Stanley Gibbons
STAMP CATALOGUE

PART 1

British Commonwealth 2001

Including post-independence issues of Ireland

103rd edition

VOLUME 2
Countries J to Z

Stanley Gibbons Ltd
London and Ringwood

By Appointment to Her Majesty The Queen
Stanley Gibbons Ltd, London
Philatelists

Published by **Stanley Gibbons Ltd**
Editorial, Publications Sales Offices and Distribution Centre:
5 Parkside, Christchurch Road, Ringwood,
Hants BH24 3SH.

© **Stanley Gibbons Ltd 2000**

Copyright Notice

ISBN: 0-85259-494-1

Item No. 2812 (01)

Text assembled by Black Bear Press Limited, Cambridge

Made and Printed in Great Britain by William Clowes Limited,
Beccles, Suffolk

Preface to the 2001 Edition

AMONG THE MEDALS

Stanley Gibbons Publications has always felt it important that its catalogues should be submitted to the Literature Classes of major International Philatelic Exhibitions, so that they could be impartially judged by leading collectors. The Catalogue Department contains medals awarded at various Exhibitions, stretching back to 1892. It is part of the firm's mythology that some of the earlier medals do actually contain gold!

2000 has seen two major philatelic exhibitions: "The Stamp Show 2000" in London and "WIPA 2000" in Vienna. Various catalogues were entered for each and the *Part 1 (British Commonwealth) Catalogue*, 2000 edition, sent to both. At "The Stamp Show 2000" it was awarded a Vermeil medal (83 marks) and at "WIPA 2000" a Large Vermeil (85 marks).

It was particularly encouraging to receive such an award from the very successful "home" International. Although patterns in the hobby continue to change in this country, the success of "The Stamp Show 2000" should leave everyone in no doubt that stamp collecting is very much alive.

One of the new aspects prominent at the exhibition was the use of the Internet as part of the hobby. In just a few months its impact as a source of information has been clearly demonstrated, and it has had a considerable effect on new issue listings for those countries who post even the most basic information on their websites. At least one country in the second volume of this edition has its new issues right up-to-date for the first time in many years, primarily because the dates of issue were provided on the Internet. It may take longer for e-commerce to become established in the philatelic trade, but in the years to come it is likely to alter our attitude to stamp collecting along with many other aspects of our everyday life.

Also evident at Earls Court were the growing problems surrounding new issues. Some countries continue to produce balanced programmes, in conjunction with their normal postal operations, which provide attractive stamps at a modest yearly cost. Such postal administrations recognise the educational aspect of their products and spend much time and effort on the research and production of their stamps, but unfortunately this is not always the case. Stamps for some other countries continue to appear in ever growing numbers, incorporating sheetlets and multiple miniature sheets, at an ever-escalating cost to the collector. There are also an increasing number of design and inscription errors, suggesting that very little effort is being made to achieve accuracy. Such instances are having a decidedly adverse effect on the ultimate purchaser, the collector, and there are growing signs that the amount spent on new issues is declining, with the purchaser being much more selective in this field than has been the case in the past.

PRICES

The market pattern outlined in last year's edition has remained unchanged over the past twelve months and continues to influence prices in these new volumes. Price rises, with some exceptions, have been solid rather than spectacular, but the continuing low level of inflation allows them to reflect the true scarcity of the stamps without the complications of wider economic factors.

Many stamps, quite common twenty or thirty years ago, are now becoming difficult to find as collectors compete for issues which were only produced in limited quantities. For errors, varieties and provisional issues, such as **Long Island** and **New Guinea** "G.R.I." overprints this leads to continuing increases year on year, but the trend is now also becoming visible for many other stamps stretching from the reign of Queen Victoria to that of King George VI. Changes in hobby trends have added emphasis to such movements. Many are neglecting "one-country" collecting, to create increased demand for such periods as King George VI or the West Indies up to 1935.

The future for stamps of the current reign is more difficult to determine. The first, recess-printed, definitive sets are probably still under-valued. Many issues from the 1960s to 1980s remain available in considerable quantities at low prices while increases for the most recent stamps are being driven largely by thematic demand. It is difficult to avoid the conclusion that a fault-line is beginning to form in the market somewhere around 1953.

This volume reflects all these trends. Many errors and varieties have increased in value, with a number of recently listed inverted watermarks priced for the first time. The West Indies revival continues, with worthwhile rises for **Jamaica**, **Leeward Islands** and **Turks and Caicos Islands** all extending to at least the King George VI issues.

A similar increase of interest is also visible for a number of the smaller African territories with many increases for **Kenya, Uganda and Tanganyika** (extending to the 1960 definitive set), **Nyasaland**, both **Northern** and **Southern Nigeria** and **Somaliland Protectorate**.

Some stamps from the classic period have done particularly well this year with rises for **Mauritius**, **New Zealand** Chalon Heads and **Uganda** to 1902. Items with links to postal history are also in demand: all prices for the stamps of India used in the **Straits Settlements** are up as are those for Gibraltar used in **Morocco Agencies** and Mauritius issues in the **Seychelles**.

Other areas of activity include **Malta** from 1863 to 1938, **Pitcairn Islands** cachets and **Ceylon** up to 1935.

In every instance there is a healthy balance between mint and fine used, indicating that there are now far more collectors ready to consider the latter than was the case even ten years ago. Stamps on cover continue to be popular.

REVISIONS FOR THIS EDITION

The coverage of "Specimen" material has been extended by the inclusion of the much sought-after "Cancelled" in oval hand-stamps applied to various issues by Perkins Bacon in 1861. Much of the detail has been taken from *Cancelled by Perkins Bacon* by Peter Jaffé, RDP, published in 1998, and I am grateful to Mr Jaffé for giving his permission for the use of this information.

Many additional watermark varieties have been listed in this edition for the first time, and further work has been done on the stamp booklet listings for **Jamaica, Kenya, Uganda and Tanganyika, Malaysia (Federated Malay States)** and **New Zealand**.

Kenya, Uganda and Tanganyika. Listings are now provided for Indian stamps used at Mombasa between July and October 1890.

Malaysia. Many additional values have been included for the modern locally produced issues, both commemoratives and the States definitives.

Pitcairn Islands. Further research has resulted in Cachet XIV being renumbered VIIIA to reflect what is believed to be the correct chronological sequence. The listing of New Zealand stamps used on the island between 1927 and 1940 has been further expanded.

St. Lucia. The notes provided for the 1930 Postage Dues have been revised and expanded based on information supplied by Henry A. Patiz of Beverly Hills.

Swaziland. The early period has been rewritten following research by Dr. Andrew Higson. Listings are now provided for South African Republic (Transvaal) stamps used in Swaziland between 1892 and 1900.

Tanzania. A modern rarity makes its first appearance in this edition with the listing of the 1984 stamp booklet which contains stamps perforated $13\frac{1}{2}$ instead of the $14 \times 14\frac{1}{2}$ from sheets.

Togo. Another new discovery is recorded with the listing of the 1916–20 2s. with watermark sideways found by Peter Duggan.

Transjordan. Extensive revisions have taken place, including a number of new variety illustrations based on the recently-published definitive study by Abed Najjar.

Vanuatu. A listing is provided for the various "V.A.T." surcharges which have appeared since December 1998. Many of these are very difficult to find outside Vanuatu and I am grateful to Peter B. Smith of Calgary for providing the information and stamps on which the listing has been based.

There are many other corrections and additions throughout the volume, and we are most grateful to those collectors, dealers and employees of postal administrations who have, as always, provided so much information for this edition.

David J. Aggersberg
Catalogue Editor

Stanley Gibbons Holdings Plc Addresses

STANLEY GIBBONS LIMITED, STANLEY GIBBONS AUCTIONS
399 Strand, London WC2R 0LX
Auction Room and Specialist Stamp Departments. Open Monday–Friday 9.30 a.m. to 5 p.m.
Shop. Open Monday–Friday 8.30 a.m. to 6 p.m. and Saturday 9.30 a.m. to 5.30 p.m.
Telephone 020 7836 8444, Fax 020 7836 7342, E-mail: enquiries @stanleygibbons.co.uk
and Internet: www.stanleygibbons.com for all departments

STANLEY GIBBONS PUBLICATIONS
5 Parkside, Christchurch Road, Ringwood, Hants BH24 3SH.
Telephone 01425 472363 (24 hour answer phone service), Fax 01425 470247 and E-mail info@stanleygibbons.co.uk
Publications Showroom (at above address). Open Monday–Friday 9 a.m. to 3 p.m.
Publications Mail Order. FREEPHONE 0800 611622. Monday–Friday 8.30 a.m. to 5 p.m.

FRASER'S
(a division of Stanley Gibbons Ltd)
399 Strand, London WC2R 0LX
Autographs, photographs, letters and documents.
Telephone 020 7836 8444, Fax 020 7836 7342, E-mail: info@frasersautographs.co.uk
and Internet:www.frasersautographs.com
Monday–Friday 9 a.m. to 5.30 p.m. and Saturday 10 a.m. to 4 p.m.

STANLEY GIBBONS PUBLICATIONS OVERSEAS REPRESENTATION

Stanley Gibbons Publications are represented overseas by the following sole distributors (*), distributors (**) or licensees (***).

Australia

Lighthouse Philatelic (Aust.) Pty Ltd*
PO Box 763
Strawberry Hills
New South Wales 2012
Australia

Stanley Gibbons (Australia) Pty Ltd***
Level 6, 36 Clarence Street
Sydney N.S.W. 2000
Australia

Belgium and Luxembourg**

Davo c/o Philac
Rue du Midi 48
Bruxelles 1000
Belgium

Canada*

Lighthouse Publications (Canada) Ltd
255 Duke Street
Montreal
Quebec
Canada H3C 2M2

Denmark**

Samlerforum/Davo
Ostergade 3
DK 7470 Karup
Denmark

Finland**

Davo
c/o Suomen Postimerkkeily
Ludvingkatu 5
SF-00130 Helsinki
Finland

France*

Davo France (Casteilla)
10 Rue Leon Foucault
78184 St Quentin Yvelines Cesex
France

Germany and Austria*

Leuchtturm Albenverlag Gmbh u. Co.
Am Spakenberg 45
Postfach 1340
D21495 Geesthacht
Germany

Hong Kong**

Po-on Stamp Service
GPO Box 2498
Hong Kong

Israel**

Capital Stamps
PO Box 3769
Jerusalem 91036
Israel

Italy*

Ernesto Marini Srl
Via Struppa 300
1-16165 Genova GE
Italy

Japan**

Japan Philatelic Co Ltd
PO Box 2
Suginami-Minami
Tokyo
Japan

Netherlands*

Davo Publications
PO Box 411
7400 AK Deventer
Netherlands

New Zealand***

Mowbray Collectables
PO Box 80
Wellington
New Zealand

Norway***

Davo Norge A/S
PO Box 738 Sentrum
N-01 05 Oslo
Norway

Singapore***

Stanley Gibbons (Singapore) Pte Ltd
Raffles City
PO Box 1689
Singapore 9117

South Africa**

Republic Stamp and Coin
  Accessories cc
Republic House
54A, Silwood Road
Bramley 2090
Republic of South Africa

Sweden*

Chr Winther Sorensen AB
Box 43
S-310 Knaered
Sweden

Switzerland**

Phila Service
Burgstrasse 160
CH 4125 Riehen
Switzerland

West Indies/Caribbean**

Hugh Dunphy
PO Box 413
Kingston 10
Jamaica
West Indies

Stanley Gibbons Stamp Catalogue
Complete List of Parts

1 British Commonwealth
(Annual in two volumes)

2 Austria & Hungary (5th edition, 1994)
Austria, Bosnia & Herzegovina, U.N. (Vienna), Hungary

3 Balkans (4th edition, 1998)
Albania, Bosnia & Herzegovina, Bulgaria, Croatia, Greece & Islands, Macedonia, Rumania, Slovenia, Yugoslavia

4 Benelux (4th edition, 1993)
Belgium & Colonies, Netherlands & Colonies, Luxembourg

5 Czechoslovakia & Poland (5th edition, 1994)
Czechoslovakia, Bohemia & Moravia, Slovakia, Poland

6 France (4th edition, 1993)
France, Colonies, Post Offices, Andorra, Monaco

7 Germany (5th edition, 1996)
Germany, States, Colonies, Post.Offices

8 Italy & Switzerland (5th edition, 1997)
Italy & Colonies, Fiume, San Marino, Vatican City, Trieste, Liechtenstein, Switzerland, U.N. (Geneva)

9 Portugal & Spain (4th edition, 1996)
Andorra, Portugal & Colonies, Spain & Colonies

10 Russia (5th edition, 1999)
Russia, Baltic States, Mongolia, Tuva

11 Scandinavia (4th edition, 1994)
Aland Island, Denmark, Faroe Islands, Finland, Greenland, Iceland, Norway, Sweden

12 Africa since Independence A-E (2nd edition, 1983)
Algeria, Angola, Benin, Bophuthatswana, Burundi, Cameroun, Cape Verde, Central African Republic, Chad, Comoro Islands, Congo, Djibouti, Equatorial Guinea, Ethiopia

13 Africa since Independence F-M (1st edition, 1981)
Gabon, Guinea, Guinea-Bissau, Ivory Coast, Liberia, Libya, Malagasy Republic, Mali, Mauritania, Morocco, Mozambique

14 Africa since Independence N-Z (1st edition, 1981)
Niger Republic, Rwanda, St. Thomas & Prince, Senegal, Somalia, Sudan, Togo, Transkei, Tunisia, Upper Volta, Venda, Zaire

15 Central America (2nd edition, 1984)
Costa Rica, Cuba, Dominican Republic, El Salvador, Guatemala, Haiti, Honduras, Mexico, Nicaragua, Panama

16 Central Asia (3rd edition, 1992)
Afghanistan, Iran, Turkey

17 China (6th edition, 1998)
China, Taiwan, Tibet, Foreign P.O.'s, Hong Kong, Macao

18 Japan & Korea (4th edition, 1997)
Japan, Ryukyus, Korean Empire, South Korea, North Korea

19 Middle East (5th edition, 1996)
Bahrain, Egypt, Iraq, Israel, Jordan, Kuwait, Lebanon, Oman, Qatar, Saudi Arabia, Syria, U.A.E., Yemen A.R., Yemen P.D.R.

20 South America (3rd edition, 1989)
Argentina, Bolivia, Brazil, Chile, Colombia, Ecuador, Paraguay, Peru, Surinam, Uruguay, Venezuela

21 South-East Asia (3rd edition, 1995)
Bhutan, Burma, Indonesia, Kampuchea, Laos, Nepal, Philippines, Thailand, Vietnam

22 United States (5th edition, 2000)
U.S. & Possessions, Canal Zone, Marshall Islands, Micronesia, Palau, U.N. (New York, Geneva, Vienna)

GREAT BRITAIN SPECIALISED CATALOGUES

Volume 1 Queen Victoria (11th edition, 1997)
Volume 2 King Edward VII to King George VI (11th edition, 1999)
Volume 3 Queen Elizabeth II Pre-decimal Issues (10th edition, 1998)
Volume 4 Queen Elizabeth II Decimal Definitive Issues (9th edition, 2000)
Volume 5 Queen Elizabeth II Decimal Special Issues (3rd edition, 1998, and 1998–99 Supplement (2000)

THEMATIC CATALOGUES

Collect Aircraft on Stamps (1st edition, 1994)
Collect Birds on Stamps (new edition in preparation)
Collect Chess on Stamps (2nd edition, 1999)
Collect Fish on Stamps (1st edition, 1999)
Collect Fungi on Stamps (2nd edition, 1997)
Collect Railways on Stamps (3rd edition, 1999)
Collect Shells on Stamps (1st edition, 1995)
Collect Ships on Stamps (new edition, 2000)

Stamps Added

Excluding new issues which have appeared in Gibbons *Stamp Monthly* Supplements, the following are the Catalogue numbers of stamps listed in this edition for the first time.

Jamaica. 94w, 124ab, 519bw, SB9a

Kenya. 117a

Kenya, Uganda and Tanganyika. Z1/8, 45w, 66x, 85b, 114ew, 145ab, 147ab

Lesotho. 722ad/b

Long Island. 17a

Malawi. 90w

Malaysia—Straits Settlements. 111w, 114b, 193bw, 202c
Federated Malay States. 64a
Malaysia. 344bw, 517w, 538w, 545a, 548b/ba, 549b, 666a, MS714a/c, MS715a/b, MS716a/ca, 723b/6b, 747a
Federal Territory. K17cw, K21ew
Johore. 29b, 89w, 109w, 123w, 204cw, 208e
Kelantan. 146cw, 146f
Malacca. 98ca, 101aw, 102e/ew
Negri Sembilan. 119ca, 123cw, 123e/ew
Pahang. 130ew, 131fw
Penang. 102cw, 104w
Perak. 201aw, 20le, 203aw
Perlis. 79cw
Selangor. 35a, 178cw, 181f, 182cw
Trengganu. 32a, 138cw
Japanese Occupation. J26a, J31a, J161e, J200a, J239a, J241a
Sabah. 462cw, J29a, J30a, J31a

Sarawak. 257fw

Malta. 112a

Mauritius. 107w, 149w, 183a, 437aw, 479w

Muscat. 1w, 7w

New Zealand. 20a, 68a, 137a/b, 138b/c, 216da, 223ab, 461a, 915c, 919c, 926a, 957ad, 1009a/b, 1010a, 1013b, 1014a, 1020a, 1202b, 1984bab, SB63ab, SB89ab/aca, O60ab, O81x, L2ax, F2w, F46a
Ross Dependency. 54a,

Nigeria. 50bw, 395a, 525ea, 619a, 620a, 621a

Pakistan. 475w, 478w, 479w, 773a/w, 775b, 777w, 913a, 915aw, 947w, 951a, 989a, 997w, 1004w/5w, 1009w, 1036w, 1046w, O76a, O77b

Palestine. 72w, 88w

Papua New Guinea—New Guinea. 21a, 42b

Pitcairn Islands. Z6, Z12/14, Z16, Z21, Z24, Z27/32, Z34/5, ZF1

St. Helena. 36a, 99dw

St. Kitts-Nevis—St. Christopher. 13b

St Lucia. 31a, D1f/g, D2d

St. Vincent. 29a, 239w

Seychelles. 14a, 21a, 226a
Zil Elwannyen Sesel. 96w

Sierra Leone. 113bx, 1028Bd/32Bd, 1033Bda, 1034Bcd

Singapore. SB2, SB8a

South Africa—Cape of Good Hope. 26ax, 53w
Natal. 22x, 103w, 106a, 148w
New Republic. 48c
Transvaal. 171b
Wolmaransstad. 1c, 2b
British Army Field Offices. Z1a, Z2a
South Africa. 30d

South Arabian Federation—Qu'aiti State in Hadhramaut. MS78a

Sri Lanka. 70by, 127w, 201aw, 1356a, 1416a

Swaziland. Z1/37, 556w

Tanzania—Tanganyika. 48w
Zanzibar. Z39, Z49, Z105, Z108, 42k
Tanzania. 320ca/ab, 320ea/eab, 320fab, SB17

Togo. H54a

Tonga. 36Af

Transjordan. 21ca, 22c, 23a, 24a, 25ba, 26b, 27b, 28a, 29ba, 30a, 32a, 33a, 36a, 39ca, 43c, 50b, 52b, 53b, 59ba, 63ca, 66a, 70c, 70e, 72a, 73a, 78bc, 79a, 81a, 90a, 105Ba, 116a, 118c, 119a, 125b/c, 126d/e, 127b, 129c/d, 130a, 131a/b, 132c, 133a/b, 134c/d, D118a, D124a, D165a, D183a,

Trinidad and Tobago. 69w, 77w, 99w, D9a, D11w, D13w, D17a

Turks and Caicos Islands. 373w, 1402a

Uganda. 8a, 341d

Zambia. 486b, 591a

Catalogue Numbers Altered

The table below is a cross-reference for stamps with catalogue numbers which have been altered in this edition.

Old	New
Jamaica	
SB11	SB10a
Kenya, Uganda and Tanganyika	
145ab	145ac
147b	147ac
SB5	*Deleted*
SB5a/ab	SB4a/ab
Kuwait	
107II/9II	107a/9a
Lesotho	
1466/84	1516/34
Malawi	
961/81	965/85
Malaysia—Straits Settlements	
142b	142c
Malaysia	
693/708a	693a/708a

Old	New
693a/708a	693/708
Selangor	
35a	35b
Japanese Occupation	
J200a/b	J200b/c
JD1B/5B	JD1a/5a
Labuan	
80bb	*Deleted*
81bb	*Deleted*
Sabah	
39a	*Deleted*
43b	*Deleted*
44c	*Deleted*
81c	*Deleted*
82c	*Deleted*
83c	*Deleted*
84b	*Deleted*
New Zealand	
SB11/a	SB11a/b

Old	New
SB13	SB11
SB14	SB12a
Nigeria	
722/6	726/30
727/32	735/40
Papua New Guinea	
853/7	857/61
Pitcairn Islands	
C17	C10A
Z6/8	Z7/11
Z9	Z15
Z10	Z18
Z11/12	Z22/3
Z13	Z26
Z13a	Z33
Z14/47	Z36/72
St Lucia	
D1a/d	D1b/e
D1e	D1h
D2a	D2b
D2b	D2a
D2d/e	D2g/h

Old	New
St. Vincent	
3982	3491
3983/91	3982/90
Sierra Leone	
1033Bda	1033Bdb
South Africa	
30d/dw	30e/ew
SB44	SB45
SB45	SB44
Tanzania—Zanzibar	
Z49/56	Z50/7
Z105/6	Z106/7
Z107/9	Z109/11
Transjordan	
22c/ca	22d/da
24a	24b
25aa/a	25a/b
25b	25c
28a/b	28b/c
30a	30b
40a	*Deleted*
42a/b	42b/c
42c	42a

Old	New
42d	42ba
43aa/a	43a/b
59a	59b
59b	59a
70c	70d
73a	73ab
78a	78ab
78c	78a
78ca	78bb
79a	79b
80f	80a
103Ac	*Deleted*
104B/a	*Deleted*
105Bb	*Deleted*
119a	119b
157a	155a
158	156b
158a	157a
Tuvalu	
822/5	827/30
826/30	822/6
Vanuatu	
793/8	798/803

Contents

General Philatelic Information

and Guidelines to the Scope of the Part 1 (British Commonwealth) Catalogue

The notes which follow seek to reflect current practice in compiling the Part 1 (British Commonwealth) Catalogue.

It scarcely needs emphasising that the *Stanley Gibbons Stamp Catalogue* has a very long history and that the vast quantity of information it contains has been carefully built up by successive generations through the work of countless individuals. Philately itself is never static and the Catalogue has evolved and developed during this long time-span. Thus, while these notes are important for today's criteria, they may be less precise the further back in the listings one travels. They are not intended to inaugurate some unwanted series of piecemeal alterations in a widely respected work, but it does seem to us useful that Catalogue users know as exactly as possible the policies currently in operation.

PRICES

The prices quoted in this Catalogue are the estimated selling prices of Stanley Gibbons Ltd at the time of publication. They are, *unless it is specifically stated otherwise*, for examples in fine condition for the issue concerned. Superb examples are worth more; those of a lower quality considerably less.

All prices are subject to change without prior notice and Stanley Gibbons Ltd may from time to time offer stamps below catalogue price. Individual low value stamps sold at 399, Strand are liable to an additional handling charge. Purchasers of new issues are asked to note that the prices charged for them contain an element for the service rendered and so may exceed the prices shown when the stamps are subsequently catalogued. Postage and handling charges are extra.

No guarantee is given to supply all stamps priced, since it is not possible to keep every catalogued item in stock. Commemorative issues may, at times, only be available in complete sets and not as individual values.

Quotation of prices. The prices in the left-hand column are for unused stamps and those in the right-hand column are for used.

A dagger (†) denotes that the item listed does not exist in that condition and a blank, or dash, that it exists, or may exist, but no market price is known.

Prices are expressed in pounds and pence sterling. One pound comprises 100 pence (£1 = 100p).

The method of notation is as follows: pence in numerals (e.g. 10 denotes ten pence); pound and pence, up to £100, in numerals (e.g. 4·25 denotes four pounds and twenty-five pence); prices above £100 expressed in whole pounds with the "£" sign shown.

Unused stamps. Great Britain and Commonwealth: the prices for unused stamps of Queen Victoria to King George V are for lightly hinged examples. Unused prices for King Edward VIII to Queen Elizabeth II issues are for unmounted mint.

Some stamps from the King George VI period are often difficult to find in unmounted mint condition. In such instances we would expect that collectors would need to pay a high proportion of the price quoted to obtain mounted mint examples. Generally speaking lightly mounted mint stamps from this reign, issued before 1945, are in considerable demand.

Mounted mint stamps from the reign of Queen Elizabeth II are frequently available at lower prices than those quoted for the stamps unmounted.

Used stamps. The used prices are normally for stamps postally used but may be for stamps cancelled-to-order where this practice exists.

A pen-cancellation on early issues can sometimes correctly denote postal use. Instances are individually noted in the Catalogue in explanation of the used price given.

Prices quoted for bisects on cover or on large piece are for those dated during the period officially authorised.

Stamps not sold unused to the public (e.g. some official stamps) are priced used only.

The use of "unified" designs, that is stamps inscribed for both postal and fiscal purposes, results in a number of stamps of very high face value. In some instances these may not have been primarily intended for postal purposes, but if they are so inscribed we include them. We only price such items used, however, where there is evidence of normal postal usage.

Cover prices. To assist collectors, cover prices are quoted for issues up to 1945 at the beginning of each country.

The system gives a general guide in the form of a factor by which the corresponding used price of the loose stamp should be multiplied when found in fine average condition on cover.

Care is needed in applying the factors and they relate to a cover which bears a single of the denomination listed; strips and blocks would need individual valuation outside the scope. If more than one denomination is present the most highly priced attracts the multiplier and the remainder are priced at the simple figure for used singles in arriving at a total.

The cover should be of non-philatelic origin, bearing the correct postal rate for the period and distance involved and cancelled with the markings normal to the offices concerned. Purely philatelic items have a cover value only slightly greater than the catalogue value for the corresponding used stamps. This applies generally to those high-value stamps used philatelically rather than in the normal course of commerce. Low-value stamps, e.g. ¼d. and ½d., are desirable when used as a single rate on cover and merit an increase in "multiplier" value.

First-day covers in the period up to 1945 are not within the scope of the system and the multiplier should not be used. As a special category of philatelic usage, with wide variations in valuation according to scarcity, they require separate treatment.

Oversized covers, difficult to accommodate on an album page, should be reckoned as worth little more than the corresponding value of the used stamps. The condition of a cover affects its value. Except for "wreck covers", serious damage or soiling reduce the value where the postal markings and stamps are ordinary ones. Conversely, visual appeal adds to the value and this can include freshness of appearance, important addresses, old-fashioned but legible hand-writing, historic town-names, etc.

The multipliers are a base on which further value would be added to take account of the cover's postal historical importance in demonstrating such things as unusual, scarce or emergency cancels, interesting routes, significant postal markings, combination usage, the development of postal rates, and so on.

For *Great Britain*, rather than multiplication factors, the cover price is shown as a third column, following the prices for unused and used stamps. It will be extended beyond King Edward VII in subsequent editions.

Minimum price. The minimum catalogue price quoted is 10p. For individual stamps prices between 10p. and 50p. are provided as a guide for catalogue users. The lowest price *charged* for individual stamps purchased from Stanley Gibbons Ltd is 50p.

Set prices. Set prices are generally for one of each value, excluding shades and varieties, but including major colour changes. Where there are alternative shades, etc., the cheapest is usually included. The number of stamps in the set is always stated for clarity. The mint prices for sets

containing *se-tenant* pieces are based on the prices quoted for such combinations, and not on those for the individual stamps.

Varieties. Where plate or cylinder varieties are priced in a used condition the price quoted is for a fine used example with the cancellation well clear of the listed flaw.

Specimen stamps. The pricing of these items is explained under that heading.

Stamp booklets. Prices are for complete assembled booklets in fine condition with those issued before 1945 showing normal wear and tear. Incomplete booklets and those which have been "exploded" will, in general, be worth less than the figure quoted.

Repricing. Collectors will be aware that the market factors of supply and demand directly influence the prices quoted in this Catalogue. Whatever the scarcity of a particular stamp, if there is no one in the market who wishes to buy it it cannot be expected to achieve a high price. Conversely, the same item actively sought by numerous potential buyers may cause the price to rise.

All the prices in this Catalogue are examined during the preparation of each new edition by expert staff of Stanley Gibbons and repriced as necessary. They take many factors into account, including supply and demand, and are in close touch with the international stamp market and the auction world.

Commonwealth cover prices and advice on postal history material originally provided by Edward B. Proud.

GUARANTEE

All stamps are guaranteed genuine originals in the following terms:

If not as described, and returned by the purchaser, we undertake to refund the price paid to us in the original transaction. If any stamp is certified as genuine by the Expert Committee of the Royal Philatelic Society, London, or by B.P.A. Expertising Ltd, the purchaser shall not be entitled to make any claim against us for any error, omission or mistake in such certificate.

Consumers' statutory rights are not affected by the above guarantee.

The recognised Expert Committees in this country are those of the Royal Philatelic Society, 41 Devonshire Place, London W1N 1PE, and B.P.A. Expertising Ltd, P.O. Box 137, Leatherhead, Surrey KT22 0RG. They do not undertake valuations under any circumstances and fees are payable for their services.

THE CATALOGUE IN GENERAL

Contents. The Catalogue is confined to adhesive postage stamps, including miniature sheets. For particular categories the rules are:

(*a*) Revenue (fiscal) stamps or telegraph stamps are listed only where they have been expressly authorised for postal duty.

(*b*) Stamps issued only precancelled are included, but normally issued stamps available additionally with precancel have no separate precancel listing unless the face value is changed.

(*c*) Stamps prepared for use but not issued, hitherto accorded full listing, are nowadays foot-noted with a price (where possible).

(*d*) Bisects (trisects, etc.) are only listed where such usage was officially authorised.

(*e*) Stamps issued only on first day covers or in presentation packs and not available separately are not listed but may be priced in a footnote.

(*f*) New printings are only included in this Catalogue where they show a major philatelic variety, such as a change in shade, watermark or paper. Stamps which exist with or without imprint dates are listed separately; changes in imprint dates are mentioned in footnotes.

(*g*) Official and unofficial reprints are dealt with by footnote.

(*h*) Stamps from imperforate printings of modern issues which also occur perforated are covered by footnotes, but are listed where widely available for postal use.

Exclusions. The following are excluded: (*a*) non-postal revenue or fiscal stamps; (*b*) postage stamps used fiscally; (*c*) local carriage labels and private local issues; (*d*) telegraph stamps; (*e*) bogus or phantom stamps; (*f*) railway or airline letter fee stamps, bus or road transport company labels; (*g*) cut-outs; (*h*) all types of non-postal labels and souvenirs; (*i*) documentary labels for the postal service, e.g. registration, recorded delivery, airmail etiquettes, etc.; (*j*) privately applied embellishments to official issues and privately commissioned items generally; (*k*) stamps for training postal officers.

Full listing. "Full listing" confers our recognition and implies allotting a catalogue number and (wherever possible) a price quotation.

In judging status for inclusion in the catalogue broad considerations are applied to stamps. They must be issued by a legitimate postal authority, recognised by the government concerned, and must be adhesives valid for proper postal use in the class of service for which they are inscribed. Stamps, with the exception of such categories as postage dues and officials, must be available to the general public, at face value, in reasonable quantities without any artificial restrictions being imposed on their distribution.

We record as abbreviated Appendix entries, without catalogue numbers or prices, stamps from countries which either persist in having far more issues than can be justified by postal need or have failed to maintain control over their distribution so that they have not been available to the public in reasonable quantities at face value. Miniature sheets and imperforate stamps are not mentioned in these entries.

The publishers of this catalogue have observed, with concern, the proliferation of "artificial" stamp-issuing territories. On several occasions this has resulted in separately inscribed issues for various component parts of otherwise united states or territories.

Stanley Gibbons Ltd have decided that where such circumstances occur, they will not, in the future, list these items in the SG catalogue without first satisfying themselves that the stamps represent a genuine political, historical or postal division within the country concerned. Any such issues which do not fulfil this stipulation will be recorded in the Catalogue Appendix only.

For errors and varieties the criterion is legitimate (albeit inadvertent) sale through a postal administration in the normal course of business. Details of provenance are always important; printers' waste and deliberately manufactured material are excluded.

Certificates. In assessing unlisted items due weight is given to Certificates from recognised Expert Committees and, where appropriate, we will usually ask to see them.

New issues. New issues are listed regularly in the Catalogue Supplement published in *Gibbons Stamp Monthly*, whence they are consolidated into the next available edition of the Catalogue.

Date of issue. Where local issue dates differ from dates of release by agencies, "date of issue" is the local date. Fortuitous stray usage before the officially intended date is disregarded in listing. For ease of reference, the Catalogue displays in the top corner the date of issue of the first set listed on each page.

Catalogue numbers. Stamps of each country are catalogued chronologically by date of issue. Subsidiary classes are placed at the end of the country, as separate lists, with a distinguishing letter prefix to the catalogue number, e.g. D for postage due, O for official and E for express delivery stamps.

The catalogue number appears in the extreme left column. The boldface Type numbers in the next column are merely cross-references to illus-

trations. Catalogue numbers in the *Gibbons Stamp Monthly* Supplement are provisional only and may need to be altered when the lists are consolidated. For the numbering of miniature sheets and sheetlets *see* section below.

Once published in the Catalogue, numbers are changed as little as possible; really serious renumbering is reserved for the occasions when a complete country or an entire issue is being rewritten. The edition first affected includes cross-reference tables of old and new numbers.

Our catalogue numbers are universally recognised in specifying stamps and as a hallmark of status.

Illustrations. Stamps are illustrated at three-quarters linear size. Stamps not illustrated are the same size and format as the value shown, unless otherwise indicated. Stamps issued only as miniature sheets have the stamp alone illustrated but sheet size is also quoted. Overprints, surcharges, watermarks and postmarks are normally actual size. Illustrations of varieties are often enlarged to show the detail. Stamp booklet covers are illustrated half-size, unless otherwise indicated.

Designers. Designers' names are quoted where known, though space precludes naming every individual concerned in the production of a set. In particular, photographers supplying material are usually named only where they also make an active contribution in the design stage; posed photographs of reigning monarchs are, however, an exception to this rule.

CONTACTING THE CATALOGUE EDITOR

The editor is always interested in hearing from people who have new information which will improve or correct the Catalogue. As a general rule he must see and examine the actual stamps before they can be considered for listing; photographs or photocopies are insufficient evidence.

Submissions should be made in writing to the Catalogue Editor, Stanley Gibbons Publications at the Ringwood office. The cost of return postage for items submitted is appreciated, and this should include the registration fee if required.

Where information is solicited purely for the benefit of the enquirer, the editor cannot undertake to reply if the answer is already contained in these published notes or if return postage is omitted. Written communications are greatly preferred to enquiries by telephone and the editor regrets that he or his staff cannot see personal callers without a prior appointment being made. Correspondence may be subject to delay during the production period of each new edition.

The editor welcomes close contact with study circles and is interested, too, in finding reliable local correspondents who will verify and supplement official information in countries where this is deficient.

> We regret we do not give opinions as to the genuineness of stamps, nor do we identify stamps or number them by our Catalogue.

TECHNICAL MATTERS

The meanings of the technical terms used in the catalogue will be found in our *Philatelic Terms Illustrated* (*new edition in preparation*).

References below to "more specialised" listings are to be taken to indicate, as appropiate, the Stanley Gibbons *Great Britain Specialised Catalogue* in 5 volumes or the *Great Britain Concise Catalogue*.

1. Printing

Printing errors. Errors in printing are of major interest to the Catalogue. Authenticated items meriting consideration would include: background, centre or frame inverted or omitted; centre or subject transposed; error of colour; error

or omission of value; double prints and impressions; printed both sides; and so on. Designs *tête-bêche*, whether intentionally or by accident, are listable. *Se-tenant* arrangements of stamps are recognised in the listings or footnotes. Gutter pairs (a pair of stamps separated by blank margin) are not included in this volume. Colours only partially omitted are not listed. Stamps with embossing omitted are reserved for our more specialised listings.

Printing varieties. Listing is accorded to major changes in the printing base which lead to completely new types. In recess-printing this could be a design re-engraved; in photogravure or photolithography a screen altered in whole or in part. It can also encompass flat-bed and rotary printing if the results are readily distinguishable.

To be considered at all, varieties must be constant.

Early stamps, produced by primitive methods, were prone to numerous imperfections: the lists reflect this, recognising re-entries, retouches, broken frames, misshapen letters, and so on. Printing technology has, however, radically improved over the years, during which time photogravure and lithography have become predominant. Varieties nowadays are more in the nature of flaws and these, being too specialised for this general catalogue, are almost always outside the scope. The development of our range of specialised catalogues allows us now to list those items which have philatelic significance in their appropriate volume.

In no catalogue, however, do we list such items as: dry prints, kiss prints, doctor-blade flaws, colour shifts or registration flaws (unless they lead to the complete omission of a colour from an individual stamp), lithographic ring flaws, and so on. Neither do we recognise fortuitous happenings like paper creases or confetti flaws.

Overprints (and surcharges). Overprints of different types qualify for separate listing. These include overprints in different colours; overprints from different printing processes such as litho and typo; overprints in totally different typefaces, etc. Major errors in machine-printed overprints are important and listable. They include: overprint inverted or omitted; overprint double (treble, etc.); overprint diagonal; overprint double, one inverted; pairs with one overprint omitted, e.g. from a radical shift to an adjoining stamp; error of colour; error of type fount; letters inverted or omitted, etc. If the overprint is handstamped, few of these would qualify and a distinction is drawn. We continue, however, to list pairs of stamps where one has a handstamped overprint and the other has not.

Varieties occurring in overprints will often take the form of broken letters, slight differences in spacing, rising spaces, etc. Only the most important would be considered for footnote mention.

Sheet positions. If space permits we quote sheet positions of listed varieties and authenticated data is solicited for this purpose.

De La Rue plates. The Catalogue classifies the general plates used by De La Rue for printing British Colonial stamps as follows:

VICTORIAN KEY TYPE

Die I

1. The ball of decoration on the second point of the crown appears as a dark mass of lines.
2. Dark vertical shading separates the front hair from the bun.
3. The vertical line of colour outlining the front of the throat stops at the sixth line of shading on the neck.
4. The white space in the coil of the hair above the curl is roughly the shape of a pin's head.

Die II

1. There are very few lines of colour in the ball and it appears almost white.
2. A white vertical strand of hair appears in place of the dark shading.
3. The line stops at the eighth line of shading.
4. The white space is oblong, with a line of colour partially dividing it at the left end.

Plates numbered 1 and 2 are both Die I. Plates 3 and 4 are Die II.

GEORGIAN KEY TYPE

Die I

A. The second (thick) line below the name of the country is cut slanting, conforming roughly to the shape of the crown on each side.
B. The labels of solid colour bearing the words "POSTAGE" and "& REVENUE" are square at the inner top corners.
C. There is a projecting "bud" on the outer spiral of the ornament in each of the lower corners.

Die II

A. The second line is cut vertically on each side of the crown.
B. The labels curve inwards at the top.
C. There is no "bud" in this position.

Unless otherwise stated in the lists, all stamps with watermark Multiple Crown CA (w **8**) are Die I while those with watermark Multiple Crown Script CA (w **9**) are Die II. The Georgian Die II was introduced in April 1921 and was used for Plates 10 to 22 and 26 to 28. Plates 23 to 25 were made from Die I by mistake.

2. Paper

All stamps listed are deemed to be on "ordinary" paper of the wove type and white in colour; only departures from this are normally mentioned.

Types. Where classification so requires we distinguish such other types of paper as, for example, vertically and horizontally laid; wove and laid bâtonné; card(board); carton; cartridge; glazed; granite; native; pelure; porous; quadrillé; ribbed; rice; and silk thread.

Wove paper   Laid paper

Granite paper   Quadrillé paper

Burelé band

The various makeshifts for normal paper are listed as appropriate. The varieties of double paper and joined paper are recognised. The security device of a printed burelé band on the back of a stamp, as in early Queensland, qualifies for listing.

Descriptive terms. The fact that a paper is handmade (and thus probably of uneven thickness) is mentioned where necessary. Such descriptive terms as "hard" and "soft"; "smooth" and 'rough"; "thick", "medium" and "thin" are applied where there is philatelic merit in classifying papers. We do not, for example, even in more specialised listings, classify paper thicknesses in the Wilding and Machin definitives of Great Britain. Weight standards for the paper apply to complete reels only, so that differences on individual stamps are acceptable to the printer provided the reel conforms overall.

Coloured, very white and toned papers. A coloured paper is one that is coloured right through (front and back of the stamp). In the Catalogue the colour of the paper is given in *italics*, thus:

black/*rose* = black design on rose paper.

Papers have been made specially white in recent years by, for example, a very heavy coating of chalk. We do not classify shades of whiteness of paper as distinct varieties. There does exist, however, a type of paper from early days called toned. This is off-white, often brownish or buffish, but it cannot be assigned any definite colour. A toning effect brought on by climate, incorrect storage or gum staining is disregarded here, as this was not the state of the paper when issued.

Modern developments. Two modern developments also affect the listings: printing on self-adhesive paper and the use of metallic foils. For self-adhesive stamps *see* under "Gum", below. Care should be taken not to damage the embossing on stamps impressed on metallic foils, such as Sierra Leone 1965–67, by subjecting the album pages to undue pressure. The possibility of faked

"missing gold heads" is noted at the appropriate places in the listing of modern Great Britain.

"Ordinary" and "Chalk-surfaced" papers. The availability of many postage stamps for revenue purposes made necessary some safeguard against the illegitimate re-use of stamps with removable cancellations. This was at first secured by using fugitive inks and later by printing on chalk-surfaced paper, both of which made it difficult to remove any form of obliteration without also damaging the stamp design.

This catalogue lists these chalk-surfaced paper varieties from their introduction in 1905. Where no indication is given, the paper is "ordinary".

Our chalk-surfaced paper is specifically one which shows a black mark when touched with a silver wire. The paper used during the Second World War for high values, as in Bermuda, the Leeward Islands, etc., was thinly coated with some kind of surfacing which does not react to silver and is therefore regarded (and listed) as "ordinary". Stamps on chalk-surfaced paper can easily lose this coating through immersion in water.

Another paper introduced during the War as a substitute for chalk-surfaced is rather thick, very white and glossy and shows little or no watermark, nor does it show a black line when touched with silver. In the Bahamas high values this paper might be mistaken for the chalk-surfaced (which is thinner and poorer-looking) but for the silver test.

Some modern coated papers show little or no reaction to the silver test and, therefore, cannot be classed as chalk-surfaced.

Glazed paper. In 1969 the Crown Agents introduced a new general-purpose paper for use in conjunction with all current printing processes. It generally has a marked glossy surface but the degree varies according to the process used, being more marked in recess-printing stamps. As it does not respond to the silver test this presents a further test where previous printings were on chalky paper. A change of paper to the glazed variety merits separate listing.

Green and yellow papers. Issues of the First World War and immediate postwar period occur on green and yellow papers and these are given separate Catalogue listing. The original coloured papers (coloured throughout) gave way to surface-coloured papers, the stamps having "white backs"; other stamps show one colour on the front and a different one at the back. Because of the numerous variations a grouping of colours is adopted as follows:

YELLOW PAPERS

(1) The original *yellow* paper (throughout), usually bright in colour. The gum is often sparse, of harsh consistency and dull-looking. Used 1912–1920.

(2) The *white backs*. Used 1913–1914.

(3) A bright *lemon* paper. The colour must have a pronounced greenish tinge, different from the "yellow" in (1). As a rule, the gum on stamps using this lemon paper is plentiful, smooth and shiny, and the watermark shows distinctly. Care is needed with stamps printed in green on yellow paper (1) as it may appear that the paper is this lemon. Used 1914–1916.

(4) An experimental *orange-buff* paper. The colour must have a distinct brownish tinge. It is not to be confused with a muddy yellow (1) nor the misleading appearance (on the surface) of stamps printed in red on yellow paper where an engraved plate has been insufficiently wiped. Used 1918–1921.

(5) An experimental *buff* paper. This lacks the brownish tinge of (4) and the brightness of the yellow shades. The gum is shiny when compared with the matt type used on (4). Used 1919–1920.

(6) A *pale yellow* paper that has a creamy tone to the yellow. Used from 1920 onwards.

GREEN PAPERS

(7) The original "green" paper, varying considerably through shades of *blue-green* and *yellow-*

green, the front and back sometimes differing. Used 1912–1916.

(8) The *white backs*. Used 1913–1914.

(9) A paper blue-green on the surface with *pale olive* back. The back must be markedly paler than the front and this and the pronounced olive tinge to the back distinguish it from (7). Used 1916–1920.

(10) Paper with a vivid green surface, commonly called *emerald-green*; it has the olive back of (9). Used 1920.

(11) Paper with *emerald-green* both back and front. Used from 1920 onwards.

3. Perforation and Rouletting

Perforation gauge. The gauge of a perforation is the number of holes in a length of 2 cm. For correct classification the size of the holes (large or small) may need to be distinguished; in a few cases the actual number of holes on each edge of the stamp needs to be quoted.

Measurement. The Gibbons *Instanta* gauge is the standard for measuring perforations. The stamp is viewed against a dark background with the transparent gauge put on top of it. Though the gauge measures to decimal accuracy, perforations read from it are generally quoted in the Catalogue to the nearest half. For example:

Just over perf $12\frac{3}{4}$ to just under $13\frac{1}{4}$ = perf 13
Perf $13\frac{1}{4}$ exactly, rounded up = perf $13\frac{1}{2}$
Just over perf $13\frac{1}{4}$ to just under $13\frac{3}{4}$ = perf $13\frac{1}{2}$
Perf $13\frac{3}{4}$ exactly, rounded up = perf 14

However, where classification depends on it, actual quarter-perforations are quoted.

Notation. Where no perforation is quoted for an issue it is imperforate. Perforations are usually abbreviated (and spoken) as follows, though sometimes they may be spelled out for clarity. This notation for rectangular stamps (the majority) applies to diamond shapes if "top" is read as the edge to the top right.

P 14: perforated alike on all sides (read: "perf 14").

P 14 × 15: the first figure refers to top and bottom, the second to left and right sides (read: "perf 14 by 15"). This is a compound perforation. For an upright triangular stamp the first figure refers to the two sloping sides and second to the base. In inverted triangulars the base is first and the second figure refers to the sloping sides.

P 14–15: perforation measuring anything between 14 and 15: the holes are irregularly spaced, thus the gauge may vary along a single line or even along a single edge of the stamp (read: "perf 14 to 15").

P 14 *irregular*: perforated 14 from a worn perforator, giving badly aligned holes irregularly spaced (read: "irregular perf 14").

P comp(ound) 14 × 15: two gauges in use but not necessarily on opposite sides of the stamp. It could be one side in one gauge and three in the other; or two adjacent sides with the same gauge. (Read: "perf compound of 14 and 15".) For three gauges or more, abbreviated as "*P* 14, $14\frac{1}{2}$, 15 *or* compound" for example.

P 14, $14\frac{1}{2}$: perforated approximately $14\frac{1}{4}$ (read: "perf 14 or $14\frac{1}{2}$"). It does *not* mean two stamps, one perf 14 and the other perf $14\frac{1}{2}$. This obsolescent notation is gradually being replaced in the Catalogue.

Imperf: imperforate (not perforated).

Imperf × *P* 14: imperforate at top and bottom and perf 14 at sides.

Perf × imperf

P 14 × *imperf*: perf 14 at top and bottom and imperforate at sides.

Such headings as "*P* 13 × 14 (*vert*) and *P* 14 × 13 (*horiz*)" indicate which perforations apply to which stamp format—vertical or horizontal.

Some stamps are additionally perforated so that a label or tab is detachable; others have been perforated suitably for use as two halves. Listings are normally for whole stamps, unless stated otherwise.

Other terms. Perforation almost always gives circular holes; where other shapes have been used they are specified, e.g. square holes; lozenge perf. Interrupted perfs are brought about by the omission of pins at regular intervals. Perforations merely simulated by being printed as part of the design are of course ignored. With few exceptions, privately applied perforations are not listed.

In the nineteenth century perforations are often described as clean cut (clean, sharply incised holes), intermediate or rough (rough holes, imperfectly cut, often the result of blunt pins).

Perforation errors and varieties. Authenticated errors, where a stamp normally perforated is accidentally issued imperforate, are listed provided no traces of perforation (blind holes or indentations) remain. They must be provided as pairs, both stamps wholly imperforate, and are only priced in that form.

In Great Britain, numerous of these part-perforated stamps have arisen from the introduction of the Jumelle Press. This has a rotary perforator with rows of pins on one drum engaging with holes on another. Engagement is only gradual when the perforating unit is started up or stopped, giving rise to perforations "fading out", a variety mentioned above as not listed.

Stamps imperforate between stamp and sheet margin are not listed in this catalogue, but such errors on Great Britain stamps will be found in the *Great Britain Specialised Catalogue*.

Pairs described as "imperforate between" have the line of perforations between the two stamps omitted.

Imperf between (*horiz pair*): a horizontal pair of stamps with perfs all around the edges but none between the stamps.

Imperf between (*vert pair*): a vertical pair of stamps with perfs all around the edges but none between the stamps.

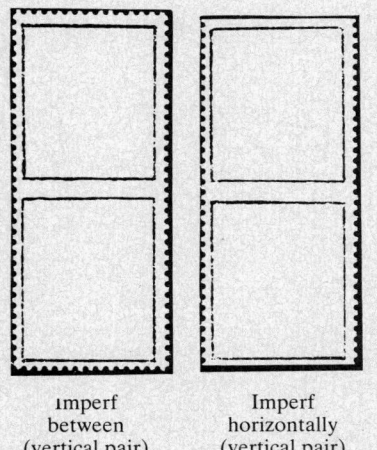

imperf
between
(vertical pair)

Imperf
horizontally
(vertical pair)

Where several of the rows have escaped perforation the resulting varieties are listable. Thus:

Imperf vert (*horiz pair*): a horizontal pair of stamps perforated top and bottom; all three vertical directions are imperf—the two outer edges and between the stamps.

Imperf horiz (*vert pair*): a vertical pair perforated at left and right edges; all three horizontal directions are imperf—the top, bottom and between the stamps.

Straight edges. Large sheets cut up before issue to post offices can cause stamps with straight edges,

i.e. imperf on one side or on two sides at right angles. They are not usually listable in this condition and are worth less than corresponding stamps properly perforated all round. This does not, however, apply to certain stamps, mainly from coils and booklets, where straight edges on various sides are the manufacturing norm affecting every stamp. The listings and notes make clear which sides are correctly imperf.

Malfunction. Varieties of double, misplaced or partial perforation caused by error or machine malfunction are not listable, neither are freaks, such as perforations placed diagonally from paper folds, nor missing holes caused by broken pins.

Centering. Well-centred stamps have designs surrounded by equal opposite margins. Where this condition affects the price the fact is stated.

Types of perforating. Where necessary for classification, perforation types are distinguished. These include:

Line perforation from one line of pins punching single rows of holes at a time.

Comb perforation from pins disposed across the sheet in comb formation, punching out holes at three sides of the stamp a row at a time.

Harrow perforation applied to a whole pane or sheet at one stroke.

Rotary perforation from toothed wheels operating across a sheet, then crosswise.

Sewing-machine perforation. The resultant condition, clean-cut or rough, is distinguished where required.

Pin-perforation is the commonly applied term for pin-roulette in which, instead of being punched out, round holes are pricked by sharp-pointed pins and no paper is removed.

Mixed perforation occurs when stamps with defective perforations are re-perforated in a different gauge.

Punctured stamps. Perforation holes can be punched into the face of the stamp. Patterns of small holes, often in the shape of initial letters, are privately applied devices against pilferage. These "perfins" are outside the scope except for Australia, Canada, Cape of Good Hope, Papua and Sudan where they were used as official stamps by the national administration. Identification devices, when officially inspired, are listed or noted; they can be shapes, or letters or words formed from holes, sometimes converting one class of stamp into another.

Rouletting. In rouletting the paper is cut, for ease of separation, but none is removed. The gauge is measured, when needed, as for perforations. Traditional French terms descriptive of the type of cut are often used and types include:

Arc roulette (*percé en arc*). Cuts are minute, spaced arcs, each roughly a semicircle.

Cross roulette (*percé en croix*). Cuts are tiny diagonal crosses.

Line roulette (*percé en ligne* or *en ligne droite*). Short straight cuts parallel to the frame of the stamp. The commonest basic roulette. Where not further described, "roulette" means this type.

Rouletted in colour or *coloured roulette* (*percé en lignes colorées* or *en lignes de couleur*). Cuts with coloured edges, arising from notched rule inked simultaneously with the printing plate.

Saw-tooth roulette (*percé en scie*). Cuts applied zigzag fashion to resemble the teeth of a saw.

Serpentine roulette (*percé en serpentin*). Cuts as sharply wavy lines.

Zigzag roulette (*percé en zigzags*). Short straight cuts at angles in alternate directions, producing sharp points on separation. U.S. usage favours "serrate(d) roulette" for this type.

Pin-roulette (originally *percé en points* and now *perforés trous d'epingle*) is commonly called pin-perforation in English.

4. Gum

All stamps listed are assumed to have gum of some kind; if they were issued without gum this is stated. Original gum (o.g.) means that which was present on the stamp as issued to the public. Deleterious climates and the presence of certain chemicals can cause gum to crack and, with early stamps, even make the paper deteriorate. Unscrupulous fakers are adept in removing it and regumming the stamp to meet the unreasoning demand often made for "full o.g." in cases where such a thing is virtually impossible.

The gum normally used on stamps has been gum arabic until the late 1960s when synthetic adhesives were introduced. Harrison and Sons Ltd for instance use *polyvinyl alcohol*, known to philatelists as PVA. This is almost invisible except for a slight yellowish tinge which was incorporated to make it possible to see that the stamps have been gummed. It has advantages in hot countries, as stamps do not curl and sheets are less likely to stick together. Gum arabic and PVA are not distinguished in the lists except that where a stamp exists with both forms this is indicated in footnotes. Our more specialised catalogues provide separate listing of gums for Great Britain.

Self-adhesive stamps are issued on backing paper, from which they are peeled before affixing to mail. Unused examples are priced as for backing paper intact, in which condition they are recommended to be kept. Used examples are best collected on cover or on piece.

5. Watermarks

Stamps are on unwatermarked paper except where the heading to the set says otherwise.

Detection. Watermarks are detected for Catalogue description by one of four methods: (1) holding stamps to the light; (2) laying stamps face down on a dark background; (3) adding a few drops of petroleum ether 40/60 to the stamp laid face down in a watermark tray; (4) by use of the Morley-Bright Detector, or other equipment, which work by revealing the thinning of the paper at the watermark (Note that petroleum ether is highly inflammable in use and can damage photogravure stamps.)

Listable types. Stamps occurring on both watermarked and unwatermarked papers are different types and both receive full listing.

Single watermarks (devices occurring once on every stamp) can be modified in size and shape as between different issues; the types are noted but not usually separately listed. Fortuitous absence of watermark from a single stamp or its gross displacement would not be listable.

To overcome registration difficulties the device may be repeated at close intervals (a *multiple watermark*), single stamps thus showing parts of several devices. Similarly, a large *sheet watermark* (or *all-over watermark*) covering numerous stamps can be used. We give informative notes and illustrations for them. The designs may be such that numbers of stamps in the sheet automatically lack watermark: this is not a listable variety. Multiple and all-over watermarks sometimes undergo modifications, but if the various types are difficult to distinguish from single stamps notes are given but not separate listings.

Papermakers' watermarks are noted where known but not listed separately, since most stamps in the sheet will lack them. Sheet watermarks which are nothing more than officially adopted papermakers' watermarks are, however, given normal listing.

Marginal watermarks, falling outside the pane of stamps, are ignored except where misplacement caused the adjoining row to be affected, in which case they are footnoted.

Watermark errors and varieties. Watermark errors are recognised as of major importance. They comprise stamps intended to be on unwatermarked paper but issued watermarked by mistake, or stamps printed on paper with the wrong watermark. Varieties showing letters omitted from the watermark are also included, but broken or deformed bits on the dandy roll are not listed unless they represent repairs.

Watermark positions. The diagram shows how watermark position is described in the Catalogue. Paper has a side intended for printing and watermarks are usually impressed so that they read normally when looked through from that printed side. However, since philatelists customarily detect watermarks by looking at the back of the stamp the watermark diagram also makes clear what is actually seen.

Illustrations in the Catalogue are of watermarks in normal positions (from the front of the stamps) and are actual size where possible.

Differences in watermark position are collectable as distinct varieties. This Catalogue now lists inverted, sideways inverted and reversed watermark varieties on Commonwealth stamps from the 1860s onwards *except* where the watermark position is completely haphazard.

Great Britain inverted and sideways inverted watermarks can be found in the *Great Britain Specialised Catalogue* and the *Great Britain Concise Catalogue*.

Where a watermark comes indiscriminately in various positions our policy is to cover this by a general note: we do not give separate listings because the watermark position in these circumstances has no particular philatelic importance. There is a general note of this sort in modern Cyprus, for example. Issues printed since 1962 by Aspioti-Elka occur with the vertical stamps having the watermark normal or inverted, while horizontal stamps are likewise found with the watermark reading upwards or downwards.

AS DESCRIBED (Read through front of stamp)		AS SEEN DURING WATERMARK DETECTION (Stamp face down and back examined)
GvR	Normal	ЯvƆ
ЯvⱭ	Inverted	Ͼᴧꓤ
ЯvƆ	Reversed	GvR
Ͼᴧꓤ	Reversed and inverted	ЯvƆ
GvR (rotated)	Sideways	ЯvⱭ (rotated)
GvR (rotated)	Sideways inverted	ЯvⱭ (rotated)

Standard types of watermark. Some watermarks have been used generally for various British possessions rather than exclusively for a single colony. To avoid repetition the Catalogue classifies 17 general types, as under, with references in the headings throughout the listings being given either in words or in the form "W w 14" (meaning "watermark type w 14"). In those cases where watermark illustrations appear in the listings themselves, the respective reference reads,

for example, W 153, thus indicating that the watermark will be found in the normal sequence of illustrations as (type) 153.

The general types are as follows, with an example of each quoted.

W	Description	Example
w 1	Large Star	St. Helena No. 1
w 2	Small Star	Turks Is. No. 4
w 3	Broad (pointed) Star	Grenada No. 24
w 4	Crown (over) CC, small stamp	Antigua No. 13
w 5	Crown (over) CC, large stamp	Antigua No. 31
w 6	Crown (over) CA, small stamp	Antigua No. 21
w 7	Crown CA (CA over Crown), large stamp	Sierra Leone No. 54
w 8	Multiple Crown CA	Antigua No. 41
w 9	Multiple Crown Script CA	Seychelles No. 158
w 9a	do. Error	Seychelles No. 158a
w 9b	do. Error	Seychelles No. 158b
w 10	V over Crown	N.S.W. No. 327
w 11	Crown over A	N.S.W. No. 347
w 12	Multiple St. Edward's Crown Block CA	Antigua No. 149
w 13	Multiple PTM	Johore No. 166
w 14	Multiple Crown CA Diagonal	Antigua No. 426
w 15	Multiple POST OFFICE	Kiribati No. 141
w 16	Multiple Crown Script CA Diagonal	Ascension No. 376
w 17	Multiple CARTOR	Brunei No. 357

CC in these watermarks is an abbreviation for "Crown Colonies" and CA for "Crown Agents". Watermarks w 1, w 2 and w 3 are on stamps printed by Perkins, Bacon; w 4 onwards on stamps from De La Rue and other printers.

w 1
Large Star

w 2
Small Star

w 3
Broad (pointed) Star

Watermark w 1, *Large Star,* measures 15 to 16 mm across the star from point to point and about 27 mm from centre to centre vertically between stars in the sheet. It was made for long stamps like Ceylon 1857 and St. Helena 1856.

Watermark w 2, *Small Star,* is of similar design but measures 12 to 13½ mm from point to point and 24 mm from centre to centre vertically. It was for use with ordinary-size stamps such as Grenada 1863–71.

When the Large Star watermark was used with the smaller stamps it only occasionally comes in the centre of the paper. It is frequently so misplaced as to show portions of two stars above and below and this eccentricity will very often help in determining the watermark.

Watermark w **3**, *Broad (pointed) Star*, resembles w **1** but the points are broader.

w **4**	w **5**
Crown (over) CC	Crown (over) CC

Two *Crown (over) CC* watermarks were used: w **4** was for stamps of ordinary size and w **5** for those of larger size.

w **6**	w **7**
Crown (over) CA	CA over Crown

Two watermarks of *Crown CA* type were used, w **6** being for stamps of ordinary size. The other, w **7**, is properly described as *CA over Crown*. It was specially made for paper on which it was intended to print long fiscal stamps: that some were used postally accounts for the appearance of w **7** in the Catalogue. The watermark occupies twice the space of the ordinary Crown CA watermark, w **6**. Stamps of normal size printed on paper with w **7** watermark show it *sideways*; it takes a horizontal pair of stamps to show the entire watermark.

w **8**	w **9**
Multiple Crown CA	Multiple Crown Script CA

Multiple watermarks began in 1904 with w **8**, *Multiple Crown CA*, changed from 1921 to w **9**, *Multiple Crown Script CA*. On stamps of ordinary size portions of two or three watermarks appear and on the large-sized stamps a greater number can be observed. The change to letters in script character with w **9** was accompanied by a Crown of distinctly different shape.

It seems likely that there were at least two dandy rolls for each Crown Agents watermark in use at any one time with a reserve roll being employed when the normal one was withdrawn for maintenance or repair.

Both the Mult Crown CA and the Mult Script CA types exist with one or other of the letters omitted from individual impressions. It is possible that most of these occur from the reserve rolls as they have only been found on certain issues. The MCA watermark experienced such problems

during the early 1920s and the Script over a longer period from the early 1940s until 1951.

During the 1920s damage must also have occurred on one of the Crowns as a substituted Crown has been found on certain issues. This is smaller than the normal and consists of an oval base joined to two upright ovals with a circle positioned between their upper ends. The upper line of the Crown's base is omitted, as are the left and right-hand circles at the top and also the cross over the centre circle.

Substituted Crown

w **9***a*: Error, Crown missing

w **9***b*: Error, St. Edward's Crown

The *Multiple Crown Script CA* watermark, w **9**, is known with two errors recurring among the 1950–52 printings of several territories. In the first a crown has fallen away from the dandy-roll that impresses the watermark into the paper pulp. It gives w **9***a*, *Crown missing*, but this omission has been found in both "Crown only" (*illustrated*) and "Crown CA" rows. The resulting faulty paper was used for Seychelles, Johore and the postage due stamps of nine colonies.

When the omission was noticed a second mishap occurred, which was to insert a wrong crown in the space, giving w **9***b*, *St. Edward's Crown*. This produced varieties in Bahamas, St. Kitts-Nevis and Singapore and the incorrect crown likewise occurs in "Crown only" and "Crown CA" rows.

w **10**	w **11**
V over Crown	Crown over A

Resuming the general types, two watermarks found in issues of several Australian States are: w **10**, *V over Crown*, and w **11**, *Crown over A*.

w **12**
Multiple St. Edward's
Crown Block CA

The *Multiple St. Edward's Crown Block CA* watermark, w **12**, was introduced in 1957 and besides the change in the Crown (from that used in *Multiple Crown Script CA*, w **9**) the letters reverted to block capitals. The new watermark began to appear sideways in 1966 and these stamps are generally listed as separate sets.

w **13**
Multiple PTM

The watermark w **13**, *Multiple PTM*, was introduced for new Malayan issues in November 1961.

w **14**
Multiple Crown CA
Diagonal

By 1974 the two dandy-rolls (the "upright" and the "sideways") for w **12** were wearing out; the Crown Agents therefore discontinued using the sideways-watermark one and retained the other only as a stand-by. A new dandy-roll with the pattern of w **14**, *Multiple Crown CA Diagonal*, was introduced and first saw use with some Churchill Centenary issues.

The new watermark has the design arranged in gradually spiralling rows. It is improved in design to allow smooth passage over the paper (the gaps between letters and rows had caused jolts in previous dandy-rolls) and the sharp corners and angles, where fibres used to accumulate, have been eliminated by rounding.

This watermark has no "normal" sideways position amongst the different printers using it. To avoid confusion our more specialised listings do not rely on such terms as "sideways inverted" but describe the direction in which the watermark points.

w 15
Multiple POST OFFICE

During 1981 w 15, *Multiple POST OFFICE,* was introduced for certain issues prepared by Philatelists Ltd, acting for various countries in the Indian Ocean, Pacific and West Indies.

w 16
Multiple Crown Script CA Diagonal

A new Crown Agents watermark was introduced during 1985, w 16, *Multiple Crown Script CA Diagonal.* This was very similar to the previous w 14, but showed "CA" in script rather than block letters. It was first used on the omnibus series of stamps commemorating the Life and Times of Queen Elizabeth the Queen Mother.

w 17
Multiple CARTOR

Watermark w 17, *Multiple CARTOR,* was used from 1985 for issues printed by this French firm for countries which did not normally use the Crown Agents watermark.

In recent years the use of watermarks has, to a small extent, been superseded by fluorescent security markings. These are often more visible from the reverse of the stamp (Cook Islands from 1970 onwards), but have occurred printed over the design (Hong Kong Nos. 415/30). In 1982 the Crown Agents introduced a new stock paper, without watermark, known as "C-Kurity" on which a fluorescent pattern of blue rosettes is visible on the reverse, beneath the gum. This paper was used for issues from Gambia and Norfolk Island.

6. Colours

Stamps in two or three colours have these named in order of appearance, from the centre moving outwards. Four colours or more are usually listed as multicoloured.

In compound colour names the second is the predominant one, thus:

orange-red = a red tending towards orange;
red-orange = an orange containing more red than usual.

Standard colours used. The 200 colours most used for stamp identification are given in the Stanley Gibbons Stamp Colour Key. The Catalogue has used the Stamp Colour Key as standard for describing new issues for some years. The names are also introduced as lists are rewritten, though exceptions are made for those early issues where traditional names have become universally established.

Determining colours. When comparing actual stamps with colour samples in the Stamp Colour Key, view in a good north daylight (or its best substitute: fluorescent "colour-matching" light). Sunshine is not recommended. Choose a solid portion of the stamp design; if available, marginal markings such as solid bars of colour or colour check dots are helpful. Shading lines in the design can be misleading as they appear lighter than solid colour. Postmarked portions of a stamp appear darker than normal. If more than one colour is present, mask off the extraneous ones as the eye tends to mix them.

Errors of colour. Major colour errors in stamps or overprints which qualify for listing are: wrong colours; one colour inverted in relation to the rest; albinos (colourless impressions), where these have Expert Committee certificates; colours completely omitted, but only on unused stamps (if found on used stamps the information is footnoted) and with good credentials, missing colours being frequently faked.

Colours only partially omitted are not recognised. Colour shifts, however spectacular, are not listed.

Shades. Shades in philately refer to variations in the intensity of a colour or the presence of differing amounts of other colours. They are particularly significant when they can be linked to specific printings. In general, shades need to be quite marked to fall within the scope of this Catalogue; it does not favour nowadays listing the often numerous shades of a stamp, but chooses a single applicable colour name which will indicate particular groups of outstanding shades. Furthermore, the listings refer to colours as issued: they may deteriorate into something different through the passage of time.

Modern colour printing by lithography is prone to marked differences of shade, even within a single run, and variations can occur within the same sheet. Such shades are not listed.

Aniline colours. An aniline colour meant originally one derived from coal-tar; it now refers more widely to colour of a particular brightness suffused on the surface of a stamp and showing through clearly on the back.

Colours of overprints and surcharges. All overprints and surcharges are in black unless stated otherwise in the heading or after the description of the stamp.

7. Specimen Stamps

Originally, stamps overprinted SPECIMEN were circulated to postmasters or kept in official records, but after the establishment of the Universal Postal Union supplies were sent to Berne for distribution to the postal administrations of member countries.

During the period 1884 to 1928 most of the stamps of British Crown Colonies required for this purpose were overprinted SPECIMEN in various shapes and sizes by their printers from typeset formes. Some locally produced provisionals were handstamped locally, as were sets prepared for presentation. From 1928 stamps were punched with holes forming the word SPECIMEN, each firm of printers using a different machine or machines. From 1948 the stamps supplied for U.P.U. distribution were no longer punctured.

Stamps of some other Commonwealth territories were overprinted or handstamped locally, while stamps of Great Britain and those overprinted for use in overseas postal agencies (mostly of the higher denominations) bore SPECIMEN overprints and handstamps applied by the Inland Revenue or the Post Office.

Some of the commoner types of overprints or punctures are illustrated here. Collectors are warned that dangerous forgeries of the punctured type exist.

The *Part 1* (*British Commonwealth*) *Catalogue* records those Specimen overprints or perforations intended for distribution by the U.P.U. to member countries. In addition the Specimen overprints of Australia and its dependent territories, which were sold to collectors by the Post Office, are also included.

Various Perkins Bacon issues exist obliterated with a "CANCELLED" within an oval of bars handstamp.

Perkins Bacon
"CANCELLED"
Handstamp

This was applied to six examples of those issues available in 1861 which were then given to members of Sir Rowland Hill's family. Seventy-five different stamps (including four from Chile) are recorded with this handstamp although others may possibly exist. The unauthorised gift of these "CANCELLED" stamps to the Hill family was a major factor in the loss of the Agent General for the Crown Colonies (the forerunner of the Crown Agents) contracts by Perkins Bacon in the following year. Where examples of these scarce items are known to be in private hands the catalogue provides a price.

For full details of these stamps see *CANCELLED by Perkins Bacon* by Peter Jaffé (published by Spink in 1998).

All other Specimens are outside the scope of this volume.

Specimens are not quoted in Great Britain as they are fully listed in the Stanley Gibbons *Great Britain Specialised Catalogue*.

In specifying type of specimen for individual high-value stamps, "H/S" means handstamped, "Optd" is overprinted and "Perf" is punctured. Some sets occur mixed, e.g. "Optd/Perf". If unspecified, the type is apparent from the date or it is the same as for the lower values quoted as a set.

Prices. Prices for stamps up to £1 are quoted in sets; higher values are priced singly after the colours, thus "(S. £20)". Where specimens exist in more than one type the price quoted is for the cheapest. Specimen stamps have rarely survived even as pairs; these and strips of three, four or five are worth considerably more than singles.

8. Luminescence

Machines which sort mail electronically have been introduced in recent years. In consequence some countries have issued stamps on fluorescent or phosphorescent papers, while others have marked their stamps with phosphor bands.

The various papers can only be distinguished by ultraviolet lamps emitting particular wavelengths. They are separately listed only when the stamps have some other means of distinguishing them, visible without the use of these lamps. Where this is not so, the papers are recorded in footnotes or headings.

For this Catalogue we do not consider it appropriate that collectors be compelled to have use of an ultraviolet lamp before being able to identify stamps by our listings. Some experience will also be found necessary in interpreting the results given by ultraviolet. Collectors using the lamps, nevertheless, should exercise great care in their use as exposure to their light is extremely dangerous to the eyes.

Phosphor bands are listable, since they are visible to the naked eye (by holding stamps at an angle to the light and looking along them, the bands appear dark). Stamps existing with and without phosphor bands or with differing numbers of bands are given separate listings. Varieties such as double bands, bands omitted, misplaced or printed on the back are not listed.

Detailed descriptions appear at appropriate places in the listings in explanation of luminescent papers; *see*, for example, Australia above No. 308, Canada above Nos. 472 and 611, Cook Is. above No. 249, etc.

For Great Britain, where since 1959 phosphors have played a prominent and intricate part in stamp issues, the main notes above Nos. 599, 723 and after the Decimal Machin issue (No. X841 onwards) should be studied, as well as the footnotes to individual listings where appropriate. In general the classification is as follows.

Stamps with *phosphor bands* are those where a separate cylinder applies the phosphor after the stamps are printed. Issues with "all-over" phosphor have the "band" covering the entire stamp. Parts of the stamp covered by phosphor bands, or the entire surface for "all-over" phosphor versions, appear matt. Stamps on *phosphorised paper* have the phosphor added to the paper coating before the stamps are printed. Issues on this paper have a completely shiny surface.

Further particularisation of phosphor—their methods of printing and the colours they exhibit under ultraviolet—is outside the scope. The more specialised listings should be consulted for this information.

9. Coil Stamps

Stamps issued only in coil form are given full listing. If stamps are issued in both sheets and coils the coil stamps are listed separately only where there is some feature (e.g. perforation or watermark sideways) by which singles can be distinguished. Coil strips containing different stamps *se-tenant* are also listed.

Coil join pairs are too random and too easily faked to permit of listing; similarly ignored are coil stamps which have accidentally suffered an extra row of perforations from the claw mechanism in a malfunctioning vending machine.

10. Stamp Booklets

Stamp booklets (with the exception of those from Great Britain, the Channel Islands and the Isle of Man, for which see the current editions of the *Great Britain Concise Catalogue* and *Collect Channel Islands and Isle of Man Stamps*) are now listed in this catalogue.

Single stamps from booklets are listed if they are distinguishable in some way (such as watermark or perforation) from similar sheet stamps.

Booklet panes are listed where they contain stamps of different denominations *se-tenant*, where stamp-size labels are included, or where such panes are otherwise identifiable. Booklet panes are placed in the listing under the lowest denomination present.

Particular perforations (straight edges) are covered by appropriate notes.

11. Miniature Sheets and Sheetlets

We distinguish between "miniature sheets" and "sheetlets" and this affects the catalogue numbering. An item in sheet form that is postally valid, containing a single stamp, pair, block or set of stamps, with wide, inscribed and/or decorative margins, is a *miniature sheet* if it is sold at post offices as an indivisible entity. As such the Catalogue allots a single **MS** number and describes what stamps make it up. (*See* Great Britain 1978 Historic Buildings, No. **MS**1058, as an example.) The *sheetlet* or *small sheet* differs in that the individual stamps are intended to be purchased separately for postal purposes. For sheetlets, all the component postage stamps are numbered individually and the composition explained in a footnote. (The 1978 Christmas Island Christmas sheetlet, Nos. 99/107, is an example.) Note that the definitions refer to post office sale—not how items may be subsequently offered by stamp dealers.

Production as sheetlets is a modern marketing development chosen by postal administrations to interest collectors in purchasing the item complete; if he has done so he should, as with all *se-tenant* arrangements, keep the sheetlet intact in his collection.

The Catalogue will in future no longer give full listing to designs, originally issued in normal sheets, which subsequently appear in sheetlets showing changes of colour, perforation, printing process or face value. Such stamps will be covered by footnotes.

12. Forgeries and Fakes

Forgeries. Where space permits, notes are considered if they can give a concise description that will permit unequivocal detection of a forgery. Generalised warnings, lacking detail, are not nowadays inserted, since their value to the collector is problematic.

Fakes. Unwitting fakes are numerous, particularly "new shades" which are colour changelings brought about by exposure to sunlight, soaking in water contaminated with dyes from adherent paper, contact with oil and dirt from a pocketbook, and so on. Fraudulent operators, in addition, can offer to arrange: removal of hinge marks; repairs of thins on white or coloured papers; replacement of missing margins or perforations; reperforating in true or false gauges; removal of fiscal cancellations; rejoining of severed pairs, strips and blocks; and (a major hazard) regumming. Collectors can only be urged to purchase from reputable sources and to insist upon Expert Committee certification where there is any kind of doubt.

The Catalogue can consider footnotes about fakes where these are specific enough to assist in detection.

1935 SILVER JUBILEE CROWN COLONY ISSUE

The Crown Colony Windsor Castle design by Harold Fleury is, surely, one of the most impressive produced in the 20th-century and its reproduction in the recess process by three of the leading stamp-printing firms of the era has provided a subject for philatelic research which has yet to be exhausted.

Each of the three, Bradbury, Wilkinson & Co. and Waterlow and Sons, who both produced fifteen issues, together with De La Rue & Co. who printed fourteen, used a series of vignette (centre) plates coupled with individual frame plates for each value. All were taken from dies made by Waterlow. Several worthwhile varieties exist on the frame plates, but most interest has been concentrated on the centre plates, each of which was used to print a considerable number of different stamps.

Sheets printed by Bradbury, Wilkinson were without printed plate numbers, but research has now identified eleven centre plates which were probably used in permanent pairings. A twelfth plate awaits confirmation. Stamps from some of these centre plates have revealed a number of prominent plate flaws, the most famous of which, the extra flagstaff, has been eagerly sought by collectors for many years.

Extra flagstaff (Plate 1" R. 9/1)   Short extra flagstaff (Plate "2" R. 2/1)

Lightning conductor (Plate "3" R. 2/5)   Flagstaff on right-hand turret (Plate "5" R. 7/1)

Double flagstaff (Plate "6" R. 5/2)

De La Rue sheets were initially printed with plate numbers, but in many instances these were subsequently trimmed off. Surviving examples do, however, enable a positive identification of six centre plates, 2A, 2B, (2A), (2B), 4 and 4/ to be made. The evidence of sheet markings and plate flaws clearly demonstrates that there were two different pairs of plates numbered 2A 2B. The second pair is designated (2A) (2B) by specialist collectors to avoid further confusion. The number of major plate flaws is not so great as on the Bradbury, Wilkinson sheets, but four examples are included in the catalogue.

Diagonal line by turret
(Plate 2A R. 10/1 and
10/2)

Dot to left of chapel
(Plate 2B R. 8/3)

Dot by flagstaff (Plate 4
R. 8/4)

Dash by turret (Plate 4/
R. 3/6)

Much less is known concerning the Waterlow centre plate system as the sheets did not show plate numbers. Ten individual plates have, so far, been identified and it is believed that these were used in pairs. The two versions of the kite and log flaw from plate "2" show that this plate exists in two states.

Damaged turret
(Plate "1" R. 5/6)

Kite and vertical log
(Plate "2A" R. 10/6)

Kite and horizontal log
(Plate "2B" R. 10/6)

Bird by turret
(Plate "7" R. 1/5)

Abbreviations

Printers

A.B.N. Co	American Bank Note Co, New York.
A. & M.	Alden & Mowbray Ltd, Oxford.
Ashton-Potter	Ashton-Potter Ltd, Toronto.
Aspioti-Elka (Aspiotis)	Aspioti-Elka, Greece.
B.A.B.N.	British American Bank Note Co, Ottawa.
B.D.T.	B.D.T. International Security Printing Ltd, Dublin, Ireland.
B.W.	Bradbury Wilkinson & Co, Ltd.
Cartor	Cartor S.A., La Loupe, France.
C.B.N.	Canadian Bank Note Co, Ottawa.
Continental B.N. Co	Continental Bank Note Co.
Courvoisier	Imprimerie Courvoisier S.A., La-Chaux-de-Fonds, Switzerland.
D.L.R.	De La Rue & Co, Ltd, London, and (from 1961) Bogota, Colombia.
Edila	Editions de l'Aubetin, S.A.
Enschedé	Joh. Enschedé en Zonen, Haarlem, Netherlands.
Format	Format International Security Printers, Ltd, London.
Harrison	Harrison & Sons, Ltd, London
Heraclio Fournier	Heraclio Fournier S.A., Vitoria, Spain.
J.W.	John Waddington Security Print Ltd., Leeds
P.B.	Perkins Bacon Ltd, London.
Questa	Questa Colour Security Printers, Ltd., London
Ueberreuter	Ueberreuter (incorporating Bruder Rosenbaum), Korneuburg, Austria.
Walsall	Walsall Security Printers, Ltd.
Waterlow	Waterlow & Sons, Ltd, London.

General Abbreviations

Alph	Alphabet
Anniv	Anniversary
Comp	Compound (perforation)
Des	Designer; designed
Diag	Diagonal; diagonally
Eng	Engraver; engraved
F.C.	Fiscal Cancellation
H/S	Handstamped
Horiz	Horizontal; horizontally
Imp, Imperf	Imperforate
Inscr	Inscribed
L	Left
Litho	Lithographed
mm	Millimetres
MS	Miniature sheet
N.Y.	New York
Opt(d)	Overprint(ed)
P or P-c	Pen-cancelled
P, Pf or Perf	Perforated
Photo	Photogravure
Pl	Plate
Pr	Pair
Ptd	Printed
Ptg	Printing
R	Right
R.	Row
Recess	Recess-printed
Roto	Rotogravure
Roul	Rouletted

S	Specimen (overprint)
Surch	Surcharge(d)
T.C.	Telegraph Cancellation
T	Type
Typo	Typographed
Un	Unused
Us	Used
Vert	Vertical; vertically
W or wmk	Watermark
Wmk s	Watermark sideways

(†)=Does not exist.

(—) (or blank price column)=Exists, or may exist, but no market price is known.

/ between colours means "on" and the colour following is that of the paper on which the stamp is printed.

Colours of Stamps

Bl (blue); blk (black); brn (brown); car, carm (carmine); choc (chocolate); clar (claret); emer (emerald); grn (green); ind (indigo); mag (magenta); mar (maroon); mult (multicoloured); mve (mauve); ol (olive); orge (orange); pk (pink); pur (purple); scar (scarlet); sep (sepia); turq (turquoise); ultram (ultramarine); verm (vermilion); vio (violet); yell (yellow).

Colour of Overprints and Surcharges

(B.) = blue, (Blk.) = black, (Br.) = brown, (C.) = carmine, (G.) = green, (Mag.) = magenta, (Mve.) = mauve, (Ol.) = olive, (O.) = orange, (P.) = purple, (Pk.) = pink, (R.)=red, (Sil.) = silver, (V.) = violet, (Vm.) or (Verm.) = vermilion, (W.) = white, (Y.) = yellow.

Arabic Numerals

As in the case of European figures, the details of the Arabic numerals vary in different stamp designs, but they should be readily recognised with the aid of this illustration.

0	1	2	3	4	5	6	7	8	9

International Philatelic Glossary

English	French	German	Spanish	Italian
Agate	Agate	Achat	Agata	Agata
Air stamp	Timbre de la poste aérienne	Flugpostmarke	Sello de correo aéreo	Francobollo per posta aerea
Apple Green	Vert-pomme	Apfelgrün	Verde manzana	Verde mela
Barred	Annulé par barres	Balkenentwertung	Anulado con barras	Sbarrato
Bisected	Timbre coupé	Halbiert	Partido en dos	Frazionato
Bistre	Bistre	Bister	Bistre	Bistro
Bistre-brown	Brun-bistre	Bisterbraun	Castaño bistre	Bruno-bistro
Black	Noir	Schwarz	Negro	Nero
Blackish Brown	Brun-noir	Schwärzlichbraun	Castaño negruzco	Bruno nerastro
Blackish Green	Vert foncé	Schwärzlichgrün	Verde negruzco	Verde nerastro
Blackish Olive	Olive foncé	Schwärzlicholiv	Oliva negruzco	Oliva nerastro
Block of four	Bloc de quatre	Viererblock	Bloque de cuatro	Bloco di quattro
Blue	Bleu	Blau	Azul	Azzurro
Blue-green	Vert-bleu	Blaugrün	Verde azul	Verde azzurro
Bluish Violet	Violet bleuâtre	Bläulichviolett	Violeta azulado	Violetto azzurrastro
Booklet	Carnet	Heft	Cuadernillo	Libretto
Bright Blue	Bleu vif	Lebhaftblau	Azul vivo	Azzurro vivo
Bright Green	Vert vif	Lebhaftgrün	Verde vivo	Verde vivo
Bright Purple	Mauve vif	Lebhaftpurpur	Púrpura vivo	Porpora vivo
Bronze Green	Vert-bronze	Bronzegrün	Verde bronce	Verde bronzo
Brown	Brun	Braun	Castaño	Bruno
Brown-lake	Carmin-brun	Braunlack	Laca castaño	Lacca bruno
Brown-purple	Pourpre-brun	Braunpurpur	Púrpura castaño	Porpora bruno
Brown-red	Rouge-brun	Braunrot	Rojo castaño	Rosso bruno
Buff	Chamois	Sämisch	Anteado	Camoscio
Cancellation	Oblitération	Entwertung	Cancelación	Annullamento
Cancelled	Annulé	Gestempelt	Cancelado	Annullato
Carmine	Carmin	Karmin	Carmín	Carminio
Carmine-red	Rouge-carmin	Karminrot	Rojo carmín	Rosso carminio
Centred	Centré	Zentriert	Centrado	Centrato
Cerise	Rouge-cerise	Kirschrot	Color de ceresa	Color Ciliegia
Chalk-surfaced paper	Papier couché	Kreidepapier	Papel estucado	Carta gessata
Chalky Blue	Bleu terne	Kreideblau	Azul turbio	Azzurro smorto
Charity stamp	Timbre de bienfaisance	Wohltätigkeitsmarke	Sello de beneficenza	Francobollo di beneficenza
Chestnut	Marron	Kastanienbraun	Castaño rojo	Marrone
Chocolate	Chocolat	Schokolade	Chocolate	Cioccolato
Cinnamon	Cannelle	Zimtbraun	Canela	Cannella
Claret	Grenat	Weinrot	Rojo vinoso	Vinaccia
Cobalt	Cobalt	Kobalt	Cobalto	Cobalto
Colour	Couleur	Farbe	Color	Colore
Comb-perforation	Dentelure en peigne	Kammzähnung, Reihenzähnung	Dentado de peine	Dentellatura e pettine
Commemorative stamp	Timbre commémoratif	Gedenkmarke	Sello conmemorativo	Francobollo commemorativo
Crimson	Cramoisi	Karmesin	Carmesí	Cremisi
Deep Blue	Bleu foncé	Dunkelblau	Azul oscuro	Azzurro scuro
Deep Bluish Green	Vert-bleu foncé	Dunkelbläulichgrün	Verde azulado oscuro	Verde azzurro scuro
Design	Dessin	Markenbild	Diseño	Disegno
Die	Matrice	Urstempel, Type, Platte	Cuño	Conio, Matrice
Double	Double	Doppelt	Doble	Doppio
Drab	Olive terne	Trüboliv	Oliva turbio	Oliva smorto
Dull Green	Vert terne	Trübgrün	Verde turbio	Verde smorto
Dull Purple	Mauve terne	Trübpurpur	Púrpura turbio	Porpora smorto
Embossing	Impression en relief	Prägedruck	Impresión en relieve	Impressione a relievo
Emerald	Vert-eméraude	Smaragdgrün	Esmeralda	Smeraldo
Engraved	Gravé	Graviert	Grabado	Inciso
Error	Erreur	Fehler, Fehldruck	Error	Errore
Essay	Essai	Probedruck	Ensayo	Saggio
Express letter stamp	Timbre pour lettres par exprès	Eilmarke	Sello de urgencia	Francobollo per espresso
Fiscal stamp	Timbre fiscal	Stempelmarke	Sello fiscal	Francobollo fiscale
Flesh	Chair	Fleischfarben	Carne	Carnicino
Forgery	Faux, Falsification	Fälschung	Falsificación	Falso, Falsificazione
Frame	Cadre	Rahmen	Marco	Cornice
Granite paper	Papier avec fragments de fils de soie	Faserpapier	Papel con filamentos	Carto con fili di seta
Green	Vert	Grün	Verde	Verde
Greenish Blue	Bleu verdâtre	Grünlichblau	Azul verdoso	Azzurro verdastro

English	French	German	Spanish	Italian
Greenish Yellow	Jaune-vert	Grünlichgelb	Amarillo verdoso	Giallo verdastro
Grey	Gris	Grau	Gris	Grigio
Grey-blue	Bleu-gris	Graublau	Azul gris	Azzurro grigio
Grey-green	Vert gris	Graugrün	Verde gris	Verde grigio
Gum	Gomme	Gummi	Goma	Gomma
Gutter	Interpanneau	Zwischensteg	Espacio blanco entre dos grupos	Ponte
Imperforate	Non-dentelé	Geschnitten	Sin dentar	Non dentellato
Indigo	Indigo	Indigo	Azul indigo	Indaco
Inscription	Inscription	Inschrift	Inscripción	Dicitura
Inverted	Renversé	Kopfstehend	Invertido	Capovolto
Issue	Émission	Ausgabe	Emisión	Emissione
Laid	Vergé	Gestreift	Listado	Vergato
Lake	Lie de vin	Lackfarbe	Laca	Lacca
Lake-brown	Brun-carmin	Lackbraun	Castaño laca	Bruno lacca
Lavender	Bleu-lavande	Lavendel	Color de alhucema	Lavanda
Lemon	Jaune-citron	Zitrongelb	Limón	Limone
Light Blue	Bleu clair	Hellblau	Azul claro	Azzurro chiaro
Lilac	Lilas	Lila	Lila	Lilla
Line perforation	Dentelure en lignes	Linienzähnung	Dentado en linea	Dentellatura lineare
Lithography	Lithographie	Steindruck	Litografía	Litografia
Local	Timbre de poste locale	Lokalpostmarke	Emisión local	Emissione locale
Lozenge roulette	Percé en losanges	Rautenförmiger Durchstich	Picadura en rombos	Perforazione a losanghe
Magenta	Magenta	Magentarot	Magenta	Magenta
Margin	Marge	Rand	Borde	Margine
Maroon	Marron pourpré	Dunkelrotpurpur	Púrpura rojo oscuro	Marrone rossastro
Mauve	Mauve	Malvenfarbe	Malva	Malva
Multicoloured	Polychrome	Mehrfarbig	Multicolores	Policromo
Myrtle Green	Vert myrte	Myrtengrün	Verde mirto	Verde mirto
New Blue	Bleu ciel vif	Neublau	Azul nuevo	Azzurro nuovo
Newspaper stamp	Timbre pour journaux	Zeitungsmarke	Sello para periódicos	Francobollo per giornali
Obliteration	Oblitération	Abstempelung	Matasello	Annullamento
Obsolete	Hors (de) cours	Ausser Kurs	Fuera de curso	Fuori corso
Ochre	Ocre	Ocker	Ocre	Ocra
Official stamp	Timbre de service	Dienstmarke	Sello de servicio	Francobollo di servizio
Olive-brown	Brun-olive	Olivbraun	Castaño oliva	Bruno oliva
Olive-green	Vert-olive	Olivgrün	Verde oliva	Verde oliva
Olive-grey	Gris-olive	Olivgrau	Gris oliva	Grigio oliva
Olive-yellow	Jaune-olive	Olivgelb	Amarillo oliva	Giallo oliva
Orange	Orange	Orange	Naranja	Arancio
Orange-brown	Brun-orange	Orangebraun	Castaño naranja	Bruno arancio
Orange-red	Rouge-orange	Orangerot	Rojo naranja	Rosso arancio
Orange-yellow	Jaune-orange	Orangegelb	Amarillo naranja	Giallo arancio
Overprint	Surcharge	Aufdruck	Sobrecarga	Soprastampa
Pair	Paire	Paar	Pareja	Coppia
Pale	Pâle	Blass	Pálido	Pallido
Pane	Panneau	Gruppe	Grupo	Gruppo
Paper	Papier	Papier	Papel	Carta
Parcel post stamp	Timbre pour colis postaux	Paketmarke	Sello para paquete postal	Francobollo per pacchi postali
Pen-cancelled	Oblitéré à plume	Federzugentwertung	Cancelado a pluma	Annullato a penna
Percé en arc	Percé en arc	Bogenförmiger Durchstich	Picadura en forma de arco	Perforazione ad arco
Percé en scie	Percé en scie	Bogenförmiger Durchstich	Picado en sierra	Foratura a sega
Perforated	Dentelé	Gezähnt	Dentado	Dentellato
Perforation	Dentelure	Zähnung	Dentar	Dentellatura
Photogravure	Photogravure, Heliogravure	Rastertiefdruck	Fotograbado	Rotocalco
Pin perforation	Percé en points	In Punkten durchstochen	Horadado con alfileres	Perforato a punti
Plate	Planche	Platte	Plancha	Lastra, Tavola
Plum	Prune	Pflaumenfarbe	Color de ciruela	Prugna
Postage Due stamp	Timbre-taxe	Portomarke	Sello de tasa	Segnatasse
Postage stamp	Timbre-poste	Briefmarke, Frei-marke, Postmarke	Sello de correos	Francobollo postale
Postal fiscal stamp	Timbre fiscal-postal	Stempelmarke als Postmarke verwendet	Sello fiscal-postal	Fiscale postale
Postmark	Oblitération postale	Poststempel	Matasello	Bollo
Printing	Impression, Tirage	Druck	Impresión	Stampa, Tiratura
Proof	Épreuve	Druckprobe	Prueba de impresión	Prova
Provisionals	Timbres provisoires	Provisorische Mark-en, Provisorien	Provisionales	Provvisori

English	*French*	*German*	*Spanish*	*Italian*
Prussian Blue	Bleu de Prusse	Preussischblau	Azul de Prusia	Azzurro di Prussia
Purple	Pourpre	Purpur	Púrpura	Porpora
Purple-brown	Brun-pourpre	Purpurbraun	Castaño púrpura	Bruno porpora
Recess-printing	Impression en taille douce	Tiefdruck	Grabado	Incisione
Red	Rouge	Rot	Rojo	Rosso
Red-brown	Brun-rouge	Rotbraun	Castaño rojizo	Bruno rosso
Reddish Lilac	Lilas rougeâtre	Rötlichlila	Lila rojizo	Lilla rossastro
Reddish Purple	Pourpre-rouge	Rötlichpurpur	Púrpura rojizo	Porpora rossastro
Reddish Violet	Violet rougeâtre	Rötlichviolett	Violeta rojizo	Violetto rossastro
Red-orange	Orange rougeâtre	Rotorange	Naranja rojizo	Arancio rosso
Registration stamp	Timbre pour lettre chargée (recommandée)	Einschreibemarke	Sello de certificado	Francobollo per lettere raccomandate
Reprint	Réimpression	Neudruck	Reimpresión	Ristampa
Reversed	Retourné	Umgekehrt	Invertido	Rovesciato
Rose	Rose	Rosa	Rosa	Rosa
Rose-red	Rouge rosé	Rosarot	Rojo rosado	Rosso rosa
Rosine	Rose vif	Lebhaftrosa	Rosa vivo	Rosa vivo
Roulette	Percage	Durchstich	Picadura	Foratura
Rouletted	Percé	Durchstochen	Picado	Forato
Royal Blue	Bleu-roi	Königblau	Azul real	Azzurro reale
Sage Green	Vert-sauge	Salbeigrün	Verde salvia	Verde salvia
Salmon	Saumon	Lachs	Salmón	Salmone
Scarlet	Écarlate	Scharlach	Escarlata	Scarlatto
Sepia	Sépia	Sepia	Sepia	Seppia
Serpentine roulette	Percé en serpentin	Schlangenliniger Durchstich	Picado a serpentina	Perforazione a serpentina
Shade	Nuance	Tönung	Tono	Gradazione de colore
Sheet	Feuille	Bogen	Hoja	Foglio
Slate	Ardoise	Schiefer	Pizarra	Ardesia
Slate-blue	Bleu-ardoise	Schieferblau	Azul pizarra	Azzurro ardesia
Slate-green	Vert-ardoise	Schiefergrün	Verde pizarra	Verde ardesia
Slate-lilac	Lilas-gris	Schieferlila	Lila pizarra	Lilla ardesia
Slate-purple	Mauve-gris	Schieferpurpur	Púrpura pizarra	Porpora ardesia
Slate-violet	Violet-gris	Schieferviolett	Violeta pizarra	Violetto ardesia
Special delivery stamp	Timbre pour exprès	Eilmarke	Sello de urgencia	Francobollo per espressi
Specimen	Spécimen	Muster	Muestra	Saggio
Steel Blue	Bleu acier	Stahlblau	Azul acero	Azzurro acciaio
Strip	Bande	Streifen	Tira	Striscia
Surcharge	Surcharge	Aufdruck	Sobrecarga	Soprastampa
Tête-bêche	Tête-bêche	Kehrdruck	Tête-bêche	Tête-bêche
Tinted paper	Papier teinté	Getöntes Papier	Papel coloreado	Carta tinta
Too-late stamp	Timbre pour lettres en retard	Verspätungsmarke	Sello para cartas retardadas	Francobollo per le lettere in ritardo
Turquoise-blue	Bleu-turquoise	Türkisblau	Azul turquesa	Azzurro turchese
Turquoise-green	Vert-turquoise	Türkisgrün	Verde turquesa	Verde turchese
Typography	Typographie	Buchdruck	Tipografia	Tipografia
Ultramarine	Outremer	Ultramarin	Ultramar	Oltremare
Unused	Neuf	Ungebraucht	Nuevo	Nuovo
Used	Oblitéré, Usé	Gebraucht	Usado	Usato
Venetian Red	Rouge-brun terne	Venezianischrot	Rojo veneciano	Rosso veneziano
Vermilion	Vermillon	Zinnober	Cinabrio	Vermiglione
Violet	Violet	Violett	Violeta	Violetto
Violet-blue	Bleu-violet	Violettblau	Azul violeta	Azzurro violetto
Watermark	Filigrane	Wasserzeichen	Filigrana	Filigrana
Watermark sideways	Filigrane couché	Wasserzeichen liegend	Filigrana acostado	Filigrana coricata
Wove paper	Papier ordinaire, Papier uni	Einfaches Papier	Papel avitelado	Carta unita
Yellow	Jaune	Gelb	Amarillo	Giallo
Yellow-brown	Brun-jaune	Gelbbraun	Castaño amarillo	Bruno giallo
Yellow-green	Vert-jaune	Gelbgrün	Verde amarillo	Verde giallo
Yellow-olive	Olive jaunâtre	Gelboliv	Oliva amarillo	Oliva giallastro
Yellow-orange	Orange jaunâtre	Gelborange	Naranja amarillo	Arancio giallastro
Zig-zag roulette	Percé en zigzag	Sägezahnartiger Durchstich	Picado en zigzag	Perforazione a zigzag

Specialist Philatelic Societies

Requests for inclusion on this page should be sent to the Catalogue Editor.

British Decimal Stamps Study Circle
Secretary—Mr. S. van Kimmenade
32 Beaufort Heights, Beaufort Road,
St. George, Bristol BS5 8JX

Great Britain Philatelic Society
Membership Secretary—Mr. A. G. Lajer
The Old Post Office, Hurst,
Berks RG10 0TR

Great Britain Decimal Stamp Book Study Circle
Membership Secretary—Mr. R. Osborne,
7 Overlord Close, Broxbourne, Herts
EN10 7TG

Great Britain Collectors' Club
Secretary/Treasurer: Ms Janet Gordon,
P.O. Box 42324, Cincinnati, Ohio
45242-0324, U.S.A.

Channel Islands Specialists Society
Membership Secretary—Mr. T. Watkins
Holmcroft, Lewes Road, Ringmer, Lewes,
East Sussex, BN8 5ES

Ascension Study Circle
Secretary—Dr. R. C. F. Baker
Greys, Tower Road, Whitstable, Kent
CT5 2ER

Australian States Study Circle
Royal Sydney Philatelic Club
Honorary Secretary—Mr. B. Palmer
G.P.O. Box 1751, Sydney, N.S.W. 1043,
Australia

British Society of Australian Philately
Secretary—Mr. A. J. Griffiths
c/o The British Philatelic Centre,
107 Charterhouse Street,
London EC1M 6PT

Society of Australasian Specialists/Oceania
Secretary—Mr. S. Leven
P.O. Box 24764, San Jose, CA 95154-4764,
U.S.A.

Bechuanalands and Botswana Society
Membership Secretary—Mr. J. Catterall
Trevessa, Upper Castle Road, St. Mawes,
Truro, Cornwall TR2 5BZ

Bermuda Collectors Society
Secretary—Mr. T. J. McMahon
P.O. Box 1949, Stuart, FL 34995, U.S.A.

British Caribbean Philatelic Study Group
Overseas Director—Mr. D. N. Druett
Pennymead Auctions, 1 Brewerton Street,
Knaresborough, North Yorkshire HG5 8AZ

British West Indies Study Circle
Membership Secretary—Mr. S. A. Sharp
34 Lovelace Drive, Pyrford, Woking, Surrey
GU22 8QY

Burma Philatelic Study Circle
Secretary—Mr. A. Meech
7208-91 Avenue, Edmonton, Alberta,
Canada T6B 0R8

Ceylon Study Circle
Secretary—Mr. R.W.P. Frost
42 Lonsdale Road, Cannington, Bridgwater,
Somerset TA5 2JS

Cyprus Study Circle
Membership Secretary— Mr. J. Wigmore,
19 Riversmeet, Appledore, Bideford,
North Devon EX39 1RE

East Africa Study Circle
Hon. Secretary—Mr. K. Hewitt
16 Ashleigh Road,
Solihull, B91 1AE

Falklands Islands Study Group
Membership Secretary—Mr. D. W. A. Jeffery
38 Bradstock Road, Stoneleigh, Epsom,
Surrey KT17 2LH

Hong Kong Study Circle
Membership Secretary—Mr. P. V. Ball
37 Hart Court, Newcastle-under-Lyme,
Staffordshire ST5 2AL

Indian Ocean Study Circle
Secretary—Mr. K. B. Fitton
50 Firlands, Weybridge, Surrey KT13 0HR

India Study Circle
Secretary—Dr. W. Fincham
10 Vallis Way, London W13 0DD

Irish Philatelic Circle
General Secretary—Mr. F. McDonald
63 Rafters Road
Drimnagh, Dublin 12, Ireland

King George V Silver Jubilee Study Circle
Secretary—Mr. N. Levinge
80 Towcester Road, Northampton
NN4 8LQ

King George VI Collectors Society
Secretary—Mr. F. R. Lockyer, OBE
98 Albany, Manor Road, Bournemouth,
Dorset BH1 3EW

Kiribati and Tuvalu Philatelic Society
Honorary Secretary—Mr. M. J. Shaw
88 Stoneleigh Avenue, Worcester Park,
Surrey KT4 8XY

Malaya Study Group
Secretary—Mr. J. Robertson
12 Lisa Court, Downsland Road,
Basingstoke, Hampshire RG21 8TU

Malta Study Circle
Hon Secretary—Mr. D. Crookes
9a Church Street
Durham DH1 3DG

New Zealand Society of Great Britain
General Secretary—Mr. K. C. Collins
13 Briton Crescent, Sanderstead,
Surrey CR2 0JN.

Orange Free State Study Circle
Secretary—Mr. J. R. Stroud
28 Oxford Street, Burnham-on-Sea,
Somerset TA8 1LQ

Pacific Islands Study Circle
Honorary Secretary—Mr. J. D. Ray
24 Woodvale Avenue, London SE25 4AE

Papuan Philatelic Society
Secretary—Mr. F. J. Prophet
5 Morcom Close, Menear Road, Boscoppa,
St. Austell, Cornwall PL25 3UF

Pitcairn Islands Study Group (U.K.)
Honorary Secretary—Mr. D. Sleep
6 Palace Gardens, 100 Court Road, Eltham,
London SE9 5NS

Rhodesian Study Circle
Secretary—Mr. R. G. Barnett
2 Cox Ley, Hatfield Heath,
Bishop's Stortford, Herts CM22 7ER

St. Helena, Ascension and Tristan da Cunha Philatelic Society
Secretary—Mr. J. Havill
205 N. Murray Blvd., #221, Colorado
Springs, CO 80916, U.S.A.

Sarawak Specialists Society (also Brunei, North Borneo and Labuan)
Secretary—Dr. J. Higgins
31 Grimston Road, South Wootton,
Kings Lynn, Norfolk PE30 3NR

South African Collectors' Society
General Secretary—Mr. R. Ross
28 Duddon Drive, Barrow-in-Furness,
Cumbria LA14 3TW

Philatelic Society of Sri Lanka
Secretary—Mr. H. Goonawardena
44A Hena Road, Mt. Lavinia 10370,
Sri Lanka.

Sudan Study Group
Secretary—Mr. N. D. Collier
34 Padleys Lane, Burton Joyce,
Nottingham NG14 5BZ

Transvaal Study Circle
Secretary—Mr. J. Woolgar
132 Dale Street, Chatham, Kent ME4 6QH

West Africa Study Circle
Secretary—Mr. J. Powell
23 Brook Street, Edlesborough, Dunstable,
Bedfordshire LU6 2JG

Select Bibliography

The literature on British Commonwealth stamps is vast, but works are often difficult to obtain once they are out of print. The selection of books below has been made on the basis of authority together with availability to the general reader, either as new or secondhand. Very specialised studies, and those covering aspects of postal history to which there are no references in the catalogue, have been excluded.

The following abbreviations are used to denote publishers:
CRL–Christie's Robson Lowe; HH–Harry Hayes; PB–Proud Bailey Co. Ltd. and Postal History Publications Co.; PC–Philip Cockrill; RSPL–Royal Philatelic Society, London; SG–Stanley Gibbons Ltd.

Where no publisher is quoted, the book is published by its author.

GENERAL. *Encyclopaedia of British Empire Postage Stamps. Vols 1–6.* Edited Robson Lowe. (CRL, 1951–1991)
Specimen Stamps of the Crown Colonies 1857–1948. Marcus Samuel. (RPSL, 1976 and 1984 Supplement)
Cancelled by Perkins Bacon. P Jaffé. (Spink & Son Ltd, 1998)
U.P.U. Specimen Stamps. J. Bendon. (1988)
King George V Key Plates of the Imperium Postage and Revenue Design. P. Fernbank. (West Africa Study Circle, 1997)
The Commemorative Stamps of the British Commonwealth. H.D.S. Haverbeck. (Faber, 1955)
Silver Jubilee of King George V Stamps Handbook. A.J. Ainscough. (Ainweel Developments, 1985)
The Printings of King George VI Colonial Stamps. W.J.W. Potter & Lt-Col R.C.M. Shelton. (1952 and later facsimile edition)
King George VI Large Key Type Stamps of Bermuda, Leeward Islands, Nyasaland. R.W. Dickgiesser and E.P. Yendall. (Triad Publications, 1985)
Madame Joseph Forged Postmarks. D. Worboys (RPSL, 1994)
G.B. Used Abroad: Cancellations and Postal Markings. J. Parmenter. (The Postal History Society, 1993)
BRITISH OCCUPATION OF GERMAN COLONIES. *G.R.I.* R.M. Gibbs. (CRL, 1989)
BRITISH POSTAL AGENCIES IN EASTERN ARABIA. *The Postal Agencies in Eastern Arabia and the Gulf.* N. Donaldson. (HH, 1975) and Supplement (Bridger & Kay Guernsey Ltd, 1994)
BRITISH WEST AFRICA. *The Postal History and Handstamps of British West Africa.* C. McCaig. (CRL, 1978)
JAMAICA. *Encyclopaedia of Jamaican Philately. Vol 1.* D Sutcliffe & S. Jarvis. (B.W.I. Study Circle, 1997)

KENYA. *British East Africa. The Stamps and Postal Stationery.* J. Minns. (RPSL, 1982 and 1990 Supplement)
The Postal History of Kenya. E.B. Proud (PB, 1992)
KIRIBATI. *Kiribati Handbook.* Edited H. Bennet. (Kiribati and Tuvalu Phil Soc., 1997)
LEEWARD ISLANDS. *The Leeward Islands— Notes for Philatelists.* M.N. Oliver (B.W.I. Study Circle, 2000)
LESOTHO. *The Cancellations and Postal Markings of Basutoland/Lesotho Post Offices.* A.H. Scott. (Collectors Mail Auctions (Pty) Ltd, 1980)
MALAWI. *The Postal History of Nyasaland.* E.B. Proud. PB, 1997)
MALAYSIA. *The Postal History of British Malaya. Vols 1–3.* E.B. Proud. (PB, 1982–84)
The Postage Stamps of Federated Malay States. W.A. Reeves. (Malaya Study Group, 1978)
Kedah and Perlis. D.R.M. Holley. (Malaya Study Group, 1995)
Kelantan. Its Stamps and Postal History. W.A. Reeves and B.E. Dexter. (Malaya Study Group, 1992)
The Postal History of the Occupation of Malaya and British Borneo 1941–1945. E.B. Proud and M.D. Rowell. (PB, 1992)
A Concise Guide to the Queen Issues of Labuan. R. Price. (Sarawak Specialists Society, 1991)
The Stamps and Postal History of North Borneo. Parts 1–3. L.H. Shipman and P.K. Cassells. (Sarawak Specialists Society, 1976–88)
The Stamps and Postal History of Sarawak. W.A. Forrester-Wood. (Sarawak Specialists Society, 1959 and 1970 Supplement)
Sarawak: The Issues of 1871 and 1875. W. Batty-Smith and W. Watterson
MALTA. *Malta. The Postal History and Postage Stamps.* Edited R.E. Martin. (CRL, 1980 and 1985 Supplement)
MAURITIUS. *The Postal History and Stamps of Mauritius.* P. Ibbotson (RPSL, 1991) revisions and additions Supplement (Indian Ocean Study Circle, 1995)
MONTSERRAT. *Montserrat to 1965.* L.E. Britnor (B.W.I. Study Circle, 2nd edition, 1998)
MOROCCO AGENCIES. *British Post Offices and Agencies in Morocco 1857–1907 and Local Posts 1891–1914.* R.K. Clough. (Gibraltar Study Circle, 1984)
NAMIBIA. *The Overprinted Stamps of South West Africa to 1930.* N. Becker. (Philatelic Holdings (Pty) Ltd, 1990)
NEW ZEALAND. *The Postage Stamps of New Zealand. Vols 1–VII.* (Royal Philatelic Society of New Zealand, 1939–98)
The Postal History and Postage Stamps of the Tokelau/Union Islands. A.H. Burgess. (Pacific Islands Study Circle, 2nd edition, 1998)
NIGERIA. *The Stamps and Postal History of the Niger Territories and the Niger Coast Protectorate.* M.P. Nicholson. (PC, 1982)
The Local Bisects and Surcharges of the Oil Rivers and Niger Coast 1893–94. M.P. Nicholson. (PC, 1982)

The Stamps and Postal History of Southern Nigeria. M.P. Nicholson. (PC, 1982)
The Postal Services of the British Nigeria Region. J. Ince and J. Sacher. (RPSL, 1992)
The Postal History of Nigeria. E.B. Proud. (PB, 1995)
PAPUA NEW GUINEA. *The Postal History of British New Guinea and Papua 1885–1942.* R. Lee. (CRL, 1983)
PITCAIRN ISLANDS. *Pitcairn Islands Philately.* D.E. Hume. (2nd edition, 1999)
RHODESIA. *Mashonaland. A Postal History 1890–96.* Dr. A. R. Drysdall and D. Collis (CRL, 1990)
Rhodesia. A Postal History. R.C. Smith. (1967 and 1970 Supplement)
ST. HELENA. *St. Helena, Postal History and Stamps.* E. Hibbert. (CRL, 1979)
ST. KITTS-NEVIS. *A Study of the King George VI Stamps of St. Kitts-Nevis.* P.L. Baldwin. (Murray Payne Ltd. 2nd edition 1997)
SAMOA. *A Postal HIstory of the Samoan Islands (Parts I and II).* Edited R. Burge. (Royal Philatelic Society of New Zealand, 1987–89)
SIERRA LEONE. *The Postal Service of Sierra Leone.* P.O. Beale. (RPSL, 1988)
The Postal History of Sierra Leone. E.B. Proud. (PB, 1994)
SOLOMON ISLANDS. *British Solomon Islands Protectorate. Its Postage Stamps and Postal History.* H.G.D. Gisburn. (T. Sanders (Philatelist) Ltd., 1956)
SOUTH ARABIA. *The Postal History of British Aden 1839–67.* Major R.W. Pratt. (PB, 1985)
SOUTH AFRICA. *Postmarks of the Cape of Good Hope.* R. Goldblatt. (Reijger Publishers (Pty) Ltd., 1984)
Stamps of the Orange Free State. Parts 1–3. G.D. Buckley & W.B. Marriott. (O.F.S. Study Circle, 1967–80)
Transvaal Philately. Edited I.B. Mathews. (Reijger Publishers (Pty) Ltd, 1986)
Transvaal. The Provisional Issues of the First British Occupation. Dr. A.R. Drysdall. (James Bendon, 1994)
SUDAN. *Sudan. The Stamps and Postal Stationery of 1867 to 1970.* E.C.W. Stagg. (HH, 1977)
TANZANIA. *The Postal History of Tanganyika. 1915-1961.* E.B. Proud. (PB, 1989)
TOGO. *Togo–The Postal History of the Anglo-French Occupation 1914-22.* J. Martin and F. Walton. (West Africa S.C., 1995)
TRANSJORDAN. *The Stamps of Jordan 1920–1965.* A.H. Najjar. (Sahara Publications Ltd, 1998)
TRINIDAD AND TOBAGO. *The Postal History of Trinidad and Tobago.* J.C. Aleong and E.B. Proud. (PB, 1997)
TRISTAN DA CUNHA. *The History and Postal History of Tristan da Cunha.* G. Crabb. (1980)
TURKS AND CAICOS ISLANDS. *Turks Islands and Caicos Islands to 1950.* J.J. Challis. (Roses Caribbean Philatelic Society, 1983)
TUVALU. *Tuvalu. A Philatelic Handbook.* M. Forand. (Tuvalu Philatelic Society, 1982)
UGANDA. *The Postal History of Uganda and Zanzibar.* E.B. Proud (PB, 1993)

Jamaica

Records show that the first local Postmaster for Jamaica on a regular basis was appointed as early as 1671, although a reasonably organised service did not evolve until 1687–8. In the early years of the 18th century overseas mail was carried by the British packets, but between 1704 and 1711 this service was run on a commercial basis by Edmund Dummer. Following the collapse of the Dummer scheme Jamaica was virtually without a Post Office until 1720 and it was not until 1755 that overseas mail was again carried by British packets.

The stamps of Great Britain were used on the island from 8 May 1858 to May 1860. Although there had been much friction between the local inhabitants and the British G.P.O. it was not until 1 August 1860 that the Jamaica authorities assumed responsibility for the postal service.

KINGSTON

Z 1

Stamps of GREAT BRITAIN *cancelled* "A 01" *as Type Z* 1.

1858 to 1860.
Z1	1d. rose-red (1857), *perf* 16 ..	£225
Z2	1d. rose-red (1857), *perf* 14 ..	32·00
Z4	4d. rose (1857)	38·00
Z5	6d. lilac (1856)	38·00
Z6	1s. green (1856)	£100

Z 2

Stamps of GREAT BRITAIN *cancelled* "A 01" *as Type Z* 2.

1859 to 1860.
Z 7	1d. rose-red (1857), *perf* 14	£170
Z 9	4d. rose (1857)	38·00
Z10	6d. lilac (1856)	38·00
Z11	1s. green (1856)	£250

Z 3

Stamps of GREAT BRITAIN *cancelled* "A 01" *as Type Z* 3.

1859 to 1860.
Z12	1d. rose-red (1857), *perf* 14 ..	£200
Z14	4d. rose (1857)	£120
	a. Thick glazed paper	£400
Z15	6d. lilac (1856)	£120
Z16	1s. green (1856)	

Cancellation "A 01" was later used by the London, Foreign Branch Office.

OTHER JAMAICA POST OFFICES

British stamps were issued to several District post offices between 8 May 1858 and 1 March 1859 (i.e. before the Obliterators A 27–A 78 were issued). These can only be distinguished (off the cover) when they have the Town's date-stamp on them. They are worth about three times the price of those with an obliteration number.

Stamps of GREAT BRITAIN *cancelled* "A 27" *to* "A 78" *as Type Z* 1

1859 to 1860.

"A 27". ALEXANDRIA
Z17	1d. rose-red (1857), *perf* 14	£425
Z17a	2d. blue (1855) Large Crown, *perf* 14 (Plate 6)	£475
Z18	4d. rose (1857)	£160
Z19	6d. lilac (1856)	£375

"A 28". ANNOTTO BAY
Z20	1d. rose-red (1857), *perf* 14	£300
Z21	4d. rose (1857)	75·00
Z22	6d. lilac (1856)	£225

"A 29". BATH
Z23	1d. rose-red (1857), *perf* 14	£120
Z24	4d. rose (1857)	85·00
Z25	6d. lilac (1856)	£400

"A 30". BLACK RIVER
Z26	1d. rose-red (1857), *perf* 14	£120
Z27	4d. rose (1857)	55·00
Z28	6d. lilac (1856)	£120

"A 31". BROWN'S TOWN
Z29	1d. rose-red (1857), *perf* 14	£160
Z30	4d. rose (1857)	£160
Z31	6d. lilac (1856)	£160

"A 32". BUFF BAY
Z32	1d. rose-red (1857), *perf* 14	£120
Z33	4d. rose (1857)	£150
Z34	6d. lilac (1856)	£120

"A 33". CHAPELTON
Z35	1d. rose-red (1857), *perf* 14	£160
Z36	4d. rose (1857)	£100
Z37	6d. lilac (1856)	£160

"A 34". CLAREMONT
Z38	1d. rose-red (1857), *perf* 14	£300
Z39	4d. rose (1857)	£150
Z40	6d. lilac (1856)	£300

"A 35". CLARENDON
(Near Four Paths)
Z41	1d. rose-red (1857), *perf* 14	£250
Z42	4d. rose (1857)	£100
Z43	6d. lilac (1856)	£160

"A 36". DRY HARBOUR
Z44	1d. rose-red (1857), *perf* 14	£375
Z45	4d. rose (1857)	£300
Z46	6d. lilac (1856)	£250

"A 37". DUNCANS
Z47	1d. rose-red (1857), *perf* 14	£375
Z48	4d. rose (1857)	£250
Z49	6d. lilac (1856)	

"A 38". EWARTON
A 38 was allocated to EWARTON but this office was closed towards the end of 1858 before the postmark arrived. A 38 was re-issued to Falmouth in 1862.

"A 39". FALMOUTH
Z53	1d. rose-red (1857), *perf* 14	85·00
Z54	4d. rose (1857)	48·00
Z55	6d. lilac (1856)	60·00
Z56	1s. green (1856)	£475

"A 40". FLINT RIVER
(Near Hopewell)
Z57	1d. rose-red (1857), *perf* 14	£150
Z58	4d. rose (1857)	£100
Z59	6d. lilac (1856)	£150
Z60	1s. green (1856)	£475

"A 41". GAYLE
Z61	1d. rose-red (1857), *perf* 14	£450
Z62	4d. rose (1857)	£120
Z63	6d. lilac (1856)	£130
Z64	1s. green (1856)	£225

"A 42". GOLDEN SPRING
(Near Stony Hill)
Z65	1d. rose-red (1857), *perf* 14	£170
Z66	4d. rose (1857)	£150
Z67	6d. lilac (1856)	£400
Z68	1s. green (1856)	£475

"A 43". GORDON TOWN
Z69	1d. rose-red (1857), *perf* 14	
Z70	4d. rose (1857)	
Z71	6d. lilac (1856)	£450

"A 44". GOSHEN
(Near Santa Cruz)
Z72	1d. rose-red (1857), *perf* 14	£120
Z73	4d. rose (1857)	£110
Z74	6d. lilac (1856)	55·00

"A 45". GRANGE HILL
Z75	1d. rose-red (1857), *perf* 14	£150
Z76	4d. rose (1857)	48·00
Z77	6d. lilac (1856)	60·00
Z77a	1s. green (1856)	£400

"A 46". GREEN ISLAND
Z78	1d. rose-red (1857), *perf* 14	£300
Z79	4d. rose (1857)	£150
Z80	6d. lilac (1856)	£250
Z81	1s. green (1856)	£475

"A 47". HIGHGATE
Z82	1d. rose-red (1857), *perf* 14	£170
Z83	4d. rose (1857)	£110
Z84	6d. lilac (1856)	£170

"A 48". HOPE BAY
Z85	1d. rose-red (1857), *perf* 14	£400
Z86	4d. rose (1857)	£150
Z87	6d. lilac (1856)	£400

"A 49". LILLIPUT
(Near Balaclava)
Z88	1d. rose-red (1857), *perf* 14	£150
Z89	4d. rose (1857)	£150
Z90	6d. lilac (1856)	75·00

"A 50". LITTLE RIVER
A 50 was allocated for use at LITTLE RIVER but this office was closed late in 1858, before the obliterator could be issued. Issued to Malvern in 1862.

"A 51". LUCEA
Z91	1d. rose-red (1857), *perf* 14	£225
Z92	4d. rose (1857)	55·00
Z93	6d. lilac (1856)	£150

"A 52". MANCHIONEAL
Z94	1d. rose-red (1857), *perf* 14	£300
Z95	4d. rose (1857)	£160
Z96	6d. lilac (1856)	

"A 53". MANDEVILLE
Z97	1d. rose-red (1857), *perf* 14	£160
Z98	4d. rose (1857)	55·00
Z99	6d. lilac (1856)	£140

"A 54". MAY HILL
(Near Spur Tree)
Z100	1d. rose-red (1857), *perf* 14	85·00
Z101	4d. rose (1857)	80·00
Z102	6d. lilac (1856)	55·00

"A 55". MILE GULLY
Z103	1d. rose-red (1857), *perf* 14	£250
Z104	4d. rose (1857)	£150
Z105	6d. lilac (1856)	£150

"A 56". MONEAGUE
Z106	1d. rose-red (1857), *perf* 14	£150
Z107	4d. rose (1857)	£190
Z108	6d. lilac (1856)	£400

"A 57". MONTEGO BAY
Z109	1d. rose-red (1857), *perf* 14	£160
Z110	4d. rose (1857)	48·00
Z111	6d. lilac (1856)	55·00
Z112	1s. green (1856)	£475

"A 58". MONTPELIER
Z113	1d. rose-red (1857), *perf* 14	
Z114	4d. rose (1857)	
Z115	6d. lilac (1856)	£650

"A 59". MORANT BAY
Z116	1d. rose-red (1857), *perf* 14	£300
Z117	4d. rose (1857)	55·00
Z118	6d. lilac (1856)	60·00

"A 60". OCHO RIOS
Z119	1d. rose-red (1857), *perf* 14	
Z120	4d. rose (1857)	80·00
Z121	6d. lilac (1856)	£140

"A 61". OLD HARBOUR
Z122	1d. rose-red (1857), *perf* 14	£150
Z123	4d. rose (1857)	£110
Z124	6d. lilac (1856)	£110

"A 62". PLANTAIN GARDEN RIVER
(Near Golden Grove)
Z125	1d. rose-red (1857), *perf* 14	£110
Z126	4d. rose (1857)	80·00
Z127	6d. lilac (1856)	£110

"A 63". PEAR TREE GROVE
No genuine specimen of A 63 has been found on a British stamp.

"A 64". PORT ANTONIO
Z131	1d. rose-red (1857), *perf* 14	£375
Z132	4d. rose (1857)	£225
Z133	6d. lilac (1856)	£225

"A 65". PORT MORANT
Z134	1d. rose-red (1857), *perf* 14	£225
Z135	4d. rose (1857)	85·00
Z136	6d. lilac (1856)	£225

"A 66". PORT MARIA
Z137	1d. rose-red (1857), *perf* 14	£150
Z138	4d. rose (1857)	60·00
Z139	6d. lilac (1856)	£225

"A 67". PORT ROYAL

Z140	1d. rose-red (1857), *perf* 14				£300
Z140a	2d. blue (1858) (plate 9)				
Z141	4d. rose (1857)				£300
Z142	6d. lilac (1856)				£300

"A 68". PORUS

Z143	1d. rose-red (1857), *perf* 14				£150
Z144	4d. rose (1857)				75·00
Z145	6d. lilac (1856)				£300

"A 69". RAMBLE

Z146	1d. rose-red (1857), *perf* 14				£150
Z147	4d. rose (1857)				£150
	a. Thick glazed paper				£400
Z149	6d. lilac (1856)				£225

"A 70". RIO BUENO

Z150	1d. rose-red (1857), *perf* 14				
Z151	4d. rose (1857)				£140
Z152	6d. lilac (1856)				90·00

"A 71". RODNEY HALL
(Now called Linstead)

Z153	1d. rose-red (1857), *perf* 14				£120
Z154	4d. rose (1857)				85·00
Z155	6d. lilac (1856)				£110

"A 72". ST. DAVID'S
(Now called Yallahs)

Z156	1d. rose-red (1857), *perf* 14				£150
Z157	4d. rose (1857)				£300
Z158	6d. lilac (1856)				

"A 73". ST. ANN'S BAY

Z159	1d. rose-red (1857), *perf* 14				£150
Z160	4d. rose (1857)				80·00
Z161	6d. lilac (1856)				£150

"A 74". SALT GUT
(Near Oracabessa)

Z162	1d. rose-red (1857), *perf* 14				£140
Z163	4d. rose (1857)				
Z164	6d. lilac (1856)				£150

"A 75". SAVANNAH-LA-MAR

Z165	1d. rose-red (1857), *perf* 14				85·00
Z166	4d. rose (1857)				50·00
Z167	6d. lilac (1856)				£150
Z168	1s. green (1856)				£425

"A 76". SPANISH TOWN

Z169	1d. rose-red (1857), *perf* 14				95·00
Z170	4d. rose (1857)				48·00
Z171	6d. lilac (1856)				85·00
Z172	1s. green (1856)				£300

"A 77". STEWART TOWN

Z173	1d. rose-red (1857), *perf* 14				£400
Z174	4d. rose (1857)				£250
Z175	6d. lilac (1856)				£150

"A 78". VERE
(Now called Alley)

Z176	1d. rose-red (1857), *perf* 14				£225
Z177	4d. rose (1857)				75·00
Z178	6d. lilac (1856)				50·00
Z179	1s. green (1856)				£475

PRICES FOR STAMPS ON COVER

Nos. 1/6	*from* × 4
Nos. 7/15	*from* × 6
Nos. 16/26	*from* × 8
Nos. 27/9	*from* × 5
No. 30	*from* × 5
Nos. 31/2	*from* × 15
Nos. 33/6	*from* × 5
Nos. 37/56	*from* × 3
No. 57	*from* × 4
Nos. 58/67	*from* × 3
Nos. 68/77	*from* × 6
Nos. 78/89	*from* × 3
Nos. 90/103	*from* × 4
Nos. 104/7	*from* × 5
Nos. 108/17	*from* × 3
Nos. 118/20	*from* × 5
Nos. 121/33a	*from* × 4
Nos. 134/40	*from* × 8
Nos. F1/9	*from* × 3
Nos. O1/5	*from* × 30

CROWN COLONY

PRINTERS. Until 1923, all the stamps of Jamaica were typographed by De La Rue & Co, Ltd, London, *unless otherwise stated.*

The official dates of issue are given, where known, but where definite information is not available the dates are those of earliest known use, etc.

1   2   3

4   5   6

7   A

1860 (23 Nov)–**70.** W 7. P 14.

1	1	1d. pale blue		60·00	15·00
		a. *Pale greenish blue*		65·00	19·00
		b. *Blue*		50·00	12·00
		c. *Deep blue* (1865)		95·00	28·00
		d. Bisected (½d.) (20.11.61) (on cover)		†	£650
		w. Wmk inverted		£100	40·00
2	2	2d. rose		£190	48·00
		a. *Deep rose*		£120	48·00
		w. Wmk inverted		—	60·00
3	3	3d. green (10.9.63)		£130	25·00
		w. Wmk inverted		£160	40·00
4	4	4d. brown-orange		£200	42·00
		a. *Red-orange*		£200	22·00
		w. Wmk inverted			
5	5	6d. dull lilac		£180	18·00
		a. *Grey-purple*		£275	32·00
		b. *Deep purple* (1870)		£800	42·00
		w. Wmk inverted		—	75·00
6	6	1s. yellow-brown		£450	24·00
		a. *Purple-brown* (1862)		£500	23·00
		b. *Dull brown* (1868)		£180	27·00
		c. "$" for "S" in "SHILLING" (A)		£1700	£600
		w. Wmk inverted		—	50·00

The diagonal bisection of the 1d. was authorised by a P.O. notice dated 20 November 1861 to pay the ½d. rate for newspapers or book post. Specimens are only of value when on original envelope or wrapper. The authority was withdrawn as from 1 December 1872. Fakes are frequently met with. Other bisections were unauthorised.

The so-called "dollar variety" of the 1s. occurs once in each sheet of stamps in all shades and in later colours, etc, on the second stamp in the second row of the left upper pane. The prices quoted above are for the dull brown shade, the prices for the other shades being proportionate to their normal value.

All values except the 3d. are known imperf, mint only.

There are two types of watermark in the 3d. and 1s., one being short and squat and the other elongated.

8   9   10

1870–83. *Wmk Crown CC.* (a) P 14.

7	8	½d. claret (29.10.72)		13·00	3·50
		a. *Deep claret* (1883)		15·00	4·75
		w. Wmk inverted		—	26·00
8	1	1d. blue (4.73)		55·00	75
		a. *Deep blue*		60·00	1·50
		w. Wmk inverted		£110	21·00
9	2	2d. rose (4.70)		55·00	70
		a. *Deep rose*		70·00	1·00
		w. Wmk inverted		75·00	21·00
10	3	3d. green (1.3.70)		90·00	8·50
		w. Wmk inverted		—	48·00
11	4	4d. brown-orange (1872)		£170	11·00
		a. *Red-orange* (1883)		£350	6·00
		w. Wmk inverted		—	42·00
12	5	6d. mauve (10.3.71)		60·00	5·50
		w. Wmk inverted		—	32·00
13	6	1s. dull brown (*to deep*) (23.2.73)		25·00	8·50
		a. "$" for "S" in "SHILLING" (A)		£1100	£600
		w. Wmk inverted		—	48·00

(b) P 12½

14	9	2s. Venetian red (27.8.75)		40·00	16·00
		w. Wmk inverted		60·00	70·00
15	10	5s. lilac (27.8.75)		90·00	£130
		w. Wmk inverted		£110	£180
7/15			Set of 9	£450	£150

The ½d., 1d., 4d., 2s. and 5s. are known imperforate.

1883–97. *Wmk Crown CA.* P 14.

16	8	½d. yellow-green (2.85)		2·25	95
		a. *Green*		80	10
		w. Wmk inverted		—	21·00
		x. Wmk reversed		—	32·00
17	1	1d. blue (1884)		£300	4·50
18		1d. rose (*to deep*) (3.3.85)		55·00	75
		a. *Carmine* (1886)		27·00	60
		w. Wmk inverted		—	32·00
19	2	2d. rose (*to deep*) (17.3.84)		£190	3·75
		w. Wmk inverted		—	42·00
20		2d. grey (1885)		75·00	2·50
		a. *Slate* (1886)		55·00	50
		w. Wmk inverted		—	21·00
21	3	3d. sage-green (11.86)		4·00	95
		a. *Pale olive-green*		2·50	1·25
22	4	4d. red-orange* (9.3.83)		£350	22·00
		aw. Wmk inverted			
		b. *Red-brown* (*shades*) (1885)		2·00	35
		bw. Wmk inverted		50·00	21·00

TWO PENCE HALF-PENNY

11   (12)

23	5	6d. deep yellow (4.10.90)		18·00	6·00
		a. *Orange-yellow*		4·00	3·50
24	6	1s. brown (*to deep*) (3.97)		5·00	6·00
		a. "$" for "S" in "SHILLING" (A)		£750	£450
		b. *Chocolate*		15·00	12·00
25	9	2s. Venetian red (2.97)		27·00	20·00
26	10	5s. lilac (2.97)		48·00	65·00
16/26			Set of 11	£550	95·00
16, 18, 20/3 Optd "Specimen"			Set of 6	£450	

*No. 22 is the same colour as No. 11a.

The 1d. carmine, 2d. slate, and 2s. are known imperf. All values to the 6d. inclusive are known perf 12. These are proofs.

1889 (8 Mar)–**91.** *Value tablet in second colour. Wmk Crown CA.* P 14.

27	11	1d. purple and mauve		2·25	20
		w. Wmk inverted		—	21·00
28		2d. green		19·00	3·50
		a. *Deep green* (*brown gum*)		4·50	6·00
		aw. Wmk inverted		42·00	
29		2½d. dull purple and blue (25.2.91)		4·75	50
		w. Wmk inverted		50·00	
27/9			Set of 3	10·50	3·75
27/9 Optd "Specimen"			Set of 3	£100	

A very wide range of shades may be found in the 1d. The headplate was printed in many shades of purple, and the dutyplate in various shades of mauve and purple and also in carmine, etc. There are fewer shades for the other values and they are not so pronounced.

1890 (4 June)–**91.** *No. 22b surch with T 12 by C. Vendyres, Kingston.*

30	4	2½d. on 4d. red-brown		27·00	8·50
		a. Spacing between lines of surch 1½ mm (2.91)		32·00	17·00
		b. Surch double		£325	£225
		c. "PFNNY" for "PENNY"		75·00	65·00
		ca. Ditto and broken "K" for "Y"		£130	£110
		w. Wmk inverted		60·00	30·00

This provisional was issued pending receipt of No. 29 which is listed above for convenience of reference.

Three settings exist. (1) Ten varieties arranged in a single vertical row and repeated six times in the pane. (2) Twelve varieties, in two horizontal rows of six, repeated five times, alternate rows show 1 and 1½ mm spacing between lines of surcharge. (3) Three varieties, arranged horizontally and repeated twenty times. All these settings can be reconstructed by examination of the spacing and relative position of the words of the surcharge and of the broken letters, etc, which are numerous.

A variety reading "PFNNK", with the "K" unbroken, is a forgery.

Surcharges misplaced either horizontally or vertically are met with, the normal position being central at the foot of the stamp with "HALF-PENNY" covering the old value.

13 Llandovery Falls, Jamaica   14 Arms of Jamaica
(photo by Dr. J. Johnston)

(Recess D.L.R.)

1900 (1 May)–**01.** *Wmk Crown CC (sideways*).* P 14.

31	13	1d. red		1·25	20
		w. Wmk Crown to left of CC		1·50	50
		x. Wmk reversed		—	32·00
32		1d. slate-black and red (25.9.01)		2·25	20
		a. *Blued paper*		£110	£100
		b. Imperf between (vert pair)		£7000	
		w. Wmk Crown to left of CC		10·00	10·00
		x. Wmk reversed		—	32·00
		y. Wmk sideways inverted and reversed			
31/2 Optd "Specimen"			Set of 2	£130	

*The normal sideways wmk shows Crown to right of CC, *as seen from the back of the stamp.*

Many shades exist of both centre and frame of the bi-coloured 1d. which was, of course, printed from two plates and the design shows minor differences from that of the 1d. red which was printed from a single plate.

(Typo D.L.R.)

1903 (16 Nov)–**04.** *Wmk Crown CA.* P 14.

33	14	½d. grey and dull green		1·50	30
		a. "SER.ET" for "SERVIET"		40·00	45·00
		w. Wmk inverted		30·00	30·00
34		1d. grey and carmine (24.2.04)		1·50	10
		a. "SER.ET" for "SERVIET"		32·00	35·00
35		2½d. grey and ultramarine		2·25	30
		a. "SER.ET" for "SERVIET"		60·00	75·00
36		5d. grey and yellow (1.3.04)		15·00	23·00
		a. "SER.ET" for "SERVIET"		£600	£700
		w. Wmk inverted		75·00	
33/6			Set of 4	18·00	23·00
33/6 Optd "Specimen"			Set of 4	75·00	

The "SER.ET" variety occurs on R. 4/2 of the left upper pane. It was corrected by De La Rue in July 1905.

The centres of the above and later bi-coloured stamps in the Arms type vary in colour from grey to grey-black.

15 Arms type redrawn   16

1905–11. *Wmk Mult Crown CA. P 14. (a) Arms types. Chalk-surfaced paper.*

37	14	½d. grey and dull green (20.11.05)		5·50	20
		a. "SER.ET" for "SERVIET"		32·00	38·00
		w. Wmk inverted			
38	15	½d. yell-grn (*ordinary paper*) (8.11.06)		7·00	40
		a. *Dull green*		3·75	20
		b. *Deep green*		4·50	20
39	14	1d. grey and carmine (20.11.05)		17·00	25
		w. Wmk inverted		—	75·00
40	16	1d. carmine (*ordinary paper*) (1.10.06)		1·25	10
		w. Wmk inverted		30·00	
41	14	2½d. grey and ultramarine (12.11.07)		2·75	2·25
42		2½d. pale ultramarine (*ordinary paper*) (21.9.10)		2·50	1·25
		a. *Deep ultramarine*		2·50	1·75
43		5d. grey and orange-yellow (24.4.07)		48·00	50·00
		a. "SER.ET" for "SERVIET"		£750	£900
44		6d. dull and bright purple (18.8.11)		12·00	12·00
45		5s. grey and violet (11.05)		40·00	30·00
37/45			*Set of 9*	£120	85·00
38, 40, 42, 44, 45 Optd "Specimen"			*Set of 5*	£140	

See note below No. 36 concerning grey centres.

(b) Queen Victoria types. Ordinary paper

46	3	3d. olive-green (3.8.05)		6·00	3·50
		a. *Sage-green* (1907)		5·00	3·00
47		3d. purple/yellow (10.3.10)		4·50	3·50
		a. Chalk-surfaced paper. *Pale purple/ yellow* (11.7.10)		2·00	1·50
		aw. Wmk inverted		42·00	42·00
48	4	4d. red-brown (6.6.08)		70·00	60·00
49		4d. black/yellow (*chalk-surfaced paper*) (21.9.10)		7·00	38·00
50		4d. red/yellow (3.10.11)		1·50	8·00
51	5	6d. dull orange (27.6.06)		15·00	24·00
		a. *Golden yellow* (9.09)		23·00	48·00
52		6d. lilac (19.11.09)		27·00	35·00
		a. Chalk-surfaced paper. *Purple* (7.10)		9·50	17·00
53	6	1s. brown (11.06)		19·00	20·00
		a. *Deep brown*		27·00	29·00
		b. "$" for "S" in "SHILLING" (A)		£900	£950
54		1s. black/green (*chalk-surfaced paper*) (21.9.10)		3·75	8·50
		a. "$" for "S" in "SHILLING" (A)		£800	£1000
55	9	2s. Venetian red (11.08)		£100	£150
56		2s. pur/bl (*chalk-surfaced paper*) (21.9.10)		6·00	3·50
46/56			*Set of 11*	£190	£300
47, 49, 50, 52, 54, 56 Optd "Specimen"			*Set of 6*	£170	

No. 38 exists in coils constructed from normal sheets.

17   18

(T 17/18 typo D.L.R.)

1911 (3 Feb). *Wmk Mult Crown CA. P 14.*

57	17	2d. grey (Optd S. £35)		2·25	13·00

1912–20. *Wmk Mult Crown CA. Chalk-surfaced paper (3d. to 5s.). P 14.*

58	18	1d. carmine-red (5.12.12)		1·25	10
		a. *Scarlet* (1916)		1·25	70
59		1½d. brown-orange (13.7.16)		1·00	60
		a. *Yellow-orange*		13·00	1·00
		b. Wmk sideways		†	£1300
60		2d. grey (2.8.12)		1·75	1·75
		a. *Slate-grey*		1·00	3·00
61		2½d. blue (13.2.13)		1·00	15
		a. *Deep bright blue*		65	95
62		3d. purple/yellow (6.3.12)		40	45
		a. *White back* (2.4.13)		55	40
		b. On lemon (25.9.16) (Optd S. £32)		3·75	1·50
		w. Wmk inverted			
63		4d. black and red/yellow (4.4.13)		50	50
		a. *White back* (7.5.14)		70	4·00
		b. On lemon (1916) (Optd S. £32)		23·00	19·00
		c. On pale yellow (1919)		22·00	15·00
64		6d. dull and bright purple (14.11.12)		4·50	9·00
		a. *Dull purple and bright mauve* (1915)		70	1·00
		b. *Dull purple & bright magenta* (1920)		3·50	2·25
65		1s. black/green (2.8.12)		2·25	2·00
		a. *White back* (4.1.15)		70	4·75
		b. On blue-green, olive back (1920)		2·25	5·50
66		2s. purple and bright blue/blue (10.1.19)		12·00	25·00
67		5s. green and red/yellow (5.9.19)		48·00	80·00
		a. On pale yellow (1920)		50·00	80·00
		b. On orange-buff (1920)		£120	£150
58/67			*Set of 10*	60·00	£100
58/67 Optd "Specimen"			*Set of 10*	£190	

No. 58 exists in coils constructed from normal sheets.
The paper of No. 67 is a bright yellow and the gum rough and dull. No. 67a is on practically the normal creamy "pale yellow" paper, and the gum is smooth and shiny. The paper of No. 67b approaches the "coffee" colour of the true "orange-buff", and the colours of both head and frame are paler, the latter being of a carmine tone.
For the ½d. and 6d. with Script wmk see Nos. 89a/90.

RED CROSS LABELS. A voluntary organization, the Jamaica War Stamp League later the Jamaica Patriotic Stamp League, was founded in November 1915 by Mr. Lewis Ashenheim, a Kingston solicitor. The aims of the League were to support the British Red Cross, collect funds for the purchase of aircraft for the Royal Flying Corps and the relief of Polish Jews.
One fund-raising method used was the sale, from 1 December 1915, of ½d. charity labels. These labels, which were available from post offices, depicted a bi-plane above a cross and were printed in red by Dennison Manufacturing Company, Framingham, U.S.A., the stamps being perforated 12 except for those along the edges of the sheet which have one side imperforate.
From 22 December 1915 supplies of the labels were overprinted "JAMAICA" in red, the colour of this overprint being changed to black from 15 January 1916. Copies sold from 11 March 1916 carried an additional "Half-Penny" surcharge, also in black.
Such labels had no postal validity when used by the general public, but, by special order of the Governor, were accepted for the payment of postage on the League's official mail. To obtain this concession the envelopes were to be inscribed "Red Cross Business" or "Jamaica Patriotic Stamp League" and the labels used endorsed with Mr. Ashenheim's signature. Such covers are rare.

WAR STAMP.	**WAR STAMP.**	**WAR STAMP.**
(19)	(20)	(21)

(T 19/21 optd Govt Printing Office, Kingston)

1916 (1 Apr–Sept). *Optd with T 19.*

68	15	½d. yellow-green		10	35
		a. No stop after "STAMP" (R. 18/2)		9·50	23·00
		b. Opt double		£100	£110
		c. Opt inverted		85·00	95·00
		d. Space between "W" and "A" (R. 20/1)		9·50	23·00
		e. *Blue-green*		10	50
		ea. No stop after "STAMP" (R. 3/11 or 11/1)		9·00	22·00
		eb. Space between "W" and "A" (R. 20/1)		10·00	24·00
		w. Wmk inverted			
69	18	3d. purple/yellow (white back)		8·00	23·00
		a. On lemon (6.16)		1·00	17·00
		ab. No stop after "STAMP" (R. 8/6 or 9/6)		23·00	75·00
		b. On pale yellow (9.16)		7·50	23·00

Minor varieties: ½d. (i) Small "P"; (ii) "WARISTAMP" (raised quad between words); (iii) Two stops after "STAMP". 3d. "WARISTAMP". There were several settings of the overprint used for each value. Where two positions are quoted for a variety these did not occur on the same sheet.

NOTE. The above and succeeding stamps with "WAR STAMP" overprint were issued for payment of a special war tax on letters and postcards or on parcels. Ordinary unoverprinted stamps could also be used for this purpose.

1916 (Sept–Dec). *Optd with T 20.*

70	15	½d. blue-green (*shades*) (2.10.16)		10	30
		a. No stop after "STAMP" (R. 5/7)		9·50	30·00
		b. Opt omitted (in pair with normal)		£1300	£1200
		c. "R" inserted by hand (R. 11/10)		£600	£550
		w. Wmk inverted		30·00	
71	18	1½d. orange (1.9.16)		10	15
		aa. Wmk sideways		†	£1200
		a. No stop after "STAMP" (R. 4/12, 8/6, 10/10, 11/1, 18/12, 19/12)		5·00	7·00
		b. "S" in "STAMP" omitted (R. 6/12)		£110	£120
		c. "S" inserted by hand		£250	
		d. "R" in "WAR" omitted (R. 1/10)		£900	£800
		e. "R" inserted by hand		£500	£450
		f. Inverted "d" for "P"		£180	£150
		w. Wmk inverted		15·00	15·00
72		3d. purple/lemon (2.10.16)		30	90
		aa. Opt inverted		£275	
		a. No stop after "STAMP" (R. 5/7)		22·00	55·00
		b. "S" in "STAMP" omitted (R. 6/12) (Dec)		£350	£325
		c. "S" inserted by hand		£180	£180
		e. On yellow (12.16)		6·00	9·00
		ea. "S" in "STAMP" omitted (R. 6/12)		£500	£450
		eb. "S" inserted by hand		£325	£250

Nos. 70c, 71c, 71e, 72c and 72eb show the missing "R" or "S" inserted by handstamp. The 3d. is known with this "S" handstamp inverted or double.
Minor varieties, such as raised quads, small stop, double stop, spaced letters and letters of different sizes, also exist in this overprint. The setting was altered several times.

1917 (March). *Optd with T 21.*

73	15	½d. blue-green (*shades*) (25.3.17)		10	20
		a. No stop after "STAMP" (R. 2/5, 8/11, 8/12)		7·50	20·00
		b. Stop inserted and "P" impressed a second time (R. 7/6)		£150	
		c. Optd on back only		£140	
		d. Opt inverted		9·50	30·00
74	18	1½d. orange (3.3.17)		10	10
		aa. Wmk sideways		†	£1300
		a. No stop after "STAMP" (R. 2/5, 8/11, 8/12)		3·00	17·00
		b. Stop inserted and "P" impressed a second time (R. 7/6)		£200	
		c. Opt double		80·00	85·00
		d. Opt inverted		80·00	75·00
		e. "WAP STAMP" (R. 6/2)			
		w. Wmk inverted		15·00	
75		3d. purple/yellow (3.3.17)		15	1·25
		a. No stop after "STAMP" (R. 2/5, 8/11, 8/12)		13·00	30·00
		b. Stop inserted and "P" impressed a second time (R. 7/6)		£170	
		c. Opt inverted		£140	
		d. Opt sideways (reading up)		£300	
		da. Opt omitted (in horiz pair with No. 75d)		£2250	

No. 75da shows the left-hand stamp as No. 75d and the right-hand stamp without overprint.
There are numerous minor varieties in this overprint with the setting being altered several times.

WAR STAMP
(22)

1919 (4 Oct)–**20.** *Optd with T 22 in red by D.L.R.*

76	15	½d. green		10	15
77	18	3d. purple/yellow		2·25	3·00
		a. *Pale purple/buff* (3.1.20)		2·00	1·25
		b. *Deep purple/buff* (1920)		5·50	6·00
76/7 Optd "Specimen"			*Set of 2*	70·00	

We list the most distinct variations in the 3d. The buff tone of the paper varies considerably in depth.

23 Jamaica Exhibition 1891   24 Arawak Woman preparing Cassava

25 War Contingent embarking, 1915   26 King's House, Spanish Town

Re-entry. Nos. 80a, 93a

The greater part of the design is re-entered, the hull showing in very solid colour and the people appear very blurred. There are also minor re-entries on stamps above (R. 7/4 and 6/4).

27 Return of War Contingent, 1919   A   B

28 Landing of Columbus, 1494   29 Cathedral, Spanish Town

34

(Typo (½d., 1d.), recess (others) D.L.R.)

1919–21. *T 23/29, 34 and similar vert designs. Wmk Mult Crown CA (sideways* on 1d., 1½d. and 10s.). Chalk-surfaced paper (½d., 1d.). P 14.*

78	23	½d. green and olive-green (12.11.20)		1·00	1·00
		w. Wmk inverted			
		x. Wmk reversed			
		y. Wmk inverted and reversed			
79	24	1d. carmine and orange (3.10.21)		1·75	1·75
		w. Wmk Crown to left of CA			

80	25	1½d. green (shades) (4.7.19) ..		40	90
		a. Major re-entry (R. 8/4) ..		65·00	
		b. "C" of "CA" missing from wmk ..		†	£225
		c. "A" of "CA" missing from wmk ..		†	—
		w. Wmk Crown to left of CA ..		20·00	
		y. Wmk sideways inverted and reversed		—	32·00
81	26	2d. indigo and green (18.2.21) ..		1·00	4·00
		w. Wmk inverted ..		35·00	
		y. Wmk inverted and reversed ..		35·00	
82	27	2½d. deep blue and blue (A) (18.2.21)		13·00	3·00
		a. Blue-black and deep blue ..		1·50	1·75
		b. "C" of "CA" missing from wmk ..			
		c. "A" of "CA" missing from wmk ..		£200	
		w. Wmk inverted ..		25·00	
		x. Wmk reversed ..		30·00	
		y. Wmk inverted and reversed ..		30·00	
83	28	3d. myrtle-green and blue (8.4.21)		1·50	2·50
		w. Wmk inverted ..		30·00	32·00
84	29	4d. brown and deep green (21.1.21)		2·50	8·50
		w. Wmk inverted ..			
		x. Wmk reversed ..			
85	—	1s. orange-yell & red-orge (10.12.20)		3·75	5·50
		a. Frame inverted ..		£19000	£14000
		b. "C" of "CA" missing from wmk ..		£275	
		c. "A" of "CA" missing from wmk ..			
		w. Wmk inverted ..			
		x. Wmk reversed ..			
86	—	2s. light blue and brown (10.12.20)		13·00	26·00
		b. "C" of "CA" missing from wmk ..			
		c. "A" of "CA" missing from wmk ..			
		w. Wmk inverted ..		32·00	40·00
		x. Wmk reversed ..			
		y. Wmk inverted and reversed ..			
87	—	3s. violet-blue and orange (10.12.20)		20·00	75·00
88	—	5s. blue and yellow-orange (15.4.21)		55·00	75·00
		a. Blue and pale dull orange ..		48·00	70·00
		w. Wmk inverted ..			
		x. Wmk reversed ..			
89	—	10s. myrtle-green (6.5.20) ..		75·00	£150
78/89			Set of 12	£150	£300
78/89 Optd "Specimen"			Set of 12	£250	

Designs: Vert.—1s. Statue of Queen Victoria, Kingston; 2s. Admiral Rodney Memorial, Spanish Town; 3s. Sir Charles Metcalfe Statue, Kingston; 5s. Jamaican scenery.

*The normal sideways wmk on Nos. 79/80 shows Crown to right of CA, as seen from the back of the stamp.

The 2½d. of the above series showed the Union Jack at left, incorrectly, as indicated in illustration A. In the issue on paper with Script wmk the design was corrected (Illustration B).

An example of the "C" omitted has been reported on an example of No. 88 overprinted "Specimen".

A 6d. stamp showing the reading of the Declaration of Freedom from Slavery in 1836 was prepared and sent out in April 1921, but for political reasons was not issued and the stock was destroyed. Copies overprinted "Specimen" are known on both the Mult CA and Script CA papers, and are worth £600 each. Price without "Specimen" on Script CA £15000.

"Bow" flaw (R.18/12)

1921 (21 Oct)–**27.** Wmk Mult Script CA. Chalk-surfaced paper (6d.). P 14.

89a	18	½d. green (Optd S. £45) (3.11.27) ..		1·50	10
		ab. Bow flaw ..		38·00	22·00
90		6d. dull pur & brt mag (Optd S. £38) ..		6·00	3·75

35 "POSTAGE & REVENUE" added

36 "Port Royal in 1853" (A. Duperly)

(Printing as before; the 6d. recess-printed)

1921–29. As Nos. 78/89. Wmk Mult Script CA (sideways* on 1d. and 1½d.). Chalk-surfaced paper (½d., 1d.). P 14.

91	23	½d. green and olive-green (5.2.22) ..		50	50
		a. Green and deep olive-green ..		25	50
		w. Wmk inverted ..		25·00	30·00
92	35	1d. carmine and orange (5.12.22) ..		1·50	10
		w. Wmk Crown to right of CA ..		15·00	15·00
		x. Wmk reversed ..		—	30·00
93	25	1½d. green (shades) (2.2.21) ..		40	45
		a. Major re-entry (R. 8/4) ..		65·00	
		w. Wmk Crown to left of CA ..		—	20·00
		x. Wmk reversed ..		20·00	20·00
		y. Wmk sideways inverted and reversed		—	40·00
94	26	2d. indigo and green (4.11.21) ..		6·00	80
		a. Indigo and grey-green (1925) ..		8·00	95
		w. Wmk inverted ..			†
95	27	2½d. deep blue and blue (B) (4.11.21)		5·50	1·75
		a. Dull blue and blue (B) ..		6·00	60
		w. Wmk inverted ..		25·00	25·00
		x. Wmk reversed ..			
		y. Wmk inverted and reversed ..			
96	28	3d. myrtle-green and blue (6.3.22) ..		2·25	70
		a. Green and pale blue ..		80	15
		x. Wmk reversed ..			

97	29	4d. brown and deep green (5.12.21) ..		75	30
		a. Chocolate and dull green ..		75	30
		w. Wmk inverted ..		25·00	
		x. Wmk reversed ..		35·00	
98	36	6d. black and blue (5.12.22) ..		12·00	2·00
		a. Grey and dull blue ..		12·00	1·50
99	—	1s. orange and red-orange (4.11.21) ..		1·75	80
		a. Orange-yellow and brown-orange ..		1·75	65
		w. Wmk inverted ..			
		x. Wmk reversed ..			
100	—	2s. light blue and brown (5.2.22) ..		3·25	65
		w. Wmk inverted ..		30·00	30·00
101	—	3s. violet-blue and orange (23.8.21) ..		11·00	9·00
102	—	5s. blue and yellow-brown (8.11.23) ..		28·00	75·00
		a. Blue and pale dull orange ..		55·00	60·00
		b. Blue and yellow-orange (1927) ..		25·00	23·00
		c. Blue and pale bistre-brown (1929) ..		25·00	22·00
		w. Wmk inverted ..		—	£110
		x. Wmk reversed ..			
103	34	10s. myrtle-green (3.22) ..		50·00	70·00
91/103			Set of 13	£100	95·00
91/103 Optd "Specimen"			Set of 13	£250	

*The normal sideways wmk shows Crown to left of CA on No. 92 or Crown to right of CA on No. 93, both as seen from the back of the stamp.

The frame of No. 102a is the same colour as that of No. 88a.

The designs of all values of the pictorial series, with the exception of the 5s. and 10s. (which originated with the Governor, Sir Leslie Probyn), were selected by Mr. F. C. Cundall, F.S.A. The 1d. and 5s. were drawn by Miss Cundall, the 3d. by Mrs. Cundall, and the 10s. by De La Rue & Co. The 6d. is from a lithograph. The other designs are from photographs, the frames of all being the work of Miss Cundall and Miss Wood.

37 **38**

39

(Centres from photos by Miss V. F. Taylor. Frames des F. C. Cundall, F.S.A., and drawn by Miss Cundall. Recess B.W.)

1923 (1 Nov). Child Welfare. Wmk Mult Script CA. P 12.

104	37	½d. + ½d. black and green ..		60	5·50
105	38	1d. + ½d. black and scarlet ..		1·75	10·00
106	39	2½d. + ½d. black and blue ..		8·50	18·00
104/6 ..			Set of 3	9·50	30·00
104/6 Optd "Specimen"			Set of 3	£120	

Sold at a premium of ½d. for the Child Welfare League, these stamps were on sale annually from 1 November to 31 January, until 31 January 1927, when their sale ceased, the remainders being destroyed on 21 February 1927.

40 **41** **42**

Die I Die II

(Recess D.L.R.)

1929–32. Wmk Mult Script CA. P 14.

108	40	1d. scarlet (Die I) (15.3.29) ..		1·75	10
		a. Die II (1932) ..		3·00	10
109	41	1½d. chocolate (18.1.29) ..		1·75	15
110	42	9d. maroon (5.3.29) ..		3·25	1·00
108/10 ..			Set of 3	6·00	1·10
108/10 Perf "Specimen"			Set of 3	75·00	

In Die I the shading below JAMAICA is formed of thickened parallel lines, and in Die II of diagonal cross-hatching.

43 Coco Palms at Don Christopher's Cove

44 Wag Water River, St. Andrew

45 Priestman's River, Portland

(Dies eng and recess Waterlow)

1932. Wmk Mult Script CA (sideways on 2d. and 2½d.). P 12½.

111	43	2d. black and green (4.11.32) ..		8·00	2·25
		a. Imperf between (vert pair) ..		£5500	
112	44	2½d. turquoise-blue & ultram (5.3.32)		1·75	1·50
		a. Imperf between (vert pair) ..		£10000	£10000
113	45	6d. grey-black and purple (4.2.32) ..		8·00	1·25
111/13			Set of 3	16·00	4·50
111/13 Perf "Specimen"			Set of 3	80·00	

46 Windsor Castle

(Des H. Fleury. Recess B.W.)

1935 (6 May). Silver Jubilee. Wmk Mult Script CA. P 11×12.

114	46	1d. deep blue and scarlet ..		20	15
		d. Flagstaff on right-hand turret ..		65·00	
		e. Double flagstaff ..		65·00	
115		1½d. ultramarine and grey-black ..		50	1·00
		a. Extra flagstaff ..		75·00	£100
		b. Short extra flagstaff ..		75·00	
		c. Lightning conductor ..		65·00	
116		6d. green and indigo ..		5·00	11·00
		a. Extra flagstaff ..		£170	£200
		b. Short extra flagstaff ..		£180	
		c. Lightning conductor ..		£150	
117		1s. slate and purple ..		4·00	7·00
		a. Extra flagstaff ..		£225	£275
		b. Short extra flagstaff ..		£250	
		c. Lightning conductor ..		£190	
114/17 ..			Set of 4	8·75	17·00
114/17 Perf "Specimen"			Set of 4	75·00	

For illustrations of plate varieties see Omnibus section following Zimbabwe.

47 King George VI and Queen Elizabeth

(Des and recess D.L.R.)

1937 (12 May). Coronation. Wmk Mult Script CA. P 14.

118	47	1d. scarlet ..		30	15
119		1½d. grey-black ..		50	30
120		2½d. bright blue ..		85	70
118/20 ..			Set of 3	1·50	1·00
118/20 Perf "Specimen"			Set of 3	55·00	

48 King George VI

49 Coco Palms at Don Christopher's Cove

50 Bananas

51 Citrus Grove **52** Kingston Harbour

53 Sugar Industry

54 Bamboo Walk

55 King George VI

56 Tobacco Growing and Cigar Making

Repaired chimney (Centre plate 1 R. 11/1)

(Recess D.L.R. (T **48**, 5s. and 10s.), Waterlow (others))

1938 (10 Oct)–52. *T* **48/56** *and as Nos.* 88, 112/13, *but with inset portrait of King George VI, as in T* **49**. *Wmk Mult Script CA. P* 13½×14 (½d., 1d., 1½d.), 14 (5s., 10s.) *or* 12½ (others).

121	48	½d. blue-green (10.10.38)	..	1·50	10
121b		a. Wmk sideways	..	† £3500	
		½d. orange (25.10.51)	..	30	90
122		1d. scarlet	..	80	10
122a		1d. blue-green (25.10.51)	..	50	10
123		1½d. brown	..	80	10
124	49	2d. grey and green (10.12.38)	..	60	60
		a. Perf 13×13½ (1939)	..	2·00	40
		ab. "C" of "CA" missing from wmk	..	£750	
		b. Perf 12½×13 (1951)	..	75	10
125	44	2½d. greenish blue & ultram (10.12.38)	..	3·00	1·50
126	50	3d. ultramarine and green (10.12.38)	..	70	1·25
		a. "A" of "CA" missing from wmk	..	£750	
126b		3d. greenish blue and ultram (15.8.49)	..	1·25	1·25
126c		3d. green and scarlet (1.7.52)	..	1·50	30
127	51	4d. brown and green (10.12.38)	..	40	10
128	45	6d. grey and purple (10.12.38)	..	3·25	30
		a. Perf 13½×13 (10.10.50)	..	1·75	10
129	52	9d. lake (10.12.38)	..	40	50
		a. "A" of "CA" missing from wmk	..	£750	
130	53	1s. green and purple-brown (10.12.38)	..	6·00	20
		a. Repaired chimney	..	£475	£100
131	54	2s. blue and chocolate (10.12.38)	..	20·00	90
132	—	5s. slate-blue & yellow-orge (10.12.38)	..	14·00	3·75
		a. Perf 14, line (1941)	..	£2750	£190
		b. Perf 13 (24.10.49)	..	6·50	3·00
		ba. Blue and orange (10.10.50)	..	6·50	3·00
133	55	10s. myrtle-green (10.12.38)	..	11·00	7·50
		aa. Perf 13 (10.10.50)	..	9·00	5·00
133a	56	£1 chocolate and violet (15.8.49)	..	27·00	26·00
121/33a			Set of 18	70·00	35·00
121/33	Perf "Specimen"		Set of 13	£200	

No. 130a occurred in conjunction with Frame plate 2 on printings between 1943 and 1951.

No. 132a shows the emergency use of a line perforation machine, giving an irregular gauge of 14–14.15, after the De La Rue works were damaged in December 1940. The normal comb measures 13.8×13.7.

Nos. 121 and 122 exist in coils constructed from normal sheets.

SELF-GOVERNMENT

57 Courthouse, Falmouth

58 King Charles II and King George VI

59 Institute of Jamaica

(Recess Waterlow)

1945 (20 Aug)–46. *New Constitution. T* **57/9** *and similar designs. Wmk Mult Script CA. P* 12½.

134	57	1½d. sepia	..	20	30
		a. Perf 12½×13 (1946)	..	3·00	50
135	58	2d. green	..	6·50	90
		a. Perf 12½×13 (1945)	..	30	50
136	59	3d. ultramarine	..	20	50
		a. Perf 13 (1946)	..	1·25	2·50
137	—	4½d. slate	..	30	30
		a. Perf 13 (1946)	..	1·50	2·00
138	—	2s. red-brown	..	30	50
139	—	5s. indigo	..	1·00	1·00
140	59	10s. green	..	85	2·25
134/40			Set of 7	2·75	4·75
134/40	Perf "Specimen"		Set of 7	£140	

Designs: Vert (as *T* **57**)—2s. "Labour and Learning". Horiz (as *T* **59**)—4½d. House of Assembly; 5s. Scroll, flag and King George VI.

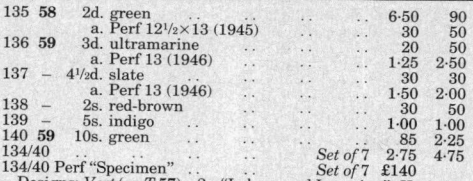

60 Houses of Parliament, London

(Des and recess D.L.R.)

1946 (14 Oct). *Victory. Wmk Mult Script CA. P* 13½×14.

141	60	1½d. purple-brown	..	2·50	10
		a. Perf 13½	..	30	65
142		3d. blue	..	2·50	2·25
		a. Perf 13½	..	30	4·25
141/2	Perf "Specimen"		Set of 2	50·00	

61 **62**
King George VI and Queen Elizabeth

(Des and photo Waterlow (T **61**). Design recess, name typo B.W. (T **62**))

1948 (1 Dec). *Royal Silver Wedding. Wmk Mult Script CA.*

143	61	1½d. red-brown (p 14×15)	..	30	10
144	62	£1 scarlet (p 11½×11)	..	24·00	45·00

63 Hermes, Globe and Forms of Transport

64 Hemispheres, Vickers Viking Airplane and Steamer

65 Hermes and Globe

66 U.P.U. Monument

(Recess Waterlow (T **63**, **66**). Design recess, name typo B.W. (T **64/5**))

1949 (10 Oct). *75th Anniv of Universal Postal Union. Wmk Mult Script CA.*

145	63	1½d. red-brown (p 13½–14)	..	30	15
146	64	2d. deep blue-green (p 11×11½)	..	1·00	1·75
147	65	3d. deep blue (p 11×11½)	..	55	1·25
148	66	6d. purple (p 13½–14)	..	65	2·50
145/8			Set of 4	2·25	5·00

67 Arms of University

68 Princess Alice

(Recess Waterlow)

1951 (16 Feb). *Inauguration of B.W.I. University College. Wmk Mult Script CA. P* 14×14½.

149	67	2d. black and red-brown	..	30	30
150	68	6d. grey-black and purple	..	35	30

69 Scout Badge and Map of Caribbean

70 Scout Badge and Map of Jamaica

(Litho B.W.)

1952 (5 Mar). *First Caribbean Scout Jamboree. Wmk Mult Script CA. P* 13½×13 (2d.) *or* 13×13½ (6d.).

151	69	2d. blue, apple-green and black	..	15	10
152	70	6d. yellow-green, carmine-red and black	..	15	50

71 Queen Elizabeth II

72 Coco Palms at Don Christopher's Cove

(Des and eng B.W. Recess D.L.R.)

1953 (2 June). *Coronation. Wmk Mult Script CA. P* 13½×13.

153	71	2d. black and deep yellow-green	..	50	10

(Recess Waterlow)

1953 (25 Nov). *Royal Visit. Wmk Mult Script CA. P* 12½×13.

154	72	2d. grey-black and green	..	40	10

73 H.M.S. *Britannia* (ship of the line) at Port Royal

(Recess D.L.R.)

1955 (10 May). *Tercentenary Issue. T* **73** *and similar horiz designs. Wmk Mult Script CA. P* 12½.

155		2d. black and olive-green	..	35	10
156		2½d. black and deep bright blue	..	15	35
157		3d. black and claret	..	15	30
158		6d. black and carmine-red	..	20	20
155/8			Set of 4	75	80

Designs:—2½d. Old Montego Bay; 3d. Old Kingston; 6d. Proclamation of Abolition of Slavery, 1838.

74 Coconut Palms

75 Mahoe

76 Blue Mountain Peak

77 Arms of Jamaica

78 Arms of Jamaica

(Recess B.W. (T **77/8**), D.L.R. (others))

1956 (1 May)–58. *T* **74/8** *and similar designs. Wmk Mult Script CA. P* 13 (½d. to 6d.), 13½ (8d. to 2s.) *or* 11½ (3s. to £1).

159	74	½d. black and deep orange-red	..	10	10
160	—	1d. black and emerald	..	10	10

161	–	2d. black and carmine-red (2.8.56)	..	10	10
162	–	2½d. black and deep bright blue (2.8.56)		30	40
163	75	3d. emerald and red-brown (17.12.56)		20	10
164	–	4d. bronze-green and blue (17.12.56)		20	10
		w. Wmk inverted	..	90·00	
165	–	5d. scarlet and bronze-green (17.12.56)		20	1·00
166	–	6d. black and deep rose-red (3.9.56)		1·25	10
167	76	8d. ultramarine & red-orge (15.11.56)		15	10
168	–	1s. yellow-green and blue (15.11.56)		60	10
169	–	1s. 6d. ultram & reddish pur (15.11.56)		80	10
170	–	2s. blue and bronze-green (15.11.56)		7·00	1·50
		a. Grey-blue & bronze-green (24.4.58)		9·50	2·00
171	77	3s. black and blue (2.8.56)		1·50	1·75
172		5s. black and carmine-red (15.8.56)		3·75	3·00
173	78	10s. black and blue-green (15.8.56)	..	25·00	13·00
174		£1 black and purple (15.8.56)	..	25·00	13·00
159/74			Set of 16	60·00	30·00

Designs: *Vert* (as T 74/5)—1d. Sugar Cane; 2d. Pineapples; 2½d. Bananas; 4d. Breadfruit; 5d. Ackee; 6d. Streamertail. *Horiz* (as T 76)—1s. Royal Botanic Gardens, Hope; 1s. 6d. Rafting on the Rio Grande; 2s. Fort Charles.

An earlier £1 value, in the design of No. 133a but showing the portrait of Queen Elizabeth II, was prepared, but not issued.

79 Federation Map

(Recess B.W.)

1958 (22 Apr). *Inauguration of British Caribbean Federation.* W w 12. P 11½×11.

175	79	2d. deep green	..	55	10
176		5d. blue	..	95	3·50
177		6d. scarlet	..	95	40
175/7			Set of 3	2·25	3·50

81 Bristol 175 Britannia 312 flying over *City of Berlin*, 1860

83 1s. Stamps of 1860 and 1956

(Recess Waterlow)

1960 (4 Jan). *Stamp Centenary.* T 81, 83 and similar design. W w 12. P 13 × 13½ (1s.) or 13½ × 14 (others).

178		2d. blue and reddish purple	..	45	10
179		6d. carmine and olive-green	..	45	25
180		1s. red-brown, yellow-green and blue		45	30
178/80			Set of 3	1·25	60

Design: As T 81—6d. Postal mule-cart and motor-van.

INDEPENDENT

1962	1962
INDEPENDENCE	INDEPENDENCE 1962
(84)	(85)

86 Military Bugler and Map

(Des V. Whiteley. Photo D.L.R. (2, 4d., 1s. 6d., 5s.))

1962 (8 Aug)–**63**. *Independence.*

(a) Nos. 159/60, 162, 171, 173/4 optd as T 84 and Nos. 163, 165/8, 170 optd with T 85

181	74	½d. black and deep orange-red		10	95
182	–	1d. black and emerald		10	10
183	–	2½d. black and deep bright blue		10	85
184	75	3d. emerald and red-brown		10	10
185	–	5d. scarlet and bronze-green		15	60
186	–	6d. black and deep rose-red		2·50	10
187	76	8d. ultram & red-orge (opt at upper left)		15	10
		a. Opt at lower left (17.9.63?)		15	15
188	–	1s. yellow-green and blue		15	10
189	–	2s. blue and bronze-green		80	1·50
		a. Dp blue & dp bronze-green (20.8.63)		6·00	2·75
190	77	3s. black and blue		90	1·50
191	78	10s. black and blue-green		2·75	4·25
192		£1 black and purple		2·75	5·50

(b) Horiz designs as T 86. W w 12. P 13

193		2d. multicoloured		75	10
194		4d. multicoloured		75	10
195		1s. 6d. black and red		2·50	85
196		5s. multicoloured		3·25	4·00
181/96			Set of 16	16·00	19·00

Designs:—2, 4d. Type 86; 1s. 6d. Gordon House and banner; 5s. Map, factories and fruit.

For these overprints on stamps watermarked w 12 see Nos. 205/13.

89 Kingston Seal, Weightlifting, Boxing, Football and Cycling

93 Farmer and Crops

(Photo Harrison)

1962 (11 Aug). *Ninth Central American and Caribbean Games, Kingston.* T 89 and similar horiz designs. W w 12. P 14½ × 14.

197		1d. sepia and carmine-red	..	20	10
198		6d. sepia and greenish blue	..	20	10
199		8d. sepia and bistre	..	20	10
200		2s. multicoloured	..	30	80
197/200			Set of 4	80	90

Designs:—6d. Kingston seal, diving, sailing, swimming and water polo; 8d. Kingston seal, pole-vaulting, javelin throwing, discus throwing, relay-racing and hurdling; 2s. Kingston coat of arms and athlete.

An imperf miniature sheet exists, but this was never available at face value or at any post office.

(Des M. Goaman. Litho D.L.R.)

1963 (4 June). *Freedom from Hunger.* P 12½.

201	93	1d. multicoloured	..	20	10
202		8d. multicoloured	..	60	60

94 Red Cross Emblem

95 Carole Joan Crawford ("Miss World 1963")

(Des V. Whiteley. Litho B.W.)

1963 (4 Sept). *Red Cross Centenary.* W w 12. P 13½.

203	94	2d. red and black	..	20	10
204		1s. 6d. red and blue	..	70	1·50

1963–64. As Nos. 181/90, but wmk w 12.

205	74	½d. black & deep orange-red (3.12.63*)	10	15
206	–	1d. black and emerald (3.4.64)	10	1·60
207	–	2½d. black and deep bright blue (3.4.64)	25	2·75
208	75	3d. emerald and red-brown (17.12.63*)	15	75
209	–	5d. scarlet and bronze-green (3.4.64)	40	2·75
210	76	8d. ultramarine and red-orange (3.4.64)	20	75
211	–	1s. yellow-green and blue (21.12.63*)	35	75
212	–	2s. dp blue & dp bronze-green (3.4.64)	60	6·50
213	77	3s. black and blue (5.2.64)	50	5·00
205/13		Set of 9	3·50	18·00

The overprint on the 8d., 1s. and 2s. is at lower left, the others are as before.

*These are the earliest known dates recorded in Jamaica.

(Des and photo D.L.R.)

1964 (14 Feb–25 May). *"Miss World 1963" Commemoration.* P 13.

214	95	3d. multicoloured	..	10	10
215		1s. multicoloured	..	15	10
216		1s. 6d. multicoloured	..	20	50
214/16			Set of 3	40	60
MS216a		153×101 mm. Nos. 214/16. Imperf (25.5.64)		1·10	2·25

96 Lignum Vitae

97 Blue Mahoe

103 Gypsum Industry

109 Arms of Jamaica

111 Multiple "J" and Pineapple

(Des V. Whiteley. Photo Harrison)

1964 (4 May)–**68**. T 96/7, 103, 109 and similar designs. W 111. P 14½ (1d., 2d., 2½d., 6d., 8d.), 14×14½ (1½d., 3d., 4d., 10s.), 14½×14 (9d., 1s., 3s., 5s., £1) or 13½×14½ (1s. 6d., 2s.).

217		1d. violet-blue, dp green & lt brn (shades)	10	10
218		1½d. multicoloured	15	10
219		2d. red, yellow and grey-green	15	10
		w. Wmk inverted	4·00	
220		2½d. multicoloured	90	60
221		3d. yellow, black and emerald	15	10
222		4d. ochre and violet	45	10
223		6d. multicoloured	2·25	10
		a. Blue omitted	55·00	
		b. Value omitted	£700	
		w. Wmk inverted	8·50	
224		8d. mult (yellowish green background)	2·25	1·50
		a. Red (beak) omitted	£100	
		b. Greyish green background (16.7.68)	6·50	3·75
225		9d. blue and yellow-bistre	1·50	10
226		1s. black and light brown	20	10
		a. Light brown omitted	£350	
		ab. Value only omitted	£450	
		b. Black omitted	£500	
		ba. "NATIONAL STADIUM" etc omitted	£600	
227		1s. 6d. black, light blue and buff	3·00	15
228		2s. red-brown, black and light blue	2·75	15
229		3s. blue and dull green	1·00	80
		aw. Wmk inverted	11·00	
		b. Perf 13½×14½	35	65
230		5s. black, ochre and blue	1·25	1·00
		w. Wmk inverted	75·00	
231		10s. multicoloured	1·25	1·25
		a. Blue ("JAMAICA", etc) omitted	£200	
232		£1 multicoloured	1·50	1·00
217/32		Set of 16	16·00	6·00

Designs: Horiz. (As T 96)—1½d. Ackee; 2½d. Land shells; 3d. National flag over Jamaica; 4d. Antillean Murex (*Murex formosus*) (shell); 6d. *Papilio homerus* (butterfly); 8d. Streamertail. As T 103—1s. National Stadium; 1s. 6d. Palisadoes International Airport; 2s. Bauxite mining; 3s. Blue Marlin (sport fishing); 5s. Exploration of sunken city, Port Royal; £1 Queen Elizabeth II and national flag.

No. 223b. Two left half sheets are known with the black printing shifted downwards to such an extent that the value is omitted from the top row.

Nos. 226a/ab came from a sheet on which the two bottom rows had the colour omitted with the next row showing it missing from the lower third of the stamps.

A similar sheet, but with the colour missing from the top two rows and part of the third produced Nos 226b/ba.

112 Scout Belt

113 Globe, Scout Hat and Scarf

114 Scout Badge and Alligator

(Photo Harrison)

1964 (27 Aug). *Sixth Inter-American Scout Conference, Kingston.* W 111. P 14 (1s.) or 14½ × 14 (others).

233	112	3d. red, black and pink	..	10	10
234	113	8d. bright blue, olive and black	..	15	25
		w. Wmk inverted		22·00	
235	114	1s. gold, deep blue and light blue		20	45
		w. Wmk inverted		20	45
233/5			Set of 3	40	70

115 Gordon House, Kingston

118 Eleanor Roosevelt

(Des V. Whiteley. Photo Harrison)

1964 (16 Nov). *Tenth Commonwealth Parliamentary Conference, Kingston.* T 115 and similar horiz designs. W 111. P 14½ × 14.

236		3d. black and yellow-green	..	10	10
237		6d. black and carmine-red	..	15	10
238		1s. 6d. black and bright blue	..	30	30
236/8			Set of 3	50	40

Designs:—6d. Headquarters House, Kingston; 1s. 6d. House of Assembly, Spanish Town.

(Des V. Whiteley. Photo Harrison)

1964 (10 Dec). *16th Anniv of Declaration of Human Rights.* W 111. P 14½ × 14.

239	118	1s. black, red and light green	..	10	10

119 Guides' Emblem on Map

120 Guide Emblems

(Photo Harrison)

1965 (17 May). *Golden Jubilee of Jamaica Girl Guides Association. W* 111 *(sideways on 3d.). P* 14 × 14½ (3d.) *or* 14 (1s.).
240	119	3d. yellow, green and light blue			10	10
241	120	1s. yellow, black and apple-green			20	40
		w. Wmk inverted	..	..	20	40

121 Uniform Cap

122 Flag-bearer and Drummer

(Photo Harrison)

1965 (23 Aug). *Salvation Army Centenary. W* 111. *P* 14 × 14½ (3d.) *or* 14½ × 14 (1s. 6d.).
242	121	3d. multicoloured		..	25	10
		w. Wmk inverted	..	..	9·50	
243	122	1s. 6d. multicoloured	..	..	50	50
		w. Wmk inverted	..	..	20·00	

123 Paul Bogle, William Gordon and Morant Bay Court House

124 Abeng-blower, "Telstar", Morse Key and I.T.U. Emblem

(Photo Enschedé)

1965 (29 Dec). *Centenary of Morant Bay Rebellion. No wmk. P* 14 × 13.
244	123	3d. light brown, ultramarine and black		10	10
245		1s. 6d. lt brown, yellow-green & black		20	10
246		3s. light brown, rose and black		30	75
244/6 ..			*Set of 3*	55	85

(Photo Harrison)

1965 (29 Dec). *I.T.U. Centenary. W* 111. *P* 14 × 14½.
247	124	1s. black, grey-blue and red		..	40	15

ROYAL VISIT MARCH 1966

(125)

126 Sir Winston Churchill

1966 (3 Mar). *Royal Visit. Nos.* 221, 223, 226/7 *optd with T* 125.
248		3d. yellow, black and emerald			15	10
249		6d. multicoloured	..	..	1·75	30
250		1s. black and light brown	..		55	10
251		1s. 6d. black, light blue and buff ..		2·00	2·00
248/51 ..			*Set of 4*	4·00	2·25

(Des Jennifer Toombs. Photo Harrison)

1966 (18 April). *Churchill Commemoration. W* 111. *P* 14.
252	126	6d. black and olive-green		50	30
253		1s. bistre-brown and deep violet-blue ..	75	80

NEW INFORMATION

The editor is always interested to correspond with people who have new information that will improve or correct the Catalogue.

---

127 Statue of Athlete and Flags

131 Bolivar's Statue and Flags of Jamaica and Venezuela

(Des V. Whiteley. Photo Harrison)

1966 (4 Aug). *Eighth British Empire and Commonwealth Games. T* 127 *and similar horiz designs. W* 111. *P* 14½ × 14.
254		3d. multicoloured			10	10
255		6d. multicoloured			40	10
		w. Wmk inverted			18·00	
256		1s. multicoloured			10	10
257		3s. bright gold and deep blue		35	45
		a. Dull gold and deep blue			
		w. Wmk inverted			18·00	
254/7			*Set of 4*	80	55

MS258   128×103 mm. *Nos.* 254/7. *Imperf* .. 4·00 7·50
Designs:—6d. Racing cyclists; 1s. National Stadium, Kingston; 3s. Games emblem.
No. MS258 has been seen with the whole printing inverted except for the brown background.

(Des and photo Harrison)

1966 (5 Dec). *150th Anniv of "Jamaica Letter". W* 111. *P* 14×15.
259	131	8d. multicoloured			20	10
		w. Wmk inverted			19·00	

132 Jamaican Pavilion

133 Sir Donald Sangster (Prime Minister)

(Des V. Whiteley. Photo Harrison)

1967 (28 Apr). *World Fair, Montreal. W* 111. *P* 14½.
260	132	6d. multicoloured			10	15
261		1s. multicoloured			10	15
		w. Wmk inverted			6·00	

(Des and photo Enschedé)

1967 (28 Aug). *Sangster Memorial Issue. P* 13½.
262	133	3d. multicoloured			10	10
263		1s. 6d. multicoloured			20	20

134 Traffic Duty

135 Personnel of the Force

(Des V. Whiteley. Photo Enschedé)

1967 (28 Nov). *Centenary of the Constabulary Force. T* 134/5 *and similar horiz design. Multicoloured. W* 111. *P* 13½ × 14.
264		3d. Type 134			40	10
		a. Wmk sideways			85	1·40
265		1s. Type 135			40	10
266		1s. 6d. Badge and Constables of 1867 and 1967 (*as T* 134)		50	75
264/6 ..			*Set of 3*	1·10	85

136 Wicket-keeping

137 Sir Alexander and Lady Bustamante

(Des V. Whiteley. Photo Harrison)

1968 (8 Feb). *M.C.C.'s West Indian Tour. T* 136 *and similar vert designs. Multicoloured. W* 111 *(sideways*). P* 14.
267		6d. Type 136			50	50
		a. Horiz strip of 3. *Nos.* 267/9		1·50	
		w. Wmk top of J to right		50	50
268		6d. Batting			50	50
		w. Wmk top of J to right		50	50
269		6d. Bowling			50	50
		w. Wmk top of J to right		50	50
267/9			*Set of 3*	1·50	1·50

*The normal sideways watermark shows the top of the "J" to left, *as seen from the back of the stamp.*
Nos. 267/9 were issued in small sheets of 9 comprising three se-tenant strips as No. 267a.
Nos. 267/9 exist on PVA gum as well as on gum arabic.

(Des and photo Harrison)

1968 (23 May). *Labour Day. W* 111. *P* 14.
270	137	3d. rose and black		..	10	15
271		1s. olive and black		..	10	15

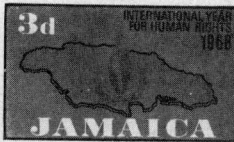

138 Human Rights Emblem over Map of Jamaica

(Photo Harrison)

1968 (3 Dec). *Human Rights Year. T* 138 *and similar multicoloured designs. W* 111. *P* 14.
272		3d. Type 138			10	10
		a. Gold (flame) omitted			90·00	
		w. Wmk inverted			4·50	
273		1s. Hands cupping Human Rights emblem (*vert*)		10	10
274		3s. Jamaican holding "Human Rights"		30	90
		a. Gold (flame) omitted			£100	
272/4			*Set of 3*	45	1·00

Three designs, showing 3d. Bowls of Grain, 1s. Abacus, 3s. Hands in Prayer, were prepared but not issued (*Price for set of 3 mint* £100).

141 ILO Emblem

142 Nurse, and Children being weighed and measured

(Des V. Whiteley. Litho Format)

1969 (23 May). *50th Anniv of International Labour Organization. P* 14.
275	141	6d. orange-yellow and blackish brown		10	10
276		3s. bright emerald and blackish brown		30	30

(Des and photo Harrison)

1969 (30 May). *20th Anniv of W.H.O. T* 142 *and similar designs. W* 111. *P* 14.
277		6d. grey, brown and orange			10	10
278		1s. black, sepia and blue-green			10	10
279		3s. grey-black, brown and pale bright blue		20	55
277/9 ..			*Set of 3*	30	60

Designs: *Horiz*—1s. Malaria eradication. *Vert*—3s. Trainee nurse.

(New Currency. 100 cents = 1 Jamaica dollar)

C-DAY 8th September 1969
1c

(145)

146 "The Adoration of the Kings" (detail, Foppa)

1969 (8 Sept). *Decimal currency. Nos.* 217, 219, 221/3 *and* 225/32 *surch as T* 145. *Sterling values unobliterated except* 1 c. *to* 4 c. *and* 8 c.
280		1 c. on 1d. violet-blue. dp green & lt brown		10	10
281		2 c. on 2d. red, yellow and grey-green		10	10
		w. Wmk inverted			2·00	
282		3 c. on 3d. yellow, black and emerald		10	10
283		4 c. on 4d. ochre and violet			1·25	10
		a. "8t" of "8th" omitted (R. 10/1)		42·00	

284	5 c. on 6d. multicoloured		1·25	10
	a. Blue omitted	.. ..	50·00	
285	8 c. on 9d. blue and yellow-bistre		10	10
286	10 c. on 1s. black and light brown		10	10
287	15 c. on 1s. 6d. black, light blue and buff		30	90
288	20 c. on 2s. red-brown, black and light blue		1·50	10
	a. "8th" omitted			
289	30 c. on 3s. blue and dull green	..	1·50	2·75
290	50 c. on 5s. black, ochre and blue	..	1·25	3·00
291	$1 on 10s. multicoloured	..	1·25	6·50
	w. Wmk inverted	..	£100	
292	$2 on £1 multicoloured	..	1·50	6·50
280/92		Set of 13	8·50	19·00

No. 281 exists with PVA gum as well as gum arabic.
Unlike the positional No. 283a the similar variety on the 20 c. on 2s. was caused by a paper fold.

(Des J. Cooter. Litho D.L.R.)

1969 (25 Oct). *Christmas. Paintings. T **146** and similar vert designs. Multicoloured. W **111**. P 13.*

293	2 c. Type **146**		20	40
294	5 c. "Madonna, Child and St. John" (Raphael)		25	40
295	8 c. "The Adoration of the Kings" (detail, Dosso Dossi)		25	40
293/5	.. .. ..	Set of 3	65	1·10

149 Half Penny, 1869

151 George William Gordon

(Des G. Drummond. Litho P.B.)

1969 (27 Oct). *Centenary of First Jamaican Coins. T **149** and similar horiz design. W **111**. P 12½.*

296	3 c. silver, black and mauve	..	15	25
	b. Wmk sideways	..	60	80
297	15 c. silver, black and light emerald	..	10	10

Design:—15 c. One penny, 1869.

(Des G. Vasarhelyi. Litho Enschedé)

1970 (11 Mar). *National Heroes. T **151** and similar vert designs. Multicoloured. P 12 × 12½.*

298	1 c. Type **151**	.. ..	10	10
	a. Yellow (from flags) omitted	.. ..	£180	
299	3 c. Sir Alexander Bustamante	..	10	10
300	5 c. Norman Manley	..	10	10
301	10 c. Marcus Garvey	..	15	10
302	15 c. Paul Bogle	.. ..	30	25
298/302		Set of 5	50	40

156 "Christ appearing to St. Peter" (Carracci)

2c

(159)

(Des G. Drummond. Photo Enschedé)

1970 (23 Mar). *Easter. T **156** and similar vert designs. Multicoloured. W **111**. P 12 × 12½.*

303	3 c. Type **156**	..	10	10
	w. Wmk inverted	..		
304	10 c. "Christ Crucified" (Antonello da Messina)	..	10	10
	w. Wmk inverted	..		
305	20 c. Easter Lily	..	20	60
303/5	.. ..	Set of 3	30	70

1970 (16 July). *No. 219 surch with T **159**.*

306	2 c. on 2d. red, yellow and grey-green		20	20

160 Lignum Vitae

161 Cable Ship Dacia

1970 (7 Sept–2 Nov). *Decimal Currency. Designs as Nos. 217/32 but inscr as T **160** in new currency. W **111** (sideways on 2, 4, 15, 20 c. and $1). P 14½ (1, 5 c.), 14 × 14½ (4 c., $1), 13½ × 14½ (15, 20 c.) or 14½ × 14 (others).*

307	1 c. violet-blue, deep green & lt brown		60	1·50
308	2 c. red, yellow and grey-green (as 2d.)		30	10
309	3 c. yellow, black and emerald (as 3d.)		45	60
310	4 c. ochre and violet (as 4d.)		2·25	10
311	5 c. multicoloured (as 6d.)		3·00	10
312	8 c. blue and yellow-bistre (as 9d.)		1·75	10
	a. Wmk sideways		1·50	45
313	10 c. black and light brown (as 1s.)		40	10
314	15 c. black, light blue and buff (as 1s. 6d.) (2.11)		2·00	2·50
315	20 c. red-brown, black & lt blue (as 2s.) (2.11)		1·25	2·25
316	30 c. blue and dull green (as 3s.) (2.11)		3·00	3·75
317	50 c. black, ochre and blue (as 5s.) (2.11)		1·25	3·75
318	$1 multicoloured (as 10s.) (2.11)		1·00	3·75
319	$2 multicoloured (as £1) (2.11)		1·25	4·00
307/19		Set of 13	16·00	20·00

(Des G. Drummond. Litho J.W.)

1970 (12 Oct). *Centenary of Telegraph Service. T **161** and similar horiz designs. W **111** (sideways). P 14½ × 14.*

320	3 c. yellow, red and black		15	10
321	10 c. black and turquoise	..	20	10
322	50 c. multicoloured	..	50	1·00
320/2		Set of 3	75	1·10

Designs:—10 c. Bright's cable gear aboard *Dacia*; 50 c. Morse key and chart.

164 Bananas, Citrus, Sugar-Cane and Tobacco

165 Locomotive *Projector* (1845)

(Des G. Drummond. Litho Questa)

1970 (2 Nov). *75th Anniv of Jamaican Agricultural Society. W **111**. P 14.*

323	**164** 2 c. multicoloured		25	60
	w. Wmk inverted	..	7·00	
324	10 c. multicoloured		45	10

(Des V. Whiteley. Litho Format)

1970 (21 Nov). *125th Anniv of Jamaican Railways. T **165** and similar horiz designs. Multicoloured. W **111** (sideways). P 13½.*

325	3 c. Type **165**.		30	10
326	15 c. Steam locomotive No. 54 (1944)		80	30
327	50 c. Diesel locomotive No. 102 (1967)		2·00	2·00
325/7		Set of 3	2·75	2·25

168 Church of St. Jago de la Vega

169 Henry Morgan and Ships

(Des R. Granger Barrett. Litho J.W.)

1971 (22 Feb). *Centenary of Disestablishment of the Church of England in Jamaica. T **168** and similar vert design. Multicoloured. W **111**. P 14½.*

328	3 c. Type **168**	.. ..	10	10
329	10 c. Type **168**	..	10	10
	w. Wmk inverted			
330	20 c. Type **168**		30	30
	w. Wmk inverted	..	38·00	
331	30 c. Emblem of Church of England in Jamaica		30	80
	w. Wmk inverted			
328/31		Set of 4	60	1·10

(Des J.W. Litho Questa)

1971 (10 May). *Pirates and Buccaneers. T **169** and similar horiz designs. Multicoloured. W **111** (sideways*). P 14.*

332	3 c. Type **169**		75	10
	w. Wmk top of J to right	..	10·00	
333	15 c. Mary Read, Anne Bonny and trial pamphlet		1·00	15
334	30 c. Pirate schooner attacking merchantman		1·75	1·25
332/4		Set of 3	3·25	1·40

*The normal sideways watermark shows the top of the "J" to left, *as seen from the back of the stamp.*

COVER PRICES

Cover factors are quoted at the beginning of each country for most issues to 1945. An explanation of the system can be found on page x. The factors quoted do not, however, apply to philatelic covers.

---

170 1s. Stamp of 1919 with Frame Inverted

171 Satellite and Dish Aerial

(Des Jennifer Toombs. Litho J.W.)

1971 (30 Oct). *Tercentenary of Post Office Establishment. T **170** and similar designs. W **111** (sideways* except 50 c.). P 13½.*

335	3 c. black and lake	..	20	20
336	5 c. grey-black and bright green		20	20
337	8 c. black and violet	..	20	10
	w. Wmk top of J to right			
338	10 c. brown, black and indigo		20	10
339	20 c. multicoloured	..	50	45
340	50 c. ochre, black and slate	..	75	1·50
335/40		Set of 6	1·90	2·25

Designs: *Horiz*—3 c. Dummer packet letter, 1705; 5 c. Pre-stamp inland letter, 1793; 8 c. Harbour St. P.O., Kingston, 1820; 10 c. Modern stamp and cancellation; 20 c. British stamps used in Jamaica, 1859.

*The normal sideways watermark shows top of J to left, *as seen from the back of the stamp.*

(Des Cable & Wireless Ltd. Litho J.W.)

1972 (17 Feb). *Opening of Jamaican Earth Satellite Station. W **111**. P 14 × 13½.*

341	**171** 3 c. multicoloured	..	15	10
	w. Wmk inverted	..	†	—
342	15 c. multicoloured	..	20	15
343	50 c. multicoloured	..	65	1·25
341/3		Set of 3	90	1·25

172 Causeway, Kingston Harbour

173 Air Jamaica Hostess and Vickers VC-10

(Des J.W. Litho Format)

1972 (17 Apr–2 Oct). *Multicoloured designs as T **172** (1 to 6 c.) or **173** (8 c. to $2). W **111** (sideways* on horiz designs). P 14½ × 14 (1, 2 c.), 14 × 14½ (3, 4, 5, 6 c.) or 13½ (others).*

344	1 c. Pimento (vert) (5.6)	..	10	10
345	2 c. Red Ginger (vert) (5.6)		10	10
346	3 c. Bauxite Industry (5.6)		10	10
	w. Wmk top of J to right	..	6·00	
347	4 c. Type **172**	..	10	10
	w. Wmk top of J to right	..	10	10
348	5 c. Oil Refinery (5.6)	..	10	10
	w. Wmk top of J to right	..	26·00	
349	6 c. Senate Building, University of the West Indies (5.6)		10	10
350	8 c. National Stadium (5.6)		30	10
351	9 c. Devon House (5.6)		10	10
352	10 c. Type **173**		20	10
	w. Wmk top of J to right	..	32·00	
353	15 c. Old Iron Bridge, Spanish Town (vert) (2.10)		2·00	10
354	20 c. College of Arts, Science and Technology (2.10)		30	15
	w. Wmk top of J to right			
355	30 c. Dunn's River Falls (vert) (2.10)		35	15
356	50 c. River rafting (5.6)	..	1·50	40
357	$1 Jamaica House (2.10)		75	1·50
	w. Wmk top of J to right			
358	$2 Kings House (2.10)		1·00	1·50
344/58		Set of 15	6·00	3·75

*The normal sideways watermark shows the top of the J to the left, *as seen from the back of the stamp.*

(174) TENTH ANNIVERSARY INDEPENDENCE 1962-1972

175 Arms of Kingston

1972 (8 Aug). *Tenth Anniv of Independence. Nos. 346, 352 and 356 optd as* T **174**.

359	3 c. Bauxite Industry	30	30
	w. Wmk top of J to right	16·00	
360	10 c. Type **173**	30	10
	w. Wmk top of J to right		
361	50 c. River rafting	75	2·00
359/61	*Set of 3*	1·25	2·25

The normal sideways watermark shows top of J to left, as seen from the back of the stamp.

(Des R. Granger Barrett. Litho J.W.)

1972 (4 Dec). *Centenary of Kingston as Capital.* W **111** (*sideways on 50 c.*). P 13½ × 14 (5 *and* 30 *c.*) *or* 14 × 13½ (50 *c.*).

362	**175** 5 c. multicoloured	10	10
363	30 c. multicoloured	20	35
364	50 c. multicoloured	40	1·75
362/4	*Set of 3*	60	2·00

The 50 c. is as T **175**, but horiz.

176 Small Indian Mongoose on Map

(Des R. Granger Barrett. Litho Questa)

1973 (9 Apr). *Centenary of Introduction of the Mongoose.* T **176** *and similar horiz designs.* W **111** (*sideways*). P 14 × 14½.

365	8 c. light apple-green, yellow-green and black	15	10
366	40 c. light cobalt, light blue and black	35	50
367	60 c. salmon-pink, brownish salmon & black	60	1·00
365/7	*Set of 3*	1·00	1·40
MS368	165 × 95 mm. Nos. 365/7	1·10	3·75

Designs:—40 c. Mongoose and rat; 60 c. Mongoose and chicken.

177 *Euphorbia punicea*

(Des Sylvia Goaman. Litho Questa)

1973 (9 July). *Flora.* T **177** *and similar diamond-shaped designs. Multicoloured.* W **111**. P 14.

369	1 c. Type **177**	10	10
370	6 c. *Hylocereus triangularis*	15	10
371	9 c. *Columnea argentea*	15	10
372	15 c. *Portlandia grandiflora*	25	15
373	30 c. *Samyda pubescens*	50	60
374	50 c. *Cordia sebestena*	80	1·25
369/74	*Set of 6*	1·75	2·00

178 *Broughtonia sanguinea*

(Des Sylvia Goaman. Litho B.W.)

1973 (8 Oct). *Orchids.* T **178** *and similar multicoloured designs.* W **111** (*sideways on 5 c., $1*). P 14×13½ (5 *c.*, $1) *or* 13½×14 (*others*).

375	5 c. Type **178**	40	10
376	10 c. *Arpophyllum jamaicense* (*vert*)	50	10
	w. Wmk inverted	14·00	
377	20 c. *Oncidium pulchellum* (*vert*)	1·25	25
378	$1 *Brassia maculata*	2·75	2·75
375/8	*Set of 4*	4·50	2·75
MS379	161×95 mm. Nos. 375/8. Wmk sideways. P 12	4·50	5·00

a. Printed on the gummed side (blue and brown plates only)

No. **MS379**a has positive impressions of the blue and brown plates printed on the reverse in addition to the normal design on the front.

STANLEY GIBBONS STAMP COLLECTING SERIES

179 *Mary*, 1808–15   **180** "Journeys"

(Des J. Cooter. Litho J.W.)

1974 (8 Apr). *Mail Packet Boats.* T **179** *and similar horiz designs. Multicoloured.* W **111** (*sideways on Nos.* 380/3, *upright on* **MS384**). P 13½ (5 c., 50 c.) *or* 14½ (*others*).

380	5 c. Type **179**	55	10
	a. Perf 14½	1·00	3·50
381	10 c. *Queensbury*, 1814–27	55	10
382	15 c. *Sheldrake*, 1829–34	90	40
383	50 c. *Thames I*, 1842	2·00	2·50
380/3	*Set of 4*	3·50	2·75
MS384	133×159 mm. Nos. 380/3. P 13½ (*sold at* 90 *c.*)	3·50	5·00

(Des R. Granger Barrett. Litho Questa)

1974 (1 Aug). *National Dance Theatre Company.* T **180** *and similar vert designs showing dance-works. Multicoloured.* W **111**. P 13½.

385	5 c. Type **180**	10	10
386	10 c. "Jamaican Promenade"	10	10
387	30 c. "Jamaican Promenade"	30	30
388	50 c. "Misa Criolla"	50	80
385/8	*Set of 4*	80	1·10
MS389	161 × 102 mm. Nos. 385/8 (*sold at* $1)	1·50	2·50

181 U.P.U. Emblem and Globe

(Des V. Whiteley. Litho J.W.)

1974 (9 Oct). *Centenary of Universal Postal Union.* W **111** (*sideways**). P 14.

390	**181** 5 c. multicoloured	10	10
391	9 c. multicoloured	10	10
392	50 c. multicoloured	35	80
	w. Wmk top of J to right		
390/2	*Set of 3*	50	90

The normal sideways watermark shows the top of the J to left, as seen from the back of the stamp.

182 Senate Building and   **183** Commonwealth Symbol
Sir Hugh Wooding

(Des R. Granger Barrett. Litho Questa)

1975 (13 Jan). *25th Anniv of University of West Indies.* T **182** *and similar horiz design. Multicoloured.* W **111** (*sideways*). P 14.

393	5 c. Type **182**	10	10
394	10 c. University Chapel and H.R.H. Princess Alice	10	10
395	30 c. Type **182**	20	25
396	50 c. As 10 c.	35	60
393/6	*Set of 4*	60	80

(Des C. Abbott. Litho Questa)

1975 (29 Apr). *Heads of Commonwealth Conference.* T **183** *and similar square designs. Multicoloured.* W **111**. P 13½.

397	5 c. Type **183**	10	10
398	10 c. Jamaican coat of arms	10	10
399	30 c. Dove of Peace	15	30
400	50 c. Jamaican flag	30	1·40
397/400	*Set of 4*	50	1·60

184 Jamaican Kite   **185** Koo Koo or Actor Boy
Swallowtail (*Eurytides marcellinus*)

(Des J. Cooter. Litho Questa)

1975 (25 Aug). *Butterflies* (1st series). T **184** *and similar vert designs showing the family Papilionidae. Multicoloured.* W **111**. P 14.

401	10 c. Type **184**	55	20
402	20 c. Orange Swallowtail (*Papilo thoas*)	1·10	1·10
403	25 c. False Androgeus Swallowtail (*Papilo thersites*)	1·25	2·00
404	30 c. Homerus Swallowtail (*Papilo homerus*)	1·40	2·75
401/4	*Set of 4*	4·00	5·50
MS405	134×179 mm. Nos. 401/4 (*sold at* 95 *c.*)	5·50	7·50

See also Nos. 429/33 and 443/47.

(Des C. Abbott. Litho J.W.)

1975 (3 Nov). *Christmas.* T **185** *and similar vert designs showing Belisario prints of "John Canoe" (Christmas) Festival* (1st series). *Multicoloured.* W **111**. P 14.

406	8 c. Type **185**	15	10
407	10 c. Red Set-girls	15	10
408	20 c. French Set-girls	35	20
409	50 c. Jaw-bone or House John Canoe	70	1·90
	w. Wmk inverted		
406/9	*Set of 4*	1·25	2·00
MS410	138×141 mm. Nos. 406/9. P 13½ (*sold at* $1)	1·75	3·25

See also Nos. 421/4.

186 Bordone Map, 1528

(Des L. Curtis. Litho Questa)

1976 (12 Mar). *16th-century Maps of Jamaica.* T **186** *and similar horiz designs.* W **111** (*sideways**). P 13½.

411	10 c. brown, light stone and light vermilion	20	10
412	20 c. multicoloured	35	25
	w. Wmk top of J to right	18·00	
413	30 c. multicoloured	60	85
414	50 c. multicoloured	85	2·25
411/14	*Set of 4*	1·75	3·00

Designs— 20 c. Porcacchi map, 1576; 30 c. DeBry map, 1594; 50 c. Langenes map, 1598.

The normal sideways watermark shows the top of the J to left, as seen from the back of the stamp.

See also Nos. 425/8.

187 Olympic Rings

(Des Sir H. McDonald: adapted V. Whiteley Studio. Litho Walsall)

1976 (14 June). *Olympic Games, Montreal.* W **111** (*sideways*). P 13½.

415	**187** 10 c. multicoloured	15	10
416	20 c. multicoloured	30	20
417	25 c. multicoloured	30	25
418	50 c. multicoloured	45	2·00
415/18	*Set of 4*	1·10	2·25

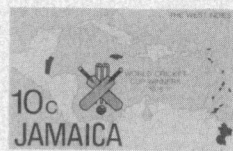

187a Map of the Caribbean

(Des PAD Studio. Litho Questa)

1976 (9 Aug). *West Indian Victory in World Cricket Cup.* T **187a** *and similar design. No wmk.* P 14.

419	10 c. multicoloured	40	50
420	25 c. black and magenta	85	1·75

Design: *Vert*—25 c. Prudential Cup.

(Des C. Abbott. Litho J.W.)

1976 (8 Nov). *Christmas. Belisario Prints* (2nd series). *Multicoloured designs as* T **185**. W **111**. P 13½.

421	10 c. Queen of the set-girls	10	10
422	20 c. Band of the Jaw-bone John Canoe	25	10
423	50 c. Koo Koo (actor-boy)	45	1·75
	w. Wmk inverted	6·50	
421/3	*Set of 3*	70	1·75
MS424	110×140 mm. Nos. 421/3. P 14×14½ (*sold at* 90 *c.*)	70	2·00

(Des L. Curtis. Litho J.W.)

1977 (28 Feb). *17th Century Maps of Jamaica. Designs as* T **186**. W **111** (*sideways*). P 13.

425	9 c. multicoloured	30	30
426	10 c. multicoloured	30	10
427	25 c. grey-black, pale blue and bright blue	70	60
428	40 c. grey-black, light turquoise and grey-blue	80	2·00
425/8	*Set of 4*	1·90	2·75

Designs:—9 c. Hickeringill map, 1661; 10 c. Ogilby map, 1671; 25 c. Visscher map, 1680; 40 c. Thornton map, 1689.

(Des J. Cooter. Litho J.W.)

1977 (9 May). *Butterflies (2nd series). Multicoloured designs as* T 184. W 111. P 13½.
429   10 c. False Barred Sulphur (*Eurema elathea*)   35   10
430   20 c. Bronze Wing (*Dynamine egaea*)   ..   75   55
431   25 c. Jamaican Harlequin (*Chlosyne pantoni*)   ..   1·00   1·50
    w. Wmk inverted   ..   ..   16·00
432   40 c. Mimic (*Hypolimnas misippus*)   ..   1·50   3·25
    w. Wmk inverted   ..   ..   38·00
429/32   ..   ..   ..   *Set of 4*   3·25   4·75
MS433   139×120 mm. Nos. 429/32. P 14½ (*sold at $1.05*)   ..   ..   4·50   7·00

188 Map, Scout Emblem and Streamertail   **189** Trumpeter

(Des Daphne Padden. Litho Questa)

1977 (5 Aug). *Sixth Caribbean Jamboree, Jamaica. Multicoloured; background colours given.* W 111 (*sideways*). P 13½.
434   **188**   new blue   35   10
435   20 c. light yellow-green   70   25
436   25 c. orange   75   35
437   50 c. light magenta   ..   ..   1·00   1·75
434/7   ..   ..   ..   *Set of 4*   2·50   2·25

(Des C. Abbott, Litho Questa)

1977 (19 Dec). *50th Anniv of Jamaica Military Band.* T 189 *and similar multicoloured designs.* W 111 (*sideways on horiz designs*). P 14.
438   9 c. Type **189**   15   10
439   10 c. Clarinet players   15   10
440   20 c. Two kettle drummers (*vert*)   ..   40   35
441   25 c. Double-bass player and trumpeter (*vert*)   55   65
438/41   ..   ..   ..   *Set of 4*   1·10   1·00
MS442   120×137 mm. Nos. 438/41. Wmk sideways (*sold at 75 c.*)   ..   2·50   4·00

(Des J. Cooter. Litho Walsall)

1978 (17 Apr). *Butterflies (3rd series). Multicoloured designs as* T 184. W 111. P 14.
443   10 c. Jamaican Hairstreak (*Callophrys crethona*)   50   10
444   20 c. Malachite (*Siproeta stelenes*)   85   20
445   25 c. Common Long-tailed Skipper (*Urbanus proteus*)   95   65
446   50 c. Troglodyte (*Anaea troglodyta*)   2·00   3·00
443/6   ..   ..   ..   *Set of 4*   3·75   3·50
MS447   100×125 mm. Nos. 443/6 (*sold at $1.15*)   ..   ..   4·50   6·00
    a. Error. Imperf £180

190 Half-figure with Canopy   **191** Norman Manley (statue)

(Des J. Cooter. Litho J.W.)

1978 (10 July). *Arawak Artefacts (1st series).* T 190 *and similar vert designs.* W 111. P 13½ × 13.
448   10 c. deep brown, yellow and black   ..   10   10
449   20 c. deep brown, mauve and black   ..   15   15
450   50 c. deep brown, apple-green and black   ..   35   35
448/50   ..   ..   ..   *Set of 3*   50   45
MS451   135 × 90 mm. Nos. 448/50. P 14 (*sold at 90 c.*)   60   1·25
Designs:—20 c. Standing figure; 50 c. Birdman.
See also Nos. 479/83.

(Des and litho J.W.)

1978 (25 Sept). *24th Commonwealth Parliamentary Conference.* T 191 *and similar vert designs. Multicoloured.* W 111. P 13.
452   10 c. Type **191**   10   10
453   20 c. Sir Alexander Bustamante (statue)   20   15
454   25 c. City of Kingston Crest   ..   20   20
455   40 c. Gordon House Chamber, House of Representatives   30   55
452/5   ..   ..   ..   *Set of 4*   70   90

192 Band and Banner   **193** "Negro Aroused" (sculpture by Edna Manley)

(Des V. Whiteley. Litho J.W.)

1978 (4 Dec). *Christmas. Centenary of Salvation Army.* T 192 *and similar horiz designs. Multicoloured.* W 111 (*sideways*). P 14.
456   10 c. Type **192**   40   10
457   20 c. Trumpeter   45   20
458   25 c. Banner   45   30
459   50 c. William Booth (founder)..   ..   80   2·50
456/9   ..   ..   ..   *Set of 4*   1·90   2·75

(Des G. Hutchins. Litho J.W.)

1978 (11 Dec). *International Anti-Apartheid Year.* W 111. P 13.
460   **193**   10 c. multicoloured   30   20

194 Tennis, Montego Bay   **195** Arms and Map of Jamaica

(Des and litho Harrison ($5). Des Walsall. Litho J.W. (others))

1979 (15 Jan)—**84**. *Vert designs as* T 194, *and* T 195. *Multicoloured. White ordinary paper* (15, 65, 75 c., $5) *or cream chalk-surfaced paper (others).* W 111 (*sideways on $5*). P 14½ × 14 ($5) *or* 13½ (*others*).
461   1 c. Type **194** (26.11.79)   ..   70   55
462   2 c. Golf, Tryall, Hanover (26.11.79)..   1·75   2·25
    a. White ordinary paper (8.84)   ..   3·00   3·25
463   4 c. Horse riding, Negril Beach (26.11.79)   ..   40   80
    a. White ordinary paper (8.84)   ..   2·50   2·50
464   5 c. Old waterwheel, Tryall, Hanover (26.11.79)   ..   55   20
    a. White ordinary paper (27.8.82)   ..   2·25   2·25
465   6 c. Fern Gully, Ocho Rios (26.11.79)   70   1·50
466   7 c. Dunn's River Falls, Ocho Rios (26.11.79)   40   30
467   8 c. Jamaican Tody (bird) (28.4.80)   1·00   65
468   10 c. Jamaican Mango (bird) (28.4.80)   1·00   20
    a. White ordinary paper (27.8.82)   ..   1·00   70
469   12 c. Yellow-billed Amazon (28.4.80)   80   1·00
470   15 c. Streamertail (bird) (28.4.80)   1·00   30
471   35 c. White-chinned Thrush (28.4.80)   1·25   30
472   50 c. Jamaican Woodpecker (28.4.80)..   1·50   30
473   65 c. Rafting, Martha Brae Trelawny (28.4.80)   70   1·50
474   75 c. Blue Marlin Fleet, Port Antonio (28.4.80)   1·25   30
475   $1 Scuba Diving, Ocho Rios (28.4.80)   1·50   1·50
    a. White ordinary paper (27.8.82)   ..   3·00   3·00
476   $2 Sailing boats, Montego Bay (28.4.80)   75   50
    a. White ordinary paper (27.8.82)   ..   3·00   3·00
477   $5 Type **195**   ..   ..   1·00   1·60
461/77   ..   ..   ..   *Set of 17*   14·50   12·00

TENTH ANNIVERSARY AIR JAMAICA 1st APRIL 1979

(196)   **197** Grinding Stone, circa 400 BC.

1979 (2 Apr). *10th Anniv of Air Jamaica. No. 352 optd with* T 196.
478   10 c. Type **173**   50   50

(Des D. Bowen. Litho Questa)

1979 (23 Apr). *Arawak Artefacts (2nd series).* T 197 *and similar multicoloured designs.* W 111 (*sideways on 10, 20 and 25 c.*). P 14.
479   5 c. Type **197**   10   10
480   10 c. Stone implements, *c.* 500 AD (*horiz*)   ..   10   10
481   20 c. Cooking pot, *c.* 300 AD (*horiz*)   ..   10   15
482   25 c. Serving boat, *c.* 300 AD (*horiz*)   ..   15   20
483   50 c. Storage jar fragment, *c.* 300 AD.   25   35
479/83   ..   ..   ..   *Set of 5*   55   70

198 1962 1s. 6d. Independence Commemorative Stamp

(Des J.W. from a local design by J. Mahfood. Litho Walsall)

1979 (13 Aug). *Death Centenary of Sir Rowland Hill.* T 198 *and similar horiz designs showing stamps and Sir Rowland Hill.* W 111 (*sideways*). P 14.
484   10 c. black, scarlet-vermilion & brt scarlet   15   10
    w. Wmk top of J to right   ..   5·00
485   20 c. orange-yellow and yellowish brown   20   15

---

486   25 c. mauve and blue   25   20
487   50 c. multicoloured   35   70
484/7   ..   ..   ..   *Set of 4*   85   1·00
MS488   146×94 mm. No. 485 (*sold at 30 c.*)   30   85
Designs:—20 c. 1920 1s. with frame inverted; 25 c. 1860 6d.; 50 c. 1968 3d. Human Rights Year commemorative.
*The normal sideways watermark has top of J to left, *when seen from the back of the stamp.*

199 Group of Children

(Des J.W. Litho Harrison)

1979 (1 Oct). *Christmas. International Year of the Child.* T 199 *and similar multicoloured designs.* W 111 (*sideways on* 10, 25 *and* 50 c.). P 14.
489   10 c. Type **199**   10   10
490   20 c. Doll (*vert*)   10   10
491   25 c. "The Family" (painting by child)   15   15
492   50 c. "House on the Hill" (painting by child)   25   40
489/92   ..   ..   ..   *Set of 4*   50   60

200 Date Tree Hall, 1886 (original home of Institute)

(Des G. Drummond. Litho Walsall)

1980 (25 Feb). *Centenary of Institute of Jamaica.* T 200 *and similar multicoloured designs.* W 111 (*sideways on* 5, 15 *and* 50 c.). P 13½.
493   5 c. Type **200**   10   10
494   15 c. Institute building, 1980 ..   15   10
495   35 c. Microfilm reader (*vert*)   ..   25   20
496   50 c. Hawksbill Turtle and Green Turtle   45   85
497   75 c. Jamaican Owl (*vert*)   ..   1·50   2·75
493/7 ..   ..   ..   *Set of 5*   2·25   3·50

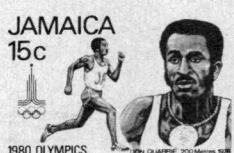

201 Don Quarrie (200 Metres, 1976)

(Des BG Studio. Litho J.W.)

1980 (21 July). *Olympic Games, Moscow. Jamaican Olympic Athletics Gold Medal Winners.* T 201 *and similar horiz designs. Multicoloured.* W 111 (*sideways**). P 13.
498   15 c. Type **201**   40   15
    w. Wmk top of J to left   ..   8·50
499   35 c. Arthur Wint (4×400 Metres Relay, 1952)   45   70
    a. Horiz strip of 4. Nos. 499/502   1·60
500   35 c. Leslie Laing (4×400 Metres Relay, 1952)   45   70
501   35 c. Herbert McKenley (4×400 Metres Relay, 1952) ..   45   70
502   35 c. George Rhoden (4×400 Metres Relay, 1952)   45   70
498/502   ..   ..   *Set of 5*   2·00   2·75
*The normal sideways watermark shows the top of J to right, *as seen from the back of the stamp.*
Nos. 499/502 were printed together, *se-tenant,* in horizontal strips of 4 throughout the sheet.

202 Parish Church   **203** Blood Cup Sponge

(Des J.W. Litho Harrison)

1980 (24 Nov). *Christmas. Churches (1st series).* T 202 *and similar horiz designs. Multicoloured.* W 111 (*sideways*). P 14.
503   15 c. Type **202**   10   10
504   20 c. Coke Memorial Church   ..   10   10
505   25 c. Church of the Redeemer   ..   15   10
506   $5 Holy Trinity Cathedral ..   ..   1·00   2·00
503/6   ..   ..   ..   *Set of 4*   1·10   2·10
MS507   120 × 139 mm. Nos. 503/6. P 14½ (*sold at $5.70*)   ..   ..   2·00   3·00
See also Nos. 537/40 and 570/2.

(Des J. Mahfood. Litho Walsall)

1981 (27 Feb). *Marine Life* (1st series). T **203** *and similar multicoloured designs.* W **111** (*sideways on 45 and 75 c.*). P 14.

508	20 c. Type **203**				15	10
509	45 c. Tube Sponge (*horiz*)				25	35
510	60 c. Black Coral				35	45
511	75 c. Tyre Reef (*horiz*)				40	75
508/11				*Set of 4*	1·00	1·50

See also Nos. 541/5.

204 Brown's Hutia
(or Indian Coney)

205 White Orchid

(Des D. Bowen. Litho Questa)

1981 (25 May). *Brown's Hutia* (or Indian Coney). T **204** *and similar horiz designs. Multicoloured.* W **111**. P 14.

512	20 c. Hutia facing right			15	20
	a. Horiz strip of 4. Nos. 512/15			55	
513	20 c. Type **204**			15	20
514	20 c. Hutia facing left and eating			15	20
515	20 c. Hutia family			15	20
512/15			*Set of 4*	55	70

Nos. 512/15 were printed together, *se-tenant*, in horizontal strips of 4 throughout the sheet.

(Des J.W. Litho Format)

1981 (29 July). *Royal Wedding.* T **205** *and similar vert designs. Multicoloured.* W w **14** (*sideways**). P 13½ ($5) or 15 (others).

516	20 c. Type **205**			10	10
	aw. Wmk Crown to right of CA			25	
	b. Perf 15×14½			25	25
	ba. Booklet pane. Nos. 516b/19b			3·50	
517	45 c. Royal Coach			15	10
	aw. Wmk Crown to right of CA			40	
	b. Perf 15×14½			50	50
518	60 c. Prince Charles and Lady Diana Spencer			20	20
	aw. Wmk Crown to right of CA			60	
	b. Perf 15×14½			60	60
519	$5 St. James' Palace			60	85
	aw. Wmk Crown to right of CA			2·25	
	b. Perf 15×14½			2·50	3·50
	bw. Wmk Crown to right of CA			2·50	
516/19			*Set of 4*	90	1·00
MS520	98×85 mm. No. 519. Wmk upright. P 13½			75	1·75
	w. Wmk inverted			2·75	

*The normal sideways watermark shows Crown to left of CA, *as seen from the back of the stamp.*

Nos. 516/18 also exist perforated 13½ (price for set of 3 70p. mint or used) from additional sheetlets of 5 stamps and one label. No. 519 exists from both normal sheets and sheetlets.

Nos. 516b/19b are from $6.25 stamp booklets.

206 Blind Man at Work

207 W.F.D. Emblem on 1964 1½d. Definitive

(Des G. Vasarhelyi. Litho J.W.)

1981 (14 Sept). *International Year for Disabled Persons.* T **206** *and similar horiz designs. Multicoloured.* W **111** (*sideways*). P 13.

521	20 c. Type **206**			15	15
522	45 c. Painting with the mouth			40	40
523	60 c. Deaf student communicating with sign language			50	75
524	$1.50, Basketball players			1·25	2·00
521/4			*Set of 4*	2·10	3·00

(Des J. Mahfood. Litho J.W.)

1981 (16 Oct). *World Food Day. Stamps on Stamps.* T **207** *and similar designs showing W.F.D. emblems on various definitives.* W **111** (*sideways on 20 c., $2 and $4*). P 13.

525	20 c. multicoloured			35	15
526	45 c. black, rose and orange			70	40
527	$2 black, violet-blue and green			2·00	1·40
528	$4 black, green and light brown			3·25	2·50
525/8			*Set of 4*	5·50	4·00

Designs: Vert as T **207**—45 c. 1922 1d. (40 × 26 mm.)—$2 As 1938 3d. but with W.F.D. emblem replacing King's head; $4 As 1938 1s. but with W.F.D. emblem replacing King's head.

Nos. 525/8 were so designed that the face values obliterated those on the stamps depicted.

MINIMUM PRICE

The minimum price quote is 10p which represents a handling charge rather than a basis for valuing common stamps. For further notes about prices see introductory pages.

208 "Survival" (song title)

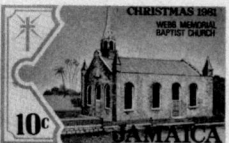

209 Webb Memorial Baptist Church

(Litho Format)

1981 (20 Oct). *Bob Marley* (musician) *Commemoration.* T **208** *and similar vert designs inscribed with song titles. In black and vermilion* ($5.25) *or multicoloured* (others). W w **14** (*sideways*). P 15.

529	1 c. Type **208**				50	40
530	2 c. "Exodus"				50	40
531	3 c. "Is this Love"				50	40
532	15 c. "Coming in from the Cold"*				2·25	30
533	20 c. "Positive Vibration"†				2·25	30
534	60 c. "War"				3·00	2·75
535	$3 "Could you be Loved"				5·50	10·00
529/35				*Set of 7*	13·00	13·00
MS536	134 × 110 mm. $5.25, Bob Marley (wmk upright)				6·00	4·75

*Part of initial "C" of song title inscription does not show on the design.

†Incorrectly inscribed "OSITIVE VIBRATION".

(Des J.W. Litho Questa)

1981 (11 Dec). *Christmas. Churches* (2nd series). T **209** *and similar horiz designs. Multicoloured.* W **111** (*sideways*). P 14.

537	10 c. Type **209**			10	10
538	45 c. Church of God in Jamaica			30	15
539	$5 Bryce United Church			1·75	2·50
537/9			*Set of 3*	1·90	2·50
MS540	120 × 168 mm. Nos. 537/9 (wmk upright). P 12			3·50	3·50

210 Gorgonian Coral

211 Cub Scout

(Des J. Mahfood; adapted PAD Studio. Litho Questa)

1982 (22 Feb). *Marine Life* (2nd series). T **210** *and similar multicoloured designs.* W **111** (*sideways on 45, 60, 75 c. and $3*). P 14.

541	20 c. Type **210**			45	10
542	45 c. Hard Sponge and diver (*horiz*)			65	25
543	60 c. American Manatee (*horiz*)			90	55
544	75 c. Plume Worm (*horiz*)			1·00	65
545	$3 Coral Banded Shrimp (*horiz*)			2·50	1·75
541/5			*Set of 5*	5·00	3·00

(Des L. Curtis. Litho J.W.)

1982 (12 July). *75th Anniv of Boy Scout Movement.* T **211** *and similar vert designs. Multicoloured.* W **111**. P 13½ × 13.

546	20 c. Type **211**			50	15
547	45 c. Scout camp			85	40
548	60 c. "Out of Many, One People"			1·10	90
549	$2 Lord Baden-Powell			1·75	2·50
546/9			*Set of 4*	3·75	3·50
MS550	80 × 130 mm. Nos. 546/9			5·00	6·00

ROYAL BABY 21.6.82

212 *Lignum vitae*
(national flower)

(212a)

(Des R. Sauer. Litho Questa)

1982 (30 Aug). *21st Birthday of Princess of Wales.* T **212** *and similar vert designs.* W **111**. P 14½ × 14.

551	20 c. Type **212**			20	20
	a. Booklet pane. Nos. 551/3			2·00	
552	45 c. Carriage ride			35	35
553	60 c. Wedding			50	60
554	75 c. Saxifraga longifolia			1·00	1·75
	a. Booklet pane. Nos. 554/6			3·00	
555	$2 Princess of Wales			1·40	1·50
556	$3 Viola gracilis major			1·40	2·75
551/6			*Set of 6*	4·25	7·00
MS557	106 × 75 mm. $5 Honeymoon photograph			1·40	2·50

Nos. 554 and 556 were printed in small sheets of 6 including one se-tenant, stamp-size, label. The other values were printed in sheets of 40.

1982 (13 Sept). *Birth of Prince William of Wales. Nos. 551/7 optd with T **212a.***

558	20 c. Type **212**			20	20
	a. Booklet pane. Nos. 558/60			80	
559	45 c. Carriage ride			30	35
560	60 c. Wedding			40	60
561	75 c. Saxifraga longifolia			70	1·00
	a. Booklet pane. Nos. 561/3			2·25	
562	$2 Princess of Wales			75	1·50
563	$3 Viola gracilis major			1·00	2·50
558/63			*Set of 6*	3·00	5·50
MS564	106 × 75 mm. $5 Honeymoon photograph			1·75	3·00

213 Prey Captured

214 Queen Elizabeth II

(Des N. Arlott. Litho Questa)

1982 (25 Oct). *Jamaican Birds* (1st series). Jamaican Lizard Cuckoo. T **213** *and similar vert designs. Multicoloured.* W **111**. P 14½.

565	$1 Type **213**			1·40	1·40
	a. Horiz strip of 5. Nos. 565/9			6·00	
566	$1 Searching for prey			1·40	1·40
567	$1 Calling prior to prey search			1·40	1·40
568	$1 Adult landing			1·40	1·40
569	$1 Adult flying in			1·40	1·40
565/9			*Set of 5*	6·00	6·00

Nos. 565/9 were printed in horizontal se-tenant strips of 5 throughout the sheet.

See also Nos. 642/5 and 707/10.

(Des and litho J.W.)

1982 (8 Dec). *Christmas. Churches* (3rd series). Horiz designs as T **209**. Multicoloured. W **111** (*sideways*). P 13.

570	20 c. United Pentecostal Church			40	10
571	45 c. Disciples of Christ Church			75	25
572	75 c. Open Bible Church			1·40	2·75
570/2			*Set of 3*	2·25	2·75

(Des D. Miller. Litho Walsall)

1983 (14 Feb). *Royal Visit.* T **214** *and similar vert design. Multicoloured.* W **111**. P 14.

573	$2 Type **214**			3·00	3·50
574	$3 Coat of Arms			4·00	5·00

215 Folk Dancing

(Des Walsall. Litho Format)

1983 (14 Mar). *Commonwealth Day.* T **215** *and similar horiz designs. Multicoloured.* W **111** (*sideways**). P 14.

575	20 c. Type **215**			15	15
576	45 c. Bauxite mining			35	35
577	75 c. World map showing position of Jamaica			45	45
578	$2 Coat of arms and family			60	1·40
	w. Wmk top of J to right			12·00	
575/8			*Set of 4*	1·40	2·10

*The normal sideways watermark has top of "J" to left, *as seen from the back of the stamp.*

216 General Cargo Ship at Wharf

217 Norman Manley and Sir Alexander Bustamante

(Des A. Theobald. Litho Format)

1983 (17 Mar). *25th Anniv of International Maritime Organization.* T **216** *and similar horiz designs. Multicoloured.* P 14.

579	15 c. Type **216**			75	30
580	20 c. Veendam (cruise liner) at Kingston			1·00	40
581	45 c. Astronomer (container ship) entering port			1·75	85
582	$1 Tanker passing International Seabed Headquarters Building			2·75	3·75
579/82			*Set of 4*	5·50	4·75

(Des D. Miller. Litho Harrison)

1983 (25 July). *21st Anniv of Independence.* W **111**. P 14.

583	**217** 15 c. multicoloured			15	20
584	20 c. multicoloured			15	25
585	45 c. multicoloured			30	50
583/5			*Set of 3*	55	85

218 Ship-to-Shore Radio

219 "Racing at Caymanas" (Sidney McLaren)

(Des Walsall. Litho Harrison)

1983 (18 Oct). *World Communications Year. T* **218** *and similar horiz designs. Multicoloured. W* **111** *(sideways). P* 14.

586	20 c. Type **218**	..	40	15
587	45 c. Postal services	..	75	40
588	75 c. Telephone communications	..	1·00	2·00
589	$1 T.V. via satellite	..	1·25	2·50
586/9	..	*Set of 4*	3·00	4·50

(Des D. Miller. Litho J.W.)

1983 (12 Dec). *Christmas. Paintings. T* **219** *and similar multicoloured designs. Multicoloured on* 15 c, 20 c. *P* 13 × 13½ (15 c, 20 c.) *or* 13½ × 13 *(others).*

590	15 c. Type **219**	..	15	10
591	20 c. "Seated Figures" (Karl Parboosingh)	..	15	10
592	75 c. "The Petitioner" (Henry Daley) (*vert*)	..	50	50
593	$2 "Banana Plantation" (John Dunkley) (*vert*)	..	1·25	2·75
590/3	..	*Set of 4*	1·90	3·00

220 Sir Alexander Bustamante

221 De Havilland D.H. 60G Gipsy Moth Seaplane

(Des D. Miller. Litho Questa)

1984 (24 Feb). *Birth Centenary of Sir Alexander Bustamante. T* **220** *and similar vert design. Multicoloured. W* **111**. *P* 14.

594	20 c. Type **220**	..	65	1·00
	a. Horiz pair. Nos. 594/5	..	1·25	2·00
595	20 c. Birthplace, Blenheim	..	65	1·00

Nos. 594/5 were printed together, *se-tenant*, in horizontal pairs throughout the sheet.

(Des A. Theobald. Litho Questa)

1984 (11 June). *Seaplanes and Flying Boats. T* **221** *and similar horiz designs. Multicoloured. W* **111** *(sideways). P* 14.

596	25 c. Type **221**	..	1·50	20
597	55 c. Consolidated Commodore flying boat	2·00	85
598	$1.50, Sikorsky S-38A flying boat	3·25	4·00
599	$3 Sikorsky S-40 flying boat *American Clipper*	4·00	6·00
596/9	..	*Set of 4*	9·50	10·00

5c

222 Cycling

223

(Des G. Vasarhelyi. Litho J.W.)

1984 (11 July). *Olympic Games, Los Angeles. T* **222** *and similar horiz designs. Multicoloured. W* **111** *(sideways). P* 14.

600	25 c. Type **222**	..	75	30
601	55 c. Relay running	..	60	30
602	$1.50, Start of race	..	1·00	2·25
603	$3 Finish of race	..	1·40	3·25
600/3	..	*Set of 4*	3·25	5·50
MS604	135 × 105 mm. Nos. 600/3 (*sold at* $5.40). *P* 13 × 13½	3·00	5·50

1984 (7 Aug). *Nos.* 465 *and* 469 *surch as T* **223**.

605	5 c. on 6 c. Fern Gully, Ocho Rios	15	40
606	10 c. on 12 c. Yellow-billed Amazon	..	85	60

224 Head of Jamaican Boa Snake

(Des I. Loe. Litho Questa)

1984 (22 Oct). *Jamaican Boa Snake. T* **224** *and similar horiz designs. Multicoloured. W* **111** *(sideways). P* 14½.

607	25 c. Type **224**	..	3·50	40
608	55 c. Boa snake on branch over stream	4·50	80
609	70 c. Snake with young	..	5·50	3·00
610	$1 Snake on log	..	6·50	3·50
607/10	..	*Set of 4*	18·00	7·00
MS611	133 × 97 mm. As Nos. 607/10 but without W.W.F. emblem (*sold at* $2.60)	6·00	3·00

225 Locomotive *Enterprise* (1845) **226** "Accompong Madonna" (Namba Roy)

(Des D. Hartley-Marjoram. Litho Enschedé)

1984 (16 Nov). *Railway Locomotives (1st series). T* **225** *and similar horiz designs. Multicoloured. W* **111** *(sideways). P* 13½ × 13.

612	25 c. Type **225**	..	1·50	30
613	55 c. Tank locomotive (1880)	..	1·75	70
614	$1.50, Kitson-Meyer tank locomotive (1904)	2·50	3·00
615	$3 Super-heated locomotive No. 40 (1916)	3·75	5·50
612/15	..	*Set of 4*	8·50	8·50

See also Nos. 634/7.

(Des G. Vasarhelyi. Litho Harrison)

1984 (6 Dec). *Christmas. Sculptures. T* **226** *and similar vert designs. Multicoloured. W* **111**. *P* 14.

616	20 c. Type **226**	..	30	10
617	25 c. "Head" (Alvin Marriott)	..	35	10
618	55 c. "Moon" (Edna Manley)	..	80	65
619	$1.50, "All Women are Five Women" (Mallica Reynolds (Kapo))	1·90	3·75
616/19	..	*Set of 4*	3·00	4·25

227 Brown Pelicans flying

228 The Queen Mother at Belfast University

(Des N. Arlott. Litho Walsall)

1985 (15 Apr). *Birth Bicentenary of John J. Audubon (ornithologist). Brown Pelican. T* **227** *and similar vert designs. Multicoloured. W* **111**. *P* 13½ × 13.

620	20 c. Type **227**	..	1·00	20
621	55 c. Diving for fish	..	1·50	40
622	$2 Young pelican taking food from adult	2·50	3·25
623	$5 "Brown Pelican" (John J. Audubon)	3·75	6·50
620/3	..	*Set of 4*	8·00	9·25
MS624	100 × 100 mm. Nos. 620/3 (*sold at* $7.85)	6·00	8·00

(Des A. Theobald ($5), C. Abbott (others). Litho Questa)

1985 (7 June). *Life and Times of Queen Elizabeth the Queen Mother. T* **228** *and similar vert designs. Multicoloured. W* **111**. *P* 14½ × 14.

625	25 c. With photograph album, 1963	20	10
626	55 c. With Prince Charles at Garter Ceremony, Windsor Castle, 1983	25	15
	w. Wmk inverted		50	
627	$1.50, Type **228**	..	50	75
628	$3 With Prince Henry at his christening (from photo by Lord Snowdon)	85	1·75
625/8	..	*Set of 4*	1·60	2·50
MS629	91 × 74 mm. $5 With the Queen, Prince Philip and Princess Anne at Ascot. Wmk sideways	1·25	1·40

229 Maps and Emblems

(Des D. Miller. Litho Harrison)

1985 (30 July). *International Youth Year and 5th Pan-American Scout Jamboree. W* **111** *(sideways). P* 14.

630	**229**	25 c. multicoloured	..	40	10
631		55 c. multicoloured	..	55	25
632		70 c. multicoloured	..	70	80
633		$4 multicoloured	..	2·50	4·50
630/3	..		*Set of 4*	3·75	5·00

(Des D. Hartley. Litho Harrison)

1985 (30 Sept). *Railway Locomotives (2nd series). Horiz designs as T* **225**. *Multicoloured. W* **111** *(sideways). P* 14.

634	25 c. Baldwin steam locomotive No. 16	1·25	30
635	55 c. Rogers locomotive	..	1·50	35
636	$1.50, Locomotive *Projector*, 1845	2·25	2·50
637	$4 Diesel locomotive No. 102	3·50	5·00
634/7	..	*Set of 4*	7·75	7·25

230 "The Old Settlement" (Ralph Campbell)

230a Princess Elizabeth and Princess Margaret, 1939

(Litho Format)

1985 (9 Dec). *Christmas. Jamaican Paintings. T* **230** *and similar multicoloured designs. W* **111** *(sideways on* 20, 75 c.). *P* 14.

638	20 c. Type **230**	..	10	10
639	55 c. "The Vendor" (Albert Huie) (*vert*)	15	15
640	75 c. "Road Menders" (Gaston Tabois)	20	35
641	$4 "Woman, must I not be about my Father's business?" (Carl Abrahams) (*vert*)	1·10	2·25
638/41	..	*Set of 4*	1·40	2·50

(Des N. Arlott. Litho B.D.T.)

1986 (10 Feb). *Jamaican Birds (2nd series). Vert designs as T* **213**. *Multicoloured. W* **111**. *P* 14.

642	25 c. Chestnut-bellied Cuckoo	50	10
643	55 c. Jamaican Becard	..	65	30
644	$1.50, White-eyed Thrush	..	85	1·75
645	$5 Rufous-tailed Flycatcher	1·75	4·00
642/5	..	*Set of 4*	3·25	5·50

(Des A. Theobald. Litho Harrison)

1986 (21 Apr). *60th Birthday of Queen Elizabeth II. T* **230a** *and similar vert designs. Multicoloured. W* **111**. *P* 14½ × 14.

646	20 c. Type **230a**	..	15	10
647	25 c. With Prince Charles and Prince Andrew, 1962	15	10
648	70 c. Queen visiting War Memorial, Montego Bay, 1983	25	25
649	$3 On state visit to Luxembourg, 1976	50	90
650	$5 At Crown Agents Head Office, London, 1983	75	1·75
646/50	..	*Set of 5*	1·60	2·75

231 Bustamante Children's Hospital

231a Prince Andrew and Miss Sarah Ferguson, Ascot, 1985

(Des D. Miller. Litho Questa)

1986 (19 May). *"Ameripex '86" International Stamp Exhibition, Chicago. T* **231** *and similar vert designs. Multicoloured. W* **111**. *P* 14½ × 14.

651	25 c. Type **231**	..	40	15
652	55 c. Air Jamaica Boeing 737 airliner and map of holiday resorts	1·00	40
653	$3 Norman Manley Law School	1·25	3·00
654	$5 Bauxite and agricultural exports	5·50	7·50
651/4	..	*Set of 4*	7·25	10·00
MS655	85 × 106 mm. Nos. 651/4 (*sold at* $8.90)	7·25	10·00

(Des D. Miller. Litho Walsall)

1986 (23 July). *Royal Wedding. T* **231a** *and similar square design. Multicoloured. W* **111**. *P* 14½ × 14.

656	20 c. Type **231a**	..	15	10
657	$5 Prince Andrew making speech, Fredericton, Canada, 1985	1·00	1·90

45c

5c

232 Richard "Shrimpy" Clarke

(233)

(Des G. Vasarhelyi. Litho Questa)

1986 (27 Oct). *Jamaican Boxing Champions. T* **232** *and similar vert designs. Multicoloured. W* **111**. *P* 14.

658	45 c. Type **232**	..	20	15
659	70 c. Michael McCallum	..	30	30
660	$2 Trevor Berbick	..	70	1·25
661	$4 "Shrimpy" Clarke, Michael McCallum and Trevor Berbick	1·25	2·25
658/61	..	*Set of 4*	2·25	3·50

1986 (3 Nov). *Nos. 472/3 surch as T 233.*
662   5 c. on 50 c. Jamaican Woodpecker   1·50   2·00
663   10 c. on 65 c. Rafting, Martha Brae Trelawny   1·00   1·40

234 Heliconia wagneriana   **235** Crown Cone (*Conus regius*)

(Des Annette Robinson. Litho B.D.T.)

1986 (1 Dec). *Christmas. Flowers (1st series). T 234 and similar multicoloured designs. W 111 (sideways on 25 c., $5). P 13½.*
664   20 c. Type 234   10   10
665   25 c. *Heliconia psittacorum* (*horiz*)   10   10
666   55 c. *Heliconia rostrata*   20   30
667   $5 *Strelitzia reginae* (*horiz*)   1·60   3·50
664/7   *Set of 4*   1·75   3·50
See also Nos. 703/6 and 739/42.

(Des A. Riley. Litho Format)

1987 (23 Feb). *Sea Shells. T 235 and similar vert designs. Multicoloured. W 111. P 15.*
668   35 c. Type 235   45   15
669   75 c. Measled Cowrie (*Cypraea zebra*)   65   60
670   $1 Atlantic Trumpet Triton (*Charonia variegata*)   75   90
671   $5 Rooster-tail Conch (*Strombus gallus*)   1·50   3·50
668/71   *Set of 4*   3·00   4·75

236 Norman Manley   **237** Arms of Jamaica

(Des C. Slania (1 c. to 90 c.). Litho Enschedé)

1987 (18 May)–97. *Vert portraits as T 236 and T 237. W 111 (sideways on $1 to $50). Cream paper (2 c. to 9 c. (Nos. 673A/80A). P 12½×13 (1 to 90 c.) or 13×13½ ($1 to $50).*

A. *Without imprint*
672A   236   1 c. scarlet and pale pink   10   30
673A   2 c. bright carmine & pale rose-pink   10   30
674A   3 c. yellow-olive and pale stone   10   30
675A   4 c. myrtle-green and pale green   10   30
676A   5 c. slate-blue and pale bluish grey   30   30
677A   6 c. dull ultram & pale lavender-grey   20   30
678A   7 c. reddish violet and pale mauve   20   30
679A   8 c. deep magenta and pale rose-pink   20   10
680A   9 c. olive-sepia and pale brown   20   10
681A   –   10 c. deep rose-red and pale pink   40   10
682A   –   20 c. reddish orange and flesh   40   10
683A   –   30 c. bright green and pale green   40   10
684A   –   40 c. dp turquoise-grn & pale turq-grn   50   20
685A   –   50 c. grey-olive and pale olive-grey   60   20
686A   –   60 c. bright blue and pale azure   30   20
687A   –   70 c. bluish violet and pale violet   30   20
688A   –   80 c. reddish violet and pale rose-lilac   30   30
689A   –   90 c. lt reddish brown & pale grey-brn   50   50
690A   237 $1 olive-sepia and cream   50   30
691A $2 bright orange and cream   50   55
692A $5 brown-olive and pale stone   60   85
693A $10 deep turquoise-blue & pale azure   70   1·25
672A/93A   *Set of 22*   6·50   6·00

B. *With imprint date at foot*
676B   236   5 c. slate-blue and pale bluish grey (6.6.88)   10   30
681B   –   10 c. dp rose-red & pale pk (11.93)   10   10
  a. Chalk-surfaced paper (10.10.94)   10   10
682B   –   20 c. reddish orange and flesh (6.6.88)   20   10
  a. Chalk-surfaced paper (5.92)   20   10
683aB   –   30 c. bright green and pale green (chalk-surfaced paper)(10.10.94)   30   30
684B   –   40 c. dp turquoise-green & pale turq-green (12.2.91)   30   20
  a. Chalk-surfaced paper (5.92)   30   20
685B   –   50 c. grey-ol & pale ol-grey (12.2.91)   30   20
  a. Chalk-surfaced paper (5.92)   30   20
685cB   –   55 c. brown-bistre and cream (chalk-surfaced paper) (10.10.94)   30   10
689B   –   90 c. light reddish brown and pale grey-brown (11.93)   60   30
  a. Chalk-surfaced paper (5.92)   60   50
690B   237 $1 olive-sepia and cream (6.6.91)   50   50
  a. Chalk-surfaced paper (30.4.97)   30   20
690cB $1.10, olive-sepia and cream (chalk-surfaced paper) (10.10.94)   40   30
691aB $2 bright orange & cream (chalk-surfaced paper) (30.4.97)   40   50
692aB $5 brown-olive & pale stone (chalk-surfaced paper) (30.4.97)   65   80
693cB $25 bluish violet and pale lavender (9.10.91)   90   1·40
693dB $50 deep mauve and pale rose-lilac (9.10.91)   1·75   2·50
676B/93dB   *Set of 13*   5·50   6·50
Designs:—10 c. to 90 c. Sir Alexander Bustamante.
Imprint dates: "1988", Nos. 676B, 682B; "1989", No. 682B; "1991", Nos. 684B/5B, 690B, 693cB/dB; "1992", Nos. 682Ba,

---

684Ba, 685Ba, 689Ba, 690B; "1993", Nos. 681B/2B, 685B, 689B/90B; "1994", Nos. 681Ba, 682Ba, 683aB, 684Ba, 685Ba, 685cB, 690cB; "1997", Nos. 690Ba, 691aB, 692aB.
The background colour on printings of Type 237 from 1992 onwards is fluorescent.

238 Jamaican Flag and Coast at Sunset   **239** Marcus Garvey

(Des D. Miller. Litho Walsall)

1987 (27 July). *25th Anniv of Independence. T 238 and similar multicoloured design. W 111 (sideways on 70 c.). P 14.*
694   55 c. Type 238   75   60
695   70 c. Jamaican flag and inscription (*horiz*)   1·00   2·00

(Des D. Miller. Litho Walsall)

1987 (17 Aug). *Birth Centenary of Marcus Garvey (founder of Universal Negro Improvement Association). T 239 and similar vert design, both black, emerald and lemon. W 111. P 14.*
696   25 c. Type 239   90   1·50
  a. Horiz pair. Nos. 696/7   1·75   3·00
697   25 c. Statue of Marcus Garvey   90   1·50
Nos. 696/7 were printed together, *se-tenant*, in horizontal pairs throughout the sheet.

240 Salvation Army School for the Blind   **241** Hibiscus Hybrid

(Des L. Curtis. Litho Walsall)

1987 (8 Oct). *Centenary of Salvation Army in Jamaica. T 240 and similar horiz designs. Multicoloured. W 111 (sideways). P 13×13½.*
698   25 c. Type 240   1·25   30
699   55 c. Col. Mary Booth and Bramwell Booth Memorial Hall   1·25   30
700   $3 Welfare Service lorry, 1929   3·25   4·25
701   $5 Col. Abram Davey and S.S. *Alene*, 1887   4·25   6·00
698/701   *Set of 4*   9·00   9·75
MS702   100×80 mm. Nos. 698/701 (*sold at $8.90*)   9·00   10·00

(Des Annette Robinson. Litho Harrison)

1987 (30 Nov). *Christmas. Flowers (2nd series). T 241 and similar vert designs. Multicoloured. W 111. P 14½×14.*
703   20 c. Type 241   15   10
704   25 c. *Hibiscus elatus*   15   10
705   $4 *Hibiscus cannabinus*   2·00   3·00
706   $5 *Hibiscus rosasinensis*   2·25   3·00
703/6   *Set of 4*   4·00   5·50

242 Chestnut-bellied Cuckoo, Black-billed Amazon and Jamaican Euphonia   **243** Blue Whales

(Des N. Arlott. Litho Walsall)

1988 (22 Jan). *Jamaican Birds (3rd series). T 242 and similar vert designs. Multicoloured. W 111. P 14.*
707   45 c. Type 242   1·75   2·25
  a. Horiz pair. Nos. 707/8   3·50   4·50
708   45 c. Black-billed Amazon, Jamaican White-eyed Vireo, Rufous-throated Solitaire and Yellow Elaenia   1·75   2·25
709   $5 Snowy Plover, Little Blue Heron and Great Blue Heron (white phase)   4·25   4·75
  a. Horiz pair. Nos. 709/10   8·50   9·50
710   $5 Black-necked Stilt, Snowy Egret, Snowy Plover and Black-crowned Night Heron   4·25   4·75
707/10   *Set of 4*   11·00   12·50
The two designs of each value were printed together, *se-tenant*, in horizontal pairs throughout the sheets, each pair forming a composite design.

(Des A. Riley. Litho Harrison)

1988 (14 Apr). *Marine Mammals. T 243 and similar horiz designs. Multicoloured. W 111 (sideways). P 14.*
711   20 c. Type 243   2·00   70
712   25 c. Gervais's Whales   2·00   70
713   55 c. Killer Whales   3·00   80
714   $5 Common Dolphins   5·00   7·50
711/14   *Set of 4*   11·00   8·75

243a Jackie Hendriks   **244** Jamaican Red Cross Workers with Ambulance

(Des D. Hartley. Litho Walsall)

1988 (6 June). *West Indian Cricket. T 243a and similar horiz designs, each showing portrait, cricket equipment and early belt buckle. Multicoloured. W 111 (sideways). P 14.*
715   25 c. Type 243a   1·50   40
716   55 c. George Headley   1·60   40
717   $2 Michael Holding   3·25   2·75
718   $3 R. K. Nunes   3·50   4·25
719   $4 Allan Rae   3·75   4·50
715/19   *Set of 5*   12·00   11·00

(Des S. Noon. Litho Walsall)

1988 (8 Aug). *125th Anniv of International Red Cross. T 244 and similar vert design. Multicoloured. W 111. P 14½ × 14.*
720   55 c. Type 244   50   30
721   $5 Henri Dunant (founder) in field hospital   2·00   3·25

245 Boxing

(Des P. Broadbent. Litho B.D.T.)

1988 (24 Aug). *Olympic Games, Seoul. T 245 and similar horiz designs. Multicoloured. W 111 (sideways). P 14.*
722   25 c. Type 245   15   10
723   45 c. Cycling   55   30
724   $4 Athletics   1·25   2·00
725   $5 Hurdling   1·25   2·00
722/5   *Set of 4*   2·75   4·00
MS726   127 × 87 mm. Nos. 722/5 (*sold at $9.90*)   2·75   4·00

246 Bobsled Team Members and Logo

(Des D. Miller. Litho B.D.T.)

1988 (4 Nov). *Jamaican Olympic Bobsled Team. T 246 and similar horiz designs. Multicoloured. W 111 (sideways*). P 14.*
727   25 c. Type 246   50   75
  a. Horiz pair. Nos. 727/8   1·00   1·50
728   25 c. Two-man bobsled   50   75
729   $5 Bobsled team members (*different*) and logo   1·40   2·25
  a. Horiz pair. Nos. 729/30   2·75   4·50
  aw. Wmk top of J to right   3·00
730   $5 Four-man bobsled   1·40   2·25
727/30   *Set of 4*   3·50   5·50
*The normal sideways watermark has top of "J" to left, *as seen from the back of the stamp.*
Nos. 727/8 and 729/30 were printed together, *se-tenant*, in horizontal pairs throughout the sheets.

+25c

HURRICANE GILBERT RELIEF FUND (247)

1988 (11 Nov). *Hurricane Gilbert Relief Fund. Nos. 722/5 surch as T 247 by Format in red or black (same price either colour).*
731   25 c. + 25 c. Type 245   10   15
732   45 c. + 45 c. Cycling   20   25
733   $4 + $4 Athletics   1·10   1·90
734   $5 + $5 Hurdling   1·10   2·25
731/4   *Set of 4*   2·25   4·00

248 Nurses and Firemen

(Des S. Noon. Litho Format)

1988 (24 Nov). *Year of the Worker. T 248 and similar horiz designs. Multicoloured. W 111 (sideways). P 14.*

735	25 c. Type **248**	45	20
736	55 c. Woodcarver	45	30
737	$3 Textile workers	1·00	2·50
738	$5 Workers on fish farm	1·25	3·00
735/8	*Set of 4*	2·75	5·50

(Des Annette Robinson. Litho Format)

1988 (15 Dec). *Christmas. Flowers (3rd series). Multicoloured designs as T 241. W 111 (sideways on 55 c., $4). P 14.*

739	25 c. Euphorbia pulcherrima	50	10
740	55 c. Spathodea campanulata (horiz)	60	15
741	$3 Hylocereus triangularis	1·10	1·60
742	$4 Broughtonia sanguinea (horiz)	1·10	1·75
739/42	*Set of 4*	3·00	3·25

 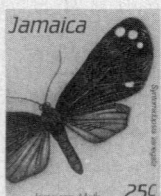

249 Old York Castle School   **250** *Syntomidopsis variegata*

(Des A. Theobald. Litho B.D.T.)

1989 (19 Jan). *Bicentenary of Methodist Church in Jamaica. T 249 and similar horiz designs. W 111 (sideways). P 13½.*

743	25 c. black and bright blue	20	10
744	45 c. black and rosine	25	10
745	$5 black and yellow-green	2·50	3·50
743/5	*Set of 3*	2·75	3·50

Designs:—45 c. Revd. Thomas Coke and Parade Chapel, Kingston; $5 Father Hugh Sherlock and St. John's Church.

(Des I. Loe. Litho B.D.T.)

1989 (30 Aug). *Jamaican Moths (1st series). T 250 and similar vert designs. Multicoloured. W 111 (sideways). P 14×13½.*

746	25 c. Type **250**	50	10
747	55 c. Himantoides perkinsae	80	30
748	$3 Arctia nigriplaga	1·50	2·75
749	$5 Sthenognatha toddi	1·90	3·50
746/9	*Set of 4*	4·25	6·00

See also Nos. 758/61 and 790/3.

251 Arawak   **252** Girl Guide
Fisherman with
Catch

(Des Josephine Martin. Litho Cartor)

1989 (22 Dec). *500th Anniv of Discovery of America by Columbus (1992) (1st issue). T 251 and similar vert designs. Multicoloured. W 111. P 13½.*

750	25 c. Type **251**	20	10
751	70 c. Arawak man smoking	45	30
752	$5 King Ferdinand and Queen Isabella inspecting caravels	2·00	2·75
753	$10 Columbus with chart	3·75	5·50
750/3	*Set of 4*	5·75	7·50
MS754	150×200 mm. Nos. 750/3. Wmk sideways. P 12½ (sold at $16.15)	10·00	10·00

No. **MS**754 also exists imperforate from a limited printing used in Presentation Packs.
See also Nos. 774/9 and 802/7.

(Des J. Sayer. Litho B.D.T.)

1990 (28 June). *75th Anniv of Girl Guide Movement in Jamaica. T 252 and similar vert designs. Multicoloured. W 111 (inverted on $5). P 14.*

755	45 c. Type **252**	75	30
756	55 c. Guide leader	85	30
757	$5 Brownie, guide and ranger	4·00	6·00
755/7	*Set of 3*	5·00	6·00

(Des I. Loe. Litho B.D.T.)

1990 (12 Sept). *Jamaican Moths (2nd series). Vert designs as T 250. Multicoloured. W 111. P 14×13½.*

758	25 c. Eunomia rubripunctata	85	35
759	55 c. Perigonia jamaicensis	1·25	35
760	$4 Uraga haemorrhoa	2·50	3·75
761	$5 Empyreuma pugione	2·50	3·75
758/61	*Set of 4*	6·25	7·50

 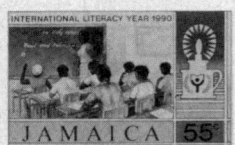

(253)   **254** Teaching English

1990 (12 Sept). *"EXPO 90" International Garden and Greenery Exhibition, Osaka. Nos. 758/61 optd with T 253.*

762	25 c. Eunomia rubripunctata	85	35
763	55 c. Perigonia jamaicensis	1·25	35
764	$4 Uraga haemorrhoa	2·50	3·75
765	$5 Empyreuma pugione	2·50	3·75
762/5	*Set of 4*	6·25	7·50

(Des G. Vasarhelyi. Litho B.D.T.)

1990 (10 Oct). *International Literacy Year. T 254 and similar horiz design. Multicoloured. W 111 (sideways). P 14.*

766	55 c. Type **254**	40	25
767	$5 Teaching maths	3·00	4·00

255 "To the Market"

(Adapted J. Mahfood and D. Miller. Litho Walsall)

1990 (7 Dec). *Christmas. Children's Paintings. T 255 and similar multicoloured designs. W 111 (sideways on horiz designs). P 14×13½ ($5) or 13½×14 (others).*

768	20 c. Type **255**	35	10
769	25 c. "House and Garden"	35	10
770	55 c. "Jack and Jill"	50	15
771	70 c. "Market"	65	40
772	$1.50, "Lonely"	1·50	2·25
773	$5 "Market Woman" (vert)	3·00	4·50
768/73	*Set of 6*	5·75	6·75

256 Map of First   **257** Weather Balloon, Dish
Voyage, 1492   Aerial and Map of Jamaica.

(Des Josephine Martin. Litho Questa)

1990 (19 Dec). *500th Anniv of Discovery of America by Columbus (1992) (2nd issue). T 256 and similar horiz designs. Multicoloured. W 111 (sideways). P 14.*

774	25 c. Type **256**	60	20
775	45 c. Map of second voyage, 1493	75	20
776	$5 Map of third voyage, 1498	3·00	3·75
777	$10 Map of fourth voyage, 1502	4·25	5·50
774/7	*Set of 4*	7·75	8·50
MS778	126×99 mm. 25, 45 c., $5, $10 Composite map of Caribbean showing routes of voyages	8·50	9·50
MS779	148×207 mm. Nos. 774/7. Imperf	8·50	9·50

Unlike the imperforate version of No. **MS**754, No. **MS**779 was freely available at face value.

(Adapted G. Vasarhelyi. Litho B.D.T.)

1991 (20 May). *11th World Meteorological Congress, Kingston. W 111 (sideways). P 14.*

780	**257** 50 c. multicoloured	50	20
781	$10 multicoloured	5·50	7·00

 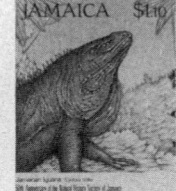

258 Bust of Mary Seacole   **259** Jamaican Iguana

(Des Jennifer Toombs. Litho B.D.T.)

1991 (24 June). *International Council of Nurses Meeting of National Representatives. T 258 and similar horiz designs. W 111 (sideways). P 13½.*

782	50 c. multicoloured	50	30
783	$1.10, multicoloured	1·25	1·75
MS784	89×60 mm. $8 agate, pale orange-brown and yellow-ochre (sold at $8.20)	2·50	3·50

Designs:—$1.10, Mary Seacole House; $8 Hospital at Scutari, 1854.

(Des I. Loe. Litho Cartor)

1991 (29 July). *50th Anniv of Natural History Society of Jamaica. Jamaican Iguana. T 259 and similar vert designs. Multicoloured. W 111. P 13.*

785	$1.10, Type **259**	55	70
	a. Horiz strip of 5. Nos. 785/9	2·50	
786	$1.10, Head of iguana looking right	55	70
787	$1.10, Iguana climbing	55	70
788	$1.10, Iguana on rock looking left	55	70
789	$1.10, Close-up of iguana's head	55	70
785/9	*Set of 5*	2·50	3·25

Nos. 785/9 were printed together, se-tenant, in horizontal strips of 5 throughout the sheet.

(Des I. Loe. Litho B.D.T.)

1991 (12 Aug). *Jamaican Moths (3rd series). Multicoloured designs as T 250. W 111. P 14×13½.*

790	50 c. Urania sloanus	65	20
791	$1.10, Phoenicoprocta jamaicensis	90	60
792	$1.40, Horama grotei	1·10	90
793	$8 Amplypterus gannascus	3·25	6·00
790/3	*Set of 4*	5·50	7·00

(260)   **261** "Doctor Bird"

1991 (23 Sept). *"Phila Nippon '91" International Stamp Exhibition, Tokyo. Nos. 790/3 optd with T 260.*

794	50 c. Urania sloanus	65	20
795	$1.10, Phoenicoprocta jamaicensis	90	60
796	$1.40, Horama grotei	1·10	90
797	$8 Amplypterus gannascus	3·25	6·00
794/7	*Set of 4*	5·50	7·00

(Adapted J. Mahfood. Litho Enschedé)

1991 (27 Nov). *Christmas. Children's Paintings. T 261 and similar horiz designs. Multicoloured. W 111 (sideways). P 14×15.*

798	50 c. Type **261**	40	10
799	$1.10, "Road scene"	80	25
800	$5 "Children and house"	2·00	2·50
801	$10 "Cows grazing"	3·25	6·00
798/801	*Set of 4*	5·75	7·00

262 Indians threatening   **263** Compasses and
Ships   Square Symbol

(Des Josephine Martin. Litho B.D.T.)

1991 (16 Dec). *500th Anniv of Discovery of America by Columbus (1992) (3rd issue). T 262 and similar horiz designs. Multicoloured. W 111 (sideways). P 13½.*

802	50 c. Type **262**	45	15
803	$1.10, Spaniards setting dog on Indians	55	30
804	$1.40, Indian with gift of pineapple	55	30
805	$25 Columbus describes Jamaica with crumpled paper	5·50	7·50
802/5	*Set of 4*	6·25	7·50
MS806	125×102 mm. Nos. 802/5 (sold at $28.20)	6·75	7·50
MS807	210×150 mm. Nos. 802/5. Imperf	6·75	7·50

(Litho Cartor)

1992 (1 May). *250th Anniv of First Provisional Grand Master of English Freemasonry in Jamaica. T 263 and similar vert designs. Multicoloured. W 111. P 13½.*

808	50 c. Type **263**	55	20
809	$1.10, Symbol in stained glass window	70	35
810	$1.40, Compasses and square on book	70	35
811	$25 Eye in triangle symbol	5·50	7·50
808/11	*Set of 4*	6·75	7·50
MS812	140×80 mm. Nos. 808/11 (sold at $28.50)	6·75	7·50

JAMAICA — 1992

264 Ship in Flooded Street

(Des J. Batchelor. Litho Cartor)

1992 (1 June). *300th Anniv of Destruction of Port Royal. T 264 and similar horiz designs. Multicoloured. W 111 (sideways). P 14×13½.*
813	50 c. Type **264**	45	30
814	$1.10, Church tower falling	60	40
815	$1.40, Houses collapsing	60	40
816	$25 Inhabitants falling into fissure	3·75	5·50
813/16	*Set of 4*	4·75	6·00
MS817	116×75 mm. $5 Contemporary broadsheet of earthquake. Wmk upright. P 13×12	2·25	2·75

No. **MS817** has a description of the broadsheet printed on the reverse under the gum.

265 Credit Union Symbol

(Des G. Vasarhelyi. Litho Enschedé)

1992 (24 Aug). *50th Anniv of Credit Union Movement. T 265 and similar horiz design. W 111 (sideways). P 14×15.*
818	50 c. dp dull bl, emer & pale turquoise-green	75	40
819	$1.40, multicoloured	1·40	1·75

Design:—$1.40, O'Hare Hall.

266 Jamaican Flag and Beach Scene   **267** "Rainbow" (Cecil Baugh)

(Des G. Vasarhelyi. Litho Cartor)

1992 (26 Oct). *30th Anniv of Independence. W 111 (sideways). P 13½.*
820	**266** 50 c. multicoloured	10	10
821	$1.10, multicoloured	20	20
822	$25 multicoloured	2·75	4·50
820/2	*Set of 3*	2·75	4·50

(Des D. Bowen. Litho Cartor)

1993 (26 Apr). *Art Ceramics and Pottery. T 267 and similar vert designs. Multicoloured. W 111. P 13½.*
823	50 c. Type **267**	10	10
824	$1.10, "Yabba Pot" (Louisa Jones)	20	20
825	$1.40, "Sculptured Vase" (Gene Pearson)	20	20
826	$25 "Lidded Form" (Norma Harrack)	3·50	4·50
823/6	*Set of 4*	3·50	4·50

268 Girls' Brigade Parade   **269** Cadet, Armoured Car and Emblem

(Des G. Vasarhelyi. Litho Cartor)

1993 (9 Aug). *Centenary of Girls' Brigade. T 268 and similar horiz design. Multicoloured. W 111 (sideways). P 14×13½.*
827	50 c. Type **268**	60	40
828	$1.10, Brigade members	65	70

(Des D. Miller. Litho B.D.T.)

1993 (8 Nov). *50th Anniv of Jamaica Combined Cadet Force. T 269 and similar multicoloured designs. W 111 (sideways on $1.10, $3). P 14.*
829	50 c. Type **269**	25	20
830	$1.10, Cadet and Britten Norman Islander light aircraft (horiz)	40	30
831	$1.40, Cadet and patrol boats	40	30
832	$3 Cadet and emblem (horiz)	60	1·40
829/32	*Set of 4*	1·50	2·00

270 Constant Spring Golf Course   **271** Norman Manley

(Des D. Miller. Litho B.D.T.)

1993 (16–21 Dec). *Golf Courses. T 270 and similar multicoloured designs. W 111 (sideways). P 14.*
833	50 c. Type **270** (21 Dec)	20	10
834	$1.10, Type **270** (21 Dec)	20	10
835	$1.40, Half Moon (21 Dec)	25	15
836	$2 As $1.40 (21 Dec)	30	35
837	$3 Jamaica Jamaica (21 Dec)	35	45
838	$10 As $3 (21 Dec)	90	1·75
833/8	*Set of 6*	2·00	2·50
MS839	66×71 mm. $25 Tryall (vert). Wmk upright (sold at $28)	2·25	3·00

(Des R. Larson. Litho B.D.T.)

1994 (12 Jan). *Birth Centenary of Norman Manley. T 271 and similar vert portrait. W 111. P 14×15.*
840	$25 multicoloured	2·00	2·75
	a. Horiz pair. Nos. 840/1	4·50	6·00
841	$50 multicoloured	2·50	3·25

Nos. 840/1 were printed together, *se-tenant*, in horizontal pairs throughout the sheet.

(272)   **273** Flags of Great Britain and Jamaica

1994 (18 Feb). *"Hong Kong '94" International Stamp Exhibition. No. MS839 optd with T 272.*
MS842	66×71 mm. $25 Tryall	3·25	3·75

(Des D. Miller. Litho B.D.T.)

1994 (1 Mar). *Royal Visit. T 273 and similar vert designs. Multicoloured. W 111. P 14×13½.*
843	$1.10, Type **273**	20	10
844	$1.40, Royal Yacht Britannia	50	20
845	$25 Queen Elizabeth II	1·50	2·50
846	$50 Queen Elizabeth and Prince Philip	2·50	3·50
843/6	*Set of 4*	4·25	5·75

274 Douglas DC-9   **275** Giant Swallowtail

(Des E. Nisbet. Litho Walsall)

1994 (26 Apr). *25th Anniv of Air Jamaica. T 274 and similar horiz designs. Multicoloured. W 111 (sideways). P 14.*
847	50 c. Type **274**	25	20
848	$1.10, Douglas DC-8	25	20
849	$5 Boeing 727	50	65
850	$50 Airbus A300	3·25	5·00
847/50	*Set of 4*	3·75	5·50

(Des N. Shewring. Litho B.D.T.)

1994 (18 Aug). *Giant Swallowtail Butterfly Conservation. T 275 and similar vert designs. Multicoloured. W 111. P 13½.*
851	50 c. Type **275**	25	20
852	$1.10, With wings closed	35	20
853	$10 On flower	1·25	2·00
854	$25 With wings spread	2·50	3·75
851/4	*Set of 4*	4·00	5·50
MS855	56×61 mm. $50 Pair of butterflies	5·50	7·00

COVER PRICES

Cover factors are quoted at the beginning of each country for most issues to 1945. An explanation of the system can be found on page x. The factors quoted do not, however, apply to philatelic covers.

276 "Royal Botanical Gardens" (Sidney McLaren)

(Des G. Vasarhelyi. Litho Questa)

1994 (7 Sept). *Tourism. T 276 and similar horiz designs. Multicoloured. W 111 (sideways). P 14.*
856	50 c. Type **276**	30	20
857	$1.10, Blue Mountains	45	30
858	$5 Tourist in hammock and water sports	1·50	2·00
856/8	*Set of 3*	2·00	2·25
MS859	105×80 mm. $25 Carolina Parakeets; $25 Silhouetted scuba diver; $25 Carolina Parakeet and foliage; $25 Tourist raft	5·00	6·00

277 Jamaican Red Poll Calf

(Des R. Watton. Litho Cartor)

1994 (16 Nov). *Jamaican Red Poll Cattle. T 277 and similar horiz designs. Multicoloured. W 111 (sideways). P 13.*
860	50 c. Type **277**	10	10
861	$1.10, Red Poll heifer	10	10
862	$25 Red Poll cow	1·25	2·25
863	$50 Red Poll bull	2·50	3·75
860/3	*Set of 4*	3·75	5·50

278 Refuse Collectors   **279** Jamaican Band-tailed Pigeon ("Ring-tailed Pigeon")

(Des D. Miller. Litho Enschedé)

1994 (1 Dec). *Christmas. Children's Paintings. T 278 and similar horiz designs. Multicoloured. W 111 (sideways). P 14×15.*
864	50 c. Type **278**	10	10
865	90 c. Hospital ward	10	10
866	$1.10, House	10	10
867	$50 Landscape	2·75	4·00
864/7	*Set of 4*	2·75	4·00

(Des N. Arlott. Litho B.D.T.)

1995 (24 Apr). *Jamaican Wild Birds. T 279 and similar vert designs. Multicoloured. W w 16. P 14.*
868	50 c. Type **279**	40	20
869	90 c. Yellow-billed Amazon ("Yellow-billed Parrot")	50	30
870	$1.10, Black-billed Amazon ("Black-billed Parrot")	50	30
871	$50 Jamaican Owl ("Brown Owl")	4·00	5·00
868/71	*Set of 4*	4·75	5·25
MS872	47×62 mm. $50 Streamertail	4·50	5·50

For No. **MS872** additionally inscribed for "Singapore '95" see No. **MS888**.

280 Graph, National Flag and Logo   **281** "Song of Freedom"

15

(Litho Cartor)

1995 (11 May). *25th Anniv of Caribbean Development Bank.*
T **280** *and similar designs. W* **111** *(sideways on horiz designs).*
P 13½.

873	280	50 c. blue-green, black & chrome-yellow	10	10
874	–	$1 blue-green, black & chrome-yellow	10	10
875	–	$1.10, multicoloured	10	10
876	–	$50 multicoloured	4·00	4·00
873/6		Set of 4	2·75	4·00

Designs: *Horiz*–$1.10, Industry, agriculture and commerce;
$50 Jamaican currency.

(Des D. Miller. Litho Questa)

1995 (31 July). *50th Birth Anniv of Bob Marley (reggae*
singer). T **281** *and similar vert designs showing record covers.*
Multicoloured. W **111**. *P* 14.

877	50 c. Type **281**	15	10
878	$1.10, "Fire"	20	15
879	$1.40, "Time will Tell"	20	15
880	$3 "Natural Mystic"	35	40
881	$10 "Live at Lyceum"	1·10	1·75
877/81	Set of 5	1·75	2·25
MS882	105×57 mm. $100 "Legend". Wmk		
	sideways	6·00	7·00

282 Queen Elizabeth   **283** Michael Manley
the Queen Mother

(Des Jennifer Toombs. Litho B.D.T.)

1995 (4 Aug). *95th Birthday of Queen Elizabeth the Queen*
Mother. Sheet 81×95 mm. *W* **111**. *P* 13½.

| MS883 | **282** $75 multicoloured | 4·50 | 5·00 |

(Des G. Vasarhelyi. Litho B.D.T.)

1995 (23 Aug). *Recipients of the Order of the Caribbean*
Community. T **283** *and similar horiz designs. Multicoloured.*
W **111** *(sideways). P* 14×15.

884	50 c. Type **283**	10	10
885	$1.10, Sir Alister McIntyre	10	10
886	$1.40, Justice P. Telford Georges	10	10
887	$50 Dame Nita Barrow	2·75	4·00
884/7	Set of 4	2·75	4·00

1995 (1 Sept). *"Singapore '95" International Stamp Exhibition.*
No. MS872 additionally inscr with exhibition emblem on sheet
margin.

| MS888 | 47×62 mm. $50 Streamertail | 3·50 | 4·25 |

284 Dish Aerial and
Landrover, Balkans

(Des A. Theobald. Litho B.D.T.)

1995 (24 Oct). *50th Anniv of United Nations. T* **284** *and*
similar horiz designs. Multicoloured. W **111** *(sideways). P* 14.

889	50 c. Type **284**	15	10
890	$1.10, Antonov An-32 aircraft, Balkans	25	15
891	$3 Bedford articulated road tanker, Balkans	40	50
892	$5 Fairchild C-119 Flying Boxcar, Korea	55	75
889/92	Set of 4	1·25	1·40
MS893	100×70 mm. $50 U.N.T.A.G. vehicles, Namibia	1·75	2·50

285 Landing of Indian   **286** Jamaican Flag
Immigrants   and U.N.I.C.E.F.
                                   Emblem

(Des K. Reece. Litho Cot Printery Ltd, Barbados)

1996 (22 May). *150th Anniv of Indian Immigration to*
Jamaica. T **285** *and similar horiz design. Multicoloured.*
W **111** *(sideways). P* 14.

| 894 | $2.50, Type **285** | 20 | 10 |
| 895 | $10 Indian musicians and traditional dancers | 60 | 80 |

(Des K. Reece. Litho Cot Printery Ltd. Barbados)

1996 (2 Sept). *50th Anniv of U.N.I.C.E.F. W* **111**. *P* 14½×14.

896	286	$2.50, multicoloured	15	10
897		$8 multicoloured	45	70
898		$10 multicoloured	50	75
896/8		Set of 3	1·00	1·40

287 Brown's Hutia

(Des W. Oliver. Litho Enschedé)

1996 (23 Sept). *Endangered Species. Brown's Hutia*
("Jamaican Hutia"). T **287** *and similar horiz designs. Multi-*
coloured. W **111** *(sideways). P* 13½.

899	$2.50, Type **287**	15	10
900	$10 Hutia on rock	50	65
901	$12.50, Female with young	60	80
902	$25 Head of Hutia	1·25	1·75
899/902	Set of 4	2·25	3·00

288 High Altar, Church of St.
Thomas the Apostle

(Des W. Wright. Litho Questa)

1997 (7 Feb). *300th Anniv of the Kingston Parish Church.*
T **288** *and similar multicoloured designs. P* 14.

903	$2 Type **288**	15	10
904	$8 Church of St. Thomas the Apostle	60	60
905	$12.50, "The Angel" (wood carving by Edna Manley) (*vert*)	90	1·25
903/5	Set of 3	1·50	1·75
MS906	106×76 mm. $60 St. Thomas the Apostle at sunset (42×56 mm)	2·75	3·50

No. 903 is inscribed "ALTER" in error.

289 Child's Face and   **290** *Coelia triptera*
U.N.E.S.C.O. Emblem

(Litho Questa)

1997 (7 Apr). *10th Anniv of Chernobyl Nuclear Disaster.*
P 13½×14.

| 907 | **289** $55 multicoloured | 1·75 | 2·25 |

(Litho Questa)

1997 (9 Oct)–**99**. *Orchids. T* **290** *and similar multicoloured*
designs. W **111** *(sideways on horiz designs). P* 14. *A. Without*
imprint date

908A	$1 Type **290**	10	10
909A	$2 *Oncidium pulchellum* (*horiz*)	10	10
910A	$2.50, *Oncidium triquetum*	10	10
911A	$3 *Broughtonia negrilensis*	10	10
912A	$4.50, *Oncidium gauntlettii* (*horiz*) (1.12.97)	10	15
913A	$5 *Encyclia fragans* (*horiz*)	15	20
914A	$8 *Broughtonia sanguinea* (*horiz*) (1.12.97)	25	30
915A	$12 *Phaius tankervilleae* (1.12.97)	35	40
916A	$25 *Cochleanthes flabelliformis* (*horiz*) (1.12.97)	1·25	1·40
917A	$50 *Broughtonia sanguinea* (three varieties) (*horiz*) (1.12.97)	1·50	1·50
908A/17A	Set of 10	3·50	4·00

B. Imprint date ("1999") at foot

| 916B | $25 *Cochleanthes flabelliformis* (*horiz*) (1.2.99) | 75 | 80 |

PRICES OF SETS

Set prices are given for many issues, generally
those containing three stamps or more. Definitive
sets include one of each value or major colour
change, but do not cover different perforations,
die types or minor shades. Where a choice is
possible the set prices are based on the cheapest
versions of the stamps included in the listings.

291 Diana, Princess   **292** University Chapel,
of Wales   Mona

(Des M. Friedman. Litho Questa)

1998 (24 Feb). *Diana, Princess of Wales Commemoration.*
T **291** *and similar vert design. Multicoloured. P* 14.

918	$20 Type **291**	85	90
	a. Sheetlet. No. 918×6	4·75	
MS919	70×100 mm. $80 Princess Diana and Mother Theresa (42×55 mm)	3·25	3·75

No. 918 was issued in sheetlets of 6 with illustrated margins.

(Litho B.D.T.)

1998 (31 July). *50th Anniv of University of West Indies. T* **292**
and similar multicoloured designs. W **111** *(sideways on horiz*
designs). P 13½.

920	Type **292**	40	40
921	$10 Philip Sherlock Centre for Creative Arts, Mona	40	40
922	$50 University arms (*vert*)	2·25	2·75
920/2	Set of 3	2·75	3·25

293 Flags of Jamaica and CARICOM

(Des R. Sauber. Litho Cartor)

1998 (17 Sept). *25th Anniv of Caribbean Community. P* 13½.

| 923 | **293** $30 multicoloured | 1·40 | 1·40 |

294 Jamaican Footballer   **295** Coral Reef

(Des D. Bowen. Litho Cartor)

1998 (25 Sept). *World Cup Football Championship, France.*
T **294** *and similar multicoloured designs. W w* **14** *(sideways*
on horiz designs). P 13½.

924	$10 Type **294**	45	40
925	$25 Jamaican team (*horiz*)	1·10	1·25
926	$100 As $25	4·00	5·00
924/6	Set of 3	5·00	6·00

(Litho Cot Printery Ltd, Barbados)

1998 (23 Dec). *Christmas. International Year of the Ocean.*
T **295** *and similar multicoloured designs. W* **111** *(sideways on*
horiz designs). P 14 ($100) *or* 14×14½ *(others).*

927	$10 Type **295**	45	40
928	$30 Fishing boats, Negril	1·25	1·25
929	$50 Black Spiny Sea Urchin	2·00	2·25
930	$100 Composite design as Nos. 927/9 (22×41 mm)	4·00	4·50
927/30	Set of 4	7·00	7·75

296 Michael Collins   **297** Lesley Ann Masterton
(astronaut)   and Fong-Yee (polo)

(Des N. Shewring. Litho Walsall)

1999 (20 July). *30th Anniv of First Manned Landing on Moon. T* **296** *and similar multicoloured designs.* W **111**. P 14×13½.

931	$7 Type **296**	30	25
932	$10 Service module docking with lunar module	40	40
933	$25 Buzz Aldrin on Moon's surface	90	95
934	$30 Command module in Earth orbit	1·00	1·10
931/4	*Set of* 4	2·40	2·40
MS935	90×80 mm. $100 Earth as seen from Moon (*circular, 40 mm diam*). Wmk sideways. P 14	3·50	4·00

(Des J. Batchelor. Litho B.D.T.)

1999 (3 Aug). *Jamaican Sporting Personalities. T* **297** *and similar multicoloured designs.* W **111** (*sideways on horiz designs*). P 13½.

936	$5 Type **297**	25	20
937	$10 Lawrence Rowe, Collie Smith and Alfred Valentine (cricket)	40	40
938	$20 Vivalyn Latty-Scott (women's cricket) (*vert*)	75	80
939	$25 Lindy Delapenha (football) (*vert*)	80	85
940	$30 Joy Grant-Charles (netball) (*vert*)	90	95
941	$50 Percy Hayles, Gerald Gray and Bunny Grant (boxing)	1·50	1·75
936/41	*Set of* 6	4·25	4·50
MS942	110×90 mm. $100 Lindy Delapenha and Joy Grant-Charles (56×42 *mm*). Wmk upright	4·00	4·50

298 *Spey* (mail ship), 1891

(Des J. Batchelor. Litho B.D.T.)

1999 (8 Oct). *125th Anniv of Universal Postal Union. T* **298** *and similar horiz designs. Multicoloured.* W **111** (*sideways*). P 14.

943	$7 Type **298**	30	25
944	$10 *Jamaica Planter* (mail ship), 1936	40	40
945	$25 Lockheed Constellation (aircraft), 1950	90	95
946	$30 Airbus A-310 (aircraft), 1999	1·00	1·10
943/6	*Set of* 4	2·40	2·40

299 Airbus A-310   300 Shih Tzu

(Litho B.D.T.)

1999 (1 Nov). *30th Anniv of Air Jamaica. T* **299** *and similar horiz designs. Multicoloured.* W **111** (*sideways*). P 14.

947	$10 Type **299**	40	40
948	$25 A-320	90	95
949	$30 A-340	1·00	1·10
947/9	*Set of* 3	2·25	2·25

(Litho Questa)

1999 (25 Nov). *Dogs. T* **300** *and similar vert designs. Multicoloured.* W **111**. P 14½.

950	$7 Type **300**	35	25
951	$10 German Shepherd	45	40
952	$30 Doberman Pinscher	1·10	1·40
950/2	*Set of* 3	1·75	1·90

301 Nelson Mandela Park   302 "The Prophet" (sculpture)

(Litho Questa)

1999 (15 Dec). *Parks and Gardens. T* **301** *and similar horiz designs. Multicoloured.* W **111** (*sideways*). P 14.

953	$7 Type **301**	20	25
954	$10 St. William Grant Park	30	35
955	$25 Seaview Park	75	80
956	$30 Holruth Park	90	95
953/6	*Set of* 4	2·10	2·25

(Litho Questa)

2000 (1 Mar). *Birth Centenary of Edna Manley (artist). T* **302** *and similar vert designs. Multicoloured.* W **111**. P 13½×14.

957	$10 Type **302**	30	35
958	$25 "Horse of the Morning"	75	80
959	$30 "The Angel"	90	95
960	$100 Edna Manley	3·00	3·25
957/60	*Set of* 4	4·75	5·25
MS961	128×159 mm. Nos. 957/60	4·75	5·25

303 Lennox Lewis

(Litho Questa)

2000 (24 Mar). *Lennox Lewis, World Heavyweight Boxing Champion. T* **303** *and similar vert designs. Multicoloured.* W **111** (*sideways*). P 14.

962	$10 Holding W.B.C. Championship belt	30	35
	a. Sheetlet. Nos. 962/70	6·00	
963	$10 In ring with right arm raised	30	35
964	$10 Holding W.B.C. belt above head	30	35
965	$25 Taking punch on chin	75	80
966	$25 Type **303**	75	80
967	$25 In corner	75	80
968	$30 With W.B.C. belt after fight	95	1·00
969	$30 Holding all four belts	95	1·00
970	$30 With belts in front of skyscraper	95	1·00
962/70	*Set of* 9	6·00	6·25

Nos. 962/70 were printed together, *se-tenant*, in sheetlets of 9.

STAMP BOOKLETS

1912. *Black on red covers. Stapled.*
SB1 2s. booklet containing twenty-four 1d. (No. 40) in
blocks of 6 (9 Mar)
SB2 2s. booklet containing twelve ½d. and eighteen 1d.
(Nos. 38, 58), each in blocks of 6 (5 Dec) .. £1300

1923 (Dec). *Black on red cover. Stapled.*
SB3 2s. booklet containing twelve ½d. (No. 91) in
blocks of 4 and eighteen 1d. (No. 92) in blocks
of 6 .. .. £850

1928 (5 Sept). *Black on red cover. Stapled.*
SB5 1s. 6d. booklet containing twelve ½d. and 1d. (Nos.
89a, 92), each in blocks of 6 ..

1929 (July)–**32.** *Black on red cover. Stapled.*
SB6 2s. booklet containing six ½d., twelve 1d. and six
1½d. (Nos. 89a, 108/9) in blocks of 6 .. £1000
a. With 1d. Die II (No. 108a) (1932) ..

1930–33. *Black on red cover. Stapled.*
SB7 2s. booklet containing twelve ½d. and eighteen 1d.
(Nos. 89a, 108), each in blocks of 6 ..
a. With 1d. Die II (No. 108a) (1933) .. £750

1935. *Silver Jubilee. Black on pink cover. Stapled.*
SB8 2s. booklet containing twenty-four 1d. (No. 114) in
blocks of 6 .. .. £1200
a. In blocks of 4 .. .. £1700

1938–40. *Black on green cover inscr "JAMAICA POSTAGE
STAMPS" in one line. Inland Postage Rates on interleaf.
Stapled.*
SB9 2s. booklet containing twelve ½d. and eighteen 1d.
(Nos. 121/2), each in blocks of 6 (inland letter
rate 1d. per oz)
a. Inland letter rate 1½d. for first 2 oz (1940) .. £350

1942–47. *Black on blue cover inscr "JAMAICA POSTAGE
STAMPS" in three lines. Inland Postage Rates on inside front
cover. Stapled.*
SB10 2s. booklet containing twelve ½d. and eighteen
1d. (Nos. 121/2), each in blocks of 6 (Inland
letter rate 1½d. for first 2 oz) .. £225
a. Black on yellow cover (1947) £130

1946. *New Constitution. Black on blue cover. Stapled.*
SB12 2s. booklet containing sixteen 1½d. (No. 134a) in
blocks of 4 .. .. £225

1952. *Black on yellow cover. Stapled.*
SB13 2s. booklet containing twelve ½d and eighteen
1d. (Nos. 121b, 122a), each in blocks of 6 .. 42·00

1956. *Black on green cover. Stitched.*
SB14 3s. booklet containing ½d., 1d., 2d. and 2½d.
(Nos. 159/62) in blocks of 6 .. .. 11·00

1965 (15 Nov). *Black on green cover. Stitched.*
SB15 3s. booklet containing 1d., 2d. and 3d. (Nos. 217,
219, 221) in blocks of 6 .. .. 5·00

1981 (29 July). *Royal Wedding. Multicoloured cover, 155×85
mm, showing Prince Charles, Lady Diana Spencer and St.
Paul's Cathedral. Stitched.*
SB16 $6.25, booklet containing se-tenant pane of 4 (No.
516ba) .. .. 3·50

1982 (30 Aug). *21st Birthday of Princess of Wales.
Multicoloured cover, 155×85 mm, showing Princess of Wales
and Highgrove House. Stitched.*
SB17 $7.50, booklet containing two different se-tenant
panes of 3 (Nos. 551a, 554a) .. .. 4·75

1982 (13 Sept). *Birth of Prince William of Wales. No. SB17
optd "ROYAL BABY 21.6.82".*
SB18 $7.50, booklet containing two different se-tenant
panes of 3 (Nos. 558a, 561a) .. .. 3·25

POSTAL FISCALS

Revenue stamps were authorised for postal use by Post Office
notice of 12 October 1887.

F 1

(Typo D.L.R.)
1865–73. *P* 14. (*a*) *Wmk Pineapple* (*T* **7**).
F1 F 1 1d. rose (1865) .. .. 75·00 95·00
a. Imperf (pair) £400
(*b*) *Wmk Crown CC*
F2 F 1 1d. rose (1871) .. .. 55·00 55·00
(*c*) *Wmk CA over Crown* (*Type* w **7** *sideways, covering two stamps*)
F3 F 1 1d. rose (1873) .. .. 18·00 7·00
a. Imperf

F 2 F 3

(Typo D.L.R.)
1855–74 (Issued). *Glazed paper. P* 14. (*a*) *No wmk.*
F4 F 2 1½d. blue/*blue* (1857) .. .. 45·00 45·00
a. Imperf (1855)
b. Blue on white .. .. 50·00 55·00
F5 3d. purple/*blue* (1857) .. .. 45·00 50·00
a. Imperf (1855)
b. Purple on lilac (1857) .. 45·00 50·00
ba. Imperf (1855)
c. Purple on white (1857) .. 50·00 50·00
(*b*) *Wmk Crown CC*
F6 F 2 3d. purple/*lilac* (1874) .. .. 12·00 15·00
All the above stamps *imperf* are exceedingly rare postally used.

1858 (1 Jan). (Issued). *No wmk. P* 15½ × 15.
F7 F 3 1s. rose/*bluish* .. .. 70·00 75·00
F8 5s. lilac/*bluish* £325 £375
F9 10s. green/*bluish* £400 £450
Telegraph stamps were also used postally, but no authority was
given for such use.

OFFICIAL STAMPS

OFFICIAL   OFFICIAL

(O 1)   (O 2)

1890 (1 Apr)–**91.** *No. 16a optd with Type* O **1** *by C. Vendryes,
Kingston.*
(*a*) "OFFICIAL" 17 *to* 17½ *mm long*
O1 8 ½d. green .. .. .. 7·00 1·00
a. "O" omitted £450
b. One "I" omitted ..
c. Both "I"s omitted £500 £500
d. "L" omitted £550 £550
e. Opt inverted .. .. .. 65·00 70·00
f. Opt double .. .. .. 65·00 70·00
g. Opt double, one inverted .. £325 £325
h. Opt double, one vertical .. £550
j. Pair, overprints *tête-bêche*
O2 8 ½d. green (3.91) .. .. 22·00 22·00
a. Opt double £500
There were five settings of the locally-overprinted Officials.
No. O1 occurred from settings I (2×10), II (3×6), IV and V (horizontal row of 6 each). No. O2 came from setting III (2×6). There
are numerous minor varieties, due to broken type, etc. (*e.g.* a
broken "E" used for "F").
Stamps with the 17–17½ mm opt were reissued in 1894
during a temporary shortage of No. O3.

1890 (1 Apr)–**91.** *Optd with Type* O **2** *by D.L.R. Wmk Crown
CA. P* 14.
O3 8 ½d. green (1891) .. .. 6·50 40
O4 11 1d. rose .. .. .. 4·00 80
O5 2d. grey .. .. .. 7·50 1·00
O3/5 Set of 3 16·00 2·00
O3/5 Optd "Specimen" Set of 3 £100
Nos. O4/5 were not issued without overprint.

The use of Official stamps ceased from 1 January 1898.

Jordan
see Transjordan

Kenya

INDEPENDENT

(Currency. 100 cents = 1 East Africa, later Kenya Shilling)

1 Cattle Ranching 2 Wood-carving

3 National Assembly

(Des V. Whiteley. Photo Harrison)

1963 (12 Dec). *Independence. T 1/3 and similar designs. P 14×15 (small designs) or 14½ (others).*

1	5 c. brown, deep blue, green and bistre	..		10	55
2	10 c. brown	..	..	10	10
3	15 c. magenta	..	..	85	10
4	20 c. black and yellow-green	..		15	15
5	30 c. black and yellow	..	..	15	10
6	40 c. brown and light blue	..		15	30
	a. Printed on the gummed side	..		75·00	
7	50 c. crimson, black and green	..		15	10
8	65 c. deep turquoise-green and yellow	..		55	65
9	1 s. multicoloured	..	..	20	10
10	1 s. 30, brown, black and yellow-green	..		4·25	10
11	2 s. multicoloured	..	..	1·25	40
12	5 s. brown, ultramarine and yellow-green	..		1·25	40
13	10 s. brown and deep blue	..		8·50	2·50
14	20 s. black and rose	..	..	5·50	7·50
1/14	..	..	Set of 14	21·00	11·50

Designs: As *T 1/2*—15 c. Heavy industry; 20 c. Timber industry; 30 c. Jomo Kenyatta and Mt Kenya; 40 c. Fishing industry; 50 c. Kenya flag; 65 c. Pyrethrum industry. As *T 3*—1 s. 30, Tourism (Treetops Hotel); 2 s. Coffee industry; 5 s. Tea industry; 10 s. Mombasa Port; 20 s. Royal College, Nairobi.

The 10 c. was produced in coils of 1000 in addition to normal sheets.

REPUBLIC

4 Cockerel

(Des M. Goaman. Photo J. Enschedé)

1964 (12 Dec). *Inauguration of Republic T 4 and similar vert designs. Multicoloured. P 13 × 12½.*

15	15 c. Type 4	..	..	20	15
16	30 c. President Kenyatta	..		20	10
17	50 c. Lion	..	..	20	10
18	1 s. 30, Hartlaub's Turaco	..		3·75	50
19	2 s. 50, Nandi flame	..	..	50	3·75
15/19	..	..	Set of 5	4·25	4·00

5 Thomson's Gazelle 6 Sable Antelope

7 Greater Kudu

(Des Rena Fennessy. Photo Harrison)

1966 (12 Dec)–**71.** *Various designs as T 5/7. Chalk-surfaced paper. P 14 × 14½ (5 c. to 70 c.) or 14½ (others).*

20	5 c. orange, black and sepia	..	..	20	20
21	10 c. black and apple-green	..		10	10
	a. Glazed, ordinary paper (13.7.71)	..	80	3·75
22	15 c. black and orange	..		10	10
	a. Glazed, ordinary paper (13.7.71)	..	80	1·00
23	20 c. ochre, black and blue	..		10	15
	a. Glazed, ordinary paper (22.1.71)	..	1·00	1·50
24	30 c. Prussian blue, blue and black	..	20	10
25	40 c. black and yellow-brown	..		60	30
	a. Glazed, ordinary paper (19.2.71)	..	1·25	2·00
26	50 c. black and red-orange	..		60	10
	a. Glazed, ordinary paper (19.2.71)	..	14·00	4·75
27	65 c. black and light green	..		1·25	2·00
28	70 c. black and claret (15.9.69)	..	6·00	1·25
	a. Glazed, ordinary paper (19.2.71)	..	20·00	13·00
29	1 s. olive-brown, black and slate-blue	..	30	10
	a. Glazed, ordinary paper (22.1.71)	..	1·25	85
30	1 s. 30, indigo, light olive-green and black	4·00	20
31	1 s. 50, black, orange-brown and dull sage-green (15.9.69)	..	4·25	2·00
	a. Glazed, ordinary paper (22.1.71)	..	3·50	6·00
32	2 s. 50, yellow, black and olive-brown	..	3·25	1·25
	a. Glazed, ordinary paper (22.1.71)	..	3·00	6·50
33	5 s. yellow, black and emerald	..	75	70
	a. Glazed, ordinary paper (22.1.71)	..	3·00	12·00
34	10 s. yellow-ochre, black and red-brown	..	1·75	3·00
35	20 s. yellow-ochre, yellow-orange, blk & gold	7·00	13·00
20/35	..	..	Set of 16	26·00	22·00
21a/33a	..	..	Set of 10	42·00	45·00

Designs: As *T 5/6*—15 c. Aardvark ("Ant Bear"); 20 c. Lesser Bushbaby; 30 c. Warthog; 40 c. Common Zebra; 50 c. African Buffalo; 65 c. Black Rhinoceros; 70 c. Ostrich. As *T 7*—1 s. 30, African Elephant; 1 s. 50, Bat-eared Fox; 2 s. 50, Cheetah; 5 s. Savanna Monkey ("Vervet Monkey"); 10 s. Giant Ground Pangolin; 20 s. Lion.

On chalk-surfaced paper, all values except 30 c., 50 c. and 2 s. 50 exist with PVA gum as well as gum arabic but the 70 c. and 1 s. 50 exist with PVA gum only. The stamps on glazed, ordinary paper exist with PVA gum only.

Nos. 21 and 26 exist in coils constructed from normal sheets.

8 Perna Tellin *(Tellina perna)* 9 Ramose Murex *(Murex ramosus)* **(10)**

50 c.	A. Inscr "Janthina globosa".
	B. Inscr "Janthina janthina".
70 c.	C. Inscr "Nautilus pompileus".
	D. Inscr "Nautilus pompilius".

(Des Rena Fennessy. Photo Harrison)

1971 (15 Dec)–**74.** *T 8/9 and similar vert designs showing seashells. Multicoloured. (a) Size as T 8. P 14½ × 14.*

36	5 c. Type 8	..	..	10	30
37	10 c. Episcopal Mitre (Mitra mitra) (yellow-green background)	..	15	10
	a. Olive-green background (21.1.74)	..	85	10
38	15 c. Purplish Clanculus (Clanculus puniceus)	..	15	20
39	20 c. Humpback Cowrie (Cypraea mauritania)	..	15	20
40	30 c. Variable Abalone (Haliotis varia)	..	20	10
41	40 c. Flame Top Shell (Trochus flammulatus)	20	10
42	50 c. Common Purple Janthina (Janthina janthina) (A)	..	30	20
43	50 c. Common Purple Janthina (Janthina janthina) (B) (21.1.74)	..	9·50	2·25
44	60 c. Bull-mouth Helmet (Cypraecassis rufa)	30	1·25
45	70 c. Chambered, Pearly Nautilus (Nautilus pompilius) (C)	..	45	1·50
46	70 c. Chambered, Pearly Nautilus (Nautilus pompilius) (D) (21.1.74)	..	9·00	4·50

(b) Size as T 9. P 14

47	1 s. Type 9 (yellow-buff background)	..	30	10
	a. Buff background (21.1.74)	..	20	10
48	1 s. 50, Trumpet Triton (Charonia tritonis)	1·00	10
49	2 s. 50, Trapezium Horse Conch (Fasciolaria trapezium)	..	1·00	10
50	5 s. Great Green Turban (Turbo marmoratus) (pale olive-yellow background)	..	1·00	10
	a. Pale olive-bistre background (13.6.73)	1·00	10
51	10 s. Textile or Cloth of Gold Cone (Conus textile)	..	3·25	15
52	20 s. Scorpion Conch (Lambis scorpius) (grey background)	..	5·00	75
	a. Bluish slate background (12.9.73)	3·25	25
36/52a	..	..	Set of 17	27·00	10·00

1975 (17 Nov). *Nos. 48/9 and 52 surch as T 10.*

53	2 s. on 1 s. 50, Trumpet Triton (Charonia tritonis)	..	6·00	4·50
54	3 s. on 2 s. 50, Trapezium Horse Conch (Fasciolaria trapezium)	..	9·50	18·00
55	40 s. on 20 s. Scorpion Conch (Lambis scorpius)	..	6·00	13·00
53/5	..	..	Set of 3	19·00	32·00

The surcharge on No. 55 does not have a dot beneath the stroke following the face value.

For commemorative stamps, issued between 1964 and 1976, inscribed "UGANDA KENYA TANGANYIKA AND ZANZIBAR" (or "TANZANIA UGANDA KENYA") see under KENYA, UGANDA AND TANGANYIKA.

---

11 Microwave Tower 12 Akii Bua, Ugandan Hurdler

(Des H. Nickelsen. Litho Format)

1976 (15 Apr). *Telecommunications Development. T 11 and similar multicoloured designs. P 14.*

56	50 c. Type 11	..	..	10	10
57	1 s. Cordless switchboard (horiz)	..	10	10
58	2 s. Telephones	..	..	20	30
59	3 s. Message Switching Centre (horiz)	25	45
56/9	..	..	Set of 4	55	75
MS60	120×120 mm. Nos. 56/9. Imperf	1·10	2·50

Nos. 56/7 and 59 exist imperforate from stock dispersed by the liquidator of Format International Security Printers Ltd.

(Des Beryl Moore. Litho Format)

1976 (7 July*). *Olympic Games, Montreal. T 12 and similar horiz designs. Multicoloured. P 14½.*

61	50 c. Type 12	..	..	10	10
62	1 s. Filbert Bayi, Tanzanian runner	..	15	10
63	2 s. Steve Muchoki, Kenyan boxer	..	45	35
64	3 s. Olympic flame and East African flags	60	50
61/4	..	..	Set of 4	1·10	85
MS65	129 × 154 mm. Nos. 61/4. P 13	6·00	7·50

*This is the local date of issue; the Crown Agents released the stamps two days earlier.

Nos. 61 and 63 exist imperforate from stock dispersed by the liquidator of Format Internationl Security Printers Ltd.

13 Diesel-hydraulic Train, Tanzania–Zambia Railway 14 Nile Perch

(Des H. Moghul. Litho Format)

1976 (4 Oct). *Railway Transport. T 13 and similar horiz designs. Multicoloured. P 14½.*

66	50 c. Type 13	..	..	35	10
67	1 s. Nile Bridge, Uganda	..	60	15
68	2 s. Nakuru Station, Kenya	..	1·75	1·25
69	3 s. Uganda Railway Class A steam locomotive, 1896	..	1·75	1·75
66/9	..	..	Set of 4	4·00	3·00
MS70	154×103 mm. Nos. 66/9. P 13	8·00	8·00

Nos. 66/70 exist imperforate from stock dispersed by the liquidator of Format International Security Printers Ltd.

(Des Adrienne Kennaway. Litho Format)

1977 (10 Jan). *Game Fish of East Africa. T 14 and similar vert designs. Multicoloured. P 14*.*

71	50 c. Type 14	..	..	25	10
72	1 s. Nile Mouthbroder ("Tilapia")	..	35	10
73	3 s. Sailfish	..	..	75	60
74	5 s. Black Marlin	..	..	90	80
71/4	..	..	Set of 4	2·00	1·40
MS75	153×129 mm. Nos. 71/4	7·50	4·00

*On No. MS75 the right-hand side of the 5 s. value is perforated 13½.

15 Maasai Manyatta (village), Kenya

(Des Rena Fennessy. Litho Questa)

1977 (15 Jan). *Second World Black and African Festival of Arts and Culture, Nigeria. T 15 and similar horiz designs. Multicoloured. P 13½.*

76	50 c. Type 15	..	..	15	10
77	1 s. "Heartbeat of Africa" (Ugandan dancers)	20	10
78	2 s. Makonde sculpture, Tanzania	..	75	1·25
79	3 s. "Early Man and Technology" (skinning hippopotamus)	..	1·00	1·75
76/9	..	..	Set of 4	1·90	2·75
MS80	132 × 109 mm. Nos. 76/9	..	4·00	5·50

16 Rally-car and Villagers

(Litho Questa)

1977 (5 Apr). *25th Anniv of Safari Rally. T **16** and similar horiz designs. Multicoloured. P 14.*

81	50 c. Type **16**		15	10
82	1 s. President Kenyatta starting rally		15	10
83	2 s. Car fording river		50	60
84	5 s. Car and elephants		1·40	1·50
81/4		Set of 4	2·00	2·00
MS85	126 × 93 mm. Nos. 81/4		3·75	6·50

17 Canon Kivebulaya

(Des Beryl Moore. Litho Questa)

1977 (30 June). *Centenary of Ugandan Church. T **17** and similar horiz designs. Multicoloured. P 14 × 13½.*

86	50 c. Type **17**		10	10
87	1 s. Modern Namirembe Cathedral		10	10
88	2 s. The first Cathedral		30	55
89	5 s. Early congregation, Kigezi		50	1·00
86/9		Set of 4	85	1·50
MS90	126 × 94 mm. Nos. 86/9		1·40	2·50

18 Sagana Royal Lodge, Nyeri, 1952

(Des G. Vasarhelyi (50s.), J. Cooter (others). Litho Questa)

1977 (20 July). *Silver Jubilee. T **18** and similar multicoloured designs. P 13½.*

91	2 s. Type **18**		15	15
92	5 s. Treetops Hotel (vert)		20	35
93	10 s. Queen Elizabeth and President Kenyatta		30	60
94	15 s. Royal visit, 1972		45	1·00
91/4		Set of 4	1·00	1·90

MS95 Two sheets: (a) 140 × 60 mm, No. 94; (b) 152 × 127 mm, 50 s. Queen and Prince Philip in Treetops Hotel .. .. *Set of 2* 2·00 1·40

19 Pancake Tortoise

(Des Rena Fennessy. Litho Questa)

1977 (26 Sept). *Endangered Species. T **19** and similar horiz designs. Multicoloured. P 14.*

96	50 c. Type **19**		30	10
97	1 s. Nile Crocodile		40	10
98	2 s. Hunter's Hartebeest		1·60	55
99	3 s. Red Colobus		1·75	70
100	5 s. Dugong		2·00	1·10
96/100		Set of 5	5·50	2·25
MS101	127 × 101 mm. Nos. 97/100		7·00	8·50

20 Kenya–Ethiopia Border Point

(Litho Questa)

1977 (10 Nov). *Nairobi–Addis Ababa Highway. T **20** and similar horiz designs. Multicoloured. P 14.*

102	50 c. Type **20**		15	10
103	1 s. Archer's Post		15	10
104	2 s. Thika Flyover		40	40
105	5 s. Marsabit Game Lodge		1·00	1·10
102/5		Set of 4	1·50	1·50
MS106	144 × 91 mm. Nos. 102/5		2·25	3·50

21 Gypsum

22 Amethyst

(Des Rena Fennessy. Photo Harrison)

1977 (10 Dec*). *Minerals. Multicoloured designs.*

(a) Vert as T **21**. P 14½ × 14

107	10 c. Type **21**		1·25	20
108	20 c. Trona		1·25	20
109	30 c. Kyanite		1·40	20
110	40 c. Amazonite		1·40	10
111	50 c. Galena		1·40	10
112	70 c. Silicified wood		5·50	40
113	80 c. Fluorite		5·50	60

(b) Horiz as T **22**. P 14

114	1s. Type **22**		1·40	10
	a. Gold (face value and inscr) omitted			
115	1s. 50, Agate		1·50	30
	a. Gold (face value and inscr) omitted			
116	2 s. Tourmaline		1·50	20
	a. Gold (face value and inscr) omitted		£200	
117	3 s. Aquamarine		1·75	55
	a. Gold (face value and inscr) omitted		£200	
118	5 s. Rhodolite Garnet		1·75	1·40
119	10 s. Sapphire		1·75	2·50
120	20 s. Ruby		6·00	3·50
121	40 s. Green Grossular Garnet		18·00	18·00
107/21		Set of 15	45·00	25·00

*This is the local issue date. The stamps were released in London on 9 December.

23 Joe Kadenge (Kenya) and Forwards

(Des H. Moghul. Litho Questa)

1978 (10 Apr). *World Cup Football Championship, Argentina. T **23** and similar horiz designs showing footballers. Multicoloured. P 14 × 13½.*

122	50 c. Type **23**		10	10
123	1 s. Mohamed Chuma (Tanzania) and Cup presentation		10	10
124	2 s. Omari Kidevu (Zanzibar) and goalmouth scene		30	70
125	3 s. Polly Ouma (Uganda) and three forwards		40	95
122/5		Set of 4	70	1·60
MS126	136 × 81 mm. Nos. 122/5		3·50	3·50

24 Boxing

(Des H. Moghul. Photo Heraclio Fournier)

1978 (17 July). *Commonwealth Games, Edmonton. T **24** and similar horiz designs. Multicoloured. P 13 × 14.*

127	50 c. Type **24**		15	10
128	1 s. Welcoming Olympic Games Team, 1968		20	10
129	3 s. Javelin throwing		60	1·00
130	5 s. President Kenyatta admiring boxer's trophy		75	1·60
127/30		Set of 4	1·50	2·50

25 "Overloading is Dangerous"

(Litho Walsall)

1978 (18 Sept). *Road Safety. T **25** and similar horiz designs. Multicoloured. P 13½.*

131	50 c. Type **25**		50	10
132	1 s. "Speed does not pay"		70	20
133	1 s. 50, "Ignoring Traffic Signs may cause death"		85	55
134	3 s. "Slow down at School Crossing"		1·25	1·00
135	3 s. "Never cross a continuous line"		1·40	2·50
136	5 s. "Approach Railway Level Crossing with extreme caution"		2·00	3·50
131/6		Set of 6	6·00	7·00

26 President Kenyatta at Mass Rally, 1963

27 Freedom Fighters, Namibia

(Des Beryl Moore. Litho J.W.)

1978 (16 Oct). *Kenyatta Day. T **26** and similar horiz designs. Multicoloured. P 14.*

137	50 c. "Harambee Water Project"		15	10
138	1 s. Handing over of Independence Instruments, 1963		15	10
139	2 s. Type **26**		40	50
140	3 s. "Harambee, 15 Great Years"		75	1·25
141	5 s. "Struggle for Independence, 1952"		1·00	2·00
137/41		Set of 5	2·25	3·25

(Des L. Curtis. Litho Questa)

1978 (11 Dec*). *International Anti-Apartheid Year. T **27** and similar horiz designs. P 14 × 14½.*

142	50 c. multicoloured		15	10
143	1 s. black and cobalt		15	10
144	2 s. multicoloured		40	30
145	3 s. multicoloured		60	65
146	5 s. multicoloured		75	1·00
142/6		Set of 5	1·90	1·90

Designs:—1 s. International seminar on apartheid, racial discrimination and colonialism in South Africa; 2 s. Steve Biko's tombstone; 3 s. Nelson Mandela; 5 s. Bishop Lamont.

*This is the local date of issue; the Crown Agents released the stamps the previous day.

28 Children Playing

(Des Beryl Moore. Litho Walsall)

1979 (5 Feb). *International Year of the Child. T **28** and similar horiz designs. Multicoloured. P 13½ × 14.*

147	50 c. Type **28**		20	10
148	2 s. Child fishing		60	60
149	3 s. Children singing and dancing		80	1·00
150	5 s. Children working with camels		1·00	1·60
147/50		Set of 4	2·40	3·00

29 "The Lion and the Jewel"

30 Blind Telephone Operator

(Des Beryl Moore. Litho Enschedé)

1979 (6 Apr). *Kenya National Theatre. T **29** and similar horiz designs. Multicoloured. P 13 × 13½.*

151	50 c. Type **29**		15	10
152	1 s. Scene from "Utisi"		15	10
153	2 s. "Entertainment past and present" (programmes from past productions)		30	30
154	3 s. Kenya National Theatre		45	45
155	5 s. Nairobi City Players production of "Genesis"		75	75
151/5		Set of 5	1·60	1·50

(Litho Harrison)

1979 (29 June*). *50th Anniv of Salvation Army Social Services. T **30** and similar multicoloured designs. P 13½ × 13 (50 c., 1s.) or 13 × 13½ (others).*

156	50 c. Type **30**		30	10
157	1 s. Care for the Aged		30	10
158	3 s. Village polytechnic (horiz)		90	1·50
159	5 s. Vocational training (horiz)		1·25	2·50
156/9		Set of 4	2·50	3·50

*This is the local date of issue; the Crown Agents released the stamps on 4 June.

MINIMUM PRICE

The minimum price quote is 10p which represents a handling charge rather than a basis for valuing common stamps. For further notes about prices see introductory pages.

31 "Father of the Nation"
(Kenyatta's funeral
procession)

32 British East Africa
Company 1890 1 a. Stamp

(Des H. Moghul. Litho Questa)

1979 (21 Aug*). *1st Death Anniv of President Kenyatta. T **31** and similar vert designs. Multicoloured. P 13½ × 14.*
160	50 c. Type 31		10	10
161	1 s. "First President of Kenya" (Kenyatta receiving independence)		10	10
162	3 s. "Kenyatta the politician" (speaking at rally)		30	50
163	5 s. "A true son of Kenya" (Kenyatta as a boy carpenter)		40	95
160/3		Set of 4	75	1·50

*This is the local date of issue; the Crown Agents did not release the stamps until 29 August.

(Des J.W. Litho Harrison)

1979 (27 Nov). *Death Centenary of Sir Rowland Hill. T **32** and similar vert designs showing stamps. P 14 × 14½.*
164	50 c. multicoloured		15	10
165	1 s. multicoloured		15	10
166	2 s. black, magenta and yellow-ochre		20	40
167	5 s. multicoloured		35	1·00
164/7		Set of 4	75	1·40

Designs:—1 s. Kenya, Uganda and Tanganyika 1935 1 s.; 2 s. Penny Black; 5 s. 1964 Inauguration of Republic 2 s. 50, commemorative.

33 Roads, Globe and Conference Emblem

(Des H. Moghul. Litho Questa)

1980 (10 Jan). *I.R.F. (International Road Federation) African Highway Conference, Nairobi. T **33** and similar horiz designs. Multicoloured. P 14 × 13½.*
168	50 c. Type 33		15	10
169	1 s. New weighbridge, Athi River		15	10
170	3 s. New Nyali Bridge, Mombasa		40	85
171	5 s. Highway to Jomo Kenyatta International Airport		50	2·00
168/71		Set of 4	1·10	2·75

34 Mobile Unit in action, Masailand

35 Statue of Sir Rowland Hill

(Des Beryl Moore. Litho Questa)

1980 (20 Mar). *Flying Doctor Service. T **34** and similar multicoloured designs. P 14½.*
172	50 c. Type 34		15	10
173	1 s. Donkey transport to Turkana airstrip (vert)		20	10
174	3 s. Surgical team in action at outstation (vert)		65	1·00
175	5 s. Emergency airlift from North Eastern Province		90	1·60
172/5		Set of 4	1·60	2·50
MS176	146 × 133 mm. Nos. 172/5		1·60	2·50

(Des J.W. Litho Questa)

1980 (6 May). *"London 1980" International Stamp Exhibition. P 14.*
177	**35** 25 s. multicoloured		1·00	2·50
MS178	114 × 101 mm. No. 177		1·00	2·75

36 Pope John Paul II

37 Blue-spotted Stingray

(Des Sister Frances Randal. Litho Italian Govt Ptg Works, Rome)

1980 (8 May). *Papal Visit. T **36** and similar multicoloured designs. P 13.*
179	50 c. Type 36		40	10
180	1 s. Pope John Paul II, cathedral and coat of arms		50	10
181	5 s. Pope John Paul II, Papal and Kenyan flags on dove symbol (vert)		1·10	70
182	10 s. President Moi, Pope John Paul II and map of Africa		1·60	1·40
179/82		Set of 4	3·25	2·00

(Des Adrienne Kennaway. Litho Harrison)

1980 (27 June). *Marine Life. T **37** and similar vert designs. Multicoloured. P 14.*
183	50 c. Type 37		30	10
184	2 s. Allard's Anemonefish		1·00	80
185	3 s. Four-coloured Nudibranch (Chromodoris quadricolor)		1·25	1·75
186	5 s. Eretmochelys imbricata		1·75	2·75
183/6		Set of 4	3·75	4·75

38 National Archives

(Des A. Odhuno; adapted L. Curtis. Litho Questa)

1980 (9 Oct). *Historic Buildings. T **38** and similar horiz designs. Multicoloured. P 14.*
187	50 c. Type 38		10	10
188	1 s. Provincial Commissioner's Office, Nairobi		15	10
189	1 s. 50, Nairobi House		20	20
190	2 s. Norfolk Hotel		25	50
191	3 s. McMillan Library		35	75
192	5 s. Kipande House		55	1·25
187/92		Set of 6	1·40	2·50

39 "Disabled Enjoys Affection"

(Des H. Moghul. Litho Enschedé)

1981 (10 Feb). *International Year for Disabled Persons. T **39** and similar horiz designs. Multicoloured. P 14 × 13.*
193	50 c. Type 39		15	10
194	1 s. President Moi presenting Kenyan flag to Disabled Olympic Games team captain		15	10
195	3 s. Blind people climbing Mount Kenya, 1975		55	65
196	5 s. Disabled artist at work		70	1·00
193/6		Set of 4	1·40	1·60

40 Longonot Complex

(Des H. Moghul. Litho Harrison)

1981 (15 Apr). *Satellite Communications. T **40** and similar horiz designs. Multicoloured. P 14 × 14½.*
197	50 c. Type 40		15	10
198	2 s. "Intelsat V"		40	35
199	3 s. "Longonot I"		45	55
200	5 s. "Longonot II"		60	85
197/200		Set of 4	1·40	1·60

41 Kenyatta Conference Centre

42 St. Paul's Cathedral

(Des L. Curtis. Litho Questa (MS206) or J.W. (others))

1981 (17 June*). *O.A.U. (Organisation of African Unity) Summit Conference, Nairobi. T **41** and similar horiz designs in black, bistre-yellow and new blue (1s.) or multicoloured (others). P 13½.*
201	50 c. Type 41		15	10
202	1 s. "Panaftel" earth stations		15	10
203	3 s. Parliament Building		40	40
204	5 s. Jomo Kenyatta International Airport		70	65
205	10 s. O.A.U. flag		80	1·00
201/5		Set of 5	2·00	2·00
MS206	110 × 110 mm. No. 205. P 14½ × 14		1·10	1·50

*This is the local date of issue; the Crown Agents did not release the stamps until 24 June.

(Des A. Theobald. Litho Questa)

1981 (29 July). *Royal Wedding. T **42** and similar vert designs. Multicoloured. P 14.*
207	50 c. Prince Charles and President Daniel Arap Moi		10	10
208	3 s. Type 42		15	20
209	5 s. Royal Yacht Britannia		25	30
210	10 s. Prince Charles on safari in Kenya		40	55
207/10		Set of 4	70	1·00
MS211	85 × 102 mm. 25 s. Prince Charles and Lady Diana Spencer		75	80

Nos. 207/10 also exist perforated 12 (price for set of 4 70p mint, £1.40 used) from additional sheetlets of five stamps and one label.

Insufficient supplies of No. MS211 were received by 29 July for a full distribution, but subsequently the miniature sheet was freely available.

43 Giraffe

44 "Technical Development"

(Des Rena Fennessy. Litho Questa)

1981 (31 Aug). *Rare Animals. T **43** and similar vert designs. Multicoloured. P 14½.*
212	50 c. Type 43		15	10
213	2 s. Bongo		35	25
214	5 s. Roan Antelope		70	1·25
215	10 s. Agile Mangabey		1·00	2·75
212/15		Set of 4	2·00	3·75

(Des H. Moghul, adapted L. Curtis. Litho Questa)

1981 (16 Oct). *World Food Day. T **44** and similar vert designs. Multicoloured. P 14.*
216	50 c. Type 44		10	10
217	1 s. "Mwea rice projects"		15	10
218	2 s. "Irrigation schemes"		30	55
219	5 s. "Breeding livestock"		60	1·75
216/19		Set of 4	1·00	2·25

45 Kamba

46 Australopithecus boisei

(Des Adrienne Kennaway. Litho Harrison)

1981 (18 Dec). *Ceremonial Costumes (1st series). T **45** and similar vert designs. Multicoloured. P 14½ × 13½.*
220	50 c. Type 45		40	10
221	1 s. Turkana		45	10
222	2 s. Giriama		1·25	85
223	3 s. Masai		1·60	2·00
224	5 s. Luo		1·75	3·00
220/4		Set of 5	5·00	5·50

See also Nos. 329/33, 413/17 and 515/19.

(Des Adrienne Kennaway. Litho Format)

1982 (19 Jan). *"Origins of Mankind". Skulls. T 46 and similar horiz designs. Multicoloured. P 13½ × 14.*

225	50 c. Type 46		1·10	20
226	2 s. *Homo erectus*		2·50	1·50
227	3 s. *Homo habilis*		3·00	3·75
228	5 s. *Proconsul africanus*		3·50	5·00
225/8		*Set of 4*	9·00	9·50

47 Tree-planting

(Des L. Curtis. Litho Harrison)

1982 (9 June). *75th Anniv of Boy Scout Movement (Nos. 229, 231, 233 and 235) and 60th Anniv of Girl Guide Movement (Nos. 230, 232, 234 and 236). T 47 and similar horiz designs. Multicoloured. P 14½.*

229	70 c. Type 47		50	65
	a. Horiz pair. Nos. 229/30		1·00	1·25
230	70 c. Paying homage		50	65
231	3 s. 50, "Be Prepared"		1·25	1·75
	a. Horiz pair. Nos. 231/2		2·50	3·50
232	3 s. 50, "International Friendship"		1·25	1·75
233	5 s. Helping disabled		1·75	2·50
	a. Horiz pair. Nos. 233/4		3·50	5·00
234	5 s. Community service		1·75	2·50
235	6 s. 50, Paxtu Cottage (Lord Baden-Powell's home)		2·00	2·75
	a. Horiz pair. Nos. 235/6		4·00	5·50
236	6 s. 50, Lady Baden-Powell		2·00	2·75
229/36		*Set of 8*	10·00	13·00
MS237	112 × 112 mm. Nos. 229, 231, 233 and 235		3·75	3·00

The two designs of each value were printed together, *se-tenant*, in horizontal pairs throughout the sheet.

48 Footballer displaying Shooting Skill

(Des local artist. Litho Harrison)

1982 (5 July). *World Cup Football Championships, Spain. T 48 and similar triangular designs showing footballers silhouetted against world map. Multicoloured. P 12½.*

238	70 c. Type 48		1·50	65
239	3 s. 50, Heading		2·75	2·75
240	5 s. Goalkeeping		3·75	4·25
241	10 s. Dribbling		5·50	8·00
238/41		*Set of 4*	12·00	14·00
MS242	101×76 mm. 20 s. Tackling. P 13×14		4·75	4·00

49 Cattle Judging   50 Micro-wave Radio System   (51)

(Des H. Moghul. Litho Harrison)

1982 (28 Sept). *80th Anniv of Agricultural Society of Kenya. T 49 and similar vert designs. Multicoloured. P 14½.*

243	70 c. Type 49		50	10
244	2 s. 50, Farm machinery		1·25	1·25
245	3 s. 50, Musical ride		1·50	1·50
246	6 s. 50, Agricultural Society emblem		2·00	4·25
243/6		*Set of 4*	4·75	7·25

(Des H. Moghul. Photo Courvoisier)

1982 (21 Oct). *I.T.U. Plenipotentiary Conference, Nairobi. T 50 and similar vert designs. Multicoloured. P 11½.*

247	70 c. Type 50		50	10
248	3 s. 50, Sea-to-shore service link		1·75	1·75
249	5 s. Rural telecommunications system		2·25	3·75
250	6 s. 50, I.T.U. emblem		2·50	4·50
247/50		*Set of 4*	6·25	9·00

1982 (22 Nov). *No. 113 surch with T 51, in white on a black panel.*

251	70 c. on 80 c. Fluorite		1·00	1·00

52 Container Cranes

(Des R. Vigurs. Litho Questa)

1983 (20 Jan). *5th Anniv of Kenya Ports Authority. T 52 and similar horiz designs. P 14.*

252	70 c. Type 52		85	10
253	2 s. Port by night		1·75	1·90
254	3 s. 50, Container cranes (*different*)		2·50	3·50
255	5 s. Map of Mombasa Port		3·25	4·50
252/5		*Set of 4*	7·50	9·00
MS256	125 × 85 mm. Nos. 252/5		7·50	9·00

53 Shada Zambarau   54 Waridi Kikuba

(Des Rena Fennessy. Photo Harrison)

1983 (15 Feb)–**85**. *Flowers. Multicoloured.*

(a) Vert designs as T 53. P 14½×14

257	10 c. Type 53		40	40
258	20 c. Kilua Kingulima		55	40
259	30 c. Mwalika Mwiya		55	40
260	40 c. Ziyungi Buluu		55	40
261	50 c. Kilua Habashia		55	30
262	70 c. Chanuo Kato		60	20
262a	80 c. As 40 c. (7.8.85)		4·00	2·75
262b	1 s. Waridi Kikuba (5.8.85*)		4·00	80

(b) Vert designs as T 54. P 14

263	1 s. Type 54		65	20
264	1 s. 50, Mshomoro Mtambazi		1·75	60
265	2 s. Papatuo Boti		1·75	60
266	2 s. 50, Tumba Mboni		2·25	60
266a	3 s. Mkuku Mrembo (12.8.85)		7·50	7·50
267	3 s. 50, Mtongo Mbeja		2·00	1·50
267b	4 s. Mnukia Muuma (7.8.85)		4·75	6·50
268	5 s. Nyungu Chepuo		2·00	1·50
268a	7 s. Mlua Miba (7.8.85)		6·50	8·50
269	10 s. Muafunili		2·00	2·00
270	20 s. Mbake Nyanza		2·00	3·00
271	40 s. Njuga Pagwa		3·75	8·00
257/71		*Set of 20*	42·00	40·00

267 3 s. 50, Gold (inscr and face value) omitted

*Earliest known postmark date.

55 Coffee Plucking   56 Examining Parcels

(Des C. Fernandes. Litho Harrison)

1983 (14 Mar). *Commonwealth Day. T 55 and similar multicoloured designs. P 14×14½ (70 c., 2 s.) or 14½×14 (others).*

272	70 c. Type 55		10	10
273	2 s. President Daniel Arap Moi		15	20
274	5 s. Satellite view of Earth (*horiz*)		35	45
275	10 s. Masai dance (*horiz*)		65	1·00
272/5		*Set of 4*	1·10	1·50

(Des H. Moghul. Litho Harrison)

1983 (11 May). *30th Anniv of Customs Co-operation Council. T 56 and similar vert designs. Multicoloured. P 14.*

276	70 c. Type 56		25	10
277	2 s. 50, Customs Headquarters, Mombasa		65	30
278	3 s. 50, Customs Council Headquarters, Brussels		75	40
279	10 s. Customs patrol boat		2·40	2·50
276/9		*Set of 4*	3·50	3·00

57 Communications via Satellite   58 *Craftsman* (freighter) in Kilindini Harbour

(Litho Harrison)

1983 (4 July). *World Communications Year. T 57 and similar multicoloured designs. P 14×14½ (70 c., 2 s. 50) or 14½×14 (others).*

280	70 c. Type 57		60	10
281	2 s. 50, "Telephone and Postal Services"		1·50	1·75
282	3 s. 50, Communications by sea and air (*horiz*)		2·00	3·00
283	5 s. Road and rail communications (*horiz*)		2·50	4·00
280/3		*Set of 4*	6·00	8·00

(Litho Harrison)

1983 (22 Sept). *25th Anniv of Intergovernmental Maritime Organization. T 58 and similar horiz designs. Multicoloured. P 14.*

284	70 c. Type 58		95	10
285	2 s. 50, Life-saving devices		2·00	1·75
286	3 s. 50, Mombasa container terminal		2·50	3·00
287	10 s. Marine park		3·50	6·50
284/7		*Set of 4*	8·00	10·00

59 President Moi signing Visitors' Book

(Litho Harrison)

1983 (31 Oct). *29th Commonwealth Parliamentary Conference. T 59 and similar multicoloured designs. P 14.*

288	70 c. Type 59		25	10
289	2 s. 50, Parliament building, Nairobi (*vert*)		90	1·10
290	5 s. State opening of Parliament (*vert*)		1·60	2·75
288/90		*Set of 3*	2·50	3·50
MS291	122 × 141 mm. Nos. 288/90		2·50	4·25

60 Kenyan and British Flags

(Des A. Theobald. Litho Harrison)

1983 (10 Nov). *Royal Visit. T 60 and similar horiz designs. Multicoloured. P 14.*

292	70 c. Type 60		50	10
293	3 s. 50, Sagana State Lodge		2·00	1·50
294	5 s. Treetops Hotel		2·25	2·50
295	10 s. Queen Elizabeth II and President Moi		3·50	6·50
292/5		*Set of 4*	7·50	9·50
MS296	126×100 mm. 25 s. Designs as Nos. 292/5, but without face values. Imperf		4·50	6·50

61 President Moi   62 White-backed Night Heron

(Des and litho Harrison)

1983 (9 Dec). *20th Anniv of Independence. T 61 and similar horiz designs. Multicoloured. P 14½.*

297	70 c. Type 61		10	10
298	2 s. President Moi planting tree		15	20
299	3 s. 50, Kenyan flag and emblem		25	35
300	5 s. School milk scheme		40	50
301	10 s. People of Kenya		75	1·10
297/301		*Set of 5*	1·50	2·00
MS302	126×93 mm. 25 s. Designs as Nos. 297 and 299/301, but without face values. Imperf		1·50	2·75

(Des Agnes Odero. Litho Harrison)

1984 (6 Feb). *Rare Birds of Kenya. T 62 and similar vert designs. Multicoloured. P 14½ × 13½.*

303	70 c. Type 62		1·75	30
304	2 s. 50, Quail Plover		3·00	2·00
305	3 s. 50, Taita Olive Thrush		3·75	3·75
306	5 s. Mufumbiri Shrike ("Yellow Gonolek")		4·25	4·25
307	10 s. White-winged Apalis		5·50	7·00
303/7		*Set of 5*	16·00	16·00

NEW INFORMATION

The editor is always interested to correspond with people who have new information that will improve or correct the Catalogue.

63 Radar Tower   **64** Running

(Des C. Fernandes. Litho Harrison)

1984 (2 Apr). *40th Anniv of International Civil Aviation Organization. T 63 and similar multicoloured designs. P 14.*
308	70 c. Type 63		15	10
309	2 s. 50, Kenya School of Aviation (*horiz*)		45	45
310	3 s. 50, Boeing 707 taking off from Moi airport (*horiz*)		65	80
311	5 s. Air traffic control centre		95	1·25
308/11		*Set of 4*	2·00	2·25

(Des and litho Harrison)

1984 (21 May). *Olympic Games, Los Angeles. T 64 and similar horiz designs. P 14½.*
312	70 c. black, bright yellow-green and bronze-green		30	10
313	2 s. 50, black, bright magenta and reddish violet		60	70
314	5 s. black, pale turquoise-blue and steel blue		1·50	2·50
315	10 s. black, bistre-yellow and brown		3·50	5·50
312/15		*Set of 4*	5·25	8·00
MS316	130×121 mm. 25 s. Designs as Nos. 312/15 but without face values. Imperf		3·25	3·25

Designs:—2 s. 50, Hurdling; 5 s. Boxing; 10 s. Hockey.

65 Conference and Kenya Library Association Logos   **66** Doves and Cross

(Des and litho Harrison)

1984 (28 June). *50th Conference of the International Federation of Library Associations. T 65 and similar horiz designs. Multicoloured. P 14½.*
317	70 c. Type 65		10	10
318	3 s. 50, Mobile library		50	60
319	5 s. Adult library		65	1·25
320	10 s. Children's library		1·00	2·50
317/20		*Set of 4*	2·00	3·75

(Des K. Bisley. Litho Harrison)

1984 (23 Aug). *4th World Conference on Religion and Peace. T 66 and similar vert designs, each showing a different central symbol. Multicoloured. P 14½.*
321	70 c. Type 66		30	10
322	2 s. 50, Arabic inscription		1·25	1·50
323	3 s. 50, Peace emblem		1·60	2·25
324	6 s. 50, Star and Crescent		2·00	3·50
321/4		*Set of 4*	4·75	6·50

67 Export Year Logo   **68** Knight and Nyayo National Stadium

(Litho Harrison)

1984 (1 Oct). *Kenya Export Year. T 67 and similar multicoloured designs. P 14½.*
325	70 c. Type 67		30	10
326	3 s. 50, Forklift truck with air cargo (*horiz*)		1·75	2·00
327	5 s. Loading ship's cargo		2·50	2·75
328	10 s. Kenyan products (*horiz*)		3·75	5·25
325/8		*Set of 4*	7·50	9·00

(Litho Harrison)

1984 (5 Nov). *Ceremonial Costumes (2nd series). Vert designs as T 45. Multicoloured. P 14½×13½.*
329	70 c. Luhya		70	15
330	2 s. Kikuyu		1·75	1·75
331	3 s. 50, Pokomo		2·25	2·25
332	5 s. Nandi		2·50	2·50
333	10 s. Rendile		3·50	5·00
329/33		*Set of 5*	9·50	10·50

(Litho Harrison)

1984 (21 Dec). *60th Anniv of International Chess Federation. T 68 and similar horiz designs showing Staunton chess pieces. Multicoloured. P 14½.*
334	70 c. Type 68		1·50	30
335	2 s. 50, Rook and Fort Jesus		2·50	1·75
336	3 s. 50, Bishop and National Monument		3·00	2·50
337	5 s. Queen and Parliament Building		3·25	3·50
338	10 s. King and Nyayo Fountain		5·00	7·00
334/8		*Set of 5*	13·50	13·50

69 Cooking with Wood-burning Stove and Charcoal Fire

(Des H. Moghul. Litho J.W.)

1985 (22 Jan). *Energy Conservation. T 69 and similar horiz designs. Multicoloured. P 13½.*
339	70 c. Type 69		20	10
340	2 s. Solar energy panel on roof		65	75
341	3 s. 50, Production of gas from cow dung		75	1·25
342	10 s. Ploughing with oxen		2·25	4·50
339/42		*Set of 4*	3·50	6·00
MS343	110×85 mm. 20 s. Designs as Nos. 339/42, but without face values		2·50	2·50

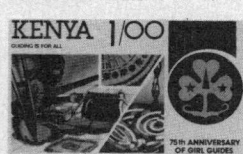

70 Crippled Girl Guide making Table-mat

(Litho J.W.)

1985 (27 Mar). *75th Anniv of Girl Guide Movement. T 70 and similar horiz designs. Multicoloured. P 13½.*
344	1 s. Type 70		75	15
345	3 s. Girl Guides doing community service		1·75	1·50
346	5 s. Lady Olave Baden-Powell (founder)		2·50	3·00
347	7 s. Girl Guides gardening		4·00	6·00
344/7		*Set of 4*	8·00	9·50

71 Stylised Figures and Globe   **72** Man with Malaria

(Des and litho Harrison)

1985 (8 May). *World Red Cross Day. T 71 and similar horiz designs. P 14½.*
348	1 s. black and rosine		80	15
349	4 s. multicoloured		3·00	3·00
350	5 s. multicoloured		3·25	3·50
351	7 s. multicoloured		4·50	6·00
348/51		*Set of 4*	10·50	11·50

Designs:—4 s. First aid team; 5 s. Hearts containing crosses ("Blood Donation"); 7 s. Cornucopia ("Famine Relief").

(Des H. Moghul. Litho Harrison)

1985 (25 June). *7th International Congress of Protozoology, Nairobi. T 72 and similar vert designs. Multicoloured. P 14½.*
352	1 s. Type 72		90	15
353	3 s. Child with Leishmaniasis		2·75	2·75
354	5 s. Cow with Trypanosomiasis		3·25	3·50
355	7 s. Dog with Babesiosis		4·75	6·50
352/5		*Set of 4*	10·50	11·50

73 Repairing Water Pipes   **74** The Last Supper

(Des J. Tobula and Harrison. Litho Harrison)

1985 (15 July). *United Nations Women's Decade Conference. T 73 and similar vert designs. Multicoloured. P 14½.*
356	1 s. Type 73		20	10
357	3 s. Traditional food preparation		60	70
358	5 s. Basket-weaving		75	1·25
359	7 s. Dressmaking		1·00	2·50
356/9		*Set of 4*	2·25	4·00

(Des Eucharistic Congress Secretariat. Litho J.W.)

1985 (17 Aug*). *43rd International Eucharistic Congress, Nairobi. T 74 and similar horiz designs. Multicoloured. P 13½.*
360	1 s. Type 74		50	10
361	3 s. Village family ("The Eucharist and the Christian Family")		2·25	2·00
362	5 s. Congress altar, Uhuru Park		2·50	2·75
363	7 s. St. Peter Claver's Church, Nairobi		3·00	4·50
360/3		*Set of 4*	7·50	8·50
MS364	117×80 mm. 25 s. Pope John Paul II		5·50	5·00

* This is the local date of issue. The Crown Agents released the stamps on 15 August and this date also appears on first day covers serviced by Kenya Posts and Telecommunications Corporation.

75 Black Rhinoceros

(Des Rena Fennessy. Litho Harrison)

1985 (10 Dec). *Endangered Animals. T 75 and similar horiz designs. Multicoloured. P 14½.*
365	1 s. Type 75		1·75	40
366	3 s. Cheetah		3·00	2·75
367	5 s. De Brazza's Monkey		3·25	3·75
368	10 s. Grevy's Zebra		5·50	7·50
365/8		*Set of 4*	12·00	13·00
MS369	129×122 mm. 25 s. Endangered species (122×114 mm). Imperf		7·00	4·50

76 Borassus aethiopum   **77** Dove and U.N. Logo (from poster)

(Des Rena Fennessy. Litho Questa)

1986 (24 Jan). *Indigenous Trees. T 76 and similar horiz designs. Multicoloured. P 14½.*
370	1 s. Type 76		65	15
371	3 s. Acacia xanthophloea		2·50	2·50
372	5 s. Ficus natalensis		3·50	3·75
373	7 s. Spathodea nilotica		4·50	6·00
370/3		*Set of 4*	10·00	11·00
MS374	117×96 mm. 25 s. Landscape with trees (109×90 mm). Imperf		3·25	4·00

(Des Advertising Link. Litho Questa)

1986 (30 Apr*). *International Peace Year. T 77 and similar multicoloured designs. P 14½.*
375	1 s. Type 77		30	10
376	3 s. U.N. General Assembly (*horiz*)		1·00	65
377	7 s. Nuclear explosion		2·25	2·75
378	10 s. Quotation from Wall of Isaiah, U.N. Building, New York (*horiz*)		3·00	3·25
375/8		*Set of 4*	6·00	6·00

*This is the local date of issue. The Crown Agents released the stamps on 17 April and this date also appears on first day covers serviced by Kenya Posts and Telecommunications Corporation.

78 Dribbling the Ball   **79** Rural Post Office and Telephone

(Des C. Fernandes. Litho Harrison)

1986 (8 May). *World Cup Football Championship, Mexico. T 78 and similar multicoloured designs. P 14½.*
379	1 s. Type 78		80	15
380	3 s. Scoring from a penalty		2·25	1·25
381	5 s. Tackling		3·00	2·00
382	7 s. Cup winners		3·75	3·50
383	10 s. Heading the ball		4·75	4·25
379/83		*Set of 5*	13·00	10·00
MS384	110×86 mm. 30 s. Harambee Stars football team (102×78 mm). Imperf		3·75	3·75

(Des H. Moghul. Litho Cartor)

1986 (11 June). *"Expo '86" World Fair, Vancouver. T 79 and similar horiz designs. Multicoloured. P 13½×13.*
385	1 s. Type 79		50	15
386	3 s. Container depot, Embakasi		2·50	1·75
387	5 s. Piper PA-30B Twin Commanche airplane landing at game park airstrip		3·50	2·75
388	7 s. Container ship		4·00	4·50
389	10 s. Transporting produce to market		4·25	5·25
385/9		*Set of 5*	13·00	13·00

On 15 July 1986 Kenya was scheduled to release a set of five stamps, 1, 3, 4, 7 and 10 s., for the Commonwealth Games at Edinburgh. A political decision was taken at the last moment not to issue the stamps, but this instruction did not reach some of the sub-post offices until the morning of 15 July. About two hundred stamps, mainly the 1 s. value, were sold by these sub-post offices before the instruction arrived. Examples of the 1 s. exist used on commercial mail from Kenyatta College sub-post office from 17 July 1986 onwards.

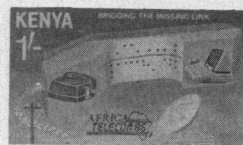

80 Telephone, Computer and Dish Aerial

(Des H. Moghul. Litho Harrison)

1986 (16 Sept). *African Telecommunications. T* 80 *and similar horiz designs. Multicoloured.* P 14½.

390	1 s. Type 80		..	35	10
391	3 s. Telephones of 1876, 1936 and 1986			1·00	85
392	5 s. Dish aerial, satellite, telephones and map of Africa			1·25	1·25
393	7 s. Kenyan manufacture of telecommunications equipment		..	1·75	2·25
390/3			*Set of 4*	4·00	4·00

81 Mashua   82 The Nativity

(Des Mukund Arts. Litho Mardon Printers Ltd, Zimbabwe)

1986 (30 Oct). *Dhows of Kenya. T* 81 *and similar horiz designs. Multicoloured.* P 14½.

394	1 s. Type 81 ..	..	..	65	20
395	3 s. Mtepe	..	..	1·75	1·50
396	5 s. Dau La Mwao	..	..	2·25	2·75
397	10 s. Jahazi	..	..	3·75	5·00
394/7			*Set of 4*	7·50	8·50
MS398	118 × 80 mm. 25 s. Lamu dhow and map of Indian Ocean			4·25	4·50

(Des Mukund Arts. Litho Courvoisier)

1986 (5 Dec). *Christmas. T* 82 *and similar multicoloured designs. Granite paper.* P 11½.

399	1 s. Type 82	..	..	30	10
400	3 s. Shepherd and sheep	..	..	1·00	55
401	5 s. Angel and slogan "LOVE PEACE UNITY" (*horiz*)			1·60	1·40
402	7 s. The Magi riding camels (*horiz*)			1·90	2·75
399/402			*Set of 4*	4·25	4·25

83 Immunization   84 Akamba Woodcarvers

(Des Judith D'Inca. Litho Harrison)

1987 (6 Jan). *40th Anniv of United Nations Children's Fund. T* 83 *and similar vert designs. Multicoloured.* P 14.

403	1 s. Type 83	..	..	45	10
404	3 s. Food and nutrition	..	..	1·00	70
405	4 s. Oral rehydration therapy	..		1·75	1·50
406	5 s. Family planning	..	..	1·75	1·50
407	10 s. Female literacy ..	..	..	2·50	3·50
403/7			*Set of 5*	6·75	6·50

(Des C. Fernandes. Litho Questa)

1987 (25 Mar). *Tourism. T* 84 *and similar horiz designs. Multicoloured.* P 14½.

408	1 s. Type 84	..	..	30	10
409	3 s. Tourists on beach	..	..	2·00	1·75
410	5 s. Tourist and guide at view point	..		2·75	3·50
411	7 s. Pride of lions	..	..	4·00	5·50
408/11			*Set of 4*	8·00	9·75
MS412	118 × 81 mm. 30 s. Geysers			7·50	8·00

(Des Mukund Arts. Litho Harrison)

1987 (20 May). *Ceremonial Costumes (3rd series). Vert designs as T* 45. *Multicoloured.* P 14½ × 13½.

413	1 s. Embu	..	..	50	10
414	3 s. Kisii	..	..	1·50	70
415	5 s. Samburu	..	..	1·75	1·40
416	7 s. Taita	..	..	2·50	2·50
417	10 s. Boran	..	..	2·75	3·00
413/17			*Set of 5*	8·00	7·00

85 Telecommunications by Satellite   86 Volleyball

(Des Mukund Arts. Litho Harrison)

1987 (1 July). *10th Anniv of Kenya Posts and Telecommunications Corporation. T* 85 *and similar triangular designs. Multicoloured.* P 13½.

418	1 s. Type 85	..	..	35	30
419	3 s. Rural post office, Kajiado	..		80	90
420	4 s. Awarding trophy, Welfare Sports			1·10	1·40
421	5 s. Village and telephone box	..		1·25	1·50
422	7 s. Speedpost labels and outline map of Kenya			1·75	2·50
418/22			*Set of 5*	4·75	6·00
MS423	110 × 80 mm. 25 s. Corporation flag			1·75	1·90

Nos. 418/22 were each printed as horizontal *tête-bêche* pairs within the sheet.

(Des C. Fernandes. Litho D.L.R.)

1987 (5 Aug). *4th All-Africa Games, Nairobi. T* 86 *and similar multicoloured designs.* P 14½ × 14.

424	1 s. Type 86	..	..	20	10
425	3 s. Cycling	..	..	25	30
426	4 s. Boxing	..	..	35	55
427	5 s. Swimming	..	..	40	60
428	7 s. Steeplechasing	..	..	50	1·10
424/8			*Set of 5*	1·50	2·25
MS429	117 × 80 mm. 30 s. Kasarani Sports Complex (*horiz*). P 14 × 14½			2·10	2·25

87 *Aloe volkensii*

(Des Advertising Link. Litho Cartor)

1987 (10 Nov). *Medicinal Herbs. T* 87 *and similar vert designs. Multicoloured.* P 13½ × 14.

430	1 s. Type 87	..	..	40	10
431	3 s. *Cassia didymobotrya*	..		1·10	1·00
432	5 s. *Erythrina abyssinica*	..		1·75	1·75
433	7 s. *Adenium obesum*	..		2·25	2·50
434	10 s. Herbalist's clinic	..		2·50	2·75
430/4			*Set of 5*	7·25	7·25

88 *Epamera sidus*   89 *Papilio rex*

(Des Rena Fennessy. Photo Harrison)

1988 (15 Feb)–**90**. *Butterflies. Multicoloured.*

   (*a*) *Vert designs as T* 88. P 15 × 14

434a	10 c. *Cyrestis camillus* (1.9.89)			90	1·50
435	20 c. Type 88	..	..	30	70
436	40 c. *Cynthia cardui*	..		40	70
437	50 c. *Colotis evippe*	..		40	70
438	70 c. *Precis westermanni*	..		40	70
439	80 c. *Colias electo*	..		40	70
440	1 s. *Eronia leda*	..		40	30
440a	1 s. 50, *Papilio dardanus* (18.5.90)			2·25	30

   (*b*) *Vert designs as T* 89. P 14½

441	2 s. Type 89	..	..	70	40
442	2 s. 50, *Colotis phisadia*	..		75	90
443	3 s. *Papilio desmondi*	..		80	90
444	3 s. 50, *Papilio demodocus*	..		80	60
445	4 s. *Papilio phorcas*	..		85	60
446	5 s. *Charaxes druceanus*	..		90	70
447	7 s. *Cymothoe teita*	..		1·00	1·75
448	10 s. *Charaxes zoolina*	..		1·25	1·75
449	20 s. *Papilio dardanus*	..		1·60	3·00
450	40 s. *Charaxes cithaeron*	..		3·00	5·50
434a/50			*Set of 18*	15·00	19·00

Examples of the 1 s. value were used in error at Kisumu from 2 February 1988.

90 Samburu Lodge and Crocodiles

(Des Advertising Link. Litho Questa)

1988 (31 May). *Kenyan Game Lodges. T* 90 *and similar horiz designs. Multicoloured.* P 14½.

451	1 s. Type 90			30	10
452	3 s. Naro Moru River Lodge and rock climbing			75	60
453	4 s. Mara Serena Lodge and zebra with foal			85	1·00
454	5 s. Voi Safari Lodge and buffalo			95	1·10
455	7 s. Kilimanjaro Buffalo Lodge and giraffes			1·25	1·75
456	10 s. Meru Mulika Lodge and rhinoceroses			1·75	2·00
451/6			*Set of 6*	5·25	5·75

91 Athletes and Stadium, Commonwealth Games, Brisbane, 1982

(Des D. Ashby. Litho Harrison)

1988 (10 June). *"Expo '88" World Fair, Brisbane, and Bicentenary of Australian Settlement. T* 91 *and similar horiz designs. Multicoloured.* P 14½.

457	1 s. Type 91			30	10
458	3 s. Flying Doctor Service De Havilland D.H.A.3 Drover 3 and Piper PA-30B Twin Commanche aircraft			1·50	1·00
459	4 s. H.M.S. *Sirius* (frigate), 1788			1·75	1·60
460	5 s. Ostrich and emu			2·00	1·90
461	7 s. Queen Elizabeth II, President Arap Moi of Kenya and Prime Minister Hawke of Australia			2·00	2·75
457/61			*Set of 5*	6·75	6·50
MS462	117 × 80 mm. 30 s. Entrance to Kenya Pavilion			1·90	2·00

92 W.H.O. Logo and Slogan   93 Handball

(Des Mukund Arts. Litho National Printing & Packaging, Zimbabwe)

1988 (1 July). *40th Anniv of World Health Organization. T* 92 *and similar horiz designs.* P 14½.

463	1 s. greenish blue, gold and ultramarine	..		25	10
464	3 s. multicoloured	..	..	85	70
465	5 s. multicoloured	..	..	1·25	1·25
466	7 s. multicoloured	..	..	1·75	2·25
463/6			*Set of 4*	3·75	3·75

Designs:—3 s. Mother with young son and nutritious food; 5 s. Giving oral vaccine to baby; 7 s. Village women drawing clean water from pump.

(Des H. Moghul. Litho D.L.R.)

1988 (1 Aug). *Olympic Games, Seoul. T* 93 *and similar vert designs. Multicoloured.* P 14½ × 14.

467	1 s. Type 93	..	..	20	10
468	3 s. Judo	..	..	45	40
469	5 s. Weightlifting	..	..	60	60
470	7 s. Javelin	..	..	75	85
471	10 s. Relay racing	..	..	90	1·25
467/71			*Set of 5*	2·50	2·75
MS472	110 × 78 mm. 30 s. Tennis			1·90	2·25

94 Calabashes   95 Pres. Arap Moi taking Oath, 1978

(Des Mukund Arts. Litho D.L.R.)

1988 (20 Sept). *Kenyan Material Culture (1st issue). T* 94 *and similar multicoloured designs.* P 14½ × 14 (*vert*) or 14 × 14½ (*horiz*).

473	1 s. Type 94	..	..	20	10
474	3 s. Milk gourds	..	..	60	55

475	5 s. Cooking pots (*horiz*)	70	65
476	7 s. Winnowing trays (*horiz*)	95	1·10
477	10 s. Reed baskets (*horiz*)	1·40	1·60
473/7	*Set of 5*	3·50	3·50
MS478	118×80 mm. 25 s. Gourds, calabash and horn (*horiz*)	1·50	1·60

See also Nos. 646/50.

(Des Mukund Arts. Litho Harrison)

1988 (13 Oct). *10th Anniv of "Nyayo" Era. T* **95** *and similar horiz designs. Multicoloured. P* 13½×14½.

479	1 s. Type **95**	25	10
480	3 s. Building soil conservation barrier	85	70
481	3 s. 50, Passengers boarding bus	1·50	1·00
482	4 s. Metalwork shop	1·25	1·25
483	5 s. Moi University, Eldoret	1·25	1·25
484	7 s. Aerial view of hospital	2·75	3·00
485	10 s. Pres. Arap Moi and Mrs. Thatcher at Kapsabet Telephone Exchange	5·00	4·50
479/85	*Set of 7*	11·50	10·50

96 Kenya Flag

(Des Mukund Arts. Photo Courvoisier)

1988 (9 Dec). *25th Anniv of Independence. T* **96** *and similar horiz designs. Multicoloured. Granite paper. P* 11½.

486	1 s. Type **96**	30	10
487	3 s. Coffee picking	50	50
488	5 s. Proposed Kenya Posts and Telecommunications Headquarters building	95	95
489	7 s. Kenya Airways Airbus Industrie A310-300 *Harambee Star*	3·00	2·00
490	10 s. New diesel locomotive No. 9401	4·25	3·50
486/90	*Set of 5*	8·00	6·25

97 Gedi Ruins, Malindi

(Des Mukund Arts. Litho National Printing & Packaging, Zimbabwe)

1989 (15 Mar). *Historic Monuments. T* **97** *and similar multicoloured designs. P* 14½.

491	1 s. 20, Type **97**	30	10
492	3 s. 40, Vasco Da Gama Pillar, Malindi (*vert*)	85	80
493	4 s. 40, Ishiakani Monument, Kiunga	95	95
494	5 s. 50, Fort Jesus, Mombasa	1·25	1·40
495	7 s. 70, She Burnan Omwe, Lamu (*vert*)	1·75	2·25
491/5	*Set of 5*	4·50	5·00

98 125th Anniversary and Kenya Red Cross Logos   **99** Female Giraffe and Calf

(Des H. Moghul. Litho Cartor)

1989 (8 May). *125th Anniv of International Red Cross. T* **98** *and similar horiz designs. Mulicoloured. P* 14×13½.

496	1 s. 20, Type **98**	30	10
497	3 s. 40, Red Cross workers with car crash victim	1·00	85
498	4 s. 40, Disaster relief team distributing blankets	1·10	1·25
499	5 s. 50, Henri Dunant (founder)	1·25	1·50
500	7 s. 70, Blood donor	1·50	2·50
496/500	*Set of 5*	4·75	5·50

(Des Doreen McGuinness. Litho Walsall)

1989 (12 July). *Reticulated Giraffe. T* **99** *and similar vert designs. Multicoloured. P* 14½.

501	1 s. 20, Type **99**	1·75	30
502	3 s. 40, Giraffe drinking	3·25	3·00
503	4 s. 40, Two giraffes	3·75	3·75
504	5 s. 50, Giraffe feeding	4·50	5·00
501/4	*Set of 4*	12·00	11·00
MS505	80×110 mm. 30 s. Designs as Nos. 501/4, but without face values	5·50	7·00

Designs from No. MS505 are without the Worldwide Fund for Nature logo.

NEW INFORMATION

The editor is always interested to correspond with people who have new information that will improve or correct the Catalogue.

100 *Lentinus sajor-caju*   **101** Independence Monuments

(Des Dvora Bochman. Litho Questa)

1989 (6 Sept). *Mushrooms. T* **100** *and similar vert designs. Multicoloured. P* 14½.

506	1 s. 20, Type **100**	1·50	30
507	3 s. 40, *Agaricus bisporus*	2·25	2·00
508	4 s. 40, *Agaricus bisporus* (different)	2·50	2·50
509	5 s. 50, *Termitomyces schimperi*	3·25	3·50
510	7 s. 70, *Lentinus edodes*	4·00	5·00
506/10	*Set of 5*	12·00	12·00

(Des Conference and Exhibitions Secretariat, Nairobi. Litho Cartor)

1989 (9 Nov). *Birth Centenary of Jawaharlal Nehru* (*Indian statesman*). *T* **101** *and similar vert designs. Multicoloured. P* 13½×14.

511	1 s. 20, Type **101**	80	30
512	3 s. 40, Nehru with graduates and open book	2·25	1·75
513	5 s. 50, Jawaharlal Nehru	3·25	3·75
514	7 s. 70, Industrial complex and cogwheels	3·75	5·00
511/14	*Set of 4*	9·00	9·75

(Des Mukund Arts. Litho Harrison)

1989 (20 Dec). *Ceremonial Costumes* (4th series). *Vert designs as T* **45**. *Multicoloured. P* 14½×13½.

515	1 s. 20, Kipsigis	75	20
516	3 s. 40, Rabai	1·75	1·50
517	5 s. 50, Duruma	2·25	2·50
518	7 s. 70, Kuria	3·00	3·50
519	10 s. Bajuni	3·25	4·00
515/19	*Set of 5*	10·00	10·50

102 EMS Speedpost Letters and Parcel

(Des Conference and Exhibitions Secretariat, Nairobi. Litho Cartor)

1990 (23 Mar). *10th Anniv of Pan African Postal Union. T* **101** *and similar multicoloured designs. P* 14×13½ (*horiz*) *or* 13½×14 (*vert*).

520	1 s. 20, Type **102**	15	10
521	3 s. 40, Mail runner	35	35
522	5 s. 50, Mandera Post Office	55	70
523	7 s. 70, EMS Speedpost Letters and globe (*vert*)	80	1·60
524	10 s. P.A.P.U. logo (*vert*)	90	1·60
520/4	*Set of 5*	2·50	3·75

103 "Stamp King" with Tweezers and Magnifying Glass   **104** Moi Golden Cup

(Des D. Miller. Photo Courvoisier)

1990 (3 May). *"Stamp World London 90" International Stamp Exhibition. T* **103** *and similar horiz designs. Granite paper. P* 11½.

525	1 s. 50, multicoloured	35	10
526	4 s. 50, multicoloured	1·25	1·25
527	6 s. 50, black, bright carmine and azure	1·40	1·60
528	9 s. multicoloured	1·75	2·75
525/8	*Set of 4*	4·25	5·00
MS529	113×77 mm. Nos. 525/8	4·50	5·50

Designs:—4 s. 50, Penny Black and Kenya Stamp Bureau postmark; 6 s. 50, Early British cancellations; 9 s. Ronald Ngala Street Post Office, Nairobi.

(Litho Harrison)

1990 (21 May). *World Cup Football Championship, Italy. Trophies. T* **104** *and similar vert designs. Multicoloured. P* 14½.

530	1 s. 50, Type **104**	60	10
531	4 s. 50, East and Central Africa Challenge Cup	1·75	1·60
532	6 s. 50, East and Central Africa Club Championship Cup	2·75	3·00
533	9 s. World Cup	3·00	4·00
530/3	*Set of 4*	7·25	8·00

105 K.A.N.U. Flag

(Des Mukund Arts. Litho Harrison)

1990 (11 June). *30th Anniv of Kenya African National Union. T* **105** *and similar horiz designs. Multicoloured. P* 14½.

534	1 s. 50, Type **105**	15	10
535	2 s. 50, Nyayo Monument	15	15
536	4 s. 50, Party Headquarters	35	35
537	5 s. Jomo Kenyatta (founder)	40	40
538	6 s. 50, President Arap Moi	50	75
539	9 s. President Moi addressing rally	70	1·40
540	10 s. Queue of voters	80	1·40
534/40	*Set of 7*	2·75	4·00

106 Desktop Computer

(Litho Questa)

1990 (12 July). *125th Anniv of International Telecommunications Union. T* **106** *and similar horiz designs. Multicoloured. P* 14½.

541	1 s. 50, Type **106**	15	10
542	4 s. 50, Telephone switchboard assembly, Gilgil	35	50
543	6 s. 50, "125 YEARS"	45	80
544	9 s. Urban and rural telecommunications	70	2·00
541/4	*Set of 4*	1·50	3·00

107 Queen Mother at British Museum, 1988   **108** Queen Elizabeth at Hospital Garden Party, 1947

(Des D. Miller. Litho Questa)

1990 (4 Aug). *90th Birthday of Queen Elizabeth the Queen Mother. P* 14×15 (10 *s.*) *or* 14½×14 (40 *s.*).

545	**107** 10 s. multicoloured	1·50	1·75
546	**108** 40 s. black and brown-olive	3·25	4·75

109 Kenya 1988 2 s. Definitive   **110** Adult Literacy Class

(Des D. Miller. Litho D.L.R.)

1990 (5 Sept). *Centenary of Postage Stamps in Kenya. T* **109** *and similar vert designs. Multicoloured. P* 14×14½.

547	1 s. 50, Type **109**	75	10
548	4 s. 50, East Africa and Uganda 1903 1 a.	1·50	90
549	6 s. 50, British East Africa Co 1890 ½ a. optd on G.B. 1d.	2·00	1·75
550	9 s. Kenya and Uganda 1922 20 c.	2·50	2·75
551	20 s. Kenya, Uganda, Tanzania 1971 2 s. 50, Railway commemorative	4·25	6·50
547/51	*Set of 5*	10·00	11·00

(Des H. Moghul. Litho Cartor)

1990 (30 Nov). *International Literacy Year. T* **110** *and similar vert designs. Multicoloured. P* 13½×14.

552	1 s. 50, Type **110**	30	10
553	4 s. 50, Teaching by radio	1·00	90
554	6 s. 50, Technical training	1·25	1·40
555	9 s. International Literacy Year logo	2·00	3·00
552/5	*Set of 4*	4·00	4·75

111 National Flag

112 Symbolic Man and Pointing Finger

(Des H. Moghul. Litho Cartor)

1991 (29 Nov). *Olympic Games, Barcelona (1992) (1st issue).
T* 111 *and similar horiz designs. Multicoloured. P* 14×13½.

556	2 s. Type 111	..	30	10
557	6 s. Basketball	..	1·75	1·25
558	7 s. Hockey	..	2·00	1·75
559	8 s. 50, Table tennis	..	2·00	2·75
560	11 s. Boxing	..	2·00	3·00
556/60		*Set of* 5	7·25	8·00

See also Nos. 580/4.

(Des H. Mogul. Litho Cartor)

1992 (31 Jan). *AIDS Day. T* 112 *and similar vert designs.
Multicoloured. P* 13½×14.

561	2 s. Type 112	..	60	15
562	6 s. Victim and drugs	..	1·50	90
563	8 s. 50, Male and female symbols	..	2·00	2·25
564	11 s. Symbolic figure and hypodermic syringe	..	2·75	3·75
561/4		*Set of* 4	6·25	6·25

...

113 Queen and Prince Philip with Pres. Moi

114 Leopard

(Des D. Miller. Litho Cartor)

1992 (6 Feb). *40th Anniv of Queen Elizabeth II's Accession.
T* 113 *and similar horiz designs. Multicoloured. P* 14×13½.

565	3 s. Type 113	..	40	10
566	8 s. Marabou Storks in tree	..	1·00	70
567	11 s. Treetops Hotel	..	1·00	90
568	14 s. Three portraits of Queen Elizabeth	..	1·10	1·25
569	40 s. Queen Elizabeth II	..	2·50	4·25
565/9		*Set of* 5	5·50	6·50

(Des Dvora Bochman. Litho National Printing & Packaging, Zimbabwe)

1992 (8 May). *Kenya Wildlife. T* 114 *and similar vert designs.
Multicoloured. P* 14×14½.

570	3 s. Type 114	..	80	30
571	8 s. Lion	..	1·75	1·50
572	10 s. Elephant	..	2·75	2·50
573	11 s. Buffalo	..	1·75	2·50
574	14 s. Black Rhinoceros	..	3·50	3·50
570/4		*Set of* 5	9·50	9·25

115 International Harvester Safari Truck, 1926

116 Kenyan Athlete winning Race

(Des Dvora Bochman. Litho National Printing & Packaging, Zimbabwe)

1992 (24 June). *Vintage Cars. T* 115 *and similar horiz designs.
Multicoloured. P* 14½×14.

575	3 s. Type 115	..	70	20
576	8 s. Fiat "509", 1924	..	1·75	1·25
577	10 s. Hupmobile, 1923	..	2·00	2·00
578	11 s. Chevrolet "Box Body", 1928	..	2·00	2·00
579	14 s. Bentley/Parkward, 1934	..	2·25	2·75
575/9		*Set of* 5	8·00	7·50

(Des Dvora Bochman. Litho National Printing & Packaging, Zimbabwe)

1992 (24 July). *Olympic Games, Barcelona (2nd series). T* 116
and similar vert designs. Multicoloured. P 14×14½.

580	3 s. Type 116	..	65	10
581	8 s. Men's judo	..	1·25	1·25

582	10 s. Kenyan women's volleyball players	..	2·00	2·00
583	11 s. Kenyan men's 4×100 metres relay runners		2·00	2·00
584	14 s. Men's 10,000 metres	..	2·25	2·75
580/4		*Set of* 5	7·25	7·25

117 Holy Child, Joseph and Animals

118 Asembo Bay Lighthouse, Lake Victoria

(Litho Cartor)

1992 (14 Dec). *Christmas. T* 117 *and similar vert designs.
Multicoloured. P* 13½×14.

585	3 s. Type 117	..	20	10
586	8 s. Mary with Holy Child	..	55	50
587	11 s. Christmas tree	..	70	80
588	14 s. Adoration of the Magi	..	1·00	1·75
585/8		*Set of* 4	2·25	2·75

(Des H. Moghul. Litho Questa)

1993 (25 Jan). *Lighthouses. T* 118 *and similar vert designs.
Multicoloured. P* 14½.

589	3 s. Type 118	..	90	30
590	8 s. Old Ras Serani lighthouse, Mombasa	1·75	1·40
591	11 s. New Ras Serani lighthouse, Mombasa	2·00	2·00
592	14 s. Gingira, Lake Victoria	..	2·50	3·00
589/92		*Set of* 4	6·50	6·00

119 Superb Starling

120 Yellow-billed Hornbill

(Des Dvora Bochman. Photo Courvoisier)

1993 (22 Feb)–96. *Birds. Multicoloured. Granite paper.*

(a) *Vert designs as T* 119. *P* 15×14.

593	50 c. Type 119	..	10	10
594	1 s. Red and Yellow Barbet	..	10	10
594a	1 s. 50, Lady Ross's Turaco (14.2.94)	10	10
595	3 s. Black-throated Honeyguide ("Greater Honeyguide")		10	10
595a	5 s. African Fish Eagle (14.2.94)	10	10
595b	6 s. Vulturine Guineafowl (30.8.96)	10	10
596	7 s. Malachite Kingfisher	..	15	20
597	8 s. Speckled Pigeon	..	15	20
598	10 s. Cinnamon-chested Bee Eater	20	25
599	11 s. Scarlet-chested Sunbird	..	20	25
600	14 s. Bagalafecht Weaver ("Reichenow's Weaver")		25	30

(b) *Vert designs as T* 120. *P* 14½

601	50 s. Type 120	..	1·00	1·10
602	80 s. Lesser Flamingo	..	1·60	1·75
603	100 s. Hadada Ibis	..	2·00	2·10
593/603		*Set of* 14	5·75	6·25

No. 595a was initially issued in coils, but was subsequently supplied in sheets.

121 Nurse bandaging Boy's Legs

122 Maendeleo House, Nairobi

(Des Conference and Exhibitions Secretariat, Nairobi. Litho National Printing & Packaging, Zimbabwe)

1993 (1 July). *17th World Congress of Rehabilitation
International. T* 121 *and similar horiz designs. P* 14½.

611	3 s. multicoloured	..	50	10
612	8 s. multicoloured	..	75	65
613	10 s. multicoloured	..	85	90
614	11 s. multicoloured	..	85	90
615	14 s. black, new blue and yellow-orange	1·10	1·60
611/15		*Set of* 5	3·50	3·75

Designs: *Horiz*—8 s. Singing group on crutches; 10 s.
Vocational training; 11 s. Wheelchair race. *Vert*—14 s. Congress emblem.

(Des Conference and Exhibitions Secretariat, Nairobi. Litho Cartor)

1994 (17 Mar). *40th Anniv of Maendeleo Ya Wanawake
Organization. T* 122 *and similar multicoloured designs.
P* 14×13½ (*horiz*) *or* 13½×14 (*vert*).

616	3 s. 50, Type 122	..	35	10
617	9 s. Planting saplings	..	60	50
618	11 s. Rural family planning clinic (*vert*)	70	70
619	12 s. 50, Women carrying water	85	1·25
620	15 s. 50, Improved wood-burning cooking stove (*vert*)	1·10	1·60
616/20		*Set of* 5	3·25	3·75

123 Ansellia africana

124 Emblem and K.I.C.C. Building, Nairobi

(Des Dvora Bochman. Litho Cartor)

1994 (27 June). *Orchids. T* 123 *and similar vert designs.
Multicoloured. P* 13½×14.

621	3 s. 50, Type 123	..	80	20
622	9 s. Aerangis luteoalba var rhodosticta	1·25	1·40
623	12 s. 50, Polystachya bella	1·40	1·50
624	15 s. 50, Brachycorythis kalbreyeri	1·75	2·00
625	20 s. Eulophia guineensis	..	2·00	2·25
621/5		*Set of* 5	6·50	6·00

(Des and litho Questa)

1994 (21 Nov). *30th Anniv of African Development Bank.
T* 124 *and similar horiz design. Multicoloured. P* 14½.

626	6 s. Type 124	..	50	25
627	25 s. Isinya-Kajiado project	..	2·00	2·75

 ...

125 Kenyan Family

126 Paul Harris (founder of Rotary)

(Des Micro General Service Ltd. Litho Questa)

1994 (22 Dec). *International Year of the Family. T* 125 *and
similar multicoloured designs. P* 14½.

628	6 s. Type 125	..	50	10
629	14 s. 50, Nurse with mother and baby	1·75	1·40
630	20 s. School children and teacher (*horiz*)	2·00	2·25
631	25 s. Emblem (*horiz*)	..	2·25	2·75
628/31		*Set of* 4	6·00	6·00

(Des Omak Design. Litho Cartor)

1994 (29 Dec). *50th Anniv of Rotary Club of Mombasa. T* 126
and similar vert designs. Multicoloured. P 13½×14.

632	6 s. Type 126	..	25	10
633	14 s. 50, Anniversary logo	..	70	70
634	17 s. 50, Administering polio vaccine	1·00	1·25
635	20 s. Women at stand pipe	..	1·00	1·40
636	25 s. Rotary emblem	..	1·10	1·60
632/6		*Set of* 5	3·50	4·50

127 Donkey

128 Male Golfer in Bunker

(Des H. Moghul. Litho Walsall)

1995 (13 Jan). *Kenya Society for Prevention of Cruelty to
Animals. T* 127 *and similar vert designs. Multicoloured.
P* 14½.

637	6 s. Type 127	..	30	10
638	14 s. 50, Cow	..	45	45
639	17 s. 50, Sheep	..	55	75
640	20 s. Dog	..	1·10	1·40
641	25 s. Cat	..	1·25	1·75
637/41		*Set of* 5	3·25	4·00

(Des Conference and Exhibitions Secretariat. Litho Questa)

1995 (28 Feb). *Golf.* T **128** *and similar vert designs. Multicoloured.* P 14½.
642	6 s. Type 128		50	15
643	17 s. 50, Female golfer on fairway		1·25	1·25
644	20 s. Male golfer teeing-off		1·40	1·75
645	25 s. Head of golf club		1·60	2·00
642/5		*Set of 4*	4·25	4·75

129 Perfume Containers

130 Tsetse Fly

(Des Lari & Loiruk Graphic Studio. Litho Cartor)

1995 (24 Mar). *Kenyan Material Culture (2nd issue).* T **129** *and similar horiz designs. Multicoloured.* P 14×13½.
646	6 s. Type 129		30	10
647	14 s. 50, Basketry		75	75
648	17 s. 50, Preserving pots		85	1·00
649	20 s. Gourds		1·10	1·50
650	25 s. Wooden containers		1·25	1·75
646/50		*Set of 5*	3·75	4·50

(Des Design Box Associates. Litho Enschedé)

1995 (29 Sept). *25th Anniv of I.C.I.P.E. Insect Pests.* T **130** *and similar vert designs. Multicoloured.* P 13½.
651	14 s. Type 130		50	30
652	26 s. Tick		80	80
653	32 s. Wild Silkmoth		95	95
654	33 s. Maize Borer		1·00	1·50
655	40 s. Locust		1·60	2·00
651/5		*Set of 5*	4·25	5·00

131 Maize

132 Kenyan and United
Nations Flags over
Headquarters, Nairobi

(Des Dvora Bochman. Litho Cartor)

1995 (16 Oct). *50th Anniv of Food and Agriculture Organization.* T **131** *and similar vert designs. Multicoloured.* P 13½×14.
656	14 s. Type 131		55	30
657	28 s. Cattle		90	80
658	32 s. Chickens		1·10	1·10
659	33 s. Fisherman with catch		1·25	1·75
660	40 s. Fruit		1·75	2·50
656/60		*Set of 5*	5·00	5·75

(Des O. Karenga. Litho Enschedé)

1995 (24 Oct). *50th Anniv of United Nations.* T **132** *and similar horiz designs.* P 13½.
661	23 s. multicoloured		70	70
662	26 s. multicoloured		80	90
663	32 s. multicoloured		95	1·10
664	40 s. brt greenish blue, dp carmine & black		1·40	2·00
661/4		*Set of 4*	3·50	4·25

Designs:—26 s. Multi-racial group with emblem; 32 s. United Nations helmet; 40 s. 50th anniversary emblem.

133 Swimming

1996 (5 Jan). *Olympic Games, Atlanta (1st issue). Events and Gold Medal Winners.* T **133** *and similar multicoloured designs. Litho.* P 14.
665	14 s. Type 133		70	80
	a. Sheetlet. Nos. 665/7 and 686/8		4·25	
666	20 s. Archery		70	80
667	20 s. Weightlifting		70	80
668	20 s. Pole vault (*vert*)		70	80
	a. Sheetlet. Nos. 668/76		5·50	
669	20 s. Equestrian (*vert*)		70	80
670	20 s. Diving (*vert*)		70	80
671	20 s. Sprinting (*vert*)		70	80

672	20 s. Athlete carrying Olympic Torch (*vert*)		70	80
673	20 s. Hurdling (*vert*)		70	80
674	20 s. Kayak (*vert*)		70	80
675	20 s. Boxing (*vert*)		70	80
676	20 s. Gymnastics (*vert*)		70	80
677	25 s. Greg Louganis (U.S.A.) (diving, 1984 and 1988) (*vert*)		70	80
	a. Sheetlet. Nos. 677/85		5·50	
678	25 s. Cassius Clay (U.S.A.) (boxing, 1960) (*vert*)		70	80
679	25 s. Nadia Comaneci (Rumania) (gymnastics, 1980) (*vert*)		70	80
680	25 s. Daley Thompson (Great Britain) (decathlon, 1980 and 1984) (*vert*)		70	80
681	25 s. Kipchoge Keino (Kenya) (running, 1968) (*vert*)		70	80
682	25 s. Kornelia Enders (Germany) (swimming, 1976) (*vert*)		70	80
683	25 s. Jackie Joyner-Kersee (U.S.A.) (long jump, 1988) (*vert*)		70	80
684	25 s. Michael Jordan (U.S.A.) (basketball, 1984) (*vert*)		70	80
685	25 s. Shun Fujimoto (Japan) (gymnastics, 1972) (*vert*)		70	80
686	32 s. Javelin		70	80
687	40 s. Fencing		80	85
688	50 s. Discus		1·00	1·10
665/88		*Set of 24*	15·00	17·00
MS689	Two sheets, each 79×109 mm. (a) 100 s. Athlete with medal (*vert*). (b) 100 s. Athlete carrying Olympic Torch (*different*)			
		Set of 2 sheets	5·25	7·00

Nos. 665/7 with 686/8, 668/76 and 677/85 were printed together, *se-tenant*, in sheetlets of 6 (Nos. 665/7, 686/8) or 9 (Nos. 668/76 and 677/85) with the backgrounds forming composite designs.
See also Nos. 702/6.

134 Lions

135 Water Buck

(Litho Cartor)

1996 (31 Jan). *Tourism. Multicoloured.* (a) Designs as T **134**. P 14×13½.
690	6 s. Type 134		30	10
691	14 s. Mt Kenya		35	30
692	20 s. Sailboards		55	70
693	25 s. Hippopotami		1·00	1·40
694	40 s. Couple in traditional dress		1·25	2·00
690/4		*Set of 5*	3·00	4·00
MS695	100×80 mm. 50 s. Female Giraffe and calf (*vert*). P 13×13½		1·75	2·50

(b) Horiz designs as T **135**. P 13×13½
696	20 s. Type 135		70	90
	a. Booklet pane. Nos. 696/701		3·75	
697	20 s. Pair of Rhinoceroses		70	90
698	20 s. Cheetah		70	90
699	20 s. Group of Oryx		70	90
700	20 s. Pair of Giraffes		70	90
701	20 s. Monkey and Bongo		70	90
696/701		*Set of 6*	3·75	4·75

Nos. 696/701 were only available from 480 s. stamp booklets. Booklet pane No. 696a exists in two versions which differ in the order of the stamps.

136 Women's
10,000 Metres

137 Red Cross
Emblem

(Des Design Box Associates. Litho Cartor)

1996 (18 July). *Olympic Games, Atlanta (2nd issue).* T **136** *and similar vert designs. Multicoloured.* P 13½×14.
702	6 s. Type 136		25	10
703	14 s. Steeple-chasing		45	30
704	20 s. Victorious athletes with flag		70	80
705	25 s. Boxing		70	1·00
706	40 s. Men's 1500 metres		1·25	2·00
702/6		*Set of 5*	3·00	3·75

(Des Dvora Bochman. Litho National Printing & Packaging, Zimbabwe)

1996 (30 Aug). *Kenya Red Cross Society.* T **137** *and similar vert designs.* P 14½.
707	6 s. scarlet-vermilion and black		25	10
708	14 s. multicoloured		45	35
709	20 s. multicoloured		70	80
710	25 s. multicoloured		80	95
711	40 s. multicoloured		1·40	2·00
707/11		*Set of 5*	3·25	3·25

Designs:—14 s. Giving blood; 20 s. Immunization; 25 s; Refugee child with food; 40 s. Cleaning the environment.

138 Impala

139 Kenya Lions
Club Logo

(Des H. Moghul. Litho Harrisons)

1996 (10 Sept). *East African Wildlife Society.* T **138** *and similar vert designs. Multicoloured.* P 14½.
712	6 s. Type 138		20	10
713	20 s. Colobus Monkey		60	60
714	25 s. African Elephant		1·10	1·25
715	40 s. Black Rhinoceros		1·75	2·25
712/15		*Set of 4*	3·25	3·75

(Des Dvora Bochman. Litho Enschedé)

1996 (31 Oct). *Work of Lions Club International in Kenya.* T **139** *and similar vert designs. Multicoloured.* P 13½.
716	6 s. Type 139		15	10
717	14 s. Eye operation		45	45
718	20 s. Two disabled children in wheelchair		70	80
719	25 s. Modern ambulance		80	1·00
716/19		*Set of 4*	1·90	2·00

140 C.O.M.E.S.A.
Logo

141 *Haplochromis cinctus*

(Des O. Katenga. Litho Cartor)

1997 (15 Jan). *Inauguration of Common Market for Eastern and Southern Africa.* T **140** *and similar vert design. Multicoloured.* P 13½×14.
720	6 s. Type 140		15	15
721	20 s. Kenyan flag and logo		70	95

(Des C. Newman. Litho Cartor)

1997 (31 Jan). *Endangered Species. Lake Victoria Cichlid Fishes.* T **141** *and similar horiz designs. Multicoloured.* P 14×13½.
722	25 s. Type 141		75	90
723	25 s. *Haplochromis* "Orange Rock Hunter"		75	90
724	25 s. *Haplochromis chilotes*		75	90
725	25 s. *Haplochromis nigricans*		75	90
722/5		*Set of 4*	2·75	3·25

142 Class 94 Diesel-electric
Locomotive No. 9401, 1981

143 Orange

(Des Design Box. Litho Cartor)

1997 (20 Feb). *Kenya Railway Locomotives.* T **142** *and similar horiz designs. Multicoloured.* P 14×13½.
726	6 s. Type 142		25	15
727	14 s. Class 87 diesel-electric No. 8721, 1964		45	40
728	20 s. Class 59 Garratt steam No. 5905, 1955		65	60
729	25 s. Class 57 Garratt steam No. 5701, 1939		70	70
730	30 s. Class 23 steam No. 2305, 1923		75	90
731	40 s. Class 10 steam No. 1001, 1914		90	1·40
726/31		*Set of 6*	3·25	3·75

(Des H. Moghul. Litho Walsall)

1997 (28 Feb). *Fruits of East Africa.* T **143** *and similar vert designs. Multicoloured.* P 14½.
732	6 s. Type 143		35	15
733	14 s. Pineapple		55	45
734	20 s. Mango		80	90
735	25 s. Pawpaw		85	1·00
732/5		*Set of 4*	2·25	2·25

144 Crocodile

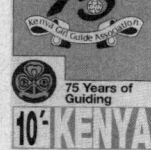

145 Girl Guides
Anniversary Logo

(Des Design Box Associates. Litho Enschedé)

1997 (9 Oct). *Local Tourist Attractions.* T **144** *and similar horiz designs. Multicoloured.* P 13½.
736	10 s. Type **144**			55	25
737	27 s. Lake Bogoria hot springs			95	90
738	30 s. Warthogs			1·00	1·00
739	33 s. Windsurfing			1·25	1·40
740	42 s. Traditional huts			1·50	2·00
736/40			*Set of 5*	4·75	5·00

(Des O. Karenga. Litho Questa)

1997 (21 Nov). *75th Anniv of Kenyan Girl Guides.* T **145** *and similar vert designs. Multicoloured.* P 14½.
741	10 s. Type **145**			30	35
	a. Horiz pair. Nos. 741/2			60	70
742	10 s. Lord Baden Powell			30	35
743	27 s. Girl Guides hiking			70	75
	a. Horiz pair. Nos. 743/4			1·40	1·50
744	27 s. Rangers in camp			70	75
745	33 s. Girl Guides planting seedlings			80	90
	a. Horiz pair. Nos. 745/6			1·60	1·75
746	33 s. Boy Scouts giving first aid			80	90
747	42 s. Boy Scouts in camp			90	1·00
	a. Horiz pair. Nos. 747/8			1·75	2·00
748	42 s. Brownies entertaining the elderly			90	1·00
741/8			*Set of 8*	4·75	5·50

Nos. 741/2, 743/4, 745/6 and 747/8 were each printed together, *se-tenant,* in horizontal pairs throughout the sheets

146 Portuguese Ships arriving at
Malindi

(Des G. Decker. Litho Cartor)

1998 (15 Apr). *500th Anniv of Vasco da Gama's Arrival at Malindi.* T **146** *and similar horiz designs. Multicoloured.* P 13½×13.
749	10 s. Type **146**			30	25
750	24 s. Portuguese ships			70	70
751	33 s. Map of Africa			90	1·10
752	42 s. Vasco da Gama Pillar and harbour			1·00	1·40
749/52			*Set of 4*	2·50	3·00

147 Lion

(Litho Questa)

1998 (10 June). *18th Anniv of Pan African Postal Union. Wildlife.* T **147** *and similar horiz designs. Multicoloured.* P 14½.
753	10 s. Type **147**			40	25
754	24 s. Buffalo			80	70
755	33 s. Grant's Gazelle			1·00	1·10
756	42 s. Cheetah			1·75	2·00
753/6			*Set of 4*	3·50	3·50
MS757	94×76 mm. 50 s. Hirola Gazelle			1·50	2·00

148 Pres. Arap Moi taking
Oath, 1998

(Litho Cartor)

1998 (8 Dec). *Daniel arap Moi's 5th Presidential Term.* P 13½.
758	**148**	14 s. multicoloured	40	40

STAMP BOOKLETS

1964. *Black on blue cover. Stitched.*
SB1 5 s. booklet containing 10 c., 15 c., 20 c., 30 c. and 50 c. (Nos. 2/5, 7) in blocks of 4 .. .. 15·00

1966 (12 Dec). *Black on bluish grey (No. SB2) or buff (No. SB3) covers. Stitched.*
SB2 3 s. booklet containing four 5 c., 10 c. and eight 30 c. (Nos. 20/1, 24), each in blocks of 4 .. .. .. 13·00
SB3 5 s. booklet containing four 5 c., 10 c., 50 c. and eight 30 c. (Nos. 20/1, 24, 26), each in blocks of 4 .. .. 15·00

1971 (13 Dec). *Black on buff (No. SB4) or dull rose (No. SB5) covers. Stitched.*
SB4 5 s. booklet containing four 10 c., 15 c., 40 c. and eight 30 c. (Nos. 37, 38, 40/1), each in blocks of 4 .. .. .. 9·00
SB5 10 s. booklet containing four 10 c., 20 c., 30 c., 50 c. and eight 70 c. (Nos. 37, 39/40, 42, 45), each in blocks of 4 .. .. .. 15·00

1977 (10 Dec). *Black on yellow (No. SB6) or bright rose (No. SB7) covers. Stitched.*
SB6 5 s. booklet containing ten 50 c. (No. 111) in two blocks of 4 and one pair .. .. 11·00
SB7 10 s. booklet containing four 10 c., 20 c., 40 c., 80 c. and eight 50 c. (Nos. 107/8, 110/11, 113), each in blocks of 4 .. .. .. 15·00

1983 (14 Feb). *Black on pale blue (No. SB8) or pale green (No. SB9) covers. Stitched.*
SB8 10 s. booklet containing four 10 c., 20 c., 30 c., 50 c. and eight 70 c. (Nos. 257/9, 261/2), each in blocks of 4 .. .. .. 6·50
SB9 20 s. booklet containing eight 10 c., 20 c., 30 c., 50 c. and sixteen 70 c. (Nos. 257/9, 261/2), each in blocks of 4 .. .. .. 11·00

1988 (15 Feb). *Black on greenish yellow (No. SB10) or yellow-orange (No. SB11) covers. Stitched.*
SB10 20 s. booklet containing eight 20 c., 50 c., 80 c., 1 s. (Nos. 435, 437, 439/40), each in blocks of 4 .. .. 3·75
SB11 40 s. booklet containing sixteen 20 c., 50 c., 80 c., 1 s. (Nos. 435, 437, 439/40), each in blocks of 4 .. .. 7·00

B 1
(Illustration reduced. Actual size 155×80 mm)

1996 (31 Jan). *Tourism. Multicoloured cover as Type B* **1**.
SB12 480 s. booklet containing four *se-tenant* panes of six (No. 696a) .. .. .. 14·00

POSTAGE DUE STAMPS

The Postage Due stamps of Kenya, Uganda and Tanganyika were used in Kenya until 2 January 1967.

D 3

(Litho D.L.R.)

1967 (3 Jan)–**70.** *Chalk-surfaced paper.* P 14×13½.
D13	D **3**	5 c. scarlet	15	2·50
		a. Perf 14. Ordinary paper. *Dull scarlet* (16.12.69)	40	4·25
D14		10 c. green	20	2·50
		a. Perf 14. Ordinary paper (16.12.69)	55	4·25
D15		20 c. blue	70	2·75
		a. Perf 14. Ordinary paper. *Deep blue* (16.12.69)	55	5·00
D16		30 c. brown	80	3·25
		a. Perf 14. Ordinary paper. *Light red-brown* (16.12.69)	80	9·00
D17		40 c. bright purple	65	6·00
		a. Perf 14. Ordinary paper. *Pale bright purple* (16.12.69)	65	9·50
D18		1 s. bright orange	1·75	7·00
		a. Perf 14. Ordinary paper. *Dull bright orange* (18.2.70)	1·50	12·00
D13/18			*Set of 6*	3·75	21·00
D13a/18a			*Set of 6*	3·75	40·00

1971 (13 July)–**73.** P 14 × 15. (a) *Chalk-surfaced paper* (13.7.71).
D19	D **3**	10 c. green	9·00	11·00
D20		20 c. deep dull blue	10·00	12·00
D21		30 c. red-brown	11·00	13·00
D22		1 s. dull bright orange	17·00	35·00
D19/22			*Set of 4*	42·00	65·00

(b) *Glazed, ordinary paper* (20.2.73).
D23	D **3**	5 c. bright scarlet	1·50	4·75
D24		10 c. dull yellow-green	1·50	4·75
D25		20 c. deep blue	1·25	5·50
D27		40 c. bright purple	1·00	8·00
D28		1 s. bright orange	1·50	12·00
D23/8			*Set of 5*	6·00	32·00

1973 (12 Dec). *Glazed, ordinary paper.* P 15.
D29	D **3**	5 c. red	30	4·00
D30		10 c. emerald	30	4·00
D31		20 c. deep blue	30	4·25
D32		30 c. red-brown	30	6·00
D33		40 c. bright purple	3·75	10·00
D34		1 s. bright orange	95	12·00
D29/34			*Set of 6*	5·50	35·00

1979 (27 Mar). *Chalk-surfaced paper.* P 14.
D35	D **3**	10 c. bright emerald	90	5·00
D36		20 c. deep dull blue	1·75	6·00
D37		30 c. dull red-brown	1·00	5·50
D38		40 c. bright reddish purple	2·00	9·00
D39		80 c. dull red	85	5·00
D40		1 s. bright reddish orange	85	5·00
D35/40			*Set of 6*	6·50	32·00

1983 (Dec). *W w 14.* P 14.
D41	D **3**	10 c. yellowish green	30	75
D42		20 c. deep blue	30	75
D43		40 c. bright purple	7·50	9·50
D41/3			*Set of 3*	7·50	10·00

(Litho Harrison)

1985 (7 Aug)–**87.** *Ordinary paper.* P 14½×14.
D44	D **3**	30 c. red-brown (9.1.87)	15	50
D45		40 c. bright magenta (9.1.87)	15	50
D46		80 c. dull vermilion (9.1.87)	20	50
D47		1 s. bright orange (1986)	1·25	1·75
D48		2 s. violet	2·00	3·00
D44/8			*Set of 5*	3·25	5·75

No. D47 was issued by the Crown Agents with Nos. D44/6, but was available in Kenya by November 1986.

(Litho Enschedé)

1993 (6 Dec). *Ordinary paper.* P 14½×14.
D49	D **3**	50 c. yellowish green	10	10
D50		1 s. yellow-orange	10	10
D51		2 s. dull violet	10	10
D52		3 s. steel-blue	10	10
D53		5 s. brown-red	10	10
D49/53			*Set of 5*	30	30

Nos. D49/53 are from re-drawn plates which differ from Harrison printings of Type D **3** in that "KENYA" is 9½ mm long on the Enschedé instead of 8½ mm and "POSTAGE DUE" 11 mm long instead of 11½ mm. There are other differences in the inner frame at bottom right.

OFFICIAL STAMPS

Intended for use on official correspondence of the Kenya Government only but there is no evidence that they were so used.

OFFICIAL

(O **4**)

(15 c. 30 c. opt typo; others in photogravure)

1964 (1 Oct). *Nos. 1/5 and 7 optd with Type O* **4**.
O21	5 c. brown, deep blue, green and bistre		10
O22	10 c. brown		10
O23	15 c. magenta		1·25
O24	20 c. black and yellow-green		20
O25	30 c. black and yellow		30
O26	50 c. crimson, black and green		2·75
O21/26		*Set of 6*	4·00

Kenya, Uganda and Tanganyika (Tanzania)

BRITISH EAST AFRICA

The area which became British East Africa had been part of the domain of the Zanzibari Sultans since 1794. In 1887 the administration of the province was granted to the British East Africa Association, incorporated as the Imperial British East Africa Company the following year.

Company post offices were established at Lamu and Mombasa in May 1890, British mails having been previously sent via the Indian post office on Zanzibar, opened in 1875.

A German postal agency opened at Lamu on 22 November 1888 and continued to operate until 31 March 1891, using German stamps. These can be identified by the "LAMU/OSTAFRIKA" cancellations and are listed under German East Africa in our *Part 7 (Germany)* catalogue.

PRICES FOR STAMPS ON COVER

Nos. 1/3	*from* × 10
Nos. 4/19	*from* × 30
Nos. 20/6	*from* × 3
Nos. 27/8	*from* × 8
Nos. 29/30	*from* × 20
No. 31	*from* × 10
No. 32	—
Nos. 33/47	*from* × 10
No. 48	*from* × 15
Nos. 49/64	*from* × 12
Nos. 65/79	*from* × 15
Nos. 80/91	*from* × 8
Nos. 92/6	*from* × 12
Nos. 97/9	—

(Currency. 16 annas = 1 rupee)

BRITISH EAST AFRICA COMPANY ADMINISTRATION

BRITISH EAST AFRICA COMPANY

BRITISH EAST AFRICA COMPANY

HALF ANNA (1)

1 ANNA (2)

(Surch D.L.R.)

1890 (23 May). *Stamps of Great Britain (Queen Victoria) surch as T* **1** *or T* **2** (1 a. *and* 4 a.).
1	½ a. on 1d. deep purple (No. 173)	£275	£200
2	1 a. on 2d. grey-green and carmine (No. 200)	£450	£275
3	4 a. on 5d. dull purple and blue (No. 207a)	£450	£275

A copy of the ½ a. with the short crossbar of "F" in "HALF" omitted exists in the Royal Collection but is the only known example.

Following the exhaustion of stocks of Nos. 1/3, stamps of India were used at Mombasa (and occasionally at Lamu) from late July 1890 until the arrival of Nos. 4/19. The following listing is for stamps clearly cancelled with the MOMBASA 21 mm circular date stamp (code "C"). Examples with LAMU circular date stamp are worth much more. Indian stamps used after October 1890, including other values, came from ship mail.

Stamps of INDIA 1882–90 (Nos. 84/101) cancelled at Mombasa between July and October 1890.
Z1	½ a. blue-green		£350
Z2	1 a. brown-purple		£300
Z3	1 a. 6 p. sepia		£500
Z4	2 a. blue		£600
Z5	3 a. orange		£600
Z6	4 a. 6 p. yellow-green		£180
Z7	8 a. dull mauve		£300
Z8	1 r. slate		£600

3

4

5 ANNAS. (5)

(Litho B.W.)

1890 (14 Oct)–95. *P* 14.
4	3	½ a. dull brown	2·50	4·00
		a. Imperf (pair)	£1000	£500
		b. *Deep brown* (21.10.93)	70	3·50
		ba. Imperf (pair)	£900	£375
		bb. Imperf between (horiz pair)	£1600	£650
		bc. Imperf between (vert pair)	£950	£500
		c. *Pale brown* (16.1.95)	1·00	5·00
5		1 a. blue-green	3·50	4·75
		aa. "ANL" (broken "D") (R. 6/3)	£450	£450
		ab. "ANL" (broken "D") (R. 6/3)	£1100	£500
		b. *Deep blue-green* (16.1.95)	75	
		ba. Imperf (pair)	£1200	£700
6		2 a. vermilion	2·75	3·75
		a. Imperf (pair)	£1500	£600

7	3	2½ a. black/*yellow-buff* (9.91)	80·00	21·00
		a. Imperf between (horiz pair)	£3500	
		b. *Black/pale buff* (9.92)	75·00	9·00
		c. *Black/bright yellow* (21.10.93)	4·50	5·00
		cb. Imperf (pair)	£1000	£400
		cc. Imperf between (horiz pair)	£1300	£400
		cd. Imperf between (vert pair)	£1300	£500
8		3 a. black/*dull red* (30.3.91)	8·50	12·00
		a. *Black/bright red* (21.10.93)	1·75	4·75
		ab. Imperf (pair)	£950	£400
		ac. Imperf between (horiz pair)	£800	£375
		ad. Imperf between (vert pair)	£600	£375
9		4 a. yellow-brown	2·50	5·00
		a. Imperf (pair)	£1700	£800
10		4 a. grey (*imperf*)	£1200	£1400
11		4½ a. dull violet (30.3.91)	35·00	14·00
		a. *Brown-purple* (21.10.93)	2·50	14·00
		ab. Imperf (pair)	£1500	£400
		ac. Imperf between (horiz pair)	£1300	£1100
		ad. Imperf between (vert pair)	£950	£475
12		8 a. blue	5·50	9·00
		a. Imperf (pair)	£2500	£700
13		8 a. grey	£275	£225
14		1 r. carmine	6·00	9·00
		a. Imperf (pair)	£3000	£800
15		1 r. grey	£225	£225
16	4	2 r. brick-red	14·00	26·00
17		3 r. slate-purple	8·50	32·00
18		4 r. ultramarine	12·00	32·00
19		5 r. grey-green	30·00	65·00
4/9, 11/19		*Set of 15*	£500	£500

For the 5 a. and 7½ a. see Nos. 29/30.

The dates quoted for these stamps are of the earliest recorded use of the various consignments based on known shipping movements. It is possible that the initial supply may have been placed on sale before 14 October 1890 as an example of the ½ a. exists postmarked on 13 October, at Mombasa.

The paper of Nos. 7, 7b, 7c, 8 and 8a is coloured on the surface only.

Printings of 1890/92 are on thin paper having the outer margins of the sheets imperf and bearing sheet watermark "PURE LINEN WOVE BANK" and "W. C. S. & Co." in a monogram, the trademark of the makers, Messrs. William Collins, Sons & Co.

1893/94 printings are on thicker coarser paper with outer margins perforated through the selvedge and without watermark. Single specimens cannot always be distinguished by lack of watermark alone. Exceptions are the 1893 printings of the 2½ a. and 3 a. which were on Wiggins Teape paper showing a sheet watermark of "1011" in figures 1 centimetre high.

Nos. 7 (coloured through) and 16/19 on thick unwatermarked paper are from a special printing made for presentation purposes.

The printings of the 4 a., 8 a. and 1 r. values in grey were intended for fiscal purposes, but in the event, were made available for postal use.

Forgeries of the 4 a., 8 a., 1 r. grey and 2 to 5 r. exist. The latter are common and can be distinguished by the scroll above "LIGHT" where there are five vertical lines of shading in the forgeries and seven in the genuine stamps. Forged cancellations exist on the commoner stamps. Beware of "imperf" stamps made by trimming margins of stamps from marginal rows.

1891. *Mombasa Provisionals.* (a) *New value handstamped in dull violet, with original face value obliterated and initials added in black manuscript*
20	3	"½ Anna" on 2 a. verm ("A.D.") (January)	£3750	£800
		a. "½ Anna" double	†	£4250
		b. Original face value not obliterated	†	£1300
21		"1 Anna" on 4 a. brn ("A.B.") (February)	£6500	£1600

(b) *Manuscript value and initials in black*
22	3	"½ Anna" on 2 a. verm ("A.D.") (original face value not obliterated) (January)	†	£1800
		a. Error. "½ Annas" ("A.D.")		
23		"½ Anna" on 2 a. vermilion ("A.B.") (February)	£3750	£800
		a. Error. "½ Annas" ("A.B.")	†	£950
24		"½ Anna" on 3 a. black/*dull red* ("A.B.") (May)	£5000	£1500
25		"1 Anna" on 3 a. black/*dull red* ("V.H.M.") (June)	£5000	£1000
26		"1 Anna" on 4 a. brown ("A.B.") (March)	£3500	£1300

A.D. = Andrew Dick, Chief Accountant.
A.B. = Archibald Brown, Cashier of the Company.
V.H.M. = Victor H. Mackenzie, Bank Manager.

(Surch B.W.)

1894 (1 Nov). *Surch as T* **5**.
27	3	5 a. on 8 a. blue	60·00	80·00
28		7½ a. on 1 r. carmine	60·00	80·00
27/28		Handstamped "Specimen"	*Set of 2*	90·00

Forgeries exist.

1895 (16 Jan). *No wmk. P* 14.
29	3	5 a. black/*grey-blue*	1·25	10·00
30		7½ a. black	1·25	13·00
29/30		Handstamped "Specimen"	*Set of 2*	75·00

The date quoted is that of earliest known use of stamps from this consignment.

These two stamps have "LD" after "COMPANY" in the inscription.

The paper of No. 29 is coloured on the surface only.

1895 (Feb). *No. 8 surch with manuscript value and initials* ("T.E.C.R."). *Original face value obliterated in manuscript.*
31	3	"½ anna" on 3 a. black/*dull red* (19.2)	£400	50·00
32		"1 anna" on 3 a. black/*dull red* (22.2)	£4000	£1900

T.E.C.R. = T. E. C. Remington, Postmaster at Mombasa.

Similar manuscript surcharges on the black/*bright red* shade (No. 8a) are believed to be forgeries.

The Company experienced considerable financial problems during 1894 with the result that the British Government agreed to assume the administration of the territory, as a protectorate, on 1 July 1895.

IMPERIAL ADMINISTRATION

BRITISH EAST AFRICA (6)

2½ (7)

(Handstamped at Mombasa)

1895 (9 July). *Handstamped with T* **6**.
33	3	½ a. deep brown	65·00	23·00
		a. *Pale brown*	95·00	38·00
		b. *Dull brown*	†	£1700
		c. Double	£425	£425
		d. Inverted	£3500	
34		1 a. blue-green	£110	85·00
		a. Double	£425	£425
		b. "ANL" (broken "D") (R. 6/3)	£1800	
35		2 a. vermilion	£160	95·00
		a. Double	£550	£475
36		2½ a. black/*bright yellow*	£170	50·00
		a. Double	£550	£425
37		3 a. black/*dull red*	75·00	42·00
38		4 a. yellow-brown	42·00	35·00
		a. Double	£450	£450
39		4½ a. dull violet	£190	95·00
		a. Double	£650	£550
		b. *Brown-purple*	£1100	£900
		ba. Double	£2250	£1800
40		5 a. black/*grey-blue*	£180	£120
		a. Double	£850	£800
		b. Inverted	†	£2750
41		7½ a. black	£100	80·00
		a. Double	£550	£550
42		8 a. blue	90·00	75·00
		a. Double	£600	£600
		b. Inverted	£3500	
43		1 r. carmine	55·00	45·00
		a. Double	£550	£550
44	4	2 r. brick-red	£375	£200
45		3 r. slate-purple	£190	£110
		a. Double	£850	£850
		b. Inverted		
46		4 r. ultramarine	£150	£140
		a. Double	£800	£800
47		5 r. grey-green	£375	£250
		a. Double	£1200	£1200
33/47		*Set of 15*	£2000	£1300

Forgeries exist.

The stamps used for this issue come from the 1893–94 printings on thicker paper, but one used example of the ½ a. is recorded on the 1890–92 thin paper printing with sheet watermark.

1895 (29 Sept). *No. 39 surch with T* **7** *by The Zanzibar Gazette.*
48	3	2½ a. on 4½ a. dull violet (R.)	£140	65·00
		a. Opt (T **6**) double	£900	£850

British East Africa (8)

British East Africa (9)

SETTING OF TYPE 8. This consisted of 120 impressions in 10 horizontal rows of 12 stamps. This matched the size of the pane for all the Indian issues to 1 r. with the exception of the 6 a. The sheets of this value contained four panes, each 8 × 10, which meant that the outer vertical margins also received the overprint.

The setting of Type 9 is not known.

Although only the one setting was used for the low values it is known that some of the overprint errors occurred, or were corrected, during the course of the various printings.

(Overprinted at the offices of *The Zanzibar Gazette*)

1895 (27 Oct)–96. *Stamps of India (Queen Victoria) optd with T* **8** *or* **9** (2 r. *to* 5 r.). W **13** (*Elephant Head*) (6 a.) *or* W **34** (*Large Star*) (*others*) *of India.*
49		½ a. blue-green (No. 85) (8.11.95)	5·50	5·50
		a. "Britlsh" for "British"	£3500	£3000
		b. "Br1tish" for "British" (R. 10/12)	£350	
		c. "Afr1ca" for "Africa" (R. 1/11)	£350	
		d. Opt double, one albino	£225	
50		1 a. plum (No. 89) (8.11.95)	4·75	5·00
		a. "Britlsh" for "British"	£4000	£2750
		b. "Br1tish" for "British" (R. 10/12)	£375	
		c. "Afr1ca" for "Africa" (R. 1/11)	£375	
51		1 a. 6 p. sepia (No. 90) (23.11.95)	3·75	4·00
		a. "Br1tish" for "British" (R. 10/12)	£450	
		b. "Afr1ca" for "Africa" (R. 1/11)	£450	
52		2 a. blue (No. 92) (8.11.95)	4·75	3·00
		a. "Britlsh" for "British"	£3250	£3500
		b. "Br1tish" for "British" (R. 10/12)	£350	£250
		c. "Afr1ca" for "Africa" (R. 1/11)	£350	£250
53		2 a. 6 p. yellow-green (No. 103)	5·50	2·50
		a. "Biitish" for "British"	£4750	
		b. "Bpitish" for "British"	£4750	
		c. "Britlsh" for "British"	†	£2750
		d. "Eas" for "East" (R. 2/12)	£950	£1200
		e. "Br1tish" for "British" (R. 10/12)	£450	£275
		f. "Afr1ca" for "Africa" (R. 1/11)	£450	£275
54		3 a. brown-orange (No. 94) (18.12.95)	8·50	10·00
		a. "Br1tish" for "British" (R. 10/12)	£475	£475
		b. "Afr1ca" for "Africa" (R. 1/11)	£475	
55		4 a. olive-green (No. 95) (18.12.95)	29·00	26·00
		a. *Slate-green*	27·00	24·00
		b. "Br1tish" for "British" (R. 10/12)	£600	£475
		c. "Afr1ca" for "Africa" (R. 1/11)	£600	£475
56		6 a. pale brown (No. 81) (18.12.95)	29·00	45·00
		a. "Br1tish" for "British" (R. 10/8)	£900	
		b. "Afr1ca" for "Africa" (R. 1/7)	£900	
		c. Opt double, one albino	£750	

57		8 a. dull mauve (No. 98) (18.12.95)		60·00	65·00
	a.	"Br1tish" for "British" (R. 10/12)		£950	
	b.	"Afr1ca" for "Africa" (R. 1/11)		£950	
	c.	*Magenta* (1896)		28·00	48·00
	ca.	"Br1tish" for "British" (R. 10/12)		£700	£650
	cb.	"Afr1ca" for "Africa" (R. 1/11)		£700	£650
	cc.	Inverted "a" for "t" of "East" (R. 2/12)		†	£6500
58		12 a. purple/*red* (No. 100) (18.12.95)		22·00	28·00
	a.	"Br1tish" for "British" (R. 10/12)		£650	£650
	b.	"Afr1ca" for "Africa" (R. 1/11)		£650	
59		1 r. slate (No. 101) (18.12.95)		75·00	65·00
	a.	"Br1tish" for "British" (R. 10/12)		£1300	
	b.	"Afr1ca" for "Africa" (R. 1/11)		£1300	
60		1 r. green & aniline carm (No. 106) (1896)		42·00	95·00
	a.	Inverted "a" for "t" of "East" (R. 2/12)		£6500	
	b.	"Br1tish" for "British" (R. 10/12)		£900	
	c.	"Afr1ca" for "Africa" (R. 1/11)		£900	
	d.	Opt double, one sideways		£425	£750
	e.	Opt double, one albino		£550	
61		2 r. carm & yellow-brn (No. 107) (18.12.95)		70·00	£110
	a.	"B" handstamped		£2750	
62		3 r. brown and green (No. 108) (18.12.95)		80·00	£120
	a.	"B" handstamped			— £2750
	b.	Opt double, one albino		£900	
63		5 r. ultramarine & vio (No. 109) (18.12.95)		£100	£140
	a.	Opt double		£1900	
	b.	"B" handstamped		£2250	£2250
49/63			*Set of 15*	£450	£650

The relative horizontal positions of the three lines of the overprint vary considerably but the distance vertically between the lines of the overprint is constant.

In both the "Br1tish" and "Afr1ca" errors the figure one is in a smaller type size.

There are other varieties, such as inverted "s" in "British", wide and narrow "B", and inverted "V" for "A" in "Africa" (R.1/1 and R.6/7).

During the overprinting of Nos. 61/3 the "B" of "British" sometimes failed to print so that only traces of the letter appeared. It was replaced by a handstamped "B" which is often out of alignment with the rest of the overprint. The handstamp is known double.

The 2, 3 and 5 r., normally overprinted in larger type than the lower values, are also known with a smaller overprint, for use as specimen stamps for the U.P.U. These were not issued for postal purposes (*Price* £400 *un per set*). The lower values were reprinted at the same time using similar type to the original overprint.

Forgeries exist.

$2\frac{1}{2}$

(10)	11

1895 (20 Dec). *No. 51 surch locally with T 10 in bright red.*

64		$2\frac{1}{2}$ on 1 $\frac{1}{2}$ a. sepia		75·00	38·00
	a.	Inverted "1" in fraction (R. 5/7, 10/7)		£900	£600
	b.	"Br1tish" for "British" (R. 10/12)		£1100	
	c.	"Afr1ca" for "Africa" (R. 1/11)		£1100	

The setting of Type 10 was in 5 horizontal rows of 12 stamps, repeated twice for each pane.

No. 51 also exists surcharged with T 12, 13 and 14 in brown-red. These stamps were sent to the Postal Union authorities at Berne, but were never issued to the public (*Price unused:* T 12 £85, T 13 £190, T 14 £140).

(Recess D.L.R.)

1896 (26 May)–1901. *Wmk Crown CA. P* 14.

65	11	$\frac{1}{2}$ a. yellow-green			1·75	80
66		1 a. carmine-rose			4·00	40
	a.	*Bright rose-red*			4·00	40
	b.	*Rosine* (1901)			22·00	4·00
	w.	Wmk inverted			80·00	
	x.	Wmk reversed			†	£100
67		2 a. chocolate			3·00	4·25
68		$2\frac{1}{2}$ a. deep blue			7·00	1·75
	a.	*Violet-blue*			9·50	2·50
	b.	Inverted "S" in "ANNAS" (R. 1/1)			95·00	50·00
69		3 a. grey			2·50	5·50
	x.	Wmk reversed			80·00	80·00
70		4 a. deep green			6·00	3·50
71		$4\frac{1}{2}$ a. orange-yellow			6·00	15·00
72		5 a. yellow-bistre			7·50	4·00
73		$7\frac{1}{2}$ a. mauve			5·00	22·00
74		8 a. grey-olive			3·00	5·50
75		1 r. pale dull blue			40·00	23·00
	a.	*Ultramarine*			55·00	55·00
76		2 r. orange			60·00	25·00
77		3 r. deep violet			60·00	30·00
78		4 r. carmine-lake			55·00	60·00
79		5 r. sepia			55·00	40·00
	a.	Thin "U" in "RUPEES" (R. 3/2)			£1100	£1100
	x.	Wmk reversed			†	£250
65/79				*Set of 15*	£275	£200
65/79 Optd "Specimen"				*Set of 15*	£275	

(Overprinted at the offices of *The Zanzibar Gazette*)

1897 (2 Jan). *Nos. 156/7, 159 and 165/7 of Zanzibar optd with T* 8. *Wmk Single Rosette.*

80		$\frac{1}{2}$ a. yellow-green and red			50·00	45·00
81		1 a. indigo and red			95·00	85·00
82		2 a. red-brown and red			32·00	21·00
83		$4\frac{1}{2}$ a. orange and red			50·00	28·00
	a.	No right serif to left-hand "4"			£450	
	b.	No fraction bar at right			£450	£300
84		5 a. bistre and red			50·00	35·00
	a.	"Bri" for "British"			£1100	£1100
85		$7\frac{1}{2}$ a. mauve and red			50·00	35·00
	a.	"Bri" for "British"			£1200	
	b.	Optd on front and back				
80/5				*Set of 6*	£300	£225

Nos. 84a and 85a appear to have occurred when the type was obscured during part of the overprinting.

The above six stamps exist with an overprint similar to T 8 but normally showing a stop after "Africa". These overprints (in red on the 1 a.) were made officially to supply the U.P.U. (*Price* £300 *un per set*). However, the stop does not always show. Pieces are

known showing overprints with and without stop *se-tenant* (including the red overprint on the 1 a.).

Stamps of Zanzibar, wmk. "Multiple Rosettes" and overprinted with T 8 are forgeries.

$2\frac{1}{2}$	$2\frac{1}{2}$	$2\frac{1}{2}$
(12)	(13)	(14)

SETTING OF TYPES 12/14. The setting of 60 (6×10) contained 26 examples of Type 12, 10 of Type 13 and 24 of Type 14.

1897 (2 Jan). *Nos. 157 and 162 of Zanzibar optd with T* 8 *and further surch locally, in red.*

86	12	$2\frac{1}{2}$ on 1 a. indigo and red			90·00	55·00
		b. Opt Type 8 double			£4500	
87	13	$2\frac{1}{2}$ on 1 a. indigo and red			£190	95·00
88	14	$2\frac{1}{2}$ on 1 a. indigo and red			£100	60·00
		a. Opt Type 8 double			£5000	
89	12	$2\frac{1}{2}$ on 3 a. grey and red			85·00	48·00
90	13	$2\frac{1}{2}$ on 3 a. grey and red			£180	90·00
91	14	$2\frac{1}{2}$ on 3 a. grey and red			95·00	50·00
86/91				*Set of 6*	£650	£350

Both the notes after No. 85 also apply here.

A special printing for U.P.U. requirements was made with the $2\frac{1}{2}$ surcharge on the 1 a. and 3 a. stamps overprinted as T 8 but *with stop* after "Africa". It also included a "2" over "1" error in T 14.

15

(Recess D.L.R.)

1897 (Nov)–1903. *Wmk Crown CC. P* 14.

92	15	1 r. grey-blue			55·00	30·00
	a.	*Dull blue* (1901)			48·00	27·00
	b.	*Bright ultramarine* (1903)			£200	£160
93		2 r. orange			75·00	75·00
94		3 r. deep violet			85·00	£100
95		4 r. carmine			£225	£275
	x.	Wmk reversed			£350	£350
96		5 r. deep sepia			£170	£225
97		10 r. yellow-bistre (S. £65)			£250	£275
98		20 r. pale green (S. £125)			£550	£1200
99		50 r. mauve (S. £250)			£1600	£4000
	x.	Wmk reversed (S. £275)			£1800	
92/6 Optd "Specimen"				*Set of 5*	£180	

On 1 April 1901 the postal administrations of British East Africa and Uganda were merged. Subsequent issues were inscribed "EAST AFRICA AND UGANDA PROTECTORATES".

EAST AFRICA AND UGANDA PROTECTORATES

For earlier issues see BRITISH EAST AFRICA and UGANDA. For the issues of the Mandated Territory of Tanganyika and the war-time issues that preceded them, see TANGANYIKA.

PRICES FOR STAMPS ON COVER TO 1945	
Nos. 1/43	*from* × 3
Nos. 44/75	*from* × 2
Nos. 76/95	*from* × 3
Nos. 96/105	
Nos. 110/23	*from* × 2
Nos. 124/7	*from* × 3
Nos. 128/30	*from* × 5
Nos. 131/54	*from* × 3
Nos. D1/12	*from* × 8

PRINTERS. All the stamps issued between 1903 and 1927 were typographed by De La Rue & Co. Ltd, London.

USED HIGH VALUES. Beware of cleaned fiscally cancelled copies with faked postmarks.

1	2

1903 (24 July)–04. *P* 14. *(a) Wmk Crown CA.*

1	1	$\frac{1}{2}$ a. green (16.2.04)			3·25	9·50
2		1 a. grey and red			1·75	90
3		2 a. dull and bright purple (24.7.03)			7·50	2·50
	w.	Wmk inverted			£100	£100
4		$2\frac{1}{2}$ a. blue			12·00	48·00
5		3 a. brown-purple and green			17·00	48·00
6		4 a. grey-green and black			11·00	18·00
7		5 a. grey and orange-brown			18·00	48·00
8		8 a. grey and pale blue			21·00	40·00

(b) *Wmk Crown CC. Ordinary paper*

9	2	1 r. green			16·00	50·00
	a.	Chalk-surfaced paper			38·00	75·00
10		2 r. dull and bright purple			60·00	65·00

11	2	3 r. grey-green and black			80·00	£160
12		4 r. grey and emerald-green			85·00	£150
13		5 r. grey and red			85·00	£160
14		10 r. grey and ultramarine			£150	£250
		a. Chalk-surfaced paper			£190	£275
		w. Wmk inverted			£325	
15		20 r. grey and stone (Optd S. £120)			£450	£900
16		50 r. grey and red-brown (Optd S. £250)			£1100	£2000
		w. Wmk inverted			£1800	
1/13				*Set of 13*	£375	£700
1/14 Optd "Specimen"				*Set of 14*	£275	

1904–07. *Wmk Mult Crown CA. Ordinary paper* ($\frac{1}{2}$ a. to 8 a.) *or chalk-surfaced paper* (1 r. to 50 r.).

17	1	$\frac{1}{2}$ a. grey-green			8·00	2·50
		a. Chalk-surfaced paper			4·50	3·00
18		1 a. grey and red			3·75	60
		a. Chalk-surfaced paper			5·50	1·00
19		2 a. dull and bright purple			3·25	2·25
		a. Chalk-surfaced paper			2·50	2·25
20		$2\frac{1}{2}$ a. blue			8·00	28·00
21		$2\frac{1}{2}$ a. ultramarine and blue			7·50	17·00
22		3 a. brown-purple and green			3·75	30·00
		a. Chalk-surfaced paper			3·75	26·00
23		4 a. grey-green and black			7·50	18·00
		a. Chalk-surfaced paper			7·50	18·00
24		5 a. grey and orange-brown			6·50	25·00
		a. Chalk-surfaced paper			6·50	25·00
25		8 a. grey and pale blue			7·00	8·50
		a. Chalk-surfaced paper			7·00	18·00
26	2	1 r. green (1907)			27·00	60·00
27		2 r. dull and bright purple (1906)			38·00	55·00
28		3 r. grey-green and black (1907)			55·00	95·00
29		4 r. grey and emerald-green (1907)			60·00	£130
30		5 r. grey and red (1907)			70·00	£100
31		10 r. grey and ultramarine (1907)			£140	£160
		w. Wmk inverted			£325	
32		20 r. grey and stone (1907)			£500	£850
33		50 r. grey and red-brown (1907)			£1200	£2250
17/30				*Set of 13*	£250	£475

(New Currency. 100 cents = 1 rupee)

1907–08. *Wmk Mult Crown CA. Chalk-surfaced paper* (10, 12, 25, 50, 75 c.). *P* 14.

34	1	1 c. brown			2·00	15
35		3 c. grey-green			8·00	50
		a. *Blue-green*			9·00	2·25
36		6 c. red			2·75	10
37		10 c. lilac and pale olive			9·00	8·50
38		12 c. dull and bright purple			9·00	2·75
39		15 c. bright blue			12·00	8·50
40		25 c. grey-green and black			6·00	7·00
41		50 c. grey-green and orange-brown			12·00	12·00
42		75 c. grey and pale blue (1908)			4·50	32·00
34/42				*Set of 9*	60·00	65·00
34/42 Optd "Specimen"				*Set of 9*	£170	

Original	Redrawn

1910. *T* 1 *redrawn. Printed from a single plate. Wmk Mult Crown CA. P* 14.

43	1	6 c. red			9·00	20

In the redrawn type a fine white line has been cut around the value tablets and above the name tablet separating the latter from the leaves above, EAST AFRICA AND UGANDA is in shorter and thicker letters and PROTECTORATES in taller letters than in No. 36.

4 cents

3	4	(5)

1912–21. *Wmk Mult Crown CA. Chalk-surfaced paper* (25 c. to 500 r.). *P* 14.

44	3	1 c. black			30	1·75
45		3 c. green			2·00	60
		a. *Deep blue-green* (1917)			4·50	1·25
		w. Wmk inverted			†	—
46		6 c. red			70	60
		a. *Scarlet* (1917)			14·00	2·25
47		10 c. yellow-orange			2·00	40
		a. *Orange* (1921)			10·00	2·50
48		12 c. slate-grey			2·75	50
49		15 c. bright blue			2·75	80
50		25 c. black and red/*yellow*			45	1·25
		a. *White back* (5.14) (Optd S. £32)			50	4·00
		b. *On lemon* (1916) (Optd S. £32)			11·00	11·00
		c. *On orange-buff* (1921)			45·00	17·00
		d. *On pale yellow* (1921)			9·00	4·75
51		50 c. black and lilac			1·50	1·25
52		75 c. black/*green*			1·50	16·00
		a. *White back* (5.14) (Optd S. £32)			90	16·00
		b. *On blue-green, ol back* (Optd S. £32)			6·00	7·00
		c. *On emerald, olive back* (1919)			42·00	£140
		d. *On emerald back* (1921)			11·00	42·00
53	4	1 r. black/*green*			1·75	4·25
		a. *On emerald back* (1919)			5·00	45·00
54		2 r. red and black/*blue*			20·00	35·00
		w. Wmk inverted			£130	
55		3 r. violet and green			20·00	70·00
56		4 r. red and green/*yellow*			45·00	£100
		a. *On pale yellow*			£100	£160
57		5 r. blue and dull purple			48·00	£120
58		10 r. red and green/*green*			85·00	£150

59	4	20 r. black and purple/*red*			£275	£300
60		20 r. purple and blue/*blue* (1918)			£300	£325
61		50 r. carmine and green (Optd S. £140)			£500	£600
		a. Ordinary paper. *Dull rose-red and dull greyish green*			£650	£700
62		100 r. purple and black/*red* (Optd S. £250)			£3500	£2250
63		500 r. green and red/*green* (Optd S. £550)			£15000	
44/58				*Set of 15*	£200	£450
44/60		Optd "Specimen"		*Set of 17*	£500	

For values in this series overprinted "G.E.A." (German East Africa) see Tanganyika Nos. 45/62.

1919 (7 Apr). *No. 46a surch with T **5** by the Swift Press, Nairobi.*

64	3	4 c. on 6 c. scarlet (*shades*)			85	15
		a. Bars omitted			38·00	65·00
		b. Surch double			£110	£180
		c. Surch inverted			£250	£325
		d. Pair, one without surch			£1100	£1200
64		H/S "Specimen"			60·00	

1921–22. *Wmk Mult Script CA. Chalk-surfaced paper (50 c. to 50 r.). P 14.*

65	3	1 c. black			40	1·75
		w. Wmk inverted			†	£180
66		3 c. green			4·75	7·00
		a. *Blue-green*			14·00	10·00
67		6 c. carmine-red			3·50	8·00
68		10 c. orange (12.21)			8·50	1·00
69		12 c. slate-grey			3·50	90·00
70		15 c. bright blue			5·50	14·00
71		50 c. black and dull purple			12·00	90·00
72	4	2 r. red and black/*blue*			60·00	£150
73		3 r. violet and green			95·00	£170
74		5 r. blue and dull purple			£120	£200
75		50 r. carmine and green (Optd S. £250)			£1900	£3500
65/74				*Set of 10*	£275	£650
65/74		Optd "Specimen"		*Set of 10*	£275	

For values in this series overprinted "G.E.A." see Tanganyika Nos. 63/73.

KENYA AND UGANDA

(New Currency. 100 cents = 1 East Africa shilling)

On 23 July 1920 Kenya became a Crown Colony with the exception of the coastal strip, previously part of the Sultan of Zanzibar's territories, which remained a protectorate.

The northern province of Jubaland was ceded to Italy on 29 June 1925 and later incorporated into Italian Somaliland.

6   **7**

1922 (1 Nov)–**27.** *Wmk Mult Script CA. P 14.*

(a) Wmk upright. Ordinary paper

76	6	1 c. pale brown			80	2·50
		a. *Deep brown* (1923)			1·50	3·00
		ax. Wmk reversed				
77		5 c. dull violet			3·25	75
		a. *Bright violet*			4·75	1·50
78		5 c. green (1927)			2·00	30
79		10 c. green			1·50	30
		w. Wmk inverted				
80		10 c. black (5.27)			4·00	20
81		12 c. jet-black			7·00	30·00
		a. *Grey-black*			3·25	26·00
82		15 c. rose-carmine			1·25	10
83		20 c. dull orange-yellow			3·25	10
		a. *Bright orange*			3·75	10
84		30 c. ultramarine			2·00	50
85		50 c. grey			2·50	10
86		75 c. olive			3·00	9·00

(b) Wmk sideways. Chalk-surfaced paper

87	7	1 s. green			3·75	2·50
88		2 s. dull purple			8·00	9·00
89		2 s. 50. brown (1.10.25)			18·00	65·00
90		3 s. brownish grey			17·00	6·50
		a. *Jet-black*			38·00	27·00
91		4 s. grey (1.10.25)			20·00	75·00
92		5 s. carmine-red			22·00	20·00
93		7 s. 50. orange-yellow (1.10.25)			60·00	£140
94		10 s. bright blue			48·00	48·00
95		£1 black and orange			£140	£200
96		£2 green and purple (1.10.25) (S. £130)			£600	
97		£3 purple and yellow (1.10.25) (S. £130)			£750	
98		£4 black & magenta (1.10.25) (S. £160)			£1400	
99		£5 black and blue (S. £200)			£1700	
100		£10 black and green (S. £250)			£7500	
101		£20 red and green (1.10.25) (S. £375)			£15000	
102		£25 black and red (S. £400)			£18000	
103		£50 black and brown (S. £450)			£25000	
104		£75 purple and grey (1.10.25) (S. £600)			£55000	
105		£100 red and black (1.10.25) (S. £650)			£55000	
76/95				*Set of 20*	£325	£550
76/95		Optd "Specimen"		*Set of 20*	£425	

Specimen copies of Nos. 96/105 are all overprinted.

STANLEY GIBBONS STAMP COLLECTING SERIES

Introductory booklets on *How to Start, How to Identify Stamps* and *Collecting by Theme.* A series of well illustrated guides at a low price.
Write for details.

KENYA, UGANDA AND TANGANYIKA

The postal administrations of Kenya, Tanganyika and Uganda were amalgamated on 1 January 1933. On the independence of the three territories the combined administration became the East African Posts and Telecommunications Corporation.

8 South African Crowned Cranes   **9** Dhow on Lake Victoria

10 Lion   **11** Kilimanjaro

12 Nile Railway Bridge, Ripon Falls   **13** Mt. Kenya

14 Lake Naivasha   I   II

(Des 1 c., 20 c., 10 s., R. C. Luck, 10 c., £1, A. Ross, 15 c., 2 s., G. Gill Holmes, 30 c., 5 s., R. N. Ambasana, 65 c., L. R. Cutts. T **10** typo, remainder recess D.L.R.).

1935 (1 May)–**37.** *Wmk Mult Script CA. Chalk-surfaced paper (10 c., £1). P 12×13 (**10**), 14 (**9** and **14**) and 13 (remainder).*

110	8	1 c. black and red-brown			50	1·50
111	9	5 c. black and green (I)			1·75	60
		a. Rope joined to sail (II) (1937)			20·00	4·50
		b. Perf 13×12 (I) (1936)			£2500	£450
		ba. Rope joined to sail (II) (1937)			£550	£160
112	10	10 c. black and yellow			3·00	60
113	11	15 c. black and scarlet			1·25	10
114	8	20 c. black and orange			2·00	20
115	12	30 c. black and blue			2·00	1·50
116	9	50 c. bright purple and black (I)			1·75	10
117	13	65 c. black and brown			2·75	2·00
118	14	1 s. black and green			1·00	65
		a. Perf 13×12 (1936)			£1000	£110
119	11	2 s. lake and purple			4·50	4·00
120	14	3 s. blue and black			6·50	15·00
		a. Perf 13×12 (1936)			£1600	
121	12	5 s. black and carmine			17·00	27·00
122	8	10 s. purple and blue			50·00	75·00
123	10	£1 black and red			£120	£140
110/23				*Set of 14*	£190	£250
110/23		Perf "Specimen"		*Set of 14*	£250	

Line through "0" of 1910 (R.4/2)

1935 (6 May). *Silver Jubilee. As Nos. 114/17 of Jamaica, but ptd by D.L.R. P 13½×14.*

124		20 c. light blue and olive-green			50	10
		f. Diagonal line by turret			60·00	
		g. Dot to left of chapel			90·00	
		h. Dot by flagstaff			90·00	
		i. Dash by turret			90·00	
125		30 c. brown and deep blue			2·50	3·50
		f. Diagonal line by turret			£100	
		g. Dot to left of chapel			£160	
		h. Dot by flagstaff			£160	
		i. Dash by turret			£160	
126		65 c. green and indigo			1·75	2·75
		f. Diagonal line by turret			£100	
		g. Dot to left of chapel			£160	
127		1 s. slate and purple			2·00	2·50
		f. Diagonal line by turret			£110	
		g. Dot to left of chapel			£170	
		h. Dot by flagstaff			£170	
		l. Line through "0" of 1910			£170	
124/7				*Set of 4*	6·00	8·00
124/7		Perf "Specimen"		*Set of 4*	£100	

For illustrations of the other plate varieties see Omnibus section following Zimbabwe.

1937 (12 May). *Coronation. As Nos. 118/20 of Jamaica.*

128		5 c. green			20	10
129		20 c. orange			40	30
130		30 c. bright blue			60	1·25
128/30				*Set of 3*	1·10	1·50
128/30		Perf "Specimen"		*Set of 3*	65·00	

15 Dhow on Lake Victoria

Damaged left-hand value tablet (Frame Pl 2–2, with Centre Pl 4B only, R. 9/6)   Retouched value tablet (Frame Pl 2–2, with Centre Pls 4B, 5, 6 or 7, R. 9/6)

Break in bird's breast (Frame Pl 2–2, with Centre Pls 4A or 4B, R. 2/5)

Damage on mountain (Pl 7B R. 6/7. August 1948 ptg. Retouched in June 1949 for 10 c. and 1 s.)   Mountain retouch (Pl 7B, R. 5/10 and 6/7. Ptgs from June 1949 onwards)

With dot   Dot removed

In the 50 c. printing of 14 June 1950, using Frame-plate 3, the dot was removed by retouching on all but five stamps (R. 5/2, 6/1, 7/2, 7/4, and 9/1). In addition, other stamps show traces of the dot where the retouching was not completely effective.

PERFORATIONS. In this issue, to aid identification, the perforations are indicated to the nearest quarter.

(T **10** typo, others recess D.L.R.)

1938 (11 Apr)–**54.** *As T **8** to **14** (but with portrait of King George VI in place of King George V, as in T **15**). Wmk Mult Script CA. Chalk-surfaced paper (£1).*

131	8	1 c. black & red-brown (p 13¾) (2.5.38)			1·75	85
		a. Perf 13¼×13¾. *Black & chocolate-brown* (1942)			30	40
		ab. "A" of "CA" missing from wmk			£1000	
		ac. Damaged value tablet			85·00	
		ad. Retouched value tablet			45·00	65·00
		ae. Break in bird's breast			75·00	
		af. *Black & dp chocolate-brn* (10.6.46)			2·25	1·75
		ag. Ditto. Retouched tablet			50·00	70·00
		ah. *Black and red-brown* (26.9.51)			2·50	1·75
132	15	5 c. black and green (II) (p 13×11¾)			2·75	50
133		5 c. reddish brown & orange (p 13×11¾) (1.6.49)			40	3·00
		a. Perf 13×12½ (14.6.50)			1·60	3·00
134	14	10 c. red-brn & orge (p 13×11¾) (2.5.38)			1·75	10
		aw. Wmk inverted				
		b. Perf 14 (22.4.41)			£110	6·50
135		10 c. black and green (p 13×11¾) (1.6.49)			30	85
		a. Mountain retouch			70·00	50·00
		b. Perf 13×12½ (14.6.50)			1·25	10
136		10 c. brown and grey (p 13×12½) (1.4.52)			75	55

137	11	15 c. black and rose-red (p 13¼) (2.5.38)	12·00	55
		a. Perf 13¾×13¼ (2.43)	3·75	3·75
		ab. "A" of "CA" missing from wmk		
138		15 c. black & green (p 13¾×13¼) (1.4.52)	1·60	3·00
139	8	20 c. black and orange (p 13¼) (2.5.38)	35·00	30
		a. Perf 14 (19.5.41)	55·00	1·75
		b. Perf 13¼×13¾ (25.2.42)	6·00	10
		ba. *Deep black and deep orange* (8.51)	11·00	1·25
		bw. Wmk inverted	†	
140	15	25 c. blk & carm-red (p 13×12¼) (1.4.52)	1·25	2·25
141	12	30 c. black and dull vio-bl (p 13¼) (2.5.38)	50·00	40
		a. Perf 14 (3.7.41)	£140	11·00
		b. Perf 13¼×13¾ (10.5.42)	2·75	10
142		30 c. dull purple and brown (p 13¼×13¾) (1.4.52)	1·50	40
143	8	40 c. black & blue (p 13¼×13¾) (1.4.52)	1·75	3·00
144	15	50 c. purple & blk (II) (p 13¼×13¾) (2.5.38)	13·00	1·00
		a. Rope not joined to sail (I) (R. 2/5)	£225	£225
		b. *Dull claret and black* (29.7.47)	28·00	4·50
		c. *Brown-purple and black* (4.48)	26·00	4·50
		d. *Reddish purple and black* (28.4.49)	20·00	2·50
		e. Ditto. Perf 13×12½ (10.49)	7·00	55
		ea. Dot removed (14.6.50)	12·00	55
		eb. Ditto. In pair with normal	£275	£100
		ew. Wmk inverted	†	£2250
145	14	1 s. black & yellowish brn (p 13×11¾) (2.5.38)	12·00	30
		a. *Black and brown* (9.42)	9·50	30
		ab. Damage on mountain	—	£250
		ac. Mountain retouch	£800	£160
		aw. Wmk inverted	†	£1900
		b. Perf 13×12½ (10.49)	10·00	60
		ba. *Deep black and brown (clearer impression)* (14.6.50)	13·00	1·50
146	11	2 s. lake-brn & brn-pur (p 13¼) (2.5.38)	£110	2·00
		a. Perf 14 (1941)	70·00	11·00
		b. Perf 13¾×13¼ (24.2.44)	15·00	30
147	14	3 s. dull ultramarine & blk (p 13×11¾) (2.5.38)	35·00	3·50
		a. *Deep violet-blue and black* (29.4.47)	45·00	7·50
		ab. Damage on mountain	£1200	
		ac. Perf 13×12½ (14.6.50)	23·00	2·00
148	12	5 s. black and carmine (p 13¼) (2.5.38)	£130	14·00
		a. Perf 14 (1941)	28·00	2·00
		b. Perf 13¾×13¼ (24.2.44)	23·00	1·00
149	8	10 s. purple and blue (p 13¼) (2.5.38)	£120	21·00
		a. Perf 14. *Reddish purple & bl* (1941)	30·00	17·00
		b. Perf 13¾×13¼ (24.2.44)	30·00	3·00
150	10	£1 black and red (p 11¾×13) (12.10.38)	£300	£120
		a. Perf 14 (1941)	17·00	15·00
		ab. Ordinary paper (24.2.44)	17·00	16·00
		b. Perf 12½ (21.1.54)	10·00	29·00
		131/50ab (*cheapest*)	Set of 20	£120 30·00
		131/50 Perf "Specimen"	Set of 13	£450

The first printing of the 50 c. utilised the King George V centre plate on which each impression had been individually corrected to show the rope joined to sail. R.2/5 was missed, however, and this continued to show Type I until replaced by a further printing from a new plate in September 1938.

Stamps perf 14, together with Nos. 131a, 137a, 139b, 141b, 146b, 148b and 149b, are the result of air raid damage to the De La Rue works which destroyed the normal perforators. Dates quoted for these stamps represent earliest known postmarks.

10c
KENYA TANGANYIKA UGANDA
(16)

A screw head in the surcharging forme appears as a crescent moon (R. 20/4)

1941 (1 July)–**42**. *Pictorial Stamps of South Africa variously surch as T 16 by Government Printer, Pretoria. Inscr alternately in English and Afrikaans.*

			Un. pair	Used pair	Used single
151		5 c. on 1d. grey & carmine (No. 56)	60	1·75	
152		10 c. on 3d. ultramarine (No. 59)	1·00	5·00	30
153		20 c. on 6d. green & verm (No. 61a)	1·00	2·25	20
154		70 c. on 1s. brown and chalky blue (No. 62) (20.4.42)	9·50	4·50	40
		a. Crescent moon flaw	60·00		
		151/4	Set of 4	11·00 12·00	95
		151/4 Handstamped "Specimen"	Set of 4	£190	

1946 (11 Nov). *Victory. As Nos. 141/2 of Jamaica.*

			Unused	Used
155		20 c. red-orange	30	10
156		30 c. blue	30	50
		155/6 Perf "Specimen"	Set of 2 55·00	

Examples of Nos. 155/6 were prereleased at Lindi on 15 October 1946.

1948 (1 Dec). *Royal Silver Wedding. As Nos. 143/4 of Jamaica.*

157		20 c. orange	15	10
158		£1 scarlet	35·00	50·00

1949 (10 Oct). *75th Anniv of Universal Postal Union. As Nos. 145/8 of Jamaica.*

159		20 c. red-orange	20	10
160		30 c. deep blue	1·50	1·25
161		50 c. grey	75	20
162		1 s. red-brown	75	40
		159/62	Set of 4	2·75 1·75

---

17 Lake Naivasha

(Recess D.L.R.)

1952 (1 Feb). *Visit of Princess Elizabeth and Duke of Edinburgh. Wmk Mult Script CA. P 13 × 12½.*

163	17	10 c. black and green	10	1·50
164		1 s. black and brown	20	1·75

1953 (2 June). *Coronation. As No. 153 of Jamaica.*

165		20 c. black and red-orange	15	10

1954 (28 Apr). *Royal Visit. As No. 171 but inscr "ROYAL VISIT 1954" below portrait.*

166		30 c. black and deep ultramarine	20	15

18 Owen Falls Dam   **19 Giraffe**

20 Royal Lodge, Sagana   **21 Queen Elizabeth II**

(Des G. Gill Holmes (10, 50 c.), H. Grieme (15 c., 1 s. 30, 5 s.), R. McLellan Sim (10 s.), De La Rue (65 c., 2 s., £1), O.C. Meronti (others). Recess D.L.R.)

1954 (1 June)–**59**. *Designs as T 18/21. Wmk Mult Script CA. P 13 (£1); others, 12½×13 (vert) or 13×12½ (horiz).*

167	18	5 c. black and deep brown	40	50
		a. Vignette inverted	†	£15000
168	19	10 c. carmine-red	75	10
169	—	15 c. black and light blue (28.3.58)	55	1·25
		a. Redrawn. Stop below "c" of "15 c" (29.4.59)	55	1·00
170	—	20 c. black and orange	80	10
		a. Imperf (pair)	£850	£950
171	18	30 c. black and deep ultramarine	80	10
		a. Vignette inverted	†	£11000
172	—	40 c. bistre-brown (28.3.58)	2·50	75
		w. Wmk inverted		
173	19	50 c. reddish purple	1·50	10
		a. Claret (23.1.57)	2·50	10
174	—	65 c. bluish green & brn-pur (1.12.55)	2·75	1·50
175	—	1 s. black and claret	1·25	10
176	—	1 s. 30, deep lilac and orange (1.12.55)	8·00	10
177	—	2 s. black and green	5·00	80
		a. *Black and bronze-green* (19.4.56)	6·50	1·00
178	—	5 s. black and orange	14·00	1·50
179	20	10 s. black and deep ultramarine	20·00	2·25
180	21	£1 brown-red and black	16·00	11·00
		a. *Venetian red and black* (19.4.56)	40·00	15·00
		167/80	Set of 14	65·00 17·00

Designs: *Vert as T 18/19*—20, 40 c., 1 s. Lion. *Horiz as T 20*—15 c., 1 s. 30, 5 s. African Elephants; 65 c., 2 s. Mount Kilimanjaro.

Only one example of No. 167a and two of No. 171a have been found, all being used.

The 5, 10 and 50 c. exist from coils made up from normal sheets.

KENYA-UGANDA
40c TANGANYIKA

25 Map of E. Africa showing Lakes

(Recess Waterlow)

1958 (30 July). *Centenary of Discovery of Lakes Tanganyika and Victoria by Burton and Speke. W w 12. P 12½.*

181	25	40 c. blue and deep green	30	40
182		1 s. 30 c. green and violet	30	1·40

COVER PRICES

Cover factors are quoted at the beginning of each country for most issues to 1945. An explanation of the system can be found on page x. The factors quoted do not, however, apply to philatelic covers.

---

26 Sisal   **27 Cotton**

28 Mt Kenya and Giant Plants   **29 Queen Elizabeth II**

(Des M. Goaman. Photo (5 c. to 65 c.), recess (others) D.L.R.)

1960 (1 Oct)–**62**. *Designs as T 26/9. W w 12. P 15×14 (5 c. to 65 c.), 13 (20 s.) or 14 (others).*

183		5 c. Prussian blue	10	15
184		10 c. yellow-green	10	10
185		15 c. dull purple	30	10
186		20 c. magenta	20	10
187		25 c. bronze-green	3·25	1·00
188		30 c. vermilion	15	10
189		40 c. greenish blue	15	10
190		50 c. slate-violet	15	10
191		65 c. yellow-olive	30	75
192		1 s. deep reddish violet and reddish purple	80	10
		a. *Blackish lilac & reddish pur* (23.1.62)	2·75	10
193		1 s. 30, chocolate and brown-red	2·50	15
194		2 s. deep grey-blue and greenish blue	2·50	30
195		2 s. 50, olive-green and deep bluish green	4·00	2·75
196		5 s. rose-red and purple	3·75	60
197		10 s. blackish green and olive-green	8·00	6·50
		a. Imperf (pair)	£800	
198		20 s. violet-blue and lake	16·00	17·00
		183/98	Set of 16	38·00 26·00

Designs: *Vert as T 26/7*—15 c. Coffee; 20 c. Blue Wildebeest; 25 c. Ostrich; 30 c. Thomson's Gazelle; 40 c. Manta; 50 c. Common Zebra; 65 c. Cheetah. *Horiz as T 28*—1 s. 30, Murchison Falls and Hippopotamus; 2 s. Mt Kilimanjaro and Giraffe; 2 s. 50, Candelabra Tree and Black Rhinoceros; 5 s. Crater Lake and Mountains of the Moon; 10 s. Ngorongoro Crater and African Buffalo.

The 10 c. and 50 c. exist in coils with the designs slightly shorter in height, a wider horizontal gutter every eleven stamps and, in the case of the 10 c. only, printed with a coarser 200 screen instead of the normal 250. (*Price for 10 c. 10p. unused.*) Plate 2 of 30 c. shows coarser 200 screen. (*Price 25p. unused.*)

KENYA UGANDA TANGANYIKA
15

30 Land Tillage

(Des V. Whiteley. Photo Harrison)

1963 (21 Mar). *Freedom from Hunger. T 30 and similar horiz design. P 14½.*

199	30	15 c. blue and yellow-olive	10	10
200	—	30 c. red-brown and yellow	20	10
201	30	50 c. blue and orange-brown	30	10
202	—	1 s. 30, red-brown and light blue	55	1·75
		199/202	Set of 4	1·00 1·75

Design:—30 c., 1 s. 30, African with Corncob.

KENYA 30
University East Africa 28 June 1963
UGANDA TANGANYIKA

31 Scholars and Open Book

(Photo Harrison)

1963 (28 June). *Founding of East African University. P 14½.*

203	31	30 c. lake, violet, black and greenish blue	10	10
204		1 s. 30, lake, blue, red & lt yellow-brown	20	20

32 Red Cross Emblem

(Des V. Whiteley. Photo Harrison)

1963 (2 Sept). *Centenary of Red Cross. P 14½.*

205	32	30 c. red and blue	1·00	10
206		50 c. red and yellow-brown	1·25	55

PRINTERS. All the following stamps were printed in photogravure by Harrison, *unless otherwise stated.*

33 Chrysanthemum Emblems 34

35 East African "Flags"

(Des V. Whiteley)

1964 (21 Oct). *Olympic Games. Tokyo.* P 14½.

207	33	30 c. yellow and reddish violet	..	10	10
208	34	50 c. deep reddish violet and yellow		15	10
209	35	1 s. 30, orange-yellow, dp green & lt blue		30	10
210		2 s. 50, magenta, deep violet-blue & lt bl		40	1·40
207/10			*Set of 4*	85	1·50

KENYA, UGANDA AND TANZANIA

The following stamps were issued by the East African Postal Administration for use in Uganda, Kenya and Tanzania, excluding Zanzibar.

36 Rally Badge   37 Cars *en route*

1965 (15 Apr*). *13th East African Safari Rally.* P 14.

211	36	30 c. black, yellow and turquoise		10	10
212		50 c. black, yellow and brown	..	10	10
		a. Imperf (pair)	..	£700	
213	37	1 s. 30, dp bluish green, yell-ochre & blue		25	10
214		2 s. 50, dp bluish green, brn-red & lt blue		40	1·50
211/14			*Set of 4*	75	1·60

*This is the local release date. The Crown Agents in London issued the stamps the previous day.

38 I.T.U. Emblem and Symbols

1965 (17 May). *I.T.U. Centenary.* P 14½.

215	38	30 c. gold, chocolate and magenta	..	20	10
216		50 c. gold, chocolate and grey	..	20	10
217		1 s. 30, gold, chocolate and blue	..	55	10
218		2 s. 50, gold, chocolate & turquoise-grn		1·00	2·25
215/18			*Set of 4*	1·75	2·25

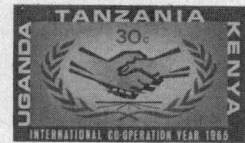

39 I.C.Y. Emblem

1965 (4 Aug). *International Co-operation Year.* P 14½ × 14.

219	39	30 c. deep bluish green and gold..		10	10
220		50 c. black and gold	..	15	10
221		1 s. 30, ultramarine and gold	..	30	10
222		2 s. 50, carmine-red and gold	..	75	2·50
219/22			*Set of 4*	1·25	2·50

40 Game Park Lodge, Tanzania

(Des Rena Fennessy)

1966 (4 Apr). *Tourism.* T **40** *and similar horiz designs. Multicoloured.* P 14½.

223		30 c. Type **40**	..	15	10
224		50 c. Murchison Falls, Uganda	..	50	10
		a. Blue omitted		£275	
225		1 s. 30, Lesser Flamingoes, Lake Nakuru, Kenya		2·25	30
226		2 s. 50, Deep Sea Fishing, Tanzania..		2·00	3·00
223/6 ..			*Set of 4*	4·50	3·00

41 Games Emblem

(Des Harrison)

1966 (2 Aug). *Eighth British Empire and Commonwealth Games Jamaica.* P 14½.

227	41	30 c. black, gold, turq-green & grey		10	10
228		50 c. black, gold, cobalt and cerise	..	15	10
229		1 s. 30, blk, gold, rosine & dp bluish grn		20	10
230		2 s. 50, black, gold, lake and ultramarine		35	1·50
227/30			*Set of 4*	70	1·50

42 U.N.E.S.C.O. Emblem

(Des Harrison)

1966 (3 Oct). *20th Anniv of U.N.E.S.C.O.* P 14½ × 14.

231	42	30 c. black, emerald and red	..	25	10
232		50 c. black, emerald and light brown		35	10
233		1 s. 30, black, emerald and grey	..	85	15
234		2 s. 50, black, emerald and yellow		1·50	3·00
231/4			*Set of 4*	2·75	3·00

43 De Havilland D.H.89 Dragon Rapide

(Des R. Granger Barrett)

1967 (23 Jan). *21st Anniv of East African Airways.* T **43** *and similar horiz designs.* P 14½.

235		30 c. slate-violet, greenish blue & myrtle-grn		30	10
236		50 c. multicoloured	.. ..	40	10
		a. Red omitted	..	£325	
237		1 s. 30, multicoloured	..	85	30
238		2 s. 50, multicoloured	..	1·25	3·00
235/8 ..			*Set of 4*	2·50	3·00

Designs:—50 c. Vickers Super VC-10; 1 s. 30, Hawker Siddeley Comet 4B; 2 s. 50, Fokker F.27 Friendship.

44 Pillar Tomb   45 Rock Painting

(Des Rena Fennessy)

1967 (2 May). *Archaeological Relics.* T **44/5** *and similar designs.* P 14½.

239		30 c. ochre, black and deep reddish purple		15	10
240		50 c. orange-red, black and greyish brown		65	10
241		1 s. 30, black, greenish, yellow and deep yellow-green		85	15
242		2 s. 50, black, ochre and brown-red		1·40	3·00
239/42			*Set of 4*	2·75	3·00

Designs:—1 s. 30, Clay head; 2 s. 50, Proconsul skull.

48 Unified Symbols of Kenya, Tanzania, and Uganda

(Des Rena Fennessy)

1967 (1 Dec). *Foundation of East African Community.* P 14½ × 14.

243	48	5 s. gold, black and grey	..	40	1·25

49 Mountaineering

(Des Rena Fennessy)

1968 (4 Mar). *Mountains of East Africa.* T **49** *and similar horiz designs. Multicoloured.* P 14.

244		30 c. Type **49**	..	15	10
245		50 c. Mount Kenya	..	30	10
246		1 s. 30, Mount Kilimanjaro	..	60	10
247		2 s. 50, Ruwenzori Mountains		90	2·25
244/7			*Set of 4*	1·75	2·25

50 Family and Rural Hospital

(Des Rena Fennessy. Litho D.L.R.)

1968 (13 May). *20th Anniv of World Health Organization.* T **50** *and similar horiz designs.* P 13½.

248		30 c. deep yellow-green, lilac and chocolate		10	10
249		50 c. slate-lilac, lilac and black	..	15	10
250		1 s. 30, yellow-brown, lilac and chocolate		20	15
251		2 s. 50, grey, black and reddish lilac..		30	1·90
248/51			*Set of 4*	60	2·00

Designs:—50 c. Family and nurse; 1 s. 30, Family and microscope; 2 s. 50, Family and hypodermic syringe.

51 Olympic Stadium, Mexico City

(Des V. Whiteley)

1968 (14 Oct). *Olympic Games, Mexico.* T **51** *and similar designs.* P 14.

252		30 c. light green and black	..	10	10
253		50 c. black and blue-green	..	15	10
254		1 s. 30, carmine-red, black and grey..		25	15
255		2 s. 50, blackish brown and yellow-brown		35	1·50
252/5			*Set of 4*	70	1·60

Designs: Horiz—50 c. High-diving boards; 1 s. 30, Running tracks. Vert—2 s. 50, Boxing ring.

52 Umoja (railway ferry)

(Des A. Grosart)

1969 (20 Jan). *Water Transport.* T **52** *and similar horiz designs.* P 14.

256		30 c. deep blue, light blue and slate-grey		40	10
		a. Slate-grey omitted	..	48·00	
257		50 c. multicoloured	..	45	10
258		1 s. 30, bronze-grn, greenish blue & blue	..	85	20
259		2 s. 50, red-orange, dp blue & pale blue	..	1·40	3·25
256/9 ..			*Set of 4*	2·75	3·25

Designs:—50 c. S.S. *Harambee*; 1 s. 30, M.V. *Victoria*; 2 s. 50, *St. Michael.*

ALTERED CATALOGUE NUMBERS

Any Catalogue numbers altered from the last edition are shown as a list in the introductory pages.

53 I.L.O. Emblem and Agriculture   **54** Pope Paul VI and Ruwenzori Mountains

(Des Rena Fennessy)

1969 (14 Apr). *50th Anniv of International Labour Organization. T 53 and similar horiz designs. P 14.*

260	30 c. black, green and greenish yellow	..	10	10
261	50 c. black, plum, cerise and rose	..	10	10
262	1 s. 30, black, orange-brown & yellow-orange		10	10
263	2 s. 50, black, ultramarine & turquoise-blue		20	90
260/3	..	*Set of 4*	35	1·00

Designs:—50 c. I.L.O. emblem and building work; 1 s. 30, I.L.O. emblem and factory workers; 2 s. 50, I.L.O. emblem and shipping.

(Des Harrison)

1969 (31 July). *Visit of Pope Paul VI to Uganda. P 14.*

264	**54**	30 c. black, gold and royal blue ..	15	10
265		70 c. black, gold and claret	20	10
266		1 s. 50, black, gold and deep blue	25	20
267		2 s. 50, black, gold and violet ..	30	1·40
264/7	..	*Set of 4*	80	1·50

55 Euphorbia Tree shaped as Africa and Emblem   **56** Marimba

(Des Rena Fennessy. Litho B.W.)

1969 (8 Dec). *Fifth Anniv of African Development Bank. P 13½.*

268	**55**	30 c. dp bluish green, gold & blue-green	10	10
269		70 c. dp bluish green, gold & reddish pur	15	10
270		1 s. 50, dp bluish grn, gold & lt turq-bl	30	10
271		2 s. 50, dp bluish grn, gold & orge-brn	35	1·00
268/71	..	..	*Set of 4*	75	1·10

(Des Rena Fennessy. Litho B.W.)

1970 (16 Feb). *Musical Instruments. T 56 and similar horiz designs. P 11 × 12.*

272	30 c. buff, yellow-brown and bistre-brown		15	10
273	70 c. olive-green, yellow-brown and yellow		25	10
274	1 s. 50, chocolate and yellow..		50	10
275	2 s. 50, salmon, yellow and chocolate		75	2·25
272/5	..	*Set of 4*	1·50	2·25

Designs:—70 c. Amadinda; 1 s. 50, Nzomari; 2 s. 50, Adeudeu.

57 Satellite Earth Station   **58** Athlete

(Des V. Whiteley. Litho J.W.)

1970 (18 May). *Inauguration of East African Satellite Earth Station. T 57 and similar horiz designs. P 14½ × 14.*

276	30 c. multicoloured	..	10	10
277	70 c. multicoloured	..	15	10
278	1 s. 50, black, slate-violet and pale orange		25	10
279	2 s. 50, multicoloured		55	2·25
276/9	..	*Set of 4*	90	2·25

Designs:—70 c. Transmitter in daytime; 1 s. 50, Transmitter at night; 2 s. 50, Earth and satellite.

(Des Rena Fennessy. Litho Walsall)

1970 (13 July). *Ninth Commonwealth Games. P 14 × 14½.*

280	**58**	30 c. orange-brown and black	10	10
281		70 c. olive-green and black	10	10
282		1 s. 50, slate-lilac and black	15	10
283		2 s. 50, turquoise-blue and black	20	1·25
280/3	..	..	*Set of 4*	40	1·40

59 "25" and U.N. Emblem

(Des Rena Fennessy)

1970 (19 Oct). *25th Anniv of United Nations. P 14½.*

284	**59**	30 c. multicoloured	..	10	10
285		70 c. multicoloured	..	10	10
286		1 s. 50, multicoloured	..	20	10
287		2 s. 50, multicoloured	..	45	2·00
284/7	..		*Set of 4*	70	2·00

60 Balance and Weight Equivalents

(Des and litho J.W.)

1971 (4 Jan). *Conversion to Metric System. T 60 and similar horiz designs. Multicoloured. P 14½ × 14.*

288	30 c. Type **60**		10	10
289	70 c. Fahrenheit and Centigrade Thermometers		10	10
290	1 s. 50, Petrol Pump and Liquid Capacities ..		15	10
291	2 s. 50, Surveyors and Land Measures		35	2·00
288/91	..	*Set of 4*	60	2·00

61 Class 11 Tank Locomotive

(Des Rena Fennessy)

1971 (5 Apr). *Railway Transport. T 61 and similar horiz designs. Multicoloured. P 14.*

292	30 c. Type **61**	..	35	10
293	70 c. Class 90 diesel-electric locomotive	..	55	10
294	1 s. 50, Class 59 steam locomotive	..	1·00	30
295	2 s. 50, Class 30 steam locomotive	..	1·75	2·75
292/5		*Set of 4*	3·25	2·75
MS296	120×88 mm. Nos. 292/5	..	6·50	10·00

62 Syringe and Cow

(Des Rena Fennessy. Litho)

1971 (5 July). *O.A.U. Rinderpest Campaign. T 62 and similar horiz design. P 14.*

297	**62**	30 c. black, pale yell-brn & pale yell-grn	10	10
298	–	70 c. black, pale slate-blue & pale yell-brn	10	10
299	**62**	1 s. 50, black, plum & pale yellow-brn	15	10
300	–	2 s. 50, black, brown-red & pale yell-brn	25	70
297/300	..	*Set of 4*	45	85

Design:—70 c., 2 s. 50, As T 62, but with bull facing right.

63 Livingstone meets Stanley

(Des and litho J.W.)

1971 (28 Oct). *Centenary of Livingstone and Stanley meeting at Ujiji. P 13½ × 14.*

301	**63**	5 s. multicoloured	..	30	75

PRICES OF SETS

Set prices are given for many issues, generally those containing three stamps or more. Definitive sets include one of each value or major colour change, but do not cover different perforations, die types or minor shades. Where a choice is possible the set prices are based on the cheapest versions of the stamps included in the listings.

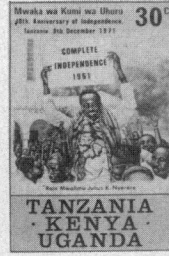

64 President Nyerere and Supporters

(Des G. Drummond. Litho J.W.)

1971 (9 Dec). *Tenth Anniv of Tanzanian Independence. T 64 and similar horiz designs. Multicoloured. P 13½.*

302	30 c. Type **64**	..	10	10
303	70 c. Ujamaa village	..	15	10
304	1 s. 50, Dar es Salaam University	..	30	25
305	2 s. 50, Kilimanjaro International Airport	1·00	3·25
302/5	..	*Set of 4*	1·40	3·25

65 Flags and Trade Fair Emblem

(Des Trade Fair Publicity Agents. Litho Questa)

1972 (23 Feb). *All-Africa Trade Fair. P 13½ × 14.*

306	**65**	30 c. multicoloured	..	10	10
307		70 c. multicoloured	..	10	10
308		1 s. 50, multicoloured	..	10	10
309		2 s. 50, multicoloured	..	25	80
306/9	..	*Set of 4*	40	90

66 Child with Cup

(Des Rena Fennessy. Litho Questa)

1972 (24 Apr). *25th Anniv of UNICEF. T 66 and similar horiz designs. Multicoloured. P 14 × 14½.*

310	30 c. Type **66**	..	10	10
311	70 c. Children with ball	..	10	10
312	1 s. 50, Child at blackboard	..	10	10
313	2 s. 50, Child and tractor	..	25	80
310/13	..	*Set of 4*	35	90

67 Hurdling

(Des G. Vasarhelyi. Litho J.W.)

1972 (28 Aug). *Olympic Games, Munich. T 67 and similar horiz designs. Multicoloured. P 14.*

314	40 c. Type **67**	..	10	10
315	70 c. Running	..	10	10
316	1 s. 50, Boxing	..	20	15
317	2 s. 50, Hockey	..	30	1·75
314/17	..	*Set of 4*	60	1·75
MS318	131 × 98 mm. Nos. 314/17	..	4·50	5·50

68 Kobs

(Des G. Drummond. Litho D.L.R.)

1972 (9 Oct). *Tenth Anniv of Ugandan Independence. T 68 and similar horiz designs. Multicoloured. P 14.*

319	40 c. Type **68**	..	30	10
320	70 c. Conference Centre	..	30	10
321	1 s. 50, Makerere University	..	65	10
322	2 s. 50, Coat of Arms ..	..	1·00	3·25
319/22	..	*Set of 4*	2·00	3·25
MS323	132 × 120 mm. Nos. 319/22. P 13 × 14	3·25	3·50

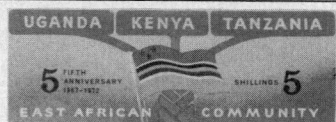

69 Community Flag

(Des Rena Fennessy. Litho)

1972 (1 Dec). *Fifth Anniv of East African Community.*
P 14½ × 14.
324 69 5 s. multicoloured .. .. .. 55 1·60

70 Run-of-the-wind Anemometer

71 "Learning by Serving"

(Des P. Powell. Litho)

1973 (1 Mar*). *I.M.O./W.M.O. Centenary. T* **70** *and similar multi-coloured designs. P 14½.*
325 40 c. Type **70** 10 10
326 70 c. Weather balloon (*vert*) 15 10
327 1 s. 50, Meteorological rocket 25 15
328 2 s. 50, Satellite receiving aerial .. .. 55 2·25
325/8 .. .. .. *Set of* 4 90 2·25
No. 325 exists with country name at foot instead of at top, and also with country name omitted (or with imprint or plate numbers in lieu). These are because of faulty registration of the perforation comb.
*This is the local release date. The Crown Agents in London did not place the stamps on sale until 5 March.

(Des Rena Fennessy. Litho)

1973 (16 July). *24th World Scout Conference, Nairobi. T* **71** *and similar vert designs. P 14.*
329 40 c. multicoloured 15 10
330 70 c. Venetian red, reddish violet and black .. 20 10
331 1 s. 50, cobalt, reddish violet and black .. 45 30
332 2 s. 50, multicoloured .. .. .. 1·00 2·25
329/32 .. .. .. *Set of* 4 1·60 2·50
Designs:—70 c. Baden-Powell's grave, Nyeri; 1 s. 50, World Scout emblem; 2 s. 50, Lord Baden-Powell.

72 Kenyatta Conference Centre

(Des Marketing Communications Ltd, Nairobi; adapted J. Cooter. Litho D.L.R.)

1973 (29 Sept*). *I.M.F./World Bank Conference. T* **72** *and similar designs. P 13½ × 14* (1 s. 50) *or 14 × 13½* (others).
333 40 c. sage-green, light greenish grey & black 10 10
334 70 c. orange-brown, greenish grey and black 10 10
335 1 s. 50, multicoloured 25 35
336 2 s. 50, orange, greenish grey and black .. 35 1·75
333/6 .. .. .. *Set of* 4 65 2·00
MS337 166 × 141 mm. Nos. 333/6. Imperf .. 1·40 3·50
Designs:—Nos. 334/6 show different arrangements of Bank emblems and the Conference Centre, the 1 s. 50 being vertical.
*This is the local release date. The Crown Agents in London issued the stamps on 24 September.

73 Police Dog-handler

74 Tea Factory

(Des C. Abbott. Litho Questa)

1973 (24 Oct)–**74**. *50th Anniv of Interpol. T* **73** *and similar vert designs. P 14.*
338 40 c. yellow, blue and black 55 15
339 70 c. turquoise-green, orange-yellow & black 90 15
340 1 s. 50, light violet, yellow and black .. 1·50 90
341 2 s. 50, light yellow-green, red-orange and black (I) .. .. .. 3·75 6·00
342 2 s. 50, light yellow-green, red-orange and black (II) (25.2.74) .. .. 3·75 6·00
338/42 .. .. .. *Set of* 4 9·50 12·00
Designs:—70 c. East African Policeman; 1 s. 50, Interpol emblem; 2 s. 50, Interpol H.Q.
Nos. 341/2. Type I inscribed "St. Clans"; Type II corrected to "St. Cloud".

(Des G. Drummond. Litho Enschedé)

1973 (12 Dec). *10th Anniv of Kenya's Independence. T* **74** *and similar horiz designs. Multicoloured. P 13 × 13½.*
343 40 c. Type **74** 10 10
344 70 c. Kenyatta Hospital 15 10
345 1 s. 50, Nairobi Airport 50 20
346 2 s. 50, Kindaruma hydro-electric scheme 65 1·75
343/6 .. .. .. *Set of* 4 1·25 1·75

75 Party H.Q.

(Des PAD Studio. Litho D.L.R.)

1974 (12 Jan). *Tenth Anniv of Zanzibar's Revolution. T* **75** *and similar horiz designs. Multicoloured. P 13½.*
347 40 c. Type **75** 10 10
348 70 c. Housing scheme 15 10
349 1 s. 50, Colour T.V. 35 30
350 2 s. 50, Amaan Stadium .. .. 70 2·50
347/50 .. .. .. *Set of* 4 1·10 2·75

76 "Symbol of Union"

(Des Jennifer Toombs. Litho Questa)

1974 (26 Apr). *Tenth Anniv of Tanganyika–Zanzibar Union. T* **76** *and similar horiz designs. Multicoloured. P 14½.*
351 40 c. Type **76** 10 10
352 70 c. Handclasp and map 15 10
353 1 s. 50, "Communications" 35 30
354 2 s. 50, Flags of Tanu, Tanzania and Afro-Shirazi Party .. .. .. 70 2·50
351/4 .. .. .. *Set of* 4 1·10 2·75

77 East African Family ("Stability of the Home")

(Des locally; adapted PAD Studio. Litho)

1974 (15 July). *17th Social Welfare Conference, Nairobi. T* **77** *and similar horiz designs. P 14½.*
355 40 c. greenish yellow, lake-brown and black 10 10
356 70 c. multicoloured 10 10
357 1 s. 50, olive-green, yellow-green and black 20 30
358 2 s. 50, light rose, reddish violet and black 1·00 2·00
355/8 .. .. .. *Set of* 4 1·25 2·25
Designs:—70 c. Dawn and drummer (U.N. Second Development Plan); 1 s. 50, Agricultural scene (Rural Development Plan); 2 s. 50, Transport and telephone ("Communications").

78 New Postal H.Q., Kampala

(Des Rena Fennessy. Litho)

1974 (9 Oct). *Centenary of Universal Postal Union. T* **78** *and similar horiz designs. Multicoloured. P 14½.*
359 40 c. Type **78** 10 10
360 70 c. Mail-train and post-van 20 10
361 1 s. 50, U.P.U. Building, Berne 15 20
362 2 s. 50, Loading mail into Vickers Super VC-10 .. .. .. 1·50
359/62 .. .. .. *Set of* 4 85 1·60

79 Family-planning Clinic

(Des C. Abbott. Litho)

1974 (16 Dec). *World Population Year. T* **79** *and similar horiz designs. P 14.*
363 40 c. multicoloured 10 10
364 70 c. deep reddish violet and scarlet .. 10 10
365 1 s. 50, multicoloured 10 10
366 2 s. 50, apple-green, blue-green & bluish blk 30 1·90
363/6 .. .. .. *Set of* 4 55 2·00
Designs:—70 c. "Tug of war"; 1 s. 50, Population "scales"; 2 s. 50, W.P.Y. emblem.

80 Seronera Wild-Life Lodge, Tanzania

(Des R. Granger Barrett. Litho)

1975 (26 Feb*). *East Africa Game Lodges. T* **80** *and similar horiz designs. Multicoloured. P 14.*
367 40 c. Type **80** 15 10
368 70 c. Mweya Safari Lodge, Uganda .. 20 10
369 1 s. 50, "Ark"—Aberdare Forest Lodge, Kenya 35 30
370 2 s. 50, Paraa Safari Lodge, Uganda .. 80 2·25
367/70 .. .. .. *Set of* 4 1·40 2·50
*This is the local release date. The Crown Agents in London issued the stamps on 24 February.

81 Kitana (wooden comb), Bajun of Kenya

82 International Airport, Entebbe

(Des Mrs. Gombe of the E.A.P.T.; adapted C. Abbott. Litho Questa)

1975 (5 May). *African Arts. T* **81** *and similar vert designs. Multicoloured. P 13½.*
371 50 c. Type **81** 10 10
372 1 s. Earring, Chaga of Tanzania .. 15 10
373 2 s. Okoco (armlet), Acholi of Uganda .. 35 70
374 3 s. Kitete (Kamba gourd), Kenya .. 65 1·40
371/4 .. .. .. *Set of* 4 1·10 2·10

(Des PAD Studio. Litho State Ptg Wks, Warsaw)

1975 (28 July). *O.A.U. Summit Conference, Kampala. T* **82** *and similar multicoloured designs. P 11.*
375 50 c. Type **82** 30 10
376 1 s. Map of Africa and flag (*vert*) .. 30 10
377 2 s. Nile Hotel, Kampala 30 85
378 3 s. Martyrs' Shrine, Namugongo (*vert*) .. 40 1·60
375/8 .. .. .. *Set of* 4 1·10 2·40

83 Ahmed ("Presidential" Elephant)

84 Maasai Manyatta (village), Kenya

(Des locally. Litho State Ptg Wks, Warsaw)

1975 (11 Sept). *Rare Animals. T* **83** *and similar vert designs. Multicoloured. P 11.*
379 50 c. Type **83** 50 10
380 1 s. Albino buffalo 50 10
381 2 s. Ahmed in grounds of National Museum 1·60 1·50
382 3 s. Abbott's Duiker .. .. 1·60 3·00
379/82 .. .. .. *Set of* 4 3·75 4·25

(Des Rena Fennessy. Litho Questa)

1975 (3 Nov). *Second World Black and African Festival of Arts and Culture, Nigeria* (1977). *T* **84** *and similar horiz designs. Multicoloured. P 13½ × 14.*
383 50 c. Type **84** 15 10
384 1 s. "Heartbeat of Africa" (Ugandan dancers) 15 10
385 2 s. Makonde sculpture, Tanzania .. 50 85
386 3 s. "Early Man and Technology" (skinning hippopotamus) .. .. .. 75 1·40
383/6 .. .. .. *Set of* 4 1·40 2·25
For similar stamps see Nos. 76/80 of Kenya and the corresponding issues of Tanzania and Uganda.

85 Fokker F.27 Friendship at Nairobi Airport

(Des local artist. Litho State Security Ptg Wks, Warsaw)

1976 (2 Jan). *30th Anniv of East African Airways. T 85 and similar triangular designs. Multicoloured. P 11½.*

387	50 c. Type **85**		1·00	30
	a. Black (aircraft) and blue omitted		†	£1400
388	1 s. Douglas DC-9 at Kilimanjaro Airport	1·10	30
389	2 s. Vickers Super VC-10 at Entebbe Airport		3·50	3·00
390	3 s. East African Airways crest		3·75	3·75
387/90			*Set of 4*	8·50	6·50

Two black plates were used for each of Nos. 387/9: one for the frame and the other for the centre. No. 387a, three used copies of which are known, has the printing from the blue and centre black plates omitted.

Further commemorative issues were released during 1976–78, using common designs, but inscribed for one republic only. These are listed under KENYA, TANZANIA, or UGANDA.

Co-operation between the postal services of the three member countries virtually ceased after 30 June 1977, the postal services of Kenya, Tanzania and Uganda then operating independently.

STAMP BOOKLETS

1912–17. *Black on pink cover. Letter rate given as 6 cents per oz. Stapled.*

SB1	1 s. 80, booklet containing twelve 3 c. and twenty-four 6 c. (Nos. 45/6), each in blocks of 6		£900
	a. Letter rate 6 cents per ½ oz. Contains Nos. 45a/6a		£900
SB2	1 s. 98, booklet containing six 3 c. and thirty 6 c. (Nos. 45/6), each in blocks of 6		£900

1938. *Black on pink cover. Stapled.*

SB3	3 s. 40, booklet containing twelve 15 c. and eight 20 c. (Nos. 137, 139), each in blocks of 4		£190

1950–52. *Blue on yellow cover. Stapled.*

SB4	1 s. booklet containing four 5 c. and eight 10 c. (Nos. 133a, 135b), each in blocks of 4		£120
	a. Stitched		50·00
	ab. Contents as No. SB4a, but 10 c. changed to No. 136 (1952)		35·00

1954 (3 Sept). *Blue on yellow cover. Stitched.*

SB6	1 s. booklet containing four 5 c. and eight 10 c. (Nos. 167/8), each in blocks of 4		3·00

1956 (16 Jan). *Black on yellow cover. Stitched.*

SB7	5 s. booklet containing four 5 c., 20 c., 30 c., 50 c. and eight 10 c. (Nos. 167, 170/1, 173), each in blocks of 4		17·00

1958 (16 Dec)–**59.** *Black on rose-red cover. Stitched.*

SB8	5 s. booklet containing 10 c., 15 c., 20 c., 30 c. and 50 c. (Nos. 168/9, 170/1, 173), in blocks of 4		24·00
	a. Contents as No. SB8, but 15 c. changed to No. 169a (20.4.59)		24·00

1961 (1 Feb). *Black on rose-red cover. Stitched.*

SB9	5 s. booklet containing 10 c., 15 c., 20 c., 30 c. and 50 c. (Nos. 184/6, 188, 190) in blocks of 4		10·00

OFFICIAL STAMPS

For use on official correspondence of the Tanganyika Government.

OFFICIAL
(O 1)

1959 (1 July). *Nos. 167/71, 173 and 175/80 optd as Type O 1.*

O 1	**18**	5 c. black and deep brown		10	60
O 2	**19**	10 c. carmine-red		15	60
O 3	—	15 c. black and light blue (No. 169a)		30	70
O 4	—	20 c. black and orange		20	20
		a. Opt double		—	£950
O 5	**18**	30 c. black and deep ultramarine		15	40
O 6	**19**	50 c. reddish purple		20	20
O 7	—	1 s. black and claret		20	40
O 8	—	1 s. 30, orange and deep lilac		1·90	1·25
O 9	—	2 s. black and bronze-green		1·25	1·00
O10	—	5 s. black and orange		3·00	2·25
O11	**20**	10 s. black and deep ultramarine		2·00	2·75
O12	**21**	£1 brown-red and black		6·50	13·00
O1/12			*Set of 12*	14·00	21·00

The 30 c., 50 c. and 1 s. exist with overprint double, but with the two impressions almost coincident.

OFFICIAL **OFFICIAL**
(O 2) (O 3)

1960 (18 Oct). *Nos. 183/6, 188, 190, 192 and 196 optd with Type O 2 (cents values) or O 3.*

O13	5 c. Prussian blue		10	75
O14	10 c. yellow-green		10	75
O15	15 c. dull purple		10	75
O16	20 c. magenta		10	10
O17	30 c. vermilion		10	10
O18	50 c. slate-violet		30	10
O19	1 s. deep reddish violet and reddish purple		30	10
O20	5 s. rose-red and purple		9·00	65
O13/20		*Set of 8*	9·00	3·00

MINIMUM PRICE

The minimum price quote is 10p which represents a handling charge rather than a basis for valuing common stamps. For further notes about prices see introductory pages.

POSTAGE DUE STAMPS

D 1

D 2

(Typo Waterlow)

1928 (Sept)–**33.** *Wmk Mult Script CA. P 15×14.*

D1	D 1	5 c. violet		2·50	50
D2		10 c. vermilion		2·50	15
D3		20 c. yellow-green		2·50	3·00
D4		30 c. brown (1931)		17·00	14·00
D5		40 c. dull blue		6·50	14·00
D6		1 s. grey-green (1933)		48·00	95·00
D1/6			*Set of 6*	70·00	£110
D1/6 Optd/Perf "Specimen"			*Set of 6*	£160	

(Typo D.L.R.)

1935 (1 May)–**60.** *Wmk Mult Script CA. P 14.*

D 7	D 2	5 c. violet		2·75	1·75
D 8		10 c. scarlet		30	50
D 9		20 c. green		40	50
D10		30 c. brown		80	50
		a. Bistre-brown (19.7.60)		3·00	7·00
D11		40 c. ultramarine		1·50	3·00
D12		1 s. grey		19·00	19·00
D7/12			*Set of 6*	22·00	23·00
D7/12 Perf "Specimen"			*Set of 6*	£110	

Kiribati
(*formerly* Gilbert Islands)

(Currency. 100 cents = 1 Australian dollar)

GILBERT ISLANDS

On 1 January 1976, the Gilbert Islands and Tuvalu (Ellice Islands) became separate Crown Colonies.

1 Charts of Gilbert Islands and Tuvalu (formerly Ellice) Islands

THE GILBERT ISLANDS
(2)

(Des J. Cooter. Litho Questa)

1976 (2 Jan). *Separation of the Islands. T 1 and similar horiz design. Multicoloured. W w 14 (sideways). P 14.*

1	4 c. Type **1**		40	75
2	35 c. Maps of Tarawa and Funafuti		70	1·50

1976 (2 Jan). *Nos. 173/86 of Gilbert & Ellice Is optd as T 2.*

(a) W w 12 *(sideways* on Nos. 5/7 and 9/10)*

3	1 c. Cutting toddy (R.)		25	30
4	2 c. Lagoon fishing (R.)		60	1·75
5	2 c. Lagoon fishing (wmk sideways) (R.)		50	30
6	3 c. Cleaning pandanus leaves (R.)		11·00	24·00
	w. Wmk Crown to the right of CA		55·00	
7	4 c. Casting nets (R.)		30	80
8	20 c. Beating a pandanus leaf (R.)		†	£110
9	20 c. Beating a pandanus leaf (wmk sideways) (R.)		5·00	3·25
10	25 c. Loading copra		28·00	50·00
	a. Opt double (Blk. + R.)		£350	
10b	50 c. Local handicrafts		£900	£950

(b) W w 14 *(sideways* on 3, 5, 20, 25 and 35 c. inverted on others)*

11	1 c. Cutting toddy (R.)		20	90
12	3 c. Cleaning pandanus leaves (R.)		40	1·00
13	5 c. Gilbertese canoe (R.)		50	80
14	6 c. De-husking coconuts (R.)		50	80
15	8 c. Weaving pandanus fronds (R.)		50	80
16	10 c. Weaving a basket (R.)		50	80
17	15 c. Tiger Shark		2·25	1·25
18	20 c. Beating a pandanus leaf (R.)		1·25	1·50
	w. Wmk Crown to right of CA		70·00	
19	25 c. Loading copra		2·00	1·25
20	35 c. Fishing at night (Gold)		2·00	1·75
21	50 c. Local handicrafts		2·00	2·75
22	$1 Weaving coconut screens (R.)		4·00	9·00
	a. Opt double		£375	
3, 4, 7 and 12/22		*Set of 14*	15·00	21·00

*The normal sideways watermark shows Crown to left of CA, as seen from the back of the stamp.

3 Teraaka (training ship)

(Des J. Cooter. Litho Questa)

1979 (1 July). *Horiz designs as T 3. Multicoloured. W w 14 (sideways*). P 14.*

23	1 c. Type **3**		40	70
24	3 c. Tautunu (inter-island freighter)		60	80
25	4 c. Moorish Idol (fish)		30	70
26	5 c. Hibiscus		30	30
27	6 c. Eastern Reef Heron		1·50	90
28	7 c. Catholic Cathedral, Tarawa		30	30
29	8 c. Frangipani		30	30
30	10 c. Maneaba, Bikenibeu		30	30
31	12 c. Betio Harbour		45	45
32	15 c. Evening scene		55	45
33	20 c. Marakei Atoll		35	35
34	35 c. G.I.P.C. Chapel, Tangintebu		35	40
35	40 c. Flamboyant Tree		40	45
36	50 c. Hypolimnas bolina (butterfly)		2·25	1·75
	w. Wmk Crown to right of CA		27·00	
37	$1 Tabakea (Tarawa Lagoon ferry)		1·60	2·50
38	$2 National flag		1·60	2·50
23/38		*Set of 16*	9·50	11·00

*The normal sideways watermark shows Crown to left of CA, as seen from the back of the stamp.

For similar designs inscribed "KIRIBATI" see Nos. 86/99b and 121/35.

4 Church
5 Porcupine Fish Helmet

(Adapted P. Powell. Litho Questa)

1976 (15 Sept). *Christmas. Children's Drawings. T 4 and similar multicoloured designs. W w 14 (sideways on 5 and 35 c.). P 14.*

39	5 c. Type **4**		25	15
40	15 c. Feasting (vert)		35	15
41	20 c. Maneaba (vert)		40	30
42	35 c. Dancing		55	45
39/42		*Set of 4*	1·40	95

(Des J. Cooter. Litho J.W.)

1976 (6 Dec). *Artefacts. T 5 and similar vert designs. Multicoloured. W w 14. P 13.*

43	5 c. Type **5**		20	15
44	15 c. Shark's teeth dagger		30	35
45	20 c. Fighting gauntlet		30	40
46	35 c. Coconut body armour		45	45
43/6		*Set of 4*	1·10	1·25
MS47	140×130 mm. Nos. 43/6. P 14		5·00	13·00

6 Queen in Coronation Robes
7 Commodore Byron and H.M.S. Dolphin

(Des J. Cooter. Litho Questa)

1977 (7 Feb). *Silver Jubilee. T 6 and similar vert designs. Multicoloured. W w 14. P 14.*

48	8 c. Prince Charles' visit, 1970		10	10
49	20 c. Prince Philip's visit, 1959		15	15
50	40 c. Type **6**		20	35
48/50		*Set of 3*	40	55

(Des J. Cooter. Litho Questa)

1977 (1 June). *Explorers. T 7 and similar horiz designs. Multicoloured. W w 14 (sideways). P 14.*

51	5 c. Type **7**		55	1·50
52	15 c. Capt. Fanning and Betsey		65	2·75
53	20 c. Admiral Bellingshausen and Vostok		65	2·75
54	35 c. Capt. Wilkes and U.S.S. Vincennes		80	4·00
51/4		*Set of 4*	2·40	10·00

8 H.M.S. Resolution and H.M.S. Discovery
9 Scout Badge and Island Scene

(Des J. Cooter. Litho Questa)

1977 (12 Sept). *Christmas and Bicentenary of Capt. Cook's Discovery of Christmas Is. T 8 and similar multicoloured designs. W w 14 (sideways on 15 and 40 c.). P 14.*

55	8 c. Type **8**		30	10
56	15 c. Logbook entry (*horiz*)		30	15
57	20 c. Capt. Cook		40	20
58	40 c. Landing party (*horiz*)		40	60
55/8		*Set of 4*	1·25	95
MS59	140 × 140 mm. Nos. 55/8. Wmk sideways		4·50	10·00

(Des J. Cooter. Litho J.W.)

1977 (5 Dec). *50th Anniv of Scouting in the Gilbert Is. T 9 and similar multicoloured designs. W w 14 (sideways on 15 and 20 c.). P 13.*

60	8 c. Type **9**		30	10
61	15 c. Patrol meeting (*horiz*)		35	20
62	20 c. Mat making (*horiz*)		40	20
63	40 c. Canoeing		50	55
60/3		*Set of 4*	1·40	95

10 Taurus (The Bull)

11 Unicorn of Scotland

(Des J. Cooter. Litho Questa)

1978 (20 Feb). *Night Sky over the Gilbert Is. (1st series). T 10 and similar vert designs. W w 14. P 14.*

64	10 c. black and light new blue		35	20
65	20 c. black and light rose-red		40	35
66	25 c. black and sage-green		40	40
67	45 c. black and orange		60	70
64/7		*Set of 4*	1·60	1·50

Designs:—20 c. Canis Major (the Great Dog); 25 c. Scorpio (the Scorpion); 45 c. Orion (the Giant Warrior).
See also Nos. 465/8.

(Des C. Abbott. Litho Questa)

1978 (21 Apr). *25th Anniv of Coronation. T 11 and similar vert designs. P 15.*

68	45 c. green, bluish violet and silver		25	40
	a. Sheetlet. Nos. 68/70 × 2		1·25	
69	45 c. multicoloured		25	40
70	45 c. green, bluish violet and silver		25	40
68/70		*Set of 3*	65	1·10

Designs:—No. 68, Type **11**; No. 69, Queen Elizabeth II; No. 70, Great Frigate Bird.
Nos. 68/70 were printed together in small sheets of 6, containing two *se-tenant* strips of 3, with horizontal gutter margin between.

12 Birds in Flight to Tarawa

(Des I. Namakin (10 c.), M. Rubennang (20 c.), K. Titi (25 c.), M. Moreti (45 c.); adapted G. Hutchins. Litho Enschedé)

1978 (5 June). *25th Anniv of Return of King George V School to Tarawa. T 12 and similar horiz designs. Multicoloured. W w 14 (sideways). P 14×13.*

71	10 c. Type **12**		10	10
72	20 c. Tarawa, Abemama and school badge		20	20
73	25 c. Rejoicing islanders		20	20
74	45 c. King George V School on Tarawa and Abemama		35	35
71/4		*Set of 4*	75	75

13 "Te Kaue ni Maie"

14 H.M.S. *Endeavour*

(Des Mrs. M. Walsh. Litho J.W.)

1978 (25 Sept). *Christmas. Kaue (traditional head decorations). T 13 and similar horiz designs. Multicoloured. W w 14 (sideways*). P 14.*

75	10 c. Type **13**		10	10
76	20 c. "Te Itera"		15	15
77	25 c. "Te Bau"		20	20
78	45 c. "Te Tai"		25	30
75/8		*Set of 4*	60	65
MS79	149×99 mm. Nos. 75/8. P 13×13½		90	4·50
	w. Wmk Crown to right of CA		£130	

*The normal sideways watermark shows Crown to left of CA, as seen from the back of the stamp.

(Des and litho (45 c. also embossed) Walsall)

1979 (22 Feb*). *Bicentenary of Captain Cook's Voyages, 1768–79. T 14 and similar vert designs. P 11.*

80	10 c. multicoloured		20	15
81	20 c. multicoloured		25	30
82	25 c. black, light green and pale lilac		25	45
83	45 c. multicoloured		25	80
80/3		*Set of 4*	85	1·50

Designs:—20 c. Green Turtle; 25 c. Quadrant; 45 c. Flaxman/Wedgwood medallion of Captain Cook.
*This was the local issue date; the stamps were released in London on 15 January.

The Gilbert Islands achieved independence on 12 July 1979 and were renamed Kiribati.

KIRIBATI

INDEPENDENT

15 Kiribati Flag

(Des G. Drummond. Litho Questa)

1979 (12 July). *Independence. T 15 and similar horiz design. Multicoloured. W w 14 (sideways). P 14.*

84	10 c. Type **15**		10	25
85	45 c. Houses of Parliament and Maneaba ni Maungatabu (House of Assembly)		20	65

16 *Teraaka* (training ship)

17 Gilbert and Ellice Islands 1911 ½d. Stamp

(Des J. Cooter. Litho Questa)

1979 (12 July)–**80**. *Multicoloured designs as Nos. 23/32 and 34/8, some with values changed, inscribed "KIRIBATI" as T 16. W w 14 (sideways*). P 14.*

86	1 c. Type **16**		10	75
	w. Wmk Crown to right of CA		90·00	
87	3 c. *Tautunu* (inter-island freighter)		30	40
	w. Wmk Crown to right of CA		4·50	
88	5 c. Hibiscus		10	20
	w. Wmk Crown to right of CA		4·50	
89	7 c. Catholic Cathedral, Tarawa		10	20
90	10 c. Maneaba, Bikenibeu		10	20
	w. Wmk Crown to right of CA		4·50	
91	12 c. Betio Harbour		15	20
92	15 c. Eastern Reef Heron (as No. 27)		35	25
	w. Wmk Crown to right of CA		£130	
93	20 c. Flamboyant Tree (as No. 35)		20	25
94	25 c. Moorish Idol (fish) (as No. 25)		30	40
95	30 c. Frangipani (as No. 29)		25	30
96	35 c. G.I.P.C. Chapel, Tangintebu		25	30
97	50 c. *Hypolimnas bolina* (butterfly)		75	55
98	$1 *Tabakea* (Tarawa Lagoon ferry)		70	75
	w. Wmk Crown to right of CA		7·50	
99	$2 Evening scene (as No. 32)		50	80
	aw. Wmk Crown to right of CA		5·50	
99*b*	$5 National flag (as No. 38) (27.8.80)		1·10	3·00
86/99*b*		*Set of 15*	4·25	7·50

*The normal sideways watermark shows Crown to left of CA, as seen from the back of the stamp.
See also Nos. 121/35.

(Des J.W. Litho Questa)

1979 (4 Oct). *Death Centenary of Sir Rowland Hill. T 17 and similar vert designs showing stamps. Multicoloured. W w 14. P 14.*

100	10 c. Type **17**		10	10
101	20 c. Gilbert and Ellice Islands 1956 2s. 6d. definitive		15	20
102	25 c. Great Britain 1902 2s. 6d.		15	20
103	45 c. Gilbert and Ellice Islands 1924 10s.		25	35
	w. Wmk inverted			
100/3		*Set of 4*	60	75
MS104	113×110 mm. Nos. 100/3		90	1·00

International Year of the Child 1979

18 Boy with Giant Clam Shell

(Des D. Bowen. Litho Enschedé)

1979 (28 Nov). *International Year of the Child. T 18 and similar multicoloured designs. W w 14 (sideways* on 20 c.). P 13×13½ (20 c.) or 13½×13 (others).*

105	10 c. Type **18**		10	10
	w. Wmk inverted			
106	20 c. Child climbing coconut tree (*horiz*)		10	10
	w. Wmk Crown to left of CA			
107	45 c. Girl reading		15	20
108	$1 Child in costume		30	50
	w. Wmk inverted			
105/8		*Set of 4*	55	75

*The normal sideways watermark shows Crown to right of CA, as seen from the back of the stamp.

19 Downrange Station, Christmas Island

(Des J. Cooter. Litho Format)

1980 (20 Feb). *Satellite Tracking. T 19 and similar multicoloured designs. P 14½.*

109	25 c. Type **19**		10	10
110	45 c. Map of South Pacific showing trajectory of Experimental Communications Satellite		15	15
111	$1 Rocket launch, Tanegashima, Japan (*vert*)		30	35
109/11		*Set of 3*	50	55

20 T.S. *Teraaka*

(Des G. Drummond. Litho Format)

1980 (30 Apr). *"London 1980" International Stamp Exhibition. T 20 and similar horiz designs. Multicoloured. P 14½.*

112	12 c. Type **20**		15	10
113	25 c. Loading Air Tungaru Britten Norman Islander, Bonriki Airport		15	10
114	30 c. Radio operator		15	10
115	$1 Bairiki Post Office		20	35
112/15		*Set of 4*	60	50
MS116	139×116 mm. Nos. 112/15. P 14×14½.		75	85

Nos. 112/15 were each printed in sheets of 12 containing *se-tenant* stamp-size labels in positions 4 and 6.
Nos. 112/16 exist imperforate from stock dispersed by the liquidator of Format International Security Printers Ltd.

21 *Achaea janata*

(Des J. Cooter. Litho Questa)

1980 (27 Aug). *Moths. T 21 and similar horiz designs. Multi-coloured. P 14.*

117	12 c. Type **21**		10	10
118	25 c. *Ethmia nigroapicella*		15	15
119	30 c. *Utetheisa pulchelloides*		15	15
120	50 c. *Anua coronata*		25	25
117/20		*Set of 4*	60	60

1980 (27 Aug)–**81**. *As Nos. 86/99b but no wmk.*

121	1 c. Type **16** (18.2.81)		10	75
122	3 c. M.V. *Tautunu* (inter-island freighter) (6.1.81)		15	30
123	5 c. Hibiscus		10	15
124	7 c. Catholic Cathedral, Tarawa		10	15
125	10 c. Maneaba, Bikenibeu (19.11.80)		10	15
126	12 c. Betio Harbour (11.12.80)		20	30
127	15 c. Eastern Reef Heron (11.12.80)		1·00	40
128	20 c. Flamboyant Tree (6.1.81)		20	40
129	25 c. Moorish Idol (fish) (19.11.80)		30	30
130	30 c. Frangipani (18.2.81)		20	1·25
131	35 c. G.I.P.C. Chapel, Tangintebu (18.2.81)		20	1·25
132	50 c. *Hypolimnas bolina* (butterfly) (18.2.81)		85	2·00
133	$1 *Tabakea* (Tarawa Lagoon ferry) (11.12.80)		50	1·00
134	$2 Evening scene (11.12.80)		50	1·00
135	$5 National flag (11.12.80)		1·00	2·50
121/35		*Set of 15*	4·50	11·00

22 Captain Cook Hotel, Christmas Island

(Des J. Cooter. Litho Format)

1980 (19 Nov). *Development. T 22 and similar horiz designs. Multicoloured. P 13½ × 14.*

136	10 c. Type 22		10	10
137	20 c. Sports Stadium		10	10
138	25 c. International Airport, Bonriki		15	10
139	35 c. National Library and Archives, Bairiki		15	10
140	$1 Otintai Hotel, Bikenibeu		20	40
136/40		Set of 5	50	65

23 *Acalypha godseffiana*

(Des J. Cooter. Litho Format)

1981 (18 Feb). *Flowers. T 23 and similar vert designs. Multicoloured. W w 15. P 14 × 13½.*

141	12 c. Type 23		10	10
142	30 c. Hibiscus schizopetalus		15	15
143	35 c. Calotropis gigantea		15	15
144	50 c. Euphorbia pulcherrima		20	20
141/4		Set of 4	55	55

25 Maps of Abaiang and Marakei, and String Figures

(Des J. Cooter. Litho Format)

1981 (6 May). *Island Maps (1st series). T 25 and similar horiz designs. Multicoloured. W w 15 (sideways). P 13½ × 14.*

145	12 c. Type 25		15	10
146	30 c. Maps of Little Makin and Butaritari, and village house		20	10
147	35 c. Map of Maiana, and coral road		25	15
148	$1 Map of Christmas Island, and Captain Cook's H.M.S. Resolution		70	75
145/8		Set of 4	1·10	1·00

See also Nos. 201/4, 215/18, 237/40 , 256/60 and 270/3.

26 *Katherine*

27 Prince Charles and Lady Diana Spencer

(Des D. Shults. Litho Questa)

1981 (13 July–26 Nov). *Royal Wedding. Horiz designs as T 26, showing Royal Yachts, and T 27. Multicoloured.*

(a) W w 15. P 14.

149	12 c. Type 26		10	15
	aw. Wmk inverted		4·50	
	b. Sheetlet. No. 149×6 and No. 150		70	
	bw. Wmk inverted		70·00	
150	12 c. Type 27		20	30
	aw. Wmk inverted		40·00	
151	50 c. Osborne		25	40
	a. Sheetlet. No. 151×6 and No. 152		1·75	
152	50 c. Type 27		50	75
153	$2 Britannia		35	80
	a. Sheetlet. No. 153×6 and No. 154		3·25	
154	$2 Type 27		1·50	2·50
149/54		Set of 6	2·50	4·50
MS155	120×109 mm. $1.20, Type 27. Wmk sideways. P 12 (26 Nov)		75	1·00

(b) Booklet stamps. No wmk. P 12 (26 Nov)

156	12 c. Type 26		15	15
	a. Booklet pane. No. 156×4 with margins all round		50	
157	50 c. Type 27		65	80
	a. Booklet pane. No. 157×2 with margins all round		1·25	

Nos. 149/54 were printed in sheetlets of seven stamps of the same face value, each containing six of the "Royal Yacht" design and one as Type 27.

Nos. 156/7 come from $1.96 stamp booklets.

28 Tuna Bait Breeding Centre, Bonriki Fish Farm

(Des G. Drummond. Litho Questa)

1981 (19 Nov). *Tuna Fishing Industry. T 28 and similar horiz designs. Multicoloured. W w 15. P 14.*

158	12 c. Type 28		15	10
159	30 c. Tuna fishing		20	20
160	35 c. Cold storage, Betio		20	25
161	50 c. Government Tuna Fishing Vessel Nei Manganibuka		30	50
158/61		Set of 4	75	55
MS162	134×99 mm. Nos. 158/61. Wmk sideways*		1·00	1·40
	w. Wmk POST OFFICE reading upwards		30·00	

*The normal sideways watermark shows "POST OFFICE" reading downwards.

29 Pomarine Skua

(Des G. Drummond. Litho Questa)

1982 (18 Feb)–**85**. *Birds. Multicoloured designs as T 29. P 14.*

163	1 c. Type 29		15	15
164	2 c. Mallard		15	15
165	4 c. Collared Petrel		20	20
166	5 c. Blue-faced Booby		20	20
167	7 c. Friendly Quail Dove		20	20
168	8 c. Common Shoveler		20	20
169	12 c. Polynesian Reed Warbler		20	20
170	15 c. American Golden Plover		25	25
171	20 c. Eastern Reef Heron		30	30
171a	25 c. Common Noddy (31.1.83)		3·00	1·50
172	30 c. Brown Booby		30	30
173	35 c. Audubon's Shearwater		30	35
174	40 c. White-throated Storm Petrel (vert)		35	40
175	50 c. Bristle-thighed Curlew (vert)		40	40
175a	55 c. White Tern (inscr "Fairy Tern") (vert) (19.11.85)		11·00	16·00
176	$1 Kuhl's Lory (vert)		70	40
177	$2 Long-tailed Koel (vert)		90	55
178	$5 Great Frigate Bird (vert)		1·75	1·25
163/78		Set of 18	18·00	21·00

30 Riley Turbo Skyliner

(Des G. Drummond. Litho Format)

1982 (18 Feb). *Inauguration of Air Tungaru Airline. T 30 and similar horiz designs. Multicoloured. W w 15 (sideways*). P 14.*

179	12 c. Type 30		15	10
	w. Wmk POST OFFICE reading upwards		30·00	
180	30 c. Britten Norman "short nose" Trislander		20	20
181	35 c. Casa C-212 Aviocar		20	25
182	50 c. Boeing 727-200		30	35
179/82		Set of 4	75	75

*The normal sideways watermark shows "POST OFFICE" reading downwards.

No. 179 is inscr "De Havilland DH114 Heron" in error.

(Des D. Shults and J. Cooter. Litho Format)

1982 (19 May). *21st Birthday of Princess of Wales. T 31 and similar vert designs. Multicoloured. W w 15. P 13½ × 14.*

183	12 c. Type 31		10	10
184	50 c. Coat of arms of Mary of Teck		20	20
	w. Wmk inverted		5·00	
185	$1 Diana, Princess of Wales		30	35
183/5		Set of 3	50	55

The 12 c. design is incorrectly dated; Mary of Teck became Princess of Wales in 1901.

1982 (14 July). *Birth of Prince William of Wales. Nos. 183/5 optd with T 19 of St. Kitts.*

186	12 c. Type 31		10	10
187	50 c. Coat of arms of Mary of Teck		25	25
	a. Opt inverted		8·00	
	w. Wmk inverted		17·00	
188	$1 Diana, Princess of Wales		40	45
186/8		Set of 3	65	70

31 Mary of Teck, Princess of Wales, 1893

32 First Aid Practice

(Des J. Cooter. Litho Format)

1982 (12 Aug). *75th Anniv of Boy Scout Movement. T 32 and similar horiz designs. Multicoloured. W w 15 (sideways). P 13½ × 14.*

189	12 c. Type 32		20	15
190	25 c. Boat repairs		20	30
191	30 c. On parade		25	35
192	50 c. Gilbert Islands 1977 8 c. Scouting stamp and "75"		25	60
189/92		Set of 4	80	1·25

33 Queen and Duke of Edinburgh with Local Dancer

(Des PAD Studio. Litho Walsall)

1982 (23 Oct). *Royal Visit. T 33 and similar horiz designs. Multicoloured. W w 15 (sideways*). P 14.*

193	12 c. Type 33		15	15
194	25 c. Queen, Duke of Edinburgh and outrigger canoe		20	20
	w. Wmk POST OFFICE reading upwards		40·00	
195	35 c. New Philatelic Bureau building		30	30
	w. Wmk POST OFFICE reading upwards		65·00	
193/5		Set of 3	60	60
MS196	88×76 mm. 50 c. Queen Elizabeth II		60	60

*The normal sideways watermark shows "POST OFFICE" reading downwards.

On No. **MS**196 the captions on the map for the islands of Teraina and Tabuaeren have been transposed.

34 "Obaia, The Feathered" (Kiribati legend)

(Des J.W. Litho Format)

1983 (14 Mar). *Commonwealth Day. T 34 and similar horiz designs. Multicoloured. W w 15 (sideways*). P 14.*

197	12 c. Type 34		10	10
	w. Wmk POST OFFICE reading upwards		10·00	
198	30 c. Robert Louis Stevenson Hotel, Abemama		15	10
	w. Wmk POST OFFICE reading upwards		7·00	
199	50 c. Container ship off Betio		15	25
	w. Wmk POST OFFICE reading upwards		5·00	
200	$1 Map of Kiribati		20	50
	w. Wmk POST OFFICE reading upwards		20·00	
197/200		Set of 4	50	90

*The normal sideways watermark shows "POST OFFICE" reading downwards.

(Des J. Cooter. Litho Format)

1983 (19 May). *Island Maps (2nd series). Multicoloured designs as T 25. W w 15 (sideways* on 12 and 25 c.). P 13½×14 (horiz) or 14×13½ (vert).*

201	12 c. Beru, Nikunau and canoe		20	15
	w. Wmk POST OFFICE reading upwards		16·00	
202	25 c. Abemama, Aranuka, Kuria and fish		20	20
	w. Wmk POST OFFICE reading upwards		8·00	
203	35 c. Nonouti and reef fishing (vert)		25	35
	w. Wmk inverted		11·00	
204	50 c. Tarawa and House of Assembly (vert)		30	50
	w. Wmk inverted		13·00	
201/4		Set of 4	85	1·00

*The normal sideways watermark shows "POST OFFICE" reading downwards.

No. 202 exists imperforate from stock dispersed by the liquidator of Format International Security Printers Ltd.

35 Collecting Coconuts

(Des G. Drummond. Litho Questa)

1983 (8 Aug). *Copra Industry. T 35 and similar horiz designs. Multicoloured. W w 15. P 14.*

205	12 c. Type 35		25	20
206	25 c. Selecting coconuts for copra		45	35
207	30 c. Removing husks		45	40
208	35 c. Drying copra		45	45
209	50 c. Loading copra at Betio		50	55
205/9		Set of 5	1·90	1·75

36 War Memorials

(Des J. Cooter. Litho Format)

1983 (17 Nov). *40th Anniv of Battle of Tarawa. T 36 and similar horiz designs. Multicoloured. W w 15 (sideways*). P 14.*
210	12 c. Type 36	15	15
211	30 c. Maps of Tarawa and Pacific Ocean	25	30
	w. Wmk POST OFFICE reading upwards	2·25	
212	35 c. Gun emplacement	25	35
	w. Wmk POST OFFICE reading upwards	20·00	
213	50 c. Modern and war-time landscapes	35	55
	w. Wmk POST OFFICE reading upwards	20·00	
214	$1 Aircraft carrier U.S.S. *Tarawa*	55	75
210/14	Set of 5	1·40	1·90

*The normal sideways watermark shows "POST OFFICE" reading downwards.

(Des J. Cooter. Litho Format)

1984 (14 Feb). *Island Maps (3rd series). Multicoloured designs as T 25. W w 15 (sideways). P 13½ × 14.*
215	12 c. Teraina and Captain Fanning's ship *Betsey*, 1799	25	15
216	30 c. Nikumaroro and Hawksbill Turtle	30	35
217	35 c. Kanton and local postmark	35	40
218	50 c. Banaba and Flying Fish	40	55
215/18	Set of 4	1·10	1·25

37 Tug *Riki*

(Des J. Cooter. Litho J.W.)

1984 (9 May). *Kiribati Shipping Corporation. T 37 and similar horiz designs. Multicoloured. W w 15 (sideways*). P 14.*
219	12 c. Type 37	50	15
	w. Wmk POST OFFICE reading downwards		
220	35 c. Ferry *Nei Nimanoa*	90	35
	w. Wmk POST OFFICE reading downwards		
221	50 c. Ferry *Nei Tebaa*	1·25	60
	w. Wmk POST OFFICE reading downwards		
222	$1 Cargo ship *Nei Momi*	1·50	1·10
219/22	Set of 4	3·75	2·00
MS223	115×98 mm. Nos. 219/22. P 13×13½	3·25	5·00
	w. Wmk POST OFFICE reading downwards		

*The normal sideways watermark shows "POST OFFICE" reading upwards.

38 Water and Sewage Schemes

(Des J. Cooter. Litho Format)

1984 (21 Aug). *"Ausipex" International Stamp Exhibition, Melbourne. T 38 and similar horiz designs. Multicoloured. W w 15 (sideways). P 13½ × 14.*
224	12 c. Type 38	20	15
225	30 c. *Nouamake* (game fishing boat)	25	30
226	35 c. Overseas training schemes	25	40
227	50 c. International communications link	35	55
224/7	Set of 4	95	1·25

39 "Tabakea supporting Banaba"

(Des Jennifer Toombs. Litho Format)

1984 (21 Nov). *Kiribati Legends (1st series). T 39 and similar horiz designs. Multicoloured. W w 15 (sideways). P 14.*
228	12 c. Type 39	15	20
229	30 c. "Nakaa, Judge of the Dead"	20	35
230	35 c. "Naareau and Dragonfly"	20	45
231	50 c. "Whistling Ghosts"	30	55
228/31	Set of 4	75	1·40

See also Nos. 245/8.

40 Sail-finned Tang

(Des G. Drummond. Litho Questa)

1985 (19 Feb). *Reef Fishes. T 40 and similar horiz designs. Multicoloured. W w 15. P 14.*
232	12 c. Type 40	60	25
	w. Wmk inverted	6·50	
233	25 c. Picasso Triggerfish	1·00	65
	w. Wmk inverted	6·50	
234	35 c. Clown Surgeonfish	1·25	85
	w. Wmk inverted		
235	80 c. Red Squirrelfish	2·00	2·50
	w. Wmk inverted		
232/5	Set of 4	4·25	3·75
MS236	140×107 mm. Nos. 232/5. Wmk sideways*	6·00	4·75
	w. Wmk POST OFFICE reading upwards	27·00	

*The normal sideways watermark shows "POST OFFICE" reading upwards.

(Des J. Cooter. Litho J.W.)

1985 (9 May). *Island Maps (4th series). Horiz designs as T 25. Multicoloured. W w 15 (sideways*). P 13½.*
237	12 c. Tabuaeran and Great Frigate Bird	75	15
	w. Wmk POST OFFICE reading downwards	32·00	
238	35 c. Rawaki and germinating coconuts	1·40	40
	w. Wmk POST OFFICE reading downwards	17·00	
239	50 c. Arorae and Xanthid Crab	1·60	65
	w. Wmk POST OFFICE reading downwards		
240	$1 Tamana and fish hook	2·25	1·25
	w. Wmk POST OFFICE reading downwards	8·00	
237/40	Set of 4	5·50	2·25

*The normal sideways watermark shows "POST OFFICE" reading upwards.

41 Youths playing Football on Beach

(Des R. Stokes. Litho Cambec Press, Melbourne)

1985 (5 Aug). *International Youth Year. T 41 and similar multicoloured designs. P 13½.*
241	15 c. Type 41	75	70
242	35 c. Logos of I.Y.Y. and Kiribati Youth Year	1·10	1·40
243	40 c. Girl preparing food (vert)	1·25	1·60
244	55 c. Map illustrating Kiribati's youth exchange links	1·40	2·25
241/4	Set of 4	4·00	5·50

(Des Jennifer Toombs. Litho Questa)

1985 (19 Nov). *Kiribati Legends (2nd series). Horiz designs as T 39. Multicoloured. P 14.*
245	15 c. "Nang Kineia and the Tickling Ghosts'	50	30
246	35 c. "Auriaria and Tituabine"	85	85
247	40 c. "The first coming of Babai at Arorae"	1·00	1·25
248	55 c. "Riiki and the Milky Way"	1·25	1·75
245/8	Set of 4	3·25	3·75

42 Map showing Telecommunications Satellite Link

(Litho Walsall)

1985 (9 Dec). *Transport and Telecommunications Decade (1st issue). T 42 and similar horiz design. Multicoloured. P 14.*
249	15 c. Type 42	1·50	1·00
250	40 c. M.V. *Moanaraoi* (Tarawa-Suva service)	2·75	3·00

See also Nos. 268/9, 293/4 and 314/15.

(Des A. Theobald. Litho Questa)

1986 (21 Apr). *60th Birthday of Queen Elizabeth II. Vert designs as T 230a of Jamaica. Multicoloured. P 14½×14.*
251	15 c. Princess Elizabeth in Girl Guide uniform, Windsor Castle, 1938	15	15
252	35 c. At Trooping the Colour, 1980	20	30
253	40 c. With Duke of Edinburgh in Kiribati, 1982	20	35
254	55 c. At banquet, Austrian Embassy, London, 1966	25	50
255	$1 At Crown Agents Head Office, London, 1983	45	1·25
251/5	Set of 5	1·10	2·25

(Des J. Cooter. Litho Questa)

1986 (17 June). *Island Maps (5th series). Horiz designs as T 25. Multicoloured. P 13½×14.*
256	15 c. Manra and Coconut Crab	1·75	85
257	30 c. Birnie and McKean Islands and cowrie shells	2·75	2·00
258	35 c. Orona and Red-footed Booby	3·25	2·25
259	40 c. Malden Island and whaling ship, 1844	3·25	3·00
260	55 c. Vostok, Flint and Caroline Islands and Bellingshausen's *Vostok*, 1820	3·25	3·50
256/60	Set of 5	13·00	10·50

 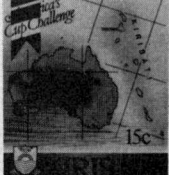

43 *Lepidodactylus lugubris*   **44** Maps of Australia and Kiribati

(Des G. Drummond. Litho Questa)

1986 (26 Aug). *Geckos. T 43 and similar horiz designs. Multicoloured. P 14.*
261	15 c. Type 43	1·50	70
262	35 c. *Gehyra mutilata*	1·75	1·50
263	40 c. *Hemidactylus frenatus*	1·90	1·75
264	55 c. *Gehyra oceanica*	2·25	2·50
261/4	Set of 4	6·75	5·75

(Des D. Miller. Litho Format)

1986 (29 Dec). *America's Cup Yachting Championship. T 44 and similar vert designs. Multicoloured. P 13½×14.*
265	15 c. Type 44	20	65
	a. Horiz strip of 3. Nos. 265/7	1·50	
266	55 c. America's Cup and map of course	50	1·25
267	$1.50, *Australia II* (1983 winner)	1·00	1·50
265/7	Set of 3	1·50	3·00

Nos. 265/7 were printed together, *se-tenant*, in horizontal strips of 3 throughout the sheet with the $1.50 at left and the 15 c. at centre of each strip.

45 Freighter *Moamoa*   (45a)

(Des and litho Questa)

1987 (31 Mar). *Transport and Telecommunications Decade (2nd issue). T 45 and similar horiz design. Multicoloured. P 13½×14.*
268	30 c. Type 45	2·25	2·25
269	55 c. Telephone switchboard and automatic exchange	3·25	3·50

(Des J. Cooter. Litho Format)

1987 (22 Sept). *Island Maps (6th series). Multicoloured designs as T 25, but vert. P 14×13½.*
270	15 c. Starbuck and White-tailed Tropic Bird	55	60
271	30 c. Enderbury and White Tern	65	65
272	55 c. Tabiteuea and Pandanus Tree	65	80
273	$1 Onotoa and okai (house)	70	2·00
270/3	Set of 4	2·25	3·50

Nos. 271/3 exist imperforate from stock dispersed by the liquidator of Format International Security Printers Ltd.

(Des G. Drummond. Litho Format)

1987 (27 Oct). *Skinks. Horiz designs as T 43. Multicoloured. P 15.*
274	15 c. *Emoia nigra*	15	20
275	35 c. *Cryptoblepharus sp.*	20	35
276	40 c. *Emoia cyanura*	25	45
277	$1 *Lipinia noctua*	40	1·00
274/7	Set of 4	90	1·75
MS278	130×114 mm. Nos. 274/7	1·10	3·25

Nos. 274/8 exist imperforate from stock dispersed by the liquidator of Format International Security Printers Ltd.

1987 (30 Nov). *Royal Ruby Wedding. Nos. 251/5 optd with T 45a in silver.*
279	15 c. Princess Elizabeth in Girl Guide uniform, Windsor Castle, 1938	15	25
280	35 c. At Trooping the Colour, 1980	20	30
281	40 c. With Duke of Edinburgh in Kiribati, 1982	25	35
282	55 c. At banquet, Austrian Embassy, London, 1966	30	45
283	$1 At Crown Agents Head Office, London, 1983	50	1·25
279/83	Set of 5	1·25	2·40

46 Henri Dunant (founder) **47** Causeway built by Australia

(Des A. Theobald. Litho Questa)

1988 (9 May). *125th Anniv of International Red Cross. T 46 and similar vert designs. Multicoloured. P 14½×14.*
284	15 c. Type **46**	80	65
285	35 c. Red Cross workers in Independence parade, 1979	1·25	1·50
286	40 c. Red Cross workers with patient	1·25	1·60
287	55 c. Gilbert & Ellice Islands 1970 British Red Cross Centenary 10 c. stamp	1·60	1·75
284/7	*Set of 4*	4·50	5·00

(Des CPE Australia Ltd ($2), D. Miller (others). Litho CPE Australia Ltd, Melbourne ($2), Format (others))

1988 (30 July). *Bicentenary of Australian Settlement and "Sydpex '88" National Stamp Exhibition, Sydney. T 47 and similar horiz designs. Multicoloured. P 14½.*
288	15 c. Type **47**	25	20
289	35 c. Capt. Cook and Pacific map	60	60
290	$1 Obverse of Australian $10 Bicentenary banknote	1·25	1·75
	a. Horiz pair. Nos. 290/1	2·50	3·50
291	$1 Reverse of $10 Bicentenary banknote	1·25	1·75
288/91	*Set of 4*	3·00	3·75
MS292	95 × 76 mm. $2 *Logistic Ace* (container ship) (37 × 26 mm). P 13½ × 14	3·00	4·00

Nos. 290/1 were printed together, *se-tenant*, in horizontal pairs throughout the sheet.
No. MS292 also commemorates the 150th anniversary of the first screw-driven steamship.

48 Manual Telephone Exchange and Map of Kiritimati

(Des A. Theobald. Litho Questa)

1988 (28 Dec). *Transport and Telecommunications Decade (3rd issue). T 48 and similar horiz design. Multicoloured. W w 14 (sideways). P 14.*
293	35 c. Type **48**	75	75
294	45 c. Betio–Bairiki Causeway	1·00	1·00

49 *Hound* (brigantine), 1835   **50** Eastern Reef Heron

(Des E. Nisbet. Litho Questa)

1989 (28 May). *Nautical History (1st series). T 49 and similar horiz designs. Multicoloured. W w 16 (sideways). P 14½.*
295	15 c. Type **49**	90	55
296	30 c. *Phantom* (brig), 1854	1·50	1·10
297	40 c. H.M.S. *Alacrity* (schooner), 1873	1·60	1·60
298	$1 *Charles W. Morgan* (whaling ship), 1851	3·00	3·75
295/8	*Set of 4*	6·25	6·25

See also Nos. 343/7 and 523/6.

(Des D. Johnstone. Litho Questa)

1989 (28 June). *Birds with Young. T 50 and similar vert designs. Multicoloured. W w 16. P 14½.*
299	15 c. Type **50**	1·25	1·50
	a. Vert pair. Nos. 299/300	2·50	3·00
300	15 c. Eastern Reef Heron chicks in nest	1·25	1·50
301	$1 White-tailed Tropic Bird	2·50	3·25
	a. Vert pair. Nos. 301/2	5·00	6·50
302	$1 Young White-tailed Tropic Bird	2·50	3·25
299/302	*Set of 4*	6·50	8·50

Nos. 299/300 and 301/2 were each printed together, *se-tenant*, in vertical pairs throughout the sheets, each pair forming a composite design.

COVER PRICES

51 House of Assembly   **51a** "Apollo 10" on Launch Gantry

(Des D. Miller. Litho Cartor)

1989 (12 July). *10th Anniv of Independence. T 51 and similar vert design. Multicoloured. W w 16 (inverted). P 13½×14.*
303	15 c. Type **51**	25	25
304	$1 Constitution	1·25	1·75

(Des A. Theobald ($2.50), D. Miller (others). Litho Questa)

1989 (20 July). *20th Anniv of First Manned Landing on Moon. T 51a and similar multicoloured designs. W w 16 (sideways on 50, 60 c.) P 14×13½ (20, 75 c.) or 14 (others).*
305	20 c. Type **51a**	30	30
306	50 c. Crew of "Apollo 10" (30×30 mm)	70	90
307	60 c. "Apollo 10" emblem (30×30 mm)	80	1·00
308	75 c. "Apollo 10" splashdown, Hawaii	95	1·25
305/8	*Set of 4*	2·50	3·00
MS309	82×100 mm. $2.50, "Apollo 11" command module in lunar orbit. P 14×13½	5·50	6·50

51b Gilbert and Ellice Islands, 1949 75th Anniv of U.P.U. 3d. Stamp   **51c** Examining Fragment of Statue

(Des D. Miller. Litho Walsall)

1989 (7 Aug*). *"Philexfrance 89" International Stamp Exhibition, Paris, and "World Stamp Expo '89", Washington (1st issue). Sheet 104×86 mm. W w 16. P 14×13½.*
MS310	**51b** $2 multicoloured	3·50	4·50

*This is the local date of issue. The agents, Caphco Ltd, placed stocks on sale in London and Paris from 7 July.

(Des D. Miller, adapted Walsall. Litho Walsall)

1989 (25 Sept). *"Philexfrance 89" International Stamp Exhibition, Paris, and "World Stamp Expo '89", Washington (2nd issue). T 51c and similar vert designs, showing Statue of Liberty. Multicoloured. W w 14. P 14×13½.*
311	35 c. Type **51c**	1·10	1·40
	a. Sheetlet. Nos. 311/13	3·00	
312	35 c. Workman drilling Statue	1·10	1·40
313	35 c. Surveyor with drawing	1·10	1·40
311/13	*Set of 3*	3·75	

Nos. 311/13 were printed, *se-tenant*, in sheetlets of 3.

52 Telecommunications Centre   (**53**)

(Des L. Curtis. Litho Questa)

1989 (16 Oct). *Transport and Telecommunications Decade (4th issue). T 52 and similar horiz design. Multicoloured. W w 16 (sideways). P 14.*
314	30 c. Type **52**	1·50	1·25
315	75 c. *Mataburo* (inter-island freighter)	3·00	3·75

1989 (21 Oct). *"Melbourne Stampshow '89". Nos. 301/2 optd with T 53.*
316	$1 White-tailed Tropic Bird	3·00	3·50
	a. Vert pair. Nos. 316/17	6·00	7·00
317	$1 Young White-tailed Tropic Bird	3·00	3·50

54 Virgin and Child (detail, "The Adoration of the Holy Child" (Denys Calvert))   **55** Gilbert and Ellice Islands 1912 1d. and G.B. Twopence Blue Stamps

(Des D. Miller. Litho Questa)

1989 (1 Dec). *Christmas. T 54 and similar vert designs showing paintings. Multicoloured. W w 16. P 14.*
318	10 c. Type **53**	65	30
319	15 c. "The Adoration of the Holy Child" (Denys Calvert)	85	40
320	55 c. "The Holy Family and St. Elizabeth" (Rubens)	2·50	1·25
321	$1 "Madonna with Child and Maria Magdalena" (School of Correggio)	3·75	6·00
318/21	*Set of 4*	7·00	7·00

(Des D. Miller. Litho Questa)

1990 (1 May). *150th Anniv of the Penny Black and "Stamp World London 90" International Stamp Exhibition. T 55 and similar horiz designs. Multicoloured. W w 16 (sideways). P 14.*
322	15 c. Type **55**	90	55
323	50 c. Gilbert and Ellice Islands 1911 ½d. and G.B. Penny Black	2·25	2·25
324	60 c. Kiribati 1982 1 c. bird and G.B. 1870 ½d.	2·25	2·25
325	$1 Gilbert Islands 1976 1 c. ship and G.B. 1841 1d. red-brown	2·75	3·25
322/5	*Set of 4*	7·25	7·50

56 Blue-barred Orange Parrotfish

(Des G. Drummond. Litho Questa)

1990 (12 July). *Fishes. T 56 and similar horiz designs. Multicoloured. W w 14 (sideways). "1990" imprint date. P 14.*
326	1 c. Type **56**	30	60
327	5 c. Honeycomb Grouper	45	60
328	10 c. Blue-finned Trevally	55	70
329	15 c. Hump-backed Snapper	70	40
330	20 c. Variegated Emperor	75	60
331	25 c. Rainbow Runner	80	65
332	30 c. Black-saddled Coral Grouper	90	65
333	35 c. Great Barracuda	1·00	75
334	40 c. Convict Tang	1·00	80
335	50 c. Violet Squirrelfish	1·25	90
336	60 c. Stocky Hawkfish	1·75	1·40
337	75 c. Pennant Coralfish	1·90	1·60
338	$1 Common Blue-striped Snapper ("Yellow and Blue Sea Perch")	2·25	1·90
339	$2 Sailfish	3·25	4·50
340	$5 White-tipped Reef Shark	6·50	9·50
326/40	*Set of 15*	21·00	23·00

For 23 c. value watermarked w 16 (sideways) see No. 356.

(Des D. Miller. Litho Questa)

1990 (4 Aug). *90th Birthday of Queen Elizabeth the Queen Mother. Vert designs as T 107 (75 c.) or 108 ($2) of Kenya. W w 16. P 14×15 (75 c.) or 14½ ($2).*
341	75 c. multicoloured	1·25	1·50
342	$2 brownish black and myrtle-green	2·75	3·50

Designs:—75 c. Queen Elizabeth the Queen Mother; $2 King George VI and Queen Elizabeth with air raid victim, London, 1940.

(Des E. Nisbet. Litho Questa)

1990 (5 Nov). *Nautical History (2nd series). Horiz designs as T 49. Multicoloured. W w 16 (sideways). P 14½.*
343	15 c. *Herald* (whaling ship), 1851	75	55
344	50 c. *Belle* (barque), 1849	1·50	1·50
345	60 c. *Supply* (schooner), 1851	1·75	2·25
346	75 c. *Triton* (whaling ship), 1848	1·75	2·25
343/6	*Set of 4*	5·25	6·00
MS347	95×75 mm. $2 *Charlotte* (convict transport), 1789	6·50	7·50

57 Manta   **58** Queen Elizabeth II

(Des G. Drummond. Litho Questa).

1991 (17 Jan). *Endangered Species. Fishes. T 57 and similar horiz designs. Multicoloured.* W w 14 (sideways). P 14.
348	15 c. Type 57	1·10	55
349	20 c. Manta Ray (different)	1·25	90
350	30 c. Whale Shark	1·75	2·00
351	35 c. Whale Shark (different)	2·00	2·25
348/51	Set of 4	5·50	5·25

1991 (30 Apr). *Horiz design as Nos. 326/40, but W w 16 (sideways). "1991" imprint date. P 14.*
356	23 c. Bennett's Pufferfish	80	80

(Des D. Miller. Litho Questa)

1991 (17 June). *65th Birthday of Queen Elizabeth II and 70th Birthday of Prince Philip. T 58 and similar vert design. Multicoloured.* W w 16 (sideways). P 14½×14.
366	65 c. Type 58	1·25	1·50
	a. Horiz pair. Nos. 366/7 separated by label	2·50	3·00
367	70 c. Prince Philip in R.A.F. uniform	1·25	1·50

Nos. 366/7 were printed together, *se-tenant*, in sheetlets of 10 (2×5) with designs alternating and the vertical rows separated by inscribed labels.

59 Aerial View of Hospital

(Des G. Vasarhelyi. Litho Questa)

1991 (16 Nov). *"Phila Nippon '91" International Stamp Exhibition, Tokyo, and Opening of Tungaru Central Hospital. T 59 and similar horiz designs. Multicoloured.* W w 16 (sideways). P 13½×14.
368	23 c. Type 59	40	30
369	50 c. Traditional dancers	75	85
370	60 c. Hospital entrance	85	1·10
371	75 c. Foundation stone and plaques	1·25	1·60
368/71	Set of 4	3·00	3·50
MS372	125×83 mm. $5 Casualty on trolley and ambulance	6·00	7·00

60 Mother and Child   **(61)**

(Des G. Vasarhelyi. Litho Questa)

1991 (2 Dec). *Christmas. T 60 and similar horiz designs. Multicoloured.* W w 14 (sideways). P 14.
373	23 c. Type 60	60	40
374	50 c. The Holy Family in Pacific setting	1·10	90
375	60 c. The Holy Family in traditional setting	1·25	1·50
376	75 c. Adoration of the Shepherds	1·50	2·00
373/6	Set of 4	4·00	4·25

(Des D. Miller. Litho Questa)

1992 (6 Feb). *40th Anniv of Queen Elizabeth II's Accession. Horiz designs as T 113 of Kenya.* W w 14 (sideways). P 14.
377	23 c. Kiribati village	30	30
378	30 c. Lagoon at sunset	40	45
379	50 c. Tarawa waterfront	60	70
380	60 c. Three portraits of Queen Elizabeth	70	90
381	75 c. Queen Elizabeth II	90	1·10
377/81	Set of 5	2·50	3·00

1992 (6 June). *"EXPO '92" Worlds Fair, Seville. Nos. 356, 336/7 and 339 optd with T 61.*
382	23 c. Bennett's Pufferfish	55	40
383	60 c. Stocky Hawkfish	1·25	1·50
384	75 c. Pennant Coralfish	1·40	1·60
385	$2 Sailfish	3·00	4·00
382/5	Set of 4	5·50	6·75

62 Marine Training Centre Sign

(Des A. Theobald. Litho Questa)

1992 (28 Aug). *25th Anniv of Marine Training Centre. T 62 and similar horiz designs. Multicoloured.* W w 16 (sideways). P 14.
386	23 c. Type 62	45	40
387	50 c. Cadets on parade	80	1·00
388	60 c. Fire school	80	1·00
389	75 c. Lifeboat training	1·10	1·40
386/9	Set of 4	2·75	3·50

---

63 Healthy Children   **64** Phoenix Petrel

(Des O. Ball. Litho Questa)

1992 (1 Dec). *United Nations World Health and Food/ Agriculture Organizations. T 63 and similar horiz designs. Multicoloured.* W w 14 (sideways). P 14.
390	23 c. Type 63	55	50
391	50 c. Fishing at night	1·00	1·00
392	60 c. Fruit	1·25	1·50
393	75 c. Papuan Chief (container ship)	1·75	2·25
390/3	Set of 4	4·00	4·75

(Des N. Arlott. Litho Questa)

1993 (28 May). *Birds. T 64 and similar vert designs. Multicoloured.* W w 14. P 14½×14.
394	23 c. Type 64	40	50
	a. Horiz pair. Nos. 394/5	80	1·00
395	23 c. Cook's Petrel	40	50
396	60 c. Pintail	90	1·10
	a. Horiz pair. Nos. 396/7	1·75	2·10
397	60 c. European Wigeon	90	1·10
398	75 c. Spectacled Tern	1·00	1·25
	a. Horiz pair. Nos. 398/9	2·00	2·50
399	75 c. Black-naped Tern	1·00	1·25
400	$1 Australian Stilt	1·25	1·40
	a. Horiz pair. Nos. 400/1	2·50	2·75
401	$1 Wandering Tattler	1·25	1·40
394/401	Set of 8	6·25	7·50

Nos. 394/5, 396/7, 398/9 and 400/1 were each printed together, *se-tenant*, in horizontal pairs throughout the sheets.

65 Chilocorus nigritus   **66** U.S. Air Reconnaissance Consolidated B-24 Liberator

(Des I. Loe. Litho Questa)

1993 (23 Aug). *Insects. T 65 and similar vert designs. Multicoloured.* W w 14. P 14½×14.
402	23 c. Type 65	85	55
403	60 c. Rodolia pumila (ladybird)	1·75	2·00
404	75 c. Rodolia cardinalis (ladybird)	2·00	2·25
405	$1 Cryptolaemus montrouzieri	2·25	2·75
402/5	Set of 4	6·25	6·75

(Des J. Batchelor. Litho Questa)

1993 (1 Nov). *50th Anniv of Battle of Tarawa. T 66 and similar horiz designs. Multicoloured.* W w 14 (sideways). P 14.
406	23 c. Type 66	60	65
	a. Sheetlet. Nos. 406/15	5·50	
407	23 c. U.S.S. Nautilus (submarine)	60	65
408	23 c. U.S.S. Indianapolis (cruiser)	60	65
409	23 c. U.S.S. Pursuit (destroyer)	60	65
410	23 c. Vought Sikorsky OS2U Kingfisher spotter seaplane	60	65
411	23 c. U.S.S. Ringgold and U.S.S. Dashiell (destroyers)	60	65
412	23 c. Sherman tank on seabed	60	65
413	23 c. Grumman F6F Hellcat fighter aircraft in lagoon	60	65
414	23 c. Naval wreck on seabed	60	65
415	23 c. First U.S. aircraft to land on Betio	60	65
416	75 c. Landing craft leaving transports	1·00	1·10
	a. Sheetlet. Nos. 416/25	9·00	
417	75 c. Marines landing on Betio	1·00	1·10
418	75 c. Landing craft approaching beach	1·00	1·10
419	75 c. Marines pinned down in surf	1·00	1·10
420	75 c. U.S.S. Maryland (battleship)	1·00	1·10
421	75 c. Aerial view of Betio Island	1·00	1·10
422	75 c. U.S. Navy memorial	1·00	1·10
423	75 c. Memorial to expatriates	1·00	1·10
424	75 c. Japanese memorial	1·00	1·10
425	75 c. Plan of Betio Island	1·00	1·10
406/25	Set of 20	14·50	16·00

Nos. 406/15 and 416/25 were each printed together, *se-tenant*, in sheetlets of 10 with the stamps arranged in two horizontal strips of 5 separated by a gutter showing Dauntless dive bomber over Betio (23 c.) and abandoned military relics (75 c.).

NEW INFORMATION

The editor is always interested to correspond with people who have new information that will improve or correct the Catalogue.

STAMPCARDS. Four Stampcards in the above design, each measuring 85×54 mm, with face values of 40 c., $1, $1.20 and $1.60, were supplied to Kiribati by the Swedish manufacturers in 1993. Each card consists of six self-adhesive stamps, separated by roulettes, with a detachable label, indicating the class of mail for which each value was valid, at left.

The four Kiribati Stampcards were announced as being issued on 1 November 1993 on a new type of postmark struck across the stamps, also carry a Betio Post Office Postage Paid mark of 20 December 1993.

It has been reported that Stampcards were only available from the Philatelic Bureau and were not accepted by the ordinary post offices as being valid for postage, although this is contradicted by the Controller of Postal Services. Covers posted by members of the general public at the Philatelic Bureau franked with stamps taken from them show both the special type of postmark and a Betio Postage Paid handstamp.

67 Shepherds and Angels

(Des G. Vasarhelyi. Litho Questa)

1993 (1 Dec). *Christmas. T 67 and similar horiz designs showing Pacific Nativity scenes. Multicoloured.* W w 14 (sideways). P 13½×14.
426	23 c. Type 67	30	25
427	40 c. Three Kings	55	60
428	60 c. Holy Family	85	1·00
429	75 c. Virgin and Child	1·10	1·40
426/9	Set of 4	2·50	3·00
MS430	100×81 mm. $3 Virgin and Child (different)	3·75	4·50

68 Group of Dogs

(Des G. Vasarhelyi. Litho Questa)

1994 (18 Feb). *"Hong Kong '94" International Stamp Exhibition. Chinese New Year ("Year of the Dog"). Sheet 120×90 mm.* W w 14 (sideways). P 14.
MS431	68 $3 multicoloured	4·00	4·50

69 Bryde's Whale and Calf   **70** Family silhouetted on Beach

(Des G. Drummond. Litho Questa)

1994 (2 May). *Whales. T 69 and similar horiz designs. Multicoloured.* W w 14 (sideways). P 14×14½.
432	23 c. Type 69	90	1·00
	a. Horiz pair. Nos. 432/3	1·75	2·00
433	23 c. Bryde's Whale with two calves	90	1·00
434	40 c. Blue Whale and calf (face value at left)	1·10	1·25
	a. Horiz pair. Nos. 434/5	2·10	2·50
435	40 c. Blue Whales and calf (face value at right)	1·10	1·25
436	60 c. Humpback Whale and calf (face value at left)	1·75	2·25
	a. Horiz pair. Nos. 436/7	3·50	4·50
437	60 c. Humpback Whale and calf (face value at right)	1·75	2·25
438	75 c. Killer Whale and calf	1·75	2·25
	a. Horiz pair. Nos.	3·50	4·50
439	75 c. Killer Whale and two calves	1·75	2·25
432/9	Set of 8	10·00	12·00

The two designs of each value were printed together, *se-tenant*, in horizontal pairs throughout the sheets.

(Des O. Ball. Litho Questa)

1994 (12 July). *15th Anniv of Independence. T* **70** *and similar horiz designs. W* w **14** (*sideways*). *P* 14½.
440	40 c.	Type 70	..	60	60
441	60 c.	Fish and coral	..	1·00	1·25
442	75 c.	Great Frigate Birds in flight		1·25	1·50
440/2			*Set of* 3	2·50	3·00

71 *Diaphania indica*

72 *Nerium oleander*

(Des R. Watton. Litho Questa)

1994 (19 Aug). *Butterflies and Moths. T* **71** *and similar vert designs. Multicoloured. W* w **14**. *P* 14½×14.
443	1 c.	Type 71	..	10	10
444	5 c.	*Herpetogramma licarsisalis*	..	10	10
445	10 c.	*Parotis suralis*	..	10	10
446	12 c.	*Sufetula sunidesalis*	..	10	10
447	20 c.	*Aedia sericea*	..	15	20
448	23 c.	*Anomis vitiensis*	..	20	25
449	30 c.	*Anticarsia irrorata*	..	25	30
450	35 c.	*Spodoptera litura*	..	25	30
451	40 c.	*Mocis frugalis*	..	30	35
452	45 c.	*Agrius convolvuli*	..	35	40
453	50 c.	*Cephonodes picus*	..	40	45
454	55 c.	*Gnathothlibus erotus*	..	40	45
455	60 c.	*Macroglossum hirundo*	..	45	50
456	75 c.	*Badamia exclamationis*	..	60	65
457	$1	*Precis villida*	..	80	85
458	$2	*Danaus plexippus*	..	1·60	1·75
459	$3	*Hypolimnas bolina* (male)	..	2·40	2·50
460	$5	*Hypolimnas bolina* (female)	..	4·00	4·50
443/60			*Set of* 18	12·50	13·50

For miniature sheet containing No. 457 see No. **MS527**.

(Des N. Shewring. Litho Questa)

1994 (31 Oct). *Seasonal Flowers. T* **72** *and similar vert designs. Multicoloured. W* w **16**. *P* 14.
461	23 c.	Type 72	..	30	30
462	60 c.	*Catharanthus roseus*	..	80	1·00
463	75 c.	*Ipomea pes-caprae*	..	1·00	1·25
464	$1	*Calophyllum inophyllum*	..	1·40	2·00
461/4			*Set of* 4	3·25	4·00

73 Gemini (The Twins)

74 Church and Traditional Meeting Hut

(Des N. Shewring. Litho Walsall)

1995 (31 Jan). *Night Sky over Kiribati* (2nd series). *T* **73** *and similar vert designs. Multicoloured. W* w **16**. *P* 14.
465	50 c.	Type 73	..	75	70
466	60 c.	Cancer (The Crab)	..	85	90
467	75 c.	Cassiopeia (The Queen of Ethiopia)	..	1·00	1·25
468	$1	Southern Cross	..	1·25	1·75
465/8			*Set of* 4	3·50	4·25

(Des D. Miller. Litho Questa)

1995 (3 Apr). *Tourism. T* **74** *and similar vert designs. Multicoloured. P* 14½. (*a*) *W* w **16** (*upright*) (*sheets*).
469	30 c.	Type 74	..	60	70
		a. Horiz strip of 5. Nos. 469/73	..	2·75	
470	30 c.	Fishermen and outrigger canoes		60	70
471	30 c.	Gun emplacement and map	..	60	70
472	30 c.	Children with marine creatures		60	70
473	30 c.	Sports	..	60	70
474	40 c.	Local girls in traditional costume		60	70
		a. Horiz strip of 5. Nos. 474/8	..	2·75	
475	40 c.	Windsurfing	..	60	70
476	40 c.	Fishermen and wood carver	..	60	70
477	40 c.	Under water sport	..	60	70
478	40 c.	Women weaving	..	60	70
469/78			*Set of* 10	5·50	6·25

(*b*) *W* w **16** (*sideways*) (*booklets*).
479	30 c.	Type 74	..	65	80
		a. Booklet pane. Nos. 479/88 plus 5 labels	6·00		
480	30 c.	Fishermen and outrigger canoes		65	80
481	30 c.	Gun emplacement and map	..	65	80
482	30 c.	Children with marine creatures		65	80
483	30 c.	Sports	..	65	80
484	40 c.	Local girls in traditional costume		65	80
485	40 c.	Windsurfing	..	65	80

486	40 c.	Fishermen and wood carver	..	65	80
487	40 c.	Under water sport	..	65	80
488	40 c.	Women weaving	..	65	80
479/88			*Set of* 10	6·00	7·00

Nos. 469/73 and 474/8 were printed together, *se-tenant*, in horizontal strips of 5 throughout the sheets.

Booklet pane No. 479a contains the ten stamps printed together, *se-tenant*, as a block of 10 with each vertical pair separated by half stamp-sized illustrated label.

75 Grumman TBF Avenger

(Des J. Batchelor (Nos. 489/94), R. Watton (No. **MS495**). Litho Cartor (Nos. 489/94) or Questa (No. **MS495**))

1995 (8 May). *50th Anniv of End of Second World War. American Aircraft. T* **75** *and similar multicoloured designs. W* w **14** (*sideways*). *P* 14×13½.
489	23 c.	Type 75	..	60	45
490	40 c.	Curtiss SOC-3-1 Seagull seaplane	..	80	70
491	50 c.	Consolidated B-24 Liberator bomber		90	90
492	60 c.	Grumman G-21 Goose amphibian		1·10	1·10
493	75 c.	Martin B-26 Marauder bomber	..	1·40	1·50
494	$1	Northrop P-61 Black Widow bomber		1·60	1·75
489/94			*Set of* 6	5·75	5·75
MS495		75×85 mm. $2 Reverse of 1939–45 War Medal (*vert*). Wmk upright. *P* 14		2·50	3·00

76 Eclectus Parrots, Great Frigate Bird and Coconut Crabs   (77)

(Des N. Shewring. Litho B.D.T.)

1995 (12 July). *Protecting the Environment. T* **76** *and similar horiz designs. Multicoloured. W* w **14** (*sideways*). *P* 14.
496	60 c.	Type 76	..	85	95
		a. Sheetlet. Nos. 496/9	..	3·00	
497	60 c.	Red-tailed Tropic Birds, Common Dolphin and Pantropical Spotted Dolphin		85	95
498	60 c.	Blue-striped Snapper ("Yellow and Blue Sea Perch"), Blue-barred Orange Parrotfish and Green Turtle		85	95
499	60 c.	Red-breasted Wrasse, Pennant Coralfish and Violet Squirrelfish		85	95
496/9			*Set of* 4	3·00	3·50

Nos. 496/9 were printed together, *se-tenant*, in sheetlets of 4 stamps and 4 labels inscribed with details of the species depicted.

1995 (19 Aug). *"Jakarta '95" Stamp Exhibition, Indonesia. Nos.* 496/9 *optd with T* **77**.
500	60 c.	Type 76	..	1·25	1·40
		a. Sheetlet. Nos. 500/3	..	4·50	
501	60 c.	Red-tailed Tropic Birds, Common Dolphin and Pantropical Spotted Dolphin		1·25	1·40
502	60 c.	Blue-striped Snapper, Blue-barred Orange Parrotfish and Green Turtle	..	1·25	1·40
503	60 c.	Red-breasted Wrasse, Pennant Coralfish and Violet Squirrelfish		1·25	1·40
500/3			*Set of* 4	4·50	5·00

78 Sow feeding Piglets

79 *Teanoai* (police patrol boat)

(Des D. Miller. Litho Cartor)

1995 (1–14 Sept). *"Singapore '95" International Stamp Exhibition and Beijing International Coin and Stamp Expo '95. Two sheets, each* 113×85 *mm, containing T* **78**. *W* w **14** (*sideways*). *P* 13.
MS504		$2 multicoloured ("Singapore '95")		2·50	3·25
MS505		$2 multicoloured ("Beijing '95") (14 Sept)		2·75	3·50

Nos. MS504/5 show the exhibition logos on the sheet margins.

(Des S. Noon. Litho Cartor)

1995 (30 Nov). *Police Maritime Unit. T* **79** *and similar vert design showing Teanoai. Multicoloured. W* w **14**. *P* 13.
506	75 c.	Type 79	..	1·40	1·50
		a. Horiz pair. Nos. 506/7	..	2·75	3·00
507	75 c.	*Teanoai* at sea	..	1·40	1·50

Nos. 506/7 were printed together, *se-tenant*, in horizontal pairs throughout the sheet.

80 Pantropical Spotted Dolphins

(Des R. Watton. Litho Walsall)

1996 (15 Jan). *Dolphins. T* **80** *and similar horiz designs. Multicoloured. W* w **16** (*sideways*). *P* 14.
508	23 c.	Type 80	..	80	55
509	60 c.	Spinner Dolphins	..	1·50	1·50
510	75 c.	Fraser's Dolphins	..	1·75	1·75
511	$1	Rough-toothed Dolphins	..	1·90	2·25
508/11			*Set of* 4	5·50	5·25

81 Tap and Top Left Segment of U.N.I.C.E.F. Emblem

(Des N. Shewring. Litho Cartor)

1996 (22 Apr). *50th Anniv of U.N.I.C.E.F. T* **81** *and similar horiz designs. Multicoloured. W* w **14** (*sideways*). *P* 13.
512	30 c.	Type 81	..	50	60
		a. Block of 4. Nos. 512/15	..	1·75	
513	30 c.	Documents and top right segment		50	60
514	30 c.	Syringe and bottom left segment		50	60
515	30 c.	Open book and bottom right segment		50	60
512/15			*Set of* 4	1·75	2·25

Nos. 512/15 were printed together, *se-tenant*, throughout the sheet with each block of 4 showing the complete emblem.

82 Chinese Dragon

(Des Jane Evans. Litho B.D.T.)

1996 (30 Apr). *"CHINA '96" 9th Asian International Stamp Exhibition, Peking. Sheet* 110×86 *mm. W* w **16** (*sideways*). *P* 13½.
MS516	82	50 c. multicoloured	..	90	1·25

83 L.M.S. No. 5609 *Gilbert and Ellice Islands* Locomotive

(Des A. Theobald. Litho Cartor)

1996 (8 June). *"CAPEX '96" International Stamp Exhibition, Toronto. Sheet* 111×80 *mm. W* w **14** (*sideways*). *P* 12.
MS517	83	$2 multicoloured	..	2·40	3·00

84 Rathbun Red Crab

(Des G. Drummond. Litho Walsall)

1996 (6 Aug). *Sea Crabs. T **84** and similar horiz designs. Multicoloured.* W w **14** (*sideways*). P 14.
518	23 c. Type 84		40	40
519	60 c. Red and White Painted Crab		80	80
520	75 c. Red-spotted Crab		95	1·10
521	$1 Red-spotted White Crab		1·40	2·25
518/21	.. ..	*Set of 4*	3·25	4·00

85 Kiribati Canoe   (86)

(Des Jane Evans. Litho Questa)

1996 (21 Oct). *"Taipei '96" International Stamp Exhibition, Taiwan. Sheet* 110×86 *mm.* W w **16** (*sideways*). P 14¹⁄₂.
MS522 **85** $1.50, multicoloured .. .. 2·25 2·50

(Des E. Nisbet. Litho Walsall)

1996 (2 Dec). *Nautical History (3rd series). Horiz designs as T **49**. Multicoloured.* W w **16** (*sideways*). P 14¹⁄₂.
523	23 c. *Potomac* (whaling ship), 1843		50	40
524	50 c. *Southern Cross IV* (missionary ship), 1890		80	80
525	60 c. *John Williams III* (missionary sailing ship), 1890		95	1·00
526	$1 H.M.S. *Dolphin* (frigate), 1765		1·40	1·75
523/6	.. ..	*Set of 4*	3·25	3·50

(Des D. Miller. Litho Questa)

1997 (12 Feb). *"HONG KONG '97" International Stamp Exhibition. Sheet* 130×90 *mm containing design as No. 457. Multicoloured.* W w **14** (*sideways*). P 14¹⁄₂×14.
MS527 $1 *Precis villida* .. .. 1·10 1·40

(Des J. Batchelor. Litho Questa)

1997 (29 May). *"Pacific '97" International Stamp Exhibition, San Francisco. Nos. 489/95 optd with T **86**.*
528	23 c. Type 75		40	35
529	40 c. Curtiss SOC.3-1 Seagull seaplane		60	55
530	50 c. Consolidated B-24 Liberator bomber		70	70
531	60 c. Grumman G-21 Goose amphibian		80	90
532	75 c. Martin B-26 Marauder bomber		90	1·10
533	$1 Northrop P-61 Black Widow bomber		1·10	1·40
528/33	.. ..	*Set of 6*	4·00	4·50
MS534 75×85 mm. $2 Reverse of 1939–45 War Medal (*vert*) .. .. .. 2·10 2·75

87 Queen Elizabeth II in 1996   **88** Young Rock Dove

(Des N. Shewring (No. **MS541**), D. Miller (others). Litho Questa (No. **MS541**), Cot Printery Ltd, Barbados (others))

1997 (10 July). *Golden Wedding of Queen Elizabeth and Prince Philip. T **87** and similar multicoloured designs.* W w **14**. P 14¹⁄₂×14.
535	50 c. Type 87		90	1·00
	a. Horiz pair. Nos. 535/6		1·75	2·00
536	50 c. Prince Philip carriage-driving at Windsor Horse Show		90	1·00
537	60 c. Queen in phaeton at Trooping the Colour		1·00	1·25
	a. Horiz pair. Nos. 537/8		2·00	2·50
538	60 c. Prince Philip on Montserrat, 1993		1·00	1·25
539	75 c. Queen Elizabeth and Prince Philip, 1989		1·25	1·40
	a. Horiz pair. Nos. 539/40		2·50	2·75
540	75 c. Prince Edward on horseback		1·25	1·40
535/40	.. ..	*Set of 6*	5·50	6·50
MS541 110×70 mm. $2 Queen Elizabeth and Prince Philip in landau (*horiz*). Wmk sideways. P 14×14¹⁄₂ .. .. .. 2·75 3·50
Nos. 535/6, 537/8 and 539/40 were each printed together, *se-tenant*, in horizontal pairs throughout the sheets with the backgrounds forming composite designs.

(Des N. Arlott. Litho Walsall)

1997 (1 Dec). *Birds. T **88** and similar vert designs. Multicoloured.* W w **16**. P 14.
542	50 c. Type 88		75	80
	a. Horiz pair. Nos. 542/3		1·50	1·60
543	50 c. Adult Rock Dove		75	80
544	60 c. Adult Pacific Pigeon		80	90
	a. Horiz pair. Nos. 544/5		1·60	1·75
545	60 c. Young Pacific Pigeon		80	90
546	75 c. Adult Micronesian Pigeon		90	1·00
	a. Horiz pair. Nos. 546/7		1·75	2·00
547	75 c. Young Micronesian Pigeon		90	1·00
542/7	.. ..	*Set of 6*	4·50	4·75
Nos. 542/3, 544/5 and 546/7 were each printed together, *se-tenant*, in horizontal pairs throughout the sheets.

(89)   **90** Spiny Lobster

1997 (5 Dec). *"ASIA '97" Stamp Exhibition, Bangkok. Nos. 542/3 and 546/7 optd with T **89**.*
548	50 c. Type 88		75	90
	a. Horiz pair. Nos. 548/9		1·50	1·75
549	50 c. Adult Rock Dove		75	90
550	75 c. Adult Micronesian Pigeon		90	1·25
	a. Horiz pair. Nos. 550/1		1·75	2·50
551	75 c. Young Micronesian Pigeon		90	1·25
548/51	.. ..	*Set of 4*	3·00	3·75

(Des Josephine Martin. Litho Cot Printery Ltd, Barbados)

1998 (2 Feb). *Endangered Species. Spiny Lobster. T **90** and similar horiz designs. Multicoloured.* W w **14** (*sideways*). P 14×14¹⁄₂.
552	25 c. Type 90		30	40
	a. Horiz strip of 4. Nos. 552/5		1·10	
553	25 c. Facing right		30	40
554	25 c. With coral in foreground		30	40
555	25 c. On sponge		30	40
552/5	.. ..	*Set of 4*	1·10	1·40
MS556 69×49 mm. $1.50, Spiny Lobster .. 1·60 2·00
Nos. 552/5 were printed either in sheets of one design or in *se-tenant* sheets of 16, containing four horizontal strips as No. 552a.
No. MS556 does not show the W.W.F. panda emblem.

91 Diana, Princess of Wales, 1992   **92** Children and Smiling Sun

(Des D. Miller. Litho Questa)

1998 (31 Mar). *Diana, Princess of Wales Commemoration. T **91** and similar vert designs. Multicoloured.* W w **16** (*No.* 557). P 14¹⁄₂×14.
557 25 c. Type 91 .. .. .. 30 40
MS558 145×70 mm. 25 c., Type **91**; 50 c., Wearing black evening dress, 1981; 60 c., With scarf over head, 1992; 75 c., Wearing brown jacket, 1993. W w **14** (*sideways*) (*sold at* $2.10 + 50 c. *charity premium*) .. .. .. 2·50 2·75

(Des R. Watton. Litho Cot Printery Ltd. Barbados)

1998 (15 Sept). *"Towards the Millennium" (1st issue). Sheet* 102×69 *mm.* W w **14** (*sideways*). P 14.
MS559 **92** $1 multicoloured .. .. 90 1·25
See also Nos. 580/4 and 594/8.

93 Indo-Pacific Humpbacked Dolphin

(Des R. Watton. Litho Cot Printery Ltd, Barbados)

1998 (1 Oct). *Whales and Dolphins. T **93** and similar horiz designs. Multicoloured.* W w **14** (*sideways*). P 14×14¹⁄₂.
560	25 c. Type 93		45	55
	a. Horiz pair. Nos. 560/1		90	1·10
561	25 c. Bottlenose Dolphin		45	55
562	60 c. Short-snouted Spinner Dolphin		80	90
	a. Horiz pair. Nos. 562/3		1·60	1·75
563	60 c. Risso's Dolphin		80	90
564	75 c. Striped Dolphin		90	1·00
	a. Horiz pair. Nos. 564/5		1·75	2·00
565	75 c. Sei Whale		90	1·00
566	$1 Fin Whale		1·00	1·25
	a. Horiz pair. Nos. 566/7		2·00	2·50
567	$1 Minke Whale		1·00	1·25
560/7	.. ..	*Set of 8*	5·50	6·50
Nos. 560/1, 562/3, 564/5 and 566/7 were each printed together, *se-tenant*, in horizontal pairs throughout the sheets.

NEW INFORMATION

The editor is always interested to correspond with people who have new information that will improve or correct the Catalogue.

94 Reuben K. Uatioa Stadium, Kiribati

(Des R. Watton. Litho Questa)

1998 (23 Oct). *"Italia '98" International Stamp Exhibition, Milan. Sheet* 110×85 *mm.* W w **14** (*sideways*). P 14.
MS568 **94** $2 multicoloured .. .. 1·75 2·00

95 Pollutants and Harmful Emissions

(Des R. Watton. Litho Cartor)

1998 (1 Dec). *The Greenhouse Effect. T **95** and similar horiz designs. Multicoloured.* W w **14** (*sideways*). P 13¹⁄₂.
569	25 c. Type 95		20	25
570	50 c. Diagram of Greenhouse Effect		40	45
571	60 c. Diagram of rising sea levels on Tarawa		45	50
572	75 c. Diagram of rising sea levels on Kiritimati		55	60
569/72	.. ..	*Set of 4*	2·50	3·00
MS573 103×69 mm. $1.50, Outrigger canoe .. 1·90 2·10

96 H.M.S. *Resolution* (Cook) at Christmas Island, 1777

(Des J. Batchelor. Litho Cot Printery Ltd, Barbados)

1999 (19 Mar). *"Australia '99" World Stamp Exhibition, Melbourne. Sheet* 136×56 *mm.* W w **14** (*sideways*). P 14.
MS574 **96** $2 multicoloured .. .. 1·75 2·00

97 Common Shoveler ("Northern Shoveler") (male)

(Des N. Shewring. Litho Enschedé)

1999 (27 Apr). *"iBRA '99" International Stamp Exhibition, Nuremberg. Ducks. T **97** and similar horiz designs. Multicoloured.* W w **14** (*sideways*). P 14.
575	25 c. Type 97		35	35
576	50 c. Common Shoveler ("Northern Shoveler") (female) and ducklings		55	55
577	60 c. Green-winged Teal (male)		65	65
578	75 c. Green-winged Teal (female) and ducklings		75	75
575/8	.. ..	*Set of 4*	2·10	2·10
MS579 100×70 mm. $3 Green-winged Teal (male) and duckling .. .. 2·75 3·00

98 Map of Millennium Island

(Des G. Vasarhelyi. Litho Cartor)

1999 (12 July). *"Towards the Millennium" (2nd issue). 20th Anniv of Independence. T **98** and similar horiz designs.* W w **14** (*sideways*). P 13¹⁄₂.
580	25 c. Type 98		35	35
581	60 c. Map of Kiribati		65	65
582	75 c. Map of Nikumaroro		75	75
583	$1 Amelia Earhart (aviator)		95	95
580/3	.. ..	*Set of 4*	2·40	2·40
MS584 100×80 mm. Nos. 582/3 .. .. 2·00 2·25
No. 581 shows Tarawa as "TAROWA" in error.

(Des N. Shewring. Litho Walsall)

1999 (20 July). *30th Anniv of First Manned Landing on Moon.*
Multicoloured designs as T 296 of Jamaica. W w 16.
P 14×13½.

585	25 c. Buzz Aldrin (astronaut)	..	35	35
586	60 c. Service module docking with lunar			
	module	..	65	65
587	75 c. "Apollo 11" on Moon's surface	..	75	75
588	$1 Command module separating from			
	service section	..	95	95
585/8		*Set of 4*	2·40	2·40

MS589 90×80 mm. $2 Kiribati as seen from
Moon (*circular, 40 mm diam*). Wmk sideways.
P 14 .. .. 1·90 2·00

99 Santa Claus in Sailing
Canoe

100 Open Hands
around Globe
("FAITH")

(Des G. Vasarhelyi. Litho Cartor)

1999 (9 Oct). *Christmas and 125th Anniv of Universal Postal*
Union. T 99 and similar horiz designs. Multicoloured. W w 14
(*sideways*). P 13½.

590	25 c. Type **99**	..	30	25
591	60 c. Santa and unloading freighter	..	55	55
592	75 c. Santa in sleigh passing aircraft	..	70	70
593	$1 Santa using computer	..	90	95
590/3		*Set of 4*	2·25	2·25

(Des F. Mint. Litho Cartor)

2000 (1 Jan). *"Towards the Millennium" (3rd issue). "A*
Region of Peace". T 100 and similar vert designs. Multi-
coloured. W w 14. P 13½×13.

594	25 c. Type **100**	..	30	30
595	40 c. Solar eclipse ("HARMONY")	..	45	45
596	60 c. Stars and Sun over Earth ("HOPE")	..	60	60
597	75 c. Sun over Earth ("ENLIGHTEN-			
	MENT")	..	75	75
598	$1 Dove over Earth ("PEACE")	..	90	90
594/8		*Set of 5*	2·75	2·75

101 Bert feeding Pigeons

(Des Children's Television Workshop. Litho Questa)

2000 (22 Mar). *Sesame Street (children's T.V. programme).*
T 101 and similar vert designs. Multicoloured. W w 14.
P 14½×15.

599	20 c. Type **101**	..	15	20
	a. Sheetlet. Nos. 599/608	..	1·25	
600	20 c. Little Bear flying kite	..	15	20
601	20 c. Grover calling	..	15	20
602	20 c. Elmo and Cookie Monster	..	15	20
603	20 c. Telly leaning out of window	..	15	20
604	20 c. Zoe painting house	..	15	20
605	20 c. Ernie with bird	..	15	20
606	20 c. Big Bird and Rosita reading	..	15	20
607	20 c. Oscar the Grouch and Slimey in			
	dustbin	..	15	20
599/607		*Set of 9*	1·25	1·75

MS608 139×86 mm. $1.50, Grover as postman.
P 14½ .. .. 1·10 1·25
Nos. 599/607 were printed together, *se-tenant*, in sheetlets of 9
with the backgrounds forming a composite design.

STAMP BOOKLETS

1981 (26 Nov). *Royal Wedding. Multicoloured cover, 105×65*
mm, showing The Katherine. *Stitched.*
SB1 $1.96, booklet containing eight 12 c. in panes of 4
(No. 156a) and two 50 c. in pane of two (No.
157a) .. .. 1·75

1983 (8 Aug). *Orange-brown, emerald and cinnamon cover,*
105×64 mm, showing sea birds. Stitched.
SB2 $3 booklet containing 25 c. and 50 c. (Nos. 171a,
174), each in block of 4 .. .. 7·50

1987 (31 Mar). *Multicoloured cover, 105×65 mm, showing sea*
birds. Stitched.
SB3 $3.40, booklet containing 15 c. (No. 170) in block
of 8 and 55 c. (No. 175a) in block of 4 .. 25·00

1995 (3 Apr). *Tourism. Multicoloured cover showing yacht at*
sunset. Pane attached by selvedge.
SB4 $3.50, booklet containing *se-tenant* pane of 10 (No.
479a) .. .. 6·00

POSTAGE DUE STAMPS

D 1 Kiribati Coat of Arms

(Litho Format)

1981 (27 Aug). P 14.

D1	D 1	1 c. black and magenta	..	10	10
D2		2 c. black and greenish blue	..	10	10
D3		5 c. black and bright green	..	10	10
D4		10 c. black and chestnut	..	10	15
D5		20 c. black and bright blue	..	15	25
D6		30 c. black and brown-ochre	..	15	35
D7		40 c. black and purple	..	20	45
D8		50 c. black and deep blue-green	..	20	50
D9		$1 black and orange-red	..	30	75
D1/9			*Set of 9*	1·00	2·25

Nos. D1/9 exist imperforate from stock dispersed by the
liquidator of Format International Security Printers Ltd.

OFFICIAL STAMPS

O.K.G.S.   O.K.G.S.
(O 1)   (O 2)

1981 (May). *Optd with Type O 1. (a) On Nos. 86, 90/3, 95 and*
97/9b, W w 14 (sideways).*

O 1	1 c. Type **16**	..	1·50	2·25
O 2	10 c. Maneaba, Bikenibeu	..	15·00	12·00
O 3	12 c. Betio Harbour	..	3·00	3·00
O 4	15 c. Eastern Reef Heron	..	16·00	11·00
O 5	20 c. Flamboyant Tree	..	10·00	11·00
O 6	30 c. Frangipani	..	4·50	6·00
O 7	50 c. *Hypolimnas bolina* (butterfly)	..	5·00	4·50
O 8	$1 *Tabakea* (Tarawa Lagoon ferry)	..	9·00	10·00
	w. Wmk Crown to right of CA	..	32·00	
O 9	$2 Evening scene	..	13·00	13·00
	w. Wmk Crown to right of CA	..	65·00	
O10	$5 National flag	..	2·00	3·00
	a. Opt inverted	..	£150	
O1/10		*Set of 10*	70·00	65·00

(*b*) On Nos. 121/35. No wmk

O11	1 c. Type **16**	..	10	30
O12	3 c. M.V. *Tautunu* (inter-island freighter)	..	10	20
O13	5 c. Hibiscus	..	10	15
O14	7 c. Catholic Cathedral, Tarawa	..	10	15
O15	10 c. Maneaba, Bikenibeu	..	10	15
	a. Opt double	..	7·00	
O16	12 c. Betio Harbour	..	30	30
O17	15 c. Eastern Reef Heron	..	1·50	30
O18	20 c. Flamboyant Tree	..	20	30
O19	25 c. Moorish Idol	..	30	30
O20	30 c. Frangipani	..	30	35
	a. Opt double	..	8·00	
O21	35 c. G.I.P.C. Chapel, Tangintebu	..	35	40
O22	50 c. *Hypolimnas bolina* (butterfly)	..	50	55
	a. Opt double	..	40·00	
	b. Opt inverted	..	60·00	
O23	$1 *Tabakea* (Tarawa Lagoon ferry)	..	75	50
O24	$2 Evening scene	..	90	70
	a. Opt double	..	£110	
O25	$5 National flag	..	2·00	2·25
O11/25		*Set of 15*	6·50	6·00

*The normal sideways watermark shows Crown to left of CA,
as seen from the back of the stamp.

1983. *Nos. 86, 90/3, 95, 97/9 and 131 optd with Type O 2.*

O26	1 c. Type **16**	..	6·00	3·00
O27	10 c. Maneaba, Bikenibeu	..	14·00	8·00
O28	12 c. Betio Harbour	..	4·00	3·50
O29	15 c. Eastern Reef Heron	..	16·00	13·00
O30	20 c. Flamboyant Tree	..	6·50	5·50
O31	30 c. Frangipani	..	9·50	4·50
O32	35 c. G.I.P.C. Chapel, Tangintebu	..	†	
O33	50 c. *Hypolimnas bolina* (butterfly)	..	9·00	4·50
O34	$1 *Tabakea* (Tarawa Lagoon ferry)	..	10·00	7·00
O35	$2 Evening scene	..	16·00	9·00

1983 (28 June). *Nos. 169, 172/3, 175 and 177 optd with Type*
O 2.

O36	12 c. Polynesian Reed Warbler	..	40	30
O37	30 c. Brown Booby	..	70	50
O38	35 c. Audubon's Shearwater	..	80	60
	a. Opt double	..	40·00	35·00
O39	50 c. Bristle-thighed Curlew	..	1·00	80
O40	$2 Long-tailed Koel	..	3·00	2·75
O36/40		*Set of 5*	5·50	4·50

Kuwait

Kuwait, an independent Arab shaikhdom since 1756, placed itself under British protection in 1899 to counter the spread of Ottoman influence in the Arabian Gulf.

The first, somewhat limited, postal service, via Bushire, commenced with the appointment of a Political Agent to Kuwait in August 1904. Because of diplomatic problems this system continued until 21 January 1915 when a regular Indian post office was established.

Limited supplies of Indian stamps were used by the Political Agency postal service, but these became available to the general public from 21 January 1915. Stamps seen postally used from Kuwait before 1923 are usually ½ a., 1 a., 1 r. or 5 r. values, with the occasional Official issue. Much more common are values to 15 r., both postage and Official, used telegraphically.

Before 1910 the name of the shaikhdom was spelt "KOWEIT" and this spelling appears on various circular postmarks used between 1915 and 1923. The more modern version of the name was first used for a postal cancellation in 1923.

1915 "KOWEIT"

1923 "KUWAIT"

On 1 August 1921 responsibility for the Kuwait postal service passed to the Iraq Post Office.

PRICES FOR STAMPS ON COVER TO 1945	
Nos. 1/15	from × 5
Nos. 16/29	from × 3
Nos. 31/51	from × 2
Nos. 52/63	from × 4
Nos. O1/27	from × 10

USED HIGH VALUES. It is necessary to emphasize that used prices quoted for high value stamps are for postally used examples.

(Currency. 16 annas = 1 rupee)

KUWAIT KUWAIT
(1)　　　(2)

1923 (1 Apr)–24. *Stamps of India (King George V), optd with T 1 or 2 (rupee values, 15½ mm) by Indian Govt Ptg Wks. W 34 (Large Star) of India. P 14.*

1	½ a. pale blue-green (No. 156)			3·00	4·25
	a. Opt double			£200	
	b. Vert pair, one without opt			£500	
2	1 a. chocolate (No. 197)			2·50	2·50
	a. Opt double			£300	
	b. Opt omitted (lower stamp of vert pair)		£850	
3	1½ a. chocolate (A) ("ANNA") (No. 163)		2·00	4·25
4	2 a. violet (No. 168)			3·25	2·50
	a. Bright purple				
5	2 a. 6 p. ultramarine (No. 171)			2·25	8·00
6	3 a. orange-brown (No. 173)			4·25	19·00
7	3 a. ultramarine (No. 200) (1924)		9·00	2·50
8	4 a. deep olive (No. 174)			8·00	24·00
	a. Olive-green				
9	6 a. yellow-bistre (No. 177)				8·00
10	8 a. purple (No. 179)			8·00	32·00
	a. Mauve				
11	12 a. claret (No. 184)			14·00	40·00
12	1 r. brown and green (No. 185)		17·00	23·00
	a. Red-brown and blue-green		19·00	26·00
13	2 r. carmine and brown (No. 187)		40·00	90·00
14	5 r. ultramarine and violet (No. 188)		80·00	£200
15	10 r. green and scarlet (No. 189)		£120	£450
1/15			*Set of 15*	£275	£750

Essays of the overprint using the obsolete spelling "KOWEIT" were prepared in 1923 and can be found on the original 14 values of the postage stamps and on the 13 stamps of the Official series. (Price per set of 27 unused £20000).

Nos. 1/4 and 6/7 are all known with inverted overprint and the overprint is also known on examples of India No. 165 ("ANNAS"). It is doubtful if such errors were actually sold at the Kuwait Post Office, although some are known on registered or ordinary covers.

KUWAIT KUWAIT
(3)　　　(4)

1929–37. *Stamps of India (King George V, Nasik printing), optd with T 3 or 4 (rupee values). W 69 (Mult Stars) of India. P 14.*

16	½ a. green (No. 202)			2·50	1·40
	aw. Wmk inverted			2·50	2·50
16b	½ a. green (No. 232) (1934)			4·50	1·10
17	1 a. chocolate (No. 203)			7·00	1·60
	aw. Wmk inverted			10·00	5·00
17b	1 a. chocolate (No. 234) (1934)			4·50	85
18	2 a. purple (No. 206)			3·00	90
19	2 a. vermilion (No. 236)			20·00	85·00
	aw. Wmk inverted			20·00	85·00
19b	2 a. vermilion (No. 236b) (1934)		16·00	6·00
19c	2 a. vermilion (small die) (No. 236c) (1937)	4·50	2·00
20	3 a. blue (No. 209)			2·75	1·75
21	3 a. carmine (No. 237)			5·50	4·25
22	4 a. sage-green (wmk inverted) (No. 211w)	25·00	80·00
22a	4 a. pale sage-green (No. 210) (1934)		5·50	13·00
22b	6 a. bistre (No. 239) (1937)		22·00	55·00
23	8 a. reddish purple (No. 212)		17·00	13·00
	w. Wmk inverted			9·00	22·00
24	12 a. claret (wmk inverted) (No. 213w) (1933)	21·00	38·00
25	1 r. chocolate and green (No. 214)		—	26·00
	a. Extended "T"			£300	
	w. Wmk inverted			10·00	
26	2 r. carm & orge (wmk inverted) (No. 215w)	10·00	65·00
	a. Extended "T"			£300	£700
27	5 r. ultramarine & purple (No. 216) (1937)	80·00	£200
	a. Extended "T"			£450	
28	10 r. green and scarlet (No. 217) (1934)	£170	£375
	a. Extended "T"			£850	
29	15 r. bl & ol (wmk inverted) (No. 218w) (1937)	£475	£750
	a. Extended "T"			£1400	
16/29			*Set of 20*	£800	£1500

The "T" of "KUWAIT" shows a ¾ mm downward extension on R. 3/2, lower left pane.

Nos. 16, 17, 18/19 and 22 are inscribed "INDIA POSTAGE & REVENUE". The remainder are inscribed "INDIA POSTAGE". No. 19b measures 19×22.6 mm and No. 19c 18.4×21.8 mm.

Examples of most values are known showing a forged Kuwait postmark dated "11 NOV 37".

1933 (Feb)–34. *Air. Nos. 220/3 of India optd as T 2 (16½ mm).*

31	2 a. deep blue-green			14·00	27·00
	w. Wmk stars to right			14·00	27·00
32	3 a. blue			2·75	2·50
	w. Wmk stars to right			2·75	3·25
33	4 a. olive-green			85·00	£170
34	6 a. bistre (2.34)			2·75	4·50
	w. Wmk stars to right			2·75	4·50
31/4			*Set of 4*	90·00	£180

The normal sideways watermark on Nos. 31/4 shows stars pointing to left, *as seen from the back of the stamp.*

The 3 a. value exists with a most pronounced lithography double print. Price £850 un., £650 used. Examples of this and other stamps with slight double prints are of little additional value.

1939. *Nos. 248, 250/1, 253, 255/63 of India (King George VI) optd with T 3 or 4 (rupee values).*

36	½ a. red-brown			7·00	1·75
38	1 a. carmine			7·00	1·50
39	2 a. vermilion			7·00	2·50
41	3 a. yellow-green			7·00	2·00
43	4 a. brown			35·00	14·00
44	6 a. turquoise-green			25·00	7·50
45	8 a. slate-violet			28·00	32·00
46	12 a. lake			20·00	48·00
47	1 r. grey and red-brown			6·50	2·75
	a. Extended "T"			£300	
	b. Opt triple, one inverted				
48	2 r. purple and brown			3·75	13·00
	a. Extended "T"			£275	
49	5 r. green and blue			12·00	18·00
	a. Extended "T"			£425	
50	10 r. purple and claret			60·00	75·00
	a. Opt double			£325	
	b. Extended "T"			£600	
51	15 r. brown and green			£130	£190
	a. Extended "T"			£850	
	w. Wmk inverted			85·00	£150
36/51w			*Set of 13*	£275	£325

On later printings the extended "T" variety was corrected in two stages.

Examples of most values are known showing a forged Kuwait postmark dated "17 NOV 39".

> Following the rebellion in Iraq control of the Kuwait postal service was assumed by the Indian authorities on 2 June 1941.
> Unoverprinted stamps of INDIA were used in Kuwait between 1941 and 1945.

1945. *Nos. 265/8 and 269a of India (King George VI, on white background) optd with T 3.*

52	3 p. slate			1·25	2·50
53	½ a. purple			1·25	2·50
54	9 p. green			2·75	7·50
55	1 a. carmine			1·50	2·00
56	1½ a. dull violet			3·25	7·50
57	2 a. vermilion			3·50	2·75
58	3 a. bright violet			3·75	3·50
59	3½ a. bright blue			4·00	7·50
60	4 a. brown			3·50	2·50
60a	6 a. turquoise-green			14·00	8·50
61	8 a. slate-violet			7·00	2·75
62	12 a. lake			7·50	3·25
63	14 a. purple			14·00	16·00
52/63			*Set of 13*	60·00	60·00

Following a short period of Pakistani control, from August 1947 the Kuwait postal service passed to British administration on 1 April 1948.

KUWAIT KUWAIT
(3)　　　(4)

KUWAIT KUWAIT

I　　　　5 RUPEES
ANNA
(5)　　　(6)

NOTE. From 1948 onwards, for stamps with similar surcharges, but without name of country, see British Postal Agencies in Eastern Arabia.

1948 (1 Apr)–49. *Nos. 470, 475, 476a/7, 478a and 485/90 of Great Britain (King George VI), surch as T 5 or 6 (rupee values).*

64	½ a. on ½d. pale green			1·25	1·25
65	1 a. on 1d. pale scarlet			1·25	1·25
66	1½ a. on 1½d. pale red-brown		1·75	75
67	2 a. on 2d. pale orange			1·25	90
68	2½ a. on 2½d. light ultramarine		1·75	1·00
69	3 a. on 3d. pale violet			1·25	30
	a. Pair, one surch albino				
70	6 a. on 6d. purple			1·25	60
71	1 r. on 1s. bistre-brown			3·00	1·00
72	2 r. on 2s. 6d. yellow-green		3·50	4·50
73	5 r. on 5s. red			5·50	4·50
73a	10 r. on 10s. ultramarine (4.7.49)		38·00	6·00
64/73a			*Set of 11*	55·00	20·00

KUWAIT KUWAIT
2½　　　　15
ANNAS　　RUPEES
(7)　　　(8)

1948 (1 May). *Royal Silver Wedding. Nos. 493/4 of Great Britain surch with T 7 or 8.*

74	2½ a. on 2½d. ultramarine			1·50	60
75	15 r. on £1 blue			30·00	30·00
	a. Short bars (R. 3/4)			£130	

No. 75a has the bars cancelling the original face value 3 mm long instead of the 3½ mm of the normal surcharge.

1948 (29 July). *Olympic Games. Nos. 495/8 of Great Britain surch as T 7, but in one line (6 a.) or two lines (others).*

76	2½ a. on 2½d. ultramarine			1·00	1·50
77	3 a. on 3d. violet			1·00	1·50
78	6 a. on 6d. bright purple			1·25	1·50
79	1 r. on 1s. brown			1·25	1·50
76/9			*Set of 4*	4·00	5·50

1949 (10 Oct). *75th Anniv of U.P.U. Nos. 499/502 of Great Britain surch "KUWAIT" and new values.*

80	2½ a. on 2½d. ultramarine			90	1·75
81	3 a. on 3d. violet			1·25	2·25
82	6 a. on 6d. bright purple			1·25	2·25
83	1 r. on 1s. brown			1·25	1·25
80/3			*Set of 4*	4·25	6·75

KUWAIT KUWAIT

2 RUPEES　2 RUPEES
Type I　　　Type II
　　(8a)

KUWAIT

　　　　Type I

10 RUPEES

KUWAIT

　　　　Type II

10 RUPEES
　(8b)

2 r. Type I　Type-set surcharge. "2" level with "RUPEES". Surcharge sharp.

Type II.　Plate-printed surcharge. "2" raised. Surcharge worn.

10 r. Type I.　Type-set surcharge. "1" and "O" spaced. Surcharge sharp and clean.

Type II.　Plate-printed surcharge. "1" and "O" closer together. Surcharge appears heavy and worn, see especially "A", "R" and "P".

KUWAIT KUWAIT

Extra bar in centre　Extra bar at top
(R. 7/2)　　　(R. 2/2)

1950 (2 Oct)–**54.** *Nos. 503/11 of Great Britain (King George VI) surch as T 5 or 8a/b (rupee values).*

84	½a. on ½d. pale orange (3.5.51)	..	..	1·75	1·50
85	1 a. on 1d. light ultramarine (3.5.51)		..	1·75	1·10
86	1½a. on 1½d. pale green (3.5.51)		..	1·75	2·25
87	2 a. on 2d. pale red-brown (3.5.51)		..	1·75	85
88	2½a. on 2½d. pale scarlet (3.5.51)		..	1·75	2·25
89	4 a. on 4d. light ultramarine		..	1·50	90
90	2 r. on 2s. 6d. yellow-green (I) (3.5.51)		..	15·00	4·50
	a. Extra bar in centre		..	£400	£350
	b. Type II surch (1954)	..	..	£180	50·00
91	5 r. on 5s. red (3.5.51)	..	..	21·00	5·00
	a. Extra bar at top	..	..	£275	£225
92	10 r. on 10s. ultramarine (I) (3.5.51)		..	29·00	6·50
	a. Type II surch (1952)	..	..	£225	50·00
84/92			*Set of 9*	65·00	22·00

No. 92a is known with surch spaced 10 mm apart instead of 9 mm.

W 153 *of Great*	W 165 *of Great*
Britain	*Britain*

1952 (10 Dec)–**54.** *Nos. 515/21, 523 and 530/1 of Great Britain (Queen Elizabeth II. W 153), surch as T 5 (in two lines only on 2½ and 6 a.).*

93	½a. on ½d. orange-red (31.8.53)		..	20	80
94	1 a. on 1d. ultramarine (31.8.53)		..	20	10
95	1½a. on 1½d. green	..	..	15	40
96	2 a. on 2d. red-brown (31.8.53)		..	35	10
97	2½a. on 2½d. carmine-red	..	..	15	40
98	3 a. on 3d. deep lilac (B.) (18.1.54)		..	40	10
99	4 a. on 4d. ultramarine (2.11.53)		..	1·25	75
100	6 a. on 6d. reddish purple (18.1.54)		..	1·25	10
101	12 a. on 1s. 3d. green (2.11.53)		..	5·00	2·50
102	1 r. on 1s. 6d. grey-blue (2.11.53)		..	4·00	35
93/102			*Set of 10*	12·00	4·50

1953 (3 June). *Coronation. Nos. 532/5 of Great Britain surch "KUWAIT" and new values.*

103	2½a. on 2½d. carmine-red	..	..	3·00	2·50
104	4 a. on 4d. ultramarine	..	..	3·00	2·50
105	12 a. on 1s. 3d. deep yellow-green		..	4·50	4·00
106	1 r. on 1s. 6d. deep grey-blue		..	4·00	1·00
103/6			*Set of 4*	13·00	9·00

KUWAIT 2 RUPEES ≡ I

KUWAIT 2 RUPEES ≡ II

(9)

KUWAIT 5 RUPEES ≡ I

KUWAIT 5 RUPEES ≡ II

(10)

KUWAIT 10 RUPEES ≡ I

KUWAIT 10 RUPEES ≡ II

(11)

Type I (9/11). Type-set overprints by Waterlow. Bold (generally thicker) letters with sharp corners and straight edges. Bars close together and usually slightly longer than in Type II.

Type II (9/11). Plate-printed overprints by Harrison. Thinner letters, rounder corners and rough edges. Bars wider apart.

1955 (23 Sept)–**57.** *Nos. 536/8 of Great Britain ("Castles" high values) surch with T 9/11.*

107	2 r. on 2s. 6d. black-brown (I)		..	7·00	2·00
	a. Type II (10.10.57)	..	..	60·00	7·00
108	5 r. on 5s. rose-carmine (I)		..	7·50	4·50
	a. Type II (10.10.57)	..	..	90·00	26·00
109	10 r. on 10s. ultramarine (I)		..	8·00	4·50
	a. Type II (10.10.57)	..	..	£150	90·00
107/9			*Set of 3*	20·00	10·00
107a/9a			*Set of 3*	£275	£110

1956. *Nos. 540/6, 548 and 555/6 of Great Britain (Queen Elizabeth II. W 165) surch as T 5 (in two lines only on 2½ and 6 a.).*

110	½a. on ½d. orange-red	..	..	30	85
111	1 a. on 1d. green	..	..	50	2·00
112	1½a. on 1½d. green	..	..	40	50
113	2 a. on 2d. red-brown	..	..	40	50
114	2½a. on 2½d. carmine-red	..	..	60	2·00
116	4 a. on 4d. ultramarine	..	..	4·75	3·25
117	6 a. on 6d. reddish purple		..	2·25	40
118	12 a. on 1s. 3d. green	..	..	9·50	8·00
119	1 r. on 1s. 6d. grey-blue		..	4·50	30
110/19			*Set of 9*	20·00	16·00

(New Currency. 100 naye paise = 1 rupee)

KUWAIT **KUWAIT** **KUWAIT**

NP 1 NP   **NP 3 NP** **75 NP**

(12) (13) (14)

1957 (1 June)–**58.** *Nos. 540/2, 543a/8, 551 and 555 of Great Britain (Queen Elizabeth II. W 165) surch as T 12 (1, 15, 25, 40, 50 n.p.), 14 (75 n.p.) or 13 (others).*

120	1 n.p. on 5d. brown	..	..	10	70
121	3 n.p. on ½d. orange-red		..	60	2·50
122	6 n.p. on 1d. ultramarine		..	60	1·25
123	9 n.p. on 1½d. green	..	..	60	2·00
124	12 n.p. on 2d. light red-brown		..	60	2·00
125	15 n.p. on 2½d. carmine-red (Type I)		..	60	2·00
	a. Type II (11.58)	..	..	28·00	65·00
126	20 n.p. on 3d. deep lilac (B.)		..	60	30
127	25 n.p. on 4d. ultramarine		..	2·25	3·25
128	40 n.p. on 6d. reddish purple		..	1·00	30
129	50 n.p. on 9d. bronze-green		..	5·50	4·00
130	75 n.p. on 1s. 3d. green		..	5·50	4·25
120/30			*Set of 11*	16·00	20·00

20 Shaikh Abdullah as-Salim as-Sabah

(Recess D.L.R.)

1958 (1 Feb). *P 12½.*

131	**20** 5 n.p. bluish green		..	50	10
132	10 n.p. rose-red	..	..	50	10
136	40 n.p. maroon	..	..	1·50	55
131/6			*Set of 3*	2·25	65

Nos. 131/6 were only valid for internal use in Kuwait prior to 1 February 1959. Further values were added to this series following the closure of the British Agency Post Offices on 31 January 1959. Responsibility of the postal service then passed to the Kuwait Government and later issues are listed in Part 19 (*Middle East*) of this catalogue.

OFFICIAL STAMPS

KUWAIT **KUWAIT**

SERVICE **SERVICE**

(O 1) (O 2)

1923–24. *Stamps of India (King George V), optd with Type O 1 or O 2 (rupee values, 15½–16 mm). W 34 (Large Star) of India. P 14.*

O 1	½a. pale blue-green (No. 156)		..	1·50	21·00
	a. Opt double, one albino		..	80·00	
O 2	1 a. chocolate (No. 197)	..	..	2·50	11·00
	a. Opt double, one albino		..	80·00	
O 3	1½a. chocolate (A) (No. 163)		..	3·25	35·00
O 4	2 a. violet (No. 168)	..	..	4·25	23·00
	a. Bright purple	..	..		
O 5	2 a. 6 p. ultramarine (No. 171)		..	4·25	50·00
O 6	3 a. orange-brown (No. 173)		..	3·50	60·00
O 7	3 a. ultramarine (No. 200) (1924)		..	5·00	48·00
O 8	4 a. olive-green (No. 175)		..	3·50	55·00
O 9	8 a. purple (No. 179)	..	..	5·50	65·00
	a. Mauve	..	..		
O10	1 r. brown and green (No. 185)		..	14·00	£130
	a. Opt double, one albino		..	£100	
O11	2 r. carmine and brown (No. 187)		..	18·00	£180
O12	5 r. ultramarine and violet (No. 188)		..	60·00	£375
	a. Opt double, one albino		..	£140	
O13	10 r. green and scarlet (No. 189)		..	£110	£350
O14	15 r. blue and olive (No. 190)		..	£180	£475
O1/14			*Set of 14*	£375	£1700

1929–33. *Nos. 203, 206, 209 and 211/18w of India (King George V, Nasik printing) optd as Types O 1 (spaced 10 mm) or O 2 (14½ mm×19–20 mm wide). W 69 (Mult Stars) of India. P 14.*

O16	1 a. chocolate	..	..		
	w. Wmk inverted	..	..	3·50	25·00
O17	2 a. purple	..	..	55·00	£150
O19	3 a. blue	..	..	4·25	38·00
O20	4 a. sage-green	..	..	4·25	65·00
	w. Wmk inverted	..	..		
O21	8 a. reddish purple	..	..	4·75	85·00
	w. Wmk inverted	..	..	4·75	
O22	12 a. claret	..	..	25·00	£150
	w. Wmk inverted	..	..		
O23	1 r. chocolate and green		..	4·00	£170
O24	2 r. carmine and orange (*wmk inverted*)		..	7·00	£300
O25	5 r. ultramarine & purple (*wmk inverted*)		..	27·00	£425
O26	10 r. green and scarlet		..	50·00	£600
O27	15 r. blue and olive (*wmk inverted*)		..	£120	£1100
O16/27			*Set of 11*	£275	£2750

Labuan
see Malaysia

Lagos
see Nigeria

Leeward Islands

The Federal Colony of the Leeward Islands was constituted in 1871 formalising links between Antigua, British Virgin Islands, Dominica, Montserrat and St. Kitts-Nevis which stretched back to the 1670s. Issues for the individual islands were superseded by those inscribed "LEEWARD ISLANDS", but were in concurrent use with them from 1903. Dominica was transferred to the Windward Islands on 31 December 1939.

PRICES FOR STAMPS ON COVER TO 1945	
Nos. 1/8	*from* × 10
Nos. 9/16	*from* × 12
Nos. 17/19	*from* × 8
Nos. 20/8	*from* × 5
Nos. 29/35	*from* × 4
Nos. 36/45	*from* × 5
Nos. 46/57	*from* × 4
Nos. 58/87	*from* × 5
Nos. 88/91	*from* × 6
Nos. 92/4	*from* × 10
Nos. 95/114	*from* × 5

PRINTERS. All the stamps of Leeward Islands were typographed by De La Rue & Co, Ltd, London, *except where otherwise stated.*

1 2

1890 (31 Oct). *Name and value in second colour. Wmk Crown CA. P 14.*

1	1	½d. dull mauve and green	..	3·25	1·25
2		1d. dull mauve and rose	..	3·25	20
3		2½d. dull mauve and blue	..	3·75	20
		w. Wmk inverted	..	†	£150
4		4d. dull mauve and orange	..	4·00	7·00
5		6d. dull mauve and brown	..	10·00	11·00
6		7d. dull mauve and slate	..	3·25	11·00
7	2	1s. green and carmine	..	16·00	40·00
8		5s. green and blue	..	£120	£225
1/8			*Set of 8*	£140	£275
1/8	Optd "Specimen"		*Set of 8*	£200	

The colours of this issue are fugitive.

 One Penny **One Penny**

(3) (4) (5)

1897 (22 July). *Queen Victoria's Diamond Jubilee. Hand-stamped with T 3.*

9	1	½d. dull mauve and green	..	3·00	10·00
		a. Opt double	..	£1200	
10		1d. dull mauve and rose	..	3·50	10·00
		a. Opt double	..	£1000	
		b. Opt triple	..	£3250	
11		2½d. dull mauve and blue	..	4·00	10·00
		a. Opt double	..	£1200	
12		4d. dull mauve and orange	..	28·00	70·00
		a. Opt double	..	£1200	
13		6d. dull mauve and brown	..	48·00	90·00
		a. Opt double	..	£1400	
14		7d. dull mauve and slate	..	48·00	90·00
		a. Opt double	..	£1400	
15	2	1s. green and carmine	..	£120	£190
		a. Opt double	..	£1800	
16		5s. green and blue	..	£450	£750
		a. Opt double	..	£5000	
9/16			*Set of 8*	£600	£1100

Beware of forgeries.

1902 (11 Aug.) *Nos. 4/6 surch.*

17	4	1d. on 4d. dull mauve and orange	..	1·75	4·75
		a. Pair, one with tall narrow "O" in "One"	..	30·00	70·00
		b. Surch double	.. ..		
18		1d. on 6d. dull mauve and brown	..	2·50	10·00
		a. Pair, one with tall narrow "O" in "One"	..	45·00	£120
19	5	1d. on 7d. dull mauve and slate	..	2·25	4·50
17/19			Set of 3	6·00	17·00

The tall narrow "O" variety occurred on R. 1/1, 5/3, 5/5 and 7/4.

6   7   8

Wide "A" (R. 6/1 of both panes)

Dropped "R" (R. 1/1 of both panes)

1902 (1 Sept.–Oct.). *Wmk Crown CA. P 14.*

20	6	¼d. dull purple and green	..	4·50	80
21		1d. dull purple and carmine	..	5·50	20
22	7	2d. dull purple and ochre (Oct)	..	2·50	4·25
23	6	2½d. dull purple and ultramarine	..	4·00	2·25
		a. Wide "A" in "LEEWARD"	..	£180	£150
24	7	3d. dull purple and black (Oct)	..	3·25	7·50
25	6	6d. dull purple and brown	..	2·00	8·00
26	8	1s. green and carmine	..	2·25	18·00
		a. Dropped "R" in "LEEWARD"			£190
27	7	2s. 6d. green and black (Oct)	..	27·00	65·00
28	8	5s. green and blue (Oct)	..	48·00	70·00
20/8			Set of 9	85·00	£160
20/8 Optd "Specimen"			Set of 9		£140

1905 (Apr)–**08**. *Wmk Mult Crown CA. Ordinary paper* (¼d., 3d.) *or chalk-surfaced paper* (others).

29	6	¼d. dull purple and green (2.06)	..	3·00	1·75
		a. Chalk-surfaced paper (25.7.08)	..	11·00	8·50
30		1d. dull purple and carmine (29.8.06)	..	6·50	70
31	7	2d. dull purple and ochre (25.7.08)	..	4·00	11·00
32	6	2½d. dull purple and ultramarine (23.7.06)	..	50·00	32·00
		a. Wide "A" in "LEEWARD"	..	£475	£300
33	7	3d. dull purple and black	..	6·50	30·00
		a. Chalk-surfaced paper (18.4.08)	..	27·00	50·00
34	6	6d. dull purple and brown (15.7.08)	..	35·00	65·00
35	8	1s. green and carmine (15.7.08)	..	42·00	85·00
29/35			Set of 7	£130	£200

1907 (14 Apr)–**11**. *Wmk Mult Crown CA. Chalk-surfaced paper* (3d. to 5s.). *P 14.*

36	7	¼d. brown ((7.8.09)	..	2·00	1·50
37	6	¼d. dull green	..	2·25	75
38		1d. bright red (7.07)	..	7·00	70
		a. Rose-carmine	..	28·00	2·25
39	7	2d. grey (3.8.11)	..	2·75	7·50
40	6	2½d. bright blue (5.07)	..	4·50	4·00
		a. Wide "A" in "LEEWARD"	..	£190	£170
41	7	3d. purple/yellow (28.10.10)	..	3·25	7·50
42	6	6d. dull and bright purple (3.8.11)	..	6·50	7·00
43	8	1s. black/green (3.8.11)	..	3·25	21·00
44	7	2s. 6d. black and red/blue (15.9.11)	..	38·00	48·00
45	8	5s. green and red/yellow (21.11.10)	..	40·00	65·00
36/45			Set of 10	£100	£150
36/45 Optd "Specimen"			Set of 10		£190

10   11

12   13

1912 (23 Oct)–**22**. *Die I* (¼d. to 3d., 6d., 1s., 2s. 6d., 5s.) *or Die II* (4d., 2s.). *Wmk Mult Crown CA. Chalk-surfaced paper* (3d. to 5s.). *P 14.*

46	10	¼d. brown	..	1·50	80
		a. Pale brown	..	3·00	1·50
47	11	½d. yellow-green (12.12)	..	4·75	2·00
		a. Deep green (1916)	..	4·25	1·25
48		1d. red	..	4·50	85
		a. Bright scarlet (1915)	..	5·00	85

49	10	2d. slate-grey (9.1.13)	.. ..	3·75	4·50
50	11	2½d. bright blue	..	2·75	7·00
		a. Deep bright blue (1914)	..	3·50	4·00
51	10	3d. purple/yellow (9.1.13)	..	1·50	10·00
		a. White back (Optd S. £42) (11.13)		48·00	95·00
		b. On lemon (1914)	..	3·50	16·00
		c. On buff (Optd S. £42) (1920)		35·00	48·00
		d. On orange-buff (1920)	..	3·50	9·00
		dw. Wmk inverted			
52		4d. blk & red/pale yell (Die II) (12.5.22)		3·25	20·00
53	11	6d. dull and bright purple (9.1.13)		2·00	8·00
54	12	1s. brown/green (9.1.13)	..	2·00	8·00
		a. White back (Optd S. £45) (11.13)		35·00	35·00
		b. On blue-green, olive back (Optd S. £45) (1917)		6·00	8·00
55	10	2s. purple & blue/blue (Die II) (12.5.22)		7·00	45·00
56		2s. 6d. black and red/blue (11.13)		11·00	38·00
57	12	5s. green and red/yellow (9.14)		42·00	80·00
		a. White back (Optd S. £48) (11.13)		42·00	75·00
		b. On lemon (1915)	..	17·00	55·00
		c. On orange-buff (1920)		85·00	£140
46/57b			Set of 12	50·00	£170
46/57 Optd "Specimen"			Set of 12		£275

Nos. 51a, 54a, and 57 were only on sale from Montserrat.

HIGH VALUE KEY TYPES. The reign of King Edward VII saw the appearance of the first in a new series of "key type" designs, initially on the issues of Malaya—Straits Settlements and Nyasaland, to be used for high value denominations where a smaller design was felt to be inappropriate. The system was extended during the reign of King George V, using the portrait as Leeward Islands Type 13, to cover Bermuda, Ceylon, Leeward Islands, Malaya—Straits Settlements, Malta and Nyasaland. A number of these territories continued to use the key type concept for high value King George VI stamps and one, Leeward Islands, for stamps of Queen Elizabeth II.

In each instance the King George V issues were printed in sheets of 60 (12×5) on various coloured papers. The system utilised a common "head" plate used with individual "duty" plates which printed the territory name and face value.

Two major plate flaws occur on the King George V head plate: the break on scroll on R. 1/12 and the broken crown and scroll on R. 2/12. Both of these occur in different states, having been repaired and then damaged once again, perhaps on several occasions. The prices quoted in the listings are for examples approximately as illustrated.

Break in scroll (R. 1/12)

Broken crown and scroll (R. 2/12)

"D I" shaved at foot 1d. R. 7/3 of left pane (all ptgs between Sept 1947 and July 1949. 1s. R. 9/6 of right pane (all ptgs between 1932 and 1938)

1921 (Oct)–**32**. *Wmk Mult Script CA or Mult Crown CA* (£1). *Chalk-surfaced paper. P 14.*

(a) Die II (1921–29)

58	10	¼d. brown (1922)	..	2·00	1·00
59	11	½d. blue-green	..	75	75
60		1d. carmine-red	..	2·00	55
61		1d. bright violet (1922)	..	2·25	1·00
62		1d. bright scarlet (1929)	..	5·50	2·25
63	10	1½d. carmine-red (10.9.26)	..	2·75	2·00
64		1½d. brown (1929)	..	75	10
65		2d. slate-grey (6.22)	..	1·50	80
		x. Wmk reversed			

66	11	2½d. orange-yellow (22.9.23)	..	6·00	45·00
67		2½d. bright blue (1.3.27)	..	2·75	1·00
68	10	3d. light ultramarine (22.9.23)	..	4·00	22·00
		a. Deep ultramarine (1925)	..	45·00	50·00
69		3d. purple/yellow (1.7.27)	..	85	6·50
70		4d. black and red/pale yellow (2.24)	..	2·50	20·00
71		5d. dull purple and olive-green (12.5.22)	..	2·25	4·25
72	11	6d. dull and bright purple (17.7.23)	..	9·00	27·00
73	12	1s. black/emerald (17.7.23)	..	5·50	8·00
74	10	2s. purple and blue/blue (12.5.22)	..	16·00	42·00
		a. Red-purple and blue/blue (1926)	..	7·00	42·00
		aw. Wmk inverted			£225
75		2s. 6d. black and red/blue (17.7.23)	..	6·50	23·00
76		3s. bright green and violet (12.5.22)	..	12·00	24·00
77		4s. black and red (12.5.22)	..	12·00	42·00
78	12	5s. green and red/pale yellow (17.7.23)	..	38·00	65·00
79	13	10s. green and red/green (1928)	..	50·00	75·00
		a. Break in scroll			£150
		b. Broken crown and scroll			£150
80		£1 purple and black/red (1928)	..	£225	£250
		a. Break in scroll			£375
		b. Broken crown and scroll			£375
58/80			Set of 22	£350	£600
58/80 Optd/Perf "Specimen"			Set of 23		£550

(b) Reversion to Die I (Plate 23) (1931–32)

81	10	¼d. brown	..	3·25	14·00
82	11	½d. blue-green	..	23·00	26·00
83		1d. bright scarlet	..	13·00	30
84	10	1½d. red-brown	..	2·75	2·75
85	11	2½d. bright blue	..	4·50	3·50
86		6d. dull and bright purple	..	14·00	70·00
87	12	1s. black/emerald	..	38·00	65·00
		a. "D I" flaw			£300
		b. "A" of "CA" missing from wmk		—	£2000
81/7			Set of 7	90·00	£160

No. 60 may not have been used locally before January 1923.

No. 68a was issued in St. Kitts-Nevis.

Nos. 59, 62 and 82/3 exist in coils, constructed from normal sheets.

Nos. 81/7 result from the use, in error, of Die I which had previously been "retired" in late 1920, to produce Plate 23.

1935 (6 May). *Silver Jubilee. As Nos. 114/17 of Jamaica, but printed by Waterlow. P 11×12.*

88		1d. deep blue and scarlet	..	1·60	1·25
89		1½d. ultramarine and grey	..	2·25	70
90		2½d. brown and deep blue	..	2·25	3·25
91		1s. slate and purple	..	5·50	14·00
		k. Kite and vertical log			£180
		l. Kite and horizontal log			£190
88/91			Set of 4	10·50	17·00
88/91 Perf "Specimen"			Set of 4		80·00

For illustrations of plate varieties see Omnibus section following Zimbabwe.

1937 (12 May). *Coronation. As Nos. 118/20 of Jamaica.*

92		1d. scarlet	..	30	15
93		1½d. buff	..	40	35
94		2½d. bright blue	..	40	45
92/4			Set of 3	1·00	85
92/4 Perf "Specimen"			Set of 3	60·00	

14   15

(Die A)   (Die B)

In Die B the figure "1" has a broader top and more projecting serif.

"ISLANDS" flaw (R. 1/2 of right pane) (Pl. 2 ptgs from November 1942 until corrected in July 1949)

Broken second "E" in "LEEWARD" (R. 4/1 of right pane) (Pl. 3 ptgs from August 1942 until corrected in June 1949)

Broken top right scroll (R. 5/11) (1942 ptg of 10s. only. Corrected on £1 value from same period)

Broken lower right scroll (R. 5/12. 1942 ptgs only)

Missing pearl
(R. 5/1. 1944 ptgs
only)

Gash in chin
(R. 2/5. 1942 ptgs
only)

1938 (25 Nov)–51. *T* **14** (*and similar type, but shaded value tablet,* ½*d.,* 1*d.,* 2½*d.,* 6*d.*) *and* **15** (10*s.,* £1). *Chalk-surfaced paper* (3*d. to* £1). *P* 14.

(a) *Wmk Mult Script CA*

95	¼d. brown			30	1·25
	a. Chalk-surfaced paper. *Dp brn* (13.6.49)			10	1·25
96	½d. emerald			60	60
	a. "ISLANDS" flaw			48·00	
97	½d. slate-grey (*chalk-surfaced paper*)				
	(1.7.49)			30	1·25
98	1d. scarlet (Die A)			9·00	1·75
99	1d. scarlet (*shades*) (Die B) (1940)			1·75	1·50
	a. "D I" flaw (9.47)			£150	
	b. Carmine (9.42)			1·00	4·25
	c. Red (13.9.48)			5·50	3·00
	ca. "D I" flaw			£150	
100	1d. blue-green (*chalk-surfaced paper*)				
	(1.7.49)			55	15
	"D I" flaw			£140	
101	1½d. chestnut			90	50
102	1½d. yellow-orange and black (*chalk-surfaced paper*) (1.7.49)			60	30
103	2d. olive-grey			2·50	1·00
	a. Slate-grey (11.42)			5·50	2·75
104	2d. scarlet (*chalk-surfaced paper*) (1.7.49)			1·40	90
	a. Vermilion (24.10.51)			15·00	9·00
105	2½d. bright blue			8·50	2·25
	a. Light bright blue (11.42)			60	1·25
106	2½d. black and purple (*chalk-surfaced paper*) (1.7.49)			55	15
107	3d. orange			35·00	2·75
	a. Ordinary paper. *Pale orange* (11.42)			40	85
108	3d. bright blue (1.7.49)			65	15
109	6d. deep dull purple and bright purple			20·00	4·75
	a. Ordinary paper (8.42)			4·50	2·25
	ab. Broken "E"			£200	
	b. Purple and deep magenta (29.9.47)			4·50	2·75
	ba. Broken "E"			£200	
110	1s. black/*emerald*			16·00	2·00
	a. "D I" flaw			£325	
	b. Ordinary paper (3.42)			4·25	90
	ba. Grey and black/emerald (8.42)			23·00	9·00
	bb. Black and grey/emerald (11.42)			£130	11·00
111	2s. reddish purple and blue/*blue*			20·00	2·25
	a. Ordinary paper (3.42)			10·00	1·50
	ab. Deep purple and blue/blue (29.9.47)			10·00	2·25
112	5s. green and red/*yellow*			48·00	15·00
	a. Ordinary paper (12.43)			32·00	14·00
	ab. Broken "E" (R. 3/4 of left pane)			£500	
	b. Bright green and red/yellow (24.10.51)			55·00	50·00
113	10s. bluish green and deep red/*green*			£190	£120
	a. Ordinary paper. *Pale green and dull red/green* (26.6.44*)			£425	£250
	ad. Broken top right scroll			£3000	
	ae. Broken lower right scroll			£3000	£3000
	af. Gash in chin			£2750	
	b. Ordinary paper. *Green and red/green* (22.2.45*)			£150	65·00
	c. Ordinary paper. *Deep green and deep vermilion/green* (17.7.48*)			£120	70·00
	ca. Missing pearl			£1200	

(b) *Wmk Mult Crown CA*

114	£1 brown-purple and black/*red*			£300	£225
	a. Purple and black/carmine (21.9.42*)			85·00	45·00
	ae. Broken lower right scroll			£1100	£550
	af. Gash in chin			£1100	£550
	b. Brown-purple & black/salmon (5.2.45*)			35·00	24·00
	ba. Missing pearl			£950	£650
	c. Perf 13. Violet & black/scarlet (4.1.52*)			32·00	38·00
	ca. Wmk sideways			£3000	
	cw. Wmk inverted			£2250	
95/114b			*Set of 19*	£190	£100
95/114 Perf "Specimen"			*Set of 13*	£500	

*Dates quoted for Nos. 113a/14c are earliest known postmark dates. Nos. 113a and 114a were despatched to the Leeward Islands in March 1942, Nos. 113b and 114b in December 1943, No. 113c in June 1944 and No. 114c on 13 December 1951.

Nos. 96, 98/9 and 99b exist in coils constructed from normal sheets.

Printings of the 10s. in March 1942 (No. 113a) and of the £1 in February and October 1942 (No. 114a) were made by Williams Lea & Co. Ltd following bomb damage to the De La Rue works in 1940.

For illustrations of Nos. 99a, 99ca, 100a and 110a see above No. 58.

1946 (1 Nov). *Victory. As Nos.* 141/2 *of Jamaica.*

115	1½d. brown			15	30
116	3d. red-orange			15	30
115/16 Perf "Specimen"			*Set of 2*	55·00	

1949 (2 Jan). *Royal Silver Wedding. As Nos.* 143/4 *of Jamaica.*

117	2½d. ultramarine			10	10
118	5s. green			3·75	2·75

1949 (10 Oct). *75th Anniv of Universal Postal Union. As Nos.* 145/8 *of Jamaica.*

119	2½d. blue-black			15	80
120	3d. deep blue			1·25	80
121	6d. magenta			30	80
122	1s. blue-green			30	80
119/22			*Set of 4*	1·75	2·75

(New Currency. 100 cents = 1 B.W.I. dollar)

1951 (16 Feb). *Inauguration of B.W.I. University College. As Nos.* 149/50 *of Jamaica.*

123	3 c. orange and black			30	60
124	12 c. rose-carmine and reddish violet		60	60

1953 (2 June). *Coronation. As No.* 153 *of Jamaica.*

125	3 c. black and green			40	1·75

16   Queen Elizabeth II   17

1954. (22 Feb). *Chalk-surfaced paper. Wmk Mult Script CA. P* 14 (*T* **16**) *or* 13 (*T* **17**)

126	**16**	½ c. brown		10	40
127		1 c. grey		50	75
128		2 c. green		50	10
129		3 c. yellow-orange and black		1·25	75
130		4 c. rose-red		1·00	10
131		5 c. black and brown-purple		1·75	75
132		6 c. yellow-orange		1·75	30
133		8 c. ultramarine		2·50	10
134		12 c. dull and reddish purple		1·75	10
135		24 c. black and green		1·75	20
136		48 c. dull purple and ultramarine		6·00	2·75
137		60 c. brown and green		6·00	2·25
138		$1.20, yellow-green and rose-red		5·00	2·75
139	**17**	$2.40, bluish green and red		6·50	5·00
140		$4.80, brown-purple and black		6·50	6·50
126/40			*Set of 15*	38·00	20·00

The 3 c., 4 c., 6 c., 8 c., 24 c., 48 c., 60 c. and $1.20 have their value tablets unshaded.

The stamps of Leeward Islands were withdrawn and invalidated on 1 July 1956 when the federal colony was dissolved.

Lesotho

(*formerly* Basutoland)

BASUTOLAND

Stamps of CAPE OF GOOD HOPE were used in Basutoland from about 1876, initially cancelled by upright oval with framed number type postmarks of that colony. Cancellation numbers known to have been used in Basutoland are 133 (Quthing), 156 (Mafeteng), 210 (Mohaleshoek), 277 (Morija), 281 (Maseru), 317 (Thlotse Heights) and 688 (Teyateyaneng).

From 1910 until 1933 the stamps of SOUTH AFRICA were in use. Stamps of the Union provinces are also known used in Basutoland during the early years of this period and can also be found cancelled-to-order during 1932–33.

The following post offices and postal agencies existed in Basutoland before December 1933. Stamps of Cape of Good Hope or South Africa with recognisable postmarks from them are worth a premium. For a few of the smaller offices or agencies there are, as yet, no actual examples recorded. Dates given are those generally accepted as the year in which the office was first opened.

Bokong (1931)	Motsekuoa (1915)
Butha Buthe (1907)	Mount Morosi (1918)
Jonathan's (1927)	Mphotos (1914)
Khabos (1927)	Peka (1908)
Khetisas (1930)	Phamong (1932)
Khukhune (1933)	Pitseng (1921)
Kolonyama (1914)	Qachasnek (1895)
Kueneng (1914)	Qalo (1923?)
Leribe (1890)	Quthing (1882)
Mafeteng (1874)	Rankakalas (1933)
Majara (1912)	Roma Mission (1913)
Makhoa (1932)	Sebapala (1930)
Makoalis (1927)	Seforong (1924)
Mamathes (1919)	Sehlabathebe (1921)
Mapoteng (1925)	Sekake (1931)
Marakabeis (1932)	Teyateyaneng (1886)
Maseru (1872)	Thaba Bosigo (1913)
Maseru Rail (1915?)	Thabana Morena (1922)
Mashai (1929)	Thabaneng (1914)
Matsaile (1930)	Thaba Tseka (1929)
Mekading (1914)	Thlotse Heights (1872)
Mofokas (1915)	Tsepo (1923)
Mohaleshoek (1873)	Tsoelike (1927)
Mokhotlong (1921)	Tsoloane (1918)
Morija (1884)	

For further details of the postal history of Basutoland see *The Cancellations and Postal Markings of Basutoland/Lesotho* by A. H. Scott, published by Collectors Mail Auctions (Pty) Ltd, Cape Town, from which the above has been, with permission, extracted.

CROWN COLONY

1   King George V,
Nile Crocodile
and Mountains

2   King George VI,
Nile Crocodile
and Mountains

(Recess Waterlow)

1933 (1 Dec). *Wmk Mult Script CA. P* 12½.

1	1	½d. emerald		80	1·75
2		1d. scarlet		60	1·00
3		2d. bright purple		90	55
4		3d. bright blue		70	60
5		4d. grey		2·00	7·00
6		6d. orange-yellow		2·25	1·50
7		1s. red-orange		2·25	4·50
8		2s. 6d. sepia		20·00	45·00
9		5s. violet		42·00	60·00
10		10s. olive-green		£110	£120
1/10			*Set of 10*	£160	£200
1/10 Perf "Specimen"			*Set of 10*	£250	

1935 (4 May). *Silver Jubilee. As Nos.* 114/17 *of Jamaica, but ptd by D.L.R. P* 13½ × 14.

11		1d. deep blue and carmine		55	25
	f. Diagonal line by turret			65·00	
12		2d. ultramarine and grey		65	75
	f. Diagonal line by turret			55·00	
	g. Dot to left of chapel			85·00	
13		3d. brown and deep blue		3·75	3·25
	g. Dot to left of chapel			£140	
	h. Dot by flagstaff			£140	
14		6d. slate and purple		3·75	3·25
	g. Dot to left of chapel			£150	
	h. Dot by flagstaff			£150	
	i. Dash by turret			£150	
11/14			*Set of 4*	8·00	6·75
11/14 Perf "Specimen"			*Set of 4*	80·00	

For illustrations of plate varieties see Omnibus section following Zimbabwe.

1937 (12 May). *Coronation. As Nos.* 118/20 *of Jamaica. P* 14.

15		1d. scarlet		35	50
16		2d. bright purple		50	85
17		3d. bright blue		60	85
15/17			*Set of 3*	1·25	2·00
15/17 Perf "Specimen"			*Set of 3*	55·00	

Tower flaw (R. 2/4)

(Recess Waterlow)

1938 (1 Apr). *Wmk Mult Script CA. P* 12½.

18	2	½d. green		30	1·00
19		1d. scarlet		50	60
	a. Tower flaw			80·00	
20		1½d. light blue		40	50
21		2d. bright purple		30	60
22		3d. bright blue		30	90
23		4d. grey		1·50	3·25
24		6d. orange-yellow		50	85
25		1s. red-orange		50	90
26		2s. 6d. sepia		8·00	7·50
27		5s. violet		22·00	9·00
28		10s. olive-green		22·00	17·00
18/28			*Set of 11*	50·00	38·00
18/28 Perf "Specimen"			*Set of 11*	£190	

Basutoland

(3)

1945 (3 Dec). *Victory. Stamps of South Africa, optd with T* **3**, *inscr alternately in English and Afrikaans.*

				Un. pair	Used pair	Used single
29	55	1d. brown and carmine		40	40	10
30	56	2d. slate-blue and violet		40	40	10
31	57	3d. deep blue and blue		40	70	15
29/31			*Set of 3*	1·10	1·40	30

4 King George VI

5 King George VI and Queen Elizabeth

6 Queen Elizabeth II as Princess, and Princess Margaret

7 The Royal Family

(Recess Waterlow)

1947 (17 Feb). *Royal Visit. Wmk Mult Script CA. P 12½.*
32	4	1d. scarlet	..	..	10	10
33	5	2d. green	..	..	10	10
34	6	3d. ultramarine	..	..	10	10
35	7	1s. mauve	..	..	15	10
32/5			*Set of 4*		40	30
32/5	Perf "Specimen"		*Set of 4*		80·00	

1948 (1 Dec). *Royal Silver Wedding. As Nos. 143/4 of Jamaica.*
36	1½d. ultramarine	..	20	10
37	10s. grey-olive	..	30·00	27·00

1949 (10 Oct). *75th Anniv of Universal Postal Union. As Nos. 145/8 of Jamaica.*
38	1½d. blue	..	30	60
39	3d. deep blue	..	1·75	1·75
40	6d. orange	..	1·50	1·75
41	1s. red-brown	..	1·00	90
38/41		*Set of 4*	4·00	4·50

1953 (3 June). *Coronation. As No. 153 of Jamaica.*
42	2d. black and reddish purple	40	50

8 Qiloane

9 Mohair (Shearing Angora Goats)

(Recess D.L.R.)

1954 (18 Oct)–58. *Designs as T 8/9. Wmk Mult Script CA. P 11½ (10s.) or 13½ (others).*
43	½d. grey-black and sepia	..	..	10	10
44	1d. grey-black and bluish green	..	..	10	10
45	2d. deep bright blue and orange	..	60	10
46	3d. yellow-green and deep rose-red	..	80	30
	a. Yellow-green and rose (27.11.58)			6·00	1·25
47	4½d. indigo and deep ultramarine	..	70	15
48	6d. chestnut and deep grey-green	..	1·25	15
49	1s. bronze-green and purple	..	1·25	30
50	1s. 3d. brown and turquoise-green	..	16·00	4·50
51	2s. 6d. deep ultramarine and crimson	13·00	7·00
	a. Brt ultram & crimson-lake (27.11.58)		40·00	16·00
52	5s. black and carmine-red	..	5·00	8·50
53	10s. black and maroon	..	18·00	23·00
43/53		*Set of 11*	48·00	40·00

Designs: *Horiz as T 8*—1d. Orange River; 2d Mosuto horseman; 3d. Basuto household; 4½d. Maletsunyane Falls; 6d. Herd-boy with Lesiba. 1s. Pastoral scene; 1s. 3d. Aeroplane over Lancers' Gap; 2s. 6d. Old Fort Leribe; 5s. Mission Cave House.

½d.

(19)

20 "Chief Moshoeshoe I" (engraving by Delangle)

1959 (1 Aug). *No. 45 surch with T 19, by South African Govt Ptr, Pretoria.*
54	½d. on 2d. deep bright blue and orange	10	15

(Des from drawings by James Walton. Recess Waterlow)

1959 (15 Dec). *Basutoland National Council. T 20 and similar vert designs. W w 12. P 13 × 13½.*
55	3d. black and yellow-olive	30	10
56	1s. carmine and yellow-green	30	10
57	1s. 3d. ultramarine and red-orange	45	45
55/7	*Set of 3*	95	95

Designs:—1s. Council house; 1s. 3d. Mosuto horseman.

(New Currency. 100 cents = 1 rand)

½C.	1c.	2c
(23)	(24)	(25)

2½c	2½c	3½c	3½c
(I)	(II)	(I)	(II)

5c	5c	10c	10c
(I)	(II)	(I)	(II)

12½c	12½c	50c	50c
(I)	(II)	(I)	(II)

25c	25c	25c
(I)	(II)	(III)

R1	R1	R1
(I)	(II)	(III)

1961 (14 Feb). *Nos. 43/53 surch with T 23 (½ c.),* **24** *(1 c.) or as T* **25** *(others) by South African Govt Printer, Pretoria.*
58	½ c. on ½d. grey-black and sepia		10	10
	a. Surch double		£325	
59	1 c. on 1d. grey-black and bluish green		10	10
60	2 c. on 2d. deep bright blue and orange	·	10	10
	a. Surch inverted		95·00	
61	2½ c. on 3d. yellow-green and rose (Type I)		10	10
	a. Type II		10	10
	b. Type II inverted		—£1100	
62	3½ c. on 4½d. indigo & deep ultram (Type I)	..	10	10
	a. Type II		2·00	4·00
63	5 c. on 6d. chestnut & dp grey-green (Type I)		10	10
	a. Type II		15	10
64	10 c. on 1s. bronze-green and purple (Type I)	..	10	10
	a. Type II		80·00	80·00
65	12½ c. on 1s. 3d. brown & turq-green (Type I)		1·00	20
	a. Type II		1·00	20
66	25 c. on 2s. 6d. bright ultramarine and crimson-lake (Type I)	..	30	30
	a. Type II		27·00	7·50
	b. Type III		30	50
67	50 c. on 5s. black and carmine-red (Type I)		1·25	1·40
	a. Type II		90	1·40
68	1 r. on 10s. black and maroon (Type I)		22·00	7·50
	a. Type II		8·50	23·00
	b. Type III		7·00	7·50
58/68b		*Set of 11*	8·50	9·00

There were two printings of the 2½ c. Type II, differing in the position of the surcharge on the stamps.
Examples of the 2 c. surcharge are known in a fount similar to Type **24** (*Price £140, unused*).

26 Basuto Household   27 Protein Foods

(Recess D.L.R.)

1961–63. *As Nos. 43/53 but values in cents as in T* **26**. *Wmk Mult Script CA. P 13½ or 11½ (1 r.).*
69	½ c. grey-black and sepia (as ½d.) (25.9.62)	10	20
	a. Imperf (pair)		£200	
70	1 c. grey-blk & bluish grn (as 1d.) (25.9.62)	10	40
71	2 c. dp brt blue & orange (as 2d.) (25.9.62)	50	1·40
72	2½ c. yellow-green & deep rose-red (14.2.61)	80	20
	a. Pale yellow-green & rose-red (22.5.62)	8·50	60
73	3½ c. indigo & dp ultram (as 4½d.) (25.9.62)	30	1·50
74	5 c. chestnut and deep grey-green (as 6d.) (10.8.62)	50	75
75	10 c. bronze-green & pur (as 1s.) (22.10.62)	30	40
76	12½ c. brown and turquoise-green (as 1s. 3d.) (17.12.62)	14·00	7·50
77	25 c. deep ultramarine and crimson (as 2s. 6d.) (25.9.62)	6·50	6·50
78	50 c. black & carmine-red (as 5s.) (22.10.62)	15·00	15·00
79	1 r. black and maroon (as 10s.) (4.2.63)	23·00	12·00
	a. Black and light maroon (16.12.63)	42·00	20·00
69/79		*Set of 11*	55·00	40·00

(Des M. Goaman. Photo Harrison)

1963 (4 June). *Freedom from Hunger. W w 12. P 14 × 14½.*
80	**27**	12½ c. reddish violet	40	15

1963 (2 Sept). *Red Cross Centenary. As Nos. 203/4 of Jamaica.*
81	2½ c. red and black	20	10
82	12½ c. red and blue	80	60

1964. *As Nos. 70, 72, 74, 76 and 78, but W w 12.*
84	1 c. grey-black and bluish green (11.8.64)	10	20
86	2½ c. pale yellow-green and rose-red (10.3.64)	15	15
88	5 c. chestnut and deep grey-green (10.11.64)	30	40
90	12½ c. brown and turquoise-green (10.11.64)	2·75	1·50
92	50 c. black and carmine-red (29.9.64)	7·25	10·00
84/92		*Set of 5*	9·50	11·00

SELF-GOVERNMENT

28 Mosotho Woman and Child   29 Maseru Border Post

1965 (10 May). *New Constitution. T* **28/9** *and similar horiz designs. Multicoloured. W w 12. P 14 × 13½.*
94	2½ c. Type 28		20	10
	w. Wmk inverted		22·00	
95	3½ c. Type 29		25	20
96	5 c. Mountain scene		25	20
	w. Wmk inverted		22·00	
97	12½ c. Legislative Buildings		45	70
94/7		*Set of 4*	1·10	1·10

30 I.T.U. Emblem   31 I.C.Y. Emblem

(Des M. Goaman. Litho Enschedé)

1965 (17 May). *I.T.U. Centenary. W w 12. P 11 × 11½.*
98	**30**	1 c. orange-red and bright purple	15	10
99		20 c. light blue and orange-brown	35	30

(Des V. Whiteley. Litho Harrison)

1965 (25 Oct). *International Co-operation Year. W w 12. P 14½.*
100	**31**	½ c. reddish purple & turquoise-green	10	10
101		12½ c. deep bluish green and lavender	45	35

32 Sir Winston Churchill and St. Paul's Cathedral in Wartime

(Des Jennifer Toombs. Photo Harrison)

1966 (24 Jan). *Churchill Commemoration. Printed in black, cerise, gold and background in colours stated. W w 12. P 14.*
102	**32**	1 c. new blue	15	30
103		2½ c. deep green	35	10
104		10 c. brown	45	30
105		22½ c. bluish violet	70	60
102/5		*Set of 4*	1·50	1·10

Basutoland attained independence on 4 October 1966 as the Kingdom of Lesotho.

LESOTHO

INDEPENDENT KINGDOM

King Moshoeshoe II, 4 October 1966–November 1990 (deposed)

33 Moshoeshoe I and Moshoeshoe II

(Des and photo Harrison)

1966 (4 Oct). *Independence. P 12½ × 13.*
106	**33**	2½ c. light brown, black and red	..	10	10
107		5 c. light brown, black and new blue	..	10	10
108		10 c. light brown, black and emerald	..	15	10
109		20 c. light brown, black & bright purple	..	20	15
106/9		*Set of 4*		45	30

LESOTHO

(34)

35 "Education Culture and Science"

1966 (1 Nov). *Stamps of Basutoland optd as T **34**. A. On Nos. 69/71 and 73/9 (Script CA wmk)*

110A	½ c. grey-black and sepia	..	10	10
111A	1 c. grey-black and bluish green	..	10	10
112A	2 c. deep bright blue and orange	..	60	10
114A	3½ c. indigo and deep ultramarine	..	30	10
115A	5 c. chestnut and deep grey-green	..	10	10
116A	10 c. bronze-green and purple	..	10	10
117A	12½ c. brown and turquoise-green	..	4·50	35
118A	25 c. deep ultramarine and crimson	..	30	20
119A	50 c. black and carmine-red	..	80	65
120A	1 r. black and maroon	..	75	3·00
	a. "LSEOTHO"	..	60·00	
	b. Opt double	..	90·00	
	ba. Ditto. "LSEOTHO"			
110A/20A		*Set of 10*	6·50	4·00

B. On Nos. 84/92 and unissued 1 r. (wmk w 12)

111B	1 c. grey-black and bluish green	..	10	10
113B	2½ c. pale yellow-green and rose-red	..	50	10
115B	5 c. chestnut and deep grey-green	..	20	10
117B	12½ c. brown and turquoise-green	..	30	20
119B	50 c. black and carmine-red	..	60	50
120B	1 r. black and maroon	..	65	75
	a. "LSEOTHO"	..	40·00	
111B/20B		*Set of 6*	2·00	1·40

(Des V. Whiteley. Litho D.L.R.)

1966 (1 Dec). *20th Anniv of U.N.E.S.C.O. P 14½ × 14.*

121	35	2½ c. orange-yellow and emerald-green	..	10	10
122		5 c. light green and olive	..	15	10
123		12½ c. light blue and red	..	35	10
124		25 c. red-orange and deep greenish blue	60	25
121/4			*Set of 4*	1·10	40

36 Maize

37 Moshoeshoe II

(Des and photo Harrison)

1967 (1 Apr). *Designs as T **36**/7. No wmk. P 14½ × 13½ (2 r.) or 13½ × 14½ (others).*

125	½ c. bluish green and light bluish violet	..	10	10
126	1 c. sepia and rose-red	..	10	10
127	2 c. orange-yellow and light green	..	10	65
128	2½ c. black and ochre	..	10	10
129	3½ c. chalky blue and yellow	..	10	20
130	5 c. bistre and new blue	..	10	10
131	10 c. yellow-brown and bluish grey	..	10	10
132	12½ c. black and red-orange	..	20	10
133	25 c. black and bright blue	..	55	20
134	50 c. black, new blue and turquoise	..	4·50	65
135	1 r. multicoloured	..	65	75
136	2 r. black, gold and magenta	..	1·00	1·75
125/36		*Set of 12*	6·25	4·00

Designs: *Horiz as T **36**—1 c. Cattle; 2 c. Agaves (wrongly inscr "Aloes"); 2½ c. Basotho Hat; 3½ c. Merino Sheep ("Wool"); 5 c. Basotho Pony; 10 c. Wheat; 12½ c. Angora Goat ("Mohair"); 25 c. Maletsunyane Falls; 50 c. Diamonds; 1 r. Arms of Lesotho. See also Nos. 147/59 and 191/203.*

46 Students and University

(Des V. Whiteley. Photo Harrison)

1967 (7 Apr). *First Conferment of University Degrees. P 14 × 14½.*

137	46	1 c. sepia, ultram & light yellow-orange	10	10
138		2½ c. sepia, ultram & light greenish blue	10	10
139		12½ c. sepia, ultramarine and rose	..	10	10
140		25 c. sepia, ultramarine and light violet	15	15
137/40			*Set of 4*	30	30

47 Statue of Moshoeshoe I

(Des and photo Harrison)

1967 (4 Oct). *First Anniv of Independence. T **47** and similar triangular designs. P 14½ × 14.*

141	2½ c. black and light yellow-green	..	10	10
142	12½ c. multicoloured	..	25	15
143	25 c. black, green and light ochre	..	35	25
141/3		*Set of 3*	65	40

Designs:—12½ c. Lesotho flag; 25 c. Crocodile (national emblem).

50 Lord Baden-Powell and Scout Saluting

(Des V. Whiteley. Photo Harrison)

1967 (1 Nov). *60th Anniv of Scout Movement. P 14 × 14½.*

144	50	15 c. multicoloured	..	20	10

51 W.H.O. Emblem and World Map

(Des G. Vasarhelyi. Photo Harrison)

1968 (7 Apr). *20th Anniv of World Health Organization. T **51** and similar horiz design. P 14 × 14½.*

145	2½ c. blue, gold and carmine-red	..	15	10
	a. Gold (emblem) omitted	..		
146	25 c. multicoloured	..	45	30

Design:—25 c. Nurse and child.

53 Basotho Hat

54 Sorghum

1968–69. *As Nos. 125/36 and T **54**, but wmk **53** (sideways on 2 r.).*

147	½ c. bluish green & lt bluish vio (26.11.68)	10	10
	a. Blue-green and violet (30.9.69)	1·25	1·25
148	1 c. sepia and rose-red (26.11.68)	..	10	10
149	2 c. orange-yellow & lt green (26.11.68)	10	10
	a. Orange-yellow & yell-grn (30.9.69)	80	90
150	2½ c. black and ochre (21.10.68)	..	15	10
	a. Black and yellow-ochre (30.9.69)	80	80
151	3 c. chocolate, green & yell-brn (1.8.68)	15	15
152	3½ c. chalky blue and yellow (26.11.68)	15	10
153	5 c. bistre and new blue (22.7.68)	30	10
154	10 c. yell-brn & pale bluish grey (26.11.68)	15	10
155	12½ c. black and red-orange (30.9.69)	60	35
156	25 c. black and bright blue (30.9.69)	1·50	1·00
157	50 c. black, new blue & turquoise (30.9.69)	11·00	2·50
158	1 r. multicoloured (26.11.68)	..	1·50	2·75
159	2 r. black, gold and magenta (30.9.69)	8·00	13·00
147/59		*Set of 13*	21·00	18·00

55 Running Hunters

(Des Jennifer Toombs. Photo Harrison)

1968 (1 Nov). *Rock Paintings. T **55** and similar designs. W **53** (sideways on 5 c., 15 c.). P 14 × 14½ (5 c., 15 c.) or 14½ × 14 (others).*

160	3 c. yellow-brown. lt blue-green & blackish green	25	10
161	3½ c. greenish yellow, yellow-olive and sepia	30	10
162	5 c. Venetian red, yell-ochre & blackish brn	35	10
163	10 c. yellow, rose and deep maroon	..	45	10
164	15 c. light buff, pale olive-yell & blackish brn	75	30
165	20 c. yellow-grn, greenish yellow & blackish brown	90	55
166	25 c. yellow, orange-brown and black	1·00	75
160/6		*Set of 7*	3·50	1·75

Designs: *Horiz*—3½ c. Baboons; 10 c. Archers; 20 c. Eland; 25 c. Hunting scene. *Vert*—5 c. Javelin throwing; 15 c. Blue Cranes.

62 Queen Elizabeth II Hospital

(Des C. R. Househam and G. Drummond. Litho P.B.)

1969 (11 Mar). *Centenary of Maseru (capital). T **62** and similar horiz designs. Multicoloured. W **53** (sideways). P 14 × 13½.*

167	2½ c. Type **62**	..	10	10
168	10 c. Lesotho Radio Station	..	10	10
169	12½ c. Leabua Jonathan Airport	..	35	10
170	25 c. Royal Palace	..	25	15
167/70		*Set of 4*	65	30

66 Rally Car passing Mosotho Horseman

(Des P. Wheeler. Photo Harrison)

1969 (26 Sept). *Roof of Africa Car Rally. T **66** and similar horiz designs. W **53**. P 14.*

171	2½ c. yellow, mauve and plum	..	15	10
172	12½ c. cobalt, greenish yellow and olive-grey	20	10
173	15 c. blue, black and mauve	..	20	10
174	20 c. black, red and yellow ..	..	20	10
171/4		*Set of 4*	65	30

Designs:—12½ c. Rally car on mountain road; 15 c. Chequered flags and mountain scenery; 20 c. Map of rally route and Rally Trophy.

71 Gryponyx and Footprints

75 Moshoeshoe I, when a Young Man

(Des Jennifer Toombs. Photo Harrison)

1970 (5 Jan). *Prehistoric Footprints (1st series). T **71** and similar designs. W **53** (sideways*). P 14×14½ (3 c.) or 14½×14 (others).*

175	3 c. pale brown, yellow-brown and sepia	..	70	70
176	5 c. dull purple, pink and sepia	..	85	30
	w. Wmk hat pointing right	..	3·25	
177	10 c. pale yellow, black and sepia	..	1·00	35
178	15 c. olive-yellow, black and sepia	..	1·60	2·25
179	25 c. cobalt and black	..	2·50	2·25
175/9		*Set of 5*	6·00	5·25

Designs: (60×23 mm)—3 c. Dinosaur footprints at Moyeni. (40×24 mm)—10 c. Plateosauravus and footprints; 15 c. Tritylodon and footprints; 25 c. Massospondylus and footprints. *The normal sideways watermark shows the hat pointing left, when seen from the back of the stamp.
See also Nos. 596/8.

(Des G. Vasarhelyi. Litho D.L.R.)

1970 (11 Mar). *Death Centenary of King Moshoeshoe I. T **75** and similar vert design. W **53**. P 13½.*

180	2½ c. pale green and magenta	..	10	10
181	25 c. pale blue and chesnut.	..	20	20

Design:—25 c. Moshoeshoe I as an old man.

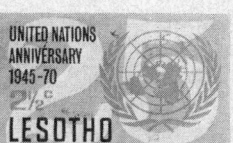

77 U.N. Emblem and "25"

(Des V. Whiteley. Litho Questa)

1970 (26 June). *25th Anniv of United Nations. T **77** and similar horiz designs. W **53** (sideways). P 14½×14.*

182	2½ c. light pink, light blue and maroon	..	10	10
183	10 c. multicoloured	..	10	10
184	12½ c. brown-red, cobalt and drab	..	10	15
185	25 c. multicoloured	..	15	30
182/5		*Set of 4*	30	50

Designs:—10 c. U.N. Building; 12½ c. "People of the World"; 25 c. Symbolic dove.

78 Basotho Hat Gift Shop, Maseru

(Des G. Drummond. Litho Questa)

1970 (27 Oct). *Tourism. T **78** and similar horiz designs. Multicoloured. P 14.*

186	2½ c. Type **78**	..	10	10
187	5 c. Trout fishing	..	20	10
188	10 c. Pony trekking	..	25	10
189	12½ c. Skiing	..	50	10
190	20 c. Holiday Inn, Maseru	..	40	50
186/90		*Set of 5*	1·25	70

79 Maize

80 Lammergeier

(Des Harrison. Litho Questa)

1971 (4 Jan–1 Apr). *As Nos. 147/58 but in new format omitting portrait of Moshoeshoe II, as in T* **79**. *4 c. and 2 r. in new designs.* W **53** *(sideways* except 2 r.).* P 14.

191	½ c. blue-green and light bluish violet	..		10	10
192	1 c. brown and orange-red	..	..	10	10
193	2 c. yellow and green	..		10	10
	w. Wmk top of hat to right				
194	2½ c. black, olive-green and yellow-ochre		10	10
195	3 c. brown, green and yellow-ochre		10	10
196	3½ c. indigo and yellow	..	..	10	10
196a	4 c. multicoloured (1.4.71)	..	..	20	10
	aw. Wmk top of hat to right				
197	5 c. yellow-brown and pale blue	..	15	10
198	10 c. orange-brown and grey-blue	..	15	10
199	12½ c. chocolate and yellow-orange	..	25	30
200	25 c. slate and pale bright blue	..	60	40
201	50 c. black, pale blue and turquoise-green	6·00	4·25
202	1 r. multicoloured	..	..	1·75	2·25
203	2 r. yellow-brown and ultramarine	..	1·75	3·00
191/203			Set of 14	10·00	9·50

Designs: *Horiz*—4 c. National flag. *Vert*—2 r. Statue of Moshoeshoe I.

**The normal sideways watermark shows top of hat to left, as seen from the back of the stamp.*

For 2 r. value without watermark see No. 401

(Des R. Granger Barrett. Litho J.W.)

1971 (1 Mar). *Birds.* T **80** *and similar vert designs. Multicoloured.* W **53**. P 14.

204	2½ c. Type 80	..	..	2·25	20
205	5 c. Bald Ibis	..	..	3·00	2·50
206	10 c. Rufous Rockjumper	..	3·00	2·00
207	12½ c. Blue Bustard	..	..	3·75	3·50
208	15 c. Painted Snipe	..	..	4·25	4·50
209	20 c. Golden-breasted Bunting	..	4·25	4·50
210	25 c. Ground Woodpecker	..	5·00	4·50
204/10			Set of 7	23·00	19·00

81 Lionel Collett Dam

(Des G. Drummond. Litho J.W.)

1971 (15 July). *Soil Conservation.* T **81** *and similar horiz designs. Multicoloured.* W **53** *(sideways).* P 14.

211	4 c. Type 81	..	..	10	10
212	10 c. Contour ridges	..	..	10	10
213	15 c. Earth dams	..	..	25	10
214	25 c. Beaver dams	..	..	35	35
211/14			Set of 4	70	50

82 Diamond Mining

(Des J.W. Litho Questa)

1971 (4 Oct). *Development.* T **82** *and similar horiz designs. Multicoloured.* W **53** *(sideways).* P 14.

215	4 c. Type 82	..	..	75	40
216	10 c. Pottery	..	..	30	10
217	15 c. Weaving	..	..	45	60
218	20 c. Construction	..	..	55	1·50
215/18			Set of 4	1·90	2·25

83 Mail Cart

84 Sprinting

(Des D. B. Picton-Phillips. Litho Questa)

1972 (3 Jan). *Post Office Centenary.* T **83** *and similar designs.* W **53** *(sideways on 5, 10 and 20 c.).* P 14 × 13½ (15 c.) or 13½ × 14 (others).

219	5 c. pale pink and black	..	..	15	20
220	10 c. multicoloured	..	..	15	10
221	15 c. pale drab, light blue and black	..	30	15
222	20 c. multicoloured	..	..	45	90
219/22			Set of 4	95	1·10

Designs: *Horiz*—10 c. Postal bus; 20 c. Maseru P.O. *Vert*—15 c. Cape of Good Hope 4d. stamp of 1876.

(Des J. W. Litho Questa)

1972 (1 Sept). *Olympic Games. Munich.* T **84** *and similar vert designs. Multicoloured.* W **53**. P 14.

223	4 c. Type 84	..	..	15	10
	w. Wmk inverted				
224	10 c. Shot putting	..	..	20	10
225	15 c. Hurdling	..	..	30	10
226	25 c. Long-jumping	..	..	35	55
223/6			Set of 4	90	70

85 "Adoration of the Shepherds" (Matthias Stomer)

(Des and litho J.W.)

1972 (1 Dec). *Christmas.* W **53** *(sideways).* P 14.

227	**85** 4 c. multicoloured	..	..	10	10
228	10 c. multicoloured	..	..	10	10
229	25 c. multicoloured	..	..	15	20
227/9			Set of 3	30	30

86 W.H.O. Emblem   (87)

O.A.U.
10th Anniversary
Freedom in Unity

(Des. J. Cooter. Litho Questa)

1973 (7 Apr). *25th Anniv of W.H.O.* W **53** *(sideways).* P 13½.

230	**86** 20 c. greenish blue and yellow	..	30	30

1973 (25 May). *Tenth Anniv of O.A.U. Nos. 194 and 196a/8 optd with T* **87** *by Govt Printer, Maseru.*

231	2½ c. black, olive-green and yellow-ochre	..	10	10
232	4 c. multicoloured	..	..	10	10
	a. Horiz pair, one without opt	..	£150	
233	5 c. yellow-brown and pale blue	..	10	10
234	10 c. orange-brown and grey-blue	..	15	15
231/4			Set of 4	35	35

88 Basotho Hat and W.F.P. Emblem

(Des locally; adapted J. Cooter. Litho Format)

1973 (1 June). *Tenth Anniv of World Food Programme.* T **88** *and similar horiz designs. Multicoloured.* W **53** *(sideways).* P 13½.

235	4 c. Type 88	..	..	10	10
236	15 c. School feeding	..	..	20	15
237	20 c. Infant feeding	..	..	20	20
	a. Imperf (pair)	..	..	£250	
238	25 c. "Food for Work"	..	..	25	25
235/8			Set of 4	65	60

89 *Aeropetes tulbaghia*

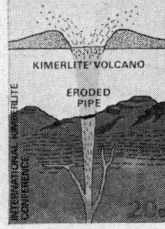

90 Kimberlite Volcano

(Des A. McLeod; artwork G. Drummond. Litho Questa)

1973 (3 Sept). *Butterflies.* T **89** *and similar horiz designs. Multicoloured.* W **53** *(sideways).* P 14.

239	4 c. Type 89	..	..	75	10
240	5 c. *Papilio demodocus*	..	85	50
241	10 c. *Cynthia cardui*	..	..	1·25	50
242	15 c. *Precis hierta*	..	..	2·25	1·75
243	20 c. *Precis oenone* ..	..	2·25	1·75
244	25 c. *Danaus chrysippus*	..	2·50	2·75
245	30 c. *Colotis evenina*	..	..	2·50	3·75
239/45			Set of 7	11·00	10·00

(Des PAD Studio. Litho Questa)

1973 (1 Oct). *International Kimberlite Conference.* T **90** *and similar multicoloured designs.* W **53** *(sideways on 10 and 15 c.).* P 13½.

246	10 c. Map of diamond mines (*horiz*)	..	2·00	2·00
247	15 c. Kimberlite-diamond rock (*horiz*)		2·25	2·25
248	20 c. Type 90	..	..	2·25	2·50
249	30 c. Diamond prospecting	..	3·75	7·00
246/9			Set of 4	9·00	11·00

Type **90** is incorrectly inscribed "KIMERLITE VOLCANO".

91 "Health"   92 Open Book and Wreath

(Des R. Granger Barrett. Litho Questa)

1974 (18 Feb). *Youth and Development.* T **91** *and similar horiz designs.* W **53** *(sideways).* P 13½.

250	4 c. Type 91	..	..	10	10
251	5 c. "Education"	..	..	15	10
252	20 c. "Agriculture"	..	..	20	10
253	25 c. "Industry"	..	..	30	20
254	30 c. "Service"	..	..	30	25
250/4			Set of 5	85	55

(Des PAD Studio. Litho Questa)

1974 (8 Apr). *Tenth Anniv of U.B.L.S.* T **92** *and similar vert designs. Multicoloured.* W **53**. P 14.

255	10 c. Type 92	..	..	15	15
256	15 c. Flags, mortar-board and scroll	..	20	20
257	20 c. Map of Africa	..	..	25	20
258	25 c. King Moshoeshoe II capping a graduate	25	50
255/8			Set of 4	75	90

93 Senqunyane River Bridge, Marakabei

(Des J. Cooter. Litho Questa)

1974 (26 June). *Rivers and Bridges.* T **93** *and similar horiz designs. Multicoloured.* W **53** *(sideways).* P 14½.

259	4 c. Type 93	..	..	10	10
260	5 c. Tsoelike River and bridge	..	10	10
261	10 c. Makhaleng River Bridge	..	20	10
262	15 c. Seaka Bridge, Orange/Senqu River	35	35
263	20 c. Masianokeng Bridge, Phuthiatsana River	40	40
264	25 c. Mahobong Bridge, Hlotse River ..	45	45
259/64			Set of 6	1·50	1·25

94 U.P.U. Emblem

(Des R. Granger Barrett. Litho Enschedé)

1974 (6 Sept). *Centenary of Universal Postal Union.* T **94** *and similar horiz designs.* W **53** *(sideways).* P 13½ × 13.

265	4 c. light emerald and black	..	10	10
266	10 c. orange, greenish yellow and black	15	10
267	15 c. multicoloured	..	..	20	60
268	20 c. multicoloured	..	..	45	85
265/8			Set of 4	80	1·40

Designs:—10 c. Map of air-mail routes; 15 c. Post Office H.Q., Maseru· 20 c. Horseman taking rural mail.

On No. 266 the inscriptions for the airstrips at Mokhotlong and Mohlanapeng were transposed in error.

95 Siege of Thaba-Bosiu

(Des Jennifer Toombs. Litho Enschedé)

1974 (25 Nov). *150th Anniv of Establishment of Thaba-Bosiu as Capital. T* **95** *and similar multicoloured designs. W* **53** *(sideways on 4 and 5 c.). P* 12½ × 12 (4 and 5 c.) or 12 × 12½ (others).

269	4 c. Type **95**			10	10
270	5 c. The wreath-laying			10	10
271	10 c. Moshoeshoe I (*vert*)			25	10
272	20 c. Makoanyane, the warrior (*vert*)			90	55
269/72			*Set of 4*	1·25	65

96 Mamokhorong

(Des PAD Studio. Litho Questa)

1975 (25 Jan). *Basotho Musical Instruments. T* **96** *and similar horiz designs. Multicoloured. W* **53** *(sideways). P* 14.

273	4 c. Type **96**			10	10
274	10 c. Lesiba			10	10
275	15 c. Setolotolo			15	15
276	20 c. Meropa			15	20
273/6			*Set of 4*	40	45
MS277	108 × 92 mm. Nos. 273/6			1·00	2·00

97 Horseman in Rock Archway   **98** Morena Moshoeshoe I

(Des J. Cooter. Litho Questa)

1975 (15 Apr). *Sehlabathebe National Park. T* **97** *and similar horiz designs. Multicoloured. W* **53** *(sideways). P* 14.

278	4 c. Type **97**			30	10
279	5 c. Mountain view through arch			30	10
280	15 c. Antelope by stream			50	40
281	20 c. Mountains and lake			50	50
282	25 c. Tourists by frozen waterfall			65	75
278/82			*Set of 5*	2·00	1·60

(Des G. Vasarhelyi. Litho Questa)

1975 (10 Sept). *Leaders of Lesotho. T* **98** *and similar vert designs. W* **53**. *P* 14.

283	3 c. black and light blue			10	10
284	4 c. black and light mauve			10	10
285	5 c. black and pink			10	10
286	6 c. black and light grey-brown			10	10
287	10 c. black and light claret			10	10
288	15 c. black and light orange-red			20	20
289	20 c. black and dull green			25	30
290	25 c. black and azure			25	40
283/90			*Set of 8*	1·00	1·10

Designs:—4 c. King Moshoeshoe II; 5 c. Morena Letsie I; 6 c. Morena Lerotholi; 10 c. Morena Letsie II; 15 c. Morena Griffith; 20 c. Morena Seeiso Griffith Lerotholi; 25 c. Mofumahali Mantsebo Seeiso, O.B.E.
The 25 c. also commemorates International Women's Year.

99 Mokhibo Dance

(Des PAD Studio. Litho Questa)

1975 (17 Dec). *Traditional Dances. T* **99** *and similar horiz designs. Multicoloured. W* **53** *(sideways). P* 14 × 14½.

291	4 c. Type **99**			15	10
292	10 c. Ndlamo			20	20
293	15 c. Baleseli			35	65
294	20 c. Mohobelo			40	85
291/4			*Set of 4*	1·00	1·50
MS295	111 × 100 mm. Nos. 291/94			3·25	3·25

100 Enrolment

(Des L. Curtis. Litho Questa)

1976 (20 Feb). *25th Anniv of the Lesotho Red Cross. T* **100** *and similar horiz designs. Multicoloured. W* **53** *(sideways). P* 14.

296	4 c. Type **100**			50	10
297	10 c. Medical aid			70	10
298	15 c. Rural service			1·00	1·25
299	25 c. Relief supplies			1·40	2·25
296/9			*Set of 4*	3·25	3·25

101 Tapestry   **102** Football

(Des V. Whiteley Studio. Litho Format)

1976 (2 June). *Multicoloured designs as T* **101**. *W* **53** *(sideways* on 2 to 50 c.*). P* 14.

300	2 c. Type **101**			10	30
	w. Wmk top of hat to right			—	40·00
301	3 c. Mosotho horseman			20	30
302	4 c. Map of Lesotho			65	10
	w. Wmk top of hat to right				
303	5 c. Lesotho Brown diamond			55	60
	w. Wmk top of hat to right				
304	10 c. Lesotho Bank			30	10
305	15 c. Lesotho and O.A.U. flags			90	65
306	25 c. Sehlabathebe National Park			60	35
307	40 c. Pottery			60	1·00
308	50 c. Prehistoric rock art			2·00	2·00
309	1 r. King Moshoeshoe II (*vert*)			75	1·75
300/9			*Set of 10*	6·00	6·25

*The normal sideways watermark shows top of hat to left when seen from the back of the stamp.
For 25 c., 40 c. and 50 c. values on unwatermarked paper, see Nos. 398/400

(Des P. Powell. Litho Questa)

1976 (9 Aug). *Olympic Games, Montreal. T* **102** *and similar vert designs. Multicoloured. W* **53**. *P* 14.

310	4 c. Type **102**			15	10
311	10 c. Weightlifting			15	10
312	15 c. Boxing			35	10
313	25 c. Throwing the discus			50	35
310/13			*Set of 4*	1·00	50

103 "Rising Sun"   **104** Telephones, 1876 and 1976

(Des L. Curtis. Litho Questa)

1976 (4 Oct). *Tenth Anniv of Independence. T* **103** *and similar vert designs. Multicoloured. W* **53**. *P* 14.

314	4 c. Type **103**			10	10
315	10 c. Open gates			10	10
316	15 c. Broken chains			40	20
317	25 c. Britten Norman Islander aircraft over hotel			50	35
314/17			*Set of 4*	1·00	55

(Des and litho J.W.)

1976 (6 Dec). *Telephone Centenary. T* **104** *and similar horiz designs. Multicoloured. W* **53** *(sideways). P* 13.

318	4 c. Type **104**			10	10
319	10 c. Early handset and telephone-user, 1976			15	10
320	15 c. Wall telephone and telephone exchange			25	15
321	25 c. Stick telephone and Alexander Graham Bell			45	40
318/21			*Set of 4*	85	55

105 *Aloe striatula*   **106** Large-toothed Rock Hyrax

(Des D. Findlay. Litho Walsall)

1977 (14 Feb). *Aloes and Succulents. T* **105** *and similar vert designs. Multicoloured. W* **53** *(inverted). P* 14.

322	3 c. Type **105**			25	10
323	4 c. *Aloe aristata*			30	10
324	5 c. *Kniphofia caulescens*			35	10
325	10 c. *Euphorbia pulvinata*			50	10
326	15 c. *Aloe saponaria*			1·50	40
327	20 c. *Caralluma lutea*			1·50	65
328	25 c. *Aloe polyphylla*			1·75	90
322/8			*Set of 7*	5·50	2·00

(Des D. Findlay. Litho Questa)

1977 (25 Apr). *Animals. T* **106** *and similar horiz designs. Multicoloured. W* **53** *(sideways). P* 14.

329	4 c. Type **106**			2·50	20
330	5 c. Cape Porcupine			2·50	30
331	10 c. Zorilla (polecat)			2·75	20
332	15 c. Klipspringer			10·00	2·25
333	25 c. Chacma Baboon			12·00	3·00
329/33			*Set of 5*	27·00	5·50

107 "Rheumatic Man"   **108** Small-mouthed Yellowfish

(Des C. Abbott. Litho Questa)

1977 (4 July). *World Rheumatism Year. T* **107** *and similar vert designs showing the "Rheumatic Man". W* **53**. *P* 14.

334	4 c. yellow and red			10	10
335	10 c. new blue and deep blue			15	10
336	15 c. yellow and blue-green			30	10
337	25 c. orange-red and black			40	45
334/7			*Set of 4*	85	65

Designs:—10 c. Man surrounded by "pain"; 15 c. Man surrounded by "chain"; 25 c. Man supporting globe.

(Des D. Findlay. Litho Questa)

1977 (28 Sept). *Fish. T* **108** *and similar horiz designs. Multicoloured. W* **53** *(sideways). P* 14.

338	4 c. Type **108**			30	10
339	10 c. Mudfish			45	10
340	15 c. Rainbow Trout			1·00	35
341	25 c. Barnard's Mudfish			1·10	60
338/41			*Set of 4*	2·50	1·00

(109)   **110** Black and White Heads

1977 (7 Dec*). *No.* 198 *surch with T* **109** *by Govt Printer, Maseru.*

342	3 c. on 10 c. yellow-brn & pale bluish grey			90	90
	a. Top obliterating bar short at left (R.2/5)			14·00	
	b. Top obliterating bar short at right (R.5/5)			14·00	
	w. Wmk top of hat to right				

*Earliest known date of use.
Nos. 342a/b occur on the upper pane.

(Des Jennifer Toombs. Litho Walsall)

1977 (12 Dec). *Decade for Action to Combat Racism. T* **110** *and similar vert designs. W* **53**. *P* 14.

343	4 c. chocolate and mauve			10	10
344	10 c. chocolate and light new blue			10	10
345	15 c. chocolate and light orange			15	15
346	25 c. chocolate and light turquoise-green			25	25
343/6			*Set of 4*	55	45

Designs:—10 c. Jigsaw pieces; 15 c. Cogwheels; 25 c. Handshake.

(Des D. Findlay. Litho Questa)

1978 (13 Feb). *Flowers. Vert designs similar to T* **105**. *Multicoloured. W* **53**. *P* 14.

347	2 c. *Papaver aculeatum*			10	20
348	3 c. *Diascia integerrima*			10	10
349	4 c. *Helichrysum trilineatum*			10	10
350	5 c. *Zaluzianskya maritima*			10	10
351	10 c. *Gladiolus natalensis*			20	20
352	15 c. *Chironia krebsii*			30	40
353	25 c. *Wahlenbergia undulata*			50	1·00
354	40 c. *Brunsvigia radulosa*			85	2·00
347/54			*Set of 8*	2·00	3·75

111 Edward Jenner
performing Vaccination

112 Tsoloane Falls

(Des G. Hutchins. Litho J.W.)

1978 (8 May). *Global Eradication of Smallpox. T* **111** *and similar vert design. Multicoloured. W* **53.** *P* 13.
355	5 c. Type 111				20	10
356	25 c. Head of child and W.H.O. emblem				70	75
	w. Wmk inverted				5·00	

(Des Kobus De Beer Art Studio. Litho Questa)

1978 (28 July). *Waterfalls. T* **112** *and similar vert designs. Multi-coloured. W* **53.** *P* 14.
357	4 c. Type 112				15	10
358	10 c. Qiloane Falls				25	10
359	15 c. Tsoelikana Falls				45	60
360	25 c. Maletsunyane Falls				75	1·50
357/60				Set of 4	1·40	2·00

113 Wright Flyer III, 1903

114 Orthetrum
farinosum

(Des L. Curtis. Litho Harrison)

1978 (9 Oct). *75th Anniv of Powered Flight. T* **113** *and similar horiz design. W* **53** *(sideways). P* 14½ × 14.
361	5 c. black, brown-ochre and new blue				15	10
362	25 c. multicoloured				40	55

Design:—25 c. Wilbur and Orville Wright.

(Des D. Findlay. Litho Questa)

1978 (18 Dec). *Insects. T* **114** *and similar vert designs. Multi-coloured. W* **53.** *P* 14.
363	4 c. Type 114				10	10
364	10 c. *Phymateus viridipes*				20	10
365	15 c. *Belonogaster lateritis*				30	40
366	25 c. *Sphodromantis gastrica*				50	80
363/6				Set of 4	1·00	1·25

115 Oudehout Branch
in flower

116 Mampharoane

(Des D. Findlay. Litho Questa)

1979 (26 Mar). *Trees. T* **115** *and similar vert designs showing branches in flower. Multicoloured. W* **53.** *P* 14.
367	4 c. Type 115				15	10
368	10 c. Wild Olive				20	10
369	15 c. Blinkblaar				35	80
370	25 c. Cape Holly				70	1·50
367/70				Set of 4	1·25	2·25

(New Currency. 100 lisente = 1(ma)loti)

(Des D. Findlay. Litho Questa)

1979 (1 June). *Reptiles. T* **116** *and similar horiz designs. Multicoloured. P* 14. A. *No wmk.*
371A	4 s. Type 116				10	10
372A	10 s. Qoaane				20	10
373A	15 s. Leupa				30	60
374A	25 s. Masumu				60	1·25
371A/4A				Set of 4	1·10	1·75

B. W **53** *(sideways)*
371B	4 s. Type 116				10	10
372B	10 s. Qoaane				20	10
373B	15 s. Leupa				30	70
374B	25 s. Masumu				60	1·50
371B/4B				Set of 4	1·10	2·10

117 Basutoland 1933 1d.
Stamp

118 Detail of Painting
"Children's Games" by
Brueghel

(Des J.W. Litho Format)

1979 (22 Oct). *Death Centenary of Sir Rowland Hill. T* **117** *and similar vert designs showing stamps. P* 14.
375	4 s. multicoloured				10	10
376	15 s. multicoloured				30	20
377	25 s. black, yellow-orange and olive-bistre				40	30
375/7				Set of 3	70	50
MS378	118 × 95 mm. 50 s. multicoloured				60	80

Designs:—15 s. Basutoland 1962 ½ c. definitive; 25 c. Penny Black; 50 s. 1972 15 c. Post Office Centenary commemorative.

(Des C. Abbott. Litho Questa)

1979 (10 Dec). *International Year of the Child. T* **118** *and similar vert designs showing details of the painting "Children's Games" by Brueghel. W* **53.** *P* 14.
379	4 s. multicoloured				10	10
380	10 s. multicoloured				10	10
381	15 s. multicoloured				15	15
379/81				Set of 3	30	30
MS382	113 × 88 mm. 25 s. multicoloured (horiz) (wmk sideways)				55	45

119 Beer Strainer, Broom and Mat

(Des Kobus de Beer Art Studio. Litho Walsall)

1980 (18 Feb). *Grasswork. T* **119** *and similar horiz designs. Multi-coloured. W* **53** *(sideways). P* 14.
383	4 s. Type 119				10	10
384	10 s. Winnowing Basket				10	10
385	15 s. Basotho Hat				20	25
386	25 s. Grain storage				35	40
383/6				Set of 4	60	70

120 Praise Poet

(Des BG Studio. Litho Walsall)

1980 (6 May). *Centenary of Gun War. T* **120** *and similar horiz designs. Multicoloured. P* 14.
387	4 s. Type 120				15	10
388	5 s. Lerotholi (commander of Basotho Army)				15	10
389	10 s. Ambush at Qalabane				20	10
390	15 s. Snider and Martini-Henry rifles				60	45
391	25 s. Map showing main areas of action				70	55
387/91				Set of 5	1·60	1·10

121 Olympic Flame, Flags and Kremlin (122)

(Des G. Vasarhelyi. Litho Format)

1980 (20 Sept). *Olympic Games, Moscow. T* **121** *and similar horiz designs. Multicoloured. P* 14½.
392	25 s. Type 121				25	25
	a. Horiz strip of 5. Nos. 392/6				1·10	
393	25 s. Doves, flame and flags				25	25
394	25 s. Football				25	25
395	25 s. Running				25	25
396	25 s. Opening ceremony				25	25
392/6				Set of 5	1·10	1·10
MS397	110 × 85 mm. 1 m. 40, Ancient and modern athletes carrying Olympic torch				1·10	1·25

Nos. 392/6 were printed together, *se-tenant*, in horizontal strips of 5 throughout the sheet.

A further series for the Moscow Olympics, printed by Walsall, showing 4 s. Javelin, 10 s. Sprinting, 15 s. Marathon and 25 s. Football, was prepared, but not issued.

1980. *As Nos. 203 and 306/8, but without wmk.*
398	25 c. Sehlabathebe National Park				75	1·40
399	40 c. Pottery				2·00	5·00
400	50 c. Prehistoric rock art				2·50	5·00
401	2 r. Statue of Moshoeshoe I (yellow-brown and ultramarine)				70	2·25
398/401				Set of 4	5·50	12·00

Two opt types of No. 409:

Type I. Cancelling bars centred on depth of "M1" (stamps surcharged in individual panes of 25 and from the righthand panes of those surcharged in sheets of 50 (2 panes 5 × 5)).

Type II. Lower cancelling bar aligns with foot of "M1" (stamps from lefthand panes of those surcharged in sheets of 50).

1980 (20 Oct)–**81.** *As Nos. 300/5, 309 and 398/401 surch as T* **122** *or with new figures of value (5 s. (No. 410A), 6, 75s., 1 and 2 m.). A. By typo (locally). (a) W* **53** *(sideways on 2, 3, 6, 10, 40, 50 and 75 s.)*
402A	2 s. on 2 c. Type 101				10	10
	w. Wmk top of hat to right				5·50	
403A	3 s. on 3 c. Mosotho horseman				20	10
404A	6 s. on 4 c. Map of Lesotho				60	10
	a. Surch double				†	
	b. Albino surch				†	—
405A	10 s. on 10 c. Lesotho Bank				80	10
405cA	25 s. on 25 c. Sehlabathebe National Park				3·25	4·50
406A	40 s. on 40 c. Pottery				45	50
407A	50 s. on 50 c. Prehistoric rock art				2·25	1·75
408A	75 s. on 15 c. Lesotho and O.A.U. flags				80	75
409A	1 m. on 1 r. King Moshoeshoe II (I) (Sil.)				80	1·00
	a. Surch double, one inverted				55·00	
	b. Opt Type II				3·75	4·00

(b) No wmk
410A	5 s. on 5 c. Lesotho Brown diamond				90	10
	a. Third surch (Basotho hat and "5 s.") double				35·00	
	b. Basotho hat and "5 s." surch albino				25·00	
	c. Basotho hat and "5 s." omitted				25·00	
	d. Basotho hat and "5 s." surch treble				40·00	
	e. Basotho hat and "5 s." surch treble, one inverted				45·00	
	f. Second surch ("6 s." and bars) albino				20·00	
412A	25 s. on 25 c. Sehlabathebe National Park				25	30
	a. Surch double				12·00	
	b. Surch triple					
	c. Surch quadruple					
413A	40 s. on 40 c. Pottery				2·50	4·25
414A	50 s. on 50 c. Prehistoric rock art				1·50	55
	a. Surch double, one inverted				30·00	
	b. Surch quadruple, one inverted				35·00	
	c. Surch omitted (in pair with normal)					
417A	2 m. on 2 r. Statue of Moshoeshoe I				80	1·40
402A/17A				Set of 14	13·50	14·00

B. *By litho (London). (a) W* **53** *(sideways on 2, 3, 6, 10, 40, 50 and 75 s.)*
402B	2 s. on 2 c. Type 101				10	10
403B	3 s. on 3 c. Mosotho horseman				20	10
404B	6 s. on 4 c. Map of Lesotho				30	10
405B	10 s. on 10 c. Lesotho Bank				5·00	5·50
406B	40 s. on 40 c. Pottery				45	50
407B	50 s. on 50 c. Prehistoric rock art				1·25	55

(b) No wmk
410B	5 s. on 5 c. Lesotho Brown diamond				60	10
411B	10 s. on 10 c. Lesotho Bank				10	10
412B	25 s. on 25 c. Sehlabathebe National Park				25	30
415B	75 s. on 15 c. Lesotho and O.A.U. flags				70	75
416B	1 m. on 1 r. King Moshoeshoe II (Blk. and Sil.)				80	1·00
417B	2 m. on 2 r. Statue of Moshoeshoe I				80	1·40
402B/17B				Set of 12	9·50	9·00

No. 410A is a further surcharge on No. 410B. Initially sheets of No. 410B were locally surcharged "6 s.", but this was later obliterated by a Basotho hat emblem and a further "5 s." surcharge added, both in typography.

The surcharge on No. 416 is similar to that on No. 409 but has the cancelling bars printed in black and the new face value in silver.

On each value except the 5 s. and 1 m. stamps, the design of the surcharge on the local printing is identical to that on the London printing. Stamps from the local printing can easily be identified from those of the London printing as indentations are clearly visible on the reverse of stamps with the typographed surcharge.

It is believed that the local surcharges were not placed on general sale before 1 December 1980. No. 410A did not appear until 20 January 1981.

Nos. 412Ab/c occurred in the same sheet which contained 5 examples of the triple surcharge, 5 of a partial quadruple surcharge and 40 with complete quadruple surcharge.

123 Beer Mug

124 Queen Elizabeth
the Queen Mother
and Prince Charles

(Des G. Vasarhelyi (No. **MS422**), Kobus de Beer Art Studio (others). Litho Format (No. **MS422**), Questa (others)).

1980 (20 Nov). *Pottery. T* **123** *and similar horiz designs. Multi-coloured. W* **53** *(sideways). P* 14.
418	4 s. Type 123				10	10
419	10 s. Beer brewing pot				10	10
420	15 s. Water pot				15	15
421	25 s. Pot shapes				25	30
418/21				Set of 4	50	50
MS422	150 × 110 mm. 40 s. × 4 Wedgwood plaques of Prince Philip; Queen Elizabeth II; Prince Charles; Princess Anne (each 22 × 35 mm). P 14 × 14½				50	90

No. **MS422** was issued to commemorate the 250th birth anniversary of Josiah Wedgwood.

(Des G. Vasarhelyi. Litho Format)

1980 (1 Dec). *80th Birthday of Queen Elizabeth the Queen Mother.*
T **124** *and similar multicoloured designs.* P 14½.

423	5 s. Type **124**	..	25	25
	a. Horiz strip of 3. Nos. 423/5		1·25	
424	10 s. Queen Elizabeth the Queen Mother		25	25
425	1 m. Basutoland 1947 Royal Visit 2d. commemorative and flags (54 × 44 *mm*)		90	90
423/5		*Set of 3*	1·25	1·25

Nos. 423/5 were printed together, *se-tenant*, in horizontal strips of 3 throughout small sheets of nine stamps.

125 Lesotho Evangelical Church, Morija

(Des G. Vasarhelyi. Litho Format (75 s., 1 m. 50), Harrison (others))

1980 (8 Dec). *Christmas. T* **125** *and similar horiz designs. Multi-coloured. No wmk* (75 s.) *or* W **53** (*others*). P 14 × 14½.

426	4 s. Type **125**	..	10	10
427	15 s. St. Agnes' Anglican Church, Teyateyaneng		10	10
428	25 s. Cathedral of Our Lady of Victories, Maseru		15	10
429	75 s. University Chapel, Roma		45	50
426/9		*Set of 4*	65	60
MS430	110 × 85 mm. 1 m. 50, Nativity scene (43 × 29 *mm*). No wmk. P 14½		50	80

126 "Voyager" Satellite and Jupiter   127 Greater Kestrel

(Des G. Vasarhelyi. Litho Format)

1981 (15 Mar). *Space Exploration. T* **126** *and similar horiz designs. Multicoloured.* P 13½ × 14.

431	25 s. Type **126**	..	30	25
	a. Horiz strip of 5. Nos. 431/5		1·40	
432	25 s. "Voyager" and Saturn		30	25
433	25 s. "Voyager" passing Saturn		30	25
434	25 s. "Space Shuttle" releasing satellite		30	25
435	25 s. "Space Shuttle" launch		30	25
431/5		*Set of 5*	1·10	1·10
MS436	111 × 85 mm. 1 m. 40, Saturn		1·75	1·00

Nos. 431/5 were printed together, *se-tenant*, in horizontal strips of 5 throughout the sheet.

No. MS436 exists imperforate from stock dispersed by the liquidator of Format International Security Printers Ltd.

(Des G. Vasarhelyi. Litho Format)

1981 (20 Apr–Dec). *Birds. Multicoloured designs as T* **127**. *With imprint date.* P 14½.

437	1 s. Type **127**	..	15	40
	a. Perf 13 (12.81)		55	30
438	2 s. Speckled Pigeon (*horiz*)		15	40
	a. Perf 13 (12.81)		65	30
439	3 s. South African Crowned Crane		20	40
440	5 s. Bokmakierie Shrike		20	40
	a. Perf 13 (12.81)		90	30
441	6 s. Cape Robin Chat		30	10
442	7 s. Yellow Canary		30	10
443	10 s. Red-billed Pintail (*horiz*)		40	10
	a. Perf 13 (12.81)		90	30
444	25 s. Malachite Kingfisher		1·00	15
445	40 s. Yellow-tufted Malachite Sunbird (*horiz*)		1·25	65
446	60 s. Cape Longclaw (*horiz*)		1·50	1·00
447	75 s. Hoopoe (*horiz*)		2·25	85
448	1 m. Red Bishop (*horiz*)		2·25	75
449	2 m. Egyptian Goose (*horiz*)		2·50	1·50
450	5 m. Lilac-breasted Roller (*horiz*)		4·00	4·00
437/50		*Set of 14*	15·00	9·50

Imprint dates: "1981", Nos. 437/50; "1982", Nos. 437/41, 443.
Nos. 437/50 exist imperforated and as progressive proofs from stock dispersed by the liquidator of Format International Security Printers Ltd.

For these stamps watermarked w **14** see Nos. 500/13.

128 Wedding Bouquet from Lesotho

(Des J.W. Litho Format)

1981 (22 July). *Royal Wedding. T* **128** *and similar vert designs. Multicoloured.* P 14.

451	25 s. Type **128**	..	10	10
	a. Booklet pane. No. 451 × 3 plus printed label		50	
	b. Booklet pane. Nos. 451/3 plus printed label		50	
452	50 s. Prince Charles riding		20	25
	a. Booklet pane. No. 452 × 3 plus printed label		55	
453	75 s. Prince Charles and Lady Diana Spencer		30	50
	a. Booklet pane. No. 453 × 3 plus printed label		70	
451/3		*Set of 3*	55	75

Nos. 451/3 also exist imperforate from a restricted printing (*price for set of 3 £5.50 mint*).
Booklet panes Nos. 451a/3a exist part perforated from stock dispersed by the liquidator of Format International Security Printers Ltd.

129 Prince Charles and Lady Diana Spencer

(Des G. Vasarhelyi. Litho Format)

1981 (5 Sept). *Royal Wedding* (2nd issue). *Sheet* 115 × 90 mm. P 14½.

MS454	**129** 1 m. 50, multicoloured		1·00	1·25

No. MS454 also exists imperforate from a restricted printing (*price £4 mint*).

130 "Santa planning his Annual Visit"   131 Duke of Edinburgh, Award Scheme Emblem and Flags

(Des G. Vasarhelyi. Litho Format)

1981 (5 Oct). *Christmas. Paintings by Norman Rockwell* (6 *to* 60 s.) *or Botticelli* (1 *m.* 25). *T* **130** *and similar multicoloured designs.* P 13½.

455	6 s. Type **130**	..	15	10
456	10 s. "Santa reading his Mail"		25	10
457	15 s. "The Little Spooners"		30	20
458	20 s. "Raleigh Rockwell Travels"		30	25
459	25 s. "Ride 'em Cowboy"		30	30
460	60 s. "The Discovery"		50	1·00
455/60		*Set of 6*	1·60	1·75
MS461	111 × 85 mm. 1 m. 25, "Mystic Nativity" (48 × 31 *mm*). P 13½ × 14		1·10	1·10

(Des G. Vasarhelyi. Litho Format)

1981 (5 Nov). *25th Anniv of Duke of Edinburgh Award Scheme. T* **131** *and similar multicoloured designs.* P 14½.

462	6 s. Type **131**	..	10	10
463	7 s. Tree planting		10	10
464	25 s. Gardening		25	20
465	40 s. Mountain climbing		40	40
466	75 s. Award Scheme emblem		70	75
462/6		*Set of 5*	1·40	1·40
MS467	111 × 85 mm. 1 m. 40, Duke of Edinburgh (45 × 30 *mm*)		1·25	1·25

132 Wild Cat

(Des G. Vasarhelyi. Litho Format)

1981 (16 Nov). *Wildlife. T* **132** *and similar multicoloured designs.* P 13½ (6, 25 s.) *or* 14½ (*others*).

468	6 s. Type **132**	..	1·25	30
469	20 s. Chacma Baboon (44 × 31 *mm*)		2·00	70
470	25 s. Eland		2·50	70
471	40 s. Cape Porcupine (44 × 31 *mm*)		3·25	1·75
472	50 s. Oribi (44 × 31 *mm*)		3·25	1·75
468/72		*Set of 5*	11·00	4·75
MS473	111 × 85 mm. 1 m. 50, Black-backed Jackal (47 × 31 *mm*). P 13½ × 14		2·75	1·90

No. MS473 exists imperforate from stock dispersed by the liquidator of Format International Security Printers Ltd.

133 Scout Bugler

(Des G. Vasarhelyi. Litho Format)

1982 (5 Mar). *75th Anniv of Boy Scout Movement. T* **133** *and similar horiz designs. Multicoloured.* P 13½.

474	6 s. Type **133**	..	50	25
	a. Booklet pane. Nos. 474/8 × 2 and MS479		8·50	
475	30 s. Scouts hiking		70	50
476	40 s. Scout sketching		75	60
477	50 s. Scout with flag		75	65
478	75 s. Scouts saluting		80	80
474/8		*Set of 5*	3·25	2·50
MS479	117 × 92 mm. 1 m. 50, Lord Baden-Powell		1·50	2·00

Nos. 474/9 exist imperforate from stock dispersed by the liquidator of Format International Security Printers Ltd.

134 Jules Rimet Trophy with Footballers and Flags of 1930 Finalists (Argentina and Uruguay)

(Des G. Vasarhelyi. Litho Format)

1982 (14 Apr). *World Cup Football Championship, Spain. T* **134** *and similar horiz designs showing World Football Cup with players and flags of countries in past finals* (Nos. 480/90). *Multicoloured.* P 14½.

480	15 s. Type **134**	..	25	25
	a. Sheetlet. Nos. 480/91		2·50	
481	15 s. Jules Rimet Trophy with Czechoslovakia and Italy, 1934		25	25
482	15 s. Jules Rimet Trophy with Hungary and Italy, 1938		25	25
483	15 s. Jules Rimet Trophy with Brazil and Uruguay, 1950		25	25
484	15 s. Jules Rimet Trophy with Hungary and West Germany, 1954		25	25
485	15 s. Jules Rimet Trophy with Sweden and Brazil, 1958		25	25
486	15 s. Jules Rimet Trophy with Czechoslovakia and Brazil, 1962		25	25
487	15 s. Jules Rimet Trophy with West Germany and England, 1966		25	25
488	15 s. Jules Rimet Trophy with Italy and Brazil, 1970		25	25
489	15 s. World Cup with Holland and West Germany, 1974		25	25
490	15 s. World Cup with Holland and Argentina, 1978		25	25
491	15 s. World Cup and map of World on footballs		25	25
480/91		*Set of 12*	2·50	2·50
MS492	118 × 93 mm. 1 m. 25, Bernabeu Stadium, Madrid (47 × 35 *mm*). P 13½		1·10	1·25

Nos. 480/91 were printed together, *se-tenant*, in sheetlets of 12.

Nos. 480/92 exist imperforate from stock dispersed by the liquidator of Format International Security Printers Ltd.

135 Portrait of George Washington   136 Lady Diana Spencer in Tetbury, May 1981

(Des G. Vasarhelyi. Litho Format)

1982 (7 June). *250th Birth Anniv of George Washington. T* **135** *and similar horiz designs. Multicoloured.* P 14 × 13½.

493	6 s. Type **135**	..	10	10
494	7 s. Washington with step-children and dog		10	10
495	10 s. Washington with Indian chief		15	10
496	25 s. Washington with troops		30	20
497	40 s. Washington arriving in New York		40	40
498	1 m. Washington on parade		1·00	1·10
493/8		*Set of 6*	1·75	1·75
MS499	117 × 92 mm. 1 m. 25, Washington crossing the Delaware		1·00	1·00

No. MS499 exists imperforate from stock dispersed by the liquidator of Format International Security Printers Ltd.

1982 (14 June). *As Nos. 437/50 but* W w **14** (*sideways on Nos. 500, 502/5 and 507*). "*1982*" *imprint date.*

500	1 s. Type **127**	..	20	50
501	2 s. Speckled Pigeon (*horiz*)		20	50
502	3 s. South African Crowned Crane		30	50
503	5 s. Bokmakierie Shrike		30	40
504	6 s. Cape Robin Chat		30	10
505	7 s. Yellow Canary		30	10
506	10 s. Red-billed Pintail (*horiz*)		30	10
507	25 s. Malachite Kingfisher		80	30

508	40 s. Yellow-tufted Malachite Sunbird (*horiz*)	1·00	45
509	60 s. Cape Longclaw (*horiz*) ..	1·25	90
510	75 s. Hoopoe (*horiz*) ..	1·75	90
511	1 m. Red Bishop (*horiz*) ..	2·00	2·75
512	2 m. Egyptian Goose (*horiz*) ..	2·75	5·00
513	5 m. Lilac-breasted Roller (*horiz*)	5·50	12·00
500/13	*Set of 14*	15·00	22·00

Nos. 500/13 exist imperforate from stock dispersed by the liquidator of Format International Security Printers Ltd.

(Des Jennifer Toombs. Litho Format)

1982 (1 July). *21st Birthday of Princess of Wales. T **136** and similar vert designs. Multicoloured. W w **14**. P 13½.*

514	30 s. Lesotho coat of arms ..	60	60
	a. Perf 13½×14 ..	40	40
515	50 s. Type **136** ..	60	60
	a. Perf 13½×14 ..	1·25	1·25
516	75 s. Wedding picture at Buckingham Palace ..	80	1·00
	a. Perf 13½×14 ..	1·00	1·00
517	1 m. Formal portrait ..	1·25	1·40
	a. Perf 13½×14 ..	1·40	1·40
514/17	*Set of 4*	3·00	3·25
514a/17a	*Set of 4*	3·50	3·50

Nos. 514/17 exist imperforate from stock dispersed by the liquidator of Format International Security Printers Ltd.

137 Mosotho reading Sesotho Bible   138 Birthday Greetings

(Des G. Vasarhelyi. Litho Format)

1982 (20 Aug). *Centenary of Sesotho Bible, T **137** and similar multicoloured designs. P 14½.*

518	6 s. Type **137** ..	15	20
	a. Horiz strip of 3. Nos. 518/20	75	
519	15 s. Sesotho Bible and Virgin Mary holding infant Jesus ..	20	25
520	1 m. Sesotho Bible and Cathedral (62 × 42 mm) ..	50	75
518/20	*Set of 3*	75	1·10

Nos. 518/20 were printed together, *se-tenant*, in horizontal strips of 3 throughout the sheet.

(Des G. Vasarhelyi. Litho Questa)

1982 (30 Sept). *Birth of Prince William of Wales. T **138** and similar vert design. Multicoloured. P 14 × 13½.*

521	6 s. Type **138** ..	2·25	2·50
	a. Sheetlet. No. 521 and 522 × 5	6·50	
522	60 s. Princess Diana and Prince William of Wales ..	1·00	1·00

Nos. 521/2 come from sheetlets of 6 containing one 6 s. and five 60 s. stamps.

139 "A Partridge in a Pear Tree"

(Litho Format)

1982 (1 Dec). *Christmas. "The Twelve Days of Christmas". T **139** and similar horiz designs depicting Walt Disney cartoon characters. Multicoloured. P 11.*

523	2 s. Type **139** ..	10	10
	a. Horiz pair. Nos. 523/4	10	10
524	2 s. "Two turtle doves" ..	10	10
525	3 s. "Three French hens" ..	10	10
	a. Horiz pair. Nos. 525/6	10	10
526	3 s. "Four calling birds" ..	10	10
527	4 s. "Five golden rings" ..	10	10
	a. Horiz pair. Nos. 527/8	15	15
528	4 s. "Six geese a-laying" ..	10	10
529	75 s. "Seven swans a-swimming" ..	1·40	1·75
	a. Horiz pair. Nos. 529/30 ..	2·75	3·50
530	75 s. "Eight maids a-milking"..	1·40	1·75
523/30	*Set of 8*	2·75	3·50

MS531 126 × 101 mm. 1 m. 50, "Nine ladies dancing, ten lords a-leaping, eleven pipers piping, twelve drummers drumming". P 13½ .. .. 2·40 2·75

Nos. 523/4, 525/6, 527/8 and 529/30 were each printed in horizontal *se-tenant* pairs throughout the sheet.

140 *Lepista caffrorum*

(Des G. Vasarhelyi. Litho Format)

1983 (11 Jan). *Fungi. T **140** and similar horiz designs. Multicoloured. P 14½.*

532	10 s. Type **140** ..	15	10
	a. Tête-bêche (vert pair)	30	30
	b. Booklet pane. Nos. 532/5	2·50	
	c. Booklet pane. Nos. 532/3	3·25	
533	30 s. Broomeia congregata	30	40
	a. Tête-bêche (vert pair)	60	80
534	50 s. Afroboletus luteolus	60	90
	a. Tête-bêche (vert pair)	1·10	1·75
535	75 s. Lentinus tuber-regium	90	1·40
	a. Tête-bêche (vert pair)	1·75	2·75
532/5	*Set of 4*	1·75	2·50

Nos. 532/5 were each printed in sheets of 36 stamps plus 4 labels as the fourth horizontal row. The stamps in horizontal rows two, six, eight and ten were inverted, forming vertical *tête-bêche* pairs.

Nos. 532/5 exist imperforate from stock dispersed by the liquidator of Format International Security Printers Ltd.

141 Ba-Leseli Dance

(Des J.W. Litho Format)

1983 (14 Mar). *Commonwealth Day. T **141** and similar multicoloured designs. P 14½.*

536	5 s. Type **141** ..	10	10
537	30 s. Tapestry weaving ..	20	30
538	60 s. Queen Elizabeth II (*vert*)..	35	65
539	75 s. King Moshoeshoe II (*vert*)	40	80
536/9	*Set of 4*	90	1·60

Nos. 536/9 exist imperforate from stock dispersed by the liquidator of Format International Security Printers Ltd.

142 "Dancers in a Trance" (rock painting from Ntloana Tsoana)

(Des G. Drummond. Litho Format)

1983 (20 May). *Rock Paintings. T **142** and similar multicoloured designs. P 14½.*

540	6 s. Type **142** ..	20	10
541	25 s. "Baboons", Sehonghong ..	55	35
542	60 s. "Hunters attacking Mountain Reedbuck", Makhetha ..	60	1·10
543	75 s. "Eland", Lehaha la Likhomo	65	1·60
540/3	*Set of 4*	1·75	2·75

MS544 166 × 84 mm. Nos. 540/3 and 10 s. "Cattle herding", Sehonghong (52 × 52 mm) .. .. 1·75 3·50

Nos. 540/4 exist imperforate from stock dispersed by the liquidator of Format International Security Printers Ltd.

143 Montgolfier Balloon, 1783

(Des J.W. Litho Format)

1983 (11 July). *Bicentenary of Manned Flight. T **143** and similar multicoloured designs. P 14½.*

545	7 s. Type **143** ..	15	10
	a. Booklet pane. Nos. 545/8	2·50	
546	30 s. Wright brothers and Flyer I ..	30	40
547	60 s. First airmail flight ..	50	1·25
548	1 m. Concorde ..	65	2·25
545/8	*Set of 4*	2·50	3·50

MS549 180×92 mm. Nos. 545/8 and 6 s. Dornier Do-28D Skyservant of Lesotho Airways (60×60 mm) .. .. 2·75 2·75

Nos. 545/9 exist imperforate from stock dispersed by the liquidator of Format International Security Printers Ltd.

144 Rev. Eugene Casalis

(Des G. Vasarhelyi. Litho Questa)

1983 (5 Sept). *150th Anniv of Arrival of the French Missionaries. T **144** and similar horiz designs. Multicoloured. P 13½ × 14.*

550	6 s. Type **144** ..	10	10
	a. Tête-bêche (vert pair)	10	15
551	25 s. The founding of Morija	10	10
	a. Tête-bêche (vert pair)	15	20
552	40 s. Baptism of Libe ..	10	15
	a. Tête-bêche (vert pair)	20	30
553	75 s. Map of Lesotho ..	20	25
	a. Tête-bêche (vert pair)	40	50
550/3	*Set of 4*	40	60

Nos. 550/3 were each issued in sheets of 20 containing two panes (2 × 5) separated by a vertical gutter. Within these sheets horizontal rows two and four are inverted forming *tête-bêche* vertical pairs.

145 Mickey Mouse and Pluto Greeted by Friends

(Litho Questa)

1983 (18 Oct). *Christmas. T **145** and similar horiz designs showing Disney cartoon characters in scenes from "Old Christmas" (Washington Irving's sketchbook). Multicoloured. P 14 × 13½.*

554	1 s. Type **145** ..	10	10
555	2 s. Donald Duck and Pluto ..	10	10
556	3 s. Donald Duck with Huey, Dewey and Louie ..	10	10
557	4 s. Goofy, Donald Duck and Mickey Mouse	10	10
558	5 s. Goofy holding turkey, Donald Duck and Mickey Mouse ..	10	10
559	6 s. Goofy and Mickey Mouse ..	10	10
560	75 s. Donald and Daisy Duck ..	2·00	2·40
561	1 m. Goofy and Clarabell ..	2·50	2·75
554/61	*Set of 8*	4·50	5·00

MS562 132 × 113 mm. 1 m. 75, Scrooge McDuck, Pluto and Donald Duck .. .. 3·25 4·50

146 *Danaus chrysippus*

(Des and litho Format)

1984 (20 Jan). *Butterflies. T **146** and similar horiz designs. Multicoloured. P 14.*

563	1 s. Type **146** ..	30	40
564	2 s. Aeropetes tulbaghia ..	30	40
565	3 s. Colotis evenina ..	35	40
566	4 s. Precis oenone ..	35	40
567	5 s. Precis hierta ..	35	10
568	6 s. Catopsilia florella ..	35	10
569	7 s. Phalanta phalantha ..	35	10
570	10 s. Acraea stenobea ..	40	10
571	15 s. Cynthia cardui ..	90	10
572	20 s. Colotis subfasciatus ..	1·00	10
573	30 s. Charaxes jasius ..	1·25	30
574	50 s. Terias brigitta ..	1·50	40
575	60 s. Pontia helice ..	1·60	50
576	75 s. Colotis regina ..	1·75	50
577	1 m. Hypolimnas misippus ..	2·00	1·50
578	5 m. Papilio demodocus ..	4·50	7·50
563/78	*Set of 16*	15·00	11·50

Nos. 563/78 exist imperforate and as progressive proofs from stock dispersed by the liquidator of Format International Security Printers Ltd.

147 "Thou Shalt not have Strange Gods before Me"

(Des G. Vasarhelyi. Litho Format)

1984 (30 Mar). *Easter. The Ten Commandments. T **147** and similar vert designs. Multicoloured. P 13½ × 14.*

579	20 s. Type **147** ..	30	30
	a. Sheetlet. Nos. 579/88	2·75	
580	20 s. "Thou shalt not take the name of the Lord thy God in vain" ..	30	30

581	20 s.	"Remember thou keep holy the Lord's Day"		30	30
582	20 s.	"Honour thy father and mother"		30	30
583	20 s.	"Thou shalt not kill"		30	30
584	20 s.	"Thou shalt not commit adultery"		30	30
585	20 s.	"Thou shalt not steal"		30	30
586	20 s.	"Thou shalt not bear false witness against thy neighbour"		30	30
587	20 s.	"Thou shalt not covet thy neighbour's wife"		30	30
588	20 s.	"Thou shalt not covet thy neighbour's goods"		30	30
579/88			Set of 10	2·75	2·75
MS589		102 × 73 mm. 1 m. 50, Moses with Tablets (45 × 28 mm). P 14.		1·00	2·25

Nos. 579/88 were printed together in small sheets of 12 including 2 se-tenant stamp-size labels.

148 Torch Bearer

(Des G. Vasarhelyi. Litho Format)

1984 (3 May). *Olympic Games, Los Angeles. T* **148** *and similar horiz designs. Multicoloured. P* 13½ × 14.

590	10 s.	Type **148**		10	10
591	30 s.	Horse-riding		10	10
592	50 s.	Swimming		15	20
593	75 s.	Basketball		20	25
594	1 m.	Running		25	30
590/4			Set of 5	70	80
MS595		101 × 72 mm. 1 m. 50, Olympic Flame and flags		1·25	2·50

Nos. 590/4 exist imperforate from stock dispersed by the liquidator of Format International Security Printers Ltd.

149 Sauropodomorph Footprints

(Des G. Drummond. Litho Format)

1984 (2 July). *Prehistoric Footprints (2nd series). T* **149** *and similar horiz designs. Multicoloured. P* 13½ × 14.

596	10 s.	Type **149**		55	30
597	30 s.	Lesothosaurus footprints		75	1·25
598	50 s.	Footprint of carnivorous dinosaur		90	2·00
596/8			Set of 3	2·00	3·25

Nos. 596/8 exist imperforate from stock dispersed by the liquidator of Format International Security Printers Ltd.

150 Wells Fargo Coach, 1852

(Des G. Vasarhelyi. Litho Format)

1984 (5 Sept). *"Ausipex" International Stamp Exhibition, Melbourne, and Bicentenary of First Mail Coach Run. T* **150** *and similar horiz designs. Multicoloured. P* 14.

599	6 s.	Type **150**		10	10
	a.	Sheetlet. Nos. 599 × 4 and No. 603		70	
600	7 s.	Basotho mail cart, circa 1900		10	10
	a.	Sheetlet. No. 600 × 4 and No. 603		80	
601	10 s.	Bath mail coach, 1784		10	10
	a.	Sheetlet. No. 601 × 4 and No. 603		90	
602	30 s.	Cobb coach, 1853		30	35
	a.	Sheetlet. No. 602 × 4 and No. 603		1·60	
603	50 s.	Exhibition logo and Royal Exhibition Buildings, Melbourne (82 × 25 mm)		50	55
599/603			Set of 5	95	1·10
MS604		147 × 98 mm. 1 m. 75, G.B. Penny Black, Basutoland 1934 "OFFICIAL" optd 6d. and Western Australia 1854 4d. with frame inverted (82 × 25 mm)		2·25	3·75

In addition to the listed sheetlets, Nos. 599/602 also exist in separate sheets of 50. No. 603 only comes from the sheetlets.

Nos. 599/602 exist imperforate from stock dispersed by the liquidator of Format International Security Printers Ltd.

151 "The Orient Express" (1900)

(Des Walsall. Litho Format)

1984 (5 Nov). *Railways of the World. T* **151** *and similar horiz designs. Multicoloured. P* 14×13½.

605	6 s.	Type **151**		40	15
606	15 s.	Class 05 streamlined steam locomotive No. 001, Germany (1935)		40	30
607	30 s.	Caledonian Railway steam locomotive Cardean (1906)		50	60
608	60 s.	Atchison, Topeka & Santa Fe "Super Chief" express (1940)		60	1·75
609	1 m.	L.N.E.R. "Flying Scotsman" (1934)		65	2·00
605/9			Set of 5	2·25	4·25
MS610		108×82 mm. 2 m. South African Railways "The Blue Train" (1972)		1·00	2·50

No. 607 exists imperforate from stock dispersed by the liquidator of Format International Security Printers Ltd.

152 Eland Calf   153 Crown of Lesotho

(Des G. Drummond. Litho Format)

1984 (20 Dec). *Baby Animals. T* **152** *and similar horiz designs. Multicoloured. P* 14 × 13½ (1 m.) or 15 (others).

611	15 s.	Type **152**		35	20
612	20 s.	Young Chacma Baboons		40	25
613	30 s.	Oribi calf		55	40
614	75 s.	Young Natal Red Hares		1·25	1·60
615	1 m.	Black-backed Jackal pups (46 × 27 mm)		1·50	2·00
611/15			Set of 5	3·50	4·00

No. 615 exists imperforate from stock dispersed by the liquidator of Format International Security Printers Ltd.

(Des G. Vasarhelyi. Litho Format)

1985 (30 Jan). *Silver Jubilee of King Moshoeshoe II. T* **153** *and similar vert designs. Multicoloured. P* 15.

616	6 s.	Type **153**		10	10
617	30 s.	King Moshoeshoe in 1960		20	30
618	75 s.	King Moshoeshoe in traditional dress, 1985		50	75
619	1 m.	King Moshoeshoe in uniform, 1985		70	1·10
616/19			Set of 4	1·25	2·00

154 Christ condemned to Death

(Des G. Vasarhelyi. Litho Format)

1985 (8 Mar). *Easter. The Stations of the Cross. T* **154** *and similar vert designs. Multicoloured. P* 11.

620	20 s.	Type **154**		20	25
	a.	Sheetlet. Nos. 620/33		2·25	
621	20 s.	Christ carrying the Cross		20	25
622	20 s.	Falling for the first time		20	25
623	20 s.	Christ meets Mary		20	25
624	20 s.	Simon of Cyrene helping to carry the Cross		20	25
625	20 s.	Veronica wiping the face of Christ		20	25
626	20 s.	Christ falling a second time		20	25
627	20 s.	Consoling the women of Jerusalem		20	25
628	20 s.	Falling for the third time		20	25
629	20 s.	Christ being stripped		20	25
630	20 s.	Christ nailed to the Cross		20	25
631	20 s.	Dying on the Cross		20	25
632	20 s.	Christ taken down from the Cross		20	25
633	20 s.	Christ being laid in the sepulchre		20	25
620/33			Set of 14	2·25	2·75
MS634		138 × 98 mm. 2 m. "The Crucifixion" (Mathias Grünewald). P 13½×14		1·50	3·50

Nos. 620/33 were printed together, se-tenant, in a sheetlet of 14 stamps with one stamp-sized label which appears in the central position.

155 Duchess of York with Princess Elizabeth, 1931

(Des G. Vasarhelyi. Litho Format)

1985 (30 May). *Life and Times of Queen Elizabeth the Queen Mother. T* **155** *and similar multicoloured designs. P* 13½ × 14.

635	10 s.	Type **155**		15	10
636	30 s.	The Queen Mother in 1975		50	50
637	60 s.	Queen Elizabeth with Queen Elizabeth and Princess Margaret, 1980		60	90
638	2 m.	Four generations of Royal Family at Prince Henry's christening, 1984		1·25	2·50
635/8			Set of 4	2·25	3·50
MS639		139 × 98 mm. 2 m. Queen Elizabeth with the Princess of Wales and her children at Prince Henry's christening (37 × 50 mm)		1·90	2·75

156 B.M.W. "732i"   157 American Cliff Swallow

(Litho Format)

1985 (10 June). *Century of Motoring. T* **156** *and similar multicoloured designs. P* 14 × 13½.

640	6 s.	Type **156**		25	15
641	10 s.	Ford "Crown Victoria"		35	15
642	30 s.	Mercedes-Benz "500SE"		75	50
643	90 s.	Cadillac "Eldorado Biarritz"		1·50	2·50
644	2 m.	Rolls-Royce "Silver Spirit"		2·00	4·00
640/4			Set of 5	4·25	6·50
MS645		139 × 98 mm. 2 m. Rolls-Royce "Silver Ghost Tourer", 1907 (37 × 50 mm). P 13½ × 14		3·75	6·00

Nos. 640/5 exist imperforate from stock dispersed by the liquidator of Format International Security Printers Ltd.

(Litho Format)

1985 (5 Aug). *Birth Bicentenary of John J. Audubon (ornithologist). T* **157** *and similar multicoloured designs showing original paintings. P* 15.

646	5 s.	Type **157**		40	30
647	6 s.	Great Crested Grebe (horiz)		40	30
648	10 s.	Vesper Sparrow (horiz)		55	30
649	30 s.	Greenshank (horiz)		1·25	75
650	60 s.	Stilt Sandpiper (horiz)		2·00	2·75
651	2 m.	Glossy Ibis (horiz)		3·50	5·50
646/51			Set of 6	7·25	9·00

Nos. 646/51 were reissued in February 1986 in sheetlets containing five stamps and one label.

158 Two Youths Rock-climbing   159 U.N. (New York) 1951 1 c. Definitive and U.N. Flag

(Des Walsall. Litho Format)

1985 (26 Sept). *International Youth Year and 75th Anniv of Girl Guide Movement. T* **158** *and similar vert designs. Multicoloured. P* 15.

652	10 s.	Type **158**		20	10
653	30 s.	Young technician in hospital laboratory		50	40
654	75 s.	Three guides on parade		1·00	1·25
655	2 m.	Guide saluting		1·75	3·00
652/5			Set of 4	3·00	4·25
MS656		138 × 98 mm. 2 m. "Olave, Lady Baden-Powell" (Grace Wheatley) (37 × 50 mm). P 13½ × 14		2·40	2·75

(Des G. Vasarhelyi. Litho Format)

1985 (15 Oct). *40th Anniv of United Nations Organization. T* **159** *and similar designs. P* 15.

657	10 s.	multicoloured		25	10
658	30 s.	multicoloured		60	35
659	50 s.	multicoloured		95	85
660	2 m.	black and bronze-green		5·00	6·50
657/60			Set of 4	6·25	7·00

Designs: *Vert*—30 s. Ha Sofonia Earth Satellite Station; 2 m. Maimonides (physician, philosopher and scholar). *Horiz*—50 s. Lesotho Airways Fokker F.27 Friendship at Maseru Airport.

160 Cosmos	160a Mrs. Jumbo and Baby Dumbo	

(Des G. Drummond. Litho Format)

1985 (11 Nov). *Wild Flowers.* T **160** *and similar vert designs. Multicoloured.* P 15.

661	6 s. Type **160**..	..	..	40	15
662	10 s. Small Agapanthus	..	..	55	15
663	30 s. Pink Witchweed..	..	..	1·10	70
664	60 s. Small Iris	..	..	1·50	2·00
665	90 s. Wild Geranium or Cranesbill	..		1·75	3·00
666	1 m. Large Spotted Orchid	..	..	3·00	5·00
661/6	..	..	*Set of 6*	7·50	10·00

(Des Walt Disney Productions. Litho Questa)

1985 (2 Dec). *150th Birth Anniv of Mark Twain.* T **160a** *and similar vert designs showing Walt Disney cartoon characters illustrating various Mark Twain quotations. Multicoloured.* P 11.

667	6 s. Type **160a**	..	..	40	15
668	50 s. Uncle Scrooge and Goofy reading newspaper	..		1·25	1·00
669	90 s. Winnie the Pooh, Tigger, Piglet and Owl			1·75	2·00
670	1 m. 50, Goofy at ship's wheel			2·75	3·00
667/70			*Set of 4*	5·50	5·50
MS671	127 × 102 mm. 1 m. 25, Mickey Mouse as astronaut. P 13½×14			4·75	3·75

No. 669 was printed in sheetlets of 8 stamps.

160b Donald Duck as the Tailor	161 Male Lammergeier on Watch

(Des Walt Disney Productions. Litho Format)

1985 (2 Dec). *Birth Bicentenaries of Grimm Brothers (folklorists).* T **160b** *and similar vert designs showing Walt Disney cartoon characters in scenes from "The Wishing Table". Multicoloured.* P 11.

672	10 s. Type **160b**	..	..	35	15
673	60 s. The second son (Dewey) with magic donkey and gold coins			1·25	1·25
674	75 s. The eldest son (Huey) with wishing table laden with food			1·50	1·50
675	1 m. The innkeeper stealing the third son's (Louie) magic cudgel			2·00	2·50
672/5			*Set of 4*	4·50	4·75
MS676	127 × 102 mm. 1 m. 50, The tailor and eldest son with wishing table. P 13½×14			4·75	5·50

No. 673 was printed in sheetlets of 8 stamps.

(Des G. Drummond. Litho Format)

1986 (20 Jan). *Flora and Fauna of Lesotho.* T **161** *and similar vert designs. Multicoloured.* P 15.

677	7 s. Type **161**..	..	..	1·25	40
678	9 s. Prickly Pear	..	..	70	20
679	12 s. Stapelia	..	..	70	20
680	15 s. Pair of Lammergeiers	..		2·00	50
681	35 s. Pig's Ears	..	..	1·10	60
682	50 s. Male Lammergeier in flight			3·50	2·50
683	1 m. Adult and juvenile Lammergeiers			3·75	4·50
684	2 m. Columnar cereus	..	..	3·75	6·00
677/84			*Set of 8*	15·00	13·00
MS685	125 ×106 mm. 2 m. Verreaux's Eagle	..		7·00	9·50

162 Two Players chasing Ball	162a Galileo and 200-inch Hale Telescope at Mt Palomar Observatory, California

---

(Des Lori Anzalone. Litho Questa)

1986 (17 Mar). *World Cup Football Championship, Mexico.* T **162** *and similar vert designs. Multicoloured.* P 14.

686	35 s. Type **162**..	..	..	1·25	50
687	50 s. Goalkeeper saving goal..	..		1·75	1·25
688	1 m. Three players chasing ball	..		3·00	2·75
689	2 m. Two players competing for ball		5·00	5·00
686/9			*Set of 4*	10·00	8·50
MS690	104×74 mm. 3 m. Player heading ball ..		9·00	8·50

(Des W. Hanson. Litho Questa)

1986 (5 Apr). *Appearance of Halley's Comet.* T **162a** *and similar horiz designs. Multicoloured.* P 14.

691	9 s. Type **162a**	..	..	50	15
692	15 s. Halley's Comet and "Pioneer Venus 2" spacecraft			75	20
693	70 s. Halley's Comet of 684 A.D. (from Nuremberg Chronicle, 1493)			1·60	1·40
694	3 m. Comet and landing of William the Conqueror, 1066			4·00	5·50
691/4			*Set of 4*	6·25	6·50
MS695	101 ×70 mm. 4 m. Halley's Comet over Lesotho	..	..	6·50	7·00

Nos. 691/3 show the face value followed by "S". Examples of these stamps without this currency abbreviation were prepared, but not issued.

163 International Year of the Child Gold Coin	163a Princess Elizabeth in Pantomime

(Litho Format)

1986 (Apr). *First Anniv of New Currency (1980).* T **163** *and similar horiz designs. Multicoloured.* P 13½×14.

696	30 s. Type **163**..	..	..	4·00	6·50
	a. Horiz strip of 5. Nos. 696/700			18·00	
697	30 s. Five maloti banknote	..		4·00	6·50
698	30 s. Fifty lisente coin	..	..	4·00	6·50
699	30 s. Ten maloti banknote	..		4·00	6·50
700	30 s. One sente coin	..	..	4·00	6·50
696/700			*Set of 5*	18·00	29·00

Nos. 696/700 were printed together, *se-tenant*, in horizontal strips of 5 throughout the sheet.

These stamps were prepared in 1980, but were not issued at that time. Due to increased postal rates a severe shortage of 30 s. stamps occurred in 1986 and Nos. 696/700 were sold for postal purposes from mid-April until early August.

(Des L. Nardo. Litho Questa)

1986 (21 Apr). *60th Birthday of Queen Elizabeth II.* T **163a** *and similar vert designs.* P 14.

701	90 s. black and yellow	..	..	50	60
702	1 m. multicoloured	..	..	55	65
703	2 m. multicoloured	..	..	90	1·40
701/3			*Set of 3*	1·75	2·40
MS704	119×85 mm. 4 m. black and grey-brown		1·75	3·25

Designs:— 1 m. Queen at Windsor Horse Show, 1971; 2 m. At Royal Festival Hall, 1971; 4 m. Princess Elizabeth in 1934.

163b Statue of Liberty and Bela Bartok (composer)

(Des J. Iskowitz. Litho Questa)

1986 (5 May). *Centenary of Statue of Liberty.* T **163b** *and similar horiz designs showing the Statue of Liberty and immigrants to the U.S.A. Multicoloured.* P 14.

705	15 s. Type **163b**	..	..	85	30
706	35 s. Felix Adler (philosopher)	..		85	30
707	1 m. Victor Herbert (composer)	..		3·00	3·00
708	3 m. David Niven (actor)	..	..	4·25	4·00
705/8			*Set of 4*	8·00	6·00
MS709	103 ×74 mm. 3 m. Statue of Liberty (*vert*)		3·50	5·00

163c Mickey Mouse and Goofy as Japanese Mail Runners

(Des Walt Disney Productions. Litho Format)

1986 (25 May). *"Ameripex" International Stamp Exhibition, Chicago.* T **163c** *and similar horiz designs showing Walt Disney cartoon characters delivering mail. Multicoloured.* P 11.

710	15 s. Type **163c**	..	..	55	20
711	35 s. Mickey Mouse and Pluto with mail sledge			90	30
712	1 m. Goofy as postman riding Harley-Davidson motorcycle			1·75	2·00
713	2 m. Donald Duck operating railway mail-bag apparatus			2·25	3·25
710/13			*Set of 4*	4·75	5·25
MS714	127 ×101 mm. 4 m. Goofy driving mail to aircraft. P 14×13½			6·50	7·00

9s	**9**s	**15**s	**35**s	**35**s
(164)	(165)	(166)	(167)	(167a)

15s	**9s**
Extra bar (R.2/5)	Long bars (R.3/8)

35s

Small "s"

Nos. 720a, 720bb, 721a, 721ca, 730ba. Occurs eleven times in the sheet of 40 on R. 1/5, 1/6, 1/8, 1/9, 2/6, 2/7, 2/8, 3/5, 4/4 4/6 and 4/8 for Nos. 720a, 720bb and 730bc or R. 1/4, 2/4, 4/4, 5/4, 6/4, 7/1, 7/4, 9/1, 9/3, 10/1 and 10/2 for Nos. 721a and 721ca.

No. 728a. Occurs thirteen times in the sheet of 49 on R. 6/2 to 7 and on all positions in Row 7.

9s	**35**s	**20**s
(168)	(169)	(170)

1986 (6 June)–**88**. *Various stamps surch (a) As T **164/7a** by Lesotho Ads, Maseru. (i) On Nos. 440, 447, 500/1, 506/7 and 509.*

715	9 s. on 10 s. Red-billed Pintail (*horiz*) (No. 506) (Type **164**)		3·00	1·25
	a. Surch on No. 443 ("1982" imprint date)		2·25	2·25
	b. Surch double		†	—
	c. Surch double, one inverted		†	
716	15 s. on 1 s. Type **127** (No. 500) (22.8.86)		7·00	3·00
	a. Extra bar			
	b. Surch on No. 437 ("1982" imprint date)		£110	
	c. Surch on No. 437a		5·00	6·00
	ca. Extra bar			
	cb. Surch double			
717	15 s. on 2 s. Speckled Pigeon (*horiz*) (22.8.86)		4·00	4·50
	a. Surch double		60·00	
	b. Surch triple			
	c. Surch omitted (in horiz pair with normal)			
718	15 s. on 5 s. Bokmakierie Shrike ("1982" imprint date) (2.11.87)		1·75	35
	a. Surch double		50·00	
719	15 s. on 60 s. Cape Longclaw (*horiz*) (No. 509) (22.8.86)		20	10
	a. Surch on No. 446		60	30
720	35 s. on 25 s. Malachite Kingfisher (No. 507) (9.87)		17·00	20·00
	a. Small "s"		32·00	35·00
	b. Surch on No. 444		50·00	50·00
	ba. Surch double		£100	
	bb. Small "s"		£100	£100
721	35 s. on 75 s. Hoopoe (*horiz*) (No. 447) (Type **167**) (9.87)		22·00	18·00
	a. Small "s"		32·00	32·00
	b. Surch double		55·00	
	c. Surch on No. 510		£110	95·00
	ca. Small "s"		£200	
721d	35 s. on 75 s. Hoopoe (*horiz*) (No. 447) (Type **167a**) (1.88)		75·00	

(ii) *On Nos. 563/5, 567, 573 and 575/6*

722	9 s. on 30 s. Charaxes jasius (Type **164**) (1.7.86)		15	10
	a. Surch with Type **165**		6·50	4·50
	ab. Surch double		†	
	ac. Surch omitted (in horiz pair with normal)			
	ad. Surch triple		75·00	
	b. Surch omitted (in horiz pair with misplaced surch)			
723	9 s. on 60 s. Pontia helice (Type **165**) (1.7.86)		4·00	4·00
	a. Surch double		50·00	
	b. Surch double, one inverted		50·00	
	c. Surch inverted			
	d. Surch triple			
724	15 s. on 1 s. Type **146** (25.6.86)		2·75	2·75
	a. Surch double			
	b. Surch omitted (in horiz pair with normal)			
725	15 s. on 2 s. Aeropetes tulbaghia (25.6.86)		20	20
726	15 s. on 3 s. Colotis evenina (25.6.86)		20	20
727	15 s. on 5 s. Precis hierta (14.8.87)		20	20
	a. Surch double		32·00	
	b. Surch omitted (in horiz pair with normal)		30·00	
728	35 s. on 75 s. Colotis regina (15.8.86)		35	35
	a. Small "s"		1·50	1·50

(b) *As T **168/70** by Epic Printers, Maseru (i) On Nos. 440 and 443*

729	9 s. on 5 s. Bokmakierie Shrike ("1982" imprint date) (30.12.87)		15	20
	a. Long bars			

730	16 s. on 25 s. Malachite Kingfisher (No. 444) (3.88)		2·25	1·00
	a. Surch on No. 507		£225	
	b. Surch on No. 720			
	ba. Small "s" in surch T 167			
731	35 s. on 25 s. Malachite Kingfisher (No. 444) (15.12.87) ..		60	60
	a. Surch on No. 507		13·00	10·00

(ii) On Nos. 566 and 569

732	20 s. on 4 s. *Precis oenone* (30.12.87)		10	10
	a. Surch double, one inverted		12·00	9·00
733	40 s. on 7 s. *Phalanta phalantha* (30.12.87)		15	20

(iii) On No. 722

734	3 s. on 9 s. on 30 s. *Charaxes jasius* (2.2.88)		15	15
	a. Surch Type 164 double		†	—
735	7 s. on 9 s. on 30 s. *Charaxes jasius* (2.2.88)		25	25
715/35		*Set of 21*	55·00	50·00

Some examples of Nos. 722a and 723 show thicker figures due to the method used to construct the artwork for the surcharge.
Nos. 730b/ba show a 16 s. surcharge as T 168 applied to stamps previously surcharged with T 167.

170a Prince Andrew and Miss Sarah Ferguson   171 Basotho Pony and Rider

(Des D. Miller. Litho Questa)

1986 (23 July). *Royal Wedding. T 170a and similar vert designs. Multicoloured.* P 14.

736	50 s. Type 170a		40	40
737	1 m. Prince Andrew ..		70	70
738	3 m. Prince Andrew piloting helicopter		2·25	2·25
736/8		*Set of 3*	3·00	3·00
MS739	88 × 88 mm. 4 m. Prince Andrew and Miss Sarah Ferguson (*different*)		3·50	4·50

(Des B. Bundock. Litho Format)

1986 (3 Oct). *20th Anniv of Independence. T 171 and similar horiz designs. Multicoloured.* P 15.

740	9 s. Type 171..		30	10
741	15 s. Basotho woman spinning mohair		30	15
742	35 s. Crossing river by rowing boat..		40	30
743	3 m. Thaba Tseka Post Office		1·00	3·00
740/3		*Set of 4*	1·75	3·25
MS744	109 × 78 mm. 4 m. King Moshoeshoe I ..		4·75	8·00

171a Chip n'Dale pulling Christmas Cracker   172 Rally Car

(Des Walt Disney Co. Litho Format)

1986 (4 Nov). *Christmas. T 171a and similar vert designs showing Walt Disney cartoon characters. Multicoloured.* P 11.

745	15 s. Type 171a		50	20
746	35 s. Mickey and Minnie Mouse ..		75	30
747	1 m. Pluto pulling Christmas taffy ..		1·50	2·25
748	2 m. Aunt Matilda baking ..		2·00	3·25
745/8		*Set of 4*	4·25	5·50
MS749	126 × 102 mm. 5 m. Huey and Dewey with gingerbread house. P 13½ × 14 ..		5·50	7·00

(Litho Questa)

1987 (28 Apr). *Roof of Africa Motor Rally. T 172 and similar vert designs. Multicoloured.* P 14.

750	9 s. Type 172..		30	10
751	15 s. Motorcyclist		35	15
752	35 s. Motorcyclist (*different*) ..		55	35
753	4 m. Rally car (*different*) ..		3·00	5·00
750/3		*Set of 4*	3·75	5·00

173 Lawn Tennis   174 Isaac Newton and Reflecting Telescope

(Des Y. Berry. Litho Questa)

1987 (29 May). *Olympic Games, Seoul (1988) (1st issue). T 173 and similar vert designs. Multicoloured.* P 14.

754	9 s. Type 173..		40	10
755	15 s. Judo		40	15
756	20 s. Athletics..		45	20
757	35 s. Boxing		60	30
758	1 m. Diving		1·00	1·60
759	3 m. Ten-pin bowling		2·00	4·50
754/9		*Set of 6*	4·25	6·00
MS760	Two sheets, each 75 × 105 mm. (a) 2 m. Lawn tennis (*different*). (b) 4 m. Football			
		Set of 2 sheets	4·25	4·50

Nos. 754/60 incorrectly show the Lesotho flag with white field and emblem at top right.
Similar stamps, with face values of 5, 10, 25, 40, 50 s., 3 m. 50 and a 4 m. miniature sheet showing the correct flag with white field and emblem at top left, were placed on philatelic sale from 30 November 1987. They were not, however, according to the Lesotho Philatelic Bureau, sold through post offices and agencies for postal purposes (*Price for set of 6 £3, mint; miniature sheet £2.75 mint*).
See also Nos. 838/42.

175 Grey Rhebuck   176 Scouts hiking

(Des Mary Walters. Litho Format)

1987 (30 June). *Great Scientific Discoveries. T 174 and similar horiz designs. Multicoloured.* P 15.

761	5 s. Type 174..		30	10
762	9 s. Alexander Graham Bell and first telephone		30	15
763	75 s. Robert Goddard and liquid fuel rocket		80	75
764	4 m. Chuck Yeager and Bell XS-1 rocket plane		2·75	4·50
761/4		*Set of 4*	3·50	5·00
MS765	98 × 68 mm. 4 m. "Mariner 10" spacecraft		2·75	3·00

(Des G. Drummond. Litho Format)

1987 (14 Aug). *Flora and Fauna. T 175 and similar multicoloured designs.* P 15.

766	5 s. Type 175.. ..		40	15
767	9 s. Cape Clawless Otter ..		40	15
768	15 s. Cape Grey Mongoose ..		55	20
769	20 s. Free State Daisy (*vert*) ..		60	20
770	35 s. River Bells (*vert*)		75	30
771	1 m. Turkey Flower (*vert*)		1·75	2·50
772	2 m. Sweet Briar (*vert*)		2·25	3·75
773	3 m. Mountain Reedbuck ..		2·75	5·00
766/73		*Set of 8*	8·50	11·00
MS774	114 × 98 mm. (a) 2 m. Pig-Lily (*vert*). (b) 4 m. Cape Wildebeest ..	*Set of 2 sheets*	4·25	7·00

(Des Mary Walters. Litho Questa)

1987 (10 Sept). *World Scout Jamboree, Australia. T 176 and similar vert designs. Multicoloured.* P 14.

775	9 s. Type 176..		50	20
776	15 s. Scouts playing football ..		55	20
777	35 s. Kangaroos		70	50
778	75 s. Scout saluting		1·50	1·25
779	4 m. Australian scout windsurfing ..		3·75	6·00
775/9		*Set of 5*	6·25	7·25
MS780	96 × 66 mm. 4 m. Outline map and flag of Australia		3·25	4·00

177 Spotted Trunkfish and Columbus' Fleet   178 "Madonna and Child" (detail)

(Des I. MacLaury. Litho Questa)

1987 (14 Dec). *500th Anniv of Discovery of America by Columbus (1992). T 177 and similar horiz designs. Multicoloured.* P 14.

781	9 s. Type 177..		45	20
782	15 s. Green Turtle and ships..		60	20
783	35 s. Columbus watching Common Dolphins from ship		80	40
784	5 m. White-tailed Tropic Bird and fleet at sea		4·25	6·50
781/4		*Set of 4*	5·50	6·50
MS785	105 × 76 mm. 4 m. *Santa Maria* and Cuban Amazon in flight ..		4·00	4·00

No. 782 is inscribed "Carribbean" in error.

(Litho Questa)

1987 (21 Dec). *Christmas. T 178 and similar vert designs showing religious paintings by Raphael. Multicoloured.* P 14.

786	9 s. Type 178..		30	10
787	15 s. "Marriage of the Virgin"		45	15
788	35 s. "Coronation of the Virgin" (detail)		90	40
789	90 s. "Madonna of the Chair"		2·00	3·50
786/9		*Set of 4*	3·25	3·75
MS790	75 × 100 mm. 3 m. "Madonna and Child enthroned with Five Saints" (detail)		3·00	3·00

179 Lesser Pied Kingfisher   (180)

(Des G. Drummond. Litho Format)

1988 (5 Apr). *Birds. T 179 and similar horiz designs. Multicoloured. "1988" imprint date, but no printer's imprint.* P 15.

791	2 s. Type 179		20	20
792	3 s. Three-banded Plover		20	30
793	5 s. Spur-winged Goose		20	30
794	10 s. Clapper Lark		20	30
795	12 s. Red-eyed Bulbul		30	10
796	16 s. Cape Weaver		30	10
797	20 s. Paradise Sparrow ("Red-headed Finch")		30	10
798	30 s. Mountain Chat		35	20
799	40 s. Stonechat		40	20
800	55 s. Pied Barbet		50	25
801	60 s. Red-shouldered Glossy Starling		55	50
802	75 s. Cape Sparrow		65	60
803	1 m. Cattle Egret		75	80
804	3 m. Giant Kingfisher		1·50	2·50
805	10 m. Helmet Guineafowl		4·00	6·00
791/805		*Set of 15*	9·50	12·00

For these stamps showing Questa imprint at bottom left see Nos. 887/99.

1988 (3 May)*. *Royal Ruby Wedding. Nos. 701/4 optd with T 180 in silver.*

806	90 s. black and yellow ..		50	65
807	1 m. multicoloured		60	80
808	2 m. multicoloured		1·00	1·40
806/8		*Set of 3*	1·90	2·50
MS809	119 × 85 mm. 4 m. black and grey-brown		2·50	2·75

*Nos. 806/9 were not available in Lesotho until the middle of 1990.

181 Mickey Mouse and Goofy outside Presidential Palace, Helsinki

(Des Walt Disney Co. Litho Questa)

1988 (2 June). *"Finlandia '88" International Stamp Exhibition, Helsinki. T 181 and similar horiz designs showing Walt Disney cartoon characters in Finland. Multicoloured.* P 14 × 13½.

810	1 s. Type 181		10	10
811	2 s. Goofy and Mickey Mouse in sauna		10	10
812	3 s. Goofy and Mickey Mouse fishing in lake		10	10
813	4 s. Mickey and Minnie Mouse and Finlandia Hall, Helsinki		10	10
814	5 s. Mickey Mouse photographing Goofy at Sibelius Monument, Helsinki		10	10
815	10 s. Mickey Mouse and Goofy pony trekking		10	10
816	3 m. Goofy, Mickey and Minnie Mouse at Helsinki Olympic Stadium		3·00	3·00
817	5 m. Mickey Mouse and Goofy meeting Santa at Arctic Circle		4·00	4·00
810/17		*Set of 8*	6·75	6·75
MS818	Two sheets, each 127 × 102 mm. (a) 4 m. Mickey Mouse and nephew as Lapps. (b) 4 m. Daisy Duck, Goofy, Mickey and Minnie Mouse by fountain, Helsinki ..	*Set of 2 sheets*	5·50	7·00

182 Pope John Paul II giving Communion   183 Large-toothed Rock Hyrax

(Litho Questa)

1988 (1 Sept). *Visit of Pope John Paul II. T 182 and similar multicoloured designs. P 14.*
819 55 s. Type 182 .. .. 40 25
820 2 m. Pope leading procession .. 1·25 1·50
821 3 m. Pope at airport .. .. 1·75 2·00
822 4 m. Pope John Paul II .. 2·25 2·75
819/22 *Set of 4* 5·00 6·00
MS823 98×79 mm. 5 m. Archbishop Morapeli (*horiz*) .. .. 5·00 4·50

(Des L. Watkins. Litho B.D.T.)

1988 (13 Oct). *Small Mammals of Lesotho. T 183 and similar vert designs. Multicoloured. P 14.*
824 16 s. Type 183 .. .. 30 15
825 40 s. Ratel and Black-throated Honeyguide (bird) 70 40
826 75 s. Small-spotted Genet .. 90 75
827 3 m. Yellow Mongoose .. .. 2·75 3·75
824/7 *Set of 4* 4·25 4·50
MS828 110×78 mm. 4 m. Meerkat .. 3·25 4·00

184 "Birth of Venus" (detail) (Botticelli)

(Litho Questa)

1988 (17 Oct). *Famous Paintings. T 184 and similar vert designs. Multicoloured. P 13½ × 14.*
829 15 s. Type 184 .. .. 30 15
830 25 s. "View of Toledo" (El Greco) .. 35 20
831 40 s. "Maids of Honour" (detail) (Velasquez) .. 45 25
832 50 s. "The Fifer" (Manet) .. 55 30
833 55 s. "Starry Night" (detail) (Van Gogh) .. 55 30
834 75 s. "Prima Ballerina" (Degas) .. 70 70
835 2 m. "Bridge over Water Lilies" (Monet) .. 1·75 2·00
836 3 m. "Guernica" (detail) (Picasso) .. 1·75 2·50
829/36 *Set of 8* 5·75 5·75
MS837 Two sheets, each 110×95 mm. (a) 4 m. "The Presentation of the Virgin in the Temple" (Titian). (b) 4 m. "The Miracle of the Newborn Infant" (Titian) .. *Set of 2 sheets* 4·00 4·50

185 Wrestling

(Des J. Martin. Litho B.D.T.)

1988 (11 Nov). *Olympic Games, Seoul (2nd issue). T 185 and similar multicoloured designs. P 14.*
838 12 s. Type 185 .. .. 10 10
839 16 s. Show jumping (*vert*) .. 10 10
840 55 s. Shooting 20 30
841 3 m. 50, As 16 s. (*vert*) .. 1·40 2·00
838/41 *Set of 4* 1·50 2·25
MS842 108×77 mm. 4 m. Olympic flame (*vert*) .. 2·75 3·50

186 Yannick Noah and Eiffel Tower, Paris
186a "The Averoldi Polyptych" (detail) (Titian)

(Des J. McDaniels. Litho Questa)

1988 (18 Nov). *75th Anniv of International Tennis Federation. T 186 and similar multicoloured designs. P 14.*
843 12 s. Type 186 .. .. 30 15
844 20 s. Rod Laver and Sydney Harbour Bridge and Opera House 35 20
845 30 s. Ivan Lendl and Prague .. 40 25
846 65 s. Jimmy Connors and Tokyo (*vert*) .. 55 40
847 1 m. Arthur Ashe and Barcelona (*vert*) .. 80 60
848 1 m. 55, Althea Gibson and New York (*vert*) .. 1·00 90
849 2 m. Chris Evert and Vienna (*vert*) .. 1·50 1·25
850 2 m. 40, Boris Becker and Houses of Parliament, London (*vert*) .. 1·75 1·75

851 3 m. Martina Navratilova and Golden Gate Bridge, San Francisco .. 1·75 2·00
843/51 *Set of 9* 7·50 6·75
MS852 98×72 mm. 4 m. Steffi Graf and Berlin 3·00 3·75
No. 844 is inscribed "SIDNEY" in error.

(Litho Questa)

1988 (1 Dec). *Christmas. 500th Birth Anniv of Titian (artist). T 186a and similar multicoloured designs. P 13½×14.*
853 12 s. Type 186a 20 10
854 20 s. "Christ and the Adulteress" (detail) .. 20 10
855 35 s. "Christ and the Adulteress" (different detail) .. 30 20
856 45 s. "Angel of the Annunciation" .. 40 30
857 65 s. "Saint Dominic" 55 50
858 1 m. "The Vendramin Family" (detail) .. 75 80
859 2 m. "Mary Magdalen" .. .. 1·25 1·75
860 3 m. "The Tribute Money" .. 1·75 2·50
853/60 *Set of 8* 4·75 5·50
MS861 (a) 94 × 110 mm. 5 m. "Mater Dolorosa". P 13½ × 14. (b) 110 × 94 mm. 5 m. "Christ and the Woman taken in Adultery" (*horiz*). P 14 × 13½ ...*Set of 2 sheets* 6·00 8·00

187 Pilatus PC-6 Turbo Porter

(Des K. Gromell. Litho Questa)

1989 (30 Jan). *125th Anniv of International Red Cross. Aircraft. T 187 and similar multicoloured designs. P 14.*
862 12 s. Type 187 .. .. 15 10
863 20 s. Unloading medical supplies from Cessna 208 Caravan I .. 20 15
864 55 s. De Havilland D.H.C.6 Twin Otter 200/300 .. .. 40 40
865 3 m. Douglas DC-3 .. .. 2·00 3·00
862/5 *Set of 4* 2·50 3·25
MS866 109×80 mm. 4 m. Red Cross logo and Douglas DC-3 (*vert*) .. 3·50 3·25

187a "Dawn Mist at Mishima" (Hiroshige)

(Litho Questa)

1989 (19 June). *Japanese Art. Paintings by Hiroshige. T 187a and similar horiz designs. Multicoloured. P 14×13½.*
867 12 s. Type 187a 30 10
868 16 s. "Night Snow at Kambara" .. 35 10
869 20 s. "Wayside Inn at Mariko Station" .. 35 10
870 35 s. "Shower at Shono" .. 55 20
871 55 s. "Snowfall on the Kisokaido near Oi" .. 65 40
872 1 m. "Autumn Moon at Seba" .. 85 85
873 3 m. 20, "Evening Moon at Ryogoku Bridge" 2·25 3·00
874 5 m. "Cherry Blossoms at Arashiyama" .. 2·75 3·75
867/74 *Set of 8* 7·25 7·50
MS875 Two sheets, each 102×76 mm. (a) 4 m. "Listening to the Singing Insects at Dokanyama". (b) 4 m. "Moonlight, Nagakubo" .. *Set of 2 sheets* 6·00 7·00
Nos. 867/74 were each printed in sheetlets of 10 containing two horizontal strips of 5 stamps separated by printed labels commemorating Emperor Hirohito.

188 Mickey Mouse as General
189 *Paxillus involutus*

(Des Walt Disney Company. Litho Questa)

1989 (10 July). *"Philexfrance 89" International Stamp Exhibition, Paris. T 188 and similar multicoloured designs showing Walt Disney cartoon characters in French military uniforms of the Revolutionary period. P 13½×14.*
876 1 s. Type 188 .. .. 10 10
877 2 s. Ludwig von Drake as infantryman .. 10 10
878 3 s. Goofy as grenadier .. 10 10

879 4 s. Horace Horsecollar as cavalryman .. 10 10
880 5 s. Pete as hussar 10 10
881 10 s. Donald Duck as marine .. 10 10
882 3 m. Gyro Gearloose as National Guard .. 3·00 3·25
883 5 m. Scrooge McDuck as admiral .. 4·00 4·25
876/83 *Set of 8* 6·75 7·00
MS884 Two sheets, each 127×102 mm. (a) 4 m. Mickey and Minnie Mouse as King Louis XVI and Marie Antoinette with Goofy as a National Guard (*horiz*). P 14×13½. (b) 4 m. Mickey Mouse as drummer. P 13½×14 .. *Set of 2 sheets* 7·50 9·00
No. 879 is inscribed "CALVARYMAN" in error.

(Litho Questa)

1989 (31 Aug)–91. *As Nos. 793, 795/7 and 803/5, but "1989" imprint date and with printer's imprint at bottom left. P 14.*
887 5 s. Spur-winged Goose (18.1.90) .. 40 55
889 12 s. Red-eyed Bulbul 50 15
890 16 s. Cape Weaver (11.11.89) .. 50 15
891 20 s. Paradise Sparrow ("Red-headed Finch") (2.12.89) .. 50 15
897 1 m. Cattle Egret (1991) .. .. 1·10 1·10
898 3 m. Giant Kingfisher (1991) .. 2·25 3·00
899 10 m. Helmet Guineafowl (1991) .. 6·00 8·00
887/99 *Set of 7* 10·00 12·00
This issue is also known perforated 12, but there is no evidence that stamps in this perforation were used for postal purposes in Lesotho.

(Des S. Wood. Litho Questa)

1989 (8 Sept). *Fungi. T 189 and similar vert designs. Multicoloured. P 14.*
900 12 s. Type 189 .. .. 20 10
901 16 s. *Ganoderma applanatum* .. 20 15
902 55 s. *Suillus granulatus* .. 45 35
903 5 m. *Stereum hirsutum* .. 3·25 4·50
900/3 *Set of 4* 3·75 4·50
MS904 96×69 mm. 4 m. *Scleroderma cepa* ("*flavidum*") .. 3·75 4·50

190 Sesotho Huts
191 Marsh Sandpiper

(Des S. Wood. Litho Questa)

1989 (18 Sept). *Maloti Mountains. T 190 and similar vert designs. Multicoloured. P 14.*
905 1 m. Type 190 .. .. 70 90
a. Horiz strip of 4. Nos. 905/8 2·50
906 1 m. American Aloe and mountains .. 70 90
907 1 m. River valley with waterfall .. 70 90
908 1 m. Sesotho tribesman on ledge .. 70 90
905/8 *Set of 4* 2·50 3·25
MS909 86×117 mm. 4 m. Spiral Aloe .. 3·00 4·00
Nos. 905/8 were printed together, *se-tenant*, in horizontal strips of 4 throughout the sheet forming a composite design.

(Des Tracy Pedersen. Litho Questa)

1989 (18 Sept). *Migrant Birds. T 191 and similar multicoloured designs. P 14.*
910 12 s. Type 191 .. .. 80 30
911 65 s. Little Stint .. .. 1·50 70
912 1 m. Ringed Plover .. .. 2·00 1·50
913 4 m. Curlew Sandpiper .. 3·50 5·50
910/13 *Set of 4* 7·00 7·25
MS914 97×69 mm. 5 m. Ruff (*vert*) .. 8·00 8·50

192 Launch of "Apollo 11"
193 English Penny Post Paid Mark, 1680

(Des G. Welker. Litho Questa)

1989 (6 Nov). *20th Anniv of First Manned Landing on Moon. T 192 and similar multicoloured designs. P 14.*
915 12 s. Type 192 .. .. 25 10
916 16 s. Lunar module *Eagle* landing on Moon (*horiz*) .. 25 15
917 40 s. Neil Armstrong leaving *Eagle* .. 45 25
918 55 s. Edwin Aldrin on Moon (*horiz*) .. 50 30
919 1 m. Aldrin performing scientific experiment (*horiz*) .. 85 85
920 2 m. *Eagle* leaving Moon (*horiz*) .. 1·50 1·75
921 3 m. Command module *Columbia* in Moon orbit (*horiz*) .. 2·00 2·25
922 4 m. Command module on parachutes .. 2·00 2·25
915/22 *Set of 8* 7·50 7·50
MS923 81×111 mm. 5 m. Astronaut on Moon .. 4·00 5·00

(Des U. Purins. Litho B.D.T.)

1989 (17 Nov). *"World Stamp Expo '89" International Stamp Exhibition, Washington (1st issue). Stamps and Postmarks.* T **193** *and similar horiz designs.* P 14.

924	75 s. brown-lake, black and stone		60	65
	a. Sheetlet. Nos. 924/32		4·75	
925	75 s. black, grey and rosine		60	65
926	75 s. dull violet, black and cinnamon		60	65
927	75 s. red-brown, black and cinnamon		60	65
928	75 s. black and olive-yellow		60	65
929	75 s. multicoloured		60	65
930	75 s. black and bright brown-lilac		60	65
931	75 s. black, bright carmine and pale brown		60	65
932	75 s. brt carmine, black & greenish yellow		60	65
924/32		*Set of 9*	4·75	5·50

Designs:— No. 925, German postal seal and feather, 1807; 926, British Post Offices in Crete 1898 20 pa. stamp; 927, Bermuda 1848 Perot 1d. provisional; 928, U.S.A. Pony Express cancellation, 1860; 929, Finland 1856 5 k. stamp; 930, Fiji 1870 *Fiji Times* 1d. stamp, 1870; 931, Sweden newspaper wrapper handstamp, 1823; 932, Bhor 1879 ½ a. stamp.

Nos. 924/32 were printed together, *se-tenant*, in sheetlets of 9.

193a Cathedral Church of St. Peter and St. Paul, Washington

193b "The Immaculate Conception" (Velazquez)

(Des Design Element. Litho Questa)

1989 (17 Nov). *"World Stamp Expo '89" International Stamp Exhibition, Washington (2nd issue). Sheet* 78×61 *mm.* P 14.

MS933	**193a** 4 m. multicoloured	2·50	3·00

(Litho Questa)

1989 (18 Dec). *Christmas. Paintings by Velazquez.* T **193b** *and similar vert designs. Multicoloured.* P 14.

934	12 s. Type **193b**		10	10
935	20 s. "St. Anthony Abbot and St. Paul the Hermit"		15	10
936	35 s. "St. Thomas the Apostle"		25	25
937	55 s. "Christ in the House of Martha and Mary"		35	10
938	1 m. "St. John writing The Apocalypse on Patmos"		60	75
939	3 m. "The Virgin presenting the Chasuble to St. Ildephonsus"		1·60	2·25
940	4 m. "The Adoration of the Magi"		2·00	2·75
934/40		*Set of 7*	4·50	6·00
MS941	71×96 mm. 5 m. "The Coronation of the Virgin"		6·00	7·00

194 Scene from 1966 World Cup Final, England

(Des G. Vasarhelyi. Litho Questa)

1989 (27 Dec). *World Cup Football Championship, Italy.* T **194** *and similar horiz designs showing scenes from past finals. Multicoloured.* P 14.

942	12 s. Type **194**		40	10
943	16 s. 1970 final, Mexico		40	15
944	55 s. 1974 final, West Germany		85	40
945	5 m. 1982 final, Spain		3·50	5·00
942/5		*Set of 4*	4·75	5·00
MS946	106×85 mm. 4 m. Player's legs and symbolic football		4·50	5·00

16 s	16 s	16 s	16 s
≡	=	Long bars (R. 6/3)	≡
(195)	**(196)**		**(196a)**

1990 (22 Feb)–**91**. *Nos. 795, 798/9 and 889 surch with* T **195/6a** *by Lesotho Ads.*

947	16 s. on 12 s. Red-eyed Bulbul (No. 795) (T **195**)		3·50	90
948	16 s. on 12 s. Red-eyed Bulbul (No. 889) (T **196**)		60	15
	a. Surch inverted		40·00	
	b. Surch double		60·00	
	c. Long bars			
	d. Surch with Type **195**			
948e	16 s. on 30 s. Mountain Chat (No. 798) (T **196a**) (18.1.91)		60	15
	ea. Surch inverted			
	eb. Lower bar omitted			
948f	16 s. on 40 s. Stonechat (No. 799) (T **196a**) (18.1.91)		60	15
	fa. Lower bar omitted			
947/8f		*Set of 4*	4·75	1·25

The lower cancelling bar is frequently completely omitted from Type **196a** on R. 4/4, although on occasions traces of it do remain.

197 *Byblia anvatara*

198 *Satyrium princeps*

(Des L. Nelson. Litho Questa)

1990 (26 Feb). *Butterflies.* T **197** *and similar vert designs. Multicoloured.* P 14.

949	12 s. Type **197**		50	15
950	16 s. *Cynthia cardui*		65	15
951	55 s. *Precis oenone*		90	40
952	65 s. *Pseudacraea boisduvali*		1·00	65
953	1 m. *Precis orithya*		1·50	1·25
954	2 m. *Precis sophia*		2·50	2·50
955	3 m. *Danaus chrysippus*		3·25	3·75
956	4 m. *Druryia antimachus*		4·25	6·00
949/56		*Set of 8*	13·00	13·00
MS957	105×70 mm. 5 m. *Papilio demodocus*		7·50	9·00

(Des B. Tear. Litho Questa)

1990 (12 Mar). *"EXPO 90" International Garden and Greenery Exhibition, Osaka. Local Orchids.* T **198** *and similar horiz designs. Multicoloured.* P 14.

958	12 s. Type **198**		55	15
959	16 s. *Huttonaea pulchra*		60	15
960	55 s. *Herschelia graminifolia*		1·25	30
961	1 m. *Ansellia gigantea*		1·75	75
962	1 m. 55, *Polystachya pubescens*		2·00	1·75
963	2 m. 40, *Penthea filicornis*		2·00	2·25
964	3 m. *Disperis capensis*		2·25	3·25
965	4 m. *Disa uniflora*		3·00	4·00
958/65		*Set of 8*	12·00	11·00
MS966	95×68 mm. 5 m. *Stenoglottis longifolia*		7·50	9·00

198a Lady Elizabeth Bowes-Lyon and Brother in Fancy Dress

199 King Moshoeshoe II and Prince Mohato wearing Seana-Marena Blankets

(Des Young Phillips Studio. Litho Questa)

1990 (5 July). *90th Birthday of Queen Elizabeth the Queen Mother.* T **198a** *and similar vert portraits, 1910–1919.* P 14.

967	1 m. 50, brownish black and bright magenta		95	1·00
	a. Strip of 3. Nos. 967/9		2·50	
968	1 m. 50, brownish black and bright magenta		95	1·00
969	1 m. 50, brownish black and bright magenta		95	1·00
967/9		*Set of 3*	2·50	2·75
MS970	90×75 mm. 5 m. dull orange-brown, brownish black and bright magenta		2·75	3·50

Designs:— No. 967, Type **198a**; No. 968, Lady Elizabeth Bowes-Lyon in evening dress; No. 969, Lady Elizabeth Bowes-Lyon wearing hat; No. MS970, Lady Elizabeth Bowes-Lyon as a child.

Nos. 967/9 were printed together, horizontally and vertically *se-tenant*, in sheetlets of 9 (3×3).

(Litho B.D.T.)

1990 (17 Aug). *Traditional Blankets.* T **199** *and similar multicoloured designs.* P 14.

971	12 s. Type **199**		10	10
972	16 s. Prince Mohato wearing Seana-Marena blanket		10	10
973	1 m. Pope John Paul II wearing Seana-Marena blanket		1·75	1·10
974	3 m. Basotho horsemen wearing Matlama blankets		2·00	2·75
971/4		*Set of 4*	3·50	3·50
MS975	85×104 mm. 5 m. Pope John Paul II wearing hat and Seana-Marena blanket (*horiz*)		4·50	4·75

200 Filling Truck at No. 1 Quarry

201 Mother breastfeeding Baby

(Litho B.D.T.)

1990 (24 Aug). *Lesotho Highlands Water Project.* T **200** *and similar vert designs. Multicoloured.* P 14.

976	16 s. Type **200**		35	10
977	20 s. Tanker lorry on Pitseng–Malibamatso road		35	10
978	55 s. Piers for Mphosong Bridge		55	30
979	2 m. Excavating Mphosong section of Pitseng–Malibamatso road		2·00	3·00
976/9		*Set of 4*	3·00	3·00
MS980	104×85 mm. 5 m. Sinking blasting boreholes on Pitseng–Malibamatso road		4·25	5·50

(Litho Questa)

1990 (26 Oct). *U.N.I.C.E.F. Child Survival Campaign.* T **201** *and similar vert designs. Multicoloured.* P 14.

981	12 s. Type **201**		40	10
982	55 s. Baby receiving oral rehydration therapy		70	45
983	1 m. Weight monitoring		1·00	2·00
981/3		*Set of 3*	1·90	2·25

King Letsie III, November 1990–25 January 1995 (abdicated)

202 Men's Triple Jump

203 "Virgin and Child" (detail, Rubens)

(Des B. Grout. Litho Questa)

1990 (5 Nov). *Olympic Games, Barcelona (1992).* T **202** *and similar multicoloured designs.* P 14.

984	16 s. Type **202**		30	10
985	55 s. Men's 200 metres race		50	25
986	1 m. Men's 5000 metres race		80	90
987	4 m. Show jumping		2·75	4·00
984/7		*Set of 4*	4·00	4·50
MS988	100×70 mm. 5 m. Olympic flame (*horiz*)		4·25	5·50

(Litho Questa)

1990 (5 Dec). *Christmas. Paintings by Rubens.* T **203** *and similar vert designs. Multicoloured.* P 13½×14.

989	12 s. Type **203**		20	10
990	16 s. "Adoration of the Magi" (detail)		20	10
991	55 s. "Head of One of the Three Kings" (detail)		45	25
992	80 s. "Adoration of the Magi" (different detail)		60	60
993	1 m. "Virgin and Child" (different detail)		70	70
994	2 m. "Adoration of the Magi" (different detail)		1·25	1·75
995	3 m. "Virgin and Child" (different detail)		2·00	2·50
996	4 m. "Adoration of the Magi" (different detail)		2·25	3·00
989/96		*Set of 8*	7·00	8·00
MS997	71×100 mm. 5 m. "Assumption of the Virgin" (detail)		4·00	5·50

204 Mickey Mouse at Nagasaki Peace Park

(Des Walt Disney Company. Litho Questa)

1991 (10 June). *"Phila Nippon '91" International Stamp Exhibition, Tokyo.* T **204** *and similar horiz designs showing Walt Disney cartoon characters in Japan. Multicoloured.* P 14×13½.

998	20 s. Type **204**		45	15
999	30 s. Mickey Mouse on Kamakura Beach		50	20
1000	40 s. Mickey and Donald Duck with Bunraku puppet		55	25
1001	50 s. Mickey and Donald eating soba		60	35
1002	75 s. Mickey and Minnie Mouse at tea house		85	70
1003	1 m. Mickey running after "Hikari" express train		1·00	1·00
1004	3 m. Mickey Mouse with deer at Todaiji Temple, Nara		2·50	3·25
1005	4 m. Mickey and Minnie outside Imperial Palace		2·75	3·50
998/1005		*Set of 8*	8·25	8·50
MS1006	Two sheets, each 127×112 mm. (a) 5 m. Mickey Mouse skiing; (b) 5 m. Mickey and Minnie having a picnic	*Set of 2 sheets*	7·00	8·00

205 Stewart Granger (*King Solomon's Mines*) **206** *Satyrus aello*

(Des R. Jung. Litho Questa)

1991 (20 June). *Famous Films with African Themes.* T **205** *and similar vert designs. Multicoloured.* P 14.

1007	12 s. Type **205**		35	20
1008	16 s. Johnny Weissmuller (*Tarzan the Ape Man*)		35	20
1009	30 s. Clark Gable with Grace Kelly (*Mogambo*)		50	35
1010	55 s. Sigourney Weaver and male gorilla (*Gorillas in the Mist*)		75	55
1011	70 s. Humphrey Bogart and Katharine Hepburn (*The African Queen*)		90	80
1012	1 m. John Wayne and capture of rhinoceros (*Hatari!*)		1·25	1·00
1013	2 m. Meryl Streep and De Havilland D.H.60G Gipsy Moth light aircraft (*Out of Africa*)		2·00	2·25
1014	4 m. Arsenio Hall and Eddie Murphy (*Coming to America*)		2·75	3·50
1007/14		*Set of 8*	8·00	8·00
MS1015	108×77 mm. 5 m. Elsa the lioness (*Born Free*)		3·75	4·50

(Des S. Heimann. Litho Cartor)

1991 (1 Aug)–**92**. *Butterflies.* T **206** *and similar horiz designs. Multicoloured.* P 14×13½. A. *Without imprint date*

1016cA	2 s. Type **206** (p 13½)		30	30
1017cA	3 s. *Erebia medusa* (p 13½)		30	30
1018A	5 s. *Melanargia galathea*		30	30
1019A	10 s. *Erebia aethiops*		30	30
1020A	20 s. *Coenonympha pamphilus*		35	30
	c. Perf 13½		35	30
1021A	25 s. *Pyrameis atalanta*		35	30
1022A	30 s. *Charaxes jasius*		40	30
	c. Perf 13½		40	30
1023A	40 s. *Colias palaeno*		40	30
1024A	50 s. *Colias cliopatra*		45	40
1025A	50 s. *Colias philodice*		60	60
1026A	70 s. *Rhumni gonepteryx*		75	75
1027cA	1 m. *Colias caesonia* (p 13½)		75	75
1028A	2 m. *Pyrameis cardui*		1·50	1·50
	c. Perf 13½		1·50	1·50
1029cA	3 m. *Danaus chrysippus* (p 13½)		1·60	1·75
1030cA	10 m. *Apatura iris* (p 13½)		4·50	5·50
1016cA/30cA		*Set of 15*	12·00	13·00

B. *With imprint date ("1992") at foot* (4.92)

1016B	2 s. Type **206**		10	20
1017B	3 s. *Erebia medusa*		10	20
1018B	5 s. *Melanargia galathea*		30	30
1019B	10 s. *Erebia aethiops*		15	10
1020B	20 s. *Coenonympha pamphilus*		35	30
	c. Perf 13½		35	30
1021B	25 s. *Pyrameis atalanta*		20	10
1022B	30 s. *Charaxes jasius*		20	10
	c. Perf 13½		20	10
1023B	40 s. *Colias palaeno*		20	10
1024B	50 s. *Colias cliopatra*		30	20
1025B	60 s. *Colias philodice*		30	20
1026B	70 s. *Rhumni gonepteryx*		40	25
1027B	1 m. *Colias caesonia*		45	30
1028B	2 m. *Pyrameis cardui*		75	70
1029A	3 m. *Danaus chrysippus*		1·25	1·00
1030B	10 m. *Apatura iris*		3·00	3·25
1016B/30B		*Set of 15*	7·00	6·50

207 Victim of Drug Abuse **208** Wattled Cranes

(Litho Cartor)

1991 (23 Sept). *"Say No To Drugs" Campaign.* P 13½×14.

1031 **207**	16 s. multicoloured	70	60

(Litho Cartor)

1991 (10 Oct). *Southern Africa Development Co-ordination Conference Tourism Promotion.* T **208** *and similar horiz designs. Multicoloured.* P 14×13½.

1032	12 s. Type **208**		70	70
1033	16 s. Butterfly on flowers		70	70
1034	25 s. Zebra and tourist bus at Mukurub (former rock formation), Namibia		85	30
1032/4		*Set of 3*	2·00	1·50
MS1035	75×117 mm. 3 m. Basotho women in ceremonial dress. P 13×12		2·75	3·50

209 De Gaulle in 1939 **210** Prince and Princess of Wales

(Des D. Miller. Litho B.D.T.)

1991 (6 Dec). *Birth Centenary of Charles de Gaulle (French statesman).* T **209** *and similar vert designs.* P 14.

1036	20 s. black and lake-brown		40	15
1037	40 s. black and purple		60	40
1038	50 s. black and yellow-olive		60	25
1039	60 s. black and greenish blue		70	65
1040	4 m. black and dull vermilion		2·25	3·75
1036/40		*Set of 5*	4·25	4·75

Designs:—40 s. General De Gaulle as Free French leader; 50 s. De Gaulle as provisional President of France 1944–46; 60 s. Charles de Gaulle in 1958; 4 m. Pres. De Gaulle, 1969.

(Des D. Miller. Litho B.D.T.)

1991 (9 Dec). *10th Wedding Anniv of Prince and Princess of Wales.* T **210** *and similar horiz designs. Multicoloured.* P 14.

1041	50 s. Type **210**		80	25
1042	70 s. Prince Charles at polo and Princess Diana holding Prince Henry		80	45
1043	1 m. Prince Charles with Prince Henry and Princess Diana in evening dress		1·00	65
1044	3 m. Prince William and Prince Henry in school uniform		1·75	2·75
1041/4		*Set of 4*	4·00	3·75
MS1045	68×91 mm. 4 m. Portraits of Prince with Princess and sons		4·00	4·25

211 "St. Anne with Mary and the Child Jesus" (Dürer) **212** Mickey Mouse and Pluto pinning the Tail on the Donkey

(Litho Walsall)

1991 (13 Dec). *Christmas. Drawings by Albrecht Dürer.* T **211** *and similar vert designs.* P 12.

1046	20 s. black and bright magenta		25	10
1047	30 s. black and new blue		35	20
1048	50 s. black and yellowish green		50	25
1049	60 s. black and vermilion		55	30
1050	70 s. black and lemon		60	45
1051	1 m. black and orange		75	75
1052	2 m. black and bright purple		1·50	2·00
1053	4 m. black and ultramarine		2·25	3·50
1046/53		*Set of 8*	6·00	6·75
MS1054	Two sheets, each 102×127 mm. (a) 5 m. black and carmine-rose. (b) 5 m. black and cobalt. P 14	*Set of 2 sheets*	4·25	5·50

Designs:—30 s. "Mary on Grass Bench"; 50 s. "Mary with Crown of Stars"; 60 s. "Mary with Child beside Tree"; 70 s. "Mary with Child beside Wall"; 1 m. "Mary in Halo on Crescent Moon"; 2 m. "Mary breastfeeding Child"; 4 m. "Mary with Infant in Swaddling Clothes"; 5 m. (No. **MS**1054a) "The Birth of Christ"; 5 m. (No. **MS**1054b) "The Holy Family with Dragonfly".

(Des Walt Disney Co. Litho Questa)

1991 (16 Dec). *Children's Games.* T **212** *and similar vert designs showing Walt Disney cartoon characters. Multicoloured.* P 13½×14.

1055	20 s. Type **212**		40	15
1056	30 s. Mickey playing mancala		45	20
1057	40 s. Mickey rolling hoop		50	20
1058	50 s. Minnie Mouse hula-hooping		55	25
1059	70 s. Mickey and Pluto throwing a frisbee		75	60
1060	1 m. Donald Duck with a diabolo		1·00	1·00
1061	2 m. Donald's nephews playing marbles		2·00	2·50
1062	3 m. Donald with Rubik's cube		2·50	3·25
1055/62		*Set of 8*	7·25	7·25
MS1063	Two sheets, each 127×112 mm. (a) 5 m. Donald's and Mickey's nephews playing tug-of-war; (b) 5 m. Mickey and Donald mock fighting	*Set of 2 sheets*	7·00	8·00

ALTERED CATALOGUE NUMBERS

Any Catalogue numbers altered from the last edition are shown as a list in the introductory pages.

213 Lanner Falcon **214** Queen Elizabeth II and Cooking at a Mountain Homestead

(Des Tracy Pedersen. Litho Questa)

1992 (10 Feb). *Birds.* T **213** *and similar vert designs. Multicoloured.* P 14½×14.

1064	30 s. Type **213**		50	50
	a. Sheetlet. Nos. 1064/83		9·00	
1065	30 s. Bateleur		50	50
1066	30 s. Paradise Sparrow ("Red-headed Finch")		50	50
1067	30 s. Lesser Striped Swallow		50	50
1068	30 s. Alpine Swift		50	50
1069	30 s. Didric Cuckoo		50	50
1070	30 s. Yellow-tufted Malachite Sunbird		50	50
1071	30 s. Burchell's Gonolek ("Crimson-breasted Shrike")		50	50
1072	30 s. Pin-tailed Whydah		50	50
1073	30 s. Lilac-breasted Roller		50	50
1074	30 s. Little Black Bustard ("Korhaan")		50	50
1075	30 s. Black-collared Barbet		50	50
1076	30 s. Secretary Bird		50	50
1077	30 s. Red-billed Quelea		50	50
1078	30 s. Red Bishop		50	50
1079	30 s. Ring-necked Dove		50	50
1080	30 s. Yellow Canary		50	50
1081	30 s. Cape Longclaw		50	50
1082	30 s. Cordon-bleu ("Blue Waxbill")		50	50
1083	30 s. Golden Bishop		50	50
1064/83		*Set of 20*	9·00	9·00

Nos. 1064/83 were printed together, *se-tenant*, as a sheetlet of 20 with the backgrounds forming a composite design.

(Des D. Miller. Litho Questa)

1992 (2 Mar). *40th Anniv of Queen Elizabeth II's Accession.* T **214** *and similar horiz designs. Multicoloured.* P 14.

1084	20 s. Type **214**		20	15
1085	30 s. View of the Lowlands		25	20
1086	1 m. Agaves and escarpment		65	65
1087	4 m. Thaba-Bosiu		2·25	3·00
1084/7		*Set of 4*	3·00	3·50
MS1088	75×97 mm. 5 m. Mountains at sunset		3·00	3·75

215 Minnie Mouse as Spanish Lady, 1540–1660

(Des Walt Disney Co. Litho Questa)

1992 (13 Apr). *International Stamp Exhibitions.* T **215** *and similar vert designs showing Walt Disney cartoon characters. Multicoloured.* P 13½×14.

(a) *"Granada 92", Spain. Traditional Spanish Costumes.*

1089	20 s. Type **215**		40	15
1090	50 s. Mickey Mouse as Don Juan at Lepanto, 1571		55	30
1091	70 s. Donald in Galician costume, 1880		70	50
1092	2 m. Daisy Duck in Aragonese costume, 1880		1·75	2·50
1089/92		*Set of 4*	3·00	3·00
MS1093	127×112 mm. 5 m. Goofy the Bullfighter		4·00	4·50

(b) *"World Columbian Stamp Expo '92". Red Indian Life.*

1094	30 s. Donald Duck making arrowheads		30	30
1095	40 s. Goofy playing lacrosse		40	40
1096	1 m. Mickey Mouse and Donald Duck planting corn		70	80
1097	3 m. Minnie Mouse doing bead work		1·60	2·50
1094/7		*Set of 4*	2·75	3·50
MS1098	127×112 mm. 5 m. Mickey paddling canoe		4·00	4·50

216 Stegosaurus **217** Men's Discus

(Des D. Burkhart. Litho Questa)

1992 (9 June). *Prehistoric Animals.* T **216** *and similar horiz designs. Multicoloured.* P 14.

1099	20 s. Type **216**		45	30
1100	30 s. Ceratosaurus		55	35
1101	40 s. Procompsognathus		65	45
1102	50 s. Lesothosaurus		55	55
1103	70 s. Plateosaurus		1·00	70
1104	1 m. Gasosaurus		1·25	1·00
1105	2 m. Massospondylus		1·75	2·00
1106	3 m. Archaeopteryx		2·00	2·50
1099/106		*Set of 8*	7·50	7·00

MS1107 Two sheets, each 105×77 mm. (a) 5 m. As 50 s. (b) 5 m. As 3 m. . . *Set of 2 sheets* 8·00 8·00

(Litho Questa)

1992 (5 Aug). *Olympic Games, Albertville and Barcelona.* T **217** *and similar multicoloured designs.* P 14.

1108	20 s. Type **217**		20	15
1109	30 s. Men's long jump		25	15
1110	40 s. Women's 4 × 100 metres relay		30	25
1111	70 s. Women's 100 metres		50	50
1112	1 m. Men's parallel bars		70	70
1113	2 m. Men's double luge (*horiz*)		1·40	1·60
1114	3 m. Women's 30k cross-country skiing (*horiz*)		1·75	2·25
1115	4 m. Men's biathlon		2·00	2·50
1108/15		*Set of 8*	6·50	7·25

MS1116 Two sheets, each 100×70 mm. (a) 5 m. Women's figure skating. (b) 5 m. Ice hockey (*horiz*) . . *Set of 2 sheets* 6·75 7·50

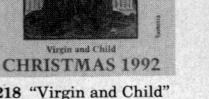

218 "Virgin and Child" (Sassetta)

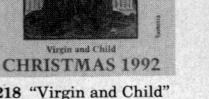

219 World Trade Centre, New York

(Litho Questa)

1992 (2 Nov). *Christmas. Religious Paintings.* T **218** *and similar vert designs. Multicoloured.* P 13½×14.

1117	20 s. Type **218**		25	15
1118	30 s. "Coronation of the Virgin" (Master of Bonastre)		30	20
1119	40 s. "Virgin and Child" (Master of SS. Cosmas and Damian)		40	25
1120	70 s. "The Virgin of Great Panagia" (detail) (12th-century Russian school)		70	55
1121	1 m. "Madonna and Child" (Vincenzo Foppa)		95	95
1122	2 m. "Madonna and Child" (School of Lippo Memmi)		1·75	2·00
1123	3 m. "Virgin and Child" (Barnaba da Modena)		2·25	2·75
1124	4 m. "Virgin and Child with Saints" (triptych) (Simone dei Crocifissi)		2·50	3·00
1117/24		*Set of 8*	8·00	8·75

MS1125 Two sheets, each 76×102 mm. (a) 5 m. "Virgin and Child with Saints" (different detail) (Simone dei Crocifissi). (b) 5 m. "Virgin and Child enthroned and surrounded by Angels" (Cimabue) . . *Set of 2 sheets* 8·00 9·00

(Des Kerri Schiff. Litho Questa)

1992 (17 Nov). *Postage Stamp Mega Event, New York. Sheet* 100×70 *mm.* P 14.

MS1126 **219** 5 m. multicoloured . . 4·00 4·50

220 Baby Harp Seal (Earth Summit '92, Rio)

(Des L. Birmingham. Litho Questa)

1993 (8 Feb). *Anniversaries and Events.* T **220** *and similar horiz designs. Multicoloured.* P 14.

1127	20 s. Type **220**		40	30
1128	30 s. Giant Panda (Earth Summit '92, Rio)		55	30
1129	40 s. Airship LZ-127 *Graf Zeppelin* over globe (75th death anniv of Count Ferdinand von Zeppelin)		55	30
1130	70 s. Woman grinding maize (International Conference on Nutrition, Rome)		55	45
1131	4 m. Lt. Robinson's Royal Aircraft Factory B.E.2C shooting down Schutte Lanz SL-11 airship (75th death anniv of Count Ferdinand von Zeppelin)		2·50	2·75
1132	5 m. Valentina Tereshkova and "Vostok 6" (30th anniv of first woman in space)		2·50	2·75
1127/32		*Set of 6*	6·25	6·25

MS1133 Two sheets, each 100×70 mm. (a) 5 m. Dr. Ronald McNair (*Challenger* astronaut) (International Space Year). (b) 5 m. South African Crowned Crane (Earth Summit '92, Rio) . . *Set of 2 sheets* 6·50 6·50

---

221 "Orpheus and Eurydice" (detail) (Poussin)

222 Aloe

(Litho Walsall)

1993 (19 Mar). *Bicentenary of the Louvre, Paris.* T **221** *and similar vert designs showing paintings. Multicoloured.* P 12.

1134	70 s. Type **221**		70	70
	a. Sheetlet. Nos. 1134/41		5·00	
1135	70 s. "Rape of the Sabine Women" (left detail) (Poussin)		70	70
1136	70 s. "Rape of the Sabine Women" (right detail) (Poussin)		70	70
1137	70 s. "The Death of Sapphira" (left detail) (Poussin)		70	70
1138	70 s. "The Death of Sapphira" (right detail) (Poussin)		70	70
1139	70 s. "Echo and Narcissus" (left detail) (Poussin)		70	70
1140	70 s. "Echo and Narcissus" (right detail) (Poussin)		70	70
1141	70 s. "Self-portrait" (Poussin)		70	70
1134/41		*Set of 8*	5·00	5·00

MS1142 70×100 mm. 5 m. "The Money Lender and his Wife" (57×89 *mm*) (Metsys). P 14½ 4·25 4·50

Nos. 1134/41 were printed together, *se-tenant*, in sheetlets of 8 stamps and one centre label.

(Des Mary Walters. Litho B.D.T.)

1993 (1 June). *Flowers.* T **222** *and similar vert designs. Multicoloured.* P 14.

1143	20 s. Type **222**		25	10
1144	30 s. Calla Lily		30	15
1145	40 s. Bird of Paradise plant		35	15
1146	70 s. Amaryllis		55	40
1147	1 m. Agapanthus		75	60
1148	2 m. Crinum		1·75	1·50
1149	4 m. Watsonia		1·90	2·25
1150	5 m. Gazania		2·00	2·50
1143/50		*Set of 8*	7·00	7·00

MS1151 Two sheets, each 98×67 mm. (a) 7 m. Plumbago. (b) 7 m. Desert Rose . . *Set of 2 sheets* 6·50 7·00

223 *Precis westermanni*

(Des L. Nelson. Litho B.D.T.)

1993 (30 June). *Butterflies.* T **223** *and similar horiz designs. Multicoloured.* P 14.

1152	20 s. Type **223**		40	15
1153	40 s. *Precis sophia*		50	20
1154	70 s. *Precis terea*		65	45
1155	1 m. *Byblia acheloia*		75	75
1156	2 m. *Papilio antimachus*		1·25	1·50
1157	5 m. *Pseudacraea boisduvali*		1·75	2·50
1152/7		*Set of 6*	4·75	5·00

MS1158 Two sheets, each 96×62 mm. (a) 7 m. *Precis oenone.* (b) 7 m. *Precis octavia* . . *Set of 2 sheets* 7·00 7·00

No. 1157 is inscribed "Pesudacraea boisduvali" in error.

224 Queen Elizabeth II at Coronation (photograph by Cecil Beaton)

(Des Kerri Schiff. Litho Questa)

1993 (30 July). *40th Anniv of Coronation.* T **224** *and similar designs.* P 13½×14.

1159	20 s. multicoloured		30	45
	a. Sheetlet. Nos. 1159/62×2		8·00	
1160	40 s. multicoloured		45	60
1161	1 m. black and bottle-green		70	90

1162	5 m. multicoloured		3·00	3·25
1159/62		*Set of 4*	4·00	4·75

MS1163 70×100 mm. 7 m. multicoloured (42½×28½ mm). P 14 4·25 4·50

Designs: *Vert*—40 s. St. Edward's Crown and Sceptre; 1 m. Queen Elizabeth the Queen Mother; 5 m. Queen Elizabeth II and family. *Horiz*—7 m. "Conversation Piece at Royal Lodge, Windsor" (detail) (Sir James Gunn).

Nos. 1159/62 were printed in sheetlets of 8, containing two *se-tenant* blocks of 4.

225 East African Railways Vulcan Steam Locomotive, 1929

226 Court-house

(Des G. Vasarhelyi. Litho B.D.T.)

1993 (31 Aug). *African Railways.* T **225** *and similar horiz designs. Multicoloured.* P 14.

1164	20 s. Type **225**		40	15
1165	30 s. Beyer-Garratt Class 15A steam locomotive, Zimbabwe Railways, 1952		50	20
1166	40 s. Class 25 steam locomotive, South African Railways, 1953		60	20
1167	70 s. Class A 58 steam locomotive, East African Railways		75	40
1168	1 m. Class 9E electric locomotives, South African Railways		90	70
1169	2 m. Class 87 diesel-electric locomotive No. 8737, East African Railways, 1971		1·40	1·25
1170	3 m. Class 92 diesel locomotive, East African Railways, 1971		1·75	1·75
1171	5 m. Class 26 steam locomotive, No. 3450, South African Railways, 1982		2·00	2·50
1164/71		*Set of 8*	7·50	6·50

MS1172 Two sheets, each 104×82 mm. (a) 7 m. Class 6E electric locomotive, South African Railways, 1969. (b) 7 m. Class 231-132BT steam locomotive, Algerian Railways, 1937 . . *Set of 2 sheets* 8·00 8·50

(Des V. Seatile Nkhomo. Litho Government Printer, Pretoria)

1993 (24 Sept). *Traditional Houses.* T **226** *and similar horiz designs. Multicoloured.* P 14×14½.

1173	20 s. Type **226**		25	10
1174	30 s. House with reed fence		30	15
1175	70 s. Unmarried girls' house		55	40
1176	4 m. Hut made from branches		2·75	3·75
1173/6		*Set of 4*	3·50	4·00

MS1177 81×69 mm. 4 m. Decorated houses 3·00 3·50

227 Black and White Shorthair

(Des V. Seatile Nkhomo. Litho Government Printer, Pretoria)

1993 (29 Oct). *Domestic Cats.* T **227** *and similar multicoloured designs.* P 14.

1178	20 s. Type **227**		30	10
1179	30 s. Shorthair Tabby lying down		30	15
1180	70 s. Head of Shorthair Tabby		45	35
1181	5 m. Black and White Shorthair with Shorthair Tabby		2·25	2·50
1178/81		*Set of 4*	3·00	2·75

MS1182 113×89 mm. 5 m. Shorthair Tabby with rat (*vert*) 1·00 1·10

228 Pluto in Chung Cheng Park, Keelung

229 Tseliso "Frisco" Khomari (Lesotho)

(Des Rosemary DeFiglio. Litho Questa)

1993 (15 Nov). *"Taipei '93" Asian International Stamp Exhibition, Taiwan.* T **228** *and similar multicoloured designs showing Walt Disney cartoon characters in Taiwan.* P 14×13½ (*horiz*) or 13½×14 (*vert*).

1183	20 s. Type **228**		30	10
1184	30 s. Donald Duck at Chiao-Tienkung Temple Festival		35	15
1185	40 s. Goofy with lantern figures		40	20
1186	70 s. Minnie Mouse shopping at temple festival		65	40
1187	1 m. Daisy Duck at Queen's Head Rock, Yehliu (*vert*)		80	70

1188	1 m. 20, Mickey and Minnie at National Concert Hall (vert)	1·00	1·00
1189	2 m. Donald at Chiang Kai-shek Memorial Hall (vert)	1·40	1·50
1190	2 m. 50, Donald and Daisy at the Grand Hotel, Taipei	1·75	2·00
1183/90	Set of 8	6·00	5·50

MS1191 Two sheets, each 128×102 mm. (a) 5 m. Goofy over National Palace Museum, Taipei. (b) 6 m. Mickey and Minnie at Presidential Palace Museum, Taipei (vert) .. .. Set of 2 sheets 8·00 8·00

(Des Rosemary DeFiglio. Litho Cartor)

1994 (1 Feb). *World Cup Football Championship '94, U.S.A. T* **229** *and similar multicoloured designs. P* 13½×14.

1192	20 s. Type 229	40	10
1193	30 s. Thato "American Spoon" Mohale (Lesotho)	45	15
1194	40 s. Jozic Davor (Yugoslavia) and Freddy Rincorn (Colombia)	55	20
1195	50 s. Lefika "Mzee" Lekhotla (Lesotho)	60	25
1196	70 s. Litsiso "House-on-fire" Khali (Lesotho)	75	55
1197	1 m. Roger Milla (Cameroun)	90	75
1198	1 m. 20, David Platt (England)	1·25	1·50
1199	2 m. Karl Heinz Rummenigge (Germany) and Soren Lerby (Denmark)	1·75	2·25
1192/9	Set of 8	6·00	5·25

MS1200 Two sheets, each 100×70 mm. (a) 6 m. Klaus Lindenberger (Czechoslovakia). (b) 6 m. Franco Baresi (Italy) and Ivan Hasek (Czechoslovakia) (horiz). P 13 .. Set of 2 sheets 8·00 8·00

230 King Letsie III signing Oath of Office 231 Aquatic River Frog

(Litho Government Printer, Pretoria)

1994 (2 Apr). *1st Anniv of Restoration of Democracy. T* **230** *and similar multicoloured designs. P* 14.

1201	20 s. Type 230	10	10
1202	30 s. Parliament building (horiz)	10	10
1203	50 s. Swearing-in of Dr. Ntsu Mokhehle as Prime Minister (horiz)	10	10
1204	70 s. Maj-Gen P. Ramaema handing Instruments of Government to Dr. Ntsu Mokhehle (horiz)	15	10
1201/4	Set of 4	45	40

(Des V. Seatile Nkhomo (Nos. 1205/8), R. Rundo (No. **MS1209**). Litho Questa)

1994 (16 Aug). *"Philakorea '94" International Stamp Exhibition, Seoul. Frogs and Toads. T* **231** *and similar multicoloured designs. P* 14×14½.

1205	35 s. Type 231	10	10
1206	50 s. Bubbling Kassina	10	10
1207	1 m. Guttural Toad	20	10
1208	1 m. 50, Common River Frog	30	40
1205/8	Set of 4	70	70

MS1209 Two sheets, each 102×72 mm. (a) 5 m. Jade frog (sculpture). (b) 5 m. Black Spotted Frog and Oriental White Eye (bird) (vert). P 14
Set of 2 sheets 2·00 2·10

232 De Havilland D.H.C.6 Twin Otter and Emblem

(Des V. Seatile Nkhomo. Litho Goverment Printer, Pretoria)

1994 (17 Nov). *50th Anniv of International Civil Aviation Organization. T* **232** *and similar horiz designs. Multicoloured. P* 14.

1210	35 s. Type 232	10	10
1211	50 s. Fokker F.27 Friendship on runway	10	10
1212	1 m. Fokker F.27 Friendship over Moshoeshoe I International Airport	20	15
1213	1 m. 50, Cessna light aircraft over mountains	30	35
1210/13	Set of 4	70	70

The new-issue supplement to this Catalogue appears each month in

GIBBONS STAMP MONTHLY

—from your newsagent or by postal subscription— details on request.

King Moshoeshoe II, 25 January 1995 (restored)– 15 January 1996

20s = (233) 234 *Tagetes minuta*

1995 (3 Mar). *No. 1022Bc surch with T* **233** *by Mazenod Ptg Wks, Lesotho.*

1214	20 s. on 30 s. *Charaxes jasius* (p 13½)	70	20
	a. Perf 14×13½ (No. 1022B)	40	20

(Des V. Seatile Nkhomo. Litho Government Printer, Pretoria)

1995 (22 May). *Medicinal Plants. T* **234** *and similar vert designs. Multicoloured. P* 14.

1215	35 s. Type 234	10	10
1216	50 s. *Plantago lanceolata*	10	10
1217	1 m. *Amaranthus spinosus*	20	25
1218	1 m. 50, *Taraxacum officinale*	30	35
1215/18	Set of 4	70	80

MS1219 120×91 mm. 5 m. *Datura stramonium* 1·00 1·10

235 Pius XII College, 1962 236 Qiloane Pinnacle, Thaba-Bosiu

(Des Sumitra Talukdar (2 m.), D. Ambrose (others). Litho Government Printer, Pretoria)

1995 (26 July). *50th Anniv of University Studies in Lesotho. T* **235** *and similar horiz designs. Multicoloured. P* 14.

1220	35 s. Type 235	10	10
1221	50 s. Campus, University of Basutoland, Bechuanaland and Swaziland, 1966	10	10
1222	70 s. Campus, University of Botswana, Lesotho and Swaziland, 1970	15	20
1223	1 m. Administration Block, University of Botswana, Lesotho and Swaziland, 1975	20	25
1224	1 m. 50, Administration Block, National University of Lesotho, 1988	30	35
1225	2 m. Procession of Vice-Chancellors, National University of Lesotho, 1995	45	50
1220/5	Set of 6	1·25	1·50

(Des M. Phakisi. Litho Government Printer, Pretoria)

1995 (28 Aug). *20th Anniv of World Tourism Organization. T* **236** *and similar multicoloured designs. P* 14.

1226	35 s. Type 236	10	10
1227	50 s. Ha Mohalenyane rock formation	10	10
1228	1 m. Botsoela Falls (vert)	20	25
1229	1 m. 50, Backpackers in Makhaleng River Gorge	30	35
1226/9	Set of 4	70	80

MS1230 143×88 mm. 4 m. Red Hot Pokers (38×57 mm) 1·00 1·10

No. MS1230, which is inscribed "RED HOT PORKERS" in error, was withdrawn in Lesotho on 12 September.

237 "Peace" 238 "Sutter's Gold" Rose

(Des V. Seatile Nkhomo. Litho Government Printer, Pretoria)

1995 (26 Sept). *50th Anniv of United Nations. T* **237** *and similar multicoloured designs. P* 14.

1231	35 s. Type 237	10	10
1232	50 s. "Justice" (scales)	10	10
1233	1 m. 50, "Reconciliation" (clasped hands) (horiz)	30	35
1231/3	Set of 3	50	55

(Des V. Seatile Nkhomo. Litho Government Printer, Pretoria)

1995 (1 Nov). *Christmas. Roses. T* **238** *and similar vert designs. Multicoloured. P* 14.

1234	35 s. Type 238	10	10
1235	50 s. "Michele Meilland"	10	10
1236	1 m. "J. Otto Thilow"	20	25
1237	2 m. "Papa Meilland"	40	45
1234/7	Set of 4	80	90

King Letsie III. 15 January 1996 (restored)

239 Part of 1911 Map showing Lephaqhoa 240 Adding Iodised Salt to Cooking Pot

(Des D. Ambrose. Litho Government Printer, Pretoria)

1996 (17 June). *Completion of New Standard Map of Lesotho (1994). T* **239** *and similar horiz designs showing map sections of the Malibamatso Valley. Multicoloured. P* 14. (a) *1911 Map*

1238	35 s. Type 239	10	10
	a. Sheetlet. Nos. 1238/47	90	
1239	35 s. Boritsa Tsuene	10	10
1240	35 s. Molapo	10	10
1241	35 s. Nkeu	10	10
1242	35 s. Three rivers flowing east	10	10
1243	35 s. Tibedi and Rafanyane	10	10
1244	35 s. Two rivers flowing east	10	10
1245	35 s. Madibatmatso River	10	10
1246	35 s. Bokung River	10	10
1247	35 s. Semena River	10	10

(b) *1978 Map*

1248	35 s. Mountains and river valley	10	10
	a. Sheetlet. Nos. 1248/57	90	
1249	35 s. Pelaneng and Lepaqoa	10	10
1250	35 s. Mamohau	10	10
1251	35 s. Ha Lejone	10	10
1252	35 s. Ha Thoora	10	10
1253	35 s. Ha Mikia	10	10
1254	35 s. Ha Kosetabole	10	10
1255	35 s. Ha Seshote	10	10
1256	35 s. Ha Rapooane	10	10
1257	35 s. Bokong Ha Kennan	10	10

(c) *1994 Map*

1258	35 s. Mafika-Lisiu Pass	10	10
	a. Sheetlet. Nos. 1258/67	90	
1259	35 s. Ha Lesaoana	10	10
1260	35 s. Ha Masaballa	10	10
1261	35 s. Ha Nkisi	10	10
1262	35 s. Ha Rafanyane	10	10
1263	35 s. Laitsoka Pass	10	10
1264	35 s. "Katse Reservoir"	10	10
1265	35 s. Seshote	10	10
1266	35 s. Sephareng	10	10
1267	35 s. Katse Dam	10	10
1238/67	Set of 30	2·75	3·00

Nos. 1238/47, 1248/57 and 1258/67 were printed together, se-tenant, in sheetlets, of 10 (2×5) each forming composite designs. Nos. 1238/67 were issued in conjunction with a schools campaign to promote use and understanding of maps.

(Des V. Seatile Nkhomo. Litho Government Printer, Pretoria)

1996 (30 July). *50th Anniv of U.N.I.C.E.F. T* **240** *and similar multicoloured designs. P* 14.

1268	35 s. Type 240	10	10
1269	50 s. Herdboys with livestock (horiz)	10	10
1270	70 s. Children in class (horiz)	15	20
1271	1 m. 50, Boys performing traditional dance (horiz)	30	35
1268/71	Set of 4	65	75

241 U.S.A. Basketball Team, 1936

(Des J. Puvillard. Litho Questa)

1996 (1 Aug). *Olympic Games, Atlanta. Previous Gold Medal Winners. T* **241** *and similar multicoloured designs. P* 14.

1272	1 m. Type 241	20	25
1273	1 m. 50, Brandenburg Gate and stadium, Berlin, 1936	30	35
1274	1 m. 50, Glen Morris (U.S.A.) (decathlon, 1936) (vert)	30	35
	a. Sheetlet. Nos. 1274/82	2·50	
1275	1 m. 50, Saidi Aouita (Morocco) (5000m running, 1984) (vert)	30	35
1276	1 m. 50, Arnie Robinson (U.S.A.) (long jump, 1976) (vert)	30	35
1277	1 m. 50, Hans Woellke (Germany) (shot put, 1936) (vert)	30	35
1278	1 m. 50, Renate Stecher (Germany) (100m running, 1972) (vert)	30	35
1279	1 m. 50, Evelyn Ashford (U.S.A.) (100m running, 1984) (vert)	30	35
1280	1 m. 50, Willie Davenport (U.S.A.) (110m hurdles, 1968) (vert)	30	35
1281	1 m. 50, Bob Beamon (U.S.A.) (long jump, 1968) (vert)	30	35
1282	1 m. 50, Heidi Rosendhal (Germany) (long jump, 1972) (vert)	30	35
1283	2 m. Jesse Owens (U.S.A.) (track and field, 1936) (vert)	40	45

1284	3 m. Speed boat racing	..	60	65
1272/84		*Set of 13*	4·00	4·75

MS1285 Two sheets, each 110×80 mm. (a) 8 m. Michael Gross (Germany) (swimming, 1984) (*vert*). (b) 8 m. Kornelia Ender (Germany) (swimming, 1976) (*vert*) .. .. *Set of 2 sheets* 3·00 3·25

No. 1273 is inscribed "BRANDEBOURG GATE" in error. No. 1274 incorrectly identifies Glen Morris as the gold medal winner in the 1936 long jump.

Nos. 1274/82 were printed together, *se-tenant*, in sheetlets of 9, the backgrounds forming a composite design.

242 Class WP Steam Locomotive (India)   **243** Mothers' Union Member, Methodist Church

(Des G. Bibi. Litho Questa)

1996 (2 Sept). *Trains of the World. T* **242** *and similar horiz designs. Multicoloured. P* 14.

1286	1 m. 50, Type **242**	.. ..	30	35
	a. Sheetlet. Nos. 1286/91		1·75	
1287	1 m. 50, Canadian Pacific steam locomotive No. 2471 (Canada)	..	30	35
1288	1 m. 50, The "Caledonian" (Great Britain)		30	35
1289	1 m. 50, Steam locomotive *William Mason* (U.S.A.)	..	30	35
1290	1 m. 50, "Trans-Siberian Express" (Russia)		30	35
1291	1 m. 50, Steam train (Switzerland)	..	30	35
1292	1 m. 50, ETR 450 high speed train (Italy)		30	35
	a. Sheetlet. Nos. 1292/7		1·75	
1293	1 m. 50, TGV express train (France)	..	30	35
1294	1 m. 50, XPT high speed train (Australia)		30	35
1295	1 m. 50, "Blue Train" (South Africa)	..	30	35
1296	1 m. 50, Intercity 225 express train (Great Britain)	..	30	35
1297	1 m. 50, "Hikari" express train (Japan)	..	30	35
1286/97		*Set of 12*	3·50	3·75

MS1298 Two sheets, each 98×68 mm. (a) 8 m. Class 52 steam locomotive (Germany) (57×43 *mm*). (b) 8 m. ICE high speed train (Germany) (57×43 *mm*) .. .. .. *Set of 2 sheets* 3·00 3·25

Nos. 1286/91 and 1292/7 were each printed together, *se-tenant* in sheetlets of 6.

(Des V. Seatile Nkhomo. Litho Goverment Printer, Pretoria)

1996 (10 Dec). *Christmas. Mothers' Unions. T* **243** *and similar vert designs. Multicoloured. P* 14.

1299	35 s. Type **243**	.. ..	10	10
1300	50 s. Roman Catholic Church	..	10	10
1301	1 m. Lesotho Evangelical Church	..	20	25
1302	1 m. 50, Anglican Church	..	30	35
1299/1302		*Set of 4*	70	75

No. 1302 is inscribed "Anglian" in error.

244 Hand Clasp (Co-operation for Development)   **245** Land Reclamation

(Des V. Seatile Nkhomo. Litho Government Printer, Pretoria)

1997 (21 Apr). *10th Anniv of Lesotho Highland Water Project* (1996). *T* **244** *and similar horiz designs. Multicoloured. P* 14.

1303	35 s. Type **244**	..	10	10
1304	50 s. Bearded Vulture and rock painting (Nature and Heritage)	..	10	10
1305	1 m. Malibamatso Bridge (Engineering) ..		20	25
1306	1 m. 50, Katse Valley in 1986 and 1996 (75×28 *mm*)		30	35
1303/6		*Set of 4*	70	80

No. 1305 is inscribed "Developement" in error.

(Des V. Seatile Nkhomo. Litho Government Printer, Pretoria)

1997 (30 June). *Environment Protection. T* **245** *and similar vert designs. Multicoloured. P* 14.

1307	35 s. Type **245**	..	10	10
1308	50 s. Throwing rubbish into bin ..		15	20
1309	1 m. Hands holding globe and tree	..	25	30
1310	1 m. 20, Recycling symbol and rubbish		30	35
1311	1 m. 50, Collecting rain water	..	40	45
1307/11		*Set of 5*	1·25	1·40

246 Schmeichel, Denmark   **247** *Spialia spio*

(Litho Questa)

1997 (3 Nov). *World Cup Football Championship, France* (1998). *T* **246** *and similar multicoloured designs. P* 13½×14.

1312	1 m. Type **246**	..	20	25
1313	1 m. 50, Bergkamp, Netherlands	..	30	35
1314	1 m. 50, Argentine players celebrating	..	30	35
	a. Sheetlet. Nos. 1314/19		1·75	
1315	1 m. 50, Argentine and Dutch players competing for ball		30	35
1316	1 m. 50, Players heading ball	..	30	35
1317	1 m. 50, Goalkeeper deflecting ball	..	30	35
1318	1 m. 50, Goalmouth melee	..	30	35
1319	1 m. 50, Argentine player kicking ball	..	30	35
1320	2 m. Southgate, England	..	40	45
1321	2 m. 50, Asprilla, Colombia	..	50	55
1322	3 m. Gascoigne, England	..	60	65
1323	4 m. Giggs, Wales	..	80	85
1312/23		*Set of 12*	4·50	5·00

MS1324 Two sheets, each 127×102 mm. (a) 8 m. Littbarski, West Germany (*horiz*). P 14×13½. (b) 8 m. Shearer, England. P 13½×14.
.. .. .. *Set of 2 sheets* 3·00 3·25

Nos. 1314/19 were printed together, *se-tenant*, in sheetlets of 6 and show scenes from the Argentina v Netherlands final of 1978.

Although First Day Covers for Nos. 1312/24 are dated 31 October 1997, the stamps were not available from Lesotho post offices before 3 November.

(Des D. Burkhart. Litho Questa)

1997 (28 Nov). *Butterflies. T* **247** *and similar horiz designs. Multicoloured. P* 14.

1325	1 m. 50, Type **247**	..	30	35
	a. Sheetlet. Nos. 1325/33		2·50	
1326	1 m. 50, *Leptotes pirithous*	..	30	35
1327	1 m. 50, *Acratea satis*	..	30	35
1328	1 m. 50, *Belenois aurota aurota*	..	30	35
1329	1 m. 50, *Spindasis natalensis*	..	30	35
1330	1 m. 50, *Torynesis orangica*	..	30	35
1331	1 m. 50, *Lepidochysops variabilis*	..	30	35
1332	1 m. 50, *Pinacopteryx eriphia*	..	30	35
1333	1 m. 50, *Anthene butleri livida*	..	30	35
1325/33		*Set of 9*	2·50	3·00

MS1334 Two sheets, each 106×76 mm. (a) 8 m. *Bematistes aganice.* (b) 8 m. *Papilio demodocus.*
.. .. *Set of 2 sheets* 3·00 3·25

Nos. 1325/33 were printed together, *se-tenant*, in sheetlets of 9 with the backgrounds forming a composite design.

No. 1326 is inscribed "Cyclyrius pirithous", No. 1332 "Pinacopteryx eriphea" and No. **MS**1334(b) "Papalio demodocus", all in error.

248 Rock Paintings and Boy   **249** Diana, Princess of Wales

(Des V. Seatile Nkhomo. Litho Government Printer, Pretoria)

1998 (30 Jan). *40th Anniv of Morija Museum and Archives. T* **248** *and similar multicoloured designs based on drawings, by Frédéric Christol. P* 14½ *(with two elliptical holes on the horiz sides (45 s. and 2 m.) or on the vert sides (others)).*

1335	35 s. Type **248**	..	10	10
1336	45 s. Hippopotamus and lower jaw bone (*horiz*)		10	15
1337	50 s. Woman and cowhide skirt ..		15	20
1338	1 m. Drum and "thomo" (musical bow)	..	25	30
1339	1 m. 50, Warrior with "khau" (gorget awarded for valour)	..	40	45
1340	2 m. Herders with ox (*horiz*)	..	50	55
1335/40		*Set of 6*	1·50	1·75

(Litho Questa)

1998 (16 Mar). *Diana, Princess of Wales Commemoration. T* **249** *and similar vert designs. Multicoloured. P* 13½.

1341	3 m. Type **249**	..	60	65
	a. Sheetlet. Nos. 1341/6		3·50	
1342	3 m. Wearing grey jacket	..	60	65
1343	3 m. Wearing white polo-necked jumper	..	60	65
1344	3 m. Wearing pearl necklace	..	60	65
1345	3 m. Wearing white evening dress	..	60	65
1346	3 m. Wearing pale blue jacket	..	60	65
1341/6		*Set of 6*	3·50	3·75

MS1347 70×100 mm. 9 m. Accepting bouquet 1·90 2·00

Nos. 1341/6 were printed together, *se-tenant*, in sheetlets of 6.

250 Atitlan Grebe   **251** Cape Vulture

(Des M. Leboeuf (Nos. 1368/76, **MS**1377d), D. Burkhart (others). Litho Questa)

1998 (14 Apr). *Fauna of the World. T* **250** *and similar multicoloured designs. (a) Vert designs as T* **250**. *P* 14.

1348	1 m. Type **250**	..	20	25
	a. Sheetlet. Nos. 1348/67		4·00	
1349	1 m. Cabot's Tragopan	..	20	25
1350	1 m. Spider Monkey	..	20	25
1351	1 m. Dibatag	..	20	25
1352	1 m. Right Whale	..	20	25
1353	1 m. Imperial Parrot	..	20	25
1354	1 m. Cheetah	..	20	25
1355	1 m. Brown-eared Pheasant	..	20	25
1356	1 m. Leatherback Turtle	..	20	25
1357	1 m. Imperial Woodpecker	..	20	25
1358	1 m. Andean Condor	..	20	25
1359	1 m. Barbary Deer	..	20	25
1360	1 m. Grey Gentle Lemur	..	20	25
1361	1 m. Cuban Parrot	..	20	25
1362	1 m. Numbat	..	20	25
1363	1 m. Short-tailed Albatross	..	20	25
1364	1 m. Green Turtle	..	20	25
1365	1 m. White Rhinoceros	..	20	25
1366	1 m. Diademed Sifaka	..	20	25
1367	1 m. Galapagos Penguin	..	20	25

(b) *Horiz designs, each* 48×31 *mm. P* 13½×14.

1368	1 m. 50, Impala	..	30	35
	a. Sheetlet. Nos. 1368/76		2·50	
1369	1 m. 50, Black Bear	..	30	35
1370	1 m. 50, American Buffalo	..	30	35
1371	1 m. 50, African Elephant	..	30	35
1372	1 m. 50, Kangaroo	..	30	35
1373	1 m. 50, Lion	..	30	35
1374	1 m. 50, Giant Panda	..	30	35
1375	1 m. 50, Tiger	..	30	35
1376	1 m. 50, Zebra	..	30	35
1348/76		*Set of 29*	6·50	8·00

MS1377 Four sheets, each 98×68 mm. (a) 8 m. White-bellied Sunbird. P 14. (b) 8 m. Golden-shouldered Parrot. P 14. (c) 8 m. Snail Darter. P 14. (d) 8 m. Monkey (47×31 *mm*). P 13½×14
.. .. .. *Set of 4 sheets* 6·00 6·50

Nos. 1348/67 and 1368/76 were each printed together, *se-tenant*, in sheetlets of 20 or 9.

(Des D. Burkhart. Litho Questa)

1998 (14 Apr). *Endangered Species. Cape Vulture. T* **251** *and similar horiz designs. Multicoloured. P* 14.

1378	1 m. Type **251**	..	20	25
	a. Horiz strip of 4. Nos. 1378/81		80	
1379	1 m. Looking towards ground	..	20	25
1380	1 m. Looking over shoulder	..	20	25
1381	1 m. Facing right	..	20	25
1378/81		*Set of 4*	80	1·00

Nos. 1378/81 were printed together, *se-tenant*, in horizontal strips of 4 throughout the sheet.

252 Siamese

(Des D. Burkhart. Litho Questa)

1998 (4 May). *Cats of the World. T* **252** *and similar horiz designs. Multicoloured. P* 14.

1382	70 s. Type **252**	..	15	20
1383	1 m. Chartreux	..	20	25
1384	2 m. Korat	..	40	45
1385	2 m. Japanese Bobtail	..	40	45
	a. Sheetlet. Nos. 1385/90		2·40	
1386	2 m. British White	..	40	45
1387	2 m. Bengal	..	40	45
1388	2 m. Abyssinian	..	40	45
1389	2 m. Snowshoe	..	40	45
1390	2 m. Scottish Fold	..	40	45
1391	2 m. Maine Coon	..	40	45
	a. Sheetlet. Nos. 1391/6		2·40	
1392	2 m. Balinese	..	40	45
1393	2 m. Persian	..	40	45
1394	2 m. Javanese	..	40	45
1395	2 m. Turkish Angora	..	40	45
1396	2 m. Tiffany	..	40	45
1397	3 m. Egyptian Mau	..	60	65
1398	4 m. Bombay	..	80	85
1399	5 m. Burmese	..	1·00	1·10
1382/99		*Set of 18*	7·75	8·75

MS1400 Two sheets, each 98×69 mm. (a) 8 m. Tonkinese. (b) 8 m. Singapura .. *Set of 2 sheets* 3·00 3·25

Nos. 1385/90 and 1391/6 were each printed together, *se-tenant*, in sheetlets of 6 with the backgrounds forming composite designs.

253 *Laccaria laccata*

(Des Rina Lyamphe. Litho Questa)

1998 (2 June). *Fungi of the World. T* **253** *and similar horiz designs. Multicoloured. P* 14.
1401	70 s. Type **253**		15	20
1402	1 m. *Mutinus caninus*		20	25
1403	1 m. *Hygrophorus psittacinus*		20	25
	a. Sheetlet. Nos. 1403/14		2·40	
1404	1 m. *Cortinarius obtusus*		20	25
1405	1 m. *Volvariella bombycina*		20	25
1406	1 m. *Cortinarius caerylescens*		20	25
1407	1 m. *Laccaria amethystina*		20	25
1408	1 m. *Tricholoma aurantium*		20	25
1409	1 m. *Amanita excelsa (spissa)*		20	25
1410	1 m. *Clavaria helvola*		20	25
1411	1 m. Unidentified species (inscr "*Cortinarius caerylescens*")		20	25
1412	1 m. *Russula queletii*		20	25
1413	1 m. *Amanita phalloides*		20	25
1414	1 m. *Lactarius deliciosus*		20	25
1415	1 m. 50, *Tricholoma lascivum*		30	35
1416	2 m. *Clitocybe geotropa*		40	45
1417	3 m. *Amanita excelsa*		60	65
1418	4 m. Red-capped Bolete		80	85
1401/18	*Set of* 18		4·75	5·75

MS1419 Two sheets, each 98×68 mm. (a) 8 m. *Amanita pantherina.* (b) 8 m. *Boletus satanas*
	Set of 2 sheets	3·00 3·25

Nos. 1403/14 were printed together, *se-tenant*, in sheetlets of 12.

Nos. 1406, 1407, 1414, 1416 and **MS**1419b are inscribed "*Continarius caerylescens*", "*Laccaria amethystea*", "*Lactarius delicious*", "*Clitocybe geotrapa*" and "*Boletys satanus*", all in error.

254 *Simba*

(Des Zina Saunders (Nos. 1420/7, **MS**1437a), J. Iskowitz (others). Litho B.D.T.)

1998 (14 July). *World Cinema. T* **254** *and similar multicoloured designs. P* 14. (a) *Films about Africa*
1420	2 m. Type **254**		40	45
	a. Sheetlet. Nos. 1420/7		3·00	
1421	2 m. *Call to Freedom*		40	45
1422	2 m. *Cry the Beloved Country*		40	45
1423	2 m. *King Solomon's Mines*		40	45
1424	2 m. *Flame and the Fire*		40	45
1425	2 m. *Cry Freedom*		40	45
1426	2 m. *Bopha!*		40	45
1427	2 m. *Zulu*		40	45

(b) *Japanese Film Stars*
1428	2 m. Takamine Hideko		40	45
	a. Sheetlet. Nos. 1428/36		3·50	
1429	2 m. James Shigeta		40	45
1430	2 m. Miyoshi Umeki		40	45
1431	2 m. May Ishimara		40	45
1432	2 m. Sessue Hayakawa		40	45
1433	2 m. Miiko Taka		40	45
1434	2 m. Mori Masayuki		40	45
1435	2 m. Hara Setsuko		40	45
1436	2 m. Kyo Machiko		40	45
1420/36	*Set of* 17		6·50	7·50

MS1437 Two sheets. (a) 68×98 mm. 10 m. Lion cubs from *Born Free* (*horiz*). (b) 70×100 mm. 10 m. Toshiro Mifune .. *Set of 2 sheets* 4·00 4·25
Nos. 1420/7 and 1428/36 were each printed together, *se-tenant*, in sheetlets of 8 or 9, with the backgrounds forming composite designs.
No. 1423 is inscribed "KING SOLOMAN'S MINES" in error.

255 *Ceresiosaurus*

(Des R. Rundo. Litho B.D.T.)

1998 (10 Aug). *Prehistoric Animals. T* **255** *and similar multicoloured designs. P* 14.
1438	2 m. Type **255**		40	45
	a. Sheetlet. Nos. 1438/46		3·50	
1439	2 m. *Rhomaleosaurus*		40	45

1440	2 m. *Anomalocaris*		40	45
1441	2 m. *Mixosaurus*		40	45
1442	2 m. *Stethacanthus*		40	45
1443	2 m. *Dunklosteus*		40	45
1444	2 m. *Tommotia*		40	45
1445	2 m. *Sanctacaris*		40	45
1446	2 m. *Ammonites*		40	45
1447	2 m. *Rhamphorhynchus*		40	45
	a. Sheetlet. Nos. 1447/55		3·50	
1448	2 m. *Brachiosaurus*		40	45
1449	2 m. *Mamenchisaurus hochuanensis*		40	45
1450	2 m. *Ceratosaurus nasicornis*		40	45
1451	2 m. *Archaeopteryx*		40	45
1452	2 m. *Leaellynasaura amicagraphica*		40	45
1453	2 m. *Chasmosaurus belli*		40	45
1454	2 m. *Deinonychus and Pachyrhinosaurus*		40	45
1455	2 m. *Deinonychus*		40	45
1456	2 m. *Nyctosaurus*		40	45
	a. Sheetlet. Nos. 1456/64		3·50	
1457	2 m. *Volcanoes*		40	45
1458	2 m. *Eudimorphodon*		40	45
1459	2 m. *Apatosaurus*		40	45
1460	2 m. *Peteinosaurus*		40	45
1461	2 m. *Tropeognathus*		40	45
1462	2 m. *Pteranodon ingens*		40	45
1463	2 m. *Ornithodesmus*		40	45
1464	2 m. *Wuerhosaurus*		40	45
1438/64	*Set of* 27		10·50	12·00

MS1465 Three sheets, each 100×70 mm. (a) 10 m. *Coelophysis* (*vert*). (b) 10 m. *Tyrannosaurus* (*vert*). (c) 10 m. Woolly Rhinoceros
	Set of 3 sheets	6·00 6·25

Nos. 1438/46, 1447/55 and 1456/64 were each printed together, *se-tenant*, in sheetlets of 9 with the backgrounds forming composite designs.

256 *Treefish*

(Des D. Burkhart. Litho Questa)

1998 (15 Oct). *Year of the Ocean. Fishes. T* **256** *and similar horiz designs. Multicoloured. P* 14.
1466	1 m. Type **256**		20	25
1467	1 m. Tigerbarb		20	25
1468	1 m. Bandtail Puffer		20	25
1469	1 m. Cod		20	25
1470	1 m. 50, Clown Loach		30	35
1471	1 m. 50, Christy's Lyretail		30	35
1472	1 m. 50, Filefish		30	35
1473	1 m. 50, Sicklefin Killie		30	35
1474	2 m. Brook Trout		40	45
1475	2 m. Emerald Betta		40	45
1476	2 m. Pacific Electric Ray		40	45
1477	2 m. Bighead Searobin		40	45
1478	2 m. Weakfish		40	45
	a. Sheetlet. Nos. 1478/85		3·25	
1479	2 m. Red Drum		40	45
1480	2 m. Blue Marlin		40	45
1481	2 m. Yellowfin Tuna		40	45
1482	2 m. Barracuda		40	45
1483	2 m. Striped Bass		40	45
1484	2 m. White Shark		40	45
1485	2 m. Permit		40	45
1486	2 m. Purple Firefish		40	45
	a. Sheetlet. Nos. 1486/93		3·25	
1487	2 m. Harlequin Sweetlips		40	45
1488	2 m. Clown Wrasse		40	45
1489	2 m. Bicolour Angelfish		40	45
1490	2 m. False Cleanerfish		40	45
1491	2 m. Mandarinfish		40	45
1492	2 m. Regal Tang		40	45
1493	2 m. Clownfish		40	45
1494	2 m. Bluegill		40	45
	a. Sheetlet. Nos. 1494/1501		3·25	
1495	2 m. Grayling		40	45
1496	2 m. Walleye		40	45
1497	2 m. Brown Trout		40	45
1498	2 m. Atlantic Salmon		40	45
1499	2 m. Northern Pike		40	45
1500	2 m. Large-mouth Bass		40	45
1501	2 m. Rainbow Trout		40	45
1502	2 m. Platy Variatus		40	45
	a. Sheetlet. Nos. 1502/9		3·25	
1503	2 m. Archerfish		40	45
1504	2 m. Clown Knifefish		40	45
1505	2 m. Angelicus		40	45
1506	2 m. Black Arowana		40	45
1507	2 m. Spotted Scat		40	45
1508	2 m. Kribensis		40	45
1509	2 m. Golden Pheasant		40	45
1510	3 m. Harlequin Tuskfish		60	65
1511	4 m. Half-moon Angelfish		80	85
1512	5 m. Spotted Trunkfish		1·00	1·10
1513	6 m. Wolf Eel		1·25	1·40
1514	7 m. Cherubfish		1·40	1·50
1466/1514	*Set of* 49		22·00	24·00

MS1515 Four sheets, each 98×73 mm. (a) 12 m. Common Carp. (b) 12 m. Sockeye Salmon. (c) 12 m. Winter Flounder. (d) 12 m. Horn Shark
	Set of 4 sheets	5·00 5·50

Nos. 1470/3 show the face value as "M1.5".
Nos. 1478/85, 1486/93, 1494/1501 and 1502/9 were each printed together, *se-tenant*, in sheetlets of 8.
Distribution of Nos. 1466/1515, and possibly also Nos. 1516/18, was delayed by unrest in Maseru.

NEW INFORMATION

The editor is always interested to correspond with people who have new information that will improve or correct the Catalogue.

257 Crowning of King Letsie III

(Des V. Seatile Nkhomo. Litho Government Printer, Pretoria)

1998 (31 Oct). *First Anniv of Coronation of King Letsie III. T* **257** *and similar horiz designs. Multicoloured. P* 14.
1516	1 m. Type **257**		20	25
	a. Horiz strip of 3. Nos. 1516/18		60	
1517	1 m. King saluting Basotho nation		20	25
1518	1 m. King Letsie in profile		20	25
1516/18	*Set of* 3		60	75

Nos. 1516/18 were printed together, *se-tenant*, in horizontal strips of 3.

258 *Pelargonium sidoides*   259 Japanese Akita

(Des Ina-Maria Harris. Litho Government Printer, Pretoria)

1998 (23 Nov). *Flowers. T* **258** *and similar vert designs. Multicoloured. P* 14.
1519	10 s. Type **258**		10	10
1520	15 s. *Aponogeton ranunculiflorus*		10	10
1521	20 s. *Sebaea leiostyla*		10	10
1522	40 s. *Sebaea grandis*		10	10
1523	50 s. *Satyrium neglectum*		10	10
1524	60 s. *Massonia jasminiflora*		10	10
1525	70 s. *Ajuga ophrydis*		15	20
1526	80 s. *Nemesia fruticans*		20	25
1527	1 m. *Aloe broomii*		20	25
1528	2 m. *Wahlenbergia androsacea*		40	45
1529	2 m. 50, *Phygelius capensis*		50	55
1530	3 m. *Dianthus basuticus*		60	65
1531	4 m. 50, *Rhodohypoxis baurii*		90	95
1532	5 m. *Turbina oblongata*		1·00	1·10
1533	6 m. *Hibiscus microcarpus*		1·10	1·40
1534	10 m. *Lobelia erinus (Moraea stricta)*		2·00	2·10
1519/34	*Set of* 16		7·50	8·50

(Des R. Francisco. Litho Questa)

1999 (18 May). *Dogs. T* **259** *and similar horiz designs. Multicoloured. P* 14.
1535	70 s. Type **259**		15	20
1536	1 m. Canaan dog		20	25
1537	2 m. Husky ("ESKIMO DOG")		40	45
1538	2 m. Cirneco dell' Etna		40	45
	a. Sheetlet. Nos. 1538/43		2·40	
1539	2 m. Afghan Hound		40	45
1540	2 m. Finnish Spitz		40	45
1541	2 m. Dalmatian		40	45
1542	2 m. Basset Hound		40	45
1543	2 m. Shar-pei		40	45
1544	2 m. Boxer		40	45
	a. Sheetlet. Nos. 1544/9		2·40	
1545	2 m. Catalan Sheepdog		40	45
1546	2 m. English Toy Spaniel		40	45
1547	2 m. Greyhound		40	45
1548	2 m. Keeshond		40	45
1549	2 m. Bearded Collie		40	45
1550	4 m. 50, Norwegian Elkhound		90	95
1535/50	*Set of* 16		6·50	7·25

MS1551 Two sheets, each 98×69 mm. (a) 8 m. Rough Collie. (b) 8 m. Borzoi .. *Set of 2 sheets* 3·25 3·50
Nos. 1538/43 and 1544/9 were each printed together, *se-tenant*, in sheetlets of 6 with the backgrounds forming composite designs.

260 Belted Kingfisher   261 *Cattleya dowiana*

(Des R. Rundo. Litho Questa)

1999 (28 June). *Birds. T* **260** *and similar multicoloured designs. P* 14.
1552	70 s. Type **260**		15	20
1553	1 m. 50, Palm Cockatoo (*vert*)		30	35
1554	2 m. Red-tailed Hawk		40	45
1555	2 m. Evening Grosbeak		40	45
	a. Sheetlet. Nos. 1555/63		3·50	

1556	2 m.	Lesser Blue-winged Pitta	40	45
1557	2 m.	Atlamira Oriole	40	45
1558	2 m.	Rose-breasted Grosbeak	40	45
1559	2 m.	Yellow Warbler	40	45
1560	2 m.	Akiapolaau	40	45
1561	2 m.	American Goldfinch	40	45
1562	2 m.	Northern Flicker	40	45
1563	2 m.	Western Tanager	40	45
1564	2 m.	Blue Jay (vert)	40	45
		a. Sheetlet. Nos. 1564/72	3·50	
1565	2 m.	Northern Cardinal (vert)	40	45
1566	2 m.	Yellow-headed Blackbird (vert)	40	45
1567	2 m.	Red Crossbill (vert)	40	45
1568	2 m.	Cedar Waxwing (vert)	40	45
1569	2 m.	Vermilion Flycatcher (vert)	40	45
1570	2 m.	Pileated Woodpecker (vert)	40	45
1571	2 m.	Western Meadowlark (vert)	40	45
1572	2 m.	Kingfisher (vert)	40	45
1573	3 m.	Tufted Puffin	60	65
1574	4 m.	Reddish Egret	80	85
1575	5 m.	Hoatzin (vert)	1·00	1·10
1552/75		Set of 24	10·50	11·50

MS1576 Two sheets. (a) 76×106 mm. 8 m. Great Egret. (b) 106×76 mm. 8 m. Chestnut-flanked White Eye (Zosterops erythropleura)
Set of 2 sheets 3·25 3·50

No. 1553 shows the face value as "M1.5".

Nos. 1555/63 and 1564/72 were each printed together, se-tenant, in sheetlet of 9 with the backgrounds forming composite designs.

(Des D. Burkhart. Litho Questa)

1999 (30 July). Orchids of the World. T 261 and similar vert designs. Multicoloured. P 14.

1577	1 m. 50, Type 261		30	35
1578	2 m.	Cochleanthes discolor	40	45
		a. Sheetlet. Nos. 1578/86	3·50	
1579	2 m.	Cischweinfia dasyandra	40	45
1580	2 m.	Ceratostylis retisquama	40	45
1581	2 m.	Comparettia speciosa	40	45
1582	2 m.	Cryptostylis subulata	40	45
1583	2 m.	Cycnoches ventricosum	40	45
1584	2 m.	Dactylorhiza maculata	40	45
1585	2 m.	Cypripedium calceolus	40	45
1586	2 m.	Cymbidium finlaysonianum	40	45
1587	2 m.	Apasia epidendroides	40	45
		a. Sheetlet. Nos. 1587/95	3·50	
1588	2 m.	Barkaria lindleyana	40	45
1589	2 m.	Bifrenaria tetragona	40	45
1590	2 m.	Bulbophyllum graveolens	40	45
1591	2 m.	Brassavola flagellaris	40	45
1592	2 m.	Bollea lawrenceana	40	45
1593	2 m.	Caladenia carnea	40	45
1594	2 m.	Catasetum macrocarpum	40	45
1595	2 m.	Cattleya aurantiaca	40	45
1596	2 m.	Dendrobium bellatulum	40	45
		a. Sheetlet. Nos. 1596/1604	3·50	
1597	2 m.	Dendrobium trigonopus	40	45
1598	2 m.	Dimerandra emarginata	40	45
1599	2 m.	Dressleria eburnea	40	45
1600	2 m.	Dracula tubeana	40	45
1601	2 m.	Disa kirstenbosch	40	45
1602	2 m.	Encyclia alata	40	45
1603	2 m.	Epidendrum pseudepidendrum	40	45
1604	2 m.	Eriopsis biloba	40	45
1605	3 m.	Diurus behrii	60	65
1606	4 m.	Ancistrochilus rothchildianus	80	85
1607	5 m.	Aerangis curnowiana	1·00	1·10
1608	7 m.	Arachnis flos-aeris	1·40	1·50
1609	8 m.	Aspasia principissa	1·60	1·75
1577/1609		Set of 33	16·00	18·00

MS1610 Four sheets, each 110×82 mm. (a) 10 m. Paphiopedilum tonsum. (b) 10 m. Ansellia africana. (c) 10 m. Laelia rubescens. (d) 10 m. Ophrys apifera
Set of 4 sheets 8·00 8·25

Nos. 1578/86, 1587/95 and 1596/1604 were each printed together, se-tenant, in sheetlets of 9.

No. 1583 was inscribed "Cycnoches ventricsum" in error.

262 "Austerity" Type Series 52 Steam Locomotive, Frankfurt, 1939

(Des B. Pevsner. Litho Questa)

1999 (16 Aug). "iBRA '99" International Stamp Exhibition, Nuremburg. Railway Locomotives. T 262 and similar horiz design. Multicoloured. P 14×14½.

1611	7 m. Type 262		1·40	1·50
1612	8 m. Adler and Brandenburg Gate, Berlin, 1835		1·60	1·75

263 "View of Sumida River in Snow" (Hokusai)   264 African Boy

(Des R. Sauber. Litho Questa)

1999 (16 Aug). 150th Death Anniv of Katsushika Hokusai (Japanese artist). T 263 and similar multicoloured designs. P 14×13½.

1613	3 m. Type 263		60	65
	a. Sheetlet. Nos. 1613/18		3·50	
1614	3 m. "Two Carp"		60	65
1615	3 m. "The Blind" (woman with eyes closed)		60	65
1616	3 m. "The Blind" (woman with one eye open)		60	65
1617	3 m. "Fishing by Torchlight"		60	65
1618	3 m. "Whaling off the Goto Islands"		60	65
1619	3 m. "Makamaro watching the Moon from a Hill"		60	65
	a. Sheetlet. Nos. 1619/24		3·50	
1620	3 m. "Peonies and Butterfly"		60	65
1621	3 m. "The Blind" (old man with open eyes)		60	65
1622	3 m. "The Blind" (old man with one eye open)		60	65
1623	3 m. "People crossing an Arched Bridge" (four people on bridge)		60	65
1624	3 m. "People crossing an Arched Bridge" (two people on bridge)		60	65
1613/24		Set of 12	7·00	7·25

MS1625 Two sheets, each 102×72 mm. (a) 10 m. "Bell-flower and Dragonfly" (vert). (b) 10 m. "Moon above Yodo River and Osaka Castle" (vert). P 13½×14
Set of 2 sheets 4·00 4·25

Nos. 1613/18 and 1619/24 were each printed together, se-tenant, in sheetlets of 6.

(Des M. Harper. Litho Questa)

1999 (16 Aug). 10th Anniv of United Nations Rights of the Child Convention. T 264 and similar vert designs. Multicoloured. P 14.

1626	2 m. Type 264		45	50
	a. Sheetlet. Nos. 1626/8		1·25	
1627	2 m. Asian girl		45	50
1628	2 m. European boy		45	50
1626/8		Set of 3	1·25	1·50

Nos. 1626/8 were printed together, se-tenant, in sheetlets of 3 with the backgrounds forming a composite design.

265 Mephistopheles appearing as Dog in Faust's Study   266 "Water Lily at Night" (Pan Tianshou)

(Des J. Iskowitz. Litho Questa)

1999 (16 Aug). 250th Birth Anniv of Johann von Goethe (German writer). T 265 and similar designs. P 14.

1629	6 m. multicoloured		1·25	1·40
	a. Sheetlet. Nos. 1629/31		3·75	
1630	6 m. deep ultramarine, slate-lilac and black		1·25	1·40
1631	6 m. multicoloured		1·25	1·40
1629/31		Set of 3	3·75	4·25

MS1632 76×106 mm. 12 m. bright crimson, reddish violet and black
2·50 2·75

Designs: Horiz—No. 1629, Type 265; No. 1630, Von Goethe and Von Schiller; No. 1631, Mephistopheles disguised as a dog scorching the Earth. Vert—No. MS1632, Mephistopheles.

Nos. 1629/31 were printed together, se-tenant, in sheetlets of 3 with enlarged illustrated margins.

No. 1629, in addition to the normal country name, shows "GUYANA" twice in violet across the centre of the design.

(Litho Questa)

1999 (16 Aug). "China '99" International Stamp Exhibition, Beijing. Paintings of Pan Tianshou (Chinese artist). T 266 and similar multicoloured designs. P 13×13½.

1633	1 m. 50, Type 266		30	35
	a. Sheetlet. Nos. 1633/42		3·00	
1634	1 m. 50, "Hen and Chicks"		30	35
1635	1 m. 50, "Plum Blossom and Orchid"		30	35
1636	1 m. 50, "Plum Blossom and Banana Tree"		30	35
1637	1 m. 50, "Crane and Pine"		30	35
1638	1 m. 50, "Swallows"		30	35
1639	1 m. 50, "Eagle on the Pine" (bird looking up)		30	35
1640	1 m. 50, "Palm Tree"		30	35
1641	1 m. 50, "Eagle on the Pine" (bird looking down)		30	35
1642	1 m. 50, "Orchids"		30	35
1633/42		Set of 10	3·00	3·50

MS1643 138×105 mm. 6 m. "Sponge Gourd" (51×39 mm); 6 m. "Dragonfly" (51×39 mm). P 13 2·10 2·25

Nos. 1633/42 were printed together, se-tenant, in sheetlets of 10.

267 Queen Elizabeth, 1938   268 Chinese Soldier firing Rocket, 1150

(Litho Questa)

1999 (17 Aug). "Queen Elizabeth the Queen Mother's Century". T 267 and similar vert designs. P 14.

1644	5 m. black and gold		1·00	1·10
	a. Sheetlet. Nos. 1644/7		4·00	
1645	5 m. multicoloured		1·00	1·10
1646	5 m. black and gold		1·00	1·10
1647	5 m. multicoloured		1·00	1·10
1644/7		Set of 4	4·00	4·25

MS1648 153×152 mm. 15 m. multicoloured. P 13½×14
3·00 3·25

Designs: (As Type 267)—No. 1644, Type 267; No. 1645, King George VI and Queen Elizabeth, 1948; No. 1646, Queen Mother wearing tiara, 1963; No. 1647, Queen Mother wearing blue hat, Canada, 1989. (37×50 mm)—No. MS1648, Queen Mother outside Clarence House.

Nos. 1644/7 were printed together, se-tenant, as a sheetlet of 4 stamps and a central label with inscribed and embossed margins.

No. MS1648 also shows the Royal Arms embossed in gold.

(Des L. Birmingham. Litho Cartor)

1999 (31 Dec). New Millennium. Events of Second Half of 12th Century. T 268 and similar multicoloured designs. P 12½.

1649	1 m. 50, Type 268		30	35
	a. Sheetlet. Nos. 1649/65		5·00	
1650	1 m. 50, Burmese temple guardian, 1150		30	35
1651	1 m. 50, Troubadour serenading Lady, 1150		30	35
1652	1 m. 50, Abbot Suger (advisor to French Kings), 1150		30	35
1653	1 m. 50, Pope Adrian IV, 1154		30	35
1654	1 m. 50, Henry II of England, 1154		30	35
1655	1 m. 50, Bust of Frederick Barbarossa, King of Germany and Holy Roman Emperor, 1155		30	35
1656	1 m. 50, Shogun Yoritomo of Japan, 1156		30	35
1657	1 m. 50, Count and Countess of Vaudemont (Crusader monument), 1165		30	35
1658	1 m. 50, Ibn Rushd (Arab translator), 1169		30	35
1659	1 m. 50, Archbishop Thomas a Becket, 1170		30	35
1660	1 m. 50, Leaning Tower of Pisa, 1174		30	35
1661	1 m. 50, Pivot windmill, 1180		30	35
1662	1 m. 50, Saladin (Saracen general), 1187		30	35
1663	1 m. 50, King Richard the Lionheart of England, 1189		30	35
1664	1 m. 50, Moal (statues), Easter Island, 1150 (59×39 mm)		30	35
1665	1 m. 50, Crusader, 1189		30	35
1649/65		Set of 17	5·00	5·75

Nos. 1649/65 were printed together, se-tenant, in sheetlets of 17 including a central label (59×39 mm) and inscribed left margin.

269 U.S.S. New Jersey (battleship)   270 King Letsie III and Miss Karabo Anne Motšoeneng

(Des F. Rivera. Litho Questa)

1999 (31 Dec). Maritime Development 1700–2000. T 269 and similar multicoloured designs. P 14.

1666	4 m. Type 269		80	85
	a. Sheetlet. Nos. 1666/71		4·75	
1667	4 m. Aquila (Italian aircraft carrier)		80	85
1668	4 m. De Zeven Provincien (Dutch cruiser)		80	85
1669	4 m. H.M.S. Formidable (aircraft carrier)		80	85
1670	4 m. Vittorio Veneto (Italian cruiser)		80	85
1671	4 m. H.M.S. Hampshire (destroyer)		80	85
1672	4 m. France (French liner)		80	85
	a. Sheetlet. Nos. 1672/7		4·75	
1673	4 m. Queen Elizabeth 2 (liner)		80	85
1674	4 m. United States (American liner)		80	85
1675	4 m. Queen Elizabeth (liner)		80	85
1676	4 m. Michelangelo (Italian liner)		80	85
1677	4 m. Mauretania (British liner)		80	85
1678	4 m. Shearwater (British hydrofoil ferry)		80	85
	a. Sheetlet. Nos. 1678/83		4·75	
1679	4 m. British Class M submarine		80	85
1680	4 m. SRN 130 hovercraft		80	85
1681	4 m. Italian Second World War submarine		80	85
1682	4 m. SRN 3 hovercraft		80	85
1683	4 m. Soucoupe Plongeante (oceanographic submersible)		80	85

1684	4 m. *James Watt* (early steamship)	..	..	80	85
	a. Sheetlet. Nos. 1684/9			4·75	
1685	4 m. *Savannah* (steam/sail ship), 1819		80	85
1686	4 m. *Amistad* (slave schooner)	..		80	85
1687	4 m. American Navy brig	..		80	85
1688	4 m. *Great Britain* (liner)			80	85
1689	4 m. *Sirius* (paddle steamer)			80	85
1666/89			*Set of 24*	19·00	20·00

MS1690 Four sheets, each 106×76 mm. (a) 15 m.
U.S.S. *Enterprise* (aircraft carrier) (*vert*); (b)
15 m. *Titanic* (liner); (c) German U-boat; (d)
15 m. E. W. Morrison (Great Lakes schooner)
(*vert*) .. .. .. 12·00 12·50
Nos. 1666/71, 1672/7, 1678/83 and 1684/9 were each printed
together, *se-tenant*, in sheetlets of 6 with enlarged illustrated
and inscribed top margins.
No. 1686 is wrongly described as "ARMISTAD" and No. 1687
"BRICK", both on the sheetlet margin.

(Des M. Friedman. Litho Questa)

2000 (18 Feb). *Wedding of King Letsie III. T* **270** *and similar
vert designs. Multicoloured. P* 14.

1691	1 m. Type 270	..	..	..	20	25
	a. Sheetlet. Nos. 1691/4		..		80	
1692	1 m. Miss Karabo Anne Motšoeneng			20	25
1693	1 m. King Letsie III	..	..		20	25
1694	1 m. King Letsie III and Miss Karabo				
	Motšoeneng in traditional dress			20	25
1691/4			*Set of 4*	80	1·00

Nos. 1691/4 were printed together, *se-tenant*, as a sheetlet of 4
stamps and a central label with enlarged illustrated margins.

1981 (20 Apr). *Multicoloured cover,* 165×100 *mm, showing
Hoopoe* (*bird*) *on front and Lesotho village scene on back.
Stapled.*
SB1 4 m. 30, booklet containing 5 s., 6 s., 7 s. and 25 s.
(Nos. 440, 441/2, 444) in blocks of 10 .. 9·00

1981 (22 July). *Royal Wedding. Multicoloured cover,* 150×100
*mm, showing Prince Charles and Lady Diana Spencer on
front and Ba-Leseli dance on back. Stitched.*
SB2 6 m. booklet containing four different panes of 3
stamps and 1 label (Nos. 451a/b, 452a, 453a) 2·00
a. Stapled .. ..

1982 (5 Mar). *75th Anniv of Boy Scout Movement.
Multicoloured cover,* 170×98 *mm, showing Lord
Baden-Powell on front and Scout with flag on back. Pane
attached by selvedge.*
SB3 5 m. 52, booklet containing *se-tenant* pane of 10
stamps and one miniature sheet (No. 474a) 8·50

1982 (14 Apr). *World Cup Football Championship, Spain.
Multicoloured cover,* 170×102 *mm, showing Championship
emblems. Stamps attached by selvedge.*
SB4 4 m. 85, booklet containing twenty-four 15 s. (Nos.
480/91) in blocks of 12 and one miniature
sheet (No. MS492) .. .. .. 6·00

1982 (14 June). *Multicoloured cover as No.* SB1. *Stapled.*
SB5 4 m. 30, booklet containing 5 s., 6 s., 7 s. and 25 s.
(Nos. 503/5, 507) in blocks of 10 .. 8·00

1983 (11 Jan). *Fungi. Multicoloured cover,* 155×80 *mm,
showing fungi on front and with biography of G. L. Vasarhelyi
on back. Panes attached by selvedge.*
SB6 3 m. 70, booklet containing two *se-tenant* panes of
4 stamps and 1 label (No 532b) and one
se-tenant pane of 2 stamps and 1 label (No.
532c) .. .. 7·50

1983 (11 July). *Bicentenary of Manned Flight. Multicoloured
cover,* 211×100 *mm, showing Montgolfier balloon. Panes
attached by selvedge.*
SB7 4 m. booklet containing *se-tenant* pane of 4 stamps
and 1 label (No. 545a) and one miniature
sheet (No. MS549) .. .. .. 5·25

OFFICIAL

(O 1)

1934 (4 May). *Nos. 1/3 and 6 optd with Type* O 1.

O1	1	½d. emerald	..			£3250	£3250
O2		1d. scarlet	..	..	..	£1400	£1000
O3		2d. bright purple	..			£800	£550
O4		6d. orange-yellow	..	..		£10000	£4750
O1/4					*Set of 4*	£14000	£8500

Collectors are advised to buy these stamps only from reliable
sources. They were not sold to the public.

D 1   Normal   Large "d."
(R. 9/6, 10/6)

(Typo D.L.R.)

1933 (1 Dec)–52. *Wmk Mult Script CA. Ordinary paper. P* 14.

D1	D 1	1d. carmine	..	..		1·75	7·00
		a. Scarlet (1938)	..	..		32·00	40·00
		b. Chalk-surfaced paper. *Deep carmine*					
		(24.10.51)	..	..		65	1·75
		ba. Error. Crown missing, W9*a*	..			£110	
		bb. Error. St. Edward's Crown, W9*b*		..		65·00	
D2		2d. violet	..	..		7·50	14·00
		a. Chalk-surfaced paper (6.11.52)		..		30	7·00
		ab. Error. Crown missing, W9*a*		..		£120	
		ac. Error. St. Edward's Crown, W9*a*	..		65·00	
		ad. Large "d"	..	..		5·50	
D1/2		Perf "Specimen"			*Set of 2*	42·00	

D 2

(Typo D.L.R.)

1956 (1 Dec). *Wmk Mult Script CA. P* 14.

D3	D 2	1d. carmine	..			30	2·75
D4		2d. deep reddish violet	..	..	..	30	5·00

5c **5c**
(I)   (II)

1961 (14 Feb). *Surch as T* 24, *but without stop.*

D5	D 2	1 c. on 1d. carmine		..		10	30
D6		1 c. on 2d. deep reddish violet				10	30
D7		5 c. on 2d. deep reddish violet (Type I)			15	30
		a. Type II	..	..		12·00	42·00
D5/7					*Set of 3*	30	80

1961 (June). *No. D2a surch as T* 24 (*without stop*).

D8	D 1	5 c. on 2d. violet	..	..		1·50	6·50
		a. Error. Missing Crown, W9*a*	..		£1000	
		b. Error. St. Edward's Crown, W9*b*	..		£225	
		c. Large "d"	..	..		15·00	

1964. *As No. D3/4 but values in cents and W w* 12 (*sideways
on* 1 *c.*).

D9	D 2	1 c. carmine	..	..	..	1·90	11·00
D10		5 c. deep reddish violet	..		..	1·90	11·00

1966 (1 Nov). *Nos. D9/10 optd as T* 34 *but smaller.*

D11	D 2	1 c. carmine	..	..	..	30	75
		a. "LSEOTHO" (R.4/7)		..		25·00	
D12		5 c. deep reddish violet		..		30	90
		a. "LSEOTHO" (R.4/7)		..		45·00	

No. D11 exists with the overprint centred near the foot of the
stamp (just above "POSTAGE DUE") (*price £50 mint*). It is believed
that this comes from a proof sheet which was issued in the normal
way. It contains the "LSEOTHO" error, which only occurred in the
first printing.

D 1   D 2

(Litho B.W.)

1967 (18 Apr). *No wmk. P* 13½.

D13	D 1	1 c. blue ..			..	..	15	3·00
D14		2 c. brown-rose		..			15	3·50
D15		5 c. emerald	..		..	..	20	3·50
D13/15						*Set of 3*	45	9·00

1976 (30 Nov). *W* 53 (*sideways*). *P* 13½.

D17	D 1	2 c. rose-red	..	..		1·50	6·00
D18		5 c. emerald	..	..		1·75	6·00

(Des G. Vasarhelyi. Litho Format)

1986. *No wmk. P* 13×13½.

D19	D 2	2 s. light green	..	..		15	70
D20		5 s. new blue	..	..		15	70
D21		25 s. violet	..	..		50	1·25
D19/21					*Set of 3*	70	2·40

Nos. D19/21 exist imperforate from stock dispersed by the
liquidator of Format International Security Printers Ltd.

POSTAL FISCAL

In July 1961 the 10s. stamp, T **9**, surcharged "R1 Revenue", was
used for postage at one post office at least, but such usage was officially unauthorised.

Appendix

The following stamps have either been issued in excess of postal
needs, or have not been made available to the public in reasonable
quantities at face value. Miniature sheets, imperforate stamps etc.,
are excluded from this section.

1981–83
15th *Anniv of Independence. Classic Stamps of the World.*
10 m. × 40, each embossed on gold foil.

Long Island

PRICES FOR STAMPS ON COVER

Most covers from Long Island are philatelic, but these are worth from ×2 (Nos. 1/3) or from ×5 (others).

The Turkish island of Chustan (or Keustan) in the Gulf of Smyrna was occupied by the Royal Navy during April 1916 and renamed Long Island.

The following stamps were provided by the Civil Administrator, Lieut.-Cmdr H. Pirie-Gordon, for the postal service inaugurated on 7 May 1916. ●

USED STAMPS. Stamps of Long Island were cancelled by hand-drawn circular date stamps in blue crayon for the Northend post office ("N") or in red crayon for Nikola post office ("S").

QUANTITIES ISSUED. The figures quoted do not include the remainders subsequently recorded as having been destroyed.

(1)　　　　　　2

1916 (7 May). *Turkish fiscal stamps surch by typewriter as in* T 1. *No wmk.* P 12.

1	½d. on 20 pa. green and buff (new value in red, remainder of surch in black)	£2250	£4000
2	1d. on 10 pa. carmine and buff	£2500	£4000
3	2½d. on 1 pi. violet and buff (R.)	£2250	£4000

Quantities issued: ½d. 25; 1d. 20; 2½d. 25.

1916 (7 May). *Typewritten as* T 2 *in various colours of ribbon and carbon. Each stamp initialled by the Civil Administrator. No gum. Imperf.*

(a) On pale green paper with horizontal grey lines. No wmk. Sheets of 12 (4×3) or 16 (4×4) with stamps initialled in red ink.

4	½d. black	£1100	£900
	a. "G.R.I." double	£1900	
	b. "7" for "&"	£3000	
5	½d. blue	£900	
	a. "G.R.I." double	£1900	
	b. "7" for "&"	£3000	
6	½d. mauve	£425	£500
	a. "G.R.I." double	£1000	
	b. "7" for "&"	£2250	

Quantity issued: 140 in all.

(b) On thin horiz laid paper with sheet wmk of "Silver Linen" in double-lined letters. Sheets of 20 (4×5) or 16 (some ptgs of 1s.) with stamps initialled in red ink.

7	½d. black	£400	£500
	a. "postage" for "Postage"	£1700	
	b. "7" for "&"	£1700	
8	½d. blue	£600	£650
	b. "7" for "&"	£1700	
9	½d. mauve	£190	£250
	a. "postage" for "Postage"	£1000	
	b. "7" for "&"	£1200	
10	1d. black	£160	£300
	a. "7" for "&"	£1200	
	b. "Rvevue" for "Revenue"	£1200	
	g. "Postagg" for "Postage"	£1700	
11	1d. blue	£225	£375
	a. "7" for "&"	£1700	
	c. "postage" for "Postage"	£1700	
	e. "G.R?I?" for "G.R.I."	£1700	
	f. "ONR" for "ONE"	£1000	
12	1d. mauve	£120	£225
	a. "7" for "&"	£1300	
	b. "Rvevue" for "Revenue"	£1700	
	c. "postage" for "Postage"	£1700	
	e. "G.R?I?" for "G.R.I."		†£1800
	f. "ONR" for "ONE"	£750	£1000
	g. "Postagg" for "Postage"	£1200	
13	1d. red	£140	£250
	a. "7" for "&"	£1200	
	c. "postage" for "Postage"	£1700	
	f. "ONR" for "ONE"	£1000	£1100
14	2½d. black	£800	
15	2½d. blue	£800	£1000
16	2½d. mauve	£1500	£1000
17	6d. black (inscr "SIX PENCE")	£1000	£1400
	a. "SIXPENCE" (one word)	£2000	
	b. Without red ink initials		†£1700
19	6d. mauve (inscr "SIX PENCE")	£375	£800
	a. "SIXPENCE" (one word)	£1500	
20	1s. black	£120	£325
	a. "ISLANA" for "ISLAND"	£1700	
	b. "Postge" for "Postage"	£950	£1400
	c. "Rebenue" for "Revenue"	£1700	
21	1s. blue	£1000	
22	1s. mauve	£110	£400
	a. "ISLANA" for "ISLAND"	£1200	
	b. "Postge" for "Postage"	£1700	
	c. "Rebenue" for "Revenue"	£1700	

Quantities issued (all colours); ½d. 237; 1d. 881; 2½d. 80; 6d. 89; 1s. 383.

(c) On thin wove paper. No wmk. Sheets of 24 with stamps initialled in indelible pencil.

23	½d. black	£300	£400
25	½d. mauve	£550	
26	1d. black	£350	£450
27	1d. red	£4500	£900
30	2d. black	£180	£450
	b. Error. 1d. and 2d. se-tenant	£3750	
	c. Initialled in red ink	£850	£950
31	2d. mauve	£180	£300
	a. Error. 1d. and 2d. se-tenant	£3500	
32	2½d. black	£400	£500
33	2½d. blue	£1000	
34	2½d. mauve	£900	£900
35	6d. black	£190	£450
	a. "Rvenne &" for "Revenue"	£1600	
	b. Error. 2d. and 6d. se-tenant, also "ISLND" for "ISLAND"	£3750	£3750
	c. "PENCC"	£1300	
36	6d. blue	£700	
	a. "Rvenne &" for "Revenue"	£2000	
	b. Error. 2d. and 6d. se-tenant, also "ISLND" for "ISLAND"	£4000	
	c. "PENCC"	£1700	

Quantities issued (all colours); ½d. 114; 1d. 120; 2d. 249; 2½d. 115; 6d. 200.

TOP SHEETS AND CARBONS. It is believed that the production sequence of the typewritten stamps was as follows:

½d. on pale green (Nos. 4/6)
　Two black top sheets of 12 (4×3) and one of 16 (4×4)
　Two blue carbon sheets of 12 (4×3) and one of 16 (4×4)
　Five mauve carbon sheets of 12, two from one top sheet and three from the other
　Varieties: "7" for "&" occurs on an unknown position from one of the sheets of 12 and "G.R.I." double occurs on R. 3/2-4 of the other

½d. on laid paper (Nos. 7/9) in sheets of 20 (4×5)
　Three black top sheets
　Three blue carbon sheets
　Eight mauve carbon sheets, two or three from each top sheet
　Varieties: "postage" occurs on R. 3/2 of one top sheet and "7" for "&" on R. 4/2 of another

1d. on laid paper (Nos. 10/13) in sheets of 20 (4×5)
　Eleven red top sheets
　Fifteen black carbon sheets, three each from five of the top sheets
　Six blue carbon sheets, one each from six of the top sheets
　Twenty-two mauve carbon sheets, probably two from each top sheet
　Varieties: "7" for "&" on R. 3/3, "postage" on R. 3/3, "Rvevue" on R. 1/3 and "Postagg" on R. 2/4, all from different top sheets. The position of "G.R?I?" is not known. "ONR" occurs from three different top sheets on R. 5/1, R. 5/2 & 4 or R. 4/1 and 5/2

2½d. on laid paper (Nos. 14/16) in sheets of 20 (4×5)
　One black top sheet
　One blue carbon sheet
　Two mauve carbon sheets

6d. on laid paper (Nos. 17/19) in sheets of 20 (4×5)
　One black top sheet
　One blue carbon sheet*
　Three mauve carbon sheets
　Variety: "SIXPENCE" occurs on R. 1/2-3

1s. on laid paper (Nos. 20/2) in sheets of 20 (4×5) and one of 16 (4×4)
　Five black top sheets, four of 20 (4×5) and one of 16 (4×4)
　Nine black carbon sheets, three each from two of the top sheets of 20 and three from the top sheet of 16
　Two blue carbon sheets, one each from two of the top sheets of 20
　Twelve mauve carbon sheets, nine from various top sheets of 20 and three from the top sheet of 16
　Varieties: "ISLANA" occurs on R. 1/2 of one of the sheets of 20 and "Postge" on R. 1/3 of the sheet of 16. "Rebenue" comes from one of the other sheets of 20

½d. on wove paper (Nos. 23/5) in sheets of 24 (4×6)
　One black top sheet
　Three black carbon sheets
　One blue carbon sheet*
　One mauve carbon sheet

1d. on wove paper (Nos. 26/7) in sheets of 24 (4×6)
　One red top sheet
　Three black carbon sheets
　One blue carbon sheet*
　One mauve carbon sheet*

2d. on wove paper (Nos. 30/1) in sheets of 24 (4×6)
　Two black top sheets
　Six black carbon sheets, three from each top sheet. One initialled in red ink
　Four mauve carbon sheets, two from each top sheet
　Variety: the "1d." error occurs on R. 5/2 from one top sheet

2½d. on wove paper (Nos. 32/4) in sheets of 24 (4×6)
　One black top sheet
　Three black carbon sheets
　One blue carbon sheet
　One mauve carbon sheet

6d. on wove paper (Nos. 35/6) in sheets of 24 (4×6)
　Two black top sheets
　Six black carbon sheets, three from each top sheet
　Two blue carbon sheets, one from each top sheet
　Varieties: the "2d." error occurs on R. 5/3 from one top sheet which also showed "PENCC" on R. 3/2, and "Rvenne &" on R. 4/1 of the other

*These carbons are described in written records, but their existence has yet to be confirmed by actual examples.

The new-issue supplement to this Catalogue appears each month in

GIBBONS STAMP MONTHLY

—from your newsagent or by postal subscription— sample copy and details on request.

Madagascar

PRICES FOR STAMPS ON COVER

Nos. 1/47	
Nos. 50/6	from × 50
Nos. 57/62	from × 30

BRITISH CONSULAR MAIL

After May 1883 mail from the British community at Antananarivo, the capital, was sent by runner to the British Consulate at Tamatave for forwarding via the French Post Office.

In March of the following year the British Vice-Consul at Antananarivo, Mr. W. C. Pickersgill, reorganised this service and issued stamps for use on both local and overseas mail. Such stamps were only gummed at one of the top corners. This was to facilitate their removal from overseas mail where they were replaced by Mauritius stamps (at Port Louis) or by French issues (at the Vice-Consulate) for transmission via Tamatave and Reunion. Local mail usually had the stamps removed also, being marked with a "PAID" or a Vice-Consular handstamp, although a few covers have survived intact.

CONDITION. Due to the type of paper used, stamps of the British Consular Mail are usually found with slight faults, especially thins. Our prices are for average examples, really fine stamps being worth a premium.

USED STAMPS. Postmarks are not usually found on these issues. Cancellations usually take the form of a manuscript line or cross in crayon, ink or pencil or as five parallel horizontal bars in black or red, approximately 15 mm long. Examples of Nos. 1/3, 5/8 and 11 showing a red diagonal line are believed to be cancelled-to-order.

1　　　　　　　　2

1884 (Mar). *Typo locally. Rouletted vertically in colour. No gum, except on one upper corner. With circular consular handstamp reading* "BRITISH VICE-CONSULATE ANTANANARIVO" *around Royal arms in black.*

(a) Inscr "LETTER".

1	1	6d. (½ oz) magenta	£400	£425
		a. Violet handstamp	£1800	
2		1s. (1 oz) magenta	£375	
3		1s. 6d. (1½ oz) magenta	£400	
4		2s. (2 oz) magenta	£600	

(b) Inscr "POSTAL PACKET"

5	1	1d. (1 oz) magenta	£400	£350
		a. Without handstamp	£4000	£4000
6		2d. (2 oz) magenta	£275	£250
7		3d. (3 oz) magenta	£275	£250
8		4d. (1 oz amended in ms to "4 oz") magenta	£650	£600
		a. Without manuscript amendment	£3250	£3250
		ab. Violet handstamp	£1100	
		ac. Without handstamp	£4000	£4000

Nos. 1/8 were printed in horizontal strips of four, each strip containing two impressions of the setting. Each strip contained two stamps with normal stops after "B.C.M." and two with a hollow stop after "B" (1d., 2d., 3d., 4d., 6d. and 2s.) or after "M" (1s. and 1s. 6d.).

Several values are known with the handstamp either inverted or double.

1886. *Manuscript provisionals.*

(a) No. 2 with "SHILLING" *erased and* "PENNY" *written above in red ink*

9	1	1d. on 1s. (1 oz) magenta		

(b) No. 2 surch "4½d." *and* "W.C.P." *in red ink with a line through the original value*

10	1	4½d. on 1s. (1 oz) magenta		

1886. *As No. 1, but colour changed. Handstamped with circular* "BRITISH VICE-CONSULATE ANTANANARIVO" *in black.*

11	1	6d. (½ oz) rose-red	£550	£500

1886. *As No. 8, but handstamped* "BRITISH CONSULAR MAIL ANTANANARIVO" *in black.*

12	1	4d. (1 oz) magenta	£1600	
		a. Violet handstamp	£3750	

1886. *Typo locally.* "POSTAGE" *and value in words printed in black. Rouletted vertically in colour. No gum, except on one upper corner.*

I. "POSTAGE" 29½ mm long. Stops after "POSTAGE" and value

(a) Handstamped "BRITISH VICE-CONSULATE ANTANANARIVO" in black

14	2	1d. rose		£100	£130
		a. Violet handstamp		£275	
15		1½d. rose		£1200	£1000
		a. Violet handstamp		£850	£750
16		2d. rose		£140	
		a. Violet handstamp		£275	
17		3d. rose		£1200	£950
		a. Violet handstamp		£350	£325
18		4½d. rose		£850	£500
		a. Violet handstamp		£450	£300
19		8d. rose		£2250	£2250
		a. Violet handstamp		£1000	£1000
20		9d. rose		£2750	£2500
		a. Violet handstamp		£950	

(b) Handstamped "BRITISH CONSULAR MAIL ANTANANARIVO" in black

21	2	1d. rose		70·00	
22		1½d. rose		70·00	
23		2d. rose		90·00	
24		3d. rose		85·00	£120
		a. Handstamp in red		†£8000	
25		4½d. rose		85·00	£120
		a. Handstamp in red		†£4750	
26		8d. rose		£100	
		a. Handstamp in violet		£1200	
27		9d. rose		£110	£160
		a. Without handstamp		£2750	
		b. Handstamp in violet		£250	

II. "POSTAGE" 29½ mm long. No stops after "POSTAGE" or value

(a) Handstamped "BRITISH VICE-CONSULATE ANTANANARIVO" in violet

28	2	1d. rose		£850	
29		1½d. rose		£1600	
30		3d. rose		£1000	
31		4½d. rose		£1500	
32		6d. rose		£1200	

(b) Handstamped "BRITISH CONSULAR MAIL ANTANANARIVO" in black

33		1d. rose		70·00	£100
		a. Without handstamp		£1800	
		b. Violet handstamp		85·00	
34		1½d. rose		65·00	95·00
		a. Without handstamp		£1900	
		b. Violet handstamp		£130	
35		2d. rose		65·00	95·00
		b. Violet handstamp		£140	
36		3d. rose		70·00	£100
		a. Without handstamp		£2750	
		b. Violet handstamp		£120	
37		4½d. rose		70·00	£100
		a. Without handstamp		£2750	
		b. Violet handstamp		£120	
38		6d. rose		70·00	£100
		a. Without handstamp		£3000	
		b. Violet handstamp		£300	

III. "POSTAGE" 24½ mm long. No stop after "POSTAGE", but stop after value.

(a) Handstamped "BRITISH VICE-CONSULATE ANTANANARIVO" in violet

39	2	4d. rose		£400	
40		8d. rose		£500	
40a		1s. rose			
41		1s. 6d. rose		£3500	
42		2s. rose		£2000	
		a. Handstamp in black			

(b) Handstamped "BRITISH CONSULAR MAIL ANTANANARIVO" in black

43		4d. rose		£180	
		a. Without handstamp		£2250	
		b. Violet handstamp		£375	
44		8d. rose		£600	
		a. Without handstamp		£2250	
		b. Violet handstamp		£500	
45		1s. rose		£450	
		a. Without handstamp		£2250	
		b. Violet handstamp		£1200	
46		1s. 6d. rose		£500	
		a. Without handstamp		£3000	
		b. Violet handstamp		£1200	
47		2s. rose		£600	
		a. Without handstamp		£3000	
		b. Violet handstamp		£1500	

The above were also printed in horizontal strips of four.

The stamps of the British Consular Mail were suppressed in 1887, but the postal service continued with the charges paid in cash.

BRITISH INLAND MAIL

In January 1895 the Malagasy government agreed that a syndicate of British merchants at Antananarivo, including the Vice-Consul, should operate an inland postal service during the war with France. Mail was sent by runner to the port of Vatomandry and forwarded via Durban where Natal stamps were added.

Nos. 50/62 were cancelled with dated circular postmarks inscribed "BRITISH MAIL".

4   5 Malagasy Runners

(Typeset London Missionary Society Press, Antananarivo)

1895 (Jan). *Rouletted in black.* (a) *Thick laid paper.*

50	4	4d. black		24·00	12·00
		a. "FUOR" for "FOUR"		—	£900

(b) *In black on coloured wove paper*

51	4	1d. blue-grey		24·00	12·00
52		6d. pale yellow		24·00	12·00
53		8d. salmon		24·00	12·00
54		1s. fawn		38·00	12·00
55		2s. bright rose		38·00	14·00
		a. Italic "2" at left		£130	60·00
56		4s. grey		55·00	12·00
50/6			Set of 7	£200	75·00

There are six types of each value, printed in blocks of 6 (2×3) separated by gutters, four times on each sheet; the upper and lower blocks being *tête-bêche*.

Nos. 50a and 55a occur in the sixth position in their respective blocks. No. 50a was soon corrected.

(Typo John Haddon & Co, London)

1895 (Mar). *The inscription in the lower label varies for each value.* P 12.

57	5	2d. blue		5·00	35·00
		a. Imperf between (pair)		£400	
58		4d. rose		5·50	35·00
		a. Imperf between (pair)		£250	
59		6d. green		6·50	35·00
		a. Imperf between (pair)		£500	
60		1s. slate-blue		6·50	45·00
		a. Imperf between (pair)		£400	
61		2s. chocolate		11·00	55·00
		a. Imperf between (pair)		£425	
62		4s. bright purple		18·00	70·00
		a. Imperf between (pair)		£1300	
57/62			Set of 6	48·00	£250

This post was suppressed when the French entered Antananarivo on 30 September 1895.

Malawi
(formerly Nyasaland)

PRICES FOR STAMPS ON COVER TO 1945	
Nos. 1/9a	from × 15
Nos. 10/19	
No. 20	from × 10
Nos. 21/6	from × 5
Nos. 27/31	
Nos. 32/7	from × 6
Nos. 38/42	
Nos. 43/7	from × 12
Nos. 48/52	
No. 53	from × 15
No. 54	from × 2
No. 55	from × 4
Nos. 55b/7a	from × 7
Nos. 57d/63	from × 6
Nos. 64/71	
Nos. 72/9	from × 5
Nos. 80/2	
Nos. 83/95	from × 4
Nos. 96/9	—
Nos. 100/57	from × 2

By 1891 the territory west of Lake Nyasa was recognised as being under British protection and the southern, eastern and northern borders had been delineated with the Portuguese and German governments.

BRITISH CENTRAL AFRICA

A protectorate under the name "Nyassaland Districts" was declared on 14 May 1891, the title being changed to the "British Central Africa Protectorate" on 22 February 1893. Such a description had been in use for some time previously and the handwritten notice of 20 July 1891, announcing the introduction of postal services, described the area as "British Central Africa".

Until 1895 the British South Africa Company contributed to the revenues of the protectorate administration which, in return, governed North-eastern Rhodesia. Stamps of the British South Africa Company overprinted "B.C.A.", in addition to use in British Central Africa, were issued to post offices at Fife, Fort Rosebery, Katwe, Johnston Falls, Rhodesia (later Kalungwisi) and Tanganyika (later Abercorn) in North-eastern Rhodesia from 1893 until 1899.

B.C.A.

B.C.A.   **FOUR SHILLINGS.**   **ONE PENNY.**

(1)   (2)   (3)

1891 (20 July)–**95.** *Stamps of Rhodesia optd as T 1.* P 14, 14½.

1	1	1d. black		3·50	4·00
2	4	2d. sea-green and vermilion		3·50	4·00
		a. Bisected (1d.) (on cover) (1895)			†£1900
3		4d. reddish chestnut and black		3·75	5·00
4	1	6d. ultramarine		45·00	20·00
5		6d. deep blue		5·50	8·00
6	4	8d. rose-lake and ultramarine		12·00	28·00
6a		8d. red and ultramarine		23·00	45·00
7	1	1s. grey-brown		13·00	11·00
8		2s. vermilion		25·00	50·00
9		2s. 6d. grey-purple		60·00	80·00
9a		2s. 6d. lilac		60·00	80·00
10	4	3s. brown and green (1895)		55·00	60·00
11		4s. grey-black and vermilion (2.93)		60·00	85·00
12	1	5s. orange-yellow		60·00	75·00
13		10s. deep green		£120	£180
14	2	£1 deep blue		£500	£500
15		£2 rose-red		£800	
16		£5 sage-green		£1400	
17		£10 brown		£3250	
1/14			Set of 13	£800	£1000

The overprint varies on values up to 10s. Sets may be made with *thin* or *thick* letters.

The bisected 2d, No. 2a, was authorised for use at Blantyre, Chiromo and Zomba in July and October 1895.

1892 (Aug)–**93.** *Stamps of Rhodesia surch as T 2.*

18	4	3s. on 4s. grey-black and vermilion (10.93)		£325	£325
19	1	4s. on 5s. orange-yellow		70·00	85·00

1895. *No. 2 surch at Cape Town with T 3.*

20	4	1d. on 2d. sea-green and vermilion		6·50	26·00
		a. Surch double		£3250	£2500

Specimens are known with double surcharge, without stop after "PENNY". These are from a trial printing made at Blantyre, but it is believed that they were not issued to the public (Price £550 un.).

5 Arms of the Protectorate   6

(Des Sir Harry Johnston. Litho D.L.R.)

1895. *No wmk.* P 14.

21	5	1d. black		12·00	7·00
22		2d. black and green		20·00	12·00
23		4d. black and reddish buff		35·00	29·00
24		6d. black and blue		55·00	7·50
25		1s. black and rose		60·00	25·00
26	6	2s. 6d. black and bright magenta		£160	£250
27		3s. black and yellow		95·00	50·00
28		5s. black and olive		£130	£160
29		£1 black and yellow-orange		£900	£375
30		£10 black and orange-vermilion		£4000	£3500
31		£25 black and blue-green		£7000	
21/8			Set of 8	£500	£475
21/9		Optd "Specimen"	Set of 9	£375	

Cancellations inscribed "BRITISH CENTRAL AFRICA" within a double-circle and with the name of a town across the centre or at foot were intended for use on stamps presented for the payment of the hut tax. Such marks can be found in black, violet or blue and are without date. Stamps with such fiscal obliterations are of little value. Prices quoted are for postally used.

1896 (Feb). *Wmk Crown CA (T 5) or CC (sideways) (T 6).* P 14.

32	5	1d. black		3·25	4·50
		y. Wmk inverted and reversed		†	£225
33		2d. black and green		14·00	5·00
34		4d. black and orange-brown		21·00	17·00
35		6d. black and blue		21·00	11·00
36		1s. black and rose		21·00	13·00
37	6	2s. 6d. black and magenta		£110	£110
38		3s. black and yellow		85·00	50·00
39		5s. black and olive		£120	£160
40		£1 black and blue		£750	£475
41		£10 black and orange (Optd S. £175)		£4750	£3500
42		£25 black and green (Optd S. £325)		£9000	
32/9			Set of 8	£350	£325
32/40		Optd "Specimen"	Set of 9	£375	

7   8

(Typo D.L.R.)

1897 (Aug)–**1900.** *T 7 (wmk Crown CA) and 8 (wmk Crown CC).* P 14.

43	7	1d. black and ultramarine		2·50	90
		w. Wmk inverted		£130	£190
44		2d. black and yellow		2·00	1·75
45		4d. black and carmine		5·50	1·50
46		6d. black and green		42·00	4·25
47		1s. black and dull purple		9·50	7·00
48	8	2s. 6d. black and ultramarine		45·00	42·00
49		3s. black and sea-green		£190	£225
50		4s. black and carmine		70·00	80·00
50a		10s. black and olive-green (1900)		£120	£130
51		£1 black and dull purple		£275	£160
52		£10 black and yellow (Optd S. £200)		£4000	£1700
43/51			Set of 10	£700	£600
43/51		Optd "Specimen"	Set of 10	£250	

ONE PENNY

(9)   **10**

1897 (31 Dec). *No. 49 surch with T 9, in red.*
53	8	1d. on 3s. black and sea-green		5·00	9·00
		a. "PNNEY" (R. 4/2)		£1900	£1900
		b. "PENN"		£1300	£1000
		c. Surch double		£450	

No. 53b shows an albino impression of the "Y".

1898 (11 Mar). *Imperf.*

(a) Setting I. The vertical frame lines of the stamps cross the space between the two rows of the sheet
  (i) With the initials "J.G." or "J.T.G." on the back in black ink
54	10	1d. vermilion and grey-blue		—	£600
		a. Without the initials		£2000	
		b. Without the initials and centre inverted		£9000	

  (ii) With a control number and letter or letters, printed in plain relief at the back
55	10	1d. vermilion and grey-blue		—	£400

(b) Setting II. The vertical frame lines do not cross the space between the rows except at the extreme ends of the sheet. Control as No. 55.
55b	10	1d. vermilion and pale ultramarine		—	80·00
		c. Control on face		—	£3250
		d. Centre omitted (vert pair with normal)		£11000	
56		1d. vermilion and deep ultramarine		—	80·00
		a. Without Control at back		£1800	£130
		b. Control doubly impressed		—	£400

1898 (June). *Setting II. Control as No. 55. P 12.*
57	10	1d. vermilion and pale ultramarine		£2000	17·00
57a		1d. vermilion and deep ultramarine		—	30·00
		ab. Without Control at back		£2000	80·00
		ac. Two different Controls on back		—	£600
		ad. Control printed in black		—	£2750

The two different settings of these stamps are each in 30 types, issued without gum.

1901. *Wmk Crown CA. P 14.*
57d	7	1d. dull purple and carmine-rose		2·00	40
57e		4d. dull purple and olive-green		8·00	11·00
58		6d. dull purple and brown		3·75	9·00
57d/8			*Set of 3*	12·50	13·00
57d/58 Optd "Specimen"			*Set of 3*	60·00	

11   **12**

(Typo D.L.R.)

1903–4. *T 11 (Wmk Crown CA) and 12 (Wmk Crown CC). P 14.*
59	11	1d. grey and carmine		4·75	1·75
60		2d. dull and bright purple		3·25	1·00
61		4d. grey-green and black		2·50	9·00
62		6d. grey and reddish buff		2·50	2·00
		aw. Wmk inverted		85·00	
62b		1s. grey and blue		2·75	10·00
63	12	2s. 6d. grey-green and green		40·00	65·00
64		4s. dull and bright purple		60·00	75·00
65		10s. green and black		90·00	£180
66		£1 grey and carmine		£225	£170
67		£10 grey and blue (Optd S. £300)		£4250	£3250
59/66			*Set of 9*	£375	£450
59/66 Optd "Specimen"			*Set of 9*	£275	

1907. *Wmk Mult Crown CA. Chalk-surfaced paper. P 14.*
68	11	1d. grey and carmine		4·50	2·50
69		2d. dull and bright purple		£9000	
70		4d. grey-green and black		£9000	
71		6d. grey and reddish buff		27·00	45·00

Nos. 69/70 were not issued in Nyasaland.

NYASALAND PROTECTORATE

The title of the Protectorate was changed again from 6 July 1907.

13   **14**

POSTAGE

Serif on "G" (R. 4/5. All ptgs of £1 Duty plate)

(Typo D.L.R.)

1908 (22 July)–**11.** *P 14. (a) Wmk Crown CA. Chalk-surfaced paper.*
72	13	1s. black/*green*		2·50	7·50

(b) Wmk Mult Crown CA. Ordinary paper (¹/₂d., 1d.) or chalk-surfaced paper (others)
73	13	¹/₂d. green		1·50	2·00
74		1d. carmine		3·50	1·00
75		3d. purple/*yellow*		1·50	3·75
		w. Wmk inverted		£140	
76		4d. black and red/*yellow*		1·50	1·50
		w. Wmk inverted		90·00	90·00
77		6d. dull purple and bright purple		3·75	10·00
78	14	2s. 6d. brownish black & carm-red/*blue*		45·00	80·00
		a. Brownish black and deep rose-red/pale blue (1911)		£170	£200
79		4s. carmine and black		80·00	£110
80		10s. green and red/*green*		£110	£190
81		£1 purple and black/*red*		£450	£550
		c. Serif on "G"		£1600	£1800
82		£10 purple & ultramarine (Optd S. £550)		£7000	£4500
72/81			*Set of 10*	£650	£850
72/81 Optd "Specimen"			*Set of 10*	£450	

15   **16**

Nick in top right scroll (R. 3/12)

"Bullet holes" flaw (R. 5/2. March 1919 ptgs)

Triangle flaw (R. 3/5. March 1919 ptg of 4s.)

1913 (1 Apr)–**19.** *Wmk Mult Crown CA. Ordinary paper (¹/₂d. to 2¹/₂d.) or chalk-surfaced paper (others). P 14.*
83	15	¹/₂d. green		60	1·50
84		¹/₂d. blue-green (1918)		90	1·50
85		1d. carmine-red		1·00	1·75
86		1d. scarlet (1916)		2·25	65
87		2d. grey (1916)		1·25	80
88		2d. slate		4·50	2·50
89		2¹/₂d. bright blue		2·25	6·50
90		3d. purple/*yellow* (1914)		4·00	4·00
		a. On pale yellow		3·75	8·50
		w. Wmk inverted			
91		4d. black and red/*yellow* (shades)		2·00	2·50
		a. On pale yellow		6·00	8·00
92		6d. dull and bright purple		2·75	8·50
92a		6d. dull purple and bright violet		9·00	10·00
93		1s. black/*green*		1·75	8·50
		a. On blue-green, olive back		5·00	1·50
		aw. Wmk inverted		80·00	£120
		b. On emerald back (Optd S. £40)		2·75	6·50
94	16	2s. 6d. black and red/*blue*		11·00	10·00
		a. Break in scroll		£120	
		b. Broken crown and scroll		£160	
		d. Nick in top right scroll		£130	
		e. "Bullet-holes" flaw		£180	
95		4s. carmine and black		13·00	48·00
		a. Break in scroll		£130	
		b. Broken crown and scroll		£170	
		d. Nick in top right scroll		£140	
		e. "Bullet-holes" flaw		£200	
		f. Triangle flaw		£200	
96		10s. pale green and deep scarlet/*green*		65·00	85·00
		d. Nick in top right scroll		£325	
		e. Green and deep scarlet/green (1919)		60·00	80·00
		ea. Break in scroll		£300	
		eb. Broken crown and scroll		£300	
		ee. "Bullet-holes" flaw		£350	
98		£1 purple and black/*red*		£150	£140
		a. Break in scroll		£500	
		b. Broken crown and scroll		£500	
		c. Serif on "G"		£550	£500
		d. Nick in top right scroll		£550	
		e. "Bullet holes" flaw		£800	
99		£10 purple & dull ultram (Optd S. £375)		£4250	
		d. Nick in top right scroll		£500	
		e. Purple and royal blue (1919)		£2750	£1700
		eb. Break in scroll		£4500	£3000
		ec. Broken crown and scroll			
		ee. "Bullet holes" flaw			
83/98			*Set of 12*	£225	£275
83/98 Optd "Specimen"			*Set of 12*	£375	

For illustrations of the other varieties on Nos. 94/9 see above Leeward Islands No. 58.
For stamps overprinted "N.F." see TANZANIA.

Break through scroll (R. 1/9. Ptgs from June 1929)

Damaged crown (R. 4/1. Ptgs from June 1924)

1921–30. *Wmk Mult Script CA. Ordinary paper (¹/₂d. to 2d.) or chalk-surfaced paper (others). P 14.*
100	15	¹/₂d. green		1·00	30
		w. Wmk inverted		—	95·00
101		1d. carmine		1·50	30
102		1¹/₂d. orange		3·25	17·00
103		2d. grey		1·00	30
105		3d. purple/*pale yellow*		9·00	3·25
106		4d. black and red/*yellow*		2·50	10·00
107		6d. dull and bright purple		3·00	3·25
108		1s. black/*emerald* (1930)		7·00	4·50
109	16	2s. purple and blue/*blue* (1926)		14·00	11·00
		a. Break in scroll		95·00	
		b. Broken crown and scroll		95·00	
		c. Break through scroll		£150	
110		2s. 6d. black and red/*blue* (1924)		18·00	15·00
		a. Break in scroll		£110	
		b. Broken crown and scroll		£110	
		c. Break through scroll		£160	
		d. Damaged crown		£180	

111	16	4s. carmine and black (1927)	..	18·00	21·00
		a. Break in scroll ..		£110	
		b. Broken crown and scroll ..		£110	
112		5s. green and red/*yellow* (1929)		35·00	75·00
		a. Break in scroll ..		£170	
		b. Broken crown and scroll ..		£170	
113		10s. green and red/*pale emerald* (1926)		80·00	95·00
		a. Break in scroll ..		£325	
		b. Broken crown and scroll ..		£325	
		c. *Green and scarlet/emerald* (1927)		£300	£475
		ca. Break in scroll ..		£900	
		cb. Broken crown and scroll ..		£900	
100/13			Set of 13	£170	£225
100/13 Optd/Perf "Specimen"			Set of 13	£350	

For illustrations of tbe other varieties on Nos. 109/13 see above Leeward Islands No. 58.

17 King George V and Symbol of the Protectorate

(Des Major H. E. Green. Recess Waterlow)

1934 (June)–**35.** *Wmk Mult Script CA.* P 12½.

114	17	½d. green	..	75	95
115		1d. brown	..	75	75
116		1½d. carmine	..	75	2·50
117		2d. pale grey	..	80	1·25
118		3d. blue	..	2·25	1·50
119		4d. bright magenta (20.5.35)		2·25	3·00
120		6d. violet	..	2·25	40
121		9d. olive-bistre (20.5.35)		5·00	9·00
122		1s. black and orange	..	7·50	13·00
114/22			Set of 9	20·00	29·00
114/22 Perf "Specimen"			Set of 9	£170	

1935 (6 May). *Silver Jubilee. As Nos. 114/17 of Jamaica, but ptd by Waterlow.* P 11×12.

123		1d. ultramarine and grey	..	1·00	1·50
		k. Kite and vertical log ..		80·00	
		m. "Bird" by turret		£100	
124		2d. green and indigo	..	1·00	70
		m. "Bird" by turret		£100	
125		3d. brown and deep blue	..	7·00	14·00
		k. Kite and vertical log ..		£170	
126		1s. slate and purple	..	16·00	32·00
		k. Kite and vertical log ..		£275	
123/6			Set of 4	12·00	42·00
123/6 Perf "Specimen"			Set of 4	£85·00	

For illustrations of plate varieties see Omnibus section following Zimbabwe.

1937 (12 May). *Coronation. As Nos. 118/20 of Jamaica, but ptd by B.W.* P 11×11½.

127		½d. green	..	30	60
128		1d. brown	..	50	40
129		2d. grey-black	..	50	1·50
127/9			Set of 3	1·10	2·25
127/9 Perf "Specimen"			Set of 3	60·00	

18 Symbol of the Protectorate   19

(T 18 recess Waterlow; T 19 typo D.L.R.)

1938 (1 Jan)–**44.** *Chalk-surfaced paper (2s. to £1).* P 12½ (T 18) or 14 (T 19). (a) *Wmk Mult Script CA*

130	18	½d. green	..	30	1·00
130a		½d. brown (12.12.42)		10	1·50
131		1d. brown	..	70	20
131a		1d. green (12.12.42)		30	60
132		1½d. carmine	..	2·00	4·50
132a		1½d. grey (12.12.42)		30	4·00
133		2d. grey	..	4·00	1·00
133a		2d. carmine (12.12.42)		30	1·25
134		3d. blue	..	60	40
135		4d. bright magenta	..	2·25	1·25
136		6d. violet	..	2·50	1·25
137		9d. olive-bistre	..	2·50	2·50
138		1s. black and orange	..	3·00	1·25
139	19	2s. purple and blue/*blue*		10·00	8·50
140		2s. 6d. black and red/*blue*		12·00	8·50
141		5s. pale green and red/*yellow*		40·00	18·00
		a. Ordinary paper. *Green and red/ pale yellow* (3.44)		85·00	85·00
142		10s. emerald and deep red/*pale green*		55·00	26·00
		a. Ordinary paper. *Bluish green and brown-red/pale green* (1.38)		£325	£225

(b) *Wmk Mult Crown CA*

143	19	£1 purple and black/*red*		30·00	26·00
		c. Serif on "G"	..	£475	£425
130/43			Set of 18	£150	95·00
130/43 Perf "Specimen"			Set of 18	£600	

No. 141a has a yellow surfacing often applied in horizontal lines giving the appearance of laid paper.

The printer's archives record the despatch of No. 142a to Nyasaland in January 1938, but no examples have been reported used before 1945. The paper coating on this printing varied considerably across the sheet. It is reported that some examples show a faint reaction to the silver test.

20 Lake Nyasa   21 King's African Rifles

(Recess B.W.)

1945 (1 Sept). *T* **20**/**1** *and similar designs. Wmk Mult Script CA (sideways on horiz designs).* P 12.

144	½d. black and chocolate	..	30	10
145	1d. black and emerald	..	40	70
146	1½d. black and grey-green	..	20	50
147	2d. black and scarlet	..	50	50
148	3d. black and light blue	..	20	30
149	4d. black and claret ..		1·25	45
150	6d. black and violet ..		1·25	40
151	9d. black and olive	..	1·50	2·50
152	1s. indigo and deep green		1·25	20
153	2s. emerald and maroon		3·75	4·25
154	2s. 6d. emerald and blue		7·50	4·25
155	5s. purple and blue	..	4·50	6·00
156	10s. claret and emerald	..	12·00	13·00
157	20s. scarlet and black	..	17·00	24·00
144/57		Set of 14	45·00	50·00
144/57 Perf "Specimen"		Set of 14	£275	

Designs: *Horiz*—1½d., 6d. Tea estate; 2d., 1s., 10s. Map of Nyasaland; 4d., 2s. 6d. Tobacco; 9d. Type **20** ; 5s., 20s. Badge of Nyasaland. *Vert*—3d., 2s. Fishing Village.

1946 (16 Dec). *Victory. As Nos. 141/2 of Jamaica.*

158	1d. green	..	10	10
159	2d. red-orange	..	30	10
158/9 Perf "Specimen"		Set of 2	55·00	

26 Symbol of the   27 Arms in 1891 and 1951
Protectorate

(Recess B.W.)

1947 (20 Oct). *Wmk Mult Script CA.* P 12.

160	26	1d. red-brown and yellow-green ..	50	20
160 Perf "Specimen"			45·00	

1948 (15 Dec). *Royal Silver Wedding. As Nos. 143/4 of Jamaica.*

161	1d. green	..	15	10
162	10s. mauve	..	15·00	25·00

1949 (21 Nov). *75th Anniv of U.P.U. As Nos. 145/8 of Jamaica.*

163	1d. blue-green	..	50	20
164	3d. greenish blue	..	2·25	2·50
165	6d. purple	..	1·00	50
166	1s. ultramarine	..	50	50
163/6 ..	..	Set of 4	3·75	3·25

(Des C. Twynam. Recess B.W.)

1951 (15 May). *Diamond Jubilee of Protectorate. Wmk Mult Script CA.* P 11 × 12.

167	27	2d. black and scarlet	1·00	1·00
168		3d. black and turquoise-blue	1·00	1·00
169		6d. black and violet	1·00	1·50
170		5s. black and indigo	2·00	7·00
167/70		Set of 4	4·50	9·50

28 Arms of Rhodesia and   29 Grading Cotton
Nyasland

(Recess Waterlow)

1953 (30 May). *Rhodes Centenary Exhibition. Wmk Mult Script CA.* P 14×13½.

171	28	6d. violet	20	30

1953 (2 June). *Coronation. As No. 153 of Jamaica, but ptd by B.W.*

172	2d. black and brown-orange ..		50	60

(Recess B.W.)

1953 (1 Sept)–**54.** *Designs previously used for King George VI issue, but with portrait of Queen Elizabeth II as in T* **29.** *Wmk Mult Script CA.* P 12.

173	½d. black and chocolate	..	10	85
	a. Perf 12 × 12½ (8.3.54) ..		10	75
174	1d. brown and bright green	..	65	20
175	1½d. black and deep grey-green		20	1·90
176	2d. black and yellow-orange		85	30
	a. Perf 12 × 12½ (8.3.54) ..		30	10
177	2½d. green and black	..	20	50
178	3d. black and scarlet	..	30	40
179	4½d. black and light blue	..	30	40
180	6d. black and violet ..		90	1·25
	a. Perf 12 × 12½ (8.3.54) ..		1·50	60
181	9d. black and deep olive	..	70	2·50
182	1s. deep blue and slate-green		1·75	40
183	2s. deep green and brown-red		2·00	3·00
184	2s. 6d. deep emerald and deep blue		3·25	4·25
185	5s. purple and Prussian blue		7·00	4·50
186	10s. carmine and deep emerald		4·25	14·00
187	20s. red and black	..	15·00	18·00
173a/87		Set of 15	32·00	45·00

Designs: *Horiz*—½d., 9d. Lake Nyasa; 1½d., 6d. Tea estate; 2d., 1s., 10s. Map of Nyasaland; 3d., 2s. 6d. Tobacco; 5s., 20s. Badge of Nyasaland. *Vert*—1d. Symbol of the protectorate; 4½d., 2s. Fishing village.

Stamps perf 12 × 12½ come from sheets comb-perforated 11.8 × 12.25. They were also issued in coils of 480 stamps made up from sheets.

For issues between 1954 and 1963, see RHODESIA AND NYASALAND.

30   (31)

(Recess B.W.)

1963 (1 Nov). *Revenue stamps optd "POSTAGE", as in T* **30,** *or additionally surch as T* **31.** P 12.

188	½d. on 1d. greenish blue	..	30	30
189	1d. green	..	30	10
190	2d. scarlet	..	30	10
191	3d. blue ..		30	10
192	6d. brown-purple	..	30	10
193	9d. on 1s. cerise	..	40	25
194	1s. purple	..	45	10
195	2s. 6d. black	..	70	1·75
196	5s. chocolate	..	2·00	1·50
197	10s. yellow-olive	..	3·25	4·50
	a. Greenish olive	..	9·50	9·50
198	£1 deep violet	..	4·25	5·00
188/98		Set of 11	11·00	13·00

32 Mother and Child   33 Chambo (fish)

34 Tea Industry   35 Nyala

(Des V. Whiteley. Photo Harrison)

1964 (1 Jan). *Designs as T* **32**/**5.** P 14½.

199	½d. reddish violet	..	10	30
200	1d. black and green	..	10	10
201	2d. light red-brown	..	10	10
202	3d. red-brown, yellow-green & bistre-brown		10	10
203	4d. indigo and orange-yellow		20	30
204	6d. purple, yellow-green and light blue		60	30
205	1s. brown, turquoise-blue and pale yellow		15	10
206	1s. 3d. bronze-green and chestnut		2·50	10
207	2s. 6d. brown and blue	..	2·50	50
208	5s. blue, green, yellow and black		1·50	1·25
209	10s. green, orange-brown and black		2·00	3·00
210	£1 deep reddish purple and yellow		7·00	5·50
199/210		Set of 12	15·00	10·00

Designs: *As T* **32**/**3**—2d. Zebu Bull; 3d. Groundnuts; 4d. Fishing. *As T* **34**—1s. Timber; 1s. 3d. Turkish tobacco industry; 2s. 6d. Cotton industry; 5s. Monkey Bay, Lake Nyasa; 10s. Forestry, Afzelia.

Nyasaland attained independence on 5 July 1964 when the country was renamed Malawi.

MALAWI

INDEPENDENT

44 Dr. H. Banda (Prime Minister)
and Independence Monument

(Des M. Goaman. Photo Harrison)

1964 (6 July). *Independence. T* **44** *and similar horiz designs.*
P 14½.
211	3d. yellow-olive and deep sepia		10	10
212	6d. red, gold, blue, carmine and lake		10	10
213	1s. 3d. red, green, black and bluish violet		35	10
214	2s. 6d. multicoloured		45	1·25
	a. Blue omitted		£400	
211/14		*Set of 4*	80	1·40

Designs:—6d. Banda and rising sun. 1s. 3d. Banda and Malawi
flag; 2s. 6d. Banda and Malawi coat of arms.
Six examples of No. 214a are known from the top horizontal
row of an otherwise normal sheet.

48 Tung Tree   49 Christmas Star
and Globe

(Des V. Whiteley. Photo Harrison)

1964 (6 July)–**65**. *As Nos.* 199/210, *but inscr* "MALAWI" *and*
T **48** (9d.). *No wmk. P* 14½.
215	½d. reddish violet		10	35
216	1d. black and green		10	10
217	2d. light red-brown		10	10
218	3d. red-brown, yellow-green & bistre-brown		15	10
219	4d. black and orange-yellow		60	15
220	6d. bluish violet, yellow-green and light blue		75	10
221	9d. bistre-brown, green and yellow		30	15
222	1s. brown, turquoise-blue and pale yellow		25	10
223	1s. 3d. bronze-green and chestnut		50	60
224	2s. 6d. brown and red		1·10	1·00
225	5s. blue, green, yellow and sepia		65	2·25
225a	5s. blue, green, yellow and sepia (1.6.65)		5·00	90
226	10s. green, orange-brown and black		1·50	2·00
227	£1 deep reddish purple and yellow		7·00	5·50
215/27		*Set of 14*	16·00	11·50

No. 225a is inscribed "LAKE MALAWI" instead of "LAKE
NYASA".
See also Nos. 252/62.

(Des V. Whiteley. Photo Harrison)

1964 (1 Dec). *Christmas. P* 14½.
228	49	3d. blue-green and gold	10	10
		a. Gold (star) omitted	£110	
229		6d. magenta and gold	10	10
230		1s. 3d. reddish violet and gold	10	10
231		2s. 6d. blue and gold	20	40
228/31		*Set of 4*	30	50
MS231a	83 × 126 mm. Nos. 228/31. Imperf	1·00	1·75

No. 228a comes from a sheet on which 41 examples had the
gold colour omitted due to a paper fold.

50 Coins   (51)

(Des V. Whiteley. Photo Enschedé)

1965 (1 Mar). *Malawi's First Coinage. Coins in black and silver.*
P 13½.
232	50	3d. green	10	10
233		9d. magenta	20	10
		a. Silver omitted	†	—
234		1s. 6d. purple	25	10
235		3s. blue	35	70
232/5		*Set of 4*	75	85
MS235a	126 × 104 mm. Nos. 232/5. Imperf	1·40	1·10

1965 (14 June). *Nos.* 223/4 *surch as T* **51**.
236	1s. 6d. on 1s. 3d. bronze-green and chestnut		10	10
237	3s. on 2s. 6d. brown and blue		20	20

On No. 237 "3/–" occurs below the bars.

52 Chilembwe leading Rebels

(Des M. Goaman. Photo Harrison)

1965 (20 Aug). *50th Anniv of 1915 Rising. P* 14 × 14½.
238	52	3d. violet and light olive-green	10	10
239		9d. olive-brown and red-orange	10	10
240		1s. 6d. red-brown and grey-blue	15	10
241		3s. turquoise-green and slate-blue	20	25
238/41		*Set of 4*	40	40
MS241a	127 × 83 mm. Nos. 238/41		5·00	6·00

53 "Learning and Scholarship"

(Des H. E. Baxter. Photo Harrison)

1965 (6 Oct). *Opening of Malawi University. P* 14½.
242	53	3d. black and emerald	10	10
243		9d. black and magenta	10	10
244		1s. 6d. black and reddish violet	10	10
245		3s. black and blue	15	40
242/5		*Set of 4*	30	50
MS246	127 × 84 mm. Nos. 242/5		2·50	2·50

54 *Papilio ophidicephalus*

(Des V. Whiteley. Photo Enschedé)

1966 (15 Feb). *Malawi Butterflies. T* **54** *and similar horiz designs.*
Multicoloured. P 13½.
247	4d. Type 54		80	10
248	9d. *Papilio desmondi* (*magdae*)		1·25	10
249	1s. 6d. *Epamera handmani*		1·75	30
250	3s. *Amauris crawshayi*		2·75	6·00
247/50		*Set of 4*	6·00	6·00
MS251	130×100 mm. Nos. 247/50		17·00	11·00

55 Cockerels

56 Burley Tobacco

57 *Cyrestis camillus* (butterfly)

(New values des V. Whiteley (1s. 6d.), M. Goaman (£2). Photo
Harrison)

1966–67. *As Nos.* 215 *etc. but W* **55** (*sideways on* ½d., 2d.), *and*
new values and designs (1s. 6d., £2). *P* 14½.
252	–	½d. reddish violet (1.4.66)	15	10
253	–	1d. black and green (1.4.66)	15	10
254	–	2d. light red-brown (4.6.66)*	15	10
255	–	3d. red-brn, yell-grn & bis-brn (4.3.67)*	20	10
256	–	6d. bluish violet, yell-grn & lt bl (2.7.66)*	1·50	50
257	48	9d. bistre-brown, green and yell (5.12.66)*	1·25	10
258	–	1s. brown, turquoise-bl & pale yell (1.4.66)	25	10
259	56	1s. 6d. chocolate & yellow-grn (15.11.66)	30	10
260	–	5s. blue, green, yellow & sepia (6.10.66)*	8·50	2·00
261	–	10s. green, orange-brown & blk (6.10.66)*	17·00	21·00
262	57	£2 black, orange-yellow, pale yellow and slate-violet (7.9.66)	25·00	24·00
252/62		*Set of 11*	45·00	42·00

*These are local dates of issue. The Crown Agents, in London,
did not distribute these printings until some time later.
No. 260 is inscribed "LAKE MALAWI".
The 2d. exists with both PVA gum and gum arabic.

58 British Central Africa   59 President Banda
6d. Stamp of 1891

(Des V. Whiteley. Photo Harrison)

1966 (4 May–10 June). *75th Anniv of Postal Services. W* **55**.
P 14½.
263	58	4d. grey-blue and yellow-green	10	10
264		9d. grey-blue and claret	15	10
265		1s. 6d. grey-blue and reddish lilac	20	10
266		3s. grey-blue and new blue	30	70
263/6		*Set of 4*	60	80
MS267	83 × 127 mm. Nos. 263/6 (10 June)		5·00	3·25

REPUBLIC

(Des M. Goaman. Photo Harrison)

1966 (6 July). *Republic Day. W* **55**. *P* 14 × 14½.
268	59	4d. brown, silver and emerald	10	10
269		9d. brown, silver and magenta	10	10
270		1s. 6d. brown, silver and violet	15	10
271		3s. brown, silver and blue	25	15
268/71		*Set of 4*	50	30
MS272	83 × 127 mm. Nos. 268/71		2·00	2·50

60 Bethlehem

(Des and photo Harrison)

1966 (12 Oct). *Christmas. W* **55**. *P* 14½.
273	60	4d. myrtle-green and gold	10	10
274		9d. brown-purple and gold	10	10
275		1s. 6d. orange-red and gold	15	10
276		3s. blue and gold	40	70
273/6		*Set of 4*	65	80

61 *Ilala I*

(Des Mrs. H. Breggar. Photo Harrison)

1967 (4 Jan). *Lake Malawi Steamers. T* **61** *and similar horiz*
designs. W **55**. *P* 14½.
277	4d. black, yellow and bright green		40	10
	a. Yellow omitted		†	£400
278	9d. black, yellow and magenta		45	10
279	1s. 6d., black, red and violet		65	20
280	3s. black, red and bright blue		1·25	1·75
277/80		*Set of 4*	2·50	1·90

Designs:—9d. *Dove*; 1s. 6d. *Chauncy Maples I* (wrongly inscr
"Chauncey"); 3s. *Gwendolen*.
No. 277a occurs on first day covers from Blantyre.

62 Golden Mbuna (female)

(Des R. Granger Barrett. Photo Enschedé)

1967 (3 May). *Lake Malawi Cichlids. T* **62** *and similar horiz designs. Multicoloured. W* **55** (*sideways*). *P* 12½×12.

281	4d. Type 62	.. ..	20	10
282	9d. Scraper-mouthed Mbuna	..	30	10
283	1s. 6d. Zebra Mbuna	.. ..	40	20
	a. Imperf (pair)		£120	
284	3s. Orange Mbuna	.. ..	1·25	1·75
	a. Imperf (pair)		£160	
281/4		*Set of 4*	1·90	1·90

63 Rising Sun and Gearwheel

(Des Jennifer Toombs. Litho D.L.R.)

1967 (5 July). *Industrial Development. P* 13½×13.

285	63	4d. black and emerald ..	10	10
286		9d. black and carmine ..	10	10
287		1s. 6d. black and reddish violet	10	10
288		3s. black and bright blue ..	15	15
285/8		*Set of 4*	30	30
MS289		134 × 108 mm. Nos. 285/8.	75	1·40

64 Mary and Joseph beside Crib

(Des Jennifer Toombs. Photo Harrison)

1967 (21 Nov–1 Dec). *Christmas. W* **55**. *P* 14 × 14½.

290	64	4d. royal blue and turquoise-green	10	10
291		9d. royal blue and light red	10	10
292		1s. 6d. royal blue and yellow ..	10	10
293		3s. royal blue and new blue ..	15	15
290/3		*Set of 4*	30	30
MS294		114 ×100 mm. Nos. 290/3. Wmk sideways. P 14 × 13½ (1 Dec)	1·00	2·50

65 *Calotropis procera*

(Des G. Drummond. Litho D.L.R.)

1968 (24 Apr). *Wild Flowers. T* **65** *and similar horiz designs. Multicoloured. W* **55** (*sideways*). *P* 13½ × 13.

295	4d. Type 65	.. ..	15	10
296	9d. *Borreria dibrachiata*	..	15	10
297	1s. 6d. *Hibiscus rhodanthus*..	15	10
298	3s. *Bidens pinnatipartita*	..	20	95
295/8		*Set of 4*	60	1·10
MS299	135 × 91 mm. Nos. 295/8.		1·25	2·75

66 Bagnall Steam Locomotive
No. 1, *Thistle*

(Des R. Granger Barrett. Photo Harrison)

1968 (24 July). *Malawi Locomotives. T* **66** *and similar horiz designs. W* **55**. *P* 14 × 14½.

300	4d. grey-green, slate-blue and red	40	10
301	9d. red, slate-blue and myrtle-green	50	15
302	1s. 6d. multicoloured	..	75	30
303	3s. multicoloured	..	1·40	3·00
300/3		*Set of 4*	2·75	3·00
MS304	120 × 88 mm. Nos. 300/3. P 14½.	3·00	6·00

Designs:—9d. Class G steam locomotive No. 49; 1s. 6d. Class "Zambesi" diesel locomotive No. 202; 3s. Diesel railcar No. DR1.

67 "The Nativity" (Piero della Francesca)

(Des and photo Harrison)

1968 (6 Nov). *Christmas. Paintings. T* **67** *and similar horiz designs. Multicoloured. W* **55** (*sideways on* 4d.). *P* 14 × 14½.

305	4d. Type 67	.. ..	10	10
306	9d. "The Adoration of the Shepherds" (Murillo)	..	10	10
307	1s. 6d. "The Adoration of the Shepherds" (Reni)	..	10	10
308	3s. "Nativity with God the Father and Holy Ghost" (Pittoni) ..	15	15
305/8		*Set of 4*	30	30
MS309	115 × 101 mm. Nos. 305/8. P 14 × 13½	35	1·40

68 Scarlet-chested Sunbird   **69** Nyasa Lovebird

70 Carmine Bee Eater

(Des V. Whiteley. Photo Harrison)

1968 (13 Nov). *Birds. T* **68/70** *and similar designs. Multicoloured. W* **55** (*sideways on* 1d. *to* 4d. *and* 3s. *to* £1). *P* 14½.

310	1d. Type 68	.. ..	15	10
311	2d. Violet Starling	..	15	10
312	3d. White-browed Robin Chat	20	10
313	4d. Red-billed Fire Finch	..	35	40
	a. Red omitted		†	—
314	6d. Type 69	.. ..	45	15
315	9d. Yellow-rumped Bishop	50	60
316	1s. Type 70	.. ..	60	15
317	1s. 6d. Grey-headed Bush Shrike	5·00	8·00
318	2s. Paradise Whydah	..	5·00	8·00
319	3s. African Paradise Flycatcher ..	4·50	4·50
320	5s. Bateleur	.. ..	7·00	4·25
321	10s. Saddle-bill Stork	..	5·50	7·50
322	£1 Purple Heron	..	10·00	18·00
323	£2 Knysna Turaco ("Livingstone's Loerie")	42·00	48·00
310/23		*Set of 14*	70·00	85·00

Sizes:—2d. to 4d. as T **68**; 9d. as T **69**; 1s. 6d., 2s, £2 as T **70**; 3s. to £1 as T **70** but vertical.

No. 310 exists in coils, constructed from normal sheets.

An example of No. 313a is known used on local cover from Limbe in September 1970.

71 I.L.O. Emblem

(Des G. Drummond. Photo, emblem die-stamped Harrison)

1969 (5 Feb). *50th Anniv of the International Labour Organization. W* **55** (*sideways on No.* **MS328**). *P* 14.

324	71	4d. gold and myrtle-green	..	10	10
325		9d. gold and chocolate	..	10	10
326		1s. 6d. gold and blackish brown	..	10	10
327		3s. gold and indigo	..	15	15
324/7		*Set of 4*	30	30
MS328		127 × 89 mm. Nos. 324/7 ..	1·25	4·75

72 White-fringed Ground Orchid   **73** African Development Bank Emblem

(Des J.W. Litho B.W.)

1969 (9 July). *Orchids of Malawi. T* **72** *and similar horiz designs. Multicoloured. W* **55**. *P* 13½ × 13.

329	4d. Type 72	.. ..	15	10
330	9d. Red Ground orchid	..	20	10
331	1s. 6d. Leopard Tree orchid	..	30	20
332	3s. Blue Ground orchid	..	60	2·00
329/32		*Set of 4*	1·10	2·00
MS333	118 × 86 mm. Nos. 329/32 ..	1·10	3·50

(Des G. Vasarhelyi. Litho D.L.R.)

1969 (10 Sept). *Fifth Anniv of African Development Bank. W* **55**. *P* 14.

334	73	4d. yellow, yellow-ochre and chocolate	10	10
335		9d. yellow, yellow-ochre & myrtle-green	10	10
336		1s. 6d. yellow, yell-ochre & blackish brn	10	10
337		3s. yellow, yellow-ochre and indigo	15	15
334/7		*Set of 4*	30	30
MS338		102 × 137 mm. Nos. 334/7	50	90

74 Dove over Bethlehem   **75** *Zonocerus elegans* (grasshopper)

(Des Jennifer Toombs. Photo Harrison)

1969 (5 Nov). *Christmas. W* **55**. *P* 14½ × 14.

339	74	2d. black and olive-yellow	..	10	10
340		4d. black and deep turquoise	..	10	10
341		9d. black and scarlet	..	10	10
342		1s. 6d. black & deep bluish violet	..	10	10
343		3s. black and ultramarine	..	15	15
339/43		*Set of 5*	30	30
MS344		130 × 71 mm. Nos. 339/43	..	1·00	1·75
		a. Ultramarine (background of 3s.) omitted	£475	

(Des V. Whiteley. Litho Format)

1970 (4 Feb). *Insects of Malawi. T* **75** *and similar vert designs. Multicoloured. W* **55**. *P* 14.

345	4d. Type 75	.. ..	15	10
346	9d. *Mylabris dicincta* (beetle)	15	10
347	1s. 6d. *Henosepilachna elaterii* (ladybird)	20	10
348	3s. *Sphodromantis speculabunda* (mantid)	35	45
345/8		*Set of 4*	75	55
MS349	86×137 mm. Nos. 345/8 ..	1·25	2·25

Rand Easter Show 1970

(76)

1970 (18 Mar). *Rand Easter Show. No.* 317 *optd with T* **76**.

350	1s. 6d. multicoloured	..	50	1·75

77 Runner

(Des J. Cooter. Litho B.W.)

1970 (3 June). *Ninth British Commonwealth Games, Edinburgh. W* **55**. *P* 13.

351	77	4d. royal blue and blue-green ..	10	10
352		9d. royal blue and carmine	..	10	10
353		1s. 6d. royal blue and dull yellow	10	10
354		3s. royal blue and new blue ..	15	15
351/4		*Set of 4*	30	30
MS355		146 × 96 mm. Nos. 351/4 ..	55	90

(New Currency, 100 tambalas = 1 kwacha)

10t (78)   **79** *Aegocera trimeni*

1970 (2 Sept). *Decimal Currency. Nos.* 316 *and* 318 *surch as T* **78**.

356	10 t. on 1s. multicoloured	..	1·75	25
	a. Surch double		†	
357	20 t. on 2s. multicoloured	..	2·25	2·50

(Des R. Granger Barrett. Litho B.W.)

1970 (30 Sept). *Moths. T 79 and similar horiz designs. Multi-coloured.* W 55. *P* 11 × 11½.

358	4d.	Type 79		20	10
359	9d.	*Faidherbia bauhiniae*		30	10
360	1s. 6d.	*Parasa karschi*		50	20
361	3s.	*Teracotona euprepia*		1·25	3·25
358/61			Set of 4	2·00	3·25
MS362	112×92 mm. Nos. 358/61			4·00	4·50

80 Mother and Child

3ot Special United Kingdom Delivery Service (81)

(Des Brother W. Meyer. Litho J.W.)

1970 (4 Nov). *Christmas.* W 55 *(sideways).* P 14.

363	80	2d. black and light yellow		10	10
364		4d. black and emerald		10	10
365		9d. black and orange-red		10	10
366		1s. 6d. black and light purple		10	10
367		3s. black and blue		15	15
363/7			Set of 5	30	30
MS368	166 × 100 mm. Nos. 363/7			1·00	2·00

1971 (8 Feb). *No. 319 surch with T 81.*

369		30 t. on 3s. multicoloured		50	2·00

No. 369 was issued for use on letters carried by an emergency airmail service from Malawi to Great Britain during the British postal strike. The fee of 30 t. was to cover the charge for delivery by a private service, and ordinary stamps to pay the normal airmail fee had to be affixed as well.

The strike ended on 8 March, when private delivery services were withdrawn.

82 Decimal Coinage and Cockerel

(Des V. Whiteley. Litho Format)

1971 (15 Feb). *Decimal Coinage.* W 55 *(sideways).* P 14.

370	82	3 t. multicoloured		15	10
371		8 t. multicoloured		20	10
372		15 t. multicoloured		25	20
373		30 t. multicoloured		35	1·50
370/3			Set of 4	85	1·60
MS374	140 × 101 mm. Nos. 370/73			1·00	1·75

83 Greater Kudu   84 Eland

(Des and litho J.W.)

1971 (15 Feb)–75. *Decimal Currency. Antelopes. Vert designs as T 83 (1 t. to 8 t.), or T 84 (others). Multicoloured.* W 55 *(sideways* on 1 t. to 8 t.). P* 13½×14 (1 t to 8 t.) or 14½ *(others).*

375		1 t. Type 83		10	10
	a.	Coil stamp. P 14½×14		15	40
	b.	Perf 14† (*wmk cockerel facing right*) (12.11.74)		45	70
376		2 t. Nyala		15	10
	w.	Wmk cockerel facing right (5.2.75)		30	30
377		3 t. Mountain Reedbuck		20	50
	a.	Perf 14† (*wmk cockerel facing right*) (12.11.74)		65	90
378		5 t. Puku		40	75
	a.	Perf 14† (*wmk cockerel facing right*) (12.11.74)		65	1·25
379		8 t. Impala		45	60
380		10 t. Type 84		60	10
381		15 t. Klipspringer		1·00	20
	w.	Wmk inverted		†	£180
382		20 t. Suni		1·50	90
383		30 t. Roan Antelope		8·00	90
384		50 t. Waterbuck		90	65
	w.	Wmk inverted (9.5.73)		90	75
385		1 k. Bushbuck		1·50	85
386		2 k. Red Forest Duiker		2·75	1·50
387		4 k. Common Duiker		20·00	18·00
375/87			Set of 13	32·00	22·00

*The normal sideways watermark shows the cockerel's head facing left *as seen from the back of the stamp.*

†These actually gauge 14.2×14 instead of 13.7×14 and are line-perforated, which in blocks they can easily be distinguished as in alternate rows across the sheet the horizontal perfs have two holes where they cross the vertical perfs.

No. 387 is incorrectly inscr "Gray Duiker".

---

85 Christ on the Cross   87 *Holarrhena febrifuga*

(Des G. Drummond. Litho Questa)

1971 (7 Apr). *Easter. Details from Painting "The Small Passion" by Dürer. T 85 and similar vert design.* W 55. *P* 13½.

388		3 t. black and green		10	20
	a.	Pair. Nos. 388/9		10	40
389		3 t. black and green		10	20
390		8 t. black and orange-red		10	20
	a.	Pair. Nos. 390/1		15	40
391		8 t. black and orange-red		10	20
392		15 t. black and violet		20	30
	a.	Pair. Nos. 392/3		40	60
393		15 t. black and violet		20	30
394		30 t. black and bright blue		25	45
	a.	Pair. Nos. 394/5		50	90
395		30 t. black and bright blue		25	45
388/95			Set of 8	95	2·00
MS396	Two sheets each 95 × 145 mm (a) Nos. 388, 390, 392 and 394; (b) Nos. 389, 391, 393 and 395			2·00	3·50

Designs:—Nos. 388, 390, 392 and 394, Type 85; Nos. 389, 391, 393 and 395, The Resurrection.

Nos. 388/9, 390/1, 392/3 and 394/5 were each printed together, se-tenant, in pairs throughout the sheet.

(Des G. Drummond. Litho J.W.)

1971 (14 July). *Flowering Shrubs and Trees. T 87 and similar vert designs. Multicoloured.* W 55. *P* 14.

397		3 t. Type 87		10	10
398		8 t. *Brachystegia spiciformis*		15	10
399		15 t. *Securidaca longepedunculata*		25	10
400		30 t. *Pterocarpus rotundifolius*		40	50
397/400			Set of 4	80	55
MS401	102 × 135 mm. Nos. 397/400			1·40	2·00

88 Drum Major   89 "Madonna and Child" (William Dyce)

(Des J.W. Litho Questa)

1971 (5 Oct). *50th Anniv of Malawi Police Force.* W 55. *P* 14 × 14½.

402	88	30 t. multicoloured		65	1·25

(Des J. Cooter. Litho Format)

1971 (10 Nov). *Christmas. T 89 and similar vert designs. Multicoloured.* W 55. *P* 14½.

403		3 t. Type 89		10	10
404		8 t. "The Holy Family" (M. Schöngauer)		15	10
405		15 t. "The Holy Family with St. John" (Raphael)		20	20
406		30 t. "The Holy Family" (Bronzino)		50	1·40
403/6			Set of 4	85	1·50
MS407	101 × 139 mm. Nos. 403/6			1·10	2·50

90 Vickers Viscount 700

(Des R. Granger Barrett. Litho Questa)

1972 (9 Feb). *Air. Malawi Aircraft. T 90 and similar horiz designs. Multicoloured.* W 55 *(sideways).* P 13½.

408		3 t. Type 90		30	10
409		8 t. Hawker Siddeley H.S.748		50	10
410		15 t. Britten Norman Islander		75	30
411		30 t. B.A.C. One Eleven		1·25	2·25
408/11			Set of 4	2·50	2·50
MS412	143×94 mm. Nos. 408/11			8·00	5·50

---

91 Figures (Chencherere Hill)   92 Boxing

(Des R. Granger Barrett. Litho Format)

1972 (10 May). *Rock Paintings. T 91 and similar horiz designs.* W 55 *(sideways). P* 13½.

413		3 t. apple-green, grey-green and black		35	10
414		8 t. red, grey and black		45	10
415		15 t. multicoloured		55	30
416		30 t. multicoloured		65	1·00
413/16			Set of 4	1·75	1·25
MS417	121 × 97 mm. Nos. 413/16. P 15			2·75	2·75

Designs:—8 t. Lizard and cat (Chencherere Hill); 15 t. Schematics (Diwa Hill); 30 t. Sun through rain (Mikolongwe Hill).

(Des local artist. Litho Harrison)

1972 (9 Aug). *Olympic Games, Munich.* W 55 *(sideways). P* 14 × 14½.

418	92	3 t. multicoloured		10	10
419		8 t. multicoloured		15	10
420		15 t. multicoloured		20	10
421		30 t. multicoloured		35	45
418/21			Set of 4	70	55
MS422	110 × 92 mm. Nos. 418/21. P 14 × 13½			1·25	1·75

93 Arms of Malawi   94 "Adoration of the Kings" (Orcagna)

(Des G. Drummond. Litho Questa)

1972 (20 Oct). *Commonwealth Parliamentary Conference.* W 55. *P* 13½.

423	93	15 t. multicoloured		30	35

(Des V. Whiteley. Litho Questa)

1972 (8 Nov). *Christmas. T 94 and similar vert designs. Multi-coloured.* W 55. *P* 14½ × 14.

424		3 t. Type 94		10	10
425		8 t. "Madonna and Child Enthroned" (Florentine School)		10	10
426		15 t. "Virgin and Child" (Crivelli)		20	10
427		30 t. "Virgin and Child with St. Anne" (Flemish School)		45	70
424/7			Set of 4	70	80
MS428	95 × 121 mm. Nos. 424/7			1·10	2·00

"MALAŴI". All issues from No. 429 onwards have a circumflex accent over the "W", to give the correct pronunciation of "Malavi".

95 *Charaxes bohemani*

(Des PAD Studio. Litho Questa)

1973 (7 Feb–5 Apr). *Butterflies. T 95 and similar horiz designs. Multicoloured.* W 55 *(sideways). P* 13½ × 14.

429		3 t. Type 95		30	10
430		8 t. *Uranothauma crawshayi*		55	10
431		15 t. *Charaxes acuminatus*		75	30
432		30 t. *Amauris ansorgei* (inscr in error "EUPHAEDRA ZADDACHI")		3·50	7·50
433		30 t. *Amauris ansorgei* (inscr corrected) (5 Apr)		3·00	7·50
429/33			Set of 5	7·25	14·00
MS434	145×95 mm. Nos. 429/32			7·00	11·50

---

96 Livingstone and Map

(Des J.W. Litho Format)

1973 (1 May). *Death Centenary of David Livingstone (1st issue).*
W 55 (*sideways*). *P* 13½ × 14.
435	96	3 t. multicoloured		..	10	10
436		8 t. multicoloured		..	15	10
437		15 t. multicoloured		..	20	10
438		30 t. multicoloured		..	35	60
435/8			*Set of 4*		70	70
MS439		144 × 95 mm. Nos. 435/8 ..			90	1·50

See also Nos. 450/**MS**451.

97 Thumb Dulcitone

(Des Jennifer Toombs. Litho Questa)

1973 (8 Aug). *Musical Instruments. T 97 and similar multi-coloured designs.* W 55 (*sideways on 8, 15 t. and* **MS**444). *P* 14.
440		3 t. Type 97		..	10	10
441		8 t. Hand zither (*vert*)		..	15	10
442		15 t. Hand drum (*vert*).		..	25	10
443		30 t. One-stringed fiddle		..	45	60
440/3			*Set of 4*		85	65
MS444		120 × 103 mm. Nos. 440/3		..	2·75	2·00

98 The Magi

(Des J.W. Litho Format)

1973 (7 Nov). *Christmas.* W 55 (*sideways*). *P* 13½.
445	98	3 t. greenish blue, dp lilac & dull ultram			10	10
446		8 t. salmon-red, bluish lilac & red-brn			10	10
447		15 t. reddish mve, greenish bl & dp mve			15	10
448		30 t. orange-yell, bluish lilac & lt lake-brn			30	70
445/8			*Set of 4*		50	75
MS449		165 × 114 mm. Nos. 445/8		..	75	1·40

99 Stained-glass Window, Livingstonia Mission

(Des PAD Studio. Litho Questa)

1973 (12 Dec). *Death Centenary of David Livingstone (2nd issue).*
W 55 (*sideways*). *P* 13½.
450	99	50 t. multicoloured		..	45	1·00
MS451		71 × 77 mm. No. 450		..	80	1·60

100 Large-mouthed Black Bass

(Des Sylvia Goaman. Litho Questa)

1974 (20 Feb). *35th Anniv of Malawi Angling Society. T 100 and similar horiz designs. Multicoloured.* W 55 (*sideways*). *P* 14.
452		3 t. Type 100		..	25	10
453		8 t. Rainbow Trout		..	30	10
454		15 t. Silver Alestes ("Lake Salmon")			55	20
455		30 t. Tigerfish		..	85	1·25
452/5			*Set of 4*		1·75	1·40
MS456		169 × 93 mm. Nos. 452/5		..	2·50	2·00

101 U.P.U. Monument and Map of Africa

(Des J. Cooter. Litho J.W.)

1974 (24 Apr). *Centenary of Universal Postal Union.* W 55 (*sideways*). *P* 13½ (*Nos. 460/**MS**461*) or 14½ × 14 (*others*).
457	101	3 t. green and ochre		..	10	10
		a. Perf 13½ (pair)		..	£200	
458		8 t. red and ochre		..	10	10
459		15 t. violet and ochre		..	15	10
460		30 t. indigo and ochre		..	30	70
457/60			*Set of 4*		60	80
MS461		115 × 146 mm. Nos. 457/60			65	1·75

No. 457a comes from normal sheets and not No. **MS**461. It can
also be identified as a marginal single.

102 Capital Hill, Lilongwe

(Des PAD Studio. Litho Questa)

1974 (3 July). *Tenth Anniv of Independence.* W 55 (*sideways*).
P 14.
462	102	3 t. multicoloured		..	10	10
463		8 t. multicoloured		..	10	10
464		15 t. multicoloured		..	10	10
465		30 t. multicoloured		..	25	35
462/5			*Set of 4*		40	40
MS466		120 × 86 mm. Nos. 462/5 ..			45	1·00

103 "Madonna of the Meadow"   104 Arms of
(Bellini)   Malawi

(Des Jennifer Toombs. Litho Enschedé)

1974 (4 Dec). *Christmas. T 103 and similar horiz designs. Multi-coloured.* W 55 (*sideways*). *P* 13 × 13½.
467	103	3 t. Type 103		..	10	10
468		8 t. "The Holy Family with Sts. John and Elizabeth" (Jordaens)			10	10
469		15 t. "The Nativity" (Pieter de Grebber)			15	10
470		30 t. "Adoration of the Shepherds" (Lorenzo di Credi)			30	50
467/70			*Set of 4*		50	50
MS471		163 × 107 mm. Nos. 467/70			60	1·25

(Des and litho Harrison)

1975 (1 Feb)–84. *Coil stamps.* W 55 (*sideways*). *P* 14½ × 14.
472	104	3 t. deep blue		..	20	40
472a		5 t. bright carmine (20.9.84)			50	1·40

105 African Snipe   106 Spur-winged Goose

(Des J.W. Litho Questa)

1975 (19 Feb). *Birds. T 105/6 and similar multicoloured designs.*
W 55 (*sideways on 2, 3, 8, 50 t., 1 k., 4 k.). White, ordinary paper.*

(a) *Size as T 105. P* 13½ × 14 (1, 5 t.) *or* 14 × 13½ (*others*)
473		1 t. Type 105		..	30	1·50
474		2 t. Double-banded Sandgrouse			50	1·50
475		3 t. Blue Quail		..	1·50	1·50
476		5 t. Bare-throated Francolin..			3·50	1·25
477		8 t. Harlequin Quail ..		..	4·75	1·00

(b) *Size as T 106. P* 14
478		10 t. Type 106		..	8·50	50
479		15 t. Barrow's Bustard		..	3·75	3·75
480		20 t. Comb Duck		..	1·00	2·25
481		30 t. Helmet Guineafowl		..	1·25	70
482		50 t. African Pigmy Goose ..			2·00	1·60
483		1 k. Garganey		..	3·00	7·50
484		2 k. White-faced Whistling Duck			13·00	15·00
485		4 k. African Green Pigeon			13·00	16·00
473/85			*Set of 13*		50·00	45·00

See also Nos. 501/4.

107 M.V. *Mpasa*   108 *Habenaria splendens*

(Des R. Granger Barrett. Litho J.W.)

1975 (12 Mar). *Ships of Lake Malawi (1st series). T 107 and
similar horiz designs. Multicoloured.* W 55 (*sideways*). *P* 13½.
486		3 t. Type 107 ..		..	30	10
487		8 t. M.V. *Ilala II*		..	40	10
488		15 t. M.V. *Chauncy Maples II*		..	75	30
489		30 t. M.V. *Nkwazi*		..	40	50
486/9			*Set of 4*		2·25	2·75
MS490		105 × 142 mm. Nos. 486/9. *P* 14			2·25	3·50

See also Nos. 728/32.

(Des Sylvia Goaman. Litho Questa)

1975 (6 June). *Malawi Orchids. T 108 and similar vert designs.
Multicoloured.* W 55. *P* 14.
491		3 t. Type 108 ..		..	40	10
492		10 t. *Eulophia cucullata*		..	50	10
493		20 t. *Disa welwitschii*		..	80	25
494		40 t. *Angraecum conchiferum*..			1·10	1·50
491/4			*Set of 4*		2·50	1·75
MS495		127 × 111 mm. Nos. 491/4		..	7·00	6·50

109 Thick-tailed Bushbaby   (110)

(Des R. Granger Barrett. Litho Walsall)

1975 (3 Sept). *Malawi Animals. T 109 and similar vert designs.
Multicoloured.* W 55 (*inverted*). *P* 14.
496		3 t. Type 109..		..	10	10
497		10 t. Leopard		..	35	10
498		20 t. Roan Antelope ..			55	35
499		40 t. Common Zebra ..			1·00	2·75
496/9			*Set of 4*		1·75	3·00
MS500		88 × 130 mm. Nos. 496/9. W 55 (*sideways*)			2·50	3·00

1975 (1 Oct). *As Nos. 473 etc, but no wmk. Toned, chalk-surfaced
paper.*
501		3 t. Blue Quail		..	3·00	1·25
502		10 t. Type 106		..	2·00	1·25
503		15 t. Barrow's Bustard		..	2·00	1·75
504		2 k. White-faced Whistling Duck			5·00	9·50
501/4			*Set of 4*		11·00	12·50

Nos. 505/13 vacant.

1975 (9 Dec). *Tenth Africa, Caribbean and Pacific Ministerial
Conference. No. 482 optd with T 110.*
514		50 t. African Pygmy Goose		..	1·00	2·00

111 "A Castle with the Adoration   112 Alexander Graham
of the Magi"   Bell

(Des PAD Studio. Litho J.W.)

1975 (12 Dec). *Christmas. T **111** and similar horiz designs showing religious medallions. Multicoloured. W **55** (sideways). P 13 × 13½.*

515	3 t.	Type **111**	10	10
516	10 t.	"The Nativity"	15	10
517	20 t.	"The Adoration of the Magi"	20	10
518	40 t.	"The Angel appearing to the Shepherds"	50	1·90
515/18		*Set of 4*	80	1·90
MS519	98 × 168 mm. Nos. 515/18. P 14		1·50	2·75

(Des C. Abbott. Litho Questa)

1976 (24 Mar). *Centenary of the Telephone. W **55**. P 14.*

520	112	3 t. black and dull green	10	10
		w. Wmk inverted	6·00	
521		10 t. black and magenta	10	10
522		20 t. black and light reddish violet	20	10
523		40 t. black and bright blue	50	90
520/3		*Set of 4*	80	1·00
MS524	137×114 mm. Nos. 520/3		1·10	1·75

113 President Banda

114 Bagnall Diesel Shunter No. 100

(Des PAD Studio. Litho J.W.)

1976 (2 July). *Tenth Anniv of the Republic. Multicoloured; frame colour given. W **55**. P 13.*

525	113	3 t. green	10	10
526		10 t. magenta	10	10
527		20 t. new blue	20	10
528		40 t. dull ultramarine	50	90
525/8		*Set of 4*	80	1·00
MS529	102 × 112 mm. Nos. 524/8. P 13½		95	1·75

(Des G. Drummond. Litho Questa)

1976 (1 Oct). *Malawi Locomotives. T **114** and similar horiz designs. Multicoloured. W **55** (sideways). P 14½ × 14.*

530	3 t.	Type **114**	40	10
531	10 t.	Class "Shire" diesel locomotive No. 503	70	10
532	20 t.	Nippon Sharyo diesel-hydraulic loco-motive No. 301	1·40	45
533	40 t.	Hunslet diesel-hydraulic locomotive No. 110	2·10	4·75
530/3		*Set of 4*	4·25	4·75
MS534	130×118 mm. Nos. 530/3		4·25	4·75

Blantyre Mission Centenary 1876-1976

(115)

116 Child on Bed of Straw

1976 (22 Oct). *Centenary of Blantyre Mission. Nos. 503 and 481 optd with T **115**.*

535	15 t. Barrow's Bustard		1·25	1·00
536	30 t. Helmet Guineafowl		1·50	2·50

(Des Jennifer Toombs. Litho Walsall)

1976 (6 Dec). *Christmas. W **55**. P 14.*

537	116	3 t. multicoloured	10	10
538		10 t. multicoloured	10	10
539		20 t. multicoloured	20	10
540		40 t. multicoloured	40	60
537/40		*Set of 4*	70	70
MS541	135 × 95 mm. Nos. 537/40		1·40	1·75

117 Man and Woman

118 Chileka Airport

(Des G. Hutchins. Litho Questa)

1977 (1 Apr). *Handicrafts. T **117** and similar multicoloured designs showing wood-carvings. W **55** (sideways on 10 and 20 t.). P 14.*

542	4 t.	Type **117**	10	10
543	10 t.	Elephant (horiz)	15	10
544	20 t.	Rhino (horiz)	20	10
545	40 t.	Deer	50	70
542/5		*Set of 4*	80	80
MS546	153 × 112 mm. Nos. 542/5. Wmk sideways		1·50	2·25

(Des Harrison. Litho Walsall)

1977 (12 July). *Transport. T **118** and similar horiz designs. Multi-coloured. W **55** (sideways). P 14½ × 14.*

547	4 t.	Type **118**	40	10
548	10 t.	Blantyre-Lilongwe Road	40	10
549	20 t.	M.V. *Ilala II*	1·25	35
550	40 t.	Blantyre-Nacala rail line	2·00	4·00
547/50		*Set of 4*	3·50	4·00
MS551	127 × 83 mm. Nos. 547/50		3·50	4·00

119 Blue-grey Mbuna

120 "Madonna and Child with St. Catherine and the Blessed Stefano Maconi" (Borgognone)

(Des R. Granger Barrett. Litho J.W.)

1997 (4 Oct). *Fish of Lake Malawi. T **119** and similar horiz designs. Multicoloured. P 13½.* A. *No wmk*

552A	4 t.	Type **119**	50	10
553A	10 t.	Livingston's Mbuna	60	10
554A	20 t.	Zebra Mbuna	1·40	30
555A	40 t.	Malawi Scale-eater	1·40	1·75
552A/5A		*Set of 4*	3·50	1·90
MS556A	147×99 mm. Nos. 552A/5A. P 13		3·00	4·00

B. *W **55** (sideways)*

552B	4 t.	Type **119**	30	10
553B	10 t.	Livingston's Mbuna	40	20
554B	20 t.	Zebra Mbuna	1·50	
555B	40 t.	Malawi Scale-eater	1·25	95
MS556B	147×99 mm. Nos. 552B/5B. P 13		5·00	7·00

(Des G. Hutchins. Litho Enschedé)

1977 (21 Nov). *Christmas. T **120** and similar vert designs. Multi-coloured; frame colours given. No wmk. P 14 × 13½.*

557	4 t.	deep blue-green	10	10
558	10 t.	light vermilion	10	10
559	20 t.	dull violet	20	10
560	40 t.	blue	50	70
557/60		*Set of 4*	2·50	2·50
MS561	150 × 116 mm. Nos. 557/60		2·50	2·50

Designs:—10 t. "Madonna and Child with the Eternal Father and Angels" (Borgognone); 20 t. Bottigella altarpiece (detail, Foppa); 40 t. "Madonna of the Fountain" (van Eyck).

121 "Entry of Christ into Jerusalem" (Giotto)

122 Nyala

(Des G. Hutchins. Litho Cartor)

1978 (1 Mar). *Easter. T **121** and similar vert designs showing paintings by Giotto. Multicoloured. P 12×12½.*

562	4 t.	Type **121**	10	10
563	10 t.	"The Crucifixion"	15	10
564	20 t.	"Descent from the Cross"	30	10
565	40 t.	"Jesus appears before Mary"	50	55
562/5		*Set of 4*	90	70
MS566	150 × 99 mm. Nos. 562/5		1·90	1·60

(Des G. Hutchins. Litho Enschedé)

1978 (1 June). *Wildlife. T **122** and similar multicoloured designs. P 13½ × 13 (4, 40 t.) or 13 × 13½ (others).*

567	4 t.	Type **122**	1·25	10
568	10 t.	Lion (horiz)	3·50	30
569	20 t.	Common Zebra (horiz)	6·50	80
570	40 t.	Mountain Reedbuck	8·00	5·50
567/70		*Set of 4*	17·00	6·00
MS571	173×113 mm. Nos. 567/70		23·00	8·50

123 Malamulo Seventh Day Adventist Church

124 Vanilla polylepis

(Des and litho Walsall)

1978 (15 Nov). *Christmas. Churches. T **123** and similar horiz designs. Multicoloured. W **55** (sideways). P 13½.*

572	4 t.	Type **123**	10	10
573	10 t.	Likoma Cathedral	10	10
574	20 t.	St. Michael's and All Angels', Blantyre	20	10
575	40 t.	Zomba Catholic Cathedral	40	60
572/5		*Set of 4*	70	70
MS576	190 × 105 mm. Nos. 572/5		70	1·50

(Des G. Drummond. Litho J.W.)

1979 (2 Jan)–82. *Orchids. Vert designs as T **124**. Multi-coloured. W **55**. P 13½.*

577	1 t.	Type **124**	50	30
578	2 t.	Cirrhopetalum umbellatum	50	30
		w. Wmk inverted	7·50	
579	5 t.	Calanthe natalensis	50	10
580	7 t.	Ansellia gigantea	50	50
581	8 t.	Tridactyle bicaudata	50	30
582	10 t.	Acampe pachyglossa	50	10
		w. Wmk inverted (14.6.82)	60	20
583	15 t.	Eulophia quartiniana	50	15
584	20 t.	Cyrtorchis arcuata (variabilis)	50	50
		w. Wmk inverted		
585	30 t.	Eulophia tricristata	1·25	30
586	50 t.	Disa hamatopetala	85	50
587	75 t.	Cynorchis glandulosa	2·00	4·25
588	1 k.	Aerangis kotschyana	1·60	1·25
589	1 k. 50,	Polystachya dendrobiiflora	1·75	2·75
590	2 k.	Disa ornithantha	1·75	2·00
591	4 k.	Cyrtorchis praetermissa	3·00	3·50
577/91		*Set of 15*	14·50	15·00

125 Tsamba

126 Train crossing Viaduct

(Des L. Curtis. Litho Questa)

1979 (21 Jan). *National Tree Planting Day. T **125** and similar vert designs. Multicoloured. W **55**. P 13½.*

592	5 t.	Type **125**	20	10
593	10 t.	Mulanje Cedar	25	10
594	20 t.	Mlombwa	40	20
595	40 t.	Mbawa	70	2·25
592/5		*Set of 4*	1·40	2·25
MS596	118 × 153 mm. Nos. 592/5		1·40	2·25

(Des J.W. Litho Questa)

1979 (17 Feb). *Opening of Salima–Lilongwe Railway. T **126** and similar horiz designs. Multicoloured. W **55** (sideways) (5 t.) or no wmk (others). P 14½.*

597	5 t.	Type **126**	25	10
598	10 t.	Diesel railcar at station	40	10
599	20 t.	Diesel train rounding bend	60	30
600	40 t.	Diesel train passing through cutting	85	1·25
597/600		*Set of 4*	1·90	1·50
MS601	153×103 mm. Nos. 597/600. W **55** (sideways)		4·00	4·50

Examples of an unissued 4 t. value as Type **126** and of a miniature sheet containing this 4 t. value exist from supplies sent to Malawi before it was decided to increase the internal postage rate to 5 t.

127 Young Child

(Des BG Studio. Litho Questa)

1979 (10 July). *International Year of the Child. T **127** and similar horiz designs showing young children. Multicoloured; back-ground colours given. W **55** (sideways). P 13½.*

602	5 t.	green	10	10
603	10 t.	red	10	10
604	20 t.	mauve	25	10
605	40 t.	blue	45	80
602/5		*Set of 4*	75	90

128 1964 3d. Independence Commemorative Stamp

(Des J.W. Litho Enschedé)

1979 (17 Sept). *Death Centenary of Sir Rowland Hill. T* **128** *and similar horiz designs showing 1964 Independence commemorative stamps. Multicoloured. W* **55** *(sideways*).* P 13×13½.*

606	5 t. Type **128**	..	10	10
607	10 t. 6d. value	..	10	10
	w. Wmk cockerel facing right	..	3·00	
608	20 t. 1s. 3d. value	..	20	10
609	40 t. 2s. 6d. value	..	35	60
606/9		*Set of 4*	65	70
MS610	163×108mm. Nos. 606/9		75	1·40

*The normal sideways watermark has the cockerel facing left, as seen from the back of the stamp.

129 River Landscape

130 Limbe Rotary Club Emblem

(Des BG Studio. Litho Format)

1979 (15 Nov). *Christmas. T* **129** *and similar horiz designs showing landscapes. Multicoloured. W* **55** *(sideways). P 13½ × 14.*

611	5 t. Type **129**	..	10	10
612	10 t. Sunset	..	10	10
613	20 t. Forest and hill	..	25	15
614	40 t. Plain and mountain	..	50	2·00
611/14		*Set of 4*	85	2·00

(Des L. Curtis. Litho J.W.)

1980 (23 Feb). *75th Anniv of Rotary International. T* **130** *and similar vert designs. W* **55**. *P 13½.*

615	5 t. multicoloured	..	10	10
616	10 t. multicoloured	..	10	10
617	20 t. multicoloured	..	30	15
618	40 t. ultramarine and gold	..	75	1·60
615/18		*Set of 4*	1·10	1·75
MS619	105 × 144 mm. Nos. 615/18. P 14 × 14½.		1·25	2·25

Designs:—10 t. Blantyre Rotary Club pennant; 20 t. Lilongwe Rotary Club pennant; 40 t. Rotary International emblem.

131 Mangochi District Post Office

132 Agate Nodule

(Des C. Abbott. Litho Walsall)

1980 (6 May). *"London 1980" International Stamp Exhibition. T* **131** *and similar horiz designs. W* **55** *(sideways). P 14½ × 14.*

620	5 t. black and blue-green	..	10	10
621	10 t. black and vermilion	..	10	10
622	20 t. black and violet	..	15	10
623	1 k. black and deep blue	..	65	1·10
620/3		*Set of 4*	80	1·10
MS624	114 × 89 mm. Nos. 620/3.		1·25	2·25

Designs:–10 t. New Blantyre Sorting Office; 20 t. Mail Transfer Hut, Walala; 1 k. First Nyasaland Post Office, Chiromo.

(Des G. Drummond. Litho J.W.)

1980 (20 Aug). *Gemstones. T* **132** *and similar vert designs. Multi-coloured. W* **55**. *P 13.*

625	5 t. Type **132**	..	60	10
626	10 t. Sunstone	..	80	10
627	20 t. Smoky Quartz	..	1·40	30
628	1 k. Kyanite crystal	..	3·50	6·00
625/8		*Set of 4*	5·75	6·00

133 Elephants

134 Suni

(Des C. Abbott. Litho J.W.)

1980 (10 Nov). *Christmas. Children's Paintings. T* **133** *and similar horiz designs. Multicoloured. W* **55** *(sideways). P 13.*

629	5 t. Type **133**	..	40	10
630	10 t. Flowers	..	30	10
631	20 t. Class "Shire" diesel train	..	75	20
632	1 k. Malachite Kingfisher	..	1·60	2·00
629/32		*Set of 4*	2·75	2·25

(Des G. Drummond. Litho Questa)

1981 (4 Feb). *Wildlife. T* **134** *and similar horiz designs. Multi-coloured. W* **55** *(sideways). P 14.*

633	7 t. Type **134**	..	15	10
634	10 t. Blue Duiker	..	20	10
635	20 t. African Buffalo	..	30	15
636	1 k. Lichtenstein's Hartebeest	..	1·25	1·60
633/6		*Set of 4*	1·75	1·75

135 "Kanjedza II" Standard "A" Earth Station

(Des L. Curtis. Litho Harrison)

1981 (24 Apr). *International Communications. T* **135** *and similar horiz designs. Multicoloured. W* **55** *(sideways). P 14½.*

637	7 t. Type **135**	..	10	10
638	10 t. Blantyre International Gateway Exchange		15	10
639	20 t. "Kanjedza I" standard "B" earth station		25	15
640	1 k. "Satellite communications"		1·50	1·90
637/40		*Set of 4*	1·75	1·90
MS641	101 × 151 mm. Nos. 637/40		1·75	3·00

136 Maize

137 "The Adoration of the Shepherds" (Murillo)

(Des Jennifer Toombs. Litho Harrison)

1981 (11 Sept). *World Food Day. Agricultural Produce. T* **136** *and similar horiz designs. Multicoloured. W* **55** *(sideways). P 14.*

642	7 t. Type **136**	..	15	10
643	10 t. Rice	..	20	10
644	20 t. Finger-millet	..	30	20
645	1 k. Wheat	..	1·00	1·40
642/5		*Set of 4*	1·50	1·50

(Des BG Studio. Litho J.W.)

1981 (26 Nov). *Christmas. Paintings. T* **137** *and similar multi-coloured designs. W* **55** *(sideways on 10 and 20 t.). P 13½ × 13 (7 t., 1 k.) or 13 × 13½ (others).*

646	7 t. Type **137**	..	20	10
647	10 t. "The Holy Family" (Lippi) (*horiz*)		25	10
648	20 t. "The Adoration of the Shepherds" (Louis le Nain) (*horiz*)		45	15
649	1 k. "The Virgin and Child, St. John the Baptist and an Angel" (Paolo Morando)		1·10	1·75
646/9		*Set of 4*	1·75	1·75

138 Impala Herd

(Des A. Theobald. Litho Harrison)

1982 (15 Mar). *National Parks. Wildlife. T* **138** *and similar horiz designs. Multicoloured. W* **55** *(sideways). P 14½ × 14.*

650	7 t. Type **138**	..	20	10
651	10 t. Lions	..	35	10
652	20 t. Greater Kudu	..	50	20
653	1 k. Greater Flamingoes	..	2·25	4·25
650/3		*Set of 4*	3·00	4·25

139 Kamuzu Academy

140 Attacker challenging Goalkeeper

(Des PAD Studio. Litho Questa)

1982 (1 July). *Kamuzu Academy. T* **139** *and similar horiz designs showing buildings. W* **55** *(sideways). P 14½.*

654	7 t. multicoloured	..	15	10
655	20 t. multicoloured	..	20	10
656	30 t. multicoloured	..	30	45
657	1 k. multicoloured	..	1·00	2·75
654/7		*Set of 4*	1·50	3·00

(Des and litho Harrison)

1982 (8 Sept). *World Cup Football Championship, Spain. T* **140** *and similar vert designs. Multicoloured. W* **55**. *P 14 × 15.*

658	7 t. Type **140**	..	75	10
659	20 t. FIFA World Cup trophy	..	1·60	1·10
660	30 t. Football stadium	..	1·90	3·25
658/60		*Set of 3*	3·75	4·00
MS661	80 × 59 mm. 1 k. Football	..	1·75	1·60

141 Blantyre War Memorial, St. Paul's Church

(Des W. Fenton. Litho Format)

1982 (5 Nov). *Remembrance Day. T* **141** *and similar horiz designs. Multicoloured. W* **55** *(sideways). P 14½ × 14.*

662	7 t. Type **141**	..	10	10
663	20 t. Zomba war memorial	..	15	10
664	30 t. Chichiri war memorial	..	20	30
665	1 k. Lilongwe war memorial	..	65	3·25
662/5		*Set of 4*	1·00	3·25

142 Kwacha International Conference Centre

143 "Christ and St. Peter"

(Des Walsall. Litho Format)

1983 (14 Mar). *Commonwealth Day. T* **142** *and similar horiz designs. Multicoloured. W* **55** *(sideways). P 14.*

666	7 t. Type **142**	..	10	10
667	20 t. Tea-picking, Mulanje	..	20	10
668	30 t. World map showing position of Malawi		25	30
669	1 k. President Dr. H. Kamuzu Banda		60	1·50
666/9		*Set of 4*	1·00	1·75

(Des C. Abbott. Litho Format)

1983 (4 Apr). *500th Birth Anniv of Raphael. Details from the cartoon for "The Miraculous Draught of Fishes" Tapestry. T* **143** *and similar multicoloured designs. W* **55** *(sideways on 30 t.). P 14.*

670	7 t. Type **143**	..	35	10
671	20 t. "Hauling in the Catch"	..	75	80
672	30 t. "Fishing Village" (*horiz*)	..	90	2·50
670/2		*Set of 3*	1·75	3·00
MS673	110 × 90 mm. 1 k. "Apostle"		1·60	1·60

144 Pair by Lake

145 Kamuzu International Airport

(Des N. Arlott. Litho Questa)

1983 (11 July). *African Fish Eagle. T* **144** *and similar vert designs. Multicoloured. W* **55**. *P 14.*

674	30 t. Type **144**	..	1·60	1·90
	a. Horiz strip of 5. Nos. 674/8	..	7·00	
675	30 t. Making gull-like call	..	1·60	1·90
676	30 t. Diving on prey	..	1·60	1·90
677	30 t. Carrying fish	..	1·60	1·90
678	30 t. Feeding on catch	..	1·60	1·90
674/8		*Set of 5*	7·00	8·50

Nos. 674/8 were printed together, *se-tenant*, in horizontal strips of 5 throughout the sheet, the backgrounds of each design forming a composite picture of Lake Malawi.

(Des A. Theobald. Litho Questa)

1983 (31 Aug). *Bicentenary of Manned Flight.* T **145** *and similar horiz designs. Multicoloured.* W **55** *(sideways).* P 14.

679	7 t. Type 145	10	10
680	20 t. Kamuzu International Airport *(different)*	25	15
681	30 t. B.A.C. One Eleven	40	45
682	1 k. Short S.23 Empire "C" Class flying boat at Cape Maclear	1·10	2·25
679/82	Set of 4	1·75	2·75
MS683	100×121 mm. Nos. 679/82	2·00	4·00

146 *Clerodendrum myricoides*   147 Golden Mbuna

(Des R. Reader. Litho J.W.)

1983 (1 Nov). *Christmas. Flowers.* T **146** *and similar vert designs. Multicoloured.* P 13 (20 t.) *or* 14 *(others).*

684	7 t. Type 146	40	10
	a. Perf 13	15·00	
685	20 t. *Gloriosa superba*	90	15
686	30 t. *Gladiolus laxiflorus*	1·25	60
687	1 k. *Aframomum angustifolium*	3·00	6·50
684/7	Set of 4	5·00	6·50

(Des L. Curtis. Litho Harrison)

1984 (2 Jan). *Fishes.* T **147** *and similar horiz designs. Multicoloured.* W **55** *(sideways). With imprint date.* P 14½×14.

688	1 t. Type 147	30	60
689	2 t. Malawi Eyebiter	30	60
690	5 t. Blue Mbuna	30	50
691	7 t. Lombardo's Mbuna	30	10
692	8 t. Golden Zebra Mbuna	30	10
693	10 t. Fairy Cichlid	30	10
694	15 t. Crabro Mbuna	30	10
695	20 t. Marbled Zebra Mbuna	30	10
696	30 t. Sky-blue Mbuna	40	20
697	40 t. Venustus Cichlid	60	30
698	50 t. Thumbi Emperor Cichlid	1·75	2·25
699	75 t. Purple Mbuna	2·25	3·50
700	1 k. Zebra Mbuna	2·50	3·50
701	2 k. Fairy Cichlid *(different)*	3·50	5·00
702	4 k. Mbenje Emperor Cichlid	4·75	8·00
688/702	Set of 15	16·00	22·00

Imprint dates: "1984", Nos. 688/702; "1986", Nos. 688, 691/7.

148 Smith's Red Hare   149 Running

(Des Garden Studios. Litho Format)

1984 (2 Feb). *Small Mammals.* T **148** *and similar horiz designs. Multicoloured.* W **55** *(sideways).* P 14.

703	7 t. Type 148	40	10
704	20 t. Gambian Sun Squirrel	65	60
705	30 t. South African Hedgehog	75	1·10
706	1 k. Large-spotted Genet	90	5·50
703/6	Set of 4	2·50	6·50

(Des C. Collins. Litho Harrison)

1984 (1 June). *Olympic Games, Los Angeles.* T **149** *and similar vert designs. Multicoloured.* W **55** *(sideways).* P 14.

707	7 t. Type 149	15	10
708	20 t. Boxing	35	20
709	30 t. Cycling	75	70
710	1 k. Long jumping	1·40	3·50
707/10	Set of 4	2·40	4·00
MS711	90 × 128 mm. Nos. 707/10. Wmk upright	2·40	4·00

150 *Euphaedra neophron*   151 "The Virgin and Child" (Duccio)

(Des and photo Courvoisier)

1984 (1 Aug). *Butterflies.* T **150** *and similar vert designs. Granite paper.* P 11½.

712	7 t. multicoloured	95	30
713	20 t. lemon, blackish brown and red	2·25	45
714	30 t. multicoloured	2·50	1·10
715	1 k. multicoloured	4·25	9·00
712/15	Set of 4	9·00	9·75

Designs:—20 t. *Papilio dardanus*; 30 t. *Antanartia schaeneia*; 1 k. *Spindasis nyassae*.

(Des C. Abbott. Litho Harrison)

1984 (22 Oct). *Christmas. Religious Paintings.* T **151** *and similar vert designs. Multicoloured.* W **55** P 14½.

716	7 t. Type 151	45	10
717	20 t. "Madonna and Child" (Raphael)	1·25	20
718	30 t. "The Virgin and Child" (ascr to Lippi)	1·75	70
719	1 k. "The Wilton Diptych"	3·25	7·50
716/19	Set of 4	6·00	7·50

152 *Leucopaxillus gracillimus*

(Des A. Jardine. Litho Harrison)

1985 (23 Jan). *Fungi.* T **152** *and similar horiz designs. Multicoloured.* W **55** *(sideways).* P 14½ × 14.

720	7 t. Type 152	1·25	30
721	20 t. *Limacella guttata*	2·50	45
722	30 t. *Termitomyces eurrhizus*	3·00	1·25
723	1 k. *Cyptotrama aspratum* ("Kerulina asprata")	5·50	9·50
720/3	Set of 4	11·00	10·50

153 Map showing Member States, and Lumberjack (Forestry)

(Des A. Theobald. Litho Harrison)

1985 (1 Apr). *5th Anniv of Southern African Development Co-ordination Conference.* T **153** *and similar horiz designs showing map and aspects of development.* W **55** *(sideways).* P 14.

724	7 t. black, yellowish green and pale green	75	10
725	15 t. black, scarlet-vermilion & salmon pink	1·25	20
726	20 t. blk, bright bluish violet & bright mauve	4·00	1·75
727	1 k. black, bright blue and cobalt	4·50	9·00
724/7	Set of 4	9·50	10·00

Designs:—15 t. Radio mast (Communications); 20 t. Diesel locomotive (Transport); 1 k. Trawler and net (Fishing).

154 M.V. *Ufulu*   155 Stierling's Woodpecker

(Des L. Curtis. Litho Cartor)

1985 (3 June). *Ships of Lake Malawi (2nd series).* T **154** *and similar horiz designs. Multicoloured.* W **55** *(sideways).* P 13½×13.

728	7 t. Type 154	90	10
729	15 t. M.V. *Chauncy Maples II*	1·75	20
730	20 t. M.V. *Mtendere*	2·25	65
731	1 k. M.V. *Ilala II*	4·50	6·00
728/31	Set of 4	8·50	6·25
MS732	120×84 mm. Nos. 728/31. P 13×12	8·00	7·00

(Des M. Stringer. Litho Harrison)

1985 (1 Aug). *Birth Bicentenary of John J. Audubon (ornithologist).* T **155** *and similar vert designs. Multicoloured.* W **55.** P 14.

733	7 t. Type 155	1·25	30
734	15 t. Lesser Seedcracker	2·25	30
735	20 t. East Coast Akelat	2·25	65
736	1 k. Boehm's Bee Eater	4·25	6·00
733/6	Set of 4	9·00	6·50
MS737	130×90 mm. Nos. 733/6. Wmk sideways	10·00	10·00

The new-issue supplement to this Catalogue appears each month in

GIBBONS STAMP MONTHLY

—from your newsagent or by postal subscription— sample copy and details on request.

CHRISTMAS 1985   Malawi 8t

MALAWI 7t

156 "The Virgin of Humility" (Jaime Serra)   157 Halley's Comet and Path of *Giotto* Spacecraft

(Photo Courvoisier)

1985 (14 Oct). *Christmas. Nativity Paintings.* T **156** *and similar vert designs. Multicoloured. Granite paper.* P 11½.

738	7 t. Type 156	30	10
739	15 t. "The Adoration of the Magi" (Stefano da Zevio)	75	15
740	20 t. "Madonna and Child" (Gerard van Honthorst)	85	25
741	1 k. "Virgin of Zbraslav" (Master of Vissy Brod)	2·25	3·75
738/41	Set of 4	3·75	3·75

(Des N. Shewring. Litho Walsall)

1986 (10 Feb). *Appearance of Halley's Comet.* T **157** *and similar vert designs. Multicoloured.* W **55.** P 14½×14.

742	8 t. Type 157	60	10
743	15 t. Halley's Comet above Earth	65	15
	w. Wmk inverted	65	
744	20 t. Comet and dish aerial, Malawi	1·00	30
745	1 k. *Giotto* spacecraft	2·00	4·00
742/5	Set of 4	3·75	4·00

158 Two Players competing for Ball   159 President Banda

(Des and photo Courvoisier)

1986 (26 May). *World Cup Football Championship, Mexico.* T **158** *and similar horiz designs. Multicoloured. Granite paper.* P 11½.

746	8 t. Type 158	70	10
747	15 t. Goalkeeper saving goal	95	20
748	20 t. Two players competing for ball *(different)*	1·10	35
749	1 k. Player kicking ball	4·00	3·50
746/9	Set of 4	6·00	3·75
MS750	108×77 mm. Nos. 746/9	10·00	11·00

(Des and litho Harrison)

1986 (30 June). *20th Anniv of the Republic.* T **159** *and similar vert designs. Multicoloured.* P 14.

751	8 t. Type 159	1·50	2·25
752	15 t. National flag	80	15
753	20 t. Malawi coat of arms	85	25
754	1 k. Kamuzu International Airport and emblem of national airline	3·50	4·50
751/4	Set of 4	6·00	6·50

It is reported that No. 751 was withdrawn locally five days after issue.

Christmas 1986   MALAWI

Malawi 8t   8t

160 "Virgin and Child" (Botticelli)   161 Wattled Crane

(Des and photo Courvoisier)

1986 (15 Dec). *Christmas.* T **160** *and similar vert designs showing paintings. Multicoloured. Granite paper.* P 11½.

755	8 t. Type 160	45	10
756	15 t. "Adoration of the Shepherds" (Guido Reni)	80	15
757	20 t. "Madonna of the Veil" (Carlo Dolci)	1·25	35
758	1 k. "Adoration of the Magi" (Jean Bourdichon)	3·75	7·50
755/8	Set of 4	5·50	7·50

(Des W. Oliver. Litho Walsall)

1987 (16 Feb)—88. *Wattled Crane.* T **161** *and similar horiz designs. Multicoloured.* P 14×14½. (a) W **55** *(sideways).*

759	8 t. Type 161	1·25	30
760	15 t. Two cranes	2·00	40
761	20 t. Cranes at nest	2·25	75
762	75 t. Crane in lake	4·50	9·00
759/62	Set of 4	9·00	9·50

(b) W w 14 *(sideways)* (10.88)

763	8 t. Type **161**		2·75	75
764	15 t. Two cranes		4·00	1·25
765	20 t. Cranes at nest		4·50	1·50
766	75 t. Cranes in lake		6·00	9·00
763/6		*Set of 4*	15·00	11·00

162 Bagnall Steam Locomotive No. 2, *Shamrock*

163 Hippopotamus grazing

(Des and litho Cartor)

1987 (25 May). *Steam Locomotives.* T **162** *and similar horiz designs. Multicoloured.* P 14×13½.

767	10 t. Type **162**		1·75	30
768	25 t. Class D steam locomotive No. 8, 1914		2·50	40
769	30 t. Bagnall steam locomotive No. 1, *Thistle*		2·75	85
770	1 k. Kitson steam locomotive, No. 6, 1903		5·00	9·00
767/70		*Set of 4*	11·00	9·50

(Des and photo Courvoisier)

1987 (24 Aug). *Hippopotamus.* T **163** *and similar vert designs. Multicoloured. Granite paper.* P 12½.

771	10 t. Type **163**		1·25	30
772	25 t. Hippopotami in water		2·00	40
773	30 t. Female and calf in water		2·00	75
774	1 k. Hippopotami and Cattle Egret		5·50	9·00
771/4		*Set of 4*	9·75	9·50
MS775	78×101 mm. Nos. 771/4		9·75	9·75

164 *Stathmostelma spectabile*

165 African and Staunton Knights

(Des and litho Harrison)

1987 (19 Oct). *Christmas. Wild Flowers.* T **164** *and similar vert designs. Multicoloured.* P 14.

776	10 t. Type **164**.		65	10
777	25 t. *Pentanisia schweinfurthii*		1·50	25
778	30 t. *Chironia krebsii.*		1·75	55
779	1 k. *Ochna macrocalyx*		3·00	7·50
776/9		*Set of 4*	6·25	7·50

(Des Jennifer Toombs. Litho Walsall)

1988 (8 Feb). *Chess.* T **165** *and similar vert designs showing local and Staunton chess pieces. Multicoloured.* W w **16**. P 14½×14.

780	15 t. Type **165**		1·00	20
781	35 t. Bishops ..		1·50	70
782	50 t. Rooks		1·75	1·50
783	2 k. Queens		5·50	8·50
780/3 ..		*Set of 4*	8·75	9·75

166 High Jumping

167 Scrub Warbler

(Des and litho Harrison)

1988 (13 June). *Olympic Games, Seoul.* T **166** *and similar vert designs. Multicoloured.* P 14.

784	15 t. Type **166**		30	10
785	35 t. Javelin throwing		50	20
786	50 t. Tennis		75	50
787	2 k. Shot-putting		1·60	3·00
784/7		*Set of 4*	2·75	3·50
MS788	91×121 mm. Nos. 784/7		3·50	3·50

(Des N. Arlott (No. 804), Courvoisier (others). Litho Questa (No. 804) or photo Courvoisier (others))

1988 (25 July)–**95**. *Birds.* T **167** *and similar vert designs. Multicoloured.* W w **14** *(sideways) (No. 804) or no wmk (others). Granite paper* (1 t. to 4 k.). P 15×14½ *(No. 804) or* 11½ *(others)*.

789	1 t. Type **167**		10	10
790	2 t. Yellow-throated Woodland Warbler		10	10
791	5 t. Moustached Green Tinkerbird		10	10
792	7 t. Waller's Red-winged Starling		10	10
793	8 t. Oriole-Finch		10	10
794	10 t. Starred Robin		1·75	30
795	15 t. Bar-tailed Trogon		10	10
796	20 t. Green-backed Twin-spot		10	10
797	30 t. African Grey Cuckoo Shrike		10	10
798	40 t. Black-fronted Bush Shrike		10	10
799	50 t. White-tailed Crested Flycatcher		2·25	60
800	75 t. Green Barbet		10	10
801	1 k. Lemon Dove ("Cinnamon Dove")		10	10
802	2 k. Silvery-cheeked Hornbill		10	15
803	4 k. Crowned Eagle		10	15
804	10 k. Anchieta's Sunbird (3.10.88)		5·00	5·50
804a	10 k. As 10 t. (1.10.95)		30	35
789/804a		*Set of 17*	9·00	6·75

167a Rebuilt Royal Exchange, 1844

168 "Madonna in the Church" (Jan van Eyck)

(Des D. Miller (15 t.), L. Curtis and D. Miller (35 t.), A. Theobald and D. Miller (50 t.), E. Nisbet and D. Miller (2 k.). Litho B.D.T.)

1988 (24 Oct). *300th Anniv of Lloyd's of London.* T **167a** *and similar multicoloured designs.* W w **14** *(sideways on 35, 50 t.).* P 14.

805	15 t. Type **167a**		30	10
806	35 t. Opening ceremony, Nkula Falls Hydro-electric Power Station		60	20
807	50 t. Air Malawi B.A.C. One Eleven airliner *(horiz)*		1·75	60
808	2 k. *Seawise University* (formerly *Queen Elizabeth*) on fire, Hong Kong, 1972		3·50	3·25
805/8 ..		*Set of 4*	5·50	3·75

(Des and litho Harrison)

1988 (28 Nov). *Christmas.* T **168** *and similar vert designs showing paintings. Multicoloured.* P 14.

809	15 t. Type **168**		60	10
810	35 t. "Virgin, Infant Jesus and St. Anna" (da Vinci)		90	25
811	50 t. "Virgin and Angels" (Cimabue)		1·25	70
812	2 k. "Virgin and Child" (Baldovinetti Apenio)		3·00	5·00
809/12		*Set of 4*	5·25	5·50

169 Robust Cichlid

(Des and litho Harrison)

1989 (10 Apr). *50th Anniv of Malawi Angling Society.* T **169** *and similar horiz designs. Multicoloured.* P 14.

813	15 t. Type **169**		50	10
814	35 t. Small-scaled Minnow ("Mpasa")		95	30
815	50 t. Large-scaled Yellowfish		1·40	1·40
816	2 k. Tigerfish		3·75	7·50
813/16		*Set of 4*	6·00	8·50

170 Independence Arch, Blantyre

(Des and litho Harrison)

1989 (26 June). *25th Anniv of Independence.* T **170** *and similar horiz designs. Multicoloured.* P 14.

817	15 t. Type **170**		70	10
818	35 t. Grain silos		1·25	30
819	50 t. Capital Hill, Lilongwe		1·75	1·50
820	2 k. Reserve Bank Headquarters		4·50	8·00
817/20		*Set of 4*	7·50	9·00

---

171 Blantyre Digital Telex Exchange

(Des and litho Harrison)

1989 (30 Oct). *25th Anniv of African Development Bank.* T **171** *and similar horiz designs. Multicoloured.* P 14.

821	15 t. Type **171**		70	10
822	40 t. Dzalanyama steer		1·25	30
823	50 t. Mikolongwe heifer		1·75	1·50
824	2 k. Zebu bull		4·50	8·00
821/4		*Set of 4*	7·50	9·00

172 Rural House with Verandah

(Des and litho Harrison)

1989 (1 Dec). *25th Anniv of Malawi–United Nations Co-operation.* T **172** *and similar horiz designs. Multicoloured.* P 14.

825	15 t. Type **172**		70	10
826	40 t. Rural house		1·25	30
827	50 t. Traditional hut and modern houses		1·75	1·50
828	2 k. Tea plantation		4·50	8·00
825/8		*Set of 4*	7·50	9·00

173 St. Michael and All Angels Church

(Des and litho Harrison)

1989 (15 Dec). *Christmas. Churches of Malawi.* T **173** *and similar horiz designs. Multicoloured.* P 14.

829	15 t. Type **173**		70	10
830	40 t. Catholic Cathedral, Limbe		1·25	30
831	50 t. C.C.A.P. Church, Nkhoma		1·75	1·50
832	2 k. Cathedral, Likoma Island		4·50	8·00
829/32		*Set of 4*	7·50	9·00

174 Ford "Sedan", 1915

175 Player heading Ball into Net

(Des and litho Cartor)

1990 (2 Apr). *Vintage Vehicles.* T **174** *and similar horiz designs. Multicoloured.* P 14×13½.

833	15 t. Type **174**		80	10
834	40 t. Two-seater Ford, 1915		1·25	30
835	50 t. Ford pick-up, 1915		1·75	1·50
836	2 k. Chevrolet bus, 1930		4·50	8·00
833/6		*Set of 4*	7·50	9·00
MS837	120×85 mm. Nos. 833/6. P 13×12		13·00	13·00

(Des and litho Questa)

1990 (14 June). *World Cup Football Championship, Italy.* T **175** *and similar vert designs. Multicoloured.* P 14.

838	15 t. Type **175**		90	10
839	40 t. Player tackling		1·40	30
840	50 t. Player scoring goal		1·90	1·50
841	2 k. World Cup		4·75	8·00
838/41		*Set of 4*	8·00	9·00
MS842	88×118 mm. Nos. 838/41		9·50	11·00

COVER PRICES

Cover factors are quoted at the beginning of each country for most issues to 1945. An explanation of the system can be found on page x. The factors quoted do not, however, apply to philatelic covers.

176 Anniversary Emblem on Map

177 *Aerangis kotschyana*

(Des and litho Questa)

1990 (24 Aug). *Tenth Anniv of Southern Africa Development Co-ordination Conference. T* **176** *and similar horiz designs. Multicoloured. P* 14.

843	15 t. Type **176**	85	10
844	40 t. Tilapia	1·40	40
845	50 t. Cedar plantation	1·75	1·50
846	2 k. Male Nyala (antelope)	4·25	8·00
843/6	*Set of* 4	7·50	9·00
MS847	174×116 mm. Nos. 843/6	9·00	9·50

(Litho Cartor)

1990 (26 Nov). *Orchids. T* **177** *and similar vert designs. Multicoloured. P* 13½×14.

848	15 t. Type **177**	1·50	20
849	40 t. *Angraecum eburneum*	2·50	70
850	50 t. *Aerangis luteo-alba rhodostica*	2·50	1·60
851	2 k. *Cyrtorchis arcuata whytei*	5·50	8·00
848/51	*Set of* 4	11·00	9·50
MS852	85×120 mm. Nos. 848/51. P 12×13	11·00	11·00

178 "The Virgin and the Child Jesus" (Raphael)

179 Buffalo

(Litho Cartor)

1990 (7 Dec). *Christmas. Paintings by Raphael. T* **178** *and similar vert designs. Multicoloured. P* 13½×14.

853	15 t. Type **178**	80	10
854	40 t. "Transfiguration" (detail)	1·50	30
855	50 t. "St. Catherine of Alexandrie" (detail)	1·60	90
856	2 k. "Transfiguration"	4·50	8·00
853/6	*Set of* 4	7·50	8·50
MS857	85×120 mm. Nos. 853/6. P 12×13	7·50	8·50

(Litho Cartor)

1991 (23 Apr). *Wildlife. T* **179** *and similar horiz designs. Multicoloured. P* 14×13½.

858	20 t. Type **179**	80	15
859	60 t. Cheetah	2·00	1·00
860	75 t. Greater Kudu	2·00	1·00
861	2 k. Black Rhinoceros	7·50	9·00
858/61	*Set of* 4	11·00	10·00
MS862	120×85 mm. Nos. 858/61. P 13×12	11·00	11·00

180 Chiromo Post Office, 1891

181 Red Locust

(Litho Cartor)

1991 (2 July). *Centenary of Postal Services. T* **180** *and similar horiz designs. Multicoloured. P* 14×13½.

863	20 t. Type **180**	70	10
864	60 t. Re-constructed mail exchange hut at Walala	1·40	85
865	75 t. Mangochi post office	1·50	95
866	2 k. Satellite Earth station	4·75	8·00
863/6	*Set of* 4	7·50	9·00
MS867	119×83 mm. Nos. 863/6. P 13×12	8·50	10·00

(Litho Cartor)

1991 (26 Sept). *Insects. T* **181** *and similar vert designs. Multicoloured. P* 13½×14.

868	20 t. Type **181**	85	20
869	60 t. Weevil	2·00	1·10
870	75 t. Cotton Stainer Bug	2·00	1·40
871	2 k. Pollen Beetle	5·50	8·50
868/71	*Set of* 4	9·25	10·00

182 Child in Manger

183 Red Bishop

(Litho Cartor)

1991 (26 Nov). *Christmas. T* **182** *and similar vert designs. Multicoloured. P* 13½×14.

872	20 t. Type **182**	65	10
873	60 t. Adoration of the Kings and Shepherds	1·60	45
874	75 t. Nativity	1·75	75
875	2 k. Virgin and Child	4·25	8·00
872/5	*Set of* 4	7·50	8·50

(Des Jennifer Toombs. Litho Questa)

1992 (7 Apr). *Birds. T* **183** *and similar horiz designs. Multicoloured. P* 14.

876	75 t. Type **183**	1·25	1·25
	a. Sheetlet. Nos. 876/95	22·00	
877	75 t. Lesser Striped Swallow	1·25	1·25
878	75 t. Long-crested Eagle	1·25	1·25
879	75 t. Lilac-breasted Roller	1·25	1·25
880	75 t. African Paradise Flycatcher	1·25	1·25
881	75 t. White-fronted Bee Eater	1·25	1·25
882	75 t. White-winged Black Tern	1·25	1·25
883	75 t. African Fire Finch	1·25	1·25
884	75 t. White-browed Robin Chat	1·25	1·25
885	75 t. African Fish Eagle	1·25	1·25
886	75 t. Malachite Kingfisher	1·25	1·25
887	75 t. Lesser Masked Weaver	1·25	1·25
888	75 t. Barn Owl	1·25	1·25
889	75 t. Variable Sunbird	1·25	1·25
890	75 t. Lesser Flamingo	1·25	1·25
891	75 t. South African Crowned Crane	1·25	1·25
892	75 t. African Pitta	1·25	1·25
893	75 t. African Darter	1·25	1·25
894	75 t. White-faced Whistling Duck	1·25	1·25
895	75 t. African Pied Wagtail	1·25	1·25
876/95	*Set of* 20	22·00	22·00

Nos. 876/95 were printed together, *se-tenant*, as a sheetlet of 20, forming a composite design.

184 Long Jumping

185 "The Angel Gabriel" (detail, "The Annunciation") (Philippe de Champaigne)

(Des G. Vasarhelyi. Litho B.D.T.)

1992 (28 July). *Olympic Games, Barcelona. T* **184** *and similar horiz designs. Multicoloured. P* 13½.

896	20 t. Type **184**	70	10
897	60 t. High Jumping	1·10	60
898	75 t. Javelin	1·40	90
899	2 k. Running	2·75	4·50
896/9	*Set of* 4	5·50	5·50
MS900	110×100 mm. Nos. 896/9	5·50	6·00

(Des D. Miller. Litho Walsall)

1992 (9 Nov). *Christmas. Religious Paintings. T* **185** *and similar vert designs. Multicoloured. P* 14.

901	20 t. Type **185**	60	10
902	75 t. "Virgin and Child" (Bernandino Luini)	1·25	50
903	95 t. "Virgin and Child" (Sassoferrato)	1·60	90
904	2 k. "Virgin Mary" (detail, "The Annunciation") (De Champaigne)	4·00	6·00
901/4	*Set of* 4	6·75	6·75

186 "Voyager 2" passing Saturn

187 *Strychnos spinosa*

(Des A. Theobald. Litho Cartor)

1992 (7 Dec). *International Space Year. T* **186** *and similar horiz designs. Multicoloured. P* 13½.

905	20 t. Type **186**	85	30
906	75 t. Centre of galaxy	1·75	90
907	95 t. Kanjedza II Standard A Earth Station	1·90	1·00
908	2 k. Communications satellite	4·00	5·50
905/8	*Set of* 4	7·75	7·00

(Des Jennifer Toombs. Litho Cartor)

1993 (21 Mar). *World Forestry Day. Indigenous Fruit Trees. T* **187** *and similar vert designs. Multicoloured. P* 13½×14.

909	20 t. Type **187**	60	15
910	75 t. *Adansonia digitata*	1·40	80
911	95 t. *Ximenia caffra*	1·50	1·00
912	2 k. *Uapaca kirkiana*	2·75	4·50
909/12	*Set of* 4	5·50	5·75

188 *Apaturopsis cleocharis*

189 The Holy Family

(Des Leta Marsden-Hugguis. Adapted D. Miller. Litho Cartor)

1993 (28 June). *Butterflies. T* **188** *and similar vert designs. Multicoloured. P* 13.

913	20 t. Type **188**	90	30
914	75 t. *Euryphura achlys*	1·75	85
915	95 t. *Cooksonia aliciae*	2·00	1·25
916	2 k. *Charaxes protoclea azota*	3·00	4·25
913/16	*Set of* 4	7·00	6·00

(Des G. Vasarhelyi. Photo Courvoisier)

1993 (30 Nov). *Christmas. T* **189** *and similar vert designs. Multicoloured. Granite paper. P* 11½.

917	20 t. Type **189**	10	10
918	75 t. Shepherds and star	20	20
919	95 t. Three Kings	25	30
920	2 k. Adoration of the Kings	65	1·50
917/20	*Set of* 4	1·10	1·90

190 Kentrosaurus

(Des E. Kapitapita and R. Larson. Litho Cartor)

1993 (30 Dec). *Prehistoric Animals. T* **190** *and similar horiz designs. Multicoloured. P* 13.

921	20 t. Type **190**	45	30
922	75 t. Stegosaurus	80	90
923	95 t. Sauropod	85	1·00
921/3	*Set of* 3	1·90	2·00
MS924	157×97 mm. 2 k. Tyrannosaurus; 2 k. Dilophosaurus; 2 k. Brachiosaurus; 2 k. Gallimimus; 2 k. Triceratops; 2 k. Velociraptor	10·00	11·00

191 Socolof's Mbuna

(Des R. Watton. Litho Enschedé)

1994 (21 Mar). *Fishes. T* **191** *and similar horiz designs. Multicoloured. P* 14×15.

925	20 t. Type **191**	20	10
926	75 t. Golden Mbuna	50	30
927	95 t. Lombardo's Mbuna	55	35
928	1 k. Scraper-mouthed Mbuna	60	70
929	2 k. Zebra Mbuna	1·25	1·75
930	4 k. Elongate Mbuna	2·00	3·25
925/30	*Set of* 6	4·50	5·75

MINIMUM PRICE

The minimum price quote is 10p which represents a handling charge rather than a basis for valuing common stamps. For further notes about prices see introductory pages.

192 *Ilala II* (lake vessel)   193 "Virgin and Child" (detail) (Dürer)

(Des N. Shewring. Litho Enschedé)

1994 (19 Oct). *Ships of Lake Malawi. T 192 and similar horiz designs. Multicoloured. P 13½×14.*

931	20 t. Type 192	..	20	10
932	75 t. *Ufulu* (tanker)	..	30	25
933	95 t. *Pioneer* (steam launch)	..	35	30
934	2 k. *Dove* (paddle-steamer)	..	60	1·25
931/4		*Set of 4*	1·25	1·60
MS935	85×51 mm. 5 k. *Monteith* (lake vessel)		2·75	3·50

(Litho Courvoisier)

1994 (30 Nov). *Christmas. Religious Paintings. T 193 and similar multicoloured designs. P 14½.*

936	20 t. Type 193	..	15	10
937	75 t. "Wise Men presenting Gifts" (Franco-Flemish Book of Hours)		30	15
938	95 t. "The Nativity" (detail) (Fra Filippo Lippi) (*horiz*)		35	15
939	2 k. "Nativity Scene with Wise Men" (Rogier van der Weyden) (*horiz*)		1·00	1·50
936/9		*Set of 4*	1·60	1·60

194 Pres. Bakili Muluzi (C.O.M.E.S.A. chairman, 1994–95)   195 Telecommunications Training

(Des and litho Courvoisier)

1995 (10 Apr). *Establishment of C.O.M.E.S.A. (Common Market for Eastern and Southern African States). P 11½.*

940	194	40 t. multicoloured	..	10	10
941		1 k. 40, multicoloured	..	20	20
942		1 k. 80, multicoloured	..	25	30
943		2 k. multicoloured	..	30	50
940/3			*Set of 4*	75	1·00

(Litho Courvoisier)

1995 (30 Oct). *50th Anniv of the United Nations. T 195 and similar horiz designs. Multicoloured. Granite paper. P 11½.*

944	40 t. Type 195	..	10	10
945	1 k. 40, Village women collecting water	..	25	20
946	1 k. 80, Mt Mulanje	..	30	40
947	2 k. Villagers in field	..	40	55
944/7		*Set of 4*	95	1·10
MS948	123×77mm. As Nos. 944/7, but ordinary paper	..	1·00	1·40

196 Teacher and Class

(Photo Courvoisier)

1995 (13 Nov). *Christmas. T 196 and similar horiz designs. Multicoloured. Granite paper. P 11½.*

949	40 t. Type 196	..	10	10
950	1 k. 40, Dispensing medicine	..	25	20
951	1 k. 80, Crowd at water pump	..	30	35
952	2 k. Refugees on ferries	..	40	55
949/52		*Set of 4*	80	1·00

197 *Precis tugela*   198 Children's Party

(Des Leta Marsden-Hugguis. Photo Courvoisoer)

1996 (5 Dec). *Butterflies. T 197 and similar horiz designs. Multicoloured. Granite paper. P 11½.*

953	60 t. Type 197	..	15	10
954	3 k. *Papilio pelodorus*	..	35	30
955	4 k. *Acrea acrita*	..	40	35
956	10 k. *Melanitis leda*	..	90	1·50
953/6		*Set of 4*	1·60	2·00

(Des G. Vasarhelyi. Photo Courvoisier)

1996 (12 Dec). *Christmas. T 198 and similar vert designs. Multicoloured. Granite paper. P 11½.*

957	10 t. Type 198	..	15	10
958	20 t. Nativity play	..	20	10
959	30 t. Children wearing party hats	..	25	15
960	60 t. Mother and child	..	40	60
957/60		*Set of 4*	90	75

199 Map of Malawi   200 Mother and Child

(Des M. Brussow. Photo Courvoisier)

1997 (6 Oct). *50th Death Anniv of Paul Harris (founder of Rotary International). T 199 and similar vert designs. Multicoloured. Granite paper. P 11½.*

961	60 t. Type 199	..	15	10
962	3 k. African Fish Eagle	..	30	75
963	4 k. 40, Leopard	..	40	50
964	5 k. Rotary International emblem	..	50	65
961/4		*Set of 4*	1·25	1·40

(Photo Courvoisier)

1997 (14 Oct). *50th Anniv of U.N.I.C.E.F. T 200 and similar horiz designs. Multicoloured. Granite paper. P 11½.*

965	60 t. Type 200	..	15	10
966	3 k. Children in class	..	30	25
967	4 k. 40, Boy with fish	..	40	50
968	5 k. Nurse inoculating child	..	50	65
965/8		*Set of 4*	1·25	1·40

201 The Nativity   202 Tattooed Rock, Mwalawamphini, Cape Maclear

(Photo Courvoisier)

1997 (15 Dec). *Christmas. T 201 and similar vert designs. Multicoloured. Granite paper. P 11½.*

969	60 t. Type 201	..	15	10
970	3 k. The Nativity (*different*)	..	30	20
971	4 k. 40, Adoration of the Magi	..	40	50
972	5 k. The Holy Family	..	50	70
969/72		*Set of 4*	1·25	1·40

(Des D. Miller. Litho Questa)

1998 (30 Nov). *Diana, Princess of Wales Commemoration. Vert designs as T 91 of Kiribati. Multicoloured. P 14½×14.*

973	60 t. Wearing red dress	..	15	10
974	6 k. Wearing lilac jacket	..	20	20
975	7 k. With headscarf	..	25	30
976	8 k. Wearing blue evening dress	..	35	45
973/6		*Set of 4*	85	95
MS977	145×70 mm. Nos. 973/6	..	1·00	1·25

(Litho Oriental Press, Bahrain)

1998 (2 Dec). *Monuments. T 202 and similar multicoloured designs. P 13½×13 (60 t., 6 k.) or 13×13½ (others).*

978	60 t. Type 202	..	10	10
979	6 k. War Memorial Tower, Zomba	..	20	20
980	7 k. Mtengatenga Postal Hut, Walala (*horiz*)		25	25
981	8 k. P.I.M. Church, Chiradzulu (*horiz*)		30	30
978/81		*Set of 4*	75	75

No. 978 is inscribed "tatooed" and No. 979 "Memoral", both in error.

COVER PRICES

Cover factors are quoted at the beginning of each country for most issues since 1945. An explanation of the system can be found on page x. The factors quoted do not, however, apply to philatelic covers.

---

203 Woman voting

(Litho Cartor)

1998 (10 Dec). *50th Anniv of Declaration of Human Rights. T 203 and similar horiz designs. Multicoloured. P 13×13½.*

982	60 t. Type 203	..	10	10
983	6 k. Books, pens and pencils ("Education")	..	20	20
984	7 k. Man and woman on scales ("Justice")	..	25	25
985	8 k. Person hugging house and land ("Property")		30	30
982/5		*Set of 4*	75	75

STAMP BOOKLETS

1954 (Jan). *Black on green cover, stitched (No. SB1) or buff cover, stapled (No. SB2). R.W. Gunson (Seeds) Ltd. advertisement on front.*

SB1	2s. 6d. booklet containing four ½d., 1d., and twelve 2d. (Nos. 173/4, 176), each in blocks of 4		27·00
SB2	5s. booklet containing eight ½d., 1d., 6d. and twelve 2d. (Nos. 173/4, 176, 180), each in blocks of 4	..	32·00

POSTAGE DUE STAMPS

D 1   D 2

(Typo D.L.R.)

1950 (1 July). *Wmk Mult Script CA. P 14.*

D1	D 1	1d. scarlet	..	3·75	18·00
D2		2d. ultramarine	..	9·00	22·00
D3		3d. green	..	9·50	6·00
D4		4d. purple	..	17·00	40·00
D5		6d. yellow-orange	..	23·00	95·00
D1/5			*Set of 5*	55·00	£160

(Litho Bradbury, Wilkinson)

1967 (1 Sept). *W 55. P 11½.*

D 6	D 2	1d. carmine	..	15	3·00
D 7		2d. sepia	..	20	3·00
D 8		4d. reddish violet	..	25	3·25
D 9		6d. blue	..	25	3·50
D10		8d. emerald	..	35	3·75
D11		1s. black	..	45	4·00
D6/11			*Set of 6*	1·50	18·00

1971 (15 Feb). *As Nos. D6/11, but values in tambalas. W 55. P 11½.*

D12	D 2	2 t. greenish drab	..	30	3·00
D13		4 t. bright mauve	..	50	3·00
D14		6 t. royal blue	..	50	3·25
D15		8 t. dull green	..	50	3·25
D16		10 t. blackish brown	..	60	3·25
D12/16			*Set of 5*	2·25	14·00

(Litho Walsall)

1975–84. *Design redrawn, with circumflex accent over "W" of "MALAWĨ". P 14. (a) W 55 (sideways).*

D17	D 2	2 t. chestnut (15.9.75)	..	1·25	6·50
D18		2 t. brown (14.6.82)	..	60	2·25
D19		4 t. deep mauve (14.6.82)	..	60	2·25
D20		6 t. royal blue (9.84)	..	1·50	2·25
D21		8 t. green (9.84)	..	1·50	2·25
D22		10 t. black (14.6.82)	..	60	2·25
D17/22			*Set of 6*	5·50	16·00

(b) No wmk

D23	D 2	2 t. brown (19.10.77)	..	5·50	5·50
D24		4 t. mauve (19.10.77)	..	5·50	5·50
D25		8 t. green (15.12.78)	..	2·25	5·50
D26		10 t. brownish grey (19.10.77)	..	5·50	6·50
D23/6			*Set of 4*	17·00	21·00

(Photo Harrison)

1989. *As Nos. D17/26, but design redrawn smaller, 17×20½ mm instead of 17½×21 mm. No wmk. P 15×14.*

D27	D 2	2 t. light brown	..	60	1·00
D28		4 t. bright purple	..	60	1·00
D29		6 t. bright blue	..	60	1·00
D31		10 t. brownish black	..	60	1·00
D27/31			*Set of 4*	2·25	3·50

Malaysia

The Federation of Malaysia was set up on 16 September 1963, and consisted of the former Malayan Federation, the State of Singapore and the two former Crown Colonies in Borneo, Sabah (North Borneo) and Sarawak. Singapore left the federation to become an independent republic on 9 August 1965.

Malaysia now consists of thirteen States (11 in Peninsular Malaysia and two in Borneo), together with the Federal Territories of Kuala Lumpur and Labuan.

The philatelic history of the component parts of the federation is most complex. Under this heading are now listed previous issues made by the present States of the Federation.

The method adopted is to show the general issues for the area first, before dealing with the issues for the individual States. The section is divided as follows:

   I. STRAITS SETTLEMENTS
  II. FEDERATED MALAY STATES
 III. MALAYAN POSTAL UNION
 IV. MALAYA (BRITISH MILITARY ADMINISTRATION)
  V. MALAYAN FEDERATION
 VI. MALAYSIA
VII. MALAYAN STATES—Johore, Kedah, Kelantan, Malacca, Negri Sembilan (with Sungei Ujong), Pahang, Penang, Perak, Perlis, Selangor, Trengganu
VIII. SIAMESE POSTS IN NORTHERN MALAYA 1887–1909
 IX. JAPANESE OCCUPATION OF MALAYA
  X. THAI OCCUPATION OF MALAYA
 XI. LABUAN
XII. SABAH (NORTH BORNEO)
XIII. JAPANESE OCCUPATION OF NORTH BORNEO
XIV. SARAWAK
 XV. JAPANESE OCCUPATION OF SARAWAK

I. STRAITS SETTLEMENTS

The three original Settlements, Malacca, Penang (with Province Wellesley) and Singapore (with Christmas Island), were formed into a Crown Colony during 1867. The Cocos (Keeling) Islands were transferred to Straits Settlements on 7 February 1886. Labuan was attached to the Colony in 1896, becoming the fourth Settlement in 1906.

The first known prestamp cover with postal markings from Penang (Prince of Wales Island) is dated March 1806 and from Malacca, under British civil administration, February 1841. The civil post office at Singapore opened on 1 February 1823.

The stamps of India were used at all three post offices from late in 1854 until the Straits Settlements became a separate colony on 1 September 1867.

The Indian stamps were initially cancelled by dumb obliterators and their use in the Straits Settlements can only be identified from complete covers. In 1856 cancellations of the ndard Indian octagonal type were issued, numbered "B 109" Malacca, "B 147" for Penang and "B 172" for Singapore.

    A   B

             C

The Penang and Singapore octagonals were replaced by a duplex type, consisting of a double-ringed datestamp and a diamond-shaped obliterator containing the office number, in 1863 and 1865 respectively.

             D

             E

PRICES. Catalogue prices in this section are for stamps with clearly legible, if partial, examples of the postmarks.

MALACCA

Stamps of INDIA *cancelled with Type A.*

1854. *(Nos. 2/34).*
Z1	½ a. blue (Die I)	£1000
Z2	1 a. red (Die I)	£850
Z3	1 a. dull red (Die II)	£900
Z4	2 a. green	£1200
Z4a	4 a. blue and pale red (Head Die I) *(cut-to-shape)*	£1300
Z5	4 a. blue and red (Head Die II) *(cut-to-shape)*	£1300
Z5a	4 a. blue and red (Head Die III) *(cut-to-shape)*	£1300

1855. *(Nos. 35/6).*
Z6	8 a. carmine (Die I)/*blue glazed*	£325

1856–64. *(Nos. 37/49).*
Z7	½ a. pale blue (Die I)	£180
Z8	1 a. brown	£140
Z8a	2 a. dull pink	£200
Z9	2 a. yellow-buff	£150
Z10	2 a. yellow	£160
Z11	4 a. green	£300
Z12	8 a. carmine (Die I)	£180

1860. *(Nos. 51/3).*
Z13	8 p. purple/*bluish*	£550
Z14	8 p. purple/*white*	£250

1865. *(Nos. 54/65).*
Z15	4 a. green	£300

PENANG

Stamps of INDIA *cancelled with Type B.*

1854. *(Nos. 2/34).*
Z20	½ a. blue (Die I)	£300
Z21	1 a. red (Die I)	£150
Z22	2 a. green	£190
Z23	4 a. blue and pale red (Head Die I)	£1100
Z24	4 a. blue and red (Head Die II)	£1100
Z25	4 a. blue and red (Head Die III)	£800

1855. *(Nos. 35/6).*
Z26	4 a. black/*blue glazed*	65·00
Z27	8 a. carmine (Die I)/*blue glazed*	55·00
	a. Bisected (4 a.) (1860) (on cover)	£42000

1856–64. *(Nos. 37/49).*
Z28	½ a. pale blue (Die I)	60·00
Z29	1 a. brown	38·00
Z30	2 a. dull pink	50·00
Z31	2 a. yellow-buff	45·00
Z32	2 a. yellow	45·00
Z33	2 a. orange	48·00
Z34	4 a. black	38·00
Z35	8 a. carmine (Die I)	45·00

1860. *(Nos. 51/3).*
Z36	8 p. purple/*white*	£100

Stamps of INDIA *cancelled with Type D.*

1854. *(Nos. 2/34).*
Z38	1 a. red (Die I)	£1900

1856–64. *(Nos. 37/49).*
Z39	½ a. pale blue (Die I)	£140
Z40	1 a. brown	38·00
Z41	2 a. yellow	45·00
Z42	4 a. black	40·00
Z43	4 a. green	£110
Z44	8 a. carmine (Die I)	42·00

1860. *(Nos. 51/3).*
Z45	8 p. purple/*white*	65·00
Z46	8 p. mauve	65·00

1865. *(Nos. 54/65).*
Z47	8 p. purple	
Z48	1 a. deep brown	38·00
Z49	2 a. yellow	45·00
Z50	4 a. green	£120
Z51	8 a. carmine (Die I)	

1866–67. *(Nos. 69/72)*
Z52	4 a. green (Die I)	£120

SINGAPORE

Stamps of INDIA *cancelled with Type C.*

1854. *(Nos. 2/34).*
Z60	½ a. blue (Die I)	£160
Z61	1 a. red (Die I)	£100
Z62	1 a. dull red (Die II)	£140
Z63	1 a. red (Die III)	£900
Z64	2 a. green	80·00
	a. Bisected (1 a.) (1857) (on cover)	£95000
Z65	4 a. blue and pale red (Head Die I)	£900
Z66	4 a. blue and red (Head Die II)	£950
Z67	4 a. blue and red (Head Die III)	£650

1855. *(Nos. 35/6).*
Z68	4 a. black/*blue glazed*	30·00
	a. Bisected (2 a.) (1859) (on cover)	£7500
Z69	8 a. carmine/*blue glazed*	32·00
	a. Bisected (4 a.) (1859) (on cover)	£35000

1856–64. *(Nos. 37/49).*
Z70	½ a. pale blue (Die I)	30·00
Z71	1 a. brown	21·00
	a. Bisected (½ a.) (1859) (on cover)	£50000
Z72	2 a. dull pink	35·00
Z73	2 a. yellow-buff	27·00
Z74	2 a. yellow	30·00
Z75	2 a. orange	35·00
Z76	4 a. black	21·00
	a. Bisected diagonally (2 a.) (1859) (on cover)	£16000
Z77	4 a. green	90·00
Z78	8 a. carmine (Die I)	27·00
	a. Bisected (4 a.) (1859) (on cover)	£38000

1860. *(Nos. 51/3).*
Z79	8 p. purple/*bluish*	£425
Z80	8 p. purple/*white*	50·00
	a. Bisected diagonally (4 p.) (1862) (on cover)	£50000
Z81	8 p. mauve	50·00

1865. *(Nos. 54/65).*
Z82	½ a. blue (Die I)	38·00
Z83	8 p. purple	90·00
Z84	1 a. deep brown	28·00
Z85	2 a. yellow	32·00
Z86	2 a. orange	32·00
Z87	4 a. green	90·00
Z88	8 a. carmine (Die I)	£225

1866–67. *(Nos. 69/72).*
Z89	4 a. green (Die I)	95·00
Z90	6 a. 8 p. slate	£180

OFFICIAL STAMPS

1866–67. *(Nos. O6/14).*
Z91	½ a. pale blue	£275
Z92	2 a. yellow	£400

Stamps of INDIA *cancelled with Type E.*

1856–64. *(Nos. 37/49).*
Z100	1 a. brown	£200
Z101	2 a. yellow	£275
Z102	4 a. black	£275
Z103	8 a. carmine (Die I)	£275

1860. *(Nos. 51/3).*
Z104	8 p. purple/*white*	£300

1865. *(Nos. 54/65).*
Z105	2 a. yellow	£250
Z106	2 a. orange	£250
Z107	4 a. green	£325

PRICES FOR STAMPS ON COVER

Nos. 1/9	*from* × 15
No. 10	—
Nos. 11/19	*from* × 8
Nos. 20/1	*from* × 20
Nos. 22/39	*from* × 10
Nos. 41/6	*from* × 20
No. 47	—
Nos. 48/9	*from* × 10
Nos. 50/62	*from* × 20
Nos. 63/71	*from* × 15
No. 72	—
Nos. 73/8	*from* × 20
No. 80	*from* × 30
Nos. 82/5	*from* × 10
Nos. 86/7	*from* × 20
Nos. 88/94	*from* × 15
Nos. 95/105	*from* × 8
Nos. 106/9	*from* × 20
Nos. 110/21	*from* × 6
No. 122	—
Nos. 123/6	*from* × 5
Nos. 127/38	*from* × 4
Nos. 139/40	—
Nos. 141/51	*from* × 15
Nos. 152/67	*from* × 4
Nos. 168/9	—
Nos. 193/212	*from* × 3
Nos. 213/15	—
Nos. 216/17	*from* × 10
Nos. 218/40a	*from* × 3
Nos. 240b/d	—
Nos. 241/55	*from* × 15
Nos. 256/9	*from* × 4
Nos. 260/98	*from* × 3
Nos. D1/6	*from* × 20

PRINTERS. All Straits Settlements issues were printed in typography by De La Rue & Co, Ltd, London, *unless otherwise stated.*

USED PRICES. The prices quoted for Nos. 1/9 are for fine used examples. Those showing parts of commercial "chops" are worth less.

(Currency. 100 cents = 1 Straits, later Malayan and Malaysian dollar)

THREE-HALF-CENTS   **32 CENTS**

    (1)   (2)

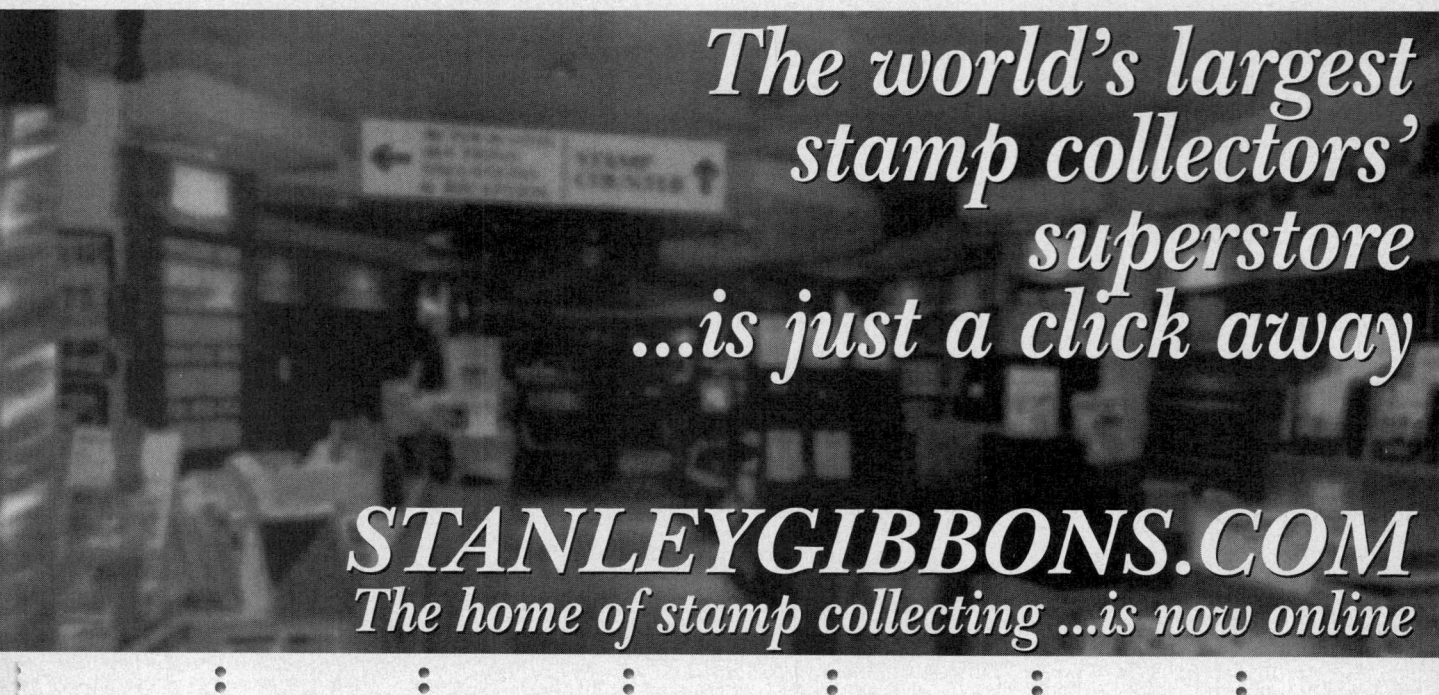

1867 (1 Sept). *Nos. 54, 59, 61, 69 and 73 of India surch as T* **1** *or* **2** *(24 c., 32 c.) by De La Rue. W* **13** *(Elephant's head) of India. P* 14.

1	1½ c. on ½ a. blue (Die I) (R.)	..	..	75·00	£180
2	2 c. on 1 a. deep brown (R.)			90·00	65·00
3	3 c. on 1 a. deep brown (B.)			95·00	70·00
4	4 c. on 1 a. deep brown (Bk.)			£190	£225
5	6 c. on 2 a. yellow (P.)			£450	£190
6	8 c. on 2 a. yellow (G.)			£140	38·00
7	12 c. on 4 a. green (R.)			£750	£250
	a. Surch double			£1400	
8	24 c. on 8 a. rose (Die II) (B.)			£300	70·00
9	32 c. on 2 a. yellow (Bk.)			£250	75·00

The 32 c. was re-issued for postal use in 1884.
No. 7a. is only known unused.

1869 (?). *No.* 1 *with* "THREE HALF" *deleted and* "2" *written above, in black manuscript.*

10	2 on 1½ c. on ½ a. blue		£7000 £3750

This stamp has been known from very early days and was apparently used at Penang, but nothing is known of its history.

5	6	7

8	9

1867 (Dec)–*72. Ornaments in corners differ for each value. Wmk Crown CC. P 14.*

11	5	2 c. brown (6.68)	..	..	20·00	3·25
		a. Yellow-brown	..	..	21·00	3·25
		b. Deep brown	..	..	60·00	9·00
		w. Wmk inverted				
12		4 c. rose (7.68)	..	..	32·00	5·50
		a. Deep rose	..	..	42·00	7·50
		w. Wmk inverted			95·00	
13		6 c. dull lilac (1.68)	..	..	60·00	13·00
		a. Bright lilac	..	..	65·00	13·00
14	6	8 c. orange-yellow	..	..	£100	8·00
		a. Orange	..	..	95·00	9·00
		w. Wmk inverted			£190	80·00
15		12 c. blue	..	..	80·00	6·00
		a. Ultramarine	..	..	85·00	8·50
		w. Wmk inverted				
16	7	24 c. blue-green	..	..	85·00	4·50
		a. Yellow-green	..	..	£180	20·00
		w. Wmk inverted				
17	8	30 c. claret (12.72)	..	..	£160	9·50
		w. Wmk inverted				
18	9	32 c. pale red	..	..	£350	60·00
		w. Wmk inverted			†	£160
19		96 c. grey	..	..	£190	35·00
		a. Perf 12½ (6.71)			£1800	£225

Five Cents.	**Seven Cents.**
(10)	(11)

1879 (May). *Nos.* 14a *and* 18 *surch with T* **10** *and* **11**.

20	6	5 c. on 8 c. orange	..	..	75·00	£110
		a. No stop after "Cents"	..	..	£550	£600
		b. "F i" spaced	..		£600	£650
21	9	7 c. on 32 c. pale red	..	..	80·00	£100
		a. No stop after "Cents"	..	..	£700	£750

The no stop error occured once in the setting.

10 cents.
(12)

	10 (a)	10 (b)	10 (c)	10 (d)
	10 (e)	10 (f)	10 (g)	10 (h)
	10 (i)	10 (j)	10 (jj)	10 (k)	10 (l)

(a) "1" thin curved serif and thin foot; "0" narrow.
(b) "1" thick curved serif and thick foot; "0" broad. Both numerals heavy.
(c) "1" as (a); "0" as (b)
(d) "1" as (a) but thicker; "0" as (a)
(e) As (a) but sides of "0" thicker.
(f) "1" as (d); "0" as (e)
(g) As (a) but "0" narrower.
(h) "1" thin, curved serif and thick foot; "0" as (g)
(i) "1" as (b); "0" as (a)
(j) "1" as (d); "0" as (g) but raised.
(jj) "1" as (a) but shorter, and with shorter serif and thicker foot; "0" as (g) but level with "1".
(k) "1" as (jj); "0" as (a)
(l) "1" straight serif; "0" as (g)

1880 (Mar). *No.* 17 *surch with T* **12** *(showing numerals (a) to (jj)).*

22	10 c. on 30 c. claret (a)		£225	55·00
23	10 c. on 30 c. claret (b)		£200	50·00
24	10 c. on 30 c. claret (c)		£2250	£425
25	10 c. on 30 c. claret (d)		£1000	£150
26	10 c. on 30 c. claret (e)		£3500	£800
27	10 c. on 30 c. claret (f)		£3500	£800
28	10 c. on 30 c. claret (g)		£1400	£300
29	10 c. on 30 c. claret (h)		£3500	£800
30	10 c. on 30 c. claret (i)		£3500	£800
31	10 c. on 30 c. claret (j)		£3500	£800
32	10 c. on 30 c. claret (jj)		£3500	£800

Nos. 22/32 come from the same setting of 60 (6 × 10) containing twenty examples of No. 22 (R.1/1-2, 1/4, 1/6, 2/1-6, 3/1, 3/3, 3/5, 4/1, 4/3-4, 10/1, 10/3-5), twenty-two of No. 23 (R.4/6, 5/1-6, 6/1-6, 7/1, 8/2-4, 9/1-5), six of No. 25 (R.1/5, 3/2, 3/4, 4/2, 4/5, 10/2), four of No. 28 (R.7/2-5), two of No. 24 (R.9/6, 10/6) and one each of Nos. 26 (R.3/6), 27 (R.1/3), 29 (R.7/6), 30 (R.8/1), 31 (R.8/6) and 32 (R.8/5).

No. 23 is known with large stop after "cents" and also with stop low.

1880 (Apr). *No.* 17 *surch as T* **12**, *but without* "cents.", *showing numerals (a) to (c), (g) to (i), (k) and (l).*

33	10 on 30 c. claret (a)			£120	42·00
	w. Wmk inverted	..	..	†	£120
34	10 on 30 c. claret (b)			£130	42·00
	w. Wmk inverted	..	..	†	£120
35	10 on 30 c. claret (c)			£400	£100
	w. Wmk inverted	..	..	†	£250
36	10 on 30 c. claret (g)			£900	£250
	aw. Wmk inverted	..	..	†	£500
36b	10 on 30 c. claret (h)			†	—
37	10 on 30 c. claret (i)			£2250	£650
38	10 on 30 c. claret (k)			£2250	£650
39	10 on 30 c. claret (l)			£2250	£650

Nos. 33/9 were surcharged from an amended setting of 60 (6×10) of which 59 positions have been identified. Of those known No. 33 occurs on twenty-four (R.6/1-6, 7/1-6, 8/1-6, 9/1-2, 9/6, 10/1-3), No. 34 on twenty-one (R.1/2-6, 2/1-6, 3/1-6, 4/3-5, 5/6), No. 35 on eight (R.1/1, 4/2, 4/6, 5/1-5), No. 36 on three (R.9/3-5) and Nos. 37 (R.10/6), 38 (R.10/4) and 39 (R.10/5) on one each. R.4/1 remains unidentified.

The existence of No. 36b, known as a single example from the 6th vertical column, and a stamp in the Royal Collection with "1" as (b) and "0" as (g) suggests that there may have been another setting.

5 cents.	5 cents.	5 cents.
(13)	(14)	(15)

1880 (Aug). *No.* 14a *surch with T* **13** *to* **15**.

41	13	5 c. on 8 c. orange	..	..	90·00	£110
42	14	5 c. on 8 c. orange	..	..	85·00	£100
43	15	5 c. on 8 c. orange	..	..	£300	£375

Surcharged in a setting of 60 (6×10) with T **13** on rows one to four, T **14** on rows five to nine and T **15** on row ten.

10 cents.	5 cents.
(16)	(17)

1880–81. *Nos.* 13, 15/a *and* 17 *surch with T* **16**.

44	10 c. on 6 c. lilac (11.81)	..	..	48·00	6·00
	a. Surch double			—	£1700
45	10 c. on 12 c. ultramarine (1.81)	..	..	50·00	16·00
	a. Blue			38·00	9·00
46	10 c. on 30 c. claret (12.80)	..	..	£275	80·00

A second printing of the 10 c. on 6 c. has the surcharge heavier and the "10" usually more to the left or right of "cents".

1882 (Jan). *No.* 12 *surch with T* **17**.

47	5 c. on 4 c. rose	..	..	£225	£250

18	19

1882 (Jan). *Wmk Crown CC. P* 14.

48	18	5 c. purple-brown	..	..	70·00	75·00
49	19	10 c. slate (Optd S. £275)	..		£275	60·00

1882. *Wmk Crown CA. P* 14.

50	5	2 c. brown (Aug)			£190	35·00
51		4 c. rose (April)			90·00	4·50
52	6	8 c. orange (Sept)	..	..	2·50	75
		w. Wmk inverted				
53	19	10 c. slate (Oct)	..	..	3·50	1·00
		w. Wmk inverted				

For the 4 c. in deep carmine see No. 98.

TWO CENTS	TWO CENTS	TWO CENTS
20a "S" wide	20b "E" and "S" wide	20c "N" wide

TWO CENTS	TWO CENTS	TWO CENTS
20d All letters narrow	20e "EN" and "S" wide	20f "E" wide

1883 (Apr). *Nos.* 52 *and* 18 *surch with T* **20**a/f.

54	20a	2 c. on 8 c. orange	..	..	£150	80·00
55	20b	2 c. on 8 c. orange	..	..	£150	80·00
56	20c	2 c. on 8 c. orange	..	..	£150	80·00
57	20d	2 c. on 8 c. orange	..	..	85·00	50·00
		a. Surch double	..	..	£2250	£950
58	20e	2 c. on 8 c. orange	..	..	£450	£250
59	20a	2 c. on 32 c. pale red	..	..	£450	£130
60	20f	2 c. on 32 c. pale red	..	..	£500	£140
		a. Surch double				

The 8 c. was surcharged using one of two triplet settings, either 54 + 55 + 56 or 57 + 57 + 57, applied to rows 2 to 10. A single handstamp, either No. 57 or No. 58, was then used to complete row 1. The 32 c. was surcharged in the same way with a triplet of 59 + 60 + 59 and a single handstamp as No. 60.

2 Cents.	4 Cents	8 Cents
(21)	(22)	(23)

1883 (June–July). *Nos.* 51 *and* 15 *surch with T* **21**.

61	2 c. on 4 c. rose	..	..	65·00	75·00
	a. "s" of "Cents" inverted	..		£900	£1000
62	2 c. on 12 c. blue (July)	..	..	£170	90·00
	a. "s" of "Cents" inverted	..		£2250	£1400

The inverted "S" error occurred once in the setting of 60.

Broken oval above "O" of "POSTAGE" (Lower right pane R. 10/5)

1883 (July)–*91. Wmk Crown CA. P* 14.

63	5	2 c. pale rose	..	..	32·00	3·00
		a. Bright rose (1889)	..		4·50	60
64		4 c. pale brown	..	..	18·00	1·25
		a. Broken oval	..		£150	35·00
		b. Deep brown	..		28·00	3·00
		ba. Broken oval	..		£250	50·00
		c. Olive-bistre	..		£350	£275
		ca. Broken oval				
		w. Wmk inverted			80·00	55·00
65	18	5 c. blue (8.83)	..	..	9·00	90
66	5	6 c. lilac (11.84)	..	..	23·00	8·50
		a. Violet	..		1·60	2·50
		aw. Wmk inverted				
67	6	6 c. brown-purple	..	..	65·00	9·00
68	7	24 c. yellow-green (2.84)	..	..	70·00	5·50
		a. Blue-green	..		3·25	3·75
69	8	30 c. claret (9.91)	..	..	7·00	7·00
		w. Wmk inverted			65·00	50·00
70	9	32 c. orange-vermilion (1.87)	..	..	6·50	2·25
		w. Wmk inverted			45·00	45·00
71		96 c. olive-grey (8.88)	..	..	75·00	38·00
63a/71				Set of 9	£170	60·00
63/5, 67 Optd "Specimen"				Set of 4	£550	

For the 4 c. in deep carmine and 12 c. in claret see Nos. 98 and 102.

1884 (Feb–Aug). *Nos.* 65, 15 *and* 67 *surch with T* **22** *or* **23**.

72	18	4 c. on 5 c. blue (Aug)	..	..	£2500	£3000
73		4 c. on 5 c. blue (R.) (Aug)			90·00	80·00
74	6	8 c. on 12 c. blue	..	..	£250	£100
		w. Wmk inverted			†	£275
75		8 c. on 12 c. brown-purple (Aug)	..	..	£200	£120
		a. Inverted "8"			†	—
		b. "s" of "Cents" low (R. 5/1)	..		£1200	£800

1884 (Aug). *No.* 65 *surch with T* **20**d/f.

76	20d	2 c. on 5 c. blue	..	..	95·00	£100
77	20e	2 c. on 5 c. blue	..	..	95·00	£100
		a. Pair, with and without surch				
		b. Surch double				
78	20f	2 c. on 5 c. blue	..	..	95·00	£100

Surcharged as a triplet, 77 + 76 + 78. On No. 76 "TS" are dropped below the line.

8	3 CENTS	THREE CENTS
(24)	(25)	(26)

1884 (Sept). *No. 75 additionally surch with large numeral as T 24 in red.*

80	6	8 on 8 c. on 12 c. dull purple	£200	£200
		a. Surch T 24 double	£3500	
		b. Surch T 23 in blue	£4750	
		c. "s" of "Cents" low	£1200	

Examples as No. 75, but with Type 23 in blue, were further surcharged in error.

A similar "4" surcharge in red on No. 73 exists from a trial printing from which seven examples are known, all used on an official's correspondence (*Price* £10000 *used*).

1885. *No. 65 and T 9 in new colour, wmk Crown CA, surch with T 25 or 26.*

82	25	3 c. on 5 c. blue (Sept)	95·00	£200
		a. Surch double	£1600	
83	26	3 c. on 32 c. pale magenta (Dec) (Optd. S. £150)	2·75	3·25
		a. Deep magenta	1·25	90

The surcharge on No. 82 was applied locally by a triplet setting. No. 83 was surcharged by De La Rue in complete panes.

3 cents (27)   2 Cents (28)

1886 (Apr). *No. 48 surch with T 27.*

84	18	3 c. on 5 c. purple-brown	£160	£170

The surcharge on No. 84 was applied by a triplet setting.

1887 (July). *No. 65 surch with T 28.*

85	18	2 c. on 5 c. blue	18·00	48·00
		a. "C" of "Cents" omitted	—	£2250
		b. Surch double	£650	£550

The surcharge on No. 85 was applied by a triplet setting.

10 CENTS (29)   THIRTY CENTS (30)

1891 (Nov). *Nos. 68 and 70 surch with T 29 and 30.*

86	7	10 c. on 24 c. yellow-green	2·00	1·25
		a. Narrow "0" in "10" (R. 4/6)	28·00	28·00
		w. Wmk inverted	38·00	42·00
87	9	30 c. on 32 c. orange-vermilion	5·50	3·50
		w. Wmk inverted		

The "R" of "THIRTY" and "N" of "CENTS" are found wide or narrow and in all possible combinations.

ONE CENT (31)   ONE CENT (32)

1892. *Stamps of 1882–91 (wmk Crown CA) surch with T 31.*

88		1 c. on 2 c. bright rose (Mar)	2·00	3·25
89		1 c. on 4 c. brown (Apr)	4·00	4·50
		a. Surch double	£850	
		b. Broken oval	75·00	75·00
		w. Wmk inverted		
90		1 c. on 6 c. lilac (Feb)	1·25	4·25
		a. Surch double, one inverted	£950	£850
		w. Wmk inverted		
91		1 c. on 8 c. orange (Jan)	1·00	1·10
92		1 c. on 12 c. brown-purple (Mar)	4·75	9·00
88/92		*Set of 5*	11·50	20·00

The three settings used for Nos. 88/92 contained various combinations of the following varieties: "ON" of "ONE" and "N" of "CENT" wide; "O" wide, "N" of "ONE" narrow and "N" of "CENT" wide; "O" narrow and both letters "N" wide; "ON" narrow, and "N" of "CENT" wide; "O" wide and both letters "N" narrow; "ON" wide and "N" of "CENT" narrow; "ON" and "N" of "CENT" narrow; "O" narrow "N" of "ONE" wide and "N" of "CENT" narrow. Antique "N" and "E" letters also occur.

1892–94. *Colours changed. Wmk Crown CA. P 14. Surch with T 32 and 26 by De la Rue.*

93	6	1 c. on 8 c. green (3.92)	90	1·50
94	9	3 c. on 32 c. carmine-rose (6.94)	2·25	70
		a. Surch omitted		
93/94		Optd "Specimen"	*Set of 2*	85·00

No. 94a comes from a sheet found at Singapore on which all stamps in the upper left pane had the surcharge omitted. Five vertical inter-panneau pairs still exist with the surcharge omitted on the upper stamps (*Price* £23000 *unused*). The only used example of the error is on cover.

(33) $5 (34)   4 cents. (35)

1892 (Mar)–99. *Wmk Crown CA. P 14.*

95	33	1 c. green (9.92)	1·75	50
		a. Malformed "S"	£150	65·00
		b. Repaired "S"	£130	55·00
96		3 c. carmine-rose (2.95)	11·00	40
		a. Malformed "S"	£225	75·00
97		3 c. brown (3.99)	4·00	60
		a. Repaired "S"	£180	75·00
		b. Yellow-brown	3·00	60

98	5	4 c. deep carmine (7.99)	3·75	1·25
		a. Broken oval	70·00	40·00
99	18	5 c. brown (6.94)	3·00	1·00
100		5 c. magenta (7.99)	2·00	2·00
101	6	8 c. ultramarine (6.94)	4·50	50
102		a. Bright blue	7·00	80
		12 c. claret (3.94)	8·00	8·50
103	33	25 c. purple-brown and green	18·00	5·00
		a. Malformed "S"	£375	£160
		b. Repaired "S"	£325	£140
		c. Dull purple and green	17·00	4·50
104		50 c. olive-green and carmine	18·00	2·50
		a. Repaired "S"	£375	£140
105	34	$5 orange and carmine (10.98)	£300	£250
		a. Repaired "S"	£1900	
95/105			*Set of 11*	£350 £250
95/101, 103/5 Optd "Specimen"			*Set of 10*	£350

For illustrations of the Repaired and Malformed "S" varieties see above No. 28 of Seychelles.

1898 (26 Dec). *T 18 and 6 surch with T 35 at Singapore.*

106		4 c. on 5 c. brown (No. 99)	2·00	4·75
107		4 c. on 5 c. blue (No. 65)	1·75	9·50
		a. Surch double	—	£1000
108		4 c. on 8 c. ultramarine (No. 101)	90	2·75
		a. Surch double	£850	£750
		b. Bright blue (No. 101a)	80	90
106/8b			*Set of 3*	4·00 13·50

Nos. 107 and 108b exist with stop spaced 1½ mm from the "S" (R. 10/6).

FOUR CENTS (36)

37   38

1899 (Mar). *T 18 (wmk Crown CA. P 14), surch with T 36 by De La Rue.*

109		4 c. on 5 c. carmine (Optd S. £40)	60	30
		a. Surch omitted	£20000	
		x. Wmk reversed	55·00	

No. 109a is only known unused.

1902 (Apr)–03. *Wmk Crown CA. P 14.*

110	37	1 c. grey-green (7.02)	2·25	2·75
		a. Pale green	4·25	3·00
111		3 c. dull purple and orange	3·50	15
		w. Wmk inverted	—	£150
112		4 c. purple/red (9.02)	4·50	30
113	38	5 c. dull purple (8.02)	4·50	85
114		8 c. purple/blue	3·25	20
115		10 c. purple and black/yellow (9.02)	18·00	1·50
116	37	25 c. dull purple and green (8.02)	11·00	5·00
117	38	30 c. grey and carmine (7.02)	16·00	8·00
118	37	50 c. deep green and carmine (9.02)	20·00	20·00
		a. Dull green and carmine	21·00	21·00
119	38	$1 dull green and black (9.02)	22·00	55·00
120	37	$2 dull purple and black (9.02)	60·00	60·00
121	38	$5 dull green & brown-orange (10.02)	£190	£150
122	37	$100 pur & grn/yell (3.03) (Optd S. £350)	£8000	
110/21			*Set of 12*	£325 £275
110/21 Optd "Specimen"			*Set of 12*	£300

39   40

41   42

(Des N. Trotter and W. Egerton)

1903 (Dec)–04. *Wmk Crown CA. P 14.*

123	39	1 c. grey-green	80	7·00
124	40	3 c. dull purple (1.04)	10·00	4·50
125	41	4 c. purple/red (4.04)	3·50	30
126	42	8 c. purple/blue (7.04)	40·00	1·25
123/6			*Set of 4*	48·00 11·50
123/6 Optd "Specimen"			*Set of 4*	£120

1904 (Aug)–10. *Wmk Multiple Crown CA. Ordinary paper (1 c. to $1 and $5) or chalk-surfaced paper ($2, $25, $100). P 14.*

127	39	1 c. deep green (9.04)	2·50	10
		a. Chalk-surfaced paper (12.05)	7·50	1·50
		w. Wmk inverted	70·00	35·00
128	40	3 c. dull purple	2·00	30
		a. Chalk-surfaced paper (8.06)	7·50	1·25
		aw. Wmk inverted	70·00	45·00
		b. Plum (2.08)	4·00	1·00
129	41	4 c. purple/red (6.05)	6·00	75
		a. Chalk-surfaced paper (10.05)	7·50	1·00
		aw. Wmk inverted	45·00	
130	38	5 c. dull purple (12.06)	6·50	2·00
		a. Chalk-surfaced paper (12.06)	12·00	5·50
131	42	8 c. purple/blue (8.05)	23·00	1·25
		a. Chalk-surfaced paper (12.05)	18·00	2·25
132	38	10 c. purple and black/yellow (8.05)	4·75	60
		a. Chalk-surfaced paper (11.05)	11·00	2·25
133	37	25 c. dull purple and green (1.05)	24·00	17·00
		a. Chalk-surfaced paper (11.05)	30·00	17·00

134	38	30 c. grey and carmine (3.05)	42·00	2·50
		a. Chalk-surfaced paper (3.06)	45·00	2·75
135	37	50 c. dull green and carmine (10.05)	48·00	14·00
		a. Chalk-surfaced paper (11.06)	27·00	14·00
136	38	$1 dull green and black (3.05)	48·00	17·00
		a. Chalk-surfaced paper (3.06)	40·00	16·00
137	37	$2 dull purple and black (10.05)	90·00	80·00
138	38	$5 dull green & brown-orange (10.05)	£160	£150
		a. Chalk-surfaced paper (1.08)	£150	£140
139	37	$25 grey-green and black (7.06) (Optd. S. £170)	£1200 £1200	
140		$100 purple and green/yellow (6.10)	£9000	
127/38			*Set of 12*	£350 £250

STRAITS SETTLEMENTS. (43)   Straits Settlements. (44)

STRAITS SETTLEMENTS.

FOUR CENTS. (45)

1906 (20 Dec)–07. *T 18 of Labuan (Nos. 117 etc.) optd with T 43 or 44 (10 c.), or additionally surch with T 45, in black (No. 145), claret (No. 151) or brown-red (others) at Singapore. P 13½–14.*

141		1 c. black and purple (p 14½–15)	50·00	£140
		a. Perf 14	£180	£300
		b. Line through "B"	£425	
142		2 c. black and green	£190	£250
		a. Perf 14½–15	£160	£250
		b. Perf 13½–14 comp 12–13	—	£850
		c. Line through "B"	£700	
143		3 c. black and carmine (1.07)	18·00	85·00
		a. Line through "B"	£200	
144		4 c. on 12 c. black and yellow	1·75	6·00
		a. No stop after "CENTS" (R. 1/8, 6/8)	£180	
		b. Line through "B"	£100	
145		4 c. on 16 c. green and brown (Blk.)	3·00	7·50
		a. "STRAITS SETTLEMENTS" in both brown-red and black	£600	£650
		b. Ditto. In vert pair with normal	£3750	
		c. Line through "B"	£110	
146		4 c. on 18 c. black and pale brown	2·50	6·00
		a. No stop after "CENTS" (R.1/8, 6/8)	£180	
		b. "FOUR CENTS" and bar double	£5500	
		c. "FOUR CENTS" and bar 1½ mm below normal position (pair with normal)	£650	
		d. Line through "B"	95·00	
147		8 c. black and vermilion	2·25	8·00
		a. Line through "B"	£100	
148		10 c. brown and slate	5·50	6·00
		a. No stop after "Settlements" (R. 1/4, 6/4)	£225	
		b. Line through "B"	£150	
149		25 c. green and greenish blue (1.07)	8·00	32·00
		a. Perf 14½–15	80·00	£110
		b. Perf 13½–14 comp 14½–15	£275	
		c. Line through "B"	£180	
150		50 c. dull purple and lilac (1.07)	11·00	70·00
		a. Line through "B"	£250	
151		$1 claret and orange (Claret) (1.07)	42·00	£110
		a. Perf 14½–15	£425	
		b. Line through "B"	£425	
141/51			*Set of 11*	£275 £650

Nos. 141/51 were overprinted by a setting of 50 (10 × 5) applied twice to the sheets of 100. The "FOUR CENTS" surcharges were applied separately by a similar setting.

No. 145a shows impressions of Type 43 in both brown-red and black. It is known from one complete sheet and the top half of another.

No. 146b occurred on row 5 from one sheet only. No. 146c occurred on R.4/10 and 9/10 of the first printing.

The line through "B" flaw occurs on R.5/10 of the basic stamp. For illustration see Labuan.

46

47

1906 (Sept)–12. *Wmk Mult Crown CA. Ordinary paper (1 c. to 10 c.) or chalk-surfaced paper (21 c. to $500). P 14.*

152	39	1 c. blue-green (3.10)	22·00	1·10
153	40	3 c. red (6.08)	1·50	10
154	41	4 c. red (7.07)	5·50	2·50
155		4 c. dull purple (2.08)	5·00	10
		a. Chalk-surfaced paper (1.12)	9·50	2·00
156		4 c. claret (9.11)	1·50	60
157	38	5 c. orange (4.09)	2·75	90
158	42	8 c. blue	3·50	90
159	38	10 c. purple/yellow (7.08)	5·00	90
		a. Chalk-surfaced paper (5.12)	13·00	4·75
160	46	21 c. dull purple and claret (11.10)	6·50	28·00
161	37	25 c. dull and bright purple (7.09)	9·50	4·25
162	38	30 c. purple and orange-yellow (11.09)	29·00	3·00
163	46	45 c. black/green (11.10)	2·50	4·00
164	37	50 c. black/green (4.10)	4·75	4·00
165	38	$1 black and red/blue (10.10)	11·00	4·25
166	37	$2 green and red/yellow (12.09)	24·00	22·00
167	38	$5 green and red/green (11.09)	£100	65·00
		w. Wmk inverted	£500	

168	47	$25 pur & blue/*bl* (5.11) (Optd S. £225)	£1100	£850
169		$500 pur & orge (5.10) (Optd S. £1000)	£65000	
152/67			Set of 16 £200	£120
153/67	Optd "Specimen"		Set of 15 £325	

Beware of dangerous forgeries of No. 169.

48   49   50

51   52   53

54

1912–23. $25, $100 and $500 as T **47**, but with head of King George V. Die I (5, 10, 25, 30, 50 c., $1, $2, $5). *Wmk Mult Crown CA. Ordinary paper* (Nos. 193/6, 198/201, 203) *or chalk-surfaced paper (others). P 14.*

193	48	1 c. green (9.12)	4.75	1.00
		a. Pale green (1.14)	5.00	1.00
		b. *Blue-green* (1917)	6.00	1.75
		bw. Wmk inverted	† £200	
194		1 c. black (2.19)	60	85
195	52	2 c. green (10.19)	50	50
196	49	3 c. red (2.13)	2.50	1.25
		a. Scarlet (2.17)	2.00	10
197	50	4 c. dull purple (3.13)	1.25	60
		a. Wmk sideways	† £1300	
198		4 c. rose-scarlet (2.19)	1.75	15
		a. Carmine	1.50	20
199	51	5 c. orange (8.12)	1.50	45
		a. Yellow-orange	2.25	80
200	52	6 c. dull claret (3.20)	1.75	50
		a. Deep claret	6.00	2.75
201		8 c. ultramarine (3.13)	80	70
202	51	10 c. purple/yellow (9.12)	1.25	80
		a. White back (1913) (Optd S. £40)	1.25	90
		b. On lemon (1916) (Optd S. £60)	15.00	1.25
		c. Wmk sideways	† £2000	
203		10 c. deep bright blue (1918)	5.50	30
		a. *Bright blue* (1919)	4.00	50
204	53	21 c. dull and bright purple (11.13)	4.25	9.50
205	54	25 c. dull purple and mauve (7.14)	7.50	6.50
		aw. Wmk inverted	70.00	
		b. *Dull purple and violet* (1919)	50.00	8.50
207	51	30 c. dull purple and orange (12.14)	8.00	1.75
208	53	45 c. black/green (*white back*) (12.14)	6.50	18.00
		a. On blue-green, olive back (7.18) (Optd S. £42)	3.25	17.00
		b. On emerald back (6.22)	3.25	13.00
209	54	50 c. black/green (7.14)	5.50	2.50
		a. On blue-green, olive back (1918)	17.00	6.00
		b. On emerald back (1921)	12.00	8.00
		c. Die II. On emerald back (1922) (Optd S. £42)	3.00	4.00
210	51	$1 black and red/*blue* (10.14)	8.50	8.00
		w. Wmk inverted	85.00	
211	54	$2 grn & red/*yell, white back* (1914)	6.50	38.00
		a. *Green and red/yellow* (1915) (Optd S. £42)	10.00	38.00
		b. On orange-buff (1921)	50.00	65.00
		c. On pale yellow (1921)	50.00	75.00
212	51	$5 grn & red/*grn, white back* (11.13)	65.00	42.00
		a. *Green and red/green* (1915) (Optd S. £60)	70.00	50.00
		b. On blue-green, olive back (1918)	£110	75.00
		c. On emerald back (1920)	£150	85.00
		d. Die II. On emerald back (1923) (Optd S. £80)	90.00	55.00
213	–	$25 purple & blue (Optd S. £170)	£900	£375
		a. Break in scroll	£1600	
		b. Broken crown and scroll	£1600	
214	–	$100 blk & car/*bl* (8.12) (Optd S. £375)	£4250	
		a. Break in scroll	£6500	
		b. Broken crown and scroll	£6500	
215	–	$500 purple and orange-brown (8.12) (Optd S. £900)	£32000	
		a. Break in scroll	£40000	
		b. Broken crown and scroll	£40000	
193/212			Set of 19 £110	£110
193/212	Optd "Specimen"		Set of 19 £500	

The 6 c. is similar to T **52**, but the head is in a beaded oval as in T **53**. The 2 c., 6 c. (and 12 c. below) have figures of value on a circular ground while in the 8 c. this is of oval shape.

For illustrations of the varieties on Nos. 213/15 see above No. 58 of Leeward Islands.

RED   CROSS

MALAYA-
BORNEO
2c.   EXHIBITION.
(55)   (56)

1917 (1 May). *Surch with T* **55**.

216	49	2 c. on 3 c. scarlet	1.75	22.00
		a. No stop (R. 2/3)	£180	£400
217	50	2 c. on 4 c. dull purple	2.00	22.00
		a. No stop (R. 2/3)	£190	£400

Nos. 216a and 217a occur in the first setting only.

Type I   Type II

The duty plate for the 25 c. value was replaced in 1926. In Type II the solid shading forming the back of the figure 2 extends to the top of the curve; the upturned end of the foot of the 2 is short; two background lines above figure 5; c close to 5; STRAITS SETTLEMENTS in taller letters.

1921–33. *Wmk Mult Script CA. Ordinary paper* (1 c. to 6 c., 10 c. (No. 230), 12 c.) *or chalk-surfaced paper (others). P 14.*

218	48	1 c. black (3.22)	40	10
219	52	2 c. green (5.21)	40	10
		w. Wmk inverted	25.00	
		y. Wmk inverted and reversed		
220		2 c. brown (12.25)	7.00	2.25
221	49	3 c. green (9.23)	1.50	70
		w. Wmk inverted	25.00	
222	50	4 c. carmine-red (10.21)	2.00	4.00
223		4 c. bright violet (8.24)	50	10
		w. Wmk inverted	25.00	
224		4 c. orange (8.29)	1.00	10
225	51	5 c. orange (Die I) (5.21)	1.25	15
		a. Wmk sideways	† £1600	
		b. Die II (1922)	2.25	1.25
		w. Wmk inverted	25.00	
226		5 c. brown (Die II) (1932)	2.00	10
		a. Die I (1933)	5.00	10
227	52	6 c. dull claret (10.22)	2.00	15
		w. Wmk inverted	25.00	30.00
228		6 c. rose-pink (2.25)	19.00	9.00
229		6 c. scarlet (1.27)	2.50	10
230	51	10 c. bright blue (Die I) (1921)	1.75	1.50
		w. Wmk inverted	25.00	
231		10 c. purple/*pale yellow* (Die I) (1923)	2.50	6.00
		a. Die II (11.26)	2.00	30
		b. *Purple/brt yellow* (Die II) (1932)		
		ba. Die I (1933)	5.50	10
232	52	12 c. bright blue (1.22)	1.00	20
		w. Wmk inverted	25.00	
233	53	21 c. dull and bright purple (2.23)	6.00	45.00
234	54	25 c. dull purple and mauve (Die I, Type I) (1921)	26.00	70.00
		a. Die II, Type I (1923)	15.00	3.00
		b. Die II, Type II (1927)	5.00	1.75
235	51	30 c. dull purple & orange (Die I) (1921)	20.00	28.00
		a. Die II (1922)	2.00	1.25
236	53	35 c. dull purple & orange-yellow (8.22)	12.00	6.00
		a. *Dull purple and orange*	3.50	5.50
237		35 c. scarlet and purple (4.31)	10.00	7.00
238	54	50 c. black/*emerald* (9.25)	1.75	40
239	51	$1 black and red/*blue* (Die II) (1921)	6.00	65
240	54	$2 grn & red/*pale yell* (Die II) (1923)	10.00	8.00
240a	51	$5 green and red/*green* (Die II) (1926)	75.00	32.00
240b	–	$25 pur & bl/*bl* (5.23) (Optd S. £140)	£500	£100
		ba. Break in scroll	£900	
		bb. Broken crown and scroll	£900	
240c	–	$100 blk & car/*bl* (5.23) (Optd S. £300)	£3000	£1200
		ca. Break in scroll	£4500	
		cb. Broken crown and scroll	£4500	
240d	–	$500 purple and orange-brown (4.23) (Optd S. £750)	£23000	
		da. Break in scroll	£30000	
		db. Broken crown and scroll	£30000	
218/40a			Set of 24 £140	£110
218/40a	ex 228 Optd/Perf "Specimen"		Set of 23 £550	

Nos. 240b/d are as Type **47**, but with portrait of George V.

An 8 c. in carmine was prepared but not issued (Optd "Specimen" £250)

The paper of Nos. 231b/ba is the normal *pale yellow* at the back, but with a bright yellow surface.

In 1926 Key and Duty plates were made of 100 (10×10) instead of the usual 60 (6×10).

For illustrations of the varieties on Nos. 240b/d see above No. 58 of Leeward Islands.

1922 (31 Mar). *Malaya–Borneo Exhibition, Singapore. T* **48** *and T* **50** *to* **54**, *overprinted with T* **56**.

(a) Wmk Mult Crown CA

241	52	2 c. green	28.00	75.00
242	50	4 c. scarlet	7.00	22.00
243	51	5 c. orange (Die I)	4.50	18.00
244	52	8 c. ultramarine	1.75	6.50
245	54	25 c. dull purple and mauve (Die I)	3.00	26.00
246	53	45 c. black/*green (olive back)*	3.00	23.00
		a. On green (white back)	£350	
247	51	$1 black and red/*blue* (Die I)	£150	£600
248	54	$2 green and red/*orange-buff* (Die I)	25.00	£100
		a. On pale yellow	60.00	£140
249	51	$5 green and red/*blue-green* (ol back)	£200	£375

(b) Wmk Mult Script CA

250	48	1 c. black	2.25	10.00
251	52	2 c. green	1.60	12.00
252	50	4 c. carmine-red	2.25	22.00
253	51	5 c. orange (Die II)	2.50	38.00
254		10 c. bright blue (Die I)	2.25	22.00
255	51	$1 black and red/*blue* (Die II)	16.00	95.00
241/55			Set of 11 £225	£650

Nos. 241/55 were overprinted by stereo which repeated a setting of 12 (6×2). The following varieties therefore occur ten times on each sheet of 120: (a) Small second "A" in "MALAYA." (b) No stop. (c) No hyphen. (d) Oval last "O" in "BORNEO," (e) "EXH.BITION".

1935 (6 May). *Silver Jubilee. As Nos. 114/17 of Jamaica, but ptd by Waterlow & Sons. P 11×12.*

256		5 c. ultramarine and grey	2.75	30
		j. Damaged turret	£150	
257		8 c. green and indigo	2.75	2.75
		j. Damaged turret	£170	
258		12 c. brown and deep blue	2.75	3.00
		j. Damaged turret	£170	
259		25 c. slate and purple	3.00	4.50
		j. Damaged turret	£200	
256/9			Set of 4 10.00	9.50
256/9	Perf "Specimen"		Set of 4 £110	

57   58

1936 (1 Jan)–37. *Chalk-surfaced paper. Wmk Mult Script CA. P 14.*

260	57	1 c. black (1.1.37)	80	20
261		2 c. green (1.2.36)	80	60
262		4 c. orange (15.6.36)	1.75	60
263		5 c. brown (1.8.36)	50	30
264		6 c. scarlet (1.2.36)	1.00	95
265		8 c. grey	1.00	60
266		10 c. dull purple (1.7.36)	1.25	30
267		12 c. bright ultramarine (1.9.36)	2.00	2.00
268		25 c. dull purple and scarlet (1.2.36)	1.00	30
269		30 c. dull purple and orange	1.25	3.25
270		40 c. scarlet and dull purple	1.25	2.50
271		50 c. black/*emerald* (1.9.36)	4.25	80
272		$1 black and red/*blue* (1.7.36)	18.00	1.00
273		$2 green and scarlet (1.4.36)	32.00	10.00
274		$5 green and red/*emerald* (1.1.37)	65.00	10.00
260/74			Set of 15 £120	30.00
260/74	Perf "Specimen"		Set of 15 £250	

1937 (12 May). *Coronation. As Nos. 118/20 of Jamaica.*

275		4 c. orange	30	10
276		8 c. grey-black	70	10
277		12 c. bright blue	1.25	60
275/7			Set of 3 2.00	65
275/7	Perf "Specimen"		Set of 3 70.00	

1937–41. *Chalk-surfaced paper. Wmk Mult Script CA. P 14 or 15×14 (15 c.). (a) Die I (printed at two operations).*

278	58	1 c. black (1.1.38)	4.00	10
279		2 c. green (6.12.37)	18.00	10
280		4 c. orange (1.1.38)	13.00	20
281		5 c. brown (19.11.37)	20.00	30
282		6 c. scarlet (10.1.38)	10.00	50
283		8 c. grey (26.1.38)	40.00	10
284		10 c. dull purple (8.11.37)	7.50	10
285		12 c. ultramarine (10.1.38)	8.00	30
286		25 c. dull purple and scarlet (11.12.37)	42.00	1.10
287		30 c. dull purple and orange (1.12.37)	30.00	2.00
288		40 c. scarlet and dull purple (20.12.37)	10.00	2.25
289		50 c. black/*emerald* (26.1.38)	10.00	10
290		$1 black and red/*blue* (26.1.38)	15.00	20
291		$2 green and scarlet (26.1.38)	30.00	4.00
292		$5 green and red/*emerald* (26.1.38)	25.00	3.25
278/98			Set of 18 £275	32.00
278/92, 294/5, 298	Perf "Specimen"		Set of 18 £375	

(b) Die II (printed at one operation)

293	58	2 c. green (28.12.38)	50.00	40
294		2 c. orange (6.10.41)	2.00	9.00
295		3 c. green (*ordinary paper*) (5.9.41)	3.25	4.00
296		4 c. orange (29.10.38)	70.00	10
297		5 c. brown (18.2.39)	28.00	10
298		15 c. ultram (*ordinary paper*) (6.10.41)	5.00	10.00

Die I. Lines of background outside central oval touch the oval and the foliage of the palm tree is usually joined to the oval frame. The downward-pointing palm frond, opposite the King's eye, has two points.

Die II. Lines of background are separated from the oval by a white line and the foliage of the palm trees does not touch the outer frame. The palm frond has only one point.

Nos. 295 and 298 were printed by Harrison and Sons following bomb damage to the De La Rue works on 29 December 1940.

The 6 c. grey, 8 c. scarlet and $5 purple and orange were only issued with the BMA overprint, but the 8 c. without overprint is known although in this state it was never issued (*Price £14*).

STAMP BOOKLETS

1914–19. *Black on blue (No. SB1) or grey (No. SB1b) covers. Stapled.*
SB1 $1 booklet containing twenty-five 4 c. dull purple (No. 197) in two blocks of 12 and one single
        a. Containing 4 c. rose-scarlet (No. 198) (1919)
SB1b $1 booklet containing four 1 c., sixteen 3 c. and twelve 4 c. (Nos. 193, 196/7) in blocks of four

1921. *Black on blue cover. Stapled.*
SB2 $1 booklet containing twenty-five 4 c. (No. 222) in two blocks of 12 and one single
        a. Contents as SB2, but four blocks of 6 and one single

1922. *Black on red cover. Stapled.*
SB3 $1 booklet containing 5 c. (No. 225) in block of 8 and 6 c. (No. 227) in block of 10 .. £900

1925–29. *Black on red cover. Stapled.*
SB4 $1.20, booklet containing thirty 4 c. bright violet (No. 223) in blocks of 10
        a. Containing 4 c. orange (No. 224) (1929)

1927. *Black on grey (No. SB5), green (No. SB6) or blue (No. SB7) covers. Stapled.*

SB5 $1 booklet containing 4 c. and 6 c. (Nos. 223, 229) in blocks of 10

SB6 $1.20, booklet containing twenty 6 c. (No. 229) in blocks of 10

SB7 $1.20, booklet containing 2 c., 4 c. and 6 c. (Nos. 219, 223, 229) in blocks of 10

1933. *Black on buff cover. Stapled.*

SB8 $1 booklet containing twenty 5 c. (No. 226a) in blocks of 10

1936. *Stapled.*

SB9 $1 booklet containing twenty 5 c. (No. 263) in blocks of 10

SB10 $1.30, booklet containing 5 c. and 8 c. (Nos. 263, 265) in blocks of 10

1938. *Black on buff (No. SB11) or black on green (No. SB12) covers. Stapled.*

SB11 $1 booklet containing twenty 5 c. (No. 281) in blocks of 10 .. .. £1200

SB12 $1.30, booklet containing 5 c. and 8 c. (Nos. 281, 283) in blocks of 10 and pane of airmail labels £1500

POSTAGE DUE STAMPS

D 1

1924 (1 Jan)**–26.** *Wmk Mult Script CA. P 14.*

D1	D 1	1 c. violet	.. ..	5·00	6·00
D2		2 c. black	.. ..	3·25	1·25
D3		4 c. green (5.26)	.. ..	2·00	4·75
D4		8 c. scarlet	.. ..	4·50	55
D5		10 c. orange	.. ..	6·00	85
D6		12 c. bright blue	.. ..	7·00	65
D1/6				*Set of 6* 25·00	12·50
D1/6 Optd "Specimen"				*Set of 6* £200	

For later issues of Postage Due stamps, see MALAYAN POSTAL UNION.

The Straits Settlements were occupied by the Japanese in 1942. After the Second World War the stamps of MALAYA (BRITISH MILITARY ADMINISTRATION) were used. In 1946 Singapore became a separate Crown Colony and Labuan was transferred to North Borneo. Separate stamps were issued for Malacca and Penang, which both joined the Malayan Federation on 1 February 1948.

II. FEDERATED MALAY STATES

On 1 July 1896, the States of Negri Sembilan, Pahang, Perak and Selangor were organised on a federal basis to be known as the Federated Malay States. For the time being each State continued with individual issues, but stamps for the use of the Federation replaced these in 1900.

PRICES FOR STAMPS ON COVER	
Nos. 1/13	*from* × 12
No. 14	
Nos. 15/22	*from* × 10
Nos. 23/5	*from* × 3
No. 26	
Nos. 27/50	*from* × 6
No. 51	
Nos. 52/81	*from* × 5
No. 82	
Nos. D1/6	*from* × 10

PRINTERS. All issues of the Federated Malay States were printed in typography by De La Rue & Co, Ltd, London, *unless otherwise stated.*

FEDERATED MALAY STATES	FEDERATED MALAY STATES
(1)	(2)

1900. *Optd with T 1 (cent values) or 2 (dollar values).*

    (a) *Stamps of Negri Sembilan (T 3)*

1	1 c. dull purple and green	2·25	4·50
2	2 c. dull purple and brown	25·00	50·00
3	3 c. dull purple and black	2·00	3·75
4	5 c. dull purple and olive-yellow	65·00	£150
5	10 c. dull purple and orange	4·25	18·00
6	20 c. green and olive	70·00	90·00
7	25 c. green and carmine	£180	£300
8	50 c. green and black	75·00	£100
1/8		*Set of 8* £375	£600
1/8 Optd "Specimen"		*Set of 8* £160	

    (b) *Stamps of Perak (T 44 and 45)*

9	5 c. dull purple and olive-yellow	11·00	48·00
10	10 c. dull purple and orange	60·00	65·00
11	$1 green and pale green	£150	£190
12	$2 green and carmine	£100	£180
13	$5 green and ultramarine	£275	£425
14	$25 green and orange (Optd S. £275)	£6500	
11/13 Optd "Specimen"		*Set of 3* £120	

The Negri Sembilan 3 c. dull purple and black does not exist without overprint Type 1.

> The stamps of STRAITS SETTLEMENTS were used in Federated Malay States from 16 July 1900 until replaced by the 1900–1 issue.

3   4

1900–1. *P 14.* (a) *T 3. Wmk Crown CA, sideways* (1901).

15	1 c. black and green	..	4·25	4·25
	a. *Grey and green*	..	2·50	30
	b. *Grey-brown and green*	..	7·00	30
16	3 c. black and brown	..	7·00	2·75
	a. *Grey and brown*	..	3·50	35
	b. *Grey-brown and brown*	..	2·50	20
17	4 c. black and carmine	..	14·00	3·50
	a. *Grey and carmine*	..	4·75	2·75
	b. *Grey-brown and carmine*	..	16·00	1·75
18	5 c. green and carmine/*yellow*	..	2·00	2·00
19	8 c. black and ultramarine	..	42·00	12·00
	a. *Grey and ultramarine*	..	20·00	3·75
	b. *Grey-brown and ultramarine*	..	23·00	3·25
20	10 c. black and claret	..	80·00	20·00
	a. *Grey and claret*	..	60·00	5·50
	b. *Black and purple*	..	95·00	20·00
	c. *Grey and purple*	..	75·00	8·00
	d. *Grey-brown and purple*	..	85·00	5·00
21	20 c. mauve and black	..	17·00	7·50
22	50 c. black and orange-brown	..	£110	90·00
	a. *Grey and orange-brown*	..	80·00	40·00
	b. *Grey-brown and orange-brown*	..	80·00	35·00
15/22			*Set of 8* £170	48·00
15/22 Optd "Specimen"			*Set of 8* £160	

Later printings in 1903–4 show the two upper lines of shading in the background at the corner nearest to the "S" of "STATE" blurred and running into one another, whereas in earlier printings these lines are distinct. Two plates were used for printing the central design of T 3. In Plate 1 the lines of background are regular throughout, but in Plate 2 they are lighter around the head and back of the tiger. The 5 c. was the only value with single wmk to be printed from Plate 2. Stamps with multiple wmk were printed for a short time from Plate 1, and show the two blurred lines of background near "S" of "STATE," but the majority of these stamps were printed from Plate 2 and later plates.

    (b) *T 4. Wmk Crown CC* (1900)

23	$1 green and pale green	..	95·00	£100
24	$2 green and carmine	..	£100	£110
25	$5 green and bright ultramarine	..	£170	£190
	a. *Green and pale ultramarine*	..	£170	£190
26	$25 green and orange (Optd S. £180)	..	£1700	£950
23/5 Optd "Specimen"			*Set of 3* £110	

Two dies for 1 c. green and 4 c. scarlet

Die I. "Head" and duty plates. Thick frame line below "MALAY" and in the 1 c. the "c" is thin whilst in the 4 c. it is thick.

Die II. Single working plate. Thin frame line below "MALAY" and in the 1 c. the "c" is thicker whilst in the 4 c. it is thinner.

1904 (10 Oct)**–22.** *T 3 and T 4 (dollar values). Wmk Mult Crown CA (sideways* on T 3). Ordinary paper (1 c. to 50 c.) or chalk-surfaced paper ($1 to $25).*

27	1 c. grey and green	..	60·00	8·00
	a. *Grey-brown and green*	..	25·00	70
28	1 c. green (Die I) (8.7.06)	..	9·50	30
29	1 c. green (Die II) (1908)	..	2·25	20
	a. *Yellow-green*	..	16·00	1·00
	aw. Wmk Crown to right of CA	..	28·00	6·50
	b. *Blue-green*	..	21·00	95
30	1 c. deep green (21.1.19)	..	2·25	90
31	2 c. green (18.2.19)	..	1·25	30
	w. Wmk Crown to right of CA	..	28·00	8·50
32	3 c. grey and brown (10.04)	..	45·00	1·00
	a. *Grey-brown and brown* (12.05)	..	28·00	1·00
	ab. Chalk-surfaced paper	..	28·00	2·00
33	3 c. brown (11.7.06)	..	6·00	15
34	3 c. carmine (2.2.09)	..	2·00	10
	aw. Wmk Crown to right of CA	..	4·50	30
	b. *Scarlet* (1.17)	..	12·00	40
	bw. Wmk Crown to right of CA	..	22·00	4·25
35	3 c. grey (29.10.18)	..	1·25	20
	w. Wmk Crown to right of CA	..	24·00	8·50

36	4 c. grey and scarlet	..	32·00	2·75
	a. *Chalk-surfaced paper. Grey and rose*	11·00	1·00
	b. *Grey-brown and scarlet*	28·00	2·25
	c. *Black and scarlet*	22·00	2·25
	d. *Black and rose*	4·00	30
	dw. Wmk Crown to right of CA	6·00	30
	e. *Black and deep rose (aniline)* (1909)	45·00	5·00
	f. *Jet black and rose* (1914)	20·00	1·50
37	4 c. scarlet (Die I) (11.2.19)	2·00	3·50
38	4 c. scarlet (Die II) (15.4.19)	1·00	15
	aw. Wmk Crown to right of CA	30·00	4·00
	b. Wmk upright (2.22)		† £325
39	5 c. green and carmine/*yellow* (5.06)	6·50	1·50
	aw. Wmk Crown to right of CA	38·00	15·00
	b. *Chalk-surfaced paper*	19·00	3·50
	c. *Deep green and carmine/yellow*	6·50	1·75
	d. *On orange-buff* (1921)	13·00	4·75
	e. *On pale yellow* (4.22)	6·00	3·25
40	6 c. orange (11.2.19)	2·25	1·50
41	8 c. grey and ultramarine (2.05)	50·00	17·00
	aw. Wmk Crown to right of CA		
	b. *Grey-brown and ultramarine* (12.05)	17·00	3·50
	ba. *Chalk-surfaced paper*	38·00	10·00
	bb. Wmk upright (3.07)	5·50	3·50
42	8 c. ultramarine (8.3.10)	13·00	90
	aw. Wmk Crown to right of CA	45·00	21·00
	b. *Deep blue* (1918)	15·00	1·25
43	10 c. grey-brown and claret	50·00	2·25
	a. *Chalk-surfaced paper* (1905)	65·00	6·00
	b. *Black and claret*	17·00	30
	bw. Wmk Crown to right of CA	29·00	1·00
	c. *Grey-brown and purple* (1905)	48·00	2·75
	d. *Black and purple*	17·00	2·00
	e. *Jet-black and bright purple* (1914)	60·00	4·00
44	10 c. deep blue (3.6.19)	6·50	1·00
	a. *Bright blue*	6·50	85
	ab. Wmk inverted		†
	aw. Wmk Crown to right of CA	35·00	16·00
45	20 c. mauve and black (3.05)	6·00	40
	a. *Chalk-surfaced paper*	8·50	2·25
	w. Wmk Crown to right of CA	42·00	16·00
46	35 c. scarlet/*pale yellow* (25.8.22)	5·50	12·00
47	50 c. grey and orange (3.05)	55·00	6·00
	aw. Wmk Crown to right of CA	£120	38·00
	b. Wmk inverted		† —
	c. *Grey-brown and orange-brown* (1906)	38·00	6·00
	ca. *Chalk-surfaced paper. Grey-brown and orange-brown*	40·00	5·00
	cb. *Grey and orange-brown*	45·00	5·50
	cc. *Black and orange-brown*	65·00	11·00
	cd. *Jet-black and orange-brown* (1914)	90·00	14·00
48	$1 grey-green and green (11.07)	50·00	38·00
	a. *Green and pale green*	70·00	38·00
	aw. Wmk inverted		
49	$2 green and carmine (4.12.07)	70·00	£100
	a. *Printed on the gummed side*		
	w. Wmk inverted		
50	$5 green and blue (1.08)	£120	£130
51	$25 green and orange (12.09)	£1100	£600
27/50		*Set of 22* £375	£250
28, 30/1, 33/5, 37, 40, 42, 44, 46 Optd "Specimen"		*Set of 11* £375	

*The normal sideways watermark shows Crown to left of CA, as seen from the back of the stamp.

Nos. 29/*b*, 30, 31, 33, 34/*b* and 35 were printed from single working plates and all the rest from double plates.

Most examples of No. 47*b* have fiscal cancellations, but at least one is known postally used.

1922–34. *Wmk Mult Script CA (sideways* on T 3). Ordinary paper (1 c. to 10 c. (No. 66), 12 c., 35 c. (No. 72)) or chalk-surfaced paper (others).*

52	3	1 c. deep brown (1.8.22)	1·50	2·50
		w. Wmk Crown to right of CA	30·00	30·00
53		1 c. black (12.6.23)	75	20
54		2 c. brown (5.8.25)	4·75	4·25
55		2 c. green (15.6.26)	2·75	10
56		3 c. grey (27.12.22)	1·75	7·00
		w. Wmk Crown to right of CA	35·00	35·00
57		3 c. green (22.1.24)	1·25	1·50
58		3 c. brown (31.5.27)	80	70
59		4 c. carmine-red (Die II) (27.11.23)	2·75	45
		w. Wmk Crown to right of CA	23·00	12·00
60		4 c. orange (9.11.26)	85	10
		a. *No watermark*	£300	£200
61		5 c. mauve/*pale yellow* (17.3.22)	85	20
		w. Wmk Crown to right of CA	30·00	27·00
62		5 c. brown (1.3.32)	2·50	10
63		6 c. orange (2.5.22)	80	45
		w. Wmk Crown to right of CA		
64		6 c. scarlet (9.11.26)	1·00	10
		a. Wmk upright		
65		10 c. bright blue (23.10.23)	1·25	7·00
		w. Wmk Crown to right of CA		
66		10 c. black and blue (18.1.24†)	2·00	75
67		10 c. purple/*pale yellow* (14.7.31)	3·50	40
68		12 c. ultramarine (12.9.22)	1·25	10
		w. Wmk Crown to right of CA	35·00	22·00
69		20 c. dull purple and black (*chalk-surfaced paper*) (3.4.23)	4·00	35
		a. Ordinary paper (29.12.26)	24·00	1·25
70		25 c. purple and bright magenta (3.9.29)	2·50	1·25
71		30 c. purple and orange-yellow (3.9.29)	3·25	2·75
72		35 c. scarlet/*pale yellow* (6.11.28)	3·25	17·00
73		35 c. scarlet and purple (29.9.31)	13·00	14·00
74		50 c. black and orange (24.4.24)	13·00	7·00
		aw. Wmk Crown to right of CA	85·00	
		b. *Black and orange-brown*	24·00	4·50
75		50 c. black/*green* (16.6.31)	4·00	2·00
76	4	$1 pale green and green (2.2.26)	21·00	80·00
		a. *Grey-green and emerald* (5.10.26)	15·00	38·00
77	3	$1 black and red/*blue* (10.3.31)	12·00	3·00
78	4	$2 green and carmine (17.8.26)	18·00	70·00
79	3	$2 green and red/*yellow* (6.2.34)	35·00	32·00
80	4	$5 green and blue (24.2.25)	75·00	£150
81	3	$5 green and red/*green* (7.34)	£140	£150
82	4	$25 grn & orge (14.2.28) (Optd S. £130)	£800	£500
52/81			*Set of 30* £325	£450
52/81 Optd/Perf "Specimen"			*Set of 30* £700	

*The normal sideways watermark shows Crown to left of CA, as seen from the back of the stamp.

†No. 66 was released in London by the Crown Agents some months earlier but this is the official date of issue in the States.

Nos. 52, 56 and 59 were printed from single working plates and the rest from double plates.

No. 55 exists in coils constructed from normal sheets.

The 5 c. mauve on white Script paper is the result of soaking early printings of No. 61 in water.

STAMP BOOKLETS

1909. *Black on pink (Nos. SB1/2) or black on buff (No. SB3) covers. Stapled.*
SB1 25 c. booklet containing twenty-four 1 c. (No. 29)
    in blocks of 6 .. .. £2000
    a. Black on green cover (1917)
    b. Black on blue cover £2000
SB2 73 c. booklet containing twenty-four 3 c. (No. 34)
    in blocks of 6 .. .. £1800
    a. Black on red cover (1917)
    b. Black on blue cover £1800
SB3 97 c. booklet containing twenty-four 4 c. (No. 36d)
    in blocks of 6 .. .. £2000

1919. *Black on green (No. SB4) or black on pink (No. SB5) covers. Stapled.*
SB4 49 c. booklet containing twenty-four 2 c. (No. 31) £5000
    in blocks of 6
SB5 97 c. booklet containing twenty-four 4 c. (No. 37)
    in blocks of 6 .. .. £1800

1922. *Black on buff cover (No. SB7). Stapled.*
SB6 $1. 21, booklet containing twenty-four 5 c. (No.
    61) in blocks of 6
SB7 $1.45, booklet containing twenty-four 6 c. (No.
    63) in blocks of 6 .. .. .. £2000

1926. *As Nos. SB4, SB3 and SB7, but sold at face value without premium. Black on green (No. SB8), black on pink (No. SB9) or black on buff (No. SB10) covers. Stapled.*
SB8 48 c. booklet containing twenty-four 2 c. (No. 55)
    in blocks of 6
SB9 96 c. booklet containing twenty-four 4 c. (No. 60)
    in blocks of 6 .. .. £2000
SB10 $1.44 booklet containing twenty-four 6 c. (No.
    64) in blocks of 6 .. .. .. £2000

1926. *Black on grey cover. Stapled.*
SB11 $1 booklet containing 4 c. and 6 c. (Nos. 60, 64)
    each in block of 10 .. .. ..

1927. *Black on bluish green cover. Stapled.*
SB12 $1.50, booklet containing 2 c., 3 c., 4 c. and 6 c.
    (Nos. 55, 58, 60, 64) each in block of 10 .. £2000

1927–30. *Black on red (No. SB13), black on green (No. SB14) or black on blue (No. SB15) covers. Stapled.*
SB13 $1.20, booklet containing thirty 4 c. (No. 60) in
    blocks of 10 .. .. £2000
    a. Black on orange cover (1930)
SB14 $1.20, booklet containing twenty 6 c. (No. 64) in
    blocks of 10 (1928) .. .. ..
SB15 $1.20, booklet containing 2 c., 4 c. and 6 c. (Nos.
    55, 60, 64) each in block of 10 (1928) ..
    a. Black on white cover (1930) .. ..

1934.
SB16 $1 booklet containing twenty 5 c. (No. 62) in
    blocks of 10 .. ..

POSTAGE DUE STAMPS

D 1

(Typo Waterlow)

1924 (1 Dec)–26. *Wmk Mult Script CA (sideways*). P 15×14.*
D1 D 1 1 c. violet .. .. .. 4·50 18·00
    w. Wmk Crown to left of CA (1926) 8·00 15·00
D2   2 c. black .. .. .. 1·75 3·25
    w. Wmk Crown to left of CA (1926) 3·25 3·25
D3   4 c. green (*wmk Crown to left of CA*)
    (27.4.26) .. .. .. 2·25 5·00
D4   8 c. red .. .. .. 4·50 20·00
    w. Wmk Crown to left of CA (1926) 9·00 17·00
D5   10 c. orange .. .. .. 8·00 16·00
    w. Wmk Crown to left of CA (1926) 14·00 13·00
D6   12 c. blue .. .. .. 9·00 21·00
    w. Wmk Crown to left of CA (1926) 12·00 14·00
D1/6 .. .. .. *Set of 6* 27·00 60·00
D1/6 Optd "Specimen" .. *Set of 6* £150
*The normal sideways watermark shows Crown to right of CA, *as seen from the back of the stamp.*

The issues of the Federated Malay States were replaced by stamps for the individual States from 1935 onwards.

III. MALAYAN POSTAL UNION

The Malayan Postal Union was organised in 1934 and, initially, covered the Straits Settlements and the Federated Malay States. Stamps of the Straits Settlements together with issues for the individual States continued to be used, but Malayan Postal Union postage due stamps were introduced in 1936.

Following the end of the Second World War the use of these postage dues spread throughout Malaya and to Singapore.

PRICES FOR STAMPS ON COVER TO 1945	
Nos. D1/6	*from* × 10
Nos. D7/13	*from* × 4

POSTAGE DUE STAMPS

D 1   **10 cents** (D 2)

(Typo Waterlow until 1961, then D.L.R.)

1936 (June)–38. *Wmk Mult Script CA. P 15×14.*
D1 D 1 1 c. slate-purple (4.38) .. 4·00 70
D2   4 c. green (9.36) .. .. 13·00 1·00
D3   8 c. scarlet .. .. .. 6·50 3·50
D4   10 c. yellow .. .. .. 9·00 30
D5   12 c. pale ultramarine (9.36) 10·00 14·00
D6   50 c. black (1.38) .. .. 28·00 6·00
D1/6 .. .. .. *Set of 6* 60·00 23·00
D1/6 Perf "Specimen" .. *Set of 6* £140
For use in Negri Sembilan, Pahang, Perak, Selangor and Straits Settlements including Singapore.

1945–49. *New values and colours. Wmk Mult Script CA. P 15×14.*
D 7 D 1 1 c. purple .. .. 2·75 1·75
D 8   3 c. green .. .. 6·00 8·50
D 9   5 c. scarlet .. .. 6·00 6·00
D10   8 c. red-orange (1949) (Perf S. £75) .. 16·00 16·00
D11   9 c. yellow-orange .. 50·00 48·00
D12   15 c. pale ultramarine .. £140 35·00
D13   20 c. blue (1948) (Perf S. £75) 8·00 5·00
D7/13 .. .. .. *Set of 7* £200 £110

1951 (8 Aug)–63. *Wmk Mult Script CA. P 14.*
D14 D 1 1 c. violet (21.8.52) .. 40 1·40
D15   2 c. deep slate-blue (16.11.53) 90 2·25
    a. Perf 12½ (15.11.60) 40 11·00
    ab. Chalk-surfaced paper (10.7.62) 35 6·50
    ac. Ditto. Imperf between (vert pair)
D16   3 c. deep green (21.8.52) 24·00 12·00
D17   4 c. sepia (16.11.53) .. 45 4·50
    a. Perf 12½ (15.11.60) 60 16·00
    ab. Chalk-surfaced paper. *Bistre-brown* (10.7.62) 70 13·00
D18   5 c. vermilion .. .. 48·00 12·00
D19   8 c. yellow-orange .. 2·00 4·25
D20   12 c. bright purple (1.2.54) 1·00 5·50
    a. Perf 12½. Chalk-surfaced paper (10.7.62) .. 1·50 62·00
D21   20 c. blue .. .. .. 4·00 6·50
    a. Perf 12½. *Deep blue* (10.12.57) 6·50 26·00
    ab. Chalk-surfaced paper (15.10.63) 3·00 32·00
D14/21 .. .. .. *Set of 8* 70·00 42·00
Nos. D7 to D21b were for use in the Federation and Singapore, and from 1963 throughout Malaysia.

1964 (14 Apr)–65. *Chalk-surfaced paper. Wmk w 12 (sideways on 1 c.). P 12½.*
D22 D 1 1 c. maroon .. .. 30 14·00
    a. Perf 12. Wmk upright (4.5.65) 30 14·00
D23   2 c. deep slate-blue .. 45 14·00
    a. Perf 12 (9.3.65) .. 75 17·00
D24   4 c. bistre-brown .. 75 14·00
    a. Perf 12 (9.3.65) .. 40 14·00
D25   8 c. yellow-orange (p 12) (4.5.65) 2·00 15·00
D27   12 c. bright purple .. 1·50 18·00
    a. Perf 12 (4.5.65) .. 4·25 28·00
D28   20 c. deep blue .. .. 2·50 35·00
    a. Perf 12 (4.5.65) .. 6·50 48·00
D22/8 .. .. .. *Set of 6* 6·25 95·00

1964 (Dec). *As No. D19 surch locally with Type D 2.*
D29 D 1 10 c. on 8 c. yellow-orange 30 2·00
First supplies of this stamp differed from No. D19 in that they had been climatically affected but later a fresh printing of No. D19 was surcharged.

1966. *Unsurfaced paper. Wmk w 12. P 15×14.*
D30 D 1 50 c. black £800 £700
Nos. D22/9 were for use throughout Malaysia and Singapore. They were superseded on 15 August 1966 by the postage dues inscribed "MALAYSIA", but continued in use, together with No. D30, for Singapore until 31 January 1968 when they were replaced by Singapore Postage Dues.

IV. MALAYA (BRITISH MILITARY ADMINISTRATION)

For use throughout all Malay States and in Singapore. From 1948 this general issue was gradually replaced by individual issues for each state. The last usage was in Kelantan where B M A overprints were not withdrawn until 10 July 1951.

B M A
MALAYA
(1)

1945 (19 Oct)–48. *T 58 of Straits Settlements from Die I (double-plate printing) or Die II (single-plate printing) optd with T 1. Wmk Mult Script CA. Chalk-surfaced paper. P 14 or 15×14 (No. 11).*
1 1 c. black (I) (R). .. .. 2·50 40
    a. Ordinary paper 10 30
2 2 c. orange (II) (8.7.47) .. 4·00 60
    a. Ordinary paper (19.10.45) 20 10
    w. Wmk inverted .. † £1300
3 2 c. orange (I) (*ordinary paper*) (9.46) 16·00 3·25
4 3 c. yellow-green (II) (*ordinary paper*) 30 50
    a. *Blue-green* (27.1.47) 3·50 3·00
    b. Chalk-surfaced paper. *Blue-grn* (8.7.47) 9·00 60
5 5 c. brown (II) (11.45) .. 70 90
6 6 c. grey (II) (22.3.48) .. 10·00 2·25
    a. Ordinary paper (19.10.45) 30 20
7 8 c. scarlet (I) (*ordinary paper*) 30 10
8 10 c. purple (I) (12.45) .. 3·25 60
    a. Ordinary paper (19.10.45) 40 10
    b. *Slate-purple* (12.45) 2·50 30
    c. *Magenta* (22.3.48) 5·50 70
9 10 c. purple (II) (28.7.48) 18·00 2·25
10 12 c. bright ultramarine (I) (11.45) 1·75 4·50
11 15 c. brt ultram (I) (*ordinary paper*) (11.45) 2·25 7·50
12 15 c. bright ultramarine (II) (R). (22.3.48) 22·00 90
    a. Ordinary paper (12.45) 75 20
    b. *Blue* (27.11.47) 45·00 85
    ba. Ordinary paper (8.7.47) 90·00 130·00
13 25 c. dull purple and scarlet (I) (22.3.48) 8·50 1·25
    a. Ordinary paper (12.45) 1·40 30
    ab. Opt double £4250
14 50 c. black/*emerald* (I) (R). (12.45) 18·00 1·50
    a. Ordinary paper .. 60 10
15 $1 black and red (I) (*ordinary paper*) (12.45) 2·00 10
16 $2 green & scar (I) (*ordinary paper*) (12.45) 2·75 75
17 $5 green and red/*emerald* (I) (11.45) 85·00 80·00
18 $5 pur & orge (I) (*ordinary paper*) (12.45) 3·75 3·00
1/18 .. .. .. *Set of 15* 90·00 80·00
1/11, 13/16, 18 Perf "Specimen" *Set of 14* £400
The 8 c. grey with "BMA" opt was prepared but not officially issued (*Price £275 unused*).

Nos. 3 and 9 do not exist without the overprint.

Initial printings on ordinary paper were produced by Harrison and Sons in 1941 following bomb damage to the De La Rue works on 29 December 1940.

No. 8 with reddish purple medallion and dull purple frame is from a 1947 printing with the head in fugitive ink which discolours with moisture.

Postal forgeries of the 50 c. value exist made by dyeing examples of the 1 c. and then altering the face value to 50 c.

In 1946 8 c. and 15 c. stamps in the Crown Colony Victory design were prepared for the Malayan Union, but not issued. Examples of the 8 c. carmine from this issue exist from unofficial leakages (*Price £275 unused*).

V. MALAYAN FEDERATION

The Malayan Federation, formed on 1 February 1948 by Malacca, Penang, the four Federated Malay States and the five Unfederated States, became an independent member of the British Commonwealth on 31 August 1957.

Commemoratives and a limited series of definitives were issued by the Federation and were used concurrently with the stamps from the individual States.

1 Tapping Rubber   4 Map of the Federation

(Centre recess, frame litho (6 c., 25 c.); centre litho, frame recess (12 c.); recess (30 c.), D.L.R.)

1957 (5 May)–63. *T 1, 4 and similar designs. W w 12. P 13×12½ (No. 4) or 13 (others).*
1 6 c. deep blue, red, yellow and grey-blue 50 10
    a. *Indigo, red, yellow and grey-blue* (20.6.61) 2·50 30
    b. *Indigo, red, yellow & slate-blue* (12.2.63) 2·75 30
    c. Yellow (star and crescent) omitted 45·00
2 12 c. red, yellow, blue, black and scarlet 85 40
3 25 c. maroon, red, yellow & dull greenish blue 2·25 10
4 30 c. orange-red and lake .. 80 20
    a. Perf 13. *Orange-red & deep lake* (20.6.61) 60 60
    ab. *Orange-red and lake* (10.7.62) 2·00 10
1/4 .. .. .. *Set of 4* 3·75 55
Designs: *Horiz*—12 c. Federation coat of arms; 25 c. Tin dredger.

NEW INFORMATION

The editor is always interested to correspond with people who have new information that will improve or correct the Catalogue.

5 Prime Minister Tunku Abdul Rahman
and Populace greeting Independence

(Des A. B. Saman. Recess Waterlow)

1957 (31 Aug). *Independence Day. Wmk Mult Script CA. P 12½.*
| 5 | 5 | 10 c. bistre-brown | .. .. | 10 | 10 |

6 United Nations Emblem **7** United Nations Emblem

(Recess D.L.R.)

1958 (5 Mar). *U.N. Economic Commission for Asia and Far East
Conference, Kuala Lumpur. W w 12. P 13½ (12 c.) or 12½ (30 c.).*
| 6 | 6 | 12 c. carmine-red | .. .. .. | 30 | 55 |
| 7 | 7 | 30 c. maroon | .. .. .. | 40 | 55 |

8 Merdeka Stadium. **9** The Yang di-Pertuan Agong
Kuala Lumpur (Tuanku Abdul Rahman)

(Photo Harrison)

1958 (31 Aug). *First Anniv of Independence. W w 12.
P 13½ × 14½ (10 c.) or 14½ × 13½ (30 c.).*
| 8 | 8 | 10 c. green, yellow, red and blue | .. | 15 | 10 |
| 9 | 9 | 30 c. red, yellow, violet-blue and green | .. | 40 | 60 |

10 "Human Rights" **11** Malayan with Torch of
Freedom

(Des J. P. Hendroff. Litho (10 c.), photo (30 c.) D.L.R.)

1958 (10 Dec). *Tenth Anniv of Declaration of Human Rights.*
(a) W w 12. P 12½ × 13
| 10 | 10 | 10 c. blue, black, carmine and orange | 15 | 10 |
(b) Wmk Mult Script CA. P 13 × 12½
| 11 | 11 | 30 c. deep green | .. | 45 | 50 |

12 Mace and
Malayan Peoples

(Photo Enschedé)

1959 (12 Sept). *Inauguration of Parliament. No wmk. P 13 × 14.*
12	12	4 c. rose-red	.. ..	10	10
13		10 c. violet	.. ..	10	10
14		25 c. yellow-green	.. ..	35	20
12/14 ..			*Set of 3*	50	30

13 **14**

(Recess D.L.R.)

1960 (7 Apr). *World Refugee Year. W w 12. P 13½ (12 c.) or
12½ × 13 (30 c.).*
| 15 | 13 | 12 c. purple | .. .. | 10 | 50 |
| 16 | 14 | 30 c. deep green | .. .. | 10 | 10 |

15 Seedling Rubber **16** The Yang
Tree and Map di-Pertuan Agong
(Tuanku Syed Putra)

(Photo Japanese Govt Ptg Wks)

1960 (19 Sept). *Natural Rubber Research Conference and 15th
International Rubber Study Group Meeting, Kuala Lumpur. T 15
and similar vert design. No wmk. P 13.*
| 17 | | 6 c. yellow-green, black, orange & red-brown | 20 | 1·00 |
| 18 | | 30 c. yellow-green, black, orange & bright blue | 50 | 60 |
No. 18 is inscribed "INTERNATIONAL RUBBER STUDY
GROUP 15th MEETING KUALA LUMPUR" at foot.

(Photo Harrison)

1961 (4 Jan). *Installation of Yang di-Pertuan Agong, Tuanku
Syed Putra. W w 12. P 14 × 14½.*
| 19 | 16 | 10 c. black and blue | .. .. | 10 | 10 |

17 Colombo Plan **18** Malaria Eradication
Emblem Emblem

(Photo Japanese Govt Ptg Works)

1961 (30 Oct). *Colombo Plan Conference, Kuala Lumpur. P 13.*
20	17	12 c. black and magenta ..	35	2·00
21		25 c. black and apple-green	80	2·00
22		30 c. black and turquoise-blue	70	30
20/2 ..		*Set of 3*	1·75	3·75

(Photo Harrison)

1962 (7 Apr). *Malaria Eradication. W w 13. P 14 × 14½.*
23	18	25 c. orange-brown	..	20	35
24		30 c. deep lilac	..	20	15
25		50 c. ultramarine	..	40	30
23/5 ..		*Set of 3*	70	70

19 Palmyra Palm Leaf **20** "Shadows of the Future"

(Photo Harrison)

1962 (21 July). *National Language Month. W w 13 (upright or
inverted). P 13½.*
26	19	10 c. light brown and deep reddish violet	15	10
27		20 c. light brown and deep bluish green	30	35
28		50 c. light brown and magenta	90	90
26/8 ..		*Set of 3*	1·25	1·25

(Photo Enschedé)

1962 (1 Oct). *Introduction of Free Primary Education. W w 13.
P 13½.*
29	20	10 c. bright purple	..	10	10
30		25 c. ochre	..	30	40
31		30 c. emerald	..	1·75	10
29/31 ..		*Set of 3*	1·90	50

21 Harvester and Fisherman **22** Dam and Pylon

(Photo Courvoisier)

1963 (21 Mar). *Freedom from Hunger. P 11½.*
32	21	25 c. carmine and apple-green	..	1·00	2·50
33		30 c. carmine and crimson	..	1·75	1·00
34		50 c. carmine and bright blue	..	1·75	2·50
32/4 ..		*Set of 3*	4·00	5·50

(Photo Harrison)

1963 (26 June). *Cameron Highlands Hydro-Electric Scheme.
W w 13. P 14.*
| 35 | 22 | 20 c. green and reddish violet | .. | 45 | 10 |
| 36 | | 30 c. blue-green and ultramarine | .. | 55 | 80 |

The definitive general issue for Malaysia and the low value sets
for the individual states superseded the stamps of the Malayan
Federation by 15 November 1965.

VI. MALAYSIA

On 16 September 1963, the Malayan Federation, Sabah
(North Borneo), Sarawak and Singapore formed the Federation
of Malaysia. Singapore left the Federation on 9 August 1965,
and became an independent republic. Stamps of Singapore
continued to be valid in Malaysia, and those of Malaysia in
Singapore, until 1 February 1967.
Individual issues for the component States continued, but were
restricted to low value definitives and the occasional "State"
commemorative. The higher value definitives and the vast
majority of commemoratives were issued on a "National" basis.

A. NATIONAL ISSUES

General issues for use throughout the Malaysian Federation.

1 Federation Map **2** Bouquet of Orchids

(Photo Harrison)

1963 (16 Sept). *Inauguration of Federation. W w 13. P 14½.*
1	1	10 c. yellow and bluish violet	..	40	10
		a. Yellow omitted	..	£100	
2		12 c. yellow and deep green	..	1·00	60
3		50 c. yellow and chocolate	..	1·40	10
1/3 ..		*Set of 3*	2·50	65

(Photo Enschedé)

1963 (3 Oct). *Fourth World Orchid Conference, Singapore. No
wmk. P 13 × 14.*
| 4 | 2 | 6 c. multicoloured | .. | 1·25 | 1·25 |
| 5 | | 25 c. multicoloured | .. | 1·25 | 25 |

4 Parliament House, Kuala Lumpur

(Des V. Whiteley. Photo Harrison)

1963 (4 Nov). *Ninth Commonwealth Parliamentary Conference,
Kuala Lumpur. W w 13 (inverted). P 13½.*
| 7 | 4 | 20 c. deep magenta and gold | .. | 65 | 40 |
| 8 | | 30 c. deep green and gold | .. | 65 | 15 |

5 "Flame of Freedom" and **6** Microwave Tower and
Emblems of Goodwill, Health I.T.U. Emblem
and Charity

(Photo Harrison)

1964 (10 Oct). *Eleanor Roosevelt Commemoration.* W w **13.**
P 14½ × 13½.

9	5	25 c. black, red and greenish blue	20	10
10		30 c. black, red and deep lilac	20	15
11		50 c. black, red and ochre-yellow	20	10
9/11		Set of 3	55	30

(Photo Courvoisier)

1965 (17 May). *I.T.U. Centenary. P* 11½.

12	6	2 c. multicoloured	15	80
13		25 c. multicoloured	1·25	50
14		50 c. multicoloured	1·75	10
12/14		Set of 3	2·75	1·25

7 National Mosque   **8** Air Terminal

(Photo Harrison)

1965 (27 Aug). *Opening of National Mosque, Kuala Lumpur.*
W w **13.** *P* 14 × 14½.

15	7	6 c. carmine	10	10
16		15 c. red-brown	20	10
17		20 c. deep bluish green	20	15
15/17		Set of 3	45	30

(Photo Harrison)

1965 (30 Aug). *Opening of International Airport, Kuala Lumpur.*
W w **13.** *P* 14½ × 14.

18	8	15 c. black, yellow-green and new blue	30	10
		a. Yellow-green omitted	23·00	
19		30 c. black, yellow-green and magenta	60	20

9 Crested Wood   **17** Sepak Raga (ball
Partridge   game) and Football

(Des A. Fraser-Brunner. Photo Harrison)

1965 (9 Sept). *T* **9** *and similar vert designs. Multicoloured.*
W w **13.** *P* 14½.

20	25 c. Type 9	50	10
	w. Wmk inverted	2·75	
21	30 c. Blue-backed Fairy Bluebird	60	10
	a. Blue (plumage) omitted	£140	
	w. Wmk inverted	4·00	
22	50 c. Black-naped Oriole	80	10
	a. Yellow omitted	85·00	
	b. Imperf (pair)	£200	
	c. Scarlet (inscr and berries) omitted	55·00	
	w. Wmk inverted	7·50	
23	75 c. Rhinoceros Hornbill	90	10
	a. Scarlet omitted*	80·00	
24	$1 Zebra Dove	1·50	10
	w. Wmk inverted	20·00	
25	$2 Great Argus Pheasant	3·50	30
	a. Imperf (pair)	£200	
	w. Wmk inverted	8·50	
26	$5 Asiatic Paradise Flycatcher	18·00	2·50
	w. Wmk inverted	22·00	
27	$10 Blue-tailed Pitta	48·00	11·00
	a. Imperf (pair)	£275	
20/7	Set of 8	65·00	12·50

*The inscription at foot is omitted and the background appears paler.
All values except the 75 c. and $10 exist with PVA gum as well as gum arabic.

(Des E. A. F. Anthony. Litho Japanese Govt Ptg Wks)

1965 (14 Dec). *Third South East Asian Peninsular Games. T* **17**
and similar vert designs. P 13 × 13½.

28	25 c. black and olive-green	40	90
29	30 c. black and bright purple	40	20
30	50 c. black and light blue	70	30
28/30	Set of 3	1·40	1·25

Designs:—30 c. Running; 50 c. Diving.

20 National Monument   **21** The Yang di-Pertuan
Agong (Tuanku Ismail
Nasiruddin Shah)

(Photo Harrison)

1966 (8 Feb). *National Monument, Kuala Lumpur.* W w **13.**
P 13½.

31	20	10 c. multicoloured	20	10
		a. Blue omitted	65·00	
32		20 c. multicoloured	30	40

(Photo Japanese Govt Ptg Wks)

1966 (11 Apr). *Installation of Yang di-Pertuan Agong, Tuanku
Ismail Nasiruddin Shah. P* 13½.

33	21	15 c. black and light yellow	10	10
34		50 c. black and greenish blue	20	20

22 School Building   **23** "Agriculture"

(Photo D.L.R.)

1966 (21 Oct). *150th Anniv of Penang Free School.* W w **13** (*sideways*). *P* 13.

35	22	20 c. multicoloured	55	10
36		50 c. multicoloured	70	10

The 50 c. is also inscr "ULANG TAHUN KE-150" at foot and
bears a shield at bottom left corner.

(Des Enche Ng Peng Nam. Photo Japanese Govt Ptg Wks)

1966 (1 Dec). *First Malaysia Plan. T* **23** *and similar horiz designs.
Multicoloured. P* 13½.

37	15 c. Type 23	20	10
38	15 c. "Rural Health"	20	10
39	15 c. "Communications"	1·25	15
40	15 c. "Education"	20	10
41	15 c. "Irrigation"	20	10
37/41	Set of 5	1·90	50

28 Cable Route Maps

(Des Enche Ng Peng Nam. Photo Japanese Govt Ptg Wks)

1967 (31 Aug). *Tenth Anniv of Independence.* W w **13.** *P* 14½.

42	28	30 c. multicoloured	80	30
43		75 c. multicoloured	2·50	3·25

29 Hibiscus and Paramount Rulers

(Photo Harrison)

1967 (31 Aug). *Tenth Anniv of Independence.* W w **13.** *P* 14½.

44	29	15 c. multicoloured	20	10
		w. Wmk inverted	3·75	
45		50 c. multicoloured	80	80

30 Mace and Shield   **31** Straits Settlements 1867 8 c.
and Malaysia 1965 25 c. Definitive

(Des Enche Ng Peng Nam. Photo Harrison)

1967 (8 Sept). *Centenary of Sarawak Council.* W w **13.** *P* 14½.

46	30	15 c. multicoloured	10	10
47		50 c. multicoloured	30	50

(Des Enche Ng Peng Nam. Photo Japanese Govt Ptg Works)

1967 (2 Dec). *Stamp Centenary. T* **31** *and similar shaped designs.
Multicoloured. P* 11½.

48	25 c. Type 31	1·40	2·25
	a. Tête-bêche (horiz pair)	2·75	4·50
49	30 c. Straits Settlements 1867 24 c. and Malaysia 1965 30 c. definitive	1·40	1·75
	a. Tête-bêche (horiz pair)	2·75	3·50
50	50 c. Straits Settlements 1867 32 c. and Malaysia 1965 50 c. definitive	2·25	2·50
	a. Tête-bêche (horiz pair)	4·50	5·00
48/50	Set of 3	4·50	6·00

Nos. 48/50 were each printed in sheets with the stamps
arranged horizontally *tête-bêche.*

34 Tapping Rubber, and   **37** Mexican Sombrero
Molecular Unit   and Blanket with
Olympic Rings

(Litho B.W.)

1968 (29 Aug). *Natural Rubber Conference, Kuala Lumpur. T* **34**
and similar horiz designs. Multicoloured. W w **13.** *P* 12.

51	25 c. Type 34	25	10
52	30 c. Tapping rubber, and export consignment	40	20
53	50 c. Tapping rubber, and aircraft tyres	40	10
51/3	Set of 3	95	35

(Litho B.W.)

1968 (12 Oct). *Olympic Games, Mexico. T* **37** *and similar vert
design. Multicoloured.* W w **13.** *P* 12 × 11½.

54	30 c. Type 37	20	10
55	75 c. Olympic rings and Mexican embroidery	55	20

39 Tunku Abdul Rahman   **40**
against background of
Pandanus Weave

(Photo Japanese Govt Ptg Wks)

1969 (8 Feb). *Solidarity Week. T* **39/40** *and similar multicoloured
design. P* 13½.

56	15 c. Type 39	15	10
57	20 c. Type 40	40	1·00
58	50 c. Tunku Abdul Rahman with pandanus pattern (*horiz*)	40	20
56/8	Set of 3	85	1·10

42 Peasant Girl with Sheaves of Paddy

(Des Enche Hoessein Anas. Photo Harrison)

1969 (8 Oct). *National Rice Year.* W w **13.** *P* 13½.

59	42	15 c. multicoloured	15	10
60		75 c. multicoloured	55	85

43 Satellite tracking Aerial

44 "Intelsat III" in Orbit

(Photo Enschedé)

1970 (6 Apr). *Satellite Earth Station.* W w **13.** *P* 14 × 13 (15 c.) or
13½ × 13 (30 c.).

61	43	15 c. multicoloured	95	15
		a. Tête-bêche (horiz pair)	1·90	2·00
62	44	30 c. multicoloured*	95	1·75
63		30 c. multicoloured*	95	1·75
61/3		Set of 3	2·50	3·25

No. 61 was issued horizontally *tête-bêche* in the sheets.
*Nos. 62/3 are of the same design, differing only in the lettering
colours (No. 62 white; No. 63 gold).

45 *Euploea leucostictus*   **46** Emblem

(Des V. Whiteley. Litho B.W. (to 1976) or Harrison)

1970 (31 Aug–16 Nov). *Butterflies. T **45** and similar vert designs. Multicoloured. P 13 × 13½.*

64	25 c.	Type 45		1·00	10
65	30 c.	*Zeuxidia amethystus*		1·50	10
66	50 c.	*Polyura athamas*		1·75	10
67	75 c.	*Papilio memnon*		2·00	10
68	$1	*Appias nero* (16.11)		2·50	10
69	$2	*Trogonoptera brookiana* (16.11)		3·50	10
70	$5	*Narathura centaurus* (16.11)		5·00	2·75
71	$10	*Terinos terpander* (16.11)		17·00	5·00
64/71			Set of 8	30·00	7·00

See also Nos. 144/5.

(Litho Harrison)

1970 (7 Sept). *50th Anniv of International Labour Organization. P 14 × 13½.*

72	46	30 c. grey and new blue		10	20
73		75 c. pink and new blue		20	30

47 U.N. Emblem encircled by Doves   **50** The Yang di-Pertuan Agong (Tuanku Abdul Halim Shah)

(Des Enche Ng Peng Nam. Litho D.L.R.)

1970 (24 Oct). *25th Anniv of United Nations. T **47** and similar horiz designs. P 13 × 12½.*

74	25 c. gold, black and brown			30	40
75	30 c. multicoloured			30	35
76	50 c. black and dull yellow-green			40	75
74/6			Set of 3	90	1·40

Designs:—30 c. Line of doves and U.N. emblem; 50 c. Doves looping U.N. emblem.

(Des Union Art Corp. Photo Harrison)

1971 (20 Feb). *Installation of Yang di-Pertuan Agong (Paramount Ruler of Malaysia). P 14½ × 14.*

77	50	10 c. black, gold and lemon		20	30
		a. Gold (value and inscr) omitted		£160	
78		15 c. black and bright mauve		20	30
79		50 c. black, gold and new blue		60	1·60
77/9			Set of 3	90	2·00

51 Bank Negara Complex

(Photo Harrison)

1971 (15 May). *Opening of Bank Negara Building. P 13½ (and around design).*

80	51	25 c. black and silver		90	90
81		50 c. black and gold		90	1·10

52 Aerial view of Parliament Buildings

(Des Union Art Corp. Litho Harrison)

1971 (13 Sept). *17th Commonwealth Parliamentary Association Conference, Kuala Lumpur. T **52** and similar multicoloured design. P 13½ (25 c.) or 12½ × 13 (75c.).*

82	25 c. Type 52		1·25	50
83	75 c. Ground view of Parliament Buildings (73 × 23½ mm)		2·75	1·75

53   **54**   **55**

Malaysian Carnival

(Des locally. Litho Harrison)

1971 (18 Sept). *Visit A.S.E.A.N.* Year. P 14½.*

84	53	30 c. multicoloured		1·50	55
		a. Horiz strip of 3. Nos. 84/6		4·00	
85	54	30 c. multicoloured		1·50	55
86	55	30 c. multicoloured		1·50	55
84/6			Set of 3	4·00	1·50

*A.S.E.A.N. = Association of South East Asian Nations.

Nos. 84/6 were printed together, *se-tenant*, in horizontal strips of 3 throughout the sheet, forming a composite design.

56 Trees, Elephant and Tiger   **57** Athletics

(Des from children's drawings. Litho Harrison)

1971 (2 Oct). *25th Anniv of U.N.I.C.E.F. T **56** and similar multicoloured designs. P 12½.*

87	15 c. Type 56			1·90	45
		a. Horiz strip of 5. Nos. 87/91		8·50	
88	15 c. Cat and kittens			1·90	45
89	15 c. Sun, flower and bird (22 × 29 mm)			1·90	45
90	15 c. Monkey, elephant and lion in jungle			1·90	45
91	15 c. Spider and butterflies			1·90	45
87/91			Set of 5	8·50	2·00

Nos. 87/91 were issued in horizontal *se-tenant* strips of 5 throughout the sheet.

(Des Union Art Corp. Litho B.W.)

1971 (11 Dec). *Sixth S.E.A.P.* Games, Kuala Lumpur. T **57** and similar horiz designs. Multicoloured. P 14½ × 14.*

92	25 c. Type 57			45	40
93	30 c. Sepak Raga players			60	50
94	50 c. Hockey			1·50	95
92/4			Set of 3	2·25	1·75

*S.E.A.P. = South East Asian Peninsula.

58   **59**   **60**

Map and Tourist Attractions

(Des locally. Litho Harrison)

1972 (31 Jan). *Pacific Area Tourist Association Conference. P 14 × 14½.*

95	58	30 c. multicoloured		2·25	70
		a. Horiz strip of 3. Nos. 95/7		6·00	
96	59	30 c. multicoloured		2·25	70
97	60	30 c. multicoloured		2·25	70
95/7			Set of 3	6·00	1·90

Nos. 95/7 were printed together, *se-tenant*, in horizontal strips of 3 throughout the sheet forming a composite design.

61 Kuala Lumpur City Hall

(Des from colour transparencies. Litho Harrison)

1972 (1 Feb). *City Status for Kuala Lumpur. T **61** and similar horiz design. Multicoloured. P 14½ × 14.*

98	25 c. Type 61			1·25	1·25
99	50 c. City Hall in floodlights			2·00	1·25

62 SOCSO Emblem   **63** W.H.O. Emblem

(Des B.W. Litho Harrison)

1973 (2 July). *Social Security Organisation. P 13½.*

100	62	10 c. multicoloured		15	15
101		15 c. multicoloured		25	10
102		50 c. multicoloured		60	1·40
100/2			Set of 3	90	1·50

(Des Union Advertising. Litho B.W.)

1973 (1 Aug). *25th Anniv of W.H.O. T **63** and similar vert design. P 13.*

103	30 c. multicoloured			65	25
104	75 c. multicoloured			1·60	1·75

64 Fireworks, National Flag and Flower   **65** Emblems of Interpol and Royal Malaysian Police

(Des Clover Associates. Litho Harrison)

1973 (31 Aug). *Tenth Anniv of Malaysia. P 13½.*

105	64	10 c. multicoloured		40	25
106		15 c. multicoloured		55	15
107		50 c. multicoloured		1·90	1·60
105/7			Set of 3	2·50	1·75

(Des Union Advertising. Litho Harrison)

1973 (15 Sept). *50th Anniv of Interpol. T **65** and similar vert design. Multicoloured. P 13½.*

108	25 c. Type 65			1·00	50
109	75 c. Emblems within "50"			2·25	2·00

66 Boeing 737 and M.A.S. Emblem

(Des Art Dept, Malaysia Airline System. Litho Harrison)

1973 (1 Oct). *Foundation of Malaysia Airline System. P 14½.*

110	66	15 c. multicoloured		35	10
111		30 c. multicoloured		65	60
112		50 c. multicoloured		95	1·60
110/12			Set of 3	1·75	2·10

67 Kuala Lumpur

(Des Malaysian Advertising Services. Litho B.W.)

1974 (1 Feb). *Establishment of Kuala Lumpur as Federal Territory. P 12½ × 13.*

113	67	25 c. multicoloured		50	85
114		50 c. multicoloured		1·00	1·75

68 Development Projects   **69** Scout Badge and Map

(Des Malaysian Advertising Services. Litho Rosenbaum Bros, Vienna)

1974 (25 Apr). *Seventh Annual Meeting of Asian Development Bank's Board of Governors, Kuala Lumpur.* P 13½.
115　68　30 c. multicoloured　..　..　..　25　50
116　　　75 c. multicoloured　..　..　80　1·75

(Des Malaysian Advertising Services. Litho Harrison)

1974 (1 Aug). *Malaysian Scout Jamboree. T* **69** *and similar multicoloured designs.* P 13 × 13½ (15 c.) or 14 × 13½ (others).
117　10 c. Type **69**　..　..　..　55　30
118　15 c. Scouts saluting and flags (46 × 24 mm)　70　30
119　50 c. Scout badge　..　..　1·75　2·25
117/19　..　..　..　Set of 3　2·75　2·50

70 Coat of Arms and Power Installations

(Des Malaysian Advertising Services. Litho Harrison)

1974 (1 Sept). *25th Anniv of National Electricity Board. T* **70** *and similar multicoloured design.* P 14 (30 c.) or 14 × 14½ (75 c.).
120　30 c. Type **70**　..　..　..　30　50
121　75 c. National Electricity Board Building (37 × 27 mm)　..　..　1·00　2·00

71 U.P.U. and Post Office Emblems within "100"

(Des Clover Associates. Litho Harrison)

1974 (9 Oct). *Centenary of Universal Postal Union.* P 14½ × 14.
122　**71**　25 c. dull yell-grn, brt yell & lt rose-carm　20　35
123　　　30 c. lt new blue, brt yell & lt rose-carm　25　35
124　　　75 c. brownish orange, bright yellow and light rose-carmine　..　..　65　1·75
122/4　..　..　..　Set of 3　1·00　2·25

72 Gravel Pump in Tin Mine　　**73** Hockey-players, World Cup and Federation Emblem

(Des Malaysian Advertising Service. Litho D.L.R.)

1974 (31 Oct). *Fourth World Tin Conference, Kuala Lumpur. T* **72** *and similar horiz designs. Multicoloured.* P 13½.
125　15 c. Type **72**　..　..　1·75　20
126　20 c. Open-cast mine　..　2·00　1·25
127　50 c. Dredger within "ingot"　..　3·75　4·50
125/7　..　..　Set of 3　6·75　5·50

(Des Malaysian Advertising Services. Litho Harrison)

1975 (1 Mar). *Third World Cup Hockey Championships.* P 13½ × 13.
128　**73**　30 c. multicoloured　..　..　90　60
129　　　75 c. multicoloured　..　2·10　2·25

74 Congress Emblem　　**75** Emblem of M.K.P.W. (Malayan Women's Organisation)

(Des Malaysian Advertising Services. Litho Harrison)

1975 (1 May). *25th Anniv of Malaysian Trade Union Congress.* P 14 × 14½.
130　**74**　20 c. multicoloured　..　20　25
131　　　25 c. multicoloured　..　30　30
132　　　30 c. multicoloured　..　45　60
130/2　..　..　Set of 3　85　1·00

(Des Malaysian Advertising Services. Litho Harrison)

1975 (25 Aug). *International Women's Year.* P 14.
133　**75**　10 c. multicoloured　..　15　25
134　　　15 c. multicoloured　..　30　25
135　　　50 c. multicoloured　..　1·25　2·25
133/5　..　..　Set of 3　1·50　2·50

76 Ubudiah Mosque, Kuala Kangsar　　**77** Plantation and Emblem

(Des Malaysian Advertising Services. Litho Harrison)

1975 (22 Sept). *Koran Reading Competition. T* **76** *and similar horiz designs. Multicoloured.* P 14.
136　15 c. Type **76**　..　..　1·60　40
　　a. Horiz strip of 5. Nos. 136/40　..　7·00
137　15 c. Zahir Mosque, Alor Star.　..　1·60　40
138　15 c. National Mosque, Kuala Lumpur　1·60　40
139　15 c. Sultan Abu Bakar Mosque, Johore Bahru　1·60　40
140　15 c. Kuching State Mosque, Sarawak　..　1·60　40
136/40　..　..　Set of 5　7·00　1·75
The above were printed together, horizontally *se-tenant* throughout the sheet.

(Des E. Sulaiman bin Haji Hassan and E. Hoh Lian Yong. Litho Harrison)

1975 (22 Oct). *50th Anniv of Malaysian Rubber Research Institute. T* **77** *and similar horiz designs. Multicoloured.* P 14 × 14½.
141　15 c. Type **77**　..　..　40　15
142　30 c. Latex cup and emblem　..　1·10　70
143　75 c. Natural rubber in test-tubes　..　2·25　2·25
141/3　..　..　Set of 3　3·25　2·75

77a *Hebomoia glaucippe*　　**78** Scrub Typhus

(Photo Harrison)

1976 (19 Jan). *Coil Stamps. T* **77a** *and similar horiz design. Multicoloured.* P 13½.
144　10 c. Type **77a**　..　2·50　6·00
145　15 c. *Precis orithya*..　..　2·50　6·00

(Des Lap Loy Fong (25 c.), Lee Eng Kee (others). Litho Harrison)

1976 (6 Feb). *75th Anniv of the Institute of Medical Research. T* **78** *and similar vert designs. Multicoloured.* P 14.
146　20 c. Type **78**　..　..　25　15
147　25 c. Malaria diagnosis　..　40　20
148　$1 Beri-beri　..　..　1·60　2·50
146/8　..　..　Set of 3　2·00　2·50

79 The Yang di-Pertuan Agong (Tuanku Yahya Petra)　　**80** State Council Complex

(Des Union Advertising. Photo Harrison)

1976 (28 Feb). *Installation of Yang di-Pertuan Agong.* P 14½ × 13½.
149　**79**　10 c. black, bistre and yellow　..　25　10
150　　　15 c. black, bistre and bright mauve　..　40　10
151　　　50 c. black, bistre and ultramarine　..　2·25　2·50
149/51　..　..　Set of 3　2·75　2·50

(Des Aini bin Abdul Rahman. Litho Harrison)

1976 (17 Aug). *Opening of the State Council Complex and Administrative Building, Sarawak.* P 12½.
152　**80**　15 c. grey-green and light yellow　..　35　10
153　　　20 c. grey-green and light bright mauve　45　40
154　　　50 c. grey-green and pale blue　..　1·00　1·40
152/4　..　..　Set of 3　1·60　1·75

81 E.P.F. Building　　**82** Blind People at Work

(Litho Harrison)

1976 (18 Oct). *25th Anniv of Employees' Provident Fund. T* **81** *and similar multicoloured designs.* P 14½ (25 c.) or 13½ × 14½ (others).
155　10 c. Type **81**　..　..　15　10
156　25 c. E.P.F. emblems (27 × 27 mm)　..　25　50
157　50 c. E.P.F. Building at night..　..　60　1·25
155/7　..　..　Set of 3　90　1·60

(Des Malayan Association for the Blind, Messrs Advertising Sales Promotion and Hexxon Grafic. Litho Harrison)

1976 (20 Nov). *25th Anniv of Malayan Association for the Blind. T* **82** *and similar horiz design. Multicoloured.* P 13½ × 14½.
158　10 c. Type **82**　..　..　15　15
159　75 c. Blind man and shadow　..　1·25　2·40

83 Independence Celebrations, 1957　　**84** F.E.L.D.A. Village Scheme

(Des Hexxon Grafic. Photo Harrison)

1977 (14 Jan). *First Death Anniversary of Tun Abdul Razak (Prime Minister). T* **83** *and similar horiz designs, each sepia and gold.* P 14.
160　15 c. Type **83**　..　..　1·50　40
　　a. Horiz strip of 5. Nos. 160/4　..　6·50
161　15 c. "Education"　..　..　1·50　40
162　15 c. Tun Razak and map ("Development")　..　1·50　40
163　15 c. "Rukunegara" (National Philosophy)　..　1·50　40
164　15 c. A.S.E.A.N. meeting　..　..　1·50　40
160/4　..　..　Set of 5　6·50　1·75
The above were printed together, horizontally *se-tenant* throughout the sheet.

(Des Halim Teh and Basyuni Sumrah. Litho Harrison)

1977 (7 July). *21st Anniv of Federal Land Development Authority (F.E.L.D.A.). T* **84** *and similar horiz design. Multicoloured.* P 13½ × 14.
165　15 c. Type **84**　..　..　30　40
166　30 c. Oil Palm settlement　..　..　80　1·50

85 Figure "10"　　**86** Games Logos

(Des Hexxon Grafic. Litho Harrison)

1977 (8 Aug). *Tenth Anniv of A.S.E.A.N. (Association of South East Asian Nations). T* **85** *and similar horiz design. Multicoloured.* P 13½ × 14½.
167　10 c. Type **85**　..　..　10　10
168　75 c. Flags of members　..　..　1·25　65

(Des PTM Communications & Co. Litho Harrison)

1977 (19 Nov). *9th South East Asia Games, Kuala Lumpur. T* **86** *and similar horiz designs. Multicoloured.* P 13½ × 14½.
169　10 c. Type **86**　..　..　15　15
170　20 c. "Ball"　..　..　20　15
171　75 c. Symbolic athletes　..　..　1·50　1·60
169/71　..　..　Set of 3　1·00　1·60

87 Islamic Development Bank Emblem　　**88** Mobile Post Office

(Des Queen's Advertising. Litho J.W.)

1978 (15 Mar). *Islamic Development Bank Board of Governors Meeting, Kuala Lumpur.* P 14.
172　**87**　30 c. multicoloured　..　..　25　15
173　　　75 c. multicoloured　..　..　65　70

(Des Hexxon Grafic. Litho J.W.)

1978 (10 July). *4th Commonwealth Postal Administrations Conference, Kuala Lumpur. T* **88** *and similar horiz designs. Multicoloured.* P 13½ × 13.
174　10 c. Type **88**　..　..　30　10
175　25 c. G.P.O., Kuala Lumpur　..　75　1·25
176　50 c. Postal delivery by motor-cycle　..　2·00　2·50
174/6　..　..　Set of 3　2·75　3·50

MINIMUM PRICE

The minimum price quote is 10p which represents a handling charge rather than a basis for valuing common stamps. For further notes about prices see introductory pages.

89 Boy Scout Emblem

90 Dome of the Rock, Jerusalem

(Des Aini bin Abdul Rahman. Litho J.W.)

1978 (26 July). *4th Malaysian Boy Scout Jamboree, Sarawak. T* **89** *and similar horiz design. Multicoloured. P* 13½ × 13.
177   15 c. Type **89** 50   10
178   $1 Bees and honeycomb .. .. 2·50   2·50

(Des Union Advertising. Litho Harrison)

1978 (21 Aug). *"Freedom for Palestine". P* 12½.
179   **90**   15 c. multicoloured 50   10
180   30 c. multicoloured .. .. .. 1·25   1·50

91 Globe and Emblems

92 "Seratus Tahun Getah Asli" and Tapping Knives Symbol

(Litho Harrison)

1978 (30 Sept). *Global Eradication of Smallpox. P* 13½ × 14½.
181   **91**   15 c. black, rosine and new blue .. 25   20
182   30 c. black, rosine and yellowish green .. 40   10
183   50 c. black, rosine and rose-pink .. 70   55
181/3 .. .. *Set of 3* 1·25   75

(Des Azmi bin Anuar. Litho J.W.)

1978 (28 Nov). *Centenary of Rubber Industry. T* **92** *and similar horiz designs. P* 13½ × 13.
184   10 c. gold and blue-green 10   10
185   20 c. ultramarine, brown & brt yellow-green .. 10   10
186   75 c. gold and blue-green 45   65
184/6 .. .. *Set of 3* 55   75
Designs:—20 c. Rubber tree seedling and part of "maxi stump"; 75 c. Graphic design of rubber tree, latex cup and globe arranged to form "100".

93 Sultan of Selangor's New Palace

(Des Queen's Advertising. Litho Harrison)

1978 (7 Dec). *Inauguration of Shah Alam New Town as State Capital of Selangor. T* **93** *and similar horiz designs. Multicoloured. P* 13½ × 14½.
187   10 c. Type **93** 10   10
188   30 c. Shah Alam (aerial view) 20   15
189   75 c. Shah Alam 55   1·50
187/9 .. .. *Set of 3* 75   1·50

94 Tiger

95 Multiple "POS" in Octagon

(Des Ong Soo Keat; adapted Malaysian Advertising Services. Litho Asher and Co, Melbourne)

1979 (4 Jan). *Wildlife. Multicoloured designs as T* **94**. *W* **95** (*inverted on* $10 *or sideways* on others*). *P* 14½.
190   30 c. Type **94** .. .. .. 1·75   10
191   40 c. Malayan Flying Lemur (*Cynocephalus variegatus*) 80   10
    w. Wmk top of letters to left
192   50 c. Lesser Malay Chevrotain (*Tragulus javanicus*) .. .. 1·75   10

193   75 c. Leathery Pangolin (*Manis javanicus*) 1·00   10
194   $1 Malayan Turtle .. .. 1·50   10
195   $2 Malayan Tapir .. .. 1·50   10
196   $5 Gaur .. .. .. 4·50   1·75
197   $10 Orang-Utan (*vert*) .. .. 7·00   3·25
190/7 .. .. *Set of 8* 18·00   5·00
*The normal sideways watermark shows the top of the letters to right, *as seen from the back of the stamp.*
For these stamps without watermark, see Nos. 272/9.

96 View of Central Bank of Malaysia

97 I.Y.C. Emblem

(Des Union Advertising. Litho J.W.)

1979 (26 Jan). *20th Anniv of Central Bank of Malaysia. T* **96** *and similar vert design showing view of bank building. P* 13.
198   10 c. multicoloured 10   10
199   75 c. multicoloured 40   75

(Des Queen's Advertising. Litho Harrison)

1979 (24 Feb). *International Year of the Child. T* **97** *and similar vert designs. P* 14½ × 14.
200   10 c. gold, blue and salmon .. 30   10
201   15 c. multicoloured 40   10
202   $1 multicoloured .. .. 2·50   3·25
200/2 .. .. *Set of 3* 2·75   3·25
Designs:—15 c. Children of different races holding hands in front of globe; $1 Children taking part in various activities.

98 Dam and Power Station

99 Exhibition Emblem

(Des National Electricity Board. Litho Harrison)

1979 (19 Sept). *Opening of Hydro-Electric Power Station, Temengor. T* **98** *and similar horiz designs showing views of power station and dam. P* 13½ × 14½.
203   15 c. multicoloured 20   15
204   25 c. multicoloured 35   60
205   50 c. multicoloured 55   1·25
203/5 .. .. *Set of 3* 1·00   1·75

(Des Malaysian Advertising Services. Litho J.W.)

1979 (20 Sept). *World Telecommunications Exhibition, Geneva. T* **99** *and similar designs. P* 14 (50 c.) *or* 13 (*others*).
206   10 c. orange, ultramarine and silver .. 10   30
207   15 c. multicoloured 15   10
208   50 c. multicoloured 40   1·75
206/8 .. .. *Set of 3* 60   1·90
Designs: (34 × 24 *mm*)—15 c. Telephone receiver joining one half of World to the other. (39 × 28 *mm*)—50 c. Communications equipment.

100 Tuanku Haji Ahmad Shah

101 Pahang and Sarawak Maps within Telephone Dials

(Des Malaysian Advertising Services. Litho Harrison)

1980 (10 July). *Installation of Yang di-Pertuan Agong (Tuanku Haji Ahmad Shah). P* 14.
209   **100**   10 c. black, gold and yellow .. 10   20
210   15 c. black, gold and bright purple .. 15   10
211   50 c. black, gold and new blue .. 40   1·50
209/11 .. .. *Set of 3* 60   1·60

(Des Malaysian Advertising Services. Litho J.W.)

1980 (31 Aug). *Kuantan-Kuching Submarine Cable Project. T* **101** *and similar horiz designs. Multicoloured. P* 13.
212   10 c. Type **101** 10   30
213   15 c. Kuantan and Kuching views within telephone dials 15   10
214   50 c. Pahang and Sarawak Maps within telephone receiver 35   1·40
212/14 .. .. *Set of 3* 50   1·60

NEW INFORMATION
The editor is always interested to correspond with people who have new information that will improve or correct the Catalogue.

102 Bangi Campus

103 Mecca

(Des Malaysian Advertising Services. Litho J.W.)

1980 (2 Sept). *10th Anniv of National University of Malaysia. T* **102** *and similar horiz designs. Multicoloured. P* 13.
215   10 c. Type **102** 15   20
216   15 c. Jalan Pantai Baru campus .. 20   10
217   75 c. Great Hall 65   2·50
215/17 .. .. *Set of 3* 90   2·50

(Des Malaysian Advertising Services. Litho J.W.)

1980 (9 Nov). *Moslem Year 1400 A.H. Commemoration. P* 13.
218   **103**   15 c. multicoloured .. 10   10
219   50 c. multicoloured 30   1·25
The 50 c. value is as T **103** but the inscriptions are in Roman lettering and the country name is to the left of the design.

104 Disabled Child learning to Walk

105 Industrial Scene

(Des Malaysian Advertising Services. Litho J.W.)

1981 (14 Feb). *International Year for Disabled Persons. T* **104** *and similar vert designs. Multicoloured. P* 13½ × 13.
220   10 c. Type **104** 30   30
221   15 c. Disabled woman sewing .. 55   10
222   75 c. Disabled athlete throwing javelin 1·50   3·25
220/2 .. .. *Set of 3* 2·10   3·25

(Des Malaysian Advertising Services. Litho J.W.)

1981 (2 May). *"Expo '81" Industrial Training Exposition, Kuala Lumpur and Seminar, Genting Highlands. T* **105** *and similar horiz designs. Multicoloured. P* 13½ × 13.
223   10 c. Type **105** 10   10
224   15 c. Worker and bulldozer .. 15   10
225   30 c. Workers at ship-building yard .. 25   35
226   75 c. Agriculture and fishing produce, workers and machinery 65   2·00
223/6 .. .. *Set of 4* 1·00   2·25

106 "25"

(Des A. Yusof and Malaysian Advertising Services. Litho J.W.)

1981 (17 June). *25th Anniv of Malaysian National Committee for World Energy Conferences. T* **106** *and similar horiz designs. Multicoloured. P* 13½ × 13.
227   10 c. Type **106** 15   20
228   15 c. Drawings showing importance of energy sources in industry .. 30   10
229   75 c. Symbols of various energy sources 1·50   2·75
227/9 .. .. *Set of 3* 1·75   2·75

107 Drawing showing development of Sabah from Village to Urbanised Area

(Des Creative Concepts. Litho J.W.)

1981 (31 Aug). *Centenary of Sabah. T* **107** *and similar horiz design. Multicoloured. P* 12.
230   15 c. Type **107** 50   15
231   80 c. Drawing showing traditional and modern methods of agriculture .. 2·00   4·00

108 Samanea saman

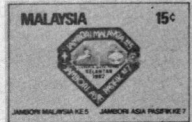
109 Jamboree Emblem

(Des Yusof bin Hadji Saman. Litho J.W.)

1981 (16 Dec). *Trees. T* **108** *and similar multicoloured designs.*
P 14.

232	15 c. Type 108	..	55	10
233	50 c. *Dyera costulata* (vert)	..	1·75	1·40
234	80 c. *Dryobalanops aromatica* (vert)	..	2·00	4·00
232/4	..	*Set of* 3	3·75	5·00

(Des P. Lim (15 c.), Datuk Syed Hashim bin Abdullah (others).
Litho J.W.)

1982 (10 Apr). *5th Malaysian/7th Asia–Pacific Boy Scout*
Jamboree. T **109** *and similar horiz designs. Multicoloured.*
P 13½×13.

235	15 c. Type 109		35	10
236	50 c. Malaysian flag and scout emblem		80	85
237	80 c. Malaysian and Asia–Pacific scout emblems		1·25	4·00
235/7		*Set of* 3	2·25	4·50

110 A.S.E.A.N. Building
and Emblem

111 Dome of the Rock,
Jerusalem

(Litho J.W.)

1982 (8 Aug). *15th Anniv Ministerial Meeting of A.S.E.A.N.*
(Association of South East Asian Nations). T **110** *and similar*
horiz design. Multicoloured. P 14.

238	15 c. Type 110		15	10
239	$1 Flags of member nations		80	2·50

(Litho J.W.)

1982 (21 Aug). *"Freedom for Palestine". P* 13½.

240	**111** 15 c. gold, blue-green and black ..		75	15
241	$1 silver, pale turquoise-green & blk ..		3·25	4·00

112 Views of Kuala Lumpur
in 1957 and 1982

(Des Ministry of Information. Litho Rosenbaum Bros, Vienna)

1982 (31 Aug). *25th Anniv of Independence. T* **112** *and similar*
horiz designs. Multicoloured. P 14 × 13½.

242	10 c. Type 112		10	10
243	15 c. Malaysian industries		15	15
244	50 c. Soldiers on parade		40	55
245	80 c. Independence ceremony ..		70	2·25
242/5		*Set of* 4	1·25	2·75
MS246	120×190 mm. Nos. 242/5 (with silver frame around centre vignette of 10 c.)		13·00	11·00
	a. Without silver frame around centre vignette of 10 c.		8·00	10·00

No. **MS**246a is from the second printing. It is without the
narrow silver frame around the centre part of the 10 c. design
which is shown on Nos. 242 and **MS**246.

113 Shadow Play

(Des N. Ajib. Litho J.W.)

1982 (30 Oct). *Traditional Games. T* **113** *and similar horiz*
designs. Multicoloured. P 13.

247	10 c. Type 113		55	30
248	15 c. Cross Top ..		55	15
249	75 c. Kite flying		2·25	4·00
247/9	..	*Set of* 3	3·00	4·00

114 Sabah Hats

(Litho Harrison)

1982 (26 Nov). *Malaysian Handicrafts. T* **114** *and similar horiz*
designs. Multicoloured. P 13 × 13½.

250	10 c. Type 114		25	30
251	15 c. Gold-threaded cloth		25	20
252	75 c. Sarawak pottery		1·25	3·00
250/2	..	*Set of* 3	1·60	3·25

115 Gas Exploitation Logo   **116** Flag of Malaysia

(Litho Security Printers (M), Malaysia)

1983 (22 Jan). *Export of Liquefied Natural Gas from Bintulu*
Field, Sarawak. T **115** *and similar horiz designs. Multicoloured.*
P 12.

253	15 c. Type 115		75	15
	a. Perf 13½		22·00	
254	20 c. *Tenaga Satu* (liquid gas tanker)		1·50	70
	a. Perf 13½		30·00	
255	$1 Gas drilling equipment		3·50	5·50
	a. Perf 13½		50·00	
253/5		*Set of* 3	5·25	5·75

Other versions of these designs, some with different face
value, were prepared, but not issued.

(Litho J.W.)

1983 (14 Mar). *Commonwealth Day. T* **116** *and similar horiz*
designs. Multicoloured. P 13½ × 14.

256	15 c. Type 116		10	10
257	20 c. The King of Malaysia		15	20
258	40 c. Oil palm tree and refinery		25	45
259	$1 Satellite view of Earth		60	2·00
256/9		*Set of* 4	1·00	2·50

117 Nile Mouthbrooder

(Des and litho Security Printers (M), Malaysia)

1983 (15 June). *Freshwater Fishes. T* **117** *and similar horiz*
designs. Multicoloured. P 12.

260	20 c. Type 117		1·50	1·75
	a. Horiz pair. Nos. 260/1		3·00	3·50
	b. Perf 13½×14		7·50	4·00
	ba. Horiz pair. Nos. 260b/1b		15·00	8·00
261	20 c. Common Carp		1·50	1·75
	b. Perf 13½×14		7·50	4·00
262	40 c. Lampan Barb ("*Puntius gonionotus*")		2·25	2·75
	a. Horiz pair. Nos. 262/3		4·50	5·50
	b. Perf 13½×14		2·50	3·25
	ba. Horiz pair. Nos. 262b/3b		5·00	6·50
263	40 c. Grass Carp ("*Ctenopharyngodon idellus*")		2·25	2·75
	b. Perf 13½×14		2·50	3·25
260/3		*Set of* 4	6·75	8·00

Nos. 260/1 and 262/3 were each printed together, *se-tenant*, in
horizontal pairs throughout the sheet.

118 Lower Pergau River Bridge

(Des Malaysian Public Works Dept. Litho Security Printers (M),
Malaysia)

1983 (11 July). *Opening of East–West Highway. T* **118** *and*
similar horiz designs. Multicoloured. P 13½.

264	15 c. Type 118		80	15
265	20 c. Perak river reservoir bridge		1·00	75
266	$1 Map showing East–West highway		3·75	5·50
264/6	..	*Set of* 3	5·00	5·75

119 Northrop F-5E Tiger II   **120** Helmeted Hornbill
Fighter

(Des and litho J.W.)

1983 (16 Sept). *50th Anniv of Malaysian Armed Forces. T* **119** *and*
similar horiz designs. Multicoloured. P 13.

267	15 c. Type 119		1·25	15
268	20 c. Missile boat		1·75	45
269	40 c. Battle of Pasir Panjang		2·25	2·50
270	80 c. Trooping the Colour		3·25	5·00
267/70		*Set of* 4	7·75	7·25
MS271	130×85 mm. Nos. 267/70. P 13½		8·50	10·00

1983 (3 Oct)–**85**.* *As Nos.* 190/7 *but without wmk.*

272	30 c. Type 94 (1984)	..	3·00	70
273	40 c. Malayan Flying Lemur (6.10.83)		2·75	60
274	50 c. Lesser Malay Chevrotain (10.4.84)		3·00	60
275	75 c. Leathery Pangolin (19.10.85) ..		4·50	7·00
276	$1 Malayan Turtle (5.10.83)		3·75	65
277	$2 Malayan Tapir ..		4·00	70
278	$5 Gaur (1985)		16·00	9·00
279	$10 Orang-Utan (vert) (3.84)		14·00	11·00
272/9		*Set of* 8	45·00	27·00

*There was no official release date for these stamps. Dates
shown are the earliest recorded from postmarks and may be
revised should earlier examples be reported.

(Des P. Ket. Litho Security Printers (M), Malaysia)

1983 (26 Oct). *Hornbills of Malaysia. T* **120** *and similar vert*
designs. Multicoloured. P 13½.

280	15 c. Type 120		1·00	15
281	20 c. Wrinkled Hornbill		1·25	50
282	50 c. Long-crested Hornbill		2·00	2·00
283	$1 Rhinoceros Hornbill		3·25	5·00
280/3	..	*Set of* 4	6·75	7·00

121 Bank Building, Ipoh   **122** Sky-scraper and Mosque,
Kuala Lumpur

(Des P. Hoong. Litho Security Printers (M), Malaysia)

1984 (26 Jan). *25th Anniv of Bank Negara. T* **121** *and similar*
horiz design. Multicoloured. P 13½ × 14.

284	20 c. Type 121	..	40	30
285	$1 Bank building, Alor Setar		2·00	3·50

(Des Mara Institute of Technology. Litho Security Printers (M),
Malaysia)

1984 (1 Feb). *10th Anniv of Federal Territory of Kuala Lumpur.*
T **122** *and similar multicoloured designs. P* 13½ × 14 (80 c.) or
14 × 13½ (others).

286	20 c. Type 122	..	80	20
287	40 c. Aerial view		1·60	1·40
288	80 c. Gardens and clock-tower (horiz)..		2·50	4·50
286/8	..	*Set of* 3	4·50	5·50

123 Map showing Industries   **124** Semenanjung Keris

(Litho Security Printers (M), Malaysia)

1984 (16 Apr). *Formation of Labuan Federal Territory. T* **123** *and*
similar vert design. Multicoloured. P 13½ × 14.

289	20 c. Type 123		75	25
290	$1 Flag and map of Labuan ..		3·75	4·50

(Des P. Ket. Litho Harrison)

1984 (30 May). *Traditional Malay Weapons. T* **124** *and similar*
vert designs. Multicoloured. P 13½ × 14.

291	40 c. Type 124	..	1·25	1·75
	a. Block of 4. Nos. 291/4		4·50	
292	40 c. Pekakak keris		1·25	1·75
293	40 c. Jawa keris		1·25	1·75
294	40 c. Lada tumbuk		1·25	1·75
291/4	..	*Set of* 4	4·50	6·00

Nos. 291/4 were printed in *se-tenant* blocks of four throughout
the sheet.

125 Map of World and Transmitter   **126** Facsimile Service

(Des Dept of Broadcasting. Litho Harrison)

1984 (23 June). *20th Anniv of Asia–Pacific Broadcasting Union.*
T **125** *and similar horiz design. Multicoloured. P* 13½ × 14½.

295	20 c. Type 125	..	40	15
296	$1 Clasped hands within "20"		2·00	3·75

(Des Mark Johan and Associates. Litho Security Printers (M),
Malaysia)

1984 (29 Oct). *Opening of New General Post Office, Kuala*
Lumpur. T **126** *and similar horiz designs. Multicoloured. P* 12.

297	15 c. Type 126	..	35	20
298	20 c. New G.P.O. building		45	45
299	$1 Mailbag conveyor		2·00	3·75
297/9	..	*Set of* 3	2·50	4·00

127 Yang di Pertuan Agong (Tuanku Mahmood)

128 White Hibiscus

(Des P. Ket. Litho Security Printers (M), Malaysia)

1984 (15 Nov). *Installation of Yang di Pertuan Agong (Tuanku Mahmood). T* **127** *and similar design. P* 12.

300	127	15 c. multicoloured	..	40	20
301	–	20 c. multicoloured	..	45	20
302	–	40 c. multicoloured	..	85	1·00
303	–	80 c. multicoloured	..	2·00	4·25
300/3			*Set of 4*	3·25	5·00

Design: *Horiz* — 40 c., 80 c. Yang di Pertuan Agong and Federal Crest.

(Litho Security Printers (M), Malaysia)

1984 (12 Dec). *Hibiscus. T* **128** *and similar vert designs. Multicoloured. P* 13½.

304		10 c. Type **128**	..	50	30
305		20 c. Red Hibiscus	..	1·00	20
306		40 c. Pink Hibiscus	..	1·75	2·00
307		$1 Orange Hibiscus	..	2·75	4·75
304/7			*Set of 4*	5·50	6·50

129 Parliament Building

130 Banded Linsang

(Des P. Ket. Litho Security Printers (M), Malaysia)

1985 (30 Mar). *25th Anniv of Federal Parliament. T* **129** *and similar multicoloured design. P* 13½ × 14 (20 c.) *or* 14 × 13½ ($1).

308		20 c. Type **129**	..	30	15
309		$1 Parliament Building (*different*) (*horiz*)	1·75	2·25

(Des P. Ket. Litho J.W.)

1985 (25 Apr). *Protected Animals of Malaysia (1st series). T* **130** *and similar multicoloured designs. P* 14.

310		10 c. Type **130**	..	60	10
311		40 c. Slow Loris (*vert*)	..	2·00	1·40
312		$1 Spotted Giant Flying Squirrel (*vert*)	4·00	5·00
310/12			*Set of 3*	6·00	6·00

See also Nos. 383/6.

131 Stylised Figures

132 Steam Locomotive No. 1, 1885

(Des Amir bin Osman. Litho Security Printers (M), Malaysia)

1985 (15 May). *International Youth Year. T* **131** *and similar horiz design. Multicoloured. P* 13.

313		20 c. Type **131**	..	30	15
314		$1 Young workers	..	3·25	4·50

(Des AMW Communications Management. Litho Security Printers (M), Malaysia).

1985 (1 June). *Centenary of Malayan Railways. T* **132** *and similar horiz designs. P* 13.

315		15 c. black, carmine-verm & pale orange	1·40	40
316		20 c. multicoloured	..	1·60	50
317		$1 multicoloured	..	3·75	5·00
315/17			*Set of 3*	6·00	5·00
MS318		119×59 mm. 80 c. multicoloured	6·50	7·50

P 13½ × 13

Designs: *Horiz* (*as T* **132**)—20 c. Class 20 diesel-electric locomotive, 1957; $1 Hitachi Class 23 diesel-electric locomotive, 1983. (48 × 31 *mm*)—80 c. Class 56 steam locomotive No. 564.18, *Seletar,* 1938.

133 Blue Proton "Saga 1.3s"

134 Penang Bridge

(Des and litho J.W.)

1985 (9 July). *Production of Proton "Saga" (Malaysian national car). T* **133** *and similar horiz designs. Multicoloured. P* 14.

319		20 c. Type **133**	..	80	15
320		40 c. White Proton "Saga 1.3s"	..	1·40	1·00
321		$1 Red Proton "Saga 1.5s"	..	2·50	4·00
319/21			*Set of 3*	4·25	4·75

(Des Kathy's Design. Litho Security Printers (M), Malaysia)

1985 (14 Sept). *Opening of Penang Bridge. T* **134** *and similar horiz designs. Multicoloured. P* 12 ($1) *or* 13 (*others*).

322		20 c. Type **134**	..	90	15
323		40 c. Penang Bridge and location map	1·75	90
324		$1 Symbolic bridge linking Penang to mainland (40 × 24 *mm*)	..	3·50	4·25
322/4			*Set of 3*	5·50	4·75

135 Offshore Oil Rig

136 Sultan Azlan Shah and Perak Royal Crest

(Des Andamaz Enterprise. Litho Security Printers (M), Malaysia)

1985 (4 Nov). *Malaysian Petroleum Production. T* **135** *and similar multicoloured designs. P* 12.

325		15 c. Type **135**	..	1·00	20
326		20 c. Malaysia's first oil refinery (*horiz*)	1·10	50
327		$1 Map of Malaysian offshore oil and gas fields (*horiz*)	..	3·50	4·50
325/7			*Set of 3*	5·00	4·75

(Des Kathy's Design. Litho J.W.)

1985 (9 Dec). *Installation of the Sultan of Perak. P* 14.

328	136	15 c. multicoloured	..	35	10
329		20 c. multicoloured	..	45	25
330		$1 multicoloured	..	2·50	4·00
328/30			*Set of 3*	3·00	4·00

137 Crested Fireback Pheasant

139 Two Kadazan Dancers, Sabah

138

(Des P. Ket. Litho Security Printers (M), Malaysia)

1986 (11 Mar). *Protected Birds of Malaysia (1st series). T* **137** *and similar multicoloured designs. W* **138** (*sideways on* 40 c.). *Phosphorised paper. P* 13½.

331		20 c. Type **137**	..	2·50	3·00
		a. Horiz pair. Nos. 331/2	5·00	6·00
332		20 c. Malaya Peacock-Pheasant	2·50	3·00
333		40 c. Bulwer's Pheasant (*horiz*)	3·00	3·50
		a. Horiz pair. Nos. 333/4	6·00	7·00
		b. Perf 12	..	2·00	3·25
		ba. Horiz pair. Nos. 333b/4b	4·00	6·50
334		40 c. Great Argus Pheasant (*horiz*)	3·00	3·50
		b. Perf 12	..	2·00	3·25
331/4			*Set of 4*	10·00	11·50

Nos. 331/2 and 333/4 were each printed together, *se-tenant*, in horizontal pairs throughout the sheets.

See also Nos. 394/7.

(Des AMC Advertising Agencies. Litho Questa)

1986 (14 Apr). *Pacific Area Travel Association Conference, Malaysia. T* **139** *and similar vert designs. Multicoloured. P* 15 × 14.

335		20 c. Type **139**	..	75	95
		a. Horiz strip of 3. Nos. 335/7	2·00	
336		20 c. Dyak dancer and longhouse, Sarawak	75	95

337		20 c. Dancers and fortress, Malacca	75	95
338		40 c. Malay dancer and Kuala Lumpur	1·10	1·40
		a. Horiz strip of 3. Nos. 338/40	3·00	
339		40 c. Chinese opera dancer and Penang Bridge	1·10	1·40
340		40 c. Indian dancer and Batu Caves	1·10	1·40
335/40			*Set of 6*	5·00	6·25

Nos. 335/7 and 338/40 were each printed together, *se-tenant*, in horizontal strips of 3 throughout the sheets.

140 Stylized Competitors

141 Rambutan

141a

(Des Design Excelsior. Litho Security Printers (M), Malaysia)

1986 (19 Apr). *Malaysia Games. T* **140** *and similar multicoloured designs. W* **138** (*sideways on* 20 c.). *Phosphorised paper. P* 12.

341		20 c. Type **140**	..	1·25	20
342		40 c. Games emblems (*vert*)	..	2·25	2·00
343		$1 National and state flags (*vert*)	6·00	7·25
341/3			*Set of 3*	8·50	8·50

(Des P. Ket)

1986 (5 June)–**94**. *Fruits of Malaysia. T* **141** *and similar vert designs. Multicoloured.*

(a) *Litho Security Printers* (M), *Malaysia. W* **138**. *Phosphorised paper. P* 12

344		40 c. Type **141**	..	15	20
		aw. Wmk inverted	..	10·00	
		b. Perf 13½×14 (1994)	..	70	20
		bw. Wmk inverted	..	8·50	
345		50 c. Pineapple	..	15	20
		aw. Wmk inverted	..	6·00	
		b. Perf 13½×14 (1994)	..	70	20
		bw. Wmk inverted	..	8·50	
346		80 c. Durian	..	25	30
		aw. Wmk inverted	..	6·00	
		b. Perf 13½×14 (1994)	..	1·00	30
347		$1 Mangosteen	..	30	35
		aw. Wmk inverted	..	7·00	
		b. Perf 13½×14 (1994)	..	1·00	35

(b) *Photo Harrison. W* **141a**. *P* 13½.

348		$2 Star Fruit	..	60	65
349		$5 Banana	..	1·60	1·75
350		$10 Mango	..	3·25	3·50
351		$20 Papaya	..	6·25	6·50
344/51			*Set of 8*	12·50	13·50

PHOSPHORISED PAPER. From No. 352 onwards all stamps were on phosphorised paper, *unless otherwise stated.*

142 Skull and Slogan "Drugs Can Kill"

143 MAS Logo and Map showing Routes

(Des Kathy's Design. Litho Security Printers (M), Malaysia)

1986 (26 June). *10th Anniv of National Association for Prevention of Drug Addiction. T* **142** *and similar multicoloured designs. W* **138** (*sideways on* 20 c., $1). *P* 13.

352		20 c. Type **142**	..	1·00	30
353		40 c. Bird and slogan "Stay Free From Drugs"	..	1·40	1·10
354		$1 Addict and slogan "Drugs Can Destroy" (*vert*)	..	2·25	3·75
352/4			*Set of 3*	4·25	4·75

(Des PTM Thompson Advertising. Litho Security Printers (M), Malaysia)

1986 (31 July). *Inaugural Flight of Malaysian Airlines Kuala Lumpur–Los Angeles Service. T* **143** *and similar horiz designs. Multicoloured. W* **138** (*sideways*). *P* 14 × 13½.

355		20 c. Type **143**	..	1·10	15
356		40 c. Logo, stylized aircraft and route diagram	..	1·75	65
357		$1 Logo and stylized aircraft	..	3·00	2·50
355/7			*Set of 3*	5·25	3·00

144 Building Construction

145 Old Seri Menanti Palace, Negri Sembilan

(Des M. Chin. Litho Security Printers (M), Malaysia)

1986 (3 Nov). *20th Anniv of National Productivity Council and 25th Anniv of Asian Productivity Organization (40 c., $1). T 144 and similar multicoloured designs. W 138 (sideways on 40 c., $1). P 13½ × 14 (20 c.) or 14 × 13½ (others).*
358	20 c. Type 144.			85	25
359	40 c. Planning and design (horiz)			1·40	1·25
360	$1 Computer-controlled car assembly line (horiz)			3·75	5·50
358/60			Set of 3	5·50	6·25

(Des P. Ket. Litho Security Printers (M), Malaysia)

1986 (20 Dec). *Historic Buildings of Malaysia (1st series). T 145 and similar horiz designs. Multicoloured. W 138 (sideways). P 13.*
361	15 c. Type 145.			50	20
362	20 c. Old Kenangan Palace, Perak			55	20
363	40 c. Old Town Hall, Malacca			1·00	70
364	$1 Astana, Kuching, Sarawak			2·25	3·50
361/4			Set of 4	3·75	4·25

See also Nos. 465/8.

146 Sompotan (bamboo pipes)

(Des Kathy Wong. Litho Security Printers (M), Malaysia)

1987 (7 Mar). *Malaysian Musical Instruments. T 146 and similar multicoloured designs. W 138 (sideways on 50, 80 c.). P 12.*
365	15 c. Type 146.			55	10
366	20 c. Sapih (four-stringed chordophone)		65	20
367	50 c. Serunai (pipes) (vert)			1·40	40
368	80 c. Rebab (three-stringed fiddle) (vert)	1·90	1·25
365/8			Set of 4	4·00	1·75

147 Modern Housing Estate

(Litho Security Printers (M), Malaysia)

1987 (6 Apr). *International Year of Shelter for the Homeless. T 147 and similar horiz design. Multicoloured. W 138. P 12.*
369	20 c. Type 147.		40	15
370	$1 Stylised families and houses		1·50	1·00

MACHINE LABELS. From 25 May 1987 gummed labels printed in red on yellow paper with an overall design of the postal logo were issued from a machine in Kuala Lumpur. Available face values ranged from 5 c. to $15.

148 Drug Addict and Family

(Des Kathy's Design. Litho Security Printers (M), Malaysia)

1987 (8 June). *International Conference on Drug Abuse, Vienna. T 148 and similar horiz designs. Multicoloured. W 138 (sideways). P 13.*
371	20 c. Type 148.			1·00	65
	a. Vert pair. Nos. 371/2		2·00	1·25
372	20 c. Hands holding drugs and damaged internal organs			1·00	65
373	40 c. Healthy boy and broken drug capsule	1·50	90
	a. Vert pair. Nos. 373/4		3·00	1·75
374	40 c. Drugs and healthy internal organs	1·50	90
371/4			Set of 4	4·50	2·75

Nos. 371/2 and 373/4 were printed together, se-tenant, in vertical pairs throughout the sheet, each pair forming a composite design.

149 Spillway and Power Station

(Des Kathy's Design. Litho Security Printers (M), Malaysia)

1987 (13 July). *Opening of Sultan Mahmud Hydro-electric Scheme, Kenyir, Trengganu. T 149 and similar horiz design. Multicoloured. W 138. P 12.*
375	20 c. Type 149.		50	10
376	$1 Dam, spillway and reservoir		2·50	1·50

150 Crossed Maces and Parliament Building, Kuala Lumpur

151 Dish Aerial, Satellite and Globe

(Des R. Zahabuddin. Litho Security Printers (M), Malaysia)

1987 (1 Sept). *33rd Commonwealth Parliamentary Conference. T 150 and similar horiz design. Multicoloured. W 138. P 12.*
377	20 c. Type 150.		25	10
378	$1 Parliament building and crossed maces emblem		1·00	1·00

(Des Mark Design. Litho Security Printers (M), Malaysia)

1987 (26 Oct). *Asia/Pacific Transport and Communications Decade. T 151 and similar horiz designs. Multicoloured. W 138 (sideways). P 13.*
379	15 c. Type 151			40	10
380	20 c. Diesel train and car			1·25	65
381	40 c. Container ships and lorry		1·50	1·25
382	$1 Malaysian Airlines Boeing 747, Kuala Lumpur Airport		2·75	4·00
379/82			Set of 4	5·50	5·50

152 Temminck's Golden Cat

153 Flags of Member Nations and "20"

(Des Ong Soo Keat. Litho Security Printers (M), Malaysia)

1987 (14 Nov). *Protected Animals of Malaysia (2nd series). T 152 and similar horiz designs. Multicoloured. W 138 (sideways on 15, 20, 40 c.). P 13.*
383	15 c. Type 152.			1·50	40
384	20 c. Flatheaded Cat			1·50	40
385	40 c. Marbled Cat			2·50	1·75
386	$1 Clouded Leopard			4·50	5·50
383/6			Set of 4	9·00	7·25

(Des P. Ket. Litho Security Printers (M), Malaysia)

1987 (14 Dec). *20th Anniv of Association of South East Asian Nations. T 153 and similar horiz design. Multicoloured. W 138. P 13.*
387	20 c. Type 153.		20	10
388	$1 Flags of member nations and globe		80	1·00

154 Mosque and Portico

155 Aerial View

(Des R. Zahabuddin. Litho Security Printers (M), Malaysia)

1988 (11 Mar). *Opening of Sultan Salahuddin Abdul Aziz Shah Mosque. T 154 and similar multicoloured designs. W 138 (sideways on 15, 20 c.). P 12.*
389	15 c. Type 154.			20	10
390	20 c. Dome, minarets and Sultan of Selangor	20	20
391	$1 Interior and dome (vert)		70	1·25
389/91			Set of 3	1·00	1·40

(Des Azmi bin Kassim. Litho Security Printers (M), Malaysia)

1988 (4 Apr). *Sultan Ismail Hydro-electric Power Station, Paka, Trengganu. T 155 and similar horiz design. Multicoloured. W 138 (sideways). P 13.*
392	20 c. Type 155.		20	10
393	$1 Power station and pylons		80	90

156 Black-naped Blue Monarch

157 Outline Map and Products of Sabah

(Des Ong Soo Keat. Litho Security Printers (M), Malaysia)

1988 (30 June). *Protected Birds of Malaysia (2nd series). T 156 and similar vert designs. Multicoloured. W 138. P 13.*
394	20 c. Type 156			1·75	1·75
	a. Horiz pair. Nos. 394/5		3·50	3·50
	w. Inverted wmk			10·00	
	wa. Horiz pair. Nos. 394w/5w		20·00	
395	20 c. Scarlet-backed Flowerpecker		1·75	1·75
	w. Inverted wmk			10·00	
396	50 c. Yellow-backed Sunbird		2·50	2·50
	a. Horiz pair. Nos. 396/7		5·00	5·00
	w. Inverted wmk			5·00	
	wa. Horiz pair. Nos. 396w/7w		10·00	
397	50 c. Black and Red Broadbill		2·50	2·50
	w. Inverted wmk			5·00	
394/7			Set of 4	7·50	7·50

The two designs of each value were printed together, se-tenant, in horizontal pairs throughout the sheets.

(Des P. Ket. Litho Security Printers (M), Malaysia)

1988 (31 Aug). *25th Anniv of Sabah and Sarawak as States of Malaysia. T 157 and similar vert designs. Multicoloured. W 138. P 13.*
398	20 c. Type 157			40	50
	a. Horiz pair. Nos. 398/9		80	1·00
399	20 c. Outline map and products of Sarawak	40	50
400	$1 Flags of Malaysia, Sabah and Sarawak (30×40 mm)		1·00	1·50
398/400			Set of 3	1·60	2·25

Nos. 398/9 were printed together, se-tenant, in horizontal pairs throughout the sheet.

158 Glossodoris atromarginata

159 Sultan's Palace, Malacca

(Litho Security Printers (M), Malaysia)

1988 (17 Dec). *Marine Life (1st series). T 158 and similar vert designs. Multicoloured. W 138. P 12.*
401	20 c. Type 158			85	90
	a. Horiz strip of 5. Nos. 401/5	3·75	
402	20 c. Ocellate Nudibranch (Phyllidia ocellata)			85	90
403	20 c. Chromodoris annae			85	90
404	20 c. Flabellina macassarana		85	90
405	20 c. Ruppell's Nudibranch (Reyfria ruppeli)	85	90
401/5			Set of 5	3·75	4·00
MS406	100×75 mm. $1 Blue-ringed Angelfish (50×40 mm). P 14		2·50	1·75

Nos. 401/5 were printed together, se-tenant, in horizontal strips of 5 throughout the sheet, forming a composite background design.
See also Nos. 410/13, 450/3, 492/7 and 559/62.

(Des P. Ket. Litho Security Printers (M), Malaysia)

1989 (15 Apr). *Declaration of Malacca as Historic City. T 159 and similar multicoloured designs. W 138 (sideways on 20 c.). P 13.*
407	20 c. Type 159			20	15
408	20 c. Independence Memorial Building		20	15
409	$1 Porta De Santiago Fortress (vert)		1·00	1·40
407/9			Set of 3	1·25	1·50

160 Tetralia nigrolineata

161 Map of Malaysia and Scout Badge

(Des P. Ket. Litho Security Printers (M), Malaysia)

1989 (29 June). *Marine Life (2nd series). Crustaceans. T 160 and similar horiz designs. Multicoloured. W 138 (sideways).*
410	20 c. Type 160			45	65
	a. Horiz pair. Nos. 410/11		90	1·25
	b. Wmk upright				
	ba. Horiz pair. Nos. 410b/11b			

411	20 c. *Neopetrolisthes maculatus* (crab)		45	65
	b. Wmk upright			
412	40 c. *Periclimenes holthuisi* (shrimp)		55	90
	a. Horiz pair. Nos. 412/13		1·10	1·75
	b. Wmk upright			
	ba. Horiz pair. Nos. 412b/13b			
413	40 c. *Synalpheus neomeris* (shrimp)		55	90
	b. Wmk upright			
410/13		Set of 4	1·75	2·75

Nos. 410/11 and 412/13 were each printed together, *se-tenant*, in horizontal pairs throughout the sheets.

(Des T. Teh Ching Seng. Litho Security Printers (M), Malaysia)

1989 (26 July). *7th National Scout Jamboree.* T **161** and similar multicoloured designs. W **138** (sideways on 10, 20 c.). P 13.

414	10 c. Type **161**		25	10
415	20 c. Saluting national flag		40	25
416	80 c. Scouts around camp fire (*horiz*)		1·25	2·50
	w. Wmk inverted		4·00	
414/16		Set of 3	1·75	2·50

162 Cycling

163 Sultan Azlan Shah

(Litho Security Printers (M), Malaysia)

1989 (20 Aug). *15th South East Asian Games, Kuala Lumpur.* T **162** and similar multicoloured designs. W **138** (sideways on 50 c., $1). P 13.

417	10 c. Type **162**		40	20
418	20 c. Athletics		30	20
419	50 c. Swimming (*vert*)		60	85
420	$1 Torch bearer (*vert*)		95	2·25
417/20		Set of 4	2·00	3·25

(Des R. Zahabuddin. Litho Security Printers (M), Malaysia)

1989 (18 Sept). *Installation of Sultan Azlan Shah as Yang di (Pertuan Agong.* W **138** (sideways). P 13.

421	**163** 20 c. multicoloured		20	15
422	40 c. multicoloured		30	35
423	$1 multicoloured		70	1·75
421/3		Set of 3	1·10	2·00

164 Putra World Trade Centre and Pan-Pacific Hotel

165 Clock Tower, Kuala Lumpur City Hall and Big Ben

(Litho Security Printers (M), Malaysia)

1989 (18 Oct). *Commonwealth Heads of Government Meeting, Kuala Lumpur.* T **164** and similar multicoloured designs. W **138** (sideways on 50 c.). P 13.

424	20 c. Type **164**		20	10
	a. Wmk sideways			
	w. Wmk inverted		2·25	
425	50 c. Traditional dancers (*vert*)		65	75
	a. Wmk upright		6·50	
426	$1 National flag and map showing Commonwealth countries		1·25	2·25
	a. Wmk sideways		6·50	
424/6		Set of 3	1·90	2·75

(Des AMC-Melewar Zecha Communications. Litho Security Printers (M), Malaysia)

1989 (2 Dec). *Inaugural Malaysia Airlines "747" Non-stop Flight to London.* T **165** and similar horiz designs, each showing Malaysia Airlines Boeing "747-400". Multicoloured. W **138**. P 13.

427	20 c. Type **165**		1·00	1·40
	a. Horiz pair. Nos. 427/9		2·00	2·75
428	20 c. Parliament Buildings, Kuala Lumpur, and Palace of Westminster		1·00	1·40
429	$1 World map showing route		2·50	2·75
427/9		Set of 3	4·00	5·00

Nos. 427/8 were printed together, *se-tenant*, in horizontal pairs throughout the sheet.

166 Sloth and Map of Park

167 Outline Map of South-east Asia and Logo

(Des Jermaine. Litho Security Printers (M), Malaysia)

1989 (28 Dec). *50th Anniv of National Park.* T **166** and similar vert design. Multicoloured. W **138**. P 12 (20 c.) or 13 ($1).

430	20 c. Type **166**		50	20
	a. Perf 14½		3·25	3·50
431	$1 Pair of Malay Ocellated Pheasants		1·75	2·75
	a. Perf 14½		3·25	4·00

(Des A. Kassim. Litho Security Printers (M), Malaysia)

1990 (1 Jan). *"Visit Malaysia Year".* T **167** and similar horiz designs. Multicoloured. W **138** (sideways). P 12.

432	20 c. Type **167**		40	15
433	50 c. Traditional drums		75	90
434	$1 Scuba diving, windsurfing and yachting		1·25	2·25
432/4		Set of 3	2·25	3·00

168 *Dillenia suffruticosa*

169 Monument and Rainbow

(Des T. Teh Chin Seng. Litho Security Printers (M), Malaysia)

1990 (12 Mar). *Wildflowers* (1st series). T **168** and similar vert designs. Multicoloured. W **138**. P 12.

435	15 c. Type **168**		25	15
436	20 c. *Mimosa pudica*		30	20
437	50 c. *Ipmoea carnea*		60	70
438	$1 *Nymphaea pubescens*		80	1·75
435/8		Set of 4	1·75	2·50

See also Nos. 505/8.

(Des CD Advertising. Litho Security Printers (M), Malaysia)

1990 (14 May). *Kuala Lumpur, Garden City of Lights.* T **169** and similar multicoloured designs. W **138** (sideways on 40 c., $1). P 12.

439	20 c. Type **169**		20	20
440	40 c. Mosque and skyscrapers at night (*horiz*)		40	55
441	$1 Kuala Lumpur skyline (*horiz*)		95	2·00
439/41		Set of 3	1·40	2·50

170 Seri Negara Building

171 Alor Setar

(Des T. Teh Chin Seng. Litho Security Printers (M), Malaysia)

1990 (1 June). *1st Summit Meeting of South–South Consultation and Co-operation Group, Kuala Lumpur.* T **170** and similar horiz design. Multicoloured. W **138** (sideways). P 13.

442	20 c. Type **170**		20	15
443	80 c. Summit logo		80	1·75

(Des Penerbit Hidayah. Litho Security Printers (M), Malaysia)

1990 (2 June). *250th Anniv of Alor Setar.* T **171** and similar multicoloured designs. W **138** (sideways on 40 c., $1). P 12.

444	20 c. Type **171**		20	20
445	40 c. Musicians and monument (*vert*)		30	35
446	$1 Zahir Mosque (*vert*)		85	1·75
444/6		Set of 3	1·25	2·10

172 Sign Language Letters

173 Leatherback Turtle

(Des S. Senika. Litho Security Printers (M), Malaysia)

1990 (8 Sept). *International Literacy Year.* T **172** and similar multicoloured designs. W **138** (sideways on 20, 40 c.). P 13 (40 c.) or 12 (others).

447	20 c. Type **172**		15	10
	a. Perf 13		13·00	
448	40 c. People reading		30	35
449	$1 Symbolic person reading (*vert*)		90	2·00
447/9		Set of 3	1·25	2·25

(Des Ong Soo Keat. Litho Security Printers (M), Malaysia)

1990 (17 Nov). *Marine Life* (3rd series). Sea Turtles. T **173** and similar horiz designs. Multicoloured. W **138** (sideways). P 12.

450	15 c. Type **173**		60	10
451	20 c. Common Green Turtle		60	15
452	40 c. Olive Ridley Turtle		1·25	80
453	$1 Hawksbill Turtle		2·25	3·00
	a. Wmk inverted			
450/3		Set of 4	4·25	3·50

174 Safety Helmet, Dividers and Industrial Skyline

175 *Eustenogaster calyptodoma*

(Litho Security Printers (M), Malaysia)

1991 (25 Apr). *25th Anniv of MARA (Council of the Indigenous People).* T **174** and similar horiz designs. Multicoloured. W **138** (sideways). P 12.

454	20 c. Type **174**		15	10
455	40 c. Documents and graph		30	35
456	$1 25th Anniversary logo		75	1·75
454/6		Set of 3	1·10	2·00

(Des Loh Wen Kong. Litho Security Printers (M), Malaysia)

1991 (29 July). *Insects. Wasps.* T **175** and similar vert designs. Multicoloured. W **138** (sideways). P 12.

457	15 c. Type **175**		25	30
	a. Wmk upright		3·25	
458	20 c. *Vespa affinis indonensis*		25	20
459	50 c. *Sceliphorn javanum*		60	70
460	$1 *Ampulex compressa*		1·00	1·75
457/60		Set of 4	1·90	2·75
MS461	130×85 mm. Nos. 457/60. Wmk sideways. P 14½×14		2·00	3·00
	a. Wmk upright. P 12		8·50	10·00

15 c. stamps from normal sheets (Nos. 457/a) show the wasp's left-hand feeler touching the edge of the design. On stamps of this value from the miniature sheet the feeler stops short of the edge.

176 Tunku Abdul Rahman Putra and Independence Rally

(Des Design Dimension. Litho Security Printers (M), Malaysia)

1991 (30 Aug). *Former Prime Ministers of Malaysia.* T **176** and similar horiz designs. Multicoloured. W **138**. P 12.

462	$1 Type **176**		70	1·00
463	$1 Tun Abdul Razak Hussein and jungle village		70	1·00
464	$1 Tun Hussein Onn and standard-bearers		70	1·00
462/4		Set of 3	1·90	2·75

177 Maziah Palace, Trengganu

178 Museum Building in 1891, Brass Lamp and Fabric

(Des A. Kassim. Litho Security Printers (M), Malaysia)

1991 (7 Nov). *Historic Buildings of Malaysia* (2nd series). T **177** and similar horiz designs. Multicoloured. W **138**. P 12.

465	15 c. Type **177**		20	10
466	20 c. Grand Palace, Johore		20	15
467	40 c. Town Palace, Kuala Langat, Selangor		45	50
468	$1 Jahar Palace, Kelantan		90	1·75
465/8		Set of 4	1·60	2·25

(Des T. Teh Chin Seng. Litho Security Printers (M), Malaysia)

1991 (21 Dec). *Centenary of Sarawak Museum.* T **178** and similar horiz design. Multicoloured. W **138**. P 12.

469	30 c. Type **178**		20	15
470	$1 Museum building in 1991, vase and fabric		80	1·25

179 Rural Postman on Cycle

180 Hill Forest and Jelutong Tree

(Des Ismail & Associates. Litho Security Printers (M), Malaysia)

1992 (1 Jan). *Inauguration of Post Office Corporation. T* **179** *and similar vert designs. Multicoloured. W* **138** *(sideways).* P 12.

471	30 c. Type **179**	..	50	65
	a. Horiz strip of 5. Nos. 471/5		2·25	
472	30 c. Urban postman on motorcycle	..	50	65
473	30 c. Inner city post van	..	50	65
474	30 c. Industrial post van	..	50	65
475	30 c. Malaysian Airlines Boeing 747 and globe	..	50	65
471/5		*Set of 5*	2·25	3·00

Nos. 471/5 were printed together, *se-tenant*, in horizontal strips of 5 throughout the sheet.

(Des T. Teh Chin Seng. Litho Security Printers (M), Malaysia)

1992 (23 Mar). *Tropical Forests. T* **180** *and similar horiz designs. Multicoloured. W* **138** *(sideways).* P 12.

476	20 c. Type **180**	..	20	10
477	50 c. Mangrove swamp and Bakau Minyak tree	..	45	50
478	$1 Lowland forest and Chengal tree	..	90	1·50
476/8		*Set of 3*	1·40	1·90

181 Tuanku Ja'afar and Coat of Arms

182 Badminton Players

(Des TIARA CDP. Litho Security Printers (M), Malaysia)

1992 (18 Apr). *25th Anniv of Installation of Tuanku Ja'afar as Yang di-Pertuan Besar of Negri Sembilan. T* **181** *and similar horiz design. W* **138** *(sideways).* P 12.

479	30 c. Type **181**	..	20	20
480	$1 Palace, Negri Sembilan	..	80	1·60

(Des T. Teh Chin Seng. Litho Security Printers (M), Malaysia)

1992 (25 July). *Malaysian Victory in Thomas Cup Badminton Championship. T* **182** *and similar multicoloured designs.* W **138**. P 12.

481	$1 Type **182**	..	55	75
	w. Wmk inverted		13·00	
482	$1 Thomas Cup and Malaysian flag	..	55	75
MS483	105×80 mm. $2 Winning team (76×28 mm). Wmk sideways		1·50	2·25

183 Women in National Costumes

184 Straits Settlements 1867 1½ c. and Malaysian Federation 1957 10 c. Stamps

(Des Image Productions. Litho Security Printers (M), Malaysia)

1992 (8 Aug). *25th Anniv of A.S.E.A.N. (Association of South East Asian Nations). T* **183** *and similar horiz designs. Multicoloured. W* **138** *(sideways).* P 12.

484	30 c. Type **183**	..	40	30
	a. Wmk inverted			
485	50 c. Regional flowers	..	65	75
486	$1 Traditional architecture	..	1·25	2·25
484/6		*Set of 3*	2·10	3·00

(Des Mega Dot. Litho Security Printers (M), Malaysia)

1992 (1 Sept). *125th Anniv of Postage Stamps and "Kuala Lumpur '92", International Stamp Exhibition. T* **184** *and similar horiz designs. Multicoloured. W* **138** *(sideways).* P 12.

487	30 c. Type **184**	..	35	50
	a. Horiz pair. Nos. 487/8		70	1·00
488	30 c. Straits Settlements 1867 2 c. and Malaysia 1963 Federation Inauguration 12 c.		35	50
489	50 c. Straits Settlements 1868 4 c. and Malaysia 1990 Kuala Lumpur 40 c.		65	80
	a. Horiz pair. Nos. 489/90		1·25	1·60
	b. Wmk inverted		4·75	
	ba. Horiz pair. Nos. 489b/90b		9·50	
490	50 c. Straits Settlements 1867 12 c. and Malaysia "Kuala Lumpur '92" $2		65	80
	b. Wmk inverted		4·75	
487/90		*Set of 4*	1·75	2·40
MS491	120×92 mm. $2 "Kuala Lumpur '92" logo on Malaysian flag. P 13×13½		1·75	2·50
	a. Perf 12		8·50	10·00

Nos. 487/8 and 489/90 were printed together, *se-tenant*, in horizontal pairs throughout the sheets.

ALTERED CATALOGUE NUMBERS

Any Catalogue numbers altered from the last edition are shown as a list in the introductory pages.

---

185 Acropora

186 Girls smiling

(Des Greenmild Advertising. Litho Security Printers (M), Malaysia)

1992 (21 Dec). *Marine Life (4th series). Corals. T* **185** *and similar multicoloured designs.* W **138**. P 12.

492	30 c. Type **185**	..	70	85
	a. Horiz strip of 5. Nos. 492/6		3·25	
493	30 c. Dendronephthya	..	70	85
494	30 c. Dendrophyllia	..	70	85
495	30 c. Sinularia	..	70	85
496	30 c. Melithaea	..	70	85
492/6		*Set of 5*	3·25	3·75
MS497	100×70 mm. $2 Subergorgia (38×28 mm). Wmk sideways		2·25	3·00
	a. Wmk upright		5·50	7·00

Nos. 492/6 were printed together, *se-tenant*, in horizontal strips of 5 throughout the sheet.

(Des Image Promotions. Litho Security Printers (M), Malaysia)

1993 (24 Apr). *16th Asian–Pacific Dental Congress. T* **186** *and similar horiz designs. Multicoloured. W* **138** *(sideways).* P 12.

498	30 c. Type **186**	..	50	65
	a. Horiz pair. Nos. 498/9		1·00	1·25
499	30 c. Girls smiling with Koala Bear		50	65
500	50 c. Dentists with Japanese, Malaysian and South Korean flags		80	1·00
	a. Horiz pair. Nos. 500/1		1·75	2·25
501	$1 Dentists with New Zealand, Thai, Chinese and Indonesian flags		1·00	1·25
498/501		*Set of 4*	2·50	3·25

Nos. 498/9 and 500/1 were each printed together, *se-tenant*, in horizontal pairs throughout the sheets.

187 View of Golf Course

188 Alpinia rafflesiana

(Des T. Teh Chin Seng. Litho Security Printers (M), Malaysia)

1993 (24 June). *Centenary of Royal Selangor Golf Club. T* **187** *and similar multicoloured designs. W* **138** *(sideways on $1).* P 12.

502	30 c. Type **187**	..	60	20
503	50 c. Old and new club houses	..	90	80
	w. Wmk inverted		15·00	
504	$1 Bunker on course (*horiz*)	..	1·75	2·00
502/4		*Set of 3*	3·00	2·75

(Des TIARA CDP. Litho Security Printers (M), Malaysia)

1993 (2 Aug). *Wildflowers (2nd series). Gingers. T* **188** *and similar vert designs. Multicoloured. W* **138**. P 12.

505	20 c. Type **188**	..	35	10
	w. Wmk inverted		12·00	
506	30 c. Achasma megalocheilos	..	45	20
507	50 c. Zingiber spectabile	..	80	80
508	$1 Costus speciosus	..	1·60	2·00
	w. Wmk inverted		16·00	
505/8		*Set of 3*	2·75	2·75

189 Forest under Magnifying Glass

190 White-breasted Kingfisher

(Des CD Advertising. Litho Security Printers (M), Malaysia)

1993 (13 Sept). *14th Commonwealth Forestry Conference, Kuala Lumpur. T* **189** *and similar multicoloured designs.* W **138** *(sideways on 30 c., 50 c.).* P 12.

509	30 c. Type **189**	..	40	20
510	50 c. Hand holding forest	..	65	70
511	$1 Forest in glass dome (*vert*)	..	1·40	2·25
509/11		*Set of 3*	2·25	2·75

Nos. 509/11 were re-issued on 1 October 1994 with the Bangkok '93 Stamp Exhibition logo incorporated in the designs. Such stamps were only available from the Malaysia stand at the exhibition and in very limited quantities from the philatelic bureaux.

(Des Ong Soo Keat. Litho Security Printers (M), Malaysia)

1993 (23 Oct). *Kingfishers. T* **190** *and similar vert designs. Multicoloured. W* **138**. P 12.

512	30 c. Type **190**	..	75	1·00
	a. Horiz pair. Nos. 512/13		1·50	2·00
513	30 c. Pair of Blue-eared Kingfishers		75	1·00
514	50 c. Chestnut-collared Kingfisher		90	1·25
	a. Horiz pair. Nos. 514/15		1·75	2·50
515	50 c. Pair of Three-toed Kingfishers		90	1·25
512/15		*Set of 4*	3·00	4·00

Nos. 512/13 and 514/15 were printed together, *se-tenant*, in horizontal pairs throughout the sheets.

191 SME MD3-160M Light Aircraft

192 Jeriau Waterfalls

(Des A. Hassan. Litho Security Printers (M), Malaysia)

1993 (7 Dec). *Langkawi International Maritime and Aerospace Exhibition '93. T* **191** *and similar horiz designs. Multicoloured. W* **138** *(sideways on 30 c.).* P 12.

516	30 c. Type **191**	..	35	20
	a. Wmk inverted		4·25	
517	50 c. Eagle X-TS light aircraft	..	65	75
	w. Wmk inverted		65	
518	$1 Kasturi (frigate)	..	1·25	2·00
	a. Wmk sideways			
516/18		*Set of 3*	2·00	2·75
MS519	120×80 mm. $2 Map of Langkawi. Wmk upright		1·60	2·25
	a. Wmk sideways		18·00	

(Des Mega Dot. Litho Security Printers (M), Malaysia)

1994 (1 Jan). *Visit Malaysia. T* **192** *and similar horiz designs. Multicoloured. W* **138** *(inverted).* P 12.

520	20 c. Type **192**	..	25	10
521	30 c. Flowers	..	30	25
522	50 c. Turtle and fishes	..	45	55
523	$1 Orang-utan and other wildlife	..	90	1·50
520/3		*Set of 4*	1·60	2·25

Nos. 520/3 were re-issued on 8 November 1994 with the "ASEANPEX '94" Stamp Exhibition logo incorporated in the designs. Such stamps were only available from the Malaysian stand at the exhibition and in very limited quantities from the philatelic bureaux.

193 Planetarium and Planets

194 Spathoglottis aurea

(Des CD Advertising and DeArt Forms. Litho Security Printers (M), Malaysia)

1994 (7 Feb). *National Planetarium, Kuala Lumpur. T* **193** *and similar horiz designs. Multicoloured. W* **138** *(inverted on 30 c.).* P 12.

524	30 c. Type **193**	..	50	20
	w. Wmk upright			
525	50 c. Static displays	..	65	75
526	$1 Planetarium auditorium	..	1·50	2·00
524/6		*Set of 3*	2·40	2·75

(Des P. Ket. Litho Security Printers (M), Malaysia)

1994 (17 Feb). *Orchids. T* **194** *and similar multicoloured designs. W* **138**. P 12.

527	20 c. Type **194**	..	35	10
528	30 c. Paphiopedilum barbatum	..	45	25
529	50 c. Bulbophyllum lobbii	..	75	85
530	$1 Aerides odorata	..	1·25	1·75
527/30		*Set of 4*	2·50	2·75
MS531	120×82 mm. $2 Grammatophyllum speciosum (*horiz*)		2·25	3·00

No. MS531 also commemorates the "Hong Kong '94" International Stamp Exhibition.

195 Decorative Bowl

196 Flock of Chickens and Vet examining Cat

(Des Assist Ad. Litho Security Printers (M), Malaysia)

1994 (17 June). *World Islamic Civilisation Festival '94, Kuala Lumpur. T* **195** *and similar vert designs. Multicoloured.* W **138**. *P* 12.

532	20 c. Type 195	..	..	15	10
533	30 c. Celestial globe	..	..	25	20
534	50 c. Dinar coins	..	..	40	55
535	$1 Decorative tile	..	..	75	1·25
532/5			Set of 4	1·40	1·90

Nos. 532/5 were re-issued on 16 August 1994 with the "Philakorea '94" Stamp Exhibition logo incorporated in the designs. Such stamps were only available from the Malaysia stand at the exhibition and in very limited quantities from the philatelic bureaux.

(Des TIARA CDP. Litho Security Printers (M), Malaysia)

1994 (26 July). *Centenary of Veterinary Services. T* **196** *and similar vert designs. Multicoloured.* W **138** *(inverted on 30 c.). P* 12.

536	30 c. Type 196	..	..	35	20
537	50 c. Vet in abattoir	..	..	60	50
538	$1 Herd of cows and veterinary equipment		1·00	1·50
	w. Wmk inverted			9·00	
536/8			Set of 3	1·75	2·00

197 Workers laying Electric Cable 198 Expressway from the Air

(Des Mega Dot. Litho Security Printers (M), Malaysia)

1994 (3 Sept). *Centenary of Electricity Supply. T* **197** *and similar horiz designs. Multicoloured.* W **138** *(sideways). P* 12.

539	30 c. Type 197	..	..	25	45
	a. Horiz pair. Nos. 539/40			50	90
540	30 c. Illuminated city	..	..	25	45
541	$1 City of the future	..	..	70	1·10
539/41			Set of 3	1·10	1·75

Nos. 539/40 were printed together, *se-tenant*, in horizontal pairs throughout the sheet.

(Des The Sharper Image. Litho Security Printers (M), Malaysia)

1994 (8 Sept). *Opening of North–South Expressway. T* **198** *and similar horiz designs. Multicoloured.* W **138** *(sideways). P* 12.

542	30 c. Type 198	..	..	20	20
543	50 c. Expressway junction	..		35	50
544	$1 Expressway bridge	..	..	80	1·25
542/4			Set of 3	1·25	1·75

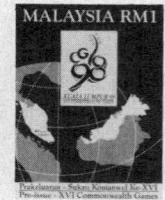

199 Sultan Tuanku Ja'afar 200 Map of Malaysia and Logo

(Des R. Yaacob. Litho Security Printers (M), Malaysia)

1994 (22 Sept). *Installation of Sultan Tuanku Ja'afar as Yang di Pertuan Agong.* W **138**. *P* 12.

545	**199**	30 c. multicoloured	..	20	20
		a. Wmk sideways	..		
		w. Wmk inverted	..	2·50	
546		50 c. multicoloured	..	40	50
547		$1 multicoloured	..	80	1·25
545/7			Set of 3	1·25	1·75

(Des Limkokwing Integrated. Litho Security Printers (M), Malaysia)

1994 (29 Oct). *16th Commonwealth Games, Kuala Lumpur (1998) (1st issue). T* **200** *and similar vert design. Multicoloured.* W **138**. *P* 12.

548	$1 Type 200	..	..	80	1·00
	a. Horiz pair. Nos. 548/9	..		1·60	2·00
	b. Perf 14½				
	ba. Horiz pair. Nos. 548b/9b		12·00	
549	$1 Wira (games mascot) holding national flag	..		80	1·00
	b. Perf 14½				

Nos. 548/9 were issued together, *se-tenant*, in sheets of 30 (6×5), showing No. 548 in vertical rows 1 and 4, No. 549 in vertical rows 3 and 6, and a stamp-size label, showing the mascot playing rugby, basketball, cricket and hockey, in vertical rows 2 and 5.

See also Nos. 575/6, 627/30, 668/71, **MS**678, 693/708 and **MS**715/16.

201 Tunku Abdul Rahman Putra and National Flag

(Des T. Teh Ching Seng. Litho Leigh-Mardon Ltd, Melbourne, Australia)

1994 (10 Nov). *5th Death Anniv of Tunku Abdul Rahman Putra (former Prime Minister). T* **201** *and simlar horiz design. Multicoloured. P* 14½.

550	30 c. Type 201	..	..	25	20
551	$1 The Residency, Kuala Lumpur	..	75	1·00

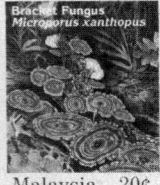

202 Library Building 203 *Microporus xanthopus*

(Des Image Promotions. Litho Security Printers (M), Malaysia)

1994 (16 Dec). *Opening of the New National Library Building. T* **202** *and similar horiz designs. Multicoloured.* W **138** *(sideways). P* 12.

552	30 c. Type 202	..	..	25	20
553	50 c. Computer plan on screen	..	45	50
554	$1 Ancient Koran	..	..	1·00	1·40
552/4			Set of 3	1·50	1·90

(Des Greenmild Advertising. Litho Enschedé)

1995 (18 Jan). *Fungi. T* **203** *and similar vert designs. Multicoloured. P* 14½×14.

555	20 c. Type 203	..	..	15	10
556	30 c. *Cookeina tricholoma*	..	25	20
557	50 c. *Phallus indusiatus* ("*Dictyophora phalloidea*")	..	45	55
558	$1 *Ramaria* sp.	..	..	90	1·50
555/8			Set of 4	1·60	2·00

204 Seafans

(Litho Security Printers (M), Malaysia)

1995 (10 Apr). *Marine Life (5th series). Corals. T* **204** *and similar horiz designs. Multicoloured.* W **138** *(sideways). P* 12.

559	20 c. Type 204	..	..	50	65
	a. Booklet pane. Nos. 559/60, each × 5	4·50	
560	20 c. Feather Stars	..	..	50	65
561	30 c. Cup Coral	..	..	50	65
	a. Booklet pane. Nos. 561/2, each × 5	4·50	
562	30 c. Soft Coral	..	..	50	65
559/62			Set of 4	1·75	2·40

Nos. 559/60 and 561/2 were only available from $2 and $3 stamp booklets.

205 Clouded Leopard on Branch

(Des A. Robinson. Litho Enschedé)

1995 (18 Apr). *Endangered Species. Clouded Leopard. T* **205** *and similar horiz designs. Multicoloured.* W w **14** *(sideways). Ordinary paper. P* 13½.

563	20 c. Type 205	..	..	25	25
	a. Strip of 4. Nos. 563/6	..		1·50	
564	30 c. With cubs	..	..	30	30
565	50 c. Crouched on branch	..	45	50
566	$1 Climbing tree	..	..	70	1·00
563/6			Set of 4	1·50	1·90

In addition to separate sheets of 50 Nos. 563/6 were also available in sheets of 16 (4×4) with the stamps *se-tenant* both vertically and horizontally.

206 Early X-Ray Equipment and X-Ray of Hand

(Des Eka IPR Agensi. Litho Security Printers (M), Malaysia)

1995 (29 May). *Centenary of Discovery of X-Rays by Wilhelm Conrad Röntgen. T* **206** *and similar horiz designs. Multicoloured.* W **138**. *P* 12.

567	30 c. Type 206	..	..	30	50
	a. Pair. Nos. 567/8	..		60	1·00
568	30 c. Body scanner and brain scan	..	30	50
569	$1 Chest X-rays	..	..	95	1·25
567/9			Set of 3	1·40	2·00

Nos. 567/8 were printed together, *se-tenant*, in horizontal and vertical pairs throughout the sheet.

207 Jembiah (curved dagger) 208 Badminton, Cricket, Shooting, Tennis, Hurdling, Hockey and Weightlifting

(Des BJ Image. Litho Questa)

1995 (1 Sept). *"Singapore '95" International Stamp Exhibition. Traditional Malay Weapons. T* **207** *and similar horiz designs. Multicoloured. P* 14.

570	20 c. Type 207	..	..	15	10
571	30 c. Keris panjang (sword)	..	25	20
572	50 c. Kerambit (curved dagger)	..	40	50
573	$1 Keris sundang (sword)	..	80	1·50
570/3			Set of 4	1·40	2·00
MS574	100×70 mm. $2 Ladig terus (dagger)	1·60	2·25

(Des Limkokwing Integrated. Litho Security Printers (M), Malaysia)

1995 (11 Sept). *16th Commonwealth Games, Kuala Lumpur (1998) (2nd issue). T* **208** *and similar vert design. Multicoloured.* W **138**. *P* 13½.

575	$1 Type 208	..	..	1·25	1·40
	a. Horiz pair. Nos. 575/6	..		2·50	2·75
	b. Perf 14½	..		3·50	3·75
	ba. Horiz pair. Nos. 575b/6b		7·00	7·50
576	$1 Cycling, bowls, boxing, basketball, rugby, gymnastics and swimming	1·25	1·40
	b. Perf 14½	..		3·50	3·75

Nos. 575/6 were issued together, *se-tenant*, in sheets of 30 (6×5), showing No. 575 in vertical rows 1 and 4, No. 576 in vertical rows 3 and 6, and a stamp-size label, showing the monkey mascot hurdling, boxing and playing badminton, in vertical rows 2 and 5.

209 Leatherback Turtle (*Dermochelys coriacea*)

(Des Choo Beng Teong. Litho Security Printers (M), Malaysia)

1995 (26 Sept). *Turtles. T* **209** *and similar horiz design. Multicoloured.* W **138** *(sideways). P* 14½.

577	30 c. Type 209	..	..	50	70
	a. Booklet pane. Nos. 577/8 each × 5	4·50	
578	30 c. Green Turtle (*Chelonia mydas*)	..	50	70

Nos. 577/8 were only issued in $3 stamp booklets.

210 Anniversary Emblem and Symbolic People around Globe 211 Boeing 747, Globe, Emblem and Malaysian Scenes

(Des PAC Advertising. Litho Southern Colour Print, Dunedin, New Zealand)

1995 (24 Oct). *50th Anniv of United Nations. T* **210** *and similar horiz design. Multicoloured. P* 13½.

579	30 c. Type 210	..	..	15	20
580	$1 United Nations emblem	..	60	80

(Des ISC Bullseye. Litho Enschedé)

1995 (30 Oct). *50th Anniv of International Air Transport Association. T* **211** *and similar vert designs, each showing Boeing 747 and globe. Multicoloured. P* 14½×14.

581	30 c. Type 211	..	..	30	40
	a. Horiz pair. Nos. 581/2	..		60	80
582	30 c. Asian and Australasian scenes	..	30	40
583	50 c. European and African scenes	..	45	65
	a. Horiz pair. Nos. 583/4	..		90	1·25
584	50 c. North and South American scenes	..	45	65
581/4			Set of 4	1·40	1·90

Nos. 581/2 and 583/4 were printed together, *se-tenant*, in horizontal pairs throughout the sheets.

212 Proton "Saga 1.5"
Saloon, 1985

213 "Ariane 4"
Launch Rocket

(Des Long's Creative. Litho Southern Colour Print, Dunedin)

1995 (23 Dec). *10th Anniv of Proton Cars. T* **212** *and similar horiz designs. Multicoloured. P* 14×14½.
585	30 c. Type **212**	..	25	30
	a. Booklet pane. Nos. 585/94	..	2·25	
586	30 c. "Iswara 1.5" aeroback, 1992	..	25	30
587	30 c. "Iswara 1.5" saloon, 1992	..	25	30
588	30 c. "Wira 1.6" saloon, 1993	..	25	30
589	30 c. "Wira 1.6" aeroback, 1993	..	25	30
590	30 c. Proton rally car, 1994	..	25	30
591	30 c. "Satria 1.6" hatchback, 1994	..	25	30
592	30 c. "Perdana 2.0" saloon, 1995	..	25	30
593	30 c. "Wira 1.6" aeroback, 1995	..	25	30
594	30 c. "Wira 1.8" saloon, 1995	..	25	30
585/94		*Set of 10*	2·25	2·75

Nos. 585/94 were only issued in $3 stamp booklets with the horizontal edges of the pane imperforate.

(Des Nerve Centre Associates. Litho Southern Colour Print, Dunedin)

1996 (13 Jan). *Launch of MEASAT I (Malaysia East Asia Satellite). T* **213** *and similar multicoloured designs. P* 13½.
595	30 c. Type **213**	..	25	20
596	50 c. Satellite over Eastern Asia	..	40	45
597	$1 Satellite Earth station, Langkawi	..	90	1·40
595/7		*Set of 3*	1·40	1·90
MS598	100×70 mm. $5 Satellite orbiting Globe (hologram) (*horiz*). P 14×14½	..	3·25	4·00

214 *Nepenthes
sanguinea*

215 Brahminy Kite

(Des P. Ket. Litho Security Printers (M), Malaysia)

1996 (6 Apr). *Pitcher Plants. T* **214** *and similar vert designs. Multicoloured. W* **138**. *P* 13½ (30 c.) *or* 14½×14 (50 c.).
599	30 c. Type **214**	..	25	35
	a. Horiz pair. Nos. 599/600	..	50	70
	b. Perf 14½×14			
	ba. Horiz pair. Nos. 599b/600b			
600	30 c. *Nepenthes macfarlanei*	..	25	35
601	50 c. *Nepenthes rajah*	..	35	50
	a. Horiz pair. Nos. 601/2	..	70	1·00
	b. Perf 13½	..	3·50	3·75
	ba. Horiz pair. Nos. 601b/2b	..	7·00	7·50
602	50 c. *Nepenthes lowii*	..	35	50
	b. Perf 13½	..	3·50	3·75
599/602	..	*Set of 4*	1·10	1·50

(Des Teh Yew Kiang)

1996 (18 May–Dec). *Birds of Prey. T* **215** *and similar multicoloured designs.* (*a*) *Litho Security Printers* (M), *Malaysia. W* **138**. *P* 13½ (30 c.) *or* 14½×14 (*others*).
603	20 c. Type **215**	..	20	15
604	30 c. Crested Serpent Eagle	..	30	25
	aw. Wmk inverted	..	20·00	
	b. Perf 14×14½	..	5·50	70
605	50 c. White-bellied Sea Eagle	..	45	55
	b. Perf 13½	..	6·00	
606	$1 Crested Hawk Eagle	..	90	1·50
	aw. Wmk inverted			
	b. Perf 13½	..	13·00	
603/6		*Set of 4*	1·75	2·25
MS607	100×70 mm. $2 Blyth's Hawk Eagle (*vert*). P 13½×14	..	2·25	2·75
	a. Perf 13½	..	8·50	9·00
	b. Perf 14	..	8·50	9·00

(*b*) *Litho Southern Colour Print, Dunedin. No wmk. P* 13½
607c	20 c. Type **215** (Dec)	..	2·50	30

No. **MS**607 also includes the "CHINA '96" 9th Asian International Stamp Exhibition logo on the sheet margin.

STANLEY GIBBONS
STAMP COLLECTING SERIES

Introductory booklets on *How to Start, How to Identify Stamps* and *Collecting by Theme.* A series of well illustrated guides at a low price.
Write for details.

---

216 Family, Globe and
Burning Drugs

217 *Graphium
sarpedon*

(Des CD Advertising. Litho Security Printers (M), Malaysia)

1996 (26 June). *International Day against Drug Abuse and Illicit Trafficking. T* **216** *and similar horiz designs. Multicoloured. W* **138** (*sideways*). *P* 14×14½.
608	30 c. Type **216**	..	25	35
	a. Horiz pair. Nos. 608/9	..	50	70
	b. Perf 13½	..	3·50	
	ba. Horiz pair. Nos. 608b/9b	..	7·00	
609	30 c. Sporting activities	..	25	35
	b. Perf 13½	..	3·50	
610	$1 Family and rainbow	..	60	80
	b. Perf 13½			
608/10		*Set of 3*	1·00	1·40

Nos. 608/9 were printed together, *se-tenant*, in horizontal pairs throughout the sheet.

(Des P. Chuah. Litho Southern Colour Print, Dunedin)

1996 (27 Sept). *"ISTANBUL '96" International Stamp Exhibition. Butterflies. T* **217** *and similar vert designs. Multicoloured. P* 14½×14.
611	30 c. Type **217**	..	40	50
	a. Booklet pane. Nos. 611/15×2	..	3·50	
612	30 c. *Terinos terpander*	..	40	50
613	30 c. *Melanocyma faunula*	..	40	50
614	30 c. *Trogonoptera brookiana*	..	40	50
615	30 c. *Delias hyparete*	..	40	50
611/15		*Set of 5*	1·75	2·25

Nos. 611/15 were only issued in $3 stamp booklets.

218 Kuala Lumpur Tower

219 C.A.P.A. Logo on
Kite

(Des The Sharper Image ($2), Akitek Akiprima (others). Litho Southern Colour Print, Dunedin)

1996 (1 Oct). *Opening of Kuala Lumpur Telecommunications Tower. T* **218** *and similar multicoloured designs. P* 13½.
616	30 c. Type **218**	..	20	20
617	50 c. Diagram of top of tower	..	30	35
618	$1 Kuala Lumpur Tower at night	..	80	1·00
616/18		*Set of 3*	1·10	1·40
MS619	70×100 mm. $2 Top of Kuala Lumpur Tower (*different*) (*vert*)	..	1·25	1·75

(Des The Sharper Image. Litho Enschedé)

1996 (7 Oct). *14th Conference of the Confederation of Asian and Pacific Accountants. T* **219** *and similar horiz design. Multicoloured. P* 14×14½.
620	30 c. Type **219**	..	20	20
621	$1 Globe and C.A.P.A logo	..	60	70

(Litho Southern Colour Print, Dunedin)

1996 (16 Oct). *"TAIPEI '96" 10th Asian International Stamp Exhibition. As No.* **MS**619, *but with exhibition logo added to bottom right-hand corner of sheet. P* 13½.
MS622	70×100 mm. $2 Top of Kuala Lumpur Tower (*vert*)	..	1·25	1·75

220 Model of D.N.A.
Molecule

221 Slow Loris

(Des The Sharper Image. Litho Southern Colour Print, Dunedin)

1996 (29 Nov). *Opening of National Science Centre, Kuala Lumpur. T* **220** *and similar horiz designs. Multicoloured. P* 13½.
623	30 c. Type **220**	..	25	20
624	50 c. Planetary model and Science Centre	..	40	40
625	$1 National Science Centre	..	90	1·25
623/5		*Set of 3*	1·40	1·60

(Des Teh Yew Kiang. Litho Southern Colour Print, Dunedin)

1996 (2 Dec). *Stamp Week. Wildlife. Sheet* 165×75 *mm containing T* **221** *and similar multicoloured designs. P* 14.
MS626	20 c. Type **221**; 30 c. Prevost's Squirrel; 50 c. Atlas Moth; $1 Rhinoceros Hornbill (60×30 mm); $1 White-handed Gibbon (30×60 mm); $2 Banded Palm Civet (60×30 mm)	..	2·75	3·50

A similar sheet, but imperforate and without face values, was also available from the Philatelic Bureau at $15.

---

222 Running

223 Pygmy Blue
Flycatcher

(Des CD Advertising. Litho Southern Colour Print, Dunedin)

1996 (21 Dec). *16th Commonwealth Games, Kuala Lumpur (1998) (3rd issue). T* **222** *and similar horiz designs. Multicoloured. P* 12.
627	30 c. Type **222**	..	20	30
	a. Vert pair. Nos. 627/8	..	40	60
628	30 c. Hurdling	..	20	30
629	30 c. High jumping	..	30	50
	a. Vert pair. Nos. 629/30	..	60	1·00
630	50 c. Javelin	..	30	50
627/30		*Set of 4*	90	1·40

Nos. 627/8 and 629/30 were each printed together, *se-tenant*, in sheets of 20 (5×4) with the first design in rows 1 and 3 and the second in rows 2 and 4. As there are horizontal gutters between rows 1 and 2 and 3 and 4, Nos. 627a and 629a only occur from rows 2 and 3.

(Des P. Chuah. Litho Enschedé)

1997 (4 Jan). *Highland Birds. T* **223** *and similar vert designs. Multicoloured. P* 13½×14.
631	20 c. Type **223**	..	25	10
632	30 c. Silver-eared Mesia	..	30	20
633	50 c. Black-sided Flower-pecker	..	40	45
634	$1 Scarlet Sunbird	..	70	1·25
631/4		*Set of 4*	1·50	1·75

(Litho Southern Colour Print, Dunedin)

1997 (12 Feb). *"HONG KONG '97" International Stamp Exhibition. As No.* **MS**626, *but with exhibition logo added to top sheet margin. P* 14.
MS635	165×75 mm. 20 c. Type **221**; 30 c. Tree Squirrel; 50 c. *Attacus atlas* (butterfly); $1 Rhinoceros Hornbill (60×30 mm); $1 Common Gibbon (30×60 mm); $2 Banded Palm Civet (60×30 mm)	..	3·25	4·25

224 Transit Train
leaving Station

225 Bowler

(Des The Sharper Image. Litho Southern Colour Print, Dunedin)

1997 (1 Mar). *Opening of Kuala Lumpur Light Rail Transit System. T* **224** *and similar horiz design. Multicoloured. P* 14×14½.
636	30 c. Type **224**	..	40	55
	a. Booklet pane. Nos. 636/7 each × 5	..	3·50	
637	30 c. Trains in central Kuala Lumpur	..	40	55

Nos. 636/7 were only issued in $3 stamp booklets

(Des P. Chuah. Litho Security Printers (M), Malaysia)

1997 (24 Mar). *International Cricket Council Trophy, Kuala Lumpur. T* **225** *and similar vert designs. Multicoloured. W* **138**. *P* 13½ ($1) *or* 14½ (*others*).
638	30 c. Type **225**	..	30	15
639	50 c. Batsman	..	45	40
	a. Perf 13½	..	4·50	
640	$1 Wicket keeper	..	80	1·00
	a. Perf 14½	..	9·00	
638/40	..	*Set of 3*	1·40	1·40

226 Boeing 747-400 over
World Map

227 *Schima
wallichii*

(Des The Sharper Image. Litho Security Printers (M), Malaysia)

1997 (2 Apr). *50th Anniv of Aviation in Malaysia. T* **226** *and similar horiz designs. Multicoloured. W* **138** (*sideways*)*. P* 13½ (30 c.) *or* 14½ (*others*).
641	30 c. Type **226**	..	40	15
	a. Perf 14½	..	1·00	
	aw. Wmk top of letters to right	..	5·00	
642	50 c. Boeing 747-400 over Kuala Lumpur	..	50	40
	aw. Wmk top of letters to right			
	b. Perf 13½	..	3·00	
643	$1 Tail fins of four airliners	..	80	1·10
	a. Perf 13½	..	3·00	
641/3		*Set of 3*	1·50	1·50

*The normal sideways watermark shows the top of the letters to left, *as seen from the back of the stamp.*

(Des The Sharper Image. Litho Southern Colour Print, Dunedin)

1997 (7 May). *Highland Flowers.* T **227** and similar vert designs. Multicoloured. P 14½×14.

644	30 c. Type 227	30	40
	a. Booklet pane. Nos. 644/8 each × 2	2·75	
645	30 c. *Aeschynanthus longicalyx*	30	40
646	30 c. *Aeschynanthus speciosa*	30	40
647	30 c. *Phyllagathis tuberculata*	30	40
648	30 c. *Didymocarpus quinquevulnerus*	30	40
644/8	Set of 5	1·40	1·75

Nos. 644/8 were only issued in $3 stamp booklets showing the outer edges of the pane imperforate.

228 World Youth Football Championship Mascot

229 Members of First Conference, 1897

(Des The Sharper Image. Litho Harrison (30 c., 50 c.), Security Printers (M), Malaysia ($1))

1997 (16 June). *9th World Youth Football Championship, Malaysia.* T **228** and similar vert designs. Multicoloured. W **138** (sideways) ($1) or no watermark (others). P 12½ ($1) or 13½×13 (others).

649	30 c. Type 228	15	10
650	50 c. Football and players	25	30
651	$1 Map of Malaysia and football	50	70
649/51	Set of 3	80	1·00

(Des R. Yaacob. Litho Southern Colour Print, Dunedin)

1997 (31 July). *Centenary of Rulers' Conference.* T **229** and similar horiz designs. Multicoloured. P 14.

652	30 c. Type 229	15	10
653	50 c. State emblems	25	30
654	$1 Seal and press	50	70
652/4	Set of 3	80	1·00

230 A.S.E.A.N. Logo and Ribbons

231 *Tubastrea* sp.

(Des R. Yaacob. Litho Security Printers (M), Malaysia)

1997 (8 Aug). *30th Anniv of Association of South-east Asian Nations.* T **230** and similar horiz designs. W **138**. P 13½.

655	30 c. Type 230	20	10
656	50 c. "30" enclosing logo	35	35
657	$1 Chevrons and logo	65	90
655/7	Set of 3	1·10	1·25

(Des The Sharper Image. Litho Southern Colour Print, Dunedin)

1997 (23 Aug). *International Year of the Coral Reefs.* T **231** and similar multicoloured designs. P 14½.

658	20 c. Type 231	15	10
	a. Perf 13½	5·50	
659	30 c. *Melithaea* sp	15	10
	a. Perf 13½	5·50	
660	50 c. *Aulostomus chinensis*	30	30
	a. Perf 13½	5·50	
661	$1 *Symphillia* sp.	45	70
	a. Perf 13½	5·50	
658/61	Set of 4	95	1·10
MS662	70×100 mm. $2 Green Turtle (horiz)	1·00	1·25

232 Women Athletes, Scientist and Politician

233 1867 12 c. on 4 anna with Malacca Postmark

(Des Eka IPR Agensi. Litho Enschedé)

1997 (25 Aug). *20th International Pan-Pacific and South-east Asia Women's Association Conference, Kuala Lumpur.* T **232** and similar vert design. Multicoloured. P 13×13½.

663	30 c. Type 232	20	30
	a. Booklet pane. Nos. 663/4, each × 5, with margins all round	1·75	
664	30 c. Family and house	20	30

Nos. 663/4 were only available from $3 stamp booklets.

(Des P. Chuah. Photo Enschedé)

1997 (9 Sept). *"Malpex '97" Stamp Exhibition, Kuala Lumpur. 50th Anniv of Organised Philately.* Sheet, 120×70 mm, containing T **233** and similar diamond-shaped designs. Multicoloured. P 12½.

MS665	20 c. Type 233; 30 c. 1997 Highland Birds set; 50 c. 1996 Wildlife miniature sheet seen through magnifying glass; $1 1867 cover to Amoy	1·00	1·25

234 Group of 15 Emblem

235 Hockey

(Des P. Ket. Litho Security Printers (M), Malaysia)

1997 (3 Nov). *7th Summit Conference of the Group of 15, Kuala Lumpur.* T **234** and similar vert design. Multicoloured. P 12 (30 c.) or 13½ (30 c.) or 13½ ($1).

666	30 c. Type 234	10	10
	a. Perf 13½		
667	$1 Flags of member countries	70	85

(Des CD Advertising. Litho Southern Colour Print, Dunedin)

1997 (15 Nov). *16th Commonwealth Games, Kuala Lumpur (1998)* (4th issue). T **235** and similar horiz designs. Multicoloured. P 12.

668	30 c. Type 235	20	30
	a. Vert pair. Nos. 668/9	40	60
669	30 c. Netball	20	30
670	50 c. Cricket	30	40
	a. Vert pair. Nos. 670/1	60	80
671	50 c. Rugby	30	40
668/71	Set of 4	90	1·25

Nos. 668/9 and 670/1 were each printed together, se-tenant, in sheets of 20 (5×4) with the first design in rows 1 and 3 and the second in rows 2 and 4. As there are horizontal gutters between rows 1 and 2 and 3 and 4, Nos. 668a and 670a only occur from rows 2 and 3.

236 False Gharial

237 Kundang

(Des Teh Yew Kiang. Litho Southern Colour Print, Dunedin)

1997 (1 Dec). *Stamp Week '97. Endangered Wildlife.* Sheet, 165×75 mm, containing T **236** and similar multicoloured designs. P 14½.

MS672	20 c. Type 236; 30 c. Western Tarsier (vert); 50 c. Indian Sambar (vert); $2 Crested Wood Partridge; $2 Malayan Bony-tongue (fish)	1·90	2·25

A second miniature sheet, incorporating a $2 tiger design, had no postal validity.

(Photo Enschedé)

1997 (15 Dec). *"INDEPEX '97" International Stamp Exhibition, New Delhi.* As No. **MS665**, but with exhibition logo added to the sheet margin, in gold, at bottom right. P 12½.

MS673	120×70 mm. 20 c. Type 233; 30 c. 1997 Highlands Bird set; 50 c. 1996 Wildlife miniature sheet seen through magnifying glass; $1 1867 cover to Amoy	75	90

(Des Eka IPR Agensi. Litho Southern Colour Print, Dunedin)

1998 (10 Jan). *Fruit.* T **237** and similar vert designs. Multicoloured. P 13½.

674	20 c. Type 237	10	10
675	30 c. Sentul	10	10
676	50 c. Pulasan	15	20
677	$1 Asam Gelugur	60	75
674/7	Set of 4	75	1·00

238 Swimming Complex

239 Mas (coin) from Trengganu, 1793–1808

(Des CD Advertising. Litho Security Printers (M), Malaysia)

1998 (23 Feb). *16th Commonwealth Games, Kuala Lumpur* (5th issue). Venues. Sheet, 120×80 mm, containing T **238** and similar horiz designs. Multicoloured. W **138**. P 13½*.

MS678	20 c. Type 238; 30 c. Hockey Stadium; 50 c. Indoor Stadium; $1 Main Stadium	75	90
	w. Wmk inverted		

*The 20 c. and 30 c. designs are perforated 14 at foot.

(Des The Sharper Image. Litho Security Printers (M), Malaysia)

1998 (11 Apr). *Gold Coins.* T **239** and similar horiz designs. Multicoloured. W **138**. P 13½ (20 c., 50 c., $1) or 14½ (30 c.).

679	20 c. Type 239	10	10
	aw. Wmk inverted	2·25	
	b. Perf 14½	2·00	
	bw. Wmk inverted	6·00	
680	30 c. Kupang from Kedah, 1661–1687	15	10
681	50 c. Kupang from Johore, 1597–1615	30	30
	a. Perf 14½	3·00	
682	$1 Kijang from Kelantan, 1400–1780	40	70
679/82	Set of 4	85	1·10

240 Red Crescent Ambulance Boat and Emblem

241 Transit Train and Boeing 747-400 at Airport

(Des P. Chuah. Litho Security Printers (M), Malaysia)

1998 (8 May). *50th Anniv of Malaysian Red Crescent Society.* T **240** and similar vert design. Multicoloured. W **138** (inverted on $1). P 13½.

683	30 c. Type 240	10	10
	a. Perf 14½	1·50	
684	$1 Ambulance and casualty	40	50
	a. Perf 14½	80	
	aw. Wmk upright	4·50	

(Des P. Chuah. Litho Security Printers (M), Malaysia)

1998 (27 June). *Opening of Kuala Lumpur International Airport.* T **241** and similar multicoloured designs, each showing control tower. W **138**. P 12.

685	30 c. Type 241	20	10
	a. Perf 12½	4·75	
686	50 c. Airport Terminals	40	30
687	$1 Airliner in flight	80	1·00
	a. Perf 12½		
685/7	Set of 3	1·25	1·25
MS688	119×70 mm. $2 Globe and control tower (22×32 mm). P 14½×14	90	95
	w. Wmk inverted	6·50	

242 *Solanum torvum*

243 Weightlifting

(Des The Sharper Image. Litho Security Printers (M), Malaysia)

1998 (18 July). *Medicinal Plants.* T **242** and similar vert designs. W **138**. P 13½ (20 c., 30 c.) or 14½ (50 c., $1).

689	20 c. Type 242	10	10
690	30 c. *Tinospora crispa*	15	10
691	50 c. *Jatropha podagrica*	25	25
692	$1 *Hibiscus rosa-sinensis*	40	70
689/92	Set of 4	75	95

(Des P. Chuah. Litho Security Printers (M), Malaysia)

1998 (11 Sept). *16th Commonwealth Games, Kuala Lumpur, Malaysia* (6th issue). Sports. T **243** and similar horiz designs. Multicoloured. W **138**. P 13½.

693	20 c. Type 243	10	10
	a. Sheetlet. Nos. 693/708	2·50	
	b. Perf 14½	30	30
	ba. Sheetlet. Nos. 693b/708b	7·50	
694	20 c. Badminton	10	10
	b. Perf 14½	30	30
695	20 c. Netball	10	10
	b. Perf 14½	30	30
696	20 c. Shooting	10	10
	b. Perf 14½	30	30
697	30 c. Men's hockey	10	10
	b. Perf 14½	30	30
698	30 c. Women's hockey	10	10
	b. Perf 14½	30	30
699	30 c. Cycling	10	10
	b. Perf 14½	30	30
700	30 c. Bowls	10	10
	b. Perf 14½	30	30
701	50 c. Gymnastics	15	20
	b. Perf 14½	50	50
702	50 c. Cricket	15	20
	b. Perf 14½	50	50

703	50 c.	Rugby			15	20
	b.	Perf 14½*			50	50
704	50 c.	Running			15	20
	b.	Perf 14½*			50	50
705	$1	Swimming			30	35
	b.	Perf 14½			95	95
706	$1	Squash			30	35
	b.	Perf 14½			95	95
707	$1	Boxing			30	35
	b.	Perf 14½*			95	95
708	$1	Ten-pin bowling			30	35
	b.	Perf 14½*			95	95
693/708			*Set of* 16		2·50	3·00

*Nos. 703a/4a and 707a/8a, which occur on the bottom row of the sheetlet, are perforated 14 at foot.

Nos. 693/708 were printed together, *se-tenant*, in sheetlets of 16 with the designs for each face value arranged as blocks of 4.

244 L.R.T. "Putra" Type Train

245 Globe and A.P.E.C. Logo

(Des P. Chuah. Litho Security Printers (M), Malaysia)

1998 (31 Oct). *Modern Kuala Lumpur Rail Transport. T* **244** *and similar horiz designs. Multicoloured. W* **138**. *P* 14½.

709	30 c.	Type 244			3·25	
	aw.	Wmk inverted			4·00	
	b.	Perf 13½			30	10
710	50 c.	L.R.T. "Star" type train			1·25	30
	b.	Perf 13½			35	20
711	$1	K.T.M commuter train			40	55
709/11			*Set of* 3		95	75

(Des The Sharper Image. Litho Security Printers (M), Malaysia)

1998 (14 Nov). *Asia–Pacific Economic Co-operation Conference. T* **245** *and similar horiz design. Multicoloured. W* **138**. *P* 13½.

712	30 c.	Type 245			80	10
	aw.	Wmk inverted			3·00	
	b.	Perf 14½			30	10
	bw.	Wmk inverted			4·00	
713	$1	Business meeting and computer office			40	50
	b.	Perf 14½			3·00	

246 *Xylotrupes gideon*

247 Nural Hudda (Women's Air Rifle Shooting)

(Des P. Chuah. Litho Security Printers (M), Malaysia)

1998 (28 Nov). *Stamp Week '98. Malaysian Insects. Sheet, 165×75 mm, containing T* **246** *and similar multicoloured designs. W* **138** *(sideways). P* 12 *($2) or* 12½ *(others).*

MS714	20 c.	Type 246; 30 c. *Pomponia imperatoria*; 50 c. *Phyllium pulchrifolium*; $2 *Hymenopus coronatus* (43×27 *mm*); $2 *Macrolyristes corporalis* (43×27 *mm*)			1·50	2·00
	a.	50 c. value perf 12 at foot				
	b.	20, 30, 50 c. values perf 12 at foot			5·00	
	c.	No wmk. 20 c. value perf 12 at foot			7·00	

(Des P. Chuah. Litho Security Printers (M), Malaysia)

1998 (12 Dec). *16th Commonwealth Games, Kuala Lumpur (7th issue). Malaysian Gold Medal Winners. Two miniature sheets, each 160×125 mm, containing multicoloured designs as T* **247**. *W* **138** *(sideways). P* 14.

MS715	$2	Malaysian team celebrating (128×80 *mm*)			60	65
	a.	Perf 14×15				
	b.	No wmk				
MS716	30 c.	Type 247; 30 c. Sapok Biki (48 kg Boxing); 30 c. G. Saravanan (50km Walk); 30 c. Mahamad Hidayat Hamidon (69kg Weightlifting); 50 c. Kenny Ang and Ben Heng (Tenpin Bowling Men's Doubles); 50 c. Kenny Ang (Tenpin Bowling Men's Singles); 50 c. Choong Tan Fook and Lee Wan Wah (Badminton Men's Doubles); 50 c. Wong Choong Hann (Badminton Men's Singles); $1 Women's Rhythmic Gymnastics team (63×26 *mm*)			1·40	1·50
	a.	Wmk upright				
	bw.	Wmk inverted				
	c.	No wmk. $1 perf 14½ at top				
	ca.	No wmk. Bottom row of stamps perf 14½ at foot				

248 Profile of Elderly Couple, World Map and Emblem

249 *Syzygium malaccense*

(Des Bowline Communications. Litho Security Printers (M), Malaysia)

1999 (28 Jan). *International Year of the Older Person. T* **248** *and similar horiz design. Multicoloured. W* **138** *(sideways). P* 14½.

717	$1	Type 248			30	35
718	$1	Four silhouettes of elderly people, world map and emblem			30	35

(Des P. Chuah. Litho Security Printers (M), Malaysia)

1999 (27 Feb). *Rare Fruits of Malaysia. T* **249** *and similar vert designs. P* 12. *(a) W* **138** *(sideways).*

719	20 c.	Type 249			10	10
720	30 c.	*Garcinia prainiana*			10	15
721	50 c.	*Mangifera caesia*			15	20
722	$1	*Salacca glabrescens*			30	35
719/22			*Set of* 4		60	75

(b) W **138** *(upright).*

723	20 c.	Type 249			10	10
	a.	Horiz strip of 4. Nos. 723/6			65	
	b.	Perf 12½			10	10
	ba.	Horiz strip of 4. Nos. 723b/6b*			65	
724	30 c.	*Garcinia prainiana*			10	15
	b.	Perf 12½			10	15
725	50 c.	*Mangifrea caesia*			15	20
	b.	Perf 12½			15	20
726	$1	*Salacca glabrescens*			30	35
	b.	Perf 12½			30	35
723/6			*Set of* 4		60	75

* Horizontal strip No. 723ba shows the final stamp, No. 726b, perforated 12 at right.

Nos. 719/22 come from sheets of 50, each of one value.

Nos. 723/6 were printed together, *se-tenant*, as horizontal strips of 4 in sheets of 20.

250 Kucing Malaysia Cat

251 Sumatran Rhinoceros

(Des P. Chuah. Litho Security Printers (M), Malaysia)

1999 (1 Apr). *Malaysian Cats. T* **250** *and similar vert designs. Multicoloured. W* **138** *(sideways). P* 12.

727	30 c.	Type 250			10	15
728	50 c.	Siamese			15	20
729	$1	Abyssinian			30	35
727/9			*Set of* 3		55	70
MS730		Two sheets, each 81×90 mm. (a) $1 British Shorthair; $1 Scottish Fold. (b) $1 Birman; $1 Persian	*Set of* 2 sheets		1·25	1·40

(Des P. Chuah. Litho Security Printers (M), Malaysia)

1999 (28 May). *Protected Mammals of Malaysia. T* **251** *and similar horiz designs. Multicoloured. (a) W* **138**. *P* 12½.

731	20 c.	Type 251			10	10
732	30 c.	Panther			10	15
733	50 c.	Sun Bear			15	20
734	$1	Indian Elephant			30	35
731/4			*Set of* 4		60	75

(b) W **138** *(sideways). P* 12.

735	20 c.	Type 251			10	10
	a.	Vert strip of 5. Nos. 735/9			1·10	
736	30 c.	Panther			10	15
737	50 c.	Sun Bear			15	20
738	$1	Indian Elephant			30	35
739	$2	Orang-utan			60	65
735/9			*Set of* 5		1·10	1·40
MS740		119×80 mm. $2 No. 739			60	65

Nos. 731/4 were printed in individual sheets of 50.

Nos. 735/9 were printed together, *se-tenant*, as vertical strips of 5 in sheets of 20.

COVER PRICES

Cover factors are quoted at the beginning of each country for most issues to 1945. An explanation of the system can be found on page x. The factors quoted do not, however, apply to philatelic covers.

252 Hearts and AIDS Ribbons

253 P. Ramlee in Traditional Dress

(Des Grey Malaysia. Litho Security Printers (M), Malaysia)

1999 (19 June). *5th International Conference on AIDS in Asia and the Pacific. T* **252** *and similar horiz designs. Each bright scarlet, bright ultramarine and black. W* **138** *(sideways). P* 14½ *(30 c.) or* 13½ *(others).*

741	30 c.	Type 252			10	15
742	50 c.	Fragmenting and stylised AIDS ribbons			15	20
743	$1	Two AIDS ribbons			30	35
741/3			*Set of* 3		55	70

(Des Eka IPR Agensi. Litho Security Printers (M), Malaysia)

1999 (24 July). *70th Birth Anniv of P. Ramlee (actor and film director). T* **253** *and similar vert designs. (a) Multicoloured. W* **138**. *P* 13½.

744	20 c.	Type 253			10	10
745	30 c.	Receiving an award			10	15
746	50 c.	Playing part of soldier in film			15	20
747	$1	Using film camera			30	35
	a.	Perf 14½			30	35
MS748		Two sheets, each 100×70 mm. (a) $1 Wearing check shirt. (b) $1 In traditional dress. Wmk sideways. P 14½×13½	*Set of* 2 sheets		60	65

(b) Designs each orange-brown, yellow-ochre and black. W **138** *(sideways). P* 13½.

749	30 c.	In traditional dress			10	15
	a.	Strip of 4. Nos. 749/52			40	
750	30 c.	With hands raised			10	15
751	30 c.	Singing into microphone			10	15
752	30 c.	Wearing army uniform			10	15
744/7, 749/52			*Set of* 8		95	1·25

Nos. 744/7 were printed in individual sheets of 100.

Nos. 749/52 were printed together, *se-tenant*, as horizontal or vertical strips of four, in sheets of 16.

STAMP BOOKLETS

B 1 Seafans and Feather Stars

1995 (10 Apr). *Marine Life (5th series). Corals. Multicoloured covers as Type B 1. Stamps attached by selvedge.*
SB1 $2 booklet containing pane of 10 20 c. stamps (No. 559a) (cover showing Type B 1) .... 4·50
SB2 $3 booklet containing pane of 10 30 c. stamps (No. 561a) (cover showing Cup Coral and Soft Coral) 4·50

B 2 Turtle swimming Underwater

1995 (26 Sept). *Turtles. Multicoloured cover as Type B 2. Stamps attached by selvedge.*
SB3 $3 booklet containing pane of ten 30 c. stamps (No. 577a) .. .. 4·50

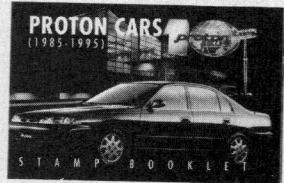

B 3 Proton Saloon Car and Factory

1995 (23 Dec). *10th Anniv of Proton Cars. Multicoloured cover as Type B 3. Stamps attached by selvedge.*
SB4 $3 booklet containing pane of ten 30 c. stamps (No. 585a) .. .. 2·25

B 4 *Pachliopta aristolochiae*

1996 (27 Feb). *"ISTANBUL '96" International Stamp Exhibition. Butterflies. Multicoloured cover as Type B 4. Stamps attached by selvedge.*
SB5 $3 booklet containing pane of ten 30 c. stamps (No. 611a) .. .. 3·50

B 5 Train leaving Station

1997 (1 Mar). *Opening of Kuala Lumpur Light Rail Transit System. Multicoloured cover as Type B 5. Stamps attached by selvedge.*
SB6 $3 booklet containing pane of ten 30 c. stamps (No. 636a) .. .. 3·50

B 6 Flowers

1997 (7 May). *Highland Flowers. Multicoloured cover as Type B 6. Stamps attached by selvedge.*
SB7 $3 booklet containing pane of ten 30 c. stamps (No. 644a) .. .. 2·75

B 7

1997 (25 Aug). *20th International Pan-Pacific and Southeast Asia Women's Association Conference, Kuala Lumpur, Multicoloured cover as Type B 7. Stamps attached by selvedge.*
SB8 $3 booklet containing pane of ten 30 c. stamps (No. 663a) .. .. 1·75

POSTAGE DUE STAMPS

Until 15 August 1966 the postage due stamps of MALAYAN POSTAL UNION were in use throughout MALAYSIA.

D 1   D 2

(Litho Harrison)

1966 (15 Aug)–71. *Ordinary paper. W w 13 (upright). P 14½ × 14.*

D1	D 1	1 c. rose	..	20	2·50
D2		2 c. indigo	.. ..	25	2·50
D3		4 c. apple-green	..	85	5·00
D4		8 c. blue-green	..	1·25	12·00
		a. Chalk-surfaced paper. *Bright blue-green* (1.6.71)		4·50	12·00
D5		10 c. bright blue	..	60	2·50
		a. Chalk-surfaced paper (1.6.71)		4·50	12·00
D6		12 c. reddish violet	..	60	4·50
D7		20 c. red-brown	..	60	4·75
		a. Chalk-surfaced paper. *Brown-purple* (22.4.69)		2·75	13·00
D8		50 c. brownish bistre	..	1·25	8·00
		a. Chalk-surfaced paper. *Olive-bistre* (1.6.71)		4·50	14·00
D1/8		..	Set of 8	5·00	38·00

1972 (23 May). *Glazed paper. W w 13 (sideways). P 14½ × 14.*

D12	D 1	8 c. turquoise-green	..	5·50	15·00
D13		10 c. dull ultramarine	..	5·50	15·00
D15		20 c. pale chocolate	..	7·00	15·00
D16		50 c. pale olive-bistre	..	7·50	20·00
D12/16			Set of 4	23·00	60·00

1980–86. *No wmk. P 14½ × 14.*

D17	D 1	2 c. indigo	..	30	2·75
D18		8 c. blue-green	..	45	3·25
D19		10 c. dull ultramarine	..	45	2·25
D19a		12 c. reddish lilac (1986)	..	11·00	16·00
D20		20 c. pale chocolate	..	55	2·75
D21		50 c. pale olive-bistre	..	90	3·50
D17/21			Set of 6	12·00	27·00

(Des Kathy Wong. Litho Security Printers (M), Malaysia)

1986 (15 Sept). P 12 × 11½.

D22	D 2	5 c. cerise and rose-lilac	..	10	10
D23		10 c. brownish black & pale olive-grey		10	10
D24		20 c. dull vermilion and cinnamon	..	10	10
D25		50 c. dp turquoise-green & turq-bl		15	20
D26		$1 ultramarine and cobalt ..		30	35
D22/6		..	Set of 5	55	70

B. FEDERAL TERRITORY ISSUES

Kuala Lumpur, previously part of Selangor state, was established as a Federal Territory on 1 February 1974.

The following stamps were produced for use there, corresponding to the low value definitives provided for the states of the federation.

The island of Labuan, formerly part of Sabah, became the second Federal Territory on 16 April 1984, when Nos. K1/14 replaced the low value definitives of Sabah previously used there.

K 1 *Rafflesia hasseltii*   K 2 Coffee

(Des M. Yusof bin Mohammed; adapted Malaysian Advertising Services. Litho Asher and Co., Melbourne)

1979 (30 Apr). *Flowers. Horiz designs as Type K 1. Multicoloured. W 95 (sideways). P 15 × 14½.*

K1	1 c. Type K 1	..	..	10	30
K2	2 c. *Pterocarpus indicus*	..		10	30
K3	5 c. *Lagerstroemia speciosa* (Type I)	..	10	30
K4	10 c. *Durio zibethinus*	..		10	10
K5	15 c. *Hibiscus rosa-sinensis*	..		20	10
	a. Vert pair, top stamp imperf				
K6	20 c. *Rhododendron scortechinii*	..	20	10
K7	25 c. *Etlingera elatior* (inscr "*Phaeomeria speciosa*")	..	40	10
K1/7		..	Set of 7	1·00	1·00

For higher values used in conjunction with this series see Nos. 190/7.

STANLEY GIBBONS STAMP COLLECTING SERIES

Introductory booklets on *How to Start, How to Identify Stamps* and *Collecting by Theme.* A series of well illustrated guides at a low price. Write for details.

I   II

Two types of 5 c.:

Type I. "5" over "i" and "c" to right of "a" in "Malaysia" (Nos. K3 and K10).

Type II. "5" over "s" and "c" aligns on "a" of "Malaysia" (No. K10a).

1983–85.* *As Nos. K3/7 but without wmk.*

K10	5 c. *Lagerstroemia speciosa* (I) (turquoise-green background) (12.12.84)	..	11·00	4·00
K10a	5 c. *Lagerstroemia speciosa* (II) (turquoise-blue background) (17.12.84)		1·50	1·00
K11	10 c. *Durio zibethinus* (9.84)	..	35	50
K12	15 c. *Hibiscus rosa-sinensis* (5.11.83)	90	15
K13	20 c. *Rhododendron scortechinii* (blackish brown background) (1983)		15·00	1·25
K13a	20 c. *Rhododendron scortechinii* (bronze-green background) (13.11.83)		80	35
K14	25 c. *Etlingera elatior* (inscr "*Phaeomeria speciosa*") (1.85)	..	5·50	3·00

*There was no official release date for these stamps. Dates shown are the earliest recorded from postmarks and may be revised if earlier examples are reported.

The 10 c., 15 c. and 20 c. (No. K13a) are also from redrawn plates and show the inscriptions or the face value in slightly different positions.

(Des Kathy Wong. Litho Security Printers (M), Malaysia)

1986 (25 Oct)–96. *Agricultural Products of Malaysia. Vert designs as Type K 2. Multicoloured. W 138. P 12.*

K15	1 c. Type K 2	..	10	10
K16	2 c. Coconuts	..	10	10
K17	5 c. Cocoa	..	10	10
	c. Perf 14×13¾ (1994)		3·25	50
	cw. Wmk inverted		4·50	
	f. Perf 14¾×14½ (1995)		1·75	10
K18	10 c. Black Pepper	..	10	10
	aw. Wmk inverted (1995)			
	b. Perf 13½×13¾		16·00	1·50
	c. Perf 14×13¾ (1994)		3·25	50
	cw. Wmk inverted		9·00	
	e. Perf 14×14½ (1994)		4·50	35
	f. Perf 14¾×14½ (1994)		2·00	35
K19	15 c. Rubber	..	10	10
	w. Wmk inverted		5·00	
K20	20 c. Oil palm	..	10	10
	aw. Wmk inverted		20·00	
	c. Perf 14×13¾ (1994)		1·00	10
	f. Perf 14¾×14½ (1994)		6·50	45
K21	30 c. Rice	..	15	20
	aw. Wmk inverted		6·50	
	b. Perf 13½×13¾ (1994)			
	c. Perf 14×13¾ (1994)		1·50	20
	cw. Wmk inverted		8·50	
	e. Perf 14×14½ (1996)		4·25	30
	ew. Wmk inverted		6·50	
	f. Perf 14¾×14½ (1994)		4·50	45
	fw. Wmk inverted (1996)		8·50	
K15/21		Set of 7	50	55

For notes concerning perforation varieties see below Johore Nos. 202/8.

STAMP BOOKLETS

1979 (1 Dec). *Cover as No. SB5 of Johore, but inscr "WILAYAH PERSEKUTUAN". Stitched.*
KSB1 $3 booklet containing eight 5 c., 10 c., and twelve 15 c., (Nos. K3/5) in blocks of 4   8·00
No. KSB1 exists with two different versions of the back cover.

JABATAN PERKHIDMATAN POS MALAYSIA
Buku Kecil ini
Mengandungi
5 Setem Harga 20 Sen Satu $1.00

KB 1

1983 (23 May). *Cover as Type KB 1. Stamps attached by selvedge.*
KSB2 $1 booklet containing 20 c. (No. K6) in strip of 5   4·00

JABATAN PERKHIDMATAN POS, MALAYSIA
Buku Kecil ini berisi setem - setem yang berikut:
3 setem harga 20 sen
Harga Jualan — 60 sen

KB 2

1986. *Black on lemon covers as Type KB 2. Stamps attached by selvedge.*
KSB3   60 c. booklet containing 20 c. (No. K13) in strip of 3   28·00
KSB4 $1.50, booklet containing 15 c. (No. K12) in pair and 20 c. (No. K13) in strip of 6   50·00

1987 (1 June). *Cover as Type B 2 of Johore, but inscr "WILAYAH PERSEKUTUAN". Stapled.*
KSB5 $2 booklet containing 5 c., 10 c., 15 c. and 20 c. (Nos. K17/20), each in block of 4   7·50

1988. *Black on rose cover as Type B 2. Stamps attached by selvedge.*
KSB6   60 c. booklet containing 20 c. (No. K20) in strip of 3   24·00

1992 (1 July). *"Kuala Lumpur '92" International Philatelic Exhibition. Cover as Type B 3 of Johore, but inscr "Wilayah Persekutuan". Stamps attached by selvedge.*
KSB7 $3 booklet containing 30 c. (No. K21) in block of 10   7·00

1993 (June). *Multicoloured on pale buff covers as Nos. SB8/9 of Johore, but inscr "Wilayah Persekutuan". Stamps attached by selvedge.*
KSB8 $2 booklet containing 20 c. (No. K20) in block of 10   1·00
KSB9 $3 booklet containing 30 c. (No. K21) in block of 10   1·50

1996. *Black on buff cover as Type B 2. Stamps attached by selvedge.*
KSB10   60 c. booklet containing 10 c. (No. K18) in strip of 3 and 15 c. (No. K19) in pair

VII. MALAYSIAN STATES

PRINTERS. All Malaysian States stamps were printed in typography by De La Rue and Co, Ltd, London, *unless otherwise stated.*

JOHORE

A British adviser was appointed to Johore in 1914. The state joined the Federation of Malaya on 1 February 1948.

Until 1 January 1899 mail for addresses outside Malaya had the external postage paid by stamps of the STRAITS SETTLEMENTS.

PRICES FOR STAMPS ON COVER TO 1945

Nos. 1/2	—
Nos. 3/5	*from* × 15
No. 6	*from* × 20
Nos. 7/8	—
Nos. 9/15	*from* × 25
No. 16	—
Nos. 17/20	*from* × 15
Nos. 21/31	*from* × 10
Nos. 32/8	*from* × 15
Nos. 39/53	*from* × 8
Nos. 54/60	*from* × 6
Nos. 61/74	*from* × 8
Nos. 75/7	—
Nos. 78/87	*from* × 8
No. 88	*from* × 10
Nos. 89/102	*from* × 6
Nos. 103/25	*from* × 5
Nos. 126/8	—
Nos. 129/30	*from* × 6
Nos. D1/5	*from* × 5

(1)

1876 (July). *No. 11 of Straits Settlements handstamped with* T 1.
1   2 c. brown £8500 £3500
No. 1 is known with the handstamp double.

From September 1878 to August 1884 no overprinted stamps were supplied by Singapore to Johore.

JOHORE
(2)

JOHORE   **JOHORE**   **JOHORE**
(3) ("H" and "E"   (4) ("H" wide, "E"   (5) ("H" and "E"
wide. "J" raised.   narrow. Opt   wide. Opt
Opt 16 mm long)   16 mm long)   16¾mm long)

JOHORE.   **JOHORE**   **JOHORE**
(6)   (7)   (8)

1884 (June)–**86**. *No. 63 of Straits Settlements optd with* T 2/8.
2   2   2 c. pale rose £3500
3   3   2 c. pale rose (8.84)   . .   £950 £425
      a. Opt double £2250
4   4   2 c. pale rose (8.84)   . .   £1200 £475
      a. Opt double £650
5   5   2 c. pale rose (8.84)   . .   £950 £425
      a. Opt double   . .   . .   —£1300
6   6   2 c. pale rose (3.85)   . .   £130 £140
      a. Opt double £650
7   7   2 c. pale rose (1885) £1900
8   8   2 c. pale rose (4.86)   . .   65·00 80·00
Nos. 3 to 7 were from triplet settings, either 3+4+5 or three examples of the same overprint. Nos. 2 and 8 are probably single unit handstamps.

JOHOR   **JOHOR**   **JOHOR**
(9) (All letters   (10)   (11) ("H" wide)
narrow)

JOHOR   **JOHOR**   **JOHOR.**
(12)   (13)   (14)

JOHOR   **JOHOR**
(15)   (16)

1884 (Aug)–**91**. *Nos. 63/a of Straits Settlements optd with* T 9/16.
9   9   2 c. pale rose   . .   . .   6·50 13·00
      a. Opt double £650
10   10   2 c. pale rose (10.84)   . .   6·50 4·50
      a. Thin, narrow "J" (R. 6/6)   95·00 80·00
      b. Opt double £650
      c. Bright rose (1890)   . .   8·50 9·00
      ca. Thin, narrow "J" (R. 6/6)   £130 £140
      cb. Opt double £750
11   11   2 c. pale rose (2.85)   . .   70·00 70·00

---

12   12   2 c. pale rose (1886)   . .   42·00 42·00
      a. Opt double £700
13   13   2 c. pale rose (1886)   . .   28·00 32·00
14   14   2 c. pale rose (1888)   . .   90·00 95·00
      a. Thin, narrow "J"   . .   £450 £275
      b. Opt double £600
15   15   2 c. bright rose (9.90)   . .   10·00 10·00
16   16   2 c. bright rose (1891)   . .   £6500
Settings:
    No. 9 — various triplets with the length of the overprint varying from 12 to 15 mm
    No. 10 — triplet or 60 (6×10)
    No. 11 — triplet 11 + 9 + 9
    No. 12 — triplet
    No. 13 — triplet
    No. 14 — 30 (3×10)
    No. 15 — 60 (6×10)
    No. 16 — not known. As no used examples are known it is possible that this stamp was not issued.

JOHOR   **JOHOR**
Two   *Two*
CENTS   CENTS
───────   ───────
(17)   (18)

JOHOR   **JOHOR**
Two   *Two*
CENTS   CENTS
───────   ───────
(19)   (20)

1891 (May). *No. 68 of Straits Settlements surch as* T 17/20.
17   17   2 c. on 24 c. green   . .   23·00 35·00
      a. "CENST" (R. 5/4)   . .   £700 £400
      w. Wmk inverted   . .   £100 £100
18   18   2 c. on 24 c. green   . .   £100 £100
      a. Thin, narrow "J" (R. 6/6)   £300 £300
19   19   2 c. on 24 c. green   . .   32·00 48·00
20   20   2 c. on 24 c. green   . .   95·00 95·00
Nos. 17/20 come from the same setting of 60. Type 17 occurs on horizontal rows 1 to 5, Type 18 on row 6, Type 19 on rows 7, 8 and 9 and Type 20 on row 10.

3 cents.

KEMAHKOTAAN

21 Sultan   (22)   (23)
Aboubakar

1891 (16 Nov)–**94**. *No wmk. P* 14.
21   21   1 c. dull purple and mauve (7.94)   30   50
22   2 c. dull purple and yellow   30   1·50
23   3 c. dull purple and carmine (7.94)   55   50
24   4 c. dull purple and black   2·75 12·00
25   5 c. dull purple and green   7·00 20·00
26   6 c. dull purple and blue   8·00 20·00
27        $1 green and carmine   . .   60·00 £130
21/7   Set of 7   70·00 £160

1894 (Mar). *Surch with* T 22.
28   21   3 c. on 4 c. dull purple and black   2·00   50
      a. No stop (R. 5/11)   . .   55·00 50·00
29   3 c. on 5 c. dull purple and green   80   2·00
      a. No stop (R. 5/11)   . .   70·00 85·00
      b. "3 cents." spaced 3½ mm from bar   £100 75·00
30   3 c. on 6 c. dull purple and blue   2·00   2·25
      a. No stop (R. 5/11)   . .   95·00 £100
31   3 c. on $1 green and carmine   10·00 48·00
      a. No stop (R. 5/11)   . .   £275 £450
28/31   Set of 4   13·00 48·00
No. 29b shows the surcharge spaced 3½ mm from the bar instead of the normal 7½ mm. It appears to come from a separate setting as a cancelled-to-order block of eight is known.

1896 (Mar). *Coronation of Sultan Ibrahim. Optd with* T 23.
32   21   1 c. dull purple and mauve   45   85
      a. "KETAHKOTAAN"   . .   3·00   5·00
33   2 c. dull purple and yellow   45   1·00
      a. "KETAHKOTAAN"   . .   2·75   5·50
34   3 c. dull purple and carmine   55   1·00
      a. "KETAHKOTAAN"   . .   6·00   7·50
35   4 c. dull purple and black   80   2·25
      a. "KETAHKOTAAN"   . .   2·75   8·00
36   5 c. dull purple and green   5·50   7·50
      a. "KETAHKOTAAN"   . .   3·25   7·50
37   6 c. dull purple and blue   3·50   6·00
      a. "KETAHKOTAAN"   . .   4·50   6·00
38        $1 green and carmine   . .   40·00 90·00
      a. "KETAHKOTAAN"   . .   27·00 £120
32/8   Set of 7   45·00 95·00
32a/8a   Set of 7   45·00 £140
Stamps overprinted "KETAHKOTAAN" (= We mourn) come from the first overprinting. The overprint was subsequently changed to the intended "KEMAHKOTAAN" (= Coronation), but both were issued together some months after the Coronation of Sultan Ibrahim had taken place.

24   Sultan Ibrahim   25

---

26   27

1896 (26 Aug)–**99**. *W* 27. *P* 14.
39   24   1 c. green   70   45
40   2 c. green and blue   . .   40   30
41   3 c. green and purple   . .   2·75 1·75
      a. *Green and dull claret*   . .   2·75 1·75
42   4 c. green and carmine   . .   50   60
43   4 c. yellow and red (1899)   . .   75   75
44   5 c. green and brown   . .   75   1·40
45   6 c. green and yellow   . .   80   2·50
46   25   10 c. green and black (1898)   . .   7·00 45·00
47   25 c. green and mauve (1898)   . .   9·00 38·00
48   50 c. green and carmine (1898)   . .   13·00 40·00
49   24 $1 dull purple and green (1898)   . .   26·00 65·00
50   26 $2 dull purple and carmine (1898)   . .   27·00 65·00
51        $3 dull purple and blue (1898)   . .   28·00 90·00
52        $4 dull purple and brown (1898)   . .   28·00 75·00
53        $5 dull purple and yellow (1898)   . .   60·00 £110
39/53   Set of 15   £180 £475

3 cents.   **10 cents.**

(28)   (29)

1903 (Apr). *Surch with* T 28 *or* 29.
54   24   3 c. on 4 c. yellow and red   . .   50 1·10
      a. Original value uncancelled   . .   3·50 14·00
55   10 c. on 4 c. green and carmine   . .   2·50 7·00
      a. Tall "1" in "10" (R. 9/12)   70·00 £100
      b. Original value uncancelled   . .   20·00 55·00
      ba. As b, with tall "1" in "10" (R. 9/12)   £850 £1000
The bars on these stamps were ruled by hand with pen and ink.

50 Cents.   **One Dollar**

(30)   (31)

1903 (Oct). *Surch with* T 30 *or* 31.
56   26   50 c. on $3 dull purple and blue   27·00 80·00
57        $1 on $2 dull purple and carmine   60·00 £110
      a. "e" of "One" inverted (R. 7/9)   . .   £1300

10 CENTS.

(32)

1904. *Surch as* T 32.
58   24   10 c. on 4 c. yellow and red (Apr)   20·00 35·00
      a. Surcharge double   . .   £6500
59   10 c. on 4 c. green and carmine (Aug)   9·00 35·00
60   26   50 c. on $5 dull purple and yellow (May)   65·00 £130
58/60   Set of 3   85·00 £180

33   34   35 Sultan Sir Ibrahim

1904 (Sept)–**10**. *W* 27. *Ordinary paper. P* 14.
61   33   1 c. dull purple and green   . .   1·75   30
      a. Chalk-surfaced paper (10.10)   3·75 4·00
62   2 c. dull purple and orange   . .   2·25 3·00
      a. Chalk-surfaced paper (10.10)   4·50 7·00
63   3 c. dull purple and olive-black   3·00   50
64   4 c. dull purple and carmine   . .   7·50 2·75
65   5 c. dull purple and sage-green   1·25 2·75
66   35   8 c. dull purple and blue   . .   3·75 8·00
67   34   10 c. dull purple and black   . .   45·00 11·00
      a. Chalk-surfaced paper (1910)   60·00 60·00
68   25 c. dull purple and green   . .   7·00 30·00
69   50 c. dull purple and red   . .   42·00 14·00
70   33 $1 green and mauve   . .   12·00 50·00
71   35 $2 green and carmine   . .   18·00 48·00
72        $3 green and blue   . .   23·00 70·00
73        $4 green and brown   . .   24·00 90·00
74        $5 green and orange   . .   32·00 80·00
75   34 $10 green and black   . .   48·00 £130
76        $50 green and ultramarine   . .   £140 £200
77        $100 green and scarlet   . .   £275 £425
61/75   Set of 15   £225 £475

1910–**19**. *Wmk Mult Rosettes (vertical). Chalk-surfaced paper.* P 14.
78   33   1 c. dull purple and green (1912)   . .   40   15
79   2 c. dull purple and orange (1912)   4·50   65
80   3 c. dull purple and olive-black (1912)   7·00   65
      a. Wmk horizontal (1910)   . .   10·00 16·00
81   4 c. dull purple and carmine (1912)   5·00   90
      a. Wmk horizontal (1910)   . .   20·00 38·00
82   5 c. dull purple and sage-green (1912)   3·25 1·00
83   35   8 c. dull purple and blue (1912)   . .   4·00 5·00
84   34   10 c. dull purple and black (1912)   . .   38·00 3·00
      a. Wmk horizontal (1911)   . .   23·00 50·00
85   25 c. dull purple and green (1912)   . .   5·50 27·00
86   50 c. dull purple and red (1919)   . .   45·00 90·00
87   33 $1 green and mauve (1918)   . .   75·00 85·00
78/87   Set of 10   £150 £190

3 CENTS.

(36)   **37** Sultan Sir Ibrahim and Sultana

1912 (Mar). *No. 66 surch with T 36.*
88	3 c. on 8 c. dull purple and blue			2·75	5·00
	a. "T" of "CENTS" omitted			†	£800
	b. Bars double			£110	

No. 88b shows the bars printed twice with the upper pair partly erased.

1918–21. *Wmk Mult Crown CA. Chalk-surfaced paper. P 14.*
89	33	2 c. dull purple and green (1919)			40	80
		w. Wmk inverted			†	
90		2 c. purple and orange (1921)			50	2·75
91		4 c. dull purple and red			90	60
92		5 c. dull purple and sage-green (1920)			2·00	4·75
		w. Wmk inverted			£110	
93	34	10 c. dull purple and blue			1·75	1·40
94		21 c. dull purple and orange (1919)			2·25	2·50
95		25 c. dull purple and green (1920)			8·00	18·00
96		50 c. dull purple and red (1920)			21·00	35·00
97	33	$1 green and mauve			10·00	60·00
98	35	$2 green and carmine			20·00	48·00
99		$3 green and blue			42·00	90·00
100		$4 green and brown			42·00	£110
101		$5 green and orange			70·00	£140
102	34	$10 green and black			£160	£275
89/102			Set of 14		£350	£700
89/102		Optd "Specimen"	Set of 14		£375	

1922–40. *Wmk Mult Script CA. Chalk-surfaced paper. P 14.*
103	33	1 c. dull purple and black			30	20
104		2 c. purple and sepia (1924)			85	3·00
105		2 c. green (1928)			40	40
106		3 c. green (1925)			1·50	40
107		3 c. purple and sepia (1928)			1·10	1·50
108		4 c. purple and carmine (1924)			2·50	20
109		5 c. dull purple and sage-green			30	30
		w. Wmk inverted				
110		6 c. dull purple and claret			40	45
111	34	10 c. dull purple and blue			16·00	28·00
112		10 c. dull purple and yellow			30	25
113	33	12 c. dull purple and blue			1·00	1·25
114		12 c. ultramarine (1940)			35·00	4·00
115	34	21 c. dull purple and orange (1928)			2·00	1·00
116		25 c. dull purple and myrtle			2·25	1·00
117	35	30 c. dull purple and orange (1936)			5·00	4·00
118		40 c. dull purple and brown (1936)			5·00	4·50
119	34	50 c. dull purple and red			3·00	1·60
120	33	$1 green and mauve			3·00	85
121	35	$2 green and carmine (1923)			5·50	3·50
122		$3 green and blue (1925)			45·00	75·00
123		$4 green and brown (1926)			75·00	£150
		w. Wmk inverted				
124		$5 green and orange			50·00	50·00
125	34	$10 green and black (1924)			£160	£250
126		$50 green and ultram (Optd S. £150)			£600	
127		$100 green and scarlet (Optd S. £250)			£1400	
128	35	$500 blue and red (1926) (Optd S. £750)			£16000	
103/25			Set of 23		£375	£500
103/25		Optd/Perf "Specimen"	Set of 23		£500	

(Recess Waterlow)

1935 (15 May). *40th Anniv of Sultan's Accession. Wmk Mult Script CA (sideways). P 12½.*
129	37	8 c. bright violet and slate			3·00	50
129		Perf "Specimen"			42·00	

38 Sultan Sir Ibrahim **39**

(Recess D.L.R.)

1940 (Feb). *Wmk Mult Script CA. P 13½.*
130	38	8 c. black and pale blue			14·00	30
130		Perf "Specimen"			42·00	

1948 (1 Dec). *Royal Silver Wedding. As Nos. 143/4 of Jamaica.*
131	10 c. violet			20	30
132	$5 green			24·00	35·00

1949 (2 May)–55. *Wmk Mult Script CA. Chalk-surfaced paper. P 17½ × 18.*
133	39	1 c. black			10	10
134		2 c. orange			10	10
		a. Orange-yellow (22.1.52)			10	60
135		3 c. green			35	60
		a. Yellow-green (22.1.52)			8·00	2·25
136		4 c. brown			10	10
136a		5 c. bright purple (1.9.52)			30	30
137		6 c. grey			20	10
		a. Pale grey (22.1.52)			30	30
		ac. Error. St. Edward's Crown W 9b			£1000	
138		8 c. scarlet			2·50	90
138a		8 c. green (1.9.52)			3·00	1·50
139		10 c. magenta			40	10
		aa. Imperf (pair)			£1500	
139a		12 c. scarlet (1.9.52)			2·25	3·00
140		15 c. ultramarine			2·00	10
141		20 c. black and green			45	1·00
141a		20 c. bright blue (1.9.52)			80	10
142		25 c. purple and orange			60	10

142a	39	30 c. scarlet and purple (5.9.55)			1·75	2·25
142b		35 c. scarlet and purple (1.9.52)			3·25	1·00
143		40 c. red and purple			3·50	7·50
144		50 c. black and blue			1·00	10
145		$1 blue and purple			3·50	1·50
146		$2 green and scarlet			14·00	3·50
147		$5 green and brown			40·00	9·00
133/47			Set of 21		70·00	27·00

1949 (10 Oct). *75th Anniv of U.P.U. As Nos. 145/8 of Jamaica.*
148	10 c. purple			30	15
149	15 c. deep blue			1·25	45
150	25 c. orange			65	2·25
151	50 c. blue-black			1·25	2·25
148/51		Set of 4		3·00	5·00

1953 (2 June). *Coronation. As No. 153 of Jamaica.*
152	10 c. black and reddish purple			50	10

40 Sultan Sir Ibrahim   **41** Sultan Sir Ismail and Johore Coat of Arms

(Recess D.L.R.)

1955 (1 Nov). *Diamond Jubilee of Sultan. Wmk Mult Script CA. P 14.*
153	40	10 c. carmine-red			10	10

(Photo Courvoisier)

1960 (10 Feb). *Coronation of Sultan. No wmk. P 11½.*
154	41	10 c. multicoloured		20	20

1960. *As T 9/19 of Kedah, but with portrait of Sultan Ismail. P 13½ ($1); others 12½ × 13 (vert) or 13 × 12½ (horiz).*
155	1 c. black (7.10.60)			10	30
156	2 c. orange-red (7.10.60)			10	50
157	4 c. sepia (19.8.60)			10	10
158	5 c. carmine-lake (7.10.60)			10	10
159	8 c. myrtle-green (9.12.60)			1·50	2·25
160	10 c. deep maroon (10.6.60)			30	10
161	20 c. blue (9.12.60)			1·00	30
162	50 c. black and bright blue (19.8.60)			30	10
163	$1 ultramarine and reddish purple (9.12.60)			1·25	2·00
164	$2 bronze-green and scarlet (9.12.60)			7·50	11·00
165	$5 brown and bronze-green (7.10.60)			24·00	25·00
155/65		Set of 11		32·00	38·00

In No. 161 there are only two figures in the boat, the steersman being missing. In the 20 c. value for all the other States there are three figures.

The 6, 12, 25 and 30 c. values used with this issue were Nos. 1/4 of Malayan Federation.

42 *Vanda hookeriana*
(Inset portrait of Sultan Ismail)

(Des A. Fraser-Brunner. Photo Harrison)

1965 (15 Nov). *T 42 and similar horiz designs. W w 13 (upright). P 14½.*
166	1 c. Type 42			10	30
	a. Black (orchid's name and part of flower) omitted			85·00	
	w. Wmk inverted			2·00	
167	2 c. *Arundina graminifolia*			10	50
168	5 c. *Paphiopedilum niveum*			10	10
	b. Yellow (flower) omitted			32·00	
169	6 c. *Spathoglottis plicata*			40	30
170	10 c. *Arachnis flos-aeris*			40	10
171	15 c. *Rhyncostylis retusa*			1·50	10
	b. Green (face value and leaves) omitted			£130	
172	20 c. *Phalaenopsis violacea*			1·50	60
	a. Bright purple (blooms) omitted			60·00	
166/72		Set of 7		3·50	1·50

The 2 c. to 15 c. exist with both PVA gum and gum arabic.

The 2 c. with black (name of state, arms and head) omitted is listed under Sarawak No. 213a as there is some evidence that a sheet was issued there; if it also exists from any of the other states it would, of course, be identical.

The higher values used with this issue were Nos. 20/27 of Malaysia (National Issues).

1970. *As No. 166 and 170 but W w 13 (sideways).*
173	1 c. multicoloured (20.11)			1·25	4·00
174	10 c. multicoloured (27.5)			1·25	2·25

44 *Delias ninus*   **45** *Rafflesia hasseltii*
(Inset portrait of Sultan Ismail)   (Inset portrait of Sultan Ismail)

(Des V. Whiteley)

1971 (1 Feb)–78. *Butterflies. T 44 and similar horiz designs. Multicoloured. No wmk. P 13½ × 13.*

(a) Litho by Bradbury, Wilkinson
175	1 c. Type 44			30	1·00
176	2 c. *Danaus melanippus*			75	1·25
177	5 c. *Parthenos sylvia*			95	20
178	6 c. *Papilio demoleus*			95	1·60
179	10 c. *Hebomoia glaucippe*			95	20
180	15 c. *Precis orithya*			95	10
181	20 c. *Valeria valeria*			95	30
175/81		Set of 7		5·25	4·00

(b) Photo Harrison (1977–78)
182	1 c. Type 44			1·50	3·00
183	2 c. *Danaus melanippus*			1·50	4·00
184	5 c. *Parthenos sylvia*			4·25	70
185	10 c. *Hebomoia glaucippe*			2·75	40
186	15 c. *Precis orithya*			4·50	25
187	20 c. *Valeria valeria*			4·75	1·00
182/7		Set of 6		17·00	8·50

The higher values used with this issue were Nos. 64/71 of Malaysia (National Issues).

DIFFERENCES BETWEEN LITHO AND PHOTO PRINTINGS. Stamps from the photogravure printings can be easily identified by the appearance of certain features. The differences are most easily observed on the face values and inscriptions. Stamps printed by lithography show straight edges to letters and figures, but when those produced by photogravure are examined under a magnifying glass it will be seen that these edges are broken by the photogravure screen.

In addition the backgrounds and portraits of those stamps of this series printed by lithography show a regular screen of dots, a feature not visible on those printed by the photogravure process.

A number of instances have come to light of photogravure stamps which have had the top colour "removed" by means of an eraser.

(Des M. Yusof bin Mohammed; adapted Malaysian Advertising Services. Litho Asher and Co., Melbourne)

1979 (30 Apr). *Flowers. Horiz designs as T 45. Multicoloured. W 95 of Malaysia (sideways). P 15 × 14½.*
188	1 c. Type 45			10	50
189	2 c. *Pterocarpus indicus*			10	50
190	5 c. *Lagerstroemia speciosa*			10	30
191	10 c. *Durio zibethinus*			15	10
192	15 c. *Hibiscus rosa-sinensis*			15	10
193	20 c. *Rhododendron scortechinii*			20	10
194	25 c. *Etlingera elatior* (inscr "*Phaeomeria speciosa*")			40	20
188/94		Set of 7		1·00	1·40

For higher values used in conjunction with this series see Nos. 190/7 of Malaysia.

1983 (16 June)–85.* *As Nos. 190/3 but without wmk.*
197	5 c. *Lagerstroemia speciosa* (20.11.83)			1·25	1·40
198	10 c. *Durio zibethinus* (11.7.85)			1·25	1·40
199	15 c. *Hibiscus rosa-sinensis* (12.83)			1·00	20
200	20 c. *Rhododendron scortechinii* (blackish brown background)			12·00	1·00
200a	20 c. *Rhododendron scortechinii* (bronze-green background) (23.9.83)			1·40	55

*There was no official release date for these stamps. Dates shown are the earliest recorded from postmarks and may be revised if earlier examples are reported.

On Nos. 197/9 and 200a the "Johor" inscription is in rounded instead of square-ended letters.

WATERMARKED AND UNWATERMARKED PRINTINGS. The first printing of the 20 c. value on unwatermarked paper was from the same plates and in the same shades as the original watermarked issue.

Subsequent no watermark printings of the 20 c. and all no watermark printings of the other values were in changed shades and can be readily identified as follows:

5 c. No watermark printing has the frame in turquoise-blue instead of the dull blue of the watermarked version.

10 c. No watermark printing shows a purple-brown background instead of the sepia of the watermarked.

15 c. No watermark printing shows stronger highlights in the design and more detail on the flowers and leaves.

20 c. Later no watermark printings have a bronze-green background instead of the blackish brown shown on the watermarked and first no watermark stamps.

25 c. No watermark printing has a deep background with more detail on the flower. The latin inscription has also been moved downwards to a more central position up the side of the vignette.

Differences also occur in the plates used to apply the state names, rulers' portraits or crests. Notes on these are provided under the individual issues.

46 Coconuts
(Inset portrait of Sultan Mahmood)

(Des Kathy Wong. Litho Security Printers (M), Malaysia)

1986 (25 Oct)–96. *Agricultural Products of Malaysia. Vert designs as T 46. Multicoloured. W 138. Phosphorised paper. P 12.*
202	1 c. Type 46			10	10
	w. Wmk inverted				
203	2 c. Coconuts			10	10
204	5 c. Cocoa			10	10
	aw. Wmk inverted				
	c. Perf 14×13¾ (1994)			3·25	30
	cw. Wmk inverted			6·50	
	f. Perf 14¾×14½ (1995)			1·00	10

205	10 c. Black pepper ..	..	..	10	10
	a. Imperf (pair)		..	£160	
	c. Perf 14×13¾ (1994)	..	..	3·25	30
	e. Perf 14×14½ (1996) ..		..	3·00	20
206	15 c. Rubber ..	..	..	10	10
207	20 c. Oil palm	..	..	10	10
	c. Perf 14×13¾ (1994)	..	..	1·75	30
	e. Perf 14×14½ (1996)	..	..	13·00	50
	f. Perf 14¾×14½ (1994)	..	..	1·00	10
208	30 c. Rice	..	..	15	20
	c. Perf 14×13¾ (1994)	..	..	3·00	30
	cw. Wmk inverted (1995)	..	..	12·00	
	e. Perf 14×14½	..	..		
	f. Perf 14¾×14½ (1994)	..	..	9·00	1·25
202/8			*Set of 7*	50	55

PERFORATION VARIETIES. Delays in the production of new definitives to replace the Agricultural Products issue led to an extended series of new printings as the postal authorities in the various states indented, on an annual basis, for fresh stocks of those values which were running short. These annual indents were identified by the plate numbers used so that 1A = 1986, 2A = 1987 etc.

Many of these printings show different perforations from the gauge 12 of the original set. Those perforations known to us have been listed. The order of listing may not show the chronological sequence parts of which remain unclear. Other perforations may well exist on these stamps.

Stamps apparently perforated 14 are now believed to result from the dimensional instability of a batch of paper, probably in 1994. These are no longer listed as the variable nature of the paper produces inaccurate perforation readings.

To assist identification the perforations are quoted to the nearest ¼. The exact decimal equivalents are as follows:

13½×13¾ = 13.5×13.75 (used 1991–1993)
14×13¾ = 14.1×13.75 (used 1993–1997)
14×14½ = 14.1×14.4 (used 1994–1997)
14¾×14½ = 14.75×14.4 (used 1994–1996)

STAMP BOOKLETS

1928. *Black on white card. Interleaved with tissue. Stapled.*
SB1 $2 booklet containing ten 1 c. and 2 c. (Nos. 103, 105), twenty 4 c. (No. 108), each in blocks of 10 and eighteen 5 c. (No. 109) in blocks of 6

1929. *Black on pink cover. Stapled.*
SB2 $1 booklet containing 2 c., 3 c. and 5 c. (Nos. 105, 107, 109) in blocks of 10   ..   ..

1930. *Black on buff cover. Stapled.*
SB3 $1 booklet containing ten 1 c. and 5 c. (Nos. 103, 109) and twenty 2 c. (Nos. 105) in blocks of 10

B 1

1973 (8 Dec). *Black on light magenta cover as Type B* **1**. *Stitched.*
SB4 $3 booklet containing eight 5 c., 10 c. and twelve 15 c. (Nos. 177, 179/80) in blocks of 4   ..   25·00

1979 (1 Dec). *Black on pink cover as Type B* **1**, *but 80×50 mm.*
SB5 $3 booklet containing eight 5 c., 10 c. and twelve 15 c. (Nos. 190/2) in blocks of 4   ..   9·00
No. SB5 exists with two different versions of the back cover.

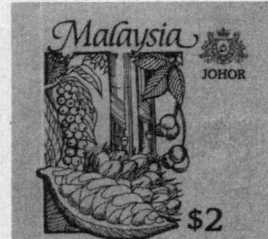

B 2 Produce

1987 (1 June). *Black on orange-yellow cover as Type B* **2**. *Stapled.*
SB6 $2 booklet containing 5 c., 10 c., 15 c. and 20 c. (Nos. 204/7) in blocks of 4   ..   8·00

B 3 Sultan Abdul Samad Building, Kuala Lumpur

1992 (1 July). *"Kuala Lumpur '92" International Philatelic Exhibition. Multicoloured cover as Type B* **3**. *Stamps attached by selvedge.*
SB7 $3 booklet containing 30 c. (No. 208) in block of 10   8·00

1993. *Multicoloured on pale green (No. SB8) or on pale buff (No. SB9) covers as Type B* **3**, *but with face values and "Kuala Lumpur" logo replaced by postal service emblem and face value, both at bottom right. Stamps attached by selvedge.*
SB8 $2 booklet containing 20 c. (No. 207) in block of 10   1·00
SB9 $3 booklet containing 30 c. (No. 208) in block of 10   1·50

POSTAGE DUE STAMPS

D 1

(Typo Waterlow)

1938 (1 Jan). *Wmk Mult Script CA. P* 12½.

D1	D 1	1 c. carmine	..	..	12·00	35·00
D2		4 c. green	..	..	40·00	40·00
D3		8 c. orange	..	..	48·00	£140
D4		10 c. brown	..	..	48·00	48·00
D5		12 c. purple	..	..	55·00	£110
D1/5		..		*Set of 5*	£180	£325
D1/5 Perf "Specimen"		..		*Set of 5*	£130	

KEDAH

Suzerainty over Kedah was transferred by Thailand to Great Britain on 15 July 1909. A Treaty of Friendship between Great Britain and Kedah was signed on 1 November 1923.
The state joined the Federation of Malaya on 1 February 1948.

For stamps of THAILAND used in Kedah between 1887 and 1909 see VIII. SIAMESE POSTS IN NORTHERN MALAYA section.
Issues of the FEDERATED MALAY STATES were used in Kedah from 16 July 1909 until 15 June 1912.

PRICES FOR STAMPS ON COVER TO 1945

Nos. 1/14	from × 15
Nos. 15/23	from × 10
Nos. 24/40	from × 8
Nos. 41/8	from × 12
Nos. 49/51	
Nos. 52/9	from × 4
Nos. 60/8	from × 3
Nos. 68a/9	from × 4

1 Sheaf of Rice   2 Malay ploughing

3 Council Chamber, Alor Star

(Recess D.L.R.)

1912 (16 June). *Wmk Mult Crown CA (sideways* on 10 c. to $5). P 14.*

1	1	1 c. black and green	50	25
2		3 c. black and red	2·75	30
3		4 c. rose and grey	9·50	25
4		5 c. green and chestnut	2·25	3·00
5		8 c. black and ultramarine	2·75	3·50
6	2	10 c. blue and sepia	1·75	90
		w. Wmk Crown to left of CA	†	—
7		20 c. black and green	3·50	4·00
		x. Wmk reversed	£110	
8		30 c. black and rose	2·25	10·00
9		40 c. black and purple	3·50	14·00
10		50 c. brown and blue	8·00	13·00
11	3	$1 black and red/*yellow*	14·00	18·00
		w. Wmk Crown to left of CA	32·00	
		x. Wmk reversed		
		y. Wmk Crown to left of CA and reversed		
12		$2 green and brown	19·00	80·00
13		$3 black and blue/*blue*	55·00	£150
		a. "A" of "CA" missing from wmk	£1000	
14		$5 black and red	55·00	£130
1/14		Set of 14	£150	£375
1/14 Optd "Specimen"		Set of 14	£275	

*The normal sideways watermark shows the Crown to right of CA, *as seen from the back of the stamp.*

Due to an increase in postal rates 1 c. and 4 c. stamps of STRAITS SETTLEMENTS were used in Kedah for some months from March 1919.

 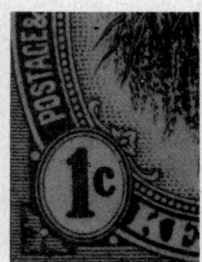

(i)   (ii)

DOUBLE AND SINGLE PLATES. (i) Printed from separate plates for frame and centre, with dotted shading extending close to the central sheaf. Soft impression of centre with little clear detail.
(ii) Printed from single plate, with white space around sheaf. Centre more deeply etched with sharp image.

1919 (June)–**21**. *New colours and values. Wmk Mult Crown CA (sideways* on 21 c., 25 c.). P 14.*

15	1	1 c. brown (ii) (18.8.19)	55	45
		w. Wmk inverted	70·00	
		y. Wmk inverted and reversed	†	£160
18		2 c. green (ii)	50	20
19		3 c. deep purple (i) (1920)	65	70
		y. Wmk inverted and reversed	60·00	80·00
20		4 c. rose (ii)	2·25	20
21		4 c. red (ii) (18.8.19)	3·25	45
		w. Wmk inverted		

22	2	21 c. mauve and purple (18.8.19)	5·50	48·00
		w. Wmk Crown to left of CA	90·00	
		y. Wmk Crown to left of CA and reversed	£160	
23		25 c. blue and purple (1921)	1·75	21·00
		a. "A" of "CA" missing from wmk	£350	
15/23		Set of 6	10·00	65·00
15/23 Optd "Specimen"		Set of 6	£140	

*The normal sideways watermark shows Crown to right of CA, *as seen from the back of the stamp.*

(4)   (5)

(Surch by Ribeiro & Co, Penang)

1919 (Mar). *Surch as T 4.*

24	3	50 c. on $2 green and brown	55·00	65·00
		a. "C" of "CENTS" inserted by handstamp (R. 6/4)	£1000	£1100
25		$1 on $3 black and blue/*blue*	20·00	85·00

Nos. 24/5 were surcharged from settings of 30 (5×6).

Two types of centre plate for Type **2** wmkd Mult Script CA:

Type I (Plate 1) (produced by electrotyping)

Type II (Plate 2) (produced by transfer die)

A new common centre plate, 2, was prepared from the original die in 1926. Stamps from Plate 2, produced using a transfer die, show considerably more detail of the ground and have the oxen, ploughman's hat and his clothing much more deeply cut as illustrated in Type II above.

1921–**32**. *Wmk Mult Script CA (sideways* on 10 c. to $5). P 14.*

26	1	1 c. brown (ii)	50	20
		w. Wmk inverted	†	£160
		y. Wmk inverted and reversed	†	£160
27		2 c. dull green (ii) (Type I)	1·25	20
28		3 c. deep purple (ii)	80	70
29		4 c. deep carmine (ii)	5·00	20
30	2	10 c. blue and sepia (I)	2·75	75
		ay. Wmk Crown to left of CA and reversed	60·00	
		b. Type I (*wmk Crown to left of CA*) (1927)	32·00	3·25
		by. Wmk Crown to right of CA and reversed	†	£160
31		20 c. black and yellow-green (I)	4·00	2·00
32		21 c. mauve and purple (I)	2·00	13·00
33		25 c. blue and purple (I)	2·25	6·00
		a. Type I (*wmk Crown to left of CA*) (1932)	50·00	4·00
34		30 c. black and rose (I) (1922)	3·00	7·00
		a. Type II (*wmk Crown to left of CA*) (1927)	32·00	3·00
35		40 c. black and purple (I)	4·25	40·00
		aw. Wmk Crown to left of CA (1924)	22·00	32·00
		b. Type II (*wmk Crown to left of CA*) (1932)	50·00	20·00
36		50 c. brown and grey-blue (I)	2·25	11·00
		aw. Wmk Crown to left of CA (1924)	23·00	14·00
		b. Type II (*wmk Crown to left of CA*) (1932)	60·00	4·50
37	3	$1 black and red/*yellow* (1924)	55·00	60·00
		w. Wmk Crown to left of CA	6·50	7·50
38		$2 myrtle and brown	13·00	80·00
		w. Wmk Crown to left of CA (1924)	19·00	80·00
39		$3 black and blue/*blue*	60·00	80·00
		w. Wmk Crown to left of CA (1924)	50·00	60·00
40		$5 black and deep carmine	75·00	£140
		w. Wmk Crown to left of CA (1926)	55·00	£110
26/40		Set of 15	£130	£275
26/40 Optd "Specimen"		Set of 15	£275	

*The normal sideways watermark shows Crown to right of CA, *as seen from the back of the stamp.*

Nos. 26/40 were produced by De La Rue using the "wet" method of recess-printing during which the stamps contracted when they were dried before gumming. From 1933 the firm adopted the "dry" method, using pre-gummed paper, with the result that stamps were up to 0.5 mm larger in size. Of the low values as Type 1 in this series only the 2 c. was still current when the "dry" method was introduced.

Stamps as Type 1 can be found perforated either comb or line. The 1 c. and 4 c. come comb only, the 3 c. line only and the 2 c. either way.

For the 2 c. Type II see No. 69.

1922 (Apr). *Malaya–Borneo Exhibition, Singapore. Optd as T 5 at Singapore.*

I. "BORNEO" 14 mm. long.

(a) Wmk Mult Crown CA

41	1	2 c. green (ii)	3·50	20·00
42	2	21 c. mauve and purple (I)	24·00	75·00
43		25 c. blue and purple (I)	24·00	75·00
		a. Overprint inverted	£900	
44		50 c. brown and grey-blue (I)	24·00	90·00

(b) Wmk Mult Script CA

45	1	1 c. brown (ii)	2·50	13·00
46		3 c. purple (ii)	3·00	35·00
47		4 c. deep carmine (ii)	3·00	25·00
48	2	10 c. blue and sepia (I)	4·50	35·00
41/8		Set of 8	80·00	£325

There are setting variations in the size and shape of the letters, stop raised, stop omitted, etc., etc.

II. "BORNEO" 15–15½ mm. long. Wmk Mult Crown CA

49	2	21 c. mauve and purple (I)	20·00	90·00
50		25 c. blue and purple (I)	22·00	£100
51		50 c. brown and grey-blue (I)	45·00	£150
49/51		Set of 3	75·00	£300

1922–**40**. *New colours, etc. Wmk Mult Script CA (sideways* on 12, 35 c.). P 14.*

52	1	1 c. black (ii) (Type I)	50	10
53		3 c. green (ii) (1924)	1·75	90
54		4 c. violet (ii) (1926)	90	10
55		5 c. yellow (ii)	1·50	10
		w. Wmk inverted	65·00	
		x. Wmk reversed	†	£130
		y. Wmk inverted and reversed	†	£130
56		6 c. carmine (ii) (1926)	70	65
		a. Carmine-red (1940)	14·00	48·00
57		8 c. grey-black (ii) (10.36)	9·50	10
58	2	12 c. black and indigo (II) (1926)	2·25	4·00
59		35 c. purple (II) (1926)	5·00	5·00
52/9		Set of 8	20·00	27·00
52/9 Optd/Perf "Specimen"		Set of 8	£190	

*The normal sideways watermark shows Crown to left of CA, *as seen from the back of the stamp.*

With the exception of the 6 c. and 8 c. the printing plates for the Type 1 values listed above were, as for the previous issue, produced by electrotyping with the face values added to the plates by pantograph. The plates for the 6 c. and 8 c. values were constructed by the more modern method of using a transfer die to enter each impression.

Printings after November 1933 were normally produced by the "dry" method as described beneath Nos. 26/40. There were late "wet" printings of the 1 c. (No. 68a) and 2 c. (No. 27) in August 1938. The 3 c. only exists from a "wet" printing, the 6 c. (No. 56a) and 8 c. from dry printings and the remainder from either method.

Stamps as Type 1 can be found perforated either comb or line. The 3 c. and 4 c. (No. 56) come comb only, the 6 c. (No. 56a) and 8 c. line only and the 1, 4 and 5 c. either way.

For the 1 c. Type II see No. 68a.

6 Sultan Abdul Hamid Halimshah

(Recess Waterlow)

1937 (30 June). *Wmk Mult Script CA. P 12½.*

60	6	10 c. ultramarine and sepia	4·00	80
61		12 c. black and violet	27·00	12·00
62		25 c. ultramarine and purple	7·50	4·50
63		30 c. green and scarlet	8·00	10·00
64		40 c. black and purple	4·00	16·00
65		50 c. brown and blue	6·00	4·00
66		$1 black and green	4·00	10·00
67		$2 green and brown	£120	90·00
68		$5 black and scarlet	32·00	£140
60/8		Set of 9	£190	£250
60/8 Perf "Specimen"		Set of 9	£200	

I   II   I   II

1938 (May)–**40**. *As Nos. 52 and 27, but face values redrawn as Types II.*

68a	1	1 c. black	80·00	3·00
69		2 c. bright green (1940)	£160	6·00

1 c. Type II. Figures "1" have square-cut corners instead of rounded, and larger top serif. Larger "C". Line perf. Produced from a new electrotyped Plate 2 with different engraved face values. Printings exist from either the "wet" or "dry" methods.

2 c. Type II. Figures "2" have circular instead of oval drops and the letters "c" are thin and tall instead of thick and rounded. Produced from a new plate, made from a transfer die, and printed by the "dry" method.

1948 (1 Dec). *Royal Silver Wedding. As Nos. 143/4 of Jamaica.*

70		10 c. violet	20	20
71		$5 carmine	25·00	32·00

1949 (10 Oct). *75th Anniv of U.P.U. As Nos. 145/8 of Jamaica.*

72		10 c. purple	25	20
73		15 c. deep blue	1·50	1·25
74		25 c. orange	65	1·25
75		50 c. blue-black	1·00	2·25
72/5		Set of 4	3·00	4·50

7 Sheaf of Rice   8 Sultan Badlishah

1950 (1 June)–**55.** *Wmk Mult Script CA. Chalk-surfaced paper.*
P 17½ × 18.

76	7	1 c. black		30	30
77		2 c. orange		30	15
78		3 c. green		1·40	1·00
79		4 c. brown		60	10
79a		5 c. bright purple (1.9.52)		60	1·25
		ab. Bright mauve (24.9.53)		60	70
80		6 c. grey		50	15
81		8 c. scarlet		1·25	2·25
81a		8 c. green (1.9.52)		75	1·75
		ab. Deep green (24.9.53)		8·00	8·50
82		10 c. magenta		50	10
82a		12 c. scarlet (1.9.52)		85	2·50
83		15 c. ultramarine		80	35
84		20 c. black and green		85	2·50
84a		20 c. bright blue (1.9.52)		85	10
85	8	25 c. purple and orange		90	30
85a		30 c. scarlet and purple (5.9.55)		1·25	1·25
85b		35 c. scarlet and purple (1.9.52)		85	1·50
86		40 c. red and purple		2·25	6·00
87		50 c. black and blue		1·75	20
88		$1 blue and purple		2·75	2·50
89		$2 green and scarlet		20·00	22·00
90		$5 green and brown		42·00	32·00
76/90			*Set of 21*	70·00	65·00

1953 (2 June). *Coronation. As No. 153 of Jamaica.*

91	10 c. black and reddish purple		65	30

9 Copra   10 Pineapples

11 Ricefield   12 Masjid Alwi Mosque, Kangar

13 East Coast Railway "Golden Blowpipe" Express   14 Tiger

15 Fishing Prau   16 Aborigines with Blowpipes

17 Government Offices   18 Bersilat

19 Weaving

(Recess D.L.R.)

1957. *Inset portrait of Sultan Badlishah. W w* 12. *P* 13 × 12½
(1 c. to 8 c.), 12½ × 13 (10 c., 20 c.), 12½ (50 c., $2, $5) *or* 13½
($1).

92	9	1 c. black (21.8)		10	35
93	10	2 c. orange-red (25.7)		10	60
94	11	4 c. sepia (21.8)		10	30
95	12	5 c. carmine-lake (21.8)		10	30

96	13	8 c. myrtle-green (21.8)		2·00	6·00
97	14	10 c. deep brown (4.8)		40	20
98	15	20 c. blue (26.6)		1·75	1·50
99	16	50 c. black and blue (25.7)		1·50	2·25
100	17	$1 ultramarine & reddish purple (25.7)		3·50	8·00
101	18	$2 bronze-green and scarlet (21.8)		19·00	21·00
102	19	$5 brown and bronze-green (26.6)		38·00	32·00
92/102			*Set of 11*	60·00	65·00

The 6, 12, 25 and 30 c. values used with this issue were Nos. 1/4
of Malayan Federation.

20 Sultan Abdul Halim Mu'Adzam Shah   21 Sultan Abdul Halim Shah

(Photo Harrison)

1959 (20 Feb). *Installation of the Sultan. W w* 12. *P* 14 × 14½.

103	20	10 c. multicoloured		10	10

1959 (1 July)–**62.** *As Nos. 92/102 but with inset portrait of Sultan Abdul Halim Shah as in T* 21.

104	21	1 c. black		10	40
105	10	2 c. orange-red		10	70
106	11	4 c. sepia		10	30
107	12	5 c. carmine-lake		10	50
108	13	8 c. myrtle-green		3·50	2·75
109	14	10 c. deep brown		75	10
109a		10 c. deep maroon (19.12.61)		3·50	30
110	15	20 c. blue		60	30
111	16	50 c. black and blue (*p* 12½)		30	90
		a. Perf 12½ × 13 (14.6.60)		30	20
112	17	$1 ultramarine and reddish purple		30	50
113	18	$2 bronze-green and scarlet		13·00	15·00
114	19	$5 brown and bronze-green (*p* 12½)		16·00	17·00
		a. Perf 13 × 12½ (26.11.62)		22·00	11·00
104/14			*Set of 12*	35·00	30·00

22 Vanda hookeriana   23 Danaus melanippus

1965 (15 Nov). *As Nos. 166/72 of Johore but with inset portrait of Sultan Abdul Halim Shah as in T* 22. *W w* 13 (*upright*).

115		1 c. multicoloured		10	50
		a. Black omitted (orchid's name and part of flower)		75·00	
116		2 c. multicoloured		10	80
		b. Yellow (flower) omitted		65·00	
117		5 c. multicoloured		10	10
		a. Black (country name and head) omitted		95·00	
118		6 c. multicoloured		15	30
119		10 c. multicoloured		30	10
		a. Red omitted		£190	
		b. Green (leaves) omitted		£190	
120		15 c. multicoloured		1·50	10
121		20 c. multicoloured		1·75	60
		a. Bright purple (blooms) omitted		£130	
		b. Yellow (leaves) omitted		27·00	
115/21			*Set of 7*	3·50	2·00

The 1 c. to 15 c. exist with PVA gum as well as gum arabic.
The 6 c. value exists with black (country name, arms and head)
omitted and is listed under Sarawak where it was issued.
The higher values used with this issue were Nos. 20/27 of
Malaysia (National Issues).

1970 (27 May). *As Nos. 115 and 119 but W w* 13 (*sideways*).

122	22	1 c. multicoloured		2·00	4·50
123	—	10 c. multicoloured		75	3·25

1971 (1 Feb)–**78.** *As Nos. 175/87 of Johore but with portrait of Sultan Abdul Halim Shah as in T* 23. (a) *Litho by Bradbury, Wilkinson.*

124		1 c. multicoloured		30	85
125		2 c. multicoloured		40	85
126		5 c. multicoloured		1·00	10
127		6 c. multicoloured		1·00	1·00
128		8 c. multicoloured		75	10
129		15 c. multicoloured		1·00	10
130		20 c. multicoloured		1·25	45
124/30			*Set of 7*	5·00	3·00

(b) *Photo by Harrison* (1977–78)

130a		2 c. multicoloured		11·00	15·00
131		5 c. multicoloured		2·75	80
132		10 c. multicoloured		6·00	30
133		15 c. multicoloured		2·00	30
134		20 c. multicoloured		3·00	1·75
130a/4			*Set of 5*	22·00	16·00

The higher values used with this issue were Nos. 64/71 of
Malaysia (National Issues).
For differences between litho and photo printings, see after
Johore No. 187.

24 Pterocarpus indicus   25 Sultan Abdul Halim Shah

1979 (30 Apr). *As Nos. 188/94 of Johore but with portrait of Sultan Abdul Halim Shah as in T* 24.

135		1 c. *Rafflesia hasseltii*		10	50
136		2 c. Type 24		10	50
137		5 c. *Lagerstroemia speciosa*		10	30
138		10 c. *Durio zibethinus*		15	10
139		15 c. *Hibiscus rosa-sinensis*		15	10
140		20 c. *Rhododendron scortechinii*		20	10
141		25 c. *Etlingera elatior* (inscr "*Phaeomeria speciosa*")		40	10
135/41			*Set of 7*	1·00	1·40

For higher values used in conjunction with this series see Nos.
190/7 of Malaysia (National Issues).

(Des and litho Security Printers (M), Malaysia)

1983 (15 July). *Silver Jubilee of Sultan. T* 25 *and similar multicoloured designs. P* 13 × 13½ (20 c.) *or* 13½ × 13 (*others*).

142		20 c. Type 25		70	30
143		40 c. Paddy fields (*horiz*)		1·75	1·00
144		60 c. Paddy fields and Mount Jerai (*horiz*)		2·50	4·25
142/4			*Set of 3*	4·50	4·50

1983 (22 Feb)–**85.** * *As Nos. 138/40 but without wmk.*

148		10 c. *Durio zibethinus* (11.5.85)		15·00	2·75
149		15 c. *Hibiscus rosa-sinensis* (12.84)		55	50
150		20 c. *Rhododendron scortechinii* (blackish brown background)		17·00	90
150a		20 c. *Rhododendron scortechinii* (bronze-green background) (16.12.83)		30	30

*There was no official release date for these stamps. Dates
shown are the earliest recorded from postmarks and may be
revised if earlier examples are reported.
For details of the shade differences between watermarked and
unwatermarked printings see after Johore No. 200a.
Nos. 148/9 and 150a show "kedah" nearer to "malaysia" than
on Nos. 135/41 and 150.

26 Cocoa

1986 (25 Oct)–**96.** *As Nos. 202/8 of Johore, but with portrait of Sultan Abdul Halim Shah as in T* 26. *P* 12.

152		1 c. Coffee		10	10
153		2 c. Coconuts		10	10
154		5 c. Type 26		10	10
		c. Perf 14×13¾ (1996)		1·00	20
		f. Perf 14¾×14½ (1994)		4·50	45
155		10 c. Black pepper		10	10
		b. Perf 13½×13¾			
		c. Perf 14×13¾ (1994)		3·75	35
		ca. No watermark (1996)		9·00	
156		15 c. Rubber		10	10
157		20 c. Oil palm		10	10
		c. Perf 14×13¾ (1994)		1·00	10
		cw. Wmk inverted (1994)		4·00	
		f. Perf 14¾×14½ (1994)		13·00	30
158		30 c. Rice		15	20
		c. Perf 14×13¾ (1994)		3·25	30
		cw. Wmk inverted (1995)		6·00	
		e. Perf 14×14½ (1996)		2·25	20
		ew. Wmk inverted		13·00	
		f. Perf 14¾×14½ (1996)		3·25	30
152/8			*Set of 7*	50	55

STAMP BOOKLETS

1973 (8 Dec). *Cover as Type B* 1 *of Johore, but inscr "KEDAH".
Stitched.*

SB1	$3 booklet containing eight 5 c., 10 c. and twelve 15 c. (Nos. 126, 128/9) in blocks of 4		25·00

1979 (1 Dec). *Cover as No. SB5 of Johore, but inscr "KEDAH".
Stitched.*

SB2	$3 booklet containing eight 5 c., 10 c., and twelve 15 c. (Nos. 137/9) in blocks of 4		9·00

No. SB2 exists with two different versions of the back cover.

1987 (1 June). *Cover as Type B* 2 *of Johore, but inscr
"KEDAH". Stapled.*

SB3	$2 booklet containing 5 c., 10 c., 15 c. and 20 c. (Nos. 154/7) in blocks of 4		8·00

1992 (1 July). *"Kuala Lumpur '92" International Philatelic
Exhibition. Cover as Type B* 3 *of Johore, but inscr "Kedah".
Stamps attached by selvedge.*

SB4	$3 booklet containing 30 c. (No. 158) in block of 10		8·00

1993. *Covers as Nos. SB8/9 of Johore, but inscr "Kedah".
Stamps attached by selvedge.*

SB5	$2 booklet containing 20 c. (No. 157) in block of 10		1·00
SB6	$3 booklet containing 30 c. (No. 158) in block of 10		1·50

KELANTAN

Suzerainty over Kelantan was transferred by Thailand to Great Britain on 15 July 1909. A British adviser was appointed in 1923.

The state joined the Federation of Malaya on 1 February 1948.

For stamps of THAILAND used in Kelantan between 1895 and 1909 see VIII. SIAMESE POSTS IN NORTHERN MALAYA section.

From 1909 until the introduction of Kelantan stamps in 1911 the issues of the FEDERATED MALAY STATES to $2 were in use.

PRICES FOR STAMPS ON COVER TO 1945

Nos. 1/11	from × 30
No. 12	—
Nos. 14/23	from × 30
Nos. 30/8	from × 15
Nos. 39/a	from × 10
Nos. 40/8	from × 30
Nos. 49/52	from × 20
No. 53	from × 3
No. 54	—

MALAYA
BORNEO
EXHIBITION

1   **(2)**

1911 (Jan)**–15.** *Wmk Mult Crown CA. Ordinary paper (1 c. to 10 c.) or chalk-surfaced paper (30 c. to $25). P 14.*

1	1	1 c. yellow-green			3·50	90
		a. *Blue-green*			2·75	30
2		3 c. red			4·00	15
3		4 c. black and red			1·50	15
4		5 c. green and red/*yellow*			9·00	75
		w. Wmk inverted			†	£350
5		8 c. ultramarine			5·50	1·00
6		10 c. black and mauve			28·00	75
7		30 c. dull purple and red			10·00	2·50
		a. *Purple and carmine*			27·00	14·00
8		50 c. black and orange			7·50	2·50
9		$1 green and emerald			45·00	48·00
9a		$1 green and brown (5.15)			35·00	2·00
10		$2 green and carmine			1·50	4·00
11		$5 green and blue			4·00	7·50
12		$25 green and orange			38·00	75·00
1/12				*Set of 13*	£170	£130
1/12 Optd "Specimen"				*Set of 13*	£225	

1921 (5 May)**–28.** *Wmk Mult Script CA. Ordinary paper (1 c. to 10 c.) or chalk-surfaced paper (30 c. to $1). P 14.*

14	1	1 c. dull green (7.21)			4·25	60
15		1 c. black (24.2.23)			50	50
16		2 c. brown (29.7.22)			4·50	3·75
16a		2 c. green (24.7.26)			1·50	40
16b		3 c. brown (5.3.27)			3·00	1·00
		ba. "C" of "CA" missing from wmk				
17		4 c. black and red (15.7.22)			1·25	10
18		5 c. green and red/*pale yellow* (12.22)			80	10
19		6 c. claret (29.7.22)			2·50	1·50
19a		6 c. scarlet (26.5.28)			4·00	5·50
20		10 c. black and mauve			2·00	10
21		30 c. purple and carmine (24.7.26)			4·00	5·50
22		50 c. black and orange (21.3.25)			5·50	45·00
23		$1 green and brown (9.2.24)			28·00	70·00
14/23				*Set of 13*	55·00	£120
14/23 Optd "Specimen"				*Set of 13*	£300	

For the 4 c., 5 c. and 6 c. surcharged, see issues under "Japanese Occupation".

1922 (31 Mar). *Malaya–Borneo Exhibition, Singapore. Optd with T 2 by Govt Survey Office, Khota Bharu.*

(a) Wmk Mult Crown CA

30	1	4 c. black and red			3·25	38·00
		a. Opt double			£2500	
31		5 c. green and red/*pale yellow*			4·50	38·00
32		30 c. dull purple and red			4·50	55·00
33		50 c. black and orange			7·50	60·00
34		$1 green and brown			22·00	80·00
35		$2 green and carmine			48·00	£150
36		$5 green and blue			£140	£300

(b) Wmk Mult Script CA

37	1	1 c. green			2·50	38·00
		a. Opt double			£2500	
38		10 c. black and mauve			4·00	48·00
30/8				*Set of 9*	£200	£700

Examples of Nos. 30a and 37a show all three lines of the overprint double.

3   Sultan Ismail   **4**

(Recess Harrison (No. 39) or D.L.R. (No. 39a))

1928–35. *Wmk Mult Script CA. P 12.*

39	3	$1 blue (Perf S. £60)			11·00	75·00
		a. Perf 14 (1935)			32·00	40·00

(Recess B.W.)

1937 (July)**–40.** *Wmk Mult Script CA. P 12.*

40	4	1 c. grey-olive and yellow			30	55
41		2 c. green			2·50	10
42		4 c. scarlet			4·75	70
43		5 c. red-brown			4·75	10
44		6 c. lake (10.37)			11·00	5·50
45		8 c. grey-olive			4·75	10
46		10 c. purple (10.37)			22·00	2·75
47		12 c. blue			3·25	4·00
48		25 c. vermilion and violet			4·75	3·50
49		30 c. violet and scarlet (10.37)			40·00	16·00
50		40 c. orange and blue-green			8·00	23·00
51		50 c. grey-olive and orange (10.37)			55·00	4·75
52		$1 violet and blue-green (10.37)			48·00	12·00
53		$2 red-brown and scarlet (3.40)			£180	£180
54		$5 vermilion and lake (3.40)			£325	£450
40/54				*Set of 15*	£650	£650
40/54 Perf "Specimen"				*Set of 15*	£400	

For above issue surcharged see issues under "Japanese Occupation".

1948 (1 Dec). *Royal Silver Wedding. As Nos. 143/4 of Jamaica.*

55		10 c. violet			60	1·75
56		$5 carmine			24·00	48·00

1949 (10 Oct). *75th Anniv of U.P.U. As Nos. 145/8 of Jamaica.*

57		10 c. purple			25	30
58		15 c. deep blue			1·50	90
59		25 c. orange			60	2·25
60		50 c. blue-black			1·00	2·25
57/60				*Set of 4*	3·00	5·00

5 Sultan Ibrahim   **6** Sultan Yahya Petra and Crest of Kelantan

Normal   No. 62a
        Tiny stop (R. 1/2)

1951 (11 July)**–55.** *Chalk-surfaced paper. Wmk Mult Script CA. P 17½ × 18.*

61	5	1 c. black			30	30
62		2 c. orange			80	35
		a. Tiny stop			22·00	
		b. *Orange-yellow* (11.5.55)			2·25	30
63		3 c. green			3·50	1·25
64		4 c. brown			40	15
65		5 c. bright purple (1.9.52)			45	50
		a. *Bright mauve* (9.12.53)			1·75	50
66		6 c. grey			40	20
67		8 c. scarlet			1·75	3·25
68		8 c. green (1.9.52)			75	1·75
69		10 c. magenta			40	10
70		12 c. scarlet (1.9.52)			75	2·25
71		15 c. ultramarine			3·25	60
72		20 c. black and green			45	5·50
73		20 c. bright blue (1.9.52)			80	25
74		25 c. purple and orange			1·00	55
75		30 c. scarlet and purple (5.9.55)			1·25	1·75
76		35 c. scarlet and purple (1.9.52)			90	1·50
77		40 c. red and purple			5·50	12·00
78		50 c. black and blue			2·00	40
79		$1 blue and purple			7·00	4·25
80		$2 green and scarlet			23·00	20·00
81		$5 green and brown			48·00	40·00
		a. *Green and sepia* (8.12.53)			75·00	80·00
61/81				*Set of 21*	90·00	80·00

1953 (2 June). *Coronation. As No. 153 of Jamaica.*

82		10 c. black and reddish purple			60	90

1957 (26 June)**–63.** *As Nos. 92/102 of Kedah but with inset portrait of Sultan Ibrahim.*

83	9	1 c. black (21.8.57)			10	30
84	10	2 c. orange-red (25.7.57)			50	60
		a. *Red-orange* (17.11.59)			5·50	5·50
85	11	4 c. sepia (21.8.57)			10	10
86	12	5 c. carmine-lake (21.8.57)			10	10
87	13	8 c. myrtle-green (21.8.57)			90	2·50
88	14	10 c. deep brown (4.8.57)			1·25	10
89		10 c. deep maroon (19.4.61)			5·50	5·50
90	15	20 c. blue (21.8.57)			1·25	30
91	16	50 c. black and blue (p 12½) (25.7.57)			50	50
		a. Perf 12½ × 13 (28.6.60)			1·00	30
92	17	$1 ultramarine & reddish pur (25.7.57)			4·50	1·50
93	18	$2 bronze-grn & scar (p 12½) (21.8.57)			11·00	6·00
		a. Perf 13 × 12½ (9.4.63)			15·00	18·00
94	19	$5 brown and bronze-green (p 12½)			15·00	12·00
		a. Perf 13 × 12½ (13.8.63)			22·00	25·00
83/94				*Set of 12*	35·00	26·00

The 6, 12, 25 and 30 c. values used with this issue were Nos. 1/4 of Malayan Federation.

(Photo Harrison)

1961 (17 July). *Coronation of the Sultan. W w 12. P 15 × 14.*

95	6	10 c. multicoloured			40	30

---

7 Sultan Yahya Petra   **8** *Vanda hookeriana*

(Recess D.L.R.)

1961–63. *As Nos. 92/8 of Kedah but with inset portrait of Sultan Yahya Petra as in T 7. W w 13. P 12½×13 (vert) or 13×12½ (horiz).*

96		1 c. black (1.3.62)			10	85
97		2 c. orange-red (1.3.62)			10	85
98		4 c. sepia (1.3.62)			20	30
99		5 c. carmine-lake (1.3.62)			20	10
100		8 c. myrtle-green (1.3.62)			6·00	7·00
		a. *Deep green* (15.1.63)			7·00	8·00
101		10 c. deep maroon (2.12.61)			80	10
102		20 c. blue (1.3.62)			3·25	55
96/102				*Set of 7*	9·50	8·50

1965 (15 Nov). *As Nos. 166/72 of Johore but with inset portrait of Sultan Yahya Petra as in T 8. W w 13 (upright).*

103		1 c. multicoloured			10	50
		b. Magenta omitted			85·00	
104		2 c. multicoloured			10	75
105		5 c. multicoloured			15	10
106		6 c. multicoloured			70	1·25
107		10 c. multicoloured			30	10
		a. Red omitted			45·00	
108		15 c. multicoloured			1·50	20
109		20 c. multicoloured			1·50	1·25
		a. Bright purple (blooms) omitted			60·00	
		b. Yellow (leaves) omitted			30·00	
103/9				*Set of 7*	3·75	3·75

The 5 c. and 10 c. exist on PVA gum as well as gum arabic.

The higher values used with this issue were Nos. 20/27 of Malaysia (National Issues).

1970 (20 Nov). *As Nos. 103 and 107 but W w 13 (sideways).*

110	8	1 c. multicoloured			1·25	6·00
111	—	10 c. multicoloured			3·00	3·75

9 *Parthenos sylvia*   **10** *Lagerstroemia speciosa*

1971 (1 Feb)**–78.** *As Nos. 175/87 of Johore but with portrait of Sultan Yahya Petra and arms, as in T 9. (a) Litho by Bradbury, Wilkinson.*

112		1 c. multicoloured			30	1·50
113		2 c. multicoloured			40	1·50
114		5 c. multicoloured			1·25	30
115		6 c. multicoloured			1·25	1·75
116		10 c. multicoloured			1·25	20
117		15 c. multicoloured			1·25	10
		a. Black (state inscription, portrait and arms) omitted			£100	
118		20 c. multicoloured			1·75	1·00
112/18				*Set of 7*	6·75	5·50

(b) Photo by Harrison (1977–78)

119		1 c. multicoloured			70	3·75
120		5 c. multicoloured			5·00	3·25
121		10 c. multicoloured			5·50	2·75
122		15 c. multicoloured			10·00	75
119/22				*Set of 4*	19·00	9·50

The higher values used with this issue were Nos. 64/71 of Malaysia (National Issues).

For differences between litho and photo printings, see after Johore No. 187.

On No. 117a only the country inscription, portrait and arms are omitted, the remainder of the black printing being as normal. The design was produced using two black plates, one for the main design, value and inscription and the other to apply the state name, head and arms. It is this plate which is omitted from No. 117a.

1979 (30 Apr). *As Nos. 188/94 of Johore but with portrait of Sultan Yahya Petra as in T 10.*

123		1 c. *Rafflesia hasseltii*			10	60
124		2 c. *Pterocarpus indicus*			10	60
125		5 c. Type **10**			10	50
126		10 c. *Durio zibethinus*			15	10
127		15 c. *Hibiscus rosa-sinensis*			15	10
128		20 c. *Rhododendron scortechinii*			20	10
129		25 c. *Etlingera elatior* (inscr "*Phaeomeria speciosa*")			40	50
123/9				*Set of 7*	1·00	2·00

For higher values used in conjunction with this series see Nos. 190/7 of Malaysia (National Issues).

11 Sultan Tengku Ismail Petra   **12** Black Pepper

(Des M. A. B. bin Saman. Litho Harrison)

1980 (30 Mar). *Coronation of Sultan Tengku Ismail Petra.* P 14.
130	**11**	10 c. multicoloured	..	40	75
131		15 c. multicoloured	.. .. ..	40	15
132		50 c. multicoloured	..	90	2·75
130/2 ..		.. .. ..	*Set of 3*	1·50	3·25

1983–86.* *As Nos. 125/6 and 128 but without wmk.*
135	5 c. Type **10** (1986) ..		.. ..	75	1·50
136	10 c. *Durio zibethinus* (18.9.84)			30	60
138	20 c. *Rhododendron scortechinii* (blackish brown background) (1983)		.. ..	19·00	1·50
138a	20 c. *Rhododendron scortechinii* (bronze-green background) (5.10.83) ..		..	50	50

*There was no official release date for these stamps. Dates shown are the earliest recorded from postmarks and may be revised if earlier examples are reported.

For details of the shade differences between watermarked and unwatermarked printings see after Johore No. 200*a*.

On Nos. 135/6 and 138*a* the portrait and state arms have been redrawn smaller.

1986 (25 Oct)–**97.** *As Nos. 202/8 of Johore, but with portrait of Sultan Ismail Petra as in T* **12.** P 12.
140	1 c. Coffee	.. ..	..	10	10
141	2 c. Coconuts	..	..	10	10
	f. Perf 14³/₄×14¹/₂ (1994)		..	3·25	50
142	5 c. Cocoa	..	..	10	10
	c. Perf 14×13³/₄	..	..	2·25	30
143	10 c. Type **12**	..	..	10	10
	c. Perf 14×13³/₄ (1995)	..	..	3·25	50
144	15 c. Rubber	..	..	10	10
145	20 c. Oil palm	..	..	10	10
	c. Perf 14×13³/₄ (1995) ..		..	3·25	50
146	30 c. Rice ..	..	..	15	20
	c. Perf 14×13³/₄ (1994) ..		..	1·00	25
	cw. Wmk inverted	..	..	6·50	
	e. Perf 14×14¹/₂ (1997) ..		..	2·25	20
	f. Perf 14³/₄×14¹/₂	..	..		
140/6	.. ..	..	*Set of 7*	50	55

STAMP BOOKLETS

1927 (June). *Black on white (No. SB1) or black on grey (No. SB2) covers. Stapled.*
SB1	36 c. booklet containing thirty-six 1 c. (No. 15) in blocks of 6		£2000
SB2	96 c. booklet containing twenty-four 4 c. (No. 17) in blocks of 6		£2000

1927 (Dec). *Black on white (No. SB3) or on grey (No. SB4) covers. Stapled.*
SB3	40 c. booklet containing forty 1 c. (No. 15) in blocks of 10		£2000
SB4	80 c. booklet containing twenty 4 c. (No. 17) in blocks of 10		£2000

1973 (8 Dec). *Cover as Type B* **1** *of Johore, but inscr* "KELANTAN". *Stitched.*
SB5	$3 booklet containing eight 5 c., 10 c. and twelve 15 c. (Nos. 114, 116/17) in blocks of 4 ..		27·00

1979 (1 Dec). *Cover as No. SB5 of Johore, but inscr* "KELANTAN". *Stitched.*
SB6	$3 booklet containing eight 5 c., 10 c., and twelve 15 c. (Nos. 125/7) in blocks of 4 ..		10·00

No. SB6 exists with two different versions of the back cover.

1987 (1 June). *Cover as Type B* **2** *of Johore, but inscr* "KELANTAN". *Stapled.*
SB7	$2 booklet containing 5 c., 10 c., 15 c. and 20 c. (Nos. 142/5) in blocks of 4		8·50

1992 (1 July). *"Kuala Lumpur '92" International Philatelic Exhibition. Cover as Type B* **3** *of Johore, but inscr* "Kelantan". *Stamps attached by selvedge.*
SB8	$3 booklet containing 30 c. (No. 146) in block of 10		8·50

1993. *Covers as Nos. SB8/9 of Johore, but inscr* "Kelantan". *Stamps attached by selvedge.*
SB9	$2 booklet containing 20 c. (No. 145) in block of 10		1·00
SB10	$3 booklet containing 30 c. (No. 146) in block of 10		1·50

MALACCA

One of the Straits Settlements.
Issues from 1965 are inscribed "MELAKA".

1948 (1 Dec). *Royal Silver Wedding. As Nos. 143/4 of Jamaica.*
1	10 c. violet	.. ..	30	70
2	$5 brown	.. ..	26·00	35·00

1949 (1 Mar)–**52**. *As T 58 of Straits Settlements, but inscr "MALACCA" at foot. Wmk Mult Script CA. Chalk-surfaced paper. P 17½ × 18.*
3	1 c. black	.. ..	30	70
4	2 c. orange	.. ..	70	45
5	3 c. green	.. ..	30	1·75
6	4 c. brown	.. ..	20	10
6a	5 c. bright purple (1.9.52)	..	45	1·50
7	6 c. grey	.. ..	60	85
8	8 c. scarlet	.. ..	30	5·50
8a	8 c. green (1.9.52)	..	85	4·50
9	10 c. purple	.. ..	20	10
9a	12 c. scarlet (1.9.52)	..	95	4·25
10	15 c. ultramarine	..	70	60
11	20 c. black and green	..	30	6·00
11a	20 c. bright blue (1.9.52)	..	1·75	2·50
12	25 c. purple and orange	..	30	70
12a	35 c. scarlet and purple (1.9.52)		1·00	3·00
13	40 c. red and purple	..	1·25	11·00
14	50 c. black and blue	..	75	1·25
15	$1 blue and purple	..	7·00	19·00
16	$2 green and scarlet..	..	20·00	21·00
17	$5 green and brown ..	..	42·00	35·00
3/17	.. ..	*Set of 20*	70·00	£110

1949 (10 Oct). *75th Anniv of U.P.U. As Nos. 145/8 of Jamaica.*
18	10 c. purple	.. ..	20	45
19	15 c. deep blue ..	..	1·40	1·75
20	25 c. orange	..	45	3·75
21	50 c. blue-black	..	1·00	4·00
18/21	.. ..	*Set of 4*	2·75	9·00

1953 (2 June). *Coronation. As No. 153 of Jamaica.*
22	10 c. black and reddish purple	..	55	75

1 Queen Elizabeth II   **2 Copra**

1954 (9 June)–**57**. *Chalk-surfaced paper. Wmk Mult Script CA. P 17½×18.*
23	**1**	1 c. black (27.4.55)	..	10	60
24		2 c. yellow-orange (27.4.55)	..	30	1·00
25		4 c. brown	..	40	10
		a. Pale brown (24.4.57)	..	5·00	3·50
26		5 c. bright purple (12.7.54)	..	30	2·00
27		6 c. grey	..	10	30
28		8 c. green (5.1.55)	..	30	2·00
29		10 c. brown-purple (1.7.54)	..	50	10
		a. Reddish purple (27.3.57)	..	1·25	30
30		12 c. rose-red (5.1.55)	..	20	2·25
31		20 c. bright blue (5.1.55)	..	20	1·00
32		25 c. brown-purple & yellow-orge (27.4.55)		20	1·00
33		30 c. rose-red and brown-purple (5.9.55)		20	30
34		35 c. rose-red and brown-purple (8.9.54)		20	80
35		50 c. black and bright blue (5.1.55)		30	1·75
36		$1 bright blue and brown-purple (8.9.54)		5·00	6·00
37		$2 emerald and scarlet (27.4.55)		22·00	30·00
38		$5 emerald and brown (27.4.55)		23·00	38·00
23/38	..		*Set of 16*	48·00	75·00

1957. *As Nos. 92/102 of Kedah but with inset portrait of Queen Elizabeth II.*
39	**9**	1 c. black (21.8)	..	10	40
40	**10**	2 c. orange-red (25.7)	..	10	40
41	**11**	4 c. sepia (21.8)	..	10	10
42	**12**	5 c. carmine-lake (21.8)	..	10	10
43	**13**	8 c. myrtle-green (21.8)	..	1·25	2·50
44	**14**	10 c. deep brown (4.8)	..	30	10
45	**15**	20 c. blue (26.6)	..	30	40
46	**16**	50 c. black and blue (25.7)	..	30	50
47	**17**	$1 ultramarine & reddish purple (25.7)		2·25	2·50
48	**18**	$2 bronze-green and scarlet (21.8)		11·00	17·00
49	**19**	$5 brown and bronze-green (26.6)		14·00	29·00
39/49			*Set of 11*	26·00	48·00

The 6, 12, 25 and 30 c. values used with this issue were Nos. 1/4 of Malayan Federation.

(Recess D.L.R.)

1960 (15 Mar)–**62**. *As Nos. 39/49, but with inset picture of Melaka tree and Pelandok (mouse deer) as in T 2. W w 12. P 13 × 12½ (1 c. to 8 c.), $2, $5), 12½ × 13 (10 c. to 50 c.) or 13½ ($1).*
50	1 c. black	.. ..	10	30
51	2 c. orange-red	..	10	40
52	4 c. sepia	..	10	10
53	5 c. carmine-lake	..	10	10
54	8 c. myrtle-green	..	2·50	2·50
55	10 c. deep maroon	..	30	10
56	20 c. blue	..	50	60
57	50 c. black and blue	..	40	60
	a. Black and ultramarine (9.1.62)	..	1·50	60
58	$1 ultramarine and reddish purple	..	1·75	2·50
59	$2 bronze-green and scarlet	..	4·50	6·50
60	$5 brown and bronze-green	..	9·00	12·00
50/60	.. ..	*Set of 11*	17·00	23·00

3 *Vanda hookeriana*   **4** *Papilio demoleus*

1965 (15 Nov)–**68**. *As Nos. 166/72 of Johore but with Arms of Malacca inset and inscr "MELAKA" as in T 3. W w 13 (upright).*
61	1 c. multicoloured	..	10	90
62	2 c. multicoloured	..	10	90
63	5 c. multicoloured	..	10	10
	b. Yellow (flower) omitted	..	28·00	
	c. Red omitted	..	40·00	
64	6 c. multicoloured	..	30	55
65	10 c. multicoloured	..	20	10
66	15 c. multicoloured	..	1·75	40
67	20 c. multicoloured (purple-brn background)		2·25	90
	a Red-brown background (2.4.68)		3·50	2·00
61/7	.. ..	*Set of 7*	4·00	3·50

The 5 c., 6 c., 10 c. and 20 c. exist with PVA gum as well as gum arabic.
The higher values used with this issue were Nos. 20/27 of Malaysia (National Issues).

1970. *As Nos. 61 and 65 but W w 13 (sideways).*
68	**3**	1 c. multicoloured (27.5.70)	..	1·50	6·50
69	—	10 c. multicoloured (20.11.70)	..	4·75	6·50

1971 (1 Feb)–**78**. *As Nos. 175/87 of Johore but with arms of Malacca and inscr "melaka", as in T 4. (a) Litho by Bradbury, Wilkinson.*
70	1 c. multicoloured	..	40	1·50
71	2 c. multicoloured	..	60	1·50
72	5 c. multicoloured	..	1·00	60
73	6 c. multicoloured	..	1·00	2·25
74	10 c. multicoloured	..	1·00	50
75	15 c. multicoloured	..	1·75	20
76	20 c. multicoloured	..	1·75	1·75
70/6	.. ..	*Set of 7*	6·75	7·50

(b) Photo by Harrison (1977–78)
77	1 c. multicoloured	..	4·50	7·00
78	5 c. multicoloured	..	1·50	1·75
79	10 c. multicoloured	..	4·50	1·50
80	15 c. multicoloured	..	12·00	50
81	20 c. multicoloured	..	4·25	3·00
77/81	.. ..	*Set of 5*	24·00	12·00

The higher values used with this issue were Nos. 64/71 of Malaysia (National Issues).
For differences between litho and photo printings, see after Johore No. 187.

5 *Durio zibethinus*   **6** Rubber

1979 (30 Apr). *As Nos. 188/94 of Johore but with Arms of Malacca and inscr "melaka" as in T 5.*
82	1 c. *Rafflesia hasseltii*	..	10	80
83	2 c. *Pterocarpus indicus*	..	10	80
84	5 c. *Lagerstroemia speciosa*	..	15	70
85	10 c. Type **5**	..	20	20
86	15 c. *Hibiscus rosa-sinensis*	..	20	10
87	20 c. *Rhododendron scortechinii*	..	25	10
88	25 c. *Etlingera elatior* (inscr "*Phaeomeria speciosa*")	..	45	60
82/8	.. ..	*Set of 7*	1·25	2·75

For higher values used in conjunction with this series see Nos. 190/7 of Malaysia (National Issues).

1983 (26 Oct)–**86.*** *As Nos. 85/7 but without wmk.*
92	10 c. Type **5** (19.4.85)	..	1·75	3·25
93	15 c. *Hibiscus rosa-sinensis* (9.86)	..	55	55
94	20 c. *Rhododendron scortechinii* (blackish brown background)	..	17·00	2·75
94a	20 c. *Rhododendron scortechinii* (bronze-green background) (13.6.84)	..	75	1·00

*There was no official release date for these stamps. Dates shown are the earliest recorded from postmarks and may be revised if earlier examples are reported.
For details of the shade differences between watermarked and unwatermarked printings see after Johore No. 200a.
On Nos. 92/3 and 94a the distance between the coat of arms and the value is greater than on Nos. 85, 87 and 94.

1986 (25 Oct)–**96**. *As Nos. 202/8 of Johore, but with Arms of Malacca and inscr "MELAKA" as in T 6. P 12.*
96	1 c. Coffee	..	10	10
	w. Wmk inverted	..		
97	2 c. Coconuts	..	10	10
98	5 c. Cocoa	..	10	10
	c. Perf 14×13¾ (1995)	..	1·00	20
	ca. Wmk sideways (1996)	..	4·25	
99	10 c. Black pepper	..	10	10
	c. Perf 14×13¾ (1995)	..	1·00	20
	f. Perf 14¾×14½ (1995)	..	1·50	10
100	15 c. Type **6**	..	10	10
	w. Wmk inverted (1991)	..	7·00	
101	20 c. Oil palm	..	10	10
	aw. Wmk inverted	..		
	c. Perf 14×13¾ (1994)	..	1·00	10
102	30 c. Rice	..	15	20
	c. Perf 14×13¾ (1994)	..	3·50	30
	cw. Wmk inverted (1996)	..	6·50	
	e. Perf 14¾×14½	..	3·75	30
	ew. Wmk inverted	..	6·50	
	f. Perf 14¾×14½ (1996)	..	5·50	40
96/102	.. ..	*Set of 7*	50	55

STAMP BOOKLETS

1973 (8 Dec). *Cover as Type B 1 of Johore, but inscr "MELAKA". Stitched.*
SB1	$3 booklet containing eight 5 c., 10 c. and twelve 15 c. (Nos. 72, 74/5) in blocks of 4	..	27·00

1979 (1 Dec). *Cover as No. SB5 of Johore, but inscr "MELAKA". Stitched.*
SB2	$3 booklet containing eight 5 c., 10 c. and twelve 15 c. (Nos. 84/6) in blocks of 4	..	10·00

No. SB2 exists with two different versions of the back cover.

1987 (1 June). *Cover as Type B 2 of Johore, but inscr "MELAKA". Stapled.*
SB3	$2 booklet containing 5 c., 10 c., 15 c. and 20 c. (Nos. 98/101) in blocks of 4	..	8·50

1992 (1 July). *"Kuala Lumpur '92" International Philatelic Exhibition. Cover as Type B 3 of Johore, but inscr "Melaka". Stamps attached by selvedge.*
SB4	$3 booklet containing 30 c. (No. 102) in block of 10		8·50

1993. *Covers as Nos. SB8/9 of Johore, but inscr "Melaka". Stamps attached by selvedge.*
SB5	$2 booklet containing 20 c. (No. 101) in block of 10		1·00
SB6	$3 booklet containing 30 c. (No. 102) in block of 10		1·50

NEGRI SEMBILAN

A federation of smaller states reconstituted in 1886. Sungei Ujong, taken under British protection in 1874, was absorbed into Negri Sembilan by Treaty of 8 August 1895. The Negri Sembilan federation joined the Federated Malay States in 1896.

A. SUNGEI UJONG

Until 1 January 1899, when the Federated Malay States joined the U.P.U., mail for addresses outside Malaya was franked with the stamps of the STRAITS SETTLEMENTS.

PRICES FOR STAMPS ON COVER

Nos. 1/14	
Nos. 15/27	*from* × 25
Nos. 28/36	*from* × 8
Nos. 37/49	*from* × 10
Nos. 50/5	*from* × 25

(1)

1878. *No. 11 of Straits Settlements handstamped with T 1.*
1 2 c. brown £1800 £2000
This overprint on India No. 54 is bogus.

SUNGEI	SUNGEI	SUNGEI
(2) (Narrow letters)	(3) ("N" wide)	(4) ("S" wide)

UJONG	UJONG	UJONG
(5) ("N" wide)	(6) (Narrow letters, "UJ" close together)	(7) Narrow letters, evenly spaced)

1881. *No. 11 of Straits Settlements optd with T 2/7.*

2	2+5	2 c. brown	.. ..	..£2750 £2500
3	3+5	2 c. brown	.. ..	..£1800 £1700
4	2+6	2 c. brown	.. ..	..£180
		a. Opt Type 6 double		..£1300
5	4+6	2 c. brown	.. ..	..£550
6	2+7	2 c. brown	.. ..	..£300

The two lines of this surcharge were applied as separate operations. On Nos. 2/3 "SUNGEI" was printed as a triplet, probably 2+3+3, "UJONG" being added by a single unit handstamp. Nos. 4 and 5 come from a similar triplet, 4+4+5, completed by another single unit handstamp. No. 6 comes from a single type triplet with the second line added as a triplet instead of by a single unit handstamp.
The 10 c. slate overprinted Types 2 + 7 is bogus.

SUNGEI	SUNGEI	SUNGEI
(8) ("N" and "E" wide)	(9) ("SUN" and "E" wide)	(10) ("SUN" wide)

SUNGEI	SUNGEI
(11) ("S" wide)	(12) (Narrow letters)

UJONG	UJONG
(13) ("U" and "NG" wide)	(14) (Narrow letters)

1881. *No. 11 of Straits Settlements optd with T 8/14.*

7	8+13	2 c. brown	.. ..	..£160
8	9+13	2 c. brown	.. ..	..£190
9	10+13	2 c. brown	.. ..	..£160
10	11+14	2 c. brown	.. ..	..£200
		a. "S" inverted		..£2500
11	12+14	2 c. brown	.. ..	..£140

Nos. 7/11 also had the two lines of the overprint applied at separate operations. "SUNGEI" as a triplet, either 7+8+9 or 10+11+11, and "UJONG" as a single unit.

S.U.

(15)

1882. *Nos. 50/1 of Straits Settlements optd as T 15.*

12	2 c. brown (with stops)..	.. ..	..£200
13	2 c. brown (without stops)	..	..£225 £275
14	4 c. rose (with stops)	.. ..	..£2250 £2250

Each of the above was applied by a triplet setting.
Examples of Straits Settlements No. 11 with a similar overprint, including stops, are trials which were not issued.

SUNGEI	SUNGEI	UJONG
(16) ("S" and "E" wide)	(17) ("E" wide)	(18) ("N" wide)

1882 (Dec)**–84.** *Nos. 12, 50, 52/3 and 63 of Straits Settlements optd with T 11/12, 14 and 16/18.*

15	12+14	2 c. brown	..	£450 £325
16	11+14	2 c. brown	..	£700 £450
17	12+14	2 c. pale rose (1884)	..	£150 £170
18	11+14	2 c. pale rose (1884)	..	£150 £170
		a. Opt Type 14 double		
19	16+14	2 c. pale rose (1884)	..	85·00 95·00
20	17+14	2 c. pale rose (1884)	..	95·00 £110
21	12+18	2 c. pale rose (1884)	..	95·00 £110
		a. Opt Type 18 double		
22	12+14	4 c. rose	..	£1000 £1100
23	11+14	4 c. rose	..	£1800 £1900
24	12+14	8 c. orange ..	..	£1200 £900
25	11+14	8 c. orange ..	..	£2250 £1500
26	12+14	10 c. slate	..	£425 £425
27	11+14	10 c. slate	..	£650 £650

Nos. 15/27 had the two lines of the overprint applied by separate triplets. Settings so far identified are Nos. 15+16+15, 17+18+19, 19+20+21, 22+23+22, 24+25+24 and 26+27+26.
The 4 c. rose overprinted Types 16+14 is now believed to be a trial.

UJONG.	UJONG.	UJONG
(19) (With stop. Narrow letters)	(20) (With stop "N" wide)	(21) (Without stop. Narrow letters)

1883–84. *Nos. 50 and 63/4 of Straits Settlements optd with T 12, 16/17 and 19/21.*

28	12+19	2 c. brown	..	40·00 90·00
29	16+19	2 c. brown	..	40·00 90·00
30	12+20	2 c. brown	..	40·00 90·00
31	16+21	2 c. pale rose (1884)	..	80·00 85·00
32	17+21	2 c. pale rose (1884)	..	80·00 85·00
33	12+21	2 c. pale rose (1884)	..	80·00 85·00
34	16+21	4 c. brown (1884)	..	£190 £250
		a. Opt Type 16 double		
		b. Opt Type 21 double		..£1300
35	17+21	4 c. brown (1884)	..	£190 £250
36	12+21	4 c. brown (1884)	..	£190 £250
		a. Opt Type 21 double		..£3750

Nos. 28/36 had the two lines of the overprint applied by separate triplets. Settings were Nos. 28+29+30, 31+32+33 and 34+35+36.
The 8 c. orange overprinted Types 12+19 is now believed to be a trial (*Price £700 unused*).

Sungei Ujong	*SUNGEI UJONG*	SUNGEI UJONG
(22)	(23)	(24)

SUNGEI UJONG	SUNGEI UJONG	SUNGEI UJONG
(25)	(26)	(27)

SUNGEI UJONG	*SUNGEI UJONG.*	SUNGEI UJONG
(28)	(29)	(30)

1885–90. *Nos. 63/a of Straits Settlements optd with T 22/30.*

37	22	2 c. pale rose	.. ..	65·00 75·00
		a. Opt double ..	..	£500 £500
38	23	2 c. pale rose	..	22·00 55·00
		a. Opt double ..		..£550
39	24	2 c. pale rose (1886)	..	95·00 £110
40	25	2 c. pale rose (1886)	..	£120 £130
		a. Opt double ..		
41	26	2 c. pale rose (1886)	..	75·00 85·00
		a. Opt double ..		
42	27	2 c. pale rose (1887)	..	8·00 25·00
43	28	2 c. pale rose (1889)	..	5·00 8·50
		a. Narrow "E" (2 mm wide) (R. 3/4 and 4/3)		..60·00
		c. Opt double ..		..£1300
		d. Bright rose (1890)		7·00 6·50
		da. Narrow "E" (2 mm wide) (R. 3/4 and 4/3) ..		..70·00
		db. Antique "N" in "UJONG" (R. 10/6)		..£110
44	29	2 c. pale rose (1889)	..	75·00 70·00
		a. "UNJOG" (R. 7/3)	..	£3250 £2750
45	30	2 c. bright rose (1890)	..	23·00 13·00
		a. Antique "G" in "SUNGEI" (R. 6/1)		..£180
		b. Antique "G" in "UJONG" (R. 8/3)	..	£180
		c. Pale rose		

All the above overprints had both lines applied at the same operation. Nos. 37/42 were from different triplet settings. The first printing of Type 28 was from a triplet (No. 43) but this was followed by two further settings of 60 (6×10), the first containing No. 43a and the second Nos. 43d/db. Nos. 44/5 were both from settings of 60.

SUNGEI UJONG Two CENTS	SUNGEI UJONG Two CENTS	SUNGEI UJONG *Two* CENTS
(31)	(32)	(33)

SUNGEI UJONG *Two* CENTS
(34)

1882 (Dec)–84. *Nos. 68 of Straits Settlements surch with T 31/4.*

46	31	2 c. on 24 c. green	.. ..	£475 £500
47	32	2 c. on 24 c. green	..	£180 £200
		w. Wmk inverted	..	£350 £375
48	33	2 c. on 24 c. green	..	£475 £500
49	34	2 c. on 24 c. green	..	£110 £130
		a. Antique "G" in "SUNGEI" (R. 6/1)		..£650
		b. Antique "G" in "UJONG" (R. 8/3)		..£650
		w. Wmk inverted		£225 £250

Nos. 46/9 come from the same setting of 60 on which "SUNGEI UJONG" was from the same type as No. 45. No. 46 occurs in row 1. No. 47 from rows 2 to 4, No. 48 from row 5 and No. 49 from rows 6 to 10.

3 CENTS

35 (36) 37

1891–94. *Wmk Crown CA. P 14.*

50	35	2 c. rose	.. ..	24·00 27·00
51		2 c. orange (1894)..	..	1·40 4·25
52		5 c. blue (1893)	.. ..	4·50 5·50
50/2			*Set of 3*	27·00 32·00
50/2 Optd "Specimen"			*Set of 3*	60·00

1894. *Surch as T 36 by De La Rue. Wmk Crown CA. P 14.*

53	35	1 c. on 5 c. green	..	65 70
54		3 c. on 5 c. rose	..	2·00 4·75

1895. *Wmk Crown CA. P 14.*

55	37	3 c. dull purple and carmine	..	6·50 2·00
53/5 Optd "Specimen"			*Set of 3*	60·00

B. NEGRI SEMBILAN

Stamps of the STRAITS SETTLEMENTS were used in Negri Sembilan during 1891, until replaced by the stamps listed below. Until the Federated Malay States joined the U.P.U. On 1 January 1899 Straits Settlements stamps continued to be used for mail to addresses outside Malaya.

PRICES FOR STAMPS ON COVER TO 1945

No. 1	*from* × 200
Nos. 2/4	*from* × 10
Nos. 5/14	*from* × 8
Nos. 15/20	*from* × 10
Nos. 21/49	*from* × 4

Negri Sembilan

(1) 2 3

1891 (Aug?). *No. 63a of Straits Settlements optd with T 1.*
1 2 c. bright rose .. .. .. 2·50 4·25

N.SEMBILAN

Short "N" in "SEMBILAN" (Top left pane R. 8/3)

1891–94. *Wmk Crown CA. P 14.*

2	1	1 c. green (1893)	.. ..	2·75 1·00
3		2 c. rose	.. ..	3·25 6·00
		a. Short "N"		..65·00
4		5 c. blue (1894)	..	28·00 40·00
2/4			*Set of 3*	30·00 42·00
2/4 Optd "Specimen"			*Set of 3*	70·00

1895–99. *Wmk Crown CA. P 14.*

5	3	1 c. dull purple and green (1899)	..	7·50 3·50
6		1 c. dull purple and brown (1898)	..	32·00 £100
7		3 c. dull purple and carmine	..	9·00 85
8		5 c. dull purple and orange-yellow (1897)	..	7·50 6·00
9		8 c. dull purple and ultramarine (1898)..		28·00 16·00
10		10 c. dull purple and orange (1897)	..	27·00 14·00
11		15 c. green and violet (1896)	..	40·00 75·00
12		20 c. green and olive (1897)	..	48·00 38·00
13		25 c. green and carmine (1896)	..	70·00 90·00
14		50 c. green and black (1896)	..	55·00 60·00
5/14			*Set of 10*	£275 £350
5/14 Optd "Specimen"			*Set of 10*	£160

Four cents.

Four cents.

(4) (5)

1898 (Dec)**–1900.** (a) *Surch as T 4.*

15	3	1 c. on 15 c. green and violet (1900)	..	80·00 £170
		a. Raised stop (R. 5/1 and R. 10/1 of each pane) ..	..	£350 £600
16	2	4 c. on 1 c. green	.. ..	1·25 15·00

17	3	4 c. on 3 c. dull purple and carmine	3·00	15·00
	a.	Horiz pair, one without surch	£3250	£3000
	b.	Surch double	£1400	£1000
	ba.	Ditto. "Four cents" albino		† £1000
	c.	Surch inverted	£1100	£1100
	d.	"cents" repeated at left	£1400	£1400
	e.	"Four" repeated at right	£1400	£1400
	f.	Without bar	£600	£475
	g.	Bar double	†	£700
18	2	4 c. on 5 c. blue	1·25	15·00

On Nos. 15 and 17 the bar is at the top of the stamp.
The surcharges were applied as a setting of 30 (6×5).

(b) Surch as T 5

19	3	4 c. on 8 c. dull purple & ultram (G.) (12.98)	2·75	4·00
	a.	Vert pair, one without surch	£3250	£2750
	b.	Surch double		£1500
	c.	Surch double (G.+R.)	£700	£700
20		4 c. on 8 c. dull purple & ultramarine (Bk.)	£900	£950

Care should be taken in distinguishing the true black surcharge, No. 20, from very deep shades of the green surcharge, No. 19.

Pending the arrival of the permanent Federated Malay States issue the stamps of SELANGOR, FEDERATED MALAY STATES provisional overprints, STRAITS SETTLEMENTS and PERAK were used at various times between October 1899 and April 1901.

The general issues for FEDERATED MALAY STATES were used in Negri Sembilan from 29 April 1901 until 1935.

---

6   Arms of Negri Sembilan   **7**

1935 (2 Dec)–**41**. *Wmk Mult Script CA. Ordinary paper (6 c. grey, 15 c.) or chalk-surfaced paper (others). P* 14.

21	6	1 c. black (1.1.36)	85	20
22		2 c. green (1.1.36)	85	20
23		2 c. orange (11.12.41)	3·75	60·00
24		3 c. green (21.8.41)	6·50	8·00
	a.	Ordinary paper	17·00	8·00
25		4 c. orange	70	10
26		5 c. brown (5.12.35)	1·50	10
27		6 c. scarlet (1.1.37)	9·50	2·50
	a.	Stop omitted at right (R. 10/4)	£275	85·00
28		6 c. grey (18.12.41)	4·25	70·00
	a.	Stop omitted at right (R. 10/4)	£120	£425
29		8 c. grey	2·00	10
30		10 c. dull purple (1.1.36)	70	10
31		12 c. bright ultramarine (1.1.36)	1·40	50
32		15 c. ultramarine (1.10.41)	9·00	48·00
33		25 c. dull purple and scarlet (1.4.36)	90	70
34		30 c. dull purple and orange (1.1.36)	3·50	2·00
35		40 c. scarlet and dull purple	85	2·00
36		50 c. black/*emerald* (1.2.36)	3·75	2·25
37		$1 black and red/*blue* (1.4.36)	2·25	3·25
38		$2 green and scarlet (16.5.36)	26·00	16·00
39		$5 green and red/*emerald* (16.5.36)	15·00	48·00
21/39			*Set of 19* 80·00	£225
21/39	Perf "Specimen"		*Set of 19* £250	

The stamps issued in 1941 were printed by Harrison and Sons following bomb damage to the De La Rue works on 29 December 1940.

An 8 c. scarlet was issued but only with opt during Japanese Occupation of Malaya. Unoverprinted specimens result from leakages.

During shortages in 1941 stamps of STRAITS SETTLEMENTS (2 c.), SELANGOR (2 c., 8 c.), PERAK (2 c., 25 c., 50 c.) and PAHANG (8 c.) were issued in Negri Sembilan.

1948 (1 Dec). *Royal Silver Wedding. As Nos. 143/4 of Jamaica.*

40		10 c. violet	15	50
41		$5 green	18·00	28·00

1949 (1 Apr)–**55**. *Chalk-surfaced paper. Wmk Mult Script CA. P* 17½ × 18.

42	7	1 c. black	10	10
43		2 c. orange	10	10
44		3 c. green	10	30
45		4 c. brown	10	10
46		5 c. bright purple (1.9.52)	30	50
	a.	Bright mauve (25.8.53)	30	45
47		6 c. grey	30	30
	a.	Pale grey (25.8.53)	3·25	30
48		8 c. scarlet	30	75
49		8 c. green (1.9.52)	1·50	1·60
50		10 c. purple	20	10
51		12 c. scarlet (1.9.52)	1·50	2·50
52		15 c. ultramarine	2·25	10
53		20 c. black and green	30	75
54		20 c. bright blue (1.9.52)	80	10
55		25 c. purple and orange	30	10
56		30 c. scarlet and purple (5.9.55)	1·25	2·50
57		35 c. scarlet and purple (1.9.52)	70	1·00
58		40 c. red and purple	80	4·75
59		50 c. black and blue	80	20
60		$1 blue and purple	3·00	2·00
61		$2 green and scarlet	12·00	15·00
62		$5 green and brown	50·00	38·00
42/62			*Set of 21* 65·00	60·00

1949 (10 Oct). *75th Anniv of U.P.U. As Nos. 145/8 of Jamaica.*

63		10 c. purple	20	10
64		15 c. deep blue	1·10	2·00
65		25 c. orange	50	2·00
66		50 c. blue-black	1·00	2·50
63/6			*Set of 4* 2·50	6·00

1953 (2 June). *Coronation. As No. 153 of Jamaica.*

67		10 c. black and reddish purple	75	30

1957 (26 June)–**63**. *As Nos. 92/102 of Kedah but with inset Arms of Negri Sembilan.*

68	9	1 c. black (21.8.57)	10	10
69	10	2 c. orange-red (25.7.57)	10	10
70	11	4 c. sepia (21.8.57)	10	10
71	12	5 c. carmine-lake (21.8.57)	10	10
72	13	8 c. myrtle-green (21.8.57)	85	1·40
73	14	10 c. deep brown (4.8.57)	1·25	10
74		10 c. deep maroon (10.1.61)	3·00	10
75	15	20 c. blue	60	10
76	16	50 c. black and blue (*p* 12½) (25.7.57)	30	85
	a.	Perf 12½ × 13 (19.7.60)	30	10
77	17	$1 ultramarine & reddish pur (25.7.57)	1·50	2·00
78	18	$2 bronze-green & scarlet (*p* 12½) (21.8.57)	5·00	12·00
	a.	Perf 13 × 12½ (15.1.63)	13·00	19·00
79	19	$5 brown and bronze-green (*p* 12½)	11·00	16·00
	a.	Perf 13 × 12½ (6.3.62)	22·00	16·00
	ab.	Perf 13 × 12½. *Brown and yellow-olive* (13.11.62)	£225	70·00
68/79			*Set of 12* 21·00	28·00

The 6, 12, 25 and 30 c. values used with this issue were Nos. 1/4 of Malayan Federation.

8 Tuanku Munawir   **9** *Vanda hookeriana*

(Photo Enschedé)

1961 (17 Apr). *Installation of Tuanku Munawir as Yang di-Pertuan Besar of Negri Sembilan. No wmk. P* 14 × 13.

80	8	10 c. multicoloured	30	40

1965 (15 Nov)–**69**. *As Nos. 166/72 of Johore but with Arms of Negri Sembilan inset and inscr* "NEGERI SEMBILAN" *as in T* 9. W w 13 (*upright*).

81		1 c. multicoloured	10	75
82		2 c. multicoloured	10	85
	w.	Wmk inverted	2·00	
83		5 c. multicoloured	40	10
	b.	Yellow omitted	32·00	
84		6 c. multicoloured	40	40
85		10 c. multicoloured	40	10
86		15 c. multicoloured	80	10
87		20 c. jet-black and multicoloured	1·25	75
	a.	Blackish brown & mult (19.12.69)	3·75	1·00
81/7			*Set of 7* 3·00	2·50

The 2 c., 6 c., 15 c. and 20 c. exist with PVA gum as well as gum arabic.

The higher values used with this issue were Nos. 20/27 of Malaysia (National Issues).

See also No. 90.

10 Negri Sembilan Crest and   **11** *Hebomoia glaucippe*
Tuanku Ja'afar

(Des Z. Noor. Photo Japanese Govt Ptg Wks)

1968 (8 Apr). *Installation of Tuanku Ja'afar as Yang di-Pertuan Besar of Negri Sembilan. P* 13.

88	10	15 c. multicoloured	15	40
89		50 c. multicoloured	30	1·25

1970 (27 May). *As No. 81 but with W w 13 (sideways).*

90	9	1 c. multicoloured	2·25	6·00

1971 (1 Feb)–**78**. *As Nos. 175/87 of Johore but with Arms of Negri Sembilan and inscr* "negeri sembilan", *as in T* 11.

(a) Litho by Bradbury, Wilkinson

91		1 c. multicoloured	40	1·25
92		2 c. multicoloured	60	1·25
93		5 c. multicoloured	90	10
94		6 c. multicoloured	90	1·50
95		10 c. multicoloured	90	10
96		15 c. multicoloured	1·25	10
97		20 c. multicoloured	1·25	40
91/7			*Set of 7* 5·50	4·00

(b) Photo by Harrison (1977–78)

98		2 c. multicoloured	95	4·50
99		5 c. multicoloured	95	1·50
100		10 c. multicoloured	9·00	1·25
101		15 c. multicoloured	12·00	30
102		20 c. multicoloured	2·50	1·75
98/102			*Set of 5* 23·00	8·50

The higher values used with issue were Nos. 64/71 of Malaysia (National Issues).

For differences between litho and photo printings, see after Johore No. 187.

COVER PRICES

Cover factors are quoted at the beginning of each country for most issues to 1945. An explanation of the system can be found on page x. The factors quoted do not, however, apply to philatelic covers.

---

12 *Hibiscus rosa-sinensis*   **13** Oil Palm

1979 (30 Apr). *As Nos. 188/94 of Johore but with Arms of Negri Sembilan and inscr* "negeri sembilan" *as in T* 12.

103		1 c. *Rafflesia hasseltii*	10	75
104		2 c. *Pterocarpus indicus*	10	75
105		5 c. *Lagerstroemia speciosa*	15	20
106		10 c. *Durio zibethinus*	20	10
107		15 c. Type 12	20	10
108		20 c. *Rhododendron scortechinii*	25	10
109		25 c. *Etlingera elatior* (inscr "*Phaeomeria speciosa*")	45	20
103/9			*Set of 7* 1·25	1·75

For higher values used in conjunction with this series see Nos. 190/7 of Malaysia (National Issues).

1983 (Oct)–**84**.* *As Nos. 105/8 but without wmk.*

112		5 c. *Lagerstroemia speciosa* (25.5.84)	1·00	1·75
113		10 c. *Durio zibethinus* (24.10.84)	30	50
114		15 c. Type 12 (11.8.84)	50	45
115		20 c. *Rhododendron scortechinii* (blackish brown background)	23·00	1·25
115a		20 c. *Rhododendron scortechinii* (bronze-green background) (1983)	30	40

*There was no official release date for these stamps. Dates shown are the earliest recorded from postmarks and may be revised if earlier examples are reported.

For details of the shade differences between watermarked and unwatermarked printings see after Johore No. 200a.

Nos. 112/14 and 115a show a larger crest, further from the face value than on Nos. 105/8 and 115.

1986 (25 Oct)–**96**. *As Nos. 202/8 of Johore, but with Arms of Negri Sembilan and inscr* "NEGERI SEMBILAN" *as in T* 13. *P* 12.

117		1 c. Coffee	10	10
118		2 c. Coconuts	10	10
119		5 c. Cocoa	10	10
	c.	Perf 14×13¾ (1996)	1·00	10
	ca.	Wmk sideways	4·25	
120		10 c. Black pepper	10	10
	c.	Perf 14×13¾ (1995)	1·00	10
	e.	Perf 14×14½ (1996)	2·25	15
	f.	Perf 14¾×14½ (1996)	7·50	40
121		15 c. Rubber	10	10
	w.	Wmk inverted (1993)	8·50	
122		20 c. Type 13	10	10
	aw.	Wmk inverted		
	c.	Perf 14×13¾ (1994)	2·50	10
123		30 c. Rice	15	20
	c.	Perf 14×13¾ (1994)	3·25	20
	cw.	Wmk inverted	8·00	
	e.	Perf 14×14½	4·50	20
	ew.	Wmk inverted	6·50	
	f.	Perf 14¾×14½ (1996)	3·25	20
117/23			*Set of 7* 50	55

STAMP BOOKLETS

1935. *Stapled.*
SB1 $1 booklet containing twenty 5 c. (No. 26) in blocks of 10

SB2 $1.30, booklet containing 5 c. and 8 c. (Nos. 26, 29), each in block of 10

1973 (8 Dec). *Cover as Type B* **1** *of Johore, but inscr* "N. SEMBILAN". *Stitched.*
SB3 $3 booklet containing eight 5 c., 10 c. and twelve 15 c. (Nos. 93, 95/6) in blocks of 4   25·00
Examples of No. SB3 exist with a white label giving revised postage rates.

1979 (1 Dec). *Cover as No. SB5 of Johore, but inscr* "NEGERI SEMBILAN". *Stitched.*
SB4 $3 booklet containing eight 5 c., 10 c., and twelve 15 c. (Nos. 105/7) in blocks of 4   9·00
No. SB4 exists with two different versions of the back cover.

1987 (1 June). *Cover as Type B* **2** *of Johore, but inscr* "NEGERI SEMBILAN". *Stapled.*
SB5 $2 booklet containing 5 c., 10 c., 15 c. and 20 c. (Nos. 119/22) in blocks of 4   8·00

1992 (1 July). "*Kuala Lumpur '92" International Philatelic Exhibition. Cover as Type B* **3** *of Johore, but inscr* "Negeri Sembilan". *Stamps attached by selvedge.*
SB6 $3 booklet containing 30 c. (No. 123) in block of 10   8·00

1993. *Covers as Nos. SB8/9 of Johore, but inscr* "Negeri Sembilan". *Stamps attached by selvedge.*
SB7 $2 booklet containing 20 c. (No. 122) in block of 10   1·00
SB8 $3 booklet containing 30 c. (No. 123) in block of 10   1·50

PAHANG

The first British Resident was appointed in 1888. Pahang joined the Federated Malay States in 1896.

Until 1 January 1899, when the Federated Malay States joined the U.P.U., mail for addresses outside Malaya was franked with stamps of the STRAITS SETTLEMENTS.

PRICES FOR STAMPS ON COVER TO 1945

No. 1	*from* × 50
Nos. 2/3	
No. 4	*from* × 100
No. 5	
No. 6	*from* × 100
Nos. 7/10	*from* × 8
Nos. 11/13	*from* × 25
Nos. 14/16	*from* × 20
Nos. 17/*a*	—
No. 18/*d*	*from* × 6
Nos. 19/24	*from* × 8
No. 25	*from* × 20
Nos. 26/7	
No. 28	*from* × 15
Nos. 29/46	*from* × 6

PAHANG   PAHANG   PAHANG

(1)   (2)   (2*a*) (Antique letters)

1889 (Jan). *Nos. 52/3 and 63 of Straits Settlements optd with T* 1.

1	2 c. pale rose		80·00	45·00
2	8 c. orange		£1600	£1400
3	10 c. slate		£225	£250

All three values were overprinted from a triplet setting, but the 2 c. also exists from a similar setting of 30 or 60.

1889. *No. 63 of Straits Settlements optd with T* 2.

4	2 c. pale rose		8·50	13·00
	a. Bright rose		3·75	8·00
	ab. Opt Type 2a. Antique letters		£225	£250

No. 4 was overprinted from a setting of 60. No. 4ab usually occurs on R. 10/1, but has also been found on R. 8/1 as the result of revision of the setting.

PAHANG   PAHANG

(3)   (4)

1890. *No. 63a of Straits Settlements optd.*

5	3	2 c. bright rose		£3250	£900
6	4	2 c. bright rose		75·00	14·00
		w. Wmk inverted			

No. 5 may have been overprinted from a triplet setting. No. 6 was from a setting of 60.

PAHANG *Two* CENTS   PAHANG *Two* CENTS

(5)   (6)

PAHANG *Two* CENTS   PAHANG *Two* CENTS

(7)   (8)

1891. *No. 68 of Straits Settlements surch with T* 5/8.

7	5	2 c. on 24 c. green		£100	£110
8	6	2 c. on 24 c. green		£475	£550
9	7	2 c. on 24 c. green		£150	£170
10	8	2 c. on 24 c. green		£475	£550

Nos. 7/10 come from one setting used to surcharge the panes of sixty. No. 7 occurs in rows 1 to 5, No. 8 on row 6, No. 9 on rows 7 to 9 and No. 10 on row 10.

9   10

1891–95. *Wmk Crown CA. P* 14.

11	9	1 c. green (1895)		3·75	3·00
12		2 c. rose		4·50	3·00
13		5 c. blue (1893)		9·50	32·00
11/13			*Set of 3*	16·00	35·00
11/13 Optd "Specimen"			*Set of 3*	60·00	

MINIMUM PRICE

The minimum price quote is 10p which represents a handling charge rather than a basis for valuing common stamps. For further notes about prices see introductory pages.

Following an increase of postage rates on 1 March 1894 1 cent stamps of STRAITS SETTLEMENTS were used in Pahang until the autumn of the following year.

1895–99. *Wmk Crown CA. P* 14.

14	10	3 c. dull purple and carmine		5·50	2·75
15		4 c. dull purple and carmine (1899)		16·00	11·00
16		5 c. dull purple and olive-yellow (1897)		20·00	20·00
14/16			*Set of 3*	38·00	30·00
14/16 Optd "Specimen"			*Set of 3*	60·00	

1897 (2 Aug). *No. 13 bisected, surch in red manuscript at Kuala Lipis and initialled "JFO". (a) Bisected horizontally.*

17	2 c. on half 5 c. blue (surch "2" and bar across "5")			—	£1400
17a	3 c. on half of 5 c. blue (surch "3")			£4000	£1400

(b) Bisected diagonally

18	2 c. on half of 5 c. blue (surch "2" and bar across "5")			£1100	£350
	a. Unsevered pair. Nos. 18 and 18d			£8500	£3750
	b. Se-tenant pair. Nos. 18 and 18d			£3500	£850
	c. Surch in black manuscript			£7500	£2750
18d	3 c. on half of 5 c. blue (surch "3")			£1100	£350
	dc. Surch in black manuscript			£7500	£2750

The initials are those of John Fortescue Owen, the District Treasurer at Kuala Lipis.

Nos. 17 and 18 only occur on the bottom half of the 5 c. and Nos. 17*a* and 18*d* on the top half. No. 18*a* is a complete example of No. 13 showing the two surcharges. No. 18*b* is a *se-tenant* pair of bisects from adjoining stamps.

Pahang.   Pahang.

(11)   (12)

1898–99. *(a) Nos. 72/5 of Perak optd with T* 11.

19	10 c. dull purple and orange		15·00	25·00
20	25 c. green and carmine		80·00	£130
21	50 c. dull purple and greenish black		£250	£275
22	50 c. green and black (1899)		£180	£190

(b) Nos. 76 and 79 of Perak optd with T 12.

23	$1 green and pale green		£275	£300
24	$5 green and ultramarine		£800	£950

Pahang   —————

Four cents   Four cents.

(13)   (14)

1898. *(a) No. 71 of Perak surch with T* 13.

25	4 c. on 8 c. dull purple and ultramarine		2·50	5·50
	a. Surch inverted		£2250	£1200
	b. Surch double		£650	

(b) T 13 *on plain paper (no stamp), but issued for postage. Imperf.*

26	4 c. black		—	£1900
27	5 c. black		£1400	

No. 26 also exists pin-perforated.

1899. *No. 16 surch with T* 14.

28	10	4 c. on 5 c. dull purple and olive-yellow		12·00	48·00

Pending the arrival of the permanent Federated Malay States issue the stamps of SELANGOR, FEDERATED MALAY STATES provisional overprints and PERAK were used at various times between November 1899 and July 1902.

The general issues for the FEDERATED MALAY STATES were used in Pahang from July 1902 until 1935.

15 Sultan Sir Abu   16 Sultan Sir Abu
     Bakar   Bakar

1935 (2 Dec)**–41.** *Chalk-surfaced paper. Wmk Mult Script CA. P* 14.

29	15	1 c. black (1.1.36)		15	40
30		2 c. green (1.1.36)		60	50
31		3 c. green (21.8.41)		12·00	13·00
		a. Ordinary paper		24·00	4·25
32		4 c. orange		30	50
33		5 c. brown (5.12.35)		60	10
34		6 c. scarlet (1.1.37)		8·50	2·25
35		8 c. grey		60	10
36		8 c. scarlet (11.12.41)		1·00	42·00
37		10 c. dull purple (1.1.36)		30	10
38		12 c. bright ultramarine (1.1.36)		1·00	1·75
39		15 c. ultram (*ordinary paper*) (1.10.41)		7·00	48·00
40		25 c. dull purple and scarlet (1.4.36)		80	1·75
41		30 c. dull purple and orange (1.1.36)		80	1·10
42		40 c. scarlet and dull purple		75	2·50
43		50 c. black/*emerald* (1.2.36)		2·75	1·75
44		$1 black and red/*blue* (1.4.36)		2·00	7·50
45		$2 green and scarlet (16.5.36)		18·00	26·00
46		$5 green and red/*emerald* (16.5.36)		70·00	50·00
29/46			*Set of 18*	55·00	£170
29/46 Perf "Specimen"			*Set of 18*	£225	

The stamps issued during 1941 were printed by Harrison and Sons following bomb damage to the De La Rue works on 29 December 1940.

A 2 c. orange and a 6 c. grey were prepared but not officially issued. (*Price mint* £4 *each*).

During shortages in 1941 stamps of STRAITS SETTLEMENTS (2 c.), SELANGOR (2 c., 8 c.) and PERAK (2 c.) were issued in Pahang.

1948 (1 Dec). *Royal Silver Wedding. As Nos. 143/4 of Jamaica.*

47	10 c. violet		15	60
48	$5 green		22·00	40·00

1949 (10 Oct). *75th Anniv of U.P.U. As Nos. 145/8 of Jamaica.*

49	10 c. purple		30	20
50	15 c. deep blue		90	70
51	25 c. orange		35	1·10
52	50 c. blue-black		70	2·00
49/52		*Set of 4*	2·00	3·50

1950 (1 June)**–56.** *Wmk Mult Script CA. Chalk-surfaced paper. P* 17½ × 18.

53	16	1 c. black		10	10
54		2 c. orange		10	10
55		3 c. green		30	60
56		4 c. brown		50	10
		a. Chocolate (24.3.54)		4·50	1·75
57		5 c. bright purple (1.9.52)		25	70
		a. Bright mauve (10.9.53)		25	15
58		6 c. grey		15	20
59		8 c. scarlet		20	1·25
60		8 c. green (1.9.52)		85	75
61		10 c. magenta		15	10
62		12 c. scarlet (1.9.52)		85	1·25
63		15 c. ultramarine		50	10
64		20 c. black and green		25	2·75
65		20 c. bright blue (1.9.52)		75	10
		a. Ultramarine (8.3.56)		4·25	2·75
66		25 c. purple and orange		30	10
67		30 c. scarlet and brown-purple (5.9.55)		1·25	35
		a. Scarlet and purple (8.3.56)		10·00	3·25
68		35 c. scarlet and purple (1.9.52)		60	25
69		40 c. red and purple		1·00	7·50
70		50 c. black and blue		1·00	10
71		$1 blue and purple		2·50	2·50
72		$2 green and scarlet		13·00	20·00
73		$5 green and brown		55·00	50·00
		a. Green and sepia (24.3.54)		85·00	85·00
53/73			*Set of 21*	70·00	75·00

1953 (2 June). *Coronation. As No. 153 of Jamaica.*

74	10 c. black and reddish purple		80	10

1957 (26 June)**–62.** *As Nos. 92/102 of Kedah but with inset portrait of Sultan Sir Abu Bakar.*

75	9	1 c. black (21.8.57)		10	10
76	10	2 c. orange-red (25.7.57)		10	10
77	11	4 c. sepia (21.8.57)		10	10
78	12	5 c. carmine-lake (21.8.57)		10	10
79	13	8 c. myrtle-green (21.8.57)		80	2·25
80	14	10 c. deep brown (4.8.57)		65	10
81		10 c. deep maroon (21.2.61)		2·25	30
82	15	20 c. blue		1·25	20
83	16	50 c. black and blue (p 12½) (25.7.57)		30	50
		a. Perf 12½ × 13 (17.5.60)		60	20
84	17	$1 ultramarine & reddish pur (25.7.57)		5·00	2·00
85	18	$2 bronze-grn & scar (p 12½) (21.8.57)		3·00	9·00
		a. Perf 13 × 12½ (13.11.62)		5·00	13·00
86	19	$5 brown and bronze-green (p 12½)		9·00	13·00
		a. Perf 13 × 12½ (17.5.60)		9·50	13·00
		b. Perf 13 × 12½. Brown and yellow-olive (23.10.62)		26·00	28·00
75/86			*Set of 12*	20·00	24·00

The 6, 12, 25 and 30 c. values used with this issue were Nos. 1/4 of Malayan Federation.

17 *Vanda hookeriana*   18 *Precis orithya*

1965 (15 Nov). *As Nos. 166/72 of Johore but with inset portrait of Sultan Sir Abu Bakar as in T* 17. W w 13 (*upright*).

87	1 c. multicoloured		10	60
	c. Grey (flower name, etc) omitted		35·00	
	w. Wmk inverted		4·25	
88	2 c. multicoloured		10	60
89	5 c. multicoloured		15	10
	c. Red (leaves, etc) omitted		42·00	
90	6 c. multicoloured		30	60
91	10 c. multicoloured		20	10
	a. Red omitted		42·00	
92	15 c. multicoloured		1·00	10
93	20 c. multicoloured		1·60	30
87/93		*Set of 7*	3·00	2·00

The 2 c., 5 c. and 6 c. exist with PVA gum as well as gum arabic. The higher values used with this issue were Nos. 20/27 of Malaysia (National Issues).

1970 (27 May). *As Nos. 87 and 91 but W w 13 (*sideways*).*

94	17	1 c. multicoloured		1·75	6·50
95	—	10 c. multicoloured		90	3·50

(Litho B.W.)

1971 (1 Feb). *As Nos. 175/81 of Johore but with portrait of Sultan Sir Abu Bakar and arms, as in T* 18.

96	1 c. multicoloured		20	1·00
97	2 c. multicoloured		40	1·00
98	5 c. multicoloured		85	50
99	6 c. multicoloured		1·50	1·40
100	10 c. multicoloured		90	20
101	15 c. multicoloured		1·00	10
102	20 c. multicoloured		1·75	30
96/102		*Set of 7*	6·00	4·00

The higher values used with this issue were Nos. 64/71 of Malaysia (National Issues).

19 Sultan Haji
Ahmad Shah

20 *Rhododendron scortechinii*

(Des Union Advertising. Litho Harrison)

1975 (8 May). *Installation of the Sultan.* P 14 × 14½.

103	**19**	10 c. slate-green, light lilac and gold		50	80
104		15 c. greenish black, yellow & dp green		60	10
105		50 c. black, light violet-bl & greenish blk		1·75	3·50
103/5			*Set of 3*	2·50	4·00

(Photo Harrison)

1977 (5 Sept)–78. *As Nos. 97/8, 100/2 but with portraits of Sultan Haji Ahmad Shah.*

106	2 c. multicoloured (1978)		40·00	40·00
107	5 c. multicoloured		60	80
108	10 c. multicoloured (10.2.78)		80	40
109	15 c. multicoloured (13.1.78)		80	30
	a. Black (face value, etc.)* omitted		£100	
110	20 c. multicoloured (1978)		4·00	1·75
106/10		*Set of 5*	42·00	40·00

*There were two black cylinders used for No. 109, one to apply the portrait and state details, the other the face value and parts of the main design.

The higher values used with this issue were Nos. 64/71 of Malaysia (National Issues).

1979 (30 Apr). *As Nos. 188/94 of Johore but with portrait of Sultan Haji Ahmad Shah as in T* **20**.

111	1 c. *Rafflesia hasseltii*		10	60
112	2 c. *Pterocarpus indicus*		10	60
113	5 c. *Lagerstroemia speciosa*		10	20
114	10 c. *Durio zibethinus*		15	10
115	15 c. *Hibiscus rosa-sinensis*		15	10
116	20 c. Type **20**		20	10
117	25 c. *Etlingera elatior* (inscr "*Phaeomeria speciosa*")		40	40
111/17		*Set of 7*	75	1·75

For higher values used in conjunction with this series see Nos. 190/7 of Malaysia (National Issues).

1983 (5 Oct)–85.* *As Nos. 113/16 but without wmk.*

120	5 c. *Lagerstroemia speciosa* (17.11.83)		40	60
121	10 c. *Durio zibethinus* (8.1.85)		1·00	1·50
123	20 c. Type **20** (blackish brown background)		21·00	1·25
123a	20 c. Type **20** (bronze-green background) (20.8.84)		75	30

*There was no official release date for these stamps. Dates shown are the earliest recorded from postmarks and may be revised if earlier examples are reported.

For details of the shade differences between watermarked and unwatermarked printings see after Johore No. 200a.

On Nos. 120/1 and 123a "pahang" is one millimetre nearer "malaysia" than on Nos. 113/16 and 123.

21 Rice

1986 (25 Oct)–96. *As Nos. 202/8 of Johore, but with portrait of Sultan Ahmad Shah as in T* **21**. P 12.

125	1 c. Coffee		10	10
	aw. Wmk inverted		3·50	
	b. Perf 13½×13¾ (1993)		7·00	40
126	2 c. Coconuts		10	10
127	5 c. Cocoa		10	10
	c. Perf 14×13¾ (1996)		1·00	10
128	10 c. Black pepper		10	10
	c. Perf 14×13¾ (1995)		2·00	50
	f. Perf 14¾×14½ (1994)		9·00	60
129	15 c. Rubber		10	10
	w. Wmk inverted (1991)		9·00	
130	20 c. Oil palm		10	10
	aw. Wmk inverted			
	c. Perf 14×13¾ (1994)		1·00	10
	e. Perf 14×14½ (1996)		6·00	20
	ew. Wmk inverted		9·50	
131	30 c. Type **21**		15	20
	aw. Wmk inverted		10·00	
	c. Perf 14×13¾ (1994)		3·25	20
	cw. Wmk inverted (1995)			
	f. Perf 14¾×14½ (1995)		7·00	60
	fw. Wmk inverted		7·00	
125/31		*Set of 7*	50	55

STAMP BOOKLETS

1935. *Stapled.*

SB1	$1 booklet containing twenty 5 c. (No. 33) in blocks of 10		
SB2	$1.30, booklet containing 5 c. and 8 c. (Nos. 33, 35) each in block of 10		

1973 (8 Dec). *Cover as Type B* **1** *of Johore, but inscr* "PAHANG". *Stitched.*

SB3	$3 booklet containing eight 5 c., 10 c. and twelve 15 c. (Nos. 98, 100/1) in blocks of 4		25·00

1979 (1 Dec). *Cover as No. SB5 of Johore, but inscr* "PAHANG". *Stitched.*

SB4	$3 booklet containing eight 5 c., 10 c., and twelve 15 c. (Nos. 113/15) in blocks of 4		9·00

No. SB4 exists with two different versions of the back cover.

1987 (1 June). *Cover as Type B* **2** *of Johore, but inscr* "PAHANG". *Stapled.*

SB5	$2 booklet containing 5 c., 10 c., 15 c. and 20 c. (Nos. 127/30) in blocks of 4		8·00

1992 (1 July). "*Kuala Lumpur '92*" *International Philatelic Exhibition. Cover as Type B* **3** *of Johore, but inscr* "Pahang". *Stamps attached by selvedge.*

SB6	$3 booklet containing 30 c. (No. 131) in block of 10		8·00

1993. *Covers as Nos. SB8/9 of Johore, but inscr* "Pahang". *Stamps attached by selvedge.*

SB7	$2 booklet containing 20 c. (No. 130) in block of 10		1·00
SB8	$3 booklet containing 30 c. (No. 131) in block of 10		1·50

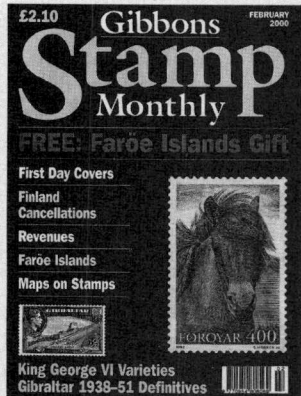

PENANG

One of the Straits Settlements.
Issues from 1965 are inscribed "PULAU PINANG".

1948 (1 Dec). *Royal Silver Wedding. As Nos. 143/4 of Jamaica.*
1	10 c. violet	30	20
2	$5 brown	30·00	28·00

1949 (21 Feb)–**52**. *As T 58 of Straits Settlements, but inscr "PENANG" at foot. Wmk Mult Script CA. Chalk-surfaced paper. P 17½ × 18.*
3	1 c. black	10	10
4	2 c. orange	55	10
5	3 c. green	20	30
6	4 c. brown	20	10
7	5 c. bright purple (1.9.52)	60	1·75
8	6 c. grey	20	20
9	8 c. scarlet	40	2·75
10	8 c. green (1.9.52)	80	1·00
11	10 c. purple	15	10
12	12 c. scarlet (1.9.52)	80	3·50
13	15 c. ultramarine	20	30
14	20 c. black and green	20	1·00
15	20 c. bright blue (1.9.52)	55	50
16	25 c. purple and orange	1·00	10
17	35 c. scarlet and purple (1.9.52)	60	80
18	40 c. red and purple	85	8·00
19	50 c. black and blue	1·25	15
20	$1 blue and purple	13·00	1·75
21	$2 green and scarlet	16·00	1·75
22	$5 green and brown	48·00	2·50
3/22	*Set of 20*	75·00	23·00

1949 (10 Oct). *75th Anniv of U.P.U. As Nos. 145/8 of Jamaica.*
23	10 c. purple	20	10
24	15 c. deep blue	1·50	1·75
25	25 c. orange	45	2·00
26	50 c. blue-black	1·50	2·75
23/6	*Set of 4*	3·25	6·00

1953 (2 June). *Coronation. As No. 153 of Jamaica.*
27	10 c. black and reddish purple	70	10

1954 (9 June)–**57**. *As T 1 of Malacca (Queen Elizabeth II) but inscr "PENANG" at foot. Chalk-surfaced paper. Wmk Mult Script CA. P 17½×18.*
28	1 c. black (5.1.55)	10	50
29	2 c. yellow-orange (8.9.54)	50	30
30	4 c. brown (1.9.54)	70	10
	a. Yellow-brown (17.7.57)	4·00	4·00
31	5 c. bright purple (1.10.54)	2·00	2·50
	a. Bright mauve (17.7.57)	4·00	4·25
32	6 c. grey	15	80
33	8 c. green (5.1.55)	20	2·50
34	10 c. brown-purple (1.9.54)	20	10
35	12 c. rose-red (5.1.55)	30	2·50
36	20 c. bright blue (1.9.54)	50	10
37	25 c. brown-purple & yellow-orange (1.12.54)	30	10
38	30 c. rose-red and brown-purple (5.9.55)	30	10
39	35 c. rose-red and brown-purple (8.9.54)	70	40
40	50 c. black and bright blue (1.12.54)	40	10
41	$1 bright blue and brown-purple (1.10.54)	2·25	10
42	$2 emerald and scarlet (1.10.54)	7·00	3·25
43	$5 emerald and brown (5.1.55)	40·00	3·25
28/43	*Set of 16*	48·00	14·50

1957. *As Nos. 92/102 of Kedah, but with inset portrait of Queen Elizabeth II.*
44	9	1 c. black (21.8)		10	70
45	10	2 c. orange-red (25.7)		10	70
46	11	4 c. sepia (21.8)		10	10
47	12	5 c. carmine-lake (21.8)		10	30
48	13	8 c. myrtle-green (21.8)		1·25	1·75
49	14	10 c. deep brown (4.8)		30	10
50	15	20 c. blue (26.6)		40	40
51	16	50 c. black and blue (25.7)		30	40
52	17	$1 ultramarine and reddish purple (25.7)		5·00	40
53	18	$2 bronze-green and scarlet (21.8)		11·00	9·00
54	19	$5 brown and bronze-green (26.6)		18·00	9·50
44/54			*Set of 11*	32·00	20·00

The note after No. 86 of Pahang also applies here.

1 Copra

2 Vanda hookeriana

(Recess D.L.R.)

1960 (15 Mar). *As Nos. 44/54, but with inset Arms of Penang as in T 1. W w 12. P 13 × 12½ (1 c. to 8 c., $2, $5), 12½ × 13 (10 c. to 50 c.) or 13½ ($1).*
55	1 c. black	10	85
56	2 c. orange-red	10	85
57	4 c. sepia	10	10
58	5 c. carmine-lake	10	10
59	8 c. myrtle-green	2·75	3·75
60	10 c. deep maroon	30	10
61	20 c. blue	40	10
62	50 c. black and blue	30	15
	a. Imperf (pair)	£400	
63	$1 ultramarine and reddish purple	4·25	1·25
64	$2 bronze-green and scarlet	4·25	4·50
65	$5 brown and bronze-green	10·00	6·50
55/65	*Set of 11*	20·00	16·00

No. 62a comes from a sheet purchased at the Penang Post Office which had the upper five horizontal rows imperforate.

1965 (15 Nov)–**68**. *As Nos. 166/72 of Johore but with Arms of Penang inset and inscr "PULAU PINANG" as in T 2. W w 13 (upright).*
66	1 c. multicoloured	10	85
67	2 c. multicoloured	10	85

68	5 c. multicoloured	20	10
	b. Yellow (flower) omitted	27·00	
	c. Red omitted	45·00	
	d. Blue (background and inscr) omitted	50·00	
	da. Blue and yellow omitted	£110	
	w. Wmk inverted	1·50	
69	6 c. multicoloured	30	85
	b. Yellow omitted	27·00	
70	10 c. grey and multicoloured	20	10
	a. Jet-black and multicoloured (12.11.68)	20	10
71	15 c. multicoloured	1·00	10
	b. Green (value and leaves) omitted	£110	
72	20 c. multicoloured	1·60	30
	a. Bright purple (blooms) omitted	£160	
	b. Yellow (leaves) omitted	£180	
66/72	*Set of 7*	3·00	2·50

The 2 c., 5 c., 6 c., 10 c. and 20 c. exist with PVA gum as well as gum arabic.
The higher values used with this issue were Nos. 20/27 of Malaysia (National Issues).

1970. *As Nos. 66 and 70 but W w 13 (sideways).*
73	2	1 c. multicoloured (27.5.70)	1·25	5·50
74	–	10 c. multicoloured (20.11.70)	5·50	4·00

3 Valeria valeria

4 Etlingera elatior (inscr "Phaeomeria speciosa")

1971 (1 Feb)–**78**. *As Nos. 175/87 of Johore, but with Arms of Penang and inscr "pulau pinang", as in T 3.*

(a) Litho by Bradbury Wilkinson
75	1 c. multicoloured	30	1·00
76	2 c. multicoloured	60	1·00
77	5 c. multicoloured	1·25	30
78	6 c. multicoloured	1·25	1·25
79	10 c. multicoloured	1·25	15
80	15 c. multicoloured	1·25	10
81	20 c. multicoloured	1·50	40
75/81	*Set of 7*	6·75	3·75

(b) Photo by Harrison (1977–78)
81a	1 c. multicoloured	5·00	7·50
82	5 c. multicoloured	2·50	60
83	10 c. multicoloured	4·75	60
84	15 c. multicoloured	11·00	30
85	20 c. multicoloured	5·00	1·00
81a/5	*Set of 5*	25·00	9·00

The higher values used with this issue were Nos. 64/71 of Malaysia (National Issues).
For differences between litho and photo printings, see after Johore No. 187.

1979 (30 Apr). *As Nos. 188/94 of Johore but with Arms of Penang and inscr "pulau pinang" as in T 4.*
86	1 c. Rafflesia hasseltii	10	60
87	2 c. Pterocarpus indicus	10	60
88	5 c. Lagerstroemia speciosa	10	15
89	10 c. Durio zibethinus	15	10
90	15 c. Hibiscus rosa-sinensis	15	10
91	20 c. Rhododendron scortechinii	20	10
92	25 c. Type 4	30	10
86/92	*Set of 7*	1·00	1·50

For higher values used in conjunction with this series see Nos. 190/7 of Malaysia (National Issues).

1983–85. * *As Nos. 88/91, but without wmk.*
95	5 c. Lagerstroemia speciosa (1.84)	30	40
96	10 c. Durio zibethinus (2.7.85)	6·00	2·50
97	15 c. Hibiscus rosa-sinensis (27.12.83)	55	40
98	20 c. Rhododendron scortechinii (blackish brown background) (27.6.84)	26·00	1·00
98a	20 c. Rhododendron scortechinii (bronze-green background) (3.84)	50	40

*There was no official release date for these stamps. Dates shown are the earliest recorded from postmarks and may be revised if earlier examples are reported.
For details of the shade differences between watermarked and unwatermarked printings see after Johore No. 200a.
On Nos. 95/7 and 98a the state arms are larger than on the watermarked printing and No. 98.

5 Cocoa

1986 (25 Oct)–**95**. *As Nos. 202/8 of Johore, but with Arms of Penang and inscr "PULAU PINANG" as in T 5. P 12.*
100	1 c. Coffee	10	10
	w. Wmk inverted (1993)	3·25	
101	2 c. Coconuts	10	10
102	5 c. Type 5	10	10
	c. Perf 14×13¾ (1994)	2·50	20
	cw. Wmk inverted	5·50	
	f. Perf 14¾×14½ (1995)	1·00	20

103	10 c. Black pepper	10	10
	aw. Wmk inverted		
	c. Perf 14×13¾ (1995)	1·00	10
	cw. Wmk inverted	5·50	
	e. Perf 14×14½ (1994)	3·25	20
	f. Perf 14¾×14½ (1995)	2·00	10
	fw. Wmk inverted	4·00	
104	15 c. Rubber	10	10
	w. Wmk inverted	8·50	
105	20 c. Oil palm	10	10
	aw. Wmk inverted	†	—
	c. Perf 14×13¾ (1994)	1·00	10
	e. Perf 14×14½ (1994)	2·50	10
	f. Perf 14¾×14½ (1994)	4·50	20
106	30 c. Rice	15	20
	aw. Wmk inverted	9·50	
	c. Perf 14×13¾ (1994)	1·00	10
	cw. Wmk inverted (1995)	2·50	
	e. Perf 14×14½ (1995)	1·75	20
	f. Perf 14¾×14½ (1994)	2·50	30
	fw. Wmk inverted		
100/6	*Set of 7*	50	55

STAMP BOOKLETS

1973 (8 Dec). *Cover as Type B 1 of Johore, but inscr "PULAU PINANG". Stitched.*
SB1	$3 booklet containing eight 5 c., 10 c. and twelve 15 c. (Nos. 77, 79/80) in blocks of 4		25·00

1979 (1 Dec). *Cover as No. SB5 of Johore, but inscr "PULAU PINANG". Stitched.*
SB2	$3 booklet containing eight 5 c., 10 c., and twelve 15 c. (Nos. 88/90) in blocks of 4		9·00

No. SB2 exists with two different versions of the back cover.

1987 (1 June). *Cover as Type B 2 of Johore, but inscr "PULAU PINANG". Stapled.*
SB3	$2 booklet containing 5 c., 10 c., 15 c. and 20 c. (Nos. 102/5) in blocks of 4		8·00

1992 (1 July). *"Kuala Lumpur '92" International Philatelic Exhibition. Cover as Type B 3 of Johore, but inscr "Pulau Pinang". Stamps attached by selvedge.*
SB4	$3 booklet containing 30 c. (No. 106) in block of 10		8·00

1993. *Covers as Nos. SB8/9 of Johore, but inscr "Pulau Pinang". Stamps attached by selvedge.*
SB5	$2 booklet containing 20 c. (No. 105) in block of 10	1·00	
SB6	$3 booklet containing 30 c. (No. 106) in block of 10	1·50	

PERAK

Perak accepted a British Resident in 1874, although he was later murdered.
The state joined the Federated Malay States in 1896.

The stamps of the STRAITS SETTLEMENTS were used in Perak during 1877/8.
Until 1 January 1899, when the Federated Malay States joined the U.P.U., mail for addresses outside Malaya was franked with stamps of the STRAITS SETTLEMENTS.

PRICES FOR STAMPS ON COVER TO 1945	
No. 1	—
Nos. 2/9	*from* × 60
Nos. 10/13	*from* × 30
Nos. 14/16	*from* × 8
Nos. 17/22	*from* × 20
No. 23	—
Nos. 24/5	—
Nos. 26/8	*from* × 15
No. 29	*from* × 75
No. 30	*from* × 20
Nos. 31/2	—
Nos. 33/40	*from* × 15
Nos. 43/60	*from* × 6
Nos. 61/5	*from* × 20
Nos. 66/79	*from* × 12
No. 80	—
Nos. 81/7	*from* × 8
Nos. 88/102	*from* × 4
Nos. 103/21	*from* × 3

The Official stamps of Perak are rare used on cover.

(1)

1878. *No. 11 of Straits Settlements handstamped with T* **1.**
1   2 c. brown £1300 £950

PERAK   **PERAK**   **PERAK**
(2)   (3)   (4)
(14½ mm long)   (11 mm long)   (10¼ mm long)

PERAK   PERAK   PERAK
(5)   (6)   (7)
(17 mm long)   ("RA" narrow)   ("R" narrow)

PERAK   **PERAK**
(8) ("P" and "K"   (9) (12 to 13½ mm
wide)   long)

1880–81. *No. 11 (wmk Crown CC) of Straits Settlements optd with T* **2/9.**
2   2   2 c. brown £800 £425
3   3   2 c. brown £750 £400
4   4   2 c. brown £425 £350
5   5   2 c. brown (1881) .. .. 25·00 45·00
6   6   2 c. brown (1881) £140 £150
7   7   2 c. brown (1881) .. .. 95·00 £120
8   8   2 c. brown (1881) £350 £325
9   9   2 c. brown (1881) .. .. 95·00 £110
Of the above No. 2 is from a single unit overprint, No. 5 from a setting of sixty and the remainder from settings applied as horizontal strips of three. Nos. 6/8 come from mixed triplets, either 6 + 7 + 7 or 7 + 7 + 8. No. 4 is believed to come from a single unit overprint in addition to a triplet.

PERAK   **PERAK**
(10) ("A" wide)   (11) ("E" wide)

1882–83. *Nos. 50 (wmk Crown CA) and 63 of Straits Settlements optd with T* **9/11.**
10   9   2 c. brown .. .. .. 19·00 38·00
   a. Opt double £475
11   2 c. pale rose (1883) .. .. 16·00 32·00
   a. Opt double £550
12 10 2 c. pale rose (1883) .. .. 16·00 45·00
13 11 2 c. pale rose (1883) .. .. 16·00 38·00
   a. Opt double £550
The above were all overprinted as triplet settings. Those for the 2 c. rose were 11 + 12 + 13, 13 + 11 + 11 and 13 + 11 + 12.

2 CENTS PERAK   **2 OENTS**
(12)   (13)

1883 (July). *No. 51 (wmk Crown CA) of Straits Settlements surch.*
(a) Surch with T **12**
14   2 c. on 4 c. rose £2250
   a. On Straits Settlements No. 12 (wmk Crown CC) £7000
(b) Optd as T **9** *or* **11** *and surch with T* **13**
15 11 2 c. on 4 c. rose £800 £350
16   9 2 c. on 4 c. rose £500 £225
It is believed that No. 14 occurred on the top row of the sheet with the remaining nine rows surcharged with a triplet containing 15 + 16 + 16.
Only one unused example, with defects, of No. 14a is recorded.

PERAK   **PERAK**   **PERAK**
(14)   (15)   (16) (12½–
("E" wide)   ("E" narrow)   13 mm long)

PERAK   **PERAK**   **PERAK**
(17) (12–   (18)   (19)
12½ mm long)   (10½ mm long)   (10 mm long)

PERAK
(20) (13 mm long)

1884–91. *Nos. 63/a of Straits Settlements optd with T* **14/20.**
17 14 2 c. pale rose .. .. .. 1·25 1·40
   a. Opt inverted £550 £550
   b. Opt inverted £325 £425
   c. Bright rose .. .. .. 2·25 1·10
18 15 2 c. pale rose .. .. .. 50·00 50·00
   b. Opt inverted £1000 £1100
   c. Opt triple £1100
   d. Bright rose £1100
19 16 2 c. pale rose (1886) .. .. 1·40 5·50
   a. Optd "FERAK" £250 £300
20 17 2 c. pale rose (1886) .. .. 3·50 17·00
   a. Opt double £1300
21 18 2 c. pale rose (1886) .. .. 85·00 95·00
   a. Bright rose .. .. ..
22 19 2 c. bright rose (1890) .. .. 8·50 35·00
23 20 2 c. bright rose (1891) £2500
Settings:
   Nos. 17/18 – triplets (either 17 + 17 + 17 or 18 + 17 + 17)
   – 30 (3 × 10) (containing twenty-eight as No. 17 and two as No. 18)
   – 60 (6 × 10) (containing either fifty-seven as No. 17 and three as No. 18 or all as No. 17)
   No. 19 – 60 (6 × 10) (No. 19a occurs on one position of the setting, it is often found amended in manuscript)
   No. 20 – triplet
   No. 21 – triplet
   No. 22 – 60 (6 × 10)
   No. 23 – not known

1 CENT
(21)

1886. *No. 17 surch with T* **21.**
24 14 1 c. on 2 c. pale rose £1900 £1900

ONE CENT PERAK   **ONE CENT PERAK.**   **ONE CFNT PERAK.**
(22)   (23)   (24) ("N" wide in "ONE"
                                                     and "CENT")

1886. *No. 63 of Straits Settlements surch with T* **22/4.**
25 22 1 c. on 2 c. pale rose £450 £475
26 23 1 c. on 2 c. pale rose .. .. 48·00 65·00
   a. Surch double £700
27 24 1 c. on 2 c. pale rose .. .. 75·00 90·00
Nos. 26/7 are from a triplet setting, 26 + 27 + 26, used on the top nine rows of the sheet. No. 25 may have been used on the bottom row.

1 CENT PERAK   **One CENT PERAK**   **ONE CENT PERAK**
(25)   (26)   (27)

1886. *No. 63 of Straits Settlements surch with T* **25.**
28   1 c. on 2 c. pale rose .. .. 90·00 £100
   a. Surch double £1500
No. 28 comes from a triplet setting.

1886. *No. 63 of Straits Settlements surch with T* **26.**
29   1 c. on 2 c. pale rose 95   7·00
   a. "One" inverted £2250
   b. Surch double £900
No. 29 comes from a triplet setting. It is believed that No. 29a occurred when the type was dropped and "One" replaced upside down.

1887. *No. 63 of Straits Settlements surch with T* **27** *in blue.*
30   1 c. on 2 c. pale rose .. .. 30·00 42·00
   a. Optd in black £1400 £950
No. 30 was printed from a setting of 60.

I CENT PERAK   **1 CENT PERAK**
(28)   (29)

1887. *No. 63 of Straits Settlements surch with T* **28.**
31   1 c. on 2 c. pale rose £400 £425
No. 31 comes from a triplet setting

1887. *No. 63 of Straits Settlements surch with T* **29.**
32   1 c. on 2 c. pale rose £1300 £1400
The size of setting used for No. 32 is not known.

One CENT PERAK   **One CENT PERAK**   **One CENT PERAK**   **One CENT PERAK**
(30)   (31)   (32)   (33)

One CENT PERAK   **One CENT PERAK**   **One CENT PERAK**   **One CENT PERAK**
(34)   (35)   (36)   (37)

1887–89. *No. 63 of Straits Settlements surch with T* **30/7.**
33 30 1 c. on 2 c. pale rose .. .. 1·00 3·00
   a. Surch double .. .. ..
   b. Bright rose .. .. .. 1·25 1·90
34 31 1 c. on 2 c. pale rose (1889) .. 95·00 £110
   b. Bright rose .. .. ..
35 32 1 c. on 2 c. pale rose (1889) .. 8·00 27·00
   a. "PREAK" (R. 6/1) £400 £450
   b. Bright rose .. .. .. 12·00 27·00
   ba. "PREAK" (R. 6/1) £500 £600
   w. Wmk inverted £100
36 33 1 c. on 2 c. pale rose (1889) .. 4·25 7·50
   b. Bright rose .. .. .. 4·25 7·50
37 34 1 c. on 2 c. pale rose (1889) .. 5·00 11·00
   b. Bright rose .. .. .. 4·25 11·00
38 35 1 c. on 2 c. bright rose (1889) .. £500 £650
39 36 1 c. on 2 c. bright rose (1889) .. £200 £250
40 37 1 c. on 2 c. pale rose (1889) .. 11·00 24·00
   b. Bright rose .. .. .. 11·00 24·00
Settings. No. 33 originally appeared as a triplet, then as a block of 30 (3 × 10) and, finally, as part of a series of composite settings of 60. Specialists recognise four such composite settings:
Setting I contained No. 33 in Rows 1 to 4, 5/1 to 5/5 and Row 7; No. 34 on R. 5/6, 6/1 and 6/2; No. 35 on R. 6/3–6; No. 36 on Row 8; No. 37 on Rows 9 and 10.
Setting II was similar, but had the example of No. 33 on R. 3/5 replaced by No. 38 and those on R. 7/4 and R. 7/6 by No. 39.
Setting III contained No. 33 in Rows 1 to 5; No. 35 in Row 6 with the "PREAK" error on the first position; No. 36 in Row 7; No. 37 in Rows 8 and 9; No. 40 in Row 10.
Setting IV was similar, but showed the "PREAK" error on R. 6/1 corrected.

ONE CENT.   **ONE CENT**
(38)   (39)

1889–90. *No. 17 surch with T* **38/9.**
41 38 1 c. on 2 c. bright rose £170 £130
42 39 1 c. on 2 c. bright rose (1890) .. — £225

PERAK Two CENTS   **PERAK One CENT**
(40)   (41)

1891. *Nos. 63a, 66 and 68 of Straits Settlements surch.*
(a) As T **30, 32/4** *and* **37,** *but with "PERAK" at top and a bar through the original value*
43 30 1 c. on 6 c. lilac .. .. 40·00 25·00
44 32 1 c. on 6 c. lilac £130 £130
45 33 1 c. on 6 c. lilac £130 £130
46 34 1 c. on 6 c. lilac .. .. 65·00 65·00
47 37 1 c. on 6 c. lilac £130 £130

(b) With T **40** *and as T* **32/4** *and* **37** *but with "PERAK" at top, all with a bar through the original value*
48 40 2 c. on 24 c. green .. .. 9·50 9·00
49 32 2 c. on 24 c. green .. .. 70·00 55·00
50 33 2 c. on 24 c. green .. .. 70·00 55·00
51 34 2 c. on 24 c. green .. .. 38·00 24·00
52 37 2 c. on 24 c. green .. .. 70·00 55·00

(c) With T **41** *and as T* **30, 34** *and* **37,** *but with "PERAK" at top.*
(i) Without bar over original value
53 30 1 c. on 2 c. bright rose £160
   a. Narrow "O" in "One" (R. 3/3) .. £1700
54 41 1 c. on 2 c. bright rose £750
55 34 1 c. on 2 c. bright rose £300
56 37 1 c. on 2 c. bright rose £750

(ii) With bar through original value
57 30 1 c. on 2 c. bright rose .. .. 55 4·00
   a. Narrow "O" in "One" (R. 3/3) .. 17·00 45·00
58 41 1 c. on 2 c. bright rose .. .. 4·50 17·00
59 34 1 c. on 2 c. bright rose .. .. 85 5·50
60 37 1 c. on 2 c. bright rose .. .. 4·50 17·00
Settings. Nos. 43/7 were arranged as Setting IV described under Nos. 33/40.
Nos. 48/52 were similar except that Type 40 replaced Type 30 on the first five rows.
The first printing of the 1 c. on 2 c. was without a bar through the original face value. Both printings, Nos. 53/60, were from the same setting with Type 30 on Rows 1 to 5, 41 on Row 6, 34 on Rows 7 to 9 and 37 on Row 10.

3 CENTS

42   (43)

1892 (1 Jan)–**95**. *Wmk Crown CA. P* 14.
61	42	1 c. green		2·25	15
62		2 c. rose		1·75	30
63		2 c. orange (9.9.95)		45	3·25
64		5 c. blue		3·25	7·50
61/4			*Set of 4*	7·00	10·00
61/4		Optd "Specimen"	*Set of 4*	75·00	

1895 (18 Apr). *Surch with T* 43. *Wmk Crown CA. P* 14.
65	42	3 c. on 5 c. rose (Optd S. £25)	1·50	1·75

44   45

1895 (2 Sept)–**99**. *P* 14. (*a*) *Wmk Crown CA.*
66	44	1 c. dull purple and green		1·25	40
67		2 c. dull purple and brown		1·00	40
68		3 c. dull purple and carmine		1·50	40
69		4 c. dull purple and carmine (1899)		8·00	4·75
70		5 c. dull purple and olive-yellow		2·75	55
71		8 c. dull purple and ultramarine		40·00	65
72		10 c. dull purple and orange		8·00	45
73		25 c. green and carmine (1897)		£110	12·00
74		50 c. dull purple and greenish black		38·00	29·00
75		50 c. green and black (2.99)		£140	£140

(*b*) *Wmk Crown CC*
76	45	$1 green and pale green (1896)		£110	£120
77		$2 green and carmine (1896)		£190	£200
78		$3 green and ochre (1898)		£225	£275
79		$5 green and ultramarine (1896)		£450	£425
80		$25 green and orange (1899?) (S. £180)		£6000	£1900
66/76			*Set of 11*	£425	£275
66/79		Optd "Specimen"	*Set of 14*	£300	

> Pending the arrival of the permanent Federated Malay States issue the stamps of FEDERATED MALAY STATES provisional overprints on SELANGOR and STRAITS SETTLEMENTS were used at various times between June 1900 and February 1901.
>
> The general issues for the FEDERATED MALAY STATES were used in Perak from 1901 until 1935.

50   Sultan Iskandar   51

1935 (2 Dec)–**37**. *Chalk-surfaced paper. Wmk Mult Script CA. P* 14.
88	50	1 c. black (1.1.36)		30	10
89		2 c. green (1.1.36)		30	10
90		4 c. orange		30	10
91		5 c. brown (5.12.35)		30	10
92		6 c. scarlet (1.1.37)		10·00	3·50
93		8 c. grey		50	10
94		10 c. dull purple (1.1.36)		30	15
95		12 c. bright ultramarine (1.1.36)		70	90
96		25 c. dull purple and scarlet (1.4.36)		1·00	85
97		30 c. dull purple and orange (1.1.36)		1·25	1·50
98		40 c. scarlet and dull purple		3·00	4·25
99		50 c. black/*emerald* (1.2.36)		3·75	1·00
100		$1 black and red/*blue* (1.4.36)		2·50	1·00
101		$2 green and scarlet (16.5.36)		15·00	8·50
102		$5 green and red/*emerald* (16.5.36)		65·00	28·00
88/102			*Set of 15*	90·00	45·00
88/102		Perf "Specimen"	*Set of 15*	£170	

No. 91 exists in coils constructed from normal sheets in 1936.

1938 (2 May)–**41**. *Wmk Mult Script CA. Chalk-surfaced paper. P* 14.
103	51	1 c. black (4.39)		6·00	10
104		2 c. green (13.1.39)		2·75	10
105		2 c. orange (30.10.41)		2·25	6·00
		a. Ordinary paper		2·50	16·00
106		3 c. green (21.8.41)		1·75	4·25
107		4 c. orange (5.39)		30·00	10
108		5 c. brown (1.2.39)		4·75	10
109		6 c. scarlet (12.39)		27·00	10
110		8 c. grey (1.12.38)		22·00	10
111		8 c. scarlet (18.12.41)		1·00	60·00
112		10 c. dull purple (17.10.38)		22·00	10
113		12 c. bright ultramarine (17.10.38)		20·00	2·00
114		15 c. brt ultram (*ordinary paper*) (8.41)		1·75	13·00
115		25 c. dull purple and scarlet (12.39)		70·00	4·25
116		30 c. dull purple and orange (17.10.38)		9·50	3·00
117		40 c. scarlet and dull purple		50·00	2·00
118		50 c. black/*emerald* (17.10.38)		27·00	75
119		$1 black and red/*blue* (7.40)		£130	16·00
120		$2 green and scarlet (9.40)		£140	60·00
121		$5 green and red/*emerald* (1.41)		£200	£275
103/21			*Set of 19*	£650	£400
103/21		Perf "Specimen"	*Set of 19*	£300	

No. 108 exists in coils constructed from normal sheets.
The stamps issued during 1941 were printed by Harrison and Sons following bomb damage to the De La Rue works on 29 December 1940.

> During shortages in 1941 stamps of STRAITS SETTLEMENTS (2 c.), SELANGOR (2 c., 3 c.) and PAHANG (8 c.) were issued in Perak.

1948 (1 Dec). *Royal Silver Wedding. As Nos.* 143/4 *of Jamaica.*
122		10 c. violet	15	10
123		$5 green	20·00	26·00

1949 (10 Oct). *75th Anniv of U.P.U. As Nos.* 145/8 *of Jamaica.*
124		10 c. purple	15	10
125		15 c. deep blue	1·00	1·25
126		25 c. orange	45	65
127		50 c. blue-black	1·75	3·00
124/7			*Set of 4*	3·00	4·50

52 Sultan Yussuf 'Izzuddin Shah   53 Sultan Idris Shah

1950 (17 Aug)–**56**. *Chalk-surfaced paper. Wmk Mult Script CA. P* 17½×18.
128	52	1 c. black		10	10
129		2 c. orange		10	10
130		3 c. green		2·00	10
		a. Yellowish green (15.11.51)		5·00	4·50
131		4 c. brown		10	10
		a. Yellow-brown (20.6.56)		3·50	10
132		5 c. bright purple (1.9.52)		50	1·00
		a. Bright mauve (10.11.54)		1·25	1·00
133		6 c. grey		10	10
134		8 c. scarlet		30	1·00
135		8 c. green (1.9.52)		1·00	60
136		10 c. purple		10	10
		a. Brown-purple (20.6.56)		3·75	30
137		12 c. scarlet (1.9.52)		1·00	2·75
138		15 c. ultramarine		30	10
139		20 c. black and green		30	30
140		20 c. bright blue (1.9.52)		75	10
141		25 c. purple and orange		30	10
142		30 c. scarlet and purple (5.9.55)		1·25	20
143		35 c. scarlet and purple (1.9.52)		70	25
144		40 c. red and purple		1·50	4·25
145		50 c. black and blue		90	10
146		$1 blue and purple		7·00	40
147		$2 green and scarlet		13·00	4·50
148		$5 green and brown		38·00	11·00
128/48			*Set of 21*	60·00	23·00

1953 (2 June). *Coronation. As No.* 153 *of Jamaica.*
149		10 c. black and reddish purple		80	10

1957 (26 June)–**61**. *As Nos.* 92/102 *of Kedah but with inset portrait of Sultan Yussuf 'Izzuddin Shah.*
150		1 c. black (21.8.57)		10	20
151		2 c. orange-red (25.7.57)		30	40
		a. Red-orange (15.12.59)		1·00	2·75
152		4 c. sepia (21.8.57)		10	10
153		5 c. carmine-lake (21.8.57)		10	10
154		8 c. myrtle-green (21.8.57)		2·00	2·50
155		10 c. deep brown (4.8.57)		65	10
156		10 c. deep maroon (21.2.61)		1·75	10
157		20 c. blue		1·50	10
158		50 c. black and blue (p 12½) (25.7.57)		40	40
		a. Perf 12½ × 13 (24.5.60)		30	10
159		$1 ultramarine and reddish purple (25.7.57)		5·00	30
160		$2 bronze-green & scar (p 12½) (21.8.57)		3·25	3·00
		a. Perf 13 × 12½ (21.2.61)		3·25	1·75
161		$5 brown and bronze-green (p 12½)		8·00	8·00
		a. Perf 13 × 12½ (24.5.60)		8·00	4·75
150/61			*Set of 12*	21·00	9·00

The 6, 12, 25 and 30 c. values used with this issue were Nos. 1/4 of Malayan Federation.

(Photo Harrison)

1963 (26 Oct). *Installation of the Sultan of Perak. W w* 13. *P* 14½.
162	53	10 c. red, black, blue and yellow		10	10

54 *Vanda hookeriana*   55 *Delias ninus*

1965 (15 Nov)–**68**. *As Nos.* 166/72 *of Johore but with inset portrait of Sultan Idris as in T* 54. *W w* 13 (*upright*).
163		1 c. multicoloured		10	30
		w. Wmk inverted		2·75	
164		2 c. multicoloured		10	10
		w. Wmk inverted		6·00	
165		5 c. pale black and multicoloured		10	10
		a. Grey-black and multicoloured (2.4.68)		65	30
		b. Yellow (flower) omitted		27·00	
166		6 c. multicoloured		15	30
167		10 c. multicoloured		15	10
168		15 c. multicoloured		80	10
		a. Black (country name and head) omitted		£180	
		c. Magenta (background) omitted		£150	
169		20 c. multicoloured		1·25	10
		a. Bright purple (blooms) omitted		45·00	
163/9			*Set of 7*	2·25	1·00

No. 168a comes from a horizontal strip of three, the centre stamp having the black completely omitted. The two outer stamps show the colour partly omitted.
The 2 c. to 15 c. exist with PVA gum as well as gum arabic.
The higher values used with this issue were Nos. 20/27 of Malaysia (National Issues).

1970. *As Nos.* 163 *and* 167, *but W w* 13 (*sideways*).
170	54	1 c. multicoloured (27.5.70)		2·00	6·00
171		10 c. multicoloured (20.11.70)		5·50	2·50

1971 (1 Feb)–**78**. *As Nos.* 175/87 *of Johore, but with portrait of Sultan Idris and arms, as in T* 55.

(*a*) *Litho by Bradbury, Wilkinson*
172		1 c. multicoloured		30	1·00
173		2 c. multicoloured		80	1·00
174		5 c. multicoloured		90	10
175		6 c. multicoloured		90	10
176		10 c. multicoloured		90	10
177		15 c. multicoloured		90	10
178		20 c. multicoloured		1·50	10
172/8			*Set of 7*	5·50	3·00

(*b*) *Photo by Harrison* (1977–78)
179		1 c. multicoloured		85	2·75
180		5 c. multicoloured		3·50	60
181		10 c. multicoloured		2·50	65
182		15 c. multicoloured		8·00	30
183		20 c. multicoloured		2·75	1·00
179/83			*Set of 5*	16·00	4·75

The higher values used with this issue were Nos. 64/71 of Malaysia (National Issues).
For differences between litho and photo printings, see after Johore, No. 187.

56 *Rafflesia hasseltii*   57 *Coffee*

1979 (30 Apr). *As Nos.* 188/94 *of Johore but with portrait of Sultan Idris as in T* 56.
184		1 c. Type 56		10	40
185		2 c. *Pterocarpus indicus*		10	40
186		5 c. *Lagerstroemia speciosa*		10	10
187		10 c. *Durio zibethinus*		15	10
188		15 c. *Hibiscus rosa-sinensis*		15	10
189		20 c. *Rhododendron scortechinii*		20	10
190		25 c. *Etlingera elatior* (inscr "*Phaeomeria speciosa*")		40	10
184/90			*Set of 7*	1·00	90

For higher values used in conjunction with this series see Nos. 190/7 of Malaysia (National Issues).

One Cent.
(46)

ONE CENT.
(47)

Three Cent.
(48)

Three Cent.
(49)

1900. *Stamps of* 1895–99 *surch.*
81	46	1 c. on 2 c. dull purple and brown (13 July*)		40	2·25
		a. Antique "e" in "One" (R. 5/2)		50·00	£120
		b. Antique "e" in "Cent" (R. 9/4)		50·00	£120
82	47	1 c. on 4 c. dull purple and carmine		65	8·00
		a. Surch double		£950	
83	46	1 c. on 5 c. dull purple & ol-yell (30 June*)		90	9·00
		a. Antique "e" in "One" (R. 5/2)		65·00	£190
		b. Antique "e" in "Cent" (R. 9/4)		65·00	£190
84	48	3 c. on 8 c. dull purple & ultram (26 Sept*)		2·50	6·50
		a. Antique "e" in "Cent" (R. 9/4)		£120	£180
		b. No stop after "Cent" (R. 9/5)		£120	£180
		c. Surch double		£425	£425
85		3 c. on 50 c. green and black (31 Aug*)		1·50	5·00
		a. Antique "e" in "Cent" (R. 9/4)		90·00	£160
		b. No stop after "Cent" (R. 9/5)		90·00	£160
86	49	3 c. on $1 green and pale green (21 Oct*)		55·00	£140
		a. Small "t" in "Cent"		£300	£500
		b. Surch double		£1300	
87		3 c. on $2 green and carmine (24 Oct*)		28·00	85·00
81/7			*Set of 7*	80·00	£225

*Earliest known postmark date.
With exception of No. 86a, whose sheet position is not known, the remaining surcharge varieties all occur in the left-hand pane.
No. 86b is also known showing the small "t" in "Cent" variety. (Price £3500 *unused*).

MINIMUM PRICE

The minimum price quote is 10p which represents a handling charge rather than a basis for valuing common stamps. For further notes about prices see introductory pages.

1983 (15 Oct)–**84.*** *As Nos. 186/9 but without wmk.*

193	5 c. *Lagerstroemia speciosa* (9.9.83)			45	40
194	10 c. *Durio zibenthinus* (1984)			30	50
195	15 c. *Hibiscus rosa-sinensis* (9.9.83)			70	30
196	20 c. *Rhododendron scortechinii* (blackish brown background)			20·00	65
196a	20 c. *Rhododendron scortechinii* (bronze-green background) (20.3.84)			85	50

*There was no official release date for these stamps. Dates shown are the earliest recorded from postmarks and may be revised if earlier examples are reported.

For details of the shade differences between watermarked and unwatermarked printings see after Johore No. 200a.

On Nos. 193/5 and 196a the portrait and arms are redrawn smaller.

1986 (25 Oct)–**96.** *As Nos. 202/8 of Johore, but with portrait of Sultan Azlan Shah as in T* **57.** *P* 12.

198	1 c. Type 57			10	10
	w. Wmk inverted			4·75	
199	2 c. Coconuts			10	10
	f. Perf 14³/₄×14¹/₂ (1994)			3·25	20
200	5 c. Cocoa			10	10
	c. Perf 14×13³/₄ (1994)			3·25	20
	f. Perf 14³/₄×14¹/₂ (1996)			2·50	30
201	10 c. Black pepper			10	10
	aw. Wmk inverted				
	c. Perf 14×13³/₄ (1995)			1·00	10
	cw. Wmk inverted			7·00	
	e. Perf 14×14¹/₂				
	f. Perf 14³/₄×14¹/₂ (1996)			2·25	20
202	15 c. Rubber			10	10
	w. Wmk inverted			9·50	
203	20 c. Oil palm			10	10
	aw. Wmk inverted				
	c. Perf 14×13³/₄ (1994)			1·50	10
	ca. No wmk			4·00	
	e. Perf 14×14¹/₂ (1996)			3·25	40
	f. Perf 14³/₄×14¹/₂ (1996)			3·25	50
204	30 c. Rice			15	20
	aw. Wmk inverted				
	c. Perf 14×13³/₄ (1994)			7·00	40
	f. Perf 14³/₄×14¹/₂ (1995)			7·00	1·25
198/204			Set of 7	50	55

STAMP BOOKLETS

1935.

SB1 $1 booklet containing twenty 5 c. (No. 91) in blocks of 10

SB2 $1.30, booklet containing 5 c. and 8 c. (Nos. 91, 93), each in block of 10

1938.

SB3 $1 booklet containing twenty 5 c. (No. 108) in blocks of 10

SB4 $1.30, booklet containing 5 c. and 8 c. (Nos. 108, 110), each in block of 10

1973 (8 Dec). *Cover as Type B* **1** *of Johore, but inscr* "PERAK". *Stitched.*

SB5 $3 booklet containing eight 5 c., 10 c. and twelve 15 c. (Nos. 174, 176/7) in blocks of 4 .. 25·00

1979 (1 Dec). *Cover as No. SB5 of Johore, but inscr* "PERAK". *Stitched.*

SB6 $3 booklet containing eight 5 c., 10 c. and twelve 15 c. (Nos. 186/8) in blocks of 4 .. 9·00

No. SB6 exists with two different versions of the back cover.

1987 (1 June). *Cover as Type B* **2** *of Johore, but inscr* "PERAK". *Stapled.*

SB7 $2 booklet containing 5 c., 10 c., 15 c. and 20 c. (Nos. 200/3) in blocks of 4 .. .. .. 8·00

1992 (1 July). *"Kuala Lumpur '92" International Philatelic Exhibition. Cover as Type B* **3** *of Johore, but inscr* "Perak". *Stamps attached by selvedge.*

SB8 $3 booklet containing 30 c. (No. 204) in block of 10 8·00

1993. *Covers as Nos. SB8/9 of Johore, but inscr* "Perak". *Stamps attached by selvedge.*

SB9 $2 booklet containing 20 c. (No. 203) in block of 10 .. .. .. 1·00

SB10 $3 booklet containing 30 c. (No. 204) in block of 10 .. .. .. 1·50

OFFICIAL STAMPS

P.G.S.   Service.
(O 1)   (O 2)

1889 (1 Nov). *Stamps of Straits Settlements optd Type O* **1.** *Wmk Crown CC (Nos. O6 and O8) or Crown CA (others).*

O1	2 c. bright rose			2·75	3·50
	a. Opt double			£750	£750
	b. Wide space between "G" and "S"		45·00	55·00
	c. No stop after "S"			45·00	55·00
O2	4 c. brown			8·00	16·00
	a. Wide space between "G" and "S"		60·00	75·00
	b. No stop after "S"			90·00	£110
	w. Wmk inverted			60·00	
O3	6 c. lilac			18·00	35·00
	a. Wide space between "G" and "S"		90·00	£130
O4	8 c. orange			24·00	65·00
	a. Wide space between "G" and "S"		£110	£170
O5	10 c. slate			75·00	75·00
	a. Wide space between "G" and "S"		£225	£250
O6	12 c. blue (CC)			£180	£190
	a. Wide space between "G" and "S"		£600	
O7	12 c. brown-purple (CA)			£200	£250
	a. Wide space between "G" and "S"		£700	
O8	24 c. green (CC)			£600	£700
	a. Wide space between "G" and "S"		£1800	
O9	24 c. green (CA)			£150	£170
	a. Wide space between "G" and "S"		£500	

Nos. O1/9 were overprinted from a setting of 30 (3 × 10). The variety "wide space between G and S" occurs on R. 10/3 and R. 10/6

of the original printing. A later printing of the 2 c. and 4 c. values had this variety corrected, but was without a stop after "S" on R. 10/1 and R. 10/4.

1894 (1 June). *No. 64 optd with Type O* **2.**

O10	5 c. blue			48·00	80
	a. Overprint inverted			£650	£450

1897. *No. 70 optd with Type O* **2.**

O11	5 c. dull purple and olive-yellow		1·50	35
	a. Overprint double			£425	£400

PERLIS

Suzerainty over Perlis was transferred by Thailand to Great Britain in 1909. A Treaty of Friendship between Great Britain and Perlis was signed on 28 April 1930.

The State joined the Federation of Malaya on 1 February 1948.

For stamps of THAILAND used in Perlis between 1894 and 1909 see VIII. SIAMESE POSTS IN NORTHERN MALAYA section.
Issues of the FEDERATED MALAY STATES were in use from 10 July 1909 until 1912 and these were replaced by the stamps of KEDAH between 1912 and 1941.

1948 (1 Dec). *Royal Silver Wedding. As Nos. 143/4 of Jamaica.*
1	10 c. violet			30	2·00
2	$5 brown			28·00	42·00

1949 (10 Oct). *75th Anniv of U.P.U. As Nos. 145/8 of Jamaica.*
3	10 c. purple			30	60
4	15 c. deep blue			1·25	3·00
5	25 c. orange			65	2·00
6	50 c. blue-black			1·40	3·75
3/6			Set of 4	3·25	8·50

1 Raja Syed Putra   2 Vanda hookeriana

1951 (26 Mar)–**55**. *Chalk-surfaced paper. Wmk Mult Script CA. P 17½ × 18.*
7	1	1 c. black		10	80
8		2 c. orange		30	40
9		3 c. green		75	2·75
10		4 c. brown		90	30
11		5 c. bright purple (1.9.52)		30	2·75
12		6 c. grey		90	1·25
13		8 c. scarlet		1·75	4·50
14		8 c. green (1.9.52)		75	2·50
15		10 c. purple		30	20
16		12 c. scarlet (1.9.52)		75	2·50
17		15 c. ultramarine		1·75	3·00
18		20 c. black and green		90	5·00
19		20 c. bright blue (1.9.52)		85	65
20		25 c. purple and orange		1·25	1·25
21		30 c. scarlet and purple (5.9.55)		1·75	8·00
22		35 c. scarlet and purple (1.9.52)		75	3·25
23		40 c. red and purple		1·50	15·00
24		50 c. black and blue		2·75	3·75
25		$1 blue and purple		6·50	17·00
26		$2 green and scarlet		13·00	24·00
27		$5 green and brown		50·00	£150
7/27			Set of 21	75·00	£150

1953 (2 June). *Coronation. As No. 153 of Jamaica.*
28	10 c. black and reddish purple			50	2·25

1957 (26 June)–**62**. *As Nos. 92/102 of Kedah but with inset portrait of Raja Syed Putra.*
29	9	1 c. black (21.8.57)		10	30
30	10	2 c. orange-red (25.7.57)		10	30
31	11	4 c. sepia (21.8.57)		10	10
32	12	5 c. carmine-lake (21.8.57)		10	10
33	13	8 c. myrtle-green (21.8.57)		2·00	1·75
34	14	10 c. deep brown (4.8.57)		50	1·50
35		10 c. deep maroon (14.3.61)		3·25	2·25
36	15	20 c. blue		1·25	2·25
37	16	50 c. black and blue (p 12½) (25.7.57)		40	2·50
		a. Perf 12½ × 13 (8.5.62)		2·00	2·75
38	17	$1 ultram & reddish purple (25.7.57)		4·50	7·50
39	18	$2 bronze-green and scarlet (25.7.57)		4·50	6·50
40	19	$5 brown and bronze-green (21.8.57)		9·00	9·50
29/40			Set of 12	23·00	30·00

The 6, 12, 25 and 30 c. values used with this issue were Nos. 1/4 of Malayan Federation.

1965 (15 Nov). *As Nos. 166/72 of Johore but with inset portrait of Tunku Bendahara Abu Bakar as in T 2.*
41	1 c. multicoloured			10	60
	w. Wmk inverted			11·00	
42	2 c. multicoloured			10	70
43	5 c. multicoloured			15	15
44	6 c. multicoloured			65	45
45	10 c. multicoloured			65	15
46	15 c. multicoloured			1·00	35
47	20 c. multicoloured			1·00	95
41/7			Set of 7	3·25	3·00

The 6 c. exists with PVA gum as well as gum arabic.
The higher values used with this issue were Nos. 20/27 of Malaysia (National Issues).

3 Danaus melanippus   4 Raja Syed Putra

1971 (1 Feb)–**78**. *As Nos. 175/87 of Johore but with portrait of Raja Syed Putra and Arms, as in T 3.*

(a) Litho by Bradbury, Wilkinson
48	1 c. multicoloured			20	80
49	2 c. multicoloured			30	1·25
50	5 c. multicoloured			1·00	70
51	6 c. multicoloured			1·00	1·75

52	10 c. multicoloured			1·00	80
53	15 c. multicoloured			1·00	30
54	20 c. multicoloured			1·00	1·50
48/54			Set of 7	5·00	6·25

(b) Photo by Harrison (1977–78)
54a	10 c. multicoloured			60·00	7·00
55	15 c. multicoloured			5·50	2·25
55a	20 c. multicoloured			30·00	26·00

The higher values used with this issue were Nos. 64/71 of Malaysia (National Issues).
For differences between litho and photo printings, see after Johore No. 187.

(Des Citizen Studio and Engravers. Litho Enschedé)

1971 (28 Mar). *25th Anniv of Installation of Raja Syed Putra. P 13½ × 13.*
56	4	10 c. multicoloured		30	1·25
57		15 c. multicoloured		30	50
58		50 c. multicoloured		80	3·25
56/8			Set of 3	1·25	4·50

5 Pterocarpus indicus   6 Coconuts

1979 (30 Apr). *As Nos. 188/94 of Johore but with portrait of Raja Syed Putra as in T 5.*
59	1 c. Rafflesia hasseltii			10	75
60	2 c. Type 5			10	75
61	5 c. Lagerstroemia speciosa			10	75
62	10 c. Durio zibethinus			15	10
63	15 c. Hibiscus rosa-sinensis			15	10
64	20 c. Rhododendron scortechinii			20	10
65	25 c. Etlingera elatior (inscr "Phaeomeria speciosa")			40	65
59/65			Set of 7	1·00	2·75

For higher values used in conjunction with this series see Nos. 190/7 of Malaysia (National Issues).

1983–84*. *As No. 64 but without wmk.*
71	20 c. Rhododendron scortechinii (blackish brown background)			28·00	5·00
71a	20 c. Rhododendron scortechinii (bronze-green background) (4.12.84)			80	1·25

*There was no official release date for these stamps. Dates shown are the earliest recorded from postmarks and may be revised if earlier examples are reported.
For details of the shade differences between watermarked and unwatermarked printings see after Johore No. 200a.
No. 71a shows the Sultan's head larger than on Nos. 64 and 71 and has "perlis" in rounded, instead of square-ended, letters.

1986 (25 Oct)–**94**. *As Nos. 202/8 of Johore, but with portrait of Raja Syed Putra as in T 6. P 12.*
73	1 c. Coffee			10	10
	w. Wmk inverted			7·00	
74	2 c. Type 6			10	10
75	5 c. Cocoa			10	10
76	10 c. Black pepper			10	10
	f. Perf 14¾ × 14½ (1994)			4·50	50
77	15 c. Rubber			10	10
78	20 c. Oil palm			10	10
79	30 c. Rice			15	20
	aw. Wmk inverted				
	c. Perf 14 × 13¾ (1994)			4·50	30
	cw. Wmk inverted			8·50	
	f. Perf 14¾ × 14½ (1994)			12·00	
73/9			Set of 7	50	55

7 Raja Syed Putra and Aspects of Perlis

(Des BJ Image Sdn Bhd. Litho Security (M), Malaysia)

1995 (4 Dec). *50th Anniv of Raja Syed Putra's Accession. T 7 and similar horiz design. Multicoloured. W 138 (sideways). P 14×14½.*
80	30 c. Type 7			30	30
	a. Perf 13½				
81	$1 Raja Syed Putra and Palace			70	1·50
	a. Perf 13½			6·50	

STAMP BOOKLETS

1973 (8 Dec). *Cover as Type B 1 of Johore, but inscr "PERLIS". Stitched.*
SB1	$3 booklet containing eight 5 c., 10 c. and twelve 15 c. (Nos. 50, 52/3) in blocks of 4		27·00

Examples of No. SB1 exist with a white label giving revised postage rates.

1979 (1 Dec). *Cover as No. SB5 of Johore, but inscr "PERLIS". Stitched.*
SB2	$3 booklet containing eight 5 c., 10 c., and twelve 15 c. (Nos. 61/3) in blocks of 4		10·00

No. SB2 exists with two different versions of the back cover.

1987 (1 June). *Cover as Type B 2 of Johore, but inscr "PERLIS". Stapled.*
SB3	$2 booklet containing 5 c., 10 c., 15 c. and 20 c. (Nos. 75/8) in blocks of 4		8·50

1992 (1 July). *"Kuala Lumpur '92" International Philatelic Exhibition. Cover as Type B 3 of Johore, but inscr "Perlis". Stamps attached by selvedge.*
SB4	$3 booklet containing 30 c. (No. 79) in block of 10		8·50

1993. *Covers as Nos. SB8/9 of Johore, but inscr "Perlis". Stamps attached by selvedge.*
SB5	$2 booklet containing 20 c. (No. 78) in block of 10		1·00
SB6	$3 booklet containing 30 c. (No. 79) in block of 10		1·50

SELANGOR

The first British Resident was appointed in 1874. Selangor joined the Federated Malay States in 1896.

The stamps of the STRAITS SETTLEMENTS were used in Selangor from 1879 until 1881.
Until 1 January 1899, when the Federated Malay States joined the U.P.U., mail for addresses outside Malaya was franked with stamps of the STRAITS SETTLEMENTS.

PRICES FOR STAMPS ON COVER TO 1945

Nos. 1/8	—
Nos. 9/19	from × 10
Nos. 20/30	from × 12
Nos. 31/3	from × 25
Nos. 34/6	from × 20
Nos. 37/8	from × 15
Nos. 38a/40	
Nos. 41/2	from × 8
No. 43	—
Nos. 44/8	from × 8
Nos. 49/53	from × 30
Nos. 54/66	from × 10
Nos. 66a/7	from × 4
Nos. 68/85	from × 3
Nos. 86/7	from × 4

The Straits Settlements 1867 2 c. brown with Crown CC watermark (No. 11) has been known since 1881 overprinted in black with a crescent and star over a capital S, all within an oval, similar in style to the overprints listed for Perak and Sungei Ujong.
The status of this item remains unclear, but it may well represent the first issue of distinctive stamps for Selangor. This overprint should not be confused with a somewhat similar cancellation used on Selangor stamps of the same period. This cancellation differs in having a circular frame with the capital S shown above the crescent and star. It is usually struck in red.
A similar overprint in red on the Straits Settlements 2 c. brown with Crown CA watermark also exists and may have been produced for sale to collectors.

SELANGOR **SELANGOR** **SELANGOR**
(1) ("S" inverted and narrow letters)   (2) ("S" wide)   (3) (narrow letters)

SELANGOR **SELANGOR** **SELANGOR**
(4) ("N" wide)   (5) ("SE" and "AN" wide)   (6) ("SEL" and "N" wide)

SELANGOR
(7) ("SELAN" wide)

1881–82. *No. 11 (wmk Crown CC) of Straits Settlements optd with T 1/7.*

1	1	2 c. brown	..	..	£350	£375
2	2	2 c. brown	..	..	£130	£140
3	3	2 c. brown	..	..	85·00	90·00
4	4	2 c. brown	..	..	†	£2000
5	5	2 c. brown (1882)	..	..	£150	£160
6	6	2 c. brown (1882)	..	..	£150	£160
7	7	2 c. brown (1882)	..	..	£150	£160

Nos. 1/3 and 5/7 have been identified as coming from triplet settings, either Nos. 1 + 2 + 3, 2 + 3 + 3 or 5 + 6 + 7. The setting for No. 4 is unknown.

S.

(8)

1882. *No. 50 (wmk Crown CA) of Straits Settlements optd with T 8.*

8	8	2 c. brown	..	..	—	£2250

SELANGOR **SELANGOR** **SELANGOR**
(9) ("SEL" and "NG" wide)   (10) ("E" and "ANG" wide)   (11) ("ELANG" wide)

SELANGOR **SELANGOR** **SELANGOR**
(12) ("S" and "L" wide)   (13) ("S" and "A" wide)   (14) ("E" wide)

SELANGOR **SELANGOR** **SELANGOR**
(15) ("EL" wide)   (16) ("SE" and "N" wide)   (17) ("S" and "N" wide)

1882–83. *No. 50 (wmk Crown CA) of Straits Settlements optd with T 2/3 and 9/17.*

9	9	2 c. brown	..	..	£170	£170
10	10	2 c. brown	..	..	£170	£170
11	11	2 c. brown	..	..	£170	£170
12	2	2 c. brown (1883)	..	..	£110	90·00
13	3	2 c. brown (1883)	..	..	£190	90·00
14	12	2 c. brown (1883)	..	..	—	£2000
15	13	2 c. brown (1883)	..	..	£375	£325
16	14	2 c. brown (1883)	..	..	£250	£190
17	15	2 c. brown (1883)	..	..	£250	£190
18	16	2 c. brown (1883)	..	..	£120	£110
19	17	2 c. brown (1883)	..	..	£120	£110

The above were all printed from triplet settings. Those so far identified are Nos. 9 + 10 + 11, 12 (with defective "G") + 13 + 13, 15 + 16 + 17 and 18 + 12 + 19. No. 14 occurs as the first position of a triplet, but the second and third units are not yet known.

SELANGOR **SELANGOR** **SELANGOR**
(18) ("E" and "A" wide)   (19) ("A" wide)   (20) ("L" wide)

SELANGOR **SELANGOR** **SELANGOR**
(21) ("L" narrow)   (22) ("A" narrow)   (23) (wide letters)

1883–85. *No. 63 of Straits Settlements optd with T 2, 4, 12, 14/15 and 18/23.*

20	12	2 c. pale rose	..	..	£140	£130
21	14	2 c. pale rose	..	..	90·00	85·00
		a. Opt double	..	..		
22	4	2 c. pale rose (1884)	..	..	£140	£130
23	15	2 c. pale rose (1884)	..	..	80·00	80·00
		a. Opt double	..	..	£700	
		b. Opt triple	..	..		
24	2	2 c. pale rose (1884)	..	..	90·00	80·00
25	18	2 c. pale rose (1884)	..	..	90·00	80·00
26	19	2 c. pale rose (1884)	..	..	£225	£150
27	20	2 c. pale rose (1884)	..	..	£300	£170
28	21	2 c. pale rose (1885)	..	..	80·00	80·00
29	22	2 c. pale rose (1885)	..	..	£130	£120
30	23	2 c. pale rose (1885)	..	..	£275	£160

The above come from triplet settings with Nos. 20 + 21 + 21, 22 + 22 + 23, 23 + 26 (with defective "A") + 26, 24 + 25 + 23 and 28 + 29 + 28 so far identified. The triplets for Nos. 27 and 30 are not known.

SELANGOR *Selangor* **SELANGOR**
(24)   (25)   (26)

SELANGOR (vert)   **SELANGOR** (vert)
(29)   (30)

SELANGOR **SELANGOR**
(27)   (28)

SELANGOR (vert)   **SELANGOR** (vert)
(31)   (32)

SELANGOR *SELANGOR*
(33)   (34)

1885–91. *Nos. 63/a of Straits Settlements optd with T 24/34.*

31	24	2 c. pale rose	..	..	7·00	15·00
		a. Opt double	..	..	£800	£700
32	25	2 c. pale rose	..	..	£850	£900
33	26	2 c. pale rose	..	..	26·00	27·00
34	27	2 c. pale rose (1886)	..	..	50·00	50·00
		a. Opt double	..	..	†	£650
35	28	2 c. pale rose (horiz opt without stop) (1887)			6·00	2·25
		a. Opt double	..	..	£650	
		b. Bright rose	..	..	6·00	2·25
36		2 c. pale rose (horiz opt with stop) (1887)		55·00	48·00
		a. Bright rose	..	..		
37	29	2 c. pale rose (1889)	..	..	£160	75·00
38	30	2 c. pale rose (vert opt) (1889)	..	60·00	6·00
		a. Bright rose	..	..		
38b		2 c. bright rose (horiz opt) (1889)	..	£3000	
39	31	2 c. pale rose (diagonal opt) (1889)	..	£1500	
40	32	2 c. pale rose (1889)	..	..	£325	22·00
41	28	2 c. brt rose (vert opt without stop) (1890)	12·00	23·00
42	33	2 c. bright rose (1890)	..	..	£100	3·00
43	34	2 c. bright rose (1891)	..	..	£300	£150

Settings:
Nos. 31/4 – each in triplet containing three examples of the same stamp
No. 35 – triplet or 60 (6×10)
No. 36 – 60 (6×10)
Nos. 37/8 – 60 (6×10) containing both overprints in an unknown combination, but with No. 38 predominating
Nos. 38b/9 – not known
Nos. 40/3 – each in 60 (6×10)

SELANGOR Two CENTS   **SELANGOR** Two CENTS   **SELANGOR** Two CENTS
(35)   (36)   (37)

SELANGOR Two CENTS   **SELANGOR** Two CENTS
(38)   (39)

1891. *No. 68 of Straits Settlements, surch with T 35/9, each with bar obliterating old value.*

44	35	2 c. on 24 c. green	..	..	19·00	60·00
45	36	2 c. on 24 c. green	..	..	£130	£180
46	37	2 c. on 24 c. green	..	..	£130	£180
47	38	2 c. on 24 c. green	..	..	70·00	£110
		a. "SELANGCR"	..	..		
48	39	2 c. on 24 c. green	..	..	£130	£180

Nos. 44/8 come from the one setting used to surcharge the panes of sixty. No. 44 occurs in rows 1 to 5, No. 45 on row 6, No. 46 on row 7, No. 47 on rows 8 and 9, and No. 48 on row 10.
The error, No. 47a, occurs in the first printing only and is No. 45 (R.8/3) on the pane.

40

3 CENTS

(41)

1891 (Nov)–95. *Wmk Crown CA. P 14.*

49	40	1 c. green (1893)	..	..	80	25
50		2 c. rose	..	..	3·50	1·00
51		2 c. orange (1895)	..	..	2·00	60
52		5 c. blue (1892)	..	..	20·00	4·50
49/52				Set of 4	24·00	5·75
49/52		Optd "Specimen"		Set of 4	70·00	

1894. *Surch with T 41. Wmk Crown CA. P 14.*

53	40	3 c. on 5 c. rose (Optd S. £30)	..	1·75	40

42   43

 (SELANGOR, dented frame)

Dented frame above "A" of "SELANGOR" (left pane R. 4/5)

1895–99. *Wmk Crown CA or Crown CC (dollar values). P 14.*

54	42	3 c. dull purple and carmine	..	6·00	30
55		5 c. dull purple and olive-yellow	..	2·00	30
56		8 c. dull purple and ultramarine (1898)	55·00	7·00
57		10 c. dull purple and orange	..	9·00	1·50
58		25 c. green and carmine (1896)	..	80·00	50·00
59		50 c. dull purple & greenish black (1896)	42·00	22·00
		a. Dented frame	..	..	£300	
60		50 c. green and black (1898)	..	£300	£110
		a. Dented frame	..	..		
61	43	$1 green and yellow-green	..	45·00	95·00
62		$2 green and carmine (1897)	..	£160	£160
63		$3 green and ochre (1897)	..	£400	£275
64		$5 green and blue	..	..	£160	£200
65		$10 green and purple (1899) (S. £95)	£450	£550
66		$25 green and orange (1899?) (S. £190)	£1900	
54/62				Set of 9	£600	£400
54/64		Optd "Specimen"		Set of 11	£275	

Pending the arrival of the permanent Federated Malay States issue the stamps of STRAITS SETTLEMENTS and PERAK were used at various times between July 1900 and March 1901.
The general issues for the FEDERATED MALAY STATES were used in Selangor from 1901 until 1935.

One cent.   **Three cents.**
(44)   (45)

1900 (Oct). *Nos. 55 and 59 surch with T 44 or 45.*

66a	42	1 c. on 5 c. dull purple & ol-yell (31 Oct*)	60·00	£100
66b		1 c. on 50 c. green and black (22 Oct*)	1·00	17·00
		bc. "cent" repeated at left	..	£1700	
		bd. Dented frame	..	..	55·00	
67		3 c. on 50 c. green and black (30 Oct*)	4·00	17·00
		a. Antique "t" in "cents"	..	£225	£325
		b. Dented frame	..	..	£180	

*Earliest known postmark date.
It is believed that these stamps were surcharged from settings of 30, repeated four times to complete the sheet of 120.
No. 66bc occurred on two separate vertical strips of five stamps where two impressions of the setting overlapped.
The position in the setting of No. 67a is not known.

46 Mosque at Palace, Klang   47 Sultan Suleiman

(Des E. J. McNaughton)

1935 (2 Dec)–41. *Wmk Mult Script CA (sideways on T 46). Chalk-surfaced paper. P 14 or 14×14½ (No. 70).*

68	46	1 c. black (1.1.36)	..	..	30	10
69		2 c. green (1.1.36)	..	..	90	10
70		2 c. orange (ordinary paper) (p 14×14½) (21.8.41)		
			..	..	3·50	75
		a. Perf 14. Ordinary paper (9.41)	20·00	6·50
		ab. Chalk-surfaced paper	..	28·00	7·00
71		3 c. green (21.8.41)	..	..	15·00	2·75
		a. Ordinary paper	..	..	1·00	7·00
72		4 c. orange	..	..	30	10
73		5 c. brown (5.12.35)	..	..	70	10
74		6 c. scarlet (1.1.37)	..	..	5·50	10

75	46	8 c. grey	.. ..	60	10
76		10 c. dull purple (1.1.36)	..	60	10
77		12 c. bright ultramarine (1.1.36)		1·00	10
78		15 c. brt ultram (*ordinary paper*) (1.10.41)	11·00	32·00
79		25 c. dull purple and scarlet (4.4.36)		1·00	10
80		30 c. dull purple and orange (1.1.36)		1·00	85
81		40 c. scarlet and dull purple		1·25	1·25
82		50 c. black/*emerald* (1.2.36)		1·00	15
83	47	$1 black and rose/*blue* (1.4.36)		7·00	80
84		$2 green and scarlet (16.5.36)		22·00	8·00
85		$5 green and red/*emerald* (16.5.36)		50·00	23·00
68/85			*Set of 18*	95·00	60·00
68/85	Perf "Specimen"		*Set of 18*	£250	

The stamps issued during 1941 were printed by Harrison and Sons following bomb damage to the De La Rue works on 29 December 1940.

Supplies of an unissued 8 c. scarlet were diverted to Australia in 1941. Examples circulating result from leakages of this supply (*Price £425*).

48　Sultan Hisamud-din Alam Shah　**49**

1941. *Wmk Mult Script CA. Chalk-surfaced paper. P* 14.
86	48	$1 black and red/*blue* (15.4.41)	..	12·00	6·00
87		$2 green and scarlet (7.7.41) (Perf S. £70)	48·00	27·00

A $5 green and red on emerald, T **48**, was issued overprinted during the Japanese occupation of Malaya. Unoverprinted examples are known, but were not issued (*Price £100*).

> During shortages in 1941 stamps of STRAITS SETTLEMENTS (2 c.) and PERAK (25 c.) were issued in Selangor.

1948 (1 Dec). *Royal Silver Wedding. As Nos. 143/4 of Jamaica.*
88	10 c. violet	..	20	10
89	$5 green	..	24·00	14·00

1949 (12 Sept)–**55.** *Wmk Mult Script CA. Chalk-surfaced paper. P* 17½×18.
90	49	1 c. black	..	10	20
91		2 c. orange	..	10	30
92		3 c. green	..	30	1·50
93		4 c. brown	..	10	10
94		5 c. bright purple (1.9.52)		30	1·10
		a. Bright mauve (17.9.53)		30	10
95		6 c. grey	..	10	10
96		8 c. scarlet	..	25	65
97		8 c. green (1.9.52)		65	80
98		10 c. purple	..	10	10
99		12 c. scarlet (1.9.52)		80	2·50
		w. Wmk inverted		£150	
100		15 c. ultramarine	..	2·00	10
101		20 c. black and green		65	10
102		20 c. bright blue (1.9.52)		80	10
103		25 c. purple and orange		1·00	10
104		30 c. scarlet and purple (5.9.55)		1·25	90
105		35 c. scarlet and purple (1.9.52)		70	1·00
106		40 c. scarlet and purple		4·00	3·75
107		50 c. black and blue		70	10
108		$1 blue and purple		2·75	30
109		$2 green and scarlet		9·50	30
110		$5 green and brown		45·00	1·75
90/110			*Set of 21*	60·00	12·00

1949 (10 Oct). *75th Anniv of U.P.U. As Nos. 145/8 of Jamaica.*
111	10 c. purple	..	30	10
112	15 c. deep blue	..	1·50	1·25
113	25 c. orange	..	2·50	2·50
114	50 c. blue-black		1·25	2·50
111/14		*Set of 4*	3·25	5·50

1953 (2 June). *Coronation. As No. 153 of Jamaica.*
115	10 c. black and reddish purple	..	80	10

1957 (26 June)–**61.** *As Nos. 92/102 of Kedah but with inset portrait of Sultan Hisamud-din Alam Shah.*
116	1 c. black (21.8.57)	..	10	1·50
117	2 c. orange-red (25.7.57)	..	10	50
	a. Red-orange (10.11.59)	..	4·25	4·25
118	4 c. sepia (21.8.57)	..	10	10
119	5 c. carmine-lake (21.8.57)	..	10	10
120	8 c. myrtle-green (21.8.57)	..	1·10	2·00
121	10 c. deep brown (4.8.57)		40	10
122	10 c. deep maroon (9.5.61)		3·00	10
123	20 c. blue	..	1·50	10
124	50 c. black and blue (p 12½) (25.7.57)	30	10
	a. Perf 12½ × 13 (10.5.60)	..	30	10
125	$1 ultramarine and reddish purple (25.7.57)	2·00	10
126	$2 bronze-green & scarlet (p 12½) (21.8.57)	2·50	1·00
	a. Perf 13 × 12½ (6.12.60)	..	2·25	1·75
127	$5 brown and bronze-green (p 12½)	7·00	2·25
	a. Perf 13 × 12½ (10.5.60)	..	4·75	1·00
116/27a		*Set of 12*	14·00	5·50

The 6, 12, 25 and 30 c. values used with this issue were Nos. 1/4 of Malayan Federation.

50　Sultan Salahuddin Abdul Aziz Shah　**51**

(Photo Harrison)

1961 (28 June). *Coronation of the Sultan. W w* **12.** *P* 15 × 14.
128	**50**	10 c. multicoloured	..	20	10
		a. Black ptg misplaced	..	£150	

No. 128a is "The Double-headed Sultan" error, from one sheet where the majority of the stamps showed considerable black printing misplacement.

1961–62. *As Nos. 92/8 of Kedah but with inset portrait of Sultan Salahuddin Abdul Aziz as in T* **51.** *W w* **13.** *P* 12½ × 13 (*vert*) *or* 13 × 12½ (*horiz*).
129	1 c. black (1.3.62)	..	10	1·25
130	2 c. orange-red (1.3.62)	..	10	1·25
131	4 c. sepia (1.3.62)	..	30	10
132	5 c. carmine-lake (1.3.62)	..	30	10
133	8 c. myrtle-green (1.3.62)	..	2·00	3·00
134	10 c. deep maroon (1.11.61)		30	10
135	20 c. blue (1.3.62)	..	3·00	40
129/35		*Set of 7*	5·50	5·50

52 *Vanda hookeriana*　　**53** *Parthenos sylvia*

1965 (15 Nov). *As Nos. 166/72 of Johore but with inset portrait of Sultan Salahuddin Abdul Aziz Shah as in T* **52.**
136	1 c. multicoloured	..	10	10
	b. Magenta omitted	..	45·00	
	w. Wmk inverted	..	50	
137	2 c. multicoloured	..	10	90
	b. Yellow (flower) omitted	..	25·00	
138	5 c. multicoloured	..	15	10
	b. Yellow (flower) omitted	..	25·00	
	c. Red (leaves, etc) omitted		£110	
139	6 c. multicoloured	..	15	10
140	10 c. multicoloured	..	15	10
	a. Red omitted	..	45·00	
141	15 c. multicoloured	..	1·25	10
	b. Green (value and leaves) omitted	£160	
142	20 c. multicoloured	..	1·90	40
	a. Bright purple (blooms) omitted	45·00	
	b. Yellow (leaves) omitted	..	27·00	
136/42		*Set of 7*	3·25	1·50

The 2 c. to 20 c. values exist with PVA gum as well as gum arabic. The higher values used with this issue were Nos. 20/27 of Malaysia (National Issues).

1970 (20 Nov). *As Nos. 136 etc. but W w* **13** (*sideways*).
143	**52**	1 c. multicoloured	..	1·25	5·50
144		10 c. multicoloured	..	4·00	1·50
145		20 c. multicoloured	..	7·50	8·00
143/5			*Set of 3*	11·50	13·50

1971 (1 Feb)–**78.** *As Nos. 175/87 of Johore but with portrait of Sultan Salahuddin Abdul Aziz Shah and Arms, as in T* **53.**

(a) Litho by Bradbury, Wilkinson
146	1 c. multicoloured	..	40	1·00
147	2 c. multicoloured	..	1·00	1·00
148	5 c. multicoloured	..	1·00	10
149	6 c. multicoloured	..	1·00	1·00
150	10 c. multicoloured	..	1·00	10
	a. Black (state inscr, portrait and arms) omitted	..	85·00	
151	15 c. multicoloured	..	1·00	10
152	20 c. multicoloured	..	1·00	30
146/52		*Set of 7*	5·75	3·00

(b) Photo by Harrison (1977–78)
153	1 c. multicoloured	..	60	3·50
154	5 c. multicoloured	..	3·25	1·75
155	10 c. multicoloured	..	6·50	1·75
156	15 c. multicoloured	..	6·50	30
157	20 c. multicoloured	..	3·50	1·00
153/7		*Set of 5*	18·00	7·50

The higher values used with this issue were Nos. 64/71 of Malaysia (National Issues).

For differences between litho and photo printings see after Johore No. 187.

A used example of No. 150 has been seen with the magenta apparently missing.

For explanation of No. 150a, see note below No. 122 of Kelantan.

54 *Lagerstroemia speciosa*　　**55** Sultan Salahuddin Abdul Aziz Shah and Royal Crest

1979 (30 Apr). *As Nos. 188/94 of Johore but with portrait of Sultan Salahuddin Abdul Aziz Shah as in T* **54.**
158	1 c. *Rafflesia hasseltii*	..	10	60
159	2 c. *Pterocarpus indicus*	..	10	60
160	5 c. Type **54**	..	10	10
161	10 c. *Durio zibethinus*	..	15	10
162	15 c. *Hibiscus rosa-sinensis*	..	15	10
163	20 c. *Rhododendron scortechinii*		20	10
164	25 c. *Etlingera elatior* (inscr "*Phaeomeria speciosa*")		40	10
158/64		*Set of 7*	1·00	1·40

For higher values used in conjunction with this series see Nos. 190/7 of Malaysia (National Issues).

1983 (6 Oct)–**85.*** *As Nos. 160/3 but without wmk.*
166	5 c. Type **54** (20.11.83)	..	50	50
167	10 c. *Durio zibethinus* (3.85)	..	75	1·00
168	15 c. *Hibiscus rosa-sinensis* (20.11.83)	70	60
169	20 c. *Rhododendron scortechinii* (blackish brown background)	20·00	90
169a	20 c. *Rhododendron scortechinii* (bronze-green background) (12.12.83)	80	55

*There was no official release date for these stamps. Dates shown are the earliest recorded from postmarks and may be revised if earlier examples are reported.

For details of the shade differences between watermarked and unwatermarked printings see after Johore No. 200a.

On Nos. 166/8 and 169a the ruler's headdress is bolder than on Nos. 160/3 and 169.

(Des P. Ket. Litho Security Printers (M), Malaysia)

1985 (5 Sept). *Silver Jubilee of Sultan. P* 13.
173	**55**	15 c. multicoloured	..	1·10	10
174		20 c. multicoloured	..	1·10	15
175		$1 multicoloured	..	5·00	6·50
173/5			*Set of 3*	6·50	6·50

56 Black Pepper

1986 (25 Oct)–**96.** *As Nos. 202/8 of Johore, but with portrait of Sultan Salahuddin Abdul Aziz Shah as in T* **56.** *P* 12.
176	1 c. Coffee	..	10	10
	w. Wmk inverted	..	10 *D*	
177	2 c. Coconuts	..	10	10
178	5 c. Cocoa	..	10	10
	c. Perf 14×13¾ (1994)	..	1·00	10
	cw. Wmk inverted	..	4·25	
	f. Perf 14¾×14½ (1994)	..	4·50	30
179	10 c. Type **56**	..	10	10
	a. Wmk sideways	..	13·00	
	bw. Wmk inverted			
	c. Perf 14×13¾ (1995)	..	3·50	20
	cw. Wmk inverted	..	10·00	
	e. Perf 14×14½ (1994)	..	5·00	
	f. Perf 14¾×14½ (1994)	..	1·25	10
180	15 c. Rubber	..	10	10
181	20 c. Oil palm	..	10	10
	aw. Wmk inverted			
	c. Perf 14×13¾ (1994)	..	1·00	10
	f. Perf 14¾×14½ (1996)	..	3·25	10
182	30 c. Rice	..	15	20
	aw. Wmk inverted			
	c. Perf 14×13¾ (1994)	..	1·00	10
	cw. Wmk inverted	..	6·00	
	e. Perf 14×14½ (1994)	..	6·50	20
	f. Perf 14¾×14½ (1995)	..	4·50	20
176/82		*Set of 7*	50	55

STAMP BOOKLETS

1935. *Stapled.*
- SB1　$1 booklet containing twenty 5 c. (No. 73) in blocks of 10
- SB2　$1.30, booklet containing 5 c. and 8 c. (Nos. 73, 75), each in block of 10

1973 (8 Dec). *Cover as Type B* **1** *of Johore, but inscr* "SELANGOR". *Stitched.*
- SB3　$3 booklet containing eight 5 c., 10 c. and twelve 15 c. (Nos. 148, 150/1) in blocks of 4 .. 25·00

1979 (1 Dec). *Cover as No. SB5 of Johore, but inscr* "SELANGOR". *Stitched.*
- SB4　$3 booklet containing eight 5 c., 10 c, and twelve 15 c. (Nos. 160/2) in blocks of 4 .. 9·00

No. SB4 exists with two different versions of the back cover.

1986. *Black on lemon cover as Type B* **2** *of Federal Territory. Stamps attached by selvedge.*
- SB5　$1.50, booklet containing 15 c. (No. 162) in pair and 20 c. (No. 169a) in block of 6 .. 9·00

1986. *Cover as No. SB5, but surch with new value and contents. Stamps attached by selvedge.*
- SB6　60 c. booklet containing 20 c. (No. 169a) in strip of 3 .. 11·00

1987. *Black on buff cover as Type B* **2** *of Federal Territory. Stamps attached by selvedge.*
- SB7　60 c. booklet containing 20 c. (No. 181) in strip of 3　3·25

1987 (1 June). *Cover as Type B* **2** *of Johore, but inscr* "SELANGOR". *Stapled.*
- SB8　$2 booklet containing 5 c., 10 c., 15 c. and 20 c. (Nos. 178/81) in blocks of 4 .. 8·00

1991. *Black on buff cover as Type B* **2** *of Federal Territory. Stamps attached by selvedge.*
- SB9　60 c. booklet containing 10 c. (No. 179) in strip of 3 and 15 c. (No. 180) in pair .. 1·75

1992 (1 July). "*Kuala Lumpur '92*" *International Philatelic Exhibition. Cover as Type B* **3** *of Johore, but inscr* "Selangor". *Stamps attached by selvedge.*
- SB10　$3 booklet containing 30 c. (No. 182) in block of 10 .. 8·00

1993 (June). *Covers as Nos. SB8/9 of Johore, but both on pale buff and inscr* "Selangor". *Stamps attached by selvedge.*
- SB11　$2 booklet containing 20 c. (No. 181) in block of 10 .. 1·00
- SB12　$3 booklet containing 30 c. (No. 182) in block of 10 .. 1·50

TRENGGANU

Suzerainty over Trengganu was transferred by Thailand to Great Britain in 1909. A British adviser was appointed in 1919. The state joined the Federation of Malaya on 1 February 1948.

PRICES FOR STAMPS ON COVER TO 1945

Nos. 1/17	*from* × 12
No. 18	—
Nos. 19/22	*from* × 10
Nos. 23/33	*from* × 12
Nos. 34/6	—
Nos. 37/47	*from* × 15
Nos. 48/60	*from* × 6
Nos. D1/4	

RED CROSS

2c.

1	Sultan Zain ul ab din **2**	**(3)**

1910 (14 Dec)—**19.** *Wmk Mult Crown CA. Ordinary paper (1 c. to 10 c.) or chalk-surfaced paper (20 c. to $25). P 14.*

1	1	1 c. blue-green	..	80	1·00
		a. Green	..	2·25	1·00
2		2 c. brown and purple (1915)	..	60	90
3		3 c. carmine-red	..	2·25	2·25
4		4 c. orange	..	3·50	5·50
5		4 c. red-brown and green (1915)	..	2·00	3·75
5a		4 c. carmine-red (1919)	..	70	1·75
6		5 c. grey	..	1·25	3·25
7		5 c. grey and brown (1915)	..	2·25	2·00
8		8 c. ultramarine	..	1·25	9·00
9		10 c. purple/*yellow*	..	5·00	12·00
		a. On pale yellow	..	3·00	4·50
10		10 c. green and red/*yellow* (1915)	..	1·00	2·25
11		20 c. dull and bright purple	..	2·75	4·25
12		25 c. green and dull purple (1915)	..	5·50	27·00
13		30 c. dull purple and black (1915)	..	6·50	48·00
14		50 c. black/*green*	..	4·50	7·00
15		$1 black and carmine/*blue*	..	16·00	18·00
16		$3 green and red/*green* (1915)	..	£120	£225
17	2	$5 green and dull purple (1912)	..	£130	£375
18		$25 rose-carm & grn (1912) (Optd S. £170)		£800	
1/17			*Set of 18*	£275	£650
1/17 Optd "Specimen"			*Set of 18*	£425	

The 8 c. is known used bisected at Kretai in December 1918. Such use was not officially authorised.

1917 (June)—**18.** *Surch with T 3.*

19	1	2 c. on 3 c. carmine-red	..	30	4·75
		a. Comma after "2 c."	..	7·50	35·00
		b. "SS" in "CROSS" inverted	..	£300	£350
		c. "CSOSS" for "CROSS"	..	80·00	£160
		d. "2" in thick block type	..	20·00	55·00
		e. Surch inverted	..	£700	£750
		f. Pair, one without surch	..	£2500	£2000
		g. "RED CROSS" omitted	..	£250	
		h. "RED CROSS" twice	..	£325	
		i. "2 c." omitted	..	£250	
		j. "2 c." twice	..	£300	
20		2 c. on 4 c. orange	..	1·00	11·00
		a. Comma after "2 c."	..	16·00	60·00
		b. "SS" in "CROSS" inverted	..	£1500	£1000
		c. "CSOSS" for "CROSS"	..	£170	£350
		d. Surch double	..	£850	
		e. "RED CROSS" omitted	..	£300	
		f. "RED CROSS" twice	..	£450	
		g. "2 c." omitted	..	£300	
		h. "2 c." twice	..	£400	
21		2 c. on 4 c. red-brown and green (1918)		2·00	28·00
		a. Pair, one without surch	..	£1700	
22		2 c. on 8 c. ultramarine (1917)	..	60	25·00
		a. Comma after "2 c."	..	11·00	80·00
		b. "SS" in "CROSS" inverted	..	£650	
		c. "CSOSS" for "CROSS"	..	£140	£375
		d. "RED CROSS" omitted	..	£300	
		e. "RED CROSS" twice	..	£400	
		f. "2 c." omitted	..	£300	
		g. "2 c." twice	..	£375	

The surcharges on Nos. 19/22 were arranged in settings of 18 (6×3) applied three times to cover the top nine rows of the sheet with the tenth row completed by a further impression so that "RED CROSS" from the centre row of the setting appears on the bottom sheet margin. Specialists recognise six different settings:

Setting I — Shows comma after "2" on both R.1/3 and 1/5, "SS" inverted on R.1/6 and "CSOSS" for "CROSS" on R.2/1. Used for 4 c. orange and 8 c.

Setting Ia — Inverted "SS" on R.1/6 corrected. Other varieties as Setting I. Used for 3 c., 4 c. orange and 8 c.

Setting II — "CSOSS" on R.2/1 corrected. Comma varieties as Setting I. Used for 3 c., 4 c. orange and 8 c.

Setting III — Both comma varieties now corrected. Used for 3 c., both 4 c. and 8 c.

Setting IIIa — "SS" inverted on R.2/5. Used for 3 c. only

Setting IV — Thick block "2" on R. 2/2. Inverted "SS" on R. 2/5 corrected. Used for 3 c. only.

Nos. 19/g/j, 20e/h and 22d/g result from the misplacement of the surcharge.

MINIMUM PRICE

The minimum price quote is 10p which represents a handling charge rather than a basis for valuing common stamps. For further notes about prices see introductory pages.

During a temporary shortage between March and August 1921 2 c., 4 c. and 6 c. stamps of the STRAITS SETTLE-MENTS were authorised for use in Trengganu.

2 CENTS

4	Sultan Suleiman **5**		**(6)**

1921–41. *Chalk-surfaced paper. P 14. (a) Wmk Mult Crown CA.*

23	4	$1 purple and blue/*blue* ..	12·00	20·00
24		$3 green and red/*emerald* ..	85·00	£180
25	5	$5 green and red/*pale yellow* ..	85·00	£250
23/5		*Set of 3*	£170	£400
23/5 Optd "Specimen"		*Set of 3*	£100	

(b) Wmk Mult Script CA

26	4	1 c. black (1926)	1·25	1·00
		a. Ordinary paper (1941)	—	17·00
27		2 c. green	1·25	1·40
		a. Ordinary paper (1941)	—	17·00
28		3 c. green (1926)	1·75	85
29		3 c. reddish brown (1938)	21·00	11·00
		a. Ordinary paper. Chestnut (1941)	—	13·00
30		4 c. rose-red	1·25	50
		a. Ordinary paper. Scarlet-verm (1941)	—	17·00
31		5 c. grey and deep brown	2·00	4·50
32		5 c. purple/*yellow* (1926)	1·75	1·00
		a. Deep reddish purple/brt yellow (1939)		
33		6 c. orange (1924)	3·25	30
		a. Ordinary paper (1941)	—	20·00
34		8 c. grey (1938)	22·00	4·25
		a. Ordinary paper (1941)	—	15·00
35		10 c. bright blue	2·00	80
36		12 c. bright ultramarine (1926)	4·25	4·25
37		20 c. dull purple and orange	2·00	1·50
38		25 c. green and deep purple	2·25	2·75
39		30 c. dull purple and black	3·25	2·25
40		35 c. carmine/*yellow* (1926)	4·75	8·00
41		50 c. green and bright carmine	5·00	2·25
42		$1 purple and blue/*blue* (1929)	9·00	3·50
43		$3 green and lake/*green* (1926)	60·00	£120
		a. Green and brown-red/green (1938)	£130	
44	5	$5 green and red/*yellow* (1938)	£250	£1300
45		$25 purple and blue (S. £100)	£650	£950
46		$50 green and yellow (S. £190)	£1500	£2500
47		$100 green and scarlet (S. £400)	£4750	£5500
26/44		*Set of 19*	£350	£1400
26/44 Optd/Perf "Specimen"		*Set of 19*	£600	

The used price quoted for No. 44 is for an example with an identifiable cancellation from 1938–41.

Printings of the 2 c. yellow-orange, 3 c. blue-green, 4 c. purple/*yellow*, 6 c. slate-grey, 8 c. rose, 15 c. ultramarine and $1 black and red/*blue* on ordinary paper were despatched to Malaya in late 1941, but did not arrive before the Japanese occupation. Unused examples are known of the 2, 3, 6, 8 and 15 c. (Prices, 3 c. £225, others £120 each, unused).

1922 (31 Mar). *Malaya–Borneo Exhibition, Singapore. Optd "MALAYA–BORNEO EXHIBITION" as T 56 of Straits Settlements at Singapore.*

48	4	2 c. green	2·75	25·00
49		4 c. rose-red	5·50	25·00
50	1	5 c. grey and brown	2·75	28·00
51		10 c. green and red/*yellow*	3·50	30·00
52		20 c. dull and bright purple	3·00	35·00
53		25 c. green and dull purple	3·00	35·00
54		30 c. dull purple and black	3·00	35·00
55		50 c. black/*green*	3·00	35·00
56		$1 black and carmine/*blue*	10·00	65·00
57		$3 green and red/*green*	£120	£350
58	2	$5 green and dull purple	£225	£750
48/58		*Set of 11*	£325	£1100

Minor varieties of this overprint exist as in Straits Settlements.

1941 (1 May). *Nos. 32a and 35 surch as T 6.*

59	4	2 c. on 5 c. deep reddish purple/*brt yellow*	6·50	3·50
60		2 c. on 10 c. bright blue ..	7·00	3·50

1948 (2 Dec). *Royal Silver Wedding. As Nos. 143/4 of Jamaica.*

61		10 c. violet ..	15	90
62		$5 carmine ..	22·00	35·00

1949 (10 Oct). *75th Anniv of U.P.U. As Nos. 145/8 of Jamaica.*

63		10 c. purple ..	30	35
64		15 c. deep blue ..	1·10	2·25
65		25 c. orange ..	55	2·25
66		50 c. blue-black ..	1·40	3·00
63/6		*Set of 4*	3·00	7·00

7 Sultan Ismail	**8** *Vanda hookeriana*	

1949 (27 Dec)—**55.** *Wmk Mult Script CA. Chalk-surfaced paper. P 17½×18.*

67	7	1 c. black ..	10	30
68		2 c. orange ..	10	30
69		3 c. green ..	30	2·25
70		4 c. brown ..	10	30
71		5 c. bright purple (1.9.52) ..	30	90
72		6 c. grey ..	40	30

73	7	8 c. scarlet ..	20	1·75
74		8 c. green (1.9.52) ..	65	1·00
		a. Deep green (11.8.53)	4·50	5·50
75		10 c. purple ..	20	10
76		12 c. scarlet (1.9.52) ..	65	1·75
77		15 c. ultramarine ..	65	30
78		20 c. black and green ..	65	2·25
79		20 c. bright blue (1.9.52) ..	80	30
80		25 c. purple and orange ..	75	90
81		30 c. scarlet and purple (5.9.55) ..	1·25	1·25
82		35 c. scarlet and purple (1.9.52) ..	70	1·60
83		40 c. red and purple ..	3·25	12·00
84		50 c. black and blue ..	80	1·25
85		$1 blue and purple ..	4·25	5·50
86		$2 green and scarlet ..	22·00	17·00
87		$5 green and brown ..	50·00	48·00
67/87		*Set of 21*	80·00	90·00

1953 (2 June). *Coronation. As No. 153 of Jamaica.*

88	10 c. black and reddish purple ..	85	85

1957 (26 June)—**63.** *As Nos. 92/102 of Kedah, but with inset portrait of Sultan Ismail.*

89	1 c. black (21.8.57)	10	20
90	2 c. orange-red (25.7.57)	1·00	30
	a. Red-orange (21.2.61)	14·00	11·00
91	4 c. sepia (21.8.57)	10	10
92	5 c. carmine-lake (21.8.57)	10	10
93	8 c. myrtle-green (21.8.57)	4·00	60
94	10 c. deep brown (4.8.57)	45	10
94a	10 c. deep maroon (21.2.61)	3·25	10
95	20 c. blue	70	80
96	50 c. black and blue (p 12½) (25.7.57)	30	1·75
	ab. Perf 12½ × 13 (17.5.60)	30	85
	ab. Black and ultramarine (20.3.62)	1·25	1·00
97	$1 ultramarine and reddish purple (25.7.57)	5·50	5·00
98	$2 bronze-green and scarlet (21.8.57)	12·00	6·00
99	$5 brown and bronze-green ..	15·00	15·00
	a. Perf 13 × 12½ (13.8.63)	18·00	15·00
89/99	*Set of 12*	38·00	25·00

The 6, 12, 25 and 30 c. values used with this issue were Nos. 1/4 of Malayan Federation.

1965 (15 Nov). *As Nos. 166/72 of Johore but with inset portrait of Sultan Ismail Nasiruddin Shah as in T 8.*

100	1 c. multicoloured	10	1·00
101	2 c. multicoloured	10	1·00
102	5 c. multicoloured	15	30
103	6 c. multicoloured	15	85
104	10 c. multicoloured	20	10
105	15 c. multicoloured	1·50	10
106	20 c. multicoloured	1·50	70
	a. Bright purple (blooms) omitted	60·00	
100/6	*Set of 7*	3·25	3·50

The 5 c. value exists with PVA gum as well as gum arabic.

No. 101a, formerly listed here, is now listed as Sarawak No. 213a. The higher values used with this issue were Nos. 20/27 of Malaysia (National Issues).

9 Sultan of Trengganu	**10** *Papilio demoleus*

(Des Enche Nik Zainal Abidin. Photo Harrison)

1970 (16 Dec). *25th Anniv of Installation of H.R.H. Tuanku Ismail Nasiruddin Shah as Sultan of Trengganu. P 14½ × 13½.*

107	9	10 c. multicoloured	50	1·25
108		15 c. multicoloured	50	90
109		50 c. multicoloured	2·00	2·25
107/9		*Set of 3*	1·75	4·00

1971 (1 Feb)—**78.** *As Nos. 175/87 of Johore but with portrait of Sultan Ismail Nasiruddin Shah and Arms, as in T 10.*

(a) Litho by Bradbury, Wilkinson

110	1 c. multicoloured	30	1·50
111	2 c. multicoloured	70	1·50
112	5 c. multicoloured	1·00	60
113	6 c. multicoloured	1·25	1·75
114	10 c. multicoloured	1·25	50
115	15 c. multicoloured	1·25	20
116	20 c. multicoloured	1·50	90
110/16	*Set of 7*	6·50	6·25

(b) Photo by Harrison (1977–78)

116a	5 c. multicoloured	22·00	9·00
117	10 c. multicoloured	6·50	3·00
117a	15 c. multicoloured	4·75	1·25

The higher values used with this issue were Nos. 64/71 of Malaysia (National Issues).

For differences between litho and photo printings, see after Johore No. 187.

11 *Durio zibethinus*	**12** Sultan Mahmud

1979 (30 Apr). *As Nos. 188/94 of Johore but with portrait of Sultan Ismail Nasiruddin Shah as in T* **11**.
118	1 c. *Rafflesia hasseltii*		10	70
119	2 c. *Pterocarpus indicus*		10	70
120	5 c. *Lagerstroemia speciosa*		10	30
121	10 c. Type **11**		15	10
122	15 c. *Hibiscus rosa-sinensis*		15	10
123	20 c. *Rhododendron scortechinii*		20	10
124	25 c. *Etlingera elatior* (inscr "*Phaeomeria speciosa*")		40	40
118/24		Set of 7	1·00	2·10

For higher values used in conjunction with this series see Nos. 190/7 of Malaysia (National Issues).

(Des Malaysian Advertising Services. Litho Harrison)
1981 (21 Mar). *Installation of Sultan Mahmud. P* 14.
125	**12**	10 c. black, gold and new blue	30	80
126		15 c. black, gold and yellow	35	35
127		50 c. black, gold and bright purple	90	2·50
125/7		Set of 3	1·40	3·25

1983 (Oct)–**86.*** *As Nos. 121/4 but without wmk.*
131	10 c. Type **11** (1.2.86)		13·00	4·00
132	15 c. *Hibiscus rosa-sinensis* (24.1.85)		75	1·00
133	20 c. *Rhododendron scortechinii* (blackish brown background)		19·00	5·00
133a	20 c. *Rhododendron scortechinii* (bronze-green background) (2.3.84)		2·75	3·00
134	25 c. *Etlingera elatior* (inscr "*Phaeomeria speciosa*") (13.11.83)		75	1·00

*There was no official release date for these stamps. Dates shown are the earliest recorded from postmarks and may be revised if earlier examples are reported.
For details of the shade differences between watermarked and unwatermarked printings see after Johore No. 200a.
On Nos. 131/2, 133a and 134 the portrait and state arms have been redrawn smaller.

13 Rubber	**14** Sultan Mizan Zainal Abidin and Istana Maziah

1986 (25 Oct)–**96.** *As Nos. 202/8 of Johore, but with portrait of Sultan Mahmud and inscr "TERENGGANU" as in T* **13**. *P* 12.
135	1 c. Coffee		10	10
	b. Perf 13½×13¾ (1993)		4·50	40
136	2 c. Coconuts		10	10
137	5 c. Cocoa		10	10
	w. Wmk inverted		10·00	
138	10 c. Black pepper		10	10
	c. Perf 14×13¾ (1995)		7·00	30
	cw. Wmk inverted		5·50	
139	15 c. Type **13**		10	10
140	20 c. Oil palm		10	10
	c. Perf 14×13¾ (1995)		7·00	30
141	30 c. Rice		15	20
	c. Perf 14×13¾ (1994)		6·50	40
	f. Perf 14¾×14½ (1995)		3·00	30
135/41		Set of 7	50	55

(Des P. Chuah. Litho Security Printers (M), Malaysia)
1999 (4 Mar). *Installation of Sultan Mizan Zainal Abidin as Sultan of Terengganu. T* **14** *and similar horiz designs. Multicoloured. W* **138**. *P* 14½ (30 c.) or 13½ (others).
142	30 c. Type **14**		10	10
143	50 c. Istana Maziah, 1903		15	20
144	$1 Mosque and minaret at night		30	35
142/4		Set of 3	55	65

STAMP BOOKLETS

1973 (8 Dec). *Cover as Type B* **1** *of Johore but inscr "TRENGGANU". Stitched.*
SB1 $3 booklet containing eight 5 c., 10 c. and twelve 15 c. (Nos. 112, 114/15) in blocks of 4 . . 27·00
Examples of No. SB1 exist with a white label giving revised postage rates.

1979 (1 Dec). *Cover as No. SB5 of Johore, but inscr "TRENGGANU". Stitched.*
SB2 $3 booklet containing eight 5 c., 10 c., and twelve 15 c. (Nos. 120/2) in blocks of 4 . . 10·00
No. SB2 exists with two different versions of the back cover.

1987 (1 June). *Cover as Type SB* **2** *of Johore, but inscr "TERENGGANU". Stapled.*
SB3 $2 booklet containing 5 c., 10 c., 15 c. and 20 c. (Nos. 137/40) in blocks of 4 . . . . 8·50

1992 (1 July). *"Kuala Lumpur '92" International Philatelic Exhibition. Cover as Type B* **3** *of Johore, but inscr "Terengganu". Stamps attached by selvedge.*
SB4 $3 booklet containing 30 c. (No. 141) in block of 10 8·50

1993. *Covers as Nos. SB8/9 of Johore, but inscr "Terengganu". Stamps attached by selvedge.*
SB5 $2 booklet containing 20 c. (No. 140) in block of 10 1·00
SB6 $3 booklet containing 30 c. (No. 141) in block of 10 1·50

POSTAGE DUE STAMPS

D **1**

1937 (10 Aug). *Wmk Mult Script CA. P* 14.
D1	D **1**	1 c. scarlet		7·50	55·00
D2		4 c. green		9·00	60·00
D3		8 c. yellow		55·00	£300
D4		10 c. brown		£110	95·00
D1/4			Set of 4	£160	£450
D1/4	Perf "Specimen"		Set of 4	£130	

VIII. SIAMESE POSTS IN NORTHERN MALAYA 1887–1909

The Thai monarchy exercised suzerainty over the northern states of the Malay Peninsula from the 16th century onwards. The extent of Thai involvement in the internal affairs of Kedah, Kelantan, Perlis and Trengganu was very variable, being dependent on the strength, or otherwise, of the Bangkok administration and the degree of co-operation of the local rulers.

The Thai public postal service, which had been inaugurated in 1883, gradually extended into the north of the Malay Peninsula from 1887 onwards and post offices were established in Kedah, Kelantan and Perlis. There is some evidence that Sultan Zainal Abidin III of Trengganu successfully blocked the use of Siamese stamps in his state.

Types of Thailand (Siam)

The following types of postmark were used on Siamese stamps from the Malay tributary states:

Type A. Single ring with date at foot (examples from 1900 show the year in manuscript)

Type B. Single ring with date in centre

Type C. Double ring. Bilingual

Type D. Double ring. English at top and ornament at foot

Type E. Double ring. English at top and bottom

PRICES are for stamps showing a large part of the postmark with the inscription clearly visible.

KEDAH

The Siamese post office at Alor Star was opened during 1887 with the first known postmark being dated 27 October. Further post offices at Kuala Muda (3 Oct 1907), Kulim (7 July 1907) and Langkawi (16 Feb 1908) followed.

A straight-line obliteration showing "KEDAH" between short vertical dashes is not believed to be genuine.

Alor Star

Stamps of SIAM *cancelled as Type A inscribed* "KEDAH".

1883. (Nos. 1/5).
Z2	1	1 att. rose-carmine	.. ..	£225
Z3		1 sio. red		£425
Z4	2	1 sik. yellow		£425

1887–91. (Nos. 11/18).
Z 6	9	1 a. green		80·00
Z 7		2 a. green and carmine		70·00
Z 8		3 a. green and blue		90·00
Z 9		4 a. green and brown		80·00
Z10		8 a. green and yellow		80·00
Z11		12 a. purple and carmine		70·00
Z12		24 a. purple and blue		80·00
Z13		64 a. purple and brown		£130

1889–91. Surch as *T 12* (Nos. Z15, Z19), *T 17* (No. Z21) or *T 18* (No. Z22) (Nos. 20/30).
Z15	9	1 a. on 2 a. green and carmine		90·00
Z19		1 a. on 3 a. green and blue		£100
Z21		2 a. on 3 a. green and blue		£130
Z22		2 a. on 3 a. green and blue		£160

1892. Surch as *T 24/5* (with or without stop) and Siamese handstamp (Nos. 33/6).
Z28	9	4 a. on 24 a. purple and blue (Type 24)	90·00
Z29		4 a. on 24 a. purple and blue (Type 25)	£110
Z30		4 a. on 24 a. purple and blue (Type 24 with stop)	£110
Z31		4 a. on 24 a. purple and blue (Type 25 with stop)	£110

1894. Surch as *T 27* with variations of English figures as *T 28* and *33* (Nos. 37/44).
Z34	9	2 a. on 64 a. purple and brown (Type 28)	90·00
Z39		2 a. on 64 a. purple and brown (Type 33)	90·00

1894. Surch with *T 34* (No. 45).
Z41	9	1 a. on 64 a. purple and brown	£110

1894–95. Surch as *T 35* with variations of English figures as *T 36/9* (Nos. 46/50).
Z42	9	1 a. on 64 a. purple and brown (Type 35)	90·00
Z43		1 a. on 64 a. purple and brown (Type 36)	90·00
Z44		2 a. on 64 a. purple and brown (Type 37)	90·00
Z45		2 a. on 64 a. purple and brown (Type 38)	90·00
Z46		10 a. on 24 a. purple and blue (Type 39)	90·00

1896. Surch as *T 39* (Siamese) and *T 40* (English) (No. 51).
Z47	9	4 a. on 12 a. purple and carmine	90·00

1897. Surch as *T 39* (Siamese) and *T 41* (English) (No. 52).
Z48	9	4 a. on 12 a. purple and carmine	90·00

1898–99. Surch as *T 42* with variations of English section as *T 44/6* (Nos. 53/62).
Z49	9	1 a. on 12 a. purple and carmine (Type 42–11½ mm long)	£120
Z52		2 a. on 64 a. purple and brown (Type 44)	£100
Z53		3 a. on 12 a. purple and carmine (Type 45–13½ mm long)	90·00
Z54		3 a. on 12 a. purple and carmine (Type 45–11½ to 11¾ mm long)	90·00
Z55		4 a. on 12 a. purple & carm (Type 46–8 mm long)	90·00
Z56		4 a. on 12 a. purple and carmine (Type 46–8½ to 9 mm long)	90·00

1899. Surch in Siamese and English with *T 48a* (Nos. 63/6).
Z62	9	2 a. on 64 a. purple and brown	£100

1899–1904. (Nos. 67/81).
Z63	49	1 a. olive-green (wide Siamese characters in face value)	90·00
Z64		2 a. grass-green	70·00
Z65		3 a. red and blue	75·00
Z66		4 a. carmine	70·00
Z67		8 a. deep green and orange	70·00
Z69		12 a. brown-purple and carmine	£110
Z70		24 a. brown-purple and blue	£160
Z71		64 a. brown-purple and chestnut	£130

1899. (Nos. 82/6).
Z72	50	1 a. green	£275
Z73		2 a. green and red	£425

Stamps of SIAM *cancelled as Type B inscr* "KEDAH" (from March 1901).

1887–91. (Nos. 11/18).
Z74	9	12 a. purple and carmine	70·00
Z75		24 a. purple and brown	70·00

1898–99. Surch with *T 42* with variations of English section as *T 45/6* (Nos. 53/62).
Z76	9	1 a. on 12 a. pur & carm (Type 42–11½ mm long)	90·00
Z81		3 a. on 12 a. purple and carmine (Type 45–11½ to 11¾ mm long)	70·00
Z83		4 a. on 12 a. purple and carmine (Type 46–8½ to 9 mm long)	70·00
Z84		4 a. on 24 a. purple and blue (Type 46)	75·00

1899–1904. (Nos. 67/81).
Z86	49	1 a. olive-green (wide Siamese characters in face value)	70·00
		a. Narrow Siamese characters in face value	65·00
Z87		2 a. grass-green	55·00
Z88		2 a. scarlet and pale blue	55·00
Z89		3 a. red and blue	65·00
Z90		3 a. deep green	65·00
Z91		4 a. carmine	55·00
Z92		4 a. chocolate and pink	60·00
Z93		8 a. deep green and orange	55·00
Z94		10 a. ultramarine	55·00
Z95		12 a. brown-purple and carmine	65·00
Z96		24 a. brown-purple and blue	£130
Z97		64 a. brown-purple and chestnut	£120

1905–09. (Nos. 92/105).
Z102	53	1 a. green and orange	55·00
Z103		2 a. grey and deep violet	55·00
Z104		3 a. green	65·00
Z105		4 a. pale red and sepia	55·00
Z106		5 a. carmine	65·00
Z107		8 a. olive-bistre and dull black	55·00
Z108		12 a. blue	65·00
Z109		24 a. red-brown	£160
Z110		1 t. bistre and deep blue	£160

Stamps of SIAM *cancelled as Type C inscr* "Kedah" *at foot (from July 1907).*

1887–91. (Nos. 11/18).
Z111	9	12 a. purple and carmine	80·00

1899–1904. (*Nos. 67/81*).
Z112 **49** 1 a. olive-green (wide Siamese characters in
    face value) .. .. 65·00
    a. Narrow Siamese characters in face value 60·00
Z113   2 a. scarlet and pale blue .. .. .. 55·00
Z114   3 a. red and blue .. .. 65·00
Z116   8 a. deep green and orange .. .. 65·00
Z117   10 a. ultramarine .. .. 60·00
Z118   12 a. brown-purple and carmine .. .. 60·00

1905–09. (*Nos. 95/105*).
Z128 **53** 1 a. green and orange .. .. .. 55·00
Z129   2 a. grey and deep violet .. .. 55·00
Z130   3 a. green .. .. 65·00
Z131   4 a. pale red and sepia .. .. .. 55·00
Z132   4 a. scarlet .. .. 55·00
Z133   5 a. carmine .. .. 65·00
Z134   8 a. olive-bistre and dull black .. 55·00
Z135   9 a. blue .. .. 55·00
Z136   18 a. red-brown .. .. 90·00
Z137   24 a. red-brown £160
Z138   1 t. bistre and deep blue £160

1907. *Surch with T* **56** (*No.* 109).
Z139 **9** 1 a. on 24 a. purple and blue .. 65·00

Kuala Muda

Stamps of SIAM *cancelled as Type B inscr* "KUALA MUDA"
(*from Oct 1907*).

1887–91. (*Nos. 11/18*).
Z143 **9** 12 a. purple and carmine £300

1899–1904. (*Nos. 67/81*).
Z144 **49** 2 a. scarlet and pale blue £300
Z145   24 a. brown-purple and blue £350

1905–09. (*Nos. 92/105*).
Z146 **53** 1 a. green and orange £300
Z147   2 a. grey and deep violet £300
Z148   3 a. green £325
Z150   5 a. carmine £325
Z151   8 a. olive-bistre and dull black .. £300

Stamps of SIAM *cancelled as Type C inscr* "Kwala Muda" *at foot*
(*from 1907*).

1887–91. (*Nos. 11/18*).
Z155 **9** 12 a. purple and carmine £140

1899–1904. (*Nos. 67/81*).
Z156 **49** 8 a. deep green and orange £170
Z157   10 a. ultramarine £170

1905–09. (*Nos. 92/105*).
Z158 **53** 1 a. green and orange £170
Z159   2 a. grey and deep violet £170
Z160   3 a. green £180
Z161   4 a. pale red and sepia £170
Z162   4 a. scarlet £170
Z163   5 a. carmine £190
Z164   8 a. olive-bistre and dull black .. £170
Z165   9 a. blue £140
Z166   24 a. red-brown £350

1907. *Surch with T* **56** (*No.* 109).
Z167 **9** 1 a. on 24 a. purple and blue £140

Kulim

Stamps of SIAM *cancelled as Type D inscr* "KULIM" (*from July
1907*).

1887–91. (*Nos. 11/18*).
Z173 **9** 12 a. purple and carmine £300

1899–1904. (*Nos. 67/81*).
Z174 **49** 8 a. deep green and orange £300

1905–09. (*Nos. 92/105*).
Z175 **53** 1 a. green and orange £325
Z176   2 a. grey and deep violet £325
Z178   4 a. pale red and sepia £300
Z179   4 a. scarlet £300
Z180   5 a. carmine £325
Z181   8 a. olive-bistre and dull black .. £300
Z182   9 a. blue £300

1907. *Surch with T* **56** (*No.* 109).
Z184 **9** 1 a. on 24 a. purple and blue £300

Stamps of SIAM *cancelled as Type C inscr* "Kulim" *at foot* (*from
Feb 1908*).

1887–91. (*Nos. 11/18*).
Z190 **9** 12 a. purple and carmine £120

1899–1904. (*Nos. 67/81*).
Z191 **49** 8 a. deep green and orange £120
Z192   10 a. ultramarine £130

1905–09. (*Nos. 92/105*).
Z196 **53** 4 a. pale red and sepia £120
Z197   4 a. scarlet £120
Z198   5 a. carmine £130
Z199   9 a. blue £130
Z200   24 a. red-brown £300
Z201   1 t. bistre and deep blue £300

1907. *Surch with T* **56** (*No.* 109).
Z202 **9** 1 a. on 24 a. purple and blue £130

Langkawi

Stamps of SIAM *cancelled as Type D inscr* "LANGKAWI" (*from
Feb 1908*).

1899–1904. (*Nos. 67/81*).
Z208 **49** 8 a. deep green and orange £300
Z209   10 a. ultramarine £300

1905–09. (*Nos. 92/105*).
Z212 **53** 3 a. green £325
Z213   4 a. pale red and sepia £300
Z215   8 a. olive-bistre and dull black .. £300

Stamps of SIAM *cancelled as Type C inscr* "Langkawi" *at foot*
(*from Nov 1908*).

1887–91. (*Nos. 11/18*).
Z219 **9** 12 a. purple and carmine £130

1899–1904. (*Nos. 67/81*).
Z220 **49** 1 a. olive-green (Type B) £140
Z221   8 a. green and orange £130

1905–09. (*Nos. 92/105*).
Z222 **53** 2 a. grey and deep violet £130
Z223   3 a. green £180
Z224   4 a. pale red and sepia £130
Z225   4 a. scarlet £140
Z226   8 a. olive-bistre and dull black .. £130
Z228   24 a. red-brown £350
Z229   1 t. bistre and deep blue £350

1907. *Surch with T* **56** (*No.* 109).
Z230 **9** 1 a. on 24 a. purple and blue £140

KELANTAN

The first Siamese post office in Kelantan opened at Kota
Bharu in 1895. It appears that in the early years this office only
accepted letters franked with stamps for delivery within
Kelantan.

The initial cancellation, of which no complete example has
been discovered, showed Thai characters only. Partial examples
have been reported on the 1887–91 8 a. and 1896 4 a. on 12 a.

The operations of the Duff Development Company in
Kelantan from 1903 led to a considerable expansion of the postal
service based on the company's river steamers. A further post
office opened at Batu Mengkebang in 1908, but may have been
preceded by manuscript endorsements of "B.M." and date known
from early 1907 onwards.

Kota Bharu

Stamps of SIAM *cancelled as Type B inscr* "KALANTAN" (*from
March 1898*).

1887–91. (*Nos. 11/18*).
Z237 **9** 2 a. green and carmine .. .. 85·00
Z238   3 a. green and blue .. .. .. 90·00
Z239   4 a. green and brown .. .. 90·00
Z240   8 a. green and yellow .. .. 90·00
Z241   12 a. purple and carmine .. .. 80·00
Z242   24 a. purple and blue .. .. 85·00

1894. *Surch as T* **27** *with variation of English figures as T* **33**
(*Nos. 37/44*).
Z251 **9** 2 a. on 64 a. purple and brown £120

1894–95. *Surch as T* **35** *with variation of English figures as*
T **36** (*Nos. 46/50*).
Z255 **9** 1 a. on 64 a. purple and brown £100

1896. *Surch as T* **39** (*Siamese*) *and T* **40** (*English*) (*No.* 51).
Z259 **9** 4 a. on 12 a. purple and carmine £100

1897. *Surch as T* **39** (*Siamese*) *and T* **41** (*English*) (*No.* 52).
Z260 **9** 4 a. on 12 a. purple and carmine £100

1898–99. *Surch as T* **42** *with variation of English section as*
T **46** (*Nos. 53/62*).
Z267 **9** 4 a. on 12 a. purple and carmine (8 mm long) £100

1899–1904. (*Nos. 67/81*).
Z275 **49** 1 a. olive-green (wide Siamese characters in
    face value) .. .. .. 85·00
Z276   2 a. grass-green .. .. .. 80·00
Z277   2 a. scarlet and pale blue .. .. 80·00
Z278   3 a. red and blue .. .. .. 90·00
Z279   4 a. carmine .. .. 80·00
Z280   4 a. chocolate and pink .. .. 90·00

Z281 **49** 8 a. deep green and orange .. .. 80·00
Z282   10 a. ultramarine .. .. .. 85·00
Z283   12 a. brown-purple and carmine .. 85·00
Z284   64 a. brown-purple and chestnut .. £180

1905–09. (*Nos. 92/105*).
Z293 **53** 1 a. green and orange .. .. 80·00
Z294   2 a. grey and deep violet .. .. 80·00
Z296   4 a. pale red and sepia .. .. 80·00
Z297   4 a. scarlet .. .. 80·00
Z298   5 a. carmine .. .. 95·00
Z299   8 a. olive-bistre and dull black .. 80·00
Z300   12 a. blue .. .. 95·00
Z301   24 a. red-brown £250
Z302   1 t. bistre and deep blue £250

1907. *Surch with T* **56** (*No.* 109).
Z303 **9** 1 a. on 24 a. purple and blue £100

Stamps of SIAM *cancelled as Type E inscr* "Kota Bahru/
Kelantan" (*from July 1908*).

1887–91. (*Nos. 11/18*).
Z307 **9** 12 a. purple and carmine .. .. 80·00
Z308   24 a. purple and blue £100

1899–1904. (*Nos. 67/81*).
Z309 **49** 8 a. deep green and orange .. .. 85·00
Z310   64 a. brown-purple and chestnut .. £120

1905–09. (*Nos. 92/105*).
Z311 **53** 1 a. green and orange .. .. 85·00
Z312   2 a. grey and deep violet .. .. 85·00
Z313   2 a. pale yellow-green .. .. 85·00
Z314   4 a. pale red and sepia .. .. 85·00
Z315   4 a. scarlet .. .. 85·00
Z316   8 a. olive-bistre and dull black .. 80·00
Z317   9 a. blue .. .. 90·00
Z318   18 a. red-brown £140

1907. *Surch with T* **56** (*No.* 109).
Z320 **9** 1 a. on 24 a. purple and blue .. .. 85·00

1908. *Surch as T* **59** (*Nos. 110/12*).
Z326 **9** 2 a. on 24 a. purple and blue £120
Z327 **53** 4 a. on 5 a. carmine £150
Z328 **49** 9 a. on 10 a. ultramarine .. .. 95·00

Batu Mengkebang

Stamps of SIAM *cancelled as Type E inscr* "Batu Menkebang/
Kelantan" (*from July 1908*).

1887–91. (*Nos. 11/18*).
Z329 **9** 12 a. purple and carmine £140

1899–1904. (*Nos. 67/81*).
Z330 **49** 8 a. deep green and orange £150

1905–09. (*Nos. 92/105*).
Z331 **53** 1 a. green and orange £140
Z332   2 a. grey and deep violet £140
Z333   2 a. pale yellow-green £150
Z334   4 a. pale red and sepia £150
Z335   4 a. scarlet £140
Z336   8 a. olive-bistre and dull black .. £120
Z337   9 a. blue £120
Z338   12 a. blue £180
Z339   24 a. red-brown £300
Z340   1 t. bistre and deep blue £325

1907. *Surch with T* **56** (*No.* 109)
Z341 **9** 1 a. on 24 a. purple and blue £120

1908. *Surch as T* **59** (*Nos. 110/12*).
Z347 **49** 9 a. on 10 a. ultramarine £180

PERLIS

The Siamese post office at Kangar is recorded as opening
during 1894. It is believed that the initial cancellation showed
Thai characters only, but no complete example has so far been
discovered.

Stamps of SIAM *cancelled as Type B inscr* "PERLIS" (*from July
1904*).

1887–91. (*Nos. 11/18*).
Z349 **9** 12 a. purple and carmine £140
Z350   24 a. purple and blue £190

1897. *Surch as T* **39** (*Siamese*) *and T* **41** (*English*) (*No.* 52).
Z351 **9** 4 a. on 12 a. purple and carmine £250

1899–1904. (*Nos. 67/81*).
Z352 **49** 1 a. olive-green (wide Siamese characters in
    face value) £170
Z353   2 a. grass-green £150
Z354   2 a. scarlet and pale blue £150
Z355   3 a. red and blue £225
Z356   4 a. carmine £150

Z357	49	4 a. chocolate and pink	..	..	£150
Z358		8 a. deep green and orange	..	..	£150
Z359		10 a. ultramarine	..	..	£150
Z360		12 a. brown-purple and carmine	..	..	£140
Z361		24 a. brown-purple and blue	..	..	£275

1905–09. (*Nos. 97/105*).

Z370	53	1 a. green and orange	..	..	£140
Z371		2 a. grey and deep violet	..	..	£140
Z372		3 a. green	..	..	£150
Z374		4 a. pale red and sepia	..	..	£140
Z375		5 a. carmine	..	..	£150
Z376		8 a. olive-bistre and dull black	..	..	£140
Z376		12 a. blue	..	..	£160
Z377		24 a. red-brown	..	..	£225

Stamps of SIAM cancelled as Type C inscr "Perlis" at foot (from Sept. 1907).

1887–91. (*Nos. 11/18*).

Z379	9	12 a. purple and carmine	..	..	£160

1899–1904. (*Nos. 67/81*).

Z380	49	1 a. olive-green (narrow Siamese characters in face value)	..	..	£170
Z381		8 a. deep green and orange	..	..	£160
Z382		10 a. ultramarine	..	..	£170

1905–09. (*Nos. 92/105*).

Z383	53	1 a. green and orange	..	..	£170
Z384		2 a. grey and deep violet	..	..	£160
Z385		3 a. green	..	..	£170
Z386		4 a. pale red and sepia	..	..	£160
Z387		4 a. scarlet	..	..	£170
Z388		5 a. carmine	..	..	£170
Z389		8 a. olive-bistre and dull black	..	..	£170
Z390		9 a. blue	..	..	£160
Z391		24 a. red-brown	..	..	£275

1907. *Surch with T 56* (*No. 109*).

Z392	9	1 a. on 24 a. purple and blue	..	..	£170

Siam transferred suzerainty over the four northern Malay States to Great Britain on 15 July 1909. Use of Siamese stamps in Kelantan and Perlis appears to have extended into early August 1909.

IX. JAPANESE OCCUPATION OF MALAYA

PRICES FOR STAMPS ON COVER	
Nos. J1/55	*from* × 10
Nos. J56/76	*from* × 12
Nos. J77/89	*from* × 20
Nos. J90/1	*from* × 15
Nos. J92/115	*from* × 6
Nos. J116/18	—
Nos. J119/32	*from* × 12
Nos. J133/45	*from* × 10
Nos. J146/223	*from* × 6
Nos. J224/58	*from* × 12
No. J259	*from* × 15
Nos. J260/96	*from* × 12
Nos. J297/310	*from* × 20
Nos. J311/17	—
Nos. JD1/10	*from* × 30
Nos. JD11/16	*from* × 12
Nos. JD17/20	*from* × 30
Nos. JD21/7	*from* × 20
Nos. JD28/33	*from* × 30
Nos. JD34/41	*from* × 60

Japanese forces invaded Malaya on 8 December 1941 with the initial landings taking place at Kota Bharu on the east coast. Penang fell, to a force which crossed the border from Thailand, on 19 December, Kuala Lumpur on 11 January 1942 and the conquest of the Malay penisula was completed by the capture of Singapore on 15 February.

During the Japanese Occupation various small Dutch East Indies islands near Singapore were administered as part of Malaya. Stamps of the Japanese Occupation of Malaya were issued to the post offices of Dabo Singkep, Puloe Samboe, Tanjong Balei, Tanjong Batu, Tanjong Pinang and Terempa between 1942 and 1945. The overprinted issues were also used by a number of districts in Atjeh (Northern Sumatra) whose postal services were administered from Singapore until the end of March 1943.

Malayan post offices were also opened in October 1943 to serve camps of civilians working on railway construction and maintenance in Thailand. Overprinted stamps of the Japanese Occupation of Malaya were used at these offices between October 1943 and the end of the year after which mail from the camps was carried free. Their postmarks were inscribed in Japanese Katakana characters, and, uniquely, showed the Japanese postal symbol.

MINIMUM PRICE

The minimum price quote is 10p which represents a handling charge rather than a basis for valuing common stamps. For further notes about prices see introductory pages.

JOHORE

The postal service in Johore was reconstituted in mid-April 1942 using Nos. J146/60 and subsequently other general issues. Stamps of Johore overprinted "DAI NIPPON 2602" were, however, only used for fiscal purposes. Overprinted Johore postage due stamps were not issued for use elsewhere in Malaya.

POSTAGE DUE STAMPS

(1) (Upright)	(2)	Second character sideways (R.6/3)

1942 (Apr). *Nos. D1/5 of Johore optd as T 1 in brown.*

JD1	D 1	1 c. carmine	..	..	60·00	85·00
		a. Black opt	..	..	25·00	70·00
JD2		4 c. green	..	..	80·00	95·00
		a. Black opt	..	..	65·00	80·00
JD3		8 c. orange	..	..	£110	£120
		a. Black opt	..	..	75·00	90·00
JD4		10 c. brown	..	..	40·00	65·00
		a. Black opt	..	..	16·00	50·00
JD5		12 c. purple	..	..	65·00	80·00
		a. Black opt	..	..	29·00	50·00

1943. *Nos. D1/5 of Johore optd with T 2.*

JD 6	D 1	1 c. carmine	..	..	4·50	20·00
		a. Second character sideways		..	£160	£325
JD 7		4 c. green	..	..	4·75	21·00
		a. Second character sideways		..	£170	£325
JD 8		8 c. orange	..	..	5·00	22·00
		a. Second character sideways		..	£200	£375
JD 9		10 c. brown	..	..	4·50	26·00
		a. Second character sideways		..	£200	£400
JD10		12 c. purple	..	..	6·00	38·00
		a. Second character sideways		..	£225	£450

KEDAH

Postal services resumed by 31 January 1942 using unoverprinted Kedah values from 1 c. to 8 c. which were accepted for postage until 13 May 1942.

During the Japanese occupation Perlis was administered as part of Kedah.

DAI NIPPON   **DAI NIPPON**

2602   **2602**

(3)   (4)

1942 (13 May)–43. *Stamps of Kedah (Script wmk) optd with T 3 (1 c. to 8 c.) or 4 (10 c. to $5), both in red.*

J 1	1	1 c. black (No. 68a)	..		3·50	5·50
J 2		2 c. bright green (No. 69)	..		24·00	30·00
J 3		4 c. violet	..		3·50	4·00
J 4		5 c. yellow	..		3·00	3·50
		a. Black opt (1943)	..		£200	£225
J 5		6 c. carmine (No. 56) (Blk.)	..		2·25	8·50
J 6		8 c. grey-black	..		2·75	1·75
J 7	6	10 c. ultramarine and sepia	..		8·00	8·00
J 8		12 c. black and violet	..		22·00	28·00
J 9		25 c. ultramarine and purple	..		7·00	9·50
		a. Black opt (1943)	..		£250	£250
J10		30 c. green and scarlet	..		65·00	75·00
J11		40 c. black and purple	..		28·00	40·00
J12		50 c. brown and blue	..		30·00	42·00
J13		$1 black and green	..		£140	£150
		a. Opt inverted	..		£600	£600
J14		$2 green and brown	..		£170	£170
J15		$5 black and scarlet	..		65·00	75·00
		a. Black opt (1943)	..		£750	£750

Nos. J1/15 were gradually replaced by issues intended for use throughout Malaya. Kedah and Perlis were ceded to Thailand by the Japanese on 19 October 1943.

KELANTAN

Postal services resumed on 1 June 1942. Stamps used in Kelantan were overprinted with the personal seals of Sunagawa, the Japanese Governor, and of Handa, the Assistant Governor.

(5) Sunagawa Seal	(6) Handa Seal

40 CENTS   **$1.00**

(7)   (8)

1 Cents

(9)

1942 (June). *Stamps of Kelantan surch*

(a) As T 7 or 8 (dollar values). Optd with T 5 in red

J16	4	1 c. on 50 c. grey-olive and orange		£225	£180
J17		2 c. on 40 c. orange and blue-green		£450	£275
J18		4 c. on 30 c. violet and scarlet		£1700	£1200
J19		5 c. on 12 c. blue (R.)		£225	£180
J20		6 c. on 25 c. vermilion and violet		£275	£190
J21		8 c. on 5 c. red-brown (R.)		£325	£140
J22		10 c. on 6 c. lake		75·00	£200
		a. "CENST" for "CENTS"		£2500	
J23		12 c. on 8 c. grey-olive (R.)		48·00	£110
J24		25 c. on 10 c. purple (R.)		£1200	£1300
J25		30 c. on 4 c. scarlet		£1800	£2000
J26		40 c. on 2 c. green (R.)		55·00	85·00
		a. Surch double (B.+R.)		£1500	
J27		50 c. on 1 c. grey-olive and yellow		£1300	£1200
J28	1	$1 on 4 c. black and red (R., bars Blk.)		50·00	75·00
J29		$2 on 5 c. green and red/*yellow*		50·00	75·00
J30		$5 on 6 c. scarlet		50·00	75·00
		a. Surch double		£350	

(b) As T 7. Optd with T 6 in red

J31	4	12 c. on 8 c. grey-olive		£140	£200
		a. Type 6 omitted (in horiz pair with normal)		£1500	

(c) As T 9. Optd with T 5 in red.

J32	4	1 c. on 50 c. grey-olive and orange	..	£130	85·00
		a. "Cents" for "Cents" (R. 5/1)		£1000	£800
J33		2 c. on 40 c. orange and blue-green		£110	90·00
		a. "Cents" for "Cents" (R. 5/1)		£950	
J34		5 c. on 12 c. blue (R.)	..	£110	£110
		a. "Cents" for "Cents" (R. 5/1)		£900	
J35		8 c. on 5 c. red-brown (R.)		£100	70·00
		a. "Cents" for "Cents" (R. 5/1)		£850	£700
J36		10 c. on 6 c. lake	..	£250	£275
		a. "Cents" for "Cents" (R. 5/1)		£1700	
J37		12 c. on 8 c. grey-olive (R.)		£425	£450
		a. "Cents" for "Cents" (R. 5/1)		£2250	
J38		30 c. on 4 c. scarlet		£2000	£2250
		a. "Cents" for "Cents" (R. 5/1)		£2250	
J39		40 c. on 2 c. green (R.)		£450	£475
		a. "Cents" for "Cents" (R. 5/1)		£2250	
J40		50 c. on 1 c. grey-olive and yellow		£1100	£1100
		a. "Cents" for "Cents" (R. 5/1)			

(d) As T 9. Optd with T 6 in red.

J41	4	1 c. on 50 c. grey-olive and orange		90·00	£130
		a. "Cente" for "Cents" (R. 5/1)		£850	
J42		2 c. on 40 c. orange and blue-green		95·00	£140
		a. "Cente" for "Cents" (R. 5/1)		£850	
J43		8 c. on 5 c. red-brown (R.)		65·00	£120
		a. "Cente" for "Cents" (R. 5/1)		£750	
J44		10 c. on 6 c. lake		85·00	£140
		a. "Cente" for "Cents" (R. 5/1)		£850	

As stamps of the above series became exhausted the equivalent values from the series intended for use throughout Malaya were introduced. Stamps as Nos. J28/30, J32/3 and J35/40, but without Type 5 or 6, are from remainders sent to Singapore or Kuala Lumpur after the state had been ceded to Thailand (*Price from £15 each unused*). Nos. J19, J21, J23 and J25/6 have also been seen without Type 5 (*Price from £50 each unused*).

Kelantan was ceded to Thailand by the Japanese on 19 October 1943.

MALACCA

Postal services from Malacca resumed on 21 April 1942, but there were no stamps available for two days.

PRICES. Those quoted are for single stamps. Blocks of four showing the complete handstamp are worth from five times the price of a single stamp.

(10) "Military Administration Malacca State Government Seal"

1942 (23 Apr). *Stamps of Straits Settlements handstamped as T 10, in red, each impression covering four stamps.*

						Single	
						Un.	Used
J45	58	1 c. black	..	..	..	80·00	65·00
J46		2 c. orange	..	..	..	55·00	65·00
J47		3 c. green	..	..	..	55·00	65·00
J48		5 c. brown	..	..	..	£110	£110
J49		8 c. grey	..	..	..	£160	£100
J50		10 c. dull purple	..	..	..	70·00	75·00
J51		12 c. ultramarine	..	..	..	90·00	95·00
J52		15 c. ultramarine	..	..	..	65·00	75·00
J53		40 c. scarlet and dull purple	..		£550	£600
J54		50 c. black/*emerald*	..	..	£850	£850
J55		$1 black and red/*blue*	..	..	£900	£850

The 30 c., $2 and $5 also exist with this overprint, but these values were not available to the public. (*Price for set of 3 £3750 unused*)

POSTAGE DUE STAMPS

1942 (23 Apr). *Postage Due stamps of Malayan Postal Union handstamped as T 10, in red, each impression covering four stamps.*

JD11	D 1	1 c. slate-purple	£180	£170
JD12		4 c. green	£225	£225
JD13		8 c. scarlet	£1700	£1400
JD14		10 c. yellow-orange	£350	£350
JD15		12 c. ultramarine	£550	£475
JD16		50 c. black	£1700	£1300

Nos. J45/55 and JD11/16 were replaced during May 1942 by the overprinted issues intended for use throughout Malaya.

PENANG

Postal services on Penang Island resumed on 30 March 1942 using Straits Settlements stamps overprinted by Japanese seals.

(11) Okugawa Seal	(12) Ochiburi Seal	(13)	DAI NIPPON 2602 PENANG

1942 (30 Mar). *Straits Settlements stamps optd.*

(a) As T 11 (three forms of the seal)

J56	58	1 c. black	9·50	11·00
J57		2 c. orange	24·00	22·00
J58		3 c. green	20·00	22·00
J59		5 c. brown	24·00	24·00
J60		8 c. grey	26·00	27·00
J61		10 c. dull purple	50·00	50·00
J62		12 c. ultramarine	27·00	38·00
J63		15 c. ultramarine	38·00	45·00
J64		40 c. scarlet and dull purple	90·00	£100
J65		50 c. black/*emerald*	£190	£200
J66		$1 black and red/*blue*	£200	£225
J67		$2 green and scarlet	£500	£500
J68		$5 green and red/*emerald*	£1500	£1400

(b) With T 12

J69	58	1 c. black	£120	£110
J70		2 c. orange	£110	85·00
J71		3 c. green	90·00	95·00
J72		5 c. brown	£1400	£1400
J73		8 c. grey	65·00	80·00
J74		10 c. dull purple	95·00	£110
J75		12 c. ultramarine	90·00	£100
J76		15 c. ultramarine	90·00	£100

Straits Settlements stamps overprinted with a similar seal impression, but circular and containing four characters, are believed to be fiscal issues.

1942 (15 Apr). *Straits Settlements stamps optd with T 13.*

J77	58	1 c. black (R.)	2·50	2·00
		a. Opt inverted	£325	£325
		b. Opt double	£275	£275
J78		2 c. orange	4·25	3·00
		a. "PE" for "PENANG"	95·00	80·00
		b. Opt inverted	£150	
		c. Opt double	£350	
J79		3 c. green (R.)	3·75	2·25
		a. Opt double, one inverted	£325	
J80		5 c. brown (R.)	2·25	4·00
		a. "N PPON"	£160	
		b. Opt double	£325	£325
J81		8 c. grey (R.)	2·25	1·40
		a. "N PPON"	50·00	55·00
		b. Opt double, one inverted	£325	
J82		10 c. dull purple (R.)	1·50	2·00
		a. Opt double	£350	£350
		b. Opt double, one inverted	£400	£400
J83		12 c. ultramarine (R.)	3·00	10·00
		a. "N PPON"	£400	
		b. Opt double	£350	
		c. Opt double, one inverted	£425	£450
J84		15 c. ultramarine (R.)	1·75	2·25
		a. "N PPON"	£100	£110
		b. Opt inverted	£400	£400
		c. Opt double	£450	£450
J85		40 c. scarlet and dull purple	4·25	10·00
J86		50 c. black/*emerald* (R.)	3·75	18·00
J87		$1 black and red/*blue*	6·00	25·00
		a. Opt inverted	£750	
J88		$2 green and scarlet	42·00	75·00
J89		$5 green and red/*emerald*	£450	£550

Nos. J77/89 were replaced by the overprinted issues intended for use throughout Malaya.

SELANGOR

Postal services resumed in the Kuala Lumpur area on 3 April 1942 and gradually extended to the remainder of the state. Stamps of the general overprinted issue were used, but the following commemorative set was only available in Selangor.

SELANGOR EXHIBITION DAI NIPPON 2602 MALAYA	(14)

1942 (3 Nov). *Selangor Agri-horticultural Exhibition. Nos. 294 and 283 of Straits Settlements optd with T 14.*

J90	58	2 c. orange	12·00	24·00
		a. "C" for "G" in "SELANGOR" (R. 1/9)	£300	£350
		b. Opt inverted	£300	£400
J91		8 c. grey	13·00	24·00
		a. "C" for "G" in "SELANGOR" (R. 1/9)	£300	£350
		b. Opt inverted	£300	£400

SINGAPORE

The first post offices re-opened in Singapore on 16 March 1942.

(15) "Malaya Military Government Division Postal Services Bureau Seal"

(Handstamped at Singapore)

1942 (16 Mar). *Stamps of Straits Settlements optd with T 15 in red.*

J92	58	1 c. black	13·00	17·00
J93		2 c. orange	13·00	13·00
		a. Pair, one without handstamp	£1100	
J94		3 c. green	50·00	70·00
J95		8 c. grey	22·00	18·00
J96		15 c. ultramarine	15·00	15·00

The overprint Type 15 has a double-lined frame, although the two lines are not always apparent, as in the illustration. Three chops were used, differing slightly in the shape of the characters, but forgeries also exist. It is distinguishable from Type 1, used for the general issues, by its extra width, measuring approximately 14 mm against 12½ mm.

The 6, 10, 30, 40, 50 c., $2 and $5 also exist with this overprint, but were not sold to the public.

Nos. J92/6 were replaced on the 3 May 1942 by the stamps overprinted with Type 1 which were intended for use throughout Malaya.

TRENGGANU

Postal services resumed in Trengganu on 5 March 1942 using unoverprinted stamps up to the 35 c. value. These remained in use until September 1942.

1942 (Sept). *Stamps of Trengganu (Script wmk) optd as T 1 at Kuala Lumpur.*

J 97	4	1 c. black	95·00	90·00
		a. Red opt	£180	£200
		b. Brown opt	£450	£275
J 98		2 c. green (No. 27a)	£140	£140
		a. Red opt	£225	£250
		b. Brown opt	£475	£325
J 99		2 c. on 5 c. deep reddish purple/*bright yellow* (No. 59)	60·00	75·00
		a. Red opt	45·00	70·00
J100		3 c. chestnut (No. 29a)	80·00	80·00
		a. Brown opt	£500	£400
J101		4 c. scarlet-vermilion (No. 30a)	£140	£140
J102		5 c. dp reddish purple/*brt yell* (No. 32a)	10·00	19·00
		a. Red opt	21·00	
J103		6 c. orange (No. 33a)	8·50	25·00
		a. Red opt	90·00	
		b. Brown opt	£450	£450
J104		8 c. grey (No. 34a)	9·00	13·00
		a. Brown to red opt	50·00	65·00
J105		8 c. on 10 c. bright blue (No. 60)	13·00	38·00
		a. Red opt	21·00	
J106		10 c. bright blue	16·00	28·00
		a. Red opt	90·00	
		b. Brown opt	£450	£450
J107		12 c. bright ultramarine	8·00	29·00
		a. Red opt	27·00	
J108		20 c. dull purple and orange	8·50	26·00
		a. Red opt	21·00	
J109		25 c. green and deep purple	7·50	32·00
		a. Red opt	22·00	
		b. Brown opt	£475	£475
J110		30 c. dull purple and black	8·00	26·00
		a. Red opt	25·00	
J111		35 c. carmine/*yellow*	22·00	38·00
		a. Red opt	24·00	
J112		50 c. green and bright carmine	65·00	75·00
J113		$1 purple and blue/*blue*	£2500	£2500
J114		$3 green & brown-red/*green* (No. 43a)	50·00	85·00
		a. Red opt	60·00	
J115	5	$5 green and red/*yellow*	£130	£180
J116		$25 purple and blue	£1000	
		a. Red opt	£3250	
J117		$50 green and yellow	£8500	
J118		$100 green and scarlet	£1100	

DAI NIPPON 2602 MALAYA	(16)

1942 (Sept). *Stamps of Trengganu (Script wmk) optd with T 16.*

J119	4	1 c. black (No. 26a)	12·00	10·00
J120		2 c. green (No. 27a)	£160	£180
J121		2 c. on 5 c. deep reddish purple/*bright yellow* (No. 59)	6·00	8·00
J122		3 c. chestnut (No. 29a)	9·00	17·00
J123		4 c. scarlet-vermilion (No. 30a)	9·00	11·00
J124		5 c. dp reddish purple/*brt yell* (No. 32a)	5·50	12·00
J125		6 c. orange (No. 33a)	5·00	12·00
J126		8 c. grey (No. 34a)	70·00	25·00
J127		8 c. on 10 c. bright blue (No. 60)	5·50	10·00
J128		12 c. bright ultramarine	5·00	20·00
J129		20 c. dull purple and orange	10·00	13·00
J130		25 c. green and deep purple	7·00	27·00
J131		30 c. dull purple and black	7·50	24·00
J132		$3 green & brown-red/*green* (No. 43a)	60·00	£110

1943. *Stamps of Trengganu (Script wmk) optd with T 2.*

J133	4	1 c. black	9·00	16·00
J134		2 c. green (No. 27a)	8·00	24·00

J135	4	2 c. on 5 c. bright reddish purple/*bright yellow* (No. 59)	6·00	18·00
J136		5 c. brt reddish purple/*brt yell* (No. 32a)	6·50	24·00
J137		6 c. orange (No. 33a)	8·00	27·00
J138		8 c. grey (No. 34a)	55·00	80·00
J139		8 c. on 10 c. bright blue (No. 60)	19·00	40·00
J140		10 c. bright blue	80·00	£180
J141		12 c. bright ultramarine	13·00	35·00
J142		20 c. dull purple and orange	15·00	35·00
J143		25 c. green and deep purple	13·00	38·00
J144		30 c. dull purple and black	16·00	40·00
J145		35 c. carmine/*yellow*	16·00	42·00

POSTAGE DUE STAMPS

1942 (Sept). *Nos. D1/4 of Trengganu optd with T 1 sideways.*

JD17	D 1	1 c. scarlet	50·00	80·00
JD18		4 c. green	75·00	95·00
		a. Brown opt	50·00	85·00
JD19		8 c. yellow	14·00	50·00
JD20		10 c. brown	14·00	50·00

The Trengganu 8 c. postage due also exists overprinted with Type 16, but this was not issued (*Price £400 unused*).

Trengganu was ceded to Thailand by the Japanese on 19 October 1943.

GENERAL ISSUES

The following stamps were produced for use throughout Malaya, except for Trengganu.

1942 (3 Apr). *Stamps optd as T 1. (a) On Straits Settlements.*

J146	58	1 c. black (R.)	3·25	3·25
		a. Black opt	£325	£325
		b. Violet opt	£550	£500
J147		2 c. green (V.)	£1700	£1700
J148		2 c. orange (R.)	3·00	2·25
		a. Black opt	£100	£110
		b. Violet opt	£180	£180
		c. Brown opt	£550	£550
J149		3 c. green (R.)	2·75	2·25
		a. Black opt	£275	£300
		b. Violet opt	£550	£550
J150		5 c. brown (R.)	22·00	28·00
		a. Black opt	£475	£475
J151		8 c. grey (R.)	3·75	2·25
		a. Black opt	£225	£225
J152		10 c. dull purple (R.)	42·00	42·00
		a. Brown opt	£650	£650
J153		12 c. ultramarine (R.)	75·00	95·00
J154		15 c. ultramarine (R.)	3·50	3·75
		a. Violet opt	£550	£550
J155		30 c. dull purple and orange (R.)	£1500	£1600
J156		40 c. scarlet and dull purple (R.)	80·00	90·00
		a. Brown opt	£500	£375
J157		50 c. black/*emerald* (R.)	45·00	48·00
J158		$1 black and red/*blue* (R.)	75·00	75·00
J159		$2 green and scarlet (R.)	£130	£140
J160		$5 green and red/*emerald* (R.)	£170	£180

(b) On Negri Sembilan.

J161	6	1 c. black (R.)	19·00	13·00
		a. Violet opt	22·00	20·00
		b. Brown opt	15·00	16·00
		c. Black opt	48·00	38·00
		d. Pair. Nos. J161/a	£275	
		e. Pair. Nos. J161 and J161b		
J162		2 c. orange (R.)	20·00	16·00
		a. Violet opt	40·00	27·00
		b. Black opt	32·00	28·00
		c. Brown opt	55·00	45·00
J163		3 c. green (R.)	27·00	20·00
		a. Violet opt	23·00	29·00
		c. Brown opt	90·00	50·00
		d. Black opt	45·00	42·00
J164		5 c. brown	28·00	21·00
		a. Pair, one without opt	£1200	
		b. Brown opt	17·00	15·00
		c. Red opt	15·00	11·00
		d. Violet opt	50·00	38·00
J165		6 c. grey	£140	£120
		a. Brown opt	£325	£325
J166		8 c. scarlet	85·00	75·00
J167		10 c. dull purple	£130	£130
		a. Red opt	£200	£200
		b. Brown opt	£325	£300
J168		12 c. bright ultramarine (Br.)	£1100	£1100
J169		15 c. ultramarine (R.)	18·00	9·00
		a. Violet opt	55·00	28·00
		b. Brown opt	27·00	12·00
J170		25 c. dull purple and scarlet	28·00	38·00
		a. Red opt	60·00	75·00
		b. Brown opt	£300	£275
J171		30 c. dull purple and orange	£180	£150
		a. Brown opt	£800	£750
J172		40 c. scarlet and dull purple	£850	£850
		a. Brown opt	£800	£800
J173		50 c. black/*emerald*	£550	£550
J174		$1 black and red/*blue*	£180	£190
		a. Red opt	£160	£180
		b. Brown opt	£450	£450
J175		$5 green and red/*emerald*	£450	£475
		a. Red opt	£650	£700

(c) On Pahang.

J176	15	1 c. black	45·00	40·00
		a. Red opt	50·00	42·00
		b. Violet opt	£300	£250
		c. Brown opt	£200	£190
J177		3 c. green	£225	£225
		a. Red opt	£225	£225
		b. Violet opt	£600	£475
J178		5 c. brown	12·00	9·00
		a. Red opt	£160	£110
		b. Brown opt	£180	£110
		c. Violet opt	£400	£250
J179		8 c. grey	£475	£425
J180		8 c. scarlet	22·00	10·00
		a. Red opt	£100	60·00
		b. Violet opt	£100	65·00
		c. Brown opt	£110	85·00

No.	Type	Description	Un	Used
J181	15	10 c. dull purple	£180	£120
		a. Red opt	£200	£200
		b. Brown opt	£325	£250
J182		12 c. bright ultramarine	£1400	£1400
		a. Red opt	£1200	£1200
J183		15 c. ultramarine	£100	£100
		a. Red opt	£225	£200
		b. Violet opt	£550	£475
		c. Brown opt	£450	£325
J184		25 c. dull purple and scarlet	19·00	29·00
J185		30 c. dull purple and orange	12·00	28·00
		a. Red opt	£140	£170
J186		40 c. scarlet and dull purple	17·00	32·00
		a. Brown opt	£275	£275
		b. Red opt	70·00	75·00
J187		50 c. black/*emerald*	£550	£550
		a. Red opt	£600	£600
J188		$1 black and red/*blue* (R.)	£110	£130
		a. Black opt	£300	£300
		b. Brown opt	£550	£550
J189		$5 green and red/*emerald*	£600	£700
		a. Red opt	£900	£950

(d) On Perak

No.	Type	Description	Un	Used
J190	51	1 c. black	50·00	32·00
		a. Violet opt	£160	£100
		b. Brown opt	80·00	80·00
J191		2 c. orange	29·00	20·00
		a. Violet opt	70·00	70·00
		b. Red opt	50·00	40·00
		c. Brown opt	55·00	55·00
J192		3 c. green	26·00	28·00
		a. Violet opt	£350	£300
		b. Brown opt	£170	£150
		c. Red opt	£300	£250
J193		5 c. brown	7·00	6·00
		a. Pair, one without opt	£1000	
		b. Brown opt	30·00	26·00
		c. Violet opt	£180	£180
		d. Red opt	£200	£200
J194		8 c. grey	50·00	42·00
		a. Red opt	£325	£225
		b. Brown opt	£325	£250
J195		8 c. scarlet	28·00	35·00
		a. Violet opt	£425	£275
J196		10 c. dull purple	26·00	24·00
		a. Red opt	£275	£225
J197		12 c. bright ultramarine	£225	£225
J198		15 c. ultramarine	24·00	30·00
		a. Red opt	£200	£200
		b. Violet opt	£300	£250
		c. Brown opt	£300	£250
J199		25 c. dull purple and scarlet	14·00	25·00
J200		30 c. dull purple and orange	17·00	32·00
		a. Pair, one without opt	£1300	
		b. Brown opt	£400	£350
		c. Red opt	32·00	55·00
J201		40 c. scarlet and dull purple	£325	£325
		a. Brown opt	£500	£475
J202		50 c. black/*emerald*	38·00	55·00
		a. Red opt	48·00	60·00
		b. Brown opt	£300	£325
J203		$1 black and red/*blue*	£400	£400
		a. Brown opt	£550	£450
J204		$2 green and scarlet	£2000	£2000
J205		$5 green and red/*emerald*	£475	
		a. Brown opt	£1500	

(e) On Selangor

No.	Type	Description	Un	Used
J206	46	1 c. black, S	12·00	22·00
		a. Red opt, SU	30·00	35·00
		b. Violet opt, SU	38·00	35·00
J207		2 c. green, SU	£900	£900
		a. Violet opt, U	£1100	£1100
J208		2 c. orange (p 14×14½), S	80·00	50·00
		a. Red opt, U	£160	£150
		b. Violet opt, U	£225	£150
		c. Brown opt, S	65·00	75·00
J209		2 c. orange (p 14), S	£100	80·00
		a. Red opt, U	£180	£160
		b. Violet opt, U	£250	£160
J210		3 c. green, SU	23·00	17·00
		a. Red opt, SU	18·00	18·00
		b. Violet opt, SU	65·00	50·00
		c. Brown opt, SU	18·00	18·00
J211		5 c. brown, SU	6·00	5·50
		a. Red opt, SU	11·00	16·00
		b. Violet opt, SU	21·00	27·00
		c. Brown opt, SU	90·00	80·00
J212		6 c. scarlet, S	£300	£300
		a. Red opt, S	£200	£250
		b. Brown opt, S	£550	
J213		8 c. grey, S	17·00	17·00
		a. Red opt, SU	42·00	32·00
		b. Violet opt, S	35·00	32·00
		c. Brown opt, S	£120	70·00
J214		10 c. dull purple, S	13·00	21·00
		a. Red opt, S	60·00	55·00
		b. Brown opt, S	£120	75·00
J215		12 c. bright ultramarine, S	60·00	60·00
		a. Red opt, S	£110	£110
		b. Brown opt, S	£110	£110
J216		15 c. ultramarine, S	16·00	22·00
		a. Red opt, SU	48·00	48·00
		b. Violet opt, U	£140	95·00
		c. Brown opt, S	80·00	60·00
J217		25 c. dull purple and scarlet, S	75·00	85·00
		a. Brown opt, S	60·00	80·00
J218		30 c. dull purple and orange, S	11·00	24·00
		a. Brown opt, S	£325	£250
J219		40 c. scarlet and dull purple, S	£130	£130
		a. Brown opt, S	£325	£225
J220		50 c. black/*emerald*, S	£110	£110
		a. Red opt, S	85·00	90·00
		b. Brown opt, S	£325	£325
J221	48	$1 black and red/*blue*	30·00	42·00
		a. Red opt	£120	£140
J222		$2 green and scarlet	35·00	60·00
		a. Pair, one without opt	£1200	
		b. Red opt	£450	£475
J223		$5 green and red/*emerald*	65·00	85·00

Nos. J161a and J163a exist with the handstamped overprint sideways.

On T **46** the overprint is normally sideways (with "top" to either right or left), but on T **48** it is always upright.

S = Sideways
U = Upright
SU = Sideways or upright (our prices being for the cheaper). Specialists recognise nine slightly different chops as Type **1**. Initial supplies with the overprint in red were produced at Singapore. Later overprintings took place at Kuala Lumpur in violet, red or brown and, finally, black. No. J155 was from the Kuala Lumpur printing only. Except where noted these overprints were used widely in Malaya and, in some instances, Sumatra.

The following stamps also exist with this overprint, but were not available to the public:
Straits Settlements (in red) 6, 25 c.
Kelantan (in black) 10 c.
Negri Sembilan 2 c. green (Blk. or Brn.), 4 c. (Blk.), 6 c. scarlet (Blk.), 8 c. grey (Blk.), 12 c. (Blk.), $2 (Blk. or Brn.)
Pahang (in black, 2 c. also in brown) 2, 4, 6 c., $2
Perak 2 c. green (R.), 6 c. (Blk.)
Selangor 4 c. (Blk.)

1942 (May). *Optd with T* **16**. *(a) On Straits Settlements.*

No.	Type	Description	Un	Used
J224	58	2 c. orange	85	50
		a. Opt inverted	9·00	17·00
		b. Opt double, one inverted	48·00	60·00
J225		3 c. green	50·00	65·00
J226		8 c. grey	3·50	2·00
		a. Opt inverted	13·00	27·00
J227		15 c. blue	9·00	6·50

(b) On Negri Sembilan

No.	Type	Description	Un	Used
J228	6	1 c. black	1·50	60
		a. Opt inverted	9·00	25·00
		b. Opt double, one inverted	35·00	50·00
J229		2 c. orange	4·00	50
J230		3 c. green	3·00	45
J231		5 c. brown	60	1·00
J232		6 c. grey	2·50	1·00
		a. Opt inverted	—	£1000
		b. Stop omitted at right (R. 10/4)	75·00	80·00
J233		8 c. scarlet	3·25	1·25
J234		10 c. dull purple	3·00	2·50
J235		15 c. ultramarine	10·00	2·50
J236		25 c. dull purple and scarlet	3·00	9·50
J237		30 c. dull purple and orange	5·00	3·00
J238		$1 black and red/*blue*	£100	£110

(c) On Pahang

No.	Type	Description	Un	Used
J239	15	1 c. black	1·50	1·50
		a. Opt omitted (in pair with normal)	£500	
J240		5 c. brown	1·00	70
J241		8 c. scarlet	25·00	2·50
		a. Opt omitted (in pair with normal)	£1000	
J242		10 c. dull purple	9·00	6·50
J243		12 c. bright ultramarine	1·25	8·00
J244		25 c. dull purple and scarlet	3·75	14·00
J245		30 c. dull purple and orange	1·90	7·00

(d) On Perak

No.	Type	Description	Un	Used
J246	51	2 c. orange	1·75	1·00
		a. Opt inverted	29·00	29·00
J247		3 c. green	60	75
		a. Opt inverted	12·00	23·00
		b. Opt omitted (in pair with normal)	£500	
J248		8 c. scarlet	60	40
		a. Opt inverted	4·50	7·00
		b. Opt double, one inverted	£200	£225
		c. Opt omitted (in horiz pair with normal)	£400	
J249		10 c. dull purple	9·00	5·50
J250		15 c. ultramarine	4·00	2·00
J251		50 c. black/*emerald*	2·00	3·00
J252		$1 black and red/*blue*	£350	£400
J253		$5 green and red/*emerald*	32·00	65·00
		a. Opt inverted	£275	£325

(e) On Selangor

No.	Type	Description	Un	Used
J254	46	3 c. green	60	2·00
J255		12 c. bright ultramarine	1·10	9·00
J256		15 c. ultramarine	3·50	1·50
J257		40 c. scarlet and dull purple	2·00	3·00
J258	48	$2 green and scarlet	10·00	30·00

On T **46** the overprint is sideways, with "top" to left or right. The following stamps also exist with this overprint, but were not available to the public.
Perak 1, 5, 30 c. (Price for set of 3 £350 *unused*).
Selangor 1, 5, 10, 30 c., $1, $5 (Price for set of 6 £600 *unused*).

DAI NIPPON	DAI NIPPON
2602	
MALAYA	YUBIN
2 Cents	**2 Cents**
(17)	(18)
	"Japanese Postal Service"

1942 (Nov). *No. 108 of Perak surch with T* **17**.

No.	Type	Description	Un	Used
J259	51	2 c. on 5 c. brown	1·25	1·75

1942 (Nov). *Perak stamps surch or opt only, as in T* **18**.

No.	Type	Description	Un	Used
J260	51	1 c. black	3·00	6·50
		a. Opt inverted	19·00	40·00
J261		2 c. on 5 c. brown	2·00	6·50
		a. "DAI NIPPON YUBIN" inverted	17·00	38·00
		b. Ditto and "2 Cents" omitted	45·00	65·00
J262		8 c. scarlet	3·50	2·25
		a. Opt inverted	11·00	24·00

A similar overprint exists on the Selangor 3 c. but this was not available to the public (Price £325 *unused*).

On 8 December 1942 contemporary Japanese 3, 5, 8 and 25 s. stamps were issued without overprint in Malaya and the 1, 2, 4, 6, 7, 10, 30 and 50 s. and 1 y. values followed on 15 February 1943.

大日本郵便
(19)

6 cts.	6 cts.	2 Cents
(20)	(21)	(22)

6 cts. $1·00
(23)   (24)

1942 (4 Dec)—**44**. *Stamps of various Malayan territories optd "Japanese Postal Service" in Kanji characters as T* **2** *or* **19**, *some additionally surch as T* **20** *to* **24**.

(a) Stamps of Straits Settlements optd with T **2**

No.	Type	Description	Un	Used
J263	58	8 c. grey (Blk.) (1943)	1·40	50
		a. Opt inverted	38·00	48·00
		b. Opt omitted (in pair with normal)	£800	
		c. Red opt	1·40	1·75
J264		12 c. ultramarine (1943)	65	6·50
J265		40 c. scarlet and dull purple (1943)	75	3·00

(b) Stamps of Negri Sembilan optd with T **2** *or surch also*

No.	Type	Description	Un	Used
J266	6	1 c. black	30	85
		a. Opt inverted	8·50	24·00
		b. Sideways second character	27·00	28·00
		ba. Opt inverted with sideways second character	£600	
J267		2 c. on 5 c. brown (surch as T 20)	50	50
J268		6 c. on 5 c. brown (surch T 21) (1943)	40	95
		a. Opt Type 2 and surch as Type 21 both inverted	£225	£225
J269		25 c. dull purple and scarlet (1943)	1·10	9·50

(c) Stamp of Pahang optd with T **2** *and surch also*

No.	Type	Description	Un	Used
J270	15	6 c. on 5 c. brown (surch T 20) (1943)	50	75
J271		6 c. on 5 c. brown (surch T 21) (1943)	1·00	1·50

(d) Stamps of Perak optd with T **2** *or surch also*

No.	Type	Description	Un	Used
J272	51	1 c. black	80	60
		a. Sideways second character	£190	£200
J273		2 c. on 5 c. brown (surch as T 20)	50	50
		a. Opt Type 2 and surch Type 20 both inverted	18·00	32·00
		b. Opt Type 2 inverted	18·00	32·00
		c. Sideways second character	50·00	50·00
J274		2 c. on 5 c. brown (surch T 22)	45	45
		a. Surch Type 22 inverted	18·00	32·00
		b. Opt Type 2 and surch Type 22 both inverted	18·00	32·00
		c. Sideways second character	25·00	32·00
		ca. Surch Type 22 inverted	£950	
		cb. Opt Type 2 with sideways second character and surch Type 22 both inverted	£950	
		d. Inverted "s" in Type 22 (R. 3/5)	50·00	
J275		5 c. brown	45	40
		a. Opt inverted	27·00	35·00
		b. Sideways second character	£400	£375
J276		8 c. scarlet	55	70
		a. Opt inverted	15·00	26·00
		b. Sideways second character	50·00	60·00
		ba. Opt inverted with sideways second character	£650	
J277		10 c. dull purple (1943)	60	50
J278		30 c. dull purple and orange (1943)	1·75	3·00
J279		50 c. black/*emerald* (1943)	3·00	13·00
J280		$5 green and red/*emerald* (1943)	50·00	80·00

(e) Stamps of Selangor optd with T **2** *(sideways on T* **46***)*

No.	Type	Description	Un	Used
J281	46	1 c. black (1943)	90	1·50
J282		3 c. green	40	45
		a. Sideways second character	17·00	25·00
J283		12 c. bright ultramarine	45	1·60
		a. Sideways second character	35·00	50·00
J284		15 c. ultramarine	2·75	3·00
		a. Sideways second character	45·00	50·00
J285	48	$1 black and red/*blue*	3·00	16·00
		a. Opt inverted	£225	£225
		b. Sideways second character	£300	£325
J286		$2 green and scarlet (1943)	10·00	38·00
J287		$5 green and red/*emerald* (1943)	22·00	70·00
		a. Opt inverted	£225	£225

(f) Stamps of Selangor optd with T **19** *or surch also*

No.	Type	Description	Un	Used
J288	46	1 c. black (R.) (1943)	35	50
J289		2 c. on 5 c. brown (surch as T 21) (R.) (1943)	30	50
J290		3 c. on 5 c. brown (surch as T 21) (1943)	30	3·00
		a. "s" in "cts." inverted (R. 4/3)	28·00	50·00
		b. Comma after "cts" (R. 9/3)	28·00	50·00
J291		5 c. brown (R.) (1944)	50	3·00
J292		6 c. on 5 c. brown (surch T 21) (1944)	30	1·00
J293		6 c. on 5 c. brown (surch T 23) (1944)	30	70
		a. "6" inverted (R. 7/8)	£700	
		b. Surch and opt double	£350	
J294		15 c. ultramarine	4·00	4·00
J295		$1 on 10 c. dull purple (surch T 24) (18.12.1944)	30	1·00
J296		$1.50 on 30 c. dull purple and orange (surch T 24) (18.12.1944)	30	1·00

The error showing the second character in Type 2 sideways occurred on R. 6/3 in the first of four settings only.

The 2 c. orange, 3 c. and 8 c. grey of Perak also exist overprinted with Type 2, but these stamps were not available to the public (Price for set of 3 £100 *unused*).

Examples of No. J275 are known postally used from the Shan States (part of pre-war Burma).

25 Tapping Rubber   26 Fruit   27 Japanese Shrine, Singapore

(Litho Kolff & Co, Batavia)

1943 (29 Apr–30 Oct). *T* **25**/**7** *and similar designs. P* 12½.

No.	Type	Description	Un	Used
J297	25	1 c. grey-green (30 Oct)	30	55
J298	26	2 c. pale emerald (1 June)	30	15
J299	25	3 c. drab (30 Oct)	15	15
J300	—	4 c. carmine-rose	65	15
J301	—	8 c. dull blue	15	15
J302	—	10 c. brown-purple (30 Oct)	15	15
J303	27	15 c. violet (30 Oct)	35	2·25
J304	—	30 c. olive-green (30 Oct)	35	35

J305	–	50 c. blue (30 Oct)	1·75	2·25
J306	–	70 c. blue (30 Oct)	16·00	10·00
J297/306		*Set of 10*	18·00	14·50

Designs: *Vert*—4 c. Tin dredger; 8 c. War Memorial, Bukit Batok, Singapore; 10 c. Fishing village; 30 c. Sago palms; 50 c. Straits of Johore. *Horiz*—70 c. Malay Mosque, Kuala Lumpur.

The 2 c. and 4 c. values exist, printed by typography, in paler shades either imperforate or rouletted. It is suggested that these may have been available in Singapore at the very end of the Japanese Occupation.

28 Ploughman   29 Rice-planting

1943 (1 Sept). *Savings Campaign. Litho. P 12½.*

J307	28	8 c. violet	7·50	2·75
J308		15 c. scarlet	6·00	2·75

(Des Hon Chin. Litho)

1944 (15 Feb). *"Re-birth" of Malaya. P 12½.*

J309	29	8 c. rose-red	10·00	2·75
J310		15 c. magenta	4·00	3·00

大日本   大日本   大日本
マライ郵便   マライ郵便   マライ郵便
50 セント   1 ドル   1½ ドル

(30)   (31)   (32)

1944 (16 Dec). *Stamps intended for use on Red Cross letters. Surch with T 30/2 in red. (a) On Straits Settlements.*

J311	58	50 c. on 50 c. black/*emerald*	11·00	24·00
J312		$1 on $1 black and red/*blue*	20·00	35·00
J313		$1.50 on $2 green and scarlet	32·00	70·00

(b) *On Johore*

J314	29	50 c. on 50 c. dull purple and red	8·00	20·00
J315		$1.50 on $2 green and carmine	5·50	14·00

(c) *On Selangor*

J316	48	$1 on $1 black and red/*blue*	4·00	14·00
J317		$1.50 on $2 green and scarlet	6·50	20·00

Nos. J311/17 were issued in Singapore but were withdrawn after one day, probably because supplies of Nos. J295/6 were received and issued on the 18 December.

A similar 6 c. surcharge exists on the Straits Settlements 5 c. but this was not available to the public (*Price £400 unused*).

STAMP BOOKLETS

1942. *Nos. SB3/4 of Perak and SB2 of Selangor with covers optd with T 1.*

SB1	$1 booklet containing twenty 5 c. (No. J193) in blocks of 10	£2000
SB2	$1.30, booklet containing 5 c. and 8 c. (Nos. J193/4), each in block of 10	£2000
SB3	$1.30, booklet containing 5 c. and 8 c. (Nos. J211 and J213), each in block of 10	£2000

POSTAGE DUE STAMPS

Postage Due stamps of the Malayan Postal Union overprinted.

1942 (3 Apr). *Handstamped as T 1 in black.*

JD21	D 1	1 c. slate-purple	12·00	20·00
		a. Red opt	85·00	85·00
		b. Brown opt	90·00	95·00
JD22		3 c. green	48·00	50·00
		a. Red opt	£130	£140
JD23		4 c. green	32·00	26·00
		a. Red opt	45·00	42·00
		b. Brown opt	£100	£100
JD24		8 c. scarlet	65·00	55·00
		a. Red opt	95·00	90·00
		b. Brown opt	£120	£120
JD25		10 c. yellow-orange	20·00	30·00
		a. Red opt	90·00	90·00
		b. Brown opt	50·00	55·00
JD26		12 c. ultramarine	20·00	38·00
		a. Red opt	£120	£120
JD27		50 c. black	50·00	65·00
		a. Red opt	£275	£300

1942. *Optd with T 16.*

JD28	D 1	1 c. slate-purple	1·60	8·00
JD29		3 c. green	9·50	15·00
JD30		4 c. green	8·50	10·00
JD31		8 c. scarlet	12·00	14·00
JD32		10 c. yellow-orange	1·60	10·00
JD33		12 c. ultramarine	1·60	23·00

The 9 c. and 15 c. also exist with this overprint, but these were not issued (*Price £425 each unused*).

1943–45. *Optd with T 2.*

JD34	D 1	1 c. slate-purple	80	2·75
JD35		3 c. green	80	2·75
		a. Opt omitted (in pair with normal)		£650
JD36		4 c. green	38·00	38·00
JD37		5 c. scarlet	70	3·25
JD38		9 c. yellow-orange	60	4·75
		a. Opt inverted	20·00	28·00
JD39		10 c. yellow-orange	70	4·50
		a. Opt inverted	50·00	50·00
JD40		12 c. ultramarine	90	9·50
JD41		15 c. ultramarine	90	5·00

X. THAI OCCUPATION OF MALAYA

Stamps issued for use in the Malay States of Kedah (renamed Syburi), Kelantan, Perlis and Trengganu, ceded by Japan to Thailand on 19 October 1943. British rule was restored on 9 (Kelantan), 18 (Perlis), 22 (Kedah) and 24 September 1945 (Trengganu). Nos. TM1/6 continued to be used for postage until replaced by the overprinted B.M.A. Malaya issues on 10 October 1945.

PRICES FOR STAMPS ON COVER	
Nos. TK1/5	*from* × 30
Nos. TM1/6	*from* × 25
Nos. TT1/29	*from* × 12

KELANTAN

TK 1

(Typo Kelantan Ptg Dept, Khota Baru)

1943 (15 Nov). *Handstamped with State arms in violet. No gum. P 11.*

TK1	TK 1	1 c. black	£190	£275
TK2		2 c. black	£225	£225
		a. Handstamp omitted		£700
TK3		4 c. black	£225	£275
		a. Handstamp omitted		£850
TK4		8 c. black	£225	£225
		a. Handstamp omitted		£550
TK5		10 c. black	£275	£375

Nos. TK1/5 were printed in sheets of 84 (12×7) and have sheet watermarks in the form of "STANDARD" in block capitals with curved "CROWN" above and "AGENTS" below in double-lined capitals. This watermark occurs four times in the sheet.

Sheets were imperforate at top and left so that stamps exist imperforate at top, left or at top and left.

Genuine examples have a solid star at the top centre of the arms, as shown in Type TK 1. Examples with a hollow outline star in this position are forgeries.

Similar stamps, but with red handstamps, were for fiscal use.

GENERAL ISSUE

TM 1 War Memorial

(Litho Defence Ministry, Bangkok)

1944 (15 Jan–4 Mar). *Thick opaque, or thin semi-transparent paper. Gummed or ungummed. P 12½.*

TM1	TM 1	1 c. yellow (4 Mar)	30·00	32·00
TM2		2 c. red-brown	12·00	20·00
		a. Imperf (pair)		£850
		b. Perf 12½×11	20·00	20·00
TM3		3 c. green (4 Mar)	20·00	38·00
		a. Perf 12½×11	30·00	42·00
TM4		4 c. purple (4 Mar)	14·00	28·00
		a. Perf 12½×11	20·00	35·00
TM5		8 c. carmine (4 Mar)	14·00	20·00
		a. Perf 12½×11	20·00	20·00
TM6		15 c. blue (4 Mar)	38·00	60·00
		a. Perf 12½×11	42·00	60·00

5 c. and 10 c. stamps in this design were prepared, but never issued.

TRENGGANU

TRENGGANU

(TT 1)

(Overprinted at Trengganu Survey Office)

1944 (1 Dec). *Various stamps optd with Type TT 1.*

(a) *On Trengganu without Japanese opt*

TT 1	4	1 c. black (26a)		
TT 2		30 c. dull purple and black (39)		

(b) *On Trengganu stamp optd as T 1 of Japanese Occupation*

TT 3	4	8 c. grey (J104)	£375	£275

(c) *On stamps optd with T 16 of Japanese Occupation.*

(i) *Pahang*

TT 4	15	12 c. bright ultramarine (J243)	£275	£120

(ii) *Trengganu*

TT 5	4	2 c. on 5 c. deep reddish purple/*bright yellow* (J121)*	£375	£375
TT 6		8 c. on 10 c. brt blue (J127) (inverted)	£300	£300
TT 7		12 c. brt ultramarine (J128) (inverted)	£300	£300

This is spelt "TRENGANU" with one "G".

(d) *On stamps optd with T 2 of Japanese Occupation.*

(i) *Straits Settlements*

TT 8	58	12 c. ultramarine (J264)	£350	£350
TT 9		40 c. scarlet and dull purple (J265)	£350	£350

(ii) *Pahang*

TT10	15	6 c. on 5 c. brown (J271)		

(iii) *Perak*

TT11	51	1 c. black (J272)		
TT12		10 c. dull purple (J277)		
TT13		30 c. dull purple and orange (J278)	£600	£350

(iv) *Selangor*

TT14	46	3 c. green (J282)	£250	£250
TT15		12 c. brt ultramarine (J283) (L. to R.)	£150	£110
TT16		12 c. brt ultramarine (J283) (R. to L.)	£150	£110
		a. Sideways second character	£1700	£1700

(e) *On Selangor stamps optd with T 19 of Japanese Occupation*

TT17	46	2 c. on 5 c. brown (J289)	£350	£350
TT18		3 c. on 5 c. brown (J290)	£350	£350

(f) *On pictorials of 1943 (Nos. J297/306)*

TT19	25	1 c. grey-green	£275	£275
TT20	26	2 c. pale emerald	£275	£150
TT21	25	3 c. drab	£180	£150
TT22	–	4 c. carmine-rose	£250	£150
TT23	–	8 c. dull blue	£400	£400
TT24	–	10 c. brown-purple	£800	£600
TT25	27	15 c. violet	£250	£150
TT26	–	30 c. olive-green	£300	£130
TT27	–	50 c. blue	£350	£250
TT28	–	70 c. blue	£750	£600

(g) *On Savings Campaign stamps (Nos. J307/8)*

TT29	28	8 c. violet	£400	£400
TT30		15 c. scarlet	£275	£160

(h) *On stamps of Japan*

TT31	–	3 s. green (No. 319)		
TT32	–	5 s. claret (No. 396)	£325	£325
TT33	–	25 c. brown and chocolate (No. 329)	£170	£110
TT34	–	30 c. blue-green (No. 330)	£325	£160

(i) *On Trengganu Postage Due stamp optd with T 1 of Japanese Occupation*

TT35	D 1	1 c. scarlet (JD17)	£1300	£1300

XI. LABUAN

CROWN COLONY

The island of Labuan, off the northern coast of Borneo, was ceded to Great Britain by the Sultan of Brunei in December 1846.

Stamps of STRAITS SETTLEMENTS were used from 1867 until 1879. Covers of 1864 and 1865 are known from Labuan franked with stamps of INDIA or HONG KONG.

PRICES FOR STAMPS ON COVER	
Nos. 1/4	—
Nos. 5/10	*from* × 30
Nos. 11/13	
Nos. 14/21	*from* × 20
Nos. 22/5	
Nos. 26/35	*from* × 30
Nos. 36/8	
Nos. 39/47	*from* × 100
Nos. 49/50	*from* × 12
Nos. 51/7	*from* × 60
Nos. 62/74	*from* × 15
Nos. 75/9	*from* × 40
Nos. 80/8	*from* × 20
Nos. 89/97	*from* × 15
Nos. 98/116	*from* × 15
Nos. 117/28	*from* × 30
Nos. 129/37	*from* × 10
Nos. 138/42	—
Nos. D1/9	*from* × 30

1   (2)   (3)

(Recess D.L.R.)

1879 (May). *Wmk CA over Crown, sideways. P 14.*

1	1	2 c. blue-green	£800	£550
2		6 c. orange-brown	£170	£170
		a. No dot at upper left (R. 2/4)	£375	£375
3		12 c. carmine	£1400	£550
		a. No right foot to second Chinese character (R. 2/3)	£2500	£1000
4		16 c. blue	50·00	£110

This watermark is always found sideways, and extends over two stamps, a single specimen showing only a portion of the Crown or the letters CA, these being tall and far apart. This paper was chiefly used for long fiscal stamps.

1880 (Jan)–**82.** *Wmk Crown CC (reversed on 8 c.). P 14.*

5	1	2 c. yellow-green	17·00	23·00
		x. Wmk reversed	32·00	42·00
		y. Wmk inverted and reversed	55·00	55·00
6		6 c. orange-brown	85·00	90·00
		a. No dot at upper left	£180	£190
		w. Wmk inverted		£150
7		8 c. carmine (4.82)	85·00	85·00
		a. No dot at lower left (R. 2/5)	£170	£170
		x. Wmk normal (not reversed)		£180
8		10 c. brown	£120	75·00
		w. Wmk inverted	95·00	80·00
9		12 c. carmine	£200	£275
		a. No right foot to second Chinese character	£400	£450
		w. Wmk inverted		£275
		x. Wmk reversed	£200	£275
10		16 c. blue (1881)	75·00	75·00
		w. Wmk inverted	£130	£130
		x. Wmk reversed	£100	£110
		y. Wmk inverted and reversed		£160
5/10		*Set of 6*	£500	£550

1880 (Aug). (*a*) *No. 9 surch with T 2 in black and with the original value obliterated by manuscript bar in red or black.*

11	8 c. on 12 c. carmine		£950	£650
	a. Type 2 inverted		£1100	£700
	b. "12" not obliterated		£1600	£1000
	c. As b. with Type 2 inverted			
	d. No right foot to second Chinese character		£1600	£1000
	x. Wmk reversed		£900	£600

(*b*) *No. 4 surch with two upright figures and No. 9 surch with two at right angles as T 3.*

12	6 c. on 16 c. blue (R.)		£1700	£700
	a. With one "6" only			
13	8 c. on 12 c. carmine		£1100	£800
	a. Both "8's" upright			
	b. Upright "8" inverted		£1200	£850
	c. No right foot to second Chinese character		£1700	£1200
	w. Wmk inverted		†	£1100
	x. Wmk reversed		£1100	£800

Eight Cents	**Eight Cents**	*one Dollar A.S.H*
(4)	(5)	(6)

1881 (Mar). *No. 9 handstamped with T 4.*

14	8 c. on 12 c. carmine		£225	£275
	a. No right foot to second Chinese character		£425	£500
	w. Wmk inverted		£300	
	x. Wmk reversed		£225	£275

1881 (June). *No. 9 surch with T 5.*

15	8 c. on 12 c. carmine		£110	£120
	a. Surch double		£1600	£1600
	b. Surch inverted		£8500	
	c. "Eighr"		£13000	
	d. No right foot to second Chinese character		£190	£225
	w. Wmk inverted		£190	
	x. Wmk reversed		£100	£110

The error "Eighr" occurred on R. 2/1 of the first printing, but was soon corrected.
Only one sheet of 10 has been reported of No. 15b, which also shows wmk inverted and reversed.

1883. *Wmk Crown CA (reversed on 8 c.). P 14.*

17	1	2 c. yellow-green		13·00	22·00
		a. Imperf between (horiz pair)		£7000	
		w. Wmk inverted		42·00	
		x. Wmk reversed		16·00	32·00
18		8 c. carmine		£200	90·00
		a. No dot at lower left		£400	£170
19		10 c. yellow-brown		23·00	38·00
		w. Wmk inverted		55·00	70·00
		x. Wmk reversed		55·00	70·00
20		16 c. blue		90·00	£160
21		40 c. amber		12·00	80·00
		x. Wmk reversed		21·00	80·00
17/21			*Set of 5*	£300	£350

1883 (May). *No. 10 surch "One Dollar A.S.H." by hand as T 6.*

22	1	$1 on 16 c. blue (R.)		£2750

The initials are those of the postmaster, Mr. A. S. Hamilton.

2 Cents	**2 Cents**	*2 Cents*
(7)	(8)	(9)

1885 (June). *Nos. 18 and 10 handstamped as T 7.*

23	1	2 c. on 8 c. carmine		£160	£350
		a. No dot at lower left		£325	
24		2 c. on 16 c. blue		£850	£750
		w. Wmk inverted		£900	

1885 (July). *No. 20 surch as T 8.*

25	1	2 c. on 16 c. blue		£110	£160
		a. Surch double		†	£3500
		b. "2" inserted		£1300	
		w. Wmk inverted			

No. 25b shows a second "2" applied by a separate handstamp to correct indistinct impressions of Type 8.

1885 (Sept). *No. 18 handstamped diag as T 9.*

26	1	2 c. on 8 c. carmine		65·00	£100
		a. No dot at lower left		£130	£225
		x. Wmk normal (not reversed)		95·00	

1885 (Sept)–86. *Wmk Crown CA. P 14.*

30	1	2 c. rose-red		1·50	8·00
		a. Pale rose-red (1886)		1·50	7·00
		x. Wmk reversed		5·00	
31		8 c. deep violet		16·00	7·00
		a. No dot at lower left		40·00	
		b. Mauve (1886)		20·00	8·00
		ba. No dot at lower left		48·00	22·00
		bw. Wmk inverted		55·00	
32		10 c. sepia (1886)		8·00	28·00
		w. Wmk inverted		32·00	
33		16 c. grey (1886)		£100	
		x. Wmk reversed		90·00	£150
30/3			*Set of 4*	£100	£170
30/3		Optd "Specimen"	*Set of 4*	£400	

ISSUES OF BRITISH NORTH BORNEO COMPANY

From 1 January 1890 while remaining a Crown Colony, the administration of Labuan was transferred to the British North Borneo Co, which issued the following stamps.

6 Cents	**Two** Cents	**Six** Cents
(10)	(11)	(12)

1891 (July)–92. *Handstamped with T 10.*

34	1	6 c. on 8 c. deep violet (No. 31)		95·00	85·00
		a. Surch inverted		£160	£150
		b. Surch double		£450	
		c. Surch double, one inverted		£750	
		d. "Cents" omitted		£400	£400
		f. Pair, one without surch, one surch inverted		£1200	
		g. No dot at lower left		£190	£180
35		6 c. on 8 c. mauve (No. 31b)		6·50	6·50
		a. Surch inverted		48·00	48·00
		b. Surch double, one inverted		£650	
		c. Surch double, both inverted		£650	
		d. "6" omitted		£425	
		e. Pair, one without surcharge		£950	£950
		f. Surch inverted with "Cents" omitted		£425	
		g. Pair, one without surch, one surch inverted		£1200	
		h. Surch double		£325	
		i. No dot at lower left		16·00	16·00
		j. Imperf between (horiz pair)			
		w. Wmk inverted		38·00	38·00
		x. Wmk reversed		26·00	
		ab. Surch inverted			
36		6 c. on 8 c. mauve (R.) (No. 31b) (2.92)		£700	£350
		a. Surch inverted		£950	£475
37		6 c. on 16 c. blue (No. 4) (3.92)		£1700	£1600
		a. Surch inverted		£6500	£4750
38		6 c. on 40 c. amber (No. 21)		£7000	£5500
		a. Surch inverted		£6000	£5500

There are two different versions of Type 10 with the lines of the surcharge either 1 mm or 2 mm apart.

(Recess D.L.R.)

1892–93. *No wmk. P 14.*

39	1	2 c. rose-lake		3·25	3·50
40		6 c. bright green		6·50	4·50
		a. No dot at upper left		17·00	15·00
41		8 c. violet		2·50	7·00
		a. Pale violet (1893)		4·00	7·00
43		10 c. brown		8·00	8·00
		a. Sepia-brown (1893)		8·00	13·00
45		12 c. bright blue		3·50	6·50
		a. No right foot to second Chinese character		11·00	18·00
46		16 c. grey		4·00	8·50
47		40 c. ochre		18·00	32·00
		a. Brown-buff (1893)		38·00	25·00
39/47			*Set of 7*	42·00	55·00

The 6 c., 12 c., 16 c. and 40 c. are in sheets of 10, as are all the earlier issues. The other values are in sheets of 30.

1892 (Dec). *Nos. 47 and 46 surch locally as T 11 or 12.*

49	1	2 c. on 40 c. ochre (13 December)		£150	90·00
		a. Surch inverted		£325	£450
50		6 c. on 16 c. grey (20 December)		£300	£140
		a. Surch inverted		£400	£225
		b. Surch sideways		£400	£225
		c. Surch "Six Cents"		£1200	

There are 10 slightly different versions of each of these surcharges which were applied in settings of 5×2, although instances of single handstamps are known.

A "SIX CENTS" handstamp with Roman "I" in "SIX" (without dot) is a clandestine surcharge, although it can be found with genuine postmarks. It also exists sideways or inverted.

The "Six Cents" surcharge of No. 50c was handstamped onto examples where the Type 12 surcharge had failed to print or where it was partially or completely albino.

CANCELLED-TO-ORDER. Prices are separately indicated, in a third price column, for stamps showing the recognisable black bars remainder cancellation. Earlier issues of the Company administration were also so treated, but, as postal cancellations were used, these cannot be identified.

(Litho D.L.R.)

1894 (Apr). *No wmk. P 14.*

51	1	2 c. carmine-pink		1·10	11·00	40
52		6 c. bright green		9·00	24·00	40
		a. Imperf between (horiz pair)		£5000		
		b. No dot at upper left		20·00	50·00	1·25
53		8 c. bright mauve		8·00	22·00	40
54		10 c. brown		27·00	32·00	40
55		12 c. pale blue		16·00	45·00	50
		a. No right foot to second Chinese character		35·00	70·00	1·25
56		16 c. grey		21·00	70·00	40
57		40 c. orange-buff		40·00	80·00	40
51/7			*Set of 7*	£110	£250	2·50
51/7		H/S "Specimen"	*Set of 7*	£110		

Collectors are warned against forgeries of this issue.

PERFORATION. There are a number of small variations in the perforation of the Waterlow issues of 1894 to 1905 which we believe to be due to irregularity of the pins rather than different perforators.

In the following lists, stamps perf 12, 12½, 13 or compound are described as perf 12–13, stamps perf 13½ or 14 are described as perf 13½–14 and those perf 14½, 15 or compound are listed as perf 14½–15. In addition the 13½–14 perforation exists compound with 14½–15 and with 12–13, whilst perf 16 comes from a separate perforator.

	LABUAN **40** CENTS
(13)	(14)

1894 (May)–96. *T 24/32 of North Borneo (colours changed), with "LABUAN" engraved on vignette plate as T 13 (8, 12, 24 c.) or horizontally (others). P 14½–15.*

(*a*) *Name and central part of design in black*

62	24	1 c. grey-mauve		1·50	6·50	50
		b. Perf 13½–14		7·00	8·50	
		ba. Imperf between (vert pair)		£600	—	£350
		c. Perf 13½–14, comp 14½–15		18·00	—	
		d. Perf 13½–14, comp 12–13		17·00	10·00	90
		e. Perf 12–13				
63	25	2 c. blue		2·50	6·50	50
		a. Imperf (pair)		£600		
		b. Perf 13½–14		3·75	6·50	
		c. Perf 13½–14, comp 14½–15		22·00		
		d. Perf 13½–14, comp 12–13				
		e. Perf 12–13		65·00		
64	26	3 c. ochre		3·75	13·00	50
		a. Perf 13½–14		6·50	9·00	
		b. Perf 13½–14, comp 14½–15				
		d. Perf 12–13		25·00		
65	27	5 c. green		26·00	18·00	65
		a. Perf 13½–14		27·00	10·00	
		ab. Imperf between (horiz pair)		£1100		
		b. Perf 13½–14, comp 12–13		38·00		
		d. Perf 12–13		75·00		
67	28	6 c. brown-lake		2·50	11·00	50
		a. Imperf (pair)		£550	†	£300
		b. Perf 13½–14		—	1·50	
		d. Perf 13½–14, comp 14½–15		—	—	
		d. Perf 13½–14, comp 12–13		—		90
		e. Perf 12–13				
68	29	8 c. rose-red		16·00	22·00	50
		a. Perf 13½–14		20·00	32·00	—
69		8 c. pink (1896)		7·00	23·00	50
		a. Perf 13½–14		23·00	29·00	50
70	30	12 c. orange-vermilion		23·00	40·00	50
		a. Perf 13½–14		55·00	60·00	2·00
		b. Perf 12–13				
		c. Perf 13½–14, comp 12–13		—	80·00	
71	31	18 c. olive-brown		22·00	45·00	50
		a. Perf 13½–14		48·00		
72		18 c. olive-bistre (1896)		48·00	60·00	50
		a. Perf 13½–14		26·00	55·00	
		b. Perf 13½–14, comp 12–13				
		c. Imperf between (vert pair)		†	†	£800

(*b*) *Name and central part in blue*

73	32	24 c. pale mauve		20·00	45·00	50
		a. Perf 13½–14		18·00	42·00	
74		24 c. dull lilac (1896)		15·00	40·00	50
		a. Perf 13½–14		13·00	38·00	50
62/74			*Set of 9*	90·00	£170	4·00
62/74		Optd "Specimen"	*Set of 9*	£140		

1895 (June). *No. 83 of North Borneo ($1 inscr "STATE OF NORTH BORNEO") surch as T 14.*

75	32c	4 c. on $1 scarlet		1·00	1·75	40
76		10 c. on $1 scarlet		2·25	1·40	40
77		20 c. on $1 scarlet		23·00	8·50	40
78		30 c. on $1 scarlet		25·00	30·00	40
79		40 c. on $1 scarlet		22·00	24·00	40
75/9			*Set of 5*	65·00	60·00	1·75
75/9		Optd "Specimen"	*Set of 5*	80·00		

No. 76 exists with the figures of the surcharge 2½ mm away from "CENTS". The normal setting has a space of 4 mm. Examples of the narrow setting have, so far, only been seen on cancelled-to-order stamps (*Price £18 c.t.o.*).

LABUAN	**1846** **JUBILEE** **1896**	**4** CENTS
(15)	(16)	(17)

1896. *T 32a to 32c of North Borneo (as Nos. 81 to 83, but colours changed) optd with T 15.*

80		25 c. green		22·00	26·00	60
		a. Opt omitted		18·00	—	1·25
		ba. Opt omitted			—	60·00
		b. Imperf (pair)		30·00		
81		50 c. maroon		22·00	26·00	60
		a. Opt omitted		16·00	—	1·25
		b. Imperf (pair)			—	60·00
		ba. Opt omitted		32·00		
82		$1 blue		50·00	45·00	60
		a. Opt omitted		22·00	—	1·25
		b. Imperf (pair)			—	60·00
		ba. Opt omitted		35·00		
80/2		Optd "Specimen"	*Set of 3*	60·00		

Nos. 80/1 showing stamps either printed double or double, one inverted, are from waste sheets subsequently sold by the British North Borneo Company to collectors.

1896 (24 Sept). *Jubilee of Cession of Labuan to Gt Britain. Nos. 62 to 68 optd with T 16. P 14½–15.*

83		1 c. black and grey-mauve		17·00	21·00	80
		b. Opt in orange		£180	£180	20·00
		c. "JEBILEE" (R. 8/7)		£950	£500	£275
		d. "JUBILE" (R. 3/10)		£1300		
		e. Perf 13½–14		19·00	22·00	
		ea. Opt double		£275	£300	—
		eb. Opt in orange		£225	£190	†
		f. Perf 13½–14, comp 12–13		25·00	18·00	†
		fa. Opt in orange		—	£190	†
		g. Perf 12–13				

84		2 c. black and blue		32·00	17·00	80
		a. Imperf horiz (vert pair)		£550	£650	†
		b. "JEBILEE" (R. 8/7)		£950	£950	—
		c. "JUBILE" (R. 3/10)		£1600		
		d. Perf 13½–14		30·00	14·00	—
		e. Perf 13½–14, comp 14½–15		—	35·00	—
		f. Perf 12–13		40·00		
85		3 c. black and mauve		30·00	22·00	80
		a. "JEBILEE" (R. 8/7)		—	£1200	£700
		b. "JUBILE" (R. 3/10)				
		d. Perf 13½–14		38·00	28·00	90
		db. Opt treble		£650		
		e. Perf 13½–14, comp 14½–15				
		f. Perf 13½–14, comp 12–13		£350	£350	£150
		fa. Opt double				
		fb. Opt treble		£650		
86		5 c. black and green		48·00	16·00	90
		a. Opt double		£425	£425	
		b. Perf 13½–14		50·00	20·00	90
		c. Perf 13½–14, comp 12–13				
87		6 c. black and brown-lake		24·00	20·00	80
		a. Opt double		£550	£450	†
		b. "JUBILE" (R. 3/10)		£1600		
		c. Perf 13½–14, comp 14½–15				
		d. Perf 13½–14		—	55·00	—
88		8 c. black and pink		40·00	13·00	80
		a. Opt double		—	£1900	†
		b. Perf 13½–14		35·00	11·00	80
		c. Perf 13½–14, comp 14½–15		48·00	18·00	—
83/8			Set of 6	£170	90·00	4·50
83/8 Optd "Specimen"			Set of 6	£150		

The normal overprint on the 1 c. varies in appearance from pure black to brownish black due to a mixing of the inks. The orange overprint on this value is in a clear, bright, unadulterated ink.

No. 84b is known in a vertical strip of 3 imperf horizontally except at the base of the bottom stamp (*Price* £5000 *unused*).

1897 (Apr)–**1901**. *T* **34/45** *of North Borneo (colours changed), with "LABUAN" engraved on vignette plate as T* **13** (8, 10, 12, 24 c.) *or horizontally (others). Name and central part in black (24 c. in blue). P* 13½–14.

89	34	1 c. dull claret (*p* 14½–15)		4·00	4·75	50
		a. Perf 13½–14, comp 14½–15				
		b. Brown (1901)		9·00	13·00	65
		ba. Perf 14½–15		3·00		
		bb. Perf 16		12·00	13·00	—
90	35	2 c. blue		11·00	4·25	40
		a. Imperf between (vert pair)		†	†	£475
		b. Imperf between (horiz pair)		†	†	£500
		c. Perf 14½–15		17·00		75
		d. Perf 13½–14, comp 12–13		27·00	17·00	—
		e. Perf 16				6·00
91	36	3 c. ochre		12·00	18·00	40
		a. Imperf between (vert pair)		£650	†	£450
		b. Perf 14½–15		8·50	6·50	40
		c. Perf 13½–14, comp 12–13		21·00	25·00	
92	38	5 c. green		45·00	45·00	60
		a. Perf 14½–15		32·00	40·00	
		b. Perf 13½–14, comp 12–13				
93	39	6 c. brown-lake		7·50	25·00	40
		a. Perf 14½–15		4·50	19·00	40
		ba. Imperf between (vert pair)		†	†	£450
		c. Perf 13½–14, comp 12–13				4·25
94	40	8 c. rose-red		40·00		40
		a. Perf 14½–15		15·00	12·00	
		b. Perf 13½–14, comp 12–13		25·00	—	2·75
		c. Vermilion		11·00		40
		ca. Perf 16				4·25
95	42	12 c. vermilion		60·00	70·00	70
		a. Perf 14½–15		25·00	45·00	70
96	44	18 c. olive-bistre		48·00	48·00	50
		a. Imperf between (vert pair)		†	†	
		b. Perf 16		15·00	40·00	50
97	45	24 c. grey-lilac		26·00	60·00	60
		a. Perf 14½–15		10·00	42·00	50
89/97			Set of 9	£110	£190	3·50
89/97 Optd "Specimen"			Set of 9	£160		

The 12, 18 and 24 c. above were errors; in the 12 c., "LABUAN" is over the value at the top; the 18 c. has "POSTAL REVENUE" instead of "POSTAGE AND REVENUE", and the 24 c. is without "POSTAGE AND REVENUE".

1897 (Nov)–**98**. (*a*) *Types of North Borneo (colours changed), with "LABUAN" engraved on the vignette plate as in T* **13**. *P* 13½–14.

98	42	12 c. black and vermilion (3.98)		†	—	2·25
		a. Perf 14½–15		38·00	42·00	—
		b. Perf 13½–14, comp 14½–15				
		c. Perf 16		48·00	50·00	
99	46	18 c. black and olive-bistre				
		a. Perf 14½–15		75·00	60·00	2·00
		b. Perf 16		†	—	8·00
100	47	24 c. blue and lilac-brown		23·00	48·00	—
		a. Perf 14½–15		23·00	48·00	
		b. Perf 13½–14, comp 12–13		—	55·00	—
		c. Perf 16		26·00		
		d. Blue and ochre (*p* 14½–15)		—	—	2·00
98/100 Optd "Specimen"			Set of 2	40·00		

In the 12 c. "LABUAN" is now correctly placed at foot of stamp. The 18 c. and 24 c. have the inscriptions on the stamps corrected. but the 18 c. still has "LABUAN" over the value at foot, and was further corrected as follows.

    (*b*) *As No. 99, but "LABUAN" at top*

101	46	18 c. black and olive-bistre (3.98)		50·00	50·00	—
		a. Perf 14½–15 (Optd S. £27)		23·00	55·00	2·75
		b. Perf 13½–14, comp 12–13		28·00	48·00	—
		c. Perf 12–13				

1899 (July). *Surch with T* **17** (*a*) *P* 14½–15.

102	38	4 c. on 5 c. (No. 92a)		30·00	26·00	
103	39	4 c. on 6 c. (No. 93b)		19·00	19·00	
		a. Perf 13½–14		26·00	26·00	
		b. Perf 13½–14, comp 12–13				
104	40	4 c. on 8 c. (No. 94a)		42·00	38·00	
		a. Perf 13½–14		22·00	32·00	
		b. Perf 13½–14, comp 12–13		26·00	32·00	
		c. Perf 12–13				
105	42	4 c. on 12 c. (No. 98a)		32·00	35·00	
		a. Perf 13½–14		32·00		
		b. Perf 16		40·00	42·00	
		c. Perf 13½–14, comp 12–13				

106	46	4 c. on 18 c. (No. 101a)		21·00	17·00	
		a. Surch double		£350	£400	
107	47	4 c. on 24 c. (No. 100a)		20·00	27·00	
		a. Perf 13½–14		16·00	28·00	
		b. Perf 13½–14, comp 12–13		24·00	23·00	
		c. Perf 16		35·00	42·00	

    (*b*) *P* 14

108	32a	4 c. on 25 c. (No. 80)			5·50	7·50
109	32b	4 c. on 50 c. (No. 81)			5·50	7·50
110	32c	4 c. on $1 (No. 82)			5·50	7·50
102/10			Set of 9	£140	£150	
102/10 Optd "Specimen"			Set of 9	£150		

A new setting of the surcharge with closer spacing (2½ mm) between "4" and "CENTS" was used for the Specimen overprints, including unissued surcharges on the 1 c., 2 c. and 3 c. values (*price* £140 *for the set of three*).

1900–02. *Types of North Borneo with "LABUAN" engraved on the vignette plate as in T* **13**, *in green on* 16 c. *P* 13½–14.

111	35	2 c. black and green		3·75	2·50	30
		a. Imperf between (horiz pair)		£1800		
		b. Perf 13½–14 (1901)				
112	37	4 c. black and yellow-brown		6·50	32·00	40
		a. Imperf between (vert pair)		£750		
		b. Perf 13½–14, comp 12–13		26·00		
113		4 c. black and carmine (8.1900)		12·00	2·75	50
		a. Perf 14½–15		6·50	7·50	40
		b. Perf 13½–14, comp 12–13		25·00	7·50	75
		c. Perf 16				
114	38	5 c. black and pale blue		25·00	18·00	65
		a. Perf 13½–14, comp 12–13		—	70·00	—
115	41	10 c. brown & slate-lilac (*p* 14½–15) (1902)		45·00	70·00	60
116	43	16 c. green and chestnut (1902)		55·00	95·00	2·50
		a. Perf 13½–14, comp 12–13		75·00	95·00	—
		b. Perf 12–13		£150		
		c. Perf 14½–15		85·00		
111/16			Set of 6	£130	£200	4·25
111/16 Optd "Specimen"			Set of 6	£140		

No. 112 was printed in an incorrect frame colour and was not issued for postal purposes in Labuan. Used examples come from dealers' stock sent to the island for cancellation.

18

Line through "B" (R.5/10)

(Recess Waterlow)

1902 (Sept)–**03.** *P* 13½–14.

117	18	1 c. black and purple (10.03)		3·50	6·50	50
		a. Perf 14½–15		—	7·00	—
		b. Perf 13½–14, comp 12–13		65·00		
		c. Line through "B"		40·00	65·00	5·00
118		2 c. black and green		3·00	4·00	30
		a. Perf 14½–15		—	5·00	—
		b. Line through "B"		40·00	50·00	5·00
119		3 c. black and sepia (10.03)		3·00	8·00	30
		a. Line through "B"		40·00	65·00	5·00
120		4 c. black and carmine		3·00	3·50	30
		a. Perf 14½–15		4·75	6·50	
		b. Perf 13½–14, comp 12–13		55·00	45·00	—
		c. Line through "B"		40·00	45·00	5·00
121		8 c. black and vermilion		7·50	8·00	50
		a. Perf 14½–15		7·00		
		b. Line through "B"		55·00	75·00	5·00
122		10 c. brown and slate-blue		3·00	8·50	30
		a. Perf 14½–15		3·75		
		ba. Imperf between (vert pair)		†	†	£600
		c. Line through "B"		40·00	75·00	5·00
123		12 c. black and yellow		3·50	10·00	30
		a. Imperf between (vert strip of 3)		†	†	£2500
		b. Perf 16		4·00	14·00	—
		c. Line through "B"		45·00	65·00	5·00
124		16 c. green and brown		4·75	14·00	30
		a. Imperf between (vert pair)		†		
		b. Line through "B"		50·00	£100	5·00
125		18 c. black and pale brown		3·25	14·00	30
		a. Line through "B"		45·00	£100	5·00
126		25 c. green and greenish blue		6·00	15·00	40
		a. Perf 14½–15		12·00	23·00	
		b. Error. Black and greenish blue		—	†	£375
		c. Line through "B"		65·00	£130	5·00
127		50 c. dull purple and lilac		10·00	40·00	60
		a. Perf 13½–14, comp 12–13		16·00	42·00	—
		b. Line through "B"		£130	£275	8·00
128		$1 claret and orange		8·00	45·00	60
		a. Perf 14½–15		10·00		
		b. Line through "B"		90·00	£275	9·00
117/28			Set of 12	50·00	£160	4·25
117/28 Optd "Specimen"			Set of 12	£180		

4
cents
(19)

1904 (Dec). *Issues of 1895 and 1897–8 surch with T* **19**.

    (*a*) *P* 14½–15

129	38	4 c. on 5 c. (No. 92a)		30·00	35·00	14·00
130	39	4 c. on 6 c. (No. 93b)		12·00	32·00	14·00
131	40	4 c. on 8 c. (No. 94a)		24·00	35·00	14·00
132	42	4 c. on 12 c. (No. 98a)		19·00	35·00	14·00
		a. Perf 16		23·00	38·00	
133	46	4 c. on 18 c. (No. 101) (*p* 13½–14)		19·00	38·00	14·00
		a. Perf 13½–14, comp 12–13		23·00	35·00	
		b. Perf 12–13				

134	47	4 c. on 24 c. (No. 100a)		16·00	38·00	14·00
		a. Perf 13½–14		—	20·00	—
		b. Perf 13½–14, comp 12–13		27·00	40·00	—
		c. Perf 16		26·00	35·00	14·00

    (*b*) *P* 14

135	32a	4 c. on 25 c. (No. 80)		8·50	21·00	14·00
136	32b	4 c. on 50 c. (No. 81)		8·50	21·00	14·00
		a. Surch double		£275		
137	32c	4 c. on $1 (No. 82)		8·50	21·00	14·00
129/37			Set of 9	£130	£225	£110

No. 136a usually shows one complete surcharge and parts of two further examples due to the position of the second impression.

The barred cancels can be found used on "philatelic" covers of this issue.

LABUAN   LABUAN
   (20)   (21)

1904 (12 Oct)–**05.** *Nos. 81, 83 (in Labuan colour), and* 84/6 *of North Borneo optd locally with T* **20** (25 c., $2) *or* **21** (*others*).

138	32a	25 c. indigo (2.05)		£950	†	
139	32c	$1 blue (2.05)				£550
140	32d	$2 dull green		£2500	£2750	—
141	14	$5 bright purple (2.05)		£5000	£5500	£1000
142	15	$10 brown (11.05)		£16000	†	£6000

Dangerous forgeries exist.
The overprint on No. 140 is 12 mm long.

POSTAGE DUE STAMPS
POSTAGE DUE
(D 1)

1901. *Optd with Type D* **1**, *reading vertically upwards. P* 13½–14.

D1	35	2 c. black and green (111)		11·00	20·00	40
		a. Opt double		£325		
		b. Perf 13½–14, comp 12–13		50·00	55·00	—
D2	36	3 c. black and ochre (91)		16·00	70·00	70
		a. Perf 13½–14, comp 12–13		50·00		
D3	37	4 c. black and carmine (113)		25·00	80·00	70
		a. Opt double		†	†	£425
		b. Perf 14½–15		25·00	80·00	45
D4	38	5 c. black and pale blue (114)		38·00	85·00	65
		a. Perf 14½–15		45·00		
		b. Perf 13½–14, comp 12–13		50·00		
D5	39	6 c. black and brown-lake (93)		18·00	75·00	65
		a. Perf 14½–15		24·00	70·00	65
		b. Perf 16		35·00		
D6	40	8 c. black and vermilion (94c)		45·00	75·00	85
		a. Frame inverted (*p* 14½–15)		†	†	£7000
		b. Perf 14½–15		38·00		85
		c. Perf 16		48·00	75·00	—
		d. Black and rose-red (94)		50·00	90·00	—
		da. Perf 14½–15		—	—	6·50
		db. Perf 13½–14, comp 12–13				
D7	42	12 c. black and vermilion (98)		65·00	85·00	2·50
		a. Opt reading downwards		†	†	£425
		b. Perf 14½–15		65·00	85·00	—
D8	46	18 c. blk & ol-bistre (101) (*p* 14½–15)		32·00	70·00	1·25
D9	47	24 c. blue and lilac-brown (100)		32·00	70·00	1·25
		a. Perf 13½–14, comp 12–13		50·00		
		b. Perf 14½–15		27·00		
		ba. Blue and ochre		48·00	—	1·25
		c. Perf 16		35·00	70·00	
D1/9			Set of 9	£225	£550	8·00

The administration of Labuan reverted to Colonial Office control, as part of an agreement with Brunei, on 1 January 1906. By Letters Patent dated 30 October 1906 Labuan was incorporated with Straits Settlements and ceased issuing its own stamps. In 1946 it became part of the Colony of North Borneo.

XII. SABAH
(*formerly* North Borneo)
NORTH BORNEO

PRICES FOR STAMPS ON COVER TO 1945		
No. 1	*from* × 100	
Nos. 2/3	*from* × 10	
Nos. 4/5	*from* × 10	
Nos. 6/19	*from* × 10	
Nos. 19b/21b		
Nos. 22/8	*from* × 50	
Nos. 29/35		
Nos. 36/44	*from* × 100	
Nos. 45/50		
Nos. 51/2	*from* × 10	
No. 54		
Nos. 55/65	*from* × 10	
Nos. 66/79	*from* × 4	
Nos. 81/6		
Nos. 87/91	*from* × 12	
Nos. 92/111	*from* × 4	
Nos. 112/26	*from* × 10	
Nos. 127/40	*from* × 6	
Nos. 141/5		
Nos. 146/57	*from* × 5	
Nos. 158/79	*from* × 8	
Nos. 181/5		
Nos. 186/8	*from* × 10	
Nos. 189/230	*from* × 4	
Nos. 231/4		
Nos. 235/49	*from* × 3	
Nos. 250/2		
Nos. 253/75	*from* × 12	
Nos. 276/92	*from* × 7	
Nos. 293/4		
Nos. 295/300	*from* × 6	
Nos. 301/2		
Nos. 303/17	*from* × 3	
Nos. 318/19	*from* × 20	
Nos. 320/34	*from* × 3	

Nos. D1/26	*from* × 25
Nos. D27/8	—
Nos. D29/35	*from* × 12
No. D35a	—
Nos. D36/65	*from* × 40
Nos. D66/70	*from* × 8

BRITISH NORTH BORNEO COMPANY ADMINISTRATION

PRINTERS. The stamps of this country up to 1894 were designed by T. Macdonald and printed in lithography by Blades, East and Blades, London.

(2)   **EIGHT CENTS**

1   (2)   (3)

1883 (Mar). *P* 12.
1   1   2 c. red-brown .. .. .. 24·00 48·00
    a. Imperf between (horiz pair)
The figure "2" varies in size.

1883 (June). *No.* 1 *surch as T* 2 *or* 3.
2   2   8 c. on 2 c. red-brown £900 £600
3   3   8 c. on 2 c. red-brown £425 £180
    a. Surch double .. .. .. † £3750
Type **2** was handstamped and stamps without stop are generally forgeries. Type **3** was a setting of 50 (10 × 5) providing ten varieties; it normally has a stop which sometimes failed to print.

CANCELLED-TO-ORDER—Prices are separately indicated in a third price column, for stamps showing the recognisable black bars remainder cancellation. The issues since 1916 have not been thus cancelled.

It should be noted, however, that a postmark of this form was in use for postal purposes up to this period, and was used at one or two of the smaller post-offices until 1949. A small oval with five bars was used to mark railway mail during 1945/55 and also as a paquebot mark at Jesselton c. 1950.

and Revenue

4   5   (6)

1883. *P* 14.
4   4   50 c. violet .. .. .. 95·00 — 20·00
    a. Inverted "L" for first "F" in "FIFTY" (R.5/2) .. .. £700 — £140
5   5 $1 scarlet .. .. .. 90·00 — 9·50

1883 (July). *P* 12.
6   1   4 c. pink .. .. .. 38·00 48·00
    a. Imperf (horiz pair) .. .. † —
7   8 c. green .. .. .. 65·00 50·00

1886. *P* 14.
8   1   ½ c. magenta .. .. .. 80·00 £170
9   1 c. orange £170 £300
    a. Imperf (pair) £275
    b. Imperf horiz (vert pair) .. £800
10   2 c. brown .. .. .. 22·00 22·00
    a. Imperf between (horiz pair) £550
11   4 c. pink .. .. .. 17·00 50·00
12   8 c. green .. .. .. 19·00 50·00
    a. Imperf between (horiz pair) £750
13   10 c. blue .. .. .. 25·00 45·00
    a. Imperf (pair) £300
8/13   *Set of* 6 £300 £550
Imperforate examples of the 4 c. pink are listed under No. 6a.

1886 (Sept). *Nos.* 8 *and* 13 *optd with T* 6.
14   ½ c. magenta .. .. .. 90·00 £170
15   10 c. blue £130 £170

3 CENTS   **5 CENTS**   **3 CENTS**
(7)   (8)   Small "3" variety (R.3/1, 3/4, 3/7)

(Surchd by *North Borneo Herald*, Sandakan)

1886 (Sept). *T* 1 *surch as T* 7/8. (*a*) *P* 12.
16   7   3 c. on 4 c. pink £140 £200
    a. Small "3" .. .. .. —£4750
17   8   5 c. on 8 c. green £160 £200

(*b*) *P* 14
18   7   3 c. on 4 c. pink .. .. 75·00 £110
    a. Small "3" £1500
19   8   5 c. on 8 c. green .. .. 80·00 £110
    a. Surch inverted £1900

9

10   11

12   13

1886–87. (*a*) *P* 14.
21b   9   ½ c. magenta .. .. 15·00 45·00
22   ½ c. rose .. .. .. 2·50 13·00
    a. Imperf (pair) .. .. 24·00
23   1 c. orange-yellow .. .. 8·00 24·00
    a. Imperf between (vert pair) .. £300
    b. Imperf (pair) .. .. 30·00
24   1 c. orange .. .. .. 2·00 8·00
    a. Imperf (pair) .. .. 24·00
25   2 c. brown .. .. .. 2·00 8·50
    a. Imperf (pair) .. .. 24·00
26   4 c. pink .. .. .. 2·50 9·00
    a. Imperf (pair) .. .. 24·00
    b. Imperf between (horiz or vert pair) £200
    c. Imperf vert (horiz pair) .. £225
    d. Error. 1 c. pink (R. 2/3) (centre stamp of strip of 3) .. £170 £425
    da. Imperf between (pair)
    db. Imperf (pair) £3000
27   8 c. green .. .. .. 8·00 16·00
    a. Imperf (pair) .. .. 24·00
28   10 c. blue .. .. .. 7·00 25·00
    a. Imperf between (vert pair) £325
    b. Imperf (pair) .. .. 24·00
29   10   25 c. indigo .. .. .. £140 10·00
    a. Imperf between (vert pair)
    b. Imperf (pair) .. .. £225 24·00
30   11   50 c. violet .. .. .. £180 12·00
    a. Imperf (pair) .. .. £300 24·00
31   12 $1 scarlet .. .. .. £200 10·00
    a. Imperf (pair) .. .. £300 24·00
32   13 $2 sage-green .. .. .. £300 17·00
    a. Imperf (pair) .. .. £200 26·00
22/32   *Set of* 10 £750 £120

(*b*) *P* 12
34   9   ½ c. magenta £140 £275
35   1 c. orange £110 £150

Nos. 21b/32 are known to have been sold as cancelled remainders, but these are difficult to distinguish from postally used. Values above 10 c. are infrequently found postally used so that the used prices quoted are for the remainders.

14

15   16

17   18

1888–92. *T* 14 (*as T* 9 *but inscr* "POSTAGE & REVENUE") *and T* 15/18 (*T* 10/13 *redrawn*). *P* 14.
36   14   ½ c. magenta (1889) .. 3·75 22·00 2·00
    a. Imperf vert (horiz pair) .. † † £200
    b. *Rose* .. .. .. 1·00 4·00 60
    ba. Imperf between (horiz pair) £350
    c. Imperf (pair) .. .. 24·00 — 8·00
37   1 c. orange (1892) .. .. 1·60 3·50 50
    a. Imperf vert (horiz pair) .. £300
    b. Imperf (pair) .. .. 24·00 — 7·00
38   2 c. brown (1889) .. .. 7·50 11·00 70
    a. Imperf between (horiz pair)
    b. *Lake-brown* .. .. 3·00 11·00 50
    c. Imperf (pair) .. .. 24·00 — 6·50
39   3 c. violet (1889) .. .. 2·50 11·00 50
    b. Imperf (pair) .. .. 18·00 — 6·50
40   4 c. rose-pink (1889) .. 4·50 24·00 50
    a. Imperf between (pair) .. — £130
    b. Imperf (pair) .. .. 24·00 — 7·00
41   5 c. slate (1889) .. .. 2·75 17·00 50
    a. Imperf between (pair)
    b. Imperf (pair) .. .. 24·00 — 7·00
42   6 c. lake (1892) .. .. 7·00 17·00 50
    a. Imperf (pair) .. .. 24·00 — 8·00
43   8 c. blue-green (1891) .. 18·00 23·00 95
    a. *Yellow-green* .. .. 15·00 21·00 50
    c. Imperf (pair) .. .. 24·00 — 8·00
44   10 c. blue (1891) .. .. 8·00 23·00 85
    a. Imperf between (vert pair) .. † † £200
    b. *Dull blue* .. .. 6·50 18·00 50
    ba. Imperf between (horiz pair)
    d. Imperf (pair) .. .. 24·00 — 8·00
45   15   25 c. indigo .. .. 40·00 80·00 75
    a. Imperf (pair) .. .. £170 — 13·00
    b. Imperf vert (horiz pair) .. † † £250
46   16   50 c. violet .. .. 70·00 £130 75
    a. Imperf (pair) .. .. £225 — 13·00
    b. *Chalky blue* .. .. † £120 †
47   17 $1 scarlet .. .. 27·00 £110 75
    a. Imperf (pair) .. .. £170 — 13·00
48   18 $2 dull green .. .. £110 £170 1·50
    a. Imperf (pair) .. .. £275 — 15·00
36b/48   *Set of* 13 £250 £550 7·50

Nos. 39, 43 and 44 showing stamps printed double or triple, one inverted, are from waste sheets subsequently sold by the British North Borneo Company to collectors.

These stamps to the 10 c. value were forged on several occasions. Most forgeries of the ½ c. value can be identified by the presence of a diagonal line joining the top two horizontal strokes of the uppermost Chinese character.

The new 25 c. has the inscription "BRITISH NORTH BORNEO" in taller capitals. In the 50 c. the "0" of the numerals "50" in the two upper corners is square-shaped at the top and bottom instead of being oval. The 1 dollar has 14 pearls instead of 13 at each side, and on the 2 dollars the word "BRITISH" measures 10½ to 11 mm in length in place of 12 mm.

19   20

1889. *P* 14.
49   19 $5 bright purple .. .. £140 £150 8·50
    a. Imperf (pair) .. .. £325 — 26·00
50   20 $10 brown .. .. .. £190 £275 12·00
    a. Imperf (pair) .. .. £450 — 30·00
    b. "DOLLAPS" for "DOLLARS" (R.2/1) £1100 £1400 £325
    ba. Ditto. Imperf (pair) .. £1900 — £700

Two Cents.   **6 cents.**   **1 cent.**
(21)   (22)   (23)

1890 (Dec). *Surch as T* 21, *in red.*
51   15   2 c. on 25 c. indigo .. 55·00 75·00
    a. Surch inverted £375 £375
52   8 c. on 25 c. indigo .. 85·00 £100
The first printing of Nos. 51/2 had the two lines of the surcharge 3.5 mm apart. On a second printing of both values this gap widened to 5 mm.

1891–92. *Surch with T* 22.
54   9   6 c. on 8 c. green (1892) .. £7000 £3750
    a. Large "s" in "cents" .. £13000
55   14   6 c. on 8 c. yellow-green .. 16·00 9·00
    a. Surch inverted £300 £350
    b. Inverted "c" in "cents" (R.5/4) £350 £400
    c. "cetns." for "cents" (R.3/7) £375 £425
    d. Large "s" in "cents" (R.2/9 or 3/7) £150 £150
56   9   6 c. on 10 c. blue .. .. 50·00 18·00
    a. Surch inverted £180 £180
    b. Surch double
    c. Surch treble £375
    d. Large "s" in "cents" .. £200 £140
57   14   6 c. on 10 c. blue .. .. £120 26·00
    a. Large "s" in "cents" .. £425 £180
Unused examples of Nos. 55 and 57 are normally without gum.

There were three settings of the surcharge for No. 55. On the first two the large "s" in "cents" occurred on R.2/9 with the other two listed varieties also included. Nos. 55b/c were corrected on the third setting and the large "s" in cents occurred on R.3/7.

1892 (Mar–Nov). *Surch as T 23 ("Cents." with capital "C" as in T 21 on No. 65), in red.*

63	14	1 c. on 4 c. rose-pink	..	.. 20·00	14·00
		a. Surch double	..		£950
		b. Surch on back and on front	..		£600
		ba. As b, but with surch double on front			
64		1 c. on 5 c. slate (Nov)	..	6·50	6·00
65	15	8 c. on 25 c. indigo (date?)	..	£130	£150

Unused examples of Nos. 63/5 are normally without gum.

24 Dyak Chief

25 Sambar Stag (*Cervus unicolor*)

26 Sago Palm

27 Great Argus Pheasant

28 Arms of the Company

29 Malay Dhow

30 Estuarine Crocodile

31 Mount Kinabalu

32 Arms of the Company with Supporters

PERFORATION. There are a number of small variations in the perforation of the Waterlow issues of 1894 to 1922 which we believe were due to irregularity of the pins rather than different perforators.

In the following lists, stamps perf 12, 12½, 13 or compound are described as perf 12–13, stamps perf 13½, 14 or compound are described as perf 13½–14 and those perf 14½, 15 or compound are listed as perf 14½–15. In addition the 13½–14 perforation exists compound with 14½–15 and with 12–13, whilst perf 15½–16 comes from a separate perforator.

(Recess Waterlow)

1894 (Feb). *P 14½–15.*

66	24	1 c. black and olive-bistre	..	1·25 8·00	50
		a. Imperf between (horiz or vert pair)			
		.. .. ..		£500	
		b. Perf 13½–14	..	1·25 8·50	50
		c. Perf 13½–14, comp 14½–15	32·00 48·00	—
		d. Perf 13½–14, comp 12–13	18·00 40·00	—
		e. Perf 12–13			
67		1 c. black and bistre-brown	..	1·75 9·00	50
		a. Perf 13½–14	..	2·25 9·00	50
		b. Perf 13½–14, comp 12–13	20·00 48·00	—
		c. Perf 12–13			
68	25	2 c. black and rose-lake	..	5·00 4·75	50
		a. Imperf between (horiz or vert pair)		£450 £500	†
		b. Perf 13½–14	..	29·00 35·00	—
69		2 c. black and lake	..	5·00 4·75	50
		a. Perf 13½–14	..	32·00 35·00	1·25
		b. Perf 13½–14, comp 12–13	25·00 26·00	—
		c. Imperf between (horiz pair)			
70	26	3 c. olive-green and dull purple	2·75 7·50	50
		a. Imperf between (horiz pair)		£375	†
		b. Bronze-green and dull purple	4·25 —	50
		c. Perf 13½–14			
71		3 c. olive-green & violet (*p* 13½–14)	14·00 42·00	—
		a. Imperf between (horiz pair)			
72	27	5 c. black and vermilion	..	12·00 11·00	60
		a. Imperf between (horiz or vert pair)		£400	
		b. Perf 13½–14	..	42·00 55·00	1·25
		c. Perf 13½–14, comp 12–13	— 60·00	5·50
		d. Perf 13½–14, comp 14½–15			
		e. Perf 12–13			
73	28	6 c. black and bistre-brown	..	55·00 75·00	60
		a. Perf 13½–14	..	4·00 15·00	60
		b. Perf 13½–14, comp 12–13	— 60·00	60
		c. Perf 13½–14, comp 14½–15	55·00	
74	29	8 c. black and dull purple	..	5·00 9·50	60
		a. Imperf between (vert pair)		£375	
		b. Perf 13½–14	..	8·50 28·00	80
		ba. Imperf between (vert pair)		£425 †	£300
		d. Perf 13½–14, comp 12–13			
75	30	12 c. black and blue	..	27·00 80·00	2·50
		a. Perf 13½–14	..	27·00 80·00	2·50
		b. Imperf between (horiz pair)	..	£700 †	£450

76	30	12 c. black and ultramarine	..	42·00 85·00	3·00
		a. Perf 13½–14	..	40·00 85·00	3·00
		b. Imperf between (pair)			
78	31	18 c. black and deep green	..	24·00 48·00	2·00
		a. Perf 13½–14	..	27·00 48·00	2·00
79	32	24 c. blue and rose-lake	..	22·00 70·00	2·00
		a. Imperf between (vert pair)	—	£300
		b. Imperf between (vert strip of 3)	† †	£400
		c. Perf 13½–14	..	22·00 70·00	2·00
		d. Perf 13½–14, comp 14½–15			
66/79		.. ..	*Set of 9*	90·00 £225	9·00

32a

32b

32c

32d

(Litho Blades, East & Blades, London)

1894 (Feb). *T 32a to 32d and T 19/20, but inscribed "THE STATE OF NORTH BORNEO". P 14.*

81		25 c. indigo	..	.. 8·50 27·00	90
		a. Imperf (pair)	..	30·00 —	7·00
		b. Imperf between (horiz or vert pair)		£650 —	90·00
82		50 c. deep slate-purple	..	15·00 50·00	1·00
		a. Imperf (pair)	..	— —	7·00
		b. Imperf between (horiz pair)			
		d. *Chalky blue*	..	— 50·00	
83		$1 scarlet	..	.. 12·00 24·00	1·00
		a. Perf 14×11	..	£180	
		b. Imperf (pair)	..	29·00 —	7·00
84		$2 dull green	..	16·00 75·00	1·50
		a. Imperf (pair)	..	—	9·50
85		$5 bright purple	..	£180 £250	13·00
		a. Imperf (pair)	..	£275 —	30·00
		b. *Dull purple*	..	£160 £225	5·50
86		$10 brown	..	£190 £275	11·00
		a. Imperf (pair)	..	£275 —	30·00
81/6			*Set of 6*	£350 £600	19·00
81/6 Optd "Specimen"			*Set of 6*	£150	

For Nos. 81 to 83 in other colours, see Labuan 80a, 81a and 82a.

Nos. 81/4 showing stamps printed double, double, one inverted, or on both sides are from waste sheets subsequently sold by the British North Borneo Company to collectors.

4

CENTS

(33 (3½ mm between lines of surcharge))

(Surcharged by Waterlow)

1895 (June). *No. 83 surch as T 33.*

87	32c	4 cents on $1 scarlet	..	4·50 1·50	40
		a. Surch double, one diagonal	£800	
88		10 cents on $1 scarlet	..	12·00 1·75	40
89		20 cents on $1 scarlet	..	30·00 14·00	40
90		30 cents on $1 scarlet	..	23·00 22·00	40
91		40 cents on $1 scarlet	..	23·00 45·00	40
87/91		..	*Set of 5*	80·00 75·00	1·75
87/91 Optd "Specimen"			*Set of 5*	85·00	

For 4 c. on $1 with wider spacing see No. 121.

No. 88 exists with the figures of the surcharge 2½ mm away from "CENTS". The normal setting has a space of 3½ mm. Examples of the narrow setting have, so far, only been seen on cancelled-to-order stamps.

34

35

36

37 Orang-Utan

38

39

40

41 Sun Bear

42

43 Borneo Railway Train

44

45

(Recess Waterlow)

1897 (Mar)–**1902.** *T 34 to 45. New frames. P 13½–14.*

92		1 c. black and bistre-brown	..	9·00 3·25	40
		aa. Perf 16	..	8·00 2·50	40
		a. Perf 14½–15	..	50·00 42·00	40
		b. Perf 13½–14, comp 12–13	..		
		c. Imperf between (horiz pair)	† †	£375
93		1 c. black and ochre	..	40·00 13·00	50
		a. Perf 14½–15	..	25·00 10·00	50
		ab. Imperf between (horiz pair)	† †	£375
		b. Perf 13½–14, comp 12–13			
94		2 c. black and lake	..	24·00 3·50	40
		a. Perf 14½–15	..	17·00 3·00	40
		ab. Imperf between (horiz pair)	† †	£400
		b. Perf 13½–14, comp 12–13	— 14·00	1·25
		c. Perf 12–13			
		d. Imperf between (vert pair)	† †	£400
95		2 c. black and green (1900)	..	42·00 1·50	40
		a. Perf 14½–15	..	70·00 11·00	—
		b. Perf 13½–14, comp 12–13	90·00 22·00	—
		c. Perf 12–13			
		d. Imperf between (pair)	..	— £550	†
96		3 c. green and rosy mauve	..	35·00 9·00	40
		a. Perf 14½–15	..	48·00 48·00	1·00
		b. Perf 13½–14, comp 12–13	65·00 65·00	—
97		3 c. green & dull mauve (*p* 14½–15)	9·50 3·00	50
98		4 c. black and green (1900)	..	9·00 —	1·50
		a. Perf 13½–14, comp 12–13			
99		4 c. black and carmine (1900)	..	30·00 6·50	50
		a. Perf 16	..	55·00 35·00	50
		a. Perf 14½–15	..	45·00 2·00	50
		c. Perf 13½–14, comp 12–13	30·00 35·00	—
		d. Perf 12–13			
100		5 c. black and orange-vermilion	..	75·00 3·50	50
		a. Perf 14½–15	..	75·00 3·00	50
		ab. Imperf between (horiz pair)	† £650	
		b. Perf 13½–14, comp 12–13	75·00 14·00	60
		c. Perf 12–13			
101		6 c. black and bistre-brown	..	35·00 17·00	50
		a. Perf 14½–15	..	15·00 3·25	50
102		8 c. black and brown-purple	..	65·00 48·00	70
		a. Perf 16	..	95·00 15·00	70
		ab. Imperf between (vert pair)	£350 £350	—
		b. Perf 14½–15	..	30·00 2·75	60
103		8 c. black and brown	..	8·50 65·00	75
		a. Perf 14½–15	..	50·00 65·00	—
		b. Perf 16	..		
104		10 c. brown and slate-lilac (1902)	..	70·00 35·00	2·00
		a. Imperf between (vert pair)			
105		10 c. brown and slate-blue (1902)	..	£160 65·00	1·50
106		12 c. black and dull blue	..	£110 48·00	1·50
		a. Imperf between (horiz pair)	† †	£425
		b. Perf 14½–15	..	80·00 32·00	1·50
		c. Perf 13½–14, comp 12–13	£140 55·00	—
		d. Perf 12–13			
107		16 c. green and chestnut (1902)	..	£120 90·00	3·00
		a. Perf 14½–15	..	£140 £130	10·00
108		18 c. black and green (*p* 16)	..	17·00 60·00	1·00
		a. Imperf vert (horiz pair)	† †	70·00
		b. Imperf between (vert pair)	† †	£250
		c. Imperf (pair)	† †	£160
109		24 c. blue and lake	..	16·00 75·00	1·60
		a. Perf 13½–14, comp 12–13	32·00 90·00	1·60
		b. Perf 12–13	..	90·00	
92/109 (*one of each value*)			*Set of 12*	£400 £275	10·00
92/109 (*excl 93, 97, 103, 105*) Optd "Specimen"			*Set of 14*	£250	

No. 98 was printed in an incorrect frame colour and it is doubtful if it was issued for postal purposes in North Borneo. Used examples come from dealers' stock sent to the territory for cancellation.

In the above the 18 c. has "POSTAL REVENUE" instead of "POSTAGE AND REVENUE" and the 24 c. has those words omitted. These stamps were replaced by others with corrected inscriptions; see Nos. 110 and 111.

46

47

1897. *Corrected inscriptions.* P 13½–14.
110	46	18 c. black and green		70·00	22·00	1·50
		a. Imperf between (horiz pair)		†	† £375
		b. Perf 14½–15		60·00	12·00	1·50
		c. Perf 13½–14, comp 12–13			
111	47	24 c. blue and lake		55·00	35·00	2·00
		a. Perf 16		95·00	95·00	2·00
		b. Perf 14½–15		40·00	50·00	2·25
		c. Perf 13½–14, comp 12–13			
		d. Perf 12–13			
110/11		Optd "Specimen"	*Set of 2* 50·00

BRITISH

4

CENTS PROTECTORATE. 4 cents

(48) (4½ mm between   (49)   (50)
lines of surcharge)

1899 (22 July–Oct). *Surch with T* **48**. (*a*) *4½ mm between lines of surch.* P 14½–15 (*Nos.* 112/17) *or* 14 (*Nos.* 118/24).
112		4 c. on 5 c. (No. 100a)		38·00	42·00
		a. Perf 13½–14		18·00	10·00
		b. Perf 13½–14, comp 12–13		28·00	28·00
113		4 c. on 6 c. (No. 101a) (date?)		18·00	23·00
		a. Perf 13½–14		14·00	40·00
114		4 c. on 8 c. (No. 102b) (Oct)		14·00	10·00
115		4 c. on 12 c. (No. 106b) (Oct)		16·00	13·00
		a. Imperf between (horiz pair)		£500	
		b. Imperf between (vert pair)			£500
		c. Perf 13½–14		29·00	
		d. Perf 12–13			
		e. Perf 13½–14, comp 12–13		25·00	
116		4 c. on 18 c. (No. 110a) (Oct)		9·50	13·00
		a. Perf 13½–14		23·00	28·00
117		4 c. on 24 c. (No. 111b) (Oct)		15·00	15·00
		a. Perf 16		42·00	50·00
		b. Perf 13½–14		15·00	35·00
		c. Perf 13½–14, comp 12–13		32·00	35·00
		d. Perf 12–13		40·00	50·00
118		4 c. on 25 c. indigo (No. 81)		5·00	8·50
		a. Imperf between (horiz strip of 3)		£850	
119		4 c. on 50 c. deep slate-purple (No. 82)		7·00	14·00
		a. Chalky blue		25·00	35·00
121		4 c. on $1 scarlet (No. 83)		5·00	10·00
122		4 c. on $2 dull green (No. 84)		5·00	12·00
123		4 c. on $5 bright purple (No. 85)		£150	£225
		a. Dull purple		£170	£225
124		4 c. on $10 brown (No. 86)		£100	£200
112/24			*Set of 12* £325 £500
112/24		Optd "Specimen"	*Set of 12* £190

(*b*) *8½ mm between lines of surch.* P 14
125		4 c. on $5 (No. 85)		5·50	12·00
126		4 c. on $10 (No. 86)		5·50	12·00

No. 121 differs only from No. 87 in having the "4" and "cents" wider apart.
Examples of the Kudat postmark dated "AU 15 1899" struck on Nos. 112/24 are generally considered to be faked.
A new setting of the surcharge, with 2½ mm between "4" and "CENTS" for values to $2 and 3½ mm on the $5 and $10, was used for the Specimen overprints, including unissued surcharges on the 1 c., 2 c. and 3 c. values (*price £100 the set of three*).

(Optd by Waterlow)

1901 (8 Oct)–**05**. *Optd as T* **49**. (*a*) *P* 13½–14.
127		1 c. (No. 92) (R.)		3·50	1·50	30
		a. Perf 14½–15		2·50	1·75	30
128		2 c. (No. 95) (R.)		3·00	1·25	30
		a. Perf 16		3·50	8·00	30
		b. Perf 14½–15		8·50	8·50	30
129		3 c. (No. 96)		1·60	4·25	30
		a. Imperf between (vert pair)			
		b. Perf 14½–15		8·00	2·25	30
		c. Perf 13½–14, comp 14½–15		45·00	
130		4 c. (No. 99) (G.)		7·00	1·50	30
		a. Perf 14½–15		17·00	1·50	30
131		5 c. (No. 100) (G.)		32·00	3·50	30
		a. Perf 14½–15		10·00	2·50	30
132		6 c. (No. 101) (R.)		40·00	50·00	1·25
		a. No stop after "Protectorate"		70·00	70·00	1·25
		b. Perf 16		3·25	11·00	70
133		8 c. (No. 103) (B.)		3·00	3·25	50
		a. No stop after "Protectorate"		3·00	22·00	1·50
		b. Perf 13½–14, comp 12–13		48·00	18·00	—
		c. Imperf between (vert pair)		†	£300
134		10 c. (No. 104) (R.) (7.02)		35·00	5·00	70
		a. Perf 14½–15		75·00	25·00	1·75
		c. Perf 13½–14. No stop after "Protectorate"		£130	
		d. Opt double		£475	† £250
		e. On 10 c. (No. 105)		£140	— 1·00
		f. Imperf vert (horiz pair)		†	£400
135		12 c. (No. 106) (R.)		40·00	12·00	1·50
136		16 c. (No. 107) (7.02)		90·00	20·00	2·25
		a. Perf 14½–15		95·00	35·00	2·25
		b. Perf 13½–14, comp 12–13		£140	50·00	—
137		18 c. (No. 110) (R.)		10·00	25·00	1·25
		a. No stop after "Protectorate"			
		b. Perf 13½–14, comp 12–13		—	1·50
138		24 c. (No. 111)		16·00	40·00	1·50
		a. Perf 14½–15		55·00	75·00	1·75
		b. Imperf between (horiz pair)			

(*b*) *P* 14
139		25 c. (No. 81) (R.)		2·00	10·00	50
		a. No stop after "Protectorate"		£120	£140	21·00
		b. Overprints tête-bêche (horiz pair)		£375	
		c. Overprint inverted		£375	
140		50 c. (No. 82) (R.)		2·75	11·00	55
		a. No stop after "Protectorate"		65·00	£110	—
		b. Chalky blue			
141		$1 (No. 83) (R.) (1.04)		10·00	60·00	—
142		$1 (No. 83)		6·50	38·00	2·50
		a. Imperf horiz (vert pair)		£475	
		b. Opt double		†	† £275
		c. Opt treble			

143		$2 (No. 84) (R.) (1903)		30·00	95·00	3·50
		a. Opt double		£1000	— £325
144		$5 (No. 85b) (R.) (2.05)		£180	£425	7·50
145		$10 (No. 86) (R.) (2.05)		£300	£550	8·50
		a. Opt inverted		£1200	† £350
127/45			*Set of 18* £650 £1100 29·00
127/40		Optd "Specimen"	*Set of 14* £275

There was more than one setting of the overprint for some of the values. Full sheets of the 6 c. and 8 c. are known, without stop throughout.

1904–5. *Surch locally with T* **50**. (*a*) *P* 14½–15.
146		4 c. on 5 c. (No. 100a)		28·00	40·00	8·00
		a. Surch omitted (in pair with normal)			
147		4 c. on 6 c. (No. 101a)		7·00	19·00	7·00
		a. Surch inverted		£190	
148		4 c. on 8 c. (No. 102b)		12·00	26·00	7·50
		a. Surch inverted		£200	
149		4 c. on 12 c. (No. 106b)		22·00	40·00	8·00
		a. Perf 13½–14		42·00	60·00	8·00
		b. Perf 13½–14, comp 12–13		24·00	60·00	—
		c. Surch omitted (in pair with normal)			
150		4 c. on 18 c. (No. 110b)		14·00	38·00	8·00
		a. Perf 13½–14			
151		4 c. on 24 c. (No. 111b)		19·00	48·00	8·00
		a. Perf 16		16·00	48·00	8·00
		b. Perf 13½–14		19·00	48·00	8·00
		c. Perf 12–13			

(*b*) *P* 14
152		4 c. on 25 c. (No. 81)		3·50	25·00	8·00
153		4 c. on 50 c. (No. 82)		4·00	38·00	8·00
154		4 c. on $1 (No. 83)		4·50	48·00	8·00
155		4 c. on $2 (No. 84)		5·50	48·00	8·00
156		4 c. on $5 (No. 85)		11·00	48·00	8·00
		a. Surch on No. 85b		30·00	48·00	—
157		4 c. on $10 (No. 86)		11·00	48·00	8·00
		a. Surch inverted		£1200	
		b. Surch omitted (in pair with normal)			
146/57			*Set of 12* £110 £425 85·00

51 Malayan Tapir

52 Travellers' Tree

53 Jesselton Railway Station

54 The Sultan of Sulu, his staff and W. C. Cowie, Managing Director of the Company

55 Indian Elephant

56 Sumatran Rhinoceros

57 Ploughing with Buffalo

58 Wild Boar

59 Palm Cockatoo

60 Rhinoceros Hornbill

61 Banteng

62 Dwarf Cassowary

(Recess Waterlow)

1909 (1 July)–**23.** *Centres in black.* P 13½–14.
158	51	1 c. chocolate-brown		4·75	1·00	30
		a. Perf 14½–15		30·00	10·00	40
159		1 c. brown		11·00	1·60	30
		a. Perf 14½–15		24·00	3·00	30
		b. Imperf between (vert pair)		£110	
160	52	2 c. green		1·00	70	30
		a. Imperf between (pair)			
		b. Perf 14½–15		2·00	70	30
161	53	3 c. lake		3·00	1·75	30
162		3 c. rose-lake		2·50	1·75	40
		a. Perf 14½–15		27·00	—	55
163		3 c. green (1923)		9·50	1·25	—
164	54	4 c. scarlet		2·75	30	30
		a. Imperf between (vert pair)			
		b. Perf 14½–15		11·00	1·75	35
165	55	5 c. yellow-brown		8·50	5·50	40
		a. Perf 14½–15			
166		5 c. dark brown		14·00	5·00	—
167	56	6 c. olive-green		6·00	1·75	30
		a. Perf 14½–15		60·00	6·50	60
168		6 c. apple-green		24·00	3·00	60
169	57	8 c. lake		2·75	1·75	40
		a. Perf 14½–15			
170	58	10 c. greyish blue		45·00	8·00	80
		a. Perf 14½–15		70·00	24·00	—
171		10 c. blue		50·00	3·50	—
172		10 c. turquoise-blue		23·00	2·00	80
		a. Perf 14½–15		45·00	5·50	—
173	59	12 c. deep blue		23·00	2·75	70
		a. Perf 14½–15			
		b. Imperf between (horiz pair)		†	† £425
173c		12 c. deep bright blue			
174	60	16 c. brown-lake		24·00	7·00	80
175	61	18 c. blue-green		90·00	30·00	1·00
176	62	24 c. deep rose-lilac		27·00	3·50	90
		a. Deep lilac		6·00	—
158/76			*Set of 13* £200 50·00			—
158/76		Optd "Specimen"	*Set of 13* £275

For this issue perf 12½ see Nos. 277, etc.

20
CENTS
(63)   64   65

1909 (7 Sept). *No.* 175 *surch with T* **63** *by Waterlow.* P 13½–14.
177		20 c. on 18 c. bl-grn (R.) (Optd S. £40)		6·00	95	20
		a. Perf 14½–15		£160	60·00	—

(Recess Waterlow)

1911 (7 Mar). *P* 13½–14.
178	64	25 c. black and yellow-green		6·50	4·00	1·50
		a. Perf 14½–15		10·00	32·00	—
		b. Imperf (pair)		45·00	
178c		25 c. black and blue-green		38·00	
179		50 c. black and steel-blue		7·00	3·75	1·75
		a. Perf 14½–15		15·00	19·00	—
		ab. Imperf between (horiz pair)		£1700	
		c. Imperf (pair)		70·00	
180		$1 black and chestnut		15·00	4·00	1·75
		a. Perf 14½–15		40·00	15·00	—
		b. Imperf (pair)		£100	
181		$2 black and lilac		45·00	15·00	4·25
182	65	$5 black and lake		95·00	£110	24·00
		a. Imperf (pair)		£170	
183		$10 black and brick-red		£250	£300	50·00
		a. Imperf (pair)		£275	
178/83			*Set of 6* £375 £375 75·00
178/83		Optd "Specimen"	*Set of 6* £250

BRITISH

2
PROTECTORATE cents
(66)   (67)   (68)

1912 (July). *Nos.* 85b *and* 86 *optd with T* **66**.
184		$5 dull purple (R.)		£850	£950	7·50
185		$10 brown (R.)		£1100		7·50
		a. Opt inverted		†	†

1916 (Feb). *Nos.* 162, 167 *and* 173 *surch as T* **67** *by Govt Printing Office, Sandakan.* P 13½–14.
186	53	2 c. on 3 c. black and rose-lake		20·00	13·00
		a. "s" inverted (R. 2/5)		95·00	95·00
		b. Surch double			
187	56	4 c. on 6 c. black and olive-green (R.)		16·00	16·00
		a. "s" inverted (R. 2/5)		95·00	95·00
		b. "s" inserted by hand		£700	
		c. Perf 14½–15		£130	£130
		ca. "s" inverted			
188	59	10 c. on 12 c. black and deep blue (R.)		48·00	50·00
		a. "s" inverted (R. 2/5)		£140	£140
		b. "s" inserted by hand		£850	
186/8			*Set of 3* 75·00 70·00
186/8		Optd "Specimen"	*Set of 3* £110

Nos. 186/8 were surcharged from a setting of 25 (5×5) on which the required face values were inserted.

1916 (May). *Stamps of 1909–11 optd with T* **68** *by Waterlow.*
P 13½–14. *Centres in black.* (a) *Cross in vermilion (thick shiny ink).*

189	51	1 c. brown	..	7·50	35·00
190	52	2 c. green	..	35·00	75·00
		a. Perf 14½–15	..	32·00	80·00
		ab. Opt double, one albino	..	£200	
191	53	3 c. rose-lake	..	27·00	48·00
		a. Nos. 191 and 204 *se-tenant* (vert pair)		£1600	
192	54	4 c. scarlet	..	5·50	32·00
		a. Perf 14½–15	..	£170	£140
193	55	5 c. yellow-brown	..	30·00	55·00
		a. Perf 14½–15	..	£170	
194	56	6 c. apple-green	..	50·00	60·00
		a. Perf 14½–15	..	£170	
195	57	8 c. lake	..	23·00	60·00
196	58	10 c. blue	..	40·00	70·00
197	59	12 c. deep blue	..	85·00	90·00
198	60	16 c. brown-lake	..	85·00	90·00
199	61	20 c. on 18 c. blue-green	..	32·00	85·00
200	62	24 c. dull mauve	..	85·00	90·00
		a. Imperf between (vert pair)		£275	£400
201	64	25 c. green (p 14½–15)	..	£275	£400
189/201			*Set of* 13	£700	£1000

(b) *Cross in shades of carmine (matt ink)*

202	51	1 c. brown	..	26·00	65·00
		a. Perf 14½–15	..	£160	
203	52	2 c. green	..	27·00	48·00
		a. Perf 14½–15	..	£160	
		ba. Opt double	..	†	—
204	53	3 c. rose-lake	..	38·00	65·00
204a	54	4 c. scarlet	..	£500	
205	55	5 c. yellow-brown	..	50·00	70·00
206	56	6 c. apple-green	..	42·00	65·00
		a. Perf 14½–15	..	£160	£180
207	57	8 c. lake	..	24·00	55·00
208	58	10 c. blue	..	48·00	65·00
209	59	12 c. deep blue	..	75·00	£100
210	60	16 c. brown-lake	..	80·00	£100
211	61	20 c. on 18 c. blue-green	..	70·00	£100
212	62	24 c. dull mauve	..	80·00	£140
213	64	25 c. green	..	£650	
		a. Perf 14½–15	..	£425	£475
202/13 (*ex 4 c.*)			*Set of* 12	£850	£1200

The British North Borneo Company donated a proportion of the above issue to be sold by the National Philatelic War Fund for the benefit of the Red Cross and St. John's Ambulance Brigade.

RED CROSS ✚

TWO CENTS   FOUR CENTS
(69)   (70)

1918 (Aug). *Stamps of 1909–11 surch as T* **69**. *P* 13½–14.

(a) *Lines of surcharge 9 mm apart*

214	51	1 c. + 2 c. brown	..	3·50	10·00
		a. Imperf between (horiz pair)		£1600	
215	52	2 c. + 2 c. green	..	1·00	8·50
		a. Imperf between (horiz or vert pair)		£1700	
		b. Imperf (pair)	..		
		c. Perf 14½–15	..		
216	53	3 c. + 2 c. rose-red	..	11·00	15·00
		a. Imperf between (horiz pair)		£1700	
		b. Perf 14½–15	..	25·00	65·00
217		3 c. + 2 c. dull rose-carmine	..	£150	
		a. Perf 14½–15	..	£180	
218	54	4 c. + 2 c. scarlet	..	70	4·00
		a. Surch inverted	..	£350	
219	55	5 c. + 2 c. deep brown	..	8·00	20·00
220		5 c. + 2 c. pale brown	..	8·50	27·00
221	56	6 c. + 2 c. olive-green	..	5·00	18·00
		a. Perf 14½–15	..	£160	£180
221b		6 c. + 2 c. apple-green	..		
		a. Perf 14½–15	..	£275	
222	57	8 c. + 2 c. lake	..	5·50	10·00
		a. Inverted figure "3" for "C" in "CENTS"			
223	58	10 c. + 2 c. blue	..	7·50	23·00
224	59	12 c. + 2 c. deep bright blue	..	18·00	42·00
		a. Surch inverted	..	£600	
225	60	16 c. + 2 c. brown-lake	..	20·00	42·00
226	62	24 c. + 2 c. mauve	..	20·00	42·00

(b) *Lines of surch 13–14 mm apart*

227	52	2 c. + 2 c. green	..	70·00	£140
228	56	6 c. + 2 c. olive-green	..	£350	£650
229	64	25 c. + 2 c. green	..	10·00	38·00
230		50 c. + 2 c. steel-blue	..	12·00	38·00
231		$1 + 2 c. chestnut	..	45·00	50·00
232		$2 + 2 c. lilac	..	70·00	95·00
233	65	$5 + 2 c. lake	..	£325	£450
234		$10 + 2 c. brick-red	..	£325	£450
214/34			*Set of* 17	£800	£1200

The above stamps were dispatched from London in three consignments, of which two were lost through enemy action at sea. Only one sheet was found of No. 228.

These stamps were sold at a premium of 2 c. per stamp, which went to the Red Cross Society.

1918 (Oct). *Stamps of 1909–11 surch with T* **70**, *in red.* *P* 13½–14.

235	51	1 c. + 4 c. chocolate	..	60	5·00
		a. Imperf between (horiz pair)		£1600	
236	52	2 c. + 4 c. green	..	65	8·00
237	53	3 c. + 4 c. rose-lake	..	90	3·75
238	54	4 c. + 4 c. scarlet	..	40	4·75
239	55	5 c. + 4 c. brown	..	2·00	18·00
240	56	6 c. + 4 c. apple-green	..	1·90	12·00
		a. Imperf between (vert pair)	..	£1500	
241	57	8 c. + 4 c. lake	..	1·25	9·50
242	58	10 c. + 4 c. turquoise-blue	..	3·75	12·00
242a		10 c. + 4 c. greenish blue	..	8·00	38·00
243	59	12 c. + 4 c. deep blue	..	10·50	14·00
		a. Surch double	..	£850	

244	60	16 c. + 4 c. brown-lake	..	7·00	16·00
245	62	24 c. + 4 c. mauve	..	9·00	20·00
246	64	25 c. + 4 c. yellow-green	..	5·00	48·00
247		25 c. + 4 c. blue-green	..	24·00	75·00
248		50 c. + 4 c. steel-blue	..	15·00	42·00
		a. Perf 14½–15	..	60·00	
249		$1 + 4 c. chestnut	..	15·00	55·00
		a. Perf 14½–15	..	85·00	
250		$2 + 4 c. lilac	..	48·00	80·00
251	65	$5 + 4 c. lake	..	£275	£400
252		$10 + 4 c. brick-red	..	£275	£400
235/52			*Set of* 17	£600	£1000

Nos. 235/52 were sold at face, plus 4 c. on each stamp for Red Cross Funds.

Examples of a double-ring "SANDAKAN N. BORNEO" postmark dated "1 NOV 1918" on these stamps are generally considered to be faked.

THREE

MALAYA-BORNEO EXHIBITION 1922.
(71)   ■CENTS■ (72)

1922 (31 Mar). *Malaya-Borneo Exhibition, Singapore. Stamps of 1909–22, some in different shades, optd as T* **71** *by Govt Printing Office, Sandakan. P* 13½–14.

253	51	1 c. brown (R.)	..	8·00	50·00
		a. "BORHEO"	..	£300	£375
		b. "BORNEQ"	..	£450	£550
		c. Stop after "EXHIBITION."		55·00	
		d. Raised stop after "1922"		£450	
		e. "EXHIBITICN." with stop		£500	
		f. Perf 14½–15	..	22·00	65·00
		fa. "BORHEO"	..	£425	
		fb. "BORNEQ"	..	£700	
		fc. Raised stop after "1922"		£650	
		fd. "EXHIBITICN." with stop		£750	
		fe. "MHLAYA" and stop after "EXHIBITION"		£2250	
		ff. Stop after "EXHIBITION."		85·00	
253g		1 c. brown (B.) (p 14½–15)		£900	
		ga. Vert pair, with and without opt		£3500	
		gb. Raised stop after "1922."		£2750	
		gc. "BORHEO"	..	£2250	
		gd. "BORNEQ"	..	£3000	
		gf. "EXHIBITICN." with stop		£3000	
		gg. "MHLAYA" and stop after "EXHIBITION"			
254		1 c. orange-brown (R.)	..	21·00	55·00
255	52	2 c. green (R.)	..	1·75	17·00
		a. Stop after "EXHIBITION."		24·00	
256	53	3 c. rose-lake (B.)	..	12·00	42·00
		a. Stop after "EXHIBITION."		55·00	
		b. "EXHIBITICN." with stop	..	£2250	
		c. Raised stop after "1922"		£1600	
257	54	4 c. scarlet (B.)	..	1·75	28·00
		a. Stop after "EXHIBITION."		24·00	
		b. Perf 14½–15	..	65·00	
		ba. Stop after "EXHIBITION."			
258	55	5 c. orange-brown (B.)	..	9·00	48·00
		a. Imperf between (vert pair) ..		£1200	£1200
		b. Stop after "EXHIBITION."		50·00	
		c. Opt double	..	£1800	
		d. Opt double (with stop)		£4250	
259		5 c. chestnut (B.)	..	18·00	55·00
		a. Stop after "EXHIBITION."		80·00	
260	56	6 c. apple-green (R.)	..	5·00	48·00
		a. Stop after "EXHIBITION."		40·00	
		b. Opt double	..	£1800	
		c. Opt double (with stop)		£4250	
261	57	8 c. dull rose (B.)	..	5·00	42·00
		a. Stop after "EXHIBITION."		48·00	
262		8 c. deep rose-lake (B.)	..	5·00	42·00
		a. Stop after "EXHIBITION."		48·00	
263	58	10 c. turquoise-blue (R.)	..	7·00	48·00
		a. Stop after "EXHIBITION."		50·00	
		b. Perf 14½–15	..	28·00	
		ba. Stop after "EXHIBITION."		£140	
264		10 c. greenish blue (R.)	..	7·50	60·00
		a. Stop after "EXHIBITION."		55·00	
265	59	12 c. deep blue (R.)	..	4·75	21·00
		a. Stop after "EXHIBITION."		48·00	£120
266		12 c. deep bright blue (R.)	..	30·00	
		a. Stop after "EXHIBITION."		£160	
267	60	16 c. brown-lake (B.)	..	13·00	50·00
		a. Stop after "EXHIBITION."		75·00	
		b. Opt in red	..	£4250	
268	61	20 c. on 18 c. blue-green (B.)	..	15·00	60·00
		a. Stop after "EXHIBITION."		£120	
269		20 c. on 18 c. blue-green (R.)	..	20·00	£130
		a. Stop after "EXHIBITION."		£200	£325
270	62	24 c. mauve (R.)	..	26·00	55·00
		a. Stop after "EXHIBITION."		£130	
271		24 c. lilac (R.)	..	26·00	55·00
		a. Stop after "EXHIBITION."		£130	
272		24 c. reddish lilac (R.)	..	38·00	70·00
		a. Stop after "EXHIBITION."		£160	
273	64	25 c. blue-green (R.)	..	14·00	50·00
		a. Stop after "EXHIBITION."		60·00	
274		25 c. yellow-green (R.)	..	4·00	50·00
		a. Stop after "EXHIBITION."		48·00	
		b. Opt double	..	£2000	
		c. Perf 14½–15	..	13·00	60·00
		ca. Stop after "EXHIBITION."		£200	
		cb. Opt double	..	£2000	
275		50 c. steel-blue (R.)	..	7·50	42·00
		a. Stop after "EXHIBITION."		65·00	
		b. Perf 14½–15	..	20·00	65·00
		ba. Stop after "EXHIBITION."			
253/75			*Set of* 14	£110	£550
253/75 Optd "Specimen"			*Set of* 14	£450	

These overprints were applied from a number of settings covering the 10, 20, 25 or 30 stamps at a time. Of the ten settings known for the horizontal stamps the earliest were only used for the 1 c. on which most of the varieties

occur. Of the others the vast majority come from settings of 20 (10 × 2) with the stop after "EXHIBITION" variety on R. 2/7, or 25 (5 × 5) on which the same variety can be found on R. 5/4. In addition the 3 c. comes from a different setting of 20 (10 × 2) on which there is a raised stop after "1922" on R. 2/8 and "EXHIBITICN." on R. 2/9.

The 1 c. sequence is complicated, but additionally includes a setting of 10 with "BORHEO" on stamps 3 and 10, "BORNEQ" on stamp 4, raised stop on stamp 8 and "EXHIBITICN." on stamp 9. A setting of 20 repeats this sequence on its bottom line as does one of 30, although in this instance "MHLAYA" replaces "EXHIBITICN." as the variety on stamp 9.

For the vertical stamps (2, 6, 10, 12, 16 and 20 c. on 18 c.) the settings were of 20 (10 × 2) or 25 (5 × 5). The stop after "EXHIBITION" occurs on R. 2/7 of the former and R. 5/4 of the latter.

The 25 c. and 50 c. high values were overprinted from a setting of 20 (10 × 2), with the stop after "EXHIBITION" on R. 2/7, or 25 (5 × 5).

1923 (Oct). *T* **54** *surch with T* **72**.

276		3 c. on 4 c. black and scarlet (Optd S. £50)	..	1·00	4·75
		a. Surch double	..	£750	

1925–28. *Designs as 1909–22 issue with centres in black and some frame colours changed. P* 12½.

277	51	1 c. chocolate-brown	..	1·00	70
		a. Imperf between (horiz pair)		£800	
278	52	2 c. claret	..	40	60
		a. Imperf between (vert pair)		—	£650
		b. Imperf between (horiz pair)			
279	53	3 c. green	..	2·75	75
		a. Imperf between (horiz pair)			
280	54	4 c. scarlet	..	45	10
		a. Imperf between (vert pair)		£275	
		b. Imperf between (horiz pair)		£650	
		c. Imperf between (vert strip of three)			
281	55	5 c. yellow-brown	..	4·50	2·75
		a. Imperf between (vert pair)		£750	
282	56	6 c. olive-green	..	5·00	90
283	57	8 c. carmine	..	3·25	50
		a. Imperf between (vert pair)		£400	
		b. Imperf between (horiz pair)			
		c. Imperf between (vert strip of four)		£1000	
284	58	10 c. turquoise-blue	..	3·25	90
		a. Imperf between (horiz pair)		£700	
		b. Imperf between (vert pair)			
285	59	12 c. deep blue	..	18·00	80
286	60	16 c. red-brown	..	28·00	£110
287	61	20 c. on 18 c. blue-green (R.)	..	6·50	3·00
288	62	24 c. violet	..	48·00	90·00
289	64	25 c. green	..	7·00	4·25
290		50 c. steel-blue	..	9·00	12·00
291		$1 chestnut	..	15·00	£180
292		$2 mauve	..	50·00	£225
293	65	$5 lake (1928)	..	£150	£550
294		$10 orange-red (1928)	..	£300	£650
277/94			*Set of* 18	£600	£1600

Examples of No. 278 were supplied for U.P.U. distribution punched with a 3½ mm diameter hole.

Examples of the 16 c., 24 c., $1, $2, $5 and $10 in this perforation were not supplied to the territory for postal purposes. Used examples exist from covers prepared by stamp dealers.

73 Head of a Murut   **76** Mount Kinabalu

(Eng J. A. C. Harrison. Recess Waterlow)

1931 (1 Jan). *50th Anniv of British North Borneo Company. T* **73**, **76** *and similar designs. P* 12½.

295		3 c. black and blue-green	..	90	80
296		6 c. black and orange	..	16·00	3·25
297		10 c. black and scarlet	..	4·00	11·00
298		12 c. black and ultramarine	..	4·25	8·00
299		25 c. black and violet	..	38·00	35·00
300		$1 black and yellow-green	..	27·00	95·00
301		$2 black and chestnut	..	48·00	£110
302		$5 black and purple	..	£140	£325
295/302			*Set of* 8	£250	£500
295/302 Optd "Specimen"			*Set of* 8	£275	

Designs: *Vert*—6 c. Orang-Utan; 10 c. Dyak warrior; $1 Badge of the Company; $5 Arms of the Company. *Horiz*—25 c. Clouded Leopard; $2 Arms of the Company.

Examples of all values are known showing a forged Jesselton postmark dated "22 AUG 1931".

81 Buffalo Transport   **82** Palm Cockatoo

(Eng J. A. C. Harrison. Recess Waterlow)

1939 (1 Jan). *T* **81/2** *and similar designs. P* 12½.

303		1 c. green and red-brown	..	1·25	1·00
304		2 c. purple and greenish blue	..	5·00	1·00
305		3 c. slate-blue and green	..	2·00	2·00
306		4 c. bronze-green and violet	..	4·00	50
307		6 c. deep blue and claret	..	3·25	5·50
308		8 c. scarlet	..	7·50	1·50

309 10 c. violet and bronze-green .. .. .. 38·00 6·00
310 12 c. green and royal blue .. .. 18·00 5·00
  a. Green and blue .. .. 32·00 6·00
311 15 c. blue-green and brown .. 17·00 7·50
312 20 c. violet and slate-blue .. 10·00 3·25
313 25 c. green and chocolate .. 13·00 9·00
314 50 c. chocolate and violet .. 16·00 7·00
315 $1 brown and carmine .. 65·00 19·00
316 $2 violet and olive-green .. £100 85·00
317 $5 indigo and pale blue .. £300 £225
303/17 Set of 15 £550 £325
303/17 Perf "Specimen" Set of 15 £275
Designs: *Vert*—3 c. Native; 4 c. Proboscis Monkey; 6 c. Mounted Bajaus; 10 c. Orang-Utan; 15 c. Dyak; $1, $2 Badge of the Company. *Horiz*—8 c. Eastern Archipelago; 12 c. Murut with blow-pipe; 20 c. River scene; 25 c. Native boat; 50 c. Mt Kinabalu; $5 Arms of the Company.

WAR TAX (96) **WAR TAX** (97)

1941 (24 Feb). Nos. 303/4 optd at Sandakan with T 96/7.
318 1 c. green and red-brown .. .. 90 2·00
  a. Optd front and back .. £300
319 2 c. purple and greenish blue .. 4·75 3·50
The 1 c. was for compulsory use on internal mail and the 2 c. on overseas mail, both in addition to normal postage.

BRITISH MILITARY ADMINISTRATION

North Borneo, including Labuan, was occupied by the Japanese in January 1942. Australian forces landed on Labuan on 10 June 1945 and by the end of the war against Japan on 14 August had liberated much of western North Borneo. The territory was placed under British Military Administration on 5 January 1946.

BMA (98) (99)

1945 (17 Dec). Nos. 303/17 optd with T 98.
320 1 c. green and red-brown .. .. 4·25 1·75
321 2 c. purple and greenish blue .. 12·00 1·75
  a. Opt double .. £5000
322 3 c. slate-blue and green .. 1·25 1·00
323 4 c. bronze-green and violet .. 16·00 14·00
324 6 c. deep blue and claret .. 1·25 75
325 8 c. scarlet .. 3·00
326 10 c. violet and bronze-green .. 3·00 40
327 12 c. green and blue .. 4·75 2·50
  a. Green and royal blue .. 7·00 1·00
328 15 c. blue-green and brown .. 1·50 1·00
329 20 c. violet and slate-blue .. 3·50 1·25
330 25 c. green and chocolate .. 5·00 1·50
331 50 c. chocolate and violet .. 3·00 1·50
332 $1 brown and carmine .. 45·00 30·00
333 $2 violet and olive-green .. 38·00 24·00
  a. Opt double .. £2750
334 $5 indigo and pale blue .. 16·00 11·00
320/34 Set of 15 £140 80·00
These stamps and the similarly overprinted stamps of Sarawak were obtainable at all post offices throughout British Borneo (Brunei, Labuan, North Borneo and Sarawak), for use on local and overseas mail.

CROWN COLONY

North Borneo became a Crown Colony on 15 July 1946.

Lower bar broken at right (R. 8/3) Lower bar broken at left (R. 8/4)

1947 (1 Sept–22 Dec). Nos. 303 to 317 optd with T 99 and bars obliterating words "THE STATE OF" and "BRITISH PROTECTORATE".
335 1 c. green and red-brown (15.12) .. 15 1·00
  b. Lower bar broken at right .. 17·00
  c. Lower bar broken at left .. 17·00
336 2 c. purple and greenish blue (22.12) .. 1·75 90
337 3 c. slate-blue and green (R.) .. 15 90
338 4 c. bronze-green and violet .. 70 40
339 6 c. deep blue and claret (R.) (22.12) .. 15 20
340 8 c. scarlet .. 20 20
  b. Lower bar broken at right .. 17·00
341 10 c. violet and bronze-green (15.12) .. 75 40
342 12 c. green and royal blue (22.12) .. 2·00 2·25
  a. Green and blue .. 3·00 3·25
343 15 c. blue-green and brown (22.12) .. 2·25 30
344 20 c. violet and slate-blue (22.12) .. 1·50 85
  b. Lower bar broken at right .. 28·00
345 25 c. green and chocolate (22.12) .. 2·50 45
  b. Lower bar broken at right .. 45·00
346 50 c. chocolate and violet (22.12) .. 1·50 85
  b. Lower bar broken at right .. 45·00
  c. Lower bar broken at left .. 45·00
347 $1 brown and carmine (22.12) .. 2·50 1·25
348 $2 violet and olive-green (22.12) .. 7·50 12·00
349 $5 indigo and pale blue (R.) (22.12) .. 16·00 12·00
  b. Lower bar broken at right .. £110
335/49 Set of 15 35·00 30·00
335/49 Perf "Specimen" Set of 15 £250

1948 (1 Nov). Royal Silver Wedding. As Nos. 143/4 of Jamaica.
350 8 c. scarlet 30 80
351 $10 mauve .. .. 20·00 35·00

1949 (10 Oct). 75th Anniv of U.P.U. As Nos. 145/8 of Jamaica.
352 8 c. carmine 40 30
353 10 c. brown .. 2·75 1·00
354 30 c. orange-brown .. 90 1·75
355 55 c. blue .. 90 2·25
352/5 Set of 4 4·50 4·75

100 Mount Kinabalu 102 Coconut Grove

(Photo Harrison)

1950 (1 July)–52. T 100, 102 and similar designs. Wmk Mult Script CA. Chalk-surfaced paper. P 13½ × 14½ (horiz), 14½ × 13½ (vert).
356 1 c. red-brown 15 70
357 2 c. blue .. 15 50
358 3 c. green .. 15 15
359 4 c. bright purple .. 15 10
360 5 c. violet .. 15 10
361 8 c. scarlet .. 75 85
362 10 c. maroon .. 60 15
363 15 c. ultramarine .. 2·00 65
364 20 c. brown .. 1·00 10
365 30 c. olive-brown .. 2·50 20
366 50 c. rose-carmine ("JESSLETON") .. 85 3·00
366a 50 c. rose-carmine ("JESSLETON") (1.5.52) .. 6·50 2·00
367 $1 red-orange .. 2·50 1·00
368 $2 grey-green .. 2·50 9·00
369 $5 emerald-green .. 12·00 16·00
370 $10 dull blue .. 35·00 45·00
356/70 Set of 16 60·00 70·00
Designs: *Horiz*—2 c. Native musical instrument; 8 c. Map; 10 c. Log pond; 15 c. Malay prau, Sandakan; 20 c. Bajau Chief; $2 Murut with blowpipe; $5 Net-fishing; $10 Arms of North Borneo. *Vert*—4 c. Hemp drying; 5 c. Cattle at Kota Belud; 30 c. Suluk river canoe, Lahad Datu; 50 c. Clock tower, Jesselton; $1 Bajau horsemen.

1953 (3 June). Coronation. As No. 153 of Jamaica.
371 10 c. black and bright scarlet .. .. 1·25 60

115 Log Pond

(Photo Harrison)

1954 (1 Mar)–59. Designs previously used for King George VI issue, but with portrait of Queen Elizabeth II as in T 115. Chalk-surfaced paper. Wmk Mult Script CA. P 14½×13½ (vert) or 13½×14½ (horiz).
372 1 c. red-brown (1.10.54) 10 30
373 2 c. blue (1.6.56) .. 60 15
374 3 c. green (1.2.57) .. 60 2·00
  a. Deep green (14.1.59) .. 3·50 4·00
375 4 c. bright purple (16.5.55) .. 75 20
376 5 c. reddish violet (1.7.54) .. 75 10
377 8 c. scarlet (1.10.54) .. 50 30
378 10 c. maroon .. 30 10
379 15 c. bright blue (16.5.55) .. 1·00 10
380 20 c. brown (3.8.54) .. 30 15
381 30 c. olive-brown (3.8.54) .. 2·00 20
382 50 c. rose-carm ("JESSLETON") (10.2.56) .. 5·00 20
  a. Rose (9.12.59) .. 14·00 1·25
  aw. Wmk inverted .. £190
383 $1 red-orange (1.4.55) .. 6·50 20
384 $2 deep green (1.10.55) .. 12·00 1·25
  a. Grey-green (21.1.58) .. 22·00 5·50
385 $5 emerald-green (1.2.57) .. 10·00 23·00
386 $10 deep blue (1.2.57) .. 23·00 35·00
372/86 Set of 15 55·00 55·00
Designs: *Horiz*—1 c. Mount Kinabalu; 2 c. Native musical instrument; 8 c. Map; 15 c. Native prahu, Sandakan; 20 c. Bajau chief; $2 Murut with blowpipe; $5 Net-fishing; $10 Arms of North Borneo. *Vert*—3 c. Coconut grove; 4 c. Hemp drying; 5 c. Cattle at Kota Belud; 30 c. Suluk boat, Lahad Datu; 50 c. Clock Tower, Jesselton; $1 Bajau horseman.
Plate 2 of the 30 c., released 10 August 1960, had a finer, 250 screen, instead of the previous 200 (price £3 mint).

116 Borneo Railway, 1902 119 Arms of Chartered Company

(Recess Waterlow)

1956 (1 Nov). 75th Anniv of British North Borneo Co. T 116, 119 and similar designs. Wmk Mult Script CA. P 13 × 13½ (horiz) or 13½ × 13 (vert).
387 10 c. black and rose-carmine .. .. 1·00 40
388 15 c. black and red-brown .. 30 30
389 35 c. black and bluish green .. 30 1·50
390 $1 black and slate .. 65 2·50
387/90 Set of 4 2·00 4·25
Designs: *Horiz*—15 c. Malay prau; 35 c. Mount Kinabalu.

120 Sambar Stag 121 Orang-Utan

(Des Chong Yun Fatt. Recess Waterlow (until 1962), then D.L.R.)

1961 (1 Feb). Horiz designs as T 120 or vert designs as T 121. W w 12. P 13.
391 1 c. emerald and brown-red 20 10
392 4 c. bronze-green and orange .. 20 90
393 5 c. sepia and violet .. 30 10
394 6 c. black and blue-green .. 50 40
395 10 c. green and red .. 30 10
396 12 c. brown and grey-green .. 30 10
397 20 c. blue-green and ultramarine .. 3·50 10
398 25 c. grey-black and scarlet .. 70 90
399 30 c. sepia and olive .. 70 20
400 35 c. slate-blue and red-brown .. 1·75 90
401 50 c. emerald and yellow-brown .. 1·75 20
402 75 c. grey-blue and bright purple .. 7·00 90
403 $1 brown and yellow-green .. 11·00 80
404 $2 brown and slate .. 25·00 3·00
405 $5 emerald and maroon .. 38·00 15·00
406 $10 carmine and blue .. 26·00 27·00
391/406 Set of 16 £100 45·00
Designs: *Horiz*—1 c. Sun Bear; 5 c. Clouded Leopard; 6 c. Dusun woman with gong; 10 c. Map of Borneo; 12 c. Banteng; 20 c. Butterfly orchid; 25 c. Sumatran Rhinoceros; 30 c. Murut with blow-pipe; 35 c. Mount Kinabalu; 50 c. Dusun and buffalo transport; 75 c. Bajau horsemen. *Vert*—$2 Rhinoceros Hornbill; $5 Crested Wood Partridge; $10 Arms of North Borneo.

1963 (4 June). Freedom from Hunger. As No. 80 of Lesotho.
407 12 c. ultramarine .. .. 1·50 75

North Borneo joined the Federation of Malaysia on 16 September 1963 and was renamed Sabah.

SABAH
STATE OF MALAYSIA

SABAH (136) **SABAH** (137)

1964 (1 July)–65. Nos. 391/406 of North Borneo (D.L.R. printings), optd with T 136 (Nos. 408/19) or T 137 (Nos. 420/3).
408 1 c. emerald and brown-red .. 10 10
409 4 c. bronze-green and orange .. 15 50
410 5 c. sepia and violet .. 15 10
  a. Light sepia and deep violet (17.8.65) .. 3·00 1·75
411 6 c. black and blue-green .. 10 10
412 10 c. green and red .. 15 10
413 12 c. brown and grey-green .. 15 10
414 20 c. blue-green and ultramarine .. 3·50 10
415 25 c. grey-black and scarlet .. 45 90
416 30 c. sepia and olive .. 25 10
417 35 c. slate-blue and red-brown .. 30 20
418 50 c. emerald and yellow-brown .. 30 10
419 75 c. grey-blue and bright purple .. 3·25 65
420 $1 brown and yellow-green .. 6·00 50
421 $2 brown and slate .. 10·00 2·00
422 $5 emerald and maroon .. 10·00 12·00
423 $10 carmine and blue .. 13·00 25·00
408/23 Set of 16 40·00 38·00
Old stocks bearing Waterlow imprints of the 4 c., 5 c., 20 c. and 35 c. to $10 were used for overprinting, but in addition new printings of all values by De La Rue using the original plates with the De La Rue imprint replacing the Waterlow imprint were specially made for overprinting.

138 *Vanda hookeriana* 139 *Hebomoia glaucippe*

1965 (15 Nov)–68. As Nos. 166/72 of Johore, but with Arms of Sabah inset as in T 138. W w 13 (upright).
424 1 c. multicoloured .. 10 70
425 2 c. multicoloured .. 10 80
426 5 c. multicoloured .. 10 10
427 6 c. multicoloured .. 30 80
428 10 c. multicoloured .. 30 10
429 15 c. multicoloured (pale black panel) .. 2·00 10
  a. Brown-black panel (20.2.68) .. 2·25 10
430 20 c. multicoloured .. 2·75 50
424/30 Set of 7 5·00 2·50
The 5 c. to 15 c. exist with PVA gum as well as gum arabic. The higher values used with this issue were Nos. 20/27 of Malaysia (National Issues).

1970 (20 Nov). *As No. 428, but W w 13 (sideways).*
431   10 c. multicoloured   ..   4·75   4·25

1971 (1 Feb)–78. *As Nos. 175/87 of Johore but with Arms of Sabah, as in T* **139**. *(a) Litho by Bradbury, Wilkinson.*
432   1 c. multicoloured   ..   30   1·75
433   2 c. multicoloured   ..   60   1·75
434   5 c. multicoloured   ..   80   30
435   6 c. multicoloured   ..   80   1·00
436   10 c. multicoloured   ..   80   10
437   15 c. multicoloured   ..   80   10
438   20 c. multicoloured   ..   1·10   70
432/8   *Set of 7*   4·75   5·00

(b) Photo by Harrison (1977–78)
439   1 c. multicoloured   ..   1·25   4·75
440   2 c. multicoloured   ..   1·25   4·50
441   5 c. multicoloured   ..   10·00   2·75
442   10 c. multicoloured   ..   1·50   85
443   15 c. multicoloured   ..   2·50   30
444   20 c. multicoloured   ..   75·00   8·00
439/44   *Set of 6*   80·00   19·00

For differences between litho and photo printings, see after Johore No. 187.
The higher values used with this issue were Nos. 64/71 of Malaysia (National Issues).

140 *Hibiscus rosa-sinensis*

141 Coffee

1979 (30 Apr). *As Nos. 188/94 of Johore but with Arms of Sabah as in T* **140**.
445   1 c. *Rafflesia hasseltii*   ..   10   75
446   2 c. *Pterocarpus indicus*   ..   10   75
447   5 c. *Lagerstroemia speciosa*   ..   15   20
448   10 c. *Durio zibethinus*   ..   30   10
449   15 c. Type **140**   ..   50   10
450   20 c. *Rhododendron scortechinii*   ..   30   10
451   25 c. *Etlingera elatior* (inscr *"Phaeomeria speciosa"*)   ..   80   10
445/51   *Set of 7*   2·00   1·50
For higher values used in conjunction with this series see Nos. 190/7 of Malaysia (National Issues).

1983–85.* *As Nos. 447/50, but without wmk.*
454   5 c. *Lagerstroemia speciosa* (1.85)   1·50   2·00
455   10 c. *Durio zibethinus* (28.7.84)   5·00   7·50
456   15 c. Type **140** (5.85)   ..   3·00   1·25
457   20 c. *Rhododendron scortechinii* (blackish brown background) (1983)   23·00   2·00
457*a*   20 c. *Rhododendron scortechinii* (bronze-green background) (29.11.83)   14·00   1·50
454/7*a*   *Set of 5*   42·00   14·00
*There was no official release date for these stamps. Dates shown are the earliest recorded from postmarks and may be revised if earlier examples are reported.
For details of the shade differences between watermarked and unwatermarked printings see after Malaysia No. 200*a*.
On Nos. 454/6 and 457*a* the state crest is redrawn larger.

1986 (25 Oct)–97. *As Nos. 202/8 of Johore, but with Arms of Sabah as in T* **141**. *P* 12.
459   1 c. Type **141**   ..   10   10
460   2 c. Coconuts   ..   10   10
   f. Perf 14¾×14½ (1994)   3·50   40
461   5 c. Cocoa   ..   10   10
462   10 c. Black pepper   ..   10   10
   c. Perf 14×13¾ (1997)   70   10
   cw. Wmk inverted   7·00
463   15 c. Rubber   ..   10   10
464   20 c. Oil palm   ..   10   10
   w. Wmk inverted
465   30 c. Rice   ..   15   20
   aw. Wmk inverted
   c. Perf 14×13¾ (1994)   1·00   20
   cw. Wmk inverted   10·00
   e. Perf 14×14½ (1996)   3·75   30
   ew. Wmk inverted
   f. Perf 14¾×14½ (1994)   4·75   30
459/65   *Set of 7*   50   55

STAMP BOOKLETS

1973 (8 Dec). *Cover as Type B* **1** *of Johore, but inscr "SABAH". Stitched.*
SB1 $3 booklet containing eight 5 c., 10 c. and twelve 15 c. (Nos. 434, 436/7) in blocks of 4   25·00

1979 (1 Dec). *Cover as No. SB5 of Johore, but inscr "SABAH". Stitched.*
SB2 $3 booklet containing eight 5 c., 10 c., and twelve 15 c. (Nos. 447/9) in blocks of 4   9·00
No. SB2 exists with two different versions of the back cover.

1987 (1 June). *Cover as Type B* **2** *of Johore, but inscr "SABAH". Stapled.*
SB3 $2 booklet containing 5 c., 10 c., 15 c. and 20 c. (Nos. 461/4) in blocks of 4   8·00

1992 (1 July). *"Kuala Lumpur '92" International Philatelic Exhibition. Cover as Type B* **3** *of Johore, but inscr "Sabah". Stamps attached by selvedge.*
SB4 $3 booklet containing 30 c. (No. 465) in block of 10   8·00

1993. *Covers as Nos. SB8/9 of Johore, but inscr "Sabah". Stamps attached by selvedge.*
SB5 $2 booklet containing 20 c. (No. 464) in block of 10   1·00
SB6 $3 booklet containing 30 c. (No. 465) in block of 10   1·50

POSTAL FISCALS

Three Cents. Revenue	Ten Cents. Revenue
(F 1)	(F 2)
(Raised stop)	

1886. *Regular issues surch as Type F* **1** *or F* **2**.
F1   **1**   3 c. on 4 c. pink (No. 6)   90·00   £130
   a. Raised stop after "Cents"   80·00   £120
F2   5 c. on 8 c. green (No. 7).   90·00   £130
   a. Raised stop after "Cents"   80·00   £120
F3   **4**   10 c. on 50 c. violet (No. 4)   £120   £140
   a. Surch double   —   £900
   b. No stop after "Cents" and stop after "Revenue."   £350   £400
   c. Inverted "L" for first "F" in "FIFTY" (R.5/2)   —   £600
It is believed that Nos. F1/2 were each surcharged from a horizontal setting of five so that the raised stop variety occurs on every stamp in the first, second, third, sixth, seventh and eighth vertical columns in the sheets of 50 (10×5).

POSTAGE DUE STAMPS

POSTAGE DUE

(D 1)

1895 (1 Aug). *Stamps of 1894 optd with Type D* **1**. *P* 14½–15.

A. Vertically (reading upwards)
D 1   **25**   2 c. black and rose-lake   16·00   32·00   2·50
   a. Opt double   †   †   £250
   b. Opt reading downwards   †   †   £300
D 2   2 c. black and lake   13·00   22·00   1·50
   a. Perf 13½–14
   b. Opt omitted (in vert pair with normal)   †   †1200
D 3   **26**   3 c. olive-green and dull purple   4·75   14·00   1·00
   a. Bronze-green and dull purple
   b. Opt reading downwards
D 3*c*   3 c. olive-green and violet
   ca. Opt double   †   †   £375
   cb. Perf 13½–14
D 4   **27**   5 c. black and vermilion   40·00   25·00   2·50
   a. Printed double   †
   b. Stop after "DUE"   65·00
   c. Opt double   £500
   d. Perf 13½–14   —   50·00   2·50
   e. Perf 13½–14, comp 12–13   —   55·00
D 5   **28**   6 c. black and bistre-brown   40·00   60·00   2·50
   a. Perf 13½–14   —   50·00   2·50
   b. Perf 12–13   10·00   38·00   2·50
   c. Perf 13½–14, comp 12–13
   d. Opt reading downwards
D 6   **31**   18 c. black and deep green   65·00   90·00   3·75
   a. Opt reading downwards   £325   £225   †
D3/4 & D6 Optd "Specimen"   *Set of 3*   90·00

B. Horizontally
D 7   **29**   8 c. black and dull purple   35·00   45·00   2·50
   a. Opt double   —   †   £325
   b. Perf 13½–14
   ba. Opt inverted   †   £180
   c. Perf 13½–14, comp 12–13   55·00
D 8   **30**   12 c. black and blue   —   50·00   2·50
   a. Opt double   †   £325
   b. Perf 13½–14   55·00   45·00   2·50
D 9   12 c. black & ultram (p 13½–14)   65·00   60·00   —
D10   **31**   18 c. black and deep green   55·00   60·00   4·00
   a. Opt inverted   £250   £350   †
   b. Perf 13½–14   60·00   75·00   4·00
   ba. Opt double   †   †   £250
D11   **32**   24 c. blue and rose-lake   55·00   75·00   4·00
   a. Opt double   †   £275
   b. Perf 13½–14   —   23·00   50·00   4·00
   c. Perf 13½–14, comp 14½–15   †
D8 & D11 Optd "Specimen"   *Set of 2*   60·00

1897. *Stamps of 1897 optd with Type D* **1**. *P* 14½–15.

A. Vertically
D12   2 c. black and lake   7·50   8·50   1·25
   a. Perf 13½–14   25·00

B. Horizontally
D13   2 c. black and lake   65·00   90·00
D14   8 c. black and brown-purple   50·00   60·00
   a. Stop after "DUE."   20·00   65·00
D12 & D14 Optd "Specimen"   *Set of 2*   48·00

1901. *Issue of 1897–1902 optd with Type D* **1**. *P* 13½–14.

A. Vertically (reading upwards)
D15   2 c. black and green..   32·00   45·00   70
   a. Perf 13½–14, comp 12–13   —   65·00   90
   b. Perf 16
   c. Perf 12–13
   d. Opt reading downwards
D16   3 c. green and rosy mauve   22·00   24·00   90
   a. Stop after "DUE"   45·00   65·00
   b. Perf 14½–15   11·00   20·00   50
   c. Perf 13½–14, comp 14½–15
   d. Opt double
   e. Opt double. Stop after "DUE"   £200
D17   3 c. green & dull mauve (p 14½–15)   11·00   27·00   1·25
   a. Stop after "DUE"   45·00   65·00
   b. Opt double. Stop after "DUE"   £225   £250
D18   4 c. black and carmine   27·00   27·00   50
   a. Perf 14½–15   85
D19   5 c. black and orange-vermilion   19·00   32·00   1·60
   a. Perf 14½–15   50·00   50·00   90
   b. Stop after "DUE"   50·00

D20   6 c. black and bistre-brown (Optd "Specimen" £27)   —   27·00   50
   a. Perf 14½–15   4·00   23·00   70
   b. Perf 13½–14, comp 12–13   —   2·00
D20*c*   8 c. black and brown-purple (p 16)
D21   8 c. black and brown
   a. Perf 14½–15   4·00   23·00   50
   ab. Opt reading downwards   †   †
D22   12 c. black and dull blue   75·00   £170   4·00
   a. Perf 14½–15   —   5·00
D23   18 c. black and green (No. 108)
   a. Perf 16   †   †   £450
D24   18 c. black and green (No. 110)   38·00   £170   4·00
   a. Perf 13½–14, comp 12–13   75·00   £170   4·00
D25   24 c. blue and lake (No. 109)   —   £180
D26   24 c. blue and lake (No. 111)
   a. Perf 14½–15   18·00   £140   2·25

B. Horizontally
D27   2 c. black and green   85·00   95·00   5·00
D28   8 c. black and brown (p 14½–15)   £100   £110   6·00
   a. Stop after "DUE".   £110   £140   —
An example of the 5 c. value, No. D19a, has been seen clearly postmarked 1899.
The stamp showing a stop after "DUE", Nos. D14a, D16a, D17a, D19b and D28a, may well represent a separate local overprint. Such stamps do not come cancelled-to-order.

1902–5. *Stamps of 1901–5 optd "British Protectorate," further optd with Type D* **1**. *P* 13½–14. A. Vertically (1902).
D29   2 c. black and green (p 16)   £225   £150
D30   3 c. green and rosy mauve   75·00   85·00
D31   5 c. black and orange-vermilion (p 14½–15)   £120   90·00
D32   8 c. black and brown   £100   80·00
D33   24 c. blue and lake   £130   75·00

B. Horizontally, at top of stamp (1904–5)
D34   2 c. black and green (p 14½–15)   85·00   50·00
   a. Perf 16   70·00   60·00
D35   4 c. black and carmine   60·00   20·00

C. Horizontally, at centre of stamp (1904–5)
D35*a*   1 c. black and bistre-brown   —   26·00
   b. Perf 14½–15   £200   26·00
D36   2 c. black and green   8·50   3·00   30
   a. Perf 14½–15   45·00   45·00   —
D37   3 c. green and rosy mauve   3·00   3·00   30
   a. Perf 14½–15   45·00   30·00   —
   ab. "POSTAGE DUE" double
D38   4 c. black and carmine   6·00   6·00   30
   a. "POSTAGE DUE" double   —   £120
   b. Perf 14½–15   4·75   11·00   30
D39   5 c. black and orange-vermilion   15·00   4·25   30
   a. No stop after "PROTECTOR-ATE"   50·00   18·00   —
   b. Perf 14½–15   50·00   23·00   —
D40   6 c. black and bistre-brown   9·00   9·00   40
   a. "POSTAGE DUE" inverted   £375   †   90·00
   b. "POSTAGE DUE" double   †
   c. No stop after "PROTECTOR-ATE"   —
   d. Perf 16   50·00   32·00
D41   8 c. black and brown   17·00   4·25   40
   a. No stop after "PROTECTOR-ATE"   45·00   42·00   —
D42   10 c. brown and slate-lilac   £140   50·00   2·25
   a. No stop after "PROTECTOR-ATE"
D42*b*   10 c. brown and slate-blue   65·00   14·00   1·40
D43   12 c. black and blue   17·00   13·00   1·50
D44   16 c. green and chestnut   28·00   18·00   1·50
D45   18 c. black and green   6·00   18·00   1·50
   a. "POSTAGE DUE" double   £425   †   50·00
   b. Imperf between (vert pair)   £375
D46   24 c. blue and lake   9·50   22·00   1·50
   a. Perf 14½–15
   b. "POSTAGE DUE" double   —

D. Horizontally. Optd locally, with stop after "DUE." (1902)
D47   1 c. black and bistre-brown   4·50   55·00
   a. With raised stop after "DUE."   60·00   60·00
No. D35a/b are usually found cancelled-to-order suggesting that they came from remainder stocks which were not issued, but we have also seen one unused example of No. D35a and several of No. D35b.

1919–24. *Stamps of 1909–23, optd with Type D* **1**. *P* 13½–14.

A. Horizontally at top of stamp
D48   4 c. black and scarlet (1919)   80·00   15·00

B. Horizontally towards foot of stamp
D49   2 c. black and green (2.24)   11·00   75·00
   a. Perf 14½–15   16·00   75·00
D50   3 c. black and green   4·25   35·00
D51   4 c. black and scarlet   80   1·00
D52   5 c. black and yellow-brown   8·00   17·00
D53   6 c. black and olive-green   6·00   7·50
D53*a*   6 c. black and apple-green
D54   8 c. black and rose-lake   1·50   1·25
   a. Opt double   £700
D55   10 c. black and turquoise-blue (7.24)   12·00   18·00
   a. Perf 14½–15   60·00   £120
D56   12 c. black and deep blue (7.24)   42·00   42·00
   a. Horiz pair, one with opt omitted   £7500
D56*b*   16 c. black and red-brown   16·00   75·00
   ba. Black and brown-lake   6·50   50·00
D49 & D56*b* Optd "Specimen"   *Set of 2*   55·00
            Set of 9   80·00   £225
Nos. D51/3 also exist with the overprint towards the centre of the stamp.

1926–31. *Stamps of 1925 optd with Type D* **1**. *P* 12½.
D57   2 c. black and claret   50   1·75
D58   3 c. black and green   5·50   18·00
D59   4 c. black and scarlet   1·25   1·25
D60   5 c. black and yellow-brown   7·00   75·00
D61   6 c. black and olive-green   4·00   2·50
D62   8 c. black and carmine   2·50   12·00
D63   10 c. black and turquoise-blue   8·00   75·00
D64   12 c. black and deep blue   28·00   £130
D65   16 c. black and red-brown (1931)   48·00   £170
D57/65   *Set of 9*   90·00   £425
Nos. D49/65 exist with two types of opt; A. Thick letters; pointed beard to "G". B. Thinner letters; square end to beard and "D" more open. No. D56b is Type B and D56ba, Type A.

D 2 Crest of the Company

(Recess Waterlow)

1939 (1 Jan). *P* 12½.
D66	D 2	2 c. brown	..	..	..	6·50	70·00
D67		4 c. scarlet	..	..	..	6·50	95·00
D68		6 c. violet	..	..	..	22·00	£120
D69		8 c. green	..	..	..	22·00	£200
D70		10 c. blue ..	..	..	..	45·00	£350
D66/70					Set of 5	90·00	£750
D66/70 Perf "Specimen"					Set of 5	£140	

XIII. JAPANESE OCCUPATION OF NORTH BORNEO

Japanese forces landed in Northern Borneo on 15 December 1941 and the whole of North Borneo had been occupied by 19 January 1942.

Brunei, North Borneo, Sarawak and, after a short period, Labuan, were administered as a single territory by the Japanese. Until September–October 1942, previous stamp issues, without overprint, continued to be used in conjunction with existing postmarks. From October 1942 onwards unoverprinted stamps of Japan were made available and examples can be found used from the area for much of the remainder of the War. Japanese Occupation issues for Brunei, North Borneo and Sarawak were equally valid throughout the combined territory but not, in practice, equally available.

PRICES FOR STAMPS ON COVER	
Nos. J1/17	*from* × 5
Nos. J18/19	*from* × 6
Nos. J20/32	*from* × 25
Nos. J33/4	*from* × 2
Nos. J35/48	*from* × 12

(1)   **2** Mt Kinabalu   **3** Borneo Scene

1942 (30 Sept). *Stamps of North Borneo handstamped with* T **1**.

(a) In violet on Nos. 303/17
J 1	1 c. green and red-brown	..	£140	£190
	a. Black opt	..	£190	£190
	ab. Pair, one without opt	..	£1400	
J 2	2 c. purple and greenish blue	..	£140	£190
	a. Black opt	..	£200	£190
J 3	3 c. slate-blue and green ..	..	£120	£190
	a. Black opt	..	£225	£200
J 4	4 c. bronze-green and violet	..	£120	£190
	a. Black opt	..	50·00	£110
J 5	6 c. deep blue and claret	..	£130	£190
	a. Black opt	..	£225	£200
J 6	8 c. scarlet	..	£130	£170
	a. Pair, one without opt	..	£1500	
	b. Black opt	..	£180	£170
J 7	10 c. violet and bronze-green	..	£140	£190
	a. Black opt	..	£200	£190
J 8	12 c. green and bright blue	..	£160	£325
	a. Black opt	..	£375	£325
J 9	15 c. blue-green and brown	..	£160	£325
	a. Pair, one without opt	..	£1600	
	b. Black opt	..	£375	£325
J10	20 c. violet and slate-blue	..	£190	£375
	a. Black opt	..	£425	£375
J11	25 c. green and chocolate	..	£190	£375
	a. Black opt	..	£425	£375
J12	50 c. chocolate and violet	..	£275	£425
	a. Black opt	..	£475	£425
J13	$1 brown and carmine	..	£275	£500
	a. Black opt	..	£600	£500
J14	$2 violet and olive-green	..	£375	£700
	a. Pair, one without opt	..	£2500	
	b. Black opt	..	£800	£700
J15	$5 indigo and pale blue	..	£450	£800
	a. Black opt	..	£900	£800

(b) In black on Nos. 318/19 ("WAR TAX")
J16	1 c. green and red-brown	..	£400	£250
	a. Pair, one without opt	..	† £2500	
	b. Violet opt	..	—£425	
J17	2 c. purple and greenish blue	..	£1100	£350
	a. Violet opt	..	—£550	

(Litho Kolff & Co., Batavia)

1943 (29 Apr). *P* 12½.
J18	**2**	4 c. red	..	14·00	32·00
J19	**3**	8 c. blue	..	14·00	32·00

NEW INFORMATION

The editor is always interested to correspond with people who have new information that will improve or correct the Catalogue.

大日本帝国郵便   大日本帝国郵便

貳
弗

北ボルネオ

(4)   (5)

("Imperial Japanese Postal Service North Borneo")

1944 (30 Sept). *Nos. 303/15 of North Borneo optd as* T **4**.
J20	1 c. green and red-brown	..	..	4·50	9·50
J21	2 c. purple and greenish blue	..	7·50	8·50	
	a. Optd on No. J2	..	..	£425	
J22	3 c. slate-blue and green	..	..	4·25	7·50
	a. Optd on No. J3	..	..	£425	
J23	4 c. bronze-green and violet	..	4·50	11·00	
	a. Optd on No. J4	..	..	£425	
J24	6 c. deep blue and claret	..	..	3·75	6·50
J25	8 c. scarlet	..	..	5·50	17·00
	a. Optd on No. J6	..	..	£425	
J26	10 c. violet and bronze-green	..	8·50	13·00	
	a. Optd on No. J7	..	..	£425	
	b. Optd on No. J7a	..	..	£180	£350
J27	12 c. green and bright blue	..	7·00	13·00	
	a. Optd on No. J8	..	..	£425	
J28	15 c. blue-green and brown	..	7·00	15·00	
	a. Optd on No. J9	..	..	£425	
J29	20 c. violet and slate-blue ..	..	17·00	40·00	
	a. Optd on No. J10	..	..	£1000	
J30	25 c. green and chocolate	..	17·00	40·00	
	a. Optd on No. J11	..	..	£1000	
J31	50 c. chocolate and violet	..	55·00	£110	
	a. Optd on No. J12	..	..	£1500	
J32	$1 brown and carmine	..	..	85·00	£150
J20/32			Set of 13	£200	£400

The spacing between the second and third lines of the overprint is 12 mm on the horizontal stamps, and 15 mm on the upright.

1944 (11 May). *No.* J1 *surch with* T **5**.
J33	**81**	$2 on 1 c. green and red-brown	..	£4500	£3750

大日本

五
弗

帝国郵便   北ボルネオ

(6)   **7** Girl War-worker   (8) ("North Borneo")

1944 (11 May). *North Borneo No.* 315 *surch with* T **6**.
J34	$5 on $1 brown and carmine	..	..	£4000	£2750
	a. Surch on No. J13	..	..	— £4000	

1944 (2 Oct)–**45**. *Contemporary stamps of Japan as* T **7** *(various subjects) optd with* T **8** *at Chinese Press, Kuching.*
J35	1 s. red-brown (No. 391) (2.45)	..	6·00	15·00
J36	2 s. scarlet (No. 318) (10.44)	..	6·00	14·00
J37	3 s. emerald-green (No. 319) (8.45)	..	5·00	15·00
J38	4 s. yellow-green (No. 395) (12.44)	..	6·00	13·00
J39	5 s. claret (No. 396) (1.45)	..	7·00	16·00
J40	6 s. orange (No. 322) (8.45)	..	8·00	17·00
	a. Opt double, one inverted	..	£350	£350
J41	8 s. violet (No. 324) (2.45)	..	5·50	17·00
J42	10 s. carmine and pink (No. 399) (11.44)	..	5·50	17·00
J43	15 s. blue (No. 401) (11.44)	..	7·50	17·00
J44	20 s. blue-slate (No. 328) (11.44)	..	90·00	85·00
J45	25 s. brown and chocolate (No. 329) (2.45)	..	55·00	70·00
J46	30 s. turquoise-blue (No. 330)	..	£160	95·00
J47	50 s. olive and bistre (No. 331) (8.45)	..	60·00	60·00
J48	1 y. red-brown & chocolate (No. 332) (5.45)	60·00	80·00	
J35/48		Set of 14	£425	£475

Designs:—2 s. General Nogi; 3 s. Hydro-electric Works; 4 s. Hyuga Monument and Mt Fuji; 5 s. Admiral Togo; 6 s. Garambi Lighthouse, Formosa; 8 s. Meiji Shrine; 10 s. Palms and map of S.E. Asia; 15 s. Airman; 20 s. Mt Fuji and cherry blossoms; 25 s. Horyu Temple; 30 s. Torii, Itsukushima Shrine at Miyajima; 50 s. Kinkaku Temple; 1 y. Great Buddha, Kamakura.

Examples of some values have been found with hand-painted forged overprints.

POSTAGE DUE STAMPS

1942 (30 Sept). *Nos.* D66/7 *and* D69 *of North Borneo handstamped with* T **1** *in black.*
JD1	D **2**	2 c. brown	..	—	£2250
JD2		4 c. scarlet	..	—	£2250
JD3		8 c. green	..	—	£2250

XIV. SARAWAK

Sarawak was placed under British protection in 1888. It was ceded to Great Britain on 1 July 1946 and was administered as a Crown Colony until 16 September 1963 when it became a state of the Federation of Malaysia.

From 1859 letters from Sarawak to overseas addresses, other than to other British possessions in Borneo and Singapore, were franked by stamps of INDIA, and subsequently STRAITS SETTLEMENTS, a stock of which was kept by the Sarawak Post Office. The stamps of Sarawak continued to have this limited validity until 1 July 1897 when the country joined the U.P.U.

PRICES FOR STAMPS ON COVER TO 1945		
No. 1		
Nos. 2/7	*from* × 50	
Nos. 8/21	*from* × 8	
Nos. 22/6	*from* × 6	
No. 27	*from* × 40	
Nos. 28/35	*from* × 6	
Nos. 36/47	*from* × 6	
No. 48	†	
No. 49	*from* × 10	
Nos. 50/61	*from* × 6	
No. 62	†	
Nos. 63/71	*from* × 4	
Nos. 72/3	*from* × 8	
Nos. 74/5		
Nos. 76/90	*from* × 7	
Nos. 91/105	*from* × 5	
Nos. 106/25	*from* × 3	
Nos. 126/45	*from* × 2	

BROOKE FAMILY ADMINISTRATION
Sir James Brooke. 1842–11 June 1868
Sir Charles Brooke. 11 June 1868–17 May 1917

UNUSED PRICES. Nos. 1/7, 27 and 32/5 in unused condition are normally found to be without gum. Prices in the unused column are for stamps in this state. Examples of these issues with original gum are worth considerably more.

1 Sir James Brooke   **2** Sir Charles Brooke

The initials in the corners of T **1** and **2** stand for "James (Charles) Brooke, Rajah (of) Sarawak".

(T **1** and **2**. Die eng Wm. Ridgway. Litho Maclure, Macdonald & Co, Glasgow)

1869 (1 Mar). *P* 11.
1	**1**	3 c. brown/*yellow*	..	..	45·00	£225

Specimens are known printed from the engraved die in orange-brown on orange surface-coloured paper, and perf 12. These were submitted to the Sarawak authorities as examples of the stamps and exist both with and without obliterations.

1871 (1 Jan). *P* 11 (irregular).
2	**2**	3 c. brown/*yellow*	..	..	1·75	3·00
		a. Stop after "THREE" ..	..	40·00	55·00	
		b. Imperf between (vert pair)	..	£450		
		c. Imperf between (horiz pair)	..	£700		

The "stop" variety, No. 2a, which occurs on R. 10/7 is of no more philatelic importance than any of the numerous other variations, such as narrow first "A" in "SARAWAK" (R. 2/7) and "R" with long tail in left lower corner (R. 9/10), but it has been accepted by collectors for many years, and we therefore retain it. The papermaker's wmk "L N L" appears once or twice in sheets of No. 2.

Specimens are known, recess-printed, similar to those mentioned in the note after No. 1.

TWO CENTS

Copies of No. 2 surcharged as above were first reported in 1876 but following the discovery of dies for forgeries and faked postmarks in 1891 it was concluded that the issue was bogus, especially as the availability of the 2 c. of 1875 made it unnecessary to issue a provisional. It has now been established that a 2 c. postal rate was introduced from 1 August 1874 for the carriage of newspapers. Moreover four examples are known with a stop after "CENTS." and showing other minor differences from the forgery illustrated. This version could be genuine and if others come to light we will reconsider listing it.

1875 (1 Jan). *P* 11½–12.
3	**2**	2 c. mauve/*lilac* (shades)	..	..	3·75	15·00
4		4 c. red-brown/*yellow*	..	..	3·25	3·00
		a. Imperf between (vert pair)	..	£600		
5		6 c. green/*green*	..	..	3·00	3·50
6		8 c. bright blue/*blue*	..	..	3·00	3·50
7		12 c. red/*pale rose*	..	..	6·50	6·50
3/7			Set of 5	18·00	28·00	

Nos. 3, 4, 6 and 7 have the watermark "L N L" in the sheet, as No. 2. No. 5 is watermarked "L N T".

All values exist imperf and can be distinguished from the proofs by shade and impression. Stamps rouletted, pin-perf, or roughly perf 6½ to 7 are proofs clandestinely perforated.

The 12 c. "laid" paper, formerly listed, is not on a true laid paper, the "laid" effect being accidental and not consistent.

The lithographic stones for Nos. 3 to 7 were made up from strips of five distinct impressions hence there are five types of each value differing mainly in the lettering of the tablets of value. There are flaws on nearly every individual stamp, from which they can be plated.

4 Sir Charles Brooke

(Typo D.L.R.)

1888 (10 Nov)–**1897.** *No wmk. P* 14.

8	**4**	1 c. purple and black (6.6.92)	..	1·25	50
9		2 c. purple and carmine (11.11.88)	..	1·00	1·25
		a. *Purple and rosine* (1897)	..	8·50	3·25
10		3 c. purple and blue (11.11.88)	..	2·00	1·75
11		4 c. purple and yellow	..	12·00	42·00
12		5 c. purple and green (12.6.91)	..	8·00	
13		6 c. purple and brown (11.11.88)	..	11·00	50·00
14		8 c. green and carmine (11.11.88)	..	6·00	2·50
		a. *Green and rosine* (1897)	..	18·00	14·00
15		10 c. green and purple (12.6.91)	..	32·00	14·00
16		12 c. green and blue (11.11.88)	..	6·00	7·50
17		16 c. green and orange (28.12.97)	..	40·00	65·00
18		25 c. green and brown (19.11.88)	..	38·00	35·00
19		32 c. green and black (28.12.97)	..	26·00	48·00
20		50 c. green (26.7.97)	..	28·00	80·00
21		$1 green and black (2.11.97)	..	55·00	75·00
8/21			*Set of* 14	£225	£375

Prepared for use but not issued

21a		$2 green and blue	..	£400
21b		$5 green and violet	..	£400
21c		$10 green and carmine	..	£400

On No. 21 the value is in black on an uncoloured ground.
The tablet of value in this and later similar issues is in the second
colour given.

One Cent. **one cent.**
(5) (6)

2c. **5c** **5c.**
(7) (8) (9)

1889 (3 Aug)–**92.** *T* **4** *surch. P* 14.

22	**5**	1 c. on 3 c. (12.1.92)	..	28·00	25·00
		a. Surch double	..	£450	£350
23	**6**	1 c. on 3 c. (2.92)	..	2·75	2·75
		a. No stop after "cent" (R. 2/6)	..	£100	
24	**7**	2 c. on 8 c. (3.8.89)	..	3·00	5·00
		a. Surch double	..	£350	
		b. Surch inverted	..	£2000	
		c. Surch omitted (in pair with normal)	..	£3250	
25	**8**	5 c. on 12 c. (with stop after "C") (17.2.91)	..	22·00	42·00
		a. No stop after "C"	..	22·00	40·00
		b. "C" omitted	..	£325	£325
		c. Surch double	..	£950	
		d. Surch double, one vertical	..	£2500	
		e. Surch omitted (in pair with normal)	..	£6500	
26	**9**	5 c. on 12 c. (17.2.91)	..	85·00	£130
		a. No stop after "C"	..	70·00	85·00
		b. "C" omitted	..	£450	£400
		c. Surch double	..	£950	

ONE CENT

(10)

1892 (23 May). *No.* 2 *surch with T* **10.**

27	**2**	1 c. on 3 c. brown/*yellow*	..	1·00	1·75
		a. Stop after "THREE."	..	26·00	32·00
		b. Imperf between (vert pair)	..	£550	
		c. Imperf horiz (vert pair)	..	£500	
		d. Bar omitted (1st ptg)	..	£160	
		e. Bar at top and bottom (1st ptg)	..	£200	
		f. Surch double (2nd ptg)	..	£325	£350

No. 27 was surcharged with a setting of 100 (10 × 10). It was
originally intended that there should be no bar at foot, but this
was then added at a second operation before the stamps were
issued. Subsequent supplies were surcharged with "ONE
CENT" and bar at one operation.
Varieties with part of the surcharge missing are due to gum on
the face of the unsurcharged stamps receiving part of the
surcharge, which was afterwards washed off.

11 **12**

13 Sir Charles Brooke **14**

(Die eng Wm. Ridgeway. Recess P.B.)

1895 (Feb–Sept). *No wmk. P* 11½–12.

28	**11**	2 c. brown-red	..	6·50	7·50
		a. Imperf between (vert pair)	..	£350	
		b. Imperf between (horiz pair)	..	£275	
		c. Second ptg. Perf 12½ (Sept)	..	7·00	4·50
		ca. Perf 12½. Imperf between (horiz pair)	..	£375	
29	**12**	4 c. black	..	6·50	3·50
		a. Imperf between (horiz pair)	..	£450	
30	**13**	6 c. violet	..	6·00	
31	**14**	8 c. green	..	22·00	6·00
28/31			*Set of* 4	38·00	21·00

Stamps of these types, printed in wrong colours, are trials and
these, when surcharged with values in "pence", are from waste
sheets that were used by Perkins, Bacon & Co as trial paper when
preparing an issue of stamps for British South Africa.

4 CENTS.

(15) **16**

1899. *Surch as T* **15.**

32	**2**	2 c. on 3 c. brown/*yellow* (19.9.99)	..	1·40	1·40
		a. Stop after "THREE"	..	45·00	48·00
		b. Imperf between (vert pair)	..	£800	
33		2 c. on 12 c. red/*pale rose* (29.6.99)	..	2·75	3·00
		a. Surch inverted	..	£750	£1100
34		4 c. on 6 c. green/*green* (R.) (16.11.99)	..	23·00	50·00
35		4 c. on 8 c. bright blue/*blue* (R.) (29.6.99)	..	3·50	6·00
32/5			*Set of* 4	27·00	55·00

A variety of surcharge with small "S" in "CENTS" may be found
in the 2 c. on 12 c. and 4 c. on 8 c. and a raised stop after "CENTS"
on the 4 c. on 6 c.
The omission of parts of the surcharge is due to gum on the
surface of the stamps (see note after No. 27).
A block of 50 of No. 35 from the right of the pane is known line
perforated 12.7 between the stamps and the margins at top and
right.

(Typo D.L.R.)

1899 (10 Nov)–**1908.** *Inscribed* "POSTAGE POSTAGE." *No wmk.
P* 14.

36	**4**	1 c. grey-blue and rosine (1.1.01)	..	1·00	1·25
		a. *Grey-blue and red*	..	4·00	1·75
		b. *Ultramarine and rosine*	..	6·00	2·25
		c. *Dull blue and carmine*	..	13·00	4·25
37		2 c. green (16.12.99)	..	1·50	90
38		3 c. dull purple (1.2.08)	..	5·00	50
39		4 c. rose-carmine (10.11.99)	..	7·00	2·50
		a. *Aniline carmine*	..	1·75	15
40		8 c. yellow and black (6.12.99)	..	1·75	80
41		10 c. ultramarine (10.11.99)	..	2·00	90
42		12 c. mauve (16.12.99)	..	4·25	4·25
		a. *Bright mauve* (1905)	..	17·00	8·00
43		16 c. chestnut and green (16.12.99)	..	2·00	1·75
44		20 c. bistre and bright mauve (4.00)	..	4·50	3·25
45		25 c. brown and blue (16.12.99)	..	3·00	4·50
46		50 c. sage-green and carmine (16.12.99)	..	18·00	22·00
47		$1 rose-carmine and green (16.12.99)	..	45·00	95·00
		a. *Rosine and pale green*	..	60·00	£100
36/47			*Set of* 12	80·00	£120

Prepared for use but not issued

48	**4**	5 c. olive-grey and green	..	12·00

The figures of value in the $1 are in colour on an uncoloured
ground.

1902. *Inscribed* "POSTAGE POSTAGE". *W* **16.** *P* 14.

49	**4**	2 c. green	..	18·00	14·00

Sir Charles Vyner Brooke. 17 May 1917–1 June 1946

17 Sir Charles Vyner Brooke

ONE cent

(18)

(Typo D.L.R.)

1918 (24 Mar–Apr). *No wmk. Chalk-surfaced paper. P* 14.

50	**17**	1 c. slate-blue and red	..	1·75	2·00
		a. *Dull blue and carmine*	..	1·75	2·00
51		2 c. green	..	2·00	1·50
52		3 c. brown-purple (Apr)	..	3·25	2·50
53		4 c. rose-carmine (Apr)	..	3·75	2·50
		a. *Rose-red*	..	4·00	2·50
54		8 c. yellow and black (Apr)	..	11·00	55·00
55		10 c. blue (*shades*) (Apr)	..	2·75	2·75
56		12 c. purple (Apr)	..	9·50	22·00
57		16 c. chestnut and green (Apr)	..	5·50	7·00
58		20 c. olive and violet (*shades*) (Apr)	..	6·50	6·50
59		25 c. brown and bright blue (Apr)	..	4·00	9·50
60		50 c. olive-green and carmine (Apr)	..	9·00	14·00
61		$1 bright rose and green (Apr)	..	15·00	28·00
50/61			*Set of* 12	65·00	£140
50/61		Optd "Specimen"	*Set of* 12	£190	

Prepared for use but not issued

62	**17**	1 c. slate-blue and slate	..	22·00

On the $1 the figures of value are in colour on an uncoloured
ground.

1922 (Jan)–**23.** *New colours and values. No wmk. Chalk-
surfaced paper. P* 14.

63	**17**	2 c. purple (5.3.23)	..	2·00	2·50
64		3 c. dull green (23.3.22)	..	1·25	1·25
65		4 c. brown-purple (10.4.23)	..	1·25	75
66		5 c. yellow-orange	..	1·25	90
67		6 c. claret	..	1·00	1·40
68		8 c. bright rose-red (1922)	..	4·50	28·00
69		10 c. black (1923)	..	2·00	3·75
70		12 c. bright blue (12.22)	..	9·50	18·00
		a. *Pale dull blue*	..	9·50	17·00
71		30 c. ochre-brown and slate	..	3·75	4·25
63/71			*Set of* 9	24·00	55·00

1923 (Jan). *Surch as T* **18.** (*a*) *First printing. Bars* 1¼ *mm
apart.*

72	**17**	1 c. on 10 c. dull blue	..	10·00	50·00
		a. "cnet" for "cent" (R. 9/5)	..	£325	£650
73		2 c. on 12 c. purple	..	6·50	35·00
		a. Thick, narrower "W" in "TWO"	..	17·00	75·00

(*b*) *Second printing. Bars* ¾ *mm apart*

74	**17**	1 c. on 10 c. dull blue	..		£250
		b. "cnet" for "cent" (R. 9/5)	..		£9500
		c. *Bright blue*	..		£110	£275
		ca. "en" of "cent" scratched out and "ne" overprinted (R. 9/5)	..		£3750
75		2 c. on 12 c. purple	..	60·00	£160
		a. Thick, narrower "W" in "TWO"	..		£130

In the 2 c. on 12 c. the words of the surcharge are about 7½ mm
from the bars.
The "cnet" error occurred on R.9/5 of all sheets from the first
printing of the 1 c. on 10 c. A single example of the error, No. 74b,
is known from the second printing, but the error was then
corrected, as shown by the evidence of a surviving plate block,
only to have the correct spelling scratched out, by a local
employee, and "ne" substituted (No. 74ca).
The thick "W" variety occurs on all stamps of the last two
horizontal rows of the first printing (12 stamps per sheet), and in
the last two vertical rows of the second (20 stamps per sheet).

1928 (7 Apr)–**29.** *W* **16** (*Multiple*). *Chalk-surfaced paper. P* 14.

76	**17**	1 c. slate-blue and carmine	..	1·00	35
77		2 c. bright purple	..	1·00	1·00
78		3 c. green	..	1·25	4·50
79		4 c. brown-purple	..	1·50	10
80		5 c. yellow-orange (7.8.29)	..	8·00	4·75
81		6 c. claret	..	1·00	30
82		8 c. bright rose-red	..	2·75	12·00
83		10 c. black	..	1·75	1·25
84		12 c. bright blue	..	2·75	18·00
85		16 c. chestnut and green	..	2·75	3·75
86		20 c. olive-bistre and violet	..	2·75	5·00
87		25 c. brown and bright blue	..	4·75	7·50
88		30 c. bistre-brown and slate	..	4·00	9·00
89		50 c. olive-green and carmine	..	4·50	9·00
90		$1 bright rose and carmine	..	14·00	23·00
76/90			*Set of* 15	48·00	90·00
76/90		Optd/Perf "Specimen"	*Set of* 15	£225	

In the $1 value is as before.

19 Sir Charles Vyner Brooke **20**

(Recess Waterlow)

1932 (1 Jan). *W* **20.** *P* 12½.

91	**19**	1 c. indigo	..	70	90
92		2 c. green	..	70	90
93		3 c. violet	..	2·50	90
94		4 c. red-orange	..	1·50	75
95		5 c. deep lake	..	5·00	1·25
96		6 c. scarlet	..	7·00	7·50
97		8 c. orange-yellow	..	3·75	7·50
98		10 c. black	..	2·25	3·25
99		12 c. deep ultramarine	..	3·75	7·00
100		15 c. chestnut	..	5·50	6·50
101		20 c. red-orange and violet	..	4·75	7·00
102		25 c. orange-yellow and chestnut	..	11·00	18·00
103		30 c. sepia and vermilion	..	7·50	18·00
104		50 c. carmine-red and olive-green	..	8·50	11·00
105		$1 green and carmine	..	15·00	28·00
91/105			*Set of* 15	70·00	£110
91/105		Perf "Specimen"	*Set of* 15	£225	

21 Sir Charles Vyner Brooke

BMA
(22)

(Recess B.W.)

1934 (1 May)–**41.** *No wmk. P* 12.

106	**21**	1 c. purple	..	30	10
107		2 c. green	..	40	10
107a		2 c. black (1.3.41)	..	1·50	1·60
108		3 c. black	..	30	10
108a		3 c. green (1.3.41)	..	3·50	4·50
109		4 c. bright purple	..	30	15
110		5 c. violet	..	60	10
111		6 c. carmine	..	1·00	60
111a		6 c. lake-brown (1.3.41)	..	4·75	8·00
112		8 c. red-brown	..	1·40	
112a		8 c. carmine (1.3.41)	..	4·50	10
113		10 c. scarlet	..	1·25	40
114		12 c. blue	..	2·00	25
114a		12 c. orange (1.3.41)	..	2·50	4·75
115		15 c. orange	..	2·25	6·00
115a		15 c. blue (1.3.41)	..	4·50	15·00
116		20 c. olive-green and carmine	..	2·25	70
117		25 c. violet and orange	..	2·25	1·50
118		30 c. red-brown and violet	..	2·25	2·50
119		50 c. violet and scarlet	..	2·25	75
120		$1 scarlet and sepia	..	60	75
121		$2 bright purple and violet	..	8·50	8·50
122		$3 carmine and green	..	25·00	25·00
123		$4 blue and scarlet	..	25·00	32·00
124		$5 scarlet and red-brown	..	25·00	32·00
125		$10 black and yellow	..	19·00	42·00
106/25			*Set of* 26	£130	£170
106/25		Perf "Specimen"	*Set of* 26	£450	

For the 3 c. green, wmkd Mult Script CA, see No. 152a.

BRITISH MILITARY ADMINISTRATION

Following the Japanese surrender elements of the British Military Administration reached Kuching on 11 September 1945. From 5 November 1945 current Australian 1d., 3d., 6d. and 1s. stamps were made available for civilian use until replaced by Nos. 126/45. Other Australian stamps were also accepted as valid for postage during this period.

1945 (17 Dec). *Optd with T 22.*

126	21	1 c. purple		40	60
127		2 c. black (R.)		40	50
		a. Opt double		† £4000	
128		3 c. green		40	40
129		4 c. bright purple		40	30
130		5 c. violet (R.)		60	90
131		6 c. lake-brown		1·00	75
132		8 c. carmine		11·00	9·00
133		10 c. scarlet		60	70
134		12 c. orange		90	3·75
135		15 c. blue		1·75	40
136		20 c. olive-green and carmine		2·25	1·40
137		25 c. violet and orange (R.)		2·25	2·75
138		30 c. red-brown and violet		5·50	2·75
139		50 c. violet and scarlet		1·25	35
140		$1 scarlet and sepia		2·50	1·25
141		$2 bright purple and violet		9·00	8·00
142		$3 carmine and green		17·00	38·00
143		$4 blue and scarlet		25·00	30·00
144		$5 scarlet and red-brown		£120	£140
145		$10 black and yellow (R.)		£120	£160
126/45			*Set of 20*	£275	£350

These stamps, and the similarly overprinted stamps of North Borneo, were obtainable at all post offices throughout British Borneo (Brunei, Labuan, North Borneo and Sarawak), for use on local and overseas mail.

The administration of Sarawak was returned to the Brooke family on 15 April 1946, but the Rajah, after consulting the inhabitants, ceded the territory to Great Britain on 1 June 1946. Values from the 1934–41 issue were used until replaced by Nos. 150/64.

23 Sir James Brooke, Sir Charles Vyner Brooke and Sir Charles Brooke (24)

(Recess B.W.)

1946 (18 May). *Centenary Issue. P 12.*

146	23	8 c. lake		1·10	30
147		15 c. blue		1·10	1·75
148		50 c. black and scarlet		1·25	1·75
149		$1 black and sepia		1·50	14·00
146/9			*Set of 4*	4·50	16·00
146/9 Perf "Specimen"			*Set of 4*	90·00	

CROWN COLONY

1947 (16 Apr). *Optd with T 24, typo by B.W. in blue-black or red. Wmk Mult Script CA. P 12.*

150	21	1 c. purple		15	30
151		2 c. black (R.)		15	15
152		3 c. green (R.)		15	15
		a. Albino opt		£4000	
153		4 c. bright purple		15	15
154		6 c. lake-brown		20	90
155		8 c. carmine		40	10
156		10 c. scarlet		20	20
157		12 c. orange		20	90
158		15 c. blue (R.)		20	40
159		20 c. olive-green and carmine (R.)		1·00	50
160		25 c. violet and orange (R.)		40	30
161		50 c. violet and scarlet (R.)		40	40
162		$1 scarlet and sepia		75	90
163		$2 bright purple and violet		1·40	3·25
164		$5 scarlet and red-brown		3·00	3·25
150/64			*Set of 15*	7·50	10·50
150/64 Perf "Specimen"			*Set of 15*	£250	

No. 152a shows an uninked impression of T 24.

1948 (25 Oct). *Royal Silver Wedding. As Nos. 143/4 of Jamaica.*

165		8 c. scarlet		30	30
166		$5 brown		30·00	32·00

1949 (10 Oct). *75th Anniv of U.P.U. As Nos. 145/8 of Jamaica.*

167		8 c. carmine		1·25	50
168		15 c. deep blue		2·50	2·25
169		25 c. deep blue-green		2·00	1·50
170		50 c. violet		2·00	4·00
167/70			*Set of 4*	7·00	7·50

25 *Trogonoptera brookiana*   26 Western Tarsier

(Recess; Arms typo B.W.)

1950 (3 Jan). *T 25/6 and similar designs. Wmk Mult Script CA. P 11½ × 11 (horiz) or 11 × 11½ (vert).*

171		1 c. black		30	30
172		2 c. red-orange		20	40
173		3 c. green		20	60
174		4 c. chocolate		20	20
175		6 c. turquoise-blue		20	15
176		8 c. scarlet		20	30
177		10 c. orange		50	3·50
178		12 c. violet		2·25	1·50
179		15 c. blue		1·00	15
180		20 c. purple-brown and red-orange		60	30
181		25 c. green and scarlet		1·50	30
182		50 c. brown and violet		1·75	15
183		$1 green and chocolate		14·00	2·75
184		$2 blue and carmine		23·00	12·00
185		$5 black, yellow, red and purple		19·00	12·00
171/85			*Set of 15*	55·00	30·00

Designs: *Horiz*—8 c. Dayak dancer; 10 c. Malayan Pangolin; 12 c. Kenyah boys; 15 c. Fire-making; 20 c. Kelemantan rice barn; 25 c. Pepper vines; $1 Kelabit smithy; $2 Map of Sarawak; $5 Arms of Sarawak. *Vert*—3 c. Kayan tomb; 4 c. Kayan girl and boy; 6 c. Bead work; 50 c. Iban woman.

40 Map of Sarawak

(Recess B.W.)

1952 (1 Feb). *Wmk Mult Script CA. P 11½ × 11.*

186	40	10 c. orange		85	40

1953 (3 June). *Coronation. As No. 153 of Jamaica.*

187		10 c. black and deep violet-blue		1·00	1·25

41 Logging   44 Malabar Pied Hornbill

51 Queen Elizabeth II   52 Queen Elizabeth II (after Annigoni)

(Des M. Thoma (1, 2 c.), R. Turrell (4 c.), J. D. Hughes (6, 12 c.), A. Hakim bin Moliti (8 c.), J. Woodcock (10 c.), J. Browning (15 c.), G. Gundersen (20 c.), K. Munich (25 c.). Recess, Arms typo ($5). B.W.)

1955 (1 June)–*59. T 41, 44, 51/2 and similar designs. Wmk Mult Script CA. P 11×11½ (1 c., 2 c., 4 c.), 12×13 (30 c., 50 c., $1, $2) or 11½×11 (others).*

188	41	1 c. green (1.10.57)		10	30
189	–	2 c. red-orange (1.10.57)		30	55
190	–	4 c. lake-brown (1.10.57)		45	60
		a. Brown-purple (18.3.59)		6·00	6·00
191	44	6 c. greenish blue (1.10.57)		3·00	2·00
192	–	8 c. rose-red (1.10.57)		30	30
193	–	10 c. deep green (1.10.57)		20	10
194	–	12 c. plum (1.10.57)		3·75	55
195	–	15 c. ultramarine (1.10.57)		1·00	30
196	–	20 c. olive and brown (1.10.57)		1·00	10
197	–	25 c. sepia and green (1.10.57)		6·50	20
198	51	30 c. red-brown and deep lilac		3·50	30
199	–	50 c. black and carmine (1.10.57)		2·00	30
200	52	$1 myrtle-green & orange-brn (1.10.57)		5·00	75
201	–	$2 violet and bronze-green (1.10.57)		12·00	3·00
202	–	$5 multicoloured (1.10.57)		16·00	8·00
188/202			*Set of 15*	48·00	15·00

Designs: *Horiz*—8 c. Shield with spears; 10 c. Kenyah ceremonial carving; 12 c. Barong panau (sailing prau); 15 c. Turtles; 20 c. Melanau basket-making; 25 c. Astana, Kuching; $5 Arms of Sarawak. *Vert (as T 41)*—2 c. Young Orang-Utan; 4 c. Kayan dancing.

1963 (4 June). *Freedom from Hunger. As No. 80 of Lesotho.*

203		12 c. sepia		1·50	85

STATE OF MALAYSIA

1964–65. *As 1955–57 but wmk w 12. Perfs as before.*

204	41	1 c. green (8.9.64)		10	50
205	–	2 c. red-orange (17.8.65)		65	9·50
206	44	6 c. greenish blue (8.9.64)		6·00	4·00
207	–	10 c. deep green (8.9.64)		1·75	1·00
208	–	12 c. plum (8.9.64)		1·50	8·00
209	–	15 c. ultramarine (17.8.65)		1·25	12·00
210	–	20 c. olive and brown (9.6.64)		50	90
211	–	25 c. deep sepia and bluish green (8.9.64)		2·50	4·25
204/11			*Set of 8*	13·00	35·00

---

53 *Vanda hookeriana*   54 *Precis orithya*

1965 (15 Nov). *As Nos. 166/72 of Johore but with Arms of Sarawak inset as in T 53.*

212		1 c. multicoloured		10	70
		c. Grey omitted		50·00	
213		2 c. multicoloured		20	90
		a. Black (country name and shield) omitted		95·00	
		c. Yellow-olive (stems) omitted		85·00	
214		5 c. multicoloured		45	10
215		6 c. multicoloured		60	1·00
		a. Black (country name and shield) omitted		95·00	
216		10 c. multicoloured		80	10
		a. Red omitted		60·00	
217		15 c. multicoloured		1·50	10
218		20 c. multicoloured		2·00	50
212/18			*Set of 7*	5·00	2·75

The 1 c., 6 c., 10 c. and 15 c. exist with PVA gum as well as gum arabic.

No. 213a was formerly listed with Trengganu No. 101 but there is evidence that it was issued in Sarawak.

A used example of No. 218 is known with the bright purple (blooms) omitted.

The higher values used with this issue were Nos. 20/7 of Malaysia (National Issues).

(Litho B.W.)

1971 (1 Feb). *As Nos. 175/81 of Johore but with Arms of Sarawak inset as in T 54.*

219		1 c. multicoloured		30	1·00
220		2 c. multicoloured		50	1·00
221		5 c. multicoloured		1·00	10
222		6 c. multicoloured		1·25	1·50
223		10 c. multicoloured		1·25	10
224		15 c. multicoloured		1·75	10
225		20 c. multicoloured		1·75	1·00
219/25			*Set of 7*	7·00	4·25

The higher values used with this issue were Nos. 64/71 of Malaysia (National Issues).

55 *Precis orithya* (different crest at right)   56 *Rhododendron scortechinii*

(Photo Harrison)

1977 (12 Feb)–*78. As Nos. 219/21 and 223/5 but ptd in photogravure showing new State Crest as T 55.*

226		1 c. multicoloured (1978)		6·50	10·00
227		2 c. multicoloured (1978)		7·00	6·50
228		5 c. multicoloured		80	70
230		10 c. multicoloured (4.4.77)		50	30
231		15 c. multicoloured (19.4.77)		1·25	20
232		20 c. multicoloured (1978)		3·00	2·25
226/32			*Set of 6*	17·00	18·00

1979 (30 Apr). *As Nos. 188/94 of Johore but with Arms of Sarawak as in T 56.*

233		1 c. *Rafflesia hasseltii*		10	40
234		2 c. *Pterocarpus indicus*		10	40
235		5 c. *Lagerstroemia speciosa*		20	20
236		10 c. *Durio zibethinus*		20	10
237		15 c. *Hibiscus rosa-sinensis*		20	10
238		20 c. Type 56		30	10
239		25 c. *Etlingera elatior* (inscr "Phaeomeria speciosa")		50	20
233/9			*Set of 7*	1·40	1·25

For higher values used in conjunction with this series see Nos. 190/7 of Malaysia (National Issues).

1983 (11 Oct)–*86.* *As Nos. 235/6 and 238 but without wmk.*

242		5 c. *Lagerstroemia speciosa* (4.4.86)		1·25	1·75
243		10 c. *Durio zibethinus* (9.9.85)		85	1·40
245		20 c. Type 56 (blackish brown background)		32·00	3·00
245a		20 c. Type 56 (bronze-green background) (2.8.84)		1·00	1·40
242/5a			*Set of 4*	32·00	6·75

* There was no official release date for these stamps. Dates shown are the earliest recorded from postmarks and may be revised if earlier examples are reported.

For details of the shade differences between watermarked and unwatermarked printings see after Malaysia–Johore No. 200a.

On Nos. 242/3 and 245a the crest is closer to the face value than on Nos. 235/6, 238 and 245.

PRICES OF SETS

Set prices are given for many issues, generally those containing three stamps or more. Definitive sets include one of each value or major colour change, but do not cover different perforations, die types or minor shades. Where a choice is possible the set prices are based on the cheapest versions of the stamps included in the listings.

57 Coffee

A

B

Two types of Arms at right.
Type A. Shield divided into three
Type B. Shield with diagonal bars

1986 (25 Oct)–**96**. *As Nos. 202/8 of Johore, but with Arms of Sarawak as in T* **57**. *P* 12. (*a*) *Arms as Type A*

247	1 c. Type **57**	..	..	..	10	10
248	2 c. Coconuts			..	10	10
249	5 c. Cocoa			..	10	10
250	10 c. Black pepper		..	..	10	10
251	15 c. Rubber			..	10	10
252	20 c. Oil palm			..	10	10
	w. Wmk inverted					
253	30 c. Rice			..	15	20
247/53	..	..	..	*Set of* 7	50	55

(*b*) *Arms as Type B* (1.9.93)

254	1 c. Type **57**			..	10	10
255	2 c. Coconuts			..	10	10
	f. Perf 14³/₄×14¹/₂ (1994)		..	3·25	30
256	5 c. Cocoa			..	10	10
	aw. Wmk inverted			8·00	
	c. Perf 14×13³/₄ (1996)		..	75	10
257	10 c. Black pepper		..	10	10
	aw. Wmk inverted			9·00	
	c. Perf 14×13³/₄ (1995)		..	2·00	20
	e. Perf 14×14¹/₂ (1996)		..	3·75	30
	f. Perf 14³/₄×14¹/₂ (1995)		..	2·00	20
	fw. Wmk inverted			5·00	
258	15 c. Rubber			..	10	10
259	20 c. Oil palm			..	10	10
	w. Wmk inverted			4·50	
260	30 c. Rice			..	15	20
	aw. Wmk inverted			4·00	
	c. Perf 14×13³/₄ (1994)		..	1·50	20
	cw. Wmk inverted (1996)			6·50	
	e. Perf 14×14¹/₂ (1994)		..	3·50	40
	f. Perf 14³/₄×14¹/₂ (1994)		..	3·25	30
254/60	..	..	..	*Set of* 7	50	55

STAMP BOOKLETS

1973 (8 Dec). *Cover as Type B* **1** *of Johore, but inscr* "SARAWAK". *Stitched.*
SB1 $3 booklet containing eight 5 c., 10 c. and twelve
15 c. (Nos. 221, 223/4) in blocks of 4 .. .. 25·00
Examples of No. SB1 exist with a white label giving revised postage rates.

1979 (1 Dec). *Cover as No. SB5 of Johore, but inscr* "SARAWAK". *Stitched.*
SB2 $3 booklet containing eight 5 c., 10 c., and twelve
15 c. (Nos. 235/7) in blocks of 4 .. .. 9·00
No. SB2 exists with two different versions of the back cover.

1987 (1 June). *Cover as Type B* **2** *of Johore, but inscr* "SARAWAK". *Stapled.*
SB3 $2 booklet containing 5 c., 10 c., 15 c. and 20 c.
(Nos. 249A/52A) in blocks of 4 .. .. 8·00

1992 (1 July). "*Kuala Lumpur '92*" *International Philatelic Exhibition. Cover as Type B* **3** *of Johore, but inscr* "Sarawak". *Stamps attached by selvedge.*
SB4 $3 booklet containing 30 c. (No. 253A) in block of
10 .. .. 8·00

1993. *Covers as Nos. SB8/9 of Johore, but inscr* "Sarawak". *Stamps attached by selvedge.*
SB5 $2 booklet containing 20 c. (No. 252B) in block of
10 .. .. 1·00
SB6 $3 booklet containing 30 c. (No. 253B) in block of
10 .. .. 1·50

XV. JAPANESE OCCUPATION OF SARAWAK

Japanese forces landed in North Borneo on 16 December 1941 and Sarawak was attacked on 23 December 1941.

Brunei, North Borneo, Sarawak and after a short period Labuan, were administered as a single territory by the Japanese. Until September–October 1942, previous stamp issues, without overprint, continued to be used in conjunction with existing postmarks. From 1 October 1942 onwards unoverprinted stamps of Japan were made available and examples can be found used from the area for much of the remainder of the War. Japanese Occupation issues for Brunei, North Borneo and Sarawak were equally valid throughout the combined territory but not, in practice, equally available.

PRICES FOR STAMPS ON COVER	
Nos. J1/21	*from* × 8
Nos. J22/6	—

大日本帝国政府

(1)

("Imperial Japanese Government")

1942 (Oct). *Stamps of Sarawak handstamped with T* **1** *in violet.*

J 1	**21**	1 c. purple	..	32·00	60·00
		a. Pair, one without opt	..	£1100	
J 2		2 c. green	..	80·00	£140
		a. Black opt	..	80·00	
J 3		2 c. black	..	75·00	85·00
		a. Black opt	..	95·00	£110
J 4		3 c. black	..	£250	£250
J 5		3 c. green	..	42·00	70·00
		a. Black opt	..	75·00	
J 6		4 c. bright purple	..	50·00	70·00
		a. Black opt	..	75·00	
J 7		5 c. violet	..	60·00	70·00
		a. Black opt	..	75·00	
J 8		6 c. carmine	..	90·00	95·00
J 9		6 c. lake-brown	..	60·00	70·00
		a. Black opt	..	75·00	85·00
J10		8 c. red-brown	..	£200	£225
		a. Black opt	..	£325	
J11		8 c. carmine	..	75·00	£110
		a. Black opt	..	£160	£180
J12		10 c. scarlet	..	55·00	75·00
		a. Black opt	..	75·00	
J13		12 c. blue	..	£120	£130
		a. Black opt	..	£160	
J14		12 c. orange	..	£120	£140
J15		15 c. orange	..	£250	£250
		a. Black opt	..	£275	
J16		15 c. blue	..	80·00	85·00
J17		20 c. olive-green and carmine	..	45·00	75·00
		a. Black opt	..	75·00	
J18		25 c. violet and orange	..	75·00	75·00
		a. Black opt	..	85·00	
J19		30 c. red-brown and violet	..	50·00	80·00
		a. Black opt	..	75·00	
J20		50 c. violet and scarlet	..	60·00	80·00
		a. Black opt	..	£160	
		b. Blue opt	..	£275	
J21		$1 scarlet and sepia	..	75·00	95·00
		a. Blue opt	..	£170	
J22		$2 bright purple and violet	..	£160	£190
		a. Blue opt	..	£225	
J23		$3 carmine and green	..	£850	£950
		a. Black opt	..	£1300	
J24		$4 blue and scarlet	..	£180	£250
J25		$5 scarlet and red-brown	..	£180	£250
J26		$10 black and yellow	..	£180	£250

The overprint, being handstamped, exists inverted or double on some values.

Stamps of T **21** optd with Japanese symbols within an oval frame are revenue stamps, while the same stamps overprinted with three Japanese characters between two vertical double rules, were used as seals.

Nos. J1/26 have been extensively forged. Recent research indicates that complete or part sets on cover cancelled by Japanese circular postmarks in violet dated "17 11 21" (21 Nov 1942) or "18 3 1" (1 Mar 1943) have forged overprints.

Maldive Islands

BRITISH PROTECTORATE

(Currency. 100 cents = 1 Ceylon rupee)

MALDIVES

(1)   2 Minaret, Juma   3
Mosque, Malé

1906 (9 Sept). *Nos. 277/9, 280a and 283/4 of Sri Lanka (Ceylon) optd with T 1. Wmk Mult Crown CA. P* 14.

1	44	2 c. red-brown	..	14·00	30·00
2	45	3 c. green	..	18·00	30·00
3		4 c. orange and ultramarine	..	32·00	70·00
4	46	5 c. dull purple	..	4·00	6·50
5	48	15 c. blue	..	60·00	£120
6		25 c. bistre	..	70·00	£130
1/6			*Set of* 6	£180	£350

Supplies of Nos. 1/6 were exhausted by March 1907 and the stamps of CEYLON were used until 1909. Overseas mail to destinations other than Ceylon or India continued to be franked with Ceylon stamps until 1967 when Maldive Islands joined the U.P.U.

(Recess D.L.R.)

1909 (May). *T* 2 (18½×22½ *mm*). *W* 3. *P* 14×13½ (2 *c.*, 5 *c.*) or 13½×14 (3 *c.*, 10 *c.*).

7	2	2 c. orange-brown	..	2·25	2·50
		a. Perf 13½×14	..	2·50	90
8		3 c. deep myrtle	..	40	70
9		5 c. purple	..	40	35
10		10 c. carmine	..	7·50	80
7/10			*Set of* 4	9·50	2·50

These stamps perforated 14×13½ (14×13.7) are from a line machine and those perforated 13½×14 (13.7×13.9) from a comb machine.

4

(Photo Harrison)

1933. *T* 2 *redrawn* (*reduced to* 18×21½ *mm*). *W* 4. *P* 15×14.

A. Wmk upright

11A	2	2 c. grey	..	2·75	2·00
12A		3 c. red-brown	..	70	2·25
14A		5 c. mauve	..	16·00	10·00
15A		6 c. scarlet	..	1·50	50
16A		10 c. green	..	85	55
17A		15 c. black	..	6·50	12·00
18A		25 c. brown	..	6·50	12·00
19A		50 c. purple	..	6·50	12·00
20A		1 r. deep blue	..	11·00	7·00
11A/20A			*Set of* 9	45·00	55·00

B. Wmk sideways

11B	2	2 c. grey	..	3·50	3·75
12B		3 c. red-brown	..	2·50	1·75
13B		5 c. claret	..	28·00	28·00
15B		6 c. scarlet	..	4·50	5·00
16B		10 c. green	..	2·50	2·50
17B		15 c. black	..	11·00	12·00
18B		25 c. brown	..	11·00	12·00
19B		50 c. purple	..	11·00	12·00
20B		1 r. deep blue	..	12·00	2·75
11B/20B			*Set of* 9	75·00	70·00

(New Currency. 100 larees=1 rupee)

5 Palm Tree and Dhow

(Recess B.W.)

1950 (24 Dec). *P* 13.

21	5	2 l. olive-green	..	1·50	40
22		3 l. blue	..	8·50	40
23		5 l. emerald-green	..	8·50	50

24	5	6 l. red-brown	..	..	70	30
25		10 l. scarlet			70	30
26		15 l. orange			70	30
27		25 l. purple			70	30
28		50 l. violet			70	30
29		1 r. chocolate			8·50	25·00
21/9				*Set of* 9	27·00	25·00

7 Fish   8 Native Products

(Recess B.W.)

1952. *P* 13.

30	7	3 l. blue	..	1·00	
31	8	5 l. emerald	..	50	1·40

SULTANATE

Sultan Mohamed Farid Didi
20 November 1953–10 November 1968

The Maldive Islands became a republic on 1 January 1953, but reverted to a sultanate on 29 November 1953.

9 Malé Harbour   10 Fort and Building

(Recess B.W.)

1956 (Feb). *P* 13½ (*T* 9) *or* 11½ × 11 (*T* 10).

32	9	2 l. purple	..	10	10
33		3 l. slate	..	10	10
34		5 l. red-brown	..	10	10
35		6 l. blackish violet	..	10	10
36		10 l. emerald	..	10	10
37		15 l. chocolate	..	10	60
38		25 l. rose-red	..	10	10
39		50 l. orange	..	10	10
40	10	1 r. bluish green	..	15	10
41		5 r. blue	..	60	30
42		10 r. magenta	..	1·50	85
32/42			*Set of* 11	2·25	1·90

11 Cycling   12 Basketball

(Des C. Bottiau. Recess and typo B.W.)

1960 (20 Aug). *Olympic Games. P* 11½ × 11 (*T* 11) *or* 11 × 11½ (*T* 12).

43	11	2 l. purple and green	..	15	10
44		3 l. greenish slate and purple	..	15	10
45		5 l. red-brown and ultramarine		15	10
46		10 l. emerald-green and brown		15	10
47		15 l. sepia and blue	..	15	25
48	12	25 l. rose-red and olive	..	15	25
49		50 l. orange and violet	..	20	40
50		1 r. emerald and purple	..	40	1·25
43/50			*Set of* 8	1·25	2·00

13 Tomb of Sultan   14 Custom House

(Recess B.W.)

1960 (15 Oct). *T* 13, 14 *and similar horiz designs. P* 11½ × 11.

51		2 l. purple	..	10	10
52		3 l. emerald-green	..	10	10
53		5 l. orange-brown	..	2·75	2·75
54		6 l. bright blue	..	10	10
55		10 l. carmine	..	10	10
56		15 l. sepia	..	10	10
57		25 l. deep violet	..	10	10
58		50 l. slate-grey	..	10	10
59		1 r. orange	..	15	10
60		5 r. deep ultramarine	..	3·00	60
61		10 r. grey-green	..	7·50	1·25
51/61			*Set of* 11	12·50	4·75

Designs:—5 l. Cowrie shells; 6 l. Old Royal Palace; 10 l. Road to Juma Mosque, Malé; 15 l. Council house; 25 l. New Government Secretariat; 50 l. Prime Minister's office; 1 r. Old Ruler's tomb; 5 r. Old Ruler's tomb (distant view); 10 r. Maldivian Port. Higher values were also issued, intended mainly for fiscal use.

---

24 "Care of Refugees"

(Recess B.W.)

1960 (15 Oct). *World Refugee Year. P* 11½ × 11.

62	24	2 l. deep violet, orange and green	..	10	10
63		3 l. brown, green and red	..	10	10
64		5 l. deep green, sepia and red	..	10	10
65		10 l. bluish green, reddish violet and red	10	10
66		15 l. reddish violet, grey-green and red	..	10	10
67		25 l. blue, red-brown and bronze-green	..	10	10
68		50 l. yellow-olive, rose-red and blue	..	10	10
69		1 r. carmine, slate and violet	..	15	35
62/9			*Set of* 8	30	45

25 Coconuts   26 Map of Malé

(Photo Harrison)

1961 (20 Apr). *P* 14 × 14½ (*Nos.* 70/74) *or* 14½ × 14 (*others*).

70	25	2 l. yellow-brown and deep green	..	10	10
71		3 l. yellow-brown and bright blue	..	10	10
72		5 l. yellow-brown and magenta	..	10	10
73		10 l. yellow-brown and red-orange	..	10	10
74		15 l. yellow-brown and black	..	10	15
75	26	25 l. multicoloured	..	15	20
76		50 l. multicoloured	..	15	30
77		1 r. multicoloured	..	20	45
70/7			*Set of* 8	55	1·10

27 5 c. Stamp of 1906   30 Malaria Eradication Emblem

(Des M. Shamir. Photo Harrison)

1961 (9 Sept). *55th Anniv of First Maldivian Stamp. T* 27 *and similar horiz designs. P* 14½ × 14.

78		2 l. brown-purple, ultramarine & lt green	..	10	10
79		3 l. brown-purple, ultramarine & lt green		10	10
80		5 l. brown-purple, ultramarine & lt green		10	10
81		6 l. brown-purple, ultramarine & lt green		10	10
82		10 l. green, claret and maroon	..	10	10
83		15 l. green, claret and maroon	..	15	15
84		20 l. green, claret and maroon	..	15	20
85		25 l. claret, green and black	..	15	20
86		50 l. claret, green and black	..	25	80
87		1 r. claret, green and black	..	40	1·75
78/87			*Set of* 10	1·00	3·00
MS87a		114 × 88 mm. No. 87 (block of four). Imperf	1·50	3·75

Designs:—2 to 6 l. Type 27; 10 to 20 l. 1906 3 c. and posthorn; 25 l. to 1 r. 1906 2 c. and olive sprig.

(Recess B.W.)

1962 (7 Apr). *Malaria Eradication. P* 13½ × 13.

88	30	2 l. chestnut	..	10	10
89		3 l. emerald	..	10	10
90		5 l. turquoise-blue	..	10	10
91		10 l. red	..	10	10
92	—	15 l. deep purple-brown	..	15	10
93	—	25 l. deep blue	..	20	15
94	—	50 l. deep green	..	25	40
95	—	1 r. purple	..	55	60
88/95			*Set of* 8	1·25	1·25

Nos. 92/5 are as T 30, but have English inscriptions at the side.

31 Children of Europe and America   33 Sultan Mohamed Farid Didi

(Des C. Bottiau. Photo Harrison)

1962 (9 Sept). *15th Anniv of U.N.I.C.E.F. T* **31** *and similar horiz design. Multicoloured. P* 14½ × 14.

96	2 l.	Type **31**	..	10	10
97	6 l.	Type **31**	..	10	10
98	10 l.	Type **31**	..	10	10
99	15 l.	Type **31**	..	10	10
100	25 l.	Children of Middle East and Far East		10	10
101	50 l.	As 25 l.	..	10	10
102	1 r.	As 25 l.	..	15	20
103	5 r.	As 25 l.	..	80	3·00
96/103			*Set of 8*	1·10	3·25

(Photo Harrison)

1962 (29 Nov). *Ninth Anniv of Enthronement of Sultan. P* 14 × 14½.

104	**33**	3 l. orange-brown and bluish green	..	10	10
105		5 l. orange-brown and indigo	..	10	10
106		10 l. orange-brown and blue	..	15	10
107		20 l. orange-brown and olive-green	..	20	20
108		50 l. orange-brown and deep magenta	..	25	40
109		1 r. orange-brown and slate-lilac	..	35	55
104/9			*Set of 6*	90	1·25

34 Royal Angelfish

(Des R. Hegeman. Photo Enschedé)

1963 (2 Feb). *Tropical Fish. T* **34** *and similar triangular designs. Multicoloured. P* 13½.

110	2 l.	Type **34**	..	10	15
111	3 l.	Type **34**	..	10	15
112	5 l.	Type **34**	..	15	15
113	10 l.	Moorish Idol	..	25	15
114	25 l.	As 10 l.	..	65	20
115	50 l.	Diadem Soldierfish	..	90	40
116	1 r.	Powder-blue Surgeonfish	..	1·25	55
117	5 r.	Racoon Butterflyfish	..	6·25	9·50
110/17			*Set of 8*	8·50	10·00

39 Fishes in Net   40 Handful of Grain

(Photo State Ptg Wks, Vienna)

1963 (21 Mar). *Freedom from Hunger. P* 12.

118	**39**	2 l. brown and deep bluish green	..	30	80
119	**40**	5 l. brown and orange-red	..	50	70
120	**39**	7 l. brown and turquoise	..	70	70
121	**40**	10 l. brown and blue	..	85	70
122	**39**	25 l. brown and brown-red	..	3·00	3·25
123	**40**	50 l. brown and violet	..	4·75	7·00
124	**39**	1 r. brown and deep magenta	..	7·50	11·00
118/24			*Set of 7*	16·00	22·00

41 Centenary Emblem   42 Maldivian Scout Badge

(Photo Harrison)

1963 (Oct). *Centenary of Red Cross. P* 14 × 14½.

125	**41**	2 l. red and deep purple	..	30	1·25
126		15 l. red and deep bluish green	..	65	80
127		50 l. red and deep brown	..	1·50	1·75
128		1 r. red and indigo	..	2·25	2·00
129		4 r. red and deep brown-olive	..	7·00	20·00
125/9			*Set of 5*	10·50	23·00

(Photo Enschedé)

1964. *World Scout Jamboree, Marathon* (1963). *P* 13½.

130	**42**	2 l. green and violet	..	10	10
131		3 l. green and bistre-brown	..	10	10
132		25 l. green and blue	..	15	15
133		1 r. green and crimson	..	55	1·50
130/3			*Set of 4*	70	1·60

NEW INFORMATION

The editor is always interested to correspond with people who have new information that will improve or correct the Catalogue.

43 Mosque, Malé   44 Putting the Shot

(Recess B.W.)

1964 (10 Aug). *"Maldives Embrace Islam". W w* **12.** *P* 11½.

134	**43**	2 l. purple	..	10	10
135		3 l. emerald-green	..	10	10
136		10 l. carmine	..	10	10
137		40 l. deep dull purple	..	30	15
138		60 l. blue	..	50	15
139		85 l. orange-brown	..	60	20
134/9			*Set of 6*	1·40	60

(Litho Enschedé)

1964 (Oct). *Olympic Games, Tokyo. T* **44** *and similar horiz design. W w* **12.** *P* 14 × 13½.

140	2 l.	deep maroon and turquoise-blue	..	10	10
141	3 l.	crimson and chestnut	..	10	10
142	5 l.	bronze-green and deep green	..	15	10
143	10 l.	slate-violet and reddish purple	..	20	10
144	15 l.	sepia and yellow-brown	..	30	10
145	25 l.	indigo and deep blue	..	50	10
146	50 l.	deep olive-green and yellow-olive	..	75	25
147	1 r.	deep maroon and olive-grey	..	1·25	50
140/7			*Set of 8*	2·75	80
MS147a	126 × 140 mm. Nos. 145/7. Imperf			2·25	2·75

Designs:—2 to 10 l. Type **44**; 15 l. to 1 r. Running.

46 Telecommunications Satellite

(Des M. Shamir. Photo Harrison)

1965 (1 July). *International Quiet Sun Years. P* 14½.

148	**46**	5 l. blue	..	15	15
149		10 l. brown	..	20	15
150		25 l. green	..	40	15
151		1 r. deep magenta	..	90	55
148/51			*Set of 4*	1·50	90

On 26 July 1965, Maldive Islands became independent and left the British Commonwealth.

47 Isis (wall carving,   48 President Kennedy
Abu Simbel)   and Doves

(Des M. and G. Shamir. Litho Harrison)

1965 (1 Sept). *Nubian Monuments Preservation. T* **47** *and similar vert design. W w* **12.** *P* 14½.

152	**47**	2 l. bluish green and brown-purple	..	10	10
153	—	3 l. lake and deep green	..	10	10
154	**47**	5 l. dull green and brown-purple	..	15	10
155	—	10 l. steel-blue and orange	..	20	10
156	**47**	15 l. red-brown and deep violet	..	35	15
157	—	25 l. reddish purple and deep blue	..	60	15
158	**47**	50 l. yellow-green and sepia	..	75	35
159	—	1 r. ochre and myrtle-green	..	1·10	55
152/9			*Set of 8*	2·75	1·25

Design:—3, 10, 25 l., 1 r. Rameses II on throne (wall carving, Abu Simbel).

(Photo State Ptg Wks, Vienna)

1965 (10 Oct). *Second Death Anniv of President Kennedy. T* **48** *and similar horiz design. P* 12.

160	**48**	2 l. black and mauve	..	10	10
161		5 l. bistre-brown and mauve	..	10	10
162		25 l. indigo and mauve	..	10	10
163	—	1 r. brt reddish purple, yellow & bl-grn		25	25
164	—	2 r. bronze-green, yellow & blue-green		40	40
160/4			*Set of 5*	75	75
MS164a	150 × 130 mm. No. 164 in block of four.				
	Imperf			2·75	3·00

Design:—1 r., 2 r. Pres. Kennedy and hands holding olive-branch.

49 "XX" and U.N. Flag   50 I.C.Y. Emblem

(Des O. Adler. Photo State Ptg Wks, Vienna)

1965 (24 Nov). *20th Anniv of U.N. P* 12.

165	**49**	3 l. turquoise-blue and red-brown	..	10	10
166		10 l. turquoise-blue and violet	..	15	10
167		1 r. turquoise-blue and bronze-green	..	65	35
165/7			*Set of 3*	75	40

(Des M. and G. Shamir. Photo State Ptg Wks, Vienna)

1965 (20 Dec). *International Co-operation Year. P* 12.

168	**50**	5 l. brown and yellow-bistre	..	15	10
169		15 l. brown and slate-lilac	..	20	10
170		50 l. brown and yellow-olive	..	45	30
171		1 r. brown and orange-red	..	1·25	55
172		2 r. brown and new blue	..	1·75	3·00
168/72			*Set of 5*	3·50	4·50
MS173	101 × 126 mm. Nos. 170/2. Imperf			6·50	6·50

51 Princely Cone Shells

(Des M. and G. Shamir. Photo State Ptg Wks, Vienna)

1966 (1 June). *T* **51** *and similar multicoloured designs. P* 12.

174	2 l.	Type **51**	..	20	40
175	3 l.	Yellow flowers	..	20	40
176	5 l.	Reticulate Distorsio and Leopard Cone shells	..	30	15
177	7 l.	Camellias	..	30	15
178	10 l.	Type **51**	..	60	15
179	15 l.	Crab Plover and Seagull	..	2·50	30
180	20 l.	As 3 l.	..	80	30
181	30 l.	Type **51**	..	2·00	35
182	50 l.	As 15 l.	..	4·50	55
183	1 r.	Type **51**	..	3·00	55
184	1 r.	As 7 l.	..	3·00	55
185	1 r. 50,	As 3 l.	..	3·50	2·00
186	2 r.	As 7 l.	..	4·75	2·50
187	5 r.	As 15 l.	..	17·00	10·00
188	10 r.	As 5 l.	..	17·00	14·00
174/88			*Set of 15*	55·00	29·00

The 3 l., 7 l., 20 l., 1 r. (No. 184), 1 r. 50 and 2 r. are diamond-shaped (43½ × 43½ mm); the others are horizontal designs as T **51**.

52 Maldivian Flag

(Des M. and G. Shamir. Litho Harrison)

1966 (26 July). *First Anniv of Independence. P* 14 × 14½.

189	**52**	10 l. green, red and turquoise	..	40	10
190		1 r. green, red, brown & orange-yellow		1·60	40

53 "Luna 9" on Moon

(Des M. and G. Shamir. Litho Harrison)

1966 (1 Nov). *Space Rendezvous and Moon Landing. T* **53** *and similar horiz designs. W w* **12.** *P* 15 × 14.

191	10 l.	light brown, grey-blue and bright blue	..	20	10
192	25 l.	green and carmine	..	30	10
193	50 l.	orange-brown and green	..	40	15
194	1 r.	turquoise-blue and chestnut	..	70	35
195	2 r.	green and violet	..	1·50	65
196	5 r.	rose-pink and deep turquoise-blue	..	2·25	1·60
191/6			*Set of 6*	4·75	2·50
MS197	108 × 126 mm. Nos. 194/6. Imperf			3·50	4·50

Designs:—25 l., 1 r., 5 r. "Gemini 6" and "7" rendezvous in space; 2 r. "Gemini" spaceship as seen from the other spaceship; 50 l. Type **53**.

54 U.N.E.S.C.O. Emblem, and Owl on Book

55 Sir Winston Churchill and Cortège

(Litho Harrison)

1966 (15 Nov). *20th Anniv of U.N.E.S.C.O. T* **54** *and similar vert designs. W w* **12.** *Multicoloured. P* 15 × 14.

198	1 l. Type **54**		10	50
199	3 l. U.N.E.S.C.O. emblem, and globe and microscope		10	50
200	5 l. U.N.E.S.C.O. emblem, and mask, violin and palette		15	30
201	50 l. Type **54**		1·75	45
202	1 r. Design as 3 l.		2·50	75
203	5 r. Design as 5 l.		8·75	13·00
198/203		*Set of 6*	12·00	14·00

(Des M. and G. Shamir. Litho Harrison)

1967 (1 Jan). *Churchill Commemoration. T* **55** *and similar horiz design. Flag in red and blue. P* 14½ × 13½.

204	**55**	2 l. olive-brown	15	40
205	—	10 l. turquoise-blue	65	10
206	**55**	15 l. green	1·00	10
207	—	25 l. violet	1·60	15
208	—	1 r. brown	4·00	75
209	**55**	2 r. 50, crimson	9·50	9·50
204/9		*Set of 6*	15·00	10·00

Design:—10 l., 25 l., 1 r. Churchill and catafalque.

IMPERFORATE STAMPS. From No. 210 onwards some sets and perforated miniature sheets exist imperforate from limited printings.

56 Footballers and Jules Rimet Cup

(Des M. and G. Shamir. Photo Govt Printer, Israel)

1967 (22 Mar). *England's Victory in World Cup Football Championship. T* **56** *and similar horiz designs. Multicoloured. P* 14×13½.

210	2 l. Type **56**		10	40
211	3 l. Player in red shirt kicking ball		10	40
212	5 l. Scoring goal		10	10
213	25 l. As 3 l.		60	10
	a. Emerald (face value and inscr) omitted		£140	
214	50 l. Making a tackle		1·00	20
215	1 r. Type **56**		2·00	55
216	2 r. Emblem on Union Jack		3·25	3·00
210/16		*Set of 7*	6·25	4·25
MS217	100×121 mm. Nos. 214/16. Imperf		7·50	6·00

57 Ornate Butterflyfish

(Des M. and G. Shamir. Photo Govt Printer, Israel)

1967 (1 May). *Tropical Fishes. T* **57** *and similar horiz designs. Multicoloured. P* 14.

218	2 l. Type **57**		10	30
219	3 l. Black-saddled Pufferfish		15	30
220	5 l. Blue Boxfish		20	10
221	6 l. Picasso Triggerfish		20	20
222	50 l. Semicircle Angelfish		3·25	30
223	1 r. As 3 l.		4·50	75
224	2 r. As 50 l.		8·50	8·00
218/24		*Set of 7*	15·00	9·00

58 Hawker Siddeley H.S.748 over Hulule Airport Building

(Des M. and G. Shamir. Photo Govt Printer, Israel)

1967 (26 July). *Inauguration of Hulule Airport. T* **58** *and similar horiz design. P* 14 × 13½.

225	2 l. reddish violet and yellow-olive		15	40
226	5 l. deep green and lavender		20	10
227	10 l. reddish violet and light turquoise-green		25	10
228	15 l. deep green and yellow-ochre		40	10
229	30 l. deep ultramarine and light blue		90	10
230	50 l. deep brown and magenta		1·50	20
231	5 r. deep ultramarine and yellow-orange		5·00	5·50
232	10 r. deep brown and blue		7·00	9·00
225/32		*Set of 8*	14·00	14·00

Designs:—2 l., 10 l., 30 l., 5 r. T **58**; 5 l., 15 l., 50 l., 10 r. Airport building and Hawker Siddeley H.S.748. Higher values were also issued, intended mainly for fiscal use.

59 "Man and Music" Pavilion

International Tourist Year 1967 **(60)**

(Des M. and G. Shamir. Photo Govt Printer, Israel)

1967 (Sept). *World Fair, Montreal. T* **59** *and similar horiz design. Multicoloured. P* 14 × 13½.

233	2 l. Type **59**		10	10
234	5 l. "Man and His Community" Pavilion		10	10
235	10 l. Type **59**		10	10
236	50 l. As 5 l.		30	20
237	1 r. Type **59**		65	40
238	2 r. As 5 l.		1·25	90
233/8		*Set of 6*	2·00	1·50
MS239	102 × 137 mm. Nos. 237/8. Imperf		2·25	3·00

1967 (1 Dec). *International Tourist Year. Nos.* 225/32 *optd as T* **60** (*in one or three lines*), *in gold*.

240	2 l. reddish violet and yellow-olive		10	30
241	5 l. deep green and lavender		15	15
242	10 l. reddish violet and light turquoise-green		20	15
243	15 l. deep green and yellow-ochre		20	15
244	30 l. deep ultramarine and light blue		30	20
245	50 l. deep brown and magenta		45	30
246	5 r. deep ultramarine and yellow-orange		3·50	3·75
247	10 r. deep brown and blue		5·00	6·00
240/7		*Set of 8*	9·00	10·00

61 Cub signalling and Lord Baden-Powell

62 French Satellite "A 1"

(Litho Harrison)

1968 (1 Jan). *Maldivian Scouts and Cubs. T* **61** *and similar vert design. P* 14 × 14½.

248	**61**	2 l. brown, green and yellow	10	30
249	—	3 l. carmine, bright blue and light blue	10	30
250	**61**	25 l. bluish violet, lake and orange-red	1·50	30
251	—	1 r. blackish green, chest & apple-green	3·50	1·60
248/51		*Set of 4*	4·50	2·25

Design:—3 l., 1 r. Scouts and Lord Baden-Powell.

(Des M. and G. Shamir. Photo Govt Printer, Israel)

1968 (27 Jan). *Space Martyrs. Triangular designs as T* **62.** *P* 14.

252	2 l. magenta and ultramarine		10	30
253	3 l. violet and yellow-brown		10	30
254	7 l. olive-brown and lake		15	30
255	10 l. deep blue, pale drab and black		15	15
256	25 l. bright emerald and reddish violet		40	15
257	50 l. blue and orange-brown		75	30
258	1 r. purple-brown and deep bluish green		1·10	50
259	2 r. deep brown, pale blue and black		1·75	1·75
260	5 r. magenta, light drab and black		2·75	3·00
252/60		*Set of 9*	6·50	6·00
MS261	110 × 155 mm. Nos. 258/9. Imperf		3·75	4·00

Designs:—2 l., 50 l. Type **62**; 3 l., 25 l. "Luna 10"; 7 l., 1 r. "Orbiter" and "Mariner"; 10 l., 2 r. Astronauts White, Grissom and Chaffee; 5 r. Cosmonaut V. M. Komarov.

63 Putting the Shot

64 "Adriatic Seascape" (Bonington)

(Des M. Shamir. Litho Harrison)

1968 (Feb). *Olympic Games, Mexico (1st issue). T* **63** *and similar vert design. Multicoloured. P* 14½.

262	2 l. Type **63**		10	15
263	6 l. Throwing the discus		10	15
264	10 l. Type **63**		10	10
265	15 l. As 6 l.		15	10
266	1 r. Type **63**		50	35
267	2 r. 50, As 6 l.		1·25	1·50
262/7		*Set of 6*	1·75	2·00

See also Nos. 294/7.

(Des M. Shamir. Litho Govt Printer, Israel)

1968 (1 Apr). *Paintings. T* **64** *and similar horiz designs. Multicoloured. P* 14.

268	50 l. Type **64**		75	30
269	1 r. "Ulysses deriding Polyphemus" (Turner)		1·25	45
270	2 r. "Sailing Boat at Argenteuil" (Monet)		2·00	1·75
271	5 r. "Fishing Boats at Les Saintes-Maries" (Van Gogh)		4·25	4·25
268/71		*Set of 4*	7·50	6·00

65 LZ-130 *Graf Zeppelin II* and Montgolfier's Balloon

(Des M. Shamir. Photo Govt Printer, Israel)

1968 (1 June). *Development of Civil Aviation. T* **65** *and similar horiz designs. P* 14 × 13½.

272	2 l. orange-brown, yellow-green & ultram		15	40
273	3 l. turquoise-blue, violet & orange-brown		15	40
274	5 l. slate-green, crimson and turquoise-blue		15	15
275	7 l. bright blue, purple and red-orange		90	55
276	10 l. brown, turquoise-blue and bright purple		35	15
277	50 l. crimson, slate-green and yellow-olive		1·50	20
278	1 r. emerald, blue and vermilion		2·25	50
279	2 r. maroon, bistre and bright blue		14·00	10·00
272/9		*Set of 8*	18·00	11·00

Designs:—3 l., 1 r. Boeing 707-420 and Douglas DC-3; 5 l., 50 l. Wright Type A and Lilienthal's glider; 7 l., 2 r. Projected Boeing 733 and Concorde; 10 l. Type **65**.

66 W.H.O. Building, Geneva

International Boy Scout Jamboree, Farragut Park, Idaho, U.S.A. August 1-9, 1967 **(67)**

(Litho Harrison)

1968 (15 July). *20th Anniv of World Health Organisation. P* 14½ × 13½.

280	**66**	10 l. violet, turquoise-bl & lt greenish bl	60	10
281		25 l. bronze-green, yell-brn & orge-yell	1·00	15
282		1 r. deep brown, emerald & brt green	3·25	90
283		2 r. bluish violet, magenta and mauve	5·25	5·50
280/3		*Set of 4*	9·00	6·00

1968 (1 Aug). *First Anniv of Scout Jamboree, Idaho. Nos.* 248/51 *optd with T* **67.**

284	2 l. brown, green and yellow		10	40
285	3 l. carmine, bright blue and light blue		10	40
286	25 l. bluish violet, lake and orange-red		1·50	40
287	1 r. blackish green, chestnut & apple-green		4·50	2·10
284/7		*Set of 4*	5·50	3·00

68 Curlew and Redshank

1968 (24 Sept). *T* **68** *and similar horiz designs. Photo. Multicoloured. P* 14×13½.

288	2 l. Type **68**		50	60
289	10 l. Pacific Grinning Tun and Papal Mitre shells		1·25	20
290	25 l. Oriental Angel Wing and Tapestry Turban shells		1·75	25
291	50 l. Type **68**		6·00	90
292	1 r. As 10 l.		4·50	95
293	2 r. As 25 l.		4·75	4·50
288/93		*Set of 6*	17·00	6·75

69 Throwing the Discus

(Des M. Shamir. Photo Govt Printer, Israel)

1968 (12 Oct). *Olympic Games, Mexico (2nd issue). T* **69** *and similar multicoloured designs. P* 14.

294	10 l. Type **69**			10	10
295	50 l. Running			20	10
296	1 r. Cycling			2·00	35
297	2 r. Basketball			2·75	1·25
294/7			Set of 4	4·50	1·60

INDEPENDENT REPUBLIC
11 November 1968

70 Fishing Dhow

71 "The Thinker" (Rodin)

(Photo Harrison)

1968 (11 Nov). *Republic Day. T* **70** *and similar horiz design. P* 14 × 14½.

298	10 l. brown, ultramarine and lt yellow-green			75	20
299	1 r. green, red and bright blue			3·00	80

Design:—1 r. National flag, crest and map.

(Des M. Shamir. Litho Rosenbaum Brothers, Vienna)

1969 (10 Apr). *U.N.E.S.C.O. "Human Rights". T* **71** *and similar vert designs, showing sculptures by Rodin. Multicoloured. P* 13½.

300	6 l. Type **71**			30	15
301	10 l. "Hands"			30	15
302	1 r. 50, "Eve"			2·00	2·25
303	2 r. 50, "Adam"			2·50	90
300/3			Set of 4	4·75	5·00
MS304	112 × 130 mm. Nos. 302/3. Imperf			5·50	6·00

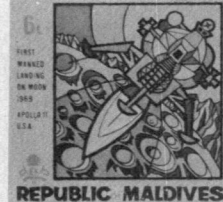

72 Module nearing Moon's Surface

(Des M. Shamir. Litho Govt Printer, Israel)

1969 (25 Sept). *First Man on the Moon. T* **72** *and similar square designs. Multicoloured. P* 14.

305	6 l. Type **72**			15	15
306	10 l. Astronaut with hatchet			15	15
307	1 r. 50, Astronaut and module			2·25	1·40
308	2 r. 50, Astronaut using camera			2·50	2·00
305/8			Set of 4	4·50	3·25
MS309	101 × 130 mm. Nos. 305/8. Imperf			2·25	3·25

Gold Medal Winner
Mohamed Gammoudi
5000 m. run
Tunisia

REPUBLIC OF MALDIVES

(73)

1969 (1 Dec). *Gold-medal Winners, Olympic Games, Mexico (1968). Nos.* 295/6 *optd with T* **73**, *or similar inscr honouring P. Trentin (cycling) of France.*

310	50 l. multicoloured			60	60
311	1 r. multicoloured			1·40	90

74 Racoon Butterflyfish

(Des M. Shamir. Litho)

1970 (Jan). *Tropical Fish. T* **74** *and similar diamond-shaped designs. Multicoloured. P* 10½.

312	2 l. Type **74**			40	70
313	5 l. Clown Triggerfish			65	40
314	25 l. Broad-barred Lionfish			2·25	40
315	50 l. Long-nosed Butterflyfish			3·00	1·00
316	1 r. Emperor Angelfish			4·00	1·00
317	2 r. Royal Angelfish			5·50	6·50
312/17			Set of 6	14·00	9·00

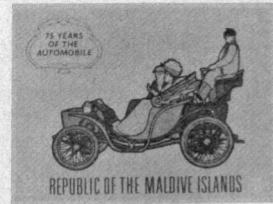

75 Columbia Dauman Victoria, 1899

(Des M. Shamir. Litho)

1970 (1 Feb). *"75 Years of the Automobile". T* **75** *and similar horiz designs. Multicoloured. P* 12.

318	2 l. Type **75**			20	30
319	5 l. Duryea phaeton, 1902			25	30
320	7 l. Packard S-24, 1906			30	30
321	10 l. Autocar Runabout, 1907			35	30
322	25 l. Type **75**			1·50	30
323	50 l. As 5 l.			2·75	55
324	1 r. As 7 l.			3·50	90
325	2 r. As 10 l.			4·50	5·50
318/25			Set of 8	12·00	7·75
MS326	95 × 143 mm. Nos. 324/5. P 11½			5·00	7·50

76 U.N. Headquarters, New York

77 Ship and Light Buoy

(Des M. Shamir. Litho Rosenbaum Brothers, Vienna)

1970 (26 June). *25th Anniv of United Nations. T* **76** *and similar horiz designs. Multicoloured. P* 13½.

327	2 l. Type **76**			10	50
328	10 l. Surgical operation (W.H.O.)			95	15
329	25 l. Student, actress and musician (U.N.E.S.C.O.)			2·00	30
330	50 l. Children at work and play (U.N.I.C.E.F.)			2·00	60
331	1 r. Fish, corn and farm animals (F.A.O.)			2·00	90
332	2 r. Miner hewing coal (I.L.O.)			5·00	5·50
327/32			Set of 6	11·00	7·25

(Des M. Shamir. Litho)

1970 (26 July). *10th Anniv of Inter-governmental Maritime Consultative Organization. T* **77** *and similar vert design. Multicoloured. P* 13½.

333	50 l. Type **77**			50	40
334	1 r. Ship and lighthouse			3·25	85

78 "Guitar-player and Masqueraders" (A. Watteau)

79 Australian Pavilion

(Des M. Shamir. Litho Govt Printer, Israel)

1970 (1 Aug). *Famous Paintings showing the Guitar. T* **78** *and similar vert designs. Multicoloured. P* 14.

335	3 l. Type **78**			10	30
336	7 l. "Spanish Guitarist" (E. Manet)			10	30
337	50 l. "Costumed Player" (Watteau)			50	35
338	1 r. "Mandoline-player" (Roberti)			85	55
339	2 r. 50, "Guitar-player and Lady" (Watteau)			2·25	2·75
340	5 r. "Mandoline-player" (Frans Hals)			4·00	4·50
335/40			Set of 6	7·00	8·00
MS341	132 × 80 mm. Nos. 339/40. Roul			6·50	7·50

(Des M. Shamir. Litho Rosenbaum Brothers, Vienna)

1970 (1 Aug). *"EXPO 70" World Fair, Osaka, Japan. T* **79** *and similar vert designs. Multicoloured. P* 13½.

342	2 l. Type **79**			10	40
343	3 l. West German Pavilion			10	40
344	10 l. U.S.A. Pavilion			30	10
345	25 l. British Pavilion			80	15
346	50 l. Soviet Pavilion			1·40	35
347	1 r. Japanese Pavilion			1·90	65
342/7			Set of 6	4·00	1·75

80 Learning the Alphabet

(Des M. Shamir. Litho Govt Printer, Israel)

1970 (7 Sept). *International Education Year. T* **80** *and similar horiz designs. Multicoloured. P* 14.

348	5 l. Type **80**			20	15
349	10 l. Training teachers			25	10
350	25 l. Geography lesson			60	15
351	50 l. School inspector			80	45
352	1 r. Education by television			1·25	90
348/52			Set of 5	2·75	1·40

Philympia
London 1970

(81)

82 Footballers

1970 (18 Sept). *"Philympia 1970" Stamp Exhibition, London. Nos.* 306/**MS**309 *optd with T* **81**, *in silver.*

353	10 l. multicoloured			10	10
354	1 r. 50, multicoloured			65	75
355	2 r. 50, multicoloured			1·00	1·50
353/5			Set of 3	1·50	2·00
MS356	101 × 130 mm. Nos. 305/8 optd. Imperf			6·00	7·00

(Des M. Shamir. Litho Rosenbaum Brothers, Vienna)

1970 (Dec). *World Cup Football Championships, Mexico. T* **82** *and similar vert designs, each showing football scenes and outline of the Jules Rimet Trophy. P* 13½.

357	3 l. multicoloured			15	40
358	6 l. multicoloured			20	40
359	7 l. multicoloured			20	30
360	25 l. multicoloured			90	20
361	1 r. multicoloured			2·50	90
357/61			Set of 5	3·50	2·00

83 Little Boy and U.N.I.C.E.F. Flag

84 Astronauts Lovell, Haise and Swigert

(Des M. Shamir. Litho State Printing Works, Budapest)

1971 (1 Apr). *25th Anniv of U.N.I.C.E.F. T* **83** *and similar vert design. Multicoloured. P* 12.

362	5 l. Type **83**			10	15
363	10 l. Little girl with U.N.I.C.E.F. balloon			10	15
364	1 r. Type **83**			1·75	85
365	2 r. As 10 l.			2·75	3·00
362/5			Set of 4	4·25	3·75

(Des M. Shamir. Litho Govt Printer, Israel)

1971 (27 Apr). *Safe Return of "Apollo 13". T 84 and similar vert designs. Multicoloured. P 14.*

366	5 l.	Type 84		20	15
367	20 l.	Explosion in Space		40	15
368	1 r.	Splashdown		1·10	50
366/8			Set of 3	1·50	70

85 "Multiracial Flower"
86 "Mme. Charpentier and her Children" (Renoir)

(Des M. Shamir. Litho)

1971 (3 May). *Racial Equality Year. P 14.*

369	85	10 l. multicoloured		10	15
370		25 l. multicoloured		20	15

1971 (Aug). *Famous Paintings showing "Mother and Child". T 86 and similar vert designs. Multicoloured. Litho. P 12.*

371	5 l.	Type 86		25	20
372	7 l.	"Susanna van Collen and her Daughter" (Rembrandt)		30	20
373	10 l.	"Madonna nursing the Child" (Titian)		40	20
374	20 l.	"Baroness Belleli and her Children" (Degas)		1·00	20
375	25 l.	"The Cradle" (Morisot)		1·00	20
376	1 r.	"Helena Fourment and her Children" (Rubens)		3·00	85
377	3 r.	"On the Terrace" (Renoir)		5·50	6·50
371/7			Set of 7	10·00	7·50

87 Alan Shepard
88 "Ballerina" (Degas)

(Photo State Ptg Works, Vienna)

1971 (11 Nov). *Moon Flight of "Apollo 14". T 87 and similar vert designs. Multicoloured. P 12½.*

378	6 l.	Type 87		30	20
379	10 l.	Stuart Roosa		35	20
380	1 r. 50,	Edgar Mitchell		4·50	3·00
381	5 r.	Mission insignia		9·50	9·50
378/81			Set of 4	13·00	11·50

(Litho Rosenbaum Brothers, Vienna)

1971 (19 Nov). *Famous Paintings showing "Dancers". T 88 and similar vert designs. Multicoloured. P 14.*

382	5 l.	Type 88		20	20
383	10 l.	"Dancing Couple" (Renoir)		25	20
384	2 r.	"Spanish Dancer" (Manet)		2·75	2·50
385	5 r.	"Ballerinas" (Degas)		5·00	5·00
386	10 r.	"La Goulue at the Moulin Rouge" (Toulouse-Lautrec)		7·50	8·00
382/6			Set of 5	14·00	14·00

ROYAL VISIT 1972

(89)
90 Book Year Emblem

1972 (13 Mar). *Visit of Queen Elizabeth II and Prince Philip. Nos. 382/6 optd with T 89.*

387	5 l. multicoloured			15	10
388	10 l. multicoloured			20	20
389	2 r. multicoloured			4·50	4·00
390	5 r. multicoloured			8·00	8·00
391	10 r. multicoloured			9·50	10·00
387/91			Set of 5	20·00	20·00

(Des M. Shamir. Litho Bradbury, Wilkinson)

1972 (1 May). *International Book Year. P 13 × 13½.*

392	90	25 l. multicoloured		15	10
393		5 r. multicoloured		1·60	2·00

91 Scottish Costume
93 Cross-country Skiing

92 Stegosaurus

(Des M. Shamir. Litho State Printing Works, Budapest)

1972 (15 May). *National Costumes of the World. T 91 and similar vert designs. Multicoloured. P 12.*

394	10 l.	Type 91		50	10
395	15 l.	Netherlands		55	15
396	25 l.	Norway		90	15
397	50 l.	Hungary		1·75	55
398	1 r.	Austria		2·25	80
399	2 r.	Spain		4·00	3·25
394/9			Set of 6	9·00	4·50

(Des M. Shamir. Litho Rosenbaum Brothers, Vienna)

1972 (31 May). *Prehistoric Animals. T 92 and similar horiz designs. Multicoloured. P 14.*

400	2 l.	Type 92		50	50
401	7 l.	Dimetrodon (inscr "Edaphosaurus")		90	40
402	25 l.	Diplodocus		1·75	40
403	50 l.	Triceratops		2·00	75
404	2 r.	Pteranodon		5·00	5·00
405	5 r.	Tyrannosaurus		9·00	9·50
400/5			Set of 6	17·00	15·00

An imperforate miniature sheet containing Nos. 404/5 also exists, but was never freely available.

(Des M. Shamir. Litho Rosenbaum Brothers, Vienna)

1972 (June). *Winter Olympic Games, Sapporo, Japan. T 93 and similar vert designs. Multicoloured. P 14.*

406	3 l.	Type 93		10	30
407	6 l.	Bob-sleighing		10	30
408	15 l.	Speed-skating		20	20
409	50 l.	Ski-jumping		1·00	45
410	1 r.	Figure-skating (pair)		1·75	70
411	2 r. 50,	Ice-hockey		5·50	3·25
406/11			Set of 6	7·50	4·75

94 Scout Saluting
95 Cycling

(Des M. Shamir. Litho Govt Printer, Israel)

1972 (1 Aug). *13th World Scout Jamboree, Asagiri, Japan (1971). T 94 and similar vert designs. Multicoloured. P 14.*

412	10 l.	Type 94		75	20
413	15 l.	Scout signalling		95	20
414	50 l.	Scout blowing bugle		3·25	1·25
415	1 r.	Scout beating drum		4·50	2·25
412/15			Set of 4	8·50	3·50

PRINTERS AND PROCESS. *Unless otherwise stated,* all the following issues to No. 1277 were lithographed by Format International Security Printers Ltd, London.

1972 (30 Oct). *Olympic Games, Munich. T 95 and similar vert designs. Multicoloured. P 14½ × 14.*

416	5 l.	Type 95		50	20
417	10 l.	Running		20	20
418	25 l.	Wrestling		30	20
419	50 l.	Hurdling		50	35
420	2 r.	Boxing		1·25	1·75
421	5 r.	Volleyball		2·75	3·25
416/21			Set of 6	5·00	5·50
MS422	92 × 120 mm. 3 r. As 50 l.; 4 r. As 10 l. P 15			5·75	7·50

96 Globe and Conference Emblem
97 "Flowers" (Van Gogh)

(Litho Harrison)

1972 (15 Nov). *U.N. Environmental Conservation Conference, Stockholm. P 14½.*

423	96	2 l. multicoloured		10	30
424		3 l. multicoloured		10	30
425		15 l. multicoloured		30	15
426		50 l. multicoloured		75	45
427		2 r. 50, multicoloured		3·25	4·00
423/7			Set of 5	4·00	4·75

(Des M. Shamir)

1973 (Mar). *Floral Paintings. T 97 and similar vert designs. Multicoloured. P 13½.*

428	1 l.	Type 97		10	30
429	2 l.	"Flowers in Jug" (Renoir)		10	30
430	3 l.	"Chrysanthemums" (Renoir)		10	30
431	50 l.	"Mixed Bouquet" (Bosschaert)		1·25	40
432	1 r.	As 3 l.		1·75	40
433	5 r.	As 2 l.		3·50	5·00
428/33			Set of 6	6·00	6·00
MS434	120 × 94 mm. 2 r. as 50 l.; 3 r. Type 97. P 15			7·00	8·50

LEMECHEV MIDDLE-WEIGHT GOLD MEDALLIST

(98)
99 Animal Care

1973 (Apr). *Gold-medal Winners, Munich Olympic Games. Nos. 420/MS422 optd with T 98 or similar commemorative inscr, in blue.*

435	2 r. multicoloured			3·00	2·25
436	5 r. multicoloured			4·00	3·50
MS437	92 × 120 mm. 3 r. multicoloured; 4 r. multicoloured			7·00	8·00

Overprints:—2 r. Type 98; 5 r. "JAPAN GOLD MEDAL WINNERS" (volleyball). Miniature sheet:—3 r. "EHRHARDT 100 METER HURDLES GOLD MEDALLIST"; 4 r. "SHORTER MARATHON GOLD MEDALLIST".

(Des M. Shamir)

1973 (Aug). *International Scouting Congress, Nairobi and Addis Ababa. T 99 and similar horiz designs. Multicoloured. P 14½.*

438	1 l.	Type 99		10	20
439	2 l.	Lifesaving		10	20
440	3 l.	Agricultural training		10	20
441	4 l.	Carpentry		10	20
442	5 l.	Playing leapfrog		10	20
443	1 r.	As 2 l.		2·75	75
444	2 r.	As 4 l.		4·00	4·75
445	3 r.	Type 99		4·50	7·00
438/45			Set of 8	10·00	12·00
MS446	101 × 79 mm. 5 r. As 3 l.			7·50	14·00

100 Blue Marlin

1973 (Aug). *Fishes. T 100 and similar horiz designs. Multicoloured. P 14½.*

447	1 l.	Type 100		10	30
448	2 l.	Skipjack Tuna		10	30
449	3 l.	Blue-finned Tuna		10	30
450	5 l.	Dolphin (fish)		10	30
451	60 l.	Humpbacked Snapper		80	40
452	75 l.	As 60 l.		1·00	40
453	1 r. 50,	Yellow-edged Lyretail		1·75	1·75
454	2 r. 50,	As 5 l.		2·25	2·75
455	3 r.	Spotted Coral Grouper		2·25	3·00
456	10 r.	Spanish Mackerel		4·75	8·00
447/56			Set of 10	11·50	16·00
MS457	119×123 mm. 4 r. As 2 l.; 5 r. Type 100			15·00	18·00

Nos. 451/2 are smaller, size 29×22 mm.

101 Golden-fronted Leafbird

102 *Lantana camara*

(Des M. Shamir)

1973 (Oct). *Fauna. T 101 and similar diamond-shaped designs. Multicoloured. P 14½.*

458	1 l. Type **101**	..	10	30
459	2 l. Indian Flying Fox	..	10	30
460	3 l. Land tortoise	..	10	30
461	4 l. *Kallima inachus* (butterfly)	..	30	30
462	50 l. As 3 l.	..	60	35
463	2 r. Type **101**	..	4·00	4·00
464	3 r. As 2 l.	..	3·50	4·00
458/64		*Set of 7*	7·75	8·50
MS465	66×74 mm. 5 r. As 4 l.	..	18·00	20·00

(Litho Questa)

1973 (19 Dec). *Flowers of the Maldive Islands. T 102 and similar vert designs. Multicoloured. P 14.*

466	1 l. Type **102**	..	10	20
467	2 l. *Nerium oleander*	..	10	20
468	3 l. *Rosa polyantha*	..	10	20
469	4 l. *Hibiscus manihot*	..	10	20
470	5 l. *Bougainvillea glabra*	..	10	20
471	10 l. *Plumera alba*	..	10	20
472	50 l. *Poinsettia pulcherrima*	..	55	30
473	5 r. *Ononis natrix*	..	3·25	6·00
466/73		*Set of 8*	3·50	6·00
MS474	110×100 mm. 2 r. As 3 l.; 3 r. As 10 l.	..	3·25	5·25

103 "Tiros" Weather Satellite

(Des M. Shamir)

1974 (10 Jan). *Centenary of World Meteorological Organization. T 103 and similar horiz designs. Multicoloured. P 14½.*

475	1 l. Type **103**	..	10	10
476	2 l. "Nimbus" satellite	..	10	10
477	3 l. *Nomad* (weather ship)	..	10	10
478	4 l. Scanner, A.P.T. Instant Weather Picture equipment	..	10	10
479	5 l. Richard's wind-speed recorder	..	10	10
480	2 r. Type **103**	..	3·00	3·50
481	3 r. As 3 l.	..	3·25	3·75
475/81		*Set of 7*	6·00	6·50
MS482	110×79 mm. 10 r. As 2 l.	..	7·50	14·00

104 "Apollo" Spacecraft and Pres. Kennedy

(Des M. Shamir)

1974 (1 Feb). *American and Russian Space Exploration Projects. T 104 and similar horiz designs. Multicoloured. P 14½.*

483	1 l. Type **104**	..	10	15
484	2 l. "Mercury" capsule and John Glenn	..	10	15
485	3 l. "Vostok 1" and Yuri Gagarin	..	10	20
486	4 l. "Vostok 6" and Valentina Tereshkova	..	10	20
487	5 l. "Soyuz 11" and "Salyut" space-station	..	10	20
488	2 r. "Skylab" space laboratory	..	3·50	3·50
489	3 r. As 2 l.	..	4·00	4·00
483/9		*Set of 7*	7·00	7·50
MS490	103×80 mm. 10 r. Type **104**	..	9·50	13·00

 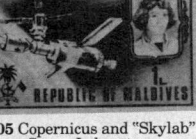

105 Copernicus and "Skylab" Space Laboratory

106 "Maternity" (Picasso)

(Des G. Vasarhelyi)

1974 (10 Apr). *500th Birth Anniv of Nicholas Copernicus (astronomer). T 105 and similar horiz designs. Multicoloured. P 14½.*

491	1 l. Type **105**	..	10	15
492	2 l. Orbital space-station of the future	..	10	15
493	3 l. Proposed "Space-shuttle" craft	..	10	15
494	4 l. "Mariner 2" Venus probe	..	10	20
495	5 l. "Mariner 4" Mars probe	..	10	20
496	25 l. Type **105**	..	90	20
497	1 r. 50, As 2 l.	..	2·50	3·25
498	5 r. As 3 l.	..	4·00	10·00
491/8		*Set of 8*	7·00	13·00
MS499	106×80 mm. 10 r. "Copernicus" orbital observatory	..	14·00	17·00

(Des M. Shamir. Litho Questa)

1974 (May). *Paintings by Picasso. T 106 and similar vert designs. Multicoloured. P 14.*

500	1 l. Type **106**	..	10	10
501	2 l. "Harlequin and Friend"	..	10	10
502	3 l. "Pierrot Sitting"	..	10	10
503	20 l. "Three Musicians"	..	25	15
504	75 l. "L'Aficionado"	..	55	40
505	5 r. "Still Life"	..	3·50	4·75
500/5		*Set of 6*	4·00	4·75
MS506	100×101 mm. 2 r. As 20 l.; 3 r. As 5 r.	..	5·50	7·00

107 U.P.U. Emblem, Steam and Diesel Locomotives

108 Footballers

(Des M. Shamir)

1974 (May). *Centenary of Universal Postal Union. T 107 and similar horiz designs. Multicoloured. P 14½.*

507	1 l. Type **107**	..	10	10
508	2 l. Paddle-steamer and modern mailboat	..	10	10
509	3 l. Airship LZ-127 *Graf Zeppelin* and Boeing 747 airliner	..	10	10
510	1 r. 50, Mailcoach and motor van	..	1·10	1·60
511	2 r. 50, As 2 l.	..	1·75	3·00
512	5 r. Type **107**	..	1·75	3·00
507/12		*Set of 6*	3·50	5·00
MS513	126×105 mm. 4 r. Type **107**	..	5·00	6·50

Nos. 507/12 were first issued in sheets of 50, but were later released in small sheets of five stamps and one label. These small sheets were perforated 13½.

(Des M. Shamir)

1974 (June). *World Cup Football Championships, West Germany. T 108 and similar vert designs, showing football scenes. P 14½.*

514	1 l. multicoloured	..	10	15
515	2 l. multicoloured	..	10	15
516	3 l. multicoloured	..	10	15
517	4 l. multicoloured	..	10	15
518	75 l. multicoloured	..	1·25	75
519	4 r. multicoloured	..	2·50	4·00
520	5 r. multicoloured	..	2·50	4·00
514/20		*Set of 7*	6·00	8·50
MS521	88×95 mm. 10 r. multicoloured	..	10·00	12·00

109 "Capricorn"

110 Churchill and Avro Type 683 Lancaster

(Des G. Vasarhelyi)

1974 (3 July). *Signs of the Zodiac. T 109 and similar horiz designs. Multicoloured. P 14½.*

522	1 l. Type **109**	..	20	30
523	2 l. "Aquarius"	..	20	30
524	3 l. "Pisces"	..	20	30
525	4 l. "Aries"	..	20	30
526	5 l. "Taurus"	..	20	30
527	6 l. "Gemini"	..	20	30
528	7 l. "Cancer"	..	20	30
529	10 l. "Leo"	..	30	30
530	15 l. "Virgo"	..	30	30
531	20 l. "Libra"	..	30	30
532	25 l. "Scorpio"	..	30	30
533	5 r. "Sagittarius"	..	6·50	12·00
522/33		*Set of 12*	8·00	13·50
MS534	119×99 mm. 10 r. "The Sun" (49×37 mm). P 13½	..	17·00	19·00

(Des M. Shamir)

1974 (30 Nov). *Birth Centenary of Sir Winston Churchill. T 110 and similar horiz designs. Multicoloured. P 14½.*

535	1 l. Type **110**	..	15	30
536	2 l. Churchill as pilot	..	15	30
537	3 l. Churchill as First Lord of the Admiralty	..	20	30
538	4 l. Churchill and H.M.S. *Eagle* (aircraft carrier)	..	20	30
539	5 l. Churchill and De Havilland D.H.98 Mosquito bombers	..	20	30
540	60 l. Churchill and anti-aircraft battery	..	2·75	1·50
541	75 l. Churchill and tank in desert	..	3·00	1·50
542	5 r. Churchill and Short S.25 Sunderland flying boat	..	11·00	12·00
535/42		*Set of 8*	16·00	15·00
MS543	113×83 mm. 10. As 4 l.	..	17·00	20·00

111 Bullmouth Helmet (*Cypraecassis rufa*)

112 Royal Throne

(Des M. Shamir)

1975 (25 Jan). *Sea Shells and Cowries. T 111 and similar multicoloured designs. P 14×13½ (60 l., 75 l.) or 14½ (others).*

544	1 l. Type **111**	..	10	30
545	2 l. Venus Comb Murex (*Murex pecten*)	..	10	30
546	3 l. Common or Major Harp (*Harpa major*)	..	10	30
547	4 l. Chiragra Spider Conch (*Lambis chiragra chiragra*)	..	10	30
548	5 l. Geography Cone (*Conus geographus*)	..	10	30
549	60 l. Dawn Cowrie (*Cypraea diluculum*) (22×30 mm)	..	3·00	2·00
550	75 l. Purplish Clanculus (*Clanculus puniceus*) (22×30 mm)	..	3·50	2·00
551	5 r. Ramose Murex (*Murex ramosus*)	..	8·50	11·00
544/51		*Set of 8*	14·00	15·00
MS552	152×126 mm. 2 r. As 3 l.; 3 r. As 2 l.	..	12·00	15·00

(Des M. Shamir. Litho Questa)

1975 (22 Feb). *Historical Relics and Monuments. T 112 and similar multicoloured designs. P 14.*

553	1 l. Type **112**	..	10	10
554	10 l. Candlesticks	..	10	10
555	25 l. Lamp-tree	..	15	10
556	60 l. Royal umbrellas	..	30	30
557	75 l. Eid-Miskith Mosque (*horiz*)	..	35	35
558	3 r. Tomb of Al-Hafiz Abu-al Barakath-al Barubari (*horiz*)	..	1·60	2·75
553/8		*Set of 6*	2·25	3·25

113 Guavas

114 *Phyllangia*

(Des M. Shamir)

1975 (Mar). *Fruits. T 113 and similar vert designs. Multicoloured. P 14½.*

559	2 l. Type **113**	..	10	30
560	4 l. Maldive mulberry	..	15	30
561	5 l. Mountain apples	..	15	30
562	10 l. Bananas	..	20	15
563	20 l. Mangoes	..	40	25
564	50 l. Papaya	..	1·00	60
565	1 r. Pomegranates	..	1·75	70
566	5 r. Coconut	..	5·50	11·00
559/66		*Set of 8*	8·00	12·00
MS567	136×102 mm. 2 r. As 10 l.; 3 r. As 2 l.	..	8·50	13·00

(Des M. Shamir)

1975 (6 June). *Marine Life. T 114 and similar triangular designs. Multicoloured. P 14½.*

568	1 l. Type **114**	..	10	10
569	2 l. *Madrepora oculata*	..	10	10
570	3 l. *Acropora gravida*	..	10	10
571	4 l. *Stylotella*	..	10	10
572	5 l. *Acrophora cervicornis*	..	10	10
573	60 l. *Strongylocentrotus purpuratus*	..	75	65
574	75 l. *Pisaster ochraceus*	..	85	70
575	5 r. *Marthasterias glacialis*	..	5·00	6·50
568/75		*Set of 8*	8·00	7·50
MS576	155×98 mm. 4 r. As 1 l. Imperf	..	11·00	14·00

PRICES OF SETS

Set prices are given for many issues, general[v] those containing three stamps or more. Definitiv[e] sets include one of each value or major colou[r] change, but do not cover different perforation[s] die types or minor shades. Where a choice [is] possible the set prices are based on the cheapes[t] versions of the stamps included in the listings.

14th Boy Scout Jamboree
July 29 — August 7, 1975

115 Clock Tower and Customs
    Building within "10"   (116)

(Des M. Shamir)

1975 (26 July). *10th Anniv of Independence. T 115 and similar horiz designs. Multicoloured. P 14½.*

577	4 l. Type 115	10	10
578	5 l. Government Offices	10	10
579	7 l. Waterfront	10	10
580	15 l. Mosque and minaret	10	10
581	10 r. Sultan Park and museum	2·25	6·00
577/81	*Set of 5*	2·25	6·00

1975 (26 July). *"Nordjamb 75" World Scout Jamboree, Norway. Nos. 443/5 and MS446 optd with T 116.*

582	1 r. multicoloured	40	40
583	2 r. multicoloured	60	60
584	3 r. multicoloured	1·25	1·25
582/4	*Set of 3*	2·00	2·00
MS585	101 × 79 mm. 5 r. multicoloured	7·00	8·00

117 Madura Prau   118 *Brahmophthalma
        wallichi* (moth)

(Des M. Shamir)

1975 (Aug). *Ships. T 117 and similar multicoloured designs. P 14½.*

586	1 l. Type 117	10	10
587	2 l. Ganges patela	10	10
588	3 l. Indian palla (*vert*)	10	10
589	4 l. Odhi (dhow) (*vert*)	10	10
590	5 l. Maldivian schooner	10	10
591	25 l. Cutty Sark	90	40
592	1 r. Maldivian baggala (*vert*)	1·50	70
593	5 r. Freighter *Maldive Courage*	5·00	6·50
586/93	*Set of 8*	5·00	6·50
MS594	99×85 mm. 10 r. As 1 r.	9·50	14·00

(Des M. Shamir)

1975 (7 Sept). *Butterflies and Moth. T 118 and similar horiz designs. Multicoloured. P 14½.*

595	1 l. Type 118	15	30
596	2 l. Teinopalpus imperialis	15	30
597	3 l. Cethosia biblis	15	30
598	4 l. Idea jasonia	15	30
599	5 l. Apatura ilia	15	30
600	25 l. Kallima horsfieldi	1·25	35
601	1 r. 50, Hebomoia leucippe	3·50	3·75
602	5 r. Papilio memnon	8·00	10·00
595/602	*Set of 8*	12·00	14·00
MS603	134×97 mm. 10 r. As 25 l.	20·00	20·00

119 "The Dying Captive" 120 Beaker and Vase

1975 (9 Oct). *500th Birth Anniv of Michelangelo. T 119 and similar vert designs. Multicoloured. P 14½.*

604	1 l. Type 119	10	10
605	2 l. Detail of "The Last Judgement"	10	10
606	3 l. "Apollo"	10	10
607	4 l. Detail of Sistine Chapel ceiling	10	10
608	5 l. "Bacchus"	10	10
609	1 r. Detail of "The Last Judgement" (*different*)	1·25	30
610	2 r. "David"	1·50	2·00
611	5 r. "Cumaean Sibyl"	2·25	5·00
604/11	*Set of 8*	6·00	8·00
MS612	123 × 113 mm. 10 r. As 2 r.	6·00	11·00

The 1, 3, 5 l. and 2, 10 r. are sculptures; the other values show details of the frescoes in the Sistine Chapel.

(Des M. Shamir. Litho Questa)

1975 (Dec). *Maldivian Lacquerware. T 120 and similar vert designs. Multicoloured. P 14.*

613	2 l. Type 120	10	30
614	4 l. Boxes	10	30
615	50 l. Jar with lid	30	20
616	75 l. Bowls with covers	40	30
617	1 r. Craftsman at work	50	40
613/17	*Set of 5*	1·10	1·40

121 Map of Maldives   122 Cross-country Skiing

(Des M. Shamir. Litho Questa)

1975 (25 Dec). *Tourism. T 121 and similar horiz designs. Multicoloured. P 14.*

618	4 l. Type 121	20	20
619	5 l. Motor launch and small craft	20	20
620	7 l. Sailing boats	20	20
621	15 l. Underwater fishing	20	20
622	3 r. Hulule Airport	2·50	2·50
623	10 r. Motor cruisers	4·50	6·50
618/23	*Set of 6*	7·00	9·00

(Des M. Shamir)

1976 (10 Jan). *Winter Olympic Games, Innsbruck, Austria. T 122 and similar vert designs. Multicoloured. P 15.*

624	1 l. Type 122	10	10
625	2 l. Speed ice-skating	10	10
626	3 l. Pairs figure-skating	10	10
627	4 l. Four-man bobsleigh	10	10
628	5 l. Ski-jumping	10	10
629	25 l. Women's figure-skating	35	10
630	1 r. 15, Slalom skiing	90	1·25
631	4 r. Ice-hockey	1·50	4·00
624/31	*Set of 8*	2·50	5·00
MS632	93 × 117 mm. 10 r. Downhill skiing	7·00	12·00

Nos. 624/31 exist imperforate from stock dispersed by the liquidator of Format International Security Printers Ltd.

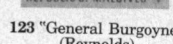

123 "General Burgoyne"   124 Thomas Edison
    (Reynolds)

(Des M. Shamir)

1976 (15 Feb). *Bicentenary of American Revolution. T 123 and similar multicoloured designs. P 15.*

633	1 l. Type 123	10	10
634	2 l. "John Hancock" (Copley)	10	10
635	3 l. "Death of General Montgomery" (Trumbull) (*horiz*)	10	10
636	4 l. "Paul Revere" (Copley)	10	10
637	5 l. "Battle of Bunker Hill" (Trumbull) (*horiz*)	10	10
638	2 r. "The Crossing of the Delaware" (Sully) (*horiz*)	2·00	2·50
639	3 r. "Samuel Adams" (Copley)	2·50	3·00
640	5 r. "Surrender of Cornwallis" (Trumbull) (*horiz*)	3·00	3·25
633/40	*Set of 8*	7·00	8·00
MS641	147 × 95 mm. 10 r. "Washington at Dorchester Heights" (Stuart)	13·00	16·00

1976 (10 Mar). *Telephone Centenary. T 124 and similar horiz designs. Multicoloured. P 15.*

642	1 l. Type 124	10	20
643	2 l. Alexander Graham Bell	10	20
644	3 l. Telephones of 1919, 1937 and 1972	10	20
645	10 l. Cable entrance into station	20	20
646	20 l. Equaliser circuit assembly	30	20
647	1 r. *Salernum* (cable ship)	1·75	55
648	10 r. "Intelsat IV-A" and Earth Station	4·75	7·50
642/8	*Set of 7*	6·50	8·00
MS649	156 × 105 mm. 4 r. Early telephones	7·50	9·00

MAY 29TH–JUNE 6TH
"INTERPHIL" 1976
    (125)   126 Wrestling

1976 (29 May). *"Interphil 76" International Stamp Exhibition, Philadelphia. Nos. 638/MS641 optd with T 125, in blue (5 r.) or silver (others).*

650	2 r. multicoloured	1·50	1·75
651	3 r. multicoloured	2·00	2·25
652	5 r. multicoloured	2·50	2·75
650/2	*Set of 3*	5·50	6·00
MS653	147 × 95 mm. 10 r. multicoloured	10·00	12·00

1976 (June). *Olympic Games, Montreal. T 126 and similar vert designs. Multicoloured. P 15.*

654	1 l. Type 126	10	10
655	2 l. Putting the shot	10	10
656	3 l. Hurdling	10	10
657	4 l. Hockey	10	10
658	5 l. Running	10	10
659	6 l. Javelin-throwing	10	10
660	1 r. 50, Discus-throwing	1·25	1·75
661	5 r. Volleyball	2·75	5·25
654/61	*Set of 8*	4·00	6·50
MS662	135 × 106 mm. 10 r. Throwing the hammer	8·50	12·00

Nos. 654/61 exist imperforate from stock dispersed by the liquidator of Format International Security Printers Ltd.

127 *Dolichos lablab*   128 "Viking" approaching Mars

(Des M. Shamir. Litho Questa)

1976 (26 July)–77. *Vegetables. T 127 and similar vert designs. Multicoloured. P 14.*

663	2 l. Type 127	10	20
664	4 l. Moringa pterygosperma	10	20
665	10 l. Solanum melongena	10	10
666	20 l. Moringa pterygosperma (1977)	1·25	1·50
667	50 l. Cucumis sativus	50	65
668	75 l. Trichosanthes anguina	55	75
669	1 r. Momordica charantia	65	85
670	2 r. Trichosanthes anguina (1977)	2·75	6·00
663/70	*Set of 8*	5·50	9·00

1976 (2 Dec). *"Viking" Space Mission. T 128 and similar horiz design. Multicoloured. P 14.*

671	5 r. Type 128	2·25	2·75
MS672	121 × 89 mm. 20 r. Landing module on Mars	10·00	14·00

129 Coronation Ceremony

1977 (6 Feb). *Silver Jubilee of Queen Elizabeth II. T 129 and similar horiz designs. Multicoloured. P 14 × 13½.*

673	1 l. Type 129	10	10
674	2 l. Queen and Prince Philip	10	10
675	3 l. Royal couple with Princes Andrew and Edward	10	10
676	1 r. 15, Queen with Archbishops	35	25
677	3 r. State coach in procession	60	55
678	4 r. Royal couple with Prince Charles and Princess Anne	60	90
673/8	*Set of 6*	1·50	1·60
MS679	120 × 77 mm. 10 r. Queen and Prince Charles	3·25	2·75

Nos. 673/8 also exist perf 12 (*Price per set of 6 £1·50 mint or used*) from additional sheetlets of five stamps and one label in changed colours.

130 Beethoven and Organ

(Des M. Shamir)

1977 (26 Mar). *150th Death Anniv of Ludwig van Beethoven (composer). T 130 and similar horiz designs. Multicoloured. P 14.*

680	1 l. Type 130	15	20
681	2 l. Portrait and manuscript of *Moonlight Sonata*	15	20
682	3 l. With Goethe at Teplitz	15	20
683	4 l. Portrait and string instruments	15	20
684	5 l. Beethoven's home, Heiligenstadt	15	20
685	25 l. Hands and gold medals	85	20
686	2 r. Portrait and part of *Missa solemnis*	2·75	3·00
687	5 r. Portrait and hearing-aids	4·75	5·00
680/7	*Set of 8*	8·25	8·25
MS688	121 × 92 mm. 4 r. Death mask and room where composer died	6·00	8·00

131 Printed Circuit and I.T.U. Emblem   132 "Miss Anne Ford" (Gainsborough)

(Des M. Shamir. Litho Questa)

1977 (17 May). *Inauguration of Satellite Earth Station. T* **131** *and similar horiz designs. Multicoloured. P* 14.

689	10 l. Type **131**	10	10
690	90 l. Central telegraph office	45	45
691	10 r. Satellite Earth station	3·00	6·00
689/91	*Set of 3*	3·25	6·00
MS692	100×85 mm. 5 r. "Intelsat IV-A" satellite over Maldives	4·25	5·50

(Des M. Shamir. Litho Questa)

1977 (20 May). *Artists' Birth Anniversaries. T* **132** *and similar vert designs. Multicoloured. P* 14.

693	1 l. Type **132** (250th anniv)	10	10
694	2 l. Group painting by Rubens (400th anniv)	10	10
695	3 l. "Girl with Dog" (Titian) (500th anniv)	10	10
696	4 l. "Mrs. Thomas Graham" (Gainsborough)	10	10
697	5 l. "Artist with Isabella Brant" (Rubens)	10	10
698	95 l. Portrait by Titian	75	40
699	1 r. Portrait by Gainsborough	75	40
700	10 r. "Isabella Brant" (Rubens)	3·75	7·00
693/700	*Set of 8*	5·00	7·50
MS701	152 × 116 mm. 5 r. "Self-portrait" (Titian)	3·75	5·50

133 Lesser Frigate Birds   134 Charles Lindbergh

(Des M. Shamir)

1977 (26 July). *Birds. T* **133** *and similar vert designs. Multicoloured. P* 14½.

702	1 l. Type **133**	20	30
703	2 l. Crab Plover	20	30
704	3 l. White-tailed Tropic Bird	20	30
705	4 l. Wedge-tailed Shearwater	20	30
706	5 l. Grey Heron	20	30
707	20 l. White Tern	90	30
708	95 l. Cattle Egret	2·25	1·60
709	1 r. 25, Black-naped Tern	2·50	2·50
710	5 r. Pheasant Coucal	6·50	8·00
702/10	*Set of 9*	12·00	12·50
MS711	124×117 mm. 10 r. Green Heron	25·00	25·00

(Des M. Shamir)

1977 (31 Oct). *50th Anniv of Lindbergh's Transatlantic Flight and 75th Anniv of First Navigable Airships. T* **134** *and similar multicoloured designs. P* 14½.

712	1 l. Type **134**	10	10
713	2 l. Lindbergh and Ryan NYP Special *Spirit of St. Louis*	10	10
714	3 l. Lindbergh's Miles Mohawk aircraft (*horiz*)	10	10
715	4 l. Lebaudy-Juillot airship *Morning Post* (*horiz*)	10	10
716	5 l. Airship LZ-127 *Graf Zeppelin* and portrait of Zeppelin	10	10
717	1 r. Airship ZR-3 *Los Angeles* (*horiz*)	60	30
718	3 r. Lindbergh and Henry Ford	1·40	1·75
719	10 r. Vickers airship R-23	2·50	5·50
712/19	*Set of 8*	4·00	7·00
MS720	148×114 mm. 5 r. Ryan NYP Special *Spirit of St. Louis*, Statue of Liberty and Eiffel Tower; 7 r. 50, Airship L-31 over *Ostfriesland* (German battleship)	12·00	17·00

No. 715 is inscr "Lebaudy I built by H. Juillot 1902".

135 Boat Building   136 Rheumatic Heart

(Des M. Shamir. Litho J.W.)

1977 (11 Nov). *Occupations. T* **135** *and similar multicoloured designs. P* 13½ × 13 (2 r.) *or* 13 × 13½ (*others*).

721	6 l. Type **135**	35	20
722	15 l. Fishing	55	20
723	20 l. Cadjan weaving	65	20
724	90 l. Mat weaving	2·00	1·40
725	2 r. Lace making (*vert*)	3·50	4·00
721/5	*Set of 5*	6·25	5·50

(Des M. Shamir. Litho Questa)

1977 (Dec). *World Rheumatism Year. T* **136** *and similar vert designs. Multicoloured. P* 14.

726	1 l. Type **136**	10	30
727	50 l. Rheumatic shoulder	40	20
728	2 r. Rheumatic fingers	75	1·25
729	3 r. Rheumatic knee	85	1·40
726/9	*Set of 4*	1·75	2·75

137 Lilienthal's Biplane Glider   138 Newgate Prison

(Des M. Shamir. Litho Questa)

1978 (27 Feb). *75th Anniv of First Powered Aircraft. T* **137** *and similar horiz designs. Multicoloured. P* 13 × 13½.

730	1 l. Type **137**	20	30
731	2 l. Chanute's glider	20	30
732	3 l. Wright testing glider No. II, 1901	20	30
733	4 l. Roe's Triplane I aircraft	20	30
734	5 l. Wright demonstrating Wright Type A aircraft to King Alfonso of Spain	20	30
735	10 l. Roe's second Avro Type D biplane	50	30
736	20 l. Wright Brothers and A. G. Bell	1·25	30
737	95 l. Hadley's triplane	3·00	2·25
738	5 r. Royal Aircraft Factory B.E.2A biplanes at Upavon, 1914	8·50	10·00
730/8	*Set of 9*	13·00	13·00
MS739	98×82 mm. 10 r. Wright Brothers' Wright Type A	14·00	16·00

No. 732 is wrongly dated "1900".

1978 (15 Mar). *World Eradication of Smallpox. T* **138** *and similar multicoloured designs. P* 14.

740	15 l. Foundling Hospital, London (*horiz*)	50	30
741	50 l. Type **138**	1·25	60
742	2 r. Edward Jenner	2·25	4·00
740/2	*Set of 3*	3·50	4·50

139 Television Set   140 Mas Odi

(Des M. Shamir. Litho J.W.)

1978 (29 Mar). *Inauguration of Television in Maldives. T* **139** *and similar multicoloured designs. P* 13 × 13½ (1 r. 50) *or* 13½ × 13 (*others*).

743	15 l. Type **139**	40	30
744	25 l. Television aerials	55	30
745	1 r. 50, Control desk (*horiz*)	2·25	2·75
743/5	*Set of 3*	2·75	3·00

(Des M. Shamir)

1978 (27 Apr). *Ships. T* **140** *and similar multicoloured designs. P* 14½.

746	1 l. Type **140**	10	15
747	2 l. Battela	10	15
748	3 l. Bandu odi (*vert*)	10	15
749	5 l. *Maldive Trader* (freighter)	20	20
750	1 r. *Fath-hul Baaree* (brigantine) (*vert*)	65	30
751	1 r. 25, Mas dhoni	85	1·00
752	3 r. Baggala (*vert*)	1·10	1·75
753	4 r. As No. 751	1·10	1·75
746/53	*Set of 8*	3·50	5·00
MS754	152 × 138 mm. 1 r. As No. 747; 4 r. As No. 751	2·50	3·75

Nos. 746/8, 750 and 752/4 exist imperforate from stock dispersed by the liquidator of Format International Security Printers Ltd.

---

141 Ampulla   142 Capt. Cook

(Des M. Shamir. Litho Questa)

1978 (15 May). *25th Anniv of Coronation of Queen Elizabeth II. T* **141** *and similar vert designs. Multicoloured. P* 14.

755	1 l. Type **141**	10	10
756	2 l. Sceptre with dove	10	10
757	3 l. Golden orb	10	10
758	1 r. 15, St. Edward's Crown	15	15
759	2 r. Sceptre with cross	20	25
760	5 r. Queen Elizabeth II	55	70
755/60	*Set of 6*	80	1·00
MS761	108×106 mm. 10 r. Anointing spoon	1·25	2·00

Nos. 755/60 were also each issued in small sheets of three stamps and one label, perf 12, in changed colours.

(Des M. Shamir)

1978 (15 July). *250th Birth Anniv of Capt. James Cook and Bicentenary of Discovery of Hawaii. T* **142** *and similar multicoloured designs. P* 14½.

762	1 l. Type **142**	10	15
763	2 l. Statue of Kamehameha I of Hawaii	10	15
764	3 l. H.M.S. *Endeavour*	10	15
765	25 l. Route of Cook's third voyage	45	45
766	75 l. H.M.S. *Resolution*, H.M.S. *Discovery* and map of Hawaiian Islands (*horiz*)	1·25	1·25
767	1 r. 50, Cook meeting Hawaiian islanders on ship (*horiz*)	2·00	2·25
768	10 r. Death of Cook (*horiz*)	5·00	10·00
762/8	*Set of 7*	8·00	13·00
MS769	100 × 92 mm. 5 r. H.M.S. *Endeavour* (*different*)	15·00	20·00

Nos. 763/4 exist imperforate from stock dispersed by the liquidator of Format International Security Printers Ltd.

143 *Schizophrys aspera*   144 "Four Apostles"

(Des M. Shamir)

1978 (30 Aug). *Crustaceans. T* **143** *and similar multicoloured designs. P* 14.

770	1 l. Type **143**	10	10
771	2 l. Atergatis floridus	10	10
772	3 l. Perenon planissimum	10	10
773	90 l. Portunus granulatus	50	40
774	1 r. Carpilius maculatus	50	40
775	2 r. Huenia proteus	1·00	1·40
776	25 r. Etisus laevimanus	7·00	13·00
770/6	*Set of 7*	8·00	14·00
MS777	147 × 146 mm. 2 r. Panulirus longipes (*vert*)	2·00	2·50

(Des BG Studio. Litho Questa)

1978 (28 Oct). *450th Death Anniv of Albrecht Dürer (artist). T* **144** *and similar designs. P* 14.

778	10 l. multicoloured	10	10
779	20 l. multicoloured	15	10
780	55 l. multicoloured	20	20
781	1 r. black, cinnamon and brown	30	30
782	1 r. 80, multicoloured	45	60
783	3 r. multicoloured	70	1·25
778/83	*Set of 6*	1·60	2·25
MS784	141 × 122 mm. 10 r. multicoloured	4·00	6·00

Designs: *Vert*—20 l. "Self-portrait at 27", 55 l. "Madonna and Child with a Pear"; 1 r. 80, "Hare"; 3 r. "Great Piece of Turf"; 10 r. "Columbine". *Horiz*—1 r. "Rhinoceros".

 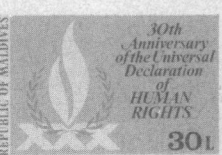

145 T.V. Tower and Building   146 Human Rights Emblem

(Des M. Shamir)

1978 (11 Nov). *Tenth Anniv of Republic.* T **145** *and similar horiz designs. Multicoloured.* P 14½.

785	1 l. Fishing boat	10	10
786	5 l. Montessori School	10	10
787	10 l. Type **145**	10	10
788	25 l. Islet	15	15
789	50 l. Boeing "737"	40	15
790	95 l. Beach scene	40	30
791	1 r. 25, Dhow at night	65	55
792	2 r. President's official residence	75	1·25
793	5 r. Masjidh Afeefuddin (mosque)	90	2·50
785/93	*Set of 9*	3·00	4·50
MS794	119 × 88 mm. 3 r. Fisherman casting net	2·25	4·00

1978 (10 Dec). *30th Anniv of Declaration of Human Rights.* P 14.

795	**146** 30 l. pale magenta, dp mauve and green	15	15
796	90 l. yellow-ochre, red-brown and green	40	60
797	1 r. 80, lt greenish blue, dp blue & grn	70	1·00
795/7	*Set of 3*	1·10	1·60

147 Great Spotted or Rare Spotted Cowrie (*Cypraea guttata*)

148 Delivery by Bellman

(Des M. Shamir. Litho Questa)

1979 (Jan). *Shells.* T **147** *and similar vert designs. Multicoloured.* P 14.

798	1 l. Type **147**	10	10
799	2 l. Imperial Cone (*Conus imperialis*)	10	10
800	3 l. Great Green Turban (*Turbo marmoratus*)	10	10
801	10 l. Giant Spider Conch (*Lambis truncata*)	45	10
802	1 r. White-toothed Cowrie (*Cypraea leucodon*)	2·00	40
803	1 r. 80, Fig Cone (*Conus figulinus*)	3·00	2·50
804	3 r. Glory of the Sea Cone (*Conus gloriamaris*)	4·50	3·75
798/804	*Set of 7*	9·00	6·00
MS805	141×110 mm. 5 r. Common Pacific Vase (*Vasum turbinellus*)	11·00	10·50

(Des M. Shamir. Litho Questa)

1979 (28 Feb). *Death Centenary of Sir Rowland Hill.* T **148** *and similar multicoloured designs.* P 14.

806	1 l. Type **148**	10	10
807	2 l. Mail coach, 1840 (*horiz*)	10	10
808	3 l. First London letter box, 1855	10	10
809	1 r. 55, Penny Black stamps and posthorn	30	50
810	5 r. Maldives 15 c. stamp, 1906, and carrier pigeon	70	1·25
806/10	*Set of 5*	90	1·75
MS811	132 × 107 mm. 10 r. Sir Rowland Hill	1·25	3·00

Nos. 806/10 were also each issued in small sheets of five stamps and one label, perf 12, in changed colours.

149 Girl with Teddy Bear

150 "White Feathers"

(Des M. Sharmir. Litho Questa)

1979 (10 May). *International Year of the Child (1st issue).* T **149** *and similar vert designs. Multicoloured.* P 14.

812	5 l. Type **149**	10	10
813	1 r. 25, Boy with model sailing boat	40	50
814	2 r. Boy with toy rocket	45	55
815	3 r. Boy with toy airship	60	75
812/15	*Set of 4*	1·40	1·60
MS816	108 × 109 mm. 5 r. Boy with toy train	1·25	2·00

See also Nos. 838/**MS**847.

(Des M. Shamir)

1979 (25 June). *25th Death Anniv of Henri Matisse (artist).* T **150** *and similar horiz designs. Multicoloured.* P 14.

817	20 l. Type **150**	15	15
818	25 l. "Joy of Life"	15	15
819	30 l. "Eggplants"	15	15
820	1 r. 50, "Harmony in Red"	45	60
821	5 r. "Still-life"	70	2·25
817/21	*Set of 5*	1·40	3·00
MS822	135 × 95 mm. 4 r. "Water Pitcher"	3·25	4·00

---

151 Sari with Overdress

152 *Gloriosa superba*

(Des M. Shamir. Litho Questa)

1979 (22 Aug). *National Costumes.* T **151** *and similar vert designs. Multicoloured.* P 14.

823	50 l. Type **151**	15	15
824	75 l. Sashed apron dress	20	20
825	90 l. Serape	25	25
826	95 l. Ankle-length printed dress	30	30
823/6	*Set of 4*	80	80

(Des M. Shamir. Litho Questa)

1979 (29 Oct). *Flowers.* T **152** *and similar vert designs. Multicoloured.* P 14.

827	1 l. Type **152**	10	10
828	3 l. Hibiscus tiliaceus	10	10
829	50 l. Barringtonia asiatica	20	15
830	1 r. Abutilon indicum	40	25
831	5 r. Guettarda speciosa	1·00	2·00
827/31	*Set of 5*	1·50	2·25
MS832	94 × 85 mm. 4 r. Pandanus odoratissimus	1·75	2·75

153 Weaving

(Litho Questa)

1979 (11 Nov). *Handicraft Exhibition.* T **153** *and similar horiz designs. Multicoloured.* P 14.

833	5 l. Type **153**	10	10
834	10 l. Lacquerwork	10	10
835	1 r. 30, Tortoiseshell jewellery	35	45
836	2 r. Carved woodwork	50	80
833/6	*Set of 4*	75	1·10
MS837	125 × 85 mm. 5 r. Gold and silver jewellery	1·25	2·25

154 Mickey Mouse attacked by Bird

(Des Walt Disney Productions)

1979 (10 Dec). *International Year of the Child (2nd issue).* T **154** *and similar multicoloured designs.* P 11.

838	1 l. Goofy delivering parcel on motor-scooter (*vert*)	10	10
839	2 l. Type **154**	10	10
840	3 l. Goofy half-covered with letters	10	10
841	4 l. Pluto licking Minnie Mouse's envelopes	10	10
842	5 l. Mickey Mouse delivering letters on roller-skates (*vert*)	10	10
843	10 l. Donald Duck placing letter in mail-box	10	10
844	15 l. Chip and Dale carrying letter	10	10
845	1 r. 50, Donald Duck on monocycle (*vert*)	75	95
846	5 r. Donald Duck with ostrich in crate (*vert*)	2·25	3·25
838/46	*Set of 9*	3·00	4·00
MS847	127 × 102 mm. 4 r. Pluto putting parcel in mail-box. P 13½	5·50	7·00

155 Post-Ramadan Dancing

(Litho Questa)

1980 (19 Jan). *National Day.* T **155** *and similar horiz designs. Multicoloured.* P 14.

848	5 l. Type **155**	10	10
849	15 l. Musicians and dancer, Eeduu Festival	10	10
850	95 l. Sultan's ceremonial band	30	30
851	2 r. Dancer and drummers, Circumcision Festival	55	85
848/51	*Set of 4*	90	1·25
MS852	131 × 99 mm. 5 r. Swordsmen	1·40	2·50

---

156 Leatherback Turtle (*Dermochelys coriacea*)

157 Paul Harris (founder)

(Des M. Shamir. Litho Questa)

1980 (17 Feb). *Turtle Conservation Campaign.* T **156** *and similar horiz designs. Multicoloured.* P 14.

853	1 l. Type **156**	10	20
854	2 l. Flatback turtle (*Chelonia depressa*)	10	20
855	5 l. Hawksbill turtle (*Eretmochelys imbricata*)	15	20
856	10 l. Loggerhead turtle (*Caretta caretta*)	20	20
857	75 l. Olive Ridley turtle (*Lepidochelys olivacea*)	80	45
858	10 r. Atlantic Ridley turtle (*Lepidochelys kempii*)	3·00	4·25
853/8	*Set of 6*	3·75	5·00
MS859	85 × 107 mm. 4 r. Green turtle (*Chelonia mydas*)	1·75	2·50

(Des J.W. Litho Questa)

1980 (7 Apr). *75th Anniv of Rotary International.* T **157** *and similar vert designs. Multicoloured.* P 14.

860	75 l. Type **157**	35	15
861	90 l. Family (Humanity)	40	20
862	1 r. Wheat (Hunger)	40	25
863	10 r. Caduceus of Hermes (Health)	2·50	4·50
860/3	*Set of 4*	3·25	4·50
MS864	109 × 85 mm. 5 r. Globe	1·50	2·50

(158)

159 Swimming

1980 (6 May). *"London 1980" International Stamp Exhibition.* Nos. 809/**MS**811 optd with T **158**.

865	1 r. 55, multicoloured	1·75	1·00
866	5 r. multicoloured	3·25	2·75
MS867	132 × 107 mm. 10 r. multicoloured	7·00	8·00

On No. **MS**867 the overprint is horizontal.

(Des J.W. Litho Questa)

1980 (4 June). *Olympic Games, Moscow.* T **159** *and similar horiz designs. Multicoloured.* P 14.

868	10 l. Type **159**	10	10
869	50 l. Running	20	20
870	3 r. Putting the shot	70	1·10
871	4 r. High jump	80	1·40
868/71	*Set of 4*	1·60	2·50
MS872	105 × 85 mm. 5 r. Weightlifting	1·25	2·25

160 White-tailed Tropic Bird

(Des A. Abbas. Litho Questa)

1980 (10 July). *Birds.* T **160** *and similar horiz designs. Multicoloured.* P 14.

873	75 l. Type **160**	25	15
874	95 l. Sooty Tern	35	30
875	1 r. Common Noddy	35	30
876	1 r. 55, Curlew	50	70
877	2 r. Wilson's Petrel	60	85
878	4 r. Caspian Tern	1·10	1·60
873/8	*Set of 6*	2·75	3·50
MS879	124 × 85 mm. 5 r. Red-footed Booby and Brown Booby	6·50	8·00

STANLEY GIBBONS STAMP COLLECTING SERIES

Introductory booklets on *How to Start, How to Identify Stamps* and *Collecting by Theme.* A series of well illustrated guides at a low price. Write for details.

161 Seal of Ibrahim II

(Litho Questa)

1980 (26 July). *Seals of the Sultans.* T **161** *and similar horiz designs. Each purple-brown and black.* P 14.
880	1 l. Type **161**		10	10
881	2 l. Mohammed Imadudeen II		10	10
882	5 l. Bin Haji Ali		10	10
883	1 r. Kuda Mohammed Rasgefaanu		30	30
884	2 r. Ibrahim Iskander I		50	70
880/4		*Set of 5*	80	1·00
MS885	131 × 95 mm. 3 r. Ibrahim Iskander I *(different)*		85	1·60

162 Queen Elizabeth the Queen Mother

(Des and litho Questa)

1980 (29 Sept). *Queen Mother's 80th Birthday.* P 14.
886	**162** 4 r. multicoloured		1·00	1·25
MS887	85 × 110 mm. **162** 5 r. multicoloured		1·60	2·25

163 Munnaru

(Des A. Abbas and M. Hassan)

1980 (9 Nov). *1400th Anniv of Hegira.* T **163** *and similar horiz designs. Multicoloured.* P 15.
888	5 l. Type **163**		15	10
889	10 l. Hukuru Miskiiy mosque		15	10
890	30 l. Medhuziyaaraiy (shrine of saint)		20	30
891	55 l. Writing tablets with verses of Koran		25	35
892	90 l. Mother teaching child Koran		45	70
888/92		*Set of 5*	1·10	1·40
MS893	124 × 101 mm. 2 r. Map of Maldives and coat of arms		80	1·60

164 Malaria Eradication

(Des J.W. Litho Questa)

1980 (30 Nov). *World Health Day.* T **164** *and similar horiz designs.* P 14.
894	15 l. black, yellow and vermilion		10	10
895	25 l. multicoloured		10	10
896	1 r. 50, orange-brown, yellow-ochre & black		1·25	1·00
897	5 r. multicoloured		2·50	2·75
894/7		*Set of 4*	3·50	3·50
MS898	68 × 85 mm. 4 r. black, greenish blue and azure		1·25	2·50

Designs:—25 l. Food (Nutrition); 1 r. 50, Molar and toothbrush (Dental health); 4, 5 r. People and medical equipment (Clinics).

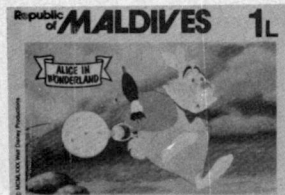

165 White Rabbit

(Des Walt Disney Productions)

1980 (22 Dec). *Scenes from Film "Alice in Wonderland".* T **165** *and similar horiz designs. Multicoloured.* P 11.
899	1 l. Type **165**		10	10
900	2 l. Alice falling into Wonderland		10	10
901	3 l. Alice too big to go through door		10	10
902	4 l. Alice and Tweedledum and Tweedledee		10	10
903	5 l. Alice and the caterpillar		10	10
904	10 l. Cheshire cat		10	10
905	15 l. Alice painting the roses		10	10
906	2 r. 50, Alice and the Queen of Hearts		2·50	2·25
907	4 r. Alice on trial		2·75	2·50
899/907		*Set of 9*	5·25	4·75
MS908	126 × 101 mm. 5 r. Alice at the Mad Hatter's tea-party. P 13½		6·00	6·50

166 Indian Ocean Ridley Turtle   **167** Pendant Lamp

(Des A. Abbas and Maniku. Litho Questa)

1980 (29 Dec). *Marine Life.* T **166** *and similar horiz designs. Multicoloured.* P 14.
909	90 l. Type **166**		2·00	60
910	1 r. 25, Pennant Coralfish		2·50	1·25
911	2 r. Spiny Lobster		3·25	1·75
909/11		*Set of 3*	7·00	3·25
MS912	140 × 94 mm. 4 r. Oriental Sweetlips and Scarlet-finned Squirrelfish		2·75	3·25

1981 (7 Jan). *National Day.* T **167** *and similar multicoloured designs.* P 14½.
913	10 l. Tomb of Ghaazee Muhammad Thakurufaan (*horiz*)		10	10
914	20 l. Type **167**		15	10
915	30 l. Chair used by Muhammad Thakurufaan		20	10
916	95 l. Muhammad Thakurufaan's palace (*horiz*)		45	30
917	10 r. Cushioned divan		2·25	4·00
913/17		*Set of 5*	2·75	4·00

168 Prince Charles and   **169** First Majlis Chamber
Lady Diana Spencer

(Des and litho J.W.)

1981 (22 June). *Royal Wedding.* T **168** *and similar vert designs. Multicoloured.* P 14.
918	1 r. Type **168**		15	15
919	2 r. Buckingham Palace		25	25
920	5 r. Prince Charles, polo player		40	50
918/20		*Set of 3*	70	80
MS921	95 × 83 mm. 10 r. State coach		75	1·10

Nos. 918/20 also exist perforated 12 (*Price for set of 3 £1 mint or used*) from additional sheets of five stamps and one label. These stamps have changed background colours.
Nos. 918/21 also exist imperforate from a restricted printing.

1981 (27 June). *50th Anniv of Citizens' Majlis (grievance rights).* T **169** *and similar multicoloured designs.* P 14½.
922	95 l. Type **169**		30	30
923	1 r. Sultan Muhammed Shamsuddin III		35	35
MS924	137 × 94 mm. 4 r. First written constitution (*horiz*)		2·00	3·75

170 "Self-portrait with   **171** Airmail Envelope
a Palette"

(Des J.W. Litho Questa)

1981 (July). *Birth Centenary of Pablo Picasso.* T **170** *and similar vert designs. Multicoloured.* P 13½ × 14.
925	5 l. Type **170**		15	10
926	10 l. "Woman in Blue"		20	10
927	25 l. "Boy with Pipe"		35	10
928	30 l. "Card Player"		35	10
929	90 l. "Sailor"		65	40
930	3 r. "Self-portrait"		1·25	1·00
931	5 r. "Harlequin"		1·75	1·75
925/31		*Set of 7*	4·25	3·25
MS932	106 × 130 mm. 10 r. "Child holding a Dove". Imperf		2·75	3·50

(Des and litho Questa)

1981 (9 Sept). *75th Anniv of Postal Service.* P 14.
933	**171** 25 l. multicoloured		10	10
934	75 l. multicoloured		20	25
935	5 r. multicoloured		70	1·25
933/5		*Set of 3*	90	1·40

172 Boeing 737 taking off   **173** Homer

(Des A. Abbas. Litho Questa)

1981 (11 Nov). *Male International Airport.* T **172** *and similar horiz designs. Multicoloured.* P 14.
936	5 l. Type **172**		20	20
937	20 l. Passengers leaving Boeing 737		40	20
938	1 r. 80, Refuelling		75	1·00
939	4 r. Plan of airport		1·00	2·00
936/9		*Set of 4*	2·10	3·00
MS940	106 × 79 mm. 5 r. Aerial view of airport		1·75	2·50

(Des J.W.)

1981 (18 Nov). *International Year of Disabled People.* T **173** *and similar vert designs. Multicoloured.* P 14½.
941	2 l. Type **173**		10	10
942	5 l. Miguel Cervantes		10	10
943	1 r. Beethoven		2·00	85
944	5 r. Van Gogh		3·00	5·00
941/4		*Set of 4*	4·50	5·50
MS945	116 × 91 mm. 4 r. Helen Keller and Anne Sullivan		3·25	5·50

174 Preparation of   **175** Collecting Bait
Maldive Fish

(Des Central Art Palace. Litho Questa)

1981 (25 Nov). *Decade for Women.* T **174** *and similar vert designs. Multicoloured.* P 14.
946	20 l. Type **174**		10	10
947	90 l. 16th century Maldive women		25	25
948	1 r. Farming		30	30
949	2 r. Coir rope making		55	1·10
946/9		*Set of 4*	1·10	1·60

(Des I. Azeez. Litho Questa)

1981 (10 Dec). *Fishermen's Day.* T **175** *and similar horiz designs. Multicoloured.* P 14.
950	5 l. Type **175**		35	15
951	15 l. Fishing boats		65	25
952	90 l. Fisherman with catch		1·25	60
953	1 r. 30, Sorting fish		1·75	1·10
950/3		*Set of 4*	3·50	1·90
MS954	147 × 101 mm. 3 r. Loading fish for export		1·50	2·50

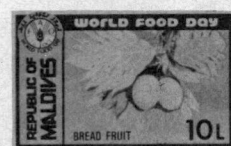

176 Bread Fruit

(Des Design Images. Litho Questa)

1981 (30 Dec). *World Food Day.* T **176** *and similar horiz designs. Multicoloured.* P 14.
955	10 l. Type **176**		25	10
956	25 l. Hen with chicks		60	15
957	30 l. Maize		60	20
958	75 l. Skipjack Tuna		1·75	65
959	1 r. Pumpkin		2·00	70
960	2 r. Coconuts		2·25	2·75
955/60		*Set of 6*	6·75	4·00
MS961	110 × 85 mm. 5 r. Eggplant		2·50	3·50

177 Pluto and Cat   **178** Balmoral

(Des Walt Disney Productions)

1982 (29 Mar). *50th Anniv of Pluto (Walt Disney cartoon character). T 177 and similar multicoloured design. P 13½.*
962	4 r. Type 177	..	3·00	2·75
MS963	127 × 101 mm. 6 r. Pluto (scene from *The Pointer*)		3·75	4·00

(Des PAD Studio. Litho Questa)

1982 (1 July). *21st Birthday of Princess of Wales. T 178 and similar vert designs. Multicoloured. P 14½ × 14.*
964	95 l. Type 178	..	20	20
965	3 r. Prince and Princess of Wales	..	60	65
966	5 r. Princess on aircraft steps	..	1·00	95
964/6		*Set of 3*	1·60	1·60
MS967	103 × 75 mm. 8 r. Princess of Wales		1·50	1·75

Nos. 964/6 also exist in sheetlets of 5 stamps and 1 label.
Nos. 964/7 and the sheetlets exist imperforate from a restricted printing.

COMMONWEALTH MEMBER
9 July 1982

179 Scout saluting and Camp-site

180 Footballer

(Des D. Miller. Litho Questa)

1982 (9 Aug). *75th Anniv of Boy Scout Movement. T 179 and similar horiz designs. Multicoloured. P 14.*
968	1 r. 30, Type 179	..	40	45
969	1 r. 80, Lighting a fire	..	50	60
970	4 r. Life-saving	..	1·10	1·40
971	5 r. Map-reading	..	1·40	1·75
968/71		*Set of 4*	3·00	3·75
MS972	128 × 66 mm. 10 r. Scout emblem and flag of the Maldives		2·00	3·00

(Des M. and S. Gerber Studio. Litho Questa)

1982 (4 Oct). *World Cup Football Championship, Spain. T 180 and similar square designs. P 13½.*
973	90 l. multicoloured	..	1·25	60
974	1 r. 50, multicoloured	..	1·75	1·10
975	3 r. multicoloured	..	2·50	1·75
976	5 r. multicoloured	..	3·25	2·50
973/6		*Set of 4*	8·00	5·50
MS977	94 × 63 mm. 10 r. multicoloured		4·50	6·00

1982 (18 Oct). *Birth of Prince William of Wales. Nos. 964/7 optd with T 212a of Jamaica.*
978	95 l. Type 178	..	15	20
979	3 r. Prince and Princess of Wales	..	45	65
980	5 r. Princess on aircraft steps	..	70	95
978/80		*Set of 3*	1·10	1·60
MS981	103 × 75 mm. 8 r. Princess of Wales		3·00	2·50

Nos. 978/80 also exist in sheetlets of 5 stamps and 1 label.
Nos. 978/81 and the sheetlets exist imperforate from a restricted printing.

181 Basic Education Scheme

182 Koch isolates the Bacillus

(Des and litho Harrison)

1982 (15 Nov). *National Education. T 181 and similar horiz designs. Multicoloured. P 14.*
982	90 l. Type 181	..	15	25
983	95 l. Primary education	..	15	25
984	1 r. 30, Teacher training	..	20	30
985	2 r. 50, Printing educational material	..	40	60
982/5		*Set of 4*	80	1·25
MS986	100 × 70 mm. 6 r. Thaana typewriter keyboard		1·00	2·00

(Des Artists International)

1982 (22 Nov). *Centenary of Robert Koch's Discovery of Tubercle Bacillus. T 182 and similar multicoloured designs. P 14.*
987	5 l. Type 182	..	10	15
988	15 l. Micro-organism and microscope	..	15	15
989	95 l. Dr. Robert Koch in 1905	..	35	45
990	3 r. Dr. Koch and plates from publication	..	85	1·50
987/90		*Set of 4*	1·25	2·00
MS991	77 × 61 mm. 5 r. Koch in his laboratory (*horiz*)		80	1·75

No. **MS**991 exists imperforate from stock dispersed by the liquidator of Format International Security Printers Ltd.

183 Blohm and Voss HA 139A Seaplane *Nordsee*

(Des W. Wright. Litho Questa)

1983 (28 July). *Bicentenary of Manned Flight. T 183 and similar horiz designs. Multicoloured. P 14.*
992	90 l. Type 183	..	2·25	70
993	1 r. 45, Macchi Castoldi MC-72 seaplane	..	2·75	1·75
994	4 r. Boeing F4B-3 biplane fighter	..	4·50	3·25
995	5 r. Renard and Kreb's airship *La France*	..	4·50	3·50
992/5		*Set of 4*	12·50	8·25
MS996	110×85 mm. 10 r. Nadar's balloon *Le Geant*		3·00	4·00

184 "Curved Dash" Oldsmobile, 1902

(Des Publishers Graphics Inc)

1983 (Aug). *Classic Motor Cars. T 184 and similar horiz designs. Multicoloured. P 14½.*
997	5 l. Type 184	..	20	40
998	30 l. Aston Martin "Tourer", 1932	..	60	40
999	40 l. Lamborghini "Muira", 1966	..	60	45
1000	1 r. Mercedes-Benz "300SL", 1945	..	1·00	70
1001	1 r. 45, Stutz "Bearcat", 1913	..	1·25	2·00
1002	5 r. Lotus "Elite", 1958	..	2·00	4·25
997/1002		*Set of 6*	5·00	7·50
MS1003	132 × 103 mm. 10 r. Grand Prix "Sunbeam", 1924. P 14½		6·00	10·00

Nos. 997/1002 were each issued in sheets of 9, including one *se-tenant* label.

185 Rough-toothed Dolphin

(Des D. Miller. Litho Questa)

1983 (6 Sept). *Marine Mammals. T 185 and similar horiz designs. Multicoloured. P 14.*
1004	30 l. Type 185	..	1·60	60
1005	40 l. Indo-Pacific Hump-backed Dolphin	..	1·60	65
1006	4 r. Finless Porpoise	..	5·00	4·00
1007	6 r. Pygmy Sperm Whale	..	10·00	7·00
1004/7		*Set of 4*	16·00	11·00
MS1008	82 × 90 mm. 5 r. Striped Dolphin		5·50	5·50

186 Dish Aerial

(Des PAD Studio. Litho Questa)

1983 (9 Oct). *World Communications Year. T 186 and similar horiz designs. Multicoloured. P 14.*
1009	50 l. Type 186	..	40	20
1010	1 r. Land, sea and air communications	..	1·00	60
1011	2 r. Ship-to-shore communication	..	1·40	1·50
1012	10 r. Air traffic controller	..	3·75	6·50
1009/12		*Set of 4*	6·00	8·00
MS1013	91 × 76 mm. 20 r. Telecommunications		3·75	4·75

187 "La Donna Gravida"

(Des M. Diamond)

1983 (25 Oct). *500th Birth Anniv of Raphael. T 187 and similar vert designs showing paintings. Multicoloured. P 13½.*
1014	90 l. Type 187	..	25	25
1015	3 r. "Giovanna d'Aragona" (detail)	..	75	1·25
1016	4 r. "Woman with Unicorn"	..	75	1·75
1017	6 r. "La Muta"	..	1·00	2·25
1014/17		*Set of 4*	2·50	5·00
MS1018	121 × 97 mm. 10 r. "The Knight's Dream" (detail)		3·00	5·00

Nos. 1014/18 exist imperforate from stock dispersed by the liquidator of Format International Security Printers Ltd.

188 Refugee Camp

(Litho Questa)

1983 (29 Nov). *Solidarity with the Palestinians. T 188 and similar horiz designs each showing the Dome of the Rock, Jerusalem. Multicoloured. P 13½ × 14.*
1019	4 r. Type 188	..	1·50	2·00
1020	5 r. Refugee holding dead child	..	1·60	2·00
1021	6 r. Child carrying food	..	1·90	2·50
1019/21		*Set of 3*	4·50	6·00

189 Education Facilities

190 Baseball

(Des I. Azeez. Litho Questa)

1983 (10 Dec). *National Development Programme. T 189 and similar horiz designs. Multicoloured. P 13½.*
1022	7 l. Type 189	..	20	10
1023	10 l. Health service and education	..	30	10
1024	5 r. Growing more food	..	1·50	1·25
1025	6 r. Fisheries development	..	2·00	1·50
1022/5		*Set of 4*	3·50	2·50
MS1026	134 × 93 mm. 10 r. Air transport		2·25	2·75

(Des PAD Studio. Litho Questa)

1984 (10 Mar). *Olympic Games, Los Angeles. T 190 and similar vert designs. Multicoloured. P 14.*
1027	50 l. Type 190	..	25	15
1028	1 r. 55, Backstroke swimming	..	55	40
1029	3 r. Judo	..	1·25	90
1030	4 r. Shot-putting	..	1·40	1·40
1027/30		*Set of 4*	3·00	2·50
MS1031	85 × 105 mm. 10 r. Team Handball		2·40	2·75

Rf **1.45**

19th UPU
CONGRESS HAMBURG
(191)   (192)

1984 (19 June). *Universal Postal Union Congress, Hamburg. Nos. 994/6 optd as T 191.*
1032	4 r. Boeing "F4B-3"	..	1·40	1·40
1033	5 r. *La France* airship	..	1·60	1·60
MS1034	110 × 85 mm. 10 r. Nadar's *Le Geant*		2·75	4·50

1984 (20 Aug). *Surch as T 192 in black or gold (same prices either colour).*

(a) On Nos. 964/7
1035	1 r. 45 on 95 l. Type 178	..	2·00	1·50
1036	1 r. 45 on 3 r. Prince and Princess of Wales	..	2·00	1·50
1037	1 r. 45 on 5 r. Princess on aircraft steps	..	2·00	1·50
1035/7		*Set of 3*	5·50	4·00
MS1038	103×75 mm. 1 r. 45 on 8 r. Princess of Wales		2·00	3·75

(b) On Nos. 978/81
1039	1 r. 45 on 95 l. Type 178	..	2·00	1·50
1040	1 r. 45 on 3 r. Prince and Princess of Wales	..	2·00	1·50
1041	1 r. 45 on 5 r. Princess on aircraft steps	..	2·00	1·50
1039/41		*Set of 3*	5·50	4·00
MS1042	103×75 mm. 1 r. 45 on 8 r. Princess of Wales		2·00	3·75

Nos. 1039/42 exist imperforate from a restricted printing.
Stamps from the sheetlets of five plus one label were also surcharged, either in black or gold using a slightly different type.

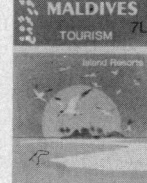

193 Hands breaking Manacles

194 Island Resort and Common Terns

198 Daisy Duck

GOLD MEDALIST THERESA ANDREWS USA

(203)

204 Queen Elizabeth the Queen Mother, 1981

1984 (26 Aug). *Namibia Day. T* **193** *and similar horiz designs. Multicoloured. P* 15.
1043	6 r. Type **193**	..	1·10	1·25
1044	8 r. Namibia family	..	1·40	1·75
MS1045	129 × 104 mm. 10 r. Map of Namibia		1·75	2·50

(Litho Questa)

1984 (12 Sept). *Tourism. T* **194** *and similar vert designs. Multicoloured. P* 14.
1046	7 l. Type **194**	..	30	10
1047	15 l. Dhow	..	30	10
1048	20 l. Snorkelling	..	30	10
1049	2 r. Wind-surfing	..	75	40
1050	4 r. Aqualung diving	..	1·25	75
1051	6 r. Night fishing	..	2·00	1·25
1052	8 r. Game fishing	..	2·25	1·50
1053	10 r. Turtle on beach	..	2·50	1·75
1046/53		Set of 8	8·75	5·25

195 Frangipani

1984 (21 Sept). *"Ausipex" International Stamp Exhibition, Melbourne. T* **195** *and similar horiz designs showing flowers. Multicoloured. P* 15.
1054	5 r. Type **195**	..	2·25	1·75
1055	10 r. Cooktown Orchid	..	4·75	3·75
MS1056	105 × 77 mm. 15 r. Sun Orchid	..	9·50	5·50

Nos. 1054/5 exist imperforate from stock dispersed by the liquidator of Format International Security Printers Ltd.

196 Facade of the Malé Mosque

1984 (11 Nov). *Opening of Islamic Centre. T* **196** *and similar multicoloured design. P* 15.
1057	2 r. Type **196**	..	45	50
1058	5 r. Malé Mosque and minaret (vert)	..	1·10	1·25

197 Air Maldives Boeing 737

(Des G. Drummond. Litho Questa)

1984 (19 Nov). *40th Anniv of International Civil Aviation Authority. T* **197** *and similar horiz designs. Multicoloured. P* 14.
1059	7 l. Type **197**	..	40	15
1060	4 r. Air Lanka Lockheed L-1011 TriStar		2·25	1·25
1061	6 r. Alitalia Douglas DC-10-30	..	2·75	1·60
1062	8 r. L.T.U. Lockheed L-1011 TriStar		3·00	2·25
1059/62		Set of 4	7·50	4·75
MS1063	110 × 92 mm. 15 r. Air Maldives Short S.7 Skyvan		3·75	4·00

(Litho Questa)

1984 (26 Nov–1 Dec). *50th Anniv of Donald Duck (Walt Disney cartoon character). T* **198** *and similar horiz designs. Multicoloured. P* 12 (5 r.) *or* 14 × 13½ (*others*).
1064	3 l. Type **198**	..	10	10
1065	4 l. Huey, Dewey and Louie	..	10	10
1066	5 l. Ludwig von Drake	..	10	10
1067	10 l. Gyro Gearloose	..	10	10
1068	15 l. Uncle Scrooge painting self portrait	..	15	10
1069	25 l. Donald Duck with camera	..	15	10
1070	5 r. Donald Duck and Gus Goose (1.12)	..	2·25	1·25
1071	8 r. Gladstone Gander	..	2·50	2·00
1072	10 r. Grandma Duck	..	3·00	2·50
1064/72		Set of 9	7·50	5·50
MS1073	102 × 126 mm. 15 r. Uncle Scrooge and Donald Duck in front of camera	..	4·75	5·00
MS1074	126 × 102 mm. 15 r. Uncle Scrooge (1.12)		4·75	5·00

No. 1070 was printed in sheetlets of 8 stamps.

199 "The Day" (detail)

200 "Edmond Iduranty" (Degas)

(Litho Questa)

1984 (10 Dec). *450th Death Anniv of Correggio (artist). T* **199** *and similar vert designs. Multicoloured. P* 14.
1075	5 r. Type **199**	..	1·00	1·50
1076	10 r. "The Night" (detail)	..	1·50	1·75
MS1077	60 × 80 mm. 15 r. "Portrait of a Man"		3·25	3·25

(Litho Questa)

1984 (15 Dec). *150th Birth Anniv of Edgar Degas (artist). T* **200** *and similar vert designs. P* 14.
1078	75 l. Type **200**	..	20	20
1079	2 r. "James Tissot"	..	50	50
1080	5 r. "Achille de Gas in Uniform"	..	1·00	1·00
1081	10 r. "Lady with Chrysanthemums"	..	1·75	2·00
1078/81		Set of 4	3·00	3·25
MS1082	100 × 70 mm. 15 r. "Self-portrait"		3·25	3·75

201 Pale-footed Shearwater

202 Squad Drilling

(Des I. MacLaury. Litho Questa)

1985 (9 Mar). *Birth Bicentenary of John J. Audubon (ornithologist) (1st issue). T* **201** *and similar multicoloured designs showing original paintings. P* 14.
1083	3 r. Type **201**	..	1·75	80
1084	3 r. 50, Little Grebe (horiz)	..	2·00	90
1085	4 r. Common Cormorant	..	2·00	1·00
1086	4 r. 50, White-faced Storm Petrel (horiz)		2·00	1·10
1083/6		Set of 4	7·00	3·50
MS1087	108 × 80 mm. 15 r. Red-necked Phalarope (horiz)		3·00	3·25

See also Nos. 1192/200.

(Des and litho Questa)

1985 (6 June). *National Security Service. T* **202** *and similar multicoloured designs. P* 13½ × 14 (*No.* 1092) *or* 14 × 13½ (*others*).
1088	15 l. Type **202**	..	40	10
1089	20 l. Combat patrol	..	40	10
1090	1 r. Fire fighting	..	1·75	40
1091	2 r. Coastguard cutter	..	2·25	1·00
1092	10 r. Independence Day Parade (vert)		3·00	3·50
1088/92		Set of 5	7·00	4·50
MS1093	128 × 85 mm. 10 r. Cannon on saluting base and National Security Service badge	..	2·25	2·25

1985 (17 July). *Olympic Games Gold Medal Winners, Los Angeles. Nos.* 1027/31 *optd as T* **203** *or in larger capitals* (50 *l.,* 10 *r.*).
1094	50 l. Type **190** (optd "JAPAN")	..	20	10
1095	1 r. 55, Backstroke swimming (opt T **203**)		40	40
1096	3 r. Judo (Optd "GOLD MEDALIST FRANK WIENEKE USA")	..	85	75
1097	4 r. Shot-putting (optd "GOLD MEDALIST CLAUDIA LOCH WEST GERMANY")	..	1·00	95
1094/7		Set of 4	2·25	2·00
MS1098	85 × 105 mm. 10 r. Team Handball (opt "U.S.A.")		1·90	2·00

(Des J.W. Litho Questa)

1985 (20 Aug). *Life and Times of Queen Elizabeth the Queen Mother. T* **204** *and similar multicoloured designs. P* 14.
1099	3 r. Type **204**	..	45	60
1100	5 r. Visiting the Middlesex Hospital (horiz)	..	65	1·00
1101	7 r. The Queen Mother	..	85	1·25
1099/101		Set of 3	1·75	2·50
MS1102	56 × 85 mm. 15 r. With Prince Charles at Garter Ceremony	..	3·50	3·25

Stamps as Nos. 1099/101, but with face values of 1 r., 4 r. and 10 r., exist from additional sheetlets of 5 plus a label issued 4 January 1986. These also have changed background colours and are perforated 12½ × 12 (4 r.) or 12 × 12½ (*others*) (*Price for set of 3 stamps £2.50 mint*).

204a Liro da Braccio

205 Mas Odi (fishing boat)

(Des Susan David. Litho Questa)

1985 (3 Sept). *300th Birth Anniv of Johann Sebastian Bach (composer). T* **204a** *and similar vert designs. P* 14.
1103	15 l. multicoloured	..	10	10
1104	2 r. multicoloured	..	50	45
1105	4 r. multicoloured	..	90	85
1106	10 r. multicoloured	..	1·90	2·25
1103/6		Set of 4	3·00	3·25
MS1107	104 × 75 mm. 15 r. black and reddish orange	..	3·00	3·50

Designs:—2 r. Tenor oboe; 4 r. Serpent; 10 r. Table organ; 15 r. Johann Sebastian Bach.

(Des H. Afeef. Litho Questa)

1985 (23 Sept). *Maldives Ships and Boats. T* **205** *and similar horiz designs. Multicoloured. P* 14.
1108	3 l. Type **205**	..	10	10
1109	5 l. Battela (dhow)	..	10	10
1110	10 l. Addu odi (dhow)	..	10	10
1111	2 r. 60, Modern dhoni (fishing boat)		1·25	1·50
1112	2 r. 70, Mas dhoni (fishing boat)	..	1·25	1·50
1113	3 r. Baththeli dhoni	..	1·40	1·60
1114	5 r. Inter 1 (inter-island vessel)	..	2·25	2·75
1115	10 r. Dhoni-style yacht	..	4·00	6·00
1108/15		Set of 8	9·25	12·00

206 Windsurfing

207 United Nations Building, New York

(Des H. Afeef. Litho Questa)

1985 (2 Oct). *10th Anniv of World Tourism Organization. T* **206** *and similar horiz designs. Multicoloured. P* 14.
1116	6 r. Type **206**	..	1·75	1·75
1117	8 r. Scuba diving	..	2·00	2·00
MS1118	171 × 114 mm. 15 r. Kuda Hithi Resort		2·75	3·00

(Litho Questa)

1985 (24 Oct). *40th Anniv of United Nations Organization and International Year of Peace. T 207 and similar multicoloured designs. P 14.*

1119	15 l. Type 207	10	10
1120	2 r. Hands releasing peace dove	40	45
1121	4 r. U.N. Security Council meeting (*horiz*)	70	85
1122	10 r. Lion and lamb	1·25	2·00
1119/22	*Set of 4*	2·25	3·00
MS1123	76×92 mm. 15 r. U.N. Building and peace dove	2·25	2·75

208 Maldivian Delegate voting in U.N. General Assembly

(Des BG Studio. Litho Questa)

1985 (24 Oct). *20th Anniv of United Nations Membership. T 208 and similar horiz design. Multicoloured. P 14.*

1124	20 l. Type 208	10	10
1125	15 r. U.N. and Maldivian flags, and U.N. Building, New York	2·00	3·00

209 Youths playing Drums

(Des BG Studio)

1985 (20 Nov). *International Youth Year. T 209 and similar multicoloured designs. P 15.*

1126	90 l. Type 209	15	20
1127	6 r. Tug-of-war	80	1·10
1128	10 r. Community service (*vert*)	1·25	2·00
1126/8	*Set of 3*	2·00	3·00
MS1129	85×84 mm. 15 r. Raising the flag at youth camp (*vert*)	2·25	3·00

210 Quotation and Flags of Member Nations

(Litho Questa)

1985 (8 Dec). *1st Summit Meeting of South Asian Association for Regional Co-operation, Dhaka, Bangladesh. P 14.*

1130	210 3 r. multicoloured	1·50	1·25

211 Frigate Mackerel   **212** Player running with Ball

(Litho Questa)

1985 (10 Dec). *Fishermen's Day. Species of Tuna. T 211 and similar horiz designs. Multicoloured. P 14.*

1131	25 l. Type 211	35	10
1132	75 l. Kakawaka ("Little Tuna")	65	15
1133	3 r. Dog-toothed Tuna	2·00	75
1134	5 r. Yellow-finned Tuna	2·50	1·25
1131/4	*Set of 4*	5·00	2·00
MS1135	130×90 mm. 15 r. Skipjack Tuna	3·50	3·50

(Des Walt Disney Productions. Litho Questa)

1985 (21 Dec). *150th Birth Anniv of Mark Twain. Vert designs as T 160a of Lesotho showing Walt Disney cartoon characters illustrating various Mark Twain quotations. Multicoloured. P 12 (4 r.) or 13½×14 (others).*

1136	2 l. Winnie the Pooh	10	10
1137	3 l. Gepetto and Figaro the cat	10	10
1138	4 l. Goofy and basket of broken eggs	10	10
1139	20 l. Goofy as doctor scolding Donald Duck	25	10
1140	4 r. Mowgli and King Louis	1·40	1·75
1141	15 r. The wicked Queen and mirror	5·00	7·00
1136/41	*Set of 6*	6·00	8·00
MS1142	126×101 mm. 15 r. Mickey Mouse as Tom Sawyer on comet's tail	6·50	7·00

No. 1140 was issued in sheetlets of 8 stamps.

(Des Walt Disney Productions. Litho Questa)

1985 (21 Dec). *Birth Bicentenaries of Grimm Brothers (folklorists). Multicoloured designs as T 160b of Lesotho, but horiz, showing Walt Disney cartoon characters in scenes from "Dr. Knowall". P 12 (3 r.) or 14×13½ (others).*

1143	1 l. Donald Duck as Crabb driving oxcart	10	10
1144	5 l. Donald Duck as Dr. Knowall	10	10
1145	10 l. Dr. Knowall in surgery	10	10
1146	15 l. Dr. Knowall with Uncle Scrooge as a lord	10	10
1147	3 r. Dr. and Mrs. Knowall in pony trap	1·10	1·50
1148	14 r. Dr. Knowall and thief	5·50	7·00
1143/8	*Set of 6*	6·00	8·00
MS1149	126×101 mm. 15 r. Donald and Daisy Duck as Dr. and Mrs. Knowall	6·50	7·00

No. 1147 was printed in sheetlets of 8 stamps.

(Des W. Hanson. Litho Questa)

1986 (29 Apr). *Appearance of Halley's Comet (1st issue). Horiz designs as T 162a of Lesotho. Multicoloured. P 14.*

1150	20 l. N.A.S.A. space telescope and Comet	50	25
1151	1 r. 50, E.S.A. *Giotto* spacecraft and Comet	1·25	1·50
1152	2 r. Japanese *Planet A* spacecraft and Comet	1·50	1·75
1153	4 r. Edmond Halley and Stonehenge	2·25	2·75
1154	5 r. Russian *Vega* spacecraft and Comet	2·25	2·75
1150/4	*Set of 5*	7·00	8·00
MS1155	101×70 mm. 15 r. Halley's Comet	7·50	9·00

See also Nos. 1206/11.

(Des J. Iskowitz. Litho Questa)

1986 (5 May). *Centenary of Statue of Liberty. Multicoloured designs as T 163b of Lesotho showing the Statue of Liberty and immigrants to the U.S.A. P 14.*

1156	50 l. Walter Gropius (architect)	40	30
1157	70 l. John Lennon (musician)	1·50	1·00
1158	1 r. George Balanchine (choreographer)	1·50	1·00
1159	10 r. Franz Werfel (writer)	3·75	6·50
1156/9	*Set of 4*	6·50	8·00
MS1160	100×72 mm. 15 r. Statue of Liberty (*vert*)	5·50	6·50

(Des Walt Disney Productions)

1986 (22 May). *"Ameripex" International Stamp Exhibition, Chicago. Horiz designs as T 163c of Lesotho showing Walt Disney cartoon characters and U.S.A. stamps. Multicoloured. P 11.*

1161	3 l. Johnny Appleseed and 1966 Johnny Appleseed stamp	10	10
1162	4 l. Paul Bunyan and 1958 Forest Conservation stamp	10	10
1163	5 l. Casey and 1969 Professional Baseball Centenary stamp	10	10
1164	10 l. Ichabod Crane and 1974 "Legend of Sleepy Hollow" stamp	10	10
1165	15 l. John Henry and 1944 75th anniv of completion of First Transcontinental Railroad stamp	15	15
1166	20 l. Windwagon Smith and 1954 Kansas Territory Centenary stamp	15	15
1167	13 r. Mike Fink and 1970 Great Northwest stamp	6·50	6·50
1168	14 r. Casey Jones and 1950 Railroad Engineers stamp	7·50	7·50
1161/8	*Set of 8*	13·00	13·00
MS1169	Two sheets, each 127×101 mm. (a) 15 r. Davy Crockett and 1967 Davy Crockett stamp. (b) 15 r. Daisy Duck as Pocahontas saving Captain John Smith (Donald Duck). P 14×13½.		
	Set of 2 sheets	12·00	15·00

(Litho Questa)

1986 (29 May). *60th Birthday of Queen Elizabeth II. Vert designs as T 163a of Lesotho. P 14.*

1170	1 r. black and chrome-yellow	30	25
1171	2 r. multicoloured	40	55
1172	12 r. multicoloured	1·50	2·50
1170/2	*Set of 3*	2·00	3·00
MS1173	120×85 mm. 15 r. black and grey-brown	3·25	4·25

Designs:—1 r. Royal Family at Girl Guides Rally, 1938; 2 r. Queen in Canada; 12 r. At Sandringham, 1970; 15 r. Princesses Elizabeth and Margaret at Royal Lodge, Windsor, 1940.

Nos. 1170/2 were each issued in sheetlets of five stamps and one stamp-size label.

(Des BG Studio. Litho Questa)

1986 (8 June). *World Cup Football Championship, Mexico. T 212 and similar vert designs. Multicoloured. P 14.*

1174	15 l. Type 212	75	30
1175	2 r. Player gaining control of ball	2·50	1·75
1176	4 r. Two players competing for ball	4·00	3·50
1177	10 r. Player bouncing ball on knee	7·50	8·00
1174/7	*Set of 4*	13·00	12·00
MS1178	95×114 mm. 15 r. Player kicking ball	4·00	5·50

(Litho Questa)

1986 (1 July). *Royal Wedding. Vert designs as T 170a of Lesotho. Multicoloured. P 14.*

1179	10 l. Prince Andrew and Miss Sarah Ferguson	15	10
1180	2 r. Prince Andrew	75	70
1181	12 r. Prince Andrew in naval uniform	3·25	3·75
1179/81	*Set of 3*	3·75	4·00
MS1182	88×88 mm. 15 r. Prince Andrew and Miss Sarah Ferguson (*different*)	4·00	4·50

NEW INFORMATION

The editor is always interested to correspond with people who have new information that will improve or correct the Catalogue.

WINNERS
Argentina 3
W.Germany 2

213 Moorish Idol and Sea Fan   (213a)

(Des Mary Walters)

1986 (22 Sept). *Marine Wildlife. T 213 and similar horiz designs. Multicoloured. P 15.*

1183	50 l. Type 213	1·25	40
1184	90 l. Regal Angelfish	1·75	55
1185	1 r. Maldive Anemonefish	1·75	55
1186	2 r. Tiger Cowrie (*Cypraea tigris*) and Stinging Coral	2·25	1·60
1187	3 r. Emperor Angelfish and Staghorn Coral	2·50	2·00
1188	4 r. Black-naped Tern	2·50	2·75
1189	5 r. Fiddler Crab and Staghorn Coral	2·50	2·75
1190	10 r. Hawksbill Turtle	3·00	5·00
1183/90	*Set of 8*	16·00	14·00
MS1191	Two sheets, each 107×76 mm. (a) 15 r. Long-nosed Butterflyfish. (b) 15 r. Oriental Trumpetfish		
	Set of 2 sheets	11·00	15·00

Nos. 1183/91 exist imperforate from stock dispersed by the liquidator of Format International Security Printers Ltd.

(Litho Questa)

1986 (9 Oct). *Birth Bicentenary of John J. Audubon (ornithologist) (1985) (2nd issue). Multicoloured designs as T 201 showing original paintings. P 14.*

1192	3 l. Little Blue Heron (*horiz*)	30	40
1193	4 l. White-tailed Kite	30	40
1194	5 l. Greater Shearwater (*horiz*)	30	40
1195	10 l. Magnificent Frigate Bird	40	40
1196	15 l. Black-necked Grebe	70	40
1197	20 l. Goosander	75	40
1198	13 r. Peregrine Falcon (*horiz*)	5·50	6·50
1199	14 r. Prairie Chicken (*horiz*)	5·50	6·50
1192/9	*Set of 8*	12·00	14·00
MS1200	Two sheets, each 74×104 mm. (a) 15 r. Fulmar. (b) 15 r. White-fronted Goose (*horiz*)		
	Set of 2 sheets	21·00	21·00

Nos. 1192/9 were each issued in sheetlets of five stamps and one stamp-size label, which appears in the centre of the bottom row.

1986 (25 Oct). *World Cup Football Championship Winners, Mexico. Nos. 1174/8 optd with T 213a in gold.*

1201	15 l. Type 212	40	30
1202	2 r. Player gaining control of ball	1·25	1·10
1203	4 r. Two players competing for ball	2·00	2·00
1204	10 r. Player bouncing ball on knee	4·25	4·25
1201/4	*Set of 4*	6·25	7·00
MS1205	95×114 mm. 15 r. Player kicking ball	3·00	4·25

(213b)   **214** Servicing Aircraft

1986 (30 Oct). *Appearance of Halley's Comet (2nd issue). Nos. 1150/5 optd with T 213b in silver.*

1206	20 l. N.A.S.A. space telescope and Comet	65	40
1207	1 r. 50, E.S.A. *Giotto* spacecraft and Comet	1·25	1·00
1208	2 r. Japanese *Planet A* spacecraft and Comet	1·50	1·50
1209	4 r. Edmond Halley and Stonehenge	2·00	2·25
1210	5 r. Russian *Vega* spacecraft and Comet	2·00	2·25
1206/10	*Set of 5*	6·75	6·75
MS1211	101×70 mm. 15 r. Halley's Comet	3·50	5·00

(Des BG Studio)

1986 (4 Nov). *40th Anniv of U.N.E.S.C.O. T 214 and similar vert designs. Multicoloured. P 15.*

1212	1 r. Type 214	60	30
1213	2 r. Boat building	70	90
1214	3 r. Children in classroom	80	1·25
1215	5 r. Student in laboratory	90	2·00
1212/15	*Set of 4*	2·75	4·00
MS1216	77×100 mm. 15 r. Diving bell on sea bed	2·75	4·00

Nos. 1212/16 exist imperforate from stock dispersed by the liquidator of Format International Security Printers Ltd.

215 *Hypholoma fasciculare*   **216** Ixora

(Des Mary Walters)

1986 (31 Dec). *Fungi of the Maldives.* T **215** *and similar multicoloured designs.* P 15.

1217	15 l.	Type **215**	..	80	25
1218	50 l.	*Kuehneromyces mutabilis* (vert)	..	1·50	45
1219	1 r.	*Amanita muscaria* (vert)	..	1·75	60
1220	2 r.	*Agaricus campestris*	..	2·50	1·50
1221	3 r.	*Amanita pantherina* (vert)	..	2·50	1·75
1222	4 r.	*Coprinus comatus* (vert)	..	2·50	2·25
1223	5 r.	*Gymnopilus junonias* ("Pholiota spectabilis")	..	2·50	2·75
1224	10 r.	*Pluteus cervinus*	..	3·75	4·50
1217/24			*Set of 8*	16·00	12·50

MS1225 Two sheets, each 100×70 mm. (a) 15 r. *Armillaria mellea.* (b) 15 r. *Stropharia aeruginosa* (vert) *Set of 2 sheets* 13·00 14·00

Nos. 1217/25 exist imperforate from stock dispersed by the liquidator of Format International Security Printers Ltd.

(Des Mary Walters)

1987 (29 Jan). *Flowers.* T **216** *and similar vert designs. Multicoloured.* P 15.

1226	10 l.	Type **216**	..	10	10
1227	20 l.	Frangipani	..	10	10
1228	50 l.	Crinum	..	90	50
1229	2 r.	Pink Rose	..	40	1·50
1230	4 r.	Flamboyant Flower	..	60	1·50
1231	10 r.	Ground Orchid	..	4·00	6·00
1226/31			*Set of 6*	5·50	8·00

MS1232 Two sheets, each 100×70 mm. (a) 15 r. Gardenia. (b) 15 r. Oleander *Set of 2 sheets* 4·75 6·50

Similar 1, 7 and 12 r. stamps were prepared but not issued. They exist from stock dispersed by the liquidator of Format International Security Printers Ltd as do Nos. 1226/32 imperforate.

217 Guides studying Wild Flowers

218 *Thespesia populnea*

(Des R. Vigurs)

1987 (4 Apr). *75th Anniv of Girl Guide Movement* (1985). T **217** *and similar horiz designs. Multicoloured.* P 15.

1233	15 l.	Type **217**	..	20	20
1234	2 r.	Guides with pet rabbits	..	55	80
1235	4 r.	Guide observing White Spoonbill	..	1·75	2·00
1236	12 r.	Lady Baden-Powell and Guide flag	..	2·00	4·50
1233/6			*Set of 4*	4·00	6·75

MS1237 104×78 mm. 15 r. Guides in sailing dinghy .. .. 2·25 3·75

Nos. 1233/7 exist imperforate from stock dispersed by the liquidator of Format International Security Printers Ltd.

(Litho Questa)

1987 (22 Apr). *Trees and Plants.* T **218** *and similar multicoloured designs.* P 14.

1238	50 l.	Type **218**	..	10	10
1239	1 r.	*Cocos nucifera*	..	15	20
1240	2 r.	*Calophyllum mophyllum*	..	30	40
1241	3 r.	*Xanthosoma indica* (horiz)	..	45	60
1242	5 r.	*Ipomoea batatas* (horiz)	..	80	1·10
1243	7 r.	*Artocarpus altilis*	..	1·10	1·75
1238/43			*Set of 6*	2·50	3·50

MS1244 75×109 mm. 15 r. *Cocos nucifera* (different) .. .. 2·25 3·25

No. 1241 is inscribed "Xyanthosoma indica" in error.

218a *Intrepid,* 1970

219 *Precis octavia*

(Des J. Iskowitz)

1987 (4 May). *America's Cup Yachting Championship.* T **218a** *and similar multicoloured designs.* P 15.

1245	15 l.	Type **218a**	..	10	10
1246	1 r.	*France II,* 1974	..	20	20
1247	2 r.	*Gretel,* 1962	..	40	60
1248	12 r.	*Volunteer,* 1887	..	2·00	3·00
1245/8			*Set of 4*	2·40	3·50

MS1249 113×83 mm. 15 r. Helmsman and crew on deck of *Defender,* 1895 (horiz) .. 2·25 3·25

Nos. 1245/9 exist imperforate from stock dispersed by the liquidator of Format International Security Printers Ltd.

1987 (16 Dec). *Butterflies.* T **219** *and similar vert designs. Multicoloured.* P 15.

1250	15 l.	Type **219**	..	45	30
1251	20 l.	*Atrophaneura hector*	..	45	30
1252	50 l.	*Teinopalpus imperialis*	..	75	40
1253	1 r.	*Kallima horsfieldi*	..	1·00	45
1254	2 r.	*Cethosia biblis*	..	1·60	1·25
1255	4 r.	*Idea jasonia*	..	2·50	2·25
1256	7 r.	*Papilio memnon*	..	3·50	4·00
1257	10 r.	*Aeropetes tulbaghia*	..	4·00	5·00
1250/7			*Set of 8*	13·00	12·50

MS1258 Two sheets, each 135×102 mm. (a) 15 r. *Acraea violae.* (b) 15 r. *Hebomoia leucippe* *Set of 2 sheets* 9·00 11·00

220 Isaac Newton experimenting with Spectrum

(Des J. Martin. Litho Questa)

1988 (10 Jan). *Great Scientific Discoveries.* T **220** *and similar multicoloured designs.* P 14.

1259	1 r. 50, Type **220**		1·25	1·00
1260	3 r.	Euclid composing *Principles of Geometry* (vert)	1·60	1·75
1261	4 r.	Mendel formulating theory of Genetic Evolution (vert)	1·75	2·00
1262	5 r.	Galileo and moons of Jupiter	3·00	3·00
1259/62		*Set of 4*	7·00	7·00

MS1263 102×72 mm. 15 r. "Apollo" lunar module (vert) .. .. 4·50 5·50

221 Donald Duck and Weather Satellite

(Des Walt Disney Co. Litho Questa)

1988 (15 Feb). *Space Exploration.* T **221** *and similar multicoloured designs showing Walt Disney cartoon characters.* P 14×13½ (horiz) or 13½×14 (vert).

1264	3 l. Type **221**		10	10
1265	4 l.	Minnie Mouse and navigation satellite	10	10
1266	5 l.	Mickey Mouse's nephews talking via communication satellite	10	10
1267	10 l.	Goofy in lunar rover (vert)	10	10
1268	20 l.	Minnie Mouse delivering pizza to flying saucer (vert)	10	10
1269	13 r.	Mickey Mouse directing spacecraft docking (vert)	5·00	5·00
1270	14 r.	Mickey Mouse and "Voyager 2"	5·00	5·00
1264/70		*Set of 7*	9·00	9·00

MS1271 Two sheets, each 127×102 mm. (a) 15 r. Mickey Mouse at first Moon landing, 1969. (b) 15 r. Mickey Mouse and nephews in space station swimming pool (vert) *Set of 2 sheets* 10·00 11·00

222 Syringe and Bacterium ("Immunization")

(Des Mary Walters. Litho Questa)

1988 (7 Apr). *40th Anniv of World Health Organization.* T **222** *and similar horiz design. Multicoloured.* P 14.

1272	2 r. Type **222**		35	40
1273	4 r. Tap ("Clean Water")		60	85

223 Water Droplet and Atoll

224 Globe, Carrier Pigeon and Letter

(Des I. Rasheed)

1988 (9 May). *World Environment Day* (1987). T **223** *and similar multicoloured designs.* P 15.

1274	15 l. Type **223**		10	10
1275	75 l. Coral reef		20	30
1276	2 r. Audubon's Shearwaters in flight		75	1·25
1274/6		*Set of 3*	95	1·50

MS1277 105×76 mm. 15 r. Banyan Tree (vert) 2·25 3·50

(Litho Questa)

1988 (31 May). *Transport and Telecommunications Decade.* T **224** *and similar horiz designs, each showing central globe. Multicoloured.* P 14.

1278	2 r. Type **224**		60	65
1279	3 r. Dish aerial and girl using telephone		1·00	1·10
1280	5 r. Satellite, television, telephone and antenna tower		1·75	2·00
1281	10 r. Car, ship and Lockheed L-1011 TriStar airliner		5·00	5·50
1278/81		*Set of 4*	7·50	8·25

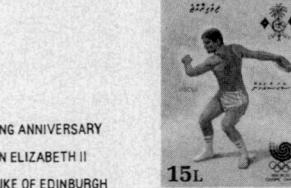

40TH WEDDING ANNIVERSARY
H.M.QUEEN ELIZABETH II
H.R.H. THE DUKE OF EDINBURGH

(225)

226 Discus-throwing

1988 (7 July). *Royal Ruby Wedding.* Nos. 1170/3 optd with T **225** *in gold.*

1282	1 r. black and chrome-yellow		35	25
1283	2 r. multicoloured		50	60
1284	12 r. multicoloured		2·50	3·50
1282/4		*Set of 3*	3·00	4·00

MS1285 120×85 mm. 15 r. black and grey-brown 3·50 4·00

(Des B. Bundock. Litho Questa)

1988 (16 July). *Olympic Games, Seoul.* T **226** *and similar multicoloured designs.* P 14.

1286	15 l. Type **226**		10	10
1287	2 r. 100 metres race		40	40
1288	4 r. Gymnastics (horiz)		70	80
1289	12 r. Three-day equestrian event (horiz)		2·25	3·25
1286/9		*Set of 4*	3·00	4·00

MS1290 106×76 mm. 20 r. Tennis (horiz) .. 3·50 4·25

227 Immunization at Clinic

228 Breadfruit

(Des A. DiLorenzo. Litho Questa)

1988 (20 July). *International Year of Shelter for the Homeless.* T **227** *and similar vert designs. Multicoloured.* P 14.

1291	50 l. Type **227**		30	30
1292	3 r. Prefab housing estate		1·10	1·40

MS1293 63×105 mm. 15 r. Building site .. 1·75 2·25

(Des G. Watkins. Litho Questa)

1988 (30 July). *10th Anniv of International Fund for Agricultural Development.* T **228** *and similar multicoloured designs.* P 14.

1294	7 r. Type **228**		1·00	1·40
1295	10 r. Mangos (vert)		1·50	1·90

MS1296 103×74 mm. 15 r. Coconut palm, fishing boat and Yellowtail Tuna .. .. 2·00 2·50

(229)

230 Pres. Kennedy and Launch of "Apollo" Spacecraft

1988 (1 Dec). *World Aids Day.* Nos. 1272/3 optd with T **229**.

1297	2 r. Type **222**		35	45
1298	4 r. Tap ("Clean Water")		65	80

(Des A. Nahigian. Litho Questa)

1989 (13 Feb). *25th Death Anniv of John F. Kennedy (American statesman)* (1988). *U.S. Space Achievements.* T **230** *and similar vert designs. Multicoloured.* P 14.
1299	5 r. Type **230**		1·75	1·90
	a. Horiz strip of 4. Nos. 1299/1302		6·25	
1300	5 r. Lunar module and astronaut on Moon		1·75	1·90
1301	5 r. Astronaut and buggy on Moon		1·75	1·90
1302	5 r. President Kennedy and spacecraft		1·75	1·90
1299/1302		*Set of 4*	6·25	7·00
MS1303	108 × 77 mm. 15 r. President Kennedy making speech		3·25	4·00

Nos. 1299/1302 were printed together, *se-tenant*, in horizontal strips of 4 throughout the sheet.

J. SCHULT DDR
(231)

ASIA-PACIFIC TELECOMMUNITY 10 YEARS
(232)

1989 (29 Apr). *Olympic Medal Winners, Seoul.* Nos. 1286/90 *optd as* T **231**.
1304	15 l. Type **226** (optd with T **231**)		20	20
1305	2 r. 100 metres race (optd "C. LEWIS USA")		65	65
1306	4 r. Gymnastics (*horiz*) (optd "MEN'S ALL AROUND V. ARTEMOV USSR")		1·25	1·25
1307	12 r. Three-day equestrian event (*horiz*) (optd "TEAM SHOW JUMPING W. GERMANY")		3·00	3·50
1304/7		*Set of 4*	4·50	5·00
MS1308	106×76 mm. 20 r. Tennis (*horiz*) (optd "OLYMPIC WINNERS MEN'S SINGLES GOLD M. MECIR CZECH. SILVER T. MAYOTTE USA BRONZE B. GILBERT USA")		4·00	4·75

On No. **MS**1308 the overprint appears on the sheet margin and not the 20 r. stamp.

(Litho Questa)

1989 (20 May). *500th Birth Anniv of Titian (artist). Vert designs as* T **186***a of Lesotho showing paintings. Multicoloured.* P 13½×14.
1309	15 l. "Benedetto Varchi"		10	10
1310	1 r. "Portrait of a Young Man"		20	15
1311	2 r. "King Francis I of France"		40	40
1312	5 r. "Pietro Aretino"		1·10	1·25
1313	15 r. "The Bravo"		4·00	5·00
1314	20 r. "The Concert" (detail)		4·00	5·50
1309/14		*Set of 6*	8·75	11·00
MS1315	Two sheets. (a) 112×96 mm. 20 r. "An Allegory of Prudence" (detail). (b) 96×110 mm. 20 r. "Francesco Maria della Rovere"			
		Set of 2 sheets	6·00	7·50

1989 (10 July). *10th Anniv of Asia-Pacific Telecommunity.* Nos. 1279/80 optd with T **232** in silver.
1316	3 r. Dish aerial and girl using telephone		1·25	1·50
1317	5 r. Satellite, television, telephone and antenna tower		1·75	2·00

(Litho Questa)

1989 (2 Sept–16 Oct). *Japanese Art. Paintings by Hokusai. Horiz designs as* T **187***a of Lesotho. Multicoloured.* P 14×13½.
1318	15 l. "Fuji from Hodogaya"		10	10
1319	50 l. "Fuji from Lake Kawaguchi"		15	15
1320	1 r. "Fuji from Owari"		25	15
1321	2 r. "Fuji from Tsukudajima in Edo"		50	40
1322	4 r. "Fuji from a Teahouse at Yoshida"		80	90
1323	6 r. "Fuji from Tagonoura"		90	1·25
1324	10 r. "Fuji from Mishima-goe"		2·25	2·75
1325	12 r. "Fuji from the Sumida River in Edo"		2·75	3·25
1318/25		*Set of 8*	6·50	7·50
MS1326	Two sheets, each 101×77 mm. (a) 18 r. "Fuji from Inume Pass" (2 Sept). (b) 18 r. "Fuji from Fukagawa in Edo" (16 Oct) *Set of 2 sheets*		7·50	8·00

Nos. 1318/25 were each printed in sheetlets of 10 containing two horizontal strips of 5 stamps separated by printed labels commemorating Emperor Hirohito.

233 Clown Triggerfish

(Des L. Birmingham. Litho Questa)

1989 (16 Oct). *Tropical Fishes.* T **233** *and similar horiz designs. Multicoloured.* P 14.
1327	20 l. Type **233**		25	20
1328	50 l. Blue-striped Snapper		35	25
1329	1 r. Powder-blue Surgeonfish		45	30
1330	2 r. Oriental Sweetlips		75	65
1331	3 r. Six-barred Wrasse		1·00	85
1332	8 r. Thread-finned Butterflyfish		2·00	2·50
1333	10 r. Bicoloured Parrotfish		2·40	2·75
1334	12 r. Scarlet-finned Squirrelfish		2·75	2·75
1327/34		*Set of 8*	8·75	9·25
MS1335	Two sheets, each 101×73 mm. (a) 15 r. Butterfly Perch. (b) 15 r. Semicircle Angelfish			
		Set of 2 sheets	11·00	12·00

234 Goofy, Mickey and Minnie Mouse with Takuri "Type 3", 1907

(Des Walt Disney Co. Litho Questa)

1989 (17 Nov). *"World Stamp Expo '89" International Stamp Exhibition, Washington (1st issue).* T **234** *and similar horiz designs showing Walt Disney cartoon characters with Japanese cars. Multicoloured.* P 14×13½.
1336	15 l. Type **234**		20	15
1337	50 l. Donald and Daisy Duck in Mitsubishi "Model A", 1917		40	30
1338	1 r. Goofy in Datsun "Roadstar", 1935		70	50
1339	2 r. Donald and Daisy Duck with Mazda, 1940		1·00	75
1340	4 r. Donald Duck with Nissan "Bluebird 310", 1959		1·50	1·25
1341	6 r. Donald and Daisy Duck with Subaru "360", 1958		1·75	1·75
1342	10 r. Mickey Mouse and Pluto in Honda "5800", 1966		3·25	3·75
1343	12 r. Mickey Mouse and Goofy in Daihatsu "Fellow", 1966		3·75	4·25
1336/43		*Set of 8*	11·50	11·50
MS1344	Two sheets, each 127×102 mm. (a) 20 r. Daisy Duck with Chip n'Dale and Isuzu "Trooper II", 1981 (b) 20 r. Mickey Mouse with tortoise and Toyota "Supra", 1985 *Set of 2 sheets*		11·00	13·00

(Des Design Element. Litho Questa)

1989 (17 Nov). *"World Stamp Expo '89" International Stamp Exhibition, Washington (2nd issue). Landmarks of Washington. Sheet* 62×78 *mm containing multicoloured designs as* T **193***a of Lesotho, but vert.* P 14.
MS1345	8 r. Marine Corps Memorial, Arlington National Cemetery		1·50	2·00

235 Lunar Module *Eagle*

(Des W. Hanson Studio. Litho Questa).

1989 (24 Nov). *20th Anniv of First Manned Landing on Moon.* T **235** *and similar multicoloured designs.* P 14.
1346	1 r. Type **235**		30	20
1347	2 r. Astronaut Aldrin collecting dust samples		50	60
1348	6 r. Aldrin setting up seismometer		1·25	1·75
1349	10 r. Pres. Nixon congratulating "Apollo 11" astronauts		1·90	2·50
1346/9		*Set of 4*	3·50	4·50
MS1350	107×75 mm. 18 r. Television picture of Armstrong about to step onto Moon (34×47 *mm*). P 13½×14		3·50	4·00

236 Jawaharlal Nehru with Mahatma Gandhi

237 Sir William van Horne (Chairman of Canadian Pacific), Locomotive and Map, 1894

(Des Design Element. Litho B.D.T.)

1989 (20 Dec)–**90**. *Anniversaries and Events.* T **236** *and similar multicoloured designs.* P 14.
1351	20 l. Type **236** (birth centenary)		90	45
1352	50 l. Opium poppies and logo (anti-drugs campaign) (*vert*)		90	45
1353	1 r. William Shakespeare (425th birth anniv) (15.2.90)		90	45
1354	2 r. Storming the Bastille (bicent of French Revolution) (*vert*) (15.2.90)		90	90
1355	3 r. Concorde (20th anniv of first flight) (15.2.90)		2·50	1·75
1356	8 r. George Washington (bicent of inauguration)		2·00	2·50
1357	10 r. William Bligh (bicent of mutiny on the *Bounty*)		4·00	4·00

1358	12 r. Hamburg Harbour (800th anniv) (*vert*) (15.2.90)		3·50	4·00
1351/8		*Set of 8*	14·00	13·00
MS1359	Two sheets. (a) 115×85 mm. 18 r. Baseball players (50th anniv of first televised game) (*vert*). (b) 110×80 mm. 18 r. Franz von Taxis (500th anniv of regular European postal services) (*vert*) (15.2.90) *Set of 2 sheets*		10·00	12·00

(Des A. Fagbohun. Litho Questa)

1989 (26 Dec). *Railway Pioneers.* T **237** *and similar vert designs. Multicoloured.* P 14.
1360	10 l. Type **237**		15	15
1361	25 l. Matthew Murray (engineer) with Blenkinsop and Murray's rack locomotive, 1810		20	20
1362	50 l. Louis Favre (railway engineer) and steam locomotive entering tunnel		25	25
1363	2 r. George Stephenson (engineer) and *Locomotion*, 1825		55	55
1364	6 r. Richard Trevithick and *Catch-Me-Who-Can*, 1808		1·50	1·50
1365	8 r. George Nagelmackers and "Orient Express" dining car		1·75	1·75
1366	10 r. William Jessop and horse-drawn wagon, Surrey Iron Railway, 1770		2·50	2·50
1367	12 r. Isambard Brunel (engineer) and G.W.R. steam locomotive, 1833		3·00	3·00
1360/7		*Set of 8*	9·00	9·00
MS1368	Two sheets, each 71×103 mm. (a) 18 r. George Pullman (inventor of sleeping cars), 1864. (b) 18 r. Rudolf Diesel (engineer) and first oil engine *Set of 2 sheets*		7·00	8·00

238 Bodu Thakurufaanu Memorial Centre, Utheemu

239 "Louis XVI in Coronation Robes" (Duplesis)

(Litho B.D.T.)

1990 (1 Jan). *25th Anniv of Independence.* T **238** *and similar horiz designs. Multicoloured.* P 14.
1369	20 l. Type **238**		10	10
1370	25 l. Islamic Centre, Malé		10	10
1371	50 l. National flag and logos of international organizations		10	10
1372	2 r. Presidential Palace, Malé		30	40
1373	5 r. National Security Service		85	1·25
1369/73		*Set of 5*	1·25	1·75
MS1374	128×90 mm. 10 r. National emblem		1·75	2·25

(Litho Questa)

1990 (11 Jan). *Bicentenary of French Revolution and "Philexfrance '89" International Stamp Exhibition, Paris. French Paintings.* T **239** *and similar multicoloured designs.* P 13½×14.
1375	15 l. Type **239**		15	15
1376	50 l. "Monsieur Lavoisier and his Wife" (David)		25	25
1377	1 r. "Madame Pastoret" (David)		35	35
1378	2 r. "Oath of Lafayette, 14 July 1790" (anon)		55	55
1379	4 r. "Madame Trudaine" (David)		1·00	1·00
1380	6 r. "Chenard celebrating the Liberation of Savoy" (Boilly)		1·40	1·60
1381	10 r. "An Officer swears Allegiance to the Constitution" (anon)		2·75	3·25
1382	12 r. "Self Portrait" (David)		3·00	3·50
1375/82		*Set of 8*	8·50	9·50
MS1383	Two sheets. (a) 104×79 mm. 20 r. "The Oath of the Tennis Court, 20 June 1789" (David) (*horiz*). P 14×13½. (b) 79×104 mm. 20 r. "Rousseau and Symbols of the Revolution" (Jeaurat). P 13½×14 *Set of 2 sheets*		8·50	9·50

239*a Donald Duck, Mickey Mouse and Goofy playing Rugby*

(Des Walt Disney Co. Litho Questa)

1990 (3 May). *"Stamp World London 90" International Stamp Exhibition.* T **239***a and similar horiz designs showing Walt Disney cartoon characters playing British sports. Multicoloured.* P 14×13½.
1384	15 l. Type **239***a		20	15
1385	50 l. Donald Duck and Chip-n-Dale curling		35	25
1386	1 r. Goofy playing polo		55	40
1387	2 r. Mickey Mouse and nephews playing soccer		80	70
1388	4 r. Mickey Mouse playing cricket		1·50	1·50
1389	6 r. Minnie and Mickey Mouse at Ascot races		1·90	1·90

1390	10 r. Mickey Mouse and Goofy playing tennis		3·25	3·50
1391	12 r. Donald Duck and Mickey Mouse playing bowls		3·25	3·50
1384/91		Set of 8	10·50	10·50

MS1392 Two sheets, each 126×101 mm. (a) 20 r. Minnie Mouse fox-hunting. (b) 20 r. Mickey Mouse playing golf .. .. Set of 2 sheets 13·00 13·00

240 Silhouettes of Queen Elizabeth II and Queen Victoria

241 Sultan's Tomb

(Des S. Pollard. Litho B.D.T.)

1990 (6 May). *150th Anniv of the Penny Black. T 240 and similar horiz designs. P 15×14.*

1393	8 r. black and olive-green		2·25	2·50
1394	12 r. black and deep dull blue		2·75	3·00

MS1395 109×84 mm. 18 r. black & yellow-brown 3·75 4·50
Designs:—12 r. As Type 240, but with position of silhouettes reversed; 18 r. Penny Black.

(Des Young Phillips Studio. Litho Questa)

1990 (8 July). *90th Birthday of Queen Elizabeth the Queen Mother. Vert designs as T 198a of Lesotho showing portraits, 1920–29. P 14.*

1396	6 r. brownish blk, brt mag & turquoise-bl		80	1·10
	a. Strip of 3. Nos. 1396/8		2·25	
1397	6 r. brownish blk, brt mag & turquoise-bl		80	1·10
1398	6 r. brownish blk, brt mag & turquoise-bl		80	1·10
1396/8		Set of 3	2·25	3·00

MS1399 90×75 mm. 18 r. multicoloured 2·50 3·25
Designs:—No. 1396, Lady Elizabeth Bowes-Lyon; No. 1397, Lady Elizabeth Bowes-Lyon wearing headband; No. 1398, Lady Elizabeth Bowes-Lyon leaving for her wedding; No. MS1399, Lady Elizabeth Bowes-Lyon wearing wedding dress.
Nos. 1396/8 were printed together, horizontally and vertically *se-tenant*, in sheetlets of 9 (3×3).

(Litho Questa)

1990 (21 July). *Islamic Heritage Year. T 241 and similar horiz designs, each black and light cobalt. P 14.*

1400	1 r. Type 241		25	35
	a. Block of 6. Nos. 1400/5		1·40	
1401	1 r. Thakurufaan's Palace		25	35
1402	1 r. Malé Mosque		25	35
1403	2 r. Veranda of Friday Mosque		25	35
1404	2 r. Interior of Friday Mosque		25	35
1405	2 r. Friday Mosque and Monument		25	35
1400/5		Set of 6	1·40	1·90

Nos. 1400/5 were printed together, *se-tenant*, in blocks of 6 (3×2) within the sheet of 36.

242 Defence of Wake Island, 1941

(Des W. Wright. Litho Questa)

1990 (9 Aug). *50th Anniv of Second World War. T 242 and similar horiz designs. Multicoloured. P 14.*

1406	15 l. Type 242		15	15
1407	25 l. Stilwell's army in Burma, 1944		20	20
1408	50 l. Normandy offensive, 1944		25	25
1409	1 r. Capture of Saipan, 1944		40	40
1410	2 r. 50, D-Day landings, 1944		70	70
1411	3 r. 50, Allied landings in Norway, 1940		90	90
1412	4 r. Lord Mountbatten, Head of Combined Operations, 1943		1·10	1·10
1413	6 r. Japanese surrender, Tokyo Bay, 1945		1·50	1·50
1414	10 r. Potsdam Conference, 1945		2·50	2·50
1415	12 r. Allied invasion of Sicily, 1943		2·75	2·75
1406/15		Set of 10	9·50	9·50

MS1416 115×87 mm. 18 r. Atlantic convoy 5·00 6·00

243 Crested Tern

(Des Mary Walters. Litho Questa)

1990 (9 Aug). *Birds. T 243 and similar horiz designs. Multicoloured. P 14.*

1417	25 l. Type 243		15	15
1418	50 l. Koel		25	25
1419	1 r. White Tern		35	35
1420	3 r. 50, Cinnamon Bittern		90	1·00
1421	6 r. Sooty Tern		1·40	1·60
1422	8 r. Audubon's Shearwater		1·60	2·00
1423	12 r. Common Noddy		2·50	3·00
1424	15 r. Lesser Frigate Bird		2·75	3·25
1417/24		Set of 8	9·00	10·50

MS1425 Two sheets, each 100×69 mm. (a) 18 r. Grey Heron. (b) 18 r. White-tailed Tropic Bird
Set of 2 sheets 8·00 10·00

244 Emblem, Dish Aerial and Sailboards

245 *Spathoglottis plicata*

(Litho Questa)

1990 (21 Nov). *Fifth South Asian Association for Regional Co-operation Summit. T 244 and similar horiz designs. P 14.*

1426	75 l. black and brown-orange		20	25
1427	3 r. 50, multicoloured		90	1·25

MS1428 112×82 mm. 20 r. multicoloured 4·50 5·50
Designs:—3 r. 50, Flags of member nations; 20 r. Global warming diagram.

(Des Dot Barlowe. Litho Questa)

1990 (9 Dec). *"EXPO '90" International Garden and Greenery Exhibition, Osaka. Flowers. T 245 and similar multicoloured designs. P 14.*

1429	20 l. Type 245		60	30
1430	75 l. Hippeastrum puniceum		90	40
1431	2 r. Tecoma stans (horiz)		1·25	90
1432	3 r. 50 Catharanthus roseus (horiz)		1·40	1·50
1433	10 r. Ixora coccinea (horiz)		2·50	3·00
1434	12 r. Clitorea ternatea (horiz)		2·75	3·25
1435	15 r. Caesalpinia pulcherrima		3·00	3·50
1429/35		Set of 7	11·00	11·50

MS1436 Four sheets, each 111×79 mm. (a) 20 r. *Plumeria obtusa* (horiz). (b) 20 r. *Jasminum grandiflorum* (horiz). (c) 20 r. *Rosa sp* (horiz). (d) 20 r. *Hibiscus tiliaceous* (horiz) Set of 4 sheets 13·00 13·00

246 The Hare and the Tortoise

(Des Walt Disney Co. Litho Questa)

1990 (11 Dec). *International Literacy Year. T 246 and similar multicoloured designs showing Walt Disney cartoon characters illustrating fables by Aesop. P 14×13½.*

1437	15 l. Type 246		30	·15
1438	50 l. The Town Mouse and the Country Mouse		50	25
1439	1 r. The Fox and the Crow		80	35
1440	3 r. 50, The Travellers and the Bear		1·60	1·60
1441	4 r. The Fox and the Lion		1·75	1·75
1442	6 r. The Mice Meeting		2·25	2·25
1443	10 r. The Fox and the Goat		2·75	3·00
1444	12 r. The Dog in the Manger		2·75	3·25
1437/44		Set of 8	11·00	11·50

MS1445 Two sheets, each 127×102 mm. (a) 20 r. The Miller, his Son and the Ass (vert). (b) 20 r. The Miser's Gold (vert). P 13½×14
Set of 2 sheets 12·00 12·00

247 East African Railways Class 31 Steam Locomotive

248 Ruud Gullit of Holland

(Des T. Agans. Litho Questa)

1990 (15 Dec). *Railway Steam Locomotives. T 247 and similar vert designs. Multicoloured. P 14.*

1446	20 l. Type 247		55	30
1447	50 l. Steam locomotive, Sudan		75	45
1448	1 r. Class GM Garratt, South Africa		1·00	60
1449	3 r. 7th Class, Rhodesia		2·00	2·00
1450	5 r. No. 229, Central Pacific Class, U.S.A.		2·25	2·25
1451	8 r. Reading Railroad No. 415, U.S.A.		2·50	2·75
1452	10 r. Porter narrow gauge, Canada		2·50	2·75
1453	12 r. Great Northern Railway No. 515, U.S.A.		2·50	3·00
1446/53		Set of 8	12·50	12·50

MS1454 Two sheets, each 90×65 mm. (a) 20 r. 19th-century standard American locomotive No. 315. (b) 20 r. East African Railways Garratt locomotive No. 5950 .. Set of 2 sheets 12·00 12·00

249 Winged Euonymus

250 "Summer" (Rubens)

(Des Young Phillips Studio. Litho Questa)

1990 (27 Dec). *World Cup Football Championship, Italy. T 248 and similar multicoloured designs. P 14.*

1455	1 r. Type 248		75	50
1456	2 r. 50, Paul Gascoigne of England		1·25	1·25
1457	3 r. 50, Brazilian challenging Argentine player		1·60	1·60
1458	5 r. Brazilian taking control of ball		2·00	2·00
1459	7 r. Italian and Austrian jumping for header		2·50	2·50
1460	10 r. Russian being chased by Turkish player		2·75	3·00
1461	15 r. Andres Brehme of West Germany		3·00	3·25
1455/61		Set of 7	12·50	12·50

MS1462 Four sheets, each 77×92 mm. (a) 18 r. Head of an Austrian player (horiz). (b) 18 r. Head of a South Korean player (horiz). (c) 20 r. Diego Maradonna of Argentina (horiz). (d) 20 r. Schilacci of Italy (horiz).. Set of 4 sheets 15·00 16·00

(Des N. Waldman. Litho Questa)

1991 (29 Jan). *Bonsai Trees and Shrubs. T 249 and similar vert designs. Multicoloured. P 14.*

1463	20 l. Type 249		30	20
1464	50 l. Japanese Black Pine		45	35
1465	1 r. Japanese Five Needle Pine		70	55
1466	3 r. 50, Flowering Quince		1·60	1·60
1467	5 r. Chinese Elm		2·00	2·00
1468	8 r. Japanese Persimmon		2·25	2·50
1469	10 r. Japanese Wisteria		2·25	2·50
1470	12 r. Satsuki Azalea		2·50	2·75
1463/70		Set of 8	11·00	11·00

MS1471 Two sheets, each 89×88 mm. (a) 20 r. Trident Maple. (b) 20 r. Sargent Juniper
Set of 2 sheets 8·50 9·50

(Litho Questa)

1991 (7 Feb). *350th Death Anniv of Rubens. T 250 and similar horiz designs. Multicoloured. P 14×13½.*

1472	20 l. Type 250		20	15
1473	50 l. "Landscape with Rainbow" (detail)		35	25
1474	1 r. "Wreck of Aeneas"		55	40
1475	2 r. 50, "Château de Steen" (detail)		1·00	1·00
1476	3 r. 50, "Landscape with Herd of Cows"		1·25	1·25
1477	7 r. "Ruins on the Palantine"		2·00	2·50
1478	10 r. "Landscape with Peasants and Cows"		2·25	2·50
1479	12 r. "Wagon fording Stream"		2·50	2·75
1472/9		Set of 8	9·00	9·75

MS1480 Four sheets, each 100×71 mm. (a) 20 r. "Landscape at Sunset". (b) 20 r. "Peasants with Cattle by a Stream". (c) 20 r. "Shepherd with Flock". (d) 20 r. "Wagon in Stream"
Set of 4 sheets 14·00 15·00

251 Greek Messenger from Marathon, 490 BC (2480th anniv)

252 Arctic Iceberg and Maldives Dhoni

(Des W. Wright. Litho Questa)

1991 (11 Mar). *Anniversaries and Events (1990). T 251 and similar multicoloured designs. P 14.*

1481	50 l. Type 251		45	25
1482	1 r. Anthony Fokker in Haarlem Spin monoplane (birth cent)		80	45
1483	3 r. 50, "Early Bird" satellite (25th anniv)		1·50	1·50
1484	7 r. Signing Reunification of Germany agreement (horiz)		1·75	2·50
1485	8 r. King John signing Magna Carta (775th anniv)		2·25	2·50
1486	10 r. Dwight D. Eisenhower (birth cent)		2·25	2·50
1487	12 r. Sir Winston Churchill (25th death anniv)		3·25	3·50
1488	15 r. Pres. Reagan at Berlin Wall (German reunification) (horiz)		2·75	3·50
1481/8		Set of 8	13·50	15·00

MS1489 Two sheets. (a) 180×81 mm. 20 r. German Junkers Ju88 bomber (50th anniv of Battle of Britain) (horiz). (b) 160×73 mm. 20 r. Brandenburg Gate (German reunification) (horiz) .. .. Set of 2 sheets 10·50 12·00

(Litho Questa)

1991 (10 Apr). *Global Warming. T 252 and similar horiz design. Multicoloured. P 14.*
1490	3 r. 50, Type 252	1·25	1·25
1491	7 r. Antarctic iceberg and *Maldive Trader* (freighter)	2·75	2·75

253 S.A.A.R.C. Emblem and Medal   **254** Children on Beach

(Litho Questa)

1991 (10 Apr). *Year of the Girl Child. P 14.*
1492	253	7 r. multicoloured	1·75	1·75

(Litho Questa)

1991 (14 Apr). *Year of the Maldivian Child. Children's Paintings. T 254 and similar horiz designs. Multicoloured. P 14.*
1493	3 r. 50, Type 254	1·50	1·25
1494	5 r. Children in a park	2·00	1·75
1495	10 r. Hungry child dreaming of food	3·00	3·50
1496	25 r. Scuba diver	5·50	8·00
1493/6	*Set of 4*	11·00	13·00

255 "Still Life: Japanese Vase with Roses and Anemones" (Van Gogh)   **256** Boy painting

(Litho Walsall)

1991 (6 June). *Death Centenary of Vincent van Gogh (artist) (1990). T 255 and similar multicoloured designs. P 13½.*
1497	15 l. Type 255	30	20
1498	20 l. "Still Life: Red Poppies and Daisies"	30	20
1499	2 r. "Vincent's Bedroom in Arles" (*horiz*)	90	80
1500	3 r. 50, "The Mulberry Tree" (*horiz*)	1·25	1·00
1501	7 r. "Blossoming Chestnut Branches" (*horiz*)	2·00	2·25
1502	10 r. "Peasant Couple going to Work" (*horiz*)	2·50	2·75
1503	12 r. "Still Life: Pink Roses" (*horiz*)	2·75	3·00
1504	15 r. "Child with Orange"	3·00	3·25
1497/1504	*Set of 8*	11·50	12·00

MS1505 Two sheets. (a) 77×101 mm. 25 r. "Houses in Auvers" (70×94 *mm*). (b) 101×77 mm. 25 r. "The Courtyard of the Hospital at Arles" (94×70 *mm*). Imperf .. *Set of 2 sheets* 12·00 12·00

(Des D. Miller. Litho Walsall)

1991 (4 July). *65th Birthday of Queen Elizabeth II. Horiz designs as T 210 of Lesotho. Multicoloured. P 14.*
1506	2 r. Queen at Trooping the Colour, 1990	75	60
1507	5 r. Queen with Queen Mother and Princess Margaret, 1973	1·50	1·50
1508	8 r. Queen and Prince Philip in open carriage, 1986	2·25	2·50
1509	12 r. Queen at Royal Estates Ball	3·00	3·25
1506/9	*Set of 4*	6·50	7·00

MS1510 68×90 mm. 25 r. Separate photographs of Queen and Prince Philip .. 5·75 6·50

(Des D. Miller. Litho Walsall)

1991 (4 July). *10th Wedding Anniv of Prince and Princess of Wales. Horiz designs as T 210 of Lesotho. Multicoloured. P 14.*
1511	1 r. Prince and Princess skiing, 1986	45	20
1512	3 r. 50, Separate photographs of Prince, Princess and sons	1·25	90
1513	7 r. Prince Henry in Christmas play and Prince William watching polo	1·50	1·75
1514	15 r. Princess Diana at Ipswich, 1990, and Prince Charles playing polo	3·00	3·00
1511/14	*Set of 4*	5·50	5·25

MS1515 68×90 mm. 25 r. Prince and Princess of Wales in Hungary, and Princes William and Henry going to school .. 5·75 6·50

(Litho Questa)

1991 (25 July). *Hummel Figurines. T 256 and similar vert designs. Multicoloured. P 14.*
1516	10 l. Type 256	15	10
1517	25 l. Boy reading at table	20	15
1518	50 l. Boy with school satchel	30	30
1519	2 r. Girl with basket	70	60
1520	3 r. 50, Boy reading	1·00	1·00
1521	8 r. Girl and young child reading	2·00	2·25
1522	10 r. School girls	2·00	2·50
1523	25 r. School boys	4·25	5·50
1516/23	*Set of 8*	9·50	11·00

MS1524 Two sheets, each 97×127 mm. (a) 5 r. As No. 1519; 5 r. As No. 1520; 5 r. As No. 1521; 5 r. As No. 1522; (b) 8 r. As Type 256; 8 r. As No. 1517; 8 r. As No. 1518; 8 r. As No. 1523
.. .. .. *Set of 2 sheets* 9·00 10·00

257 Class C57 Steam Locomotive   **258** *Salamis temora* and *Vanda caerulea*

(Litho B.D.T.)

1991 (25 Aug). *"Phila Nippon '91" International Stamp Exhibition, Tokyo. Japanese Steam Locomotives. T 257 and similar multicoloured designs. P 14.*
1525	15 l. Type 257	25	15
1526	25 l. Class 6250 locomotive, 1915 (*horiz*)	35	25
1527	1 r. Class D51, locomotive, 1936	60	40
1528	3 r. 50, Class 8620 locomotive, 1914 (*horiz*)	1·25	1·10
1529	5 r. Class 10 locomotive, 1889 (*horiz*)	1·50	1·50
1530	7 r. Class C61 locomotive, 1947	1·75	2·25
1531	10 r. Class 9600 locomotive, 1913 (*horiz*)	2·00	2·50
1532	12 r. Class D52 locomotive, 1943 (*horiz*)	2·40	3·00
1525/32	*Set of 8*	9·00	10·00

MS1533 Two sheets, each 118×80 mm. (a) 20 r. Class C56 locomotive, 1935 (*horiz*). (b) 20 r. Class 1080 locomotive, 1925 (*horiz*) .. *Set of 2 sheets* 8·00 8·00

(Litho Questa)

1991 (2 Dec). *Butterflies and Flowers. T 258 and similar horiz designs. Multicoloured. P 14.*
1534	10 l. Type 258	40	40
1535	25 l. *Meneris tulbaghia* and *Incarvillea younghusbandii*	55	30
1536	50 l. *Polyommatus icarus* and *Campsis grandiflora*	75	40
1537	2 r. *Danaus plexippus* and *Thunbergia grandiflora*	1·25	90
1538	3 r. 50, *Colias interior* and *Medinilla magnifica*	1·75	1·75
1539	5 r. *Ascalapha ordorata* and *Meconopsis horridula*	2·00	2·00
1540	8 r. *Papilio memnon* and *Dillenia obovata*	2·50	3·00
1541	10 r. *Precis octavia* and *Thespesia populnea*	2·50	3·00
1534/41	*Set of 8*	10·50	10·50

MS1542 Two sheets, each 100×70 mm. (a) 20 r. *Bombax ceiba* and *Phyciodes tharos*. (b) 20 r. *Amauris niavius* and *Bombax insigne*
.. .. .. *Set of 2 sheets* 9·25 9·50

259 "H-II" Rocket

(Des K. Gromell. Litho Questa)

1991 (11 Dec). *Japanese Space Programme. T 259 and similar multicoloured designs. P 14.*
1543	15 l. Type 259	40	20
1544	20 l. Projected "H-II" orbiting plane	40	20
1545	2 r. Satellite "GMS-5"	1·00	75
1546	3 r. 50, Satellite "MOMO-1"	1·40	1·40
1547	7 r. Satellite "CS-3"	2·25	2·50
1548	10 r. Satellite "BS-2a, 2b"	2·50	2·75
1549	12 r. "H-I" Rocket (*vert*)	2·75	3·00
1550	15 r. Space Flier unit and U.S. space shuttle	2·75	3·00
1543/50	*Set of 8*	12·00	12·50

MS1551 Two sheets. (a) 116×85 mm. 20 r. Dish aerial, Katsura Tracking Station (*vert*). (b) 85×116 mm. 20 r. "M-3SII" rocket (*vert*)
.. .. .. *Set of 2 sheets* 10·00 11·00

260 Williams "FW-07"

(Litho B.D.T.)

1991 (28 Dec). *Formula 1 Racing Cars. T 260 and similar horiz designs. Multicoloured. P 14.*
1552	20 l. Type 260	30	20
1553	50 l. Brabham/BMW "BT50" turbo	45	30
1554	1 r. Williams/Honda "FW-11"	60	45
1555	3 r. 50, Ferrari "312 T3"	1·25	1·25
1556	5 r. Lotus/Honda "99T"	1·75	1·75
1557	7 r. Benetton/Ford "B188"	2·00	2·25
1558	10 r. Tyrrell "P34" six-wheeler	2·25	2·50
1559	21 r. Renault "RE-30B" turbo	4·00	5·00
1552/9	*Set of 8*	11·50	12·50

MS1560 Two sheets, each 84×56 mm. (a) 25 r. Brabham/BMW "BT50" turbo (*different*). (b) 25 r. Ferrari "F189" .. *Set of 2 sheets* 11·00 12·00

261 "Testa Rossa", 1957   **262** Franklin D. Roosevelt

(Litho Questa)

1991 (28 Dec). *Ferrari Cars. T 261 and similar horiz designs. Multicoloured. P 14.*
1561	5 r. Type 261	1·50	1·75
	a. Sheetlet. Nos. 1561/9	12·00	
1562	5 r. "275GTB", 1966	1·50	1·75
1563	5 r. "Aspirarta", 1951	1·50	1·75
1564	5 r. "Testarossa"	1·50	1·75
1565	5 r. Enzo Ferrari	1·50	1·75
1566	5 r. "Dino 246", 1958	1·50	1·75
1567	5 r. "Type 375", 1952	1·50	1·75
1568	5 r. Nigel Mansell's Formula 1 racing car	1·50	1·75
1569	5 r. "312T", 1975	1·50	1·75
1561/9	*Set of 9*	12·00	14·00

Nos. 1561/9 were printed together, *se-tenant*, in sheetlets of 9 (3×3).

(Des R. Jung. Litho Questa)

1991 (30 Dec). *50th Anniv of Japanese Attack on Pearl Harbor. American War Leaders. T 262 and similar horiz designs. Multicoloured. P 14½.*
1570	3 r. 50, Type 262	1·25	1·40
	a. Sheetlet. Nos. 1570/9	11·00	
1571	3 r. 50, Douglas MacArthur and map of Philippines	1·25	1·40
1572	3 r. 50, Chester Nimitz and Pacific island	1·25	1·40
1573	3 r. 50, Jonathan Wainwright and barbed wire	1·25	1·40
1574	3 r. 50, Ernest King and U.S.S. *Hornet* (aircraft carrier)	1·25	1·40
1575	3 r. 50, Claire Chennault and Curtiss P-40B Tomahawk II fighters	1·25	1·40
1576	3 r. 50, William Halsey and U.S.S. *Enterprise* (aircraft carrier)	1·25	1·40
1577	3 r. 50, Marc Mitscher and U.S.S. *Hornet* (aircraft carrier)	1·25	1·40
1578	3 r. 50, James Doolittle and North American B-25B Mitchell bomber	1·25	1·40
1579	3 r. 50, Raymond Spruance and Douglas SBD Dauntless dive bomber	1·25	1·40
1570/9	*Set of 10*	11·00	12·00

Nos. 1570/9 were printed together, *se-tenant*, in sheetlets of 10 with the stamps arranged in two horizontal strips of 5 separated by a gutter showing Japanese fighters attacking Pearl Harbor and Admiral Isoroku Yamamoto.

263 Brandenburg Gate and Postcard commemorating Berlin Wall   **264** Mickey Mouse on Flying Carpet, Arabia

(Des L. Fried (Nos. 1580, 1583, 1585, 1597, **MS**1599b/d), J. Iskowitz (Nos. 1581/2, 1584, 1586/7, 1589, 1593, 1598, **MS**1599a,f). W. Hanson (Nos. 1594/5, **MS**1599e,h), W. Wright (others). Litho Questa)

1992 (30 Jan). *Anniversaries and Events. T 263 and similar multicoloured designs. P 14.*
1580	20 l. Type 263	10	10
1581	50 l. Schwarzenburg Palace	15	10
1582	1 r. Spa at Baden	20	15
1583	1 r. 75, Berlin Wall and man holding child	30	30
1584	2 r. Royal Palace, Berlin	35	35
1585	4 r. Demonstrator and border guards	75	75
1586	5 r. Viennese masonic seal	2·00	1·50
1587	6 r. De Gaulle and Normandy landings, 1944 (*vert*)	2·00	1·75
1588	6 r. Lilienthal's signature and *Flugzeug Nr. 16*	2·00	1·75
1589	7 r. St. Marx	2·00	1·75
1590	7 r. Trans-Siberian Railway Class VL80T electric locomotive No. 1406 (*vert*)	2·00	1·75
1591	8 r. Kurt Schwitters (artist) and Landes-museum	2·00	1·75
1592	9 r. Map of Switzerland and man in Uri traditional costume	2·00	1·75
1593	10 r. De Gaulle in Madagascar, 1958	2·00	1·75

1594	10 r. Scouts exploring coral reef ..	2·00	2·00
1595	11 r. Scout salute and badge (vert)	2·00	2·00
1596	12 r. Trans-Siberian Railway steam locomotive	2·25	2·25
1597	15 r. Imperial German badges	2·00	2·00
1598	20 r. Josepsplatz, Vienna	2·75	2·75
1580/98	Set of 19	26·00	24·00

MS1599 Eight sheets. (a) 76×116 mm. 15 r. General de Gaulle during Second World War (vert). (b) 101×72 mm. 18 r. Ancient German helmet. (c) 101×72 mm. 18 r. 19th-century shako. (d) 101×72 mm. 18 r. Helmet of 1939. (e) 90×117 mm. 18 r. Postcard of Lord Baden-Powell carried by rocket, 1937 (brownish grey, black and magenta) (vert). (f) 75×104 mm. 20 r. Bust of Mozart (vert). (g) 115×85 mm. 20 r. Trans-Siberian Railway Class P36 steam locomotive stopped at signal (57×43 mm). (h) 117×90 mm. 20 r. Czechoslovakia 1918 10 h. "Scout Post" stamp (vert) .. Set of 8 sheets 26·00 27·00

Anniversaries and Events:—Nos. 1580, 1583, 1585, 1597, MS1599b/d, Bicentenary of Brandenburg Gate, Berlin; Nos. 1581/2, 1584, 1586, 1589, 1598, MS1599f, Death bicentenary of Mozart (1991); Nos. 1587, 1593, MS1599a, Birth centenary of Charles de Gaulle (French statesman) (1990); No. 1588, Centenary of Otto Lilienthal's first gliding experiments; Nos. 1590, 1596, MS1599g, Centenary of Trans-Siberian Railway; No. 1591, 750th anniv of Hannover; No. 1592, 700th anniv of Swiss Confederation; Nos. 1594/5, MS1599e,h, 17th World Scout Jamboree, Korea.

(Des Walt Disney Co. Litho B.D.T.)

1992 (4 Feb). *Mickey's World Tour.* T **264** *and similar multicoloured designs showing Walt Disney cartoon characters in different countries.* P 13.

1600	25 l. Type 264	30	20
1601	50 l. Goofy and Big Ben, Great Britain	40	25
1602	1 r. Mickey wearing clogs, Netherlands	50	35
1603	2 r. Pluto eating pasta, Italy	85	65
1604	3 r. Mickey and Donald doing Mexican hat dance	1·10	1·10
1605	3 r. 50, Mickey, Goofy and Donald as tiki, New Zealand	1·25	1·25
1606	5 r. Goofy skiing in Austrian Alps	1·50	1·50
1607	7 r. Mickey and city gate, Germany	1·75	2·00
1608	10 r. Donald as samurai, Japan	2·00	2·25
1609	12 r. Mickey as heroic statue, Russia	2·25	2·50
1610	15 r. Mickey, Donald, Goofy and Pluto as German band	2·50	2·75
1600/10	Set of 11	13·00	13·00

MS1611 Three sheets, each 83×104 mm. (a) 25 r. Donald chasing leprechaun, Ireland (horiz). (b) 25 r. Baby kangaroo surprising Pluto, Australia. (c) 25 r. Mickey and globe .. Set of 3 sheets 13·00 14·00

265 Whimbrel

266 Powder-blue Surgeonfish

(Des D. Delouise. Litho B.D.T. (6 r. 50 + 50, 30 r., 40 r.) or Questa (others))

1992 (17 Feb)–**98**. *Birds.* T **265** *and similar vert designs. Multicoloured.* P 13 (6 r. 50 + 50 l., 30 r., 40 r.) or 14½ (others).

1612	10 l. Type 265	10	10
1613	25 l. Great Egret	10	10
1614	50 l. Grey Heron	10	10
1615	2 r. Shag	20	25
1616	3 r. 50, Roseate Tern	35	40
1617	5 r. Greenshank	50	55
1617a	6 r. 50 + 50 l. Egyptian Vulture (1.1.94)	70	75
1618	8 r. Hoopoe	80	85
1619	10 r. Black-shouldered Kite	1·00	1·10
1620	25 r. Scarlet Ibis	2·50	2·75
1620a	30 r. Peregrine Falcon (1.1.94)	3·00	3·25
1620b	40 r. Black Kite (1.1.94)	4·00	4·25
1621	50 r. Grey Plover	5·00	5·50
1621a	100 r. Common Shoveler (26.10.98)	10·00	10·50
1612/21a	Set of 14	28·00	30·00

Nos. 1617a, 1620a/b and 1621a are larger, 23×32 mm.

(Des D. Miller. Litho Questa)

1992 (3 Mar). *40th Anniv of Queen Elizabeth II's Accession. Horiz designs as* T **214** *of Lesotho. Multicoloured.* P 14.

1622	1 r. Palm trees on beach	40	25
1623	3 r. 50, Path leading to jetty	1·25	1·00
1624	7 r. Tropical plant	2·00	2·50
1625	10 r. Palm trees on beach (different)	2·40	3·00
1622/5	Set of 4	5·50	6·00

MS1626 Two sheets each 74×97 mm. (a) 18 r. Dhow. (b) 18 r. Palm trees on beach (different) Set of 2 sheets 8·50 9·50

(Litho B.D.T.)

1992 (23 Mar). *Fishes.* T **266** *and similar horiz designs. Multicoloured.* P 14.

1627	7 l. Type 266	30	20
1628	20 l. Catalufa	40	25
1629	50 l. Yellow-finned Tuna	1	30
1630	1 r. Twin-spotted Snapper	75	35
1631	3 r. 50, Hawaiian Squirrelfish	1·50	1·25
1632	5 r. Picasso Triggerfish	2·00	2·00
1633	8 r. Bennett's Butterflyfish	2·25	2·50
1634	10 r. Parrotfish	2·50	2·75
1635	12 r. Coral Hind	2·75	3·00
1636	15 r. Skipjack Tuna	2·75	3·00
1627/36	Set of 10	14·00	14·00

MS1637 Four sheets, each 116×76 mm. (a) 20 r. Thread-finned Butterflyfish. (b) 20 r. Oriental Sweetlips. (c) 20 r. Two-banded Anemonefish ("Clownfish"). (d) 20 r. Clown Triggerfish
Set of 4 sheets 13·00 15·00

(Des Walt Disney Co. Litho Questa)

1992 (15 Apr). *International Stamp Exhibitions. Multicoloured designs as* T **215** *of Lesotho, showing Walt Disney cartoon characters.* P 13½×14.

(a) "Granada '92", Spain. The Alhambra

1638	2 r. Minnie Mouse in Court of the Lions	90	60
1639	5 r. Goofy in Lions Fountain	1·75	1·50
1640	8 r. Mickey Mouse at the Gate of Justice	2·25	2·50
1641	12 r. Donald Duck serenading Daisy at the Vermilion Towers	2·75	3·00
1638/41	Set of 4	7·00	7·00

MS1642 127×102 mm. 25 r. Goofy pushing Mickey in wheelbarrow .. 5·50 6·00

(b) "World Columbian Stamp Expo '92". Chicago Landmarks

1643	1 r. Mickey meeting Jean Baptiste du Sable (founder)	60	35
1644	3 r. 50, Donald Duck at Old Chicago Post Office	1·50	1·00
1645	7 r. Donald at Old Fort Dearborn	2·25	2·50
1646	15 r. Goofy in Field Museum of Natural History	3·00	3·50
1643/6	Set of 4	6·50	6·50

MS1647 127×102 mm. 25 r. Mickey and Minnie Mouse at Columbian Exposition, 1893 (horiz). P 14×13½ .. 5·50 6·00
On No. 1646 the design is wrongly captioned as the Science and Industry Museum.

267 Coastguard Patrol Boats   **268** Flowers of the United States of America

(Litho Questa)

1992 (21 Apr). *Centenary of National Security Service.* T **267** *and similar horiz designs. Multicoloured.* P 14.

1648	3 r. 50, Type 267	1·50	1·25
1649	7 r. Infantry in training	2·00	1·75
1650	10 r. Aakoatey fort	2·25	2·50
1651	15 r. Fire Service	2·75	3·00
1648/51	Set of 4	9·75	10·00

MS1652 100×68 mm. 20 r. Ceremonial procession, 1892 .. 6·00 7·00

(Des W. Wright. Litho Questa)

1992 (26 Apr). *National Flowers.* T **268** *and similar multicoloured designs.* P 14½.

1653	25 l. Type 268	40	20
1654	50 l. Australia	60	30
1655	2 r. England	1·10	75
1656	3 r. 50, Brazil	1·50	1·25
1657	5 r. Holland	2·00	2·00
1658	8 r. France	2·25	2·50
1659	10 r. Japan	2·50	2·75
1660	15 r. Africa	2·75	3·00
1653/60	Set of 8	12·00	11·50

MS1661 Two sheets, each 114×85 mm. (a) 25 r. Plumieria rubra, Classia fistula and Eugenia malaccensis (57×43 mm). (b) 25 r. Bauhinia variegata, Catharanthus roseus and Plumieria alba (57×43 mm). P 14 .. Set of 2 sheets 9·00 10·00

269 Laetiporus sulphureus   **270** Hurdling

(Litho Walsall)

1992 (14 May). *Fungi.* T **269** *and similar vert designs. Multicoloured.* P 14.

1662	10 l. Type 269	30	30
1663	25 l. Coprinus atramentarius	40	30
1664	50 l. Ganoderma lucidum	60	40
1665	3 r. 50, Russula aurata	1·25	1·00
1666	5 r. Gifola umbellata ("Polyporus umbellatus")	1·75	1·75
1667	8 r. Suillus grevillei	2·25	2·50
1668	10 r. Clavaria zollingeri	2·50	2·50
1669	25 r. Boletus edulis	6·00	6·00
1662/9	Set of 8	12·50	13·00

MS1670 Two sheets, each 100×70 mm. (a) 25 r. Marasmius oreades; (b) 25 r. Pycnoporus cinnabarinus ("Trametes cinnabarina") Set of 2 sheets 12·00 13·00

(Litho Questa)

1992 (1 June–5 Oct). *Olympic Games, Albertville and Barcelona (1st issue). Multicoloured designs as* T **216** *of Lesotho.* P 14.

1671	10 l. Pole vault	20	10
1672	25 l. Men's pommel horse (horiz)	25	15
1673	50 l. Men's shot put	30	25

1674	1 r. Men's horizontal bar (horiz)	35	30
1675	2 r. Men's triple jump (horiz)	80	65
1676	3 r. 50, Table tennis	1·10	1·10
1677	5 r. Two-man bobsled (5 Oct)	1·40	1·40
1678	7 r. Freestyle wrestling (horiz)	1·75	2·00
1679	8 r. Freestyle ski-jump (5 Oct)	1·75	2·00
1680	9 r. Baseball	2·00	2·25
1681	10 r. Women's cross-country Nordic skiing (5 Oct)	2·00	2·25
1682	12 r. Men's 200 metres backstroke (horiz)	2·00	2·25
1671/82	Set of 12	12·50	13·00

MS1683 Three sheets. (a) 100×70 mm. 25 r. Decathlon (horiz). (b) 100×70 mm. 25 r. Women's slalom skiing (horiz) (5 Oct). (c) 70×100 mm. 25 r. Men's figure skating (5 Oct)
Set of 3 sheets 12·00 13·00

(Litho Walsall)

1992 (1 June). *Olympic Games, Barcelona (2nd issue).* T **270** *and similar vert designs. Multicoloured.* P 14.

1684	10 l. Type 270	10	10
1685	1 r. Boxing	30	30
1686	3 r. 50, Women's sprinting	80	70
1687	5 r. Discus	1·25	1·25
1688	7 r. Basketball	2·50	2·25
1689	10 r. Long-distance running	2·00	2·25
1690	12 r. Aerobic gymnastics	2·25	2·50
1691	20 r. Fencing	3·00	3·75
1684/91	Set of 8	11·00	12·00

MS1692 Two sheets, each 70×100 mm. (a) 25 r. Olympic symbol and national flags. (b) 25 r. Olympic symbol and flame .. Set of 2 sheets 8·50 9·00

271 Deinonychus   **272** Destruction of LZ-129 Hindenburg (airship), 1937

(Des D. Ben-Ami. Litho Questa)

1992 (15 Sept). *"Genova '92" International Thematic Stamp Exhibition. Prehistoric Animals.* T **271** *and similar vert designs. Multicoloured.* P 14.

1693	5 l. Type 271	30	20
1694	10 l. Styracosaurus	30	20
1695	25 l. Mamenchisaurus	40	30
1696	50 l. Stenonychosaurus	50	30
1697	1 r. Parasaurolophus	60	40
1698	1 r. 25, Scelidosaurus	70	50
1699	1 r. 75, Tyrannosaurus	75	55
1700	2 r. Stegosaurus	85	60
1701	3 r. 50, Iguanodon	1·00	80
1702	4 r. Anatosaurus	1·00	90
1703	5 r. Monoclonius	1·25	1·00
1704	7 r. Tenontosaurus	1·40	1·40
1705	8 r. Brachiosaurus	1·40	1·50
1706	10 r. Euoplocephalus	1·40	1·50
1707	25 r. Triceratops	2·75	3·50
1708	50 r. Apatosaurus	5·50	6·50
1693/1708	Set of 16	18·00	17·00

MS1709 Four sheets, each 116×85 mm. (a) 25 r. Hadrosaur hatchling. (b) 25 r. Iguanodon fighting Allosaurus. (c) 25 r. Tyrannosaurus attacking Triceratops. (d) 25 r. Brachiosaurus and Iguanodons .. Set of 4 sheets 14·00 15·00

(Des Kerri Schiff. Litho Questa)

1992 (28 Oct). *Postage Stamp Mega Event, New York. Sheet 100×70 mm containing multicoloured design as* T **219** *of Lesotho, but horiz.* P 14.
MS1710 20 r. New York Public Library .. 2·50 3·00

(Des K. Grommell. Litho B.D.T.)

1992 (28 Oct). *Mysteries of the Universe.* T **272** *and similar multicoloured designs, each in separate miniature sheet.* P 14.
MS1711 Sixteen sheets, each 100×71 mm. (a) 25 r. Type 272. (b) 25 r. Loch Ness Monster. (c) 25 r. Crystal skull. (d) 25 r. Space craft in Black Hole. (e) 25 r. Ghosts (vert). (f) 25 r. Flying saucer, 1947 (vert). (g) 25 r. Bust of Plato (Atlantis). (h) 25 r. U.F.O, 1973. (i) 25 r. Crop circles. (j) 25 r. Mil Mi-26 Russian helicopter at Chernobyl nuclear explosion. (k) 25 r. Figure from Plain of Nazca. (l) 25 r. Stonehenge (vert). (m) 25 r. Yeti footprint (vert). (n) 25 r. The Pyramid of Giza. (o) 25 r. Marie Celeste (brigantine) (vert). (p) 25 r. American Grumman TBF Avenger fighter aircraft (Bermuda Triangle)
Set of 16 sheets 55·00 55·00

273 Zubin Mehta (musical director)   **274** Friedrich Schmiedl

(Litho B.D.T.)

1992 (9 Nov). *150th Anniv of New York Philharmonic Orchestra. Sheet 100×70 mm. P 14.*
MS1712 **273** 20 r. multicoloured .. .. 4·00 4·50

(Litho B.D.T.)

1992 (1 Dec). *90th Birth Anniv of Friedrich Schmiedl (rocket mail pioneer). Sheet 104×69 mm. P 14½×14.*
MS1713 **274** 25 r. multicoloured .. 5·50 6·00

275 Goofy in *Father's Weekend*, 1953

(Des Walt Disney Co. Litho Questa)

1992 (7 Dec). *60th Anniv of Goofy (Disney cartoon character). T 275 and similar multicoloured designs showing Goofy in various cartoon films. P 14×13½ (horiz) or 13½×14 (vert).*

1714	10 l. Type **275**		10	10
1715	50 l. *Symphony Hour*, 1942		35	20
1716	75 l. *Frank Duck Brings 'Em Back Alive, 1946*		45	20
1717	1 r. *Crazy with the Heat*, 1947		45	20
1718	2 r. *The Big Wash*, 1948		70	60
1719	3 r. 50, *How to Ride a Horse*, 1950		1·25	1·25
1720	5 r. *Two Gun Goofy*, 1952		1·50	1·50
1721	8 r. *Saludos Amigos*, 1943 (*vert*)		2·00	2·25
1722	10 r. *How to be a Detective*, 1952		2·00	2·25
1723	12 r. *For Whom the Bulls Toil*, 1953		2·25	2·50
1724	15 r. *Double Dribble*, 1946 (*vert*)		2·25	2·50
1714/24		Set of 11	12·00	12·00

MS1725 Three sheets, each 127×102 mm. (a) 20 r. *Double Dribble*, 1946 (*different*) (*vert*). (b) 20 r. *The Goofy Success Story*, 1955 (*vert*). (c) 20 r. *Mickey and the Beanstalk*, 1947
.. .. Set of 3 sheets 9·00 9·50

276 Minnie Mouse in "Le Missioner" (Toulouse-Lautrec)

(Des Euro-Disney, Paris. Litho Cartor)

1992 (7 Dec). *Opening of Euro-Disney Resort, France. T 276 and similar multicoloured designs showing Disney cartoon characters superimposed on Impressionist paintings. P 14×13½.*

1726	5 r. Type **276**		1·40	1·50
	a. Sheetlet. Nos. 1726/34		11·00	
1727	5 r. Goofy in "The Card Players" (Cezanne)		1·40	1·50
1728	5 r. Mickey and Minnie Mouse in "The Cafe Terrace, Place du Forum" (Van Gogh)		1·40	1·50
1729	5 r. Mickey in "The Bridge at Langlois" (Van Gogh)		1·40	1·50
1730	5 r. Goofy in "Chocolate Dancing" (Toulouse-Lautrec)		1·40	1·50
1731	5 r. Mickey and Minnie in "The Seine at Asnieres" (Renoir)		1·40	1·50
1732	5 r. Minnie in "Ball at the Moulin Rouge" (Toulouse-Lautrec)		1·40	1·50
1733	5 r. Mickey Mouse in "Wheatfield with Cypresses" (Van Gogh)		1·40	1·50
1734	5 r. Minnie in "When will you Marry?" (Gauguin)		1·40	1·50
1726/34		Set of 9	11·00	12·00

MS1735 Four sheets. (a) 128×100 mm. 20 r. Minnie as can-can dancer. P 14×13½. (b) 128×100 mm. 20 r. Goofy as cyclist. P 14×13½. (c) 100×128 mm. 20 r. Mickey as artist. P 14×13½. (d) 100×128 mm. 20 r. Donald as Frenchman (*vert*). P 13½×14 .. Set of 4 sheets 12·00 13·00
Nos. 1726/34 were printed together, *se-tenant*, in sheetlets of 9.

277 Rivers

278 Jürgen Klinsmann (Germany)

(Litho Questa)

1992 (30 Dec). *South Asian Association for Regional Co-operation Year of the Environment. T 277 and similar horiz designs showing natural and polluted environments. Multicoloured. P 14.*

1736	25 l. Type **277**	..	..	..	15	10
1737	50 l. Beaches			..	25	10
1738	5 r. Oceans			..	80	1·00
1739	10 r. Weather			..	1·50	2·00
1736/9				Set of 4	2·40	2·75

(Litho Questa)

1993 (7 Jan). *World Cup Football Championship, U.S.A. (1994) (1st issue). T 278 and similar multicoloured designs showing German players and officials. P 14.*

1740	10 l. Type **278**		15	20
1741	25 l. Pierre Littbarski		20	20
1742	50 l. Lothar Matthaus		30	20
1743	1 r. Rudi Voller		35	25
1744	2 r. Thomas Hassler		60	60
1745	3 r. 50, Thomas Berthold		1·00	1·00
1746	4 r. Jurgen Kohler		1·25	1·25
1747	5 r. Berti Vogts		1·40	1·40
1748	6 r. Bodo Illgner		1·60	1·90
1749	7 r. Klaus Augenthaler		1·75	2·00
1750	8 r. Franz Beckenbauer		1·75	2·00
1751	10 r. Andreas Brehme		2·00	2·25
1752	12 r. Guido Buchwald		2·00	2·50
1740/52		Set of 13	13·00	14·00

MS1753 Two sheets, each 103×73 mm. (a) 35 r. German players celebrating (*horiz*). (b) 35 r. Rudi Voller (*horiz*) .. Set of 2 sheets 13·00 14·00
See also Nos. 1990/8 and 2089/101.

279 German Navy Airship L-13 bombing London, 1914–18

280 Elvis Presley

(Des W. Wright and W. Hanson (Nos. 1754, 1766, MS1767a), W. Wright (others). Litho B.D.T.)

1993 (7 Jan). *Anniversaries and Events. T 279 and similar horiz designs. Multicoloured. P 14.*

1754	1 r. Type **279**		55	30
1755	3 r. 50, Radio telescope		70	70
1756	3 r. 50, Chancellor Adenauer and Pres. De Gaulle		70	70
1757	6 r. Indian Rhinoceros		2·00	1·50
1758	6 r. Columbus and globe		1·50	1·25
1759	7 r. Conference emblems		1·00	1·00
1760	8 r. Green Seaturtle		1·40	1·40
1761	10 r. *America* (yacht), 1851		1·75	1·75
1762	10 r. Melvin Jones (founder) and emblem		1·75	1·75
1763	12 r. Columbus landing on San Salvador		2·00	2·00
1764	15 r. "Voyager I" approaching Saturn		3·50	3·50
1765	15 r. Adenauer, N.A.T.O. flag and Lockheed F-104G Starfighter aircraft		3·50	3·50
1766	20 r. *Graf Zeppelin* over New York, 1929		3·50	3·50
1754/66		Set of 13	21·00	21·00

MS1767 Five sheets, each 111×80 mm. (a) 20 r. Count Ferdinand von Zeppelin. (b) 20 r. "Landsat" satellite. (c) 20 r. Konrad Adenauer. (d) 20 r. Scarlet Macaw. (e) 20 r. *Santa Maria*
.. Set of 5 sheets 19·00 20·00
Anniversaries and Events:—Nos. 1754, 1766, MS1767a, 75th death anniv of Count Ferdinand von Zeppelin; Nos. 1755, 1764, MS1767b, International Space Year; Nos. 1756, 1765, MS1767c, 25th death anniv of Konrad Adenauer; Nos. 1757, 1760, MS1767d, Earth Summit '92, Rio; Nos. 1758, 1763, MS1767e, 500th anniv of Discovery of America by Columbus; No. 1759, International Conference on Nutrition, Rome; No. 1761, Americas Cup Yachting Championship; No. 1762, 75th anniv of International Association of Lions Clubs.

(Des A. Nahigian. Litho Questa)

1993 (7 Jan). *15th Death Anniv of Elvis Presley (singer). T 280 and similar vert designs. Multicoloured. P 14.*

1768	3 r. 50, Type **280**		70	70
	a. Strip of 3. Nos. 1768/70		1·90	
1769	3 r. 50, Elvis with guitar		70	70
1770	3 r. 50, Elvis with microphone		70	70
1768/70		Set of 3	1·90	1·90

Nos. 1768/70 were printed together, horizontally and vertically *se-tenant*, in sheetlets of 9 (3×3).

(Litho Walsall)

1993 (7 Jan). *Bicentenary of the Louvre, Paris. Multicoloured designs as T 221 of Lesotho. P 12.*

1771	8 r. "The Study" (Fragonard)		90	95
	a. Sheetlet. Nos. 1771/8		7·00	
1772	8 r. "Denis Diderot" (Fragonard)		90	95
1773	8 r. "Marie-Mádelaine Guimard" (Fragonard)		90	95
1774	8 r. "Inspiration" (Fragonard)		90	95
1775	8 r. "Waterfalls, Tivoli" (Fragonard)		90	95
1776	8 r. "The Music Lesson" (Fragonard)		90	95
1777	8 r. "The Bolt" (Fragonard)		90	95
1778	8 r. "Blind-man's Buff" (Fragonard)		90	95
1779	8 r. "Self-portrait" (Corot)		90	95
	a. Sheetlet. Nos. 1779/86		7·00	
1780	8 r. "Woman in Blue" (Corot)		90	95
1781	8 r. "Woman with a Pearl" (Corot)		90	95
1782	8 r. "Young Girl at her Toilet" (Corot)		90	95
1783	8 r. "Haydée" (Corot)		90	95

1784	8 r. "Chartres Cathedral" (Corot)		90	95
1785	8 r. "The Belfry of Douai" (Corot)		90	95
1786	8 r. "The Bridge of Mantes" (Corot)		90	95
1787	8 r. "Madame Sériziat" (David)		90	95
	a. Sheetlet. Nos. 1787/94		7·00	
1788	8 r. "Pierre Sériziat" (David)		90	95
1789	8 r. "Madame De Verninac" (David)		90	95
1790	8 r. "Madame Récamier" (David)		90	95
1791	8 r. "Self-portrait" (David)		90	95
1792	8 r. "General Bonaparte" (David)		90	95
1793	8 r. "The Lictors bringing Brutus his Son's Body" (David) (left detail)		90	95
1794	8 r. "The Lictors bringing Brutus his Son's Body" (David) (right detail)		90	95
1771/94		Set of 24	21·00	22·00

MS1795 Two sheets, each 100×70 mm. (a) 20 r. "Gardens of the Villa D'Este, Tivoli" (Corot) (85×52 mm). (b) 20 r. "Tiger Cub playing with its Mother" (Delacroix) (85×52 mm). P 14½
.. .. Set of 2 sheets 7·50 8·00
Nos. 1771/8, 1779/86 and 1787/94 were each printed together, *se-tenant*, in sheetlets of 8 stamps and one centre label.

281 James Stewart and Marlene Dietrich (*Destry Rides Again*)

(Des P. Wolff and D. Lewis. Litho Questa)

1993 (18 Jan). *Famous Western Films. T 281 and similar vert designs. Multicoloured. P 13½×14.*

1796	5 r. Type **281**		80	80
	a. Sheetlet. Nos. 1796/1803		5·75	
1797	5 r. Gary Cooper (*The Westerner*)		80	80
1798	5 r. Henry Fonda (*My Darling Clementine*)		80	80
1799	5 r. Alan Ladd (*Shane*)		80	80
1800	5 r. Kirk Douglas and Burt Lancaster (*Gunfight at the O.K. Corral*)		80	80
1801	5 r. Steve McQueen (*The Magnificent Seven*)		80	80
1802	5 r. Robert Redford and Paul Newman (*Butch Cassidy and The Sundance Kid*)		80	80
1803	5 r. Jack Nicholson and Randy Quaid (*The Missouri Breaks*)		80	80
1796/1803		Set of 8	5·75	5·75

MS1804 Two sheets, each 134×120 mm. (a) 20 r. John Wayne (*The Searchers*) (French poster). (b) 20 r. Clint Eastwood (*Pale Rider*) (French poster)
.. Set of 2 sheets 6·50 6·50
Nos. 1796/1803 were printed together, *se-tenant*, in sheetlets of 8.

(Des Kerri Schiff. Litho Questa)

1993 (2 June). *40th Anniv of Coronation. Vert designs as T 224 of Lesotho. P 13½×14.*

1805	3 r. 50, multicoloured		1·00	1·10
	a. Sheetlet. Nos. 1805/8×2		9·50	
1806	5 r. multicoloured		1·25	1·40
1807	10 r. indigo and black		1·50	1·75
1808	10 r. indigo and black		1·50	1·75
1805/8		Set of 4	4·75	5·50

Designs:—No. 1805, Queen Elizabeth II at Coronation (photograph by Cecil Beaton); No. 1806, St. Edward's Crown; No. 1807, Guests in the Abbey; No. 1808, Queen Elizabeth II and Prince Philip.
Nos. 1805/8 were printed together in sheetlets of 8, containing two *se-tenant* blocks of 4.

282 Blue Goatfish

(Des S. Barlowe. Litho Cartor)

1993 (30 June). *Fishes. T 282 and similar multicoloured designs. P 14×13½.*

1809	3 r. 50, Type **282**		60	70
	a. Sheetlet. Nos. 1809/20		6·50	
1810	3 r. 50, Emperor Angelfish		60	70
1811	3 r. 50, Madagascar Butterflyfish		60	70
1812	3 r. 50, Regal Angelfish		60	70
1813	3 r. 50, Forceps Fish ("Longnose Butterflyfish")		60	70
1814	3 r. 50, Racoon Butterflyfish		60	70
1815	3 r. 50, Harlequin Filefish		60	70
1816	3 r. 50, Rectangle Triggerfish		60	70
1817	3 r. 50, Yellow-tailed Anemonefish		60	70
1818	3 r. 50, Clown Triggerfish		60	70
1819	3 r. 50, Zebra Lionfish		60	70
1820	3 r. 50, Maldive Anemonefish ("Clownfish")		60	70
1821	3 r. 50, Black-faced Butterflyfish		60	70
	a. Sheetlet. Nos. 1821/32		6·50	
1822	3 r. 50, Bird Wrasse		60	70

1823	3 r. 50, Checkerboard Wrasse			60	70
1824	3 r. 50, Yellow-faced Angelfish			60	70
1825	3 r. 50, Masked Bannerfish			60	70
1826	3 r. 50, Thread-finned Butterflyfish			60	70
1827	3 r. 50, Painted Triggerfish			60	70
1828	3 r. 50, Coral Hind			60	70
1829	3 r. 50, Pennant Coralfish			60	70
1830	3 r. 50, Black-backed Butterflyfish			60	70
1831	3 r. 50, Red-toothed Triggerfish			60	70
1832	3 r. 50, Melon Butterflyfish			60	70
1809/32			*Set of 24*	13·00	15·00

MS1833 Two sheets. (a) 69×96 mm. 25 r. Klein's Butterflyfish (*vert*). (b) 96×69 mm. 25 r. Brown Anemonefish (*vert*). P 12×13 . . *Set of 2 sheets* 8·00 8·50

Nos. 1809/20 and 1821/32 were printed together, *se-tenant*, in sheetlets of 12 with the backgrounds forming composite designs. Nos. 1810 and 1824 are both inscribed "Anglefish" in error.

283 Gull-billed Tern

284 Precious Wentletrap (*Epitonium scalare*)

(Des S. Barlowe. Litho Cartor)

1993 (5 July). *Birds. T* **283** *and similar multicoloured designs.* P 14×13½ (*horiz*) or 13½×14 (*vert*).

1834	3 r. 50, Type **283**			60	70
	a. Sheetlet. Nos. 1834/45			6·50	
1835	3 r. 50, White-tailed Tropic Bird			60	70
1836	3 r. 50, Great Frigate Bird			60	70
1837	3 r. 50, Wilson's Petrel			60	70
1838	3 r. 50, White Tern			60	70
1839	3 r. 50, Brown Booby			60	70
1840	3 r. 50, Marsh Harrier			60	70
1841	3 r. 50, Common Noddy			60	70
1842	3 r. 50, Green Heron ("Little Heron")			60	70
1843	3 r. 50, Turnstone			60	70
1844	3 r. 50, Curlew			60	70
1845	3 r. 50, Crab Plover			60	70
1846	3 r. 50, Pallid Harrier (*vert*)			60	70
	a. Sheetlet. Nos. 1846/57			6·50	
1847	3 r. 50, Cattle Egret (*vert*)			60	70
1848	3 r. 50, Koel (*vert*)			60	70
1849	3 r. 50, Tree Pipit (*vert*)			60	70
1850	3 r. 50, Short-eared Owl (*vert*)			60	70
1851	3 r. 50, Common Kestrel ("European Kestrel") (*vert*)			60	70
1852	3 r. 50, Yellow Wagtail (*vert*)			60	70
1853	3 r. 50, Grey Heron ("Common Heron") (*vert*)			60	70
1854	3 r. 50, Black Bittern (*vert*)			60	70
1855	3 r. 50, Common Snipe (*vert*)			60	70
1856	3 r. 50, Little Egret (*vert*)			60	70
1857	3 r. 50, Little Stint (*vert*)			60	70
1834/57			*Set of 24*	13·00	15·00

MS1858 Two sheets, each 105×75 mm. (a) 25 r. Caspian Tern. (b) 25 r. Audubon's Shearwater. P 13×12 . . . . *Set of 2 sheets* 8·50 9·00

Nos. 1834/45 and 1846/57 were printed together, *se-tenant*, in sheetlets of 12 with the backgrounds forming composite designs.

(Litho Questa)

1993 (15 July). *Shells. T* **284** *and similar vert designs. Multicoloured.* P 14.

1859	7 l. Type **284**			20	20
1860	15 l. Common Purple Janthina (*Janthina janthina*)			25	20
1861	50 l. Asiatic Arabian Cowrie (*Cypraea arabica asiatica*)			40	20
1862	3 r. 50, Common or Major Harp (*Harpa major*)			1·25	1·00
1863	4 r. Amplustre or Royal Paper Bubble (*Aplustrum amplustre*)			1·50	1·25
1864	5 r. Sieve Cowrie (*Cypraea cribraria*)			1·75	1·40
1865	6 r. Episcopal Mitre (*Mitra mitra*)			1·90	1·75
1866	7 r. Camp Pitar Venus (*Lioconcha castrensis*)			2·00	2·00
1867	8 r. Spotted or Eyed Auger (*Terebra guttata*)			2·00	2·25
1868	10 r. Exposed Cowrie (*Cypraea succincta*)			2·00	2·25
1869	12 r. Geographic Map Cowrie (*Cypraea mappa geographus*)			2·25	2·75
1870	20 r. Bramble Murex (*Murex tribulus*)			2·50	3·50
1859/70			*Set of 12*	16·00	17·00

MS1871 Three sheets, each 104×75 mm. (a) 25 r. Black-striped Triton (*Cymatium hepaticum*). (b) 25 r. Scorpion Conch (*Lambis scorpio*). (c) 25 r. Bull-mouth Helmet (*Cypraecassis rufa*)
. . . . *Set of 3 sheets* 16·00 17·00

285 Sifaka Lemur

286 Symbolic Heads and Arrows

(Litho Questa)

1993 (20 July). *Endangered Species. T* **285** *and similar vert designs. Multicoloured.* P 14.

1872	7 l. Type **285**			30	20
1873	10 l. Snow Leopard			30	20
1874	15 l. Numbat			30	20
1875	25 l. Gorilla			50	30
1876	2 r. Koala			70	55
1877	3 r. 50, Cheetah			90	90
1878	5 r. Yellow-footed Rock Wallaby			1·25	1·25
1879	7 r. Orang-Utan			1·75	2·00
1880	8 r. Black Lemur			1·75	2·00
1881	10 r. Black Rhinoceros			2·00	2·25
1882	15 r. Humpback Whale			2·25	2·50
1883	20 r. Mauritius Parakeet			2·75	3·00
1872/83			*Set of 12*	13·00	14·00

MS1884 Three sheets, each 104×75 mm. (a) 25 r. Giant Panda. (b) 25 r. Tiger. (c) 25 r. Indian Elephant . . . . *Set of 3 sheets* 16·00 17·00

(Litho Questa)

1993 (25 July). *Productivity Year. T* **286** *and smilar vert design. Multicoloured.* P 14.

1885	7 r. Type **286**			1·25	1·40
1886	10 r. Abstract			1·60	1·75

287 Early Astronomical Equipment

288 *Limenitis procris* and *Mussaenda*

(Des Kerri Schiff (Nos. 1890, 1894, 1896, 1898, **MS**1899d/e). Litho Questa)

1993 (11 Oct). *Anniversaries and Events. T* **287** *and similar multicoloured designs.* P 14.

1887	3 r. 50, Type **287**			70	70
1888	3 r. 50, "Still Life with Pitcher and Apples" (Picasso)			70	70
1889	3 r. 50, "Zolte Roze" (Menasze Seiden-beurel)			70	70
1890	3 r. 50, Prince Naruhito and engagement photographs (*horiz*)			70	70
1891	5 r. "Bowls and Jug" (Picasso)			80	80
1892	5 r. Krysztofory Palace, Cracow			80	80
1893	8 r. "Jabtka i Kotara" (Waclaw Borowski)			1·40	1·40
1894	8 r. Marina Kiehl (Germany) (women's downhill skiing)			1·40	1·40
1895	10 r. "Bowls of Fruit and Loaves on a Table" (Picasso)			1·60	1·60
1896	10 r. Masako Owada and engagement photographs (*horiz*)			1·60	1·60
1897	15 r. American astronaut in space			2·25	2·25
1898	15 r. Vegard Ulvang (Norway) (30km cross-country skiing)			2·25	2·25
1887/98			*Set of 12*	13·00	13·00

MS1899 Five sheets. (a) 105×75 mm. 20 r. Copernicus. (b) 105×75 mm. 20 r. "Green Still Life" (detail) (Picasso) (*horiz*). (c) 105×75 mm. 25 r. "Pejzaz Morski-Port z Doplywajacym Ststkiem" (detail) (Roman Sielski) (*horiz*). (d) 75×105 mm. 25 r. Masako Owada. (e) 105×75 mm. 25 r. Ice hockey goalkeeper *Set of 5 sheets* 16·00 17·00

Anniversaries and Events:—Nos. 1887, 1897, **MS**1899a, 450th death anniv of Copernicus (astronomer); Nos. 1888, 1891, 1895, **MS**1899b, 20th death anniv of Picasso (artist); Nos. 1889, 1892/3, **MS**1899c, "Polska '93" International Stamp Exhibition, Poznan; Nos. 1890, 1896, **MS**1899d, Marriage of Crown Prince Naruhito of Japan; Nos. 1894, 1898, **MS**1899e, Winter Olympic Games '94, Lillehammer.

(Des Tracy Pedersen. Litho B.D.T.)

1993 (25 Oct). *Butterflies and Flowers. T* **288** *and similar multicoloured designs.* P 14.

1900	7 l. Type **288**			30	20
1901	20 l. *Danaus limniace* and *Thevetia neriifolia*			45	20
1902	25 l. *Amblypodia centaurus* and *Clitoria ternatea*			45	20
1903	50 l. *Papilio crino* and *Crossandra infundibuliformis*			60	20
1904	5 r. *Mycalesis patnia* and *Thespesia populnia*			1·75	1·40
1905	6 r. 50 + 50 l. *Idea jasonia* and *Cassia glauca*			2·00	2·25
1906	7 r. *Catopsilia pomona* and *Calotropis*			2·00	2·25
1907	10 r. *Precis orithyia* and *Thunbergia grandiflora*			2·25	2·50
1908	12 r. *Vanessa cardui* and *Caesalpinia pulcherrima*			2·50	3·00
1909	15 r. *Papilio polymnestor* and *Nerium oleander*			2·75	3·25
1910	18 r. *Cirrochroa thais* and *Vinca rosea*			3·00	3·50
1911	20 r. *Pachliopta hector* and *Ixora coccinea*			3·00	3·50
1900/11			*Set of 12*	19·00	20·00

MS1912 Three sheets, each 105×72 mm. (a) 25 r. *Cheritra freja* and *Bauhinia purpurea* (*vert*). (b) 25 r. *Rohana parisatis* and *Plumeria acutifolia* (*vert*). (c) 25 r. *Hebomoia glaucippe* and *Punica granatum* (*vert*) . . *Set of 3 sheets* 15·00 16·00

289 Airship LZ-127 *Graf Zeppelin* in Searchlights

290 Ford Model "T"

(Litho Walsall)

1993 (22 Nov). *Aviation Anniversaries. T* **289** *and similar multicoloured designs.* P 14.

1913	3 r. 50, Type **289**			80	55
1914	5 r. Homing pigeon and message from Santa Catalina mail service, 1894			1·00	90
1915	10 r. Eckener and airship LZ-127 *Graf Zeppelin*			1·75	1·75
1916	15 r. Pilot's badge and loading Philadelphia–Washington mail, 1918			2·50	3·00
1917	20 r. U.S.S. *Macon* (airship) and mooring mast, 1933			2·50	3·00
1913/17			*Set of 5*	7·75	8·25

MS1918 Two sheets. (a) 70×100 mm. 25 r. Santos Dumont's airship *Balloon No. 5* and Eiffel Tower. 1901. (b) 100×70 mm. 25 r. Jean-Pierre Blanchard's balloon, 1793 (*vert*) . . *Set of 2 sheets* 6·00 7·00

Anniversaries:—Nos. 1913, 1915, 1917, **MS**1918a, 125th birth anniv of Hugo Eckener (airship pioneer); Nos. 1914, 1916, **MS**1918b, Bicent of First Airmail Flight.

(Litho Questa)

1993 (22 Nov). *Centenaries of Henry Ford's First Petrol Engine* (Nos. 1919/30, **MS**1943a) *and Karl Benz's First Four-wheeled Car* (others). *T* **290** *and similar horiz designs.* P 14.

1919	3 r. 50, multicoloured			70	70
	a. Sheetlet. Nos. 1919/30			7·50	
1920	3 r. 50, multicoloured			70	70
1921	3 r. 50, black and reddish violet			70	70
1922	3 r. 50, multicoloured			70	70
1923	3 r. 50, multicoloured			70	70
1924	3 r. 50, multicoloured			70	70
1925	3 r. 50, multicoloured			70	70
1926	3 r. 50, multicoloured			70	70
1927	3 r. 50, multicoloured			70	70
1928	3 r. 50, multicoloured			70	70
1929	3 r. 50, multicoloured			70	70
1930	3 r. 50, black, light brown & reddish violet			70	70
1931	3 r. 50, multicoloured			70	70
	a. Sheetlet. Nos. 1931/42			7·50	
1932	3 r. 50, multicoloured			70	70
1933	3 r. 50, greenish black, black & reddish vio			70	70
1934	3 r. 50, multicoloured			70	70
1935	3 r. 50, multicoloured			70	70
1936	3 r. 50, multicoloured			70	70
1937	3 r. 50, multicoloured			70	70
1938	3 r. 50, multicoloured			70	70
1939	3 r. 50, multicoloured			70	70
1940	3 r. 50, multicoloured			70	70
1941	3 r. 50, multicoloured			70	70
1942	3 r. 50, black, light brown & reddish violet			70	70
1919/42			*Set of 24*	15·00	15·00

MS1943 Two sheets, each 100×70 mm. (a) 25 r. multicoloured. (b) 25 r. multicoloured
. . . . *Set of 2 sheets* 9·00 9·50

Designs:—No. 1920, Henry Ford; No. 1921, Plans of first petrol engine; No. 1922, Ford "Probe GT", 1993; No. 1923, Front of Ford "Sportsman", 1947; No. 1924, Back of Ford "Sportsman"; No. 1925, Advertisement of 1915; No. 1926, Ford "Thunderbird", 1955; No. 1927, Ford logo; No. 1928, Ford "Edsel Citation", 1958; No. 1929, Ford half-ton pickup, 1941; No. 1930, Silhouette of early Ford car; No. 1931, Daimler-Benz "Straight 8", 1937; No. 1932, Karl Benz; No. 1933, Mercedes-Benz poster; No. 1934, Mercedes "38-250SS", 1929; No. 1935, Benz "Viktoria", 1893; No. 1936, Benz logo; No. 1937, Plan of Mercedes engine; No. 1938, Mercedes-Benz "300SL Gullwing", 1952; No. 1939, Mercedes-Benz "SL", 1993; No. 1940, Front of Benz 4-cylinder car, 1906; No. 1941, Back of Benz 4-cylinder car and advertisement; No. 1942, Silhouette of early Benz car; No. **MS**1943a, Ford Model "Y", 1933; No. **MS**1943b, Mercedes "300S", 1955.

Nos. 1919/30 and 1931/42 were printed together, *se-tenant*, in sheetlets of 12 each forming a composite design.

291 Ivan, Sonia, Sasha and Peter in the Snow

(Des Rosemary DeFiglio. Litho Questa)

1993 (20 Dec). *Peter and the Wolf. T* **291** *and similar horiz designs showing scenes from Walt Disney's cartoon film. Multicoloured.* P 14×13½.

1944	7 l. Type **291**			15	15
1945	15 l. Grandpa and Peter			20	20
1946	20 l. Peter on bridge			20	20
1947	25 l. Yascha, Vladimir and Mischa			20	20
1948	50 l. Sasha on lookout			30	20
1949	1 r. The Wolf			35	25

1950	3 r. 50, Peter dreaming	60	60
	a. Sheetlet. Nos. 1950/8 ..	4·75	
1951	3 r. 50, Peter taking gun ..	60	60
1952	3 r. 50, Peter with gun in snow ..	60	60
1953	3 r. 50, Sasha and Peter ..	60	60
1954	3 r. 50, Sonia and Peter ..	60	60
1955	3 r. 50, Peter with Ivan and Sasha	60	60
1956	3 r. 50, Ivan warning Peter of the Wolf	60	60
1957	3 r. 50, Ivan, Peter and Sasha in tree	60	60
1958	3 r. 50, Wolf below tree ..	60	60
1959	3 r. 50, Wolf and Sonia ..	60	60
	a. Sheetlet. Nos. 1959/67 ..	4·75	
1960	3 r. 50, Sasha attacking the Wolf ..	60	60
1961	3 r. 50, Sasha walking into Wolf's mouth	60	60
1962	3 r. 50, Peter firing pop gun at Wolf ..	60	60
1963	3 r. 50, Wolf chasing Sonia ..	60	60
1964	3 r. 50, Ivan tying rope to Wolf's tail	60	60
1965	3 r. 50, Peter and Ivan hoisting Wolf	60	60
1966	3 r. 50, Sasha and the hunters ..	60	60
1967	3 r. 50, Ivan and Peter on Wolf hanging from tree ..	60	60
1944/67	*Set of 24*	11·00	11·00

MS1968 Two sheets. (a) 102×127 mm. 25 r. Sonia as an angel. (b) 127×102 mm. 25 r. Ivan looking proud .. *Set of 2 sheets* 8·00 8·50

Nos. 1950/8 and 1959/67 were printed together, *se-tenant*, in sheetlets of 9.

292 "Girl with a Broom" (Rembrandt)

(Des Kerri Schiff. Litho Cartor)

1994 (2 Feb). *Famous Paintings by Rembrandt and Matisse. T 292 and similar multicoloured designs. P 13.*

1969	50 l. Type 292 ..	30	15
1970	2 r. "Girl with Tulips" (Matisse)	65	50
1971	3 r. 50, "Young Girl at half-open Door" (Rembrandt) ..	1·00	90
1972	3 r. 50, "Portrait of Greta Moll" (Matisse)	1·00	90
1973	5 r. "The Prophetess Hannah" (Rembrandt) ..	1·25	1·00
1974	6 r. 50, "The Idol" (Matisse) ..	1·50	1·50
1975	7 r. "Woman with a Pink Flower" (Rembrandt) ..	1·50	1·50
1976	9 r. "Mme Matisse in a Japanese Robe" (Matisse) ..	1·75	2·00
1977	10 r. "Portrait of Mme Matisse" (Matisse)	1·75	2·00
1978	12 r. "Lucretia" (Rembrandt) ..	2·00	2·25
1979	15 r. "Lady with an Ostrich Feather Fan" (Rembrandt) ..	2·00	2·50
1980	15 r. "The Woman with the Hat" (Matisse)	2·00	2·50
1969/80	*Set of 12*	15·00	16·00

MS1981 Three sheets. (a) 106×132 mm. 25 r. "The Music-makers" (detail) (Rembrandt). (b) 132×106 mm. 25 r. "Married Couple with Three Children" (detail) (Rembrandt) (*horiz*). (c) 132×106 mm. 25 r. "The Painter's Family" (detail) (Matisse) .. *Set of 3 sheets* 13·00 14·00

No. 1979 is inscribed "The Lady with an Ostich Feather Fan" in error.

293 Hong Kong 1983 $1 Space Museum Stamp and Moon-lantern Festival

294 Vase

(Des W. Hanson. Litho Questa)

1994 (18 Feb). *"Hong Kong '94" International Stamp Exhibition (1st issue). T 293 and similar horiz design. Multicoloured. P 14.*

1982	4 r. Type 293 ..	50	70
	a. Horiz pair. Nos. 1982/3 ..	1·00	1·40
1983	4 r. Maldive Islands 1976 5 r. "Viking" space mission stamp and Moon-lantern Festival ..	50	70

Nos. 1982/3 were printed together, *se-tenant*, in horizontal pairs throughout the sheet with the centre part of each pair forming a composite design.

(Des Kerri Schiff. Litho Questa)

1994 (18 Feb). *"Hong Kong '94" International Stamp Exhibition (2nd issue). Ching Dynasty Cloisonné Enamelware. T 294 and similar vert designs. Multicoloured. P 14.*

1984	2 r. Type 294 ..	35	35
	a. Sheetlet. Nos. 1984/9 ..	1·90	
1985	2 r. Flower holder ..	35	35

1986	2 r. Elephant with vase on back ..	35	35
1987	2 r. Tibetan style lama's teapot ..	35	35
1988	2 r. Fo-Dog ..	35	35
1989	2 r. Teapot with swing handle ..	35	35
1984/9	*Set of 6*	1·90	1·90

Nos. 1984/9 were printed, *se-tenant*, in sheetlets of 6.

295 Windischmann (U.S.A.) and Giannini (Italy)

296 Humpback Whale

(Litho Questa)

1994 (28 Feb). *World Cup Football Championship, U.S.A. (2nd issue). T 295 and similar multicoloured designs. P 14.*

1990	7 l. Type 295 ..	20	15
1991	20 l. Carnevale (Italy) and Gascoigne (England) ..	30	20
1992	25 l. England players congratulating Platt	30	20
1993	3 r. 50, Koeman (Holland) and Klinsmann (Germany) ..	85	70
1994	5 r. Quinn (Ireland) and Maldini (Italy)	1·10	90
1995	7 r. Lineker (England) ..	1·50	1·50
1996	15 r. Hassam (Egypt) and Moran (Ireland)	2·50	3·00
1997	18 r. Canniggia (Argentina) ..	2·75	3·00
1990/7	*Set of 8*	8·50	8·75

MS1998 Two sheets, each 103×73 mm. (a) 25 r. Ogris (Austria). (b) 25 r. Conejo (Costa Rica) (*horiz*) .. *Set of 2 sheets* 9·00 9·50

(Litho Questa)

1994 (20 May). *Centenary of Sierra Club (environmental protection society) (1992). Endangered Species. T 296 and similar multicoloured designs. P 14.*

1999	6 r. 50, Type 296 ..	1·25	1·25
	a. Sheetlet. Nos. 1999/2004 ..	6·50	
2000	6 r. 50, Ocelot crouched in grass	1·25	1·25
2001	6 r. 50, Ocelot sitting ..	1·25	1·25
2002	6 r. 50, Snow Monkey ..	1·25	1·25
2003	6 r. 50, Prairie Dog ..	1·25	1·25
2004	6 r. 50, Golden Lion Tamarin ..	1·25	1·25
2005	6 r. 50, Prairie Dog eating (*horiz*)	1·25	1·25
	a. Sheetlet. Nos. 2005/10 ..	6·50	
2006	6 r. 50, Prairie Dog outside burrow (*horiz*)	1·25	1·25
2007	6 r. 50, Herd of Woodland Caribou (*horiz*)	1·25	1·25
2008	6 r. 50, Woodland Caribou facing left (*horiz*) ..	1·25	1·25
2009	6 r. 50, Woodland Caribou facing right (*horiz*) ..	1·25	1·25
2010	6 r. 50, Pair of Galapagos Penguins (*horiz*)	1·25	1·25
2011	6 r. 50, Galapagos Penguin facing right	1·25	1·25
	a. Sheetlet. Nos. 2011/18 ..	9·00	
2012	6 r. 50, Galapagos Penguin looking straight ahead ..	1·25	1·25
2013	6 r. 50, Bengal Tiger looking straight ahead ..	1·25	1·25
2014	6 r. 50, Bengal Tiger looking right	1·25	1·25
2015	6 r. 50, Philippine Tarsier with tree trunk at left ..	1·25	1·25
2016	6 r. 50, Philippine Tarsier with tree trunk at right ..	1·25	1·25
2017	6 r. 50, Head of Philippine Tarsier	1·25	1·25
2018	6 r. 50, Sierra Club Centennial emblem (black, buff and deep turquoise-green)	1·25	1·25
2019	6 r. 50, Golden Lion Tamarin between two branches (*horiz*) ..	1·25	1·25
	a. Sheetlet. Nos. 2019/26 ..	9·00	
2020	6 r. 50, Golden Lion Tamarin on tree trunk (*horiz*) ..	1·25	1·25
2021	6 r. 50, Tail fin of Humpback Whale and coastline (*horiz*) ..	1·25	1·25
2022	6 r. 50, Tail fin of Humpback Whale at night (*horiz*) ..	1·25	1·25
2023	6 r. 50, Bengal Tiger (*horiz*) ..	1·25	1·25
2024	6 r. 50, Ocelot (*horiz*) ..	1·25	1·25
2025	6 r. 50, Snow Monkey in water climbing out of pool (*horiz*) ..	1·25	1·25
2026	6 r. 50, Snow Monkey swimming (*horiz*)	1·25	1·25
1999/2026	*Set of 28*	30·00	30·00

Nos. 1999/2004, 2005/10, 2011/18 and 2019/26 were each printed together, *se-tenant*, as two sheetlets of 6 (Nos. 1999/2010) or two sheetlets of 8 (Nos. 2011/18).

297 Dome of the Rock, Jerusalem

298 Elasmosaurus

(Litho Cartor)

1994 (10 June). *Solidarity with the Palestinians. P 13½×14.*

2027	297 8 r. multicoloured ..	1·40	1·50

(Des L. Birmingham. Litho B.D.T.)

1994 (20 June). *Prehistoric Animals. T 298 and similar multicoloured designs. P 14.*

2028/59	25 l., 50 l., 1 r., 3 r. x 24, 5 r., 8 r., 10 r., 15 r., 20 r. .. *Set of 32*	26·00	26·00

MS2060 Two sheets, each 106×76 mm. (a) 25 r. Gallimimus. (b) 25 r. Plateosaurus (*vert*) .. *Set of 2 sheets* 8·00 8·50

Nos. 2031/42 and 2043/54 were each printed together, *se-tenant*, in sheetlets of 12 forming composite designs. The species depicted are, in addition to Type 298, Dilophosaurus, Avimimus, Dimorphodon, Megalosaurus, Kuehneosaurus, Dryosaurus, Kentrosaurus, Baraposaurus, Tenontosaurus, Elaphrosaurus, Maiasaura, Huayangosaurus, Rutiodon, Pianitzkysaurus, Quetzalcoatlus, Daspletosaurus, Pleurocoelus, Baryonyx, Pentaceratops, Kritosaurus, Microvenator, Nodosaurus, Montanaceratops, Dromiceiomimus, Drypto-saurus, Parkosaurus, Chasmosaurus, Edmontonia, Anatosaurus, Velociraptor and Spinosaurus.

299 Mallet Steam Locomotive, Indonesia

300 Japanese Bobtail

(Des K. Gromell. Litho B.D.T.)

1994 (4 July). *Railway Locomotives of Asia. T 299 and similar multicoloured designs. P 14.*

2061	25 l. Type 299 ..	20	20
2062	50 l. Class C62 steam locomotive, Japan, 1948 ..	25	20
2063	1 r. Class D51 steam locomotive, Japan, 1936 (*horiz*) ..	30	20
2064	5 r. Steam locomotive, India (*horiz*) ..	90	90
2065	6 r. 50 + 50 l. Class W steam locomotive, India (*horiz*) ..	1·25	1·50
	a. Sheetlet. Nos. 2065/70 ..	6·50	
2066	6 r. 50 + 50 l. Class C53 steam locomotive, Indonesia (*horiz*) ..	1·25	1·50
2067	6 r. 50 + 50 l. Class C10 steam locomotive, Japan (*horiz*) ..	1·25	1·50
2068	6 r. 50 + 50 l. Hanomag steam locomotive, India (*horiz*) ..	1·25	1·50
2069	6 r. 50 + 50 l. Hikari express train, Japan (*horiz*) ..	1·25	1·50
2070	6 r. 50 + 50 l. Class C55 steam locomotive, Japan, 1935 (*horiz*) ..	1·25	1·50
2071	8 r. Class 485 electric locomotive, Japan (*horiz*) ..	1·50	1·75
2072	10 r. Class WP steam locomotive, India (*horiz*) ..	1·75	2·00
2073	15 r. Class RM steam locomotive, China (*horiz*) ..	2·00	2·25
2074	20 r. Class C57 steam locomotive, Japan, 1937 ..	2·25	2·50
2061/74	*Set of 14*	15·00	17·00

MS2075 Two sheets, each 110×80 mm. (a) 25 r. Steam locomotive pulling goods train, Indonesia (*horiz*). (b) 25 r. Class 8620 steam locomotive, Japan, 1914 (*horiz*) .. *Set of 2 sheets* 8·00 8·50

Nos. 2065/70 were printed together, *se-tenant* in sheetlets of 6. No. 2069 is inscribed "Hakari" in error.

(Litho Questa)

1994 (11 July). *Cats. T 297 and similar multicoloured designs. P 14.*

2076	7 l. Type 297 ..	20	20
2077	20 l. Siamese (*vert*) ..	35	20
2078	25 l. Persian Longhair ..	35	20
2079	50 l. Somali (*vert*) ..	40	20
2080	3 r. 50, Oriental Shorthair ..	1·00	80
2081	5 r. Burmese ..	1·25	1·00
2082	7 r. Bombay carrying kitten ..	1·50	1·50
2083	10 r. Turkish Van (*vert*) ..	1·50	1·75
2084	12 r. Javanese (*vert*) ..	1·75	2·00
2085	15 r. Singapura (*vert*) ..	2·00	2·50
2086	18 r. Turkish Angora (*vert*) ..	2·25	2·75
2087	20 r. Egyptian Mau (*vert*) ..	2·25	2·75
2076/87	*Set of 12*	13·00	14·00

MS2088 Three sheets. (a) 70×100 mm. 25 r. Birman (*vert*). (b) 70×100 mm. 25 r. Korat (*vert*). (c) 100×70 mm. 25 r. Abyssinian (*vert*) .. *Set of 3 sheets* 12·00 13·50

301 Franco Baresi (Italy) and
Stuart McCall (Scotland)

(Litho Questa)

1994 (4 Aug). *World Cup Football Championship, U.S.A. (3rd issue).* T **301** *and similar multicoloured designs.* P 14.

(a) Horiz designs

2089	10 l. Type 301		40	40
	a. Sheetlet. Nos. 2089/94		4·75	
2090	25 l. Mick McCarthy (Ireland) and Gary Lineker (England)		50	50
2091	50 l. J. Helt (Denmark) and R. Gordillo (Spain)		50	50
2092	5 r. Martin Vasquez (Spain) and Enzo Scifo (Belgium)		1·00	1·00
2093	10 r. Championship emblem		1·40	1·40
2094	12 r. Tomas Brolin (Sweden) and Gordon Durie (Scotland)		1·60	1·60

(b) Vert designs

2095	6 r. 50, Bebeto (Brazil)		1·10	1·10
	a. Sheetlet. Nos. 2095/100		6·00	
2096	6 r. 50, Lothar Matthaus (Germany)		1·10	1·10
2097	6 r. 50, Diego Maradona (Argentina)		1·10	1·10
2098	6 r. 50, Stephane Chapuasti (Switzerland)		1·10	1·10
2099	6 r. 50, George Hagi (Rumania)		1·10	1·10
2100	6 r. 50, Carlos Valderama (Colombia)		1·10	1·10
2089/100		*Set of 12*	10·50	10·50
MS2101	100×70 mm. 10 r. Egyptian players		3·50	3·50

Nos. 2089/94 and 2095/100 were each printed together, *se-tenant*, in sheetlets of 6.

302 Crew of "Apollo 11"

303 Linford Christie (Great Britain) (100 metres), 1992

(Des W. Hanson. Litho B.D.T.)

1994 (8 Aug). *25th Anniv of First Moon Landing.* T **302** *and similar multicoloured designs.* P 14.

2102	5 r. Type 302		90	90
	a. Sheetlet. Nos. 2102/7		4·75	
2103	5 r. "Apollo 11" mission logo		90	90
2104	5 r. Edwin Aldrin (astronaut) and *Eagle*		90	90
2105	5 r. Crew of "Apollo 12"		90	90
2106	5 r. "Apollo 12" mission logo		90	90
2107	5 r. Alan Bean (astronaut) and equipment		90	90
2108	5 r. Crew of "Apollo 16"		90	90
	a. Sheetlet. Nos. 2108/13		4·75	
2109	5 r. "Apollo 16" mission logo		90	90
2110	5 r. Astronauts with U.S. flag		90	90
2111	5 r. Crew of "Apollo 17"		90	90
2112	5 r. "Apollo 17" mission logo		90	90
2113	5 r. Launch of "Apollo 17"		90	90
2102/13		*Set of 12*	9·50	9·50
MS2114	100×76 mm. 25 r. Launch of Russian rocket from Baikonur (*vert*)		3·50	4·00

Nos. 2102/7 and 2108/13 were printed together, *se-tenant*, in sheetlets of 6.

(Des Kerri Schiff. Litho Questa)

1994 (8 Aug). *Centenary of International Olympic Committee. Gold Medal Winners.* T **303** *and similar vert designs. Multicoloured.* P 14.

2115	7 r. Type 303		1·50	1·25
2116	12 r. Koji Gushiken (Japan) (gymnastics), 1984		1·75	2·00
MS2117	106×71 mm. 25 r. George Hackl (Germany) (single luge), 1994		3·50	4·00

304 U.S. Amphibious DUKW

(Des J. Batchelor. Litho Questa)

1994 (8 Aug). *50th Anniv of D-Day.* T **304** *and similar horiz designs. Multicoloured.* P 14.

2118	2 r. Type 304		45	30
2119	4 r. Tank landing craft unloading at Sword Beach		75	60
2120	18 r. Infantry landing craft at Omaha Beach		3·00	4·00
2118/20		*Set of 3*	3·75	4·50
MS2121	105×76 mm. 25 r. Landing craft with Canadian commandos		3·75	4·25

305 Duckpond, Suwan Folk Village

306 U.S. "Voyager 2" Satellite

(Des Kerri Schiff. Litho B.D.T. (3 r.) or Questa (others))

1994 (8 Aug). *"Philakorea '94" International Stamp Exhibition, Seoul.* T **305** *and similar multicoloured designs.* P 13½×14 (Nos. 2123/30) or 14 (others).

2122	50 l. Type 305		15	15
2123	3 r. Pear-shaped bottle		45	45
	a. Sheetlet. Nos. 2123/30		3·25	
2124	3 r. Vase with dragon decoration		45	45
2125	3 r. Vase with repaired lip		45	45
2126	3 r. Stoneware vase with floral decoration		45	45
2127	3 r. Celadon-glazed vase		45	45
2128	3 r. Unglazed stone vase		45	45
2129	3 r. Ritual water sprinkler		45	45
2130	3 r. Long-necked celadon-glazed vase		45	45
2131	3 r. 50, Yongduson Park		50	50
2132	20 r. Ploughing with ox, Hahoe		3·00	3·75
2122/32		*Set of 11*	6·50	7·25
MS2133	70×102 mm. 25 r. "Hunting" (detail from eight-panel painted screen (*vert*)		3·25	4·00

Nos. 2123/30, each 24×47 mm, were printed together, *se-tenant*, in sheetlets of 8.

(Des Outsiders Group. Litho Questa)

1994 (8 Aug). *Space Exploration.* T **306** *and similar multicoloured designs.* P 14.

2134	5 r. Type 306		85	85
	a. Sheetlet. Nos. 2134/45		9·00	
2135	5 r. Russian "Sputnik" satellite		85	85
2136	5 r. "Apollo-Soyuz" mission		85	85
2137	5 r. "Apollo 10" on parachutes		85	85
2138	5 r. "Apollo 11" mission flag		85	85
2139	5 r. Hubble space telescope		85	85
2140	5 r. Edwin "Buzz" Aldrin (astronaut)		85	85
2141	5 r. RCA lunar camera		85	85
2142	5 r. Lunar Rover (space buggy)		85	85
2143	5 r. Jim Irwin (astronaut)		85	85
2144	5 r. "Apollo 12" lunar module		85	85
2145	5 r. Astronaut holding equipment		85	85
2134/45		*Set of 12*	9·00	9·00
MS2146	Two sheets. (a) 70×100 mm. 25 r. David Scott (astronaut) in open hatch of "Apollo 9". (b) 100×70 mm. 25 r. Alan Shepherd Jr. (astronaut) (*horiz*)		*Set of 2 sheets*	8·50 9·00

Nos. 2134/45 were printed together, *se-tenant*, in sheetlets of 12 forming a composite design.

307 Mother, Child, Old Man and Town Skyline

(Litho Questa)

1994 (24 Oct). *United Nations Development Programme.* T **307** *and similar horiz design. Multicoloured.* P 14.

2147	1 r. Type 307		15	10
2148	8 r. Fisherman with son and island		1·40	1·50

308 School Band

(Litho Questa)

1994 (28 Nov). *50th Anniv of Aminiya School. Children's Paintings.* T **308** *and similar multicoloured designs.* P 14.

2149	15 l. Type 308		10	10
2150	50 l. Classroom		20	15
2151	1 r. School emblem and hand holding book (*vert*)		30	15
2152	8 r. School girls holding books (*vert*)		1·75	2·00
2153	10 r. Sporting activities		1·75	2·00
2154	11 r. School girls holding crown (*vert*)		1·90	2·25
2155	13 r. Science lesson		1·90	2·25
2149/55		*Set of 7*	7·00	8·00

309 Boeing 747

(Des W. Wright. Litho B.D.T.)

1994 (31 Dec). *50th Anniv of International Civil Aviation Organization.* T **309** *and similar horiz designs. Multicoloured.* P 14.

2156	50 l. Type 309		30	15
2157	1 r. Hawker Siddeley ("de Havilland") Comet 4		35	20
2158	2 r. Male International Airport		60	50
2159	3 r. Lockheed L.1649 Super Star		75	75
2160	8 r. European Airbus		1·40	1·50
2161	10 r. Dornier Do-228		1·50	1·60
2156/61		*Set of 6*	4·50	4·25
MS2162	100×70 mm. 25 r. Concorde		3·75	4·00

310 Pintail ("Northern Pintail")

(Des Outsiders Group. Litho Questa)

1995 (27 Feb). *Ducks.* T **310** *and similar multicoloured designs.* P 14.

2163	5 r. Type 310		75	75
	a. Sheetlet. Nos. 2163/71		6·00	
2164	5 r. Comb Duck		75	75
2165	5 r. Ruddy Shelduck		75	75
2166	5 r. Garganey		75	75
2167	5 r. Indian Whistling Duck ("Lesser Whistling Duck")		75	75
2168	5 r. Green-winged Teal		75	75
2169	5 r. Fulvous Whistling Duck		75	75
2170	5 r. Common Shoveler ("Northern Shoveler")		75	75
2171	5 r. Cotton Pygmy Goose		75	75
2172	6 r. 50 + 50 l. European Pochard (*vert*)		85	85
	a. Sheetlet. Nos. 2172/80		7·00	
2173	6 r. 50 + 50 l. Mallard (*vert*)		85	85
2174	6 r. 50 + 50 l. European Wigeon (*vert*)		85	85
2175	6 r. 50 + 50 l. Common Shoveler ("Northern Shoveler") (*vert*)		85	85
2176	6 r. 50 + 50 l. Pintail (*vert*)		85	85
2177	6 r. 50 + 50 l. Garganey (*vert*)		85	85
2178	6 r. 50 + 50 l. Tufted Duck (*vert*)		85	85
2179	6 r. 50 + 50 l. Red-crested Pochard ("Ferruginous Duck") (*vert*)		85	85
2180	6 r. 50 + 50 l. Ferruginous Duck ("Red-crested Pochard") (*vert*)		85	85
2163/80		*Set of 18*	13·00	13·00
MS2181	Two sheets. (a) 100×71 mm. 25 r. Spotbill Duck ("Garganey"). (b) 73×100 mm. 25 r. Cotton Pygmy Goose (*vert*) *Set of 2 sheets*			7·50 7·50

Nos. 2163/71 and 2172/80 were printed together, *se-tenant*, in sheetlets of 9, each with enlarged top margin, forming composite designs.

311 Taj Mahal, India

(Litho Questa)

1995 (28 Feb). *Famous Monuments of the World.* T **311** *and similar multicoloured designs.* P 14.

2182	7 l. Type 311		10	10
2183	10 l. Washington Monument, U.S.A.		10	10
2184	15 l. Mount Rushmore, U.S.A.		10	10
2185	25 l. Arc de Triomphe, Paris (*vert*)		10	10
2186	50 l. Sphinx, Egypt (*vert*)		20	20
2187	5 r. El Castillo, Toltec pyramid, Yucatan		70	70
2188	8 r. Toltec statue, Tula, Mexico (*vert*)		1·00	1·25
2189	12 r. Victory Column, Berlin (*vert*)		1·40	1·75
2182/9		*Set of 8*	3·25	3·75
MS2190	Two sheets, each 112×85 mm. (a) 25 r. Easter Island statue (42×56 mm). (b) 25 r. Stonehenge, Wiltshire (85×28 mm) *Set of 2 sheets*			7·50 7·50

PRICES OF SETS

Set prices are given for many issues, generally those containing three stamps or more. Definitive sets include one of each value or major colour change, but do not cover different perforations, die types or minor shades. Where a choice is possible the set prices are based on the cheapest versions of the stamps included in the listings.

312 Donald Duck driving Chariot

(Des Rosemary DeFiglio. Litho B.D.T.)

1995 (22 Mar). *History of Wheeled Transport.* T **312** *and similar multicoloured designs showing scenes from Disney cartoon film* Donald and the Wheel. *P* 13.

2191	3 l.	Type 312	10	10
2192	4 l.	Donald with log	10	10
2193	5 l.	Donald driving Stephenson's *Rocket*	10	10
2194	10 l.	Donald pondering over circle (*vert*)	10	10
2195	20 l.	Donald in crashed car (*vert*)	10	10
2196	25 l.	Donald listening to early gramophone	10	10
2197	5 r.	Donald on Mammoth	75	75
2198	20 r.	Donald pushing early car	2·75	3·25
2191/8		*Set of 8*	3·50	4·00

313 Donald Duck playing Saxophone   **314 Islamic Centre, Malé**

(Des Alvin White Studios. Litho B.D.T)

1995 (22 Mar). *60th Birthday of Donald Duck.* T **313** *and similar multicoloured designs showing Walt Disney cartoon characters. P* 13.

2199	5 r.	Type 313	80	80
		a. Sheetlet. Nos. 2199/206	5·50	
2200	5 r.	Moby Duck playing fiddle	80	80
2201	5 r.	Feathry Duck with banjo and drum	80	80
2202	5 r.	Daisy Duck playing harp	80	80
2203	5 r.	Gladstone Gander with clarinet	80	80
2204	5 r.	Huey, Dewey and Louie with bassoon	80	80
2205	5 r.	Gus Goose playing flute	80	80
2206	5 r.	Prof. Ludwig von Drake playing trombone	80	80
2207	5 r.	Daisy picking flowers	80	80
		a. Sheetlet. Nos. 2207/14	5·50	
2208	5 r.	Donald with backpack	80	80
2209	5 r.	Grandma Duck with kitten	80	80
2210	5 r.	Gus Goose and pie	80	80
2211	5 r.	Gyro Gearloose in space	80	80
2212	5 r.	Huey, Dewey and Louie photographing porcupine	80	80
2213	5 r.	Prof. Ludwig von Drake	80	80
2214	5 r.	Scrooge McDuck with money	80	80
2199/214		*Set of 16*	11·00	11·00

MS2215 Four sheets. (a) 108×130 mm. 25 r. Donald playing banjo. (b) 133×108 mm. 25 r. Donald posing for photo. (c) 108×130 mm. 25 r. Donald conducting (*horiz*). (d) 102×121 mm. 25 r. Huey, Dewey and Louie (*horiz*)

Set of 4 sheets 14·00 15·00

Nos. 2199/206 and 2207/14 were printed together, *se-tenant*, in sheetlets of 8.

(Litho Questa)

1995 (1 May). *Eid Greetings.* T **314** *and similar vert designs. Multicoloured. P* 14.

2216	1 r.	Type 314	15	15
2217	1 r.	Rose	15	15
2218	8 r.	Orchid	1·25	1·25
2219	10 r.	Orchid (*different*)	1·25	1·25
2216/19		*Set of 4*	2·50	2·50

315 Killer Whale

(Des K. Gromell. Litho Questa)

1995 (16 May). *"Singapore '95" International Stamp Exhibition* (1st issue). *Whales, Dolphins and Porpoises.* T **315** *and similar horiz designs. Multicoloured. P* 14.

2220	1 r.	Type 315	20	20
2221	2 r.	Bottlenose Dolphins	35	35
2222	3 r.	Right Whale	50	50
		a. Sheetlet. Nos. 2222/33	5·50	
2223	3 r.	Pair of Killer Whales	50	50
2224	3 r.	Humpback Whale	50	50
2225	3 r.	Pair of Belugas	50	50
2226	3 r.	Narwhal	50	50

2227	3 r.	Head of Blue Whale	50	50
2228	3 r.	Bowhead Whale	50	50
2229	3 r.	Head of Fin Whale	50	50
2230	3 r.	Pair of Pilot Whales	50	50
2231	3 r.	Grey Whale	50	50
2232	3 r.	Sperm Whale	50	50
2233	3 r.	Pair of Goosebeaked Whales	50	50
2234	3 r.	Hourglass Dolphin	50	50
		a. Sheetlet. Nos. 2234/45	5·50	
2235	3 r.	Bottlenose Dolphin (*different*)	50	50
2236	3 r.	Dusky Dolphin	50	50
2237	3 r.	Spectacled Porpoise	50	50
2238	3 r.	Fraser's Dolphin	50	50
2239	3 r.	Camerson's Dolphin	50	50
2240	3 r.	Pair of Spinner Dolphins	50	50
2241	3 r.	Pair of Dalls Dolphins	50	50
2242	3 r.	Spotted Dolphin	50	50
2243	3 r.	Indus River Dolphin	50	50
2244	3 r.	Hector's Dolphin	50	50
2245	3 r.	Amazon River Dolphin	50	50
2246	8 r.	Humpback Whale and calf	1·00	1·00
2247	10 r.	Common Dolphin	1·25	1·25
2220/47		*Set of 28*	13·00	13·00

MS2248 Two sheets, each 100×70 mm. (a) 25 r. Sperm Whale (*different*). (b) 25 r. Pair of Hourglass Dolphins ... *Set of 2 sheets* 7·50 7·50

Nos. 2222/33 and 2234/45 were printed together, *se-tenant*, in sheetlets of 12.

See also Nos. 2302/10.

316 Scout Camp and National Flag

(Des B. Hargreaves. Litho Questa)

1995 (6 July). *18th World Scout Jamboree, Netherlands.* T **316** *and similar multicoloured designs. P* 14.

2249	10 r.	Type 316	1·40	1·50
		a. Horiz strip of 3. Nos. 2249/51	4·00	
2250	12 r.	Campfire cooking	1·50	1·60
2251	15 r.	Scouts erecting tent	1·60	1·75
2249/51		*Set of 3*	4·00	4·25

MS2252 102×72 mm. 25 r. Scouts around camp fire (*vert*) ... 3·50 4·00

Nos. 2249/51 were printed in sheets of 9 containing three *se-tenant* horizontal strips, each forming a composite design.

317 Soviet Heavy Howitzer Battery

(Des W. Wright. Litho Questa)

1995 (6 July). *50th Anniv of End of Second World War in Europe.* T **317** *and similar horiz designs. Multicoloured. P* 14.

2253	5 r.	Type 317	75	75
		a. Sheetlet. Nos. 2253/60	5·50	
2254	5 r.	Ruins of Berchtesgaden	75	75
2255	5 r.	U.S. Boeing B-17 Flying Fortress dropping food over the Netherlands	75	75
2256	5 r.	Soviet Ilyushin Il-1 bomber	75	75
2257	5 r.	Liberation of Belsen	75	75
2258	5 r.	Supermarine Spitfire and V-1 flying bomb	75	75
2259	5 r.	U.S. tanks advancing through Cologne	75	75
2260	5 r.	Reichstag in ruins	75	75
2253/60		*Set of 8*	5·50	5·50

MS2261 107×76 mm. 25 r. Soviet and U.S. troops celebrating ... 3·50 3·50

Nos. 2253/60 were printed together, *se-tenant*, in sheetlets of 8 with the stamps arranged in two horizontal strips of 4 separated by a gutter showing R.A.F. Lancasters over Dresden.

318 Asian Child and Dove   **319 United Nations Emblem**

(Des J. Iskowitz. Litho)

1995 (6 July). *50th Anniv of United Nations* (1st issue). T **318** *and similar vert designs. Multicoloured. P* 14.

2262	6 r. 50 + 50 l.	Type 318	90	1·00
		a. Horiz strip of 3. Nos. 2262/4	2·75	
2263	8 r.	Globe and dove	1·00	1·10
2264	10 r.	African child and dove	1·10	1·25
2262/4		*Set of 3*	2·75	3·00

MS2265 72×102 mm. 25 r. United Nations emblem and dove ... 2·75 3·25

Nos. 2262/4 were printed in sheets of 9 containing three *se-tenant* horizontal strips, each forming a composite design.

(Litho Questa)

1995 (6 July). *50th Anniv of United Nations* (2nd issue). T **319** *and similar horiz designs. P* 14.

2266	30 l.	black, bright blue and green	10	10
2267	8 r.	multicoloured	1·00	1·10
2268	11 r.	multicoloured	1·25	1·40
2269	13 r.	black, grey and rosine	1·60	1·75
2266/9		*Set of 4*	3·50	3·75

Designs:—8 r. Symbolic women, flag and map; 11 r. U. N. soldier and symbolic dove; 13 r. Gun barrels, atomic explosion and bomb sight.

320 Asian Child eating Rice   **321 Queen Elizabeth the Queen Mother**

(Des J. Iskowitz. Litho)

1995 (6 July). *50th Anniv of Food and Agriculture Organization* (1st issue). T **320** *and similar multicoloured designs. P* 14.

2270	6 r. 50 + 50 l.	Type 320	90	1·00
		a. Horiz strip of 3. Nos. 2270/2	2·75	
2271	8 r.	F.A.O. emblem	1·00	1·10
2272	10 r.	African mother and child	1·10	1·25
2270/2		*Set of 3*	2·75	3·00

MS2273 72×102 mm. 25 r. African child and symbolic hand holding maize ... 2·75 3·25

Nos. 2270/2 were printed in sheets of 9 containing three *se-tenant* horizontal strips.

See also Nos. 2311/12.

(Litho Questa)

1995 (6 July). *95th Birthday of Queen Elizabeth the Queen Mother.* T **321** *and similar vert designs. P* 13½×14.

2274	5 r.	orange-brown, pale brown and black	80	85
		a. Sheetlet. Nos. 2274/7×2	5·50	
2275	5 r.	multicoloured	80	85
2276	5 r.	multicoloured	80	85
2277	5 r.	multicoloured	80	85
2274/7		*Set of 4*	2·75	3·00

MS2278 125×100 mm. 25 r. multicoloured ... 3·50 3·75

Designs:—No. 2274, Queen Elizabeth the Queen Mother (pastel drawing); No. 2275, Without hat; No. 2276, At desk (oil painting); No. 2277, Type **321**; No. **MS2278**, Wearing lilac hat and dress.

Nos. 2274/7 were printed together in sheetlets of 8 containing two *se-tenant* horizontal strips of 4.

(Des J. Batchelor. Litho Questa)

1995 (6 July). *50th Anniv of End of Second World War in the Pacific. Horiz designs as* T **317**. *P* 14.

2279	6 r. 50 + 50 l.	Grumman F6F-3 Hellcat aircraft	1·00	1·00
		a. Sheetlet. Nos. 2279/84	5·50	
2280	6 r. 50 + 50 l.	F4-U1 fighter aircraft attacking beach	1·00	1·00
2281	6 r. 50 + 50 l.	Douglas SBD Dauntless aircraft	1·00	1·00
2282	6 r. 50 + 50 l.	American troops in landing craft, Guadalcanal	1·00	1·00
2283	6 r. 50 + 50 l.	U.S. marines in Alligator tanks	1·00	1·00
2284	6 r. 50 + 50 l.	U.S. landing ship	1·00	1·00
2279/84		*Set of 6*	5·50	5·50

MS2285 106×74 mm. 25 r. F4-U1 fighter aircraft ... 3·50 3·75

Nos. 2279/84 were printed together, *se-tenant*, in sheetlets of 6 with the stamps arranged in two horizontal strips of 3 separated by a gutter showing U.S. marines in landing craft.

322 Students using Library

(Litho Questa)

1995 (12 July). *50th Anniversary of National Library.* T **322** *and similar horiz designs. Multicoloured. P* 14.

2286	2 r.	Type 322	25	25
2287	8 r.	Students using library (*different*)	1·00	1·25

MS2288 105×75 mm. 10 r. Library entrance (100×70 mm). Imperf ... 1·40 1·60

MINIMUM PRICE

The minimum price quote is 10p which represents a handling charge rather than a basis for valuing common stamps. For further notes about prices see introductory pages.

323 Spur-thighed Tortoise

(Des D. Burkhardt. Litho Questa)

1995 (22 Aug). *Turtles and Tortoises. T 323 and similar horiz designs. Multicoloured. P 14.*

2289	3 r.	Type 323	..	50	50
	a.	Sheetlet. Nos. 2289/96		3·50	
2290	3 r.	Aldabra Turtle	..	50	50
2291	3 r.	Loggerhead Turtle	..	50	50
2292	3 r.	Olive Ridley Turtle	..	50	50
2293	3 r.	Leatherback Turtle	..	50	50
2294	3 r.	Green Turtle	..	50	50
2295	3 r.	Atlantic Ridley Turtle	..	50	50
2296	3 r.	Hawksbill Turtle	..	50	50
2297	10 r.	Hawksbill Turtle on beach	..	1·40	1·40
	a.	Vert strip of 4. Nos. 2297/300		5·00	
2298	10 r.	Pair of Hawksbill Turtles	..	1·40	1·40
2299	10 r.	Hawksbill Turtle climbing out of water		1·40	1·40
2300	10 r.	Hawksbill Turtle swimming	..	1·40	1·40
2289/2300			*Set of 12*	8·50	8·50

MS2301 100×70mm. 25 r. Green Turtle .. 3·50 4·00
Nos. 2289/96 were printed together, *se-tenant*, in sheetlets of 8 forming a composite design.
Nos. 2297/2300, which include the W.W.F. Panda emblem, were printed together in sheets of 12 (3×4) containing 3 vertical *se-tenant* strips.

324 *Russula aurata* (fungi) and *Papilio demodocus* (butterfly)

325 Planting Kaashi

(Des L. Nelson. Litho Questa)

1995 (18 Oct). *"Singapore '95" International Stamp Exhibition (2nd issue). Butterflies and Fungi. T 324 and similar multicoloured designs. P 14.*

2302	2 r.	Type 324	..	35	35
	a.	Sheetlet. Nos. 2302/5		1·25	
2303	2 r.	*Lepista saeva* and *Kallimoides rumia*		35	35
2304	2 r.	*Lepista nuda* and *Hypolimnas salmacis*		35	35
2305	2 r.	*Xerocomus subtomentosus* ("Boletus subtomentosus") and *Precis octavia*	..	35	35
2306	2 r.	*Gyroporus castaneus* and *Hypolimnas salmacis*		85	95
	a.	Sheetlet. Nos. 2306/9		4·00	
2307	8 r.	*Gomphidius glutinosus* and *Papilio dardanus*		1·10	1·25
2308	10 r.	*Russula olivacea* and *Precis octavia*		1·25	1·40
2309	12 r.	*Boletus edulis* and *Prepona praeneste*		1·25	1·40
2302/9			*Set of 8*	5·25	5·75

MS2310 Two sheets, each 105×76 mm. (a) 25 r. *Amanita muscaria* and *Kallimoides rumia* (vert). (b) 25 r. *Boletus rhodoxanthus* and *Hypolimnas salmacis* (vert) .. .. *Set of 2 sheets* 7·50 7·50
Nos. 2302/5 and 2306/9 were each printed together, *se-tenant*, in sheetlets of 4, forming composite designs.
No. 2304 is inscribed "Lapista" in error.

(Litho Questa)

1995 (2 Nov). *50th Anniv of Food and Agriculture Organization (2nd issue). T 325 and similar vert design. Multicoloured. P 14.*

2311	7 r.	Type 325	..	90	90
2312	8 r.	Fishing boat	..	1·10	1·10

326 Ballade Tulip

327 John Lennon with Microphone

(Des L. Fried. Litho Questa)

1995 (4 Dec). *Flowers. T 326 and similar multicoloured designs. P 14.*

2313	1 r.	Type 326	..	20	15
2314	3 r.	White Mallow	..	50	50
2315	5 r.	Regale Trumpet Lily	..	75	75
2316	5 r.	*Dendrobium* "Waipahu Beauty"	..	75	75
	a.	Sheetlet. Nos. 2316/24		6·00	
2317	5 r.	*Brassocattleya* "Jean Murray"		75	75
2318	5 r.	*Cymbidium* "Fort George"		75	75
2319	5 r.	*Paphiopedilum malipoense*		75	75
2320	5 r.	*Cycnoches chlorochilon*		75	75
2321	5 r.	*Rhyncholaelia digbgana*		75	75
2322	5 r.	*Lycaste deppei*		75	75
2323	5 r.	*Masdevallia constricta*		75	75
2324	5 r.	*Paphiopedilum* "Clair de Lune"		75	75
2325	7 r.	Lilactime Dahlia	..	1·00	1·00
2326	8 r.	Blue Ideal Iris	..	1·10	1·10
2327	10 r.	Red Crown Imperial	..	1·25	1·25
2313/27			*Set of 15*	10·50	10·50

MS2328 Two sheets, each 106×76 mm. (a) 25 r. *Encyclia cochleata* (vert). (b) 25 r. *Psychopsis kramerina* (vert) .. .. *Set of 2 sheets* 7·50 7·50
Nos. 2316/24 were printed together, *se-tenant*, in sheetlets of 9.

(Litho Questa)

1995 (8 Dec). *15th Death Anniv of John Lennon (musician). T 327 and similar vert designs. Multicoloured. P 14.*

2329	5 r.	Type 327	..	1·25	1·25
	a.	Sheetlet. Nos. 2329/34		6·50	
2330	5 r.	With glasses and moustache	..	1·25	1·25
2331	5 r.	With guitar	..	1·25	1·25
2332	5 r.	With guitar and wearing glasses		1·25	1·25
2333	5 r.	Wearing sun glasses and red jacket		1·25	1·25
2334	5 r.	Wearing headphones	..	1·25	1·25
2329/34			*Set of 6*	6·50	6·50

MS2335 88×117 mm. 2, 3, 8, 10 r. Different portraits of John Lennon .. .. 5·00 5·00
MS2336 102×72 mm. 25 r. John Lennon performing .. .. .. 5·50 5·50
Nos. 2329/34 were printed together, *se-tenant*, in sheetlets of 6.

328 Elvis Presley with Microphone

329 Johannes van der Waals (1919 Physics)

(Des R. Martin. Litho Questa)

1995 (8 Dec). *60th Birth Anniv of Elvis Presley (entertainer). T 328 and similar multicoloured designs. P 13¹/₂×14.*

2337	5 r.	Type 328	..	75	75
	a.	Sheetlet. Nos. 2337/45		6·00	
2338	5 r.	Wearing red jacket	..	75	75
2339	5 r.	Wearing blue jacket	..	75	75
2340	5 r.	With microphone and wearing blue jacket		75	75
2341	5 r.	In army uniform	..	75	75
2342	5 r.	Wearing yellow bow tie	..	75	75
2343	5 r.	In yellow shirt	..	75	75
2344	5 r.	In light blue shirt	..	75	75
2345	5 r.	Wearing red and white high-collared jacket		75	75
2337/45			*Set of 9*	6·00	6·00

MS2346 80×110 mm. 25 r. Elvis Presley (horiz). P 14×13¹/₂ .. .. .. 3·50 3·75
Nos. 2337/45 were printed together, *se-tenant*, in sheetlets of 9.

(Des R. Rundo. Litho Questa)

1995 (28 Dec). *Centenary of Nobel Prize Trust Fund. T 329 and similar vert designs. Multicoloured. P 14.*

2347/55	5 r. × 9 (Type 329; Charles Guillaume (1920 Physics); Sir James Chadwick (1935 Physics); Willem Einthoven (1924 Medicine); Henrik Dam (1943 Medicine); Sir Alexander Fleming (1945 Medicine); Hermann Muller (1946 Medicine); Rodney Porter (1972 Medicine); Werner Arber (1978 Medicine))	
	a. Sheetlet. Nos. 2347/55	4·50
2356/64	5 r. × 9 (Niels Bohr (1922 Physics); Ben Mottelson (1975 Physics); Patrick White (1973 Literature); Elias Canetti (1981 Literature); Theodor Kocher (1909 Medicine); August Krogh (1920 Medicine); William Murphy (1934 Medicine); John Northrop (1946 Chemistry); Luis Leloir (1970 Chemistry))	
	a. Sheetlet. Nos. 2356/64	4·50
2365/73	5 r. × 9 (Dag Hammarskjöld (1961 Peace); Alva Myrdal (1982 Peace); Archbishop Desmond Tutu (1984 Peace); Rudolf Eucken (1908 Literature); Aleksandr Solzhenitsyn (1970 Literature); Gabriel Márquez (1982 Literature); Chen Yang (1957 Physics); Karl Müller (1987 Physics); Melvin Schwartz (1988 Physics))	
	a. Sheetlet. Nos. 2365/73	4·50

2374/82	5 r. × 9 (Robert Millikan (1923 Physics); Louis de Broglie (1929 Physics); Ernest Walton (1951 Physics); Richard Willstätter (1915 Chemistry); Lars Onsager (1968 Chemistry); Gerhard Herzberg (1971 Chemistry); William B. Yeats (1923 Literature); George Bernard Shaw (1925 Literature); Eugene O'Neill (1936 Literature))	
	a. Sheetlet. Nos. 2374/82	4·50
2383/91	5 r. × 9 (Bernardo Houssay (1947 Medicine); Paul Müller (1948 Medicine); Walter Hess (1949 Medicine); Sir MacFarlane Burnet (1960 Medicine); Baruch Blumberg (1976 Medicine); Daniel Nathans (1978 Medicine); Glenn Seaborg (1951 Chemistry); Ilya Prigogine (1977 Chemistry); Kenichi Fukui (1981 Chemistry))	
	a. Sheetlet. Nos. 2383/91	4·50
2392/400	5 r. × 9 (Carl Spitteler (1919 Literature); Henri Bergson (1927 Literature); Johannes Jensen (1944 Literature); Antoine-Henri Becquerel (1903 Physics); Sir William H. Bragg (1915 Physics); Sir William L. Bragg (1915 Physics); Frederik Bajer (1908 Peace); Léon Bourgeois (1920 Peace); Karl Benning (1921 Peace))	
	a. Sheetlet. Nos. 2392/3000	4·50
2347/2400	*Set of 54*	27·00 29·00

MS2401 Six sheets. (a) 80×110 mm. 25 r. Konrad Bloch (1964 Medicine). (b) 80×110 mm. 25 r. Samuel Beckett (1969 Literature). (c) 80×110 mm. 25 r. Otto Wallach (1910 Chemistry). (d) 110×80 mm. 25 r. Hideki Yukawa (1949 Physics). (e) 110×80 mm. 25 r. Eisaku Sato (1974 Peace). (f) 110×80 mm. 25 r. Robert Koch (1905 Medicine) .. *Set of 6 sheets* 19·00 20·00
Nos. 2347/55, 2356/64, 2365/73, 2374/82, 2383/91 and 2392/2400 were printed together, *se-tenant*, in sheetlets of 9.

330 Rhythmic Gymnast and Japanese Fan

(Des L. Fried. Litho Questa)

1996 (25 Jan). *Olympic Games, Atlanta (1st issue). T 330 and similar multicoloured designs. P 14.*

2402	1 r.	Type 330	..	20	15
2403	3 r.	Archer and Moscow Olympics logo	..	50	50
2404	5 r.	Diver and Swedish flag	..	75	75
2405	5 r.	Canadian Maple Leaf	..	75	75
	a.	Sheetlet. Nos. 2405/13		6·00	
2406	5 r.	Shot putting (Decathlon)	..	75	75
2407	5 r.	Moscow Olympic medal and ribbon		75	75
2408	5 r.	Fencer	..	75	75
2409	5 r.	Gold medal	..	75	75
2410	5 r.	Equestrian competitor	..	75	75
2411	5 r.	Sydney Opera House	..	75	75
2412	5 r.	Athlete on starting blocks	..	75	75
2413	5 r.	South Korean flag	..	75	75
2414	7 r.	High jumper and Tower Bridge, London		1·00	1·00
2415	10 r.	Athlete on starting blocks and Brandenburg Gate, Germany		1·10	1·10
2416	12 r.	Hurdler and Amsterdam Olympic logo		1·25	1·40
2402/16			*Set of 15*	10·50	10·50

MS2417 Two sheets, each 113×80 mm. (a) 25 r. Red Olympic Flame (vert). (b) 25 r. Multicoloured Olympic Flame (vert) .. *Set of 2 sheets* 7·00 7·50
Nos. 2405/13 were printed together, *se-tenant*, in sheetlets of 9.

See also Nos. 2469/88.

331 "Self Portrait" (Degas)

(Litho Questa)

1996 (22 Apr). *125th Anniv of Metropolitan Museum of Art, New York. T 331 and similar multicoloured designs. P 13¹/₂×14.*

2418/25	4 r. × 8 (Type 331; "Andromache and Astyanax" (Prud'hon); "René Grenier" (Toulouse-Lautrec); "The Banks of the Biévre near Bicétre" (Rousseau); "The Repast of the Lion" (Rousseau); "Portrait of Yves Gobillard-Morisot" (Degas); "Sunflowers" (Van Gogh); "The Singer in Green" (Degas)	
	a. Sheetlet. Nos. 2418/25	4·50

2426/33   4 r. × 8 ("Still Life" (Fantin-Latour); "Portrait of a Lady in Grey" (Degas); "Apples and Grapes" (Monet); "The Englishman" (Toulouse-Lautrec); "Cypresses" (Van Gogh); "Flowers in a Chinese Vase" (Redon); "The Gardener" (Seurat); "Large Sunflowers I" (Nolde))
    a. Sheetlet. Nos. 2426/33   ..   4·50

2434/41   4 r. × 8 (All by Manet: "The Spanish Singer"; "Young Man in Costume of Majo"; "Mademoiselle Victorine"; "Boating"; "Peonies"; "Woman with a Parrot"; "George Moore"; "The Monet Family in their Garden")
    a. Sheetlet. Nos. 2434/41   ..   4·50

2442/9   4 r. × 8 ("Goldfish" (Matisse); "Spanish Woman: Harmony in Blue" (Matisse); "Nasturtiums and the "Dance" II" (Matisse); "The House behind Trees" (Braque); "Mada Primavesi" (Klimt); "Head of a Woman" (Picasso); "Woman in White" (Picasso); "Harlequin" (Picasso))
    a. Sheetlet. Nos. 2442/9   ..   4·50

2418/49   ..   *Set of 32*   16·00   17·00
MS2450   Four sheets, each 95×70 mm containing horiz designs, 81×53 mm. P 14. (a) 25 r. "Northeaster" (Homer). (b) 25 r. "The Fortune Teller" (De La Tour). (c) 25 r. "Santo (Sanzio), Ritratto de Andrea Navagero e Agostino Beazzano" (Raphael). (d) 25 r. "Portrait of a Woman" (Rubens)   ..   *Set of 4 sheets*   14·00   15·00
Nos. 2418/25, 2426/33, 2434/41 and 2442/9 were each printed together, *se-tenant*, in sheetlets of 8 stamps and one centre label.

332   Mickey Mouse on Great Wall of China

(Des Walt Disney Company Asia Pacific Ltd. Litho Questa)

1996 (10 May).   *"CHINA '96" 9th Asian International Stamp Exhibition, Peking. T* **332** *and similar multicoloured designs showing Walt Disney cartoon characters in China.* P 14×13½ (*horiz*) or 13½×14 (*vert*).
2451   2 r. Type **332**   ..   55   55
    a. Sheetlet. Nos. 2451/6   ..   3·00
2452   2 r. Pluto with temple guardian   55   55
2453   2 r. Minnie Mouse with Pandas   55   55
2454   2 r. Mickey windsurfing near junks   55   55
2455   2 r. Goofy cleaning Grottoe statue   55   55
2456   2 r. Donald and Daisy Duck at Marble Boat   ..   55   55
2457   2 r. Mickey with terracotta warriors   55   55
    a. Sheetlet. Nos. 2457/62   ..   3·00
2458   2 r. Goofy with geese and masks   55   55
2459   2 r. Donald and Goofy on traditional fishing boat   ..   55   55
2460   2 r. Mickey and Minnie in dragon boat   55   55
2461   2 r. Donald at Peking opera   ..   55   55
2462   2 r. Mickey and Minnie in Chinese garden   55   55
2463   3 r. Mickey and Minnie at the Ice Pagoda (*vert*)   ..   65   65
    a. Sheetlet. Nos. 2463/7   ..   3·00
2464   3 r. Donald and Mickey flying Chinese kites (*vert*)   ..   65   65
2465   3 r. Goofy playing anyiwu (*vert*)   65   65
2466   3 r. Paper cutouts of Mickey and Goofy (*vert*)   ..   65   65
2467   3 r. Donald and Mickey in dragon dance (*vert*)   ..   65   65
2451/67   ..   *Set of 17*   9·00   9·00
MS2468   Three sheets. (a) 108×133 mm. 5 r. Mickey pointing. (b) 133×108 mm. 7 r. Mickey and Minnie watching Moon. (c) 133×108 mm. 8 r. Donald using chopsticks   *Set of 3 sheets*   4·00   4·25
Nos. 2451/6, 2457/62 and 2463/7 were each printed together, *se-tenant*, in sheetlets of 6 (Nos. 2451/6, 2457/62) or 5 stamps and one label (Nos. 2463/7).

333   Stella Walsh (Poland) (100m sprint, 1932) on Medal

(Litho B.D.T.)

1996 (27 May).   *Olympic Games, Atlanta (2nd issue). Previous Gold Medal Winners. T* **333** *and similar multicoloured designs.* P 14.
2469   1 r. Type **333**   ..   10   10
2470   3 r. Emile Zatopek (Czechoslovakia) (10,000m running, 1952) and Olympic torch (*vert*)   ..   30   35
2471   5 r. Yanko Rousseu (Bulgaria) (lightweight, 1980) (*vert*)   ..   50   55
    a. Sheetlet. Nos. 2471/9   ..   4·50
2472   5 r. Peter Baczako (Hungary) (middle heavyweight, 1980) (*vert*)   ..   50   55

2473   5 r. Leonid Taranenko (Russia) (heavyweight, 1980) (*vert*)   ..   50   55
2474   5 r. Aleksandr Kurlovich (Russia) (heavyweight, 1988) (*vert*)   ..   50   55
2475   5 r. Assen Zlateu (Bulgaria) (middleweight, 1980) (*vert*)   ..   50   55
2476   5 r. Zeng Guoqiang (China) (flyweight, 1984) (*vert*)   ..   50   55
2477   5 r. Yurik Vardanyan (Russia) (heavyweight, 1980) (*vert*)   ..   50   55
2478   5 r. Sultan Rakhmanov (Russia) (super heavyweight, 1980) (*vert*)   ..   50   55
2479   5 r. Vassily Alexeev (Russia) (super heavyweight, 1972) (*vert*)   ..   50   55
2480   5 r. Ethel Catherwood (Canada) (high jump, 1928)   ..   50   55
    a. Sheetlet. Nos. 2480/5   ..   3·00
2481   5 r. Mildred Didrikson (U.S.A.) (javelin, 1932)   ..   50   55
2482   5 r. Francina Blankers-Koen (Netherlands) (80m hurdles, 1948)   ..   50   55
2483   5 r. Tamara Press (Russia) (shot put, 1960)   ..   50   55
2484   5 r. Lia Manoliu (Rumania) (discus, 1968)   50   55
2485   5 r. Rosa Mota (Portugal) (marathon, 1988)   ..   50   55
2486   10 r. Olga Fikotova (Czechoslovakia) (discus, 1956) on medal   ..   1·00   1·10
2487   12 r. Joan Benoit (U.S.A.) (marathon, 1984) on medal   ..   1·25   1·40
2469/87   ..   *Set of 19*   10·00   11·00
MS2488   Two sheets. (a) 76×106 mm. 25 r. Naeem Suleymanoglu (Turkey) (weightlifting, 1988) (*vert*). (b) 105×75 mm. 25 r. Irena Szewinska (Poland) (400m running, 1976) on medal   ..   *Set of 2 sheets*   5·00   5·25
Nos. 2471/9 (weightlifters) and Nos. 2480/5 (women's track and field as T **333**) were each printed together, *se-tenant*, in sheetlets of 9 or 6.
No. 2469 identifies the event as 10 metres in error.

334   Queen Elizabeth II   335   African Child

(Litho Questa)

1996 (10 July).   *70th Birthday of Queen Elizabeth II. T* **334** *and similar vert designs showing different photographs. Multicoloured.* P 13½×14.
2489   8 r. Type **334**   ..   80   85
    a. Strip of 3. Nos. 2489/91   2·40
2490   8 r. Wearing hat   ..   80   85
2491   8 r. At desk   ..   80   85
2489/91   ..   *Set of 3*   2·40   2·50
MS2492   125×103 mm. 25 r. Queen Elizabeth and Queen Mother on Buckingham Palace Balcony   ..   2·40   2·50
Nos. 2489/91 were printed together, *se-tenant*, in horizontal and vertical strips of 3 throughout sheets of 9.

(Litho B.D.T. (No. 2495) or Questa (others))

1996 (10 July).   *50th Anniv of U.N.I.C.E.F. T* **335** *and similar vert designs. Multicoloured.* P 14.
2493   5 r. Type **335**   ..   50   55
2494   7 r. European girl   ..   70   75
2495   7 r. Maldivian boy   ..   70   75
2496   10 r. Asian girl   ..   1·00   1·10
2493/6   ..   *Set of 4*   2·75   3·25
MS2497   114×74 mm. 25 r. Baby with toy   2·50   2·75

336   "Sputnik 1" Satellite

1996 (10 July).   *Space Exploration. T* **336** *and similar multicoloured designs.* Litho. P 14.
2498   6 r. Type **336**   ..   60   65
    a. Sheetlet. Nos. 2498/503   3·50
2499   6 r. "Apollo 11" command module   60   65
2500   6 r. "Skylab"   ..   60   65
2501   6 r. Astronaut Edward White walking in Space   ..   60   65
2502   6 r. "Mariner 9"   ..   60   65
2503   6 r. "Apollo" and "Soyuz" docking   60   65
2498/503   ..   *Set of 6*   3·50   3·75
MS2504   104×74 mm. 25 r. Launch of "Apollo 8" (*vert*)   ..   2·50   2·75
Nos. 2498/503 were printed together, *se-tenant*, in sheetlets of 6, the background forming a composite design.

337   *Epiphora albida*

1996 (10 July).   *Butterflies. T* **337** *and similar multicoloured designs.* Litho. P 14.
2505   7 r. Type **337**   ..   70   75
    a. Sheetlet. Nos. 2505/10   4·00
2506   7 r. *Satyrus dryas*   ..   70   75
2507   7 r. *Satyrus lena*   ..   70   75
2508   7 r. *Papilio tynderaeus*   ..   70   75
2509   7 r. *Urota suraka*   ..   70   75
2510   7 r. *Satyrus nercis*   ..   70   75
2511   7 r. *Papilio troilus* (*vert*)   ..   70   75
    a. Sheetlet. Nos. 2511/18   5·50
2512   7 r. *Papilio cresphontes* (*vert*)   70   75
2513   7 r. Lime Swallowtail caterpillar (*vert*)   70   75
2514   7 r. *Cynthia virginiensis* (*vert*)   70   75
2515   7 r. Monarch caterpillar (*vert*)   70   75
2516   7 r. *Danaus plexippus* (*vert*)   70   75
2517   7 r. Monarch caterpillar and pupa (*vert*)   70   75
2518   7 r. *Chlosyne harrisii* (*vert*)   70   75
2519   7 r. *Cymothoe coccinata* (*vert*)   70   75
    a. Sheetlet. Nos. 2519/22×2   2·75
2520   7 r. *Morpho rhetenor* (*vert*)   70   75
2521   7 r. *Callicore lidwina* (*vert*)   70   75
2522   7 r. *Heliconius erato reductimacula* (*vert*)   70   75
2505/22   ..   *Set of 18*   12·00   13·50
MS2523   Two sheets, each 106×76 mm. (a) 25 r. *Heliconius charitonius* (*vert*). (b) 25 r. *Heliconius cydno* (*vert*)   *Set of 2 sheets*   5·00   5·25
Nos. 2505/10, 2511/18 and 2519/22 were each printed together, *se-tenant*, in sheetlets of 6 or 8.

338   Amtrak F40H Diesel-electric Locomotive, U.S.A.   339   Bongo

1996 (2 Sept).   *Trains of the World. T* **338** *and similar horiz designs. Multicoloured.* Litho. P 14.
2524   3 r. Type **338**   ..   30   35
    a. Sheetlet. Nos. 2524/32   2·50
2525   3 r. Stephenson's *Experiment*   30   35
2526   3 r. Indian-Pacific Intercontinental, Australia   ..   30   35
2527   3 r. Stephenson's Killingworth type steam locomotive, 1815   ..   30   35
2528   3 r. George Stephenson   ..   30   35
2529   3 r. Stephenson's *Rocket*, 1829   30   35
2530   3 r. High Speed Train 125, Great Britain, 1975   ..   30   35
2531   3 r. First rail passenger coach *Experiment*, 1825   ..   30   35
2532   3 r. Union Pacific Class U25B diesel locomotive (inscr "Tofac"), U.S.A.   30   35
2533   3 r. Southern Pacific "Daylight" express, U.S.A., 1952   ..   30   35
    a. Sheetlet. Nos. 2533/41   2·50
2534   3 r. Timothy Hackworth's *Sans Pareil*, 1829   ..   30   35
2535   3 r. Chicago and North Western diesel locomotive, U.S.A.   ..   30   35
2536   3 r. Richard Trevithick's *Pen-y-Darren* locomotive, 1804   ..   30   35
2537   3 r. Isambard Kingdom Brunel   30   35
2538   3 r. Great Western locomotive, 1838   30   35
2539   3 r. Vistadome observation car, Canada   30   35
2540   3 r. Mohawk and Hudson Railroad *Experiment*, 1832   ..   30   35
2541   3 r. ICE high speed train, Germany   30   35
2542   3 r. Electric container locomotive, Germany   ..   30   35
    a. Sheetlet. Nos. 2542/50   2·50
2543   3 r. John Blenkinsop's rack locomotive, 1811   ..   30   35
2544   3 r. Diesel-electric locomotive, Western Australia   ..   30   35
2545   3 r. Timothy Hackworth's *Royal George*, 1827   ..   30   35
2546   3 r. Robert Stephenson   ..   30   35
2547   3 r. Trevithick's *Newcastle*   ..   30   35
2548   3 r. Deltic diesel-electric locomotive, Great Britain   ..   30   35
2549   3 r. Stockton and Darlington Railway locomotive No. 5 Stockton, 1826   30   35
2550   3 r. Channel Tunnel "Le Shuttle" train   30   35
2524/50   ..   *Set of 27*   8·00   9·25
MS2551   Three sheets, each 96×91 mm. (a) 25 r. Peter Cooper's *Tom Thumb*, 1829. (b) 25 r. John Jarvis's *De Witt Clinton*, 1831. (c) 25 r. William Hudson's *The General*, 1855   *Set of 3 sheets*   8·25   8·50
Nos. 2524/32, 2533/41 and 2542/50 were printed together, *se-tenant*, in sheetlets of 9.
No. 2524 is inscribed "F4 OPH" in error.

1996 (9 Sept). *Wildlife of the World.* T **339** *and similar multicoloured designs. Litho.* P 14.

2552	5 r. Type **339**		50	55
	a. Sheetlet. Nos. 2552/9		4·00	
2553	5 r. Bushbuck		50	55
2554	5 r. Namaqua Dove		50	55
2555	5 r. Hoopoe		50	55
2556	5 r. African Fish Eagle		50	55
2557	5 r. Egyptian Goose		50	55
2558	5 r. Saddle-bill Stork		50	55
2559	5 r. Blue-breasted Kingfisher		50	55
2560	5 r. Yellow Baboon		50	55
	a. Sheetlet. Nos. 2560/7		4·00	
2561	5 r. Banded Duiker ("Zebra Duiker")		50	55
2562	5 r. Yellow-backed Duiker		50	55
2563	5 r. Pygmy Hippopotamus		50	55
2564	5 r. Large-spotted Genet		50	55
2565	5 r. African Spoonbill		50	55
2566	5 r. White-faced Whistling Duck		50	55
2567	5 r. Helmet Guineafowl		50	55
2568	7 r. Cotton-headed Tamarin (*horiz*)		70	75
	a. Sheetlet. Nos. 2568/76		6·25	
2569	7 r. European Bison (*horiz*)		70	75
2570	7 r. Tiger (*horiz*)		70	75
2571	7 r. Capercaillie (*horiz*)		70	75
2572	7 r. Giant Panda (*horiz*)		70	75
2573	7 r. *Trogonoptera brookiana* (butterfly) (*horiz*)		70	75
2574	7 r. American Beaver (*horiz*)		70	75
2575	7 r. *Leiopelma hamiltoni* (frog) (*horiz*)		70	75
2576	7 r. Manatee (*horiz*)		70	75
2552/76		*Set of 25*	14·00	15·00
MS2577	106×76 mm. 25 r. Chimpanzee (*horiz*)		2·50	2·75

Nos. 2552/9, 2560/7 and 2568/76 were each printed together, *se-tenant*, in sheetlets of 8 or 9, the backgrounds forming composite designs.

No. 2553 is inscribed "BUSHBACK" in error.

340 Giant Panda

1996 (9 Sept). *Endangered Species.* T **340** *and similar multicoloured designs. Litho.* P 14.

2578	5 r. Type **340**		50	55
	a. Sheetlet. Nos. 2578/83		3·00	
2579	5 r. Indian Elephant		50	55
2580	5 r. Arrow-poison Frog		50	55
2581	5 r. Mandrill		50	55
2582	5 r. Snow Leopard		50	55
2583	5 r. California Condor		50	55
2584	5 r. Whale-headed Stork ("Shoebill Stork")		50	55
	a. Sheetlet. Nos. 2584/9		3·00	
2585	5 r. Red-billed Hornbill		50	55
2586	5 r. Hippopotamus		50	55
2587	5 r. Gorilla		50	55
2588	5 r. Lion		50	55
2589	5 r. South African Crowned Crane		50	55
2578/89		*Set of 12*	6·00	6·50
MS2590	Two sheets, each 110×80 mm. (a) 25 r. Tiger (*vert*). (b) 25 r. Leopard	*Set of 2 sheets*	5·00	5·25

Nos. 2578/83 and 2584/9 were each printed togther, *se-tenant*, in sheetlets of 6.

341 Mickey Mouse climbing out of Puddle

(Des Alvin White Studio, Litho Questa)

1996 (2 Dec). *Centenary of the Cinema.* T **341** *and similar horiz designs showing a series of cartoon frames from* The Little Whirlwind *(Nos. 2591/2607) and* Pluto and the Flypaper *(Nos. 2608/24). Multicoloured.* P 14×13½.

2591	4 r. Type **341**		90	90
	a. Sheetlet. Nos. 2591/8 and 1 label		6·50	
2592	4 r. Frame 2		90	90
2593	4 r. Frame 3		90	90
2594	4 r. Frame 4		90	90
2595	4 r. Frame 5		90	90
2596	4 r. Frame 6		90	90
2597	4 r. Frame 7		90	90
2598	4 r. Frame 8		90	90
2599	4 r. Frame 9		90	90
	a. Sheetlet. Nos. 2599/607		7·00	
2600	4 r. Frame 10		90	90
2601	4 r. Frame 11		90	90
2602	4 r. Frame 12		90	90
2603	4 r. Frame 13		90	90
2604	4 r. Frame 14		90	90
2605	4 r. Frame 15		90	90
2606	4 r. Frame 16 (Mickey holding fish above head)		90	90
2607	4 r. Frame 17 (Mickey throwing fish into pool)		90	90
2608	4 r. Frame 1 (Pluto)		90	90
	a. Sheetlet. Nos. 2608/15 and 1 label		6·50	
2609	4 r. Frame 2		90	90
2610	4 r. Frame 3		90	90
2611	4 r. Frame 4		90	90

2612	4 r. Frame 5		90	90
2613	4 r. Frame 6		90	90
2614	4 r. Frame 7		90	90
2615	4 r. Frame 8		90	90
2616	4 r. Frame 9		90	90
	a. Sheetlet. Nos. 2616/24		7·00	
2617	4 r. Frame 10		90	90
2618	4 r. Frame 11		90	90
2619	4 r. Frame 12		90	90
2620	4 r. Frame 13		90	90
2621	4 r. Frame 14		90	90
2622	4 r. Frame 15		90	90
2623	4 r. Frame 16		90	90
2624	4 r. Frame 17		90	90
2591/624		*Set of 34*	27·00	27·00
MS2625	Two sheets, 111×131 mm. (a) 25 r. Frame 18 (*The Little Whirlwind*). (b) 25 r. Frame 18 (*Pluto and the Flypaper*)	*Set of 2 sheets*	10·00	10·50

Nos. 2591/8, 2599/2607, 2608/15 and 2616/24 were printed together, *se-tenant*, in sheets of 8 or 9. It is intended that the stamps should be separated and used as a flip book to produce a moving image.

342 Letter "O" with Chinese Character

343 California Condor

(Des M. Friedman. Litho Questa)

1997 (12 Feb). *"HONG KONG '97" International Stamp Exhibition.* T **342** *and similar multicoloured designs.* P 13½×14.

2626	5 r. Letter "H" and Chinese couple		50	55
	a. Sheetlet. Nos. 2626/33		4·00	
2627	5 r. Type **342**		50	55
2628	5 r. Letter "N" and Chinese dragon		50	55
2629	5 r. Letter "G" and carnival dragon		50	55
2630	5 r. Letter "K" and modern office block		50	55
2631	5 r. Letter "O" and Chinese character (*different*)		50	55
2632	5 r. Letter "N" and Chinese fan cases		50	55
2633	5 r. Letter "G" and Chinese junk		50	55
2626/33		*Set of 8*	4·00	4·25
MS2634	106×125 mm. 25 r. "HONG KONG" as on Nos. 2626/33 (76×38 mm)		2·75	3·00

Nos. 2626/33 were printed together, *se-tenant*, in sheetlets of 8.

1997 (12 Feb). *Birds of the World.* T **343** *and similar vert designs. Multicoloured. Litho.* P 14.

2635	5 r. Type **343**		50	55
	a. Sheetlet. Nos. 2635/43		4·50	
2636	5 r. Audouin's Gull		50	55
2637	5 r. Atlantic Puffin		50	55
2638	5 r. Resplendent Quetzal		50	55
2639	5 r. Puerto Rican Amazon		50	55
2640	5 r. Lesser Bird of Paradise		50	55
2641	5 r. Japanese Crested Ibis		50	55
2642	5 r. Mauritius Kestrel		50	55
2643	5 r. Kakapo		50	55
2635/43		*Set of 9*	4·50	4·75
MS2644	76×106 mm. 25 r. Ivory-billed Woodpecker		2·50	2·75

Nos. 2635/43 were printed together, *se-tenant*, in sheetlets of 9 with the backgrounds forming a composite design.

344 Ye Qiabo (China) (women's 500/100m speed skating, 1992)

345 Crowned Solitary Eagle

(Litho Questa)

1997 (13 Mar). *Winter Olympic Games, Nagano, Japan (1998).* T **344** *and similar vert designs. Multicoloured.* P 14.

2645	2 r. Type **344**		20	25
2646	3 r. Leonhard Stock (Austria) (downhill skiing, 1980)		30	35
2647	5 r. Herma von Szabo-Planck (Austria) (figure skating, 1924)		50	55
	a. Sheetlet. Nos. 2647/50×2		4·00	
2648	5 r. Katarina Witt (Germany) (figure skating, 1988)		50	55
2649	5 r. Natalia Bestemianova and Andrei Bukin (Russia) (pairs ice dancing, 1988)		50	55

2650	5 r. Jayne Torvill and Christopher Dean (Great Britain) (pairs ice dancing, 1984)		50	55
2651	8 r. Bjorn Daehlie (Norway) (cross-country skiing, 1992)		80	85
2652	12 r. Wolfgang Hoppe (Germany) (bobsleigh, 1984)		1·25	1·40
2645/52		*Set of 8*	4·50	5·00
MS2653	Two sheets, each 76×106 mm. (a) 25 r. Sonja Henie (Norway) (figure skating, 1924). (b) 25 r. Andree Joly and Pierre Brunet (France) (pairs ice dancing, 1932)	*Set of 2 sheets*	5·00	5·25

Nos. 2645/52 were printed together, *se-tenant*, in sheetlets of 8 containing two of each design.

(Litho Questa)

1997 (20 Mar). *Eagles.* T **345** *and similar multicoloured designs.* P 14.

2654	1 r. Type **345**		10	15
2655	2 r. African Hawk Eagle (*horiz*)		20	25
2656	3 r. Lesser Spotted Eagle		30	35
2657	5 r. Stellar's Sea Eagle		50	55
2658	5 r. Bald Eagle attacking		50	55
	a. Sheetlet. Nos. 2658/63		3·00	
2659	5 r. Bald Eagle on branch		50	55
2660	5 r. Bald Eagle looking left		50	55
2661	5 r. Bald Eagle looking right		50	55
2662	5 r. Bald Eagle sitting on branch with leaves		50	55
2663	5 r. Bald Eagle soaring		50	55
2664	8 r. Spanish Imperial Eagle (*horiz*)		80	85
2665	10 r. Harpy Eagle		1·00	1·10
2666	12 r. Crested Serpent Eagle (*horiz*)		1·25	1·40
2654/66		*Set of 13*	7·00	6·00
MS2667	Two sheets. (a) 73×104 mm. 25 r. Bald Eagle. (b) 104×73 mm. 25 r. American Bald Eagle (*horiz*)	*Set of 2 sheets*	5·00	5·25

Nos. 2658/63 were printed together, *se-tenant*, in sheetlets of 6.

346 Blitzer Benz, 1911

1997 (27 Mar). *Classic Cars.* T **346** *and similar horiz designs. Multicoloured. Litho.* P 14.

2668	5 r. Type **346**		50	55
	a. Sheetlet. Nos. 2668/73		3·00	
2669	5 r. Datsun, 1917		50	55
2670	5 r. Auburn 8-120, 1929		50	55
2671	5 r. Mercedes-Benz C280, 1996		50	55
2672	5 r. Suzuki UR-1		50	55
2673	5 r. Chrysler Atlantic		50	55
2674	5 r. Mercedes-Benz 190SL, 1961		50	55
	a. Sheetlet. Nos. 2674/9		3·00	
2675	5 r. Kwaishinha D.A.T., 1916		50	55
2676	5 r. Rolls-Royce Roadster 20/25		50	55
2677	5 r. Mercedes-Benz SLK, 1997		50	55
2678	5 r. Toyota Camry, 1996		50	55
2679	5 r. Jaguar MK 2, 1959		50	50
2668/79		*Set of 12*	6·00	6·50
MS2680	Two sheets, each 100×70 mm. (a) 25 r. Volkswagen, 1939. (b) 25 r. Mazda RX-01	*Set of 2 sheets*	5·00	5·25

Nos. 2668/73 and 2674/9 were each printed together, *se-tenant*, in sheetlets of 6.

No. **MS**2680b is inscribed "MAZADA" in error.

347 *Patris II,* Greece (1926)

(Des D. Miller. Litho Questa)

1997 (1 Apr). *Passenger Ships.* T **347** *and similar multicoloured designs.* P 14.

2681	1 r. Type **347**		10	15
2682	2 r. *Infanta Beatriz,* Spain (1928)		20	25
2683	3 r. *Vasilefs Constantinos,* Greece (1914)		30	35
	a. Sheetlet. Nos. 2683/91		2·50	
2684	3 r. *Cunene,* Portugal (1911)		30	35
2685	3 r. *Selandia,* Denmark (1912)		30	35
2686	3 r. *President Harding,* U.S.A. (1921)		30	35
2687	3 r. *Ulster Monarch,* Great Britain (1929)		30	35
2688	3 r. *Matsonia,* U.S.A. (1913)		30	35
2689	3 r. *France,* France (1911)		30	35
2690	3 r. *Campania,* Great Britain (1893)		30	35
2691	3 r. *Klipfontein,* Holland (1922)		30	35
2692	3 r. *Eridan,* France (1929)		30	35
	a. Sheetlet. Nos. 2692/700		2·50	
2693	3 r. *Mount Clinton,* U.S.A. (1921)		30	35
2694	3 r. *Infanta Isabel,* Spain (1912)		30	35
2695	3 r. *Suwa Maru,* Japan (1914)		30	35
2696	3 r. *Yorkshire,* Great Britain (1920)		30	35
2697	3 r. *Highland Chieftain,* Great Britain (1929)		30	35
2698	3 r. *Sardinia,* Norway (1920)		30	35
2699	3 r. *San Guglielmo,* Italy (1911)		30	35
2700	3 r. *Avila,* Great Britain (1927)		30	35

2701	8 r. *Stavangerfjord*, Norway (1918) ..	80	85
2702	12 r. *Baloeran*, Netherlands (1929) ..	1·25	1·40
2681/702	*Set of 22*	7·75	8·75

MS2703 Four sheets. (a) 69×69 mm. 25 r. *Mauritania*, Great Britain (1907). (b) 69×69 mm. 25 r. *United States*, U.S.A. (1952). (c) 69×69 mm. 25 r. *Queen Mary*, Great Britain (1930). (d) 91×76 mm. 25 r. *Royal Yacht Britannia* and Chinese junk, Hong Kong (56×42 mm) .. .. .. *Set of 4 sheets* 10·00 10·50

Nos. 2683/91 and 2692/700 were each printed together, *se-tenant*, in sheetlets of 9.

No. MS2703d is inscribed "BRITTANIA" in error.

348 Prayer Wheels, Lhasa

(Des M. Freedman and Dena Rubin. Litho Questa)

1997 (7 Apr). *50th Anniv of U.N.E.S.C.O. T* **348** *and similar multicoloured designs.* P 14×13½ (*horiz*) or 13½×14 (*vert*).

2704	1 r. Type **348** ..	10	15
2705	2 r. Ruins of Roman Temple of Diana, Portugal (*horiz*) ..	20	25
2706	3 r. Santa Maria Cathedral, Hildesheim, Germany (*horiz*)	30	35
2707	5 r. Vivunga National Park, Zaire ..	50	55
	a. Sheetlet. Nos. 2707/14 and central label	4·00	
2708	5 r. Valley of Mai Nature Reserve, Seychelles ..	50	55
2709	5 r. Kandy, Sri Lanka ..	50	55
2710	5 r. Taj Mahal, India ..	50	55
2711	5 r. Istanbul, Turkey ..	50	55
2712	5 r. Sana'a, Yemen ..	50	55
2713	5 r. Bleinheim Palace, England ..	50	55
2714	5 r. Grand Canyon National Park, U.S.A.	50	55
2715	5 r. Tombs, Gondar, Ethiopia ..	50	55
	a. Sheetlets. Nos. 2715/22 and central label	4·00	
2716	5 r. Bwindi National Park, Uganda ..	50	55
2717	5 r. Bemaraha National Reserve, Madagascar ..	50	55
2718	5 r. Buddhist ruins at Takht-I-Bahi, Pakistan ..	50	55
2719	5 r. Anuradhapura, Sri Lanka ..	50	55
2720	5 r. Cairo, Egypt ..	50	55
2721	5 r. Ruins, Petra, Jordan ..	50	55
2722	5 r. Volcano, Ujung Kulon National Park, Indonesia ..	50	55
2723	5 r. Terrace, Mount Taishan, China ..	50	55
	a. Sheetlet. Nos. 2723/30 and central label	4·00	
2724	5 r. Temple, Mount Taishan, China ..	50	55
2725	5 r. Temple turret, Mount Taishan, China	50	55
2726	5 r. Standing stones, Mount Taishan, China ..	50	55
2727	5 r. Courtyard, Mount Taishan, China ..	50	55
2728	5 r. Staircase, Mount Taishan, China ..	50	55
2729	5 r. Terracotta Warriors, China ..	50	55
2730	5 r. Head of Terracotta Warrior, China	50	55
2731	7 r. Doorway, Abu Simbel, Egypt ..	70	75
2732	8 r. Mandraki, Rhodes, Greece (*horiz*) ..	80	85
2733	8 r. Agios Stefanos Monastery, Meteora, Greece (*horiz*)	80	85
	a. Sheetlet. Nos. 2733/7 and label ..	4·00	
2734	8 r. Taj Mahal, India (*horiz*) ..	80	85
2735	8 r. Cistercian Abbey of Fontenay, France (*horiz*)	80	85
2736	8 r. Yarushima, Japan (*horiz*) ..	80	85
2737	8 r. Cloisters, San Gonzalo Convent, Portugal (*horiz*)	80	85
2738	8 r. Olympic National Park, U.S.A. (*horiz*)	80	85
	a. Sheetlet. Nos. 2738/42 and label	4·00	
2739	8 r. Waterfall, Nahanni National Park, Canada (*horiz*)	80	85
2740	8 r. Mountains, National Park, Argentina (*horiz*)	80	85
2741	8 r. Bonfin Salvador Church, Brazil (*horiz*)	80	85
2742	8 r. Convent of the Companions of Jesus, Morelia, Mexico (*horiz*)	80	85
2743	8 r. Two-storey Temple, Horyu Temple, Japan (*horiz*)	80	85
	a. Sheetlet. Nos. 2743/7 and label ..	4·00	
2744	8 r. Summer house, Horyu Temple, Japan (*horiz*)	80	85
2745	8 r. Temple and cloister, Horyu Temple, Japan (*horiz*)	80	85
2746	8 r. Single storey Temple, Horyu Temple, Japan (*horiz*)	80	85
2747	8 r. Well, Horyu Temple, Japan (*horiz*) ..	80	85
2748	10 r. Scandola Nature Reserve, France (*horiz*)	1·00	1·10
2749	12 r. Temple on the Lake, China (*horiz*)	1·25	1·40
2704/49	*Set of 46*	28·00	30·00

MS2750 Four sheets, each 127×102 mm. (a) 25 r. Fatehpur Sikri Monument, India (*horiz*). (b) 25 r. Temple, Chengde, China (*horiz*). (c) 25 r. Serengeti National Park, Tanzania (*horiz*). (d) 25 r. Buddha, Anuradhapura, Sri Lanka (*horiz*)
Set of 4 sheets 10·00 10·50

Nos. 2707/14, 2715/22 and 2723/30 were each printed together, *se-tenant*, in sheetlets of 8 stamps with a central label and Nos. 2733/7, 2738/42 and 2743/7 in sheetlets of 5 stamps with a top left-hand corner label.

No. 2717 is inscribed "MADAGASGAR" and No. 2737 "COVENT", both in error.

---

349 White Doves and S.A.A.R.C. Logo

(Litho Security Printers (M), Malaysia)

1997 (12 May). *9th South Asian Association for Regional Co-operation Summit, Malé. T* **349** *and similar horiz design.* Multicoloured. P 13.

2751	3 r. Type **349** ..	30	35
2752	5 r. Flags of member countries ..	50	55

350 Queen Elizabeth II

(Litho Questa)

1997 (12 June). *Golden Wedding of Queen Elizabeth and Prince Philip. T* **350** *and similar horiz designs.* Multicoloured. P 14.

2753	5 r. Type **350** ..	50	55
	a. Sheetlet. Nos. 2753/8	3·00	
2754	5 r. Royal coat of arms ..	50	55
2755	5 r. Queen Elizabeth and Prince Philip at opening of Parliament	50	55
2756	5 r. Queen Elizabeth and Prince Philip with Prince Charles, 1948	50	55
2757	5 r. Buckingham Palace from the garden	50	55
2758	5 r. Prince Philip	50	55
2753/8	*Set of 6*	3·00	3·25

MS2759 100×70 mm. 25 r. Queen Elizabeth II 2·50 2·75

Nos. 2753/8 were printed together, *se-tenant*, in sheetlets of 6.

351 Early Indian Mail Messenger

352 "Dawn at Kanda Myojin Shrine"

(Des J. Iskowitz. Litho Questa)

1997 (12 June). *"Pacific '97" International Stamp Exhibition, San Francisco. Death Centenary of Heinrich von Stephan (founder of the U.P.U.). T* **351** *and similar horiz designs.* P 14.

2760	2 r. turquoise-green and black ..	20	25
	a. Sheetlet. Nos. 2760/2	60	
2761	2 r. chestnut and black ..	20	25
2762	2 r. violet ..	20	25
2760/2	*Set of 3*	60	75

Designs:—No. 2760, Type **351**; No. 2761, Von Stephan and Mercury; No. 2762, Autogyro, Washington.

Nos. 2760/2 were printed together, *se-tenant*, in sheetlets of 3 with enlarged right-hand margin.

(Litho Questa)

1997 (12 June). *Birth Bicentenary of Hiroshige (Japanese painter). "One Hundred Famous Views of Edo". T* **352** *and similar vert designs.* Multicoloured. P 13½×14.

2763	8 r. Type **352** ..	80	85
	a. Sheetlet. Nos. 2763/8	4·75	
2764	8 r. "Kiyomizu Hall and Shinobazu Pond at Ueno"	80	85
2765	8 r. "Ueno Yamashita" ..	80	85
2766	8 r. "Moon Pine, Ueno" ..	80	85
2767	8 r. "Flower Pavilion, Dango Slope, Sendagi"	80	85
2768	8 r. "Shitaya Hirokoji" ..	80	85
2763/8	*Set of 6*	4·75	5·00

MS2769 Two sheets, each 102×127 mm. (a) 25 r. "Hilltop View, Yushima Tenjin Shrine". (b) 25 r. "Seido and Kanda River from Shohei Bridge"
Set of 2 sheets 5·00 5·25

Nos. 2763/8 were printed together, *se-tenant*, in sheetlets of 6.

The new-issue supplement to this Catalogue appears each month in

GIBBONS STAMP MONTHLY

—from your newsagent or by postal subscription— sample copy and details on request.

---

353 Common Noddy

354 *Canarina eminii*

(Des M. Lebouef. Litho B.D.T.)

1997 (17 June). *Birds. T* **353** *and similar vert designs.* Multicoloured. P 14.

2770	30 l. Type **353** ..	10	10
2771	1 r. Spectacled Owl ..	10	10
2772	2 r. Malay Fish Owl ..	20	25
2773	3 r. Peregrine Falcon ..	30	35
2774	5 r. Golden Eagle ..	50	55
2775	7 r. Ruppell's Parrot ..	70	75
	a. Sheetlet. Nos. 2775/80	4·00	
2776	7 r. Blue-headed Parrot ..	70	75
2777	7 r. St. Vincent Amazon ..	70	75
2778	7 r. Grey Parrot ..	70	75
2779	7 r. Masked Lovebird ..	70	75
2780	7 r. Sun Conure ..	70	75
2781	8 r. Bateleur ..	80	85
2782	10 r. Whiskered Tern with chicks ..	1·00	1·10
2783	10 r. Common Caracara ..	1·00	1·10
2784	15 r. Red-footed Booby ..	1·50	1·60
2770/84	*Set of 15*	9·50	10·50

MS2785 Two sheets, each 67×98 mm. (a) 25 r. American Bald Eagle. (b) 25 r. Secretary Bird
Set of 2 sheets 5·00 5·25

Nos. 2775/80 were printed together, *se-tenant*, in sheetlets of 6.

(Litho Questa)

1997 (24 June). *Flowers. T* **354** *and similar multicoloured designs.* P 14½×14 (*vert*) or 14×14½ (*horiz*).

2786	1 r. Type **354** ..	10	10
2787	2 r. *Delphinium macrocentron* ..	20	25
2788	3 r. *Leucadendron discolor* ..	30	35
2789	5 r. *Nymphaea caerulea* ..	50	55
2790	7 r. *Rosa multiflora polyantha* (20×23 mm) ..	70	75
2791	8 r. *Bulbophyllum barbigerum* ..	80	85
2792	8 r. *Acacia seyal* (*horiz*) ..	80	85
	a. Sheetlet. Nos. 2792/7	4·75	
2793	8 r. *Gloriosa superba* (*horiz*) ..	80	85
2794	8 r. *Gnidia subcordata* (*horiz*) ..	80	85
2795	8 r. *Platycelyphium voense* (*horiz*) ..	80	85
2796	8 r. *Aspilia mossambicensis* (*horiz*) ..	80	85
2797	8 r. *Adenium obesum* (*horiz*) ..	80	85
2798	12 r. *Hibiscus vitifolius* ..	1·25	1·40
2786/98	*Set of 13*	8·50	9·25

MS2799 Two sheets, each 105×76 mm. (a) 25 r. *Aerangis rhodosticta* (*horiz*). (b) 25 r. *Dichrostachys cinerea* and two sailing boats (*horiz*)
Set of 2 sheets 5·00 5·25

Nos. 2792/7 were printed together, *se-tenant*, in sheetlets of 6 with the backgrounds forming a composite design.

355 Archaeopteryx

356 Pres. Nelson Mandela

(Des. J Ruff and M Leboeuf. Litho Questa)

1997 (20 Nov). *Prehistoric Animals.* Multicoloured. P 14. (a) T **355** *and similar horiz designs.*

2800	5 r. Type **355** ..	50	55
2801	7 r. Diplodocus ..	70	75
	a. Sheetlet. Nos. 2801/6	4·00	
2802	7 r. Tyrannosaurus rex ..	70	75
2803	7 r. Pteranodon ..	70	75
2804	7 r. Montanceratops ..	70	75
2805	7 r. Dromaeosaurus ..	70	75
2806	7 r. Oviraptor ..	70	75
2807	8 r. Mosasaurus ..	80	85
2808	12 r. Deinonychus ..	1·25	1·40
2809	15 r. Triceratops ..	1·50	1·60

(b) *Square designs,* 31×31 mm.

2810	7 r. Troodon ..	70	75
	a. Sheetlet. Nos. 2810/15	4·00	
2811	7 r. Brachiosaurus ..	70	75
2812	7 r. Saltasaurus ..	70	75
2813	7 r. Oviraptor ..	70	75
2814	7 r. Parasaurolophus ..	70	75
2815	7 r. Psittacosaurus ..	70	75
2816	7 r. Triceratops ..	70	75
	a. Sheetlet. Nos. 2816/21	4·00	
2817	7 r. Pachycephalosaurus ..	70	75
2818	7 r. Iguanodon ..	70	75
2819	7 r. Tyrannosaurus rex ..	70	75
2820	7 r. Corythosaurus ..	70	75
2821	7 r. Stegosaurus ..	70	75
2822	7 r. Euophlocephalus ..	70	75
	a. Sheetlet. Nos. 2822/7	4·00	

2823	7 r.	Compsognathus	..	70	75
2824	7 r.	Herrerasaurus	..	70	75
2825	7 r.	Styracosaurus	..	70	75
2826	7 r.	Baryonyx	..	70	75
2827	7 r.	Lesothosaurus	..	70	75
2800/27			*Set of 28*	20·00	22·00

MS2828 Two sheets. (a) 99×79 mm. 25 r. Tyrannosaurus rex (42×28 *mm*). (b) 73×104 mm. 25 r. Archaeopteryx (31×31 *mm*)
Set of 2 sheets 10·00 10·50

Nos. 2801/6, 2810/15 2816/21 and 2822/7 were each printed together, *se-tenant*, in sheetlets of 6, with the backgrounds forming composite designs (Nos. 2801/6 and 2810/15) or with enlarged illustrated margins (Nos. 2816/21 and 2822/7).

(Litho Questa)

1997 (10 Dec). *World Cup Football Championship, France. Designs as T 246 of Lesotho.* P 14×13½.

2829	1 r.	black	..	10	15
2830	2 r.	black	..	25	25
2831	3 r.	multicoloured	..	30	35
2832/9	3 r. × 8 (brownish black; brownish black; multicoloured; multicoloured; brownish black; multicoloured; brownish black; multicoloured)				
	a. Sheetlet. Nos. 2832/9 and central label			2·40	
2840/7	3 r. × 8 (multicoloured; multicoloured; brownish black; brownish black; brownish black; multicoloured; multicoloured; brownish black)				
	a. Sheetlet. Nos. 2840/7 and central label			2·40	
2848/55	3 r. × 8 (multicoloured; multicoloured; multicoloured; brownish black; brownish black; multicoloured; multicoloured; multicoloured)				
	a. Sheetlet. Nos. 2848/55 and central label			2·40	
2856	7 r.	black	..	70	75
2857	8 r.	black	..	80	85
2858	10 r.	multicoloured	..	1·00	1·10
2829/58			*Set of 30*	10·00	11·50

MS2859 Three sheets. (a) 103×128 mm. 25 r. multicoloured. P 13½×14. (b) 103×128 mm. 25 r. multicoloured. P 14×13½. (c) 128×103 mm. 25 r. multicoloured. P 13½×14
Set of 3 sheets 7·50 7·75

Designs: *Horiz*—No. 2829, Brazilian team, 1994; No. 2830, German player, 1954; No. 2831, Maradona holding World Cup, 1986; No. 2832, Brazilian team, 1958; No. 2833, Luis Bellini, Brazil, 1958; No. 2834, Brazilian team, 1962; No. 2835, Carlos Alberto, Brazil, 1970; No. 2836, Mauro, Brazil, 1962; No. 2837, Brazilian team, 1970; No. 2838, Dunga, Brazil, 1994; No. 2839, Brazilian team, 1994; No. 2840, Paulo Rossi, Italy, 1982; No. 2841, Zoff and Gentile, Italy, 1982; No. 2842, Angelo Schavio, Italy; No. 2843, Italian team, 1934; No. 2844, Italian team with flag, 1934; No. 2845, Italian team, 1982; No. 2846, San Paolo Stadium, Italy; No. 2847, Italian team, 1938; No. 2848, English player with ball, 1966; No. 2849, Wembley Stadium, London; No. 2850, English player heading ball, 1966; No. 2851, English players celebrating, 1966; No. 2852, English and German players chasing ball, 1966; No. 2853, English player wearing No. 21 shirt, 1966; No. 2854, English team with Jules Rimet trophy, 1966; No. 2855, German player wearing No. 5 shirt, 1966; No. 2856, Argentine player holding trophy, 1978; No. 2857, English players with Jules Rimet trophy, 1966; No. 2858, Brazilian player with trophy, 1970; No. **MS**2859*c*, Klinsmann, Germany. *Vert*—No. **MS**2859*a*, Ronaldo, Brazil; No. **MS**2592*b*, Schmeichel, Denmark.

Nos. 2832/9, 2840/7 and 2848/55 were each printed together, *se-tenant*, in sheetlets of 8 stamps and a central label.

(Litho Questa)

1998 (9 Feb). *Diana, Princess of Wales Commemoration. Vert designs as T 249 of Lesotho.* Multicoloured (except Nos. 2864, 2870, 2872, 2877 *and* MS2878b). P 13½.

2860	7 r.	Laughing	..	70	75
	a. Sheetlet. Nos. 2860/5			4·00	
2861	7 r.	With Prince William and Prince Harry		70	75
2862	7 r.	Carrying bouquets	..	70	75
2863	7 r.	In white evening dress	..	70	75
2864	7 r.	Wearing bowtie (chestnut and black)		70	75
2865	7 r.	Wearing black jacket	..	70	75
2866	7 r.	With Indian child on lap	..	70	75
	a. Sheetlet. Nos. 2866/71			4·00	
2867	7 r.	Wearing blue evening dress	..	70	75
2868	7 r.	Wearing blue jacket and poppy		70	75
2869	7 r.	Wearing cream jacket	..	70	75
2870	7 r.	Wearing blouse and jacket (lake-brown and black)		70	75
2871	7 r.	Wearing red jacket	..	70	75
2872	7 r.	Wearing hat (new blue and black)		70	75
	a. Sheetlet. Nos. 2872/7			4·00	
2873	7 r.	Wearing red evening dress	..	70	75
2874	7 r.	With Sir Richard Attenborough	..	70	75
2875	7 r.	Wearing jeans and white shirt	..	70	75
2876	7 r.	Wearing white jacket	..	70	75
2877	7 r.	Carrying bouquet (orange-brown and black)		70	75
2860/77			*Set of 18*	12·50	13·50

MS2878 Three sheets. (a) 100×70 mm. 25 r. On ski-lift. (b) 100×70 mm. 25 r, Wearing polkadot dress (brown and black). (c) 70×100 mm. 25 r. Wearing garland of flowers . . *Set of 3 sheets* 7·50 7·75

Nos. 2860/5, 2866/71 and 2872/7 were printed together, *se-tenant*, in sheetlets of 6.

Two 50 r. values embossed on gold foil also exist from limited printings.

(Des Zina Saunders. Litho Questa)

1998 (1 Mar). *80th Birthday of Nelson Mandela (President of South Africa).* P 14.

2879	**356**	7 r. multicoloured	..	70	75

357 Pres. John F. Kennedy

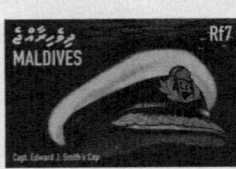

358 Yakovlev Yak-18 (from 1947)

(Des M. Bennett. Litho Questa)

1998 (1 Mar). *Pres. John F. Kennedy Commemoration. T 357 and similar vert portraits.* Multicoloured: background colours given. P 13½×14.

2880	5 r.	deep turquoise-green (Type 357)	..	50	55
	a. Sheetlet. Nos. 2880/8			4·50	
2881	5 r.	turquoise-green	..	50	55
2882	5 r.	ochre (inscr at right)	..	50	55
2883	5 r.	pale lemon	..	50	55
2884	5 r.	bluish violet	..	50	55
2885	5 r.	violet-blue	..	50	55
2886	5 r.	lavender-grey	..	50	55
2887	5 r.	drab (inscr at left)	..	50	55
2888	5 r.	cobalt (value at bottom right)	..	50	55
2880/8			*Set of 9*	4·50	4·75

Nos. 2880/8 were printed together, *se-tenant*, in sheetlets of 9 with enlarged illustrated right-hand margin.

(Des W. Wright. Litho Questa)

1998 (1 Mar). *Aircraft in Longest Continuous Production. T 358 and similar horiz designs.* Multicoloured. P 14.

2889	5 r.	Type 358	..	50	55
	a. Sheetlet. Nos. 2889/97			4·50	
2890	5 r.	Beechcraft Bonanza (from 1947)	..	50	55
2891	5 r.	Piper Cub (1937–82)	..	50	55
2892	5 r.	Tupolev Tu-95 (1954–90)	..	50	55
2893	5 r.	Lockheed C-130 Hercules (from 1954)		50	55
2894	5 r.	Piper PA-28 Cherokee (from 1961)		50	55
2895	5 r.	Mikoyan Gurevich MiG-21 (from 1959)		50	55
2896	5 r.	Pilatus PC-6 Turbo Porter (from 1960)		50	55
2897	5 r.	Antonov An-2 (from 1949)	..	50	55
2889/97			*Set of 9*	4·50	4·75

MS2898 120×90 mm. 25 r. Boeing KC-135E (from 1956) (84×28 *mm*) . . 2·50 2·75

Nos. 2889/97 were printed together, *se-tenant*, in sheetlets of 9 with enlarged margin at foot containing text.

359 White American Shorthair

360 Boeing 737 HS

(Des R. Martin. Litho Questa)

1998 (1 June). *Cats. T 359 and similar multicoloured designs.* P 14.

2899	5 r.	Type 359	..	50	55
2900	7 r.	American Curl and Maine Coon (*horiz*)		70	75
	a. Sheetlet. Nos. 2900/5			4·00	
2901	7 r.	Maine Coon (*horiz*)	..	70	75
2902	7 r.	Siberian (*horiz*)	..	70	75
2903	7 r.	Somali (*horiz*)	..	70	75
2904	7 r.	European Burmese (*horiz*)	..	70	75
2905	7 r.	Nebelung (*horiz*)	..	70	75
2906	7 r.	Bicolor British Shorthair (*horiz*)		70	75
	a. Sheetlet. Nos. 2906/11			4·00	
2907	7 r.	Manx (*horiz*)	..	70	75
2908	7 r.	Tabby American Shorthair (*horiz*)		70	75
2909	7 r.	Silver Tabby Persian (*horiz*)	..	70	75
2910	7 r.	Oriental White (*horiz*)	..	70	75
2911	7 r.	Norwegian Forest Cat (*horiz*)	..	70	75
2912	8 r.	Sphynx Cat	..	80	85
2913	10 r.	Tabby American Shorthair	..	1·00	1·10
2914	12 r.	Scottish Fold	..	1·25	1·25
2899/914			*Set of 16*	11·50	12·50

MS2915 Two sheets, each 98×68 mm. (a) 30 r. Norwegian Forest Cat. (b) 30 r. Snowshoe
Set of 2 sheets 6·00 6·25

Nos. 2900/5 and 2906/11 were each printed together, *se-tenant*, in sheetlets of 6, forming composite designs.

(Des S. Gardner. Litho Questa)

1998 (10 Aug). *Aircraft. T 360 and similar horiz designs.* Multicoloured. P 14.

2916	2 r.	Type 360	..	20	25
2917	5 r.	CL-215 (flying boat)	..	50	55
	a. Sheetlet. Nos. 2917/24			4·00	
2918	5 r.	Orion	..	50	55
2919	5 r.	Yakolev Yak-54	..	50	55
2920	5 r.	Cessna sea plane	..	50	55
2921	5 r.	CL-215 (amphibian)	..	50	55
2922	5 r.	CL-215 SAR (amphibian)	..	50	55
2923	5 r.	Twin Otter	..	50	55
2924	5 r.	Rockwell Quail	..	50	55

2925	5 r.	F.S.W. fighter	..	50	55
	a. Sheetlet. Nos. 2925/32			4·00	
2926	5 r.	V-Jet II	..	50	55
2927	5 r.	Pilatus PC-12	..	50	55
2928	5 r.	Citation Exel	..	50	55
2929	5 r.	Stutz Bearcat	..	50	55
2930	5 r.	Cessna T-37 (B)	..	50	55
2931	5 r.	Peregrine Business Jet	..	50	55
2932	5 r.	Beech 58 Baron	..	50	55
2933	7 r.	Boeing 727	..	70	75
2934	8 r.	Boeing 747-400	..	80	85
2935	10 r.	Boeing 737	..	1·00	1·10
2916/35			*Set of 20*	10·50	11·50

MS2936 Two sheets, each 98×68 mm. (a) 25 r. Beechcraft Model 18. (b) 25 r. Falcon Jet
Set of 2 sheets 5·00 5·25

Nos. 2917/24 and 2925/32 were each printed together, *se-tenant*, in sheetlets of 8.

361 Captain Edward Smith's Cap

(Des Zina Saunders. Litho Cartor)

1998 (27 Sept). *Titanic Commemoration. T 361 and similar horiz designs.* Multicoloured. P 14.

2937	7 r.	Type 361	..	70	75
	a. Sheetlet. Nos. 2937/42			4·00	
2938	7 r.	Deck chair	..	70	75
2939	7 r.	Fifth Officer Harold Lowe's coat button		70	75
2940	7 r.	Lifeboat	..	70	75
2941	7 r.	*Titanic's* wheel	..	70	75
2942	7 r.	Passenger's lifejacket	..	70	75
2937/42			*Set of 6*	4·00	4·50

MS2943 110×85 mm. 25 r. *Titanic* from newspaper picture . . 2·50 2·75

Nos. 2937/42 were printed together, *se-tenant*, in sheetlets of 6 with enlarged illustrated top margin.

362 Guava Tree

(Litho B.D.T)

1998 (30 Nov). *20th Anniv of International Fund for Agriculture. T 362 and similar horiz designs.* Multicoloured. P 14.

2944	1 r.	Type 362	..	10	15
2945	5 r.	Selection of fruit	..	50	55
2946	7 r.	Fishing boat	..	70	75
2947	8 r.	Papaya Tree	..	80	85
2948	10 r.	Vegetable produce	..	1·00	1·10
2944/8			*Set of 5*	3·00	3·25

363 Thread-finned Butterflyfish

(Des T. Wood. Litho Questa)

1998 (10 Dec). *Fish. T 363 and similar horiz designs.* Multicoloured. P 14.

2949	50 l.	Type 363	..	10	10
2950	50 l.	Queen Angelfish	..	10	10
2951	1 r.	Oriental Sweetlips	..	10	15
2952	3 r.	Mandarin Fish	..	30	35
	a. Sheetlet. Nos. 2952/60			2·75	
2953	3 r.	Copper-banded Butterflyfish	..	30	35
2954	3 r.	Harlequin Tuskfish	..	30	35
2955	3 r.	Yellow-tailed Demoiselle	..	30	35
2956	3 r.	Wimplefish	..	30	35
2957	3 r.	Red Emperor Snapper	..	30	35
2958	3 r.	Clown Triggerfish	..	30	35
2959	3 r.	Common Clown	..	30	35
2960	3 r.	Palette Surgeonfish ("Regal Tang")		30	35
2961	5 r.	Emperor Angelfish	..	50	55
	a. Sheetlet. Nos. 2961/9			4·50	
2962	5 r.	Common Squirrelfish ("Diadem Squirrelfish")		50	55
2963	5 r.	Lemon-peel Angelfish	..	50	55
2964	5 r.	Powder-blue Surgeonfish	..	50	55
2965	5 r.	Moorish Idol	..	50	55
2966	5 r.	Bicolor Angelfish ("Bicolor Cherub")		50	55
2967	5 r.	Duboulay's Angelfish ("Scribbled Angelfish")		50	55
2968	5 r.	Two-banded Anemonefish	..	50	55
2969	5 r.	Yellow Tang	..	50	55
2970	7 r.	Red-tailed Surgeonfish ("Achilles Tang")		70	75
2971	7 r.	Bandit Angelfish	..	70	75
2972	8 r.	Hooded Butterflyfish ("Red-headed Butterflyfish")		80	85
2973	50 r.	Blue-striped Butterflyfish	..	5·00	5·50
2949/73			*Set of 25*	14·50	16·00

MS2974 Two sheets, each 110×85 mm. (a) 25 r. Long-nosed Butterflyfish. (b) 25 r. Porkfish.
Set of 2 sheets 5·00 5·25

Nos. 2952/60 and 2961/9 were each printed together, *se-tenant*, in sheetlets of 9.

364 Baden-Powell inspecting
Scouts, Amesbury, 1909

365 Diana, Princess of
Wales

(Des J. Iskowitz. Litho Questa)

1998 (15 Dec). *19th World Scout Jamboree, Chile. T 364 and similar multicoloured designs. P 14.*

2975	12 r. Type 364	..	1·25	1·40
	a. Sheetlet. Nos. 2975/7		3·75	
2976	12 r. Sir Robert and Lady Baden-Powell with children, 1927	..	1·25	1·40
2977	12 r. Sir Robert Baden-Powell awarding merit badges, Chicago, 1926		1·25	1·40
2975/7		*Set of 3*	3·75	4·00

Nos. 2975/7 were printed together, *se-tenant*, in sheetlets of 3 with enlarged illustrated margins at top and right.

1998 (15 Dec). *1st Death Anniv of Diana, Princess of Wales. Litho. P 14½×14.*

2978	365 10 r. multicoloured	..	1·00	1·10
	a. Sheetlet of 6		6·00	

No. 2978 was printed in sheetlets of 6 with an enlarged illustrated left margin.

366 Triton Shell

(Litho Questa)

1999 (1 Apr). *International Year of the Ocean. Marine Life. T 366 and similar horiz designs. Multicoloured. Litho. P 14.*

2979	25 l. Type 366	..	10	10
	a. Sheetlet. Nos. 2979/82 and 2992/3		1·90	
2980	50 l. Napoleon Wrasse	..	10	10
2981	1 r. Whale Shark	..	10	15
2982	3 r. Grey Reef Shark	..	30	35
2983	5 r. Harp Seal	..	50	55
	a. Sheetlet. Nos. 2983/91		4·50	
2984	5 r. Killer Whale	..	50	55
2985	5 r. Sea Otter	..	50	55
2986	5 r. Beluga	..	50	55
2987	5 r. Narwhal	..	50	55
2988	5 r. Walrus	..	50	55
2989	5 r. Sea Lion	..	50	55
2990	5 r. Humpback Salmon	..	50	55
2991	5 r. Emperor Penguin	..	50	55
2992	7 r. Blue Whale	..	70	75
2993	7 r. Skipjack Tuna	..	70	75
	a. Sheetlet. No. 2993×6		4·25	
2994	8 r. Ocean Sunfish	..	80	85
	a. Sheetlet. Nos. 2994/7		3·25	
2995	8 r. Opalescent Squid	..	80	85
2996	8 r. Electric Ray	..	80	85
2997	8 r. Corded Neptune	..	80	85
2979/97		*Set of 19*	8·25	9·00

MS2998 Three sheets, each 110×85 mm. (a) 25 r. Horseshoe Crab. (b) 25 r. Blue Whale. (c) 25 r. Triton shell .. .. *Set of 3 sheets* 7·50 7·75

Nos. 2979/82 and 2992/3 were printed together, *se-tenant*, in sheetlets of 6. No. 2993 was also available in a sheetlet containing 6 examples of the one design. Nos. 2983/91 and 2994/7 were each printed together, *se-tenant*, in sheetlets of 9 (Nos. 2983/91, with the backgrounds forming a composite design) or 4 (Nos. 2994/7).

367 Broderip's Cowrie

(Litho Questa)

1999 (1 Apr). *Marine Life. T 367 and similar horiz designs. Multicoloured. P 14.*

2999	30 l. Type 367	..	10	10
3000	1 r. White Tern	..	10	15
3001	3 r. Green Heron	..	30	35
3002	5 r. Manta Ray	..	50	55
	a. Sheetlet. Nos. 3002/10		4·50	
3003	5 r. Green Turtle	..	50	55
3004	5 r. Spotted Dolphins	..	50	55
3005	5 r. Moorish Idols	..	50	55
3006	5 r. Threadfin Anthias	..	50	55
3007	5 r. Goldbar Wrasse	..	50	55
3008	5 r. Palette Surgeonfish	..	50	55
3009	5 r. Three-spotted Angelfish	..	50	55
3010	5 r. Oriental Sweetlips	..	50	55
3011	5 r. Brown Booby	..	50	55
	a. Sheetlet. Nos. 3011/19		4·50	
3012	5 r. Red-tailed Tropic Bird	..	50	55
3013	5 r. Sooty Tern	..	50	55

3014	5 r. Striped Dolphin	..	50	55
3015	5 r. Spinner Dolphin	..	50	55
3016	5 r. Crab Plover	..	50	55
3017	5 r. Hawksbill Turtle	..	50	55
3018	5 r. Indo-Pacific Sergeant	..	50	55
3019	5 r. Yellow-finned Tuna	..	50	55
3020	7 r. Blackflag Sandperch	..	70	75
3021	8 r. Coral Hind	..	80	85
3022	10 r. Olive Ridley Turtle	..	1·00	1·10
2999/3022		*Set of 24*	12·00	13·00

MS3023 Two sheets, each 110×85 mm. (a) 25 r. Cinnamon Bittern. (b) 25 r. Blue-faced Angelfish .. .. *Set of 2 sheets* 5·00 5·25

Nos. 3002/10 and 3011/19 were each printed together, *se-tenant*, in sheetlets of 9 with the backgrounds forming composite designs.

368 Mickey Mouse

1999 (27 May). *70th Anniv of Mickey Mouse (Disney cartoon character). T 368 and similar multicoloured designs. Litho. P 13½×14.*

3024/9	5 r. × 6 (Mickey Mouse: Type 368; laughing; looking tired; frowning; smiling; winking)		
	a. Sheetlet. Nos. 3024/9		3·00
3030/5	5 r. × 6 (Minnie Mouse: facing left and smiling; with eyes closed; with hand on head; looking surprised; smiling; looking cross)		
	a. Sheetlet. Nos. 3030/5		3·00
3036/41	7 r. × 6 (Donald Duck: facing left and smiling; laughing; looking tired; looking cross; smiling; winking)		
	a. Sheetlet. Nos. 3036/41		4·25
3042/7	7 r. × 6 (Daisy Duck: with half closed eyes; laughing; looking shocked; looking cross; facing forwards; with head on one side)		
	a. Sheetlet. Nos. 3042/7		4·25
3048/53	7 r. × 6 (Goofy: facing right and smiling; with eyes closed; with half closed eyes; looking shocked; looking puzzled; looking thoughtful)		
	a. Sheetlet. Nos. 3048/53		4·25
3054/9	7 r. × 6 (Pluto: looking shocked; with eyes closed; smiling; scowling; with tongue out (orange background); with tongue out (green background))		
	a. Sheetlet. Nos. 3054/9		4·25
3024/59		*Set of 36*	23·00 25·00

MS3060 Six sheets, each 127×102 mm. (a) 25 r. Minnie Mouse wearing necklace. (b) 25 r. Mickey with hand on head. (c) 25 r. Mickey wearing baseball hat. (d) Mickey facing right (*horiz*). (e) 25 r. Minnie looking left (includes label showing Mickey with bouquet). (f) 25 r. Minnie drinking through straw. P 13½×14 (*vert*) or 14×13½ (*horiz*) .. .. .. *Set of 6 sheets* 15·00 16·00

Nos. 3024/9, 3030/5, 3036/41, 3042/7, 3048/53 and 3054/9 were each printed together, *se-tenant*, in sheetlets of 6 stamps, with enlarged illustrated margins.

369 Great Orange Tip

(Litho Questa)

1999 (8 June). *Butterflies. T 369 and similar multicoloured designs. P 14.*

3061	50 l. Type 369	..	10	10
3062	1 r. Large Green Aporandria	..	10	15
3063	2 r. Common Mormon	..	20	25
3064	3 r. African Migrant	..	30	35
3065	5 r. Common Pierrot	..	50	55
3066	7 r. Crimson Tip (*vert*)	..	70	75
	a. Sheetlet. Nos. 3066/71		4·25	
3067	7 r. Tawny Rajah (*vert*)	..	70	75
3068	7 r. Leafwing Butterfly (*vert*)	..	70	75
3069	7 r. Great Egg-fly (*vert*)	..	70	75
3070	7 r. Blue Admiral (*vert*)	..	70	75
3071	7 r. African Migrant (*vert*)	..	70	75
3072	7 r. Common Red Flash (*vert*)	..	70	75
	a. Sheetlet. Nos. 3072/7		4·25	
3073	7 r. Burmese Lascar (*vert*)	..	70	75
3074	7 r. Common Perriot (*vert*)	..	70	75
3075	7 r. Baron (*vert*)	..	70	75
3076	7 r. Leaf Blue (*vert*)	..	70	75
3077	7 r. Great Orange Tip (*vert*)	..	70	75
3078	10 r. Giant Red-eye	..	1·00	1·10
3061/78		*Set of 18*	10·50	11·50

MS3079 Two sheets, each 70×100 mm. (a) 25 r. Crimson Tip. (b) 25 r. Large Oak Blue .. .. .. *Set of 2 sheets* 5·00 5·25

Nos. 3066/71 and 3072/7 were each printed together, *se-tenant*, in sheetlets of 6 with backgrounds forming composite designs.

370 Scelidosaurus

(Litho Questa)

1999 (22 June). *Prehistoric Animals. T 370 and similar horiz designs. Multicoloured. P 14.*

3080	1 r. Type 370	..	10	15
3081	3 r. Yansudaurus	..	30	35
3082	5 r. Ornitholestes	..	50	55
3083	7 r. Dimorphodon (*vert*)	..	70	75
	a. Sheetlet. Nos. 3083/8		4·25	
3084	7 r. Rhamphorhynchus (*vert*)	..	70	75
3085	7 r. Allosaurus (*vert*)	..	70	75
3086	7 r. Leaellynasaura (*vert*)	..	70	75
3087	7 r. Troodon (*vert*)	..	70	75
3088	7 r. Syntarsus (*vert*)	..	70	75
3089	7 r. Anchisaurus (*vert*)	..	70	75
	a. Sheetlet. Nos. 3089/94		4·25	
3090	7 r. Pterenodon (*vert*)	..	70	75
3091	7 r. Barosaurus (*vert*)	..	70	75
3092	7 r. Iguanodon (*vert*)	..	70	75
3093	7 r. Archaeopteryx (*vert*)	..	70	75
3094	7 r. Ceratosaurus (*vert*)	..	70	75
3095	7 r. Stegosaurus (*vert*)	..	70	75
	a. Sheetlet. Nos. 3095/100		4·25	
3096	7 r. Corythosaurus	..	70	75
3097	7 r. Cetiosaurus	..	70	75
3098	7 r. Avimimus	..	70	75
3099	7 r. Styracosaurus	..	70	75
3100	7 r. Massospondylus	..	70	75
3101	8 r. Astrodon	..	80	85
3080/101		*Set of 22*	14·50	15·50

MS3102 Two sheets, each 116×81 mm. (a) 25 r. Megalosaurus (*vert*). (b) 25 r. Brachiosaurus (*vert*) .. .. .. *Set of 2 sheets* 5·00 5·25

Nos. 3083/8, 3089/94 and 3095/100 were each printed together, *se-tenant*, in sheetlets of 6, forming composite designs.

371 Express Locomotive, Egypt,
1856

(Litho Questa)

1999 (26 Oct). *Trains of the World. T 371 and similar horiz designs. Multicoloured. P 14.*

3103	50 l. Type 371	..	10	10
3104	1 r. Channel Tunnel Le Shuttle, France, 1994	..	10	15
3105	2 r. Gowan and Marx locomotive, U.S.A., 1839	..	20	25
3106	3 r. TGV train, France, 1981	..	30	35
3107	5 r. "Ae 6/6" electric locomotive, Switzerland, 1954	..	50	55
3108	7 r. Stephenson's long-boilered locomotive, Great Britain, 1846 (red livery)	..	70	75
	a. Sheetlet. Nos. 3108/13		4·25	
3109	7 r. *Cornwall*, Great Britain, 1847	..	70	75
3110	7 r. First locomotive, Germany, 1848	..	70	75
3111	7 r. Great Western locomotive, Great Britain, 1846	..	70	75
3112	7 r. Standard Stephenson locomotive, France, 1837	..	70	75
3113	7 r. *Meteor*, Great Britain, 1843	..	70	75
3114	7 r. Class 4T diesel-electric locomotive, Great Britain, 1940–65	..	70	75
	a. Sheetlet. Nos. 3114/19		4·25	
3115	7 r. Mainline diesel-electric locomotive No. 20101, Malaya, 1940–65	..	70	75
3116	7 r. Class 7000 high-speed electric locomotive, France, 1949	..	70	75
3117	7 r. Diesel hydraulic express locomotive, Thailand, 1940–65	..	70	75
3118	7 r. Diesel hydraulic locomotive, Burma, 1940–65	..	70	75
3119	7 r. "Hikari" super express train, Japan, 1940–65	..	70	75
3120	8 r. Stephenson's long-boilered locomotive, Great Britain, 1846 (orange and green livery)	..	80	85
3121	10 r. *Philadelphia*, Austria, 1838	..	1·00	1·10
3122	15 r. S.E. and C. Railway Class E steam locomotive, Great Britain, 1940	..	1·50	1·60
3103/22		*Set of 20*	12·50	13·50

MS3123 Two sheets, each 110×85 mm. (a) 25 r. Passenger locomotive, France, 1846. (b) 25 r. Southern Railway Class "King Arthur", steam locomotive, Great Britain, 1940 .. *Set of 2 sheets* 5·00 5·25

Nos. 3108/13 and 3114/19 were each printed together, *se-tenant*, in sheetlets of 6 containing two horizontal strips of 3.

MINIMUM PRICE

The minimum price quote is 10p which represents a handling charge rather than a basis for valuing common stamps. For further notes about prices see introductory pages.

(Litho Questa)

1999 (1 Dec). *"Queen Elizabeth the Queen Mother's Century".*
*Vert designs as T **267** of Lesotho. P 14.*
3124   7 r.   black and gold   70   75
     a. Sheetlet. Nos. 3124/7   ..   ..   2·75
3125   7 r.   black and gold   70   75
3126   7 r.   multicoloured   70   75
3127   7 r.   multicoloured   70   75
3124/7   *Set of 4*   2·75   3·00
MS3128   153×157 mm.   25 r.   multicoloured.
   P 13½×14   ..   ..   2·50   2·75
Designs: (As *Type* **267** *of Lesotho*)—No. 3124, King George VI
and Queen Elizabeth, 1936; No. 3125, Queen Elizabeth, 1941;
No. 3126, Queen Elizabeth in evening dress, 1960; No. 3127,
Queen Mother at Ascot, 1981. *(37×50 mm)*—No. **MS**3128,
Queen Mother in Garter robes.
   Nos. 3124/7 were printed together, *se-tenant,* as a sheetlet of 4
stamps and a central label with inscribed and embossed
margins. No. **MS**3128 also shows the Royal Arms embossed in
gold.
   A 50 r. value embossed on gold foil also exists from a limited
printing.

(Litho Questa)

1999 (23 Dec). *"iBRA '99" International Stamp Exhibition,
Nuremberg. Horiz designs as T **262** of Lesotho. Multicoloured.
P 14×14½.*
3129   12 r. *Adler*   (first   German   railway
     locomotive), 1833   ..   ..   1·25   1·40
3130   15 r. *Drache* (Henshell and Sohn's first
     locomotive), 1848   ..   ..   1·50   1·60
The captions on Nos. 3129/30 are transposed.

(Litho Questa)

1999 (23 Dec). *150th Death Anniv of Katsushika Hokusai,
(Japanese artist). Designs as T **263** of Lesotho. Multicoloured
(except No. 3133). P 14×13½.*
3131   7 r.   "Haunted House"   70   75
     a. Sheetlet. Nos. 3131/6   ..   4·25
3132   7 r.   "Juniso Shrine at Yotsuya"   ..   70   75
3133   7 r.   Drawing of bird (blk, lt sage-grn & gold)   70   75
3134   7 r.   Drawing of two women   70   75
3135   7 r.   "Lover in the Snow"   70   75
3136   7 r.   "Mountain Tea House"   ..   70   75
3137   7 r.   "A Coastal View"   70   75
     a. Sheetlet. Nos. 3137/42   ..   4·25
3138   7 r.   "Bath House by a Lake"   ..   70   75
3139   7 r.   Drawing of a horse   70   75
3140   7 r.   Drawing of two birds on branch   ..   70   75
3141   7 r.   "Evening Cool at Ryogoku"   ..   70   75
3142   7 r.   "Girls boating"   70   75
3131/42   *Set of 12*   8·25   9·00
MS3143   Two sheets, each 100×70 mm. (a) 25 r.
   "Girls gathering Spring Herbs" (*vert*). (b) 25 r.
   "Scene in the Yoshiwara" (*vert*). P 13½×14
            Set of 2 sheets   5·00   5·25
   Nos. 3131/6 and 3137/42 were each printed together,
se-tenant, in sheetlets of 6.

(Litho Questa)

1999 (23 Dec). *10th Anniv of United Nations Rights of the
Child Convention. Vert designs as T **264** of Lesotho.
Multicoloured. P 14.*
3144   10 r.   Baby boy and young mother   ..   1·00   1·10
     a. Sheetlet. Nos. 3144/6   ..   3·00
3145   10 r.   Young girl laughing   ..   1·00   1·10
3146   10 r.   Three children   ..   ..   1·00   1·10
3144/6   *Set of 3*   3·00   3·25
MS3147   110×85 mm. 25 r. Sir Peter Ustinov
   (Goodwill ambassador for U.N.I.C.E.F.)   2·50   2·75

372 Standard Stephenson Railway
Locomotive *Versailles*, 1837

(Litho Questa)

1999 (23 Dec). *"PhilexFrance '99" International Stamp
Exhibition, Paris. Railway Locomotives. Two sheets, each
106×81 mm, containing T **372** and similar horiz design.
Multicoloured. P 14×13½.*
MS3148   (a) 25 r. Type **372**. (b) 25 r. Stephenson
   long-boilered locomotive, 1841 .. *Set of 2 sheets*   5·00   5·25

373 Phobos and Demos (Martian
Moons)

(Litho Questa)

2000 (24 Jan). *Future Colonisation of Mars. T **373** and similar
multicoloured designs. P 14.*
3149   5 r.   Type **373**   50   55
     a. Sheetlet. Nos. 3149/57   ..   4·50
3150   5 r.   Improved Hubble Telescope   ..   50   55

3151   5 r.   Passenger shuttle   ..   50   55
3152   5 r.   Skyscrapers on Mars   50   55
3153   5 r.   Martian taxi   50   55
3154   5 r.   Martian landing facilities   ..   50   55
3155   5 r.   Vegetation in Martian bio-sphere   ..   50   55
3156   5 r.   Walking on Mars and bio-sphere   ..   50   55
3157   5 r.   Mars rover   50   55
3158   5 r.   Russian Phobos 25 satellite   ..   50   55
     a. Sheetlet. Nos. 3158/66   ..   4·50
3159   5 r.   Earth and Moon   50   55
3160   5 r.   Space shuttle leaving Earth   ..   50   55
3161   5 r.   Lighthouse on Mars   50   55
3162   5 r.   Mars excursion space liner   ..   50   55
3163   5 r.   Mars shuttle and skyscrapers   ..   50   55
3164   5 r.   Viking Lander   50   55
3165   5 r.   Mars air and water purification plant   50   55
3166   5 r.   Family picnic on Mars   ..   50   55
3149/66   *Set of 18*   9·00   9·75
MS3167   Two sheets, each 110×85 mm. (a) 25 r.
   Astronaut with jet-pack; (b) 25 r. Mars
           Set of 2 sheets   5·00   5·25
   Nos. 3149/57 and 3158/66 were each printed together,
se-tenant, in sheetlets of 9 with the backgrounds forming
composite designs and inscribed top margins.

374 Coconuts

(Litho Questa)

2000 (1 Feb). *"Destination 2000 – Maldives" Tourism
Campaign. T **374** and similar horiz designs. Multicoloured.
P 14×13½.*
3168   7 r.   Type **374**   70   75
     a. Sheetlet. Nos. 3168/73   ..   4·00
3169   7 r.   Shoal of Skipjack Tuna   ..   70   75
3170   7 r.   Seaplane and traditional dhow   ..   70   75
3171   7 r.   *Plumera alba*   70   75
3172   7 r.   Lionfish   70   75
3173   7 r.   Windsurfers   70   75
3168/73   *Set of 6*   4·00   4·50
   Nos. 3168/73 were printed together, *se-tenant,* in sheetlets of 6
with an enlarged illustrated and inscribed left margin.

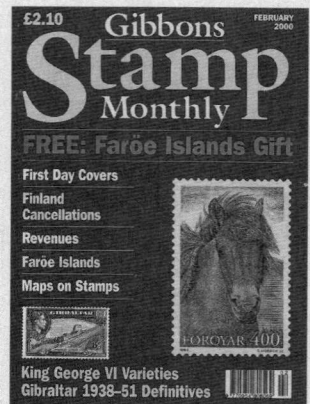

Malta

Early records of the postal services under the British Occupation are fragmentary, but it is known that an Island Postmaster was appointed in 1802. A British Packet Agency was established in 1806 and it later became customary for the same individual to hold the two appointments together. The inland posts continued to be the responsibility of the local administration, but the overseas mails formed part of the British G.P.O. system.

The stamps of Great Britain were used on overseas mails from September 1857. Previously during the period of the Crimean War letters franked with Great Britain stamps from the Crimea were cancelled at Malta with a wavy line obliterator. Such postmarks are known between April 1855 and September 1856.

The British G.P.O. relinquished control of the overseas posts on 31 December 1884 when Great Britain stamps were replaced by those of Malta.

Z 1

Z 2

1855–56. *Stamps of* GREAT BRITAIN *cancelled with wavy lines obliteration, Type Z 1.*

Z1	1d. red-brown (1854), Die I, *wmk* Small Crown, *perf* 16	£800
Z2	1d. red-brown (1855), Die II, *wmk* Small Crown, *perf* 14	£800
	a. Very blued paper	
Z3	1d. red-brown (1855), Die II, *wmk* Large Crown, *perf* 16	£800
Z3a	1d. red-brown (1855), Die II, *wmk* Large Crown, *perf* 14	£800
Z4	2d. blue (1855), *wmk* Large Crown, *perf* 14 Plate No. 5	
Z5	6d. (1854) embossed	£4000
Z6	1s. (1847) embossed	£4500

It is now established that this obliterator was sent to Malta and used on mail in transit emanating from the Crimea.

1857 (18 Aug)–**59.** *Stamps of* GREAT BRITAIN *cancelled* "M", *Type Z 2.*

Z 7	1d. red-brown (1841)	£1300
Z 8	1d. red-brown, Die I, *wmk* Small Crown, *perf* 16	90·00
Z 9	1d. red-brown, Die II, *wmk* Small Crown, *perf* 16	£800
Z10	1d. red-brown, Die II (1855) *wmk* Small Crown, *perf* 14	£170
Z11	1d. red-brown, Die II (1855) *wmk* Large Crown, *perf* 14	70·00
Z12	1d. rose-red (1857), *wmk* Large Crown, *perf* 14	20·00
Z13	2d. blue (1841), *imperf*	£2500
Z14	2d. blue (1854) *wmk* Small Crown, *perf* 16 Plate No. 4.	£650
Z15	2d. blue (1855), *wmk* Large Crown, *perf* 14 *From* 48·00 Plate Nos. 5, 6.	
Z16	2d. blue (1858), *wmk* Large Crown, *perf* 16 Plate No. 6.	£250
Z17	2d. blue (1858) (Plate Nos. 7, 8, 9) *From* 35·00	
Z18	4d. rose (1857)	35·00
	a. Thick glazed paper	£170
Z19	6d. violet (1854), embossed	£1700
Z20	6d. lilac (1856)	40·00
	a. Thick paper	£190
Z21	6d. lilac (1856) (blued *paper*)	£850
Z22	1s. green (1856)	£110
	a. Thick paper	£160

Z 3

Z 6

Z 4

Z 5

Z 7

1860–84. *Stamps of* GREAT BRITAIN *cancelled* "A 25" *as in Types Z 3/7.*

Z23	½d. rose-red (1870–79)	*From*	18·00
	Plate Nos. 4, 5, 6, 8, 9, 10, 11, 12, 13, 14, 15, 19, 20.		
Z24	1d. red-brown (1841), *imperf*		£2250
Z25	1d. red-brown (1854), *wmk* Small Crown, *perf* 16		£250
Z26	1d. red-brown (1855), *wmk* Large Crown, *perf* 14		60·00
Z27	1d. rose-red (1857), *wmk* Large Crown, *perf* 14		7·50
Z28	1d. rose-red (1861), Alphabet IV		£450
Z29	1d. rose-red (1864–79)	*From*	12·00
	Plate Nos. 71, 72, 73, 74, 76, 78, 79, 80, 81, 82, 83, 84, 85, 86, 87, 88, 89, 90, 91, 92, 93, 94, 95, 96, 97, 98, 99, 100, 101, 102, 103, 104, 105, 106, 107, 108, 109, 110, 111, 112, 113, 114, 115, 116, 117, 118, 119, 120, 121, 122, 123, 124, 125, 127, 129, 130, 131, 132, 133, 134, 135, 136, 137, 138, 139, 140, 141, 142, 143, 144, 145, 146, 147, 148, 149, 150, 151, 152, 153, 154, 155, 156, 157, 158, 159, 160, 161, 162, 163, 164, 165, 166, 167, 168, 169, 170, 171, 172, 173, 174, 175, 176, 177, 178, 179, 180, 181, 182, 183, 184, 185, 186, 187, 188, 189, 190, 191, 192, 193, 194, 195, 196, 197, 198, 199, 200, 201, 202, 203, 204, 205, 206, 207, 208, 209, 210, 211, 212, 213, 214, 215, 216, 217, 218, 219, 220, 221, 222, 223, 224.		
Z31	1½d. lake-red (1870–79) (Plate Nos. 1, 3)	*From*	£300
Z32	2d. blue (1841), *imperf*		£3500
Z33	2d. blue (1855) *wmk* Large Crown *perf* 14		60·00
Z34	2d. blue (1858–69)	*From*	15·00
	Plate Nos. 7, 8, 9, 12, 13, 14, 15.		
Z35	2½d. rosy mauve (1875) (blued *paper*)	*From*	60·00
	Plate Nos. 1, 2.		
Z36	2½d. rosy mauve (1875–76) (Plate Nos. 1, 2, 3)	*From*	30·00
Z37	2½d. rosy mauve (*Error of Lettering*)		£2250
Z38	2½d. rosy mauve (1876–79)	*From*	16·00
	Plate Nos. 3, 4, 5, 6, 7, 8, 9, 10, 11, 12, 13, 14, 15, 16, 17.		
Z39	2½d. blue (1880–81) (Plate Nos. 17, 18, 19, 20)	*From*	10·00
Z40	2½d. blue (1881) (Plate Nos. 21, 22, 23)	*From*	7·00
Z41	3d. carmine-rose (1862)		£100
Z42	3d. rose (1865) (Plate No. 4)		55·00
Z43	3d. rose (1867–73)	*From*	19·00
	Plate Nos. 4, 5, 6, 7, 8, 9, 10.		
Z44	3d. rose (1873–76)	*From*	23·00
	Plate Nos. 11, 12, 14, 15, 16, 17, 18, 19, 20.		
Z45	3d. rose (1881) (Plate Nos. 20, 21)		£800
Z46	3d. on 3d. lilac (1883)		£450
Z47	4d. rose (or rose-carmine) (1857)		27·00
	a. Thick glazed paper		£110
Z48	4d. red (1862) (Plate Nos. 3, 4)	*From*	30·00
Z49	4d. vermilion (1865–73)	*From*	16·00
	Plate Nos. 7, 8, 9, 10, 11, 12, 13, 14.		
Z50	4d. vermilion (1876) (Plate No. 15)		£160
Z51	4d. sage-green (1877) (Plate Nos. 15, 16)	*From*	85·00
Z52	4d. grey-brown (1880) *wmk* Large Garter Plate No. 17.		£120
Z53	4d. grey-brown (1880) *wmk* Crown	*From*	30·00
	Plate Nos. 17, 18.		
Z54	6d. violet (1854), embossed		£1600
Z55	6d. lilac (1856)		35·00
	a. Thick paper		
Z56	6d. lilac (1862) (Plate Nos. 3, 4)	*From*	30·00
Z57	6d. lilac (1865–67) (Plate Nos. 5, 6)	*From*	28·00
Z58	6d. lilac (1865–67) (*Wmk error*)		£1200
Z59	6d. lilac (1867) (Plate No. 6)		32·00
Z60	6d. violet (1867–70) (Plate Nos. 6, 8, 9)	*From*	25·00
Z61	6d. buff (1872–73) (Plate Nos. 11, 12)	*From*	£100
Z62	6d. chestnut (1872) (Plate No. 11)		30·00
Z63	6d. grey (1873) (Plate No. 12)		75·00
Z64	6d. grey (1873–80)	*From*	26·00
	Plate Nos. 13, 14, 15, 16, 17.		
Z65	6d. grey (1881–82) (Plate Nos. 17, 18)	*From*	40·00
Z66	6d. on 6d. lilac (1883)		£110
Z67	8d. orange (1876)		£275
Z68	9d. straw (1862)		£550
Z69	9d. bistre (1862)		£500
Z70	9d. straw (1865)		£500
Z71	9d. straw (1867)		£650
Z72	10d. red-brown (1867)		£130
Z73	1s. (1847), embossed		£1900
Z74	1s. green (1856)		70·00
Z75	1s. green (1856) (thick *paper*)		£250
Z76	1s. green (1862)		60·00
Z77	1s. green ("K" variety)		£2250
Z78	1s. green (1865) (Plate No. 4)		40·00
Z79	1s. green (1867–73) (Plate Nos. 4, 5, 6, 7)	*From*	15·00
Z80	1s. green (1873–77)	*From*	32·00
	Plate Nos. 8, 9, 10, 11, 12, 13.		
Z81	1s. orange-brown (1880) (Plate No. 13)		£225
Z82	1s. orange-brown (1881) (Plate Nos. 13, 14)	*From*	60·00
Z83	2s. blue (*shades*) (1867)	*From*	£100
Z84	2s. brown (1880)		£1800
Z85	5s. rose (1867–74) (Plate Nos. 1, 2)	*From*	£300
Z86	5s. rose (1882) (Plate No. 4), blue *paper*		£1100
Z87	5s. rose (1882) (Plate No. 4), white *paper*.		£1000
Z88	10s. grey-green (1878)		£1600

1880.

Z89	½d. deep green	10·00
Z90	½d. pale green	10·00
Z91	1d. Venetian red	9·00
Z92	1½d. Venetian red	£275
Z93	2d. pale rose	30·00
Z94	2d. deep rose	30·00
Z95	5d. indigo	50·00

1881.

Z96	1d. lilac (14 *dots*)	16·00
Z97	1d. lilac (16 *dots*)	6·00

1883–84.

Z 98	½d. slate-blue	11·00
Z 99	1½d. lilac	
Z100	2d. lilac	65·00
Z101	2½d. lilac	10·00
Z102	3d. lilac	
Z103	4d. dull green	£110
Z104	5d. dull green	£120
Z105	6d. dull green	
Z106	9d. dull green	
Z107	1s. dull green	
Z108	5s. rose (*blued paper*)	£1000
Z109	5s. rose (*white paper*)	£750

POSTAL FISCALS

Z109a	1d. reddish lilac (Type F 8) (1867) *wmk* Anchor	
Z110	1d. purple (Type F 12) (1871) *wmk* Anchor	£750
Z111	1d. purple (Type F 12) (1881) *wmk* Orb	£600

PRICES FOR STAMPS ON COVER TO 1945

Nos. 1/3	*from* × 4
Nos. 4/19	*from* × 5
Nos. 20/9	*from* × 6
No. 30	
Nos. 31/3	*from* × 4
Nos. 34/7	*from* × 10
Nos. 38/88	*from* × 4
Nos. 92/3	*from* × 5
Nos. 97/103	*from* × 3
Nos. 104/5	—
Nos. 106/20	*from* × 3
No. 121	—
Nos. 122/38	*from* × 3
Nos. 139/40	—
Nos. 141/72	*from* × 4
Nos. 173/209	*from* × 3
Nos. 210/31	*from* × 2
Nos. D1/10	*from* × 30
Nos. D11/20	*from* × 15

CROWN COLONY

PRINTERS. Nos. 1/156. Printed by De La Rue; typographed *except where otherwise stated.*

1

Type 1

The first Government local post was established on 10 June 1853 and, as an experiment, mail was carried free of charge. During 1859 the Council of Government decided that a rate of ½d. per ½ ounce should be charged for this service and stamps in Type I were ordered for this purpose. Both the new rate and the stamps were introduced on 1 December 1860. Until 1 January 1885 the ½d. stamps were intended for the local service only; mail for abroad being handled by the British Post Office on Malta, using G.B. stamps.

Specialists now recognise 29 printings in shades of yellow and one in green during the period to 1884. These printings can be linked to the changes in watermark and perforation as follows:

Ptg 1—Blued paper without wmk. P 14.
Ptgs 2 and 3—White paper without wmk. P 14.
Ptgs 4 to 9, 11, 13 to 19, 22 to 24—Crown CC wmk. P 14.
Ptg 10—Crown CC wmk. P 12½ (rough).
Ptg 12—Crown CC wmk. P 12½ (clean-cut).
Ptgs 20 and 21—Crown CC wmk. P 14 × 12½.
Ptgs 25 to 28, 30—Crown CA wmk. P 14.
Ptg 29—In green (No. 20).

(Des E. Fuchs)

1860 (1 Dec)–**63.** *No wmk. P 14. (a) Blued paper.*

1	½d. buff (1.12.60)			£850 £425

(b) Thin, hard white paper

2	½d. brown-orange (11.61)			£800 £325
3	½d. buff (1.63)			£550 £275
	a. Pale buff			£550 £275

No. 1 is printed in fugitive ink. It is known imperforate but was not issued in that state (*Price* £9000 *unused*).

The printing on No. 2 gives a very blurred and muddy impression; on Nos. 3/3a the impression is clear.

Specks of carmine can often be detected with a magnifying glass on Nos. 2/3a, and also on No. 4. Examples also exist on which parts of the design are in pure rose, due to defective mixing of the ink.

1863–81. *Wmk Crown CC. (a) P 14.*

4	½d. buff (6.63)			80·00 48·00
	w. Wmk inverted			£250 £250
	x. Wmk reversed			£550
5	½d. bright orange (11.64)			£350 £110
	w. Wmk inverted			† £425
6	½d. orange-brown (4.67)			£300 80·00
7	½d. dull orange (4.70)			£180 65·00
	w. Wmk inverted			† £275
8	½d. orange-buff (5.72)			£130 55·00
9	½d. golden yellow (aniline) (10.74)			£250 £300
10	½d. yellow-buff (9.75)			60·00 55·00
11	½d. pale buff (3.77)			£150 55·00
	w. Wmk inverted			† £325
12	½d. bright orange-yellow (4.80)			£130 70·00
13	½d. yellow (4.81)			80·00 48·00
	w. Wmk inverted			† £275

(b) P 12½ rough (No. 14) or clean-cut (No. 15).

14	½d. buff-brown (11.68)			95·00 85·00
15	½d. yellow-orange (5.71)			£250 £150

(c) P 14×12½

16		½d. yellow-buff (7.78) ..	..	£150 85·00
17		½d. yellow (2.79)	..	£170 90·00

Examples of No. 4 from the 1863 printing are on thin, surfaced paper; later printings in the same shade were on unsurfaced paper.

The ink used for No. 5 is mineral and, unlike that on No. 9, does not stain the paper.

Some variations of shade on No. 6 may be described as chestnut. The ink of No. 6 is clear and never muddy, although some examples are over-inked. Deeper shades of No. 4, with which examples of No. 6 might be confused, have muddy ink.

It is believed that there are no surviving pairs of the buff-brown imperforate between variety previously listed.

The Royal Collection contains an unused horizontal pair of the yellow-buff perforated 12½×14.

1882 (Mar)–**84.** *Wmk Crown CA. P* 14.

18		½d. orange-yellow ..	..	27·00 35·00
19		½d. red-orange (9.84)..	..	17·00 48·00

2   3

4   5

1885 (1 Jan)–**90.** *Wmk Crown CA. P* 14.

20	1	½d. green	..	1·90 50
		w. Wmk inverted ..	..	90·00 75·00
21	2	1d. rose	..	85·00 26·00
22		1d. carmine (*shades*) (1890) ..		2·25 35
		w. Wmk inverted ..	..	† £800
23	3	2d. grey	..	5·00 1·40
24	4	2½d. dull blue ..	..	55·00 2·50
25		2½d. bright blue ..	..	35·00 1·00
26		2½d. ultramarine ..	..	35·00 90
27	3	4d. brown ..	..	11·00 3·00
		a. Imperf (pair) ..	..	£4750 £4750
28		1s. violet	..	35·00 9·00
29		1s. pale violet (1890) ..	..	55·00 19·00
		w. Wmk inverted ..	..	£475 £200
20/9			Set of 6	80·00 14·00
20/8 Optd "Specimen"			Set of 6	£2250

Although not valid for postage until 1 January 1885 these stamps were available at the G.P.O., Valletta from 27 December 1884.

Three unused examples of the ½d. green, No. 20, are known line perforated 12. It is believed that these originated from proof books, the stamp not being issued for use with this perforation.

The Royal Collection includes an example of the 1d. carmine printed on the gummed side.

1886 (1 Jan). *Wmk Crown CC. P* 14.

30	5	5s. rose (Optd S. £450) ..	..	£110 80·00
		w. Wmk inverted ..	..	£140 £110

6 Harbour of   7 Gozo Fishing   8 Galley of Knights
Valletta   Boat   of St. John

9 Emblematic figure of   10 Shipwreck of
Malta   St. Paul

(T 6/10 recess)

1899 (4 Feb)–**1901.** *P* 14. (*a*) *Wmk Crown CA* (*sideways* on* ¼d.).

31	6	¼d. brown (4.1.01) ..	..	2·50 2·25
		a. Red-brown ..	..	1·25 40
		w. Wmk Crown to left of CA	..	2·25 75
		x. Wmk sideways reversed ..		32·00 20·00
		y. Wmk Crown to left of CA and reversed ..	..	42·00 25·00
32	7	4½d. sepia ..	..	14·00 10·00
33	8	5d. vermilion ..	..	32·00 15·00
		x. Wmk reversed ..	..	£110 £110

(b) *Wmk Crown CC*

34	9	2s. 6d. olive-grey ..	..	40·00 12·00
35	10	10s. blue-black ..	..	85·00 60·00
		x. Wmk reversed ..	..	— £275
		w. Wmk inverted and reversed ..		£250 £190
31/5			Set of 5	150·00 85·00
31/5 Optd "Specimen"			Set of 5	£225

*The normal sideways watermark shows Crown to right of CA, *as seen from the back of the stamp.*

**One
Penny**

(11)   12

1902 (4 July). *Nos.* 24 *and* 25 *surch locally at Govt Ptg Office with T* 11.

36		1d. on 2½d. dull blue (Optd S. £70)..		90 1·25
		a. Surch double ..	..	—£3750
		b. "One Pnney" (R. 9/2) ..		28·00 55·00
		ba. Surch double, with "One Pnney"		
37		1d. on 2½d. bright blue ..	..	90 1·75
		a. "One Pnney" (R. 9/2) ..		30·00 55·00

(Des E. Fuchs)

1903 (12 Mar)–**04.** *Wmk Crown CA. P* 14.

38	12	½d. green ..	..	7·00 75
39		1d. blackish brown and red (7.5.03)		14·00 40
40		2d. purple and grey ..	..	23·00 6·00
41		2½d. maroon and blue (9.03) ..		15·00 4·00
42		3d. grey and purple (26.3.03) ..		1·75 50
43		4d. blackish brown and brown (19.5.04)		25·00 15·00
44		1s. grey and violet (6.4.03) ..		14·00 7·00
38/44			Set of 7	90·00 30·00
38/44 Optd "Specimen"			Set of 7	£130

1904–14. *Wmk Mult Crown CA* (*sideways* on* ¼d.). *P* 14.

45	6	¼d. red-brown (10.10.05) ..		2·50 40
		a. Deep brown (2.4.10†) ..		1·75 10
		aw. Wmk Crown to left of CA ..		5·50 1·50
		ax. Wmk reversed ..	..	
		ay. Wmk Crown to left of CA and reversed ..	..	
47	12	½d. green (6.11.04) ..	..	3·50 30
		aw. Wmk inverted ..	..	
		b. Deep green (1909) ..		3·25 10
		bw. Wmk inverted ..	..	
48		1d. black and red (24.4.05) ..		11·00 20
49		1d. red (2.4.07) ..	..	1·75 10
50		2d. purple and grey (22.2.05) ..		7·50 1·75
51		2d. grey (4.10.11) ..	..	3·00 5·00
52		2½d. maroon and blue (10.04) ..		15·00 50
53		2½d. bright blue (15.1.11) ..		5·00 2·50
54		4d. black and brown (1.4.06) ..		10·00 5·50
		w. Wmk inverted ..	..	
55		4d. black and red/*yellow* (21.11.11)		3·75 3·25
57	7	4½d. brown (27.2.05) ..	..	24·00 5·50
		w. Wmk inverted ..	..	£160 £160
58		4½d. orange (16.3.12†) ..		4·25 3·50
59	8	5d. vermilion (20.2.05) ..		26·00 5·00
60		5d. pale sage-green (1909) ..		4·00 3·50
		a. Deep sage-green (1914) ..		11·00 14·00
61	12	1s. grey and violet (14.12.04) ..		50·00 1·75
62		1s. black/*green* (15.3.11) ..		6·50 2·50
63		5s. green and red/*yellow* (22.3.11)		65·00 70·00
45/63			Set of 17	£225 95·00
45*a*, 47*b*, 49, 51, 53, 55, 58, 60, 62/3 Optd "Specimen"			Set of 10	£300

*The normal sideways watermark shows Crown to right of CA, *as seen from the back of the stamp.*

†These are the earliest known dates of use.

13   14   15

1914–21. *Wmk Mult Crown CA. Ordinary paper* (¼d. *to* 2½d., 2s. 6d.) *or chalk-surfaced paper* (*others*). *P* 14.

69	13	¼d. brown (2.1.14) ..	..	70 10
		a. Deep brown (1919) ..		70 50
		x. Wmk reversed ..	..	† £375
71		½d. green (20.1.14) ..	..	2·00 30
		aa. Wmk sideways ..	..	† £3500
		a. Deep green (1919) ..		1·90 60
		aw. Wmk inverted ..	..	† £160
73		1d. carmine-red (15.4.14) ..		1·25 10
		a. Scarlet (1915) ..	..	1·50 40
		w. Wmk inverted ..	..	† £160
75		2d. grey (12.8.14) ..	..	6·00 3·00
		aw. Wmk inverted ..	..	† £375
		b. Deep slate (1919) ..		8·00 11·00
77		2½d. bright blue (11.3.14) ..		2·00 50
		w. Wmk inverted ..	..	† £110
78	14	3d. purple/*yellow* (1.5.20) ..		2·50 8·00
		a. On orange-buff ..	..	40·00 40·00
79	6	4d. black (21.8.15) ..	..	14·00 3·00
		a. Grey-black (28.10.16) ..		23·00 8·00
80	13	6d. dull and bright purple (10.3.14)		10·00 16·00
		a. Dull purple and magenta (1918)		13·00 16·00
		w. Wmk inverted ..	..	
81	14	1s. black/*green* (*white back*) (2.1.14)		12·00 20·00
		a. On grn, grn back (Optd S. £45) (1915)		11·00 14·00
		ab. Wmk sideways ..	..	† £1800
		b. On blue-green, olive back (1918)		18·00 19·00
		c. On emerald surface (1920) ..		8·50 21·00
		d. On emerald back (1921) ..		28·00 50·00
86	15	2s. purple and bright blue/*blue* (15.4.14)		50·00 29·00
		a. Break in scroll ..	..	£225
		b. Broken crown and scroll ..		£275
		c. Dull purple and blue/blue (1921)		70·00 48·00
		ca. Break in scroll ..	..	£300
		cb. Broken crown and scroll ..		£350
87	9	2s. 6d. olive-green (1919) ..		55·00 75·00
		a. Olive-grey (1920) ..		60·00 95·00

88	15	5s. green and red/*yellow* (21.3.17)		80·00 95·00
		a. Break in scroll ..	..	£350
		b. Broken crown and scroll ..		£400
69/88			Set of 12	£200 £200
69/88 (*excl* 87) Optd "Specimen"			Set of 11	£400

The design of Nos. 79/*a* differs in various details from that of Type 6.

We have only seen one copy of No. 71*aa*; it is in used condition.

A 3d. purple on yellow on white back, Type 14, was prepared for use but not issued. It exists overprinted "Specimen" (*Price* £250).

An example of the 2s. 6d. olive-grey with bottom margin attached exists with the "A" omitted from "CA" in the watermark on the margin.

For illustrations of the varieties on Nos. 86 and 88 see above No. 58 of Leeward Islands.

WAR TAX

(16)   17   18

1917–18. *Optd with T* 16 *by De La Rue.*

92	13	½d. deep green (14.12.17*) ..		70 15
		w. Wmk inverted ..	..	£350
93	12	3d. grey and purple (15.2.18*) ..		1·40 7·50
92/3 Optd "Specimen"			Set of 2	£130

*These are the earliest known dates of use.

(T 17 recess)

1919 (6 Mar). *Wmk Mult Crown CA. P* 14.

96	17	10s. black (Optd S. £750) ..		£2500 £3500

Dark flaw on scroll   Lines omitted from scroll
(R. 2/4 1st state)   (R. 2/4 2nd state)

1921 (16 Feb)–**22.** *Wmk Mult Script CA. Chalk-surfaced paper* (6d., 2s.) *or ordinary paper* (*others*). *P* 14.

97	13	¼d. brown (12.1.22) ..	..	1·00 25·00
98		½d. green (19.1.22) ..	..	1·25 17·00
99		1d. scarlet (24.12.21) ..		1·50 1·60
		w. Wmk inverted ..	..	£375 £130
100	18	2d. grey	..	2·50 1·75
101	13	2½d. bright blue (15.1.22) ..		2·75 23·00
102		6d. dull purple & brt purple (19.1.22)		28·00 65·00
103	15	2s. purple and blue/*blue* (19.1.22)		60·00 £180
		a. Break in scroll ..	..	£200
		b. Broken crown and scroll ..		£200
		c. Dark flaw on scroll ..		£1600
		d. Lines omitted from scroll ..		£350
104	17	10s. black (19.1.22) ..	..	£300 £550
97/104			Set of 8	£350 £750
97/104 Optd "Specimen"			Set of 8	£400

For illustrations of other varieties on No. 103 see above No. 58 of Leeward Islands.

Examples of all values are known showing a forged G.P.O. Malta postmark dated "MY 10 22".

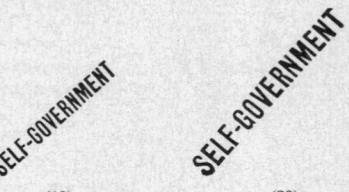

(19)   (20)

1922 (12 Jan–Apr). *Optd with T* 19 *or T* 20 (*large stamps*), *at Govt Printing Office, Valletta.* (*a*) *On No.* 35. *Wmk Crown CC.*

105	10	10s. blue-black (R.) ..	..	£180 £275

(b) *On Nos.* 71, 77, 78*a*, 80, 81*d*, 86*c*, 87*a and* 88. *Wmk Mult Crown CA*

106	13	½d. green ..	..	70 1·50
		w. Wmk inverted ..	..	60·00
107		2½d. bright blue ..	..	7·50 26·00
108	14	3d. purple/*orange-buff* ..		2·00 14·00
109	13	6d. dull and bright purple ..		2·00 14·00
		x. Wmk reversed ..	..	† £550
110	14	1s. black/*emerald* ..		3·00 13·00
111	15	2s. purple and blue/*blue* (R.) ..		£200 £400
		a. Break in scroll ..	..	£600
		b. Broken crown and scroll ..		£600
112	9	2s. 6d. olive-grey ..	..	22·00 40·00
		a. "C" of "CA" missing from wmk ..		£850
113	15	5s. green and red/*yellow* ..		50·00 75·00
		a. Break in scroll ..	..	£225
		b. Broken crown and scroll ..		£225
		c. Lines omitted from scroll ..		£300
106/13			Set of 8	£250 £500

(c) On Nos. 97/104. Wmk Mult Script CA

114	13	¼d. brown		20	75
115		½d. green (29.4)		1·25	5·00
116		1d. scarlet		70	15
117	18	2d. grey		2·00	45
118	13	2½d. bright blue (15.1)		85	80
119		6d. dull and bright purple (19.4)		7·50	26·00
120	15	2s. purple and blue/blue (R.) (25.1)		40·00	75·00
		a. Break in scroll		£170	
		b. Broken crown and scroll		£170	
		c. Lines omitted from scroll		£250	
121	17	10s. black (R.) (9.3)		£110	£160
114/21		Set of 8		£140	£225

Examples of all values are known showing a forged G.P.O. Malta postmark dated "MY 10 22".

One Farthing

(21) 22 23

1922 (15 Apr). No. 100 surch with T 21, at Govt Printing Office, Valletta.

122	18	¼d. on 2d. grey		65	30

(Des C. Dingli (T 22) and G. Vella (23))

1922 (1 Aug)–26. Wmk Mult Script CA (sideways* on T 22, except No. 140). P 14. (a) Typo. Chalk-surfaced paper.

123	22	¼d. brown (22.8.22)		1·75	60
		a. Chocolate-brown		2·25	40
		w. Wmk Crown to right of CA		—	50·00
124		½d. green		1·75	10
		w. Wmk Crown to right of CA		—	50·00
125		1d. orange and purple		2·50	15
		w. Wmk Crown to right of CA		—	40·00
126		1d. bright violet (25.4.24)		2·50	80
127		1½d. brown-red (1.10.23)		2·50	10
128		2d. bistre-brown & turquoise		2·50	90
		w. Wmk Crown to right of CA		—	75·00
129		2½d. ultramarine (16.2.26)		2·00	6·50
130		3d. cobalt (28.8.22)		2·75	90
		a. Bright ultramarine		2·75	1·50
131		3d. black/yellow (16.2.26)		2·50	9·00
132		4d. yellow and bright blue (28.8.22)		1·25	2·00
		w. Wmk Crown to right of CA		£100	
133		6d. olive-green and reddish violet		2·75	1·75
134	23	1s. indigo and sepia		4·75	2·50
135		2s. brown and blue		8·00	8·50
136		2s. 6d. brt magenta & black (28.8.22)		9·50	15·00
137		5s. orange-yell & brt ultram (28.8.22)		21·00	32·00
138		10s. slate-grey and brown (28.8.22)		55·00	£130

(b) Recess

139	22	£1 black and carmine-red (wmk sideways) (28.8.22)		£120	£275
140		£1 black and bright carmine (wmk upright) (14.5.25)		90·00	£250
123/39		Set of 17		£180	£400
123/39	Optd "Specimen"		Set of 17	£450	

*The normal sideways watermark shows Crown to left of CA, as seen from the back of the stamp.

Two pence halfpenny

POSTAGE

(24) (25)

1925. Surch with T 24, at Govt Printing Office, Valletta.

141	22	2½d. on 3d. cobalt (3 Dec)		1·50	2·50
142		2½d. on 3d. bright ultramarine (9 Dec)		1·60	2·50

1926 (1 Apr). Optd with T 25 at Govt Printing Office, Valletta.

143	22	¼d. brown		45	2·50
144		½d. green		50	15
		w. Wmk Crown to right of CA		50·00	
145		1d. bright violet		75	25
146		1½d. brown-red		75	50
147		2d. bistre-brown and turquoise		60	40
148		2½d. ultramarine		1·00	70
149		3d. black/yellow		60	70
		a. Opt inverted		£170	£475
150		4d. yellow and bright blue		4·25	13·00
151		6d. olive-green and violet		2·75	2·50
152	23	1s. indigo and sepia		4·75	9·00
153		2s. brown and blue		48·00	£130
154		2s. 6d. bright magenta and black		9·50	25·00
155		5s. orange-yellow & brt ultramarine		8·50	27·00
156		10s. slate-grey and brown		7·00	15·00
143/56		Set of 14		80·00	£200

26   27 Valletta Harbour

28 St. Publius   33 St. Paul

(T 26 typo, others recess Waterlow)

1926 (6 Apr)–27. T 26/8, 33 and similar designs. Inscr "POSTAGE". Wmk Mult Script CA. P 15×14 (T 26) or 12½ (others).

157	26	¼d. brown		80	15
158		½d. yellow-green (5.8.26)		50	15
		a. Printed on the gummed side		£350	
		w. Wmk inverted			
159		1d. rose-red (1.4.27)		2·75	90
160		1½d. chestnut (7.10.26)		1·75	10
161		2d. greenish grey (1.4.27)		4·25	8·50
162		2½d. blue (1.4.27)		3·75	45
162a		3d. violet (1.4.27)		4·00	2·25
163		4d. black and red		2·75	8·00
164		4½d. lavender and ochre		3·25	2·50
165		6d. violet and scarlet (5.5.26)		4·00	2·50
166	27	1s. black		6·50	3·25
167	28	1s. 6d. black and green		6·50	13·00
168	—	2s. black and purple		6·50	15·00
169	—	2s. 6d. black and vermilion		15·00	42·00
170	—	3s. black and blue		17·00	28·00
171	—	5s. black and green (5.5.26)		22·00	60·00
172	33	10s. black and carmine (9.2.27)		55·00	£100
157/72		Set of 17		£130	£250
157/72	Optd "Specimen"		Set of 17	£275	

Designs: Vert—2s. 6d. Gozo fishing boat; 3s. Neptune; Horiz—2s. Mdina (Notabile); 5s. Neolithic temple, Mnajdra.

POSTAGE

AIR MAIL	AND	POSTAGE AND
	REVENUE	REVENUE.
(34)	(35)	(36)

1928 (1 Apr). Air. Optd with T 34.

173	26	6d. violet and scarlet		1·50	90

1928 (1 Oct–5 Dec). As Nos. 157/72, optd.

174	35	¼d. brown		1·50	10
175		½d. yellow-green		1·50	10
176		1d. rose-red		1·75	3·00
177		1d. chestnut (5.12.28)		4·50	10
178		1½d. chestnut		1·75	50
179		1½d. rose-red (5.12.28)		4·25	10
180		2d. greenish grey		4·00	8·50
181		2½d. blue		1·75	10
182		3d. violet		1·75	40
183		4d. black and red		1·75	1·50
184		4½d. lavender and ochre		2·25	1·00
185		6d. violet and scarlet		2·25	1·25
186	36	1s. black (R.)		4·75	2·50
187		1s. 6d. black and green (R.)		5·50	9·50
188		2s. black and purple (R.)		22·00	50·00
189		2s. 6d. black and vermilion (R.)		17·00	23·00
190		3s. black and blue (R.)		19·00	30·00
191		5s. black and green (R.)		27·00	65·00
192		10s. black and carmine (R.)		55·00	90·00
174/92		Set of 19		£150	£250
174/92	Optd "Specimen"		Set of 19	£300	

1930 (20 Oct). As Nos. 157/172, but inscr "POSTAGE (&) REVENUE".

193		¼d. brown			50	10
194		½d. yellow-green			50	10
195		1d. chestnut			60	10
196		1½d. rose-red			70	10
197		2d. greenish grey			1·00	30
198		2½d. blue			2·00	10
199		3d. violet			1·50	20
200		4d. black and red			1·25	3·50
201		4½d. lavender and ochre			3·00	1·00
202		6d. violet and scarlet			2·25	1·00
203		1s. black			9·50	11·00
204		1s. 6d. black and green			7·50	18·00
205		2s. black and purple			9·50	18·00
206		2s. 6d. black and vermilion			17·00	48·00
207		3s. black and blue			24·00	55·00
208		5s. black and green			30·00	65·00
209		10s. black and carmine			65·00	£120
193/209		Set of 17		£150	£300	
193/209	Perf "Specimen"		Set of 17	£275		

1935 (6 May). Silver Jubilee. As Nos. 114/17 of Jamaica.

210		½d. black and green		40	50
		a. Extra flagstaff		22·00	
		b. Short extra flagstaff		35·00	
		c. Lightning conductor		30·00	
211		2½d. brown and deep blue		2·50	4·00
		a. Extra flagstaff		£130	
		b. Short extra flagstaff		£130	
		c. Lightning conductor		£100	
212		6d. light blue and olive-green		7·00	4·00
		a. Extra flagstaff		£180	
		b. Short extra flagstaff		£190	
		c. Lightning conductor		£140	
213		1s. slate and purple		11·00	16·00
		a. Extra flagstaff		£425	
		b. Short extra flagstaff		£350	
		c. Lightning conductor		£250	
210/13		Set of 4		19·00	22·00
210/13	Perf "Specimen"		Set of 4	£130	

For illustrations of plate varieties see Omnibus section following Zimbabwe.

Sheets from the second printing of the ½d., 6d. and 1s. in November 1935 had the extra flagstaff partially erased from the stamp with a sharp point.

1937 (12 May). Coronation. As Nos. 118/20 of Jamaica.

214		½d. green		10	10
215		1½d. scarlet		50	20
		a. Brown-lake		£550	£550
216		2½d. bright blue		50	40
214/16		Set of 3		1·00	60
214/16	Perf "Specimen"		Set of 3	60·00	

---

37 Grand Harbour, Valletta   38 H.M.S. St. Angelo

39 Verdala Palace   40 Hypogeum, Hal Saflieni

Broken cross
(Right pane R. 5/7)   Extra windows (R. 2/7)
                          (corrected in 1945)

Damaged value
tablet (R. 4/9)   Semaphore flaw
                       (R. 2/7)

(Recess Waterlow)

1938 (17 Feb*)–43. T 37/40 and similar designs. Wmk Mult Script CA (sideways on No. 217). P 12½.

217	37	¼d. brown		10	10
218	38	½d. green		1·75	30
218a		½d. red-brown (8.3.43)		55	30
219	39	1d. red-brown		4·25	30
219a		1d. green (8.3.43)		60	10
220	40	1½d. scarlet		1·00	30
		a. Broken cross		70·00	
220b		1½d. slate-black (8.3.43)		30	15
		ba. Broken cross		50·00	
221	—	2d. slate-black		40	1·75
		a. Extra windows		35·00	
221b	—	2d. scarlet (8.3.43)		40	20
		ba. Extra windows		35·00	
222	—	2½d. greyish blue		75	45
222a	—	2½d. dull violet (8.3.43)		60	10
223	—	3d. dull violet		45	80
223a	—	3d. blue (8.3.43)		30	10
224	—	4½d. olive-green and yellow-brown		50	10
225	—	6d. olive-green and scarlet		75	30
226	—	1s. black		75	30
227	—	1s. 6d. black and olive-green		7·00	3·75
228	—	2s. green and deep blue		4·00	3·75
229	—	2s. 6d. black and scarlet		7·50	5·00
		a. Damaged value tablet		£150	
230	—	5s. black and green		4·50	5·50
		a. Semaphore flaw		65·00	
231	—	10s. black and carmine		15·00	15·00
217/31		Set of 21		45·00	32·00
217/31	Perf "Specimen"		Set of 21	£350	

Designs: Horiz (as T 39)—2d. Victoria and citadel, Gozo; 2½d. De l'Isle Adam entering Mdina; 4½d. Ruins at Mnajdra; 1s. 6d. St. Publius; 2s. Mdina Cathedral; 2s. 6d. Statue of Neptune, Vert (as T 40)—3d. St. John's Co-Cathedral; 6d. Statue of Manoel de Vilhena; 1s. Maltese girl wearing faldetta; 5s. Palace Square, Valletta; 10s. St. Paul.

*This is the local date of issue but the stamps were released in London on 15 February.

1946 (3 Dec). Victory. As Nos. 141/2 of Jamaica, but inscr "MALTA" between Maltese Cross and George Cross.

232		1d. green		15	10
233		3d. blue		20	40
232/3	Perf "Specimen"		Set of 2	50·00	

SELF-GOVERNMENT

(52)   "NT" joined
            (R. 4/10)

Halation flaw (Pl 2 R. 2/5)
(ptg of 8 Jan 1953)

Cracked plate (Pl 2 R. 5/1) (ptg of 8 Jan 1953)

(Optd by Waterlow)

1948 (25 Nov)–53. *New Constitution. As Nos. 217/31 but optd as T 52; reading up on ½d. and 5s., down on other values, and smaller on ¼d. value.*

234	37	¼d. brown		20	20
235	38	½d. red-brown		20	10
		a. "NT" joined		17·00	
236	39	1d. green		20	10
236a		1d. grey (R.) (8.1.53)		20	10
237	40	1½d. blue-black (R.)		75	10
		a. Broken cross		60·00	
237b		1½d. green (8.1.53)		30	10
		ba. Albino opt		† £10000	
238	—	2d. scarlet		85	10
		a. Extra windows		38·00	
238b	—	2d. yellow-ochre (8.1.53)		30	10
		ba. Halation flaw		£110	
		bc. Cracked plate		£100	
239	—	2½d. dull violet (R.)		80	10
239a	—	2½d. scarlet-vermilion (8.1.53)		30	85
240	—	3d. blue (R.)		45	15
240a	—	3d. dull violet (R.) (8.1.53)		35	15
241	—	4½d. olive-green and yellow-brown		2·00	1·50
241a	—	4½d. olive-grn & dp ultram (R.) (8.1.53)		50	90
242	—	6d. olive-green and scarlet		1·75	45
243	—	1s. black		2·25	40
244	—	1s. 6d. black and olive-green		2·50	45
245	—	2s. green and deep blue (R.)		5·00	1·50
246	—	2s. 6d. black and scarlet		12·00	2·50
		a. Damaged value tablet		£325	
247	—	5s. black and green (R.)		17·00	3·50
		a. "NT" joined		£170	£100
		b. Semaphore flaw		—	£1600
248	—	10s. black and carmine		17·00	21·00
234/48			*Set of 21*	55·00	30·00

1949 (4 Jan). *Royal Silver Wedding. As Nos. 143/4 of Jamaica, but inscr "MALTA" between Maltese Cross and George Cross and with £1 ptd in recess.*

249		1d. green		50	10
250		£1 indigo		38·00	35·00

1949 (10 Oct). *75th Anniv of U.P.U. As Nos. 145/8 of Jamaica, but inscr "MALTA" in recess.*

251		2½d. violet		30	10
252		3d. deep blue		3·25	50
253		6d. carmine-red		1·00	50
254		1s. blue-black		1·00	1·75
251/4			*Set of 4*	5·00	2·50

53 Queen Elizabeth II when Princess

54 "Our Lady of Mount Carmel" (attrib Palladino)

(T 53/4. Recess B.W.)

1950 (1 Dec). *Visit of Princess Elizabeth to Malta. Wmk Mult Script CA. P 12 × 11½.*

255	53	1d. green		10	10
256		3d. blue		20	10
257		1s. black		55	60
255/7			*Set of 3*	70	70

1951 (12 July). *Seventh Centenary of the Scapular. Wmk Mult Script CA. P 12 × 11½.*

258	54	1d. green		10	10
259		3d. violet		20	10
260		1s. black		60	40
258/60			*Set of 3*	80	50

1953 (3 June). *Coronation. As No. 153 of Jamaica.*

261		1½d. black and deep yellow-green		30	10

55 St. John's Co-Cathedral

56 "Immaculate Conception" (Caruana) (altar-piece, Cospicua)

(Recess Waterlow)

1954 (3 May). *Royal Visit. Wmk Mult Script CA. P 12½.*

262	55	3d. violet		30	10

(Photo Harrison)

1954 (8 Sept). *Centenary of Dogma of the Immaculate Conception. Wmk Mult Script CA. Chalk-surfaced paper. P 14½ × 14.*

263	56	1½d. emerald		10	10
264		3d. bright blue		10	10
265		1s. grey-black		35	20
263/5			*Set of 3*	45	30

57 Monument of the Great Siege, 1565

62 Auberge de Castile

(Recess Waterlow (2s. 6d. to £1). B.W. (others))

1956 (23 Jan)–58. *T 57, 62 and similar designs. Wmk Mult Script CA. P 14×13½ (2s. 6d. to £1) or 11½ (others).*

266		¼d. violet		20	10
267		½d. orange		50	10
268		1d. black (9.2.56)		1·25	10
269		1½d. bluish green (9.2.56)		30	10
270		2d. brown (9.2.56)		1·25	10
		a. Deep brown (26.2.58)		2·75	10
271		2½d. orange-brown		55	30
272		3d. rose-red (22.3.56)		75	10
		w. Wmk inverted		†	£500
273		4½d. deep blue		1·00	20
274		6d. indigo (9.2.56)		50	10
		w. Wmk inverted		£100	
275		8d. bistre-brown		1·50	1·00
276		1s. deep reddish violet		50	10
277		1s. 6d. deep turquoise-green		9·50	20
278		2s. olive-green		11·00	80
279		2s. 6d. chestnut (22.3.56)		7·50	2·25
280		5s. green (11.10.56)		13·00	2·75
281		10s. carmine-red (19.11.56)		35·00	9·50
282		£1 yellow-brown (5.1.57)		35·00	22·00
266/82			*Set of 17*	95·00	35·00

Designs: *Vert*—½d. Wignacourt aqueduct horsetrough; 1d. Victory church; 1½d. Second World War memorial; 2d. Mosta Church; 3d. The King's Scroll; 4½d. Roosevelt's Scroll; 8d. Vedette (tower); 1s. Mdina gate; 1s. 6d. "Les Gavroches" (statue); 2s. Monument of Christ the King; 2s. 6d. Grand Master Cottoner's monument; 5s. Grand Master Perellos's monument; 10s. St. Paul; £1 Baptism of Christ. *Horiz*—6d. Neolithic Temples at Tarxien.
See also Nos. 314/15.

74 "Defence of Malta"

75 Searchlights over Malta

(Des E. Cremona. Photo Harrison)

1957 (15 Apr). *George Cross Commemoration. Cross in silver. T 74/5 and similar design. Wmk Mult Script CA. P 14½ × 14 (3d.) or 14 × 14½ (others).*

283		1½d. deep dull green		15	10
284		3d. vermilion		15	10
285		1s. reddish brown		15	10
283/5			*Set of 3*	40	20

Design: *Vert*—1s. Bombed buildings.

77 "Design"

(Des E. Cremona. Photo Harrison)

1958 (15 Feb). *Technical Education in Malta. T 77 and similar designs. W w 12. P 14 × 14½ (3d.) or 14½ × 14 (others).*

286		1½d. black and deep green		10	10
287		3d. black, scarlet and grey		10	10
288		1s. grey, bright purple and black		15	10
286/8			*Set of 3*	30	15

Designs: *Vert*—3d. "Construction". *Horiz*—1s. Technical School, Paola.

ALTERED CATALOGUE NUMBERS

Any Catalogue numbers altered from the last edition are shown as a list in the introductory pages.

80 Bombed-out Family

81 Sea Raid on Grand Harbour, Valletta

(Des E. Cremona. Photo Harrison)

1958 (15 Apr). *George Cross Commemoration. Cross in first colour, outlined in silver. T 80/1 and similar design. W w 12. P 14 × 14½ (3d.) or 14½ × 14 (others).*

289		1½d. blue-green and black		15	10
290		3d. red and black		15	10
291		1s. reddish violet and black		15	10
		a. Silver (outline) omitted		£375	
289/91			*Set of 3*	40	15

Design: *Horiz*—1s. Searchlight crew.

83 Air Raid Casualties

84 "For Gallantry"

(Des E. Cremona. Photo Harrison)

1959 (15 Apr). *George Cross Commemoration. T 83/4 and similar design. W w 12. P 14½ × 14 (3d.) or 14 × 14½ (others).*

292		1½d. grey-green, black and gold		20	10
293		3d. reddish violet, black and gold		20	10
294		1s. blue-grey, black and gold		70	80
292/4			*Set of 3*	1·00	80

Design: *Vert*—1s. Maltese under bombardment.

86 Shipwreck of St. Paul   87 Statue of St. Paul, Rabat, Malta (after Palombi)

(Des E. Cremona. Photo Harrison)

1960 (9 Feb). *19th Centenary of the Shipwreck of St. Paul. T 86/7 and similar designs. W w 12. P 13 (1½d., 3d., 6d.) or 14×14½ (others).*

295		1½d. blue, gold and yellow-brown		15	10
		a. Gold (dates and crosses) omitted		55·00	
296		3d. bright purple, gold and blue		15	10
		a. Printed on the gummed side			
297		6d. carmine, gold and pale grey		25	10
298		8d. black and gold		30	50
299		1s. maroon and gold		25	10
300		2s. 6d. blue, deep bluish green and gold		1·00	2·00
		a. Gold omitted		£350	
295/300			*Set of 6*	1·90	2·50

Designs: *Vert as T 86*—3d. Consecration of St. Publius (first Bishop of Malta) (after Palombi); 6d. Departure of St. Paul (after Palombi). *Diamond shaped as T 87*—1s. Angel with *Acts of the Apostles*; 2s. 6d. St. Paul with *Second Epistle to the Corinthians*.

92 Stamp of 1860

(Centre litho; frame recess. Waterlow)

1960 (1 Dec). *Stamp Centenary. W w 12. P 13½.*

301	92	1½d. buff, pale blue and green		25	10
		a. Buff, pale bl & myrtle (white paper)		3·00	1·75
302		3d. buff pale blue and deep carmine		30	10
		a. Blank corner		£160	
303		6d. buff, pale blue and ultramarine		40	1·00
301/3			*Set of 3*	85	1·00

Examples of the 1½d. apparently with the blue omitted are from sheets with a very weak printing of this colour.

No. 302a shows the right-hand bottom corner of the 1860 stamp blank. It occurs on R. 4/7 from early trial plates and sheets containing the error should have been destroyed, but some were sorted into good stock and issued at a post office.

93 George Cross

(Photo Harrison)

1961 (15 Apr). *George Cross Commemoration. T* **93** *and similar designs showing medal. W* w **12**. *P* 15 × 14.
304	1½d. black, cream and bistre		15	10
305	3d. olive-brown and greenish blue.		30	10
306	1s. olive-green, lilac & dp reddish violet		75	1·40
304/6	.. .. *Set of 3*		1·10	1·40

96 "Madonna Damascena"

(Photo Harrison)

1962 (7 Sept). *Great Siege Commemoration. T* **96** *and similar vert designs. W* w **12**. *P* 13 × 12.
307	2d. bright blue		10	10
308	3d. red		10	10
309	6d. bronze-green		25	10
310	1s. brown-purple		25	40
307/10	*Set of 4*		55	50

Designs:—3d. Great Siege Monument; 6d. Grand Master La Valette; 1s. Assault on Fort St. Elmo.

1963 (4 June). *Freedom from Hunger. As No.* 80 *of Lesotho.*
311	1s. 6d. sepia		2·25	2·50

1963 (2 Sept). *Red Cross Centenary. As Nos.* 203/4 *of Jamaica.*
312	2d. red and black		25	15
313	1s. 6d. red and blue		3·00	3·75

1963 (15 Oct)–**64**. *As Nos.* 268 *and* 270, *but wmk* w **12**.
314	**59** 1d. black		50	30
315	**61** 2d. deep brown (11.7.64*)		1·75	2·25

*This is the earliest known date recorded in Malta.

**100 Bruce, Zammit   101 Goat and
and Microscope   Laboratory Equipment**

(Des E. Cremona. Photo Harrison)

1964 (14 April). *Anti-Brucellosis Congress. W* w **12**. *P* 14.
316	**100** 2d. light brown, black and bluish green		10	10
	a. Black (microscope, etc) omitted		£250	
317	**101** 1s. 6d. black and maroon		90	30

**102 "Nicola Cotoner tending Sick Man"
(M. Preti)**

**105 Maltese Cross
(Upright)**

In this illustration the points of the crosses meet in a vertical line. When the watermark is sideways they meet in a horizontal line.

(Des E. Cremona. Photo Harrison)

1964 (5 Sept). *First European Catholic Doctors' Congress, Vienna. T* **102** *and similar horiz designs. W* **105** *(sideways). P* 13½ × 11½.
318	2d. red, black, gold and grey-blue		20	10
319	6d. red, black, gold and bistre		50	15
320	1s. 6d. red, black, gold and reddish violet		1·10	1·90
318/20	*Set of 3*		1·60	1·90

Designs:—6d. St. Luke and Hospital; 1s. 6d. Sacra Infermeria, Valletta.

INDEPENDENT

**106 Dove and British   109 "The Nativity"
Crown**

(Des E. Cremona. Photo Harrison)

1964 (21 Sept). *Independence. T* **106** *and similar vert designs. W* **105**. *P* 14½ × 13½.
321	2d. olive-brown, red and gold		30	10
	a. Gold omitted		70·00	
322	3d. brown-purple, red and gold		30	10
	a. Gold omitted		70·00	
323	6d. slate, red and gold		70	15
324	1s. blue, red and gold		70	15
325	1s. 6d. indigo, red and gold		2·00	1·00
326	2s. 6d. deep violet-blue, red and gold		2·00	2·25
321/6	*Set of 6*		5·50	3·25

Designs:—2d., 1s. Type **106**; 3d., 1s. 6d. Dove and Pope's Tiara; 6d., 2s. 6d. Dove and U.N. emblem.

(Des E. Cremona. Photo D.L.R.)

1964 (3 Nov). *Christmas. W* **105** *(sideways). P* 13 × 13½.
327	**109** 2d. bright purple and gold		10	10
328	4d. bright blue and gold		20	15
329	8d. deep bluish green and gold		45	45
327/9	*Set of 3*		65	60

**110 Neolithic Era   117 Galleys of Knights
of St. John**

119 British Rule

(Des E. Cremona. Photo Harrison)

1965 (7 Jan)–**70**. *Chalk-surfaced paper. T* **110**, **117**, **119** *and similar designs. W* **105**. *P* 14×14½ (vert) or 14½ (horiz).
330	½d. multicoloured		10	10
	a. "½d." (white) printed twice†		10·00	
	b. Rose-pink ("MALTA") printed twice		10·00	
	c. White (face value) omitted		42·00	
331	1d. multicoloured		10	10
	a. Gold (ancient lettering) omitted		60·00	
	b. White (Greek lettering and "PUNIC") omitted		60·00	
	c. White ptg double		20·00	
	d. "PUNIC" omitted		90·00	
332	1½d. multicoloured		30	10
333	2d. multicoloured		10	10
	a. Gold omitted		22·00	
	b. Imperf (pair)		£275	
334	2½d. multicoloured		55	10
	a. Orange omitted*		75·00	
	b. Gold ("SARACENIC") omitted		55·00	
	c. Salmon printed twice†		65·00	
335	3d. multicoloured		10	10
	a. Gold (windows) omitted		85·00	
	b. "MALTA" (silver) omitted		26·00	
	c. "MALTA" (silver) printed twice		£300	
	d. Bright lilac ("SICULO NORMAN") omitted		£300	
	e. Imperf (pair)		£300	
336	4d. multicoloured		40	10
	a. "KNIGHTS OF MALTA" (silver) omitted		50·00	
	b. "MALTA" (silver) omitted		60·00	
	c. Black (shield surround) omitted		55·00	
	d. Imperf (pair)		£160	
337	4½d. multicoloured		1·00	40
	a. Silver ("MALTA", etc) omitted		£300	
337b	5d. multicoloured (1.8.70)		30	20
	ba. "FORTIFICATIONS" (gold) omitted		75·00	
338	6d. multicoloured		20	10
	a. "MALTA" (silver) omitted		42·00	
	b. Black omitted		75·00	

339	8d. multicoloured		50	10
	a. Gold (centre) omitted		35·00	
	b. Gold (frame) omitted		60·00	
339c	10d. multicoloured (1.8.70)		45	1·60
	ca. "NAVAL ARSENAL" (gold) omitted		£170	
340	1s. multicoloured		30	10
	a. Gold (centre) omitted		£140	
	b. Gold (framework) omitted		42·00	
341	1s. 3d. multicoloured		2·00	1·40
	a. Gold (centre) omitted		55·00	
	b. Gold (framework) omitted		£120	
	c. Imperf (pair)		£350	
342	1s. 6d. multicoloured		60	10
	a. Head (black) omitted		£225	
	b. Gold (centre) omitted		40·00	
	c. Gold (frame) omitted		70·00	
343	2s. multicoloured		70	10
	a. Gold (centre) omitted		£140	
	b. Gold (framework) omitted		50·00	
344	2s. 6d. multicoloured		70	50
345	3s. multicoloured		1·50	75
	a. Gold (framework) omitted		30·00	
346	5s. multicoloured		6·00	1·00
	a. Gold (HAFMED emblem) omitted		80·00	
	b. Gold (framework) omitted		75·00	
347	10s. multicoloured		3·00	3·00
	a. Gold (centre) omitted		£130	
348	£1 multicoloured		3·75	5·00
	a. Pink omitted		26·00	
330/48	*Set of 21*		19·00	12·50

Designs: *Vert*—1d. Punic era; 1½d. Roman era; 2d. Proto Christian era; 2½d. Saracenic era; 3d. Siculo Norman era; 4d. Knights of Malta; 5d. Fortifications; 6d. French occupation. *Horiz*—10d. Naval arsenal; 1s. Maltese corps of the British army; 1s. 3d. International Eucharistic congress, 1913; 1s. 6d. Self-government, 1921; 2s. Gozo civic council; 2s. 6d. State of Malta; 3s. Independence, 1964; 5s. HAFMED (Allied forces, Mediterranean); 10s. The Maltese Islands (map); £1 Patron saints.

*The effect of this is to leave the Saracenic pattern as a pink colour.

†On the ½d. the second impression is 6½ mm lower or 3 mm to the left, and on the 2½d. 1 mm lower so that it falls partly across "MALTA" and "2½d". Stamps with almost coincidental double impression are common.

The ½d. and 1d. had white printing plates. Two silver plates were used on the 4d., one for "KNIGHTS OF MALTA" and the other for "MALTA". Two gold plates were used for the 8d. to 10s., one for the framework and the other for the gold in the central part of the designs.

No. 337a comes from a sheet on which the silver printing was so misplaced that it missed the top horizontal row entirely.

The ½d. to 4d., 1s. and 1s. 6d. to 5s. values exist with PVA gum as well as gum arabic and the 5d. and 10d. have PVA gum only.

129 "Dante" (Raphael)

(Des E. Cremona. Photo Govt Ptg Works, Rome)

1965 (7 July). 700*th Birth Anniv of Dante. P* 14.
349	**129** 2d. indigo		10	10
350	6d. bronze-green		25	10
351	2s. chocolate		1·10	1·50
349/51	*Set of 3*		1·25	1·50

130 Turkish Camp   131 Turkish Fleet

(Des E. Cremona. Photo Harrison)

1965 (1 Sept). 400*th Anniv of Great Siege. T* **130**/1 *and similar designs. W* **105** *(sideways). P* 13 (6d., 1s.) or 14½×14 (others).
352	2d. olive-green, red and black		30	10
353	3d. olive-green, red, black and light drab		30	10
354	6d. multicoloured		50	10
	a. Gold (framework and dates) omitted		£200	
	b. Black (on hulls) omitted		£200	
355	8d. red, gold, indigo and blue		90	90
	a. Gold (flag and dates) omitted		£100	
356	1s. red, gold and deep grey-blue		50	10
357	1s. 6d. ochre, red and black		1·50	30
358	2s. 6d. sepia, black, red and yellow-olive		1·75	3·25
352/8	*Set of 7*		5·25	4·25

Designs: *Square (as T* **130**)—3d. Battle scene; 8d. Arrival of relief force; 1s. 6d. "Allegory of Victory" (from mural by M. Preti); 2s. 6d. Victory medal. *Vert (as T* **131**)—1s. Grand Master J. de La Valette's arms.

NEW INFORMATION

The editor is always interested to correspond with people who have new information that will improve or correct the Catalogue.

137 "The Three Kings" 138 Sir Winston Churchill

(Des E. Cremona. Photo Enschedé)

1965 (7 Oct). *Christmas.* W 105 (*sideways*). P 11 × 11½.
359	137	1d. slate-purple and red		10	10
360		4d. slate-purple and blue	.. ..	30	25
361		1s. 3d. slate-purple and bright purple		30	30
359/61			*Set of 3*	60	50

(Des E. Cremona. Photo Harrison)

1966 (24 Jan). *Churchill Commemoration.* T **138** *and similar square design.* W **105** (*sideways*). P 14½ × 14.
362	138	2d. black, red and gold	..	20	10
363	–	3d. bronze-green, yellow-olive and gold		20	10
364	138	1s. maroon, red and gold	.. ..	25	10
		a. Gold (shading) omitted		£150	
365	–	1s. 6d. chalky blue, violet-blue and gold		35	40
362/5	..		*Set of 4*	90	55

Design:—3d., 1s. 6d. Sir Winston Churchill and George Cross.

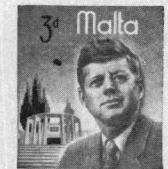

140 Grand Master La Valette 145 President Kennedy and Memorial

(Des E. Cremona. Photo State Ptg Works, Vienna)

1966 (28 Mar). *400th Anniv of Valletta.* T **140** *and similar square designs. Multicoloured.* W **105** (*sideways*). P 12.
366		2d. Type **140** ..		10	10
367		3d. Pope Pius V	.. ..	10	10
		a. Gold omitted	.. ..	£275	
368		6d. Map of Valletta	..	15	10
369		1s. Francesco Laparelli (architect) ..		15	10
370		2s. 6d. Girolamo Cassar (architect) ..		35	50
366/70	..		*Set of 5*	65	65

(Des E. Cremona. Photo Harrison)

1966 (28 May). *President Kennedy Commemoration.* W **105** (*sideways*). P 15 × 14.
371	145	3d. olive, gold and black	..	10	10
		a. Gold inscr omitted	..	£150	
372		1s. 6d. Prussian blue, gold and black		10	10

146 "Trade"

(Des E. Cremona. Photo D.L.R.)

1966 (16 June). *Tenth Malta Trade Fair.* W **105** (*sideways*). P 13½.
373	146	2d. multicoloured	.. ..	10	10
374		8d. multicoloured	.. ..	30	25
375		2s. 6d. multicoloured ..	.. ..	30	25
373/5	..	.. ..	*Set of 3*	65	50

147 "The Child in the Manger" 148 George Cross

(Des E. Cremona. Photo D.L.R.)

1966 (7 Oct). *Christmas.* W **105**. P 13½.
376	147	1d. black, gold, turquoise-bl & slate-pur		10	10
377		4d. black, gold, ultramarine & slate-pur		10	10
378		1s. 3d. black, gold, brt pur & slate-pur		10	10
		a. Gold omitted	..	60·00	
376/8	..	.. ..	*Set of 3*	15	10

(Des E. Cremona. Photo Harrison)

1967 (1 Mar). *25th Anniv of George Cross Award to Malta.* W **105** (*sideways*). P 14½ × 14.
379	148	2d. multicoloured	..	10	10
380		4d. multicoloured	..	10	10
381		3s. multicoloured	..	15	15
379/81	..	.. ..	*Set of 3*	20	15

149 Crucifixion of St. Peter

150 Open Bible and Episcopal Emblems

(Des E. Cremona. Photo Harrison)

1967 (28 June). *1900th Anniv of Martyrdom of Saints Peter and Paul.* T **149**/50 *and similar design.* W **105** (*sideways*). P 13½ × 14½ (8d.) or 14½ (others).
382		2d. chestnut, orange and black	..	10	10
383		8d. yellow-olive, gold and black		15	10
384		3s. blue, light blue and black	..	20	15
382/4		.. ..	*Set of 3*	30	20

Design:—*Square as* T **149**—3s. Beheading of St. Paul.

152 "St. Catherine of Siena" 156 Temple Ruins, Tarxien

(Des E. Cremona. Photo Enschedé)

1967 (1 Aug). *300th Death Anniv of Melchior Gafa (sculptor).* T **152** *and similar horiz designs. Multicoloured.* W **105** (*sideways*). P 13½ × 13.
385		2d. Type **152** ..	..	10	10
386		4d. "St. Thomas of Villanova"	..	10	10
387		1s. 6d. "Baptism of Christ" (detail) ..		15	10
388		2s. 6d. "St. John the Baptist" (from "Baptism of Christ")		15	10
385/8	..	.. .. ..	*Set of 4*	30	15

(Des E. Cremona. Photo Harrison)

1967 (12 Sept). *15th International Historical Architecture Congress, Valletta.* T **156** *and similar square designs. Multicoloured.* W **105**. P 15 × 14½.
389		2d. Type **156**	..	10	10
390		6d. Facade of Palazzo Falzon, Notabile		10	10
391		1s. Parish Church, Birkirkara	..	10	10
392		3s. Portal, Auberge de Castille		25	25
389/92	..	.. ..	*Set of 4*	30	30

160 "Angels" 161 "Crib" 162 "Angels"

(Des E. Cremona. Photo D.L.R.)

1967 (20 Oct). *Christmas.* W **105** (*sideways*). P 14.
393	160	1d. multicoloured	..	10	10
		a. Horiz strip of 3. Nos. 393/5	..	40	20
		b. White stars (red omitted)	..	70·00	
394	161	8d. multicoloured	..	20	10
395	162	1s. 4d. multicoloured	..	20	10
393/5		.. ..	*Set of 3*	40	20

Nos. 393/5 were issued in sheets of 60 of each value (arranged *tête-bêche*), and also in sheets containing the three values *se-tenant*, thus forming a triptych of the Nativity.

163 Queen Elizabeth II and Arms of Malta

(Des E. Cremona. Photo Harrison)

1967 (13 Nov). *Royal Visit.* T **163** *and similar designs.* W **105** (*sideways on* 2d., 3s.). P 14×15 (4d.) or 15×14 (others).
396		2d. multicoloured	..	10	10
		a. Grey-brown omitted*			
397		4d. black, brown-purple and gold ..		10	10
398		3s. multicoloured	..	20	25
396/8		.. ..	*Set of 3*	30	30

Designs: *Vert*—4d. Queen in Robes of Order of St. Michael and St. George. *Horiz*—3s. Queen and outline of Malta.
*This affects the Queen's face.

166 Human Rights Emblem and People 167

(Des E. Cremona. Photo Harrison)

1968 (2 May). *Human Rights Year.* W **105**. P 12½ (6d.) or 14½ (others).
399	166	2d. multicoloured	.. ..	10	10
400	167	6d. multicoloured	.. ..	10	10
401		2s. multicoloured	.. ..	10	10
399/401			*Set of 3*	15	10

The design of the 2s. value is a reverse of Type **166**.

169 Fair "Products"

(Des E. Cremona. Photo Harrison)

1968 (1 June). *Malta International Trade Fair.* W **105** (*sideways*). P 14½ × 14.
402	169	4d. multicoloured	.. ..	10	10
403		8d. multicoloured	.. ..	10	10
404		3s. multicoloured	.. ..	15	10
402/4		.. ..	*Set of 3*	20	15

170 Arms of the Order of St. John and La Valette 171 "La Valette" (A. de Favray)

172 La Valette's Tomb 173 Angels and Scroll bearing Date of Death

(Des E. Cremona. Photo Govt Printer, Israel)

1968 (1 Aug). *Fourth Death Centenary of Grand Master La Valette.* W **105** (*upright,* 1s. 6d.; *sideways, others*). P 13 × 14 (1d., 1s. 6d.) or 14 × 13 (others).
405	170	1d. multicoloured	..	10	10
406	171	8d. multicoloured	..	15	10
407	172	1s. 6d. multicoloured	..	15	10
408	173	2s. 6d. multicoloured	..	20	20
405/8	..	.. ..	*Set of 4*	45	30

174 Star of Bethlehem and Angel waking Shepherds 177 "Agriculture"

(Des E. Cremona. Photo Harrison)

1968 (3 Oct). *Christmas. T* **174** *and similar shaped designs. Multicoloured. W* **105** (*sideways*). *P* 14½ × 14.
409   1d. Type **174** 10 10
410   8d. Mary and Joseph with shepherd watching over cradle 15 10
411   1s. 4d. Three Wise Men and Star of Bethlehem 15 20
409/11 .. .. *Set of* 3 30 30
The shortest side at top and the long side at the bottom both gauge 14½, the other three sides are 14. Nos. 409/11 were issued in sheets of 60 arranged in ten strips of six, alternately upright and inverted.

(Des E. Cremona. Photo Enschedé)

1968 (21 Oct). *Sixth Food and Agricultural Organization Regional Conference for Europe. T* **177** *and similar vert designs. Multicoloured. W* **105** (*sideways*). *P* 12½ × 12.
412   4d. Type **177** 10 10
413   1s. F.A.O. emblem and coin 10 10
414   2s. 6d. "Agriculture" sowing seeds .. 10 15
412/14 .. .. *Set of* 3 15 20

180 Mahatma Gandhi   **181** I.L.O. Emblem

(Des E. Cremona. Photo Enschedé)

1969 (24 Mar). *Birth Centenary of Mahatma Gandhi. W* **105**. *P* 12 × 12½.
415 **180** 1s. 6d. blackish brown, black and gold 15 10

(Des E. Cremona. Photo Harrison)

1969 (26 May). *50th Anniv of International Labour Organization. W* **105** (*sideways*). *P* 13½ × 14½.
416 **181** 2d. indigo, gold and turquoise .. 10 10
417   6d. sepia, gold and chestnut .. 10 10

182 Robert Samut

1969 (26 July). *Birth Centenary of Robert Samut* (*composer of Maltese National Anthem*). *W* **105** (*sideways*). *P* 13.
418 **182** 2d. multicoloured 10 10

183 Dove of Peace, U.N. Emblem and Sea-Bed

(Des E. Cremona. Photo D.L.R.)

1969 (26 July). *United Nations Resolution on Oceanic Resources. W* **105** (*sideways*). *P* 13.
419 **183** 5d. multicoloured 10 10

184 "Swallows" returning to Malta

(Des E. Cremona. Photo D.L.R.)

1969 (26 July). *Maltese Migrants' Convention. W* **105** (*sideways*). *P* 13.
420 **184** 10d. black, gold and yellow-olive .. 10 10

185 University Arms and Grand Master de Fonseca (founder)

(Des E. Cremona. Photo D.L.R.)

1969 (26 July). *Bicentenary of University of Malta. W* **105** (*sideways*). *P* 13.
421 **185** 2s. multicoloured 15 20

186 1919 Monument   **187** Flag of Malta and Birds

(Des E. Cremona. Photo Enschedé)

1969 (20 Sept). *Fifth Anniv of Independence. T* **186/7** *and similar designs. W* **105** (*upright on* 5d., *sideways others*). *P* 13½ × 12½ (2d.), 12 × 12½ (5d.), *or* 12½ × 12 (*others*).
422   2d. multicoloured 10 10
423   5d. black, red and gold 10 10
424   10d. black, turquoise-blue and gold .. 10 10
425   1s. 6d. multicoloured 20 35
426   2s. 6d. black, olive-brown and gold .. 25 45
422/6 .. .. *Set of* 5 50 90
Designs:—Vert as T **187**—10d. "Tourism"; 1s. 6d. U.N. and Council of Europe emblems; 2s. 6d. "Trade and Industry".

191 Peasants playing Tambourine and Bagpipes

(Des E. Cremona. Litho D.L.R.)

1969 (8 Nov). *Christmas. Children's Welfare Fund. T* **191** *and similar horiz designs. Multicoloured. W* **105** (*sideways*). *P* 12½.
427   1d. + 1d. Type **191** 10 20
    a. Gold omitted .. .. .. 90·00
    b. Horiz strip of 3. Nos. 427/9 .. 30 75
428   5d. + 1d. Angels playing trumpet and harp 15 20
429   1s. 6d. + 3d. Choir boys singing .. 15 45
427/9 .. .. *Set of* 3 30 75
Nos. 427/9 were issued in sheets of 60 of each value, and also in sheets containing the three values *se-tenant*, thus forming the triptych No. 427b.

194 "The Beheading of St. John" (Caravaggio)

(Des E. Cremona. Photo Enschedé)

1970 (21 Mar). *13th Council of Europe Art Exhibition. T* **194** *and similar multicoloured designs. W* **105** (*upright,* 10d., 2s.; *sideways, others*). *P* 14 × 13 (1d., 8d.), 12 (10d., 2s.) *or* 13 × 13½ (*others*).
430   1d. Type **194** 10 10
431   2d. "St. John the Baptist" (M. Preti) (45 × 32 *mm*) 10 10
432   5d. Interior of St. John's Co-Cathedral, Valletta (39 × 39 *mm*) .. 10 10
433   6d. "Allegory of the Order" (Neapolitan School) (45 × 32 *mm*) .. 15 10
434   8d. "St. Jerome" (Caravaggio) .. 15 30
435   10d. Articles from the Order of St. John in Malta (63 × 21 *mm*) .. 15 10
436   1s. 6d. "The Blessed Gerard receiving Godfrey de Bouillon" (A. de Favray) (45 × 35 *mm*) 25 35
437   2s. Cape and Stolone (16th-century) (63 × 21 *mm*) 25 45
430/37 .. .. *Set of* 8 90 1·10

202 Artist's Impression of Fujiyama

(Des E. Cremona. Photo D.L.R.)

1970 (29 May). *World Fair, Osaka. W* **105** (*sideways*). *P* 15.
438 **202** 2d. multicoloured 10 10
439   5d. multicoloured 10 10
440   3s. multicoloured 15 15
438/40 .. .. *Set of* 3 20 20

203 "Peace and Justice"   **204** Carol-Singers, Church and Star

(Des J. Casha. Litho Harrison)

1970 (30 Sept). *25th Anniv of United Nations. W* **105**. *P* 14 × 14½.
441 **203** 2d. multicoloured 10 10
442   5d. multicoloured 10 10
443   2s. 6d. multicoloured 15 15
441/3 .. .. *Set of* 3 15 15

(Des E. Cremona. Photo Govt Printer, Israel)

1970 (7 Nov). *Christmas. T* **204** *and similar vert designs. Multicoloured. W* **105** (*sideways*). *P* 14 × 13.
444   1d. + ½d. Type **204** 10 10
445   10d. + 2d. Church, star and angels with Infant 15 20
446   1s. 6d. + 3d. Church, star and nativity scene 20 35
444/6 .. .. *Set of* 3 30 60

207 Books and Quill   **208** Dun Karm, Books, Pens and Lamp

(Des H. Alden (1s. 6d.), A. Agius (2s.). Litho D.L.R.)

1971 (20 Mar). *Literary Anniversaries. Death Bicentenary* (1970) *of De Soldanis* (*historian*) (1s. 6d.) *and Birth Centenary of Dun Karm* (*poet*) (2s.). *W* **105** (*sideways*). *P* 13 × 13½.
447 **207** 1s. 6d. multicoloured 10 10
448 **208** 2s. multicoloured 10 15

209 Europa "Chain"

(Des H. Haflidason; adapted E. Cremona. Litho Harrison)

1971 (3 May). *Europa. W* **105** (*sideways*). *P* 13½ × 14½.
449 **209** 2d. orange, black and yellow-olive .. 10 10
450   5d. orange, black and vermilion .. 10 10
451   1s. 6d. orange, black and slate .. 45 90
449/51 .. .. *Set of* 3 55 90

210 "St. Joseph, Patron of the Universal Church" (G. Cali)   **211** *Centaurea spathulata*

(Des E. Cremona. Litho D.L.R.)

1971 (24 July). *Centenary of Proclamation of St. Joseph as Patron Saint of Catholic Church, and 50th Anniv of the Coronation of the Statue of "Our Lady of Victories". T* **210** *and similar horiz design. Multicoloured. W* **105** (*sideways*). *P* 13 × 13½.
452   2d. Type **210** 10 10
453   5d. Statue of "Our Lady of Victories" and galley 10 10
454   10d. Type **210** 15 10
455   1s. 6d. As 5d. 30 40
452/5 .. .. *Set of* 4 45 50

(Des Reno Psaila. Litho Harrison)

1971 (18 Sept). *National Plant and Bird of Malta. T* **211** *and similar horiz design. Multicoloured. W* **105** (*sideways on* 5d. *and* 10d.). *P* 14½ × 14.
456   2d. Type **211** 10 10
457   5d. Blue Rock Thrush 20 10
458   10d. As 5d. 30 15
459   1s. 6d. Type **211** .. .. .. 30 1·25
456/9 .. .. *Set of* 4 75 1·40

212 Angel

(Des E. Cremona. Litho Format)

1971 (8 Nov). *Christmas. T* **212** *and similar horiz designs. Multicoloured.* W **105** (*sideways*). P 13½ × 14.

460	1d. + ½d. Type 212	..	10	10
461	10d. + 2d. Mary and the Child Jesus	..	15	20
462	1s. 6d. + 3d. Joseph lying awake	..	20	30
460/2		*Set of 3*	35	55
MS463	131 × 113 mm. Nos. 460/2. P 15	..	75	2·50

213 Heart and W.H.O. Emblem   214 Maltese Cross

(Des A. Agius. Litho Format)

1972 (20 Mar). *World Health Day.* W **105**. P 13½ × 14.

464	213	2d. multicoloured	10	10
465		10d. multicoloured	15	10
466		2s. 6d. multicoloured	40	80
464/6		*Set of 3*	55	85

(New Currency. 10 mils = 1 cent; 100 cents = 1 Maltese pound)

(Des G. Pace. Litho Format)

1972 (16 May). *Decimal Currency. T* **214** *and similar vert designs showing decimal coins. Multicoloured.* P **14** (2 *m.*, 3 *m.*, 2 *c.*), 14½ × 14 (5 *m.*, 1 *c.*, 5 *c.*) *or* 13½ (10 *c.*, 50 *c.*).

467	2 m. Type 214	..	10	10
468	3 m. Bee on honeycomb	..	10	10
469	5 m. Earthen lampstand	..	10	10
470	1 c. George Cross	..	10	10
471	2 c. Classical head	..	10	10
472	5 c. Ritual altar	..	10	10
473	10 c. Grandmaster's galley	..	20	10
474	50 c. Great Siege Monument	..	1·25	1·25
467/74		*Set of 8*	1·60	1·25

Sizes:—2 m., 3 m. and 2 c. as T **214**; 5 m., 1 c. and 5 c. 22 × 27 mm; 10 c. and 50 c. 27 × 35 mm.

No. 467 exists imperforate from stock dispersed by the liquidator of Format International Security Printers Ltd.

(215)

= 1c3

216 "Communications"

1972 (30 Sept). *Nos. 337a, 339 and 341 surch as T* **215**, *by Govt. Printing Works, Valletta.*

475	1 c. 3 on 5d. multicoloured	..	10	10
476	3 c. on 8d. multicoloured	..	15	10
	a. Surch inverted	..	60·00	
	b. Gold (frame) omitted	..	65·00	
477	5 c. on 1s. 3d. multicoloured	..	15	20
	a. Surch double	..	55·00	
	b. Surch inverted	..	35·00	
	c. Gold (centre) omitted	..	45·00	
475/7		*Set of 3*	30	35

PRINTERS. All stamps between Nos. 478 and 1093 were printed in lithography by Printex Ltd. Malta.

(Des P. Huovinen; adapted G. Pace)

1972 (11 Nov). *Europa.* W **105** (*sideways*). P 13.

478	216	1 c. 3, multicoloured	10	10
479		3 c. multicoloured	10	10
480		5 c. multicoloured	15	35
481		7 c. 5, multicoloured	20	75
478/81		*Set of 4*	50	1·10

Nos. 478/81 were each printed in sheets including two *se-tenant* stamp-size labels in the second and third positions of the top row.

217 Angel

(Des E. Cremona)

1972 (9 Dec). *Christmas. T* **217** *and similar horiz designs.* W **105** (*sideways*). P 13½.

482	8 m. + 2 m. dull sepia, brownish grey & gold	10	10
483	3 c. + 1 c. plum, lavender and gold		15	40
484	7 c. 5 + 1 c. 5, indigo, azure and gold	..	20	50
482/4		*Set of 3*	35	85
MS485	137×113 mm. Nos. 482/4		2·25	4·25

Designs:—No. 483, Angel with tambourine; No. 484, Singing angel.

See also Nos. 507/10.

218 Archaeology   219 Europa "Posthorn"

(Des E. Cremona)

1973 (31 Mar)—76. *T* **218** *and similar designs. Multicoloured.* W **105** (*sideways*). P 13½ × 14 (*Nos.* 500/*a*) *or* 13½ (*others*).

486	2 m. Type 218	..	10	10
487	4 m. History	..	10	10
	a. Gold (inscr and decoration) omitted	..	75·00	
	b. Imperf (pair)	..	£325	
488	5 m. Folklore	..	10	10
489	8 m. Industry	..	10	10
490	1 c. Fishing industry	..	10	10
491	1 c. 3, Pottery	..	10	10
492	2 c. Agriculture	..	10	10
493	3 c. Sport	..	10	10
494	4 c. Yacht marina	..	15	10
495	5 c. Fiesta	..	15	10
496	7 c. 5, Regatta	..	25	25
497	10 c. Voluntary service	..	25	10
498	50 c. Education	..	75	1·00
499	£1 Religion	..	2·25	2·75
500	£2 Coat of arms (*horiz*)	..	12·00	17·00
	a. Gold omitted	..		
500*b*	£2 National Emblem (*horiz*) (28.1.76)	7·50	14·00
486/500*b*		*Set of 16*	21·00	32·00

Nos. 500/*b* are larger, 32 × 27 mm.

(Des L. Anisdahl; adapted G. Pace)

1973 (2 June). *Europa.* W **105**. P 14.

501	219	3 c. multicoloured	15	10
502		5 c. multicoloured	15	35
503		7 c. 5, multicoloured	25	60
501/3		*Set of 3*	50	95

Nos. 501/3 were each printed in sheets containing two *se-tenant* stamp-size labels.

220 Emblem, and Woman   221 Girolamo Cassar
holding Corn   (architect)

(Des H. Alden)

1973 (6 Oct). *Anniversaries. T* **220** *and similar vert designs showing emblem and allegorical figures.* W **105** (*sideways*). P 13½.

504	1 c. 3, multicoloured	..	10	10
505	7 c. 5, multicoloured	..	25	40
506	10 c. multicoloured	..	30	50
504/6		*Set of 3*	55	85

Anniversaries:—1 c. 3, Tenth Anniv of World Food Programme; 7 c. 5, 25th Anniv of W.H.O.; 10 c. 25th Anniv of Universal Declaration of Human Rights.

(Des E. Cremona)

1973 (10 Nov). *Christmas. Horiz designs as T* **217**. *Multicoloured.* W **105** (*sideways*). P 13½.

507	8 m. + 2 m. Angels and organ pipes	15	10
508	3 c. + 1 c. Madonna and Child	..	25	55
509	7 c. 5 + 1 c. 5, Buildings and Star	45	1·00
507/9		*Set of 3*	75	1·50
MS510	137 × 112 mm. Nos. 507/9	..	4·75	7·00

(Des E. Cremona)

1974 (12 Jan). *Prominent Maltese. T* **221** *and similar vert designs.* W **105**. P 14.

511	1 c. 3, dull myrtle-grn, dull grey-grn & gold	10	10
512	3 c. deep turquoise, grey-blue and gold	15	10
513	5 c. dull sepia, deep slate-green and gold	20	15
514	7 c. 5, slate-blue, light slate-blue and gold	20	30
515	10 c. purple, dull purple and gold	20	40
511/15		*Set of 5*	70	85

Designs:—3 c. Giuseppe Barth (ophthalmologist); 5 c. Nicolo' Isouard (composer); 7 c. 5, John Borg (botanist); 10 c. Antonio Sciortino (sculptor).

222 "Air Malta" Emblem

(Des E. Cremona)

1974 (30 Mar). *Air. T* **222** *and similar horiz design. Multicoloured.* W **105** (*sideways*). P 13½.

516	3 c. Type 222	..	15	10
517	4 c. Boeing 720B	..	15	10
518	5 c. Type 222	..	20	10
519	7 c. 5, As 4 c.	..	25	10
520	20 c. Type 222	..	80	60
521	25 c. As 4 c.	..	80	60
522	35 c. Type 222	..	1·10	1·40
516/22		*Set of 7*	3·00	2·50

223 Prehistoric Sculpture

(Des E. Cremona)

1974 (13 July). *Europa. T* **223** *and similar designs.* W **105** (*sideways on Nos.* 523 *and* 525). P 13½.

523	1 c. 3, slate-blue, grey-black and gold	..	15	10
524	3 c. light bistre-brown, grey-black and gold	20	15
525	5 c. purple, grey-black and gold	..	25	50
526	7 c. 5, dull green, grey-black and gold	..	35	1·00
523/6		*Set of 4*	85	1·60

Designs:—*Vert*—3 c. Old Cathedral Door, Mdina; 7 c. 5, "Vetlina" (sculpture by A. Sciortino). *Horiz*—5 c. Silver Monstrance.

Nos. 523/6 were each printed in sheets including two *se-tenant* stamp-size labels.

224 Heinrich von Stephan   225 Decorative Star
(founder) and Land Transport   and Nativity Scene

(Des S. and G. Sullivan)

1974 (20 Sept). *Centenary of Universal Postal Union. T* **224** *and similar horiz designs.* W **105** (*sideways*). P 13½ × 14.

527	1 c. 3, blue-green, lt violet-blue & yell-orge	30	10
528	5 c. brown, dull vermilion and yellow-green	30	10
529	7 c. 5, dp dull blue, lt violet-blue & yell-grn	35	20
530	50 c. purple, dull vermilion and yellow-orange	1·00	1·25
527/30		*Set of 4*	1·75	1·50
MS531	126 × 91 mm. Nos. 527/30	..	4·50	6·50

Designs (each containing portrait as T **224**):—5 c. *Washington* (paddle-steamer) and *Royal Viking Star* (liner); 7 c. 5, Balloon and Boeing 747-100; 50 c. U.P.U. Buildings, 1874 and 1974.

(Des E. Cremona)

1974 (22 Nov). *Christmas. T* **225** *and similar vert designs, each with decorative star. Multicoloured.* W **105** (*sideways*). P 14.

532	8 m. + 2 m. Type 225	..	10	10
533	3 c. + 1 c. "Shepherds"	..	15	20
534	5 c. + 1 c. "Shepherds with gifts"	..	20	35
535	7 c. 5 + 1 c. 5, "The Magi"	..	30	40
532/5		*Set of 4*	65	95

REPUBLIC

226 Swearing-in of Prime Minister

(Des E. Cremona)

1975 (31 Mar). *Inauguration of Republic. T* **226** *and similar horiz designs.* W **105** (*sideways*). P 14.

536	1 c. 3, multicoloured	..	10	10
537	5 c. rose-red and grey-black	..	20	10
538	25 c. multicoloured	..	60	1·00
536/8		*Set of 3*	75	1·00

Designs:—5 c. National flag; 25 c. Minister of Justice, President and Prime Minister.

227 Mother and Child ("Family Life")

(Des D. Friggieri)

1975 (30 May). *International Women's Year. T* **227** *and similar horiz design.* W **105**. P 13½ × 14.

539	227	1 c. 3, light violet and gold	..	15	10
540	—	3 c. light blue and gold	..	20	10
541	227	5 c. dull olive-sepia and gold	..	30	20
542	—	20 c. chestnut and gold	..	1·10	2·75
539/42		*Set of 4*	1·60	2·75

Design:—3 c., 20 c. Office secretary ("Public Life").

228 "Allegory of Malta" (Francesco de Mura)

(Des E. Cremona)

1975 (15 July). *Europa. T* **228** *and similar horiz design. Multicoloured. W* **105.** *P* 14 × 13½.
543   5 c. Type **228** 30   10
544   15 c. "Judith and Holofernes" (Valentin de
          Boulogne) 50   75
The 15 c. is a smaller design than the 5 c. (47 × 23 mm), though the perforated area is the same.
Nos. 543/4 were each printed in sheets including two *se-tenant* stamp-size labels.

229 Plan of Ggantija Temple

(Des R. England)

1975 (16 Sept). *European Architectural Heritage Year. T* **229** *and similar horiz designs. W* **105** *(sideways). P* 13½.
545   1 c. 3, brownish black and light orange-red ..   10   10
546   3 c. dull purple, lt orange-red & blackish brn   20   10
547   5 c. blackish brown and light orange-red   30   25
548   25 c. dull grey-olive, light orange-red and
          brownish black .. .. ..   1·10   3·00
545/8 .. .. *Set of 4*   1·50   3·00
Designs:—3 c. Mdina skyline; 5 c. View of Victoria, Gozo; 25 c. Silhouette of Fort St. Angelo.

230 Farm Animals   **231** "The Right to Work"

(Des E. Cremona)

1975 (4 Nov). *Christmas. T* **230** *and similar multicoloured designs. W* **105** *(sideways). P* 13½.
549   8 m. + 2 m. Type **230**   30   25
          a. Horiz strip of 3. Nos. 549/51 ..   1·25   3·25
550   3 c. + 1 c. Nativity scene (50×23 mm)   50   75
551   7 c. 5 + 1 c. 5, Approach of the Magi   60   1·40
549/51 .. .. .. *Set of 3*   1·25   2·25
Nos. 549/51 were issued in sheets of 50 of each value, and also in sheets containing the three values horizontally *se-tenant*, thus forming the triptych No. 549a which is a composite design of "The Nativity" by Master Alberto.

(Des A. de Giovanni)

1975 (12 Dec). *First Anniv of Republic. T* **231** *and similar vert designs. W* **105.** *P* 14.
552   1 c. 3, multicoloured   10   10
553   5 c. multicoloured   20   10
554   25 c. deep rose, light steel-blue and black ..   70   1·10
552/4 .. .. *Set of 3*   80   1·10
Designs:—5 c. "Safeguarding the Environment"; 25 c. National Flag.

232 "Festa Tar-Rahal"   **233** Water Polo

(Des M. Camilleri)

1976 (26 Feb). *Maltese Folklore. T* **232** *and similar multicoloured designs. W* **105** *(sideways on 5 c. and 7 c. 5). P* 14.
555   1 c. 3, Type **232**   10   10
556   5 c. "L-Imnarja" (*horiz*)   15   10
557   7 c. 5, "Il-Karnival" (*horiz*) ..   35   70
558   10 c. "Il-Gimgha L-Kbira" ..   55   1·40
555/8 .. .. *Set of 4*   1·00   2·00

(Des H. Alden)

1976 (28 Apr). *Olympic Games, Montreal. T* **233** *and similar horiz designs. Multicoloured. W* **105.** *P* 13½ × 14.
559   1 c. 7, Type **233**   10   10
560   5 c. Sailing   25   10
561   30 c. Athletics   85   1·50
559/61 .. .. .. *Set of 3*   1·10   1·50

234 Lace-making

(Des F. Portelli)

1976 (8 July). *Europa. T* **234** *and similar horiz design. Multicoloured. W* **105** *(sideways). P* 13½ × 14.
562   7 c. Type **234**   20   35
563   15 c. Stone carving   25   60
Nos. 562/3 were each printed in sheets including two *se-tenant* stamp-size labels.

235 Nicola Cotoner

(Des E. Cremona)

1976 (14 Sept). *300th Anniv of School of Anatomy and Surgery. T* **235** *and similar horiz designs. Multicoloured. W* **105** *(sideways). P* 13½.
564   2 c. Type **235**   10   10
565   5 c. Arm   15   10
566   7 c. Giuseppe Zammit   20   10
567   1 c. Sacra Infermeria   35   65
564/7 .. .. .. *Set of 4*   70   75

236 St. John the Baptist and St. Michael   **237** Jean de la Valette's Armour   **(238)**

1c7 ▬

(Des E. Cremona)

1976 (23 Nov). *Christmas. Designs showing portions of "Madonna and Saints" by Domenico di Michelino. Multicoloured. W* **105** *(sideways on No. 571). P* 13½ × 14 (*No. 571*) *or* 13½ (*others*).
568   1 c. + 5 m. Type **236** ..   15   20
569   5 c. + 1 c. Madonna and Child ..   20   60
570   7 c. + 1 c. 5, St. Christopher and St. Nicholas   30   80
571   10 c. + 2 c. Complete painting (32 × 27 mm) ..   40   1·25
568/71 .. .. .. *Set of 4*   95   2·50

(Des J. Briffa)

1977 (20 Jan). *Suits of Armour. T* **237** *and similar vert designs. Multicoloured. W* **105.** *P* 13½.
572   2 c. Type **237**   10   10
573   7 c. Aloph de Wignacourt's armour ..   20   10
574   11 c. Jean Jacques de Verdelin's armour ..   25   50
572/4 .. .. .. *Set of 3*   45   60

1977 (24 Mar). *No. 336 surch with T* **238** *by Govt Printing Press, Malta.*
575   116   1 c. 7 on 4d. multicoloured ..   25   25
          a. "KNIGHTS OF MALTA" (silver)
             omitted .. .. ..   75·00

239 "Annunciation"   **240** Map and Radio Aerial

(Des E. Cremona)

1977 (30 Mar). *400th Birth Anniversary of Rubens. Flemish tapestries (1st series) showing his paintings as T* **239.** *Multicoloured. W* **105** *(sideways). P* 14.
576   2 c. Type **239**   10   10
577   7 c. "Four Evangelists"   25   10
578   11 c. "Nativity"   45   45
579   20 c. "Adoration of the Magi" ..   80   1·00
576/9 .. .. .. *Set of 4*   1·40   1·50
See also Nos. 592/5, 615/18 and 638/40.

(Des H. Borg)

1977 (17 May). *World Telecommunication Day. T* **240** *and similar design. W* **105** *(sideways on 1 and 6 c.). P* 14 × 13½ (*1 and 6 c.*) *or* 13½ × 14 (*others*).
580   240   1 c. black, green and vermilion ..   10   10
581   6 c. black, grey-blue and vermilion ..   20   10
582   —   8 c. black, chestnut and vermilion ..   30   10
583   —   17 c. black, dull mauve and vermilion ..   60   40
580/3 .. .. .. *Set of 4*   1·00   55
Design: *Horiz*—8 and 17 c. Map, aerial and aeroplane tail-fin.

241 Ta' L-Isperanza   **242** "Aid to Handi-capped Workers" (detail from Workers' Monument)

(Des G. French)

1977 (5 July). *Europa. T* **241** *and similar horiz design. Multicoloured. W* **105** *(sideways). P* 13½.
584   7 c. Type **241**   30   15
585   20 c. Is-Salini   35   1·00
Nos. 584/5 were each printed in sheets including two *se-tenant* stamp-size labels.

(Des A. Agius)

1977 (12 Oct). *Maltese Worker Commemoration. T* **242** *and similar designs. W* **105** *(sideways on 20 c.). P* 13½.
586   2 c. orange-brown and light brown ..   10   10
587   7 c. chestnut and brown   15   10
588   20 c. multicoloured .. .. *Set of 3*   40   60
586/8 .. .. .. *Set of 3*   55   60
Designs: *Vert*—7 c. "Stoneworker, modern industry and ship-building" (monument detail). *Horiz*—20 c. "Mother with Dead Son" and Service Medal.

243 The Shepherds   **244** "Young Lady on Horseback and Trooper"

(Des E. Cremona)

1977 (16 Nov). *Christmas. T* **243** *and similar horiz designs. Multicoloured. W* **105** *(sideways). P* 13½ × 14.
589   1 c. + 5 m. Type **243**   10   20
          a. Vert strip of 3. Nos. 589/91 ..   40
590   7 c. + 1 c. The Nativity   15   30
591   11 c. + 1 c. 5, Flight into Egypt ..   20   45
589/91 .. .. .. *Set of 3*   40   85
Nos. 589/91 were issued in sheets of 50 of each value, and also in sheets containing the three values *se-tenant*.

(Des E. Cremona)

1978 (26 Jan). *Flemish Tapestries (2nd series). Horiz designs similar to T* **239.** *Multicoloured. W* **105** *(sideways). P* 14.
592   2 c. "The Entry into Jerusalem" (artist
          unknown)   10   10
593   7 c. "The Last Supper" (after Poussin) ..   25   10
594   11 c. "The Raising of the Cross" (after Rubens)   30   25
595   25 c. "The Resurrection" (after Rubens) ..   70   80
592/5 .. .. .. *Set of 4*   1·25   1·10

(Des A. Camilleri)

1978 (7 Mar). *450th Death Anniv of Albrecht Dürer. T* **244** *and similar vert designs. W* **105.** *P* 14.
596   1 c. 7, black, vermilion and deep blue ..   10   10
597   8 c. black, vermilion and slate ..   15   10
598   17 c. black, vermilion and deep slate ..   40   45
          a. Vermilion (monogram) omitted ..   75·00
596/8 .. .. .. *Set of 3*   55   55
Designs:—8 c. "The Bag-piper"; 17 c. "The Virgin and Child with a Monkey".

PRICES OF SETS

Set prices are given for many issues, generally those containing three stamps or more. Definitive sets include one of each value or major colour change, but do not cover different perforations, die types or minor shades. Where a choice is possible the set prices are based on the cheapest versions of the stamps included in the listings.

245 Monument to Grand Master Nicola Cotoner (Foggini)　　**246** Goalkeeper

(Des E. Cremona)

1978 (26 Apr). *Europa. Monuments. T 245 and similar vert design. Multicoloured. W 105. P 14 × 13½.*
599　7 c. Type 245　　　　　　　15　10
600　25 c. Monument to Grand Master Ramon Perellos (Mazzuoli)　　35　90
　Nos. 599/600 were each printed in sheets including two *se-tenant* stamp-size labels.

(Des A. de Giovanni)

1978 (6 June). *World Cup Football Championship, Argentina. T 246 and similar vert designs. Multicoloured. W 105 (sideways). P 14 × 13½.*
601　2 c. Type 246　　　　　　　10　10
602　11 c. Players heading ball　　　15　10
603　15 c. Tackling　　　　　　　25　35
601/3　　　　　　　*Set of 3*　45　45
MS604　125 × 90 mm. Nos. 601/3　　1·75　2·75

247 Boeing 707 over Megalithic Temple

(Des R. Caruana)

1978 (3 Oct). *Air. Horiz designs as T 247. Multicoloured. W 105 (sideways). P 13½.*
605　5 c. Type 247　　　　　　　20　10
606　7 c. Air Malta Boeing 720B　　20　10
607　11 c. Boeing 747 taking off from Luqa Airport　　　　　35　10
608　17 c. Type 247　　　　　　　45　30
609　20 c. As 7 c.　　　　　　　60　40
610　75 c. As 11 c.　　　　　　　1·75　2·75
605/10　　　　　　*Set of 6*　3·25　3·25

248 Folk Musicians and Village Church　　**249** Luzzu and Aircraft Carrier

(Des E. Cremona)

1978 (9 Nov). *Christmas. T 248 and similar multicoloured designs. W 105 (sideways). P 13½ (11 c.) or 14 (others).*
611　1 c. + 5 m. Type 248　　　　　10　10
612　5 c. + 1 c. Choir of Angels　　　15　20
613　7 c. + 1 c. 5, Carol singers　　　20　35
614　11 c. + 3 c. Folk musicians, church, angels and carol singers (58 × 23 mm)　25　45
611/14　　　　　　*Set of 4*　60　1·00
　The 1, 5 and 7 c. values depict details of the complete design shown on the 11 c. value.

(Des E. Cremona)

1979 (24 Jan). *Flemish Tapestries (3rd series). Horiz designs as T 239 showing paintings by Rubens. Multicoloured. W 105 (sideways). P 14.*
615　2 c. "The Triumph of the Catholic Church"　　10　10
616　7 c. "The Triumph of Charity"　　20　10
617　11 c. "The Triumph of Faith"　　30　25
618　25 c. "The Triumph of Truth"　　95　80
615/18　　　　　　*Set of 4*　1·40　1·10

(Des E. Cremona)

1979 (31 Mar). *End of Military Facilities Agreement. T 249 and similar vert designs. Multicoloured. W 105 (sideways). P 13½.*
619　2 c. Type 249　　　　　　　10　10
620　5 c. Raising the flag ceremony　　10　10
621　7 c. Departing soldier and olive sprig　15　10
622　8 c. Type 249　　　　　　　40　40
623　17 c. As 5 c.　　　　　　　55　60
624　20 c. As 7 c.　　　　　　　55　60
619/24　　　　　　*Set of 6*　1·60　1·60

250 Speronara (fishing boat) and Tail of Air Malta Airliner　　**251** Children on Globe

(Des E. Cremona)

1979 (9 May). *Europa. Communications. T 250 and similar vert design. Multicoloured. W 105 (sideways). P 14.*
625　7 c. Type 250　　　　　　　20　10
626　25 c. Coastal watch tower and radio link towers　40　75
　Nos. 625/6 were each printed in sheets including two *se-tenant* stamp-size labels.

(Des A. Bonnici (2 c.), A. Pisani (7 c.), M. French (11 c.))

1979 (13 June). *International Year of the Child. T 251 and similar multicoloured designs. W 105 (sideways). P 14 × 13½ (2 c.) or 14 (others).*
627　2 c. Type 251　　　　　　　10　10
628　7 c. Children flying kites (27 × 33 mm)　15　10
629　11 c. Children in circle (27 × 33 mm).　20　35
627/9　　　　　　　*Set of 3*　35　45

252 Shells (*Gibbula nivosa*)

(Des R. Pitré)

1979 (10 Oct). *Marine Life. T 252 and similar horiz designs. Multicoloured. W 105. P 13½.*
630　2 c. Type 252　　　　　　　10　10
631　5 c. Loggerhead Turtle (*Garetta garetta*)　20　10
632　7 c. Dolphin (fish) (*Coryphaena hippurus*)　25　10
633　25 c. Noble Pen Shell (*Pinna nobilis*)　90　1·25
630/3　　　　　　　*Set of 4*　1·25　1·25

253 "The Nativity" (detail)

(Des E. Cremona)

1979 (14 Nov). *Christmas. Paintings by G. Cali. T 253 and similar horiz designs. Multicoloured. W 105. P 14 × 13½.*
634　1 c. + 5 m. Type 253　　　　　10　10
635　5 c. + 1 c. "The Flight into Egypt" (detail)　10　15
636　7 c. + 1 c. 5, "The Nativity"　　15　20
637　11 c. + 3 c. "The Flight into Egypt" (Rubens)　25　50
634/7　　　　　　　*Set of 4*　50　85

(Des E. Cremona)

1980 (30 Jan). *Flemish Tapestries (4th series). Horiz designs as T 239 taken from paintings. Multicoloured. W 105 (sideways). P 14.*
638　2 c. "The Institution of Corpus Domini" (Rubens)　　10　10
639　8 c. "The Destruction of Idolatry" (Rubens)　　20　20
MS640　114 × 86 mm. 50 c. "Grand Master Perellos with St. Jude and St. Simon" (unknown Maltese artist) (*vert*)　　80　1·60

254 Hal Saflieni Hypogeum, Paola　　**255** Dun Gorg Preca

1980 (15 Feb). *International Restoration of Maltese Monuments Campaign. T 254 and similar multicoloured designs. W 105 (sideways on 8 and 12 c.). P 14.*
641　2 c. 5, Type 254　　　　　　10　15
642　6 c. Vilhena Palace, Mdina　　25　20
643　8 c. Victoria Citadel, Gozo (*horiz*)　30　40
644　12 c. Fort St. Elmo, Valletta (*horiz*)　40　60
641/4　　　　　　　*Set of 4*　95　1·25

(Des R. Pitré)

1980 (12 Apr). *Birth Centenary of Dun Gorg Preca (founder of Society of Christian Doctrine). W 105 (sideways). P 14 × 13½.*
645　255　2 c. 5, black and grey　　　10　10

256 Ruzar Briffa (poet)　　**257** "Annunciation"

(Des V. Apap)

1980 (29 Apr). *Europa. Personalities. T 256 and similar horiz design. W 105 (sideways). P 13½ × 14.*
646　8 c. black, brown-ochre and bronze-green　　20　10
647　30 c. brown, brown-olive and brown-lake　　55　1·25
　Design:—30 c. Nikiol Anton Vassalli (scholar and patriot).
　Nos. 646/7 were each printed in sheets including two *se-tenant* stamp-size labels.

(Des R. Pitré)

1980 (7 Oct). *Christmas. Paintings by A. Inglott. T 257 and similar multicoloured designs. W 105 (sideways on 12 c.). P 14 (12 c.) or 13½ (others).*
648　2 c. + 5 m. Type 257　　　　　10　10
649　6 c. + 1 c. "Conception"　　　20　20
650　8 c. + 1 c. 5, "Nativity"　　　25　40
651　12 c. + 3 c. "Annunciation", "Conception" and "Nativity" (47 × 38 mm)　　30　70
648/51　　　　　　*Set of 4*　75　1·25
　The paintings from the 2, 6 and 8 c. values are united to form the triptych on the 12 c. value.

258 Rook and Pawn　　**259** Barn Owl (*Tyto alba*)

(Des H. Borg)

1980 (20 Nov). *24th Chess Olympiad and International Chess Federation Congress, Malta. T 258 and similar multicoloured designs. W 105 (sideways on 30 c.) P 14×13½ (30 c.) or 13½×14 (others).*
652　2 c. 5, Type 258　　　　　　25　20
653　8 c. Bishop and Pawn　　　　65　20
654　30 c. King, Queen and Pawn (*vert*)　1·00　1·50
652/4　　　　　　　*Set of 3*　1·75　1·75

(Des M. Burlò)

1981 (20 Jan). *Birds. T 259 and similar vert designs. Multicoloured. W 105 (sideways). P 13½.*
655　3 c. Type 259　　　　　　　30　25
656　8 c. Sardinian Warbler (*Sylvia melanocephala*)　　50　25
657　12 c. Woodchat Shrike (*Lanius senator*)　60　80
658　23 c. British Storm Petrel (*Hydrobates pelagicus*)　　1·10　1·75
655/8　　　　　　　*Set of 4*　2·25　2·75

260 Traditional Horse Race　　**261** Stylised "25"

(Des H. Borg)

1981 (28 Apr). *Europa. Folklore. T 260 and similar vert design. Multicoloured. W 105 (sideways). P 14.*
659　8 c. Type 260　　　　　　　20　10
660　30 c. Attempting to retrieve flag from end of "gostra" (greasy pole)　　40　65
　The two values were each printed in sheets including two *se-tenant* stamp-size labels.

(Des A. de Giovanni)

1981 (12 June). *25th Maltese International Trade Fair. W 105 (sideways). P 13½.*
661　261　4 c. multicoloured　　　15　15
662　25 c. multicoloured　　　50　60

OMNIBUS ISSUES

Details, together with prices for complete sets, of the various Omnibus issues from the 1935 Silver Jubilee series to date are included in a special section following Zimbabwe at the end of Volume 2.

262 Disabled Artist
at Work

263 Wheat Ear in
Conical Flask

(Des A. Camilleri)

1981 (17 July). *International Year for Disabled Persons.* T **262**
and similar vert design. Multicoloured. W **105** *(sideways).* P 13½.
663   3 c. Type **262** 20   10
664   35 c. Disabled child playing football .. 90   75

(Des R. Caruana)

1981 (16 Oct). *World Food Day.* W **105** *(sideways).* P 14.
665 **263**   8 c. multicoloured 15   15
666   23 c. multicoloured 60   50

264 Megalithic Building

265 Children and
Nativity Scene

(Des F. Portelli)

1981 (31 Oct). *History of Maltese Industry. Horiz designs as* T **264**.
Multicoloured. W **105**. P 14.
667   5 m. Type **264** 10   50
668   1 c. Cotton production 10   10
669   2 c. Early ship-building 70   10
670   3 c. Currency minting 30   10
671   5 c. "Art" 30   25
672   6 c. Fishing 90   25
673   7 c. Agriculture 30   90
674   8 c. Stone quarrying 45   35
675 -10 c. Grape pressing 35   50
676   12 c. Modern ship-building .. .. 1·50   1·50
677   15 c. Energy 70   1·25
678   20 c. Telecommunications 70   75
679   25 c. "Industry" 90   1·60
680   50 c. Drilling for water .. .. 2·00   2·50
681   £1 Sea transport .. .. 6·50   7·00
682   £3 Air transport .. .. 11·00 17·00
667/82 .. .. .. *Set of 16* 24·00 30·00

(Des A. Bugeja)

1981 (18 Nov). *Christmas.* T **265** *and similar multicoloured
designs.* W **105** *(sideways).* P 14.
683   2 c. + 1 c. Type **265** 20   10
684   8 c. + 2 c. Christmas Eve procession *(horiz)* .. 30   20
685   20 c. + 3 c. Preaching midnight sermon .. 55   75
683/5 .. .. *Set of 3* 95   95

266 Shipbuilding

267 Elderly Man and Has-Serh
(home for elderly)

(Des N. Attard)

1982 (29 Jan). *Shipbuilding Industry.* T **266** *and similar vert
designs showing different scenes.* W **105** *(sideways).* P 13½.
686   3 c. multicoloured 15   10
687   8 c. multicoloured 30   30
688   13 c. multicoloured 55   55
689   27 c. multicoloured .. .. 1·25   1·25
686/9 .. .. *Set of 4* 2·00   2·00

(Des R. Pitré)

1982 (16 Mar). *Care of Elderly.* T **267** *and similar horiz design.
Multicoloured.* W **105**. P 14 × 13½.
690   8 c. Type **267** 40   20
691   30 c. Elderly woman and Has-Zmien (hospital
for elderly) .. .. .. 1·40   1·40

268 Redemption of Islands by Maltese, 1428

(Des F. Portelli)

1982 (29 Apr). *Europa. Historical Events.* T **268** *and similar horiz
design. Multicoloured.* W **105**. P 14 × 13½.
692   8 c. Type **268** 40   20
693   30 c. Declaration of rights by Maltese, 1802 .. 1·00   1·40
Nos. 692/3 were each printed in sheets containing 2 *se-tenant*
stamp-size labels.

269 Stylised Footballer

(Des R. Caruana)

1982 (11 June). *World Cup Football Championship, Spain.* T **269**
and similar horiz designs showing stylised footballers. W **105**.
P 14.
694   3 c. multicoloured 20   10
695   12 c. multicoloured 60   55
696   15 c. multicoloured 70   65
694/6 .. .. *Set of 3* 1·40   1·25
MS697   125 × 90 mm. Nos. 694/6 .. .. 2·50   3·50

270 Angel appearing to Shepherds

(Des J. Mallia)

1982 (8 Oct). *Christmas.* T **270** *and similar multicoloured
designs.* W **105** *(sideways).* P 14 *(No. 700) or* 13½ *(others).*
698   2 c. + 1 c. Type **270** 15   15
699   8 c. + 2 c. Nativity and Three Wise Men
bearing gifts 50   50
700   20 c. + 3 c. Nativity scene *(larger 45 × 37 mm)* 1·00   1·00
698/700 .. .. .. *Set of 3* 1·50   1·50
The designs from the 2 and 8 c. values are united to form the
design of the 20 c. stamp.

271 Ta' Salvo Serafino
(oared brigantine), 1531

(Des N. Attard)

1982 (13 Nov). *Maltese Ships (1st series).* T **271** *and similar horiz
designs. Multicoloured.* W **105**. P 14 × 13½.
701   3 c. Type **271** 40   10
702   8 c. *La Madonna del Rosaria* (tartane),
1740 80   30
703   12 c. *San Paulo* (xebec), 1743 .. 1·25   55
704   20 c. *Ta' Pietro Saliba* (xprunara), 1798 .. 1·60   90
701/4 .. .. .. *Set of 4* 3·50   1·60
See also Nos. 725/8, 772/5, 792/5 and 809/12.

272 Locomotive *Manning Wardle,*
1883

(Des R. Caruana)

1983 (21 Jan). *Centenary of Malta Railway.* T **272** *and similar
horiz designs. Multicoloured.* W **105**. P 14 × 13½.
705   3 c. Type **272** 45   15
706   13 c. Locomotive *Black Hawthorn*, 1884 .. 1·00   1·00
707   27 c. Beyer Peacock locomotive, 1895 .. 2·00   3·25
705/7 .. .. *Set of 3* 3·00   4·00

273 Peace Doves leaving Malta

(Des C. Cassar)

1983 (14 Mar). *Commonwealth Day.* T **273** *and similar multicoloured designs.* W **105** *(sideways on vert designs).* P 14 × 13½
(8, 12 c.) or 13½ × 14 *(others).*
708   8 c. Type **273** 25   30
709   12 c. Tourist landmarks 40   60
710   15 c. Holiday beach *(vert)* 45   75
711   23 c. Ship-building *(vert)* 70   1·00
708/11 .. .. .. *Set of 4* 1·60   2·40

---

274 Ggantija Megalithic Temples, Gozo

(Des T. Bugeja (8 c.), R. Caruana (30 c.))

1983 (5 May). *Europa.* T **274** *and similar horiz design. Multicoloured.* W **105**. P 14 × 13½.
712   8 c. Type **274** 40   40
713   30 c. Fort St. Angelo .. .. 1·00   2·40
Nos. 712/13 were each printed in sheets including two *se-tenant*
stamp-size labels.

275 Dish Aerials (World
Communications Year)

(Des D. Friggieri)

1983 (14 July). *Anniversaries and Events.* T **275** *and similar horiz
designs. Multicoloured.* W **105** *(sideways).* P 13½ × 14.
714   3 c. Type **275** 45   15
715   7 c. Ships' prows and badge (25th anniv of
I.M.O. Convention) 70   55
716   13 c. Container lorries and badge (30th anniv
of Customs Co-operation Council) .. 90   90
717   20 c. Stadium and emblem (9th Mediterranean
Games) .. .. 1·00   2·25
714/17 .. .. .. *Set of 4* 2·75   3·50

276 Monsignor Giuseppe
de Piro

277 Annunciation

(Des E. Barthet)

1983 (1 Sept). *50th Death Anniv of Monsignor Giuseppe de Piro.*
W **105** *(sideways).* P 14.
718 **276**   3 c. multicoloured 15   15

(Des N. Attard)

1983 (6 Sept). *Christmas.* T **277** *and similar vert designs. Multicoloured.* W **105** *(sideways).* P 13½ × 14.
719   2 c. + 1 c. Type **277** 30   15
720   8 c. + 2 c. The Nativity 75   60
721   20 c. + 3 c. Adoration of the Magi .. 1·40   2·25
719/21 .. .. .. *Set of 3* 2·25   2·75

278 Workers at Meeting

(Des F. Portelli)

1983 (5 Oct). *40th Anniv of General Workers' Union.* T **278** *and
similar horiz designs. Multicoloured.* W **105**. P 14 × 13½.
722   3 c. Type **278** 25   10
723   8 c. Worker with family 50   40
724   27 c. Union H.Q. Building .. .. 1·50   1·75
722/4 .. .. *Set of 3* 2·00   2·00

(Des N. Attard)

1983 (17 Nov). *Maltese Ships (2nd series). Horiz designs as* T **271**.
Multicoloured. W **105**. P 14 × 13½.
725   2 c. *Strangier* (full-rigged ship), 1813 .. 30   25
726   12 c. *Tigre* (topsail schooner), 1839 .. 1·25   1·25
727   13 c. *La Speranza* (brig), 1844 .. 1·25   1·25
728   20 c. *Wignacourt* (barque), 1844 .. 1·75   2·75
725/8 .. .. .. *Set of 4* 4·00   5·00

279 Boeing 737

(Des R. Caruana)

1984 (26 Jan). *Air. T* **279** *and similar horiz designs. Multicoloured. W* 105. *P* 14 × 13½.
729	7 c.	Type **279**	..	50	30
730	8 c.	Boeing 720B	..	60	35
731	16 c.	Vickers 953 Vanguard	..	1·25	70
732	23 c.	Vickers Viscount 700	..	1·50	70
733	27 c.	Douglas DC-3	..	1·75	80
734	38 c.	Armstrong Whitworth A.W.15 Atalanta *Artemis*		2·25	2·75
735	75 c.	Marina Fiat MF.5 flying boat		3·25	5·00
729/35			Set of 7	10·00	9·50

280 C.E.P.T. 25th Anniversary Logo   281 Early Policeman

(Des J. Larrivière and L. Borg)

1984 (27 Apr). *Europa. W* 105. *P* 13½.
736	**280**	8 c. green, black and gold	..	35	35
737		30 c. carmine-lake, black and gold		1·25	1·25

Nos. 736/7 were each printed in sheets including two *se-tenant* stamp-size labels.

(Des T. Bugeja)

1984 (14 June). *170th Anniv of Malta Police Force. T* **281** *and similar vert designs. Multicoloured. W* 105. *P* 14 × 13½.
738	3 c.	Type **281**	..	65	15
739	8 c.	Mounted police	..	1·50	65
		a. Pale Venetian red (background) omitted		£110	
740	11 c.	Motorcycle policeman	..	1·75	2·00
741	25 c.	Policeman and fireman	..	2·75	3·75
738/41			Set of 4	6·00	6·00

282 Running   283 "The Visitation" (Pietru Caruana)

(Des L. Micallef)

1984 (26 July). *Olympic Games, Los Angeles. T* **282** *and similar vert designs. Multicoloured. W* 105 *(sideways). P* 14.
742	7 c.	Type **282**	..	25	30
743	12 c.	Gymnastics	..	50	70
744	23 c.	Swimming	..	85	1·25
742/4			Set of 3	1·50	2·00

(Des L. Micallef)

1984 (5 Oct). *Christmas. Paintings from Church of Our Lady of Porto Salvo, Valletta. T* **283** *and similar multicoloured designs. W* 105 *(sideways on horiz designs). P* 14.
745	2 c. + 1 c.	Type **283**	55	55
746	8 c. + 2 c.	"The Epiphany" (Rafel Caruana) (*horiz*)	1·00	1·25
747	20 c. + 3 c.	"Jesus among the Doctors" (Rafel Caruana) (*horiz*)	2·00	3·75
745/7		Set of 3	3·25	5·00

284 Dove on Map   285 1885 ½d. Green Stamp

(Des L. Micallef)

1984 (12 Dec). *10th Anniv of Republic. T* **284** *and similar vert designs. Multicoloured. W* 105 *(sideways). P* 14.
748	3 c.	Type **284**	40	20
749	8 c.	Fort St. Angelo	75	65
750	30 c.	Hands	2·50	4·75
748/50		Set of 3	3·25	5·00

(Des N. Attard)

286 Boy, and Hands planting Vine

1985 (2 Jan). *Centenary of Malta Post Office. T* **285** *and similar vert designs showing stamps of 1885. Multicoloured. W* 105. *P* 14.
751	3 c.	Type **285**	..	45	15
752	8 c.	1885 1d. rose	..	65	45
753	12 c.	1885 2½d. dull blue		90	1·40
754	20 c.	1885 4d. brown	..	1·40	3·00
751/4			Set of 4	3·00	4·50
MS755	165 × 90 mm. Nos. 751/4. Wmk sideways			3·25	5·00

(Des T. Bugeja)

1985 (7 Mar). *International Youth Year. T* **286** *and similar multicoloured designs. W* 105 *(sideways on* 13 *c.). P* 14.
756	2 c.	Type **286**	..	15	15
757	13 c.	Young people and flowers (*vert*)		85	60
758	27 c.	Girl holding flame in hand	..	1·75	1·40
756/8			Set of 3	2·50	1·90

287 Nicolo Baldacchino (tenor)   288 Guzeppi Bajada and Manwel Attard (victims)

(Des L. Micallef)

1985 (25 Apr). *Europa. European Music Year. T* **287** *and similar vert design. Multicoloured. W* 105. *P* 14.
759	8 c.	Type **287**	2·00	50
760	30 c.	Francesco Azopardi (composer)	3·50	5·00

Nos. 759/60 were each printed in sheets including two *se-tenant* stamp-size labels.

(Des L. Micallef)

1985 (7 June). *66th Anniv of 7 June 1919 Demonstrations. T* **288** *and similar multicoloured designs. W* 105 *(sideways on* 3 *c.,* 7 *c.). P* 14.
761	3 c.	Type **288**	35	15
762	7 c.	Karmnu Abela and Wenzu Dyer (victims)	75	40
763	35 c.	Model of projected Demonstration monument by Anton Agius (*vert*)	2·50	2·75
761/3		Set of 3	3·25	3·00

289 Stylized Birds   290 Giorgio Mitrovich (nationalist) (Death Centenary)

(Des D. Friggieri)

1985 (26 July). *40th Anniv of United Nations Organization. T* **289** *and similar horiz designs. Multicoloured. W* 105 *(sideways). P* 13½ × 14.
764	4 c.	Type **289**	25	15
765	11 c.	Arrow-headed ribbons	85	1·25
766	31 c.	Stylized figures	2·00	3·25
764/6		Set of 3	2·75	4·25

(Des R. Pitre)

1985 (3 Oct). *Celebrities' Anniversaries. T* **290** *and similar vert design. Multicoloured. W* 105 *(sideways). P* 14.
767	8 c.	Type **290**	80	35
768	12 c.	Pietru Caxaru (poet and administrator) (400th death anniv)	1·60	2·50

COVER PRICES

Cover factors are quoted at the beginning of each country for most issues to 1945. An explanation of the system can be found on page x. The factors quoted do not, however, apply to philatelic covers.

---

291 The Three Wise Men   292 John XXIII Peace Laboratory and Statue of St. Francis of Assisi

(Des G. Bonnici)

1985 (10 Oct). *Christmas. T* **291** *and similar vert designs showing details of terracotta relief by Ganni Bonnici. Multicoloured. W* 105 *(sideways). P* 14.
769	2 c. + 1 c.	Type **291**	55	75
770	8 c. + 2 c.	Virgin and Child	1·25	1·75
771	20 c. + 3 c.	Angels	2·50	4·00
769/71		Set of 3	3·75	6·00

(Des N. Attard)

1985 (27 Nov). *Maltese Ships (3rd series). Steamships. Horiz designs as T* **271**. *Multicoloured. W* 105. *P* 14.
772	3 c.	*Scotia* (paddle-steamer), 1844	..	75	20
773	7 c.	*Tagliaferro* (screw steamer), 1882	..	1·40	1·00
774	15 c.	*Gleneagles* (screw steamer), 1885	..	2·00	3·25
775	23 c.	*L'Isle Adam* (screw steamer), 1886	..	2·75	4·00
772/5			Set of 4	6·25	7·50

(Des A. Agius (8 c.), T. Bugeja (11, 27 c.))

1986 (28 Jan). *International Peace Year. T* **292** *and similar horiz designs. Multicoloured. W* 105 *(sideways). P* 14 (8, 27 *c.) or* 13½ × 14 (11 *c.).*
776	8 c.	Type **292**	..	1·25	50
777	11 c.	Dove and hands holding olive branch (40 × 19 *mm*)	..	1·50	2·50
778	27 c.	Map of Africa, dove and two heads	..	3·25	4·75
776/8			Set of 3	5·50	7·00

293 Symbolic Plant and *Cynthia cardui, Vanessa atalanta* and *Polyommatus icarus* (butterflies)   294 Heading the Ball

(Des M. Burló)

1986 (3 Apr). *Europa. Environmental Conservation. T* **293** *and similar vert design. Multicoloured. W* 105. *P* 14.
779	8 c.	Type **293**	1·75	50
780	35 c.	Island, Neolithic frieze, sea and sun	3·25	6·00

Nos. 779/80 were each printed in sheets including two *se-tenant* stamp-size labels.

(Des T. Bugeja)

1986 (30 May). *World Cup Football Championship, Mexico. T* **294** *and similar horiz designs. Multicoloured. W* 105. *P* 14.
781	3 c.	Type **294**	..	60	20
782	7 c.	Saving a goal	..	1·25	1·00
783	23 c.	Controlling the ball	..	4·00	6·50
781/3			Set of 3	5·25	7·00
MS784	125 × 90 mm. Nos. 781/3. Wmk sideways			7·00	8·50

295 Father Diegu   296 "Nativity"

(Des L. Micallef)

1986 (28 Aug). *Maltese Philanthropists. T* **295** *and similar vert designs. Multicoloured. W* 105. *P* 14.
785	2 c.	Type **295**	..	40	30
786	3 c.	Adelaide Cini	..	50	30
787	8 c.	Alfonso Maria Galea	..	1·25	60
788	27 c.	Vincenzo Bugeja	..	3·25	6·00
785/8			Set of 4	5·00	6·50

(Des L. Micallef)

1986 (10 Oct). *Christmas. T* **296** *and similar multicoloured designs showing paintings by Giuseppe D'Arena. W* **105** *(sideways on horiz designs). P* 14.

789	2 c. + 1 c. Type **296** ..	90	1·00
790	8 c. + 2 c. "Nativity" (detail) (*vert*) ..	2·50	3·00
791	20 c. + 3 c. "Epiphany" ..	3·75	5·50
789/91	*Set of 3*	6·50	8·50

(Des N. Attard)

1986 (19 Nov). *Maltese Ships (4th series). Horiz designs as T* **271**. *Multicoloured. W* **105**. *P* 14.

792	7 c. *San Paul* (freighter), 1921 ..	1·25	50
793	10 c. *Knight of Malta* (mail steamer), 1930	1·50	1·75
794	12 c. *Valetta City* (freighter), 1948 ..	1·75	2·75
795	20 c. *Saver* (freighter), 1959 ..	3·00	4·50
792/5	*Set of 4*	6·75	8·50

297 European Robin

(Des R. Caruana)

1987 (26 Jan). *25th Anniv of Malta Ornithological Society. T* **297** *and similar multicoloured designs. W* **105** *(sideways on 3, 23 c.). P* 14.

796	3 c. Type **297**. ..	1·00	50
797	8 c. Peregrine Falcon (*vert*)..	2·25	1·00
798	13 c. Hoopoe (*vert*) ..	3·00	4·00
799	23 c. Cory's Shearwater ..	3·50	6·00
796/9	*Set of 4*	8·75	10·50

298 Aquasun Lido   299 16th-century Pikeman

(Des R. England)

1987 (15 Apr). *Europa. Modern Architecture. T* **298** *and similar vert design. Multicoloured. W* **105**. *P* 14.

800	8 c. Type **298**. ..	1·25	75
801	35 c. Church of St. Joseph, Manikata ..	3·50	6·25

Nos. 800/1 were each printed in sheets including two *se-tenant* stamp-size labels.

(Des L. Micallef)

1987 (10 June). *Maltese Uniforms (1st series). T* **299** *and similar vert designs. Multicoloured. W* **105** *(sideways). P* 14.

802	3 c. Type **299**. ..	65	40
803	7 c. 16th-century officer ..	1·25	90
804	10 c. 18th-century standard bearer ..	1·50	2·25
805	27 c. 18th-century General of the Galleys ..	3·25	4·75
802/5	*Set of 4*	6·00	7·50

See also Nos. 832/5, 851/4, 880/3 and 893/6.

300 Maltese Scenes, Wheat Ears and Sun
(European Environment Year)

(Des A. Camilleri)

1987 (18 Aug). *Anniversaries and Events. T* **300** *and similar horiz designs. Multicoloured. W* **105** *(sideways). P* 14.

806	5 c. Type **300**. ..	1·00	50
807	8 c. Esperanto star as comet (Centenary of Esperanto) ..	1·25	60
808	23 c. Family at house door (International Year of Shelter for the Homeless) ..	3·00	3·00
806/8	*Set of 3*	4·75	3·75

(Des N. Attard)

1987 (16 Oct). *Maltese Ships (5th series). Horiz designs as T* **271**. *Multicoloured. W* **105**. *P* 14.

809	2 c. *Medina* (freighter), 1969 ..	60	60
810	11 c. *Rabat* (container ship), 1974 ..	2·25	2·50
811	13 c. *Ghawdex* (passenger ferry), 1979 ..	2·50	2·75
812	20 c. *Pinto* (car ferry), 1987 ..	3·50	4·00
809/12	*Set of 4*	8·00	9·00

301 "The Visitation"

(Des R. Caruana)

1987 (6 Nov). *Christmas. T* **301** *and similar horiz designs, each showing illuminated illustration, score and text from 16th-century choral manuscript. Multicoloured. W* **105** *(sideways). P* 14.

813	2 c. + 1 c. Type **301** ..	50	50
814	8 c. + 2 c. "The Nativity" ..	2·00	2·75
815	20 c. + 3 c. "The Adoration of the Magi" ..	3·25	4·50
813/15	*Set of 3*	5·25	7·00

302 Dr. Arvid Pardo   303 Ven. Nazju Falzon
(U.N. representative)   (Catholic catechist)

(Des S. Mallia)

1987 (18 Dec). *20th Anniv of United Nations Resolution on Peaceful Use of the Seabed. T* **302** *and similar vert design. Multicoloured. W* **105**. *P* 14.

816	8 c. Type **302**. ..	1·00	75
817	12 c. U.N. emblem and sea ..	1·75	3·00
MS818	125×90 mm. Nos. 816/17. Wmk sideways. P 13×13½ ..	3·00	3·75

(Des E. Barthet)

1988 (23 Jan). *Maltese Personalities. T* **303** *and similar vert designs. Multicoloured. W* **105**. *P* 14.

819	2 c. Type **303** ..	25	30
820	3 c. Mgr. Sidor Formosa (philanthropist) ..	25	30
821	4 c. Sir Luigi Preziosi (ophthalmologist) ..	40	30
822	10 c. Fr. Anastasju Cuschieri (poet) ..	80	85
823	25 c. Mgr. Pietru Pawl Saydon (Bible translator) ..	2·25	3·25
819/23	*Set of 5*	3·50	4·50

304 "St. John Bosco   305 Bus, Ferry
with Youth" (statue)   and Airliner
(Death Centenary)

(Des F. Portelli)

1988 (5 Mar). *Religious Anniversaries. T* **304** *and similar vert designs. Multicoloured. W* **105** *(sideways). P* 14.

824	10 c. Type **304** ..	1·00	1·00
825	12 c. "Assumption of Our Lady" (altarpiece by Perugino, Ta' Pinu, Gozo) (Marian Year) ..	1·25	1·50
826	14 c. "Christ the King" (statue by Sciortino) (75th anniv of International Eucharistic Congress, Valletta) ..	1·75	2·50
824/6	*Set of 3*	3·50	4·50

(Des F. Fenech)

1988 (9 Apr). *Europa. Transport and Communications. T* **305** *and similar vert design. Multicoloured. W* **105** *(sideways). P* 13½.

827	10 c. Type **305** ..	1·25	75
828	35 c. Control panel, dish aerial and pylons	2·75	4·50

Nos. 827/8 were each printed in sheets including two *se-tenant* stamp-size labels.

NEW INFORMATION

The editor is always interested to correspond with people who have new information that will improve or correct the Catalogue.

306 Globe and Red Cross   307 Athletics
Emblems (125th anniv of
International Red Cross)

(Des M. Cremona)

1988 (28 May). *Anniversaries and Events. T* **306** *and similar horiz designs. Multicoloured. W* **105**. *P* 13½.

829	4 c. Type **306** ..	40	50
830	18 c. Divided globe (Campaign for North-South Interdependence and Solidarity) ..	1·75	2·50
831	19 c. Globe and symbol (40th anniv of World Health Organization) ..	1·75	2·50
829/31	*Set of 3*	3·50	5·00

(Des L. Micallef)

1988 (23 July). *Maltese Uniforms (2nd issue). Vert designs as T* **299**. *Multicoloured. W* **105** *(sideways). P* 14.

832	3 c. Private, Maltese Light Infantry, 1800	30	30
833	4 c. Gunner, Malta Coast Artillery, 1802 ..	35	35
834	10 c. Field Officer, 1st Maltese Provincial Battalion, 1805 ..	85	1·25
835	25 c. Subaltern, Royal Malta Regiment, 1809 ..	2·25	4·25
832/5	*Set of 4*	3·25	5·50

(Des R. Gauci)

1988 (17 Sept). *Olympic Games, Seoul. T* **307** *and similar vert designs. Multicoloured. W* **105** *(sideways). P* 14×13½.

836	4 c. Type **307** ..	30	30
837	10 c. Diving ..	70	1·00
838	35 c. Basketball ..	2·00	3·25
836/8	*Set of 3*	2·75	4·00

308 Shepherd with   309 Commonwealth
Flock   Emblem

(Des R. Gauci)

1988 (5 Nov). *Christmas. T* **308** *and similar vert designs. Multicoloured. W* **105**. *P* 14.

839	3 c. + 1 c. Type **308** ..	30	30
840	10 c. + 2 c. The Nativity ..	70	1·25
841	25 c. + 3 c. Three Wise Men ..	1·75	2·75
839/41	*Set of 3*	2·50	3·75

(Des F. Portelli)

1989 (28 Jan). *25th Anniv of Independence. T* **309** *and similar multicoloured designs. W* **105** *(sideways). P* 14 (25 c.) or 13½ (others).

842	2 c. Type **309** ..	25	35
843	3 c. Council of Europe flag ..	25	35
844	4 c. U. N. flag ..	30	35
845	10 c. Workers hands gripping ring and national flag ..	75	95
846	12 c. Scales and allegorical figure of Justice	90	1·40
847	25 c. Prime Minister Borg Olivier with Independence constitution (42 × 28 mm) ..	1·90	3·25
842/7	*Set of 6*	4·00	6·00

310 New State Arms   311 Two Boys
flying Kite

(Des F. Portelli)

1989 (25 Mar). *W* **105**. *P* 14.

848	**310** £1 multicoloured ..	4·00	4·50

(Des R. Gauci)

1989 (6 May). *Europa. Children's Games. T* **311** *and similar vert design. Multicoloured. W* **105** *(sideways). P* 13½.

849	10 c. Type **311** ..	1·25	75
850	35 c. Two girls with dolls ..	3·25	4·50

Nos. 849/50 were each printed in sheets including two *se-tenant* stamp-size labels.

(Des L. Micallef)

1989 (24 June). *Maltese Uniforms (3rd series). Vert designs as T* **299.** *Multicoloured.* W **105** *(sideways).* P 14.

851	3 c.	Officer, Maltese Veterans, 1815	45	45
852	4 c.	Subaltern, Royal Malta Fencibles, 1839	50	50
853	10 c.	Private, Malta Militia, 1856	1·50	1·50
854	25 c.	Colonel, Royal Malta Fencible Artillery, 1875	2·75	3·75
851/4		Set of 4	4·75	5·50

312 Human Figures and Buildings

313 Angel and Cherub

(Des L. Casha)

1989 (17 Oct). *Anniversaries and Commemorations. T* **312** *and similar horiz designs showing logo and stylized human figures. Multicoloured.* W **105** *(sideways).* P 14.

855	3 c.	Type **312** (20th anniv of U.N. Declaration on Social Progress and Development)	30	30
856	4 c.	Workers and figure in wheelchair (Malta's Ratification of European Social Charter)	35	35
857	10 c.	Family (40th anniv of Council of Europe)	80	1·25
858	14 c.	Teacher and children (70th anniv of Malta Union of Teachers)	1·00	1·75
859	25 c.	Symbolic knights (Knights of the Sovereign Military Order of Malta Assembly)	2·25	3·50
855/9		Set of 5	4·25	6·50

(Des J. Mallia)

1989 (11 Nov). *Christmas. T* **313** *and similar horiz designs showing vault paintings by Mattia Preti from St. John's Co-Cathedral, Valletta. Multicoloured.* W **105.** P 13½.

860	3 c.	+ 1 c. Type **313**	60	50
861	10 c.	+ 2 c. Two angels	1·50	1·75
862	20 c.	+ 3 c. Angel blowing trumpet	2·00	3·25
860/2		Set of 3	3·50	5·00

314 Presidents Bush and Gorbachev

315 General Post Office, Auberge d'Italie, Valletta

1989 (2 Dec). *U.S.A.–U.S.S.R. Summit Meeting, Malta.* W **105.** P 14.

863	**314** 10 c. multicoloured		1·00	1·25

(Des R. Caruana)

1990 (9 Feb). *Europa. Post Office Buildings. T* **315** *and similar multicoloured design.* W **105** *(sideways on 10 c.).* P 14.

864	10 c.	Type **315**	75	50
865	35 c.	Branch Post Office, Zebbug (horiz)	2·25	3·50

Nos. 864/5 were each printed in sheets including two se-tenant stamp-size labels.

316 Open Book and Letters from Different Alphabets (International Literacy Year)

317 Samuel Taylor Coleridge (poet) and Government House

(Des T. Bugeja)

1990 (7 Apr). *Anniversaries and Events. T* **316** *and similar multicoloured designs.* W **105** *(sideways on 4, 19 c.).* P 14.

866	3 c.	Type **316**	25	25
867	4 c.	Count Roger of Sicily and Norman soldiers (900th anniv of Sicilian rule) (horiz)	45	30
868	19 c.	Communications satellite (25th anniv of International Telecommunication Union membership) (horiz)	1·75	2·50
869	20 c.	Football and map of Malta (Union of European Football Associations 20th Ordinary Congress, Malta)	1·75	2·50
866/9		Set of 4	3·75	5·00

(Des A. Grech)

1990 (3 May). *British Authors. T* **317** *and similar horiz designs. Multicoloured.* W **105** *(sideways).* P 13½.

870	4 c.	Type **317**	35	30
871	10 c.	Lord Byron (poet) and map of Valletta	70	70
872	12 c.	Sir Walter Scott (novelist) and Great Siege	80	95
873	25 c.	William Makepeace Thackeray (novelist) and Naval Arsenal	1·50	2·25
870/3		Set of 4	3·00	3·75

318 St. Paul

319 Flags and Football

(Des N. Bason)

1990 (25 May). *Visit of Pope John Paul II. T* **318** *and similar vert design showing bronze bas-reliefs.* W **105** *(sideways).* P 14.

874	4 c.	brownish black, flesh and carmine	50	1·50
	a.	Pair. Nos. 874/5	2·00	3·25
875	25 c.	brownish black, flesh and carmine	1·50	1·75

Design:—25 c. Pope John Paul II.

Nos. 874/5 were printed together in a sheet of 12 (4×3) containing 10 stamps, se-tenant horizontally or vertically, and two stamp-size labels on R. 2/1 and 2/4.

(Des T. Bugeja)

1990 (8 June). *World Cup Football Championship, Italy. T* **319** *and similar horiz designs. Multicoloured.* W **105.** P 14.

876	5 c.	Type **319**	35	30
877	10 c.	Football in net	65	1·00
878	14 c.	Scoreboard and football	1·00	1·75
876/8		Set of 3	1·75	2·75
MS879	123×90 mm. Nos. 876/8. Wmk sideways		2·75	3·50

(Des L. Micallef)

1990 (25 Aug). *Maltese Uniforms (4th series). Vert designs as T* **299.** *Multicoloured.* W **105** *(sideways).* P 14.

880	3 c.	Captain, Royal Malta Militia, 1889	65	55
881	4 c.	Field officer, Royal Malta Artillery, 1905	70	60
882	10 c.	Labourer, Malta Labour Corps, 1915	1·75	1·50
883	25 c.	Lieutenant, King's Own Malta Regiment of Militia, 1918	2·75	3·00
880/3		Set of 4	5·25	5·00

320 Innkeeper

321 1919 10s. Stamp under Magnifying Glass

(Des J. Smith)

1990 (10 Nov). *Christmas. Figures from Crib by Austin Galea, Marco Bartolo and Rosario Zammit. T* **320** *and similar multicoloured designs.* W **105** *(sideways).* P 14×14½ (10 c.) or 13½×14 (others).

884	3 c.	+ 1 c. Type **320**	30	40
885	10 c.	+ 2 c. Nativity (41×28 mm)	70	1·25
886	25 c.	+ 3 c. Shepherd with sheep	1·60	2·25
884/6		Set of 3	2·40	3·50

(Des J. Mallia)

1991 (6 Mar). *25th Anniv of Philatelic Society of Malta.* W **105** *(sideways).* P 14.

887	**321** 10 c. multicoloured		60	70

322 "Eurostar" Satellite and V.D.U. Screen

323 St. Ignatius Loyola (founder of Jesuits) (500th birth anniv)

(Des R. Caruana)

1991 (16 Mar). *Europa. Europe in Space. T* **322** *and similar vert design. Multicoloured.* W **105** *(sideways).* P 14.

888	10 c.	Type **322**	1·00	70
889	35 c.	"Ariane 4" rocket and projected HOTOL aerospaceplane	2·00	2·75

Nos. 888/9 were each printed in sheets including two se-tenant stamp-size labels.

(Des J. Mallia)

1991 (29 Apr). *Religious Commemorations. T* **323** *and similar multicoloured designs.* W **105** *(sideways on 3, 30 c.).* P 14.

890	3 c.	Type **323**	30	20
891	4 c.	Abbess Venerable Maria Adeodata Pisani (185th birth anniv) (vert)	35	25
892	30 c.	St. John of the Cross (400th death anniv)	2·00	2·25
890/2		Set of 3	2·40	2·40

(Des L. Micallef)

1991 (13 Aug). *Maltese Uniforms (5th series). Vert designs as T* **299.** *Multicoloured.* W **105** *(sideways).* P 14.

893	3 c.	Officer with colour, Royal Malta Fencibles, 1860	30	25
894	10 c.	Officer with colour, Royal Malta Regiment of Militia, 1903	70	60
895	19 c.	Officer with Queen's colour, King's Own Malta Regiment, 1968	1·40	1·75
896	25 c.	Officer with colour, Malta Armed Forces, 1991	1·75	2·00
893/6		Set of 4	3·75	4·25

324 Interlocking Arrows

325 Honey Buzzard

(Des N. Attard)

1991 (23 Sept). *25th Anniv of Union Haddiema Maghqudin (public services union).* W **105** *(sideways).* P 13½.

897	**324** 4 c. multicoloured		30	30

(Des H. Borg)

1991 (3 Oct). *Endangered Species. Birds. T* **325** *and similar vert designs. Multicoloured.* W **105.** P 14.

898	4 c.	Type **325**	1·75	2·00
	a.	Horiz strip of 4. Nos. 898/901	6·00	
899	4 c.	Marsh Harrier	1·75	2·00
900	10 c.	Eleonora's Falcon	1·75	2·00
901	10 c.	Lesser Kestrel	1·75	2·00
898/901		Set of 4	6·00	7·00

Nos. 898/901 were printed together, se-tenant, in horizontal strips of 4 throughout the sheet.

326 Three Wise Men

327 Ta' Hagrat Neolithic Temple

(Des H. Borg)

1991 (6 Nov). *Christmas. T* **326** *and similar vert designs. Multicoloured.* W **105.** P 14.

902	3 c.	+ 1 c. Type **326**	30	30
903	10 c.	+ 2 c. Holy Family	75	90
904	25 c.	+ 3 c. Two shepherds	1·50	2·50
902/4		Set of 3	2·25	3·25

(Des F. Portelli)

1991 (9 Dec). *National Heritage of the Maltese Islands. T* **327** *and similar multicoloured designs.* W **105** *(sideways on £2).* P 13½.

905	1 c.	Type **327**	15	10
906	2 c.	Cottoner Gate	20	10
907	3 c.	St. Michael's Bastion, Valletta	20	10
908	4 c.	Spinola Palace, St. Julian's	30	20
909	5 c.	Birkirkara Church	30	20
910	10 c.	Mellieha Bay	50	35
911	12 c.	Wied iz-Zurrieq	65	45
912	14 c.	Mgarr harbour, Gozo	75	50
913	20 c.	Yacht marina	1·25	65
914	50 c.	Gozo Channel	2·25	1·60
915	£1	"Arab Horses" (sculpture by Antonio Sciortino)	3·75	3·50
916	£2	Independence Monument (Ganni Bonnici) (vert)	7·00	7·00
905/16		Set of 12	15·00	14·00

MINIMUM PRICE

The minimum price quote is 10p which represents a handling charge rather than a basis for valuing common stamps. For further notes about prices see introductory pages.

328 Aircraft Tailfins and Terminal

(Des. H. Borg)

1992 (8 Feb). *Opening of International Air Terminal. T 328 and similar horiz design. W 105 (sideways). P 14.*
917   4 c. Type 328 .. .. .. 45 30
918   10 c. National flags and terminal 65 65

329 Ships of Columbus   **330** George Cross and Anti-aircraft Gun Crew

(Des H. Borg)

1992 (20 Feb). *Europa. 500th Anniv of Discovery of America by Columbus. T 329 and similar horiz design. W 105 (sideways). P 14.*
919   10 c. Type 329 .. .. .. 75 55
920   35 c. Columbus and map of Americas .. 2·00 2·25
Nos. 919/20 were each printed in sheets including two se-tenant stamp-size labels.

(Des H. Borg)

1992 (15 Apr). *50th Anniv of Award of George Cross to Malta. T 330 and similar vert designs. Multicoloured. W 105. P 14.*
921   4 c. Type 330 .. .. .. 65 30
922   10 c. George Cross and memorial bell .. 1·25 1·00
923   50 c. Tanker *Ohio* entering Grand Harbour 5·00 6·50
921/3   .. .. *Set of 3* 6·25 7·00

331 Running   **332** Church of the Flight into Egypt

(Des H. Borg)

1992 (24 June). *Olympic Games, Barcelona. T 331 and similar horiz designs. Multicoloured. W 105 (sideways). P 14.*
924   3 c. Type 331 .. .. .. 45 20
925   10 c. High jumping 95 80
926   30 c. Swimming .. .. 2·25 3·75
924/6   .. .. *Set of 3* 3·25 4·25

(Des N. Attard)

1992 (5 Aug). *Rehabilitation of Historical Buildings. T 332 and similar designs. W 105 (sideways on 4, 25 c.). P 14.*
927   3 c. black, pale stone and bluish grey .. 30 20
928   4 c. black, pale stone and flesh .. 35 20
929   19 c. black, pale stone and pale rose-lilac .. 1·75 2·25
930   25 c. black, pale stone and pale grey-olive 2·00 2·25
927/30   .. .. *Set of 4* 4·00 4·50
Designs: *Horiz*—4 c. St. John's Co-Cathedral; 25 c. Auberge de Provence. *Vert*—19 c. Church of Madonna del Pillar.

333 "The Nativity" (Giuseppe Cali)   **334** Malta College Building, Valletta

(Des L. Buttigieg)

1992 (22 Oct). *Christmas. Religious Paintings by Giuseppe Cali from Mosta Church. T 333 and similar horiz designs. Multicoloured. W 105 (sideways). P 14.*
931   3 c. + 1 c. Type 333 .. .. 60 60
932   10 c. + 2 c. "Adoration of the Magi" .. 1·50 1·50
933   25 c. + 3 c. "Christ with the Elders in the Temple" .. .. 2·75 3·75
931/3   .. .. *Set of 3* 4·25 5·25

(Des L. Buttigieg)

1992 (12 Nov). *400th Anniv of University of Malta. T 334 and similar multicoloured design. W 105 (sideways on 30 c.). P 14.*
934   4 c. Type 334 .. .. .. 50 25
935   30 c. Modern University complex, Tal-Qroqq (*horiz*) .. .. 2·25 3·25

335 Lions Club Emblem   **336** Untitled Painting by Paul Carbonaro

(Des H. Borg)

1993 (4 Feb). *75th Anniv of International Association of Lions Club. T 335 and similar horiz design. Multicoloured. W 105. P 13½.*
936   4 c. Type 335 .. .. 50 25
937   50 c. Eye (Sight First Campaign) .. 2·75 3·50

1993 (7 Apr). *Europa. Contemporary Art. T 336 and similar multicoloured design. W 105 (sideways on 35 c.). P 14.*
938   10 c. Type 336 .. .. 1·00 50
939   35 c. Untitled painting by Alfred Chircop (*horiz*) .. .. 2·50 4·00
Nos. 938/9 were each printed in sheets including two stamp-size labels.

337 Mascot holding Flame   **338** Learning First Aid

(Des R. Caruana)

1993 (4 May). *5th Small States of Europe Games. T 337 and similar horiz designs. Multicoloured. W 105. P 13½×14.*
940   3 c. Type 337 .. .. 20 20
941   4 c. Cycling 60 30
942   10 c. Tennis .. .. 1·25 1·00
943   35 c. Yachting .. .. 2·50 3·50
940/3   .. .. *Set of 4* 4·00 4·50
MS944   120×80 mm. Nos. 940/3. Wmk sideways 3·50 4·00

(Des L. Micallef)

1993 (21 July). *50th Anniv of Award of Bronze Cross to Maltese Scouts and Guides. T 338 and similar vert designs. Multicoloured. W 105. P 14.*
945   3 c. Type 338 .. .. 30 15
946   4 c. Bronze Cross 30 20
947   10 c. Scout building camp fire .. 80 80
948   35 c. Governor Lord Gort presenting Bronze Cross, 1943 .. .. 2·25 3·25
945/8   .. .. *Set of 4* 3·25 4·00

339 *Papilio machaon*   **340** G.W.U. Badge and Interlocking "50"

(Des M. Burlo)

1993 (23 Sept). *European Year of the Elderly. Butterflies. T 339 and similar vert design. Multicoloured. W 105. P 14.*
949   5 c. Type 339 .. .. 35 20
950   35 c. *Vanessa atalanta* .. .. 1·75 2·25

(Des H. Borg)

1993 (5 Oct). *50th Anniv of General Workers Union. W 105 (sideways). P 13½.*
951 340   4 c. multicoloured 35 40

341 Child Jesus and Star

(Des H. Borg)

1993 (5 Nov). *Christmas. T 341 and similar vert designs. Multicoloured. W 105. P 14.*
952   3 c. + 1 c. Type 341 .. .. 30 30
953   10 c. + 2 c. Christmas tree 85 95
954   25 c. + 3 c. Star in traditional window 1·60 2·25
952/4   .. .. *Set of 3* 2·50 3·25

342 Council Arms (face value top left)

(Des J. Mizzi)

1993 (20 Nov). *Inauguration of Local Community Councils. Sheet 110×93 mm. containing T 342 and similar horiz designs showing different Council Arms. Multicoloured. W 105 (sideways). P 14.*
MS955   5 c. Type 342; 5 c. Face value top right; 5 c. Face value bottom left; 5 c. Face value bottom right .. .. .. 1·50 2·25

343 Symbolic Tooth and Probe   **344** Sir Themistocles Zammit (discoverer of Brucella microbe)

(Des F. Ancilleri)

1994 (12 Feb). *50th Anniv of Maltese Dental Association. T 343 and similar vert design. Multicoloured. W 105. P 14.*
956   5 c. Type 343 .. .. 35 30
957   44 c. Symbolic mouth and dental mirror .. 3·00 3·00

(Des H. Borg)

1994 (29 Mar). *Europa. Discoveries. T 344 and similar vert design. Multicoloured. W 105. P 14.*
958   14 c. Type 344 .. .. 50 30
959   30 c. Bi-lingually inscribed candelabrum of 2nd century B.C. (deciphering of ancient Phoenician language) .. 1·90 3·00
Nos. 958/9 were each printed in sheets including two se-tenant stamp-size labels.

345 Family in Silhouette (International Year of the Family)   **346** Football and Map

(Des F. Ancilleri)

1994 (10 May). *Anniversaries and Events. T* **345** *and similar multicoloured designs. W* **105** *(sideways on 25 c.). P* 14.
960	5 c.	Type **345**	30	20
961	9 c.	Stylised Red Cross (International Recognition of Malta Red Cross Society)	60	50
962	14 c.	Animals and crops (150th anniv of Agrarian Society)	90	80
963	20 c.	Worker in silhouette (75th anniv of International Labour Organization)	1·25	1·60
964	25 c.	St. Paul's Anglican Cathedral (155th anniv) (*vert*)	1·40	1·75
960/4		*Set of 5*	4·00	4·25

(Des F. Ancilleri)

1994 (9 June). *World Cup Football Championship, U.S.A. T* **346** *and similar horiz designs. Multicoloured. W* **105**. *P* 14.
965	5 c.	Type **346**	40	20
966	14 c.	Ball and goal	1·00	80
967	30 c.	Ball and pitch superimposed on map	2·50	3·00
965/7		*Set of 3*	3·50	3·50
MS968	123×88 mm. Nos. 965/7. Wmk sideways		3·50	3·50

347 Falcon Trophy, Twin Comanche and Auster (25th anniv of Malta International Rally)

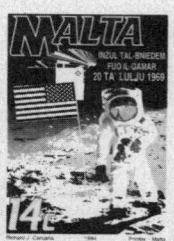
348 National Flags and Astronaut on Moon

(Des R. Caruana)

1994 (2 July). *Aviation Anniversaries and Events. T* **347** *and similar horiz designs. Multicoloured. W* **105** *(sideways). P* 14.
969	5 c.	Type **347**	50	20
970	14 c.	Alouette helicopter, display teams and logo (Malta International Airshow)	1·75	85
971	20 c.	De Havilland Dove *City of Valetta* and Avro York aircraft with logo (50th anniv of International Civil Aviation Organization)	1·90	1·75
972	25 c.	Airbus 320 *Nicolas Cottoner* and De Havilland Comet aircraft with logo (50th anniv of I.C.A.O.)	1·90	1·90
969/72		*Set of 4*	5·50	4·25

After printing it was found that all examples of the 20 c. were inscribed "Anniverarju" in error. These were withdrawn before issue and replaced by stock showing the word correctly spelt as "Anniversarju". It is reported that all sheets of the incorrect printing were destroyed.

(Des R. Caruana)

1994 (20 July). *25th Anniv of First Moon Landing. W* **105**. *P* 14.
973	**348** 14 c. multicoloured		1·10	95

349 Virgin Mary and Child with Angels

350 Helmet-shaped Ewer

(Des H. Borg)

1994 (26 Oct). *Christmas. T* **349** *and similar multicoloured designs. W* **105** *(sideways on 5 c.). P* 13½ (5 c.) or 14 (others).
974	5 c.	Type **349**	25	10
975	9 c. + 2 c.	Angel in pink (*vert*)	65	60
976	14 c. + 3 c.	Virgin Mary and Child (*vert*)	90	1·25
977	20 c. + 3 c.	Angel in green (*vert*)	1·60	2·25
974/7		*Set of 4*	3·00	3·75

Nos. 975/7 are larger, 28×41 mm, and depict details from Type 349.

(Des M. Burlo)

1994 (12 Dec). *Maltese Antique Silver Exhibition. T* **350** *and similar vert designs. Multicoloured. W* **105**. *P* 14.
978	5 c.	Type **350**	25	20
979	14 c.	Balsamina	70	80
980	20 c.	Coffee pot	1·25	1·40
981	25 c.	Sugar box	1·50	1·75
978/81		*Set of 4*	3·25	3·75

351 "60 plus" and Hands touching

352 Hand holding Leaf and Rainbow

(Des Anna Grima)

1995 (27 Feb). *Anniversaries and Events. T* **351** *and similar vert designs. Multicoloured. W* **105** *(sideways). P* 14.
982	2 c.	Type **351** (25th anniv of National Association of Pensioners)	15	15
983	5 c.	Child's drawing (10th anniv of National Youth Council)	25	20
984	14 c.	Conference emblem (4th World Conference on Women, Peking, China)	70	80
985	20 c.	Nurse and thermometer (50th anniv of Malta Memorial District Nursing Association)	1·25	1·40
986	25 c.	Louis Pasteur (biologist) (death centenary)	1·50	1·75
982/6		*Set of 5*	3·50	3·75

(Des H. Borg)

1995 (29 Mar). *Europa. Peace and Freedom. T* **352** *and similar multicoloured design. W* **105** *(sideways on 30 c.). P* 14.
987	14 c.	Type **352**	75	55
988	30 c.	Peace doves (*horiz*)	1·50	2·00

Nos. 987/8 were each printed in sheets including two stamp-size labels.

353 Junkers Ju 87B "Stuka" Dive Bombers over Valletta and Anti-aircraft Gun

354 Light Bulb

(Des F. Ancilleri)

1995 (21 Apr). *Anniversaries. T* **353** *and similar multicoloured designs. W* **105** *(sideways on horiz designs). P* 14.
989	5 c.	Type **353** (50th anniv of end of Second World War)	25	25
990	14 c.	Silhouetted people holding hands (50th anniv of United Nations)	70	80
991	35 c.	Hands holding bowl of wheat (50th anniv of Food and Agriculture Organization) (*vert*)	2·00	2·25
989/91		*Set of 3*	2·75	3·00

(Des M. Burlo)

1995 (15 June). *Maltese Electricity and Telecommunications. T* **354** *and similar vert designs. Multicoloured. W* **105** *(sideways). P* 13½.
992	2 c.	Type **354**	15	15
993	5 c.	Symbolic owl and binary codes	25	25
994	9 c.	Dish aerial	45	50
995	14 c.	Sun and rainbow over trees	70	80
996	20 c.	Early telephone, satellite and Moon's surface	1·25	1·50
992/6		*Set of 5*	2·50	2·75

355 Rock Wall and Girna

356 Pinto's Turret Clock

(Des M. Burlo)

1995 (26 July). *European Nature Conservation Year. T* **355** *and similar horiz designs. Multicoloured. W* **105** *(sideways). P* 14.
997	5 c.	Type **355**	35	25
998	14 c.	Maltese Wall Lizards	1·00	80
999	44 c.	Aleppo Pine	3·00	3·00
997/9		*Set of 3*	4·00	3·50

(Des F. Ancilleri)

1995 (5 Oct). *Treasures of Malta. Antique Maltese Clocks. T* **356** *and similar vert designs. Multicoloured. W* **105**. *P* 14.
1000	1 c.	Type **356**	10	10
1001	5 c.	Michelangelo Sapiano (horologist) and clocks	30	25
1002	14 c.	Arlogg tal-lira clock	90	80
1003	25 c.	Sundials	1·75	2·50
1000/3		*Set of 4*	2·75	3·25

357 Children's Christmas Eve Procession

(Des H. Borg)

1995 (15 Nov). *Christmas. T* **357** *and simlar multicoloured designs. W* **105** *(sideways on 5 c.). P* 14×13½.
1004	5 c.	Type **357**	25	10
1005	5 c. + 2 c.	Children with crib (*vert*)	30	40
1006	14 c. + 3 c.	Children with lanterns (*vert*)	85	90
1007	25 c. + 3 c.	Boy with lantern and balustrade (*vert*)	1·60	1·75
1004/7		*Set of 4*	2·75	2·75

Nos. 1005/7 are 27×32 mm and depict details from Type 357.

358 Silhouetted Children and President's Palace, San Anton

(Des F. Ancilleri)

1996 (29 Feb). *Anniversaries. T* **358** *and similar horiz designs. Multicoloured. W* **105** *(sideways). P* 14.
1008	5 c.	Type **358** (35th anniv of the President's Award)	25	25
1009	14 c.	Father Nazzareno Camilleri and St. Patrick's Church, Salesjani (90th birth anniv)	65	65
1010	20 c.	St. Mary Euphrasia and convent (Birth bicentenary)	1·00	1·10
1011	25 c.	Silhouetted children and fountain (50th anniv of U.N.I.C.E.F.)	1·25	1·40
1008/11		*Set of 4*	2·75	3·00

359 Carved Figures from Skorba

360 Mabel Strickland (politician and journalist)

(Des H. Borg)

1996 (29 Mar). *Maltese Prehistoric Art Exhibition. T* **359** *and similar multicoloured designs. W* **105** *(sideways on horiz designs). P* 14.
1012	5 c.	Type **359**	30	20
1013	14 c.	Temple carving, Gozo	80	85
1014	20 c.	Carved figure of a woman, Skorba (*vert*)	1·10	1·25
1015	35 c.	Ghar Dalam pot (*vert*)	1·90	2·25
1012/15		*Set of 4*	3·75	4·00

(Des Catherine Cavallo)

1996 (24 Apr). *Europa. Famous Women. T* **360** *and similar vert design. Multicoloured. W* **105**. *P* 14.
1016	14 c.	Type **360**	70	55
1017	30 c.	Inez Soler (artist, musician and writer)	1·75	2·00

PRICES OF SETS

Set prices are given for many issues, generally those containing three stamps or more. Definitive sets include one of each value or major colour change, but do not cover different perforations, die types or minor shades. Where a choice is possible the set prices are based on the cheapest versions of the stamps included in the listings.

361 Face and Emblem (United Nations Decade against Drug Abuse)

362 Judo

(Des D. Nicolas)

1996 (5 June). *Anniversaries and Events.* T **361** *and similar vert designs. Multicoloured.* W **105**. *P* 14.
1018	5 c. Type 361		25	25
1019	5 c. "Fi" and emblem (50th anniv of Malta Federation of Industry)		25	25
1020	14 c. Commemorative plaque and national flag (75th anniv of Self-government)		80	80
1021	44 c. Guglielmo Marconi and early radio equipment (Centenary of radio)		2·25	2·50
1018/21		*Set of 4*	3·25	3·50

(Des L. Micallef)

1996 (10 July). *Olympic Games, Atlanta.* T **362** *and similar horiz designs. Multicoloured.* W **105** (*sideways*). *P* 14.
1022	2 c. Type 362		10	10
1023	5 c. Athletics		30	25
1024	14 c. Diving		80	80
1025	25 c. Rifle-shooting		1·40	1·60
1022/5		*Set of 4*	2·40	2·50

363 "Harvest Time" (Cali)

(Des Debbie Dingli)

1996 (22 Aug). *150th Birth Anniv of Guiseppe Cali (painter).* T **363** *and similar multicoloured designs.* W **105** (*sideways on 5, 14 c.*). *P* 14.
1026	5 c. Type 363		30	25
1027	14 c. "Dog" (Cali)		80	70
1028	20 c. "Countrywoman in a Field" (Cali) (*vert*)		1·10	1·10
1029	25 c. "Cali at his Easel" (Edward Dingli) (*vert*)		1·25	1·25
1026/9		*Set of 4*	3·00	3·00

364 Bus No. 1990 *Diamond Star,* 1920s

(Des R. Caruana)

1996 (26 Sept). *Buses.* T **364** *and similar horiz designs. Multicoloured.* W **105** (*sideways*). *P* 14.
1030	2 c. Type 364		25	10
1031	5 c. No. 434 *Tom Mix,* 1930s		50	25
1032	14 c. No. 1764 *Verdala,* 1940s		1·00	80
1033	30 c. No. 3495, 1960s		1·75	2·00
1030/3		*Set of 4*	3·25	2·75

365 Stained Glass Window

(Des H. Borg)

1996 (1 Nov). *Christmas.* T **365** *and similar multicoloured designs.* W **105** (*sideways on 5 c.*). *P* 14×13½.
1034	5 c. Type 365		35	10
1035	5 c. + 2 c. Madonna and Child (29×35 mm)		40	45
1036	14 c. + 3 c. Angel facing right (29×35 mm)		1·25	1·40
1037	25 c. + 3 c. Angel facing left (29×35 mm)		1·25	1·40
1034/7		*Set of 4*	2·50	2·50

Nos. 1035/7 show details from Type **365**.

366 Hompesch Arch and Arms, Zabbar

367 Captain-General of the Galleys' Sedan Chair

(Des R. Caruana)

1997 (20 Feb). *Bicentenary of Maltese Cities.* T **366** *and similar vert designs. Multicoloured.* W **105**. *P* 14.
1038	6 c. Type 366		30	25
1039	16 c. Statue, church and arms, Siggiewi		70	70
1040	26 c. Seated statue and arms, Zejtun		1·10	1·10
1038/40		*Set of 3*	1·90	1·90
MS1041	125×90 mm. As Nos. 1038/40. Wmk sideways		2·40	2·40

1997 (11 Apr). *Treasures of Malta. Sedan Chairs.* T **367** *and similar multicoloured designs.* W **105** (*sideways on horiz designs*). *P* 14.
1042	2 c. Type 367		15	15
1043	6 c. Cotoner Grandmasters' chair		30	30
1044	16 c. Chair from Cathedral Museum, Mdina (*vert*)		70	70
1045	27 c. Chevalier D'Arezzo's chair (*vert*)		1·10	1·10
1042/5		*Set of 4*	2·00	2·00

368 Gahan carrying Door

369 Modern Sculpture (Antonio Sciortino)

(Des J. Mallia)

1997 (5 May). *Europa. Tales and Legends.* T **368** *and similar vert design. Multicoloured.* W **105** (*sideways*). *P* 14.
1046	16 c. Type 368		75	75
1047	35 c. St. Dimitrius appearing from painting		1·25	1·50

Nos. 1046/7 were each printed in sheets of 10 and two stamp-size labels.

1997 (10 July). *Anniversaries.* T **369** *and similar multicoloured designs.* W **105** (*sideways on horiz designs*). *P* 14.
1048	1 c. Type 369		10	15
1049	6 c. Joseph Calleia and film reel (*horiz*)		40	40
1050	6 c. Gozo Cathedral (*horiz*)		40	40
1051	11 c. City of Gozo (*horiz*)		60	50
1052	16 c. Sculpture of head (Sciortino)		80	70
1053	22 c. Joseph Calleia and film camera (*horiz*)		1·00	1·00
1048/53		*Set of 6*	3·00	2·75

Anniversaries; 1 c., 16 c. 50th death anniv of Antonio Sciortino (sculptor); 6 c. (No. 1049), 22 c., Birth centenary of Joseph Calleia (actor); 6 c. (No. 1050), 11 c. 300th anniv of construction of Gozo Cathedral

370 Dr. Albert Laferla

371 The Nativity

(Des Debbie Dingli)

1997 (24 Sept). *Pioneers of Education.* T **370** *and similar vert designs. Multicoloured.* W **105**. *P* 14.
1054	6 c. Type 370		30	25
1055	16 c. Sister Emilie de Vialar		70	70
1056	19 c. Mgr. Paolo Pullicino		80	80
1057	26 c. Mgr. Tommaso Gargallo		1·00	1·10
1054/7		*Set of 4*	2·50	2·50

(Des H. Borg)

1997 (12 Nov). *Christmas.* T **371** *and similar multicoloured designs.* W **105** (*sideways on 6 c.*). *P* 14.
1058	6 c. Type 371		30	10
1059	6 c. + 2 c. Mary and baby Jesus (*vert*)		35	40
1060	16 c. + 3 c. Joseph with donkey (*vert*)		80	85
1061	26 c. + 3 c. Shepherd with lamb (*vert*)		1·25	1·60
1058/61		*Set of 4*	2·40	2·75

Nos. 1059/61 show details from Type **371**.

372 Plan of Fort and Soldiers in Victoria Lines

373 "Maria Amelia Grognet" (Antoine de Favray)

1997 (5 Dec). *Anniversaries.* T **372** *and similar horiz designs. Multicoloured (except 6 c.).* W **105** (*sideways*). *P* 14.
1062	2 c. Type 372		20	10
1063	6 c. Sir Paul Boffa making speech (black and scarlet)		30	25
1064	16 c. Plan of fort and gun crew		90	65
1065	37 c. Queue of voters		1·50	2·00
1062/5		*Set of 4*	2·50	2·75

Anniversaries; 2 c., 16 c. Centenary of Victoria Lines; 6 c., 37 c. 50th anniv of 1947 Self-Government Constitution

(Des F. Ancilleri)

1998 (26 Feb). *Treasures of Malta. Costumes and Paintings.* T **373** *and similar vert designs.* W **105**. *P* 14.
1066	6 c. Type 373		40	40
1067	6 c. Gentleman's waistcoat, c. 1790–1810		40	40
1068	16 c. Lady's dinner dress, c. 1880		70	80
1069	16 c. "Veneranda, Baroness Abela, and her Grandson" (De Favray)		70	80
1066/9		*Set of 4*	2·00	2·25
MS1070	123×88 mm. 26 c. City of Valletta from old print (39×47 mm). Wmk sideways. P 13×13½		1·40	1·40

374 Grand Master Ferdinand von Hompesch

375 Racing Two-man Luzzus

(Des J. Mizzi)

1998 (28 Mar). *Bicentenary of Napoleon's Capture of Malta.* T **374** *and similar horiz designs. Multicoloured.* W **51** (*sideways*). *P* 14.
1071	6 c. Type 374		30	40
	a. Vert pair. Nos. 1071/2		60	80
1072	6 c. French fleet		30	40
1073	16 c. French landing		75	90
	a. Vert pair. Nos. 1073/4		1·50	1·75
1074	16 c. General Napoleon Bonaparte		75	90
1071/4		*Set of 4*	1·90	2·40

Nos. 1071/2 and 1073/4 were each printed together, *se-tenant,* in horizontal pairs throughout the sheets

(Des R. Caruana)

1998 (22 Apr). *Europa. Sailing Regatta, Grand Harbour.* T **375** *and similar horiz design. Multicoloured.* W **51**. *P* 14.
1075	16 c. Type 375		85	55
1076	35 c. Racing four-man luzzus		1·40	1·75

376 Dolphin and Diver

377 Goalkeeper saving Goal

(Des Isabelle Borg)

1998 (27 May). *International Year of the Ocean.* T **376** *and similar multicoloured designs.* W **105** (*sideways on 16 and 27 c.*). *P* 14.
1077	2 c. Type 376		20	15
1078	6 c. Diver and sea-urchin		40	25
1079	16 c. Jacques Cousteau and diver (*horiz*)		85	70
1080	27 c. Two divers (*horiz*)		1·25	1·50
1077/80		*Set of 4*	2·40	2·40

(Des R. Caruana)

1998 (10 June). *World Cup Football Championship, France.* T **377** *and similar horiz designs showing players and flags. Multicoloured.* W **105**. *P* 14.
1081	6 c. Type 377		40	25
1082	16 c. Two players and referee		85	70
1083	22 c. Two footballers		1·25	1·40
1081/3		*Set of 3*	2·25	2·10
MS1084	122×87 mm. Nos. 1081/3. Wmk sideways		2·25	2·50

378 Ships' Wheels (50th anniv of Int Maritime Organization)

379 "Rest on the Flight to Egypt"

(Des H. Borg)

1998 (17 Sept). *Anniversaries. T* **378** *and similar horiz designs. Multicoloured.* W **105** (*sideways*). *P* 14.
1085	1 c. Type **378**		10	10
1086	6 c. Symbolic family (50th anniv of Universal Declaration of Human Rights)		30	25
1087	11 c. "GRTU" and cogwheels (50th anniv of General Retailers and Traders Union)		45	40
1088	19 c. Mercury (50th anniv of Chamber of Commerce)		70	75
1089	26 c. Aircraft tailfins (25th anniv of Air Malta)		1·10	1·25
1085/9		*Set of* 5	2·40	2·50

1998 (19 Nov). *Christmas. Paintings by Mattia Preti. T* **379** *and similar vert designs. Multicoloured.* W **105**. *P* 14.
1090	6 c. Type **379**		30	10
1091	6 c. + 2 c. "Virgin and Child with Sts. Anthony and John the Baptist"		35	40
1092	16 c. + 3 c. "Virgin and Child with Sts. Raphael, Nicholas and Gregory"		80	85
1093	26 c. + 3 c. "Virgin and Child with Sts. John the Baptist and Nicholas"		1·25	1·40
1090/3		*Set of* 4	2·40	2·50

PRINTERS. All stamps from No. 1094 onwards were printed in lithography by German State Printing Works, Berlin.

380 Fort St. Angelo

(Des F. Ancilleri)

1999 (26 Feb). *900th Anniv of the Sovereign Military Order of Malta. T* **380** *and similar multicoloured designs. P* 14.
1094	2 c. Type **380**		15	10
1095	6 c. Grand Master De l'Isle Adam (*vert*)		30	25
1096	16 c. Grand Master La Valette (*vert*)		65	55
1097	27 c. Auberge de Castille		1·00	1·40
1094/7		*Set of* 4	1·90	2·00

381 Little Ringed Plover, Ghadira Nature Reserve

(Des R. Caruana)

1999 (6 Apr). *Europa. Parks and Gardens. T* **381** *and similar horiz design. Multicoloured. P* 14.
1098	16 c. Type **381**		75	55
1099	35 c. Common Kingfisher, Simar Nature Reserve		1·25	1·50

382 Council of Europe Assembly

(Des R. Caruana)

1999 (6 Apr). *50th Anniv of the Council of Europe. T* **382** *and similar horiz design. Multicoloured. P* 14.
1100	6 c. Type **382**		30	25
1101	16 c. Council of Europe Headquarters, Strasbourg		70	55

383 U.P.U. Emblem and Marsamxett Harbour, Valletta

384 Couple in Luzzu

(Des A. Spratte)

1999 (2 June). *125th Anniv of Universal Postal Union. T* **383** *and similar horiz designs. Multicoloured. P* 13½.
1102	6 c. Type **383**		40	45
	a. Horiz strip of 5. Nos. 1102/6		3·75	
1103	16 c. Nuremberg and "iBRA '99" International Stamp Exhibition emblem		75	80
1104	22 c. Paris and "Philexfrance '99" International Stamp Exhibition emblem		90	1·00
1105	27 c. Peking and "China '99" International Stamp Exhibition emblem		1·00	1·10
1106	37 c. Melbourne and "Australia '99" International Stamp Exhibition emblem		1·10	1·25
1102/6		*Set of* 5	3·75	4·25

Nos. 1102/6 were printed together, *se-tenant*, as horizontal strips of 5 in sheets of 10.

(Des G. Mallia)

1999 (16 June). *Tourism. T* **384** *and similar multicoloured designs. P* 14.
1107	6 c. Type **384**		30	25
1108	16 c. Tourist taking photograph		65	55
1109	22 c. Man sunbathing (*horiz*)		85	90
1110	27 c. Couple with horse-drawn carriage (*horiz*)		95	1·00
1111	37 c. Caveman at Ta' Hagrat Neolithic temple (*horiz*)		1·25	1·50
1107/11		*Set of* 5	3·50	3·75

385 Common Jellyfish

(Des A. Micallef)

1999 (25 Aug). *Marine Life of the Mediterranean. T* **385** *and similar square designs. Multicoloured. P* 13½.
1112	6 c. Type **385**		35	35
	a. Sheetlet. Nos. 1112/27		5·00	
1113	6 c. Peacock Wrasse		35	35
1114	6 c. Common Cuttlefish		35	35
1115	6 c. Violet Sea-urchin		35	35
1116	6 c. Dusky Grouper		35	35
1117	6 c. Common Two-banded Seabream		35	35
1118	6 c. Star-coral		35	35
1119	6 c. Spiny Spider Crab		35	35
1120	6 c. Rainbow Wrasse		35	35
1121	6 c. Octopus		35	35
1122	6 c. Atlantic Trumpet Triton		35	35
1123	6 c. Mediterranean Parrotfish		35	35
1124	6 c. Long-snouted Seahorse		35	35
1125	6 c. Deep-water Hermit Crab		35	35
1126	6 c. Mediterranean Moray		35	35
1127	6 c. Common Starfish		35	35
1112/27		*Set of* 16	5·00	5·00

Nos. 1112/27 were printed together, *se-tenant*, in sheetlets of 16, forming a composite design.

386 Father Mikiel Scerri

(Des J. Mizzi)

1999 (6 Oct). *Bicentenary of Maltese Uprising against the French. T* **386** *and similar horiz designs. Multicoloured. P* 14.
1128	6 c. Type **386**		20	25
	a. Pair. Nos. 1128/9		40	50
1129	6 c. "L-Eroj Maltin" (statue)		20	25
1130	16 c. General Belgrand de Vaubois (French commander)		50	55
	a. Pair. Nos. 1130/1		1·00	1·10
1131	16 c. Captain Alexander Ball R.N.		50	55
1128/31		*Set of* 4	1·40	1·60

Nos. 1128/9 and 1130/1 were each printed together, *se-tenant*, as horizontal or vertical pairs in sheets of 10.

387 "Wolfgang Philip Guttenberg interceding with The Virgin" (votive painting)

(Des J. Mizzi)

1999 (6 Oct). *Mellieha Sanctuary Commemoration. T* **387** *and similar multicoloured design. P* 14.
1132	35 c. Type **387**		1·00	1·10
MS1133	123×88 mm. 6 c. "Mellieha Virgin and Child" (rock painting) (*vert*)		30	30

388 Pancratium maritimum

389 Madonna and Child

(Des M. Burlo)

1999 (20 Oct). *Maltese Flowers. T* **388** *and similar square designs. Multicoloured. P* 14.
1134	2 c. Type **388**		10	10
1135	4 c. *Iris pseudopumila*		10	15
1136	6 c. *Narcissus tazetta*		20	25
1137	16 c. *Crocus longiflorus*		50	55
1138	25 c. *Ornithogalum arabicum*		75	80
1139	46 c. *Tulipa sylvestris*		1·40	1·50
1134/9		*Set of* 6	3·00	3·25

(Des H. Borg)

1999 (27 Nov). *Christmas. T* **389** *and similar square designs. Multicoloured. P* 14.
1146	6 c. Type **389**		20	25
1147	6 c. + 3 c. Carol singers		25	30
1148	16 c. + 3 c. Santa Claus		60	65
1149	26 c. + 3 c. Christmas decorations		90	95
1146/9		*Set of* 4	1·90	2·10

390 Parliament Chamber and Symbolic Luzzu

(Des R. Caruana)

1999 (10 Dec). *25th Anniv of Republic. T* **390** *and similar horiz designs. Multicoloured. P* 14.
1150	6 c. Type **390**		20	25
1151	11 c. Parliament in session and Council of Europe emblem		30	35
1152	16 c. Church and Central Bank of Malta building		50	55
1153	19 c. Aerial view of Gozo and emblems		60	65
1154	26 c. Computer and shipyard		75	80
1150/4		*Set of* 5	2·25	2·50

391 Gift and Flowers

(Des H. Borg)

2000 (9 Feb). *Greetings Stamps. T* **391** *and similar horiz designs. Multicoloured. P* 14.

1155	3 c. Type **391**		10	15
1156	6 c. Photograph, envelope and rose		20	25
1157	16 c. Flowers and silver heart		50	55
1158	20 c. Champagne and pocket watch		60	65
1159	22 c. Wedding rings and roses		65	70
1155/9		*Set of* 5	2·00	2·25

Nos. 1155/9 were printed with greetings labels on the vertical sheet margins.

392 Luzzu and Cruise Liner

(Des F. Ancilleri)

2000 (7 Mar). *Malta during the 20th Century. T* **392** *and similar horiz designs. Multicoloured. P* 14.

1160	6 c. Type **392**	20	25
1161	16 c. Street musicians and modern street carnival	50	55
1162	22 c. Family in 1900 and illuminated quayside	65	70
1163	27 c. Rural occupations and Citadel, Victoria	80	85
1160/3		*Set of* 4	2·10	2·25

393 Footballers and Trophy
(Centenary of Malta Football Association)

(Des L. Flask)

2000 (28 Mar). *Sporting Events. T* **393** *and similar horiz designs. Multicoloured. P* 14.

1164	6 c. Type **393**	20	25
1165	16 c. Swimming and sailing (Olympic Games, Sydney)	50	55
1166	26 c. Judo, shooting and running (Olympic Games, Sydney)	75	80
1167	37 c. Football (European Championship)	1·00	1·10
1164/7		*Set of* 4	2·40	2·50

STAMP BOOKLETS

B 1

1970 (16 May). *Brownish black on brownish grey cover as Type* B 1 *depicting G.P.O. Palazzo Parisio, Valletta. Stitched.*

SB1	2s. 6d. booklet containing six 1d. and twelve 2d. (Nos. 331, 333) in blocks of 6		4·50

1970 (18 May). *Black on pink cover as Type* B 1 *depicting Magisterial Palace, Valletta. Stitched.*

SB2	2s. 6d. booklets containing six 1d. and twelve 2d. (Nos. 331, 333) in blocks of 6		4·00

1971 (29 May). *Black on green cover as Type* B 1 *depicting Auberge d'Aragon, Valletta. Stitched.*

SB3	2s. 6d. booklet containing six 1d. and twelve 2d. (Nos. 331, 333) in blocks of 6		10·00

1971 (3 July). *Black on white cover as Type* B 1 *depicting Fort St. Angelo. Stitched.*

SB4	5s. booklet containing twelve 5d. (No. 337b) in blocks of 6		9·00

B 2

1994 (2 Nov). *Multicoloured covers as Type* B 2. *Stamps attached by selvedge.*

SB5	50 c. booklet containing 5 c. (No. 909) in block of 10, (cover showing Malta 1926 2s. Mdina (Notabile) stamp)		2·00
SB6	70 c. booklet containing 14 c. (No. 912) in strip of 5 with 6 airmail labels (cover showing Malta 1926 1s. Valleta Harbour stamp)		2·75

POSTAGE DUE STAMPS

D 1   D 2   D 3 Maltese Lace

1925 (16 Apr). *Type-set by Govt Printing Office, Valletta. Imperf.*

D 1	D 1	½d. black	1·25	5·00
		a. *Tête-bêche* (horiz pair)	5·00	15·00
D 2		1d. black	3·25	2·50
		a. *Tête-bêche* (horiz pair)	10·00	11·00
D 3		1½d. black	3·00	3·50
		a. *Tête-bêche* (horiz pair)	10·00	14·00
D 4		2d. black	6·00	10·00
		a. *Tête-bêche* (horiz pair)	15·00	30·00
D 5		2½d. black	2·75	2·75
		a. "2" of "½" omitted	£800	£1200
		b. *Tête-bêche* (horiz pair)	12·00	14·00
D 6		3d. black/grey	9·00	12·00
		a. *Tête-bêche* (horiz pair)	30·00	40·00
D 7		4d. black/buff	5·00	9·50
		a. *Tête-bêche* (horiz pair)	17·00	35·00
D 8		6d. black/buff	5·00	14·00
		a. *Tête-bêche* (horiz pair)	17·00	48·00
D 9		1s. black/buff	7·50	18·00
		a. *Tête-bêche* (horiz pair)	25·00	55·00
D10		1s. 6d. black/buff	13·00	55·00
		a. *Tête-bêche* (horiz pair)	40·00	£130
D1/10		*Set of* 10	48·00	£120

Nos. D1/10 were each issued in sheets containing 4 panes (6×7) printed separately, the impressions in the two right-hand panes being inverted. Fourteen horizontal *tête-bêche* pairs occur from the junction of the left and right-hand panes.

No. D5a occurred on R. 4/4 of the last 2½d. pane position to be printed. Forgeries exist, but can be detected by comparison with a normal example under ultra-violet light. They are often found in pair with normal, showing forged cancellations of "VALLETTA AP20 25" or "G.P.O" MY 7 25".

(Typo B.W.)

1925 (20 July). *Wmk Mult Script CA* (sideways). *P* 12.

D11	D 2	½d. green		1·25	60
D12		1d. violet		1·25	45
D13		1½d. brown		1·50	80
D14		2d. grey		11·00	1·00
D15		2½d. orange		2·00	1·25
		x. Wmk reversed		75·00	
D16		3d. blue		3·25	1·25
D17		4d. olive-green		12·00	15·00
D18		6d. purple		3·00	3·25
D19		1s. black		6·50	10·00
D20		1s. 6d. carmine		8·50	24·00
D11/20			*Set of* 10	45·00	50·00
D11/20	Optd "Specimen"		*Set of* 10	£200	

1953 (5 Nov)–**63**. *Wmk Mult Script CA* (sideways). *Chalk-surfaced paper. P* 12.

D21	D 2	½d. emerald		70	2·00
D22		1d. purple		70	1·25
		a. *Deep purple* (17.9.63)		75	3·50
D23		1½d. yellow-brown		3·00	8·50
D24		2d. grey-brown (20.3.57)		5·00	8·50
		a. *Blackish brown* (3.4.62)		20·00	13·00
D25		3d. deep slate-blue		1·50	2·00
D26		4d. yellow-olive		4·50	8·00
D21/6			*Set of* 6	14·00	27·0

1966 (Oct). *As No. D24, but wmk w* **12** (sideways).

D27	D 2	2d. grey-brown		16·00	25·00

1967–70. *Ordinary paper. W* **105** (sideways).

(a) P 12, *line* (9.11.67)

D28	D 2	½d. emerald		4·00	9·00
D29		1d. purple		4·00	9·00
D30		2d. blackish brown		4·00	9·00
D31		4d. yellow-olive		45·00	90·00
D28/31			*Set of* 4	50·00	£100

(b) P 12½, *comb* (30.5.68–70)

D32	D 2	½d. emerald		35	1·75
D33		1d. purple		30	1·75
D34		1½d. yellow-brown		35	3·00
		a. *Orange-brown* (23.10.70)		90	3·00
D35		2d. blackish brown		85	70
		a. *Brownish black* (23.10.70)		2·00	3·00
D36		2½d. yellow-orange		60	70
D37		3d. deep slate-blue		60	60
D38		4d. yellow-olive		1·00	80
D39		6d. purple		75	1·25
D40		1s. black		90	1·50
D41		1s. 6d. carmine		2·25	6·00
D32/41			*Set of* 10	7·00	15·00

The above are the local release dates. In the 12½ perforation the London release dates were 21 May for the ½d. to 4d. and 4 June for the 6d. to 1s. 6d.

Nos. D34a and D35a are on glazed paper.

(Des G. Pace. Litho Printex Ltd, Malta)

1973 (28 Apr). *W* **105**. *P* 13 × 13½.

D42	D 3	2 m. grey-brown and reddish brown		10	10
D43		3 m. dull orange and Indian red		10	15
D44		5 m. rose and bright scarlet		15	20
D45		1 c. turquoise and bottle green		30	35
D46		2 c. slate and black		30	35
D47		3 c. light yellow-brown and red-brown		30	35
D48		5 c. dull blue and royal blue		55	70
D49		10 c. reddish lilac and plum		75	1·00
D42/9			*Set of* 8	2·25	2·75

D 4

(Des M. Bonavia. Litho Printex Ltd, Malta)

1993 (4 Jan). *W* **105** (sideways). *P* 14.

D50	D 4	1 c. magenta and pale magenta		10	10
D51		2 c. new blue and pale blue		15	15
D52		5 c. blue-green & pale turquoise-green		20	20
D53		10 c. yellow-orange and greenish yellow		35	35
D50/3			*Set of* 4	70	70

Mauritius

GREAT BRITAIN STAMPS USED IN MAURITIUS. We no longer list the Great Britain stamps with obliteration "B 53" as there is no evidence that British stamps were available from the Mauritius Post Office.

See under SEYCHELLES for stamps of Mauritius used at Victoria with "B 64" cancellations between 1861 and 1890.
A similar "B 65" cancellation was used on the island of Rodrigues, a dependency of Mauritius, from 11 December 1861 onwards.

PRICES FOR STAMPS ON COVER TO 1945

Nos. 1/5	*from* × 2
Nos. 6/9	*from* × 3
Nos. 10/15	*from* × 4
Nos. 16/25	*from* × 5
Nos. 26/9	*from* × 3
Nos. 30/1	*from* —
Nos. 32/5	*from* × 4
Nos. 36/44	*from* × 5
Nos. 46/72	*from* × 3
Nos. 76/82	*from* × 5
Nos. 83/91	*from* × 6
Nos. 92/100	*from* × 4
Nos. 101/11	*from* × 3
Nos. 117/24	*from* × 8
Nos. 127/32	*from* × 7
No. 133	*from* × 6
Nos. 134/5	*from* × 10
No. 136	*from* × 8
Nos. 137/56	*from* × 6
Nos. 157/63	*from* × 5
Nos. 164/221	*from* × 3
No. 222	*from* —
Nos. 223/41	*from* × 3
Nos. 242/4	*from* × 10
Nos. 245/8	*from* × 3
Nos. 249/63	*from* × 2
Nos. E1/6	*from* × 10
Nos. D1/7	*from* × 40
Nos. R1/3	*from* × 15

CROWN COLONY

Nos. 1/25b and 36/44 were printed in Mauritius.

1
("POST OFFICE")

2
("POST PAID")

(Engraved on copper by J. O. Barnard)

1847 (21 Sept). *Head of Queen on groundwork of diagonal and perpendicular lines. Imperf.*

1	1	1d. orange-red		— £450000
2		2d. deep blue		— £550000

A single plate contained one example of each value.
It is generally agreed that fifteen examples of No. 1 have survived (including two unused) and twelve of No. 2 (including four unused). Most are now in permanent museum collections.

NOTE. Our prices for early Mauritius are for stamps in very fine condition. Exceptional copies are worth more, poorer copies considerably less.

(Engraved on copper by J. O. Barnard)

1848 (June)—**59**. *Imperf.*

A. *Earliest impressions. Design deep, sharp and clear. Diagonal lines predominate. Thick paper (Period of use: 1d. 1853–54, 2d. 1848–49).*

3	2	1d. orange-vermilion/*yellowish*		£35000 £13000
4		2d. indigo-blue/*grey to bluish*		£30000 £15000
		a. "PENOE" for "PENCE" (R. 3/1)		£60000 £23000
5		2d. deep blue/*grey to bluish*		£30000 £15000
		a. "PENOE" for "PENCE" (R. 3/1)		£60000 £26000

B. *Early impressions. Design sharp and clear but some lines slightly weakened. Paper not so thick, grey to yellowish white or bluish (Period of use: 1d. 1853–55, 2d. 1849–54).*

6	2	1d. vermilion		£15000 £5500
7		1d. orange-vermilion		£16000 £5000
8		2d. blue		£17000 £6000
		a. "PENOE" for "PENCE" (R. 3/1)		£27000 £9500
9		2d. deep blue		£21000 £6500

C. *Intermediate impressions. White patches appear where design has worn. Paper yellowish white, grey or bluish, of poorish quality (Period of use: 1d and 2d. 1854–57)*

10	2	1d. bright vermilion		£7500 £2000
11		1d. dull vermilion		£7500 £2000
12		1d. red		£7500 £2000
13		2d. deep blue		£10000 £3000
14		2d. blue		£7500 £2250
		a. "PENOE" for "PENCE" (R. 3/1) *from*		£13000 £4750
15		2d. light blue		£7500 £2250

D. *Worn impressions. Much of design worn away but some diagonal lines distinct. Paper yellowish, grey or bluish, of poorish quality (Period of use: 1d. 1857–59, 2d. 1855–58)*

16	2	1d. red/*yellowish or grey*		£2250 £425
17		1d. red-brown/*yellowish or grey*		£2250 £425
18		1d. red/*bluish*		£1700 £375
		a. Doubly printed		
19		1d. red-brown/*bluish*		£1700 £375
20		2d. blue (*shades*)/*yellowish or grey*		£2500 £800
		a. "PENOE" for "PENCE" (R. 3/1) .. *from*		—£1300
21		2d. grey-blue/*yellowish or grey*		£2750 £750
22		2d. blue (*shades*)/*bluish*		£2500 £750
		a. Doubly printed		

E. *Latest impressions. Almost none of design showing except part of Queen's head and frame. Paper yellowish, grey or bluish, of poorish quality (Period of use: 1d. 1859, 2d. 1856–58)*

23	2	1d. red		£1400 £375
24		1d. red-brown		£1400 £375
25		2d. grey-blue/*bluish*		£1900 £500
		a. "PENOE" for "PENCE" (R. 3/1)		£3500 £900

Earliest known use of the 2d. value is on 19 June 1848, but the 1d. value is not known used before 27 September 1853.
There were separate plates for the 1d. and 2d. values, each of 12 (3×4).

3

(4)

5

(Eng G. Fairman. Recess P.B.)

1858*. *Surch with T 4. Imperf.*

26	3	4d. green		£750 £375

*Although originally gazetted for use from 8 April 1854, research into the archives indicates that No. 26 was not actually issued until 1858, when the stamps were mentioned in an ordinance of 30 April. The earliest dated postmark known is 27 March 1858.

PERKINS BACON "CANCELLED". For notes on these handstamps, showing "CANCELLED" between horizontal bars forming an oval, see Catalogue Introduction.

1858–62. *No value expressed. Imperf.*

27	3	(4d.) green		£425 £200
28		(6d.) vermilion		26·00 45·00
29		(9d.) dull magenta (1859)		£550 £200
		a. Reissued as (1d.) value (11.62)	†	£160

Prepared for use but not issued

30	3	(No value), red-brown		11·00
31		(No value), blue (H/S "CANCELLED" in oval £5000)		3·00

Use of the dull magenta as a 1d. value can be confirmed by the presence of the "B 53" cancellation which was first introduced in 1861.
Remainders of Nos. 30/1, overprinted "L.P.E. 1890" in red, were perforated at the London Philatelic Exhibition and sold as souvenirs.

(Recess P.B.)

1859–61. *Imperf.*

32	5	6d. bl (H/S "CANCELLED" in oval £7000)		£550 32·00
33		6d. dull purple-slate (1861)		20·00 32·00
34		1s. vermilion (H/S "CANCELLED" in oval £4000)		£2000 45·00
35		1s. yellow-green (1861)		£425 95·00

The 1859 printings had the colours transposed by mistake.

6

7

8

(Engraved on copper by J. Lapirot)

1859 (Mar–Nov). *Imperf.* (a) *Early impressions.*

36	6	2d. deep blue		£4750 £1800
37		2d. blue		£3750 £1600

(b) *Intermediate prints. Lines of background, etc, partly worn away (July)*

38	6	2d. blue		£2500 £600

(c) *Worn impressions, bluish-paper (Oct)*

39	6	2d. blue		£1100 £400

(d) *Retouched impression (Nov)*

39a	6	2d. blue		† —
		ab. "MAURITIUS" (R.2/4)	†	£100000
		ac. "MAURITUS" (R.3/1)	†	£100000

Nos. 36/9a were printed from a plate of 12 (4×3). The plate became worn through use, and was eventually extensively re-engraved. Only two pairs (one on cover) have been recorded from this retouched impression. The errors made in the re-engraving of the inscriptions probably resulted in it being withdrawn from use.

(1848 plate re-engraved by R. Sherwin)

1859 (Oct). *Bluish paper. Imperf.*

40	7	2d. deep blue		£100000 £4000

The 1d. plate was also re-engraved, but was not put into use. Reprints in black were made in 1877 from both 1d. and 2d. re-engraved plates. Coloured autotype illustrations were prepared from these reprints and 600 were included in the R.P.S.L. handbook on British Africa in 1900. Further reprints in black were made in 1911 after the plates had been presented to the R.P.S.L. and defaced.

(Lithographed by L. A. Dardenne)

1859 (12 Dec). *White laid paper. Imperf.*

41	8	1d. deep red		£5000 £1500
41a		1d. red		£4000 £850
42		1d. dull vermilion		£3000 £750
43		2d. slate-blue		£3250 £700
43a		2d. blue		£1600 £475
44		2d. pale blue		£1500 £375
		a. Heavy retouch on neck		—£1100
		b. Retouched below "TWO"		—£600

The neck retouch shows a prominent curved white line running from the base of the chignon to the nape of the neck. No. 44b shows several diagonal lines in the margin below "TWO".

9

10

(Typo D.L.R.)

1860 (7 Apr)—**63.** *No wmk. P 14.*

46	9	1d. purple-brown		£140 18·00
47		2d. blue		£180 28·00
48		4d. rose		£180 23·00
49		6d. green (1862)		£600 £100
50		6d. slate (1863)		£180 75·00
51		9d. dull purple		85·00 38·00
52		1s. buff (1862)		£225 65·00
53		1s. green (1863)		£550 £150

1862. *Intermediate perf 14 to 16.*

54	5	6d. slate		17·00 45·00
		a. Imperf between (horiz pair)		£4500
55		1s. deep green		£1800 £325

1863–72. *Wmk Crown CC. P 14.*

56	9	1d. purple-brown		50·00 9·00
		w. Wmk inverted		75·00 20·00
57		1d. brown		65·00 5·50
58		1d. bistre (1872)		85·00 7·00
		w. Wmk inverted		
59		2d. pale blue		65·00 7·50
		w. Wmk inverted		90·00 20·00
		x. Wmk reversed		
		y. Wmk inverted and reversed		
60		2d. bright blue		65·00 7·50
		a. Imperf (pair)		£1300 £1800
61		3d. deep red		£120 22·00
61a		3d. dull red		40·00 9·00
		aw. Wmk inverted		85·00 25·00
62		4d. rose		80·00 3·00
		w. Wmk inverted		£100 15·00
63		6d. dull violet		£160 24·00
		w. Wmk inverted		
		x. Wmk reversed		
64		6d. yellow-green (1865)		£130 11·00
65		6d. blue-green		95·00 4·00
		w. Wmk inverted		£150 25·00
		y. Wmk inverted and reversed		
66		9d. yellow-green (1872)		£100 £170
		w. Wmk inverted		
67	10	10d. maroon (1872)		£180 30·00
		w. Wmk inverted		
68	9	1s. yellow		£150 18·00
		w. Wmk inverted		£180 35·00
69		1s. blue (1866)		£130 18·00
		w. Wmk inverted		— 38·00
		x. Wmk reversed		
70		1s. orange (1872)		£140 12·00
		y. Wmk inverted and reversed		— 35·00
71		5s. rosy mauve		£150 48·00
72		5s. bright mauve (1865)		£190 48·00
		w. Wmk inverted		£250

HALF
PENNY
(11)

½ d

HALF PENNY
(12)

1876. (a) *Nos. 51 and 67 surch with T 11 locally.*

76	9	½d. on 9d. dull purple		6·50 9·50
		a. Surch inverted		£375
		b. Surch double		—£1100
77	10	½d. on 10d. maroon		1·75 14·00
		y. Wmk inverted and reversed		

(b) *Prepared for use, but not issued. No. 51 surch with T 12.*

78	9	½d. on 9d. dull purple (R.)		£750
		a. "PRNNY"		
		b. Black surch		£1100

HALF PENNY
(13)

One Penny
(14)

One Shilling
(15)

Shill
Wrong fount "S"

1877 (Apr–Dec). *Nos. 62, 67 (colour changed) and 71/2 surch T 13 by D.L.R. or T 14/15 locally.*

79	10	½d. on 10d. rose		3·00 26·00
		w. Wmk inverted		
80	9	1d. on 4d. rose-carmine (6 Dec)		7·50 12·00
		w. Wmk inverted		— 45·00

81	9	1s. on 5s. rosy mauve (6 Dec)	..	..	£225	90·00
		w. Wmk inverted			£300	
82		1s. on 5s. bright mauve (6 Dec)	..		£200	£100
		a. Wrong fount "S"			£300	£170
		w. Wmk inverted				

(New Currency. 100 cents = 1 rupee)

"CANCELLED" OVERPRINTS. Following the change of currency in 1878 various issues with face values in sterling were overprinted "CANCELLED" in serifed type and sold as remainders. The stamps involved were Nos. 51, 56/62, 65, 67/8, 71/2, 76, 78/b, 79 and 81/2.

Examples of such overprints on stamps between Nos. 51 and 72 are worth about the same as the prices quoted for used, on Nos. 78/b they are worth 12% of the unused price, on No. 79 65% and on Nos. 81/2 20%.

| **2 CENTS** | **2 RS. 50 C.** |
| (16) | (17) |

1878 (3 Jan). *Surch as T 16 or 17 (No. 91). Wmk Crown CC. P 14.*

83	10	2 c. dull rose (lower label blank)	..	5·50	4·50
		w. Wmk inverted		—	30·00
84	9	4 c. on 1d. bistre	..	7·50	4·50
85		8 c. on 2d. blue	..	65·00	1·50
		w. Wmk inverted			
86		13 c. on 3d. orange-red	..	7·50	24·00
87		17 c. on 4d. rose	..	£140	2·00
88		25 c. on 6d. slate-blue	..	£170	4·75
89		38 c. on 9d. pale violet	..	18·00	48·00
90		50 c. on 1s. green	..	85·00	2·50
		w. Wmk inverted			
91		2 r. 50 on 5s. bright mauve	..	12·00	14·00
83/91		..	Set of 9	£450	95·00

| 18 | 19 | 20 |

| 21 | 22 | 23 |

| 24 | 25 | 26 |

(Typo D.L.R.)

1879 (Mar)–80. *Wmk Crown CC. P 14.*

92	18	2 c. Venetian red (1.80)	..	32·00	11·00
93	19	4 c. orange	..	65·00	3·50
		w. Wmk inverted			
94	20	8 c. blue (1.80)	..	13·00	2·25
		w. Wmk inverted		—	75·00
95	21	13 c. slate (1.80)	..	£120	£160
96	22	17 c. rose (1.80)	..	50·00	4·75
		w. Wmk inverted		—	£100
97	23	25 c. olive-yellow	..	£250	8·00
98	24	38 c. bright purple (1.80)	..	£150	£190
99	25	50 c. green (1.80)	..	3·75	2·75
		w. Wmk inverted		75·00	
100	26	2 r. 50, brown-purple (1.80)	..	30·00	55·00
92/100		..	Set of 9	£650	£375

27

(Typo D.L.R.)

1893–94. *Wmk Crown CA. P 14.*

101	18	1 c. pale violet (1893)	..	1·75	45
102		2 c. Venetian red	..	30·00	4·75
103		2 c. green (1885)	..	2·25	60
104	19	4 c. orange	..	65·00	2·50
		w. Wmk inverted			
105		4 c. carmine (1885)	..	2·75	60
		w. Wmk inverted			
106	20	8 c. blue (1891)	..	2·00	90
		w. Wmk inverted			
		x. Wmk reversed			
107	27	15 c. chestnut (1893)	..	4·00	1·25
		w. Wmk inverted		—	75·00
108		15 c. blue (1894)	..	5·50	90
109		16 c. chestnut (1885)	..	4·00	1·00

110	23	25 c. olive-yellow	..	4·50	1·75
		w. Wmk inverted			
111	25	50 c. orange (1887)	..	28·00	8·00
		w. Wmk inverted			
101/11			Set of 11	£140	20·00
101, 103, 105, 107/9, 111 Optd "Specimen"	Set of 7	£400	

| **16 CENTS** | **SIXTEEN CENTS** |
| (28) | (29) |

(a) Surcharge 14 mm long and 3 high.
(b) Surcharge 15 mm long and 3½ high.
(c) Surcharge 15 mm long and 2½ high.

1883 (26 Feb). *No. 96 surch as T 28 locally.*

112	22	16 c. on 17 c. rose (a)	..	£130	50·00
		a. Surch double		†	£1500
113		16 c. on 17 c. rose (b)	..	£140	50·00
114		16 c. on 17 c. rose (c)	..	£275	£100

1883 (14 July). *Surch with T 29 by D.L.R. Wmk Crown CA. P 14.*

| 115 | 22 | 16 c. on 17 c. rose | .. | 60·00 | 1·00 |
| | | w. Wmk inverted | | | |

| **2 CENTS** | **2 CENTS** |
| (30) | (31) |

1885 (11 May). *No. 98 surch with T 30 locally.*

116	24	2 c. on 38 c. bright purple	..	85·00	32·00
		a. Without bar			£130
		b. Surch inverted		£450	£450
		c. Surch double		£550	

1887 (6 July). *No. 95 surch with T 31 locally.*

117	21	2 c. on 13 c. slate (R.)	..	38·00	70·00
		a. Surch inverted		£130	£150
		b. Surch double		—	£475
		c. Surch double, one on back of stamp		£550	

| **TWO CENTS** | **TWO CENTS** |
| (32) | (33) |

1891 (10–16 Sept). *Nos. 88, 96, 98 and 105 surch locally as T 32 (Nos. 118/19, 121) or T 33 (No. 120).*

118	19	2 c. on 4 c. carmine (No. 105) (12 Sept)	1·50	60
		a. Surch inverted		70·00	
		b. Surch double		75·00	70·00
		c. Surch double, one inverted	..	75·00	70·00
119	22	2 c. on 17 c. rose (No. 96) (16 Sept)	90·00	90·00
		a. Surch inverted		£250	
		b. Surch double		£475	£475
120	9	2 c. on 38 c. on 9d. pale violet (No. 89) (16 Sept)	..	1·90	3·50
		a. Surch inverted		£250	
		b. Surch double		£475	£475
		c. Surch double, one inverted		£100	£110
121	24	2 c. on 38 c. bright purple (No. 98)	2·50	3·75
		a. Surch inverted		£500	
		b. Surch double		£120	
		c. Surch double, one inverted	..	£120	

Minor varieties are also known with portions of the surcharge missing, due to defective printing.

| **ONE CENT** | **ONE CENT** |
| (34) | (35) |

1893 (1–7 Jan). *Surch with T 34 by D.L.R. or T 35 locally. Wmk Crown CA. P 14.*

123	18	1 c. on 2 c. pale violet (Optd S. £28)	1·25	50
124	27	1 c. on 16 c. chestnut (7 Jan)	..	1·25	2·75
		w. Wmk inverted		35·00	

| 36 | 37 |

(Typo D.L.R.)

1895–9. *Wmk Crown CA. P 14.*

127	36	1 c. dull purple and ultramarine (8.7.97)	75	1·25
128		2 c. dull purple and orange (8.7.97)	..	2·00	50
129		3 c. dull purple and deep purple	60	50
130		4 c. dull purple and emerald (8.7.97)	..	3·75	70
131		6 c. green and rose-red (1899)	..	4·00	4·00
132		18 c. green and ultramarine (8.7.97)	6·50	5·00
127/32			Set of 6	16·00	10·50
127/32 Optd "Specimen"	..	Set of 6	85·00	

(Des L. Duvergé. Typo D.L.R.)

1898 (15 Apr). *Diamond Jubilee. Wmk CA over Crown (sideways). P 14.*

| 133 | 37 | 36 c. orange and ultramarine (Optd S. £45) | 10·00 | 15·00 |

| **6 CENTS** | **15 CENTS** |
| (38) | (39) |

1899 (23–28 May). *Nos. 132/3 surcharged with T 38/9 locally.*

134	36	6 c. on 18 c. green and ultramarine (R.)	1·00	1·00
		a. Surch inverted		£300	£170
135	37	15 c. on 36 c. orge & ultram (B.) (28 May)	1·40	1·75
		a. Bar of surch omitted		£250	

The space between "6" and "CENTS" varies from 2½ to 4 mm.

| 40 | 4 Cents |
| 40 Admiral Mahé de Labourdonnais, Governor of Mauritius, 1735–46 | (41) |

(Recess D.L.R.)

1899 (13 Dec). *Birth Bicentenary of Labourdonnais. Wmk Crown CC. P 14.*

| 136 | 40 | 15 c. ultramarine (Optd S. £70) | .. | 10·00 | 3·25 |
| | | w. Wmk inverted | | 50·00 | |

1900. *No. 109 surch with T 41 locally.*

| 137 | 27 | 4 c. on 16 c. chestnut | .. | 2·50 | 8·00 |

| 42 | 12 CENTS |
| | (43) |

(Typo D.L.R.)

1900–05. *Wmk Crown CC (1 r.) or Crown CA (others) (sideways on 2 r. 50, 5 r.). Ordinary paper. P 14.*

138	36	1 c. grey and black (1901)		50	10
139		2 c. dull purple and bright purple (4.01)	75	20
140		3 c. green and carmine/yellow (1902)	3·50	1·25
141		4 c. purple and carmine/yellow	1·50	40
		w. Wmk inverted			
142		4 c. grey-green and violet (1903)	60	2·00
		w. Wmk inverted			
143		4 c. black and carmine/blue (14.10.04)	5·00	60
		w. Wmk inverted		15·00	15·00
144		5 c. dull purple & brt pur/buff (8.10.02)	6·00	50·00
145		5 c. dull purple and black/buff (2.03)	2·50	2·50
146		6 c. purple and carmine/red (1902)	1·50	80
		w. Wmk inverted		20·00	15·00
147		8 c. green and black/buff (16.7.02)	1·75	6·00
148		12 c. grey-black and carmine (16.7.02)	1·75	2·25
149		15 c. green and orange	10·00	6·00
		w. Wmk inverted			
150		15 c. black and blue/blue (1905)	48·00	1·25
151		25 c. green and carmine/green (1902)	8·50	17·00
		a. Chalk-surfaced paper		2·75	11·00
152		50 c. dull green & dp green/yellow (1902)	16·00	29·00
153	42	1 r. grey-black and carmine (1902)	48·00	42·00
		w. Wmk inverted		80·00	
154		2 r. 50, green and black/blue (1902)	16·00	75·00
155		5 r. purple and carmine/red (1902)	55·00	75·00
138/55			Set of 18	£200	£275
138/55 Optd "Specimen"		Set of 18	£275	

1902. *No. 132 surch with T 43.*

| 156 | 36 | 12 c. on 18 c. green and ultramarine | 1·75 | 5·00 |

The bar cancelling the original value seems in some cases to be one thick bar and in others two thin ones.

Postage & Revenue.

(43)

1902 (7 July). *Various stamps optd with T 44 locally.*

157	36	4 c. purple and carmine/yellow (No. 141)	75	20
158		6 c. green and rose-red (No. 131)	75	2·50
159		15 c. green and orange (No. 149)	..	2·00	30
160	23	25 c. olive-yellow (No. 110)	..	2·00	2·50
161	25	50 c. green (No. 99)	..	3·75	2·50
162	26	2 r. 50, brown-purple (No. 100)	..	75·00	95·00
157/62			Set of 6	75·00	95·00

Nos. 157/62 were overprinted to make surplus stocks of postage stamps available for revenue (fiscal) purposes also.

1902 (22 Sept). *No. 133 surch as T 43, but with longer bar.*

| 163 | 37 | 12 c. on 36 c. orange and ultramarine | .. | 1·25 | 1·25 |
| | | a. Surch inverted | | £425 | £325 |

The note below No. 156 also applies to No. 163.

Forged double surcharge errors show a straight, instead of a curved, serif to the "1" of "12".

1904–7. *Wmk Mult Crown CA. Ordinary paper (2 c., 4 c., 6 c.) or chalk-surfaced paper (others). P 14.*

164	36	1 c. grey and black (1907)	..	8·00	3·25
165		2 c. dull and bright purple (1905)	..	19·00	2·75
		a. Chalk-surfaced paper		19·00	1·75
166		3 c. green and carmine/yellow	..	21·00	8·50
167		4 c. black and carmine/blue	..	9·00	1·50
		a. Chalk-surfaced paper		1·75	10

168	36	6 c. purple and carmine/*red*	..	6·50	30
171		15 c. black and blue/*blue* (1907)		4·00	35
174		50 c. green and deep green/*yellow*		1·50	2·25
175	42	1 r. grey-black and carmine (1907)		20·00	45·00
164/75			*Set of 8*	65·00	55·00

46

47

(Typo D.L.R.)

1910 (17 Jan). *Wmk Mult Crown CA. Ordinary paper (1 c. to 15 c.) or chalk-surfaced paper (25 c. to 10 r.). P 14.*

181	46	1 c. black	..	2·50	30
182		2 c. brown	..	2·50	10
183		3 c. green	..	2·75	10
		a. "A" of "CA" missing from wmk		†	—
		w. Wmk inverted		20·00	
184		4 c. pale yellow-green and carmine		3·25	10
		w. Wmk inverted		—	30·00
185	47	5 c. grey and carmine		2·50	2·75
186	46	6 c. carmine-red		2·00	20
		a. *Pale red*		2·50	95
		ab. "A" of "CA" missing from wmk		†	
187		8 c. orange	..	2·75	1·25
188	47	12 c. greyish slate		1·75	2·50
189	46	15 c. blue		16·00	20
190	47	25 c. black and red/*yellow*		1·75	11·00
191		50 c. dull purple and black		1·75	17·00
192		1 r. black/*green*		6·00	11·00
193		2 r. 50 black and blue/*blue*		10·00	60·00
194		5 r. green and red/*yellow*		26·00	85·00
195		10 r. green and red/*green*		85·00	£170
181/95			*Set of 15*	£150	£325
181/95 Optd "Specimen"			*Set of 15*	£250	

On Nos. 188, 190 and 195 the value labels are as in T **49**.

48

49

(Typo D.L.R.)

1913–22. *Die I. Wmk Mult Crown CA. Ordinary paper (5 c., 12 c.) or chalk-surfaced paper (others). P 14.*

196	48	5 c. grey and carmine (1913)	..	1·75	3·75
		a. *Slate-grey and carmine*		10·00	10·00
198	49	12 c. greyish slate (1914)		4·00	85
199		25 c. black and red/*yellow* (1913)		40	1·40
		a. *White back* (1914)		50	13·00
		aw. Wmk inverted and reversed		25·00	
		b. *On orange-buff* (1920)		32·00	60·00
		c. *On pale yellow* (1921) (Optd S. £30)		32·00	40·00
		cw. Wmk inverted		75·00	
		d. *Die II. On pale yellow* (1921) (Optd S. £30)		60	15·00
200	48	50 c. dull purple and black (1920)		35·00	60·00
201		1 r. black/*blue-green* (*olive back*) (1917)		3·25	17·00
		a. *On emerald* (*olive back*) (1921)		7·50	48·00
		b. *Die II. On emerald* (*emerald back*) (1921) (Optd S. £30)		2·25	6·50
202		2 r. 50, black and blue/*blue* (1916)		16·00	45·00
203		5 r. green and red/*orange-buff* (1921)		65·00	£100
		a. *On pale yellow* (1921)		55·00	£100
		b. *Die II. On pale yellow* (1922)		45·00	£130
204	49	10 r. grn & red/*grn* (*bl-grn back*) (1913)		55·00	£110
		a. *On blue-green* (*olive back*) (1919)		£750	
		b. *On emerald* (*olive back*) (1921)		65·00	£100
		c. *On emerald* (*emerald back*) (1921)		40·00	£110
		d. *Die II. On emerald* (*emerald back*) (1922) (Optd. S. £38)		26·00	90·00
196/204			*Set of 8*	£120	£275
196/202, 203a, 204 Optd "Specimen"			*Set of 8*	£180	

1921–26. *Wmk Mult Script CA. Chalk-surfaced paper (50 r.). P 14.*

205	46	1 c. black		1·00	90
		w. Wmk inverted			
206		2 c. brown		1·00	10
		w. Wmk inverted			
207		2 c. purple/*yellow* (1926)		60	20
		w. Wmk inverted		15·00	
208		3 c. green (1926)		2·75	40
209		4 c. pale olive-green and carmine		1·50	1·75
		x. Wmk reversed			
210		4 c. green (1922)		1·00	10
		w. Wmk inverted			
		x. Wmk reversed			
211		4 c. brown (1926)		2·75	1·25
212		6 c. carmine		12·00	6·50
		x. Wmk reversed		50·00	
213		6 c. bright mauve (1922)		1·25	10
214		8 c. orange (1925)		2·25	16·00
215		10 c. grey (1922)		2·00	3·25
216		10 c. carmine-red (1926)		3·75	1·25
217		12 c. carmine-red (1922)		1·50	40
218		12 c. grey (1926)		1·75	3·00
219		15 c. blue		5·50	4·50
		ax. Wmk reversed		50·00	
		b. *Cobalt* (1926)		75	25
220		20 c. blue (1922)		2·00	80
221		20 c. purple (1926)		8·50	10·00
222	—	50 r. dull purple and green (1924) (Optd S. £190)		£700	£1300
205/21			*Set of 17*	42·00	42·00
205/21 Optd "Specimen"			*Set of 17*	£300	

No. 222 is as Type **46**, but measures 25×35 mm.

Normal   Open "C" (R. 9/6 of right pane)

A   B

Two types of duty plate in the 12 c. In Type B the letters of "MAURITIUS" are larger; the extremities of the downstroke and the tail of the "2" are pointed, instead of square, and the "c" is larger.

1921–34. *Die II. Wmk Mult Script CA. Chalk-surfaced paper (25 c. to 10 r.). P 14.*

223	49	1 c. black (1926)		80	1·00
224		2 c. brown (1926)		70	10
225		3 c. green (1926)		70	30
226		4 c. sage-green and carmine (1926)		60	30
		a. Open "C"		32·00	
		b. Die I (1932)		6·00	32·00
		ba. Open "C"		80·00	
226c		4 c. green (Die I) (1932)		4·50	45
		ca. Open "C"		65·00	
227	48	5 c. grey and carmine (1922)		90	10
		a. Die I (1932)		5·00	5·00
228	49	6 c. sepia (1927)		1·00	60
229		8 c. orange (1926)		75	9·00
230		10 c. carmine-red (1926)		1·00	20
		a. Die I (1932)		6·00	7·00
231		12 c. grey (Type A) (1922)		1·00	11·00
232		12 c. carmine-red (Type A) (1922)		30	3·00
232a		12 c. pale grey (Type A) (1926) (Optd S. £32)		1·40	11·00
232b		12 c. grey (Type B) (1934)		4·25	20
233		15 c. Prussian blue (1926)		80	20
234		20 c. purple (1926)		55	40
235		20 c. Prussian blue (Die I) (1932)		9·50	80
		a. Die II (1934)		11·00	30
236		25 c. black and red/*pale yellow* (1922)		30	15
		a. Die I (1932)		2·75	27·00
237	48	50 c. dull purple and black (1921)		7·50	3·50
238		1 r. black/*emerald* (1924)		3·50	40
		a. Die I (1932)		15·00	26·00
239		2 r. 50, black and red/*blue* (1922)		19·00	6·00
240		5 r. green and red/*yellow* (1924)		27·00	60·00
241	49	10 r. green and red/*emerald* (1924)		60·00	£150
223/41			*Set of 20*	£120	£200
223/41 Optd/Perf "Specimen"			*Set of 20*	£375	

3
Cents

(50)   51

1925 (25 Nov). *Nos. 210, 217 and 220 surch locally as T* **50.**

242	46	3 c. on 4 c. green		2·50	3·75
243		10 c. on 12 c. carmine-red		30	30
244		15 c. on 20 c. blue		55	20
242/4			*Set of 3*	3·00	3·75
242/4 Optd "Specimen"			*Set of 3*	75·00	

1935 (6 May). *Silver Jubilee. As Nos. 114/17 of Jamaica but ptd by D.L.R. P* 13½×14.

245		5 c. ultramarine and grey		50	10
		f. Diagonal line by turret		40·00	
		g. Dot to left of chapel		70·00	
		h. Dot by flagstaff		70·00	
246		12 c. green and indigo		4·50	10
		f. Diagonal line by turret		80·00	
		g. Dot to left of chapel		£130	
247		20 c. brown and deep blue		4·50	20
		f. Diagonal line by turret		90·00	
		g. Dot to left of chapel		£130	
248		1 r. slate and purple		29·00	40·00
		h. Dot by flagstaff		£350	
245/8			*Set of 4*	35·00	40·00
245/8 Perf "Specimen"			*Set of 4*	85·00	

For illustrations of plate varieties see Omnibus section following Zimbabwe.

Line through sword (R. 2/2)   Line by sceptre (R. 5/3)

1937 (12 May). *Coronation. As Nos. 118/20 of Jamaica.*

249		5 c. violet		40	10
250		12 c. scarlet		40	1·50
251		20 c. bright blue		40	10
		a. Line through sword		55·00	
		b. Line by sceptre		55·00	
249/51			*Set of 3*	1·10	1·50
249/51 Perf "Specimen"			*Set of 3*	55·00	

Sliced "S" at right (R. 2/2, 3/2, right pane)   Sliced "S" at top (R. 4/1, left pane and R. 8/4, right pane)

Broken frame under "A" of "MAURITIUS" (R. 9/3 left pane, Key Plate 2)

"IJ" flaw (R. 3/6 of right pane)   Battered "A" (R. 6/1 of right pane)

(Typo D.L.R.)

1938–49. *T* **51** *and similar types. Wmk Mult Script CA. Chalk-surfaced paper (25 c. to 10 r.). P 14.*

252		2 c. olive-grey (9.3.38)		30	10
		a. Perf 15×14 (1942)		1·00	10
253		3 c. reddish purple and scarlet (27.10.38)		2·00	1·75
		a. Sliced "S" at right		70·00	
		b. *Reddish lilac and red* (4.43)		2·75	2·75
		ba. Sliced "S" at right		8·00	
254		4 c. dull green (26.2.38)		2·50	1·75
		a. Open "C"		80·00	
		b. *Deep dull green* (4.43)		1·00	1·75
		ba. Open "C"		55·00	
255		5 c. slate-lilac (23.2.38)		7·50	70
		a. *Pale lilac* (shades) (4.43)		2·25	20
		b. Perf 15×14 (1942)		45·00	10
256		10 c. rose-red (9.3.38)		2·25	20
		a. Sliced "S" at top		85·00	
		b. *Deep reddish rose* (shades) (4.43)		2·25	10
		ba. Sliced "S" at top		85·00	
		c. Perf 15×14. *Pale reddish rose* (1942)		27·00	90
		ca. Sliced "S" at top		£275	
257		12 c. salmon (shades) (26.2.38)		1·00	20
		a. Perf 15×14 (1942)		50·00	75
258		20 c. blue (26.2.38)		1·00	10
		a. Broken frame		£130	
259		25 c. brown-purple (2.3.38)		8·00	20
		a. "IJ" flaw		£190	
		b. Ordinary paper (8.4.43)		5·00	10
		ba. "IJ" flaw		£130	
260		1 r. grey-brown (2.3.38)		22·00	1·50
		a. Battered "A"		£300	
		b. Ordinary paper (8.4.43)		16·00	90
		ba. Battered "A"		£225	
		c. *Drab* (4.49)		24·00	4·00
		ca. Battered "A"		£300	
261		2 r. 50, pale violet (2.3.38)		38·00	11·00
		a. Ordinary paper (8.4.43)		27·00	10·00
		b. *Slate-violet* (4.48)		45·00	24·00
262		5 r. olive-green (2.3.38)		48·00	22·00
		a. Ordinary paper. *Sage-green* (8.4.43)		27·00	22·00
263		10 r. reddish purple (shades) (2.3.38)		42·00	28·00
		a. Ordinary paper (8.4.43)		11·00	22·00
252/63a			*Set of 12*	85·00	50·00
252/63 Perf "Specimen"			*Set of 12*	£180	

The stamps perf 15 × 14 were printed by Bradbury, Wilkinson from De La Rue plates and issued only in the colony in 1942. De La Rue printings of the 2 c. to 20 c. in 1943–45 were on thin, whiter paper. 1943–45 printings of the 25 c. to 10 r. were on unsurfaced paper.

1946 (20 Nov). *Victory. As Nos. 141/2 of Jamaica.*

264		5 c. lilac		10	10
265		20 c. blue		10	10
264/5 Perf "Specimen"			*Set of 2*	50·00	

52 1d. "Post Office" Mauritius and King George VI

(Recess B.W.)

1948 (22 Mar). *Centenary of First British Colonial Postage Stamp. Wmk Mult Script CA. P* 11½×11.

266	52	5 c. orange and magenta		10	30
267		12 c. orange and green		10	10
268	—	20 c. blue and light blue		10	10
269	—	1 r. blue and red-brown		15	30
266/9			*Set of 4*	40	60
266/9 Perf "Specimen"			*Set of 4*	95·00	

Design:—20 c., 1 r. As T **52** but showing 2d. "Post Office" Mauritius.

1948 (25 Oct). *Royal Silver Wedding. As Nos. 143/4 of Jamaica.*

270		5 c. violet		10	10
271		10 r. magenta		9·50	22·00

1949 (10 Oct). *75th Anniv of U.P.U. As Nos. 145/8 of Jamaica.*

272	12 c. carmine		40	65
273	20 c. deep blue		1·75	1·50
274	35 c. purple		40	65
275	1 r. sepia		40	20
272/5		Set of 4	2·75	2·75

53 Labourdonnais Sugar Factory   **55** Aloe Plant

(Photo Harrison)

1950 (1 July). *T* **53, 55** *and similar designs. Wmk Mult Script CA. Chalk surfaced paper. P* 13½ × 14½ (*horiz*), 14½ × 13½ (*vert*).

276	1 c. bright purple		10	50
277	2 c. rose-carmine		15	10
278	3 c. yellow-green		60	2·50
279	4 c. green		20	1·25
280	5 c. blue		15	10
281	10 c. scarlet		30	75
282	12 c. olive-green		1·25	2·00
283	20 c. ultramarine		60	15
284	25 c. brown-purple		1·25	40
285	35 c. violet		30	10
286	50 c. emerald-green		2·00	50
287	1 r. sepia		4·25	10
288	2 r. 50, orange		12·00	6·50
289	5 r. red-brown		14·00	14·00
290	10 r. dull blue		14·00	18·00
276/290		Set of 15	45·00	40·00

Designs: *Horiz*—2 c. Grand Port; 5 c. Rempart Mountain; Transporting cane; 12 c. Mauritius Dodo and map; 35 c. Government House, Reduit; 1 r. Timor Deer; 2 r. 50, Port Louis; 5 r. Beach scene; 10 r. Arms of Mauritius. *Vert*—4 c. Tamarind Falls; 20 c. Legend of Paul and Virginie (inscr "VIRGINIA"); 25 c. Labourdonnais statue; 50 c. Pieter Both Mountain.

The latitude is incorrectly shown on No. 282. This was corrected before the same design was used for No. 302a.

1953 (2 June). *Coronation. As No. 153 of Jamaica.*

291	10 c. black and emerald		70	15

68 Tamarind Falls   **69** Historical Museum, Mahebourg

(Photo Harrison)

1953 (3 Nov)–**58**. *Designs previously used for King George VI issue, but with portrait of Queen Elizabeth II as in T* **68/9**. *Wmk Mult Script CA. Chalk-surfaced paper. P* 13½×14½ (*horiz*) *or* 14½×13½ (*vert*).

293	2 c. bright carmine (1.6.54)		10	10
294	3 c. yellow-green (1.6.54)		30	40
295	4 c. bright purple		10	60
	w. Wmk inverted		27·00	
296	5 c. Prussian blue (1.6.54)		10	10
297	10 c. bluish green		20	10
	a. Yellowish green (9.2.55)		20	10
298	15 c. scarlet		10	10
299	20 c. brown-purple		15	20
	w. Wmk inverted		6·00	
300	25 c. bright ultramarine		1·50	10
	a. Bright blue (19.6.57)		3·25	30
301	35 c. reddish violet (1.6.54)		20	10
	w. Wmk inverted			
302	50 c. bright green		55	75
302a	60 c. deep green (2.8.54)		10·00	10
	ab. Bronze-green (27.8.58)		11·00	10
303	1 r. sepia		30	10
	a. Deep grey-brown (19.6.57)		2·00	65
	w. Wmk inverted		£130	
304	2 r. 50, orange (1.6.54)		14·00	9·00
305	5 r. red-brown (1.6.54)		14·00	9·00
	a. Orange-brown (19.6.57)		25·00	11·00
306	10 r. deep grey-blue (1.6.54)		13·00	10·00
293/306		Set of 15	48·00	19·00

Designs: *Horiz*—2 c. Grand Port; 4 c. Sugar factory; 5 c. Rempart Mountain; 35 c. Government House; 60 c. Mauritius Dodo and map; 1 r. Timor Deer; 2 r. 50, Port Louis; 5 r. Beach scene; 10 r. Arms of Mauritius. *Vert*—20 c. Aloe plant; 25 c. Labourdonnais statue; 25 c. Legend of Paul and Virginie; 50 c. Pieter Both Mountain.

Nos. 296 and 300 exist in coils, constructed from normal sheets.
See also Nos. 314/16.

70 Queen Elizabeth II and King George III (after Lawrence)

(Litho Enschedé)

1961 (11 Jan). *150th Anniv of British Post Office in Mauritius. W* w **12**. *P* 13½ × 14.

307	**70**	10 c. black and brown-red	10	10
		w. Wmk inverted	70·00	15·00
308		20 c. ultramarine and light blue	30	25
		w. Wmk inverted	38·00	
309		35 c. black and yellow	40	25
310		1 r. deep maroon and green	60	25
		w. Wmk inverted		
307/10			Set of 4	1·25	70

1963 (4 June). *Freedom from Hunger. As No. 80 of Lesotho.*

311	60 c. reddish violet		40	10

1963 (2 Sept). *Red Cross Centenary. As Nos. 203/4 of Jamaica.*

312	10 c. red and black		15	10
313	60 c. red and blue		60	20

1963 (12 Nov)–**65**. *As Nos. 297, 302ab and 304 but wmk w* **12**.

314	**68**	10 c. bluish green (1964)	15	10
		a. Yellowish green (21.1.65)	25	10
315	—	60 c. bronze-green (28.5.64)	1·75	10
316	—	2 r. 50, orange	5·50	8·50
314/16			Set of 3	6·75	8·50

71 Bourbon White Eye

(Des D. M. Reid-Henry. Photo Harrison)

1965 (16 Mar). *Horiz designs as T* **71**. *W* w **12** (*upright*). *Multicoloured; background colours given. P* 14½×14.

317	2 c. lemon		40	15
	a. Grey (leg) omitted		£120	
	w. Wmk inverted		9·00	
318	3 c. brown		1·00	15
	a. Black (eye and beak) omitted		£110	
	w. Wmk inverted		26·00	
319	4 c. light reddish purple		30	15
	a. Mauve-pink omitted*		45·00	
	b. Pale grey omitted		£110	
	c. Orange omitted		£160	
	w. Wmk inverted		4·00	
320	5 c. grey-brown		3·25	10
	w. Wmk inverted		50·00	
321	10 c. light grey-green		30	10
	w. Wmk inverted		6·00	
322	15 c. pale grey		2·00	40
	a. Red (beak) omitted		85·00	
	w. Wmk inverted		28·00	
323	20 c. light yellow-bistre		2·00	10
	w. Wmk inverted		9·50	
324	25 c. bluish grey		2·00	30
	w. Wmk inverted		7·50	
325	35 c. greyish blue		3·25	10
	w. Wmk inverted		55·00	
326	50 c. light yellow-buff		50	40
	w. Wmk inverted		40·00	
327	60 c. light greenish yellow		60	10
	w. Wmk inverted		1·50	
328	1 r. light yellow-olive		5·50	10
	a. Pale orange omitted		£130	
	b. Light grey (ground) omitted		£170	
329	2 r. 50, pale stone		5·00	6·00
330	5 r. pale grey-blue		14·00	9·50
	a. Brown-red omitted		£140	
331	10 r. pale bluish green		26·00	19·00
317/31		Set of 15	55·00	32·00

Designs:—3 c. Rodriguez Fody; 4 c. Mauritius Olive White Eye; 5 c. Mascarene Paradise Flycatcher; 10 c. Mauritius Fody; 15 c. Mauritius Parakeet; 20 c. Mauritius Greybird; 25 c. Mauritius Kestrel; 35 c. Pink Pigeon; 50 c. Reunion Bulbul; 60 c. Mauritius Blue Pigeon (extinct); 1 r. Mauritius Dodo (extinct); 2 r. 50, Rodriguez Solitaire (extinct); 5 r. Mauritius Red Rail (extinct); 10 r. Broad-billed Parrot (extinct).

*On the 4 c. the background is printed in two colours so that in No. 319a the background colour is similar to that of the 5 c.

On No. 317a it is the deep grey which is missing, affecting the leg, beak and part of the branch. On No. 319c the missing orange affects the under breast of the bird, which appears much paler. On No. 328a the omission affects the legs and part of the body and on No. 330a the whole of the bird appears in the same colour as the legs.

The 50 c. and 2 r. 50 exist with PVA gum as well as gum arabic. Nos. 320 and 324 exist in coils, constructed from normal sheets.

See also Nos. 340/1 and 370/5.

1965 (17 May). *I.T.U. Centenary. As Nos. 98/9 of Lesotho.*

332	10 c. red-orange and apple-green		15	10
333	60 c. yellow and bluish violet		60	20

1965 (25 Oct). *International Co-operation Year. As Nos. 100/1 of Lesotho.*

334	10 c. reddish purple and turquoise-green		15	10
335	60 c. deep bluish green and lavender		30	20

1966 (24 Jan). *Churchill Commemoration. As Nos. 102/5 of Lesotho.*

336	2 c. new blue		10	2·25
	w. Wmk inverted		32·00	
337	10 c. deep green		25	10
	w. Wmk inverted		23·00	
338	60 c. brown		1·10	20
	w. Wmk inverted		8·00	
339	1 r. bluish violet		1·25	20
336/9		Set of 4	2·40	2·50

1966–67. *As Nos. 320, 325 but wmk w* **12** *sideways*.

340	5 c. grey-brown (1966)		40	15
	w. Wmk Crown to right of CA		30·00	
341	35 c. greyish blue (27.6.67)		30	15

*The normal sideways watermark shows Crown to left of CA, as seen from the back of the stamp.
No. 340 exists in coils, constructed from normal sheets.

72 "Education"

73 "Science"

74 "Culture"

(Des Jennifer Toombs. Litho Harrison)

1966 (1 Dec). *20th Anniv of U.N.E.S.C.O. W* w **12** (*sideways*). *P* 14.

342	**72**	5 c. slate-violet, red, yellow and orange	15	30
343	**73**	10 c. orange-yellow, violet and deep olive	25	10
344	**74**	60 c. black, bright purple and orange	95	15
342/4			Set of 3	1·25	45

SELF-GOVERNMENT

86 Red-tailed Tropic Bird

(Des D. M. Reid-Henry. Photo Harrison)

1967 (1 Sept). *Self-Government. T* **86** *and similar horiz designs. Multicoloured. W* w **12**. *P* 14½.

345	2 c. Type **86**		20	1·25
	w. Wmk inverted		9·50	
346	10 c. Rodriguez Brush Warbler		60	10
347	60 c. Rose-ringed Parakeet (extinct)		70	10
348	1 r. Grey-rumped Swiftlet		70	10
345/8		Set of 4	2·00	1·40

SELF GOVERNMENT 1967

(90)

1967 (1 Dec). *Self-Government. As Nos. 317/31 but wmk sideways* *on Nos. 352/3 and 357. Optd with T* **90**. *P* 14×14½.

349	2 c. lemon		10	50
	w. Wmk inverted		6·00	
350	3 c. brown		10	50
	w. Wmk inverted		9·00	
351	4 c. light reddish purple		10	50
	a. Orange omitted		80·00	
352	5 c. grey-brown		10	10
353	10 c. light grey-green		10	10
	w. Wmk Crown to right of CA		9·00	
354	15 c. pale grey		10	30
355	20 c. light yellow-bistre		15	10
	w. Wmk inverted		6·50	
356	25 c. bluish grey		15	10
357	35 c. greyish blue		20	10
	w. Wmk Crown to right of CA		45·00	
358	50 c. light yellow-buff		30	15
359	60 c. light greenish yellow		30	10
	w. Wmk inverted		3·50	
360	1 r. light yellow-olive		50	10
361	2 r. 50, pale stone		1·00	2·25
362	5 r. pale grey-blue		6·00	3·25
363	10 r. pale bluish green		8·00	20·00
349/63		Set of 15	15·00	20·00

*The normal sideways watermark shows Crown to left of CA, as seen from the back of the stamp.

INDEPENDENT

91 Flag of Mauritius

(Litho D.L.R.)

1968 (12 Mar). *Independence. T 91 and similar horiz design.*
P 13½ × 13.

364	91	2 c. multicoloured			10	1·50
365	–	3 c. multicoloured			15	1·50
366	91	15 c. multicoloured			20	10
367	–	20 c. multicoloured			50	10
368	91	60 c. multicoloured			60	10
369	–	1 r. multicoloured			95	10
364/9				Set of 6	2·25	2·75

Design:—3 c., 20 c. and 1 r. Arms and Mauritius Dodo emblem.

1968 (12 July). *As Nos. 317/18, 322/3 and 327/8 but background colours changed as below.*

370		2 c. olive-yellow			20	1·75
	a.	Black printed double			£120	
	b.	Grey printed double			80·00	
371		3 c. cobalt			1·75	3·75
	w.	Wmk inverted			55·00	
372		15 c. cinnamon			55	20
	a.	Greenish blue omitted			£160	
373		20 c. buff			3·50	3·00
374		60 c. rose			1·50	15
	w.	Wmk inverted			30·00	
375		1 r. reddish purple			2·50	1·25
370/5				Set of 6	9·00	9·00

93 Dominique rescues Paul and Virginie

(Des V. Whiteley, from prints. Litho Format)

1968 (2 Dec). *Bicentenary of Bernardin de St. Pierre's Visit to Mauritius. Multicoloured designs as T 93. P 13½.*

376		2 c. Type 93			10	80
377		15 c. Paul and Virginie crossing the river			25	10
378		50 c. Visit of Labourdonnais to Madame de la Tour (*horiz*)			40	10
379		60 c. Meeting of Paul and Virginie in Confidence (*vert*)			40	10
380		1 r. Departure of Virginie for Europe (*horiz*)			50	20
381		2 r. 50, Bernardin de St. Pierre (*vert*)			1·50	3·50
376/81				Set of 6	2·75	4·25

99 Black-spotted Emperor

(Des J. Vinson (3 c., 20 c., 1 r.), R. Granger Barrett (others). Photo Harrison)

1969 (12 Mar)–73. *W w 12 (sideways* on 2, 3, 4, 5, 10, 15, 60 and 75 c). Chalk-surfaced paper. P 14.*

382		2 c. multicoloured			10	1·75
	a.	Pale green printed double**			50·00	
383		3 c. multicoloured			10	2·50
	w.	Wmk Crown to right of CA			8·00	
384		4 c. multicoloured			1·40	2·75
	w.	Wmk Crown to right of CA			9·00	
385		5 c. multicoloured			30	10
386		10 c. scarlet, black and flesh			1·00	10
	w.	Wmk Crown to right of CA			8·00	
387		15 c. ochre, black and cobalt			30	10
	w.	Wmk Crown to right of CA			1·75	
388		20 c. multicoloured			65	70
	a.	Glazed ordinary paper (20.2.73)			45	6·00
389		25 c. red, black and pale apple-green			30	2·00
	a.	Glazed ordinary paper (22.1.71)			3·75	4·75
	w.	Wmk inverted			4·00	
390		30 c. multicoloured			1·50	1·50
	a.	Glazed, ordinary paper (20.3.73)			6·50	10·00
391		35 c. multicoloured			1·75	1·25
	a.	Glazed ordinary paper (3.2.71)			90	2·25
	aw.	Wmk inverted			2·50	
392		40 c. multicoloured			35	1·25
	a.	Glazed ordinary paper (20.2.73)			6·50	10·00
	aw.	Wmk inverted			11·00	
393		50 c. multicoloured			1·00	10
	a.	Red omitted			90·00	
	b.	Glazed ordinary paper (22.1.71)			1·50	20
	ba.	Red printed double				
	bw.	Wmk inverted			1·50	20
394		60 c. black, rose and ultramarine			1·50	10
395		75 c. multicoloured			1·50	2·25
	w.	Wmk Crown to right of CA			17·00	
396		1 r. multicoloured			60	10
	a.	Glazed ordinary paper (22.1.71)			2·25	15
	aw.	Wmk inverted			50·00	
397		2 r. 50, multicoloured			3·00	8·50
	a.	Glazed ordinary paper (20.2.73)			2·00	11·00
398		5 r. multicoloured			8·00	9·50
	a.	Glazed ordinary paper (22.1.71)			12·00	5·50
	aw.	Wmk inverted			25·00	
399		10 r. multicoloured			2·50	4·75
	w.	Wmk inverted (26.1.72)			2·50	3·00
382/99				Set of 18	22·00	32·00
388a/98a				Set of 9	32·00	45·00

Designs:—3 c. Red Reef Crab; 4 c. Episcopal Mitre (*Mitra mitra*); 5 c. Black-saddled Pufferfish ("Bourse"); 10 c. Starfish; 15 c. Sea Urchin; 20 c. Fiddler Crab; 25 c. Spiny Shrimp; 30 c. Single Harp Shells and Double Harp Shell; 35 c. Common Paper

Nautilus (*Argonauta argo*); 40 c. Spanish Dancer (*Hexabranchus sanguineus*); 50 c. Orange Spider Conch (*Lambis crocata*) and Violet Spider Conch (*Lambis violacea*); 60 c. Blue Marlin; 75 c. *Conus clytospira*; 1 r. Dolphin (fish); 2 r. 50, Spiny Lobster; 5 r. Ruby Snapper ("Sacré Chien Rouge"); 10 r. Yellow-edged Lyretail ("Croissant Queue Jaune").

*The normal sideways watermark shows Crown to left of CA, *as seen from the back of the stamp.*

**No. 382a occurs from a sheet on which a second printing of the pale green appears above the normal.

Nos. 385/6 and 389 exist in coils constructed from normal sheets.

See also Nos. 437/54 and 475/91.

117 Gandhi as Law Student 124 Frangourinier Cane-crusher (18th cent)

(Des J. W. Litho Format)

1969 (1 July). *Birth Centenary of Mahatma Gandhi. T 117 and similar vert designs. Multicoloured. W w 12. P 13½.*

400		2 c. Type 117			10	10
401		15 c. Gandhi as stretcher-bearer during Zulu Revolt			25	10
402		50 c. Gandhi as Satyagrahi in South Africa			30	40
403		60 c. Gandhi at No. 10 Downing Street, London			30	10
404		1 r. Gandhi in Mauritius, 1901			40	10
405		2 r. 50, Gandhi, the "Apostle of Truth and Non-Violence"			90	1·75
400/5				Set of 6	2·00	2·25
MS406		153 × 153 mm. Nos. 400/5			2·50	7·50

(Des V. Whiteley. Photo Enschedé)

1969 (22 Dec).* *150th Anniv of Telfair's Improvements to the Sugar Industry. T 124 and similar multicoloured designs. W w 12 (sideways on 2 c. to 1 r.), P 11½ × 11 (2 r. 50) or 11 × 11½ (others).*

407		2 c. Three-roller Vertical Mill			10	20
408		15 c. Type 124			10	10
409		60 c. Beau Rivage Factory, 1867			10	10
410		1 r. Mon Désert-Alma Factory, 1969			10	10
411		2 r. 50, Dr. Charles Telfair (*vert*)			25	1·00
407/11				Set of 5	45	1·25
MS412		159 × 88 mm. Nos. 407/11†. Wmk sideways. P 11 × 11½			1·25	2·25

*This was the local release date but the Crown Agents issued the stamps on 15 December.

† In the miniature sheet the 2 r. 50 is perf 11 at the top and imperf on the other three sides.

EXPO '70' OSAKA

(128) 129 Morne Plage, Mountain and Boeing 707

1970 (7 Apr). *World Fair, Osaka. Nos. 394 and 396 optd with T 128 by Harrison & Sons.*

413		60 c. black, rose and ultramarine			10	10
	w.	Wmk Crown to right of CA			50·00	
414		1 r. multicoloured			10	10

(Des H. Rose. Litho G. Gehringer, Kaiserslautern, Germany)

1970 (2 May). *Inauguration of Lufthansa Flight, Mauritius-Frankfurt. T 129 and similar multicoloured design. P 14.*

415		25 c. Type 129			10	10
416		50 c. Boeing 707 and Map (*vert*)			10	10

131 Lenin as a Student 133 2d. "Post Office" Mauritius and original Post Office

(Photo State Ptg Works, Moscow)

1970 (15 May). *Birth Centenary of Lenin. T 131 and similar vert design. P 12 × 11½.*

417		15 c. blackish green and silver			10	10
418		75 c. blackish brown and gold			20	20

Design:—75 c. Lenin as Founder of U.S.S.R.

(Des and litho D.L.R.)

1970 (15 Oct). *Port Louis, Old and New. T 133 and similar horiz designs. Multicoloured. W w 12 (sideways). P 14.*

419		5 c. Type 133			10	10
420		15 c. G.P.O. Building (built 1870)			10	10
421		50 c. Mail Coach (*c.* 1870)			40	10
422		75 c. Port Louis Harbour (1970)			55	10
423		2 r. 50, Arrival of Pierre A. de Suffren (1783)			70	70
419/23				Set of 5	1·60	80
MS424		165 × 95 mm. Nos. 419/23			2·75	7·00

138 U.N. Emblem and Symbols

(Des Jennifer Toombs. Litho Format)

1970 (24 Oct). *25th Anniv of United Nations. W w 12 (sideways). P 14½.*

425	138	10 c. multicoloured			10	10
426		60 c. multicoloured			40	10

139 Rainbow over Waterfall

(Des R. Granger Barrett from local ideas (60 c.), R. Granger Barrett from local ideas and adapted by N. Mossae (others). Litho Format)

1971 (12 Apr). *Tourism. T 139 and similar horiz designs. Multicoloured. W w 12 (sideways*). P 14.*

427		10 c. Type 139			35	10
428		15 c. Trois Mamelles Mountains			35	10
	w.	Wmk Crown to right of CA			14·00	
429		60 c. Beach scene			55	10
430		2 r. 50, Marine life			1·50	1·50
427/30				Set of 4	2·50	1·50

*The normal sideways watermark shows Crown to left of CA, *as seen from the back of the stamp.*

Nos. 427/30 are inscribed on the reverse with details of tourist attractions in Mauritius.

140 "Crossroads" of Indian Ocean

(Des R. Granger Barrett (60 c.) or V. Whiteley (others). Litho Harrison)

1971 (23 Oct). *25th Anniv of Plaisance Airport. T 140 and similar horiz designs. Multicoloured. W w 12 (sideways* on 15 c.). P 14.*

431		15 c. Type 140			20	10
	w.	Wmk Crown to right of CA			24·00	
432		60 c. Boeing 707 and Terminal Buildings			40	10
	w.	Wmk inverted			2·50	
433		1 r. Air hostesses on gangway			45	10
	w.	Wmk inverted			3·00	90
434		2 r. 50, Farman F.190 Roland Garros airplane, Choisy Airfield, 1937			1·75	3·75
431/4				Set of 4	2·50	3·75

*The normal sideways watermark shows Crown to left of CA, *as seen from the back of the stamp.*

141 Princess Margaret Orthopaedic Centre

(Des and litho Harrison)

1971 (2 Nov). *Third Commonwealth Medical Conference. T 141 and similar horiz design. Multicoloured. W w 12. P 14 × 13½.*

435		10 c. Type 141			10	10
	w.	Wmk inverted			6·50	
436		75 c. Operation Theatre in National Hospital			20	20

1972 (10 Jan)–74. *As Nos. 382/99 but W w 12 upright (2, 3, 4, 5, 10, 15, 60, 75 c.) or sideways* (others). Glazed, ordinary paper (2, 3, 5, 10, 15, 60, 75 c.) or chalk-surfaced paper (others).*

437		2 c. multicoloured (20.2.73)			30	2·75
	a.	Chalk-surfaced paper (13.6.74)			1·50	4·25
	aw.	Wmk inverted			40·00	
438		3 c. multicoloured (20.2.73)			3·75	5·50
	a.	Chalk-surfaced paper (13.6.74)			40	2·00
439		4 c. multicoloured (13.6.74)			9·50	9·50
440		5 c. multicoloured			4·00	30
	aw.	Wmk inverted			60	
	b.	Chalk-surfaced paper (25.2.74)			30	10

441	10 c. scarlet, black and flesh	..	4·25	30
	a. Chalk-surfaced paper (8.11.73)	..	9·00	2·00
	aw. Wmk inverted		22·00	
442	15 c. ochre, black and cobalt (20.2.73)	..	50	90
	aw. Wmk inverted		38·00	
	b. Chalk-surfaced paper (25.2.74)		35	40
443	20 c. multicoloured (8.11.73)	..	35	2·00
	c. Printed on the gummed side		45·00	†
444	25 c. red, black and apple-green (12.12.73)		35	2·75
	w. Wmk Crown to right of CA		38·00	
445	30 c. multicoloured (8.11.73)	..	3·50	8·00
446	35 c. multicoloured (8.11.73)	..	6·00	75
	a. Orange-brown omitted		£100	
	w. Wmk Crown to right of CA		11·00	
447	40 c. multicoloured (8.11.73)	..	6·50	10·00
448	50 c. multicoloured (12.12.73)	..	45	10
	a. Red omitted		95·00	
	w. Wmk Crown to right of CA		30·00	30·00
449	60 c. black, rose and ultramarine (20.2.73)		60	60
	aw. Wmk inverted		17·00	
	b. Chalk-surfaced paper (25.2.74)		65	10
	ba. Rose omitted		70·00	
450	75 c. multicoloured (20.2.73)	..	1·75	10·00
	a. Chalk-surfaced paper (8.11.73)		3·00	1·25
451	1 r. multicoloured (8.11.73)	..	1·25	30
452	2 r. 50, multicoloured (12.12.73)	..	2·00	4·00
453	5 r. multicoloured (12.12.73)	..	3·00	2·00
	a. Greenish blue printed double		55·00	
454	10 r. multicoloured (8.11.73)	..	5·00	8·00
437/54		*Set of 18*	42·00	48·00

*The normal sideways watermark shows Crown to left of CA, as seen from the back of the stamp.

Nos. 440b and 444 exist in coils, constructed from normal sheets.

142 Queen Elizabeth and Prince Philip

(Des and photo Harrison)

1972 (24 Mar). *Royal Visit. T* **142** *and similar multicoloured design. W w* **12**. *P* 14.

455	15 c. Type **142**	..	15	10
456	2 r. 50, Queen Elizabeth II (*vert*)	..	2·50	2·50

143 Theatre Façade

(Des and litho Harrison)

1972 (26 June). *150th Anniversary of Port Louis Theatre. T* **143** *and similar horiz design. Multicoloured. W w* **12**. *P* 14.

457	10 c. Type **143**	..	10	10
	w. Wmk inverted		3·50	
458	1 r. Theatre Auditorium	..	40	20
	w. Wmk inverted	..	5·50	

144 Pirate Dhow

(Des and litho Harrison)

1972 (17 Nov). *Pirates and Privateers. T* **144** *and similar multicoloured designs. W w* **12** (*sideways on* 60 c. *and* 1 r.). *P* 14½ × 14 (60 c., 1 r.) *or* 14 × 14½ (*others*).

459	15 c. Type **144**	..	65	15
460	60 c. Treasure chest (*vert*)	..	1·00	20
461	1 r. Lemene and *L'Hirondelle* (*vert*)	..	1·25	20
462	2 r. 50, Robert Surcouf	..	4·50	7·50
459/62		*Set of 4*	6·75	7·50

145 Mauritius University   146 Map and Hands

(Des and litho Harrison)

1973 (10 Apr). *Fifth Anniv of Independence. T* **145** *and similar horiz designs. Multicoloured. W w* **12** (*sideways**). *P* 14.

463	15 c. Type **145**	..	10	10
	w. Wmk Crown to right of CA		30·00	
464	60 c. Tea Development	..	15	15
465	1 r. Bank of Mauritius	..	15	15
463/5		*Set of 3*	30	30

*The normal sideways watermark shows Crown to left of CA, as seen from the back of the stamp.

(Des and litho Harrison)

1973 (25 Apr). *O.C.A.M.* Conference. T* **146** *and similar multicoloured design. W w* **12** (*sideways on* 10 c.). *P* 14½ × 14 (10 c.) *or* 14 × 14½ (2 r. 50).

466	10 c. O.C.A.M. emblem (*horiz*)	..	10	10
467	2 r. 50, Type **146**	..	40	45

*O.C.A.M. = Organisation Commune Africaine Malgache et Mauricienne.

147 W.H.O. Emblem

(Des and litho Harrison)

1973 (20 Nov). *25th Anniv of W.H.O. W w* **12**. *P* 14.

468	**147** 1 r. multicoloured	..	10	10
	a. Wmk sideways	..	20	10

148 Meteorological Station, Vacoas.

(Des and litho Harrison)

1973 (27 Nov). *I.M.O./W.M.O. Centenary. W w* **12** (*sideways*). *P* 14.

469	**148** 75 c. multicoloured	..	30	60

149 Capture of the *Kent*, 1800   150 P. Commerson (naturalist)

(Des and litho Harrison)

1974 (21 Mar). *Birth Bicent of Robert Surcouf (privateer). W w* **12** (*sideways*). *P* 14.

470	**149** 60 c. multicoloured	..	50	85

(Des and litho Harrison)

1974 (18 Apr). *Death Bicent of Philibert Commerson (1973). W w* **12**. *P* 14½.

471	**150** 2 r. 50, multicoloured	..	30	40

151 Cow being Milked

(Des and litho Harrison)

1974 (23 Oct). *Eighth F.A.O. Regional Conference for Africa, Mauritius. W w* **12** (*sideways*). *P* 14.

472	**151** 60 c. multicoloured	..	20	20

152 Mail Train

(Des and litho Harrison)

1974 (4 Dec). *Centenary of Universal Postal Union. T* **152** *and similar horiz design. Multicoloured. W w* **12**. *P* 14.

473	15 c. Type **152**	..	40	15
474	1 r. New G.P.O., Port Louis	..	40	20

1975–77. *As Nos. 382/99 but W w* **14** (*sideways* on* 2 *to* 15 c., 60 c. *and* 75 c.). *Chalk-surfaced paper.*

475	2 c. multicoloured (16.8.77)	..	7·00	1·50
476	3 c. multicoloured (16.8.77)	..	7·00	1·50
	w. Wmk Crown to right of CA		28·00	
477	4 c. multicoloured (16.8.77)	..	8·00	1·50
478	5 c. multicoloured (19.3.75)	..	1·25	40
	w. Wmk Crown to right of CA		6·50	
479	15 c. ochre, black and cobalt (21.1.75)		2·25	1·25
	w. Wmk Crown to right of CA		8·00	
480	20 c. multicoloured (19.3.76)	..	70	30
	a. Grey (background) omitted		£200	
481	25 c. red, black and apple-green (19.3.75)		1·00	6·00
482	30 c. multicoloured (21.1.75)	..	35	7·50
	a. Yellow omitted		£100	
483	35 c. multicoloured (19.3.76)	..	1·00	15
	a. Orange-brown omitted		70·00	
484	40 c. multicoloured (19.3.76)	..	1·00	60
485	50 c. multicoloured (19.3.76)	..	1·00	10
	w. Wmk inverted		20·00	
486	60 c. black, rose and ultramarine (16.8.77)		7·50	25
487	75 c. multicoloured (19.4.77)	..	1·25	1·50
488	1 r. multicoloured (19.3.76)	..	1·00	20
	a. Deep bluish green (fin and tail markings) omitted		£140	
489	2 r. 50, multicoloured (16.8.77)	..	17·00	4·00
	w. Wmk inverted		21·00	
490	5 r. multicoloured (21.1.75)	..	5·00	15·00
	w. Wmk inverted		70·00	
491	10 r. multicoloured (21.1.75)	..	7·50	12·00
475/91		*Set of 17*	60·00	48·00

*The normal sideways watermark shows Crown to left of CA, as seen from the back of the stamp.

153 "Cottage Life" (F. Leroy)

(Des and litho Harrison)

1975 (6 Mar). *Aspects of Mauritian Life. T* **153** *and similar multicoloured designs showing paintings. W w* **14** (*sideways* on* 15 c., 60 c. *and* 2 r. 50). *P* 14.

493	15 c. Type **153**	..	10	10
	w. Wmk Crown to right of CA	..		
494	60 c. "Milk Seller" (A. Richard) (*vert*)		35	10
	a. Brown and stone (ornaments and frame) double			
495	1 r. "Entrance of Port Louis Market" (Thuillier)		35	10
496	2 r. 50, "Washerwoman" (Max Bouleé) (*vert*)		95	80
	w. Wmk Crown to right of CA		5·00	
493/6		*Set of 4*	1·60	85

*The normal sideways watermark shows Crown to left of CA, as seen from the back of the stamp.

154 Mace across Map

(Des Harrison. Litho Questa)

1975 (21 Nov). *French-speaking Parliamentary Assemblies Conference. Port Louis. W w* **14** (*sideways*). *P* 14.

497	**154** 75 c. multicoloured	..	30	1·00

155 Woman with Lamp ("The Light of the World")

(Des A. H. Abdoolah; adapted Harrison. Litho Questa)

1975 (5 Dec). *International Women's Year. W w* **14** (*sideways*). *P* 14½.

498	**155** 2 r. 50, multicoloured	..	35	1·25

156 Parched Landscape

(Des Harrison (50 c.), J.W. Ltd (60 c.) Litho Questa)

1976 (26 Feb). *Drought in Africa. T* **156** *and similar design. Multicoloured. W w* **14** (*sideways on* 50 c.). *P* 14.

499	50 c. Type **156**	..	15	15
500	60 c. Map of Africa and carcass (*vert*)	..	15	15

157 *Pierre Loti, 1953–70*

(Des J. W. Litho Questa)

1976 (2 July). *Mail Carriers to Mauritius.* T **157** *and similar horiz designs. Multicoloured.* W w **14** (*sideways**). P 14½×14.
501	10 c. Type **157**	55	10
502	15 c. Secunder, 1907	80	10
	w. Wmk Crown to right of CA	40·00	
503	50 c. Hindoostan, 1842	1·25	15
504	60 c. St. Geran, 1740	1·40	15
505	2 r. 50, Maën, 1638	3·25	6·50
501/5	*Set of 5*	6·50	6·50
MS506	115×138 mm. Nos. 501/5	7·00	9·00

*The normal sideways watermark shows Crown to left of CA, as seen from the back of the stamp.

158 "The Flame of Hindi carried across the Seas" **159** Conference Logo and Map of Mauritius

(Des N. Nagalingum (Type **158**), C. R. Prakashi and R. B. Kailash (1 r. 20); adapted J. W. Litho Questa)

1976 (28 Aug). *Second World Hindi Convention.* T **158** *and similar horiz design. Multicoloured.* W w **14** (*sideways*). P 14.
507	10 c. Type **158**	10	10
508	75 c. Type **158**	10	15
509	1 r. 20, Hindi script	20	70
507/9	*Set of 3*	30	80

(Des J. W. Litho Questa)

1976 (22 Sept). *22nd Commonwealth Parliamentary Association Conference.* T **159** *and similar vert design. Multicoloured.* W w **14**. P 14.
510	1 r. Type **159**	25	10
511	2 r. 50, Conference logo	50	1·25

160 King Priest and Breastplate **161** Sega Scene

(Des J. W. Litho Walsall)

1976 (15 Dec). *Moenjodaro Excavations, Pakistan.* T **160** *and similar vert designs. Multicoloured.* W w **14**. P 14.
512	60 c. Type **160**	30	10
513	1 r. House with well and goblet	50	10
514	2 r. 50, Terracotta figurine and necklace	1·25	80
512/14	*Set of 3*	1·75	85

(Des BG Studio. Litho J.W.)

1977 (20 Jan). *Second World Black and African Festival of Arts and Culture, Nigeria.* W w **14** (*sideways*). P 13.
515	**161** 1 r. multicoloured	30	15

162 The Queen with Sceptre and Rod **163** *Hugonia tomentosa*

(Des L. Curtis. Litho Harrison)

1977 (7 Feb). *Silver Jubilee.* T **162** *and similar vert designs. Multicoloured.* W w **14** (*sideways*). P 14½ × 14.
516	50 c. The Queen at Mauritius Legislative Assembly, 1972	15	10
517	75 c. Type **162**	20	10
518	5 r. Presentation of Sceptre and Rod	55	75
516/18	*Set of 3*	80	75

(Des Jennifer Toombs. Litho Questa)

1977 (22 Sept). *Indigenous Flowers.* T **163** *and similar multicoloured designs.* W w **14** (*sideways on 20 c. and 1 r. 50*). P 14.
519	20 c. Type **163**	20	10
520	1 r. Ochna mauritiana (vert)	40	10
521	1 r. 50, Dombeya acutangula	50	20
522	5 r. Trochetia blackburniana (vert)	1·10	1·25
519/22	*Set of 4*	2·00	1·40
MS523	130 × 130 mm. Nos. 519/22. Wmk sideways	3·00	6·00

164 De Havilland D.H.C.6 Twin Otter 200/300 **165** Portuguese Map of Mauritius, 1519

(Des A. Theobald. Litho Questa)

1977 (31 Oct). *Inaugural International Flight of Air Mauritius.* T **164** *and similar horiz designs. Multicoloured.* W w **14** (*sideways**). P 14½×14.
524	25 c. Type **164**	60	10
	w. Wmk Crown to right of CA	3·50	
525	50 c. De Havilland D.H.C.6 Twin Otter 200/300 and Air Mauritius emblem	80	10
	w. Wmk Crown to right of CA	3·75	
526	75 c. Piper PA-31 Navajo and Boeing 747-100	95	15
	w. Wmk Crown to right of CA	4·00	
527	5 r. Boeing 707	3·00	3·25
	w. Wmk Crown to right of CA	11·00	
524/7	*Set of 4*	4·75	3·25
MS528	110×152 mm. Nos. 524/7	6·00	6·00

*The normal sideways watermark shows Crown to left of CA, as seen from back of the stamp.

(Des Harrison. Litho J.W.)

1978 (12 Mar)–**85**. *Designs as* T **165** *in light brown, chestnut and black* (25 r.) *or multicoloured* (others). W w **14** (*sideways* on horiz designs*). P 13½. A. *Without imprint date.*
529A	10 c. Type **165**	50	1·50
530A	15 c. Dutch Occupation, 1638–1710 (horiz)	1·50	2·25
531A	20 c. Van Keulen's map, c. 1700 (horiz)	80	2·25
	w. Wmk Crown to left of CA	27·00	
532A	25 c. Settlement on Rodriguez, 1691	60	75
	w. Wmk inverted	4·25	
533A	35 c. French charter, 1715	30	1·25
	w. Wmk inverted	13·00	
534A	50 c. Construction of Port Louis, c. 1736 (horiz)	50	60
535A	60 c. Pierre Poivre, 1767	60	2·00
536A	70 c. Bellin's map, 1763 (horiz)	2·75	3·00
537A	75 c. First coinage, 1794	2·00	2·75
538A	90 c. Battle of Grand Port, 1810 (horiz)	2·75	3·00
539A	1 r. British landing, 1810 (horiz)	60	50
540A	1 r. 20, Government House, c. 1840 (horiz)	1·75	2·75
541A	1 r. 25, Lady Gomm's ball, 1847	1·50	40
542A	1 r. 50, Indian immigration, 1835 (horiz)	1·00	1·50
543A	2 r. Race course, c. 1870 (horiz)	60	40
	w. Wmk Crown to left of CA	3·75	
544A	3 r. Place d'Armes, c. 1880 (horiz)	60	40
545A	5 r. Royal Visit postcard, 1901 (horiz)	60	1·00
	w. Wmk Crown to left of CA	25·00	
546A	10 r. Royal College, 1914 (horiz)	1·00	1·00
547A	15 r. Unfurling Mauritian flag, 1968	1·50	2·25
548A	25 r. First Mauritian Prime Minister and Governor-General (horiz)	2·00	3·00
529A/48A	*Set of 20*	21·00	29·00

B. *With imprint date at foot.*
529B	10 c. Type **165** (11.84)	75	90
532B	25 c. Settlement on Rodriguez, 1691 (11.84)	1·25	40
533B	35 c. French charter, 1715 (1.84)	1·00	20
534B	50 c. Construction of Port Louis, c. 1736 (horiz) (11.84)	1·25	20
537B	75 c. First coinage, 1794 (15.6.83)	1·75	2·25
539B	1 r. British landing, 1810 (horiz) (4.85)	1·75	20
541B	1 r. 25, Lady Gomm's ball, 1847 (15.6.83)	1·50	20
543B	2 r. Race course, c. 1870 (horiz) (15.6.83)	1·25	30
545B	5 r. Royal Visit postcard, 1901 (horiz) (8.5.85)	5·50	6·00
529B/45B	*Set of 9*	14·00	9·50

*The normal sideways watermark shows Crown to right of CA, as seen from the back of the stamp.
Imprint dates: "1983", Nos. 533B, 537B, 541B, 543B; "1985", Nos. 529B, 532B/4B, 537B, 539B, 541B, 543B, 545B.
For 35 c. as No. 533B, but perforated 14½ see No. 737 and for values watermarked w **16** see Nos. 740/57.

COVER PRICES

Cover factors are quoted at the beginning of each country for most issues to 1945. An explanation of the system can be found on page x. The factors quoted do not, however, apply to philatelic covers.

---

166 Mauritius Dodo **167** Problem of Infection, World War I

(Des Jennifer Toombs. Litho Questa)

1978 (21 Apr). *25th Anniv of Coronation.* T **166** *and similar vert designs.* P 15.
549	3 r. grey-blue, black and new blue	25	45
	a. Sheetlet, Nos. 549/51, each × 2	1·75	
550	3 r. multicoloured	25	45
551	3 r. grey-blue, black and new blue	25	45
549/51	*Set of 3*	65	1·25

Designs:—No. 549, Antelope of Bohun; 550, Queen Elizabeth II. Nos. 549/51 were printed together in small sheets of 6, containing two *se-tenant* strips of 3 with horizontal gutter margin between.

(Des Jennifer Toombs. Litho Enschedé)

1978 (3 Aug). *50th Anniv of Discovery of Penicillin.* T **167** *and similar horiz designs.* W w **14** (*sideways*). P 13½ × 14.
552	20 c. multicoloured	50	10
553	1 r. multicoloured	1·10	10
554	1 r. 50, black, olive-bistre & dp bluish grn	1·50	1·40
555	5 r. multicoloured	2·25	2·25
552/5	*Set of 4*	4·75	6·25
MS556	150 × 90 mm. Nos. 552/5	6·00	7·00

Designs:—1 r. First mould-growth, 1928; 1 r. 50, *Penicillium chrysogenum* ("*notatum*"); 5 r. Sir Alexander Fleming.

168 *Papilio manlius* (butterfly) **169** Ornate Table

(Des G. Drummond. Litho Walsall)

1978 (21 Sept). *World Wildlife.* T **168** *and similar horiz designs. Multicoloured.* W w **14** (*sideways*). P 13½ × 14.
557	20 c. Type **168**	1·50	10
558	1 r. Geckos	90	10
559	1 r. 50 Greater Mascarene Flying Fox	1·25	75
560	5 r. Mauritius Kestrel	11·00	6·50
557/60	*Set of 4*	13·00	6·50
MS561	154×148 mm. Nos. 557/60	27·00	14·00

(Des C. Abbott. Litho Questa)

1978 (21 Dec). *Bicentenary of Reconstruction of Chateau Le Réduit.* T **169** *and similar vert designs. Multicoloured.* W w **14**. P 14½ × 14.
562	15 c. Type **169**	10	10
563	75 c. Chateau Le Réduit	10	10
564	3 r. Le Réduit gardens	30	45
562/4	*Set of 3*	40	50

170 Whitcomb Diesel Locomotive 65 H.P., 1949 **171** Father Laval and Crucifix

(Des G. Hutchins. Litho Questa)

1979 (1 Feb). *Railway Locomotives.* T **170** *and similar horiz designs. Multicoloured.* W w **14** (*sideways*). P 14½.
565	20 c. Type **170**	20	10
566	1 r. Sir William, 1922	40	10
567	1 r. 50, Kitson type, 1930	60	45
568	2 r. Garratt type, 1927	75	85
565/8	*Set of 4*	1·75	1·25
MS569	128 × 128 mm. Nos. 565/8	2·50	3·75

(Des J. W. Litho Questa)

1979 (30 Apr). *Beatification of Father Laval* (*missionary*). T **171** *and similar multicoloured designs.* W w **14** (*sideways on 5 r.*). P 14.
570	20 c. Type **171**	10	10
571	1 r. 50, Father Laval	10	10
572	5 r. Father Laval's tomb (horiz)	35	50
570/2	*Set of 3*	40	55
MS573	150 × 96 mm. Nos. 570/2 (wmk upright)	1·40	2·25

MAURITIUS — 1979

172 Astronaut descending from Lunar Module
173 Great Britain 1855 4d. Stamp and Sir Rowland Hill

(Manufactured by Walsall)

1979 (20 July). *10th Anniv of Moon Landing. T* **172** *and similar vert designs. Multicoloured. Imperf×roul 5*. Self-adhesive.*

574	20 c. Type 172	..	25	30
	a. Booklet pane. Nos. 574/6.	..	3·00	
	b. Booklet pane. Nos. 574/5, each × 3		2·50	
575	3 r. Astronaut performing experiment on Moon		70	90
576	5 r. Astronaut on Moon	..	2·50	4·50
574/6		*Set of 3*	3·00	5·00

*Nos. 574/6 are separated by various combinations of rotary-knife (giving a straight edge) and roulette.
Nos. 574/6 were only issued in 17 r. 80 stamp booklets.

(Des J. W. Litho Questa)

1979 (27 Aug). *Death Centenary of Sir Rowland Hill. T* **173** *and similar vert designs showing stamps and Sir Rowland Hill. Multicoloured. W w* **14**. *P* **14**.

577	25 c. Type 173	..	10	10
578	2 r. 1954 60 c. definitive	..	55	50
579	5 r. 1847 1d. "POST OFFICE"	..	1·00	1·25
577/9		*Set of 3*	1·50	1·60
MS580	120 × 89 mm. 3 r. 1847 2d. "POST OFFICE"	..	1·10	1·75

174 Young Child being Vaccinated

(Des V. Whiteley Studio. Litho Questa)

1979 (11 Oct). *International Year of the Child. T* **174** *and similar designs in black, ultramarine and bright blue (1 r.) or multicoloured (others). W w* **14** *(sideways on 15, 25 c., 1 r. 50, and 3 r.). P* 14½ × 14.

581	15 c. Type 174	..	10	10
582	25 c. Children playing	..	10	10
583	1 r. I.Y.C. emblem (*vert*)	..	15	10
584	1 r. 50, Girls in chemistry laboratory		30	20
585	3 r. Boy operating lathe	..	50	50
581/5		*Set of 5*	1·00	75

175 The Liénard Obelisk
176 *Emirne* (French steam packet)

(Des L. Curtis. Litho Questa)

1980 (24 Jan). *Pamplemousses Botanical Gardens. T* **175** *and similar horiz designs. Multicoloured. W w* **14** *(sideways*). *P* 14×14½.

586	20 c. Type 175	..	10	10
587	25 c. Poivre Avenue	..	10	10
	w. Wmk Crown to right of CA	..	22·00	
588	1 r. Varieties of Vacoas	..	20	10
589	2 r. Giant Water Lilies	..	45	55
590	5 r. Mon Plaisir (mansion)	..	80	2·25
586/90		*Set of 5*	1·50	2·75
MS591	152×105mm. Nos. 586/90		2·75	3·75

*The normal watermark shows Crown to left of CA, *as seen from the back of the stamp.*

(Des J.W. Litho Walsall)

1980 (6 May). *"London 1980" International Stamp Exhibition. Mail-carrying Ships. T* **176** *and similar horiz designs. Multicoloured. W w* **14** *(sideways*). *P* 14½×14.

592	25 c. Type 176	..	30	10
	w. Wmk Crown to right of CA	..	9·50	
593	1 r. *Boissevain* (cargo liner)	..	50	10
594	2 r. *La Boudeuse* (Bougainville)	..	70	60
595	5 r. *Sea Breeze* (English clipper)	..	95	2·00
592/5		*Set of 4*	2·25	2·50

*The normal sideways watermark shows Crown to left of CA, *as seen from the back of the stamp.*

NEW INFORMATION

The editor is always interested to correspond with people who have new information that will improve or correct the Catalogue.

177 Blind Person Basket-making
178 Prime Minister Sir Seewoosagur Ramgoolam

(Des J. W. Litho Harrison)

1980 (27 June). *Birth Centenary of Helen Keller (campaigner for the handicapped). T* **177** *and similar vert designs. Multicoloured. W w* **14**. *P* 14.

596	25 c. Type 177	..	20	10
597	1 r. Deaf child under instruction	..	45	10
598	2 r. 50, Helen reading braille	..	70	35
599	5 r. Helen at graduation, 1904	..	1·25	1·25
596/9		*Set of 4*	2·40	1·50

(Des Walsall. Litho and gold foil embossed Questa)

1980 (18 Sept). *80th Birthday and 40th Year in Parliament of Prime Minister Sir Seewoosagur Ramgoolam. W w* **14**. *P* 13½.

600	178	15 r. multicoloured	..	1·00	1·40

No. 600 was printed in sheets of 4 stamps.

179 Headquarters, Mauritius Institute

(Des BG Studio. Litho J.W.)

1980 (1 Oct). *Centenary of Mauritius Institute. T* **179** *and similar horiz designs. Multicoloured. W w* **14** *(sideways*). *P* 13.

601	25 c. Type 179	..	15	10
602	2 r. Rare copy of Veda	..	40	20
603	2 r. 50, Glory of India Cone shell	..	55	25
604	5 r. "Le Torrent" (painting by Harpignies)	65	90
601/4		*Set of 4*	1·60	1·25

180 *Hibiscus liliiflorus*
181 Beau-Bassin/Rose Hill

(Des Jennifer Toombs. Litho Questa)

1981 (15 Jan). *Flowers. T* **180** *and similar vert designs. Multicoloured. W w* **14**. *P* 14.

605	25 c. Type 180	..	20	10
606	2 r. *Erythrospermum monticolum*	..	70	65
607	2 r. 50, *Chasalia boryana*	..	80	1·25
608	5 r. *Hibiscus columnaris*	..	1·40	2·75
605/8		*Set of 4*	2·75	4·25

(Des L. Curtis. Litho J.W.)

1981 (10 Apr). *Coats of Arms of Mauritius Towns. T* **181** *and similar vert designs. Multicoloured. W w* **14**. *P* 13½ × 13.

609	25 c. Type 181	..	10	10
610	1 r. 50, Curepipe	..	25	20
611	2 r. Quatre-Bornes	..	30	25
612	2 r. 50, Vacoas/Phoenix	..	35	30
613	5 r. Port Louis	..	55	75
609/13		*Set of 5*	1·40	1·40
MS614	130×130 mm. Nos. 609/13. P 14		2·40	5·00
	w. Wmk inverted	..	£120	

182 Prince Charles as Colonel-in-Chief, Royal Regiment of Wales
183 Emmanuel Anquetil and Guy Rozemont

(Des J. W. Litho Questa)

1981 (22 July). *Royal Wedding. T* **182** *and similar vert designs. Multicoloured. W w* **14**. *P* 14.

615	25 c. Wedding bouquet from Mauritius	..	10	10
616	2 r. 50, Type 182	..	40	15
617	10 r. Prince Charles and Lady Diana Spencer	80	90
615/17		*Set of 3*	1·10	1·00

(Des G. Vasarhelyi. Litho Questa)

1981 (27 Aug). *Famous Politicians and Physician (5 r). T* **183** *and similar horiz designs. W w* **14** *(sideways*). *P* 14½.

618	20 c. black and carmine	..	10	10
619	25 c. black and lemon	..	10	10
620	1 r. 25, black and emerald	..	30	15
621	1 r. 50, black and rose-red	..	35	15
622	2 r. black and ultramarine	..	45	20
623	2 r. 50, black and orange-brown	..	50	30
624	5 r. black and turquoise-blue	..	75	60
618/24		*Set of 7*	2·75	1·60

Designs:—25 c. Remy Ollier and Sookdeo Bissoondoyal; 1 r. 25, Maurice Curé and Barthélemy Ohsan; 1 r. 50, Sir Guy Forget and Renganaden Seeneevassen; 2 r. Sir Abdul Razak Mohamed and Jules Koenig; 2 r. 50, Abdoollatiff Mahomed Osman and Dazzi Rama (Pandit Sahadeo); 5 r. Sir Thomas Lewis and electrocardiogram.

184 Drummer and Piper
185 "Skills"

(Des Jennifer Toombs. Litho Format)

1981 (16 Sept). *Religion and Culture. T* **184** *and similar multicoloured designs. W w* **14** *(sideways on 20 c. and 5 r.). P* 14 × 13½ (20 c.), 13½ × 14 (2 r.) or 13½ (5 r.).

625	20 c. Type 184	..	10	10
626	2 r. Swami Sivananda (*vert*)	..	1·00	1·00
627	5 r. Chinese Pagoda	..	1·25	90
625/7		*Set of 3*	2·00	3·50

The 20 c. value commemorates the World Tamil Culture Conference (1980).

(Des BG Studio. Litho Questa)

1981 (15 Oct). *25th Anniv of Duke of Edinburgh Award Scheme. T* **185** *and similar vert designs. Multicoloured. W w* **14**. *P* 14.

628	25 c. Type 185	..	10	10
629	1 r. 25, "Service"	..	10	10
	w. Wmk inverted	..	13·00	
630	5 r. "Expeditions"	..	20	30
631	10 r. Duke of Edinburgh	..	40	70
628/31		*Set of 4*	60	1·00

186 Ka'aba (sacred shrine, Great Mosque of Mecca)
187 Scout Emblem

(Des Jennifer Toombs. Litho Questa)

1981 (26 Nov). *Moslem Year 1400 A.H. Commemoration. T* **186** *and similar vert designs. Multicoloured. W w* **14**. *P* 14½ × 14.

632	25 c. Type 186	..	30	10
633	2 r. Mecca	..	80	80
634	5 r. Mecca and Ka'aba	..	1·40	2·75
632/4		*Set of 3*	2·25	3·25

(Des C. Abbott. Litho Walsall)

1982 (22 Feb). *75th Anniv of Boy Scout Movement and 70th Anniv of Scouting in Mauritius. T* **187** *and similar horiz designs. W w* **14** *(sideways*). *P* 14 × 14½.

635	25 c. deep lilac and light green	..	10	10
636	2 r. deep brown and brown-ochre	..	40	30
637	5 r. deep green and yellow-olive	..	85	1·00
638	10 r. deep green and new blue	..	1·25	2·00
635/8		*Set of 4*	2·25	3·00

Designs:—2 r. Lord Baden-Powell and Baden-Powell House; 5 r. Grand Howl; 10 r. Ascent of Pieter Both.

188 Charles Darwin
189 Bride and Groom at Buckingham Palace

(Des L. Curtis. Litho Questa)

1982 (19 Apr). *150th Anniv of Charles Darwin's Voyage. T* **188** *and similar horiz designs. Multicoloured. W* w **14** *(sideways). P* 14.

639	25 c. Type **188**	10	10
	a. Yellow (background to side panels) omitted		
640	2 r. Darwin's telescope	30	45
641	2 r. 50, Darwin's elephant ride	35	55
642	10 r. H.M.S. *Beagle* beached for repairs	1·40	2·75
639/42	*Set of 4*	1·90	3·50

(Des Jennifer Toombs. Litho J. W.)

1982 (1 July). *21st Birthday of Princess of Wales. T* **189** *and similar vert designs. Multicoloured. W* w **14**. *P* 13.

643	25 c. Mauritius coat of arms	10	10
644	2 r. 50, Princess Diana in Chesterfield, November 1981	60	35
645	5 r. Type **189**	75	90
646	10 r. Formal portrait	2·50	2·50
643/6	*Set of 4*	3·50	3·50

190 Prince and Princess of Wales with Prince William   191 Bois Fandamane Plant

(Des Harrison. Litho Walsall)

1982 (22 Sept). *Birth of Prince William of Wales. W* w **14** *(sideways). P* 14 × 14½.

647	**190** 2 r. 50, multicoloured	75	30

(Des Harrison. Litho Format)

1982 (15 Dec). *Centenary of Robert Koch's Discovery of Tubercle Bacillus. T* **191** *and similar vert designs. Multicoloured. W* w **14**. *P* 14.

648	25 c. Type **191**	10	10
649	1 r. 25, Central market, Port Louis	40	40
650	2 r. Bois Banane plant	65	75
651	5 r. Platte de Lézard plant	75	2·25
652	10 r. Dr. Robert Koch	1·25	3·75
648/52	*Set of 5*	2·75	6·50

192 Arms and Flag of Mauritius   193 Early Wall-mounted Telephone

(Des and litho J.W.)

1983 (14 Mar). *Commonwealth Day. T* **192** *and similar horiz designs. Multicoloured. W* w **14** *(sideways). P* 13.

653	25 c. Type **192**	10	10
654	2 r. 50, Satellite view of Mauritius	20	30
655	5 r. Harvesting sugar cane	30	75
656	10 r. Port Louis harbour	95	1·50
653/6	*Set of 4*	1·40	2·40

(Des G. Vasarhelyi. Litho Format)

1983 (24 June). *World Communications Year. T* **193** *and similar multicoloured designs. W* w **14** *(sideways on* 1 r. 25 *and* 10 r.). *P* 14.

657	25 c. Type **193**	10	10
658	1 r. 25, Early telegraph apparatus (*horiz*)	35	20
659	2 r. Earth satellite station	45	50
660	10 r. First hot-air balloon in Mauritius, 1784 (*horiz*)	80	2·75
657/60	*Set of 4*	1·50	3·25

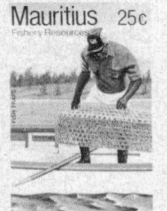

194 Map of Namibia   195 Fish Trap

(Des J. W. Litho Questa)

1983 (26 Aug). *Namibia Day. T* **194** *and similar vert designs. Multicoloured. W* w **14**. *P* 14.

661	25 c. Type **194**	45	10
662	2 r. 50, Hands breaking chains	1·50	75
663	5 r. Family and settlement	2·00	2·25
664	10 r. Diamond mining	4·75	3·75
661/4	*Set of 4*	8·00	6·00

(Des Walsall. Litho Format)

1983 (25 Sept). *Fishery Resources. T* **195** *and similar multicoloured designs. W* w **14** *(sideways on* 1 r. *and* 10 r.). *P* 14.

665	25 c. Type **195**	15	10
666	1 r. Fishing boat (*horiz*)	40	15
667	5 r. Game fishing	75	2·50
668	10 r. Octopus drying (*horiz*)	1·00	4·00
665/8	*Set of 4*	2·10	6·00

196 Swami Dayananda   197 Adolf von Plevitz

(Des A. Theobald. Litho Questa)

1983 (3 Nov). *Death Centenary of Swami Dayananda. T* **196** *and similar vert designs. Multicoloured. W* w **14**. *P* 14.

669	25 c. Type **196**	10	10
670	35 c. Last meeting with father	10	10
671	2 r. Receiving religious instruction	50	65
672	5 r. Swami demonstrating strength	90	2·25
673	10 r. At a religious gathering	1·40	3·50
669/73	*Set of 5*	2·75	6·00

(Des L. Curtis. Litho Harrison)

1983 (8 Dec). *125th Anniv of the Arrival in Mauritius of Adolf von Plevitz (social reformer). T* **197** *and similar horiz designs. Multicoloured. W* w **14** *(sideways). P* 14 × 14½.

674	25 c. Type **197**	10	10
675	1 r. 25, La Laura Government school	30	30
676	5 r. Von Plevitz addressing 1872 Commission of Enquiry	1·00	2·50
677	10 r. Von Plevitz with Indian farm workers	1·75	3·75
674/7	*Set of 4*	2·75	6·50

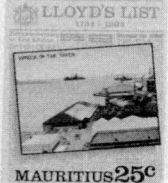

198 Courtship Chase   199 Wreck of S.S. *Tayeb*

(Des N. Arlott. Litho Format)

1984 (26 Mar). *Mauritius Kestrel. T* **198** *and similar multicoloured designs. W* w **14** *(sideways on* 25 c. *and* 2 r. 50). *P* 14.

678	25 c. Type **198**	85	30
679	2 r. Kestrel in tree (*vert*)	2·00	1·25
680	2 r. 50, Young Kestrel	2·25	2·25
681	10 r. Head (*vert*)	3·25	8·00
678/81	*Set of 4*	7·50	10·50

(Des M. Joyce. Litho Questa)

1984 (23 May). *250th Anniv of "Lloyd's List" (newspaper). T* **199** *and similar vert designs. Multicoloured. W* w **14**. *P* 14½ × 14.

682	25 c. Type **199**	30	10
683	1 r. S.S. *Taher*	95	15
684	5 r. East Indiaman *Triton*	3·00	3·25
685	10 r. M.S. *Astor*	3·50	6·00
682/5	*Set of 4*	7·00	9·00

200 Blue Latan Palm   201 Slave Girl

(Des Jennifer Toombs. Litho Format)

1984 (23 July). *Palm Trees. T* **200** *and similar vert designs. Multicoloured. W* w **14**. *P* 14½.

686	25 c. Type **200**	10	10
687	50 c. *Hyophorbe vaughanii*	20	20
688	2 r. 50, *Tectiphiala ferox*	1·25	1·50
689	5 r. Round Island Bottle-palm	2·00	3·00
690	10 r. *Hyophorbe amaricaulis*	3·25	5·25
686/90	*Set of 5*	6·25	9·00

(Des C. Abbott. Litho Walsall)

1984 (20 Aug). *150th Anniv of the Abolition of Slavery and of the Introduction of Indian Immigrants. T* **201** *and similar designs. W* w **14** *(sideways on* 2 r., 10 r.). *P* 14½.

691	25 c. deep rose-lilac, rose-lilac and bistre	15	10
692	1 r. deep rose-lilac, rose-lilac and bistre	70	10
693	2 r. deep rose-lilac and rose-lilac	1·50	1·00
694	10 r. deep rose-lilac and rose-lilac	5·00	8·00
691/4	*Set of 4*	6·50	8·00

Designs: *Vert*—1 r. Slave market. *Horiz*—2 r. Indian immigrant family; 10 r. Arrival of Indian immigrants.

202 75th Anniversary Production of *Faust* and Leoville L'Homme   203 The Queen Mother on Clarence House Balcony, 1980

(Des Walsall. Litho Questa)

1984 (10 Sept). *Centenary of Alliance Francaise (cultural organization). T* **202** *and similar horiz designs. Multicoloured. W* w **14** *(sideways). P* 14½ × 14.

695	25 c. Type **202**	20	10
696	1 r. 25, Prize-giving ceremony and Aunauth Beejadbur	70	50
697	5 r. First headquarters and Hector Clarenc	2·00	3·00
698	10 r. Lion Mountain and Labourdonnais	2·50	5·00
695/8	*Set of 4*	4·75	7·75

(Des A. Theobald (15 r.), C. Abbott (others). Litho Questa)

1985 (7 June). *Life and Times of Queen Elizabeth the Queen Mother. T* **203** *and similar vert designs. Multicoloured. W* w **16**. *P* 14½ × 14.

699	25 c. The Queen Mother in 1926	20	10
700	2 r. With Princess Margaret at Trooping the Colour	60	30
701	5 r. Type **203**	75	1·40
702	10 r. With Prince Henry at his christening (from photo by Lord Snowdon)	1·25	2·75
699/702	*Set of 4*	2·50	4·00
MS703	91 × 73 mm. 15 r. Reopening the Stratford Canal, 1964. Wmk sideways	4·00	3·25

204 High Jumping   205 Adult and Fledgling Pink Pigeons

(Des Joan Thompson. Litho Walsall)

1985 (24 Aug). *2nd Indian Ocean Islands Games. T* **204** *and similar vert designs. Multicoloured. W* w **14**. *P* 14½.

704	25 c. Type **204**	20	10
705	50 c. Javelin-throwing	50	30
706	1 r. 25, Cycling	2·75	1·60
707	10 r. Wind surfing	6·00	8·50
704/7	*Set of 4*	8·50	9·50

(Des N. Arlott. Litho Walsall)

1985 (2 Sept). *Endangered Species. Pink Pigeon. T* **205** *and similar vert designs. Multicoloured. W* w **16**. *P* 14.

708	25 c. Type **205**	2·00	30
709	2 r. Pink Pigeon displaying at nest	4·25	1·75
710	2 r. 50, On nest	4·75	3·50
711	5 r. Pair preening	9·00	10·00
708/11	*Set of 4*	18·00	14·00

206 Caverne Patates, Rodrigues

(Des D. Miller. Litho Walsall)

1985 (27 Sept). *10th Anniv of World Tourism Organization T* **206** *and similar horiz designs. Multicoloured. W* w **16** *(sideways). P* 14½.

712	25 c. Type **206**	50	10
713	35 c. Coloured soils, Chamarel	50	30
714	5 r. Serpent Island	4·00	4·50
715	10 r. Coin de Mire Island	6·00	8·50
712/15	*Set of 4*	10·00	12·00

207 Old Town Hall, Port Louis

(Des Jennifer Toombs. Litho J.W.)

1985 (22 Nov). *250th Anniv of Port Louis. T **207** and similar horiz designs. Multicoloured. W w **16** (sideways). P 13 × 13½.*

716	25 c. Type **207**	10	10
717	1 r. Al-Aqsa Mosque (180th anniv)	1·00	
718	2 r. 50, Vase and trees (250th anniv of settlement of Tamil-speaking Indians)	1·25	1·50
719	10 r. Port Louis Harbour	6·50	8·50
716/19	*Set of 4*	8·00	9·00

208 Edmond Halley and Diagram   **209** Maize (World Food Day)

(Des D. Hartley. Litho Walsall)

1986 (21 Feb). *Appearance of Halley's Comet. T **208** and similar horiz designs. Multicoloured. W w **16** (sideways). P 14.*

720	25 c. Type **208**	40	10
721	1 r. 25, Halley's Comet (1682) and Newton's Reflector	1·10	50
722	3 r. Halley's Comet passing Earth	1·60	2·00
723	10 r. *Giotto* spacecraft	3·50	6·00
720/3	*Set of 4*	6·00	7·75

(Des A. Theobald. Litho Harrison)

1986 (21 Apr). *60th Birthday of Queen Elizabeth II. Vert designs as T **230a** of Jamaica. Multicoloured. W w **16**. P 14½×14.*

724	25 c. Princess Elizabeth wearing badge of Grenadier Guards, 1942	10	10
725	75 c. Investiture of Prince of Wales, 1969	10	10
726	2 r. With Prime Minister of Mauritius, 1972	20	25
727	3 r. In Germany, 1978	30	40
728	15 r. At Crown Agents Head Office, London, 1983	1·25	2·00
724/8	*Set of 5*	1·60	2·50

(Des O. Bell. Litho Walsall)

1986 (25 July). *International Events. T **209** and similar vert designs. Multicoloured. W w **16**. P 14.*

729	25 c. Type **209**	10	10
	w. Wmk inverted	25·00	
730	1 r. African Regional Industrial Property Organization emblem (10th anniv)	35	10
731	1 r. 25, International Peace Year emblem	65	50
732	10 r. Footballer and Mauritius Football Association emblem (World Cup Football Championship, Mexico)	5·50	7·50
729/32	*Set of 4*	6·00	7·50

210 *Cryptopus elatus*   **211** Hesketh Bell Bridge

(Des Harrison. Litho Walsall)

1986 (3 Oct). *Orchids. T **210** and similar vert designs. Multicoloured. W w **16**. P 14½×14.*

733	25 c. Type **210**	40	10
734	2 r. *Jumellea recta*	1·10	45
735	2 r. 50, *Angraecum mauritianum*	1·25	60
736	10 r. *Bulbophyllum longiflorum*	2·25	3·00
733/6	*Set of 4*	4·50	3·75

1986 (Nov). *As No. 533B but printed litho by Questa. "1986" imprint date. P 14½.*

737	35 c. French charter, 1715	2·25	2·00

(Litho Questa)

1987 (11 Jan)–**89**. *As Nos. 531/2, 534, 543/5 and 548 but W w **16** (sideways on horiz designs). Imprint date. P 14½.*

740	20 c. Van Keulen's map, c. 1700 (horiz)	2·00	1·40
741	25 c. Settlement on Rodriguez, 1691	2·00	1·40
743	50 c. Construction of Port Louis, c. 1736 (horiz) (16.1.89)	1·40	30
752	2 r. Race course, c. 1870 (horiz)	1·40	40
753	3 r. Place d'Armes, c. 1880 (horiz) (16.1.89)	3·00	3·00
754	5 r. Royal Visit postcard, 1901 (horiz) (16.1.89)	5·00	5·00
757	25 r. First Mauritian Governor-General and Prime Minister (horiz) (16.1.89)	5·50	8·00
740/57	*Set of 7*	18·00	17·00

Imprint dates: "1987", Nos. 740/1, 752; "1989", Nos. 743, 752/3, 754, 757.

(Des D. Hartley. Litho Format)

1987 (22 May). *Mauritius Bridges. T **211** and similar horiz designs. Multicoloured. W w **16** (sideways). P 14½.*

758	25 c. Type **211**	25	10
759	50 c. Sir Colville Deverell Bridge	35	20
760	2 r. 50, Cavendish Bridge	70	75
761	5 r. Tamarin Bridge	90	2·00
762	10 r. Grand River North West Bridge	1·25	2·50
758/62	*Set of 5*	3·00	5·00

212 Supreme Court, Port Louis   **213** Dodo Mascot

(Des N. Shewring. Litho Walsall)

1987 (2 June). *Bicentenary of the Mauritius Bar. T **212** and similar horiz designs. Multicoloured. W w **16** (sideways). P 14×14½.*

763	25 c. Type **212**	10	10
764	1 r. District Court, Flacq	40	10
765	1 r. 25, Statue of Justice	50	20
766	10 r. Barristers of 1787 and 1987	2·00	2·25
763/6	*Set of 4*	2·75	2·25

(Des O. Bell. Litho Format)

1987 (5 Sept). *International Festival of the Sea. T **213** and similar multicoloured designs. W w **16** (sideways on 25 c., 5 r.). P 14×14½ (vert) or 14½×14 (horiz).*

767	25 c. Type **213**	20	10
768	1 r. 50, Yacht regatta (horiz)	1·00	90
769	3 r. Water skiing (horiz)	2·00	2·75
770	5 r. *Svanen* (barquentine)	2·75	4·25
767/70	*Set of 4*	5·50	7·25

214 Toys   **215** Maison Ouvriere (Int Year of Shelter for the Homeless)

(Des G. Vasarhelyi. Litho Walsall)

1987 (30 Oct). *Industrialisation. T **214** and similar horiz designs. Multicoloured. W w **14** (sideways). P 14.*

771	20 c. Type **214**	10	10
772	35 c. Spinning factory	10	10
773	50 c. Rattan furniture	10	10
774	2 r. 50, Spectacle factory	85	80
775	10 r. Stone carving	2·50	2·75
771/5	*Set of 5*	3·25	3·25

(Des D. Miller. Litho Walsall)

1987 (30 Dec). *Art and Architecture. T **215** and similar horiz designs. W w **16** (sideways). P 14×14½.*

776	25 c. multicoloured	10	10
777	1 r. black and brownish grey	25	10
778	1 r. 25, multicoloured	30	30
779	2 r. multicoloured	55	55
780	5 r. multicoloured	1·00	1·25
776/80	*Set of 5*	2·00	2·00

Designs:—1 r. "Paul et Virginie" (lithograph); 1 r. 25, Chateau de Rosnay; 2 r. "Vielle Ferme" (Boulle); 5 r. "Trois Mamelles".

216 University of Mauritius   **217** Breast Feeding

(Des A. Theobald. Litho B.D.T.)

1988 (11 Mar). *20th Anniv of Independence. T **216** and similar horiz designs. Multicoloured. W w **14** (sideways). P 13½.*

781	25 c. Type **216**	10	10
782	75 c. Anniversary gymnastic display	20	10
783	2 r. 50, Hurdlers and aerial view of Sir Maurice Rault Stadium	70	55
784	5 r. Air Mauritius aircraft at Sir Seewoosagur Ramgoolam International Airport	1·40	1·60
785	10 r. Governor-General Sir Veerasamy Ringadoo and Prime Minister Aneerood Jugnauth	2·25	2·75
781/5	*Set of 5*	4·25	4·50

(Des D. Ashby. Litho B.D.T.)

1988 (1 July). *40th Anniv of World Health Organization. T **217** and similar vert designs. Multicoloured. W w **14**. P 13½.*

786	20 c. Type **217**	15	10
787	2 r. Baby under vaccination umbrella and germ droplets	1·25	70
788	3 r. Nutritious food	1·40	1·25
789	10 r. W.H.O. logo	2·75	3·25
786/9	*Set of 4*	5·00	4·75

218 Modern Bank Building   **219** Olympic Rings and Athlete

(Des N. Shewring (25 r.). Litho B.D.T.)

1988 (1 Sept). *150th Anniv of Mauritius Commercial Bank Ltd. T **218** and similar multicoloured designs. W w **14** (sideways on 1, 25 r.). P 13½.*

790	25 c. black, blue-green and new blue	10	10
791	1 r. black and brown-lake	15	10
792	1 r. 25, multicoloured	30	30
793	25 r. multicoloured	6·50	7·00
790/3	*Set of 4*	6·50	7·00

Designs: Horiz—1 r. Mauritius Commercial Bank, 1897; 25 r. Fifteen dollar bank note of 1838. Vert—1 r. 25, Bank arms.

(Des P. Broadbent. Litho B.D.T.)

1988 (1 Oct). *Olympic Games, Seoul. T **219** and similar horiz designs. Multicoloured. W w **14** (sideways). P 14.*

794	25 c. Type **219**	10	10
795	35 c. Wrestling	15	15
796	1 r. 50, Long distance running	75	60
797	10 r. Swimming	2·50	3·75
794/7	*Set of 4*	3·25	4·00

220 Nature Park   **221** La Tour Sumeire, Port Louis

(Des D. Miller. Litho Harrison (40 c. (No. 809), 3 r., 4 r. (No. 804A), 6 r. (No. 805A), 10 r. (to 1997)), D.L.R. (6 r. (No. 805B), 10 r. (from 1998)) or B.D.T. (others))

1989 (11 Mar)–**98**. *Protection of the Environment. T **220** and similar multicoloured designs. P 14.*

I. W w **14** (sideways on horiz designs). A. *Without imprint date*

798A	15 c. View beneath the sea (29.11.90)	40	20
802A	1 r. 50, Whimbrel (29.11.90)	10	10
803A	3 r. Marine life	15	20
804A	4 r. Fern Tree (vert)	40	40
805A	6 r. Ecological scenery (vert)	40	40
807A	25 r. Migratory birds and map (vert) (29.11.90)	2·50	2·75
798A/807A	*Set of 6*	3·50	3·50

B. *With imprint date*

798B	15 c. View beneath the sea (26.7.94)	10	10
799B	20 c. As 15 c. (19.3.96)	10	10
800B	30 c. Greenshank (15.8.95)	10	10
801B	40 c. Type **220** (19.2.91)	10	10
801cB	60 c. As 50 c. (19.3.96)	10	10
804B	4 r. Fern Tree (vert) (20.9.94*)	20	25
804aB	5 r. Rivière du Poste estuary (26.10.98*)	30	35
805B	6 r. Ecological scenery (vert) (29.12.98*)	35	40
806B	10 r. *Phelsuma ornata* (gecko) on plant (vert) (5.12.95)	55	60
806aB	15 r. Benarès waves (12.10.98*)	80	85
807B	25 r. Migratory birds and map (vert) (28.4.98*)	1·40	1·50
798B/807B	*Set of 11*	4·00	4·00

II. W w **16** (sideways on horiz designs). A. *Without imprint date*

808A	30 c. Greenshank (29.11.90)	90	15
809A	40 c. Type **220**	50	30
810A	50 c. Round Island (vert) (4.10.91)	10	10
811A	75 c. Bassin Blanc (4.10.91)	10	10
812A	1 r. Mangrove (vert) (29.11.90)	10	10
813A	2 r. Le Morne (4.10.91)	10	15
814A	5 r. Rivière du Poste estuary (4.10.91)	30	35
815A	10 r. *Phelsuma ornata* (gecko) on plant (vert)	55	70
816A	15 r. Benarès waves (4.10.91)	90	1·25
808A/16A	*Set of 9*	3·00	2·75

B. *With imprint date*

812B	1 r. Mangrove (vert) (10.11.98)	10	10
817B	25 r. Migratory birds and map (vert) (6.2.96)	1·60	2·00

*Local date of issue.

Imprint dates: "1991", No. 801B; "1993", No. 801B; "1994", Nos. 798B, 801B, 804B; "1995", Nos. 798B, 800B, 806B; "1996", Nos. 799B, 801cB, 817B; "1997", Nos. 801B, 801cB, 806B, 817B; "1998", Nos. 804B/7B, 812B.

(Des A. Theobald. Litho B.D.T.)

1989 (14 July). *Bicentenary of the French Revolution. T **221** and similar vert designs. W w **14**. P 14.*

818	30 c. black, emerald & pale greenish yellow	10	10
819	1 r. black, orange-brown and cinnamon	20	10
820	8 r. multicoloured	1·50	1·50
821	15 r. multicoloured	2·00	2·25
818/21	*Set of 4*	3·50	3·50

Designs:—1 r. Salle de Spectacle du Jardin; 8 r. Portrait of Comte de Malartic; 15 r. Bicentenary logo.

222 Cardinal Jean
Margeot

223 Nehru

(Des L. Curtis. Litho B.D.T.)

1989 (13 Oct). *Visit of Pope John Paul II. T* **222** *and similar vert designs. Multicoloured.* W w 14. P 14×13¹⁄₂.

822	30 c. Type **222**		30	10
823	40 c. Pope John Paul II and Prime Minister Jugnauth, Vatican, 1988		70	25
824	3 r. Mère Marie Magdeleine de la Croix and Chapelle des Filles de Marie, Port Louis, 1864		1·25	1·25
825	6 r. St. Francois d'Assise Church, Pamplemousses, 1756		2·00	2·25
826	10 r. Pope John Paul II		4·50	5·00
822/6		*Set of 5*	8·00	8·00

(Des K. Clarkson. Litho B.D.T.)

1989 (14 Nov). *Birth Centenary of Jawaharlal Nehru (Indian statesman). T* **223** *and similar horiz designs. Multicoloured.* W w 16 *(sideways).* P 14.

827	40 c. Type **223**		70	20
828	1 r. 50, Nehru with daughter, Indira, and grandsons		1·50	70
829	3 r. Nehru and Gandhi		2·50	2·50
830	4 r. Nehru with Presidents Nasser and Tito		2·50	2·75
831	10 r. Nehru with children		4·50	6·00
827/31		*Set of 5*	10·50	11·00

224 Cane cutting

225 Industrial Estate

(Des D. Miller. Litho B.D.T.)

1990 (10 Jan). *350th Anniv of Introduction of Sugar Cane to Mauritius. T* **224** *and similar horiz designs. Multicoloured.* W w 16 *(sideways).* P 13¹⁄₂.

832	30 c. Type **224**		10	10
833	40 c. Sugar factory, 1867		15	10
834	1 r. Mechanical loading of cane		30	10
835	25 r. Modern sugar factory		8·00	9·00
832/5		*Set of 4*	8·00	9·00

(Des L. Curtis. Litho B.D.T.)

1990 (29 Mar). *60th Birthday of Prime Minister Sir Anerood Jugnauth. T* **225** *and similar horiz designs. Multicoloured.* W w 14 *(sideways).* P 13¹⁄₂.

836	35 c. Type **225**		10	10
837	40 c. Sir Anerood Jugnauth at desk		10	10
838	1 r. 50, Mauritius Stock Exchange symbol		30	30
839	4 r. Jugnauth with Governor-General Sir Seewoosagur Ramgoolam		1·50	2·25
840	10 r. Jugnauth greeting Pope John Paul II		5·50	6·00
836/40		*Set of 5*	6·50	8·50

226 Desjardins (naturalist) (150th death anniv)

227 Letters from Alphabets

(Des D. Miller. Litho B.D.T.)

1990 (5 July). *Anniversaries. T* **226** *and similar multicoloured designs.* W w 14 *(sideways on 35 c., 8 r.).* P 14.

841	30 c. Type **226**		20	10
842	35 c. Logo on TV screen (25th anniv of Mauritius Broadcasting Corporation) *(horiz)*		20	10
843	6 r. Line Barracks (now Police Headquarters) (250th anniv)		3·50	3·75
844	8 r. Town Hall, Curepipe (centenary of municipality) *(horiz)*		3·50	4·00
841/4		*Set of 4*	6·75	7·00

(Des G. Vasarhelyi. Litho B.D.T.)

1990 (28 Sept). *International Literacy Year. T* **227** *and similar horiz designs. Multicoloured.* W w 14 *(sideways).* P 14.

845	30 c. Type **227**		15	10
846	1 r. Blind child reading Braille		85	15
847	3 r. Open book and globe		1·75	1·75
848	10 r. Book showing world map with quill pen		4·50	6·50
845/8		*Set of 4*	6·50	7·75

(Des D. Miller. Litho Questa)

1991 (17 June). *65th Birthday of Queen Elizabeth II and 70th Birthday of Prince Philip. Vert designs as T* **58** *of Kiribati. Multicoloured.* W w 16 *(sideways).* P 14¹⁄₂×14.

849	8 r. Queen Elizabeth II		1·40	2·00
	a. Horiz pair. Nos. 849/50 separated by label		2·75	4·00
850	8 r. Prince Philip in Grenadier Guards ceremonial uniform		1·40	2·00

Nos. 849/50 were printed together in a similar sheet format to Nos. 366/7 of Kiribati.

228 City Hall, Port Louis (25th anniv of City status)

229 *Euploea euphon*

(Des G. Vasarhelyi. Litho Questa)

1991 (18 Aug). *Anniversaries and Events. T* **228** *and similar multicoloured designs.* W w 14 *(sideways on 40 c., 10 r.).* P 14.

851	40 c. Type **228**		10	10
852	4 r. Colonel Draper (race course founder) (150th death anniv) *(vert)*		1·75	1·75
853	6 r. Joseph Barnard (engraver) and "POST PAID" 2d. stamp (175th birth anniv) *(vert)*		2·00	2·25
854	10 r. Supermarine Spitfire *Mauritius II* (50th anniv of Second World War)		4·50	6·00
851/4		*Set of 4*	7·50	9·00

(Des I. Loe. Litho Walsall)

1991 (15 Nov). *"Phila Nippon '91" International Stamp Exhibition, Tokyo. Butterflies. T* **229** *and similar horiz designs.* W w 14 *(sideways).* P 14×14¹⁄₂.

855	40 c. Type **229**		60	20
856	3 r. *Hypolimnas misippus* (female)		1·90	1·00
857	3 r. *Papilio manlius*		3·50	4·00
858	10 r. *Hypolimnas misippus* (male)		3·50	4·25
855/8		*Set of 4*	8·50	8·50

230 Green Turtle, Tromelin

(Des G. Vasarhelyi. Litho Walsall)

1991 (13 Dec). *Indian Ocean Islands. T* **230** *and similar horiz designs. Multicoloured.* W w 14 *(sideways).* P 14.

859	40 c. Type **230**		50	20
860	1 r. Glossy Ibis, Agalega		1·50	40
861	2 r. Takamaka flowers, Chagos Archipelago		1·60	1·10
862	15 r. Violet Spider Conch (*Lambis violacea*) sea shell, St. Brandon		7·00	8·50
859/62		*Set of 4*	9·50	9·25

231 Pres. Veerasamy Ringadoo and President's Residence

232 Ticolo (mascot)

(Des G. Vasarhelyi. Litho Walsall)

1992 (12 Mar). *Proclamation of Republic. T* **231** *and similar horiz designs.* W w 14 *(sideways).* P 13¹⁄₂×14.

863	40 c. Type **231**		10	10
864	4 r. Prime Minister Anerood Jugnauth and Government House		80	1·25
865	8 r. Children and rainbow		1·75	2·75
866	10 r. Presidential flag		2·00	3·00
863/6		*Set of 4*	4·25	6·25

(Des G. Vasarhelyi. Litho B.D.T.)

1992 (25 June). *8th African Athletics Championships, Port Louis. T* **232** *and similar multicoloured designs.* W w 14 *(sideways on 4, 5 r.).* P 13¹⁄₂.

867	40 c. Type **232**		10	10
868	4 r. Sir Anerood Jugnauth Stadium *(horiz)*		65	95
869	5 r. High jumping *(horiz)*		75	1·10
870	6 r. Championships emblem		90	1·60
867/70		*Set of 4*	2·10	3·25

---

233 Bouquet (25th anniv of Fleurir Maurice)

234 Bank of Mauritius Headquarters

(Des D. Miller. Litho B.D.T.)

1992 (13 Aug). *Local Events and Anniversaries. T* **233** *and similar multicoloured designs.* W w 14 *(sideways on 2, 3, 15 r.).* P 13¹⁄₂.

871	40 c. Type **233**		10	10
872	1 r. Swami Krishnanandji Maharaj (25th anniv of arrival)		40	10
873	2 r. Boy with dog (humane education) *(horiz)*		1·10	75
874	3 r. Commission Headquarters (10th anniv of Indian Ocean Commission) *(horiz)*		1·10	1·00
875	15 r. Radio telescope antenna, Bras d'Eau (project inauguration) *(horiz)*		4·50	6·00
871/5		*Set of 5*	6·50	7·00

(Des D. Miller. Litho Walsall)

1992 (29 Oct). *25th Anniv of Bank of Mauritius. T* **234** *and similar multicoloured designs).* P 14¹⁄₂.

876	40 c. Type **234**		10	10
877	4 r. Dodo gold coin *(horiz)*		1·50	90
878	8 r. First bank note issue *(horiz)*		2·25	2·75
879	15 r. Graph of foreign exchange reserves, 1967–92 *(horiz)*		4·00	5·50
876/9		*Set of 4*	7·00	8·25

235 Housing Development

236 Bell 206B JetRanger Helicopter

(Des G. Vasarhelyi. Litho B.D.T.)

1993 (12 Mar). *25th Anniv of National Day. T* **235** *and similar vert designs. Multicoloured.* W w 14. P 15×14.

880	30 c. Type **235**		10	10
881	40 c. Gross domestic product graph on computer screen		10	10
882	3 r. National colours on map of Mauritius		40	50
883	4 r. Ballot box		45	60
884	15 r. Grand Commander's insignia for Order of Star and Key of the Indian Ocean		1·75	3·00
880/4		*Set of 5*	2·50	3·75

(Des N. Shewring. Litho B.D.T.)

1993 (14 June). *25th Anniv of Air Mauritius Ltd. T* **236** *and similar horiz designs. Multicoloured.* W w 14 *(sideways).* P 14.

885	40 c. Type **236**		60	30
886	3 r. Boeing 747SP		1·00	1·00
887	4 r. Aerospatiale/Aeritalia ATR 42		1·25	1·25
888	10 r. Boeing 767-200ER		2·50	4·00
885/8		*Set of 4*	4·75	6·00
MS889	150×91 mm. Nos. 885/8		5·25	6·50

40cs ═

(237)

1993 (15 Sept). *No. 811A surch with T* **237**

890	40 c. on 75 c. Bassin Blanc		30	30

238 French Royal Charter, 1715, and Act of Capitulation, 1810

239 *Scotia* (cable ship) and Map of Cable Route

(Des D. Miller. Litho B.D.T.)

1993 (16 Oct). *5th Summit of French-speaking Nations. T 238 and similar vert designs. Multicoloured.* W w **14**. *P* 13.

891	1 r. Type **238**		30	10
892	5 r. Road signs		1·75	1·50
893	6 r. Code Napoléon		1·75	2·00
894	7 r. Early Mauritius newspapers		1·75	2·25
891/4		Set of 4	5·00	5·25

(Des N. Shewring. Litho Cartor)

1993 (25 Nov). *Centenary of Telecommunications. T 239 and similar horiz designs. Multicoloured.* W w **14** (*sideways*). *P* 13.

895	40 c. Type **239**		30	10
896	3 r. Morse key and code		70	70
897	4 r. Signal Mountain Earth station		85	1·00
898	8 r. Communications satellite		1·60	2·50
895/8		Set of 4	3·00	3·75

240 Indian Mongoose
241 Dr. Edouard Brown-Séquard (physiologist) (death cent)

(Des A. Robinson. Litho Questa)

1994 (9 Mar). *Mammals. T 240 and similar horiz designs. Multicoloured.* W w **16** (*sideways*). *P* 14½.

899	40 c. Type **240**		30	10
900	2 r. Indian Black-naped Hare		60	40
901	8 r. Pair of Crab-eating Macaque		1·75	2·50
902	10 r. Adult and infant Common Tenrec		2·00	2·75
899/902		Set of 4	4·25	5·25

(Des N. Shewring. Litho B.D.T.)

1994 (16 June). *Anniversaries and Events. T 241 and similar vert designs. Multicoloured.* W w **14**. *P* 14.

903	40 c. Type **241**		10	10
904	4 r. Family in silhouette (International Year of the Family)		45	55
905	8 r. World Cup and map of U.S.A. (World Cup Football Championship, U.S.A.)		1·00	1·50
906	10 r. Control tower, SSR International Airport (50th anniv of Civil Aviation Organization)		1·25	1·75
903/6		Set of 4	2·50	3·50

242 *St. Géran* leaving L'Orient for Isle de France, 1744

(Des Jennifer Toombs. Litho Questa)

1994 (18 Aug). *250th Anniv of Wreck of* St. Géran (*sailing packet*). *T 242 and similar multicoloured designs.* W w **16** (*sideways*). *P* 14.

907	40 c. Type **242**		20	10
908	5 r. In rough seas off Isle de France		65	70
909	6 r. Bell and main mast		75	1·00
910	10 r. Artifacts from wreck		1·25	2·25
907/10		Set of 4	2·50	3·50
MS911	119×89 mm. 15 r. St Géran leaving L'Orient (*vert*)		2·75	3·50

243 Ring-a-ring-a-roses
244 Nutmeg

(Des G. Vasarhelyi. Litho B.D.T.)

1994 (25 Oct). *Children's Games and Pastimes. T 243 and similar horiz designs showing children's paintings. Multicoloured.* W w **14** (*sideways*). *P* 13½.

912	30 c. Type **243**		10	10
913	40 c. Skipping and ball games		10	10
914	8 r. Water sports		1·25	1·75
915	10 r. Blind man's buff		1·25	1·75
912/15		Set of 4	2·40	3·25

(Des I. Loe. Litho Enschedé)

1995 (10 Mar). *Spices. T 244 and similar vert designs. Multicoloured.* W w **14**. *P* 13×14½.

916	40 c. Type **244**		10	10
917	4 r. Coriander		55	65
918	5 r. Cloves		65	75
919	10 r. Cardamom		1·25	2·25
916/19		Set of 4	2·25	3·25

(Des A. Theobald. Litho B.D.T)

1995 (8 May). *50th Anniv of End of Second World War. Designs as T 75 of Kiribati, but 35×28 mm. Multicoloured.* W w **14** (*sideways*). *P* 13½.

920	5 r. H.M.S. *Mauritius* (cruiser)		1·00	1·40
921	5 r. Mauritian soldiers and map of North Africa		1·00	1·40
922	5 r. Consolidated PBY-5 Catalina flying boat, Tombeau Bay		1·00	1·40
920/2		Set of 3	2·75	3·75

245 Mare Longue Reservoir
246 Ile Plate Lighthouse

(Des A. Theobald. Litho B.D.T.)

1995 (8 May). *Anniversaries. T 245 and similar horiz designs. Multicoloured.* W w **14** (*sideways*). *P* 13½.

923	40 c. Type **245** (50th anniv of construction)		10	10
924	4 r. Mahebourg to Curepipe road (bicentenary of construction)		60	70
925	10 r. Buildings on fire (centenary of Great Fire of Port Louis)		1·25	2·00
923/5		Set of 3	1·75	2·50

(Des N. Shewring. Litho Enschedé)

1995 (28 Aug). *Lighthouses. T 246 and similar vert designs. Multicoloured.* W w **14**. *P* 13×14½.

926	30 c. Type **246**		40	20
927	40 c. Pointe aux Caves		40	20
928	8 r. Ile aux Fouquets		1·75	2·25
929	10 r. Pointe aux Canonniers		2·00	2·25
926/9		Set of 4	4·00	4·50
MS930	130×100 mm. Nos. 926/9		4·00	4·75

247 Symbolic Children under U.N.I.C.E.F. Umbrella
248 C.O.M.E.S.A. Emblem

(Des E. Nisbet. Litho B.D.T.)

1995 (24 Oct). *50th Anniv of United Nations. T 247 and similar horiz designs. Multicoloured.* W w **14** (*sideways*). *P* 13½.

931	40 c. Type **247**		10	10
932	4 r. Hard hat and building construction (I.L.O.)		35	45
933	8 r. Satellite picture of cyclone (W.M.O.)		70	1·10
934	10 r. Bread and grain (F.A.O.)		90	1·40
931/5		Set of 4	1·90	2·75

(Des E. Nisbet. Litho Cartor)

1995 (8 Dec). *Inauguration of Common Market for Eastern and Southern Africa.* W w **14**. *P* 13×13½.

935	248	60 c. black and rose		10	10
936		4 r. black and cobalt		35	45
937		8 r. black and lemon		70	1·10
938		10 r. black and bright emerald		90	1·40
935/8			Set of 4	1·90	2·75

249 *Pachystyla bicolor*

(Des I. Loe. Litho Cartor)

1996 (11 Mar). *Snails. T 249 and similar horiz designs. Multicoloured.* W w **14** (*sideways*). *P* 14×13½.

939	60 c. Type **249**		15	10
940	4 r. Gonidomus pagodus		45	50
941	5 r. Harmogenanina implicata		45	60
942	10 r. Tropidophora eugeniae		85	1·60
939/42		Set of 4	1·75	2·50

250 Boxing

(Des R. Watton. Litho B.D.T.)

1996 (26 June). *Centenary of Modern Olympic Games. T 250 and similar horiz designs. Multicoloured.* W w **16** (*sideways*). *P* 13½.

943	60 c. Type **250**		10	10
944	4 r. Badminton		45	50
945	5 r. Basketball		60	65
946	10 r. Table tennis		1·00	1·50
943/6		Set of 4	1·90	2·40

251 *Zambezia* (freighter)

(Des J. Batchelor. Litho B.D.T.)

1996 (30 Sept). *Ships. T 251 and similar horiz designs. Multicoloured.* W w **14** (*sideways*). *P* 14.

947	60 c. Type **251**		15	10
948	4 r. Sir Jules (coastal freighter)		45	50
949	5 r. Mauritius (cargo liner)		50	60
950	10 r. Mauritius Pride (container ship)		1·00	1·50
947/50		Set of 4	1·90	2·40
MS951	125×91 mm. Nos. 947/50		1·90	2·75

252 Posting a Letter
253 Vavang

(Des D. Miller. Litho B.D.T.)

1996 (2 Dec). *150th Anniv of the Post Office Ordinance. T 252 and similar horiz designs. Multicoloured.* W w **16** (*sideways*). *P* 13½.

952	60 c. Type **252**		10	10
953	4 r. "B53" duplex postmark		45	50
954	5 r. Modern mobile post office		55	60
955	10 r. Carriole (19th-century horse-drawn postal carriage)		1·00	1·50
952/5		Set of 4	1·75	2·50

(Des I. Loe. Litho Cartor)

1997 (10 Mar). *Fruits. T 253 and similar vert designs. Multicoloured.* W w **14**. *P* 13×13½.

956	60 c. Type **253**		10	10
957	4 r. Pom Zako		45	50
958	5 r. Zambos		55	60
959	10 r. Sapot Negro		1·00	1·50
956/9		Set of 4	1·75	2·50

254 Governor Mahé de la Bourdonnais and Map

(Des G. Vasarhelyi. Litho B.D.T.)

1997 (9 June). *Aspects of Mauritius History. T 254 and similar horiz designs. Multicoloured.* W w **14** (*sideways*). *P* 13½.

960	60 c. Type **254**		20	15
961	1 r. La Pérouse and map of Pacific		30	15
962	4 r. Governor Sir William Gomm and Lady Gomm's Ball, 1847		55	50
963	6 r. George Clark discovering skeleton of dodo, 1865		80	80
964	10 r. Professor Brian Abel-Smith and Social Policies report of 1960		1·00	1·50
960/4		Set of 5	2·50	2·75

255 1d. "POST OFFICE"
Mauritius

(Des D. Miller. Litho B.D.T.)

1997 (22 Sept). *150th Anniv of "POST OFFICE" Stamps. T* **255** *and similar horiz designs. Multicoloured. W* w **14** *(sideways). P* 13½.

965	60 c. Type 255	20	10
	a. Sheetlet. Nos. 965×7 and 966×5	2·75	
	b. Booklet pane of 10 with margins all round	2·00	
966	4 r. 2d. "POST OFFICE" Mauritius	40	40
	a. Booklet pane of 10 with margins all round	3·75	
967	5 r. "POST OFFICE" 1d. and 2d. on gold background	50	50
	a. Booklet pane of 10 with margins all round	4·50	
968	10 r. "POST OFFICE" 2d. and 1d. on silver background	90	1·40
	a. Booklet pane of 10 with margins all round	8·00	
965/8	*Set of 4*	1·75	2·25
MS969	127×90 mm. 20 r. "POST OFFICE" stamps on cover to Bordeaux	1·50	2·00

Nos. 965/8 were issued in separate sheets, but Nos. 965/6 also exist as a sheetlet of 12 (3×4), containing seven 60 c. and five 4 r.

256 Wheelwright

(Des N. Shewring. Litho Walsall)

1997 (1 Dec). *Small Businesses. T* **256** *and similar horiz designs. Multicoloured. W* w **14** *(sideways). P* 14½.

970	60 c. Type 256	10	10
971	4 r. Laundryman	30	30
972	5 r. Shipwright	40	40
973	15 r. Quarryman	1·25	1·75
970/3	*Set of 4*	1·90	2·25

257 *Phelsuma guentheri* (gecko)

(Des W. Oliver. Litho B.D.T.)

1998 (11 Mar). *Geckos. T* **257** *and similar horiz designs. Multicoloured. W* w **14** *(sideways). P* 13½.

974	1 r. Type 257	15	10
975	6 r. *Nactus serpensinsula durrelli*	45	50
976	7 r. *Nactus coindemirensis*	55	65
977	8 r. *Phelsuma edwardnewtonii*	65	80
974/7	*Set of 4*	1·60	1·75

258 Steam Train on Viaduct   259 President Nelson Mandela

(Litho B.D.T.)

1998 (15 June). *Inland Transport. T* **258** *and similar horiz designs. Multicoloured. W* w **14** *(sideways). P* 13½.

978	40 c. Type 258	15	10
979	5 r. Early lorry	45	45
980	6 r. Bus in town street	50	60
981	10 r. Sailing barge at wharf	1·50	2·00
978/81	*Set of 4*	2·40	2·75

(Litho Walsall)

1998 (10 Sept). *State Visit of President Nelson Mandela of South Africa. W* w **16**. *P* 14½.

982	259	25 r. multicoloured	1·60	2·00

260 Count Maurice of Nassau and Dutch Landing

(Des A. Theobald. Litho Enschedé)

1998 (18 Sept). *400th Anniv of Dutch Landing on Mauritius. T* **260** *and similar horiz designs. W* w **14** *(sideways). P* 13½.

983	50 c. Type 260	10	10
984	1 r. Fort Frederik Hendrik and sugar cane	10	10
985	7 r. Dutch map of Mauritius (1670)	65	75
986	8 r. Diagram of landing	70	80
983/6	*Set of 4*	1·40	1·60
MS987	105×80 mm. 25 r. Two Dutch ships	2·00	2·50

261 Cascade Balfour

(Des N. Shewring. Litho B.D.T.)

1998 (16 Nov). *Waterfalls. T* **261** *and similar multicoloured designs. W* w **16** *(sideways on 1, 5 r.). P* 13½.

988	1 r. Type 261	10	10
989	5 r. Rochester Falls	30	35
990	6 r. Cascade G.R.S.E. (*vert*)	35	40
991	10 r. 500 ft. Cascade (*vert*)	55	75
988/91	*Set of 4*	1·25	1·40

262 Plan of Le Réduit

(Des D. Miller. Litho Questa)

1998 (14 Dec). *250th Anniv of Château Le Réduit. T* **262** *and similar horiz designs. Multicoloured. W* w **14** *(sideways). P* 14½.

992	1 r. Type 262	10	10
993	4 r. "Le Château du Réduit, 1814" (P. Thuillier)	20	25
994	5 r. "Le Réduit, 1998" (Hassen Edun)	30	35
995	15 r. Commemorative monument	80	1·25
992/5	*Set of 4*	1·40	1·75

263 Governor Mahé de la Bourdonnais on 15 c. Stamp of 1899

(Litho Cartor)

1999 (11 Feb). *300th Birth Anniv of Governor Mahé de la Bourdonnais. W* w **14** *(sideways). P* 13×13½.

996	263	7 r. dp ultramarine, black & brt crimson	45	55

264 *Clerodendron laciniatum*

(Des Lynn Chadwick. Litho B.D.T.)

1999 (10 Mar). *Local Plants. T* **264** *and similar horiz designs. Multicoloured. W* w **14** *(sideways). P* 13½.

997	1 r. Type 264	10	10
998	2 r. *Senecio lamarckianus*	10	15
999	5 r. *Cylindrocline commersonii*	35	35
1000	9 r. *Psiadia pollicina*	60	75
997/1000	*Set of 4*	1·00	1·25

265 "The Washerwomen" (Hervé Masson)   266 Old Chimney, Alma

(Des N. Shewring. Litho Enschedé)

1999 (18 June). *Mauritius through Local Artists' Eyes. T* **265** *and similar horiz designs. Multicoloured. W* w **14** *(sideways). P* 14×15.

1001	1 r. Type 265	10	10
1002	3 r. "The Casino" (Gaetan de Rosnay)	25	25
1003	4 r. "The Four Elements" (Andrée Poilly)	30	30
1004	6 r. "Going to Mass" (Xavier Le Juge de Segrais)	45	50
1001/4	*Set of 4*	95	1·00

(Des N. Shewring. Litho Questa)

1999 (17 Sept). *Old Sugar Mill Chimneys. T* **266** *and similar vert designs. Multicoloured. W* w **16**. *P* 14½.

1005	1 r. Type 266	10	10
1006	2 r. Antoinette	15	15
1007	5 r. Belle Mare	40	40
1008	7 r. Grande Rosalie	50	60
1005/8	*Set of 4*	95	1·00
MS1009	132×100 mm. Nos. 1005/8. W w **14**	95	1·10

267 Mosquito and Sprayer (Eradication of Malaria)

(Des N. Shewring (2 r.), O. Bell (others). Litho Cartor)

1999 (7 Dec). *20th-century Achievements. T* **267** *and similar horiz designs. Multicoloured. W* w **14** *(sideways). P* 13½×13.

1010	1 r. Type 267	10	10
1011	2 r. Judge's robes, silhouette and airliner (emancipation of women)	15	15
1012	5 r. Conference room (international conference centre)	40	40
1013	9 r. Spoons full of sugar (development of sugar industry)	75	85
1010/13	*Set of 4*	1·25	1·40

268 Crest

(Litho Enschedé)

2000 (25 Jan). *150th Anniv of Mauritius Chamber of Commerce and Industry. T* **268** *and similar triangular designs. Multicoloured. W* w **14** *(sideways). P* 13½.

1014	1 r. Type 268	10	10
1015	2 r. Unity, Vision and Service logos	10	15
1016	7 r. Francis Channell (First Secretary, 1850–72)	40	45
1017	15 r. Louis Léchelle (First President, 1850)	80	85
1014/17	*Set of 4*	1·40	1·50

269 *Cratopus striga* (beetle)

(Des R. Watton. Litho Questa)

2000 (29 Mar). *Beetles. T* **269** *and similar horiz designs. Multicoloured. W* w **14** *(sideways). P* 14½.

1018	1 r. Type 269	10	10
1019	2 r. *Cratopus armatus*	10	15
1020	3 r. *Cratopus chrysochlorus*	15	20
1021	15 r. *Cratopus nigrogranatus*	80	85
1018/21	*Set of 4*	1·10	1·25
MS1022	130×100 mm. Nos. 1018/21	1·10	1·25

STAMP BOOKLETS

1953 (10 Oct). *Black on white cover. Stapled.*
SB1   5 r. booklet containing four 5 c., eight 10 c. and
        50 c. (Nos. 280, 286, 291) in blocks of 4 and one
        pane of 4 air mail labels £180

1954 (23 Sept). *Black on white or grey cover. Stapled.*
SB2   5 r. booklet containing four 5 c., eight 10 c. and
        50 c. (Nos. 296/7, 302) in blocks of 4 and one
        pane of 4 air mail labels   . .   . .   . .   35·00

1955. *Black on grey cover. Stapled.*
SB3   5 r. booklet containing four 5 c., eight 10 c. and
        50 c. (Nos. 296, 297a, 302) in block of 4 and
        one pane of 4 air mail labels   . .   . .   40·00

1979 (20 July). *Tenth Anniv of Moon Landing. Multicoloured
cover, 165×92 mm, showing astronauts on front and Lunar
Module above Moon on back. Stitched.*
SB4   17 r. 80, booklet containing se-tenant panes of 3 or
        6 (Nos. 574a/b)   . .   . .   5·50

Booklet of 10 Postage Stamps – Rs6

B 1 Port Louis Post Office
(Illustration reduced. Actual size 125×71 mm)

1997 (22 Sept). *150th Anniv of "POST OFFICE" Stamps.
Covers as Type B 1. Panes attached by selvedge.*
SB5   6 r. booklet containing pane of ten 60 c. (No.
        965b)   . .   . .   2·00
SB6   40 r. booklet containing pane of ten 4 r. (No.
        966a)   . .   . .   3·75
SB7   50 r. booklet containing pane of ten 5 r. (No.
        967a)   . .   . .   4·50
SB8   100 r. booklet containing pane of ten 10 r. (No.
        968a)   . .   . .   8·00

EXPRESS DELIVERY STAMPS

EXPRESS DELIVERY 15 c.
(E 1)

EXPRESS DELIVERY (INLAND) 15 c.
(E 2)

EXPRESS DELIVERY (INLAND) 15 c.
(E 3)

EXPRESS DELIVERY (INLAND) 15 c
(E 4)

Type E 2. "(INLAND)" was inserted at a second printing on stamps
already surcharged with Type E 1 (No. E1).
Type E 3. New setting made at one printing. More space above and
below "(INLAND)".
Type E 4. New setting with smaller "15 c" and no stop.

1903 (10 Aug)–04. *No. 136 surch locally in red.*
E1   E 1   15 c. on 15 c. ultramarine   . .   . .   6·50   18·00
E2   E 2   15 c. on 15 c. ultramarine (28.3.04)   30·00   38·00
            a. "A" inverted £650   £550
            b. "(INLAND)" inverted   . .   . .   †   £950
E3   E 3   15 c. on 15 c. ultramarine (4.04)   . .   7·50   2·50
            a. Surch inverted £400   £400
            aw. Surch and wmk inverted   . .   —   £400
            b. Surch double, both inverted   . .   £950   £950
            c. Imperf between (vert pair)   . .   £2750
            w. Wmk inverted
E4   E 4   15 c. on 15 c. ultramarine (1904)   . .   £375   £375
            a. Surch inverted   . .   . .   —   £900
            b. Surch double
            c. Surch double, both inverted   . .
            d. "c" omitted   . .   . .   . .   —   £1500

(FOREIGN) EXPRESS DELIVERY 18 CENTS
(E 5)

1904. *T 42 (without value in label), surch with Type E 5 locally.
Wmk Crown CC. P 14.*
E5   18 c. green   . .   . .   . .   1·50   20·00
        a. Exclamation mark for "I" in "FOREIGN"   £425

1904. *T 42 (without value in label) surch with Type E 3 locally.*
E6   15 c. grey-green (R.)   . .   . .   . .   3·50   3·50
        a. Surch inverted £600   £550
        b. Surch double £425   £450
        c. Surch double, one "LNIAND"   . .   £450   £475

POSTAGE DUE STAMPS

D 1

POSTAGE DUE 10c
(D 2)

(Typo Waterlow)

1933–54. *Wmk Mult Script CA. P 15 × 14.*
D1   D 1   2 c. black   . .   . .   . .   1·25   50
D2   4 c. violet   40   65
D3   6 c. scarlet   40   80
D4   10 c. green   60   70
D5   20 c. bright blue   50   1·00
D6   50 c. deep magenta (1.3.54)   . .   55   15·00
D7   1 r. orange (1.3.54)   70   15·00
D1/7   Set of 7   4·00   30·00
D1/5 Perf "Specimen"   Set of 5   65·00

(Typo D.L.R.)

1966–72. *Wmk w 12. Chalk-surfaced paper. P 13½×14 (2 c.) or
15×14 (others).*
D 8   D 1   2 c. black (11.7.67)   . .   . .   2·50   2·50
D 9   4 c. slate-lilac (7.1.69)   . .   1·75   8·00
D10   6 c. red-orange (7.1.69)   . .   6·50   18·00
            a. Perf 13½×14   . .   . .   22·00   40·00
D11   10 c. yellow-green (16.2.67)   . .   30   2·00
D12   20 c. blue (3.1.66)   . .   . .   2·25   4·50
            a. Deep blue (7.1.69)   . .   2·25   12·00
D13   50 c. deep magenta (7.1.69)   . .   75   12·00
            a. Magenta (10.1.72)   . .   1·75   16·00
D8/13   Set of 6   12·50   42·00

1982 (25 Oct). *Nos. 530A/1A, 535A, 540A, 542A and 547A optd
as Type D 2, by J. W. Dunn Printers Ltd.*
D14   10 c. on 15 c. Dutch Occupation, 1638–1710   20   30
D15   20 c. on 20 c. Van Keulen's map, circa 1700 . .   30   30
D16   50 c. on 60 c. Pierre Poivre, circa 1767   . .   30   30
D17   1 r. on 1 r. 20, Government House, circa 1840   40   30
D18   1 r. 50 on 1 r. 50, Indian immigration, 1835   50   75
D19   5 r. on 15 r. Unfurling Mauritian flag, 1968   1·00   2·00
D14/19   . .   . .   Set of 6   2·40   3·50

FISCALS USED FOR POSTAGE

INLAND REVENUE
(F 1)

INLAND
(F 2)

REVENUE

F 3

1889. *T 19, wmk Crown CA, optd. P 14.*
R1   F 1   4 c. carmine   . .   . .   11·00   5·00
R2   F 2   4 c. lilac   . .   . .   . .   2·50   10·00

(Typo D.L.R.)

1896. *Wmk Crown CA. P 14.*
R3   F 3   4 c. dull purple . .   . .   . .   20·00   25·00

Montserrat

A local post office operated on Montserrat from 1702, although the first recorded postal marking does not occur until 1791. A branch of the British G.P.O. was established at Plymouth, the island capital, in 1852.

The stamps of Great Britain were used from 1858 until the overseas postal service reverted to local control on 1 April 1860.

In the interim period between 1860 and the introduction of Montserrat stamps in 1876 No. CC1 and a similar "uncrowned" handstamp were again used.

PLYMOUTH
CROWNED-CIRCLE HANDSTAMPS

C 1

CC1 C 1 MONTSERRAT (R.) (15.7.1852) *Price on cover* £2500
No. CC1 was used as an emergency measure, struck in black, during 1886.

Stamps of GREAT BRITAIN *cancelled* "A 08" *as Type Z 1 of Jamaica.*

1858 (8 May) *to* 1860.
Z1	1d. rose-red (1857), *perf 14*	.. .. ..	£1100
Z2	4d. rose (1857)	.. .. ..	
Z3	6d. lilac (1856)	.. .. ..	£450
Z4	1s. green (1856)		

PRICES FOR STAMPS ON COVER TO 1945
Nos. 1/2	*from* × 40
No. 3	†
Nos. 4/5	*from* × 8
Nos. 6/13	*from* × 12
Nos. 14/22	*from* × 4
No. 23	—
Nos. 24/33	*from* × 4
Nos. 35/47	*from* × 3
No. 48	—
Nos. 49/59	*from* × 3
Nos. 60/2	*from* × 15
Nos. 63/83	*from* × 3
Nos. 84/93	*from* × 4
Nos. 94/7	*from* × 3
Nos. 98/100	*from* × 8
Nos. 101/12	*from* × 5

1		(2)	3 (Die I)

(T 1 recess D.L.R.)

1876 (Sept)–83. *Stamps of Antigua optd with T 2. Wmk Crown CC. P 14.*
1	1	1d. red	.. ..	22·00 15·00
		a. Bisected (½d.) (1883) (on cover)	..	† £1400
		b. Inverted "S"	.. ..	£1000 £750
		w. Wmk inverted		
		x. Wmk reversed	.. ..	27·00 20·00
		y. Wmk inverted and reversed	..	42·00
2		6d. green	.. ..	55·00 40·00
		a. Trisected (used as 2d.) (12.83)	..	† £5000
		b. Inverted "S"	.. ..	£1300 £1000
		x. Wmk reversed	.. ..	— 75·00
3		6d. blue-green	.. ..	£1000
		a. Inverted "S"	.. ..	£6000

Nos. 1/3 were overprinted either from a setting of 120 (12×10) or from a setting of 60 (6×10) applied twice to each sheet. This setting of 60 had an inverted "S" on R. 2/3. The same setting was subsequently used for some sheets of Nos. 6 and 8.

No. 1 was bisected and used for a ½d. in 1883. This bisected stamp is found surcharged with a small "½" in *black* and also in *red*; both were unofficial and they did not emanate from the Montserrat P.O.

The 6d. in blue-green is only known unused.

(T 3 typo D.L.R.)

1880 (Jan). *Wmk Crown CC. P 14.*
4	3	2½d. red-brown	.. ..	£250 £180
5		4d. blue	.. ..	£140 40·00
		w. Wmk inverted	.. ..	— £100
		x. Wmk reversed	.. ..	£250

1883 (Mar). *Wmk Crown CA. P 12.*
6	1	1d. red	.. ..	70·00 50·00
		a. Inverted "S"	.. ..	£1800 £1300
		b. Bisected (½d.) (on cover)	..	† £1600
		x. Wmk reversed	.. ..	— 75·00

Top left triangle detached
(Pl 2 R.3/3 of right pane)

1884–85. *Wmk Crown CA. P 14.*
7	3	½d. dull green	.. ..	1·00 7·00
		a. Top left triangle detached	..	48·00
8	1	1d. red	.. ..	14·00 18·00
		a. Inverted "S"	.. ..	£850 £850
		bx. Wmk reversed	.. ..	— 25·00
		c. Rose-red (1885)	.. ..	15·00 14·00
		ca. Bisected vert (½d.) (on cover)		† £1300
		cb. Inverted "S"	.. ..	£950 £950
		cx. Wmk reversed	.. ..	20·00 20·00
9	3	2½d. red-brown	.. ..	£225 65·00
10		2½d. ultramarine (1885)	.. ..	19·00 18·00
		a. Top left triangle detached	..	£250
		w. Wmk inverted	.. ..	80·00
11		4d. blue	.. ..	£1800 £250
12		4d. mauve (1885)	.. ..	4·50 3·00
		a. Top left triangle detached	..	£120
	10, 12 Optd "Specimen"		*Set of 2*	£325

The stamps for Montserrat were superseded by the general issue for Leeward Islands in November 1890, but the following issues were in concurrent use with the stamps inscribed "LEEWARD ISLANDS" until 1 July 1956, when Leeward Islands stamps were withdrawn and used.

4 Device of the Colony   5

(Typo D.L.R.)

1903 (Aug). (a) *Wmk Crown CA. P 14.*
14	4	½d. grey-green and green	..	75 14·00
15		1d. grey-black and red	..	75 40
		w. Wmk inverted		
16		2d. grey and brown	..	5·00 24·00
17		2½d. grey and blue	..	1·50 1·75
18		3d. dull orange and deep purple		4·00 25·00
19		6d. dull purple and olive	..	4·00 40·00
20		1s. green and bright purple	..	10·00 17·00
21		2s. green and brown-orange	..	24·00 17·00
22		2s. green and black	..	18·00 32·00

(b) *Wmk Crown CC. P 14*
23	5	5s. black and scarlet	..	90·00 £150
	14/23		*Set of 10*	£140 £275
	14/23 Optd "Specimen"	..	*Set of 10*	£160

1904–08. *Wmk Mult Crown CA. Ordinary paper (½d., 2d., 3d., 6d.) or chalk-surfaced paper (others). P 14.*
24	4	½d. grey-green and green	..	3·00 1·50
		a. Chalk-surfaced paper (3.06)		40 1·00
25		1d. grey-black and red (11.07)		12·00 23·00
26		2d. grey and brown	..	65 4·00
		a. Chalk-surfaced paper (5.06)		1·75 1·00
27		2½d. grey and blue (12.05)	..	2·50 6·50
28		3d. dull orange and deep purple		6·50 6·00
		a. Chalk-surfaced paper (5.08)		7·00 2·50
29		6d. dull purple and olive	..	3·50 18·00
		a. Chalk-surfaced paper (5.08)		7·00 5·50
30		1s. green and bright purple (5.08)		8·50 7·00
31		2s. green and orange (5.08)	..	29·00 42·00
32		2s. 6d. green and black (5.08)	..	40·00 48·00
33	5	5s. black and red (9.07)	..	80·00 £110
	24/33		*Set of 10*	£160 £225

1908 (June)–14. *Wmk Mult Crown CA. Ordinary paper (½d. to 2½d.) or chalk-surfaced paper (3d. to 5s.). P 14.*
35	4	½d. deep green (4.10)	..	5·00 1·00
36		1d. rose-red	..	1·40 30
38		2d. greyish slate (9.09)	..	1·75 14·00
39		2½d. blue	..	2·25 3·50
40		3d. purple/yellow (9.09)	..	1·00 17·00
		a. White back (1.14) (Optd S. £25)		3·50 26·00
43		6d. dull and deep purple (9.09)		6·50 48·00
		a. Dull and bright purple (1914)		9·50 48·00
44		1s. black/green (9.09)	..	8·50 45·00
45		2s. purple and bright blue/blue (9.09)		25·00 55·00
46		2s. 6d. black and red/blue (9.09)		30·00 70·00
47	5	5s. red and green/yellow (9.09)		50·00 70·00
	35/47		*Set of 10*	£110 £275
	35/47 Optd "Specimen"	..	*Set of 10*	£190

Examples of most values are known showing forged Montserrat postmarks dated "OC 16 1909" or "NO 26 1910".

7		8	WAR STAMP (9)

(T 7/8 typo D.L.R.)

1914. *Wmk Mult Crown CA. Chalk-surfaced paper. P 14.*
48	7	5s. red and green/yellow	..	60·00 90·00
48	Optd "Specimen"	..		75·00

1916 (10 Oct)–22. *Wmk Mult Crown CA. Ordinary paper (½d. to 2½d.) or chalk-surfaced paper (3d. to 5s.). P 14.*
49	8	½d. green	.. ..	30 2·50
50		1d. scarlet	.. ..	45 75
		a. Carmine-red	.. ..	16·00 6·00
51		2d. grey	.. ..	1·75 4·00
52		2½d. bright blue	.. ..	1·50 16·00
53		3d. purple/yellow	.. ..	1·00 6·50
		a. On pale yell (13.7.22) (Optd S. £22)		75 10·00
54		4d. grey-black & red/pale yell (13.7.22)		5·50 32·00
55		6d. dull and deep purple	..	2·75 18·00
56		1s. black/blue-green (olive back)		3·00 19·00
57		2s. purple and blue/blue	..	13·00 26·00
58		2s. 6d. black and red/blue	..	22·00 48·00
59		5s. green and red/yellow	..	38·00 48·00
	49/59		*Set of 11*	75·00 £200
	49/59 Optd "Specimen"		*Set of 11*	£160

1917 (8 Oct)–18. *No. 49 optd with T 9.*
60	8	½d. green (R.)	..	10 1·00
		a. Short opt (right pane R. 10/1)		10·00
		y. Wmk inverted and reversed		50·00
61		½d. green (Blk.) (5.18)	..	30 2·00
		a. Short opt (right pane R. 10/1)		12·00
		b. Deep green (10.18)	..	15 1·25
		ba. "C" and "A" missing from wmk		
		bb. Short opt (right pane R. 10/1)		10·00
		w. Wmk inverted		

Nos. 60a, 61a, and 61bb show the overprint 2 mm high instead of 2½ mm.

No. 61ba shows the "C" omitted from one impression and the "A" missing from the next.

1919 (6 Mar). T 8. *Special printing in orange. Value and "WAR STAMP" as T 9 inserted in black at one printing.*
62		1½d. black and orange	..	10 30
	60/2 Optd "Specimen"		*Set of 3*	80·00

1922 (13 July)–29. *Wmk Mult Script CA. Ordinary paper (¼d. to 3d. (No. 73) or chalk-surfaced paper (others). P 14.*
63	8	¼d. brown	..	15 5·50
64		½d. green (5.4.23)	..	20 30
65		1d. bright violet (5.4.23)	..	30 60
66		1d. carmine (1929)	..	75 1·50
67		1½d. orange-yellow	..	1·75 9·50
68		1½d. carmine (5.4.23)	..	30 3·25
69		1½d. red-brown (1929)	..	90 50
70		2d. grey	..	45 1·75
71		2½d. deep bright blue	..	8·00 16·00
		a. Pale brt blue (17.8.26) (Optd S. £30)		60 90
72		2½d. orange-yellow (5.4.23)	..	1·25 19·00
73		3d. dull blue (5.4.23)	..	60 15·00
74		3d. purple/yellow (2.1.27)	..	1·10 4·75
75		4d. black and red/pale yellow		60 11·00
76		5d. dull purple and olive	..	2·75 10·00
77		6d. pale and bright purple (5.4.23)		2·50 7·00
78		1s. black/emerald (5.4.23)	..	3·00 7·00
79		2s. purple and blue/blue	..	7·00 13·00
80		2s. 6d. black and red/blue (5.4.23)		12·00 48·00
81		3s. green and violet	..	12·00 18·00
82		4s. black and scarlet	..	15·00 32·00
83	5	5s. green and red/pale yellow (6.23)		24·00 38·00
	63/83		*Set of 21*	75·00 £225
	63/83 Optd/Perf "Specimen"		*Set of 21*	£275

10 Plymouth

(Recess D.L.R.)

1932 (18 Apr). *300th Anniv of Settlement of Montserrat. Wmk Mult Script CA. P 14.*
84	10	½d. green	..	75 6·00
85		1d. scarlet	..	75 5·50
86		1½d. red-brown	..	1·25 2·50
87		2d. grey	..	1·50 15·00
88		2½d. ultramarine	..	1·25 13·00
89		3d. orange	..	1·50 14·00
90		6d. violet	..	2·25 26·00
91		1s. olive-brown	..	12·00 35·00
92		2s. 6d. purple	..	48·00 70·00
93		5s. chocolate	..	£100 £160
	84/93		*Set of 10*	£150 £300
	84/93 Perf "Specimen"		*Set of 10*	£225

Examples of all values are known showing a forged G.P.O. Plymouth postmark dated "MY 13 32".

1935 (6 May). *Silver Jubilee. As Nos. 114/17 of Jamaica, but ptd by Waterlow & Sons. P 11×12.*
94		1d. deep blue and scarlet	..	85 3·25
95		1½d. ultramarine and grey	..	1·50 2·75
96		2½d. brown and deep blue	..	2·25 3·25
97		1s. slate and purple	..	3·00 14·00
	94/7		*Set of 4*	7·00 21·00
	94/7 Perf "Specimen"		*Set of 4*	75·00

1937 (12 May). *Coronation. As Nos. 118/20 of Jamaica.*

98	1d. scarlet	30	50
99	1½d. yellow-brown	40	30
100	2½d. bright blue	40	75
98/100	Set of 3	1·00	1·40
98/100 Perf "Specimen"	Set of 3	50·00	

11 Carr's Bay

12 Sea Island Cotton

13 Botanic Station

(Recess D.L.R.)

1938 (2 Aug)–48. *Wmk Mult Script CA. P 12 (10s., £1) or 13 (others).*

101	11	½d. blue-green	2·50	1·50
		a. Perf 14 (1942)	15	20
102	12	1d. carmine	2·00	40
		a. Perf 14 (1943)	30	30
103		1½d. purple	10·00	50
		a. Perf 14 (1942)	30	50
		ab. "A" of "CA" missing from wmk		
104	13	2d. orange	10·00	60
		a. Perf 14 (1942)	85	70
105	12	2½d. ultramarine	65	60
		a. Perf 14 (1943)	40	30
106	11	3d. brown	1·75	40
		a. Perf 14. Red-brown (1942)	1·75	40
		ab. Deep brown (1943)	1·75	4·25
107	13	6d. violet	8·00	80
		a. Perf 14 (1943)	2·50	60
108	11	1s. lake	10·00	70
		a. Perf 14 (1942)	2·00	30
109	13	2s. 6d. slate-blue	20·00	80
		a. Perf 14 (1943)	17·00	2·50
110	11	5s. rose-carmine	27·00	8·00
		a. Perf 14 (1943)	21·00	3·00
111	13	10s. pale blue (1.4.48)	13·00	17·00
112	11	£1 black (1.4.48)	13·00	27·00
101a/12		Set of 12	65·00	45·00
101/12 Perf "Specimen"		Set of 12	£250	

Nos. 101/2 exist in coils constructed from normal sheets.

1946 (1 Nov). *Victory. As Nos. 141/2 of Jamaica.*

113	1½d. purple	10	10
114	3d. chocolate	10	10
113/14 Perf "Specimen"	Set of 2	55·00	

1949 (3 Jan). *Royal Silver Wedding. As Nos. 143/4 of Jamaica.*

115	2½d. ultramarine	10	10
116	5s. carmine	4·75	6·50

1949 (10 Oct). *75th Anniv of U.P.U. As Nos. 145/8 of Jamaica.*

117	2½d. ultramarine	20	30
118	3d. brown	1·75	30
119	6d. purple	40	30
120	1s. purple	40	40
117/20	Set of 4	2·50	1·10

(New Currency. 100 cents = 1 West Indies, later Eastern Caribbean dollar)

1951 (16 Feb). *Inauguration of B.W.I. University College. As Nos. 149/50 of Jamaica.*

121	3 c. black and purple	20	60
122	12 c. black and violet	20	60

14 Government House

18 Badge of Presidency

(Recess B.W.)

1951 (17 Sept). *T 14, 18 and similar horiz designs. Wmk Mult Script CA. P 11½ × 11.*

123	14	1 c. black	10	1·50
124	–	2 c. green	15	70
125	–	3 c. orange-brown	30	70
126	–	4 c. carmine	30	50
127	–	5 c. reddish violet	30	70
128	18	6 c. olive-brown	30	30
129	–	8 c. deep blue	35	20
130	–	12 c. blue and chocolate	35	30
131	–	24 c. carmine and yellow-green	95	30
132	–	60 c. black and carmine	6·00	2·50
133	–	$1.20, yellow-green and blue	6·00	4·50
134	–	$2.40, black and green	5·00	12·00
135	18	$4.80, black and purple	16·00	16·00
123/135		Set of 13	32·00	35·00

Designs:—2 c., $1.20, Sea Island cotton: cultivation; 3 c. Map of colony; 4, 24 c. Picking tomatoes; 5, 12 c. St. Anthony's Church; 8, 60 c. Sea Island cotton: ginning; $2.40, Government House.

1953 (2 June). *Coronation. As No. 153 of Jamaica.*

136	2 c. black and deep green	40	15

19 Government House

20 Shakespeare and Memorial Theatre, Stratford-upon-Avon

Two Types of ½ c., 3 c., 6 c. and $4.80: I. Inscr "PRESIDENCY". II. Inscr "COLONY".

(Recess B.W.)

1953 (15 Oct)–62. *As King George VI issue, but with portrait of Queen Elizabeth II as in T 19. Wmk Mult Script CA. P 11½×11.*

136a	–	½ c. deep violet (I) (3.7.56)	50	10
136b	–	½c. deep violet (II) (1.9.58)	70	10
137	19	1 c. black	10	10
138	–	2 c. green	15	10
139	–	3 c. orange-brown (I)	50	10
139a	–	3 c. orange-brown (II) (1.9.58)	70	1·25
140	–	4 c. carmine-red (1.6.55)	30	20
141	–	5 c. reddish lilac (1.6.55)	30	30
142	18	6 c. deep bistre-brown (I) (1.6.55)	30	10
142a		6 c. deep bistre-brown (II) (1.9.58)	40	15
		ab. Deep sepia-brown (30.7.62)	7·00	4·75
143	–	8 c. deep bright blue (1.6.55)	1·00	10
144	–	12 c. blue and red-brown (1.6.55)	1·50	10
145	–	24 c. carmine-red (1.6.55)	1·50	20
145a	–	48 c. yellow-olive and purple (15.10.57)	12·00	2·25
146	–	60 c. black and carmine (1.6.55)	7·00	2·00
147	–	$1.20, green and greenish blue (1.6.55)	14·00	4·25
148	–	$2.40, black and bluish green (1.6.55)	12·00	10·00
149	18	$4.80, black & deep purple (I) (1.6.55)	6·00	10·00
149a		$4.80, black & deep purple (II) (1.9.58)	12·00	7·50
136a/49		Set of 15	50·00	24·00

Extra designs:—½, 3 c. Map of colony; 48 c. Sea Island cotton cultivation.
See also No. 157.

1958 (22 Apr). *Inauguration of British Caribbean Federation. As Nos. 175/7 of Jamaica.*

150	3 c. deep green	55	20
151	6 c. blue	75	60
152	12 c. scarlet	90	15
150/2	Set of 3	2·00	85

1963 (8 July). *Freedom from Hunger. As No. 80 of Lesotho.*

153	12 c. reddish violet	30	15

1963 (2 Sept). *Red Cross Centenary. As Nos. 203/4 of Jamaica.*

154	4 c. red and black	15	20
155	12 c. red and blue	35	50

(Des R. Granger Barrett. Photo Harrison)

1964 (23 Apr). *400th Birth Anniv of William Shakespeare. W w 12. P 14×14½.*

156	20	12 c. indigo	10	10

1964 (29 Oct). *As No. 138 but wmk w 12.*

157	2 c. green	40	20

1965 (17 May). *I.T.U. Centenary. As Nos. 98/9 of Lesotho.*

158	4 c. vermilion and violet	15	10
159	48 c. light emerald and carmine	30	20

21 Pineapple

22 Avocado

(Des Sylvia Goaman. Photo Harrison)

1965 (16 Aug). *T 21/2 and similar vert designs showing vegetables, fruit or plants. Multicoloured. W w 12 (upright). P 15×14.*

160		1 c. Type 21	10	10
		w. Wmk inverted	1·00	1·25
161		2 c. Type 22	10	10
162		3 c. Soursop	10	10
163		4 c. Pepper	10	10
164		5 c. Mango	10	10
165		6 c. Tomato	10	10
166		8 c. Guava	10	10
167		10 c. Ochro	10	10
168		12 c. Lime	15	10
		w. Wmk inverted	—	28·00
169		20 c. Orange	20	10
170		24 c. Banana	20	10
171		42 c. Onion	75	60
172		48 c. Cabbage	1·50	75
173		60 c. Pawpaw	2·25	90
174		$1.20, Pumpkin	2·00	2·50
175		$2.40, Sweet potato	6·00	5·50
176		$4.80, Egg plant	6·00	9·00
160/76		Set of 17	17·00	18·00

See also Nos. 213/22.

1965 (25 Oct). *International Co-operation Year. As Nos. 100/1 of Lesotho.*

177	2 c. reddish purple and turquoise-green	10	20
178	12 c. deep bluish green and lavender	25	10

1966 (26 Jan). *Churchill Commemoration. As Nos. 102/5 of Lesotho.*

179	1 c. new blue	10	10
	a. Cerise (sky) omitted	£275	
180	2 c. deep green	10	10
181	24 c. brown	20	10
182	42 c. bluish violet	25	15
179/82	Set of 4	50	30

23 Queen Elizabeth II and Duke of Edinburgh

(Des H. Baxter. Litho B.W.)

1966 (4 Feb). *Royal Visit. W w 12. P 11×12.*

183	23	14 c. black and ultramarine	50	15
184		24 c. black and magenta	75	15

24 W.H.O. Building

(Des M. Goaman. Litho Harrison)

1966 (20 Sept). *Inauguration of W.H.O. Headquarters, Geneva. W w 12 (sideways). P 14.*

185	24	12 c. black, yellow-green and light blue	15	10
186		60 c. black, light purple and yellow-brown	35	60

1966 (1 Dec). *20th Anniv of U.N.E.S.C.O. As Nos. 342/4 of Mauritius.*

187	4 c. slate-violet, red, yellow and orange	10	10
	a. Orange omitted	70·00	
188	60 c. orange-yellow, violet and deep olive	35	10
189	$1.80, black, bright purple and orange	1·40	70
187/9	Set of 3	1·60	75

On No. 187a the omission of the orange only affects the squares of the lower case letters so that they appear yellow, the same as the capital squares.

25 Yachting
(26)

$1.00

(Des and photo Harrison)

1967 (29 Dec). *International Tourist Year. T 25 and similar multicoloured designs. W w 12 (sideways on 15 c.). P 14.*

190	5 c. Type 25	15	10
191	15 c. Waterfall near Chance Mountain (vert)	20	10
192	16 c. Fishing, skin-diving and swimming	25	40
193	24 c. Playing golf	1·60	45
190/3	Set of 4	2·00	90

1968 (6 May). *Nos. 168, 170, 172 and 174/6 surch as T 26. W w 12 (upright).*

194	15 c. on 12 c. Lime	20	15
195	25 c. on 24 c. Banana	25	15
196	50 c. on 48 c. Cabbage	45	15
197	$1 on $1.20, Pumpkin	80	40
198	$2.50 on $2.40, Sweet potato	1·25	3·25
199	$5 on $4.80, Egg plant	1·40	3·75
194/9	Set of 6	4·00	7·00

See also Nos. 219 etc.

27 Sprinting

28 Sprinting, and Aztec Pillars

(Des G. Vasarhelyi. Photo Harrison)

1968 (31 July). *Olympic Games, Mexico. T 27/8 and similar designs. W w 12 (sideways on $1). P 14.*

200	15 c. deep claret, emerald and gold	10	10
201	25 c. blue, orange and gold	15	10
202	50 c. green, red and gold	25	10
203	$1 multicoloured	35	30
200/3	Set of 4	70	40

Designs: Horiz as T 27—25 c. Weightlifting; 50 c. Gymnastics.

31 Alexander Hamilton

(Des and photo Harrison)

1968 (6 Dec*). *Human Rights Year. T* **31** *and similar horiz designs. Multicoloured.* W w **12**. *P* 14 × 14½.

204	5 c. Type 31			10	10
205	15 c. Albert T. Marryshow			10	10
206	25 c. William Wilberforce			10	10
207	50 c. Dag Hammarskjöld			10	10
208	$1 Dr. Martin Luther King			25	30
204/8			Set of 5	40	45

*Although first day covers were postmarked 2 December, these stamps were not put on sale in Montserrat until 6 December.

32 "The Two Trinities" (Murillo) 33 "The Adoration of the Kings" (detail, Botticelli)

(Des and photo Harrison)

1968 (16 Dec). *Christmas.* W w **12** (*sideways*). *P* 14½ × 14.

209	**32**	5 c. multicoloured		10	10
210	**33**	15 c. multicoloured		10	10
211	**32**	25 c. multicoloured		10	10
212	**33**	50 c. multicoloured		25	20
209/12			Set of 4	40	30

1969–70. *As Nos.* 160/4, 167, 167 *and* 194/6 *but wmk* w **12** *sideways*.

213	1 c. Type **21** (24.6.69)		10	10
214	2 c. Type **22** (23.4.70)		70	85
215	3 c. Soursop (24.6.69)		30	15
	w. Wmk Crown to right of CA		15.00	
216	4 c. Pepper (24.6.69)		60	15
217	5 c. Mango (23.4.70)		1·00	85
218	10 c. Ochro (24.6.69)		50	15
	w. Wmk Crown to right of CA		60·00	
219	15 c. on 12 c. Lime (24.6.69)		60	30
220	20 c. Orange (17.3.69)		75	30
221	25 c. on 24 c. Banana (24.6.69)		90	40
222	50 c. on 48 c. Cabbage (24.6.69)		4·50	9·50
213/22		Set of 10	9·00	11·50

*The normal sideways watermark shows Crown to left of CA, as seen from the back of the stamp.

The 1 c., 3 c., 4 c., 10 c., 15 c. and 20 c. exist with PVA gum as well as gum arabic, but the 2 c. and 5 c. exist with PVA gum only.

34 Map showing "CARIFTA" Countries 35 "Strength in Unity"

(Des J. Cooter. Photo Harrison)

1969 (27 May). *First Anniv of CARIFTA (Caribbean Free Trade Area).* W w **12** (*sideways** on T **34**). *P* 14.

223	**34**	15 c. multicoloured		10	10
224		20 c. multicoloured		10	10
		w. Wmk Crown to right of CA		1·60	
225	**35**	35 c. multicoloured		10	10
226		30 c. multicoloured		15	15
223/6			Set of 4	30	30

*The normal sideways watermark shows Crown to left of CA, as seen from the back of the stamp.

36 Telephone Receiver and Map of Montserrat 40 Dolphin (fish)

(Des R. Reid, adapted by V. Whiteley. Litho P.B.)

1969 (29 July). *Development Projects. T* **36** *and similar vert designs. Multicoloured.* W w **12**. *P* 13½.

227	15 c. Type **36**		10	10
228	25 c. School symbols and map		10	10
229	50 c. Hawker Siddeley H.S.748 aircraft and map		15	10
230	$1 Electricity pylon and map		25	40
227/30		Set of 4	35	50

(Des Harrison. Photo Enschedé)

1969 (1 Nov). *Game Fish. T* **40** *and similar horiz designs. Multicoloured.* *P* 13 × 13½.

231	5 c. Type **40**		35	10
232	15 c. Atlantic Sailfish		50	10
233	25 c. Black-finned Tuna		60	10
234	40 c. Spanish Mackerel		80	55
231/4		Set of 4	2·00	75

41 King Caspar before the Virgin and Child (detail) (Norman 16th-cent stained glass window) 42 "Nativity" (Leonard Limosin)

(Des J. Cooter. Litho D.L.R.)

1969 (10 Dec). *Christmas. Paintings multicoloured; frame colours given.* W w **12** (*sideways on* 50 c.). *P* 13.

235	**41**	15 c. black, gold and violet		10	10
236		25 c. black and vermilion		10	10
237	**42**	50 c. black, ultramarine & yellow-orange		15	15
235/7			Set of 3	30	30

43 "Red Cross Sale"

(Des and litho J.W.)

1970 (13 Apr). *Centenary of British Red Cross. T* **43** *and similar horiz designs. Multicoloured.* W w **12** (*sideways*). *P* 14½ × 14.

238	3 c. Type **43**		10	15
239	4 c. School for deaf children		10	15
240	15 c. Transport services for disabled		10	20
241	20 c. Workshop		10	60
238/41		Set of 4	30	90

44 Red-footed Booby 45 "Madonna and Child with Animals" (Brueghel the Elder, after Dürer)

(Des V. Whiteley. Photo Harrison)

1970 (2 July)–**74**. *Birds. T* **44** *and similar multicoloured designs.* W w **12** (*sideways** *on vert designs and upright on horiz designs. Glazed, ordinary paper ($10) or chalk-surfaced paper (others).* P 14×14½ (*horiz*) or 14½×14 (*vert*).

242	1 c. Type **44**		10	10
	w. Wmk inverted		14·00	
243	2 c. American Kestrel (*vert*)		15	15
	a. Glazed, ordinary paper (22.1.71)		1·25	3·00
244	3 c. Magnificent Frigate Bird (*vert*)		15	15
	w. Wmk Crown to right of CA			
245	4 c. Great Egret (*vert*)		1·00	15
246	5 c. Brown Pelican (*vert*)		2·00	10
	aw. Wmk Crown to right of CA		2·50	
	b. Glazed, ordinary paper (22.1.71)		1·50	2·00
	bw. Wmk Crown to right of CA			
247	10 c. Bananaquit (*vert*)		40	10
	a. Glazed, ordinary paper (22.1.71)		1·50	2·00
248	15 c. Smooth-billed Ani		30	15
	a. Glazed, ordinary paper (22.1.71)		4·50	5·00
	aw. Wmk inverted		4·50	
249	20 c. Red-billed Tropic Bird		35	15
	a. Glazed, ordinary paper (22.1.71)		1·50	2·00
250	25 c. Montserrat Oriole		50	50
	a. Glazed, ordinary paper (22.1.71)		5·00	6·00
251	50 c. Green-throated Carib (*vert*)		5·00	1·25
	a. Glazed, ordinary paper (22.1.71)		4·00	4·50

252	$1 Antillean Crested Hummingbird		6·50	1·00
	aw. Wmk inverted		19·00	
	b. Glazed, ordinary paper (22.1.71)		4·25	5·00
253	$2.50, Little Blue Heron (*vert*)		5·50	10·00
	a. Glazed, ordinary paper (22.1.71)		8·00	10·00
254	$5 Purple-throated Carib		7·50	11·00
	a. Glazed, ordinary paper (22.1.71)		13·00	18·00
254c	$10 Forest Thrush (30.10.74)			
242/54c		Set of 14	35·00	35·00

*The normal sideways watermark shows Crown to left of CA, as seen from the back of the stamp.
See also Nos. 295/302.

(Des G. Drummond. Litho D.L.R.)

1970 (1 Oct).* *Christmas. T* **45** *and similar multicoloured design.* W w **12**. *P* 13½ × 14.

255	5 c. Type **45**		10	10
	w. Wmk inverted		22·00	
256	15 c. "The Adoration of the Shepherds" (Domenichino)		10	10
257	20 c. Type **45**		10	10
	w. Wmk inverted		4·00	
258	$1 As 15 c.		35	1·25
255/8		Set of 4	55	1·40

*This was the local date of issue but the stamps were released by the Crown Agents on 21 September.

46 War Memorial 47 Girl Guide and Badge

(Des V. Whiteley. Litho J.W.)

1970 (30 Nov). *Tourism. T* **46** *and similar horiz designs. Multicoloured.* W w **12** (*sideways**). *P* 14½×14.

259	5 c. Type **46**		10	10
260	15 c. Plymouth from Fort St. George		10	10
261	25 c. Carr's Bay		15	15
262	50 c. Golf Fairway		1·00	1·40
	w. Wmk Crown to right of CA		5·50	
259/62		Set of 4	1·25	1·50
MS263	135×109mm. Nos. 259/62		2·50	2·00

*The normal sideways watermark shows Crown to left of CA, as seen from the back of the stamp.

(Des V. Whiteley. Litho Questa)

1970 (31 Dec). *Diamond Jubilee of Montserrat Girl Guides. T* **47** *and similar vert design. Multicoloured.* W w **12**. *P* 14.

264	10 c. Type **47**		10	10
265	15 c. Brownie and Badge		10	10
266	25 c. As 15 c.		15	10
267	40 c. Type **47**		20	60
264/7		Set of 4	50	75

48 "Descent from the Cross" (Van Hemessen) 49 D.F.C. and D.F.M. in Searchlights

(Des J.W. Photo Enschedé)

1971 (22 Mar). *Easter. T* **48** *and similar vert design. Multicoloured.* W w **12**. *P* 13½.

268	5 c. Type **48**		10	10
269	15 c. "Noli me tangere" (Orcagna)		10	10
270	20 c. Type **48**		10	10
271	40 c. As 15 c.		15	30
268/71		Set of 4	30	50

(Des Col. A. Maynard. Litho Questa)

1971 (8 July). *Golden Jubilee of Commonwealth Ex-Services League. T* **49** *and similar vert designs. Multicoloured.* W w **12**. *P* 14.

272	10 c. Type **49**		10	10
273	20 c. M.C., M.M. and jungle patrol		15	10
274	40 c. D.S.C., D.S.M. and submarine action		20	15
275	$1 V.C. and soldier attacking bunker		50	70
272/5		Set of 4	85	85

OMNIBUS ISSUES

Details, together with prices for complete sets, of the various Omnibus issues from the 1935 Silver Jubilee series to date are included in a special section following Zimbabwe at the end of Volume 2.

50 "The Nativity with Saints" (Romanino)

51 Piper PA-23 Apache

(Des G. Drummond. Litho Questa)

1971 (16 Sept). *Christmas. T 50 and similar vert design. Multi-coloured.* W w 12. P 14 × 13½.

276	5 c. Type 50	10	10
277	15 c. "Choir of Angels" (Simon Marmion)	10	10
278	20 c. Type 50	10	10
279	$1 As 15 c.	35	40
276/9	Set of 4	50	50

(Des and litho J.W.)

1971 (16 Dec). *14th Anniv of Inauguration of L.I.A.T. (Leeward Islands Air Transport). T 51 and similar horiz designs. Multi-coloured.* W w 12 (*sideways*). P 13½.

280	5 c. Type 51	10	10
281	10 c. Beech 50 Twin Bonanza	15	15
282	15 c. De Havilland D.H.114 Heron 2	30	15
283	20 c. Britten Norman Islander	35	15
284	40 c. De Havilland D.H.C.6 Twin Otter 100	65	45
285	75 c. Hawker Siddeley H.S.748	2·00	2·25
280/5	Set of 6	3·25	3·00
MS286	203×102 mm. Nos. 280/5	8·00	13·00

52 "Chapel of Christ in Gethsemane", Coventry Cathedral

53 Lizard

(Des G. Drummond. Litho A. & M.)

1972 (9 Mar). *Easter. T 52 and similar horiz design. Multi-coloured.* W w 12. P 13.

287	5 c. Type 52	10	10
288	10 c. "The Agony in the Garden" (Bellini)	10	10
289	20 c. Type 52	10	10
290	75 c. As 10 c.	35	50
287/90	Set of 4	45	60

(Des G. Drummond. Litho Questa)

1972 (20 July). *Reptiles. T 53 and similar multicoloured designs.* W w 12 (*sideways on 40 c. and $1*). P 14½.

291	15 c. Type 53	15	10
292	20 c. Mountain Chicken (frog)	20	10
293	40 c. Iguana (*horiz*)	35	20
294	$1 Tortoise (*horiz*)	1·50	1·50
291/4	Set of 4	2·00	1·60

1972 (21 July)–74. *As No. 242 etc., but* W w 12, *sideways* on horiz designs* (1, 15, 20, 25 c.) *and upright on vert designs (others). Glazed, ordinary paper.*

295	1 c. Type 44	1·25	45
	a. Chalk-surfaced paper (4.2.74)	80	45
296	2 c. American Kestrel	1·50	45
	aw. Wmk inverted	9·00	
	b. Chalk-surfaced paper (4.2.74)	3·25	45
297	3 c. Magnificent Frigate Bird	12·00	10·00
298	4 c. Great Egret (*chalk-surfaced paper*) (4.2.74)	1·00	3·00
	w. Wmk inverted	5·00	
299	5 c. Brown Pelican (8.3.73)	1·75	30
	a. Chalk-surfaced paper (4.2.74)	60	55
300	15 c. Smooth-billed Ani (8.3.73)	50	45
	a. Chalk-surfaced paper (2.10.73)	85	1·00
	aw. Wmk Crown to left of CA (17.5.74)	2·50	2·25
301	20 c. Red-billed Tropic Bird (*chalk-surfaced paper*) (2.10.73)	1·40	1·50
302	25 c. Montserrat Oriole (*chalk-surfaced paper*) (17.5.74)	3·25	3·50
295/302	Set of 8	19·00	18·00

*The normal sideways watermark shows Crown to left of CA on 1 c and 20 c., and to right on 15 c and 25 c., *as seen from the back of the stamp.*

In 1973–74, during shortages of the 5 c. value, letters can be found posted unstamped and franked with a "postage paid" mark. Other covers exist with the word "paid" in manuscript.

54 "Madonna of the Chair" (Raphael)

(Des J. Cooter. Litho Format)

1972 (18 Oct). *Christmas. T 54 and similar horiz designs. Multi-coloured.* W w 12. P 13½.

303	10 c. Type 54	10	10
304	35 c. "Virgin and Child with Cherub" (Fungai)	20	10
305	50 c. "Madonna of the Magnificat" (Botticelli)	30	30
306	$1 "Virgin and Child with St. John and an Angel" (Botticelli)	40	65
303/6	Set of 4	80	90

55 Lime, Tomatoes and Pawpaw

56 Passiflora herbertiana

(Des from photographs by D. Groves) and photo Harrison)

1972 (20 Nov). *Royal Silver Wedding. Multicoloured; background colour given.* W w 12. P 14 × 14½.

307	55 35 c. rose	10	10
308	$1 bright blue	20	20
	w. Wmk inverted	38·00	

(Des J. Cooter. Litho Walsall)

1973 (9 Apr). *Easter. T 56 and similar vert designs showing passion-flowers. Multicoloured.* W w 12. P 13½.

309	20 c. Type 56	25	10
310	35 c. P. vitifolia	30	10
311	75 c. P. amabilis	50	75
312	$1 P. alata-caerulea	60	80
309/12	Set of 4	1·50	1·60

Nos. 309/12 are inscribed on the reverse with information about the passion-flower.

57 Montserrat Monastery, Spain

58 "Virgin and Child" (School of Gerard David)

(Des J. Cooter. Litho Format)

1973 (9 July). *480th Anniv of Columbus's Discovery of Montserrat. T 57 and similar horiz designs. Multicoloured.* W w 12. P 13½.

313	10 c. Type 57	15	10
314	35 c. Columbus sighting Montserrat	30	15
315	60 c. Santa Maria off Montserrat	1·10	1·10
316	$1 Colony badge and map of voyage	1·25	1·10
313/16	Set of 4	2·50	2·25
MS317	126×134 mm. Nos. 313/16. Wmk inverted	11·00	13·00
	w. Wmk upright	75·00	

(Des J. Cooter. Litho Questa)

1973 (22 Oct). *Christmas. T 58 and similar vert designs. Multi-coloured.* W w 12 (*sideways*). P 13½.

318	20 c. Type 58	25	10
319	35 c. "The Holy Family with St. John" (Jordaens)	30	10
320	50 c. "Virgin and Child" (Bellini)	45	50
321	90 c. "Virgin and Child with Flowers" (Dolci)	65	1·00
318/21	Set of 4	1·50	1·40

58a Princess Anne and Captain Mark Phillips

59 Steel Band

(Des PAD Studio. Litho Questa)

1973 (14 Nov). *Royal Wedding. Centre multicoloured.* W w 12 (*sideways*). P 13½.

322	58a 35 c. sage-green	10	10
323	$1 violet-blue	20	20

(Des J. W. Litho Questa)

1974 (8 Apr). *25th Anniv of University of West Indies. T 59 and similar designs. Multicoloured.* W w 12 (*sideways on 20 c., $1 and MS328*).

324	20 c. Type 59	15	10
325	35 c. Masqueraders (*vert*)	15	10
326	60 c. Student weaving (*vert*)	25	45
	w. Wmk inverted	†	£100
327	$1 University Centre, Montserrat	30	55
324/7	Set of 4	75	1·00
MS328	130×89 mm. Nos. 324/7	1·75	6·00

60 Hands with Letters

(61)

(Des P. Powell. Litho Walsall)

1974 (3 July). *Centenary of Universal Postal Union. T 60 and similar horiz design.* W w 12. P 14½ × 14.

329	60	1 c. multicoloured	10	10
330		2 c. lt rose-red, orange-verm & blk	10	10
331	60	3 c. multicoloured	10	10
332		5 c. lt yellow-orange, reddish orge & blk	10	10
333	60	50 c. multicoloured	20	20
334		$1 pale blue, turquoise-blue and black	40	65
329/34		Set of 6	75	90

Designs:—2 c., 5 c., $1 Figures from U.P.U. Monument.

1974 (2 Oct). *Various stamps surch as T 61.*

335	2 c. on $1 (No. 252b)	30	1·50
	w. Wmk inverted	40·00	
336	5 c. on 50 c. (No. 333)	30	60
337	10 c. on 60 c. (No. 326)	65	1·75
	a. Surch double		
338	20 c. on $1 (No. 252b)	30	1·25
	a. "2" with serifs (Pl 1B R. 3/1)	13·00	
	b. Bottom bar of surch omitted (Pl 1B R. 5/1-5)	4·25	
339	35 c. on $1 (No. 334)	40	1·25
335/9	Set of 5	1·75	5·75

62 Churchill and Houses of Parliament

63 Carib "Carbet"

(Des R. Granger Barrett. Litho D.L.R.)

1974 (30 Nov). *Birth Centenary of Sir Winston Churchill. T 62 and similar vert design. Multicoloured. No wmk.* P 13 × 13½.

340	15 c. Type 62	15	10
341	70 c. Churchill and Blenheim Palace	20	20
MS342	81 × 85 mm. Nos. 340/1	50	70

(Des C. Abbott. Litho Walsall)

1975 (3 Mar). *Carib Artefacts. T 63 and similar horiz designs.*

(a) W w 12 (*sideways*). *From sheets.* P 14

343	5 c. lake-brown, yellow and black	10	10
344	20 c. black, lake-brown and yellow	10	10
345	35 c. black, yellow and lake-brown	15	10
346	70 c. yellow, lake-brown and black	45	40
343/6	Set of 4	70	60

(b) No wmk. Self-adhesive with advertisements on the reverse. From booklets. Rouletted

347	5 c. lake-brown, yellow and black	15	25
	a. Booklet pane. Nos. 347/50 se-tenant	90	
348	20 c. black, lake-brown and yellow	15	25
	a. Booklet pane. Nos. 348 × 3 and No. 349 × 3	90	
349	35 c. black, yellow and lake-brown	15	25
350	70 c. yellow, lake-brown and black	55	80
347/50	Set of 4	90	1·40

Designs:—20 c. "Caracoli"; 35 c. Club or mace; 70 c. Canoe.

64 One-Bitt Coin

(Des J. Cooter. Litho Questa)

1975 (1 Sept). *Local Coinage, 1785–1801. T 64 and similar diamond-shaped designs.* W w 14 (*sideways*). P 13½.
351	5 c. black, light violet-blue and silver	..	..	10	10
352	10 c. black, salmon and silver		..	15	10
353	35 c. black, light blue-green and silver	..	..	20	15
354	$2 black, bright rose and silver	..	..	90	1·50
351/4			*Set of 4*	1·25	1·60
MS355	142 × 142 mm. Nos. 351/4		..	1·25	2·75

Designs:—10 c. Eighth dollar; 35 c. Quarter dollar; $2 One dollar.

No. **MS355** has details of the coins depicted printed on the reverse side, beneath the gum.

65 1d. and 6d. Stamps of 1876

66 "The Trinity"

(Des J. Cooter. Litho J. W.)

1976 (5 Jan). *Centenary of First Montserrat Postage Stamp. T 65 and similar horiz designs.* W w 12 (*sideways*). P 13.
356	5 c. deep carmine, yellowish green and black		15	10
357	10 c. light yellow-ochre, scarlet and black		20	10
358	40 c. multicoloured	..	..	50	40
359	55 c. deep mauve, yellowish green and black		60	50
360	70 c. multicoloured	..	..	70	70
361	$1.10, yellowish green, brt blue & grey-blk.		1·00	1·00
356/61			*Set of 6*	2·75	2·50
MS362	170 × 159 mm. Nos. 356/61. P 13½		3·00	5·50

Designs:—10 c. G.P.O. and bisected 1d. stamp; 40 c. Bisects on cover; 55 c. G.B. 6d. used in Montserrat and local 6d. of 1876; 70 c. Stamps for 2½d. rate, 1876; $1.10, Packet boat *Antelope* and 6d. stamp.

(Des J. Cooter. Litho Questa)

1976 (5 Apr). *Easter. Unissued stamps prepared for Easter 1975 with values and date obliterated by black bars. T 66 and similar vert designs showing paintings by Orcagna. Multicoloured.* W w 14. P 13½.
363	15 c. on 5 c. Type 66	..	..	10	10
	a. Surch omitted	..	..	40·00	
364	40 c. on 35 c. "The Resurrection"		15	15
	a. Surch omitted	..	..	40·00	
365	55 c. on 70 c. "The Ascension"		15	15
	a. Surch omitted	..	..	40·00	
366	$1.10 on $1 "Pentecost"	..	..	30	40
	a. Surch omitted	..	..	40·00	
363/6			*Set of 4*	55	65
MS367	160 × 142 mm. Nos. 363/6	..	1·25	2·25
	a. Surch omitted	..	..	£160	

For No. 363 the "1" was added to the original 5 c. to make 15 c.

(67)   **68** White Frangipani

1976 (12 Apr). *Nos. 244 and 246/7 surch as T 67.*
368	2 c. on 5 c. Brown Pelican	..		10	15
369	30 c. on 10 c. Bananaquit	..		30	20
370	45 c. on 3 c. Magnificent Frigate Bird		40	25
	a. Surch triple				
	b. Surch double	..	..	32·00	
368/70			*Set of 3*	70	55

(Des J. Cooter. Litho Questa)

1976 (5 July)–**80**. *Various horiz designs showing Flowering Trees as T 68. Multicoloured. Ordinary paper.* W w 14 (*sideways**). P 13½.
371	1 c. Type 68	..	..	10	10
372	2 c. Cannon-ball Tree	..	..	10	10
	w. Wmk Crown to right of CA	..	65·00	
373	3 c. Lignum vitae	..	..	10	10
374	5 c. Malay apple	..	..	15	10
	w. Wmk Crown to right of CA	..	24·00	
375	10 c. Jacaranda	..	..	30	10
376	15 c. Orchid Tree	..	..	50	10
	a. Chalk-surfaced paper (8.80)	..	1·25	2·00
377	20 c. Manjak	..	..	30	10
	a. Chalk-surfaced paper (8.80)	..	1·25	2·00
378	25 c. Tamarind	..	..	60	50
379	40 c. Flame of the Forest	..	..	40	10
380	55 c. Pink Cassia	..	..	50	30
381	70 c. Long John	..	..	50	30
382	$1 Saman	..	..	65	60
383	$2.50, Immortelle	..	..	1·25	1·50
384	$5 Yellow Poui	..	..	1·75	2·25
	w. Wmk Crown to right of CA	..	10·00	
385	$10 Flamboyant	..	..	2·50	4·25
371/85			*Set of 15*	8·00	9·00

*The normal sideways watermark shows Crown to left of CA, as seen from the back of the stamp.

69 Mary and Joseph   **70** Hudson River Review, 1976

(Des L. Curtis. Litho Format)

1976 (4 Oct). *Christmas. T 69 and similar vert designs. Multicoloured.* W w 14. P 14.
386	15 c. Type 69	..	..	10	10
387	20 c. The Shepherds	..	..	10	10
388	55 c. Mary and Jesus	..	..	15	10
389	$1.10, The Magi	..	..	30	50
386/9			*Set of 4*	50	65
MS390	95 × 135 mm. Nos. 386/9 ..		60	2·25

(Des and litho J.W.)

1976 (13 Dec). *Bicentenary of American Revolution. T 70 and similar vert designs. Multicoloured.* W w 14. P 13.
391	15 c. Type 70	..	..	40	20
	a. Horiz pair. Nos. 391 and 394		1·75	80
392	40 c. *Raleigh* (American frigate), 1777*	70	40
	a. Horiz pair. Nos. 392/3	..	1·40	80
393	75 c. H.M.S. *Druid* (frigate), 1777*	70	40
394	$1.25, Hudson River Review	..	1·25	60
391/4			*Set of 4*	2·75	1·40
MS395	95×145 mm. Nos. 391/4. P 13½	2·75	2·75

*The date is wrongly given on the stamps as "1776".

Nos. 392/3 and 391 with 394 were each printed in horizontal *se-tenant* pairs throughout the sheets, the pairs forming composite designs.

71 The Crowning   **72** *Ipomoea alba*

(Des G. Vasarhelyi. Litho J.W.)

1977 (7 Feb). *Silver Jubilee. T 71 and similar horiz designs. Multicoloured.* W w 14 (*sideways*). P 13.
396	30 c. Royal Visit, 1966..	..	10	10
397	40 c. Cannons firing salute	..	15	10
398	$1 Type 71	..	..	25	50
396/8			*Set of 3*	45	60

(Des J. Cooter. Litho Questa)

1977 (1 June). *Flowers of the Night. T 72 and similar multi-coloured designs.* W w 14 (*sideways on 40 and 55 c.*). P 14.
399	15 c. Type 72	..	..	20	10
400	40 c. *Epiphyllum hookeri* (horiz)	..	30	30
401	55 c. *Cereus hexagonus* (horiz)	..	30	30
402	$1.50, *Cestrum nocturnum*	..	80	1·40
399/402			*Set of 4*	1·40	1·90
MS403	126 × 130 mm. Nos. 399/402. Wmk sideways		1·60	3·25

73 Princess Anne laying Foundation Stone of Glendon Hospital

(Des BG Studio. Litho Questa)

1977 (3 Oct). *Development. T 73 and similar horiz designs. Multicoloured.* W w 14 (*sideways**). P 14½×14.
404	20 c. Type 73	..	..	15	10
405	35 c. *Statesman* (freighter) at Plymouth	35	15
406	55 c. Glendon Hospital	..	35	20
	w. Wmk Crown to right of CA	..	32·00	
407	$1.50, Jetty at Plymouth Port	..	90	1·00
404/7			*Set of 4*	1·60	1·25
MS408	146×105 mm. Nos. 404/7 ..		2·00	2·50

*The normal sideways watermark shows Crown to left of CA, as seen from the back of the stamp.

ALTERED CATALOGUE NUMBERS

Any Catalogue numbers altered from the last edition are shown as a list in the introductory pages.

$1.00

SILVER JUBILEE 1977

ROYAL VISIT

TO THE CARIBBEAN

(74)

1977 (28 Oct). *Royal Visit. Nos. 380/1 and 383 surch locally with T 74.*
409	$1 on 55 c. Pink Cassia	..	..	30	45
410	$1 on 70 c. Long John	..	..	30	45
411	$1 on $2.50, Immortelle	..	..	30	45
	a. Surch double				
	b. Surch omitted (top stamp of vert pair)		
409/11			*Set of 3*	80	1·25

On No. **411b** the lower stamp in the pair also shows the surcharge bars omitted.

75 The Stable at Bethlehem   **76** Four-eyed Butterflyfish

(Des L. Curtis. Litho Walsall)

1977 (14 Nov). *Christmas. T 75 and similar vert designs. Multi-coloured.* W w 14. P 14 × 14½.
412	5 c. Type 75	..	..	10	10
413	40 c. The Three Kings	..	..	15	10
414	55 c. Three Ships	..	..	20	10
415	$2 Three Angels	..	..	65	1·25
412/15			*Set of 4*	90	1·40
MS416	119 × 115 mm. Nos. 412/15		1·00	2·25

(Des J.W. Litho Walsall)

1978 (15 Mar). *Fish. T 76 and similar horiz designs. Multi-coloured.* W w 14 (*sideways*). P 14.
417	30 c. Type 76	..	..	55	10
418	40 c. French Angelfish	..	..	60	15
419	55 c. Blue Tang	..	..	70	15
420	$1.50, Queen Triggerfish	..	1·10	1·25
417/20			*Set of 4*	2·75	1·40
MS421	152 × 102 mm. Nos. 417/20	..	2·75	3·00

77 St. Paul's Cathedral   **78** *Alpinia speciosa*

(Des G. Drummond. Litho J.W.)

1978 (2 June). *25th Anniv of Coronation. T 77 and similar horiz designs. Multicoloured.* W w 14 (*sideways*). P 13.
422	40 c. Type 77	..	..	10	10
423	55 c. Chichester Cathedral	..	10	10
424	$1 Lincoln Cathedral	..	..	20	25
425	$2.50, Llandaff Cathedral	..	40	50
422/5			*Set of 4*	65	75
MS426	130 × 102 mm. Nos. 422/5. P 13½ × 14	70	1·25

Nos. 422/5 were each printed in sheets including two *se-tenant* stamp-size labels.

(Des J. Cooter. Litho J.W.)

1978 (18 Sept). *Flowers. T 78 and similar vert designs. Multi-coloured.* W w 14. P 13½ × 13.
427	40 c. Type 78	..	..	20	10
428	55 c. *Allamanda cathartica*	..	25	15
429	$1 *Petrea volubilis*	..	..	45	45
430	$2 *Hippeastrum puniceum*	..	70	80
427/30			*Set of 4*	1·40	1·40

79 Private, 21st (Royal North British Fusiliers), 1796   **80** Cub Scouts

(Des J.W. Litho Questa)

1978 (20 Nov). *Military Uniforms* (1st series). T **79** and similar vert designs showing soldiers from British infantry regiments. Multicoloured. W w 14. P 14 × 14½.
431	30 c. Type **79**		15	15
432	40 c. Corporal, 86th (Royal County Down), 1831		20	15
433	55 c. Sergeant, 14th (Buckinghamshire) 1837		30	20
434	$1.50, Officer, 55th (Westmorland), 1784		75	80
431/4		Set of 4	1.25	1.10
MS435	140 × 89 mm. Nos. 431/4		2.00	2.75

See also Nos. 441/5.

(Des J. W. Litho Walsall)

1979 (2 Apr). *50th Anniv of Boy Scout Movement on Montserrat.* T **80** and similar multicoloured designs. W w 14 (sideways on 40 and 55 c). P 14.
436	40 c. Type **80**		20	10
437	55 c. Scouts with signalling equipment		30	20
438	$1.25, Camp fire (vert)		50	55
439	$2 Oath ceremony (vert)		65	1.00
436/9		Set of 4	1.50	1.75
MS440	120 × 110 mm. Nos. 436/9		1.75	2.25

(Des J.W. Litho Questa)

1979 (4 June). *Military Uniforms* (2nd series). Vert designs as T **79** showing soldiers from infantry regiments. Multicoloured. W w 14. P 14 × 14½.
441	30 c. Private, 60th (Royal American), 1783		15	15
442	40 c. Private, 1st West India, 1819		20	15
443	55 c. Officer, 5th (Northumberland), 1819		30	25
444	$2.50, Officer, 93rd (Sutherland Highlanders), 1830		1.00	1.10
441/4		Set of 4	1.50	1.50
MS445	139 × 89 mm. Nos. 441/4		1.50	2.50

81 Child reaching out to Adult

(Des G. Vasarhelyi. Litho Questa)

1979 (17 Sept). *International Year of the Child.* W w 14 (sideways). P 13½ × 14.
446	**81**	$2 black, orange-brown and flesh	50	55
MS447	85 × 99 mm. No. 446		50	1.10

82 Sir Rowland Hill with Penny Black and Montserrat 1876 1d. Stamp

83 Plume Worm

(Des G. Vasarhelyi. Litho Questa)

1979 (1 Oct). *Death Centenary of Sir Rowland Hill and Centenary of U.P.U. Membership.* T **82** and similar horiz designs. Multicoloured. W w 14 (sideways). P 14.
448	40 c. Type **82**		20	10
449	55 c. U.P.U. emblem and notice announcing Leeward Islands entry into Union		20	15
450	$1 1883 Letter following U.P.U. membership		30	50
451	$2 Great Britain Post Office Regulations notice and Sir Rowland Hill		40	80
448/51		Set of 4	1.00	1.40
MS452	135 × 154 mm. Nos. 448/51		1.25	2.25

(Des G. Drummond. Litho Walsall)

1979 (26 Nov). *Marine Life.* T **83** and similar vert designs. Multicoloured. W w 14. P 14.
453	40 c. Type **83**		30	15
454	55 c. Sea Fans		40	20
455	$2 Coral and Sponge		1.00	2.10
453/5		Set of 3	1.50	2.25

84 Tree Frog

(Des J. Cooter. Litho Rosenbaum Bros, Vienna)

1980 (4 Feb). *Reptiles and Amphibians.* T **84** and similar horiz designs. Multicoloured. W w 14 (sideways*). P 13½.
456	40 c. Type **84**		20	15
	w. Wmk Crown to right of CA		20	
457	55 c. Tree Lizard		25	25
	w. Wmk Crown to right of CA		30	
458	$1 Crapaud		45	50
	w. Wmk Crown to right of CA		55	
459	$2 Wood Slave		80	90
	w. Wmk Crown to right of CA		90	
456/9		Set of 4	1.50	1.60

*The normal sideways watermark shows Crown to left of CA, as seen from the back of the stamp.

85 Marquess of Salisbury and 1838 Handstamps

75th Anniversary of Rotary International

(**86**)

(Des BG Studio. Litho Questa)

1980 (14 Apr). *"London 1980" International Stamp Exhibition.* T **85** and similar horiz designs. Multicoloured. W w 14 (sideways). P 14.
460	40 c. Type **85**		20	15
461	55 c. Hawker Siddeley H.S.748 aircraft and 1976 55 c. definitive		25	25
462	$1.20, La Plata (liner) and 1903 5s. stamp		30	45
463	$1.20, Lady Hawkins (packet steamer) and 1932 Tercentenary 5s. commemorative		30	45
464	$1.20, Avon (paddle-steamer) and Penny Red stamp with "A 08" postmark		30	45
465	$1.20, Aeronca Champion 17 airplane and 1953 $1.20 definitive		30	45
460/5		Set of 6	1.50	2.00
MS466	115×110 mm. Nos. 460/5. P 12		1.60	2.50

Nos. 460/5 were each printed in sheets of 4 stamps and two *se-tenant* stamp-size labels.

Some sheets of No. 462 showed the red colour omitted from the map in the right-hand label.

1980 (7 July). *75th Anniv of Rotary International.* No. 383 optd with T **86**.
467	$2.50, Immortelle		55	85

87 Greek, French and U.S.A. Flags

(Des A. Theobald. Litho Questa)

1980 (7 July). *Olympic Games, Moscow.* T **87** and similar horiz designs. Multicoloured. W w 14 (sideways). P 13½ × 14.
468	40 c. Type **87**		20	30
469	55 c. Union, Swedish and Belgian flags		20	30
470	70 c. French, Dutch and U.S.A. flags		30	40
471	$1 German, Union and Finnish flags		35	40
472	$1.50, Australian, Italian and Japanese flags		45	70
473	$2 Mexican, West German and Canadian flags		50	70
474	$2.50, "The Discus Thrower" (sculpture by Miron)		55	1.00
468/74		Set of 7	2.25	3.50
MS475	150 × 100 mm. Nos. 468/74		2.25	3.50
	a. Bottom row of stamps in miniature sheet imperf on 3 sides		£475	

Nos. 468/74 were each printed in small sheets of 4 including one se-tenant stamp-size label.

No. MS475a shows the three stamps in the bottom row of the miniature sheet imperforate vertically and with no perforations between the stamps and the bottom margin.

(**88**)

89 Lady Nelson, 1928

1980 (30 Sept). *Nos. 371, 373, 376 and 379 surch as T **88**.*
476	5 c. on 3 c. Lignum vitae		10	10
	a. Surch double, one inverted		35.00	
477	35 c. on 1 c. Type **68**		15	15
	a. Surch omitted (in vert pair with normal)		35.00	
478	35 c. on 3 c. Lignum vitae		15	15
479	35 c. on 15 c. Orchid Tree		15	15
480	55 c. on 40 c. Flame of the Forest		15	15
	a. Surch inverted		50.00	
481	$5 on 40 c. Flame of the Forest		85	2.00
476/81		Set of 6	1.40	2.25

The surcharge omitted error, No. 477a, occurs on the lower stamp of a vertical pair. On the upper stamp the surcharge is at the foot of the design.

For 30 c. on 15 c. and $2.50 on 40 c. see Nos. O33a and O39a.

(Des J.W. Litho Walsall)

1980 (3 Nov). *Mail Packet Boats* (1st series). T **89** and similar horiz designs. Multicoloured. W w 14 (sideways). P 14.
482	40 c. Type **89**		30	15
483	55 c. Chignecto, 1913		40	25
484	$1 Solent II, 1878		80	60
485	$2 Dee, 1841		1.10	1.25
482/5		Set of 4	2.40	2.00

See also Nos. 615/19.

90 Heliconius charithonia

91 Atlantic Spadefish

(Des J.W. Litho Questa)

1981 (2 Feb). *Butterflies.* T **90** and similar square designs. Multicoloured. W w 14 (inverted). P 14.
486	50 c. Type **90**		60	40
	w. Wmk upright		1.75	
487	65 c. Pyrgus oileus		70	45
488	$1.50, Phoebis agarithe		90	45
489	$2.50, Danaus plexippus		1.25	50
486/9		Set of 4	3.00	2.50

Nos. 486/9 were each printed in sheets including two se-tenant stamp-size labels.

(Des G. Drummond. Litho J.W.)

1981 (20 Mar). *Fishes.* Vert designs as T **91**. Multicoloured. W w 14. No imprint date. P 13½×13.
490	5 c. Type **91**		70	30
491	10 c. Hogfish and Neon Goby		70	30
492	15 c. Creole Wrasse		80	30
493	20 c. Three-spotted Damselfish		90	30
494	25 c. Sergeant Major		90	30
495	35 c. Fin-spot Wrasse		80	30
496	45 c. Schoolmaster		80	40
497	55 c. Striped Parrotfish		1.10	45
498	65 c. Bigeye		80	60
499	75 c. French Grunt		80	60
	w. Wmk inverted		8.00	
500	$1 Rock Beauty		1.00	70
501	$2 Blue Chromis		1.50	1.10
502	$3 Royal Gramma ("Fairy Basslet") and Blueheads		1.60	1.75
503	$5 Cherub Angelfish		2.25	2.75
	w. Wmk inverted		13.00	
504	$7.50, Long-jawed Squirrelfish		3.00	4.75
505	$10 Caribbean Long-nosed Butterflyfish		3.50	6.50
490/505		Set of 16	19.00	19.00

For stamps watermarked with W w 15 see Nos. 555/70.

92 Fort St. George

(Des J. Cooter. Litho Format)

1981 (18 May). *National Trust.* T **92** and similar horiz designs. Multicoloured. W w 14 (sideways). P 13½ × 14.
506	50 c. Type **92**		25	20
507	65 c. Bird sanctuary, Fox's Bay		45	40
508	$1.50, Museum		50	65
509	$2.50, Bransby Point Battery, circa 1780		60	1.10
506/9		Set of 4	1.60	2.10

(Des D. Shults. Litho Questa)

1981 (17 July–19 Nov). *Royal Wedding.* Horiz designs as T **26/27** of Kiribati. Multicoloured. (a) W w **15**. P 14.
510	90 c. Charlotte		25	25
	aw. Wmk inverted		9.00	
	b. Sheetlet. No. 510×6 and No. 511		2.10	
	bw. Wmk inverted		70.00	
511	90 c. Prince Charles and Lady Diana Spencer		85	85
	aw. Wmk inverted		25.00	
512	$3 Portsmouth		60	60
	aw. Wmk inverted		5.50	
	b. Sheetlet. No. 512×6 and No. 513		4.50	
	bw. Wmk inverted		48.00	
513	$3 As No. 511		1.50	1.50
	aw. Wmk inverted		20.00	
514	$4 Britannia		75	75
	aw. Wmk inverted		8.00	
	b. Sheetlet. No. 514×6 and No. 515		5.50	
	bw. Wmk inverted		65.00	
515	$4 As No. 511		1.75	1.75
	aw. Wmk inverted		25.00	
510/15		Set of 6	5.25	5.25
MS516	120×109 mm. $5 As No. 511. Wmk sideways. P 12 (19 Nov)		1.00	1.00

(b) *Booklet stamps. No wmk. P 12 (19 Nov)*

517	90 c. As No. 510		30	45
	a. Booklet pane. No. 517×4 with margins all round		1·10	
518	$3 As No. 513		1·40	1·75
	a. Booklet pane. No. 518×2 with margins all round		2·75	

Nos. 510/15 were printed in sheetlets of seven stamps of the same face value, each containing six of the "Royal Yacht" design and one of the larger design showing Prince Charles and Lady Diana.

Nos. 517/18 come from $13.20 stamp booklets.

93 H.M.S. *Dorsetshire* and Fairey IIIF Firefly Seaplane

94 Methodist Church, Bethel

(Des Court House Advertising Ltd. Litho Questa)

1981 (31 Aug). *50th Anniv of Montserrat Airmail Service. T* **93** *and similar horiz designs. Multicoloured. W w* **14** *(sideways). P* 14.

519	50 c. Type 93		40	30
520	65 c. Beech 50 Twin Bonanza		55	50
521	$1.50, De Havilland D.H.89 Dragon Rapide *Lord Shaftesbury*		80	1·75
522	$2.50, Hawker Siddeley H.S.748 and maps of Montserrat and Antigua		1·00	2·75
519/22		*Set of 4*	2·50	4·75

(Des J. Cooter. Litho Walsall)

1981 (16 Nov). *Christmas. Churches. T* **94** *and similar vert designs. Multicoloured. W w* **14**. P 14 × 13½.

523	50 c. Type 94		15	15
524	65 c. St George's Anglican Church, Harris		20	15
525	$1.50, St Peter's Anglican Church, St Peters		45	60
526	$2.50, St Patrick's R.C. Church, Plymouth		55	1·00
523/6		*Set of 4*	1·25	1·75
MS527	176 × 120 mm. Nos. 523/6		2·25	3·00

95 Rubiaceae (*Rondeletia buxifolia*)

96 Plymouth

(Des local artist. Litho Questa)

1982 (18 Jan). *Plant Life. T* **95** *and similar multicoloured designs. W w* **14** *(sideways on 65 c. and $2.50). P* 14½.

528	50 c. Type 95		20	30
529	65 c. Boraginaceae (*Heliotropium ternatum*) (horiz)		25	40
530	$1.50, Simarubaceae (*Picramnia pentandra*)		50	85
531	$2.50, Ebenaceae (*Diospyrus revoluta*) (horiz)		70	1·25
528/31		*Set of 4*	1·50	2·50

(Litho Format)

1982 (17 Apr). *350th Anniv of Settlement of Montserrat by Sir Thomas Warner. W w* **14** *(sideways). P* 14½.

532	**96** 40 c. green		25	30
533	55 c. red		30	35
534	65 c. chestnut		35	50
535	75 c. olive-grey		40	60
536	85 c. bright blue		40	75
537	95 c. bright orange		40	80
538	$1 bright reddish violet		40	80
539	$1.50, brown-olive		45	1·25
540	$2 deep claret		55	1·50
541	$2.50, bistre-brown		60	1·50
532/41		*Set of 10*	3·50	7·50

Nos. 532/41 are based on the 1932 Tercentenary set.

97 Catherine of Aragon, Princess of Wales, 1501

98 Local Scout

(Des D. Shults and J. Cooter. Litho Format)

1982 (16 June). *21st Birthday of Princess of Wales. T* **97** *and similar vert designs. Multicoloured. W w* **15**. P 13½ × 14.

542	75 c. Type 97		15	15
543	$1 Coat of arms of Catherine of Aragon		15	15
	w. Wmk inverted		11·00	
544	$5 Diana, Princess of Wales		80	1·25
542/4		*Set of 3*	1·00	1·40

(Des D. Shults. Litho Format)

1982 (13 Sept). *75th Anniv of Boy Scout Movement. T* **98** *and similar vert design. Multicoloured. W w* **15**. P 14.

545	$1.50, Type 98		50	50
546	$2.50, Lord Baden-Powell		60	75

Nos. 545/6 exist imperforate from stock dispersed by the liquidator of Format International Security Printers Ltd.

99 Annunciation

(Des Jennifer Toombs. Litho Walsall)

1982 (18 Nov). *Christmas. T* **99** *and similar horiz designs. Multicoloured. W w* **14** *(sideways). P* 14.

547	35 c. Type 99		15	15
548	75 c. Shepherd's Vision		25	35
549	$1.50, The Stable		45	85
550	$2.50, Flight into Egypt		55	1·10
547/50		*Set of 4*	1·25	2·25

100 *Lepthemis vesiculosa*

101 Blue-headed Hummingbird

(Des J. Cooter. Litho Walsall)

1983 (19 Jan). *Dragonflies. T* **100** *and similar horiz designs. Multicoloured. W w* **14** *(sideways). P* 13½ × 14.

551	50 c. Type 100		40	20
552	65 c. Orthemis ferruginea		50	25
553	$1.50, Triacanthagyna trifida		1·00	1·25
554	$2.50, Erythrodiplax umbrata		1·40	2·00
551/4		*Set of 4*	3·00	3·25

1983 (12 Apr). *As Nos. 490/505, but W w* **15** *and imprint date "1983" added. P* 13½ × 13.

555	5 c. Type 91		20	10
556	10 c. Hogfish and Neon Goby		25	10
559	25 c. Sergeant Major		35	20
560	35 c. Fin-spot Wrasse		45	30
564	75 c. French Grunt		75	55
565	$1 Rock Beauty		85	65
568	$5 Cherub Angelfish		2·25	3·00
570	$10 Caribbean Long-nosed Butterflyfish		3·75	6·00
555/70		*Set of 8*	8·00	10·00

(Des G. Drummond. Litho Format)

1983 (24 May). *Hummingbirds. T* **101** *and similar vert designs. Multicoloured. W w* **14**. P 14.

571	35 c. Type 101		1·50	35
572	75 c. Green-throated Carib		1·75	85
573	$2 Antillean Crested Hummingbird		2·75	2·75
574	$3 Purple-throated Carib		3·00	3·75
571/4		*Set of 4*	8·00	7·00

102 Montserrat Emblem

(103)

(Litho Harrison)

1983 (25 July). *W w* **14**. P 14½.

575	102 $12 royal blue and rose		4·25	5·00
576	$30 rose and royal blue		9·00	12·00

1983 (15 Aug). *Various stamps surch as T* **103**. (a) *Nos. 491, 498, 501 (all W w* **14**), 559, 564 (both W w* **15**).

577	40 c. on 25 c. Sergeant Major (No. 559)		30	30
	a. Surch inverted		15·00	
	b. Surch on No. 494		4·00	9·00
	c. Error. Surch on 10 c. (No. 491)		11·00	
	d. Surch double		40·00	
578	70 c. on 10 c. Hogfish and Neon Goby (No. 491)		45	45
	a. Surch inverted		14·00	
	b. Surch on No. 556		24·00	24·00
	c. Surch omitted (in pair with normal)		£130	
	d. Surch double		24·00	
579	90 c. on 65 c. Bigeye (No. 498)		55	60
	a. Error. Surch on 10 c. (No. 491)		80·00	
	b. Error. Surch on 75 c. (No. 499)		80·00	
	c. Surch double		40·00	
580	$1.15 on 75 c. French Grunt (No. 564)		65	70
	a. Surch on No. 499		9·50	11·00
	b. Error. Surch on 25 c. (No. 559)		40·00	
	c. Surch inverted		25·00	
581	$1.50 on $2 Blue Chromis (No. 501)		85	90
	a. Surch inverted		60·00	
	b. Error. Surch on 75 c. (No. 499)		80·00	
	c. Error. Surch on 75 c. (No. 564)			

(b) *Nos. 512/15*

582	70 c. on $3 *Portsmouth*		40	85
	aw. Wmk inverted		15·00	
	b. Sheetlet. No. 582×6 and No. 583		3·00	
	bw. Wmk inverted		£120	
	c. Surch double		5·00	
	d. Surch inverted		17·00	
	e. Surch inverted (horiz pair)		35·00	
583	70 c. on $3 Prince Charles and Lady Diana Spencer		1·00	2·25
	aw. Wmk inverted		55·00	
	b. Surch double		32·00	
	c. Surch inverted		90·00	
584	$1.15 on $4 *Britannia*		50	1·25
	aw. Wmk inverted		15·00	
	b. Sheetlet. No. 584×6 and No. 585		3·75	
	bw. Wmk inverted		£120	
	c. Surch double		20·00	
	d. Surch inverted		11·00	
	e. Surch inverted (horiz pair)		22·00	
	f. Error. Surch on $3 (No. 512)		5·50	
585	$1.15 on $4 As No. 583		1·25	2·50
	aw. Wmk inverted		55·00	
	b. Surch double		30·00	
	c. Surch inverted		65·00	
	f. Error. Surch on $3 (No. 513)		70·00	
577/85		*Set of 9*	5·50	8·75

Nos. 582e and 584e show the long surcharge intended for Nos. 583 or 585 inverted across horizontal pairs of the smaller design. Nos. 583c and 585c show two examples of the smaller surcharge inverted.

104 Montgolfier Balloon, 1783

105 Boys dressed as Clowns

(Des A. Theobald. Litho Format)

1983 (19 Sept). *Bicentenary of Manned Flight. T* **104** *and similar multicoloured designs. W w* **14** *(sideways* on 75 c. to $2). P* 14.

586	35 c. Type 104		15	15
587	75 c. De Havilland D.H.C.6 Twin Otter 200/300 (horiz)		25	30
588	$1.50, Lockheed Vega V (horiz)		40	75
	w. Wmk Crown to right of CA		35·00	
589	$2 Beardmore airship R-34 (horiz)		60	1·25
586/9		*Set of 4*	1·25	2·25
MS590	109×145 mm. Nos. 586/9. Wmk sideways		1·25	2·75

*The normal sideways watermark shows Crown to left of CA, as seen from the back of the stamp.

Nos. 586/9 were re-issued on 15 December 1983 overprinted "INAUGURAL FLIGHT Montserrat–Nevis–St. Kitts". It is understood that all but approximately 100 sets were used on Flown First Flight/Day Covers (*Price for set of 4 on First Flight Cover* £30).

(Des Jennifer Toombs. Litho Format)

1983 (18 Nov). *Christmas. Carnival. T* **105** *and similar horiz designs. Multicoloured. W w* **15** *(sideways). P* 14.

591	55 c. Type 105		10	10
592	90 c. Girls dressed as silver star bursts		15	20
593	$1.15, Flower girls		20	35
594	$2 Masqueraders		35	80
591/4		*Set of 4*	70	1·25

106 Statue of Discus-thrower

107 Cattle Egret

(Des Court House Studio. Litho Questa)

1984 (26 Mar). *Olympic Games, Los Angeles. T **106** and similar vert designs. Multicoloured. W w 15 (sideways*). P 14.*

595	90 c. Type 106	30	35
	w. Wmk POST OFFICE reading upwards	2·50	
596	$1 Olympic torch	35	45
	w. Wmk POST OFFICE reading upwards	4·50	
597	$1.15, Olympic Stadium, Los Angeles	40	50
	w. Wmk POST OFFICE reading upwards	4·50	
598	$2.50, Olympic and American flags	65	1·00
	w. Wmk POST OFFICE reading upwards	4·50	
595/8		1·50	2·10
MS599	110×110 mm. Nos. 595/8. Wmk upright	1·50	2·25
	w. Wmk inverted	16·00	

*The normal sideways watermark shows "POST OFFICE" reading downwards.

(Des G. Drummond. Litho Walsall)

1984 (28 May). *Birds of Montserrat. T **107** and similar multicoloured designs. W w 15 (sideways* on 5 c. to 90 c.). P 14.*

600	5 c. Type 107	30	30
601	10 c. Carib Grackle	30	30
	a. Printed on the gummed side	75·00	
602	15 c. Moorhen ("Common Gallinule")	30	30
	w. Wmk POST OFFICE reading upwards	3·50	
603	20 c. Brown Booby	40	30
604	25 c. Black-whiskered Vireo	40	40
605	40 c. Scaly-breasted Thrasher	60	50
606	55 c. Laughing Gull	75	30
607	70 c. Glossy Ibis	90	45
608	90 c. Green Heron	1·00	60
609	$1 Belted Kingfisher (vert)	1·25	70
610	$1.15, Bananaquit (vert)	1·50	1·40
	w. Wmk inverted	4·50	
611	$3 American Kestrel ("Sparrow Hawk") (vert)	3·25	5·00
612	$5 Forest Thrush (vert)	4·50	7·00
613	$7.50, Black-crowned Night Heron (vert)	6·00	12·00
614	$10 Bridled Quail Dove (vert)	7·00	13·00
600/14		*Set of 15*	26·00	38·00

*The normal sideways watermark shows "POST OFFICE" reading downwards.

(Des J.W. Litho Format)

1984 (9 July). *Mail Packet Boats (2nd series). Multicoloured designs as T **89**. W w 15 (sideways*). P 14.*

615	55 c. Tagus II, 1907	20	40
	w. Wmk POST OFFICE reading upwards	11·00	
616	90 c. Cobequid, 1913	30	50
	w. Wmk POST OFFICE reading upwards	11·00	
617	$1.15, Lady Drake, 1942	40	70
618	$2 Factor, 1948	60	1·25
615/18		*Set of 4*	1·40	2·50
MS619	152×100 mm. Nos. 615/18	2·00	5·00

*The normal sideways watermark shows "POST OFFICE" reading downwards.

No. **MS619** also commemorates the 250th anniversary of *Lloyd's List* (newspaper).

108 Hermit Crab and West Indian Top Shell (*Cittarium pica*)

(Des G. Drummond. Litho Questa)

1984 (24 Sept). *Marine Life. T **108** and similar horiz designs. Multicoloured. W w 15 (sideways). P 14.*

620	90 c. Type 108	1·50	1·00
621	$1.15, Rough File Shell (Lima scabra)	1·75	1·40
622	$1.50, True Tulip (Fasciolaria tulipa)	2·50	3·00
623	$2.50, Queen or Pink Conch (Strombus gigas)	3·25	4·75
620/3		*Set of 4*	8·00	9·00

109 "Bull Man"

110 Mango

(Des Jennifer Toombs. Litho Questa)

1984 (12 Nov). *Christmas. Carnival Costumes. T **109** and similar horiz designs. Multicoloured. W w 15 (sideways). P 14.*

624	55 c. Type 109	50	25
625	$1.15, Masquerader Captain	1·50	1·25
626	$1.50, "Fantasy" Carnival Queen	1·75	1·25
627	$2.30, "Ebony and Ivory" Carnival Queen	2·50	4·00
624/7		*Set of 4*	5·75	7·00

(Des G. Drummond. Litho Format)

1985 (8 Feb). *National Emblems. T **110** and similar vert designs. Multicoloured. W w 15. P 14.*

628	$1.15, Type 110	30	60
629	$1.50, Lobster Claw	40	1·00
630	$3 Montserrat Oriole	60	2·00
628/30		*Set of 3*	1·10	3·25

IMPERFORATES AND MISSING COLOURS. Various issues between Nos. 631 and 695 exist either imperforate or with colours omitted. Such items are not listed as there is no evidence that they fulfil the criteria outlined on page xi of this catalogue.

111 *Oncidium urophyllum*

112 Queen Elizabeth the Queen Mother

(Des J. Cooter. Litho Format)

1985 (9 May). *Orchids of Montserrat. T **111** and similar vert designs. Multicoloured. W w 15. P 14.*

631	90 c. Type 111	45	55
632	$1.15, Epidendrum difforme	50	80
633	$1.50, Epidendrum ciliare	55	1·10
634	$2.50, Brassavola cucullata	75	2·50
631/4		*Set of 4*	2·00	4·50
MS635	120×140 mm. Nos. 631/4	4·25	6·50

(Des D. Ewart ($2), Maxine Marsh (others). Litho Format)

1985 (7 Aug). *Life and Times of Queen Elizabeth the Queen Mother. Various vertical portraits as T **112**. P 12½.*

636	55 c. multicoloured	25	30
	a. Horiz pair. Nos. 636/7	50	60
637	55 c. multicoloured	25	30
638	90 c. multicoloured	25	40
	a. Horiz pair. Nos. 638/9	50	80
639	90 c. multicoloured	25	40
640	$1.15, multicoloured	25	40
	a. Horiz pair. Nos. 640/1	50	80
641	$1.15, multicoloured	25	40
642	$1.50, multicoloured	30	40
	a. Horiz pair. Nos. 642/3	60	80
643	$1.50, multicoloured	30	40
636/43		*Set of 8*	1·90	2·75
MS644	85×113 mm. $2 multicoloured; $2 multicoloured	65	1·90

The two designs of each value were issued, *se-tenant*, in horizontal pairs within the sheets. Each *se-tenant* pair shows a floral pattern across the bottom of the portraits which stops short of the left-hand edge on the left-hand stamp and of the right-hand edge on the right-hand stamp.

Designs as Nos. 636/7 and 642/3 but with face values of $6×2 and $3.50×2, also exist in additional miniature sheets from a restricted printing issued 10 January 1986.

Nos. 636/43 and an unissued 15 c. also exist in separate miniature sheets, combining the two designs for each value, from stock dispersed by the liquidator of Format International Security Printers Ltd.

113 Cotton Plants

(Des G. Drummond. Litho Format)

1985 (18 Oct). *Montserrat Sea Island Cotton Industry. T **113** and similar horiz designs. Multicoloured. W w 15. P 15.*

645	90 c. Type 113	25	45
646	$1 Operator at carding machine	25	50
647	$1.15, Threading loom	25	65
648	$2.50, Weaving with hand loom	50	2·25
645/8		*Set of 4*	1·10	3·50
MS649	148×103 mm. Nos. 645/8. Wmk sideways	3·00	3·75

CARIBBEAN ROYAL VISIT 1985

(**114**)

115 Black-throated Blue Warbler

1985 (25 Oct). *Royal Visit. Nos. 514/15, 543, 587/8 and 640/1 optd as T **114** or surch also.*

650	75 c. multicoloured (No. 587)	2·75	2·50
651	$1 multicoloured (No. 543)	4·25	3·50
652	$1.15, multicoloured (No. 640)	4·25	5·00
	a. Horiz pair. Nos. 652/3	8·50	10·00
653	$1.15, multicoloured (No. 641)	4·25	5·00
654	$1.50, multicoloured (No. 588)	6·00	6·00

655	$1.60 on $4 multicoloured (No. 514)	2·00	3·75
	a. Sheetlet. No. 655×6 and No. 656	22·00	
	ab. Sheetlet. No. 655×6 and No. 656a	25·00	
	abw. Sheetlet. Wmk inverted		
656	$1.60 on $4 multicoloured (No. 515) (surch $1.60 only)	13·00	16·00
	a. Additionally optd "CARIBBEAN ROYAL VISIT—1985"	16·00	24·00
650/6		*Set of 7*	32·00	38·00

No. 656 shows a new face value only; "CARIBBEAN ROYAL VISIT" being omitted from the surcharge. No. 656a is the corrected version issued subsequently.

(Des R. Vigurs. Litho Format)

1985 (29 Nov). *Leaders of the World. Birth Bicentenary of John J. Audubon (ornithologist). T **115** and similar vert designs showing original paintings. Multicoloured. P 12½.*

657	15 c. Type 115	15	30
	a. Horiz pair. Nos. 657/8	30	40
658	15 c. Palm Warbler	15	20
659	30 c. Bobolink	15	30
	a. Horiz pair. Nos. 659/60	30	60
660	30 c. Lark Sparrow	15	30
661	55 c. Chipping Sparrow	20	40
	a. Horiz pair. Nos. 661/2	40	80
662	55 c. Northern Oriole	20	40
663	$2.50, American Goldfinch	40	1·25
	a. Horiz pair. Nos. 663/4	80	2·50
664	$2.50, Blue Grosbeak	40	1·25
657/64		*Set of 8*	1·60	4·00

Nos. 657/8, 659/60, 661/2 and 663/4 were printed together, *se-tenant*, in horizontal pairs throughout the sheets.

116 Herald Angel appearing to Goatherds

117 Lord Baden-Powell

(Des Jennifer Toombs. Litho Format)

1985 (2 Dec). *Christmas. T **116** and similar horiz designs showing a Caribbean Nativity. Multicoloured. P 15.*

665	70 c. Type 116	15	15
666	$1.15, Three Wise Men following the Star	25	40
667	$1.50, Carol singing around War Memorial, Plymouth	30	70
668	$2.30, Praying to "Our Lady of Montserrat" Church of Our Lady, St. Patrick's Village	45	1·60
665/8		*Set of 4*	1·00	2·50

(Des G. Vasarhelyi. Litho Format)

1986 (11 Apr). *50th Anniv of Montserrat Girl Guide Movement. T **117** and similar vert designs. Multicoloured. W w 15 (sideways). P 15.*

669	20 c. Type 117	15	40
	a. Horiz pair. Nos. 669/70	30	80
670	20 c. Girl Guide saluting	15	40
671	75 c. Lady Baden-Powell	25	75
	a. Horiz pair. Nos. 671/2	50	1·50
672	75 c. Guide assisting in old people's home	25	75
673	90 c. Lord and Lady Baden-Powell	30	75
	a. Horiz pair. Nos. 673/4	60	1·50
674	90 c. Guides serving meal in old people's home	30	75
675	$1.15, Girl Guides of 1936	40	80
	a. Horiz pair. Nos. 675/6	80	1·60
676	$1.15, Two Guides saluting	40	80
669/76		*Set of 8*	2·00	4·75

Nos. 669/70, 671/2, 673/4 and 675/6 were each printed together, *se-tenant*, in horizontal pairs throughout the sheets.

117a Queen Elizabeth II

(Des Court House Studio. Litho Format)

1986 (21 Apr). *60th Birthday of Queen Elizabeth II. T **117a** and similar multicoloured designs. P 12½.*

677	10 c. Type 117a	10	10
678	$1.50, Princess Elizabeth in 1928	25	50
679	$3 In Antigua, 1977	40	85
680	$6 In Canberra, 1982 (vert)	65	1·75
677/80		*Set of 4*	1·25	2·75
MS681	85×115 mm. $8 Queen with bouquet	3·25	5·50

The 10 c., $1.50 and $3 also exist watermarked w **16** (sideways), but no examples of these used from Montserrat have been seen.

Nos. 677/80 also exist in individual miniature sheets from stock dispersed by the liquidator of Format International Security Printers Ltd.

118 King Harold and
Halley's Comet, 1066
(from Bayeux Tapestry)

(Des Court House Studio. Litho Format)

1986 (9 May). *Appearance of Halley's Comet. T* **118** *and similar horiz designs. Multicoloured. P* 14 × 13½.

82	35 c. Type **118**. .		25	25
83	50 c. Comet of 1301 (from Giotto's "Adoration of the Magi")		30	30
84	70 c. Edmond Halley and Comet of 1531 . .		30	40
85	$1 Comets of 1066 and 1910		30	40
86	$1.15, Comet of 1910 . .		40	50
87	$1.50, E.S.A. *Giotto* spacecraft and Comet		40	80
88	$2.30, U.S. Space Telescope and Comet . .		50	1·75
89	$4 Computer reconstruction of 1910 Comet		60	2·75
82/9		*Set of 8*	2·75	6·50
MS690	Two sheets, each 140×115 mm. (a) 40 c. Type **118**; $1.75, As No. 683; $2 As No. 684; $3 As No. 685. (b) 55 c. As No. 686; 60 c. As No. 687; 80 c. As No. 688; $5 As No. 689 *Set of 2 sheets*		4·50	9·00

118a Prince Andrew 119 *Antelope* being attacked by *L'Atalante*

(Des Court House Studio. Litho Format)

1986 (23 July–15 Oct). *Royal Wedding (1st issue). T* **118a** *and similar multicoloured designs. P* 12½.

691	70 c. Type **118a**		25	35
	a. Pair. Nos. 691/2 . .		50	70
692	70 c. Miss Sarah Ferguson		25	35
693	$2 Prince Andrew wearing stetson (*horiz*)		40	80
	a. Pair. Nos. 693/4 . .		80	1·60
694	$2 Miss Sarah Ferguson on skiing holiday (*horiz*)		40	80
691/4		*Set of 4*	1·10	2·10
MS695	115×85 mm. $10 Duke and Duchess of York on Palace balcony after wedding (*horiz*) (15.10)		3·00	4·75

Nos. 691/2 and 693/4 were printed together, *se-tenant*, in horizontal and vertical pairs throughout the sheets.

Nos. 691/4 imperforate come from souvenir stamp booklets.

See also Nos. 705/8.

A set of eight was prepared for the 1986 World Cup Football Championships, but was not issued. Examples exist from stock dispersed by the liquidator of Format International Security Printers Ltd.

(Des T. Hadler. Litho Questa)

1986 (29 Aug). *Mail Packet Sailing Ships. T* **119** *and similar horiz designs. Multicoloured. W* w **15**. *P* 14.

696	90 c. Type **119**		2·00	1·50
697	$1.15, *Montagu* (1810)		2·25	2·00
698	$1.50, *Little Catherine* being pursued by *L'Etoile* (1813)		2·75	2·75
699	$2.30, *Hinchingbrook I* (1813)		3·50	5·00
696/9		*Set of 4*	9·50	10·00
MS700	165×123 mm. Nos. 696/9, Wmk sideways		10·00	11·00

120 Radio Montserrat
Building, Dagenham

(Des G. Vasarhelyi. Litho Questa)

1986 (29 Sept). *Communications. T* **120** *and similar horiz designs. Multicoloured. W* w **15**. *P* 14.

701	70 c. Type **120**. .		1·00	70
702	$1.15, Radio Gem dish aerial, Plymouth . .		1·50	1·50
703	$1.50, Radio Antilles studio, O'Garro's . .		1·75	2·25
704	$2.30, Cable and Wireless building, Plymouth		2·25	4·25
701/4 . .		*Set of 4*	6·00	8·00

Congratulations to
***T.R.H. The Duke
& Duchess of York***

(121) 121a Statue of Liberty

1986 (14 Nov). *Royal Wedding (2nd issue). Nos.* 691/4 *optd as T* **121** *in silver.*

705	70 c. Type **118a**		70	1·25
	a. Pair. Nos. 705/6 . .		1·40	2·50
706	70 c. Miss Sarah Ferguson		70	1·25
707	$2 Prince Andrew wearing stetson (*horiz*)		1·25	1·75
	a. Pair. Nos. 707/8 . .		2·50	3·50
708	$2 Miss Sarah Ferguson on skiing holiday (*horiz*)		1·25	1·75
705/8 . .		*Set of 4*	3·50	5·50

(Des Court House Studio. Litho Format)

1986 (18 Nov). *Centenary of Statue of Liberty. Vert views of Statue as T* **121a** *in separate miniature sheets. Multicoloured. P* 14×13½.

MS709	Three sheets, each 85×115 mm. $3; $4.50; $5		4·50	9·00
		Set of 3 sheets		

122 Sailing and Windsurfing 123 Christmas Rose

(Des J. Cooter. Litho Format)

1986 (10 Dec). *Tourism. T* **122** *and similar horiz designs. Multicoloured. P* 15.

710	70 c. Type **122**. .		40	70
711	$1.15, Golf		80	1·50
712	$1.50, Plymouth market . .		80	2·00
713	$2.30, Air Recording Studios		1·25	3·00
710/13		*Set of 4*	3·00	6·50

(Des Jennifer Toombs. Litho Questa)

1986 (12 Dec). *Christmas. Flowering Shrubs. T* **123** *and similar vert designs. Multicoloured. P* 14.

714	70 c. Type **123**. .		70	40
715	$1.15, Candle Flower		95	85
716	$1.50, Christmas Tree Kalanchoe		1·50	1·50
717	$2.30, Snow on the Mountain		2·00	4·50
714/17		*Set of 4*	4·75	6·50
MS718	150×110 mm. Nos. 714/17. P 12		7·50	8·00

124 Tiger Shark (125)

(126)

127 *Phoebis trite*

(Des M. Hillier. Litho Questa)

1987 (2 Feb). *Sharks. T* **124** *and similar horiz designs. Multicoloured. W* w **15**. *P* 14.

719	40 c. Type **124**		1·50	55
720	90 c. Lemon Shark		2·50	1·50
721	$1.15, Great White Shark		2·75	2·00
722	$3.50, Whale Shark		5·50	8·00
719/22		*Set of 4*	11·00	11·00
MS723	150×102 mm. Nos. 719/22. Wmk sideways. P 12		12·00	14·00

1987 (6 Apr). *Nos.* 601, 603, 607/8 *and* 611 *surch as T* **125**.

724	5 c. on 70 c. Glossy Ibis		50	1·00
725	$1 on 20 c. Brown Booby		1·75	90
726	$1.15 on 10 c. Carib Grackle		2·00	1·40
727	$1.50 on 90 c. Green Heron		2·25	2·50
728	$2.30 on $3 American Kestrel (*vert*)		3·25	5·50
724/8 . .		*Set of 5*	8·75	10·00

1987 (13 June). *"Capex '87" International Stamp Exhibition, Toronto. No.* **MS**690 *optd with T* **126** *in black and red.*

MS729	Two sheets. As No. **MS**690			
		Set of 2 sheets	4·50	10·00

No. **MS**729 also carries an overprint commemorating the exhibition on the lower sheet margins.

No. **MS**729 exists imperforate from stock dispersed by the liquidator of Format International Security Printers Ltd.

(Des M. Hillier. Litho Questa)

1987 (10 Aug). *Butterflies. T* **127** *and similar square designs. Multicoloured. W* w **15**. *P* 14.

730	90 c. Type **127**		2·00	1·10
731	$1.15, *Biblis hyperia*		2·50	1·60
732	$1.50, *Polygonus leo*		3·00	2·50
733	$2.50, *Hypolimnas misippus*		4·50	6·50
730/3		*Set of 4*	11·00	10·50

128 *Oncidium variegatum*

(Des R. Vigurs. Litho Questa)

1987 (13 Nov). *Christmas. Orchids. T* **128** *and similar multicoloured designs. P* 14×13½ (90 c., $1.50) *or* 13½×14 (*others*).

734	90 c. Type **128**. .		60	45
735	$1.15, *Vanilla planifolia* (*horiz*) . .		85	55
736	$1.50, *Gongora quinquenervis* . .		1·10	1·10
737	$3.50, *Brassavola nodosa* (*horiz*) . .		2·00	4·50
734/7 . .		*Set of 4*	4·00	6·00
MS738	100×75 mm. $5 *Oncidium lanceanum* (*horiz*)		9·00	11·00

**40th Wedding Anniversary
HM Queen Elizabeth II
HRH Duke of Edingburgh.
November 1987.**

$2.30 ==

(129) 130 Free-tailed Bat

1987 (29 Nov–18 Dec). *Royal Ruby Wedding. Nos.* 601, 604/5 *and* 608 *surch as T* **129**. **A.** *Surch* "Edingburgh".

739A	5 c. on 90 c. Green Heron		1·50	1·75
740A	$1.15 on 10 c. Carib Grackle		3·25	3·25
741A	$2.30 on 25 c. Black-whiskered Vireo		6·00	7·00
742A	$5 on 40 c. Scaly-breasted Thrasher		9·00	11·00
739A/42A		*Set of 4*	18·00	21·00

B. *Surch* "Edinburgh" (18 Dec)

739B	5 c. on 90 c. Green Heron		30	40
740B	$1.15 on 10 c. Carib Grackle		1·00	1·00
741B	$2.30 on 25 c. Black-whiskered Vireo		1·75	2·25
742B	$5 on 40 c. Scaly-breasted Thrasher		3·50	4·50
739B/42B		*Set of 4*	6·00	7·25

Nos. 739A/42A were from the first printing using Type **129**. After the spelling mistake was noticed it was corrected on sheets subsequently surcharged.

(Des M. Pollard. Litho Questa)

1988 (8 Feb). *Bats. T* **130** *and similar vert designs. Multicoloured. W* w **15** (*sideways*). *P* 14.

743	55 c. Type **130**. .		80	40
744	90 c. *Chiroderma improvisum* (fruit bat) . .		1·25	90
745	$1.15, Fisherman Bat		1·60	1·50
746	$2.30, *Brachyphylla cavernarum* (fruit bat)		3·00	5·50
743/6 . .		*Set of 4*	6·00	7·50
MS747	133×110 mm. $2.50, Funnel-eared Bat. Wmk upright		5·50	7·00

131 Magnificent
Frigate Bird

132 Discus throwing

(Des R. Vigurs. Litho Questa)

1988 (2 Apr). *Easter. Birds. T* **131** *and similar vert designs. Multicoloured. P* 14×13½.

748	90 c. Type 131	..	60	45
749	$1.15, Caribbean Elaenia	..	80	75
750	$1.50, Glossy Ibis	..	1·00	1·50
751	$3.50, Purple-throated Carib	..	2·00	4·00
748/51		Set of 4	4·00	6·00
MS752	100 × 75 mm. $5 Brown Pelican		2·50	3·50

(Des R. Vigurs. Litho Questa)

1988 (29 July). *Olympic Games, Seoul. T* **132** *and similar horiz designs. Multicoloured. P* 13½×14.

753	90 c. Type 132	..	60	50
754	$1.15, High jumping	..	70	60
755	$3.50, Athletics	..	2·00	3·25
753/5		Set of 3	3·00	4·00
MS756	103×77 mm. $5 Rowing		2·75	2·75

133 Golden Tulip (*Pleuroploca aurantiaca*)

134 University Crest

(Des R. Vigurs. Litho Questa)

1988 (30 Aug). *Sea Shells. T* **133** *and similar horiz designs. Multicoloured. P* 14.

757	5 c. Type 133		30	30
758	10 c. Little Knobbed Scallop (*Chlamys imbricata*)		40	40
759	15 c. Sozoni's Cone (*Conus delessertii*)		40	40
760	20 c. Globular Coral Shell (*Coralliophila aberrans*)		50	40
761	25 c. American or Common Sundial (*Architectonica nobilis*)		50	40
762	40 c. King Helmet (*Cassis tuberosa*)		60	40
763	55 c. Channelled Turban (*Turbo canaliculatus*)		80	40
764	70 c. True Tulip (*Fasciolaria tulipa*)		1·00	75
765	90 c. Music Volute (*Voluta musica*)		1·25	75
766	$1 Flame Auger (*Terebra taurina*)		1·40	80
767	$1.15, Rooster-tail Conch (*Strombus gallus*)		1·50	90
768	$1.50, Queen or Pink Conch (*Strombus gigas*)		1·60	1·40
769	$3 Teramachi's Slit Shell (*Perotrochus teramachii*)		2·50	4·00
770	$5 Common or Florida Crown Conch (*Melongena corona*)		3·50	6·50
771	$7.50, Beau's Murex (*Murex beauii*)		4·50	10·00
772	$10 Atlantic Trumpet Triton (*Charonia variegata*)		5·50	10·00
757/72		Set of 16	22·00	35·00

(Des R. Vigurs. Litho Questa)

1988 (14 Oct). *40th Anniv of University of West Indies. P* 14×13½.

773	134 $5 multicoloured	2·40	3·25

1988 (10 Nov). *Princess Alexandra's Visit. Nos.* 763, 766 *and* 769/70 *surch as T* **135**.

774	40 c. on 55 c. Channelled Turban (*Turbo canaliculatus*)		45	45
775	90 c. on $1 Flame Auger (*Terebra taurina*)		70	80
776	$1.15 on $3 Teramachi's Slit Shell (*Perotrochus teramachii*)		85	95
	a. Surch double		55·00	
777	$1.50 on $5 Common or Florida Crown Conch (*Melongena corona*)		1·10	1·50
774/7		Set of 4	2·75	3·25

It was intended that Nos. 774/7 were to be issued on 9 November, but the day before it was found that the surcharge contained the error "ALEXANDRIA". The issue was postponed until 10 November to allow replacements to be printed, but examples of the error exist from pre-release stock sent to dealers overseas.

Christmas 1988

136 Spotted Sandpiper

MONTSERRAT 90c

(Des R. Vigurs. Litho Questa)

1988 (4 Dec). *Christmas. Sea Birds. T* **136** *and similar horiz designs. Multicoloured. P* 13½×14.

778	90 c. Type 136		70	55
779	$1.15, Turnstone		85	70
780	$3.50, Red-footed Booby		2·00	3·75
778/80		Set of 3	3·25	4·50
MS781	105×79 mm. $5 Audubon's Shearwater		2·75	3·75

137 Handicapped Children in Classroom

(Des R. Vigurs. Litho Questa)

1988 (16 Dec). *125th Anniv of International Red Cross. P* 13½ × 14.

782	137 $3.50, multicoloured	..	1·50	2·25

138 Drum Major in Ceremonial Uniform

139 Amazon Lily

(Des R. Vigurs. Litho Questa)

1989 (24 Feb). *75th Anniv of Montserrat Defence Force* (1988). *Uniforms. T* **138** *and similar vert designs. Multicoloured. P* 14×13½.

783	90 c. Type 138		70	55
784	$1.15, Field training uniform		85	75
785	$1.50, Cadet in ceremonial uniform		1·25	1·75
786	$3.50, Gazetted Police Officer in ceremonial uniform		2·50	3·50
783/6		Set of 4	4·75	6·00
MS787	102×76 mm. $5 Island Girl Guide Commissioner and Brownie		3·50	4·25

(Litho Questa)

1989 (21 Mar). *Easter. Lilies. T* **139** *and similar multicoloured designs. P* 13½×14 (90 c.) *or* 14×13½ (*others*).

788	90 c. Type 139		50	50
789	$1.15, Salmon Blood Lily (*vert*)		70	70
790	$1.50, Amaryllis (*Hippeastrum vittatum*) (*vert*)		85	1·25
791	$3.50, Amaryllis (*Hippeastrum* hybrid) (*vert*)		1·90	2·75
788/91		Set of 4	3·90	4·75
MS792	103×77 mm. $5 Resurrection Lily (*vert*)		4·00	6·00

140 *Morning Prince* (schooner), 1942

141 The Scarecrow

(Des R. Vigurs. Litho Questa)

1989 (30 June). *Shipbuilding in Montserrat. T* **140** *and similar horiz designs. Multicoloured. P* 13½×14.

793	90 c. Type 140		90	60
794	$1.15, Western Sun (inter-island freighter)		1·40	1·10
795	$1.50, *Kim G* (inter-island freighter) under construction		1·75	2·00
796	$3.50, *Romaris* (island ferry), c. 1942		2·75	4·50
793/6		Set of 4	6·00	7·50

(Litho Questa)

1989 (22 Sept). *50th Anniv of The Wizard of Oz* (*film*). *T* **141** *and similar multicoloured designs. P* 14.

797	90 c. Type 141		40	45
798	$1.15, The Lion		55	60
799	$1.50, The Tin Man		70	85
800	$3.50, Dorothy		1·60	2·50
797/800		Set of 4	3·00	4·00
MS801	113×84 mm. $5 Characters from film (*horiz*)		2·40	3·50

1989 (20 Oct). *Hurricane Hugo Relief Fund. Nos.* 795/6 *surch with T* **142**.

802	$1.50 + $2.50, *Kim G* (inter-island freighter) under construction		2·25	3·00
803	$3.50 + $2.50, *Romaris* (island ferry), c. 1942		2·50	4·00

143 "Apollo 11" above Lunar Surface

(Litho Questa)

1989 (19 Dec). *20th Anniv of First Manned Landing on Moon. T* **143** *and similar multicoloured designs. P* 13½×14.

804	90 c. Type 143		35	40
805	$1.15, Astronaut alighting from lunar module *Eagle*		45	50
806	$1.50, *Eagle* and astronaut conducting experiment		60	80
807	$3.50, Opening "Apollo 11" hatch after splashdown		1·40	2·25
804/7		Set of 4	2·50	3·50
MS808	101×76 mm. $5 Astronaut on Moon. P 14 ×13½		4·25	5·50

144 *Yamato* (Japanese battleship)

145 The Empty Tomb

(Litho Questa)

1990 (12 Feb). *World War II Capital Ships. T* **144** *and similar horiz designs. Multicoloured. P* 14.

809	70 c. Type 144		1·75	70
810	$1.15, U.S.S. *Arizona* at Pearl Harbour		2·25	95
811	$1.50, *Bismarck* (German battleship) in action		2·75	2·50
812	$3.50, H.M.S. *Hood* (battle cruiser)		4·25	7·00
809/12		Set of 4	10·00	10·00
MS813	118×90 mm. $5 *Bismarck* and map of North Atlantic		7·50	9·00

(Des R. Vigurs. Litho Questa)

1990 (12 Apr). *Easter. T* **145** *and similar vert designs showing stained glass windows from St. Michael's Parish Church, Bray, Berkshire. Multicoloured. P* 14×15.

814	$1.15, Type 145		1·25	1·50
	a. Horiz strip of 3. Nos. 814/16		4·00	
815	$1.50, The Ascension		1·50	1·75
816	$3.50, The Risen Christ with Disciples		1·75	2·25
814/16		Set of 3	4·00	5·00
MS817	65×103 mm. $5 The Crucifixion		4·00	5·00

Nos. 814/16 were printed together, *se-tenant*, in sheets of 6 (3×2).

1990 (3 May). *"Stamp World London 90" International Stamp Exhibition. Nos.* 460/4 *surch as T* **146** *in bright purple.*

818	70 c. on 40 c. Type 85		50	50
819	90 c. on 55 c. Hawker Siddeley H.S.748 aircraft and 1976 55 c. definitive		70	70
820	$1 on $1.20, *La Plata* (liner) and 1903 5s. stamp		80	90
821	$1.15 on $1.20, *Lady Hawkins* (packet steamer) and 1932 Tercentenary 5s. commemorative		90	1·10
822	$1.50 on $1.20, *Avon* (paddle-steamer) and Penny Red stamp with "A 08" postmark		1·25	1·75
818/22		Set of 5	3·75	4·50

Nos. 818/22 also show the "Stamp World London 90" emblem overprinted on one of the *se-tenant* labels.

147 General Office, Montserrat,
and 1884 ½d. Stamp

(Litho Questa)

1990 (1 June). *150th Anniv of the Penny Black. T 147 and similar multicoloured designs. P 13½×14 (horiz) or 14×13½ (vert).*

823	90 c. Type 147	65	65
824	$1.15, Sorting letters and Montserrat 1d. stamp of 1876 (vert)	85	90
825	$1.50, Posting letters and Penny Black (vert)	1·25	1·75
826	$3.50, Postman delivering letters and 1840 Twopence Blue	3·00	4·50
823/6	Set of 4	5·25	7·00
MS827	102×75 mm. $5 Montserrat soldier's letter of 1836 and Penny Black	6·00	7·00

148 Montserrat v. Antigua
Match

(Litho Questa)

1990 (8 July). *World Cup Football Championship, Italy. T 148 and similar multicoloured designs. P 14.*

828	90 c. Type 148	65	55
829	$1.15, U.S.A v. Trinidad match	85	75
830	$1.50, Montserrat team	1·25	1·50
831	$3.50, West Germany v. Wales match	2·25	3·25
828/31	Set of 4	4·50	5·50
MS832	77×101 mm. $5 World Cup trophy (vert)	4·50	6·50

149 Spinner Dolphin

(Des Jennifer Toombs. Litho Questa)

1990 (25 Sept). *Dolphins. T 149 and similar horiz designs. Multicoloured. P 14.*

833	90 c. Type 149	1·50	85
834	$1.15, Common Dolphin	1·75	1·25
835	$1.50, Striped Dolphin	2·50	2·50
836	$3.50, Atlantic Spotted Dolphin	3·75	5·00
833/6	Set of 4	8·50	8·75
MS837	103×76 mm. $5 Atlantic White-sided Dolphin	7·50	8·50

150 Spotted Goatfish   (151)

(Litho Questa)

1991 (7 Feb). *Tropical Fishes. T 150 and similar horiz designs. Multicoloured. P 13½×14.*

838	90 c. Type 150	1·50	85
839	$1.15, Cushion Star	1·75	1·25
840	$1.50, Rock Beauty	2·50	2·50
841	$3.50, French Grunt	3·75	5·00
838/41	Set of 4	8·50	8·75
MS842	103×76 mm. $5 Buffalo Trunkfish	5·50	7·00

1991 (27 Feb). *Nos. 760/1, 768 and 771 surch as T 151.*

843	5 c. on 20 c. Globular Coral Shell (Coralliophila aberrans)	65	1·25
844	5 c. on 25 c. American or Common Sundial (Architectonica nobilis)	65	1·25
845	$1.15 on $1.50, Queen or Pink Conch (Strombus gigas)	2·75	3·25
846	$1.15 on $7.50, Beau's Murex (Murex beauii)	2·75	3·25
843/6	Set of 4	6·00	8·00

152 Duck   153 Panaeolus
antillarum

(Des K. West. Litho Questa)

1991 (29 May). *Domestic Birds. T 152 and similar horiz designs. Multicoloured. P 14.*

847	90 c. Type 152	60	60
848	$1.15, Hen and chicks	80	90
849	$1.50, Red Junglefowl	1·10	1·50
850	$3.50, Helmet Guineafowl	2·40	3·50
847/50	Set of 4	4·50	6·00

(Des M. Pollard. Litho Questa)

1991 (13 June). *Fungi. T 153 and similar square designs. P 14.*

851	90 c. olive-grey	1·25	1·00
852	$1.15, rosine	1·50	1·25
853	$1.50, yellow-brown	2·25	2·25
854	$2 maroon	2·50	3·25
855	$3.50, dull ultramarine	3·75	5·00
851/5	Set of 5	10·00	11·50

Designs:—$1.15, *Cantharellus cinnabarinus*; $1.50, *Gymnopilus chrysopellus*; $2, *Psilocybe cubensis*; $3.50, *Leptonia caeruleocapitata*.

154 Red Water   155 Tree Frog
Lily

(Des M. Pollard. Litho Questa)

1991 (8 Aug). *Lilies. T 154 and similar vert designs. Multicoloured. P 14.*

856	90 c. Type 154	65	65
857	$1.15, Shell Ginger	75	85
858	$1.50, Early Day Lily	1·00	1·60
859	$3.50, Anthurium	2·50	3·50
856/9	Set of 4	4·50	6·00

(Des M. Pollard. Litho B.D.T.)

1991 (9 Oct). *Frogs and Toad. T 155 and similar multicoloured designs. P 14.*

860	$1.15, Type 155	2·25	1·25
861	$2 Crapaud Toad	3·25	3·75
862	$3.50, Mountain Chicken (frog)	5·50	6·50
860/2	Set of 3	10·00	10·50
MS863	110×110 mm. $5 Tree Frog, Crapaud Toad and Mountain Chicken (76½×44 mm). P 15×14	6·50	7·50

156 Black British Shorthair
Cat

(Des M. Pollard. Litho B.D.T.)

1991 (5 Dec). *Cats. T 156 and similar horiz designs. Multicoloured. P 14.*

864	90 c. Type 156	1·50	90
865	$1.15, Seal Point Siamese	1·75	1·10
866	$1.50, Silver Tabby Persian	2·25	2·25
867	$2.50, Birman Temple Cat	3·00	3·75
868	$3.50, Egyptian Mau	4·00	5·00
864/8	Set of 5	11·00	11·50

157 Navigational Instruments   158 Runner with
Olympic Flame

(Des M. Pollard. Litho Questa)

1992 (16 Jan). *500th Anniv of Discovery of America by Columbus. T 157 and similar horiz designs. Multicoloured. P 14.*

869	$1.50, Type 157	1·25	1·50
	a. Sheetlet. Nos. 869/75	8·50	
870	$1.50, Columbus and coat of arms	1·25	1·50
871	$1.50, Landfall on the Bahamas	1·25	1·50
872	$1.50, Petitioning Queen Isabella	1·25	1·50
873	$1.50, Tropical birds	1·25	1·50
874	$1.50, Tropical fruits	1·25	1·50
875	$3 Ships of Columbus (81×26 mm)	1·75	2·00
869/75	Set of 7	8·50	10·00

Nos. 869/75 were printed together, *se-tenant*, in sheetlets of 7 with decorative margins.

For these designs, some with different face values, inscr "500TH ANNIVERSARY DISCOVERY OF MONTSERRAT", see Nos. 915/21.

(Des M. Pollard. Litho B.D.T.)

1992 (10 Apr). *Olympic Games, Barcelona. T 158 and similar square designs. Multicoloured. P 14.*

876	$1 Type 158	90	60
877	$1.15, Montserrat, Olympic and Spanish flags	1·25	90
878	$2.30, Olympic flame on map of Montserrat	2·25	2·75
879	$3.60, Olympic events	2·75	4·00
876/9	Set of 4	6·50	7·50

159 Tyrannosaurus

(Des M. Pollard. Litho Questa)

1992 (1 May). *Death Centenary of Sir Richard Owen (zoologist). T 159 and similar multicoloured designs. P 14.*

880	$1 Type 159	2·00	1·25
881	$1.15, Diplodocus	2·25	1·40
882	$1.50, Apatosaurus	2·75	2·75
883	$3.45, Dimetrodon	5·50	8·00
880/3	Set of 4	11·00	12·00
MS884	114×84 mm. $4.60, Sir Richard Owen and dinosaur bone (vert)	8·50	10·00

160 Male Montserrat Oriole

(Des R. Vigurs. Litho Questa)

1992 (30 June). *Montserrat Oriole. T 160 and similar horiz designs. Multicoloured. P 14.*

885	$1 Type 160	1·10	1·10
886	$1.15, Male and female Orioles	1·40	1·40
887	$1.50, Female Oriole with chicks	1·75	2·00
888	$3.60, Map of Montserrat and male Oriole	3·50	5·00
885/8	Set of 4	7·00	8·50

161 Psophus stridulus
(grasshopper)

(Des M. Pollard. Litho B.D.T.)

1992 (20 Aug). *Insects. T 161 and similar horiz designs. Multicoloured. P 15×14.*

889	5 c. Type 161	30	40
890	10 c. *Gryllus campestris* (field cricket)	35	40
891	15 c. *Lepthemis vesiculosa* (dragonfly)	40	40
892	20 c. *Orthemis ferruginea* (red skimmer)	45	45
893	25 c. *Gerris lacustris* (pond skater)	45	45
894	40 c. *Byctiscus betulae* (leaf weevil)	60	50
895	55 c. *Atta texana* (leaf-cutter ants)	60	40
896	70 c. *Polistes fuscatus* (paper wasp)	70	60
897	90 c. *Sparmopolius fulvus* (bee fly)	80	60
898	$1 *Chrysopa carnea* (lace wing)	1·25	65
899	$1.15, *Phoebis philea* (butterfly)	2·00	90
900	$1.50, *Cynthia cardui* (butterfly)	2·25	1·75
901	$3 *Utetheisa bella* (moth)	3·00	4·00
902	$5 *Alucita pentadactyla* (moth)	4·25	5·50
903	$7.50, *Anartia jatropha* (butterfly)	5·50	7·50
904	$10 *Heliconius melpomene* (butterfly)	5·50	7·50
889/904	Set of 16	24·00	29·00

162 Adoration of the Magi

(Des M. Pollard. Litho Questa)

1992 (26 Nov). *Christmas. T* **162** *and similar horiz design. Multicoloured. P* 13½×14.
905   $1.15, Type **162**   ..   ..   1·75   75
906   $4.60, Appearance of angel to shepherds   ..   4·25   6·50

163   $1 Coin and $20 Banknote

164   Columbus meeting Amerindians

(Des R. Vigurs. Litho Questa)

1993 (10 Feb). *East Caribbean Currency. T* **163** *and similar vert designs. Multicoloured. P* 14.
907   $1 Type **163**   90   70
908   $1.15, 10 c. and 25 c. coins with $10 bank-note   ..   ..   1·25   85
909   $1.50, 5 c. coin and $5 banknote   ..   1·75   2·00
910   $3.60, 1 c. and 2 c. coins with $1 banknote   4·00   6·00
907/10   ..   ..   ..   *Set of 4*   7·00   8·50

(Des M. Pollard. Litho Questa)

1993 (10 Mar). *Organization of East Caribbean States. 500th Anniv of Discovery of America by Columbus. T* **164** *and similar square design. Multicoloured. P* 14.
911   $1 Type **164**   ..   ..   1·10   90
912   $2 Ships approaching island   ..   2·00   2·75

165   Queen Elizabeth II on Montserrat with Chief Minister W. H. Bramble, 1966

(Des M. Pollard. Litho Questa)

1993 (2 June). *40th Anniv of Coronation. T* **165** *and similar horiz design. Multicoloured. P* 14.
913   $1.15, Type **165**   ..   ..   1·50   75
914   $4.60, Queen Elizabeth II in State Coach, 1953   ..   ..   4·50   5·50

1993 (5 Oct). *500th Anniv of Discovery of Montserrat. Designs as Nos. 869/75, some with new values, each showing "500th ANNIVERSARY DISCOVERY" of MONTSERRAT" at foot and with additional historical inscr across the centre. P* 14.
915   $1.15, multicoloured (As Type **157**)   ..   1·25   1·50
      a. Sheetlet. Nos. 915/21   ..   ..   10·00
916   $1.15, multicoloured (As No. **870**)   ..   1·25   1·50
917   $1.15, multicoloured (As No. **871**)   ..   1·25   1·50
918   $1.50, multicoloured (As No. **872**)   ..   1·60   1·90
919   $1.50, multicoloured (As No. **873**)   ..   1·60   1·90
920   $1.50, multicoloured (As No. **874**)   ..   1·60   1·90
921   $3.45, multicoloured (As No. **875**)   ..   2·50   3·25
915/21   ..   ..   *Set of 7*   10·00   12·00
Additional inscriptions:—No. 915, "PRE-COLUMBUS CARIB NAME OF ISLAND ALLIOUAGANA"; No. 916, "COLUMBUS NAMED ISLAND SANTA MARIA DE MONTSERRATE"; No. 917, "COLUMBUS SAILED ALONG COASTLINE 11th NOV. 1493"; No. 918, "ISLAND OCCUPIED BY FRENCH BRIEFLY IN 1667"; No. 919, "ISLAND DECLARED ENGLISH BY TREATY OF BREDA 1667"; No. 920, "AFRICAN SLAVES BROUGHT IN DURING 1600's"; No. 921, "IRISH CATHOLICS FROM ST. KITTS AND VIRGINIA SETTLED ON ISLAND BETWEEN 1628–1634".
Nos. 915/21 were printed together, *se-tenant,* in sheetlets of 7, with decorative margins.

MINIMUM PRICE

The minimum price quote is 10p which represents a handling charge rather than a basis for valuing common stamps. For further notes about prices see introductory pages.

166   Boeing E-3 Sentry, 1993

(Des A. Theobald. Litho Questa)

1993 (17 Nov). *75th Anniv of Royal Air Force. T* **166** *and similar horiz designs. Multicoloured. W w* 14 *(sideways). P* 14.
922   15 c. Type **166**   45   20
923   55 c. Vickers Valiant B Mk 1, 1962   65   40
924   $1.15, Handley Page H.P.67 Hastings C Mk 2, 1958   ..   ..   1·25   75
925   $3 Lockheed PV-1 Ventura, 1943   2·50   4·00
922/5   ..   ..   ..   *Set of 4*   4·25   4·75
MS926   117×78 mm. $1.50, Felixstowe F5, 1921; $1.50, Armstrong Whitworth Atlas, 1934; $1.50, Fairey Gordon, 1935; $1.50, Boulton & Paul Overstrand, 1936   ..   ..   4·50   5·50

167   Ground Beetle

168   *Gossypium barbadense*

(Des M. Pollard. Litho B.D.T.)

1994 (21 Jan). *Beetles. T* **167** *and similar horiz designs. Multicoloured. P* 15×14.
927   $1 Type **167**   65   65
928   $1.15, Click Beetle   80   80
929   $1.50, Harlequin Beetle   ..   1·25   1·50
930   $3.45, Leaf Beetle   ..   ..   3·00   4·25
927/30   ..   ..   *Set of 4*   5·25   6·50
MS931   68×85 mm. $4.50, Scarab Beetle   3·50   3·50

(Des R. Vigurs. Litho Questa)

1994 (22 Mar). *Flowers. T* **168** *and similar vert designs. Multicoloured. P* 14×13½.
932   90 c. Type **168**   ..   ..   1·00   80
933   $1.15, *Hibiscus sabdariffa*   ..   1·25   1·00
934   $1.50, *Hibiscus esculentus*   ..   1·60   1·75
935   $3.50, *Hibiscus rosa-sinensis*   ..   3·50   5·00
932/5   ..   ..   *Set of 4*   6·50   7·75

169   Coaching Young Players and Logo

(Litho Questa)

1994 (20 Apr). *World Cup Football Championship, U.S.A. T* **169** *and similar horiz designs. Multicoloured. P* 14×14½.
936   90 c. Type **169**   ..   ..   1·25   1·75
      a. Vert strip of 4. Nos. 936/9   ..   6·00
937   $1 United States scoring against England, 1950   ..   ..   1·25   1·75
938   $1.15, Rose Bowl stadium, Los Angeles, and trophy   ..   ..   1·25   1·75
939   $3.45, German players celebrating with trophy, 1990   ..   ..   2·75   3·25
936/9   ..   ..   *Set of 4*   6·00   7·75
MS940   114×85 mm. $2 Jules Rimet (founder) and Jules Rimet Trophy; $2 Bobby Moore (England) holding trophy, 1966; $2 Lew Jaschin (U.S.S.R); $2 Sepp Herberger (Germany) and German players celebrating, 1990   ..   7·00   8·00
Nos. 936/9 were printed together, *se-tenant,* in vertical strips of 4, each sheet containing two such strips separated by a gutter of 4 stamp-size labels showing Montserrat flag, championship mascot and logos.

170   Elasmosaurus

(Des M. Pollard. Litho B.D.T.)

1994 (6 May). *Aquatic Dinosaurs. T* **170** *and similar horiz designs. Multicoloured. P* 15×14.
941   $1 Type **170**   ..   ..   1·75   2·00
      a. Horiz strip of 4. Nos. 941/4   ..   8·00
942   $1.15, Plesiosaurus   ..   1·75   2·00
943   $1.50, Nothosaurus   ..   2·25   2·50
944   $3.45, Mosasaurus   ..   3·00   3·75
941/4   ..   ..   *Set of 4*   8·00   9·00
Nos. 941/4 were printed together, *se-tenant,* in horizontal strips of 4 throughout the sheet.

Space Anniversaries
Columbia
First Space Shuttle
April 12, 1981
$2 30

(171)

1994 (20 July). *Space Anniversaries. Nos. 804/7 surch in black and red or optd in red only as T* **171**, *each including "Space Anniversaries".*
945   40 c. on 90 c. Type **143**   ..   1·25   70
946   $1.15, Astronaut alighting from lunar module *Eagle*   ..   2·00   1·25
947   $1.50, *Eagle* and astronaut conducting experiment   ..   2·50   2·50
948   $2.30 on $3.50, Opening "Apollo 11" hatch after splashdown   ..   3·75   5·50
945/8   ..   ..   *Set of 4*   8·50   9·00
Surcharges and overprints:—No. 945, "Juri Gagarin First man in space April 12, 1961"; No. 946, "First Joint US Soviet Mission July 15, 1975"; No. 947 "25th Anniversary First Moon Landing Apollo XI – July 20, 1994".
Nos. 945 and 948 show the face value obliterated in black and the rest of the surcharge in red.

172   1969 Festival Logo

173   Sea Fan

(Des A. Skolnick and Barbara Pensoy. Litho The Mansfield Press)

1994 (20 Oct). *25th Anniv of Woodstock Music Festival. T* **172** *and similar vert design. Multicoloured. P* 12½.
949   $1.15, Type **172**   ..   ..   1·00   1·00
950   $1.50, 1994 anniversary festival logo   ..   1·25   1·25

(Des M. Pollard. Litho B.D.T.)

1995 (14 Feb). *Marine Life. T* **173** *and simlar vert designs. Multicoloured. P* 14×15.
951   $1 Type **173**   60   50
952   $1.15, Sea Lily   70   60
953   $1.50, Sea Pen   90   1·00
954   $3.45, Sea Fern   ..   ..   2·00   2·75
951/4   ..   ..   *Set of 4*   3·75   4·25
MS955   88×96 mm. $4.50, Sea Rose   ..   3·00   3·75

174   Marilyn Monroe

175   Jesse Owens (U.S.A.)

(Des S. Bickel (No. **MS965**), Lisa Egeli (others). Litho)

1995 (13 June). *Centenary of Cinema. T* **174** *and similar vert designs showing portraits of Marilyn Monroe (film star). Multicoloured. P* 12½.
956   $1.15, Type **174**   90   1·00
      a. Sheetlet. Nos. 956/64   ..   7·00
957   $1.15, Puckering lips   ..   90   1·00
958   $1.15, Laughing in brown evening dress and earrings   ..   90   1·00
959   $1.15, Wearing red earrings   ..   90   1·00

960	$1.15, In brown dress without earrings	90	1·00
961	$1.15, With white boa	90	1·00
962	$1.15, In red dress	90	1·00
963	$1.15, Wearing white jumper	90	1·00
964	$1.15, Looking over left shoulder	90	1·00
956/64		*Set of 9* 7·00	8·00

MS965 102×132 mm. $6 With Elvis Presley (50×56 *mm*) .. .. .. 4·50 4·75
Nos. 956/64 were printed together, *se-tenant*, in sheetlets of 9.

(Des M. Morck. Litho B.D.T.)

1995 (3 Aug). *5th International Amateur Athletic Federation Games, Göteborg. Sheet 181×103 mm, containing T 175 and similar vert designs. P 14.*
MS966 $1.50, black and pink (Type 175); $1.50, black and pale orange (Eric Lemming (Sweden)); $1.50, black and chrome-yellow (Rudolf Harbig (Germany)); $1.50, black and bright yellow-green (young Montserrat athletes) .. 4·50 5·50

176 Atmospheric Sounding Experiments using V2 Rockets

177 Ears of Wheat ("Food")

(Des M. Pollard. Litho Cot Printery Ltd, Barbados)

1995 (15 Aug). *50th Anniv of End of Second World War. Scientific Achievements. T 176 and similar horiz designs. Multicoloured. P 14.*

967	$1.15, Type 176	80	1·00
	a. Horiz pair. Nos. 967/8	1·60	2·00
968	$1.15, American Space Shuttle *Challenger*	80	1·00
969	$1.15, Nuclear experiment, Chicago, 1942	80	1·00
	a. Horiz pair. Nos. 969/70	1·60	2·00
970	$1.15, Calder Hall Atomic Power Station, 1956	80	1·00
971	$1.50, Radar-equipped Ju 88G 7a night-fighter	1·00	1·25
	a. Horiz pair. Nos. 971/2	2·00	2·50
972	$1.50, Boeing E6 A.W.A.C.S. aircraft	1·00	1·25
973	$1.50, Gloster G.41 Meteor Mk III jet fighter	1·00	1·25
	a. Horiz pair. Nos. 973/4	2·00	2·50
974	$1.50, Concorde (airliner)	1·00	1·25
967/74		*Set of 8* 6·50	8·00

Nos. 967/8, 969/70, 971/2 and 973/4 were each printed together, *se-tenant*, in horizontal pairs throughout the sheets.

(Des M. Pollard. Litho Cot Printery Ltd, Barbados)

1995 (14 Sept). *50th Anniv of United Nations. T 177 and similar vert designs. Multicoloured. P 14.*

975	$1.15, Type 177	90	75
976	$1.50, Open book ("Education")	1·25	1·00
977	$2.30, P.T. class ("Health")	1·75	2·25
978	$3 Dove ("Peace")	2·25	3·50
975/8		*Set of 4* 5·50	6·75

MS979 105×75 mm. $6 Scales ("Justice") .. 3·75 5·00

178 Headquarters Building

(Litho Cot Printery Ltd, Barbados)

1995 (15 Nov). *25th Anniv of Montserrat National Trust. T 178 and similar multicoloured designs. P 14.*

980	$1.15, Type 178	80	75
981	$1.50, 17th-century cannons, Bransby Point	1·25	1·00
982	$2.30, Impression of Galways Sugar Mill (*vert*)	2·25	2·50
983	$3 Great Alps Falls (*vert*)	3·50	4·50
980/3		*Set of 4* 7·00	8·00

25TH ANNIVERSARY 1970 - 1995

+$5⁰⁰

(179)

1995 (29 Dec). *25th Anniv of Air Recording Studios. No. 713 surch with T 179 in red.*
984 $2.30 + $5 Air Recording Studios .. 4·25 4·75
The $5 premium on No. 984 was for relief following a volcanic eruption.

180 Bull Shark

(Des M. Pollard. Litho B.D.T.)

1996 (14 Feb). *Scavengers of the Sea. T 180 and similar horiz designs. Multicoloured. P 15×14.*

985	$1 Type 180	80	70
986	$1.15, Sea Mouse	90	80
987	$1.50, Bristleworm	1·25	1·50
988	$3.45, Prawn *Xiphocaris*	2·50	3·50
985/8		*Set of 4* 5·00	6·00

MS989 69×95 mm. $4.50, Man of War Fish .. 3·00 3·75

181 Marconi and Radio Equipment, 1901

(Des M. Pollard. Litho Cot Printery Ltd, Barbados)

1996 (19 Mar). *Centenary of Radio. T 181 and similar horiz designs. Multicoloured. P 14.*

990	$1.15, Type 181	90	80
991	$1.50, Marconi's steam yacht *Elettra*	1·25	1·00
992	$2.30, Receiving first Transatlantic radio message, Newfoundland, 1901	1·75	2·25
993	$3 Imperial Airways airplane at Croydon Airport, 1920	2·25	3·25
990/3		*Set of 4* 5·50	6·50

MS994 74×105 mm. $4.50, Radio telescope, Jodrell Bank .. 3·00 3·75

182 Paul Masson (France) (Cycling)

(Litho B.D.T.)

1996 (24 June). *Olympic Games, Atlanta. Gold Medal Winners of 1896. T 182 and similar diamond-shaped designs. Multicoloured. P 14.*

995	$1.15, Type 182	80	80
996	$1.50, Robert Garrett (U.S.A.) (Discus)	1·00	1·00
997	$2.30, Spyridon Louis (Greece) (Marathon)	1·50	1·75
998	$3 John Boland (Great Britain) (Tennis)	2·00	3·00
995/8		*Set of 4* 4·75	6·00

183 James Dean

184 Leprechaun

(Des T. Kelly. Litho)

1996 (28 June). *James Dean (film star) Commemoration. T 183 and similar designs. Multicoloured. P 12½.*

999	$1.15, Type 183	80	85
	a. Sheetlet. Nos. 999/1007	6·50	
1000	$1.15, Wearing stetson facing right	80	85
1001	$1.15, Wearing blue sweater	80	85
1002	$1.15, Wearing black sweater	80	85
1003	$1.15, Full face portrait wearing stetson	80	85
1004	$1.15, Wearing fawn jacket	80	85
1005	$1.15, Wearing red wind-cheater	80	85
1006	$1.15, Smoking a cigarette	80	85
1007	$1.15, In open-necked shirt and green jumper	80	85
999/1007		*Set of 9* 6·50	7·00

MS1008 169×133 mm. $6 As No. 1000 (51×57 mm) .. 4·50 5·50
Nos. 999/1007 were printed together, *se-tenant*, in sheetlets of 9.

(Litho Cot Printery Ltd, Barbados)

1996 (15 Aug). *Mythical Creatures. T 184 and similar vert designs. Multicoloured. P 14.*

1009	5 c. Type 184	10	10
1010	10 c. Pegasus	10	10
1011	15 c. Griffin	10	10
1012	20 c. Unicorn	10	10
1013	25 c. Gnomes	10	15
1014	40 c. Mermaid	15	20
1015	55 c. Cockatrice	25	30
1016	70 c. Fairy	30	35
1017	90 c. Goblin	40	45
1018	$1 Faun	45	50
1019	$1.15, Dragon	50	55
1020	$1.50, Giant	65	70
1021	$3 Elves	1·25	1·40
1022	$5 Centaur	2·10	2·25
1023	$7.50, Phoenix	3·25	3·50
1024	$10 Erin	4·25	4·50
1009/24		*Set of 16* 14·00	15·00

185 Blue and Green Teddybears

186 Turkey Vulture

1996 (21 Oct). *Jerry Garcia and the Grateful Dead (rock group) Commemoration. T 185 and similar vert designs. Multicoloured. Litho. P 12½.*

1025	$1.15, Type 185	1·00	1·00
	a. Horiz strip of 3. Nos. 1025/7	2·75	
1026	$1.15, Green and yellow teddybears	1·00	1·00
1027	$1.15, Brown and pink teddybears	1·00	1·00
1028	$6 Jerry Garcia (37×50 mm)	5·50	5·50
1025/8		*Set of 4* 7·75	7·75

Nos. 1025/7 were printed together, *se-tenant*, in horizontal strips of 3 throughout the sheet, each strip forming a composite design.

(Des M. Pollard. Litho B.D.T.)

1997 (28 Jan). *Scavengers of the Sky. T 186 and similar horiz designs. Multicoloured. P 15×14.*

1029	$1 Type 186	75	70
1030	$1.15, American Crow	90	70
1031	$1.50, Great Skua	1·25	1·50
1032	$3.45, Kittiwake	2·25	3·00
1029/32		*Set of 4* 4·75	5·50

MS1033 74×95 mm. $4.50, King Vulture .. 2·40 3·00

HONG KONG '97
(187)

(Litho Cambridge Security Press Ltd)

1997 (26 Mar). *"HONG KONG '97" International Stamp Exhibition. Nos. 1025/7 overprinted with T 187 in deep blue across horizontal strips of three.*

1034	$1.15, Type 185	70	90
	a. Horiz strip of 3. Nos. 1034/6	1·90	
1035	$1.15, Green and yellow teddybears	70	90
1036	$1.15, Brown and pink teddybears	70	90
1034/6		*Set of 3* 1·90	2·40

Type **187** falls across the three stamps with "HO" on No. 1034, "NG KONG" on No. 1035 and "'97" on No. 1036.

(188)

189 Heavy Ash Eruption over Plymouth, 1995

1997 (2 June). *"Pacific '97" International Stamp Exhibition, San Francisco. Nos. 999/1007 optd with T 188 with each impression falling across two stamps.*

1037	$1.15, Type 183	80	90
	a. Sheetlet. Nos. 1037/45	6·50	
1038	$1.15, Wearing stetson facing right	80	90
1039	$1.15, Wearing blue sweater	80	90
1040	$1.15, Wearing black sweater	80	90
1041	$1.15, Full-face portrait wearing stetson	80	90
1042	$1.15, Wearing fawn jacket	80	90
1043	$1.15, Wearing red wind-cheater	80	90
1044	$1.15, Smoking a cigarette	80	90
1045	$1.15, In open-necked shirt and green jumper	80	90
1037/45		*Set of 9* 6·50	7·25

(Des M. Pollard. Litho Cot Printery, Barbados)

1997 (23 June). *Eruption of Soufriere Volcano. T 189 and similar vert designs. Multicoloured. P 14½×14.*

1046	$1.50, Type 189	1·10	1·25
	a. Sheetlet. Nos. 1046/54	9·00	
1047	$1.50, Burning rock flow entering sea	1·10	1·25

1048	$1.50, Double venting at Castle Peak		1·10	1·25
1049	$1.50, Mangrove Cuckoo		1·10	1·25
1050	$1.50, Lava flow at night, 1996		1·10	1·25
1051	$1.50, Antillean Crested Hummingbird		1·10	1·25
1052	$1.50, Ash cloud over Plymouth		1·10	1·25
1053	$1.50, Lava spine, 1996		1·10	1·25
1054	$1.50, Burning rock flows forming new land		1·10	1·25
1046/54		Set of 9	9·00	10·00

Nos. 1046/54 were printed together, se-tenant, in sheetlets of 9.

No. 1046a was reissued on 29 December 1997 overprinted "MUSIC FOR / IN AID OF THE VICTIMS OF SOUFRIERE HILLS VOLCANO / ROYAL ALBERT HALL LONDON / 15th SEPTEMBER 1997" in black on top, left and right margins.

190 Elvis Presley

191 Untitled Painting by Frama

(Litho Cambridge Security Press Ltd)

1997 (29 Aug). *Rock Legends. T* **190** *and similar vert designs. Multicoloured. P* 12½.

1055	$1.15, Type 190		1·00	1·10
1056	$1.15, Jimi Hendrix		1·00	1·10
1057	$1.15, Jerry Garcia		1·00	1·10
1058	$1.15, Janis Joplin		1·00	1·10
1055/8		Set of 4	3·50	4·00

Nos. 1055/8 were each printed in sheets of 8 containing two blocks of four separated by a vertical gutter.

(Litho Cambridge Security Press Ltd)

1997 (29 Aug). *Frama Exhibition at Guggenheim Museum, New York. P* 12½.

1059	191	$1.50, multicoloured	85	95
	a. Sheetlet. No. 1059×8		6·00	

No. 1059 was printed in sheetlets of 8 stamps, containing two blocks of four separated by an illustrated margin.

(192)

193 Prickly Pear

194 Eva and Juan Perón (Argentine politicians)

1997 (21 Nov). *No. 1028 surch with T* **192** *in black on gold by Benjies Printery, Antigua.*

1060	$1.50 on $6 Jerry Garcia (37×50 mm)		85	90

(Des M. Pollard. Litho Questa)

1998 (30 Mar). *Medicinal Plants. T* **193** *and similar vert designs. Multicoloured. P* 15×14½.

1061	$1 Type 193		55	50
1062	$1.15, Pomme Coolie		65	55
1063	$1.50, Aloe		75	75
1064	$3.45, Bird Pepper		1·75	2·00
1061/4		Set of 4	3·25	3·50

(Litho Cambridge Security Press)

1998 (18 May). *Famous People of the 20th Century. T* **194** *and similar multicoloured designs. P* 12½.

1065	$1.15, Type 194		70	80
	a. Sheetlet of 4		2·50	
1066	$1.15, Pablo Picasso (painter)		70	80
	a. Sheetlet of 4		2·50	
1067	$1.15, Wernher von Braun (space scientist)		70	80
	a. Sheetlet of 4		2·50	
1068	$1.15, David Ben Gurion (Israeli statesman)		70	80
	a. Sheetlet of 4		2·50	
1069	$1.15, Jean Henri Dunant (founder of Red Cross)		70	80
	a. Sheetlet of 4		2·50	
1070	$1.15, Dwight Eisenhower (President of U.S.A.)		70	80
	a. Sheetlet of 4		2·50	
1071	$1.15, Mahatma Gandhi (leader of Indian Independence movement)		70	80
	a. Sheetlet of 4		2·50	
1072	$1.15, King Leopold III and Queen Astrid of Belgium		70	80
	a. Sheetlet of 4		2·50	
1073	$1.15, Grand Duchess Charlotte and Prince Felix of Luxembourg		70	80
	a. Sheetlet of 4		2·50	

1074	$1.50, Charles Augustus Lindbergh (pioneer aviator)		80	90
	a. Sheetlet of 4		2·75	
1075	$1.50, Mao Tse-tung (Chinese communist leader)		80	90
	a. Sheetlet of 4		2·75	
1076	$1.50, Earl Mountbatten (last Viceroy of India)		80	90
	a. Sheetlet of 4		2·75	
1077	$1.50, Konrad Adenauer (German statesman)		80	90
	a. Sheetlet of 4		2·75	
1078	$1.50, Anne Frank (Holocaust victim)		80	90
	a. Sheetlet of 4		2·75	
1079	$1.50, Queen Wilhelmina of the Netherlands		80	90
	a. Sheetlet of 4		2·75	
1080	$1.50, King George VI of Great Britain		80	90
	a. Sheetlet of 4		2·75	
1081	$1.50, King Christian X of Denmark		80	90
	a. Sheetlet of 4		2·75	
1082	$1.50, King Haakon VII and Crown Prince Olav of Norway		80	90
	a. Sheetlet of 4		2·75	
1083	$1.50, King Alfonso XIII of Spain		80	90
	a. Sheetlet of 4		2·75	
1084	$1.50, King Gustavus V of Sweden		80	90
	a. Sheetlet of 4		2·75	
1065/84		Set of 20	13·50	15·00
MS1085	115×63 mm. $3 John F. Kennedy (President of U.S.A.) (50×32 mm)		1·60	2·00

Nos. 1065/84 were each printed in sheetlets of 4 with enlarged illustrated right margins.

195 Jerry Garcia

(Litho Cambridge Security Press Ltd)

1998 (6 Aug). *Rock Music Legends. T* **195** *and similar vert designs. Multicoloured. P* 12½.

(a) Jerry Garcia

1086	$1.15, In long-sleeved blue shirt		70	80
	a. Sheetlet. Nos. 1086/94		5·50	
1087	$1.15, With drum kit in background		70	80
1088	$1.15, Type 195		70	80
1089	$1.15, Wearing long-sleeved black t-shirt		70	80
1090	$1.15, Close-up with left hand in foreground		70	80
1091	$1.15, With purple and black background		70	80
1092	$1.15, Holding microphone		70	80
1093	$1.15, In short-sleeved blue t-shirt		70	80
1094	$1.15, In sunglasses with cymbal in background		70	80

(b) Bob Marley. Predominant colour for each design given

1095	$1.15, Pointing (green)		70	80
	a. Sheetlet. Nos. 1095/103, and 1 central label		5·00	
1096	$1.15, Wearing neck chain (green)		70	80
1097	$1.15, Singing into microphone (green)		70	80
1098	$1.15, Singing with eyes closed (yellow)		70	80
1099	$1.15, Facing audience (yellow)		70	80
1100	$1.15, In striped t-shirt with fingers on chin (red)		70	80
1101	$1.15, In Rastafarian hat (red)		70	80
1102	$1.15, In striped t-shirt with hand closed (red)		70	80
1086/1102		Set of 17	10·50	12·00
MS1103	152×101 mm. $5 Jerry Garcia (50×75 mm)		2·50	3·00

Nos. 1086/94 and 1095/102 were each printed together, se-tenant, in sheetlets of 9 or 8 stamps and one label.

196 Ash Eruption from Soufriere Hills Volcano

(Litho Cambridge Security Press Ltd)

1998 (21 Sept). *Total Eclipse of the Sun on 26 February. T* **196** *and similar multicoloured designs. P* 12½.

1104	$1.15, Type 196		90	90
1105	$1.15, Volcano emitting black cloud		90	90
1106	$1.15, Village below volcano		90	90
1107	$1.15, Lava flow and wrecked house		90	90
1104/7		Set of 4	3·25	3·25
MS1108	152×102 mm. $6 Solar eclipse (vert)		3·25	3·25

Nos. 1104/7 were each printed in small sheets of 4.

197 Princess Diana on Wedding Day, 1981

(198)

(Des M. Pollard. Litho Cambridge Security Press Ltd)

1998 (23 Nov). *Diana, Princess of Wales Commemoration. T* **197** *and similar horiz designs. Multicoloured. P* 12½.

1109	$1.15, Type 197		75	70
1110	$1.50, Accepting bouquet from children		90	90
1111	$3 At Royal Ascot		1·75	2·00
1109/11		Set of 3	3·00	3·25
MS1112	133×100 mm. $6 Diana and "Princess of Wales" rose (50×37 mm)		3·00	3·50

1998 (29 Dec). *19th World Scout Jamboree, Chile. Nos.* 669/72 *optd with T* **198** *in red.*

1113	20 c. Type 117		20	25
	a. Horiz pair. Nos. 1113/14		40	50
1114	20 c. Girl Guide saluting		20	25
1115	75 c. Lady Baden-Powell		65	75
	a. Horiz pair. Nos. 1115/16		1·25	1·50
1116	75 c. Guide assisting in old people's home		65	75
1113/16		Set of 4	1·50	1·75

199 Jerry Garcia

(Litho Cambridge Security Press Ltd)

1999 (9 Apr–7 May). *Jerry Garcia (rock musician) Commemoration. T* **199** *and similar multicoloured designs. P* 12½.

1117	$1.15, Type 199		75	75
	a. Sheetlet. Nos. 1117/19, each × 3		6·00	
1118	$1.15, In front of drum kit (bluish violet background)		75	75
1119	$1.15, Singing into microphone		75	75
1120	$1.15, Playing guitar, facing right (vert)		75	75
	a. Sheetlet. Nos. 1120/2, each × 3		6·00	
1121	$1.15, Singing with eyes closed (vert)		75	75
1122	$1.15, Singing in white spotlight (vert)		75	75
1123	$1.15, In front of drum kit (deep turquoise-green background) (7 May)		75	75
	a. Sheetlet. Nos. 1123/5, each × 3		6·00	
1124	$1.15, In long-sleeved black shirt (7 May)		75	75
1125	$1.15, In red shirt (7 May)		75	75
1126	$1.15, In short-sleeved black t-shirt (without frame) (vert) (7 May)		75	75
	a. Sheetlet. Nos. 1126/8, each × 3		6·00	
1127	$1.15, In blue t-shirt (oval frame) (vert) (7 May)		75	75
1128	$1.15, In short-sleeved black t-shirt (oval frame) (vert) (7 May)		75	75
1117/28		Set of 12	8·00	8·00
MS1129	Two sheets. (a) 115×153 mm. $6 Jerry Garcia in concert (50×75 mm). (b) 153×115 mm. $6 Singing into microphone (75×50 mm) (7 May)			
		Set of 2 sheets	7·00	8·00

Nos. 1117/19, 1120/2, 1123/5 and 1126/8 were each printed together, se-tenant, in sheetlets of 9 containing three of each design.

(200)

201 Mango

1999 (27 Apr). *"iBRA '99" International Stamp Exhibition, Nuremberg. Nos.* 975/6 *optd with T* **200**.

1130	$1.15, Type 200		75	75
1131	$1.50, Open book ("Education")		90	90

(Des M. Pollard. Litho Cambridge Security Press Ltd)

1999 (5 July). *Tropical Caribbean Fruits. T* **201** *and similar square designs. Multicoloured. P* 12½.

1132	$1.15, Type 201		75	70
1133	$1.50, Breadfruit		90	80
1134	$2.30, Papaya		1·40	1·40
1135	$3 Lime		1·75	1·90
1136	$6 Akee		3·50	4·00
1132/6		Set of 5	7·50	8·00
MS1137	134×95 mm. Nos. 1132/6		8·50	9·00

202 Yorkshire Terrier   203 Pupil's Equipment
and World Map

(Des M. Pollard. Litho Cambridge Security Press Ltd)

1999 (27 Sept). *Dogs. T* **202** *and similar square designs. Each black. P* 12½.

1138	70 c. Type 202	..	..	..	55	40
1139	$1 Welsh Corgi	..	..	..	65	55
1140	$1.15, King Charles Spaniel	..	..	75	70
1141	$1.50, Poodle	..	..	..	90	90
1142	$3 Beagle	..	..	..	1·75	2·00
1138/42	..	..	..	Set of 5	4·25	4·00
MS1143	133×95 mm. Nos. 1138/42	..			4·25	4·50

(Des M. Pollard. Litho Cambridge Security Press Ltd)

1999 (5 Oct). *World Teachers' Day. T* **203** *and similar square designs. Multicoloured. P* 12½.

1144	$1 Type 203	..	..	..	65	55
1145	$1.15, Teacher and class	..	..	75	70
1146	$1.50, Emblems of vocational training	..	90	90
1147	$5 Scientific equipment	..	..	3·25	3·75
1144/7	..	..	..	Set of 4	5·00	5·50

204 Great Hammerhead
Shark

(Des R. Watton. Litho Impressor)

1999 (29 Nov). *Endangered Species. Great Hammerhead Shark. T* **204** *and similar horiz designs. Multicoloured. P* 13½.

1148	50 c. Type 204	..	..	..	20	25
	a. Strip of 4. Nos. 1148/51				80	
1149	50 c. Two Hammerhead Sharks among fish	20	25
1150	50 c. Two Hammerhead Sharks on sea-bed	20	25
1151	50 c. Three Hammerhead Sharks		20	25
1148/51	..	..	..	Set of 4	80	1·00

Nos. 1148/51 were printed together, *se-tenant*, both horizontally and vertically, in sheets of 16.

STAMP BOOKLETS

1975 (3 Mar). *Carib Artefacts. Multicoloured cover. Stitched.*
SB1 $2.95, booklet containing *se-tenant* panes of 4 and 6 (Nos. 347a/8a) .. .. 1·90

1977 (7 Feb). *Silver Jubilee. Black on white cover. Stapled.*
SB2 $7 booklet containing 30 c., 45 c. and $1 (Nos. 396/8), each in block of 4 .. .. 5·00

1978 (2 June). *25th Anniv of Coronation. Multicoloured cover, 82×52 mm, showing Coronation ceremony on the front and Westminster Abbey on the reverse. Stapled.*
SB3 $8.90, booklet containing 40 c., 55 c., $1 and $2.50 (Nos. 422/5), each in pair .. .. .. 1·25

1981. *Black and blue cover, 102×64 mm, showing stylized fishes design. Stitched.*
SB4 $5.80, booklet containing 35 c., 45 c. and 65 c. (Nos. 495/6, 498), each in block of 4 .. 4·50

1981 (19 Nov). *Royal Wedding. Multicoloured cover, 105×65 mm, showing The Charlotte. Stitched.*
SB5 $13.20, booklet containing eight 90 c. in panes of 4 (No. 517a) and two $3 in pane of 2 (No. 518a) 4·25

1986 (23 July). *Royal Wedding. Gold (No. SB6) or silver (No. SB7) on greenish yellow covers. Stapled.*
SB6 $8.40, booklet (Westminster Abbey) containing twelve 70 c. (Nos. 691/2) .. .. 3·50
SB7 $10.80, booklet (State Coach) containing 70 c. and $2 (Nos. 691/4, but imperf), each value in block of 4 .. .. 4·75

OFFICIAL STAMPS

O.H.M.S. **O.H.M.S.**
(O 1) (O 2)

1976 (12 Apr). *Various stamps, some already surcharged, optd locally with Type O 1.*

O1	5 c. multicoloured (No. 246)	..	†	65
O2	10 c. multicoloured (No. 247)	..	†	75
	a. Opt double	..	†	12·00
	b. Horiz pair, one stamp without opt	†	£250
O3	30 c. on 10 c. multicoloured (No. 369)	†	1·50
	a. Opt double	..	†	25·00
	w. Wmk Crown to right of CA	†	25·00
O4	45 c. on 3 c. multicoloured (No. 370)	†	2·00
O5	$5 multicoloured (No. 254)	..	†	£100
O6	$10 multicoloured (No. 254c)	..	†	£550
O1/6		*Set of 6*	†	£600

These stamps were issued for use on mail from the Montserrat Philatelic Bureau. They were not available for sale in either unused or used condition.

1976 (1 Oct)–80. *Nos. 374/8, 380/2 and 384/5 optd with Type O 2 locally.*

O 7	5 c. Malay Apple	..	†	15
	a. Opt inverted	..	†	—
	b. Missing stop after "S"	†	1·50
O 8	10 c. Jacaranda	..	†	20
	a. Missing stop after "S"	†	1·50
O 9	15 c. Orchid Tree	..	†	25
	a. Opt inverted	..	†	70·00
	b. Missing stop after "S"	†	1·50
	w. Wmk Crown to right of CA	†	25·00
O10	20 c. Manjak	..	†	30
	a. Opt inverted	..	†	70·00
	b. Missing stop after "S"	†	1·50
	c. Chalk-surfaced paper (1980)	†	—
O11	25 c. Tamarind	..	†	35
	a. Missing stop after "S"	†	1·50
O12	55 c. Pink Cassia	..	†	55
	a. Opt inverted	..	†	—
	b. Opt double	..	†	—
	c. Missing stop after "S"	†	2·50
O13	70 c. Long John	..	†	60
	a. Missing stop after "S"	†	3·50
O14	$1 Saman	..	†	75
	a. Opt inverted	..	†	—
	b. Missing stop after "S"	†	5·00
O15	$5 Yellow Poui	..	†	2·00
	a. Missing stop after "S"	†	11·00
	w. Wmk Crown to right of CA	†	10·00
O16	$10 Flamboyant (14.4.80)	..	†	3·75
	a. Missing stop after "S"	†	20·00
O7/16		*Set of 10*	†	8·00

Nos. O7/16 were not available in an unused condition, but were sold to the public cancelled-to-order.
The missing stop after "S" variety occurs on R. 1/3 and 3/5.

O.H.M.S. O.H.M.S. O.H.M.S.
(O 3) (O 4) 45¢ (O 5)

1980 (7 July). *Nos. 374/8, 380/2 and 384/5 optd with Type O 3 in Great Britain.*

O17	5 c. Malay Apple	..	†	10
	a. Opt double	..	†	—
O18	10 c. Jacaranda	..	†	10
O19	15 c. Orchid Tree	..	†	10
O20	20 c. Manjak	..	†	10
	a. Opt double	..	†	70·00
O21	25 c. Tamarind	..	†	15
O22	55 c. Pink Cassia	..	†	35
	a. Opt double	..	†	11·00
O23	70 c. Long John	..	†	45
O24	$1 Saman	..	†	60

O25	$5 Yellow Poui	..	†	2·00
O26	$10 Flamboyant	..	†	3·00
O17/26		*Set of 10*	†	6·00

Nos. O17/26 were not available in an unused condition, but were sold to the public cancelled-to-order. At least two values, the 20 c. and $1 are, however, known uncancelled.

These stamps were originally intended for issue on 3 November 1980, but certain values were placed on sale from 7 July onwards to meet shortages. Bulk supplies did not arrive on the island until early December 1980.

O.H.M.S.
Spaced "H" and "M" (R. 3/4)

1980 (30 Sept). *Nos. 374/82, 384/5 and 476, together with surcharges on Nos. 372, 376 and 379, optd as Type O 4 locally.*

O27	5 c. Malay Apple	..	†	30
O28	5 c. on 3 c. Lignum vitae	..	†	30
O29	10 c. Jacaranda	..	†	30
O30	15 c. Orchid Tree	..	†	30
	a. Opt double	..	†	—
O31	20 c. Manjak	..	†	40
	a. Opt double	..	†	11·00
O32	25 c. Tamarind	..	†	40
O33	30 c. on 15 c. Orchid Tree	..	†	40
	a. "O.H.M.S." opt omitted	..	†	—
O34	35 c. on 2 c. Cannon-ball Tree	..	†	40
	a. Spaced "H" and "M"			3·50
O35	40 c. Flame of the Forest	..	†	50
O36	55 c. Pink Cassia	..	†	45
O37	70 c. Long John	..	†	60
O38	$1 Saman	..	†	60
O39	$2.50 on 40 c. Flame of the Forest	†	1·75
	a. "O.H.M.S." opt omitted			£160
O40	$5 Yellow Poui	..	†	2·00
O41	$10 Flamboyant	..	†	3·00
	a. Opt double	..	†	75·00
O27/41		*Set of 15*	†	10·50

Nos. O27/41 were not available in an unused condition, but were sold to the public cancelled-to-order. No. O39a was, however, found amongst supplies of the postage series.

1981 (20 Mar). *Nos. 490/4, 496, 498, 500, 502/3 and 505 optd with Type O 4.*

O42	5 c. Type 91	..	10	10
	a. Opt inverted	..	15·00	
O43	10 c. Hogfish and Neon Goby	..	10	10
O44	15 c. Creole Wrasse	..	10	10
	a. Opt double	..	†	
O45	20 c. Three-spotted Damselfish		15	15
O46	25 c. Sergeant Major	..	15	15
O47	45 c. Schoolmaster	..	25	20
	a. Opt double	..	16·00	
	ab. Opt double, one on reverse	11·00	
	b. Opt inverted	..	20·00	
O48	65 c. Bigeye	..	35	30
	a. Opt inverted	..	65·00	
O49	$1 Rock Beauty	..	65	65
O50	$3 Royal Gramma ("Fairy Basslet") and Blueheads	..	1·75	1·75
O51	$5 Cherub Angelfish	..	2·50	2·25
	w. Wmk inverted		30·00	
O52	$10 Caribbean Long-nosed Butterflyfish	4·00	2·25
	w. Wmk inverted		32·00	
O42/52		*Set of 11*	9·00	7·00

O.H.M.S.
45¢ (O 5)

1982 (17 Nov). *Nos. 510/15 surch as Type O 5 (in one line on Nos. O54, O56 and O58).*

O53	45 c. on 90 c. *Charlotte*		20	30
	a. Sheetlet. No. O53×6 and No. O54	1·60	
	b. Surch double	..	18·00	
	c. Surch inverted	..	12·00	
	d. Surch inverted (horiz pair)	32·00	
	e. Horiz pair, one without surch	70·00	
O54	45 c. on 90 c. Prince Charles and Lady Diana Spencer		60	70
	b. Surch double	..	70·00	
	c. Surch inverted	..	50·00	
O55	75 c. on $3 *Portsmouth*	..	25	35
	aw. Wmk inverted	..	6·00	
	b. Sheetlet. No. O55×6 and No. O56	2·25	
	bw. Wmk inverted	..	60·00	
	c. Surch double	..	27·00	
	d. Surch inverted	..	13·00	
	e. Surch inverted (horiz pair)	23·00	
	f. Horiz pair, one without surch	70·00	
	g. Error. Surch on $4 (No. 514)	12·00	
	ga. Sheetlet. No. O55g×6 and No. O56g	£130	
O56	75 c. on $3 Prince Charles and Lady Diana Spencer	..	90	1·00
	aw. Wmk inverted	..	30·00	
	c. Surch double	..	75·00	
	d. Surch inverted	..	22·00	
	g. Error. Surch on $4 (No. 515)	70·00	
O57	$1 on $4 *Britannia*	..	35	50
	aw. Wmk inverted	..	7·00	
	b. Sheetlet. No. O57×6 and No. O58	2·75	
	bw. Wmk inverted	..	65·00	
	c. Surch double	..	32·00	
	d. Surch inverted	..	7·50	
	e. Surch inverted (horiz pair)	21·00	
	f. Horiz pair, one without surch		
O58	$1 on $4 Prince Charles and Lady Diana Spencer	..	1·00	1·10
	aw. Wmk inverted	..	32·00	
	c. Surch double	..	80·00	
	d. Surch inverted	..	23·00	
O53/8		*Set of 6*	3·00	3·50

Nos. O53d, O55e and O57e show the long surcharge, intended for Nos. O54, O56 or O58, inverted across horizontal pairs of the smaller design. Nos. O54c, O56d and O58d show two examples as Type O 5 inverted on the same stamp.

NEW INFORMATION

The editor is always interested to correspond with people who have new information that will improve or correct the Catalogue.

═══ 70¢

O.H.M.S. O.H.M.S. O.H.M.S.
(O 6) (O 7) (O 8)

1983 (19 Oct). *Nos. 542/4 surch as Type O 6 or optd only ($1).*

O59	70 c. on 75 c. Type 97	..	60	40
O60	$1 Coat of Arms of Catherine of Aragon	70	50
	a. Opt inverted		32·00	
O61	$1.50 on $5 Diana, Princess of Wales	1·00	80
O59/61		*Set of 3*	2·10	1·60

1985 (12 Apr). *Nos. 600/12 and 614 opt with Type O 7 (horizontally on Nos. O71/5).*

O62	5 c. Type 107	..	60	70
O63	10 c. Carib Grackle	..	60	70
O64	15 c. Moorhen	..	70	70
O65	20 c. Brown Booby	..	75	60
O66	25 c. Black-whiskered Vireo	..	75	60
O67	40 c. Scaly-breasted Thrasher	1·00	60
	a. Opt double	..	†	
O68	55 c. Laughing Gull	..	1·25	65
O69	70 c. Glossy Ibis	..	1·40	80
O70	90 c. Green Heron	..	1·75	80
O71	$1 Belted Kingfisher	..	1·75	60
O72	$1.15, Bananaquit	..	2·50	90
O73	$3 American Kestrel	..	3·75	2·50
O74	$5 Forest Thrush	..	4·50	2·50
O75	$10 Bridled Quail Dove	..	6·50	2·50
O62/75		*Set of 14*	25·00	13·50

1989 (9 May). *Nos. 757/70 and 772 optd with Type O 8.*

O76	5 c. Type 133	..	25	30
O77	10 c. Little Knobbed Scallop (*Chlamys imbricata*)	25	30
O78	15 c. Sozoni's Cone (*Conus delessertii*)	30	30
O79	20 c. Globular Coral Shell (*Coralliophila aberrans*)	35	30
O80	25 c. American or Common Sundial (*Architectonica nobilis*)	35	30
O81	40 c. King Helmet (*Cassis tuberosa*)	45	40
O82	55 c. Channelled Turban (*Turbo canaliculatus*)	50	40
O83	70 c. True Tulip (*Fasciolaria tulipa*)	60	60
	a. Horiz pair, left-hand stamp without opt		
O84	90 c. Music Volute (*Voluta musica*)	75	75
O85	$1 Flame Auger (*Terebra taurina*)	80	70
O86	$1.15, Rooster-tail Conch (*Strombus gallus*)	90	80
O87	$1.50, Queen or Pink Conch (*Strombus gigas*)	1·10	1·10
O88	$3 Teramachi's Slit Shell (*Perotrochus teramachii*)	1·75	1·90
O89	$5 Common or Florida Crown Conch (*Melongena corona*)	3·00	3·00
O90	$10 Atlantic Trumpet Triton (*Charonia variegata*)	5·50	5·50
O76/90		*Set of 15*	15·00	15·00

▉ 70¢

OHMS OHMS 70¢
(O 9) (O 10)

1989 (26 May). *Nos. 578 and 580/1 surch with Type O 9.*

O91	70 c. on 10 c. Hogfish and Neon Goby	1·50	1·50
O92	$1.15 on 75 c. French Grunt	2·00	1·50
O93	$1.50 on $2 Blue Chromis	2·25	2·75
O91/3		*Set of 3*	5·25	5·25

1992 (3 July–Nov). *Nos. 838/41, 847/50 and 856/9 surch or optd only as Type O 10 ("OHMS" vert on Nos. O96, O98/9, O102/3 and O105) by Benjies Printery, Antigua.*

O94	70 c. on 90 c. Type 150	..	1·25	1·25
O95	70 c. on 90 c. Type 152	..	1·25	1·25
	a. Vert opt (11.92)			
O96	70 c. on 90 c. Type 154	..	1·25	1·25
O97	70 c. on $3.50, French Grunt	1·25	1·25
O98	$1 on $3.50, Helmet Guineafowl	1·40	1·40
O99	$1 on $3.50, Anthurium	1·40	1·40
O100	$1.15, Cushion Star	..	1·40	1·40
	a. Vert opt (11.92)			
O101	$1.15, Hen and Chicks	..	1·40	1·40
O102	$1.15, Shell Ginger	..	1·40	1·40
O103	$1.50, Rock Beauty	..	1·50	1·50
O104	$1.50, Red Junglefowl	..	1·50	1·50
O105	$1.50, Early Day Lily	..	1·50	1·50
O94/105		*Set of 12*	15·00	15·00

OHMS O.H.M.S.
(O 11) (O 12)

1993 (14 Apr). *Nos. 889/902 and 904 optd with Type O* **11** *in red.*

O106	5 c. Type **161**		40	60
O107	10 c. *Gryllus campestris* (field cricket)		40	60
O108	15 c. *Lepthemis vesiculosa* (dragonfly)		50	60
O109	20 c. *Orthemis ferruginea* (Red Skimmer)		50	50
O110	25 c. *Gerris lacustris* (pond skater)		50	50
O111	40 c. *Byctiscus betulae* (leaf weevil)		60	40
O112	55 c. *Atta texana* (Leaf-cutter Ants)		65	40
O113	70 c. *Polistes fuscatus* (Paper Wasp)		70	70
O114	90 c. *Sparmopolius fulvus* (Bee Fly)		80	70
O115	$1 *Chrysopa carnea* (lace wing)		1·00	70
O116	$1.15, *Phoebis philea* (butterfly)		1·75	1·50
O117	$1.50, *Cynthia cardui* (butterfly)		2·00	2·25
O118	$3 *Utetheisa bella* (moth)		2·50	3·00
O119	$5 *Alucita pentadactyla* (moth)		3·50	3·75
O120	$10 *Heliconius melpomene* (butterfly)		5·50	6·00
O106/20	..	*Set of 15*	19·00	20·00

1997 (21 Nov). *Nos. 1009/22 and 1024 optd with Type O* **12** *in red.*

O121	5 c. Type **184**		10	10
O122	10 c. Pegasus		10	10
O123	15 c. Griffin		10	10
O124	20 c. Unicorn		10	10
O125	25 c. Gnomes		10	15
O126	40 c. Mermaid		15	20
O127	55 c. Cockatrice		25	30
O128	70 c. Fairy		30	35
O129	90 c. Goblin		40	45
O130	$1 Faun		45	50
O131	$1.15, Dragon		50	55
O132	$1.50, Giant		65	70
O133	$3 Elves		1·25	1·40
O134	$5 Centaur		2·10	2·25
O135	$10 Erin		4·25	4·50
O121/35	..	*Set of 15*	10·50	11·50

Morocco Agencies
(British Post Offices)

With the growth of trade and commerce during the 19th century European powers opened post offices or postal agencies in various ports along the Moroccan coast from the early 1850's onwards. French and, in the north, Spanish influence eventually became predominant, leading to the protectorates of 1912. The British, who had inaugurated a regular postal service between Gibraltar and Tangier or Tetuan in May 1778, established their first postal agency in 1857. German offices followed around the turn of the century.

Before 1892 there was no indigenous postal service and those towns where there was no foreign agency were served by a number of private local posts which continued to flourish until 1900. In November 1892 the Sultan of Morocco established the Cherifian postal service, but this was little used until after its reorganization at the end of 1911. The Sultan's post was absorbed by the French postal service on 1 October 1913. Issues of the local posts and of the Sultan's post can occasionally be found used on cover in combination with stamps of Gibraltar or the Morocco Agencies.

In 1857 the first British postal agency was established at Tangier within the precincts of the Legation and was run by the official interpreter. From 1 March 1858 all letters for Great Britain sent via the British mail packets from Gibraltar required franking with Great Britain stamps.

In 1872 the Tangier office was relocated away from the Legation and the interpreter was appointed British Postal Agent. At the same time the agency was placed under the control of the Gibraltar postmaster. When the colonial posts became independent of the British G.P.O. on 1 January 1886 Gibraltar retained responsibility for the Morocco Agencies. Further offices, each under the control of the local Vice-Consul, were opened from 1886 onwards.

I. GIBRALTAR USED IN MOROCCO

Details of the various agencies are given below. Type C, the "A26" killer, is very similar to postmarks used at Gibraltar during this period. In addition to the town name postmarks as Types A, B and D from Fez, Mazagan, Saffi and Tetuan were also inscribed "MOROCCO".

Postmark Types used on Gibraltar issues.

Type A
Circular datestamp

Type C
"A26" killer

Type B
Duplex cancellation

Type D
Registered oval

BISECTS. The 10 c., 40 c. and 50 c. values of the 1889 surcharges and of the 1889–96 issue are known bisected and used for half their value from various of the Morocco Agencies. These bisects were never authorised by the Gibraltar Post Office.

CASABLANCA

The British postal agency opened on 1 January 1887 and was initially supplied with ½d., 4d. and 6d. stamps from the Gibraltar 1886 overprinted on Bermuda issue and 1d., 2d. and 2½d. values from the 1886–87 set.

Stamps of GIBRALTAR cancelled with Types A (without code or code "C"), B (without code or code "A") or D.

1886. *Optd on Bermuda (Nos. 1/7).*

Z1	½d. dull green			65·00
Z2	4d. orange-brown			£300
Z3	6d. deep lilac			£300

1886–87. *Queen Victoria £sd issue (Nos. 8/14).*

Z 4	½d. dull green			29·00
Z 5	1d. rose			32·00
Z 6	2d. brown-purple			70·00
Z 7	2½d. blue			42·00
Z 8	4d. orange-brown			£100
Z10	1s. bistre			£300

1889. *Surch in Spanish currency (Nos. 15/21).*

Z11	5 c. on ½d. green			48·00
Z12	10 c. on 1d. rose			40·00
Z13	25 c. on 2d. brown-purple			60·00
Z14	25 c. on 2½d. bright blue			38·00
Z15	40 c. on 4d. orange-brown			£110
Z16	50 c. on 6d. bright lilac			£100
Z17	75 c. on 1s. bistre			£130

1889–96. *Queen Victoria Spanish currency issue (Nos. 22/33).*

Z18	5 c. green			13·00
Z19	10 c. carmine			13·00
Z20	20 c. olive-green and brown			30·00
Z22	25 c. ultramarine			13·00
Z23	40 c. orange-brown			35·00
Z24	50 c. bright lilac			27·00
Z25	75 c. olive-green			80·00
Z26	1 p. lilac			70·00
Z28	1 p. bistre and ultramarine			35·00
Z29	2 p. black and carmine			50·00

FEZ

The British postal agency in this inland town opened on 24 February 1892 and was initially supplied with stamps up to the 50 c. value from the Gibraltar 1889–96 issue.

Stamps of GIBRALTAR cancelled with Types A (without code) or D.

1889–96. *Queen Victoria Spanish currency issue (Nos. 22/33).*

Z31	5 c. green			28·00
Z32	10 c. carmine			30·00
Z33	20 c. olive-green and brown			55·00
Z35	25 c. ultramarine			42·00
Z36	40 c. orange-brown			75·00
Z37	50 c. bright lilac			55·00

LARAICHE

The British postal agency at Laraiche opened in March 1886, although the first postmark, an "A26" killer, was not supplied until May.

Stamps of GIBRALTAR cancelled with Types B (without code) or D.

1886. *Optd on Bermuda (Nos. 1/7).*

Z39	½d. dull green			
Z40	1d. rose-red			
Z41	2½d. ultramarine			

1886–87. *Queen Victoria £sd issue (Nos. 8/14).*

Z42	½d. dull green			90·00
Z43	1d. rose			85·00
Z45	2½d. blue			90·00

1889. *Surch in Spanish currency (Nos. 15/21).*

Z47	5 c. on ½d. green			60·00
Z48	10 c. on 1d. rose			
Z49	25 c. on 2½d. bright blue			

It is believed that the other surcharges in this series were not supplied to Laraiche.

1889–96. *Queen Victoria Spanish currency issue (Nos. 22/33).*

Z50	5 c. green			30·00
Z51	10 c. carmine			40·00
Z52	20 c. olive-green and brown			
Z54	25 c. ultramarine			40·00
Z55	40 c. orange-brown			
Z56	50 c. bright-lilac			80·00
Z57	1 p. bistre and ultramarine			

MAZAGAN

This was the main port for the inland city of Marrakesh. The British postal agency opened on 1 March 1888 and was initially supplied with stamps from the Gibraltar 1886–87 series.

Stamps of GIBRALTAR cancelled with Types A (codes "A" or "C") or D (without code, code "A" or code "C").

1886–87. *Queen Victoria £sd issue (Nos. 8/14).*

Z58	½d. dull green			30·00
Z59	1d. rose			30·00
Z60	2d. brown-purple			
Z61	2½d. blue			38·00
Z62	4d. orange-brown			£110
Z63	6d. lilac			£130

1889. *Surch in Spanish currency (Nos. 15/21).*

Z64	5 c. on ½d. green			
Z65	10 c. on 1d. rose			
Z66	25 c. on 2½d. bright blue			

It is believed that the other surcharges in this series were not supplied to Mazagan.

1889–96. *Queen Victoria Spanish currency issue (Nos. 22/33).*

Z67	5 c. green			19·00
Z68	10 c. carmine			17·00
Z69	20 c. olive-green and brown			50·00
Z70	25 c. ultramarine			42·00
Z71	40 c. orange-brown			75·00
Z72	50 c. bright lilac			
Z74	1 p. bistre and ultramarine			
Z75	2 p. black and carmine			

MOGADOR

The British postal agency at this port opened in May 1887 and was initially supplied with stamps from the Gibraltar 1886–87 series.

Stamps of GIBRALTAR cancelled with Types A (code "C"), B (code "C") or D.

1886–87. *Queen Victoria £sd issue (Nos. 8/14).*

Z76	½d. dull green			29·00
Z77	1d. rose			38·00
Z78	2d. brown-purple			70·00
Z79	2½d. blue			38·00

1889. *Surch in Spanish currency (Nos. 15/21).*

Z80	5 c. on ½d. green			48·00
Z81	10 c. on 1d. rose			48·00
Z82	25 c. on 2½d. bright blue			48·00

It is believed that the other surcharges in this series were not supplied to Mogador.

1889–96. *Queen Victoria Spanish currency issue (Nos. 22/33).*

Z83	5 c. green			13·00
Z84	10 c. carmine			15·00
Z85	20 c. olive-green and brown			
Z87	25 c. ultramarine			19·00
Z88	40 c. orange-brown			32·00
Z89	50 c. bright lilac			32·00

RABAT

The British postal agency at this port on the north-west coast of Morocco opened in March 1886, although the first cancellation, an "A26" killer, was not supplied until May. The initial stock of stamps was from the Gibraltar 1886 overprinted on Bermuda issue.

Stamps of GIBRALTAR cancelled with Types B (code "O") or D.

1886. *Optd on Bermuda (Nos. 1/7).*

Z92	½d. dull green			
Z93	1d. rose-red			
Z94	2½d. ultramarine			£130

1886–87. *Queen Victoria £sd issue (Nos. 8/14).*

Z 95	½d. dull green			29·00
Z 96	1d. rose			29·00
Z 97	2d. brown-purple			70·00
Z 98	2½d. blue			40·00
Z101	1s. bistre			£350

1889. *Surch in Spanish currency (Nos. 15/21).*

Z102	5 c. on ½d. green			48·00
Z103	10 c. on 1d. rose			42·00
Z104	25 c. on 2½d. bright blue			48·00

It is believed that the other surcharges in this series were not supplied to Rabat.

1889–96. *Queen Victoria Spanish currency issue (Nos. 22/33).*

Z105	5 c. green			18·00
Z106	10 c. carmine			18·00
Z107	20 c. olive-green and brown			40·00
Z108	25 c. ultramarine			19·00
Z109	40 c. orange-brown			45·00
Z110	50 c. bright lilac			40·00

SAFFI

The British postal agency at this port opened on 1 July 1891 and was supplied with stamps from the Gibraltar 1889–96 series.

Stamps of GIBRALTAR cancelled with Types B (code "C") or D (code "C").

1889–96. *Queen Victoria Spanish currency issue (Nos. 22/33).*

Z111	5 c. green	..	..	..	19·00
Z112	10 c. carmine	..	..	..	19·00
Z113	20 c. olive-green and brown	..	..	45·00
Z115	25 c. ultramarine	..	..	..	21·00
Z116	40 c. orange-brown	..	..	..	75·00
Z117	50 c. bright lilac	..	..	..	55·00
Z118	1 p. bistre and ultramarine	..	..	60·00
Z119	2 p. black and carmine	..	..	70·00

TANGIER

The British postal agency in Tangier opened on 1 April 1857 and from 1 March of the following year letters from it sent via the packet service to Great Britain required franking with Great Britain stamps.

No identifiable postmark was supplied to Tangier until 1872 and all earlier mail was cancelled with one of the Gibraltar marks. In April 1872 a postmark as Type A was supplied on which the "N" of "TANGIER" was reversed. A corrected version, with code letter "A", followed in 1878, but both were used as origin or arrival marks and the Great Britain stamps continued to be cancelled with Gibraltar obliterators. The Type A postmarks generally fell into disuse after 1880 and very few identifiable marks occur on mail from Tangier until the introduction of Gibraltar stamps in 1886.

Stamps of GIBRALTAR cancelled with Types A (codes "A" or "C"), B (code "A") or D.

1886. *Optd on Bermuda (Nos. 1/7).*

Z120	½d. dull green	..	..	..	42·00
Z121	1d. rose-red	..	..	..	65·00
Z122	2d. purple-brown	..	..	..	£140
Z123	2½d. ultramarine	..	..	..	42·00
Z124	4d. orange-brown	..	..	..	£170
Z125	6d. deep lilac	..	..	..	£225
Z126	1s. yellow-brown	..	..	..	£500

1886–87. *Queen Victoria £sd issue (Nos. 8/14).*

Z127	½d. dull green	..	..	..	18·00
Z128	1d. rose	..	..	..	18·00
Z129	2d. brown-purple	..	..	..	48·00
Z130	2½d. blue	..	..	..	27·00
Z131	4d. orange-brown	..	..	..	80·00
Z132	6d. lilac	..	..	..	£120
Z133	1s. bistre	..	..	..	£275

1889. *Surch in Spanish currency (Nos. 15/21).*

Z134	5 c. on ½d. green	..	..	29·00
Z135	10 c. on 1d. rose	..	..	20·00
Z136	25 c. on 2d. brown-purple	..	..	38·00
Z137	25 c. on 2½d. bright blue	..	..	29·00
Z138	40 c. on 4d. orange-brown	..	..	95·00
Z139	50 c. on 6d. bright lilac	..	..	90·00
Z140	75 c. on 1s. bistre	..	..	£120

1889–96. *Queen Victoria Spanish currency issue (Nos. 22/33).*

Z141	5 c. green	..	..	..	5·00
Z142	10 c. carmine	..	..	..	5·00
Z143	20 c. olive-green and brown	..	..	21·00
Z144	20 c. olive-green	..	..	..	55·00
Z145	25 c. ultramarine	..	..	..	8·00
Z146	40 c. orange-brown	..	..	..	13·00
Z147	50 c. bright lilac	..	..	..	12·00
Z148	75 c. olive-green	..	..	..	50·00
Z149	1 p. bistre	..	..	..	60·00
Z150	1 p. bistre and ultramarine	..	..	20·00
Z151	2 p. black and carmine	..	..	40·00
Z152	5 p. slate-grey	..	..	..	£110

TETUAN

The British postal agency in this northern town was opened in 1890 and was supplied with stamps from the Gibraltar 1889–96 series.

Stamps of GIBRALTAR cancelled with Types A (code "C"), B (code "C" often inverted) or D (code "C").

1889–96. *Queen Victoria Spanish currency issue (Nos. 22/33).*

Z153	5 c. green	..	..	..	24·00
Z154	10 c. carmine	..	..	..	28·00
Z155	20 c. olive-green and brown	..	..	50·00
Z157	25 c. ultramarine	..	..	..	32·00
Z158	40 c. orange-brown	..	..	..	60·00
Z159	50 c. bright lilac	..	..	..	60·00
Z161	1 p. bistre and ultramarine	..	..	

PRICES FOR STAMPS ON COVER TO 1945

Nos. 1/16	from × 7
Nos. 17/30	from × 3
Nos. 31/74	from × 3
Nos. 75/6	from × 4
Nos. 112/24	from × 4
No. 125	—
Nos. 126/35	from × 5
Nos. 136/42	from × 2
Nos. 143/59	from × 3
Nos. 160/75	from × 8
Nos. 191/9	from × 5
Nos. 200/1	from × 3
Nos. 202/11	from × 4
Nos. 212/15	from × 5
Nos. 216/24	from × 8
Nos. 225/6	from × 2
Nos. 227/30	from × 8
Nos. 231/52	from × 6

The above prices apply to stamps used on cover from Morocco. Examples of Nos. 31/76 and 231/52 used on cover in Great Britain after 1950 have little additional value.

II. GIBRALTAR ISSUES OVERPRINTED

With the reversion of Gibraltar to sterling in 1898 it became necessary to provide separate issues for the Morocco Agencies which continued to use Spanish currency.

The following were used in all the British postal agencies.

Morocco	Morocco
Agencies	Agencies
(1)	(2)

Agencies	Agencies
Inverted "V" for "A" (Right-hand pane R.6/6)	Long tail to "S" (Right-hand pane R.8/2)

Broken "M" (Pl 2 R. 4/5)

Flat top to "C" (Pl 2 R. 4/4)

1898 (1 June)–1900. *Nos. 22/8 and 31/2 (Queen Victoria) of Gibraltar optd with T 1 (wide "M" and ear of "g" projecting upwards), in black at Gibraltar Chronicle office.*

1	5 c. green	1·50	1·50
	a. Inverted "V" for "A"	25·00	28·00
	b. Long tail to "S"	25·00	28·00
	c. Broken "M" in "CENTIMOS"	30·00	
2	10 c. carmine	2·25	30
	b. Bisected (5 c.) (on cover)	† £1100	
	c. Inverted "V" for "A"	£225	£275
	d. Long tail to "S"	£225	
	e. Lines of opt 5 mm apart (6.00)	3·25	2·25
	ea. Opt double	£500	
3	20 c. olive-green and brown	4·00	1·25
	a. Inverted "V" for "A"	35·00	35·00
	b. Long tail to "S"	35·00	35·00
3c	20 c. olive-green	5·00	5·00
	ca. Opt double	£450	
	cb. Inverted "V" for "A"	42·00	48·00
	cc. Long tail to "S"	42·00	48·00
	cd. Flat top to "C" in "CENTIMOS"	55·00	
4	25 c. ultramarine	2·50	60
	a. Inverted "V" for "A"	£100	£120
	b. Long tail to "S"	£100	£120
5	40 c. orange-brown (2.6.98)	4·00	3·25
	a. Inverted "V" for "A"	£150	£180
	b. Long tail to "S"	£150	£180
	c. Blue opt (7.98)	35·00	32·00
6	50 c. bright lilac (2.6.98)	15·00	23·00
	a. Inverted "V" for "A"	£250	£275
	b. Long tail to "S"	£250	£275
	c. Blue opt (7.98)	11·00	12·00
7	1 p. bistre and ultramarine (2.6.98)	12·00	26·00
	a. Inverted "V" for "A"	£190	£275
	b. Long tail to "S"	£190	£275
	c. Blue opt (7.98)	£140	£180
8	2 p. black and carmine (4.6.98)	13·00	26·00
	a. Inverted "V" for "A"	£225	£275
	b. Long tail to "S"	£225	£275
1/8		*Set of 8* 45·00 65·00	

The blue overprint can be easily distinguished by looking through the stamp in front of a strong light.

The listed varieties of overprint occur from the first setting. They were corrected on the second setting of July 1898, which produced Nos. 5c, 6c, 7c and further supplies of No. 8. The corrected type was subsequently used to produce additional stocks of Nos. 1/2. Numerous more minor varieties exist from these settings.

No. 2e comes from two further printings in 1900 using a third setting on which the two lines of the overprint were 5 mm apart instead of the 4 mm space used previously.

Agencies	Morocco	Agencies
"CD" sideways flaw (Left-hand pane R.1/5)	Broad top to "M" (Left-hand pane R.7/3)	Hyphen between "nc" (Right-hand pane R.3/5)

1899 (Feb)–1902. *Nos. 22/3, 25/8 and 31/2 (Queen Victoria) of Gibraltar optd with T 2 (narrow "M" and ear of "g" horizontal), in black by D.L.R., London.*

9	5 c. green (4.99)	30	40
	a. "CD" sideways	11·00	11·00
	b. Broad top to "M"	8·00	8·00
	c. Hyphen between "nc"	8·00	8·00
	d. Broken "M" in "CENTIMOS"	13·00	
10	10 c. carmine	55	30
	a. "CD" sideways	11·00	11·00
	b. Broad top to "M"	8·00	8·00
	c. Hyphen between "nc"	8·00	8·00
	d. Opt double	£700	£700
11	20 c. olive-green (5.02)	4·00	70
	b. Broad top to "M"	26·00	26·00
	c. Hyphen between "nc"	26·00	26·00
	d. Flat top to "C" in "CENTIMOS"	35·00	
12	25 c. ultramarine (10.99)	6·50	90
	a. "CD" sideways	38·00	38·00
	b. Broad top to "M"	32·00	32·00
	c. Hyphen between "nc"	32·00	32·00

13	40 c. orange-brown (3.02)	38·00	23·00
	b. Broad top to "M"	£190	£180
	c. Hyphen between "nc"	£190	£180
14	50 c. bright lilac (4.99)	6·50	3·50
	b. Broad top to "M"	90·00	£110
	c. Hyphen between "nc"	90·00	£110
15	1 p. bistre and ultramarine (4.99)	23·00	32·00
	b. Broad top to "M"	£130	£160
	c. Hyphen between "nc"	£130	£160
16	2 p. black and carmine (3.01)	38·00	48·00
	b. Broad top to "M"	£250	£325
	c. Hyphen between "nc"	£250	£325
9/16		*Set of 8* £100 95·00	
9/16	Optd "Specimen"	*Set of 8* £180	

1903–5. *As Nos. 46/51 (King Edward VII) of Gibraltar, but with value in Spanish currency, optd with T 2. Wmk Crown CA. P 14.*

17	5 c. grey-green and green (1.03)	6·50	2·25
	a. "CD" sideways	35·00	35·00
	b. Broad top to "M"	35·00	35·00
	c. Hyphen between "nc"	35·00	35·00
18	10 c. dull purple/red (8.03)	6·00	
	a. "CD" sideways	32·00	32·00
	b. Broad top to "M"	32·00	32·00
	c. Hyphen between "nc"	32·00	32·00
	w. Wmk inverted	30·00	
19	20 c. grey-green and carmine (9.04)	11·00	45·00
	a. "CD" sideways	75·00	£150
	b. Broad top to "M"	75·00	£150
	c. Hyphen between "nc"	75·00	£150
20	25 c. purple and black/blue (1.7.03)	5·00	20
	a. "CD" sideways	38·00	38·00
	b. Broad top to "M"	38·00	38·00
	c. Hyphen between "nc"	38·00	38·00
21	50 c. purple and violet (3.7.05)	85·00	£160
	a. "CD" sideways	£300	£500
	b. Broad top to "M"	£300	£500
	c. Hyphen between "nc"	£300	£500
22	1 p. black and carmine (19.11.05)	45·00	£150
	a. "CD" sideways	£225	£450
	b. Broad top to "M"	£225	£450
	c. Hyphen between "nc"	£225	£450
23	2 p. black and blue (19.11.05)	50·00	£120
	a. "CD" sideways	£250	£425
	b. Broad top to "M"	£250	£425
	c. Hyphen between "nc"	£250	£425
17/23		*Set of 7* £190 £425	
17/23	Optd "Specimen"	*Set of 7* £180	

Examples of Nos. 19 and 21/3 are known showing a forged Registered Mazagan postmark dated "15 SP 10".

1905 (Jan)–06. *As Nos. 17/23 but wmk Mult Crown CA. Ordinary paper (5, 10, 20 c.) or chalk-surfaced paper (others).*

24	5 c. grey-green and green (4.05)	4·75	2·75
	a. "CD" sideways	35·00	35·00
	b. Broad top to "M"	35·00	35·00
	c. Hyphen between "nc"	£600	£650
	d. Chalk-surfaced paper (1.06)	4·75	3·25
	da. "CD" sideways	35·00	35·00
	db. Broad top to "M"	35·00	35·00
25	10 c. dull purple/red	6·00	90
	a. "CD" sideways	35·00	26·00
	b. Broad top to "M"	35·00	26·00
	cw. Wmk inverted	25·00	
	d. Chalk-surfaced paper (12.05)	1·75	90
	da. "CD" sideways	23·00	23·00
	db. Broad top to "M"	23·00	23·00
26	20 c. grey-green and carmine (1.06)	3·00	25·00
	a. "CD" sideways	35·00	£100
	b. Broad top to "M"	35·00	£100
27	25 c. purple and black/blue (6.06)	30·00	6·50
	a. "CD" sideways	£200	£120
	b. Broad top to "M"	£200	£120
28	50 c. purple and violet (7.06)	6·00	35·00
	a. "CD" sideways	£130	£200
	b. Broad top to "M"	£130	£200
29	1 p. black and carmine (11.05)	24·00	75·00
	a. "CD" sideways	£180	£300
	b. Broad top to "M"	£180	£300
30	2 p. black and blue (11.05)	15·00	35·00
	a. "CD" sideways	£160	£225
	b. Broad top to "M"	£160	£225
24/30		*Set of 7* 75·00 £160	

Examples of Nos. 26 and 28/30 are known showing a forged Registered Mazagan postmark dated "15 SP 10".

Control of the British postal agencies in Morocco returned to the G.P.O., London, from 1 January 1907.

All the following issues are overprinted on Great Britain

III. BRITISH CURRENCY

Stamps overprinted "MOROCCO AGENCIES" only were primarily intended for use on parcels (and later, air-mail correspondence), and were on sale at British P.Os throughout Morocco including Tangier, until 1937.

PRICES. Our prices for used stamps with these overprints are for specimens used in Morocco. These stamps could be used in the United Kingdom, with official sanction, from the summer of 1950 onwards with U.K. postmarks are worth about 50 per cent less.

MOROCCO AGENCIES (4)	MOROCCO AGENCIES (5)	MOROCCO AGENCIES (6)

1907 (30 Apr)–13. *King Edward VII optd as T 4 or 5 (2s. 6d.).*

(a) De La Rue printings. Ordinary paper (½d., 1d., 4d. (No. 35) or chalk-surfaced paper (others)

31	½d. pale yellowish green (1.6.07)	1·50	7·00
32	1d. scarlet (5.5.07)	7·50	4·00
33	2d. pale grey-green and carmine-red	6·50	4·50
34	4d. green and chocolate-brown (29.10.07)	3·75	3·25
35	4d. pale orange (3.12)	8·50	8·50
	a. Orange-red	8·50	8·50

36	6d. pale dull purple (5.5.07)	..	..	12·00	14·00
	a. Dull purple		..	12·00	14·00
37	1s. dull green and carmine (5.5.07)		..	26·00	17·00
38	2s. 6d. pale dull purple (5.5.07)	..	..	65·00	£110
	a. Dull purple		..	65·00	£110
31/8			Set of 8	£120	£150
37/8	Optd "Specimen"		Set of 2	£140	

(b) Harrison printing. Ordinary paper

40	4d. bright orange (No. 286) (1913)	..	16·00	20·00

(c) Somerset House printing. Ordinary paper

41	2s. 6d. dull greyish purple (No. 315) (1913)	90·00	£160

1914–31. *King George V.*

(a) W 100 (Simple Cypher). Optd with T 4

42	½d. green	..	..	2·00	45
43	1d. scarlet	..	..	60	10
44	1½d. red-brown (1921)	..	2·25	11·00
45	2d. orange (Die I)	..	2·25	35
46	3d. bluish violet (1921)	..	1·00	35
47	4d. grey-green (1921)	..	2·25	80
48	6d. reddish purple (chalk-surfaced paper) (1921)	..	4·00	13·00
49	1s. bistre-brown (1917)	..	5·00	75
	a. Opt triple, two albino		£100	

(b) W 110 (Single Cypher). Optd with T 6.

50	2s. 6d. sepia-brown (Waterlow ptg) (No. 400) (1914)	..	42·00	55·00
	a. Re-entry (R. 2/1)		£650	£650
	b. Opt double, one albino		£160	
51	2s. 6d. yellow-brown (D.L.R. ptg) (No. 406) (1917)	..	45·00	28·00
	a. Opt double		£1500	£1000
	b. Pale brown (No. 407)		30·00	50·00
53	2s. 6d. chocolate-brown (B.W. ptg) (No. 414)	32·00	25·00
	a. Opt double, one albino*		£160	
54	5s. rose-red (B.W. ptg) (No. 416) (1931)	50·00	80·00
	a. Opt triple, two albino		£200	
42/54		Set of 10	90·00	£120
49/50, 54	Optd "Specimen"	Set of 3	£200	

*The albino overprint is quite clear, with the "MOROCCO" appearing just below "AGENCIES" of the normal overprint and a little to the right as seen from the back. There is also a second faint albino impression just below the normal overprint.

MOROCCO AGENCIES **S** (7) (A) MOROCCO AGENCIES **S** (8) (B)

Type 7: Opt 14 mm long; ends of "s" cut off diagonally.
Type 8: Opt 15½ mm long; ends of "s" cut off horizontally

1925–36. *King George V (W 111 (Block Cypher)) optd with T 8 (4d.) or 7 (others).*

55	½d. green	..	..	60	30
	aw. Wmk inverted	..	..	75·00	
	b. Optd with Type 8	..	4·25	28·00
56	1½d. chestnut (1931)	..	10·00	13·00
57	2d. orange	..	..	2·00	1·00
58	2½d. blue	..	..	2·00	5·00
	a. Optd with Type 8	..	£100	30·00
59	4d. grey-green (1.36)	..	5·50	30·00
60	6d. purple (1931) ..	..	2·00	8·50
	a. Optd with Type 8	..	55	60
61	1s. bistre-brown	..	15·00	50·00
	a. Optd with Type 8	..	50·00	55·00
55/61		Set of 7	32·00	50·00
61	Optd "Specimen"	..	..	60·00	

1935 (8 May). *Silver Jubilee (Nos. 453/6) optd "MOROCCO AGENCIES" only, as in T 17.*

62	½d. green (B.)	..	1·25	6·50
63	1d. scarlet (B.)	..	1·25	6·50
64	1½d. red-brown (B.)	..	2·25	9·00
65	2½d. blue (R.)	..	2·50	2·50
62/5		Set of 4	6·50	22·00

1935–37. *King George V. (a) Harrison photo ptgs (Nos. 440/5 and 449). W 111 (Block Cypher). Optd with T 8.*

66	1d. scarlet (4.35)	..	3·25	8·00
67	1½d. red-brown (28.4.36)	..	3·00	12·00
68	2d. orange (1.5.36)	..	40	4·25
69	2½d. ultramarine (11.2.36)	..	1·75	4·25
70	3d. violet (2.3.36)	..	40	20
71	4d. deep grey-green (14.5.36)	..	40	20
72	1s. bistre-brown (31.8.36)	..	80	1·75

(b) Waterlow re-engraved ptgs. W 110 (Single Cypher) optd with T 6.

73	2s. 6d. chocolate-brown (No. 450)	..	40·00	48·00
74	5s. bright rose-red (No. 451) (2.3.37)	..	23·00	85·00
66/74		Set of 9	65·00	£150
72/3	Optd "Specimen"	Set of 2	£130	

1936 (26 Oct)–**37.** *King Edward VIII, optd "MOROCCO AGENCIES" only, as in T 18 with "MOROCCO" 14¼ mm long.*

75	1d. scarlet	..	10	30
	a. "MOROCCO" 15¼ mm long (5.1.37)	5·50	12·00
76	2½d. bright blue	..	10	15
	a. "MOROCCO" 15¼ mm long (5.1.37)	80	4·25

The first two printings of both values showed all the stamps with the short overprint, Nos. 75/6.

On 5 January 1937 a further printing of both values was placed on sale in London which had the 24 stamps from the bottom two horizontal rows (Rows 19 and 20) with the long overprint, Nos. 75a/6a. Subsequent printings increased the number of long overprints in the sheet to 25 by the addition of R. 8/9, and finally, to 31 (R. 1/7, R. 7/1, R. 8/1, R. 13/3, 4 and 10, R. 14/6, but without R. 8/9).

For the 1d. printings cylinder 2 show the first setting. Sheets from cylinder 6 were also used for the first, and for all subsequent settings. The 2½d. value was overprinted on sheets from cylinder 2 throughout.

From 3 June 1937 unoverprinted stamps of Great Britain were supplied to the post offices at Tangier and Tetuan (Spanish Zone) as local stocks of issues overprinted "MOROCCO AGENCIES" were exhausted.

Type E   Type F

Stamps of GREAT BRITAIN *cancelled as Types E or F at Tangier.*

1937. *King George V.*

Z170	1½d. red-brown (No. 441)	..	..	10·00
Z171	2d. orange (No. 442)	..	..	10·00
Z172	3d. violet (No. 444)	..	..	10·00
Z173	4d. deep grey-green (No. 445)	..	8·00
Z174	6d. purple (No. 426a)	..	8·00
Z175	1s. bistre-brown (No. 449)	..	30·00
Z176	2s. 6d. chocolate-brown (No. 450)	..	65·00
Z177	5s. bright rose-red (No. 451)	..	

1937–39. *King George VI (Nos. 462/75).*

Z178	½d. green	..	..	12·00
Z179	1d. scarlet	..	..	12·00
Z180	1½d. red-brown	..	..	10·00
Z181	2d. orange	..	..	10·00
Z182	2½d. ultramarine	..	..	8·00
Z183	3d. violet	..	..	8·00
Z184	4d. grey-green	..	..	8·00
Z185	5d. brown	..	..	10·00
Z186	6d. purple	..	..	5·00
Z187	7d. emerald-green	..	..	8·00
Z188	8d. bright carmine	..	..	15·00
Z189	9d. deep olive-green	..	10·00
Z190	10d. turquoise-blue	..	15·00
Z191	1s. bistre-brown	..	..	5·00

1939–42. *King George VI (Nos. 476/8a).*

Z192	2s. 6d. brown	..	..	40·00
Z193	2s. 6d. yellow-green	..	12·00
Z194	5s. red	..	..	18·00
Z195	10s. dark blue	..	..	75·00
Z196	10s. ultramarine	..	..	32·00

1941–42. *King George VI pale colours (Nos. 485/90).*

Z197	½d. pale green	..	..	8·00
Z198	1d. pale scarlet	..	..	8·00
Z199	1½d. pale red-brown	..	8·00
Z200	2d. pale orange	..	..	8·00
Z201	2½d. light ultramarine	..	7·00
Z202	3d. pale violet	..	..	5·00

1946. *Victory (Nos. 491/2).*

Z203	2½d. ultramarine	..	..	7·00
Z204	3d. violet	..	..	7·00

Type G

Stamps of GREAT BRITAIN *cancelled as Type G at Tetuan.*

1937. *King George V.*

Z208	4d. deep grey-green (No. 445)	..	18·00
Z209	6d. purple (No. 426a)	..	
Z210	1s. bistre-brown (No. 449)	..	

1937–39. *King George VI (Nos. 465/75).*

Z211	2d. orange	..	..	15·00
Z212	2½d. ultramarine	..	..	
Z213	3d. violet	..	..	
Z214	4d. grey-green	..	..	15·00
Z215	6d. purple	..	..	10·00
Z216	9d. deep olive-green	..	
Z217	1s. bistre-brown	..	..	10·00

1939–42. *King George VI (Nos. 476/7).*

Z218	2s. 6d. brown	..	..	
Z219	2s. 6d. yellow-green	..	32·00
Z220	5s. red	..	..	42·00

1941. *King George VI pale colours (Nos. 485/90).*

Z221	½d. pale green	..	..	
Z222	2d. pale orange	..	..	
Z223	2½d. light ultramarine	..	
Z224	3d. pale violet	..	..	10·00

Other unoverprinted stamps of Great Britain are known with Morocco Agencies postmarks during this period, but it is believed that only Nos. Z170/224 were sold by the local post offices.

The use of unoverprinted stamps in Tangier ceased with the issue of Nos. 261/75 on 1 January 1949. Stamps overprinted "MOROCCO AGENCIES" replaced the unoverprinted values at Tetuan on 16 August 1949.

MOROCCO AGENCIES (9)   MOROCCO AGENCIES (10)

1949 (16 Aug). *King George VI, optd with T 9 or 10 (2s. 6d., 5s.).*

77	½d. pale green	..	..	1·75	40
78	1d. pale scarlet	..	..	2·75	9·00
79	1½d. pale red-brown	..	2·75	8·50
80	2d. pale orange	..	..	3·00	9·00
81	2½d. light ultramarine	..	3·25	10·00
82	3d. pale violet	..	..	1·50	1·60
83	4d. grey-green	..	..	45	90
84	5d. brown ..	..	..	3·00	15·00
85	6d. purple	..	..	1·50	1·00
86	7d. emerald-green	..	40	16·00
87	8d. bright carmine	..	3·00	6·50
88	9d. deep olive-green	..	40	11·00
89	10d. turquoise-blue	..	40	6·00
90	11d. plum	..	..	70	6·00
91	1s. bistre-brown	..	2·75	6·00
92	2s. 6d. yellow-green	..	12·00	29·00
93	5s. red	..	..	28·00	55·00
77/93		Set of 17	60·00	£170

1951 (3 May). *King George VI (Nos. 503/7, 509/10), optd with T 9 or 10 (2s. 6d., 5s.).*

94	½d. pale orange	..	..	1·75	50
95	1d. light ultramarine	..	1·75	65
96	1½d. pale green	..	1·75	1·75
97	2d. pale red-brown	..	1·75	3·25
98	2½d. pale scarlet	..	1·75	3·00
99	2s. 6d. yellow-green (H.M.S. Victory)	12·00	18·00
100	5s. red (Dover)	..	12·00	19·00
94/100		Set of 7	29·00	42·00

1952–55. *Queen Elizabeth II. W 153 (Tudor Crown). Optd with T 9.*

101	½d. orange-red (31.8.53)	..	10	10
102	1d. ultramarine (31.8.53)	..	15	1·00
103	1½d. green (5.12.52)	..	15	20
104	2d. red-brown (31.8.53)	..	20	1·25
105	2½d. carmine-red (5.12.52)	..	15	60
106	4d. ultramarine (1.3.55)	..	85	3·25
107	5d. brown (6.7.53)	..	65	60
108	6d. reddish purple (1.3.55)	..	85	3·25
109	8d. magenta (6.7.53)	..	70	1·00
110	1s. bistre-brown (6.7.53)	..	70	60
101/10		Set of 10	4·00	10·50

1956 (10 Sept). *Queen Elizabeth II. W 165 (St. Edward's Crown). Optd with T 9.*

111	2½d. carmine-red (No. 544)	..	55	2·50

Stamps overprinted "MOROCCO AGENCIES" were withdrawn from sale on 31 December 1956.

IV. SPANISH CURRENCY

Stamps surcharged in Spanish currency were sold at British P.Os. throughout Morocco until the establishment of the French Zone and the Tangier International Zone, when their use was confined to the Spanish Zone.

During this period further British postal agencies were opened at Alcazar (1907–1916), Fez–Mellah (Jewish quarter) (1909), Marrakesh (1909), Marrakesh–Mellah (Jewish quarter) (1909–17) and Mequinez (1907–1916).

MOROCCO AGENCIES   MOROCCO AGENCIES

5 CENTIMOS (11)   6 PESETAS (12)

1907 (1 Jan)–**12.** *King Edward VII surch as T 11 (5 c. to 1 p.) or 12 (3 p. to 12 p.).*

(a) De La Rue printings. Ordinary paper (Nos. 112/13, 116, 118, 122/3) or chalk-surfaced paper (others)

112	5 c. on 1d. pale yellowish green	..	3·50	20
	a. Yellowish green		3·50	20
113	10 c. on 1d. scarlet	..	6·50	10
	a. Bright scarlet		6·50	10
114	15 c. on 1½d. pale dull purple and green	2·75	40
	a. Slate-purple and bluish green	1·75	20
	b. "1" of "15" omitted		£3500	
115	20 c. on 2d. pale grey-green and carmine-red	1·00	60
	a. Pale grey-green and scarlet	1·60	30
116	25 c. on 2½d. ultramarine	..	1·75	20
	a. Pale ultramarine		1·25	20
117	40 c. on 4d. green & chocolate-brn (29.10.07)	1·00	2·00
	a. Deep green and chocolate-brown	1·50	1·75
118	40 c. on 4d. pale orange (12.5.10)	..	1·50	75
	a. Orange-red		90	60
119	50 c. on 5d. dull purple and ultramarine	3·00	2·00
	a. Slate-purple and ultramarine	1·25	1·25
120	1 p. on 10d. dull purple and carmine	18·00	9·00
	a. Slate-purple and carmine	18·00	8·00
	b. No cross on crown			
121	3 p. on 2s. 6d. pale dull purple	..	20·00	24·00
	a. Dull purple		20·00	24·00
122	6 p. on 5s. bright carmine	..	35·00	45·00
	a. Deep bright carmine		35·00	45·00
123	12 p. on 10s. ultramarine (30.4.07)	75·00	75·00
112/23		Set of 12	£150	£140
117, 123	Optd "Specimen"	Set of 2	£140	

(b) Harrison printing. Ordinary paper

124	25 c. on 2½d. bright blue (No. 283) (1912)	25·00	21·00
	a. Dull blue		23·00	21·00

(c) Somerset House printing. Ordinary paper

125	12 p. on 10s. blue (No. 319) (1912)	£160	£225

No. 114b occurred on stamps from the first vertical row of one sheet.

1912. *King George V (W 49 (Imperial Crown)) surch as T 11.*

126	5 c. on ½d. green (No. 339)	2·50	10
127	10 c. on 1d. scarlet (No. 342)	90	10
	a. No cross on crown	£110	55·00

MOROCCO AGENCIES

3 CENTIMOS
(13)

MOROCCO AGENCIES

10 CENTIMOS
(14)

MOROCCO AGENCIES

MOROCCO AGENCIES

15 CENTIMOS
(15)

6 PESETAS
(16)

1914–26. *King George V. (a) W 100 (Simple Cypher). Surch as T 11 (5 c.), 13 (3 c. and 40 c.)*, 15 (15 c.) and 14 (remainder).*

128	3 c. on ½d. green (1917)	50	3·25
129	5 c. on ½d. green	50	10
130	10 c. on 1d. scarlet	70	10
	y. Wmk inverted and reversed		
131	15 c. on 1½d. red-brown (1915)	70	10
	a. Surch double, one albino	80·00	
132	20 c. on 2d. orange (Die I)	60	25
	a. Surch double, one albino	80·00	
133	25 c. on 2½d. blue (shades)	1·50	25
	w. Wmk inverted		
134	40 c. on 4d. grey-green (1917)	1·75	4·00
	a. Surch double, one albino		
135	1 p. on 10d. turquoise-blue	1·75	4·25

*The surcharge on Nos. 134, 148 and 158 is as T 13 for the value and T 15 for "MOROCCO AGENCIES".

(b) W 110 (Single Cypher). Surch as T 16. (i) Waterlow printings

136	6 p. on 5s. rose-carmine	29·00	48·00
	a. Surch double, one albino	£130	
	b. Surch triple, two albino	£140	
137	6 p. on 5s. pale rose-carmine	£130	£180
	a. Surch double, one albino	£180	
138	12 p. on 10s. indigo-blue (R.)	£110	£160
	a. Surch double, one albino	£225	
	b. Surch triple, two albino		
	136, 138 Optd "Specimen" *Set of 2*	£180	

(ii) De La Rue printings

139	3 p. on 2s. 6d. grey-brown (1918)	35·00	95·00
	a. Surch double, one albino		
140	3 p. on 2s. 6d. yellow-brown	27·00	£120
	a. Surch double, one albino		
141	12 p. on 10s. blue (R.)	£110	£160
	a. Surch double, one albino	£275	

(iii) Bradbury Wilkinson printings

142	3 p. on 2s. 6d. chocolate-brown (1926)	23·00	75·00
	128/42 *Set of 11*	£150	£275

1925–31. *King George V (W 111 (Block Cypher), surch as T 11, 13, 14 or 15.*

143	5 c. on ½d. green (1931)	1·50	10·00
144	10 c. on 1d. scarlet (1929)	15·00	20·00
145	15 c. on 1½d. red-brown	7·50	20·00
146	20 c. on 2d. orange (1931)	3·00	7·50
	a. Surch double, one albino	85·00	
147	25 c. on 2½d. blue	1·25	1·50
	w. Wmk inverted	50·00	
148	40 c. on 4d. grey-green (1930)	1·25	1·50
	a. Surch double, one albino		
	143/8 *Set of 6*	27·00	55·00

MOROCCO AGENCIES

10 CENTIMOS
(17)

MOROCCO AGENCIES

10 CENTIMOS
(18)

1935 (8 May). *Silver Jubilee (Nos. 453/6). Surch as T 17.*

149	5 c. on ½d. green (B.)	1·00	65
150	10 c. on 1d. scarlet (B.)	2·75	2·25
	a. Pair, one with "CENTIMES"	£1200	£1300
151	15 c. on 1½d. red-brown (B.)	5·00	16·00
152	25 c. on 2½d. blue (R.)	4·00	2·25
	149/52 *Set of 4*	11·50	19·00

No. 150a occurred on R. 5/4 of a small second printing made in June 1935. The error can only be identified when se-tenant with a normal No. 150. Beware of forgeries.

1935–37. *King George V Harrison photo ptgs (Nos. 439/43, 445 and 448). W 111 (Block Cypher). Surch as T 11, 13, 14 or 15.*

153	5 c. on ½d. green (9.6.36)	75	14·00
154	10 c. on 1d. scarlet (11.36)	2·50	5·00
155	15 c. on 1½d. red-brown (4.35)	4·00	3·25
156	20 c. on 2d. orange (26.10.36)	40	25
157	25 c. on 2½d. ultramarine (8.9.36)	1·25	3·75
158	40 c. on 4d. deep grey-green (18.5.37)	45	3·00
159	1 p. on 10d. turquoise-blue (14.4.37)	4·00	30
	153/9 *Set of 7*	12·00	26·00

1936 (26 Oct)–37. *King Edward VIII surch as T 18 with "MOROCCO" 14¼ mm long.*

160	5 c. on ½d. green	10	10
161	10 c. on 1d. scarlet	50	1·50
	a. "MOROCCO" 15¼ mm long (5.1.37)	3·25	9·00
162	15 c. on 1½d. red-brown	10	10
163	25 c. on 2½d. bright blue	10	10
	160/3 *Set of 4*	65	1·60

The first three printings of the 10 c. on 1d. (from cyls 4, 5 and 6) showed all stamps with the short surcharge (No. 161).

On 5 January 1937 a further printing was placed on sale in London which had 49 stamps in the sheet (R. 1/2 to 11, R. 2/1, 5 and 6, 8 and 9, R. 3/5, R. 4/5, R. 5/4 and 5, 10, R. 6/6 and 7, R. 7/8, R. 8/8, R. 9/8, R. 11/7, 9, R. 13/2 to 5, 7 and 8, R. 14/1, 7, R.15/7, 11, R. 16/5, 10, R. 17/4, 10 and 11, R. 18/1, R. 19/2, R. 20/1 and 2, 3, 7, 9) with long surcharge (No. 161a). The next printing increased the number of long surcharges in the sheet to 50 (R. 10/2), but the final version. although retaining 50 long surcharges, showed them on R. 1/2 to 11, R. 17/5 to 8 and the entire rows 18, 19 and 20. The first two printings with long surcharges were from cylinder 6 and the last from cylinder 13.

MOROCCO

15 CENTIMOS
(19)

1937 (13 May). *Coronation (No. 461), surch as T 19.*

164	15 c. on 1½d. maroon (B.)	50	30

MOROCCO AGENCIES

MOROCCO AGENCIES

10 CENTIMOS
(20)

10 CENTIMOS
(21)

1937 (June)–52. *King George VI (Nos. 462/4, 466, 468, 471 and 474), surch as T 20.*

165	5 c. on ½d. green (B.)	55	15
166	10 c. on 1d. scarlet	50	10
167	15 c. on 1½d. red-brown (B.) (4.8.37)	55	25
168	25 c. on 2½d. ultramarine	60	50
169	40 c. on 4d. grey-green (9.40)	28·00	10·00
170	70 c. on 7d. emerald-green (9.40)	60	9·00
171	1 p. on 10d. turquoise-blue (16.6.52)	1·00	3·50
	165/71 *Set of 7*	29·00	21·00

1940 (6 May). *Centenary of First Adhesive Postage Stamps (Nos. 479/81 and 483), surch as T 21.*

172	5 c. on ½d. green (B.)	30	1·75
173	10 c. on 1d. scarlet	2·75	2·00
174	15 c. on 1½d. red-brown (B.)	40	2·00
175	25 c. on 2½d. ultramarine	40	60
	172/5 *Set of 4*	3·50	5·50

25 CENTIMOS
(22)

45 PESETAS MOROCCO AGENCIES
(23)

1948 (26 Apr). *Silver Wedding (Nos. 493/4), surch with T 22 or 23.*

176	25 c. on 2½d. ultramarine	40	15
177	45 p. on £1 blue	17·00	22·00

1948 (29 July). *Olympic Games (Nos. 495/8), variously surch as T 22.*

178	25 c. on 2½d. ultramarine	40	60
179	30 c. on 3d. violet	40	60
180	60 c. on 6d. bright purple	40	60
181	1 p. 20 c. on 1s. brown	55	60
	a. Surch double	£700	
	178/81 *Set of 4*	1·60	2·25

1951 (3 May)–52. *King George VI (Nos. 503/5 and 507/8), surch as T 20.*

182	5 c. on ½d. pale orange	2·00	2·25
183	10 c. on 1d. light ultramarine	3·25	4·00
184	15 c. on 1½d. pale green	1·75	12·00
185	25 c. on 2½d. pale scarlet	1·75	4·00
186	40 c. on 4d. light ultramarine (26.5.52)	60	9·00
	182/6 *Set of 5*	8·50	28·00

1954–55. *Queen Elizabeth II. W 153 (Tudor Crown). Surch as T 20.*

187	5 c. on ½d. orange-red (1.9.54)	20	2·50
188	10 c. on 1d. ultramarine (1.3.55)	50	75

1956. *Queen Elizabeth II. W 165 (St. Edward's Crown). Surch as T 20.*

189	5 c. on ½d. orange-red (June)	15	1·00
190	40 c. on 4d. ultramarine (15 Aug)	70	1·75

The British postal agency at Laraiche closed on 30 June 1938. Stamps surcharged in Spanish currency were withdrawn from sale when the Tetuan agency closed on 31 December 1956.

V. FRENCH CURRENCY

For use in the British postal agencies at Casablanca (closed 14.8.37), Fez (closed 8.1.38), Fez–Mellah (closed after 1930), Marrakesh (closed 14.8.37), Mazagan (closed 14.8.37), Mogador (closed 31.10.33), Rabat (closed 8.1.38) and Saffi (closed 14.8.37).

MOROCCO AGENCIES

MOROCCO AGENCIES

25 CENTIMES
(24)

1 FRANC
(25)

1917–24. *King George V (W 100 (Simple Cypher)), surch as T 24 or 25 (1 f.).*

191	3 c. on ½d. green (R.)	60	2·50
192	5 c. on ½d. green	30	10
193	10 c. on 1d. scarlet	3·00	15
194	15 c. on 1½d. red-brown	2·25	15
195	25 c. on 2½d. blue	1·75	15
196	40 c. on 4d. slate-green	2·25	15
197	50 c. on 5d. yellow-brown (1923)	70	2·75
198	75 c. on 9d. olive-green (1924)	60	75
199	1 f. on 10d. turquoise-blue	5·00	1·75
	a. Surch double, one albino	85·00	
	191/9 *Set of 9*	15·00	8·00

1924–32. *King George V (B. W. ptg). W 110 (Single Cypher), surch as T 25, but closer vertical spacing.*

200	3 f. on 2s. 6d. chocolate-brown	7·50	1·50
	b. Major re-entry (R. 1/2)	£350	£350
	b. Surch double, one albino		
	c. Reddish brown	13·00	10·00
201	6 f. on 5s. rose-red (1932)	38·00	42·00
	200/1 Optd "Specimen" *Set of 2*	£120	

1925–34. *King George V (W 111 (Block Cypher), surch as T 24 or 25 (1 f.).*

202	5 c. on ½d. green	30	6·50
203	10 c. on 1d. scarlet	30	85
204	15 c. on 1½d. red-brown	85	1·75
205	25 c. on 2½d. blue	40	40
206	40 c. on 4d. grey-green	50	80
207	50 c. on 5d. yellow-brown	50	10
	w. Wmk inverted	75·00	
208	75 c. on 9d. olive-green	1·75	15
	w. Wmk inverted		
209	90 c. on 9d. olive-green	11·00	4·50
210	1 f. on 10d. turquoise-blue	70	10
211	1 f. 50 on 1s. bistre-brown (Optd S. £50)	6·50	2·25
	202/11 *Set of 10*	20·00	15·00

1935 (8 May). *Silver Jubilee (Nos. 453/6), surch as T 17, but in French currency.*

212	5 c. on ½d. green (B.)	15	15
213	10 c. on 1d. scarlet (B.)	2·25	50
214	15 c. on 1½d. red-brown (B.)	30	50
215	25 c. on 2½d. blue (R.)	30	15
	212/15 *Set of 4*	2·75	1·10

1935–37. *King George V (Harrison photo ptgs. W 111 (Block Cypher)), surch as T 24 or 25 (1 f.).*

216	5 c. on ½d. green (10.35)	45	4·00
217	10 c. on 1d. scarlet (2.3.36)	35	30
218	15 c. on 1½d. red-brown	3·00	3·50
219	25 c. on 2½d. ultramarine (25.9.36)	30	15
220	40 c. on 4d. deep grey-green (2.12.36)	30	15
221	50 c. on 5d. yellow-brown (15.9.36)	30	15
222	90 c. on 9d. deep olive-green (15.2.37)	35	1·00
223	1 f. on 10d. turquoise-blue (10.2.37)	30	30
224	1 f. 50 on 1s. bistre-brown (20.7.37) (Optd S. £50)	40	2·25

1935–36. *King George V (Waterlow re-engraved ptgs. W 100 (Single Cypher), surch as T 25, but closer vertical spacing.*

225	3 f. on 2s. 6d. chocolate-brown (No. 450)	4·75	12·00
226	6 f. on 5s. bright rose-red (No. 451) (17.6.36)	6·00	21·00
	216/26 *Set of 11*	15·00	40·00
	225/6 Optd "Specimen" *Set of 2*	£120	

1936 (26 Oct). *King Edward VIII, surch as T 18, but in French currency.*

227	5 c. on ½d. green	10	15
	a. Bar through "POSTAGE"	£450	
228	15 c. on 1½d. red-brown	10	15

1937 (13 May). *Coronation (No. 461), surch as T 19, but in French currency.*

229	15 c. on 1½d. maroon (B.)	30	20

1937 (June). *King George VI, surch as T 20, but in French currency.*

230	5 c. on ½d. green (B.)	1·25	1·40

Stamps surcharged in French currency were withdrawn from sale on 8 January 1938.

VI. TANGIER INTERNATIONAL ZONE

By an agreement between Great Britain, France and Spain Tangier was declared an international zone in 1924. Stamps overprinted "Morocco Agencies" or surcharged in Spanish currency were used there until replaced by Nos. 231/4.

PRICES. Our note re U.K. usage (at beginning of Section III) also applies to "TANGIER" optd stamps.

TANGIER

(26)   **(27)**

1927. *King George V (W 111 (Block Cypher)), optd with T 26.*
231	½d. green	1·25	10
	a. Opt double, one albino		
232	1d. scarlet	1·50	10
	a. Inverted "Q" for "O" (R. 20/3)	£800	
233	1½d. chestnut	3·75	2·25
234	2d. orange	3·25	10
	a. Opt double, one albino	80·00	
231/4	Set of 4	8·75	2·25

1934 (Dec)–35. *King George V (Harrison photo ptgs. W 111 (Block Cypher)), optd with T 26.*
235	½d. green (2.35)	1·00	1·40
236	1d. scarlet	2·00	70
237	1½d. red-brown	15	10
235/7	Set of 3	2·75	2·00

1935 (8 May). *Silver Jubilee (Nos. 453/5), optd with T 27.*
238	½d. green (B.)	1·00	2·75
239	1d. scarlet	13·50	11·00
240	1½d. red-brown (B.)	1·25	40
238/40	Set of 3	14·00	13·00

1936 (26 Oct). *King Edward VIII, optd with T 26.*
241	½d. green	10	15
242	1d. scarlet	10	10
243	1½d. red-brown	15	10
241/3	Set of 3	30	30

(28)   **(29)**

1937 (13 May). *Coronation (No. 461), optd with T 28.*
244	1½d. maroon (B.)	40	30

1937. *King George VI (Nos. 462/4), optd with T 29.*
245	½d. green (B.) (June)	1·25	40
246	1d. scarlet (June)	3·75	30
247	1½d. red-brown (B.) (4 Aug)	1·00	10
245/7	Set of 3	5·50	70

(30)   **(31)**

1940 (6 May). *Centenary of First Adhesive Postage Stamps (Nos. 479/81), optd with T 30.*
248	½d. green (B.)	30	3·25
249	1d. scarlet	45	50
250	1½d. red-brown (B.)	2·00	2·75
248/50	Set of 3	2·50	6·00

1944. *King George VI pale colours (Nos. 485/6), optd with T 29.*
251	½d. pale green (B.)	7·00	2·50
252	1d. pale scarlet	7·00	2·25

1946 (11 June). *Victory (Nos. 491/2), optd as T 31.*
253	2½d. ultramarine	30	20
254	3d. violet	30	55

The opt on No. 254 is smaller (23×2½ mm).

1948 (26 Apr). *Royal Silver Wedding (Nos. 493/4), optd with T 30.*
255	2½d. ultramarine	30	15
	a. Opt omitted (in vert pair with stamp optd at top)	£3000	
256	£1 blue	25·00	25·00

No. 255a comes from a sheet on which the overprint is misplaced downwards resulting in the complete absence of the opt from the six stamps of the top row. On the rest of the sheet the opt falls at the top of each stamp instead of at the foot (*Price* £250, *unused*).

1948 (29 July). *Olympic Games (Nos. 495/8), optd with T 30.*
257	2½d. ultramarine	75	1·25
258	3d. violet	75	1·25
259	6d. bright purple	75	1·25
260	1s. brown	75	60
257/60	Set of 4	2·75	4·00

1949 (1 Jan). *King George VI, optd with T 29.*
261	2d. pale orange	4·00	4·00
262	2½d. light ultramarine	60	2·75
263	3d. pale violet	35	65
264	4d. grey-green	7·50	10·00
265	5d. brown	3·50	11·00
266	6d. purple	35	30
267	7d. emerald-green	90	10·00
268	8d. bright carmine	3·50	8·50
269	9d. deep olive-green	70	11·00
270	10d. turquoise-blue	70	11·00
271	11d. plum	70	8·50
272	1s. bistre-brown	70	1·75
273	2s. 6d. yellow-green	4·25	11·00
274	5s. red	13·00	38·00
275	10s. ultramarine	38·00	95·00
261/75	Set of 15	70·00	£200

1949 (10 Oct). *75th Anniv of U.P.U. (Nos. 499/502), optd with T 30.*
276	2½d. ultramarine	50	1·25
277	3d. violet	50	85
278	6d. bright purple	50	85
279	1s. brown	50	1·75
276/9	Set of 4	1·75	4·25

1950 (2 Oct)–51. *King George VI, optd with T 29 or 30 (shilling values).*
280	½d. pale orange (3.5.51)	60	1·00
281	1d. light ultramarine (3.5.51)	70	2·50
282	1½d. pale green (3.5.51)	70	14·00
283	2d. pale red-brown (3.5.51)	70	2·00
284	2½d. pale scarlet (3.5.51)	70	3·25
285	4d. light ultramarine	1·50	2·50
286	2s. 6d. yell-grn (H.M.S. Victory) (3.5.51)	4·00	4·50
287	5s. red (Dover) (3.5.51)	14·00	15·00
288	10s. ultramarine (St. George) (3.5.51)	19·00	15·00
280/8	Set of 9	42·00	55·00

1952–54. *Queen Elizabeth II (W 153 (Tudor Crown)), optd with T 29.*
289	½d. orange-red (31.8.53)	10	40
290	1d. ultramarine (31.8.53)	15	40
291	1½d. green (5.12.52)	10	30
292	2d. red-brown (31.8.53)	20	30
293	2½d. carmine-red (5.12.52)	10	40
294	3d. deep lilac (B.) (18.1.54)	20	40
295	4d. ultramarine (2.11.53)	45	3·25
296	5d. brown (6.7.53)	60	90
297	6d. reddish purple (18.1.54)	45	15
298	7d. bright green (18.1.54)	80	2·00
299	8d. magenta (6.7.53)	60	1·50
300	9d. bronze-green (8.2.54)	1·40	75
301	10d. Prussian blue (8.2.54)	1·40	2·75
302	11d. brown-purple (8.2.54)	1·40	3·25
303	1s. bistre-brown (6.7.53)	50	30
304	1s. 3d. green (2.11.53)	65	2·50
305	1s. 6d. grey-blue (2.11.53)	1·00	1·75
289/305	Set of 17	9·00	19·00

1953 (3 June). *Coronation (Nos. 532/5), optd with T 30.*
306	2½d. carmine-red	50	30
307	4d. ultramarine	1·00	30
308	1s. 3d. deep yellow-green	1·25	1·25
309	1s. 6d. deep grey-blue	1·25	85
306/9	Set of 4	3·50	2·50

1955 (23 Sept). *Queen Elizabeth II, Castle high values (W 165 (St. Edward's Crown)), optd with T 30.*
310	2s. 6d. black-brown	3·50	7·00
311	5s. rose-red	5·50	14·00
312	10s. ultramarine	19·00	21·00
310/12	Set of 3	25·00	38·00

1956. *Queen Elizabeth II (W 165 St. Edward's Crown)), optd with T 29.*
313	½d. orange-red (21 March)	10	20
314	1d. ultramarine (13 April)	20	30
315	1½d. green (22 Oct)	40	90
316	2d. red-brown (25 July)	1·25	1·75
317	2d. light red-brown (10 Dec)	70	30
318	2½d. carmine-red (19 Dec)	40	30
319	3d. deep lilac (B.) (22 Oct)	40	1·75
320	4d. ultramarine (25 June)	65	2·00
321	6d. reddish purple (22 Oct)	50	1·75
322	1s. 3d. green (26 Nov)	1·75	12·00
313/22	Set of 10	5·50	19·00

1857-1957

TANGIER

1857-1957 TANGIER

(32)   **(33)**

1957 (1 Apr). *Centenary of British Post Office in Tangier.*

(a) Nos. 540/2 and 543b/56 (W 165 (St. Edward's Crown)), optd as T 32 or 33 (7d).
323	½d. orange-red	10	10
324	1d. ultramarine	10	10
325	1½d. green	10	10
326	2d. light red-brown	10	10
327	2½d. carmine-red	15	60
328	3d. deep lilac (B.)	15	10
329	4d. ultramarine	30	20
330	5d. brown	30	35
331	6d. reddish purple	30	15
332	7d. bright green	30	30
333	8d. magenta	30	70
334	9d. bronze-green	30	30
	a. "TANGIER" omitted	£4000	
335	10d. Prussian blue	30	30
336	11d. brown-purple	30	30
337	1s. bistre-brown	30	30
338	1s. 3d. green	45	2·50
339	1s. 6d. grey-blue	50	1·00

(b) Nos. 536/8 (W 165 (St. Edward's Crown)), optd as T 32.
340	2s. 6d. black-brown	2·00	3·00
	a. Hyphen omitted	65·00	
	b. Hyphen inserted	20·00	
341	5s. rose-red	2·75	4·25
	a. Hyphen omitted	65·00	
	b. Hyphen inserted	10·00	
342	10s. ultramarine	5·50	6·00
	a. Hyphen omitted	80·00	
	b. Hyphen inserted	15·00	
323/42	Set of 20	13·00	18·00

Nos. 340a/b, 341a/b and 342a/b occur on R.9/2 in the sheet of 40 (4×10). They are best collected in marginal blocks of four from the bottom left corner of the sheet. Specialists recognise two forms of No. 340b; one where the hyphen on R.9/2 was inserted separately to correct the error, No. 340a; the other from a later printing where a new and corrected overprinting plate was used. (*Price* £12 *un.*).

All stamps overprinted "TANGIER" were withdrawn from sale on 30 April 1957.

Mosul
see Iraq

Mozambique

The Republic of Mozambique joined the Commonwealth on 12 November 1995.

(Currency. 100 centavos = 1 metical)

PRINTERS. All stamps are printed in lithography by the State Printing Works, Maputo, *unless otherwise stated.*

267 Child wearing Blue Cloak   268 Player scoring Goal

(Des F. Jofane)

1995 (22 Nov). *20th Anniv of U.N.I.C.E.F. in Mozambique.* P 11½×11.
1417	267	5000 m. multicoloured	60	65

(Des F. Jofane)

1996 (5 Apr). *Football. T 268 and similar horiz designs. Multicoloured.* P 11×11½.
1418		1000 m. Type 268	10	15
1419		2000 m. Goalkeeper holding ball	20	25
1420		4000 m. Referee admonishing players	40	45
1421		6000 m. Two players tackling for ball	60	65
1418/21		Set of 4	1·25	1·50

269 Mask   270 "Mae Africa" (De Malangatana)

1996 (2 July). *Local Masks. T 269 and similar vert designs showing different local masks.* P 11½×11.
1422	1000 m. Type 269	10	15
1423	2000 m. multicoloured	20	25
1424	4000 m. multicoloured	40	45
1425	6000 m. multicoloured	60	65
1422/5	Set of 4	1·25	1·50

1996 (10 July). *15th Anniv of Mozambique Red Cross.* P 11½×11.
1426	270	5000 m. multicoloured	50	55

271 African Elephant   272 Mine Field

1996 (3 Sept). *Wild Animals. T 271 and similar vert designs. Multicoloured.* P 11½×11.
1427	1000 m. Type 271	35	20
1428	2000 m. White Rhinoceros	50	35
1429	4000 m. Leopard	70	65
1430	6000 m. Pel's Fishing Owl	1·00	1·00
1427/30	Set of 4	2·25	2·00

1996 (9 Nov). *Land Mine Clearance Campaign. T 272 and similar vert designs. Multicoloured. P 11½×11.*
1431	2000 m. Type **272**	..	20	25
1432	6000 m. Warning sign		60	65
1433	8000 m. Soldier with mine detector		80	85
1434	10000 m. Soldier lifting mine		1·00	1·10
1431/4	.. ..	Set of 4	2·50	2·75

273 City Street

274 5 r. Stamp of 1876 and Magnifying Glass

1996 (16 Dec). *"Keeping the City Clean". P 11½×11.*
1435	**273** 2000 m. multicoloured	..	20	25

(Des F. Jofane)

1996 (16 Dec). *120th Anniv of Mozambique Stamps. P 11½×11.*
1436	**274** 2000 m. multicoloured	..	20	25

275 Mitumbui   276 Village Scene

1997 (10 Apr). *Local Boats. T 275 and similar horiz designs. Multicoloured. P 11×11½.*
1437	2000 m. Type **275**	..	20	25
1438	6000 m. Muterere	..	60	65
1439	8000 m. Lancha ..	..	80	85
1440	10000 m. Dhow	..	1·00	1·10
1437/40	.. .. ..	Set of 4	2·50	2·75

1997 (1 June). *International Children's Day. P 11×11½.*
1441	**276** 2000 m. multicoloured	..	20	25

277 Enaretta conifera   278 Yellow-billed Stork

1997 (5 July). *Beetles. T 277 and similar horiz designs. Multicoloured. P 11×11½.*
1442	2000 m. Type **277**	..	20	25
1443	6000 m. Zographus hieroglyphicus	..	60	65
1444	8000 m. Tragiscoschema bertolonii	..	80	85
1445	10000 m. Tragocephala ducalis	..	1·00	1·10
1442/5	.. ..	Set of 4	2·50	2·75
MS1446	97×105 mm. Nos. 1442/5		2·50	2·75

No. **MS1446** also commemorates the "LUBRAPEX 97" International Stamp Exhibition, Brazil.

1997 (16 July). *Aquatic Birds. T 278 and similar multicoloured designs. P 11½×11 (vert) or 11×11½ (horiz).*
1447	2000 m. Type **278**	..	35	25
1448	4000 m. Black-winged Stilt		55	45
1449	8000 m. Long-toed Stint (horiz)		95	85
1450	10000 m. Eastern White Pelican	..	1·10	1·10
1447/50	.. .. ..	Set of 4	2·75	2·75

279 Abstract Patterns   280 Sun and Globe

(Des P. Barbosa)

1997 (5 Sept). *Centenary of João Ferreira dos Santos Group. P 11×11½.*
1451	**279** 2000 m. multicoloured	..	20	25

1997 (18 Sept). *Protection of Ozone Layer. P 11½×11.*
1452	**280** 2000 m. multicoloured	..	20	25

282 Coelacanth   283 Woman with Food Products

(Des P. Antonio)

1998 (22 May). *"EXPO '98" International Stamp Exhibition, Lisbon. P 11×11½.*
1454	**282** 2000 m. multicoloured	..	20	25

1998 (1 June). *Food Production. P 11×11½.*
1455	**283** 2000 m. multicoloured	..	20	25

Muscat

An independent Arab Sultanate in Eastern Arabia with an Indian postal administration.

The Indian post office at Muscat town is officially recorded as having opened on 1 May 1864. Stamps of India were provided for its use, most surviving examples being of the ½ a. value, although others to the 8 a. are known.

The office was initially included in the Bombay Postal Circle and the first postmark, so far only recorded on stampless covers, was a single circle, 21½ mm in diameter, broken at the top by "MUSCAT" and with the date in two lines across the centre. This was followed by a cancellation showing the post office number, "309", within a diamond of 13, later 16, bars. It is believed that this was used in conjunction with a single ring date stamp inscribed "MUSCAT".

1864 Diamond

In 1869 the office was transferred to the Sind Circle, assigned a new number, "23", and issued with a duplex cancellation. Major reorganisation of the postal service in 1873 resulted in Muscat becoming office "K-4". For ten years from 1873 the cancellations do not, very confusingly, carry any indication of the year of use.

1869 Duplex

1873 Duplex

Muscat rejoined the Bombay Circle in 1879 and was issued with a cancellation showing a "B" within a square of horizontal bars. The date stamp used at this time was unique in that it carried the inscription "MASKAT", although the spelling reverted to the more usual form by 1882. The square cancellation had been replaced by a similar circular mark by 1884.

Subsequent postmarks were of various circular types, all inscribed "MUSCAT".

There was only one Indian post office in Muscat, but a further office did exist, from 12 April 1868, at the Muscat dependency of Guadur, a port on the Mekran coast of Baluchistan.

No cancellations have been reported from Guadur before its transfer to the Sind Circle in 1869. Cancellations are all similar in style to those for Muscat, Guadur being initially assigned number "24", although an office in Southern India is also known to have used this numeral. The 1869 duplex is interesting in that it is inscribed "GWADUR". Under the 1873 reorganisation the office became "4/K-1", this postmark using the "GUADUR" spelling.

1869 Duplex

PRICES FOR STAMPS ON COVER
Nos. 1/15   *from* ×50
Nos. O1/10   *from* ×75

(Currency 12 pies = 1 anna; 16 annas = 1 Indian rupee)

(1)   (2)

1944 (20 Nov). *Bicentenary of Al-Busaid Dynasty. Nos. 259/60, 265/8 and 269a/77 (King George VI) of India optd ("AL BUSAID 1363" in Arabic script) as T 1 or 2 (rupee values).*

1	3 p. slate		30	5·00
	w. Wmk inverted		15·00	
2	½ a. purple		30	5·00
3	9 p. green		30	5·00
4	1 a. carmine		30	5·00
5	1½ a. dull violet		30	5·00
6	2 a. vermilion		30	5·00
7	3 a. bright violet		50	5·00
	w. Wmk inverted		20·00	
8	3½ a. bright blue		50	5·00
9	4 a. brown		50	5·00
10	6 a. turquoise-green		65	5·00
11	8 a. slate-violet		65	5·00
12	12 a. lake		80	5·00
13	14 a. purple		2·00	7·00
14	1 r. grey and red-brown		50	9·00
15	2 r. purple and brown		1·50	15·00
1/15		*Set of 15*	8·50	80·00

OFFICIAL STAMPS

1944 (20 Nov). *Bicentenary of Al-Busaid Dynasty. Nos. O138, O143, O144a/6 and 146b/50 of India optd as T 1 or 2 (1 r.).*

O 1	3 p. slate		50	9·50
O 2	½ a. purple		50	9·50
O 3	9 p. green		50	9·50
O 4	1 a. carmine		50	9·50
O 5	1½ a. dull violet		50	9·50
O 6	2 a. vermilion		50	9·50
O 7	2½ a. bright violet		1·50	9·50
O 8	4 a. brown		1·00	9·50
O 9	8 a. slate-violet		2·00	11·00
O10	1 r. grey and red-brown		2·25	19·00
O1/10		*Set of 10*	8·75	95·00

From December 1947 there was a Pakistani postal administration and stamps of Pakistan were used until 31 March 1948. The subsequent British administration operated from 1 April 1948 to 29 April 1966 when the stamps of the BRITISH POSTAL AGENCIES IN EASTERN ARABIA were used.

Later issues for this area will be found listed under OMAN in Part 19 (*Middle East*) of this catalogue.

Nagaland

Labels inscribed "NAGALAND" with currency in cents and chaplees are considered to be propaganda labels.

Namibia

(*formerly* South West Africa)

SOUTH WEST AFRICA

The stamps of Germany were used in the colony from July 1886 until the introduction of issues for GERMAN SOUTH-WEST AFRICA in May 1897. Following occupation by South African forces in 1914–15 the issues of SOUTH AFRICA were used, being replaced by the overprinted issues in 1923.

Walvis (or Walfish) Bay, the major anchorage on the South West Africa coast, was claimed by Great Britain as early as 1796. In 1878 the 430 sq mile area around the port, together with a number of offshore islands, was annexed to Cape Province, passing to the Union of South Africa in 1910.

Stamps of the Cape of Good Hope and South Africa were used at Walfish Bay, often cancelled with numeral obliterator 300, until the enclave was transferred to the South West Africa administration on 1 October 1922.

The Walfish Bay territory reverted to South Africa on 30 August 1977 and from that date the stamps of South Africa were, once again, in use.

PRICES FOR STAMPS ON COVER TO 1945
Nos. 1/40a	*from* × 6
Nos. 41/133	*from* × 2
Nos. D1/5	*from* × 10
Nos. D6/51	*from* × 20
Nos. O1/4	*from* × 3
Nos. O5/20	*from* × 15
No. O21	*from* × 2
No. O22	*from* × 15

INSCRIPTIONS. Most of the postage stamps up to No. 140 are inscribed alternately in English and Afrikaans throughout the sheets and the same applies to all the Official stamps and to Nos. D30/33.

PRICES for Nos. 1/140 are for unused horizontal pairs, used horizontal pairs or used singles (either inscr), *unless otherwise indicated.*

OVERPRINT SETTINGS. Between 1923 and 1928 the King George V definitives of South Africa, Types 2 and 3, and the various postage due stamps were issued overprinted for use in South West Africa. A number of overprint settings were used:

Setting I – Overprint Types 1 and 2 ("Zuid-West Afrika"). 14 mm between lines of overprint. See Nos. 1/12 and D1/9
Setting II – As Setting I, but 10 mm between lines of overprint. See Nos. 13/15 and D10/13
Setting III – Overprint Types 3 ("Zuidwest Afrika") and 4. "South West" 14 mm long. "Zuidwest" 11 mm long. 14 mm between lines of overprint. See Nos. 16/27 and D14/17
Setting IV – As Setting III, but "South West" 16 mm long, "Zuidwest" 12 mm long and 14 mm between lines of overprint. See Nos. 28 and D17a/20
Setting V – As Setting IV, but 12 mm between lines of overprint. See Nos. D21/4
Setting VI – As Setting IV, but 9½ mm between lines of overprint. See Nos. 29/40 and D25/32.

South West	Zuid-West
Africa.	Afrika.
(1)	(2)

1923 (1 Jan–17 June). *Nos. 3/4, 6 and 9/17 of South Africa optd alternately with T 1 and 2 by typography.*

			Un pair	Us pair	Us single
	(a) Setting I (14 *mm between lines of overprint*)				
1	½d. green		2·25	8·00	1·00
	a. "Wes" for "West" (R. 20/8)		80·00	£120	
	b. "Afr ica" (R. 20/2)		£120		
	c. Litho opt in shiny ink (17 June)		8·50	45·00	4·75
2	1d. rose-red		3·00	8·00	1·00
	a. Opt inverted		£450		
	b. "Wes" for "West" (R. 12/2)		£170		
	c. "Af.rica" for "Africa" (R. 20/6)		£140	£170	
	d. Opt double		£750		
	e. "Afr ica" (R. 20/2)		£120		
	f. "Afrika" without stop (R. 17/8)		£225		
3	2d. dull purple		4·00	10·00	1·50
	a. Opt inverted		£500	£550	
	b. "Wes" for "West" (R. 20/8)		£225		
	c. Litho opt in shiny ink (30 Mar)		35·00	90·00	10·00
4	3d. ultramarine		7·50	16·00	2·75
5	4d. orange-yellow and sage-green		13·00	45·00	4·00
	a. Litho opt in shiny ink (19 Apr)		35·00	70·00	8·00
6	6d. black and violet		8·00	38·00	4·00
	a. Litho opt in shiny ink (19 Apr)		35·00	70·00	7·50
7	1s. orange-yellow		23·00	48·00	5·00
	a. Litho opt in shiny ink (19 Apr)		60·00	£100	11·00
	b. "Afrika" without stop (R. 17/8)				
8	1s. 3d. pale violet		30·00	55·00	5·50
	a. Opt inverted		£300		
	b. Litho opt in shiny ink (19 Apr)		75·00	£130	14·00
9	2s. 6d. purple and green		70·00	£130	18·00
	a. Litho opt in shiny ink (19 Apr)		£150	£275	35·00
10	5s. purple and blue		£160	£325	50·00
11	10s. blue and olive-green		£1600	£2500	£400
12	£1 green and red		£900	£1600	£250
1/12		*Set of 12*	£2500	£4250	£650
1/12	Optd "Specimen" . *Set of 12 singles* £1500				

Nos. 1/12 were overprinted in complete sheets of 240 (4 panes 6×10).

No. 3b shows traces of a type spacer to the right of where the "t" should have been. This spacer is not visible on Nos. 1a and 2b.

Minor varieties, such as broken "t" in "West", were caused by worn type. Stamps showing one line of overprint only or with the lower line above the upper line due to overprint misplacement may also be found. All values exist showing a faint stop after "Afrika" on R. 17/8, but only examples of the 1d. and 1s. have been seen with it completely omitted.

	(b) Setting II (10 *mm between lines of opt*) (31 Mar)				
13	5s. purple and blue		£140	£250	45·00
	a. "Afrika" without stop (R.6/1)		£1200	£1300	
14	10s. blue and olive-green		£500	£850	£140
	a. "Afrika" without stop (R.6/1)		£2250	£2750	
15	£1 green and red		£1000	£1400	£200
	a. "Afrika" without stop (R.6/1)		£5000	£5000	£900
13/15		*Set of 3*	£1500	£2250	£350

Nos. 13/15 were overprinted in separate panes of 60 (6×10).

Zuidwest	South West
Afrika.	Africa.
(3)	(4)

1923 (15 July)–**26**. *Nos. 3/4, 6 and 9/17 of South Africa optd as T 3 ("Zuidwest" in one word, without hyphen) and 4 alternately.*

	(a) Setting III ("South West" 14 *mm long, "Zuidwest" 11 mm long, 14 mm between lines of opt*)				
16	½d. green (5.9.24)		5·50	35·00	3·75
	a. "outh" for "South" (R. 1/1)		£1400		
17	1d. rose-red (28.9.23)		5·50	8·50	1·40
	a. "outh" for "South" (R. 1/1)		£1400		
18	2d. dull purple (28.9.23)		5·50	8·50	1·25
	a. Opt double		£850		
19	3d. ultramarine		5·00	8·50	1·25
20	4d. orange-yellow and sage-green		6·00	19·00	2·75
	w. Wmk inverted		†	†	
21	6d. black and violet (28.9.23)		14·00	42·00	5·00
22	1s. orange-yellow		14·00	42·00	5·00
23	1s. 3d. pale violet		29·00	45·00	5·00
24	2s. 6d. purple and green		45·00	80·00	10·00
25	5s. purple and blue		70·00	£130	18·00

26	10s. blue and olive-green	..	£200	£300	50·00
27	£1 green and red (28.9.23)	..	£350	£475	70·00
16/27		*Set of 12*	£650	£1000	£150

Nos. 16/27 were overprinted in complete sheets of 240 (4 panes 6×10).

Two sets may be made with this overprint, one with bold lettering, and the other from September 1924, with thinner lettering and smaller stops.

(b) *Setting IV* ("South West" 16 mm long, "Zuidwest" 12 mm long, 14 mm between lines of opt)

28	2s. 6d purple and green (29.6.24)		80·00	£150	28·00

No. 28 was overprinted on two panes of 60 horizontally side by side.

(c) *Setting VI* ("South West" 16 mm long, "Zuidwest" 12 mm long, 9½ mm between lines of opt)

29	½d. green (16.12.25)	..	7·00	40·00	5·00
30	1d. rose-red (9.12.24)	..	3·25	9·50	1·40
	a. Opt omitted (in pair with normal)		£1200		
31	2d. dull purple (9.12.24)	..	5·00	20·00	1·75
32	3d. ultramarine (31.1.26)	..	4·50	28·00	2·75
	a. Deep bright blue (20.4.26)		55·00	95·00	12·00
33	4d. orge-yellow & sage-grn (9.12.24)	6·50	40·00	4·00
34	6d. black and violet (9.12.24)		8·50	48·00	5·00
35	1s. orange-yellow (9.12.24)		11·00	48·00	5·00
36	1s. 3d. pale violet (9.12.24)		15·00	48·00	5·00
37	2s. 6d. purple and green (9.12.24)	..	35·00	70·00	10·00
38	5s. purple and blue (31.1.26)	..	55·00	£100	14·00
39	10s. blue and olive-green (9.12.24)	..	85·00	£130	20·00
40	£1 green and red (9.1.26)	..	£300	£450	70·00
	a. Pale olive-green and red (8.11.26)	£250	£450	90·00
29/40a		*Set of 12*	£425	£850	£140
35, 39/40 H/S "Specimen" ..		*Set of 3*	£500		

Nos. 29/40 were overprinted in complete sheets of 240 (4 panes of 6×10) with, initially, "South West Africa" 16½ mm long on the upper two panes and 16 mm long on the lower two. This order was subsequently reversed. For printings from 8 November 1926 all four panes showed the 16½ mm measurement. No. 40a only comes from this printing.

Suidwes Afrika.	South West Africa.
(5)	**(6)**

1926 (1 Jan–1 May). *Nos. 30/2 of South Africa optd with T 5 (on stamps inscr in Afrikaans) and 6 (on stamps inscr in English) sideways, alternately in black.*

41	½d. black and green	..	3·75	8·50	1·00
42	1d. black and carmine	..	3·00	7·50	80
43	6d. green and orange (1 May)	..	30·00	48·00	7·00
41/3		*Set of 3*	32·00	55·00	8·00

SOUTH WEST AFRICA	SUIDWES-AFRIKA
(7)	**(8)**

1926. *No. 33 of South Africa, imperf, optd.* (a) *With T 7 (English)*

Single stamps

44A	4d. grey-blue			65	3·00

(b) *With T 8 (Afrikaans)*

44B	4d. grey-blue			65	3·00

1927. *As Nos. 41/3, but Afrikaans opt on stamp inscr in English and vice versa.*

45	½d. black and green		1·60	5·50	80
	a. "Africa" without stop (R.13/8) ..	£150		
46	1d. black and carmine		1·60	2·50	50
	a. "Africa" without stop (R.13/8)	£225		
47	6d. green and orange		14·00	25·00	3·00
	a. "Africa" without stop (R.13/8) ..	£170		
45/7		*Set of 3*	15·00	30·00	3·75

SOUTH WEST AFRICA	S.W.A.	S.W.A.
(9)	**(10)**	**(11)**

1927. *As No. 44A, but overprint T 9.*

Single stamps

48	4d. grey-blue (H/S. S. £70)		7·50	19·00

1927 (Apr). *Nos. 34/9 of South Africa optd alternately as T 5 and 6, in blue, but with lines of overprint spaced 16 mm.*

49	2d. grey and purple	..	4·75	15·00	1·75
50	3d. black and red	..	4·75	25·00	2·50
51	1s. brown and blue	..	15·00	32·00	4·00
52	2s. 6d. green and brown	..	45·00	85·00	13·00
53	5s. black and green	..	75·00	£150	20·00
54	10s. blue and bistre-brown	..	85·00	£130	20·00
49/54		*Set of 6*	£200	£400	50·00
49/51, 54 H/S "Specimen" ..		*Set of 4*	£350		

A variety of Nos. 49, 50, 51 and 54, with spacing 16½ mm between lines of overprint, occurs in the third vertical row of each sheet.

1927. *As No. 44, but perf 11½ by John Meinert Ltd, Windhoek.*

(a) *Optd with T 7 (English)*

Single stamps

55A	4d. grey-blue	..	80	4·00
	a. Imperf between (pair)	..	32·00	70·00
55A H/S "Specimen" ..			70·00	

(b) *Optd with T 8 (Afrikaans)*

55B	4d. grey-blue	..	80	4·00
	a. Imperf between (pair)	..	32·00	70·00
55B H/S "Specimen" ..	..	70·00	

1927 (Aug)–30. *Optd with T 10.* (a) *On Nos. 13 and 17a of South Africa.*

Single stamps

56	1s. 3d. pale violet (H/S S. £70)		1·25	6·00
	a. Without stop after "A" (R.3/4)	..	90·00	
57	£1 pale olive-green and red		£120	£180
	a. Without stop after "A" (R.3/4)	£1800	£2500

(b) *On Nos. 30/2 and 34/9 of South Africa*

		Un pair	Us pair	Us single
58	½d. black and green	2·00	6·50	80
	a. Without stop after "A" ..	50·00	75·00	
	b. "S.W.A." opt above value	2·75	14·00	2·25
	c. As b, in vert pair, top stamp without opt	£475		
59	1d. black and carmine	1·25	3·25	55
	a. Without stop after "A" ..	50·00	75·00	
	b. "S.W.A." opt at top (30.4.30)	1·75	13·00	1·60
	c. As b, in vert pair, top stamp without opt	£375		
60	2d. grey and maroon	8·00	21·00	1·50
	c. Perf 14×13½ ..	15·00	28·00	
	ca. Without stop after "A" ..	75·00	£110	
	cb. Opt double, one inverted	£650	£850	
61	3d. black and red	6·00	23·00	3·25
	a. Without stop after "A" ..	75·00	£120	
	b. Perf 14×13½ ..	11·00	35·00	
	ba. Without stop after "A" ..	75·00	£120	
	bb. Without stop after "W"			
62	4d. brown (4.28)	18·00	48·00	7·00
	a. Without stop after "A" ..	85·00	£130	
	b. Perf 14×13½ ..	24·00	48·00	
63	6d. green and orange	13·00	22·00	2·75
	a. Without stop after "A" ..	£110		
64	1s. brown and deep blue ..	24·00	48·00	5·00
	b. Perf 14×13½ ..	50·00	75·00	
	ba. Without stop after "A" ..	£1700		
65	2s. 6d. green and brown ..	45·00	85·00	12·00
	a. Without stop after "A" ..	£160	£250	
	b. Perf 14×13½ ..	65·00	£100	
	ba. Without stop after "A" ..	£180	£275	
66	5s. black and green ..	65·00	£120	18·00
	a. Without stop after "A" ..	£225	£350	
	b. Perf 14×13½ ..	85·00	£140	
	ba. Without stop after "A" ..	£225	£350	
67	10s. bright blue and brown ..	£120	£190	28·00
	a. Without stop after "A" ..	£325	£500	
58/67		*Set of 10*	£250	£500	70·00
58/61, 63/7 H/S "Specimen" ..		*Set of 9*	£550		

On the ½d., 1d. and 6d. the missing stop variety occurs three times on each sheet, R.1/7, 13/4 and one position not yet identified. For the other values it comes on R.2/3 of the right pane, and, for the 2s. 6d., 5s. and 10s., on R.8/1 of the left pane. The missing stop after "W" on the 3d. occurs on R. 10/5 of the right pane.

The overprint is normally found at the base of the ½d., 1d., 6d., 1s. 3d. and £1 values and at the top on the remainder.

1930–31. *Nos. 42 and 43 of South Africa (rotogravure printing) optd with T 10.*

68	½d. black and green (1931)	..	8·00	26·00	2·75
69	1d. black and carmine	..	6·00	25·00	2·75

1930 (27 Nov–Dec). *Air. Nos. 40/1 of South Africa optd.*

(a) *As T 10.*

		Un single	Us single
70	4d. green (*first printing*)	14·00	28·00
	a. No stop after "A" of "S.W.A." ..	80·00	£110
	b. Later printings ..	7·00	28·00
71	1s. orange (*first printing*)	70·00	£120
	a. No stop after "A" of "S.W.A." ..	£400	£500
	b. Later printings ..	15·00	50·00

First printing: Thick letters, blurred impression. Stops with rounded corners.

Later printings: Thinner letters, clear impression. Clean cut, square stops.

(b) *As T 11* (12.30)

72	4d. green	.. ..	1·25	6·00
	a. Opt double	.. ..	£150	
	b. Opt inverted	.. ..	£140	
73	1s. orange	.. ..	3·75	15·00
	a. Opt double	.. ..	£500	

12 Kori Bustard

13 Cape Cross

14 Bogenfels

15 Windhoek

16 Waterberg

17 Luderitz Bay

---

18 Bush Scene

19 Elands

20 Mountain Zebra and Blue Wildebeests

21 Herero Huts

22 Welwitschia Plant

23 Okuwahaken Falls

24 Monoplane over Windhoek

25 Biplane over Windhoek

(*Recess B.W.*)

1931 (5 Mar). *T 12 to 25 (inscr alternately in English and Afrikaans). W 9 of South Africa. P 14 × 13½.* (a) *Postage.*

74	½d. black and emerald	..	2·25	2·25	10
75	1d. indigo and scarlet	..	2·25	2·25	10
76	2d. blue and brown	..	70	3·50	15
	w. Wmk inverted ..		£350		
77	3d. grey-blue and blue	..	70	4·00	15
78	4d. green and purple	..	1·75	7·00	20
79	6d. blue and brown	..	1·50	8·00	20
80	1s. chocolate and blue	..	1·50	8·00	25
81	1s. 3d. violet and yellow	..	9·50	11·00	50
82	2s. 6d. carmine and grey	..	24·00	24·00	1·75
83	5s. sage-green and red-brown	..	20·00	40·00	2·75
84	10s. red-brown and emerald	..	55·00	60·00	7·00
85	20s. lake and blue-green	..	£110	£110	12·00

(b) *Air*

86	3d. brown and blue	..	32·00	40·00	3·50
87	10d. black and purple-brown	..	45·00	85·00	9·00
74/87		*Set of 14*	£275	£350	32·00

26

(*Recess B.W.*)

1935 (1 May). *Silver Jubilee. Inscr bilingually. W 9 of South Africa. P 14 × 13½.*

			Un single	Us single
88	26	1d. black and scarlet	1·00	25
89		2d. black and sepia	1·00	25
90		3d. black and blue	13·00	18·00
91		6d. black and purple	6·00	10·00
88/91		*Set of 4*	19·00	26·00

1935–36. *Voortrekker Memorial Fund. Nos. 50/3 of South Africa optd with T 10.*

92	½d. + ½d. black and green	..	1·00	5·50	75
	a. Opt inverted	..	£300		
93	1d. + ½d. grey-black and pink	..	1·50	3·25	40
94	2d. + 1d. grey-green and purple	..	5·50	6·00	80
	a. Without stop after "A"	..	£200		
	b. Opt double	..	£190		
95	3d. + 1½d. grey-green and blue	..	16·00	32·00	4·00
	a. Without stop after "A"	..	£250	£300	
92/5		*Set of 4*	22·00	42·00	5·50

27 Mail Train

28

(*Recess B.W.*)

1937 (1 Mar). *W 9 of South Africa. P 14 × 13½.*

96	27	1½d. purple-brown	..	19·00	3·00	25

(Recess B.W.)

1937 (12 May). *Coronation. W 9 of South Africa (sideways).*
P 13½ × 14.

97	**28**	½d. black and emerald			50	15	10
98		1d. black and scarlet			50	15	10
99		1½d. black and orange			50	15	10
100		2d. black and brown			50	15	10
101		3d. black and blue			50	15	10
102		4d. black and purple			50	20	10
103		6d. black and yellow			60	2·00	20
104		1s. black and grey-black			80	2·50	25
97/104				Set of 8	4·00	5·00	65

1938 (14 Dec). *Voortrekker Centenary Memorial. Nos. 76/9 of South Africa optd as T 11.*

105	½d. + ½d. blue and green			8·00	15·00	1·75
106	1d. + 1d. blue and carmine			18·00	8·00	1·00
107	1½d. + 1½d. chocolate & blue-green		22·00	20·00	2·75
108	3d. + 3d. bright blue			42·00	50·00	6·50
105/8			Set of 4	80·00	85·00	11·00

1938 (14 Dec). *Voortrekker Commemoration. Nos. 80/1 of South Africa optd as T 11.*

109	1d. blue and carmine			10·00	14·00	1·50
	a. Three bolts in wheel rim		40·00		
110	1½d. greenish blue and brown		12·00	16·00	1·75

1939 (17 July). *250th Anniv of Landing of Huguenots in South Africa and Huguenot Commemoration Fund. Nos. 82/4 of South Africa optd as T 11.*

111	½d. + ½d. brown and green			12·00	12·00	1·10
112	1d. + 1d. green and carmine		15·00	12·00	1·25
113	1½d. + 1½d. blue-green and purple		22·00	12·00	1·25
111/13			Set of 3	45·00	32·00	3·25

SWA **SWA** SWA **S W A**

(29) (30) (31) (32)

1941 (1 Oct)–**43**. *War Effort. Nos. 88/96 of South Africa optd with T 29 or 30 (3d. and 1s.). (a) Inscr alternately.*

114	½d. green (1.12.41)			75	2·75	15
	a. *Blue-green* (1942)			65	2·00	15
115	1d. carmine (1.11.41)			55	2·25	15
	a. "Stain" on uniform		7·00		
116	1½d. myrtle-green (21.1.42)		55	2·25	15
117	3d. blue			22·00	17·00	1·00
	a. Cigarette flaw		60·00		
118	4d. orange-brown			6·50	12·00	1·00
	a. *Red-brown*			18·00	24·00	3·00
119	6d. red-orange			2·50	3·25	50
120	1s. 3d. olive-brown (15.1.43)		11·00	14·00	1·25

(b) *Inscr bilingually*

				Un single	Us single
121	2d. violet			50	40
122	1s. brown (17.11.41)			60	40
114/22	Set of 7 pairs and 2 singles	40·00	48·00	

1943–**44**. *War Effort (reduced sizes). Nos. 97/104 of South Africa, optd with T 29 (1½d. and 1s., No. 130), or T 31 (others). (a) Inscr alternately*

				Un unit	Us unit single	Us single
123	½d. blue-green (T)			40	3·00	10
	a. *Green*			3·75	4·25	15
	b. *Greenish blue*			3·75	4·25	
124	1d. carmine-red (T)			1·25	3·00	10
	a. *Bright carmine*			2·25	4·00	
125	1½d. red-brown (P)			45	60	10
126	2d. violet (P)			5·50	3·50	
	a. *Reddish violet*			6·50	3·75	10
	b. Apostrophe flaw		20·00			
127	3d. blue (T)			3·25	14·00	45
128	6d. red-orange (P)			5·50	2·75	30
	a. Opt inverted			£425		

(b) *Inscr bilingually*

129	4d. slate-green (T)			2·00	15·00	45
	a. Opt inverted			£450	£300	50·00
130	1s. brown (opt T 29) (P)		11·00	23·00	2·00
	a. Opt inverted			£425	£300	
	b. Opt T 31 (1944)			4·00	5·00	30
	c. Opt T 31 inverted		£375	£275	40·00
	d. "Bursting shell"			30·00		
123/30b			Set of 8	20·00	42·00	1·75

The "units" referred to above consist of pairs (P) or triplets (T).
No. 128 exists with another type of opt as Type 31, but with broader "s", narrower "w" and more space between the letters.

1945. *Victory. Nos. 108/10 of South Africa optd with T 30.*

131	1d. brown and carmine			25	50	10
	a. Opt inverted			£225	£250	
132	2d. slate-blue and violet			30	55	10
133	3d. deep blue and blue			1·25	90	10
131/3			Set of 3	1·60	1·75	20

1947 (17 Feb). *Royal Visit. Nos. 111/13 of South Africa optd as T 31, but 8½ × 2 mm.*

134	1d. black and carmine			10	10	10
135	2d. violet			10	20	10
	a. "Bird" on "2"		6·00			
136	3d. blue			15	20	10
134/6			Set of 3	30	45	15

1948 (26 Apr). *Royal Silver Wedding. No. 125 of South Africa, optd as T 31, but 4 × 2 mm.*

137	3d. blue and silver			1·50	35	10

1949 (1 Oct). *75th Anniv of U.P.U. Nos. 128/30 of South Africa optd as T 30, but 13 × 4 mm.*

138	1d. blue-green			1·00	2·00	25
139	1½d. brown-red			1·00	1·00	15
140	3d. bright blue			1·50	1·50	25
	a. Serif on "C"		22·00			
	b. "Lake" in East Africa		27·00			
138/40			Set of 3	3·25	4·00	60

1949 (1 Dec). *Inauguration of Voortrekker Monument, Pretoria. Nos. 131/3 of South Africa optd with T 32.*

				Un single	Us single
141	1d. magenta			10	10
142	1½d. blue-green			10	10
143	3d. blue			15	25
141/3			Set of 3	30	30

1952 (14 Mar). *Tercentenary of Landing of Van Riebeeck. Nos. 136/40 of South Africa optd as T 30, but 8 × 3½ mm (1d., 4½d.) or 11 × 4 mm (others).*

144	½d. brown-purple and olive-grey		10	50
145	1d. deep blue-green			10	10
146	2d. deep violet			50	10
147	4½d. blue			30	2·75
148	1s. brown			1·25	20
144/8			Set of 5	2·00	3·25

PRINTERS. The following stamps were printed by the Government Printer, Pretoria, in photogravure (Nos. 149/234) or lithography (subsequent issues), *unless stated otherwise*.

33 Queen Elizabeth II and *Catophracies Alexandri*

1953 (2 June). *Coronation. T 33 and similar horiz designs. W 9 of South Africa. P 14.*

149	1d. bright carmine			60	10
150	2d. deep bluish green			60	10
151	4d. magenta			80	55
152	6d. dull ultramarine			80	1·25
153	1s. deep orange-brown			80	40
149/53			Set of 5	3·25	2·25

Designs:—2d. *Bauhinia macrantha*, 4d. *Caralluma nebrownii*, 6d. *Gloriosa virescens*, 1s. *Rhigozum tricholotum*.

34 "Two Bucks"
(rock painting)

36 "Rhinoceros Hunt"
(rock painting)

38 Karakul Lamb

39 Ovambo Woman blowing Horn

(Des O. Schroeder (1d. to 4d.), M. Vandenschen (4½d. to 10s.))

1954 (15 Nov). *T 34, 36, 38/9 and similar designs. W 9 of South Africa (sideways* on vert designs). P 14.*

154	1d. brown-red			30	10
	w. Wmk horns of springbok to right	15·00	7·00
155	2d. deep brown			35	10
156	3d. dull purple			2·25	10
157	4d. blackish olive			2·50	10
158	4½d. deep blue			1·25	20
159	6d. myrtle-green			1·25	50
	w. Wmk horns of springbok to right	60·00	32·00
160	1s. deep mauve			1·25	50
161	1s. 3d. cerise			4·00	1·00
162	1s. 6d. purple			4·00	50
163	2s. 6d. bistre-brown			7·00	70
164	5s. deep bright blue			10·00	2·75
165	10s. deep myrtle-green			42·00	15·00
154/65			Set of 12	65·00	19·00

Designs: *Vert (as T 34)*—2d. "White Lady" (rock painting). (*As T 38*)—2s. Lioness; 5s. Gemsbok; 10s. African Elephant. (*As T 39*)—1s. Ovambo woman; 1s. 3d. Herero woman; 1s. 6d. Ovambo girl. *Horiz (as T 36)*—4d. "White Elephant and Giraffe" (rock painting).

*The normal sideways watermark shows the horns of the springbok pointing left, *as seen from the back of the stamp.*

1960. *As Nos. 154/7, 162, but W 102 of South Africa (sideways on vert designs). P 14.*

166	1d. brown-red			55	1·50
167	2d. deep brown			70	1·50
168	3d. dull purple			1·40	4·50
169	4d. blackish olive			4·25	4·75
170	1s. 6d. purple			26·00	15·00
166/70			Set of 5	30·00	24·00

MINIMUM PRICE

The minimum price quote is 10p which represents a handling charge rather than a basis for valuing common stamps. For further notes about prices see introductory pages.

(New Currency. 100 cents = 1 South African rand)

46 G.P.O. Windhoek   47 Finger Rock

48 Mounted Soldier Monument   49 Quivertree

50 S.W.A. House, Windhoek   50a Greater Flamingoes and Swakopmund Lighthouse

51 Fishing Industry   52 Greater Flamingo   53 German Lutheran Church, Windhoek

54 Diamond   55 Fort Namutoni

55a Hardap Dam   56 Topaz

57 Tourmaline   58 Heliodor

1961 (14 Feb)–**63**. *Unsurfaced paper. W 102 of South Africa (sideways on vert designs). P 14.*

171	**46**	½ c. brown and pale blue			60	10
172	47	1 c. sepia and reddish lilac		15	10
173	48	1½ c. slate-violet and salmon		20	10
174	49	2 c. deep green and yellow		75	90
175	50	2½ c. red-brown and light blue		35	10
176	50a	3 c. ultramarine and rose-red (1.10.62)	4·25	40
177	51	3½ c. indigo and blue-green		85	15
178	52	5 c. scarlet and grey-blue		6·50	10
179	53	7½ c. sepia and pale lemon		70	15
180	54	10 c. blue and greenish yellow		1·75	30
181	55	12½ c. indigo and lemon		85	30
182	55a	15 c. chocolate and light blue (16.3.63)	14·00	3·25
183	56	20 c. brown and red-orange		6·50	30
184	57	50 c. deep bluish green & yellow-orge	8·50	1·50
185	58	1 r. yellow, maroon and blue		55·00	5·00
171/185				Set of 15	55·00	19·00

See also Nos. 186/91, 202/16, 224/6 and 240.

1962–**66**. *As No. 171, etc., but without watermark.*

186	**46**	½ c. brown and pale blue (8.62)		50	1·75
187	48	1½ c. slate-violet and salmon (9.62)	5·00	45
188	49	2 c. deep green and yellow (5.62)	3·50	4·00
189	50	2½ c. red-brown and light blue (1964)	5·00	5·00
190	51	3½ c. indigo and blue-green (1966)	13·00	4·50
191	52	5 c. scarlet and grey-blue (9.62)	7·00	1·25
186/91			Set of 6	30·00	15·00

59 "Agricultural Development"

60 Centenary Emblem and Map

61 Centenary Emblem and part of Globe

1963 (16 Mar). *Opening of Hardap Dam. W 102 of South Africa (sideways). P 14.*
192   59   3 c. chocolate and light green 30 15

1963 (30 Aug). *Centenary of Red Cross. P 14.*
193 60 7½ c. red, black and light blue .. 7·00 6·00
194 61 15 c. red, black and orange-brown .. 11·00 9·00

62 Interior of Assembly Hall

63 Calvin

1964 (14 May). *Opening of Legislative Assembly Hall, Windhoek. W 102 of South Africa. P 14.*
195   62   3 c. ultramarine and salmon 50 30

1964 (1 Oct). *400th Death Anniv of Calvin (Protestant reformer). P 14.*
196 63 2½ c. brown-purple and gold 50 15
197   15 c. deep bluish green and gold . .. 2·75 3·50

64 Mail Runner of 1890

65 Kurt von François (founder)

66 Dr. H. Vedder

(Des D. Aschenborn)

1965 (18 Oct). *75th Anniv of Windhoek. Chalk-surfaced paper. W 127 of South Africa (sideways). P 14.*
198 64 3 c. sepia and scarlet 50 15
199 65 15 c. red-brown and blue-green .. 1·25 2·25

1966 (4 July). *90th Birth Anniv of Dr. H. Vedder (philosopher and writer). Chalk-surfaced paper. W 127 of South Africa (sideways). P 14.*
200 66 3 c. blackish green and salmon .. 50 15
201   15 c. deep sepia and light blue .. 1·25 65
Nos. 200/1 exist on Swiss-made paper with *tête-bêche* watermark from a special printing made for use in presentation albums for delegates to the U.P.U. Congress in Tokyo in 1969, as supplies of the original Harrison paper were by then exhausted (*Set of 2 price £22 mint*).

1966–72. *As 1961–66 but chalk-surfaced paper and W 127 of South Africa* (sideways† on vert designs).*
202 46 ½ c. brown and pale blue (1967) .. 1·25 10
203 47 1 c. sepia and light reddish lilac (1967) 1·50 10
       a. Grey-brown and lilac (9.72) .. 3·00 10
204 48 1½ c. slate-violet and salmon (1968) .. 7·00 30
205 49 2 c. deep bluish green and yellow .. 4·50 10
206 50 2½ c. dp red-brown & lt turquoise-blue 2·50 30
       a. Dp red-brown & pale blue (1967) .. 70 10
207 50a 3 c. ultramarine and rose-red (1970) 8·50 60
208 51 3½ c. indigo and blue-green (1967) .. 4·00 5·00
209 50 4 c. dp red-brown & lt turq-bl (1.4.71) 1·50 2·50
210 52 5 c. scarlet and grey-blue (1968) .. 4·00 10
211 53 6 c. sepia & greenish yellow (31.8.71) 8·50 11·00
212   7½ c. sepia and pale lemon (1967) .. 3·50 30
       w. Wmk top of triangle to right .. 3·50 30
213 55 9 c. indigo & greenish yellow (1.7.71) 8·50 11·00
214 54 10 c. brt blue & greenish yellow (6.70) 18·00 1·50
       a. Whiter background** (9.72) .. 18·00 2·25
215 55a 15 c. chocolate and light blue (1.72) 20·00 6·50
216 56 20 c. brown and red-orange (1968) .. 18·00 1·75
202/16 .. .. *Set of 15* 95·00 35·00

*The watermark in this issue is indistinct but the stamps can be distinguished from the stamps without watermark by their shades and the chalk-surfaced paper which is appreciably thicker and whiter. The 1, 1½, 3, 4, 5, 6, 9, 10, 15 and 20 c. are known only with the watermark *tête-bêche* but the ½ c. and 2½ c. exist with both forms, the remainder being as illustrated.

†The normal sideways watermark shows top of triangle pointing to left, *as seen from the back of the stamp.*

**No. 214a, printed from sheets, has a much whiter background around the value and behind "SOUTH WEST AFRICA" compared with No. 214, which was issued in coils only.
See also Nos. 224/6 and 240.

67 Camelthorn Tree

(Des D. Aschenborn (2½ c., 3 c.), Govt Printer, Pretoria (15 c.))

1967 (6 Jan). *Verwoerd Commemoration. Chalk-surfaced paper. T 67 and similar designs. W 127 of South Africa (sideways on vert designs). P 14.*
217 2½ c. black and emerald-green .. 20 10
218 3 c. brown and new blue 30 10
219 15 c. blackish brown and reddish purple 1·10 45
217/19 .. .. *Set of 3* 1·40 60
Designs: Vert.—3 c. Waves breaking against rock; 15 c. Dr. H. F. Verwoerd.

70 President Swart   **71** President and Mrs. Swart

1968 (2 Jan). *Swart Commemoration. Chalk-surfaced paper. W 127 of South Africa (tête-bêche, sideways). P 14 × 15.*
220 70 3 c. orange-red, black & turquoise-blue
       G. Inscribed in German 45 15
       A. Inscribed in Afrikaans .. 45 15
       E. Inscribed in English .. 45 15
221 71 15 c. red, blackish olive and dull green
       G. Inscribed in German .. .. 1·50 1·75
       A. Inscribed in Afrikaans .. 1·50 1·75
       E. Inscribed in English .. 1·50 1·75
       a. Red, brownish olive & bronze-green
       G. Inscribed in German .. .. 3·00 2·25
       A. Inscribed in Afrikaans .. 3·00 2·25
       E. Inscribed in English .. 3·00 2·25
220/1 .. *Set of 2 values in strips of three* 12·00
       Set of 6 singles 5·00 5·00
The three languages appear, *se-tenant*, both horizontally and vertically, throughout the sheet.

1970 (14 Feb). *Water 70 Campaign. As Nos. 299/300 of South Africa, but without phosphor band and inscr "SWA".*
222 2½ c. green, bright blue and chocolate 75 30
223 3 c. Prussian blue, royal blue and buff 75 30

72 G.P.O., Windhoek   **73** "Red Sand-dunes, Eastern South West Africa"

1970–71. *As Nos. 202 and 204/5 but "POSGELD INKOMSTE" omitted and larger figure of value as in T 72. W 127 of South Africa (tête-bêche, sideways on 1½ and 2 c.).*
224 72 ½ c. brown and pale blue (6.70).. 1·50 30
225 – 1½ c. slate-violet and salmon (1.6.71) 13·00 16·00
226 – 2 c. deep bluish green and lemon (11.70) 5·00 40
224/6 .. .. *Set of 3* 18·00 16·00

1970 (24 Aug). *150th Anniv of Bible Society of South Africa. As Nos. 301/2 of South Africa, but inscr "SWA".*
228 2½ c. multicoloured .. .. 1·50 10
229 12½ c. gold, black and blue .. 7·00 8·00
No. 228 has a phosphor frame, probably added in error.
A mint example of No. 229 exists with a second, blind, impression of the die-stamped features.

1971 (31 May). *"Interstex" Stamp Exhibition, Cape Town. As No. 303A of South Africa, but without phosphor frame and inscr "SWA".*
230 5 c. light greenish blue, black and pale yellow 4·00 1·50

1971 (31 May). *Tenth Anniv of Antarctic Treaty. As No. 304 of South Africa, but without phosphor frame, and inscr "SWA".*
231 12½ c. blue-black, greenish blue & orge-red 32·00 21·00

1971 (31 May). *Tenth Anniv of the South African Republic. As Nos. 305/6 of South Africa, but without phosphor frame, and inscr "SWA".*
232 2 c. pale flesh and brown-red .. 3·25 75
233 4 c. green and black .. .. 3·25 75

1972 (19 Sept). *Centenary of S.P.C.A. As No. 312 of South Africa, but inscr "SWA".*
234 5 c. multicoloured .. .. 3·00 65

WATERMARK. All issues from this date are on unwatermarked paper.

(Lettering by E. de Jong)

1973 (1 May). *Scenery. T 73 and similar multicoloured designs showing paintings by Adolph Jentsch. P 11½ × 12½ (10 and 15 c.) or 12½ × 11½ (others).*
235 2 c. Type 73 .. .. .. 75 75
236 4 c. "After the Rain" .. .. 1·10 1·25
237 5 c. "Barren Country" .. .. 1·25 1·50
238 10 c. "Schaap River" (*vert*) .. 1·75 2·25
239 15 c. "Namib Desert" (*vert*) .. 3·00 3·75
235/9 .. .. *Set of 5* 7·00 8·50

1973 (28 May). *As Nos. 207 but without wmk. Phosphorised paper.*
240 50a 3 c. ultramarine and rose-red .. 2·50 1·25
No. 240 is also distinguishable in that the lettering of "SOUTH WEST AFRICA" is whiter.

---

74 *Sarcocaulon rigidum*   **75** *Euphorbia virosa*

(Des D. Findlay)

1973 (1 Sept)–79. *Succulents. Various multicoloured designs as T 74/5. Phosphorised glossy paper (original printing of all values) or ordinary paper (1, 2, 3, 4, 5, 9, 10, 15, 20, 30, 50 c.).*

(a) *As T 74. P 12½.*
241 1 c. Type 74 .. .. 15 10
     a. Black (face value, etc.) omitted .. £200
242 2 c. *Lapidaria margaretae* 90 50
     a. Perf 14 × 13½ (4.8.79) .. 20 10
243 3 c. *Titanopsis schwantesii* 20 10
     a. Black (face value, etc.) omitted 80·00
     b. Perf 14 × 13½ (8.8.79) .. 30 15
244 4 c. *Lithops karasmontana* .. 25 10
245 5 c. *Caralluma lugardii* 40 30
     a. Black (face value, etc.) omitted £140
     b. Perf 14 × 13½ (12.12.79) .. 50 20
246 6 c. *Dinteranthus microspermus* .. 1·50 1·75
247 7 c. *Conophytum gratum* .. .. 75 1·75
248 9 c. *Huernia oculata* .. .. 65 2·00
249 10 c. *Gasteria pillansii*.. .. 1·00 45
     a. Black (face value, etc.) omitted £200
     b. Perf 14 × 13½ (8.3.79).. 40 30
250 14 c. *Stapelia pedunculata* .. 1·50 2·50
251 15 c. *Fenestraria aurantiaca* .. 65 30
252 20 c. *Decabelone grandiflora* .. 4·50 2·75
253 25 c. *Hoodia bainii* .. .. 3·25 2·25

(b) *As T 75. P 11½×12½ (30 c., 1 r.) or 12½×11½ (50 c.)*
254 30 c. Type 75 .. .. 1·00 80
     a. Perf 13½×14 (27.12.79) .. 90 90
255 50 c. *Pachypodium namaquanum* (*vert*) 1·25 2·25
     a. Perf 14×13½ (18.12.79) .. 1·25 1·25
256 1 r. *Welwitschia bainesii* .. 1·50 5·00
241/56 .. .. .. *Set of 16* 16·00 18·00

1973 (1 Sept)–80. *Coil stamps. As Nos. 241/2 and 245 but photo, colours changed. P 14.*
257 1 c. black and light mauve .. 70 60
     a. Chalk-surfaced paper (7.76?) .. 1·00 40
     b. Imperf × perf 14. Chalk-surfaced paper (1980) .. 4·75 5·50
258 2 c. black and yellow 50 50
     a. Chalk-surfaced paper (7.76?) .. 1·00 50
     b. Imperf × perf 14. Chalk-surfaced paper (1.79) .. 1·00 40
259 5 c. black and light rose-red .. 1·75 60
     a. Imperf × perf 14. Chalk-surfaced paper (8.2.78) .. 1·25 60
257/9 .. .. *Set of 3* 2·25 1·25
Coils of Nos. 257b, 258b and 259a come with every fifth stamp numbered on the reverse.

76 Chat-shrike   **77** Giraffe, Antelope and Spoor

(Des D. Findlay)

1974 (13 Feb). *Rare Birds. T 76 and similar vert designs. Multicoloured. P 12½ × 11½.*
260 4 c. Type 76 .. .. 3·25 1·00
261 5 c. Peach-faced Lovebirds .. 4·25 1·50
262 10 c. Damaraland Rock Jumper .. 11·00 5·50
263 15 c. Rüppell's Parrots .. 15·00 9·50
260/3 .. .. *Set of 4* 30·00 16·00

(Des O. Schröder)

1974 (10 Apr). *Twyfelfontein Rock-engravings. T 77 and similar multicoloured designs. P 11½ × 12½ (15 c.) or 12½ (others).*
264 4 c. Type 77 .. .. 1·50 50
265 5 c. Elephant, hyena, antelope and spoor 1·50 80
     a. Black (value and "SWA") omitted .. £1000
266 15 c. Kudu Cow (38 × 21 mm) .. 7·00 7·50
264/6 .. .. .. *Set of 3* 9·00 8·00

78 Cut Diamond   **79** Wagons and Map of the Trek

(Des M. Barnett)

1974 (30 Sept). *Diamond Mining.* T **78** *and similar vert design. Multicoloured.* P 12½ × 11½.
267 10 c. Type **78** .. .. 5·00 6·00
268 15 c. Diagram of shore workings .. 5·00 6·00

(Des K. Esterhuysen)

1974 (13 Nov). *Centenary of Thirstland Trek.* P 11½ × 12½.
269 **79** 4 c. multicoloured .. .. 75 1·00

80 Peregrine Falcon   81 Kolmannskop (ghost town)

(Des D. Findlay)

1975 (19 Mar). *Protected Birds of Prey.* T **80** *and similar vert designs. Multicoloured.* P 12½ × 11½.
270 4 c. Type **80** .. .. .. 2·00 1·25
271 5 c. Verreaux's Eagle .. .. 2·25 1·75
272 10 c. Martial Eagle .. .. 6·00 5·50
273 15 c. Egyptian Vulture .. .. 7·50 8·00
270/3 .. .. .. Set of 4 16·00 15·00

(Des A. H. Barrett)

1975 (23 July). *Historic Monuments.* T **81** *and similar horiz designs. Multicoloured.* P 11½ × 12½.
274 5 c. Type **81** 30 15
275 9 c. "Martin Luther" (steam tractor) .. 50 60
276 15 c. Kurt von François and Old Fort, Windhoek .. .. .. 1·00 1·00
274/6 .. .. .. Set of 3 1·60 1·60

82 "View of Lüderitz"

(Des J. Hoekstra)

1975 (15 Oct). *Otto Schröder.* T **82** *and similar horiz designs showing his paintings. Multicoloured.* P 11½ × 12½.
277 15 c. Type **82** 50 60
　　a. Block of 4. Nos. 277/80 .. 1·75
278 15 c. "View of Swakopmund" .. 50 60
279 15 c. "Harbour Scene" 50 60
280 15 c. "Quayside, Walvis Bay" .. 50 60
277/80 .. .. Set of 4 1·75 2·25
MS281 122 × 96 mm. Nos. 277/80 .. 1·75 3·50
Nos. 277/80 were printed together, in *se-tenant* blocks of four within the sheet.

83 Elephants

(Des H. Pager)

1976 (31 Mar). *Prehistoric Rock Paintings.* T **83** *and similar horiz designs. Multicoloured.* P 11½ × 12½.
282 4 c. Type **83** 50 15
283 10 c. Rhinoceros 75 70
284 15 c. Antelope 90 85
285 20 c. Man with bow and arrow .. 1·25 1·40
282/5 .. .. .. Set of 4 3·00 2·75
MS286 121 × 95 mm. Nos. 282/5 .. 3·00 4·00

84 Schwerinsburg

(Des H. Pager)

1976 (14 May). *Castles.* T **84** *and similar horiz designs. Multicoloured.* P 11½ × 12½.
287 10 c. Type **84** 40 30
288 15 c. Schloss Duwisib 55 60
289 20 c. Heynitzburg 75 90
287/9 .. .. .. Set of 3 1·50 1·60

85 Large-toothed Rock Hyrax

(Des D. Findlay)

1976 (16 July). *Fauna Conservation.* T **85** *and similar horiz designs. Multicoloured.* P 11½ × 12½.
290 4 c. Type **85** 50 20
291 10 c. Kirk's Dik-Dik .. .. 1·25 90
292 15 c. Kuhl's Tree Squirrel .. 2·00 2·25
290/2 .. .. .. Set of 3 3·25 3·00

86 The Augustineum, Windhoek

(Des H. Pager)

1976 (17 Sept). *Modern Buildings.* T **86** *and similar horiz design.* P 11½ × 12½.
293 15 c. black and yellow 50 65
294 20 c. black and light yellow .. 60 75
Design:—20 c. Katutura Hospital, Windhoek.

87 Ovambo Water Canal System

(Des A. H. Barrett)

1976 (19 Nov). *Water and Electricity Supply.* T **87** *and similar horiz design. Multicoloured.* P 11½ × 12½.
295 15 c. Type **87** 40 40
296 20 c. Ruacana Falls Power Station .. 50 50

88 Coastline near Pomona

(Des A. H. Barrett)

1977 (29 Mar). *Namib Desert.* T **88** *and similar horiz designs. Multicoloured.* P 12½.
297 4 c. Type **88** 20 15
298 10 c. Bush and dunes, Sossusvlei .. 30 30
299 15 c. Plain near Brandberg .. 50 50
300 20 c. Dunes, Sperr Gebiet .. 60 60
297/300 .. .. Set of 4 1·40 1·40

89 Kraal

(Des A. H. Barrett)

1977 (15 July). *The Ovambo People.* T **89** *and similar horiz designs.* P 11½ × 12½.
301 4 c. multicoloured 10 10
302 10 c. black, dull orange and cinnamon .. 30 20
303 15 c. multicoloured 30 25
304 20 c. multicoloured 35 45
301/4 .. .. .. Set of 4 95 90
Designs—10 c. Grain baskets; 15 c. Pounding grain; 20 c. Women in tribal dress.

90 Terminal Buildings

(Des H. Pager and A. H. Barrett)

1977 (22 Aug). *J. G. Strijdom Airport, Windhoek.* P 12½.
305 **90** 20 c. multicoloured 40 30

91 Drostdy, Lüderitz   92 Side-winding Adder

(Des A. H. Barrett)

1977 (4 Nov). *Historic Houses.* T **91** *and similar horiz designs. Multicoloured.* P 12 × 12½.
306 5 c. Type **91** 15 10
307 10 c. Woermannhaus, Swakopmund .. 25 30
308 15 c. Neu-Heusis, Windhoek .. 30 35
309 20 c. Schmelenhaus, Bethanie .. 40 40
306/9 .. .. .. Set of 4 1·00 1·10
MS310 122 × 96 mm. Nos. 306/9 .. 1·00 2·00

(Des D. Findlay)

1978 (6 Feb). *Small Animals.* T **92** *and similar horiz designs. Multicoloured.* P 12½.
311 4 c. Type **92** 15 10
312 10 c. Grant's Desert Golden Mole .. 30 30
313 15 c. Palmato Gecko 50 30
314 20 c. Namaqua Chameleon .. 65 40
311/14 .. .. .. Set of 4 1·40 1·00

93 Ostrich Hunting

(Des A. H. Barrett)

1978 (14 Apr). *The Bushmen.* T **93** *and similar horiz designs in light grey-brown, stone and black.* P 12 × 12½.
315 4 c. Type **93** 30 10
316 10 c. Woman carrying ostrich eggs .. 30 20
317 15 c. Hunters kindling fire .. 45 30
318 20 c. Woman with musical instrument .. 55 40
315/18 .. .. .. Set of 4 1·40 90

94 Lutheran Church, Windhoek

ALGEMENE STEMREG
(95)

(Des A. H. Barrett)

1978 (16 June). *Historic Churches.* T **94** *and similar horiz designs.* P 12½.
319 4 c. grey-black and cinnamon .. 10 10
320 10 c. grey-black and ochre .. 15 20
321 15 c. grey-black and light brown-rose .. 20 25
322 20 c. grey-black and light grey-blue .. 30 35
319/22 .. .. .. Set of 4 65 80
MS323 125 × 90 mm. Nos. 319/22 .. 75 1·75
Designs:—10 c. Lutheran Church, Swakopmund; 15 c. Rhenish Mission Church, Otjimbingwe; 20 c. Rhenish Missionary Church, Keetmanshoop.

1978 (1 Nov). *Universal Suffrage. Designs as Nos. 244/5, 249 and 251/3 optd with* T **95** *(or similar inscr in English or German).*
324 4 c. *Lithops karasmontana* .. .. ..
　　A. Opt in Afrikaans 10 10
　　E. Opt in English 10 10
　　G. Opt in German 10 10
325 5 c. *Caralluma lugardii* .. .. ..
　　A. Opt in Afrikaans 10 10
　　E. Opt in English 10 10
　　G. Opt in German 10 10
326 10 c. *Gasteria pillansii* .. .. ..
　　A. Opt in Afrikaans 10 10
　　E. Opt in English 10 10
　　G. Opt in German 10 10
327 15 c. *Fenestraria aurantiaca* .. .. ..
　　A. Opt in Afrikaans 15 15
　　E. Opt in English 15 15
　　G. Opt in German 15 15
328 20 c. *Decabelone grandiflora* .. .. ..
　　A. Opt in Afrikaans 15 15
　　E. Opt in English 15 15
　　G. Opt in German 15 15
329 25 c. *Hoodia bainii* .. .. ..
　　A. Opt in Afrikaans 15 15
　　E. Opt in English 15 15
　　G. Opt in German 15 15
324/9 .. .. Set of 18 (6 strips of 3) 1·75 1·75
Nos. 324A/G, 325A/G, 326A/G, 327A/G, 328A/G and 329A/G were each printed together, *se-tenant*, in horizontal and vertical strips of 3 throughout the sheets.

OMNIBUS ISSUES

Details, together with prices for complete sets, of the various Omnibus issues from the 1935 Silver Jubilee series to date are included in a special section following Zululand at the end of the catalogue.

96 Greater Flamingo   **97** Silver Topaz

(Des D. Findlay)

1979 (5 Apr). *Water Birds. T* **96** *and similar vert designs. Multicoloured. P* 14.
330	4 c. Type **96**	20	10
331	15 c. White-breasted Cormorant	45	25
332	20 c. Chestnut-banded Sand Plover	50	35
333	25 c. Eastern White Pelican	55	40
330/3	*Set of* 4	1·50	1·00

(Des H. Botha)

1979 (26 Nov). *Gemstones. T* **97** *and similar horiz designs. Multicoloured. P* 14.
334	4 c. Type **97**	30	10
335	15 c. Aquamarine	65	20
336	20 c. Malachite	70	25
337	25 c. Amethyst	70	30
334/7	*Set of* 4	2·10	75

98 Killer Whale   **99** Impala

(Des A. H. Barrett)

1980 (25 Mar). *Whales. T* **98** *and similar multicoloured designs. P* 14.
338	4 c. Type **98**	35	20
339	5 c. Humpback Whale (38 × 22 *mm*)	40	20
340	10 c. Black Right Whale (38 × 22 *mm*)	55	30
341	15 c. Sperm Whale (58 × 22 *mm*)	1·00	75
342	20 c. Fin Whale (58 × 22 *mm*)	1·25	90
343	25 c. Blue Whale (88 × 22 *mm*)	1·60	1·25
338/43	*Set of* 6	4·50	3·25
MS344	202 × 95 mm. Nos. 338/43	5·50	6·00

(Des P. Bosman)

1980 (25 June). *25th Anniv of Division of Nature Conservation and Tourism. Antelopes. T* **99** *and similar horiz designs. Multicoloured. P* 14.
345	5 c. Type **99**	15	10
346	10 c. Topi	20	10
347	15 c. Roan Antelope	40	15
348	20 c. Sable Antelope	50	20
345/8	*Set of* 4	1·10	45

100 Black-backed Jackal   **101** Meerkat

(Des Sheila Nowers (11, 12, 14, 16 c.), P. Bosman (others))

1980 (1 Oct)–**89**. *Wildlife. Multicoloured designs as T* **100**. *Ordinary paper. P* 14.
349	1 c. Type **100**	15	10
	a. Chalk-surfaced paper (11.6.85)	1·00	1·00
350	2 c. Hunting Dog	30	10
	a. Chalk-surfaced paper (4.6.86)	1·25	1·25
351	3 c. Brown Hyena	20	10
	a. Chalk-surfaced paper (10.2.88)	80	1·00
352	4 c. Springbok	20	10
	a. Chalk-surfaced paper (29.7.87)	80	1·00
353	5 c. Gemsbok	20	10
	a. Chalk-surfaced paper (11.6.85)	1·75	1·75
354	6 c. Greater Kudu	20	10
	a. Chalk-surfaced paper (8.8.88)	2·25	2·25
355	7 c. Mountain Zebra (*horiz*)	40	20
	a. Chalk-surfaced paper (19.3.86)	2·00	2·25
356	8 c. Cape Porcupine (*horiz*)	30	10
	a. Chalk-surfaced paper (11.6.85)	2·25	2·25
357	9 c. Ratel (*horiz*)	30	10
	a. Chalk-surfaced paper (10.2.88)	2·25	2·25
358	10 c. Cheetah (*horiz*)	30	10
358*a*	11 c. Blue Wildebeest (2.4.84)	40	30
358*b*	12 c. African Buffalo (*horiz*) (1.4.85)	70	1·25
	ba. Booklet pane of 10 with margins all round (1.8.85)	4·50	
358*c*	14 c. Caracal (*horiz*) (*chalk-surfaced paper*) (1.4.86)	3·00	2·25

359	15 c. Hippopotamus (*horiz*)	30	10
	a. Chalk-surfaced paper (10.2.88)	80	1·25
359*b*	16 c. Warthog (*horiz*) (*chalk-surfaced paper*) (1.4.87)	1·75	1·75
	ba. Ordinary paper (15.2.89)	3·50	3·50
360	20 c. Eland (*horiz*)	30	10
	a. Chalk-surfaced paper (11.6.85)	80	1·25
361	25 c. Black Rhinoceros (*horiz*)	50	20
	a. Chalk-surfaced paper (11.6.85)	80	1·25
362	30 c. Lion (*horiz*)	80	20
	a. Chalk-surfaced paper (4.6.86)	1·75	2·00
363	50 c. Giraffe	50	30
	a. Chalk-surfaced paper (21.4.88)	1·25	1·75
364	1 r. Leopard	1·00	55
	a. Chalk-surfaced paper (4.6.86)	2·25	2·50
365	2 r. African Elephant	1·00	90
	a. Chalk-surfaced paper (10.2.88)	3·00	3·25
349/65	*Set of* 21	11·50	8·00

Some printings of the 4, 15 and 25 c. from 1983/4 were on phosphorescent paper. The same paper was used for printings of the 1, 2, 3, 8, 9, 10, 16 c. (No. 359ba), 20, 30 c. and 1 r. during 1989.

For $1.20 design as No. 359*b* see No. **MS675** and for $1.30 as No. 358*c* see No. **MS685**.

(Des P. Bosman. Photo)

1980 (1 Oct). *Coil stamps. Wildlife. Vert designs as T* **101**. *Imperf × perf* 14.
366	1 c. yellow-brown	20	20
367	2 c. deep dull blue	20	20
368	5 c. yellow-olive	30	30
366/8	*Set of* 3	65	65

Designs:—2 c. Savanna Monkey; 5 c. Chacma Baboon.

102 Von Bach

(Des A. H. Barrett)

1980 (25 Nov). *Water Conservation. Dams. T* **102** *and similar horiz designs. Multicoloured. P* 14.
369	5 c. Type **102**	10	10
370	10 c. Swakoppoort	15	10
371	15 c. Naute	20	20
372	20 c. Hardap	25	25
369/72	*Set of* 4	60	60

103 View of Fish River Canyon   **104** *Aloe erinacea*

(Des A. H. Barrett)

1981 (20 Mar). *Fish River Canyon. T* **103** *and similar horiz designs showing various views of canyon. P* 14.
373	5 c. multicoloured	10	10
374	15 c. multicoloured	20	20
375	20 c. multicoloured	25	25
376	25 c. multicoloured	30	30
373/6	*Set of* 4	75	70

(Des D. Findlay)

1981 (14 Aug). *Aloes. T* **104** *and similar vert designs. Multicoloured. P* 14 × 13½.
377	5 c. Type **104**	15	10
378	15 c. *Aloe viridiflora*	35	25
379	20 c. *Aloe pearsonii*	40	25
380	25 c. *Aloe littoralis*	50	30
377/80	*Set of* 4	1·25	75

105 Paul Weiss-Haus

(Des A. H. Barrett)

1981 (16 Oct). *Historic Buildings of Lüderitz. T* **105** *and similar horiz designs. Multicoloured. P* 14.
381	5 c. Type **105**	10	10
382	15 c. Deutsche Afrika Bank	20	20
383	20 c. Schroederhaus	30	30
384	25 c. Altes Postamt	30	35
381/4	*Set of* 4	75	80
MS385	125 × 90 mm. Nos. 381/4	85	90

106 Salt Pan   **107** Kalahari Starred Tortoise (*Psammobates oculifer*)

(Des A. H. Barrett)

1981 (4 Dec). *Salt Industry. T* **106** *and similar horiz designs. Multicoloured. P* 14.
386	5 c. Type **106**	10	10
387	15 c. Dumping and washing	20	20
388	20 c. Loading by conveyor	25	30
389	25 c. Dispatch to refinery	30	35
386/9	*Set of* 4	70	80

(Des A. H. Barrett)

1982 (12 Mar). *Tortoises. T* **107** *and similar horiz designs. Multicoloured. P* 14.
390	5 c. Type **107**	15	10
391	15 c. Leopard Tortoise (*Geochelone pardalis*)	25	25
392	20 c. Angulate Tortoise (*Chersina angulata*)	30	35
393	25 c. Speckled Padloper (*Homopus signatus*)	40	45
390/3	*Set of* 4	1·00	1·00

108 Mythical Sea-monster

(Des Sheila Nowers)

1982 (28 May). *Discoverers of South West Africa. (1st series). Bartolomeu Dias. T* **108** *and similar horiz designs. Multicoloured. P* 14.
394	15 c. Type **108**	20	20
395	20 c. Bartolomeu Dias and map of Africa showing voyage	40	30
396	25 c. Dias' caravel	65	40
397	30 c. Dias erecting commemorative cross, Angra das Voltas, 25 July 1488	70	45
394/7	*Set of* 4	1·75	1·25

See also Nos. 455/8.

109 Brandberg   **110** Otjikaeva Head-dress of Herero Woman

(Des A. H. Barrett)

1982 (3 Aug). *Mountains of South West Africa. T* **109** *and similar horiz designs. Multicoloured. P* 13½ × 14.
398	6 c. Type **109**	10	10
399	15 c. Omatako	20	20
400	20 c. Die Nadel	25	30
401	25 c. Spitzkuppe	30	35
398/401	*Set of* 4	75	85

(Des A. H. Barrett)

1982 (15 Oct). *Traditional Head-dresses of South West Africa. (1st series). T* **110** *and similar vert designs. Multicoloured. P* 14.
402	6 c. Type **110**	10	10
403	15 c. Ekori head-dress of Himba	25	35
404	20 c. Oshikoma hair-piece and iipando plaits of Ngandjera	35	45
405	25 c. Omhatela head-dress of Kwanyama	35	60
402/5	*Set of* 4	95	1·40

See also Nos. 427/30.

111 Fort Vogelsang   **112** Searching for Diamonds, Kolmanskop, 1908

(Des J. van Ellinckhuijzen)

1983 (16 Mar). *Centenary of Lüderitz. T* **111** *and similar designs. P* 14.
406	6 c. brownish black and deep carmine-red	10	10
407	20 c. brownish black and yellow-brown	20	20
408	25 c. brownish black and chestnut	25	25
409	30 c. brownish black and brown-purple	25	30
410	40 c. brownish black and bright green	35	45
406/10	*Set of* 5	1·00	1·25

Designs: *Vert* (23 × 29 *mm*)—20 c. Chief Joseph Fredericks; 30 c. Heinrich Vogelsang (founder); 40 c. Adolf Lüderitz (colonial promoter). *Horiz* (*As T* 111)—25 c. Angra Pequena.

(Des J. van Ellinckhuijzen)

1983 (8 June). *75th Anniv of Discovery of Diamonds.* T **112** *and similar designs.* P 13½ × 14 (10, 20 c.) or 14 × 13½ (others).

411	10 c. deep brown and pale stone		15	15
412	20 c. maroon and pale stone		30	40
413	25 c. Prussian blue and pale stone		35	40
414	40 c. brownish black and pale stone		55	70
411/14		Set of 4	1·25	1·50

Designs: *Horiz* (34 × 19 *mm*)—20 c. Digging for diamonds, Kolmanskop, 1908. *Vert* (19 × 26 *mm*)—25 c. Sir Ernest Oppenheimer (industrialist); 40 c. August Stauch (prospector).

113 "Common Zebras drinking"   114 The Rock Lobster
(J. van Ellinckhuijzen)

1983 (1 Sept). *Painters of South West Africa.* T **113** *and similar horiz designs. Multicoloured.* P 13½ × 14.

415	10 c. Type 113..		15	15
416	20 c. "Rossing Mountain" (H. Henckert)		25	30
417	25 c. "Stampeding African Buffalo" (F. Krampe)..		30	35
418	40 c. "Erongo Mountains" (J. Blatt)..		50	55
415/18		Set of 4	1·10	1·25

(Des J. van Ellinckhuijzen)

1983 (23 Nov). *Lobster Industry.* T **114** *and similar horiz designs. Multicoloured.* P 13½ × 14.

419	10 c. Type 114..		15	15
420	20 c. Mother ship and fishing dinghies		25	30
421	25 c. Netting lobsters from dinghy		30	35
422	40 c. Packing lobsters		50	55
419/22		Set of 4	1·10	1·25

115 Hohenzollern House

(Des A. H. Barrett)

1984 (8 Mar). *Historic Buildings of Swakopmund.* T **115** *and similar horiz designs.* P 14.

423	10 c. grey-black and orange-brown		15	15
424	20 c. grey-black and new blue..		30	25
425	25 c. grey-black and yellow-green		30	30
426	30 c. grey-black and ochre		35	30
423/6		Set of 4	1·00	90

Designs:—20 c. Railway Station; 25 c. Imperial District Bureau; 30 c. Ritterburg.

(Des A. H. Barrett)

1984 (25 May). *Traditional Head-dresses of South West Africa (2nd series). Multicoloured designs as* T **110**. P 14.

427	11 c. Eendjushi head-dress of Kwambi		25	15
428	20 c. Bushman woman		40	25
429	25 c. Omulenda head-dress of Kwaluudhi		45	30
430	30 c. Mbukushu women		45	30
427/30		Set of 4	1·40	90

116 Map and German Flag   117 Sweet Thorn

(Des J. van Ellinckhuijzen)

1984 (7 Aug). *Centenary of German Colonisation.* T **116** *and similar horiz designs. Multicoloured.* P 14 × 14½.

431	11 c. Type 116..		25	15
432	25 c. Raising the German flag, 1884		50	50
433	30 c. German Protectorate boundary marker		50	60
434	45 c. *Elizabeth* and *Leipzig* (German corvettes)		1·25	1·75
431/4		Set of 4	2·25	2·75

(Des Eva-Maria Linsmayer)

1984 (22 Nov). *Spring in South West Africa.* T **117** *and similar vert designs. Multicoloured.* P 14.

435	11 c. Type 117		25	15
436	25 c. Camel Thorn		35	35
437	30 c. Hook Thorn		40	45
438	45 c. Candle-pod Acacia		50	70
435/8		Set of 4	1·40	1·50

NEW INFORMATION

The editor is always interested to correspond with people who have new information that will improve or correct the Catalogue.

118 Head of Ostrich

(Des J. van Ellinckhuijzen)

1985 (15 Mar). *Ostriches.* T **118** *and similar horiz designs. Multicoloured.* P 14.

439	11 c. Type 118..		40	10
440	25 c. Ostrich on eggs		70	30
441	30 c. Newly-hatched chick and eggs		80	50
442	50 c. Mating dance		1·10	75
439/42		Set of 4	2·75	1·50

119 Kaiserstrasse

(Des A. H. Barrett)

1985 (6 June). *Historic Buildings of Windhoek.* T **119** *and similar horiz designs.* P 14.

443	12 c. black and brown-ochre..		25	10
444	25 c. black and grey-olive		45	25
445	30 c. black and brown		45	30
446	50 c. black and yellow-brown		55	30
443/6		Set of 4	1·90	1·25

Designs:—25 c. Turnhalle; 30 c. Old Supreme Court Building; 50 c. Railway Station.

120 Zwilling Locomotive   121 Lidumu-dumu
(keyboard instrument)

(Des J. van Ellinckhuijzen)

1985 (2 Aug). *Narrow-gauge Railway Locomotives.* T **120** *and similar horiz designs. Multicoloured.* P 14.

447	12 c. Type 120..		30	10
448	25 c. Feldspur side-tank locomotive		60	25
449	30 c. Jung and Henschel side-tank locomotive		70	35
450	50 c. Henschel Hd locomotive		90	60
447/50		Set of 4	2·25	1·10

(Des J. van Ellinckhuijzen)

1985 (17 Oct). *Traditional Musical Instruments.* T **121** *and similar horiz designs. Multicoloured.* P 14.

451	12 c. Type 121..		10	10
452	25 c. Ngoma (drum)		20	20
453	30 c. Okambulumbumbwa (stringed instrument)		25	25
454	50 c. // Gwashi (stringed instrument)		35	35
451/4		Set of 4	80	80

122 Erecting Commemorative   123 Ameib, Erongo
Pillar at Cape Cross, 1486   Mountains

(Des J. van Ellinckhuijzen)

1986 (24 Jan). *Discoverers of South West Africa (2nd series). Diogo Cao.* T **122** *and similar horiz designs.* P 14.

455	12 c. black, brownish grey & deep dull green	35	10
456	20 c. black, brownish grey & pale red-brown	55	25
457	25 c. black, brownish grey and dull blue	70	35
458	30 c. black, brownish grey & dull reddish pur	85	60
455/8		Set of 4	2·25	1·10

Designs:—20 c. Diogo Cao's coat of arms; 25 c. Caravel; 30 c. Diogo Cao.

(Des J. van Niekerk)

1986 (24 Apr). *Rock Formations.* T **123** *and similar horiz designs. Multicoloured.* P 14.

459	14 c. Type 123..		60	15
460	20 c. Vingerklip, near Outjo		70	25
461	25 c. Petrified sand dunes, Kuiseb River		85	40
462	30 c. Orgelpfeifen, Twyfelfontein		95	55
459/62		Set of 4	2·75	1·25

PHILATELIC FOUNDATION MINIATURE SHEETS. These miniature sheets were issued by the Philatelic Foundation of Southern Africa and not the postal administration. They could be purchased by post or from a limited number of philatelic offices, mainly in South Africa, at a premium in aid of various national and international stamp exhibitions.

124 Model wearing   125 Pirogue, Lake
Swakara Coat   Liambezi

(Des J. van Ellinckhuijzen)

1986 (10 July). *Karakul Industry.* T **124** *and similar vert designs. Multicoloured.* P 14.

463	14 c. Type 124..		35	15
464	20 c. Weaving karakul wool carpet		55	30
465	25 c. Flock of karakul ewes on veld..		55	45
466	30 c. Karakul rams		75	60
463/6		Set of 4	2·00	1·40

The 30 c. value exists as a Philatelic Foundation miniature sheet.

1986 (6 Nov). *Life in the Caprivi Strip.* T **125** *and similar horiz designs. Multicoloured.* P 14.

467	14 c. Type 125..		50	15
468	20 c. Ploughing with oxen		80	80
469	25 c. Settlement in Eastern Caprivi		1·00	1·25
470	30 c. Map of Caprivi Strip		1·25	2·00
467/70		Set of 4	3·25	3·75

126 "Gobabis Mission Station", 1863   127 *Garreta nitens*
(beetle)

1987 (19 Feb). *Paintings by Thomas Baines.* T **126** *and similar horiz designs. Multicoloured.* P 14.

471	14 c. Type 126..		50	15
472	20 c. "Outspan at Koobie", 1861		90	90
473	25 c. "Outspan under Oomahaama Tree", 1862		1·25	1·50
474	30 c. "Swakop River", 1861		1·50	2·50
471/4		Set of 4	3·75	4·50

The 25 c. value exists as a Philatelic Foundation miniature sheet.

(Des E. Holm)

1987 (7 May). *Useful Insects.* T **127** *and similar horiz designs. Multicoloured.* P 14.

475	16 c. Type 127..		60	15
476	20 c. *Alcimus stenurus* (fly)		95	95
477	25 c. *Anthophora caerulea* (bee)		1·25	1·75
478	30 c. *Hemiempusa capensis* (mantid)		1·60	2·50
475/8		Set of 4	4·00	4·75

128 Okaukuejo

(Des J. van Niekerk)

1987 (23 July). *Tourist Camps.* T **128** *and similar horiz designs. Multicoloured.* P 14½ × 14.

479	16 c. Type 128..		55	15
480	20 c. Daan Viljoen		70	75
481	25 c. Ai-Ais		80	1·40
482	30 c. Hardap		85	1·60
479/82		Set of 4	2·50	3·50

129 Wreck of *Hope*   130 Bartolomeu Dias
(Dutch whaling
schooner), 1804

(Des Sheila Nowers)

1987 (15 Oct). *Shipwrecks.* T **129** *and similar horiz designs. Multicoloured.* P 14.

483	16 c. Type 129		60	15
484	30 c. *Tilly* (brig), 1885		1·00	1·00
485	40 c. *Eduard Bohlen* (steamer), 1909		1·25	2·25
486	50 c. *Dunedin Star* (liner), 1942		1·50	1·50
483/6		Set of 4	4·00	5·50

(Des Sheila Nowers)

1988 (7 Jan). *500th Anniv of Discovery of Cape of Good Hope by Bartolomeu Dias. T* **130** *and similar vert designs. Multicoloured. P* 14.

487	16 c. Type **130**. .	..	45	15
488	30 c. Caravel	..	85	55
489	40 c. Map of South West Africa, c. 1502		1·00	70
490	50 c. King João II of Portugal	..	1·00	75
487/90	.. .. ..	*Set of* 4	3·00	2·00

131 Sossusvlei

(Des J. van Niekerk)

1988 (3 Mar). *Landmarks of South West Africa. T* **131** *and similar horiz designs. Multicoloured. P* 14.

491	16 c. Type **131**.	..	45	15
492	30 c. Sesriem Canyon	..	80	65
493	40 c. Hoaruseb "clay castles"	..	95	1·10
494	50 c. Hoba meteorite	..	1·00	1·40
491/4	..	*Set of* 4	2·75	3·00

MACHINE LABELS. From 30 March 1988 gummed labels in the above design numbered "PT01", ranging in value from 1 c. to 99 r. 99, were available from a machine located at the Windhoek Post Office. During 1989 three further machines at Windhoek Ausspanplatz (PT02) (6 March), Swakopmund (PT03) (10 March) and Keepmanshoop (PT04) (14 March) were added. Machines PT01/2 were withdrawn on 23 November 1990 and the other two followed four days later. A commemorative design, without code number, was used at the "OTYIMBINGUE 100" philatelic exhibition, Windhoek, between 7 and 9 July 1988.

132 First Postal Agency, Otyimbingue, 1888	133 Herero Chat

(Des H. Pulon)

1988 (7 July). *Centenary of Postal Service in South West Africa. T* **132** *and similar horiz designs. Multicoloured. P* 14.

495	16 c. Type **132**	..	45	15
496	30 c. Post Office, Windhoek, 1904	..	80	55
497	40 c. Mail-runner and map	..	90	75
498	50 c. Camel mail, 1904	..	1·00	1·00
495/8	..	*Set of* 4	2·75	2·25

The 50 c. value exists as a Philatelic Foundation miniature sheet.

(Des G. Arnott)

1988 (3 Nov). *Birds of South West Africa. T* **133** *and similar vert designs. Multicoloured. P* 14.

499	16 c. Type **133**	..	70	20
500	30 c. Gray's Lark	..	1·10	75
501	40 c. Rüppell's Bustard	..	1·25	1·10
502	50 c. Monteiro's Hornbill	..	1·25	1·25
499/502	..	*Set of* 4	3·75	3·00

134 Dr. C. H. Hahn and Gross-Barmen Mission	135 Beech Commuter 1900

(Des H. Pulon)

1989 (16 Feb). *Missionaries. T* **134** *and similar horiz designs. Multicoloured. P* 14.

503	16 c. Type **134**	..	30	10
504	30 c. Revd. J. G. Krönlein and Berseba Mission		60	60
505	40 c. Revd. F. H. Kleinschmidt and Rehoboth Mission		70	70
506	50 c. Revd. J. H. Schmelen and Bethanien Mission		70	85
503/6		*Set of* 4	2·10	2·00

(Des M. Botha)

1989 (18 May). *75th Anniv of Aviation in South West Africa. T* **135** *and similar horiz designs. Multicoloured. P* 14.

507	18 c. Type **135**	..	40	15
508	30 c. Ryan Navion	..	70	50

509	40 c. Junkers F-13	..	80	55
510	50 c. Pfalz Otto biplane	..	90	70
507/10		*Set of* 4	2·50	1·75

The 50 c. value exists as a Philatelic Foundation miniature sheet.

136 Barchan Dunes

(Des A. H. Barrett)

1989 (14 Aug). *Namib Desert Sand Dunes. T* **136** *and similar horiz designs. Multicoloured. P* 14.

511	18 c. Barchan dunes	..	30	15
512	30 c. Star dunes (36×20 *mm*)	..	50	40
513	40 c. Transverse dunes	..	60	60
514	50 c. Crescentic dunes (36×20 *mm*)		80	80
511/14		*Set of* 4	2·00	1·75

137 Ballot Box and Outline Map of South West Africa

1989 (24 Aug). *South West Africa Constitutional Election. P* 14.

515	**137** 18 c. purple-brown and salmon	..	30	15
516	35 c. deep grey-blue and pale emerald		50	40
517	45 c. plum and lemon	..	70	60
518	60 c. dull green and deep yellow-ochre		80	80
515/18		*Set of* 4	2·10	1·75

138 Gypsum	139 Oranjemund Alluvial Diamond Field

(Des J. van Niekerk)

1989 (16 Nov)–**90.** *Minerals. T* **138/9** *and similar multicoloured designs. Phosphorised paper (25 c.) or chalk-surfaced paper (30, 35, 50 c., 1 r.). P* 14.

519	1 c. Type **138**	..	10	10
520	2 c. Fluorite	..	15	10
521	5 c. Mimetite	..	20	10
522	7 c. Cuprite	..	20	10
523	10 c. Azurite	..	25	10
524	18 c. Boltwoodite (inscr "K (H3O) (UO2) (SiO4)")		25	10
	a. Formula corrected to "K2 (UO2) 2 (SiO3) 2 (OH) 2 5 H2O" (25.10.90)		11·00	2·00
525	20 c. Dioptase	..	40	15
526	25 c. Type **139**	..	50	15
527	30 c. Tsumeb lead and copper complex		65	20
528	35 c. Rosh Pinah zinc mine	..	65	20
529	40 c. Diamonds	..	85	30
530	45 c. Wulfenite	..	85	30
531	50 c. Uis tin mine	..	1·00	40
532	1 r. Rössing uranium mine	..	1·75	1·00
533	2 r. Gold	..	2·75	2·00
519/33		*Set of* 15	9·50	4·50

The 1, 2, 5, 7, 10, 18, 20, 40, 45 c. and 2 r. are vertical as T **138**, and the 25, 30, 35, 50 c. and 1 r. horizontal as T **139**.

140 Arrow Poison

(Des Eva-Maria Linsmayer)

1990 (1 Feb). *Flora. T* **140** *and similar vert designs. Multicoloured. P* 14.

534	18 c. Type **140**	..	35	10
535	35 c. Baobab flower	..	70	40
536	45 c. Sausage Tree flowers	..	75	50
537	60 c. Devil's Claw	..	90	90
534/7		*Set of* 4	2·50	1·75

The 60 c. value exists as a Philatelic Foundation miniature sheet.

NAMIBIA

South West Africa became independent, as Namibia, on 21 March 1990.

The Walvis Bay Territory was ceded by South Africa to Namibia on 1 March 1994.

PRINTERS. The following stamps were printed in lithography by the Government Printer, Pretoria, South Africa.

141 Pres. Sam Nujoma, Map of Namibia and National Flag	142 Fish River Canyon

(Des T. Marais)

1990 (21 Mar). *Independence. T* **141** *and similar multicoloured designs. P* 14.

538	18 c. Type **141**	..	30	15
539	45 c. Hands releasing dove and map of Namibia (*vert*)		70	1·00
540	60 c. National flag and map of Africa		1·25	1·75
538/40		*Set of* 3	2·00	2·50

(Des J. van Ellinckhuijzen)

1990 (26 Apr). *Namibia Landscapes. T* **142** *and similar horiz designs. Multicoloured. P* 14.

541	18 c. Type **142**	..	35	20
542	35 c. Quiver-tree forest, Keetmanshoop		65	35
543	45 c. Tsaris Mountains	..	75	55
544	60 c. Dolerite boulders, Keetmanshoop		85	65
541/4		*Set of* 4	2·40	1·60

The 60 c. value exists as a Philatelic Foundation miniature sheet.

143 Stores on Kaiser Street, c. 1899	144 Maizefields

(Des J. van Ellinckhuijzen)

1990 (26 July). *Centenary of Windhoek. T* **143** *and similar horiz designs. Multicoloured. P* 14.

545	18 c. Type **143**	..	25	20
546	35 c. Kaiser Street, 1990	..	45	35
547	45 c. City Hall, 1914	..	55	65
548	60 c. City Hall, 1990	..	70	1·00
545/8		*Set of* 4	1·75	2·00

1990 (11 Oct). *Farming. T* **144** *and similar horiz designs. Multicoloured. P* 14.

549	20 c. Type **144**	..	25	20
550	35 c. Sanga bull	..	45	35
551	50 c. Damara ram	..	60	45
552	65 c. Irrigation in Okavango	..	75	60
549/52		*Set of* 4	1·90	1·40

145 Gypsum	146 Radiosonde Weather Balloon

(Des J. van Niekerk)

1991 (2 Jan–14 June). *Minerals. Designs as Nos.* 519/21 *and* 523/33, *some with values changed, and new design (5 r.), inscr* "Namibia" *as T* **145**. *Multicoloured. Chalk-surfaced paper (25, 30, 35, 50 c., 1 r.). P* 14.

553	1 c. Type **145**	..	10	10
554	2 c. Fluorite	..	15	10
555	5 c. Mimetite	..	20	10
556	10 c. Azurite	..	30	10
557	20 c. Dioptase	..	35	10
558	25 c. Type **139**	..	35	15
	a. Ordinary paper (14 June)		35	15
559	30 c. Tsumeb lead and copper complex		50	20
560	35 c. Rosh Pinah zinc mine	..	50	20
561	40 c. Diamonds	..	65	25
562	50 c. Uis tin mine	..	65	25
563	65 c. Boltwoodite	..	65	35
564	1 r. Rössing uranium mine	..	70	50
565	1 r. 50, Wulfenite	..	1·00	70
566	2 r. Gold	..	1·50	1·10
567	5 r. Willemite (vert as T **145**)	..	2·00	2·75
553/67		*Set of* 15	9·50	6·00

Printings of the 5 c. and 10 c. in 1992 were on phosphorescent paper.

(Des L. Kriedemann)

1991 (1 Feb). *Centenary of Weather Service. T* **146** *and similar horiz designs. Multicoloured. P* 14.

568	20 c. Type **146**	..	30	20
569	35 c. Sunshine recorder	..	45	30
570	50 c. Measuring equipment	..	60	50
571	65 c. Meteorological station, Gobabeb		70	60
568/71		*Set of* 4	1·90	1·40

147 Herd of Zebras   148 Karas Mountains

1991 (18 Apr). *Endangered Species. Mountain Zebra. T* **147** *and similar horiz designs. Multicoloured. P* 14.

572	20 c. Type **147**		1·10	60
573	25 c. Mare and foal		1·25	70
574	45 c. Zebras and foal		2·00	1·75
575	60 c. Two zebras		2·50	3·00
572/5		*Set of 4*	6·00	5·50

The 45 c. value exists as a Philatelic Foundation miniature sheet.

(Des A. H. Barrett)

1991 (18 July). *Mountains of Namibia. T* **148** *and similar horiz designs. Multicoloured. P* 14.

576	20 c. Type **148**		35	20
577	25 c. Gamsberg Mountains		40	30
578	45 c. Mount Brukkaros		70	70
579	60 c. Erongo Mountains		80	1·00
576/9		*Set of 4*	2·00	2·00

149 Bernabe de la Bat   150 Artist's Pallet
Camp

(Des J. van Niekerk)

1991 (24 Oct). *Tourist Camps. T* **149** *and similar horiz designs. Multicoloured. P* 14.

580	20 c. Type **149**		45	30
581	25 c. Von Bach Dam Recreation Resort		55	45
582	45 c. Gross Barmen Hot Springs		85	65
583	60 c. Namutoni Rest Camp		1·00	1·00
580/3		*Set of 4*	2·50	2·25

(Des H. Pulon)

1992 (30 Jan). *21st Anniv of Windhoek Conservatoire. T* **150** *and similar horiz designs. Multicoloured. P* 14.

584	20 c. Type **150**		20	15
585	25 c. French horn and cello		25	20
586	45 c. Theatrical masks		50	60
587	60 c. Ballet dancers		65	1·00
584/7		*Set of 4*	1·40	1·75

151 Mozambique   152 Old Jetty
Mouthbrooder

(Des B. Jackson)

1992 (16 Apr). *Freshwater Angling. T* **151** *and similar horiz designs. Multicoloured. P* 14.

588	20 c. Type **151**		40	20
589	25 c. Large-mouthed Yellowfish		45	20
590	45 c. Common Carp		85	50
591	60 c. Sharp-toothed Catfish		95	65
588/91		*Set of 4*	2·40	1·40

The 45 c. value exists as a Philatelic Foundation miniature sheet.

1992 (2 July). *Centenary of Swakopmund. T* **152** *and similar horiz designs. Multicoloured. P* 14.

592	20 c. Type **152**		25	25
593	25 c. Recreation centre		25	25
594	45 c. State House and lighthouse		80	60
595	60 c. Sea front		85	75
592/5		*Set of 4*	1·90	1·60
MS596	118×93 mm. Nos. 592/5		2·75	2·75

153 Running   154 Wrapping
English
Cucumbers

(Des B. Jackson)

1992 (24 July). *Olympic Games, Barcelona. T* **153** *and similar horiz designs. Multicoloured. P* 14.

597	20 c. Type **153**		25	20
598	25 c. Map of Namibia, Namibian flag and Olympic rings		30	20
599	45 c. Swimming		50	40
600	60 c. Olympic Stadium, Barcelona		1·50	1·25
597/600		*Set of 4*	1·50	1·25
MS601	115×75 mm. Nos. 597/600 (*sold at 2 r.*)		2·25	2·75

1992 (10 Sept). *Integration of the Disabled. T* **154** *and similar horiz designs. Multicoloured. P* 14.

602	20 c. Type **154**		20	15
603	25 c. Weaving mats		20	15
604	45 c. Spinning thread		40	30
605	60 c. Preparing pot plants		55	50
602/5		*Set of 4*	1·25	1·00

155 Elephants in Desert   156 Herd of Simmentaler
Cattle

(Des D. Murphy)

1993 (25 Feb). *Namibia Nature Foundation. Rare and Endangered Species. T* **155** *and similar horiz designs. Multicoloured. P* 14.

606	20 c. Type **155**		40	20
607	25 c. Sitatunga in swamp		30	20
608	45 c. Black Rhinoceros		65	50
609	60 c. Hunting Dogs		65	60
606/9		*Set of 4*	1·75	1·40
MS610	217×59 mm. Nos. 606/9 (*sold at 2 r.* 50)		3·50	3·50

(Des Carola Kronsbein-Goldbeck)

1993 (16 Apr). *Centenary of Simmentaler Cattle in Namibia. T* **156** *and similar horiz designs. Multicoloured. P* 14.

611	20 c. Type **156**		30	10
612	25 c. Cow and calf		30	15
613	45 c. Bull		60	40
614	60 c. Cattle on barge		85	75
611/14		*Set of 4*	1·90	1·25

The 45 c. value exists as a Philatelic Foundation miniature sheet.

157 Sand Dunes,   158 Smiling Child
Sossusvlei

(Des J. van Ellinckhuijzen)

1993 (4 June). *Namib Desert Scenery. T* **157** *and similar horiz designs. Multicoloured. P* 14.

615	30 c. Type **157**		25	20
616	40 c. Blutkuppe		25	20
617	65 c. River Kuiseb, Homeb		40	45
618	85 c. Desert landscape		60	65
615/18		*Set of 4*	1·40	1·40

(Des J. van Ellinckhuijzen)

1993 (6 Aug). *S.O.S. Child Care in Namibia. T* **158** *and similar horiz designs. Multicoloured. P* 14.

619	30 c. Type **158**		30	20
620	40 c. Family		35	20
621	65 c. Modern house		60	55
622	85 c. Young artist with mural		80	80
619/22		*Set of 4*	1·90	1·60

(New Currency. 100 cents = 1 Namibia dollar)

159 *Charaxes*   160 White Seabream
jasius

(Des A. Ainslie)

1993 (1 Oct). *Butterflies. T* **159** *and similar vert designs. Multicoloured. P* 14.

623	5 c. Type **159**		20	20
624	10 c. *Acraea anemosa*		20	20
625	20 c. *Papilio nireus*		30	10
626	30 c. *Junonia octavia*		30	10
627	40 c. *Hypolimnus misippus*		30	10
628	50 c. *Physcaeneura panda*		40	20
629	65 c. *Charaxes candiope*		40	30
630	85 c. *Junonia hierta*		50	40
631	90 c. *Colotis cellmene*		50	40
632	$1 *Cacyreus dicksoni*		55	35
633	$2 *Charaxes bohemani*		80	80
634	$2.50, *Stugeta bowkeri*		1·00	1·10
635	$5 *Byblia anvatara*		1·50	1·75
623/35		*Set of 13*	6·25	5·50

For similar design inscribed "STANDARDISED MAIL" see No. 648.

For 5 c. and 50 c. with elliptical perforations see Nos. 707/8.

(Des B. Jackson)

1994 (4 Feb). *Coastal Angling. T* **160** *and similar horiz designs. Multicoloured. P* 14.

636	30 c. Type **160**		25	25
637	40 c. Kob		25	25
638	65 c. West Coast Steenbras		40	40
639	85 c. Galjoen		60	60
636/9		*Set of 4*	1·40	1·40
MS640	134×89 mm. Nos. 636/9 (*sold at $2.50*)		2·00	2·50

161 Container Ship at   162 *Adenolobus*
Wharf   *pechuelii*

(Des Liza van der Wal (85 c.))

1994 (1 Mar). *Incorporation of Walvis Bay Territory into Namibia. T* **161** *and similar vert designs. Multicoloured. P* 14.

641	30 c. Type **161**		40	30
642	65 c. Aerial view of Walvis Bay		60	80
643	85 c. Map of Namibia		95	1·25
641/3		*Set of 3*	1·75	2·10

(Des Auriol Batten)

1994 (8 Apr). *Flowers. T* **162** *and similar vert designs. Multicoloured. P* 14.

644	35 c. Type **162**		30	25
645	40 c. *Hibiscus elliottiae*		30	25
646	65 c. *Pelargonium cortusifolium*		55	40
647	85 c. *Hoodia macrantha*		75	60
644/7		*Set of 4*	1·60	1·40

1994 (8 Apr). *Butterflies. Vert design as T* **159**, *but inscr* "STANDARDISED MAIL". *Multicoloured. P* 14.

648	(–) *Graphium antheus*		15	20

No. 648 was initially sold at 35 c., but this was subsequently increased to reflect changes in postal rates.

163 Yellow-billed   164 Steam Railcar, 1908
Stork

(Des A. Barrett)

1994 (3 June). *Storks. T* **163** *and similar vert designs. Multicoloured. P* 14.

649	35 c. Type **163**		40	30
650	40 c. Abdim's Stork		40	30
651	80 c. African Open-bill Stork		70	50
652	$1.10, White Stork		80	65
649/52		*Set of 4*	2·10	1·60

(Des H. Botha)

1994 (5 Aug). *Steam Locomotives. T* **164** *and similar horiz designs. Multicoloured. P* 14.

653	35 c. Type **164**		45	30
654	70 c. Krauss side-tank locomotive No. 106, 1904		70	50
655	80 c. Class 24 locomotive, 1948		75	55
656	$1.10, Class 7C locomotive, 1914		1·10	90
653/6		*Set of 4*	2·75	1·90

The 80 c. value exists as a Philatelic Foundation miniature sheet.

165 Cape Cross Locomotive No.   166 National Arms
84 *Prince Edward*, 1895

(Des H. Botha)

1995 (8 Mar–1 Nov). *Centenary of Railways in Namibia. T* **165** *and similar horiz designs. Multicoloured. P* 14.

657	35 c. Type **165**		45	25
658	70 c. Steam locomotive, German South West Africa		70	35
659	80 c. South African Railways Class 8 steam locomotive		75	40

660	$1.10, Trans-Namib Class 33-400 diesel-electric locomotive	.. ..	1·10	55
657/60		*Set of 4*	2·75	1·40
MS661	101×94 mm. Nos. 657/60	.. ..	2·75	1·75
	a. Optd "November 1995" on sheet margin (1 Nov)		2·75	2·25

(Des B. Wepener)

1995 (21 Mar). *5th Anniv of Independence.* P 14.

662 **166**	(–) multicoloured	.. ..	30	30

No. 662 is inscribed "STANDARDISED MAIL" and was initially sold for 35 c., but this was subsequently increased to reflect changes in postal rates.

167 Living Tortoise and *Geochelone stromeri* (fossil)

168 Martii Rautanen and Church

(Des L. Kriedemann)

1995 (24 May). *Fossils.* T **167** *and similar vert designs. Multicoloured.* P 14.

663	40 c. Type **167**	..	50	25
664	80 c. Ward's Diamond Bird and *Diamantornis wardi* (fossil eggs)		80	60
665	90 c. Hyraxes and *Prohyrax hendeyi* skull		90	70
666	$1.20, Crocodiles and *Crocodylus lloydi* skull	..	1·10	90
663/6		*Set of 4*	3·00	2·25

The 80 c. value exists as a Philatelic Foundation miniature sheet.

(Des H. Pulon)

1995 (10 July). *125th Anniv of Finnish Missionaries in Namibia.* T **168** *and similar horiz designs. Multicoloured.* P 14.

667	40 c. Type **168**	..	25	20
668	80 c. Albin Savola and hand printing press		50	50
669	90 c. Karl Weikkolin and wagon	..	60	65
670	$1.20, Dr. Selma Rainio and Onandjokwe Hospital		85	95
667/70		*Set of 4*	2·00	2·10

169 Ivory Buttons

170 U.N. Flag

(Des H. Pulon)

1995 (16 Aug). *Personal Ornaments.* T **169** *and similar vert designs. Multicoloured.* P 14.

671	40 c. Type **169**	..	20	20
672	80 c. Conus shell pendant	..	45	45
673	90 c. Cowrie shell headdress	..	55	55
674	$1.20, Shell button pendant	..	85	95
671/4		*Set of 4*	1·90	2·00

(Des Sheila Nowers)

1995 (1 Sept). *"Singapore '95" International Stamp Exhibition. Sheet, 110×52 mm, containing designs as No. 359b with altered face value and inscription.* P 14.

MS675	$1.20, multicoloured	.. ..	1·10	1·25

No. **MS675** shows the exhibition emblem printed on the sheet margin.

(Des J. van Niekerk)

1995 (24 Oct). *50th Anniv of the United Nations.* P 14.

676 **170**	40 c. new blue and black	.. ..	20	20

171 Bogenfels Arch

172 Sister Leoni Kreitmeier and Döbra Education and Training Centre

(Des Christine Marais. Litho Harrison)

1996 (1 Apr). *Tourism.* T **171** *and similar horiz designs. Multicoloured.* P 15×14.

677	(–) Type **171**	..	15	15
678	90 c. Ruacana Falls	..	30	30
679	$1 Epupa Falls	..	30	30
680	$1.30, Herd of wild horses	..	35	50
677/80		*Set of 4*	1·00	1·10

No. 677 is inscribed "Standardised Mail" and was initially sold at 45 c.

(Des J. van Niekerk. Litho Harrison)

1996 (27 May). *Centenary of Catholic Missions in Namibia.* T **172** *and similar horiz designs. Multicoloured.* P 15×14.

681	50 c. Type **172**	..	20	20
682	95 c. Father Johann Malinowski and Heirachabis Mission		30	40
683	$1 St. Mary's Cathedral, Windhoek		30	40
684	$1.30, Archbishop Joseph Gotthardt and early church, Ovamboland		35	80
681/4		*Set of 4*	1·00	1·60

(Des Sheila Nowers)

1996 (8 June). *"CAPEX '96" International Stamp Exhibition, Toronto. Sheet, 105×45 mm, containing design similar to No. 358c with new face value and inscription.* P 14½×14.

MS685	$1.30, multicoloured	.. ..	85	90

173 Children and U.N.I.C.E.F. Volunteer

(Des A. Ainslie. Litho Harrison)

1996 (14 June). *50th Anniv of U.N.I.C.E.F.* T **173** *and similar horiz design. Multicoloured.* P 15×14.

686	(–) Type **173**	..	15	15
687	$1.30, Girls in school	..	60	60

No. 686 is inscribed "STANDARD POSTAGE" and was initially sold at 50 c.

174 Boxing

175 Scorpius

(Des B. Jackson. Litho Harrison)

1996 (27 June). *Centennial Olympic Games, Atlanta.* T **174** *and similar horiz designs. Multicoloured.* P 15×14.

688	(–) Type **174**	..	15	15
689	90 c. Cycling	..	30	40
690	$1 Swimming	..	30	40
691	$1.30, Running	..	35	55
688/91		*Set of 4*	1·00	1·40

No. 688 is inscribed "Standard Postage" and was initially sold at 50 c.

(Des J. van Ellinckhuijzen. Litho Harrison)

1996 (12 Sept). *Stars in the Namibian Sky.* T **175** *and similar horiz designs. Multicoloured.* P 15×14.

692	(–) Type **175**	..	15	15
693	90 c. Sagittarius	..	25	30
694	$1 Southern Cross	..	30	30
695	$1.30, Orion	..	35	50
692/5		*Set of 4*	95	1·10
MS696	100×80 mm. No. 694		1·50	1·75

No. 692 is inscribed "Standard Postage" and was initially sold at 50 c.

For No. **MS696** revalued to $3.50 see No. **MS706**

176 Urn-shaped Pot

177 Khauxa!nas Ruins

(Des Sheila Nowers. Litho Harrison)

1996 (17 Oct). *Early Pottery.* T **176** *and similar vert designs. Multicoloured.* P 14×15.

697	(–) Type **176**	..	15	15
698	90 c. Decorated storage pot	..	25	40
699	$1 Reconstructed cooking pot	..	30	40
700	$1.30, Storage pot	..	35	70
697/700		*Set of 4*	95	1·50

No. 697 is inscribed "Standard Postage" and was initially sold at 50 c.

(Des J. van Ellinckhuijzen. Litho Harrison)

1997 (6 Feb). *Khaux!nas Ruins.* T **177** *and similar horiz designs showing different views.* P 15×14.

701	(–) multicoloured	..	25	20
702	$1 multicoloured	..	50	50
703	$1.10, multicoloured	..	60	65
704	$1.50, multicoloured	..	85	1·00
701/4		*Set of 4*	2·00	2·10

No. 701 is inscribed "Standard postage" and was initially sold at 50 c.

178 Ox

179 Heinrich von Stephan

(Des J. van Ellinckhuijzen. Litho Harrison)

1997 (12 Feb). *"HONG KONG '97" International Stamp Exhibition and Chinese New Year ("Year of the Ox"). Sheet, 103×67 mm.* P 15×14.

MS705 178	$1.30, multicoloured	.. ..	1·10	1·10

1997 (17 Feb). *Support for Organised Philately.* No. **MS696** *with margin additional inscr "Reprint February 17 1997. Sold in aid of organized Philately N$3.50".*

MS706	$1 Southern Cross (sold at $3.50)	.. ..	1·75	2·00

(Litho Harrison)

1997 (26 Mar). *As Nos. 623 and 628, but* P 14½ *(with two elliptical holes on each vertical side).*

707	5 c. Type **159**	..	10	10
708	50 c. *Physcaeneura panda*	..	40	40

(Des J. van Ellinckhuijzen. Litho Harrison)

1997 (8 Apr). *Death Centenary of Heinrich von Stephan (founder of U.P.U.).* P 14×15.

709 **179**	$2 multicoloured	.. ..	85	85

180 Cinderella Waxbill

181 Helmet Guineafowl

(Des Julia Birkhead. Photo Harrison)

1997 (6 May). *Waxbills.* T **180** *and similar horiz design. Multicoloured.* P 14×14½ *(with one elliptical hole on each horizontal side).*

710	50 c. Type **180**	..	20	30
	a. Booklet pane. Nos. 710/11, each × 5		2·00	
711	60 c. Black-cheeked Waxbill	..	20	30

Nos. 710/11 were only issued in $5.50 stamp booklets.

(Des Isabel van der Ploeg. Photo Enschedé)

1997 (6 May). *Greetings Stamp.* P 15×14.

712 **181**	$1.20, multicoloured	..	30	35

For similar designs see Nos. 743/6

182 Jackass Penguins calling

183 Caracal

(Des D. Thorpe. Litho Harrison)

1997 (15 May). *Endangered Species. Jackass Penguin.* T **182** *and similar vert designs. Multicoloured.* P 14×15.

713	(–) Type **182**	..	25	30
714	$1 Incubating egg	..	40	40
715	$1.10, Adult with chick	..	50	50
716	$1.50, Penguins swimming	..	55	55
713/16		*Set of 4*	1·50	1·50
MS717	101×92 mm. As Nos. 713/16, but without the WWF symbol (*sold at $5*)		1·50	1·50

No. 713 is inscribed "STANDARD POSTAGE" and was initially sold for 50 c.

(Des Sheila Nowers. Litho Harrison)

1997 (12 June). *Wildcats.* T **183** *and similar horiz designs. Multicoloured.* P 15×14.

718	(–) Type **183**	..	20	20
719	$1 *Felis lybica*	..	30	30
720	$1.10, Serval	..	35	40
721	$1.50, Black-footed Cat	..	55	55
718/21		*Set of 4*	1·25	1·25
MS722	100×80 mm. $5 As No. 721		2·00	2·25

No. 718 is inscribed "STANDARD POSTAGE" and was initially sold at 50 c.

No. **MS722** was sold in aid of organised philately in Southern Africa.

184 *Catophractes alexandri*   185 Collecting Bag

(Des T. Breckwoldt (Nos 723/7), Isabel van der Ploeg (others). Litho Enschedé)

1997 (27 June). *Greeting Stamps. Flowers and Helmet Guineafowl. T* **184** *and similar horiz designs. Multicoloured. P* 14×13½.

723	(–) Type 184	15	20
	a. Booklet pane. Nos. 723/7, each × 2, and 10 labels		1·50
724	(–) *Crinum paludosum*	15	20
725	(–) *Gloriosa superba*	15	20
726	(–) *Tribulus zeyheri*	15	20
727	(–) *Aptosimum pubescens*	15	20
728	50 c. Helmet Guineafowl raising hat	15	20
	a. Booklet pane. Nos. 728/32, each × 2, and 10 labels		1·75
729	50 c. Holding bouquet	15	20
730	50 c. Ill in bed	15	20
731	$1 With heart round neck	25	20
732	$1 With suitcase and backpack	25	20
723/32	Set of 10	1·75	2·25

These stamps only come from $5 (Nos. 723/7) or $7 (Nos. 728/32) stamp booklets where they occur in panes of 10 (5×2) with margins all round and greetings labels at top and bottom. Nos. 723/7 are inscribed "Standard Postage" and were initially sold at 50 c. each.

(Des J. van Niekerk. Litho Harrison)

1997 (8 July). *Basket Work. T* **185** *and similar vert designs. Multicoloured. P* 14×15.

733	50 c. Type 185	20	20
734	90 c. Powder basket	30	30
735	$1.20, Fruit basket	35	35
736	$2 Grain basket	70	75
733/6	Set of 4	1·40	1·40

186 Veterinary Association Coat of Arms

(Litho Harrison)

1997 (12 Sept). *50th Anniv of Namibian Veterinary Association. P* 14×14½.

737	186 $1.50, multicoloured	50	50
	a. Tête-bêche pair	1·00	1·00

No. 737 was issued in sheets of 10 containing one row of tête-bêche pairs.

187 Head of Triceratops   188 German South West Africa Postman

(Des J. van Ellinckhuijzen. Litho Enschedé)

1997 (27 Sept). *Youth Philately. Dinosaurs. Sheet* 82×56 *mm. P* 12½×13.

MS738	187 $5 multicoloured	1·50	1·75

(Des J. Madisia. Litho Enschedé)

1997 (9 Oct). *World Post Day. P* 14×15

739	188 (–) multicoloured	20	20

No. 739 is inscribed "STANDARD POSTAGE" and was initially sold at 50 c.

STANLEY GIBBONS STAMP COLLECTING SERIES

Introductory booklets on *How to Start, How to Identify Stamps* and *Collecting by Theme*. A series of well illustrated guides at a low price. Write for details.

---

189 False Mopane   190 Flame Lily

(Des Auriol Batten. Litho Enschedé)

1997 (10 Oct). *Trees. T* **189** *and similar vert designs. Multicoloured. P* 14×15.

740	(–) Type 189	15	20
741	$1 Ana Tree	30	40
742	$1.10, Shepherd's Tree	35	55
743	$1.50, Kiaat	50	70
740/3	Set of 4	1·10	1·60

No. 740 is inscribed "STANDARD POSTAGE" and was initially sold at 50 c.

(Des Isabel van der Ploeg. Litho Enschedé)

1997 (3 Nov). *Christmas. Multicoloured designs as T* **181** *showing Helmet Guineafowl, each with festive frame. P* 13×12½.

744	(–) Guineafowl facing right	15	20
745	$1 Guineafowl in grass	30	30
746	$1.10, Guineafowl on rock	35	40
747	$1.50, Guineafowl in desert	50	55
744/7	Set of 4	1·10	1·25
MS748	110×80 mm. $5 Helmet Guineafowl (vert). P 12½×13	2·00	2·00

No. 744 is inscribed "standard postage" and was initially sold at 50 c.

(Des D. Murphy. Litho Enschedé)

1997 (3 Nov). *Flora and Fauna. T* **190** *and similar vert designs. Multicoloured.* (a) *P* 13½.

749	5 c. Type 190	10	10
	a. Booklet pane. Nos. 749/66 with margins all round		6·50
750	10 c. Bushman Poison	10	10
751	20 c. Camel's Foot	10	10
752	30 c. Western Rhigozum	10	10
753	40 c. Blue-cheeked Bee-eater	10	10
754	50 c. Laughing Dove	10	10
755	(–) Peach-faced Lovebird	10	10
	a. Booklet pane. No. 755×10 with margins all round		1·00
756	60 c. Lappet-faced Vulture	10	10
757	90 c. Yellow-billed Hornbill	20	25
758	$1 Lilac-breasted Roller	20	25
759	$1.10, Hippopotamus	20	25
760	$1.20, Giraffe	30	35
761	(–) Leopard	30	35
	a. Booklet pane. No. 761×10 with margins all round		3·00
762	$1.50, Elephant	30	35
763	$2 Lion	40	45
764	$4 Buffalo	80	85
765	$5 Black Rhinoceros	1·00	1·10
766	$10 Cheetah	2·00	2·10
749/66	Set of 18	6·50	7·00

(b) *Self-adhesive. P* 12×12½.

767	(–) As No. 755	15	20
768	$1 As No. 758	25	30
769	(–) As No. 761	30	35
767/9	Set of 3	70	85

Nos. 755 and 767 are inscribed "standard postage" and were each initially sold at 50 c., Nos. 761 and 769 are inscribed "postcard rate" and were each initially sold at $1.20.

191 John Muafangejo   192 Gabriel B. Taapopi

(Des J. van Ellinckhuijzen. Litho Harrison)

1997 (27 Nov). *10th Death Anniv of John Muafangejo (artist). P* 14×15.

770	191 (–) multicoloured	30	30

No. 770 is inscribed "STANDARD POSTAGE" and was initially sold at 50 c.

(Des J. van Ellinckhuijzen. Litho Enschedé)

1998 (15 Jan). *Gabriel B. Taapopi (educator) Commemoration. P* 14×15.

771	192 (–) silver and reddish brown	20	20

No. 771 is inscribed "STANDARD POSTAGE" and was sold for 50 c.

---

193 Year of the Tiger

(Litho Enschedé)

1998 (19 Jan). *International Stamp and Coin Exhibition* 1997, *Shanghai. Sheets,* 165×125 *mm or* 97×85 *mm, containing multicoloured designs as T* **193**.

(a) *Lunar New Year*

MS772	165×125 mm. $2.50 × 6. Type 193; Light green tiger and circular symbol; Yellow tiger and head symbol; Blue tiger and square symbol; Emerald tiger and square symbol; Mauve tiger and triangular symbol (61×29 mm). P 13½×13½	3·00	3·25
MS773	97×85 mm. $6 Symbolic tiger designs (71×40 mm). P 12½	1·25	1·40

(b) *Chinese Calendar*

MS774	165×125 mm. $2.50 × 6. Various calendar symbols (24×80 mm). P 14×13½	3·00	3·25
MS775	97×85 mm. $6 Soft toy tigers (71×36 mm). P 12½	1·25	1·40

(c) *25th Anniv of Shanghai Communique*

MS776	165×125 mm. $3.50 × 4. Pres. Nixon's visit to China, 1972; Vice Premier Deng Xiaoping's visit to U.S.A., 1979; Pres. Regan's visit to China, 1984; Pres. Bush's visit to China, 1989 (61×32 mm). P 13½×12½	2·75	3·00
MS777	97×85 mm. $6 China–U.S.A. Communique, 1972 (69×36 mm). P 14½×13	1·25	1·40

(d) *Pres. Deng Xiaoping's Project for Unification of China*

MS778	165×125 mm. $3.50 × 4. Beijing as national capital; Return of Hong Kong; Return of Macao; Links with Taiwan (37×65 mm). P 14×13	2·75	3·00
MS779	97×85 mm. $6 Reunified China (71×41 mm). P 12½	1·25	1·40

(e) *Return of Macao to China,* 1999

MS780	Two sheets, each 165×120 mm. (a) $4.50 × 3 Carnival dragon and modern Macao (44×33 mm). P 13½. (b) $4.50 × 3 Ruins of St. Paul's Church, Macao (62×29 mm). P 13½×12½		
	Set of 2 sheets	5·25	5·50
MS781	Two sheets, each 97×85 mm. (a) $6 Carnival dragon and modern Macao (62×32 mm). P 13½×12½. (b) $6 Deng Xiaoping and ruins of St. Paul's Church, Macao (71×36 mm). P 12½		
	Set of 2 sheets	2·50	2·75

194 Leopard   195 Narra Plant

(Des Sheila Nowers. Litho Enschedé)

1998 (26 Jan). *Large Wild Cats. T* **194** *and similar horiz designs. Multicoloured. P* 13×12½.

782	$1.20, Type 194	40	25
783	$1.90, Lioness and cub	60	55
784	$2 Lion	60	60
785	$2.50, Cheetah	70	90
782/5	Set of 4	2·10	2·10
MS786	112×98 mm. Nos. 782/5	2·25	2·25

(Des Christine Marais. Litho Enschedé)

1998 (9 Feb). *Narra Cultivation. P* 12½.

787	195 $2.40, multicoloured	35	40

196 Collecting Rain Water   197 White-faced Scops Owl

(Des J. van Ellinckhuijzen. Litho Enschedé)

1998 (23 Mar). *World Water Day. P* 14×15.

788	196 (–) multicoloured	30	30

No. 788 is inscribed "STANDARD POSTAGE" and was initially sold at 50 c. On 1 April 1998 the standard postage rate was increased to 55 c.

(Des D. Miller. Litho Questa)

1998 (31 Mar). *Diana, Princess of Wales Commemoration. Sheet, 145×70 mm, containing four vert designs as T 91 of Kiribati. Multicoloured. P 14¹⁄₂×14.*
MS789 $1 Princess Diana wearing protective mask; $1 Wearing Red Cross badge; $1 Wearing white shirt; $1 Comforting crippled child .. 1·25 1·40

(Des Helge Denker. Litho Enschedé)

1998 (1 Apr). *Owls of Namibia. T 197 and similar multicoloured designs. P 13¹⁄₂×12¹⁄₂.*
790	55 c. Black-tailed Tree Rat (20×24 mm) ..		30	30
	a. Booklet pane. Nos. 790/4 ..		2·25	
791	$1.50, Type 197		55	55
792	$1.50, Barred Owl ..		55	55
793	$1.90, Spotted Eagle Owl ..		55	55
794	$1.90, Barn Owl (61×24 mm) ..		55	55
790/4		Set of 5	2·25	2·25

Nos. 790/4 were only issued in $7.35 stamp booklets.
For miniature sheet containing $11 as No. 794 see No. MS850.

198 *Patella ganatina* (Limpet)

(Des Mary Volkmann. Litho Enschedé)

1998 (14 May). *Shells. T 198 and similar horiz designs. Multicoloured. P 13×12¹⁄₂.*
795	(–) Type 198		20	10
796	$1.10, Cymatium cutaceum africanum (Triton)		40	30
797	$1.50, Conus mozambicus (Cone) ..		60	55
798	$6 Venus verrucosa (Venus Clam) ..		1·75	2·00
795/8		Set of 4	2·75	2·75
MS799	109×84 mm. Nos. 795/8 ..		2·75	2·75

No. 795 is inscribed "Standard Postage" and was initially sold at 55 c.

199 Underwater Diamond Excavator

200 "Chinga" (cheetah)

(Des S. Williams. Litho Questa)

1998 (18 May). *Marine Technology. Sheet 70×90 mm. P 14¹⁄₂×14.*
MS800 199 $2.50, multicoloured .. .. 90 1·00

(Litho Enschedé)

1998 (5 June). *Wildlife Conservation. "Racing for Survival" (Olympic sprinter Frank Frederiks v cheetah). Sheet 108×80 mm. P 13.*
MS801 200 $5 multicoloured .. .. 1·25 1·40

201 Namibian Beach

202 Two Footballers

(Litho Cartor)

1998 (5 June). *World Environment Day. T 201 and similar horiz designs. Multicoloured. P 13×13¹⁄₂.*
802	(–) Type 201 ..		10	10
803	$1.10, Okavango sunset ..		20	25
804	$1.50, Sossusvlei ..		30	35
805	$1.90, African Moringo tree ..		40	45
802/5		Set of 4	1·00	1·10

No. 802 is inscribed "STANDARD POSTAGE" and was initially sold at 55 c.

(Des J. Madisia. Litho Enschedé)

1998 (15 June). *World Cup Football Championship, France. Sheet 80×56 mm. P 14×13¹⁄₂.*
MS806 202 $5 multicoloured .. .. 1·00 1·10

NEW INFORMATION

The editor is always interested to correspond with people who have new information that will improve or correct the Catalogue.

---

203 Chacma Baboon

204 Carmine Bee-eater

(Des D. Murphy. Litho Cartor)

1998 (18 June). *Animals with their Young. Sheet, 176×60 mm, containing T 203 and similar vert designs. P 13¹⁄₂×13.*
MS807 $1.50, Type 203; $1.50, Blue Wildebeest; $1.50, Meercat (suricate); $1.50, African Elephant; $1.50, Burchell's Zebra .. 1·50 1·60

(Des Mary Volkmann. Litho Cartor)

1998 (26 Sept). *Wildlife of the Caprivi Strip. T 204 and similar multicoloured designs. P 12¹⁄₂.*
808	60 c. Type 204		20	20
	a. Sheetlet. Nos. 808/17 ..		1·75	
809	60 c. Sable Antelope (40×40 mm) ..		20	20
810	60 c. Lechwe (40×40 mm) ..		20	20
811	60 c. Woodland Waterberry ..		20	20
812	60 c. Nile Monitor (40×40 mm) ..		20	20
813	60 c. African Jacana ..		20	20
814	60 c. African Fish Eagle ..		20	20
815	60 c. Woodland Kingfisher ..		20	20
816	60 c. Nile Crocodile (55×30 mm) ..		20	20
817	60 c. Black Mamba (32×30 mm) ..		20	20
808/17		Set of 10	1·75	1·75

Nos. 808/17 were printed together, *se-tenant*, in sheetlets of 10 with the backgrounds forming a composite design.

205 Black Rhinoceros and Calf

(Des Helge Denker. Litho Cartor)

1998 (20 Oct). *"ILSAPEX '98" International Stamp Exhibition, Johannesburg. Sheet 103×68 mm. P 13.*
MS818 205 $5 multicoloured .. .. 1·00 1·10

206 Blue Whale

207 Damara Dik-dik

(Des Mary Butterfield. Litho Questa)

1998 (23 Oct). *Whales of the Southern Oceans (joint issue with Norfolk Island and South Africa). Sheet 103×70 mm. P 13¹⁄₂×14.*
MS819 206 $5 multicoloured .. .. 1·25 1·40

(Des L. Voight. Litho Enschedé)

1999 (18 Jan). *"Fun Stamps for Children". Animals. T 207 and similar multicoloured design. P 14×13¹⁄₂ ($1.80) or 13¹⁄₂×14 ($2.65).*
820	$1.80, Type 207 ..		50	50
821	$2.65, Striped Tree Squirrel (26×36 mm) ..		75	75

208 Yoka perplexed

209 Windhuk (liner)

(Des J. van Ellinckhuijzen. Litho Enschedé)

1999 (1 Feb). *"Yoka the Snake" (cartoon). T 208 and similar multicoloured designs. Self-adhesive. P 5.*
822	$1.60, Type 208 ..		30	35
	a. Booklet pane. Nos. 822/31 ..		3·00	
823	$1.60, Yoka under attack (33×27 mm) ..		30	35
824	$1.60, Yoka caught on branch ..		30	35
825	$1.60, Yoka and wasps (33×27 mm) ..		30	35

826	$1.60, Yoka and footprint ..		30	35
827	$1.60, Yoka and tail of red and white snake		30	35
828	$1.60, Mouse hunt (33×27 mm) ..		30	35
829	$1.60, Snakes entwined ..		30	35
830	$1.60, Red and white snake singing ..		30	35
831	$1.60, Yoka sulking (33×27 mm) ..		30	35
822/31		Set of 10	3·00	3·50

Nos. 822/31 were only printed, *se-tenant*, in $16 stamp booklets on which the backing paper forms the cover.
See also No. MS835.

(Litho German State Ptg Wks, Berlin)

1999 (18 Mar). *Windhuk (liner) Commemoration. Sheet 110×90 mm. P 14.*
MS832 209 $5.50, multicoloured .. .. 1·25 1·40

210 Zögling Glider, 1928

211 Yoka the Snake with Toy Zebra

(Des D. Bagnall. Litho Cartor)

1999 (13 Apr). *Gliding in Namibia. T 210 and similar horiz design. Multicoloured. P 13.*
833	$1.60, Type 210 ..		40	40
834	$1.80, Schleicher glider, 1998 ..		50	50

(Des J. van Ellinckhuijzen. Litho German State Ptg Wks, Berlin)

1999 (27 Apr). *"iBRA '99" International Stamp Exhibition, Nuremberg. Sheet 110×84 mm. P 14.*
MS835 211 $5.50, multicoloured .. .. 1·25 1·40

212 Greater Kestrel

(Des H. Denker. Litho Cartor)

1999 (18 May). *Birds of Prey. T 212 and similar horiz designs. Multicoloured. P 13¹⁄₂.*
836	60 c. Type 212 ..		20	15
837	$1.60, Common Kestrel ("Rock Kestrel") ..		45	40
838	$1.80, Red-headed Falcon ..		45	45
839	$2.65, Lanner Falcon ..		70	80
836/9		Set of 4	1·60	1·60

213 Wattled Crane

214 Termitomyces schimperi (fungus)

(Des C. van Rooyen. Litho Enschedé)

1999 (28 June). *Wetland Birds. T 213 and similar horiz designs. Multicoloured. P 13×12¹⁄₂.*
840	$1.60, Type 213 ..		45	40
841	$1.80, Variegated Sandgrouse ("Burchell's Sandgrouse") ..		45	45
842	$1.90, Pratincole ..		50	50
843	$2.65, Eastern White Pelican ..		70	80
840/3		Set of 4	1·90	1·90

(Des C. van Rooyen. Litho Enschedé)

1999 (2 July). *"PhilexFrance '99" International Stamp Exhibition, Paris. Sheet 79×54 mm. P 14×13¹⁄₂.*
MS844 214 $5.50, multicoloured .. .. 1·00 1·10

215 *Eulophia hereroensis* (orchid)

216 Johanna Gertze

(Des Mary Volkmann. Litho and embossed Cartor)

1999 (21 Aug). *"China '99" International Philatelic Exhibition, Beijing. Orchids. T 215 and similar diamond-shaped designs. Multicoloured. P 12½.*

845	$1.60, Type **215**	..	..	..	45	35
846	$1.80, *Ansellia africana*	..	..	45	40
847	$2.65, *Eulophia leachii*	..	..	70	70
848	$3.90, *Eulophia speciosa*	..	..	90	1·00
845/8				Set of 4	2·25	2·25
MS849	72×72 mm. $5.50, *Eulophia walleri*	..	1·00	1·10

(Des H. Denker. Litho Cartor)

1999 (30 Sept). *Winning entry in 5th Stamp World Cup, France. Sheet 120×67 mm design as No. 794, but with changed face value. Multicoloured. P 13½×12½.*

MS850	$11 Barn Owl (61×24 *mm*)	..	2·25	2·40

(Des Inge Madlé. Litho Enschedé)

1999 (1 Oct). *Johanna Gertze Commemoration. P 12½×13.*

851	**216** $20 Indian red, flesh and bright new blue	4·00	4·25

217 Sunset over Namibia

(Des J. van Ellinckhuijzen. Litho Enschedé)

1999 (31 Dec). *New Millennium. T 217 and similar multi-coloured designs. P 13½.*

852	$2.20, Type **217**	..	..	40	45
853	$2.40, Sunrise over Namibia	..	45	50
MS854	77×54 mm. $9 Globe (hologram) (37×44 *mm*). P 14×13½		1·90	2·00

=

218 South African Shelduck **(219)**

(Des P. Huebsch. Litho Enschedé)

2000 (18 Feb). *Ducks of Namibia. T 218 and similar horiz designs. Multicoloured. P 13.*

855	$2 Type **218**	..	..	40	45
856	$2.40, White-faced Whistling Duck	..	45	50
857	$3 Comb Duck ("Knobbilled duck")	..	60	65
858	$7 Cape Shoveler	..	..	1·50	1·60
855/8			Set of 4	2·75	3·00

No. 858 is inscribed "Cape shoveller" in error.

2000 (1 Mar). *Nos. 749/52 optd as T 219.*

859	(—) on 5 c. Type **190**	..	..	15	20
860	$1.80, on 30 c. Western Rhigozum	..	35	40
861	$3 on 10 c. Bushman Poison	..	60	65
862	$6 on 20 c. Camel's Foot	..	1·10	1·25
859/62			Set of 4	2·10	2·50

No. 859 was initially sold at 65 c. The other surcharges show face values.

220 Namibian Children   **221** Actor playing Jesus wearing Crown of Thorns

(Des Saatchi and Saatchi. Litho Enschedé)

2000 (21 Mar). *10th Anniv of Independence. T 220 and similar square design. Multicoloured. P 13½×14.*

863	65 c. Type **220**	..	15	20
864	$3 Namibian flag	..	60	65

(Des J. van Ellinckhuijzen. Litho Enschedé)

2000 (1 Apr). *Easter Passion Play. T 221 and similar horiz design. Multicoloured. P 13½×14.*

865	$2.10, Type **221**	..	40	45
866	$2.40, On the way to Calvary	..	45	50

STAMP BOOKLETS

B 1 Buffalo
(Illustration further reduced. Actual size 125×74 mm)

1985 (1 Aug). *Multicoloured cover as Type B 1. Pane attached by selvedge.*

SB1	1 r. 20, booklet containing pane of 10 12 c. (No. 358ba)	..	4·50

1986 (Feb). *Multicoloured cover as Type B 1 but smaller, 125×70 mm, showing herd of buffaloes. Pane attached by selvedge.*

SB2	1 r. 20, booklet containing pane of 10 12 c. (No. 358ba)		4·50

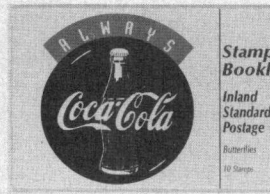

B 2

1997 (1 Feb). *Multicoloured cover as Type B 2. Stamps attached by selvedge.*

SB3	($5) booklet containing block of 10 "STANDARDISED MAIL" (No. 648)	1·50
SB4	$5 booklet containing two strips of 5 "STANDARDISED MAIL" (No. 662)	2·25

B 3

1997 (6 May). *Waxbills. Multicoloured cover as Type B 3. Stamps attached by selvedge.*

SB5	$5.50, booklet containing block of 10 (2×5) (No. 710a)	2·00

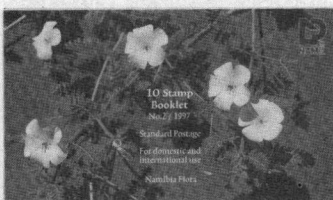

B 4 *Tribulus zeyheri*
(Illustration further reduced. Actual size 132×80 mm)

1997 (27 June). *Greetings Stamps. Multicoloured covers as Type B 4. Panes attached by selvedge.*

SB6	($5) booklet containing pane of 10 (5×2) (No. 723a) (Type B 4)	1·50
SB7	$7 booklet containing pane of 10 (5×2) (No. 728a) (cover showing Helmet Guineafowl and chicks)	1·75

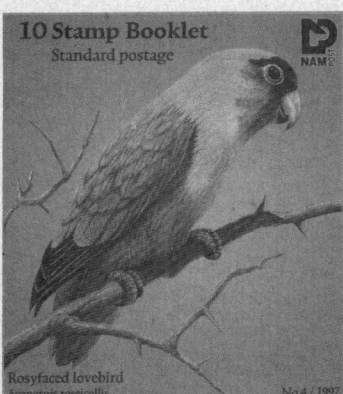

B 5 Peach-faced Lovebird

1997 (3 Nov). *Flora and Fauna. Multicoloured covers as Type B 5. Panes attached by selvedge.*

SB8	($5) booklet containing pane of 10 (5×2) (No. 755a) (cover showing Peach-faced Lovebird)	1·00
SB9	($12) booklet containing pane of 10 (5×2) (No. 761a) (cover showing Leopard)	2·50
SB10	($30.55) booklet containing pane of 18 (9×2) (No. 749a) (cover showing animals and birds)	6·25

B 6 Eagle Owl

1998 (1 Apr). *Owls of Namibia. Multicoloured cover as Type B 6. Pane attached by selvedge.*

SB11	$7.35, booklet containing *se-tenant* pane (No. 790a)	2·25

B 7 Yoka the Snake

1999 (1 Feb). *Yoka the Snake. Multicoloured cover as Type B 7. Self-adhesive.*

SB12	$16 booklet containing *se-tenant* pane (No. 822a)	3·25

POSTAGE DUE STAMPS

PRICES for Nos. D1/39 are for unused horizontal pairs, used horizontal pairs and used singles.

1923 (1 Jan–July). *Optd with T* **1** *and* **2** *alternately.*

(a) *Setting I* (14 *mm between lines of overprint*) (i) *On Nos. D5/6 of Transvaal*

D1	5d. black and violet	4·00	48·00	11·00
	a. "Wes" for "West" (R. 8/6, 10/2 left pane)			£130
	b. "Afrika" without stop (R. 6/1)			80·00
D2	6d. black and red-brown	17·00	48·00	11·00
	a. "Wes" for "West" (R. 10/2)			£225
	b. "Afrika" without stop (R. 6/1, 7/2)			£140

(ii) *On Nos. D3/4 and D6 of South Africa (De La Rue printing)*

D3	2d. black and violet	23·00	45·00	10·00
	a. "Wes" for "West" (R. 10/2)		£160	£225
	b. "Afrika" without stop (R. 6/1, 7/2)			£160
D4	3d. black and blue	11·00	45·00	10·00
	a. "Wes" for "West" (R. 10/2)			£120
D5	6d. black and slate (20 Apr)	26·00	50·00	13·00
	a. "Wes" for "West" (R. 8/6)			£150

(iii) *On Nos. D9/10, D11 and D14 of South Africa (Pretoria printings)*

D6	½d. black and green (p 14)	5·50	25·00	5·50
	a. Opt inverted			£400
	b. Opt double		£750	£800
	c. "Wes" for "West" (R. 10/2)			75·00
	d. "Afrika" without stop (R. 6/1, 7/2)			75·00
D7	1d. black and rose (*roul*)	7·00	27·00	6·00
	a. "Wes" for "West" (R. 10/2)			85·00
	b. "Afrika" without stop (R. 6/1)			85·00
	c. Imperf between (horiz pair)			£950
D8	1½d. black and yellow-brown (*roul*)	1·00	13·00	2·75
	a. "Wes" for "West" (R. 8/6, 10/2)			70·00
	b. "Afrika" without stop (R. 6/1)			70·00
D9	2d. black and violet (*p* 14) (21 June)	3·50	24·00	5·00
	a. "Wes" for "West" (R. 8/6)			85·00
	b. "Afrika" without stop (R. 6/1)			£100

Nos. D1/9 were initially overprinted as separate panes of 60, but some values were later done as double panes of 120.

A variety of Nos. D1, D4/5 and D9 with 15 mm between the lines of overprint occurs on four positions in each pane from some printings.

(b) *Setting II* (10 *mm between lines of overprint*). (i) *On No. D5 of Transvaal*

D10	5d. black and violet (20 Apr)		55·00	£140

(ii) *On Nos. D3/4 of South Africa (De La Rue printing)*

D11	2d. black and violet (20 Apr)	16·00	40·00	9·00
	a. "Afrika" without stop (R.6/1)			£140
D12	3d. black and blue (20 Apr)	7·50	25·00	5·50
	a. "Afrika" without stop (R.6/1)			80·00

(iii) *On No. D9 of South Africa (Pretoria printing). Roul*

D13	1d. black and rose (July)	£8500 — £1500

1923 (30 July)–**26**. *Optd as T* **3** ("*Zuidwest*" *in one word without hyphen*) *and* **4**.

(a) *Setting III* ("*South West*" 14 *mm long,* "*Zuidwest*" 11 *mm long and* 14 *mm between lines of overprint*).

(i) *On No. D6 of Transvaal*

D14	6d. black and red-brown	21·00	80·00	20·00

(ii) *On Nos. D9 and D11/12 of South Africa (Pretoria printing)*

D15	½d. black and green (p 14)	11·00	26·00	5·50
D16	1d. black and rose (*roul*)	3·75	26·00	5·50
D17	1d. black and rose (p 14) (2.8.23)	12·00	26·00	5·50

(b) *Setting IV* ("*South West*" 16 *mm long,* "*Zuidwest*" 12 *mm long and* 14 *mm between lines of overprint*).

(i) *On No. D5 of Transvaal*

D17a	5d. black and violet (1.7.24)		£425	£850

(ii) *On Nos. D11/12 and D16 of South Africa (Pretoria printing). P* 14

D18	½d. black and green (1.7.24)	6·50	26·00	5·50
D19	1d. black and rose (1.7.24)	5·00	26·00	5·50
D20	6d. black and slate (1.7.24)	2·25	40·00	9·00
	a. "Africa" without stop (R.9/5)			£100

(c) *Setting V* (12 *mm between lines of overprint*).

(i) *On No. D5 of Transvaal*

D21	5d. black and violet (6.8.24)	3·75	42·00	9·00

(ii) *On No. D4 of South Africa (De La Rue printing)*

D22	3d. black and blue (6.8.24)	15·00	48·00	11·00

(iii) *On Nos. D11 and D13 of South Africa (Pretoria printing). P* 14

D23	½d. black and green (6.8.24)	2·50	27·00	6·50
D24	1½d. black & yellow-brown (6.8.24)	4·50	30·00	7·00

(d) *Setting VI* (9½ *mm between lines of overprint*).

(i) *On No. D5 of Transvaal*

D25	5d. black and violet (7.9.24)	2·50	17·00	3·50
	a. "Africa" without stop (R. 9/5)			65·00

(ii) *On No. D4 of South Africa (De La Rue printing)*

D26	3d. black and blue (3.2.26)	6·50	48·00	11·00

(iii) *On Nos. D11/16 of South Africa (Pretoria printing). P* 14

D27	½d. black and green (1.3.26)	8·50	32·00	7·50
D28	1d. black and rose (16.3.25)	2·00	9·00	1·60
	a. "Africa" without stop (R. 9/5 right pane)			75·00
D29	1½d. black & yellow-brown (1.10.26)	4·50	28·00	6·50
	a. "Africa" without stop (R. 9/5 right pane)			80·00
D30	2d. black and violet (7.9.24)	2·50	17·00	3·50
	a. "Africa" without stop (R. 9/5 right pane)			65·00
D31	3d. black and blue (6.5.26)	4·50	18·00	3·75
	a. "Africa" without stop (R. 9/5 right pane)			70·00
D32	6d. black and slate (1.10.26)	9·00	48·00	14·00
	a. "Africa" without stop (R. 9/5 right pane)			£120
D27/32		Set of 6	28·00	£140	32·00

For Setting VI the overprint was applied to sheets of 120 (2 panes of 60) of the 1d., 3d. and 6d., and to individual panes of 60 for the other values. The two measurements of "South West", as detailed under No. 40, also occur on the postage dues. Nos. D25 and D31/2 show it 16 mm long, No. 27 16½ mm long and the other stamps can be found with either measurement. In addition to the complete panes the 16½ mm long "South West" also occurs on R.2/4 in the 16 mm left pane for Nos. D28 and D30/2.

Suidwes	**South West**

Afrika.	**Africa.**
(D **1**)	(D **2**)

1927 (14 May–27 Sept). *Optd as Types* D **1** *and* D **2**, *alternately,* 12 *mm between lines of overprint.* (a) *On No. D5 of Transvaal.*

D33	5d. black and violet (27 Sept)	19·00	85·00	23·00

(b) *On Nos. D13/16 of South Africa (Pretoria printing). P* 14

D34	1½d. black and yellow-brown	80	15·00	3·25
D35	2d. black and pale violet (27 Sept)	4·50	13·00	3·25
	a. Black and deep violet	7·00	14·00	3·50
D37	3d. black and blue (27 Sept)	13·00	40·00	11·00
D38	6d. black and slate (27 Sept)	7·50	30·00	8·50

(c) *On No. D18 of South Africa (Pretoria printing). P* 14

D39	1d. black and carmine	1·00	9·50	2·25
D33/9		Set of 6	42·00	£160	45·00

No. D33 was overprinted in panes of 60 and the remainder as complete sheets of 120.

Examples of all values can be found with very small or very faint stops from various positions in the sheet.

1928–29. *Optd with T* **10**. (a) *On Nos. D15/16 of South Africa*

		Un Single	Us Single
D40	3d. black and blue	1·50	12·00
	a. Without stop after "A" (R.3/6)	30·00	
D41	6d. black and slate	6·00	25·00
	a. Without stop after "A" (R.3/6)	£120	

(b) *On Nos. D17/21 of South Africa*

D42	½d. black and green	40	7·50
D43	1d. black and carmine	40	3·25
	a. Without stop after "A" (R.3/6)	40·00	
D44	2d. black and mauve	40	4·25
	a. Without stop after "A" (R.3/6)	55·00	
D45	3d. black and blue	2·25	24·00
	a. Without stop after "A" (R.3/6)	24·00	
D46	6d. black and slate	1·50	19·00
	a. Without stop after "A" (R.3/6)	45·00	
D42/6		Set of 5	4·50	50·00

D **3**	D **4**	D **5**

(Litho B.W.)

1931 (23 Feb). *Inscribed bilingually. W* **9** *of South Africa. P* 12.

D47	D **3**	½d. black and green	80	9·00
D48		1d. black and scarlet	80	1·25
D49		2d. black and violet	80	2·75
D50		3d. black and blue	3·75	17·00
D51		6d. black and slate	13·00	27·00
D47/51			Set of 5	17·00	50·00

PRINTER. The following issues have been printed by the South African Government Printer, Pretoria.

1959 (18 May). *Centre typo; frame roto. W* **9** *of South Africa. P* 15 × 14.

D52	D **4**	1d. black and scarlet	1·50	15·00
D53		2d. black and reddish violet	1·50	15·00
D54		3d. black and blue	1·50	15·00
D52/4			Set of 3	4·00	40·00

1960 (Dec). *As Nos. D52 and D54 but W* **102** *of South Africa.*

D55	1d. black and scarlet	2·50	4·50
D56	3d. black and blue	2·50	6·50

1961 (14 Feb). *As Nos. D52 etc, but whole stamp roto, and value in cents. W* **102** *of South Africa.*

D57	1 c. black and blue-green	70	3·75
D58	2 c. black and scarlet	70	3·75
D59	4 c. black and reddish violet	70	3·75
D60	5 c. black and light blue	1·00	4·25
D61	6 c. black and green	1·25	6·50
D62	10 c. black and yellow	3·25	8·00
D57/62		Set of 6	7·00	27·00

1972 (22 Mar). *W* **127** (*sideways tête-bêche*). *Phosphorised chalk-surfaced paper. P* 14 × 13½.

D63	D **5**	1 c. emerald	75	5·00
D64		8 c. ultramarine	3·00	8·50

The use of Postage Due stamps ceased in April 1975.

NEW INFORMATION

The editor is always interested to correspond with people who have new information that will improve or correct the Catalogue.

OFFICIAL STAMPS

OFFICIAL	**OFFISIEEL**

(table headers reading vertically: South West / Africa. / Suidwes / Afrika)

(O **1**)	(O **2**)

1926 (Dec). *Nos. 30, 31, 6 and 32 of South Africa optd with Type* O **1** *on English stamp and* O **2** *on Afrikaans stamp alternately.*

		Un pair	Us pair	Us single
O1	½d. black and green	70·00	£160	30·00
O2	1d. black and carmine	70·00	£160	30·00
O3	2d. dull purple		£160	£250	45·00
O4	6d. green and orange	90·00	£150	30·00
O1/4		Set of 4	£350	£650	£120

OFFICIAL	**OFFISIEEL**

S.W.A.	**S.W.A.**
(O **3**)	(O **4**)

1929 (May). *Nos. 30, 31, 32 and 34 of South Africa optd with Type* O **3** *on English stamp and* O **4** *on Afrikaans stamp.*

O5	½d. black and green	1·00	14·00	2·75
O6	1d. black and carmine	1·00	14·00	2·75
O7	2d. grey and purple	1·50	18·00	3·50
	a. Pair, stamp without stop after "OFFICIAL"	5·50	40·00	
	b. Pair, stamp without stop after "OFFISIEEL"	5·50	40·00	
	c. Pair, comprising a and b	16·00	75·00	
O8	6d. green and orange	3·00	19·00	3·75
O5/8		Set of 4	6·00	60·00	11·50

Types O **3** and O **4** are normally spaced 17 mm between lines on all except the 2d. value, which is spaced 13 mm.

Except on No. O7, the words "OFFICIAL" or "OFFISIEEL" normally have no stops after them.

OFFICIAL	**OFFISIEEL**
S.W.A.	**S.W.A.**
(O **5**)	(O **6**)

OFFICIAL.	**OFFISIEEL.**
S.W.A.	**S.W.A.**
(O **7**)	(O **8**)

1929 (Aug). *Nos. 30, 31 and 32 of South Africa optd with Types* O **5** *and* O **6**, *and No. 34 with Types* O **7** *and* O **8**, *languages to correspond.*

O 9	½d. black and green	65	14·00	2·75
O10	1d. black and carmine	75	14·00	2·75
O11	2d. grey and purple	90	14·00	3·25
	a. Pair, one stamp without stop after "OFFICIAL"	3·75	38·00	
	b. Pair, one stamp without stop after "OFFISIEEL"	3·75	38·00	
	c. Pair, comprising a and b	18·00	75·00	
O12	6d. green and orange	3·00	27·00	6·50
O9/12		Set of 4	4·75	60·00	13·50

OFFICIAL	**OFFISIEEL**
(O **9**)	(O **10**)

1931. *English stamp optd with Type* O **9** *and Afrikaans stamp with Type* O **10** *in red.*

O13	12	½d. black and emerald	10·00	17·00	3·50
O14	13	1d. indigo and scarlet	75	17·00	3·50
O15	14	2d. blue and brown	1·75	10·00	2·25
O16	17	6d. blue and brown	2·25	14·00	3·25
O13/16			Set of 4	13·00	50·00	11·50

OFFICIAL	**OFFISIEEL**
(O **11**)	(O **12**)

1938 (1 July). *English stamp optd with Type* O **11** *and Afrikaans with Type* O **12** *in red.*

O17	27	1½d. purple-brown	24·00	45·00	6·00

OFFICIAL	**OFFISIEEL**
(O **13**)	(O **14**)

1945–50. *English stamp optd with Type* O **13**, *and Afrikaans stamp with Type* O **14** *in red.*

O18	12	½d. black and emerald	13·00	27·00	5·00
O19	13	1d. indigo and scarlet (1950)	4·25	16·00	3·25
		a. Opt double			£425
O20	27	1½d. purple-brown	45·00	40·00	6·50
O21	14	2d. blue and brown (1947?)	£450	£600	£100
O22		6d. blue and brown	13·00	45·00	7·00
O18/20, O22			Set of 4	65·00	£110	20·00

OFFICIAL   OFFISIEEL

(O 15)   (O 16)

1951 (16 Nov)–**52**. *English stamp optd with Type* O **15** *and Afrikaans stamp with Type* O **16**, *in red*.

O23	12	½d. black and emerald (1952)		12·00	20·00	4·50
O24	13	1d. indigo and scarlet		4·00	13·00	1·75
O25	27	1½d. purple-brown		24·00	24·00	5·00
		a. Opts transposed		70·00	80·00	
O26	14	2d. blue and brown		1·50	16·00	3·50
		a. Opts transposed		45·00	£100	
O27	17	6d. blue and brown		2·75	38·00	7·50
		a. Opts transposed		22·00	£110	
O23/7		*Set of 5*	40·00	£100	20·00	

The above errors refer to stamps with the English overprint on Afrikaans stamp and *vice versa*.

The use of official stamps ceased in January 1955.

Natal
see South Africa

Nauru

Stamps of MARSHALL ISLANDS were used in Nauru from the opening of the German Colonial Post Office on 14 July 1908 until 8 September 1914.

Following the occupation by Australian forces on 6 November 1914 the "N.W. PACIFIC ISLANDS" overprints on Australia (see NEW GUINEA) were used from 2 January 1915.

PRICES FOR STAMPS ON COVER TO 1945

Nos. 1/12	*from* ×10
Nos. 13/16	*from* ×4
Nos. 17/25	—
Nos. 26/39	*from* × 6
Nos. 40/3	*from* × 10
Nos. 44/7	*from* × 15

BRITISH MANDATE

NAURU (1)   **NAURU** (2)   **NAURU** (3)

1916 (2 Sept)–**23**. *Stamps of Great Britain (1912–22) overprinted at Somerset House.*

(a) With T 1 (12½ mm long) at foot

1	½d. yellow-green			1·75	6·50
	a. "NAUP.U"			£350	
	b. Double opt, one albino			60·00	
2	1d. bright scarlet			1·50	4·50
	a. "NAUP.U"			£600	
2b	1d. carmine-red			11·00	
	bb. Double opt, one albino			£225	
3	1½d. red-brown (1923)		55·00	80·00	
4	2d. orange (Die I)			2·00	11·00
	a. "NAUP.U"			£350	£425
	b. Double opt, one albino			£110	
	y. Wmk inverted and reversed			£100	
5	2d. orange (Die II) (1923)		70·00	£100	
6	2½d. blue			2·75	7·00
	a. "NAUP.U"			£400	£475
	b. Double opt, one albino			£225	
7	3d. bluish violet			2·00	3·50
	a. "NAUP.U"			£425	£500
	b. Double opt, one albino			£225	
8	4d. slate-green			2·00	8·50
	a. "NAUP.U"			£550	£700
	b. Double opt, one albino			£225	
9	5d. yellow-brown			2·25	8·50
	a. "NAUP.U"			£800	
	b. Double opt, one albino			£150	
10	6d. purple (*chalk-surfaced paper*)			3·25	10·00
	a. "NAUP.U"			£750	
	b. Double opt, one albino			£250	
11	9d. agate			8·50	20·00
	a. Double opt, one albino			£250	
12	1s. bistre-brown (Optd S. £130)			7·00	19·00
	a. Double opt, one albino			£275	
1/12		*Set of 11*	75·00	£150	

(b) With T 2 (13½ mm long) at centre (1923)

13	½d. green			4·50	40·00
14	1d. scarlet			18·00	30·00
15	1½d. red-brown			23·00	40·00
	a. Double opt, one albino			£100	
16	2d. orange (Die II)			30·00	60·00
13/16		*Set of 4*	65·00	£150	

The "NAUP.U" errors occur on R.6/2 from Control I 16 only. The ink used on this batch of overprints was shiny jet-black.

There is a constant variety consisting of short left stroke to "N" which occurs on Nos. 1, 2, 2b, 4 (£30 *each*); 3 (£175); 5 (£200); 6, 7 (£40 *each*); 8, 9, 10 (£60 *each*); 11, 12 (£85 *each*). All unused prices.

(c) With T 3. (i) Waterlow printing

17	5s. rose-carmine		£2250	£1600
18	10s. indigo-blue (R.) (Optd S. £1000)		£6000	£4500
	a. Double opt, one albino		£7000	£7000

(ii) De La Rue printing

19	2s. 6d. deep brown (Optd S. £275)		£600	£700
	a. Double opt, one albino		£1300	
	b. Treble opt, two albino		£1400	
20	2s. 6d. yellow-brown		65·00	95·00
21	2s. 6d. pale brown (worn plate) (Optd S. £250)		70·00	90·00
	a. Re-entry (R. 2/1)			
22	5s. bright carmine (*shades*) (Optd S. £250)		£100	£140
	a. Treble opt, two albino		£600	
23	10s. pale blue (R.)		£250	£325
	a. Treble opt (Blk. + R. + albino)		£2250	
	b. Double opt, one albino		£900	
23c	10s. deep bright blue (R.)		£500	£550

(iii) Bradbury, Wilkinson printing (1919)

24	2s. 6d. chocolate-brown		75·00	£110
	a. Major re-entry (R. 1/2)			
	b. Double opt, one albino		£375	
25	2s. 6d. pale brown		65·00	95·00
	a. Double opt, one albino		£350	

Examples of most values between Nos. 1 and 25 are known showing a forged P.O. Pleasant Island postmark dated "NO 2 21".

AUSTRALIAN MANDATE

4 Century (freighter)

(Des R. A. Harrison. Eng T. S. Harrison. Recess Note Printing Branch of the Treasury, Melbourne and from 1926 by the Commonwealth Bank of Australia)

1924–48. *No wmk. P 11.*

A. Rough surfaced, greyish paper (1924–34).

26A	4	½d. chestnut			1·50	2·75
27A		1d. green			3·25	2·75
28A		1½d. scarlet			4·00	4·00
29A		2d. orange			4·00	11·00
30A		2½d. slate-blue			5·50	19·00
		c. Greenish blue (1934)			5·50	14·00
31A		3d. pale blue			3·00	13·00
32A		4d. olive-green			7·00	16·00
33A		5d. brown			3·75	6·50
34A		6d. dull violet			4·25	12·00
35A		9d. olive-brown			9·00	19·00
36A		1s. brown-lake			6·00	13·00
37A		2s. 6d. grey-green			27·00	45·00
38A		5s. claret			50·00	90·00
39A		10s. yellow			£110	£150
26A/39A			*Set of 14*	£200	£350	

B. Shiny surfaced, white paper (1937–48)

26B	4	½d. chestnut			8·00	13·00
		c. Perf 14 (1947)			1·40	9·50
27B		1d. green			2·50	3·00
28B		1½d. scarlet			90	1·50
29B		2d. orange			1·75	8·00
30dB		2½d. dull blue (1948)			2·00	4·00
		da. Imperf between (vert pair)		£4500	£4500	
		db. Imperf between (horiz pair)		£4500	£4500	
31cB		3d. greenish grey (1947)			2·75	10·00
32B		4d. olive-green			4·25	12·00
33B		5d. brown			3·50	4·00
34B		6d. dull violet			3·25	4·50
35B		9d. olive-brown			7·50	20·00
36B		1s. brown-lake			5·50	2·75
37B		2s. 6d. grey-green			25·00	35·00
38B		5s. claret			35·00	50·00
39B		10s. yellow			£100	£130
26B/39B			*Set of 14*	£170	£250	

HIS MAJESTY'S JUBILEE.

1910 - 1935

(5)   6

1935 (12 July). *Silver Jubilee. T 4 (shiny surfaced, white paper) optd with T 5.*

40	1½d. scarlet			75	80
41	2d. orange			1·25	4·00
42	2½d. dull blue			1·50	1·50
43	1s. brown-lake			5·00	3·50
40/3		*Set of 4*	7·75	9·00	

(Recess John Ash, Melbourne)

1937 (10 May). *Coronation. P 11.*

44	6	1½d. scarlet			45	1·25
45		2d. orange			45	1·75
46		2½d. blue			45	60
47		1s. purple			65	90
44/7			*Set of 4*	1·75	4·00	

Japanese forces invaded Nauru on 26 August 1942 and virtually all the inhabitants were removed to Truk in the Caroline Islands.

The Australian army liberated Nauru on 13 September 1945. After an initial period without stamps Australian issues were supplied during October 1945 and were used from Nauru until further supplies of Nos. 26/39 became available. The deportees did not return until early in 1946.

7 Nauruan Netting Fish   8 Anibare Bay

15 Map of Nauru

(Recess Note Printing Branch, Commonwealth Bank, Melbourne, and from 1960 by Note Ptg Branch, Reserve Bank of Australia, Melbourne)

1954 (6 Feb)–**65**. *T 7/8, 15 and similar designs. Toned paper. P 13½×14½ (horiz) or 14½×13½ (vert).*

48	½d. deep violet			20	40
	a. Violet (8.5.61)			20	40
49	1d. bluish green			30	50
	a. Emerald-green (8.5.61)			20	40
	b. Deep green (1965)			85	50
50	3½d. scarlet			1·50	60
	a. Vermilion (1958)			3·00	60
51	4d. grey-blue			1·50	1·75
	a. Deep blue (1958)			6·00	2·50
52	6d. orange			70	20
53	9d. claret			60	20
54	1s. deep purple			30	20
55	2s. 6d. deep green			2·75	1·25
56	5s. magenta			9·00	3·00
48/56		*Set of 9*	15·00	7·00	

Designs: *Horiz*—3½d. Loading phosphate from cantilever; 4d. Great Frigate Bird; 6d. Nauruan canoe; 9d. Domaneab (meeting-house); 2s. 6d. Buada lagoon. *Vert*—1s. Palm trees.

Nos. 48a, 49a/b, 50a and 51a are on white paper.

16 Micronesian Pigeon   17 Poison Nut

20 Capparis   21 White Tern

(Recess (10d., 2s. 3d.) or photo (others) Note Ptg Branch, Reserve Bank of Australia, Melbourne)

1963–65. *T 16/17, 20/1 and similar designs. P 13½ × 13 (5d.), 13 × 13½ (8d.), 14 × 13½ (10d.), 15 × 14½ (1s. 3d.) or 13½ (others).*

57	2d. black, blue, red-brn & orge-yell (3.5.65)			75	2·25
58	3d. multicoloured (16.4.64)			55	35
59	5d. multicoloured (22.4.63)			55	75
60	8d. black and green (1.7.63)			2·50	80
61	10d. black (16.4.64)			50	30
62	1s. 3d. blue, black & yellow-green (3.5.65)			2·75	4·00
63	2s. 3d. ultramarine (16.4.64)			3·50	55
64	3s. 3d. multicoloured (3.5.65)			2·75	2·75
57/64		*Set of 8*	12·00	10·50	

Designs: *Vert*—5d. "Iyo" (*calophyllum*). *Horiz*—8d. Black Lizard; 2s. 3d. Coral pinnacles; 3s. 3d. Finsch's Reed Warbler.

22 "Simpson and his Donkey"

(Des C. Andrew (after statue, Shrine of Remembrance, Melbourne. Photo Note Ptg Branch, Reserve Bank of Australia, Melbourne)

1965 (14 Apr). *50th Anniv of Gallipoli Landing. P 13½.*

65	22	5d. sepia, black and emerald		15	10

(New Currency. 100 cents = 1 Australian dollar)

24 Anibare Bay   25 "Iyo" (*calophyllum*)

(Recess (1, 2, 3, 5, 8, 19, 25 c. and $1) or photo (others))

1966 (14 Feb–25 May). *Decimal Currency. Various stamps with values in cents and dollars as T 24/5 and some colours changed. Recess printed stamps on helecon paper.*

66	24	1 c. deep blue	15	10
67	7	2 c. brown-purple (25 May)	15	40
68	—	3 c. bluish green (as 3½d.) (25 May)	30	1·25
69	25	4 c. multicoloured	25	10
70	—	5 c. deep ultramarine (as 1s.) (25 May)	25	60
71	—	7 c. black and chestnut (as 8d.)	30	10
72	20	8 c. olive-green	30	10
73	—	10 c. red (as 4d.)	40	10
74	21	15 c. blue, black and yellow-green (25 May)	80	1·50
75	—	25 c. deep brown (as 2s. 3d.) (25 May)	45	60
76	17	30 c. multicoloured	70	30
77	—	35 c. multicoloured (as 3s. 3d.) (25 May)	1·25	35
78	16	50 c. multicoloured	2·50	80
79	—	$1 magenta (as 5s.)	1·50	1·00
66/79		*Set of 14*	8·00	6·00

The 25 c. is as No. 63, but larger, 27½×24½ mm.

REPUBLIC

Nauru became independent on 31 January 1968 and was later admitted into special membership of the Commonwealth.

REPUBLIC OF NAURU
(26)

1968 (31 Jan–15 May). *Nos. 66/79 optd with T 26.*

80	24	1 c. deep blue (R.)	10	30
81	7	2 c. brown-purple	10	10
82	—	3 c. bluish green	15	10
83	25	4 c. multicoloured (15.5.68)	15	10
84	—	5 c. deep ultramarine (R.)	15	10
85	—	7 c. black and chestnut (R.) (15.5.68)	25	10
86	20	8 c. olive-green (R.)	25	10
87	—	10 c. red	30	15
88	21	15 c. blue, black and yellow-green (R.)	2·25	2·50
89	—	25 c. deep brown (R.)	30	15
90	17	30 c. multicoloured (15.5.68)	55	15
91	—	35 c. multicoloured (15.5.68)	2·00	30
92	16	50 c. multicoloured	2·00	50
93	—	$1 magenta	1·25	75
80/93		*Set of 14*	8·00	4·50

27 "Towards the Sunrise"   28 Planting Seedling, and Map

(Des H. Fallu (5 c.), Note Ptg Branch (10 c.). Photo Note Ptg Branch, Reserve Bank of Australia, Melbourne)

1968 (11 Sept). *Independence.* P 13½.

94	27	5 c. black, slate-lilac, orange-yellow and yellow-green	10	10
95	28	10 c. black, yellow-green and new blue	10	10

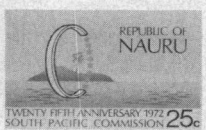

29 Flag of Independent Nauru   30 Island, "C" and Stars

(Des J. Mason. Photo Note Ptg Branch, Reserve Bank of Australia, Melbourne)

1969 (31 Jan). P 13½.

96	29	15 c. yellow, orange and royal blue	50	15

This is a definitive issue which was put on sale on the first anniversary of Independence.

(Des R. Brooks, Litho Format)

1972 (7 Feb). *25th Anniv of South Pacific Commission.* P 14½ × 14.

97	30	25 c. multicoloured	30	30

Independence 1968-1973
(31)

1973 (31 Jan). *Fifth Anniv of Independence. No. 96 optd with T 31 in gold.*

98	29	15 c. yellow, orange and royal blue	20	30

---

32 Denea   33 Artefacts and Map

(Des locally; adapted G. Vasarhelyi. Litho Format)

1973 (28 Mar*–25 July). *Various multicoloured designs as T 32 (1 to 5 c.) or T 33 (others). P 14 (1 to 5 c.), 14½×14 (7, 8, 10, 30, 50 c.) or 14×14½ (others).*

99	1 c. Ekwenababae			40	20
100	2 c. Kauwe Iud			45	20
101	3 c. Rimone			45	20
102	4 c. Type 32			45	40
103	5 c. Erekogo			45	40
104	7 c. Racoon Butterflyfish ("Ikimago") (25.7)			30	50
105	8 c. Catching flying-fish (23.5)			30	20
106	10 c. Itsibweb (ball game) (23.5)			30	20
107	15 c. Nauruan wrestling (23.5)			35	20
108	20 c. Snaring Great Frigate Birds (23.5)			50	50
109	25 c. Nauruan girl (25.7)			40	30
110	30 c. Catching Common Noddy Birds (25.7)			60	40
111	50 c. Great Frigate Birds (25.7)			80	75
112	$1 Type 33			80	75
99/112		*Set of 14*		6·00	4·75

*This is the local release date but the Crown Agents issued the stamps on 21 March.

The 1 to 5 c. show flowers, and the 7, 8, 10, 30, 50 c. are horiz designs.

Nos. 99/112 exist imperforate from stock dispersed by the liquidator of Format International Security Printers Ltd.

34 Co-op Store   35 Phosphate Mining

(Des G. Vasarhelyi. Litho Format)

1973 (20 Dec). *50th Anniv of Nauru Co-operative Society. T 34 and similar multicoloured designs. P 14 × 14½ (50 c.) or 14½ × 14 (others).*

113	5 c. Type 34			20	30
114	25 c. Timothy Detudamo (founder)			20	15
115	50 c. N.C.S. trademark (*vert*)			45	55
113/15		*Set of 3*		75	90

(Des G. Vasarhelyi (7 c. from original by J. Mason; 10 c. from original by K. Depaune). Litho Format)

1974 (21 May). *175th Anniv of First Contact with the Outside World. T 35 and similar horiz designs. Multicoloured. P 13 × 13½ (7, 35, 50 c.) or 13½ × 13 (others).*

116	7 c. *Eigamoiya* (bulk carrier) (70×22 mm)	80	90
117	10 c. Type 35	60	25
118	15 c. Fokker F. 28 Fellowship *Nauru Chief*	80	30
119	25 c. Nauruan chief in early times	60	35
120	35 c. Capt. Fearn and 18th-century frigate (70×22 mm)	3·00	2·50
121	50 c. 18th-century frigate off Nauru (70×22 mm)	1·50	1·40
116/21	*Set of 6*	6·50	5·25

The ship on the 35 c. and 50 c. is wrongly identified as the *Hunter* (snow).

36 Map of Nauru   37 Rev. P. A. Delaporte

(Des G. Vasarhelyi. Litho Format)

1974 (23 July). *Centenary of Universal Postal Union. T 36 and similar multicoloured designs. P 13½ × 14 (5 c.), 13 × 13½ ($1) or 13½ × 13 (others).*

122	5 c. Type 36			15	20
123	8 c. Nauru Post Office			15	20
124	20 c. Nauruan postman			15	10
125	$1 U.P.U. Building and Nauruan flag			40	60
122/5		*Set of 4*		75	1·00
MS126	157 × 105 mm. Nos. 122/5. Imperf			2·00	5·50

The 8 and 20 c. are horiz (33 × 21 mm), and the $1 is vert (21 × 33 mm).

(Des J.W. Litho Format)

1974 (10 Dec). *Christmas and 75th Anniv of Rev. Delaporte's Arrival.* P 14½.

127	37	15 c. multicoloured	20	20
128		20 c. multicoloured	30	30

---

38 Map of Nauru, Lump of Phosphate Rock and Albert Ellis   39 Micronesian Outrigger

(Des M. and Sylvia Goaman. Litho Format)

1975 (23 July). *Phosphate Mining Anniversaries. T 38 and similar horiz designs. Multicoloured. P 14½×14.*

129	5 c. Type 38			25	40
130	7 c. Coolies and mine			35	40
131	15 c. Electric phosphate train, barges and ship			1·00	1·40
132	25 c. Modern ore extraction			1·25	1·50
129/32		*Set of 4*		2·50	3·25

Anniversaries:—5 c. 75th Anniv of discovery; 7 c. 70th Anniv of Mining Agreement; 15 c. 55th Anniv of British Phosphate Commissioners; 25 c. 5th Anniv of Nauru Phosphate Corporation.

(Des M. and Sylvia Goaman. Litho Format)

1975 (1 Sept). *South Pacific Commission Conference, Nauru (1st issue). T 39 and similar horiz designs. Multicoloured. P 13½ × 14.*

133	20 c. Type 39			75	40
	a. Block of 4. Nos. 133/6			2·75	
134	20 c. Polynesian double-hull			75	40
135	20 c. Melanesian outrigger			75	40
136	20 c. Polynesian outrigger			75	40
133/6		*Set of 4*		2·75	1·40

Nos. 133/6 were printed in *se-tenant* blocks of four throughout the sheet.

40 New Civic Centre   41 "Our Lady" (Yaren Church)

(Des M. and Sylvia Goaman. Litho Format)

1975 (29 Sept). *South Pacific Commission Conference, Nauru (2nd issue). T 40 and similar horiz design. Multicoloured. P 14.*

137	30 c. Type 40			15	15
138	50 c. Domaneab (meeting-house)			30	30

(Des M. and Sylvia Goaman. Litho Format)

1975 (7 Nov). *Christmas. T 41 and similar vert design showing stained-glass window. Multicoloured. P 14½ × 14.*

139	5 c. Type 41			15	15
140	7 c. "Suffer little children. . ." (Orro Church)			15	15
141	15 c. As 7 c.			20	55
142	25 c. Type 41			25	70
139/42		*Set of 4*		65	1·40

42 Flowers floating towards Nauru

(Des M. and Sylvia Goaman. Litho Format)

1976 (31 Jan*). *30th Anniv of the Return from Truk. T 42 and similar horiz designs. Multicoloured. P 14½.*

143	10 c. Type 42			10	10
144	14 c. Nauru encircled by garland			15	10
145	25 c. Finsch's Reed Warbler and maps			35	25
146	40 c. Return of the islanders			45	35
143/6		*Set of 4*		95	65

*This is the local date of issue; the Crown Agents released the stamps one day earlier.

Nos. 143/6 exist imperforate from sets of progressive proofs.

43 3d. and 9d. Stamps of 1916

(Des M. and Sylvia Goaman. Litho Format)

1976 (6 May). *60th Anniv of Nauruan Stamps. T* **43** *and similar horiz designs. Multicoloured. P* 13½.

147	10 c. Type **43**	.. .. ..	15	15
148	15 c. 6d. and 1s. stamps	.. ..	20	15
149	25 c. 2s. 6d. stamp	.. ..	30	25
150	50 c. 5s. "Specimen" stamp	..	40	35
147/50		*Set of 4*	95	80

Nos. 147/8 show stamps with errors; the 3d. "Short N" and the 6d. "P" for "R".

Nos. 147/50 exist imperforate from sets of progressive proofs.

44 *Pandanus mei* and *Enna G* (cargo liner)

(Des M. and Sylvia Goaman. Litho Format)

1976 (26 July). *South Pacific Forum, Nauru. T* **44** *and similar horiz designs. Multicoloured. P* 13½.

151	10 c. Type **44**		15	10
152	20 c. *Tournefortia argentea* with Boeing 737 and Fokker F.28 Fellowship aircraft		20	15
153	30 c. *Thespesia populnea* and Nauru Tracking Station		25	15
154	40 c. *Cordia subcordata* and produce		35	25
151/4		*Set of 4*	85	60

Nos. 151/4 exist imperforate from sets of progressive proofs.

45 Nauruan Choir   **46** Nauru House and Coral Pinnacles

(Des G. Vasarhelyi. Litho Format)

1976 (17 Nov). *Christmas. T* **45** *and similar vert designs. Multicoloured. P* 13½.

155	15 c. Type **45**	.. ..	10	10
	a. Horiz pair. Nos. 155/6		20	20
156	15 c. Nauruan choir		10	10
157	20 c. Angel in white dress	..	15	15
	a. Horiz pair. Nos. 157/8		30	30
158	20 c. Angel in red dress	..	15	15
155/8		*Set of 4*	50	50

Nos. 155/6 and 157/8 were printed horizontally *se-tenant* throughout the sheet, both forming composite designs.

(Des D. Gentleman. Photo Harrison)

1977 (25 Apr*). *Opening of Nauru House, Melbourne. T* **46** *and similar vert design. Multicoloured. P* 14.

159	15 c. Type **46**	.. ..	15	15
160	30 c. Nauru House and Melbourne skyline	..	25	25

*This is the local release date. The London agency released the stamps on 14 April.

47 Cable Ship *Anglia*   **48** Father Kayser and First Catholic Church

(Des D. Gentleman. Photo Harrison)

1977 (7 Sept). *75th Anniv of First Trans-Pacific Cable and 20th Anniv of First Artificial Earth Satellite. T* **47** *and similar vert designs. P* 14 × 14½.

161	7 c. multicoloured	.. ..	20	10
162	15 c. light blue, grey and black	..	30	15
163	20 c. light blue, grey and black	..	30	20
164	25 c. multicoloured	..	30	20
161/4		*Set of 4*	1·00	60

Designs:—15 c. Tracking station, Nauru; 20 c. Stern of *Anglia*; 25 c. Dish aerial.

(Des D. Gentleman. Photo Harrison)

1977 (28 Nov). *Christmas. T* **48** *and similar vert designs. Multicoloured. P* 14½.

165	15 c. Type **48**	.. ..	10	10
166	25 c. Congregational Church, Orro	..	15	15
167	30 c. Catholic Church, Arubo	..	15	15
165/7		*Set of 3*	30	30

No. 165 also commemorates the 75th anniversary of the Catholic Church on Nauru.

---

49 Arms of Nauru   **4c** =   (50)

(Des G. Vasarhelyi. Litho Format)

1978 (31 Jan). *Tenth Anniv of Independence. P* 14½.

168	**49** 15 c. multicoloured	.. ..	20	15
169	60 c. multicoloured	..	35	30

1978 (29 Mar). *Nos. 159/60 surch as T* **50** *by Format.*

170	4 c. on 15 c. Type **46**	..	55	1·50
171	5 c. on 15 c. Type **46**	..	55	1·50
172	8 c. on 30 c. No. 160	..	55	1·50
173	10 c. on 30 c. No. 160	..	55	1·50
170/3		*Set of 4*	2·00	5·50

51 Collecting Shellfish   **52** A.P.U. Emblem

(Des D. Gentleman. Photo Harrison)

1978 (17 May)–*79. Horiz designs as T* **51** *in brown, blue and black (4 c.), grey, black and light blue (20 c., $5) or multicoloured (others). P* 14½.

174	1 c. Type **51**	.. ..	50	30
175	2 c. Coral outcrop (6.6.79)	..	50	30
176	3 c. Reef scene (6.6.79)	..	1·00	40
177	4 c. Girl with fish (6.6.79)	..	50	30
178	5 c. Eastern Reef Heron (6.6.79)	..	1·75	40
179	7 c. Catching fish, Buada Lagoon	..	30	65
180	10 c. Ijuw Lagoon	..	30	20
181	15 c. Girl framed by coral	..	40	30
182	20 c. Pinnacles, Anibare Bay reef	..	30	30
183	25 c. Pinnacle at Meneng	..	30	30
184	30 c. Head of Great Frigate Bird	..	1·50	45
185	32 c. White-capped Noddy in coconut palm	..	2·25	65
186	40 c. Wandering Tattler	..	1·50	1·75
187	50 c. Great Frigate Birds on perch	..	85	75
188	$1 Old coral pinnacles at Topside	..	70	55
189	$2 New pinnacles at Topside	..	95	1·00
190	$5 Blackened pinnacles at Topside	..	1·50	2·25
174/90		*Set of 17*	13·50	9·75

(Litho Toppan Ptg Co, Ltd)

1978 (28 Aug). *14th General Assembly of Asian Parliamentarians' Union. T* **52** *and similar vert design. P* 13.

191	15 c. multicoloured	..	20	25
192	20 c. black, deep ultramarine and gold	..	20	25

Design:—20 c. As T **52** but different background.

53 Virgin and Child   **54** Baden-Powell and Cub Scout

(Des R. Vigurs. Litho Format)

1978 (1 Nov). *Christmas. T* **53** *and similar multicoloured design. P* 14.

193	7 c. Type **53**	.. ..	10	10
194	15 c. Angel in sun-rise scene (*horiz*)	..	10	10
195	20 c. As 15 c.	..	15	15
196	30 c. Type **53**	..	20	20
193/6		*Set of 4*	40	40

(Des J. Charles. Litho Format)

1978 (1 Dec). *70th Anniv of Boy Scout Movement. T* **54** *and similar horiz designs. Multicoloured. P* 13½.

197	20 c. Type **54**	.. ..	20	15
198	30 c. Baden-Powell and Boy Scout	..	25	20
199	50 c. Baden-Powell and Rover Scout	..	35	30
197/9		*Set of 3*	70	60

COVER PRICES

Cover factors are quoted at the beginning of each country for most issues to 1945. An explanation of the system can be found on page x. The factors quoted do not, however, apply to philatelic covers.

---

55 Wright Flyer I over Nauru

(Des D. Gentleman. Litho Format)

1979 (24 Jan). *Flight Anniversaries. T* **55** *and similar horiz designs. Multicoloured. P* 14.

200	10 c. Type **55**	..	20	15
201	15 c. Fokker F.VIIa/3m *Southern Cross* superimposed on nose of Boeing 737		30	20
	a. Pair. Nos. 201/2		60	40
202	15 c. Fokker F.VIIa/3m *Southern Cross* and Boeing 737 (front view)		30	20
203	30 c. Wright Flyer I over Nauru airfield	..	55	30
200/3		*Set of 4*	1·25	75

Commemorations:—10, 30 c. 75th anniversary of powered flight; 15 c. 50th anniversary of Kingsford-Smith's Pacific flight.

Nos. 201/2 were printed together, *se-tenant*, in horizontal and vertical pairs throughout the sheet.

No. 203 exists with black (inscription) omitted from stock dispersed by the liquidator of Format International Security Printers Ltd.

56 Sir Rowland Hill and Marshall Islands 10 pf. Stamp of 1901

(Des R. Granger Barrett. Litho Format)

1979 (27 Feb). *Death Centenary of Sir Rowland Hill. T* **56** *and similar horiz designs showing stamps and Sir Rowland Hill. Multicoloured. P* 14½.

204	5 c. Type **56**	..	15	10
	a. Imperf (pair)		60·00	
205	15 c. "NAURU" opt on Great Britain 10s. "Seahorse" of 1916–23		25	20
	a. Imperf (pair)		60·00	
206	60 c. 1978 10th Anniversary of Independence 60 c. commemorative		55	40
	a. Imperf (pair)		60·00	
204/6		*Set of 3*	85	60
MS207	159 × 101 mm. Nos. 204/6	..	85	1·25
	a. Error. Imperf		£150	

57 Dish Antenna, Transmitting Station and Radio Mast   **58** Smiling Child

(Des G. Vasarhelyi. Litho Format)

1979 (22 Aug). *50th Anniv of International Consultative Radio Committee. T* **57** *and similar horiz designs. Multicoloured. P* 14½.

208	7 c. Type **57**	..	15	10
209	32 c. Telex operator	..	35	25
210	40 c. Radio operator	..	40	25
208/10		*Set of 3*	80	55

(Des G. Vasarhelyi. Litho Format)

1979 (3 Oct). *International Year of the Child. T* **58** *and similar vert designs showing smiling children. P* 14½.

211	8 c. multicoloured	..	10	10
	a. Horiz strip of 5. Nos. 211/15		70	
212	15 c. multicoloured	..	15	15
213	25 c. multicoloured	..	20	20
214	32 c. multicoloured	..	20	20
215	50 c. multicoloured	..	25	25
211/15		*Set of 5*	70	70

Nos. 211/15 were printed together, *se-tenant*, in horizontal strips of 5 throughout the sheet, forming a composite design.

59 Ekwenababae (flower), Scroll inscribed "Peace on Earth" and Star

(Des G. Vasarhelyi. Litho Format)

1979 (14 Nov). *Christmas. T* **59** *and similar horiz designs. Multicoloured. P* 14½.

216	7 c. Type **59**	..	10	10
217	15 c. *Thespia populnea* (flower), scroll inscribed "Goodwill toward Men" and star		10	10

218 20 c. Denea (flower), scroll inscribed "Peace on Earth" and star 10 10
219 30 c. Erekogo (flower), scroll inscribed "Good-will toward Men" and star 20 20
216/19 .. .. *Set of 4* 40 40
Nos. 216/19 exist imperforate from sets of progressive proofs.

TENTH ANNIVERSARY OF AIR NAURU

60 Dassault Breguet Mystère Falcon 50 over Melbourne

(Des G. Vasarhelyi. Litho Format)

1980 (28 Feb). *10th Anniv of Air Nauru. T* **60** *and similar horiz designs. Multicoloured. P* 14½.
220 15 c. Type **60** 35 15
221 20 c. Fokker F.28 Fellowship over Tarawa 40 15
222 25 c. Boeing 727-100 over Hong Kong 40 15
223 30 c. Boeing 737 over Auckland .. 40 15
220/3 .. .. *Set of 4* 1·40 55
Nos. 220/2 exist imperforate from stock dispersed by the liquidator of Format International Security Printers Ltd.

61 Steam Locomotive

(Des G. Vasarhelyi. Litho Format)

1980 (6 May). *10th Anniv of Nauru Phosphate Corporation. Railway Locomotives. T* **61** *and similar horiz designs. Multicoloured. P* 14½.
224 8 c. Type **61** 10 10
225 32 c. Electric locomotives 20 20
226 60 c. Diesel-hydraulic locomotive .. 35 35
224/6 .. .. *Set of 3* 60 60
MS227 168×118 mm. Nos. 224/6. P 13 .. 1·40 2·50
No. **MS227** also commemorates the "London 1980" International Stamp Exhibition.

62 Verse 10 from Luke, Chapter 2 in English

(Des C. Abbott. Litho Format)

1980 (24 Sept). *Christmas. T* **62** *and similar square designs showing verses from Luke, chapter 2. Multicoloured. P* 14½.
228 20 c. Type **62** 10 10
  a. Horiz pair. Nos. 228/9 .. .. 20 20
229 20 c. Verse 10 in Nauruan 10 10
230 30 c. Verse 14 in English 15 15
  a. Horiz pair. Nos. 230/1 .. .. 30 30
231 30 c. Verse 14 in Nauruan 15 15
228/31 .. .. *Set of 4* 50 50
Nos. 228/9 and 230/1 were each printed together, *se-tenant*, in horizontal pairs throughout the sheet.
Nos. 228/31 exist imperforate from stock dispersed by the liquidator of Format International Security Printers Ltd.
See also Nos. 248/51.

63 Nauruan, Australian, Union and New Zealand Flags on Aerial View of Nauru

(Des H. Woods. Litho Format)

1980 (3 Dec)–**81**. *20th Anniv of U.N. Declaration on the Granting of Independence to Colonial Countries and Peoples. T* **63** *and similar multicoloured designs. P* 14½ (25 c.) *or* 13½ *(others)*.
232 25 c. Type **63** 15 15
233 30 c. U.N. Trusteeship Council (72 × 23 *mm*) (11.2.81) 15 15
234 50 c. Nauru independence ceremony, 1968 (72 × 23 *mm*) 25 25
232/4 .. .. *Set of 3* 50 50
The 25 c. value was printed in sheets including 5 *se-tenant* stamp-size labels; the other two values were each printed in sheets including 5 *se-tenant* half stamp-size labels.
Nos. 233/4 exist imperforate from stock dispersed by the liquidator of Format International Security Printers Ltd.

64 Timothy Detudamo

(Des R. Granger Barrett. Litho Format)

1981 (11 Feb). *30th Anniv of Nauru Local Government Council. Head Chiefs. T* **64** *and similar horiz designs. Multicoloured. P* 14½.
235 20 c. Type **64** 15 15
236 30 c. Raymond Gadabu 15 15
237 50 c. Hammer DeRoburt 25 25
235/7 .. .. *Set of 3* 50 50
Nos. 235/7 exist imperforate from stock dispersed by the liquidator of Format International Security Printers Ltd.

65 Casting Net by Hand

(Litho Questa)

1981 (22 May). *Fishing. T* **65** *and similar horiz designs. Multicoloured. P* 12 × 11½.
238 8 c. Type **65** 10 10
239 20 c. Outrigger canoe.. .. .. 20 15
240 32 c. Outboard motor boat 25 20
241 40 c. Trawler 30 25
238/41 .. .. *Set of 4* 75 60
MS242 167 × 116 mm. No. 241 × 4. P 14 .. 2·25 2·00
No. **MS242** was issued to commemorate the "WIPA 1981" International Stamp Exhibition, Vienna.

66 Bank of Nauru Emblem and Building **67** Inaugural Speech

(Des H. Woods. Litho Harrison)

1981 (21 July). *Fifth Anniv of Bank of Nauru. P* 14 × 14½.
243 **66** $1 multicoloured 60 60

(Des G. Vasarhelyi. Litho Questa)

1981 (24 Oct). *U.N. Day. E.S.C.A.P. (United Nations Economic and Social Commission for Asia and the Pacific) Events. T* **67** *and similar square designs. Multicoloured. P* 14 × 14½.
244 15 c. Type **67** 15 15
245 20 c. Presenting credentials 15 15
246 25 c. Unveiling plaque 20 20
247 30 c. Raising U.N. flag 25 25
244/7 .. .. *Set of 4* 65 65

(Des C. Abbott. Litho Format)

1981 (14 Nov). *Christmas. Bible Verses. Square designs as T* **62**. *Multicoloured. P* 14½.
248 20 c. Matthew 1, 23 in English .. 15 15
  a. Horiz pair. Nos. 248/9 .. .. 30 30
249 20 c. Matthew 1, 23 in Nauruan .. 15 15
250 30 c. Luke 2, 11 in English 20 20
  a. Horiz pair. Nos. 250/1 .. .. 40 40
251 30 c. Luke 2, 11 in Nauruan 20 20
248/51 .. .. *Set of 4* 70 70
Nos. 248/9 and 250/1 were each printed together, *se-tenant*, in horizontal pairs throughout the sheet.
Nos. 248/51 exist imperforate from stock dispersed by the liquidator of Format International Security Printers Ltd.

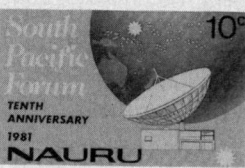

68 Earth Satellite Station

(Des M. Rickards. Litho Format)

1981 (9 Dec). *Tenth Anniv of South Pacific Forum. T* **68** *and similar horiz designs. Multicoloured. P* 13½ × 14.
252 10 c. Type **68** 20 15
253 20 c. *Enna G* (cargo liner) 25 20
254 30 c. Boeing 737 airliner 25 25
255 40 c. Local produce 25 30
252/5 .. .. *Set of 4* 85 80

69 Nauru Scouts leaving for 1935 Frankston Scout Jamboree

(Des C. Abbott. Litho Format)

1982 (23 Feb). *75th Anniv of Boy Scout Movement. T* **69** *and similar multicoloured designs. P* 14.
256 7 c. Type **69** 15 15
257 8 c. Two Nauru scouts on *Nauru Chief*, 1935 (*vert*) 15 15
258 15 c. Nauru scouts making pottery, 1935 (*vert*) 15 20
259 20 c. Lord Huntingfield addressing Nauru scouts, Frankston Jamboree, 1935 20 25
260 25 c. Nauru cub and scout, 1982 .. 20 30
261 40 c. Nauru cubs, scouts and scouters, 1982 .. .. .. 30 45
256/61 .. .. *Set of 6* 1·00 1·40
MS262 152 × 114 mm. Nos. 256/61. Imperf 1·25 2·25
No. **MS262** also commemorates Nauru's participation in the "Stampex" National Stamp Exhibition, London.
Nos. 256/61 were each printed in sheets including four *se-tenant* stamp-size labels.

70 100kw Electricity Generating Plant under Construction (left side)

(Litho Irish Security Stamp Printing Ltd)

1982 (10 June). *Ocean Thermal Energy Conversion. T* **70** *and similar horiz designs. Multicoloured. P* 13½.
263 25 c. Type **70** 50 30
  a. Horiz pair. Nos. 263/4 .. .. 1·00 60
264 25 c. 100kw Electricity Generating Plant under construction (right side) 50 30
265 40 c. Completed plant (left) 70 40
  a. Horiz pair. Nos. 265/6 .. .. 1·40 80
266 40 c. Completed plant (right) .. 70 40
263/6 .. .. *Set of 4* 2·25 1·25
Nos. 263/4 and 265/6 were printed together, *se-tenant*, in horizontal pairs forming composite designs throughout sheets which also included two stamp-size and twelve half stamp-size labels.

71 S.S. *Fido* **72** Queen Elizabeth II on Horseback

(Des R. Littleford (5 c.), Debbie Ryder (10, 30 c.), Cecilia Eales (60 c.), Jane Evans ($1). Litho Format)

1982 (11 Oct). *75th Anniv of Phosphate Shipments. T* **71** *and similar horiz designs. Multicoloured. P* 14.
267 5 c. Type **71** 55 10
268 10 c. Steam locomotive *Nellie* .. 80 30
269 30 c. Class "Clyde" diesel locomotive 90 50
270 60 c. M.V. *Eigamoiya* (bulk carrier) 95 80
267/70 .. .. *Set of 4* 2·75 1·40
MS271 165×107 mm. $1 *Eigamoiya, Rosie-D* and *Kolle-D* (bulk carriers) (67 × 27 *mm*) 1·50 2·25
No. **MS271** was issued to commemorate "ANPEX 82" National Stamp Exhibition, Brisbane.
Nos. 267/71 exist imperforate from stock dispersed by the liquidator of Format International Security Printers Ltd.

(Des G. Vasarhelyi. Litho Format)

1982 (21 Oct). *Royal Visit. T* **72** *and similar multicoloured designs. P* 14½.
272 20 c. Type **72** 35 30
273 50 c. Prince Philip, Duke of Edinburgh 45 60
274 $1 Queen Elizabeth II and Prince Philip (*horiz*) .. .. .. 60 1·25
272/4 .. .. *Set of 3* 1·25 1·90

73 Father Bernard Lahn **74** Speaker of the Nauruan Parliament

(Des G. Vasarhelyi. Litho Format)

1982 (17 Nov). *Christmas. T* **73** *and similar horiz designs. Multicoloured. P* 14½.
275 20 c. Type **73** 20 30
276 30 c. Reverend Itubwa Amram .. 20 45
277 40 c. Pastor James Aingimen .. 25 70
278 50 c. Bishop Paul Mea .. .. 30 1·00
275/8 .. .. *Set of 4* 85 2·25
Nos. 275/8 were printed in sheets of 25 including 5 *se-tenant* stamp-size, labels.

(Des G. Vasarhelyi. Litho Walsall)

1983 (23 Mar). *15th Anniv of Independence. T* **74** *and similar multicoloured designs. W w* 14 *(sideways on* 30, 50 *c.). P* 14.

279	15 c. Type **74**	.. ..	15	15
280	20 c. Family Court in session	..	20	20
281	30 c. Law Courts building (*horiz*)	..	25	25
282	50 c. Parliamentary chamber (*horiz*)	..	40	40
279/82		*Set of 4*	90	90

75 Nauru Satellite Earth Station

(Des C. Abbott. Litho Questa)

1983 (11 May). *World Communications Year. T* **75** *and similar horiz designs. Multicoloured. W w* 14 *(sideways). P* 14.

283	5 c. Type **75**	.. ..	20	10
284	10 c. Omni-directional range installation	..	20	15
285	20 c. Emergency short-wave radio	..	25	25
286	25 c. Radio Nauru control room	..	40	30
287	40 c. Unloading air mail	..	90	45
283/7	..	*Set of 5*	1·75	1·10

76 Return of Exiles from Truk on M.V. *Trienza*, 1946

77 "The Holy Virgin, the Holy Child and St. John" (School of Raphael)

(Des D. Slater. Litho Format)

1983 (14 Sept). *Angam Day. T* **76** *and similar multicoloured designs. W w* 14 *(sideways on* 15 *c.). P* 13½ (15 c.) *or* 14 (*others*).

288	15 c. Type **76**	.. ..	20	25
289	20 c. Mrs. Elsie Agio (exile community leader)	..	20	25
290	30 c. Child on scales	..	35	40
291	40 c. Nauruan children	..	45	50
288/91		*Set of 4*	1·10	1·25

Nos. 289/91 are vertical designs, each 25 × 41 mm.

(Des L. Curtis. Litho Questa)

1983 (16 Nov). *Christmas. T* **77** *and similar multicoloured designs. W w* 14 *(sideways on* 50 *c.). P* 14 × 14½ (50 c.) *or* 14½ × 14 (*others*).

292	5 c. Type **77**	.. ..	10	10
293	15 c. "Madonna on the Throne surrounded by Angels" (School of Seville)	..	20	15
294	50 c. "The Mystical Betrothal of St. Catherine with Jesus" (School of Veronese) (*horiz*)	..	60	40
292/4	..	*Set of 3*	75	55

78 S.S. *Ocean Queen*

79 1974 U.P.U. $1 Stamp

(Des Beverley Barnard and L. Curtis. Litho Questa)

1984 (23 May). *250th Anniv of "Lloyd's List" (newspaper). T* **78** *and similar vert designs. Multicoloured. W w* 14. *P* 14½ × 14.

295	20 c. Type **78**	.. ..	40	30
296	25 c. M.V. *Enna G*	..	45	35
297	30 c. M.V. *Baron Minto*	..	50	40
298	40 c. Sinking of M.V. *Triadic*, 1940	..	75	55
295/8	..	*Set of 4*	1·90	1·40

(Des L. Curtis. Litho Format)

1984 (4 June). *Universal Postal Union Congress, Hamburg. W w* 14. *P* 14.

299	**79** $1 multicoloured	.. ..	90	1·25

80 *Hypolimnas bolina* (female)

(Des I. Loe. Litho B.D.T.)

1984 (24 July). *Butterflies. T* **80** *and similar horiz designs. Multicoloured. W w* 14 *(sideways). P* 14.

300	25 c. Type **80**	.. ..	50	40
301	30 c. *Hypolimnas bolina* (male)	..	55	55
302	50 c. *Danaus plexippus*	..	70	85
300/2		*Set of 3*	1·60	1·60

81 Coastal Scene

82 Buada Chapel

(Des A. Theobald. Litho Enschedé)

1984 (21 Sept). *Life in Nauru. T* **81** *and similar multicoloured designs. W w* 14 *(sideways on horiz designs). P* 13½ × 14 (1, 5, 10, 25, 40 c., $2) *or* 14 × 13½ (*others*).

303	1 c. Type **81**	..	10	40
304	3 c. Nauruan woman (*vert*)	..	15	40
305	5 c. Modern trawler	..	40	50
306	10 c. Golfer on the links	..	90	50
307	15 c. Excavating phosphate (*vert*)	..	90	65
308	20 c. Surveyor (*vert*)	..	65	55
309	25 c. Air Nauru Boeing 727 airliner	..	80	55
310	40 c. Elderly Nauruan (*vert*)	..	50	50
311	40 c. Loading hospital patient on to Boeing 727 aircraft	..	90	55
312	50 c. Skin-diver with fish (*vert*)	..	1·00	80
313	$1 Tennis player (*vert*)	..	2·50	3·25
314	$2 Anabar Lagoon	..	2·50	3·75
303/14		*Set of 12*	10·00	11·00

Nos. 303/14 were each issued in sheets of 9 with decorative margins.

(Des L. Curtis. Litho Format)

1984 (14 Nov). *Christmas. T* **82** *and similar multicoloured designs. W w* 14 *(sideways on* 50 *c.). P* 14.

315	30 c. Type **82**	.. ..	40	50
316	40 c. Detudamo Memorial Church	..	50	65
317	50 c. Candle-light service, Kayser College (*horiz*)	..	60	70
315/17	..	*Set of 3*	1·40	1·75

83 Air Nauru Boeing 737 Jet on Tarmac

(Des L. Curtis. Litho Walsall)

1985 (26 Feb). *15th Anniv of Air Nauru. T* **83** *and similar multicoloured designs. W w* 14 *(sideways on* 20 *c.,* 40 *c.). P* 14.

318	20 c. Type **83**	.. ..	65	35
319	30 c. Stewardess on Boeing 727 aircraft steps (*vert*)	..	85	60
320	40 c. Fokker F.28 Fellowship over Nauru		1·10	75
321	50 c. Freight being loaded onto Boeing 727 (*vert*)	..	1·25	85
318/21	..	*Set of 4*	3·50	2·25

84 Open Cut Mining

85 Mother and Baby on Beach

(Des L. Curtis. Litho B.D.T.)

1985 (31 July). *15th Anniv of Nauru Phosphate Corporation. T* **84** *and similar horiz designs. Multicoloured. W w* 14 *(sideways). P* 14.

322	20 c. Type **84**	.. ..	80	60
323	25 c. Diesel locomotive hauling crushed ore		1·50	1·00
324	30 c. Phosphate drying plant	..	1·50	1·00
325	50 c. Early steam locomotive	..	2·25	1·75
322/5	..	*Set of 4*	5·50	4·00

(Des A. Theobald. Litho Questa)

1985 (15 Nov). *Christmas. T* **85** *and similar vert design. Multicoloured. W w* 16 *(sideways). P* 14.

326	50 c. Beach scene	..	1·10	2·00
	a. Horiz pair. Nos. 326/7	..	2·10	4·00
327	50 c. Type **85**	.. ..	1·10	2·00

Nos. 326/7 were printed in sheets of 16 made up of two strips of four *se-tenant* pairs, each pair forming a composite design. The two strips were divided by a horizontal gutter.

86 Adult Common Noddy with Juvenile

(Des N. Arlott. Litho Questa)

1985 (31 Dec). *Birth Bicentenary of John J. Audubon (ornithologist). Common "Brown" Noddy. T* **86** *and similar horiz designs. Multicoloured. W w* 16. *P* 14.

328	10 c. Type **86**	.. ..	35	35
	w. Wmk inverted	..	25·00	
329	20 c. Adult and immature birds in flight	..	50	70
	w. Wmk inverted		25·00	
330	30 c. Adults in flight	..	65	85
	w. Wmk inverted		25·00	
331	50 c. "Brown Noddy" (John J. Audubon)	..	80	1·00
328/31		*Set of 4*	2·10	2·75

87 Douglas Motor Cycle

(Des M. Joyce. Litho Questa)

1986 (5 Mar). *Early Transport on Nauru. T.* **87** *and similar horiz designs. Multicoloured. W w* 16. *P* 14.

332	15 c. Type **87**	.. ..	80	70
333	20 c. Primitive lorry	..	95	95
334	30 c. German-built steam locomotive, 1910		1·50	1·50
335	40 c. "Baby" Austin car	..	1·75	1·75
332/5		*Set of 4*	4·50	4·50

88 Island and Bank of Nauru

89 *Plumeria rubra*

(Des G. Vasarhelyi. Litho Format)

1986 (21 July). *10th Anniv of Bank of Nauru. Children's Paintings. T* **88** *and similar horiz designs. Multicoloured. W w* 16 *(sideways). P* 14.

336	20 c. Type **88**	.. ..	20	30
337	25 c. Borrower with notes and coins	..	25	35
338	30 c. Savers	..	30	40
339	40 c. Customers at bank counter	..	35	55
336/9	..	*Set of 4*	1·00	1·40

(Des Doreen McGuinness. Litho Questa)

1986 (30 Sept). *Flowers. T* **89** *and similar horiz designs. Multicoloured. W w* 16. *P* 14.

340	20 c. Type **89**	.. ..	55	70
341	25 c. *Tristellateia australis*	..	65	85
342	30 c. *Bougainvillea* cultivar	..	75	1·00
343	40 c. *Delonix regia*	..	1·00	1·25
340/3	..	*Set of 4*	2·75	3·50

90 Carol Singers

91 Young Girls Dancing

(Des M. Joyce. Litho Questa)

1986 (8 Dec). *Christmas. T* **90** *and similar horiz design. Multicoloured. W w* 16 *(sideways). P* 14.

344	20 c. Type **90**	.. ..	40	30
345	$1 Carol singers and hospital patient	..	1·60	3·00

(Des Joan Thompson. Litho Questa)

1987 (31 Jan). *Nauruan Dancers. T* **91** *and similar multicoloured designs. W w* 16 *(sideways on* 20, 30 *c.). P* 14.

346	20 c. Type **91**	.. ..	80	80
347	30 c. Stick dance	..	1·00	1·25
348	50 c. Boy doing war dance (*vert*)	..	1·75	2·50
346/8	..	*Set of 3*	3·25	4·00

92 Hibiscus Fibre Skirt

93 U.P.U. Emblem and Air Mail Label

(Des L. Curtis. Litho B.D.T.)

1987 (30 July). *Personal Artifacts. T 92 and similar horiz designs. Multicoloured. W w 16 (sideways). P 14.*
349	25 c. Type 92	..	75	75
350	30 c. Headband and necklets	..	85	85
351	45 c. Decorative necklets	..	1·10	1·10
352	60 c. Pandanus leaf fan	..	1·60	1·60
349/52		Set of 4	3·75	3·75

(Des D. Miller. Litho Format)

1987 (20 Oct). *World Post Day. T 93 and similar multicoloured design. W w 16. P 14½×14.*
353	40 c. Type 93	..	90	75
	w. Wmk inverted	..	14·00	
MS354	122×82mm. $1 U.P.U. emblem and map of Pacific showing mail routes (114×74 mm). Wmk sideways. Imperf	..	2·50	3·25

94 Open Bible

95 Nauruan Children's Party

(Des Janet Boschen. Litho Walsall)

1987 (5 Nov). *Centenary of Nauru Congregational Church. W w 14. P 13×13½.*
355	**94** 40 c. multicoloured	..	75	1·00

(Des M. Joyce. Litho Format)

1987 (27 Nov). *Christmas. T 95 and similar horiz design. Multicoloured. W w 16 (sideways). P 14.*
356	20 c. Type 95	..	75	50
357	$1 Nauruan Christmas dinner	..	2·75	3·25

96 Loading Phosphate on Ship

97 Map of German Marshall Is. and 1901 5 m. Yacht Definitive

(Des B. Clinton. Litho CPE Australia Ltd, Melbourne)

1988 (31 Jan). *20th Anniv of Independence. T 96 and similar multicoloured designs. P 13½×14 (25 c.), 14×13½ (40, 55 c.) or 13 ($1).*
358	25 c. Type 96	..	1·00	1·00
359	40 c. Tomano flower (vert)	..	1·50	1·50
360	55 c. Great Frigate Bird (vert)	..	2·25	2·25
361	$1 Arms of Republic (35×35 mm)	..	2·50	3·50
358/61		Set of 4	6·50	7·50

(Des O. Bell. Litho Format)

1988 (29 July). *80th Anniv of Nauru Post Office. T 97 and similar horiz designs. Multicoloured. W w 16 (sideways). P 14.*
362	30 c. Type 97	..	75	75
363	50 c. Letter and post office of 1908	..	1·00	1·25
364	70 c. Nauru Post Office and airmail letter	..	1·25	1·50
362/4		Set of 3	2·75	3·25

98 "Itubwer" (mat)

99 U.P.U. Emblem and National Flag

(Des Jennifer Toombs. Litho CPE Australia Ltd, Melbourne)

1988 (1 Aug). *String Figures. T 98 and similar horiz designs. Multicoloured. P 13½ × 14.*
365	25 c. Type 98	..	35	35
366	40 c. "Etegerer–the Pursuer"	..	50	60
367	55 c. "Holding up the Sky"	..	65	70
368	80 c. "Manujie's Sword"	..	1·00	1·25
365/8		Set of 4	2·25	2·50

(Des Elisabeth Innes. Litho CPE Australia Ltd, Melbourne)

1988 (1 Oct). *Centenary of Nauru's Membership of Universal Postal Union. P 13½ × 14.*
369	**99** $1 multicoloured	..	1·25	1·25

NEW INFORMATION

The editor is always interested to correspond with people who have new information that will improve or correct the Catalogue.

100 "Hark the Herald Angels"

101 Logo (15th anniv of Nauru Insurance Corporation)

(Des Elisabeth Innes. Litho CPE Australia Ltd, Melbourne)

1988 (28 Nov). *Christmas. T 100 and similar square designs showing words and music from "Hark the Herald Angels Sing". P 13.*
370	20 c. black, orange-vermilion and lemon	..	40	30
371	60 c. black, orange-vermilion and mauve	..	1·00	85
372	$1 black, orange-vermilion & bright green	..	1·60	1·40
370/2		Set of 3	2·75	2·25

(Litho Note Ptg Branch, Reserve Bank of Australia)

1989 (19 Nov). *Anniversaries and Events. T 101 and similar vert designs. Multicoloured. P 14×15.*
373	15 c. Type 101	..	30	30
374	50 c. Logos (World Telecommunications Day and 10th anniv of Asian Pacific Tele-community)	..	75	85
375	$1 Photograph of island scene (150 years of photography)	..	1·75	2·00
376	$2 Capitol and U.P.U. emblem (20th U.P.U. Congress, Washington)	..	2·75	3·75
373/6		Set of 4	5·00	6·25

102 Mother and Baby

103 Eigigu working while Sisters play

(Des Robin White. Litho Note Ptg Branch, Reserve Bank of Australia)

1989 (15 Dec). *Christmas. T 102 and similar vert design. Multicoloured. P 14×15.*
377	20 c. Type 102	..	50	30
378	$1 Children opening presents	..	2·25	3·00

(Des Anita Cecil. Litho Note Ptg Branch, Reserve Bank of Australia)

1989 (22 Dec). *20th Anniv of First Manned Landing on Moon. Legend of Eigigu, the Girl in the Moon. T 103 and similar vert designs. Multicoloured. P 14×15.*
379	25 c. Type 103	..	2·50	2·50
380	30 c. Eigigu climbing tree	..	2·75	2·75
381	50 c. Eigigu stealing toddy from blind woman	..	4·75	4·75
382	$1 Eigigu on Moon	..	7·00	7·00
379/82		Set of 4	15·00	15·00

104 Early Mining by Hand

105 Sunday School Class

(Des Robin White. Litho Note Ptg Branch, Reserve Bank of Australia)

1990 (3 July). *20th Anniv of Nauru Phosphate Corporation. T 104 and similar vert design. Multicoloured. P 14×15.*
383	50 c. Type 104	..	75	75
384	$1 Modern mining by excavator	..	1·25	1·50

(Litho Note Ptg Branch, Reserve Bank of Australia)

1990 (26 Nov). *Christmas. T 105 and similar vert design. Multicoloured. P 14×15.*
385	25 c. Type 105	..	90	1·00
	a. Horiz pair. Nos. 385/6	..	1·75	2·00
386	25 c. Teacher telling Christmas story	..	90	1·00

Nos. 385/6 were printed together, *se-tenant*, in horizontal pairs throughout the sheet, each pair forming a composite design.

106 Eoiyepiang laying Baby on Mat

107 Oleander

(Des Robin White. Litho Note Ptg Branch, Reserve Bank of Australia)

1990 (24 Dec). *Legend of "Eoiyepiang, the Daughter of Thunder and Lightning". T 106 and similar vert designs. Multicoloured. P 14×15.*
387	25 c. Type 106	..	1·00	60
388	30 c. Eoiyepiang making floral decoration	..	1·25	70
389	50 c. Eoiyepiang left on snow-covered mountain	..	1·75	2·00
390	$1 Eoiyepiang and warrior	..	2·75	3·50
387/90		Set of 4	6·00	6·00

(Litho Leigh-Mardon Ltd, Melbourne)

1991 (22 July). *Flowers. T 107 and similar multicoloured designs. P 14½.*
391	15 c. Type 107	..	10	15
392	20 c. Lily	..	15	20
393	25 c. Passion Flower	..	20	25
394	30 c. Lily (different)	..	25	30
395	35 c. Caesalpinia	..	30	35
396	40 c. Clerodendron	..	30	35
397	45 c. Baubina pinnata	..	35	40
398	50 c. Hibiscus (vert)	..	40	45
399	75 c. Apocymaceae	..	60	65
400	$1 Bindweed (vert)	..	80	85
401	$2 Tristellateia (vert)	..	1·60	1·75
402	$3 Impala Lily (vert)	..	2·40	2·50
391/402		Set of 12	7·50	8·25

108 Jesus Christ and Children (stained glass window)

109 Star and Symbol of Asian Development Bank

(Des R. Varma. Litho Leigh-Mardon Ltd, Melbourne)

1991 (12 Dec). *Christmas. Sheet 124×82 mm. P 14.*
MS403	**108** $2 multicoloured	..	4·00	4·50

(Des R. Varma. Litho Leigh-Mardon Ltd, Melbourne)

1992 (4 May). *25th Annual Meeting of Asian Development Bank. P 14×14½.*
404	**109** $1.50, multicoloured	..	2·00	2·50

110 Gifts under Christmas Tree

111 Hammer DeRoburt

(Des B. Clinton. Litho Printset Cambec Pty Ltd, Australia)

1992 (23 Nov). *Christmas. Children's Paintings. T 110 and similar horiz design. Multicoloured. P 14½×14.*
405	45 c. Type 110	..	75	75
406	60 c. Father Christmas in sleigh	..	1·00	1·50

(Des B. Clinton. Litho McPherson's Ptg Group. Mulgrave)

1993 (31 Jan). *25th Anniv of Independence and Hammer DeRoburt (former President) Commemoration. P 14×14½.*
407	**111** $1 multicoloured	..	2·00	2·50

112 Running,
Constitution Day
Sports

(Des B. Clinton. Litho McPherson's Ptg Group, Mulgrave)

1993 (17 May). *15th Anniv of Constitution Day. T 112 and similar vert design. Multicoloured. P 14×14½.*
408 70 c. Type 112 .. .. 75 75
409 80 c. Part of Independence Proclamation .. 1·00 1·25

113 Great Frigate Birds, Flying
Fish and Island

(Litho McPherson's Printing Group, Mulgrave)

1993 (9 Aug). *24th South Pacific Forum Meeting, Nauru. T 113 and similar horiz designs. Multicoloured. P 14½×14.*
410 60 c. Type 113 .. .. 1·40 1·50
 a. Block of 4. Nos. 410/13 .. 5·00
411 60 c. Red-tailed Tropic Bird, Great Frigate
  Bird, dolphin and island .. 1·40 1·50
412 60 c. Racoon Butterflyfish ("Ikimago"), coral
  and sea urchins .. 1·40 1·50
413 60 c. Three different types of fish with corals 1·40 1·50
410/13 *Set of 4* 5·00 5·50
MS414 140×130 mm. Nos. 410/13 .. 6·50 7·00
Nos. 410/13 were printed together, *se-tenant*, in blocks of 4 throughout the sheet with each block forming a composite design.

114 "Peace on Earth, Goodwill to
Men" and Star

(Litho Leigh-Mardon Ltd, Melbourne)

1993 (29 Nov). *Christmas. T 114 and similar horiz design. Multicoloured. P 14½×14.*
415 55 c. Type 114 .. .. 85 85
416 65 c. "Hark the Herald Angels Sing" and
  star 90 90
Nos. 415/16 were printed in sheets containing the two values in blocks of 9 (3×3) separated by a horizontal gutter.

115 Girls with Dogs   **116** Weightlifting

(Des B. Clinton. Litho McPherson's Ptg Group, Mulgrave)

1994 (10 Feb). *"Hong Kong '94" International Stamp Exhibition. Chinese New Year ("Year of the Dog"). T 115 and similar vert designs. Multicoloured. P 14×14½.*
417 $1 Type 115 .. .. 1·50 1·75
 a. Horiz pair. Nos. 417/18 .. 3·00 3·50
418 $1 Boys with dogs .. .. 1·50 1·75
MS419 100×75 mm. Nos. 417/18 .. 3·00 3·75
 a. Optd with exhibition logo on margin at
  bottom right .. .. 2·50 3·75
Nos. 417/18 were printed together, *se-tenant*, in horizontal pairs throughout the sheet of 12.

1994 (31 Aug). *"Singpex '94" National Stamp Exhibition, Singapore. No. MS419 optd "SINGPEX '94" and emblem in gold on sheet margin.*
MS420 100×75 mm. Nos. 417/18 .. 3·00 3·75

(Des R. Innes. Litho Printset Cambec Pty Ltd, Melbourne)

1994 (8 Sept). *15th Commonwealth Games, Victoria, Canada. P 14×14½.*
421 **116** $1.50, multicoloured .. .. 1·40 1·75

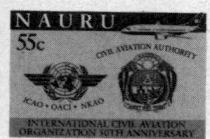

117 Peace Dove   **118** Air Nauru Airliner
and Star over   and Emblems
Island

(Des Passmore Design. Litho McPherson's Ptg Group, Mulgrave)

1994 (20 Nov). *Christmas. T 117 and similar vert design. Multicoloured. P 14½×14.*
422 65 c. Type 117 .. .. 60 65
423 75 c. Star over Bethlehem 70 85

(Litho Printset Cambec Pty Ltd, Melbourne)

1994 (14 Dec). *50th Anniv of International Civil Aviation Organization. T 118 and similar horiz designs. Multicoloured. P 14×14½.*
424 55 c. Type 118 .. .. 50 55
425 65 c. Control tower, Nauru International
  Airport 60 65
426 80 c. D.V.O.R. equipment .. .. 70 1·00
427 $1 Crash tenders .. .. 90 1·10
424/7 *Set of 4* 2·50 3·00
MS428 165×127 mm. Nos. 424/7 .. 3·50 4·00

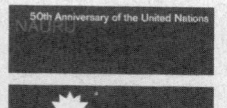

119 Emblem and   **120** Nauruan Flag
Olympic Rings

(Des D. Sharma. Litho McPherson's Ptg Group, Mulgrave)

1994 (27 Dec). *Nauru's Entry into International Olympic Committee. P 14×14½.*
429 **119** 50 c. multicoloured 45 50

(Litho McPherson's Ptg Group, Mulgrave)

1995 (1 Jan). *50th Anniv of United Nations (1st issue). T 120 and similar horiz designs. Multicoloured. P 14×14½.*
430 75 c. Type 120 .. .. 90 1·10
 a. Block of 4. Nos. 430/3 .. 3·25
431 75 c. Arms of Nauru .. .. 90 1·10
432 75 c. Outrigger canoe on coastline .. 90 1·10
433 75 c. Airliner over phosphate freighter .. 90 1·10
430/3 *Set of 4* 3·25 4·00
MS434 110×85 mm. Nos. 430/3 .. 4·00 5·00
Nos. 430/3 were printed together, *se-tenant*, in blocks of 4 with Nos. 432/3 forming a composite design.
See also Nos. 444/5.

121 Signing Phosphate   **(122)**
Agreement, 1967

(Des B. Clinton. Litho Printset Cambec Pty Ltd, Melbourne)

1995 (1 July). *25th Anniv of Nauru Phosphate Corporation. T 121 and similar horiz designs. Multicoloured. P 14×14½.*
435 60 c. Type 121 .. .. 80 1·00
 a. Horiz pair. Nos. 435/6 .. 1·60 2·00
436 60 c. Pres. Bernard Dowiyogo and Prime
  Minister Keating of Australia shaking
  hands .. .. 80 1·00
MS437 120×80 mm. $2 Excavating phosphate 2·75 3·25
Nos. 435/6 were printed together, *se-tenant*, in horizontal pairs throughout the sheet.

1995 (19 Aug). *International Stamp Exhibitions. No. 309 surch as T 122.*
438 50 c. on 25 c. mult (surch with T 122) .. 90 1·10
 a. Horiz strip of 3. Nos. 438/40 .. 2·40
439 $1 on 25 c. mult (surch "at Jakarta") .. 90 1·40
440 $1 on 25 c. mult (surch "at Singapore") .. 90 1·40
438/40 *Set of 3* 2·40 3·50
Nos. 438/40 were surcharged together, *se-tenant*, as horizontal strips of 3 on the sheets of 9.

Nauru   **Nauru**
123 Sea Birds (face   **124** Children playing on Gun
value at top right)

(Litho Southern Colour Print, Dunedin)

1995 (1 Sept). *Olympic Games, Atlanta. Sheet 140×121 mm, containing T 123 and similar vert designs. Multicoloured. P 12.*
MS441 60 c. + 15 c. Type 123; 60 c. + 15 c. Sea
  birds (face value at top left); 60 c. + 15 c. Four
  dolphins; 60 c. + 15 c. Pair of dolphins .. 4·00 4·50
The premiums on No. MS441 were for Nauru sport development.

(Des Passmore Design. Litho Questa)

1995 (13 Sept). *50th Anniv of Peace. T 124 and similar horiz design. Multicoloured. P 14×13½.*
442 75 c. Type 124 .. .. 1·25 1·50
 a. Horiz pair. Nos. 442/3 and label .. 3·00
 b. Vert pair. Nos. 442/3 .. 3·00
443 $1.50, Children making floral garlands .. 1·75 2·00
Nos. 442/3 were printed together, *se-tenant*, in sheets of 12 (3×4) containing 8 stamps and 4 labels. The labels, which show a dove or a war memorial, occur in the centre vertical row.
Nos. 442/3 were reissued on 23 February 1996 with the centre labels overprinted in gold with the "HONGPEX '96" logo or a mouse.

125 Nauru Crest,   **126** Young Girl
Coastline and U.N.   praying
Anniversary Emblem

(Des and litho Courvoisier)

1995 (24 Oct). *50th Anniv of United Nations (2nd issue). T 125 and similar horiz design. Multicoloured. P 14½×14.*
444 75 c. Type 125 .. .. 90 1·00
445 $1.50, Aerial view of Nauru and U.N.
  Headquarters, New York .. 1·60 2·00

(Litho Questa)

1995 (7 Dec). *Christmas. T 126 and similar vert design. Multicoloured. P 14½.*
446 60 c. Type 126 .. .. 90 1·00
 a. Horiz pair. Nos. 446/7 .. 1·75 2·00
447 70 c. Man praying .. .. 90 1·00
Nos. 446/7 were printed together, *se-tenant*, in horizontal pairs throughout the sheet.

127 Returning Refugees and
Head Chief Timothy Detudamo

(Des P. Arnold. Litho Southern Colour Print, Dunedin)

1996 (31 Jan). *50th Anniv of Nauruans' Return from Truk. P 12.*
448 **127** 75 c. multicoloured .. .. 90 1·00
449 $1.25, multicoloured .. .. 1·60 2·00
MS450 120×80 mm. Nos. 448/9 .. 2·75 3·25

**STANLEY GIBBONS
STAMP COLLECTING SERIES**

Introductory booklets on *How to Start, How to Identify Stamps* and *Collecting by Theme.* A series of well illustrated guides at a low price.
Write for details.

128 Nanjing Stone Lion   **129** Symbolic Athlete

(Litho Southern Colour Print, Dunedin)

1996 (20 Mar). *"CHINA '96" 9th Asian International Stamp Exhibition, Peking. Sheet* 130×110 *mm. P* 12.

MS451 **128** 45 c. multicoloured   80   1·00

(Des and litho Courvoisier)

1996 (21 July). *Centenary of Modern Olympic Games. T* **129** *and similar multicoloured designs. P* 14.

452	40 c. Type **129**	..	..	70	70
453	50 c. Symbolic weightlifter	..	..	80	90
454	60 c. Weightlifter (*horiz*)	..	..	90	1·00
455	$1 Athlete (*horiz*)	..	..	1·40	2·00
452/5			Set of 4	3·50	4·25

130 The Nativity and Angel   **131** Dolphin (fish)

(Des G. Vasarhelyi. Litho Courvoisier)

1996 (16 Dec). *Christmas. T* **130** *and similar horiz design. Multicoloured. P* 14.

456	50 c. Type **130**	..	..	60	60
457	70 c. Angel, world map and wild animals	..	80	1·00

(Des and litho Courvoisier)

1997 (12 Feb). *Endangered Species. Fishes. T* **131** *and similar horiz designs. Multicoloured. P* 11½.

458	20 c. Type **131**	..	..	60	60
	a. Strip of 4. Nos. 458/61	..	..	2·50	
459	30 c. Wahoo	..	..	70	70
460	40 c. Sailfish	..	..	75	75
461	50 c. Yellow-finned Tuna	..	..	80	80
458/61			Set of 4	2·50	2·50

Nos. 458/61 were printed together, *se-tenant*, as horizontal or vertical strips of 4 in sheets of 16.

132 Statue of Worshipper with Offering   **133** Princess Elizabeth and Lieut. Philip Mountbatten, 1947

(Litho Southern Colour Print, Dunedin)

1997 (12 Feb). *"HONG KONG '97" International Stamp Exhibition. T* **132** *and similar vert designs showing statues of different worshippers* (1 c. to 15 c.) *or Giant Buddha of Hong Kong* (25 c.). *P* 14.

462	1 c. multicoloured	..	..	20	20
	a. Sheetlet. Nos. 462/8	..	1·75	
463	2 c. multicoloured	..	..	20	20
464	5 c. multicoloured	..	..	25	25
465	10 c. multicoloured	..	..	30	30
466	12 c. multicoloured	..	..	30	30
467	15 c. multicoloured	..	..	30	30
468	25 c. multicoloured	..	..	40	40
462/8			Set of 7	1·75	1·75

No. 468 is larger, 59×79 mm, and was printed with Nos. 462/7 in *se-tenant* sheetlets of 7.

(Des Colleen Corlett. Litho and embossed Southern Colour Print, Dunedin)

1997 (15 July). *Golden Wedding of Queen Elizabeth and Prince Philip. T* **133** *and similar vert design. P* 13½.

469	80 c. black and gold	..	..	90	1·00
470	$1.20, multicoloured	..	..	1·40	1·60
MS471	150×110 mm. Nos. 469/70 (sold at $3)		3·00	3·25

Design:—$1.20, Queen Elizabeth and Prince Philip, 1997.

134 Conference Building

(Des Patricia Altman. Litho Southern Colour Print, Dunedin)

1997 (24 July). *28th Parliamentary Conference of Presiding Officers and Clerks. Sheet* 150×100 *mm. P* 14.

MS472 **134** $2 multicoloured   ..   ..   1·75   1·90

135 Commemorative Pillar   **136** Weightlifter

(Des Audrey Bascand. Litho Southern Colour Print, Dunedin)

1997 (5 Nov). *Christmas. 110th Anniv of Nauru Congregational Church. T* **135** *and similar horiz design. Multicoloured. P* 13½.

473	60 c. Type **135**	..	..	60	55
474	80 c. Congregational Church	..	80	90

(Des Patricia Altman. Litho Southern Colour Print, Dunedin)

1998 (25 Mar). *Commonwealth, Oceania and South Pacific Weightlifting Championships, Nauru. Sheet* 180×100 *mm, containing T* **136** *and similar vert designs showing weightlifters. P* 14.

MS475 40 c., 60 c., 80 c., $1.20, multicoloured   2·25   2·40

137 Juan Antonio Samaranch and Aerial View   **138** Diana, Princess of Wales

(Litho Southern Colour Print, Dunedin)

1998 (17 May). *Visit of International Olympic Committee President. P* 13½.

476 **137** $2 multicoloured   ..   ..   1·75   2·00

(Litho Questa)

1998 (31 Aug). *Diana, Princess of Wales Commemoration. T* **138** *and similar vert designs. Multicoloured. P* 14.

477	70 c. Type **138**	..	..	55	60
	a. Sheetlet. Nos. 477/82	..	3·25	
478	70 c. Wearing white shirt	..	55	60
479	70 c. With tiara	..	..	55	60
480	70 c. In white jacket	..	55	60
481	70 c. Wearing pink hat	..	55	60
482	70 c. In white suit	..	..	55	60
477/82			Set of 6	3·25	3·50

Nos. 477/82 were printed together, *se-tenant*, in sheetlets of 6.

139 Gymnastics   **140** Sqn. Ldr. Hicks (composer of Nauru's National Anthem) conducting

(Des K. Tamon. Litho Security Printers (M), Malaysia)

1998 (11 Sept). *16th Commonwealth Games, Kuala Lumpur, Malaysia. T* **139** *and similar vert designs. Multicoloured. P* 13½.

483	40 c. Type **139**	..	..	30	35
484	60 c. Athletics	..	..	45	50
485	70 c. Sprinting	..	..	55	60
486	80 c. Weightlifting	..	..	60	65
483/6			Set of 4	1·90	2·10
MS487	153×130 mm. Nos. 483/6. P 14½×14	1·90	2·00

(Des Patricia Altman. Litho Southern Colour Print, Dunedin)

1998 (26 Oct). *30th Anniv of Independence. T* **140** *and similar horiz design. Multicoloured. P* 14.

488	$1 Type **140**	..	..	85	
489	$2 Sqn. Ldr. Hicks and score	..	1·75	2·4
MS490	175×110 mm. Nos. 488/9	..	2·50	3·

141 Palm Trees, Fish, Festive Candle and Flower

(Des G. Douran. Litho Security Printers (M), Malaysia)

1998 (9 Nov). *Christmas. T* **141** *and similar horiz desig. Multicoloured. P* 13.

491	85 c. Type **141**	..	..	80	8
492	95 c. Flower, present, fruit and island scene	85	9

142 18th-century Frigate

(Des Mary Butterfield. Litho Southern Colour Print, Dunedin)

1998 (1 Dec). *Bicent of First Contact with the Outside World T* **142** *and similar square design. P* 12.

493	$1.50, Type **142**	..	..	1·25	1·5
	a. Horiz pair. Nos. 493/4	..	2·50	3·0
494	$1.50, Capt. John Fearn	..	1·25	1·5
MS495	173×131 mm. Nos. 493/4	..	3·00	3·00

Nos. 493/4 were printed together, *se-tenant*, in horizontal pairs throughout the sheet.

The ship on No. 493 is wrongly identified as the *Hunter* (snow).

143 H.M.A.S. *Melbourne* (cruiser)   **144** Emblem and Forms of Transport

(Des G. Douran. Litho Southern Colour Print, Dunedin)

1999 (19 Mar). *"Australia '99" World Stamp Exhibition, Melbourne. Ships. Sheet* 101×120 *mm, containing T* **143** *and similar multicoloured designs. P* 12.

MS496 70 c. Type **143**; 80 c. H.M.A.S. *D'Amantina* (frigate); 90 c. *Alcyone* (experimental ship); $1 *Rosie-D* (bulk carrier); $1.10, Outrigger canoe (80×30 *mm*)   ..   4·25   4·50

(Des N. Shewring. Litho Walsall)

1999 (20 July). *30th Anniv of First Manned Landing on Moon. Multicoloured designs as T* **296** *of Jamaica. P* 14×13½.

497	70 c. Neil Armstrong (astronaut)	..	65	65
498	80 c. Service and lunar module on way to Moon	..	70	70
499	90 c. Aldrin and "Apollo 11" on Moon's surface	..	85	85
500	$1 Command module entering Earth's atmosphere	..	90	90
497/500			Set of 4	2·75	2·75
MS501	90×80 mm. $2 Earth as seen from Moon (circular, 40 mm diam). P 14		1·90	2·00

(Litho Courvoisier)

1999 (23 Aug). *125th Anniv of Universal Postal Union. P* 11½.

502 **144** $1 multicoloured   90   95

OMNIBUS ISSUES

Details, together with prices for complete sets, of the various Omnibus issues from the 1935 Silver Jubilee series to date are included in a special section following Zimbabwe at the end of Volume 2.

145 Killer Whale   146 Girl holding Candle

1999 (30 Aug). *"China '99" International Philatelic Exhibition, Beijing. Sheet, 185×85 mm, containing T 145 and similar vert design. Multicoloured. Litho. P 12½.*
MS503   50 c. Type 145; 50 c. Swordfish   ..   80   85

(Litho Security Printers (M), Malaysia)
1999 (17 Nov). *Christmas. T 146 and similar vert design. Multicoloured. W 138 of Malaysia (sideways). P 13½.*
504   65 c. Type 146   50   55
505   70 c. Candle and Christmas tree   55   60

147 Nauruan Woman in Traditional Dress and Canoes

(Litho Security Printers (M), Malaysia)
2000 (1 Jan). *New Millennium. T 147 and similar horiz designs. Multicoloured. W 138 of Malaysia. P 12.*
506   70 c. Type 147   55   60
507    $1.10, Aspects of modern Nauru   ..   85   90
508    $1.20, Woman holding globe and man at computer   90   95
506/8   ..   ..   ..   Set of 3   2·25   2·40
MS509   149×88 mm. Nos. 506/8. Wmk sideways   2·25   2·40

Nevis
see St. Kitts-Nevis

New Brunswick
see Canada

Newfoundland
see Canada

New Guinea
see Papua New Guinea

New Hebrides
see Vanuatu

New Republic
see South Africa

New South Wales
see Australia

New Zealand

From 1831 mail from New Zealand was sent to Sydney, New South Wales, routed through an unofficial postmaster at Kororareka.

The first official post office opened at Kororareka in January 1840 to be followed by others at Auckland, Britannia, Coromandel Harbour, Hokianga, Port Nicholson, Russell and Waimate during the same year. New South Wales relinquished control of the postal service when New Zealand became a separate colony on 3 May 1841.

The British G.P.O. was responsible for the operation of the overseas mails from 11 October 1841 until the postal service once again passed under colonial control on 18 November 1848.

CC 1 CC 2

AUCKLAND
CROWNED-CIRCLE HANDSTAMPS

CC1	CC 1	AUCKLAND NEW ZEALAND (R.) (31.10.1846)	.. Price on cover	£275

NELSON
CROWNED-CIRCLE HANDSTAMPS

CC2	CC 1	NELSON NEW ZEALAND (R.) (31.10.1846)	Price on cover	£950

NEW PLYMOUTH
CROWNED-CIRCLE HANDSTAMPS

CC3	CC 1	NEW PLYMOUTH NEW ZEALAND (R. or Black) (31.10.1846) .. Price on cover	£1800
CC3a	CC 2	NEW PLYMOUTH NEW ZEALAND (R. or Black) (1854) Price on cover	£2250

OTAGO
CROWNED-CIRCLE HANDSTAMPS

CC4	CC 2	OTAGO NEW ZEALAND (R.) (1851) Price on cover	£1800

PETRE
CROWNED-CIRCLE HANDSTAMPS

CC5	CC 1	PETRE NEW ZEALAND (R.) (31.10.1846) Price on cover	£1200

PORT VICTORIA
CROWNED-CIRCLE HANDSTAMPS

CC6	CC 2	PORT VICTORIA NEW ZEALAND (R.) (1851) Price on cover	£1000

RUSSELL
CROWNED-CIRCLE HANDSTAMPS

CC7	CC 1	RUSSELL NEW ZEALAND (R.) (31.10.1846) Price on cover	£3000

WELLINGTON
CROWNED-CIRCLE HANDSTAMPS

CC8	CC 1	WELLINGTON NEW ZEALAND (R.) (31.10.1846) .. .. Price on cover	£300

A similar mark for Christchurch as Type CC 2 is only known struck, in black, as a cancellation after the introduction of adhesive stamps.

No. CC3a is a locally-cut replacement with the office name around the circumference, but a straight "PAID AT" in the centre.

PRICES FOR STAMPS ON COVER TO 1945

Nos. 1/125	from × 2
Nos. 126/36	from × 3
Nos. 137/9	from × 2
No. 140	—
No. 141	from × 2
No. 142	—
Nos. 143/8	from × 2
Nos. 149/51	from × 10
Nos. 152/84	from × 2
Nos. 185/6	—
Nos. 187/203	from × 3
Nos. 205/7e	—
Nos. 208/13	from × 2
Nos. 214/16j	—
Nos. 217/58	from × 3
No. 259	—
Nos. 260/9	from × 3
No. 270	—
Nos. 271/6	from × 3
Nos. 277/307	from × 2
Nos. 308/16	from × 3
No. 317	—
Nos. 318/28	from × 3
Nos. 329/48	from × 5
No. 349	—
Nos. 350/1	—
No. 352	from × 5
Nos. 353/69	—
Nos. 370/86	from × 2
No. 387	from × 4
Nos. 388/99	from × 3
Nos. 400/666	from × 2
Nos. E1/5	from × 5
No. E6	from × 10
Nos. D1/8	from × 3
Nos. D9/16	from × 5
Nos. D17/20	from × 3
Nos. D21/47	from × 6
Nos. O1/24	from × 12
Nos. O59/66	from × 4
Nos. O67/8	—
Nos. O69/81	from × 5
Nos. O82/7	—
Nos. O88/93	from × 20
Nos. O94/9	from × 12
Nos. O100/11	from × 5
Nos. O112/13	—
Nos. O115/19	from × 15
Nos. O120/33	from × 10
Nos. O134/51	from × 4
Nos. P1/7	from × 8
Nos. L1/9	from × 10
Nos. L9a/12	—
Nos. L13/20	from × 15
Nos. L21/3	—
Nos. L24/41	from × 12
No. F1	—
No. F2	from × 5
Nos. F3/144	—
Nos. F145/58	from × 3
Nos. F159/68	—
Nos. F169/79	from × 3
Nos. F180/6	—
Nos. F187/90	from × 2

Nos. F191/203	from × 3
Nos. F204/11	—
Nos. F212/18	from × 2
Nos. A1/3	from × 2

CROWN COLONY

PERKINS BACON "CANCELLED". For notes on these handstamps, showing "CANCELLED" between horizontal bars forming an oval, see Catalogue Introduction.

1 2

(Eng by Humphreys. Recess P.B.)

1855 (18 July). *Wmk Large Star, W w 1. Imperf.*

1	1	1d. dull carmine (white paper) (H/S "CANCELLED" in oval £15000) ..	£32000	£9000
2		2d. dull blue (blued paper) (H/S "CANCELLED" in oval £10000)	£14000	£550
3		1s. pale yellow-green (blued paper) (H/S "CANCELLED" in oval £10000)	£25000	£5000
		a. Bisected (6d.) (on cover)		† £30000

The 2d. and 1s. on white paper formerly listed are now known to be stamps printed on blued paper which have had the bluing washed out.

Nos. 3a and 6a were used at Dunedin between March 1857, when the rate for ½ oz. letters to Great Britain was reduced to 6d., and August 1859. All known examples are bisected vertically.

(Printed by J. Richardson, Auckland, N.Z.)

1855 (Dec). *First printing. Wmk Large Star. White paper. Imperf.*

3b		1d. orange		£18000

1855 (Dec)–57. *No wmk. Blue paper. Imperf.*

4	1	1d. red	£7500	£1500
5		2d. blue (3.56)	£2500	£300
		a. Without value		
6		1s. green (9.57)	£21000	£3500
		a. Bisected (6d.) (on cover)		† £20000

These stamps on blue paper may occasionally be found watermarked double-lined letters, being portions of the paper-maker's name.

1857 (Jan). *Wmk Large Star. White paper similar to the issue of July 1855.*

7	1	1d. dull orange		† £13000

This stamp is in the precise shade of the 1d. of the 1858 printing by Richardson on *no wmk* white paper. An unsevered pair is known with Dunedin cancellation on a cover front showing an Auckland arrival postmark of 19.1.1857.

1857–63. *Hard or soft white paper. No wmk.* (a) *Imperf.*

8	1	1d. dull orange (1858)	£1800	£475
8a		2d. deep ultramarine (1858)	£1700	£800
9		2d. pale blue	£800	£180
10		2d. blue (12.57)	£800	£180
11		2d. dull deep blue	£1200	£275
12		6d. bistre-brown (8.59)	£2500	£500
13		6d. brown	£1500	£300
14		6d. pale brown	£1500	£300
15		6d. chestnut	£2750	£550
16		1s. dull emerald-green (1858)	£11000	£1200
17		1s. blue-green	£10000	£1200

(b) *Pin-roulette, about 10 at Nelson* (1860)

18	1	1d. dull orange	†	£4500
19		2d. blue	†	£3000
20		6d. brown	†	£3750
20a		1s. dull emerald-green	†	£5500
21		1s. blue-green	†	£5500

(c) *Serrated perf about 16 or 18 at Nelson* (1862)

22	1	1d. dull orange ..	†	£3750
23		2d. blue ..	†	£2750
24		6d. brown	†	£2750
25		6d. chestnut	†	£5500
26		1s. blue-green	†	£4750

(d) *Rouletted 7 at Auckland* (April 1859)

27	1	1d. dull orange ..	£5500	£4000
28		2d. blue ..	£6000	£2750
29		6d. brown	£5000	£2250
		a. Imperf between (pair)	£13000	£9000
30		1s. dull emerald-green	†	£3500
31		1s. blue-green	†	£3500

(e) *P 13 at Dunedin* (1863)

31a	1	1d. dull orange	†	£4500
31b		2d. pale blue	£3250	£2000
32		6d. pale brown	†	£5000

(f) *"H" roulette 16 at Nelson*

32a		2d. blue	†	£3500
32b		6d. brown	†	£3750

(g) *"Y" roulette 18 at Nelson*

32c	1	1d. dull orange	†	£4000
32d		2d. blue	†	£3250
32e		6d. brown	†	£3750
32f		6d. chestnut	†	£3750
32g		1s. blue-green	†	£6000

(h) *Oblique roulette 13 at Wellington*

32h	1	1d. dull orange	†	£4500

The various separations detailed above were all applied by hand to imperforate sheets. The results were often poorly cut and badly aligned. Nos. 32a/b and 32c/g were produced using roulette wheels fitted with cutting edges in the shape of "H" or "Y".

(Printed by John Davies at the G.P.O., Auckland, N.Z.)

1862 (Feb–Dec). *Wmk Large Star.* (a) *Imperf.*

33	1	1d. orange-vermilion	£500	£190
34		1d. vermilion	£425	£190
35		1d. carmine-vermilion	£375	£225

36	1	2d. deep blue (Plate I)	..	£375	70·00
		a. Double print	..	—	£2500
37		2d. slate-blue (Plate I)	..	£1500	£180
37a		2d. milky blue (Plate I, worn)	..	—	£225
38		2d. pale blue (Plate I, worn)	..	£300	90·00
39		2d. blue (to deep) (Plate I, very worn)		£275	70·00
40		3d. brown-lilac (Dec 1862)	..	£325	£120
41		6d. black-brown	..	£900	90·00
42		6d. brown	..	£800	90·00
43		6d. red-brown	..	£700	90·00
44		1s. green	..	£1000	£200
45		1s. yellow-green	..	£900	£250
46		1s. deep green	..	£1100	£300

The 2d. in a distinctive deep bright blue on white paper wmkd. Large Star is believed by experts to have been printed by Richardson in 1861 or 1862. This also exists doubly printed and with serrated perf.

No. 37 shows traces of plate wear to the right of the Queen's head. This is more pronounced on Nos. 37a/8 and quite extensive on No. 39.

(b) Rouletted 7 at Auckland (5.62)

47	1	1d. orange-vermilion	..	£3750	£700
48		1d. vermilion	..	£2250	£700
48a		1d. carmine-vermilion	..	£3750	£850
49		2d. deep blue	..	£2250	£425
50		2d. slate-blue	..	£3250	£750
51		2d. pale blue	..	£1800	£550
52		3d. brown-lilac	..	£2250	£700
53		6d. black-brown	..	£2500	£450
54		6d. brown	..	£2250	£550
55		6d. red-brown	..	£2250	£450
56		1s. green	..	£2500	£650
57		1s. yellow-green	..	£3500	£650
58		1s. deep green	..	£3500	£750

(c) Serrated perf 16 or 18 at Nelson (8.62)

59	1	1d. orange-vermilion	..	£6500	£1500
60		2d. deep blue	..	†	£950
		a. Imperf between (pair)	..	£8000	£3500
61		2d. slate-blue	..		
62		3d. brown-lilac	..	£3000	£1500
63		6d. black-brown	..	†	£1600
64		6d. brown	..	†	£1700
65		1s. yellow-green	..	†	£2750

(d) Pin-perf 10 at Nelson (8.62)

66	1	2d. deep blue	..	†	£2250
67		6d. black-brown	..	†	£3250

(e) "H" roulette 16 at Nelson

67a	1	2d. deep blue (Plate I)	..	†	£1800
67b		6d. black-brown	..	†	£1800
67c		1s. green	..	—	£2250

(f) "Y" roulette 18 at Nelson

67d	1	1d. orange-vermilion	..	†	£1600
67e		2d. deep blue (Plate I)	..	†	£1700
67f		2d. slate-blue (Plate I)	..	†	£1700
67g		3d. brown-lilac	..	†	£1800
67h		6d. black-brown	..	†	£1700
67i		6d. brown	..	†	£1700
67j		1s. yellow-green	..	†	£2250

(g) Oblique roulette 13 at Wellington

67k	1	2d. deep blue (Plate I)	..	†	£1700
67l		2d. slate-blue (Plate I)	..	†	£2000
67m		3d. brown-lilac	..	†	£1700
67n		6d. black-brown	..	†	£1800

(h) Square roulette 14 at Auckland

67o	1	1d. orange-vermilion	..	†	£1500
67p		2d. deep blue (Plate I)	..	†	£1700
67q		3d. brown-lilac	..	†	£2000
67r		6d. black-brown	..	†	£1800

(i) Serrated perf 13 at Dunedin

67s	1	1d. orange-vermilion	..	†	£1900
67t		2d. deep blue (Plate I)	..	†	£1700
67u		3d. brown-lilac	..	—	£1600
67v		6d. black-brown	..	†	£1700
67w		1s. yellow-green	..	†	£2500

The dates put to above varieties are the earliest that have been met with.

1862. *Wmk Large Star. P 13 (at Dunedin).*

68	1	1d. orange-vermilion	..	£1000	£275
		a. Imperf between (horiz pair)	..	†	£6000
69		1d. carmine-vermilion	..	£1000	£275
70		2d. deep blue (Plate I)	..	£325	75·00
71		2d. slate-blue (Plate I)	..	†	£600
72		2d. blue (Plate I)	..	£250	55·00
72a		2d. milky blue (Plate I)	..	—	£500
73		2d. pale blue (Plate I)	..	£250	55·00
74		3d. brown-lilac	..	£1000	£300
75		6d. black-brown	..	£900	£170
		a. Imperf between (horiz pair)	..		
76		6d. brown	..	£750	85·00
77		6d. red-brown	..	£700	70·00
78		1s. dull green	..	£1000	£300
79		1s. deep green	..	£1100	£275
80		1s. yellow-green	..	£1100	£250

See also Nos. 110/25 and the note that follows these.

1862–63. *Pelure paper. No wmk. (a) Imperf.*

81	1	1d. orange-vermilion (1863)	..	£6500	£1900
82		2d. ultramarine	..	£3500	£800
83		2d. pale ultramarine	..	£3250	£750
84		3d. lilac	..	£27000	†
85		6d. black-brown	..	£1600	£250
86		1s. deep green	..	£6500	£950

The 3d. is known only unused.

(b) Rouletted 7 at Auckland

87	1	1d. orange-vermilion	..	†	£4500
88		6d. black-brown	..	£2250	£475
89		1s. deep green	..	£7500	£1500

(c) P 13 at Dunedin

90	1	1d. orange-vermilion	..	£10000	£3000
91		2d. ultramarine	..	£4500	£700
92		2d. pale ultramarine	..	£4500	£700
93		6d. black-brown	..	£3500	£400
94		1s. deep green	..	£8000	£1400

(d) Serrated perf 16 at Nelson

95	1	6d. black-brown	..	—	£4250

(e) Serrated perf 13 at Dunedin

95a	9	1d. orange-vermilion	..	†	£6500

1863 (early). *Thick soft white paper. No wmk. (a) Imperf.*

96	1	2d. dull deep blue (shades)	..	£2250	£800

(b) P 13

96a	1	2d. dull deep blue (shades)	..	£1600	£475

These stamps show slight beginnings of wear of the printing plate in the background to right of the Queen's ear, as one looks at the stamps. By the early part of 1864, the wear of the plate had spread, more or less, all over the background of the circle containing the head. The major portion of the stamps of this printing appears to have been consigned to Dunedin and to have been there perforated 13.

1864. *Wmk "N Z", W 2. (a) Imperf.*

97	1	1d. carmine-vermilion	..	£700	£225
98		2d. pale blue (Plate I worn)	..	£750	£225
99		6d. red-brown	..	£3000	£500
100		1s. green	..	£1000	£250

(b) Rouletted 7 at Auckland

101	1	1d. carmine-vermilion	..	£4500	£2750
102		2d. pale blue (Plate I worn)	..	£1400	£750
103		6d. red-brown	..	£4500	£2750
104		1s. green	..	£2750	£1000

(c) P 13 at Dunedin

104a	1	1d. carmine-vermilion	..	£6500	£4500
105		2d. pale blue (Plate I worn)	..	£550	£160
106		1s. green	..	£1200	£450
		a. Imperf between (horiz pair)			£8500

(d) "Y" roulette 18 at Nelson

106b	1	1d. carmine-vermilion	..	—	£4500

(e) P 12½ at Auckland

106c	1	1d. carmine-vermilion	..	£6500	£4000
107		2d. pale blue (Plate I worn)	..	£225	50·00
108		6d. red-brown	..	£250	38·00
109		1s. yellow-green	..	£4250	£2250

1864–67. *Wmk Large Star. P 12½ (at Auckland).*

110	1	1d. carmine-vermilion (1864)	..	£110	26·00
111		1d. pale orange-vermilion	..	£140	26·00
		a. Imperf (pair)	..	£2500	£1600
112		2d. orange	..	£325	75·00
113		2d. pale blue (Plate I worn) (1864)		£140	21·00
114		2d. deep blue (Plate II) (1866)	..	£110	18·00
		a. Imperf vert (horiz pair)	..	†	£3000
115		2d. blue (Plate II)	..	£110	18·00
		a. Retouched (Plate II) (1867)	..	£180	45·00
		c. Imperf (pair) (Plate II)	..	£1600	£1400
		d. Retouched. Imperf (pair)	..	£2500	£2750
116		3d. brown-lilac (1864)	..	£1500	£600
117		3d. lilac	..	90·00	27·00
		a. Imperf (pair)	..	£3000	£1600
118		3d. deep mauve	..	£400	65·00
		a. Imperf (pair)	..	£3000	£1600
119		4d. deep rose (1865)	..	£2250	£250
120		4d. yellow (1865)	..	£130	90·00
121		4d. orange	..	£1700	£900
122		6d. red-brown (1864)	..	£160	24·00
122a		6d. brown	..	£180	35·00
		b. Imperf (pair)	..	£1500	£1600
123		1s. deep green (1864)	..	£600	£275
124		1s. green	..	£300	£100
125		1s. yellow-green	..	£140	80·00

The above issue is sometimes difficult to distinguish from Nos. 68/80 because the vertical perforations usually gauge 12¾ and sometimes a full 13. However stamps of this issue invariably gauge 12½ horizontally, whereas the 1862 stamps measure a full 13.

Nos. 111a, 115c/d, 117a, 118a and 122b were issued during problems with the perforation machine which occurred in 1866–67, 1869–70 and 1871–73. Imperforate sheets of the 1s. were also released, but these stamps are very similar to Nos. 44/6.

The new plate of the 2d. showed signs of deterioration during 1866 and thirty positions in rows 13 and 16 to 20 were retouched by a local engraver.

The 1d., 2d. and 6d. were officially reprinted imperforate, without gum, in 1884 for presentation purposes. They can be distinguished from the errors listed by their shades which are pale orange, dull blue and dull chocolate-brown respectively, and by the worn state of the plates from which they were printed (*Prices £65 each unused*).

1871. *Wmk Large Star. (a) P 10.*

126	1	1d. brown	..	£450	85·00

(b) P 12½ × 10

127	1	1d. deep brown	..	†	£2500

(c) P 10 × 12½

128	1	1d. brown	..	£160	38·00
		a. Perf 12½ comp 10 (1 side)	..	£375	£130
129		2d. deep blue (Plate II)	..	†	£7000
		a. Perf 10*	..	†	£12000
130		2d. vermilion	..	£160	30·00
		a. Retouched	..	£250	48·00
		b. Perf 12½ comp 10 (1 side)	..	£400	
		c. Perf 10*	..	†	£12000
131		6d. deep blue	..	£1400	£650
		a. Blue	..	£950	£240
		b. Imperf between (vert pair)	..	—	£5000
		c. Perf 12½ comp 10 (1 side)	..	£800	£350
		ca. Imperf vert (horiz pair)	..	†	—

(d) P 12½

132	1	1d. red-brown	..	£100	28·00
		a. Brown (shades, worn plate)	..	£100	28·00
		b. Imperf horiz (vert pair)	..	—	£3500
133		2d. orange	..	95·00	25·00
		a. Retouched	..	£150	45·00
134		2d. vermilion	..	£120	28·00
		a. Retouched	..	£190	55·00
135		6d. blue	..	£150	48·00
136		6d. pale blue	..	£110	48·00

*Only one used copy each of Nos. 129a and 130c have been reported.

1872. *No wmk. P 12½.*

137	1	1d. brown	..	£475	£100
		a. Watermarked (script letters)*	..	£3000	£2000
		b. Watermarked (double-lined capitals)*		£1500	£500
138		2d. vermilion	..	85·00	48·00
		a. Retouched	..	£160	70·00
		b. Watermarked (script letters)*	..	£3000	£1300
		c. Watermarked (double-lined capitals)*		£1500	£750
139		4d. orange-yellow	..	£140	£650
		a. Watermarked (double-lined capitals)*			£200

*In or about 1872 1d., 2d. and 4d. stamps were printed on paper showing sheet watermarks of either "W. T. & Co." (Wiggins Teape & Co.) in script letters or "T. H. Saunders" in double-lined capitals; portions of these letters are occasionally found on stamps.

1872. *Wmk "N Z", W 2. P 12½.*

140	1	1d. brown	..	†	£4000
141		2d. vermilion	..	£500	£170
		a. Retouched	..	£800	£250

1872. *Wmk Lozenges, with "INVICTA" in double-lined capitals four times in the sheet. P 12½.*

142	1	2d. vermilion	..	£2750	£500
		a. Retouched	..	£4000	£750

3   4

(Des John Davies. Die eng on wood in Melbourne. Printed from electrotypes at Govt Ptg Office, Wellington)

1873 (1 Jan). *(a) Wmk "NZ", W 2.*

143	3	½d. pale dull rose (p 10)	..	75·00	35·00
144		½d. pale dull rose (p 12½)	..	£180	65·00
145		½d. pale dull rose (p 12½×10)	..	£110	65·00
		a. Perf 10×12½	..	£130	75·00

(b) No wmk

146	3	½d. pale dull rose (p 10)	..	£110	45·00
147		½d. pale dull rose (p 12½)	..	£200	75·00
148		½d. pale dull rose (p 12½×10)	..	£150	70·00
		a. Perf 10×12½	..	†	—

As the paper used for Nos. 143/5 was originally intended for fiscal stamps which were more than twice as large, about one-third of the impressions fall on portions of the sheet showing no watermark, giving rise to varieties Nos. 146/8. In later printings of No. 151 a few stamps in each sheet are without watermark. These can be distinguished from No. 147 by the shade.

1875 (Jan). *Wmk Star, W 4.*

149	3	½d. pale dull rose (p 12½)	..	13·00	1·40
		a. Imperf horiz (vert pair)	..	£700	£375
		b. Imperf between (horiz pair)	..	†	£600
150		½d. dull pale rose (p nearly 12)	..	60·00	11·00

1892 (May). *Wmk "NZ and Star". W 12b. P 12½.*

151	3	½d. bright rose (shades)	..	8·00	70
		a. No wmk	..	14·00	7·50
		w. Wmk inverted	..	50·00	30·00
		x. Wmk reversed	..	—	90·00

5   6   7

8   9   10

11   12   12a 6 mm

12b 7 mm   12c 4 mm

(T **5/10** eng De La Rue. T **11** and **12** des, eng & plates by W. R. Bock. Typo Govt Ptg Office, Wellington)

1874 (2 Jan)–78. *W 12a. A. White paper.* (*a*) *P* 12½.
152	5	1d. lilac	..	..	48·00	3·75
		a. Imperf	..	..	£400	
		w. Wmk inverted	..	..	†	40·00
		x. Wmk reversed	..	..	†	90·00
153	6	2d. rose	..	..	50·00	2·00
154	7	3d. brown	..	..	£100	55·00
155	8	4d. maroon	..	..	£275	65·00
156	9	6d. blue	..	..	£180	10·00
		w. Wmk inverted	..	..		50·00
		x. Wmk reversed	..	..	—	50·00
157	10	1s. green	..	..	£650	28·00
		w. Wmk inverted	..	..		

(b) Perf nearly 12
158	6	2d. rose (1878)	..	..	£600	£180

(c) Perf compound of 12½ *and* 10
159	5	1d. lilac	..	..	£150	40·00
		w. Wmk inverted	..	..	—	60·00
160	6	2d. rose	..	..	£400	40·00
		w. Wmk inverted	..	..	—	£100
161	7	3d. brown	..	..	£160	65·00
162	8	4d. maroon	..	..	£400	£110
163	9	6d. blue	..	..	£225	45·00
		w. Wmk inverted	..	..	—	75·00
164	10	1s. green	..	..	£550	£110
		a. Imperf between (vert pair)	..	..	†	—
		bw. Wmk inverted	..	..	†	£250

(d) Perf nearly 12×12½
164c	5	1d. lilac (1875)	..	..	£650	£250
165	6	2d. rose (1878)	..	..	£650	£190

B. Blued paper. (*a*) *P* 12½
166	5	1d. lilac	..	..	85·00	30·00
167	6	2d. rose	..	..	£110	34·00
		w. Wmk inverted	..	..	—	50·00
		x. Wmk reversed	..	..	†	75·00
168	7	3d. brown	..	..	£225	85·00
169	8	4d. maroon	..	..	£425	£110
170	9	6d. blue	..	..	£325	50·00
171	10	1s. green	..	..	£1000	£190

(b) Perf compound of 12½ *and* 10
172	5	1d. lilac	..	..	£190	55·00
173	6	2d. rose	..	..	£550	85·00
174	7	3d. brown	..	..	£225	80·00
175	8	4d. maroon	..	..	£500	£130
176	9	6d. blue	..	..	£325	95·00
177	10	1s. green	..	..	£1000	£225

1875. *Wmk Large Star, W w* 1. *P* 12½.
178	5	1d. deep lilac	..	..	£650	£110
179	6	2d. rose	..	..	£300	18·00

1878. *W 12a. P* 12 × 11½ (*comb*).
180	5	1d. mauve-lilac	..	..	38·00	3·00
181	6	2d. rose	..	..	38·00	1·60
182	8	4d. maroon	..	..	£140	40·00
183	9	6d. blue	..	..	80·00	10·00
184	10	1s. green	..	..	£120	35·00
185	11	2s. deep rose (1 July)	..	£325	£275
186	12	5s. grey (1 July)	..	£350	£275

This perforation is made by a horizontal "comb" machine, giving a gauge of 12 horizontally and about 11¾ vertically. Single specimens can be found apparently gauging 11½ all round or 12 all round, but these are all from the same machine. The perforation described above as "nearly 12" was from a single-line machine.

13	14	15
16	17	18
19	20	21
	22	

Description of Watermarks

W12a. 6 mm between "N Z" and star; broad irregular star; comparatively wide "N"; "N Z" 11½ mm wide.
W12b. 7 mm between "N Z" and star; narrower star; narrow "N"; "N Z" 10 mm wide.
W12c. 4 mm between "N Z" and star; narrow star; wide "N"; "N Z" 11½ mm wide.

Description of Papers

1882–88.	Smooth paper with horizontal mesh. W 12a.
1888–98.	Smooth paper with vertical mesh. W 12b.
1890–91.	Smooth paper with vertical mesh. W 12c.
1898.	Thin yellowish toned, coarse paper with clear vertical mesh. W 12b. Perf 11 only.

In 1899–1900 stamps appeared on medium to thick white coarse paper but we do not differentiate these (except where identifiable by shade) as they are more difficult to distinguish.

PAPER MESH. This shows on the back of the stamp as a series of parallel grooves, either vertical or horizontal. It is caused by the use of a wire gauze conveyor-belt during paper-making.

Description of Dies

1d.

Die 1

Die 2

Die 3

1882.	Die 1.	Background shading complete and heavy.
1886.	Die 2.	Background lines thinner. Two lines of shading weak or missing left of Queen's forehead.
1889.	Die 3.	Shading on head reduced; ornament in crown left of chignon clearer, with unshaded "arrow" more prominent.

2d.

Die 1

Die 2

Die 3

1882.	Die 1.	Background shading complete and heavy.
1886.	Die 2.	Weak line of shading left of forehead and missing shading lines below "TA".
1889.	Die 3.	As Die 2 but with comma-like white notch in hair below "&".

6d.

Die 1

Die 2

1882.	Die 1.	Shading heavy. Top of head merges into shading.
1892.	Die 2.	Background lines thinner. Shading on head more regular with clear line of demarcation between head and background shading.

STAMPS WITH ADVERTISEMENTS. During November 1891 the New Zealand Post Office invited tenders for the printing of advertisements on the reverse of the current 1d. to 1s. stamps. The contract was awarded to Messrs Miller, Truebridge & Reich and the first sheets with advertisements on the reverse appeared in February 1893.

Different advertisements were applied to the backs of the individual stamps within the sheets of 240 (four panes of 60).

On the first setting those in a vertical format were inverted in relation to the stamps and each of the horizontal advertisements had its base at the left-hand side of the stamp when seen from the back. For the second and third settings the vertical advertisements were the same way up as the stamps and the bases of those in the horizontal format were at the right as seen from the back. The third setting only differs from the second in the order of the individual advertisements.

The experiment was not, however, a success and the contract was cancelled at the end of 1893.

(Des F. W. Sears (½d.), A. E. Cousins (2½d.), A. W. Jones (5d.); others adapted from 1874 issue by W. H. Norris. Dies eng A. E. Cousins (½d., 2½d., 5d.), W. R. Bock (others). Typo Govt Ptg Office)

1882–1900. *Inscr* "POSTAGE & REVENUE".

A. W **12a**. Paper with horiz mesh (1.4.82–86). (*a*) *P* 12×11½
187	14	1d. rose *to* rose-red (Die 1)		35·00	5·00
		a. Imperf (pair)		£350	
		b. Imperf between (vert pair)		£375	
		cw. Wmk inverted			
		d. Die 2. *Pale rose to carm-rose* (1886)	30·00	5·00
		dw. Wmk inverted		†	25·00
		dx. Wmk reversed		60·00	25·00
188	15	2d. lilac *to* lilac-purple (Die 1)		40·00	4·00
		a. Imperf (pair)		£375	
		b. Imperf between (vert pair)		£375	
		cw. Wmk inverted		60·00	12·00
		d. Die 2. *Lilac* (1886)		50·00	7·00
189	17	3d. yellow (1884)		50·00	5·50
190	18	4d. blue-green		70·00	5·00
191	20	6d. brown (Die 1)		80·00	3·75
		w. Wmk inverted		£150	25·00
192	21	8d. blue (1885)		70·00	45·00
193	22	1s. red-brown		85·00	12·00

(b) P 12½ (1884?)
193a	14	1d. rose *to* rose-red (Die 1)		£170	85·00

B. W **12b**. Paper with vert mesh (1888–95)

(a) P 12×11½ (1888–95)
194	13	½d. black (1.4.95)		25·00	75·00
195	14	1d. rose *to* rosine (Die 2)		35·00	3·50
		aw. Wmk inverted		£150	15·00
		b. Die 3. *Rose to carmine* (1889)	35·00	3·50
		bb. Red-brn advert (1st setting) (2.93)	50·00	12·00
		bc. Red advert (1st setting) (3.93)	50·00	12·00
		bd. Blue advert (2nd setting) (4.93)	65·00	35·00
		be. Mauve advert (2nd setting) (5.93)	40·00	7·00
		bf. Green advert (2nd setting) (6.93)		
		bg. Brn-red advert (3rd setting) (9.93)	40·00	7·00
		bw. Wmk inverted		60·00	15·00
		bx. Wmk reversed		70·00	20·00
196	15	2d. lilac (Die 2)		42·00	4·25
		a. Die 3. *Lilac to purple* (1889)	42·00	4·25
		ab. Red advert (1st setting) (3.93)	60·00	16·00
		ac. Mauve advert (2nd setting) (5.93)	50·00	16·00
		ad. Sepia advert (2nd setting) (5.93)	50·00	22·00
		ae. Green advert (2nd setting) (6.93)	—	75·00
		af. Brn-red advert (3rd setting) (9.93)	50·00	16·00
		aw. Wmk inverted		60·00	8·00
197	16	2½d. pale blue (1891)		55·00	5·50
		a. Brn-red advert (2nd setting) (4.93)	70·00	16·00
		ax. Wmk reversed		£110	30·00
		b. *Ultramarine* (green advert. 2nd setting) (6.93)	70·00	18·00
198	17	3d. yellow		42·00	6·50
		a. Brn-red advert (2nd setting) (4.93)	70·00	18·00
		b. Sepia advert (2nd setting) (5.93)		
199	18	4d. green *to* bluish green		50·00	3·00
		a. Sepia advert (2nd setting) (5.93)	65·00	12·00
		aw. Wmk inverted		†	
200	19	5d. olive-black (1.2.91)		42·00	9·00
		a. Imperf (pair)		£400	
		b. Brn-pur advert (3rd setting) (9.93)	60·00	30·00
201	20	6d. brown (Die 1)		70·00	2·25
		a. Die 2 (1892)		£110	50·00
		ab. Sepia advert (2nd setting) (5.93)		
		ac. Brn-red advert (3rd setting) (9.93)	£150	70·00
		ax. Wmk reversed		†	—
202	21	8d. blue		65·00	45·00
203	22	1s. red-brown		80·00	6·00
		a. Black advert (2nd setting) (5.93)	£300	£150
		b. Brn-pur advert (3rd setting) (9.93)	£110	16·00
		w. Wmk inverted		£120	15·00

(b) P 12½ (1888–91)
204	14	1d. rose (Die 2)		£190	85·00
		a. Die 3 (1889)			

(c) P 12½ (1888–89)
205	14	1d. rose (Die 3) (1889)		£160	95·00
		a. Mauve advert (2nd setting) (5.93)		
		x. Wmk reversed		†	—
206	15	2d. lilac (Die 2)		£120	85·00
		a. Die 3. *Deep lilac* (1889)		90·00	65·00
		ab. Brn-red advert (3rd setting) (9.93)	£160	85·00
207	16	2½d. blue (1891)		£170	95·00

(d) Mixed perfs 12×11½ *and* 12½ (1891–93)
207a	14	1d. rose (Die 3) (brn-red advert. 3rd setting)		†	50·00
207b	15	2d. lilac (Die 3)		†	—
		ba. Brn-red advert (3rd setting) (9.93)	†	
207c	18	4d. green		†	50·00
207d	19	5d. olive-black		†	95·00
207e	20	6d. brown (Die I)		†	£100
		ea. Die 2		†	£150

C. W **12c**. Paper with vert mesh (1890). (*a*) *P* 12×11½
208	14	1d. rose (Die 3)		70·00	6·50
209	15	2d. purple (Die 3)		70·00	7·00
		x. Wmk reversed			
210	16	2½d. ultramarine (27.12)		65·00	11·00
		x. Wmk reversed		†	20·00

211	17	3d. yellow		70·00	16·00
		a. Lemon-yellow		70·00	18·00
212	20	6d. brown (Die 1)		£120	24·00
213	22	1s. deep red-brown		£130	55·00

(b) P 12½

214	14	1d. rose (Die 3)		£170	£100
215	15	2d. purple (Die 3)		£150	£100
216	16	2½d. ultramarine		£200	£100

(c) P 12×12½

216a	20	6d. brown (Die 1)		£180	£140

D. Continuation of W 12b. Paper with vert mesh (1891–1900)

(a) P 10×12½ (1891–94)

216b	14	1d. rose (Die 3)		£180	90·00
		ba. Perf 12½×10		£200	90·00
		bb. Red-brn advert (1st setting) (2.93)	£250	£120
		bc. Brn-red advert (2nd setting) (4.93)	£250	£100
		bd. Mauve advert (2nd setting) (5.93)	£250	£100
		be. Green advert (2nd setting) (6.93)	£250	£140
216c	15	2d. lilac (Die 3)		£150	60·00
216d	16	2½d. blue (1893)		£130	65·00
		da. Perf 12½×10		£150	
216e	17	3d. yellow		£150	75·00
216f	18	4d. green		£170	£140
216g	19	5d. olive-black (1894)		£180	£170
		ga. Perf 12½×10		£200	£170
216h	20	6d. brown (Die II)		£190	£190
		i. Die 2 (1892)		£150	£150
		ia. Brn-pur advert (3rd setting) (9.93)	£200	£180
216j	22	1s. red-brown		£170	£170
		ja. Perf 12½×10		†	—

(b) P 10 (1891–95)

217	13	½d. black (1895)		4·00	50
218	14	1d. rose (Die 3)		4·50	10
		a. Carmine		9·00	1·25
		b. Imperf (pair)		£300	£300
		c. Imperf between (pair)		£350	
		d. Imperf horiz (vert pair)		£275	
		e. Mixed perfs 10 and 12½	£250	£120
		f. Red-brn advert (1st setting) (2.93)	15·00	4·00
		g. Red advert (1st setting) (3.93)	15·00	5·00
		h. Brown-red advert (2nd and 3rd settings) (4.93)	8·50	2·50
		i. Blue advert (2nd setting) (4.93)	60·00	26·00
		j. Mauve advert (2nd setting) (5.93)	8·50	2·50
		k. Green advert (2nd setting) (6.93)	50·00	16·00
		l. Brn-pur advert (3rd setting) (9.93)	8·50	2·75
		w. Wmk inverted		30·00	6·00
		x. Wmk reversed		18·00	8·00
219	15	2d. lilac (Die 3)		11·00	40
		a. Purple		12·00	40
		b. Imperf between (pair)		£350	
		c. Mixed perfs 10 and 12½	—	90·00
		d. Red-brn advert (1st setting) (2.93)	24·00	7·00
		e. Red advert (1st setting) (3.93)	24·00	5·50
		f. Brown-red advert (2nd and 3rd settings) (4.93)	13·00	2·75
		g. Sepia advert (2nd setting) (5.93)	16·00	3·25
		h. Green advert (2nd setting) (6.93)	35·00	9·00
		i. Brn-pur advert (3rd setting) (9.93)	13·00	2·75
		w. Wmk reversed		24·00	8·00
220	16	2½d. blue (1892)		48·00	3·50
		a. Ultramarine		48·00	4·00
		b. Mixed perfs 10 and 12½	£170	90·00
		c. Mauve advert (2nd setting) (5.93)	65·00	8·50
		d. Green advert (2nd setting) (6.93)	75·00	10·00
		e. Brn-pur advert (3rd setting) (9.93)	65·00	8·00
		w. Wmk reversed		†	25·00
221	17	3d. pale orange-yellow		40·00	8·50
		a. Orange		40·00	10·00
		b. Lemon-yellow		40·00	12·00
		c. Mixed perfs 10 and 12½	£160	£120
		d. Brown-red advert (2nd and 3rd settings) (4.93)	65·00	13·00
		e. Sepia advert (2nd setting) (5.93)	75·00	26·00
		f. Brn-pur advert (3rd setting) (9.93)	65·00	11·00
222	18	4d. green (1892)		45·00	2·50
		a. Blue-green		50·00	3·75
		b. Mixed perfs 10 and 12½	£190	80·00
		c. Brn-red advert (2nd setting) (4.93)	65·00	4·00
		d. Brn-pur advert (3rd setting) (9.93)	65·00	4·00
223	19	5d. olive-black (1893)		45·00	11·00
		a. Brn-pur advert (3rd setting) (9.93)	65·00	16·00
		ab. Mixed perfs 10 and 12½	£100	60·00
224	20	6d. brown (Die 1)		85·00	20·00
		a. Mixed perfs 10 and 12½		
		b. Die 2 (1892)		45·00	5·50
		ba. Black-brown		50·00	6·00
		bb. Imperf (pair)		£375	
		bc. Mixed perfs 10 and 12½	90·00	50·00
		bd. Sepia advert (2nd setting) (4.93)	85·00	10·00
		be. Brn-red advert (3rd setting) (9.93)	85·00	10·00
		bf. Brn-pur advert (3rd setting) (9.93)	85·00	10·00
		bx. Wmk reversed (with brown-purple advert)	†	30·00
225	21	8d. blue (brown-purple advert. 3rd setting) (9.93)	65·00	45·00
226	22	1s. red-brown		75·00	5·50
		a. Imperf between (pair)		£650	
		b. Mixed perfs 10 and 12½	£150	£110
		c. Sepia advert (2nd setting) (5.93)	£100	16·00
		d. Black advert (2nd setting) (5.93)	£180	£110
		e. Brn-red advert (3rd setting) (9.93)	£100	16·00
		f. Brn-pur advert (3rd setting) (9.93)	£100	16·00

(c) P 10×11 (1895–97)

227	13	½d. black (1896)		3·25	50
		a. Mixed perfs 10 and 11	85·00	30·00
		b. Perf 11×10		28·00	12·00
228	14	1d. rose (Die 3)		4·75	15
		a. Mixed perfs 10 and 11	85·00	50·00
		b. Perf 11×10		55·00	8·00
		x. Wmk reversed		£100	50·00
229	15	2d. purple (Die 3)		10·00	30
		a. Mixed perfs 10 and 11	60·00	50·00
230	16	2½d. blue (1896)		48·00	3·75
		a. Ultramarine		48·00	4·50
		b. Mixed perfs 10 and 11	—	65·00
231	17	3d. lemon-yellow (1896)		60·00	9·00
232	18	4d. pale green (1896)		70·00	12·00
		a. Mixed perfs 10 and 11	—	85·00
233	19	5d. olive-black (1897)		48·00	10·00

234	20	6d. deep brown (Die 2) (1896)	65·00	5·50
		a. Mixed perfs 10 and 11		
		b. Perf 11×10		£160	50·00
235	22	1s. red-brown (1896)		75·00	9·00
		a. Mixed perfs 10 and 11	£140	70·00

(d) P 11 (1895–1900)

236	13	½d. black (1897)		3·25	15
		aw. Wmk inverted		40·00	15·00
		ax. Wmk reversed		50·00	20·00
		b. Thin coarse toned paper (1898)	22·00	2·25
		ba. Wmk sideways		—	£160
237	14	1d. rose (Die 3)		3·75	10
		a. Deep carmine		5·50	1·50
		b. Imperf between (pair)		£375	
		c. Dp carm/thin coarse toned (1898)	8·00	1·50
		ca. Wmk sideways		—	£225
		w. Wmk inverted		15·00	15·00
		x. Wmk reversed		15·00	5·00
		y. Wmk inverted and reversed	25·00	25·00
238	15	2d. mauve (Die 3)		8·00	30
		a. Purple		8·50	30
		b. Dp purple/thin coarse toned (1898)	8·50	2·00
		ba. Wmk sideways		—	£180
		w. Wmk inverted		15·00	5·00
		x. Wmk reversed		25·00	8·00
239	16	2½d. blue (1898)		45·00	3·75
		a. Thin coarse toned paper (1898)	55·00	13·00
240	17	3d. pale yellow (1897)		50·00	4·75
		a. Pale dull yellow/thin coarse toned (1898)	60·00	11·00
		b. Orange (1899)		42·00	8·50
		c. Dull orange-yellow (1900)	48·00	13·00
241	18	4d. yellowish green		48·00	3·50
		a. Bluish green (1897)		48·00	3·25
		w. Wmk inverted		75·00	10·00
242	19	5d. olive-black/thin coarse toned (1899)	50·00	22·00
243	20	6d. brown (Die 2) (1897)		65·00	3·00
		a. Black-brown		65·00	3·00
		b. Brown/thin coarse toned (1898)	80·00	6·00
		x. Wmk reversed		†	20·00
244	21	8d. blue (1898)		65·00	45·00
245	22	1s. red-brown (1897)		75·00	7·00

Only the more prominent shades have been included.

Stamps perf compound of 11 and 12½ exist but we do not list them as there is some doubt as to whether they are genuine.

For the ½d. and 2d. with double-lined watermark, see Nos. 271/2.

23 Mount Cook or Aorangi

24 Lake Taupo and Mount Ruapehu

25 Pembroke Peak, Milford Sound

26 Lake Wakatipu and Mount Earnslaw, inscribed "WAKITIPU"

27 Lake Wakatipu and Mount Earnslaw, inscribed "WAKATIPU"

28 Sacred Huia Birds

29 White Terrace, Rotomahana

30 Otira Gorge and Mount Ruapehu

31 Brown Kiwi

32 Maori War Canoe

33 Pink Terrace, Rotomahana

34 Kea and Kaka

35 Milford Sound

36 Mount Cook

(Des H. Young (½d.), J. Gaut (1d.), W. Bock (2d., 3d., 9d., 1s.), E. Howard (4d., 6d., 8d.), E. Luke (others). Eng A. Hill (2½d., 1s.), J. A. C. Harrison (5d.), Rapkin (others). Recess Waterlow)

1898 (5 Apr). *No wmk. P 12 to 16.*

246	23	½d. purple-brown		4·75	60
		a. Imperf between (pair)	£650	£700
		b. Purple-slate		4·75	60
		c. Purple-black		7·00	2·50
247	24	1d. blue and yellow-brown	3·50	20
		a. Imperf between (pair)	£700	
		b. Imperf vert (horiz pair)	£500	£550
		c. Imperf horiz (vert pair)	£500	£550
		d. Blue and brown		3·75	80
		da. Imperf between (pair)	£650	
248	25	2d. lake		26·00	20
		a. Imperf vert (horiz pair)	£400	
		b. Rosy lake		26·00	20
		ba. Imperf between (pair)	£600	
		bb. Imperf vert (horiz pair)	£400	
249	26	2½d. sky-blue (inscr "WAKITIPU")	7·00	24·00
		a. Blue		7·00	24·00
250	27	2½d. blue (inscr "WAKATIPU")	23·00	2·25
		a. Deep blue		23·00	2·25
251	28	3d. yellow-brown		23·00	7·00
252	29	4d. bright rose		12·00	16·00
		a. Lake-rose		15·00	17·00
		b. Dull rose		12·00	16·00
253	30	5d. sepia		65·00	£160
		a. Purple-brown		40·00	15·00
254	31	6d. green		50·00	26·00
		a. Grass-green		65·00	65·00
255	32	8d. indigo		38·00	35·00
		a. Prussian blue		38·00	28·00
256	33	9d. purple		40·00	24·00
257	34	1s. vermilion		55·00	19·00
		a. Dull red		55·00	19·00
		ab. Imperf between (pair)	£1800	
258	35	2s. grey-green		£100	£100
		a. Imperf between (vert pair)	£1800	£1800
259	36	5s. vermilion		£170	£275
246/59			Set of 13	£500	£475

For these designs with face values in cents and dollars see the centenary issue Nos. 2158/71.

37 Lake Taupo and Mount Ruapehu

(Recess Govt Printer, Wellington)

1899 (May)–03. *Thick, soft ("Pirie") paper. No wmk. P 11.*

260	27	2½d. blue (6.99)		13·00	3·25
		a. Imperf between (pair)	£550	
		b. Imperf horiz (vert pair)	£350	
		c. Deep blue		13·00	3·25
261	28	3d. yellow-brown (5.00)		27·00	2·00
		a. Imperf between (pair)	£800	
		b. Imperf vert (horiz pair)	£425	
		c. Deep brown		27·00	2·00
		ca. Imperf between (pair)	£800	
262	37	4d. indigo and brown (8.99)		5·50	2·75
		a. Bright blue and chestnut	5·50	2·75
		b. Deep blue and bistre-brown	5·50	2·75
263	30	5d. purple-brown (6.99)		24·00	2·75
		a. Deep purple-brown		24·00	2·75
		ab. Imperf between (pair)	£950	
264	31	6d. deep green		55·00	60·00
		a. Yellow-green		70·00	95·00
265		6d. pale rose (5.5.00)		35·00	3·75
		a. Imperf vert (horiz pair)	£375	
		b. Rose-red		35·00	3·75
		ba. Printed double		£425	£450
		bb. Imperf between (pair)	£600	
		bc. Imperf vert (horiz pair)	£250	
		bd. Showing part of sheet wmk (7.02)*	75·00	45·00
		c. Scarlet		55·00	12·00
		ca. Imperf vert (horiz pair)	£450	
266	32	8d. indigo		27·00	12·00
		a. Prussian blue		27·00	11·00
267	33	9d. deep purple (8.99)		45·00	25·00
		a. Rosy purple		35·00	9·50
268	34	1s. red (5.00)		48·00	8·50
		a. Dull orange-red		48·00	3·00
		b. Dull brown-red		48·00	8·50
		c. Bright red		60·00	26·00
269	35	2s. blue-green (7.99)		75·00	32·00
		a. Laid paper (1.03)		£180	£200
		b. Grey-green		85·00	42·00
270	36	5s. vermilion (7.99)		£170	£200
		a. Carmine-red		£275	£325
260/70			Set of 11	£425	£275

*No. 265bd is on paper without general watermark, but showing the words "LISBON SUPERFINE" wmkd once in the sheet; the paper was obtained from Parsons Bros, an American firm with a branch at Auckland.

38

900. *Thick, soft ("Pirie") paper. Wmk double-lined "NZ" and Star, W 38 (sideways*). P 11.*

71	13	½d. black	..	7·50	8·50
		x. Wmk reversed	..	40·00	30·00
72	15	2d. bright purple	..	17·00	8·50
		w. Wmk sideways inverted	..	28·00	11·00
		y. Wmk sideways inverted and reversed		—	22·00

*The normal sideways wmk on Nos. 271/2 shows the star to the right of NZ, *as seen from the back of the stamp.*

39 White Terrace, Rotomahana   **41**

40 Commemorative of the New Zealand Contingent in the South African War

(Des J. Nairn (1½d.). Recess Govt Printer, Wellington)

900 (Mar–Dec). *Thick, soft ("Pirie") paper. W 38. P 11.*

273	23	½d. pale yellow-green (7.3.00)	..	8·00	3·50
		a. Yellow-green	..	5·50	70
		b. Green	..	4·75	30
		ba. Imperf between (pair)	..	£300	
		c. Deep green	..	4·75	30
		w. Wmk inverted	..	20·00	10·00
		y. Wmk inverted and reversed	..	40·00	20·00
274	39	1d. crimson (7.3.00)	..	13·00	10
		a. Rose-red	..	13·00	10
		ab. Imperf between (pair)	..	£650	£650
		ac. Imperf vert (horiz pair)	..	£375	
		b. Lake	..	25·00	3·50
		w. Wmk inverted	..	†	—
		x. Wmk reversed	..	†	—
275	40	1½d. khaki (7.12.00)	..	£800	£550
		a. Brown	..	50·00	50·00
		ab. Imperf vert (horiz pair)	..	£500	
		ac. Imperf (pair)	..	£600	
		b. Chestnut	..	9·00	4·00
		ba. Imperf vert (horiz pair)	..	£500	
		bb. Imperf horiz (vert pair)	..	£650	
		c. Pale chestnut	..	9·00	4·00
		ca. Imperf (pair)	..	£600	
276	41	2d. dull violet (3.00)	..	7·50	65
		a. Imperf between (pair)	..	£700	
		b. Mauve	..	9·00	1·50
		c. Purple	..	7·00	65
		ca. Imperf between (pair)	..	£600	

The above ½d. stamps are slightly smaller than those of the previous printing. A new plate was made to print 240 stamps instead of 120 as previously, and to make these fit the watermarked paper the border design was redrawn and contracted, the centre vignette remaining as before. The 2d. stamp is also from a new plate providing smaller designs.

42

(Des G. Bach and G. Drummond. Eng J. A. C. Harrison. Recess Waterlow)

1901 (1 Jan). *Universal Penny Postage. No wmk. P 12 to 16.*

277	42	1d. carmine	..	4·00	3·00

All examples of No. 277 show a small dot above the upper left corner of the value tablet which is not present on later printings.

(Recess Govt Printer, Wellington)

1901 (Feb–Dec). *Thick, soft ("Pirie") paper. W 38. (a) P 11.*

278	42	1d. carmine	..	6·00	15
		a. Imperf vert (horiz pair)	..	£250	
		b. Deep carmine	..	6·00	15
		ba. Imperf vert (horiz pair)	..	£250	
		c. Carmine-lake	..	20·00	8·00
		x. Wmk reversed	..	†	—
		y. Wmk inverted and reversed		—	50·00

(b) P 14

279	23	½d. green (11.01)	..	11·00	3·75
280	42	1d. carmine	..	40·00	9·50
		a. Imperf vert (horiz pair)	..	£225	
		y. Wmk inverted and reversed	..	75·00	35·00

(c) P 14×11

281	23	½d. green	..	8·00	5·50
		a. Deep green	..	8·00	5·50
		b. Perf 11×14	..	11·00	13·00
282	42	1d. carmine	..	£250	75·00
		a. Perf 11×14	..	£1100	£300

(d) P 11 and 14 mixed*

283	23	½d. green	..	40·00	45·00
284	42	1d. carmine	..	£250	75·00

*The term "mixed" is applied to stamps from sheets which were at first perforated 14, or 14×11, and either incompletely or defectively perforated. These sheets were patched on the back with strips of paper, and re-perforated 11 in those parts where the original perforation was defective.

Nos. 278/84 were printed from new plates supplied by Waterlow. These were subsequently used for Nos. 285/307 with later printings on Cowan paper showing considerable plate wear.

WATERMARK VARIETIES. The watermark on the Basted Mills version of the W 38 paper used for Nos. 285/92 occurs indiscriminately normal, reversed, inverted etc.

(Recess Govt Printer, Wellington)

1901 (Dec). *Thin, hard ("Basted Mills") paper. W 38. (a) P 11.*

285	23	½d. green	..	50·00	60·00
286	42	1d. carmine	..	65·00	80·00

(b) P 14

287	23	½d. green	..	25·00	18·00
		a. Imperf vert (horiz pair)	..	£325	
288	42	1d. carmine	..	14·00	3·00
		a. Imperf vert (horiz pair)	..	£250	
		b. Imperf horiz (vert pair)	..	£250	

(c) P 14×11

289	23	½d. green	..	20·00	40·00
		a. Deep green	..	20·00	40·00
		b. Perf 11×14	..	20·00	40·00
290	42	1d. carmine	..	17·00	6·50
		a. Perf 11×14	..	12·00	3·25

(d) Mixed perfs

291	23	½d. green	..	50·00	60·00
292	42	1d. carmine	..	75·00	65·00

(Recess Govt Printer, Wellington)

1902 (Jan). *Thin, hard ("Cowan") paper. No wmk. (a) P 11.*

293	23	½d. green	..	95·00	£170

(b) P 14

294	23	½d. green	..	9·00	3·75
295	42	1d. carmine	..	12·00	2·00

(c) P 14×11

296	23	½d. green	..	65·00	£120
		a. Perf 11×14	..	75·00	£130
297	42	1d. carmine	..	£110	£110
		a. Perf 11×14	..	£110	£130

(d) Mixed perfs

298	23	½d. green	..	90·00	£130
299	42	1d. carmine	..	£120	£120

43 "Single" Wmk

SIDEWAYS WATERMARKS. In its sideways format the single NZ and Star watermark, W 43, exists indiscriminately sideways, sideways inverted, sideways reversed and sideways inverted plus reversed.

(Recess Govt Printer, Wellington)

1902 (Apr). *Thin, hard ("Cowan") paper. W 43. (a) P 11.*

300	23	½d. green	..	55·00	85·00
301	42	1d. carmine	..	£600	£450

(b) P 14

302	23	½d. green	..	5·50	40
		a. Imperf vert (horiz pair)	..	£180	
		b. Deep green	..	5·50	60
		ba. Imperf vert (horiz pair)	..	£180	
		c. Yellow-green	..	6·00	60
		d. Pale yellow-green	..	13·00	2·75
		w. Wmk inverted	..	20·00	10·00
		x. Wmk reversed	..	30·00	18·00
		y. Wmk inverted and reversed	..	40·00	24·00
303	42	1d. carmine	..	3·00	10
		a. Imperf horiz (vert pair)	..	£170	
		b. Booklet pane of 6 (21.8.02)	..	£200	
		c. Pale carmine	..	3·00	10
		ca. Imperf horiz (vert pair)	..	£170	
		cb. Booklet pane of 6	..	£200	
		d. Deep carmine*	..	32·00	4·00
		w. Wmk inverted	..	60·00	35·00
		x. Wmk reversed	..	60·00	35·00
		y. Wmk inverted and reversed	..	35·00	15·00

(c) P 14×11

304	23	½d. green	..	19·00	
		a. Deep green	..	25·00	
		b. Perf 11×14	..	17·00	
305	42	1d. carmine	..	£100	80·00
		a. Perf 11×14	..	£120	90·00
		ab. Deep carmine*	..	£400	£300

(d) Mixed perfs

306	23	½d. green	..	24·00	40·00
		a. Deep green	..	30·00	
307	42	1d. carmine	..	24·00	32·00
		a. Pale carmine	..	24·00	32·00
		b. Deep carmine*	..	£250	£250
		y. Wmk inverted and reversed			

*Nos. 303d, 305a and 307b were printed from a plate made by Waterlow & Sons, known as the "Reserve" plate. The stamps do not show evidence of wearing and the area surrounding the upper part of the figure is more deeply shaded. This plate was subsequently used to produce Nos. 362, 364, and 366/9.

A special plate, made by W. R. Royle & Sons, showing a minute dot between the horizontal rows, was introduced in 1902 to print the booklet pane, No. 303b. A special characteristic of the booklet pane was that the pearl in the top left-handed corner was large. Some panes exist with the outer edges imperforate.

(Recess Govt Printer, Wellington)

1902 (28 Aug)–09. *Thin, hard ("Cowan") paper. W 43 (sideways on 3d., 6d., 8d., 1s. and 5s.). (a) P 11*

308	27	2½d. blue (5.03)	..	11·00	12·00
		a. Deep blue	..	13·00	12·00
		w. Wmk inverted	..	80·00	50·00
		x. Wmk reversed	..	50·00	25·00
		y. Wmk inverted and reversed	..	70·00	40·00
309	28	3d. yellow-brown	..	23·00	1·00
		a. Bistre-brown	..	23·00	1·00
		b. Pale bistre	..	35·00	3·25
310	37	4d. dp blue & dp brn/bluish (27.11.02)	6·00	55·00
		a. Imperf vert (horiz pair)	..	£450	
311	30	5d. red-brown (4.03)	..	24·00	7·00
		a. Deep brown	..	22·00	4·75
		b. Sepia	..	38·00	15·00
312	31	6d. rose (9.02)	..	35·00	5·00
		a. Rose-red	..	35·00	6·00
		ab. Wmk upright	..	£550	£350
		b. Rose-carmine	..	40·00	6·00
		ba. Imperf vert (horiz pair)	..	£425	
		c. Bright carmine-pink	..	50·00	7·00
		d. Scarlet	..	60·00	16·00
313	32	8d. blue (2.03)	..	28·00	9·00
		a. Steel-blue	..	28·00	9·00
		ab. Imperf vert (horiz pair)	..	£700	
		ac. Imperf horiz (vert pair)	..	£700	
314	33	9d. purple (5.03)	..	45·00	12·00
		w. Wmk inverted	..	65·00	40·00
		x. Wmk reversed	..	85·00	75·00
		y. Wmk inverted and reversed	..	70·00	40·00
315	34	1s. brown-red (11.02)	..	48·00	8·50
		a. Bright red	..	48·00	9·50
		b. Orange-red	..	48·00	4·25
		ba. Error. Wmk W 12b (inverted)	..	†	£1400
		c. Orange-brown	..	60·00	11·00
316	35	2s. green (4.03)	..	80·00	50·00
		a. Blue-green	..	70·00	42·00
		w. Wmk inverted	..	£225	60·00
317	36	5s. deep red (6.03)	..	£170	£200
		a. Wmk upright	..	£200	£250
		b. Vermilion	..	£170	£200
		ba. Wmk upright	..	£200	£250
		w. Wmk inverted	..	£475	£375

(b) P 14

318	40	1½d. chestnut (2.07)	..	15·00	45·00
319	41	2d. grey-purple (12.02)	..	5·50	1·25
		a. Purple	..	5·50	1·25
		ab. Imperf vert (horiz pair)	..	£375	
		ac. Imperf horiz (vert pair)	..	£375	
		b. Bright reddish purple	..	6·50	2·00
320	27	2½d. blue (1906)	..	11·00	2·75
		a. Deep blue	..	11·00	2·75
		w. Wmk reversed	..	†	
321	28	3d. bistre-brown (1906)	..	27·00	3·00
		a. Imperf vert (horiz pair)	..	£550	
		b. Bistre	..	27·00	3·00
		c. Pale yellow-bistre	..	48·00	9·50
322	37	4d. dp blue & dp brown/bluish (1903)	6·00	2·75
		a. Imperf vert (horiz pair)	..	£400	
		b. Imperf horiz (vert pair)	..	£400	
		c. Centre inverted	..		
		d. Blue and chestnut/bluish	..	4·00	1·75
		e. Blue and ochre-brown/bluish	..	4·00	1·75
		w. Wmk inverted	..	20·00	7·00
		x. Wmk reversed	..	15·00	5·00
		y. Wmk inverted and reversed	..	40·00	12·00
323	30	5d. black-brown (1906)	..	50·00	17·00
		a. Red-brown	..	26·00	7·00
324	31	6d. bright carmine-pink (1906)	..	50·00	8·50
		a. Imperf vert (horiz pair)	..	£500	
		b. Rose-carmine	..	50·00	9·00
325	32	8d. steel-blue (1907)	..	27·00	8·00
326	33	9d. purple (1906)	..	27·00	6·00
		w. Wmk inverted	..	60·00	20·00
327	34	1s. orange-brown (1906)	..	60·00	6·50
		a. Orange-red	..	55·00	6·50
		b. Pale red	..	80·00	35·00
328	35	2s. green (1.06)	..	65·00	22·00
		a. Blue-green	..	70·00	28·00
		aw. Wmk inverted	..	£200	60·00
		ax. Wmk reversed	..	†	—
329	36	5s. deep red (1906)	..	£170	£190
		a. Wmk upright	..	£200	£225
		b. Dull red	..	£170	£190
		ba. Wmk upright	..	£190	£225

(c) Perf compound of 11 and 14

330	40	1½d. chestnut (1907)	..	£700	
331	41	2d. purple (1903)	..	£275	
332	28	3d. bistre-brown (1906)	..	£550	£450
333	37	4d. blue and yellow-brown (1903)	..	£300	£300
334	30	5d. red-brown (1906)	..	£550	£550
335	31	6d. rose-carmine (1907)	..	£325	£200
336	32	8d. steel-blue (1907)	..	£650	
337	33	9d. purple (1906)	..	£900	£900
338	36	5s. deep red (1906)	..	£1800	

(d) Mixed perfs

339	40	1½d. chestnut (1907)	..	£700	
340	41	2d. purple (1903)	..	£150	
341	28	3d. bistre-brown (1906)	..	£550	£450
342	37	4d. blue and chestnut/bluish (1904)	..	£250	£250
		a. Blue and yellow-brown/bluish	..	£250	£250
343	30	5d. red-brown (1906)	..	£450	£450
344	31	6d. rose-carmine (1907)	..	£275	£200
		a. Bright carmine-pink	..	£300	£200
345	32	8d. steel-blue (1907)	..	£650	
346	33	9d. purple (1906)	..	£800	£800
347	35	2s. blue-green (1906)	..	£1000	£1000
348	36	5s. vermilion (wmk upright) (1906)	..	£1600	
		w. Wmk inverted			

Two sizes of paper were used for the above stamps:—

(1) A sheet containing 240 wmks, with a space of 9 mm between each.

(2) A sheet containing 120 wmks, with a space of 24 mm between each vertical row.

Size (1) was used for the ½d., 1d., 2d., and 4d., and size (2) for 2½d., 5d., 9d., and 2s. The paper in each case exactly fitted the plates, and had the watermark in register, though in the case of the 4d., the plate of which contained only 80 stamps, the paper was cut up to print it. The 3d., 6d., 8d., and 1s. were printed on variety (1), but with watermark sideways: by reason of this, specimens from the margins of the sheets show parts of the words "NEW ZEALAND POSTAGE" in large letters, and some copies have no watermark at all. For the 1½d. and 5s. stamps variety (1) was also used, but two watermarks appear on each stamp.

The only known example of No. 322c, postmarked at Picton on 21 March 1904, was purchased for the New Zealand Post archive collection in 1998.

(Recess Govt Printer, Wellington)

1904 (Feb). *Printed from new "dot" plates made by W.R. Royle & Sons. Thin, hard ("Cowan") paper.* W 43. *(a)* P 14.

349	42	1d. rose-carmine	..	7·50	40
		a. Pale carmine	..	7·50	40
		w. Wmk inverted	..	75·00	95·00
		y. Wmk inverted and reversed		85·00	35·00

(b) P 11×14

350	42	1d. rose-carmine	..	£120	£110

(c) Mixed perfs

351	42	1d. rose-carmine	..	26·00	27·00
		a. Pale carmine	..	26·00	27·00

These plates have a minute dot in the horizontal margins between the rows, centred under each stamp, but it is frequently cut out by the perforations. However, they can be further distinguished by the notes below.

In 1906 fresh printings were made from four new plates, two of which, marked in the margin "W1" and "W2", were supplied by Waterlow Bros and Layton, and the other two, marked "R1" and "R2", by W. R. Royle & Son. The intention was to note which pair of plates wore the best and produced the best results. They can be distinguished as follows:—

(a) (b) (c)

(d) (e) (f)

(a) Four o'clock flaw in rosette at top right corner. Occurs in all these plates but not in the original Waterlow plates.
(b) Pearl at right strong.
(c) Pearl at right weak.
(d) Dot at left and S-shaped ornament unshaded.
(e) S-shaped ornament with one line of shading within.
(f) As *(e)* but with line from left pearl to edge of stamp.
"Dot" plates comprise *(a)* and *(d)*.
Waterlow plates comprise *(a)*, *(b)* and *(e)*.
Royle plates comprise *(a)*, *(c)* and *(e)* and the line in *(f)* on many stamps but not all.

(Recess Govt Printer, Wellington)

1906. *Thin, hard ("Cowan") paper.* W 43.

(a) Printed from new Waterlow plates. (i) P 14

352	42	1d. deep rose-carmine	..	24·00	1·25
		a. Imperf horiz (vert pair)	..	£200	
		b. Aniline carmine	..	23·00	1·25
		ba. Imperf vert (horiz pair)	..	£200	
		c. Rose-carmine	..	23·00	1·25
		y. Wmk inverted and reversed			

(ii) P 11

353	42	1d. aniline carmine	..	£550	£650

(iii) P 11×14

354	42	1d. rose-carmine	..	£425	
		a. Perf 14×11	..	—	£750

(iv) Mixed perfs

355	42	1d. deep rose-carmine	..	£400	

(b) Printed from new Royle plates. (i) P 14

356	42	1d. rose-carmine	..	10·00	1·25
		a. Imperf horiz (vert pair)	..	£225	£225
		b. Bright rose-carmine	..	12·00	1·40
		w. Wmk inverted	..		
		y. Wmk inverted and reversed			

(ii) P 11

357	42	1d. bright rose-carmine	..	£100	£150

(iii) P 11×14

358	42	1d. rose-carmine	..	£100	
		a. Perf 14×11	..	£100	

(iv) Mixed perfs

359	42	1d. rose-carmine	..	£100	

(v) P 14×14½ (*comb*)

360	42	1d. bright rose-carmine	..	60·00	45·00
		a. Rose-carmine	..	60·00	45·00

Nos. 360/*a* are known both with and without the small dot. See also No. 386.

1905 (15 June)–06. *Stamps supplied to penny-in-the-slot machines.*

(i) *"Dot" plates* of 1904. (ii) Waterlow *"reserve" plate* of 1902

(a) Imperf top and bottom; zigzag roulette 9½ on one or both sides, two large holes at sides

361	42	1d. rose-carmine (i)	..	£140	
362		1d. deep carmine (ii)	..	£160	

(b) As last but rouletted 14½ (8.7.05)

363	42	1d. rose-carmine (i)	..	£150	
364		1d. deep carmine (ii)	..	£300	

(c) Imperf all round, two large holes each side (6.3.06)

365	42	1d. rose-carmine (i)	..	£120	
366		1d. deep carmine (ii)	..	£120	

(d) Imperf all round (21.6.06)

367	42	1d. deep carmine (ii)	..	£130	

(e) Imperf all round. Two small indentations on back of stamp (1.06)

368	42	1d. deep carmine (ii)	..	£160	£140

(f) Imperf all round; two small pin-holes in stamp (21.6.06)

369	42	1d. deep carmine (ii)	..	£140	£140

No. 365 *only* exists from strips of Nos. 361 or 363 (resulting from the use of successive coins) which have been separated by scissors. Similarly strips of Nos. 362 and 364 can produce single copies of No. 366 but this also exists in singles from a different machine. Most used copies of Nos. 361/7 are forgeries and they should only be collected on cover.

44 Maori Canoe, *Te Arawa*

(Des L. J. Steele. Eng W. R. Bock. Typo Govt Printer, Wellington)

1906 (1–17 Nov). *New Zealand Exhibition, Christchurch.* T **44** *and similar horiz designs.* W 43 (*sideways*). P 14.

370	½d. emerald-green	..	18·00	28·00
371	1d. vermilion	..	15·00	16·00
	a. Claret	..	£6000	£9000
372	3d. brown and blue	..	48·00	75·00
373	6d. pink and olive-green (17.11)		£170	£250
370/3		Set of 4	£225	£325

Designs:—1d. Maori art; 3d. Landing of Cook; 6d. Annexation of New Zealand.

The 1d. in claret was the original printing, which was considered unsatisfactory.

47 (T **28** reduced)   **48** (T **31** reduced)   **49** (T **34** reduced)

(New plates (except 4d.) supplied by Perkins Bacon. Recess Govt Printer, Wellington).

1907–8. *Thin, hard ("Cowan") paper.* W 43. *(a)* P 14 (*line*)

374	23	½d. green (1907)	..	25·00	9·00
		a. Imperf (pair)	..	£130	
		b. Yellow-green	..	17·00	2·75
		c. Deep yellow-green	..	17·00	2·75
375	47	3d. brown (6.07)	..	48·00	23·00
376	48	6d. carmine-pink (3.07)	..	45·00	7·00
		a. Red	..	60·00	35·00

(b) P 14×13, 13½ (*comb*)

377	23	½d. green (1907)	..	17·00	9·00
		a. Yellow-green	..	8·00	2·50
378	47	3d. brown (2.08)	..	48·00	26·00
		a. Yellow-brown ..		48·00	28·00
379	37	4d. blue and yellow-brown/*bluish* (6.08)	28·00	26·00
380	48	6d. pink (2.08)	..	£275	£100
381	49	1s. orange-red (12.07)	..	£130	48·00

(c) P 14×15 (*comb*)

382	23	½d. yellow-green (1907)	..	8·00	85
		y. Wmk inverted and reversed		—	£150
383	47	3d. brown (8.08)	..	35·00	14·00
		a. Yellow-brown	..	35·00	14·00
384	48	6d. carmine-pink (8.08)	..	40·00	10·00
385	49	1s. orange-red (8.08)	..	£120	24·00
		a. Deep orange-brown	..	£325	£475

The ½d. stamps of this 1907–8 issue have a minute dot in the margin between the stamps, where not removed by the perforation. (See note after No. 351*a*.) Those perforated 14 can be distinguished from the earlier stamps, Nos. 302/*d*, by the absence of plate wear. This is most noticeable on the 1902 printings as a white patch at far left, level with the bottom of the "P" in "POSTAGE". Such damage is not present on the new plates used for Nos. 374/*c*.

Stamps of T **47**, **48** and **49** also have a small dot as described in note after No. 351*a*.

TYPOGRAPHY PAPERS. 1908–30. *De La Rue paper* is chalk-surfaced and has a smooth finish. The watermark is as illustrated. The gum is toned and strongly resistant to soaking. **Jones paper** is chalk-surfaced and has a coarser texture, is poorly surfaced and the ink tends to peel. The outline of the watermark commonly shows on the surface of the stamp. The gum is colourless or only slightly toned and washes off readily. **Cowan paper** is chalk-surfaced and is white and opaque. The watermark is usually smaller than in the "Jones" paper and is often barely visible. **Wiggins Teape paper** is chalk-surfaced and is thin and hard. It has a vertical mesh with a narrow watermark, whereas the other papers have a horizontal mesh and a wider watermark.

50

(Typo Govt Printer, Wellington, from Perkins Bacon plate).

1908 (1 Dec). *De La Rue chalk-surfaced paper.* W 43. P 14×15 (*comb*).

386	50	1d. carmine	..	22·00	70
		w. Wmk inverted	..	—	50·00

The design of Type 50 differs from Type 42 by alterations in the corner rosettes and by the lines on the globe which are diagonal instead of vertical.

51   **52**   **53**

(Eng. P.B. Typo Govt Printer, Wellington)

1909 (8 Nov)–12. *De La Rue chalk-surfaced paper with toned gum.* W 43. P 14×15 (*comb*)

387	51	½d. yellow-green	..	3·75	20
		aa. Deep green	..	3·75	30
		a. Imperf (pair)	..	£170	
		b. Booklet pane. Five stamps plus label in position 1 (4.10)	£500	
		c. Ditto, but label in position 6 (4.10)	£500	
		d. Booklet pane of 6 (4.10)	£160	
		e. Ditto, but with coloured bars on selvedge (5.12)	£150	
		w. Wmk inverted	..	†	£300

Stamps with blurred and heavy appearance are from booklets.

(Eng W. R. Royle & Son, London. Recess Govt Printer, Wellington)

1909 (8 Nov)–16. T **52** *and similar portraits.*

(a) W 43. P 14×14½ (*comb*)

388	2d. mauve	..	14·00	6·50
	a. Deep mauve	..	18·00	6·50
	w. Wmk inverted	..	†	
389	3d. chestnut	..	23·00	80
390	4d. orange-red	..	26·00	27·00
	a. Orange-yellow (1912)	..	7·00	6·00
	aw. Wmk inverted	..	£250	75·00
391	5d. brown (1910)	..	17·00	2·00
	a. Red-brown	..	15·00	2·00
	w. Wmk inverted	..	†	
392	6d. carmine (1910)	..	40·00	80
	a. Deep carmine (29.10.13)	..	42·00	2·50
393	8d. indigo-blue	..	10·00	65
	a. Deep bright blue	..	13·00	65
	w. Wmk inverted	..	35·00	20·00
394	1s. vermilion (1910)	..	48·00	1·75
	w. Wmk inverted	..	£150	50·00
388/94		Set of 8	£160	40·00

(b) W 43. P 14 (*line*)*

395	3d. chestnut (1910)	..	40·00	7·00
396	4d. orange (1910)	..	20·00	13·00
397	5d. brown	..	24·00	4·25
	a. Red-brown (15.9.11)	..	26·00	4·75
	w. Wmk inverted	..		
398	6d. carmine	..	48·00	9·50
399	1s. vermilion	..	48·00	12·00
395/9		Set of 5	£160	40·00

(c) W 43 (*sideways*) (*paper with widely spaced watermark as used for Nos. 308 and 320 — see note below No. 348*). P 14 (*line*)*

400	8d. indigo-blue (8.16) ..	18·00	48·00
	a. No wmk	60·00	£140

(d) W 43. P 14×13½ (*comb*)†

401	3d. chestnut (1915)	60·00	75·00
	a. Vert pair. P 14×13½ and 14×14½	£225	£275
	w. Wmk inverted	£120	£120
402	5d. red-brown (1916)	19·00	2·50
	a. Vert pair. P 14×13½ and 14×14½	50·00	70·00
403	6d. carmine (1915)	70·00	75·00
	a. Vert pair. P 14×13½ and 14×14½	£225	£275
404	8d. indigo-blue (3.16)	24·00	2·50
	a. Vert pair. P 14×13½ and 14×14½	50·00	70·00
	b. Deep bright blue	26·00	2·50
	ba. Vert pair. P 14×13½ and 14×14½	50·00	70·00
	w. Wmk inverted	35·00	20·00
401/4	Set of 4	£150	£140

*In addition to showing the usual characteristics of a line perforation, these stamps may be distinguished by their vertical perforation which measures 13.8. Nos. 388/94 generally measure vertically 14 to 14.3. An exception is 13.8 one vertical side but 14 the other.

†The 3d. and 6d. come in full sheets perf 14×13½. The 3d., 5d. and 6d. values also exist in two combinations: (*a*) five top rows perf 14×13½ with five bottom rows perf 14×14½ and (*b*) four top rows perf 14×13½ with six bottom rows perf 14×14½. The 8d. perf 14×13½ only exists from combination (*b*).

(Eng P.B. Typo Govt Printer, Wellington)

1909 (8 Nov)–26. P 14×15 (*comb*).

(a) W 43. *De La Rue chalk-surfaced paper with toned gum*

405	53	1d. carmine	..	1·25	10
		a. Imperf (pair)	..	£275	
		b. Booklet pane of 6 (4.10)	£140	
		c. Ditto, but with coloured bars on selvedge (5.12)	£110	
		w. Wmk inverted	..	25·00	20·00
		y. Wmk inverted and reversed			

(b) W 43. *Jones chalk-surfaced paper with white gum*

406	53	1d. deep carmine (6.24)		12·00	4·75
		a. On unsurfaced paper. *Pale carmine*		£325	
		b. Booklet pane of 6 with bars on selvedge (1.12.24)		£100	
		w. Wmk inverted		35·00	25·00

(c) W 43. *De La Rue unsurfaced medium paper with toned gum*

407	53	1d. rose-carmine (4.25)		28·00	£100

(d) W 43 (sideways). *De La Rue chalk-surfaced paper with toned gum*

408	53	1d. bright carmine (4.25)		7·00	35·00
		a. No wmk		20·00	55·00
		b. Imperf (pair)		55·00	

(e) *No wmk, but bluish "NZ" and Star lithographed on back. Art paper*

409	53	1d. rose-carmine (7.25)		2·25	2·50
		a. "NZ" and Star in black		13·00	
		b. "NZ" and Star colourless		24·00	

(f) W 43. *Cowan thick, opaque, chalk-surfaced paper with white gum*

410	53	1d. deep carmine (8.25)		5·00	1·00
		a. Imperf (pair)		75·00	85·00
		b. Booklet pane of 6 with bars and adverts on selvedge		£100	
		w. Wmk inverted		30·00	20·00
		x. Wmk reversed (1926)		6·00	1·75
		y. Wmk inverted and reversed (1926)		30·00	20·00

(g) W 43. *Wiggins Teape thin, hard, chalk-surfaced paper with white gum*

411	53	1d. rose-carmine (6.26)		24·00	12·00
		w. Wmk inverted		35·00	20·00

Examples of No. 405 with a blurred and heavy appearance are from booklets.

No. 406a comes from a sheet on which the paper coating was missing from the right-hand half.

Many stamps from the sheets of No. 408 were without watermark or showed portions of "NEW ZEALAND POSTAGE" in double-lined capitals.

AUCKLAND EXHIBITION, 1913.

(59)   60

1913 (1 Dec). *Auckland Industrial Exhibition. Nos. 387aa, 389, 392 and 405 optd with T 59 by Govt Printer, Wellington.*

412	51	½d. deep green		13·00	40·00
413	53	1d. carmine		19·00	38·00
414	52	3d. chestnut		£130	£250
415		6d. carmine		£140	£275
412/15			*Set of 4*	£275	£550

These overprinted stamps were only available for letters in New Zealand and to Australia.

(Des H. L. Richardson. Recess Govt Printer, Wellington, from plates made in London by P.B.)

1915 (30 July)–30. (a) W 43, *Cowan unsurfaced paper.* P 14×13½ (comb) (see notes below).

416	60	1½d. grey-slate		2·25	1·75
		a. Perf 14×14½ (1915)		3·50	1·75
		aw. Wmk inverted		40·00	35·00
		b. Vert pair. Nos. 416/a		35·00	60·00
417		2d. bright violet		7·00	32·00
		a. Perf 14×14½		7·00	28·00
		b. Vert pair. Nos. 417/a		24·00	£120
418		2d. yellow (15.1.16)		5·00	26·00
		a. Perf 14×14½		5·00	26·00
		b. Vert pair. Nos. 418/a		18·00	£150
419		2½d. blue		3·25	3·50
		a. Perf 14×14½ (1916)		9·50	17·00
		b. Vert pair. Nos. 419/a		35·00	80·00
420		3d. chocolate		9·00	1·25
		aw. Wmk inverted		£110	65·00
		ax. Wmk reversed			
		b. Perf 14×14½		9·00	1·75
		bw. Wmk inverted		£110	65·00
		bx. Wmk reversed		£120	
		c. Vert pair. Nos. 420 and 420b		35·00	80·00
		cw. Wmk inverted			
		cx. Wmk reversed			
421		4d. yellow		4·25	48·00
		a. Re-entry (Pl 20 R. 1/6)		32·00	
		b. Re-entry (Pl 20 R. 4/10)		38·00	
		c. Perf 14×14½		4·25	50·00
		d. Vert pair. Nos. 421 and 421c		26·00	£160
422		4d. bright violet (7.4.16)		8·50	40
		a. Imperf (horiz pair)		£850	
		b. Re-entry (Pl 20 R. 1/6)		38·00	20·00
		c. Re-entry (Pl 20 R. 4/10)		42·00	24·00
		dx. Wmk reversed			
		e. Perf 14×14½		7·00	40
		ew. Wmk inverted		†	—
		ex. Wmk reversed		—	£100
		f. Vert pair. Nos. 422 and 422e		35·00	75·00
		fx. Wmk reversed			
423		4½d. deep green		12·00	15·00
		a. Perf 14×14½ (1915)		15·00	30·00
		b. Vert pair. Nos. 423/a		48·00	90·00
424		5d. light blue (4.22)		6·50	1·00
		a. Imperf (pair)		£130	£160
		bw. Wmk inverted		—	95·00
		c. Perf 14×14½		14·00	38·00
		d. Pale ultramarine (5.30)		8·50	7·00
		da. Perf 14×14½		12·00	17·00
		db. Vert pair. Nos. 424d/da		55·00	£110
425		6d. carmine		7·00	40
		a. Imperf three sides (top stamp of vert pair)		£1300	
		bw. Wmk inverted		£110	65·00
		bx. Wmk reversed		—	£110
		by. Wmk inverted and reversed			
		c. Carmine-lake (11.27)		£500	£275
		d. Perf 14×14½ (1915)		8·50	60
		dw. Wmk inverted		50·00	40·00
		e. Vert pair. Nos. 425 and 425d		65·00	£120

426	60	7½d. red-brown		13·00	23·00
		a. Perf 14×14½ (10.20)		20·00	50·00
		b. Vert pair. Nos. 426/a		50·00	£120
427		8d. indigo-blue (19.4.21)		14·00	45·00
		a. Perf 14×14½		15·00	45·00
		b. Vert pair. Nos. 427/a		38·00	£140
428		8d. red-brown (3.22)		18·00	1·50
429		9d. sage-green		17·00	2·25
		a. Imperf (pair)		£850	
		b. Imperf three sides (top stamp of vert pair)		£1400	
		c. Yellowish olive (12.25)		28·00	9·50
		d. Perf 14×14½		21·00	10·00
		e. Vert pair. Nos. 429 and 429d		70·00	£140
430		1s. vermilion		13·00	2·25
		a. Imperf (pair)		£2250	
		bw. Wmk inverted		£225	£130
		c. Perf 14×14½ (1915)		14·00	50
		ca. Pale orange-red (4.24)		30·00	15·00
		cb. Imperf (pair)		£325	
		cc. Orange-brown (1.2.28)		£500	£250
		cw. Wmk inverted		£225	
		d. Vert pair. Nos. 430 and 430c		75·00	£150
		dw. Wmk inverted			
416/30			*Set of 15*	£120	£170

(b) W 43 (sideways on 2d., 3d. and 6d.). *Thin paper with widely spaced watermark as used for Nos. 308 and 320 (see note below No. 348.)* P 14×13½ (comb) (see notes below) (1½d.) or 14 (line) (others)

431	60	1½d. grey-slate (3.16)		1·75	5·50
		a. No wmk		2·75	11·00
		b. Perf 14×14½		1·75	5·50
		ba. No wmk		2·75	11·00
		by. Wmk inverted and reversed			
		c. Vert pair. Nos. 431 and 431b		20·00	60·00
		ca. Vert pair. Nos. 431a and 431ba		38·00	90·00
432		2d. yellow (6.16)		4·50	48·00
		a. No wmk		35·00	£100
433		3d. chocolate (6.16)		6·50	24·00
		a. No wmk		32·00	75·00
434		6d. carmine (6.16)		8·00	48·00
		a. No wmk		65·00	£140
431/4			*Set of 4*	19·00	£110

The 1½d., 2½d., 4½d. and 7½d. have value tablets as shown in Type 60. For the other values the tablets are shortened and the ornamental border each side of the crown correspondingly extended.

With the exception of Nos. 432/4 stamps in this issue were comb-perforated 14×13½, 14×14½ or a combination of the two. The 1½d. (No. 416), 2½d., 4d. (both), 4½d., 5d., 6d., 7½d., 8d. red-brown, 9d. and 1s. are known to have been produced in sheets perforated 14×13½ throughout with the 4d. bright violet, 5d., 6d. and 1s. known perforated 14×14½ throughout.

On the sheets showing the two perforations combined the top four rows are usually perforated 14×13½ and the bottom six 14×14½. Combination sheets are known to have been produced in this form for the 1½d. (Nos. 416 and 431), 2d. (both), 2½d., 3d., 4d. (both), 4½d., 6d., 7½d., 8d. indigo-blue, 9d. and 1s. On a late printing of the 4d. bright violet and 5d. pale ultramarine the arrangement is different with the top five rows perforated 14×14½ and the bottom five 14×13½.

With the exception of Nos. 432/4 any with perforations measuring 14×14 or nearly must be classed as 14×14½, this being an irregularity of the comb machine, and not a product of the 14-line machine.

During the laying-down of plate 20 for the 4d., from the roller-die which also contained dies of other values, an impression of the 4½d. value was placed on R. 1/6 and of the 2½d. on R. 4/10. These errors were subsequently corrected by re-entries of the 4d. impression, but on R. 1/6 traces of the original impression can be found in the right-hand value tablet and above the top frame line, while on R. 4/10 the foot of the "2" is visible in the left-hand value tablet with traces of "½" to its right.

61   62   (63)

WAR STAMP

Type 62 (from local plates) can be identified from Type 61 (prepared by Perkins Bacon) by the shading on the portrait. This is diagonal on Type 62 and horizontal on Type 61.

(Die eng W. R. Bock. Typo Govt Printer, Wellington, from plates made by P.B. (T 61) or locally (T 62))

1915 (30 July)–33. P 14×15.

(a) W 43. *De La Rue chalk-surfaced paper with toned gum.*

435	61	½d. green		90	10
		a. Booklet pane of 6 with bars on selvedge		£110	
		b. Yellow-green		3·75	1·40
		ba. Booklet pane of 6 with bars on selvedge		90·00	
		c. Very thick, hard, highly surfaced paper with white gum (12.15)		12·00	32·00
		w. Wmk inverted		30·00	60·00
		x. Wmk reversed		—	50·00
		y. Wmk inverted and reversed		—	50·00
436	62	1½d. grey-black (4.16)		5·50	85
		a. Black		6·50	95
		y. Wmk inverted and reversed		—	£110
437	61	1½d. slate (5.9.16)		6·50	10
		w. Wmk inverted		—	£110
438		1½d. orange-brown (9.18)		2·25	10
		w. Wmk inverted		75·00	60·00
		x. Wmk reversed		†	—
		y. Wmk inverted and reversed		£100	80·00
439		2d. yellow (9.16)		1·75	10
		a. Pale yellow		3·75	60
		w. Wmk inverted		75·00	
440		3d. chocolate (5.19)		7·00	75
435/40			*Set of 6*	21·00	1·75

(b) W 43. *Jones chalk-surfaced paper with white gum*

441	61	½d. green (10.24)		6·50	7·50
		a. Booklet pane of 6 with bars on selvedge (1.12.24)		£100	
		w. Wmk inverted		40·00	
442		2d. dull yellow (7.24)		6·00	24·00
		w. Wmk inverted		30·00	
443		3d. deep chocolate (3.25)		19·00	11·00
441/3			*Set of 3*	28·00	38·00

(c) *No wmk, but bluish "NZ" and Star lithographed on back. Art paper*

444	61	½d. apple-green (4.25)		1·50	2·00
		a. "NZ" and Star almost colourless		4·25	
445		2d. yellow (7.25)		6·50	4·00

(d) W 43. *Cowan thick, opaque, chalk-surfaced paper with white gum*

446	61	½d. green (4.25)		50	15
		a. Booklet pane of 6 with bars and adverts on selvedge		90·00	
		ab. Booklet pane of 6 with bars on selvedge (1928)		£250	
		bw. Wmk inverted		35·00	25·00
		bx. Wmk reversed (1926)		3·50	1·50
		by. Wmk inverted and reversed (1926)		35·00	20·00
		c. Perf 14 (1927)		60	20
		ca. Booklet pane of 6 with bars on selvedge (1928)		85·00	
		cb. Booklet pane of 6 with bars and adverts on selvedge (1928)		85·00	
		cw. Wmk inverted		40·00	25·00
447		1½d. orange-brown (p 14) (8.29)		8·50	17·00
		a. Perf 14×15 (7.33)		40·00	60·00
448		2d. yellow (8.25)		5·00	30
		ax. Wmk reversed (1927)		10·00	40·00
		ay. Wmk inverted and reversed (1927)		£100	
		b. Perf 14 (1929)		2·75	10
		bw. Wmk inverted		35·00	20·00
449		3d. chocolate (8.25)		7·50	40
		aw. Wmk inverted		60·00	
		b. Perf 14 (1929)		7·50	2·75
446/9			*Set of 4*	17·00	15·00

(e) W 43. *Wiggins Teape thin, hard, chalk-surfaced paper*

450	61	1½d. orange-brown (p 14) (1930)		32·00	65·00
451		2d. yellow (5.26)		7·50	16·00
		aw. Wmk inverted		24·00	
		b. Perf 14 (10.27)		6·50	16·00
		bw. Wmk inverted		30·00	30·00

The designs of these stamps also differ as described beneath No. 434.

Stamps from booklet panes often have blurred, heavy impressions. Different advertisements can be found on the listed booklet panes.

1915 (24 Sept). No. 435 optd with T 63.

452	61	½d. green		1·60	30

64 "Peace" and Lion   65 "Peace" and Lion

(Des and typo D.L.R. from plates by P.B., Waterlow and D.L.R.)

1920 (27 Jan). *Victory. T 64/5 and similar designs.* W 43 (sideways on ½d., 1½d., 3d. and 1s.). *De La Rue chalk-surfaced paper.* P 14.

453		½d. green		3·00	2·25
		a. Pale yellow-green		25·00	25·00
454		1d. carmine-red		4·00	40
		a. Bright carmine		6·00	50
		w. Wmk inverted		15·00	4·00
		x. Wmk reversed		48·00	10·00
455		1½d. brown-orange		3·50	30
456		3d. chocolate		13·00	12·00
457		6d. violet		15·00	16·00
		a. Wmk sideways		†	£325
		x. Wmk inverted		—	£110
458		1s. orange-red		24·00	48·00
453/8			*Set of 6*	55·00	70·00

Designs: *Horiz* (as T 65)—1½d. Maori chief. (As T 64)—3d. Lion; 1s. King George V. *Vert* (as T 64)—6d. "Peace" and "Progress".

The above stamps were placed on sale in London in November, 1919.

2d.   2d.

TWOPENCE

(68)   69

1922 (Mar). No. 453 surch with T 68.

459	64	2d. on ½d. green (R.)		3·25	1·40

(Des and eng W. R. Bock. Typo Govt Printer, Wellington)

1923 (1 Oct)–25. *Restoration of Penny Postage.* W 43. P 14×15.

(a) *De La Rue chalk-surfaced paper with toned gum*

460	69	1d. carmine		2·75	50

(b) *Jones chalk-surfaced paper with white gum*

461	69	1d. carmine (3.24)		6·00	3·75
		a. Wmk sideways		50·00	†
		w. Wmk inverted		50·00	40·00

(c) *Cowan unsurfaced paper with very shiny gum*

462	69	1d. carmine-pink (4.25)		27·00	27·00

The paper used for No. 462 is similar to that of Nos. 416/30.

70 Exhibition Buildings

(Des H. L. Richardson. Eng and typo Govt Printer, Wellington)

1925 (17 Nov). *Dunedin Exhibition. W* **43**. *Cowan chalk-surfaced paper. P* 14 × 15.

463	70	½d. yellow-green/*green*	..	..	3·00	11·00
		w. Wmk inverted			£225	£100
464		1d. carmine/*rose*	..	..	3·25	5·50
		w. Wmk inverted			£225	£100
465		4d. mauve/*pale mauve*			40·00	70·00
		a. "POSTAGF" at right (R. 1/2, R 10/1)		£120	£170
463/5	..	..	..	*Set of* 3	42·00	80·00

71   **72**

(Des H. L. Richardson; plates by B.W. (1d. from sheets), P.B. (1d. from booklets), Royal Mint, London (others). Typo Govt Printer, Wellington)

1926 (12 July)–**34**. *W* **43**. *P* 14. (*a*) *Jones chalk-surfaced paper with white gum.*

466	72	2s. deep blue	..	..	48·00	55·00
		w. Wmk inverted			48·00	55·00
467		3s. mauve	..		70·00	£150
		w. Wmk inverted			70·00	£150

(*b*) *Cowan thick, opaque, chalk-surfaced paper with white gum*

468	71	1d. rose-carmine (15.11.26)			55	10
		a. Imperf (pair)			£100	
		b. Booklet pane of 6 with bars on selvedge (1928)		75·00	
		c. Booklet pane of 6 with bars and adverts on selvedge (1928)		75·00	
		dw. Wmk inverted			20·00	10·00
		e. Perf 14×15 (3.27)			55	10
		ea. Booklet pane of 6 with bars and adverts on selvedge (1934)		85·00	
		ew. Wmk inverted			20·00	10·00
		ex. Wmk reversed			10·00	
469	72	2s. light blue (5.27)			48·00	20·00
470		3s. pale mauve (9.27)			80·00	£130
468/70	..	..	..	*Set of* 3	£120	£140

(*c*) *Wiggins Teape thin, hard, chalk-surfaced paper with white gum*

471	71	1d. rose-carmine (6.30)			15·00	7·00
		w. Wmk inverted			30·00	15·00

No. 468ex exists in a range of colours including scarlet and deep carmine to magenta but we have insufficient evidence to show that these were issued.

Following the reduction of the postage rate to ½d. on 1 June 1932 the firm of R. H. White & Co. Ltd. of Stratford returned a quantity of envelopes stamped with 1d. stamps to the local post office who surcharged the stamps "HALFPENNY" in purple using a handstamp. The covers were then returned to the firm for normal use. A similar local surcharge was applied to a smaller quantity of 1d. stamps at Greymouth where "HALFPENNY" was applied, diagonally, in blue.

73 Nurse   **74** Smiling Boy

(Typo Govt Printing Office, Wellington)

1929–30. *Anti-Tuberculosis Fund. T* **73** *and similar design. W* **43**. *P* 14.

(*a*) *Inscribed* "HELP STAMP OUT TUBERCULOSIS".

544		1d. + 1d. scarlet (11.12.29)		11·00	18·00
		w. Wmk inverted	..	£190	£190

(*b*) *Inscribed* "HELP PROMOTE HEALTH"

545		1d. + 1d. scarlet (29.10.30)		22·00	32·00

(Des L. C. Mitchell. Dies eng and plates made Royal Mint, London (1d.), Govt Ptg Office, Wellington from W. R. Bock die (2d.). Typo Govt Ptg Office, Wellington)

1931 (31 Oct). *Health Stamps. W* **43** (*sideways*). *P* 14½ × 14.

546	74	1d. + 1d. scarlet		75·00	75·00
547		2d. + 1d. blue	..	75·00	60·00

COVER PRICES

Cover factors are quoted at the beginning of each country for most issues to 1945. An explanation of the system can be found on page x. The factors quoted do not, however, apply to philatelic covers.

---

75 New Zealand Lake Scenery   **FIVE PENCE**   (**76**)

(Des L. C. Mitchell. Plates, Royal Mint, London. Typo Govt Ptg Office)

1931 (10 Nov)–**35**. *Air. W* **43**. *P* 14×14½.

548	75	3d. chocolate			24·00	13·00
		a. Perf 14×15 (4.35)			£130	£425
549		4d. blackish purple			24·00	17·00
550		7d. brown-orange			27·00	8·00
548/50				*Set of* 3	65·00	35·00

1931 (18 Dec). *Air. Surch with T* **76**. *W* **43**. *P* 14×14½.

551	75	5d. on 3d. green (R.)			12·00	8·00

77 Hygeia,
Goddess of Health   **78** The Path to Health

(Des R. E. Tripe and W. J. Cooch. Eng H. T. Peat. Recess Govt Printing Office, Wellington)

1932 (18 Nov). *Health Stamp. W* **43**. *P* 14.

552	77	1d. + 1d. carmine			23·00	27·00
		w. Wmk inverted			£225	£120
		x. Wmk reversed			†	£275

(Des J. Berry. Eng H. T. Peat. Recess Govt Printing Office, Wellington)

1933 (8 Nov). *Health Stamp. W* **43**. *P* 14.

553	78	1d. + 1d. carmine			13·00	17·00
		w. Wmk inverted			£150	£110

TRANS-TASMAN
AIR MAIL
"FAITH IN AUSTRALIA."
(**79**)   **80** Crusader

1934 (17 Jan). *Air. T* **75** *in new colour optd with T* **79**. *W* **43**. *P* 14×14½.

554	75	7d. light blue (B.)			35·00	40·00

(Des J. Berry. Recess D.L.R.)

1934 (25 Oct). *Health Stamp. W* **43** (*sideways*). *P* 14×13½.

555	80	1d. + 1d. carmine			11·00	17·00

81 Collared Grey
Fantail   **82** Brown Kiwi   **83** Maori Woman

84 Maori Carved House   **85** Mt Cook

86 Maori Girl   **87** Mitre Peak

88 Striped Marlin   **89** Harvesting

---

90 Tuatara Lizard   **91** Maori Panel   **92** Tui

93 Capt. Cook at Poverty Bay   **94** Mt Egmont

Die I   Die II

**CAPTAIN COQK
AT POVERTY BAY
OCTOBER 8** 1769

"Captain Coqk"
(R. 1/4)

(Des J. Fitzgerald (½d., 4d.), C. H. and R. J. G. Collins (1d.), M. Matthews (1½d.), H. W. Young (2d.), L. C. Mitchell (2½d. 3d., 8d., 1s., 3s.), W. J. Cooch and R. E. Tripe (5d.), T. I. Archer (6d.), I. F. Calder (9d.) and I. H. Jenkins (2s.). Litho Waterlow (9d.). Recess D.L.R. (remainder))

1935 (1 May)–**36**. *W* **43** (*sideways on* 8d.).

556	81	½d. bright green, *p* 14×13½		1·50	50
		w. Wmk inverted		2·25	1·75
557	82	1d. scarlet (Die I), *p* 14×13½		1·50	30
		aw. Wmk inverted		2·25	1·50
		b. Perf 13½×14 (1936)		75·00	45·00
		c. Die II. Perf 14×13½ (1935)		5·50	2·75
		ca. Booklet pane of 6 with adverts on selvedge		40·00	
		w. Wmk inverted		12·00	3·00
558	83	1½d. red-brown, *p* 14×13½		6·00	8·50
		a. Perf 13½×14 (1935)		4·75	5·50
		ay. Wmk inverted and reversed (2.36)	18·00	22·00
559	84	2d. orange, *p* 14×13½		2·75	40
		w. Wmk inverted		75·00	20·00
560	85	2½d. chocolate and slate, *p* 13–14×13½	55·00	22·00
		aw. Wmk inverted		20·00	32·00
		b. Perf 13½×14 (11.35)		4·00	17·00
		bx. Wmk reversed		†	£425
561	86	3d. brown, *p* 14×13½		12·00	1·50
		w. Wmk inverted		—	£110
562	87	4d. black and sepia, *p* 14		3·50	1·50
		w. Wmk inverted		£200	80·00
563	88	5d. ultramarine, *p* 13–14×13½		23·00	23·00
		aw. Wmk inverted		†	85·00
		b. Perf 13½×14		24·00	30·00
564	89	6d. scarlet, *p* 13½×14		6·50	4·75
		w. Wmk inverted		—	55·00
565	90	8d. chocolate, *p* 14×13½		9·50	8·00
566	91	9d. scarlet and black, *p* 14×14½		11·00	3·25
567	92	1s. deep green, *p* 14×13½		20·00	9·50
		w. Wmk inverted		—	70·00
568	93	2s. olive-green, *p* 13–14½×13½		35·00	32·00
		a. "CAPTAIN COQK"		80·00	
		bw. Wmk inverted		70·00	40·00
		c. Perf 13½×14 (1935)		42·00	38·00
		ca. "CAPTAIN COQK"		90·00	
569	94	3s. choc & yell-brn, *p* 13–14×13½		15·00	45·00
		a. Perf 13½×14 (11.35)		19·00	45·00
		aw. Wmk inverted		†	£180
		ay. Wmk inverted and reversed (1936)	£300	£325
556/69	..	..	*Set of* 14	£130	£130

Some stamps from sheets perforated 14×13½ by De La Rue sometimes show the horizontal perforations nearer 13½.

In the 2½d., 5d., 2s. and 3s. perf 13–14×13½ the horizontal perforations of each stamp are in two sizes, one half of each horizontal side measuring 13 and the other 14.

See also Nos. 577/90 and 630/1.

95 Bell Block Aerodrome   **96** King George V
and Queen Mary

(Des J. Berry. Eng Stamp Printing Office, Melbourne. Recess Govt Printing Office, Wellington)

1935 (4 May). *Air.* W **43**. P 14.
570	95	1d. carmine	..	1·00	50
		w. Wmk inverted	..	60·00	40·00
571		3d. violet	..	5·00	3·00
		w. Wmk inverted	..	75·00	40·00
572		6d. blue	..	9·50	2·50
		w. Wmk inverted	..	85·00	60·00
570/2			*Set of 3*	14·00	5·50

(Frame by J. Berry. Recess B.W.)

1935 (7 May). *Silver Jubilee.* W **43**. P 11×11½.
573	96	½d. green	..	75	90
574		1d. carmine	..	1·25	70
575		6d. red-orange	..	21·00	23·00
573/5			*Set of 3*	21·00	23·00

97 "The Key to Health"   **98** "Multiple Wmk"

(Des S. Hall. Recess John Ash, Melbourne)

1935 (30 Sept). *Health Stamp.* W **43**. P 11.
576	97	1d. + 1d. scarlet	..	2·50	2·75

WATERMARKS. In W **43** the wmk units are in vertical columns widely spaced and the sheet margins are unwatermarked or wmkd "NEW ZEALAND POSTAGE" in large letters.

In W **98** the wmk units are arranged alternately in horizontal rows closely spaced and are continued into the sheet margins. Stamps with W **98** sideways show the star to the left of NZ, *as seen from the back*. Sideways inverted varieties have the star to right *as seen from the back*.

Litho Govt Ptg Office, Wellington (9d). Recess Waterlow or D.L.R. (others))

1936–42. W **98**.
577	81	½d. bright green, p 14×13½	..	2·75	10
		w. Wmk inverted	..	5·00	1·50
578	82	1d. scarlet (Die II), p 14×13½ (4.36)	..	2·25	10
		w. Wmk inverted	..	7·00	2·50
579	83	1½d. red-brown, p 14×13½ (6.36)	..	9·00	5·50
580	84	2d. orange, p 14×13½ (3.36)	..	30	10
		aw. Wmk inverted	..	80·00	27·00
		b. Perf 12½* (6.41)	..	3·75	10
		bw. Wmk inverted	..		
		c. Perf 14 (6.41)	..	25·00	90
		d. Perf 14×15 (6.41)	..	38·00	18·00
581	85	2½d. chocolate and slate, p 13–14×13½	..	3·75	14·00
		aw. Wmk inverted	..	20·00	30·00
		b. Perf 14 (11.36)	..	4·00	1·50
		bw. Wmk inverted	..	13·00	16·00
		c. Perf 14×13½ (11.42)	..	50	4·00
582	86	3d. brown, p 14×13½	..	35·00	55
		w. Wmk inverted	..	60·00	27·00
583	87	4d. black and sepia, p 14×13½	..	4·75	40
		aw. Wmk inverted	..	14·00	7·50
		b. Perf 12½* (1941)	..	27·00	9·50
		bw. Wmk inverted	..		†
		c. Perf 14, line (1941)	..	65·00	95·00
		d. Perf 14×14½ comb (7.42)	..	90	10
		dw. Wmk inverted	..	90·00	
584	88	5d. ultramarine, p 13–14×13½ (8.36)	..	15·00	1·90
		aw. Wmk inverted	..	30·00	13·00
		b. Perf 12½*† (7.41)	..	20·00	3·00
		c. Perf 14×13½ (11.42)	..	3·00	75
		cw. Wmk inverted	..	90·00	70·00
585	89	6d. scarlet, p 13½×14 (8.36)	..	11·00	80
		aw. Wmk inverted	..	35·00	5·00
		b. Perf 12½* (10.41)	..	3·00	3·50
		c. Perf 14½×14 (6.42)	..	1·00	10
		cw. Wmk inverted	..	£225	65·00
586	90	8d. choc, p 14×13½ (*wmk sideways*)	..	10·00	3·00
		aw. Wmk sideways inverted	..	25·00	9·00
		b. Perf 12½* (*wmk sideways*) (7.39)	..	4·00	3·00
		bw. Wmk inverted	..		
		c. Perf 12½* (*wmk sideways*) (7.41)	..	3·75	1·50
		d. Perf 14×14½ (*wmk sideways*) (7.42)	..	3·75	70
		dw. Wmk sideways inverted	..	—	35·00
587	91	9d. red and grey, p 14×15 (*wmk sideways*)	..	40·00	3·25
		ay. Wmk sideways inverted and reversed	..	—	75·00
		b. Wmk upright. *Red and grey-black*, p 13½×14 (1.3.38)	..	65·00	3·25
		bw. Wmk inverted	..	90·00	24·00
588	92	1s. deep green, p 14×13½	..	2·50	60
		aw. Wmk inverted	..	55·00	10·00
		b. Perf 12½* (11.41)	..	65·00	15·00
589	93	2s. olive-green, p 13–14×13½ (8.36)	..	35·00	5·00
		a. "CAPTAIN COQK"	..	60·00	
		bw. Wmk inverted	..	£100	28·00
		c. Perf 13½×14 (3.39)	..	£275	3·00
		ca. "CAPTAIN COQK"	..	£275	
		d. Perf 12½*† (7.41)	..	26·00	6·00
		da. "CAPTAIN COQK"	..	60·00	
		e. Perf 14×13½ (10.42)	..	10·00	1·50
		ea. "CAPTAIN COQK"	..	80·00	
		ew. Wmk inverted	..	—	85·00

590	94	3s. chocolate & yell-brn, p 13–14×13½		42·00	6·00
		aw. Wmk inverted	..	65·00	16·00
		b. Perf 12½* (1941)	..	80·00	48·00
		c. Perf 14×13½ (1942)	..	5·00	2·25
577/90c			*Set of 14*	£100	14·00

*†Stamps indicated with an asterisk were printed and perforated by Waterlow; those having a dagger were printed by D.L.R. and perforated by Waterlow. No. 580d was printed by D.L.R. and perforated by Harrison and No. 583c was printed by Waterlow and perforated by D.L.R. These are all known as "Blitz perfs" because De La Rue were unable to maintain supplies after their works were damaged by enemy action. All the rest, except the 9d., were printed and perforated by D.L.R.

On stamps printed and perforated by De La Rue the perf 14×13½ varies in the sheet and is sometimes nearer 13½. 2d. perf 14×15 is sometimes nearer 14×14½.

2½d., 5d., 2s. and 3s. In perf 13–14×13½ one half the length of each horizontal perforation measures 13 and the other 14. In perf 14×13½ the horizontal perforation is regular.

4d. No. 583c. is line-perf measuring 14 exactly and has a blackish sepia frame. No. 583d is a comb-perf measuring 14×14.3 or 14×14.2 and the frame is a warmer shade.

2s. No. 589c is comb-perf and measures 13.5×13.75.

For 9d. typographed, see Nos. 630/1.

99 N.Z. Soldier at Anzac Cove   **100** Wool

(Des L. C. Mitchell. Recess John Ash, Melbourne)

1936 (27 Apr). *Charity. 21st Anniv of "Anzac" Landing at Gallipoli.* W **43**. P 11.
591	99	½d. + ½d. green	..	60	1·75
592		1d. + 1d. scarlet	..	60	1·40

(Des L. C. Mitchell. Recess John Ash, Melbourne)

1936 (1 Oct). *Congress of British Empire Chambers of Commerce, Wellington. Industries Issue.* T **100** and similar horiz designs. W **43** (*sideways*). P 11½.
593	½d. emerald-green	..	30	30
594	1d. scarlet	..	30	20
595	2½d. blue	..	1·00	8·00
596	4d. violet	..	80	5·50
597	6d. red-brown	..	2·00	4·50
593/7		*Set of 5*	4·00	17·00

Designs:—1d. Butter; 2½d. Sheep; 4d. Apples; 6d. Exports.

105 Health Camp   **106** King George VI and Queen Elizabeth

(Des J. Berry. Recess John Ash, Melbourne)

1936 (2 Nov). *Health Stamp.* W **43** (*sideways*). P 11.
598	105	1d. + 1d. scarlet	..	1·50	3·75

(Recess B.W.)

1937 (13 May). *Coronation.* W **98**. P 14 × 13½.
599	106	1d. carmine	..	30	10
600		2½d. Prussian blue	..	1·00	2·25
601		6d. red-orange	..	1·50	2·00
599/601			*Set of 3*	2·50	3·75

107 Rock climbing   **108** King George VI   **108a**

(Des G. Bull and J. Berry. Recess John Ash, Melbourne)

1937 (1 Oct). *Health Stamp.* W **43**. P 11.
602	107	1d. + 1d. scarlet	..	2·25	3·25

ALTERED CATALOGUE NUMBERS

Any Catalogue numbers altered from the last edition are shown as a list in the introductory pages.

Broken ribbon flaw (R. 6/6 of Pl 8)

(Des W. J. Cooch. Recess B.W.)

1938–44. W **98**. P 14×13½.
603	108	½d. green (1.3.38)	..	6·50	10
		w. Wmk inverted	..	12·00	2·50
604		½d. orange-brown (10.7.41)	..	20	20
		w. Wmk inverted	..		
605		1d. scarlet (1.7.38)	..	5·00	10
		a. Broken ribbon	..	50·00	
		w. Wmk inverted	..	12·00	2·50
606		1d. green (21.7.41)	..	20	10
		w. Wmk inverted	..	30·00	18·00
607	108a	1½d. purple-brown (26.7.38)	..	26·00	2·00
		w. Wmk inverted	..	38·00	3·75
608		1½d. scarlet (1.2.44)	..	20	30
		w. Wmk inverted	..	—	60·00
609		3d. blue (26.9.41)	..	20	10
		w. Wmk inverted	..	—	45·00
603/9			*Set of 7*	35·00	2·25

For other values see Nos. 680/9.

109 Children playing   **110** Beach Ball

(Des J. Berry. Recess B.W.)

1938 (1 Oct). *Health Stamp.* W **98**. P 14 × 13½.
610	109	1d. + 1d. scarlet	..	4·00	2·50

(Des S. Hall. Recess Note Printing Branch, Commonwealth Bank of Australia, Melbourne)

1939 (16 Oct). *Health Stamps. Surcharged with new value.* W **43**. P 11.
611	110	1d. on ½d. + ½d. green	..	3·75	4·00
612		2d. on 1d. + 1d. scarlet	..	3·75	4·00

111 Arrival of the Maoris, 1350   **115** Signing Treaty of Waitangi, 1840

(Des L. C. Mitchell (½d., 3d., 4d.); J. Berry (others). Recess B.W.)

1940 (2 Jan–8 Mar). *Centenary of Proclamation of British Sovereignty.* T **111**, **115** and similar designs. W **98**. P 14 × 13½ (2½d.), 13½ × 14 (5d.) or 13½ (others).
613	½d. blue-green	..	30	10
614	1d. chocolate and scarlet	..	2·75	10
615	1½d. light blue and mauve	..	30	30
616	2d. blue-green and chocolate	..	1·50	10
617	2½d. blue-green and blue	..	1·75	75
618	3d. purple and carmine	..	3·50	75
619	4d. chocolate and lake	..	16·00	1·25
620	5d. pale blue and brown	..	7·00	3·50
621	6d. emerald-green and violet	..	13·00	90
622	7d. black and red	..	1·50	3·75
623	8d. black and red (8.3)	..	13·00	2·75
624	9d. olive-green and orange	..	7·50	1·75
625	1s. sage-green and deep green	..	17·00	3·50
613/25		*Set of 13*	75·00	17·00

Designs: *Horiz* (as T **111**)—1d. *Endeavour*, Chart of N.Z., and Capt. Cook; 1½d. British Monarchs; 2d. Tasman with his ship and chart; 3d. Landing of immigrants, 1840; 4d. Road, Rail, Sea and Air Transport; 6d. *Dunedin* and "Frozen Mutton Route" to London; 7d., 8d. Maori council; 9d. Gold mining in 1861 and 1940. (As T **115**)—5d. H.M.S. *Britomar* at Akaroa, 1840. *Vert* (as T **111**)—1s. Giant Kauri tree.

1940 (1 Oct). *Health Stamps. As T **110**, but without extra surcharge.* W **43**. P 11.
626	110	1d. + ½d. blue-green	..	13·00	14·00
627		2d. + 1d. brown-orange	..	13·00	14·00

1ᴰ 1ᴰ

2ᴰ **1941**

(123)   Inserted "2"   (124)

1941. *Nos. 603 and 607 surch as T 123.*
628	108	1d. on ½d. green (1.5.41)	..	90	10
629	108a	2d. on 1½d. purple-brown (4.41)	..	90	10
		a. Inserted "2"	..	£550	£300

The surcharge on No. 629 has only one figure, at top left, and there is only one square to obliterate the original value at bottom right.

The variety "Inserted 2" occurs on the 10th stamp, 10th row. It is identified by the presence of remnants of the damaged "2", and by the spacing of "2" and "D" which is variable and different from the normal.

(Typo Govt Printing Office, Wellington)

1941. *As T 91, but smaller (17½×20½ mm). Chalk-surfaced paper. P 14×15. (a) W 43.*
630	91	9d. scarlet and black (5.41)	..	95·00	25·00
		w. Wmk inverted	..	†	£200

(b) W 98
631	91	9d. scarlet and black (29.9.41)	..	3·25	2·25
		w. Wmk inverted	..	£120	75·00

1941 (4 Oct). *Health Stamps. Nos. 626/7 optd with T 124.*
632	110	1d. + ½d. blue-green	..	30	2·00
633		2d. + 1d. brown-orange	..	30	2·00

125 Boy and Girl on Swing

126 Princess Margaret

(Des S. Hall. Recess Note Printing Branch, Commonwealth Bank of Australia, Melbourne)

1942 (1 Oct). *Health Stamps. W 43. P 11.*
634	125	1d. + ½d. blue-green	..	30	90
635		2d. + 1d. orange-red	..	30	90

(Des J. Berry. Recess B.W.)

1943 (1 Oct). *Health Stamps. T 126 and similar triangular design. W 98. P 12.*
636		1d. + ½d. green	..	20	1·10
		a. Imperf between (vert pair)		£6500	
637		2d. + 1d. red-brown	..	20	20
		a. Imperf between (vert pair)		£8000	£8000

Design:—2d. Queen Elizabeth II as Princess.

✠ TENPENCE ✠

(128)

1944 (1 May). *No. 615 surch with T 128.*
662	10d. on 1½d. light blue and mauve	..	15	20

129 Queen Elizabeth II as Princess and Princess Margaret

130 Statue of Peter Pan, Kensington Gardens

(Recess B.W.)

1944 (9 Oct). *Health Stamps. W 98. P 13½.*
663	129	1d. + ½d. green	..	25	40
664		2d. + 1d. blue	..	25	30

(Des J. Berry. Recess B.W.)

1945 (1 Oct). *Health Stamps. W 98. P 13½.*
665	130	1d. + ½d. green and buff	..	15	20
		w. Wmk inverted	..	50·00	35·00
666		2d. + 1d. carmine and buff	..	15	20
		w. Wmk inverted	..	60·00	45·00

131 Lake Matheson

132 King George VI and Parliament House, Wellington

---

133 St. Paul's Cathedral

139 "St. George" (Wellington College War Memorial Window)

Printer's guide mark (R. 12/3)

Completed rudder (R. 2/4 of Pl 42883 and R. 3/2 of Pl 42796)

(Des J. Berry. Photo Harrison (1½d. and 1s.). Recess B.W. (1d. and 2d.) and Waterlow (others))

1946 (1 Apr). *Peace issue. T 131/3, 139 and similar designs. W 98 (sideways on 1½d.). P 13 (1d., 2d.), 14×14½ (1½d., 1s.), 13½ (others).*
667		½d. green and brown	..	20	40
		a. Printer's guide mark	..	7·50	
		w. Wmk inverted	..	55·00	40·00
668		1d. green	..	10	10
		w. Wmk inverted	..	38·00	23·00
669		1½d. scarlet	..	10	30
		w. Wmk sideways inverted	..	10	10
670		2d. purple	..	15	10
671		3d. ultramarine and grey	..	30	15
		a. Completed rudder	..	6·50	
672		4d. bronze-green and orange	..	20	20
		w. Wmk inverted	..	90·00	42·00
673		5d. green and ultramarine	..	40	60
674		6d. chocolate and vermilion	..	15	30
675		8d. black and carmine	..	15	20
676		9d. blue and black	..	15	20
677		1s. grey-black	..	15	20
667/77			*Set of 11*	1·75	2·40

Designs: *Horiz (as T 132)*—2d. The Royal Family. *(As T 131)*—3d. R.N.Z.A.F. badge and airplanes; 4d. Army badge, tank and plough; 5d. Navy badge, H.M.N.Z.S. *Achilles* (cruiser) and *Dominion Monarch* (liner); 6d. N.Z. coat of arms, foundry and farm; 9d. Southern Alps and Franz Josef Glacier. *Vert (as T 139)*—1s. National Memorial Campanile.

142 Soldier helping Child over Stile

(Des J. Berry. Recess Waterlow)

1946 (24 Oct). *Health Stamps. W 98. P 13½.*
678	142	1d. + ½d. green and orange-brown	..	15	15
		a. Yellow-green and orange-brown	..	4·50	5·00
		w. Wmk inverted	..	13·00	13·00
679		2d. + 1d. chocolate and orange-brown	..	15	15

144 King George VI

145 Statue of Eros

Plate 1

Plate 2

(Des W. J. Cooch. Recess T 108a, B.W.; T 144, D.L.R.)

1947–52. *W 98 (sideways on "shilling" values). (a) P 14×13½.*
680	108a	2d. orange	..	15	10
		w. Wmk inverted	..	80·00	
681		4d. bright purple	..	70	30
682		5d. slate	..	50	70
683		6d. carmine	..	40	10
		w. Wmk inverted	..	75·00	16·00
684		8d. violet	..	65	30
685		9d. purple-brown	..	1·75	30
		w. Wmk inverted	..	38·00	12·00

(b) P 14
686	144	1s. red-brown and carmine (Plate 1)	..	1·40	80
		aw. Wmk sideways inverted	..	13·00	8·50
		b. Wmk upright (Plate 1)	..	50	70
		c. Wmk upright (Plate 2)	..	2·25	80
		cw. Wmk inverted	..	60·00	23·00
687		1s. 3d. red-brown and blue (Plate 2)	..	1·25	80
		aw. Wmk sideways inverted	..	7·50	5·50
		b. Wmk upright (14.1.52)	..	2·25	4·00
		bw. Wmk inverted			
688		2s. brown-orange and green (Plate 1)	..	3·00	2·00
		aw. Wmk sideways inverted	..	15·00	11·00
		b. Wmk upright (Plate 1)	..	4·00	6·50
689		3s. red-brown and grey (Plate 2)	..	3·25	3·25
		w. Wmk sideways inverted	..	29·00	14·00
680/9			*Set of 10*	11·00	7·50

In head-plate 2 the diagonal lines of the background have been strengthened and result in the upper corners and sides appearing more deeply shaded.

(Des J. Berry. Recess Waterlow)

1947 (1 Oct). *Health Stamps. W 98 (sideways). P 13½.*
690	145	1d. + ½d. green	..	15	15
		w. Wmk sideways inverted	..	25·00	25·00
691		2d. + 1d. carmine	..	15	15
		w. Wmk sideways inverted	..	38·00	38·00

146 Port Chalmers, 1848

148 First Church, Dunedin

(Des J. Berry. Recess B.W.)

1948 (23 Feb). *Centennial of Otago. T 146, 148 and similar designs. W 98 (sideways on 3d.). P 13½.*
692		1d. blue and green	..	20	20
		w. Wmk inverted	..	30·00	30·00
693		2d. green and brown	..	20	20
694		3d. purple	..	20	40
695		6d. black and rose	..	20	40
		w. Wmk inverted	..		£170
692/5			*Set of 4*	70	1·10

Designs: *Horiz*—2d. Cromwell, Otago; 6d. University of Otago.

150 Boy Sunbathing and Children Playing

151 Nurse and Child

(Des E. Linzell. Recess B.W.)

1948 (1 Oct). *Health Stamps. W 98. P 13½.*
696	150	1d. + ½d. blue and green	..	15	15
		w. Wmk inverted	..	20·00	20·00
697		2d. + 1d. purple and scarlet	..	15	15

1949 ROYAL VISIT ISSUE. Four stamps were prepared to commemorate this event: 2d. Treaty House, Waitangi; 3d. H.M.S. *Vanguard*; 5d. Royal portraits; 6d. Crown and sceptre. The visit did not take place and the stamps were destroyed, although a few examples of the 3d. later appeared on the market. A similar set was prepared in 1952, but was, likewise, not issued.

(Des J. Berry. Photo Harrison)

1949 (3 Oct). *Health Stamps. W 98. P 14 × 14½.*
698	151	1d. + ½d. green	..	20	20
699		2d. + 1d. ultramarine	..	20	20
		a. No stop below "D" of "1D." (R.1/2)		6·50	15·00

PRICES OF SETS

Set prices are given for many issues, generally those containing three stamps or more. Definitive sets include one of each value or major colour change, but do not cover different perforations, die types or minor shades. Where a choice is possible the set prices are based on the cheapest versions of the stamps included in the listings.

1½d.

POSTAGE

(152)

153 Queen Elizabeth II and Prince Charles

1950 (28 July). *As Type F 6, but without value, surch with T 152. W 98 (inverted). Chalk-surfaced paper. P 14.*
700 F 6 1½d. carmine 30 30
    w. Wmk upright .. .. .. 2·50 3·00

(Des J. Berry and R. S. Phillips. Photo Harrison)
1950 (2 Oct). *Health Stamps. W 98. P 14×14½.*
701 153 1d. +½d. green 15 15
    w. Wmk inverted .. .. 4·75 4·75
702 2d. +1d. plum 15 15
    w. Wmk inverted .. .. 16·00 16·00

154 Christchurch Cathedral   155 Cairn on Lyttleton Hills

(Des L. C. Mitchell (2d.), J. A. Johnstone (3d.) and J. Berry (others). Recess B.W.)
1950 (20 Nov). *Centennial of Canterbury, N.Z. T 154/5 and similar designs. W 98 (sideways on 1d. and 3d.). P 13½.*
703 1d. green and blue 20 40
704 2d. carmine and orange 20 40
705 3d. dark blue and blue 20 60
706 6d. brown and blue 20 60
707 1s. reddish purple and blue .. 20 80
703/7 .. .. .. *Set of 5* 90 2·50
Designs: *Vert* (as T 154)—3d. John Robert Godley. *Horiz* (as T 155)—6d. Canterbury University College; 1s. Aerial view of Timaru.

159 "Takapuna" class Yachts

(Des J. Berry and R. S. Phillips. Recess B.W.)
1951 (1 Nov). *Health Stamps. W 98. P 13½.*
708 159 1½d. +½d. scarlet and yellow .. 15 70
709 2d. + 1d. deep green and yellow .. 15 10
    w. Wmk inverted .. .. 45·00 45·00

160 Princess Anne   161 Prince Charles   (162)

3D

(From photographs by Marcus Adams. Photo Harrison)
1952 (1 Oct). *Health Stamps. W 98. P 14 × 14½.*
710 160 1½d. +½d. carmine-red 15 30
711 161 2d. + 1d. brown 15 20

1952–53. *Nos. 604 and 606 surch as T 162.*
712 108 1d. on ½d. brown-orange (11.9.53) .. 20 85
    a. "D" omitted .. .. .. †
713 3d. on 1d. green (12.12.52*) .. 10 10
*Earliest known date used.

163 Buckingham Palace   164 Queen Elizabeth II

(Des L. C. Mitchell (1s. 6d.), J. Berry (others). Recess D.L.R. (2d., 4d.), Waterlow (1s. 6d.) Photo Harrison (3d., 8d.))
1953 (25 May). *Coronation. T 163/4 and similar designs. W 98. P 13 (2d., 4d.), 13½ (1s. 6d.) or 14×14½ (3d., 8d.).*
714 2d. deep bright blue 30 30
715 3d. brown 30 10
716 4d. carmine .. .. 1·25 2·50
717 8d. slate-grey .. .. .. 80 1·60
718 1s. 6d. purple and ultramarine .. 2·00 2·75
714/18 .. .. .. *Set of 5* 4·25 6·50
Designs: *Horiz* (as T 163)—4d. Coronation State Coach; 1s. 6d. St. Edward's Crown and Royal Sceptre. *Vert* (as T 164)—8d. Westminster Abbey.

168 Girl Guides   169 Boy Scouts

(Des J. Berry. Photo Harrison)
1953 (7 Oct). *Health Stamps. W 98. P 14 × 14½.*
719 168 1½d. + ½d. blue 15 10
720 169 2d. + 1d. deep yellow-green .. 15 40
    a. Imperf 3 sides (block of 4) .. £1500
No. 720a shows the left-hand vertical pair imperforate at right and the right-hand pair imperforate at left, top and bottom.

170 Queen Elizabeth II   171 Queen Elizabeth II and Duke of Edinburgh

(Des L. C. Mitchell. Recess Waterlow)
1953 (9 Dec). *Royal Visit. W 98. P 13×14 (3d.) or 13½ (4d.).*
721 170 3d. dull purple 10 10
    w. Wmk inverted .. .. — 38·00
722 171 4d. deep ultramarine 10 60

172   173 Queen Elizabeth II 174

Die I   Die II

(Des L. C. Mitchell (T 172/3), J. Berry (T 174). Recess D.L.R. (T 173), B.W. (others))
1953 (15 Dec)–59. *W 98. P 14×13½ (T 172), 14 (T 173) or 13½ (T 174).*
723 172 ½d. slate-black (1.3.54) 15 30
724 1d. orange (1.3.54) 15 10
    w. Wmk inverted 30 60
725 1½d. brown-lake 20 10
726 2d. bluish green (1.3.54) .. 20 10
    w. Wmk inverted .. .. † £300
727 3d. vermilion (1.3.54) 20 10
    w. Wmk inverted 40 60
728 4d. blue (1.3.54) 40 40
729 6d. purple (1.3.54) .. .. 70 1·40
    w. Wmk inverted £250 £150
730 8d. carmine (1.3.54) 60 60
    w. Wmk inverted £450 £300
731 173 9d. brown and bright green (1.3.54) .. 60 30
    w. Wmk inverted £250 £150
732 1s. black & carm-red (Die I) (1.3.54) .. 65 10
    aw. Wmk inverted £250 £200
    b. Die II (1958) .. .. 75·00 17·00
733 1s. 6d. black and bright blue (1.3.54) .. 1·25 50
    aw. Wmk inverted £250 £160
733b 1s. 9d. black and red-orange (1.7.57) .. 8·50 1·25
    bw. Wmk inverted £350 £250
    c. White opaque paper (2.2.59) .. 7·00 1·25

733d 174 2s. 6d. brown (1.7.57) .. .. 27·00 8·00
734 3s. bluish green (1.3.54) .. 12·00 30
    w. Wmk inverted £450 £300
735 5s. carmine (1.3.54) .. .. 20·00 4·25
736 10s. deep ultramarine (1.3.54) .. 45·00 18·00
723/36 .. .. .. *Set of 16* £100 32·00

1s. Dies I and II. The two dies of the Queen's portrait differ in the shading on the sleeve at right. The long lines running upwards from left to right are strong in Die I and weaker in Die II. In the upper part of the shading the fine cross-hatching is visible in Die I only between the middle two of the four long lines, but in Die II it extends clearly across all four lines.
In the lower part of the shading the strength of the long lines in Die I makes the cross-hatching appear subdued, whereas in Die II the weaker long lines make the cross-hatching more prominent.
Centre plates 1A, 1B and 2B are Die I; 3A and 3B are Die II.
For stamps as T 172 but with larger figures of value see Nos. 745/51.

WHITE OPAQUE PAPER. A new white opaque paper first came into use in August 1958. It is slightly thicker than the paper previously used, but obviously different in colour (white, against cream) and opacity (the previous paper being *relatively* transparent).

175 Young Climber and Mts Aspiring and Everest

(Des J. Berry. Recess; vignette litho B.W.)
1954 (4 Oct). *Health Stamps. W 98. P 13½.*
737 175 1½d. + ½d. sepia and deep violet .. 15 30
738 2d. + 1d. sepia and blue-black .. 15 30

176 Maori Mail-carrier   177 Queen Elizabeth II

178 Douglas DC-3 Airliner

(Des R. M. Conly (2d.), J. Berry (3d.), A. G. Mitchell (4d.). Recess D.L.R.)
1955 (18 July). *Centenary of First New Zealand Postage Stamps. W 98. P 14 (2d.), 14 × 14½ (3d.) or 13 (4d.).*
739 176 2d. sepia and deep green 10 10
    w. Wmk inverted .. .. — £100
740 177 3d. brown-red 10 10
741 178 4d. black and bright blue 35 80
739/41 .. .. .. *Set of 3* 50 85

179 Children's Health Camps Federation Emblem   180

(Des E. M. Taylor. Recess B.W.)
1955 (3 Oct). *Health Stamps. W 98 (sideways). P 13½ × 13.*
742 179 1½d. + ½d. sepia and orange-brown .. 10 40
743 2d. + 1d. red-brown and green .. 10 20
744 3d. + 1d. sepia and deep rose-red .. 15 10
    a. Centre omitted
742/4 .. .. .. *Set of 3* 30 65

1955–59. *As Nos. 724/30 but larger figures of value with stars omitted from lower right corner and new colour (8d.).*
745 180 1d. orange (12.7.56) 50 10
    aw. Wmk inverted .. .. 1·25 1·00
    b. White opaque paper (2.6.59) .. 50 10
    bw. Wmk inverted 80 80
746 1½d. brown-lake (1.12.55) .. 60 60
747 2d. bluish green (19.3.56) .. 40 10
    a. White opaque paper (10.11.59) .. 55 10

748	180	3d. vermilion (1.5.56)	..	..	1·50	75
		aw. Wmk inverted ..	..	..	1·50	90
		b. White opaque paper (20.6.59)		..	75	10
		bw. Wmk inverted ..	..	..	1·75	1·25
749		4d. blue (3.2.58)	..	..	1·50	70
		a. White opaque paper (9.9.59)		..	2·00	70
750		6d. purple (20.10.55)	..	..	9·50	10
751		8d. chestnut (white opaque paper)				
		(1.12.59)	..	..	6·50	8·00
745/51				Set of 7	18·00	8·50

See note re white opaque paper after No. 736.

181 "The Whalers of Foveaux Strait"   183 Takahe

(Des E. R. Leeming (2d.), L. C. Mitchell (3d.), M. R. Smith (8d.). Recess D.L.R.)

1956 (16 Jan). *Southland Centennial. T 181, 183 and similar design. W 98. P 13½ × 13 (8d.) or 13 × 12½ (others).*

752		2d. deep blue-green	..	..	30	15
753		3d. sepia	..	..	10	10
		w. Wmk inverted ..	..	..	—	80·00
754		8d. slate-violet and rose-red	..		1·25	1·75
752/4				Set of 3	1·50	1·75

Design: *Horiz—3d. "Farming".*

184 Children picking Apples

(Des L. C. Mitchell, after photo by J. F. Louden. Recess B.W.)

1956 (24 Sept). *Health Stamps. W 98. P 13 × 13½.*

755	184	1½d. + ½d. purple-brown	..	..	15	60
		a. Blackish brown	..	..	1·25	6·50
756		2d. + 1d. blue-green ..	..	..	15	50
757		3d. + 1d. claret	..	..	15	15
755/7 ..				Set of 3	40	1·10

185 New Zealand Lamb   186 Lamb, *Dunedin* and
and Map   *Port Brisbane* (refrigerated
    freighter)

(Des M. Goaman. Photo Harrison)

1957 (15 Feb). *75th Anniv of First Export of N.Z. Lamb. W 98 (sideways inverted on 4d.). P 14 × 14½ (4d.) or 14½ × 14 (8d.).*

758	185	4d. blue	..	..	50	1·00
		w. Wmk sideways	..	..	8·00	13·00
759	186	8d. deep orange-red	..	..	75	1·25

187 Sir Truby King

(Des M. R. Smith. Recess B.W.)

1957 (14 May). *50th Anniv of Plunket Society. W 98. P 13.*

760	187	3d. bright carmine-red	..	..	10	10
		w. Wmk inverted	..	..	75·00	

188 Life-savers in Action   189 Children on Seashore

(Des L. Cutten (2d.), L. C. Mitchell (3d.). Recess Waterlow)

1957 (25 Sept). *Health Stamps. W 98 (sideways). P 13½.*

761	188	2d. + 1d. black and emerald	..	15	60
762	189	3d. + 1d. ultramarine and rose-red	..	15	15
MS762b		Two sheets each 112 × 96 mm with Nos.			
		761 and 762 in blocks of 6 (2 × 3) ..	Per pair	9·00	23·00
MS762c		As last but with wmk upright	Per pair	13·00	40·00

2d
●
(190)

191 Girls' Life Brigade   192 Boys' Brigade
Cadet   Bugler

1958 (6 Jan–Mar). *No. 746 surch as T 190.*

763	180	2d. on 1½d. brown-lake	..	..	70	10
		a. Smaller dot in surch	..	..	15	10
		b. Error. Surch on No. 725 (3.58)		£110	£160

Diameter of dot on No. 763 is 4¼ mm; on No. 763a 3¾ mm.
Forgeries of No. 763b are known.

(Des J. Berry. Photo Harrison)

1958 (20 Aug). *Health Stamps. W 98. P 14 × 14½.*

764	191	2d. + 1d. green	..	..	20	40
765	192	3d. + 1d. blue	..	..	20	40
MS765a		Two sheets each 104 × 124 mm with Nos.			
		764/5 in blocks of 6 (3 × 2).	Per pair	11·00	15·00

193 Sir Charles   194 Seal of Nelson
Kingsford-Smith and
Fokker F.VIIa/3m
Southern Cross

(Des J. E. Lyle. Eng F. D. Manley. Recess Commonwealth Bank of Australia Note Ptg Branch)

1958 (27 Aug). *30th Anniv of First Air Crossing of the Tasman Sea. W 98 (sideways). P 14 × 14½.*

766	193	6d. deep ultramarine	..	..	50	65

(Des M. J. Macdonald. Recess B.W.)

1958 (29 Sept). *Centenary of City of Nelson. W 98. P 13½ × 13.*

767	194	3d. carmine	..	..	10	10

195 "Pania"   196 Australian Gannets on
Statue, Napier   Cape Kidnappers

(Des M. R. Smith (2d.), J. Berry (3d.), L. C. Mitchell (8d.). Photo Harrison)

1958 (3 Nov). *Centenary of Hawke's Bay Province. T 195/6 and similar design. W 98 (sideways on 3d.). P 14½ × 14 (3d.) or 13½ × 14½ (others).*

768		2d. yellow-green	..	..	10	10
769		3d. blue	..	..	20	10
770		8d. red-brown	..	..	55	1·50
768/70 ..				Set of 3	75	1·50

Design:—*Vert 8d. Maori sheep-shearer.*

197 "Kiwi" Jamboree   198 Careening H.M.S.
Badge   *Endeavour* at Ship Cove

(Des Mrs. S. M. Collins. Recess B.W.)

1959 (5 Jan). *Pan-Pacific Scout Jamboree, Auckland. W 98. P 13½ × 13.*

771	197	3d. sepia and carmine	..	..	30	10

(Des G. R. Bull and G. R. Smith. Photo Harrison)

1959 (2 Mar). *Centenary of Marlborough Province. T 198 and similar horiz designs. W 98 (sideways). P 14½ × 14.*

772		2d. green	..	..	30	10
773		3d. deep blue	..	..	30	10
774		8d. light brown	..	..	1·00	2·25
772/4 ..				Set of 3	1·40	2·25

Designs:—*3d. Shipping wool, Wairau Bar, 1857; 8d. Salt industry. Grassmere.*

---

201 Red Cross Flag

(Photo Harrison)

1959 (3 June). *Red Cross Commemoration. W 98 (sideways). P 14½ × 14.*

775	201	3d. + 1d. red and ultramarine ..	..	20	10
		a. Red Cross omitted ..	..	..	£1100	

202 Grey Teal   203 New Zealand
    Stilt

(Des Display Section, G.P.O. Photo Harrison)

1959 (16 Sept). *Health Stamps. W 98 (sideways). P 14 × 14½.*

776	202	2d. + 1d. greenish yellow, ol & rose-red	40	65
777	203	3d. + 1d. black, pink and light blue ..	40	65
		a. Pink omitted ..	..	£100	
		bw. Wmk sideways inverted ..	..	16·00	16·00
MS777c		Two sheets, each 95×109 mm. with Nos.		
		776/7 in blocks of 6 (3×2) ..	Per pair	7·50	20·00

204 "The Explorer"   205 "The Gold Digger"

(Des G. R. Bull and G. R. Smith. Photo Harrison)

1960 (16 May). *Centenary of Westland Province. T 204/5 and similar vert design. W 98. P 14 × 14½.*

778		2d. deep dull green	..	..	20	10
779		3d. orange-red	..	..	20	10
780		8d. grey-black	..	..	1·10	3·00
778/80				Set of 3	1·40	3·00

Design:—*8d. "The Pioneer Woman".*

207 Manuka   214 National Flag   216 Rainbow
(Tea Tree)   Trout

219 Taniwha   220 Butter Making
(Maori Rock Drawing)

221 Tongariro National Park   221a Tongariro National Park
and Château   and Château

(Des Harrison (½d.), G. F. Fuller (1d., 3d., 6d.), A. G. Mitchell (2d., 4d., 5d., 8d., 3s., 10s., £1), P.O. Public Relations Division (7d.), P.O. Publicity Section (9d.), J. Berry (1s., 1s. 6d.), R. E. Barwick (1s. 3d.), J. C. Boyd (1s. 9d.), D. F. Kee (2s.), L. C. Mitchell (2s. 6d., 5s.). Photo D.L.R. (½d., 1d., 2d., 3d., 4d., 6d., 8d.) or Harrison (others))

1960 (11 July)–66. T 207, 214, 216, 219/21a and similar designs. Chalk-surfaced paper (2½d., 5d., 7d., 1s. 9d. (No. 795), 3s. (No. 799). W 98 (sideways on 5d., 1s. 3d., 1s. 6d., 2s. 6d., 3s. and 10s. or sideways inverted (2½d.)). P 14×14½ (1s. 3d., 1s. 6d., 2s., 5s., £1) or 14½×14 (others).

781	207	½d. grey, green and cerise (1.9.60)	10	10
		a. Grey omitted	90·00	
		b. Green omitted	£150	
782	–	1d. orge, green, lake & brn (1.9.60)	10	10
		a. Orange omitted	£225	
		b. Coil. Perf 14½×13. Wmk sideways (11.63)	1·25	2·50
		c. Chalk-surfaced paper (1965?)	10	75
783	–	2d. carmine, black, yellow & green	10	10
		a. Black omitted	£225	
		b. Yellow omitted	£275	
784	–	2½d. red, yellow, blk & grn (1.11.61)	90	10
		a. Red omitted	£375	
		b. Yellow omitted	£120	
		c. Green omitted	£150	
		d. Red and green omitted	£475	
		w. Wmk sideways	–	40·00
785	–	3d. yellow, green, yellow-brown and deep greenish blue (1.9.60)	30	10
		a. Yellow omitted	£110	
		b. Green omitted	£130	
		c. Yellow-brown omitted	£110	
		e. Coil. Perf 14½×13. Wmk sideways (3.10.63)	1·25	2·25
		f. Chalk-surfaced paper (1965?)	30	90
786	–	4d. purple, buff, yellow-green & lt bl	40	10
		a. Purple omitted	£200	
		b. Buff omitted	£275	
		d. Chalk-surfaced paper (1965?)	£550	10·00
787	–	5d. yell, dp grn, blk & vio (14.5.62)	1·25	10
		a. Yellow omitted	£190	
		w. Wmk sideways inverted	–	45·00
788	–	6d. lilac, green and deep bluish green (1.9.60)	60	10
		a. No wmk	30·00	
		ab. Lilac omitted	£200	
		ac. Green omitted	£180	
		c. Chalk-surfaced paper (1966?)	65	2·50
788d	–	7d. red, green, yellow and pale red (16.3.66)	45	1·25
		dw. Wmk inverted	3·50	4·50
789	–	8d. rose-red, yellow, green and grey (1.9.60)	40	10
790	214	9d. red and ultramarine (1.9.60)	40	10
		a. Red omitted	£275	
791	–	1s. brown and deep green	30	10
792	216	1s. 3d. carmine, sepia & bright blue	3·25	50
		a. Carmine omitted	£350	
		b. Carmine, sepia and greyish blue	1·50	20
		w. Wmk sideways inverted	£200	£110
793	–	1s. 6d. olive-green & orange-brown	1·00	10
794	–	1s. 9d. bistre-brown	16·00	15
795	–	1s. 9d. orange-red, blue, green and yellow (4.11.63)	8·50	1·00
		a. Wmk sideways	£375	
		w. Wmk inverted	£500	
796	219	2s. black and orange-buff	3·50	10
		a. Chalk-surfaced paper (1966)	2·50	2·50
797	220	2s. 6d. yellow and light brown	1·75	95
		a. Yellow omitted	£400	
798	221	3s. blackish brown	32·00	75
799	221a	3s. bistre, blue and green (1.4.64)	6·50	1·75
		w. Wmk sideways inverted	28·00	30·00
800	–	5s. blackish green	5·50	80
		a. Chalk-surfaced paper (1966)	2·25	4·75
801	–	10s. steel-blue	9·00	3·25
		a. Chalk-surfaced paper (1966)	5·00	11·00
802	–	£1 deep magenta	14·00	6·00
781/802		Set of 23	80·00	14·00

Designs: Vert (as T 207)—1d. Karaka; 2d. Kowhai Ngutu–kaka (Kaka Beak); 2½d. Titoki; 3d. Kowhai; 4d. Puarangi (Hibiscus); 5d. Matua Tikumu (Mountain Daisy); 6d. Pikiarero (Clematis); 7d. Koromiko; 8d. Rata. (As T 216)—1s. 6d. Tiki. (As T 219)—5s. Sutherland Falls; £1 Pohutu Geyser. Horiz (as T 214)—1s. Timber industry—1s. 9d. Aerial top dressing. (As T 221)—10s. Tasman Glacier.

Nos. 782b and 785e were replaced by coils with upright watermark perf 14½×14 in 1966.

CHALKY PAPER. The chalk-surfaced paper is not only whiter but also thicker, making the watermark difficult to see. Examples of the 4d. value can be found on a thick surfaced paper. These should not be confused with the rare chalk-surfaced printing, No. 786d, which can be identified by its positive reaction to the silver test.

225 Sacred Kingfisher

226 New Zealand Pigeon

(Des Display Section, G.P.O. Recess B.W.)

1960 (10 Aug). Health Stamps. W 98. P 13½.

803	225	2d. + 1d. sepia and turquoise-blue	90	65
804	226	3d. + 1d. deep purple-brown and orange	90	65
MS804b		Two sheets each 95 × 107 mm with Nos. 803 and 804 in blocks of 6. P 11½ × 11 Per pair	30·00	35·00

227 "The Adoration of the Shepherds" (Rembrandt)

(Photo Harrison)

1960 (1 Nov). Christmas. W 98. P 12.

805	227	2d. red and deep brown/cream	15	10
		a. Red omitted	£225	

228 Great Egret

229 New Zealand Falcon

(Des Display Section, G.P.O. Recess B.W.)

1961 (2 Aug). Health Stamps. W 98. P 13½.

806	228	2d. + 1d. black and purple	65	65
807	229	3d. + 1d. deep sepia and yellow-green	65	65
MS807a		Two sheets each 97 × 121 mm with Nos. 806/7 in blocks of 6 (3 × 2) Per pair	25·00	27·00

2½d (230)   2½d (231)

≡ (230)   ≡ (231)

232 "Adoration of the Magi" (Dürer)

1961 (1 Sept). No. 748 surch with T 230 (wide setting).

808	180	2½d. on 3d. vermilion	15	15
		a. Narrow setting (T 231)	15	15
		b. Pair, wide and narrow	16·00	26·00

The difference in the settings is in the overall width of the new value, caused by two different spacings between the "2", "½" and "d".

(Photo Harrison)

1961 (16 Oct). Christmas. W 98 (sideways). P 14½×14.

809	232	2½d. multicoloured	10	10
		w. Wmk sideways inverted	45·00	14·00

233 Morse Key and Port Hills, Lyttleton

(Des A. G. Mitchell (3d.) and L. C. Mitchell (8d.). Photo Harrison)

1962 (1 June). Telegraph Centenary. T 233 and similar horiz design. W 98 (sideways). P 14½ × 14.

810		3d. sepia and bluish green	10	10
		a. Bluish green omitted	£600	
811		8d. black and brown-red	90	55
		a. Imperf (pair)	£1000	
		b. Black omitted	£500	

Design:—8d. Modern teleprinter.

No. 811a comes from a sheet with the two top rows imperforate and the third row imperforate on three sides.

235 Red-fronted Parakeet

236 Tieke Saddleback

(Des Display Section, G.P.O. Photo D.L.R.)

1962 (3 Oct). Health Stamps. W 98. P 15×14.

812	235	2½d. + 1d. multicoloured	50	65
		a. Orange omitted	£300	
		b. Printed on the gummed side	£300	
		w. Wmk inverted	48·00	65·00
813	236	3d. + 1d. multicoloured	50	65
		a. Orange omitted	£1300	
MS813b		Two sheets, each 96×101 mm with Nos. 812/13 in blocks of 6 (3×2) Per pair	45·00	50·00

No. 812b comes from a miniature sheet.

237 "Madonna in Prayer" (Sassoferrato)

(Photo Harrison)

1962 (15 Oct). Christmas. W 98. P 14½ × 14.

814	237	2½d. multicoloured	10	10

238   Prince Andrew   239

(Design after photographs by Studio Lisa, London. Recess D.L.R.)

1963 (7 Aug). Health Stamps. W 98. P 14.

815	238	2½d. + 1d. dull ultramarine	30	70
		a. Ultramarine	40	80
		b. Deep blue	30	80
816	239	3d. + 1d. carmine	30	10
MS816a		Two sheets each 93×100 mm with Nos. 815/16 in blocks of 6 (3 × 2) Per pair	26·00	32·00

240 "The Holy Family" (Titian)

(Photo Harrison)

1963 (14 Oct). Christmas. W 98 (sideways). P 12½.

817	240	2½d. multicoloured	10	10
		a. Imperf (pair)	£200	
		b. Yellow omitted	£250	
		w. Wmk sideways inverted	40	40

241 Steam Locomotive Pilgrim (1863) and Class DG Diesel Locomotive   242 Diesel Express and Mt Ruapehu

(Des Commercial Art Section, N.Z. Railways. Photo D.L.R.)

1963 (25 Nov). Railway Centenary. W 98 (sideways). P 14.

818	241	3d. multicoloured	40	10
		a. Blue (sky) omitted	£275	
819	242	1s. 9d. multicoloured	2·25	1·50
		a. Red (value) omitted	£1100	

243 "Commonwealth Cable"

(Des P. Morriss. Photo Note Printing Branch, Reserve Bank of Australia)

1963 (3 Dec). Opening of COMPAC (Trans-Pacific Telephone Cable). No wmk. P 13½.

820	243	8d. red, blue and yellow	50	1·25

244 Road Map and Car Steering-wheel   245 Silver Gulls

(Des L. C. Mitchell. Photo Harrison)

1964 (1 May). *Road Safety Campaign.* W 98. P 15 × 14.
821 244 3d. black, ochre-yellow and blue   30   10

(Des Display Section G.P.O., after Miss T. Kelly. Photo Harrison)

1964 (5 Aug). *Health Stamps.* T 245 *and similar horiz design. Multicoloured.* W 98. P 14½.
822 2½d. + 1d. Type 245   40   50
   a. Red (beak and legs) omitted   £160
   w. Wmk inverted   † £225
823 3d. + 1d. Little Penguin   40   50
   aw. Wmk inverted   £100
MS823b Two sheets each 171×84 mm with Nos
  822/3 in blocks of 8 (4×2)   *Per pair* 48·00 55·00
   bw. Wmk inverted (No. 823 only)

246 Rev. S. Marsden taking first Christian service at Rangihoua Bay, 1814

7D

POSTAGE

(247)

(Des L. C. Mitchell. Photo Harrison)

1964 (12 Oct). *Christmas.* W 98 (*sideways*). P 14 × 13½.
824 246 2½d. multicoloured   10   10

1964 (14 Dec). *As Type F 6, but without value, surch with T 247.* W 98. *Unsurfaced paper.* P 14 × 13½.
825 F 6 7d. carmine-red   70 1·25

248 Anzac Cove

(Des R. M. Conly. Photo Harrison)

1965 (14 Apr). *50th Anniv of Gallipoli Landing.* T 248 *and similar horiz design.* W 98. P 12½.
826 4d. yellow-brown   10   10
827 5d. green and red   10   60
   Design:—5d. Anzac Cove and poppy.

249 I.T.U. Emblem and Symbols   250 Sir Winston Churchill

(Photo Harrison)

1965 (17 May). *I.T.U. Centenary.* W 98. P 14½×14.
828 249 9d. blue and pale chocolate   55   35

(Des P. Morriss from photograph by Karsh. Photo Note Ptg Branch, Reserve Bank of Australia)

1965 (24 May). *Churchill Commemoration.* P 13½.
829 250 7d. black, pale grey and light blue   30   50

251 Wellington Provincial Council Building

(Des from painting by L. B. Temple (1867). Photo Harrison)

1965 (26 July). *Centenary of Government in Wellington.* W 98 (*sideways*). P 14½ × 14.
830 251 4d. multicoloured   20   10

252 Kaka   253 Collared Grey Fantail (after Miss T. Kelly)

(Des Display Section, G.P.O. Photo Harrison)

1965 (4 Aug). *Health Stamps.* W 98. P 14×14½.
831 252 3d. + 1d. multicoloured   40   50
   w. Wmk inverted
832 253 4d. + 1d. multicoloured   40   50
   a. Green ("POSTAGE HEALTH" and on leaves) omitted   £325
MS832b Two sheets each 100×109 mm with Nos.
  831/2 in blocks of 6 (3×2)   *Per pair* 42·00 50·00
   bw. Wmk inverted (No. 831 only)

254 I.C.Y. Emblem   255 "The Two Trinities" (Murillo)

(Litho D.L.R.)

1965 (28 Sept). *International Co-operation Year.* W 98 (*sideways*). P 14.
833 254 4d. carmine-red and light yellow-olive   20   10
   w. Wmk sideways inverted   4·25 1·75

(Photo Harrison)

1965 (11 Oct). *Christmas.* W 98. P 13½ × 14.
834 255 3d. multicoloured   10   10
   a. Gold (frame) omitted   £600

256 Arms of New Zealand   259 "Progress" Arrowhead

(Des Display Section, G.P.O. Photo D.L.R.)

1965 (30 Nov). *11th Commonwealth Parliamentary Conference.* T 256 *and similar horiz designs. Multicoloured.* P 14.
835 4d. Type 256   25   20
   a. Blue (incl value) omitted   £400
   b. Printed on the gummed side
836 9d. Parliament House, Wellington and Badge   65 1·25
837 2s. Wellington from Mt Victoria   4·50 6·00
   a. Carmine omitted   £375
835/7   *Set of 3* 4·75 6·75

(Des Display Section, G.P.O. Photo Harrison)

1966 (5 Jan). *Fourth National Scout Jamboree, Trentham.* W 98. P 14 × 15.
838 259 4d. gold and myrtle-green   15   10
   a. Gold (arrowhead) omitted   £475

260 New Zealand Bell Bird   262 "The Virgin with Child" (Maratta)

(Des Display Section, G.P.O. Photo Harrison)

1966 (3 Aug). *Health Stamps.* T 260 *and similar vert design. Multicoloured.* W 98 (*sideways*). P 14×14½.
839 3d. + 1d. Type 260   40   65
   w. Wmk sideways inverted   80·00
840 4d. + 1d. Weka Rail   40   65
   a. Deep brown (values and date) omitted   £1100
   w. Wmk sideways inverted   50·00
MS841 Two sheets, each 107×91 mm. Nos.
  839/40 in blocks of 6 (3×2)   *Per pair* 20·00 45·00
   In No. 840a besides the value, "1966" and "Weka" are also omitted and the bird, etc. appears as light brown.

(Photo Harrison)

1966 (3 Oct). *Christmas.* W 98 (*sideways*). P 14½.
842 262 3d. multicoloured   10   10
   a. Red omitted   £150

263 Queen Victoria and Queen Elizabeth II   264 Half-sovereign of 1867 and Commemorative Dollar Coin

(Des Display Section, G.P.O. Photo Harrison)

1967 (3 Feb). *Centenary of New Zealand Post Office Savings Bank.* W 98 (*sideways on 4d.*). P 14 × 14½.
843 263 4d. black, gold and maroon   10   10
   w. Wmk sideways inverted   50·00 16·00
844 264 9d. gold, silver, black, lt blue & dp grn   10   20
   w. Wmk inverted

(New Currency. 100 cents = 1 New Zealand Dollar)

265 Manuka (Tea Tree)   266 Pohutu Geyser

1967 (10 July). *Decimal Currency. Designs as 1960–66 issue, but with values inscr in decimal currency as T 265/6. Chalky paper.* W 98 (*sideways on 8 c., 10 c., 20 c., 50 c. and $2*). P 13½×14 (½ c. to 3 c., 5 c. and 7 c.), 14½×14 (4 c., 6 c., 8 c., 10 c., 25 c. and $1) *or* 14×14½ (15 c., 20 c., 50 c. and $2).
845 265 ½ c. pale blue, yellow-green & cerise   10   10
846 — 1 c. yellow, carmine, green and light brown (as 1d.)   10   10
   a. Booklet pane. Five stamps plus one printed label   2·25
847 — 2 c. carmine, black, yellow, and green (as 2d.)   10   10
848 — 2½ c. yellow, green, yellow-brown, and deep bluish green (as 3d.)   10   10
   a. Deep bluish green omitted*   £650
   b. Imperf (pair)†   £100
849 — 3 c. purple, buff, yellow-green and light greenish blue (as 4d.)   10   10
850 — 4 c. yellow, deep green, black and violet (as 5d.)   30   10
851 — 5 c. lilac, yellow-olive and bluish green (as 6d.)   65   10
852 — 6 c. red, green, yell & lt pink (as 7d.)   70   30
853 — 7 c. rose-red, yell, grn & grey (as 8d.)   85   30
   w. Wmk inverted
854 214 8 c. red and ultramarine   85   10
   a. Red omitted   £350
855 — 10 c. brown and deep green (as 1s.)   90   10
   w. Wmk sideways inverted
856 — 15 c. olive-grn & orge-brn (as 1s. 6d.)   1·50   90
   w. Wmk inverted   4·50 7·50
857 219 20 c. black and buff   2·50   10
858 220 25 c. yellow and light brown   2·50 1·75
859 221a 30 c. olive-yellow, green & greenish bl   2·50   25
   w. Wmk inverted   90·00 45·00
860 — 50 c. blackish green (as 5s.)   2·75   75
861 — $1 Prussian blue (as 10s.)   10·00 1·25
   w. Wmk inverted   £170 £100
862 266 $2 deep magenta   6·00 9·00
845/62   *Set of 18* 28·00 13·50

*This occurred on one horizontal row of ten, affecting the background colour so that the value is also missing. In the row above and the row below, the colour was partially omitted. The price is for a vertical strip.
   The 2½ c. value has been seen with the yellow omitted, but only on a used example.
†This comes from a sheet of which the six right-hand vertical rows were completely imperforate and the top, bottom and left-hand margins had been removed.
   The 4 c., 30 c. and 50 c. exist with PVA gum as well as gum arabic. No. 859a exists with PVA gum only.
   For $4 to $10 in the "Arms" type, see under Postage Fiscal stamps.
   For other versions of 15 c., 30 c., and $2 see Nos. 870/9.

268 Running with Ball

(Des L. C. Mitchell. Photo Harrison)

1967 (2 Aug). *Health Stamps. Rugby Football.* T **268** *and similar multicoloured design.* W **98** *(sideways on* 2½ c.*).* P 14½ × 14 (2½ c.) *or* 14 × 14½ (3 c.).
867   2½ c. + 1 c. Type **268**   15   15
868   3 c. + 1 c. Positioning for a place-kick (*horiz*)   15   15
MS869 Two sheets; (*a*) 76 × 130 mm (867); (*b*) 130 × 76 mm (868). Containing blocks of six .. .. *Per pair* 23·00 38·00

270 *Kaita* (trawler) and Catch   **271** Brown Trout

276 Dairy Farm, Mt Egmont and Butter Consignment   **277** Fox Glacier, Westland National Park

(Des Display Section, G.P.O. (7, 8, 10, 18, 20, 25 c. and 28 c. from photo), R. M. Conly (7½ c.). Litho B.W. (7, 8, 18, 20 c.) or photo D.L.R. (7½ c.) and Harrison (10, 25, 28 c.). Others (15 c., 30 c., $2) as before)

1967–70. T **270/1, 276/7** *and similar designs. Chalky paper* (except 7, 8, 18, 20 c.). *No wmk* (7, 8, 20, 30 c.) *or* W **98** (*sideways inverted on* 7½ c., *sideways on* 10, 15, 25 c., *upright on* 18, 28 c., $2). P 13½ (7, 7½ c.), 13×13½ (8, 18, 20 c.), 14½×14 (10, 25, 30 c.) *or* 14×14½ (15, 28 c., $2).
870   **270**   7 c. multicoloured (3.12.69) ..   1·50   90
871   **271**   7½ c. multicoloured* (29.8.67) ..   45   70
        a. Wmk upright (10.68) ..   50   90
872   —   8 c. multicoloured (8.7.69) ..   75   70
873   —   10 c. multicoloured (2.4.68) ..   50   10
        a. Green (background) omitted ..   £400
        w. Wmk sideways inverted ..   †   —
874   —   15 c. apple-green, myrtle-green and carm (as No. 856†) (19.3.68)   1·00   90
        w. Wmk sideways inverted ..   †   —
875   —   18 c. multicoloured (8.7.69) ..   1·00   55
        a. Printed on the gummed side ..   —
876   —   20 c. multicoloured (8.7.69) ..   1·00   20
877   **276**   25 c. multicoloured (10.12.68) ..   2·50   2·00
878   **277**   28 c. multicoloured (30.7.68) ..   60   10
        aw. Wmk inverted ..   †   —
878*b* **221***a*   30 c. olive-green, green & greenish blue (as No. 859) (2.6.70) ..   2·75   3·75
879   **266** $2 black, ochre and pale blue (as No. 862) (10.12.68) ..   18·00 15·00
870/9   .. .. *Set of* 11 26·00 22·00
Designs: *Horiz*—8 c. Apples and orchard; 10 c. Forest and timber; 18 c. Sheep and the "Woolmark"; 20 c. Consignments of beef and herd of cattle.
*No. 871 was originally issued to commemorate the introduction of the brown trout into New Zealand.
† No. 874 is slightly larger than No. 856, measuring 21 × 25 mm and the inscriptions and numerals differ in size.

278 "The Adoration of the Shepherds" (Poussin)   **279** Mount Aspiring, Aurora Australis and Southern Cross   **280** Sir James Hector (founder)

(Photo Harrison)

1967 (3 Oct). *Christmas.* W **98** (*sideways*). P 13½ × 14.
880   **278**   2½ c. multicoloured   10   10

(Des J. Berry. Litho D.L.R.)

1967 (10 Oct). *Centenary of the Royal Society of New Zealand.* W **98** (*sideways on* 4 c.). P 14 (4 c) *or* 13 × 14 (8 c.).
881   **279**   4 c. multicoloured   25   20
        w. Wmk sideways inverted ..   7·50   7·00
882   **280**   8 c. multicoloured   25   80

281 Open Bible   **282** Soldiers and Tank

(Des Display Section, G.P.O. Litho D.L.R.)

1968 (23 Apr). *Centenary of Maori Bible.* W **98**. P 13½.
883   **281**   3 c. multicoloured   10   10
        a. Gold (inscr etc.) omitted ..   £140
        w. Wmk inverted .. .. ..   27·00

(Des L. C. Mitchell. Litho D.L.R.)

1968 (7 May). *New Zealand Armed Forces.* T **282** *and similar horiz designs. Multicoloured.* W **98** (*sideways*). P 14 × 13½.
884   4 c. Type **282**   30   15
        w. Wmk sideways inverted ..   9·00 11·00
885   10 c. Airmen, Fairey Firefly and English Electric Canberra aircraft ..   50   70
886   28 c. Sailors and H.M.N.Z.S. *Achilles*, 1939, and H.M.N.Z.S. *Waikato*, 1968 ..   70   2·50
        w. Wmk sideways inverted ..   5·00   7·50
884/6   .. .. *Set of* 3   1·40   3·00

285 Boy breasting Tape, and Olympic Rings   **287** Placing Votes in Ballot Box

(Des L. C. Mitchell. Photo Harrison)

1968 (7 Aug). *Health Stamps.* T **285** *and similar horiz design. Multicoloured.* P 14½ × 14.
887   2½ c. + 1 c. Type **285**   20   15
888   3 c. + 1 c. Girl swimming and Olympic rings   20   15
        a. Red (ring) omitted ..   £900
        b. Blue (ring) omitted ..   £475
MS889 Two sheets each 145×95 mm. Nos. 887/8 in blocks of six .. .. *Per pair* 16·00 40·00
No. 888*a* occurred in one miniature sheet. Six examples are known, one being used. No. 888*b* occurred from a second miniature sheet.

(Des J. Berry. Photo Japanese Govt Ptg Bureau, Tokyo)

1968 (19 Sept). *75th Anniv of Universal Suffrage in New Zealand.* P 13.
890   **287**   3 c. ochre, olive-green and light blue ..   10   10

288 Human Rights Emblem   **289** "Adoration of the Holy Child" (G. van Honthorst)

(Photo Japanese Govt Ptg Bureau, Tokyo)

1968 (19 Sept). *Human Rights Year.* P 13.
891   **288**   10 c. scarlet, yellow and deep green ..   10   30

(Photo Harrison)

1968 (1 Oct). *Christmas.* W **98** (*sideways*). P 14 × 14½.
892   **289**   2½ c. multicoloured   10   10

290 I.L.O. Emblem

(Photo Harrison)

1969 (11 Feb). *50th Anniv of International Labour Organization.* W **98** (*sideways*). P 14½ × 14.
893   **290**   7 c. black and carmine-red ..   15   30

---

291 Supreme Court Building, Auckland   **292** Law Society's Coat of Arms

(Des R. M. Conly. Litho B.W.)

1969 (8 Apr). *Centenary of New Zealand Law Society.* T **291/2** *and similar design.* P 13½ × 13 (3 c.) *or* 13 × 13½ (others).
894   3 c. multicoloured (*shades*) ..   10   10
895   10 c. multicoloured   35   60
896   18 c. multicoloured (*shades*) ..   45   1·25
894/6   .. .. *Set of* 3   80   1·75
Design:—*Vert*—18 c. "Justice" (from Memorial Window in University of Canterbury, Christchurch).

295 Student being conferred with Degree

(Des R. M. Conly. Litho B.W.)

1969 (3 June). *Centenary of Otago University* T **295** *and similar multicoloured design.* P 13 × 13½ (3 c.) *or* 13½ × 13 (10 c.).
897   3 c. Otago University (*vert*) ..   10   10
898   10 c. Type **295**   20   25

296 Boys playing Cricket   **298** Dr. Elizabeth Gunn (founder of First Children's Health Camp)

(Des R. M. Conly (4 c.); L. C. Mitchell (others). Litho B.W.)

1969 (6 Aug). *Health Stamps.* T **296** *and similar horiz design and* T **298**. P 12½ × 13 (No. 901) *or* 13 × 12½ (others).
899   2½ c. + 1 c. multicoloured ..   40   50
900   3 c. + 1 c. multicoloured ..   40   50
901   4 c. + 1 c. brown and ultramarine ..   40   2·00
899/901   .. .. .. *Set of* 3   1·10   2·75
MS902 Two sheets each 144 × 84 mm. Nos. 899/900 in blocks of six .. *Per pair* 20·00 48·00
Design:—3 c. Girls playing cricket.

299 Oldest existing House in New Zealand, and Old Stone Mission Store, Kerikeri

(Litho D.L.R.)

1969 (18 Aug). *Early European Settlement in New Zealand, and 150th Anniv of Kerikeri.* T **299** *and similar horiz design. Multicoloured.* W **98** (*sideways*). P 13 × 13½.
903   4 c. Type **299**   20   25
904   6 c. View of Bay of Islands ..   30   1·75

301 "The Nativity" (Federico Fiori (Barocci))   **302** Captain Cook, Transit of Venus and "Octant"

(Photo Harrison)

1969 (1 Oct). *Christmas.* W **98**. P 13×14.
905   **301**   2½ c. multicoloured   10   10
        a. No wmk   10   15

(Des Eileen Mayo. Photo; portraits embossed Harrison)

1969 (9 Oct). *Bicentenary of Captain Cook's Landing in New Zealand. T 302 and similar horiz designs.* P 14½×14.
906		4 c. black, cerise and blue		1·00	35
	a.	Imperf (pair)			
907		6 c. slate-green, purple-brown and black		1·25	2·75
908		18 c. purple-brown, slate-green and black		2·25	2·75
909		28 c. cerise, black and blue		3·25	4·75
906/9			Set of 4	7·00	9·50
MS910		109×90 mm. Nos. 906/9		18·00	35·00

Designs:—6 c. Sir Joseph Banks (naturalist) and outline of H.M.S. *Endeavour*; 18 c. Dr. Daniel Solander (botanist) and his plant; 28 c. Queen Elizabeth II and Cook's chart, 1769.

The miniature sheet exists additionally inscribed on the selvedge at bottom. "A SOUVENIR FROM NEW ZEALAND STAMP EXHIBITION, NEW PLYMOUTH 6TH—11TH OCTOBER. 1969". These were not sold from Post Offices.

306 Girl, Wheat Field and C.O.R.S.O. Emblem

307 Mother feeding her Child, Dairy Herd and C.O.R.S.O. Emblem

(Des L. C. Mitchell. Photo Japanese Govt Printing Bureau, Tokyo)

1969 (18 Nov). *25th Anniv of C.O.R.S.O. (Council of Organizations for Relief Services Overseas).* P 13.
911	306	7 c. multicoloured		70	1·40
912	307	8 c. multicoloured		70	1·40

308 "Cardigan Bay" (champion trotter)

(Des L. C. Mitchell. Photo Courvoisier)

1970 (28 Jan). *Return of "Cardigan Bay" to New Zealand.* P 11½.
913	308	10 c. multicoloured		30	30

309 Vanessa gonerilla (butterfly)

310 Queen Elizabeth II and New Zealand Coat of Arms

(Des Enid Hunter (½ c., 1 c., 2 c., 18 c., 20 c.), Eileen Mayo (2½ c. to 7 c.), D. B. Stevenson (7½ c., 8 c.), M. Cleverley (10 c., 15 c., 25 c., 30 c., $1, $2), M. V. Askew (23 c., 50 c.). Photo Harrison (½ c. to 20 c.), Enschedé (23 c., 50 c.), Courvoisier ($1, $2) or Litho B.W. (25 c., 30 c.))

1970 (12 Mar)–**76**. *Various designs at T 309/10.* W 98 (sideways on 10 c., or sideways inverted on 15 c., 20 c.) or No wmk (23 c. to $2).

(a) Size as T 309. P 13½×13
914	½ c. multicoloured (2.9.70)		10	20
	w. Wmk inverted		—	£110
915	1 c. multicoloured (2.9.70)		10	10
	aw. Wmk inverted		40·00	27·00
	b. Wmk sideways inverted (booklets) (6.7.71)		80	1·50
	ba. Booklet pane. No. 915b×3 with three se-tenant printed labels		2·25	
	c. Blue omitted (booklets)		£150	
916	2 c. multicoloured (2.9.70)		10	10
	a. Black (inscr, etc) omitted		£200	
	w. Wmk inverted		2·75	1·50
917	2½ c. multicoloured (2.9.70)		40	10
918	3 c. black, brown and orange (2.9.70)		15	10
	aw. Wmk inverted		2·50	2·75
	b. Wmk sideways inverted (booklets) (6.7.71)		55	1·25
	bw. Wmk sideways		24·00	24·00
919	4 c. multicoloured (2.9.70)		15	10
	aw. Wmk inverted		3·00	1·75
	b. Wmk sideways inverted (booklets) (6.7.71)		55	1·25
	bw. Wmk sideways		70·00	60·00
	c. Bright green (wing veins) omitted			
920	5 c. multicoloured (4.11.70)		45	10
	w. Wmk inverted		†	
921	6 c. blackish grn, yell-grn & carm (4.11.70)		45	20
922	7 c. multicoloured (4.11.70)		55	55
	w. Wmk inverted		—	50·00
923	7½ c. multicoloured (4.11.70)		1·00	1·50
	w. Wmk inverted			
924	8 c. multicoloured (4.11.70)		65	80

(b) Size as T 310. Various perfs
925	10 c. multicoloured (p 14½×14)		40	15
	w. Wmk sideways inverted		6·00	3·00
926	15 c. black, flesh & pale brown (p 13½×13) (20.1.71)		1·00	50
	a. Pale brown omitted		£250	
	w. Wmk sideways		38·00	30·00

927	18 c. chestnut, blk & apple-grn (p 13×13½) (20.1.71)		1·00	40
	w. Wmk inverted		38·00	30·00
928	20 c. black & yell-brn (p 13½×13) (20.1.71)		1·00	15
929	23 c. multicoloured (p 13½×12½) (1.12.71)		80	30
930	25 c. multicoloured (p 13×13½) (1.9.71)		1·00	40
	b. Perf 14 (11.76?)		70	40
	ba. Printed on the gummed side		£400	
931	30 c. multicoloured (p 13×13½) (1.9.71)		75	15
	a. Perf 14 (9.76?)		1·25	1·75
932	50 c. multicoloured (p 13½×12½) (1.9.71)		60	20
	a. Apple green (hill) omitted		28·00	
	b. Buff (shore) omitted		55·00	
933	$1 multicoloured (p 11½) (14.4.71)		1·75	1·00
934	$2 multicoloured (p 11½) (14.4.71)		2·75	1·50
914/34		Set of 21	13·00	7·25

Designs: *Vert*—½ c. *Lycaena salustius* (butterfly); 2 c. *Argyrophenga antipodum* (butterfly); 2½ c. *Nyctemera annulata* (moth); 3 c. *Detunda egregia* (moth); 4 c. *Charagia virescens* (moth); 5 c. Scarlet Wrasse ("Scarlet Parrot Fish"); 6 c. Big-bellied Sea Horses; 7 c. Leather-jacket (fish); 7½ c. Intermediate Halfbeak ("Garfish"); 8 c. John Dory (fish); 18 c. Maori club; 25 c. Hauraki Gulf Maritime Park; 30 c. Mt Cook National Park. *Horiz*—10 c. Type 310; 15 c. Maori fish hook; 20 c. Maori tattoo pattern; 23 c. Egmont National Park; 50 c. Abel Tasman National Park; $1 Geothermal Power; $2 Agricultural Technology.

Although issued as a definitive No. 925 was put on sale on the occasion of the Royal Visit to New Zealand.

See also Nos. 1008, etc.

311 Geyser Restaurant

312 U.N. H.Q. Building

(Des M. Cleverley. Photo Japanese Govt Printing Bureau, Tokyo)

1970 (8 Apr). *World Fair, Osaka. T 311 and similar horiz designs. Multicoloured.* P 13.
935	7 c. Type 311		40	1·00
936	8 c. New Zealand Pavilion		40	1·00
937	18 c. Bush Walk		60	1·00
935/7		Set of 3	1·25	2·75

(Des R. M. Conly (3 c.), L. C. Mitchell (10 c.). Litho D.L.R.)

1970 (24 June). *25th Anniv of United Nations. T 312 and similar vert design.* P 13½.
938	3 c. multicoloured		10	10
939	10 c. scarlet and yellow		20	20

Design:—10 c. Tractor on horizon.

313 Soccer

(Des L. C. Mitchell. Litho D.L.R.)

1970 (5 Aug). *Health Stamps. T 313 and similar multicoloured design.* P 13½.
940	2½ c. + 1 c. Netball (vert)		30	65
941	3 c. + 1 c. Type 313		30	65
MS942	Two sheets: (a) 102×125 mm (940); (b) 125×102 mm (941), containing blocks of six			
		Per pair	18·00	42·00

314 "The Virgin adoring the Child" (Correggio)

315 "The Holy Family" (stained glass window, Invercargill Presbyterian Church)

(Litho D.L.R.)

1970 (1 Oct). *Christmas. T 314/15 and similar design.* P 12½.
943	2½ c. multicoloured		10	10
944	3 c. multicoloured		10	10
	a. Green (inscr and value) omitted		£225	
945	10 c. black, orange and silver		30	75
943/5		Set of 3	35	75

Design: *Horiz*—10 c. Tower of Roman Catholic Church, Sockburn.

No. 943 exists as an imperforate proof with the country inscription and face value omitted.

316 Chatham Islands Lily

(Des Eileen Mayo. Photo Japanese Govt Printing Bureau, Tokyo)

1970 (2 Dec). *Chatham Islands. T 316 and similar horiz design. Multicoloured.* P 13.
946	1 c. Type 316		10	35
947	2 c. Shy Albatross		30	40

317 Country Women's Institute Emblem

(Des L. C. Mitchell. Photo Japanese Govt Ptg Bureau, Tokyo)

1971 (10 Feb). *50th Anniversaries of Country Women's Institutes and Rotary International in New Zealand. T 317 and similar horiz design. Multicoloured.* P 13.
948	4 c. Type 317		10	10
949	10 c. Rotary emblem and map of New Zealand		20	40

318 Rainbow II (yacht)

(Des J. Berry (5 c.), G. F. Fuller (8 c.). Litho B.W.)

1971 (3 Mar). *One Ton Cup Racing Trophy. T 318 and similar horiz design. Multicoloured.* P 13½ × 13.
950	5 c. Type 318		25	25
951	8 c. One Ton Cup		35	1·25

319 Civic Arms of Palmerston North

(Des R. M. Conly. Photo Japanese Govt Ptg Bureau, Tokyo)

1971 (12 May). *City Centenaries. T 319 and similar horiz designs. Multicoloured.* P 13.
952	3 c. Type 319		10	10
953	4 c. Arms of Auckland		10	10
954	5 c. Arms of Invercargill		15	90
952/4		Set of 3	30	1·00

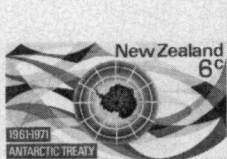

320 Antarctica on Globe

321 Child on Swing

(Des Eileen Mayo. Photo Japanese Govt Ptg Bureau, Tokyo)

1971 (9 June). *Tenth Anniv of Antarctic Treaty.* P 13.
955	320	6 c. multicoloured	1·00	1·00

(Des Eileen Mayo. Photo Japanese Govt Ptg Bureau, Tokyo)

1971 (9 June). *25th Anniv of U.N.I.C.E.F.* P 13.
956	321	7 c. multicoloured	50	70

4c 4c 4c

= = =

(322) (322a) (322b)

T 322. Photo, showing screening dots; thin bars, wide apart.
T 322a. Typo, without screening dots; thick bars, closer together.
T 322b. Typo; bars similar to T 322.

1971–73. *No. 917 surcharged.*

(a) In photogravure, by Harrison (23.6.71)*
957	322	4 c. on 2½ c. multicoloured	15	10

(b) Typographically, by Harrison (13.7.72*)

957a	322a	4 c. on 2½ c. multicoloured ..	45	10
		ab. Albino surch		£110
		ac. Surch double, one albino	15·00	
		ad. Pair, one without surch	..	£225

(c) Typographically, locally (18.6.73*)

957b	322b	4 c. on 2½ c. multicoloured ..	15	10

*Earliest known postmarks.

323 Satellite-tracking Aerial

(Des M. Cleverley. Photo Courvoisier)

1971 (14 July). *Opening of Satellite Earth Station. T 323 and similar horiz design. P 11½.*

958	8 c. black, drab-grey and vermilion ..	60	1·25
959	10 c. black, turquoise-grn & pale bluish vio ..	65	1·00

Design:—10 c. Satellite.

324 Girls playing Hockey

(Des L. C. Mitchell. Litho Harrison)

1971 (4 Aug). *Health Stamps. T 324 and similar horiz designs. Multicoloured. W 98 (sideways on 5 c.). P 13½ × 13.*

960	3 c. + 1 c. Type 324	45	50
961	4 c. + 1 c. Boys playing hockey	45	50
962	5 c. + 1 c. Dental Health	1·10	2·00
960/2	*Set of 3*	1·75	2·75

MS963 Two sheets, each 122×96 mm. Nos. 960/1 in blocks of six .. .. *Per pair* 19·00 42·00

325 "Madonna bending over the Crib" (Maratta)   **326** "Tiffany" Rose

(Des Enid Hunter (10 c.), D. A. Hatcher (others). Photo Harrison)

1971 (6 Oct). *Christmas. T 325 and similar vert designs. Multicoloured. P 13 × 13½.*

964	3 c. Type 325	10	10
965	4 c. "The Annunciation" (stained-glass window) (21½ × 38 mm)	10	10
966	10 c. "The Three Kings" (21½ × 38 mm)	70	1·25
964/6 ..	*Set of 3*	80	1·25

(Des A. G. Mitchell. Photo Courvoisier)

1971 (3 Nov). *First World Rose Convention, Hamilton. T 326 and similar vert designs showing roses. Multicoloured. P 11½.*

967	2 c. Type 326 ..	15	30
968	5 c. "Peace"	35	35
969	8 c. "Chrysler Imperial"	60	1·10
967/9 ..	*Set of 3*	1·00	1·60

327 Lord Rutherford and Alpha Particles   **328** Benz (1895)

(Des M. Cleverley. Litho B.W.)

1971 (1 Dec). *Birth Centenary of Lord Rutherford (scientist). T 327 and similar horiz design. Multicoloured. P 13½ × 13.*

970	1 c. Type 327	25	50
971	7 c. Lord Rutherford and formula ..	85	1·50

(Des A. G. Mitchell. Litho B.W.)

1972 (2 Feb). *International Vintage Car Rally. T 328 and similar horiz designs. Multicoloured. P 14.*

972	3 c. Type 328	20	10
973	4 c. Oldsmobile (1904)	25	10
974	5 c. Ford "Model T" (1914)	25	10
975	6 c. Cadillac Service car (1915)	35	45
976	8 c. Chrysler (1924)	75	1·90
977	10 c. Austin "7" (1923)	75	1·40
972/7 ..	*Set of 6*	2·25	3·50

329 Coat of Arms of Wanganui   **330** Black Scree Cotula

(Des M. Cleverley. Litho Harrison)

1972 (5 Apr). *Anniversaries. T 329 and similar designs. P 13 × 13½ (3, 5 and 8 c.) or 13½ × 13 (others).*

978	3 c. multicoloured	15	10
979	4 c. red-orange, brown-bistre and black	15	10
980	5 c. multicoloured	25	10
981	8 c. multicoloured	65	1·25
982	10 c. multicoloured	65	1·25
978/82	*Set of 5*	1·75	2·50

Designs and Events: *Vert*—3 c. Type **329** (centenary of Wanganui Council govt); 5 c. De Havilland D.H.89 Dragon Rapide and Boeing 737 (25th anniv of National Airways Corp); 8 c. French frigate and Maori palisade (bicent of landing by Marion du Fresne). *Horiz*—4 c. Postal Union symbol (10th anniv of Asian-Oceanic Postal Union); 10 c. Stone cairn (150th anniv of New Zealand Methodist Church).

(Des Eileen Mayo. Litho Harrison)

1972 (7 June). *Alpine Plants. T 330 and similar vert designs. Multicoloured. P 13½.*

983	4 c. Type 330	30	10
984	6 c. North Island Edelweiss	40	40
985	8 c. Haast's Buttercup	60	65
986	10 c. Brown Mountain Daisy	70	1·25
983/6	*Set of 4*	1·75	2·25

331 Boy playing Tennis   **332** "Madonna with Child" (Murillo)

(Des L. C. Mitchell. Litho Harrison)

1972 (2 Aug). *Health Stamps. T 331 and similar vert design. P 13 × 13½.*

987	3 c. + 1 c. light grey and chestnut	30	45
988	4 c. + 1 c. light red-brown, grey and lemon	30	45

MS989 Two sheets each 107 × 123 mm. Nos. 987/8 in blocks of six .. *Per pair* 18·00 38·00

Design:—No. 988, Girl playing tennis.

(Des D. A. Hatcher. Photo Courvoisier)

1972 (4 Oct). *Christmas. T 332 and similar vert designs. Multicoloured. P 11½.*

990	3 c. Type 332	10	10
991	5 c. "The Last Supper" (stained-glass window, St. John's Church, Levin)	15	10
992	10 c. Pohutukawa flower	35	70
990/2 ..	*Set of 3*	50	70

333 Lake Waikaremoana   **334** Old Pollen Street

(Des D. A. Hatcher. Photo Courvoisier)

1972 (6 Dec). *Lake Scenes. T 333 and similar vert designs. Multicoloured. P 11½.*

993	6 c. Type 333	1·00	1·25
994	8 c. Lake Hayes	1·10	1·25
995	18 c. Lake Wakatipu	1·50	2·25
996	23 c. Lake Rotomahana	1·75	2·75
993/6 ..	*Set of 4*	4·75	6·75

(Des Miss V. Jepsen (3 c.), B. Langford (others). Litho Harrison)

1973 (7 Feb). *Commemorations. T 334 and similar horiz designs. Multicoloured (except 8 c.). P 13½ × 13.*

997	3 c. Type 334	10	10
998	4 c. Coal-mining and pasture	15	10
999	5 c. Cloister	15	15
1000	6 c. Forest, birds and lake	60	65
1001	8 c. Rowers (light grey, indigo and gold)	50	65
1002	10 c. Graph and people	70	1·00
997/1002	*Set of 6*	2·00	2·25

Events:—3 c. Centennial of Thames Borough; 4 c. Centennial of Westport Borough; 5 c. Centennial of Canterbury University; 6 c. 50th Anniv of Royal Forest and Bird Protection Society; 8 c. Success of N.Z. Rowers in 1972 Olympics; 10 c. 25th Anniv of E.C.A.F.E.

335 Class W Locomotive   **336** "Maori Woman and Child"

(Des R. M. Conly. Litho Harrison)

1973 (4 Apr). *New Zealand Steam Locomotives. T 335 and similar horiz designs. Multicoloured. P 14 × 14½.*

1003	3 c. Type 335	40	10
1004	4 c. Class X	40	10
1005	5 c. Class Ab	40	10
1006	10 c. Class Ja No. 1274	2·25	1·40
1003/6	*Set of 4*	3·00	1·40

1973–76. *As Nos. 915 etc., but no wmk.*

1008	1 c. multicoloured (7.9.73)	60	1·10
	a. Booklet pane. No. 1008×3 with three se-tenant printed labels (8.74)	2·40	
	b. Red (wing markings) omitted	£180	
	c. Blue (spots on wings) omitted	£120	
1009	2 c. multicoloured (6.73?)	30	10
	a. Purple and yellow omitted		
	b. Black (inscr, etc) omitted	£225	
1010	3 c. black, light brown and orange (1974)	2·25	1·50
	a. Orange omitted	£200	
1011	4 c. multicoloured (7.9.73)	45	10
	a. Bright green (wing veins) inverted	£325	
	b. Purple-brown omitted	£190	
	c. Orange-yellow omitted	£250	
	d. Greenish blue (background) omitted	£200	
	e. Bright green (wing veins) omitted	6·00	
	f. Apple green (wings) omitted	£180	
1012	5 c. multicoloured (1973)	2·25	1·75
1013	6 c. blackish green, yellow-green and rose-carmine (7.9.73)	60	45
	a. Yellow-grn (part of sea horse) omitted	£200	
	b. Rose-carmine omitted	£400	
1014	7 c. multicoloured (1974)	4·00	2·50
	a. Black omitted	£200	
1015	8 c. multicoloured (1974)	5·00	1·75
	a. Blue-green (background) omitted	£350	
1017	10 c. multicoloured, p 13½×13 (6.73?)	1·00	10
	a. Silver (Arms) omitted	£130	
	b. Imperf (vert pair)	£190	
	c. Deep blue (Queen's head, face value etc.) omitted	£225	
	d. Red (hair ribbon) omitted	17·00	
1018	15 c. black, flesh & pale brown, p 13½×13 (2.8.76)	2·25	10
1019	18 c. chestnut, black & apple-green (1974)	1·25	1·25
	a. Black (inscr, etc) omitted	£225	
1020	20 c. black and yellow-brown (1974)	80	9·50
	a. Black omitted	£250	
1008/20	*Set of 12*	18·00	9·50

(Des and photo Courvoisier)

1973 (6 June). *Paintings by Frances Hodgkins. T 336 and similar vert designs. Multicoloured. P 11½.*

1027	5 c. Type 336	40	15
1028	8 c. "Hilltop"	60	75
1029	10 c. "Barn in Picardy"	80	1·25
1030	18 c. "Self Portrait Still Life"	1·25	2·50
1027/30	*Set of 4*	2·75	4·25

337 Prince Edward   **338** "Tempi Madonna" (Raphael)

(Des and litho Harrison)

1973 (1 Aug). *Health Stamps. P 13 × 13½.*

1031	**337** 3 c. + 1 c. dull yellowish green and reddish brown	30	30
1032	4 c. + 1 c. rose-red and blackish brown	30	30

MS1033 Two sheets each 96 × 121 mm with Nos. 1031/2 in blocks of 6 (3 × 2) .. *Per pair* 16·00 32·00

(Des A. G. Mitchell. Photo Enschedé)

1973 (3 Oct). *Christmas. T 338 and similar vert designs. Multicoloured. P 12½ × 13½.*

1034	3 c. Type 338	10	10
1035	5 c. "Three Kings" (stained-glass window, St. Theresa's Church, Auckland)	10	10
1036	10 c. Family entering church	25	50
1034/6	*Set of 3*	40	50

ALTERED CATALOGUE NUMBERS

Any Catalogue numbers altered from the last edition are shown as a list in the introductory pages.

339 Mitre Peak   **340** Hurdling

(Des D. A. Hatcher. Photo Enschedé)

1973 (5 Dec). *Mountain Scenery.* T **339** and similar multicoloured designs. P 13 × 13½ (6, 8 c.) or 13½ × 13 (others).

1037	6 c. Type 339	70	80
1038	8 c. Mt Ngauruhoe	80	1·00
1039	18 c. Mt Sefton (*horiz*)	1·10	2·25
1040	23 c. Burnett Range (*horiz*)	1·25	2·50
1037/40	*Set of 4*	3·50	6·00

(Des M. Cleverley. Litho Harrison)

1974 (9 Jan). *Tenth British Commonwealth Games, Christchurch.* T **340** and similar vert designs. 5 c. black and violet-blue, others multicoloured. P 13 × 14.

1041	4 c. Type 340	10	10
1042	5 c. Ball-player	15	10
1043	10 c. Cycling	20	15
1044	18 c. Rifle-shooting	25	50
1045	23 c. Bowls	35	70
1041/5	*Set of 5*	85	1·40

No. 1042 does not show the Games emblem, and commemorates the Fourth Paraplegic Games, held at Dunedin.

341 Queen Elizabeth II   **342** "Spirit of Napier" Fountain

(Des D. A. Hatcher and A. G. Mitchell. Litho Harrison)

1974 (5 Feb). *New Zealand Day.* Sheet 131 × 74 mm. *containing* T **341** *and similar horiz designs, size* 37 × 20 mm. *Multicoloured.* P 13.

MS1046	4 c. × 5 Treaty House, Waitangi; Signing Waitangi Treaty; Type 341; Parliament Buildings Extensions; Children in Class	90	2·50

(Des Miss V. Jepsen. Photo Courvoisier)

1974 (3 Apr). *Centenaries of Napier and U.P.U.* T **342** *and similar vert designs. Multicoloured.* P 11½.

1047	4 c. Type 342	10	10
1048	5 c. Clock Tower, Berne	20	30
1049	8 c. U.P.U. Monument, Berne	80	1·60
1047/9	*Set of 3*	1·00	1·75

343 Boeing Seaplane, 1919   **344** Children, Cat and Dog

(Des R. M. Conly. Litho Harrison)

1974 (5 June). *History of New Zealand Airmail Transport.* T **343** *and similar horiz designs. Multicoloured.* P 14 × 13.

1050	3 c. Type 343	30	10
1051	4 c. Lockheed 10 Electra *Kauha*, 1937	35	10
1052	5 c. Bristol Type 170 Freighter Mk 31, 1958	40	30
1053	23 c. Short S.30 modified "G" Class flying-boat *Aotearoa*, 1940	1·75	2·50
1050/3	*Set of 4*	2·50	2·75

(Des B. Langford. Litho Harrison)

1974 (7 Aug). *Health Stamps.* P 13 × 13½.

1054	**344** 3 c. + 1 c. multicoloured	20	35
1055	— 4 c. + 1 c. multicoloured	25	35
1056	— 5 c. + 1 c. multicoloured	1·00	1·50
1054/6	*Set of 3*	1·25	2·00
MS1057	145 × 123 mm. No. 1055 in block of ten	21·00	35·00

Nos. 1055/6 are as T **344**, showing children and pets.

345 "The Adoration" of the Magi" (Konrad Witz)   **346** Great Barrier Island

(Des Eileen Mayo. Photo Courvoisier)

1974 (2 Oct). *Christmas.* T **345** and similar horiz designs. Multicoloured. P 11½.

1058	3 c. Type 345	10	10
1059	5 c. "The Angel Window" (stained-glass window, Old St. Pauls Church, Wellington)	10	10
1060	10 c. Madonna Lily	30	80
1058/60	*Set of 3*	40	85

(Des D. A. Hatcher. Photo Enschedé)

1974 (4 Dec). *Off-shore Islands.* T **346** and similar horiz designs. Multicoloured. P 13½ × 13.

1061	6 c. Type 346	30	40
1062	8 c. Stewart Island	50	1·25
1063	10 c. White Island	70	1·25
1064	23 c. The Brothers	75	1·50
1061/4	*Set of 4*	2·00	4·00

347 Crippled Child

(Des Miss V. Jepsen (3 c., 5 c.), A. G. Mitchell (10 c., 18 c.). Litho Harrison)

1975 (5 Feb). *Anniversaries and Events.* T **347** and similar horiz designs. Multicoloured. P 13½.

1065	3 c. Type 347	10	10
1066	5 c. Farming family	15	10
1067	10 c. I.W.Y. symbols	20	65
1068	18 c. Medical School Building, Otago University	55	1·75
1065/8	*Set of 4*	90	2·25

Commemorations:—3 c. 40th Anniv. of N.Z. Crippled Children Society; 5 c. 50th Anniv of Women's Division, Federated Farmers of N.Z.; 10 c. International Women's Year; 18 c. Centenary of Otago Medical School.

348 Scow *Lake Erie*

(Des R. M. Conly. Litho Harrison)

1975 (2 Apr). *Historic Sailing Ships.* T **348** and similar horiz designs. P 13½ × 13.

1069	4 c. black and red	30	10
1070	5 c. black and turquoise-blue	30	10
1071	8 c. black and yellow	55	60
1072	10 c. black and olive-yellow	60	60
1073	18 c. black and light brown	1·00	2·00
1074	23 c. black and slate-lilac	1·10	2·00
1069/74	*Set of 6*	3·50	4·75

Ships:—5 c. Schooner *Herald*; 8 c. Brigantine *New Zealander*; 10 c. Topsail schooner *Jessie Kelly*; 18 c. Barque *Tory*; 23 c. Full-rigged clipper *Rangitiki*.

349 Lake Sumner Forest Park

(Des and photo Enschedé)

1975 (4 June). *Forest Park Scenes.* T **349** and similar horiz designs. Multicoloured. P 13.

1075	6 c. Type 349	50	70
1076	8 c. North-west Nelson	60	1·00
1077	18 c. Kaweka	1·00	1·75
1078	23 c. Coromandel	1·25	2·00
1075/8	*Set of 4*	3·00	5·00

COVER PRICES

Cover factors are quoted at the beginning of each country for most issues to 1945. An explanation of the system can be found on page x. The factors quoted do not, however, apply to philatelic covers.

350 Girl feeding Lamb   **351** "Virgin and Child" (Zanobi Machiavelli)

(Des Margaret Chapman. Litho Harrison)

1975 (6 Aug). *Health Stamps.* T **350** and similar horiz designs. Multicoloured. P 13½ × 13.

1079	3 c. + 1 c. Type 350	20	30
1080	4 c. + 1 c. Boy with hen and chicks	20	30
1081	5 c. + 1 c. Boy with duck and duckling	60	1·50
1079/81	*Set of 3*	90	1·90
MS1082	123 × 146 mm. No. 1080 × 10	14·00	35·00

(Des Enid Hunter. Photo Harrison)

1975 (1 Oct). *Christmas.* T **351** and similar horiz designs. Multicoloured. P 13 × 13½ (3 c.) or 13½ × 13 (others).

1083	3 c. Type 351	10	10
	a. Red omitted*	£200	
1084	5 c. "Cross in Landscape" (stained-glass window, Greendale Church)	10	10
	a. Brown (face value) omitted	£170	
1085	10 c. "I saw three ships . . ." (carol)	35	65
1083/5	*Set of 3*	60	65

*This occurred in the last two vertical rows of the sheet with the red partially omitted on the previous row.

Used copies of No. 1083 have been seen with the orange ("Christmas 1975") omitted.

352 "Sterling Silver"   **353** Queen Elizabeth II (photograph by W. Harrison)   **353a** Maripi (knife)

353b Rainbow Abalone or Paua   **353c** "Beehive" (section of Parliamentary Buildings, Wellington)

(Des A. G. Mitchell (1 to 14 c.), I. Hulse (20 c. to $2), R. Conly ($5). Photo Harrison (1 to 10 c.), Courvoisier (11 to 14 c.), Heraclio Fournier (20 c. to $5))

1975 (26 Nov)–81. (*a*) *Vert designs as* T **352** *showing garden roses. Multicoloured.* P 14½ (6 to 8 c.) or 14½×14 (others).

1086	1 c. Type 352	10	10
1087	2 c. "Lilli Marlene"	10	10
1088	3 c. "Queen Elizabeth"	60	10
	a. Perf 14½ (8.79)	85	10
1089	4 c. "Super Star"	10	20
1090	5 c. "Diamond Jubilee"	10	10
1091	6 c. "Cresset"	70	1·00
	a. Perf 14½×14 (8.76)	40	70
1092	7 c. "Michele Meilland"	85	60
	a. Perf 14½×14 (5.76)	40	10
1093	8 c. "Josephine Bruce"	85	90
	a. Perf 14½×14 (8.76)	45	10
1094	9 c. "Iceberg"	30	40

(*b*) Type **353**. P 14½×14 (7.12.77)

1094a	10 c. multicoloured	45	20
	ab. Perf 14½ (1.79)	30	10

(*c*) *Vert designs as* T **353a** *showing Maori artefacts. Granite paper.* P 11½ (24.11.76)

1095	11 c. reddish brown, lemon & blackish brown	30	50
1096	12 c. reddish brown, lemon & blackish brown	30	15
1097	13 c. reddish brown, greenish blue and blackish brown	40	65
1098	14 c. reddish brown, lemon & blackish brown	30	20

Designs:—12 c. Putorino (flute); 13 c. Wahaika (club); 14 c. Kotiate (club).

(*d*) *Horiz designs as* T **353b** *showing sea shells. Multicoloured.* P 13

1099	20 c. Type 353b (29.11.78)	15	20
1100	30 c. Toheroa Clam (29.11.78)	25	30
1101	40 c. Old Woman or Coarse Dosina (29.11.78)	30	35
1102	50 c. New Zealand or Spiny Murex (29.11.78)	40	45
1103	$1 New Zealand Scallop (26.11.79)	70	95
	a. Imperf between (vert pair)	£450	
1104	$2 Circular Saw (26.11.79)	1·00	1·75

1105 $5 multicoloured .. .. 2·50 1·50
a. Imperf (vert pair)
1086/105 *Set of 21* 8·00 7·00
Faked "missing colour errors" exist of No. 1094a, involving parts of the portrait.

Used examples of No. 1099 exists with the black colour omitted so that the body of the shell appears in blue instead of green.

No. 1103a occurs on the top two rows of the sheet; the lower stamp being imperforate on three edges except for two perforation holes at the foot of each vertical side.

354 Family and League of Mothers Badge

(Des A. P. Derrick. Litho J.W.)

1976 (4 Feb). *Anniversaries and Metrication.* T **354** *and similar horiz designs. Multicoloured.* P 13½ × 14.
1110 6 c. Type **354** 10 10
1111 7 c. Weight, temperature, linear measure
and capacity 10 10
1112 8 c. *William Bryan* (immigrant ship),
mountain and New Plymouth .. 15 10
1113 10 c. Two women shaking hands and
Y.W.C.A. badge 15 50
1114 25 c. Map of the world showing cable links.. 30 1·25
1110/14 .. .. *Set of 5* 70 1·75
Anniversaries:—6 c. League of Mothers, 50th Anniv; 7 c. Metrication; 8 c. Centenary of New Plymouth; 10 c. 50th Anniv of New Zealand Y.W.C.A.; 25 c. Centenary of link with International Telecommunications Network.

355 Gig   **356** Purakaunui Falls

(Des G. F. Fuller. Litho Harrison)

1976 (7 Apr). *Vintage Farm Transport.* T **355** *and similar horiz designs. Multicoloured.* P 13½ × 13.
1115 6 c. Type **355** 15 40
1116 7 c. Thornycroft lorry 20 10
1117 8 c. Scandi wagon 40 20
1118 9 c. Traction engine 30 50
1119 10 c. Wool wagon 30 50
1120 25 c. Cart .. .. 85 2·25
1115/20 .. .. *Set of 6* 2·00 3·50

(Des and photo Courvoisier)

1976 (2 June). *Waterfalls.* T **356** *and similar vert designs. Multicoloured.* P 11½.
1121 10 c. Type **356** 35 10
1122 14 c. Marakopa Falls 60 95
1123 15 c. Bridal Veil Falls .. .. 65 1·10
1124 16 c. Papakorito Falls .. .. 70 1·25
1121/4 .. .. .. *Set of 4* 2·10 3·00

357 Boy and Pony   **358** "Nativity"
                    (Spanish carving)

(Des Margaret Chapman. Litho Harrison)

1976 (4 Aug). *Health Stamps.* T **357** *and similar vert designs. Multicoloured.* P 13 × 13½.
1125 7 c. + 1 c. Type **357** 20 30
1126 8 c. + 1 c. Girl and calf 20 30
1127 10 c. + 1 c. Girls and bird .. 40 90
1125/7 .. .. .. *Set of 3* 70 1·40
MS1128 96 × 121 mm. Nos. 1125/7 × 2 .. 3·75 7·00

(Des Margaret Chapman (18 c.), D. A. Hatcher (others). Photo Harrison)

1976 (6 Oct). *Christmas.* T **358** *and similar horiz designs. Multicoloured.* P 14 × 14½ (7 c.) or 14½ × 14 (others).
1129 7 c. Type **358** 15 10
1130 11 c. "Resurrection" (stained-glass window,
St. Joseph's Catholic Church, Grey Lynn) 25 30
1131 18 c. Angels 40 90
1129/31 .. .. *Set of 3* 70 1·10

---

359 Arms of Hamilton   **360** Queen Elizabeth II

(Des P. L. Blackie. Litho Harrison)

1977 (19 Jan). *Anniversaries.* T **359** *and similar vert designs. Multicoloured.* P 13 × 13½.
1132 8 c. Type **359** 15 10
a. Horiz strip of 3, Nos. 1132/4 45
1133 8 c. Arms of Gisborne 15 10
1134 8 c. Arms of Masterton 15 10
1135 10 c. A.A. emblem 15 40
a. Horiz pair. Nos. 1135/6 .. 30 1·00
1136 10 c. Arms of the College of Surgeons .. 15 40
1132/6 .. .. *Set of 5* 75 1·00
Events:—Nos. 1132/4, City Centenaries; No. 1135, 75th Anniv of the Automobile Association in New Zealand; No. 1136, 50th Anniv of Royal Australasian College of Surgeons.
Designs of each value were printed in the same sheet horizontally *se-tenant.*

(Des and photo Harrison from photographs by Warren Harrison)

1977 (23 Feb). *Silver Jubilee.* Sheet 178 × 82 *mm containing* T **360** *and similar vert designs showing different portraits.* P 14 × 14½.
MS1137 8 c. × 5 multicoloured .. .. 65 1·60
a. Imperf £1200
ab. Ditto, and silver omitted .. £2000
b. Silver omitted £800
c. Indian red omitted £300

361 Physical Education   **(362)**
and Maori Culture

(Des A. G. Mitchell. Litho Harrison)

1977 (6 Apr). *Education.* T **361** *and similar vert designs. Multicoloured.* P 13 × 13½.
1138 8 c. Type **361** 40 70
a. Horiz strip of 5, Nos. 1138/42 .. 1·75
1139 8 c. Geography, science and woodwork 40 70
1140 8 c. Teaching the deaf, kindergarten and
woodwork 40 70
1141 8 c. Tertiary and language classes .. 40 70
1142 8 c. Home science, correspondence school and
teacher training 40 70
1138/42 .. .. *Set of 5* 1·75 3·25
Nos. 1138/42 were printed horizontally *se-tenant* throughout the sheet.

1977 (Apr). *Coil stamps for use in stamp-fixing machines. Nos.* 1010/11 *surch as* T **362** *by Govt Printer, Wellington.*
1143 7 c. on 3 c. *Detunda egregia* (moth) (18.4) 40 70
1144 8 c. on 4 c. *Charagia virescens* (moth)
(20.4) 40 70
a. Bright green (wing veins) omitted .. £275
Forged "7 c." surcharges, similar to No. 1143, but in smaller type, are known applied to Nos. 918 and 1010.

363 Karitane Beach   **364** Girl with Pigeon

(Des D. A. Hatcher. Photo Heraclio Fournier)

1977 (1 June). *Seascapes.* T **363** *and similar horiz designs. Multicoloured.* P 14½.
1145 10 c. Type **363** 15 10
1146 16 c. Ocean Beach, Mount Maunganui .. 30 30
1147 18 c. Piha Beach 30 30
1148 30 c. Kaikoura Coast 35 40
1145/8 .. .. *Set of 4* 1·00 1·00

(Des A. P. Derrick. Litho Harrison)

1977 (3 Aug). *Health Stamps.* T **364** *and similar vert designs. Multicoloured.* P 13 × 13½.
1149 7 c. + 2 c. Type **364** 20 30
1150 8 c. + 2 c. Boy with frog 25 45
1151 10 c. + 2 c. Girl with butterfly .. 45 1·00
1149/51 .. .. *Set of 3* 80 1·60
MS1152 97 × 120 mm. Nos. 1149/51 × 2 .. 2·50 7·00
Stamps from the miniature sheet are without white border and together form a composite design.

365 "The Holy Family" (Correggio)

(Des Margaret Chapman (23 c.), graphics for all values produced by printer. Photo Courvoisier)

1977 (5 Oct). *Christmas.* T **365** *and similar vert designs. Multicoloured.* P 11½.
1153 7 c. Type **365** 15 10
1154 16 c. "Madonna and Child" (stained-glass
window, St. Michael's and All Angels,
Dunedin) 25 25
1155 23 c. "Partridge in a Pear Tree" .. 40 1·25
1153/5 .. .. *Set of 3* 70 1·40

366 Merryweather Manual   **367** Town Clock and
Pump, 1860   Coat of Arms,
                              Ashburton

(Des R. M. Conly. Litho Harrison)

1977 (7 Dec). *Fire Fighting Appliances.* T **366** *and similar horiz designs. Multicoloured.* P 14 × 13.
1156 10 c. Type **366** 15 10
1157 11 c. 2-wheel hose, reel and ladder, 1880 .. 15 25
1158 12 c. Shand Mason steam fire engine, 1873 .. 20 30
1159 23 c. Chemical fire engine, 1888 .. 30 70
1156/9 .. .. *Set of 4* 70 1·25

(Des P. L. Blackie (No. 1162), Harrison (No. 1163), P. J. Durrant (others), Litho Harrison)

1978 (8 Mar). *Centenaries.* T **367** *and similar multicoloured designs.* P 14.
1160 10 c. Type **367** 15 10
a. Horiz pair. Nos. 1160/1 .. 30 50
1161 10 c. Stratford and Mt Egmont .. 15 10
1162 12 c. Early telephone 15 15
1163 20 c. Bay of Islands (*horiz*) .. 20 30
1160/3 .. .. *Set of 4* 60 60
Centenaries commemorate are those of the towns of Ashburton and Stratford, of the telephone in New Zealand, and of the Bay of Islands County.
The 10 c. values were printed together, *se-tenant*, in horizontal pairs throughout the sheet.

368 Students and   **369**   **370** Maui Gas
Ivey Hall, Lincoln   Drilling Platform
College

(Des A. P. Derrick. Litho Harrison)

1978 (26 Apr). *Land Resources and Centenary of Lincoln College of Agriculture.* T **368** *and similar vert designs. Multicoloured.* P 14½.
1164 10 c. Type **368** 15 10
1165 12 c. Sheep grazing 15 25
1166 15 c. Fertiliser ground spreading .. 15 30
1167 16 c. Agricultural Field Days .. 15 30
1168 20 c. Harvesting grain 20 40
1169 30 c. Dairy farming 30 70
1164/9 .. .. *Set of 6* 1·00 1·90

(Photo Harrison)

1978 (3 May–13 June). *Coil Stamps.* P 14½ × 14 (10 c.) or 14×13 (others).
1170 **369** 1 c. bright purple (13 June) .. 10 40
1171 2 c. bright orange (13 June) .. 10 40
1172 5 c. red-brown (13 June) .. 10 40
1173 10 c. bright blue 30 75
1170/3 .. .. *Set of 4* 45 1·75

(Des R. M. Conly. Litho Harrison)

1978 (7 June). *Resources of the Sea.* T **370** *and similar vert designs. Multicoloured.* P 13 × 14.
1174	12 c.	Type 370	20	15
1175	15 c.	Trawler	25	30
1176	20 c.	Map of 200 mile fishing limit	30	40
1177	23 c.	Humpback Whale and Bottle-nosed Dolphins	40	50
1178	35 c.	Kingfish, snapper, grouper and squid	60	75
1174/8		Set of 5	1·60	1·90

371 First Health Charity Stamp

372 "The Holy Family" (El Greco)

373 Sir Julius Vogel

(Des A. G. Mitchell. Litho Harrison)

1978 (2 Aug). *Health Stamps. Health Services Commemorations.* T **371** *and similar vert design.* P 13 × 14.
1179	10 c. + 2 c. black, red and gold		30	35
1180	12 c. + 2 c. multicoloured		30	40
MS1181	97 × 124 mm. Nos. 1179/80 × 3.		1·75	4·50

Designs and commemorations:—10 c. Type **371** (50th anniversary of health charity stamps); 12 c. Heart operation (National Heart Foundation).

(Des R. M. Conly. Photo Courvoisier)

1978 (4 Oct). *Christmas.* T **372** *and similar multicoloured designs.* P 11½.
1182	7 c.	Type 372	10	10
1183	16 c.	All Saints' Church, Howick (horiz)	25	35
1184	23 c.	Beach scene (horiz)	30	50
1182/4		Set of 3	60	80

(Des A. G. Mitchell. Litho J.W.)

1979 (7 Feb). *Statesmen.* T **373** *and similar vert designs in sepia and drab.* P 13 × 13½.
1185	10 c.	Type 373	30	65
	a.	Horiz strip of 3, Nos. 1185/7	90	
1186	10 c.	Sir George Grey	30	65
1187	10 c.	Richard John Seddon	30	65
1185/7		Set of 3	90	1·75

Nos. 1185/7 were printed together, *se-tenant,* in horizontal strips of 3 throughout the sheet.
Nos. 1185/7 have matt, almost invisible gum.

374 Riverlands Cottage, Blenheim

375 Whangaroa Harbour

(Des P. Leitch. Litho Enschedé)

1979 (4 Apr). *Architecture (1st series).* T **374** *and similar horiz designs.* P 13½ × 13.
1188	10 c.	black, new blue and deep blue	10	10
1189	12 c.	black, pale green and bottle green	15	25
1190	15 c.	black and grey	20	30
1191	20 c.	black, yellow-brown and sepia	25	30
1188/91		Set of 4	65	90

Designs:—12 c. The Mission House, Waimate North; 15 c. "The Elms", Tauranga; 20 c. Provincial Council Buildings, Christchurch.
See also Nos. 1217/20 and 1262/5.

(Photo Heraclio Fournier)

1979 (6 June). *Small Harbours.* T **375** *and similar multicoloured designs.* P 13.
1192	15 c.	Type 375	15	10
1193	20 c.	Kawau Island	20	40
1194	23 c.	Akaroa Harbour (vert)	20	50
1195	35 c.	Picton Harbour (vert)	30	70
1192/5		Set of 4	75	1·50

376 Children with Building Bricks

(Des W. Kelsall. Litho J.W.)

1979 (6 June). *International Year of the Child.* P 14.
1196	376	10 c. multicoloured	15	10

377 Two-spotted Chromis   (**378**)

(Des P. Blackie (12 c.), G. Fuller (others). Litho Harrison)

1979 (25 July). *Health Stamps. Marine Life.* T **377** *and similar multicoloured designs.* P 13 × 13½ (12 c.) or 13½ × 13 (others).
1197	10 c. + 2 c.	Type 377	30	60
	a.	Horiz pair. Nos. 1197/8	60	1·10
1198	10 c. + 2 c.	Sea Urchin	30	60
1199	12 c. + 2 c.	Red Goatfish and underwater cameraman (vert)	30	60
1197/9		Set of 3	80	1·60
MS1200	144×72 mm. Nos. 1197/9, each × 2.			
	P 14×14½ (12 c.) or 14½×14 (others)		1·75	4·00

Nos. 1197/8 were printed together, *se-tenant,* in horizontal pairs throughout the sheet.

1979 (31 Aug)–80. *Nos. 1091a, 1092a, 1093a and 1094ab surch as* T **378** *by Govt Printer, Wellington.*
1201	4 c. on 8 c. "Josephine Bruce" (24.9.79)		10	20
	a. Surch double		35·00	
1202	14 c. on 10 c. Type 353		30	20
	a. Surch double, one albino		£140	
	b. Surch inverted			
1203	17 c. on 6 c. "Cresset" (8.10.79)		30	70
1203a	20 c. on 7 c. "Michele Meilland" (29.9.80)		30	10
1201/3a		Set of 4	80	1·10

Neither of the impressions of the surcharge on No. 1201a are properly inked.

379 "Madonna and Child" (sculpture by Ghiberti)

380 Chamber, House of Representatives

(Des D. Hatcher. Photo Courvoisier)

1979 (3 Oct). *Christmas.* T **379** *and similar vert designs. Multicoloured.* P 11½.
1204	10 c.	Type 379	15	10
1205	25 c.	Christ Church, Russell	30	40
1206	35 c.	Pohutukawa (tree)	40	55
1204/6		Set of 3	75	90

(Des D. Hatcher. Litho J.W.)

1979 (26 Nov). *25th Commonwealth Parliamentary Conference, Wellington.* T **380** *and similar vert designs. Multicoloured.* P 13½.
1207	14 c.	Type 380	15	10
1208	20 c.	Mace and Black Rod	20	30
1209	30 c.	Wall hanging from the "Beehive"	30	70
1207/9		Set of 3	60	95

381 1855 1d. Stamp

(Des D. Hatcher (14 c. (all designs)), R. M. Conly (others). Litho Harrison)

1980 (7 Feb). *Anniversaries and Events.* T **381** *and similar designs.* P 13½×13 (14 c. (all designs)) or 14 (others).
1210	14 c. black, brown-red and yellow		20	30
	a. Horiz strip of 3. Nos. 1210/12		60	
	ab. Black (inscription) omitted (strip of 3)		£250	
1211	14 c. black, deep turquoise-blue and yellow		20	30
1212	14 c. black, dull yellowish green and yellow		20	30
1213	17 c. multicoloured		20	30
1214	25 c. multicoloured		25	35
1215	30 c. multicoloured		25	40
1210/15		Set of 6	1·10	1·75
MS1216	146×96 mm. Nos. 1210/12 (as horiz strip). P 14½×14 (sold at 52 c.)		1·25	4·00

Designs and commemorations; (38 × 22 *mm*)—No. 1210, Type **381**; No. 1211, 1855 2d. stamp; No. 1212, 1855 1s. stamp (125th anniversary of New Zealand stamps). (40 × 23 *mm*)—No. 1213, Geyser, wood-carving and building (centenary of Rotorua (town)); No. 1214, *Earina autumnalis* and *thelymitra venosa* (International Orchid Conference, Auckland); No. 1215; Ploughing and Golden Plough Trophy (World Ploughing Championships, Christchurch).
The premium on No. MS1216 was used to help finance the "Zeapex 80" International Stamp Exhibition, Auckland.
Nos. 1210/12 were printed together, *se-tenant,* in horizontal strips of 3 throughout the sheet.

382 Ewelme Cottage, Parnell

383 Auckland Harbour

(Des P. Leitch. Litho Enschedé)

1980 (2 Apr). *Architecture (2nd series).* T **382** *and similar horiz designs. Multicoloured.* P 13½ × 12½.
1217	14 c.	Type 382	15	10
1218	17 c.	Broadgreen, Nelson	15	25
1219	25 c.	Courthouse, Oamaru	20	30
1220	30 c.	Government Buildings, Wellington	25	35
1217/20		Set of 4	65	90

(Des D. Hatcher. Photo Heraclio Fournier)

1980 (4 June). *Large Harbours.* T **383** *and similar horiz designs. Multicoloured.* P 13.
1221	25 c.	Type 383	25	20
1222	30 c.	Wellington Harbour	30	30
1223	35 c.	Lyttelton Harbour	30	35
1224	50 c.	Port Chalmers	50	65
1221/4		Set of 4	1·25	1·40

384 Surf-fishing

385 "Madonna and Child with Cherubim" (sculpture by Andrea della Robbia)

(Des Margaret Chapman. Litho Enschedé)

1980 (6 Aug). *Health Stamps. Fishing.* T **384** *and similar horiz designs. Multicoloured.* P 13 × 12½.
1225	14 c. + 2 c.	Type 384	30	70
	a.	Horiz pair. Nos. 1225/6	60	1·40
1226	14 c. + 2 c.	Wharf-fishing	30	70
1227	17 c. + 2 c.	Spear-fishing	30	55
1225/7		Set of 3	80	1·75
MS1228	148 × 75 mm. Nos. 1225/7 each × 2. P 13½ × 13		1·60	3·25

Nos. 1225/6 were printed together, *se-tenant,* in horizontal pairs throughout the sheet.

(Des P. Durrant. Photo Courvoisier)

1980 (1 Oct). *Christmas.* T **385** *and similar vert designs. Multicoloured.* P 11½.
1229	10 c.	Type 385	15	10
1230	25 c.	St. Mary's Church, New Plymouth	25	25
1231	35 c.	Picnic scene	40	80
1229/31		Set of 3	70	1·00

386 Te Heu Heu (chief)

387 Lt.-Col. the Hon W. H. A. Feilding and Borough of Feilding Crest

(Des R. M. Conly. Litho Heraclio Fournier)

1980 (26 Nov). *Maori Personalities. Vert designs as* T **386**. *Multicoloured.* P 12½×13.
1232	15 c.	Type 386	10	10
1233	25 c.	Te Hau (chief)	15	20
1234	35 c.	Te Puea (princess)	20	20
1235	45 c.	Ngata (politician)	30	20
1236	60 c.	Te Ata-O-Tu (warrior)	35	25
1232/6		Set of 5	1·00	70

(Des R. M. Conly. Litho Harrison)

1981 (4 Feb). *Commemorations.* T **387** *and similar horiz design.* P 14½.
1237	20 c.	multicoloured	20	20
1238	25 c.	black and brown-ochre	25	25

Designs and Commemorations:—20 c. Type **387** (Centenary of Feilding (town)); 25 c. I.Y.D. emblem and cupped hands (International Year of the Disabled).

388 The Family at Play

389 Kaiauai River

(Des A. Derrick. Litho J.W.)

1981 (1 Apr). *"Family Life." T **388** and similar vert designs. Multicoloured. P 13½ × 13.*

1239	20 c.	Type 388		..	15	10
1240	25 c.	The family, young and old			20	20
1241	30 c.	The family at home		..	20	30
1242	35 c.	The family at church		..	25	45
1239/42				*Set of 4*	70	95

(Des D. Hatcher. Photo Heraclio Fournier)

1981 (3 June). *River Scenes. T **389** and similar multicoloured designs. P 13½ × 13 (30, 35 c.) or 13 × 13½ (others).*

1243	30 c.	Type 389		..	25	25
1244	35 c.	Mangahao		..	30	30
1245	40 c.	Shotover (*horiz*) ..			35	40
1246	60 c.	Cleddau (*horiz*)		..	55	65
1243/6				*Set of 4*	1·25	1·40

390 St. Paul's Cathedral   391 Girl with Starfish

(Des and litho Harrison)

1981 (29 July). *Royal Wedding. T **390** and similar horiz design. Multicoloured. P 13½.*

1247	20 c.	Type 390		..	30	30
	a.	Pair. Nos. 1247/8			60	60
	ab.	Deep grey (inscriptions and date) omitted £800				
1248	20 c.	Prince Charles and Lady Diana Spencer			30	30

Nos. 1247/8 were printed together, *se-tenant*, in horizontal and vertical pairs throughout the sheet.

(Des P.O. Litho Harrison)

1981 (5 Aug). *Health Stamps. Children playing by the Sea. T **391** and similar vert designs. Multicoloured. P 14½.*

1249	20 c. + 2 c.	Type 391		..	25	50
	a.	Horiz pair. Nos. 1249/50			50	1·00
1250	20 c. + 2 c.	Boy fishing		..	25	50
1251	25 c. + 2 c.	Children exploring rock pool		..	25	35
1249/51				*Set of 3*	70	1·25
MS1252	100 × 125 mm.	Nos. 1249/51, each × 2		..	1·25	3·00

The 20 c. values were printed together, *se-tenant*, in horizontal pairs throughout the sheet, forming a composite design.

The stamps from No. **MS**1252 were printed together, *se-tenant*, in two horizontal strips of 3, each forming a composite design.

392 "Madonna Suckling the Child"   393 Tauranga
(painting, d'Oggiono)   Mission House

(Des Margaret Chapman. Photo Courvoisier)

1981 (7 Oct). *Christmas. T **392** and similar vert designs. Multicoloured. P 11½.*

1253	14 c.	Type 392		..	15	10
1254	30 c.	St. John's Church, Wakefield		..	20	25
1255	40 c.	Golden Tainui (flower)		..	35	35
1253/5				*Set of 3*	65	60

(Des A. Derrick. Litho Walsall)

1982 (3 Feb). *Commemorations. T **393** and similar vert designs. Multicoloured. P 14½.*

1256	20 c.	Type 393		..	25	10
	a.	Horiz pair. Nos. 1256/7 ..			50	60
1257	20 c.	Water tower, Hawera		..	25	10
1258	25 c.	Cat		..	35	35
1259	30 c.	Dunedin (refrigerated sailing ship)			35	40
1260	35 c.	Scientific research equipment		..	40	45
1256/60				*Set of 5*	1·40	1·25

Commemorations:—No. 1256, Centenary of Tauranga (town); No. 1257, Centenary of Hawera (town); No. 1258, Centenary of S.P.C.A. (Society for the Prevention of Cruelty to Animals in New Zealand); No. 1259, Centenary of Frozen Meat Exports; No. 1260, International Year of Science.

The 20 c. values were printed together, *se-tenant*, in horizontal pairs throughout the sheet.

394 Map of New Zealand   395 Alberton, Auckland

(Des A. G. Mitchell. Litho Leigh-Mardon Ltd, Melbourne)

1982 (1 Apr–13 Dec). *P 12½.*

1261	**394**	24 c. pale yellowish green and ultram			30	10
	a.	Perf 14½ × 14 (13.12.82)			35	10

(Des P. Leitch. Litho Walsall)

1982 (7 Apr). *Architecture (3rd series). T **395** and similar horiz designs. Multicoloured. P 14 × 14½.*

1262	20 c.	Type 395		..	20	15
1263	25 c.	Caccia Birch, Palmerston North			25	25
1264	30 c.	Railway station, Dunedin		..	50	30
1265	35 c.	Post Office, Ophir		..	40	40
1262/5				*Set of 4*	1·25	1·00

396 Kaiteriteri Beach,   397 Labrador
Nelson (Summer)

(Des D. Hatcher. Photo Heraclio Fournier)

1982 (2 June). *"The Four Seasons". New Zealand Scenes. T **396** and similar horiz designs. Multicoloured. P 13 × 13½.*

1266	35 c.	Type 396		..	30	30
1267	40 c.	St. Omer Park, Queenstown (Autumn)			35	35
1268	45 c.	Mt Ngauruhoe, Tongariro National Park (Winter)			40	40
1269	70 c.	Wairarapa farm (Spring)		..	60	60
1266/9				*Set of 4*	1·50	1·50

(Des R. M. Conly. Litho Enschedé)

1982 (4 Aug). *Health Stamps. Dogs. T **397** and similar vert designs. Multicoloured. P 13×13½.*

1270	24 c. + 2 c.	Type 397		..	80	1·00
	a.	Horiz pair. Nos. 1270/1 ..			1·60	2·00
1271	24 c. + 2 c.	Border Collie		..	80	1·00
1272	30 c. + 2 c.	Cocker Spaniel		..	80	1·00
1270/2				*Set of 3*	2·25	2·75
MS1273	98 × 125 mm.	Nos. 1270/2, each × 2.				
	P 14 × 13½				4·25	6·50

The 24 c. values were printed together, *se-tenant*, in horizontal pairs throughout the sheet.

398 "Madonna with Child
and Two Angels"
(painting by Piero di Cosimo)

(Des Margaret Chapman. Photo Heraclio Fournier)

1982 (6 Oct). *Christmas. T **398** and similar vert designs. Multicoloured. P 14 × 13½.*

1274	18 c.	Type 398		..	20	10
1275	35 c.	Rangiatea Maori Church, Otaki			35	30
1276	45 c.	Surf life-saving		..	50	40
1274/6				*Set of 3*	95	65

399 Nephrite   399a Grapes

399b Kokako

(Des P. Durrant (Nos. 1277/82), D. Little (Nos. 1283/7), Janet Marshall (Nos. 1288/97). Litho Leigh-Mardon Ltd. Melbourne)

1982 (1 Dec)–**89**. *Multicoloured. P 14½×14 (Nos. 1277/87) or 14½ (Nos. 1288/97).*

*(a) Minerals. T **399** and similar vert designs*

1277	1 c.	Type 399		..	10	10
	a.	Perf 12½			45	20
1278	2 c.	Agate		..	10	10
	a.	Perf 12½			1·00	1·50
1279	3 c.	Iron Pyrites		..	10	10
1280	4 c.	Amethyst		..	10	10
1281	5 c.	Carnelian		..	10	10
1282	9 c.	Native Sulphur		..	20	10

*(b) Fruits. T **399a** and similar vert designs*

1283	10 c.	Type 399a (7.12.83)			50	10
1284	20 c.	Citrus Fruit (7.12.83)			35	10
1285	30 c.	Nectarines (7.12.83)			30	10
1286	40 c.	Apples (7.12.83)		..	35	10
1287	50 c.	Kiwifruit (7.12.83)		..	40	10

*(c) Native Birds. T **399b** and similar vert designs. Phosphorised paper ($1, $2)*

1288	30 c.	Kakapo (1.5.86)		..	50	25
1289	40 c.	Mountain ("Blue") Duck (2.2.87)			60	35
1290	45 c.	New Zealand Falcon (1.5.86)			1·00	35
1291	60 c.	New Zealand Teal (2.2.87)			1·00	40
1292	$1	Type 399b (24.4.85)		..	1·00	30
1293	$2	Chatham Island Robin (24.4.85)			1·75	50
1294	$3	Stitchbird (23.4.86)		..	1·75	1·40
1295	$4	Saddleback (23.4.86)		..	2·00	2·50
1296	$5	Takahe (20.4.88)		..	3·25	3·00
1297	$10	Little Spotted Kiwi (19.4.89)			6·00	6·75
1277/97				*Set of 21*	20·00	15·00
1292/7 Optd "Specimen"				*Set of 6*	7·50	

Nos. 1292/7 overprinted "Specimen" come from a special "NEW ZEALAND 1990" Presentation Pack issued on 19 April 1989.

A miniature sheet containing No. 1293 was only available from the New Zealand stand at "PHILEXFRANCE '89" International Stamp Exhibition or the Philatelic Bureau at Wanganui.

Versions of the $3 with narrow face value and of the $4 in horizontal format were prepared, but not issued for postal purposes.

For No. 1297 in a miniature sheet for "POST X 95" Postal History Exhibition see No. **MS**1854.

400 Old Arts Building,   401 Queen Elizabeth II
Auckland University

(Des G. Emery (35 c.), P. Durrant (others). Litho Cambec Press, Melbourne (35 c.), J.W. (others))

1983 (2 Feb). *Commemorations. T **400** and similar vert designs. Multicoloured. P 13 × 13½ (35 c.) or 14 × 13½ (others).*

1303	24 c.	Salvation Army Centenary logo			20	10
1304	30 c.	Type 400		..	25	35
1305	35 c.	Stylised Kangaroo and Kiwi			30	35
1306	40 c.	Rainbow Trout		..	30	45
1307	45 c.	Satellite over Earth		..	35	50
1303/7				*Set of 5*	1·25	1·50

Commemorations:—24 c. Centenary of Salvation Army; 30 c. Centenary of Auckland University; 35 c. Closer Economic Relationship agreement with Australia; 40 c. Centenary of introduction of Rainbow Trout into New Zealand; 45 c. World Communications Year.

(Des P. Durrant. Litho Harrison)

1983 (14 Mar). *Commonwealth Day. T **401** and similar horiz designs. Multicoloured. P 13½.*

1308	24 c.	Type 401		..	20	10
1309	35 c.	Maori rock drawing		..	30	50
1310	40 c.	Woolmark and wool-scouring symbols ..			30	80
1311	45 c.	Coat of arms		..	30	80
1308/11				*Set of 4*	1·00	2·00

402 "Boats, Island Bay"   403 Mt Egmont
(Rita Angus)

(Des D. Hatcher. Litho Leigh-Mardon Ltd, Melbourne)

1983 (6 Apr). *Paintings by Rita Angus. T **402** and similar vert designs. Multicoloured. P 14½.*

1312	24 c.	Type 402		..	35	10
1313	30 c.	"Central Otago Landscape"			40	45
1314	35 c.	"Wanaka Landscape"		..	50	50
1315	45 c.	"Tree"		..	70	70
1312/15				*Set of 4*	1·75	1·60

(Des P. Durrant. Photo Heraclio Fournier)

1983 (1 June). *Beautiful New Zealand. T **403** and similar multi-coloured designs. P 13.*

1316	35 c.	Type 403		..	30	35
1317	40 c.	Cooks Bay		..	35	40
1318	45 c.	Lake Matheson (*horiz*)			40	45
1319	70 c.	Lake Alexandrina (*horiz*)			65	70
1316/19				*Set of 4*	1·50	1·75

404 Tabby   **405** "The Family of the Holy Oak Tree" (Raphael)

(Des R. M. Conly. Litho Harrison)

1983 (3 Aug). *Health Stamps. Cats.* T **404** *and similar vert designs. Multicoloured.* P 14.

1320	24 c. + 2 c. Type 404	..	..	40	50
	a. Horiz pair. Nos. 1320/1	..	..	80	1·00
1321	24 c. + 2 c. Siamese	..	..	40	50
1322	30 c. + 2 c. Persian	..	..	75	90
1320/2			*Set of 3*	1·40	1·75
MS1323	100 × 126 mm. Nos. 1320/2, each × 2			2·25	2·25

The 24 c. values were printed together, *se-tenant*, in horizontal pairs throughout the sheet.

(Des R. M. Conly (45 c.), M. Wyatt (others). Photo Courvoisier)

1983 (5 Oct). *Christmas.* T **405** *and similar vert designs. Multicoloured.* P 12×11½.

1324	18 c. Type 405			15	10
1325	35 c. St. Patrick's Church, Greymouth			40	40
1326	45 c. "The Glory of Christmas" (star and flowers)			55	55
1324/6			*Set of 3*	1·00	90

406 Geology

(Des R. M. Conly. Litho Cambec Press, Melbourne)

1984 (1 Feb). *Antarctic Research.* T **406** *and similar horiz designs. Multicoloured.* P 13½×13.

1327	24 c. Type 406	..	..	35	10
1328	40 c. Biology	..	..	45	40
1329	58 c. Glaciology	..	..	60	55
1330	70 c. Meteorology	..	..	70	70
1327/30			*Set of 4*	1·90	1·60
MS1331	126 × 110 mm. Nos. 1327/30			1·90	3·25

407 Mountaineer, Lake Wakatipu   **408** Mount Hutt

(Des M. Wyatt. Litho Cambec Press, Melbourne)

1984 (4 Apr). *New Zealand Ferry Boats.* T **407** *and similar horiz designs. Multicoloured.* P 13½ × 13.

1332	24 c. Type 407	..	..	25	10
1333	40 c. *Waikana*, Otago	..	..	30	45
1334	58 c. *Britannia*, Waitemata	..	..	40	1·10
1335	70 c. *Wakatere*, Firth of Thames	..	..	55	85
1332/5			*Set of 4*	1·40	2·25

(Des D. Little. Litho Cambec Press, Melbourne)

1984 (6 June). *Ski-slope Scenery.* T **408** *and similar horiz designs. Multicoloured.* P 13½ × 13.

1336	35 c. Type 408	..	..	30	25
1337	40 c. Coronet Park	..	..	30	30
1338	58 c. Turoa	..	..	35	30
1339	70 c. Whakapapa	..	..	60	75
1336/9			*Set of 4*	1·40	1·40

409 Hamilton's Frog

(Des A. G. Mitchell. Litho Cambec Press, Melbourne)

1984 (11 July). *Amphibians and Reptiles.* T **409** *and similar horiz designs. Multicoloured.* P 13½.

1340	24 c. Type 409	..	..	30	30
	a. Horiz pair. Nos. 1340/1	..	..	60	60
1341	24 c. Great Barrier Skink	..	..	30	30
1342	30 c. Harlequin Gecko	..	..	35	35
1343	58 c. Otago Skink	..	..	70	70
1344	70 c. Gold-striped Gecko	..	..	75	75
1340/4			*Set of 5*	2·25	2·25

Nos. 1340/1 were printed together, *se-tenant*, in horizontal pairs throughout the sheet.

---

410 Clydesdales ploughing Field

(Des Margaret Chapman. Litho Harrison)

1984 (1 Aug). *Health Stamps. Horses.* T **410** *and similar horiz designs. Multicoloured.* P 14½.

1345	24 c. + 2 c. Type 410	..	..	30	50
	a. Horiz pair. Nos. 1345/6	..	..	60	1·00
1346	24 c. + 2 c. Shetland ponies	..	..	30	50
1347	30 c. + 2 c. Thoroughbreds	..	..	45	50
1345/7			*Set of 3*	1·00	1·40
MS1348	148 × 75 mm. Nos. 1345/7, each × 2			1·60	2·50

Nos. 1345/6 were printed together, *se-tenant*, in horizontal pairs throughout the sheet.

MACHINE LABELS. An automatic machine dispensing labels, ranging in value from 1 c. to $99.99, was installed at the Queen Street Post Office, Auckland, on 3 September 1984 for a trial period. The oblong designs, framed by simulated perforations at top and bottom and vertical rules at the sides, showed the "Southern Cross", face value and vertical column of six horizontal lines between the "NEW ZEALAND" and "POST-AGE" inscriptions. The trial period ended abruptly on 16 October 1984.

Similar labels, with the face value and inscriptions within a plain oblong, were introduced on 12 February 1986 and from 22 August 1988 they were printed on paper showing New Zealand flags. On 12 September 1990 the design printed on the paper was changed to show seaplanes and on 12 August 1992 to a Maori pattern. A further Maori pattern, taken from rafters, in green and grey appeared on 21 February 1996.

A commemorative label was available at "NEW ZEALAND '90" held at Auckland between 24 August and 2 September 1990.

411 "Adoration of the Shepherds" (Lorenzo di Credi)

(Des R. M. Conly (45 c.), P. Durrant (others). Photo Heraclio Fournier)

1984 (26 Sept). *Christmas.* T **411** *and similar multicoloured designs.* P 13½×14 (18 c.) or 14×13½ (others).

1349	18 c. Type 411			15	10
1350	35 c. Old St. Paul's, Wellington (*vert*)			30	30
1351	45 c. "The Joy of Christmas" (*vert*)			40	65
1349/51			*Set of 3*	75	85

412 Mounted Riflemen, South Africa, 1901

(Des R. M. Conly. Litho Harrison)

1984 (7 Nov). *New Zealand Military History.* T **412** *and similar horiz designs. Multicoloured.* P 15×14.

1352	24 c. Type 412			25	10
1353	40 c. Engineers, France, 1917			35	45
1354	58 c. Tanks of 2nd N.Z. Divisional Cavalry, North Africa, 1942			50	90
1355	70 c. Infantryman in jungle kit, and 25-pounder gun, Korea and South-East Asia, 1950–72			60	80
1352/5			*Set of 4*	1·50	2·00
MS1356	122 × 106 mm. Nos. 1352/5			1·25	2·25

413 St. John Ambulance Badge

(Des Lindy Fisher. Litho J.W.)

1985 (16 Jan). *Centenary of St. John Ambulance in New Zealand.* P 14.

1357	**413** 24 c. black, gold and bright rosine			25	15
1358	30 c. black, sil & bright ultram			35	45
1359	40 c. black and grey			40	1·10
1357/9			*Set of 3*	90	1·50

The colours of the badge depicted are those for Bailiffs and Dames Grand Cross (24 c.), Knights and Dames of Grace (30 c.) and Officer Brothers and Sisters (40 c.).

---

414 Nelson Horse Tram, 1862   **415** Shotover Bridge

(Des R. M. Conly. Litho Cambec Press, Melbourne)

1985 (6 Mar). *Vintage Trams.* T **414** *and similar horiz designs. Multicoloured.* P 13½.

1360	24 c. Type 414	..	..	40	10
1361	30 c. Graham's Town steam tram, 1871	..	..	50	60
1362	35 c. Dunedin cable car, 1881	..	..	50	70
1363	40 c. Auckland electric tram, 1902	..	..	50	70
1364	45 c. Wellington electric tram, 1904	..	..	60	90
1365	58 c. Christchurch electric tram, 1905	..	..	70	1·75
1360/5			*Set of 6*	2·75	4·25

TARAPEX '86. To support this National Philatelic Exhibition the New Zealand Post Office co-operated with the organisers in the production of a set of "postage imprint labels". Five of the designs showed drawings of Maoris, taken from originals by Arthur Herbert Messenger and the sixth the Exhibition logo.

The sheetlets of 6 gummed and perforated labels were released by the Exhibition organisers on 3 April 1985. Although such labels were valid for postage, and could be so used by the general public, the sheetlets were not available from any New Zealand post office or from the Philatelic Bureau.

(Des R. Freeman. Photo Courvoisier)

1985 (12 June). *Bridges of New Zealand.* T **415** *and similar multicoloured designs. Granite paper.* P 11½.

1366	35 c. Type 415	..	..	60	60
1367	40 c. Alexandra Bridge	..	..	65	60
1368	45 c. South Rangitikei Railway Bridge (*vert*)			70	1·25
1369	70 c. Twin Bridges (*vert*)	..	..	90	1·25
1366/9			*Set of 4*	2·50	3·25

416 Queen Elizabeth II (from photo by Camera Press)   **417** Princess of Wales and Prince William

(Des B. Clinton. Litho Leigh-Mardon Ltd, Melbourne)

1985 (1 July). *Multicoloured, background colours given.* P 14½ × 14.

1370	**416** 25 c. rosine	..	..	50	10
1371	35 c. new blue.	..	..	90	10

Examples of the 25 c. value exist with the orders on the sash omitted. These are believed to originate from unissued sheets sent for destruction in March 1986.

(Des D. Little. Litho Cambec Press, Melbourne)

1985 (31 July). *Health Stamps.* T **417** *and similar vert designs showing photographs by Lord Snowdon. Multicoloured.* P 13½.

1372	25 c. + 2 c. Type 417	..	..	90	1·10
	a. Horiz pair. Nos. 1372/3	..	..	1·75	2·10
1373	25 c. + 2 c. Princess of Wales and Prince Henry			90	1·10
1374	35 c. + 2 c. Prince and Princess of Wales with Princes William and Henry			90	1·10
1372/4			*Set of 3*	2·50	3·00
MS1375	118 × 84 mm. Nos. 1372/4, each × 2	..		4·25	5·50

Nos. 1372/3 were printed together, *se-tenant*, in horizontal pairs throughout the sheet.

418 The Holy Family in the Stable   **419** H.M.N.Z.S. *Philomel* (1914–47)

(Des Eileen Mayo. Photo Enschedé)

1985 (18 Sept). *Christmas.* T **418** *and similar vert designs. Multicoloured.* P 13½×12½.

1376	18 c. Type 418	..	..	20	10
1377	40 c. The shepherds	..	..	40	85
1378	50 c. The angels	..	..	45	1·00
1376/8			*Set of 3*	95	1·75

Examples of the 18 c. and 50 c. stamps exist showing the spelling error "CRISTMAS". These are believed to originate from unissued sheets sent for destruction in March 1986. The New Zealand Post Office has stated that no such stamps were issued and that existing examples "were removed unlawfully during the destruction process".

(Des P. Durrant. Litho Cambec Press, Melbourne)

1985 (6 Nov). *New Zealand Naval History.* T **419** *and similar horiz designs. Multicoloured.* P 13½.

1379	25 c. Type **419**	70	15
1380	45 c. H.M.N.Z.S. *Achilles* (1936–46)	1·10	1·40
1381	60 c. H.M.N.Z.S. *Rotoiti* (1949–65)..	1·40	2·00
1382	75 c. H.M.N.Z.S. *Canterbury* (from 1971)	1·75	2·25
1379/82	*Set of 4*	4·50	5·25
MS1383	124×108 mm. Nos. 1379/82	4·50	5·25

420 Police Computer Operator   **421** Indian "Power Plus" 1000cc Motor Cycle (1920)

(Des A. Mitchell. Litho Leigh-Mardon Ltd, Melbourne)

1986 (15 Jan). *Centenary of New Zealand Police.* T **420** *and similar vert designs, each showing historical aspects above modern police activities. Multicoloured.* P 14½×14.

1384	25 c. Type **420**	35	50
	a. Horiz strip of 5. Nos. 1384/8	1·60	
1385	25 c. Detective and mobile control room	35	50
1386	25 c. Policewoman and badge	35	50
1387	25 c. Forensic scientist, patrol car and policeman with child	35	50
1388	25 c. Police College, Porirua, Patrol boat *Lady Elizabeth II* and dog handler	35	50
1384/8	*Set of 5*	1·60	2·25

Nos. 1384/8 were printed together, *se-tenant*, in horizontal strips of 5 throughout the sheet.

(Des M. Wyatt. Litho J.W.)

1986 (5 Mar). *Vintage Motor Cycles.* T **421** *and similar horiz designs. Multicoloured.* P 13×12½.

1389	35 c. Type **421**	55	45
1390	45 c. Norton "CS1" 500cc (1927)	65	65
1391	60 c. B.S.A. "Sloper" 500cc (1930)	85	1·50
1392	75 c. Triumph "Model H" 550cc (1915)	95	1·50
1389/92	*Set of 4*	2·75	3·50

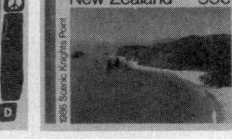

422 Tree of Life   **423** Knights Point

(Des Margaret Clarkson. Litho J.W.)

1986 (5 Mar). *International Peace Year.* T **422** *and similar horiz design. Multicoloured.* P 13×12½.

1393	25 c. Type **422**	30	30
	a. Horiz pair. Nos. 1393/4	60	60
1394	25 c. Peace dove	30	30

Nos. 1393/4 were printed together, *se-tenant*, in horizontal pairs throughout the sheet.

(Des P. Durrant. Photo Heraclio Fournier)

1986 (11 June). *Coastal Scenery.* T **423** *and similar horiz designs. Multicoloured.* P 14.

1395	55 c. Type **423**	55	65
1396	60 c. Becks Bay	55	80
1397	65 c. Doubtless Bay	60	90
1398	80 c. Wainui Bay	75	1·25
1395/8	*Set of 4*	2·25	3·25
MS1399	124×99 mm. No. 1398 (*sold at* $1.20) ..	1·40	1·25

The 40 c. premium on No. **MS**1399 was to support "New Zealand 1990" International Stamp Exhibition, Auckland.

No. **MS**1399 exists overprinted for "Stockholmia". Such miniature sheets were only available at this International Stamp Exhibition in Stockholm and were not placed on sale in New Zealand.

424 "Football" (Kylie Epapara)   **425** "A Partridge in a Pear Tree"

(Litho Leigh-Mardon Ltd, Melbourne)

1986 (30 July). *Health Stamps. Children's Paintings* (1st series). T **424** *and similar multicoloured designs.* P 14½×14 (30 c.) or 14×14½ (45 c.).

1400	30 c. + 3 c. Type **424**	40	40
	a. Horiz pair. Nos. 1400/1	80	80
1401	30 c. + 3 c. "Children at Play" (Philip Kata)	40	40
1402	45 c. + 3 c. "Children Skipping" (Mia Flannery) (horiz)	50	50
1400/2	*Set of 3*	1·10	1·10
MS1403	144×81 mm. Nos. 1400/2, each×2	2·25	2·25

Nos. 1400/1 were printed together, *se-tenant*, in horizontal pairs throughout the sheet.

No. **MS**1403 exists overprinted for "Stockholmia". Such miniature sheets are only available at this International Stamp Exhibition in Stockholm and were not placed on sale in New Zealand.

See also Nos. 1433/6.

(Des Margaret Halcrow-Cross. Photo Heraclio Fournier)

1986 (17 Sept). *Christmas. "The Twelve Days of Christmas"* (carol). T **425** *and similar vert designs. Multicoloured.* P 14½.

1404	25 c. Type **425**	20	10
1405	55 c. "Two turtle doves"	45	45
1406	65 c. "Three French hens"	50	50
1404/6	*Set of 3*	1·00	95

426 Conductor and Orchestra   **427** Jetboating

(Des R. Freeman. Litho Leigh-Mardon Ltd, Melbourne)

1986 (5 Nov). *Music in New Zealand.* T **426** *and similar vert designs.* P 14½×14.

1407	30 c. multicoloured	25	10
	a. Imperf (pair)	£250	
1408	60 c. black, new blue and yellow-orange	45	70
1409	80 c. multicoloured	70	1·40
1410	$1 multicoloured	80	1·10
1407/10	*Set of 4*	2·00	3·00

Designs:—60 c. Cornet and brass band; 80 c. Piper and Highland pipe band; $1 Guitar and country music group.

(Des M. Wyatt. Litho Leigh-Mardon Ltd, Melbourne)

1987 (14 Jan). *Tourism.* T **427** *and similar vert designs. Multicoloured.* P 14½×14.

1411	60 c. Type **427**	50	50
1412	70 c. Sightseeing flights	60	60
1413	80 c. Camping	70	75
1414	85 c. Windsurfing	70	75
1415	$1.05, Mountaineering	90	1·00
1416	$1.30, River rafting	1·10	1·25
1411/16	*Set of 6*	4·00	4·25

428 Southern Cross Cup

(Des R. Proud. Litho Leigh-Mardon Ltd, Melbourne)

1987 (2 Feb). *Yachting Events.* T **428** *and similar horiz designs showing yachts. Multicoloured.* P 14×14½.

1417	40 c. Type **428**	35	15
1418	80 c. Admiral's Cup..	70	80
1419	$1.05, Kenwood Cup	85	1·25
1420	$1.30, America's Cup	1·10	1·40
1417/20	*Set of 4*	2·75	3·25

429 Hand writing Letter and Postal Transport

(Des Communication Arts Ltd. Litho C.P.E. Australia Ltd, Melbourne)

1987 (1 Apr). *New Zealand Post Ltd Vesting Day.* T **429** *and similar horiz designs. Multicoloured.* P 13½.

1421	40 c. Type **429**	1·00	1·40
	a. Horiz pair. No. 1421/2	2·00	2·25
1422	40 c. Posting letter, train and mailbox	1·00	1·40

Nos. 1421/2 were printed together, *se-tenant*, in horizontal pairs throughout the sheet.

---

430 Avro Type 626 and Wigram Airfield, 1937   **431** Urewera National Park and Fern Leaf

(Des P. Leitch. Litho Leigh-Mardon Ltd, Melbourne)

1987 (15 Apr). *50th Anniv of Royal New Zealand Air Force.* T **430** *and similar horiz designs. Multicoloured.* P 14×14½.

1423	40 c. Type **430**	65	15
1424	70 c. Curtiss P-40E Kittyhawk I over World War II Pacific airstrip	90	1·50
1425	80 c. Short S.25 Sunderland flying boat and Pacific lagoon	1·00	1·50
1426	85 c. Douglas A-4F Skyhawk and Mt Ruapehu	1·10	1·25
1423/6	*Set of 4*	3·25	4·00
MS1427	115×105 mm. Nos. 1423/6	4·50	4·00

No. **MS**1427 overprinted on the selvedge with the "CAPEX" logo was only available from the New Zealand stand at this International Philatelic Exhibition in Toronto.

(Des Tracey Purkis. Litho Leigh-Mardon Ltd, Melbourne)

1987 (17 June). *Centenary of National Parks Movement.* T **431** *and similar vert designs. Multicoloured.* P 14½.

1428	70 c. Type **431**	70	55
1429	80 c. Mt Cook and buttercup	75	60
1430	85 c. Fiordland and pineapple shrub	80	65
1431	$1.30, Tongariro and tussock	1·40	95
1428/31	*Set of 4*	3·25	2·50
MS1432	123×99 mm. No. 1431 (*sold at* $1.70)	1·25	1·75

The 40 c. premium on No. **MS**1432 was to support "New Zealand 1990" International Stamp Exhibition, Auckland.

No. **MS**1432 overprinted on the selvedge with the "CAPEX" logo was only available from the New Zealand stand at this International Philatelic Exhibition in Toronto.

432 "Kite Flying" (Lauren Baldwin)   **433** "Hark the Herald Angels Sing"

(Adapted D. Little. Litho Leigh-Mardon Ltd, Melbourne)

1987 (29 July). *Health Stamps. Children's Paintings* (2nd series). T **432** *and similar multicoloured designs.* P 14½.

1433	40 c. + 3 c. Type **432**	80	1·25
	a. Horiz pair. No. 1433/4	1·60	2·50
1434	40 c. + 3 c. "Swimming" (Ineke Schoneveld)	80	1·25
1435	60 c. + 3 c. "Horse Riding" (Aaron Tylee) (vert)	1·25	1·50
1433/5	*Set of 3*	2·50	3·50
MS1436	100×117 mm. Nos. 1433/5, each×2	5·00	6·50

Nos. 1433/4 were printed together, *se-tenant*, in horizontal pairs throughout the sheet.

(Des Ellen Giggenbach. Litho Leigh-Mardon Ltd, Melbourne)

1987 (16 Sept). *Christmas.* T **433** *and similar vert designs. Multicoloured.* P 14½.

1437	45 c. Type **433**	45	10
1438	70 c. "Away in a Manger"	90	55
1439	85 c. "We Three Kings of Orient Are"	1·10	65
1437/9	*Set of 3*	2·25	1·25

434 Knot ("Pona")   **435** "Geothermal"

(Des Nga Puna Waihanga. Litho Security Printers (M), Malaysia)

1987 (4 Nov). *Maori Fibre-work.* T **434** *and similar vert designs. Multicoloured.* W **138** of Malaysia. P 12.

1440	40 c. Type **434**	35	10
1441	60 c. Binding ("Herehere")	45	55
1442	80 c. Plait ("Whiri")	60	90
1443	85 c. Cloak weaving ("Korowai") with flax fibre ("Whitau")	65	95
1440/3	*Set of 4*	1·90	2·25

(Des Fay McAlpine. Litho Leigh-Mardon Ltd, Melbourne)

1988 (13 Jan). *Centenary of Electricity.* T **435** *and similar horiz designs, each showing radiating concentric circles representing energy generation.* P 14×14½.

1444	40 c. multicoloured	30	35
1445	60 c. black, rosine and brownish black	40	45
1446	70 c. multicoloured	50	55
1447	80 c. multicoloured	55	60
1444/7	*Set of 4*	1·60	1·75

Designs:—60 c. "Thermal"; 70 c. "Gas"; 80 c. "Hydro".

436 Queen Elizabeth II and 1882 Queen Victoria 1d. Stamp

437 "Mangopare"

(Des A. G. Mitchell (40 c.), R. M. Conly and M. Stanley ($1). Litho Leigh-Mardon Ltd., Melbourne)

1988 (13 Jan). *Centenary of Royal Philatelic Society of New Zealand. T 436 and similar multicoloured designs. P 14×14½.*

1448	40 c. Type **436**		35	50
	a. Horiz pair. Nos. 1448/9		70	1·00
1449	40 c. As Type **436**, but 1882 Queen Victoria 2d.		35	50
MS1450	107×160 mm. $1 "Queen Victoria" (Chalon) (*vert*). P 14½×14		2·75	3·00

Nos. 1448/9 were printed together, *se-tenant*, in horizontal pairs throughout the sheet.

No. MS1450 overprinted on the selvedge with the "SYDPEX" logo was only available from the New Zealand stand at this International Philatelic Exhibition in Sydney and from the Philatelic Bureau at Wanganui.

(Des S. Adsett. Litho Leigh-Mardon Ltd, Melbourne)

1988 (2 Mar). *Maori Rafter Paintings. T 437 and similar vert designs. Multicoloured. P 14½.*

1451	40 c. Type **437**		40	40
1452	40 c. "Koru"		40	40
1453	40 c. "Raupunga"		40	40
1454	60 c. "Koiri"		55	65
1451/4		*Set of 4*	1·60	1·75

438 "Good Luck"

439 Paradise Shelduck

(Des Communication Arts Ltd. Litho CPE Australia Ltd, Melbourne)

1988 (18 May). *Greetings Stamps. T 438 and similar multicoloured designs. P 13½.*

1455	40 c. Type **438**		60	70
	a. Booklet pane. Nos. 1455/9		2·75	
1456	40 c. "Keeping in touch"		60	70
1457	40 c. "Happy birthday"		60	70
1458	40 c. "Congratulations" (41 × 27 *mm*)		60	70
1459	40 c. "Get well soon" (41 × 27 *mm*)		60	70
1455/9		*Set of 5*	2·75	3·25

Nos. 1455/9 were only issued in $2 stamp booklets.

(Des Pauline Morse. Litho Southern Colour Print, Dunedin (Nos. 1467ab/ac) or Leigh-Mardon Ltd, Melbourne (others))

1988 (7 June)–95. *Native Birds. T 439 and similar vert designs. Multicoloured. Phosphorised paper (5, 45 c.). P 14½×14.*

1459a	5 c. Sooty Crake (1.7.91)		10	10
1460	10 c. Double-banded Plover ("Banded Dotterel") (2.11.88)		10	10
1461	20 c. Yellowhead (2.11.88)		15	20
	a. Perf 14 (22.9.95)		45	30
1462	30 c. Grey-backed White Eye ("Silvereye") (2.11.88)		30	30
1463	40 c. Brown Kiwi (2.11.88)		35	40
	a. Perf 13½×13 (8.11.89)		90	1·25
	ab. Pack pane. No. 1463a×10 with margins all round		8·50	
1463b	45 c. Rock Wren (1.7.91)		60	60
	ba. Booklet pane. No. 1463b×10 with horiz sides of pane imperf (1.10.91)		5·00	
1464	50 c. Sacred Kingfisher (2.11.88)		50	50
1465	60 c. Spotted Cormorant ("Spotted Shag") (2.11.88)		50	55
	a. Perf 13½ (22.9.95)		70	70
1466	70 c. Type **439**		55	90
1467	80 c. Fiordland Crested Penguin (2.11.88)		80	70
1467a	80 c. New Zealand Falcon (31.3.93)		1·00	90
	ab. Perf 12 (7.94)		90	90
	ac. Booklet pane. No. 1467ab×10		9·00	
1468	90 c. New Zealand Robin (2.11.88)		1·25	80
1459a/68		*Set of 12*	5·00	5·00

No. 1463a was only issued in panes of ten with margins on all four sides. These panes were initially included in "Stamp Pads" of 50 such panes, but subsequently appeared in $4 stamp packs.

A miniature sheet containing No. 1466 was only available from the New Zealand stand at "WORLD STAMP EXPO '89" International Exhibition or the Philatelic Bureau, Wanganui. It was subsequently overprinted with the "New Zealand 1990" emblem.

No. 1467a was originally issued in $8 booklets on 31 March 1993, but appeared in sheets on 18 February 1994.

No. 1467ab was only issued in $8 stamp booklets and shows the vertical edges of the pane imperforate.

For 40 c. and 45 c. stamps in similar designs, but self-adhesive, see Nos. 1589/a.

For Nos. 1459a/65 in miniature sheet for the "Philakorea '94" International Stamp Exhibition see No. MS1830.

440 Milford Track

441 Kiwi and Koala at Campfire

(Des H. Thompson. Litho Leigh-Mardon Ltd, Melbourne)

1988 (8 June). *Scenic Walking Trails. T 440 and similar vert designs. Multicoloured. P 14½.*

1469	70 c. Type **440**		50	60
1470	80 c. Heaphy Track		55	75
1471	85 c. Copland Track		60	80
1472	$1.30, Routeburn Track		90	1·25
1469/72		*Set of 4*	2·25	3·00
MS1473	124 × 99 mm. No. 1472 (*sold at $1.70*)		1·50	1·50

The 40 c. premium on No. MS1473 was to support "New Zealand 1990" International Stamp Exhibition, Auckland.

(Des R. Harvey. Litho Leigh-Mardon Ltd, Melbourne)

1988 (21 June). *Bicentenary of Australian Settlement. P 14½.*

1474	**441** 40 c. multicoloured		40	35

A stamp in a similar design was also issued by Australia.

 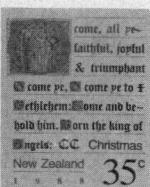

442 Swimming

443 "O Come All Ye Faithful"

(Des R. Proud. Litho Leigh-Mardon Ltd, Melbourne)

1988 (27 July). *Health Stamps. Olympic Games, Seoul. T 442 and similar horiz designs. Multicoloured. P 14½.*

1475	40 c. + 3 c. Type **442**		40	65
1476	60 c. + 3 c. Athletics		60	1·00
1477	70 c. + 3 c. Canoeing		70	1·00
1478	80 c. + 3 c. Show-jumping		90	1·25
1475/8		*Set of 4*	2·40	3·50
MS1479	120 × 90 mm. Nos. 1475/8		3·25	4·00

(Des Fay McAlpine. Litho Leigh-Mardon Ltd, Melbourne)

1988 (14 Sept). *Christmas. Carols. T 443 and similar vert designs, each showing illuminated verses. Multicoloured. P 14½.*

1480	35 c. Type **443**		30	30
1481	70 c. "Hark the Herald Angels Sing"		50	65
1482	80 c. "Ding Dong Merrily on High"		50	70
1483	85 c. "The First Nowell"		55	80
1480/3		*Set of 4*	1·75	2·25

444 "Lake Pukaki" (John Gully)

445 Brown Kiwi

(Litho Leigh-Mardon Ltd, Melbourne)

1988 (5 Oct). *New Zealand Heritage (1st issue). The Land. T 444 and similar horiz designs showing 19th-century paintings. Multicoloured. P 14 × 14½.*

1484	40 c. Type **444**		35	35
1485	60 c. "On the Grass Plain below Lake Arthur" (William Fox)		45	45
1486	70 c. "View of Auckland" (John Hoyte)		55	55
1487	80 c. "Mt. Egmont from the Southward" (Charles Heaphy)		60	60
1488	$1.05, "Anakiwa, Queen Charlotte Sound" (John Kinder)		80	80
1489	$1.30, "White Terraces, Lake Rotomahana" (Charles Barraud)		95	95
1484/9		*Set of 6*	3·25	3·25

See also Nos. 1505/10, 1524/9, 1541/6, 1548/53 and 1562/7.

(Des A. Mitchell. Eng. G. Prosser of B.A.B.N. Recess Leigh-Mardon Ltd, Melbourne)

1988 (19 Oct)–93. *Phosphorised paper (No. 1490b). P 14½ (and 13 around design).*

1490	**445** $1 bronze-green		2·00	2·75
	a. Booklet pane. No. 1490×6		11·00	
1490b	$1 bright scarlet (17.4.91)		1·40	1·50
1490c	$1 blue (9.6.93)		1·00	1·25
1490/c		*Set of 3*	4·00	5·00

Nos. 1490/c were each printed within a square margin, perforated vertically for No. 1490 and on all four sides for Nos. 1490b/c, and with a further circular perforation around the design.

No. 1490 was only issued in $6 stamp booklets with the horizontal edges of the booklet pane imperforate.

Nos. 1490b/c were printed in sheets of 24 (6×4).

For miniature sheets containing similar stamps, some printed in lithography, see Nos. MS1745 and MS1786.

For $1 violet and $1.10 see Nos. 2090/a.

446 Humpback Whale and Calf

447 Clover

(Des Lindy Fisher. Litho Govt Ptg Office, Wellington)

1988 (2 Nov). *Whales. T 446 and similar horiz designs. Multicoloured. P 13½.*

1491	60 c. Type **446**		80	85
1492	70 c. Killer Whales		1·00	1·10
1493	80 c. Southern Right Whale		1·10	1·25
1494	85 c. Blue Whale		1·25	1·50
1495	$1.05, Southern Bottlenose Whale and calf		1·50	2·00
1496	$1.30, Sperm Whale		1·60	2·00
1491/6		*Set of 6*	6·50	8·00

Although inscribed "ROSS DEPENDENCY" Nos. 1491/6 were available from post offices throughout New Zealand.

(Des Heather Arnold. Litho Leigh-Mardon Ltd, Melbourne)

1989 (18 Jan). *Wild Flowers. T 447 and similar horiz designs. Multicoloured. P 14½.*

1497	40 c. Type **447**		40	35
1498	60 c. Lotus		50	60
1499	70 c. Montbretia		60	80
1500	80 c. Wild Ginger		70	90
1497/1500		*Set of 4*	2·00	2·40

448 Katherine Mansfield

449 Moriori Man and Map of Chatham Islands

(Des A. G. Mitchell. Litho Harrison)

1989 (1 Mar). *New Zealand Authors. T 448 and similar vert designs. Multicoloured. P 12½.*

1501	40 c. Type **448**		30	35
1502	60 c. James K. Baxter		40	50
1503	70 c. Bruce Mason		50	60
1504	80 c. Ngaio Marsh		55	70
1501/4		*Set of 4*	1·60	1·90

(Des D. Gunson. Litho Leigh-Mardon Ltd, Melbourne)

1989 (17 May). *New Zealand Heritage (2nd issue). The People. T 449 and similar horiz designs. P 14×14½.*

1505	40 c. multicoloured		45	35
1506	60 c. orge-brn, brownish grey & reddish brn		60	70
1507	70 c. yellow-grn, brownish grey & dp olive		65	75
1508	80 c. bright greenish blue, brownish grey and deep dull blue		75	85
1509	$1.05, grey, brownish grey & grey-black		1·00	1·10
1510	$1.30, bright rose-red, brownish grey, and lake-brown		1·25	1·40
1505/10		*Set of 6*	4·25	4·50

Designs:—60 c. Gold prospector; 70 c. Settler ploughing; 80 c. Whaling; $1.05, Missionary preaching to Maoris; $1.30, Maori village.

450 White Pine (Kahikatea)

451 Duke and Duchess of York with Princess Beatrice

(Des D. Gunson. Litho Questa)

1989 (7 June). *Native Trees. T 450 and similar vert designs. Multicoloured. P 14×14½.*

1511	80 c. Type **450**		75	80
1512	85 c. Red Pine (Rimu)		80	85
1513	$1.05, Totara		1·00	1·10
1514	$1.30, Kauri		1·25	1·40
1511/14		*Set of 4*	3·50	3·75
MS1515	102×125 mm. No. 1514 (*sold at $1.80*)		1·75	1·75

The 50 c. premium on No. MS1515 was to support "New Zealand 1990" International Stamp Exhibition, Auckland.

(Des and litho Leigh-Mardon Ltd, Melbourne)

1989 (26 July). *Health Stamps. T 451 and similar vert designs. Multicoloured. P 14½.*

1516	40 c. + 3 c. Type **451**		80	1·25
	a. Horiz pair. Nos. 1516/17		1·60	2·50
1517	40 c. + 3 c. Duchess of York with Princess Beatrice		80	1·25

1518	80 c. + 3 c. Princess Beatrice	1·40	1·75
1516/18	*Set of 3*	2·75	3·75
MS1519	120×89 mm. Nos. 1516/18, each ×2	5·50	7·00

Nos. 1516/17 were printed together, *se-tenant*, in horizontal pairs throughout the sheet.

No. **MS**1519 overprinted on the selvedge with the "WORLD STAMP EXPO '89" logo was only available from the New Zealand stand at this International Stamp Exhibition and from the Philatelic Bureau at Wanganui.

452 One Tree Hill, Auckland, through Bedroom Window   **453** Windsurfing

(Des H. Chapman. Litho Leigh-Mardon Ltd, Melbourne)

1989 (13 Sept). *Christmas. T* **452** *and similar vert designs showing Star of Bethlehem. Multicoloured. P* 14½.

1520	35 c. Type 452	40	30
1521	65 c. Shepherd and dog in mountain valley	75	70
1522	80 c. Star over harbour	95	90
1523	$1 Star over globe	1·25	1·40
1520/3	*Set of 4*	3·00	3·00

(Des M. Bailey. Litho Leigh-Mardon Ltd, Melbourne)

1989 (11 Oct). *New Zealand Heritage (3rd issue). The Sea. T* **453** *and similar horiz designs. Multicoloured. P* 14×14½.

1524	40 c. Type 453	40	30
1525	60 c. Fishes of many species	70	70
1526	65 c. Striped Marlin and game fishing launch	75	75
1527	80 c. Rowing boat and yachts in harbour	85	85
1528	$1 Coastal scene	1·10	1·10
1529	$1.50, *Rotoiti* (container ship) and tug	1·50	1·60
1524/9	*Set of 6*	4·75	4·75

454 Games Logo

(Des Heather Arnold. Litho Leigh-Mardon Ltd, Melbourne)

1989 (8 Nov)–**90**. *14th Commonwealth Games. Auckland. T* **454** *and similar horiz designs. Multicoloured. P* 14½.

1530	40 c. Type 454	40	35
1531	40 c. Goldie (games kiwi mascot)	40	35
1532	40 c. Gymnastics	40	35
1533	50 c. Weightlifting	50	55
1534	65 c. Swimming	65	70
1535	80 c. Cycling	80	90
1536	$1 Lawn bowling	1·00	1·25
1537	$1.80, Hurdling	1·75	1·90
1530/7	*Set of 8*	5·50	5·75

MS1538 Two sheets, each 105×92 mm. with different margin designs. (a) Nos. 1530/1 (horiz pair). (b) Nos. 1530/1 (vert pair) (24.1.90).
	Set of 2 sheets 5·00	3·50

455 Short S.30 Modified "G" Class Flying Boat *Aotearoa* and Boeing 747-200   **456** Chief Kawiti signing Treaty

(Des R. Proud. Litho Enschedé)

1990 (17 Jan). *50th Anniv of Air New Zealand. P* 13×14½.

1539	455 80 c. multicoloured	1·40	1·10

(Des A. G. Mitchell from painting by L. C. Mitchell. Litho Enschedé)

1990 (17 Jan). *150th Anniv of Treaty of Waitangi. Sheet* 80×118 mm, *containing T* **456** *and similar multicoloured design. P* 13½.

MS1540 40 c. Type **456**; 40 c. Chief Hone Heke (first signatory) and Lieut-Governor Hobson (*horiz*) .. 3·25 3·25

NEW INFORMATION

The editor is always interested to correspond with people who have new information that will improve or correct the Catalogue.

---

457 Maori Voyaging Canoe   **458** *Thelymitra pulchella*

(Des G. Fuller. Litho Leigh-Mardon Ltd, Melbourne)

1990 (7 Mar). *New Zealand Heritage (4th issue). The Ships. T* **457** *and similar horiz designs. Multicoloured. P* 14×14½.

1541	40 c. Type 457	60	35
1542	50 c. H.M.S. *Endeavour* (Cook), 1769	85	80
1543	60 c. *Tory* (barque), 1839	95	90
1544	80 c. *Crusader* (full-rigged immigrant ship), 1871	1·40	1·40
1545	$1 *Edwin Fox* (full-rigged immigrant ship), 1873	1·60	1·40
1546	$1.50, *Arawa* (steamer), 1884	2·00	2·75
1541/6	*Set of 6*	6·75	6·75

A miniature sheet containing No. 1542 was only available from the New Zealand stand at "Stamp World London '90" International Stamp Exhibition or from the Philatelic Bureau, Wanganui.

(Des Lindy Fisher. Litho Leigh-Mardon Ltd, Melbourne)

1990 (18 Apr). *"New Zealand 1990" International Stamp Exhibition, Auckland. Native Orchids. Sheet* 179×80 mm. *containing T* **458** *and similar vert designs. Multicoloured. P* 14½.

MS1547 40 c. Type **458**; 40 c. *Corybas macranthus*; 40 c. *Dendrobium cunninghamii*; 40 c. *Pterostylis banksii*; 80 c. *Aporostylis bifolia* (*sold at* $4.90) .. .. 4·50 4·50

The stamps in No. **MS**1547 form a composite design.

The $2.50 premium on No. **MS**1547 was used to support the Exhibition.

Miniature sheets as No. **MS**1547, but imperforate are from a limited printing distributed to those purchasing season tickets for the exhibition.

459 Grace Neill (social reformer) and Maternity Hospital, Wellington   **460** Akaroa

(Des Elspeth Williamson. Litho Leigh-Mardon Ltd, Melbourne)

1990 (16 May). *New Zealand Heritage (5th issue). Famous New Zealanders. T* **459** *and similar horiz designs. Multicoloured. P* 14×14½.

1548	40 c. Type 459	55	30
1549	50 c. Jean Batten (pilot) and Percival P.3 Gull Six aircraft	65	75
1550	60 c. Katherine Sheppard (suffragette) and 19th-century women	85	1·25
1551	80 c. Richard Pearse (inventor) and early flying machine	1·10	1·25
1552	$1 Lt.-Gen. Sir Bernard Freyberg and tank	1·25	1·25
1553	$1.50, Peter Buck (politician) and Maori pattern	1·50	2·00
1548/53	*Set of 6*	5·50	6·25

(Des Lindy Fisher. Litho Leigh-Mardon Ltd, Melbourne)

1990 (13 June). *150th Anniversary of European Settlements. T* **460** *and similar vert designs. Multicoloured. P* 14½.

1554	80 c. Type 460	75	75
1555	$1 Wanganui	95	95
1556	$1.50, Wellington	1·40	2·25
1557	$1.80, Takapuna Beach, Auckland	1·60	2·25
1554/7	*Set of 4*	4·25	5·50
MS1558	125×100 mm. No. 1557 (*sold at* $2.30)	3·50	3·50

The 50 c. premium on No. **MS**1558 was to support "New Zealand 1990" International Stamp Exhibition, Auckland.

461 Jack Lovelock (athlete) and Race   **462** Creation Legend of Rangi and Papa

(Des T. Crilley. Litho Questa)

1990 (25 July). *Health Stamps. Sportsmen (1st series). T* **461** *and similar horiz design. Multicoloured. P* 14½×13½.

1559	40 c. + 5 c. Type 461	50	75
1560	80 c. + 5 c. George Nepia (rugby player) and match	75	1·25
MS1561	115×96 mm. Nos. 1559/60, each × 2	2·50	3·25

See also Nos. 1687/9.

(Des K. Hall. Litho Leigh-Mardon Ltd, Melbourne)

1990 (24 Aug). *New Zealand Heritage (6th issue). The Maori. T* **462** *and similar horiz designs. Multicoloured. P* 14×14½.

1562	40 c. Type 462	40	30
	a. Violet-blue (face value) omitted	£275	
1563	50 c. Pattern from Maori feather cloak	55	70
1564	60 c. Maori women's choir	60	80
1565	80 c. Maori facial tattoos	75	90
1566	$1 War canoe prow (detail)	90	1·10
1567	$1.50, Maori haka	1·40	2·50
1562/7	*Set of 6*	4·25	5·75

463 Queen Victoria   **464** Angel

(Des A. G. Mitchell. Recess Leigh-Mardon Ltd, Melbourne)

1990 (29 Aug). *150th Anniv of the Penny Black. Sheet* 169×70 mm *containing T* **463** *and similar vert designs. P* 14½×14.

MS1568 40 c. ×6 indigo (Type **463**, King Edward VII, King George V, King Edward VIII, King George VI, Queen Elizabeth II) .. 4·00 4·50

(Des Sally Simons. Litho Leigh-Mardon Ltd, Melbourne)

1990 (12 Sept). *Christmas. T* **464** *and similar vert designs showing angels. P* 14½.

1569	40 c. purple, dp greenish bl & dp yellow-brn	40	30
1570	$1 purple, blue-green & dp yellow-brown	80	80
1571	$1.50, pur, brt crimson & dp yellow-brn	1·40	1·75
1572	$1.80, purple, red and deep yellow-brown	1·60	1·75
1569/72	*Set of 4*	3·75	4·25

465 Antarctic Petrel   **466** Coopworth Ewe and Lambs

(Des Janet Luxton. Litho Heraclio Fournier)

1990 (7 Nov). *Antarctic Birds. T* **465** *and similar vert designs. Multicoloured. P* 13½×13.

1573	40 c. Type 465	80	30
1574	50 c. Wilson's Petrel	90	55
1575	60 c. Snow Petrel	1·10	85
1576	80 c. Southern Fulmar	1·25	85
1577	$1 Chinstrap Penguin	1·40	85
1578	$1.50, Emperor Penguin	1·60	2·25
1573/8	*Set of 6*	6·25	5·25

Although inscribed "Ross Dependency" Nos. 1573/8 were available from post offices throughout New Zealand.

(Des Lindy Fisher. Litho Leigh-Mardon Ltd, Melbourne)

1991 (23 Jan). *New Zealand Farming and Agriculture. Sheep Breeds. T* **466** *and similar vert designs. Multicoloured. P* 14½×14.

1579	40 c. Type 466	40	40
1580	60 c. Perendale	55	75
1581	80 c. Corriedale	70	85
1582	$1 Drysdale	85	90
1583	$1.50, South Suffolk	1·25	2·00
1584	$1.80, Romney	1·50	2·00
1579/84	*Set of 6*	4·75	6·25

467 Moriori, Royal Albatross, Nikau Palm and Artefacts   **468** Goal and Footballers

(Des K. Hall. Litho Southern Colour Print Ltd, Dunedin)

1991 (6 Mar). *Bicentenary of Discovery of Chatham Islands. T* **467** *and similar vert design. Multicoloured. P* 13½.

1585	40 c. Type 467	50	50
1586	80 c. Carvings, H.M.S. *Chatham*, Moriori house of 1870, and Tommy Solomon	1·25	1·60

(Des T. Crilley. Litho Southern Colour Print Ltd, Dunedin)

1991 (6 Mar). *Centenary of New Zealand Football Association. T 468 and similar horiz design. Multicoloured. P 13½.*
1587	80 c. Type 468	..	1·00	1·40
	a. Horiz pair. Nos. 1587/8	..	2·00	2·75
1588	80 c. Five footballers and referee	..	1·00	1·40

Nos. 1587/8 were printed together, *se-tenant*, in horizontal pairs throughout the sheet, each pair forming a composite design.

(Des Pauline Morse. Litho Printset-Cambec Pty Ltd, Melbourne (40 c., 45 c. (No. 1589a) or Leigh-Mardon Ltd, Melbourne (45 c. (No. 1589ab))

1991 (17 Apr–Dec). *As Nos. 1463/b, but self-adhesive. Phosphorised paper. P 11½.*
1589	40 c. Brown Kiwi	..	70	80
1589a	45 c. Rock Wren (1 July)	..	30	45
	ab. Perf 11 (Dec)	..	30	45

Nos. 1589/a were only available in coils of 100, each stamp, with die-cut perforations, being separate on the imperforate backing paper. Initially the 45 c. showed the surplus surface paper removed, but from December 1991 supplies of No. 1589ab had the stamps surrounded by white selvedge. The format was changed again in March 1992 when the coils again appeared without the white selvedge. Part of the March 1992 printing, and all subsequent supplies, had the stamps interlocked with no backing paper visible between them.

A limited quantity of the 45 c. (No. 1589a) in sheets of 200 (8×25) was produced for use on official first day covers. It is reported that a small number of such sheets were subsequently sold by a few post offices.

469 Tuatara on Rocks   **470** Clown

(Des Pauline Morse. Litho Leigh-Mardon Ltd, Melbourne)

1991 (17 Apr). *Endangered Species. The Tuatara. T 469 and similar horiz designs. Multicoloured. P 14½.*
1590	40 c. Type 469	..	40	55
1591	40 c. Tuatara in crevice	..	40	55
1592	40 c. Tuatara with foliage	..	40	55
1593	40 c. Tuatara in dead leaves	..	40	55
1590/3		Set of 4	1·40	2·00

(Des Helen Crawford. Litho Leigh-Mardon Ltd, Melbourne)

1991 (15 May–1 July). *"Happy Birthday". T 470 and similar multicoloured designs. P 13½.*
1594	40 c. Type 470	..	55	60
	a. Booklet pane. Nos. 1594/8	..	2·50	
1595	40 c. Balloons	..	55	60
1596	40 c. Party hat	..	55	60
1597	40 c. Birthday present (41×27 mm)	..	55	60
1598	40 c. Birthday cake (41×27 mm)	..	55	60
1599	45 c. Type 470 (1 July)	..	55	60
	a. Booklet pane. Nos. 1599/1603	..	2·50	
1600	45 c. As No. 1595 (1 July)	..	55	60
1601	45 c. As No. 1596 (1 July)	..	55	60
1602	45 c. As No. 1597 (1 July)	..	55	60
1603	45 c. As No. 1598 (1 July)	..	55	60
1594/1603		Set of 10	5·00	5·50

The above were only issued in $2 (Nos. 1594/8) or $2.25 (Nos. 1599/1603) stamp booklets.

471 Cat at Window   **472** Punakaiki Rocks

(Des Jennifer Lautusi. Litho Leigh-Mardon Ltd, Melbourne)

1991 (15 May–1 July). *"Thinking of You". T 471 and similar multicoloured designs. P 13½.*
1604	40 c. Type 471	..	55	60
	a. Booklet pane. Nos. 1604/8	..	2·50	
1605	40 c. Cat playing with slippers	..	55	60
1606	40 c. Cat with alarm clock	..	55	60
1607	40 c. Cat in window (41×27 mm)	..	55	60
1608	40 c. Cat at door (41×27 mm)	..	55	60
1609	45 c. Type 471 (1 July)	..	55	60
	a. Booklet pane. Nos. 1609/13	..	2·50	
1610	45 c. As No. 1605 (1 July)	..	55	60
1611	45 c. As No. 1606 (1 July)	..	55	60
1612	45 c. As No. 1607 (1 July)	..	55	60
1613	45 c. As No. 1608 (1 July)	..	55	60
1604/13		Set of 10	5·00	5·50

The above were only issued in $2 (Nos. 1604/8) or $2.25 (Nos. 1609/13) stamp booklets.

(Des H. Thompson. Litho Leigh-Mardon Ltd, Melbourne)

1991 (12 June). *Scenic Landmarks. T 472 and similar horiz designs. Multicoloured. P 14½.*
1614	40 c. Type 472	..	40	30
1615	50 c. Moeraki Boulders	..	55	55
1616	80 c. Organ Pipes	..	85	85
1617	$1 Castle Hill	..	95	95
1618	$1.50, Te Kaukau Point	..	1·50	1·60
1619	$1.80, Ahuriri River Clay Cliffs	..	1·75	1·90
1614/19		Set of 6	5·50	5·50

473 Dolphins Underwater   **474** Children's Rugby

(Des Heather Arnold. Litho Leigh-Mardon Ltd, Melbourne)

1991 (24 July). *Health Stamps. Hector's Dolphin. T 473 and similar horiz design. Multicoloured. P 14½.*
1620	45 c. + 5 c. Type 473	..	90	1·00
1621	80 c. + 5 c. Dolphins leaping	..	1·25	1·75
MS1622	115×100 mm. Nos. 1620/1, each × 2		4·50	5·50

(Des A.G. Mitchell. Litho Leigh-Mardon Ltd, Melbourne)

1991 (21 Aug). *World Cup Rugby Championship. T 474 and similar vert designs. Multicoloured. P 14½×14.*
1623	80 c. Type 474	..	1·00	1·25
1624	$1 Women's rugby	..	1·10	95
1625	$1.50, Senior rugby	..	1·75	2·50
1626	$1.80, "All Blacks" (national team)	..	2·00	2·50
1623/6		Set of 4	5·25	6·50
MS1627	113×90 mm. No. 1626 (sold at $2.40)		4·00	4·00

No. MS1627 additionaly inscribed "PHILA NIPPON '91" was available, at $1·80, from the New Zealand stand at this International Stamp Exhibition in Tokyo and from the Philatelic Bureau at Wanganui.

475 Three Shepherds   **476** Dodonidia helmsii

(Des Designworks Communications. Litho Southern Colour Print, Dunedin)

1991 (18 Sept). *Christmas. T 475 and similar vert designs. Multicoloured. P 13½.*
1628	45 c. Type 475	..	55	75
	a. Block of four. Nos 1628/31	..	2·00	
1629	45 c. Two Kings on camels	..	55	75
1630	45 c. Mary and Baby Jesus	..	55	75
1631	45 c. King with gift	..	55	75
1632	65 c. Star of Bethlehem	..	70	80
1633	$1 Crown	..	85	95
1634	$1.50, Angel	..	1·40	2·00
1628/34		Set of 7	4·50	6·00

Nos. 1628/31 were printed together, *se-tenant*, in blocks of four throughout the sheet.

(Des Pauline Morse)

1991 (6 Nov)–97. *Butterflies. T 476 and similar vert designs. Multicoloured. (a) Litho Leigh-Mardon Ltd, Melbourne. Phosphorised paper ($4, $5). P 14½*
1635	$1 Type 476	..	1·00	60
1636	$2 Zizina otis oxleyi	..	2·00	1·50
1637	$3 Vanessa itea	..	2·75	2·50
1638	$4 Lycaena salustius (25.1.95)	..	4·00	3·75
1639	$5 Bassaris gonerilla (25.1.95)	..	4·75	4·50
1635/9		Set of 5	13·00	11·50

(b) Litho Questa. P 13½×14
1640	$1 As Type 476 (6.11.96)	..	90	80
1641	$2 As No. 1636 (6.11.96)	..	2·00	1·75
1642	$3 As No. 1637 (8.96)	..	2·75	3·00
	a. Grey (inscrs) and apple-green (frame) omitted		£325	
1643	$4 As No. 1638 (10.97)	..	3·25	3·50
1644	$5 As No. 1639 (9.10.96)	..	3·75	4·00
1640/4		Set of 5	11·50	11·50

(c) Booklet stamps. Litho Southern Colour Print, Dunedin. P 14×14½
1645	$1 Type 476 (1.9.95)	..	2·75	3·00
	a. Booklet pane. No. 1645×5 and five "airPOST" labels		13·00	

Nos. 1640/2 are from the 3 kiwi printings and Nos. 1643/4 from the 1 kiwi. The designs of Nos. 1640/1 are redrawn.

No. 1645 only exists imperforate at foot and was issued in $5 stamp booklets in which the airmail labels were vertically *se-tenant* with the stamps.

A miniature sheet containing No. 1637 was only available from the New Zealand stand at "PHILA NIPPON '91" International Stamp Exhibition, Tokyo, or the Philatelic Bureau, Wanganui.

(Des R. Proud. Litho Leigh-Mardon Ltd, Melbourne)

1992 (22 Jan). *New Zealand Challenge for America's Cup. T 479 and similar horiz designs. Multicoloured. P 14.*
1655	45 c. Type 479	..	45	35
1656	80 c. Yacht New Zealand, 1988	..	80	70
1657	$1 Yacht America, 1851	..	95	85
1658	$1.50, "America's Cup" Class yacht, 1992	1·60	1·40
1655/8		Set of 4	3·50	3·00

(Des G. Fuller. Litho Enschedé)

1992 (12 Mar). *Great Voyages of Discovery. T 480 and similar horiz designs. Multicoloured. P 13×14½.*
1659	45 c. Type 480	..	55	35
1660	80 c. Zeehan	..	90	85
1661	$1 Santa Maria	..	1·25	85
1662	$1.50, Pinta and Nina	..	1·50	1·60
1659/62		Set of 4	3·75	3·25

Nos. 1659/60 commemorate the 350th anniversary of Tasman's discovery of New Zealand and Nos. 1661/2 the 500th anniversary of discovery of America by Columbus.

A miniature sheet containing stamps as Nos. 1661/2, but perforated 14, was only available from the New Zealand stand at "World Columbian Stamp Expo '92", Chicago, and from the Philatelic Bureau at Wanganui.

481 Sprinters   **482** Weddell Seal and Pup

(Des Sheryl McCammon. Litho Southern Colour Print, Dunedin)

1992 (3 Apr). *Olympic Games, Barcelona (1st issue). P 13½.*
1663	481 45 c. multicoloured	..	50	40

See also Nos. 1670/4.

(Des Lindy Fisher. Litho Southern Colour Print, Dunedin)

1992 (8 Apr). *Antarctic Seals. T 482 and similar horiz designs. Multicoloured. P 13½.*
1664	45 c. Type 482	..	70	40
1665	50 c. Crabeater Seals swimming	..	80	40
1666	65 c. Leopard Seal and Adelie Penguins	1·00	85
1667	80 c. Ross Seal	..	1·25	90
1668	$1 Southern Elephant Seal and harem	1·40	95
1669	$1.80, Hooker's Sea Lion and pup	2·25	2·25
1664/9		Set of 6	6·75	5·25

Although inscribed "ROSS DEPENDENCY" Nos. 1664/9 were available from post offices throughout New Zealand.

483 Cycling   **484** Ice Pinnacles, Franz Josef Glacier

(Des M. Bailey. Litho Southern Colour Print, Dunedin)

1992 (13 May). *Olympic Games, Barcelona (2nd issue). T 483 and similar horiz designs. Multicoloured. P 13½.*
1670	45 c. Type 483	..	65	35
1671	80 c. Archery	..	90	70
1672	$1 Equestrian three-day eventing	..	1·00	85
1673	$1.50, Sailboarding	..	1·50	1·40
1670/3		Set of 4	3·50	3·00
MS1674	125×100 mm. Nos. 1670/3. P 14×14½		3·50	4·00

No. MS1674 exists overprinted with the emblem of the "World Columbian, Stamp Expo '92" and was only available from the New Zealand stand at this International Stamp Exhibition in Chicago and from the Philatelic Bureau at Wanganui.

(Des A. Hollows. Litho Southern Colour Print, Dunedin)

1992 (12 June). *Glaciers. T 484 and similar horiz designs. Multicoloured. P 13½.*
1675	45 c. Type 484	..	40	35
1676	50 c. Tasman Glacier	..	50	45
1677	80 c. Snowball glacier, Marion Plateau	70	70
1678	$1 Brewster Glacier	..	85	85
1679	$1.50, Fox Glacier	..	1·40	1·40
1680	$1.80, Franz Josef Glacier	..	1·50	1·60
1675/80		Set of 6	4·75	4·75

479 Yacht *Kiwi Magic*, 1987   **480** Heemskerk

485 "Grand Finale" Camellia   **486** Tree and Hills

(Des Patricia Altman. Litho Leigh-Mardon Ltd, Melbourne)
1992 (8 July). *Camellias.* T **485** *and similar vert designs. Multicoloured.* P 14½.
1681	45 c. Type **485**		40	35
1682	50 c. "Showa-No-Sakae"		50	45
1683	80 c. "Sugar Dream"		70	70
1684	$1 "Night Rider"		85	85
1685	$1.50, "E.G. Waterhouse"		1·40	1·75
1686	$1.80, "Dr. Clifford Parks"		1·50	2·00
1681/6		Set of 6	4·75	5·50

(Des T. Crilley. Litho Southern Colour Print, Dunedin)
1992 (12 Aug). *Health Stamps. Sportsmen (2nd series). Horiz designs as* T **461**. *Multicoloured.* P 13½.
1687	45 c. + 5 c. Anthony Wilding (tennis player) and match		80	85
1688	80 c. + 5 c. Stewie Dempster (cricketer) and batsman		95	1·40
MS1689	115×96 mm. Nos. 1687/8, each × 2. P 14		4·00	4·25

(Des Van de Roer Design. Litho Leigh-Mardon Ltd, Melbourne)
1992 (1 Sept). *Landscapes.* T **486** *and similar horiz designs. Multicoloured.* P 14×14½.
1690	45 c. Type **486**		40	50
	a. Booklet pane. Nos. 1690/9		3·75	
1691	45 c. River and hills		40	50
1692	45 c. Hills and mountain		40	50
1693	45 c. Glacier		40	50
1694	45 c. Hills and waterfall		40	50
1695	45 c. Tree and beach		40	50
1696	45 c. Estuary and cliffs		40	50
1697	45 c. Fjord		40	50
1698	45 c. River delta		40	50
1699	45 c. Ferns and beach		40	50
1690/9		Set of 10	3·75	4·50
Nos. 1690/9 were only issued in $4.50 stamp booklets with the pane forming a composite design.

487 Reindeer over Houses   488 1920s Fashions

(Des K. Hall. Litho Leigh-Mardon Ltd, Melbourne)
1992 (16 Sept). *Christmas.* T **487** *and similar vert designs. Multicoloured.* P 14½.
1700	45 c. Type **487**		70	85
	a. Block of 4. Nos. 1700/3		2·50	
1701	45 c. Santa Claus on sleigh over houses		70	85
1702	45 c. Christmas tree in window		70	85
1703	45 c. Christmas wreath and children at window		70	85
1704	65 c. Candles and fireplace		80	90
1705	$1 Family going to church		1·00	1·00
1706	$1.50, Picnic under Pohutukawa tree		1·75	2·25
1700/6		Set of 7	5·75	6·75
Nos. 1700/3 were printed together, *se-tenant*, in blocks of four throughout the sheet.

(Des T. Crilley. Litho Southern Colour Print, Dunedin)
1992 (4 Nov). *New Zealand in the 1920s.* T **488** *and similar vert designs. Multicoloured.* P 13½.
1707	45 c. Type **488**		50	35
1708	50 c. Dr. Robert Jack and early radio announcer		55	55
1709	80 c. "All Blacks" rugby player, 1924		85	85
1710	$1 Swaggie and dog		95	95
1711	$1.50, Ford "Model A" car and young couple		1·75	1·75
1712	$1.80, Amateur aviators and biplane		2·00	2·50
1707/12		Set of 6	6·00	6·25

489 "Old Charley" Toby Jug   490 Women's Fashions of the 1930s

(Des Brand New Ltd. Litho Leigh-Mardon Ltd, Melbourne)
1993 (20 Jan). *Royal Doulton Ceramics Exhibition, New Zealand.* T **489** *and similar designs. Multicoloured.* P 13.
1713	45 c. Type **489**		50	35
1714	50 c. "Bunnykins" nursery plate		55	50
1715	80 c. "Maori Art" tea set		85	75
1716	$1 "Ophelia" handpainted plate		1·00	90
1717	$1.50, "St. George" figurine		1·60	2·00
1718	$1.80, "Lambeth" saltglazed stoneware vase		1·90	2·25
1713/18		Set of 6	5·75	6·00
MS1719	125×100 mm. No. 1718		1·60	2·25

(Des R. Jones. Litho Leigh-Mardon Ltd, Melbourne)
1993 (17 Feb). *New Zealand in the 1930s.* T **490** *and similar vert designs. Multicoloured.* P 14½×14.
1720	45 c. Type **490**		50	45
1721	50 c. Unemployed protest march		55	75
1722	80 c. "Phar Lap" (racehorse)		85	95
1723	$1 State housing project		1·00	1·00
1724	$1.50, Boys drinking free school milk		1·75	2·25
1725	$1.80, Cinema queue		1·90	2·00
1720/5		Set of 6	6·00	6·50

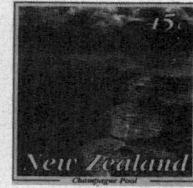

491 Women signing Petition   492 Champagne Pool

(Des Lindy Fisher. Litho Southern Colour Print, Dunedin)
1993 (31 Mar). *Centenary of Women's Suffrage.* T **491** *and similar vert designs. Multicoloured.* P 13½.
1726	45 c. Type **491**		50	35
1727	80 c. Aircraft propeller and woman on tractor		1·00	85
1728	$1 Housewife with children		1·00	95
1729	$1.50, Modern women		1·60	1·60
1726/9		Set of 4	3·50	3·25

(Des A. Hollows. Litho Southern Colour Print, Dunedin)
1993 (5 May). *Thermal Wonders, Rotorua.* T **492** *and similar square designs. Multicoloured.* P 12.
1730	45 c. Type **492**		60	40
1731	50 c. Boiling mud		60	40
1732	80 c. Emerald Pool		85	70
1733	$1 Hakereteke Falls		95	80
1734	$1.50, Warbrick Terrace		1·50	1·50
1735	$1.80, Pohutu Geyser		1·60	1·75
1730/5		Set of 6	5·50	5·00
For miniature sheet containing $1.80 see No. MS1770.

493 Yellow-eyed Penguin, Hector's Dolphin and New Zealand Fur Seal   494 Boy with Puppy

(Des Donna McKenna. Litho Southern Colour Print, Dunedin (No. 1740) or Leigh-Mardon Ltd, Melbourne (others))
1993 (9 June). *Endangered Species Conservation.* T **493** *and similar horiz designs. Multicoloured.* P 13½ (No. 1740) or 14×14½ (others).
1736	45 c. Type **493**		55	70
	a. Block of 4. Nos. 1736/9		2·00	
1737	45 c. Chatham Island Taiko (bird), Mount Cook Lily and Mountain Duck		55	70
1738	45 c. Giant Snail, Rock Wren and Hamilton's Frog		55	70
1739	45 c. Kaka (bird), New Zealand Pigeon and Giant Weta		55	70
1740	45 c. Tusked Weta (23×28 mm)		55	70
1736/40		Set of 5	2·50	3·25
Nos. 1736/9 were issued either in sheets of one design or in sheets containing *se-tenant* blocks of four, as No. 1736a, each forming a composite design.
No. 1740 was only issued in $4.50 stamp booklets.

(Des Karen Odiam. Litho Southern Colour Print, Dunedin)
1993 (21 July). *Health Stamps. Children's Pets.* T **494** *and similar vert design. Multicoloured.* P 13½.
1741	45 c. + 5 c. Type **494**		60	70
1742	80 c. + 5 c. Girl with kitten		90	1·40
MS1743	115×96 mm. Nos. 1741/2, each × 2. P 14½		2·50	3·50
No. MS1743 exists surcharged "STAMPEX '93 NATIONAL YOUTH PHILATELIC EXHIBITION CHRISTCHURCH 19TH–21ST AUGUST 1993 $6·00" in ultramarine. Such miniature sheets were prepared by the organisers and sold at the Exhibition P.O. philatelic counter.

(Recess and litho Leigh-Mardon Ltd, Melbourne (No. MS1745))
1993 (14 Aug). *"Taipei '93" Asian International Stamp Exhibition, Taiwan.*
  (a) No. MS1743 optd "TAIPEI '93" and emblem on sheet margin
MS1744	Nos. 1741/2, each × 2		10·00	11·00
  (b) Sheet 125×100 mm containing No. 1490c (recess) and two similar designs as Nos. 1490/b, but litho. P 13 (around design)
MS1745	445 $1 deep green, $1 blue, $1 rosine		4·50	4·50
Unlike previous miniature sheets produced by New Zealand Post for international stamp exhibitions overseas Nos. MS1744/5, and all subsequent issues of this type, were supplied to collectors in New Zealand and abroad by standing order.

495 Christmas Decorations (value at left)   496 Rainbow Abalone or Paua

(Des Kristine Cotton. Litho Southern Colour Print, Dunedin (Nos. 1746b/9b) or Leigh-Mardon Ltd, Melbourne (others))
1993 (1 Sept–3 Nov). *Christmas.* T **495** *and similar vert designs. Multicoloured.* P 14½×14.
1746	45 c. Type **495**		60	80
	a. Block of 4. Nos. 1746/9		2·25	
	b. Perf 12 (3 Nov)		1·25	1·40
	ba. Booklet pane. Nos. 1746b/7a, each × 3, and 1748a/9a, each × 2		11·00	
1747	45 c. Christmas decorations (value at right)		60	80
	a. Perf 12 (3 Nov)		1·25	1·40
1748	45 c. Sailboards, gifts and Christmas pudding (value at left)		60	80
	a. Perf 12 (3 Nov)		1·25	1·40
1749	45 c. Sailboards, gifts and Christmas pudding (value at right)		60	80
	a. Perf 12 (3 Nov)		1·25	1·40
1750	$1 Sailboards, baubles and Christmas cracker		1·50	1·25
1751	$1.50, Sailboards, present and wreath		2·00	2·75
1746/51		Set of 6	5·50	6·50
Nos. 1746/9 were printed together, *se-tenant*, in blocks of four throughout the sheet.
Booklet pane No. 1746ba contains two *se-tenant* blocks of 4 and a horizontal pair.

(Des R. Youmans. Litho Southern Colour Print, Dunedin)
1993 (1 Sept). *Marine Life.* T **496** *and similar horiz designs. Multicoloured.* P 13½.
1752	45 c. Type **496**		75	75
	a. Booklet pane. Nos. 1752/61 and two stamp-size labels		6·50	
1753	45 c. Green Mussels		75	75
1754	45 c. Tarakihi		75	75
1755	45 c. Salmon		75	75
1756	45 c. Southern Blue-finned Tuna, Yellow-finned Tuna and Kahawai		75	75
1757	45 c. Rock Lobster		75	75
1758	45 c. Snapper		75	75
1759	45 c. Grouper		75	75
1760	45 c. Orange Roughy		75	75
1761	45 c. Squid, Hoki and Black Oreo		75	75
1752/61		Set of 10	6·50	6·50
Nos. 1752/61 were only issued in $4.50 stamp booklets with the *se-tenant* pane, which includes two inscribed labels at left, forming a composite design.

497 Sauropod   498 Soldiers, National Flag and Pyramids

(Des G. Cox. Litho Southern Colour Print, Dunedin)
1993 (1 Oct). *Prehistoric Animals.* T **497** *and similar multicoloured designs.* P 12 (No. 1763) or 13½ (others).
1762	45 c. Type **497**		45	45
1763	45 c. Carnosaur and Sauropod (30×25 mm)		50	50
	a. Booklet pane of 10 and two labels		4·75	
1764	80 c. Pterosaur		85	85
1765	$1 Ankylosaur		95	95
1766	$1.20, Mauisaurus		1·40	1·50
1767	$1.50, Carnosaur		1·50	1·75
1762/7		Set of 6	5·00	5·50
MS1768	125×100 mm. $1.50, As No. 1767. P 14½×14		1·75	1·75
No. 1763 was only issued in $4.50 stamp booklets.
A used example of No. 1762 is known with the yellow omitted.

(Des A. Hollows (No. MS1770). Litho Southern Colour Print, Dunedin)
1993 (1 Oct). *"Bangkok '93" International Stamp Exhibition, Thailand.*
  (a) No. MS1768 optd "BANGKOK '93" and emblem on sheet margin
MS1769	$1.50, As No. 1767		1·60	2·00
  (b) Sheet 115×100 mm. containing No. 1735
MS1770	$1.80, multicoloured		2·50	3·25

(Des P. Andrews. Litho Questa)
1993 (3 Nov). *New Zealand in the 1940s.* T **498** *and similar vert designs. Multicoloured.* P 14.
1771	45 c. Type **498**		60	40
1772	50 c. Aerial crop spraying		60	50
1773	80 c. Hydro-electric scheme		90	80
1774	$1 Marching majorettes		1·00	90
1775	$1.50, American troops		1·60	1·50
1776	$1.80, Crowd celebrating victory		1·75	1·60
1771/6		Set of 6	5·75	5·25

499 Bungy Jumping   **500** *New Zealand Endeavour* (yacht)

(Des G. Taylor. Litho Southern Colour Print, Dunedin)

1994 (19 Jan). *Tourism. T 499 and similar multicoloured designs. P 12.*

1777	45 c. Type **499**	50	40
1778	45 c. White water rafting (25×25 mm)	50	55
	a. Booklet pane of 10 plus 4 half stamp-size greetings labels	4·50	
1779	80 c. Trout fishing	70	70
1780	$1 Jet boating (horiz)	80	80
1781	$1.50, Tramping	1·40	1·40
1782	$1.80, Heli-skiing	1·90	2·00
1777/82	Set of 6	5·25	5·25

No. 1778 was only issued in $4.50 stamp booklets.
For miniature sheet containing the $1.80 see No. **MS1785**.

(Des B. Hall. Litho Leigh-Mardon Ltd, Melbourne)

1994 (19 Jan). *Round the World Yacht Race. P 14½ (and 13 around design).*

1783	**500** $1 multicoloured	1·40	1·40

No. 1783 was printed in sheets of 24 (6×4) with each stamp within a square perforated margin and with a further circular perforation around the design..

501 Mt Cook and New Zealand Symbols

502

(Des Heather Arnold. Engraved C. Slania. Recess and die-stamped (gold) Leigh-Mardon Ltd, Melbourne)

1994 (18 Feb). *W 502. Phosphorised paper. P 14½×15.*

1784	**501** $20 deep violet-blue and gold	12·50	13·50

No. 1784 shows a fluorescent security pattern of "New Zealand Post" printed beneath the design.

(Des G. Taylor (No. **MS1785**), Karen Odiam (No. **MS1786**). Litho Southern Colour Print, Dunedin (No. **MS1785**) or Leigh-Mardon Ltd, Melbourne (No. **MS1786**))

1994 (18 Feb). *"Hong Kong '94" International Stamp Exhibition. P 12 (No. **MS1785**) or 13 (No. **MS1786**).*

MS1785	95×115 mm. $1.80, mult (No. 1782)	3·00	3·00
MS1786	100×125 mm. $1 deep green, $1 rosine, $1 blue (As Nos. 1490/c, but all printed litho)	4·50	4·50

503 Rock and Roll Dancers   **504** Mt Cook and Mt Cook Lily ("Winter")

(Des Karen Odiam. Litho Leigh-Mardon Ltd, Melbourne)

1994 (23 Mar). *New Zealand in the 1950s. T 503 and similar vert designs. Multicoloured. P 14½×14.*

1787	45 c. Type **503**	45	40
1788	80 c. Sir Edmund Hillary on Mt Everest	75	75
1789	$1 Aunt Daisy (radio personality)	85	85
1790	$1.20, Queen Elizabeth II during 1953 royal visit	1·25	1·25
1791	$1.50, Children playing with Opo the dolphin	1·60	1·60
1792	$1.80, Auckland Harbour Bridge	1·90	2·00
1787/92	Set of 6	6·25	6·25

(Des R. Youmans. Litho Southern Colour Print, Dunedin)

1994 (27 Apr). *The Four Seasons. T 504 and similar horiz designs. Multicoloured. P 12.*

1793	45 c. Type **504**	45	40
	a. Horiz strip of 4. Nos. 1793/6	3·75	
1794	70 c. Lake Hawea and Kowhai ("Spring")	65	65
1795	$1.50, Opononi Beach and Pohutukawa ("Summer")	1·40	1·40
1796	$1.80, Lake Pukaki and Puriri ("Autumn")	1·75	1·75
1793/6	Set of 4	3·75	3·75

In addition to separate sheets of 100 (10×10) Nos. 1793/6 were also printed together, *se-tenant*, in horizontal strips of 4 throughout sheets of 80 (8×10).

505 Rainbow Abalone or Paua Shell   **506** Maui pulls up Te Ika

(Des D. Gunson. Litho Southern Colour Print, Dunedin)

1994 (27 Apr). *New Zealand Life. T 505 and similar multi-coloured designs. P 12.*

1797	45 c. Type **505** (25×20 mm)	35	40
	a. Booklet pane. Nos. 1797/1806	3·50	
1798	45 c. Pavlova dessert (35×20 mm)	35	40
1799	45 c. Hokey pokey ice cream (25×20 mm)	35	40
1800	45 c. Fish and chips (35×20 mm)	35	40
1801	45 c. Jandals (30×20 mm)	35	40
1802	45 c. Bush shirt (25×30½ mm)	35	40
1803	45 c. Buzzy Bee (toy) (35×30½ mm)	35	40
1804	45 c. Gumboots and black singlet (25×30½ mm)	35	40
1805	45 c. Rugby boots and ball (35×30½ mm)	35	40
1806	45 c. Kiwifruit (30×30½ mm)	35	40
1797/1806	Set of 10	3·50	4·00

Nos. 1797/1806 were only issued in $4.50 stamp booklets.

(Des Manu Kopere Society. Litho Leigh-Mardon Ltd, Melbourne)

1994 (8 June). *Maori Myths. T 506 and similar vert designs. Multicoloured. P 13.*

1807	45 c. Type **506**	50	40
1808	80 c. Rona snatched up by Marama	85	85
1809	$1 Maui attacking Tuna	1·00	1·00
1810	$1.20, Tane separating Rangi and Papa	1·40	1·75
1811	$1.50, Matakauri slaying the Giant of Wakatipu	1·50	2·00
1812	$1.80, Panenehu showing crayfish to Tangaroa	1·75	2·00
1807/12	Set of 6	6·25	7·25

507 1939 2d. on 1d. + 1d. Health Stamp and Children playing with Ball   **508** Astronaut on Moon (hologram)

(Des D. Gunson. Litho Leigh-Mardon Ltd, Melbourne)

1994 (20 July). *Health Stamps. 75th Anniv of Children's Health Camps. T 507 and similar vert designs. Multicoloured. P 14½.*

1813	45 c. + 5 c. Type **507**	50	70
1814	45 c. + 5 c. 1949 1d. + ½d. stamp and nurse holding child	50	70
1815	45 c. + 5 c. 1969 4 c. + 1 c. stamp and children reading	50	70
1816	80 c. + 5 c. 1931 2d. + 1d. stamp and child in cap	75	90
1813/16	Set of 4	2·00	2·75
MS1817	130×90 mm. Nos. 1813/16	2·00	2·75

(Des Brand New Ltd, Wellington. Litho Southern Colour Print, Dunedin (hologram by Woodmansterne Ltd, Watford))

1994 (20 July). *25th Anniv of First Moon Landing. P 12.*

1818	**508** $1.50, multicoloured	1·25	1·50

509 "people reaching people"   **510** African Elephants

Two types of Type **509**:
Type I: "w" of "new" partly in blue. "i" of "reaching" without dot.
Type II: "w" of "new" all in magenta. "i" of "reaching" with dot.

(Des Van de Roer Designs. Litho Leigh-Mardon Ltd, Melbourne (Nos. 1818a, 1819) or SNP Cambec (Nos. 1818ab, 1819a))

1994 (20 July)–**95**. *Self-adhesive. Phosphorised paper (Nos. 1818ab, 1819a). P 11.*

1818a	**509** 40 c. multicoloured (I) (2.10.95)	1·50	1·50
	ab. Perf 11½. Type II (11.95)	45	40
1819	45 c. multicoloured (I)	50	45
	a. Perf 11½. Type II (8.95)	70	50

Nos. 1818a/19a were each available in coils of 100. On Nos. 1818a and 1819 the vertical die-cut perforations interlock, but on No. 1818ab and 1819a the stamps are separate on the backing paper.

(Des Denise Durkin. Litho Leigh-Mardon Ltd, Melbourne)

1994 (16 Aug). *Stamp Month. Wild Animals. T 510 and similar horiz designs. Multicoloured. P 14×14½.*

1820	45 c. Type **510**	60	60
	a. Block of 10. Nos. 1820/9	5·50	
1821	45 c. White Rhinoceros	60	60
1822	45 c. Lions	60	60
1823	45 c. Common Zebras	60	60
1824	45 c. Giraffe and calf	60	60
1825	45 c. Siberian Tiger	60	60
1826	45 c. Hippopotami	60	60
1827	45 c. Spider Monkey	60	60
1828	45 c. Giant Panda	60	60
1829	45 c. Polar Bear and cub	60	60
1820/9	Set of 10	5·50	5·50

Nos. 1820/9 were printed together, *se-tenant*, in sheets of 100 so arranged as to provide horizontal or vertical strips of 10 or blocks of 10 (5×2) showing all the designs.

(Des Pauline Morse (No. **MS1830**), Denise Durkin (No. **MS1831**). Litho Leigh-Mardon Ltd, Melbourne)

1994 (16 Aug). *"Philakorea '94" International Stamp Exhibition, Seoul. Multicoloured. P 14½×14 (No. **MS1830**) or 14×14½ (No. **MS1831**).*

MS1830	125×100 mm. Nos. 1459a/65.	5·00	4·50
MS1831	125×100 mm. Nos. 1820, 1822, 1824/5 and 1828/9	3·75	4·00

511 Children with Crib   **512** Batsman

(Des Karen Odiam. Litho Southern Colour Print, Dunedin (No. 1832) or Leigh-Mardon Ltd, Melbourne (others))

1994 (21 Sept). *Christmas. T 511 and similar horiz designs. Multicoloured. P 12 (No. 1832) or 14½ (others).*

1832	45 c. Father Christmas and children (30×25 mm)	45	40
1833	45 c. Type **511**	45	40
1834	70 c. Man and toddler with crib	65	60
1835	80 c. Three carol singers	70	85
1836	$1 Five carol singers	90	90
1837	$1.50, Children and candles	1·25	1·75
1838	$1.80, Parents with child	1·60	2·00
1832/8	Set of 7	5·50	6·25
MS1839	125×100 mm. Nos. 1833/6	2·75	2·75

No. 1832 was only issued in $4.50 stamp booklets.

(Des M. Bailey (Nos. 1840/9), P. Andrews (others). Litho Southern Colour Print, Dunedin)

1994 (2 Nov). *Centenary of New Zealand Cricket Council.*

(a) Horiz designs, each 30×25 mm. Multicoloured. P 12

1840	45 c. Bathers catching balls	40	60
	a. Booklet pane of 10. Nos. 1840/9	3·50	
1841	45 c. Child on surf board at top	40	60
1842	45 c. Young child with rubber ring at top	40	60
1843	45 c. Man with beach ball at top	40	60
1844	45 c. Woman with cricket bat at right	40	60
1845	45 c. Boy in green cap with bat	40	60
1846	45 c. Man in spotted shirt running	40	60
1847	45 c. Woman in striped shorts with bat	40	60
1848	45 c. Boy in wet suit with surf board at right	40	60
1849	45 c. Sunbather with newspaper at right	40	60

(b) T 512 and similar vert designs. Multicoloured. P 13½

1850	45 c. Type **512**	45	40
1851	80 c. Bowler	80	80
1852	$1 Wicket keeper	1·00	1·00
1853	$1.80, Fielder	1·75	1·75
1840/53	Set of 14	7·25	9·00

Nos. 1840/9 were only issued in $4.50 stamp booklets.

(Litho Leigh-Mardon Ltd, Melbourne)

1995 (3 Feb). *"POST X '95" Postal History Exhibition, Auckland. Sheet 130×90 mm, containing No. 1297 and a reproduction of No. 557 optd "SPECIMEN". P 14½.*

MS1854	$10 multicoloured	17·00	17·00

COVER PRICES

Cover factors are quoted at the beginning of each country for most issues to 1945. An explanation of the system can be found on page x. The factors quoted do not, however, apply to philatelic covers.

513 Auckland

514 The 15th Hole, Waitangi

(Des Red Cactus Design. Litho Southern Colour Print, Dunedin)

1995 (22 Feb). *New Zealand by Night.* T **513** *and similar horiz designs. Multicoloured.* P 12.

1855	45 c. Type **513**	..	..	45	40
1856	80 c. Wellington	..	..	75	65
1857	$1 Christchurch	..	..	90	85
1858	$1.20, Dunedin	..	..	1·10	1·00
1859	$1.50, Rotorua	..	..	1·25	1·25
1860	$1.80, Queenstown	..	..	1·50	1·50
1855/60		*Set of 6*		5·50	5·50

See also No. **MS1915**.

(Des R. Jones. Litho Leigh-Mardon Ltd, Melbourne)

1995 (22 Mar). *New Zealand Golf Courses.* T **514** *and similar vert designs. Multicoloured.* P 14½×14.

1861	45 c. Type **514**	..	..	65	40
1862	80 c. The 6th hole, New Plymouth			1·00	90
1863	$1.20, The 9th hole, Rotorua			1·50	1·75
1864	$1.80, The 5th hole, Queenstown			2·40	2·75
1861/4	.. ..	*Set of 4*		5·00	5·25

515 New Zealand Pigeon and Nest

516 Teacher with Guitar and Children

(Des Niki Hill. Litho Southern Colour Print, Dunedin)

1995 (22 Mar). *Environment.* T **515** *and similar horiz designs. Multicoloured.* P 12.

1865	45 c. Type **515**	..	..	60	60
	a. Booklet pane. Nos. 1865/74			5·50	
1866	45 c. Planting sapling	..	..	60	60
1867	45 c. Dolphins and whales	..		60	60
1868	45 c. Thunder storm	..	..	60	60
1869	45 c. Backpackers	..	..	60	60
1870	45 c. Animal pests	..	..	60	60
1871	45 c. Noxious plants	..	..	60	60
1872	45 c. Undersized fish and shellfish			60	60
1873	45 c. Pollution from factories			60	60
1874	45 c. Family at picnic site	..		60	60
1865/74		*Set of 10*		5·50	5·50

Nos. 1865/74 were only issued in $4.50 stamp booklets with the vertical edges of the pane imperforate. Each vertical pair forms a composite design.

(Des M. Kopere. Litho Southern Colour Print, Dunedin)

1995 (3 May). *Maori Language Year.* T **516** *and similar vert designs. Multicoloured.* P 13½.

1875	45 c. Type **516**	..	..	50	45
1876	70 c. Singing group	..	..	75	75
1877	80 c. Mother and baby	..	..	85	85
1878	$1 Women performing traditional welcome	..		1·10	1·10
1879	$1.50, Grandfather reciting family genealogy	..		1·75	1·75
1880	$1.80, Tribal orator	..	..	2·00	2·00
1875/80		*Set of 6*		6·25	6·00

In addition to sheets containing stamps of one value Nos. 1875/80 also exist in sheetlets of 24 containing four of each value *se-tenant.* These sheetlets were only available from Limited Edition Collectors Packs costing NZ$135.

517 Map of Australasia and Asia

518 *Black Magic* (yacht)

(Des Cue Design. Litho Southern Colour Print, Dunedin)

1995 (3 May). *Meetings of Asian Development Bank Board of Governors and International Pacific Basin Economic Council, Auckland.* T **517** *and similar horiz design. Multicoloured.* P 13½.

1881	$1 Type **517**	..	..	1·25	1·00
1882	$1.50, Map of Australasia and Pacific			1·75	2·50

(Des A. Hollows. Litho Southern Colour Print, Dunedin)

1995 (16 May). *New Zealand's Victory in 1995 America's Cup.* P 12.

1883	518	45 c. multicoloured	..	55	55

No. 1883 was issued in small sheets of 10 with a seascape printed on the margins. This sheetlet also exists numbered and overprinted in gold foil from a Limited Edition Collectors Pack costing NZ$25.

519 Boy on Skateboard

520 Lion Red Cup and Players

(Des P. Martinson. Litho Leigh-Mardon Ltd, Melbourne)

1995 (21 June). *Health Stamps. Children's Sports.* T **519** *and similar triangular design. Multicoloured.* P 14½.

1884	45 c. + 5 c. Type **519**	..		65	70
	a. *Tête-bêche* (pair)	..		1·25	1·40
1885	80 c. + 5 c. Girl on bicycle	..		1·25	1·40
	a. *Tête-bêche* (pair)	..		2·50	2·75
MS1886	130×90 mm. Nos. 1884/5, each × 2			3·75	4·00

Nos. 1884/5 were each printed in sheets with the horizontal rows made up of *tête-bêche* pairs.

1995 (1 July). *"Stampex '95" National Stamp Exhibition, Wellington. No.* **MS1886** *additionally inscr with "Stampex '95" and emblem on sheet margin.*

MS1887 130×90 mm. Nos. 1884/5, each × 2   3·75 4·50

(Des Heather Arnold. Litho Southern Colour Print, Dunedin (No. 1888) or Enschedé (others))

1995 (26 July). *Centenary of Rugby League.* T **520** *and similar horiz designs. Multicoloured.* P 12 (*No.* 1888) or 14×14½ (*others*).

1888	45 c. Trans Tasman test match (30×25 mm)			50	45
	a. Booklet pane. No. 1888×10			4·00	
1889	45 c. Type **520**	..		50	45
1890	$1 Children's rugby and mascot			1·25	1·10
1891	$1.50, George Smith, Albert Baskerville and early match			2·00	2·00
1892	$1.80, Courtney Goodwill Trophy and match against Great Britain			2·25	2·25
1888/92		*Set of 5*		6·00	5·75
MS1893	125×100 mm. No. 1892			2·50	2·50

No. 1888 was only issued in $4.50 stamp booklets and has the vertical edges of the pane imperforate.

No. **MS1893** imperforate comes from a Limited Edition Collectors Pack costing NZ$135.

521 Sheep and Lamb

522 Archangel Gabriel

(Des Joanne Kreyl. Litho Southern Colour Print, Dunedin)

1995 (1 Sept–2 Oct). *Farmyard Animals.* T **521** *and similar horiz designs.* P 14×14½.

1894	40 c. Type **521** (2 Oct)	..		60	65
	a. Booklet pane. Nos. 1894/1903			5·50	
1895	40 c. Deer (2 Oct)	..		60	65
1896	40 c. Mare and foal (2 Oct)	..		60	65
1897	40 c. Cow with calf (2 Oct)	..		60	65
1898	40 c. Goats and kid (2 Oct)	..		60	65
1899	40 c. Common Turkey (2 Oct)	..		60	65
1900	40 c. Ducks (2 Oct)	..		60	65
1901	40 c. Red Junglefowl (2 Oct)	..		60	65
1902	40 c. Sow with piglets (2 Oct)	..		60	65
1903	40 c. Border Collie (2 Oct)	..		60	65
1904	45 c. Type **521**	..		60	65
	a. Booklet pane. Nos. 1904/13			5·50	
1905	45 c. As No. 1895	..		60	65
1906	45 c. As No. 1896	..		60	65
1907	45 c. As No. 1897	..		60	65
1908	45 c. As No. 1898	..		60	65
1909	45 c. As No. 1899	..		60	65
1910	45 c. As No. 1900	..		60	65
1911	45 c. As No. 1901	..		60	65
1912	45 c. As No. 1902	..		60	65
1913	45 c. As No. 1903	..		60	65
1894/1913		*Set of 20*		11·00	12·00

Nos. 1894/1903 and 1904/13 were only issued in $4 (Nos. 1894/1903) and $4.50 (Nos. 1904/13) stamp booklets in which the horizontal edges of the booklet panes are imperforate.

(Des Joanne Kreyl (No. **MS1914**), Red Cactus Design (No. **MS1915**). Litho Southern Colour Print, Dunedin)

1995 (1 Sept). *"Singapore '95" International Stamp Exhibition.* P 12.

MS1914	170×70 mm. Nos. 1909/13	..		2·75	3·00
MS1915	148×210 mm. Nos. 1855/60	..		8·00	9·00

No. **MS1915** also includes the "JAKARTA '95" logo.

(Des K. Hall. Litho Southern Colour Print, Dunedin)

1995 (1 Sept–9 Nov). *Christmas. Stained Glass Windows from St. Mary's Anglican Church, Merivale (Nos.* 1916/18), *The Lady Chapel of St. Luke's Anglican Church, Christchurch (Nos.* 1919/22) *or St. John the Evangelist Church, Cheviot (No.* 1923). *Multicoloured.* (a) *As* T **522**. P 12.

1916	40 c. Type **522** (2 Oct)			60	40
1917	45 c. Type **522**	..		60	45
1918	70 c. Virgin Mary	..		90	90
1919	80 c. Shepherds	..		1·00	1·00
1920	$1 Virgin and Child	..		1·25	1·10
1921	$1.50, Two Wise Men	..		2·00	2·50
1922	$1.80, Wise Man kneeling	..		2·25	2·50

(b) *Smaller design,* 25×30 mm. P 14½×14

1923	40 c. Angel with Trumpet (9 Nov)		55	50
	a. Booklet pane. No. 1923×10		5·00	
1916/23		*Set of 8*	8·00	8·25

No. 1923 was only issued in $4 stamp booklets which show the outer edges of the pane imperforate.

Nos. 1916 and 1918/22 also exist as a miniature sheet, only available as part of a joint Phone Card and Stamp Collectors Pack produced in a limited quantity and costing NZ$115.

523 Face and Nuclear Disarmament Symbol

524 Mount Cook

(Des C. Martin. Litho Southern Colour Print, Dunedin)

1995 (1 Sept). *Nuclear Disarmament.* P 13½.

1924	523	$1 multicoloured	1·00	1·00

(Des Red Cactus Design. Litho Enschedé ($10) or Southern Colour Print, Dunedin (others))

1995 (2 Oct)–2000. *New Zealand Scenery.* T **524** *and similar multicoloured designs.* P 13½×14 ($10) or 13½ (*others*).

1925	5 c. Type **524** (27.3.96)	..	10	10
1926	10 c. Champagne Pool (27.3.96)	..	10	10
1927	20 c. Cape Reinga (27.3.96)	..	15	20
1928	30 c. Mackenzie Country (27.3.96)	..	20	25
1929	40 c. Mitre Peak (*vert*)	..	25	30
1930	50 c. Mount Ngauruhoe (27.3.96)	..	30	35
1931	60 c. Lake Wanaka (*vert*) (27.3.96)	..	40	45
1932	70 c. Giant Kauri tree (*vert*) (27.3.96)	..	45	50
1933	80 c. Doubtful Sound (*vert*) (27.3.96)	..	50	55
1934	90 c. Waitomo Limestone Cave (*vert*) (27.3.96)		55	60
1934a	$1 Taiaroa Head (29×24 mm) (6.3.00)		65	70
1934b	$1.10, Kaikoura Coast (29×24 mm) (6.3.00)		70	75
1934c	$2 Great Barrier Island (29×24 mm) (6.3.00)		1·25	1·40
1934d	$3 Cape Kidnappers (29×24 mm) (6.3.00)		1·90	2·00
1935	$10 Mt Ruapehu (40×34 mm) (12.2.97)		6·25	6·50
1925/35		*Set of 15*	13·50	14·50

For miniature sheets containing some of these designs see Nos. **MS1978**, **MS1998** and **MS2005**.

For similar self-adhesive designs see Nos. 1984/91.

525 Dame Kiri te Kanawa (opera singer)

526 National Flags, Peace Dove and "50"

(Des Karen Odiam. Litho Southern Colour Print, Dunedin)

1995 (4 Oct). *Famous New Zealanders.* T **525** *and similar horiz designs. Multicoloured.* P 12.

1936	40 c. Type **525**		65	40
1937	80 c. Charles Upham, V.C. (war hero)	..	90	85
1938	$1 Barry Crump (author)	..	1·25	1·00
1939	$1.20, Sir Brian Barratt-Boyes (surgeon)	1·50	1·25
1940	$1.50, Dame Whina Cooper (Maori leader)	..	1·75	1·75
1941	$1.80, Sir Richard Hadlee (cricketer)	..	2·50	2·25
1936/41		*Set of 6*	7·75	6·75

Nos. 1936/41 were issued in sheets with each stamp *se-tenant* horizontally with a 10×30 mm label inscribed "STAMP MONTH October 1995".

(Des S. Fuller. Litho Leigh-Mardon Ltd, Melbourne)

1995 (4 Oct). *50th Anniv of United Nations.* P 15.

1942	526	$1.80, multicoloured	2·25	1·90

527 Fern and Globe

(Des Red Cactus Design. Litho Leigh-Mardon Ltd, Melbourne)

1995 (9 Nov). *Commonwealth Heads of Government Meeting, Auckland. T 527 and similar horiz design. Multicoloured. P 14.*
1943	40 c. Type **527**	..	..	60	40
1944	$1.80, Fern and New Zealand flag	..		2·50	2·00

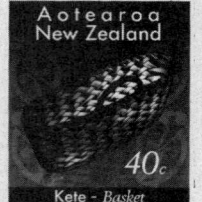

528 "Kiwi" **529 Kete (basket)**

(Des Communication Arts Ltd. Litho Enschedé)

1996 (24 Jan). *Famous Racehorses. T 528 and similar horiz designs. Multicoloured. P 14×14½.*
1945	40 c. Type **528**	..	..	55	40
1946	80 c. "Rough Habit"	..	..	95	95
1947	$1 "Blossom Lady"	..	..	1·25	1·25
1948	$1.20, "Il Vicolo"	..	..	1·60	1·60
1949	$1.50, "Horlicks"	..	..	1·75	1·75
1950	$1.80, "Bonecrusher"	..		2·50	2·50
1945/50			*Set of 6*	7·75	7·75
MS1951	Seven sheets, each 162×110 mm. (a)				

No. 1945. (b) No. 1946. (c) No. 1947. (d) No. 1948.
(e) No. 1949. (f) No. 1950. (g) Nos. 1945/50
	Set of 7 sheets	16·00	18·00

Nos. **MS**1951a/g were only available from $13.70 stamp booklets, with each miniature sheet showing a line of roulettes at left.

An overprinted and numbered miniature sheet containing Nos. 1945/50 comes from a Limited Edition Collectors Pack costing NZ$135.

"BEST OF '96". Sets of three miniature sheets with this inscription and containing Nos. 1950, 1957, 1983, 1997, 2012, 2017, 2025, 2033 and 2042 were distributed by the Philatelic Bureau to customers who had purchased a certain amount of philatelic material from them during the year. These miniature sheets were printed in lithography by Southern Colour Print, Dunedin, and a number of the stamps they contain show different perforations from the examples in normal sheets. They could not be purchased by the general public at post offices.

(Des G. Hubbard. Litho Enschedé)

1996 (21 Feb). *Maori Crafts. T 529 and similar vert designs. Multicoloured. P 14×13½.*
1952	40 c. Type **529**	..	..	50	40
1953	80 c. Head of Taiaha (spear)	..	..	90	90
1954	$1 Taniko (embroidery)	..	..	1·25	1·25
1955	$1.20, Pounamu (greenstone)	..		1·50	1·50
1956	$1.50, Hue (gourd)	..	..	1·75	1·75
1957	$1.80, Korowai (feather cloak)	..		2·00	2·25
1952/7			*Set of 6*	7·25	7·25

For miniature sheet containing some of these designs see No. **MS**2049.

530 Black-backed Gulls **531 Fire and Ambulance Services**

(Des Sue Wickison)

1996 (21 Feb–7 Aug). *Seaside Environment. T 530 and similar horiz designs. Multicoloured.*

(a) *Litho Southern Colour Print, Dunedin. P 14×14½.*
1958	40 c. Type **530**	..	..	45	50
	a. Booklet pane of 10. Nos. 1958/67			4·25	
1959	40 c. Children, Sea Cucumber and Spiny Starfish			45	50
1960	40 c. Yacht, gull and Common Shrimps	..		45	50
1961	40 c. Gaudy Nudibranch			45	50
1962	40 c. Large Rock Crab and Clingfish			45	50
1963	40 c. Snake Skin Chiton and Red Rock Crab			45	50
1964	40 c. Estuarine Triplefin and Cat's-eye shell			45	50
1965	40 c. Cushion Star and Sea Horses			45	50

1966	40 c. Blue-eyed Triplefin and Yaldwyn's Triplefin			45	50
1967	40 c. Common Octopus	..	..	45	50
1958/67		..	*Set of 10*	4·25	4·50

Nos. 1958/67 were only issued in $4 stamp booklets in which the horizontal edges of the pane are imperforate.

(b) *Litho SNP Cambec, Australia. Self-adhesive. P 11½* (7 Aug)
1968	40 c. Type **530**	..	..	45	50
	a. Booklet pane of 10. Nos. 1968/77			4·25	
1969	40 c. Children, Sea Cucumber and Spiny Starfish			45	50
1970	40 c. Yacht, gull and Common Shrimps			45	50
1971	40 c. Gaudy Nudibranch			45	50
1972	40 c. Large Rock Crab and Clingfish			45	50
1973	40 c. Snake Skin Chiton and Red Rock Crab			45	50
1974	40 c. Estuarine Triplefin and Cat's-eye shell			45	50
1975	40 c. Cushion Star and Sea Horses			45	50
1976	40 c. Blue-eyed Triplefin and Yaldwyn's Triplefin			45	50
1977	40 c. Common Octopus	..	..	45	50
1968/77			*Set of 10*	4·25	4·50

Nos. 1958/67 were only issued in $4 stamp booklets in which the horizontal edges of the pane are imperforate.

Nos. 1968/77 were only issued in $4 self-adhesive stamp booklets, containing No. 1968a on which the surplus self-adhesive paper around each stamp was retained.

The phosphor, which shows pink under U.V. light, forms an irregular frame on two sides of each design.

(Litho Southern Colour Print, Dunedin)

1996 (15 Mar). *"SOUTHPEX '96" Stamp Show, Invercargill. Sheet 100×215 mm, containing No. 1929×10. P 12.*
MS1978	40 c. × 10 multicoloured	..	5·50	5·50

(Des Dave Clark Design Associates. Litho Southern Colour Print, Dunedin)

1996 (27 Mar). *Rescue Services. T 531 and similar vert designs. Multicoloured. P 14½×15.*
1979	40 c. Type **531**	..	..	50	40
1980	80 c. Civil Defence	..	..	90	90
1981	$1 Air-sea rescue	..	..	1·10	1·10
1982	$1.50, Air ambulance and rescue helicopter			1·60	1·60
1983	$1.80 Mountain rescue and Red Cross			2·25	2·40
1979/83			*Set of 5*	5·75	5·75

532 Mt Egmont, Taranaki **533 Yellow-eyed Penguin**

(Des Red Cactus Design. Litho Southern Colour Print, Dunedin (Nos. 1984b/9b) or SNP Cambec, Australia (others))

1996 (1 May)–98. *New Zealand Scenery. Self-adhesive. T 532 and similar multicoloured designs. Phosphor frame. P 11½.*
1984	40 c. Type **532**	..	..	25	30
	a. Sheetlet of 10. Nos. 1984/9 (one each of two designs and two each of the remainder)			20·00	
	b. Perf 10 (14.1.98)	..	..	25	30
	ba. Booklet pane. Nos. 1984b×2, 1985b, 1986b×2, 1987b and 1988b/9b each ×2			2·50	
	bab. Booklet pane. Printed on the backing paper			60·00	
1985	40 c. Piercy Island, Bay of Islands			25	30
	b. Perf 10 (14.1.98)	..	..	25	30
1986	40 c. Tory Channel, Marlborough Sounds			25	30
	b. Perf 10 (14.1.98)	..	..	25	30
	ba. "Marlborough Sounds" inscr omitted			20·00	
1987	40 c. *Earnslaw* (ferry), Lake Wakatipu			25	30
	b. Perf 10 (14.1.98)	..	..	25	30
1988	40 c. Lake Matheson	..	..	25	30
	b. Perf 10 (14.1.98)	..	..	25	30
1989	40 c. Fox Glacier	..	..	25	30
	b. Perf 10 (14.1.98)	..	..	25	30
1990	80 c. Doubtful Sound (as No. 1933) (*vert*) (13.11.96)			50	55
	a. Booklet pane. No. 1990×10			5·00	
1991	$1 Pohutukawa tree (33×22 *mm*) (7.8.96)			65	70
	a. Booklet pane. No. 1991×5			3·25	
1984/91			*Set of 8*	2·50	3·00

Nos. 1984/9 occur in rolls of 100, with the surplus self-adhesive paper around each stamp removed.

No. 1984a comes from the residue of special sheet stock used to prepare first day covers and subsequently sold as $4 "hang-sell" sheetlets.

Nos. 1984b/9b come from $4 stamp booklets, containing No. 1984ba, on which the surplus self-adhesive paper was retained.

No. 1984bab occurred when the self-adhesive paper "sandwich" became reversed so that the designs were printed on what should have been the back of the booklet. This results in the gum being attached to the backing paper instead of the stamps. Normal versions of the booklet show the paper around the stamps, outside the phosphor frames, as white with a strong fluorescent content. On the error this paper is off white and non-fluorescent.

No. 1986ba occurs on one of the examples of this design in 2% of the original printing of booklet pane No. 1984ba.

Nos. 1990/1 come from stamp booklets on which the surplus self-adhesive paper around each stamp was retained.

The phosphor, which shows pink under U.V. light, appears as an irregular frame to each design.

(Des Sea Sky Design. Litho Southern Colour Print, Dunedin)

1996 (1 May). *Marine Wildlife. T 533 and similar multicoloured designs. P 14.*
1992	40 c. Type **533**	..	..	50	50
	a. Block of 6. Nos. 1992/7			6·75	
1993	80 c. Royal Albatross (*horiz*)	..		90	90
1994	$1 White Herons (*horiz*)	..		1·10	1·10
1995	$1.20, Flukes of Sperm Whale (*horiz*)			1·40	1·40
1996	$1.50, Fur Seals	..	..	1·60	1·60
1997	$1.80, Bottlenose Dolphin	..		2·00	2·00
1992/7			*Set of 6*	6·75	6·75

In addition to separate sheets of 100 Nos. 1992/7 were also issued in *se-tenant* blocks of 6 which also contained two irregular-shaped labels.

For miniature sheets containing these designs see Nos. **MS**1999 and **MS**2037.

(Des Diane Prosser (No. **MS**1998), Sea Sky Design (No. **MS**1999). Litho Southern Colour Print, Dunedin)

1996 (18 May). *"CHINA '96" 9th International Stamp Exhibition, Peking. Multicoloured. P 13½ (No. **MS**1998) or 14 (No. **MS**1999).*
MS1998	180×80 mm. Nos. 1926/8 and 1930	..	1·75	2·00
MS1999	140×90 mm. Nos. 1994 and 1996	..	2·75	3·00

No. **MS**1999 also shows designs as Nos. 1992/3, 1995 and 1997, but without face values.

534 Baby in Car Seat

(Des Helen Casey)

1996 (5 June). *Health Stamps. Child Safety. T 534 and similar vert design. Multicoloured. (a) Litho Southern Colour Print, Dunedin (No. 2000), Enschedé (Nos. 2000a, 2001) or SNP Cambec (No. **MS**2002). P 13½.*
2000	40 c. + 5 c. Type **534**	..	..	50	50
	a. As Type **534**, but teddy bear at top right and face value at bottom left			£500	£500
2001	80 c. + 5 c. Child and adult on zebra crossing			90	90
MS2002	130×90 mm. Nos. 2000/1, each × 2. P 14×14½			2·75	2·75

(b) *Litho SNP Cambec. Self-adhesive. Phosphor frame on three sides. P 11½*
2003	40 c. + 5 c. Type **534**	..	..	50	50
	a. As Type **534**, but teddy bear at top right and face value at bottom left	..		£600	£600

The original versions (Nos. 2000a and 2003a) of the 40 c. + 5 c. showed a teddy bear at top right and the face value above the inscription at bottom left. As depicted the design breached New Zealand safety guidelines and both versions were redrawn as shown in Type **534**. All the original versions should have been withdrawn from post office stocks before the release date, but examples were sold from at least two New Zealand Post outlets at Royal Oak (Auckland) and Te Ngae (Rotorua) and used for postal purposes.

Two examples of the miniature sheet, one with the "CAPEX '96" overprint, including the teddy bear, were sold in the Netherlands during 1997. There is no evidence to link these two miniature sheets with New Zealand.

Stamps from No. **MS**2002 are slightly larger with "NEW ZEALAND" and the face values redrawn.

No. 2003 is smaller, 21½×38 mm, and occurs in rolls of 100 with the surplus self-adhesive paper around each stamp removed. The phosphor shows pink under U.V. light.

(Des Diane Prosser (No. **MS**2005). Litho SNP Cambec (No. **MS**2004) or Southern Colour Print, Dunedin (No. **MS**2005))

1996 (8 June). *"CAPEX '96" International Stamp Exhibition, Toronto.*

(a) *No. **MS**2002 optd "CAPEX '96" and emblem on sheet margin*
MS2004	Nos. 2000/1, each × 2	..	3·25	2·75

(b) *Sheet 180×80 mm, containing Nos. 1931/4. P 13½*
MS2005	$3 multicoloured	..	3·25	3·25

535 Violin

(Des M. Bailey. Litho and gold die-stamped Southern Colour Print, Dunedin)

1996 (10 July). *50th Anniv of New Zealand Symphony Orchestra. T 535 and similar horiz design. Multicoloured. P 15×14½.*
2006	40 c. Type **535**	..	..	40	40
2007	80 c. French horn	..	..	1·00	1·50

536 Swimming   **537** *Hinemoa*

(Des S. Fuller. Litho Southern Colour Print, Dunedin)

1996 (10 July). *Centennial Olympic Games, Atlanta. T* **536** *and similar circular designs. Multicoloured. P* 14½ *(and 14 around design).*

2008	40 c. Type **536**	..	50	40
2009	80 c. Cycling	..	1·25	90
2010	$1 Running	..	1·25	1·00
2011	$1.50, Rowing	..	1·75	2·00
2012	$1.80, Dinghy sailing	..	2·00	2·25
2008/12		*Set of 5*	6·00	6·00
MS2013	120×80 mm. No. 2008/12		6·00	6·00

A miniature sheet containing Nos. 2008/12 both perforated and imperforate comes from a Limited Edition Collectors Pack costing NS$135.

(Des Eyework Design and Production. Litho Southern Colour Print, Dunedin (prize labels printed by Sabre Print))

1996 (7 Aug). *Centenary of New Zealand Cinema. T* **537** *and similar vert designs. Multicoloured. P* 14½.

2014	40 c. Type **537**	..	50	40
2015	80 c. *Broken Barrier*	..	1·00	80
2016	$1.50, *Goodbye Pork Pie*	..	1·75	2·00
2017	$1.80, *Once Were Warriors*	..	1·75	2·00
2014/17		*Set of 4*	4·50	4·75

Nos. 2014/17 were printed in sheets of 25, each stamp being *se-tenant* with a "Scratch and Win" stamp-size label.

538 Danyon Loader (swimmer) and Blyth Tait (horseman)   **539** Beehive Ballot Box

(Des Red Cactus Design. Litho Southern Colour Print, Dunedin)

1996 (28 Aug). *New Zealand Olympic Gold Medal Winners, Atlanta. P* 14½ *(and 14 around design).*

2018	**538** 40 c. multicoloured	..	45	45

No. 2018 was printed in sheets of 36 (6×6) with each stamp within a square perforated margin showing a pattern of Olympic rings and fern leaves.

(Des Gatehaus Design. Litho Southern Colour Print, Dunedin)

1996 (4 Sept). *New Zealand's First Mixed Member Proportional Representation Election. P* 12.

2019	**539** 40 c. black, scarlet and pale yellow		45	45

No. 2019 was printed in sheets of 10 (2×5) with decorated margins.

540 King following Star   **541** Adzebill

(Des Lindy Fisher)

1996 (4 Sept). *Christmas. T* **540** *and similar horiz designs. Multicoloured. (a) Litho Questa. Designs* 35×35 *mm. P* 14.

2020	40 c. Type **540**		50	40
2021	70 c. Shepherd and Baby Jesus	..	80	80
2022	80 c. Angel and shepherd		90	90
2023	$1 Mary, Joseph and Baby Jesus		1·25	1·00
2024	$1.50, Mary and Joseph with donkey	..	2·00	2·00
2025	$1.80, The Annunciation		2·00	2·25
2020/5		*Set of 6*	6·75	6·75

(b) Litho SNP Cambec, Australia. Smaller designs, 30×24 *mm. Self-adhesive. P* 11½

2026	40 c. Angels with trumpets	..	45	60
2027	40 c. King with gift	..	45	50
	a. Booklet pane. No. 2027×10	..	4·25	

No. 2026 comes from rolls of 100, on which the surplus self-adhesive paper around each stamp was removed, and No. 2027 from $4 booklets, containing No. 2027a on which the surplus paper was retained.

The phosphor, which shows pink under U.V. light, appears as a three-sided frame on stamps from both rolls and booklets.

(Des G. Cox)

1996 (2 Oct). *Extinct Birds. T* **541** *and similar horiz designs. Multicoloured. (a) Litho Southern Colour Print, Dunedin. Designs* 40×28 *mm. P* 13½.

2028	40 c. Type **541**	..	60	40
2029	80 c. South Island Whekau ("Laughing Owl")	..	1·25	1·25
2030	$1 Piopio	..	1·25	1·10
2031	$1.20, Huia	..	1·50	1·60
2032	$1.50, Giant Eagle	..	1·75	2·00
2033	$1.80, Giant Moa	..	2·00	2·00
2028/33		*Set of 6*	7·50	7·50
MS2034	105×92 mm. No. 2033. P 14		2·00	2·00

(b) Litho SNP Cambec, Australia. Smaller design, 30×24 *mm. Self-adhesive. P* 11½

2035	40 c. Stout-legged Wren	..	45	50
	a. Booklet pane. No. 2035×10		4·25	

No. 2035 comes from $4 booklets, containing No. 2035a on which the surplus self-adhesive paper was retained.

The phosphor, which shows orange under U.V. light, appears as a vertical band at the right of the stamp.

(Des G. Cox (No. **MS**2036), Sea Sky Design (No. **MS**2037). Litho Southern Colour Print, Dunedin)

1996 (21 Oct). *"TAIPEI '96" 10th Asian International Stamp Exhibition, Taiwan. (a) No.* **MS**2034 *overprinted with "TAIPEI '96" logo on sheet margin.*

MS2036	105×92 mm. No. 2033	..	2·75	2·75

(b) Sheet 140×90 *mm containing Nos.* 1993 *and* 1997. *Multicoloured. P* 14.

MS2037	Nos. 1993 and 1997	..	2·75	2·75

No. **MS**2037 also shows designs as Nos. 1992 and 1994/6, but without face values

542 Seymour Square, Blenheim   **543** Holstein Friesian Cattle

(Des H. Thompson. Litho Walsall)

1996 (13 Nov). *Scenic Gardens. T* **542** *and similar vert designs. Multicoloured. P* 13½.

2038	40 c. Type **542**		50	40
2039	80 c. Pukekura Park, New Plymouth	..	1·00	1·00
2040	$1 Wintergarden, Auckland	..	1·25	1·10
2041	$1.50, Botanic Garden, Christchurch	..	1·75	2·00
2042	$1.80, Marine Parade Gardens, Napier	..	1·90	2·00
2038/42		*Set of 5*	5·75	6·00

(Des Lindy Fisher. Litho Questa)

1997 (15 Jan). *Cattle Breeds. T* **543** *and similar vert designs. Multicoloured. P* 14×14½.

2043	40 c. Type **543**	..	50	40
2044	80 c. Jersey	..	1·00	1·00
2045	$1 Simmental	..	1·25	1·00
2046	$1.20, Ayrshire	..	1·50	1·60
2047	$1.50, Angus	..	1·60	2·00
2048	$1.80, Hereford	..	1·90	2·00
2043/8		*Set of 6*	7·00	7·25

"BEST OF '97". A further set of three miniature sheets, as described below No. **MS**1951, was distributed by the Philatelic Bureau in 1997 to customers purchasing a certain amount of philatelic material. The stamps shown for 1997 were Nos. 2048, 2056, 2062, 2077, 2085, 2090, 2096, 2102 and 2121.

(Des Red Cactus Design (No. **MS**2049), Lindy Fisher (No. **MS**2050) Litho Southern Colour Print, Dunedin (**MS**2049) or Questa (**MS**2050))

1997 (12 Feb). *"HONG KONG '97" International Stamp Exhibition. P* 13 *(No.* **MS**2049) *or* 14×14½ *(No.* **MS**2050).

MS2049	130×110 mm. Nos. 1952/3 and 1956	3·00	3·00
MS2050	101×134 mm. Nos. 2044/5 and 2047	3·50	3·50

No. **MS**2050 is also inscribed for the Chinese New Year ("Year of the Ox").

544 James Cook and Sextant

(Des Red Cactus Design. Litho Southern Colour Print, Dunedin)

1997 (12 Feb). *Millennium Series (1st issue). Discoverers of New Zealand. T* **544** *and similar multicoloured designs. P* 14½×14 *($1, $1.20) or* 14×14½ *(others).*

2051	40 c. Type **544**	..	70	45
2052	80 c. Kupe and ocean-going canoe	..	1·00	90
2053	$1 Carved panel depicting Maui (*vert*)	1·25	1·00
2054	$1.20, Anchor and Jean de Surville's *St. Jean Baptiste* (*vert*)	..	1·50	1·60
2055	$1.50, Dumont d'Urville, crab and *L'Astrolabe*	..	1·75	2·00
2056	$1.80, Abel Tasman and illustration from journal	..	1·90	2·00
2051/6		*Set of 6*	7·25	7·25

A miniature sheet containing Nos. 2051/6 comes from a Limited Edition Millennium Collection costing NZ$129.

See also Nos. 2140/5, 2216/21, 2239/44, 2304/9 and 2310.

---

545 Rippon Vineyard, Central Otago   **546** Cottage Letterbox

(Des Dianne Prosser from paintings by Nancy Tichborne. Litho Southern Colour Print, Dunedin)

1997 (19 Mar). *New Zealand Vineyards. T* **545** *and similar horiz designs. Multicoloured. P* 14.

2057	40 c. Type **545**	..	60	40
2058	80 c. Te Mata Estate, Hawke's Bay	..	1·00	90
2059	$1 Cloudy Bay Vineyard, Marlborough	1·25	1·00
2060	$1.20, Pegasus Bay Vineyard, Waipara	1·50	1·60
2061	$1.50, Milton Vineyard, Gisborne	1·75	2·00
2062	$1.80, Goldwater Estate, Waiheke Island	1·90	2·00
2057/62		*Set of 6*	7·25	7·25
MS2063	Seven sheets, each 150×110 mm. (a) No. 2057; (b) No. 2058; (c) No. 2059; (d) No. 2060; (e) No. 2061; (f) No. 2062; (g) Nos. 2057/62			
		Set of 7 sheets	12·00	13·00

Nos. **MS**2063a/g were only available from $13.40 stamp booklets with each miniature sheet showing a line of roulettes at left.

An overprinted and numbered miniature sheet containing Nos. 2057/62 comes from a Limited Edition Collectors Pack costing NZ$135.

For a further miniature sheet containing Nos. 2057, 2059 and 2061 see No. **MS**2081.

(Des Communication Arts. Litho SNP Cambec, Australia)

1997 (19 Mar). *Curious Letterboxes. T* **546** *and similar vert designs. Multicoloured. Self-adhesive. Phosphor frame. P* 11½.

2064	40 c. Type **546**	..	45	50
	a. Booklet pane of 10. Nos. 2064/73	4·25	
	b. Sheetlet of 10. Nos. 2064/73	..	18·00	
2065	40 c. Owl letterbox	..	45	50
2066	40 c. Blue whale letterbox	..	45	50
2067	40 c. "Kilroy is Back" letterbox	..	45	50
2068	40 c. Nesting box letterbox	..	45	50
2069	40 c. Piper letterbox	..	45	50
2070	40 c. Diver's helmet letterbox	..	45	50
2071	40 c. Aircraft letterbox	..	45	50
2072	40 c. Water tap letterbox	..	45	50
2073	40 c. Indian palace letterbox	..	45	50
2064/73		*Set of 10*	4·25	4·50

The phosphor, which shows orange under U.V. light, appears as a frame on two adjacent sides of each design.

Nos. 2064/73 were only issued in $4 stamp booklets in which the booklet pane, No. 2064a, shows the surplus self-adhesive paper around each stamp retained.

No. 2064b comes from the residue of special sheet stock used to prepare first day covers and subsequently sold as $4 "hang-sell" sheetlets. The stamps are on plain backing paper with the surplus self-adhesive paper around each stamp removed.

547 "The Promised Land", 1948 (Colin McCahon)

(Des H. Thompson. Litho Southern Colour Print, Dunedin)

1997 (7 May). *Contemporary Paintings by Colin McCahon. T* **547** *and similar horiz designs. Multicoloured. P* 14.

2074	40 c. Type **547**	..	50	35
2075	$1 "Six Days in Nelson and Canterbury", 1950	..	1·10	90
2076	$1.50, "Northland Panels" (detail), 1958	1·75	2·25
2077	$1.80, "Moby Dick is sighted off Muriwai Beach", 1972	..	2·25	2·25
2074/7		*Set of 4*	5·00	5·25

548 Carrier Pigeon (based on 1899 "Pigeon-gram" local stamp)

(Des S. Fuller. Litho Southern Colour Print, Dunedin)

1997 (7 May). *Centenary of Great Barrier Island Pigeon Post. P* 14×13½.

2078	**548** 40 c. scarlet	..	50	70
	a. Tête-bêche pair	..	1·00	1·40
2079	80 c. deep dull blue	..	90	1·25
	a. Tête-bêche pair	..	1·75	2·50

Nos. 2078/9 were each issued in sheets of 50 on which the stamps were arranged both horizontally and vertically *tête-bêche*.

For these stamps in miniature sheets see Nos. **MS**2080 and **MS**2122.

(Des S. Fuller (No. **MS2080**), Dianne Prosser (No. **MS2081**). Litho Southern Colour Print, Dunedin)

1997 (29 May). *"Pacific '97" International Stamp Exhibition, San Francisco.* P 14×13½ (No. **MS2080**) or 14 (No. **MS2081**).
MS2080   137×120 mm. Nos. 2078/9, each × 2   2·50   2·50
MS2081   140×100 mm. Nos. 2057, 2059 and 2061   3·00   3·00
No. MS2080 is in a triangular format.

549 Rainbow Trout and Red Setter Fly

(Des Joanne Kreyl. Litho Southern Colour Print, Dunedin)

1997 (18 June). *Fly Fishing.* T **549** *and similar horiz designs. Multicoloured.* P 13.
2082   40 c. Type **549**   40   35
2083 $1 Sea-run Brown Trout and Grey Ghost fly   90   90
2084 $1.50, Brook Charr and Twilight Beauty fly   ..   ..   1·40   1·75
2085 $1.80, Brown Trout and Hare and Cooper fly   ..   ..   1·60   2·00
2082/5   ..   ..   Set of 4   3·75   4·50
For miniature sheet containing Nos. 2082 and 2085 see No. MS2172.

550 "Beach Scene" (Fern Petrie)

(Adapted Communication Arts Ltd. Litho Southern Colour Print, Dunedin)

1997 (18 June). *Children's Health.* T **550** *and similar multicoloured designs showing children's paintings.* (a) P 14.
2086   40 c. + 5 c. Type **550**   ..   45   45
2087   80 c. + 5 c. "Horse-riding on the Waterfront" (Georgia Dumergue)   ..   80   85
MS2088   130×90 mm. Nos. 2086/7 and 40 c. + 5 c. As No. 2089 (25×36 mm). P 14½ (as No. 2089) or 14 (others)   ..   1·75   1·75

(b) *Self-adhesive.* P 10×10½
2089   40 c. + 5 c. "Picking Fruit" (Anita Pitcher)   45   45
2086/9   ..   Set of 3   1·60   1·75
No. 2089 comes from rolls of 100 on which the surplus self-adhesive paper around each stamp was removed. This design with traditional gum was only available as part of No. MS2088.

(Des A. Mitchell. Litho Southern Colour Print, Dunedin)

1997 (6 Aug)–**2000**. P 14½ (*and* 14 *around design*).
2090   445 $1 violet   75   80
2090a $1.10, gold (6.3.00)   ..   70   75
Nos. 2090/a were printed in sheets of 36 with each stamp within a square margin perforated on all four sides and with a further circular perforation around the design.
Sheets of No. 2090 were re-issued on 31 December 1999 with a pattern of gold suns overprinted on the margins around each stamp to mark the Millennium.

551 The "Overlander" at Paremata, Wellington

552 Samuel Marsden's *Active*, Bay of Islands

(Des R. Jones. Litho Southern Colour Print, Dunedin)

1997 (6 Aug). *Scenic Railway Services.* T **551** *and similar horiz designs. Multicoloured.* P 14×14½.
2091   40 c. Type **551**   50   35
2092   80 c. The "Tranz Alpine" in the Southern Alps   ..   90   80
2093 $1 The "Southerner" at Canterbury   ..   1·00   90
2094 $1.20, The "Coastal Pacific" on the Kaikoura Coast   ..   1·40   1·75
2095 $1.50, The "Bay Express" at Central Hawke's Bay   ..   1·60   2·00
2096 $1.80, The "Kaimai Express" at Tauranga Harbour   ..   1·75   2·00
2091/6   ..   Set of 6   6·50   7·00
For miniature sheet containing Nos. 2092/3 and 2095 see No. MS2173.
A miniature sheet containing Nos. 2091/6 comes from a Limited Edition Collectors Pack costing NZ$135.

(Des Fifi Colston. Litho Southern Colour Print, Dunedin)

1997 (3 Sept). *Christmas.* T **552** *and similar vert designs. Multicoloured.* (a) P 14.
2097   40 c. Type **552**   45   40
  a. Block of 6. Nos. 2097/102   ..   5·75
2098   70 c. Revd. Marsden preaching   ..   75   65
2099   80 c. Marsden and Maori chiefs   ..   85   75
2100 $1 Maori family   ..   ..   1·00   90
2101 $1.50, Handshake and cross   ..   1·60   1·75
2102 $1.80, Pohutukawa (flower) and Rangihoua Bay   ..   1·75   2·00
(b) *Self-adhesive. Smaller design, 29×24 mm.* P 10
2103   40 c. Memorial cross, Pohutukawa and Bay of Islands   ..   40   40
  a. Booklet pane of 10   ..   4·00
2097/103   ..   Set of 7   6·00   6·25
In addition to separate sheets Nos. 2097/102 were also issued as *se-tenant* blocks of 6.
No. 2103 comes from either rolls of 100, on which the surplus adhesive paper was removed, or from $4 booklets on which the surplus paper was retained.

553 Huhu Beetle   **554** *Rosa rugosa*

(Des D. Gunson. Litho SNP Cambec, Australia)

1997 (1 Oct). *Insects.* T **553** *and similar horiz designs. Multicoloured. Self-adhesive. Two phosphor bands.* P 11½.
2104   40 c. Type **553**   45   45
  a. Booklet pane. Nos. 2104/13   ..   4·00
  b. Sheetlet of 10. Nos. 2104/13   ..   13·00
2105   40 c. Giant Land Snail   45   45
2106   40 c. Giant Weta   45   45
2107   40 c. Giant Dragonfly   45   45
2108   40 c. Peripatus   45   45
2109   40 c. Cicada   45   45
2110   40 c. Puriri Moth   45   45
2111   40 c. Veined Slug   45   45
2112   40 c. Katipo   45   45
2113   40 c. Flax Weevil   45   45
2104/13   ..   Set of 10   4·00   4·00
The phosphor, which shows pink under U.V. light, appears as horizontal bands across the top and bottom of each design.
Nos. 2104/13 were only issued in $4 stamp booklets in which the booklet pane, No. 2104a, shows the surplus self-adhesive paper around each stamp retained.
No. 2104b comes from the residue of special sheet stock used to prepare first day covers and subsequently sold as $4 "hang-sell" sheetlets. The stamps are on plain backing paper, with the surplus self-adhesive paper around each stamp removed.

(Des Z. Guizheng. Litho Southern Colour Print, Dunedin)

1997 (9 Oct). *New Zealand–China Joint Issue. Roses.* T **554** *and similar vert design. Multicoloured.* P 14.
2114   40 c. Type **554**   40   40
  a. Horiz pair. Nos. 2114/15   ..   80   80
2115   40 c. Aotearoa   40   40
MS2116   115×95 mm. 80 c. Nos. 2114/15   85   85
Nos. 2114/15 were printed together, *se-tenant*, in horizontal pairs throughout the sheet.
Stamps in similar designs were also issued by China.

555 Queen Elizabeth II and Prince Philip

556 Cartoon Kiwi on Busy-bee

(Des Red Cactus Design. Litho Southern Colour Print, Dunedin)

1997 (12 Nov). *Golden Wedding of Queen Elizabeth and Prince Philip.* P 12.
2117   555   40 c. multicoloured   ..   40   35
No. 2117 was printed in sheets of 10 (2×5) with decorated margins.

(Des G. Tremain (40 c.), J. Hubbard ($1), E. Heath ($1.50), B. Silver ($1.80). Litho Southern Colour Print, Dunedin)

1997 (12 Nov). *New Zealand Cartoons. "Kiwis taking on the World".* T **556** *and similar horiz designs. Multicoloured.* P 14.
2118   40 c. Type **556**   45   35
2119 $1 "Let's have 'em for Breakfast"   85   80
2120 $1.50, Kiwi dinghy winning race   1·25   1·50
2121 $1.80, "CND" emblem cut in forest   1·60   1·75
2118/21   ..   Set of 4   3·75   4·00

(Des S. Fuller. Litho Southern Colour Print, Dunedin)

1997 (13 Nov). *"Aupex '97" National Stamp Exhibition, Auckland. Sheet* 140×120 mm. P 14×13½.
MS2122   Nos. 2078/9, each × 2   ..   2·10   2·10
No. MS2122 is in a triangular format

1997 (19 Nov). *International Stamp and Coin Exhibition 1997, Shanghai. Sheet as No.* **MS2116** *but redrawn to include* "Issued by New Zealand Post to commemorate the International Stamp and Coin Expo. Shanghai, China. 19–23 November 1997" *inscr in English and Chinese with additional die-stamped gold frame and logo.*
MS2123   115×95 mm. Nos. 2114/15   ..   70   70

557 Modern Dancer

(Des N. Childs. Litho Southern Colour Print, Dunedin)

1998 (14 Jan). *Performing Arts.* T **557** *and similar vert designs. Multicoloured.* P 13½.
2124   40 c. Type **557**   50   35
2125   80 c. Trombone player   ..   85   75
  a. Perf 14
2126 $1 Opera singer   ..   ..   1·00   85
2127 $1.20, Actor   ..   ..   1·50   1·50
2128 $1.50, Singer   ..   ..   1·75   1·90
2129 $1.80, Ballet dancer   ..   2·00   2·25
  a. Perf 14
2124/9   ..   Set of 6   7·00   7·00
MS2130   Seven sheets, each 150×110 mm. (a) No. 2124; (b) No. 2125; (c) No. 2126; (d) No. 2127; (e) No. 2128; (f) No. 2129; (g) Nos. 2124/9. P 12 (Nos. MS2130c, MS2130g) or 13½ (others)
  Set of 7 sheets   14·00   16·00
Nos. 2130a/g were only available from $13.40 stamp booklets, with each miniature sheet showing a line of roulettes at left.

"**BEST OF '98**". A further set of three miniature sheets, as described below No. **MS1951**, was distributed by the Philatelic Bureau in 1998 to customers purchasing a certain amount of philatelic material. The stamps shown for 1998 were Nos. 2129, 2132, 2138, 2147, 2171, 2177, 2187, 2194 and 2221.

558 Museum of New Zealand

(Des Joanne Kreyl. Litho Southern Colour Print, Dunedin)

1998 (11 Feb). *Opening of Museum of New Zealand, Wellington.* T **558** *and similar diamond-shaped design. Multicoloured.* P 14½.
2131   40 c. Type **558**   30   35
2132 $1.80, Museum and seabirds   ..   1·40   1·40

559 Domestic Cat   **560** Maoris and Canoe

(Des Julie Grieg. Litho Southern Colour Print, Dunedin)

1998 (11 Feb). *Cats.* T **559** *and similar vert designs. Multicoloured.* P 13½.
2133   40 c. Type **559**   40   35
2134   80 c. Burmese   75   80
2135 $1 Birman   85   80
2136 $1.20, British Blue   ..   1·00   1·10
2137 $1.50, Persian   ..   ..   1·25   1·50
2138 $1.80, Siamese   ..   ..   1·75   2·00
2133/8   ..   Set of 6   5·50   6·00

(Des Julie Grieg. Litho Southern Colour Print, Dunedin)

1998 (11 Feb). *Chinese New Year ("Year of the Tiger").* P 13½.
MS2139   100×135 mm. Nos. 2133, 2135 and 2138   2·75   2·75

(Des T. Crilley. Litho Southern Colour Print, Dunedin)

1998 (18 Mar). *Millennium Series (2nd issue). Immigrants.*
T 560 and similar vert designs. Multicoloured. P 14½×14.

2140	40 c. Type 560		30	35
2141	80 c. 19th-century European settlers and immigrant ship		60	65
2142	$1 Gold miners and mine		75	80
2143	$1.20, Post 1945 European migrants and liner		90	95
2144	$1.50, Pacific islanders and church		1·10	1·25
2145	$1.80, Asian migrant and jumbo jet		1·25	1·40
2140/5		*Set of 6*	5·00	5·25

Miniature sheets containing Nos. 2140/5 come from a Limited Edition Collectors Pack costing NZ$135 or a Limited Edition Millennium Collection costing NZ$129.

561 "With Great Respect   562 Mother and
to the Mehmetcik"   Son hugging
Statue, Gallipoli

(Des Dianne Prosser. Litho Southern Colour Print, Dunedin)

1998 (18 Mar). *Joint Issue New Zealand–Turkey. Memorial*
Statues. T 561 and similar vert design. Multicoloured. P 13½.

2146	40 c. Type 561		30	35
2147	$1.80, "Mother with Children", National War Memorial, Wellington		1·25	1·40

(Des Colenso Communications Ltd. Litho Southern Colour Print, Dunedin)

1998 (15 Apr). *"Stay in Touch" Greetings Stamps. T 562 and*
similar multicoloured designs. Self-adhesive. Phosphorised
paper. P 10½×10 (horiz) or 10×10½ (vert).

2148	40 c. Type 562		25	30
	a. Booklet pane. Nos. 2148/57		2·50	
	b. Sheetlet of 4. Nos. 2148/51		3·25	
2149	40 c. Couple on beach		25	30
2150	40 c. Boys shaking hands		25	30
2151	40 c. Grandmother and grandson		25	30
2152	40 c. Young boys in pool (horiz)		25	30
	b. Sheetlet of 6. Nos. 2152/7		4·75	
2153	40 c. "I'LL MISS YOU... PLEASE WRITE" (horiz)		25	30
2154	40 c. Symbolic couple and clouds (horiz)		25	30
2155	40 c. Young couple kissing (horiz)		25	30
2156	40 c. Couple sat on sofa (horiz)		25	30
2157	40 c. Maoris rubbing noses (horiz)		25	30
2148/57		*Set of 10*	2·50	3·00

Nos. 2148/57 were only available from $4 stamp booklets, containing No. 2148a on which the surplus self-adhesive paper was retained.

Nos. 2148b and 2152b come from the residue of special sheet stock used to prepare first day covers and subsequently sold as $4 "hang-sell" packs containing the two sheetlets. The stamps are on plain backing paper, with the surplus self-adhesive paper around each stamp removed.

563 Mount Cook   564 "Wounded at Cassino"
or Aorangi

(Adapted R. Jones. Litho Southern Colour Print, Dunedin)

1998 (20 May). *Centenary of 1898 Pictorial Stamps. Designs as*
T 23/36 with modern face values as T 563. P 14×14½ (Nos.
2158/65) or P 14½ (others).

2158	563	40 c. purple-brown		40	40
2159	24	40 c. deep blue and orange-brown		40	40
2160	25	40 c. lake-brown		40	40
2161	28	40 c. chestnut		40	40
2162	29	40 c. deep rose-red		40	40
2163	31	40 c. deep green		40	40
2164	32	40 c. indigo		40	40
2165	34	40 c. red-orange		40	40
2166	26	80 c. steel-blue (inscr "LAKE WAKITIPU") (35×23 mm)		75	75
2167	27	80 c. steel-blue (inscr "LAKE WAKATIPU") (35×23 mm)		75	75
2168	30	$1 reddish brown (23×35 mm)		85	85
2169	33	$1.20, purple-brown (35×23 mm)		90	90
2170	35	$1.50, deep blue-green (35×23 mm)		1·25	1·25
2171	36	$1.80, dull vermilion (23×35 mm)		1·40	1·40
2158/71			*Set of 14*	8·00	8·00

For miniature sheets containing Nos. 2166/7 and 2170 see Nos. MS2188 and MS2214.

Sheets of Nos. 2158/71 numbered and with the margins decorated in gold come from special Centenary Collections.

(Des Joanne Kreyl (No. MS2172), R. Jones (No. MS2173). Litho Southern Colour Print, Dunedin)

1998 (20 May). *"Israel '98" World Stamp Exhibition, Tel Aviv.*
P 13 (No. MS2172) or 14×14½ (No. MS2173).

MS2172	112×90 mm. Nos. 2082 and 2085	2·50	2·75
MS2173	125×100 mm. Nos. 2092/3 and 2095	4·00	4·00

(Des H. Thompson. Litho Southern Colour Print, Dunedin)

1998 (24 June). *Paintings by Peter McIntyre. T 564 and*
similar horiz designs. Multicoloured. P 13½.

2174	40 c. Type 564		35	30
2175	$1 "The Cliffs of Rangitikei"		85	75
2176	$1.50, "Maori Children, King Country"		1·25	1·40
2177	$1.80, "The Anglican Church, Kakahi"		1·40	1·50
2174/7		*Set of 4*	3·50	3·50

For Nos. 2176/7 in miniature sheet for "Italia '98" see No. MS2215. A similar miniature sheet, but with the exhibition logo replaced by the Limited Edition symbol at bottom right, comes from Limited Edition Collectors Packs costing NZ$135.

565 Girl wearing Lifejacket

(Des Sea Sky Design)

1998 (24 June). *Children's Health. Water Safety. T 565 and*
similar vert design. Multicoloured. (a) Litho Southern Colour
Print, Dunedin. P 13½.

2178	40 c. + 5 c. Type 565		40	40
2179	80 c. + 5 c. Boy learning to swim		60	60
MS2180	125×90 mm. Nos. 2178/9, each × 2. P 14½×14		2·00	2·00

(b) *Litho SNP Cambec. Smaller design, 25×37 mm. Self-*
adhesive. Phosphor on inscr panel and background. P 11½.

2181	40 c. + 5 c. Type 565		30	35

No. 2181, on which the phosphor shows pink under U.V. light, comes from rolls of 100 on which the surplus self-adhesive paper around each stamp was removed. Examples without printer's imprint on the reverse come from $4.35 "hang-sell" packs containing Nos. 2178/81.

566 Sunrise near Cambridge

(Des Cato Design. Litho Southern Colour Print, Dunedin)

1998 (29 July). *Scenic Skies. T 566 and similar horiz designs.*
Multicoloured. P 15×14½.

2182	40 c. Type 566		35	30
2183	80 c. Clouds over Lake Wanaka		65	65
2184	$1 Sunset over Mount Maunganui		75	75
2185	$1.20, Rain clouds over South Bay, Kaikoura		90	90
2186	$1.50, Sunset near Statue of Wairaka, Whakatane Harbour		1·25	1·25
2187	$1.80, Cloud formation above Lindis Pass		1·60	1·75
2182/7		*Set of 6*	5·00	5·00

For Nos. 2182 and 2187 in miniature sheet for "Australia '99" see No. MS2245.

(Des R. Jones. Litho Southern Colour Print, Dunedin)

1998 (7 Aug). *"TARAPEX '98" National Stamp Exhibition,*
New Plymouth. P 14½.

MS2188	90×80 mm. Nos. 2166/7	1·60	1·75

567 Virgin Mary and   568 Lemon and Mineral
Christ Child   Water Bottle, Paeroa

(Des Sally Simons)

1998 (2 Sept). *Christmas. T 567 and similar vert designs.*
Multicoloured.

(a) *Litho Southern Colour Print, Dunedin. P 13½.*

2189	40 c. Type 567		35	30
2190	70 c. Shepherds approaching the stable		55	55
2191	80 c. Virgin Mary, Joseph and Christ Child		65	65
2192	$1 Magi with gift of gold		80	80
2193	$1.50, Three magi		1·25	1·25
2194	$1.80, Angel and shepherds		1·40	1·50
2189/94		*Set of 6*	4·50	4·50

(b) *Litho SNP Cambec, Australia. Smaller design, 24×29 mm.*
Self-adhesive. P 11½.

2195	40 c. Type 567		35	30
	a. Booklet pane of 10		3·00	

No. 2195, which shows a broad band of pink phosphor over both the right-hand part of the centre design and "NEW ZEALAND", comes from either rolls of 100, on which the surplus adhesive paper was removed, or from $4 booklets on which the surplus paper was retained.

(Des Donna McKenna. Litho SNP Cambec, Melbourne)

1998 (7 Oct). *Town Icons. T 568 and similar vert designs.*
Multicoloured. Self-adhesive. Phosphor backgrounds. P 11
(Nos. 2202/5) or 11½ (others).

2196	40 c. Type 568		35	35
	a. Booklet pane of 10. Nos. 2196/205		3·00	
	b. Sheetlet of 10. Nos. 2196/205		9·00	
2197	40 c. Carrot, Ohakune		35	35
2198	40 c. Brown Trout, Gore (25×36 mm)		35	35
2199	40 c. Crayfish, Kaikoura (25×36 mm)		35	35
2200	40 c. Sheep-shearer, Te Kuiti (25×36 mm)		35	35
2201	40 c. "Pania of the Reef" (Maori legend), Napier (25×36 mm)		35	35
2202	40 c. Paua Shell, Riverton (24×29 mm)		35	35
2203	40 c. Kiwifruit, Te Puke (24×29 mm)		35	35
2204	40 c. Border Collie, Lake Tekapo (24×29 mm)		35	35
2205	40 c. "Big Cow", Hawera (24×29 mm)		35	35
2196/205		*Set of 10*	3·00	3·00

Nos. 2196/205 were only issued in $4 self-adhesive stamp booklets containing No. 2196a on which the surplus self-adhesive paper was retained.

The phosphor, which shows pink under U.V. light, covers most of the background on each design.

No. 2196b comes from the residue of special sheet stock used to prepare first day covers and subsequently sold as $4 "hang-sell" sheetlets. The stamps are on plain backing paper with the surplus self-adhesive paper around each stamp removed. Similar "hang-sell" packs, selling at $9.60, were prepared containing blocks or pairs of the individual designs for sale at the towns depicted. On these blocks or pairs the surplus self-adhesive paper was retained.

569 Moonfish   570 Wellington in 1841 and
1998

(Des G. Cox. Litho Southern Colour Print, Dunedin)

1998 (7 Oct). *International Year of the Ocean. T 569 and*
similar vert designs. P 14.

2206	40 c. Type 569		35	35
	a. Block of 4. Nos. 2206/9		1·25	
2207	40 c. Mako Shark		35	35
2208	40 c. Yellowfin Tuna		35	35
2209	40 c. Giant Squid		35	35
2210	80 c. Striped Marlin		60	60
	a. Block of 4. Nos. 2210/3		2·25	
2211	80 c. Porcupine Fish		60	60
2212	80 c. Eagle Ray		60	60
2213	80 c. Sandager's Wrasse		60	60
2206/13		*Set of 8*	3·50	3·50

Nos. 2206/9 and 2210/13 were each printed together, *se-tenant*, in blocks of four, forming composite designs.

A miniature sheet containing Nos. 2206/13 comes from a Limited Edition Collectors Pack costing NS$135.

For Nos. 2206/7 and 2210/11 in miniature sheet for "Australia '99" see No. MS2246 and for Nos. 2208/9 and 2212/13 in a miniature sheet for "PhilexFrance 99" see No. MS2277.

(Adapted R. Jones. Litho Southern Colour Print, Dunedin)

1998 (23 Oct). *"Italia '98" International Philatelic Exhibition,*
Milan. P 13½ (No. MS2214) or 14 (No. MS2215).

MS2214	90×80 mm. Nos. 2167 and 2170	3·00	3·25
MS2215	112×90 mm. Nos. 2176/7	2·00	2·25

(Des Niki Hill. Litho Southern Colour Print, Dunedin)

1998 (11 Nov). *Millennium Series (3rd issue). Urban*
Transformations. T 570 and similar horiz designs.
Multicoloured. P 14×14½.

2216	40 c. Type 570		40	30
2217	80 c. Auckland in 1852 and 1998		65	55
2218	$1 Christchurch in 1851 and 1998		75	70
2219	$1.20, Westport in 1919 and 1998		85	1·00
2220	$1.50, Tauranga in 1880 and 1998		1·25	1·40
2221	$1.80, Dunedin in 1862 and 1998		1·40	1·60
2216/21		*Set of 6*	4·75	5·00

A miniature sheet containing Nos. 2216/21 comes from a Limited Edition Millennium Collection costing NZ$129.

"BEST OF '99". A further set of three miniature sheets, as described below No. MS1951, was distributed by the Philatelic Bureau to customers purchasing a certain amount of philatelic material. The stamps shown for 1999 were Nos. 2227, 2230, 2237, 2244, 2271, 2284, 2293, 2301 and 2309.

OMNIBUS ISSUES

Details, together with prices for complete sets, of the various Omnibus issues from the 1935 Silver Jubilee series to date are included in a special section following Zimbabwe at the end of Volume 2.

571 *Fuchsia excorticata*

572 Civic Theatre, Auckland

(Des Sue Wickison. Litho Southern Colour Print, Dunedin)

1999 (13 Jan). *Flowering Trees of New Zealand. T **571** and similar vert designs. Multicoloured. P 14½×14.*

2222	40 c. Type **571**		40	30
2223	80 c. *Solanum laciniatum*		65	55
2224	$1 *Sophora tetraptera*		75	70
2225	$1.20, *Carmichaelia stevensonii*		85	1·00
2226	$1.50, *Olearia angustfolia*		1·25	1·40
2227	$1.80, *Metrosideros umbellata*		1·40	1·60
2222/7		*Set of* 6	4·75	5·00

A miniature sheet containing Nos. 2226/7 comes from a Limited Edition Collectors Pack costing NZ$135.
For Nos. 2222/3 in miniature sheet for "China '99" see No. MS2286.

(Des Donna McKenna. Litho Southern Colour Print, Dunedin)

1999 (10 Feb). *Art Deco Architecture. T **572** and similar vert designs. Multicoloured. P 14½×14.*

2228	40 c. Type **572**		40	30
2229	$1 Masonic Hotel, Napier		1·00	80
2230	$1.50, Medical and Dental Chambers, Hastings		1·25	1·40
2231	$1.80, Buller County Chambers, Westport		1·40	1·60
2228/31		*Set of* 4	3·50	3·50

573 Labrador Puppy and Netherland Dwarf Rabbit

574 Toy Fire Engine and Marbles

(Des Lindy Fisher. Litho Southern Colour Print, Dunedin)

1999 (10 Feb). *Popular Pets. T **573** and similar vert designs. Multicoloured. P 14.*

2232	40 c. Type **573**		40	30
2233	80 c. Netherland Dwarf Rabbit		80	55
2234	$1 Tabby kitten and Netherland Dwarf Rabbit		90	70
2235	$1.20, Lamb		1·25	1·25
2236	$1.50, Welsh pony		1·40	1·50
2237	$1.80, Two Budgerigars		1·50	1·60
2232/7		*Set of* 6	5·50	5·50
MS2238	100×135 mm. Nos. 2232/4		1·75	1·75

No. **MS**2238 also commemorates the Chinese New Year ("Year of the Rabbit").
For Nos. 2232 and 2234 in miniature sheet for "China '99" see No. **MS**2287.

(Des Siren Communications Ltd. Litho Southern Colour Print, Dunedin)

1999 (10 Mar). *Millennium Series (4th issue). Nostalgia. T **574** and similar horiz designs. Multicoloured. P 14×14½.*

2239	40 c. Type **574**		40	30
2240	80 c. Commemorative tin of biscuits and cereal packet		70	55
2241	$1 Tram, tickets and railway crockery		85	70
2242	$1.20, Radio and *Woman's Weekly* magazine		1·00	1·25
2243	$1.50, Coins, postcards and stamps		1·25	1·40
2244	$1.80, Lawn mower and seed packets		1·40	1·60
2239/44		*Set of* 6	5·00	5·25

A miniature sheet containing Nos. 2239/44 comes from a Limited Edition Millennium Collection costing NZ$129.

(Des Cato Design (No. **MS**2245), G. Cox (No. **MS**2246). Litho Southern Colour Print, Dunedin)

1999 (19 Mar). *"Australia '99" World Stamp Exhibition, Melbourne. P 15×14½ (No. **MS**2245) or 14 (No. **MS**2246).*

MS2245	130×70 mm. Nos. 2182 and 2187		1·90	1·90
MS2246	130×90 mm. Nos. 2206/7 and 2210/11		2·00	2·00

NEW INFORMATION

The editor is always interested to correspond with people who have new information that will improve or correct the Catalogue.

---

575 Hunter Building, Victoria University

576 Auckland Blues Player kicking Ball

(Litho Southern Colour Print)

1999 (7 Apr). *Centenary of Victoria University, Wellington. P 14×14½.*

2247	**575**	40 c. multicoloured		30	30

(Des P. Martinson and Diane Prosser)

1999 (7 Apr). *New Zealand U-Bix Rugby Super 12 Championship. T **576** and similar vert designs. Multicoloured.*

(a) Litho Southern Colour Print. P 14½.

2248	40 c. Type **576**		35	35
	a. Sheetlet. Nos. 2248/57		3·00	
2249	40 c. Auckland Blues player being tackled		35	35
2250	40 c. Chiefs player being tackled		35	35
2251	40 c. Chiefs lineout jump		35	35
2252	40 c. Wellington Hurricanes player being tackled		35	35
2253	40 c. Wellington Hurricanes player passing ball		35	35
2254	40 c. Canterbury Crusaders lineout jump		35	35
2255	40 c. Canterbury Crusaders player kicking ball		35	35
2256	40 c. Otago Highlanders diving for try		35	35
2257	40 c. Otago Highlanders player running with ball		35	35
2248/57		*Set of* 10	3·00	3·00

(b) Litho SNP Ausprint. Self-adhesive. Phosphor frame. P 11½

2258	40 c. Type **576**		35	35
	a. Booklet pane. Nos. 2258/9, each × 5		3·00	
2259	40 c. Auckland Blues player being tackled		35	35
2260	40 c. Chiefs player being tackled		35	35
	a. Booklet pane. Nos. 2260/1, each × 5		3·00	
2261	40 c. Chiefs lineout jump		35	35
2262	40 c. Wellington Hurricanes player being tackled		35	35
	a. Booklet pane. Nos. 2262/3, each × 5		3·00	
2263	40 c. Wellington Hurricanes player passing ball		35	35
2264	40 c. Canterbury Crusaders lineout jump		35	35
	a. Booklet pane. Nos. 2264/5, each × 5		3·00	
2265	40 c. Canterbury Crusaders player kicking ball		35	35
2266	40 c. Otago Highlanders diving for try		35	35
	a. Booklet pane. Nos. 2266/7, each × 5		3·00	
2267	40 c. Otago Highlanders player running with ball		35	35
2258/67		*Set of* 10	3·00	3·00

Nos. 2248/57 were printed together, *se-tenant*, in sheetlets of 10 (2×5).
Nos. 2258/67, on which the phosphor shows pink under U.V. light, were only issued in $4 booklets (one for each team) on which the surplus self-adhesive paper was retained.
Examples on plain backing paper with the surplus self-adhesive paper around each stamp removed come from the residue of special sheet stock used to prepare first day covers and subsequently sold as $4 "hang-sell" packs containing five separate panes.

577 "The Lake, Tuai"

(Des H. Thompson. Litho Southern Colour Print, Dunedin)

1999 (16 June). *Paintings by Doris Lusk. T **577** and similar horiz designs. Multicoloured. P 14.*

2268	40 c. Type **577**		35	30
2269	$1 "The Pumping Station"		80	70
2270	$1.50, "Arcade Awning, St. Mark's Square, Venice (2)"		1·10	1·25
2271	$1.80, "Tuam St. II"		1·25	1·40
2268/71		*Set of* 4	3·25	3·25

For Nos. 2268 and 2271 in miniature sheet for "PhilexFrance '99" see No. **MS**2276.

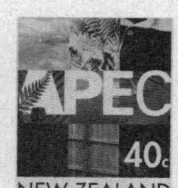

578 "A Lion in the Meadow" (Margaret Mahy)

579 "APEC"

(Des Ann Adams from book illustrations. Litho Southern Colour Print, Dunedin)

1999 (16 June). *Children's Health. Children's Books. T **578** and similar horiz designs. Multicoloured. Phosphorised paper.*

(a) P 14

2272	40 c. + 5 c. Type **578**		40	40
2273	80 c. + 5 c. "Greedy Cat" (Joy Cowley)		60	60
MS2274	130×90 mm. 40 c. + 5 c. Type **578**; 40 c. + 5 c. As No. 2275 (37×25 *mm*); 80 c. + 5 c. No. 2273		1·40	1·40

(b) Self-adhesive. P 10

2275	40 c. + 5 c. "Hairy Maclary's Bone" (Lynley Dodd) (37×25 *mm*)		35	35

No. 2275 comes only in rolls of 100 on which the surplus self-adhesive paper around each stamp was removed.

(Des G. Cox (No. **MS**2276), H. Thompson (No. **MS**2277). Litho Southern Colour Print, Dunedin)

1999 (2 July). *"PhilexFrance '99" International Stamp Exhibition, Paris. P 14.*

MS2276	112×90 mm. Nos. 2268 and 2271		1·75	1·75
MS2277	130×90 mm. Nos. 2208/9 and 2212/13		2·00	2·00

(Des S. Fuller. Litho Southern Colour Print, Dunedin)

1999 (21 July). *10th Asia-Pacific Economic Co-operation Meeting, New Zealand. P 14.*

2278	**579**	40 c. multicoloured		30	30

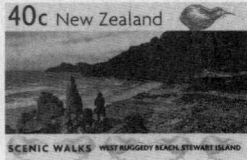

580 West Ruggedy Beach, Stewart Island

(Des Ocean Design. Litho Southern Colour Print, Dunedin)

1999 (28 July). *Scenic Walks. T **580** and similar horiz designs. Multicoloured. P 14.*

2279	40 c. Type **580**		25	30
2280	80 c. Ice lake, Butler Valley, Westland		50	55
2281	$1 Tonga Bay, Abel Tasman National Park		65	70
2282	$1.20, East Matakitaki Valley, Nelson Lakes National Park		75	80
2283	$1.50, Great Barrier Island		95	1·00
2284	$1.80, Mt. Egmont, Taranaki		1·10	1·25
2279/84		*Set of* 6	4·25	4·50
MS2285	Seven sheets, each 150×110 mm. (a) No. 2279. (b) No. 2280. (c) No. 2281. (d) No. 2282. (e) No. 2283. (f) No. 2284. (g) Nos. 2279/84			
		Set of 2 sheets	8·50	9·00

Nos. **MS**2285a/g were only available from $13.40 stamp booklets, with each miniature sheet showing a line of roulettes at left.
For No. 2284 in miniature sheet for "Palmpex '99" see No. **MS**2295.

(Des Lindy Fisher (No. **MS**2286), Sue Wickison (No. **MS**2287). Litho Southern Colour Print, Dunedin)

1999 (21 Aug). *"China '99" International Stamp Exhibition, Peking. P 14½×14 (No. **MS**2286) or 14 (No. **MS**2287).*

MS2286	112×90 mm. Nos. 2222/3		1·00	1·00
MS2287	100×135 mm. Nos. 2232 and 2234		1·00	1·00

581 Baby Jesus with Animals

582 "P" Class Dinghy

(Des Lindy Fisher. Litho Southern Colour Print, Dunedin)

1999 (8 Sept–1 Nov). *Christmas. (a) T **581** and similar square designs. Multicoloured. P 13.*

2288	40 c. Type **581**		25	30
2289	80 c. Virgin Mary praying		50	55
2290	$1.10, Mary and Joseph on way to Bethlehem		70	75
2291	$1.20, Angel playing harp		75	80
2292	$1.50, Three shepherds		95	1·00
2293	$1.80, Three wise men with gifts		1·10	1·25
2288/93		*Set of* 6	4·25	4·50

(b) Smaller multicoloured design, 23×28 mm. Self-adhesive. Phosphor frame. P 9½

2294	40 c. Type **581**		25	30
	a. Booklet pane. No. 2294×10 (1 Nov)		2·50	

No. 2294, on which the phosphor shows pink under UV light, comes from rolls of 100 on which the surplus self-adhesive paper around each stamp was removed or from booklet pane No. 2294a where the surplus paper was retained.

(Des Ocean Design. Litho Southern Colour Print, Dunedin)

1999 (1 Oct). *"Palmpex '99" National Stamp Exhibition, Palmerston North. Sheet 130×90 mm containing No. 2284. Multicoloured. P 14.*

MS2295	$1.80, Mt Egmont, Taranaki		1·40	1·40

(Des BNA Design, Litho Southern Colour Print, Dunedin)

1999 (20 Oct). *Yachting. T* **582** *and similar vert designs. Phosphorised paper. Multicoloured.* (a) *Size* 28×39 *mm. P* 14
2296	40 c. Type **582**	25	30
2297	80 c. Laser dinghy	50	55
2298	$1.10, 18' skiff	70	75
2299	$1.20, Hobie catamaran	75	80
2300	$1.50, Racing yacht	95	1·00
2301	$1.80, Cruising yacht	1·10	1·25
2296/301	Set of 6	4·25	4·50
MS2302	125×100 mm. Nos. 2296/301	4·25	4·50

(b) *Self-adhesive. Size* 23×28 *mm. P* 9½
2303	40 c. Optimist dinghy	25	30
	a. Booklet pane. No. 2303×10	2·50	

No. 2303 was only issued in $4 stamp booklets, containing No. 2303a, on which the surplus self-adhesive paper was retained.

583 Group of Victorian Women (female suffrage, 1893)

(Des Deirdre Cassell. Litho Southern Colour Print, Dunedin)

1999 (17 Nov). *Millennium Series* (5th issue). *New Zealand Achievements. T* **583** *and similar horiz designs. Phosphorised paper. Multicoloured. P* 14×14½.
2304	40 c. Type **583**	25	30
2305	80 c. Richard Pearse's aircraft (powered flight, 1903)	50	55
2306	$1.10, Lord Rutherford (splitting the atom, 1919)	70	75
2307	$1.20, Boat on lake (invention of jet boat, 1953)	75	80
2308	$1.50, Sir Edmund Hillary (conquest of Everest, 1953)	95	1·00
2309	$1.80, Protesters and warship (nuclear free zone, 1987)	1·10	1·25
2304/9	Set of 6	4·25	4·50

A miniature sheet containing Nos. 2304/9 comes from a Limited Edition Millennium Collection costing NZ$129.

584 Sunrise and World Map   **585** Araiteuru (North Island sea guardian)

(Des Diane Prosser. Litho Southern Colour Print, Dunedin)

2000 (1 Jan). *Millennium Series* (6th issue). *Phosphorised paper. P* 14×14½.
2310	**584** 40 c. multicoloured	25	30
	a. Sheetlet. No. 2310×10	2·50	
	b. New Zealand Millennium logo missing from bottom left (sheetlet R. 3/1)	2·50	

No. 2310 was printed in sheets of 50 (5×10) and in sheetlets of 10 (2×5) with an enlarged right margin separated from the block of stamps by a line of roulettes. No. 2310b, which shows the map of New Zealand and rays omitted from beside the time at bottom left, occurs on R. 3/1 of the sheetlet only.
A miniature sheet containing six examples of No. 2310 comes from a Limited Edition Millennium Collection costing NZ$129.

(Des M. Smith. Litho Southern Colour Print, Dunedin)

2000 (9 Feb). *Chinese New Year* ("Year of the Dragon"). *Maori Spirits and Guardians. T* **585** *and similar vert designs. Multicoloured. P* 14.
2311	40 c. Type **585**	25	30
2312	80 c. Kurangaituku (giant bird woman)	50	55
2313	$1.10, Te Hoata and Te Pupu (volcanic taniwha sisters)	70	75
2314	$1.20, Patupaiarehe (mountain fairy tribe)	75	80
2315	$1.50, Te Ngarara-huarau (giant first lizard)	95	1·00
2316	$1.80, Tuhirangi (South Island sea guardian)	1·10	1·25
2311/16	Set of 6	4·25	4·50
MS2317	125×90 mm. Nos. 2315/16	4·25	4·50

A further miniature sheet, containing Nos. 2313/14, comes from a Limited Edition Collection Pack costing NZ$135.

Index to New Zealand Stamp Designs from 1946

The following index is intended to facilitate the identification of all New Zealand stamps from 1946 onwards. Portrait stamps are usually listed under surnames only, views under the name of the town or city and other issues under the main subject or a prominent word and date chosen from the inscription. Simple abbreviations have occasionally been resorted to and when the same design or subject appears on more than one stamp, only the first of each series is indicated.

STAMP BOOKLETS

Nos. SB1 to SB24 are stapled.

Nos. SB1/5 were sold at ½d. above the face value of the stamps to cover the cost of manufacture.

1901 (1 Apr). *White card covers with postage rates.*
SB1   1s. ½d. booklet containing twelve 1d. (No. 278) in blocks of 6 .. .. £2250
SB2   2s. 6½d. booklet containing thirty 1d. (No. 278) in blocks of 6 .. .. £2750
Original printings of Nos. SB1/2 showed the face value on the cover in small figures. Subsequent printings show large figures of value on the covers and the prices quoted are for this type.

1902 (21 Aug)–05. *White card covers with postage rates.*
SB3   1s. ½d. booklet containing twelve 1d. in panes of 6 (Nos. 303b or 303cb) £1800
SB4   2s. ½d. booklet containing twenty-four 1d. in panes of 6 (Nos. 303b or 303cb) (21.3.05) .. £2000
SB5   2s. 6½d. booklet containing thirty 1d. in panes of 6 (Nos. 303b or 303cb) £2750

1910 (Apr). *White card cover with postage rates.*
SB6   2s. booklet containing eleven ½d. in pane of 5 with 1 label (Nos. 387b or 387c) and pane of 6 (No. 387d), and eighteen 1d. in three panes of 6 (No. 405b) £3750

1912 (May). *White card cover.*
SB7   2s. booklet containing twelve ½d. and eighteen 1d. in panes of 6 with bars on the selvedge (Nos. 387e, 405c) £2750

1915 (Feb). *Red card cover.*
SB8   2s. booklet containing twelve ½d. and eighteen 1d. in panes of 6 with bars on the selvedge (Nos. 435a or 435ba, 405c) £1300
   a. Grey cover
   b. Blue cover
   c. Yellow-buff cover
   d. Purple-buff cover

1924 (1 Dec)–25. *Cover inscription within frame.*
SB9   2s. booklet containing twelve ½d. and eighteen 1d. in panes of 6 with bars on the selvedge (Nos. 441a, 406b) (lilac cover) .. £1400
   a. Grey cover
SB10   2s. booklet containing twelve ½d. and eighteen 1d. in panes of 6 with bars and advertisements on the selvedge (Nos. 446a, 410b) (1925) (yellow-buff cover) £1500
   a. Grey-green cover £1500
   b. Grey-buff cover £1500
   c. Grey-pink cover £1800

1928–34.
SB11   2s. booklet containing twelve ½d. (p 14×15) and eighteen 1d. in panes of 6 with bars on the selvedge (Nos. 446ab, 468b) .. £2000
   a. As No. SB11, but ½d. (p 14) (Nos. 446ca, 468b) £1300
   b. As No. SB11 but panes with bars and advertisements on the selvedge (Nos. 446cb, 468c) £1300
SB12   2s. booklet containing twenty-four 1d (p 14) in panes of 6 with bars and advertisements on the selvedge (No. 468c) (1930) £1300
   a. As No. SB12, but 1d. (p 14×15) (No. 468ea) (1934) £1200

1935.
SB15   2s. booklet containing twenty-four 1d. in panes of 6 with advertisements on the selvedge (No. 557ca) £375

1936.
SB16   2s. booklet containing twenty-four 1d. (No. 578) in blocks of 6 .. .. £250

B 1

1938 (1 July). *Cream cover as Type B 1.*
SB17   2s. booklet containing twenty-four 1d. (No. 605) in blocks of 6 .. .. .. £300

1938 (Nov). *Cream (No. SB18) or blue (No. SB19) covers as Type B 1.*
SB18   2s. booklet containing twelve ½d. and eighteen 1d. (Nos. 603, 605) in blocks of 6 .. £350
SB19   2s. 3d. booklet containing eighteen 1½d. (No. 607) in blocks of 6 .. .. .. £325

B 2

1954 (Apr). *Black and green on cream cover as Type B 2.*
SB20   4s. booklet containing twelve 1d. and 3d. (Nos. 724, 727), each in blocks of 6 .. .. 6·00
   a. Contents as SB20 but with one pane of airmail labels .. .. .. 18·00

1956 (1 May). *Black and green on cream cover as Type B 2.*
SB21   4s. booklet containing twelve 1d. and 3d. (Nos. 724, 748), each in blocks of 6, and one pane of air mail labels .. .. .. 13·00

1957 (5 Sept). *Black and green on cream cover as Type B 2.*
SB22   4s. booklet containing twelve 1d. and 3d. (Nos. 745, 748), each in blocks of 6, and one pane of air mail labels .. .. .. 12·00

B 3

1960 (1 Sept). *Black and red on cream cover as Type B 3.*
SB23   4s. booklet containing twelve 1d. and 3d. (Nos. 782, 785), each in blocks of 6, and one pane of air mail labels .. .. .. 15·00

1962 (21 May). *Black and red on cream cover as Type B 3.*
SB24   4s. 6d. booklet containing twelve ½d., 1d. and 3d. (Nos. 781, 782, 785), each in blocks of 6, and one pane of air mail labels .. .. 45·00

1964. *Black and carmine on cream cover as Type B 3. Stitched.*
SB25   4s. 3d. booklet containing six ½d. and twelve 1d. and 3d. (Nos. 781/2, 785), each in blocks of 6, and one pane of air mail labels .. .. 18·00

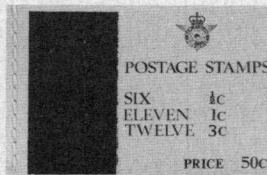

B 4 Maori Art

1967 (10 July). *Black and carmine on pale lemon cover as Type B 4. Stitched.*
SB26   50 c. booklet containing ½d. (No. 845) in block of 6, eleven 1 c. in block of 6 (No. 846) and pane of 5 stamps and 1 label (No. 846a), and twelve 3 c. (No. 849) in blocks of 6 .. 8·00

B 5 Native Trees

1971 (6 July). *Multicoloured cover as Type B 5. Stitched.*
SB27   75 c. booklet containing nine 1 c. (No. 915b) in block of 6 and in pane of 3 stamps and three labels (No. 915ba), six 3 c. (No. 918b) and twelve 4 c. (No. 919b), each in blocks of 6 with sideways inverted or sideways watermarks .. .. 8·00

1974 (Aug). *Multicoloured cover as Type B 5. Stitched.*
SB28   75 c. booklet. As No. SB27 but containing stamps without watermark (Nos. 1008/a, 1010/11) .. 8·00

All booklets from No. SB29 onwards have their panes attached by the selvedge, *unless otherwise stated.*

B 6 Garden Rose "Josephine Bruce"

1977 (May). *Multicoloured cover as Type B 6.*
SB29   80 c. booklet containing 8 c. (No. 1093a) in block of 10 .. .. 3·50

B 7

1977 (May). *Blue and black printed cover as Type B 7.*
SB30 $1 booklet containing 10 c. (No. 1017) in block of 10 .. .. 7·50

B 8

Two Settings of Booklet Cover for No. SB31:
   Setting I. Inscription at foot. "c" aligned at top of "10" (similar to Type B 8).
   Setting II. Inscription at top. "c" aligned on bottom of "10".

1978 (Aug)–79. *Black and ultramarine printed cover as Type B 8.*
SB31 $1 booklet containing 10 c. (No. 1094a) in block of 10 (Cover Setting I) .. .. .. 9·50
   a. Cover Setting II .. .. .. 18·00
   b. Containing 10 c. (No. 1094ab) (Cover Setting I) (1979) .. .. .. 15·00

1978 (Aug). *Black and orange cover as Type B 8.*
SB32 $1.20, booklet containing 12 c. (No. 1096) in block of 10 .. .. 4·00

1980 (Mar). *Black and red cover as Type B 8.*
SB33 $1.40, booklet containing 14 c. (No. 1098) in block of 10 .. .. 4·00

B 9

1980 (12 May). *Black and green cover as Type B 9.*
SB34 $1.40, booklet containing 14 c. (No. 1098) in block of 10 .. .. 3·50
The cover of No. SB34 is inscribed "$1.54" which included a premium payable when purchased from commercial outlets authorized to sell booklets. It was available at $1.40 (value of contents) from the Post Office Philatelic Bureau.

B 10

1981. *Black and blue cover as Type* B **10**.
SB35 $2 booklet containing 20 c. (No. 1099) in block
of 10 .. .. 3·25

B 11

1981. *Black and green cover as Type* B **11**.
SB36 $2 booklet containing 20 c. (No. 1099) in block
of 10 .. .. 3·00
The cover of No. SB36 is inscribed "$2.20". See note below No.
SB34.

1982 (1 Apr)–**83.** *Black and green cover as Type* B **8**.
SB37 $2.40, booklet containing 24 c. (p 12½) (No.
1261) in block of 10 .. .. .. 4·25
a. Containing 24 c. (p 14½×14) (No. 1261a)
(3.83) .. .. 9·50

1982 (1 Apr)–**85.** *Black and blue cover as Type* B **9**.
SB38 $2.40, booklet containing 24 c. (p 12½) (No.
1261) in block of 10 .. .. .. 4·00
a. Containing 24 c. (p 14½×14) (No. 1261a)
(3.85) .. .. 15·00
The covers of Nos. SB38/a are inscribed "$2.64". See note
below No. SB34.

B 12 Lake Tekapo, South Island

1985 (1 July). *Multicoloured cover as Type* B **12** *with design
continuing on back cover.*
SB39 $2.50, booklet (Type B **12**) containing 25 c. (No.
1370) in block of 10 .. .. .. 6·00
SB40 $2.50, booklet (Tongariro Park, North Island)
containing 25 c. (No. 1370) in block of 10 .. 7·00
The cover of No. SB40 is inscribed "$2.75". See note below No.
SB34.

1986 (1 May). *Multicoloured covers as Type* B **12**, *but* 115×60
mm, with the design continuing on back cover.
SB41 $3 booklet (Matukituki Valley, Otago) contain-
ing 30 c. (No. 1288) in block of 10 .. .. 7·00
SB42 $3 booklet (Stream and native bush, Canter-
bury) containing 30 c. (No. 1288) in block of 10 7·00
The cover of No. SB42 is inscribed "$3.30". See note below No.
SB34.
Nos. SB41/2 exist overprinted on the front cover with the
"Stockholmia" logo for sale at the International Philatelic
Exhibition in Sweden.

1987 (2 Feb–June). *Multicoloured covers as Type* B **12**, *but*
115×60 *mm, with the design continuing on back cover.*
SB43 $4 booklet (Ahuriri Valley, Otago) containing
40 c. (No. 1289) in block of 10 .. .. 11·00
a. Revised "NZ POST" logo without crown (June) 11·00
SB44 $4 booklet (Totaranui Beach, Abel Tasman
National Park, Nelson) containing 40 c. (No.
1289) in block of 10 .. .. .. 11·00
a. Revised "NZ POST" logo without crown (June) 17·00
The covers of booklets Nos. SB44/a are inscribed "$4.40". See
note below No. SB34.
Nos. SB43a and SB44a exist overprinted on the front cover
with the "CAPEX" logo for sale at the International Philatelic
Exhibition in Toronto.

1987 (Nov). *Multicoloured covers as Type* B **12**, *but* 115×60
*mm, with the design continuing on back cover. New "NZ
POST" logo as shown on Type* B **14**.
SB45 $4 booklet (Wellington by night) containing 40 c.
(No. 1289) in block of 10 .. .. 7·00
SB46 $4 booklet (Katiki Point) containing 40 c. (No.
1289) in block of 10 .. .. .. 27·00
The cover of No. SB46 is inscribed "$4.40". See note below No.
SB34.

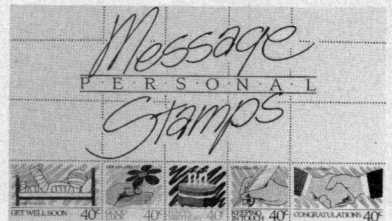

B 13

1988 (18 May). *"Personal Message Stamps". Multicoloured
cover as Type* B **13**.
SB47 $2 booklet containing pane of 5 different 40 c.
(No. 1455a) .. .. 2·75
No. SB47 exists overprinted on the front cover with the
"WORLD STAMP EXPO '89" logo for sale at the International
Stamp Exhibition in Washington, U.S.A.

B 14

1988 (7 June). *"Fast Post" Service. Black, bright scarlet and
new blue cover as Type* B **14**.
SB48 $7 booklet containing 70 c. (No. 1466) in block
of 10 .. .. 6·50

B 15

1988 (14 Sept). *Christmas. Multicoloured cover as Type* B **15**.
SB49 $3.50, booklet containing 35 c. (No. 1480) in
block of 10 .. .. 4·00

B 16

1988 (19 Oct). *Multicoloured cover as Type* B **16**.
SB50 $6 booklet containing pane of 6 $1 (No. 1490a) 11·00

B 17 Mt Cook from the Hooker Valley,
South Canterbury

1988 (2 Nov). *Multicoloured cover as Type* B **17** *with design
continuing on back cover.*
SB51 $4 booklet containing 40 c. (No. 1463) in block
of 10 .. .. 5·50
No. SB51 exist overprinted on the front cover with the "Stamp
World London'90" logo for sale at the International Stamp
Exhibition in Great Britain.

1989 (13 Sept). *Christmas. Multicoloured cover as Type* B **17**.
SB52 $3.50, booklet containing 35 c. (No. 1520) in
block of 10 .. .. 5·50

B 18

1990 (Aug). *Black and white cover as Type* B **18** *showing
multicoloured stamp No.* 1463.
SB53 $4 booklet containing 40 c. (No. 1463) in block of
10 with three fastPOST labels .. .. 7·50
No. SB53 has a slot in the cover for hanging display. Booklets
in this format were produced for self-service sales.

B 19

1991 (15 May). *"Happy Birthday". Multicoloured cover as Type*
B **19**.
SB54 $2 booklet containing pane of 5 different 40 c.
(No. 1594a) .. .. 2·50

B 20

1991 (15 May). *"Thinking of You". Multicoloured cover as Type*
B **20**.
SB55 $2 booklet containing pane of 5 different 40 c.
(No. 1604a) .. .. 2·50

1991 (1 July). *Blue and white cover as Type* B **18** *showing
multicoloured stamp No.* 1463b.
SB56 $4.50, booklet containing 45 c. (No. 1463b) in
block of 10 .. .. 4·00

1991 (1 July). *"Happy Birthday". Multicoloured vert cover as
Type* B **19**, *but in hanging display format as Type* B **18**.
SB57 $2.25, booklet containing pane of 5 different 45 c.
(No. 1599a) .. .. 2·50

1991 (1 July). *"Thinking of You". Multicoloured cover as Type*
B **20**, *but in hanging display format as Type* B **18**.
SB58 $2.25, booklet containing pane of 5 different 45 c.
(No. 1609a) .. .. 2·50

BARCODES. All booklets from No. SB59 show a barcode on
the reverse, *unless indicated otherwise.*

B 21

1991 (1 Oct)–*92. Bright red and black cover as Type B 21 showing multicoloured stamp No. 1463b. Roman "I" on back.*
SB59 $4.50, booklet containing 45 c. (No. 1463b) in block of 10   4·00
   a. Roman "II" on back (5.92)   5·50
   b. With additional slotted tab at right. Containing 45 c. in pane of 10 (No. 1463ba) ("I" on back)   5·00
   ba. Containing 45 c. (No. 1463b) in block of 10 ("II" on back)   6·50

1992 (Mar–27 May). *Bright blue and black cover as Type B 21, but without stamp design. No barcode on reverse.*
SB60 $4 booklet containing 80 c. (No. 1467) in strip of 5 and pane of six fastPOST labels   4·00
SB61 $8 booklet containing 80 c. (No. 1467) in block of 10 and pane of ten fastPOST labels   22·00
   a. Barcode on back (27 May)   8·00

1992 (1 Sept)–*93. Landscapes. Bright red and black cover as Type B 21 showing multicoloured stamp No. 1690. Roman "I" on back.*
SB62 $4.50, booklet containing pane of 10 different 45 c. (No. 1690a)   4·00
   a. Roman "II" on back (1993)   8·50
   b. Roman "III" on back (1993)   17·00
   c. With additional slotted tab at right ("I" on back)   3·75
   ca. Roman "II" on back (1993)   10·00
   cb. Roman "III" on back (1993)   17·00

1993 (31 Mar)–*95. Bright blue and black cover as Type B 21, but without stamp design.*
SB63 $8 booklet containing 80 c. (No. 1467a) in block of 10 and block of 10 fastPOST labels   5·75
   a. Containing pane No. 1467ab (p 12) (7.94)   9·00
   ab. With additional slotted tab at right (7.95)   ..

1993 (9 June). *Endangered Species Conservation. Cover as Type B 21 showing multicoloured illustration of Tusked Weta.*
SB64 $4.50, booklet containing 45 c. (No. 1740) in block of 10   5·00
   a. With additional slotted tab at right   5·00

1993 (1 Sept). *Marine Life. Bright red and black cover as Type B 21 showing multicoloured illustration of Groper (fish).*
SB65 $4.50, booklet containing pane of 10 different 45 c. (No. 1752a)   6·50
   a. With additional slotted tab at right   7·50

1993 (1 Oct). *Prehistoric Animals. Cover as Type B 21 showing multicoloured illustration of Carnosaur.*
SB66 $4.50, booklet containing pane of ten 45 c. plus two labels (No. 1763a)   4·75
   a. With additional slotted tab at right   4·75

1993 (3 Nov). *Christmas. Bright red and black cover as Type B 21 showing multicoloured illustration of Christmas Pudding.*
SB67 $4.50, booklet containing pane of ten 45 c. (No. 1746ba)   11·00
   a. With additional slotted tab at right   11·00

1994 (19 Jan–Aug). *Tourism. Bright red and black cover as Type B 21 showing multicoloured illustration of White Water Rafting.*
SB68 $4.50, booklet containing pane of ten 45 c. and four half stamp-size labels (No. 1778a) (horiz format)   4·50
   a. Roman "II" on back (Aug)   6·50
   b. Vert format with additional slotted tab at top   6·50
   ba. Roman "II" on back (Aug)   6·50

1994 (27 Apr). *New Zealand Life. Bright red and black cover as Type B 21 showing multicoloured illustration of Buzzy Bee.*
SB69 $4.50, booklet containing pane of ten different 45 c. (No. 1797a) (horiz format)   3·50
   a. Vert format with additional slotted tab at right   3·50

1994 (21 Sept). *Christmas. Multicoloured covers as Type B 21 showing illustration of Father Christmas and children.*
SB70 $4.50, booklet containing 45 c. (No. 1832) in block of 10 (horiz format)   3·50
   a. Vert format with additional slotted tab at top   4·00

1994 (2 Nov). *Centenary of New Zealand Cricket Council. Multicoloured covers as Type B 21 showing illustration of father and son playing cricket.*
SB71 $4.50, booklet containing pane of ten 45 c. (No. 1840a) (horiz format)   3·50
   a. Vert format with additional slotted tab at top   4·00

B 22   **B 23**

1995 (22 Mar). *Environment. Bright red and black cover as Type B 22 showing multicoloured illustration of backpackers.*
SB72 $4.50, booklet containing pane of ten 45 c. (No. 1865a) inserted sideways in the vertical cover   5·50

1995 (26 July). *Centenary of Rugby League. Multicoloured cover as Type B 21 showing New Zealand and Australian Players.*
SB73 $4.50, booklet containing pane of ten 45 c. (No. 1889)   4·75

1995 (1 Sept). *Black and bright royal blue cover as Type B 23 inscribed "airPOST INTERNATIONAL".*
SB74 $5 booklet containing pane of five $1 and five labels (No. 1645a) inserted sideways in the cover   13·00

1995 (1 Sept–2 Oct). *Farmyard Animals. Multicoloured covers as Type B 22 showing illustration of sow and piglets.*
SB75 $4 booklet containing pane of ten 40 c. (No. 1894a) inserted sideways in the cover (2 Oct)   5·50
SB76 $4.50, booklet containing pane of ten 45 c. (No. 1904a) inserted sideways in the cover   5·50

1995 (9 Nov). *Christmas. Multicoloured cover as Type B 22 showing illustration of Angel holding trumpet.*
SB77 $4 booklet containing pane of ten 40 c. (No. 1923a)   5·00

B 24
(Illustration reduced. Actual size 166×110 mm)

1996 (24 Jan). *Famous Racehorses. Multicoloured cover as Type B 24 showing illustrations of harness and horse races.*
SB78 $13.40, booklet containing seven miniature sheets (Nos. MS1951a/g)   16·00

1996 (21 Feb). *Seaside Environment. Multicoloured cover as Type B 21, but vert, showing illustration of sea shore.*
SB79 $4 booklet containing pane of ten 40 c. (No. 1958a)   4·25

1996 (7 Aug). *Seaside Environment. Multicoloured cover as No. SB79, but 58×78 mm. Self-adhesive.*
SB80 $4 booklet containing pane of ten 40 c. (No. 1968a)   4·25

B 25

1996 (7 Aug)–*99. Multicoloured cover as Type B 25 showing illustration of Pohutukawa tree. "New Zealand Post" and logo in white on ultramarine background. Self-adhesive.*
SB81 $5 booklet containing pane of five $1 (No. 1991a)   4·50
   a. "New Zealand Post" and logo redrawn larger in black and red on white panel (2.99)   3·25

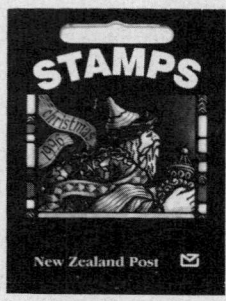

B 26

1996 (4 Sept). *Christmas. Multicoloured cover as Type B 26 showing illustration of King. Self-adhesive.*
SB82 $4 booklet containing pane of ten 40 c. (No. 2027a)   4·25

1996 (2 Oct). *Extinct Birds. Multicoloured cover as Type B 26 showing illustration of Stout-legged Wren. Self-adhesive.*
SB83 $4 booklet containing pane of ten 40 c. (No. 2035a)   4·25

1996 (13 Nov)–*99. Multicoloured cover as Type B 25 but smaller, 59×78 mm, inscr "fastPOST" with illustration of Doubtful Sound. Self-adhesive.*
SB84 $8 booklet containing pane of ten 80 c. (No. 1990a) incorporating ten half-width "fastPOST" labels on the inner cover   7·00
   a. Incorporating ten full width "fastPOST" labels with barcode on inner cover (1.99)   5·00
No. S84a also shows "New Zealand Post" and logo redrawn larger.

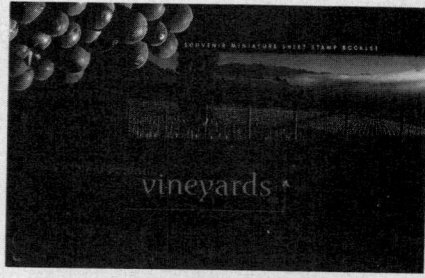

B 27
(Illustration reduced. Actual size 116×110 mm)

1997 (19 Mar). *New Zealand Vineyards. Multicoloured cover as Type B 27.*
SB85 $13.40, booklet containing seven miniature sheets (Nos. MS2063a/g)   12·00

1997 (19 Mar). *Curious Letterboxes. Multicoloured cover as Type B 26 showing letterbox. Self-adhesive.*
SB86 $4 booklet containing pane of ten 40 c. (No. 2064a)   4·25

1997 (3 Sept). *Christmas. Multicoloured cover as Type B 26 showing illustration of Memorial Cross, Pohutukawi, and Bay of Islands. Self-adhesive.*
SB87 $4 booklet containing pane of ten 40 c. (No. 2103a)   4·00

1997 (1 Oct). *Insects. Multicoloured cover as Type B 26 showing illustration of Grasshopper's head. Self-adhesive.*
SB88 $4 booklet containing pane of ten 40 c. (No. 2104a)   4·00

1998 (14 Jan)–*99. Multicoloured (background vermilion) cover as Type B 26 showing New Zealand scenery. Self-adhesive.*
SB89 $4 booklet containing pane of ten 40 c. (No. 1984ba) (Motoring Guide advertisement on inner cover)   3·00
   a. Background of cover deep rose-red (Scenic Skies presentation pack advertisement on inner cover) (8.98)   2·50
   ab. Town Icon's presentation pack advertisement on inner cover (5.99)   2·50
   ac. U-BIX Rugby Super 12 Championship stamp packs advertisement on inner cover (7.99)   2·50
   aca. Stamps printed on backing paper
Nos. SB89a/ac also show "New Zealand" and logo redrawn larger.
For explanation of No. SB89aca see after Nos. 1984/91.

NEW INFORMATION

The editor is always interested to correspond with people who have new information that will improve or correct the Catalogue.

B 28
(Illustration reduced. Actual size 164×110 mm)

1998 (14 Jan). *Performing Arts. Multicoloured cover as Type B 28 showing illustration of performers.*
SB90 $13.40, booklet containing seven miniature sheets (Nos. MS2130a/g)   ..   ..   13·00

1998 (15 Apr). *"Stay in Touch" Greetings Stamps. Multicoloured cover as Type B 26 showing couple on beach. Self-adhesive.*
SB91 $4 booklet containing pane of ten 40 c. (No. 2148a)   ..   ..   ..   2·50

1998 (2 Sept). *Christmas. Multicoloured cover as Type B 26 showing illustration of Virgin Mary and Christ Child. Self-adhesive.*
SB92 $4 booklet containing pane of ten 45 c. (No. 2195a)   ..   ..   ..   3·00

1998 (7 Oct). *Town Icons. Multicoloured cover as B 26, but 60×99 mm, showing illustration of town symbols. Self-adhesive.*
SB93 $4 booklet containing se-tenant pane of ten 40 c. (No. 2196a)   ..   ..   3·00

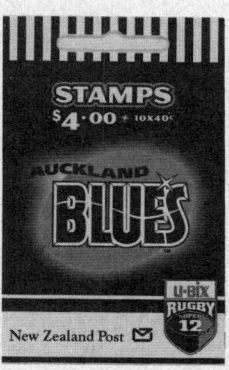

B 29

1999 (7 Apr). *New Zealand U-Bix Rugby Super 12 Championship. Multicoloured covers as Type B 29 showing team logos. Self-adhesive.*
SB94 $4 booklet containing pane of ten 40 c. (No. 2258a) (Type B 29)   ..   ..   3·00
SB95 $4 booklet containing pane of ten 40 c. (No. 2260a) (Chiefs)   ..   ..   3·00
SB96 $4 booklet containing pane of ten 40 c. (No. 2262a) (Wellington Hurricanes)   ..   3·00
SB97 $4 booklet containing pane of ten 40 c. (No. 2264a) (Canterbury Crusaders)   ..   3·00
SB98 $4 booklet containing pane of ten 40 c. (No. 2266a) (Otago Highlanders)   ..   3·00

B 30
(Illustration reduced. Actual size 168×110 mm)

1999 (28 July). *Scenic Walks. Multicoloured cover as Type B 30 showing illustration of man reading map.*
SB99 $13.40, booklet containing seven miniature sheets (Nos. MS2285a/g)   ..   ..   8·50

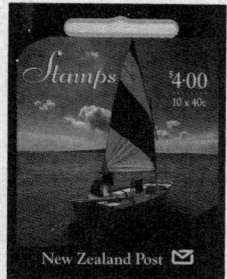

B 31 "Optimist" Sailing Dinghy

1999 (20 Oct). *Yachting. Multicoloured cover as Type B 31. Self-adhesive.*
SB100 $4 booklet containing pane of ten 40 c. (No. 2303a)   ..   ..   ..   2·50

B 32 Baby Jesus with Animals

1999 (1 Nov). *Christmas. Multicoloured cover as Type B 32. Self-adhesive.*
SB101 $4 booklet containing pane of ten 40 c. (No. 2294a)   ..   ..   ..   2·50

EXPRESS DELIVERY STAMPS

E 1

(Typo Govt Printing Office, Wellington)

1903 (9 Feb). *Value in first colour.* W 43 *(sideways).* P 11.
E1 E 1 6d. red and violet .. .. .. 35·00 22·00

1926–36. *Thick, white, opaque chalk-surfaced "Cowan" paper.*
W 43.

(a) P 14×14½
E2 E 1 6d. vermilion and bright violet .. 42·00 24·00
  w. Wmk inverted £110

(b) P 14×15 (1936)
E3 E 1 6d. carmine and bright violet .. 55·00 55·00

1937–39. *Thin, hard, chalk-surfaced "Wiggins Teape" paper.*

(a) P 14 × 14½
E4 E 1 6d. carmine and bright violet .. 85·00 48·00

(b) P 14 × 15 (1939)
E5 E 1 6d. vermilion and bright violet .. £140 £200

E 2 Express Mail Delivery Van

(Des J. Berry. Eng Stamp Ptg Office, Melbourne Recess Govt Ptg
Office, Wellington)

1939 (16 Aug). W 43. P 14.
E6 E 2 6d. violet .. .. .. 1·50 1·75
  w. Wmk inverted .. .. 70·00

POSTAGE DUE STAMPS

D 1

(I)

N.Z.

(II)

(a)   (b)
Large "D"   Small "D"

(Typo Govt Printing Office, Wellington)

1899 (1 Dec). W 12b. *Coarse paper.* P 11.

I. *Type I.* Circle of 14 ornaments, 17 dots over "N.Z.", "N.Z." large.

(a) Large "D"
D1 D 1 ½d. carmine and green .. .. 12·00 24·00
  a. No stop after "D" (Right pane R. 2/3) 85·00 £140
D2   8d. carmine and green .. .. 60·00 75·00
D3   1s. carmine and green .. .. 65·00 85·00
D4   2s. carmine and green £120 £140
D1/4   Set of 4 £225 £275

To avoid further subdivision the 1s. and 2s. are placed with the
pence values, although the two types of "D" do not apply to the
higher values.

(b) Small "D"
D6 D 1 5d. carmine and green .. .. 21·00 22·00
D7   6d. carmine and green .. .. 28·00 24·00
D8   10d. carmine and green .. .. 70·00 85·00
D6/8   Set of 3 £100 £110

II. *Type II.* Circle of 13 ornaments, 15 dots over "N.Z.", "N.Z." small.

(a) Large "D"
D9 D 1 ½d. vermilion and green .. .. 2·75 16·00
  a. No stop after "D" (Right pane R. 2/3) .. 55·00 95·00
D10   1d. vermilion and green .. .. 9·50 1·25
D11   2d. vermilion and green .. 48·00 9·00
D12   3d. vermilion and green .. .. 13·00 3·50
D9/12   Set of 4 65·00 26·00

(b) Small "D"
D14 D 1 1d. vermilion and green .. .. 14·00 1·50
D15   2d. vermilion and green .. .. 45·00 4·75
D16   4d. vermilion and green .. .. 32·00 9·00
D14/16   Set of 3 80·00 14·00

Nos. D9/16 were printed from a common frame plate of 240 (4
panes of 60) used in conjunction with centre plates of 120 (2
panes of 60) for the ½d. and 2d. or 240 for the other values.
Sheets of the 1d. and 2d. each contained two panes with large
"D" and two panes with small "D".

D 2   D 3

(Des W. R. Bock. Typo Govt Printing Office)

1902 (28 Feb). *No wmk.* P 11.
D17 D 2 ½d. red and deep green .. .. 1·75 6·00

1904–08. *"Cowan" unsurfaced paper.* W 43 *(sideways).* (a) P 11.
D18 D 2 ½d. red and green (4.04) .. 1·75 1·50
  a. Imperf between (horiz pair) .. £600
D19   1d. red and green (5.12.05) .. 8·50 3·50
D20   2d. red and green (5.4.06) .. 90·00 95·00
D18/20 .. .. .. Set of 3 90·00 95·00

(b) P 14
D21 D 2 1d. carmine and green (12.06) .. 12·00 1·50
  a. Rose-pink and green (9.07) .. 11·00 1·50
D22   2d. carmine and green (10.06) .. 9·00 5·50
  a. Rose-pink and green (6.08) .. 5·00 1·50

1919 (Jan)–**20.** *"De La Rue" chalky paper. Toned gum.* W 43.
P 14×15.
D23 D 2 ½d. carmine and green (6.19) .. 3·25 3·75
D24   1d. carmine and green .. 7·00 50
  w. Wmk inverted .. .. †
D25   2d. carmine and green (8.20) .. 11·00 2·50
D23/5   Set of 3 19·00 6·00

1925 (May). *"Jones" chalky paper. White gum.* W 43. P 14×15.
D26 D 2 ½d. carmine and green .. .. 35·00 40·00

1925 (July). *No wmk, but bluish "N Z" and Star lithographed on
back.* P 14 × 15.
D27 D 2 ½d. carmine and green .. .. 2·00 23·00
D28   2d. carmine and green .. .. 3·50 20·00

1925 (Nov)–**35.** *"Cowan" thick, opaque chalky paper.* W 43.

(a) P 14 × 15
D29 D 2 ½d. carmine and green (12.26) .. 1·75 8·00
D30   1d. carmine and green .. .. 3·75 80
D31   2d. carmine and green (6.26) .. 18·00 4·25
D32   3d. carmine and green (6.35) .. 48·00 55·00
D29/32   Set of 4 65·00 60·00

(b) P 14
D33 D 2 ½d. carmine and green (10.28) .. 42·00 30·00
D34   1d. rose and pale yellow-green (6.28) 4·00 1·25
D35   2d. carmine and green (10.29) .. 7·00 3·00
D36   3d. carmine and green (5.28) .. 15·00 42·00
D33/6 ..   Set of 4 60·00 70·00

1937–38. *"Wiggins Teape" thin, hard chalky paper.* W 43.
P 14×15.
D37 D 2 ½d. carmine and yellow-green (2.38) .. 18·00 32·00
D38   1d. carmine and yellow-green (1.37) .. 11·00 3·75
D39   2d. carmine and yellow-green (6.37) .. 30·00 13·00
D40   3d. carmine and yellow-green (11.37) 85·00 55·00
D37/40   Set of 4 £130 95·00

(Des J. Berry. Typo Govt Printing Office, Wellington)

1939–49. P 15×14. (a) W 43 *(sideways inverted)* (16.8.39).
D41 D 3 ½d. turquoise-green .. .. 5·00 5·00
D42   1d. carmine .. .. .. 2·75 30
  w. Wmk sideways .. .. £100 1·50
D43   2d. bright blue .. .. 6·00 2·75
D44   3d. orange-brown .. 23·00 25·00
  w. Wmk sideways
D41/4   Set of 4 32·00 30·00

(b) W 98 *(sideways* (1d.)*, sideways inverted* (2d.) *or upright*
(3d.)
D45 D 3 1d. carmine (4.49) .. .. 16·00 5·50*
D46   2d. bright blue (12.46) .. .. 7·50 1·40
  w. Wmk sideways (4.49) .. 2·75 8·00
D47   3d. orange-brown (1943) .. 42·00 32·00
  a. Wmk sideways inverted (6.45) 17·00 5·00
  aw. Wmk sideways (28.11.49) .. 9·00 8·00
D45/7   Set of 3 25·00 10·00*

*The use of Postage Due stamps ceased on 30 September
1951, our used price for No. D45 being for stamps postmarked
after this date (price for examples clearly cancelled 1949–51,
£27).

OFFICIAL STAMPS

1891 (Dec)–**1906.** *Contemporary issues handstamped "O.P.
S.O." diagonally.* (a) *Stamps of 1873 type.* W 12b. P 12½.
O 1 3 ½d. rose (V.) .. .. .. — £450

(b) *Stamps of 1882–97 optd in rose or magenta.* W 12b.
O 2 13 ½d. black (p 10) .. .. — £180
  a. Violet opt .. .. .. — £225
O 3   ½d. black (p 10 × 11) .. — £180
O 4 14 1d. rose (p 12 × 11½) .. — £180
O 5   1d. rose (p 11) .. .. — £180
O 6 15 2d. purple (p 11) .. .. — £325
O 7   2d. mauve-lilac (p 10) .. — £325
  a. Violet opt .. .. — £325
O 8 16 2½d. blue (p 11) .. .. — £225
O 9   2½d. ultramarine (p 10) .. — £225
O10   2½d. ultramarine (p 10 × 11) — £225
O11 19 5d. olive-black (p 12 × 11½) — £375
O12 20 6d. brown (p 12 × 11½) .. — £500

(c) *Stamps of 1898–1903 optd in violet.* P 11. (i) *No wmk*
O13 23 ½d. green (p 14) (No. 294) .. — £180
O14 26 2½d. blue (p 12–16) (No. 249a) .. — £400
O15 27 2½d. blue (No. 260) .. .. — £325
O16 37 4d. indigo and brown (No. 262) .. — £375
O17 30 5d. purple-brown (No. 263) .. — £400
  a. Green opt .. .. — £375
O18 32 8d. indigo (No. 266) .. .. — £475

(ii) W 38
O19 42 1d. carmine (No. 278) .. — £180

(iii) W 43 *(sideways on 3d., 1s.)*
O20 42 1d. carmine (p 14) (No. 303) .. — £180
  a. Green opt .. .. — £180
O21 27 2½d. blue (No. 308) .. .. — £275
O22 28 3d. yellow-brown (No. 309) .. — £400
O23 34 1s. orange-red (No. 315b) .. — £800
O24 35 2s. green (No. 316) .. .. — £1200

The letters signify "On Public Service Only", and stamps so
overprinted were used by the Post Office Department on official
correspondence between the department and foreign countries.

(O 3)

1907. *Stamps of 1902–6 optd with Type O 3 (vertically
upwards).* W 43 *(sideways on 3d., 6d., 1s. and 5s.).* P 14.
O59 23 ½d. yellow-green .. .. 8·00 50
  a. Perf 11×14 .. .. 95·00
  b. Mixed perfs .. .. 95·00
O60 42 1d. carmine (No. 303) (1.7.07*) .. 7·00 10·00
  a. Booklet pane of 6 .. 42·00
  ab. Imperf horiz (booklet pane of 6) £1400
O60b   1d. rose-carmine (Waterlow) (No. 352) 8·50 30
  ba. Perf 11×14 .. .. — £250
  bb. Mixed perfs .. .. — £250
O60c   1d. carmine (Royle) .. 16·00 30
  ca. Perf 11×14 .. .. £225
  cb. Mixed perfs £225
O61 41 2d. purple .. .. 9·00 1·75
  a. Bright reddish purple .. 8·50 1·40
  ab. Mixed perfs £190 £200
O63 28 3d. bistre-brown .. .. 42·00 1·75
O64 31 6d. bright carmine-pink .. £130 18·00
  a. Imperf vert (horiz pair) .. £800
  b. Mixed perfs £475 £425
O65 34 1s. orange-red .. .. 85·00 15·00
O66 35 2s. blue-green .. .. 70·00 48·00
  a. Imperf between (pair) .. £1500
  b. Imperf vert (horiz pair) .. £1200
  w. Wmk inverted £250
O67 36 5s. deep red £150 £170
  a. Wmk upright £700 £750

*Though issued in 1907, a large quantity of booklets was
mislaid and not utilized until they were found in 1930.

1908–09. *Optd as Type O 3.* W 43.
O69 23 ½d. green (p 14 × 15) .. 7·50 1·75
O70 50 1d. carmine (p 14 × 15) .. 65·00 2·50
O71 48 6d. pink (p 14 × 13, 13½) .. £140 45·00
O72   6d. pink (p 14 × 15) (1909) .. £110 35·00
O72a F 4 £1 rose-pink (p 14) (No. F89) .. £500 £400

1910. *No. 387 optd with Type O 3.*
O73 51 ½d. yellow-green .. .. 4·25 30
  a. Opt inverted (reading downwards) † £1400

1910–16. *Nos. 389 and 392/4 optd with Type O 3.* P 14×14½.
O74 52 3d. chestnut .. .. 14·00 80
  a. Perf 14×13½ (1915) .. 60·00 70·00
  ab. Vert pair. Nos. O74/a .. £300 £350
O75 — 6d. carmine .. .. 19·00 4·75
  a. Perf 14 (line) (No. 398) .. †
  b. Deep carmine .. .. 25·00 5·00
  w. Wmk inverted
O76 — 8d. indigo-blue (R.) (5.16) .. 14·00 18·00
  aw. Wmk inverted .. .. 30·00 30·00
  b. Perf 14×13½ .. .. 14·00 18·00
  ba. Vert pair. Nos. O76 and O76b 45·00 70·00
  bw. Wmk inverted .. .. 30·00 30·00
O77 — 1s. vermilion .. .. 30·00 15·00
O74/7   Set of 4 85·00 35·00

1910–26. *Optd with Type O 3.* (a) W 43. *De La Rue chalk-
surfaced paper with toned gum.*
O78 53 1d. carmine (No. 405) .. .. 3·25 10
  y. Wmk inverted and reversed

(b) W 43. *Jones chalk-surfaced paper with white gum*
O79 53 1d. deep carmine (No. 406) (1925) .. 10·00 6·50

(c) *No wmk, but bluish "NZ" and Star lithographed on back. Art
paper*
O80 53 1d. rose-carmine (No. 409) (1925) .. 6·00 10·00

(d) W 43. *Cowan thick, opaque, chalk-surfaced paper with
white gum*
O81 53 1d. deep carmine (No. 410) (1925) .. 8·00 1·25
  x. Wmk reversed (1926) .. 25·00 20·00

1913–25. *Postal Fiscal stamps optd with Type O 3.*
(i) *Chalk-surfaced De La Rue paper.* (a) P 14 (1913–14)
O82 F 4 2s. blue (30.9.14) .. .. 48·00 38·00
O83   5s. yellow-green (13.6.13) .. 75·00 90·00
O84   £1 rose-carmine (1913) .. £550 £500
O82/4 ..   Set of 3 £600 £550

(b) P 14½ × 14, comb (1915)
O85 F 4 2s. deep blue (Aug) .. .. 55·00 38·00
  a. No stop after "OFFICIAL" .. £120 95·00
O86   5s. yellow-green (Jan) .. 65·00 75·00
  a. No stop after "OFFICIAL" .. £200 £225

(ii) *Thick, white, opaque chalk-surfaced Cowan paper.*
P 14½ × 14 (1925)
O87 F 4 2s. blue .. .. 80·00 70·00
  a. No stop after "OFFICIAL" .. £180 £180

The overprint on these last, and on Nos. O69 and O72a, is
from a new set of type, giving a rather sharper impression than
Type O 3, but otherwise resembling it closely.

1915 (12 Oct)–**34.** *Optd with Type O 3.* P 14×15. (a) On Nos.
435/40 (De La Rue chalk-surfaced paper with toned gum).
O88 61 ½d. green .. .. 1·25 10
O89 62 1½d. grey-black (6.16) .. 6·50 2·50
O90 61 1½d. slate (12.16) .. 4·25 80
O91   1½d. orange-brown (4.19) .. 4·25 30
O92   2d. yellow (4.17) .. 4·25 10
O93   3d. chocolate (11.19) .. 11·00 90
O88/93   Set of 6 28·00 4·00

(b) On Nos. 441 and 443 (Jones chalk-surfaced paper with white
gum)
O94 61 ½d. green (1924) .. .. 4·50 3·25
O95   3d. deep chocolate (1924) .. 35·00 9·50

(c) On Nos. 446/7 and 448a/9 *(Cowan thick, opaque, chalk-surfaced paper with white gum)*

O96	61	½d. green (1925)		80	10
		ax. Wmk reversed (1927)		8·00	10·00
		ay. Wmk inverted and reversed (1927)		30·00	20·00
		b. Perf 14 (1929)		3·50	35
		ba. No stop after "OFFICIAL"		23·00	32·00
O97		1½d. orange-brown (p 14) (1929)		9·50	11·00
		a. No stop after "OFFICIAL"		48·00	60·00
		b. Perf 14×15 (1934)		22·00	28·00
O98		2d. yellow (p 14) (1931)		2·00	40
		a. No stop after "OFFICIAL"		35·00	38·00
O99		3d. chocolate (1925)		4·00	40
		a. No stop after "OFFICIAL"		65·00	45·00
		b. Perf 14 (1930)		35·00	1·75
		ba. No stop after "OFFICIAL"		£120	50·00
O96/9		*Set of 4*		14·50	11·00

1915 (Dec)–**27**. *Optd with Type O 3. P 14×13½. (a) Nos. 420, 422, 425, 428 and 429/30 (Cowan unsurfaced paper).*

O100	60	3d. chocolate		4·25	1·25
		aw. Wmk inverted		13·00	4·00
		b. Perf 14×14½		4·25	1·25
		bw. Wmk inverted		13·00	4·00
		c. Vert pair, Nos. O100 and O100b		35·00	60·00
		cw. Wmk inverted		75·00	
O101		4d. bright violet (4.25)		14·00	3·25
		a. Re-entry (Pl 20 R. 1/6)		42·00	20·00
		b. Re-entry (Pl 20 R. 4/10)		48·00	28·00
		c. Perf 14×14½ (4.27)		27·00	1·00
O102		6d. carmine (6.16)		5·00	75
		aw. Wmk inverted		85·00	
		b. Perf 14×14½		6·00	95
		c. Vert pair, Nos. O102 and O102b		50·00	85·00
O103		8d. red-brown (8.22)		70·00	£110
O104		9d. sage-green (4.25)		38·00	32·00
O105		1s. vermilion (9.16)		17·00	13·00
		aw. Wmk inverted		£180	£120
		b. Perf 14×14½		7·00	2·00
		ba. Pale orange-red		28·00	20·00
		bw. Wmk inverted		£180	£120
		c. Vert pair, Nos. O105 and O105b		65·00	£110
		cw. Wmk inverted		£425	
O100/5		*Set of 6*		£120	£130

(b) No. 433 *(Thin paper with widely spaced sideways wmk)*

O106	60	3d. chocolate (p 14) (7.16)		3·00	8·00
		a. No wmk		35·00	55·00

1927–33. *Optd with Type O 3. W 43. P 14.*

O111	71	1d. rose-carmine (No. 468)		2·00	10
		a. No stop after "OFFICIAL"		22·00	26·00
		bw. Wmk inverted		†	25·00
		c. Perf 14×15		1·50	10
O112	72	2s. light blue (No. 469) (2.28)		70·00	£100
O113	F 6	5s. green (1933)		£250	£300
O111/13		*Set of 3*		£300	£350

Official   *Official*
(O 4)   (O 5)

1936–61. *Pictorial issue optd horiz or vert (2s.) with Type O 4.*

(a) W 43 *(Single "N Z" and Star)*

O115	82	1d. scarlet (Die I) (p 14×13½)		2·50	80
		a. Perf 13½×14		75·00	60·00
O116	83	1½d. red-brown (p 13½×14)		21·00	25·00
		a. Perf 14×13½		£5500	
O118	92	1s. deep green (p 14×13½)		26·00	40·00
		w. Wmk inverted		†	80·00
O119	F 6	5s. green (p 14) (12.38)		£130	40·00
O115/19		*Set of 4*		£160	95·00

The watermark of No. O119 is almost invisible.
Only four examples of No. O116a exist. The error occurred when a sheet of No. 558a was found to have a block of four missing. This was replaced by a block of No. 558 and the sheet was then sent for overprinting.

(b) W 98 *(Mult "N Z" and Star)*

O120	81	½d. bright green, p 14×13½ (7.37)		6·50	4·50
O121	82	1d. scar (Die II), p 14×13½ (11.36)		3·75	50
		w. Wmk inverted		7·50	4·50
O122	83	1½d. red-brown, p 14×13½ (7.36)		16·00	4·25
O123	84	2d. orange, p 14×13½ (1.38)		2·25	10
		aw. Wmk inverted		—	£110
		b. Perf 12½ (1942)		£190	55·00
		c. Perf 14 (1942)		48·00	15·00
O124	85	2½d. chocolate & slate, p 13–14×13½ (26.7.38)		48·00	75·00
		a. Perf 14 (1938)		14·00	21·00
O125	86	3d. brown, p 14×13½ (1.3.38)		48·00	3·25
		w. Wmk inverted		—	27·00
O126	87	4d. black and sepia, p 14×13½ (8.36)		8·50	1·10
		a. Perf 14 (8.41)		7·50	4·00
		b. Perf 12½ (1941)		5·00	5·00
		c. Perf 14×14½ (10.42)		3·75	85
		cw. Wmk inverted		—	45·00
O127	89	6d. scar. t, p 13½×14 (12.37)		15·00	70
		aw. Wmk inverted			
		b. Perf 12½ (1941)		15·00	5·50
		c. Perf 14½×14 (7.42)		8·00	30
O128	90	8d. chocolate, p 12½ (wmk sideways) (1942)		14·00	17·00
		a. Perf 14×14½ (wmk sideways) (1945)		8·00	16·00
		b. Perf 14×13½		† £1600	
O129	91	9d. red & grey-black (G.) (No. 587a), p 13½×14 (1.3.38)		60·00	38·00
O130		9d. scar & blk (chalk-surfaced paper) (Blk.) (No. 631), p 14×15 (1943)		20·00	22·00
O131	92	1s. deep green p 14×13½ (2.37)		45·00	1·50
		aw. Wmk inverted		—	85·00
		b. Perf 14 (1942)		2·25	1·00
O132	93	2s. olive-green, p 13–14×13½ (5.37)		80·00	30·00
		a. "CAPTAIN COQK"		95·00	
		b. Perf 13½×14 (1939)		£170	6·50
		ba. "CAPTAIN COQK"		£180	
		c. Perf 12½ (1942)		90·00	27·00
		ca. "CAPTAIN COQK"		£110	
		d. Perf 14×13½ (1944)		42·00	7·00
		da. "CAPTAIN COQK"		£225	

O133	F 6	5s. green (chalk-surfaced paper), p 14 (3.43)		38·00	5·00
		aw. Wmk inverted		38·00	5·00
		b. Perf 14×13½. Yellow-green (ordinary paper) (10.61)		17·00	32·00
O120/33		*Set of 14*		£250	£110

The opt on No. O127a was sometimes applied at the top of the stamp, instead of always at the bottom, as on No. O127.
All examples of No. O128b were used by a government office in Whangerei.
The 5s. value on ordinary paper perforated 14×13½ does not exist without the "Official" overprint.
See notes on perforations after No. 590b.

1938–51. *Nos. 603 etc., optd with Type O 4.*

O134	108	½d. green (1.3.38)		16·00	2·25
O135		½d. brown-orange (1946)		1·60	3·00
O136		1d. scarlet (1.7.38)		16·00	15
O137		1d. green (10.7.41)		2·25	10
O138	108a	1½d. purple-brown (26.7.38)		75·00	18·00
O139		1½d. scarlet (2.4.51)		9·00	5·00
O140		3d. blue (16.10.41)		2·25	10
O134/40		*Set of 7*		£110	25·00

1940 (2 Jan–8 Mar). *Centennial. Nos. 613, etc., optd with Type O 5.*

O141		½d. blue-green (R.)		1·75	35
		a. "ff" joined, as Type O 4		50·00	60·00
O142		1d. chocolate and scarlet		4·00	10
		a. "ff" joined, as Type O 4		50·00	60·00
O143		1½d. light blue and mauve		2·75	2·00
O144		2d. blue-green and chocolate		4·00	10
		a. "ff" joined, as Type O 4		60·00	60·00
O145		2½d. blue-green and ultramarine		4·00	2·75
		a. "ff" joined, as Type O 4		50·00	65·00
O146		3d. purple and carmine (R.)		8·00	90
		a. "ff" joined, as Type O 4		42·00	48·00
O147		4d. chocolate and lake		40·00	2·00
		a. "ff" joined, as Type O 4		£120	80·00
O148		6d. emerald-green and violet		25·00	2·00
		a. "ff" joined, as Type O 4		70·00	70·00
O149		8d. black and red (8.3)		30·00	17·00
		a. "ff" joined, as Type O 4		70·00	£100
O150		9d. olive-green and vermilion		11·00	7·00
O151		1s. sage-green and deep green		48·00	4·00
O141/51		*Set of 11*		£160	35·00

For this issue the Type O 4 overprint occurs on R.4/3 of the 2½d. and on R.1/10 of the other values.

1947–49. *Nos. 680, etc., optd with Type O 4.*

O152	108a	2d. orange		1·75	10
O153		4d. bright purple		4·25	1·75
O154		6d. carmine		11·00	40
O155		8d. violet		8·00	6·50
O156		9d. purple-brown		9·00	6·50
O157	144	1s. red-brown and carmine (wmk upright) (Plate 1)		17·00	95
		a. Wmk sideways (Plate 1) (1949)		8·50	9·00
		aw. Wmk sideways inverted		35·00	
		b. Wmk upright (Plate 2)		24·00	7·00
		bw. Wmk inverted (Plate 1)		65·00	28·00
O158		2s. brown-orange and green (wmk sideways) (Plate 1)		23·00	16·00
		a. Wmk upright (Plate 1)		32·00	40·00
O152/8		*Set of 7*		60·00	28·00

O 6   (O 7)
Queen Elizabeth II

(Des J. Berry. Recess B.W.)

1954 (1 Mar)–**63.** *W 98. P 14×13½.*

O159	O 6	1d. orange		60	40
		a. White opaque paper (8.7.59)		50	20
O160		1½d. brown-lake		3·50	4·50
O161		2d. bluish green		40	20
		a. White opaque paper (11.12.58)		40	20
O162		2½d. olive (white opaque paper) (1.3.63)		4·25	1·50
O163		3d. vermilion		70	10
		a. White opaque paper (1960)		40	10
		aw. Wmk inverted		25·00	16·00
O164		4d. blue		1·25	40
		a. Printed on the gummed side		£130	
		b. White opaque paper (1.9.61)		1·00	50
O165		9d. carmine		7·00	90
O166		1s. purple		1·00	10
		a. White opaque paper (2.10.61)		2·50	75
O167		3s. slate (white opaque paper) (1.3.63)		35·00	48·00
O159/67		*Set of 9*		48·00	48·00

See note re white opaque paper after No. 736.

1959 (1 Oct). *No. O160 surch with Type O 7.*

O168	O 6	6d. on 1½d. brown-lake		40	1·10

1961 (1 Sept). *No. O161 surch as Type O 7.*

O169	O 6	2½d. on 2d. bluish green		95	1·50

Owing to the greater use of franking machines by Government Departments, the use of official stamps was discontinued on 31 March 1965, but they remained on sale at the G.P.O. until 31 December 1965.

STAMP BOOKLET

1907 (1 July). *White card cover.*

OB1	10s. booklet containing one hundred and twenty 1d. in panes of 6 (No. O60a)		£1000

PROVISIONALS ISSUED AT REEFTON AND USED BY THE POLICE DEPARTMENT

1907 (Jan). *Current stamps of 1906, optd "Official", in red manuscript, and handstamped with a circular "Greymouth—PAID—3", P 14.*

P1	23	½d. green		£1000	£1200
P2	40	1d. carmine		£1100	£1100
P3	38a	2d. purple		£1300	£1500
P4	28	3d. bistre		£1600	£1800
P5	31	6d. pink		£1600	£1800
P6	34	1s. orange-red		£2000	£2250
P7	35	2s. green		£6000	

LIFE INSURANCE DEPARTMENT

L 1   Lighthouse   L 2

(Des W. B. Hudson and J. F. Rogers; eng A. E. Cousins. Typo Govt Printing Office, Wellington)

1891 (2 Jan)–**98.** *A. W 12c. P 12×11½.*

L 1	L 1	½d. bright purple		60·00	6·00
		x. Wmk reversed		†	
L 2		1d. blue		55·00	4·00
		ax. Wmk reversed			
		ay. Wmk inverted and reversed		†	32·00
		b. Wmk 12b		90·00	20·00
		bx. Wmk reversed		†	
L 3		2d. brown-red		85·00	7·00
		ax. Wmk reversed		†	80·00
		b. Wmk 12b		95·00	13·00
L 4		3d. deep brown		£160	20·00
L 5		6d. green		£275	60·00
L 6		1s. rose		£500	£120
L1/6		*Set of 6*		£1000	£200

B. W 12b (1893–98). (a) P 10 (1893)

L 7	L 1	½d. bright purple		55·00	8·50
L 8		1d. blue		55·00	1·25
L 9		2d. brown-red		80·00	3·75
L7/9		*Set of 3*		£170	12·00

(b) P 11×10

L10	L 1	½d. bright purple (1896)		90·00	26·00
		a. Perf 10×11		£150	60·00
L11		1d. blue (1897)		†	—
		a. Perf 10×11		60·00	12·00

(c) Mixed perfs 10 and 11 (1897)

L12	L 1	2d. brown-red		£550	£550

(d) P 11 (1897–98)

L13	L 1	½d. bright purple		55·00	3·00
		a. Thin coarse toned paper (1898)		75·00	5·50
L14		1d. blue		55·00	75
		a. Thin coarse toned paper (1898)		70·00	1·75
		x. Wmk reversed		£110	12·00
		y. Wmk inverted and reversed		£110	22·00
L15		2d. brown-red		75·00	3·50
		a. Chocolate		£110	24·00
		b. Thin coarse toned paper (1898)		£120	3·50
L13/15		*Set of 3*		£170	6·50

1902–04. *W 43 (sideways). (a) P 11.*

L16	L 1	½d. bright purple (1903)		55·00	4·75
L17		1d. blue (1902)		55·00	1·00
L18		2d. brown-red (1904)		90·00	7·50
L16/18		*Set of 3*		£180	12·00

(b) P 14×11

L19	L 1	½d. bright purple (1903)		£1300	
L20		1d. blue (1904)		95·00	11·00

Nos. L16/17 and L20 are known without watermark from the margins of the sheet.

1905–6. *Redrawn, with "V.R." omitted. W 43 (sideways). (a) P 11.*

L21	L 2	2d. brown-red (12.05)		£1000	80·00

(b) P 14

L22	L 2	1d. blue (7.06)		£160	30·00

(c) P 14×11

L23	L 2	1d. blue (7.06)		£475	£150
		a. Mixed perfs		†	£375

Between January 1907 and the end of 1912 the Life Insurance Department used ordinary Official stamps.

1913 (2 Jan)–**37.** *New values and colours. W 43.*

(a) "De La Rue" paper. P 14×15

L24	L 2	½d. green		10·00	1·00
		a. Yellow-green		10·00	1·00
L25		1d. carmine		8·00	1·00
		a. Carmine-pink		15·00	1·40
L26		1½d. black (1917)		40·00	6·50
L27		1½d. chestnut-brown (1919)		1·50	2·25
L28		2d. bright purple		48·00	26·00
		w. Wmk inverted		†	75·00
L29		2d. yellow (1920)		5·50	2·00
L30		3d. yellow-brown		45·00	24·00
L31		6d. carmine-pink		35·00	22·00
L24/31		*Set of 8*		£170	75·00

(b) "Cowan" paper. (i) P 14×15

L31a	L 2	½d. yellow-green (1925)		26·00	4·00
L31b		1d. carmine-pink (1925)		28·00	3·50
		bw. Wmk inverted		35·00	5·00

(ii) P 14

L32	L 2	½d. yellow-green (1926)		9·00	1·75
		w. Wmk inverted		†	10·00
L33		1d. scarlet (1931)		7·50	1·50
		w. Wmk inverted		13·00	2·75
L34		2d. yellow (1937)		6·00	4·75
		w. Wmk inverted		30·00	25·00
L35		3d. brown-lake (1931)		18·00	22·00
L36		6d. pink (1925)		32·00	38·00
L32/6		*Set of 5*		65·00	60·00

(c) "Wiggins Teape" paper. P 14×15
L36a	L 2	½d. yellow-green (3.37)	7·00	9·50
L36b		1d. scarlet (3.37)	15·00	3·25
L36c		6d. pink (7.37)	35·00	40·00
L36a/c		Set of 3	50·00	48·00

For descriptions of the various types of paper, see after No. 385.

In the 1½d. the word "POSTAGE" is in both the side-labels instead of at left only.

1944–47. W 98. P 14×15.
L37	L 2	½d. yellow-green (7.47)	4·50	9·00
L38		1d. scarlet (6.44)	3·25	2·00
L39		2d. yellow (1946)	10·00	13·00
L40		3d. brown-lake (10.46)	15·00	35·00
L41		6d. pink (7.47)	11·00	12·00
L37/41		Set of 5	40·00	80·00

L 3 Castlepoint Lighthouse   L 6 Cape Campbell Lighthouse

(Des J. Berry. Recess B.W.).

1947 (1 Aug)–65. Type L 3, L 6 and similar designs. W 98 (sideways on 1d., 2d., 2½d.). P 13½.
L42		½d. grey-green and orange-red	1·00	60
L43		1d. olive-green and pale blue	1·00	65
L44		2d. deep blue and grey-black	70	50
L45		2½d. black and bright blue (white opaque paper) (4.11.63)	9·50	12·00
L46		3d. mauve and pale blue	2·50	35
L47		4d. brown and yellow-orange	3·25	1·25
		a. Wmk sideways (white opaque paper) (13.10.65)	5·00	13·00
L48		6d. chocolate and blue	3·50	1·75
L49		1s. red-brown and blue	3·50	2·75
L42/49		Set of 8	22·00	19·00

Designs: Horiz (as Type L 3)–1d Taiaroa lighthouse; 2d. Cape Palliser lighthouse; 6d. The Brothers lighthouse. Vert (as Type L 6)–3d. Eddystone lighthouse; 4d. Stephens Island lighthouse; 1s. Cape Brett lighthouse.

1967 (10 July)–68. Decimal currency. Stamps of 1947–65, surch as Type L 12 or L 11 (2 c.).
L50		1 c. on 1d. (No. L43)	2·25	4·25
		a. Wmk upright (white opaque paper) (10.5.68)	1·40	4·25
L51		2 c. on 2½d. (No. L45)	11·00	13·00
L52		2½ c. on 3d. (No. L46)	2·00	4·50
		a. Horiz pair, one without surcharge	£2000	
		b. Wmk sideways (white opaque paper) (4.68?)	2·40	4·75
L53		3 c. on 4d. (No. L47a)	4·50	5·50
		w. Wmk sideways inverted	†	
L54		5 c. on 5d. (No. L48)	1·00	6·00
		a. White opaque paper	1·50	6·50
L55		10 c. on 1s. (No. L49)	2·00	10·00
		a. Wmk sideways (white opaque paper)	1·00	4·00
		aw. Wmk sideways inverted	†	—
L50/5a		Set of 6	19·00	32·00

See note re white paper below No. 736.

L 13 Moeraki Point Lighthouse   L 14 Puysegur Point Lighthouse

(Des J. Berry. Litho B.W.).

1969 (27 Mar)–77. Types L 13/14 and similar designs. No wmk. Chalk-surfaced paper (8, 10 c.), ordinary paper (others). P 14 (8, 10 c.) or 13½ (others).
L56		½ c. greenish yellow, red and deep blue	90	1·75
L57		2½ c. ultramarine, green and pale buff	75	1·25
L58		3 c. reddish brown and yellow	75	75
		a. Chalk-surfaced paper (16.6.77)	50	2·25
L59		4 c. lt new blue, yellowish grn & apple-grn	75	1·00
		a. Chalk-surfaced paper (16.6.77)	50	2·25
L60		8 c. multicoloured (17.11.76)	45	2·75
L61		10 c. multicoloured (17.11.76)	45	2·75
L62		15 c. black, light yellow and ultramarine	60	2·00
		a. Chalk-surfaced paper (3.75)	20·00	22·00
		ab. Perf 14 (24.12.76)	90	2·25
L56/62		Set of 7	3·75	11·00

Designs: Horiz–4 c. Cape Egmont Lighthouse; Vert–3c. Baring Head Lighthouse; 8 c. East Cape; 10 c. Farewell Spit; 15 c. Dog Island Lighthouse.

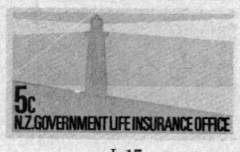

(L 16)   L 17

1978 (8 Mar). No. L 57 surch with Type L 16. Chalky paper.
L63	L 14	25 c. on 2½ c. ultramarine, grn & buff	75	1·75

(Des A. G. Mitchell. Litho Harrison)

1981 (3 June). P 14½.
L64	L 17	5 c. multicoloured	10	10
L65		10 c. multicoloured	10	10
L66		20 c. multicoloured	15	15
L67		30 c. multicoloured	25	25
L68		40 c. multicoloured	35	30
L69		50 c. multicoloured	45	35
L64/9		Set of 6	1·25	1·00

Issues for the Government Life Insurance Department were withdrawn on 1 December 1989 when it became the privatised Tower Corporation.

POSTAL FISCAL STAMPS

As from 1 April 1882 fiscal stamps were authorised for postal use and conversely postage stamps became valid for fiscal use. Stamps in the designs of 1867 with "STAMP DUTY" above the Queen's head were withdrawn and although some passed through the mail quite legitimately they were mainly "philatelic" and we no longer list them. The issue which was specifically authorised in 1882 was the one which had originally been put on sale for fiscal use in 1880.

Although all fiscal stamps were legally valid for postage only values between 2s. and £1 were stocked at ordinary post offices. Other values could only be obtained by request from the G.P.O., Wellington or from offices of the Stamp Duties Department. Later the Arms types above £1 could also be obtained from the head post offices in Auckland, Christchurch, Dunedin and also a branch post office at Christchurch North where there was a local demand for them.

It seems sensible to list under Postal Fiscals the Queen Victoria stamps up to the £1 value and the Arms types up to the £5 because by 1931 the higher values were genuinely needed for postal purposes. Even the £10 was occasionally used on insured airmail parcels.

Although 2s. and 5s. values were included in the 1898 pictorial issue, it was the general practice for the Postal Department to limit the postage issues to 1s. until 1926 when the 2s. and 3s. appeared. These were then dropped from the fiscal issues and when in turn the 5s. and 10s. were introduced in 1953 and the £1 in 1960 no further printings of these values occurred in the fiscal series.

FORGED POSTMARKS. Our prices are for stamps with genuine postal cancellations. Beware of forged postmarks on stamps from which fiscal cancellations have been cleaned off.

Many small post offices acted as agents for government departments and it was the practice to use ordinary postal date-stamps on stamps used fiscally, so that when they are removed from documents they are indistinguishable from postally used specimens unless impressed with the embossed seal of the Stamp Duties Department.

Date-stamps very similar to postal date-stamps were sometimes supplied to offices of the Stamp Duties Department and it is not clear when this practice ceased. Prior to the Arms types the only sure proof of the postal use of off-cover fiscal stamps is when they bear a distinctive duplex, registered or parcel post cancellation, but beware of forgeries of the first two.

F 1   F 2   F 3

(Die eng W. R. Bock. Typo Govt Ptg Office)

1882 (Feb). W 12a. P 12×11½.
F1	F 1	1d. lilac	£225	£325
F2		1d. blue	£110	25·00
		w. Wmk inverted		

The 1d. fiscal was specifically authorised for postal use in February 1882 owing to a shortage of the 1d. Type 5 and pending the introduction of the 1d. Type 14 on 1 April.

The 1d. lilac fiscal had been replaced by the 1d. blue in 1878 but postally used copies with 1882 duplex postmarks are known although most postally used examples are dated from 1890 and these must have been philatelic.

(Des and dies eng W. R. Bock. Typo Govt Ptg Office)

1882 (early). W 12a. P 12 × 11½.
F3	F 2	1s. grey-green		
F4	F 3	1s. grey-green and red		

Copies of these are known postally used in 1882 and although not specifically authorised for postal use it is believed that their use was permitted where there was a shortage of the 1s. postage stamp.

The 2s. value Type F 3 formerly listed is not known with 1882–83 postal date-stamps.

WMK TYPE F 5. The balance of the paper employed for the 1867 issue was used for early printings of Type F 4 introduced in 1880 before changing over to the "N Z" and Star watermark. The values we list with this watermark are known with 1882–83 postal date stamps. Others have later dates and are considered to be philatelic but should they be found with 1882–83 postal dates we would be prepared to add them to the list.

In the following list the 4d., 6d., 8d. and 1s. are known with early 1882 postal date-stamps and, like Nos. F3/4, it is assumed that they were used to meet a temporary shortage of postage stamps.

F 4   F 5

The 12s. 6d. value has the head in an oval (as Type 10), and the 15s. and £1 values have it in a broken circle (as Type 7).

(Dies eng W. R. Bock. Typo Govt Ptg Office)

1882 (1 Apr). Type F 4 and similar types. "De La Rue" paper.

A. W 12a (6 mm). (a) P 12 (1882)
F 5		4d. orange-red (Wmk F 5)	—	£160
F 6		4d. lake-brown	—	£160
F 7		8d. green (Wmk F 5)		
F 8		1s. pink		
F 9		2s. blue	50·00	4·50
F10		2s. 6d. grey-brown	85·00	4·50
		a. Wmk F 5		
F11		3s. mauve	£110	6·00
F12		4s. brown-rose	£110	11·00
F13		5s. green	£140	12·00
		a. Yellow-green	£140	12·00
F14		6s. rose	£150	29·00
F15		7s. ultramarine	£160	50·00
F16		7s. 6d. bronze-grey	£250	85·00
F17		8s. deep blue	£170	60·00
F18		9s. orange	£190	55·00
F19		10s. brown-red	£140	20·00
		a. Wmk F 5		
F20		15s. green	£250	85·00
F21		£1 rose-pink	£190	50·00

(b) P 12½ (1886)
F22		2s. blue	50·00	4·50
F23		2s. 6d. grey-brown	85·00	4·50
F24		3s. mauve	£110	6·00
F25		4s. purple-claret	£110	11·00
		a. Brown-rose	£110	11·00
F26		5s. green	£140	12·00
		a. Yellow-green	£140	12·00
F27		6s. rose	£150	29·00
F28		7s. ultramarine	£160	50·00
F29		8s. deep blue	£170	60·00
F30		9s. orange	£190	55·00
F31		10s. brown-red	£140	20·00
F32		15s. green	£250	85·00
F33		£1 rose-pink	£190	50·00

B. W 12b (7 mm). P 12½ (1888)
F34		2s. blue	45·00	4·50
F35		2s. 6d. grey-brown	80·00	4·50
F36		3s. mauve	£100	6·00
F37		4s. brown-rose	£100	11·00
		a. Brown-red	£100	11·00
F38		5s. green	£130	12·00
		a. Yellow-green	£130	12·00
F39		6s. rose	£150	29·00
F40		7s. ultramarine	£160	50·00
F41		7s. 6d. bronze-grey	£250	85·00
F42		8s. deep blue	£170	60·00
F43		9s. orange	£190	55·00
F44		10s. brown-red	£140	18·00
		a. Maroon	£140	18·00
F45		£1 pink	£190	50·00

C. W 12c (4 mm). P 12½ (1890)
F46		2s. blue	75·00	11·00
F46a		2s. 6d. grey-brown	£110	13·00
F47		3s. mauve	£150	27·00
F48		4s. brown-red	£120	15·00
F49		5s. green	£140	13·00
F50		6s. rose	£160	29·00
F51		7s. ultramarine	£170	50·00
F52		8s. deep blue	£180	60·00
F53		9s. orange	£200	65·00
F54		10s. brown-red	£150	20·00
F55		15s. green	£275	£100

D. Continuation of W 12b. P 11 (1895–1901)
F56		2s. blue	27·00	5·50
F57		2s. 6d. grey-brown	80·00	4·50
		a. Inscr "COUNTERPART" (1901)*	£160	£180
F58		3s. mauve	£100	6·00
F59		4s. brown-red	£100	10·00
F60		5s. yellow-green	£130	13·00
F61		6s. rose	£140	29·00
F62		7s. pale blue	£160	50·00
F63		7s. 6d. bronze-grey	£250	85·00
F64		8s. deep blue	£170	60·00
F65		9s. orange	£190	55·00
		a. Imperf between (horiz pair)	£850	
F66		10s. brown-red	£140	18·00
		a. Maroon	£140	18·00
F67		15s. green	£250	85·00
F68		£1 rose-pink	£190	50·00

*The plate normally printed in yellow and inscribed "COUNTERPART" just above the bottom value panel, was for use on the counterparts of documents but was issued in error in the colour of the normal fiscal stamp and accepted for use.

E. W 43 (sideways)
(i) Unsurfaced "Cowan" paper. (a) P 11 (1903)
F69		2s. 6d. grey-brown	80·00	4·50
F70		3s. mauve	£100	6·00
F71		4s. orange-red	£100	10·00
F72		6s. rose	£140	29·00
F73		7s. pale blue	£160	50·00
F74		8s. deep blue	£170	60·00
F75		10s. brown-red	£130	20·00
		a. Maroon	£130	20·00
F76		15s. green	£250	85·00
F77		£1 rose-pink	£170	50·00

(b) P 14 (1906)

78	2s. 6d. grey-brown	..	80·00	4·50
79	3s. mauve	..	£100	6·00
80	4s. orange-red	..	£100	7·50
81	5s. yellow-green	..	90·00	8·50
82	6s. rose	..	£140	29·00
83	7s. pale blue	..	£150	60·00
84	7s. 6d. bronze-grey	..	£250	85·00
85	8s. deep blue	..	£170	60·00
86	9s. orange	..	£180	55·00
87	10s. maroon	..	£130	18·00
88	15s. green	..	£250	85·00
89	£1 rose-pink	..	£170	50·00

(c) P 14½ × 14, comb (clean-cut) (1907)

90	2s. blue	..	25·00	4·00
91	2s. 6d. grey-brown	..	80·00	4·50
92	3s. mauve	..	£100	6·00
93	4s. orange-red	..	90·00	7·50
94	6s. rose	..	£140	29·00
95	10s. maroon	..	£130	18·00
96	15s. green	..	£250	85·00
97	£1 rose-pink	..	£170	50·00

(ii) Chalk-surfaced "De La Rue" paper. (a) P 14 (1913)

98	2s. blue	..	25·00	4·00
99	2s. 6d. grey-brown	..	27·00	4·50
100	3s. purple	..	70·00	6·00
101	4s. orange-red	..	70·00	7·00
102	5s. yellow-green	..	70·00	8·50
*103	6s. rose	..	£110	15·00
*104	7s. pale blue	..	£120	25·00
*105	7s. 6d. bronze-grey	..	£250	85·00
*106	8s. deep blue	..	£150	30·00
*107	9s. orange	..	£180	55·00
*108	10s. maroon	..	£130	16·00
*109	15s. green	..	£250	85·00
*110	£1 rose-carmine	..	£170	50·00

(b) P 14½ × 14, comb (1913–21)

*111	2s. deep blue	..	25·00	4·00
*112	2s. 6d. grey-brown	..	27·00	4·50
*113	3s. purple	..	70·00	6·00
*114	4s. orange-red	..	70·00	7·00
*115	5s. yellow-green	..	70·00	8·50
*116	6s. rose	..	£110	15·00
*117	7s. pale blue	..	£120	25·00
*118	8s. deep blue	..	£150	30·00
*119	9s. orange	..	£170	55·00
*120	10s. maroon	..	£130	16·00
*121	12s. 6d. deep plum (1921)	..	£3750	£1500
*122	15s. green	..	£250	85·00
*123	£1 rose-carmine	..	£170	50·00

The "De La Rue" paper has a smooth finish and has toned gum which is strongly resistant to soaking.

(iii) Chalk-surfaced "Jones" paper. P 14½ × 14, comb (1924)

*124	2s. deep blue	..	30·00	5·00
*125	2s. 6d. deep grey-brown	..	32·00	5·50
*126	3s. purple	..	80·00	6·50
*127	5s. yellow-green	..	80·00	9·00
*128	10s. brown-red	..	£140	16·00
*129	12s. 6d deep purple	..	£3750	£1500
*130	15s. green	..	£275	95·00

The "Jones" paper has a coarser texture, is poorly surfaced and the ink tends to peel. The outline of the watermark commonly shows on the surface of the stamp. The gum is colourless or only slightly toned and washes off readily.

(iv) Thick, opaque, chalk-surfaced "Cowan" paper. P 14½×14, comb (1925–30)

F131	2s. blue	..	27·00	5·00
F132	2s. 6d. deep grey-brown	..	30·00	5·50
F133	3s. mauve	..	£100	10·00
F134	4s. orange-red	..	70·00	10·00
F135	5s. yellow-green	..	70·00	12·00
	x. Wmk reversed (1927)	..	£100	20·00
F136	6s. rose	..	£110	18·00
F137	7s. pale blue	..	£120	25·00
F138	8s. deep blue	..	£150	30·00
	a. Error. Blue (as 2s.) (1930)		£500	
F139	10s. brown-red	..	£130	16·00
	x. Wmk reversed (1927)	..	£200	£150
F140	12s. 6d. blackish purple	..	£3750	£1500
F141	15s. green	..	£275	95·00
F142	£1 rose-pink	..	£170	50·00

The "Cowan" paper is white and opaque and the watermark, which is usually smaller than in the "Jones" paper, is often barely visible.

(v) Thin, hard, chalk-surfaced "Wiggins Teape" paper. P 14½ × 14, comb (1926)

F143	4s. orange-red	..	80·00	13·00
F144	£1 rose-pink	..	£180	95·00

The "Wiggins Teape" paper has a vertical mesh with narrow watermark, whereas other chalk-surfaced papers with this perforation have a horizontal mesh and wider watermark.

35/-

F 6   (F 7)

(Des H. L. Richardson. Typo Govt Ptg Office)

1931–40. *As Type F 6 (various frames). W 43. P 14.*

(i) Thick, opaque, chalk-surfaced "Cowan" paper, with horizontal mesh (1931–35)

F145	1s. 3d. lemon (4.31)	..	8·00	35·00
F146	1s. 3d. orange-yellow	..	5·50	5·50
F147	2s. 6d. deep brown	..	13·00	4·00
F148	4s. red	..	14·00	4·75
F149	5s. green	..	17·00	7·50
F150	6s. carmine-rose	..	32·00	12·00
F151	7s. blue	..	27·00	20·00
F152	7s. 6d. olive-grey	..	60·00	80·00
F153	8s. slate-violet	..	28·00	28·00
F154	9s. brown-orange	..	30·00	28·00

F155	10s. carmine-lake	..	24·00	8·00
F156	12s. 6d. deep plum (9.35)	..	£140	£140
F157	15s. sage-green	..	60·00	35·00
F158	£1 pink	..	60·00	19·00
F159	25s. greenish blue	..	£250	£375
F160	30s. brown (1935)	..	£250	£140
F161	35s. orange-yellow	..	£2500	£2750
F162	£2 bright purple	..	£300	60·00
F163	£2 10s. red	..	£250	£300
F164	£3 green	..	£325	£170
F165	£3 10s. rose (1935)	..	£1300	£1000
F166	£4 light blue (1935)	..	£325	£130
F167	£4 10s. deep olive-grey (1935)	..	£1000	£1100
F168	£5 indigo-blue	..	£325	90·00

(ii) Thin, hard "Wiggins Teape" paper with vertical mesh (1936–40)

(a) Chalk-surfaced (1936–39)

F169	1s. 3d. pale orange-yellow	..	13·00	3·25
F170	2s. 6d. dull brown	..	48·00	3·25
F171	4s. pale red-brown	..	55·00	6·00
F172	5s. green	..	65·00	7·00
	w. Wmk inverted			
F173	6s. carmine-rose	..	70·00	25·00
F174	7s. pale blue	..	80·00	28·00
F175	8s. slate-violet	..	£100	45·00
F176	9s. brown-orange	..	£110	65·00
F177	10s. pale carmine-lake	..	£120	6·50
F178	15s. sage-green	..	£170	50·00
F179	£1 pink	..	£130	24·00
F180	30s. brown (1.39)	..	£350	£140
F181	35s. orange-yellow	..	£3000	£3000
F182	£2 bright purple (1937)	..	£475	80·00
	w. Wmk inverted			
F183	£3 green (1937)	..	£500	£200
F184	£5 indigo-blue (1937)	..	£700	£160

(b) Unsurfaced (1940)

F185	7s. 6d. olive-grey	..	£150	90·00

Not all values listed above were stocked at ordinary post offices as some of them were primarily required for fiscal purposes but all were valid for postage.

1939. *No. F161 surch with Type F 7.*

F186	35/- on 35s. orange-yellow	..	£400	£225

Because the 35s. orange-yellow could so easily be confused with the 1s. 3d. in the same colour it was surcharged.

1940 (June). *New values surch as Type F 7. W 43. "Wiggins Teape" chalk-surfaced paper. P 14.*

F187	3/6 on 3s. 6d. deep-green	..	50·00	16·00
F188	5/6 on 5s. 6d. lilac	..	80·00	45·00
F189	11/- on 11s. yellow	..	£140	£110
F190	22/- on 22s. scarlet	..	£350	£250
F187/90		*Set of 4*	£550	£375

These values were primarily needed for fiscal use.

1940–58. *As Type F 6 (various frames). W 98.*

(i) P 14. "Wiggins Teape" chalk-surfaced paper with vertical mesh (1940–56)

F191	1s. 3d. orange-yellow	..	8·00	1·50
	w. Wmk inverted			
F192	1s. 3d. yellow and black (*wmk inverted*) (14.6.55)	..	1·50	80
	aw. Wmk upright (9.9.55)	..	27·00	27·00
	b. Error. Yellow and blue (*wmk inverted*) (7.56)	..	4·00	5·50
F193	2s. 6d. deep brown	..	8·00	60
	w. Wmk inverted (3.49)	..	8·00	30
F194	4s. red-brown	..	12·00	90
	w. Wmk inverted (3.49)	..	14·00	70
F195	5s. green	..	17·00	80
	w. Wmk inverted (1.5.50)	..	22·00	80
F196	6s. carmine-rose	..	30·00	3·25
	w. Wmk inverted (1948)	..	32·00	2·75
F197	7s. pale blue	..	30·00	4·75
F198	7s. 6d. ol-grey (*wmk inverted*) (21.12.50)	..	60·00	50·00
F199	8s. slate-violet	..	48·00	17·00
	w. Wmk inverted (6.12.50)	..	45·00	17·00
F200	9s. brown-orange (1946)	..	22·00	38·00
	w. Wmk inverted (9.1.51)	..	45·00	38·00
F201	10s. carmine-lake	..	28·00	2·25
	w. Wmk inverted (4.50)	..	28·00	2·50
F202	15s. sage-green	..	42·00	18·00
	w. Wmk inverted (8.12.50)	..	55·00	25·00
F203	£1 pink	..	27·00	3·75
	w. Wmk inverted (1.2.50)	..	38·00	4·25
F204	25s. greenish blue (1946)	..	£325	£350
	w. Wmk inverted (7.53)	..	£375	£400
F205	30s. brown (1946)	..	£225	£100
	w. Wmk inverted (9.49)	..	£200	£100
F206	£2 bright purple (1946)	..	80·00	20·00
	w. Wmk inverted (17.6.52)	..	80·00	20·00
F207	£2 10s. red (*wmk inverted*) (9.8.51)	..	£250	£250
F208	£3 green (1946)	..	£110	48·00
	w. Wmk inverted (17.6.52)	..	£100	45·00
F209	£3 10s. rose (11.48)	..	£1500	£1000
	w. Wmk inverted (5.52)	..	£1600	£1000
F210	£4 light blue (*wmk inverted*) (12.2.52)	..	£130	95·00
	w. Wmk upright		†	
F211	£5 indigo-blue	..	£225	48·00
	w. Wmk inverted (11.9.50)	..	£160	45·00
F191/211		*Set of 21*	£2500	£1700

THREE SHILLINGS   I.

THREE SHILLINGS   II.

3s. 6d.

Type I. Broad serifed capitals
Type II. Taller capitals, without serifs

Surcharged as Type F 7

F212	3/6 on 3s. 6d. grey-green (I) (1942)	..	20·00	7·00
	w. Wmk inverted (12.10.50)	..	32·00	18·00
F213	3/6 on 3s. 6d. grey-green (II) (6.53)	..	13·00	38·00
	w. Wmk inverted (6.53)	..	35·00	40·00

F214	5/6 on 5s. 6d. lilac (1944)	..	48·00	18·00
	w. Wmk inverted (13.9.50)	..	48·00	18·00
F215	11/- on 11s. yellow (1942)	..	75·00	48·00
F216	22/- on 22s. scarlet (1945)	..	£250	£130
	w. Wmk inverted (1.3.50)	..	£250	£130
F212/16		*Set of 5*	£350	£200

(ii) P 14×13½. "Wiggins Teape" unsurfaced paper with horizontal mesh (1956–58)

F217	1s. 3d. yellow and black (11.56)		1·75	1·75
	w. Wmk inverted		18·00	17·00
F218	£1 pink (20.10.58)		32·00	12·00

No. F192b had the inscription printed in blue in error but as many as 378,000 were printed.

From 1949–53 inferior paper had to be used and for technical reasons it was necessary to feed the paper into the machine in a certain way which resulted in whole printings with the watermark inverted for most values.

F 8

1967 (10 July)–**68.** *Decimal currency. W 98 (sideways inverted). Unsurfaced paper. P 14.*

F219	F 8	$4 deep reddish violet	..	10·00	7·00
		w. Wmk sideways (17.9.68)		3·00	1·50
F220		$6 emerald	..	12·00	12·00
		w. Wmk sideways (17.9.68)		4·50	3·00
F221		$8 light greenish blue	..	19·00	19·00
		w. Wmk sideways (20.6.68)		6·00	4·50
F222		$10 deep ultramarine	..	25·00	20·00
		w. Wmk sideways (20.6.68)		7·50	4·50
F219/22			*Set of 4*	60·00	50·00
F219w/22w			*Set of 4*	19·00	12·00

The original printings were line perforated on paper with the sideways watermark inverted ("N Z" to right of star when viewed from the front). In 1968 the stamps appeared comb perforated with the normal sideways watermark. A further comb perforated printing in July 1984 showed the watermark sideways inverted.

1986 (Apr). *As Nos. F220/2 but without wmk. Chalk-surfaced paper.*

F223	F 8	$6 bright green	..	5·50	4·00
F224		$8 light greenish blue	..	7·00	14·00
F225		$10 deep ultramarine	..	8·00	6·00
F223/5			*Set of 3*	18·00	22·00

ANTARCTIC EXPEDITIONS

VICTORIA LAND

These issues were made under authority of the New Zealand Postal Department and, while not strictly necessary, they actually franked correspondence to New Zealand. They were sold to the public at a premium.

1908 (15 Jan). *Shackleton Expedition. T 42 of New Zealand (p 14), optd "King Edward VII Land", in two lines, reading up, by Coulls, Culling and Co., Wellington.*

A1	1d. rose-carmine (No. 356 Royle) (G.)	..	£400	35·00
	a. Opt double			†£1500
A1b	1d. rose-carmine (No. 352c Waterlow) (G.)	..	£1300	£800

Nos. A1/1b were used on board the expedition ship, *Nimrod*, and at the Cape Royds base in McMurdo Sound. Due to adverse conditions Shackleton landed in Victoria Land rather than King Edward VII Land the intended destination.

1911 (9 Feb)–**13.** *Scott Expedition. Stamps of New Zealand optd "VICTORIA LAND.", in two lines by Govt Printer, Wellington.*

A2	51	½d. deep green (No. 387aa) (18.1.13)	£550	£650
A3	53	1d. carmine (No. 405)	45·00	85·00
		a. No stop after "LAND" (R. 7/5)	£275	£600

Nos. A2/3 were used at the Cape Evans base on McMurdo Sound or on the *Terra Nova*.

ROSS DEPENDENCY

This comprises a sector of the Antarctic continent and a number of islands. It was claimed by Great Britain on 30 July 1923 and soon afterward put under the jurisdiction of New Zealand.

1 H.M.S. *Erebus*

2 Shackleton and Scott

3 Map of Ross Dependency and New Zealand

4 Queen Elizabeth II

(Des E. M. Taylor (3d.), L. C. Mitchell (4d.), R. Smith (8d.), J.Berry (1s. 6d.). Recess D.L.R.)

1957 (11 Jan). W **98** *of New Zealand* (*Mult N Z and Star*). P 13 (1s. 6d.) or 14 (others).

1	1	3d. indigo		1·50	1·00
2	2	4d. carmine-red		1·50	75
3	3	8d. bright carmine-red and ultramarine		1·50	1·00
		a. Bright carmine-red and blue		5·50	4·50
4	4	1s. 6d. slate-purple		1·50	1·25
1/4			Set of 4	5·50	3·50

(New Currency. 100 cents = 1 New Zealand dollar)

5 H.M.S. *Erebus*

1967 (10 July). *Decimal currency. As Nos. 1/4 but with values inscr in decimal currency as T* **5**. *Chalky paper* (except 15 c.). W **98** *of New Zealand* (*sideways on 7 c.*). P 13 (15 c.) or 14 (others).

5	5	2 c. indigo		12·00	4·75
		a. Deep blue		16·00	7·00
6	2	3 c. carmine-red		7·00	4·75
		w. Wmk inverted		65·00	
7	3	7 c. bright carmine-red and ultramarine		9·00	7·50
8	4	15 c. slate-purple		9·00	12·00
		w. Wmk inverted		85·00	
5/8			Set of 4	32·00	26·00

6 McCormick's Skua

7 Scott Base

(Des M. Cleverley. Litho B.W.)

1972 (18 Jan)–**79**. *Horiz design as T* **6** (3 to 8 c.) or **7** (10, 18 c.). *Ordinary paper.* P 14½ × 14 (10, 18 c.) or 13 (others).

9		3 c. black, brownish grey and pale blue		1·50	1·40
		a. Chalk-surfaced paper (2.79)		1·50	1·60
10		4 c. black, royal blue and violet		65	1·40
		a. Chalk-surfaced paper (2.79)		30	1·60
11		5 c. black, brownish grey and rose-lilac		50	1·40
		a. Chalk-surfaced paper (2.79)		20	1·60
12		8 c. black, yellow-brown and brownish grey		50	1·40
		a. Chalk-surfaced paper (2.79)		20	1·60
13		10 c. black, turquoise-green and slate-green		80	1·50
		a. Perf 13½ × 13. Chalk-surfaced paper (2.79)		30	1·60
14		18 c. black, violet and bright violet		1·75	2·50
		a. Perf 13½ × 13. Chalk-surfaced paper (2.79)		30	1·60
9/14			Set of 6	4·00	8·50
9a/14a			Set of 6	2·50	8·50

Designs:—4 c. Lockheed C-130 Hercules airplane at Williams Field; 5 c. Shackleton's Hut; 8 c. Supply ship H.M.N.Z.S. *Endeavour*; 18 c. Tabular ice floe.

8 Adelie Penguins

9 McCormick's Skua

(Des R. Conly. Litho Asher and Co, Melbourne)

1982 (20 Jan). *Horiz designs as T* **8**. *Multicoloured.* P 15½.

15		5 c. Type **8**		1·25	1·25
16		10 c. Tracked vehicles		40	40
17		20 c. Scott Base		40	40
18		30 c. Field party		40	40
19		40 c. Vanda Station		40	40
20		50 c. Scott's hut, Cape Evans		40	40
15/20			Set of 6	3·00	3·00

The post office at Scott Base closed on 30 September 1987 and Nos. 15/20 were withdrawn from sale at philatelic counters in New Zealand on 31 December 1987. Local stamps were subsequently issued by the Armed Forces Canteen Council to cover the cost of mail carriage from Scott Base to New Zealand. These are not listed as they had no national or international validity.

Sets of stamps, showing whales, Antarctic birds and seals,

inscribed "NEW ZEALAND ROSS DEPENDENCY", were issued in 1988, 1990 and 1992. These were available from post offices throughout New Zealand, but not in the Ross Dependency.

Separate issues for Ross Dependency were resumed in November 1994. Such stamps were only valid on mail from Scott Base, but were not postmarked until arrival at the New Zealand Post Ross Dependency Agency situated at Christchurch.

(Des G. Millen. Litho Southern Colour Print, Dunedin)

1994 (2 Nov)–**95**. *Wildlife. T* **9** *and similar horiz designs. Multicoloured.* P 13½.

21	5 c. Type **9**			10	10
22	10 c. Snow Petrel chick			10	10
23	20 c. Black-browed Albatross			15	20
24	40 c. Emperor Penguins (2.10.95)			25	30
25	45 c. As 40 c.			30	35
26	50 c. Chinstrap Penguins			30	35
27	70 c. Adelie Penguin			45	50
28	80 c. Elephant Seals			50	55
29	$1 Leopard Seal			65	70
30	$2 Weddell Seal			1·25	1·40
31	$3 Crabeater Seal pup			1·90	2·00
21/31			Set of 11	5·75	6·75

10 Capt. James Cook with H.M.S. *Resolution* and H.M.S. *Adventure*

11 Inside Ice Cove

(Des G. Fuller. Litho Questa)

1995 (9 Nov). *Antarctic Explorers. T* **10** *and similar horiz designs. Multicoloured.* P 14½.

32	40 c. Type **10**			75	75
33	80 c. James Clark Ross with H.M.S. *Erebus* and H.M.S. *Terror*			1·25	1·25
34	$1 Roald Amundsen and *Fram*			1·40	1·40
35	$1.20, Robert Scott with *Terra Nova*			1·75	1·75
36	$1.50, Ernest Shackleton with *Endurance*			2·00	2·00
37	$1.80, Richard Byrd with Ford 4-AT-B Trimotor *Floyd Bennett* (airplane)			2·00	2·00
32/7			Set of 6	8·25	8·25

(Des Diane Prosser. Litho Enschedé)

1996 (13 Nov). *Antarctic Landscapes. T* **11** *and similar multicoloured designs.* P 14½×14 (vert) or 14×14½ (horiz).

38	40 c. Type **11**			40	35
39	80 c. Base of glacier			70	65
40	$1 Glacier ice fall			85	80
41	$1.20, Climbers on crater rim (*horiz*)			1·00	95
42	$1.50, Pressure ridges (*horiz*)			1·25	1·25
43	$1.80, Fumarole ice tower (*horiz*)			1·40	1·40
38/43			Set of 6	5·50	5·50

12 Snow Petrel

13 Sculptured Sea Ice

(Des P. Martinson. Litho Southern Colour Print, Dunedin)

1997 (12 Nov). *Antarctic Seabirds. T* **12** *and similar vert designs. Multicoloured.* P 14. (a) With "WWF" panda emblem.

44	40 c. Type **12**			40	40
45	80 c. Cape Petrel			70	70
46	$1.20, Antarctic Fulmar			1·00	1·00
47	$1.50, Antarctic Petrel			1·25	1·25

(b) Without "WWF" panda emblem

48	40 c. Type **12**			40	40
	a. Block of 6. Nos. 48/53			5·00	
49	80 c. Cape Petrel			70	70
50	$1 Antarctic Prion			90	90
51	$1.20, Antarctic Fulmar			1·00	1·00
52	$1.50, Antarctic Petrel			1·25	1·40
53	$1.80, Antarctic Tern			1·25	1·50
44/53			Set of 10	8·00	8·50

Nos. 44/7 were printed in sheets containing stamps of one value.

Nos. 48/53 were printed in sheets containing the six values together, *se-tenant*, with the backgrounds forming a composite design. In addition the $1 and $1.80 were also produced in separate sheets.

(Des S. Fuller. Litho Southern Colour Print, Dunedin)

1998 (11 Nov). *Ice Formations. T* **13** *and similar horiz designs. Multicoloured.* P 14.

54	40 c. Type **13**			50	35
	a. Block of 6. Nos. 54/9			5·25	
55	80 c. Glacial tongue			70	60
56	$1 Stranded tabular iceberg			90	80
57	$1.20, Autumn at Cape Evans			1·00	90
58	$1.50, Sea ice in summer thaw			1·25	1·10
59	$1.80, Sunset at tabular icebergs			1·40	1·40
54/9			Set of 6	5·25	4·75

Nos. 54/9 were printed in sheets of one value or together, *se-tenant*, in blocks of 6.

14 Sea Smoke, McMurdo Sound

(Des G. Millen. Litho Southern Colour Print, Dunedin)

1999 (17 Nov). *Night Skies. T* **14** *and similar horiz designs. Multicoloured.* P 14.

60	40 c. Type **14**			25	30
61	80 c. Alpenglow, Mount Erebus			50	55
62	$1.10, Sunset, Black Island			70	75
63	$1.20, Pressure ridges, Ross Sea			75	80
64	$1.50, Evening light, Ross Island			1·10	1·25
65	$1.80, Mother of pearl clouds, Ross Island			1·25	1·40
60/5			Set of 6	4·50	5·00

TOKELAU

Formerly known as the Union Islands, and administered as part of the Gilbert & Ellice Islands Colony, Tokelau was transferred to New Zealand on 4 November 1925 and administered with Western Samoa. The islands were finally incorporated in New Zealand on 1 January 1949 and became a dependency. The name Tokelau was officially adopted on 7 May 1946.

Stamps of GILBERT AND ELLICE ISLANDS were used in Tokelau from February 1911 until June 1926 when they were replaced by those of SAMOA. These were current until 1948. The post office on Atafu opened in 1911, but the cancellations for the other two islands, Fakaofo and Nukunono, did not appear until 1926.

1 Atafu Village and Map

(Des J. Berry from photographs by T. T. C. Humphrey. Recess B.W.)

1948 (22 June). *T* **1** *and similar horiz designs. Wmk T* **98** *of New Zealand* (Mult N Z *and Star*). *P* 13½.

1	½d. red-brown and purple	..	15	40
2	1d. chestnut and green	..	15	30
	w. Wmk inverted	..	£275	
3	2d. green and ultramarine	..	15	30
1/3		*Set of 3*	40	90

Designs:—1d. Nukunono hut and map; 2d. Fakaofo village and map.
Covers are known postmarked 16 June 1948, but this was in error for 16 July.

1953 (16 June*). *Coronation. As No.* 715 *of New Zealand, but inscr* "TOKELAU ISLANDS".

4	164	3d. brown	2·00	2·00

*This is the date of issue in Tokelau. The stamps were released in New Zealand on 25 May.

ONE SHILLING

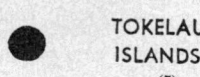

(4)   (5)

1956 (27 Mar). *No.* 1 *surch with T* **4** *by Govt Printer, Wellington.*

5	1	1s. on ½d. red-brown and purple	1·50	2·00

1966 (8 Nov). *Postal fiscal stamps of New Zealand (Type F* **6**)*, but without value, surch as T* **5** *by Govt Printer, Wellington. W* **98** *of New Zealand. P* 14.

6	6d. light blue	..	40	80
7	8d. light emerald	..	50	80
8	2s. light pink	..	50	80
6/8		*Set of 3*	1·25	2·25

(New Currency. 100 cents = 1 New Zealand dollar)

(6)   (7)

1967 (4 Sept*). *Decimal currency.*

(*a*) *Nos.* 1/3 *surch in decimal currency as T* **6** *by Govt Printer, Wellington*

9	1c. on 1d.	..	50	60
10	2 c. on 2d.	..	75	1·00
11	10 c. on 10d.	..	1·50	2·00

(*b*) *Postal Fiscal stamps of New Zealand (Type F* **6**)*, but without value, surch as T* **7** *by Govt Printer, Wellington. W* **98** *of New Zealand (sideways). P* 14 (line or comb)

12	F **6**	3 c. reddish lilac	30	30
13		5 c. light blue	30	30
14		7 c. light emerald	30	30
15		20 c. light pink	30	40
9/15		*Set of 7*	3·50	4·50

*This is the date of issue in Tokelau. The stamps were released in New Zealand on 10 July.

8 British Protectorate **12** H.M.S. *Dolphin*, 1765
(1877)

(Des New Zealand P.O. artists from suggestions by Tokelau Administration. Litho B.W.)

1969 (8 Aug). *History of Tokelau. T* **8** *and similar horiz designs. W* **98** *of New Zealand. P* 13 × 12½.

16	5 c. ultramarine, yellow and black	..	30	10
17	10 c. vermilion, yellow and black	..	35	10
18	15 c. green, yellow and black	..	40	15
19	20 c. yellow-brown, yellow and black	..	60	15
16/19		*Set of 4*	1·50	45

Designs:—10 c. Annexed to Gilbert and Ellice Islands, 1916; 15 c. New Zealand Administration, 1925; 20 c. New Zealand Territory, 1948.

1969 (14 Nov*). *Christmas. As T* **301** *of New Zealand, but inscr* "TOKELAU ISLANDS". *W* **98** *of New Zealand. P* 13½×14½.

20	2 c. multicoloured		10	15

*This is the date of issue in Tokelau. The stamps were released in New Zealand on 1 October.

1970 (15 Nov*). *Christmas. As T* **314** *of New Zealand, but inscr* "TOKELAU ISLANDS". *P* 12½.

21	2 c. multicoloured		10	20

*This is the date of issue in Tokelau. The stamps were released in New Zealand on 1 October.

(Des D. B. Stevenson. Litho B.W.)

1971 (9 Feb*). *Discovery of Tokelau. T* **12** *and similar multicoloured designs. P* 13½.

22	5 c. Type **12**		1·00	35
23	10 c. H.M.S. *Pandora*, 1791		1·00	35
24	25 c. *General Jackson* (American whaling ship), 1835 (*horiz*)		2·50	70
22/4		*Set of 3*	4·00	1·25

*This is the date of issue in Tokelau. The stamps were released in New Zealand on 9 December 1970.

13 Fan   **14** Windmill Pump

(Des Enid Hunter. Litho Harrison)

1971 (20 Oct). *Various horiz designs as T* **13** *showing handicrafts. Multicoloured. P* 14.

25	1 c. Type **13**		20	20
26	2 c. Hand-bag		30	30
27	3 c. Basket		30	40
28	5 c. Hand-bag		35	65
29	10 c. Shopping-bag		35	80
30	15 c. Fishing box		50	1·50
31	20 c. Canoe		50	1·75
32	25 c. Fishing hooks		50	1·75
25/32		*Set of 8*	2·75	6·50

(Des A. G. Mitchell. Litho Questa)

1972 (6 Sept). *25th Anniversary of South Pacific Commission. T* **14** *and similar vert designs. Multicoloured. P* 14 × 13½.

33	5 c. Type **14**		45	70
34	10 c. Community well		55	80
35	15 c. Pest eradication		80	1·40
36	20 c. Flags of member nations		85	1·40
33/6		*Set of 4*	2·40	3·75

On No. 35 "PACIFIC" is spelt "PACFIC".

15 Horny Coral   **16** Hump-back Cowrie

(Des Eileen Mayo. Litho B.W.)

1973 (12 Sept). *Coral. T* **15** *and similar vert designs. Multicoloured. P.* 13.

37	3 c. Type **15**		80	80
38	5 c. Soft Coral		80	90
39	15 c. Mushroom Coral		1·25	1·50
40	25 c. Staghorn Coral		1·50	1·75
37/40		*Set of 4*	4·00	4·50

(Des G. F. Fuller. Litho Questa)

1974 (13 Nov). *"Shells of the Coral Reef". T* **16** *and similar horiz designs. Multicoloured. P* 14.

41	3 c. Type **16**		1·00	1·25
42	5 c. Tiger Cowrie		1·10	1·25
43	15 c. Mole Cowrie		1·50	2·50
44	25 c. Eyed Cowrie		1·75	2·75
41/4		*Set of 4*	4·75	7·00

---

17 Moorish Idol   **18** Canoe Building

(Des Eileen Mayo. Litho Questa)

1975 (19 Nov). *Fishes. T* **17** *and similar vert designs. Multicoloured. P* 14.

45	5 c. Type **17**		40	1·00
46	10 c. Long-nosed Butterflyfish		45	1·25
47	15 c. Lined Butterflyfish		55	1·50
48	25 c. Lionfish ("Red Fire Fish")		60	1·75
45/8		*Set of 4*	1·75	5·00

(Des F. Paulo. Litho Questa)

1976 (27 Oct)–81. *T* **18** *and similar multicoloured designs showing local life. P* 14 × 13½ (9 c. to $1) *or* 13½ × 14 (*others*).

49	1 c. Type **18**		40	1·25
50	2 c. Reef fishing		10	15
51	3 c. Weaving preparation		30	1·60
	a. Perf 14½ × 15 (15.7.81)		25	75
52	5 c. Umu (kitchen)		10	15
	a. Perf 14½ × 15 (15.7.81)		30	75
53	9 c. Carving (*vert*)		10	15
	a. Perf 15 × 14½ (15.7.81)		10	1·00
54	20 c. Husking coconuts (*vert*)		10	15
	a. Perf 15 × 14½ (15.7.81)		15	80
55	50 c. Wash day (*vert*)		15	20
	a. Perf 15 × 14½ (15.7.81)		20	90
56	$1 Meal time (*vert*)		20	20
	a. Perf 15 × 14½ (15.7.81)		35	2·25
49/56		*Set of 8*	1·60	8·25
49a/56a		*Set of 7*	95	1·10

19 White Tern   **20** Westminster Abbey

(Des F. Paulo. Litho Questa)

1977 (16 Nov). *Birds of Tokelau. T* **19** *and similar horiz designs. Multicoloured. P* 14½.

57	8 c. Type **19**		40	50
58	10 c. Turnstone		45	55
59	15 c. White-capped Noddy		70	1·00
60	30 c. Common Noddy		90	1·60
57/60		*Set of 4*	2·25	3·25

(Des Eileen Mayo. Litho Questa)

1978 (28 June). *25th Anniv of Coronation. T* **20** *and similar vert designs. Multicoloured. P* 14.

61	8 c. Type **20**		20	20
62	10 c. King Edward's Chair		20	20
63	15 c. Coronation regalia		30	35
64	30 c. Queen Elizabeth II		50	60
61/4		*Set of 4*	1·10	1·25

21 Canoe Race   **22** Rugby

(Des F. Paulo. Photo Heraclio Fournier)

1978 (8 Nov). *Canoe Racing. T* **21** *and similar horiz designs showing races. P* 13½ × 14.

65	8 c. multicoloured		20	30
66	12 c. multicoloured		25	35
67	15 c. multicoloured		30	40
68	30 c. multicoloured		50	70
65/8		*Set of 4*	1·10	1·60

(Des F. Paulo. Photo Heraclio Fournier)

1979 (7 Nov). *Sports. T* **22** *and similar horiz designs. Multicoloured. P* 13½.

69	10 c. Type **22**		20	25
70	15 c. Cricket		55	75
71	20 c. Rugby (*different*)		55	80
72	30 c. Cricket (*different*)		70	1·00
69/72		*Set of 4*	1·75	2·50

NEW INFORMATION

The editor is always interested to correspond with people who have new information that will improve or correct the Catalogue.

23 Surfing 24 Pole Vaulting

(Des F. Paulo. Litho J.W.)

1980 (5 Nov). *Water Sports.* T **23** *and similar horiz designs. Multi-coloured. P* 13.

73	10 c. Type **23**	..	..	10	15
74	20 c. Surfing (*different*)	..	..	15	20
75	30 c. Swimming	..	..	20	25
76	50 c. Swimming (*different*)	..	..	25	35
73/6			*Set of* 4	60	85

(Des F. Paulo. Photo Heraclio Fournier)

1981 (4 Nov). *Sports.* T **24** *and similar vert designs. Multi-coloured. P* 14 × 13½.

77	10 c. Type **24**	..	..	10	10
78	20 c. Volleyball	..	..	20	20
79	30 c. Running	..	..	25	30
80	50 c. Volleyball (*different*)	..	..	30	35
77/80	..		*Set of* 4	75	85

25 Wood Carving 26 Octopus Lure

(Des R. Conly. Litho Enschedé)

1982 (5 May). *Handicrafts.* T **25** *and similar vert designs. Multi-coloured. P* 14 × 13½.

81	10 s. Type **25**	..	..	10	15
82	22 s. Bow-drilling sea shell	..	..	15	30
83	34 s. Bowl finishing	..	..	20	40
84	60 s. Basket weaving	..	..	35	70
81/4			*Set of* 4	70	1·40

(Des R. Conly. Litho Questa)

1982 (3 Nov). *Fishing Methods.* T **26** *and similar vert designs. Multicoloured. P* 14.

85	5 s. Type **26**	..	..	15	10
86	18 s. Multiple-hook fishing	..	..	35	20
87	23 s. Ruvettus fishing	..	..	40	25
88	34 s. Netting flyingfish	..	..	45	30
89	63 s. Noose fishing	..	..	55	40
90	75 s. Bonito fishing	..	..	60	45
85/90			*Set of* 6	2·25	1·50

27 Outrigger Canoe 28 Javelin Throwing

(Des R. Conly. Litho Cambec Press, Melbourne)

1983 (4 May). *Transport.* T **27** *and similar horiz designs. Multicoloured. P* 13 × 13½.

91	5 s. Type **27**	..	..	10	10
92	18 s. Wooden whaleboat	..	..	15	15
93	23 s. Aluminium whaleboat	..	..	15	20
94	34 s. *Alia* (fishing catamaran)	..	..	25	25
95	63 s. *Frysna* (freighter)	..	..	35	40
96	75 s. Grumman MacKinnon G-21C Goose flying boat	..	..	45	50
91/6			*Set of* 6	1·25	1·40

(Des R. Conly. Litho Questa)

1983 (2 Nov). *Traditional Pastimes.* T **28** *and similar horiz designs. Multicoloured. P* 14.

97	5 s. Type **28**	..	..	10	10
98	18 s. String game	..	..	15	15
99	23 s. Fire making	..	..	15	20
100	34 s. Shell throwing	..	..	15	25
101	63 s. Hand-ball game	..	..	25	40
102	75 s. Mass wrestling	..	..	30	50
97/102			*Set of* 6	1·00	1·40

OMNIBUS ISSUES

Details, together with prices for complete sets, of the various Omnibus issues from the 1935 Silver Jubilee series to date are included in a special section following Zimbabwe at the end of Volume 2.

29 Planting and Harvesting 30 Convict Tang ("Manini")

(Des R. Conly. Litho J.W.)

1984 (2 May). *Copra Industry.* T **29** *and similar vert designs. Multicoloured. P* 13½ × 13.

103	48 s. Type **29**	..	..	30	40
	a. Horiz strip of 5. Nos. 103/7			1·40	
104	48 s. Husking and splitting	..	..	30	40
105	48 s. Drying	..	..	30	40
106	48 s. Bagging	..	..	30	40
107	48 s. Shipping	..	..	30	40
103/7			*Set of* 5	1·40	1·75

Nos. 103/7 were printed together, *se-tenant*, in horizontal strips of 5 throughout the sheet.

(Des R. Conly. Litho B.D.T.)

1984 (5 Dec). *Fishes.* T **30** *and similar horiz designs. Multicoloured. P* 15 × 14.

108	1 s. Type **30**	..	..	15	10
109	2 s. Flyingfish ("Hahave")	..	..	15	10
110	5 s. Surge Wrasse (" Uloulo")	..	..	20	10
111	9 s. Unicornfish ("Ume ihu")	..	..	20	10
112	23 s. Wrasse ("Lafilafi")	..	..	50	20
113	34 s. Red Snapper ("Fagamea")	..	..	60	25
114	50 s. Yellow-finned Tuna ("Kakahi")	..	..	80	40
115	75 s. Oilfish ("Palu po")	..	..	1·10	55
116	$1 Grey Shark ("Mokoha")	..	..	1·50	70
117	$2 Black Marlin ("Hakula")	..	..	2·00	1·40
108/17			*Set of* 10	6·50	3·25

Examples of Nos. 108/17 are known postmarked at Nukunonu on 23 November 1984.

The 50 s., No. 114 was sold at the "STAMPEX 86" Stamp Exhibition, Adelaide, overprinted "STAMPEX 86 4–10 AUGUST 1986" in three lines. These overprinted stamps were not available from post offices in Tokelau. Used examples come from dealers' stocks subsequently sent to the islands for cancellation.

31 *Ficus tinctoria* ("Mati") 32 Administration Centre, Atafu

(Des R. Conly. Litho Wyatt and Wilson Ltd, Christchurch, N.Z.)

1985 (26 June). *Native Trees.* T **31** *and similar vert designs. Multicoloured. P* 13.

118	5 c. Type **31**	..	..	10	10
119	18 c. *Morinda citrifolia* ("Nonu")	..	..	15	15
120	32 c. Breadfruit Tree ("Ulu")	..	..	20	25
121	48 c. *Pandanus tectorius* ("Fala")	..	..	35	40
122	60 c. *Cordia subcordata* ("Kanava")	..	..	40	45
123	75 c. Coconut Palm ("Niu")	..	..	50	55
118/23			*Set of* 6	1·50	1·60

Nos. 118/23 were issued with matt, almost invisible PVA gum.

(Des R. Conly. Litho Questa)

1985 (4 Dec). *Tokelau Architecture (1st series). Public Buildings.* T **32** *and similar horiz designs. Multicoloured. P* 14.

124	5 c. Type **32**	..	..	10	10
125	18 c. Administration Centre, Nukunonu	..	..	15	15
126	32 c. Administration Centre, Fakaofo	..	..	20	25
127	48 c. Congregational Church, Atafu	..	..	35	40
128	60 c. Catholic Church, Nukunonu	..	..	40	45
129	75 c. Congregational Church, Fakaofo	..	..	50	55
124/9			*Set of* 6	1·50	1·60

33 Atafu Hospital

(Des R. Conly. Litho Cambec Press, Melbourne)

1986 (7 May). *Tokelau Architecture (2nd series). Hospitals and Schools.* T **33** *and similar horiz designs. Multicoloured. P* 13½.

130	5 c. Type **33**	..	..	10	15
131	18 c. St. Joseph's Hospital, Nukunonu	..	..	15	15
132	32 c. Fenuafala Hospital, Fakaofo	..	..	20	30
133	48 c. Matauala School, Atafu	..	..	35	45
134	60 c. Matiti School, Nukunonu	..	..	40	60
135	75 c. Fenuafala School, Fakaofo	..	..	50	90
130/5			*Set of* 6	1·50	2·25

34 Coconut Crab

(Des R. Conly. Litho Questa)

1986 (3 Dec). *Agricultural Livestock.* T **34** *and similar horiz designs. Multicoloured. P* 14.

136	5 c. Type **34**	..	..	10	10
137	18 c. Pigs	..	..	15	15
138	32 c. Chickens	..	..	25	25
139	48 c. Reef Hawksbill Turtle	..	..	40	40
140	60 c. Goats	..	..	45	45
141	75 c. Ducks	..	..	60	60
136/41			*Set of* 6	1·75	1·75

35 *Scaevola taccada* ("Gahu")

(Des R. Conly. Litho Questa)

1987 (6 May). *Tokelau Flora.* T **35** *and similar horiz designs. Multicoloured. P* 14.

142	5 c. Type **35**	..	..	45	50
143	18 c. *Hernandia nymphaeifolia* ("Puka")	..	..	70	80
144	32 c. *Pandanus tectorius* ("Higano")	..	1·00	1·10
145	48 c. *Gardenia taitensis* ("Tialetiale")	..	1·25	1·40
146	60 c. *Pemphis acidula* ("Gagie")	..	1·60	1·75
147	75 c. *Guettarda speciosa* ("Puapua")	..	1·75	1·90
142/7			*Set of* 6	6·00	6·75

36 Javelin-throwing

(Des F. Paulo. Litho Leigh-Mardon Ltd, Melbourne)

1987 (2 Dec). *Tokelau Olympic Sports.* T **36** *and similar horiz designs. Multicoloured. P* 14 × 14½.

148	5 c. Type **36**	..	..	25	30
149	18 c. Shot-putting	..	..	45	50
150	32 c. Long jumping	..	..	70	90
151	48 c. Hurdling	..	..	85	1·10
152	60 c. Sprinting	..	..	1·25	1·75
153	75 c. Wrestling	..	..	1·50	1·90
148/53			*Set of* 6	4·50	5·75

37 Small Boat Flotilla in Sydney Harbour 38 Island Maps and Ministerial Representatives

(Des and litho CPE Australia Ltd, Melbourne)

1988 (30 July). *Bicentenary of Australian Settlement and "Sydpex '88" National Stamp Exhibition, Sydney.* T **37** *and similar square designs. Multicoloured. P* 13.

154	50 c. Type **37**	..	..	1·75	2·00
	a. Horiz strip of 5. Nos. 154/8			8·00	
155	50 c. Sailing ships and liners	..	..	1·75	2·00
156	50 c. Sydney skyline and Opera House	..	1·75	2·00
157	50 c. Sydney Harbour Bridge	..	..	1·75	2·00
158	50 c. Sydney waterfront	..	..	1·75	2·00
154/8			*Set of* 5	8·00	9·00

Nos. 154/8 were printed together, *se-tenant*, in horizontal strips of five throughout the sheet, forming a composite aerial view of the re-enactment of First Fleet's arrival.

(Des F. Paulo. Litho Leigh-Mardon Ltd, Melbourne)

1988 (10 Aug). *Political Development.* T **38** *and similar horiz designs. Multicoloured. P* 14½.

159	5 c. Type **38** (administration transferred to N.Z. Foreign Affairs Ministry, 1975)	..	25	35
160	18 c. General Fono (island assembly) meeting, 1977		35	40
161	32 c. Arms of New Zealand (first visit by New Zealand Prime Minister, 1985)		60	70
162	48 c. U.N. logo (first visit by U.N. representative, 1976)		75	85
163	60 c. Canoe and U.N. logo (first Tokelau delegation to U.N., 1987)		90	1·25
164	75 c. Secretary and N.Z. flag (first islander appointed as Official Secretary, 1987)		1·00	1·25
159/64			*Set of* 6	3·50	4·25

TOKELAU 5c

39 Three Wise Men in
Canoe and Star

(Des F. Paulo. Litho Govt Ptg Office, Wellington)

1988 (7 Dec). *Christmas. T **39** and similar horiz designs
showing Christmas in Tokelau. Multicoloured. P 13½.*

165	5 c. Type 39			25	25
166	20 c. Tokelau Nativity			30	30
167	40 c. Flight to Egypt by canoe			60	60
168	60 c. Children's presents			80	1·00
169	70 c. Christ child in Tokelauan basket			90	1·10
170	$1 Christmas parade			1·10	1·40
165/70			*Set of 6*	3·50	4·25

40 Launching Outrigger   **41** Basketwork
Canoe

(Des F. Paulo. Litho Leigh-Mardon Ltd, Melbourne)

1989 (28 June). *Food Gathering. T **40** and similar horiz
designs. Multicoloured. P 14×14½.*

171	50 c. Type 40			1·40	1·60
	a. Horiz strip of 3. Nos. 171/3			3·75	
172	50 c. Paddling canoe away from shore			1·40	1·60
173	50 c. Fishing punt and sailing canoe			1·40	1·60
174	50 c. Canoe on beach			1·40	1·60
	a. Horiz strip of 3. Nos. 174/6			3·75	
175	50 c. Loading coconuts into canoe			1·40	1·60
176	50 c. Tokelauans with produce			1·40	1·60
171/6			*Set of 6*	7·50	8·50

Nos. 171/3 and 174/6 were each printed together, *se-tenant*, in
horizontal strips of three throughout the sheets. forming
composite designs.

A $3 miniature sheet commemorating the 150th anniversary
of the Penny Black and "Stamp World London 90" International
Stamp Exhibition exists, but was not issued or used by the New
Zealand Post offices on the islands. Examples were subsequently
offered to collectors in January 1994.

(Des F. Paulo. Litho Leigh-Mardon Ltd, Melbourne)

1990 (2 May). *Women's Handicrafts. T **41** and similar
designs. Multicoloured. P 14½.*

177	5 c. Type 41			55	55
178	20 c. Preparing cloth			95	95
179	40 c. Tokelau fabrics			1·40	1·40
180	60 c. Mat weaving			1·75	2·00
181	80 c. Weaving palm fronds			2·50	3·00
182	$1 Basket making			2·75	3·25
177/82			*Set of 6*	9·00	10·00

42 Man with Adze and Wood   **43** Swimming
Blocks

(Des F. Paulo. Litho Wyatt & Wilson, Christchurch)

1990 (1 Aug). *Men's Handicrafts. T **42** and similar horiz
designs. Multicoloured. P 13½.*

183	50 c. Type 42			1·75	2·00
	a. Horiz strip of 3. Nos. 183/5			4·75	
184	50 c. Making fishing boxes			1·75	2·00
185	50 c. Fixing handles to fishing boxes			1·75	2·00
186	50 c. Two men decorating fishing boxes			1·75	2·00
	a. Horiz strip of 3. Nos. 186/8			4·75	
187	50 c. Canoe building (two men)			1·75	2·00
188	50 c. Canoe building (three men)			1·75	2·00
183/8			*Set of 6*	9·50	11·00

Nos. 183/5 and 186/8 were each printed together, *se-tenant*, in
horizontal strips of 3 throughout the sheets, and have matt,
almost invisible, gum.

Under the terms of the Tokelau Post Office Regulations which
came into force on 1 March 1991 the responsibility for providing
postage stamps for the islands passed from New Zealand Post to
the Administrator of Tokelau, based at the Ministry of External
Relations, Wellington.

(Des R. Roberts. Litho Southern Colour Print, Dunedin)

1992 (8 July). *Olympic Games, Barcelona. T **43** and similar
vert designs. Multicoloured. P 13½.*

189	40 c. Type 43			60	60
190	60 c. Longjumping			80	90
191	$1 Volleyball			1·60	1·75
192	$1.80, Running			2·25	3·25
189/92			*Set of 4*	4·75	6·00

44 *Santa Maria*   **45** Queen Elizabeth II in
1953

(Des R. Roberts. Litho Southern Colour Print, Dunedin)

1992 (18 Dec). *500th Anniv of Discovery of America by
Columbus. T **44** and similar horiz designs. Multicoloured.
P 13½.*

193	40 c. Type 44			80	80
194	60 c. Christopher Columbus			1·10	1·25
195	$1.20, Fleet of Columbus			2·50	2·75
196	$1.80, Columbus landing in the New World			3·50	3·75
193/6			*Set of 4*	7·00	7·75

(Des M. Conly. Litho Southern Colour Print, Dunedin)

1993 (8 July). *40th Anniv of Coronation. T **45** and similar
horiz designs. Multicoloured. P 13½.*

197	25 c. Type 45			70	70
198	40 c. Prince Philip			90	90
199	$1 Queen Elizabeth II in 1993			1·60	1·75
200	$2 Queen Elizabeth II and Prince Philip			2·75	3·00
197/200			*Set of 4*	5·50	5·75

46 Bristle-thighed Curlew

(Des M. Conly. Litho Southern Colour Print, Dunedin)

1993 (15 Dec). *Birds of Tokelau. T **46** and similar horiz
designs. Multicoloured. P 13½.*

201	25 c. Type 46			75	75
202	40 c. Red-tailed Tropic Bird			1·10	1·10
203	$1 Eastern Reef Heron			1·75	1·75
204	$2 American Golden Plover			2·50	3·25
201/4			*Set of 4*	5·50	6·25

(Des M. Conly. Litho Southern Colour Print, Dunedin)

1994 (18 Feb). *"Hong Kong '94" International Stamp
Exhibition. Multicoloured. P 14×14½.*

MS205 125×100 mm. As Nos. 201/4 (sold at $5) 5·00 6·00

47 Great Egret ("White Heron")

(Des M. Conly. Litho Southern Colour Print, Dunedin)

1994 (16 Aug). *"Philakorea '94" International Stamp
Exhibition, Seoul. P 12.*

206	47 $2 multicoloured			2·50	3·00
MS207	110×76 mm. No. 206			3·50	3·75

 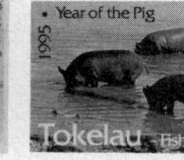

48 Model Outrigger   **49** Fishing Pigs
Canoe

(Des M. Conly. Litho Southern Colour Print, Dunedin)

1994 (19 Dec). *Handicrafts. T **48** and similar horiz designs.
Multicoloured. P 13½.*

208	5 c. Type 48			10	10
209	25 c. Plaited fan			15	20
210	40 c. Plaited baskets			25	30
211	50 c. Fishing box			30	35
212	80 c. Water bottle			50	55
213	$1 Fishing hook			65	70
214	$2 Coconut gourds			1·25	1·40
215	$5 Shell necklace			3·25	3·50
208/15			*Set of 8*	6·25	7·00

(Des M. Conly. Litho Southern Colour Print, Dunedin)

1995 (3 Feb). *Chinese New Year ("Year of the Pig"). Sheet
100×75 mm. P 14×14½.*

MS218 49 $5 multicoloured 6·50 7·00

1995 (3 Feb). *"PostX '95" National Stamp Exhibition,
Auckland. No. **MS**218 optd with "PostX '95" emblem on sheet
margin in red.*

MS219 49 $5 multicoloured 7·00 8·00

50 Pacific Pigeon on Branch   **51** Long-nosed
Butterflyfish

(Des Patricia Altman. Litho Southern Colour Print, Dunedin)

1995 (27 Apr). *Endangered Species. Pacific Pigeon. T **50** and
similar horiz designs. Multicoloured. P 13½.*

220	25 c. Type 50			60	60
221	40 c. On branch (different)			85	85
222	$1 On branch with berries			1·40	1·60
223	$2 Chick in nest			2·40	3·00
220/3			*Set of 4*	4·75	5·50

(Des R. Youmans. Litho Southern Colour Print, Dunedin)

1995 (1 Sept). *Reef Fishes. T **51** and similar horiz designs.
Multicoloured. P 12.*

224	25 c. Type 51			45	55
225	40 c. Emperor Angelfish			70	75
226	$1 Moorish Idol			1·40	1·60
227	$2 Lined Butterflyfish			2·40	3·00
224/7			*Set of 4*	4·50	5·50
MS228	130×90 mm. Lionfish (39×34 mm)			3·25	3·75

No. **MS**228 includes the "Singapore '95" International Stamp
Exhibition logo on the sheet margin.

1995 (1 Sept). *"Singapore '95" International Stamp Exhibition.
No. **MS**218 optd with exhibition emblem in red on sheet
margin.*

MS229 49 $5 multicoloured 5·50 6·50

52 *Danaus plexippus*   **53** Hawksbill Turtle

(Des Patricia Altman. Litho Southern Colour Print, Dunedin)

1995 (16 Oct). *Butterflies and Moths. T **52** and similar vert
designs. Multicoloured. P 12.*

230	25 c. Type 52			65	65
231	40 c. Precis villida samoensis			90	90
232	$1 Hypolimnas bolina			2·00	2·25
233	$2 Euploea lewenii			3·00	3·50
230/3			*Set of 4*	6·00	6·50

(Des Patricia Altman. Litho Southern Colour Print, Dunedin)

1995 (27 Nov). *Year of the Sea Turtle. T **53** and similar horiz
designs. Multicoloured. P 12.*

234	25 c. Type 53			65	65
235	40 c. Leatherback Turtle			90	90
236	$1 Green Turtle			2·00	2·25
237	$2 Loggerhead Turtle			3·00	3·50
234/7			*Set of 4*	6·00	6·50
MS238	130×90 mm. $3 As $2 (50×40 mm)			4·00	5·00

54 Pacific Rat

(Des Patricia Altman. Litho Southern Colour Print, Dunedin)

1996 (19 Feb). *Chinese New Year ("Year of the Rat"). Sheet
128×97 mm. P 12.*

MS239 54 $3 multicoloured 3·25 4·00

COVER PRICES

Cover factors are quoted at the beginning of each
country for most issues to 1945. An explanation of
the system can be found on page x. The factors
quoted do not, however, apply to philatelic covers.

55 Queen Elizabeth
II and Nukunonu

56 Fraser's Dolphin

(Des D. Miller. Litho Enschedé)

1996 (22 Apr). *70th Birthday of Queen Elizabeth II. T* **55** *and
similar vert designs, each incorporating a different
photograph of the Queen. Multicoloured. P* 13½.

240	40 c. Type **55**	..	50	50
241	$1 Atafu at night	..	1·40	1·50
242	$1.25, Atafu	..	1·60	1·75
243	$2 Atafu village ..	..	2·00	2·50
240/3		*Set of* 4	5·00	5·75
MS244	64×66 mm. $3 Queen Elizabeth II	..	3·25	3·75

1996 (18 May). *"CHINA '96" 9th Asian International Stamp
Exhibition, Peking. No.* MS239 *optd with exhibition emblem
on sheet margin in red.*
MS245 128×97 mm. $3 Type **54** .. 3·75 4·50

(Des R. Youmans. Litho Southern Colour Print, Dunedin)

1996 (15 July). *Dolphins. T* **56** *and similar horiz designs.
Multicoloured. P* 14.

246	40 c. Type **56**	..	1·00	1·00
247	$1 Common Dolphin	..	2·50	2·50
248	$1.25, Striped Dolphin	..	2·50	2·50
249	$2 Spotted Dolphin	..	3·50	3·50
246/9		*Set of* 4	8·50	8·50

57 Mole Cowrie

58 Ox

(Des Patricia Altman. Litho Southern Colour Print, Dunedin)

1996 (16 Oct). *Sea Shells. T* **57** *and similar horiz designs.
Multicoloured. P* 12.

250	40 c. Type **57**	..	60	60
251	$1 Humpback Cowrie	..	1·50	1·50
252	$1.25, Eyed Cowrie	..	1·60	1·75
253	$2 Tiger Cowrie ..	..	2·25	2·75
250/3		*Set of* 4	5·50	6·00
MS254	123×83 mm. $3 Humpback Cowrie *(different)* (50×40 *mm*)		3·50	4·00

1996 (16 Oct). *"TAIPEI '96" 10th Asian International Stamp
Exhibition, Taiwan. No.* MS239 *optd with exhibition emblem
on sheet margin in red.*
MS255 128×97 mm. $3 Type **54** .. 3·25 3·75

(Des Patricia Altman. Litho Southern Colour Print, Dunedin)

1997 (12 Feb). *Chinese New Year ("Year of the Ox"). Sheet*
120×78 *mm. P* 15×14½.
MS256 **58** $2 multicoloured .. .. 2·25 2·75

1997 (12 Feb). *"HONG KONG '97" International Stamp
Exhibition. No.* MS256 *optd with "HONG KONG '97 STAMP
EXHIBITION" in gold on sheet margin.*
MS257 120×78 mm. **58** $2 multicoloured .. 2·25 2·75

1997 (29 May). *"Pacific '97" International Stamp Exhibtion,
San Francisco. No.* MS256 *optd with exhibition emblem in red
on sheet margin.*
MS258 120×78 mm. **58** $2 multicoloured .. 2·25 2·75

59 Humpback Whale

60 Church by Lagoon

(Des Patricia Altman. Litho Southern Colour Print, Dunedin)

1997 (10 June). *Humpback Whales. T* **59** *and similar horiz
designs. Multicoloured. P* 12.

259	40 c. Type **59**	..	60	55
260	$1 Family of Humpback Whales	..	1·10	1·10
261	$1.25, Humpback Whale feeding	..	1·40	1·60
262	$2 Humpback whale and calf	..	2·25	2·50
259/62		*Set of* 4	4·75	5·25
MS263	135×87 mm. $3 Head of Humpback Whale		2·75	3·00

(Des R. Youmans. Litho Southern Colour Print, Dunedin)

1997 (17 Sept). *50th Anniv of South Pacific Commission. T* **60**
*and similar horiz designs showing views of Tokelau.
Multicoloured. P* 14.

264	40 c. Type **60**	..	45	45
265	$1 Boy looking across lagoon	..	90	90
266	$1.25, Bungalow on small island	..	1·25	1·50
267	$2 Tokelau from the air	..	1·90	2·25
264/7		*Set of* 4	4·00	4·50

61 Gorgonian Coral and
Emperor Angelfish

62 Tiger

(Des Patricia Altman. Litho Southern Colour Print, Dunedin)

1997 (20 Oct). *Pacific Year of the Coral Reef. T* **61** *and similar
horiz designs. Multicoloured. P* 13½.

268	$1 Type **61**	..	1·00	1·25
	a. Horiz strip of 5. Nos. 268/72	..	4·50	
269	$1 Soft Coral	..	1·00	1·25
270	$1 Mushroom Coral	..	1·00	1·25
271	$1 Staghorn Coral	..	1·00	1·25
272	$1 Staghorn Coral and Moorish Idols	..	1·00	1·25
268/72		*Set of* 5	4·50	5·50

Nos. 268/72 were printed together, *se-tenant*, in horizontal
strips of five with the backgrounds forming a composite design.

(Des Patricia Altman. Litho Southern Colour Print, Dunedin)

1997 (13 Nov). *"Aupex '97" National Stamp Exhibition,
Auckland. No.* MS263 *optd "AUPEX '97 13–16 NOVEMBER
NZ NATIONAL STAMP EXHIBITION" on sheet margin in
black. P* 12.
MS273 135×87 mm. $3 Head of Humpback Whale 2·75 3·00

(Des S. Chan. Litho Southern Colour Print, Dunedin)

1998 (28 Jan). *Chinese New Year ("Year of the Tiger"). Sheet*
130×95 *mm. P* 14×14½.
MS274 **62** $2 multicoloured .. .. 1·75 2·00

(Des D. Miller. Litho Questa)

1998 (31 Mar). *Diana, Princess of Wales Commemoration. Vert
designs as T* **91** *of Kiribati. Multicoloured. P* 14½×14.
275 $1 Carrying yellow bouquet .. 80 85
MS276 145×70 mm. $1 Wearing red polka-dot
dress; $1 Wearing matching pink hat and jacket;
$1 No. 275; $1 In pink and yellow jacket with
flowers *(sold at* $4 + 50 c. *charity premium)* .. 3·50 3·75

63 1948 ½d. Atafu
Village Stamp

64 *Oryctes rhinoceros*

(Des Sea Sky Design Studio. Litho Southern Colour Print,
Dunedin)

1998 (22 June). *50th Anniv of Tokelau Postage Stamps. Sheet,*
105×80 *mm, containing T* **63** *and similar horiz designs.
Multicoloured. P* 14½.
MS277 $1 Type **63**; $1 1948 1d. Nukunono hut
stamp; $1 1948 2d. Fakaofo village stamp .. 2·25 2·40

(Des Patricia Altman. Litho Southern Colour Print, Dunedin)

1998 (23 Aug). *Beetles. T* **64** *and similar horiz designs.
Multicoloured. P* 14.

278	40 c. Type **64**	..	55	55
279	$1 *Tribolium castaneum*	..	1·10	1·10
280	$1.25, *Coccinella repanda*	..	1·25	1·25
281	$2 *Amarygmus hydrophiloides*	..	1·90	2·25
278/81		*Set of* 4	4·25	4·75
MS282	125×86 mm. $3 *Coccinella repanda (different)*		2·25	2·40

65 *Ipomoea pes-caprae*

(Des Patricia Altman. Litho Southern Colour Print, Dunedin)

1998 (18 Nov). *Tropical Flowers. T* **65** *and similar horiz
designs. Multicoloured. P* 14.

283	40 c. Type **65**	..	40	40
284	$1 *Ipomoea littoralis*	..	85	85
285	$1.25, *Scaevola taccada*	..	1·00	1·00
286	$2 *Thespesia populnea*	..	1·60	1·90
283/6		*Set of* 4	3·50	3·75

66 Rabbit

(Des Stan Chan Graphics. Litho Southern Colour Print,
Dunedin)

1999 (16 Feb). *Chinese New Year ("Year of the Rabbit"). Sheet*
105×70 *mm. P* 14.
MS287 **66** $3 multicoloured .. .. 1·90 2·00

67 H.M.S. *Pandora* (frigate)

1999 (19 Mar). *"Australia '99" International Stamp Exhibition,
Melbourne. Sheet* 119×80 *mm. P* 14.
MS288 **67** $3 multicoloured .. .. 1·90 2·00

1999 (27 Apr). *"iBRA '99" International Stamp Exhibition,
Nuremberg. No.* MS287 *optd with the "iBRA" logo on the sheet
margin.*
MS289 105×70 mm. **66** $3 multicoloured .. 1·90 2·00

68 Coconut Crab

69 Lift-off

(Litho Southern Colour Print, Dunedin)

1999 (10 Aug). *Pacific Crabs. T* **68** *and similar horiz designs.
Multicoloured. P* 14½.

290	40 c. Type **68**	..	40	40
291	$1 Ghost Crab	..	85	85
292	$1.25, Land Hermit Crab	..	1·00	1·00
293	$2 Purple Hermit Crab ..	..	1·60	1·90
290/3		*Set of* 4	3·50	3·75
MS294	127×89 mm. $3 Ghost Crab *(different)*		1·90	2·00

(Des N. Shewring. Litho Southern Colour Print, Dunedin)

1999 (31 Aug). *30th Anniv of First Manned Landing on Moon.
T* **69** *and similar vert designs. Multicoloured. P* 13½.

295	25 c. Type **69**	..	40	40
296	50 c. Rocket stage separation	..	60	60
297	75 c. Aldrin deploying experiment	..	70	70
298	$1 Planting the flag	..	85	85
299	$1.25, Separation of command module	..	1·00	1·00
300	$2 Recovery of astronauts	..	1·50	1·75
295/300		*Set of* 6	4·50	4·75
MS301	90×65 mm. $3 Lunar module, Earth and Jupiter ..		1·90	2·00

Nigeria

LAGOS

A British Consul was established at Lagos during 1853 as part of the anti-slavery policy, but the territory was not placed under British administration until occupied by the Royal Navy in August 1861. From 19 February 1866 Lagos was administered with Sierra Leone and from July 1874 as part of Gold Coast. It became a separate colony on 13 January 1886.

Although a postal service had been established by the British G.P.O. in April 1852 no postal markings were supplied to Lagos until 1859. The British G.P.O. retained control of the postal service until June 1863, when it became the responsibility of the colonial authorities.

CROWNED-CIRCLE HANDSTAMPS

CC 1

CC1 CC 1 LAGOS (19.12.1859).. .. *Price on cover* £1600
First recorded use of No. CC1 is 12 December 1871. It is later known used as a cancellation.

PRICES FOR STAMPS ON COVER

Nos. 1/9	*from* × 10	
Nos. 10/26	*from* × 8	
Nos. 27/9		
Nos. 30/8	*from* × 10	
Nos. 39/41		
No. 42	*from* × 20	
Nos. 44/50	*from* × 8	
Nos. 51/3	—	
Nos. 54/60	*from* × 8	
Nos. 61/3	—	

PRINTERS. All the stamps of Lagos were typographed by D.L.R.

1

1874 (10 June)–**75.** *Wmk Crown CC. P* 12½.

1	1	1d. lilac-mauve	55·00	30·00
2		2d. blue	55·00	26·00
3		3d. red-brown (2.75)	95·00	42·00
4		3d. red-brown and chestnut	80·00	48·00
5		4d. carmine	65·00	40·00
6		6d. blue-green	85·00	11·00
8		1s. orange (value 15½ mm) (2.75)	£350	£140
9		1s. orange (value 16½ mm) (7.75)	£250	60·00
1/9			*Set of* 6 £550	£180

1876–79. *Wmk Crown CC. P* 14.

10	1	1d. lilac-mauve	38·00	18·00
11		2d. blue	38·00	12·00
12		3d. red-brown	95·00	18·00
13		3d. chestnut	£110	35·00
14		4d. carmine	£170	11·00
		a. Wmk sideways	£950	£130
15		6d. green	90·00	6·00
16		1s. orange (value 16½ mm long) (1879)	£500	80·00
10/16			*Set of* 6 £850	£130

1882 (June). *Wmk Crown CA. P* 14.

17	1	1d. lilac-mauve	18·00	10·00
18		2d. blue	£130	4·75
19		3d. chestnut	14·00	5·00
20		4d. carmine	£120	12·00
17/20			*Set of* 4 £250	29·00

1884 (Dec)–**86.** *New values and colours. Wmk Crown CA. P* 14.

21	1	½d. dull green (1885)	2·00	80
22		1d. rose-carmine	2·00	80
		w. Wmk inverted	—	75·00
23		2d. grey	55·00	5·00
24		4d. pale violet	95·00	8·50
25		6d. olive-green	8·00	35·00
26		1s. grey (3.85)	7·00	20·00
27		2s. 6d. olive-black (1886)	£275	£250
28		5s. blue (1886)	£475	£400
29		10s. purple-brown (1886)	£1200	£800
21/9			*Set of* 9 £1800	£1300
27/9 Optd "Specimen"			*Set of* 3 £400	

We would warn collectors against clever forgeries of Nos. 27 to 29 on genuinely watermarked paper.

2½ PENNY	A
2½ PENNY	B

1887 (Mar)–**1902.** *Wmk Crown CA. P* 14.

30	1	2d. dull mauve and blue	2·75	2·00
31		2½d. ultramarine (A) (1891)	3·50	1·75
		a. Larger letters of value (B)	22·00	17·00
		b. *Blue* (A)	80·00	50·00
32		3d. dull mauve and chestnut (4.91)	2·50	3·25
33		4d. dull mauve and black	2·25	1·75
34		5d. dull mauve and green (2.94)	2·00	11·00
35		6d. dull mauve and mauve	4·75	3·00
		a. *Dull mauve and carmine* (10.02)	4·75	12·00
36		7½d. dull mauve and carmine (2.94)	2·00	26·00
37		10d. dull mauve and yellow (2.94)	3·25	13·00
38		1s. yellow-green and black	5·00	23·00
		a. *Blue-green and black*	4·75	24·00
39		2s. 6d. green and carmine	22·00	75·00
40		5s. green and blue	38·00	£140
41		10s. green and brown	65·00	£180
30/41			*Set of* 12 £130	£425
30/41 Optd "Specimen"			*Set of* 12 £225	

HALF PENNY

(2)   3

1893 (2 Aug). *No. 33 surch with T* **2** *locally.*

42	1	½d. on 4d. dull mauve and black	4·00	2·50
		a. Surch double	55·00	55·00
		b. Surch treble	£120	
		c. Error. ½d. on 2d. (No. 30)	—£15000	

There were two separate settings of No. 42. The most common, of which there were five separate printings, shows "HALF PENNY" 16 mm long and was applied as a horizontal pair or triplet. The scarcer setting, also applied as a triplet, shows "HALF PENNY" 16½ mm long.

Three examples of No. 42c are known, two unused and one used. Only the latter is in private hands.

1904 (22 Jan–Nov). *Wmk Crown CA. P* 14.

44	3	½d. dull green and green	1·50	5·50
45		1d. purple and black/*red*	1·00	15
46		2d. dull purple and blue	6·00	7·00
47		2½d. dull purple and blue/*blue* (B)	1·00	1·60
		aw. Wmk inverted	—	55·00
		b. Smaller letters of value as A	4·50	8·50
		bw. Wmk inverted		
48		3d. dull purple and brown	2·00	1·75
49		6d. dull purple and mauve	35·00	10·00
50		1s. green and black	35·00	42·00
51		2s. 6d. green and carmine	80·00	£180
52		5s. green and blue	£150	£275
53		10s. green and brown (Nov)	£275	£750
44/53			*Set of* 10 £500	£1100
44/53 Optd "Specimen"			*Set of* 10 £180	

1904–06. *Wmk Mult Crown CA. Ordinary paper. P* 14.

54	3	½d. dull green and green (30.10.04)	7·50	2·50
		a. Chalk-surfaced paper (12.3.06)	9·50	1·75
		w. Wmk inverted		
55		1d. purple and black/*red* (22.10.04)	6·00	10
		a. Chalk-surfaced paper (21.9.05)	1·25	10
		aw. Wmk inverted	—	55·00
56		2d. dull purple and blue (2.05)	2·25	1·75
		a. Chalk-surfaced paper (25.9.06)	13·00	6·50
		aw. Wmk inverted	80·00	
57		2½d. dull purple and blue/*blue* (B) (*chalk-surfaced paper*) (13.10.05)	1·75	16·00
		a. Smaller letters of value as A	55·00	£120
58		3d. dull purple and brown (27.4.05)	3·50	90
		a. Chalk-surfaced paper (2.8.06)	15·00	1·75
		w. Wmk inverted		
59		6d. dull purple and mauve (31.10.04)	6·50	2·00
		a. Chalk-surfaced paper (1.3.06)	4·25	1·25
		w. Wmk inverted		
60		1s. green and black (15.10.04)	12·00	15·00
		a. Chalk-surfaced paper (4.06)	20·00	2·25
		w. Wmk inverted		
61		2s. 6d. green and carmine (3.12.04)	13·00	42·00
		a. Chalk-surfaced paper (21.10.06)	32·00	42·00
62		5s. green and blue (1.05)	22·00	95·00
		a. Chalk-surfaced paper (21.10.06)	50·00	£130
63		10s. green and brown (3.12.04)	55·00	£180
		a. Chalk-surfaced paper (12.3.06)	75·00	£180
54/63			*Set of* 10 £110	£300

Lagos was incorporated into the Colony and Protectorate of Southern Nigeria, previously formed from Niger Coast Protectorate and part of the Niger Company territories, on 16 February 1906. Stamps of Lagos were then authorised for use throughout Southern Nigeria.

NIGER COAST PROTECTORATE

OIL RIVERS PROTECTORATE

A British consulate for the Bights of Benin and Biafra was established in 1849 on the off-shore Spanish island of Fernando Po. In 1853 the appointment was divided with a consul for the Bight of Benin at Lagos. The consulate for the Bight of Biafra was transferred to Old Calabar in 1882.

A British protectorate was proclaimed over the coastal area, with the exceptions of the colony of Lagos and the centre of the Niger delta, on 5 June 1885. It was not, however, until July 1891 that steps were taken to set up an administration with a consul-general at Old Calabar and vice-consuls at some of the river ports.

The consulate-general at Old Calabar and the vice-consulates at Benin, Bonny, Brass, Forcados and Opobo acted as collection and distribution centres for mail from November 1891, but were not recognised as post offices until 20 July 1892.

For a few months from July 1892 local administrative handstamps, as Type Z **1**, were in use either as obliterators or in conjunction with the c.d.s.

Z 1

These oval handstamps are usually found on the 1892 overprinted issue, but the following are known on unoverprinted stamps of Great Britain:

1892

BENIN

Stamps of GREAT BRITAIN *cancelled with oval postmark, Type* Z **1**, *inscribed* "BENIN".

Z1	2½d. purple/*blue* (V.)	£1000

BONNY

Stamps of GREAT BRITAIN *cancelled with oval postmark, Type* Z **1**, *inscribed* "BONNY".

Z2	2½d. purple/*blue* (V.)	£1000

BRASS RIVER

Stamps of GREAT BRITAIN *cancelled with oval postmark, Type* Z **1**, *inscribed* "BRASS".

Z3	2½d. purple/*blue* (Blk.)	£750

OLD CALABAR RIVER

Stamps of GREAT BRITAIN *cancelled with oval postmark, Type* Z **1**, *inscribed* "OLD CALABAR".

Z4	2½d. purple/*blue* (Blk.)	£750

Stamps of GREAT BRITAIN *cancelled* "BRITISH VICE-CONSULATE OLD CALABAR" *within double-lined circle.*

Z5	2½d. purple/*blue* (V.)	£450
Z6	5d. dull purple and blue (V.)	

For later use of Type Z **1** and the circular Vice-Consulate marks see note beneath No. 6.

Z 2.

Unoverprinted stamps of Great Britain remained officially valid for postage in the Protectorate until 30 September 1892, but were available from post offices in the Niger Company Territories up to the end of 1899. The two areas were so closely linked geographically that offices in the Protectorate continued to accept letters franked with Great Britain stamps until the reorganisation of 1900. The listing below covers confirmed examples, known on cover or piece, the prices quoted being for the latter.

1892 to 1899

Stamps of GREAT BRITAIN *cancelled with circular postmarks as Type* Z **2**.

BENIN RIVER

Z 7	2d. green and carmine	
Z 8	2½d. purple/*blue*	£500
Z 9	3d. purple/*yellow*	£500
Z10	5d. dull purple and blue	
Z11	1s. green	

BONNY RIVER

Z12	½d. vermilion	£350
Z12a	1d. lilac	£300
Z13	2½d. purple/*blue*	£250
Z14	5d. dull purple and blue	£350
Z15	6d. deep purple/*red*	£350

BRASS RIVER

Z16	1½d. dull purple and green	£750
Z17	2½d. purple/*blue*	£650
Z17a	2½d. purple/*blue* (squared-circle cancellation)	£850
Z18	6d. purple/*red*	£700

FORCADOS RIVER

Z19	1d. lilac	£550
Z20	2½d. purple/*blue*	
Z21	5d. dull purple and blue (m/s cancellation)	
Z22	10d. dull purple and carmine	

OLD CALABAR RIVER

Z23	½d. vermilion	£300
Z24	1d. lilac	£250
Z25	2½d. dull purple and green	£350
Z26	2d. green and vermilion	£350
Z27	2½d. purple/*blue*	£250
Z28	5d. dull purple and blue	£350
Z29	6d. purple/*red*	£350
Z30	1s. green	£450

OPOBO RIVER

Z31	2½d. purple/*blue*		£300
Z32	10d. dull purple and carmine		£600

Some later covers are known franked with G.B. stamps, but the origin of the stamps involved is uncertain.

PRICES FOR STAMPS ON COVER

Nos. 1/6	*from* × 12
Nos. 7/36	*from* × 4
Nos. 37/44	—
Nos. 45/50	*from* × 10
Nos. 51/6	*from* × 12
Nos. 57/65	*from* × 3
Nos. 66/73	*from* × 12

BRITISH PROTECTORATE

(1)   (2)

OIL RIVERS

1892 (20 July)–94. *Nos. 172, 197, 200/1, 207a and 211 of Great Britain optd by D.L.R. with T* **1.**

1	½d. vermilion		9·00	5·00
2	1d. lilac		5·50	6·50
	a. Opt reversed "OIL RIVERS" at top	£4250		
	b. Bisected (½d.) (on cover)		† £2500	
3	2d. grey-green and carmine		18·00	8·00
	a. Bisected (1d.) (on cover)		† £2500	
4	2½d. purple/*blue*		6·50	2·25
5	5d. dull purple and blue (Die II (No. 207a)	7·50	7·50
	a. On Die I (No. 207)			
6	1s. dull green		55·00	75·00
1/6		*Set of* 6	90·00	90·00
1/6 H/S "Specimen"		*Set of* 6 £250		

Nos. 2b and 3a were used at Bonny River during August and September 1894.

Die II of the 5d. shows thin vertical lines to the right of "5d.". On Die I there are square dots in this position.

OVAL HANDSTAMPS. In addition to Nos. Z1/4 postmarks as Type **Z 1** are also known used on the 1892–94 overprinted issue from the following offices:

Bakana (Nos. 2, 4/6)
Benin (Nos. 1/6)
Bonny (No. 2)
Brass (Nos. 3/5)
Buguma (Nos. 4 and 6)
Old Calabar (No. 4)
Opobo (Nos. 1/3)
Sombreiro River (Nos. 1/6)

The Vice-Consulate marks, as No. Z5/6, are also known struck on examples of No. 4 from Bonny, Forcados or Old Calabar.

Nos. 2 to 6 surcharged locally

1893 (3 Sept). *Issued at Old Calabar. Surch with T* **2** *and then bisected.*

7	½d. on half of 1d. (R.)		£150	£140
	a. Unsevered pair		£450	£425
	ab. Surch inverted and dividing line reversed (unsevered pair)	—	£8500
	b. Surch reversed (dividing line running from left to right) (unsevered pair)	—	£8500
	c. Straight top to "1" in ½	£350	£350
	d. "½" omitted			
	e. Surch double (unsevered pair with normal)	—	£1600
	f. Vert *se-tenant* pair. Nos. 7a/8a	—£11000
8	½d. on half of 1d. (V.)		£3750	£3500
	a. Unsevered pair		£9000	£8500
	b. Surch double (pair)		£14000	

The surcharge was applied in a setting covering one horizontal row at a time. Violet ink was used for the top row in the first sheet, but was then replaced with red.

HALF PENNY.   HALF PENNY.

(3)   (4)

In T 3 "HALF" measures 9½ mm and "PENNY" 12½ mm with space 1½ mm between the words. Bar 14½ mm ending below the stop. The "F" is nearly always defective.

In T 4 "HALF" is 8½ mm, "PENNY" 12½ mm, spacing 2½ mm, and bar 16 mm, extending beyond the stop.

HALF PENNY.   HALF PENNY

5 (Stop after "N")   6 (No stop after "N")

In T 5 the "P" and "Y" are raised, and the space between the words is about 4 mm. Bar is short, approx 13½ mm. T **6** is similar but without the stop after "N".

Half Penny   *Half Penny*

(7)   (8)

In T **7** the "a" and "e" are narrow and have a short upward terminal hook. The "l" has a very small hook. The letters "nny" have curved serifs, and the distance between the words is 5½ mm.

In T **8** the "a" and "e" are wider. The "l" has a wider hook. The letters "nny" have straight serifs, and the distance between the words is 4¼ mm.

HALF PENNY.   *HALF PENNY*

(9)   (10)

1893 (Dec). *Issued at Old Calabar. Nos. 3/4 handstamped.*

(a) With T **3**

9	½d. on 2d. (V.)		£600	£300
	a. Surch inverted		£4000	
	b. Surch diagonal (up or down)	£2250	
	c. Surch vertical (up or down)	£2750	
10	½d. on 2½d. (Verm.)		£8500	
10a	½d on 2½d. (C.)		£20000	

(b) With T **4**

11	½d. on 2½d. (G.)		£250	£225
	a. Surch double		£2000	£2000
	b. Surch diagonally inverted	£2750	
12	½d. on 2½d. (Verm.)		£600	£300
13	½d. on 2½d. (C.)		£350	£325
	a. Surch omitted (in pair)	£3500	
14	½d. on 2½d. (B.)		£325	£400
15	½d. on 2½d. (Blk.)		£3500	
	a. Surch inverted		£5500	
	b. Surch diagonal inverted (up or down)	£4000	
16	½d. on 2½d. (B.-Blk.)		£3250	

(c) With T **5**

17	½d. on 2½d. (Verm.)		£600	£200
	a. Surch double		—	£1300
	b. Surch vertical (up)		—	£2750

(d) With T **6**

18	½d. on 2d. (V.)		£600	£350
19	½d. on 2½d. (Verm.)		£275	£300
	a. Surch inverted		£2250	
	b. Surch double		—	£1600
	c. Surch diagonal (up or down)	£1400	
	d. Surch omitted (in strip of 3)	£11000	
	e. Surch vertical (up or down)	£1800	
	f. Surch diagonal, inverted (up or down)	£1800	

(e) With T **7**

20	½d. on 2d. (V.)		£300	£225
	a. Surch double		—	£5500
	b. Surch vertical (up or down)	£2500	
	c. Surch diagonal (up or down)	£2000	
	d. Surch diagonal (inverted)	£3250	
	e. Surch inverted			
21	½d. on 2½d. (Verm.)		£275	£180
	a. Surch double		£4000	
	b. Surch vertical (up or down)	£1800	
	c. Surch inverted		£2250	
	d. Surch diagonal (up or down)	£1300	
	e. Surch diagonal, inverted (up)	£3250	
22	½d. on 2½d. (B.)		£8500	£8500
23	½d. on 2½d. (C.)		£8000	
24	½d. on 2½d. (V.)		£4000	

(f) With T **8**

25	½d. on 2½d. (Verm.)		£425	£550
	a. Surch diagonal (up)	£1900	
26	½d. on 2½d. (B.)		£20000	
27	½d. on 2½d. (G.)		£350	£450
	a. Surch double		£5000	
28	½d. on 2½d. (C.)		£15000	£15000

(g) With T **9**

29	½d. on 2d. (V.)		£300	£325
30	½d. on 2d. (B.)		£1200	£600
	a. Surch double			
31	½d. on 2½d. (Verm.)		£450	£500
	a. Surch double			
32	½d. on 2½d. (B.)		£300	£300
33	½d. on 2½d. (G.)		£300	£350
	a. Surch double (G.)	£1600	
	b. Surch double (G. + Verm.)	£3750	
34	½d. on 2½d. (V.)		£3750	

(h) With T **10**

35	½d. on 2½d. (G.)		£400	£450
36	½d. on 2½d. (Verm.)		£5500	

Various types of surcharges on Nos. 9 to 36 were printed on the same sheet, and different types in different colours may be found *se-tenant* (Prices, *from* £1700 *per pair, unused*).

One Shilling   5/-

(11)   (12)

1893 (Dec). *Issued at Old Calabar. Nos. 3 and 5/6 handstamped.*

(a) With T **11**

37	1s. on 2d. (V.)		£400	£350
	a. Surch inverted		£4250	
	b. Surch vertical (up or down)	£3500	
	c. Surch diagonal (up or down)	£2500	
	d. Surch diagonal, inverted (up or down)	£4000	
	e. Pair, Nos. 37 and 38	£2000	
38	1s. on 2d. (Verm.)		£550	£3750
	a. Surch inverted		£6000	
	b. Surch diagonal (up or down)	£4000	
	c. Surch vertical (up or down)	£6000	

39	1s. on 2d. (Blk.)		£5500	
	a. Surch inverted		£10000	
	b. Surch vertical (up or down)	£8500	
	c. Surch diagonal (up or down)	£6500	

(b) As T **12**

40	5s. on 2d. (V.)		£9000	£10000
	a. Surch inverted		£14000	
	b. Surch vertical (up or down)	£14000	£14000
	c. Surch diagonal (down)	£14000	
41	10s. on 5d. (Verm.)		£6000	£8000
	a. Surch inverted		£13000	
	b. Surch vertical (up or down)	£13000	
	c. Surch diagonal (down)			
42	20s. on 1s. (V.)		£70000	
	a. Surch inverted		£85000	
43	20s. on 1s. (Verm.)		£70000	
44	20s. on 1s. (Blk.)		£70000	

There are two main settings of the "One Shilling" surcharge:—

Type A. The "O" is over the "hi" of "Shilling" and the downstrokes on the "n" in "One", if extended, would meet the "ll" of "Shilling". The "g" is always raised. Type A is known in all three colours from one sheet of 120.

Type B. The "O" is over the first "i" of "Shilling" and the downstrokes of the "n" would meet the "li" of "Shilling". Type B is known in violet (two sheets) and vermilion (one sheet).

NIGER COAST PROTECTORATE

The protectorate was extended into the interior and the name changed to Niger Coast Protectorate on 12 May 1893.

PERFORATION. There are a number of small variations in the perforation of the Waterlow issues of 1893 to 1898 which were due to irregularity of the pins rather than different perforators.

In the following lists, stamps perf 12, 12½, 13 or compound are described as perf 12–13, stamps perf 13½, 14 or compound are described as perf 13½–14 and those perf 14½, 15 or compound are listed as perf 14½–15. In addition the 13½–14 perforation exists compound with 14½–15 and with 12–13, whilst perf 15½–16 comes from a separate perforator.

13   14

(Des G. D. Drummond. Recess Waterlow)

1894 (1 Jan). *T* **13** (*with* "OIL RIVERS" *obliterated and* "NIGER COAST" *in top margin*). *Various frames. No wmk. Thick and thin papers. P* 14½–15.

45	½d. vermilion		4·00	3·75
	a. Perf 13½–14		6·00	6·00
46	1d. pale blue		5·50	3·25
	a. Bisected (½d.) (on cover)	† £550	
	b. *Dull blue*		3·75	3·25
	ba. Bisected (½d.) (on cover)	† £450	
	c. Perf 13½–14		4·00	
	d. Perf 13½–14, comp 12–13			
47	2d. green		23·00	20·00
	a. Imperf between (horiz pair)	† £4250	
	b. Bisected (1d.) (on cover)	† £700	
	c. Perf 14½–15, comp 12–13			
	d. Perf 13½–14		18·00	13·00
	e. Perf 13½–14, comp 12–13	30·00	27·00
	d. Perf 12–13			
48	2½d. carmine-lake		8·00	3·50
	a. Perf 13½–14		10·00	8·00
	b. Perf 13½–14, comp 12–13			
	c. Perf 12–13			
49	5d. grey-lilac		15·00	12·00
	a. *Lilac* (1894)		13·00	16·00
	b. Perf 13½–14		13·00	13·00
50	1s. black		14·00	12·00
	a. Perf 14½–15, comp 12–13			
	b. Perf 13½–14		22·00	18·00
	c. Perf 13½–14, comp 12–13	26·00	
45/50		*Set of* 6	55·00	42·00

There were three printings of each value, in November 1893, Jan 1894 and March 1894.

Nos. 46a, 46ba and 47b were used at Bonny River during August and September 1894.

(Recess Waterlow)

1894 (May). *T* **14** (*various frames*). *No wmk. P* 14½–15.

51	½d. yellow-green		4·50	4·50
	a. *Deep green*		5·00	4·50
	b. Perf 14½–15, comp 13½–14			
	c. Perf 13½–14		6·00	7·00
	d. Perf 13½–14, comp 12–13	16·00	
52	1d. orange-vermilion		15·00	10·00
	a. *Vermilion*		11·00	7·00
	b. Bisected diagonally (½d.) (on cover)	† £500	
	c. Perf 15½–16			
	d. Perf 13½–14		16·00	
	e. Perf 13½–14, comp 12–13			
53	2d. lake		25·00	6·50
	a. Bisected diagonally (1d.) (on cover)			
	b. Perf 13½–14		26·00	6·50
	c. Perf 13½–14, comp 12–13	32·00	
54	2½d. blue		13·00	3·75
	a. *Pale blue*		8·50	7·50
	b. Perf 13½–14		17·00	
55	5d. purple		6·00	5·50
	a. *Deep violet*		6·00	5·50
56	1s. black		30·00	15·00
	a. Perf 13½–14		30·00	7·00
	b. Perf 13½–14, comp 12–13	30·00	
51/6		*Set of* 6	75·00	30·00

Nos. 52b and 53a were used at Bonny River during August and September 1894.

| | ½ (15) | 1 (16) | ONE HALF PENNY (17) |

1894. *Provisionals. Issued at Opobo.*

(a) Nos. 46b and 46 *bisected vertically and surch with T 15* (May–June)

57	"½" on half of 1d dull blue (R.) (May)	.. £1000 £375
	a. Surch inverted (in strip of 3 with normals)	£9000
58	"½" on half of 1d. pale blue (R.) (June)	.. £700 £275
	a. Surch tête-bêche (pair)	
	b. Surcharge inverted	.. £3500

(b) No. 3 *bisected vertically and surch*

(i) With T 16 (12 mm high) (June–Oct)

59	"1" on half of 2d. (Verm.)	.. £1400 £275
	a. Surch double	.. £2500 £1200
	b. Surch inverted	— £1500
	c. Unsevered pair	† —

(ii) Smaller "1" (4¾ mm high)

| 60 | "1" on half of 2d. (C.) | —£4250 |

(iii) Smaller "1" (3¾ mm high)

| 61 | "1" on half of 2d. (C.) | |

Nos. 60 and 61 exist *se-tenant.* (Price £20000 used)

(c) No. 52a *bisected, surch with T 15 (Aug–Sept)*

62	½ on half of 1d. vermilion (Blk.)	.. £3000 £750
63	½ on half of 1d. vermilion (V.)	.. £2000 £450
64	½ on half of 1d. vermilion (B.)	.. £1700 £350
	a. "½" double	—£2500

The stamp is found divided down the middle and also diagonally.

1894 (10 Aug). *Issued at Old Calabar. No. 54 surch with T 17 and two bars through value at foot.*

65	½d. on 2½d. blue	£350 £225
	a. Surch double	.. £2750 £1500
	b. "OIE" for "ONE"	.. £1500 £1000
	c. Ditto. Surch double	—£3750

There are eight types in the setting of Type 17, arranged in a horizontal row. No. 65b occurred on No. 8 in the setting at some point during surcharging.

(Recess Waterlow)

1897 (Mar)–98. As T 14 *(various frames). Wmk Crown CA. P 14½–15.*

66	½d. green (7.97)	.. .. .. 3·25 1·50
	a. Sage-green	.. .. 4·00 2·25
	b. Perf 13½–14	.. .. 2·75 3·00
	c. Perf 15½–16	.. .. 12·00 6·50
	d. Perf 13½–14, comp 12–13	.. 16·00
	x. Wmk reversed	.. 75·00
67	1d. orange-vermilion	.. .. 3·75 1·50
	a. Vermilion	.. .. 3·75 1·50
	b. Imperf vert (horiz pair)	£4000
	c. Perf 15½–16	.. .. 8·00
	d. Perf 13½–14	.. .. 2·50 2·75
	e. Perf 13½–14, comp 12–13	— 10·00
68	2d. lake (7.97)	.. .. 1·75 1·25
	a. Perf 15½–16	.. .. 4·00 2·25
	b. Perf 13½–14	.. .. 4·00 3·25
	c. Perf 13½–14, comp 12–13	.. 21·00
	x. Wmk reversed	.. 75·00
69	2½d. slate-blue (8.97)	.. 7·00 2·00
	a. Deep bright blue	.. 7·50 1·50
	b. Perf 13½–14	.. 6·00 3·75
	w. Wmk inverted	
70	5d. red-violet (p 13½–14) (1898)	8·50 55·00
	a. Purple	.. 8·50 60·00
	b. Perf 13½–14, comp 12–13	.. 18·00
71	6d. yellow-brown (6.98)	.. 7·00 6·50
	a. Perf 13½–14	.. 8·50
	b. Perf 15½–16	— 15·00
	x. Wmk reversed	
72	1s. black (1898)	.. 15·00 26·00
	a. Perf 13½–14	.. 14·00 26·00
	b. Perf 13½–14, comp 12–13	.. 32·00
73	2s. 6d. olive-bistre (6.98)	.. 42·00
	a. Perf 15½–16	.. 42·00
	b. Perf 13½–14	.. 22·00 75·00
74	10s. deep violet (6.98)	.. 90·00 £160
	a. Bright violet	.. 90·00 £160
	b. Perf 13½–14	.. 80·00 £160
66/74		Set of 9 £130 £275
71, 73/4 Optd "Specimen"		Set of 3 £225

Owing to temporary shortages in Southern Nigeria, the above issue was again in use at various times from 1902 until 1907.

On 1 January 1900 the Niger Coast Protectorate together with the southern portion of the Niger Company Territories became the protectorate of Southern Nigeria.

NIGER COMPANY TERRITORIES

Following the development of trade along the Niger, British commercial interests formed the United African Company in 1879 which became the National African Company in 1882 and the Royal Niger Company in 1886. A charter was granted to the Company in the same year to administer territory along the Rivers Niger and Benue over which a British protectorate had been proclaimed in June 1885. The Company's territories extended to the Niger delta to provide access to the interior.

Post Offices were opened at Akassa (1887), Burutu (1896), Lokoja (1899) and Abutshi (1899). The stamps of Great Britain were used from 1888.

On the establishment of postal services in 1887 the Company arranged with the British G.P.O. that unstamped mail marked with their handstamps would be delivered in Great Britain, the recipients only being charged the normal rate of postage from West Africa. This system was difficult to administer, however, so the British authorities agreed in 1888 to the supply of G.B. stamps for use at the Company post offices.

Initially the stamps on such covers were left uncancelled until the mail arrived in the United Kingdom, the Company handstamp being struck elsewhere on the address side. This method continued

to be used until early 1896, although a number of covers from the twelve months prior to that date do show the Company handstamp cancelling the stamps. Some of these covers were later recancelled on arrival in Great Britain. From May 1896 the postage stamps were cancelled in the Niger Territories.

In the following listings no attempt has been made to cover the use of the Company marks on the reverse of envelopes.

Dates given are those of earliest known postmarks. Colour of postmarks in brackets. Where two or more colours are given, price is for cheapest. Illustrations are reduced to two-thirds linear of the actual size.

Stamps of GREAT BRITAIN cancelled as indicated below.

ABUTSHI

1899. *Cancelled as T 8, but inscribed "THE ROYAL NIGER CO. C. & L. ABUTSHI" with "CUSTOMS (date) OFFICE" in central oval.*

Z1	½d. vermilion (V.)	.. .. £500
Z2	1d. lilac (V.)	.. .. £375
Z3	2½d. purple/blue (V.)	.. .. £500
Z4	5d. dull purple and blue (V.)	.. .. £550
Z5	10d. dull purple and carmine (V.)	.. £650
Z6	2s. 6d. deep lilac (V.)	.. .. £750

AKASSA

The listings for Nos. Z7/15a are for *covers* on which the Akassa handstamp appears on the front, but is *not* used as a cancellation for the G.B. stamps. Examples of Nos. Z16/26 occur, from 1895–96, with the handstamp struck on the front of the cover away from the stamps, or, from 1896, used as a cancellation. The prices quoted are for *single stamps* showing the cancellation; covers from either period being worth considerably more. On Nos. Z29/42b the handstamp was used as a cancellation and the prices quoted are for *single stamps*.

1888–90. *Cancelled as T 3, but with Maltese cross each side of "AKASSA". Size 36×22 mm.*

| Z7 | 6d. deep purple/red (V.) | .. .. £1100 |

1889–94. *Size 39×24 mm.*

Z8	1	2½d. purple/blue (V.)	.. .. £600
Z9		3d. purple/yellow (V.)	..
Z10		5d. dull purple and blue (V.)	..
Z11		6d. deep purple/red (V.)	.. .. £400
Z12		10d. dull purple and carmine (V.)	..
Z12a		1s. green (V.)	..
Z13		2s. 6d. lilac (V.)	

1894–95.

Z14	2	1d. lilac (V.)	.. .. £350
Z15		2½d. purple/lilac (V.)	..
Z15a		2s. 6d. lilac (V.)	

1895. *Size 39×25 mm.*

| Z16 | 3 | 2½d. purple/blue (V.) | .. .. |

1895–99.

Z17	4	½d. vermilion (V.)	.. .. 65·00
Z18		1d. lilac (V.)	.. .. 55·00
Z19		2d. green and vermilion (V.)	.. £350
Z20		2½d. purple/blue (V.)	.. 35·00
Z21		3d. purple/yellow (V.)	.. £225
Z22		5d. dull purple and blue (V.)	.. 48·00
Z23		6d. deep purple/red (V.)	.. £225
Z24		9d. dull purple and blue (V.)	.. £300
Z25		10d. dull purple and carmine (V.)	80·00
Z26		2s. 6d. deep lilac (V.)	.. £190

1897–99.

Z29	5	½d. vermilion (V.)	.. .. 48·00
Z30		1d. lilac (V.)	.. .. 42·00
		a. "RECD" for year in postmark	.. £500
Z31		2d. green and vermilion (V.)	.. £180
Z32		2½d. purple/blue (V.)	.. 48·00
		a. "RECD" for year in postmark (1898)	£500
Z33		3d. purple/yellow (V.)	.. £170
Z34		4d. green and brown (V.)	.. £225
Z35		4½d. green and carmine (V.)	.. £700
Z36		5d. dull purple and blue (V.)	.. 60·00
Z37		6d. deep purple/red (V.)	.. £190
Z38		9d. dull purple and blue (V.)	.. £325
Z39		10d. dull purple and carmine (V.)	£150
Z40		1s. green (V.)	.. £600
Z41		2s. 6d. deep lilac (V.)	.. £275

1899. *Cancelled as T 7, but inscribed "AKASSA".*

| Z42 | 5d. dull purple and blue (V.) | .. £1000 |

1899. *Cancelled as T 4, but "CUSTOMS DEPT" in place of "POST OFFICE".*

| Z42a | 1d. lilac (V.) | .. .. £600 |
| Z42b | 2½d. purple/blue (V.) | .. .. £600 |

BURUTU

1896–99. *Cancelled as T 6, "BURUTU" in sans-serif caps. Size 44×24 mm.*

Z43	6	½d. vermilion (V., Blk.)	.. 85·00
Z44		1d. lilac (V., Blk.)	.. 75·00
Z45		1½d. dull purple and green (V.)	.. £300
Z46		2d. green and carmine (V.)	.. £180
Z47		2½d. purple/blue (V., Blk.)	.. 35·00
Z48		3d. purple/yellow (V., Blk.)	.. £180
Z49		4d. green and brown (V.)	.. £180
Z50		5d. dull purple and blue (V., Blk.)	65·00
Z51		6d. deep purple/red (V.)	.. £200
Z52		9d. dull purple and blue (V.)	.. £325
Z53		10d. dull purple and carmine (V., Blk.)	£110
Z54		1s. green (V.)	.. £550
Z55		2s. 6d. lilac (V.)	.. £225

1898–99. *Cancelled as T 4, but inscribed "BURUTU" in serifed caps. Size 44×27 mm.*

Z56		½d. vermilion (V., Blk.)	.. 60·00
Z57		1d. lilac (V., Blk.)	.. 48·00
Z58		2d. green and vermilion (V.)	.. £250
Z59		2½d. purple/blue (V., Blk.)	.. 42·00
Z60		3d. purple/yellow (V.)	.. £200
Z61		4d. green and brown (V.)	.. £200
Z62		4½d. green and carmine (V.)	.. £700
Z63		5d. dull purple and blue (V.)	.. 65·00
Z64		6d. deep purple/red (V.)	.. £225
Z65		9d. dull purple and blue (V.)	.. £350
Z66		10d. dull purple and carmine (V., Blk.)	£110
Z67		2s. 6d. lilac (V., Blk.)	.. £275

1898–99.

| Z68 | 7 | 1d. lilac (V.) | .. |
| Z69 | | 2½d. purple/blue (V.) | .. £325 |

1899. *Cancelled as T 4, but inscribed "CUSTOM DEPT. BURUTU".*

| Z70 | 1d. lilac (V.) | .. |

LOKOJA

1899.

Z71	8	½d. vermilion (V.)	.. £110
Z72		1d. lilac (V.)	.. 80·00
Z73		2½d. purple/blue (V.)	.. £250
Z74		5d. dull purple and blue (V.)	.. £375
Z75		10d. dull purple and carmine (V.)	£400
Z76		2s. 6d. deep lilac (V.)	.. £475

AGENT GENERAL NIGER TERRITORIES

The listings for Nos. Z78/9 are for covers showing a handstamp struck on the address side, but *not* used as a cancellation for the G.B. stamp.

1894–99. *Cancelled as T 8, but inscribed "AGENT GENERAL NIGER TERRITORIES".*

| Z77 | 1d. lilac (V.) | .. |
| Z78 | 2½d. purple/blue (V.) | .. £1000 |

1895–96. *Cancelled as T 7, but inscribed as Nos. Z77/8.*

Z79	2½d. purple/blue (V.)	.. £1000
Z80	5d. dull purple and blue (V.)	..
Z81	10d. dull purple and carmine (V.)	
Z82	2s. 6d. deep lilac (V.)	..

It is now believed that these cancellations may have been used at Asaba. They all occur on covers with Akassa handstamps, often of different dates.

The British Government purchased the Royal Niger Company territories and from 1 January 1900 they were incorporated into the protectorates of Northern and Southern Nigeria. Of the post offices listed above only Lokoja was then situated in Northern Nigeria, the remainder joining Niger Coast in forming Southern Nigeria.

Issues for Northern Nigeria did not reach Lokoja until sometime in March 1900 and the post office there continued to use unoverprinted stamps of Great Britain until these supplies arrived.

NORTHERN NIGERIA

The protectorate of Northern Nigeria was formed on 1 January 1900 from the northern part of the Niger Company Territories. Only one post office existed in this area, at Lokoja, and this continued to use unoverprinted stamps of GREAT BRITAIN until the arrival of Nos. 1/9 during April 1900.

PRICES FOR STAMPS ON COVER

Nos. 1/7	*from* × 6
Nos. 8/9	—
Nos. 10/16	*from* × 5
Nos. 17/19	—
Nos. 20/6	*from* × 5
No. 27	—
Nos. 28/37	*from* × 5
Nos. 38/9	—
Nos. 40/9	*from* × 5
Nos. 50/2	—

PRINTERS. All issues were typographed by De La Rue & Co.

1   2

1900 (Apr). *Wmk Crown CA. P 14.*

1	1	½d. dull mauve and green	..	2·25	9·50
2		1d. dull mauve and carmine	..	2·75	3·50
3		2d. dull mauve and yellow	..	9·00	32·00
4		2½d. dull mauve and ultramarine	..	7·00	32·00
5	2	5d. dull mauve and chestnut	..	17·00	32·00
6		6d. dull mauve and violet	..	15·00	25·00
7	1	1s. green and black	..	20·00	60·00
8		2s. 6d. green and ultramarine	..	80·00	£375
9		10s. green and brown	..	£200	£475
1/9			*Set of 9*	£325	£950
1/9 Optd "Specimen"			*Set of 9*	£180	

Examples of all values are known showing a forged Northern Nigeria postmark dated "AU 14 1900".

3   4

1902 (1 July). *Wmk Crown CA. P 14.*

10	3	½d. dull purple and green	..	2·00	1·00
11		1d. dull purple and carmine	..	2·00	60
12		2d. dull purple and yellow	..	2·00	2·75
13		2½d. dull purple and ultramarine..		1·50	6·50
14	4	5d. dull purple and chestnut	..	2·00	5·00
15		6d. dull purple and violet	..	5·00	4·50
16	3	1s. green and black	..	3·00	5·50
17		2s. 6d. green and ultramarine	..	8·00	35·00
18		10s. green and brown	..	48·00	55·00
10/18			*Set of 9*	£65·00	£100
10/18 Optd "Specimen"			*Set of 9*	£150	

1904 (Apr). *Wmk Mult Crown CA. P 14.*

19	4	£25 green and carmine	..	£38000

No. 19, although utilising the "POSTAGE & REVENUE" Key type, was intended to pay the fiscal fee for liquor licences.

1905 (Aug)–07. *Wmk Mult Crown CA. Ordinary paper. P 14.*

20	3	½d. dull purple and green (10.05)	..	12·00	8·00
		a. Chalk-surfaced paper (1906)		5·50	5·00
21		1d. dull purple and carmine		14·00	65
		a. Chalk-surfaced paper (1906)		4·00	90
22		2d. dull purple and yellow (10.05)		10·00	28·00
		a. Chalk-surfaced paper (1907)		18·00	21·00
23		2½d. dull purple and ultramarine (10.05)		6·00	7·50
24	4	5d. dull purple and chestnut (10.05)		21·00	50·00
		a. Chalk-surfaced paper (1907)		29·00	50·00
25		6d. dull purple and violet (10.05)		23·00	38·00
		a. Chalk-surfaced paper (1906)		29·00	29·00
26	3	1s. green and black (10.05)		55·00	80·00
		a. Chalk-surfaced paper (1906)		22·00	48·00
27		2s. 6d. green and ultramarine (10.05)		48·00	48·00
		a. Chalk-surfaced paper (1906)		30·00	48·00
20/7			*Set of 8*	£110	£190

1910 (30 Jan)–11. *Wmk Mult Crown CA. Ordinary paper (½d. to 2½d.) or chalk-surfaced paper (others). P 14.*

28	3	½d. green (15.4.10)	..	1·75	1·25
29		1d. carmine	..	1·75	1·00
30		2d. grey (26.10.11)	..	3·25	2·25
31		2½d. blue (10.10.)	..	1·75	6·50
32	4	3d. purple/*yellow* (10.9.11)	..	3·00	50
34		5d. dull purple and olive-green (26.2.11)		3·75	8·00
35		6d. dull purple and purple (10.11.10)		5·50	14·00
		a. Dull and bright purple (1911)		3·75	6·00
36	3	1s. black/*green* (10.11.10)	..	2·00	75
37		2s. 6d. black and red/*blue* (15.3.11)		9·50	27·00
38	4	5s. green and red/*yellow* (10.9.11)		23·00	75·00
39	3	10s. green and red/*green* (15.3.11)		42·00	48·00
28/39			*Set of 11*	85·00	£160
28/39 Optd "Specimen"			*Set of 11*	£225	

5   6

1912. *Wmk Mult Crown CA. Ordinary paper (½d., 1d., 2d.) or chalk-surfaced paper (others). P 14.*

40	5	½d. deep green	..	85	60
41		1d. red	.. ..	85	60
42		2d. grey	..	3·00	5·00
43	6	3d. purple/*yellow*	..	2·25	1·25
44		4d. black and red/*yellow*	..	75	2·00
45		5d. dull purple and olive-green	..	4·00	6·00
46		6d. dull purple and purple	..	4·00	4·00
47		9d. dull purple and carmine	..	2·00	10·00
48	5	1s. black/*green*	..	4·00	2·25
49		2s. 6d. black and red/*blue*	..	7·00	32·00
50	6	5s. green and red/*yellow*	..	19·00	75·00
51	5	10s. green and red/*green*	..	38·00	48·00
52	6	£1 black and red/*red*	..	£170	£110
40/52			*Set of 13*	£225	£275
40/52 Optd "Specimen"			*Set of 13*	£200	

Examples of most values are known showing forged postmarks of Lokoja dated "MR 22 12" or Minna dated "JN 16 1913". These forged postmarks have also been seen on examples of earlier issues.

On 1 January 1914 Northern Nigeria became part of Nigeria.

SOUTHERN NIGERIA

The Colony and Protectorate of Southern Nigeria was formed on 1 January 1900 by the amalgamation of Niger Coast Protectorate with the southern part of the Niger Territories. Lagos was incorporated into the territory on 1 May 1906.

The stamps of NIGER COAST PROTECTORATE were used in Southern Nigeria until the introduction of Nos. 1/9, and also during a shortage of these values in mid-1902. The issues of LAGOS were utilized throughout Southern Nigeria after 1 May 1906 until supplies were exhausted.

PRICES FOR STAMPS ON COVER

Nos. 1/7	*from* × 8
Nos. 8/9	—
Nos. 10/18	*from* × 4
Nos. 19/20	—
Nos. 21/30	*from* × 4
Nos. 31/2	—
Nos. 33/42	*from* × 4
Nos. 43/4	—
Nos. 45/53	*from* × 4
Nos. 55/6	—

PRINTERS. All issues of Southern Nigeria were typographed by De La Rue & Co, Ltd, London.

1   2   3

1901 (Mar)–02. *Wmk Crown CA. P 14.*

1	1	½d. black and pale green	..	1·75	2·25
		a. Sepia and green (1902)		2·25	2·00
2		1d. black and carmine	..	1·40	1·50
		a. Sepia and carmine (1902)		2·00	1·50
3		2d. black and red-brown	..	3·00	3·75
4		4d. black and sage-green	..	2·50	12·00
5		6d. black and purple	..	2·50	6·50
6		1s. green and black	..	7·50	24·00
7		2s. 6d. black and brown	..	42·00	75·00
8		5s. black and orange-yellow	..	48·00	90·00
9		10s. black and purple/*yellow*	..	85·00	£140
1/9			*Set of 9*	£170	£325
1/9 Optd "Specimen"			*Set of 9*	£140	

1903 (Mar)–04. *Wmk Crown CA. P 14.*

10	2	½d. grey-black and pale green	..	70	30
		w. Wmk inverted			
11		1d. grey-black and carmine	..	1·25	60
12		2d. grey-black and chestnut	..	6·00	1·50
13		2½d. grey-black and blue (1904)	..	2·00	75
14		4d. grey-black and olive-green	..	2·25	5·50
15		6d. grey-black and purple	..	3·50	8·00
16		1s. green and black	..	27·00	19·00
17		2s. 6d. grey-black and brown	..	20·00	50·00
18		5s. grey-black and yellow	..	55·00	£110
19		10s. grey-black and purple/*yellow*	..	27·00	85·00
20		£1 green and violet	..	£275	£500
10/20			*Set of 11*	£375	£700
10/20 Optd "Specimen"			*Set of 11*	£180	

Two Dies of Head Plate:

A   B

In Head A the fifth line of shading on the king's cheek shows as a line of dots and the lines of shading up to the king's hair are broken in places. In Head B the lines of shading are more regular, especially the fifth line.

1904 (June)–09. *Head Die A. Wmk Mult Crown CA. Ordinary paper. P 14.*

21	2	½d. grey-black and pale green	..	50	10
		a. Chalk-surfaced paper (1905)		85	80
22		1d. grey-black and carmine	..	10·00	20
		a. Chalk-surfaced paper (1905)		11·00	10
23		2d. grey-black and chestnut (1905)		2·50	45
		a. Pale grey and chestnut (Head Die B) (1907)		3·50	40
24		2½d. grey-black and bright blue (9.09)		1·00	95
25		3d. orange-brown and bright purple (*chalk-surfaced paper*) (Head Die B) (18.8.07) (Optd S. £20)		9·00	1·25
26		4d. grey-black and olive-green (12.05)		14·00	25·00
		a. Chalk-surfaced paper (1906)		25·00	27·00
		ab. Grey-black and pale olive-green (Head Die B) (1907)		32·00	25·00
27		6d. grey-black and bright purple (12.05)		10·00	2·75
		a. Chalk-surfaced paper (1906)		12·00	3·00
		ab. Head Die B (1907)		17·00	1·75
28		1s. grey-green and black (19.9.07)		3·00	3·25
		a. Chalk-surfaced paper (Head Die B) (1907)		26·00	3·00
29		2s. 6d. grey-black and brown (30.4.06)		20·00	15·00
		a. Chalk-surfaced paper (1906)		32·00	12·00
		ab. Head Die B (1907)		27·00	12·00
30		5s. grey-black and yellow (10.12.07)		38·00	70·00
		a. Chalk-surfaced paper (Head Die B) (1908)		48·00	70·00
31		10s. grey-black and purple/*yellow* (*chalk-surfaced paper*) (Head Die B) (9.08)		95·00	£160
32		£1 green and violet (19.3.06)		£170	£200
		a. Chalk-surfaced paper (1906)		£180	£200
		ab. Head Die B (1907)		£140	£180
21/32			*Set of 12*	£300	£400

I   II

Die I. Thick "1", small "d". (double working plate).
Die II. Thinner "1", larger "d" (single working plate).

1907–11. *Colours changed. Head Die B. Ordinary paper (½d. to 2½d.) or chalk-surfaced paper (others). Wmk Mult Crown CA. P 14.*

33	2	½d. pale green (1907)	..	1·00	20
		a. Head Die A		4·50	30
		b. Blue-green (1910)		1·50	20
34		1d. carmine (I) (12.8.07)	..	2·50	80
		a. Head Die A		6·00	30
		ab. Die II. *Carmine-red* (1910)		50	10
35		2d. greyish slate (9.09)	..	2·25	70
36		2½d. blue (9.09)	..	1·50	3·75
37		3d. purple/*yellow* (7.09)	..	1·50	30
38		4d. black and red/*yellow* (9.09)	..	1·75	80
39		6d. dull purple and purple (9.09)	..	21·00	3·25
		a. Dull purple and bright purple (1911)		25·00	3·25
		aw. Wmk inverted			
40		1s. black/*green* (7.09)	..	7·00	40
41		2s. 6d. black and red (9.09)	..	4·50	90
42		5s. green and red/*yellow* (9.09)	..	35·00	48·00
43		10s. green and red/*green* (9.09)	..	60·00	90·00
44		£1 purple and black/*red* (9.09)	..	£180	£190
33/44			*Set of 12*	£275	£300
33/44 Optd "Specimen"			*Set of 12*	£225	

1912. *Wmk Mult Crown CA. P 14.*

45	3	½d. green	..	1·50	10
46		1d. red	..	1·00	10
		w. Wmk inverted			
47		2d. grey	..	60	85
48		2½d. bright blue	..	2·50	2·75
49		3d. purple/*yellow*	..	75	30
50		4d. black and red/*yellow*	..	70	2·00
51		6d. dull and bright purple	..	75	1·25
52		1s. black/*green*	..	2·75	75
53		2s. 6d. black and red/*blue*	..	7·50	26·00
54		5s. green and red/*yellow*	..	19·00	65·00
55		10s. green and red/*green*	..	45·00	85·00
56		£1 purple and black/*red*	..	£170	£180
45/56			*Set of 12*	£225	£325
45/56 Optd "Specimen"			*Set of 12*	£200	

STAMP BOOKLETS

1904. *Black on red cover. Stapled.*

SB1	2s. 1d. booklet containing twenty-four 1d (No. 11) in blocks of 6 ..	..

1905 (1 June)–06. *Black on red cover. Stapled.*

SB2	2s. 1d. booklet containing twenty-four 1d (No. 22) in blocks of 6 ..	
	a. As No. SB2 but containing No. 22a (1906)	£1500

1907 (7 Oct). *Black on red cover. Stapled.*

SB3	2s. 1d. booklet containing twenty-four 1d (No. 34) in blocks of 6 ..	£2000

1910 (19 Sept). *Black on red cover. Stapled.*

SB4	2s. booklet containing eleven ½d. and eighteen 1d. (Nos. 33b, 34ab) in blocks of 6 or 5 ..	

1912 (Oct). *Black on red cover. Stapled.*

SB5	2s. booklet containing twelve ½d. and eighteen 1d. (Nos. 45/6) in blocks of 6 ..	£1500

On 1 January 1914 Southern Nigeria became part of Nigeria.

COVER PRICES

Cover factors are quoted at the beginning of each country for most issues to 1945. An explanation of the system can be found on page x. The factors quoted do not, however, apply to philatelic covers.

NIGERIA

Nigeria was formed on 1 January 1914 from the former protectorates of Northern and Southern Nigeria.

PRICES FOR STAMPS ON COVER TO 1945	
Nos. 1/10	from × 3
Nos. 11/12	from × 3
Nos. 15/28	from × 3
Nos. 29/a	—
Nos. 30/3	from × 3
Nos. 34/59	from × 2

CROWN COLONY

1   2

(Typo D.L.R.)

1914 (1 June)–**29.** *Die I. Wmk Mult Crown CA. Ordinary paper (¹⁄₂d. to 2¹⁄₂d.) or chalk-surfaced paper (others).* P 14.

1	1	¹⁄₂d. green	3·75	70
2		1d. carmine-red	4·25	10
		a. Scarlet (1916)	5·50	15
		w. Wmk inverted	60·00	
3		2d. grey	7·00	1·50
		a. Slate-grey (1918)	8·50	75
4		2¹⁄₂d. bright blue	4·25	2·50
		a. Dull blue (1915)	8·00	3·00
5	2	3d. purple/yellow (white back)	3·25	9·00
		a. Lemon back (19.8.15)	1·50	2·75
		b. On deep yellow (yellow back) (thick paper) (1915) (Optd S. £38)	25·00	7·50
		c. On orange-buff (1920)	9·00	21·00
		d. On buff (1920)	11·00	
		e. On pale yellow (1921)	11·00	15·00
6		4d. black and red/yellow (white back)	1·40	9·00
		a. Lemon back (19.8.15)	1·00	4·25
		b. On deep yellow (yellow back) (thick paper) (1915) (Optd S. £38)	25·00	7·50
		c. On orange-buff (1920)	11·00	8·50
		d. On buff (1920)	11·00	
		e. On pale yellow (1921)	10·00	17·00
7		6d. dull purple and bright purple	9·00	9·00
8	1	1s. black/blue-green (white back)	1·25	17·00
		a. On yellow-green (white back) (1915)	£120	
		b. Yellow-green back (19.8.15)	28·00	29·00
		c. Blue-green back (1915) (Optd S. £38)	1·00	8·50
		d. Pale olive back (1917)	22·00	22·00
		dw. Wmk inverted		
		e. On emerald (pale olive back) (1920)	7·50	26·00
		f. On emerald (emerald back) (1920)	1·25	14·00
9		2s. 6d. black and red/blue	14·00	6·00
10	2	5s. green and red/yellow (white back)	12·00	42·00
		a. Lemon back (19.8.15)	18·00	48·00
		b. On deep yellow (yellow back) (thick paper) (1915) (Optd S. £42)	45·00	60·00
		c. On orange-buff (1920)	35·00	75·00
		d. On buff (1920)	45·00	
		e. On pale yellow (1921)	55·00	£110
11	1	10s. green and red/blue-green (white back)	45·00	£130
		a. Blue-grn back (19.8.15) (Optd S. £48)	48·00	80·00
		b. Pale olive back (1917)	£650	£1100
		c. On emerald (pale olive back) (1920)	95·00	£140
		d. On emerald (emerald back) (1921)	38·00	90·00
12	2	£1 deep purple and black/red	£150	£200
		a. Purple and black/red (1917)	£160	£190
		b. Die II. Dp purple & blk/red (19.1.27)	£160	£250
		ba. Purple and black/red (1929)	£180	£250
1/12		Set of 12	£200	£275
1/12	Optd "Specimen"	Set of 12	£300	

The ¹⁄₂d. and 1d. were printed in sheets of 240 using two plates one above the other.

1921–32. *Wmk Mult Script CA. Ordinary paper (¹⁄₂d. to 3d.) or chalk-surfaced paper (others).* P 14.

15	1	¹⁄₂d. green (Die I) (1921)	1·00	40
		aw. Wmk inverted	60·00	
		b. Die II (1925)	3·75	85
		c. Vert gutter pair. Die I and Die II. Nos. 15/b (1925)	£140	
16		1d. rose-carmine (Die I) (1921)	3·00	30
		aw. Wmk inverted	55·00	55·00
		b. Die II (1925)	1·75	55
		c. Vert gutter pair. Die I and Die II. Nos. 16/b (1925)	£140	
17	2	2¹⁄₂d. orange (Die II) (1.4.31)	3·75	15
18	1	2d. grey (Die I) (1921)	1·50	3·75
		a. Die II (1924)	7·50	40
19		2d. chestnut (Die II) (1.10.27)	4·25	1·00
20		2d. chocolate (Die II) (1.7.28)	1·25	15
		a. Die I (1932)	5·50	75
21		2¹⁄₂d. bright blue (Die I) (1921)	1·00	5·00
22	2	3d. bright violet (Die I) (1924)	5·00	3·25
		a. Die II (1925)	10·00	1·50
23		3d. bright blue (Die II) (1.4.31)	6·00	1·50
24		4d. black & red/pale yellow (Die II) (1923)	65	55
		a. Die I (1932)	5·50	7·00
25		6d. dull purple & brt purple (Die I) (1921)	12·00	14·00
		a. Die II (1923)	7·00	8·00
		aw. Wmk inverted	70·00	
26	1	1s. black/emerald (Die II) (1924)	1·25	2·00
27		2s. 6d. black and red/blue (Die II) (1925)	6·50	23·00
		a. Die I (1932)	40·00	60·00
28	2	5s. green & red/pale yellow (Die I) (1926)	15·00	65·00
		a. Die I (1932)	60·00	£150
29	1	10s. green and red/green (Die II) (1925)	55·00	£170
		a. Die I (1932)	£100	£350
15/29		Set of 15	95·00	£250
15/19, 21/9	Optd/Perf "Specimen"	Set of 14	£350	

The ¹⁄₂d. and 1d., together with the 1¹⁄₂d. from 1932, were printed in sheets of 240 using two plates one above the other. Nos. 15c and 16c come from printings in November 1924 which combined Key Plate No. 7 (Die I) above Key Plate No. 12 (Die II).

1935 (6 May). *Silver Jubilee. As Nos. 114/17 of Jamaica, but ptd by Waterlow.* P 11×12.

30		1¹⁄₂d. ultramarine and grey	80	65
31		2d. green and indigo	1·50	65
		k. Kite and vertical log	65·00	
32		3d. brown and deep blue	3·00	9·00
33		1s. slate and purple	3·00	24·00
30/3		Set of 4	7·50	30·00
30/3	Perf "Specimen"	Set of 4	75·00	

For illustration of plate variety see Omnibus section following Zimbabwe.

3 Apapa Wharf   4 Fishing Village

5 Victoria-Buea Road

(Recess D.L.R.)

1936 (1 Feb). *Designs as T 3/5. Wmk Mult Script CA.*

(a) P 11¹⁄₂ × 13

34		¹⁄₂d. green	1·50	1·40
35		1d. carmine	40	40
36		1¹⁄₂d. brown	1·75	40
		a. Perf 12¹⁄₂ × 13¹⁄₂	42·00	3·50
37		2d. black	40	80
38		3d. blue	1·75	1·25
		a. Perf 12¹⁄₂ × 13¹⁄₂	85·00	24·00
39		4d. red-brown	1·75	2·00
40		6d. dull violet	40	60
41		1s. sage-green	1·50	4·50

(b) P 14

42		2s. 6d. black and ultramarine	3·50	19·00
43		5s. black and olive-green	6·00	24·00
44		10s. black and grey	45·00	65·00
45		£1 black and orange	70·00	£140
34/45		Set of 12	£120	£225
34/45	Perf "Specimen"	Set of 12	£225	

Designs: *Vert as T 3/4*—1d. Cocoa; 1¹⁄₂d. Tin dredger; 2d. Timber industry; 4d. Cotton ginnery; 6d. Habe minaret; 1s. Fulani Cattle. *Horiz as T 5*—5s. Oil Palms; 10s. River Niger at Jebba; £1, Canoe pulling.

1937 (12 May). *Coronation. As Nos. 118/20 of Jamaica, but ptd by B.W. & Co.* P 11×11¹⁄₂.

46		1d. carmine	30	1·50
47		1¹⁄₂d. brown	1·25	2·25
48		3d. blue	1·40	2·25
46/8		Set of 3	2·75	5·50
46/8	Perf "Specimen"	Set of 3	55·00	

15 King George VI   16 Victoria-Buea Road

(Recess B.W. (T 15), D.L.R. (others))

1938 (1 May)–**51.** *Designs as T 15/16. Wmk Mult Script CA.* P 12 (T 15) or 13×11¹⁄₂ (others).

49	15	¹⁄₂d. green	10	10
		a. Perf 11¹⁄₂ (15.2.50)	60	20
50		1d. carmine	19·00	2·50
		a. Rose-red (shades) (1940)	75	30
50b		1d. bright purple (1.12.44)	10	20
		ba. Perf 11¹⁄₂ (15.2.50)	30	50
		bw. Wmk inverted (p 12)		
51		1¹⁄₂d. brown	20	10
		a. Perf 11¹⁄₂ (15.11.50)	10	10
52		2d. black	10	1·00
52a		2d. rose-red (1.12.44)	10	80
		ab. Perf 11¹⁄₂ (15.2.50)	10	40
52b		2¹⁄₂d. orange (4.41)	10	70
53		3d. blue	10	10
		a. Wmk sideways	†	£3000
53b		3d. black (1.12.44)	15	40
54		4d. orange	48·00	2·75
54a		4d. blue (1.12.44)	15	1·75
55		6d. blackish purple	40	10
		a. Perf 11¹⁄₂ (17.4.51)	60	60
56		1s. sage-green	60	10
		a. Perf 11¹⁄₂ (14.6.50)	15	10
57		1s. 3d. light blue (1940)	90	30
		a. Perf 11¹⁄₂ (14.6.50)	80	70
		ab. Wmk sideways	†	£2750

58	16	2s. 6d. black and blue	60·00	13·00
		a. Perf 13¹⁄₂ (6.42)	3·75	4·25
		ab. Black and deep blue (1947)	55·00	50·00
		b. Perf 14 (1942)	2·25	3·00
		c. Perf 12 (15.8.51)	1·75	3·50
59	—	5s. black and orange	£110	12·00
		a. Perf 13¹⁄₂ (8.42)	5·50	4·50
		b. Perf 14 (1948)	6·00	3·00
		c. Perf 12 (19.5.49)	5·50	4·00
49/59c		Set of 16	50·00	12·00
49/52a, 53/9	Perf "Specimen"	Set of 15	£200	

Design: *Horiz as T 16*—5s. R. Niger at Jebba.
The 1d., No. 50ba, exists in coils constructed from normal sheets.

1946 (21 Oct). *Victory. As Nos. 141/2 of Jamaica.*

60		1¹⁄₂d. chocolate	25	10
61		4d. blue	25	1·25
60/1	Perf "Specimen"	Set of 2	55·00	

1948 (20 Dec). *Royal Silver Wedding. As Nos. 143/4 of Jamaica.*

62		1d. bright purple	35	30
63		5s. brown-orange	5·00	8·00

1949 (10 Oct). *75th Anniv of U.P.U. As Nos. 145/8 of Jamaica.*

64		1d. bright reddish purple	20	10
65		3d. deep blue	1·25	2·50
66		6d. purple	70	2·25
67		1s. olive	80	1·75
64/7		Set of 4	2·75	6·00

1953 (2 June). *Coronation. As No. 153 of Jamaica, but ptd by B.W.*

68		1¹⁄₂d. black and emerald	40	10
		w. Wmk inverted	†	—

18 Old Manilla Currency   21 "Tin"

Die I   Die Ia
Flat-bed   Rotary

Two types of 1d.:
The Belgian rotary printings have thicker lines of shading giving blotches of black colour instead of fine lines, particularly in the stirrups.

Major re-entry showing duplication of steps of the terraces (Pl 3, R. 1/5)

Type A   Type B
Gap in row of dots   Unbroken row of dots

Two types of 2d. slate-violet:
Nos. 72c/cc. The original cylinder used was Type A (July 1956); later Type B (Sept 1957). The above illustrations will help classification, but two stamps per sheet of 60 of Type A show faint dots. However, one of these has the "2d." re-entry which does not exist in Type B sheets, and shades are distinctive.

Die I Flat-bed

Die 1a Rotary

Two types of 3d.:
As in the 1d. the Belgian rotary printings have thicker lines of shading and this is particularly noticeable in the dark hills in the background.

24 Ife Bronze

26 Victoria Harbour

29 New and Old Lagos

(Des M. Fievet. Recess Waterlow)

1953 (1 Sept)–58. T 18, 21, 24, 26, 29 and similar designs. Wmk Mult Script CA. P 14.

69	18	½d. black and orange	15	30
70	—	1d. black and bronze-green (Die I)	20	10
		a. Die Ia (1.9.58)	20	10
71	—	1½d. blue-green	50	40
72	21	2d. black and yellow-ochre	4·00	30
		a. Black and ochre (18.8.54)	4·25	30
		b. Re-entry	90·00	
72c		2d. slate-violet (Type A) (23.7.56)	3·00	1·75
		ca. Slate-blue (shades) (Type A)	7·50	40
		cb. Bluish grey (Type B) (25.9.57)	3·50	40
		cc. Grey (shades) (Type B)	4·50	30
73		3d. black and purple (Die I)	55	10
		a. Die Ia. Black & reddish pur (1.9.58)	55	10
		b. Imperf (pair)	£200	
74	—	4d. black and blue	2·50	20
75	24	6d. orange-brown and black	30	10
		a. Chestnut and black (18.8.54)	1·50	10
76	—	1s. black and maroon	40	10
77	26	2s. 6d. black and green	6·00	50
		a. Black and deep green (18.8.54)	9·00	50
78	—	5s. black and red-orange	3·50	1·25
79	—	10s. black and red-brown	13·00	2·00
80	29	£1 black and violet	22·00	7·00
69/80		Set of 13	48·00	11·50

Designs: Horiz (as T 18)—1d. Bornu horsemen; 1½d. "Groundnuts"; 3d. Jebba Bridge and R. Niger; 4d. "Cocoa"; 1s. "Timber". (As T 26)—5s. "Palm-oil"; 10s. "Hides and skins".
Nos. 70a, 72c/cc and 73a were printed on rotary machines by a subsidiary company, Imprimerie Belge de Sécurité, in Belgium.
Nos. 72ca and 72cc were only available in Nigeria.
The ½d. and 1d. (Die I) exist in coils constructed from sheets. Coils containing the 1d. (Die Ia) and 2d. (Type A) appeared in 1958 from continuously printed reels.

ROYAL VISIT 1956
(30)

31 Victoria Harbour

1956 (28 Jan). Royal Visit. No. 72a optd with T 30.

81	21	2d. black and ochre	40	30
		a. Opt inverted	£180	

(Recess Waterlow)

1958 (1 Dec). Centenary of Victoria. W w 12. P 13½ × 14.

82	31	3d. black and purple	20	30

32 Lugard Hall

(Recess Waterlow)

1959 (14 Mar). Attainment of Self-Government, Northern Region of Nigeria. T 32 and similar horiz design. W w 12. P 13½ (3d.) or 13½ × 14 (1s.).

83		3d. black and purple	15	10
84		1s. black and green	55	85

Design:—1s. Kano Mosque.

INDEPENDENT FEDERATION

34

35 Legislative Building

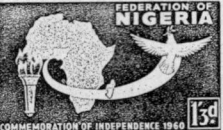

38 Dove, Torch and Map

(Des L. J. Wittington (1d.), R. Crawford (3d.), R. D. Baxter (6d.), J. White (1s. 3d.), Photo Waterlow)

1960 (1 Oct). Independence. T 35, 38 and similar horiz designs. W 34. P 13½ (1s. 3d.) or 14 (others).

85		1d. black and scarlet	10	10
86		3d. black and greenish blue	15	10
87		6d. green and red-brown	20	20
88		1s. 3d. bright blue and yellow	40	20
85/8		Set of 4	70	50

Designs: (As T 35)—3d. African paddling canoe; 6d. Federal Supreme Court.

39 Groundnuts

48 Central Bank

1961 (1 Jan). T 39, 48, and similar designs. W 34. P 15 × 14 (½d. to 1s 3d.) or 14½ (others).

89		½d. emerald	10	50
90		1d. reddish violet	80	10
91		1½d. carmine-red	70	2·25
92		2d. deep blue	30	10
93		3d. deep green	40	10
94		4d. blue	40	75
95		6d. yellow and black	80	10
		a. Yellow omitted	—	£650
96		1s. yellow-green	4·50	10
97		1s. 3d. orange	1·25	10
98		2s. 6d. black and yellow	2·50	15
99		5s. black and emerald	65	85
100		10s. black and ultramarine	2·00	2·25
101		£1 black and carmine-red	9·50	11·00
		w. Wmk inverted		
89/101		Set of 13	21·00	16·00

Designs: Vert (as T 39)—1d. Coal mining; 1½d. Adult education; 2d. Pottery; 3d. Oyo carver; 4d. Weaving; 6d. Benin mask; 1s. Yellow-casqued Hornbill; 1s. 3d. Camel train. Horiz (as T 48)—5s. Nigeria Museum; 10s. Kano airport; £1 Lagos railway station.

PRINTERS. The above and all following issues to No. 206 were printed in photogravure by Harrison & Sons, except where otherwise stated.

52 Globe and Diesel-electric Locomotive

56 Coat of Arms

(Des M. Goaman)

1961 (25 July). Admission of Nigeria into U.P.U. T 52 and similar horiz designs. W 34. P 14½.

102		1d. red-orange and blue	30	10
103		3d. olive-yellow and black	30	10
104		1s. 3d. blue and carmine-red	80	20
105		2s. 6d. deep green and blue	85	2·00
102/5		Set of 4	2·00	2·00

Designs:—3d. Globe and mail-van; 1s. 3d. Globe and Bristol 175 Britannia aircraft; 2s. 6d. Globe and liner.

(Des S. Bodo (3d.), R. Hopeman (4d.), C. Adesina (6d.), M. Shamir (1s. 6d.), B. Enweonwu (2s. 6d.))

1961 (1 Oct). First Anniv of Independence. T 56 and similar designs. W 34. P 14½.

106		3d. multicoloured	10	10
107		4d. yellow-green and yellow-orange	20	10
108		6d. emerald-green	30	10
109		1s. 3d. grey, emerald and blue	35	40
110		2s. 6d. green and grey-blue	40	1·75
106/10		Set of 5	1·25	1·90

Designs: Horiz—4d. Natural resources and map; 6d. Nigerian Eagle; 1s. 3d. Eagles in flight; 2s. 6d. Nigerians and flag.
A used copy of No. 106 has been seen with both the silver (large "Y" appearing grey) and the yellow (appearing white) omitted.

61 "Health"

66 Malaria Eradication Emblem and Parasites

(Des M. Shamir)

1962 (25 Jan). Lagos Conference of African and Malagasy States. T 61 and similar vert designs. W 34. P 14 × 14½.

111		1d. yellow-bistre	10	10
112		3d. deep reddish purple	10	10
113		6d. deep green	15	10
114		1s. brown	20	10
115		1s. 3d. blue	25	20
111/15		Set of 5	65	40

Designs:—3d. "Culture"; 6d. "Commerce"; 1s. "Communications"; 1s. 3d. "Co-operation".

1962 (7 Apr). Malaria Eradication. T 66 and similar horiz designs. W 34. P 14½.

116		3d. green and orange-red	15	10
117		6d. blue and bright purple	20	10
118		1s. 3d. magenta and violet-blue	20	10
119		2s. 6d. blue and yellow-brown	30	80
116/19		Set of 4	75	90

Designs:—6d. Insecticide spraying; 1s. 3d. Aerial spraying; 2s. 6d. Mother, child and microscope.

70 National Monument

71 Benin Bronze

(Des S. Bodo (3d.), B. Enweonwu (5s.))

1962 (1 Oct). Second Anniv of Independence. W 34. P 14½ × 14 (3d.) or 14 × 14½ (5s.).

120	70	3d. emerald and blue	10	10
		a. Emerald omitted		
121	71	5s. red, emerald and violet	1·00	70

72 Fair Emblem

73 "Cogwheels of Industry"

(Des M. Goaman (1d., 2s. 6d.), J. O. Gbagbeolu and M. Goaman (6d.), R. Hegeman (1s.))

1962 (27 Oct). International Trade Fair, Lagos. W 34. T 72/3 and similar designs. P 14½.

122		1d. olive-brown and orange-red	10	10
123		6d. carmine-red and black	15	10
124		1s. orange-brown and black	15	10
125		2s. 6d. ultramarine and yellow	60	20
122/5		Set of 4	85	30

Designs: Horiz as T 73—1s. "Cornucopia of Industry"; 2s. 6d. Oilwells and tanker.

76 "Arrival of Delegates"   **77** Mace as Palm Tree

(Des S. Akosile (2½d.), M. Goaman (others))

1962 (5 Nov). *Eighth Commonwealth Parliamentary Conference, Lagos.* T **76/77** *and similar design.* W **34**. P 14½.
126	2½d. greenish blue	..	15	20
127	4d. indigo and rose-red	..	15	15
128	1s. 3d. sepia and lemon	..	20	20
126/8	..	*Set of 3*	45	50

Design: *Horiz*—4d. National Hall.

80 Tractor and Maize   **81** Mercury Capsule and Kano Tracking Station

(Des M. Goaman)

1963 (21 Mar). *Freedom from Hunger.* T **80** *and similar design.* W **34**. P 14.
129	3d. olive-green	..	1·00	20
130	6d. magenta	..	1·50	20

Design: *Vert*—3d. Herdsman.

(Des R. Hegeman)

1963 (21 June). *"Peaceful Use of Outer Space".* T **81** *and similar vert design.* W **34**. P 14½ × 14.
131	6d. blue and yellow-green	..	25	10
132	1s. 3d. black and blue-green.	..	35	20

Design:—1s. 3d. Satellite and Lagos Harbour.

83 Scouts shaking Hands

(Des S. Apostolou (3d.), G. Okiki (1s.))

1963 (1 Aug). *11th World Scout Jamboree, Marathon.* T **83** *and similar triangular-shaped design.* W **34**. P 14.
133	3d. red and bronze-green	..	30	15
134	1s. black and red	..	95	80
MS134a	93 × 95 mm. Nos. 133/4	..	1·75	1·75
ab.	Red omitted (on 3d. value)	..	£275	

Design:—1s. Campfire.

85 Emblem and First Aid Team   **88** President Azikiwe and State House

(Des M. Goaman)

1963 (1 Sept). *Red Cross Centenary.* T **85** *and similar horiz designs.* W **34**. P 14½.
135	3d. red and deep ultramarine	..	75	10
136	6d. red and deep green	..	1·25	10
137	1s. 3d. red and deep sepia	..	1·75	70
135/7	..	*Set of 3*	3·25	80
MS137a	102 × 102 mm. No. 137 (block of four)		8·50	11·00

Designs:—6d. Emblem and "Hospital Services"; 1s. 3d. Patient and emblem.

(Des M. Shamir. Photo Govt Printer, Israel)

1963 (1 Oct). *Republic Day.* T **88** *and similar vert designs showing administrative buildings and President Azikiwe.* P 14 × 13.
138	3d. yellow-olive and grey-green	..	10	10
139	1s. 3d. yellow-brown and sepia	..	10	10
	a. Yellow-brown (portrait) omitted			
140	2s. 6d. turquoise-blue and deep violet-blue	..	15	15
138/40	..	*Set of 3*	30	30

Designs:—1s. 3d. Federal Supreme Court Building; 2s. 6d. Parliament Building.

89 Charter and Broken Whip   **90** "Freedom of Worship"

(Des S. Apostolou (3d.), Mrs. F. P. Effiong (others). Photo D.L.R.)

1963 (10 Dec). *15th Anniv of Declaration of Human Rights.* T **89/90** *and similar designs.* W **34**. P 13.
141	3d. vermilion	..	10	10
142	6d. blue-green	..	15	10
143	1s. 3d. ultramarine	..	30	10
144	2s. 6d. bright purple	..	45	30
141/4		*Set of 4*	85	35

Designs: *Vert as* T **90**—1s. 3d. "Freedom from want"; 2s. 6d. "Freedom of speech".

93 Queen Nefertari   **94** Rameses II

(Des M. Shamir)

1964 (8 Mar). *Nubian Monuments Preservation.* W **34**. P 14½.
145	**93**	6d. yellow-olive and emerald	..	50	10
146	**94**	2s. 6d. brown, deep olive and emerald	2·25	2·00

95 President Kennedy

(Des M. Shamir (1s. 3d.), M. Goaman (2s. 6d.), Mr. Bottiau (5s.). Photo Govt Printer, Israel (1s. 3d.); litho Lewin-Epstein, Bat Yam, Israel (others))

1964 (27 Aug). *President Kennedy Memorial Issue.* T **95** *and similar horiz designs.* P 13 × 14 (1s. 3d.) or 14 (others).
147	1s. 3d. light violet and black	..	50	15
148	2s. 6d. black, red, blue and green	..	70	55
149	5s. black, deep blue, red and green	..	1·25	1·60
147/9		*Set of 3*	2·25	2·10
MS149a	154 × 135 mm. No. 149 (block of four).			
	Imperf	..	10·00	12·00

Designs:—2s. 6d. President Kennedy and flags; 5s. President Kennedy (U.S. coin head) and flags.

98 President Azikiwe   **99** Herbert Macaulay

(Des S. Apostolou (3d.), W. H. Irvine (others). Photo Govt Printer, Israel (others))

1964 (1 Oct). *First Anniv of Republic.* T **98** *or* **99** *and similar vert design.* P 14 × 13 (3d.) or 14½ (others).
150	3d. red-brown	..	10	10
151	1s. 3d. green	..	35	10
152	2s. 6d. deep grey-green	..	70	90
150/2		*Set of 3*	1·00	1·00

Design:—2s. 6d. King Jaja of Opobo.

101 Boxing Gloves

102 Hurdling

(Des A. Adalade (3d.), S. Medahunsi (6d.), M. Shamir (1s. 3d.), M. Goaman (2s. 6d.))

1964 (10 Oct). *Olympic Games, Tokyo.* T **101** *and similar designs, and* T **102**. W **34**. P 14 (2s. 6d.) or 14½ (others).
153	3d. sepia and olive-green	..	45	10
154	6d. emerald and indigo	..	60	10
155	1s. 3d. sepia and yellow-olive	..	1·25	15
156	2s. 6d. sepia and chestnut	..	2·25	3·75
153/6		*Set of 4*	4·00	3·75
MS156a	102 × 102 mm. No. 156 (block of four).			
	Imperf		3·00	4·25

Designs: *Horiz*—6d. High-jumping. *Vert*—1s. 3d. Running.

105 Scouts on Hill-top

(Des S. Apostolou (1d., 1s. 3d.), H. N. G. Cowham and Eagle Scout N. A. Lasisi (3d.), W. H. Irvine (6d.))

1965 (1 Jan). *50th Anniv of Nigerian Scout Movement.* T **105** *and similar vert designs.* P 14 × 14½.
157	1d. brown	..	10	10
158	3d. red, black and emerald	..	15	10
159	6d. red, sepia and yellow-green	..	25	20
160	1s. 3d. bistre-brown, greenish yellow and black-green	..	40	85
157/60		*Set of 4*	75	1·10
MS160a	76 × 104 mm. No. 160 (block of four).			
	Imperf		5·00	8·50

Designs:—3d. Scout badge on shield; 6d. Scout badges; 1s. 3d. Chief Scout and Nigerian scout.

109 "Telstar"   **110** Solar Satellite

(Des M. Shamir. Photo Govt Printer, Israel)

1965 (1 Apr). *International Quiet Sun Years.* P 14½ × 13.
161	**109**	6d. reddish violet and turquoise-blue	..	15	15
162	**110**	1s. 3d. green and reddish lilac	..	15	15

111 Native Tom-tom and Modern Telephone

(Des C. Botham (5s.), H. N. G. Cowham (others). Photo Enschedé)

1965 (2 Aug). *I.T.U. Centenary.* T **111** *and similar designs.* P 11½ × 11 (1s. 3d.) or 11 × 11½ (others).
163	3d. black, carmine and yellow-brown	..	20	10
164	1s. 3d. black, blue-green and chalky blue	..	2·00	1·00
165	5s. black, carmine, blue & brt greenish blue	5·00	7·00
163/5		*Set of 3*	6·50	7·25

Designs: *Vert*—1s. 3d. Microwave aerial. *Horiz*—5s. Telecommunications satellite and part of globe.

114 I.C.Y. Emblem and Diesel-hydraulic Locomotive   **117** Carved Frieze

(Des W. H. Irvine. Photo D.L.R.)

1965 (1 Sept). *International Co-operation Year.* T **114** *and similar horiz designs.* W **34**. P 14 × 15.
166	3d. green, red and orange	..	3·00	20
167	1s. black, bright blue and lemon	..	3·00	40
168	2s. 6d. green, bright blue and yellow	..	9·00	7·00
166/8		*Set of 3*	13·50	7·25

Designs:—1s. Students and Lagos Teaching Hospital; 2s. 6d. Kainji (Niger) Dam.

(Des S. Apostolou (3d.), W. H. Irvine (others). Photo D.L.R.)

1965 (1 Oct). *2nd Anniv of Republic. T* **117** *and similar designs.*
P 14 × 15 (3d.) *or* 15 × 14 (others).

169	3d. black, red and orange-yellow		10	10
170	1s. 3d. red-brown, dp green & lt ultramarine		50	10
171	5s. brown, blackish brown and light green		1·00	1·25
169/71		*Set of 3*	1·40	1·25

Designs: *Vert*—1s. 3d. Stone images at Ikom; 5s. Tada bronze.

120 Lion and Cubs

121 African Elephants

132 Hippopotamus

133 African Buffalo

(Des M. Fievet. Photo Harrison (1d., 2d., 3d., 4d. (No. 177a), 9d.) or
Delrieu (others))

1965 (1 Nov)–**66**. *T* **120/1**, **132/3** *and similar designs. Without
printer's imprint. Chalk-surfaced paper* (1d., 2d., 3d., 4d., 9d.)
P 12 × 12½ (½d., 6d.), 12½ × 12 (1½d., 4d.), 14 × 13½
(1d., 2d., 3d., 9d.) *or* 12½ (others).

172	½d. multicoloured (1.11.65)		80	2·00
173	1d. multicoloured (1.11.65)		40	15
174	1½d. multicoloured (2.5.66)		6·00	7·00
175	2d. multicoloured (1.4.66)		3·00	15
176	3d. multicoloured (17.10.66)		1·25	30
177	4d. multicoloured (2.5.66)		50	2·75
	a. Perf 14 × 13½ (1966)		30	10
178	6d. multicoloured (2.5.66)		2·00	40
179	9d. Prussian blue and orange-red (17.10.66)		3·00	60
180	1s. multicoloured (2.5.66)		2·50	70
181	1s. 3d. multicoloured (2.5.66)		8·50	1·00
182	2s. orange-brown, buff and brown (2.5.66)		75	1·25
183	5s. chestnut, light yellow and brown (2.5.66)		1·75	2·75
	a. Pale chestnut, yellow and brown-purple (1966)		2·25	2·75
184	10s. multicoloured (2.5.66)		6·50	3·00
185	£1 multicoloured (2.5.66)		15·00	9·00
172/85		*Set of 14*	45·00	26·00

Designs: *Horiz* (as *T* **121**)—1½d. Splendid Sunbird; 2d. Village
Weaver and Red-headed Malimbe; 3d. Cheetah; 4d. Leopards; 9d.
Grey Parrots. (As *T* **133**)—1s. Blue-breasted Kingfishers; 1s. 3d.
Crowned Cranes; 2s. 6d. Kobs; 5s. Giraffes. *Vert* (as *T* **120**)—6d.
Saddle-bill Stork.

The 2d. and 3d. exist with PVA gum as well as gum arabic.
See also Nos. 220, etc.

The 1d., 3d., 4d. (No. 177a), 1s., 1s. 3d., 2s. 6d., 5s. and £1
values exist overprinted "F.G.N." (Federal Government of
Nigeria) twice in black. They were prepared during 1968 at the
request of one of the State Governments for use as official
stamps, but the scheme was abandoned and meter machines
were used instead. Some stamps held at Lagos Post Office were
sold over the counter in error and passed through the post in
October 1968. The Director of Posts made limited stocks of all
values, except the 1s., available from the Philatelic Bureau from
11 April 1969 "in order not to create an artificial scarcity", but
they had no postal validity. Covers do, however, exist showing
the 4d. value used by Lagos Federal Income Tax Office in April
1969 and others from the Office of the Secretary to the Military
Government in 1973 carry the 3d., 4d. and 2s. 6d. values.

COMMONWEALTH
P. M. MEETING
11. JAN. 1966

(134)

135 Y.M.C.A. Emblem
and H.Q., Lagos

1966 (11 Jan). *Commonwealth Prime Ministers' Meeting, Lagos.
No* 98 *optd with T* **134** *by the Nigerian Security Printing and
Minting Co, Lagos, in red.*

186	**48**	2s. 6d. black and yellow	30	30

(Des S. B. Ajayi. Litho Nigerian Security Printing & Minting Co
Ltd)

1966 (1 Sept). *Nigerian Y.W.C.A.'s Diamond Jubilee. P* 14.

187	**135**	4d. yellow-orange, ultramarine, orange-brown and yellow-green	15	10
188		9d. yellow-orange, ultramarine, brown and turquoise-green	15	60

137 Telephone Handset and
Linesman

139 "Education, Science and
Culture"

(Des S. B. Ajayi (4d.), N. Lasisi (1s. 6d.), B. Enweonwu (2s. 6d.))

1966 (1 Oct). *Third Anniv of Republic. T* **137** *and similar designs.
W* **34**. *P* 14½ × 14.

189		4d. green	10	10
190		1s. 6d. black, brown and reddish violet	45	50
191		2s. 6d. indigo, blue, yellow and green	1·25	2·25
189/91		*Set of 3*	1·60	2·50

Designs: *Vert*—4d. Dove and flag. *Horiz*—2s. 6d. North
Channel Bridge over Niger, Jebba.

(Des V. Whiteley from sketch by B. Salisu)

1966 (4 Nov). *20th Anniv of U.N.E.S.C.O. W* **34** (sideways).
P 14½ × 14.

192	**139**	4d. black, lake and orange-yellow	40	10
193		1s. 6d. black, lake and turquoise-green	1·75	2·50
194		2s. 6d. black, lake and rose-pink	2·75	5·00
192/4		*Set of 3*	4·50	7·00

140 Children drinking

(Des V. Whiteley, after M. O. Afamefuna (4d.), I. U. Anawanti
(1s. 6d.) and S. Adeyemi (2s. 6d.))

1966 (1 Dec). *Nigerian Red Cross. T* **140** *and similar designs.
W* **34**. *P* 14 × 14½ (1s. 6d.) *or* 14½ × 14 (others).

195		4d. + 1d. black, reddish violet and red	40	30
196		1s. 6d. + 3d. multicoloured	1·00	3·75
197		2s. 6d. + 3d. multicoloured	1·10	4·25
195/7		*Set of 3*	2·25	7·50

Designs: *Vert*—1s. 6d. Tending patient. *Horiz*—2s. 6d. Tending
casualties, and badge.

143 Surveying

(Des M. Goaman)

1967 (1 Feb). *International Hydrological Decade. T* **143** *and
similar multicoloured design. W* **34**. *P* 14½ × 14 (4d.) *or*
14 × 14½ (2s. 6d.).

198		4d. Type **143**	10	10
199		2s. 6d. Water gauge on dam (*vert*)	25	1·00

145 Globe and Weather Satellite

147 Eyo Masqueraders

(Des M. Shamir (4d.), S. Bodo (1s. 6d.))

1967 (23 Mar). *World Meteorological Day. T* **145** *and similar
horiz design. W* **34**. *P* 14½ × 14.

200		4d. magenta and blue	15	10
201		1s. 6d. black, yellow and blue	65	90

Design:—1s. 6d. Passing storm and sun.

(Des G. A. Okiki (4d.), A. B. Saka Lawal (1s. 6d.), S. Bodo (2s. 6d.).
Photo Enschedé)

1967 (1 Oct). *4th Anniv of Republic. T* **147** *and similar multicoloured designs. P* 11½ × 11 (2s. 6d.) *or* 11 × 11½ (others).

202		4d. Type **147**	15	10
203		1s. 6d. Crowd watching acrobat	50	1·50
204		2s. 6d. Stilt dancer (*vert*)	75	3·00
202/4		*Set of 3*	1·25	4·25

150 Tending Sick Animal

151 Smallpox Vaccination

(Des G. Drummond)

1967 (1 Dec). *Rinderpest Eradication Campaign. P* 14½ × 14.

205	**150**	4d. multicoloured	10	10
206		1s. 6d. multicoloured	55	1·50

PRINTERS AND PROCESS. Nos. 207/89 were printed in photogravure by the Nigerian Security Printing and Minting Co Ltd,
unless otherwise stated.

(Des J. Owei. Litho)

1968 (7 Apr). *20th Anniv of World Health Organization. T* **151**
and similar horiz design. P 14.

207		4d. magenta and black	15	10
208		1s. 6d. orange, lemon and black	55	40

Design:—1s. 6d. African and mosquito.

153 Chained Hands and Outline
of Nigeria

155 Hand grasping at
Doves of Freedom

(Des Jennifer Toombs)

1968 (1 July). *Human Rights Year. T* **153** *and similar design.
P* 14.

209		4d. greenish blue, black and yellow	10	10
210		1s. 6d. myrtle-green, orange-red and black	20	50

Design: *Vert*—1s. 6d. Nigerian flag and Human Rights emblem.

(Des G. Vasarhelyi)

1968 (1 Oct). *5th Anniv of Federal Republic. P* 13½ × 14.

211	**155**	4d. multicoloured	10	10
212		1s. 6d. multicoloured	20	20

156 Map of Nigeria and
Olympic Rings

158 G.P.O., Lagos

(Des J. Owei)

1968 (14 Oct). *Olympic Games, Mexico. T* **156** *and similar horiz
design. P* 14.

213		4d. black, green and scarlet	10	10
214		1s. 6d. multicoloured	20	20

Design:—1s. 6d. Nigerian athletes, flag and Olympic rings.

(Des D.L.R.)

1969 (11 Apr). *Inauguration of Philatelic Service. P* 14.

215	**158**	4d. black and green	10	10
216		1s. 6d. black and blue	20	20

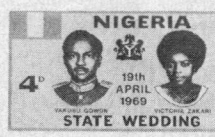

159 Yakubu Gowon and Victoria Zakari

(Des adapted from photo by Jackie Phillips. Litho)

1969 (20 Sept). *Wedding of General Gowon. P* 13 × 13½.

217	**159**	4d. chocolate and emerald	10	10
218		1s. 6d. black and emerald	50	20

1969–72. (a) *As No.* 173 *etc, but printed by Nigerian Security
Printing and Minting Co Ltd. With printer's imprint* "N.S.P. &
M. CO. LTD." *P* 13½ (6d.) *or P* 13 × 13½ (others).

220		1d. multicoloured	3·00	2·25
222		2d. multicoloured	1·75	90
		a. Smaller imprint (13.1.71)	1·00	1·75
223		3d. multicoloured (7.71)	65	1·50
		a. Larger imprint (22.10.71)	1·00	1·50
224		4d. multicoloured	8·00	10
		a. Smaller imprint	50·00	
225		6d. multicoloured (1971)	1·75	20
226		9d. Prussian blue and orange-red (1970)	6·00	50
		a. "TD" of "LTD" omitted from imprint (Pl. 1B, R. 10/2)	40·00	
227		1s. multicoloured (8.71)	2·00	20
228		1s. 3d. multicoloured (1971)	11·00	3·75
229		2s. 6d. multicoloured (1972)	8·50	70
230		5s. multicoloured (1972)	3·00	13·00
220/30		*Set of 10*	40·00	26·00

*On No. 222a the designer's name measures 4¾ mm. On No.
223a the imprints measure 9 and 8½ mm respectively. The normal
imprints on Nos. 222/3 both measure 5½ mm.
The date given for Nos. 222a and 223a are for the earliest known
used copies.

†No. 224 has the left-hand imprint 6 mm long and the
right-hand 5½ mm. On No. 224a the imprints are 5½ mm and
4½ mm respectively. The width of the design is also ½ mm
smaller.

Postal forgeries of the 2s. 6d. exist printed by lithography and
roughly perforated 11–12.
Imperforate proofs of similar 10s. and £1 values are known.

(b) *As Nos.* 222 *and* 224, *but redrawn, and printed by Enschedé. No
printer's imprint; designer's name at right. P* 14½ × 13.

231		2d. multicoloured (9.70)	29·00	2·00
232		4d. multicoloured (3.71)	75	30

In the 2d. the face value is white instead of yellow, and in the 4d.
the white lettering and value are larger.

160 Bank Emblem and
"5th Anniversary"
261 Bank Emblem
and Rays

(Des J. Owei (4d.), B. Salisu (1s. 6d.). Litho)

1969 (18 Oct). *Fifth Anniv of African Development Bank.* P 14.
233	160	4d. orange, black and blue	..	10	10
234	161	1s. 6d. lemon, black and plum	..	20	50

162 I.L.O. Emblem
164 Olumo Rock

(Des D. West)

1969 (15 Nov). *50th Anniv of International Labour Organisation.*
T **162** *and similar horiz design.* P 14.
235	4d. black and bright reddish violet	..	10	10
236	1s. 6d. emerald and black	..	75	1·00

Design:—1s. 6d. World map and I.L.O. emblem.

(Des A. Onwudimegwu)

1969 (30 Dec). *International Year of African Tourism. T* **164** *and
similar designs.* P 14.
237	4d. multicoloured	..	15	10
238	1s. black and bright emerald	..	20	10
239	1s. 6d. multicoloured	..	1·25	50
237/9		*Set of 3*	1·40	55

Designs: Vert—1s. Traditional musicians; 1s. 6d. Assob Falls.

167 Symbolic Tree
168 U.P.U. H.Q. Building

(Des E. Emokpae (4d., 1s., 2s.), B. Onobrakpeya (1s. 6d.). Photo
Enschedé)

1970 (28 May). *"Stamp of Destiny"; End of Civil War. T* **167** *and
similar designs.* P 11 × 11½ (2s.) or 11½ × 11 (others).
240	4d. gold, new blue and black	..	10	10
241	1s. multicoloured	..	10	10
242	1s. 6d. yellow-green and black	..	15	10
243	2s. multicoloured	..	20	20
240/3		*Set of 4*	40	30

Designs: Vert—1s. Symbolic Wheel; 1s. 6d. United Nigerians
supporting Map. Horiz—2s. Symbolic Torch.

(Des A. Onwudimegwu)

1970 (29 June). *New U.P.U. Headquarters Building.* P 14.
244	168	1s. reddish violet and greenish yellow ..	10	10
245		1s. 6d. light greenish blue and deep blue	40	20

169 Scroll
170 Oil Rig

(Des A. Onwudimegwu)

1970 (1 Sept). *25th Anniv of United Nations. T* **169** *and similar
vert design.* P 14.
246	4d. orange-brown, buff and black	..	10	10
247	1s. 6d. steel-blue, cinnamon and gold	..	30	20

Design:—1s. 6d. U.N. Building.

(Des E. Emokpae. Litho Enschedé)

1970 (30 Sept). *Tenth Anniv of Independence. T* **170** *and similar
vert designs. Multicoloured.* P 13½ × 13.
248	Type 170	..	25	10
249	4d. University Graduate	..	15	10
250	6d. Durbar Horsemen	..	30	10
251	1s. Servicemen raising Flag..	..	40	10
252	1s. Footballer	..	40	10

253	1s. 6d. Parliament Building..	..	40	40
254	2s. Kainji Dam	..	70	90
255	2s. 6d. Agricultural Produce	..	70	1·00
248/55		*Set of 8*	3·00	2·40

171 Children and Globe
172 Ibibio
Face Mask

(Des E. Emokpae and A. Onwudimegwu. Photo Enschedé)

1971 (21 Mar). *Racial Equality Year. T* **171** *and similar multicoloured designs.* P 13 × 13½ (4d., 2s.) or 13½ × 13 (others).
256	4d. Type 171	..	10	10
257	1s. Black and white men uprooting "Racism"			
	(vert)	..	10	10
258	1s. 6d. The world in black and white (vert)	..	15	60
259	2s. Black and white men united	..	15	85
256/9		*Set of 4*	35	1·50

(Des A. Onwudimegwu)

1971 (30 Sept). *Antiquities of Nigeria. T* **172** *and similar vert
designs.* P 13½ × 14.
260	4d. black and pale blue	..	10	10
261	1s. 3d. blackish brown and ochre	..	15	30
262	1s. 9d. emerald, sepia and olive-yellow	..	20	80
260/2		*Set of 3*	35	1·00

Designs:—1s. 3d. Benin bronze; 1s. 9d. Ife bronze.

173 Children and
Symbol
174 Mast and Dish
Aerial

(Des E. Emokpae)

1971 (11 Dec). *25th Anniv of U.N.I.C.E.F. T* **173** *and similar
vert designs, each incorporating the U.N.I.C.E.F. symbol.*
P 13½ × 14.
263	4d. multicoloured	..	10	10
264	1s. 3d. yellow-orange, orge-red & carm-lake	15	40
265	1s. 9d. pale greenish blue & dp greenish blue	15	85
263/5		*Set of 3*	30	1·25

Designs:—1s. 3d. Mother and child; 1s. 9d. Mother carrying
child.

(Des A. Onwudimegwu)

1971 (30 Dec). *Opening of Nigerian Earth Satellite Station. T* **174**
and similar horiz designs. P 14.
266	174	4d. multicoloured	..	15	10
267	—	1s. 3d. green, blue and black	..	30	50
268	—	1s. 9d. brown, orange and black	..	40	1·00
269	—	3s. mauve, black and magenta	..	85	2·00
266/9			*Set of 4*	1·50	3·25

Designs:—Nos. 267/9, as T **174**, but showing different views of
the Satellite Station.
The 4d. has been seen on a cover from Ilorin, postmarked
23.12.71.

175 Trade Fair
Emblem
176 Traffic

(Des E. Emokpae (4d.), A. Onwudimegwu (others). Litho D.L.R.)

1972 (23 Feb). *All-Africa Trade Fair. T* **175** *and similar designs.*
P 13.
270	4d. multicoloured	..	10	10
271	1s. 3d. deep lilac, lemon and gold	..	15	35
272	1s. 9d. yellow-orange, orange-yellow & black	15	90
270/2		*Set of 3*	30	1·25

Designs: Horiz—1s. 3d. Map of Africa with pointers to Nairobi.
Vert—1s. 9d. Africa on globe.

(Des A. Onwudimegwu (4d., 3s.), E. Emokpae (1s. 3d.), J. Owei
(1s. 9d.). Litho D.L.R.)

1972 (23 June). *Change to Driving on the Right. T* **176** *and similar
horiz designs. Multicoloured (except 4d.).* P 13.
273	4d. Type 176 (yellow-orge, dp chest & black)	50	10
274	1s. 3d. Roundabout	..	1·25	70
275	1s. 9d. Highway	..	1·40	10
276	3s. Road junction	..	2·25	3·00
273/6		*Set of 4*	4·75	4·50

---

177 Nok Style
Terracotta Head
178 Hides and Skins

(Des G. Okiki (1s. 3d.), A. Aiyegbusi (others). Litho D.L.R.)

1972 (1 Sept). *All-Nigeria Arts Festival. T* **177** *and similar multicoloured designs.* P 13.
277	4d. Type 177	..	10	10
278	1s. 3d. Bronze pot from Igbo-Ukwu ..	..	25	60
279	1s. 9d. Bone harpoon (horiz)..	..	30	1·50
277/9		*Set of 3*	60	2·00

(New Currency. 100 kobo = 1 naira)

(Des E. Emokpae (8, 25, 30, 50 k., 1 n.), A. Onwudimegwu (others))

1973–74. *T* **178** *and similar designs.* P 14.

(a) Photo. Left-hand imprint 5¼ mm long (2 Jan–2 Apr)
280	1 k. multicoloured (deep green foliage)	..	90	70
	a. Light emerald foliage* (2.4.73)	..	20	10
281	2 k. black, pale turquoise-blue and bright			
	purple	..	35	10
282	5 k. multicoloured (emerald hills)	..	60	60
	a. Bright yellow-green hills* (2.4.73)	..	50	10
283	10 k. black, orange-yellow and lilac	..	70	80
284	12 k. black, pale emerald and deep cobalt	..	12·00	10·00
285	18 k. multicoloured	..	12·00	2·00
286	20 k. multicoloured	..	12·00	3·00
287	30 k. black, chrome-yellow and new blue	..	12·00	7·50
288	50 k. multicoloured (black background and			
	figure)	..	2·50	2·75
	a. Deep chocolate background and figure*			
	(2.4.73)	..	75	90
289	1 n. multicoloured	..	2·50	6·00
280/9		*Set of 10*	48·00	27·00

(b) Litho. Left-hand imprint 6 mm long (2 Apr 1973†–74)
290	1 k. multicoloured (8.73)	..	10	20
291	2 k. black, pale turquoise-blue and bright			
	purple (27.6.74)**	..	2·50	90
292	3 k. multicoloured	..	15	10
293	5 k. multicoloured (shades) (2.74)	..	3·75	70
294	7 k. multicoloured	..	30	1·25
295	8 k. multicoloured	..	40	10
296	10 k. black, orange-yellow and lilac (8.73)	..	4·50	20
297	12 k. black, green and cobalt (shades)	..	30	2·25
298	15 k. multicoloured	..	30	60
299	18 k. multicoloured	..	50	30
300	20 k. multicoloured	..	65	30
301	25 k. multicoloured	..	85	45
302	30 k. black, chrome-yellow and new blue	..	40	1·50
303	35 k. multicoloured	..	6·00	4·25
305	1 n. multicoloured (shades)	..	50	75
306	2 n. multicoloured (shades)..	..	1·25	2·00
290/306		*Set of 16*	19·00	14·00

Designs: Horiz—2 k. Natural gas tanks; 3 k. Cement works; 5 k.
Cattle-ranching; 7 k. Timber mill; 8 k. Oil refinery; 10 k.
Cheetahs, Yankari Game Reserve; 12 k. New Civic Building;
15 k. Sugar-cane harvesting; 20 k. Vaccine production; 25 k.
Modern wharf; 35 k. Textile machinery; 1 n. Eko Bridge; 2 n.
Teaching Hospital, Lagos. Vert—18 k. Palm oil production; 30 k.
Argungu Fishing Festival; 50 k. Pottery.
*On Nos. 280a, 282a and 288a other colours also differ, but the
shades can best be identified by the distinctive features noted.
†Although First Day Covers of Nos. 290/306 were dated 1
April the stamps were not placed on sale until 2 April. Later,
post-dated, covers included No. 291.
**This is the earliest known postmark date. No. 291 was not
released by the Crown Agents in London until 11 September 1975.
Differences between printings:
1 k. In photogravure printings the stretched hide at left is in
brownish black; on the litho stamps this hide is brown and
yellow.
2 k. On the litho stamp the line of division between the black and
pale blue colours of the gas tanks is a regular curve; on the
photogravure printing it is horizontal and irregular. The
litho stamp also has a wider mauve border at top.
5 k. The litho printing differs from the photogravure (Nos. 282/a)
in having brown on the herdsman, instead of black.
10 k. The litho version has much less black on the cheetahs and
tree trunk. It also shows black details at the left-hand end of
the trunk, which do not appear on the photogravure version.
12 k. No. 284 is much darker than the litho version, especially
within the building and amongst the trees at right.
18 k. The lithographed printing shows two oildrums in the foreground which are not present on the photogravure stamp.
20 k. The lithographed printing includes a brown plate not
present on the photogravure version and this shows on the
chemist. The liquid in the flasks is grey-blue instead of
black. On the watermarked version, No. 348, the liquid is
turquoise-blue.
30 k. No. 287 is much darker, with greater use of black in the
design.
50 k. The litho version (No. 352) has solid shading on the potter's
upper arm and lacks a black inner frame-line beneath the
potter's wheel. No. 352 has a green printer's imprint at foot
(instead of black) and its background is similar to that of No.
288a.
1 n. On the photogravure stamp the traffic is shown driving on
the left. For the litho version the traffic is corrected to show
it driving on the right.
Used copies of No. 282a have been seen with orange omitted.
Postal forgeries of the 10 k. Yankari Game Reserve design
exist crudely printed by lithography on unwatermarked paper
and roughly perforated 11–12.
See also Nos. 338/54.

PROCESS. From No. 307 onwards all stamps were lithographed
by the Nigerian Security Printing and Minting Co Ltd.

179 Athlete

1973 (8 Jan). *Second All-African Games. Lagos. T* **179** *and similar multicoloured designs (except 5 k.).* P 13.
307 5 k. Type 179 (lt lilac, lt greenish bl & blk) .. 15 10
308 12 k. Football .. 25 50
309 18 k. Table-tennis .. 60 1·00
310 25 k. National Stadium (*vert*) .. 70 1·50
307/10 .. .. *Set of 4* 1·50 2·75

180 All-Africa House, Addis Ababa

181 Dr. Hansen

1973 (25 May). *Tenth Anniv of O.A.U. T* **180** *and similar vert designs. Multicoloured.* P 14.
311 5 k. Type 180 .. .. 10 10
312 18 k. O.A.U. flag 30 40
313 30 k. O.A.U. emblem and symbolic flight of ten stairs .. 50 80
311/13 .. .. .. *Set of 3* 70 1·10

(Des A. Onwudimegwu)

1973 (30 July). *Centenary of Discovery of Leprosy Bacillus.* P 14.
314 **181** 5 k. + 2 k. lt red-brown, flesh & black .. 30 70

182 W.M.O. Emblem and Weather-vane

183 University Complex

(Des O. I. Oshiga)

1973 (4 Sept). *I.M.O./W.M.O. Centenary.* P 14.
315 **182** 5 k. multicoloured 30 10
316 30 k. multicoloured .. .. 1·50 2·25

(Des A. Onwudimegwu (5, 18 k.), C. Okechukwu (12 k.), O. I. Oshiga (30 k.))

1973 (17 Nov). *25th Anniv of Ibadan University. T* **183** *and similar multicoloured designs.* P 13½ × 14 (12 k.) or 14 × 13½ (*others*).
317 5 k. Type 183 .. .. 10 10
318 12 k. Students' population growth (*vert*) 15 20
319 18 k. Tower and students .. 25 35
320 30 k. Teaching Hospital .. 35 65
317/20 .. .. .. *Set of 4* 75 1·10

184 Lagos 1d. Stamp of 1874

(Des A. Onwudimegwu (30 k.), S. Eluare (others))

1974 (10 June). *Stamp Centenary. T* **184** *and similar horiz designs.* P 14 × 13½.
321 5 k. light emerald, yellow-orange and black 15 10
322 12 k. multicoloured 40 40
323 18 k. light yellowish green, mauve and black 60 70
324 30 k. multicoloured .. .. 1·75 2·00
321/4 .. .. .. *Set of 4* 2·50 2·75
Designs:—5 k. Graph of mail traffic growth; 12 k. Northern Nigeria £25 stamp of 1904; 30 k. Forms of mail transport.

185 U.P.U. Emblem on Globe

186 Starving and Well-fed Children

(Des S. Eluare (5 k.), A. Onwudimegwu (18 k.), O. I. Oshiga (30 k.))

1974 (9 Oct). *Centenary of Universal Postal Union. T* **185** *and similar horiz designs.* P 14.
325 5 k. lt greenish blue, yellow-orange & black 15 10
326 18 k. multicoloured .. .. 2·00 60
327 30 k. bistre-brown, lt greenish blue & black 1·75 1·75
325/7 .. .. .. *Set of 3* 3·50 3·25
Designs:—18 k. World transport map; 30 k. U.P.U. emblem and letters.

(Des A. Onwudimegwu (12 k.), S. Eluare (others))

1974 (25 Nov). *Freedom from Hunger Campaign. T* **186** *and similar designs.* P 14.
328 5 k. apple-green, buff and grey-black .. 10 10
329 12 k. multicoloured 30 50
330 30 k. multicoloured .. .. 80 1·75
328/30 .. .. .. *Set of 3* 1·00 2·00
Designs: *Horiz*—12 k. Poultry battery. *Vert*—30 k. Water-hoist.

187 Telex Network and Teleprinter

188 Queen Amina of Zaria

(Des S. Eluare)

1975 (3 July). *Inauguration of Telex Network. T* **187** *and similar vert designs.* P 13½ × 14.
331 5 k. black, yellow-orange & light olive-green 10 10
332 12 k. black, lemon and orange-brown .. 20 20
333 18 k. multicoloured 30 30
334 30 k. multicoloured 50 50
331/4 .. .. .. *Set of 4* 1·00 1·00
Nos. 332/4 are as T **187** but have the motifs arranged differently.

(Des A. Onwudimegwu)

1975 (18 Aug). *International Women's Year.* P 14.
335 **188** 5 k. deep olive, light yellow and azure 20 10
336 18 k. purple, pale blue and light mauve .. 80 80
337 30 k. multicoloured .. .. 95 1·60
335/7 .. .. .. *Set of 3* 1·75 2·25

WATERMARK VARIETIES. Issues printed by Nigerian Security Printing and Minting Co. Ltd. on W **189** show the horizontal stamps with the watermark upright or inverted and the vertical stamps with it reading up or down.

189

1975–82*. *As Nos. 290 etc., but* W **189** (*sideways on* 18, 50 k.).
338 1 k. multicoloured (6.4.77) .. 1·00 1·25
339 2 k. black, pale turq-bl & bright purple (9.75) 1·00 10
340 3 k. multicoloured (10.75) .. 15 10
341 5 k. multicoloured (1.76) .. 1·25 10
342 7 k. multicoloured (16.5.80) .. 2·25 2·00
343 8 k. multicoloured (12.76) .. 2·00 90
344 10 k. blk, orange-yell & lilac (*shades*) (7.4.76) 1·00 20
346 15 k. multicoloured (5.82) .. — 1·75
347 18 k. multicoloured (12.78) .. 3·00 2·75
348 20 k. multicoloured (9.79) .. 3·00 2·75
349 25 k. multicoloured (21.3.77) .. 3·25 30
352 50 k. multicoloured (2.9.77) .. 4·25 3·50
354 2 n. multicoloured (11.77) .. 5·00 6·00
*Earliest known dates of issue.
Some values of this series, including the 50 k., were re-issued in 1992 during shortages of the current definitive set.

190 Alexander Graham Bell

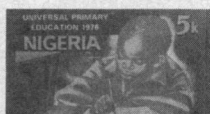
191 Child Writing

(Des A. Onwudimegwu)

1976 (10 Mar). *Telephone Centenary. T* **190** *and similar designs.* W **189** (*sideways on* 5 *and* 25 k.). P 13½.
355 5 k. multicoloured 10 10
356 18 k. multicoloured 40 60
357 25 k. royal blue, pale blue and blackish brown 70 1·00
  a. No wmk .. .. 10·00
355/7 .. .. .. *Set of 3* 1·10 1·50
Designs: *Horiz*—18 k. Gong and modern telephone system. *Vert*—25 k. Telephones, 1876 and 1976.

(Des A. Onwudimegwu (5 k.), S. Eluare (18 k.), N. Lasisi (25 k.))

1976 (20 Sept). *Launching of Universal Primary Education. T* **191** *and similar designs.* W **189** (*sideways on* 18 *and* 25 k.). P 14.
358 5 k. lemon, light violet and bright mauve .. 10 10
359 18 k. multicoloured 45 60
360 25 k. multicoloured 70 85
358/60 .. .. .. *Set of 3* 1·10 1·40
Designs: *Vert*—18 k. Children entering school; 25 k. Children in class.

192 Festival Emblem

(Des O. I. Oshiga (5 k., 30 k.), A. Onwudimegwu (10 k., 12 k.), N. Lasisi (18 k.))

1976–77. *Second World Black and African Festival of Arts and Culture, Nigeria. T* **192** *and similar horiz designs.* W **189.** P 14.
361 5 k. gold and blackish brown (1.11.76) 25 10
362 10 k. lt red-brown, lt yellow & black (15.1.77) 35 40
363 12 k. multicoloured (15.1.77) .. 60 55
364 18 k. chrome-yellow, lt brown & blk (1.11.76) 80 80
365 30 k. magenta and black (15.1.77) .. 1·00 1·50
361/5 .. .. .. *Set of 5* 2·75 3·00
Designs:—10 k. National Arts Theatre; 12 k. African hair styles; 18 k. Musical instruments; 30 k. "Nigerian arts and crafts".

193 General Murtala Muhammed and Map of Nigeria

194 Scouts Saluting

(Des A. Onwudimegwu (5, 18 k.), O. I. Oshiga (30 k.))

1977 (13 Feb). *First Death Anniv of General Muhammed (Head of State). T* **193** *and similar vert designs. Multicoloured.* W **189** (*sideways on* 18 *and* 30 k.). P 14.
366 5 k. Type 193 .. .. 10 10
367 18 k. General in dress uniform .. 20 35
368 30 k. General in battle dress .. 30 70
366/8 .. .. .. *Set of 3* 50 1·00

(Des N. Lasisi (18 k.), A. Onwudimegwu (others))

1977 (2 Apr). *First All-Africa Scout Jamboree, Jos, Nigeria. T* **194** *and similar horiz designs. Multicoloured.* W **189** (*sideways on* 5 k.). P 14.
369 5 k. Type 194 .. .. 15 10
370 18 k. Scouts cleaning street .. 60 70
371 25 k. Scouts working on farm .. 70 1·25
372 30 k. Jamboree emblem and map of Africa 80 2·00
369/72 .. .. .. *Set of 4* 2·00 3·50

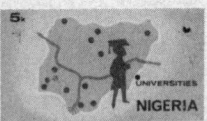
195 Trade Fair Complex

(Des S. Eluare (5 k.), A. Onwudimegwu (others))

1977 (27 Nov). *1st Lagos International Trade Fair. T* **195** *and similar horiz designs.* W **189.** P 14.
373 5 k. black, new blue and yellow-green .. 10 10
374 18 k. black, new blue and magenta .. 20 25
375 30 k. multicoloured 30 45
373/5 .. .. .. *Set of 3* 50 70
Designs:—18 k. Globe and Trade Fair emblem; 30 k. Weaving and basketry.

196 Map showing Nigerian Universities

(Des M. O. Shadare (5 k.), C. Okechukwu (12 k.), A. Onwudimegwu (18 k.), N. Lasisi (30 k.))

1978 (28 Apr). *Global Conference on Technical Co-operation between Developing Countries, Buenos Aires. T* **196** *and similar horiz designs.* W **189.** P 14.
376 5 k. multicoloured 10 10
377 12 k. multicoloured 15 15
378 18 k. multicoloured 25 25
379 30 k. yellow, bluish violet and black .. 45 60
376/9 .. .. .. *Set of 4* 80 1·00
Designs:—12 k. Map of West African highways and telecommunications; 18 k. Technologists undergoing training; 30 k. World map.

197 Microwave Antenna

1978 (17 May). *10th World Telecommunications Day.* W **189**. P 14.
380 197 30 k. multicoloured 50 60

198 Students on "Operation Feed the Nation"

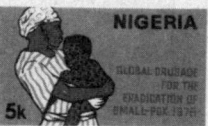

199 Mother with Infected Child

(Des J. Salisu (5 k.), N. Lasisi (18 k.), A. Onwudimegwu (30 k.))

1978 (7 July). *"Operation Feed the Nation" Campaign.* T **198** and similar multicoloured designs. W **189** (sideways on 30 k.). P 14.
381 5 k. Type 198 .. .. .. 10 10
382 18 k. Family backyard farm 20 20
383 30 k. Plantain farm (vert) 35 60
381/3 Set of 3 55 75

(Des G. Osuji (30 k.), N. Lasisi (others))

1978 (31 Aug). *Global Eradication of Smallpox.* T **199** and similar designs. W **189** (sideways on 30 k.). P 14.
384 5 k. black, orange-brown and rose-lilac 15 10
385 12 k. multicoloured 25 20
386 18 k. black, lake-brown and greenish yellow 40 40
387 30 k. black, silver and rose-pink .. 55 70
384/7 Set of 4 1·25 1·25
Designs: *Horiz*—12 k. Doctor and infected child; 18 k. Group of children being vaccinated. *Vert*—30 k. Syringe.

200 Nok Terracotta Human Figure, Bwari (900 B.C.–200 A.D.)

201 Anti-Apartheid Emblem

(Des local artists)

1978 (27 Oct). *Antiquities.* T **200** and similar designs. W **189** (sideways on 5, 18 and 30 k.). P 14.
388 5 k. black, new blue and carmine-red 10 10
389 12 k. multicoloured 15 10
390 18 k. black, greenish blue and carmine-red 20 15
391 30 k. multicoloured 25 20
388/91 Set of 4 60 45
Designs: *Horiz*—12 k. Igbo-Ukwu bronze snail shell, Igbo Isaiah (9th-century A.D.). *Vert*—18 k. Ife bronze statue of king (12th–15th century A.D.); 30 k. Benin bronze equestrian figure (about 1700 A.D.).

(Des A. Onwudimegwu)

1978 (10 Dec). *International Anti-Apartheid Year.* W **189** (sideways). P 14.
392 201 18 k. black, greenish yellow & vermilion 15 15

202 Wright Brothers and Wright Type A

203 Murtala Muhammed Airport

(Des A. Onwudimegwu)

1978 (28 Dec). *75th Anniv of Powered Flight.* T **202** and similar horiz design. W **189**. P 14.
393 5 k. multicoloured 20 10
394 18 k. black, ultramarine and light blue 60 20
Design:—18 k. Nigerian Air Force formation.

(Des A. Onwudimegwu)

1979 (15 Mar). *Opening of Murtala Muhammed Airport.* W **189**. P 14.
395 203 5 k. black, grey-blk & brt greenish blue 40 30
a. Printed on the gummed side .. 11·00

MINIMUM PRICE

The minimum price quote is 10p which represents a handling charge rather than a basis for valuing common stamps. For further notes about prices see introductory pages.

---

204 Child with Stamp Album

205 Mother and Child

1979 (11 Apr). *10th Anniv of National Philatelic Service.* W **189**. P 14.
396 204 5 k. multicoloured 10 10

1979 (28 June). *International Year of the Child.* T **205** and similar multicoloured designs. W **189** (sideways on 25 k.). P 14.
397 5 k. Type 205 .. .. .. 10 10
398 18 k. Children studying 35 30
399 25 k. Children playing (vert) .. 40 50
397/9 Set of 3 75 80

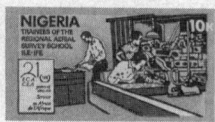

206 Trainee Teacher making Audio Visual Aid Materials

207 Necom House

(Des M. Shadare and O. Oshiga)

1979 (25 July). *50th Anniv of International Bureau of Education.* T **206** and similar vert design. Multicoloured. W **189** (sideways). P 14.
400 10 k. Type 206 .. .. 10 10
401 30 k. Adult education class .. 25 30

(Des A. Onwudimegwu)

1979 (20 Sept). *50th Anniv of Consultative Committee of International Radio.* W **189** (sideways). P 14.
402 207 10 k. multicoloured 15 20

208 Trainees of the Regional Aerial Survey School, Ile-Ife

(Des A. Onwudimegwu)

1979 (12 Dec). *21st Anniv of the Economic Commission for Africa.* W **189**. P 14.
403 208 10 k. multicoloured 20 20

209 Football, Cup and Map of Nigeria

210 Wrestling

(Des G. Akinola (10 k.), Mrs. O. Adeyeye (30 k.))

1980 (8 Mar). *African Cup of Nations Football Competition, Nigeria.* T **209** and similar multicoloured design. W **189** (sideways on 30 k.). P 14.
404 10 k. Type 209 .. .. 20 10
405 30 k. Footballer (vert) 60 50

(Des M. Shadare (10 k.), Mrs. O. Adeyeye (others))

1980 (19 July). *Olympic Games, Moscow.* T **210** and similar designs. W **189** (sideways on 10, 20 and 45 k.). P 14.
406 10 k. multicoloured 10 10
407 20 k. black and bright yellow-green 10 10
408 30 k. black, reddish orange and blue 15 15
409 45 k. multicoloured 20 20
406/9 Set of 4 45 45
Designs: *Vert*—20 k. Long jump; 45 k. Netball. *Horiz*—30 k. Swimming.

211 Figures supporting O.P.E.C. Emblem

212 Tank Locomotive No. 2, Wushishi Tramway

(Des G. Oluwasegun)

1980 (15 Sept). *20th Anniv of O.P.E.C. (Organization of Petroleum Exporting Countries).* T **211** and similar design. W **189** (sideways on 45 k.). P 14.
410 10 k. black, ultramarine and greenish yellow 15 10
411 45 k. black, deep turquoise-blue and magenta 70 60
Design: *Vert*—45 k. O.P.E.C. emblem on globe.

1980 (2 Oct). *25th Anniv of Nigerian Railway Corporation.* T **212** and similar horiz designs. Multicoloured. W **189**. P 14.
412 10 k. Type 212 .. .. .. 75 10
413 20 k. Loading goods train .. 1·50 85
414 30 k. Freight train .. .. 2·00 1·25
412/14 Set of 3 3·75 2·00

213 Metric Scales

214 "Communications" Symbols and Map of West Africa

(Des G. Akinola (10 k.), M. Shadare (30 k.))

1980 (14 Oct). *World Standards Day.* T **213** and similar design. W **189** (sideways on 10 k.). P 14.
415 10 k. red and black 10 10
416 30 k. multicoloured 35 40
Design: *Horiz*—30 k. Quality control.

1980 (5 Nov). *5th Anniv of E.C.O.W.A.S. (Economic Community of West African States).* T **214** and similar horiz designs showing symbols of economic structure and map of West Africa. W **189**. P 14.
417 10 k. black, yellow-orange and grey-olive 10 10
418 25 k. black, emerald and bright rose 30 10
419 30 k. black, greenish yellow and yellow-brown 20 15
420 45 k. black, turquoise-blue and bright blue 25 25
417/20 Set of 4 70 50
Designs:—25 k. "Transport"; 30 k. "Agriculture"; 45 k. "Industry".

215 Disabled Woman Sweeping

216 President launching "Green Revolution" (food production campaign)

(Des N. Lasisi (10 k.), G. Akinola (30 k.))

1981 (25 June). *International Year for Disabled Persons.* T **215** and similar vert design. W **189** (sideways). P 14.
421 10 k. multicoloured 20 10
422 30 k. black, chestnut and new blue 65 65
Design:—30 k. Disabled man filming.

(Des Mrs. A. Adeyeye (10 k.), G. Akinola (30 k.), S. Eluare (others))

1981 (16 Oct). *World Food Day.* T **216** and similar designs. W **189** (sideways on 25 and 30 k.). P 14.
423 10 k. multicoloured 10 10
424 25 k. black, greenish yellow and emerald 20 50
425 30 k. multicoloured 25 55
426 45 k. black, yellow-brown and orange-yellow 45 85
423/6 Set of 4 85 1·75
Designs: *Vert*—25 k. Food crops; 30 k. Harvesting tomatoes. *Horiz*—45 k. Pig farming.

217 Rioting in Soweto

218 "Preservation of Wildlife"

(Des G. Osuji)

1981 (10 Dec). *Anti-Apartheid Movement.* T **217** and similar design. W **189** (sideways on 45 k.). P 14.
427 30 k. multicoloured 35 55
428 45 k. black, vermilion and light green 50 95
Design: *Vert*—45 k. "Police brutality".

(Des G. Akinola)

1982 (22 Feb). *75th Anniv of Boy Scout Movement.* T **218** and similar horiz design. Multicoloured. W **189**. P 14.
429 30 k. Type 218 .. .. .. 50 55
430 45 k. Lord Baden-Powell taking salute 75 95

219 Early Inoculation

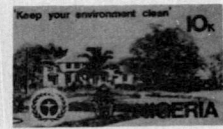
220 "Keep your Environment Clean"

(Des G. Osuji (10 k.), C. Ogbebor (30 k.), N. Lasisi (45 k.))

1982 (24 Mar). *Centenary of Robert Koch's Discovery of Tubercle Bacillus. T* **219** *and similar designs. W* **189** *(sideways on 45 k.). P* 14.

431	10 k. multicoloured		20	15
432	30 k. grey-black, brown and turquoise-green		50	65
433	45 k. grey-black, light brown and bright green		80	1·40
431/3		*Set of* 3	1·40	2·00

Designs: *Horiz*—30 k. Technician and microscope. *Vert*—45 k. Patient being X-rayed.

(Des C. Ogbebor (10 k.), N. Lasisi (others))

1982 (10 June). *10th Anniv of U.N. Conference on Human Environment. T* **220** *and similar horiz designs. W* **189**. *P* 14.

434	10 k. multicoloured		10	10
435	20 k. yellow-orange, greenish grey and black		20	40
436	30 k. multicoloured		35	60
437	45 k. multicoloured		55	85
434/7		*Set of* 4	1·10	1·75

Designs:—20 k. "Check air pollution"; 30 k. "Preserve natural environment"; 45 k. "Reafforestation concerns all".

221 *Salamis parhassus*

222 Carving of "Male and Female Twins"

(Des G. Akinola)

1982 (15 Sept). *Nigerian Butterflies. T* **221** *and similar horiz designs. Multicoloured. W* **189**. *P* 14.

438	10 k. Type **221**		15	10
439	20 k. *Iterus zalmoxis*		30	30
440	30 k. *Cymothoe beckeri*		40	40
441	45 k. *Papilio hesperus*		70	70
438/41		*Set of* 4	1·40	1·40

(Des C. Ogbebor (10 k.), G. Akinola (20 k.), S. Eluare (30 k.), N. Lasisi (45 k.))

1982 (18 Nov). *25th Anniv of National Museum. T* **222** *and similar multicoloured designs. W* **189** *(sideways on 10, 30, 45 k.). P* 14.

442	10 k. Type **222**		10	10
443	20 k. Royal bronze leopard (*horiz*)		20	35
444	30 k. Soapstone seated figure		35	90
445	45 k. Wooden helmet mask		50	1·50
442/5		*Set of* 4	1·10	2·50

223 Three Generations

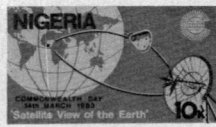
224 Satellite View of Globe

(Des G. Akinola)

1983 (8 Mar). *Family Day. T* **223** *and similar multicoloured design. W* **189** *(sideways on 30 k.). P* 14.

446	10 k. Type **223**		15	10
447	30 k. Parents with three children (*vert*)		50	65

(Des N. Lasisi (30 k.), C. Ogbebor (others))

1983 (14 Mar). *Commonwealth Day. T* **224** *and similar designs. W* **189** *(sideways on 30, 45 k.). P* 14.

448	10 k. yellow-brown and black		10	10
449	25 k. multicoloured		20	30
450	30 k. black, magenta and pale grey		55	35
451	45 k. multicoloured		35	45
448/51		*Set of* 4	1·10	1·10

Designs: *Horiz*—25 k. National Assembly Buildings. *Vert*—30 k. Drilling for oil; 45 k. Athletics.

225 Corps Members on Building Project

226 Postman on Bicycle

(Des Mrs. A. Adeyeye (25 k.), G. Akinola (others))

1983 (25 May). *10th Anniv of National Youth Service Corps. T* **225** *and similar multicoloured designs. P* 14.

452	10 k. Type **225**		15	10
453	25 k. On the assault-course (*vert*)		30	30
454	30 k. Corps members on parade (*vert*)		40	40
452/4		*Set of* 3	75	70

(Des N. Lasisi (25 k.), O. Ogunfowora (30 k.), Mrs. A. Adeyeye (others))

1983 (20 July). *World Communications Year. T* **226** *and similar multicoloured designs. W* **189** *(sideways on 10 k.). P* 14.

455	10 k. Type **226**		15	10
456	25 k. Newspaper kiosk (*horiz*)		30	40
457	30 k. Town crier blowing elephant tusk (*horiz*)		35	45
458	45 k. T.V. newsreader (*horiz*)		45	55
455/8		*Set of* 4	1·10	1·25

227 Pink Shrimp

228 On Parade

(Des Hilda Woods (10 k.), G. Osuji (25 k.), Mrs. A. Adeyeye (30 k.), O. Ogunfowora (45 k.))

1983 (22 Sept). *World Fishery Resources. T* **227** *and similar horiz designs. W* **189**. *P* 14.

459	10 k. rose, new blue and black		15	10
460	25 k. multicoloured		30	40
461	30 k. multicoloured		30	45
462	45 k. multicoloured		40	70
459/62		*Set of* 4	1·00	1·40

Designs:—25 k. Long-necked Croaker; 30 k. Barracuda; 45 k. Fishing techniques.

(Des F. Nwaije (10 k.), Mrs A. Adeyeye (30 k.), G. Osuji (45 k.))

1983 (14 Oct). *Boys' Brigade Centenary and 75th Anniv of Movement in Nigeria. T* **228** *and similar multicoloured designs. W* **189** *(sideways on 10 k.). P* 14.

463	10 k. Type **228**		40	10
464	30 k. Members working on cassava plantation (*horiz*)		1·50	1·50
465	45 k. Skill training (*horiz*)		2·25	2·75
463/5		*Set of* 3	3·75	4·00

229 Crippled Child

230 Waterbuck

(Des S. Eluare (10 k.), G. Osuji (others))

1984 (29 Feb). *Stop Polio Campaign. T* **229** *and similar designs. W* **189** *(sideways on 10 k. and 30 k.). P* 14.

466	10 k. light blue, black and light brown		20	15
467	25 k. pale orange, black and greenish yellow		40	75
468	30 k. carmine-rose, black and orange-brown		60	1·10
466/8		*Set of* 3	1·10	1·75

Designs: *Horiz*—25 k. Child receiving vaccine. *Vert*—30 k. Healthy child.

(Des O. Ogunfowora (30 k.), Mrs. A. Adeyeye (45 k.), N. Lasisi (others))

1984 (25 May). *Nigerian Wildlife. T* **230** *and similar designs. W* **189** *(inverted on 30 k., sideways on 10 k., 45 k.). P* 14.

469	10 k. light green, light brown and black		20	10
470	25 k. multicoloured		40	50
471	30 k. yellow-brown, black and light green		50	90
472	45 k. new blue, pale orange and black		60	1·25
469/72		*Set of* 4	1·50	2·50

Designs: *Horiz*—25 k. Hartebeest; 30 k. African Buffalo. *Vert*—45 k. Diademed Monkey ("African Golden Monkey").

231 Obverse and Reverse of 1969 £1 Note

232 Boxing

1984 (2 July). *25th Anniv of Nigerian Central Bank. T* **231** *and similar horiz designs. W* **189** *(inverted on 30 k.). P* 14.

473	10 k. multicoloured		20	10
474	25 k. deep cinnamon, black and light green		45	50
475	30 k. light rose, black and grey-olive		55	60
473/5		*Set of* 3	1·10	1·10

Designs:—25 k. Central Bank; 30 k. Obverse and reverse of 1959 £5 note.

1984 (20 July). *Olympic Games, Los Angeles. T* **232** *and similar vert designs. Multicoloured. W* **189** *(sideways). P* 14.

476	10 k. Type **232**		15	10
477	25 k. Discus-throwing		35	50
478	30 k. Weightlifting		40	60
479	45 k. Cycling		60	90
476/9		*Set of* 4	1·40	1·90

233 Irrigation Project, Lesotho

234 Pin-tailed Whydah

(Des Mrs. A. Adeyeye (10 k.), S. Eluare (25 k.), Hilda Woods (30 k.), O. Ogunfowora (45 k.))

1984 (10 Sept). *20th Anniv of African Development Bank. T* **233** *and similar designs. W* **189** *(sideways on 10 k.). P* 14.

480	10 k. multicoloured		15	10
481	25 k. multicoloured		30	50
482	30 k. black, chrome yell & bright greenish bl		35	60
483	45 k. black, orange-brn & bright greenish bl		1·75	90
480/3		*Set of* 4	2·25	1·90

Designs: *Horiz*—25 k. Bomi Hills Road, Liberia; 30 k. School building project, Seychelles; 45 k. Coal mining, Niger.

(Des S. Eluare (25 k.), O. Ogunfowora (45 k.), F. Isibor (others))

1984 (24 Oct). *Rare Birds. T* **234** *and similar vert designs. Multicoloured. W* **189** *(sideways). P* 14.

484	10 k. Type **234**		75	20
485	25 k. Spur-winged Plover		1·50	70
486	30 k. Red Bishop		1·50	1·75
487	45 k. Double-spurred Francolin		1·75	2·50
484/7		*Set of* 4	5·00	4·75

235 Boeing 747 Airliner taking-off

236 Office Workers and Clocks ("Punctuality")

(Des. F. Isibor (10 k.), O. Ogunfowora (45 k.))

1984 (7 Dec). *40th Anniv of International Civil Aviation Organization. T* **235** *and similar horiz design. Multicoloured. W* **189** *(inverted on 45 k.). P* 14.

488	10 k. Type **235**		40	10
489	45 k. Boeing 707 airliner circling globe		1·50	2·25

(Des O. Ogunfowora)

1985 (27 Feb). *"War against Indiscipline". T* **236** *and similar horiz design. Multicoloured. W* **189** *(inverted on 20 k.). P* 14.

490	20 k. Type **236**		30	35
491	50 k. Cross over hands passing banknotes ("Discourage Bribery")		55	75

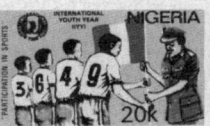
237 Footballers receiving Flag from Major-General Buhari

238 Rolling Mill

(Des F. Isibor (50 k.), G. Akinola (others))

1985 (5 June). *International Youth Year. T* **237** *and similar multicoloured designs. W* **189** *(sideways on 50, 55 k.). P* 14.

492	20 k. Type **237**		30	20
493	50 k. Girls of different tribes with flag (*vert*)		55	70
494	55 k. Members of youth organizations with flags (*vert*)		55	80
492/4		*Set of* 3	1·25	1·50

(Des O. Ogunfowora (50 k.), Mrs. A. Adeyeye (others))

1985 (2 Sept). *25th Anniv of Independence. T* **238** *and similar horiz designs. Multicoloured. W* **189**. *P* 14.

495	20 k. Type **238**		25	10
496	50 k. Map of Nigeria		40	35
497	55 k. Remembrance Arcade		40	40
498	60 k. Eleme, first Nigerian oil refinery		1·00	50
495/8		*Set of* 4	1·90	1·25
MS499	101×101 mm. Nos. 495/8. Wmk sideways		5·00	6·50

239 Globe and O.P.E.C. Emblem   **240** Waterfall

1985 (15 Sept). *25th Anniv of Organization of Petroleum Exporting Countries. T 239 and similar design. W 189 (sideways on 20 k.). P 14.*

500	20 k. greenish blue and orange-vermilion	75	35
501	50 k. black and ultramarine	1·50	75

Design: *Horiz*—50 k. World map and O.P.E.C. emblem.

(Des S. Eluare (55 k.), F. Isibor (60 k.), Mrs. A. Adeyeye (others))

1985 (27 Sept). *World Tourism Day. T 240 and similar multicoloured designs. W 189 (sideways on 20, 55, 60 k., inverted on 50 k.). P 14.*

502	20 k. Type 240	35	10
503	50 k. Pottery, carved heads and map of Nigeria (*horiz*)	45	50
504	55 k. Calabash carvings and Nigerian flag	45	50
505	60 k. Leather work	45	55
502/5	Set of 4	1·50	1·50

241 Map of Nigeria and National Flag   **242** Rock Python

(Des N. Lasisi (20 k.), Mrs. A. Adeyeye (50 k.), O. Ogunfowora (55 k.))

1985 (7 Oct). *40th Anniv of United Nations Organization and 25th Anniv of Nigerian Membership. T 241 and similar designs. W 189 (sideways on 20 k., inverted on 50 k.). P 14.*

506	20 k. black, light green and pale blue	20	10
507	50 k. black, dull ultramarine and cerise	35	50
508	55 k. black, new blue and carmine	35	60
506/8	Set of 3	80	1·10

Designs: *Horiz*—50 k. United Nations Building, New York; 55 k. United Nations logo.

IMPERFORATE STAMPS. Nos. 509/12, 528/38, 543/6, 555/7, 560/79, 582/94, 599/603, 607/16, 619/37, 642/74 and 685/6 exist imperforate from restricted printings. Such printings may also exist for other issues.

(Des Hilda Woods (10, 30 k.), G. Akinola (20 k.), F. Isibor (25 k.))

1986 (15 Apr). *African Reptiles. T 242 and similar horiz designs. W 189. P 14.*

509	10 k. multicoloured	30	10
510	20 k. black, orange-brown and pale new blue	50	70
511	25 k. multicoloured	50	80
512	30 k. multicoloured	50	80
509/12	Set of 4	1·60	2·25

Designs:—20 k. Long Snouted Crocodile; 25 k. Gopher Tortoise; 30 k. Chameleon.

243 Social Worker with Children   **244** Emblem and Globe

(Des G. Akinola (1, 35 k.), S. Eluare (5 k., 20 n.), O. Ogunfowora (10, 15 k.), Mrs. A. Adeyeye (40, 45 k., 50 n.), G. Osuji (50 k.), Hilda Woods (10 n.), F. Abdul (500 n.), C. Ogbebor (all other values except 100 n.))

1986 (16 June)–**98**. *Nigerian Life. T 243 and similar multicoloured designs. W 189 (sideways on 1, 10, 20, 40 k., 100 n.). P 14.*

513	1 k. Type 243	10	20
514	2 k. Volkswagen motor assembly line (*horiz*)	10	20
515	5 k. Modern housing estate (*horiz*)	10	20
516	10 k. Harvesting oil palm fruit	10	10
517	15 k. Unloading freighter (*horiz*)	10	10
518	20 k. Tecoma stans (flower)	10	10
519	25 k. Hospital ward (*horiz*)	10	10
519a	30 k. Birom dancers (*horiz*)	10	10
520	35 k. Telephonists operating switchboard (*horiz*)	10	10
521	40 k. Nkpokiti dancers	10	10
522	45 k. Hibiscus (*horiz*)	10	10
523	50 k. Post Office counter (*horiz*)	30	20
	a. No wmk (1992)	10	10
524	1 n. Stone quarry (*horiz*)	10	10
	a. No wmk (1993)	10	10
525	2 n. Students in laboratory (*horiz*)	30	30
	a. No wmk (1993)	10	10
525b	10 n. Lekki Beach (*horiz*) (1.92)	2·00	1·25
	ba. No wmk (1992)	55	60
525c	20 n. Ancient wall, Kano (*horiz*) (5.90)	4·00	1·50
525d	50 n. Rock bridge (*horiz*) (5.90)	2·75	3·00
	da. No wmk (1997?)		
525e	100 n. Ekpe masquerader (5.90)	5·50	5·75
	ea. No wmk (1998?)	5·50	5·75
525f	500 n. National Theatre (*horiz*) (5.90)	27·00	28·00
513/25f	Set of 19	35·00	38·00

Nos. 513/25 were originally scheduled for issue during 1984, but were delayed. The 5 k., 10 k. and 20 k. appear to have been released earlier for postal purposes and are known postmarked from 2 November 1984 (5 k.), 14 October 1985 (10 k.) or December 1983 (20 k.). The 30 k. value, No. 519a, was not included in the 1986 philatelic release.

Postal forgeries exist, in some quantity, of the 50 k., 10 n. and 20 n. These were often produced by photocopying on unwatermarked paper with either rough perforations or roulettes. They appear to have been produced in bulk for use on bogus financial offers sent to addresses overseas.

(Des Mrs. A. Adeyeye)

1986 (20 June). *International Peace Year. T 244 and similar horiz design. Multicoloured. W 189. P 14.*

526	10 k. Type 244	20	10
527	20 k. Hands of five races holding globe	60	1·00

245 *Goliathus goliathus* (beetle)   **246** Oral Rehydration Therapy

(Des Hilda Woods (25 k.), S. Eluare (others))

1986 (14 July). *Nigerian Insects. T 245 and similar horiz designs. Multicoloured. W 189. P 14.*

528	10 k. Type 245	30	10
529	20 k. *Vespa vulgaris* (wasp)	40	40
530	25 k. *Acheta domestica* (cricket)	45	70
531	30 k. *Anthrenus verbasci* (beetle)	55	1·00
528/31	Set of 4	1·50	2·00
MS532	119×101 mm. Nos. 528/31. Wmk sideways	4·50	6·50

(Des N. Lasisi (10 k.), F. Isibor (30 k.), Mrs. A. Adeyeye (others))

1986 (11 Nov). *40th Anniv of United Nations Children's Fund. T 246 and similar vert designs. W 189 (sideways). P 14.*

533	10 k. multicoloured	30	10
534	20 k. black, reddish brown & greenish yellow	40	40
535	25 k. multicoloured	45	70
536	30 k. multicoloured	55	1·00
533/6	Set of 4	1·50	2·00

Designs:—20 k. Immunisation; 25 k. Breast feeding; 30 k. Mother and child.

247 Stylized Figures on Wall ("International Understanding")   **248** Freshwater Clam

(Des S. Eluare (20 k.), Hilda Woods (30 k.))

1986 (12 Dec). *25th Anniv of Nigerian Institute of International Affairs. T 247 and similar design. W 189 (sideways on 30 k.). P 14.*

537	20 k. black, greenish blue and light green	50	50
538	30 k. multicoloured	75	1·25

Design: *Vert*—30 k. "Knowledge" (bronze sculpture).

(Des G. Osuji (20 k.), F. Isibor (others))

1987 (31 Mar). *Shells. T 248 and similar horiz designs. W 189 (inverted on 10, 25 k.). P 14.*

539	10 k. multicoloured	65	10
540	20 k. black, reddish brown & pale rose-pink	1·25	1·75
541	25 k. multicoloured	1·25	2·00
542	30 k. multicoloured	1·50	2·50
539/42	Set of 4	4·25	5·50

Design:—20 k. Periwinkle; 25 k. Bloody Cockle (inscr "BLODDY COCKLE"); 30 k. Mangrove Oyster.

249 *Clitoria ternatea*   **250** Doka Hairstyle

(Des S. Eluare (10 k.), Hilda Woods (20 k.), Mrs. A. Adeyeye (others))

1987 (28 May). *Nigerian Flowers. T 249 and similar vert designs. W 189 (sideways). P 14.*

543	10 k. multicoloured	10	10
544	20 k. lake-brown, greenish yellow & emerald	15	15
545	25 k. multicoloured	15	20
546	30 k. multicoloured	20	40
543/6	Set of 4	55	70

Designs:—20 k. *Hibiscus tiliaceus*; 25 k. *Acanthus montanus*; 30 k. *Combretum racemosum*.

(Des G. Akinola (25 k.), S. Eluare (30 k.), Mrs. A. Adeyeye (others))

1987 (15 Sept). *Women's Hairstyles. T 250 and similar vert designs. W 189 (sideways). P 14.*

547	10 k. black, orange-brown and olive-grey	10	10
548	20 k. multicoloured	15	20
549	25 k. black, brown and vermilion	20	35
550	30 k. multicoloured	20	40
547/50	Set of 4	60	90

Designs:—20 k. Eting; 25 k. Agogo; 30 k. Goto.

251 Family sheltering under Tree   **252** Red Cross Worker distributing Food

(Des S. Nwasike (20 k.), Mrs. A. Adeyeye (30 k.))

1987 (10 Dec). *International Year of Shelter for the Homeless. T 251 and similar vert design. Multicoloured. W 189 (sideways). P 14.*

551	20 k. Type 251	15	15
552	30 k. Family and modern house	15	30

(Des G. Osuji)

1988 (17 Feb). *125th Anniv of International Red Cross. T 252 and similar vert design. Multicoloured. W 189 (sideways). P 14.*

553	20 k. Type 252	65	30
554	30 k. Carrying patient to ambulance	65	95

253 Doctor vaccinating Baby   **254** O.A.U. Logo

(Des C. Ogbebor (10 k.), G. Osuji (others))

1988 (7 Apr). *40th Anniv of World Health Organization. T 253 and similar horiz designs. Multicoloured. W 189 (inverted). P 14.*

555	10 k. Type 253	25	10
556	20 k. W.H.O. logo and outline map of Nigeria	60	60
557	30 k. Doctor and patients at mobile clinic	60	60
555/7	Set of 3	1·25	1·10

(Des O. Ojo (10 k.), Mrs. A. Adeyeye (20 k.))

1988 (25 May). *25th Anniv of Organization of African Unity. T 254 and similar vert design. W 189 (sideways). P 14.*

558	10 k. olive-bistre, emerald and bright orange	15	15
559	20 k. multicoloured	15	15

Design:—20 k. Four Africans supporting map of Africa.

255 Pink Shrimp   **256** Weightlifting

(Des S. Eluare)

1988 (2 June). *Shrimps. T 255 and similar horiz designs. W 189. P 14.*

560	10 k. multicoloured	25	10
561	20 k. black and pale yellow-olive	40	15
562	25 k. black, orange-vermilion & yell-brown	45	25
563	30 k. reddish orange, olive-bistre and black	55	50
560/3	Set of 4	1·50	90
MS564	120 × 101 mm. Nos. 560/3. Wmk sideways	1·50	2·00

Designs:—20 k. Tiger Shrimp; 25 k. Deepwater Roseshrimp; 30 k. Estuarine Prawn.

(Des G. Osuji (30 k.), Mrs. A. Adeyeye (others))

1988 (6 Sept). *Olympic Games, Seoul. T 256 and similar multicoloured designs. W 189 (sideways on 30 k.). P 14.*

565	10 k. Type 256	25	10
566	20 k. Boxing	35	35
567	30 k. Athletics (*vert*)	45	55
565/7	Set of 3	95	90

257 Banknote Production Line

(Des Mrs. A. Adeyeye (25 k.), G. Akinola (30 k.), O. Ojo (others))

1988 (28 Oct). *25th Anniv of Nigerian Security Printing and Minting Co Ltd.* T **257** *and similar designs.* W **189** *(inverted on 10 k.).* P 14.
568	10 k. multicoloured	10	10
569	20 k. black, silver and emerald	20	20
570	25 k. multicoloured	30	30
571	30 k. multicoloured	45	45
568/71	*Set of 4*	95	95

Designs: *Horiz (as T 257)*—20 k. Coin production line. *Vert (37 × 44 mm)*—25 k. Montage of products; 30 k. Anniversary logos.

258 Tambari

259 Construction of Water Towers, Mali

(Des S. Nwasike (10 k.), N. Lasisi (20 k.), S. Eluare (others))

1989 (29 June). *Nigerian Musical Instruments.* T **258** *and similar horiz designs.* W **189** *(inverted).* P 14.
572	10 k. multicoloured	10	10
573	20 k. multicoloured	20	20
574	25 k. chestnut, bronze-green and black	30	30
575	30 k. red-brown and black	45	45
572/5	*Set of 4*	95	95

Designs:—20 k. Kundung, 25 k. Ibid; 30 k. Dundun.

(Des Hilda Woods (10 k.), F. Abdul (20, 25 k.), S. Eluare (30 k.))

1989 (10 Sept). *25th Anniv of African Development Bank.* T **259** *and similar multicoloured designs.* W **189** *(inverted on 10, 25 k. and sideways on 30 k.)* P 14.
576	10 k. Type 259	10	10
577	20 k. Paddy field, Gambia	15	15
578	25 k. Bank Headquarters, Abidjan, Ivory Coast	25	25
579	30 k. Anniversary logo (*vert*)	35	35
576/9	*Set of 4*	75	75

260 Lighting Campfire

261 Etubom Costume

(Des F. Abdul (10 k.), Mrs. A. Adeyeye (20 k.))

1989 (16 Sept). *70th Anniv of Nigerian Girl Guides Association.* T **260** *and similar multicoloured design.* W **189** *(inverted on 10 k. and sideways on 20 k.).* P 14.
580	10 k. Type 260	30	10
581	20 k. Guide on rope bridge (*vert*)	60	60

(Des S. Eluare (10 k.), Mrs. A. Adeyeye (20 k.), F. Abdul (others))

1989 (26 Oct). *Traditional Costumes.* T **261** *and similar vert designs. Multicoloured.* W **189** *(sideways).* P 14.
582	10 k. Type 261	15	10
583	20 k. Fulfulde	25	25
584	25 k. Aso-Ofi	35	40
585	30 k. Fuska Kura	45	60
582/5	*Set of 4*	1·10	1·25

262 Dove with Letter and Map of Africa

263 Oil Lamps

1990 (18 Jan). *10th Anniv of Pan African Postal Union.* T **262** *and similar vert design. Multicoloured.* W **189** *(sideways).* P 14.
586	10 k. Type 262	25	10
587	20 k. Parcel and map of Africa	50	50

1990 (24 May). *Nigerian Pottery.* T **263** *and similar horiz designs.* W **189** *(inverted on 10 k.).* P 14.
588	10 k. brownish black, orange-brn & slate-vio	10	10
589	20 k. brownish black, red-brown & slate-vio	20	20
590	25 k. reddish brown and slate-violet	25	25
591	30 k. multicoloured	35	35
588/91	*Set of 4*	75	75
MS592	120×100 mm. Nos. 588/91. Wmk sideways	80	90

Designs:—20 k. Water pots; 25 k. Musical pots; 30 k. Water jugs.

264 Teacher and Class

(Des Mrs. A. Adeyeye (20 k.), G. Osuji (30 k.))

1990 (8 Aug). *International Literacy Year.* T **264** *and similar horiz design.* W **189** *(inverted).* P 14.
593	20 k. multicoloured	20	10
594	30 k. blackish brn, greenish bl & orange-yell	30	30

Design:—30 k. Globe and book.

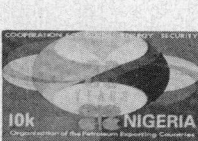

265 Globe and OPEC Logo

266 Grey Parrot

1990 (14 Sept). *30th Anniv of the Organisation of Petroleum Exporting Countries.* T **265** *and similar multicoloured designs.* W **189** *(inverted on 10, 25 k. and sideways on others).* P 14.
595	10 k. Type 265	10	10
596	20 k. Logo and flags of member countries (*vert*)	20	20
597	25 k. World map and logo	25	25
598	30 k. Logo within inscription "Co-operation for Global Energy Security" (*vert*)	35	35
595/8	*Set of 4*	75	75

(Des C. Ogbebor (20 k.), G. Osuji (30 k, 2 n. 50), S. Eluare (1 n. 50))

1990 (8 Nov). *Wildlife.* T **266** *and similar vert designs. Multicoloured.* W **189** *(sideways).* P 14.
599	20 k. Type 266	20	10
600	30 k. Roan Antelope	20	10
601	1 n. 50, Grey-necked Bald Crow ("Rock-fowl")	60	80
602	2 n. 50, Mountain Gorilla	85	1·25
599/602	*Set of 4*	1·75	2·00
MS603	118×119 mm. Nos. 599/602. Wmk inverted	1·75	2·25

267 Eradication Treatment

268 Hand holding Torch (Progress)

(Des C. Ogbebor (20 k.), G. Osuji (others))

1991 (20 Mar). *National Guineaworm Eradication Day.* T **267** *and similar multicoloured designs.* W **189** *(sideways on 10, 30 k.).* P 14.
604	10 k. Type 267	15	10
605	20 k. Women collecting water from river (*horiz*)	25	25
606	30 k. Boiling pot of water	25	25
604/6	*Set of 3*	60	55

1991 (26 May). *Organization of African Unity Heads of State and Governments Meeting, Abuja.* T **268** *and similar vert designs each showing outline map of Africa. Multicoloured.* W **189** *(sideways).* P 14.
607	20 k. Type 268	15	10
608	30 k. Cogwheel (Unity)	20	25
609	50 k. O.A.U. flag (Freedom)	20	45
607/9	*Set of 3*	50	70

MINIMUM PRICE

The minimum price quote is 10p which represents a handling charge rather than a basis for valuing common stamps. For further notes about prices see introductory pages.

269 National Flags

270 Electric Catfish

(Des G. Osuji)

1991 (4 July). *Economic Community of West African States Summit Meeting, Abuja.* T **269** *and similar horiz design. Multicoloured.* W **189** *(inverted).* P 14.
610	20 k. Type 269	15	10
611	50 k. Map showing member states	30	45

(Des R. Adeyemi (10 k.), C. Ogbebor (20 k.), N. Lasisi (others))

1991 (30 July). *Nigerian Fishes.* T **270** *and similar horiz designs. Multicoloured.* W **189** *(inverted on 20 k.).* P 14.
612	10 k. Type 270	15	10
613	20 k. Nile Perch	25	25
614	30 k. Nile Mouthbrooder ("Talapia")	35	35
615	50 k. Sharp-toothed Catfish	50	55
612/15	*Set of 4*	1·10	1·10
MS616	121×104 mm. Nos. 612/15. Wmk sideways	1·50	1·75

Postal forgeries of the 50 k. value exist crudely printed by lithography and roughly perforated 11–12.

271 Telecom '91 Emblem

272 Boxing

(Des S. Eluare)

1991 (7 Oct). *"Telecom '91" 6th World Telecommunication Exhibition, Geneva.* T **271** *and similar design.* W **189** *(sideways on 50 k.).* P 14.
617	20 k. black, deep green and deep violet	30	10
618	50 k. multicoloured	40	30

Design: *Vert*—50 k. Emblem and patchwork.

(Des G. Akinola (2 n.), G. Osuji (others))

1992 (24 Jan). *Olympic Games, Barcelona (1st issue).* T **272** *and similar horiz designs.* W **189** *(2 n.) or no wmk (others). Multicoloured.* P 14.
619	50 k. Type 272	15	15
	a. Wmk 189		
620	1 n. Nigerian athlete winning race	25	25
	a. Wmk 189		
621	1 n. 50, Table tennis	35	35
	a. Wmk 189		
622	2 n. Taekwondo	45	45
619/22	*Set of 4*	1·10	1·10
MS623	120×117 mm. Nos. 619/22. W 189 (sideways)	1·75	2·00

273 Football

274 Blood Pressure Gauge

(Des A. Olusola)

1992 (3 Apr). *Olympic Games, Barcelona (2nd issue).* W **189** *(sideways).* P 14.
624	273	1 n. 50, multicoloured	50	50

(Des Mrs. A. Adeyeye (50 k., 1 n.), G. Osuji (others))

1992 (7 Apr). *World Health Day.* T **274** *and similar vert designs. No wmk. Multicoloured.* P 14.
625	50 k. Type 274	15	15
626	1 n. World Health Day '92 emblem	20	20
627	1 n. 50, Heart and lungs	30	30
628	2 n. Interior of heart	40	40
625/8	*Set of 8*	95	95
MS629	123×111 mm. Nos. 625/8	1·10	1·25

275 Map of World and Stamp on Globe

276 Gathering Plantain Fruit

(Des Mrs. A. Adeyeye)

1992 (3 July). *"Olymphilex '92" Olympic Stamp Exhibition, Barcelona. T **275** and similar horiz design. Multicoloured. W **189**. P 14.*

630	50 k. Type **275**	..	..	20	10
631	1 n. 50, Examining stamps	..		40	40
MS632	120×109 mm. Nos. 630/1. No wmk	..	1·40	1·60

(Des S. Eluare (50 k., 1 n.), N. Lasisi (1 n. 50), G. Osuji (2 n.))

1992 (17 July). *25th Anniv of International Institute of Tropical Agriculture. T **276** and similar designs. P 14.*

633	50 k. multicoloured	..	..	10	10
634	1 n. multicoloured	..	..	15	15
635	1 n. 50, black, reddish brown and emerald	20	20
636	2 n. multicoloured	..	..	25	25
633/6			*Set of 4*	60	60
MS637	121×118 mm. Nos. 633/6	..	1·25	1·50

Designs: *Vert*—1 n. 50, Harvesting cassava tubers; 2 n. Stacking yams. *Horiz*—1 n. Tropical foods

277 Centre Emblem   **278** Healthy Food and Emblem

(Des Mrs. A. Adeyeye (50 k., 2 n.), G. Osuji (others))

1992 (16 Oct). *Commissioning of Maryam Babangida National Centre for Women's Development. T **277** and similar designs. P 14.*

638	50 k. gold, emerald and blue-green	..	10	10
639	1 n. multicoloured	..	..	15	15
640	1 n. 50, multicoloured	..	..	20	20
641	2 n. multicoloured	..	..	30	30
638/41			*Set of 4*	65	65

Designs: *Vert*—1 n. Women working in fields; 2 n. Woman at loom. *Horiz*—1 n. 50, Maryam Babangida National Centre.

All examples of No. 641 are without a "NIGERIA" inscription.

1992 (1 Dec). *International Conference on Nutrition, Rome. T **278** and similar multicoloured designs. P 14.*

642	50 k. Type **278**	..	..	10	10
643	1 n. Child eating	..	..	15	15
644	1 n. 50, Fruit (*vert*)	..	..	20	20
645	2 n. Vegetables	..	..	25	25
642/5			*Set of 4*	60	60
MS646	120×100 mm. Nos. 642/5	..	1·50	1·75

279 Sabada Dance   **280** African Elephant

(Des S. Eluare (50 k.), Mrs A. Adeyeye (1 n.), G. Osuji (1 n. 50), G. Akinola (2 n.))

1992 (15 Dec). *Traditional Dances. T **279** and similar vert designs. Multicoloured. P 14.*

647	50 k. Type **279**	..	..	10	10
648	1 n. Sato	..	..	15	15
649	1 n. 50, Asian Ubo Ikpa	..	..	20	20
650	2 n. Dundun	..	..	25	25
647/50			*Set of 4*	60	60
MS651	126×107 mm. Nos. 647/50	..	1·50	1·75

(Des G. Osuji (1 n. 50), S. Eluare (5 n.), D. Ogunfowora (20 n.), F. Abdul (30 n.))

1993 (Feb). *Wildlife. T **280** and similar multicoloured designs. P 14.*

652	1 n. 50, Type **280**	..	..	10	10
653	5 n. Stanley Crane (*vert*)	..	..	25	30
654	20 n. Roan Antelope	..	..	1·10	1·25
655	30 n. Lion	..	..	1·60	1·75
652/5			*Set of 4*	3·00	3·25

Postal forgeries exist of the 20 n. and 30 n. values produced on colour photocopies and rouletted.

281 Suburban Garden   **282** Oni Figure

(Des A. Lasisi (1 n., 1 n. 50), S. Eluare (5 n.), Mrs. A. Adeyeye (10 n.))

1993 (4 June). *World Environment Day. T **281** and similar horiz designs. Multicoloured. P 14.*

656	1 n. Type **281**	..	..	10	10
657	1 n. 50, Water pollution	..	..	15	10
658	5 n. Forest road	..	..	50	50
659	10 n. Rural house	..	..	90	90
656/9			*Set of 4*	1·50	1·40

(Des G. Osuji (1 n.), O. Ogunfowora (others))

1993 (28 July). *50th Anniv of National Museums and Monuments Commission. T **282** and similar multicoloured designs. P 14.*

660	1 n. Type **282**	..	..	10	10
661	1 n. 50, Bronze head of Queen Mother	10	10
662	5 n. Bronze pendant (*horiz*)	..	30	35
663	10 n. Nok head	..	..	70	75
660/3			*Set of 4*	1·10	1·10

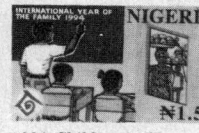

283 *Bulbophyllum distans*   **284** Children in Classroom and Adults carrying Food

1993 (28 Oct). *Orchids. T **283** and similar vert designs. Multicoloured. P 14.*

664	1 n. Type **283**	..	..	10	10
	a. Booklet pane. Nos. 664/7 with margins all round		1·10	
665	1 n. 50, *Eulophia cristata*	..	15	10
666	5 n. *Eulophia horsfalli*	..	45	45
667	10 n. *Eulophia quartiniana*	..	1·00	1·10
664/7			*Set of 4*	1·50	1·50
MS668	103×121 mm. Nos. 664/7	..	1·75	2·00

1994 (30 Mar). *International Year of the Family. T **284** and similar horiz design. Multicoloured. P 14.*

669	1 n. 50, Type **284**	..	..	10	10
670	10 n. Market	..	..	1·00	1·00

285 Hand with Tweezers holding 1969 4d. Philatelic Service Stamp   **286** "I Love Stamps"

1994 (11 Apr). *25th Anniv of National Philatelic Service. T **285** and similar horiz designs. Multicoloured. P 14.*

671	1 n. Type **285**	..	..	10	10
672	1 n. 50, Philatelic Bureau	..	15	10
673	5 n. Stamps forming map of Nigeria	45	45
674	10 n. Philatelic counter	..	1·00	1·10
671/4			*Set of 4*	1·50	1·50

1994 (10 June). *120th Anniv of First Postage Stamps in Nigeria. T **286** and similar horiz designs. Multicoloured. P 14.*

675	1 n. Type **286**	..	..	10	10
676	1 n. 50, "I Collect Stamps"	..	15	10
677	5 n. 19th-century means of communication	45	45
678	10 n. Lagos stamp of 1874	..	1·00	1·10
675/8			*Set of 4*	1·50	1·50

287 Magnifying Glass over Globe   **288** Geryon Crab

1994 (16 Aug). *"Philakorea '94" International Stamp Exhibition, Seoul. P 14.*

679	**287** 30 n. multicoloured	1·75	2·40
MS680	127×115 mm. **287** 30 n. multicoloured. Roul 9 ..	2·75	4·00

1994 (12 Aug). *Crabs. T **288** and similar horiz designs. Multicoloured. P 14.*

681	1 n. Type **288**	..	..	10	10
682	1 n. 50, Spider Crab	..	..	10	10
683	5 n. Red Spider Crab	..	..	45	45
684	10 n. Geryon Maritae Crab	..	90	90
681/4			*Set of 4*	1·40	1·40

---

289 Sewage Works   **290** Letterbox

1994 (16 Sept). *30th Anniv of African Development Bank. T **289** and similar horiz design. Multicoloured. P 14.*

685	1 n. 50, Type **289**	..	..	15	10
686	30 n. Development Bank emblem and flowers		1·75	2·40

1995 (1 Jan). *10th Anniv of Nigerian Post and Tele-communication Corporations. T **290** and similar multi-coloured designs. P 14.*

687	1 n. Type **290**	..	..	10	10
688	1 n. 50, Letter showing "1 JAN 1985" postmark (*horiz*)		10	10
689	5 n. Nipost and Nitel emblems (*horiz*)	..	30	35
690	10 n. Mobile telephones	..	60	65
687/90			*Set of 4*	1·10	1·25

Postal forgeries of the 10 n. exist produced on colour photocopiers and separated by fine roulettes.

291 Woman preparing Food   **292** "Candlestick" Telephone

(Des F. Abdul (1 n. 50), S. Eluare (5 n), G. Osuji (1, 10 n))

1995 (20 July). *Family Support Programme. T **291** and similar horiz designs. Multicoloured. P 14.*

691	1 n. Type **291**	..	..	10	10
692	1 n. 50, Mother teaching children	..	10	10
693	5 n. Family meal	..	..	30	35
694	10 n. Agricultural workers and tractor	60	65
691/4			*Set of 4*	1·10	1·25

1995 (9 Oct). *Centenary of First Telephone in Nigeria. T **292** and similar vert design. Multicoloured. P 14.*

695	1 n. 50, Type **292**	..	..	10	10
696	10 n. Early equipment	..	..	60	65

293 F.A.O. Emblem   **294** "Justice" and 50th Anniversary Emblem

1995 (16 Oct). *50th Anniv of Food and Agriculture Organ-ization. T **293** and similar horiz design. Multicoloured. P 14.*

697	1 n. 50, Type **293**	..	..	10	10
698	30 n. Fishing canoes	..	..	1·90	2·00

1995 (24 Oct). *50th Anniv of United Nations. T **294** and similar multicoloured designs. P 14.*

699	1 n. Type **294**	..	..	10	10
700	1 n. 50, Toxic waste (*horiz*)	..	10	10
701	5 n. Tourist hut (*horiz*)	..	30	35
702	10 n. Nigerian armoured car on U.N. duty (*horiz*)		90	95
699/702			*Set of 4*	1·25	1·25

295 Container Ship in Dock   **296** Scientist and Crops

1996 (29 Apr). *10th Anniv of Niger Dock. T **295** and similar horiz designs. Multicoloured. P 14.*

703	5 n. Type **295**	..	..	35	30
704	10 n. *Badagri* (tourist launch) on crane	65	60
705	20 n. Shipping at dock	..	1·25	1·50
706	30 n. *Odoragushin* (ferry)	..	2·00	2·50
703/6			*Set of 4*	3·75	4·50

(Des O. Ogunfowora (5 n.), S. Eluare (30 n.))

1996 (28 May). *21st Anniv of E.C.O.W.A.S. (Economic Community of West African States). T 296 and similar horiz design. Multicoloured. P 14.*

707	5 n. Type 296	..	30	30
708	30 n. Queue at border crossing	..	1·50	2·00

297 Judo   **298** Nigerian Flag and Exhibition Emblem

1996 (28 June). *Olympic Games, Atlanta. T 297 and similar vert designs. Multicoloured. P 14.*

709	5 n. Type 297	..	35	30
710	10 n. Tennis	..	80	60
711	20 n. Relay race	..	1·25	1·50
712	30 n. Football	..	1·75	2·25
709/12		Set of 4	3·75	4·25

1996 (10 Oct). *"ISTANBUL '96" International Stamp Exhibition. P 14.*

713	**298**	30 n. cerise, light green and black	1·50	2·00

299 Volvariella esculenta   **300** Boy with Toys

1996 (19 Nov). *Fungi. T 299 and similar horiz designs. Multicoloured. P 14.*

714	5 n. Type 299	..	45	30
715	10 n. Lentinus subnudus	..	90	60
716	20 n. Tricholoma lobayensis	..	1·50	1·50
717	30 n. Pleurotus tuber-regium	..	2·00	2·25
714/17		Set of 4	4·25	4·25

1996 (10 Dec). *50th Anniv of U.N.I.C.E.F. T 300 and similar multicoloured design. P 14.*

718	5 n. Type 300	..	30	30
719	30 n. Girl reading book *(horiz)*	..	1·50	2·00

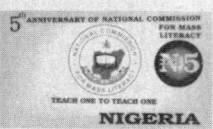

301 Literacy Logo   **302** Three Footballers

1996 (30 Dec). *5th Anniv of Mass Literacy Commission. T 301 and similar horiz design. P 14.*

720	5 n. emerald, light green and black		30	30
721	30 n. emerald, light green and black		1·50	2·00

Design—30 n. Hands holding book and literacy logo.

(Des A. Felix (5 n.), A. Adeyeye (10 n.), Hilda Woods (20 n.) and V. Leneke (30 n.))

1998 (10 June). *World Cup Football Championship, France. T 302 and similar multicoloured designs. P 13.*

722	5 n. Type 302	..	25	30
	a. Perf 14			
723	10 n. Player with ball *(vert)*	..	55	60
724	20 n. Player receiving ball *(vert)*	..	1·10	1·25
725	30 n. Two opposing players	..	1·60	1·75
722/5		Set of 4	3·50	3·75

303 University Tower and Complex   **304** Ship and Logo

1998 (17 Nov). *50th Anniv of Ibadan University. T 303 and similar horiz design. P 14.*

726	5 n. Type 303	..	25	30
727	30 n. Anniversary logo and University crest	1·60	1·75

1998 (30 Nov). *8th Anniv of Economic Community of West African States Military Arm (ECOMOG). T 304 and similar horiz designs. Multicoloured. P 14.*

728	5 n. Type 304		25	30
729	30 n. Logo and original member states		1·60	1·75
730	50 n. Current member states		2·75	3·00
728/30		Set of 3	4·50	5·00

305 Caged Steam Locomotive   **306** Football and Globe

1999 (20 Jan). *Centenary of Nigerian Railway Corporation. T 305 and similar horiz designs. Multicoloured. P 14 (20 n.) or 13 (others).*

731	5 n. Type 305	..	25	30
732	10 n. Iddo Terminus	..	55	60
733	20 n. Diesel locomotive No. 2131	..	1·10	1·25
734	30 n. Passenger train pulling into station	..	1·60	1·75
731/4		Set of 4	3·50	3·75

(Des A. Adekunle)

1999 (31 Mar). *11th World Youth Football Championship, Nigeria. T 306 and similar horiz designs. Multicoloured. P 13×14.*

735	5 n. + 5 n. Type 306	..	15	20
736	10 n. + 5 n. Player throwing ball	..	20	25
737	20 n. + 5 n. Player scoring goal	..	35	40
738	30 n. + 5 n. Map of Nigeria showing venues	50	55
739	40 n. + 5 n. World Youth Football Championship logo	..	60	65
740	50 n. + 5 n. Player being tackled	..	75	80
735/40		Set of 6	2·50	2·75
MS741	120×115 mm. Nos. 735/40		2·50	2·75

Postal forgeries of the 40 n. + 5 n. exist produced on colour photocopiers.

307 Sea Life and F. E. P. A. Emblem   **308** Nicon Emblem

1999 (8 June). *10th Anniv of Federal Environmental Protection Agency. T 307 and similar horiz designs. Multicoloured. P 14 (10 n.) or 13 (others).*

742	5 n. Type 307	..	25	30
743	10 n. Forest	..	55	60
744	20 n. Monkeys	..	1·10	1·25
745	30 n. Villagers and wildlife	..	1·60	1·75
742/5		Set of 4	3·50	3·75

1999 (31 Aug). *30th Anniv of Nicon Insurance Corporation. T 308 and similar multicoloured design. P 13.*

746	5 n. Type 308	..	25	30
747	30 n. Emblem and Nicon Building *(horiz)*	1·60	1·75

STAMP BOOKLETS

1915. *Crimson cover.*
SB1 2s. booklet containing twelve ½d. and eighteen 1d. (Nos. 1/2) in blocks of 6

1921. *Crimson cover.*
SB2 4s. booklet containing twelve 1d. and eighteen 2d. (Nos. 16, 18) in blocks of 6

1924. *Scarlet cover.*
SB3 4s. booklet containing twelve 1d. and eighteen 2d. (Nos. 16, 18a) in blocks of 6 ..

1926.
SB4 4s. booklet containing twelve 1d. and eighteen 2d. (Nos. 16a, 18a) in blocks of 6 .. ..

1928. *Crimson cover.*
SB5 4s. booklet containing twelve 1d. and eighteen 2d. (Nos. 16a, 19) in blocks of 6 .. ..

1929.
SB6 4s. booklet containing twelve 1d. and eighteen 2d. (Nos. 16a, 20) in blocks of 6 .. ..

1931 (Jan).
SB7 4s. booklet containing twelve 1d. and twenty-four 1½d. (Nos. 16a, 17) in blocks of 6 ..

1957 (Aug). *Black on green cover. Stitched.*
SB8 2s. booklet containing four 1d. and eight ½d. and 2d. (Nos. 69/70, 72c) in blocks of 4 .. 24·00
a. Contents as No. SB8, but containing No. 72cb 45·00

1957 (Oct). *Black on buff cover. Stitched.*
SB9 10s. booklet containing eight 3d. and 1s. (Nos. 73, 76) in blocks of 4 and a pane of air mail labels 28·00

1963. *Black on green (No. SB10) or buff (No. SB11) covers. Stitched.*
SB10 2s. booklet containing 1d. and 3d. (Nos. 90, 93) in blocks of 6 .. 5·50
SB11 10s. 6d. booklet containing six 1s. 3d. and twelve 3d. (Nos. 93, 97) in blocks of 6 and two panes of air mail labels .. 15·00

1966. *Black on green cover. Stitched.*
SB12 3s. booklet containing four 1d. and 4d. and eight 2d. (Nos. 173, 175, 177a) in blocks of 4 .. 35·00

1993 (28 Oct). *Orchids. Multicoloured cover. Stapled.*
SB13 35 n. booklet containing pane No. 664a×2 .. 2·10

POSTAGE DUE STAMPS

D 1

(Litho B.W.)

1959 (4 Jan). *Wmk Mult Script CA. P 14½×14.*

D1	D 1	1d. red-orange	..	15	75
D2		2d. red-orange	..	20	80
D3		3d. red-orange	..	25	1·40
D4		6d. red-orange	..	25	5·00
D5		1s. grey-black	..	50	6·50
D1/5			Set of 5	1·25	13·00

1961 (1 Aug). *W 34. P 14½ × 14.*

D 6	D 1	1d. red	..	15	40
D 7		2d. light blue	..	20	45
D 8		3d. emerald	..	25	60
D 9		6d. yellow	..	30	1·40
D10		1s. blue *(shades)*	..	50	2·25
D6/10		..	Set of 5	1·25	4·50

(Litho Nigerian Security Printing & Minting Co)

1973 (3 May)–**94.** *New Currency. No wmk. P 12½×13½.*

D11	D 1	2 k. red	..	10	10
		a. Roul 9 (1990)	..	1·50	1·50
D12		3 k. blue *(shades)*	..	10	10
D13		5 k. orange-yellow *(shades)*	..	10	10
		a. Roul 9 (1994)	..	3·00	3·00
D14		10 k. light apple-green *(shades)*	..	10	10
		a. Roul 9. *Emerald* (1987)	..	4·00	4·00
D11/14			Set of 4	20	20

Nos. D11a and D14a are known postally used at Ibadan in January 1990 and August 1987.

BIAFRA

The following stamps were issued by Biafra (the Eastern Region of Nigeria) during the civil war with the Federal Government, 1967–70.

They were in regular use within Biafra from the time when supplies of Nigerian stamps were exhausted; and towards the end of the conflict they began to be used on external mail carried by air via Libreville.

1 Map of Republic **2** Arms, Flag and Date of Independence **3** Mother and Child

(Typo and litho Mint, Lisbon)

1968 (5 Feb). *Independence.* P 12½.
1	1	2d. multicoloured	..	15	65
2	2	4d. multicoloured	..	15	65
3	3	1s. multicoloured	..	15	1·75
1/3			*Set of 3*	40	2·75

(4)

1968 (Apr). *Nos. 172/5 and 177/85 of Nigeria optd as T **4*** (*without* "SOVEREIGN" *on 10s.*).
4		½d. multicoloured (No. 172)	..	1·50	3·00
5		1d. multicoloured (No. 173)	..	1·50	4·50
	a.	Opt double	..	£200	
	b.	Opt omitted (in pair with normal)	..	£400	
6		1½d. multicoloured (No. 174)	..	6·50	9·50
7		2d. multicoloured (No. 175)	..	21·00	45·00
8		4d. multicoloured (No. 177a)	..	17·00	45·00
9		6d. multicoloured (No. 178)	..	5·50	9·50
10		9d. Prussian blue and orange-red (No. 179)	3·00	2·50
11		1s. multicoloured (Blk. + R.) (No. 180)	60·00	£110
12		1s. 3d. multicoloured (Blk. + R.) (No. 181)	35·00	50·00
	a.	Black opt omitted	..	£300	
	b.	Red opt omitted	..	£300	
13		2s. 6d. orange-brown, buff and brown (Blk. + R.) (No. 182)	1·75	10·00
	a.	Red opt omitted	..	£200	
14		5s. chestnut, light yellow and brown (Blk. + R.) (No. 183)	2·25	9·00
	a.	Red opt omitted	..	£200	
	b.	Black opt omitted	..	£200	
	c.	Red opt double	..	£300	
	d.	*Pale chestnut, yell & brn-pur (No. 183a)*	2·25	9·00
15		10s. multicoloured (No. 184)	..	10·00	32·00
16		£1 multicoloured (Blk. + R.) (No. 185)	10·00	32·00
	a.	Black ("SOVEREIGN BIAFRA") opt omitted	..	£200	
	b.	Red (coat of arms) opt omitted	..	£200	
4/16			*Set of 13*	£150	£325

Nos. 172/3 of Nigeria also exist surcharged "BIAFRA – FRANCE FRIENDSHIP 1968 SOVEREIGN BIAFRA", clasped hands and "+5/-" (½d.) or "+£1" (1d.). There is no evidence that these two surcharges were used for postage within Biafra (*Price for set of 2 £20 mint*).

5 Weapon Maintenance **8** Biafran Arms and Banknote **9** Orphaned Child

(Litho Mint, Lisbon)

1968 (30 May). *First Anniv of Independence. T **5**, **8/9** and similar vert designs.* P 12½.
17	4	4d. multicoloured	..	15	10
18		1s. multicoloured	..	20	20
19		2s. 6d. multicoloured	..	45	2·50
20		5s. multicoloured	..	60	3·00
	a.	Indigo (banknote) omitted	..	60·00	
	b.	Red (from flag) omitted	..	50·00	
21		10s. multicoloured	..	1·00	3·50
	a.	Bright green (from flag) omitted	..	35·00	
17/21			*Set of 5*	2·10	8·50

Designs:—1s. Victim of atrocity; 2s. 6d. Nurse and refugees.

Nos. 17/21 also exist surcharged "HELP BIAFRAN CHILDREN" and different charity premium ranging from 2d. on the 4d. to 2s. 6d. on the 10s. There is no evidence that these surcharges were used for postage within Biafra (*Price for set of 5 £2 mint*).

In late 1968 a set of four values, showing butterflies and plants, was offered for sale outside Biafra. The same stamps also exist overprinted "MEXICO OLYMPICS 1968" and Olympic symbol. There is no evidence that either of these issues were used for postage within Biafra (*Price for set of 4 £4 (Butterflies and Plants) or £3.50 (Olympic overprints), both mint*).

CANCELLED-TO-ORDER. Many issues of Biafra, including the three unissued sets mentioned above, were available cancelled-to-order with a special "UMUAHIA" handstamp. This was the same diameter as postal cancellations, but differed from them by having larger letters, 3 mm. high, and the year date in full. Where such cancellations exist on issued stamps the used prices quoted are for c-t-o examples. Postally used stamps are worth considerably more.

16 Child in Chains and Globe **17** Pope Paul VI, Map of Africa and Papal Arms

1969 (30 May). *Second Anniv of Independence. Multicoloured; frame colours given.* Litho. P 13 × 13½.
35	16	2d. yellow-orange	..	1·25	3·75
36		4d. red-orange	..	1·25	3·75
	a.	Green (wreath) and orange (Sun) omitted	..	£190	
37		1s. new blue	..	1·75	6·00
38		2s. 6d. emerald	..	2·50	12·00
35/8			*Set of 4*	6·00	23·00

A miniature sheet with a face value of 10s. was also released.

1969 (1 Aug). *Visit of Pope Paul to Africa. T **17** and similar vert designs. Multicoloured.* Litho. P 13 × 13½.
39		4d. Type **17**	..	40	2·50
40		6d. Pope Paul VI, Map of Africa and arms of the Vatican	55	5·50
41		9d. Pope Paul VI, map of Africa and St. Peter's Basilica, Vatican..	75	7·50
42		3s. Pope Paul VI, map of Africa and Statue of St. Peter	2·25	12·00
39/42			*Set of 4*	3·50	25·00

A miniature sheet with a face value of 10s. was also released. No. 42 has a magenta background. This value is also known with the background in brown-red or brown.

Biafra was overrun by Federal troops on 10 January 1970 and surrender took place on 15 January.

On 17 December the French Agency released a Christmas issue consisting of Nos. 39/42 overprinted "CHRISTMAS 1969 PEACE ON EARTH AND GOODWILL TO ALL MEN" together with the miniature sheet overprinted "CHRISTMAS 1969" and surcharged £1. Later Nos. 35/38 were released overprinted in red "SAVE BIAFRA 9TH JAN 1970" with a premium of 8d., 1s. 4d., 4s., and 10s. respectively together with the miniature sheet with a premium of £1. We have no evidence that these issues were actually put on sale in Biafra before the collapse, but it has been reported that the 4d. Christmas issue and 2d. + 8d. Save Biafra exist genuinely used before capitulation.

Nos. 40/41 have been seen surcharged "+ 10/–HUMAN RIGHTS" and the United Nations emblem but it is doubtful if they were issued.

No. 81 of Nigeria has also been reported with the original "ROYAL VISIT 1956" overprint, together with "NIGERIA" from the basic stamp, obliterated and a "SERVICE" overprint added. Such stamps were not used for official mail in Biafra, although an example is known with the "UMUAHIA" c-t-o mark.

Niue

Niue became a British Protectorate on 20 April 1900 and was transferred to New Zealand control on 11 June 1901. There was considerable local resentment at attempts to incorporate Niue into the Cook Islands and, in consequence, the island was recognised as a separate New Zealand dependency from 1902.

PRICES FOR STAMPS ON COVER TO 1945	
No. 1	*from × 3*
Nos. 2/5	*from × 8*
Nos. 6/7	—
Nos. 8/9	*from × 30*
Nos. 10/12	—
Nos. 13/31	*from × 3*
Nos. 32/7c	—
Nos. 38/47	*from × 5*
Nos. 48/9	—
No. 50	*from × 15*
Nos. 51/4	—
Nos. 55/61	*from × 8*
Nos. 62/8	*from × 12*
Nos. 69/71	*from × 3*
Nos. 72/4	*from × 10*
Nos. 75/8	*from × 8*
Nos. 79/88	—
Nos. 89/97	*from × 2*

NEW ZEALAND DEPENDENCY
Stamps of New Zealand overprinted

NIUE

(1)

1902 (4 Jan). *Handstamped with T **1**, in green or bluish green. Pirie paper. Wmk double-lined "N Z" and Star, W **38** of New Zealand.* P 11.
1	**42**	1d. carmine	..	£300	£300

A few overprints were made with a *greenish violet* ink. These occurred only in the first vertical row and part of the second row of the first sheet overprinted owing to violet ink having been applied to the pad (*Price £1400 un*).

NIUE. **NIUE.** **NIUE.**
½ PENI. **TAHA PENI.** **2½ PENI.**
(2) (3) 1d. (4)

1902 (4 Apr). *Type-set surcharges. T **2**, **3**, and **4**.*
(i) Pirie paper. No wmk. P 11.
2	**27**	2½d. blue (R.)	..	1·25	4·00
	a.	No stop after "PENI"	..	25·00	48·00
	b.	Surch double	..	£2000	

*(ii) Basted Mills paper. Wmk double-lined "N Z" and Star, W **38** of New Zealand.*
(a) P 14
3	**23**	½d. green (R.)	..	2·25	4·00
	a.	Spaced "U" and "E" (R. 3/3, 3/6, 8/3, 8/6)	10·00	17·00
	b.	Surch inverted	..	£300	£475
	c.	Surch double	..	£850	
4	**42**	1d. carmine (B.)	..	16·00	19·00
	a.	Spaced "U" and "E" (R. 3/3, 3/6, 8/6)	90·00	£100
	b.	No stop after "PENI" (R. 9/3)	£225	£250
	c.	Varieties a. and b. on same stamp (R. 8/3)	£225	£250

(b) P 11×14
5	**42**	1d. carmine (B.)	..	1·75	2·50
	b.	Spaced "U" and "E" (R. 3/3, 3/6, 8/6)	12·00	14·00
	c.	No stop after "PENI" (R. 9/3)	32·00	42·00
	d.	Varieties b. and c. on same stamp (R. 8/3)	32·00	42·00

(c) Mixed perfs
6	**23**	½d. green (R.)	..	£950
7	**42**	1d. carmine (B.)	..	£650

1902 (2 May). *Type-set surcharges, T **2**, **3**. Cowan paper. Wmk single-lined "N Z" and Star, W **43** of New Zealand. (a)* P 14.
8	**23**	½d. green (R.)	..	75	80
	a.	Spaced "U" and "E" (R. 3/3, 3/6, 8/3, 8/6)	6·00	7·00
9	**42**	1d. carmine (B.)	..	50	70
	a.	Surch double	..	£1100	
	b.	Spaced "U" and "E" (R. 3/3, 3/6, 8/6)	9·00	12·00
	c.	No stop after "PENI" (R. 5/3, 7/3, 9/3, 10/3, 10/6)	9·00	12·00
	d.	Varieties b. and c. on same stamp (R. 8/3)	28·00	38·00
	e.	"I" of "NIUE" omitted (R. 6/5 from end of last ptg)		

(b) P 14×11
10	**23**	½d. green (R.)	..	

(c) Mixed perfs
11	**23**	½d. green (R.)	..	£950
12	**42**	1d. carmine (B.)	..	£180
	a.	Spaced "U" and "E" (R. 3/3, 3/6, 8/3, 8/6)	£475	
	b.	No stop after "PENI" (R. 5/3, 7/3, 9/3, 10/3, 10/6)	£475	

NIUE. **Tolu e Pene.**
(5) (6) 3d.

Ono e Pene. **Taha e Sileni.**
(7) 6d. (8) 1s.

1903 (2 July). *Optd with name at top, T **5**, and values at foot, T **6/8**, in blue. W **43** of New Zealand (sideways).* P 11.
13	**28**	3d. yellow-brown	..	9·50	5·00
14	**31**	6d. rose-red	..	12·00	11·00
15	**34**	1s. brown-red ("Tahae" joined)..	£650	
16		1s. bright red	..	35·00	35·00
	a.	*Orange-red*	..	45·00	48·00
13/16	..		*Set of 3*	50·00	45·00

NIUE. **NIUE.** **NIUE.**
½ PENI. **2½ PENI.**
(9) (9a) (10)

1911 (30 Nov). *½d. surch with T **9**, others optd at top as T **5** and values at foot as T **7**, **8**. W **43** of New Zealand.* P 14×15 (½d.) or 14×14½ (others).
17	**51**	½d. green (C.)	..	45	40
18	**52**	6d. carmine (B.)..	..	2·00	7·00
19		1s. vermilion (B.)	..	6·50	45·00
17/19			*Set of 3*	8·00	48·00

1915 (Sept). *Surch with T **9a**. W **43** of New Zealand.* P 14.
20	**27**	2½d. deep blue (C.)	..	15·00	27·00

1917 (Aug). *1d. surch as T **3**, 3d. optd as T **5** with value as T **6**. W **43** of New Zealand.*
21	**53**	1d. carmine (p 14×15) (Br.)	..	8·50	5·50
	a.	No stop after "PENI" (R. 10/16)	£275	
22	**60**	3d. chocolate (p 14×14½) (B.)..	48·00	80·00
	a.	No stop after "Pene" (R. 10/4)	£600	
	b.	Perf 14×13½	..	60·00	90·00
	c.	Vert pair, Nos. 22/b	..	£180	

1917–21. Optd with T **10**. W **43** of New Zealand. (a) P 14×15.

23	**61**	½d. green (R.) (2.20)		70	2·25
24	**53**	1d. carmine (B.) (10.17)		8·00	7·50
25	**61**	1½d. slate (R.) (11.17)		90	2·25
26		1½d. orange-brown (R.) (2.19)		70	3·75
27		3d. chocolate (B.) (6.19)		1·40	23·00

(b) P 14×13½

28	**60**	2½d. blue (R.) (10.20)		2·25	5·50
		a. Perf 14×14½		1·25	3·00
		b. Vert pair, Nos. 28/a		18·00	48·00
29		3d. chocolate (B.) (10.17)		1·60	2·00
		a. Perf 14×14½		1·25	1·50
		b. Vert pair, Nos. 29/a		27·00	42·00
30		6d. carmine (B.) (8.21)		5·50	21·00
		a. Perf 14×14½		4·75	21·00
		b. Vert pair, Nos. 30/a		38·00	85·00
31		1s. vermilion (B.) (10.18)		8·50	21·00
		a. Perf 14×14½		5·50	21·00
		b. Vert pair, Nos. 31/a		42·00	85·00
23/31			Set of 9	22·00	75·00

1918–29. Postal Fiscal stamps as Type F **4** of New Zealand optd with T **10**. W **43** of New Zealand (sideways).

(i) Chalk-surfaced "De La Rue" paper. (a) P 14

32		5s. yellow-green (R.) (7.18)		£100	£110

(b) P 14½ × 14, comb

33		2s. deep blue (R.) (9.18)		15·00	32·00
34		2s. 6d. grey-brown (B.) (2.23)		21·00	48·00
35		5s. yellow-green (R.) (10.18)		25·00	50·00
36		10s. maroon (B.) (2.23)		90·00	100
37		£1 rose-carmine (B.) (2.23)		£130	£160
33/7			Set of 5	£250	£350

(ii) Thick, opaque, white chalk-surfaced "Cowan" paper. P 14½ × 14

37a		5s. yellow-green (R.) (10.29)		27·00	50·00
37b		10s. brown-red (B.) (2.27)		75·00	95·00
37c		£1 rose-pink (B.) (2.28)		£130	£160
37a/c			Set of 3	£200	£275

11 Landing of Captain Cook

12 Landing of Captain Cook

R.2/8   R.3/6   R.5/2

Double derrick flaws

(Des, eng and recess P.B.)

1920 (23 Aug). T **11** and similar designs. No wmk. P 14.

38		½d. black and green		3·75	3·75
39		1d. black and dull carmine		2·00	1·25
		a. Double derrick flaw (R.2/8, 3/6 or 5/2)		6·50	
40		1½d. black and red		2·50	6·50
41		3d. black and blue		60	12·00
42		6d. red-brown and green		1·75	18·00
43		1s. black and sepia		1·75	18·00
38/43			Set of 6	11·00	55·00

Designs: Vert—1d. Wharf at Avarua; 1½d. "Capt Cook (Dance)"; 3d. Palm tree. Horiz—6d. Huts at Arorangi; 1s. Avarua Harbour.

Examples of the 6d. with inverted centre were not supplied to the Post Office.

1925–27. As Nos. 38/9 and new values. W **43** of New Zealand. P 14.

44		½d. black and green (1927)		1·50	7·50
45		1d. black and deep carmine (1925)		1·75	75
		a. Double derrick flaw (R.2/8, 3/6 or 5/2)		5·50	
46		2½d. black and blue (10.27)		4·25	11·00
47		4d. black and violet (10.27)		7·00	17·00
44/7			Set of 4	13·00	32·00

Designs: Vert—2½d. Te Po, Rarotongan chief. Horiz—4d. Harbour, Rarotonga, and Mount Ikurangi.

1927–28. Admiral type of New Zealand optd as T **10**. W **43** of New Zealand. P 14.

(a) "Jones" paper

48	**72**	2s. deep blue (2.27) (R.)		19·00	45·00
		w. Wmk inverted		15·00	45·00

(b) "Cowan" paper

49	**72**	2s. light blue (R.) (2.28)		18·00	32·00

1931 (Apr). No. 40 surch as T **18** of Cook Is.

50		2d. on 1½d. black and red		2·25	1·00

1931 (12 Nov). Postal Fiscal stamps as Type F **6** of New Zealand optd as T **10**. W **43** of New Zealand. Thick, opaque, chalk-surfaced "Cowan" paper. P 14.

51		2s. 6d. deep brown (B.)		4·00	11·00
52		5s. green (R.)		29·00	55·00
53		10s. carmine-lake (B.)		35·00	85·00
54		£1 pink (B.)		55·00	£120
51/4			Set of 4	£110	£250

See also Nos. 79/82 for different type of overprint.

(Des L. C. Mitchell. Recess P.B.)

1932 (16 Mar). T **12** and similar designs inscr "NIUE" and "COOK ISLANDS". No wmk. P 13.

55		½d. black and emerald		9·50	21·00
		a. Perf 13×14×13×13		£250	
56		1d. black and deep lake		1·00	40
57		2d. black and red-brown		2·00	4·00
		a. Perf 14×13×13×13		£100	£160
58		2½d. black and slate-blue		8·00	65·00
59		4d. black and greenish blue		14·00	48·00
		a. Perf 14		15·00	45·00
60		6d. black and orange-vermilion		2·50	24·00
61		1s. black and purple (p 14)		2·25	50·00
55/61			Set of 7	35·00	£130

Designs: Vert—1d. Capt. Cook; 1s. King George V. Horiz—2d. Double Maori canoe; 2½d. Islanders working cargo; 4d. Port of Avarua; 6d. R.M.S. Monowai.

Examples of the 2½d. with inverted centre were not supplied to the Post Office.

Nos. 55a and 57a are mixed perforations, each having one side perforated 14 where the original perforation, 13, was inadequate.

(Recess from Perkins, Bacon's plates at Govt Ptg Office, Wellington, N.Z.)

1932–36. As Nos. 55/61, but W **43** of New Zealand. P 14.

62		½d. black and emerald		50	2·50
63		1d. black and deep lake		50	1·25
		w. Wmk inverted		45·00	
64		2d. black and yellow-brown (1.4.36)		40	1·25
		w. Wmk inverted		25·00	
65		2½d. black and slate-blue		40	4·25
		w. Wmk inverted		45·00	
66		4d. black and greenish blue		1·75	2·75
		w. Wmk inverted			
67		6d. black and red-orange (1.4.36)		70	75
68		1s. black and purple (1.4.36)		8·00	19·00
62/8			Set of 7	11·00	28·00

Imperforate proofs of No. 65 are known used on registered mail from Niue postmarked 30 August 1945 or 29 October 1945.

See also Nos. 89/97.

SILVER JUBILEE OF KING GEORGE V 1910-1935.

Normal letters   B K E N

Narrow letters   B K E N

(13)

1935 (7 May). Silver Jubilee. Designs as Nos. 63, 65 and 67 (colours changed) optd with T **13** (wider vertical spacing on 6d.). W **43** of New Zealand. P 14.

69		1d. red-brown and lake		60	3·00
		a. Narrow "K" in "KING"		2·75	8·50
		b. Narrow "B" in JUBILEE		2·75	8·50
70		2½d. dull and deep blue (R.)		3·25	6·00
		a. Narrow first "E" in "GEORGE"		4·00	13·00
71		6d. green and orange		3·25	6·00
		a. Narrow "N" in "KING"		15·00	13·00
69/71			Set of 3	6·50	13·50

Examples of No. 70 imperforate horizontally are from proof sheets not issued through the Post and Telegraph Department (Price £300 for vert pair).

NIUE

(14)

15 King George VI

16 Tropical Landscape

1937 (13 May). Coronation. Nos. 599/601 of New Zealand optd with T **14**.

72		1d. carmine		30	10
73		2½d. Prussian blue		40	50
74		6d. red-orange		40	20
72/4			Set of 3	1·00	70

1938 (2 May). T **15** and similar designs inscr "NIUE COOK ISLANDS". W **43** of New Zealand. P 14.

75		1s. black and violet		7·00	7·00
76		2s. black and red-brown		12·00	16·00
77		3s. light blue and emerald-green		32·00	16·00
75/7			Set of 3	45·00	35·00

Designs: Vert—2s. Island village. Horiz—3s. Cook Islands canoe.

1940 (2 Sept). Unissued stamp surch as in T **16**. W **98** of New Zealand. P 13½×14.

78		3d. on 1½d. black and purple		50	20

NIUE.

(17)

1941–67. Postal Fiscal stamps as Type F **6** of New Zealand with thin opt, T **17**. P 14.

(i) Thin, hard, chalk-surfaced "Wiggins Teape" paper with vertical mesh (1941–43). (a) W **43** of New Zealand

79		2s. 6d. deep brown (B.) (4.41)		60·00	70·00
80		5s. green (R.) (4.41)		£250	£180
81		10s. pale carmine-lake (B.) (6.42)		£120	£180
82		£1 pink (B.) (2.43?)		£180	£275
79/82			Set of 4	£550	£650

(b) W **98** of New Zealand (1944–54)

83		2s. 6d. deep brown (B.) (3.45)		3·50	9·00
		w. Wmk inverted (11.51)		9·00	12·00
84		5s. green (R.) (11.44)		7·50	11·00
		w. Wmk inverted (19.5.54)		7·50	11·00
85		10s. carmine-lake (B.) (11.45)		55·00	90·00
		w. Wmk inverted		55·00	90·00
86		£1 pink (B.) (6.42)		42·00	55·00
83/6			Set of 4	95·00	£150

(ii) Unsurfaced "Wiggins Teape" paper with horizontal mesh. W **98** of New Zealand (1957–67)

87		2s. 6d. deep brown (p 14 × 13½) (1.11.57)		7·50	10·00
88		5s. pale yellowish green (wmk sideways) (6.67)		28·00	75·00

No. 88 came from a late printing made to fill demands from Wellington, but no supplies were sent to Niue. It exists in both line and comb perf.

1944–46. As Nos. 62/7 and 75/7, but W **98** of New Zealand (sideways on ½d., 1d., 1s. and 2s.).

89	**12**	½d. black and emerald		50	1·75
90	—	1d. black and deep lake		50	80
91	—	2d. black and red-brown		5·50	6·50
92	—	2½d. black and slate-blue (1946)		60	85
93	—	4d. black and greenish blue		3·50	90
		w. Wmk inverted and reversed		16·00	
94	—	6d. black and red-orange		1·50	1·40
95	**15**	1s. black and violet		1·25	85
96	—	2s. black and red-brown (1945)		8·50	2·75
97	—	3s. light blue and emerald-green (1945)		15·00	7·00
89/97			Set of 9	32·00	21·00

1946 (4 June). Peace. Nos. 668, 670, 674/5 of New Zealand optd as T **17** without stop (twice, reading up and down on 2d.).

98		1d. green (Blk.)		20	10
99		2d. purple (B.)		20	10
100		6d. chocolate and vermilion (Blk.)		20	40
		a. Opt double, one albino		£200	
101		8d. black and carmine (B.)		30	40
98/101			Set of 4	80	80

Nos. 102/112 are no longer used.

18 Map of Niue

19 H.M.S. Resolution

23 Bananas

24 Matapa Chasm

(Des J. Berry. Recess B.W.)

1950 (3 July). T **18/19**, **23/24** and similar designs. W **98** of New Zealand (sideways inverted on 1d., 2d., 3d., 4d., 6d. and 1s.). P 13½×14 (horiz) or 14×13½ (vert).

113		½d. orange and blue		10	50
114		1d. brown and blue-green		2·25	1·50
115		2d. black and carmine		60	60
116		3d. blue and violet-blue		10	15
117		4d. olive-green and purple-brown		60	60
118		6d. green and brown-orange		60	60
119		9d. orange and brown		10	60
120		1s. purple and black		10	15
121		2s. brown-orange and dull green		1·00	3·75
122		3s. blue and black		1·50	2·50
113/22			Set of 10	8·00	10·50

Designs: Horiz (as T **19**)—2d. Alofi landing; 3d. Native hut; 4d. Arch at Hikutavake; 6d. Alofi bay; 1s. Cave, Makefu. Vert (as T **18**)—9d. Spearing fish.

1953 (25 May). Coronation. As Nos. 715 and 717 of New Zealand, but inscr "NIUE".

123		3d. brown		65	40
124		6d. slate-grey		95	40

(New Currency. 100 cents = 1 New Zealand dollar)

(25)   **26**

1967 (10 July–7 Aug). Decimal currency. (a) Nos. 113/22 surch as T **25**.

125		½ c. on ½d.		10	10
126		1 c. on 1d.		1·10	15
127		2 c. on 2d.		10	10
128		2½ c. on 3d.		10	10
129		3 c. on 4d.		10	10
130		5 c. on 6d.		10	10
131		8 c. on 9d.		10	10
132		10 c. on 1s.		10	10
133		20 c. on 2s.		35	1·00
134		30 c. on 3s.		65	1·50
125/34			Set of 10	2·00	2·50

(b) Arms type of New Zealand without value, such as in T **26**. W **98** of New Zealand (sideways). P 14.

135	**26**	25 c. deep yellow-brown		40	55
		a. Rough perf 11		6·00	13·00
136		50 c. pale yellowish green		70	80
		a. Rough perf 11		7·00	14·00
137		$1 magenta		45	1·25
		a. Rough perf 11		9·00	13·00

138	26	$2 light pink	..	..	70	2·00
		a. Rough perf 11			11·00	14·00
135/8			Set of 4		2·00	4·25
135a/8a			Set of 4		30·00	48·00

The 25 c., $1 and $2 perf 14 exist both line and comb perforated.
The 50 c. is comb perforated only. The perf 11 stamps resulted from
an emergency measure in the course of printing.

1967 (3 Oct). *Christmas. As T 278 of New Zealand, but inscr
"NIUE". W 98 (sideways) of New Zealand. P 13½×14.*

139	2½ c. multicoloured	..	..	10	10
	w. Wmk sideways inverted	..	..	15	30

1969 (1 Oct). *Christmas. As T 301 of New Zealand, but inscr
"NIUE". W 98 of New Zealand. P 13½ × 14½.*

140	2½ c. multicoloured	..	..	10	10

27 "Pua"

37 Kalahimu

(Des Mrs. K. W. Billings. Litho Enschedé)

1969 (27 Nov). *T 27 and similar vert designs. Multicoloured.
P 12½ × 13½.*

141	½ c. Type 27	..	..	10	10
142	1 c. "Golden Shower"	..	..	10	10
143	2 c. Flamboyant	..	..	10	10
144	2½ c. Frangipani	..	..	10	10
145	3 c. Niue Crocus	..	..	10	10
146	5 c. Hibiscus	..	..	10	10
147	8 c. "Passion Fruit"	..	..	10	10
148	10 c. "Kampui"	..	..	10	10
149	20 c. Queen Elizabeth II (after Anthony Buckley)			75	1·25
150	30 c. Tapeu Orchid	..	..	1·50	1·75
141/150		Set of 10		2·50	3·00

For 20 c. design as 5 c. see No. 801.

(Des G. F. Fuller. Photo Enschedé)

1970 (19 Aug). *Indigenous Edible Crabs. T 37 and similar horiz
designs. Multicoloured. P 13½ × 12½.*

151	3 c. Type 37	..	..	10	10
152	5 c. Kalavi	..	..	10	10
153	30 c. Unga	..	..	30	25
151/3		Set of 3		45	40

1970 (1 Oct). *Christmas. As T 314 of New Zealand, but inscr
"NIUE".*

154	2½ c. multicoloured	..	..	10	10

38 Outrigger Canoe and
Fokker F.27 Friendship
Aircraft over Jungle

39 Spotted Triller

(Des L. C. Mitchell. Litho B.W.)

1970 (9 Dec). *Opening of Niue Airport. T 38 and similar horiz
designs. Multicoloured. P 13½.*

155	3 c. Type 38	..	..	10	15
156	5 c. Tofua II (cargo liner) and Fokker F.27 Friendship over harbour	..		15	15
157	8 c. Fokker F.27 Friendship over Airport	..		15	20
155/7		Set of 3		35	45

(Des A. G. Mitchell. Litho B.W.)

1971 (23 June). *Birds. T 39 and similar horiz designs. Multicoloured. P 13½.*

158	5 c. Type 39	..	..	15	20
159	10 c. Purple-capped Fruit Dove	..		70	20
160	20 c. Blue-crowned Lory	..		80	20
158/60		Set of 3		1·50	55

1971 (6 Oct). *Christmas. As T 325 of New Zealand, but inscr
"Niue".*

161	3 c. multicoloured	..	..	10	10

40 Niuean Boy

41 Octopus Lure

(Des L. C. Mitchell. Litho Harrison)

1971 (17 Nov). *Niuean Portraits. T 40 and similar vert designs.
Multicoloured. P 13 × 14.*

162	4 c. Type 40	..	..	10	10
163	6 c. Girl with garland	..	..	10	15
164	9 c. Man	..	..	10	35
165	14 c. Woman with garland	..		15	60
162/5		Set of 4		35	1·00

(Des A. G. Mitchell. Litho B.W.)

1972 (3 May). *South Pacific Arts Festival, Fiji. T 41 and similar
multicoloured designs. P 13½.*

166	3 c. Type 41	..	..	10	10
167	5 c. War weapons	..	..	15	15
168	10 c. Sika throwing (horiz)	..		20	15
169	25 c. Vivi dance (horiz)	..		30	25
166/9		Set of 4		65	55

42 Alofi Wharf

(Des A. G. Mitchell. Litho Questa)

1972 (6 Sept). *25th Anniversary of South Pacific Commission.
T 42 and similar horiz designs. Multicoloured. P 14.*

170	4 c. Type 42	..	..	10	10
171	5 c. Medical Services	..	..	15	10
172	6 c. Schoolchildren	..	..	15	10
173	18 c. Dairy cattle	..	..	25	20
170/3		Set of 4		60	40

1972 (4 Oct). *Christmas. As T 332 of New Zealand but inscr
"NIUE".*

174	3 c. multicoloured	..	..	10	10

43 Silver Sweeper

44 "Large Flower Piece"
(Jan Brueghel)

(Des G. F. Fuller. Litho Harrison)

1973 (27 June). *Fishes. T 43 and similar horiz designs. Multicoloured. P 14 × 13½.*

175	8 c. Type 43	..	..	25	25
176	10 c. Peacock Hind ("Loi")	..		30	30
177	15 c. Yellow-edged Lyretail ("Malau")	..		40	40
178	20 c. Ruby Snapper ("Palu")	..		45	45
175/8		Set of 4		1·25	1·25

(Des and litho Enschedé)

1973 (21 Nov). *Christmas. T 44 and similar vert designs showing
flower studies by the artists listed. Multicoloured. P 14 × 13½.*

179	4 c. Type 44	..	..	10	10
180	5 c. Bollongier	..	..	10	10
181	10 c. Ruysch	..	..	20	20
179/81		Set of 3		30	30

45 Capt. Cook and Bowsprit

46 King Fataaiki

(Des A. G. Mitchell. Litho Questa)

1974 (20 June). *Bicentenary of Capt. Cook's Visit. T 45 and
similar horiz designs each showing Cook's portrait. Multicoloured. P 13½ × 14.*

182	2 c. Type 45	..	..	20	20
183	3 c. Niue landing place	..		20	20
184	8 c. Map of Niue	..	..	20	30
185	20 c. Ensign of 1774 and Administration Building	..		30	65
182/5		Set of 4		80	1·25

SELF-GOVERNMENT

(Des A. G. Mitchell. Litho Questa)

1974 (19 Oct). *Self-Government. T 46 and similar multicoloured
designs. P 14 × 13½ (4 and 8 c.) or 13½ × 14 (others).*

186	4 c. Type 46	..	..	10	10
187	8 c. Annexation Ceremony, 1900	..		10	10
188	10 c. Legislative Assembly Chambers (horiz)	..		10	10
189	20 c. Village meeting (horiz)	..		15	15
186/9		Set of 4		35	30

47 Decorated Bicycles

48 Children going to Church

(Des B. C. Strong. Litho D.L.R.)

1974 (13 Nov). *Christmas. T 47 and similar vert designs. P 12½.*

190	3 c. multicoloured	..	..	10	10
191	10 c. multicoloured	..	..	10	10
192	20 c. dull red-brown, slate and black	..		20	30
190/2		Set of 3		30	40

Designs:—10 c. Decorated motorcycles; 20 c. Motor transport to
church.

(Des Enid Hunter. Litho Questa)

1975 (29 Oct). *Christmas. T 48 and similar horiz designs. Multicoloured. P 14.*

193	4 c. Type 48	..	..	10	10
194	5 c. Child with balloons on bicycle	..		10	10
195	10 c. Balloons and gifts on tree	..		20	20
193/5		Set of 3		30	30

49 Hotel Buildings

50 Preparing Ground for Taro

(Des B. C. Strong. Litho Harrison)

1975 (19 Nov). *Opening of Tourist Hotel. T 49 and similar horiz
design. Multicoloured. P 13½ × 13.*

196	8 c. Type 49	..	..	10	10
197	20 c. Ground-plan and buildings	..		20	20

(Des A. G. Mitchell. Litho Questa)

1976 (3 Mar). *T 50 and similar horiz designs showing food gathering. Multicoloured. P 13½ × 14.*

198	1 c. Type 50	..	..	10	10
199	2 c. Planting taro	..	..	10	10
200	3 c. Banana gathering	..		10	10
201	4 c. Harvesting taro	..		10	10
202	5 c. Gathering shell fish	..		30	10
203	10 c. Reef fishing	..	..	20	10
204	20 c. Luku gathering	..		20	15
205	50 c. Canoe fishing	..		30	60
206	$1 Coconut husking	..		35	80
207	$2 Uga gathering	..		60	1·40
198/207		Set of 10		1·75	2·75

See also Nos. 249/58 and 264/73.

51 Water

52 Christmas Tree, Alofi

(Des A. G. Mitchell. Litho Questa)

1976 (7 July). *Utilities. T 51 and similar vert designs. Multicoloured. P 14.*

208	10 c. Type 51	..	..	10	10
209	15 c. Telecommunications	..		15	15
210	20 c. Power	..	..	15	15
208/10		Set of 3		30	30

(Des A. G. Mitchell. Litho Questa)

1976 (15 Sept). *Christmas. T 52 and similar horiz design. Multicoloured. P 14.*

211	9 c. Type 52	..	..	15	15
212	15 c. Church Service, Avatele	..		15	15

53 Queen Elizabeth II and Westminster Abbey

(Des and photo Heraclio Fournier)

1977 (7 June). *Silver Jubilee. T 53 and similar horiz design.
Multicoloured. P 13½.*

213	$1 Type 53	..	..	60	50
214	$2 Coronation regalia	..		80	75
MS215	72 × 104 mm. Nos. 213/14	..		1·10	1·60

Stamps from the miniature sheet have a blue border.

OMNIBUS ISSUES

Details, together with prices for complete sets,
of the various Omnibus issues from the 1935
Silver Jubilee series to date are included in a
special section following Zimbabwe at the end of
Volume 2.

54 Child Care   **55** "The Annunciation"

(Des R. M. Conly. Litho Questa)

1977 (29 June). *Personal Services.* T **54** *and similar horiz designs. Multicoloured.* P 14½.

216	10 c. Type **54**	..	15	10
217	15 c. School dental clinic	..	20	20
218	20 c. Care of the aged	..	20	20
216/18		Set of 3	50	45

(Des and photo Heraclio Fournier)

1977 (15 Nov). *Christmas.* T **55** *and similar vert designs showing paintings by Rubens. Multicoloured.* P 13.

219	10 c. Type **55**	..	20	10
220	12 c. "Adoration of the Magi"	..	20	15
221	20 c. "Virgin in a Garland"	..	35	40
222	35 c. "The Holy Family"	..	55	90
219/22		Set of 4	1·10	1·40
MS223	82 × 129 mm. Nos. 219/22		1·50	2·25

12c

(56)

1977 (15 Nov). *Nos.* 198 *etc.,* 214, 216 *and* 218 *surch as* T **56** *by New Zealand Govt Printer.*

224	12 c. on 1 c. Type **50**	..	25	25
225	16 c. on 2 c. Planting taro	..	30	30
226	30 c. on 3 c. Banana gathering	..	40	40
227	35 c. on 4 c. Harvesting taro	..	45	45
228	40 c. on 5 c. Gathering shell fish	..	45	50
229	60 c. on 20 c. Luku gathering	..	45	55
230	70 c. on $1 Coconut husking	..	45	55
231	85 c. on $2 Uga gathering	..	45	60
232	$1.10 on 10 c. Type **54**	..	45	60
233	$2.60 on 20 c. Care of the aged	..	50	70
234	$3.20 on $2 Coronation regalia (Gold)	..	60	80
224/34		Set of 11	4·25	5·00

57 "An Island View in Atooi"

(Photo Heraclio Fournier)

1978 (18 Jan). *Bicentenary of Discovery of Hawaii.* T **57** *and similar horiz designs showing paintings by John Webber. Multicoloured.* P 13.

235	12 c. Type **57**	..	85	40
236	16 c. "View of Karakaooa, in Owhyhee"	..	95	50
237	20 c. "Offering before Capt. Cook in the Sandwich Islands"	..	1·00	60
238	30 c. "Tereeboo, King of Owhyhee bringing presents to Capt. Cook"	..	1·10	70
239	35 c. "Canoe in the Sandwich Islands, the rowers masked"	..	1·25	80
235/9		Set of 5	4·75	2·75
MS240	121 × 121 mm. Nos. 235/9		4·75	2·75

Nos. 235/9 were each printed in small sheets of 6, including 1 se-tenant stamp-size label.

58 "The Deposition of   **59** Flags of Niue and U.K.
Christ" (Caravaggio)

(Photo Heraclio Fournier)

1978 (15 Mar). *Easter. Paintings from the Vatican Galleries.* T **58** *and similar vert design. Multicoloured.* P 13.

241	10 c. Type **58**	..	30	10
242	20 c. "The Burial of Christ" (Bellini)	..	60	25
MS243	102 × 68 mm. Nos. 241/2	..	90	1·00

1978 (15 Mar). *Easter. Children's Charity. Designs as Nos.* 241/2 *in separate miniature sheets* 64 × 78 *mm, each with a face value of* 70 c. + 5 c. P 13.

MS244	As Nos. 241/2	..	Set of 2 sheets	1·00	2·00

(Photo Heraclio Fournier)

1978 (26 June). *25th Anniv of Coronation.* T **59** *and similar horiz designs. Multicoloured. With white or turquoise borders (same prices either colour).* P 13.

245	$1.10, Type **59**	..	60	90
246	$1.10, Coronation portrait by Cecil Beaton	..	60	90
247	$1.10, Queen's personal flag for New Zealand	..	60	90
245/7		Set of 3	1·60	2·40
MS248	87×98 mm. Nos. 245/7 with white borders		2·50	1·50

Nos. 245/7 were printed together, *se-tenant*, in sheets of 6, containing two strips of 3, with horizontal gutter between. The upper strip has white borders, the lower turquoise-green.

(Litho Questa)

1978 (27 Oct). *Designs as Nos.* 198/207 *but margin colours changed and silver frame.* P 13½ × 14.

249	12 c. Type **50**	..	20	20
250	16 c. Planting taro	..	20	20
251	30 c. Banana gathering	..	30	25
252	35 c. Harvesting taro	..	30	30
253	40 c. Gathering shell fish	..	30	40
254	60 c. Reef fishing	..	30	35
255	75 c. Luku gathering	..	30	40
256	$1.10 Coconut husking	..	35	80
257	$3.20, Coconut husking	..	50	90
258	$4.20, Uga gathering	..	55	95
249/58		Set of 10	3·00	4·25

See also Nos. 264/73.

60 "Festival of the Rosary"

(Des and photo Heraclio Fournier)

1978 (30 Nov). *Christmas. 450th Death Anniv of Dürer.* T **60** *and similar horiz designs. Multicoloured.* P 13.

259	20 c. Type **60**	..	40	20
260	30 c. "The Nativity"	..	50	30
261	35 c. "Adoration of the Magi"	..	60	35
259/61		Set of 3	1·40	75
MS262	143 × 82 mm. Nos. 259/61		1·50	1·75

Nos. 259/61 were each printed in small sheets of 6.

1978 (30 Nov). *Christmas. Children's Charity. Designs as Nos.* 259/61 *in separate miniature sheets* 74 × 66 *mm., each with a face value of* 60 c. + 5 c. P 13.

MS263	As Nos. 259/61		Set of 3 sheets	1·00	2·00

(Litho Questa)

1979 (26 Feb–28 May). *Air. Designs as Nos.* 249/58 *but gold frames and additionally inscr "AIRMAIL".* P 13½ × 14.

264	15 c. Planting taro	..	20	15
265	20 c. Banana gathering	..	25	15
266	23 c. Harvesting taro	..	30	15
267	50 c. Canoe fishing	..	70	20
268	90 c. Reef fishing	..	80	35
269	$1.35, Type **50** (30.3)	..	80	1·50
270	$2.10, Gathering shell fish (30.3)	..	80	1·75
271	$2.60, Luku gathering (30.3)	..	80	1·75
272	$5.10, Coconut husking (28.5)	..	80	1·75
273	$6.35, Uga gathering (28.5)	..	80	1·75
264/73		Set of 10	5·50	8·50

PRINTERS. The following stamps were printed in photogravure by Heraclio Fournier, Spain, *except where otherwise stated.*

61 "Pietà" (Gregorio Fernandez)   **62** "The Nurse and Child"
(Franz Hals)

1979 (2 Apr). *Easter. Paintings.* T **61** *and similar horiz design. Multicoloured.* P 13.

274	30 c. Type **61**	..	30	25
275	35 c. "Burial of Christ" (Pedro Roldan)	..	35	25
MS276	82 × 82 mm. Nos. 274/5	..	1·25	1·25

1979 (2 Apr). *Easter. Children's Charity. Designs as Nos.* 274/5 *in separate miniature sheets* 86 × 69 *mm., each with a face value of* 70 c. + 5 c. P 13.

MS277	As Nos. 274/5	..	Set of 2 sheets	1·10	1·75

1979 (31 May). *International Year of the Child. Details of Paintings.* T **62** *and similar vert designs. Multicoloured.* P 14 × 13½.

278	16 c. Type **62**	..	20	15
279	20 c. "Child of the Duke of Osuna" (Goya)	..	20	20
280	30 c. "Daughter of Robert Strozzi" (Titian)	..	35	35
281	35 c. "Children eating Fruit" (Murillo)	..	45	40
278/81		Set of 4	1·10	1·00
MS282	80 × 115 mm. Nos. 278/81. P 13	..	1·60	2·25

1979 (31 May). *International Year of the Child. Children's Charity. Designs as Nos.* 278/81 *in separate miniature sheets* 99 × 119 *mm each with a face value of* 70 c. + 5 c. P 13.

MS283	As Nos. 278/81	..	Set of 4 sheets	1·00	1·50

---

63 Penny Black Stamp   **64** Cook's Landing at Botany Bay

1979 (3 July). *Death Centenary of Sir Rowland Hill.* T **63** *and similar vert designs. Multicoloured.* P 14×13½.

284	20 c. Type **63**	..	20	15
285	20 c. Sir Rowland Hill and original Bath mail coach	..	20	15
286	30 c. Basel 1845 2½ r. stamp	..	30	20
287	30 c. Rowland Hill and Alpine village coach	..	30	20
288	35 c. U.S.A. 1847 5 c. stamp	..	35	20
289	35 c. Sir Rowland Hill and *Washington* (first Transatlantic U.S.A. mail vessel)	..	35	20
290	50 c. France 1849 20 c. stamp	..	40	30
291	50 c. Sir Rowland Hill and French Post Office railway van, 1849	..	40	30
292	60 c. Bavaria 1849 1 k. stamp	..	40	30
293	60 c. Sir Rowland Hill and Bavarian coach with mail	..	40	30
284/93		Set of 10	3·00	2·10
MS294	143×149 mm. Nos. 284/93		3·00	3·75

Nos. 284/5, 286/7, 288/9, 290/1 and 292/3 were each printed together, *se-tenant*, in horizontal pairs throughout the sheet forming composite designs.

1979 (30 July). *Death Bicentenary of Captain Cook.* T **64** *and similar horiz designs. Multicoloured.* P 14.

295	20 c. Type **64**	..	55	30
296	30 c. Cook's men during a landing on Erromanga	..	75	40
297	35 c. H.M.S. *Resolution* and H.M.S. *Discovery* in Queen Charlotte's Sound	..	85	45
298	75 c. Death of Captain Cook, Hawaii	..	1·50	70
295/8		Set of 4	3·25	1·75
MS299	104 × 80 mm. Nos. 295/8. P 13½	..	3·75	3·00

65 Launch of "Apollo 11"   **66** "Virgin of Tortosa"
(P. Serra)

1979 (27 Sept). *10th Anniv of First Moon Landing.* T **65** *and similar vert designs. Multicoloured.* P 13½.

300	20 c. Type **65**	..	35	20
301	35 c. Lunar module on Moon	..	45	25
302	60 c. Sikorsky S-61B SH-3 Sea King helicopter, recovery ship and command module after splashdown	..	60	40
300/2		Set of 3	1·25	75
MS303	120 ×82 mm. Nos. 300/2		1·25	1·60

Stamps from No. **MS303** have the inscription in gold on a blue panel.

1979 (29 Nov). *Christmas. Paintings.* T **66** *and similar vert designs. Multicoloured.* P 13.

304	20 c. Type **66**	..	10	10
305	25 c. "Virgin with Milk" (R. di Mur)	..	15	15
306	30 c. "Virgin and Child" (S. di G. Sassetta)	..	20	20
307	50 c. "Virgin and Child" (J. Huguet)	..	25	25
304/7		Set of 4	60	60
MS308	95 × 113 mm. Nos. 304/7		75	1·25

1979 (29 Nov). *Christmas. Children's Charity. Designs as Nos.* 304/7 *in separate miniature sheets,* 49 × 84 *mm, each with a face value of* 85 c. + 5 c. P 13.

MS309	As Nos. 304/7	..	Set of 4 sheets	1·00	2·00

HURRICANE RELIEF
Plus 2c

(67)   **68** "Pietà" (Bellini)

1980 (25 Jan). *Hurricane Relief. Various stamps surch as* T **67** *in black (Nos.* 310/19) *or silver (*320/30*).*

   (a) *Nos.* 284/93 (*Death Centenary of Sir Rowland Hill*)

310	20 c. + 2 c. Type **63**	..	30	30
311	20 c. + 2 c. Sir Rowland Hill and original Bath mail coach	..	30	30
312	30 c. + 2 c. Basel 1845 2½ r. stamp	..	35	35
313	30 c. + 2 c. Sir Rowland Hill and Alpine village coach	..	35	35
314	35 c. + 2 c. U.S.A. 1847 5 c. stamp	..	40	40

315	35 c. + 2 c. Sir Rowland Hill and *Washington* (first Transatlantic U.S.A. mail vessel)		40	40
316	50 c. + 2 c. France 1849 20 c. stamp		55	55
317	50 c. + 2 c. Sir Rowland Hill and French Post Office railway van, 1849		55	55
318	60 c. + 2 c. Bavaria 1849 1 k. stamp.		65	65
319	60 c. + 2 c. Sir Rowland Hill and Bavarian coach with mail		65	65

(b) Nos. 295/8 (Death Bicentenary of Captain Cook)

320	20 c. + 2 c. Type **64**		40	40
321	30 c. + 2 c. Cook's men during a landing on Erromanga		50	50
322	35 c. + 2 c. H.M.S. *Resolution* and H.M.S. *Discovery* in Queen Charlotte's Sound		55	55
323	75 c. + 2 c. Death of Captain Cook, Hawaii		1·00	1·00

(c) Nos. 300/2 (10th Anniv of First Moon Landing)

324	30 c. + 2 c. Type **65**		35	35
325	35 c. + 2 c. Lunar module on Moon		40	40
326	60 c. + 2 c. Sikorsky S-61B SH-3 Sea King helicopter, recovery ship and command module after splashdown		65	65

(d) Nos. 304/7 (Christmas)

327	20 c. + 2 c. Type **66**		25	25
328	25 c. + 2 c. "Virgin with Milk" (R. de Mur)		30	30
329	30 c. + 2 c. "Virgin and Child" (S. di G. Sassetta)		35	35
330	50 c. + 2c. "Virgin and Child" (J. Huguet)		55	55
310/30		Set of 21	9·00	9·00

On Nos. 310/19 "HURRICANE RELIEF" covers the two designs of each value.

1980 (2 Apr). *Easter. Paintings. T* **68** *and similar horiz designs showing "Pietà" paintings by various artists. Multicoloured. P 13½ × 13.*

331	25 c. Type **68**		30	15
332	30 c. Botticelli		35	20
333	35 c. Antony van Dyck		35	20
331/3		Set of 3	90	50
MS334	75 × 104 mm. As Nos. 331/3, but each with additional premium of "+ 2 c."		55	90

The premiums on No. **MS334** were used to support Hurricane Relief.

1980 (2 Apr). *Easter. Hurricane Relief. Designs as Nos. 331/3 in separate miniature sheets, 75 × 52 mm, each with a face value of 85 c. + 5 c. P 13 × 14.*

MS335	As Nos. 331/3	Set of 3 sheets	1·00	1·50

69 Ceremonial Stool, New Guinea

1980 (30 July). *South Pacific Festival of Arts, New Guinea. T* **69** *and similar vert designs. Multicoloured. P 13.*

336	20 c. Type **69**		10	10
337	20 c. Ku-Tagwa plaque, New Guinea		10	10
338	20 c. Suspension hook, New Guinea		10	10
339	20 c. Ancestral board, New Guinea		10	10
340	25 c. Platform post, New Hebrides		10	10
341	25 c. Canoe ornament, New Ireland		10	10
342	25 c. Carved figure, Admiralty Islands		10	10
343	25 c. Female with child, Admiralty Islands		10	10
344	30 c. The God A'a, Rurutu (Austral Islands)		15	15
345	30 c. Statue of Tangaroa, Cook Islands		15	15
346	30 c. Ivory pendant, Tonga		15	15
347	30 c. Tapa (Hiapo) cloth, Niue		15	15
348	35 c. Feather box (Waka), New Zealand		15	15
349	35 c. Hei-Tiki amulet, New Zealand		15	15
350	35 c. House post, New Zealand		15	15
351	35 c. Feather image of god Ku, Hawaii		15	15
336/51		Set of 16	1·60	1·60
MS352	Four sheets, each 86 × 124 mm. (a) Nos. 336, 340, 344, 348; (b) Nos. 337, 341, 345, 349; (c) Nos. 338, 342, 346, 350; (d) Nos. 339, 343, 347, 351. Each stamp with an additional premium of 2 c.	Set of 4 sheets	1·75	2·00

Nos. 336/9, 340/3, 344/7 and 348/51 were each printed together, *se-tenant*, in horizontal strips of 4 throughout the sheet.

NEW ZEALAND STAMP EXHIBITION

ZEAPEX '80 AUCKLAND

(70)   (71)

1980 (22 Aug). *"Zeapex '80" International Stamp Exhibition, Auckland. Nos. 284, 286, 288, 290 and 292 optd with T* **70** *and Nos. 285, 287, 289, 291 and 293 optd with T* **71**, *both in black on silver background.*

353	20 c. Type **63**		30	20
354	20 c. Sir Rowland Hill and original Bath mail coach		30	20
355	30 c. Basel 1845 2½ r. stamp.		30	20
356	30 c. Sir Rowland Hill and Alpine village coach		30	20
357	35 c. U.S.A. 1847 5 c. stamp		30	20
358	35 c. Sir Rowland Hill and *Washington* (first Transatlantic U.S.A. mail vessel)		30	20
359	50 c. Sir Rowland Hill and France 1849 20 c. stamp.		40	25
360	50 c. Sir Rowland Hill and French Post Office railway van, 1849		40	25
361	60 c. Bavaria 1849 1 k. stamp.		40	25
362	60 c. Sir Rowland Hill and Bavarian coach with mail		40	25
353/62		Set of 10	3·00	2·00
MS363	143 × 149 mm. Nos. 353/62, each additionally surcharged "+ 2 c."		4·00	3·25

72 Queen Elizabeth the Queen Mother   **73** 100 Metre Dash

1980 (15 Sept). *80th Birthday of Queen Elizabeth the Queen Mother. P 13.*

364	**72** $1.10 multicoloured		80	1·50
MS365	55 × 80 mm. **72** $3 multicoloured		1·00	1·75

No. 364 was printed in small sheets of 6 including one *se-tenant* stamp-size label.

1980 (30 Oct). *Olympic Games, Moscow. T* **73** *and similar horiz designs. Multicoloured. P 14 × 13½.*

366	20 c. Type **73**		20	15
367	20 c. Allen Wells, Great Britain (winner of 100 metre dash)		20	15
368	25 c. } 400 metre freestyle (winner, Ines Diers,		20	20
369	25 c. } D.D.R.)		20	20
370	30 c. } "Soling" Class Yachting (winner,		25	20
371	30 c. } Denmark)		25	20
372	35 c. } Football (winner, Czechoslovakia)		25	25
373	35 c. }		25	25
366/73		Set of 8	1·60	1·40
MS374	119 × 128 mm. Nos. 366/73, each stamp including premium of 2 c.		1·25	1·50

Nos. 366/7, 368/9, 370/1 and 372/3 were each printed together, *se-tenant*, in horizontal pairs throughout the sheet, forming composite designs. On the 25 c. and 35 c. stamps the face value is at right on the first design and at left on the second in each pair. For the 30 c. No. 370 has a yacht with a green sail at left and No. 371 a yacht with a red sail.

74 "The Virgin and Child"   **75** *Phalaenopsis sp.*

1980 (28 Nov). *Christmas and 450th Death Anniv of Andrea del Sarto (painter). T* **74** *and similar vert designs showing different "The Virgin and Child" works. P 13.*

375	20 c. multicoloured		15	15
376	25 c. multicoloured		15	15
377	30 c. multicoloured		20	20
378	35 c. multicoloured		20	20
375/8		Set of 4	60	60
MS379	87 × 112 mm. Nos. 375/8		85	1·25

1980 (28 Nov). *Christmas. Children's Charity. Designs as Nos. 375/8 in separate miniature sheets 62 × 84 mm, each with a face value of 80 c. + 5 c. P 13.*

MS380	As Nos. 375/8	Set of 4 sheets	1·25	1·75

1981 (2 Apr)-82. *Flowers (1st series). Horiz designs as T* **75**. *Multicoloured. P 13.*

381	2 c. Type **75**		10	10
382	2 c. Moth Orchid		10	10
383	5 c. *Euphorbia pulcherrima*		10	10
384	5 c. Poinsettia		10	10
385	10 c. *Thunbergia alata*		10	10
386	10 c. Black-eyed Susan		10	10
387	15 c. *Cochlospermum hibiscoides*		15	15
388	15 c. Buttercup Tree		15	15
389	20 c. *Begonia sp.*		20	20
390	20 c. Begonia		20	20
391	25 c. *Plumeria sp.*		25	25
392	25 c. Frangipani		25	25
393	30 c. *Strelitzia reginae* (26 May)		30	30
394	30 c. Bird of Paradise (26 May)		30	30
395	35 c. *Hibiscus syriacus* (26 May)		30	30
396	35 c. Rose of Sharon (26 May)		30	30
397	40 c. *Nymphaea sp.* (26 May)		35	35
398	40 c. Water Lily (26 May)		35	35
399	50 c. *Tibouchina sp.* (26 May).		45	45
400	50 c. Princess Flower (26 May)		45	45
401	60 c. *Nelumbo sp.* (26 May)		55	55
402	60 c. Lotus (26 May)		55	55
403	80 c. *Hybrid hibiscus* (26 May)		75	75
404	80 c. Yellow Hibiscus (26 May)		75	75
405	$1 Golden Shower Tree (*Cassia fistula*) (9.12.81)		1·25	1·00
406	$2 *Orchid var.* (9.12.81)		3·50	2·50
407	$3 *Orchid sp.* (9.12.81)		4·50	3·50
408	$4 *Euphorbia pulcherrima* poinsettia (15.1.82)		3·50	4·00
409	$6 *Hybrid hibiscus* (15.1.82)		5·50	6·00
410	$10 Scarlet Hibiscus (*Hibiscus rosasinensis*) (12.3.82)		8·50	9·00
381/410		Set of 30	30·00	30·00

The two designs of the 2 c. to 80 c. show different drawings of the same flower, one inscribed with its name in Latin, the other giving the common name. These were printed together, *se-tenant*, in horizontal and vertical pairs throughout the sheet.

Nos. 405/10 are larger, 47 × 33 mm.

See also Nos. 527/36.

76 "Jesus Defiled" (El Greco)   **77** Prince Charles

1981 (10 Apr). *Easter. Details of Paintings. T* **76** *and similar horiz designs. Multicoloured. P 14.*

425	35 c. Type **76**		40	30
426	50 c. "Pietà" (Fernando Gallego)		60	50
427	60 c. "The Supper of Emmaus" (Jacopo da Pontormo)		65	55
425/7		Set of 3	1·50	1·25
MS428	69 × 111 mm. As Nos. 425/7, but each with charity premium of 2 c. P 13½		1·40	1·75

1981 (10 Apr). *Easter. Children's Charity. Designs as Nos. 425/7 in separate miniature sheets 78 × 86 mm, each with a face value of 80 c. + 5 c. P 13½ × 14.*

MS429	As Nos. 425/7	Set of 3 sheets	1·25	2·00

1981 (26 June). *Royal Wedding. T* **77** *and similar vert designs. Multicoloured. P 14.*

430	75 c. Type **77**		25	60
431	95 c. Lady Diana Spencer		30	70
432	$1.20, Prince Charles and Lady Diana		30	80
430/2		Set of 3	75	1·90
MS433	78 × 85 mm. Nos. 430/2		2·00	2·50

Nos. 430/2 were each printed in small sheets of 6, including one *se-tenant* stamp-size label.

78 Footballer Silhouettes   +5c   (79)

1981 (16 Oct). *World Cup Football Championship, Spain (1982). T* **78** *and similar horiz designs showing footballer silhouettes. P 13.*

434	30 c. blue-green, gold & new blue (Type **78**)		20	20
435	30 c. blue-green, gold and new blue (gold figure 3rd from left of stamp)		20	20
436	30 c. blue-green, gold and new blue (gold figure 4th from left)		20	20
437	35 c. new blue, gold and reddish orange (gold figure 3rd from left)		20	20
438	35 c. new blue, gold and reddish orange (gold figure 4th from left)		20	20
439	35 c. new blue, gold and reddish orange (gold figure 2nd from left)		20	20
440	40 c. reddish orange, gold and blue-green (gold figure 3rd from left, displaying close control)		20	20
441	40 c. reddish orange, gold and blue-green (gold figure 2nd from left)		20	20
442	40 c. reddish orange, gold and blue-green (gold figure 3rd from left, heading)		20	20
434/42		Set of 9	1·60	1·60
MS443	162 × 122 mm. 30 c. + 3 c., 35 c. + 3 c., 40 c. + 3 c. (each × 3). As Nos. 434/42		1·60	2·00

The three designs of each value were printed together, *se-tenant*, in horizontal strips of 3 throughout the sheets.

1981 (3 Nov). *International Year for Disabled Persons. Nos. 430/3 surch as T* **79**.

444	75 c. + 5 c. Type **77**		50	85
445	95 c. + 5 c. Lady Diana Spencer		60	1·00
446	$1.20 + 5 c. Prince Charles and Lady Diana		60	1·25
444/6		Set of 3	1·50	2·75
MS447	78×85 mm. As Nos. 444/6, with each surcharged "+ 10 c."		1·75	4·50

Nos. 444/6 have a commemorative inscription overprinted on the sheet margins.

OMNIBUS ISSUES

Details, together with prices for complete sets, of the various Omnibus issues from the 1935 Silver Jubilee series to date are included in a special section following Zimbabwe at the end of Volume 2.

80 "The Holy
Family with Angels"
(detail)

81 Prince of Wales

1981 (11 Dec). *Christmas and 375th Birth Anniv of Rembrandt. T* **80** *and similar vert designs. Multicoloured. P* 14 × 13.

448	20 c. Type **80**		65	45
449	35 c. "Presentation in the Temple"		85	55
450	50 c. "Virgin and Child in Temple"		95	1·10
451	60 c. "The Holy Family"		1·25	1·50
448/51		Set of 4	3·25	3·25
MS452	79 × 112 mm. Nos. 448/51		3·25	3·50

1982 (22 Jan). *Christmas. Children's Charity. Designs as Nos. 448/51 in separate miniature sheets 66 × 80 mm, each with a face value of 80 c. + 5 c. P* 14 × 13.

MS453	As Nos. 448/51	Set of 4 sheets	2·00	2·50

1982 (1 July). *21st Birthday of Princess of Wales. T* **81** *and similar horiz designs. Multicoloured. P* 14.

454	50 c. Type **81**		40	55
455	$1.25, Prince and Princess of Wales		60	90
456	$2.50, Princess of Wales		1·50	1·40
454/6		Set of 3	2·25	2·50
MS457	81 × 101 mm. Nos. 454/6		4·75	3·50

Nos. 454/6 were each printed in small sheets of 6 including one *se-tenant* stamp-size label.

The stamps from No. **MS457** are without white borders.

(82)   83 Infant

1982 (23 July). *Birth of Prince William of Wales (1st issue). Nos. 430/3 optd as T* **82**.

458	75 c. Type **77** (optd with T **82**)		1·50	2·00
	a. Pair. Nos. 458/9		3·00	4·00
459	75 c. Type **77** (optd "BIRTH OF PRINCE WILLIAM OF WALES 21 JUNE 1982")		1·50	2·00
	a. Pair. Nos. 460/1		5·00	5·00
460	95 c. Lady Diana Spencer (optd with T **82**)		2·50	2·50
461	95 c. Lady Diana Spencer (optd "BIRTH OF PRINCE WILLIAM OF WALES 21 JUNE 1982")		2·50	2·50
462	$1.20, Prince Charles and Lady Diana Spencer (optd with T **82**)		2·50	2·75
	a. Pair. Nos. 462/3		5·00	5·50
463	$1.20, Prince Charles and Lady Diana Spencer (optd "BIRTH OF PRINCE WILLIAM OF WALES 21 JUNE 1982")		2·50	2·75
458/63		Set of 6	11·50	13·00
MS464	78 × 85 mm. Nos. 430/2 each optd "PRINCE WILLIAM OF WALES 21 JUNE 1982"		6·00	6·00

Nos. 458/9, 460/1 and 462/3 were each printed *se-tenant* in small sheets of 6, containing three stamps overprinted with Type **82**, two with "BIRTH OF PRINCE WILLIAM OF WALES 21 JUNE 1982" and one stamp-size label.

1982 (10 Sept). *Birth of Prince William of Wales (2nd issue). Designs as Nos. 454/7 but with changed inscriptions. Multicoloured. P* 14.

465	50 c. Type **81**		45	55
466	$1.25, Prince and Princess of Wales		85	1·25
467	$2.50, Princess of Wales		3·00	2·50
465/7		Set of 3	3·75	3·75
MS468	81 × 101 mm. As Nos. 465/7		6·00	5·50

Nos. 465/7 were each printed in small sheets of 6 including one *se-tenant*, stamp-size, label.

1982 (3 Dec). *Christmas. Paintings of Infants by Bronzino, Murillo and Boucher. T* **83** *and similar horiz designs. P* 13 × 14½.

469	40 c. multicoloured		1·25	60
470	52 c. multicoloured		1·40	75
471	83 c. multicoloured		2·25	2·00
472	$1.05, multicoloured		2·50	2·25
469/72		Set of 4	6·50	5·00
MS473	110 × 76 mm. Designs as Nos. 469/72 (each 31 × 27 mm), but without portrait of Princess and Prince William. P 13½		5·00	2·75

MINIMUM PRICE

The minimum price quote is 10p which represents a handling charge rather than a basis for valuing common stamps. For further notes about prices see introductory pages.

---

84 Prince and Princess of
Wales with Prince William

85 Prime Minister Robert Rex

1982 (3 Dec). *Christmas. Children's Charity. Sheet 72 × 58 mm. P* 13 × 13½.

MS474	84	80 c. + 5 c. multicoloured	1·50	1·50

No. **MS474** occurs with four different designs in the sheet margin.

1983 (14 Mar). *Commonwealth Day. T* **85** *and similar horiz designs. Multicoloured. P* 13.

475	70 c. Type **85**		50	55
476	70 c. H.M.S. *Resolution* and H.M.S. *Adventure* off Niue, 1774		50	55
477	70 c. Passion flower		50	55
478	70 c. Limes		50	55
475/8		Set of 4	1·75	2·00

Nos. 475/8 were issued together, *se-tenant*, in blocks of four throughout the sheet.

86 Scouts signalling   (87)

1983 (28 Apr). *75th Anniv of Boy Scout Movement and 125th Birth Anniv of Lord Baden-Powell. T* **86** *and similar vert designs. Multicoloured. P* 13.

479	40 c. Type **86**		35	40
480	50 c. Planting sapling		45	50
481	83 c. Map-reading		85	90
479/81		Set of 3	1·50	1·60
MS482	137 × 90 mm. As Nos. 479/81, but each with premium of 3 c.		1·60	1·75

1983 (14 July). *15th World Scout Jamboree, Alberta, Canada. Nos. 479/82 optd with T* **87**, *in black on silver background.*

483	40 c. Type **86**		35	40
484	50 c. Planting sapling		45	50
485	83 c. Map-reading		85	90
483/5		Set of 3	1·50	1·60
MS486	137 × 90 mm. As Nos. 483/5, but each with premium of 3 c.		1·60	1·75

88 Black Right Whale

1983 (15 Aug). *Protect the Whales. T* **88** *and similar horiz designs. Multicoloured. P* 13 × 14.

487	12 c. Type **88**		75	65
488	25 c. Fin Whale		95	80
489	35 c. Sei Whale		1·50	1·25
490	40 c. Blue Whale		1·75	1·50
491	58 c. Bowhead Whale		1·90	1·60
492	70 c. Sperm Whale		2·25	1·75
493	83 c. Humpback Whale		2·50	2·25
494	$1.05, Minke Whale ("Lesser Rorqual")		3·00	2·50
495	$2.50, Grey Whale		4·25	4·00
487/95		Set of 9	17·00	15·00

89 Montgolfier Balloon, 1783

90 "The Garvagh Madonna"

1983 (14 Oct). *Bicentenary of Manned Flight. T* **89** *and similar horiz designs. Multicoloured. (a) Postage. P* 13½.

496	25 c. Type **89**		35	25
497	40 c. Wright Brothers Flyer 1, 1903		80	45
498	58 c. Airship LZ-127 *Graf Zeppelin*, 1928		1·00	60
499	70 c. Boeing 247, 1933		1·40	85
500	83 c. "Apollo 8", 1968		1·40	1·00
501	$1.05, Space shuttle *Columbia*, 1982		1·60	1·40
496/501		Set of 6	6·00	4·00

(b) *Air. Inscr* "AIRMAIL"

MS502	118 × 130 mm. Nos. 496/501. P 13		3·00	3·25

1983 (25 Nov). *Christmas. 500th Birth Anniv of Raphael. T* **90** *and similar vert designs. Multicoloured. P* 14 × 13½.

503	30 c. Type **90**		50	30
504	40 c. "Madonna of the Granduca"		55	35
505	58 c. "Madonna of the Goldfinch"		75	50
506	70 c. "The Holy Family of Francis I"		90	60
507	83 c. "The Holy Family with Saints"		1·10	70
503/7		Set of 5	3·50	2·25
MS508	120 × 114 mm. As Nos. 503/7 but each with a premium of 3 c.		3·25	2·75

83c

(90a)

1983 (30 Nov). *Various stamps surch as T* **90a**.

(a) *Nos. 393/4, 399/404 and* 407

509	52 c. on 30 c. *Strelitzia reginae*		60	45
510	52 c. on 30 c. Bird of Paradise		60	45
511	58 c. on 50 c. *Tibouchina sp.*		70	55
512	58 c. on 50 c. Princess Flower		70	55
513	70 c. on 60 c. *Nelumbo sp.*		75	60
514	70 c. on 60 c. Lotus		75	60
515	83 c. on 80 c. *Hybrid hibiscus*		90	75
516	83 c. on 80 c. Yellow Hibiscus		90	75
517	$3.70 on $3 *Orchid sp.*		5·00	3·25

(b) *Nos. 431/2 and* 455/6

518	$1.10 on 95 c. Lady Diana Spencer		2·50	2·25
	a. Error. Surch on No. 458		6·00	6·00
	ab. Pair. Nos. 518a/b		13·00	13·00
	b. Error. Surch on No. 459		7·00	7·00
519	$1.10 on $1.25, Prince and Princess of Wales (Gold on Blk.)		2·00	2·00
520	$2.60 on $1.20, Prince Charles and Lady Diana		4·00	3·50
	a. Error. Surch on No. 462		6·00	6·00
	ab. Pair. Nos. 520a/b		13·00	13·00
	b. Error. Surch on No. 463		7·00	7·00
521	$2.60 on $2.50, Princess of Wales (Gold on Blk.)		2·75	3·25
509/21		Set of 13	20·00	17·00

1983 (29 Dec). *Christmas. 500th Birth Anniv of Raphael. Children's Charity. Designs as Nos. 503/7 in separate miniature sheets, 65 × 80 mm, each with face value of 85 c. + 5 c. P* 13½.

MS522	As Nos. 503/7	Set of 5 sheets	3·25	2·75

91 Morse Key Transmitter

92 *Phalaenopsis sp.*

1984 (23 Jan). *World Communications Year. T* **91** *and similar vert designs. Multicoloured. P* 13 × 13½.

523	40 c. Type **91**		30	35
524	52 c. Wall-mounted phone		40	45
525	83 c. Communications satellite		60	65
523/5		Set of 3	1·10	1·25
MS526	114 × 90 mm. Nos. 523/5		1·10	1·50

1984 (20 Feb–23 July). *Flowers (2nd series). Designs as Nos. 381 etc., but with gold frames and redrawn inscr as in T* **92**. *Multicoloured. P* 13 *(Nos.* 537/42*) or* 13 × 13½ *(others).*

527	12 c. Type **92**		25	15
528	25 c. *Euphorbia pulcherrima*		35	20
529	30 c. *Cochlospermum hibiscoides*		40	25
530	35 c. *Begonia sp.*		40	25
531	40 c. *Plumeria sp.*		50	30
532	52 c. *Strelitzia reginae*		65	40
533	58 c. *Hibiscus syriacus*		70	45
534	70 c. *Tibouchina sp.*		1·00	60
535	83 c. *Nelumbo sp.*		1·10	70
536	$1.05, *Hybrid hibiscus*		1·25	85
537	$1.75, *Cassia fistula* (10.5)		2·00	1·50
538	$2.30, *Orchid var.* (10.5)		3·50	2·00
539	$3.90, *Orchid sp.* (10.5)		5·00	4·00
540	$5 *Euphorbia pulcherrima poinsettia* (18.6)		6·50	4·50
541	$6.60, *Hybrid hibiscus* (18.6)		7·00	6·00
542	$8.30, *Hibiscus rosasinensis* (23.7)		8·00	7·00
527/42		Set of 16	35·00	26·00

Nos. 537/42 are larger, 39 × 31 mm.

93 Discus-throwing   94 Koala

1984 (15 Mar). *Olympic Games, Los Angeles. T* **93** *and similar multicoloured designs showing ancient Greek sports. P* 14.

547	30 c. Type **93**		25	30
548	35 c. Sprinting (*horiz*)		30	35
549	40 c. Horse racing (*horiz*)		35	40
550	58 c. Boxing (*horiz*)		50	55
551	70 c. Javelin-throwing		60	65
547/51		Set of 5	1·75	2·00

1984 (24 Aug). *"Ausipex" International Stamp Exhibition, Melbourne* (1st issue). P 14. (*a*) *Postage. Vert designs as T* **94** *showing Koala Bears.*

552	25 c. multicoloured		60	30
553	35 c. multicoloured		65	35
554	40 c. multicoloured		70	40
555	58 c. multicoloured		90	65
556	70 c. multicoloured		1·10	75

(*b*) *Air. Vert designs showing Red Kangaroos*

557	83 c. multicoloured		1·25	85
558	$1.05, multicoloured		1·50	1·25
559	$2.50, multicoloured		3·00	3·50
552/9		Set of 8	8·75	7·25
MS560	110 × 64 mm. $1.75, Wallaby; $1.75, Koala Bear. P 13½		4·00	4·00

See also Nos. MS566/7.

Discus Throw
Rolf Danneberg
Germany

(**95**)

96 Niue National Flag and Premier Sir Robert Rex

1984 (7 Sept). *Olympic Gold Medal Winners, Los Angeles. Nos.* 547/51 *optd as T* **95** *in red* (35 c.) *or gold* (*others*).

561	30 c. Type **93** (opt T **95**)		35	30
562	35 c. Sprinting (optd "1,500 Metres Sebastian Coe Great Britain")		40	35
563	40 c. Horse racing (optd "Equestrian Mark Todd New Zealand")		45	35
564	58 c. Boxing (optd "Boxing Tyrell Biggs United States")		50	50
565	70 c. Javelin-throwing (optd "Javelin Throw Arto Haerkoenen Finland")		55	60
561/5		Set of 5	2·00	1·90

1984 (20 Sept). *"Ausipex" International Stamp Exhibition, Melbourne* (2nd issue). *Designs as Nos.* 552/60 *in miniature sheets of six or four. Multicoloured. P* 13½.

MS566	109 × 105 mm. Nos. 552/6 and $1.75, Koala Bear (as No. MS560)	6·00	4·75
MS567	80 × 105 mm. Nos. 557/9 and $1.75, Wallaby (as No. MS560)	6·00	4·75

1984 (19 Oct). *10th Anniv of Self-Government. T* **96** *and similar horiz designs. Multicoloured. P* 13.

568	40 c. Type **96**		70	35
569	58 c. Map of Niue and Premier Rex		75	50
570	70 c. Premier Rex receiving proclamation of self-government		75	60
568/70		Set of 3	2·00	2·00
MS571	110 × 83 mm. Nos. 568/70		2·00	2·00
MS572	100 × 74 mm. $2.50, As 70 c. (50 × 30 mm)		2·00	2·00

$2
Prince Henry

IIII
IIII

15. 9. 84

(**97**)

98 "The Nativity" (A. Vaccaro)

1984 (22 Oct). *Birth of Prince Henry. Nos.* 430 *and* 454 *optd as T* **97**.

573	$2 on 50 c. Type 81 (Sil.)		2·50	1·75
574	$2 on 75 c. Type 77 (R.)		2·50	1·75

1984 (23 Nov). *Christmas. T* **98** *and similar vert designs. Multicoloured. P* 13 × 13½.

575	40 c. Type **98**		50	35
576	58 c. "Virgin with Fly" (anon, 16th-century)		65	50
577	70 c. "The Adoration of the Shepherds" (B. Murillo)		75	60
578	83 c. "Flight into Egypt" (B. Murillo)		85	70
575/8		Set of 4	2·50	1·90
MS579	115 × 111 mm. As Nos. 575/8 but each stamp with a 5 c. premium		2·50	2·25
MS580	Four sheets, each 66 × 98 mm. As Nos. 575/8, but each stamp 30 × 42 mm. with a face value of 95 c. + 10 c. P 13½ Set of 4 sheets		3·25	3·00

99 House Wren

1985 (15 Apr). *Birth Bicentenary of John J. Audubon (ornithologist). T* **99** *and similar horiz designs showing original paintings. Multicoloured. P* 14.

581	40 c. Type **99**		2·75	1·00
582	70 c. Veery		3·00	1·60
583	83 c. Grasshopper Sparrow		3·25	2·00
584	$1.05, Henslow's Sparrow		3·50	2·25
585	$2.50, Vesper Sparrow		5·00	4·25
581/5		Set of 5	16·00	10·00
MS586	Five sheets, each 54 × 60 mm. As Nos. 581/5 but each stamp 34 × 26 mm. with a face value of $1.75 and without the commemorative inscription Set of 5 sheets		12·00	8·50

100 The Queen Mother in Garter Robes

1985 (14 June). *Life and Times of Queen Elizabeth the Queen Mother. T* **100** *and similar horiz designs. Multicoloured. P* 13.

587	70 c. Type **100**		55	60
588	$1.15, In open carriage with the Queen		80	95
589	$1.50, With Prince Charles during 80th birthday celebrations		90	1·25
587/9		Set of 3	2·00	2·50
MS590	70 × 70 mm. $3 At her desk in Clarence House (38 × 35 mm)		3·50	2·50

Nos. 587/9 were each issued in sheetlets of five stamps and one stamp-size label at top left, showing the Queen Mother's arms. For Nos. 587/9 in miniature sheet see No. MS627.

MINI SOUTH PACIFIC GAMES, RAROTONGA

52 c

(**101**)

1985 (26 July). *South Pacific Mini Games, Rarotonga. Nos.* 547/8 *and* 550/1 *surch as T* **101** *in black and gold.*

591	52 c. on 70 c. Javelin-throwing		40	45
592	83 c. on 58 c. Boxing		65	70
593	95 c. on 35 c. Sprinting		75	80
594	$2 on 30 c. Type **93**		1·50	1·60
591/4		Set of 4	3·00	3·25

On Nos. 591/4 the new face values and inscriptions are surcharged in black on gold panels. The Games emblem is in gold only.

PACIFIC ISLANDS CONFERENCE, RAROTONGA

(**102**)

103 "R. Strozzi's Daughter" (Titian)

1985 (26 July). *Pacific Islands Conference, Rarotonga. Nos.* 475/8 *optd with T* **102** *in black on silver.*

595	70 c. Type **85**		55	60
596	70 c. *Resolution* and *Adventure* off Niue, 1774		55	60
597	70 c. Passion flower		55	60
598	70 c. Limes		55	60
595/8		Set of 4	2·00	2·25

No. 595 also shows an overprinted amendment to the caption which now reads "Premier Sir Robert Rex K.B.E.".

1985 (11 Oct). *International Youth Year. T* **103** *and similar vert designs. Multicoloured. P* 13.

599	58 c. Type **103**		1·25	90
600	70 c. "The Fifer" (E. Manet)		1·50	1·00
601	$1.15, "Portrait of a Young Girl" (Renoir)		2·25	1·90
602	$1.50, "Portrait of M. Berard" (Renoir)		2·50	2·50
599/602		Set of 4	6·75	5·75
MS603	Four sheets, each 63 × 79 mm. As Nos. 599/602 but each with a face value of $1.75 + 10 c. Set of 4 sheets		12·00	11·00

104 "Virgin and Child"

1985 (29 Nov). *Christmas. Details of Paintings by Correggio. T* **104** *and similar vert designs. Multicoloured. P* 13 × 13½.

604	58 c. Type **104**		1·50	85
605	85 c. "Adoration of the Magi"		1·75	1·40
606	$1.05, "Virgin with Child and St. John"		2·25	2·50
607	$1.45, "Virgin and Child with St. Catherine"		2·75	3·50
604/7		Set of 4	7·50	7·50
MS608	83 × 123 mm. As Nos. 604/7, but each stamp with a face value of 60 c. + 10 c.		3·00	2·75
MS609	Four sheets, each 80 × 90 mm. 65 c. Type **104**; 95 c. As No. 605; $1.20, As No. 606; $1.75, As No. 607 (each stamp 49 × 59 mm). Imperf Set of 4 sheets		4·00	4·00

105 "The Constellations" (detail)   106 Queen Elizabeth II and Prince Philip

1986 (24 Jan). *Appearance of Halley's Comet. T* **105** *and similar horiz designs showing details from ceiling painting "The Constellations" by Giovanni de Vecchi. Nos.* 611/13 *show different spacecraft at top left. P* 13½.

610	60 c. multicoloured		50	50
611	75 c. multicoloured (*Vega* spacecraft)		65	65
612	$1.10, multicoloured (*Planet A* spacecraft)		90	90
613	$1.50, multicoloured (*Giotto* spacecraft)		1·25	1·25
610/13		Set of 4	3·00	3·00
MS614	125 × 91 mm. As Nos. 610/13 but each stamp with a face value of 95 c.		4·75	4·25

Stamps from No. MS614 are without borders.

1986 (28 Apr). *60th Birthday of Queen Elizabeth II. T* **106** *and similar vert designs. Multicoloured. P* 14½ × 13.

615	$1.10, Type **106**		80	1·00
616	$1.50, Queen and Prince Philip at Balmoral		1·00	1·25
617	$2 Queen at Buckingham Palace		1·50	1·75
615/17		Set of 3	3·00	3·50
MS618	110 × 70 mm. As Nos. 615/17, but each with a face value of 75 c.		2·75	3·25
MS619	58 × 89 mm. $3 Queen and Prince Philip at Windsor Castle		3·50	4·25

107 U.S.A. 1847 Franklin 5 c. Stamp and Washington Sculpture, Mt. Rushmore, U.S.A.   108 "Statue under Construction, Paris, 1883" (Victor Dargaud)

1986 (22 May). *"Ameripex '86" International Stamp Exhibition, Chicago. T 107 and similar vert design. Multicoloured. P 14.*
620 $1 Type **107** .. .. .. 3·00 3·00
   a. Horiz pair. Nos. 620/1 .. .. 6·00 6·00
621 $1 Flags of Niue and U.S.A. and Mt. Rushmore sculptures .. .. 3·00 3·00
Nos. 620/1 were printed together, *se-tenant*, in horizontal pairs, within sheetlets of 8 stamps, each pair forming a composite design.

1986 (4 July). *Centenary of Statue of Liberty (1st issue). T 108 and similar vert design. Multicoloured. P 13 × 13½.*
622 $1 Type **108** .. .. .. 2·00 2·00
623 $2.50, "Unveiling of the Statue of Liberty" (Edmund Morand) .. .. 2·75 2·75
MS624 107×73 mm. As Nos. 622/3, but each stamp with a face value of $1.25 .. 2·50 3·00
See also No. **MS648**.

109 Prince Andrew, Miss Sarah Ferguson and Westminster Abbey

1986 (23 July). *Royal Wedding. T 109 and similar horiz design. Multicoloured. P 13½ × 13.*
625 $2.50, Type **109** .. .. 3·25 3·25
MS626 106×68 mm. $5 Prince Andrew and Miss Sarah Ferguson (43×30 mm) .. 7·50 8·00

1986 (4 Aug). *86th Birthday of Queen Elizabeth the Queen Mother. Nos. 587/9 in miniature sheet, 109×83 mm. P 13.*
MS627 Nos. 587/9 .. .. .. 8·50 9·00

110 Great Egret   111 "Virgin and Child" (Perugino)

1986 (4 Aug). *"Stampex '86" Stamp Exhibition, Adelaide. Australian Birds. T 110 and similar multicoloured designs. P 13×13½ (40, 75 c., $1, $2.20) or 13½×13 (others).*
628 40 c. Type **110** .. .. .. 2·50 1·75
629 60 c. Painted Finch (*horiz*) .. .. 2·75 2·00
630 75 c. Australian King Parrot .. 3·00 2·25
631 80 c. Variegated Wren (*horiz*) .. 3·25 2·50
632 $1 Peregrine Falcon .. .. 3·75 2·75
633 $1.65, Azure Kingfisher (*horiz*) .. 5·00 4·00
634 $2.20, Budgerigars .. .. 6·00 6·00
635 $4.25, Emu (*horiz*) .. .. 7·50 7·50
628/35 .. .. .. *Set of 8* 30·00 26·00

1986 (14 Nov). *Christmas. Paintings from the Vatican Museum. T 111 and similar vert designs. Multicoloured. P 14.*
636 80 c. Type **111** .. .. 2·00 1·75
637 $1.15, "Virgin of St. N. dei Frari" (Titian) 2·25 2·00
638 $1.80, "Virgin with Milk" (Lorenzo di Credi) .. .. .. 3·25 3·50
639 $2.60, "Madonna of Foligno" (Raphael) .. .. 4·00 4·00
636/9 .. .. .. *Set of 4* 10·50 10·50
MS640 87×110 mm. As Nos. 636/9, but each stamp with a face value of $1.50. P 13½ .. 8·00 6·00
MS641 70×100 mm. $7.50, As No. 639, but 27×43 mm. P 14½×13 .. .. 8·00 9·00

(112)

1986 (21 Nov). *Visit of Pope John Paul II to South Pacific. Nos. 636/41 surch as T 112 in black on silver.*
642 8⁰ c. + 1⁰ c. Type **111** .. 2·75 2·50
643 $1.15 + 10 c. "Virgin of St. N. dei Frari" (Titian) .. .. 3·25 3·00
644 $1.80 + 10 c. "Virgin with Milk" (Lorenzo di Credi) .. .. 4·25 4·00
645 $2.60 + 10 c. "Madonna of Foligno" (Raphael) .. .. 5·50 5·00
642/5 .. .. .. *Set of 4* 14·00 13·00
MS646 87×110 mm. As Nos. 642/5, but each stamp with a face value of $1.50 + 10 c. .. 12·00 11·00
MS647 70×100 mm. $7.50 + 50 c. As No. 645, but 27×43 mm .. .. 12·00 11·00

1987 (20 May). *Centenary of Statue of Liberty (1986) (2nd issue). Two sheets, each 122×122 mm, containing multicoloured designs as T 63 of Cook Islands (Penrhyn). Litho. P 13½×14 (horiz) or 14×13½ (vert).*
MS648 Two sheets. (a) 75 c. Sailing ship under Brooklyn Bridge; 75 c. Restoring Statue's flame; 75 c. Steam-cleaning Statue's torch; 75 c. *Esmerelda* (Chilean cadet barquentine) off Manhattan; 75 c. Cadet barque at dusk. (b) 75 c. Statue of Liberty at night (*vert*); 75 c. Statue at night (side view) (*vert*); 75 c. Cleaning Statue's crown (*vert*); 75 c. Statue at night (rear view) (*vert*); 75 c. Cleaning a finial (*vert*) *Set of 2 sheets* 5·00 6·00

113 Boris Becker, Olympic Rings and Commemorative Coin

(Des G. Vasarhelyi. Litho Questa)

1987 (25 Sept). *Olympic Games, Seoul (1988). Tennis (1st issue). T 113 and similar horiz designs showing Boris Becker in play. P 13½×14.*
649 80 c. multicoloured .. .. 2·25 2·00
650 $1.15, multicoloured .. .. 2·50 2·25
651 $1.40, multicoloured .. .. 2·75 2·50
652 $1.80, multicoloured .. .. 3·50 3·25
649/52 .. .. .. *Set of 4* 10·00 9·00

(Des G. Vasarhelyi. Litho Questa)

1987 (20 Oct). *Olympic Games, Seoul (1988). Tennis (2nd issue). Horiz designs as T 113, but showing Steffi Graf. P 13½×14.*
653 85 c. multicoloured .. .. 1·75 1·25
654 $1.05, multicoloured .. .. 2·00 1·50
655 $1.30, multicoloured .. .. 2·25 1·75
656 $1.75, multicoloured .. .. 2·75 2·00
653/6 .. .. .. *Set of 4* 8·00 6·00

40TH WEDDING ANNIV.

4.85

(114)   115 "The Nativity"

1987 (20 Nov). *Royal Ruby Wedding. Nos. 616/17 optd with T 114.*
657 $4.85 on $1.50, Queen and Prince Philip at Balmoral .. .. 4·00 4·50
658 $4.85 on $2 Queen at Buckingham Palace .. 4·00 4·50
On Nos. 657/8 the original values are obliterated in gold.

1987 (4 Dec). *Christmas. Religious Paintings by Dürer. T 115 and similar horiz designs. Multicoloured. P 13½.*
659 80 c. Type **115** .. .. 1·50 1·25
660 $1.05, "Adoration of the Magi" .. 1·75 1·75
661 $2.80, "Celebration of the Rosary" .. 3·25 3·50
659/61 .. .. .. *Set of 3* 6·00 6·00
MS662 100×140 mm. As Nos. 659/61, but each size 48×37 mm with a face value of $1.30 5·50 4·50
MS663 90×80 mm. $7.50, As No. 661, but size 51×33 mm .. .. 7·00 7·00
Nos. 659/61 each include a detail of an angel with lute as in T 115. Stamps from the miniature sheets are without this feature.

116 Franz Beckenbauer in Action

(Des G. Vasarhelyi. Litho Questa)

1988 (20 June). *West German Football Victories. T 116 and similar horiz designs. Multicoloured. P 13½×14.*
664 20 c. Type **116** 70 70
665 40 c. German "All Star" team in action .. 90 90
666 60 c. Bayern Munich team with European Cup, 1974 .. .. 1·10 1·10
667 80 c. World Cup match, England, 1966 .. 1·40 1·40
668 $1.05, World Cup match, Mexico, 1970 .. 1·60 1·60
669 $1.30, Beckenbauer with pennant, 1974 2·00 2·00
670 $1.80, Beckenbauer and European Cup, 1974 .. .. 2·25 2·25
664/70 .. .. .. *Set of 7* 9·00 9·00

NEW INFORMATION

The editor is always interested to correspond with people who have new information that will improve or correct the Catalogue.

Australia 24 Jan 88
French Open 4 June 88

(117)   118 Angels

1988 (14 Oct). *Steffi Graf's Tennis Victories. Nos. 653/6 optd as T 117.*
671 85 c. multicoloured (optd with T 117) 1·60 1·50
672 $1.05, mult (optd "Wimbledon 2 July 88 U S Open 10 Sept. 88") .. 1·90 1·75
673 $1.30, mult (optd "Women's Tennis Grand Slam: 10 September 88") .. 2·00 1·90
674 $1.75, multicoloured (optd "Seoul Olympic Games Gold Medal Winner") .. 2·25 2·10
671/4 .. .. .. *Set of 4* 7·00 6·50

1988 (28 Oct). *Christmas. T 118 and similar vert designs showing details from "The Adoration of the Shepherds" by Rubens. Multicoloured. P 13½.*
675 60 c. Type **118** .. .. 1·75 1·50
676 80 c. Shepherds .. .. 2·00 1·75
677 $1.05, Virgin Mary .. .. 2·75 2·50
678 $1.30, Holy Child .. .. 3·50 3·00
675/8 .. .. .. *Set of 4* 9·00 8·00
MS679 83 × 103 mm. $7.20, The Nativity (38 × 49 mm) .. .. 6·00 7·00

119 Astronaut and "Apollo 11" Emblem

(Des G. Vasarhelyi)

1989 (20 July). *20th Anniv of First Manned Landing on Moon. T 119 and similar horiz designs. Multicoloured. P 14.*
680 $1.50, Type **119** .. .. 4·00 4·00
   a. Horiz strip of 3. Nos. 680/2 .. 11·00
681 $1.50, Earth and Moon .. .. 4·00 4·00
682 $1.50, Astronaut and "Apollo 1" emblem 4·00 4·00
680/2 .. .. .. *Set of 3* 11·00 11·00
MS683 160×64 mm. As Nos. 680/2, but each stamp with a face value of $1.15. P 13 5·00 5·00
Nos. 680/2 were printed together, *se-tenant*, in horizontal strips of 3 throughout the sheet.

120 Priests

1989 (22 Nov). *Christmas. T 120 and similar multicoloured designs showing details from "Presentation in the Temple" by Rembrandt. P 13.*
684 70 c. Type **120** .. .. 2·25 2·25
685 80 c. Virgin and Christ Child in Simeon's arms .. .. .. 2·25 2·25
686 $1.05, Joseph .. .. 2·75 2·75
687 $1.30, Simeon and Christ Child .. 3·25 3·25
684/7 .. .. .. *Set of 4* 9·50 9·50
MS688 84×110 mm. $7.20, "Presentation in the Temple" (39×49 mm). P 13½ .. 10·50 11·00

121 Fritz Walter

1990 (5 Feb). *World Cup Football Championship, Italy. German Footballers. T 121 and similar horiz designs. Multicoloured. P 13½×13.*
689 80 c. Type **121** .. .. 2·50 2·50
690 $1.15, Franz Beckenbauer .. 2·75 2·75
691 $1.40, Uwe Seeler .. .. 3·00 3·00
692 $1.80, German team emblem and signatures of former captains .. 4·00 4·00
689/92 .. .. .. *Set of 4* 11·00 11·00

122 "Merchant Maarten Looten" (Rembrandt)

123 Queen Elizabeth the Queen Mother

1990 (2 May). *150th Anniv of the Penny Black. T 122 and similar vert designs showing Rembrandt paintings. Multicoloured. P 13½.*
693	80 c. Type 122	2·25	2·25
694	$1.05, "Rembrandt's Son Titus with Pen in Hand"	2·50	2·50
695	$1.30, "The Shipbuilder and his Wife"	2·75	2·75
696	$1.80, "Bathsheba with King David's Letter"	3·00	3·00
693/6	*Set of 4*	9·50	9·50
MS697	82×143 mm. As Nos. 693/6, but each with a face value of $1.50	7·50	7·50

1990 (23 July). *90th Birthday of Queen Elizabeth the Queen Mother. P 13×13½.*
698	123 $1.25, multicoloured	4·00	3·75
MS699	84×64 mm. 123 $7 multicoloured	13·00	11·00

124 "Adoration of the Magi" (Dirk Bouts)

(125)

(Litho Questa)

1990 (27 Nov). *Christmas. Religious Paintings. T 124 and similar vert designs. Multicoloured. P 14.*
700	70 c. Type 124	2·25	2·25
701	80 c. "Holy Family" (Fra Bartolommeo)	2·50	2·50
702	$1.05, "Nativity" (Memling)	2·75	2·75
703	$1.30, "Adoration of the Kings" (Bruegel the Elder)	3·50	3·50
700/3	*Set of 4*	10·00	10·00
MS704	100×135 mm. $7.20, "Virgin and Child Enthoned" (detail, Cosimo Tura)	11·00	12·00

1990 (5 Dec). *"Birdpex '90" Stamp Exhibition, Christchurch, New Zealand. No. 410 optd with T 125 in silver.*
705	$10 Scarlet Hibiscus	11·00	12·00

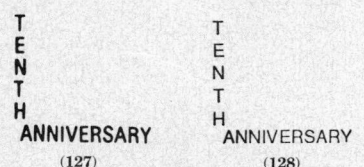

SIXTY FIFTH BIRTHDAY QUEEN ELIZABETH II
(126)

1991 (22 Apr). *65th Birthday of Queen Elizabeth II. No. 409 optd with T 126.*
706	$6 Hybrid hibiscus	8·50	10·00

TENTH ANNIVERSARY (127)

TENTH ANNIVERSARY (128)

1991 (26 June). *10th Wedding Anniv of Prince and Princess of Wales. Nos. 430/2 optd. A. With T 127 in typography (75 c. in silver).*
707A	75 c. Type 77	1·75	1·75
708A	95 c. Lady Diana Spencer	2·75	2·75
709A	$1.20, Prince Charles and Lady Diana	2·75	2·75
707A/9A	*Set of 3*	6·50	6·50

B. With T 128 in lithography (75 c. in black).
707B	75 c. Type 77	1·75	1·75
708B	95 c. Lady Diana Spencer	2·75	2·75
709B	$1.20, Prince Charles and Lady Diana	2·75	2·75
707B/9B	*Set of 3*	6·50	6·50

Nos. 707A/9A come from small sheets of 6, including one se-tenant stamp-size label, and Nos. 707B/9B from uncut sheets containing four such small sheets.

129 "The Virgin and Child with Sts Jerome and Dominic" (Lippi)

130 Banded Rail

(Des G. Vasarhelyi. Litho Questa)

1991 (11 Nov). *Christmas. Religious Paintings. T 129 and similar vert designs. Multicoloured. P 14.*
710	20 c. Type 129	65	65
711	50 c. "The Isenheim Altarpiece" (M. Grunewald)	1·25	1·25
712	$1 "The Nativity" (G. Pittoni)	2·25	2·50
713	$2 "Adoration of the Kings" (J. Brueghel the Elder)	3·00	3·25
710/13	*Set of 4*	6·50	7·00
MS714	79×104 mm. $7 "Adoration of the Shepherds" (G. Reni)	8·50	10·00

(Litho B.D.T.)

1992 (19 Feb)–93. *Birds. T 130 and similar vert designs. Multicoloured. P 13 ($7, $10, $15) or 14 (others).*
718	20 c. Type 130	45	35
719	50 c. Red-tailed Tropic Bird	60	40
720	70 c. Purple Swamphen	80	60
721	$1 Pacific Pigeon	1·00	80
722	$1.50, White-collared Kingfisher (20.3.92)	1·50	1·50
723	$2 Blue-crowned Lory (20.3.92)	2·00	2·00
724	$3 Purple-capped Fruit Dove (16.4.92)	2·50	2·50
726	$5 Barn Owl (15.5.92)	3·75	3·75
727	$7 Longtailed Koel ("Cockoo") (26.3.93)	4·50	5·00
728	$10 Eastern Reef Heron (16.4.93)	6·25	6·50
729	$15 Spotted Triller ("Polynesian Triller") (10.8.93)	9·50	9·75
718/29	*Set of 11*	29·00	30·00

Nos. 727/9 are larger, 48½×35 mm, and show a silhouette portrait of Queen Elizabeth II at right.

131 Columbus before King Ferdinand and Queen Isabella

(Des G. Vasarhelyi. Litho B.D.T.)

1992 (22 May). *500th Anniv of Discovery of America by Columbus. T 131 and similar horiz designs. Multicoloured. P 13½×13.*
731	$2 Type 131	2·75	2·75
732	$3 Fleet of Columbus	4·50	4·50
733	$5 Claiming the New World for Spain	6·00	6·00
731/3	*Set of 3*	12·00	12·00

132 Tennis and $10 Commemorative Coin

(Des G. Vasarhelyi. Litho B.D.T.)

1992 (22 July). *Olympic Games, Barcelona. T 132 and similar horiz designs. Multicoloured. P 13.*
734	$2.50, Type 132	4·50	4·50
	a. Horiz strip of 3. Nos. 734/6	12·00	
735	$2.50, Olympic flame and national flags	4·50	4·50
736	$2.50, Gymnastics and different $10 coin	4·50	4·50
734/6	*Set of 3*	12·00	12·00
MS737	152×87 mm. $5 Water polo	8·00	9·00

Nos. 734/6 were printed together, se-tenant, in horizontal strips of 3 throughout the sheet.

134 "St. Catherine's Mystic Marriage" (detail) (Memling)

1992 (30 Sept). *6th Festival of Pacific Arts, Rarotonga. Nos. 336/51 surch with T 133.*
738	$1 on 20 c. Type 69	1·00	1·00
739	$1 on 20 c. Ku-Tagwa plaque, New Guinea	1·00	1·00
740	$1 on 20 c. Suspension hook, New Guinea	1·00	1·00
741	$1 on 20 c. Ancestral board, New Guinea	1·00	1·00
742	$1 on 25 c. Platform post, New Hebrides	1·00	1·00
743	$1 on 25 c. Canoe ornament, New Ireland	1·00	1·00
744	$1 on 25 c. Carved figure, Admiralty Islands	1·00	1·00
745	$1 on 25 c. Female with child, Admiralty Islands	1·00	1·00
746	$1 on 30 c. The God A'a, Rurutu (Austral Islands)	1·00	1·00
747	$1 on 30 c. Statue of Tangaroa, Cook Islands	1·00	1·00
748	$1 on 30 c. Ivory pendant, Tonga	1·00	1·00
749	$1 on 30 c. Tapa (Hiapo) cloth, Niue	1·00	1·00
750	$1 on 35 c. Feather box (Waka), New Zealand	1·00	1·00
751	$1 on 35 c. Hei-Tiki amulet, New Zealand	1·00	1·00
752	$1 on 35 c. House post, New Zealand	1·00	1·00
753	$1 on 35 c. Feather image of god Ku, Hawaii	1·00	1·00
738/53	*Set of 16*	14·50	14·50

1992 (18 Nov). *Christmas. Different details from "St. Catherine's Mystic Marriage" by Hans Memling. T 134 and similar vert designs. Litho. P 13½.*
754	20 c. Type 134	65	50
755	50 c. multicoloured	1·10	1·00
756	$1 multicoloured	1·75	1·75
757	$2 multicoloured	2·75	3·50
754/7	*Set of 4*	5·50	6·00
MS758	87×101 mm. $7 multicoloured (as 50 c., but larger (36×47 mm))	8·00	9·00

135 Queen on Official Visit

136 Rough-toothed Dolphin

(Litho B.D.T.)

1992 (7 Dec). *40th Anniv of Queen Elizabeth II's Accession. T 135 and similar vert designs. Multicoloured. P 14.*
759	70 c. Type 135	1·50	1·50
760	$1 Queen in green evening dress	2·00	2·00
761	$1.50, Queen in white embroidered evening dress	2·50	2·50
762	$2 Queen with bouquet	2·75	2·75
759/62	*Set of 4*	8·00	8·00

(Des G. Drummond. Litho B.D.T.)

1993 (13 Jan). *Endangered Species. South Pacific Dolphins. T 136 and similar horiz designs. Multicoloured. P 14.*
763	20 c. Type 136	1·25	90
764	50 c. Fraser's Dolphin	2·00	1·60
765	75 c. Pantropical Spotted Dolphin	2·50	2·75
766	$1 Risso's Dolphin	3·00	3·50
763/6	*Set of 4*	8·00	8·00

(137)

138 Queen Elizabeth II in Coronation Robes and St. Edward's Crown

1993 (15 Mar). *Premier Sir Robert Rex Commemoration. Nos. 568/70 optd or surch as T 137.*
767	40 c. Type 96	1·25	1·25
768	58 c. Map of Niue and Premier Rex	1·50	1·50
769	70 c. Premier Rex receiving proclamation of self-government	1·50	1·50
770	$1 on 40 c. Type 96	1·75	1·75
771	$1 on 58 c. Map of Niue and Premier Rex	1·75	1·75
772	$1 on 70 c. Premier Rex receiving proclamation of self-government	1·75	1·75
767/72	*Set of 6*	8·50	8·50

(Litho B.D.T.)

1993 (2 June). *40th Anniv of Coronation. P 14.*
773	138 $5 multicoloured	7·50	8·00

MINIMUM PRICE

The minimum price quote is 10p which represents a handling charge rather than a basis for valuing common stamps. For further notes about prices see introductory pages.

139 "Virgin of the
Rosary" (detail)
(Guido Reni)

(Litho Fournier)

1993 (29 Oct). *Christmas. Different details of "Virgin of the Rosary" (Reni). T 139 and similar vert designs. P 13½ ($3) or 14 (others).*

774	20 c. multicoloured				65	50
775	70 c. multicoloured				1·50	1·00
776	$1 multicoloured				1·75	1·25
777	$1.50, multicoloured				2·50	3·00
778	$3 multicoloured (32×47 mm)				4·25	5·00
774/8				*Set of 5*	9·50	9·75

140 World Cup and Globe with Flags of
U.S.A. and Previous Winners

(Des G. Vasarhelyi. Litho B.D.T.)

1994 (17 June). *World Cup Football Championship, U.S.A. P 14.*

779	**140**	$4 multicoloured			6·50	7·00

141 "Apollo 11" and Astronaut on Moon

(Litho B.D.T.)

1994 (20 July). *25th Anniv of First Moon Landing. T 141 and similar horiz designs. Multicoloured. P 14.*

780	$2.50, Type **141**				6·00	6·00
	a. Horiz strip of 3. Nos. 780/2				16·00	
781	$2.50, Astronaut and flag				6·00	6·00
782	$2.50, Astronaut and equipment				6·00	6·00
780/2				*Set of 3*	16·00	16·00

Nos. 780/2 were printed together, *se-tenant*, in horizontal strips of 3 throughout the sheet.

142 "The Adoration of the
Kings" (Jan Gossaert)

143 Long John Silver
and Jim Hawkins
(Treasure Island)

(Litho B.D.T.)

1994 (28 Nov). *Christmas. Religious Paintings. T 142 and similar horiz designs. Multicoloured. P 14.*

783	70 c. Type **142**				1·00	1·25
	a. Block of 4. Nos. 783/6				3·50	
784	70 c. "Madonna and Child with Sts. John and Catherine" (Titian)				1·00	1·25
785	70 c. "The Holy Family and Shepherd" (Titian)				1·00	1·25
786	70 c. "The Virgin and Child with Saints" (Gerard David)				1·00	1·25
787	$1 "The Adoration of the Shepherds" (cherubs detail) (Poussin)				1·25	1·50
	a. Block of 4. Nos. 787/90				4·50	
788	$1 "The Adoration of the Shepherds" (Holy Family detail) (Poussin)				1·25	1·50

789	$1 "Madonna and Child with Sts. Joseph and John" (Sebastiano)					
790	$1 "The Adoration of the Kings" (Veronese)				1·25	1·50
					1·25	1·50
783/90				*Set of 8*	8·00	10·00

Nos. 783/6 and 787/90 were printed together, *se-tenant*, on blocks of 4 throughout the sheets.

(Des G. Vasarhelyi. Litho B.D.T.)

1994 (14 Dec). *Death Centenary of Robert Louis Stevenson (author). T 143 and similar vert designs. Multicoloured. P 15×14.*

791	$1.75, Type **143**				2·50	2·75
	a. Block of 4. Nos. 791/4				9·00	
792	$1.75, Transformation of Dr. Jekyll (Dr. Jekyll and Mr. Hyde)				2·50	2·75
793	$1.75, Attack on David Balfour (Kidnapped)				2·50	2·75
794	$1.75, Robert Louis Stevenson, tomb and inscription				2·50	2·75
791/4				*Set of 4*	9·00	10·00

Nos. 791/4 were printed together, *se-tenant*, in blocks of 4 throughout the sheet.

**XXX
50c**

(144)

145 Tapeu Orchid

1996 (19 Feb). *Nos. 720 and 722 surch as T 144 by Tonga Govt Printers.*

795	50 c. on 70 c. Purple Swamphen			2·75	1·75
796	$1 on $1.50, White-collared Kingfisher		4·00	3·25

(Litho Questa)

1996 (10 May). *Flowers. T 145 and similar vert designs. Multicoloured. P 14½.*

797	70 c. Type **145**				80	80
798	$1 Frangipani				1·00	1·00
799	$1.20, "Golden Shower"				1·40	1·60
800	$1.50, "Pua"				1·90	2·25
797/800				*Set of 4*	4·50	5·00

(Litho Photopress International, Norfolk Island)

1996 (22 Aug). *Redrawn design as No. 146. Roul 7.*

801	20 c. rosine and green				20	30
	a. Booklet pane of 10 with margins all round				2·00	

No. 801 was only issued in $2 stamp booklets.

146 Jackfish (yacht)   **147** Desert Star (ketch)

(Des Mary Butterfield. Litho Questa)

1996 (30 Sept). *Sailing Ships. T 146 and similar square designs. Multicoloured. P 14½.*

802	70 c. Type **146**				90	90
803	$1 Jennifer (yacht)				1·40	1·40
804	$1.20, Mikeva (yacht)				1·75	2·00
805	$2 Eye of the Wind (cadet brig)			2·25	2·50
802/5				*Set of 4*	5·50	6·00

(Litho Southern Colour Print, Dunedin)

1996 (31 Oct). *"Taipei '96" International Philatelic Exhibition, Taiwan. Sheet 90×80 mm. P 14.*

MS806	**147**	$1.50, multicoloured			1·75	2·00

148 Acropora gemmifera   **149** Ox

(Des Sue Wickison. Litho Southern Colour Print, Dunedin)

1996 (20 Dec). *Corals. T 148 and similar horiz designs. Multicoloured. P 14.*

807	20 c. Type **148**				15	20
808	50 c. Acropora nobilis				30	35
809	70 c. Goniopora lobata				45	50
810	$1 Stylaster sp.				65	70
811	$1.20, Alveopora catalai				75	80
812	$1.50, Fungia scutaria				95	1·00
813	$2 Porites solida				1·25	1·40
814	$3 Millepora sp.				1·90	2·00
815	$4 Pocillopora eydouxi				2·50	2·75
816	$5 Platygyra pini				3·25	3·50
807/16				*Set of 10*	12·00	13·00

(Des Tracey Yager. Litho Southern Colour Print, Dunedin)

1997 (10 Feb). *"HONG KONG '97" International Stamp Exhibition. Chinese New Year ("Year of the Ox"). Sheet 120×90 mm. P 13.*

MS817	**149**	$1.50, multicoloured			1·50	1·75

150 Steps to Lagoon

(Des M. Cross. Litho Questa)

1997 (18 Apr). *Island Scenes. T 150 and similar horiz designs. Multicoloured. P 13½×14.*

818	$1 Type **150**				1·00	1·10
	a. Block of 4. Nos. 818/21				3·75	
819	$1 Islands in lagoon				1·00	1·10
820	$1 Beach with rocks in foreground				1·00	1·10
821	$1 Over-hanging rock on beach				1·00	1·10
818/21				*Set of 4*	3·75	4·00

Nos. 818/21 were printed together, *se-tenant*, in blocks of 4 forming a composite design.

151 Humpback Whale

(Des Sue Wickison. Litho Southern Colour Print, Dunedin)

1997 (29 May). *Whales (1st series). T 151 and similar multicoloured designs. P 14.*

822	20 c. Type **151**				30	25
823	$1 Humpback Whale and calf (vert)				1·10	1·10
824	$1.50, Humpback Whale surfacing (vert)			1·60	1·75
822/4				*Set of 3*	3·00	3·00
MS825	120×90 mm. Nos. 822/4				3·00	3·25

No. **MS825** shows the "Pacific '97" International Stamp Exhibition, San Francisco, emblem on the margin.
See also Nos. 827/9.

152 Niue 1902
Ovpt on New
Zealand 1d.

153 Niue 1918–29
Overprint on New
Zealand £1

1997 (9 June). *"Aupex '97" Stamp Exhibition, Auckland (1st issue). Sheet 136×90 mm. Litho. P 14×15.*

MS826	**152**	$2+20 c. multicoloured			2·10	2·50

(Des Sue Wickison. Litho Southern Colour Print, Dunedin)

1997 (3 Sept). *Whales (2nd series). Multicoloured designs as T 151, but vert. P 14.*

827	50 c. Killer Whale				70	70
828	70 c. Minke Whale				90	90
829	$1.20, Sperm Whale				1·25	1·25
827/9				*Set of 3*	2·50	2·50

1997 (13 Nov). *"Aupex '97" Stamp Exhibition, Auckland (2nd issue). Sheet 90×135 mm. Litho. P 14½×15.*

MS830	**153**	$2 + 20 c. multicoloured			1·90	2·25

154 Floral Display in Woven Basket

155 Divers and Turtle

(Des Neline Pasisi. Litho Southern Colour Print, Dunedin)

1997 (26 Nov). *Christmas. Floral Displays. T 154 and similar vert designs. Multicoloured. P 14.*
831	20 c. Type **154**		35	30
832	50 c. Display in white pot		60	50
833	70 c. Display in white basket		80	80
834	$1 Display in purple vase		1·00	1·25
831/4		*Set of 4*	2·50	2·50

(Des D. Miller. Litho Questa)

1998 (31 Mar). *Diana, Princess of Wales Commemoration. Sheet 145×70 mm, containing vert designs as T 91 of Kiribati. Multicoloured. P 14¹/₂×14.*
MS835   20 c. Wearing white jacket, 1992; 50 c. Wearing pearl-drop earrings, 1988; $1 In raincoat, 1990; $2 With Mother Theresa, 1992 (*sold at $3·70 + 50 c. charity premium*)   ..   3·00   3·25

156 Mult "Triangle" Crosses

(Des M. Cross. Litho Southern Colour Print, Dunedin)

1998 (20 May). *Diving. T 155 and similar multicoloured designs. W 156. P 14¹/₂.*
836	20 c. Type **155**		30	30
837	70 c. Diver exploring coral reef		65	65
838	$1 Exploring underwater chasm (*vert*)		80	80
839	$1·20, Divers and coral fronds		90	90
840	$1·50, Divers in cave		1·25	1·25
836/40		*Set of 5*	3·50	3·50

157 Pacific Black Duck

(Des R. Yeoman. Litho Southern Colour Print, Dunedin)

1998 (23 July). *Coastal Birds. T 157 and similar multicoloured designs. W 156. P 14×14¹/₂ ($1) or 14¹/₂×14 (others).*
841	20 c. Type **157**		45	40
842	70 c. Fairy Tern		80	75
843	$1 Great Frigate Bird (*vert*)		1·00	1·00
844	$1·20, Lesser Golden Plover		1·25	1·40
845	$2 Brown Noddy		1·75	2·00
841/5		*Set of 5*	4·75	5·00

158 Golden Cowrie

(Des M. Cross. Litho Southern Colour Print, Dunedin)

1998 (23 Sept). *Shells. T 158 and similar horiz designs. Multicoloured. P 14¹/₂.*
846	20 c. Type **158**		40	30
847	70 c. Cowrie shell		75	65
848	$1 Spider conch		1·00	1·00
849	$5 Helmet shell		5·00	5·50
846/9		*Set of 4*	6·50	6·75

159 Clubs

(Des C. Abbott. Litho Southern Colour Print, Dunedin)

1998 (18 Nov). *Ancient Weapons. T 159 and similar horiz designs. Multicoloured. P 14×14¹/₂.*
850	20 c. Type **159**		30	30
851	$1·20, Three spears (59×24 mm)		1·00	1·00
852	$1·50, Five spears (59×24 mm)		1·25	1·40
853	$2 Throwing stones		1·50	1·75
850/3		*Set of 4*	3·50	4·00

160 Outrigger Canoe (first migration of Niue Fekai)

(Litho Southern Colour Print, Dunedin)

1999 (24 Feb). *"Australia '99" World Stamp Exhibition, Melbourne. Maritime History. T 160 and similar horiz designs. Each bright violet-blue. P 14¹/₂×14.*
854	70 c. Type **160**		55	50
855	$1 H.M.S. *Resolution* (Cook)		90	90
856	$1·20, *John Williams* (missionary sailing ship)		1·00	1·25
857	$1·50, Captain James Cook		1·40	1·50
854/7		*Set of 4*	3·50	3·75

161 *Risbecia tryoni*

162 Togo Chasm

(Des Mary Butterfield. Litho Southern Colour Print, Dunedin)

1999 (17 Mar). *Endangered Species. Nudibranchs. T 161 and similar horiz designs. Multicoloured. P 14¹/₂.*
858	20 c. Type **161**		30	30
859	$1 *Chromodoris lochi*		85	85
860	$1·20, *Chromodoris elizabethina*		95	1·10
861	$1·50, *Chromodoris bullocki*		1·25	1·40
858/61		*Set of 4*	3·00	3·25
MS862	190×105 mm. Nos. 858/61×2		5·50	6·00

(Des R. Youmans. Litho Questa)

1999 (16 June). *Scenic Views. T 162 and similar multicoloured designs. P 14.*
863	$1 Type **162**		75	75
864	$1·20, Matapa Chasm		90	90
865	$1·50, Tufukia (*horiz*)		1·10	1·25
866	$2 Talava Arches (*horiz*)		1·40	1·60
863/6		*Set of 4*	3·75	4·00

163 Shallow Baskets

(Des C. Abbott. Litho Southern Colour Print, Dunedin)

1999 (18 Sept). *Woven Baskets. T 163 and similar multicoloured designs. P 12.*
867	20 c. Type **163**		25	30
	a. Horiz pair. Nos. 867 and 869		90	1·00
868	70 c. Tray and bowl		65	70
	a. Horiz pair. Nos. 868 and 870		2·75	2·75
869	$1 Tall basket and deep bowls (44×34 mm)		65	70
870	$3 Tall basket and shallow bowls (44×34 mm)		2·10	2·25
867/70		*Set of 4*	3·25	3·50

Nos. 867 with 869 and 868 with 870 were printed together, *se-tenant*, in horizontal pairs throughout separate sheets.

164 Children, Yachts and Forest

(Des D. Gunson. Litho and die-stamped Southern Colour Print, Dunedin)

1999 (1 Dec). *25th Anniv of Self-Government. Sheet, 120×74 mm, containing T 164 and similar horiz design. Multicoloured. P 15.*
MS871   20 c. Type **164**; $5 Scuba diver, young child and sunset   ..   3·25   3·50
On No. **MS**871 the horizontal edges of the miniature sheet are cut to resemble a flying flag.

165 Family and Man in Canoe

(Des Sea Sky Design Studio. Litho Southern Colour Print, Dunedin)

1999 (31 Dec). *New Millennium. T 165 and similar circular designs. Multicoloured. P 14¹/₂×15 (and 15 around design).*
872	20 c. Type **165**		15	20
	a. Horiz strip of 3. Nos. 872/4		3·00	
873	70 c. People pointing up		45	50
874	$4 Diver and man in traditional dress		2·50	2·75
872/4		*Set of 3*	3·00	3·25

Nos. 872/4 were printed together, *se-tenant*, in horizontal strips of 3 with the backgrounds forming a composite design. Each stamp is within a square margin perforated on all four sides and with a further circular perforation around the design.

1982 (June). *Royal Wedding. Multicoloured cover, 129×74 mm, showing Prince and Princess of Wales. Stitched.*

SB1 $8.50, booklet containing 75 c. and 95 c. (Nos. 430/1), each in block of 5 stamps and 1 label   7·00

B 2
(Illustration reduced. Actual size 170×80 mm)

1996 (22 Aug). *Flowers. Multicoloured cover as Type B* **2**. *Stamps attached by selvedge.*

SB2 $2 booklet containing pane of ten 20 c. (No. 801a)   2·00

OFFICIAL STAMPS

O.H.M.S.   O.H.M.S.
(O 1)   (O 2)

1985 (1 July)–**87**. *Nos. 408/10 optd with Type O* **2** *in gold and Nos. 527/42 optd with Type O* **1** *in blue, all by foil embossing.*

O 1	12 c. Type **92**	..	..	35	30
O 2	25 c. *Euphorbia pulcherrima*	..	..	40	35
O 3	30 c. *Cochlospermum hibiscoides*	..	45	35
O 4	35 c. *Begonia sp.*	..	..	50	40
O 5	40 c. *Plumeria sp.*	..	..	50	45
O 6	52 c. *Strelitzia reginae*	..	..	60	50
O 7	58 c. *Hibiscus syriacus*	..	..	60	55
O 8	70 c. *Tibouchina sp.*	..	..	75	70
O 9	83 c. *Nelumbo sp.*	..	..	90	80
O10	$1.05, *Hybrid hibiscus*	..	..	1·25	1·00
O11	$1.75, *Cassia fistula*	..	..	1·75	1·75
O12	$2.30, *Orchid var.* (29.11.85)	..	5·50	2·75
O13	$3.90, *Orchid sp.* (29.11.85)	..	6·00	4·25
O14	$4 *Euphorbia pulcherrima poinsettia* (1.4.86)	..	..	5·50	6·00
O15	$5 *Euphorbia pulcherrima poinsettia* (1.4.86)	..	..	5·50	6·00
O16	$6 *Hybrid hibiscus* (29.4.87)	..	6·50	7·50
O17	$6.60, *Hybrid hibiscus* (15.9.86)	..	6·50	7·50
O18	$8.30, *Hibiscus rosasinensis* (15.9.86)	..	7·50	8·50
O19	$10 Scarlet Hibiscus (29.4.87)	..	8·50	9·50
O1/19	..	..	..	*Set of* 19	55·00	55·00

O.H.M.S.
(O 3)

1993 (10 Dec)–**94**. *Nos. 718/29 optd with Type O* **3** *(larger, 25×4 mm, on Nos. 727/9) in gold by foil embossing.*

O20	20 c. Type **130**	..	..	50	50
O21	50 c. Red-tailed Tropic Bird	..	..	60	60
O22	70 c. Purple Swamphen	..	..	1·25	80
O23	$1 Pacific Pigeon	..	..	1·50	1·25
O24	$1.50, White-collared Kingfisher	..	1·75	1·75
O25	$2 Blue-crowned Lory	..	..	2·00	2·00
O26	$3 Crimson-crowned Fruit Dove (27.4.94)	2·25	2·50
O27	$5 Barn Owl (27.4.94)	..	..	5·00	5·00
O28	$7 Longtailed Cuckoo (48½×35 mm) (1.9.94)	..	5·50	6·00
O29	$10 Eastern Reef Heron (48½×35 mm) (1.9.94)	..	7·00	8·00
O30	$15 Spotted Triller ("Polynesian Triller") (48½×35 mm) (30.9.94)	10·00	11·00
O20/30	..	..	..	*Set of* 11	35·00	35·00

Norfolk Island
see after Australia

North Borneo
see Malaysia

Northern Nigeria
see Nigeria

Northern Rhodesia
see Zambia

North-West Pacific Islands
see Papua New Guinea

Nova Scotia
see Canada

Nyasaland Protectorate
see Malawi

Orange Free State
see South Africa

Pakistan

(Currency. 12 pies = 1 anna; 16 annas = 1 rupee)

DOMINION

PAKISTAN (1)	PAKISTAN (2)

1947 (1 Oct). *Nos. 259/68 and 269a/77 (King George VI) of India optd by litho at Nasik, as T* **1** (3 p. to 12 a.) *or* **2** (14 a. and rupee values).

1	3 p. slate	..	..	10	10
2	½ a. purple	..	..	10	10
3	9 p. green	..	..	10	10
4	1 a. carmine	..	..	10	10
5	1½ a. dull violet	..	..	10	10
	w. Wmk inverted				
6	2 a. vermilion	..	..	10	20

7	3 a. bright violet	..	..	10	20
8	3½ a. bright blue	..	..	65	2·25
9	4 a. brown	..	..	20	10
10	6 a. turquoise-green	..	..	1·00	75
11	8 a. slate-violet	..	..	30	60
12	12 a. lake	..	..	1·00	20
13	14 a. purple	..	..	2·50	1·25
14	1 r. grey and red-brown	..	..	1·75	70
15	2 r. purple and brown	..	..	3·25	1·25
16	5 r. green and blue	..	..	4·00	3·75
17	10 r. purple and claret	..	..	4·00	2·00
18	15 r. brown and green	..	..	48·00	75·00
19	25 r. slate-violet and purple	..	..	55·00	42·00
1/19			Set of 19	£110	£110

Numerous provisional "PAKISTAN" overprints, both hand-stamped and machine-printed, in various sizes and colours, on Postage and Official stamps, also exist.

These were made under authority of Provincial Governments, District Head Postmasters or Local Postmasters and are of considerable philatelic interest.

The 1 a. 3 p. (India No. 269) exists only as a local issue (*Price,* Karachi opt 90p. *unused*; £1.75 *used*).

The 12 a., as No. 12 but overprinted at Karachi, exists with overprint inverted (*Price £60 unused*).

The 1 r. value with local overprint exists with overprint inverted (*Price £150 unused*) or as a pair with one stamp without overprint (*Price £600 unused*).

3 Constituent Assembly Building, Karachi
6 Crescent and Stars

(Des A. Chughtai (1 r.). Recess D.L.R.)

1948 (9 July). *Independence. T* **3**, **6** *and similar horiz designs. P* 13½ × 14 *or* 11½ (1 r.).

20	1½ a. ultramarine	..	..	70	50
21	2½ a. green	..	..	70	10
22	3 a. purple-brown	..	..	70	20
23	1 r. scarlet	..	..	70	50
	a. Perf 14 × 13½	..	..	4·50	13·00
20/3			Set of 4	2·50	1·10

Designs:—2½ a. Karachi Airport entrance; 3 a. Gateway to Lahore Fort.

7 Scales of Justice   8 Star and Crescent   9 Lloyds Barrage

10 Karachi Airport   13 Khyber Pass

(Des M. Suharwardi (T **8**). Recess Pakistan Security Ptg Corp Ltd, Karachi (P 13 and 13½); D.L.R. (others))

1948 (14 Aug)—56? *T* **7/10**, **13** *and similar designs. P* 13½×14 *or* 11½ (1 r.).

24	**7**	3 p. red (*p* 12½)	..	10	10
		a. Perf 13½ (1954?)	..	20	50
25		6 p. violet (*p* 12½)	..	80	10
		a. Perf 13½ (1954?)	..	2·00	1·75
26		9 p. green (*p* 12½)	..	50	10
		a. Perf 13½ (1954?)	..	75	75
27	**8**	1 a. blue (*p* 12½)	..	10	50
28		1½ a. grey-green (*p* 12½)	..	10	10
29		2 a. red (*p* 12½)	..	40	50
30	**9**	2½ a. green (*p* 14×13½)	..	2·75	6·00
31	**10**	3 a. green (*p* 14)	..	7·50	65
32	**9**	3½ a. bright blue (*p* 14×13½)	..	3·50	5·00
33		4 a. reddish brown (*p* 12½)	..	50	10
34	—	6 a. blue (*p* 14×13½)	..	50	50
35	—	8 a. black (*p* 12½)	..	50	50
36	**10**	10 a. scarlet (*p* 14)	..	4·50	7·00
37	—	12 a. scarlet (*p* 14×13½)	..	6·50	80
38	—	1 r. ultramarine (*p* 14)	..	5·50	10
		a. Perf 13½ (1954?)	..	14·00	2·75
39	—	2 r. chocolate (*p* 14)	..	20·00	30
		a. Perf 13½ (1954?)	..	24·00	1·50
40	—	5 r. carmine (*p* 14)	..	15·00	60
		a. Perf 13½ (7.53)	..	9·00	20
41	**13**	10 r. magenta (*p* 14)	..	9·00	15·00
		a. Perf 12	..	70·00	5·00
		b. Perf 13 (1951)	..	18·00	30
42		15 r. blue-green (*p* 12)	..	17·00	12·00
		a. Perf 14	..	15·00	32·00
		b. Perf 13 (1956?)	..	18·00	12·00
43		25 r. violet (*p* 14)	..	55·00	80·00
		a. Perf 12	..	27·00	30·00
		b. Perf 13 (1954)	..	40·00	20·00
24/43			Set of 20	£100	48·00

Designs: *Vert* (as T **7**)—6 a., 8 a., 12 a. Karachi Port Trust. (As T **10**)—1 r., 2 r., 5 r. Salimullah Hostel, Dacca.

For 25 r. with W **98**, see No. 210.

---

14 Star and Crescent   15 Karachi Airport

(Recess Pakistan Security Ptg Corp (P 13½), D.L.R. (others).

1949 (Feb)—53? *Redrawn. Crescent moon with points to left as T* **14/15**.

44	**14**	1 a. blue (*p* 12½)	..	4·00	70
		a. Perf 13½ (1953?)	..	3·50	10
45		1½ a. grey-green (*p* 12½)	..	3·75	70
		a. Perf 13½ (1952?)	..	3·00	10
		ab. Printed on the gummed side		50·00	
46		2 a. red (*p* 12½)	..	4·00	10
		a. Perf 13½ (1953?)	..	3·50	10
47	**15**	3 a. green (*p* 14)	..	8·50	65
48	—	6 a. blue (as No. 34) (*p* 14×13½)	..	8·50	60
49	—	8 a. black (as No. 35) (*p* 12½)	..	4·50	1·00
50	**15**	10 a. scarlet (*p* 14)	..	15·00	1·50
51	—	12 a. scarlet (as No. 37) (*p* 14×13½)	..	18·00	30
44/51			Set of 8	55·00	3·50

16

(Recess D.L.R.)

1949 (11 Sept). *First Death Anniv of Mohammed Ali Jinnah. T* **16** *and similar design. P* 14.

52	**16**	1½ a. brown	..	1·25	90
53		3 a. green	..	1·25	90
54		10 a. black	..	4·00	6·50
52/4			Set of 3	6·00	7·50

Design:—10 a. Similar inscription reading "QUAID-I-AZAM/ MOHAMMAD ALI JINNAH" etc.

17 Pottery   18 Aeroplane and Hour-glass

Two Types of 3½ a.:

I   II

19 Saracenic Leaf Pattern   20 Archway and Lamp

(Des A. Chughtai. Recess D.L.R., later printings, Pakistan Security Ptg Corp)

1951 (14 Aug)—56. *Fourth Anniv of Independence. P* 13.

55	**17**	2½ a. carmine	..	1·00	50
56	**18**	3 a. purple	..	50	10
57	**17**	3½ a. blue (I)	..	75	3·25
57a		3½ a. blue (II)(12.56)	..	3·25	3·00
58	**19**	4 a. green	..	35	10
59		6 a. brown-orange	..	45	10
60	**20**	8 a. sepia	..	4·00	10
61		10 a. violet	..	80	80
62	**18**	12 a. slate	..	90	10
55/62			Set of 9	11·00	7·00

The above and the stamps issued on the 14 August 1954, 1955 and 1956, are basically definitive issues, although issued on the Anniversary date of Independence.

3ᴬˢ CENTENARY 1ˢᵗ POSTAGE STAMP ᴀˢ ᵳ

21 "Scinde Dawk" stamp and Ancient and Modern Transport

(Recess D.L.R.)

1952 (14 Aug). *Centenary of "Scinde Dawk" Issue of India. P* 13.

63	**21**	3 a. deep olive/*yellow-olive*	..	75	85
64		12 a. deep brown/*salmon*	..	1·00	15

PRINTERS. All issues up to No. 219 were recess-printed by the Pakistan Security Printing Corporation, *unless otherwise stated.*

22 Kaghan Valley

23 Mountains, Gilgit

24 Tea Plantation, East Pakistan

1954 (14 Aug). *Seventh Anniv of Independence. T* **22**/**4** *and similar designs. P* 13½ (14 a., 1 r., 2 r.) *or* 13 (*others*).

65		6 p. reddish violet		10	10
66		9 p. blue		3·25	1·50
67		1 a. carmine		10	10
68		1½ a. red		10	10
69		14 a. deep green		55	10
70		1 r. green		11·00	10
71		2 r. red-orange		2·75	10
65/71			*Set of 7*	16·00	1·50

Designs: *As T* **22**—1½ a. Mausoleum of Emperor Jehangir, Lahore. *As T* **23**—1 a. Badshahi Mosque, Lahore. *As T* **24**—1 r. Cotton plants, West Pakistan; 2 r. Jute fields and river, East Pakistan.

29 View of K 2

1954 (25 Dec). *Conquest of K 2* (*Mount Godwin-Austen*). *P* 13.

72	**29**	2 a. deep violet		30	30

30 Karnaphuli Paper Mill, Type I (Arabic fraction on left) Type II (Arabic fraction on right)

1955 (14 Aug)–56. *Eighth Anniv of Independence. T* **30** *and similar horiz designs. P* 13.

73		2½ a. scarlet (I)		50	1·10
73a		2½ a. scarlet (II) (12.56)		30	1·10
74		6 a. deep ultramarine		1·00	10
75		8 a. deep reddish violet		3·75	10
76		12 a. carmine and orange		4·00	10
73/6			*Set of 5*	8·50	2·00

Designs:—6 a. Textile mill, West Pakistan; 8 a. Jute mill, East Pakistan; 12 a. Main Sui gas plant.

TENTH
ANNIVERSARY
UNITED NATIONS

24. 10. 55.

(34)

35 Map of West Pakistan

TENTH
ANNIVERSARY
UNITED NATIONS

24. 10. 55.

"UNITED NATIONS"
shifted 1 mm to left
(1½ a. R. 7/10; 12 a.
R. 1/8, 3/8, 5/8, 7/8, 9/8)

1955 (24 Oct). *Tenth Anniv of United Nations. Nos.* 68 *and* 76 *optd as T* **34**.

77		1½ a. red (B.)		1·50	5·00
78		*a.* "UNITED NATIONS" 1 mm to left		3·75	7·00
		12 a. carmine and orange (B.)		50	3·50
		a. "UNITED NATIONS" 1 mm to left		3·75	7·00

Forgeries exist of the overprint on No. 77. These are in very uneven thin type and measure 20×18 mm instead of the genuine 19½×19 mm.

1955 (7 Dec). *West Pakistan Unity. P* 13½.

79	**35**	1½ a. myrtle-green		15	20
80		2 a. sepia		15	10
81		12 a. deep rose-red		75	20
79/81			*Set of 3*	95	40

REPUBLIC

36 Constituent Assembly Building, Karachi

(Litho D.L.R.)

1956 (23 Mar). *Republic Day. P* 13.

82	**36**	2 a. myrtle-green		80	10

37 38 Map of East Pakistan

1956 (14 Aug). *Ninth Anniv of Independence. P* 13½.

83	**37**	2 a. scarlet		65	10
		a. Printed on the gummed side		6·50	

1956 (15 Oct). *First Session of National Assembly of Pakistan at Dacca. P* 13½.

84	**38**	1½ a. myrtle-green		30	1·00
85		2 a. sepia		30	10
86		12 a. deep rose-red		30	1·10
84/6			*Set of 3*	80	2·00

39 Karnaphuli Paper Mill, East Bengal 40 Pottery

41 Orange Tree

1957 (23 Mar). *First Anniv of Republic. P* 13.

87	**39**	2½ a. scarlet		20	10
88	**40**	3½ a. blue		30	10
89	**41**	10 r. myrtle-green and yellow-orange		80	20
87/9			*Set of 3*	1·10	30

The above and No. 95 are primarily definitive issues, although issued on the Anniversary of Republic Day.
For 10 r. with W **98**, see No. 208.

42 Pakistani Flag 43 Pakistani Industries

(Des Ahsan. Litho D.L.R.)

1957 (10 May). *Centenary of Struggle for Independence* (*Indian Mutiny*). *P* 13.

90	**42**	1½ a. bronze-green		50	10
91		12 a. light blue		1·25	10

(Litho D.L.R.)

1957 (14 Aug). *Tenth Anniv of Independence. P* 14.

92	**43**	1½ a. ultramarine		20	30
93		4 a. orange-red		40	1·00
94		12 a. mauve		40	50
92/4			*Set of 3*	90	1·60

---

44 Coconut Tree 45

1958 (23 Mar). *Second Anniv of Republic. P* 13.

95	**44**	15 r. red and deep reddish purple		3·50	3·00

This is a definitive issue, see note below No. 89.
See No. 209 for this stamp with W **98**.

(Photo Harrison)

1958 (21 Apr). *20th Death Anniv of Mohammed Iqbal* (*poet*). *P* 14½ × 14.

96	**45**	1½ a. yellow-olive and black		55	30
97		2 a. orange-brown and black		55	10
98		14 a. turquoise-blue and black		90	10
96/8			*Set of 3*	1·75	40

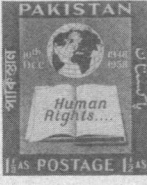

PAKISTAN
BOY SCOUT
2nd NATIONAL
JAMBOREE

CHITTAGONG
Dec. 58—Jan. 59

46 U.N. Charter and Globe (47)

1958 (10 Dec). *Tenth Anniv of Declaration of Human Rights. P* 13.

99	**46**	1½ a. turquoise-blue		10	10
100		14 a. sepia		65	10

1958 (28 Dec). *Second Pakistan Boy Scouts National Jamboree, Chittagong. Nos.* 65 *and* 75 *optd with T* **47**.

101		6 p. reddish violet		30	10
102		8 a. deep reddish violet		65	10

REVOLUTION
DAY
Oct. 27, 1959

(48)

49 "Centenary of An Idea"

1959 (27 Oct). *Revolution Day. No.* 74 *optd with T* **48** *in red.*

103		6 a. deep ultramarine		80	10

1959 (19 Nov). *Red Cross Commemoration. Recess; cross typo. P* 13.

104	**49**	2 a. red and green		30	10
105		10 a. red and deep blue		55	10

50 Armed Forces Badge 51 Map of Pakistan

(Litho D.L.R.)

1960 (10 Jan). *Armed Forces Day. P* 13½ × 13.

106	**50**	2 a. red, ultramarine and blue-green		60	10
107		14 a. red and bright blue		1·50	10

1960 (23 Mar). *P* 13 × 13½.

108	**51**	6 p. deep purple		40	10
109		2 a. brown-red		60	10
110		8 a. deep green		1·25	10
111		1 r. blue		2·00	10
		a. Printed on the gummed side			
108/11			*Set of 4*	3·75	20

52 Uprooted Tree 53 Punjab Agricultural College

1960 (7 Apr). *World Refugee Year. P* 13.

112	**52**	2 a. rose-carmine		20	10
113		10 a. green		30	10

1960 (10 Oct). *Golden Jubilee of Punjab Agricultural College, Lyallpur. T 53 and similar horiz design. P 12½ × 14.*
114		2 a. slate-blue and carmine-red	10	10
115		8 a. bluish green and reddish violet	20	10

Design:—8 a. College arms.

55 "Land Reforms, Rehabilitation and Reconstruction"

56 Caduceus

(Des M. Hanjra. Photo D.L.R.)

1960 (27 Oct). *Revolution Day. P 13×13½.*
116	55	2 a. green, pink and brown	10	10
		a. Green and pink omitted	14·00	
		b. Pink omitted	5·00	
117		14 a. green, yellow and ultramarine	50	60

(Photo D.L.R.)

1960 (16 Nov). *Centenary of King Edward Medical College, Lahore. P 13.*
118	56	2 a. yellow, black and blue	50	10
119		14 a. emerald, black and carmine	1·75	70

57 "Economic Co-operation"

58 Zam-Zama Gun, Lahore ("Kim's Gun," after Rudyard Kipling)

1960 (5 Dec). *International Chamber of Commerce C.A.F.E.A. Meeting, Karachi. P 13.*
120	57	14 a. orange-red	45	10

(Centre typo, background recess Pakistan Security Ptg Corp)

1960 (24 Dec). *Third Pakistan Boy Scouts National Jamboree, Lahore. P 12½ × 14.*
121	58	2 a. carmine, yellow & dp bluish green	80	10

(New Currency. 100 paisa=1 rupee)

1 PAISA

(59)

1961 (1 Jan–14 Feb). *Nos. 24a, 67/8, 83 and 108/9, surch as T 59. Nos. 123/4 and 126 surch by Pakistan Security Ptg Corp and others by the Times Press, Karachi.*
122		1 p. on 1½ a. red (10.1)	30	10
		a. Printed and surch on the gummed side		
123		2 p. on 3 p. red	10	10
124		3 p. on 6 p. deep purple	15	10
		a. "PASIA" for "PAISA"	4·00	
125		7 p. on 1 a. carmine (14.2)	30	10
126		13 p. on 2 a. brown-red (14.2)	30	10
		a. "PAIS" for "PAISA"	4·00	
127		13 p. on 2 a. scarlet (14.2)	30	10
			Set of 6 1·25	30

No. 122. Two settings were used, the first with figure "1" 2½ m. tall and the second 3 mm.

On the 1 p. with tall "1" and the 13 p. (No. 127), the space between the figures of value and "P" of "PAISA" varies between 1½ mm and 3 mm.

See also Nos. 262/4.

ERRORS. In the above issue and the corresponding official stamps we have listed errors in the stamps surcharged by the Pakistan Security Printing Corp but have not included the very large number of errors which occurred in the stamps surcharged by the less experienced Times Press. This was a very hurried job and there was no time to carry out the usual checks. It is also known that some errors were not issued to the public but came on the market by other means.

NOTE. Stamps in the old currency were also *handstamped* with new currency equivalents and issued in various districts but these local issues are outside the scope of this catalogue.

60 Khyber Pass

61 Shalimar Gardens, Lahore

62 Chota Sona Masjid (gateway)

(a)	(b)	(c)

Types (a) and (b) show the first letter in the top right-hand inscription; (a) wrongly engraved, "SH" (b) corrected to "P".

On Nos. 131/2 and 134 the corrections were made individually on the plate, so that each stamp in the sheet may be slightly different. Type (c) refers to No. 133a only.

1961–63. *No wmk. P 13 (T 62) or 14 (others).*

(a) Inscribed "SHAKISTAN" in Bengali
128	60	1 p. violet (1.1.61)	1·50	10
129		2 p. rose-red (12.1.61)	1·50	10
130		5 p. ultramarine (23.3.61)	2·50	10

(b) Inscribed "PAKISTAN" in Bengali
131	60	1 p. violet	70	10
		a. Printed on the gummed side		
132		2 p. rose-red	70	10
133		3 p. reddish purple (27.10.61)	30	10
		a. Re-engraved. First letter of Bengali inscription as Type (c) (1963)	3·50	3·50
134		5 p. ultramarine	3·50	10
		a. Printed on the gummed side		
135		7 p. emerald (23.3.61)	1·25	10
136	61	10 p. brown (14.8.61)	20	10
137		13 p. slate-violet (14.8.61)	15	10
138		25 p. deep blue (1.1.62)	4·75	10
139		40 p. deep purple (1.1.62)	1·50	10
140		50 p. deep bluish green (1.1.62)	35	10
141		75 p. carmine-red (23.3.62)	40	20
142		90 p. yellow-green (1.1.62)	50	20
143	62	1 r. vermilion (7.1.63)	2·00	10
		a. Imperf (pair)		
144		1 r. 25, reddish violet (27.10.61)	75	55
144a		2 r. orange (7.1.63)	5·50	15
144b		5 r. green (7.1.63)	6·00	2·00
128/44b		*Set of 19*	30·00	3·25

See also Nos. 170/81 and 204/7.

LAHORE STAMP EXHIBITION 1961

(63)

64 Warsak Dam and Power Station

1961 (12 Feb). *Lahore Stamp Exhibition. No. 110 optd with T 63.*
145	51	8 a. deep green (R.)	90	1·50

(Des A. Ghani)

1961 (1 July). *Completion of Warsak Hydro-Electric Project. P 12½×14.*
146	64	40 p. black and blue	60	10

65 Narcissus	66 Ten Roses

(Des A. Ghani)

1961 (2 Oct). *Child Welfare Week. P 14.*
147	65	13 p. turquoise-blue	40	10
148		90 p. bright purple	1·10	20

(Des A. Ghani)

1961 (4 Nov). *Co-operative Day. P 13.*
149	66	13 p. rose-red and deep green	50	10
150		90 p. rose-red and blue	1·25	50

67 Police Crest and "Traffic Control"

68 Locomotive *Eagle*, 1861

(Photo D.L.R.)

1961 (30 Nov). *Police Centenary. P 13.*
151	67	13 p. silver, black and blue	50	10
152		40 p. silver, black and red	1·00	20

(Des M. Thoma. Photo D.L.R.)

1961 (31 Dec). *Railway Centenary. T 68 and similar horiz design. P 14.*
153		13 p. green, black and yellow	1·00	80
154		50 p. yellow, black and green	1·25	1·00

Design:—50 p. Diesel locomotive No. 20 and tracks forming "1961".

FIRST JET FLIGHT KARACHI-DACCA

13 Paisa

(70)

71 *Anopheles sp* (mosquito)

1962 (6 Feb). *First Karachi–Dacca Jet Flight. No. 87 surch with T 70.*
155	39	13 p. on 2½ a. scarlet (R.)	1·50	90

(Photo D.L.R.)

1962 (7 Apr). *Malaria Eradication. T 71 and similar horiz design. P 14.*
156		10 p. black, yellow and red	50	10
157		13 p. black, greenish yellow and red	50	10

Design:—13 p. Mosquito pierced by blade.

73 Pakistan Map and Jasmine

(Photo Courvoisier)

1962 (8 June). *New Constitution. P 12.*
158	73	40 p. yellow-green, bluish green and grey	1·00	10

74 Football

78 Marble Fruit Dish and Bahawalpuri Clay Flask

(Des A. Ghani and M. Bhatti)

1962 (14 Aug). *Sports. T 74 and similar horiz designs. P 12½×14.*
159		7 p. black and blue	10	10
160		13 p. black and green	60	60
161		25 p. black and purple	20	10
162		40 p. black and orange-brown	2·00	2·25
159/62		*Set of 4*	2·50	2·75

Designs:—13 p. Hockey; 25 p. Squash; 40 p. Cricket.

(Des A. Ghani and M. Bhatti)

1962 (10 Nov). *Small Industries. T 78 and similar vert designs. P 13.*
163		7 p. brown-lake	10	10
164		13 p. deep green	4·00	2·25
165		25 p. reddish violet	10	10
166		40 p. yellow-green	10	10
167		50 p. deep red	10	10
163/7		*Set of 5*	4·00	2·25

Designs:—13 p. Sports equipment; 25 p. Camel-skin lamp and brassware; 40 p. Wooden powderbowl and basket-work; 50 p. Inlaid cigarette-box and brassware.

83 "Child Welfare"

(Des M. Thoma. Photo D.L.R.)

1962 (11 Dec). *16th Anniv of U.N.I.C.E.F. P 14.*
168	83	13 p. black, light blue and maroon	35	10
169		40 p. black, yellow and turquoise-blue	35	10

Nos. 170, etc.	Nos. 131/42

1962–70. *As T 60/1 but with redrawn Bengali inscription at top right. No wmk.*
170	60	1 p. violet (1963)	10	10
171		2 p. rose-red (1964)	85	10
		a. Imperf (pair)	3·00	
172		3 p. reddish purple (1970)	5·00	3·50
173		5 p. ultramarine (1963)	10	10
		a. Printed on the gummed side	12·00	
174		7 p. emerald (1964)	6·50	3·50
175	61	10 p. brown (1963)	10	10
		a. Printed on the gummed side	12·00	
176		13 p. slate-violet	10	10
176a		15 p. bright purple (31.12.64)	15	10
		ab. Imperf (pair)	4·50	
		ac. Printed on the gummed side		

PAKISTAN — 1962

176b	61	20 p. myrtle-green (26.1.70)		30	10
		ba. Imperf (pair)		3·50	
		bb. Printed on the gummed side		15·00	
177		25 p. deep blue (1963)		8·00	10
		a. Imperf (pair)			
178		40 p. deep purple (1964)		15	20
		a. Imperf (pair)		6·50	
179		50 p. deep bluish green (1964)		15	10
		a. Printed on the gummed side			
180		75 p. carmine-red (1964)		30	70
		a. Printed on the gummed side		12·00	
181		90 p. yellow-green (1964)		30	90
170/81		Set of 14		19·00	7·50

Other values in this series and the high values (Nos. 204/10) are known imperforate but we are not satisfied as to their status.

(84) — 85 "Dancing" Horse, Camel and Bull

1963 (15 Feb). *Pakistan U.N. Force in West Irian.* No. 176 optd with T **84**.
182 **61** 13 p. slate-violet (R.) 10 30

(Des S. Jahangir. Photo Courvoisier)
1963 (13 Mar). *National Horse and Cattle Show.* P 11½.
183 **85** 13 p. blue, sepia and cerise .. 10 10

86 Wheat and Tractor

1963 (21 Mar). *Freedom from Hunger.* T **86** and similar horiz design. P 12½ × 14.
184 13 p. orange-brown .. .. 2·00 10
185 50 p. bistre-brown .. .. 3·50 55
Design:—50 p. Rice.

 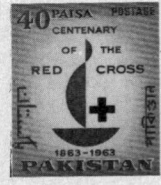

(88) — 89 Centenary Emblem

1963 (23 Mar). *2nd International Stamp Exhibition, Dacca.* No. 109 surch with T **88**.
186 **51** 13 p. on 2 a. brown-red .. 75 10

1963 (25 June). *Centenary of Red Cross. Recess; cross typo.* P 13.
187 **89** 40 p. red and deep olive .. 2·00 15

90 Paharpur (94)

(Des A. Ghani)
1963 (16 Sept). *Archaeological Series.* T **90** and similar designs. P 14×12½ (13 p.) or 12½×15 (others).
188 7 p. ultramarine 45 10
189 13 p. sepia 45 10
190 40 p. carmine 80 10
191 50 p. deep reddish violet .. 85 10
188/91 Set of 4 2·25 30
Designs: *Vert*—13 p. Moenjodaro; *Horiz*—40 p. Taxila; 50 p. Mainamati.

1963 (7 Oct). *Centenary of Public Works Department.* No. 133 surch with T **94** by typography.
192 **60** 13 p. on 3 p. reddish purple .. 10 10
Forged surcharges applied in *lithography* exist.

95 Ataturk's Mausoleum

(Des A. Ghani)
1963 (10 Nov). *25th Death Anniv of Kemal Ataturk.* P 13½.
193 **95** 50 p. red 80 10

96 Globe and U.N.E.S.C.O. Emblem

(Photo D.L.R.)
1963 (10 Dec). *15th Anniv of Declaration of Human Rights.* P 14.
194 **96** 50 p. brown, red and ultramarine .. 40 10

97 Thermal Power Installations

(Des A. Ghani)
1963 (25 Dec). *Completion of Multan Thermal Power Station.* P 12½×14.
195 **97** 13 p. ultramarine .. 10 10

98 Multiple Star and Crescent — 99 Temple of Thot, Queen Nefertari and Maids

1963–79. As Nos. 43b, 89, 95 and 143/4b, but W **98** (sideways* on 15 r.).
204	62	1 r. vermilion		30	10
		a. Printed on the gummed side		7·50	
		b. Imperf (pair)		1·25	
		w. Wmk inverted		1·25	
205		1 r. 25, reddish violet (1964)		1·50	10
		aw. Wmk inverted		2·25	
		b. Purple (1975?)		1·50	10
		ba. Imperf (pair)		6·00	
206		2 r. orange (1964)		55	15
		a. Imperf (pair)		8·00	
		w. Wmk inverted		1·75	
207		5 r. green (1964)		4·50	55
		a. Imperf (pair)		11·00	
		w. Wmk inverted		4·50	
208	41	10 r. myrtle-green & yellow-orge (1968)		3·25	3·75
		a. Imperf (pair)			
		bw. Wmk inverted			
		c. Wmk sideways		1·50	1·50
209	44	15 r. red & deep reddish purple (20.3.79)		1·50	2·00
		a. Imperf (pair)		13·00	
		w. Wmk tips of crescent pointing downwards			
210	13	25 r. violet (1968)		6·00	9·00
		aw. Wmk inverted		13·00	
		b. Wmk sideways		3·00	4·00
		ba. Imperf (pair)		15·00	
204/10b		Set of 7		11·50	7·50

*The normal sideways watermark shows the tips of the crescent pointing upwards, *when viewed from the back of the stamp.*

(Des A. Ghani)
1964 (30 Mar). *Nubian Monuments Preservation.* T **99** and similar horiz design. P 13×13½.
211 13 p. turquoise-blue and red .. 75 10
212 50 p. bright purple and black .. 1·25 10
Design:—50 p. Temple of Abu Simbel.

101 "Unisphere" and Pakistan Pavilion — 103 Shah Abdul Latif's Mausoleum

(Des A. Ghani)
1964 (22 Apr). *New York World's Fair.* T **101** and similar design. P 12½×14 (13 p.) or 14×12½ (1 r. 25).
213 13 p. ultramarine .. 10 10
214 1 r. 25, ultramarine and red-orange .. 40 20
Design: *Vert*—1 r. 25, Pakistan Pavilion on "Unisphere".

(Des A. Ghani)
1964 (25 June). *Death Bicentenary of Shah Abdul Latif of Bhit.* P 13½×13.
215 **103** 50 p. bright blue and carmine-lake .. 80 10

104 Mausoleum of Quaid-i-Azam — 105 Mausoleum

(Des A. Ghani)
1964 (11 Sept). *16th Death Anniv of Mohammed Ali Jinnah (Quaid-i-Azam).* P 13½ (15 p.) or 13 (50 p.).
216 **104** 15 p. emerald-green .. 75 10
217 **105** 50 p. bronze-green .. 1·75 10

106 Bengali and Urdu Alphabets — 107 University Building

(Des N. Rizvi)
1964 (5 Oct). *Universal Children's Day.* P 13.
218 **106** 15 p. brown .. 10 10

(Des N. Rizvi)
1964 (21 Dec). *First Convocation of the West Pakistan University of Engineering and Technology, Lahore.* P 12½×14.
219 **107** 15 p. chestnut .. 10 10

PROCESS. All the following issues were lithographed by the Pakistan Security Printing Corporation, *unless otherwise stated.*

108 "Help the Blind" — 109 "I.T.U. Emblem and Symbols"

(Des A. Chughtai)
1965 (28 Feb). *Blind Welfare.* P 13.
220 **108** 15 p. ultramarine and yellow .. 20 10

(Des N. Rizvi. Recess)
1965 (17 May). *I.T.U. Centenary.* P 12½×14.
221 **109** 15 p. reddish purple .. 1·50 30

110 I.C.Y. Emblem

1965 (26 June). *International Co-operation Year.* P 13 × 13½.
222 **110** 15 p. black and light blue .. 50 15
223 50 p. green and yellow .. 1·00 40

111 "Co-operation"

112 Globe and Flags of Turkey, Iran and Pakistan

1965 (21 July). *First Anniv of Regional Development Co-operation Pact.* P 13½ × 13 (15 p.) or 13 (50 p.).
224 **111** 15 p. multicoloured .. 20 10
225 **112** 50 p. multicoloured .. 1·10 10

336

113 Soldier and Tanks

(Des S. Ghori (7 p.), N. Rizvi (15 p.), A. Ghani (50 p.))

1965 (25 Dec). *Pakistan Armed Forces.* T **113** *and similar horiz designs. Multicoloured.* P 13½×13.
226	7 p. Type 113					75	30
227	15 p. Naval officer and *Tughril* (destroyer)				1·50	10
228	50 p. Pilot and Lockheed F-104C Starfighters					2·50	30
226/8					*Set of 3*	4·25	60

116 Army, Navy and Air Force Crests

117 Atomic Reactor, Islamabad

(Des A. Ghani)

1966 (13 Feb). *Armed Forces Day.* P 13½×13.
229	**116** 15 p. royal blue, dull grn, brt blue & buff	65	10

(Des A. Ghani. Recess)

1966 (30 Apr). *Inauguration of Pakistan's First Atomic Reactor.* P 13.
230	**117** 15 p. black			10	10

118 Bank Crest

119 Children

(Des A. Ghani)

1966 (25 Aug). *Silver Jubilee of Habib Bank.* P 12½×14.
231	**118** 15 p. blue-green, yellow-orange & sepia	10	10

(Des S. Nagi)

1966 (3 Oct). *Universal Children's Day.* P 13½.
232	**119** 15 p. black, red and pale yellow	10	10

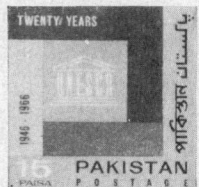

120 U.N.E.S.C.O. Emblem

1966 (24 Nov). *20th Anniv of U.N.E.S.C.O.* P 14.
233	**120** 15 p. multicoloured	2·75	30

121 Flag, Secretariat Building and President Ayub

(Des A. Ghani)

1966 (29 Nov). *Islamabad (new capital).* P 13.
234	**121** 15 p. deep bluish green, chestnut, light blue and bistre-brown	25	10
235	50 p. deep bluish green, chestnut, light blue and black	60	10

122 Avicenna

123 Mohammed Ali Jinnah

(Des A. Ghani)

1966 (3 Dec). *Foundation of Health and Tibbi Research Institute.* P 13×13½.
236	**122** 15 p. dull green and salmon	40	10
	a. Imperf (pair)	65·00	

(Des A. Ghani. Recess and litho)

1966 (25 Dec). *90th Birth Anniv of Mohammed Ali Jinnah.* T **123** *and similar design bearing same portrait, but in different frame.* P 13.
237	**123** 15 p. black, orange and greenish blue	20	10
238	– 50 p. black, purple and ultramarine	50	10

124 Tourist Year Emblem

125 Emblem of Pakistan T.B. Association

(Des A. Ghani)

1967 (1 Jan). *International Tourist Year.* P 13½×13.
239	**124** 15 p. black, light blue and yellow-brown	10	10

1967 (10 Jan). *Tuberculosis Eradication Campaign.* P 13½ × 13.
240	**125** 15 p. red, sepia and chestnut	10	10

126 Scout Salute and Badge

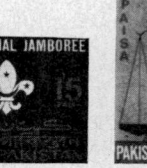

127 "Justice"

(Des A. Rauf. Photo)

1967 (29 Jan). *4th National Scout Jamboree.* P 12½×14.
241	**126** 15 p. light orange-brown and maroon	15	10

(Des A. Rauf)

1967 (17 Feb). *Centenary of West Pakistan High Court.* P 13.
242	**127** 15 p. black, slate, light red and slate-blue	10	10

128 Dr. Mohammed Iqbal (philosopher)

(Des A. Rauf)

1967 (21 Apr). *Iqbal Commemoration.* P 13.
243	**128** 15 p. sepia and light red	15	10
244	1 r. sepia and deep green	60	10

129 Hilal-i-Isteqlal Flag

(Des A. Rahman)

1967 (15 May). *Award of Hilal-i-Isteqlal (for Valour) to Lahore, Sialkot, and Sargodha.* P 13.
245	**129** 15 p. multicoloured	10	10

130 "20th Anniversary"

(Des F. Karim. Photo)

1967 (14 Aug). *20th Anniv of Independence.* P 13.
246	**130** 15 p. red and deep bluish green	10	10

131 "Rice Exports"

132 Cotton Plant, Yarn and Textiles

(Des S. Nagi (10 p.), F. Karim (others). Photo)

1967 (26 Sept). *Pakistan Exports.* T **131/2** *and similar design.* P 13×13½.
247	10 p. yellow, deep bluish green and deep blue	10	15
248	15 p. multicoloured	10	10
	a. Pale orange (top panel) omitted	10·00	
249	50 p. multicoloured	20	15
247/9	*Set of 3*	30	30

Design: *Vert as* T **132**—50 p. Raw jute, bale and bags.

134 Clay Toys

(Des F. Karim)

1967 (2 Oct). *Universal Children's Day.* P 13.
250	**134** 15 p. multicoloured	10	10

135 Shah and Empress of Iran and Gulistan Palace, Teheran

(Des S. Ghori. Recess and litho)

1967 (26 Oct). *Coronation of Shah Mohammed Riza Pahlavi and Empress Farah of Iran.* P 13.
251	**135** 50 p. purple, blue and light yellow-ochre	70	10

136 "Each For All—All For Each"

(Des A. Rauf)

1967 (4 Nov). *Co-operative Day.* P 13.
252	**136** 15 p. multicoloured	10	10

137 Mangla Dam

(Des S. Nagi)

1967 (23 Nov). *Indus Basin Project.* P 13.
253 **137** 15 p. multicoloured 10 10

138 Crab pierced by Sword   139 Human Rights Emblem

(Des F. Karim)

1967 (26 Dec). *The Fight against Cancer.* P 13.
254 **138** 15 p. red and black 70 10

1968 (31 Jan). *Human Rights Year.* Photo. P 14 × 13.
255 **139** 15 p. red and deep turquoise-blue .. 10 15
256   50 p. red, yellow and silver-grey.. 10 15

140 Agricultural University, Mymensingh   141 W.H.O. Emblem

(Des S. Ghori. Photo)

1968 (28 Mar). *First Convocation of East Pakistan Agricultural University.* P 13¹/₂×13.
257 **140** 15 p. multicoloured 10 10

(Des A. Salahuddin. Photo)

1968 (7 Apr). *20th Anniv of World Health Organization.* P 14×13.
258 **141** 15 p. green and orange-red .. 10 15
    a. "PAIS" for "PAISA" (R. 4/5) .. 1·50
259   50 p. red-orange and indigo .. 10 15

142   Kazi Nazrul Islam (poet, composer and patriot)

(Des F. Karim. Recess and litho)

1968 (25 June). *Nazrul Islam Commemoration.* P 13.
260 **142** 15 p. sepia and pale yellow .. 30 15
261   50 p. sepia and pale rose-red .. 60 15
    Nos. 260/1 with a two-line inscription giving the wrong date of birth ("1889") were prepared but not issued. Some are known to have been released in error.

4 PAISA
(143)

1968 (18 July–Aug). *Nos. 56, 74 and 61 surch as T 143.*
262   4 p. on 3 a. purple .. .. 65 1·25
263   4 p. on 6 a. deep ultramarine (R.) (Aug) .. 1·00 1·25
264   60 p. on 10 a. violet (R.) 50 35
    a. Surch in black 30 70
    b. Surch triple .. .. 30·00
262/4 .. .. *Set of 3* 1·90 2·50

ALTERED CATALOGUE NUMBERS

Any Catalogue numbers altered from the last edition are shown as a list in the introductory pages.

144 Children running with Hoops

(Des A. Rauf)

1968 (7 Oct). *Universal Children's Day.* P 13.
265 **144** 15 p. multicoloured 10 10

145 "National Assembly"

(Des M. Khatoon)

1968 (27 Oct). *"A Decade of Development".* T 145 and similar horiz designs. P 13.
266   10 p. multicoloured 10 10
267   15 p. multicoloured 15 10
268   50 p. multicoloured .. .. 2·25 20
269   60 p. light blue, dull purple and vermilion .. 1·00 35
266/9 .. .. *Set of 4* 3·00 65
    Designs:—15 p. Industry and agriculture; 50 p. Army, Navy and Air Force; 60 p. Minaret and atomic reactor plant.

149 Chittagong Steel Mill

(Des M. Khatoon)

1969 (7 Jan). *Pakistan's First Steel Mill, Chittagong.* P 13.
270 **149** 15 p. grey, light blue & pale yellow-olive 10 10

150 "Family"   151 Olympic Gold Medal and Hockey Player

(Des M. Khatoon)

1969 (14 Jan). *Family Planning.* P 13¹/₂×13.
271 **150** 15 p. bright purple & pale greenish blue 10 10

(Des S. Ghori. Photo)

1969 (30 Jan). *Olympic Hockey Champions.* P 13¹/₂.
272 **151** 15 p. black, gold, dp green & pale blue 1·00 50
273   1 r. black, gold, dp green & flesh-pink 2·50 1·00

152 Mirza Ghalib and Lines of Verse

(Des A. Rauf)

1969 (15 Feb). *Death Centenary of Mirza Ghalib (poet).* P 13.
274 **152** 15 p. multicoloured 20 15
275   50 p. multicoloured 50 15
    The lines of verse on No. 275 are different from those in T 152.

153 Dacca Railway Station

(Des F. Karim)

1969 (27 Apr). *First Anniv of New Dacca Railway Station.* P 13.
276 **153** 15 p. multicoloured 30 10

154 I.L.O. Emblem and "1919–1969"   155 "Lady on Balcony" (18th-cent Mogul)

(Des R-ud Din)

1969 (15 May). *50th Anniv of International Labour Organization.* P 13¹/₂.
277 **154** 15 p. buff and bluish green .. 10 10
278   50 p. cinnamon and cerise .. 40 10

(Des S. Ghori, A. Rauf, F. Karim, A. Salahuddin, N. Mohammad and M. Khatoon)

1969 (21 July). *Fifth Anniv of Regional Co-operation for Development.* T 155 and similar vert designs showing miniatures. Multicoloured. P 13.
279   20 p. Type 155 .. .. 15 10
280   50 p. "Kneeling Servant" (17th-cent Persian) 15 10
281   1 r. "Suleiman the Magnificent holding Audience" (16th-cent Turkish) 20 10
279/81 .. .. .. *Set of 3* 45 30

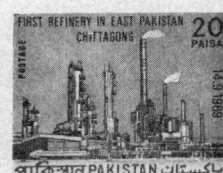

158 Eastern Refinery, Chittagong

(Des M. Khatoon. Photo)

1969 (14 Sept). *First Oil Refinery in East Pakistan.* P 13¹/₂×13.
282 **158** 20 p. multicoloured 10 10

159 Children playing Outside "School"

(Des M. Khatoon. Photo)

1969 (6 Oct). *Universal Children's Day.* P 13.
283 **159** 20 p. multicoloured 10 10

160 Japanese Doll and P.I.A. Air Routes

(Des N. Mohammad)

1969 (1 Nov). *Inauguration of P.I.A. Pearl Route, Dacca–Tokyo.* P 13¹/₂×13.
284 **160** 20 p. multicoloured 60 10
    a. Yellow and pink omitted .. 8·00
285   50 p. multicoloured 90 40
    a. Yellow and pink omitted .. 8·00

161 "Reflection of Light" Diagram

(Des A. Rauf. Photo)

1969 (4 Nov). *Millenary Commemorative of Ibn-al-Haitham (physicist).* P 13.
286 **161** 20 p. black, lemon and light blue .. 10 10

172 Vickers Vimy and
Karachi Airport

163 Flags, Sun Tower and
Expo Site Plan

(Des N. Mohammad. Photo)

1969 (2 Dec). *50th Anniv of First England–Australia Flight.* P 13½×13.
287 **162** 50 p. multicoloured .. .. 1·00 35

(Des R-ud Din)

1970 (15 Mar). *World Fair, Osaka.* P 13.
288 **163** 50 p. multicoloured 20 30

164 New U.P.U. H.Q. Building

(Des R-ud Din)

1970 (20 May). *New U.P.U. Headquarters Building.* P 13½×13.
289 **164** 20 p. multicoloured 15 10
290 50 p. multicoloured 25 25
The above, in a miniature sheet, additionally inscr "U.P.U. Day 9th Oct, 1971", were put on sale on that date in very limited numbers.

165 U.N. H.Q. Building

(Des A. Rauf)

1970 (26 June). *25th Anniv of United Nations.* T **165** and similar horiz design. Multicoloured. P 13×13½.
291 20 p. Type **165** 15 10
292 50 p. U.N. emblem 15 20

167 I.E.Y. Emblem, Book and Pen

(Des M. Khatoon)

1970 (6 July). *International Education Year.* P 13.
293 **167** 20 p. multicoloured 10 10
294 50 p. multicoloured 20 20

168 Saiful Malook Lake (Pakistan)

1970 (21 July). *Sixth Anniv of Regional Co-operation for Development.* T **168** and similar square designs. Multicoloured. P 13.
295 20 p. Type **168** 15 10
296 50 p. Seeyo-Se-Pol Bridge, Esfahan (Iran) .. 20 10
297 1 r. View from Fethiye (Turkey) .. 20 15
295/7 .. .. *Set of 3* 50 30

171 Asian Productivity Symbol

172 Dr. Maria Montessori

1970 (18 Aug). *Asian Productivity Year.* Photo. P 12½ × 14.
298 **171** 50 p. multicoloured 20 20

(Des M. Khatoon)

1970 (31 Aug). *Birth Centenary of Dr. Maria Montessori (educationist).* P 13.
299 **172** 20 p. multicoloured 15 10
300 50 p. multicoloured 15 30

173 Tractor and Fertilizer Factory

1970 (12 Sept). *Tenth Near East F.A.O. Regional Conference, Islamabad.* P 13.
301 **173** 20 p. bright green, and orange-brown 15 20

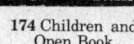

174 Children and
Open Book

175 Pakistan Flag
and Text

(Des F. Karim. Photo)

1970 (5 Oct). *Universal Children's Day.* P 13.
302 **174** 20 p. multicoloured 15 10

(Des A. Salahuddin)

1970 (7 Dec). *General Elections for National Assembly.* P 13½×13.
303 **175** 20 p. green and bluish violet .. 15 10

(Des A. Salahuddin)

1970 (17 Dec). *General Elections for Provincial Assemblies.* As No. 303, but inscr "PROVINCIAL ASSEMBLIES 17TH DEC., 1970".
304 **175** 20 p. green and pale magenta .. 15 10

176 Conference Crest and burning Al-Aqsa Mosque

(Des R-ud Din)

1970 (26 Dec). *Conference of Islamic Foreign Ministers, Karachi.* P 13.
305 **176** 20 p. multicoloured 15 15

177 Coastal Embankments

(Des N. Mohammad)

1971 (25 Feb). *Coastal Embankments in East Pakistan Project.* P 13.
306 **177** 20 p. multicoloured 15 15

178 Emblem and United
Peoples of the World

180 Chaharbagh School (Iran)

179 Maple Leaf Cement Factory, Daudkhel

(Des M. Khatoon)

1971 (21 Mar). *Racial Equality Year.* P 13.
307 **178** 20 p. multicoloured 10 15
308 50 p. multicoloured 20 45

(Des M. Khatoon)

1971 (1 July). *20th Anniv of Colombo Plan.* P 13.
309 **179** 20 p. brown, black and reddish violet .. 10 10

(Des A. Rauf)

1971 (21 July). *Seventh Anniv of Regional Co-operation for Development.* T **180** and similar horiz designs. Multicoloured. P 13.
310 10 p. Selimiye Mosque (Turkey) .. 10 15
311 20 p. Badshahi Mosque (Lahore) .. 20 25
312 50 p. Type **180** 30 35
310/12 .. .. .. *Set of 3* 55 65

181 Electric Train and Boy with Toy Train

(Des A. Rauf)

1971 (4 Oct). *Universal Children's Day.* P 13.
313 **181** 20 p. multicoloured .. .. 1·75 50

182 Horseman and Symbols

(Des N. Mohammad)

1971 (15 Oct). *2500th Anniv of Persian Monarchy.* P 13.
314 **182** 10 p. multicoloured 35 30
315 20 p. multicoloured 45 40
316 50 p. multicoloured 55 75
314/16 *Set of 3* 1·25 1·25
The above exist in a miniature sheet, but only a very limited quantity was placed on sale.

183 Hockey-player and Trophy

(Des F. Karim)

1971 (24 Oct). *World Cup Hockey Tournament, Barcelona.* P 13.
317 **183** 20 p. multicoloured .. .. .. 1·75 65

184 Great Bath, Moenjodaro

(Des A. Salahuddin)

1971 (4 Nov). *25th Anniv of U.N.E.S.C.O. and Campaign to save the Moenjodaro Excavations.* P 13.
318 **184** 20 p. multicoloured 20 30

185 U.N.I.C.E.F. Symbol

(Des F. Karim)

1971 (11 Dec). *25th Anniv of U.N.I.C.E.F.* P 13.
319 **185** 50 p. multicoloured 30 60

186 King Hussein and Jordanian Flag

(Des F. Karim)

1971 (25 Dec). *50th Anniv of Hashemite Kingdom of Jordan.* P 13.
320 **186** 20 p. multicoloured 15 20

187 Badge of Hockey Federation and Trophy
188 Reading Class

(Des F. Karim)

1971 (31 Dec). *Hockey Championships Victory.* P 13.
321 **187** 20 p. multicoloured .. .. 2·50 90

(Des M. Khatoon)

1972 (15 Jan). *International Book Year.* P 13½.
322 **188** 20 p. multicoloured 20 30

OUTSIDE THE COMMONWEALTH

On 30 January 1972 Pakistan left the Commonwealth.

189 View of Venice

(Des A. Salahuddin)

1972 (7 Feb). *U.N.E.S.C.O. Campaign to Save Venice.* P 13.
323 **189** 20 p. multicoloured 30 30

190 E.C.A.F.E. Emblem and Discs
191 Human Heart

(Des F. Karim)

1972 (28 Mar). *25th Anniv of E.C.A.F.E. (Economic Commission for Asia and the Far East).* P 13.
324 **190** 20 p. multicoloured 15 30

(Des M. Khatoon)

1972 (7 Apr). *World Health Day.* P 13×13½.
325 **191** 20 p. multicoloured 20 30

192 "Only One Earth"
193 "Fisherman" (Cevat Dereli)

(Des R-ud Din)

1972 (5 June). *U.N. Conference on the Human Environment, Stockholm.* P 13×13½.
326 **192** 20 p. multicoloured 20 30

(Des F. Karim)

1972 (21 July). *Eighth Anniv of Regional Co-operation for Development.* T **193** *and similar vert designs. Multicoloured.* P 13.
327 10 p. Type **193** 20 20
328 20 p. "Iranian Woman" (Behzad) .. 35 25
329 50 p. "Will and Power" (A. R. Chughtai) .. 55 70
a. Brown-ochre (border) omitted 17·00
327/9 .. .. *Set of 3* 1·00 1·00

194 Mohammed Ali Jinnah and Tower
195 Donating Blood

(Des Mukhtar Ahmad and T. Sultana)

1972 (14 Aug). *25th Anniv of Independence.* T **194** *and similar horiz designs. Multicoloured.* P 13 (10 and 60 p.) or 14×12½ (20 p.).
330 10 p. Type **194** 10 10
331 20 p. "Land Reform" (74×23½ mm) .. 15 25
a. Vert strip of 4. Nos. 331/4 .. 55
332 20 p. "Labour Reform" (74×23½ mm) .. 15 25
333 20 p. "Education Policy" (74×23½ mm) .. 15 25
334 20 p. "Health Policy" (74×23½ mm) .. 15 25
335 60 p. National Assembly Building (46×28 mm) .. 25 35
330/5 *Set of 6* 80 1·25
Nos. 331/4 were printed vertically *se-tenant* throughout the sheet.

(Des M. Khatoon)

1972 (6 Sept). *National Blood Transfusion Service.* P 13½×12½.
336 **195** 20 p. multicoloured .. 20 30

196 People and Squares

(Des Munawar Ahmad)

1972 (16 Sept). *Centenary of Population Census.* P 13½.
337 **196** 20 p. multicoloured 20 20

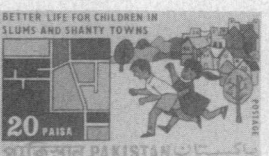

197 Children from Slums

(Des Mukhtar Ahmad)

1972 (2 Oct). *Universal Children's Day.* P 13.
338 **197** 20 p. multicoloured 20 30

198 People and Open Book

(Des T. Sultana)

1972 (23 Oct). *Education Week.* P 13.
339 **198** 20 p. multicoloured 20 30

199 Nuclear Power Plant

1972 (28 Nov). *Inauguration of Karachi Nuclear Power Plant.* P 13.
340 **199** 20 p. multicoloured 20 30

200 Copernicus in Observatory

(Des M. Sultana)

1973 (19 Feb). *500th Birth Anniv of Nicholas Copernicus (astronomer).* P 13.
341 **200** 20 p. multicoloured 20 30

201 Moenjodaro Excavations
202 Elements of Meteorology

(Des A. Salahuddin)

1973 (23 Feb). *50th Anniv of Moenjodaro Excavations.* P 13½×13½.
342 **201** 20 p. multicoloured 20 30

(Des T. Sultana)

1973 (23 Mar). *I.M.O./W.M.O. Centenary.* P 13.
343 202 20 p. multicoloured 20 30

203 Prisoners-of-war

(Des Mukhtar Ahmad)

1973 (18 Apr). *Prisoners-of-war in India.* P 13.
344 203 1 r. 25, multicoloured .. .. .. 1·50 2·25

204 National Assembly Building
and Constitution Book

(Des Mukhtar Ahmad)

1973 (21 Apr). *Constitution Week.* P 12½×13½.
345 204 20 p. multicoloured 50 40

205 Badge and State Bank Building

(Des A. Salahuddin)

1973 (1 July). *25th Anniv of Pakistan State Bank.* P 13.
346 205 20 p. multicoloured 15 30
347 1 r. multicoloured 30 50

206 Lut Desert Excavations   **207** Constitution Book
(Iran)   and Flag

(Des A. Salahuddin)

1973 (21 July). *9th Anniv of Regional Co-operation for Development.* T **206** and similar vert designs. Multicoloured. P 13×13½.
348 20 p. Type **206** 30 20
349 60 p. Main Street, Moenjodaro (Pakistan) 55 50
350 1 r. 25, Mausoleum of Antiochus I (Turkey) 75 1·25
348/50 .. .. .. *Set of 3* 1·40 1·75

(Des Mukhtar Ahmad)

1973 (14 Aug). *Independence Day and Enforcement of the Constitution.* P 13.
351 **207** 20 p. multicoloured 15 30

208 Mohammed Ali Jinnah   **209** Wallago
(Quaid-i-Azam)

1973 (11 Sept). *25th Death Anniv of Mohammed Ali Jinnah.* P 13.
352 **208** 20 p. light emerald, pale yellow and black 15 30

1973 (24 Sept). *Fishes.* T **209** *and similar horiz designs. Multi-coloured.* P 13½.
353 10 p. Type **209** .. .. 1·10 1·10
    a. Horiz strip of 4. Nos. 353/6 .. 4·75
354 20 p. Rohu .. .. .. 1·25 1·25
355 60 p. Mozambique Mouthbrooder .. 1·40 1·40
356 1 r. Catla .. .. .. 1·40 1·40
353/6 .. .. *Set of 4* 4·75 4·75
Nos. 353/6 were printed within one sheet, horizontally se-tenant.

210 Children's Education

1973 (1 Oct). *Universal Children's Day.* P 13.
357 **210** 20 p. multicoloured 15 30

211 Harvesting

(Des A. Salahuddin)

1973 (15 Oct). *Tenth Anniv of World Food Programme.* P 13.
358 **211** 20 p. multicoloured 60 40

212 Ankara and Kemal Atatürk

(Des Mukhtar and Munawar Ahmad)

1973 (29 Oct). *50th Anniv of Turkish Republic.* P 13.
359 **212** 50 p. multicoloured 45 35

213 Boy Scout   **214** "Basic Necessities"

(Des T. Sultana)

1973 (11 Nov). *National Silver Jubilee Scout Jamboree.* P 13.
360 **213** 20 p. multicoloured .. .. .. 1·75 50

(Des Munawar Ahmad)

1973 (16 Nov). *25th Anniv of Declaration of Human Rights.* P 13.
361 **214** 20 p. multicoloured 30 30

215 Al-Biruni and Nandana Hill   **216** Dr. Hansen, Microscope and Bacillus

(Des Mukhtar Ahmad)

1973 (26 Nov). *Al-Biruni Millennium Congress.* P 13.
362 **215** 20 p. multicoloured 40 20
363 1 r. 25, multicoloured .. .. 1·10 75

1973 (29 Dec). *Centenary of Hansen's Discovery of Leprosy Bacillus.* P 13.
364 **216** 20 p. multicoloured .. .. .. 1·00 60

217 Family and Emblem   **218** Conference Emblem

(Des M. Saeed)

1974 (1 Jan). *World Population Year.* P 13.
365 **217** 20 p. multicoloured 10 10
366 1 r. 25, multicoloured 30 40

(Des I. Gilani (20 p.), M. Saeed (65 p.), A. Salahuddin (No. MS369))

1974 (22 Feb). *Islamic Summit Conference, Lahore.* T **218** *and similar design.* P 14×12½ (20 p.) or 13 (65 p.).
367 20 p. Type **218** .. 10 10
368 65 p. Emblem on "Sun" (42 × 30 *mm*). .. 25 60
MS369 102 × 102 mm. Nos. 367/8. Imperf 1·50 4·75

219 Units of Weight and   **220** "Chand Chauthai" Carpet,
Measurement   Pakistan

(Des M. Saeed)

1974 (1 July). *Adoption of International Weights and Measures System.* P 13.
370 **219** 20 p. multicoloured 15 25

(Des I. Gilani)

1974 (21 July). *Tenth Anniv of Regional Co-operation for Development. Vert designs as* T **220** *showing carpets from member countries. Multicoloured.* P 13.
371 20 p. Type **220** .. 20 15
372 60 p. Persian carpet, 16th-century .. 40 55
373 1 r. 25, Anatolian carpet, 15th-century 65 1·25
371/3 .. .. *Set of 3* 1·10 1·75

221 Hands protecting Sapling   **222** Torch and Map

(Des Munawar Ahmad)

1974 (9 Aug). *Tree Planting Day.* P 13.
374 **221** 20 p. multicoloured 50 50

(Des G. Parwar)

1974 (26 Aug). *Namibia Day.* P 13.
375 **222** 60 p. multicoloured 35 60

223 Highway Map

(Des I. Gilani)

1974 (23 Sept). *Shahrah-e-Pakistan (Pakistan Highway).* P 13.
376 **223** 20 p. multicoloured 90 60

224 Boy at Desk   **225** U.P.U. Emblem

(Des A. Salahuddin)

1974 (7 Oct). *Universal Children's Day. P 13.*
377 **224** 20 p. multicoloured 30 30

(Des T. Sultana (20 p.), Mukhtar Ahmad (2 r. 25))

1974 (9 Oct). *Centenary of Universal Postal Union. T 225 and similar vert design. Multicoloured. P 13×13½ (20 p.) or 13 (2 r. 25).*
378 20 p. Type **225** 20 20
379 2 r. 25, U.P.U. emblem, Boeing 707 and mail-wagon (30×41 *mm*) .. .. 55 1·40
MS380 100×101 mm. Nos. 378/9. Imperf .. 1·75 5·50

226 Liaquat Ali Khan **227** Dr. Mohammed Iqbal (poet and philosopher)

(Des Munawar Ahmad)

1974 (16 Oct). *Liaquat Ali Khan (First Prime Minister of Pakistan). P 13×13½.*
381 **226** 20 p. black and light vermilion .. 30 30

(Des Munawar Ahmad)

1974 (9 Nov). *Birth Centenary of Dr. Iqbal (1977) (1st issue). P 13.*
382 **227** 20 p. multicoloured 30 30
See also Nos. 399, 433 and 445/9.

228 Dr. Schweitzer and River Scene

(Des Mukhtar Ahmad)

1975 (14 Jan). *Birth Centenary of Dr. Albert Schweitzer. P 13.*
383 **228** 2 r. 25, multicoloured .. .. 2·75 3·25

229 Tourism Year Symbol

(Des A. Salahuddin)

1975 (15 Jan). *South East Asia Tourism Year. P 13.*
384 **229** 2 r. 25, multicoloured 55 80

230 Assembly Hall, Flags and Prime Minister Bhutto

(Des A. Salahuddin)

1975 (22 Feb). *First Anniv of Islamic Summit Conference, Lahore. P 13.*
385 **230** 20 p. multicoloured 35 35
386 1 r. multicoloured .. .. .. 75 1·40

231 "Scientific Research" **232** "Globe" and Algebraic Symbol

(Des A. Salahuddin (20 p.), Mukhtar Ahmad (2 r. 25))

1975 (15 June). *International Women's Year. T 231 and similar horiz design. Multicoloured. P 13.*
387 20 p. Type **231** 20 25
388 2 r. 25, Girl teaching woman ("Adult Education") .. .. .. 1·10 2·00

(Des Mukhtar Ahmad)

1975 (14 July). *International Congress of Mathematical Sciences, Karachi. P 13.*
389 **232** 20 p. multicoloured 50 50

233 Pakistani Camel-skin Vase **234** Sapling and Dead Trees

(Des I. Gilani)

1975 (21 July). *Eleventh Anniv of Regional Co-operation for Development. T 233 and similar multicoloured designs. P 13.*
390 20 p. Type **233** 25 30
391 60 p. Iranian tile (*horiz*) .. .. 50 1·00
392 1 r. 25, Turkish porcelain vase .. 75 1·50
390/2 .. .. *Set of 3* 1·40 2·50

(Des Munawar Ahmad)

1975 (9 Aug). *Tree Planting Day. P 13×13½.*
393 **234** 20 p. multicoloured 35 40

235 Black Partridge **236** "Today's Girls"

(Des A. Salahuddin)

1975 (30 Sept). *Wildlife Protection (1st series). P 13.*
394 **235** 20 p. multicoloured .. .. 1·25 35
395 2 r. 25, multicoloured .. .. 4·00 4·75
See also Nos. 400/1, 411/12, 417/18, 493/6, 560, 572/3, 581/2, 599, 600, 605, 621/2, 691, 702, 752, 780/3, 853 and 1027.

(Des N. Sultana)

1975 (6 Oct). *Universal Children's Day. P 13.*
396 **236** 20 p. multicoloured 30 30

237 Hazrat Amir Khusrau, Sitar and Tabla

(Des A. Salahuddin)

1975 (24 Oct). *700th Birth Anniv of Hazrat Amir Khusrau (poet and musician). P 13½ × 12½.*
397 **237** 20 p. multicoloured 20 45
398 2 r. 25, multicoloured .. .. 75 1·60

238 Dr. Mohammed Iqbal **239** Urial (wild sheep)

(Des A. Salahuddin)

1975 (9 Nov). *Birth Centenary of Dr. Iqbal (1977) (2nd issue). P 13.*
399 **238** 20 p. multicoloured 30 30

(Des Munawar Ahmad)

1975 (31 Dec). *Wildlife Protection (2nd series). P 13.*
400 **239** 20 p. multicoloured 30 30
401 3 r. multicoloured .. .. .. 1·75 3·25

240 Moenjodaro Remains **241** Dome and Minaret of Rauza-e-Mubarak

(Des A. Salahuddin)

1976 (29 Feb). *"Save Moenjodaro" (1st series). T 240 and similar vert designs. Multicoloured. P 13.*
402 10 p. Type **240** 65 75
   a. Horiz strip of 5. Nos. 402/6 .. 3·25
403 20 p. Remains (*different*) 75 85
404 65 p. The Citadel 75 85
405 3 r. Well inside a house 75 85
406 4 r. The "Great Bath" 85 95
402/6 .. .. *Set of 5* 3·25 3·75
Nos. 402/6 were printed horizontally *se-tenant* within the sheet, the five stamps forming a composite design of the excavations. See also Nos. 414 and 430.

(Des A. Ghani. Photo)

1976 (3 Mar). *International Congress on Seerat. P 13 × 13½.*
407 **241** 20 p. multicoloured 15 20
408 3 r. multicoloured 55 90

242 Alexander Graham Bell and Telephone Dial

(Des M. Saeed. Photo)

1976 (10 Mar). *Telephone Centenary. P 13.*
409 **242** 3 r. multicoloured .. .. 1·25 2·00

243 College Arms within "Sun"

(Des A. Salahuddin)

1976 (15 Mar). *Centenary of National College of Arts, Lahore. P 13.*
410 **243** 20 p. multicoloured 30 40

COVER PRICES

Cover factors are quoted at the beginning of each country for most issues to 1945. An explanation of the system can be found on page x. The factors quoted do not, however, apply to philatelic covers.

244 Common Peafowl

(Des A. Salahuddin)

1976 (31 Mar). *Wildlife Protection* (3rd series). P 13.
411 244 20 p. multicoloured .. .. .. 1·00 35
412 3 r. multicoloured .. .. .. 3·50 4·50

245 Human Eye

(Des M. Saeed)

1976 (7 Apr). *Prevention of Blindness*. P 13.
413 245 20 p. multicoloured 70 70

246 Unicorn and Ruins

(Des I. Gilani)

1976 (31 May). *"Save Moenjodaro"* (2nd series). P 13.
414 246 20 p. multicoloured 30 35

247 Jefferson Memorial   248 Ibex

(Des I. Gilani (90 p.), A. Salahuddin (4 r.))

1976 (4 July). *Bicentenary of American Revolution*. T 247 and similar horiz design. Multicoloured. P 13 (90 p.) or 13½ (4 r.).
415 90 p. Type 247 .. .. 75 60
416 4 r. "Declaration of Independence" (47 × 36 mm) .. .. 3·00 5·00

(Des Mukhtar Ahmad)

1976 (12 July). *Wildlife Protection* (4th series). P 13.
417 248 20 p. multicoloured 30 35
418 3 r. multicoloured .. .. .. 1·75 2·50

249 Mohammed Ali Jinnah

(Des A. Salahuddin)

1976 (21 July). *Twelfth Anniv of Regional Co-operation for Development*. T 249 and similar diamond-shaped designs. Multicoloured. P 14.
419 20 p. Type 249 .. .. .. 80 80
  a. Vert strip of 3. Nos. 419/21 .. 2·25
420 65 p. Reza Shah the Great (Iran) .. 80 80
421 90 p. Kemal Atatürk (Turkey) .. 80 80
419/21 *Set of 3* 2·25 2·25
Nos. 419/21 were printed vertically *se-tenant* throughout the sheet.

250 Urdu Text

251 Mohammed Ali Jinnah and Wazir Mansion

(Des A. Salahuddin)

1976 (14 Aug). *Birth Centenary of Mohammed Ali Jinnah* (1st issue). P 13. (a) Type 250.
422 5 p. black, new blue and yellow .. 20 25
  a. Block of 8. Nos. 422/9 .. 1·75
423 10 p. black, yellow and magenta .. 20 25
424 15 p. black and violet-blue .. 20 25
425 1 r. black, yellow and new blue .. 30 30

(b) *Multicoloured designs as T 251, different buildings in the background*
426 20 p. Type 251 .. .. 20 25
427 40 p. Sind Madressah 20 25
428 50 p. Minar Qarardad-e-Pakistan .. 20 25
429 3 r. Mausoleum 45 50
422/9 *Set of 8* 1·75 2·10
Nos. 422/9 were printed in *se-tenant* blocks of 8 throughout the sheet.
See also No. 436.

252 Dancing-girl, Ruins and King Priest

(Des A. Salahuddin)

1976 (31 Aug). *"Save Moenjodaro"* (3rd series). P 14.
430 252 65 p. multicoloured 35 60

253 U.N. Racial Discrimination Emblem

(Des A. Salahuddin)

1976 (15 Sept). *U.N. Decade to Combat Racial Discrimination*. P 12½ × 13½.
431 253 65 p. multicoloured 30 60

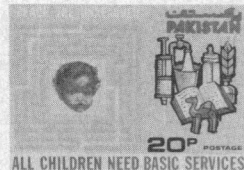

254 Child in Maze and Basic Services

(Des Mukhtar Ahmad)

1976 (4 Oct). *Universal Children's Day*. P 13.
432 254 20 p. multicoloured 30 30

Stamps commemorating the visit of King Khalid of Saudi Arabia and showing the Islamabad Mosque were prepared for release on 11 October 1976, but withdrawn before issue. Some are known to have been released in error.

255 Verse from "Allama Iqbal"   256 Mohammed Ali Jinnah giving Scout Salute

(Des M. Javed)

1976 (9 Nov). *Birth Centenary of Dr. Iqbal* (1977) (3rd issue). P 13.
433 255 20 p. multicoloured 15 30

(Des I. Gilani)

1976 (20 Nov). *Quaid-i-Azam Centenary Jamboree*. P 13½.
434 256 20 p. multicoloured 75 30

257 Children Reading   258 Mohammed Ali Jinnah

(Des Mukhtar Ahmad)

1976 (15 Dec). *Children's Literature*. P 13.
435 257 20 p. multicoloured 40 30

(Litho and embossed Cartor S.A., France)

1976 (25 Dec). *Birth Centenary of Mohammed Ali Jinnah* (2nd issue). P 12½.
436 258 10 r. emerald and gold .. .. 2·50 3·50

259 Rural Family   260 Turkish Vase, 1800 B.C.

(Des Mukhtar Ahmad)

1977 (14 Apr). *Social Welfare and Rural Development Year*. P 13.
437 259 20 p. multicoloured 15 10

(Des A. Salahuddin)

1977 (21 July). *13th Anniv of Regional Co-operation for Development*. T 260 and similar horiz designs. P 13.
438 20 p. red-orange, violet-blue and black .. 35 10
439 65 p. multicoloured 55 40
440 90 p. multicoloured .. .. 80 1·50
438/40 *Set of 3* 1·50 1·75
Designs:—60 p. Pakistani toy bullock cart, Moenjodaro; 90 p. Pitcher with spout, Sialk Hill, Iran.

261 Forest   262 Desert Scene

(Des A. Ahmed)

1977 (9 Aug). *National Tree Plantation Campaign*. P 13.
441 261 20 p. multicoloured 20 30

(Des M. Javed)

1977 (5 Sept). *U.N. Conference on Desertification, Nairobi*. P 13.
442 262 65 p. multicoloured 60 30

PRICES OF SETS

Set prices are given for many issues, generally those containing three stamps or more. Definitive sets include one of each value or major colour change, but do not cover different perforations, die types or minor shades. Where a choice is possible the set prices are based on the cheapest versions of the stamps included in the listings.

263 "Water for the Children of the World"   **264** Aga Khan III

(Des A. Salahuddin)

1977 (3 Oct). *Universal Children's Day.* P 13½ × 12½.
443 **263** 50 p. multicoloured 40 30

(Des A. Rauf)

1977 (2 Nov). *Birth Centenary of Aga Khan III.* P 13.
444 **264** 2 r. multicoloured .. .. 55 1·00

265 Iqbal and Spirit of the Poet Roomi (from painting by Behzad)   **266** The Holy "Khana-Kaaba" (House of God, Mecca)

(Des A. Ahmed)

1977 (9 Nov). *Birth Centenary of Dr. Mohammed Iqbal* (4th issue). T **265** *and similar vert designs. Multicoloured.* P 13.
445 20 p. Type **265** 40 50
   a. Horiz strip of 5. Nos. 445/9 .. 2·10
446 65 p. Iqbal looking at Jamaluddin Afghani and
    Saeed Haleem Pasha at prayer (Behzad) 40 50
447 1 r. 25, Urdu verse 45 55
448 2 r. 25, Persian verse. 50 65
449 3 r. Iqbal 55 75
445/9 .. .. *Set of 5* 2·10 2·75
Nos. 445, 448/9, 447 and 446 (in that order) were issued in horizontal *se-tenant* strips of 5.

(Des I. Gilani)

1977 (21 Nov). *Haj* (*pilgrimage to Mecca*). P 14.
450 **266** 65 p. multicoloured 30 30

267 Rheumatic Patient and Healthy Man   **268** Woman in Costume of Rawalpindi-Islamabad

(Des T. Hameed)

1977 (19 Dec). *World Rheumatism Year.* P 13.
451 **267** 65 p. turquoise-blue, black and yellow .. 30 20

(Des A. Salahuddin)

1978 (5 Feb). *Indonesia–Pakistan Economic and Cultural Co-operation Organization.* P 12½ × 13½.
452 **268** 75 p. multicoloured 30 20

269 Human Body and Sphygmomanometer   **270** Henri Dunant

(Des A. Salahuddin)

1978 (20 Apr). *World Hypertension Month.* P 13.
453 **269** 20 p. multicoloured 15 10
454 — 2 r. multicoloured 60 90
The 2 r. value is as T **269**, but has the words "Down with high blood pressure" instead of the Urdu inscription at bottom left.

(Des A. Salahuddin)

1978 (8 May). *150th Birth Anniv of Henri Dunant* (*founder of Red Cross*). P 14.
455 **270** 1 r. black, new blue and vermilion .. 1·00 20

271 Red Roses (Pakistan)   **272** "Pakistan, World Cup Hockey Champions"

(Des A. Salahuddin)

1978 (21 July). *14th Anniv of Regional Co-operation for Development.* T **271** *and similar vert designs. Multicoloured.* P 13½.
456 20 p. Type **271** 35 20
   a. Horiz strip of 3. Nos. 456/8 .. 1·40
457 90 p. Pink roses (Iran) 50 20
458 2 r. Yellow rose (Turkey) 75 25
456/8 .. .. *Set of 3* 1·40 60
Nos. 456/8 were printed together, *se-tenant*, in horizontal strips of 3 throughout the sheet.

(Des Munawar Ahmad)

1978 (26 Aug). *"Riccione '78" International Stamp Fair.* T **272** *and similar vert design. Multicoloured.* P 13.
459 1 r. Type **272** .. .. 1·25 25
460 2 r. Fountain at Plazza Turismo .. 50 35

273 Cogwheels within Globe Symbol   **274** St. Patrick's Cathedral

(Des A. Salahuddin)

1978 (3 Sept). *U.N. Technical Co-operation amongst Developing Countries Conference.* P 13.
461 **273** 75 p. multicoloured 15 10

(Des A. Salahuddin)

1978 (29 Sept). *Centenary of St. Patrick's Cathedral, Karachi.* T **274** *and similar vert design. Multicoloured.* P 13.
462 1 r. Type **274** 10 10
463 2 r. Stained glass window 25 25

275 Minar-i-Qarardad-e-Pakistan   **276** Tractor

276a Mausoleum of Ibrahim Khan Makli, Thatta

Die I   Die II

Two Dies of 75 p. value:

Die I. Size of design 26½ × 21½ mm. Figures of value large; "p" small. Plough does not touch left-hand frame.
Die II. Size of design 25½ × 21 mm. Smaller figures; larger "p". Plough touches left-hand frame.

(Des A. Salahuddin. Litho (10, 25, 40, 50, 90 p.), recess (others))

1978 (7 Nov)–81. *No wmk* (2 to 90 p.) *or* W **98** (1 to 5 r.).
P 14×13½ (2 to 5 p.), 13½×14 (10 to 90 p.) or 13 (1 to 5 r.).
464 **275** 2 p. deep grey-green 10 10
   a. Printed on the gummed side ..
465 3 p. black 10 10
   a. Imperf (pair) .. .. 5·00
   b. Printed on the gummed side ..
466 5 p. deep ultramarine 10 10
   a. Printed on the gummed side .. 8·00
467 **276** 10 p. new blue & greenish bl (7.10.79) 10 10
468 20 p. deep yellow-green (25.3.79) 50 10
469 25 p. dp green & dull mag (19.3.79) 80 10
470 40 p. new blue and magenta (16.12.78) 10 10
471 50 p. slate-lilac & turq-green (19.3.79) 30 10
   a. Printed on the gummed side .. 6·00
472 60 p. black (16.12.78) 10 10
   a. Imperf (pair) .. .. 5·00
473 75 p. dull vermilion (I) (16.12.78) .. 60 10
   a. Imperf (pair) .. .. 16·00
   b. Die II (1980) 55 10
   ba. Imperf (pair) .. .. 6·00
   bb. Printed on the gummed side
474 90 p. magenta and new blue (16.12.78) 20 10
   a. Printed on the gummed side .. 18·00
475 **276a** 1 r. bronze-green (2.8.80) .. 10 10
   a. Imperf (pair) .. .. 14·00
   w. Wmk inverted
476 1 r. 50, red-orange (17.11.79) .. 10 10
   a. Imperf (pair) .. .. 6·00
   w. Wmk inverted
477 2 r. carmine-red (17.11.79) .. 10 10
   a. Imperf (pair) .. .. 7·00
   b. Printed on the gummed side .. 10·00
   w. Wmk inverted
478 3 r. blue-black (4.6.80) 15 10
   a. Imperf (pair) .. .. 9·00
   w. Wmk inverted
479 4 r. black (1.1.81) 15 10
   a. Imperf (pair) .. .. 9·00
   w. Wmk inverted
480 5 r. sepia (1.1.81) 20 10
   a. Imperf (pair) .. .. 9·00
   w. Wmk inverted
464/80 .. .. .. *Set of 17* 3·25 75
The remaining values as Type **276** printed in recess, are from Die II.
Postal forgeries exist of the 2 r. and 3 r. values. These are poorly printed with perforations which do not match those of the genuine stamps.
Later printings of all but the 75 p. Type I occur with matt, almost invisible gum of a PVA type, instead of the gum arabic used previously.

277 Emblem and "United Races" Symbol   **278** Maulana Mohammad Ali Jauhar

(Des M. Munawar)

1978 (20 Nov). *International Anti-Apartheid Year.* P 13.
481 **277** 1 r. multicoloured 15 15

(Des A. Salahuddin)

1978 (10 Dec). *Birth Centenary of Maulana Mohammad Ali Jauhar* (*patriot*). P 13.
482 **278** 50 p. multicoloured 40 20

NEW INFORMATION

The editor is always interested to correspond with people who have new information that will improve or correct the Catalogue.

279 Panavia MRCA Tornado,
De Havilland D.H.89 Dragon
Rapide and Wright Flyer I

(Des A. Salahuddin)

1978 (24 Dec). *75th Anniv of Powered Flight. T* **279** *and similar diamond-shaped designs. Multicoloured. P* 13.
483	65 p. Type **279**	..	..	1·25	1·75
	a. Block of 4. Nos. 483/6		..	5·00	
484	1 r. McDonnell Douglas F-4A Phantom II, Lockheed L-1011 TriStar 500 and Wright Flyer I			1·40	1·75
485	2 r. North American X-15, Tupolev Tu-104 and Wright Flyer I			1·50	2·00
486	2 r. 25, Mikoyan Gurevich MiG-15, Concorde and Wright Flyer I			1·50	2·25
483/6			*Set of 4*	5·00	7·00

Nos. 483/6 were printed together, *se-tenant*, in blocks of 4 throughout the sheet.

280 "Holy Koran illuminating Globe" and Raudha-e-Mubarak (mausoleum)

281 "Aspects of A.P.W.A."

(Des A. Salahuddin)

1979 (10 Feb). *"12th Rabi-ul-Awwal" (Prophet Mohammed's birthday). P* 13.
487	**280**	20 p. multicoloured	..	30	15

(Des M. Saeed)

1979 (25 Feb). *30th Anniv of A.P.W.A. (All Pakistan Women's Association). P* 13.
488	**281**	50 p. multicoloured	..	60	15

282 Tippu Sultan Shaheed of Mysore

(Des A. Rauf)

1979 (23 Mar). *Pioneers of Freedom (1st series). T* **282** *and similar diamond-shaped designs. Multicoloured. W* **98**. *P* 14.
490	10 r. Type **282**	..	..	75	1·25
	a. Horiz strip of 3. Nos. 490/2	..	3·00		
491	15 r. Sir Syed Ahmad Khan	..	1·00	1·75	
492	25 r. Altaf Hussain Hali	..	1·50	2·00	
490/2			*Set of 3*	3·00	4·50

Nos. 490/2 were printed together, *se-tenant*, in the same sheet; there being ten horizontal strips of 3 values and ten additional 10 r. stamps.

See also Nos. 757, 801/27, 838/46, 870/2, 904/6, 921/8, 961/2, 1007, 1019/20 and 1075/7.

283 Himalayan Monal Pheasant

(Des Mukhtar Ahmad)

1979 (17 June). *Wildlife Protection (5th series). Pheasants. T* **283** *and similar horiz designs. Multicoloured. P* 13.
493	20 p. Type **283**	..	..	1·25	60
494	25 p. Kalij	..	..	1·25	80
495	40 p. Koklass	..	..	1·60	1·75
496	1 r. Cheer	..	..	3·00	2·00
493/6			*Set of 4*	6·25	4·75

284 "Pakistan Village Scene" (Ustad Bakhsh)

(Des A. Rauf)

1979 (21 July). *15th Anniv of Regional Co-operation for Development. Paintings. T* **284** *and similar horiz designs. Multicoloured. P* 14 × 12½.
497	40 p. Type **284**	..	20	25
	a. Vert strip of 3. Nos. 497/9	..	60	
498	75 p. "Iranian Goldsmith" (Kamal al Molk)	20	25	
499	1 r. 60, "Turkish Harvest" (Namik Ismail)	..	25	30
497/9		*Set of 3*	60	70

Nos. 497/9 were printed together, *se-tenant*, in vertical strips of 3 throughout the sheet.

285 Guj Embroidered Shirt (detail)

(Des A. Salahuddin)

1979 (23 Aug). *Handicrafts (1st series). T* **285** *and similar horiz designs. Multicoloured. P* 14×12½.
500	40 p. Type **285**	..	..	20	20
	a. Block of 4. Nos. 500/3	..	1·00		
501	1 r. Enamel inlaid brass plate	..	25	25	
502	1 r. 50, Baskets	..	30	30	
503	2 r. Chain-stitch embroidered rug (detail)	..	40	40	
500/3			*Set of 4*	1·00	1·00

Nos. 500/3 were printed together, *se-tenant*, in blocks of 4 throughout the sheet.

See also Nos. 578/9, 595/6 and 625/8.

286 Children playing on Climbing Frame

(Des A. Rauf)

1979 (10 Sept). *S.O.S. Children's Village, Lahore (orphanage). P* 13.
504	**286**	50 p. multicoloured	..	40	40

287 "Island" (Z. Maloof)

(Des A. Salahuddin)

1979 (22 Oct). *International Year of the Child. Children's Paintings. T* **287** *and similar horiz designs. Multicoloured. P* 14 × 12½.
505	40 p. Type **287**	..	15	15
	a. Block of 4. Nos. 505/8	..	85	
506	75 p. "Playground" (R. Akbar)	..	25	25
507	1 r. "Fairground" (M. Azam)	..	25	25
508	1 r. 50, "Hockey Match" (M. Tayyab)	30	30	
505/8		*Set of 4*	85	85
MS509	79 × 64 mm. 2 r. "Child looking at Faces in the Sky" (M. Mumtaz) (*vert*). Imperf	1·00	2·00	

Nos. 505/8 were printed together, *se-tenant*, in blocks of 4 throughout the sheet.

Examples of No. **MS**509 are known overprinted in gold for the "PHILEXFRANCE" International Stamp Exhibition in 1982. The Pakistan Post Office has declared such overprints to be bogus.

288 Warrior attacking Crab **289** Pakistan Customs Emblem

(Des A. Salahuddin)

1979 (12 Nov). *Fight Against Cancer. P* 14.
510	**288**	40 p. black, greenish yellow and magenta	70	70

(Des A. Salahuddin)

1979 (10 Dec). *Centenary of Pakistan Customs Service. P* 13 × 13½.
511	**289**	1 r. multicoloured	..	30	30

290 Boeing 747-200 and Douglas DC-3 Airliners **291** Islamic Pattern

(Des A. Salahuddin)

1980 (10 Jan). *25th Anniv of Pakistan International Air Lines. P* 13.
512	**290**	1 r. multicoloured	..	1·75	90

(Des and litho Secura, Singapore)

1980 (15 Jan–10 Mar). *Matt, almost invisible PVA gum. P* 12.
513	**291**	10 p. slate-green and orange-yellow	10	10
514		15 p. slate-green & bright yellow-green	10	10
515		25 p. violet and brown-red (10.3)	10	30
516		35 p. carmine & brt yellow-green (10.3)	10	10
517	—	40 p. rosine and olive-sepia	15	10
	a. Printed on the gummed side			
518	—	50 p. violet and dull yellow-green (10.3)	10	30
519	—	80 p. bright yellow-green & black (10.3)	15	40
513/19		*Set of 7*	70	1·25

The 40 to 80 p. values also show different Islamic patterns, the 40 p. being horizontal and the remainder vertical.

292 Young Child **293** Conference Emblem

(Des M. Saeed)

1980 (16 Feb). *5th Asian Congress of Paediatric Surgery, Karachi. P* 13.
530	**292**	50 p. multicoloured	..	75	1·50

(Des A. Salahuddin)

1980 (17 May). *11th Islamic Conference of Foreign Ministers, Islamabad. P* 13.
531	**293**	1 r. multicoloured	..	65	50

294 Karachi Port

(Des A. Salahuddin)

1980 (15 July). *Centenary of Karachi Port Authority. P* 13 × 13½.
532	**294**	1 r. multicoloured	..	1·75	1·40

PRICES OF SETS

Set prices are given for many issues, generally those containing three stamps or more. Definitive sets include one of each value or major colour change, but do not cover different perforations, die types or minor shades. Where a choice is possible the set prices are based on the cheapest versions of the stamps included in the listings.

RICCIONE 80
(295)

296 College Emblem with
Old and New Buildings

1980 (30 Aug). *"Riccione 80" International Stamp Exhibition. Nos. 505/8 optd with T 295 in red.*
533	40 p. Type **287**	.. ..	30	60
	a. Block of 4. Nos. 533/6	..	1·60	
534	75 p. "Playground" (R. Akbar)	..	40	70
535	1 r. "Fairground" (M. Azam)	..	45	75
536	1 r. 50, "Hockey Match" (M. Tayyab)	60	90
533/6	.. .. .. *Set of 4*	1·60	2·75

(Des Munawar Ahmad)

1980 (18 Sept). *75th Anniv of Command and Staff College, Quetta. P 13.*
537	**296**	1 r. multicoloured	..	10	15

WORLD TOURISM CONFERENCE
MANILA 80
(297)

1980 (27 Sept). *World Tourism Conference, Manila. No. 496 optd with T 297.*
538	1 r. Cheer	..	75	30

298 Birth Centenary Emblem

(Des A. Salahuddin)

1980 (5 Oct). *Birth Centenary of Hafiz Mahmood Shairani. P 13.*
539	**298**	40 p. multicoloured	..	30	75

299 Shalimar Gardens, Lahore

(Des A. Salahuddin)

1980 (23 Oct). *Aga Khan Award for Architecture. P 13.*
540	**299**	2 r. multicoloured	..	40	75

 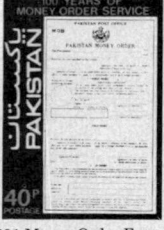

300 Rising Sun   301 Money Order Form

(Des S. Ahmed (40 p.), J. Sultana (2 r.), A. Salahuddin (others))

1980 (10 Nov). *1400th Anniv of Hegira (1st issue). T 300 and similar multicoloured designs. P 14 (2 r.) or 13 (others).*
541	40 p. Type **300**		10	10
542	2 r. Ka'aba and symbols of Moslem achievement (34 × 34 mm)		25	40
543	3 r. Holy Koran illuminating World (31 × 54 mm)		30	60
541/3	.. .. *Set of 3*	55	95
MS544	106 × 84 mm. 4 r. Candles. Imperf	..	45	1·00

See also No. 549.

(Des A. Ahmed)

1980 (20 Dec). *Centenary of Money Order Service. P 13.*
545	**301**	40 p. multicoloured	..	20	60

302 Postcards
encircling Globe

303 Heinrich von Stephan
and U.P.U. Emblem

(Des A. Ahmed)

1980 (27 Dec). *Centenary of Postcard Service. P 13.*
546	**302**	40 p. multicoloured	..	20	60

(Des J. Sultana)

1981 (7 Jan). *150th Birth Anniv of Heinrich von Stephan (founder of U.P.U.). P 13.*
547	**303**	1 r. multicoloured	..	30	20

304 Aircraft and Airmail Letters

(Des J. Sultana)

1981 (15 Feb). *50th Anniv of Airmail Service. P 13.*
548	**304**	1 r. multicoloured	..	60	20

305 Mecca   306 Conference Emblem and
Afghan Refugees

(Des A. Salahuddin)

1981 (7 Mar). *1400th Anniv of Hegira (2nd issue). P 13.*
549	**305**	40 p. multicoloured	..	20	60

(Des Z. Akhlaq (Nos. 550 and 552), A. Ahmed (Nos. 551 and 553), M. Jafree (No. 554))

1981 (29 Mar). *Islamic Summit Conference (1st issue). T 306 and similar multicoloured designs. P 13.*
550	40 p. Type **306**	30	10
551	40 p. Conference emblem encircled by flags and Afghan refugees (28 × 58 mm)	30	10
552	1 r. Type **306**	50	10
553	1 r. As No. 551	50	10
554	2 r. Conference emblem and map showing Afghanistan (48 × 32 mm)	65	50
550/4	.. .. .. *Set of 5*	2·00	75

307 Conference Emblem   308 Kemal Atatürk

(Des A. Salahuddin (Nos. 555, 557), A. Irani (Nos. 556, 558))

1981 (20 Apr). *Islamic Summit Conference (2nd issue). T 307 and similar multicoloured design. P 13.*
555	40 p. Type **307**	10	10
556	40 p. Conference emblem and flags (28 × 46 mm)	10	10
557	85 p. Type **307**	20	40
558	85 p. As No. 556	20	40
555/8	.. .. *Set of 4*	55	90

(Des A. Salahuddin)

1981 (19 May). *Birth Centenary of Kemal Atatürk (Turkish statesman). P 13.*
559	**308**	1 r. multicoloured	..	50	15

309 Green Turtle   310 Dome of the Rock

(Des Jamal. Litho Secura, Singapore)

1981 (20 June). *Wildlife Protection (6th series). Matt, almost invisible PVA gum. P 12 × 11½.*
560	**309**	40 p. multicoloured	..	1·25	40

(Des A. Salahuddin)

1981 (25 July). *Palestinian Welfare. P 13.*
561	**310**	2 r. multicoloured	..	35	35

311 Malubiting West

(Des A. Salahuddin. Litho Secura, Singapore)

1981 (20 Aug). *Mountain Peaks (1st series). Karakoram Range. T 311 and similar multicoloured designs. Matt, almost invisible PVA gum. P 14×13½.*
562	40 p. Type **311** ..	40	40
	a. Horiz pair. Nos. 562/3	80	80
563	40 p. Malubiting West (24 × 31 mm)	40	40
564	1 r. Haramosh	75	75
	a. Horiz pair. Nos. 564/5 ..	1·50	1·50
565	1 r. Haramosh (24 × 31 mm)	75	75
566	1 r. 50, K6	90	1·00
	a. Horiz pair. Nos. 566/7 ..	1·75	2·00
567	1 r. 50, K6 (24 × 31 mm)	90	1·00
568	2 r. K2, Broad Peak, Gasherbrum 4 and Gasherbrum 2	1·00	1·40
	a. Horiz pair. Nos. 568/9 ..	2·00	2·75
569	2 r. K2 (24×31 mm)	1·00	1·40
562/9	*Set of 8*	5·50	6·50

The two designs of each value were printed together, *se-tenant*, in horizontal pairs throughout the sheet.
See also Nos. 674/5.

312 Pakistan Steel   313 Western Tragopan
"Furnace No. 1"

(Des A. Ahmed)

1981 (31 Aug). *First Firing of Pakistan Steel "Furnace No. 1", Karachi. P 13.*
570	**312**	40 p. multicoloured	..	25	10
571		2 r. multicoloured	..	65	1·25

(Litho Secura, Singapore)

1981 (15 Sept). *Wildlife Protection (7th series). Matt, almost invisible PVA gum. P 14.*
572	**313**	40 p. multicoloured	..	1·50	75
573		2 r. multicoloured	..	3·50	4·25

The 2 r. value is as Type **313** but the background design shows a winter view.

---

314 Disabled People and
I.Y.D.P. Emblem

315 World Hockey Cup below
flags of participating Countries

(Des M. Saeed)

1981 (12 Dec). *International Year for Disabled Persons. P* 13.
574 **314** 40 p. multicoloured 30 50
575 2 r. multicoloured .. .. .. 95 1·75

(Des A. Salahuddin)

1982 (31 Jan). *Pakistan—World Cup Hockey Champions. T* **315**
and similar vert design. Multicoloured. P 13.
576 1 r. Type **315** .. .. .. 2·00 1·50
577 1 r. World Hockey Cup above flags of participating countries .. .. .. 2·00 1·50

316 Camel Skin Lamp

317 Chest X-Ray of Infected
Person

(Des A. Salahuddin. Litho Secura, Singapore)

1982 (20 Feb). *Handicrafts* (2nd series). *T* **316** *and similar vert
design. Multicoloured. P* 14.
578 1 r. Type **316** 70 70
579 1 r. Hala pottery 70 70
See also Nos. 595/6.

(Des A. Ahmed)

1982 (24 Mar). *Centenary of Robert Koch's Discovery of Tubercle
Bacillus. P* 13.
580 **317** 1 r. multicoloured .. .. 1·25 90

318 Indus Dolphin

(Des A. Salahuddin. Litho Secura, Singapore)

1982 (24 Apr). *Wildlife Protection* (8th series). *P* 12 × 11½.
581 **318** 40 p. multicoloured .. .. 1·50 1·00
582 — 1 r. multicoloured .. .. 3·00 2·25
The 1 r. value is as Type **318** but the design is reversed.

319 "Apollo–Soyuz" Link-up, 1975

(Des A. Salahuddin)

1982 (7 June). *Peaceful Uses of Outer Space. P* 13.
583 **319** 1 r. multicoloured .. .. 2·00 1·25

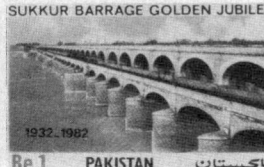

320 Sukkur Barrage

(Des A. Salahuddin)

1982 (17 July). *50th Anniv of Sukkur Barrage. P* 13.
584 **320** 1 r. multicoloured 30 30

RICCIONE – 82.
(322)

321 Pakistan National Flag
and Stylised Sun

(Des A. Ahmed)

1982 (14 Aug). *Independence Day. T* **321** *and similar vert design.
Multicoloured. P* 13.
585 40 p. Type **321** 10 30
586 85 p. Map of Pakistan and stylised torch 20 50

1982 (28 Aug). *"Riccione 82" International Stamp Exhibition. No.
584 optd with T* **322**.
587 **320** 1 r. multicoloured 20 20

323 Arabic Inscription and University Emblem

(Des Syed Tanwir Rizvi)

1982 (14 Oct). *Centenary of the Punjab University. P* 13½ × 13.
588 **323** 40 p. multicoloured 75 30

324 Scout Emblem and Tents   325 Laying Pipeline

(Des M. Saeed)

1982 (23 Dec). *75th Anniv of Boy Scout Movement. P* 13.
589 **324** 2 r. multicoloured 50 45

(Des A. Salahuddin)

1983 (6 Jan). *Inauguration of Quetta Natural Gas Pipeline
Project. P* 13.
590 **325** 1 r. multicoloured 30 20

326 Papilio polyctor

(Litho Secura, Singapore)

1983 (15 Feb). *Butterflies. T* **326** *and similar horiz designs. Multicoloured. Matt, almost invisible PVA gum. P* 13½.
591 40 p. Type **326** .. .. .. 1·25 20
592 50 p. *Atrophaneura aristolochiae* .. 1·50 20
593 60 p. *Danaus chrysippus* .. .. 1·75 60
594 1 r. 50, *Papilio demoleus* .. .. 2·50 2·25
591/4 Set of 4 6·25 3·00

(Litho Secura, Singapore)

1983 (9 Mar). *Handicrafts* (3rd series). *Vert designs as T* **316**.
Multicoloured. Matt, almost invisible PVA gum. P 14.
595 1 r. Five flower motif needlework, Sind .. 15 15
596 1 r. Straw mats 15 15

ALTERED CATALOGUE NUMBERS

Any Catalogue numbers altered from the last
edition are shown as a list in the introductory
pages.

---

327 School of Nursing and University Emblem

(Des A. Salahuddin)

1983 (16 Mar). *Presentation of Charter to Aga Khan University,
Karachi. P* 13½ × 13.
597 **327** 2 r. multicoloured 40 30
No. 597 was issued in sheets of 8 (2 × 4), each horizontal pair
being separated by a different *se-tenant* label showing views of the
University.

328 Yak Caravan crossing
Zindiharam-Darkot Pass, Hindu Kush

(Des A. Salahuddin)

1983 (28 Apr). *Trekking in Pakistan. P* 13.
598 **328** 1 r. multicoloured .. .. 1·50 60

329 Marsh Crocodile

(Litho Secura, Singapore)

1983 (19 May). *Wildlife Protection* (9th series). *Matt, almost invisible PVA gum. P* 13½.
599 **329** 3 r. multicoloured .. .. 3·50 2·00

330 Goitred Gazelle   331 Floral Design

(Litho Secura, Singapore)

1983 (20 June). *Wildlife Protection* (10th series). *Matt, almost
invisible PVA gum. P* 14 × 13½.
600 **330** 1 r. multicoloured .. .. 2·50 2·00

(Des A. Ahmed)

1983 (14 Aug). *36th Anniv of Independence. T* **331** *and similar
vert design. Multicoloured. P* 13.
601 60 p. Type **331** 10 10
602 4 r. Hand holding flaming torch .. 40 45

332 Traditional Weaving, Pakistan

(Des A. Salahuddin)

1983 (19 Aug). *Indonesian–Pakistan Economic and Cultural Co-
operation Organization, 1969–1983. T* **332** *and similar horiz
design. Multicoloured. P* 13.
603 2 r. Type **332** 20 25
604 2 r. Traditional weaving, Indonesia .. 20 25

333 "Siberian Cranes" (Great White Cranes) (Sir Peter Scott)

1983 (8 Sept). *Wildlife Protection* (11th series). P 13.
605 333 3 r. multicoloured .. .. .. 3·00 3·00

334 W.C.Y. Emblem

(Des J. Sultana)

1983 (9 Oct). *World Communications Year. T* **334** *and similar multicoloured design. P* 13 (2 r.) *or* 14 (3 r.).
606 2 r. Type **334** 20 25
607 3 r. W.C.Y. emblem (*different*) (33 × 33 *mm*) 30 35

335 Farm Animals

336 Agricultural Produce and Fertiliser Factory

(Des A. Salahuddin)

1983 (24 Oct). *World Food Day. T* **335** *and similar horiz designs. Multicoloured. P* 13.
608 3 r. Type **335** .. .. .. 1·50 1·75
    a. Horiz strip of 4. Nos. 608/11 5·50
609 3 r. Fruit .. .. .. 1·50 1·75
610 3 r. Crops .. .. .. 1·50 1·75
611 3 r. Sea food .. .. .. 1·50 1·75
608/11 .. .. .. *Set of* 4 5·50 6·00
Nos. 608/11 were printed together, *se-tenant*, in horizontal strips of four throughout the sheet.

(Des J. Sultana)

1983 (24 Oct). *National Fertiliser Corporation. P* 13 × 13½.
612 336 60 p. multicoloured 15 30

337 Lahore, 1852

338 Winner of "Enterprise" Event

(Des A. Salahuddin)

1983 (13 Nov). *National Stamp Exhibition, Lahore. T* **337** *and similar vert designs showing panoramic view of Lahore in* 1852. *Multicoloured. P* 13 × 13½.
613 60 p. Musti Durwaza Dharmsala .. 60 70
    a. Horiz strip of 6. Nos. 613/18 3·25
614 60 p. Khabgha 60 70
615 60 p. Type **337** 60 70
616 60 p. Summan Burj Hazuri .. 60 70
617 60 p. Flower Garden, Samadhi Northern Gate 60 70
618 60 p. Budda Darya, Badshahi Masjid .. 60 70
613/18 .. .. .. *Set of* 6 3·25 3·75
Nos. 613/18 were printed together, *se-tenant* in sheets of twelve, containing two horizontal strips of six.

(Des J. Sultana)

1983 (31 Dec). *Yachting Champions, Asian Games, Delhi. T* **338** *and similar vert design. Multicoloured. P* 13.
619 60 p. Type **338** .. .. .. 1·75 1·75
620 60 p. Winner of "OK" Dinghy event .. 1·75 1·75

339 Snow Leopard

(Litho Secura, Singapore)

1984 (21 Jan). *Wildlife Protection* (12th series). *Matt, almost invisible PVA gum. P* 14.
621 339 40 p. multicoloured .. .. 1·75 90
622 1 r. 60, multicoloured .. .. 4·75 6·00

340 Jahangir Khan (World Squash Champion)

341 P.I.A. Boeing 707 Airliner

(Des A. Salahuddin)

1984 (17 Mar). *Squash. P* 13.
623 340 3 r. multicoloured .. .. 2·25 1·75

(Des A. Salahuddin)

1984 (29 Apr). *20th Anniv of Pakistan International Airways' Service to China. P* 13.
624 341 3 r. multicoloured .. .. 5·00 5·00

342 Glass-work

343 Attock Fort

(Des A. Salahuddin. Litho Secura, Singapore)

1984 (31 May). *Handicrafts* (4th series). *T* **342** *and similar designs showing glass-work in Sheesh Mahal, Lahore Fort. P* 13½.
625 1 r. multicoloured (blue frame) .. 25 15
626 1 r. multicoloured (red frame) .. 25 15
627 1 r. multicoloured (green frame) (*horiz*) 25 15
628 1 r. multicoloured (violet frame) (*horiz*) 25 15
625/8 .. .. .. *Set of* 4 90 55

(Des S. Hyder (15 p.), J. Sultana (others))

1984 (16 June)–**86**. *Forts. T* **343** *and similar horiz designs. P* 11.
629 5 p. brownish black & brown-pur (1.11.84) 10 10
630 10 p. brownish black and rose-red (25.9.84) 10 10
631 15 p. reddish violet & bistre-brown (1.12.86) 10 10
632 20 p. black and bright reddish violet 10 10
    a. Black ptd double .. ..
633 50 p. sepia and Venetian red (10.4.86) 50 10
634 60 p. blackish brown and light brown 30 10
635 70 p. greenish blue (3.8.86) .. 40 10
636 80 p. bistre-brown and dull scarlet (1.7.86) 55 10
629/36 .. .. .. *Set of* 8 1·75 40
Design:—5 p. Kot Diji Fort; 10 p. Rohtas Fort; 15 p. Bala Hissar Fort; 50 p. Hyderabad Fort; 60 p. Lahore Fort; 70 p. Sibi Fort; 80 p. Ranikot Fort.
No. 632a appears to have received two distinct impressions of the black plate rather than an offset from the litho "blanket".
No. 636 can be found on the matt, almost invisible PVA gum in addition to the usual gum arabic.

344 Shah Rukn i Alam's Tomb, Multan

(Des A. Salahuddin)

1984 (26 June). *Aga Khan Award for Architecture. P* 13.
647 344 60 p. multicoloured .. .. 1·75 1·75

345 Radio Mast and Map of World

(Des J. Sultana)

1984 (1 July). *20th Anniv of Asia–Pacific Broadcasting Union. P* 13.
648 345 3 r. multicoloured 80 60

346 Wrestling

(Des A. Salahuddin)

1984 (31 July). *Olympic Games, Los Angeles. T* **346** *and similar horiz designs. P* 13.
649 3 r. Type **346** .. .. .. 1·50 1·50
650 3 r. Boxing .. .. .. 1·50 1·50
651 3 r. Athletics .. .. .. 1·50 1·50
652 3 r. Hockey .. .. .. 1·50 1·50
653 3 r. Yachting .. .. .. 1·50 1·50
649/53 .. .. .. *Set of* 5 6·75 6·75

347 Jasmine (National flower) and Inscription

348 Gearwheel Emblem and Flags of Participating Nations

(Des M. Munawar)

1984 (14 Aug). *Independence Day. T* **347** *and similar horiz design. Multicoloured. P* 13.
654 60 p. Type **347** 10 10
655 4 r. Symbolic torch 45 50

(Des A. Zafar)

1984 (1 Sept). *Pakistan International Trade Fair. P* 13.
656 348 60 p. multicoloured 60 80

349 Interior of Main Dome

(Des A. Salahuddin)

1984 (5 Nov). *Tourism Convention. Shahjahan Mosque, Thatta. T* **349** *and similar horiz designs. Multicoloured. P* 13½.
657 1 r. Type **349** 50 60
    a. Horiz strip of 5. Nos. 657/61 2·25
658 1 r. Brick and glazed tile work .. 50 60
659 1 r. Gateway 50 60
660 1 r. Symmetrical archways .. 50 60
661 1 r. Interior of a dome 50 60
657/61 .. .. .. *Set of* 5 2·25 2·75
Nos. 657/61 were printed together, *se-tenant*, in horizontal strips of 5 throughout the sheet

350 Bank Emblem in Floral Pattern

(Des A. Zafar)

1984 (7 Nov). *25th Anniv of United Bank Ltd. P 13½.*
662 350 60 p. multicoloured 70 70

351 Conference Emblem

352 Postal Life Insurance Emblem within Hands

(Des A. Salahuddin)

1984 (24 Dec). *20th United Nations Conference on Trade and Development. P 14.*
663 351 60 p. multicoloured 70 40

(Des A. Zafar (60 p.), J. Sultana (1 r.))

1984 (29 Dec). *Centenary of Postal Life Insurance. T 352 and similar vert design. Multicoloured. P 13½.*
664 60 p. Type 352 .. .. .. 45 15
665 1 r. "100" and Postal Life Insurance emblem 55 15

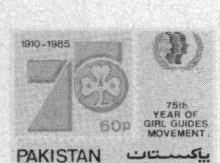

353 Bull (Wall painting)

354 International Youth Year Emblem and "75"

(Des A. Salahuddin and M. Munawar)

1984 (31 Dec). *U.N.E.S.C.O. Save Moenjadoro Campaign. T 353 and similar vert design. Multicoloured. P 13½.*
666 2 r. Type 353 .. .. .. 1·40 1·00
       a. Horiz pair. Nos. 666/7 .. 2·75 2·00
667 2 r. Bull (seal).. .. .. 1·40 1·00
Nos. 666/7 were printed together, *se-tenant*, in horizontal pairs throughout the sheet.

(Des A. Salahuddin)

1985 (6 Jan). *75th Anniv of Girl Guide Movement. P 13½.*
668 354 60 p. multicoloured .. 2·50 1·25

355 Smelting Ore

356 Map of Pakistan and Rays of Sun

(Des Munawar Ahmad (60 p.), J. Sultana (1 r.))

1985 (15 Jan). *Inauguration of Pakistan Steel Corporation. T 355 and similar multicoloured design. P 13.*
669 60 p. Type 355 .. .. 65 25
670 1 r. Pouring molten steel from ladle (28 × 46 mm) .. .. 1·10 25

(Des A. Salahuddin)

1985 (20 Mar). *Presidential Referendum of 19 December 1984. P 13.*
671 356 60 p. multicoloured .. .. 1·00 55

357 Ballot Box and Voting Paper

(Des A. Salahuddin (No. 672), Sultana Shamim Haider (No. 673))

1985 (23 Mar). *March Elections. T 357 and similar multicoloured design. P 13.*
672 1 r. Type 357 .. .. .. 65 15
673 1 r. Minar-e-Qarardad-e-Pakistan Tower, and word "Democracy" (31 × 43 mm) .. 65 15

(Des and litho Secura, Singapore)

1985 (27 May). *Mountain Peaks (2nd series). Horiz designs as T 311. Multicoloured. Matt, almost invisible PVA gum. P 14 × 13½.*
674 40 p. Rakaposhi (Karakoram Range) .. 1·75 75
675 2 r. Nangaparbat (Western Himalayas) .. 3·75 5·00

358 Trophy and Medals from Olympic Games 1984, Asia Cup 1985 and World Cup 1982

(Des A. Salahuddin)

1985 (5 July). *Pakistan Hockey Team "Grand Slam" Success. P 13.*
676 358 1 r. multicoloured .. .. 2·50 1·50

359 King Edward Medical College

(Des Sultana Shamim Haider)

1985 (28 July). *125th Anniv of King Edward Medical College, Lahore. P 13.*
677 359 3 r. multicoloured .. .. 1·75 65

360 Illuminated Inscription in Urdu

(Des A. Salahuddin)

1985 (14 Aug). *Independence Day. T 360 and similar horiz design. Multicoloured. P 13.*
678 60 p. Type 360 .. .. .. 40 50
       a. Sheetlet. Nos. 678/9 × 2 .. 1·40
679 60 p. Illuminated "XXXVIII" (inscr in English).. .. .. .. 40 50
Nos. 678/9 were issued *se-tenant*, both horizontally and vertically, in sheetlets of four stamps and four stamp-size labels inscribed in Urdu.

361 Sind Madressah-tul-Islam, Karachi

(Des A. Salahuddin)

1985 (1 Sept). *Centenary of Sind Madressah-tul-Islam (theological college), Karachi. P 13.*
680 361 2 r. multicoloured .. .. 1·75 70

362 Jamia Masjid Mosque by Day

(Des A. Salahuddin)

1985 (14 Sept). *Inauguration of New Jamia Masjid Mosque, Karachi. T 362 and similar horiz design. Multicoloured. P 13.*
681 1 r. Type 362 .. .. .. 90 35
682 1 r. Jamia Masjid illuminated at night .. 90 35

363 Lawrence College, Murree

(Des A. Salahuddin)

1985 (21 Sept). *125th Anniv of Lawrence College, Murree. P 13.*
683 363 3 r. multicoloured .. .. 2·00 65

364 United Nations Building, New York

(Des A. Salahuddin)

1985 (24 Oct). *40th Anniv of United Nations Organization. T 364 and similar diamond-shaped design. Multicoloured. P 14.*
684 1 r. Type 364 .. .. 30 15
685 2 r. U.N. Building and emblem .. 40 25

365 Tents and Jamboree Emblem

(Des A. Salahuddin)

1985 (8 Nov). *10th National Scout Jamboree. P 13.*
686 365 60 p. multicoloured .. 2·25 2·25

366 Islamabad

367 Map of S.A.A.R.C. Countries and National Flags

(Des H. Durrani)

1985 (30 Nov). *25th Anniv of Islamabad. P 14½ × 14.*
687 366 3 r. multicoloured .. .. 2·00 45

(Des A. Salahuddin)

1985 (8 Dec). *1st Summit Meeting of South Asian Association for Regional Cooperation, Dhaka, Bangladesh. T 367 and similar multicoloured design. P 13½ × 13 (1 r.) or 13 (2 r.).*
688 1 r. Type 367 .. .. .. 1·75 4·50
689 2 r. National flags (39 × 39 mm) .. 1·25 2·25
No. 688 is reported to have been withdrawn on 9 December 1985.

368 Globe and Peace Dove

369 Peregrine Falcon

(Des A. Salahuddin)

1985 (14 Dec). *25th Anniv of U.N. General Assembly's Declaration on Independence for Colonial Territories. P* 13.
690 368 60 p. multicoloured .. .. 1·00 60

(Des and litho Secura, Singapore)

1986 (20 Jan). *Wildlife Protection* (13th series). *Peregrine Falcon. Matt, almost invisible PVA gum. P* 13½.
691 369 1 r. 50, multicoloured .. 4·25 4·25

370 A.D.B.P. Building, Islamabad

(Des A. Salahuddin)

1986 (18 Feb). *25th Anniv of Agricultural Development Bank of Pakistan. P* 13.
692 370 60 p. multicoloured .. .. .. 1·00 50

371 Government S.E. College   **372** Emblem and Bar Graph

(Des Sultana Shamim Haider)

1986 (25 Apr). *Centenary of Government Sadiq Egerton College, Bahawalpur. P* 13.
693 371 1 r. multicoloured .. .. .. 1·75 40

(Des Sultana Shamim Haider)

1986 (11 May). *25th Anniv of Asian Productivity Organization. P* 13½.
694 372 1 r. multicoloured .. .. .. 1·75 30

373 "1947 1986"   **374** Open Air Class

(Des A. Salahuddin (80 p.), M. Munawar (1 r.))

1986 (14 Aug). *39th Anniv of Independence. T* **373** *and similar vert design. Multicoloured. P* 14.
695 80 p. Type **373**. 65 15
696 1 r. Illuminated inscription in Urdu .. 65 15

(Des Sultana Shamim Haider)

1986 (8 Sept). *International Literacy Day. P* 13.
697 374 1 r. multicoloured 85 30

375 Mother and Child   **376** Aitchison College

1986 (28 Oct). *U.N.I.C.E.F. Child Survival Campaign. P* 13½ × 13.
698 375 80 p. multicoloured .. .. .. 1·50 30

(Des A. Salahuddin)

1986 (3 Nov). *Centenary of Aitchison College, Lahore. P* 13½.
699 376 2 r. 50, multicoloured 45 30

377 Two Doves carrying Olive Branches   **378** Table Tennis Players

(Des Sultana Shamim Haider)

1986 (20 Nov). *International Peace Year. P* 13.
700 377 4 r. multicoloured 50 50

(Des A. Salahuddin)

1986 (25 Nov). *4th Asian Cup Table Tennis Tournament, Karachi. P* 14.
701 378 2 r. multicoloured .. .. .. 2·00 65

379 Argali

(Des M. Jamal. Litho Secura, Singapore)

1986 (4 Dec). *Wildlife Protection* (14th series). *Argali. Matt, almost invisible PVA gum. P* 14.
702 379 2 r. multicoloured .. .. .. 3·00 3·00

380 Selimiye Mosque, Edirne, Turkey

(Des A. Salahuddin)

1986 (20 Dec). *"Ecophilex '86" International Stamp Exhibition, Islamabad. T* **380** *and similar vert designs. Multicoloured. P* 13.
703 3 r. Type **380** .. .. .. 1·40 1·60
  a. Horiz strip of 3. Nos. 703/5 .. .. 3·75
704 3 r. Gawhar Shad Mosque, Mashhad, Iran .. 1·40 1·60
705 3 r. Grand Mosque, Bhong, Pakistan .. 1·40 1·60
703/5 .. .. *Set of* 3 3·75 4·25
Nos. 703/5 were printed together, *se-tenant*, in horizontal strips of three, within sheetlets of 12.

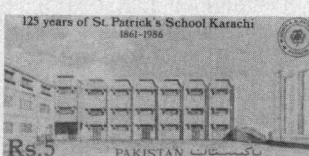

381 St. Patrick's School

(Des A. Salahuddin)

1987 (29 Jan). *125th Anniv of St. Patrick's School, Karachi. P* 13.
706 381 5 r. multicoloured .. .. .. 1·75 90

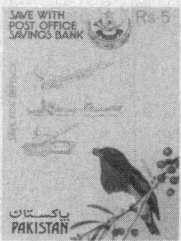

382 Mistletoe Flowerpecker and Defence Symbols

(Des A. Salahuddin)

1987 (21 Feb). *Post Office Savings Bank Week. T* **382** *and similar vert designs, each showing a different bird. Multicoloured. P* 13.
707 5 r. Type **382** .. .. .. 1·10 70
  a. Block of 4. Nos. 707/10 .. .. 4·00
708 5 r. Spotted Pardalote and laboratory apparatus .. .. 1·10 70
709 5 r. Black-throated Blue Warbler and agriculture symbols .. .. .. 1·10 70
710 5 r. Red-capped Manakin and industrial skyline .. .. 1·10 70
707/10 .. .. *Set of* 4 4·00 2·50
Nos. 707/10 were printed together, *se-tenant*, in blocks of four throughout the sheet of 32 which contained six blocks of four and eight labels in the left and right-hand vertical columns.

383 New Parliament House, Islamabad

(Des A. Salahuddin)

1987 (23 Mar). *Inauguration of New Parliament House, Islamabad. P* 13.
711 383 3 r. multicoloured 30 30

384 Opium Poppies and Flames

(Des A. Salahuddin)

1987 (30 June). *Campaign against Drug Abuse. P* 13.
712 384 1 r. multicoloured 45 20

385 Flag and National Anthem Score

(Des A. Salahuddin)

1987 (14 Aug). *40th Anniv of Independence. T* **385** *and similar horiz design. Multicoloured. P* 13.
713 80 p. Type **385**. 35 10
714 3 r. Text of speech by Mohammed Ali Jinnah, Minar-e-Qardad-e-Pakistan Tower and arms 90 25

386 Hawker Tempest Mk II

(Des M. Hussaini and A. Salahuddin)

1987 (7 Sept). *Air Force Day. T* **386** *and similar horiz designs showing military aircraft. Multicoloured. P* 13½.
715 3 r. Type **386** .. .. .. 1·25 1·25
  a. Sheetlet. Nos. 715/24 .. .. 11·00
716 3 r. Hawker Fury .. .. .. 1·25 1·25
717 3 r. Supermarine Attacker .. .. 1·25 1·25
718 3 r. North American F-86 Sabre .. 1·25 1·25
719 3 r. Lockheed F-104C Starfighter .. 1·25 1·25
720 3 r. Lockheed C-130 Hercules .. 1·25 1·25
721 3 r. Shenyang/Tianjin F-6 .. .. 1·25 1·25
722 3 r. Dassault Mirage III .. .. 1·25 1·25
723 3 r. North American A-5A Vigilante .. 1·25 1·25
724 3 r. General Dynamics F-16 Fighting Falcon .. .. 1·25 1·25
715/24 .. .. *Set of* 10 11·00 11·00
Nos. 715/24 were printed together, *se-tenant*, in sheetlets of 10.

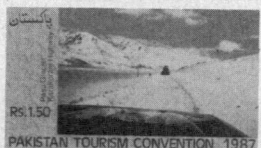

387 Pasu Glacier

(Des A. Salahuddin)

1987 (1 Oct). *Pakistan Tourism Convention.* T **387** *and similar horiz designs showing views along Karakoram Highway. Multicoloured.* P 13.

725	1 r. 50, Type 387	..	..	60	40
	a. Block of 4. Nos. 725/8	..	..	2·25	
726	1 r. 50, Apricot trees	..	..	60	40
727	1 r. 50, Karakoram Highway	..	..	60	40
728	1 r. 50, View from Khunjerab Pass	..	60	40
725/8			*Set of* 4	2·25	1·40

Nos. 725/8 were printed together, *se-tenant*, in blocks of four throughout the sheet of 24.

388 Shah Abdul Latif Bhitai Mausoleum

(Des A. Salahuddin)

1987 (8 Oct). *Shah Abdul Latif Bhitai (poet) Commemoration.* P 13.

729	388	80 p. multicoloured	..	20	20

389 D. J. Sind Science College, Karachi

(Des Sultana Shamim Haider)

1987 (7 Nov). *Centenary of D. J. Sind Science College, Karachi.* P 13.

730	389	80 p. multicoloured	..	20	20

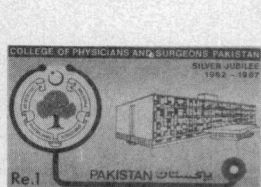

390 College Building   391 Homeless People, Houses and Rising Sun

(Des Sultana Shamim Haider)

1987 (9 Dec). *25th Anniv of College of Physicians and Surgeons.* P 13.

731	390	1 r. multicoloured	..	50	20

(Des Sultana Shamim Haider)

1987 (15 Dec). *International Year of Shelter for the Homeless.* P 13.

732	391	3 r. multicoloured	..	30	30

392 Cathedral Church of the Resurrection, Lahore

(Des A. Salahuddin)

1987 (20 Dec). *Centenary of Cathedral Church of the Resurrection, Lahore.* P 13.

733	392	3 r. multicoloured	..	30	30

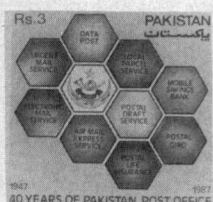

393 Honeycomb and Arms

(Des A. Salahuddin)

1987 (28 Dec). *40th Anniv of Pakistan Post Office.* P 13.

734	393	3 r. multicoloured	..	30	30

394 Corporation Emblem

(Des A. Salahuddin)

1987 (31 Dec). *Radio Pakistan's New Programme Schedules.* P 13.

735	394	80 p. multicoloured	..	15	15

395 Jamshed Nusserwanjee Mehta and Karachi Municipal Corporation Building   396 Leprosy Symbols within Flower

(Des A. Salahuddin)

1988 (7 Jan). *Birth Centenary (1986) of Jamshed Nusserwanjee Mehta (former President of Karachi Municipal Corporation).* P 13.

736	395	3 r. multicoloured	..	30	30

(Des Sultana Shamim Haider)

1988 (31 Jan). *World Leprosy Day.* P 13.

737	396	3 r. multicoloured	..	75	30

397 W.H.O. Building, Geneva

(Des A. Salahuddin)

1988 (7 Apr). *40th Anniv of World Health Organization.* P 13.

738	397	4 r. multicoloured	..	60	35

398 Globe   399 Crescent, Leaf Pattern and Archway

1988 (8 May). *125th Anniv of International Red Cross and Crescent.* P 13.

739	398	3 r. multicoloured	..	30	30

(Des A. Salahuddin)

1988 (14 Aug). *Independence Day.* P 13½.

740	399	80 p. multicoloured	..	10	10
741		4 r. multicoloured	..	25	30

400 Field Events

(Des A. Salahuddin)

1988 (17 Sept). *Olympic Games, Seoul.* T **400** *and similar horiz designs. Multicoloured.* P 13.

742	10 r. Type 400	..	..	1·10	1·10
	a. Sheetlet. Nos. 742/51	..	10·00	
743	10 r. Track events	..	..	1·10	1·10
744	10 r. Jumping and pole vaulting	..	1·10	1·10
745	10 r. Gymnastics	..	..	1·10	1·10
746	10 r. Table tennis, tennis, hockey and baseball		1·10	1·10
747	10 r. Volleyball, football, basketball and handball		1·10	1·10
748	10 r. Wrestling, judo, boxing and weight-lifting		1·10	1·10
749	10 r. Shooting, fencing and archery	..	1·10	1·10
750	10 r. Water sports	..	..	1·10	1·10
751	10 r. Equestrian events and cycling	..	1·10	1·10
742/51		*Set of* 10	10·00	10·00

Nos. 742/51 were issued, *se-tenant*, in sheetlets of ten stamps and thirty-six half stamp-size labels.

401 Markhor

(Litho Secura, Singapore)

1988 (29 Oct). *Wildlife Protection (15th series). Markhor. Matt, almost invisible PVA gum.* P 14.

752	401	2 r. multicoloured	..	40	40

402 Islamia College, Peshawar

(Des A. Salahuddin)

1988 (22 Dec). *75th Anniv of Islamia College, Peshawar.* P 13½.

753	402	3 r. multicoloured	..	30	30

403 Symbols of Agriculture, Industry and Education with National Flags

(Des Sultana Shamim Haider (25 r.), G. M. Shaikh (50 r.), A. Salahuddin (75 r.))

1988 (29 Dec). *South Asian Association for Regional Co-operation, 4th Summit Meeting, Islamabad.* T **403** *and similar multicoloured designs.* P 13 (25 r.), 14 (50 r.) or 13½×13 (75 r.).

754	25 r. Type 403	..	1·50	1·50
755	50 r. National flags on globe and symbols of communications (33×33 mm)		3·25	3·25
756	75 r. Stamps from member countries (52×29 mm)		4·50	4·50
754/6		*Set of* 3	8·25	8·25

No. 755 was printed in sheets of eight stamps and stamp-size label, showing the S.A.A.R.C. emblem, in the central position.

(Des A. Salahuddin)

1989 (23 Jan). *Pioneers of Freedom (2nd series). Diamond-shaped design as* T **282**. *Multicoloured.* W **98**. P 14.

757	3 r. Maulana Hasrat Mohani	..	15	20

404 Logo

405 Zulfikar Ali Bhutto

(Des A. Salahuddin)

1989 (18 Feb). *"Adasia 89" 16th Asian Advertising Congress, Lahore.* P 13.
758	404	1 r. mult ("Pakistan" in yellow)	..	95	95
		a. Sheetlet. Nos. 758/60, each × 3	7·00		
759		1 r. mult ("Pakistan" in turquoise-bl)		95	95
760		1 r. mult ("Pakistan" in white)		95	95
758/60			Set of 3	2·50	2·50

Nos. 758/60 were printed together, *se-tenant*, in horizontal and vertical strips of three within the sheetlets of nine.

(Des A. Munir (1 r.), A. Salahuddin (2 r.))

1989 (4 Apr). *10th Death Anniv of Zulfikar Ali Bhutto (statesman). T* **405** *and similar vert design. Multicoloured.* P 13.
761		1 r. Type **405**	..	15	10
762		2 r. Zulfikar Ali Bhutto *(different)*	..	20	20

406 "Daphne" Class Submarine

(Des A. Salahuddin)

1989 (1 June). *25 Years of Pakistan Navy Submarine Operations. T* **406** *and similar horiz designs. Multicoloured.* P 13½.
763		1 r. Type **406**	..	1·10	1·10
		a. Vert strip of 3. Nos. 763/5	..	3·00	
764		1 r. "Fleet Snorkel" class submarine	..	1·10	1·10
765		1 r. "Agosta" class submarine	..	1·10	1·10
763/5			Set of 3	3·00	3·00

Nos. 763/5 were printed together, *se-tenant*, in vertical strips of three throughout the sheet.

407 "The Oath of the Tennis Court" (David)

(Des A. Salahuddin)

1989 (24 June). *Bicentenary of French Revolution.* P 13½.
766	407	7 r. multicoloured	..	1·75	90

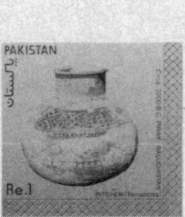

408 Pitcher, *c.* 2200 B.C.

409 Satellites and Map of Asian Telecommunications Network

(Des A. Salahuddin)

1989 (28 June). *Archaeological Artifacts. T* **408** *and similar square designs showing terracotta pottery from Baluchistan Province. Multicoloured.* P 14.
767		1 r. Type **408**		15	15
		a. Block of 4. Nos. 767/70		55	
768		1 r. Jar, *c.* 2300 B.C.	..	15	15
769		1 r. Vase, *c.* 3600 B.C.	..	15	15
770		1 r. Jar, *c.* 2600 B.C.	..	15	15
767/70			Set of 4	55	55

Nos. 767/70 were printed together, *se-tenant*, in blocks of four throughout the sheet.

(Des G. Shaikh)

1989 (1 July). *10th Anniv of Asia-Pacific Telecommunity.* P 13½.
771	409	3 r. multicoloured	..	30	30

410 Container Ship at Wharf

411 Mohammed Ali Jinnah

(Des A. Salahuddin)

1989 (5 Aug). *Construction of Integrated Container Terminal, Port Qasim.* P 14.
772	410	6 r. multicoloured	..	3·00	3·50

(Des A. Salahuddin. Eng A. Munir. Recess and litho)

1989 (14 Aug). W **98**. P 13.
773	411	1 r. multicoloured	..	35	10
		a. Wmk sideways	..		
		w. Wmk inverted	..		
774		1 r. 50, multicoloured		45	20
775		2 r. multicoloured		55	30
		a. Head omitted	..		
		b. Wmk sideways	..		
776		3 r. multicoloured	..	70	40
777		4 r. multicoloured	..	85	45
		w. Wmk inverted	..		
778		5 r. multicoloured	..	95	60
773/8			Set of 6	3·50	1·90

No. 775a occurs on the last vertical row of a sheet and shows the sepia head completely omitted together with almost all the oval frame.

Examples of Nos. 773/8 overprinted "NATIONAL SEMINAR ON PHILATELY MULTAN 1992" as a continuous pattern were available at this event on 15 and 16 April 1992.

Details of authorisation by the Pakistan Post Offices and of availability at Multan are disputed, but, even if officially sanctioned, these overprints do not fulfil the criteria for catalogue listing due to their limited availability. They were not available from any post office other than Multan and, it is reported, only forty-five sheets of each of the three higher values were overprinted.

412 Mausoleum of Shah Abdul Latif Bhitai

413 Asiatic Black Bear

(Des A. Salahuddin)

1989 (16 Sept). *300th Birth Anniv of Shah Abdul Latif Bhitai (poet).* P 13.
779	412	2 r. multicoloured	..	20	20

COMMONWEALTH MEMBER

Pakistan rejoined the Commonwealth on 1 October 1989.

(Des A. McCoy)

1989 (7 Oct). *Wildlife Protection (16th series). Asiatic Black Bear. T* **413** *and similar horiz designs. Multicoloured.* P 13½.
780		4 r. Type **413**	..	90	1·10
		a. Block of 4. Nos. 780/3	..	3·25	
781		4 r. Bear among boulders	..	90	1·10
782		4 r. Standing on rock	..	90	1·10
783		4 r. Sitting by trees	..	90	1·10
780/3			Set of 4	3·25	4·00

Nos. 780/3 were printed together, *se-tenant*, in blocks of 4 throughout the sheet.

414 Ear of Wheat encircling Globe

415 Games Emblem and Flags of Member Countries

(Des A. Salahuddin)

1989 (16 Oct). *World Food Day.* P 14×12½.
784	414	1 r. multicoloured	..	35	35

(Des A. Salahuddin)

1989 (20 Oct). *4th South Asian Sports Federation Games, Islamabad.* P 13.
785	415	1 r. multicoloured	..	35	35

416 Patchwork Kamblee (cloth) entering Gate of Heaven

(Des Farah and Fareeda Batul)

1989 (20 Oct). *800th Birth Anniv of Baba Farid (Muslim spiritual leader).* P 13.
786	416	3 r. multicoloured	..	30	30

417 Pakistan Television Logo

418 Family of Drug Addicts in Poppy Bud

(Des A. Salahuddin)

1989 (26 Nov). *25th Anniv of Television Broadcasting in Pakistan.* P 13½.
787	417	3 r. multicoloured	..	30	30

(Des M. Munawar)

1989 (8 Dec). *South Asian Association for Regional Co-operation Anti-Drugs Campaign.* P 13.
788	418	7 r. multicoloured	..	1·40	85

419 Murray College, Sialkot

(Des A. Salahuddin)

1989 (18 Dec). *Centenary of Murray College, Sialkot.* P 14.
789	419	6 r. multicoloured	..	50	70

420 Government College, Lahore

(Des N. Sheikh)

1989 (21 Dec). *125th Anniv of Government College, Lahore.* P 13.
790	420	6 r. multicoloured	..	50	80

421 Fields, Electricity Pylons and Rural Buildings

(Des A. Salahuddin)

1989 (31 Dec). *10th Anniv of Centre for Asia and Pacific Integrated Rural Development.* P 13.
791 421 3 r. multicoloured 55 65

422 Emblem and Islamic Patterns

(Des A. Salahuddin)

1990 (9 Feb). *20th Anniv of Organization of the Islamic Conference.* P 13.
792 422 1 r. multicoloured 50 20

423 Hockey Match

(Des M. Khan)

1990 (12 Feb). *7th World Hockey Cup, Lahore.* P 13½.
793 423 2 r. multicoloured .. .. .. 3·75 3·75

424 Mohammed Iqbal addressing Crowd and Liaquat Ali Khan taking Oath

(Des A. Zafar (1 r.), A. Salahuddin (7 r.))

1990 (23 Mar). *50th Anniv of Passing of Pakistan Resolution. T* 424 *and similar multicoloured designs.* P 13 (1 r.) or 13½ (7 r.).
794 1 r. Type 424 .. .. 80 90
  a. Horiz strip of 3. Nos. 794/6 .. 2·25
795 1 r. Maulana Mohammad Ali Jauhar and Mohammed Ali Jinnah with banner .. 80 90
796 1 r. Women with Pakistan flag, and Mohammed Ali Jinnah taking Governor-General's oath. 1947 .. 80 90
797 7 r. Minar-i-Qarardad-e-Pakistan Monument and Resolution in Urdu and English (86×42 mm) .. .. 1·75 2·25
794/7 .. .. .. Set of 4 3·75 4·50
Nos. 794/6 were printed together, *se-tenant*, in horizontal strips of 3 throughout the sheet, each strip forming a composite design.

425 Pregnant Woman resting

(Des Family Planning Association of Pakistan)

1990 (24 Mar). *"Safe Motherhood" South Asia Conference, Lahore.* P 13½.
798 425 5 r. multicoloured 75 75

PRICES OF SETS

Set prices are given for many issues, generally those containing three stamps or more. Definitive sets include one of each value or major colour change, but do not cover different perforations, die types or minor shades. Where a choice is possible the set prices are based on the cheapest versions of the stamps included in the listings.

426 "Decorated Verse by Ghalib" (Shakir Ali)

(Des A. Salahuddin)

1990 (19 Apr). *Painters of Pakistan (1st series). Shakir Ali.* P 13½×13.
799 426 1 r. multicoloured .. .. 1·25 75
See also Nos. 856/7.

427 Satellite in Night Sky

(Des S. Afsar)

1990 (26 July). *Launch of "Badr 1" Satellite.* P 13.
800 427 3 r. multicoloured .. .. 2·50 2·50

428 Allama Mohammed Iqbal

(Des S. Akhtar)

1990 (14 Aug). *Pioneers of Freedom (3rd series). T* 428 *and similar vert designs. Each brown and green.* P 13.
801 1 r. Type 428 .. .. .. 25 25
  a. Sheetlet. Nos. 801/9 .. 2·00
802 1 r. Mohammed Ali Jinnah .. 25 25
803 1 r. Sir Syed Ahmad Khan .. 25 25
804 1 r. Nawab Salimullah .. 25 25
805 1 r. Mohtarma Fatima Jinnah .. 25 25
806 1 r. Aga Khan III .. 25 25
807 1 r. Nawab Mohammad Ismail Khan 25 25
808 1 r. Hussain Shaheed Suhrawardy .. 25 25
809 1 r. Syed Ameer Ali .. 25 25
810 1 r. Nawab Bahadur Yar Jung .. 25 25
  a. Sheetlet. Nos. 810/18 .. 2·00
811 1 r. Khawaja Nazimuddin .. 25 25
812 1 r. Maulana Obaidullah Sindhi .. 25 25
813 1 r. Sahibzada Abdul Qaiyum Khan 25 25
814 1 r. Begum Jahanara Shah Nawaz .. 25 25
815 1 r. Sir Ghulam Hussain Hidayatullah 25 25
816 1 r. Qazi Mohammad Isa .. 25 25
817 1 r. Sir M. Shahnawaz Khan Mamdot 25 25
818 1 r. Pir Sahib of Manki Sharif .. 25 25
819 1 r. Liaquat Ali Khan .. 25 25
  a. Sheetlet. Nos. 819/27 .. 2·00
820 1 r. Maulvi A. K. Fazl-ul-Haq .. 25 25
821 1 r. Allama Shabbir Ahmad Usmani 25 25
822 1 r. Sadar Abdur Rab Nishtar .. 25 25
823 1 r. Bi Amma .. 25 25
824 1 r. Sir Abdullah Haroon .. 25 25
825 1 r. Chaudhry Rahmat Ali .. 25 25
826 1 r. Raja Sahib of Mahmudabad .. 25 25
827 1 r. Hassanally Effendi .. 25 25
801/27 .. .. Set of 27 6·00 6·00
Nos. 801/9, 810/18 and 819/27 were printed together, *se-tenant*, in sheetlets of nine.
See also Nos. 838/46, 870/2, 904/6, 921/8, 961/2, 1007, 1019/20 and 1075/7.

429 Cultural Aspects of Indonesia and Pakistan

(Des J. Engineer)

1990 (19 Aug). *Indonesia–Pakistan Economic and Cultural Cooperation Organization.* P 13.
828 429 7 r. multicoloured .. .. 1·00 1·00

430 Globe, Open Book and Pen

(Des S. Afsar)

1990 (8 Sept). *International Literacy Year.* P 13.
829 430 3 r. multicoloured .. 90 1·25

431 College Crests   432 Children and Globe

(Des I. Gilani)

1990 (22 Sept). *Joint Meeting between Royal College of Physicians, Edinburgh, and College of Physicians and Surgeons, Pakistan.* P 13.
830 431 2 r. multicoloured 60 45

(Des A. Salahuddin)

1990 (29 Sept). *U. N. World Summit for Children, New York.* P 13.
831 432 7 r. multicoloured 55 75

433 Girl within Members' Flags

(Des A. Salahuddin)

1990 (21 Nov). *South Asian Association for Regional Co-operation Year of Girl Child.* P 13½.
832 433 2 r. multicoloured 70 75

434 Paper passing over Rollers   435 Civil Defence Worker protecting Islamabad

(Des I. Gilani)

1990 (8 Dec). *25th Anniv of Security Papers Limited.* P 13.
833 434 3 r. multicoloured .. .. 1·00 1·25
  a. Red ("25 YEARS OF SECURITY PAPERS LTD") omitted .. 60·00

(Des I. Jillani)

1991 (1 Mar). *International Civil Defence Day.* P 13.
834 435 7 r. multicoloured .. .. 1·25 1·50

436 Logo and Flags of Member Countries

(Des A. Salahuddin)

1991 (12 Mar). *South and West Asia Postal Union Commemoration.* P 13.
835 **436** 5 r. multicoloured .. .. 1·60 1·90

437 Globe and Figures

(Des S. Afsar)

1991 (11 July). *World Population Day.* P 13.
836 **437** 10 r. multicoloured .. .. 1·90 2·25

438 Mentally   **439** Habib Bank
Handicapped Athlete   Headquarters and Emblem

(Des A. Salahuddin)

1991 (19 July). *Pakistan Participation in Special Olympic Games.* P 13.
837 **438** 7 r. multicoloured .. .. 1·75 2·25

1991 (14 Aug). *Pioneers of Freedom (4th series). Vert designs as T 428. Each brown and green.* P 13.
838   1 r. Maulana Zafar Ali Khan .. 30 30
   a. Sheetlet. Nos. 838/46 .. 2·40
839   1 r. Maulana Mohamed Ali Jauhar 30 30
840   1 r. Chaudhry Khaliquzzaman .. 30 30
841   1 r. Hameed Nizami .. 30 30
842   1 r. Begum Ra'ana Liaquat Ali Khan 30 30
843   1 r. Mirza Abol Hassan Ispahani .. 30 30
844   1 r. Raja Ghazanfar Ali Khan .. 30 30
845   1 r. Malik Barkat Ali .. 30 30
846   1 r. Mir Jaffer Khan Jamali .. 30 30
838/46   *Set of 9* 2·40 2·40
Nos. 838/46 were printed together, *se-tenant*, as a sheetlet of nine.

(Des I. Jillani)

1991 (25 Aug). *50th Anniv of Habib Bank.* P 13.
847 **439** 1 r. multicoloured 40 10
848   5 r. multicoloured .. .. 2·25 2·75

440 St. Joseph's Convent School

(Des A. Salahuddin)

1991 (8 Sept). *130th Anniv (1992) of St. Joseph's Convent School, Karachi.* P 13.
849 **440** 5 r. multicoloured .. .. 2·25 2·50

441 Emperor Sher   **442** Jinnah Antarctic Research
Shah Suri   Station

(Des S. Akhtar)

1991 (5 Oct). *Emperor Sher Shah Suri (founder of road network) Commemoration. Multicoloured.* P 13.
850   5 r. Type **441** .. .. 1·50 2·00
MS851 92×80 mm. 7 r. Emperor on horseback and portrait as Type **441**. Imperf .. 1·40 2·25

(Des I. Jillani)

1991 (28 Oct). *Pakistan Scientific Expedition to Antarctica.* P 13.
852 **442** 7 r. multicoloured .. .. 2·50 2·25

443 Houbara Bustard   **444** Mosque

1991 (4 Nov). *Wildlife Protection (17th series).* P 13.
853 **443** 7 r. multicoloured .. .. 2·00 2·25

(Des I. Jillani)

1991 (22 Nov). *300th Death Anniv of Hazrat Sultan Bahoo.* P 13.
854 **444** 7 r. multicoloured 70 80

445 Development
Symbols and Map of
Asia

(Des G. Shaikh)

1991 (19 Dec). *25th Anniv of Asian Development Bank.* P 13.
855 **445** 7 r. multicoloured .. .. 1·50 1·75

(Des A. Salahuddin)

1991 (24 Dec). *Painters of Pakistan (2nd series). Horiz designs as T 426. Multicoloured.* P 13½×13.
856   1 r. "Procession" (Haji Muhammad Sharif) 1·25 1·25
857   1 r. "Women harvesting" (Ustad Allah Bux) 1·25 1·25

446 American Express Travellers Cheques of 1891 and
1991

(Des A. Salahuddin)

1991 (26 Dec). *Centenary of American Express Travellers Cheques.* P 13½.
858 **446** 7 r. multicoloured .. .. 1·75 2·00

447 Flag, Banknote and Banking
Equipment

1992 (8 Apr). *1st Anniv of Muslim Commercial Bank Privatisation. T 447 and similar horiz design. Multicoloured.* P 13.
859   1 r. Type **447** 10 10
860   7 r. Flag with industrial and commercial scenes 45 60

448 Imran Khan   **449** "Rehber-1" Rocket and
(team captain) and   Satellite View of Earth
Trophy

(Des I. Jillani (2 r.), A. Salahuddin (5 r.), M. Ahmed (7 r.))

1992 (27 Apr). *Pakistan's Victory in World Cricket Championship. T 448 and similar multicoloured designs.* P 13.
861   2 r. Type **448** 70 70
862   5 r. Trophy and national flags (*horiz*) 1·50 1·50
863   7 r. Pakistani flag, trophy and symbolic cricket ball .. .. 1·75 1·75
861/3   *Set of 3* 3·50 3·50

(Des I. Jillani (1 r.), S. Afsar (2 r.))

1992 (7 June). *International Space Year. T 449 and similar horiz design. Multicoloured.* P 13.
864   1 r. Type **449** 15 10
865   2 r. Satellite orbiting Earth and logo 20 20

450 Surgical Instruments   **451** Globe and Symbolic Family

(Des S. Afsar)

1992 (5 July). *Industries. T 450 and similar horiz designs. Multicoloured.* P 13½.
866   10 r. Type **450** 60 80
   a. Horiz strip of 3. Nos. 866/8 .. 2·40
867   15 r. Leather goods .. .. 75 1·00
868   25 r. Sports equipment .. .. 1·25 1·50
866/8   *Set of 3* 2·40 3·00
Nos. 866/8 were printed together, *se-tenant*, in horizontal strips of three throughout the sheet.

(Des S. Afsar)

1992 (25 July). *Population Day.* P 13.
869 **451** 6 r. multicoloured 80 90

(Des S. Akhtar)

1992 (14 Aug). *Pioneers of Freedom (5th series). Vert designs as T 428. Each brown and green.* P 13.
870   1 r. Syed Suleman Nadvi .. 75 75
   a. Horiz strip of 3. Nos. 870/2 .. 2·00
871   1 r. Nawab Iftikhar Hussain Khan Mamdot 75 75
872   1 r. Maulana Muhammad Shibli Naumani 75 75
870/2   *Set of 3* 2·00 2·00
Nos. 870/2 were printed together, *se-tenant*, in horizontal strips of three throughout a sheetlet of nine.

452 Scout Badge   **453** College Building
and Salute

(Des I. Jillani)

1992 (23 Aug). *6th Islamic Scout Jamboree and 4th Islamic Scouts Conference. T 452 and similar vert design. Multicoloured.* P 14×13.
873   6 r. Type **452** 50 75
874   6 r. Conference centre and scout salute .. 50 75

1992 (1 Nov). *Centenary of Islamia College, Lahore.* P 13.
875 **453** 3 r. multicoloured 35 50

454 *Viola odorata* (flower) and
Symbolic Drug Manufacture

(Des S. Afsar)

1992 (22 Nov). *Medicinal Plants (1st series).* P 13.
876 **454** 6 r. multicoloured .. .. 1·25 1·40
See also Nos. 903, 946, 1010, 1026, 1037 and 1099.

NEW INFORMATION

The editor is always interested to correspond with people who have new information that will improve or correct the Catalogue.

455 Emblem

(Des A. Salahuddin)

1992 (28 Nov). *Extraordinary Ministerial Council Session of Economic Co-operation Organization, Islamabad. P* 13.
877 455 7 r. multicoloured .. .. .. 85 1·00

456 Emblems and Field   457 Alhambra Palace,
Granada, Spain

(Des A. Salahuddin)

1992 (5 Dec). *International Conference on Nutrition, Rome. P* 14.
878 456 7 r. multicoloured 70 90

(Des A. Salahuddin)

1992 (14 Dec). *Cultural Heritage of Muslim Granada. P* 13.
879 457 7 r. multicoloured 70 90

458 Mallard   459 Baluchistan
Costume

Four different versions of designs as T **458**:
Type A. "Rs.5" at right with rainbow 8 mm beneath "P" of "PAKISTAN"
Type B. "Rs.5" at right with rainbow 2 mm beneath "P"
Type C. "Rs.5" at left with rainbow 2 mm beneath "N" of "PAKISTAN"
Type D. "Rs.5" at left with rainbow 8 mm beneath "N"

(Des A. Salahuddin)

1992 (31 Dec). *Water Birds. T* **458** *and similar vert designs. Multicoloured. P* 14×13.
880   5 r. Type 458 (A) 60 60
     a. Sheetlet. Nos. 880/95 .. .. 8·50
881   5 r. Type 458 (B) 60 60
882   5 r. Type 458 (C) 60 60
883   5 r. Type 458 (D) 60 60
884   5 r. Greylag Goose (A) 60 60
885   5 r. As No. 884 (B) 60 60
886   5 r. As No. 884 (C) 60 60
887   5 r. As No. 884 (D) 60 60
888   5 r. Gadwall (A) .. (A) 60 60
889   5 r. As No. 888 (B) 60 60
890   5 r. As No. 888 (C) 60 60
891   5 r. As No. 888 (D) 60 60
892   5 r. Common Shelduck (A) 60 60
893   5 r. As No. 892 (B) 60 60
894   5 r. As No. 892 (C) 60 60
895   5 r. As No. 892 (D) 60 60
880/95 .. .. *Set of* 16 8·50 8·50
Nos. 880/95 were printed together, *se-tenant,* in sheetlets of 16 (4×4). Stamps in the first two vertical rows show the face value at right and those in the last two show it at left. Each horizontal row shows a rainbow which curves across the tops of the designs. The four different bird designs are repeated in different positions on each horizontal row. Row 1 contains Nos. 880 (A), 885 (B), 890 (C) and 895 (D). Row 2 commences with No. 884 (A) and ends with No. 883 (D) and the sequence continues on the other rows.

(Des S. Rahman)

1993 (10 Mar). *Women's Traditional Costumes. T* **459** *and similar vert designs. Multicoloured. P* 13.
896   6 r. Type 459 .. .. .. 1·25 1·50
897   6 r. Punjab .. .. .. 1·25 1·50
898   6 r. Sindh .. .. .. 1·25 1·50
899   6 r. North-west Frontier Province .. 1·25 1·50
896/9 .. .. *Set of* 4 4·50 5·50

 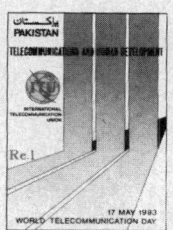

460 Clasped Hands and   461 I.T.U. Emblem
Islamic Symbols

(Des I. Jillani)

1993 (25 Apr). *21st Conference of Islamic Foreign Ministers, Karachi. P* 13.
900 460 1 r. multicoloured 30 10
901   6 r. multicoloured .. .. .. 95 1·25

(Des Pakistan Telecommunication Corporation, Islamabad)

1993 (17 May). *25th Anniv of World Telecommunication Day. P* 13.
902 461 1 r. multicoloured 65 30

(Des S. Afsar)

1993 (20 June). *Medicinal Plants* (*2nd series*). *Horiz design as T* **454**. *Multicoloured. P* 13.
903   6 r. Fennel and symbolic drug manufacture 1·75 1·75

(Des S. Akhtar)

1993 (14 Aug). *Pioneers of Freedom* (*6th series*). *Vert designs as T* **428**. *Each brown and vermilion. P* 13.
904   1 r. Ghulam Mohammad Bhurgri .. 75 75
     a. Horiz strip of 3. Nos. 904/6 .. 2·00
905   1 r. Ahmed Yar Khan 75 75
906   1 r. Mohammad Pir Sahib Zakori Sharif 75 75
904/6 .. .. .. *Set of* 3 2·00 2·00
Nos. 904/6 were printed together, *se-tenant,* in horizontal strips of three throughout a sheetlet of nine.

462 College Building and Arms

(Des Nargis Munir)

1993 (1 Sept). *Centenary of Gordon College, Rawalpindi. P* 13.
907 462 2 r. multicoloured 80 80

463 Juniper Forest   464 Globe, Produce and
Emblem

(Des A. Salahuddin)

1993 (30 Sept)–**95**. *Campaign to Save the Juniper Forest, Ziarat. P* 13.
907a 463 1 r. multicoloured (14.2.95) .. 50 30
908   7 r. multicoloured .. .. 2·00 2·25

(Des Jawaiduddin)

1993 (16 Oct). *World Food Day. P* 14.
909 464 6 r. multicoloured 70 80

465 Burn Hall   466 Peace Dove
Institution, Abbottabad   carrying Letter and
National Flags

(Des I. Jillani)

1993 (28 Oct). *50th Anniv of Burn Hall Institutions. P* 13.
910 465 7 r. multicoloured .. .. 1·25 1·50

(Des F. Amir)

1993 (18 Nov). *South and West Asia Postal Union Commemoration. P* 13.
911 466 7 r. multicoloured .. .. 1·25 1·50

467 Congress Emblem   468 Wazir Mansion
(birthplace)

1993 (10 Dec). *Pakistan College of Physicians and Surgeons International Medical Congress. P* 13.
912 467 1 r. multicoloured 60 30

(Des A. Siddique)

1993 (25 Dec). *45th Death Anniv of Mohammed Ali Jinnah. W* **98**. *P* 13½×13.
913 468 1 r. multicoloured 60 30
     a. Wmk sideways .. ..

469 Emblem and National Flag

(Des A. Salahuddin)

1994 (11 Apr). *75th Anniv of International Labour Organization. W* **98** (*sideways*). *P* 13.
914 469 7 r. multicoloured 75 80

470 Ratan Jot (flower)   471 Silhouette of
Family and Emblem

(Des I. Jillani)

1994 (20 Apr). *Ratification of International Biological Diversity Convention. T* **470** *and similar horiz designs. Multicoloured. W* **98**. *P* 13½.
915   6 r. Type 470 .. .. .. 35 35
     a. Horiz strip of 4. Nos. 915/18 .. 1·25
     aw. Wmk inverted
916   6 r. Wetlands habitat 35 35
917   6 r. Golden Mahseer (*Tor puttitora*) (fish) 35 35
918   6 r. Brown Bear 35 35
915/18 .. .. .. *Set of* 4 1·25 1·25
Nos. 915/18 were printed together, *se-tenant,* in horizontal strips of 4 throughout the sheet.

(Des Nargis Munir)

1994 (15 May). *International Year of the Family. W* **98**. *P* 13.
919 471 7 r. multicoloured 40 40

472 Symbolic Globe and Logo

1994 (11 July). *World Population Day. W* **98**. *P* 13.
920 472 7 r. multicoloured 40 40

PAKISTAN—1994

(Des S. Akhtar)

1994 (14 Aug). *Pioneers of Freedom (7th series). Vert designs as T 428. Each brown and green. P 13.*

921	1 r. Nawab Mohsin-Ul-Mulk	..	10	10
	a. Sheetlet. Nos. 921/8	..	80	
922	1 r. Sir Shahnawaz Bhutto	..	10	10
923	1 r. Nawab Viqar-Ul-Mulk	..	10	10
924	1 r. Pir Ilahi Bux	..	10	10
925	1 r. Sheikh Abdul Qadir	..	10	10
926	1 r. Dr. Sir Ziauddin Ahmed	..	10	10
927	1 r. Jam Mir Ghulam Qadir Khan	..	10	10
928	1 r. Sardar Aurangzeb Khan	..	10	10
921/8		Set of 8	80	80

Nos. 921/8 were printed together, *se-tenant*, in sheetlets of 8 stamps and one centre label showing the Pakistan flag.

473 Hala Pottery, Pakistan

474 Boy writing and Globe

(Des A. Siddique (No. 929))

1994 (19 Aug). *Indonesia–Pakistan Economic and Cultural Co-operation Organization. T 473 and similar vert design. Multicoloured. W 98 (sideways). P 13.*

929	10 r. Type 473	..	45	50
	a. Horiz pair. Nos. 929/30	..	90	1·00
930	10 r. Lombok pottery, Indonesia	..	45	50

Nos. 929/30 were printed together, *se-tenant*, in horizontal pairs throughout the sheet.

(Des Nargis Munir)

1994 (8 Sept). *International Literacy Day. W 98 (sideways). P 13½.*

931	474	7 r. multicoloured	30	35

475 Mohammed Ali Jinnah and Floral Pattern

476 Gateway and Emblem

(Des A. Salahuddin. Eng Z. Ali. Recess and litho)

1994 (11 Sept). *W 98 (sideways). P 13.*

932	475	1 r. multicoloured	10	10
933		2 r. multicoloured	10	10
934		3 r. multicoloured	10	10
935		4 r. multicoloured	10	10
936		5 r. multicoloured	10	15
937		7 r. multicoloured	15	20
938		10 r. multicoloured	25	30
939		12 r. multicoloured	35	40
940		15 r. multicoloured	40	45
941		20 r. multicoloured	50	55
942		25 r. multicoloured	60	65
943		30 r. multicoloured	70	75
932/43		Set of 12	3·25	3·75

(Des Nargis Munir)

1994 (22 Sept). *2nd South Asian Association for Regional Co-operation and 12th National Scout Jamborees, Quetta. W 98. P 13.*

944	476	7 r. multicoloured	50	55

477 Engraver

478 Henbane

1994 (7 Oct). *First International Festival of Islamic Artisans at Work. W 98 (sideways). P 13½.*

945	477	2 r. multicoloured	40	30

(Des F. Amir)

1994 (18 Oct). *Medicinal Plants (3rd series). W 98. P 13.*

946	478	6 r. multicoloured	55	60

---

479 Abu-I Kasim Firdausi (poet)

480 Museum Building

(Des F. Amir)

1994 (27 Oct). *Millenary of Shahnama (poem). W 98. P 13.*

947	479	1 r. multicoloured	15	15
		w. Wmk inverted		

(Des A. Siddique)

1994 (27 Dec). *Centenary of Lahore Museum. W 98 (sideways). P 13.*

948	480	4 r. multicoloured	40	40

481 World Cup Trophies for 1971, 1978, 1982 and 1994

(Des Jawaiduddin)

1994 (31 Dec). *Victory of Pakistan in World Cup Hockey Championship. W 98 (sideways). P 13½×13.*

949	481	5 r. multicoloured	50	50

482 Tourist Attractions

(Des Nargis Munir)

1995 (2 Jan). *20th Anniv of World Tourism Organization. W 98. P 13.*

950	482	4 r. multicoloured	40	40

483 Khan Khushal of Khattak and Army

484 E.C.O. Emblem

(Des S. Afsar)

1995 (28 Feb). *Khan Khushal of Khattak (poet) Commemoration. W 98. P 13.*

951	483	7 r. multicoloured	65	65
		a. Wmk sideways		

1995 (14 Mar). *3rd Economic Co-operation Organization Summit, Islamabad. W 98 (sideways). P 14.*

952	484	6 r. multicoloured	55	55

485 Common Indian Krait

486 Globe and Environments

(Des M-ur Rehman (Nos. 953, 955), A. Siddique (Nos. 954, 956))

1995 (15 Apr). *Snakes. T 485 and similar horiz designs. Multicoloured. P 13½.*

953	6 r. Type 485	..	70	70
	a. Block of 4. Nos. 953/6		2·50	
954	6 r. Indian Cobra	..	70	70
955	6 r. Indian Python	..	70	70
956	6 r. Russell's Viper	..	70	70
953/6		Set of 4	2·50	2·50

Nos. 953/6 were printed together, *se-tenant*, in blocks of 4 throughout the sheet.

(Des A. Siddique)

1995 (20 Apr). *Earth Day. W 98 (sideways). P 13.*

957	486	6 r. multicoloured	55	55

487 Victoria Carriage, Karachi

(Des F. Amir)

1995 (22 May). *Traditional Transport. W 98 (sideways). P 13.*

958	487	5 r. multicoloured	50	50

488 Prime Minister Tansu Ciller of Turkey and Rose

(Des J. Siddiqui)

1995 (1 Aug). *First Muslim Women Parliamentarians' Conference, Islamabad. T 488 and similar horiz design. Multicoloured. P 13.*

959	5 r. Type 488	..	55	65
	a. Horiz pair. Nos. 959/60		1·10	1·25
960	5 r. Prime Minister Benazir Bhutto and jasmine	..	55	65

Nos. 959/60 were printed together, *se-tenant*, in horizontal pairs throughout the sheet.

(Des S. Akhtar)

1995 (14 Aug). *Pioneers of Freedom (8th series). Vert designs as T 428. Each brown and myrtle-green. P 13.*

961	1 r. Maulana Shaukat Ali	..	30	30
	a. Pair. Nos. 961/2		60	60
962	1 r. Chaudhry Ghulam Abbas	..	30	30

Nos. 961/2 were printed together, *se-tenant*, in sheetlets of 8 stamps and one centre label showing the Pakistani flag.

489 Oil Sardine

490 Erasmia pulchella

(Des Nargis Munir)

1995 (1 Sept). *Fishes. T 489 and similar horiz designs. Multicoloured. W 98. P 13½.*

963	6 r. Type 489	..	50	60
	a. Horiz strip of 4. Nos. 963/6		1·75	
964	6 r. Mozambique Mouthbrooder ("Tilapia")	..	50	60
965	6 r. Brown Trout	..	50	60
966	6 r. Rohu	..	50	60
963/6		Set of 4	1·75	2·25

Nos. 963/6 were printed together, *se-tenant*, in horizontal strips of 4 throughout the sheet.

(Des A. Salahuddin)

1995 (1 Sept). *Butterflies. T 490 and similar horiz designs. Multicoloured. W 98 (sideways). P 13½.*

967	6 r. Type 490	..	50	60
	a. Horiz strip of 4. Nos. 967/70		1·75	
968	6 r. Callicore astarte (inscr "CATO-GRAMME")	..	50	60
969	6 r. Ixias pyrene	..	50	60
970	6 r. Heliconius	..	50	60
967/70		Set of 4	1·75	2·25

Nos. 967/70 were printed together, *se-tenant*, in horizontal strips of 4 throughout the sheet.

NEW INFORMATION

The editor is always interested to correspond with people who have new information that will improve or correct the Catalogue.

491 Major Raja Aziz Bhatti
Shaheed and Medal

(Des A. Zafar)

1995 (6 Sept). *Defence Day.* W **98**. *P* 13.
971 **491** 1 r. 25, multicoloured 65 50
    w. Wmk inverted

492 Presentation Convent
School, Rawalpindi
493 Women Soldiers,
Golfer and Scientist

(Des I. Gilani)

1995 (8 Sept). *Centenary of Presentation Convent School,
Rawalpindi.* W **98**. *P* 13½.
972 **492** 1 r. 25, multicoloured 30 20

(Des A. Salahuddin)

1995 (15 Sept). *4th World Conference on Women, Peking.*
T **493** *and similar vert designs. Multicoloured.* W **98**
(sideways). P 13.
973   1 r. 25, Type **493** 20 20
     a. Horiz strip of 4. Nos. 973/6 .. 70
974   1 r. 25, Women graduates, journalist,
     computer operator and technicians .. 20 20
975   1 r. 25, Sewing machinist and women at
     traditional crafts 20 20
976   1 r. 25, Army officer and women at
     traditional tasks 20 20
973/6 .. .. .. *Set of* 4 70 70
Nos. 973/6 were printed together, *se-tenant,* in horizontal
strips of 4 throughout the sheet.

494 "Louis Pasteur in
Laboratory" (Edelfelt)
495

1995 (28 Sept). *Death Centenary of Louis Pasteur (chemist).*
W **98** *(sideways). P* 13.
977 **494** 5 r. multicoloured 50 60

1995 (28 Sept)–96. *P* 13½.
978 **495** 5 p. blue, yellow-orange and reddish
     brown (10.10.95) 10 10
979   15 p. yellow-orange, dull violet and
     reddish brown (10.10.95) .. 10 10
980   25 p. cobalt, cerise and purple .. 10 10
981   75 p. bright green, red-brown and
     reddish brown (15.5.96) .. 10 10
978/81 .. .. .. *Set of* 4 10 10

496 Liaquat Ali Khan

(Des A. Salahuddin)

1995 (1 Oct). *Birth Centenary (1995) of Liaquat Ali Khan*
(statesman). W **98**. *P* 13.
987 **496** 1 r. 25, multicoloured 20 10

497 Village and Irrigated Fields

(Des Nargis Munir)

1995 (16 Oct). *50th Anniv of Food and Agriculture*
Organization. W **98**. *P* 13.
988 **497** 1 r. 25, multicoloured 20 10

498 Pakistani Soldier treating
Somali Refugees
499 Education
Emblem

1995 (24 Oct). *50th Anniv of United Nations.* W **98**. *P* 13½.
989 **498** 7 r. multicoloured 50 50
     a. Wmk sideways

1995 (3 Nov). *80th Anniv (1993) of Kinnaird College for*
Women, Lahore. W **98** *(sideways). P* 14×13.
990 **499** 1 r.25, multicoloured 20 10

500 Hand holding Book,
Eye and Pen Nib
501 Children holding
Hands and S.A.A.R.C.
Logo

1995 (30 Nov). *International Conference of Writers and*
Intellectuals, Islamabad. W **98** *(sideways). P* 14.
991 **500** 1 r. 25, multicoloured 20 10

(Des Nargis Munir)

1995 (8 Dec). *10th Anniv of South Asian Association for*
Regional Co-operation. W **98** *(sideways). P* 13.
992 **501** 1 r. 25, multicoloured 20 10

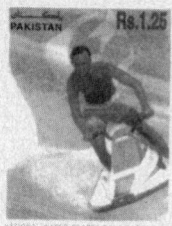

502 Jet Skier

(Des F. Siddiqui and M-ur Rehman)

1995 (14 Dec). *National Water Sports Gala, Karachi. T* **502**
and similar vert designs. Multicoloured. W **98** *(sideways).*
P 13.
993   1 r. 25, Type **502** 20 20
     a. Block of 4. Nos. 993/6 .. 70
994   1 r. 25, Local punts 20 20
995   1 r. 25, Wind surfers 20 20
996   1 r. 25, Water skier 20 20
993/6 .. .. .. *Set of* 4 70 70
Nos. 993/6 were printed together, *se-tenant,* in blocks of four
throughout the sheet.

The new-issue supplement to this Catalogue
appears each month in

GIBBONS STAMP MONTHLY

—from your newsagent or by postal subscription—
sample copy and details on request.

---

503 Mortar Board and Books

(Des A. Siddique)

1995 (16 Dec). *20th Anniv of Allama Iqbal Open University.*
W **98**. *P* 13.
997 **503** 1 r. 25, multicoloured .. 20 10
     w. Wmk inverted

504 Balochistan Quetta
University Building
505 Zulfikar Ali Bhutto,
Flag and Crowd

(Des I. Jillani)

1995 (31 Dec). *25th Anniv of Balochistan Quetta University.*
W **98**. *P* 13.
998 **504** 1 r. 25, multicoloured 20 10

(Des A. Salahuddin)

1996 (4 Apr). *17th Death Anniv of Zulfikar Ali Bhutto (former*
Prime Minister). T **505** *and similar multicoloured designs.*
W **98** *(sideways* on* 4 *r.). P* 13.
999   1 r. 25, Type **505** 40 10
1000   4 r. Zulfikar Ali Bhutto and flag (53×31
     mm) .. .. .. 1·25 1·40
MS1001   118×74 mm. 8 r. Zulfikar Ali Bhutto
   and crowd (118×74 *mm*). Wmk sideways. Imperf 1·40 1·40
     w. Wmk tips of crescent pointing
     downwards
     *The normal sideways watermark shows the tips of the
crescent pointing upwards, *when viewed from the back of the*
stamp.

506 Wrestling

(Des F. Siddiqui and Nargis Munir)

1996 (3 Aug). *Olympic Games, Atlanta. T* **506** *and similar*
horiz designs. Multicoloured. W **98** *(sideways*). P* 13.
1002   5 r. Type **506** 40 40
1003   5 r. Boxing 40 40
1004   5 r. Pierre de Coubertin .. 40 40
     w. Wmk tips of crescent pointing
     downwards 40 40
1005   5 r. Hockey 40 40
     w. Wmk tips of crescent pointing
     downwards
1002/5 .. .. .. *Set of* 4 1·40 1·40
MS1006   112×100 mm. 25 r. Designs as Nos.
   1002/5, but without face values. Imperf 2·00 2·25
     w. Wmk tips of crescent pointing
     downwards
     *The normal sideways watermark shows the tips of the
crescent pointing upwards, *when viewed from the back of the*
stamp.

(Des S. Akhtar)

1996 (14 Aug). *Pioneers of Freedom (9th series). Vert design as*
T **425** *showing Allama Abdullah Yousuf Ali. P* 13.
1007   1 r. brown and myrtle-green .. 10 10

507 G.P.O. Building,
Lahore
508 Symbolic Open Book
and Text

(Des A. Salahuddin)

1996 (21 Aug). *Restoration of G.P.O. Building, Lahore.* W **98**.
P 14.
1008 **507** 5 r. multicoloured 30 35

1996 (8 Sept). *International Literacy Day.* W **98**. *P* 13.
1009 **508** 2 r. multicoloured 20 15
   w. Wmk inverted ..

509 Yarrow   510 Faiz Ahmed Faiz

(Des F. Amir)

1996 (25 Nov). *Medicinal Plants (4th series).* W **98** *(sideways).*
P 13.
1010 **509** 3 r. multicoloured 60 50

(Des S. Akhtar)

1997 (12 Feb). *86th Birth Anniv of Faiz Ahmed Faiz (poet).*
P 13.
1011 **510** 3 r. multicoloured 10 15

511 Golden Jubilee   512 Amir Timur
and O.I.C. Emblems

1997 (23 Mar). *Special Summit Conference of Organization of
Islamic Countries commemorating 50th anniv of Pakistan.*
P 13.
1012 **511** 2 r. multicoloured 10 10

1997 (8 Apr). *660th Birth Anniv of Timur (founder of Timurid
Empire). P* 13.
1013 **512** 3 r. multicoloured 10 15

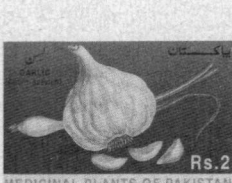

513 Jalal-al-din   514 Apple
Moulana Rumi

(Des Javeduddin)

1997 (21 Apr). *Pakistan–Iran Joint Issue.* T **513** *and similar
vert design. P* 13½.
1014   3 r. Type **513** 10 15
1015   3 r. Allama Mohammad Iqbal (poet) .. 10 15

(Des A. Salahuddin)

1997 (8 May). *Fruit. P* 13.
1016 **514** 2 r. multicoloured 10 10

515 People on Globe   516 Stylised Dove of
Peace

(Des M-ur Rehman)

1997 (11 July). *World Population Day. P* 13.
1017 **515** 2 r. multicoloured 10 10

(Des Nargis Munir)

1997 (29 July). *40th Anniv of Co-operation between
International Atomic Energy Agency and Pakistan Atomic
Energy Corporation. P* 14.
1018 **516** 2 r. multicoloured 10 10

(Des S. Akhtar)

1997 (14 Aug). *Pioneers of Freedom (10th series). Vert designs
as* T **428**. *Each deep brown and myrtle-green. P* 13.
1019   1 r. Mohammad Ayub Khuhro .. 10 10
1020   1 r. Begum Salma Tassaduq Hussain 10 10

517 Mohammed Ali   518 College Building
Jinnah

(Des Nargis Munir)

1997 (14 Aug). *50th Anniv of Independence.* T **517** *and similar
vert designs. Multicoloured. P* 13.
1021   3 r. Type **517** 15 20
   a. Block of 4. Nos. 1021/4 with two labels 55
1022   3 r. Allama Mohammad Iqbal .. 15 20
1023   3 r. Mohtarma Fatima Jinnah .. 15 20
1024   3 r. Liaquat Ali Khan .. 15 20
1021/4   *Set of 4* 55 70
   Nos. 1021/4 were printed together, *se-tenant,* in sheets of 48
stamps and 24 stamp-size labels. The labels, which show either
the Pakistan flag or the anniversary logo, alternate in vertical
rows 2, 5, 8 and 11. Nos. 1021 and 1023 alternate in vertical
rows 1, 4, 7 and 10 with Nos. 1022 and 1024 in vertical rows 3, 6,
9 and 12.

1997 (23 Sept). *75th Anniv of Lahore College for Women. P* 13.
1025 **518** 3 r. multicoloured 20 10

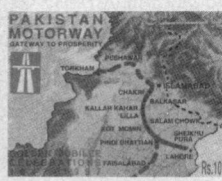

519 Garlic   520 Himalayan Monal
Pheasant

(Des A. Siddique)

1997 (22 Oct). *Medicinal Plants (5th series). P* 13.
1026 **519** 2 r. multicoloured 10 10

(Des A. Salahuddin)

1997 (29 Oct). *Wildlife Protection (18th series). P* 13.
1027 **520** 2 r. multicoloured 30 10

521 Globe and   522 Map of Pakistan
Cracked Ozone Layer   Motorway Project

(Des Nargis Munir)

1997 (15 Nov). *Save Ozone Layer Campaign. P* 13.
1028 **521** 3 r. multicoloured 10 10

(Des A. Salahuddin)

1997 (26 Nov). *Pakistan Motorway Project. P* 13½.
1029 **522** 10 r. multicoloured 30 40
MS1030 117×97 mm. No. 1029 *(sold at 15 r.)* 95 1·10

---

523 Emblem and Disabled People

(Des Nargis Munir)

1997 (3 Dec). *International Day for the Disabled. P* 13.
1031 **523** 4 r. multicoloured 20 20

524 Karachi Grammar   525 Mirza Ghalib
School

(Des F. Amir)

1997 (30 Dec). *150th Anniv of Karachi Grammar School.
P* 13½.
1032 **524** 2 r. multicoloured 10 10

(Des F. Siddiqui)

1998 (15 Feb). *Birth Bicentenary (1997) of Mirza Ghalib (poet).*
W **98**. *P* 13.
1033 **525** 2 r. multicoloured 10 10
   No. 1033 is inscribed "DEATH ANNIVERSARY".

526 Servicemen, Pakistan
Flag and "50"

1998 (23 Mar). *50th Anniv (1997) of Armed Forces.* W **98**.
P 13½.
1034 **526** 7 r. multicoloured 30 40

527 Sir Syed Ahmed Khan

(Des A. Salahuddin)

1998 (27 Mar). *Death Centenary of Sir Syed Ahmed Khan
(social reformer).* W **98**. *P* 14.
1035 **527** 7 r. chocolate, emerald and yellow-ochre 30 40

The new-issue supplement to this Catalogue
appears each month in

GIBBONS
STAMP MONTHLY

—from your newsagent or by postal subscription—
sample copy and details on request.

528 Olympic Torch and Sports

529 Thornapple

(Des A. Salahuddin)

1998 (22 Apr). *27th National Games, Peshawar.* W **98**. *P* 13.
1036 528 7 r. multicoloured 30 40
w. Wmk inverted 40

(Des S. Afsar)

1998 (27 Apr). *Medicinal Plants (6th series).* W **98**. *P* 13.
1037 529 2 r. multicoloured 10 10

530 Silver Jubilee Emblem

531 Mohammed Ali Jinnah

1998 (6 Aug). *25th Anniv of Senate.* W **98** *(sideways). P* 13½.
1038 530 2 r. multicoloured 10 10
1039 5 r. multicoloured 10 15

1998 (14 Aug). *Recess and litho.* W **98** *(sideways). P* 14.
1040 531 2 r. dull ultramarine and carmine 10 10
1041 3 r. deep grey-green and red-brown 10 10
1042 4 r. blackish purple and orange .. 10 10
1043 5 r. deep brown and deep green .. 10 15
1044 6 r. deep blue-green and light blue .. 15 20
1045 7 r. orange-red and bright violet .. 15 20
1040/5 *Set of 6* 60 80

532 College Building

533 Mohammed Ali Jinnah

1998 (14 Aug). *Centenary of Government College, Faisalabad.* W **98**. *P* 13.
1046 532 5 r. multicoloured 10 15
w. Wmk inverted

1998 (11 Sept). *50th Death Anniv of Mohammed Ali Jinnah.* W **98**. *P* 13½.
1047 533 15 r. multicoloured 35 40
MS1048 72×100 mm. 533 15 r. multicoloured. No wmk *(sold at* 20 *r.)* 50 55

534 Cross-section of Eye

1998 (12 Sept). *21st International Ophthalmology Congress, Islamabad.* W **98** *(sideways). P* 13.
1049 534 7 r. multicoloured 15 20

OMNIBUS ISSUES

Details, together with prices for complete sets, of the various Omnibus issues from the 1935 Silver Jubilee series to date are included in a special section following Zimbabwe at the end of Volume 2.

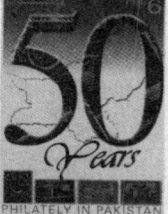

535 United Nations Emblems and Bukhari

536 Map, "50 years" and Stamps

1998 (1 Oct). *Birth Centenary of Syed Ahmed Shah Patrus Bukhari.* W **98**. *P* 13.
1050 535 5 r. multicoloured 10 15

1998 (4 Oct). *50th Anniv of Philately in Pakistan.* W **98** *(sideways). P* 13.
1051 536 6 r. multicoloured 15 20

537 Mother and Child

538 Dr. Abdus Salam

1998 (16 Oct). *World Food Day.* W **98**. *P* 13.
1052 537 6 r. multicoloured 15 20

1998 (21 Nov). *Scientists of Pakistan (1st series). Dr. Abdus Salam. P* 13.
1053 538 2 r. multicoloured 10 10
See also No. 1068.

539 Satellite Dish Aerial

540 Globe and Human Rights Emblem

1998 (27 Nov). *"Better Pakistan" Development Plan. T* 539 *and similar horiz designs. Multicoloured. P* 13×14.
1054 2 r. Type 539 .. .. 10 10
1055 2 r. Combine harvester 10 10
1056 2 r. Airliner 10 10
1057 2 r. Children and doctor 10 10
1054/7 *Set of 4* 20 25

1998 (10 Dec). *50th Anniv of Universal Declaration of Human Rights.* W **98**. *P* 12½×14.
1058 540 6 r. multicoloured 15 20

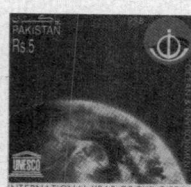

541 Pakistani Woman carrying Water Pot

542 Earth seen from Space

1998 (11 Dec). *50th Anniv of U.N.I.C.E.F. in Pakistan. T* 541 *and similar square designs. Multicoloured.* W **98**. *P* 14.
1059 2 r. Type 541 .. .. 10 10
a. Block of 4. Nos. 1059/62 20 25
1060 2 r. Woman reading 10 10
1061 2 r. Woman with goitre 10 10
1062 2 r. Young boy receiving oral vaccine 10 10
1059/62 *Set of 4* 20 25
Nos. 1059/62 were printed together, *se-tenant,* in blocks of 4 with the U.N.I.C.E.F. symbol in the centre.

1998 (15 Dec). *International Year of the Ocean.* W **98**. *P* 14.
1063 542 5 r. multicoloured 10 15

543 Marchers and Route Map

544 Centenary Logo

1998 (16 Dec). *Qaumi Parcham March, Khyber to Chaghi.* W **98**. *P* 13.
1064 543 2 r. multicoloured 10 10

1999 (27 Jan). *Centenary of Saud Dynasty of Saudi Arabia. T* 544 *and similar vert design. Multicoloured. P* 13½.
1065 2 r. Type 544 .. .. 10 10
1066 15 r. As Type 544, but with mosaic pattern in corners 35 40
MS1067 73×100 mm. 15 r. No. 1066 *(sold at* 20 *r.)* 50 55

545 Dr. Salimuz Zaman Siddiqui

546 Mountains and Pakistan Flag

1999 (14 Apr). *Scientists of Pakistan (2nd series). Dr. Salimuz Zaman Siddiqui. P* 13.
1068 545 5 r. multicoloured 10 15

1999 (28 May). *"Atoms for Peace". P* 13.
1069 546 5 r. multicoloured 10 15

547 Plan and View of Mosque

548 Fasting Buddha Statue (drapery on left knee)

1999 (31 May). *Completion of Data Darbar Mosque Complex, Lahore. P* 13.
1070 547 7 r. multicoloured 15 20

1999 (21 July). *Archaeological Heritage. T* 548 *and similar vert design. Multicoloured.* W **98** *(sideways). P* 13½.
1071 7 r. Type 548 .. .. 15 20
1072 7 r. Fasting Buddha (drapery on right knee) 15 20
MS1073 107×90 mm. Nos. 1071/2. Wmk upright *(sold at* 25 *r.)* 60 65
No. MS1073 includes the "China '99" International Stamp Exhibition, Beijing, logo on the margin.

549 Red Cross International Committee Emblem and "50"

1999 (12 Aug). *50th Anniv of Geneva Conventions. P* 13×14.
1074 549 5 r. orange-red and black 10 15

1999 (14 Aug). *Pioneers of Freedom (11th series). Vert designs as T* 428. *Each sepia and deep dull green. P* 13.
1075 2 r. Maulana Abdul Hamid Badayuni .. 10 10
1076 2 r. Chaudhry Muhammad Ali .. 10 10
1077 2 r. Sir Adamjee Haji Dawood .. 10 10
1075/7 *Set of 3* 15 20

550 Ustad Nusrat Fateh Ali Khan

551 Islamic Development Bank Building

1999 (16 Aug). *Ustad Nusrat Fateh Ali Khan (musician) Commemoration.* P 13.
1078 550 2 r. multicoloured 10 10

1999 (18 Sept). *25th Anniv of Islamic Development Bank.* W 98. P 13.
1079 551 5 r. multicoloured 10 15

552 Crowd celebrating

553 "Enterprise" Sailing Dinghy

1999 (21 Sept). *50th Anniv of People's Republic of China. T 552 and similar multicoloured design.* W 98. P 13.
1080 2 r. Type 552 .. .. 10 10
1081 15 r. Bust of Mao Tse-tung (Chinese leader) and emblem (horiz) .. 35 40

1999 (28 Sept). *9th Asian Sailing Championship. Sailing Craft. T 553 and similar vert designs. Multicoloured.* P 13½.
1082 2 r. Type 553 .. .. 10 10
　　a. Strip of 5. Nos. 1082/6 25
1083 2 r. "470" dinghy .. 10 10
1084 2 r. "Optimist" dinghy .. 10 10
1085 2 r. "Laser" dinghy .. 10 10
1086 2 r. "Mistral" sail board .. 10 10
1082/6 Set of 5 25 30
　Nos. 1082/6 were printed together, *se-tenant*, as horizontal or vertical strips of 5.

554 "Optimist" Sailing Dinghies

555 U.P.U. Emblem

1999 (7 Oct). *10th Asian "Optimist" Sailing Championship.* P 13½.
1087 554 2 r. multicoloured .. 10 10
　No. 1087 was printed *se-tenant* with a half stamp-size label showing the Championship emblem.

1999 (9 Oct). *125th Anniv of Universal Postal Union.* W 98. P 14.
1088 555 10 r. multicoloured 25 30

556 Hakim Mohammed Said

557 National Bank of Pakistan Building

1999 (17 Oct). *First Death Anniv of Hakim Mohammed Said.* P 13.
1089 556 5 r. multicoloured 10 15

1999 (8 Nov). *50th Anniv of National Bank of Pakistan.* W 98. P 13½×14.
1090 557 5 r. multicoloured 10 15

558 Evolution of the "Shell" Emblem

559 Profiles of Children in "10"

1999 (15 Nov). *Centenary of Shell in Pakistan.* W 98. P 13.
1091 558 4 r. multicoloured 10 10

1999 (20 Nov). *10th Anniv of United Nations Rights of the Child Convention.* P 13×13½.
1092 559 2 r. emerald, bright green and rosine 10 10

560 Science Equipment, Books and Computer

561 Josh Malihabadi

1999 (20 Nov). *25th Anniv of Allama Iqbal Open University. T 560 and similar horiz designs. Multicoloured.* P 13.
1093 2 r. Type 560 .. .. 10 10
1094 3 r. Scholastic symbols as Type 560 10 10
1095 5 r. Map of Pakistan .. 10 15
1093/5 Set of 3 25 30

1999 (5 Dec). *Birth Centenary of Josh Malihabadi (poet).* P 13.
1096 561 5 r. multicoloured 10 15

562 Dr. Afzal Qadri and Locusts

563 Ghulam Bari Aleeg

1999 (6 Dec). *25th Death Anniv of Dr. Afzal Qadri (entomologist).* P 13.
1097 562 3 r. multicoloured 10 10

1999 (6 Dec). *50th Death Anniv of Ghulam Bari Aleeg (writer).* P 13.
1098 563 5 r. multicoloured 10 15

564 Plantain

1999 (20 Dec). *Medicinal Plants (7th series).* P 13.
1099 564 5 r. multicoloured 10 15

565 Mosque

1999 (24 Dec). *Eid-ul-Fitr Greetings.* P 13½.
1100 565 2 r. multicoloured 10 10
1101 15 r. multicoloured 35 40

NEW INFORMATION
The editor is always interested to correspond with people who have new information that will improve or correct the Catalogue.

STAMP BOOKLETS

1956 (23 Mar). *Black on green cover. Stapled.*
SB1 1 r. 08, booklet containing twelve 6 p. and 1½ a. (Nos. 65, 68) in blocks of 4 .. .. .. 9·00

1994 (1 Feb). *Maroon on bright greenish blue cover with "window" showing contents. Stamps affixed by selvedge.*
SB2 15 r. booklet containing fourteen 1 r. (No. 913) in block of 14 50

OFFICIAL STAMPS

PAKISTAN

(O 1)

1947. *Nos. O138/41 and O143/50 (King George VI) of India, optd as Type O 1 (Nos. O1/9) or as T 2 (Nos. O10/13) both in litho by Nasik.*

O 1	3 p. slate			80	10
O 2	½ a. purple	..		30	10
O 3	9 p. green			4·00	2·50
O 4	1 a. carmine			30	10
O 5	1½ a. dull violet			30	10
	w. Wmk inverted			20·00	
O 6	2 a. vermilion			30	10
O 7	2½ a. bright violet			6·00	7·50
O 8	4 a. brown			1·25	30
O 9	8 a. slate-violet			1·50	1·25
O10	1 r. grey and red-brown			80	85
O11	2 r. purple and brown			3·50	3·00
O12	5 r. green and blue			15·00	26·00
O13	10 r. purple and claret			40·00	85·00
O1/13			Set of 13	65·00	£110

See note after No. 19. The 1 a. 3 p. (India No. O146a) exists as a local issue (*Price, Karachi opt, £4.25 mint, £12 used*).

SERVICE   SERVICE   SERVICE
    (O 2)   (O 3)   (O 4)

NOTE. Apart from a slight difference in size, Types O 2 and O 3 can easily be distinguished by the difference in the shape of the "c". Type O 4 is taller and thinner in appearance.

PRINTERS. Type O 2 was overprinted by De La Rue and Types O 3 and O 4 by the Pakistan Security Ptg Corp.

1948 (14 Aug)–54? *Optd with Type O 2.*

O14	7	3 p. red (No. 24)		10	10
O15		6 p. violet (No. 25) (R.)		10	10
O16		9 p. green (No. 26) (R.)		10	10
O17	8	1 a. blue (No. 27) (R.)		3·75	10
O18		1½ a. grey-green (No. 28) (R.)		3·50	10
O19		2 a. red (No. 29)		1·50	10
O20	10	3 a. green (No. 31)		24·00	6·00
O21	9	4 a. reddish brown (No. 33)		80	10
O22		8 a. black (No. 35) (R.)		1·50	6·00
O23		1 r. ultramarine (No. 38)		1·00	10
O24		2 r. chocolate (No. 39)		13·00	6·50
O25		5 r. carmine (No. 40)		26·00	6·50
O26	13	10 r. magenta (No. 41)		14·00	40·00
		a. Perf 12 (10.10.51)		15·00	40·00
		b. Perf 13 (1954?)		13·00	48·00
O14/26			Set of 13	80·00	60·00

1949. *Optd with Type O 2.*

O27	1 a. blue (No. 44) (R.)			1·25	10
O28	1½ a. grey-green (No. 45) (R.)			40	10
	a. Opt inverted			£250	40·00
O29	2 a. red (No. 46)			1·25	10
	a. Opt omitted (in pair with normal)			—	£120
O30	3 a. green (No. 47)			20·00	4·50
O31	8 a. black (No. 49) (R.)			14·00	14·00
O27/31			Set of 5	48·00	17·00

1951 (14 Aug). *4th Anniv of Independence. As Nos. 56, 58 and 60, but inscr "SERVICE" instead of "PAKISTAN POSTAGE".*

O32	18	3 a. purple		6·00	8·00
O33	19	4 a. green		1·50	10
O34	20	8 a. sepia		7·00	2·50
O32/4			Set of 3	13·00	9·50

1953. *Optd with Type O 3.*

O35	3 p. red (No. 24a)			10	10
O36	6 p. violet (No. 25a) (R.)			10	10
O37	9 p. green (No. 26a) (R.)			10	10
O38	1 a. blue (No. 44a) (R.)			10	10
O39	1½ a. grey-green (No. 45a) (R.)			10	10
O40	2 a. red (No. 46a) (1953?)			15	10
O41	1 r. ultramarine (No. 38a)			9·00	3·00
O42	2 r. chocolate (No. 39a)			3·50	10
O43	5 r. carmine (No. 40a)			26·00	12·00
O44	10 r. magenta (No. 41b) (date?)			21·00	48·00
O35/44			Set of 10	55·00	55·00

1954 (14 Aug). *Seventh Anniv of Independence. Nos. 65/71 optd with Type O 3.*

O45	6 p. reddish violet (R.)			10	2·00
O46	9 p. blue (R.)			90	6·50
O47	1 a. carmine			15	1·75
O48	1½ a. red			15	1·75
O49	14 a. deep green (R.)			60	5·50
O50	1 r. green (R.)			75	10
O51	2 r. red-orange (R.)			10	
O45/51			Set of 7	3·50	16·00

1955 (14 Aug). *Eighth Anniv of Independence. No. 75 optd with Type O 3.*
O52 8 a. deep reddish violet (R.) 30 10

1957 (Jan)–59. *Nos. 65/71 optd with Type O 4.*

O53	6 p. reddish violet (R.)			10	10
	a. Opt inverted			†	
O54	9 p. blue (R.) (1.59)			10	10
	a. Opt inverted			23·00	

O55	1 a. carmine			10	10
	a. Opt inverted			—	60·00
	b. Printed on the gummed side				
O56	1½ a. red			10	10
	a. Opt double				
	b. Printed on the gummed side				
O57	14 a. deep green (R.) (2.59)			40	3·50
O58	1 r. green (R.) (4.58)			40	10
O59	2 r. red-orange (4.58)			5·50	10
O53/9			Set of 7	6·00	3·50

1958 (Jan)–61. *Optd with Type O 4.*

O60	7	3 p. red (No. 24a)		10	10
O61		5 r. carmine (No. 40a) (7.59)		7·00	15
O62	41	10 r. myrtle-green and yellow-orange (No. 89) (R.) (1961)		7·00	8·00
		a. Opt inverted		17·00	
O60/2			Set of 3	12·50	8·00

1958 (Jan)–61. *Nos. 74/5 optd with Type O 4.*

O63	6 a. deep ultramarine (R.) (4.61)			15	10
O64	8 a. deep reddish violet (R.)			15	10

1959 (Aug). *No. 83 optd with Type O 4.*
O65 37 2 a. scarlet 10 10

1961 (Apr). *Nos. 110/11 optd with Type O 4.*

O66	51	8 a. deep green		20	10
O67		1 r. blue		20	10
		a. Opt inverted		7·50	

NEW CURRENCY. In addition to the local *handstamped* surcharges mentioned in the note above No. 122, the following *typographed* surcharges were made at the Treasury at Mastung and issued in the Baluchi province of Kalat: 6 p. on 1 a. (No. O55), 9 p. on 1½ a. (No. O56) and 13 p. on 2 a. (No. O65). They differ in that the surcharges are smaller and "PAISA" is expressed as "Paisa". Being locals they are outside the scope of this catalogue.

1961. *Optd with Type O 4.*

O68	1 p. on 1½ a. (No. 122)			10	10
	a. Optd with Type O 3			3·25	1·25
O69	2 p. on 3 p. (No. 123) (1.1.61)			10	10
	a. Surch double				
	b. Optd with Type O 3			4·75	3·25
O70	3 p. on 6 p. (No. 124)			10	10
O71	7 p. on 1 a. (No. 125)			10	10
	a. Optd with Type O 3			4·75	5·50
O72	13 p. on 2 a. (No. 126)			10	10
O73	13 p. on 2 a. (No. 127)			10	10
O68/73			Set of 6	30	30

No. O68 exists with small and large "1" (see note below Nos. 122/7, etc.).

ERRORS. See note after No. 127.

SERVICE   SERVICE
    (O 5)   (O 6)

1961–63. *Nos. 128/44b optd with Type O 4 (rupee values) or O 5 (others). (a) Inscribed "SHAKISTAN".*

O74	1 p. violet (R.) (1.1.61)			10	10
O75	2 p. rose-red (R.) (12.1.61)			10	10
O76	5 p. ultramarine (R.) (23.3.61)			15	10
	a. Opt inverted				

(b) Inscribed "PAKISTAN"

O77	1 p. violet (R.)			2·25	10
	a. Printed on the gummed side				
	b. Opt inverted				
O78	2 p. rose-red (R.)			10	10
	a. Printed on the gummed side				
O79	3 p. reddish purple (27.10.61)			10	10
O80	5 p. ultramarine (R.)			6·00	10
O81	7 p. emerald (R.) (23.3.61)			10	10
O82	10 p. brown (R.)			10	10
	a. Opt inverted				
O83	13 p. slate-violet (R.) (14.2.61)			10	10
O85	40 p. deep purple (R.) (1.1.62)			10	10
O86	50 p. deep bluish green (R.) (1.1.62)			15	10
	a. Opt double			†	—
O87	75 p. carmine-red (R.) (23.3.62)			20	10
	a. Opt double				
O88	1 r. vermilion (7.1.63)			35	10
	a. Opt double			12·00	
	b. Opt as Type O 3			11·00	11·00
	c. Opt inverted			10·00	
O89	2 r. orange (7.1.63)			1·50	20
O90	5 r. green (R.) (7.1.63)			4·25	6·50
O74/90			Set of 16	13·00	6·50

1963–78? *Nos. 170, etc., optd with Type O 5, in red.*

O 91	1 p. violet			10	10
O 92	2 p. rose-red (1965)			10	10
	a. Opt inverted			2·75	
	b. Albino opt				
	c. Opt double, one albino				
O 93	3 p. reddish purple (1967)			2·50	80
	a. Opt double			7·50	
	b. Opt inverted			2·75	
	c. Printed on the gummed side				
O 94	5 p. ultramarine			10	10
	a. Opt inverted			1·75	
	ab. Vert pair, top stamp without opt, lower with opt inverted				
O 95	7 p. emerald (date?)			11·00	9·00
O 96	10 p. brown (1965)			10	10
	a. Opt inverted			3·00	
O 97	13 p. slate-violet			10	10
O 98	15 p. bright purple (31.12.64)			10	70
O 99	20 p. myrtle-green (26.1.70)			10	30
	a. Opt double			22·00	
O100	25 p. deep blue (1977)			6·00	2·25
O101	40 p. deep purple (1972?)			11·00	4·50
O102	50 p. deep bluish green (1965)			10	15
O103	75 p. carmine-red (date?)			9·00	9·50
O104	90 p. yellow-green (5.78?)			3·75	3·75
O91/104			Set of 14	40·00	27·00

1968–(?). *Nos. 204, 206 and 207 optd with Type O 4.*

O105	62	1 r. vermilion		2·25	50
		a. Opt inverted		11·00	
		b. Printed and overprinted on the gummed side		11·00	
		w. Wmk inverted		11·00	
O107		2 r. orange (date?)		10·00	1·00
		a. Opt inverted		11·00	
O108		5 r. green (R.) (date?)		14·00	5·50
		a. Opt inverted		15·00	
O105/8			Set of 3	24·00	6·25

1979–85. *Nos. 464/72, 473b and 475/80 optd as Type O 5 in black (2 r.) or in red (reading vertically downwards on 2, 3 and 5 p.) (others).*

O109	275	2 p. deep grey-green		10	10
		a. Opt reading upwards			
		ab. Horiz pair, one with opt reading upwards, the other with opt omitted			
		b. Printed on the gummed side			
O110		3 p. black		10	10
		a. Opt reading upwards		3·00	90
O111		5 p. deep ultramarine		10	10
		a. Opt reading upwards		1·50	1·50
		b. Vert pair, top stamp without opt		3·00	
O112	276	10 p. new blue and greenish blue		10	10
O113		20 p. deep yellow-green		10	10
O114		25 p. deep green and dull magenta		10	10
O115		40 p. new blue and magenta		30	10
		a. Opt inverted		8·00	
		b. Albino opt		10·00	
O116		50 p. slate-lilac and turquoise-green		10	10
O117		60 p. black		1·00	10
		a. Printed on the gummed side			
O118		75 p. dull vermilion (Die II) (1980)		1·00	10
O119	276a	1 r. bronze-green (1980)		2·25	10
O120		1 r. 50, red-orange (1979)		10	10
		w. Wmk inverted			
O121		2 r. carmine-red (1979)		15	10
		w. Wmk inverted			
O122		3 r. blue-black (1980)		20	20
O123		4 r. black (1985)		1·50	25
O124		5 r. sepia (1985)		1·50	30
O109/24			Set of 16	7·50	1·50

Examples of Nos. O109/10, O111a and O115/21 occur with matt, almost invisible gum of a P.V.A. type, as well as the usual gum arabic.

(Des and litho Secura, Singapore)

1980 (15 Jan–10 Mar). *As Nos. 513/19 but inscr "SERVICE". P 12.*

O125	291	10 p. slate-green and orange-yellow		1·00	10
O126		15 p. slate-green & brt yellow-green		1·00	10
O127		25 p. violet and brown-red (10 Mar)		15	10
O128		35 p. carmine & brt yell-grn (10 Mar)		20	10
O129	—	40 p. rosine and olive-sepia		1·00	10
O130	—	50 p. violet & dull yell-green (10 Mar)		20	10
O131	—	80 p. brt yellow-green & blk (10 Mar)		30	80
O125/31			Set of 7	3·50	1·10

1984 (25 Sept)–89. *Nos. 629/30 and 632/6 optd with Type O 6 in red.*

O132	—	5 p. brownish blk & brn-pur (1989?)		10	10
O133	—	10 p. brownish black and rose-red		10	10
O135	343	20 p. black and bright reddish violet (opt at right) (20.11.84)		10	10
		a. Opt at left		10	10
O136	—	50 p. sepia and Venetian red (1988?)		20	10
O137	—	60 p. lt brown & blackish brown (1985)		20	20
O138	—	70 p. greenish blue (1988?)		20	20
O139	—	80 p. bistre-brown & dull scar (1988)		20	20
O132/9			Set of 7	90	75

1989 (24 Dec). *No. 773 optd with Type O 5.*
O140 411 1 r. multicoloured .. .. 2·00 60

Other values of this series overprinted with a different "SERVICE" are reported to be bogus.

O 7 State Bank of Pakistan Building, Islamabad

1990 (12 Apr)–99. *W 98 (sideways*). P 13½.*

O141	O 7	1 r. carmine and dull green		10	10
		w. Wmk tips of crescent pointing downwards			
O142		2 r. carmine and rose-carmine		10	10
O143		3 r. carmine and ultramarine		10	10
O144		4 r. carmine and red-brown		10	10
O145		5 r. carmine and reddish purple (*wmk tips of crescent pointing downwards*)		20	25
		w. Wmk tips of crescent pointing upwards			
O146		10 r. carmine and deep brown (6.2.99)		25	30
O141/6			Set of 6	70	75

*The normal sideways watermark for Nos. O141/4 and O146 shows the tips of the crescent pointing upwards and for No. O145 pointing downwards, *both* when viewed from the back of the stamp.

BAHAWALPUR

Bahawalpur, a former feudatory state situated to the west of the Punjab, was briefly independent following the partition of India on 15 August 1947 before acceding to Pakistan on 3 October of the same year.

East India Company and later Indian Empire post offices operated in Bahawalpur from 1854. By a postal agreement of 1879 internal mail from the state administration was carried unstamped, but this arrangement was superseded by the issue of Official stamps in 1945.

These had been preceded by a series of pictorial stamps prepared in 1933–34 on unwatermarked paper. It was intended that these would be used as state postage stamps, but permission for such use was withheld by the Indian Government so they were used for revenue purposes. The same designs were utilised for the 1945 Official series, Nos. O1/6, on paper watermarked Star and Crescent. Residual stocks of the unwatermarked 1 a., 8 a., 1 r. and 2 r. were used for the provisional Officials, Nos. O7 and O11/13.

A commemorative 1 a. Receipt stamp was produced to mark the centenary of the alliance with Great Britain. This may not have been ready until 1935, but an example of this stamp is known used on cover from Deh Rawal to Sadiq Garh and postmarked 14 August 1933. Both this 1 a. and the same value from the unwatermarked set also exist with Official Arabic overprint in black. These were not issued for postal purposes although one used example of the latter has been recorded postmarked 22 February 1933 also from Deh Rawal.

Stamps of India were overprinted in the interim period between 15 August and 3 October 1947. After the state joined Pakistan postage stamps were issued for internal use until 1953.

PRICES FOR STAMPS ON COVER

The postage and Official stamps of Bahawalpur are rare used on cover.

Nawab (from 1947 Amir) Sadiq Mohammad Khan Abbasi V, 1907–1966

(1)

1947 (15 Aug). *Nos. 265/8, 269a/77 and 259/62 (King George VI) of India optd locally with T **1**.*

1	3 p. slate (R.)			14·00
2	½ a. purple			14·00
3	9 p. green (R.)			14·00
4	1 a. carmine			14·00
5	1½ a. dull violet (R.)			14·00
6	2 a. vermilion			14·00
	a. Opt double			£850
7	3 a. bright violet (R.)			14·00
8	3½ a. bright blue (R.)			14·00
9	4 a. brown			14·00
10	6 a. turquoise-green (R.)			14·00
	a. Opt double			£850
11	8 a. slate-violet (R.)			14·00
12	12 a. lake			14·00
13	14 a. purple			48·00
14	1 r. grey and red-brown			19·00
15	2 r. purple and brown (R.)			£900
16	5 r. green and blue (R.)			£900
17	10 r. purple and claret			£900
1/17			*Set of 17*	£2500

Nos. 1/17 were issued during the interim period, following the implementation of the Indian Independence Act, during which time Bahawalpur was part of neither of the two Dominions created. The Amir acceded to the Dominion of Pakistan on 3 October 1947 and these overprinted stamps of India were then withdrawn.

The stamps of Bahawalpur only had validity for use within the state. For external mail Pakistan stamps were used.

PRINTERS. All the following issues were recess-printed by De La Rue & Co, Ltd, London.

2 Amir Muhammad Bahawal Khan I Abbasi

3

1947 (1 Dec). *Bicentenary Commemoration. W **3** (sideways). P 12½ × 11½.*

18	**2**	½ a. black and carmine		1·25	1·25

---

4 H.H. the Amir of Bahawalpur

5 The Tombs of the Amirs

6 Mosque in Sadiq-Garh

7 Fort Derawar from the Lake

8 Nur-Mahal Palace

9 The Palace, Sadiq-Garh

10 H.H. the Amir of Bahawalpur

11 Three Generations of Rulers; H.H. the Amir in centre

1948 (1 Apr). *W **3** (sideways on vert designs). P 12½ (T **4**), 11½ × 12½ (T **5**, **7**, **8** and **9**), 12½ × 11½ (T **6** and **10**) or 13½ × 14 (T **11**).*

19	**4**	3 p. black and blue		75	15·00
20		½ a. black and claret		75	15·00
21		9 p. black and green		75	15·00
22		1 a. black and carmine		75	15·00
23		1½ a. black and violet		75	12·00
24	**5**	2 a. green and carmine		1·00	16·00
25		4 a. orange and brown		1·25	16·00
26	**7**	6 a. violet and blue		1·25	16·00
27	**8**	8 a. carmine and violet		1·25	16·00
28	**9**	12 a. green and carmine		1·50	22·00
29	**10**	1 r. violet and brown		16·00	32·00
30		2 r. green and claret		32·00	50·00
31		5 r. black and violet		32·00	65·00
32	**11**	10 r. scarlet and black		32·00	80·00
19/32			*Set of 14*	£110	£350

12 H.H. The Amir of Bahawalpur and Mohammed Ali Jinnah

13 Soldiers of 1848 and 1948

1948 (3 Oct). *First Anniv of Union of Bahawalpur with Pakistan. W **3**. P 13.*

33	**12**	1½ a. carmine and blue-green		60	1·25

1948 (15 Oct). *Multan Campaign Centenary. W **3**. P 11½.*

34	**13**	1½ a. black and lake		70	7·50

1948. *As Nos. 29/32, but colours changed.*

35	**10**	1 r. deep green and orange		70	15·00
36		2 r. black and carmine		1·00	18·00
37		5 r. chocolate and ultramarine		1·10	32·00
38	**11**	10 r. red-brown and green		1·25	38·00
35/8			*Set of 4*	3·50	90·00

14 Irrigation

17 U.P.U. Monument, Berne

1949 (3 Mar). *Silver Jubilee of Accession of H.H. the Amir of Bahawalpur. T **14** and similar horiz designs. W **3**. P 14.*

39	3 p. black and ultramarine		10	8·00
40	½ a. black and brown-orange		10	8·00
41	9 p. black and green		10	8·00
42	1 a. black and carmine		10	8·00
39/42		*Set of 4*	30	29·00

Designs:—½ a. Wheat; 9 p. Cotton; 1 a. Sahiwal bull.
Nos. 39/42 exist imperforate (*Prices, £15 per pair, unused*).

1949 (10 Oct). *75th Anniv of Universal Postal Union. W **3**. P 13.*

43	**17**	9 p. black and green		20	2·00
		a. Perf 17½ × 17		2·50	14·00
44		1 a. black and magenta		20	2·00
		a. Perf 17½ × 17		2·50	14·00
45		1½ a. black and orange		20	2·00
		a. Perf 17½ × 17		2·50	14·00
46		2½ a. black and blue		20	2·00
		a. Perf 17½ × 17		2·50	14·00
43/6			*Set of 4*	70	7·00
43a/6a			*Set of 4*	9·00	50·00

Nos. 43/6 exist imperforate (*Prices, £10 per pair, unused*).

OFFICIAL STAMPS

O 1 Panjnad Weir

O 2 Dromedary and Calf

O 3 Blackbuck

O 3 Blackbuck — O 4 Eastern White Pelicans

O 5 Friday Mosque, Fort Derawar — O 6 Temple at Pattan Munara

1945 (1 Mar). *Various horizontal pictorial designs, with red Arabic opt. W **3**. P 14.*

O1	O **1**	½ a. black and green		2·75	10·00
O2	O **2**	1 a. black and carmine		3·75	6·00
		a. Opt omitted		†	£750
O3	O **3**	2 a. black and violet		3·25	9·50
O4	O **4**	4 a. black and olive-green		7·50	22·00
O5	O **5**	8 a. black and brown		18·00	12·00
O6	O **6**	1 r. black and orange		18·00	12·00
O1/6			*Set of 6*	48·00	65·00

Permission for the introduction of Nos. O1/6 was granted by the Imperial Government as from 1 January 1945, but the stamps were not used until 1 March. First Day covers exist showing the January date.

Examples of No. O2a come from a sheet used at Rahimya Khan.

It is believed that examples of Nos. O1/2 in different shades and with white gum appeared in 1949 and were included in the Silver Jubilee Presentation Booklet.

O 7 Baggage Camels — (O 8)

1945 (10 Mar). *Revenue stamp with red Arabic opt. No wmk. P 14.*

O7	O **7**	1 a. black and brown		29·00	48·00

1945 (Mar–June). *Surch as Type O **8** (at Security Printing Press, Nasik) instead of red Arabic opt. No wmk. P 14.*

O11	O **5**	½ a. on 8 a. black and purple		4·25	3·50
O12	O **6**	1½ a. on 1 r. black and orange		32·00	9·00
O13	O **1**	1½ a. on 2 r. black and blue (1 June)	£120	10·00
O11/13			*Set of 3*	£140	20·00

The stamps used as a basis for Nos. O7 and O11/13 were part of the Revenue series issued in 1933–34.

SERVICE

(O 9) — O 10 H.H. the Amir of Bahawalpur

1945. *Optd with Type O 9 (by D.L.R.) instead of red Arabic opt. No wmk. P 14.*

O14	O 1	½ a. black and carmine..		1·25	10·00
O15	O 2	1 a. black and carmine..		2·00	13·00
O16	O 3	2 a. black and orange..		3·25	38·00
O14/16			*Set of 3*	6·00	55·00

1945. *P 14.*

O17	O 10	3 p. black and blue		2·50	7·00
O18		1½ a. black and violet..		14·00	7·00

O 11 Allied Banners

(Des E. Meronti. Recess, background litho)

1946 (1 May). *Victory. P 14.*

O19	O 11	1½ a. green and grey		2·00	3·00

1948. *Nos. 19, 22, 24/5 and 35/8 optd as Nos. O1/6.*

O20	4	3 p. black and blue (R.)		60	10·00
O21		1 a. black and carmine (Blk.)		60	9·00
O22	5	2 a. green and carmine (Blk.)		60	10·00
O23	6	4 a. orange and brown (Blk.)		60	14·00
O24	10	1 r. deep green and orange (R.)		60	16·00
O25		2 r. black and carmine (R.)		60	22·00
O26		5 r. chocolate and ultramarine (R.)		60	35·00
O27	11	10 r. red-brown and green (R.)		60	35·00
O20/7			*Set of 8*	4·25	£130

1949 (10 Oct). *75th Anniv of Universal Postal Union. Nos. 43/6 optd as Nos. O1/6.*

O28	17	9 p. black and green		15	4·50
		aw. Wmk inverted		†	£100
		b. Perf 17½×17		2·00	25·00
O29		1 a. black and magenta		15	4·50
		b. Perf 17½×17		2·00	25·00
O30		1½ a. black and orange		15	4·50
		b. Perf 17½×17		2·00	25·00
O31		2½ a. black and blue		15	4·50
		b. Perf 17½×17		2·00	25·00
O28/31			*Set of 4*	55	16·00
O28b/31b..			*Set of 4*	7·50	90·00

Nos. O28/31 exist imperforate (*Prices, £10 per pair, unused*)

From 1947 stamps of Pakistan were used on all external mail. Bahawalpur issues continued to be used on internal mail until 1953.

Palestine

The stamps of TURKEY were used in Palestine from 1865. In addition various European Powers, and Egypt, maintained post offices at Jerusalem (Austria, France, Germany, Italy, Russia), Jaffa (Austria, Egypt, France, Germany, Russia) and Haifa (Austria, France) using their own stamps or issues specially prepared for Levant post offices. All foreign post offices had closed by the time of the British Occupation.

PRICES FOR STAMPS ON COVER TO 1945

No. 1	*from* × 6	
No. 2	*from* × 4	
Nos. 3/4	*from* × 5	
Nos. 5/15	*from* × 4	
Nos. 16/29	*from* × 3	
Nos. 30/42	*from* × 2	
No. 43	—	
Nos. 44/57	*from* × 2	
Nos. 58/9	—	
Nos. 60/8	*from* × 3	
Nos. 69/70	—	
Nos. 71/89	*from* × 3	
Nos. 90/103	*from* × 4	
Nos. 104/11	*from* × 8	
Nos. D1/5	*from* × 30	
Nos. D6/20	*from* × 10	

BRITISH MILITARY OCCUPATION

British and allied forces invaded Palestine in November 1917 capturing Gaza (7 November), Jaffa (16 November) and Jerusalem (9 December). The front line then stabilised until the second British offensive of September 1918.

Nos. 1/15 were issued by the British military authorities for use by the civilian population in areas they controlled previously part of the Ottoman Empire. Before the issue of Nos. 1/2 in February 1918 civilian mail was carried free. In addition to Palestine the stamps were available from E.E.F. post offices in Syria (including what subsequently became Transjordan) from 23 September 1918 to 23 February 1922, Lebanon from 21 October 1918 to September 1920 and Cilicia from 2 September 1919 to 16 July 1920. Use in the following post offices outside Palestine is recorded in *British Empire Campaigns and Occupations in the Near East, 1914–1924* by John Firebrace:

Adana, Cilicia	Babitoma, Syria
Akkari ("Akkar"), Syria	Behamdoun, Lebanon
Aleppo ("Alep, Halep"), Syria	Beit ed Dine, Lebanon
Aleih ("Alie"), Lebanon	Bekaa, Lebanon
Alexandretta, Syria	Beyrouth, Lebanon
Antakie, Syria	Beit Mery, Beyrouth
Ba'abda, Lebanon	Lebanon
Baalbek, Lebanon	Bouzanti, Syria
Bab, Syria	Broumana, Lebanon

Damascus ("Damas"), Syria	Massel el Chouf ("Moussalc"),
Damour ("Damor"), Lebanon	Lebanon
Der'a ("Deraa"), Syria	Merdjajoun, Lebanon
Deurt-Yol, Syria	Mersina ("Mersine"), Cilicia
Djey Han, Syria	Mounboudje, Syria
Djezzin ("Djezzine"), Lebanon	Nabatti, Lebanon
Djon, Lebanon	Nebk ("Nebik"), Syria
Djounie, Lebanon	Payass, Syria
Djubeil, Lebanon	Racheya, Lebanon
Douma, Syria	Safita, Syria
Edleb, Syria	Savour, Tyre, Lebanon
Feke, Turkey	Selimie, Syria
Habib Souk, Syria	Sidan ("Saida (Echelle)"),
Hajjin ("Hadjin"), Cilicia	Lebanon
Hama, Syria	Suweidiya ("Suvedie"), Syria
Hasbaya, Lebanon	Talia, Syria
Hasine, Cilicia	Tarsous, Cilicia
Hommana, Lebanon	Tartous, Syria
Homs, Syria	Tibnin, Lebanon
Kozan, Cilicia	Tripoli, Syria
Lattakia ("Laskie,	Zahle, Lebanon
Lattaquie"), Syria	Zebdani, Syria

This information is reproduced here by permission of the publishers, Robson Lowe Publications.

(Currency. 10 milliemes = 1 piastre)

1	(2)	3

"E.E.F." = Egyptian Expeditionary Force

W 100 of Great
Britain

(Des G. Rowntree. Litho Typographical Dept, Survey of Egypt, Giza, Cairo)

1918 (10 Feb). *Wmk Royal Cypher in column (W 100 of Great Britain). Ungummed. Roul 20.*

1	1	1 p. indigo (Optd S. £300)		£180	£100
		a. Deep blue		£150	90·00
		b. Blue		£150	90·00
		Control: A 18 (*Prices, corner block of 4*; No. 1 £850. No. 1a, £750. No. 1b, £850).			

1918 (16 Feb). *As last (ungummed) surch with T 2.*

2	1	5 m. on 1 p. cobalt-blue (Optd S. £300)		90·00	£475
		a. "MILLILMES" (No. 10 in sheet)		£3250	£9000
		w. Wmk inverted			
		Control: B 18 A (*Corner block, £1100*).			

1918 (5 Mar). *As No. 1 but colour changed. With gum.*

3	1	1 p. ultramarine (*shades*)		2·00	2·00
		w. Wmk inverted		£160	£150
		Control: C 18. (*Corner block, £70*).			

1918 (5 Mar *and* 13 May). *No. 3 surch with T 2.*

4	1	5 m. on 1 p. ultramarine		3·00	2·75
		a. Arabic surch wholly or partly missing (No. 11 in sheet)		£350	£400
		w. Wmk inverted			£250
		Controls: C 18 B (Mar). (*Corner block, £700*).			
		D 18 C (May). (*Corner block, £200*).			

(Typo Stamping Dept, Board of Inland Revenue, Somerset House, London)

1918 (16 July–27 Dec). *Wmk Royal Cypher in column (W 100 of Great Britain). P 15×14.*

5	3	1 m. sepia		30	40
		a. Deep brown		40	40
6		2 m. blue-green		30	45
		a. Deep green		90	80
7		3 m. yellow-brown (17 Dec)		35	35
		a. Chestnut		10·00	6·00
8		4 m. scarlet		35	40
9		5 m. yellow-orange (25 Sept)		1·00	30
		a. Orange		65	45
		w. Wmk inverted			—£1500
10		1 p. deep indigo (9 Nov)		35	25
		w. Wmk inverted		£150	£160
11		2 p. pale olive		60	60
		a. Olive		1·50	1·10
12		5 p. purple		1·75	2·25
13		9 p. ochre (17 Dec)		2·50	4·50
14		10 p. ultramarine (17 Dec)		2·25	3·00
		w. Wmk inverted			£400
15		20 p. pale grey (27 Dec)		11·00	16·00
		a. Slate-grey		15·00	22·00
5/15			*Set of 11*	18·00	25·00

There are two sizes of the design of this issue:
19 × 23 mm. 1, 2, and 4 m., and 2 and 5 p.
18 × 21½ mm. 3 and 5 m., and 1, 9, 10 and 20 p.
There are numerous minor plate varieties in this issue, such as stops omitted in "E.E.F.", malformed Arabic characters, etc.

CIVIL ADMINISTRATION UNDER BRITISH HIGH COMMISSIONER

Palestine was placed under civil administration by a British High Commissioner on 1 July 1920.

(4)	(5)	(6)

Differences:—
T 5. 20 mm vert and 7 mm between English and Hebrew.
T 6. 19 mm and 6 mm respectively.

(Optd at Greek Orthodox Convent, Jerusalem)

1920 (1 Sept). *Optd with T 4 (Arabic 8 mm long). (a) P 15×14.*

16	3	1 m. sepia		2·00	1·90
17		2 m. blue-green		6·00	4·50
18		3 m. chestnut		4·50	4·75
		a. Opt inverted		£450	£600
19		4 m. scarlet		1·00	1·25
20		5 m. yellow-orange		11·00	4·25
21		1 p. deep indigo (Sil.)		1·00	80
		w. Wmk inverted		60·00	60·00
22		2 p. deep olive		1·75	1·90
23		5 p. deep purple		11·00	17·00
24		9 p. ochre		8·00	20·00
25		10 p. ultramarine		10·00	17·00
26		20 p. pale grey		18·00	42·00
		(b) P 14			
27	3	2 m. blue-green		1·40	1·40
28		3 m. chestnut		48·00	48·00
29		5 m. orange		1·40	90
16/29			*Set of 14*	£100	£140

Two settings of T 4 are known to specialists, the first, of 24, being used for all values perforated 15×14 (but only on one sheet of the 1 p.) and the second, of 12, for all values in both perforations.

Apart from minor varieties due to broken type, there are three major errors which are rare in some values. These are (a) two Hebrew characters at left transposed (all values of first setting only); (b) diamond-shaped dot over the Arabic "t" making the word read "Faleszin" for "Falestin" (2 p. to 20 p. of first setting and 1 m. and 3 m. perf 15 × 14, and 5 m. perf 14 of second setting); (c) "B" for final "E" of "PALESTINE" (2 p. to 20 p. of first setting and all values of second setting except 3 m. perf 14).

Faulty registration of the overprint in this issue has resulted in numerous misplaced overprints, either vertically or horizontally, which are not of great importance with the exception of Nos. 21 and 29 which exist with the overprint out of sequence, i.e. Hebrew/Arabic/English or English/Arabic/Hebrew or English/Hebrew only. Also all values are known with Arabic/English only.

1920 (22 Sept)–21. *Optd with T 5* (Arabic 10 mm long).*

		(a) P 15×14			
30	3	1 m. sepia (27.12.20)		1·00	1·00
		a. Opt inverted		£400	†
31		2 m. blue-green (27.12.20)		6·00	4·00
		a. Opt double			
32		3 m. yellow-brown (27.12.20)		1·25	1·00
33		4 m. scarlet (27.12.20)		1·25	1·25
34		5 m. yellow-orange		2·25	75
35		1 p. deep indigo (Silver) (21.6.21)		£425	25·00
36		2 p. olive (21.6.21)		60·00	25·00
37		5 p. deep purple (21.6.21)		28·00	9·50
		(b) P 14			
38	3	1 m. sepia		£500	£700
39		2 m. blue-green		2·50	4·00
40		4 m. scarlet		55·00	75·00
41		5 m. orange		85·00	9·00
		a. Yellow-orange		3·50	1·10
42		1 p. deep indigo (Silver)		30·00	1·25
43		5 p. purple		£200	£450

*In this setting the Arabic and Hebrew characters are badly worn and blunted, the Arabic "S" and "T" are joined (i.e. there is no break in the position indicated by the arrow in our illustration); the letters of "PALESTINE" are often irregular or broken; and the space between the two groups of Hebrew characters varies from 1 mm to over 1¾ mm. The " character in the left-hand Hebrew word extends above the remainder of the line (*For clear, sharp overprint, see Nos. 47/59*).

The dates of issue given are irrespective of the perforations, i.e. one or both perfs could have been issued on the dates shown. Nos. 31 and 39 exist with any one line of the overprint partly missing.

1920 (6 Dec). *Optd with T 6. (a) P 15 × 14.*

44	3	3 m. yellow-brown		35·00	32·00
44a		5 m. yellow-orange		£14000	£12000
		(b) P 14			
45	3	1 m. sepia		35·00	32·00
46		5 m. orange		£350	30·00

(6a)	(7)	(8)

1921 (29 May–4 Aug). *Optd as T 6a. (a) P 15×14.*

47	3	1 m. sepia (23.6)		7·00	3·50
48		2 m. blue-green (23.6)		11·00	5·50
49		3 m. yellow-brown (23.6)		24·00	3·00
		a. "PALESTINE" omitted			£2500

50	3	4 m. scarlet (23.6)..		22·00	3·50
51		5 m. yellow-orange		32·00	1·00
52		1 p. deep indigo (Silver) (July)		18·00	75
53		2 p. olive (4.8)		21·00	6·00
54		5 p. purple (4.8)		25·00	4·00
55		9 p. ochre (4.8)		40·00	90·00
56		10 p. ultramarine (4.8)		42·00	14·00
57		20 p. pale grey (4.8)		75·00	50·00
47/57			Set of 11	£275	£160

(b) P 14

58	3	1 m. sepia		—	£2000
59		20 p. pale grey		£12000	£2500

In this setting the Arabic and Hebrew characters are sharp and pointed and there is usually a break between the Arabic "S" and "T", though this is sometimes filled with ink. The space between the two groups of Hebrew characters is always 1¾ mm. The top of the " character in the Hebrew aligns with the remainder of the word.

1921 (Sept–Oct). *Optd with T 7 ("PALESTINE" in sans-serif letters) by Stamping Dept, Board of Inland Revenue, Somerset House, London. Wmk Royal Cypher in column (W 100 of Great Britain). P 15×14.*

60	3	1 m. sepia		85	30
61		2 m. blue-green		85	30
62		3 m. yellow-brown		1·00	30
63		4 m. scarlet		1·00	60
64		5 m. yellow-orange		1·00	30
65		1 p. bright turquoise-blue		1·00	35
66		2 p. olive		1·75	40
67		5 p. deep purple		5·50	5·00
68		9 p. ochre		14·00	14·00
69		10 p. ultramarine		19·00	£500
		w. Wmk inverted		†	
70		20 p. pale grey		50·00	£1200
60/70			Set of 11	85·00	

(Printed and optd by Waterlow & Sons from new plates)

1922 (Sept–Nov). *T 3 (redrawn), optd with T 8. Wmk Mult Script CA. (a) P 14.*

71	3	1 m. sepia		30	30
		a. Deep brown		60	30
		b. Opt inverted		—	£12000
		c. Opt double		£225	£425
		w. Wmk inverted		15·00	10·00
72		2 m. yellow		45	30
		a. Orange-yellow		2·25	50
		b. Wmk sideways		†	
		w. Wmk inverted		—	35·00
73		3 m. greenish blue		45	15
		w. Wmk inverted		30·00	30·00
74		4 m. carmine-pink		40	20
		w. Wmk inverted		38·00	38·00
75		5 m. orange		65	50
		w. Wmk inverted		50·00	38·00
76		6 m. blue-green		80	30
		w. Wmk inverted		40·00	40·00
77		7 m. yellow-brown		80	30
		w. Wmk inverted		£150	£150
78		8 m. scarlet		80	30
		w. Wmk inverted		45·00	50·00
79		1 p. grey		80	30
		w. Wmk inverted		50·00	50·00
80		13 m. ultramarine		75	15
		w. Wmk inverted		30·00	20·00
81		2 p. olive		1·50	35
		a. Opt inverted		£300	£500
		b. Ochre		£120	6·50
		w. Wmk inverted		£150	£120
82		5 p. deep purple		4·75	1·25
		aw. Wmk inverted		—	£400
82b		9 p. ochre		£900	£200
83		10 p. light blue		35·00	9·50
		a. "E.F.F." for "E.E.F." in bottom panel (R. 10/3)		£600	£400
84		20 p. bright violet		£120	90·00

(b) P 15×14

86	3	5 p. deep purple		40·00	4·00
87		9 p. ochre		9·00	9·00
88		10 p. light blue		7·50	2·50
		a. "E.F.F." for "E.E.F." in bottom panel (R. 10/3)		£375	£275
		w. Wmk inverted		—	£225
89		20 p. bright violet		9·00	5·50
71/89		Optd "Specimen"	Set of 15	£400	

Most values can be found on thin paper.

In this issue the design of all denominations is the same size, 18 mm × 21½ mm. Varieties may be found with one or other of the stops between "E.E.F." missing.

BRITISH MANDATE TO THE LEAGUE OF NATIONS

The League of Nations granted a mandate to Great Britain for the administration of Palestine on 29 September 1923.

(New Currency. 1,000 mils = 1 Palestine pound)

9 Rachel's Tomb

10 Dome of the Rock

11 Citadel, Jerusalem

12 Sea of Galilee

(Des F. Taylor. Typo Harrison)

1927 (1 June)–45. *Wmk Mult Script CA. P 13½ × 14½ (2 m. to 20 m.) or 14.*

90	9	2 m. greenish blue (14.8.27)		30	10
		w. Wmk inverted		—	£400
91		3 m. yellow-green		40	10
		w. Wmk inverted		—	£200
92	10	4 m. rose-pink (14.8.27)		3·25	1·25
93	11	5 m. orange (14.8.27)		65	10
		a. From coils. Perf 14½×14 (1935)		14·00	18·00
		b. Yellow (12.44)		65	15
		c. Yellow. From coils. Perf 14½×14 (1945)		30·00	27·00
		w. Wmk inverted		15·00	18·00
94	10	6 m. pale green (14.8.27)		3·00	1·75
		a. Deep green		50	20
95	11	7 m. scarlet (14.8.27)		4·00	60
96	10	8 m. yellow-brown (14.8.27)		12·00	6·00
97	9	10 m. slate (14.8.27)		40	10
		a. Grey. From coils. Perf 14½×14 (11.38)		20·00	24·00
		aw. Wmk inverted			
		b. Grey (1944)		75	10
98	10	13 m. ultramarine		4·00	30
99	11	20 m. dull olive-green (14.8.27)		1·00	15
		a. Bright olive-green (12.44)		1·00	15
		w. Wmk inverted		—	£275
100	12	50 m. deep dull purple (14.8.27)		1·00	30
		a. Bright purple (12.44)		1·25	30
		w. Wmk inverted			
101		90 m. bistre (14.8.27)		55·00	60·00
102		100 m. turquoise-blue (14.8.27)		2·00	70
103		200 m. deep violet (14.8.27)		8·00	5·00
		a. Bright violet (1928)		27·00	16·00
		b. Blackish violet (12.44)		6·00	3·50
90/103b			Set of 14	80·00	65·00
90/103 H/S "Specimen"			Set of 14	£325	

Three sets may be made of the above issue; one on thin paper, one on thicker paper with a ribbed appearance, and another on thick white paper without ribbing.

2 m. stamps in the grey colour of the 10 m., including an example postmarked in 1935, exist as do 50 m. stamps in blue, but it has not been established whether they were issued.

Nos. 90/1 and 93 exist in coils, constructed from normal sheets.

1932 (1 June)–44. *New values and colours. Wmk Mult Script CA. P 13½ × 14½ (4 m. to 15 m.) or 14.*

104	10	4 m. purple (1.11.32)		65	10
		w. Wmk inverted		—	£400
105	11	7 m. deep violet		45	10
106	10	8 m. scarlet		60	20
		w. Wmk inverted		—	£500
107		13 m. bistre (1.8.32)		70	10
108		15 m. ultramarine (1.8.32)		1·75	10
		a. Grey-blue (12.44)		1·00	40
		b. Greenish blue		1·10	40
		w. Wmk inverted		—	£500
109	12	250 m. brown (15.1.42)		3·75	1·75
110		500 m. scarlet (15.1.42)		4·50	3·00
111		£P1 black (15.1.42)		5·00	3·50
104/11			Set of 8	15·00	8·00
104/11 Perf "Specimen"			Set of 8	£375	

No. 108 exists in coils, constructed from normal sheets.

STAMP BOOKLETS

1929. *Blue cover inscr "PALESTINE POSTAGE STAMP BOOKLET" and contents in English. Without advertisements on front. Stitched.*

SB1	150 m. booklet containing twelve 2 m., 3 m. and eighteen 5 m. (Nos. 90/1, 93) in blocks of 6	£2000
	a. As No. SB1, but stapled	£1600

1930. *Blue cover inscr "PALESTINE POSTS & TELEGRAPHS POSTAGE STAMP BOOKLET" and contents all in English, Arabic and Hebrew. Without advertisements on front. Stapled.*

SB2	150 m. booklet. Contents as No. SB1	

1937–38. *Red cover inscr "POSTAGE STAMP BOOKLET" and contents in English, Hebrew and Arabic. With advertisements on front. Stapled.*

SB3	150 m. booklet containing 2 m., 3 m., 5 m. and 15 m. (Nos. 90/1, 93, 108) in blocks of 6	£1600
	a. Blue cover (1938)	£1600

1939. *Pink cover inscr "POSTAGE STAMP BOOKLET" and contents in English, Hebrew and Arabic. With advertisements on front. Stapled.*

SB4	120 m. booklet containing six 10 m. and twelve 5 m. (Nos. 93, 97) in blocks of 6	£1500

POSTAL FISCALS

Type-set stamps inscribed "O.P.D.A." (= Ottoman Public Debt Administration) or "H.J.Z." (Hejaz Railway); British 1d. stamps of 1912–24 and Palestine stamps overprinted with one or other of the above groups of letters, or with the word "Devair", with or without surcharge of new value, are fiscal stamps. They are known used as postage stamps, alone, or with other stamps to make up the correct rates, and were passed by the postal authorities, although they were not definitely authorised for postal use.

POSTAGE DUE STAMPS

D 1

D 2 (MILLIEME)

D 3 (MIL)

(Typo Greek Orthodox Convent Press, Jerusalem)

1923 (1 Apr.) *P 11.*

D1	D 1	1 m. yellow-brown		27·00	40·00
		a. Imperf (pair)		£300	
		b. Imperf between (horiz pair)		£1100	
D2		2 m. blue-green		19·00	27·00
		a. Imperf (pair)		£400	
D3		4 m. scarlet		22·00	35·00
D4		8 m. mauve		15·00	26·00
		a. Imperf (pair)		£120	
		b. Imperf between (horiz pair)		—	£1800
D5		13 m. steel blue		15·00	26·00
		a. Imperf between (horiz pair)		£850	
D1/5			Set of 5	90·00	£140

Perfectly centred and perforated stamps of this issue are worth considerably more than the above prices, which are for average specimens.

(Types D 2/3. Typo D.L.R.)

1924 (1 Dec). *Wmk Mult Script CA. P 14.*

D 6	D 2	1 m. deep brown		90	2·00
D 7		2 m. yellow		2·00	1·75
		w. Wmk inverted		—	£400
D 8		4 m. green		2·00	1·25
D 9		8 m. scarlet		3·00	90
D10		13 m. ultramarine		2·75	2·50
D11		5 p. violet		8·50	1·75
D6/11			Set of 6	17·00	9·00
D6/11 Optd "Specimen"			Set of 6	£275	

1928 (1 Feb)–45. *Wmk Mult Script CA. P 14.*

D12	D 3	1 m. brown		45	85
		a. Perf 15×14 (1944)		32·00	60·00
D13		2 m. yellow		55	60
		w. Wmk inverted		†	£400
D14		4 m. green		80	1·60
		a. Perf 15×14 (1945)		55·00	75·00
D15		6 m. orange-brown (10.33)		12·00	8·50
D16		8 m. carmine		1·75	90
D17		10 m. pale grey		1·25	60
D18		13 m. ultramarine		1·50	1·75
D19		20 m. pale olive-green		1·60	1·25
D20		50 m. violet		2·50	1·25
D12/20			Set of 9	20·00	16·00
D12/20 Perf (D15) or Optd (others) "Specimen"			Set of 9	£300	

Nos. D12a and D14a were printed and perforated by Harrison and Sons following bomb damage to the De La Rue works on 29 December 1940.

The British Mandate terminated on 14 May 1948. Later issues of stamps and occupation issues will be found listed under Gaza, Israel and Jordan in Part 19 (*Middle East*) of this catalogue.

Papua New Guinea

NEW GUINEA

Stamps of Germany and later of GERMAN NEW GUINEA were used in New Guinea from 1888 until 1914.

During the interim period between the "G.R.I." surcharges and the "N.W. PACIFIC ISLANDS" overprints, stamps of AUSTRALIA perforated "OS" were utilised.

PRICES FOR STAMPS ON COVER

Nos. 1/30	from × 3
Nos. 31/2	—
Nos. 33/49	from × 3
Nos. 50/9	from × 2
Nos. 60/2	—
Nos. 63/4	from × 2
Nos. 64c/q	—
Nos. 65/81	from × 5
Nos. 83/5	—
Nos. 86/97	from × 5
No. 99	—
Nos. 100/16	from × 4
Nos. 117/18	—
Nos. 119/24	from × 4
Nos. 125/203	from × 2
Nos. 204/5	—
Nos. 206/11	from × 8
Nos. 212/25	from × 2
Nos. O1/33	from × 8

AUSTRALIAN OCCUPATION

Stamps of German New Guinea surcharged

G.R.I.	G.R.I.	
2d.	1s.	1
(1)	(2)	(3)

SETTINGS. The "G.R.I." issues of New Guinea were surcharged on a small hand press which could only accommodate one horizontal row of stamps at a time. In addition to complete sheets the surcharges were also applied to multiples and individual stamps which were first lightly affixed to plain paper backing sheets. Such backing sheets could contain a mixture of denominations, some of which required different surcharges.

Specialists recognise twelve settings of the low value surcharges (1d. to 8d.):

Setting 1 (Nos. 1/4, 7/11) shows the bottom of the "R" 6 mm from the top of the "d"

Setting 2 (Nos. 16/19, 22/6) shows the bottom of the "R" 5 mm from the top of the "d"

Setting 3 was used for the Official stamps (Nos. O1/2)

Setting 4, which included the 2½d. value for the first time, and Setting 5 showed individual stamps with either 6 mm or 5 mm spacing.

These five settings were for rows of ten stamps, but the remaining seven, used on odd stamps handed in for surcharging, were applied as strips of five only. One has, so far, not been reconstructed, but of the remainder three show the 6 mm spacing, two the 5 mm and one both.

On the shilling values the surcharges were applied as horizontal rows of four and the various settings divide into two groups, one with 3½ to 4½ mm between the bottom of the "R" and the top of numeral, and the second with 5½ mm between the "R" and numeral. The first group includes the very rare initial setting on which the space is 4 to 4½ mm.

G.R.I.	G.R.I.	G.R.I.
2d.	**1d.**	**1s.**
"1" for "I" (Setting 1)	Short "1" (Setting 1)	Large "S" (Setting 1)

1914 (17 Oct)–15. *Stamps of 1901 surch.*

(a) As T 1. "G.R.I." and value 6 mm apart

1	1d. on 3 pf. brown	£300	£350
	a. "1" for "I"	£750	
	b. Short "1"	£750	
	c. "1" with straight top serif (Setting 6)	£750	
	d. "I" for "1" (Setting 12)	£1000	
2	1d. on 5 pf. green	42·00	50·00
	a. "1" for "I"	£190	£250
	b. Short "1"	£190	£250
	c. "1" with straight top serif (Settings 6 and 9)	£300	£350
3	2d. on 10 pf. carmine	48·00	70·00
	a. "1" for "I"	£225	£300
4	2d. on 20 pf. ultramarine	48·00	50·00
	a. "1" for "I"	£200	£250
	e. Surch double, one "G.R.I." albino	£2500	
	f. Surch inverted	£4750	
5	2½d. on 10 pf. carmine (27.2.15)	65·00	£140
	a. Fraction bar omitted (Setting 9)	£1200	£1300
6	2½d. on 20 pf. ultramarine (27.2.15)	70·00	£140
	a. Fraction bar omitted (Setting 9)	£750	
7	3d. on 25 pf. black and red/*yellow*	£190	£250
	a. "1" for "I"	£650	£700
8	3d. on 30 pf. black and orange/*buff*	£225	£250
	a. "1" for "I"	£700	
	e. Surch double	£4500	£4250
9	4d. on 40 pf. black and carmine	£250	£300
	a. "1" for "I"	£800	
	e. Surch double	£1000	£1500
	f. Surch inverted	£4750	
10	5d. on 50 pf. black and purple/*buff*	£450	£650
	a. "1" for "I"	£1200	£1500
	e. Surch double	£4750	
11	8d. on 80 pf. black and carmine/*rose*	£650	£850
	a. "1" for "I"	£1700	
	d. No stop after "d"	£2250	
	e. Error. Surch "G.R.I. 4d."	£4000	

(b) As T 2. "G.R.I." and value 3½ to 4 mm apart

12	1s. on 1 m. carmine	£1500	£2000
	a. Large "s"	£4750	£4750
13	2s. on 2 m. blue	£1700	£2500
	a. Large "s"	£5000	£6000
	c. Error. Surch "G.R.I. 5s."	£14000	
	d. Error. Surch "G.R.I. 2d." corrected by handstamped "S"	£14000	
14	3s. on 3 m. violet-black	£3250	£4250
	a. Large "s"	£6000	
	b. No stop after "I" (Setting 3)	£6500	£6500
15	5s. on 5 m. carmine and black	£6500	£8500
	a. Large "s"	£13000	
	b. No stop after "I" (Setting 3)	£9500	£12000
	c. Error. Surch "G.R.I. 1s."	£20000	

G.R.I.	G.R.I.
3d.	**5d.**
Thick "3" (Setting 2)	Thin "5" (Setting 2)

1914 (16 Dec)–15. *Stamps of 1901 surch.*

(a) As T 1. "G.R.I." and value 5 mm apart

16	1d. on 3 pf. brown	45·00	55·00
	a. "I" for "1" (Setting 11)	£400	
	b. Short "1" (Setting 2)	£200	
	c. "1" with straight top serif (Settings 2 and 6)	75·00	90·00
	e. Surch double	£450	£650
	f. Surch double, one inverted	£1900	
	g. Surch inverted	£1100	£1500
	h. Error. Surch "G.R.I. 4d."	£4500	
17	1d. on 5 pf. green	18·00	28·00
	b. Short "1" (Setting 2)	£110	£160
	c. "1" with straight top serif (Setting 2)	35·00	60·00
	e. "d" inverted	† £1000	
	f. "1d" inverted	† £3500	
	g. "G.R.I." without stops or spaces	£3500	
	ga. "G.R.I." without stops, but with normal spaces	—	£3500
	h. "G.I.R." instead of "G.R.I."	£4500	£4750
	i. Surch double	£1200	

18	2d. on 10 pf. carmine	24·00	38·00
	e. No stop after "d" (Setting 2)	£130	£180
	f. Stop before, instead of after, "G" (Settings 4 and 5)	£3500	
	g. Surch double	£4750	£4750
	h. Surch double, one inverted	—	£3000
	i. In vert pair with No. 20	£11000	
	j. In horiz pair with No. 20	£11000	
	k. Error. Surch "G.R.I. 3d."	£3500	£3000
	l. Error. Surch "G.I.R. 3d."	£4500	
19	2d. on 20 pf. ultramarine	28·00	42·00
	e. No stop after "d" (Setting 2)	95·00	£130
	f. No stop after "I" (Setting 11)	£750	
	g. "R" inverted (Settings 4 and 5)	—	£3250
	h. Surch double	£950	£1600
	i. Surch double, one inverted	£1500	£1800
	j. Surch inverted	£3000	£3500
	k. Albino surch (in horiz pair with normal)	£8500	
	l. In vert pair with No. 21	£7500	£9000
	m. Error. Surch "G.R.I. 1d."	£4500	£4500
20	2½d. on 10 pf. carmine (27.2.15)	£160	£250
21	2½d. on 20 pf. ultramarine (27.2.15)	£1500	£1800
	a. Error. Surch "G.R.I. 3d." (in vert pair with normal)	£8500	
22	3d. on 25 pf. black and red/*yellow*	£100	£140
	e. Thick "3"	£500	
	f. Surch double	£3500	£4250
	g. Surch inverted	£3500	£4250
	h. Surch omitted (in horiz pair with normal)	£8500	
	i. Error. Surch "G.R.I. 1d."	£8000	
23	3d. on 30 pf. black and orange/*buff*	85·00	£120
	e. No stop after "d" (Setting 2)	£550	
	f. Thick "3"	£475	
	g. Surch double	£1100	£1600
	h. Surch double, one inverted	£1400	£1800
	i. Surch double, both inverted	£3500	£4250
	j. Surch inverted	£3000	
	k. Albino surch	£6000	
	l. Surch omitted (in vert pair with normal)	£4500	
	m. Error. Surch "G.R.I. 1d."	£3500	£4500
24	4d. on 40 pf. black and carmine	£100	£140
	e. Surch double	£950	
	f. Surch double, one inverted	£1800	
	g. Surch double, both inverted	£4000	
	h. Surch inverted	£2250	
	i. Error. Surch "G.R.I. 1d."	£2250	
	ia. Surch "G.R.I. 1d." inverted	£4000	
	j. Error. Surch "G.R.I. 3d." double	£6500	
	k. No stop after "I" (Setting 11)	£1800	
25	5d. on 50 pf. black and purple/*buff*	£140	£180
	e. Thin "5"	£750	£1300
	f. Surch double	£1400	
	g. Surch double, one inverted	£3000	£4250
	h. Surch double, both inverted	£3500	£4250
	i. Surch inverted	£2250	
	j. Error. Surch "G.I.R. 3d."	£7000	
26	8d. on 80 pf. black and carmine/*rose*	£325	£400
	e. Surch double	£2250	£2750
	f. Surch double, one inverted	£2250	£2750
	g. Surch triple	£2500	£3000
	h. Surch inverted	£3750	£4250
	i. Error. Surch "G.R.I. 3d."	£7500	

(b) As T 2. "G.R.I." and value 5½ mm apart

27	1s. on 1 m. carmine	£2500	£3500
	a. No stop after "I" (Setting 7)	£5000	
28	2s. on 2 m. blue	£2750	£4250
	a. No stop after "I" (Setting 7)	£5000	
29	3s. on 3 m. violet-black	£4500	£7500
	a. G.R.I." double	£14000	
30	5s. on 5 m. carmine and black	£16000	£18000

1915 (Jan). *Nos. 18 and 19 further surch with T 3.*

31	1d. on 2d. on 10 pf.	£14000	£14000
32	1d. on 2d. on 20 pf.	£13000	£8500

OFFICIAL STAMPS

O. S.

G.R.I.

1d.

(O 3a)

1915 (27 Feb). *Stamps of 1901 surch as Type O 3a. "G.R.I." and value 3½ mm apart.*

O1	1d. on 3 pf. brown	25·00	70·00
	a. "1" and "d" spaced	75·00	£160
	b. Surch double	£2250	
O2	1d. on 5 pf. green	80·00	£140
	a. "1" and "d" spaced	£160	£300

German New Guinea Registration Labels surcharged

4	4a

G.R.I.

3d.

Sans serif "G" and different "3"

1915 (Jan). *Registration Labels surch "G.R.I. 3d." in settings of five or ten and used for postage. Each black and red on buff. Inscr "(Deutsch Neuguinea)" spelt in various ways as indicated. P 14 (No. 43) or 11½ (others).*

I. With name of town in sans-serif letters as T 4

33	Rabaul "(Deutsch Neuguinea)"	£180	£200
	a. "G.R.I. 3d." double	£1900	£2500
	b. No bracket before "Deutsch"	£700	£900
	ba. No bracket and surch double	£4750	
	d. "(Deutsch-Neuguinea)"	£250	£375
	da. "G.R.I. 3d." double	£4750	£4750
	db. No stop after "I"	£650	
	dc. "G.R.I. 3d" inverted	£4750	
	dd. No bracket before "Deutsch"	£1000	£1400
	de. No bracket after "Neuguinea"	£1000	£1400
34	Deulon "(Deutsch Neuguinea)"	£12000	
35	Friedrich-Wilhelmshafen "(Deutsch Neuguinea)"	£170	£450
	a. No stop after "d"	£325	
	b. "G" omitted	£2750	
	c. Sans-serif "G"	£5000	
	d. Sans-serif "G" and different "3"	£4500	
	e. Surch inverted	† £4750	
	f. "(Deutsch-Neuguinea)"	£180	£450
	fa. No stop after "d"	£375	
36	Herbertshöhe "(Deutsch Neuguinea)"	£190	£500
	a. No stop after "d"	£400	
	b. No stop after "I"	£700	
	c. "G" omitted	£3000	
	d. Surch omitted (in horiz pair with normal)	£6500	
	e. "(Deutsch Neu-Guinea)"	£350	£600
37	Käwieng "(Deutsch-Neuguinea)"	£550	
	a. No bracket after "Neuguinea"	£2500	
	b. "Deutsch Neu-Guinea"	£250	£475
	ba. No stop after "d"	£425	
	bb. "G.R.I." double	£2250	
	bc. "3d." double	£2250	
	bd. "G" omitted	£3500	
38	Kieta "(Deutsch-Neuguinea)"	£350	£600
	a. No bracket before "Deutsch"	£1200	£1800
	b. No stop after "d"	£650	
	c. Surch omitted (righthand stamp of horiz pair)	£5500	
	e. No stop after "I"	£950	
	f. "G" omitted	£3250	
39	Manus "(Deutsch Neuguinea)"	£200	£550
	a. "G.R.I. 3d." double	£2750	
	b. No bracket before "Deutsch"	£900	£1400
40	Stephansort "(Deutsch Neu-Guinea)"	† £1800	
	a. No stop after "d"	† £3750	

II. With name of town in letters with serifs as T 4a

41	Friedrich Wilhelmshafen "(Deutsch-Neuguinea)"	£160	£425
	b. No stop after "d"	£325	£700
	c. No stop after "I"	£650	£1000
	d. No bracket before "Deutsch"	£1000	£1500
	e. No bracket after "Neuguinea"	£1000	£1500
42	Käwieng "(Deutsch Neuguinea)"	£150	£400
	a. No stop after "d"	£375	
	b. No stop after "I"	£375	
43	Manus "(Deutsch-Neuguinea)"	£2000	£3000
	a. No stop after "I"	£3500	£3500

Stamps of Marshall Islands surcharged

SETTINGS. The initial supply of Marshall Islands stamps, obtained from Nauru, was surcharged with Setting 2 (5 mm between "R" and "d") on the penny values and with the 3½ to 4 setting on the shilling stamps.

Small quantities subsequently handed in were surcharged, often on the same backing sheet as German New Guinea values, with Settings 6, 7 or 12 (all 6 mm between "R" and "d") for the penny values and with a 5½ mm setting for the shilling stamps.

1914 (16 Dec). *Stamps of 1901 surch.*

(a) As T 1. "G.R.I." and value 5 mm apart

50	1d. on 3 pf. brown	48·00	80·00
	c. "1" with straight top serif (Setting 2)	£110	£180
	d. ".G.R.I." and "1" with straight top serif (Settings 4 and 5)	† £4250	
	e. Surch inverted	£2500	
51	1d. on 5 pf. green	50·00	55·00
	c. "1" with straight top serif (Settings 2 and 11)	£100	£120
	d. "I" for "1" (Setting 11)	£650	
	e. "1" and "d" spaced	£325	£350
	f. Surch double	£1000	£1700
	g. Surch inverted	£1300	
52	2d. on 10 pf. carmine	17·00	26·00
	e. No stop after "G" (Setting 2)	£550	
	f. Surch double	£1000	£1700
	g. Surch double, one inverted	£1300	£1700
	h. Surch inverted	£2000	
	i. Surch sideways	£3750	
53	2d. on 20 pf. ultramarine	18·00	30·00
	e. No stop after "d" (Setting 2)	45·00	80·00
	f. Surch double	£1300	£1800
	g. Surch double, one inverted	£2500	£2750
	h. Surch inverted	£3250	£3250
54	3d. on 25 pf. black and red/*yellow*	£275	£375
	e. No stop after "d" (Settings 2 and 11)	£500	£700
	f. Thick "3"	£750	
	g. Surch double	£1300	£1800
	h. Surch double, one inverted	£1300	
	i. Surch inverted	£3250	
55	3d. on 30 pf. black and orange/*buff*	£300	£400
	e. No stop after "d" (Setting 2)	£550	£700
	f. Thick "3"	£800	
	g. Surch inverted	£2250	£2750
	h. Surch double	£2000	
56	4d. on 40 pf. black and carmine	£100	£130
	e. No stop after "d" (Setting 2)	£250	£400
	f. "d" omitted (Setting 2)	† £3750	
	g. Surch double	£2250	£2750
	h. Surch triple	£4000	
	i. Surch inverted	£2750	
	j. Error. Surch "G.R.I. 1d."	£5500	
	k. Error. Surch "G.R.I. 3d."	£5500	

57	5d. on 50 pf. black and purple/*buff*	..	£140	£180
	e. Thin "5"	..		£2500
	f. "d" omitted (Setting 2)	..		£1400
	g. Surch double	..		£3500
	h. Surch inverted	..		£4000
58	8d. on 80 pf. black and carmine/*rose*	..	£400	£500
	e. Surch double	..		£2750
	f. Surch double, both inverted	..	£3500	£4000
	g. Surch triple	..		£4250
	h. Surch inverted	..		£3250

(b) As T 2. "G.R.I." and value 3½–4 mm apart

59	1s. on 1 m. carmine	..	£1800	£3000
	b. No stop after "I"	..	£3250	£4500
	e. Surch double	..		£10000
60	2s. on 2 m. blue	..	£1200	£2000
	b. No stop after "I"	..	£2500	£3750
	e. Surch double	..		£10000
	f. Surch double, one inverted	..	£9500	£9500
61	3s. on 3 m. violet-black	..	£3250	£4750
	b. No stop after "I"	..		£4500
	e. Surch double	..	£11000	£14000
62	5s. on 5 m. carmine and black	..	£6500	£8500
	e. Surch double, one inverted	..		†£18000

1915 (Jan). *Nos. 52 and 53 further surch with T 3.*

63	1d. on 2d. on 10 pf. carmine	..	£140	£170
	a. "1" double	..		£8000
	b. "1" inverted	..	£8500	£8500
	c. Small "1"	..		£350
64	1d. on 2d. on 20 pf. ultramarine	..	£3000	£2250
	a. On No. 53e	..	£5000	£3000
	b. "1" inverted	..	£9000	£9000

The surcharged "1" on No. 63c is just over 4 mm tall. Type 3 is 6 mm tall.

1915. *Stamps of 1901 surch.*

(a) As T 1. "G.R.I." and value 6 mm apart

64c	1d. on 3 pf. brown	..		£950
	cc. "1" with straight top serif (Setting 6)			
	cd. "I" for "1" (Setting 12)	..		£1400
	ce. Surch inverted	..		£4250
64d	1d. on 5 pf. green	..		£1000
	dc. "1" with straight top serif (Setting 6)			£1400
	dd. "I" for "1" (Setting 12)	..		£1400
	de. Surch inverted	..		£4250
	df. Surch double	..		£4250
64e	2d. on 10 pf. carmine	..		£1500
	ea. Surch sideways	..		£4750
64f	2d. on 20 pf. ultramarine	..		£1300
	fe. Surch inverted	..		£4250
64g	2½d. on 10 pf. carmine	..		£7000
64h	2½d. on 20 pf. ultramarine	..		£10000
64i	3d. on 25 pf. black and red/*yellow*	..		£1700
64j	3d. on 30 pf. black and orange/*buff*	..		£1700
	je. Error. Surch "G.R.I. 1d."	..		£5500
64k	4d. on 40 pf. black and carmine	..		£1700
	ke. Surch double	..		£4500
	kf. Surch inverted	..		£4500
64l	5d. on 50 pf. black and purple/*buff*	..		£1500
	le. Surch double	..		£4500
64m	8d. on 80 pf. black and carmine/*rose*	..		£2250
	me. Surch inverted	..		£5000

(b) As T 2. "G.R.I." and value 5½ mm apart

64n	1s. on 1 m. carmine	..		£6500
	na. Large "s" (Setting 5)	..		£8000
	nb. No stop after "I" (Setting 7)	..		£8000
64o	2s. on 2 m. blue	..		£5000
	oe. Surch double, one inverted	..		£18000
64p	3s. on 3 m. violet-black	..		£9500
	pa. Large "s" (Setting 5)	..		£13000
	pb. No stop after "I" (Setting 7)	..		£13000
	pe. Surch inverted	..		£18000
64q	5s. on 5 m. carmine and black	..		£16000
	qa. Large "s" (Setting 5)	..		£19000

Stamps of Australia overprinted

T 1 of Australia   T 5a of Australia

W 2 of Australia   W 5 of Australia

W 6 of Australia

N. W.   N. W.   N. W.
PACIFIC   PACIFIC   PACIFIC
ISLANDS.   ISLANDS.   ISLANDS.

(a)   (b)   (c)

(6)

1915–16. *Stamps of Australia optd in black as T 6 (a), (b) or (c).*

(i) T 5a. W 5 of Australia. P 14 (4 Jan–15 March 1915)

65	½d. green	..	2·50	7·50
	a. Bright green	..	3·00	8·50
	aw. Wmk inverted			
67	1d. pale rose (Die I) (4.1)	..	6·00	6·00
	a. Dull red	..	7·00	6·50
	b. Carmine-red	..	6·50	6·00
	ba. Substituted cliché (Pl 2 rt pane R. 6/5)		£1200	£750
	c. Die II. Carmine-red	..	£180	£140
	ca. Substituted cliché (Pl 2 rt pane R. 6/4)		£1200	£750
70	4d. yellow-orange	..	4·00	14·00
	a. Pale orange-yellow	..	17·00	28·00
	b. Chrome-yellow	..	£250	£275
	c. Line through "FOUR PENCE" (Pl 2 rt pane R. 2/6) (*all shades*)	*from*	£350	£550
72	5d. brown	..	3·25	16·00

(ii) T 1. W 2 of Australia. P 12 (4 Jan 1915–March 1916)

73	2d. grey (Die I)	..	18·00	42·00
74	2½d. indigo (Die II) (4.1.15)	..	2·75	16·00
76	3d. yellow-olive (Die I)	..	20·00	45·00
	a. Die II	..	£300	£400
	ab. In pair with Die I	..	£500	£700
	c. Greenish olive	..	£190	£275
	ca. Die II	..		£1300
	cb. In pair with Die I	..		£2250
78	6d. ultramarine (Die II)	..	42·00	55·00
	a. Retouched "E"	..	£5000	£5500
	w. Wmk inverted	..		80·00
79	9d. violet (Die II)	..	42·00	55·00
81	1s. green (Die II)	..	42·00	55·00
83	5s. grey and yellow (Die II) (3.16)	..	£750	£1100
84	10s. grey and pink (Die II) (12.15)	..	£110	£160
85	£1 brown and ultramarine (Die II) (12.15)	..	£425	£600

(iii) T 1. W 5 of Australia. P 12 (Oct 1915–July 1916)

86	2d. grey (Die II)	..	13·00	17·00
87	2½d. indigo (Die II) (7.16)	..	£10000	£10000
88	6d. ultramarine (Die II)	..	10·00	12·00
89	9d. violet (Die II) (12.15)	..	16·00	20·00
90	1s. emerald (Die II) (12.15)	..	11·00	24·00
91	2s. brown (Die II) (12.15)	..	80·00	£100
92	5s. grey and yellow (Die II) (12.15)	..	70·00	£100

(iv) T 1. W 6 of Australia. P 12 (Dec 1915–1916)

94	2d. grey (Die I)	..	5·00	13·00
	a. In pair with Die IIA	..	£300	
96	3d. yellow-olive (Die I)	..	5·00	11·00
	a. Die II	..	75·00	£120
	ab. In pair with Die I	..	£160	
97	2s. brown (Die II) (8.16)	..	27·00	45·00
	w. Wmk inverted	..		35·00
99	£1 chocolate and dull blue (Die II) (8.16)	..	£250	£400

Dates for Nos. 67 and 74 are issue dates at Rabaul. The stamps were in use from 2 January 1915 on Nauru. All other dates are those of despatch. Nos. 65/6, 68/73, 76/81 were despatched on 15 March 1915.

For Die IIA of 2d. see note below Australia No. 45.

SETTINGS. Type 6 exists in three slightly different versions, illustrated above as (a), (b), and (c). These differ in the letters "S" of "ISLANDS" as follows:

(a) Both "SS" normal.
(b) First "S" with small head and large tail and second "S" normal.
(c) Both "SS" with small head and large tail.

Type 11, which also shows the examples of "S" as the normal version, can be identified from Type 6(a) by the relative position of the second and third lines of the overprint. On Type 6a the "P" of "PACIFIC" is exactly over the first "S" of "ISLANDS". On Type 11 the "P" appears over the space between "I" and "S".

It has been established, by the study of minor variations, that there are actually six settings of the "N.W. PACIFIC ISLANDS" overprint, including that represented by T 11, but the following are the different arrangements of Type 6(a), (b), and (c) which occur.

A. Horizontal rows 1 and 2 all Type (a). Row 3 all Type (b). Rows 4 and 5 all Type (c).

B. (½d. green only). As A, except that the types in the bottom row run (c) (c) (c) (c) (b) (c).

C. As A, but bottom row now shows types (a) (c) (c) (c) (b) (c). Horizontal strips and pairs showing varieties (a) and (c), or (b) and (c) se-tenant are scarce.

The earliest printing of the 1d. and 2½d. values was made on sheets with margin attached on two sides, the later printings being on sheets from which the margins had been removed. In this printing the vertical distances between the overprints are less than in later printings, so that in the lower horizontal rows of the sheet the overprint is near the top of the stamp.

The settings used on King George stamps and on the Kangaroo type are similar, but the latter stamps being smaller the overprints are closer together in the vertical rows.

PURPLE OVERPRINTS. We no longer differentiate between purple and black overprints in the above series. In our opinion the two colours are nowadays insufficiently distinct to warrant separation.

PRICES. The prices quoted for Nos. 65 to 101 apply to stamps with opts Types 6 (a) or 6 (c). Stamps with opt Type 6 (b) are worth a 25 per cent premium. Vertical strips of three, showing (a), (b) and (c), are worth from four times the prices quoted for singles as Types 6 (a) or 6 (c).

N. W.
PACIFIC
One Penny   ISLANDS.

(10)   (11)

1918 (23 May). *Nos. 72 and 81 surch locally with T 10.*

100	1d. on 5d. brown	..	90·00	80·00
101	1d. on 1s. green	..	90·00	75·00

Types 6 (a), (b), (c) occur on these stamps also.

1918–23. *Stamps of Australia optd with T 11 ("P" of "PACIFIC" over space between "I" and "S" of "ISLANDS").*

(i) T 5a. W 5 of Australia. P 14

102	½d. green	..	1·00	3·50
103	1d. carmine-red (Die I)	..	2·50	1·60
	a. Substituted cliché (Pl 2 rt pane R. 6/5)		£650	£375
	b. Die II	..	£110	48·00
	ba. Substituted cliché (Pl 2 rt pane R. 6/4)		£650	£375
104	4d. yellow-orange (1919)	..	3·25	16·00
	a. Line through "FOUR PENCE" (Pl 2 rt pane R. 2/6)		£800	£1200
105	5d. brown (1919)	..	1·75	12·00

(ii) T 1. W 6 of Australia. P 12

106	2d. grey (Die I) (1919)	..	7·00	18·00
	a. Die II	..	10·00	38·00
107	2½d. indigo (Die II) (1919)	..	3·00	16·00
	a. "1" of "½" omitted	..	£5500	£7000
	b. Blue (1920)	..	7·00	25·00
109	3d. greenish olive (Die I) (1919)	..	21·00	24·00
	a. Die II	..	48·00	60·00
	ab. In pair with Die I	..	£325	£400
	b. Light olive (Die IIB) (1923)	..	21·00	29·00
110	6d. ultramarine (Die II) (1919)	..	4·50	14·00
	a. Greyish ultramarine (1922)	..	42·00	65·00
112	9d. violet (Die IIB) (1919)	..	7·50	35·00
113	1s. emerald (Die II)	..	6·50	30·00
	a. Pale blue-green	..	14·00	30·00
115	2s. brown (Die II) (1919)	..	21·00	38·00
116	5s. grey and yellow (Die II) (1919)	..	60·00	65·00
117	10s. grey and bright pink (Die II) (1919)	..	£150	£200
118	£1 bistre-brown & grey-bl (Die II) (1922)	..	£2750	£4000

(iii) T 5a. W 5 of Australia. Rough, unsurfaced paper, locally gummed. P 14

118a	1d. rosine (Die I)	..	£400	£120
	ab. Substituted cliché (Pl 2 rt pane R. 6/5)			
	b. Die II	..	£1100	£400
	ba. Substituted cliché (Pl 2 rt pane R. 6/4)			

(iv) T 5a. W 6a of Australia (Mult Crown A). P 14

119	½d. green (1919)	..	75	3·50
	w. Wmk inverted	..		35·00

(v) T 5a. W 5 of Australia. Colour changes and new value

120	1d. violet (*shades*) (1922)	..	1·25	6·50
121	2d. orange (1921)	..	4·50	3·25
122	2d. rose-scarlet (1922)	..	8·50	4·50
123	4d. violet (1922)	..	29·00	48·00
	a. "FOUR PENCE" in thinner letters (Pl 2 rt pane R. 2/6)		£750	£1000
124	4d. ultramarine (1922)	..	11·00	50·00
	a. "FOUR PENCE" in thinner letters (Pl 2 rt pane R. 2/6)			£750
120/4		*Set of 5*	48·00	£100

Type 11 differs from Type 6 (a) in the position of the "P" of "PACIFIC", which is further to the left in Type 11. Nos. 118a/ba only exist perforated "O S".

MANDATED TERRITORY OF NEW GUINEA

PRINTERS. See note at the beginning of Australia.

12 Native Village   (13)

(Des R. Harrison. Eng T. Harrison. Recess Note Printing Branch, Treasury, Melbourne, from 1926 Note Ptg Branch, Commonwealth Bank of Australia, Melbourne)

1925 (23 Jan)–**28.** *P 11.*

125	12	½d. orange	..	2·50	6·00
126		1d. green	..	2·50	5·50
126a		1½d. orange-vermilion (1926)	..	3·25	2·50
127		2d. claret	..	2·50	4·50
128		3d. blue	..	4·50	4·00
129		4d. olive-green	..	13·00	18·00
130		6d. dull yellow-brown	..	20·00	48·00
		a. Olive-bistre (1927)	..	6·00	48·00
		b. Pale yellow-bistre (1928)	..	4·50	48·00
131		9d. dull purple (*to violet*)	..	13·00	45·00
132		1s. dull blue-green (6.4.25)	..	15·00	24·00
133		2s. brown-lake (6.4.25)	..	30·00	48·00
134		5s. olive-bistre (6.4.25)	..	48·00	65·00
135		10s. dull rose (6.4.25)	..	£100	£160
136		£1 dull olive-green (6.4.25)	..	£180	£250
125/36			*Set of 13*	£375	£550

1931 (8 June). *Air. Optd with T 13. P 11.*

137	12	½d. orange	..	1·00	5·00
138		1d. green	..	1·60	4·50
139		1½d. orange-vermilion	..	1·00	5·00
140		2d. claret	..	1·00	7·00
141		3d. blue	..	1·75	13·00
142		4d. olive-green	..	1·25	8·50
143		6d. pale yellow-bistre	..	1·75	13·00
144		9d. violet	..	3·00	17·00
145		1s. dull blue-green	..	3·00	17·00
146		2s. brown-lake	..	7·00	40·00
147		5s. olive-bistre	..	20·00	65·00
148		10s. bright pink	..	75·00	£100
149		£1 olive-grey	..	£120	£200
137/49			*Set of 13*	£200	£450

14 Raggiana Bird of Paradise (Dates either side of value)

(15)

(Recess John Ash, Melbourne)

1931 (2 Aug). *Tenth Anniv of Australian Administration. T* **14** *(with dates). P* 11.

150	**14**	1d. green			3·25	80
151		1½d. vermilion			4·25	10·00
152		2d. claret			4·75	2·25
153		3d. blue			4·75	4·75
154		4d. olive-green			6·50	16·00
155		5d. deep blue-green			4·75	17·00
156		6d. bistre-brown			4·75	17·00
157		9d. violet			8·00	17·00
158		1s. pale blue-green			6·00	15·00
159		2s. brown-lake			10·00	27·00
160		5s. olive-brown			40·00	50·00
161		10s. bright pink			75·00	£120
162		£1 olive-grey			£170	£225
150/62				*Set of* 13	£300	£450

1931 (2 Aug). *Air. Optd with T* **15**.

163	**14**	½d. orange			3·00	3·25
164		1d. green			3·75	4·50
165		1½d. vermilion			3·75	9·50
166		2d. claret			2·50	3·00
167		3d. blue			6·00	6·00
168		4d. olive-green			6·00	6·00
169		5d. deep blue-green			6·00	9·50
170		6d. bistre-brown			7·00	25·00
171		9d. violet			8·00	15·00
172		1s. pale blue-green			7·00	15·00
173		2s. dull lake			16·00	48·00
174		5s. olive-brown			42·00	65·00
175		10s. bright pink			60·00	£110
176		£1 olive-grey			£100	£190
163/76				*Set of* 14	£200	£450

1932 (30 June)–**1934**. *T* **14** *(redrawn without dates). P* 11.

177		1d. green			90	20
178		1½d. claret			1·00	10·00
179		2d. vermilion			1·25	20
179a		2½d. green (14.9.34)			5·00	16·00
180		3d. blue			1·75	80
180a		3½d. aniline carmine (14.9.34)			11·00	9·00
181		4d. olive-green			90	5·00
182		5d. deep blue-green			1·25	70
183		6d. bistre-brown			2·50	3·00
184		9d. violet			9·50	21·00
185		1s. blue-green			4·00	10·00
186		2s. dull lake			4·00	17·00
187		5s. olive			27·00	45·00
188		10s. pink			48·00	70·00
189		£1 olive-grey			95·00	£100
177/89				*Set of* 15	£190	£250

1932 (30 June)–34. *Air. T* **14** *(redrawn without dates), optd with T* **15**. *P* 11.

190		½d. orange			50	1·50
191		1d. green			80	1·50
192		1½d. claret			1·25	6·00
193		2d. vermilion			90	30
193a		2½d. green (14.9.34)			4·75	2·25
194		3d. blue			2·50	2·50
194a		3½d. aniline carmine (14.9.34)			4·00	3·25
195		4d. olive-green			4·25	9·00
196		5d. deep blue-green			7·00	7·50
197		6d. bistre-brown			4·25	13·00
198		9d. violet			6·00	9·00
199		1s. pale blue-green			6·00	8·50
200		2s. dull lake			9·00	45·00
201		5s. olive-brown			45·00	55·00
202		10s. pink			75·00	75·00
203		£1 olive-grey			75·00	55·00
190/203				*Set of* 16	£200	£225

The ½d. orange redrawn without dates exists without overprint, but it is believed that this was not issued (*Price* £125 *un*).

16 Bulolo Goldfields

(Recess John Ash, Melbourne)

1935 (1 May). *Air. P* 11.

204	**16**	£2 bright violet			£200	£120
205		£5 emerald-green			£500	£375

HIS MAJESTY'S JUBILEE. 1910 — 1935

(17)

18

1935 (27 June). *Silver Jubilee. As Nos.* 177 *and* 179, *but shiny paper. Optd with T* **17**.

206		1d. green			60	35
207		2d. vermilion			1·75	35

(Recess John Ash, Melbourne)

1937 (18 May). *Coronation. P* 11.

208	**18**	2d. scarlet			50	30
209		3d. blue			50	55
210		5d. green			50	55
		a. Re-entry (design completely duplicated) (Pl 2a R. 5/2)			55·00	80·00
211		1s. purple			50	35
208/11				*Set of* 4	1·75	1·60

(Recess John Ash, Melbourne)

1939 (1 Mar). *Air. Inscr* "AIR MAIL POSTAGE" *at foot. P* 11.

212	**16**	½d. orange			3·00	6·00
213		1d. green			3·25	4·00
214		1½d. claret			3·25	7·50
215		2d. vermilion			7·50	3·50
216		3d. blue			9·50	18·00
217		4d. yellow-olive			10·00	8·00
218		5d. deep green			8·00	2·75
219		6d. bistre-brown			19·00	15·00
220		9d. violet			19·00	20·00
221		1s. pale blue-green			19·00	18·00
222		2s. dull lake			50·00	48·00
223		5s. olive-brown			£120	95·00
224		10s. pink			£325	£225
225		£1 olive-green			£100	£110
212/25				*Set of* 14	£600	£500

OFFICIAL STAMPS

Australian stamps perforated "O S" exist with overprint Type **11** for use in New Guinea. We do not list such varieties.

O S O s

(O 1)   **(O 2)**

1925 (6 Apr)–**31**. *Optd with Type* O **1**. *P* 11.

O 3	**12**	1d. green			1·00	4·50
O 4		1½d. orange-vermilion (1931)			5·50	17·00
O 5		2d. claret			1·75	3·75
O 6		3d. blue			3·50	6·50
O 7		4d. olive-green			4·50	8·50
O 8		6d. olive-bistre			19·00	35·00
		a. Pale yellow-bistre (1931)			7·00	35·00
O 9		9d. violet			4·00	35·00
O10		1s. dull blue-green			5·50	35·00
O11		2s. brown-lake			28·00	60·00
O3/11				*Set of* 9	55·00	£180

1931 (2 Aug). *Optd with Type* O **2**. *P* 11.

O12	**14**	1d. green			4·25	13·00
O13		1½d. vermilion			5·00	12·00
O14		2d. claret			8·50	7·00
O15		3d. blue			6·00	6·00
O16		4d. olive-green			4·25	8·50
O17		5d. deep blue-green			10·00	12·00
O18		6d. bistre-brown			13·00	17·00
O19		9d. violet			16·00	28·00
O20		1s. pale blue-green			16·00	28·00
O21		2s. brown-lake			40·00	65·00
O22		5s. olive-brown			90·00	£150
O12/22				*Set of* 11	£190	£325

1932 (30 June)–34. *T* **14** *(redrawn without dates), optd with Type* O **2**. *P* 11.

O23		1d. green			4·50	4·50
O24		1½d. claret			5·50	12·00
O25		2d. vermilion			5·50	3·00
O26		2½d. green (14.9.34)			3·25	6·00
O27		3d. blue			6·50	21·00
O28		3½d. aniline carmine (14.9.34)			3·25	9·00
O29		4d. olive-green			5·50	15·00
O30		5d. deep blue-green			5·50	15·00
O31		6d. bistre-brown			8·00	32·00
O32		9d. violet			10·00	40·00
O33		1s. pale blue-green			15·00	28·00
O34		2s. dull lake			35·00	75·00
O35		5s. olive-brown			£120	£160
O23/35				*Set of* 13	£190	£375

Civil Administration in New Guinea was suspended in 1942, following the Japanese invasion.

Various New Guinea stamps exist overprinted with an anchor and three Japanese characters in a style similar to the Japanese Naval Control Area overprints found on the stamps of Netherlands Indies. These overprints on New Guinea are bogus. Two different versions are known, one produced in Japan during 1947 and the other in Australia during the late 1980s.

On resumption, after the Japanese defeat in 1945, Australian stamps were used until the appearance of the issue for the combined territories of Papua & New Guinea.

PRICES OF SETS

Set prices are given for many issues, generally those containing three stamps or more. Definitive sets include one of each value or major colour change, but do not cover different perforations, die types or minor shades. Where a choice is possible the set prices are based on the cheapest versions of the stamps included in the listings.

PAPUA (BRITISH NEW GUINEA)

Stamps of QUEENSLAND were used in British New Guinea (Papua) from at least 1885 onwards. Post Offices were opened at Daru (1894), Kulumadau (Woodlarks) (1899), Nivani (1899), Port Moresby (1885), Samarai (1888), Sudest (1899) and Tamata (1899). Stamps were usually cancelled "N.G." (at Port Moresby from 1885) or "BNG" (without stops at Samarai or with stops at the other offices) from 1888. Queensland stamps were replaced in Papua by the issue of 1901.

PRICES FOR STAMPS ON COVER	
Nos. 1/7	*from* × 15
No. 8	—
Nos. 9/15	*from* × 20
No. 16	—
Nos. 17/27	*from* × 6
No. 28	—
Nos. 39/45a	*from* × 5
Nos. 47/71	*from* × 8
Nos. 72/4	—
Nos. 75/92a	*from* × 8
Nos. 93/103	*from* × 6
Nos. 104/5	—
Nos. 106/11	*from* × 10
Nos. 112/14	*from* × 6
No. 115	—
Nos. 116/28	*from* × 5
Nos. 130/53	*from* × 4
Nos. 154/7	*from* × 12
Nos. 158/67	*from* × 4
No. 168	*from* × 3
Nos. O1/54	*from* × 10
Nos. O55/66a	*from* × 7

1 Lakatoi (trading canoe) with Hanuabada Village in Background

2 (Horizontal)

Deformed "d" at left (R. 4/3)

(Recess D.L.R.)

1901 (1 July)–**05**. *Wmk Mult Rosettes, W* **2**. *P* 14.

   A. *Wmk horizontal. Thick paper. Line perf*

1	**1**	½d. black and yellow-green			9·00	14·00
		a. Thin paper			£170	£140
2		1d. black and carmine			7·00	9·00
3		2d. black and violet			8·00	7·00
4		2½d. black and ultramarine			16·00	10·00
		a. Thin paper			£225	£160
		ab. Black and dull blue			£500	£350
5		4d. black and sepia			48·00	35·00
		a. Deformed "d" at left			£250	£200
6		6d. black and myrtle-green			45·00	35·00
7		1s. black and orange			60·00	65·00
8		2s. 6d. black and brown (1.1.05)			£600	£550

   B. *Wmk vertical. Medium to thick paper. Line or comb perf*

9	**1**	½d. black and yellow-green			5·50	3·75
		a. Thin paper (*comb perf*) (1905)			14·00	23·00
10		1d. black and carmine			3·50	2·00
11		2d. black and violet			9·50	4·00
		a. Thin paper (*comb perf*) (1905)			48·00	16·00
12		2½d. black and ultramarine (*shades*)			9·50	12·00
13		4d. black and sepia			32·00	48·00
		a. Deformed "d" at left			£200	£275
		b. Thin paper (*comb perf*) (1905)			£190	
		ba. Deformed "d" at left			£850	
14		6d. black and myrtle-green			48·00	70·00
		a. Thin paper (*comb perf*) (1905)			£600	
15		1s. black and orange			55·00	80·00
		a. Thin paper (*comb perf*) (1905)			£550	
16		2s. 6d. black and brown (1905)			£3000	£2250
		a. Thin paper (*comb perf*)			£550	£1000
1/16				*Set of* 8	£650	£650

The paper used for Nos. 1/8 is white, of consistent thickness and rather opaque. The thin paper used for the horizontal watermark printings is of variable thickness, readily distinguishable from the thick paper by its greater transparency and by the gum which is thin and smooth.

Nos. 9/16 were initially printed on the same thick paper as the stamps with horizontal watermark and were line perforated. Values from ½d. to 2½d. were subsequently printed on medium paper on which the watermark was more visible. These were comb perforated. The thin paper with vertical watermark, produced in 1905, is much more transparent and has smooth gum. Printings were made on this paper for all values except the 2½d., but only the ½d. and 2d. were issued in Papua although used examples of the 2s. 6d. are also known. The entire printing of the 1d. on thin paper with vertical watermark was used for subsequent overprints.

The sheets of the ½d., 2d. and 2½d. show a variety known as "white leaves" on R. 4/5 while the 2d. and 2½d. (both R. 6/2) and the ½d. and 1s. (both R. 6/3) show what is known as the "unshaded leaves" variety.

Papua. (3) Papua. (4)

1906–07. I. *Optd with T 3 (large opt), at Port Moresby (8 Nov 1906).*

A. *Wmk horizontal. Thick paper. Line perf*

17	1	4d. black and sepia	£190 £150
		a. Deformed "d" at left	£600 £500
18		6d. black and myrtle-green	38·00 42·00
19		1s. black and orange	20·00 38·00
20		2s. 6d. black and brown	£140 £150

B. *Wmk vertical. Thin paper (½d., 1d., 2d.) or medium to thick paper (others). Comb perf (½d. to 2½d.) or line perf (others)*

21	1	½d. black and yellow-green	4·50 20·00
22		1d. black and carmine	8·00 16·00
23		2d. black and violet	4·75 3·00
24		2½d. black and ultramarine	3·75 15·00
25		4d. black and sepia	£170 £130
		a. Deformed "d" at left	£550
26		6d. black and myrtle-green	28·00 55·00
27		1s. black and orange	£1200 £900
28		2s. 6d. black and brown	£7500 £6500
17/28		Set of 8	£325 £375

II. *Optd with T 4 (small opt), at Brisbane (May–June 1907)*

A. *Wmk horizontal. Thick paper. Line perf*

34	1	½d. black and yellow-green	
		a. Thin paper	60·00 80·00
35		2½d. black and ultramarine	
		a. Thin paper	30·00 60·00
		ac. Black and dull blue	£140 £150
36		1s. black and orange	£150 £200
37		2s. 6d. black and brown	32·00 48·00
		a. Opt reading downwards	£4000
		c. Opt double (horiz)	† £3000
		d. Opt triple (horiz)	† £2500

B. *Wmk vertical. Thin paper (½d., 1d., 2d., 4d., 6d.) or medium to thick paper (2½d., 1s., 2s. 6d.). Line or comb perf (2½d.), line perf (1s., 2s. 6d.) or comb perf (others)*

38	1	½d. black and yellow-green	6·00 8·00
		a. Opt double	£1700
39		1d. black and carmine	3·50 5·00
		a. Opt reading upwards	£1900 £1200
40		2d. black and violet	4·50 2·25
41		2½d. black and ultramarine	8·50 18·00
42		4d. black and sepia	25·00 48·00
		a. Deformed "d" at left	£170 £275
43		6d. black and myrtle-green	25·00 40·00
		a. Opt double	£2250 £4000
44		1s. black and orange	60·00 75·00
		b. Thin paper (comb perf)	27·00 40·00
		ba. Opt double, one diagonal	£6500 £4000
45		2s. 6d. black and brown	£6000 £4500
		a. Thin paper (comb perf)	38·00 60·00
34/45 (cheapest)		Set of 8	£110 £180

In the setting of this overprint Nos. 10, 16, and 21 have the "p" of "Papua" with a defective foot or inverted "d" for "p", and in No. 17 the "pua" of "Papua" is a shade lower than the first "a".

No. 37a comes from a single sheet on which the overprints were sideways. Examples exist showing one, two or four complete or partial overprints.

PRINTERS. All the following issues were printed at Melbourne by the Stamp Ptg Branch (to 1928) or Note Ptg Branch.

WATERMARK VARIETIES. When printing the lithographed issues, Nos. 47/83, little attention was paid to the position of the watermark. Nos. 47, 49/58 and 75/83 all come either upright or inverted while Nos. 48 and 59/71 all occur with watermark sideways to left or right. Nos. 51/2 are known with watermark reversed and others may well exist.

5 Large "PAPUA"   B   C

Three types of the 2s. 6d.:—
A. Thin top to "2" and small ball. Thin "6" and small ball. Thick uneven stroke.
B. Thin top to "2" and large, well shaped ball. Thin "6" and large ball. Very thick uneven stroke.
C. Thick top to "2" and large, badly shaped ball. Thick "6" and uneven ball. Thin even line.
Type A is not illustrated as the stamp is distinguishable by perf and watermark.
The litho stones were prepared from the engraved plates of the 1901 issue, value for value except the 2s. 6d. for which the original plate was mislaid. No. 48 containing Type A was prepared from the original ½d. plate with the value inserted on the stone and later a fresh stone was prepared from the 1d. plate and this contained Type B. Finally, the original plate of the 2s. 6d. was found and a third stone was prepared from this, and issued in 1911. These stamps show Type C.

6 Small "PAPUA"

(Litho Stamp Ptg Branch, Melbourne, from transfers taken from original engraved plates)

1907–10. *Wmk Crown over A, W w 11.*

A. *Large "PAPUA". (a) Wmk upright. P 11*

47	5	½d. black and yellow-green (11.07)	1·25 3·50

(b) *Wmk sideways. P 11*

48	5	2s. 6d. black and chocolate (A) (12.09)	48·00 60·00
		a. "POSTAGIE" at left (R. 1/5)	£550 £650

B. *Small "PAPUA"*

I. *Wmk upright. (a) P 11 (1907–8)*

49	6	1d. black and rose (6.08)	4·75 4·50
50		2d. black and purple (10.08)	7·50 4·50
51		2½d. black and bright ultramarine (7.08)	16·00 24·00
		a. Black and pale ultramarine	5·50 6·50
52		4d. black and sepia (20.11.07)	4·25 8·50
		a. Deformed "d" at left	28·00 42·00
53		6d. black and myrtle-green (4.08)	11·00 16·00
54		1s. black and orange (10.08)	19·00 20·00

(b) *P 12½ (1907–9)*

55	6	2d. black and purple (10.08)	16·00 6·50
56		2½d. black and bright ultramarine (7.08)	£120 £130
		b. Black and pale ultramarine	48·00 75·00
57		4d. black and sepia (20.11.07)	8·00 8·00
		a. Deformed "d" at left	45·00 45·00
58		1s. black and orange (1.09)	60·00 85·00

II. *Wmk sideways. (a) P 11 (1909–10)*

59	6	½d. black and yellow-green (12.09)	2·25 2·75
		a. Black and deep green (1910)	28·00 42·00
60		1d. black and carmine (1.10)	8·50 7·50
61		2d. black and purple (1.10)	8·00 8·00
62		2½d. black and dull blue (1.10)	4·25 17·00
63		4d. black and sepia (1.10)	4·50 7·50
		a. Deformed "d" at left	24·00 40·00
64		6d. black and myrtle-green (11.09)	10·00 16·00
65		1s. black and orange (3.10)	42·00 60·00

(b) *P 12½ (1909–10)*

66	6	½d. black and yellow-green (12.09)	1·60 3·25
		a. Black and deep green (1910)	30·00 38·00
67		1d. black and carmine (12.09)	6·00 11·00
68		2d. black and purple (1.10)	3·50 4·50
69		2½d. black and dull blue (1.10)	8·50 30·00
70		6d. black and myrtle-green (11.09)	£2750 £3750
71		1s. black and orange (3.10)	12·00 30·00

(c) *Perf compound of 11 and 12½*

72	6	½d. black and yellow-green	£2250 £2250
73		2d. black and purple	£850

(d) *Mixed perfs 11 and 12½*

74	6	4d. black and sepia	£5500

Compound perforations on the 4d. are fakes.
The only known examples of No. 74 come from the top row of a sheet perforated 11 and with an additional line perf 12½ in the top margin.

(Litho Stamp Ptg Branch, Melbourne, by J. B. Cooke, from new stones made by fresh transfers)

1910 (Sept)**–11.** *Large "PAPUA". W w 11 (upright). P 12½.*

75	5	½d. black and green (12.10)	3·50 11·00
76		1d. black and carmine	9·00 7·50
77		2d. black & dull purple (shades) (12.10)	4·00 5·00
		a. "C" for "O" in "POSTAGE" (R. 4/3)	65·00 65·00
78		2½d. black and blue-violet (10.10)	4·50 17·00
79		4d. black and sepia (10.10)	4·50 10·00
		a. Deformed "d" at left	22·00 50·00
80		6d. black and myrtle-green	7·50 7·50
81		1s. black and deep orange (12.10)	5·50 18·00
82		2s. 6d. black and brown (B)	35·00 45·00
83		2s. 6d. black and brown (C) (1911)	42·00 55·00
75/82		Set of 8	65·00 £110

A variety showing a white line or "rift" in clouds occurs on R. 5/3 in Nos. 49/74 and the "white leaves" variety mentioned below No. 22 occurs on the 2d. and 2½d. values in both issues. They are worth about three times the normal price.

ONE PENNY
8   (9)

(Eng S. Reading. Typo J. B. Cooke)

1911–15. *Printed in one colour. W 8 (sideways*).*

(a) *P 12½ (1911–12)*

84	6	½d. yellow-green	1·00 3·50
		a. Green	40 2·25
		w. Wmk Crown to right of A	10·00
85		1d. rose-pink	70 75
		w. Wmk Crown to right of A	20·00 20·00
86		2d. bright mauve	70 75
		w. Wmk Crown to right of A	— 40·00
87		2½d. bright ultramarine	4·75 8·50
		a. Dull ultramarine	5·50 8·50
		aw. Wmk Crown to right of A	50·00
88		4d. pale olive-green	2·25 11·00
		w. Wmk Crown to right of A	— 40·00
89		6d. orange-brown	3·75 5·00
90		1s. yellow	9·00 15·00
		w. Wmk Crown to right of A	75·00
91		2s. 6d. rose-carmine	32·00 38·00
		w. Wmk Crown to right of A	— £170
84/91		Set of 8	48·00 70·00

(b) *P 14*

92	6	1d. rose-pink (6.15)	22·00 6·00
		a. Pale scarlet	6·50 2·00
		w. Wmk Crown to right of A	— 40·00

*The normal sideways watermark shows Crown to left of A, as seen from the back of the stamp.

(Typo J. B. Cooke (1916–18), T. S. Harrison (1918–26), A. J. Mullett (No. 95b only) (1926–27), or John Ash (1927–31))

1916 (Aug)**–31.** *Printed in two colours. W 8 (sideways*). P 14.*

93	6	½d. myrtle and apple green (Harrison and Ash) (1919)	80 1·00
		a. Myrtle and pale olive-green (1927)	1·75 2·00
		w. Wmk Crown to right of A	5·00 5·00
94		1d. black and carmine-red	1·40 1·25
		a. Grey-black and red (1918)	1·60 1·75
		aw. Wmk Crown to right of A	3·00 40
		b. Intense black and red (Harrison) (wmk Crown to right of A) (1926)	2·50 2·50
95		1½d. pale grey-blue (shades) & brn (1925)	2·00 80
		aw. Wmk Crown to right of A	15·00 5·00
		b. Cobalt and light brown (Mullett) (wmk Crown to right of A) (1927)	6·00 3·25
		c. Bright blue and bright brown (1929)	2·75 2·00
		d. "POSTACE" at right (R. 1/1) (all printings) .. From	32·00 32·00
96		2d. brown-purple & brown-lake (1919)	1·75
		a. Deep brown-purple and lake (1931)	25·00 1·75
		aw. Wmk Crown to right of A	30·00 1·75
		b. Brown-purple and claret (1931)	2·00 75
97		2½d. myrtle and ultramarine (1919)	4·75 12·00
98		3d. black and bright blue-green (12.16)	1·25 1·75
		a. Error. Black and deep greenish Prussian blue†	£500 £500
		b. Sepia-black & brt bl-grn (Harrison)	22·00 19·00
		c. Black and deep blue-green (1927)	4·50 8·00
99		4d. brown and orange (1919)	2·50 5·00
		a. Light brown and orange (1927)	8·00 15·00
		aw. Wmk Crown to right of A	7·50 14·00
100		5d. bluish slate and pale brown (1931)	4·25 16·00
101		6d. dull and pale purple (wmk Crown to right of A) (1919)	3·25 9·50
		aw. Wmk Crown to left of A	10·00
		b. Dull purple and red-purple (wmk Crown to left of A) (1927)	10·00 16·00
		c. "POSTACE" at left (R. 6/2) (all printings) .. From	70·00 £100
102		1s. sepia and olive (1919)	3·50 6·50
		a. Brown and yellow-olive (1927)	6·50 13·00
103		2s. 6d. maroon and pale pink (1919)	18·00 40·00
		a. Maroon & brt pink (shades) (1927)	19·00 50·00
104		5s. black and deep green (12.16)	40·00 48·00
105		10s. green and pale ultramarine (1925)	£140 £180
93/105		Set of 13	£200 £250

*The normal sideways watermark shows Crown to left of A, as seen from the back of the stamp.
†Beware of similar shades produced by removal of yellow pigment. No. 98a is a colour trial, prepared by Cooke, of which, it is believed, five sheets were sold in error.
The printers of various shades can be determined by their dates of issue. The Ash printings are on whiter paper.
For 9d. and 1s. 3d. values, see Nos. 127/8.

1917 (Oct). *Nos. 84, 86/9 and 91 surch with T 9 by Govt Ptg Office, Melbourne.*

106	6	1d. on ½d. yellow-green	1·25 1·60
		a. Green	65 1·25
		w. Wmk Crown to right of A	4·00 4·00
107		1d. on 2d. bright mauve	12·00 15·00
108		1d. on 2½d. ultramarine	1·25 3·75
109		1d. on 4d. pale olive-green	1·75 4·50
		w. Wmk Crown to right of A	— 40·00
110		1d. on 6d. orange-brown	8·00 17·00
111		1d. on 2s. 6d. rose-carmine	1·50 6·00
106/11		Set of 6	22·00 42·00

AIR MAIL
(10)   (11)

1929 (Oct)**–30.** *Air. Optd with T 10 by Govt Printer, Port Moresby.*

(a) *Cooke printing. Yellowish paper*

112	6	3d. black and bright blue-green	1·25 9·50
		a. Opt omitted in vert pair with normal	£3000

(b) *Harrison printing. Yellowish paper*

113	6	3d. sepia-black and bright blue-green	50·00 65·00

(c) *Ash printing. White paper*

114	6	3d. black and blue-green	90 7·00
		a. Opt omitted (in horiz pair with normal)	£3500
		b. Ditto, but vert pair	£3000
		c. Opt vertical, on back	£3000
		d. Opts tête-bêche (vert pair)	£3000

1930 (15 Sept). *Air. Optd with T 11, in carmine by Govt Printer, Port Moresby. (a) Harrison printings. Yellowish paper*

115	6	3d. sepia-black and bright blue-green	£1600 £2750
116		6d. dull and pale purple	3·00 16·00
		a. "POSTACE" at left (R. 6/2)	65·00 £110
117		1s. sepia and olive	8·00 23·00
		a. Opt inverted	£4500

(b) *Ash printings. White paper*

118	6	3d. black and blue-green	90 6·00
119		6d. dull purple and red-purple	7·00 10·00
		a. "POSTACE" at left (R. 6/2)	70·00 £100
120		1s. brown and yellow-olive	4·25 15·00
118/20		Set of 3	11·00 28·00

The rare Harrison printing with this overprint, No. 115, should not be confused with examples of the Ash printing, No. 118, which have been climatically toned.

5d.

TWO PENCE   FIVE PENCE
(12)   (13)

1931 (1 Jan). *Surch with T 12 by Govt Printer, Port Moresby.*

(a) Mullett printing

121	6	2d. on 1½d. cobalt and light brown		12·00	24·00
		a. "POSTACE" at right (R. 1/1)		£140	£225

(b) Ash printing

122	6	2d. on 1½d. bright blue and bright brown		1·00	2·00
		a. "POSTACE" at right (R. 1/1)		25·00	42·00

1931. *Surch as T 13 by Govt Printer, Port Moresby.*

(a) Cooke printing

123	6	1s. 3d. on 5s. black and deep green		4·00	9·00

(b) Harrison printing. Yellowish paper

124	6	9d. on 2s. 6d. maroon and pale pink (Dec)	6·00	18·00

(c) Ash printings. White paper

125	6	5d. on 1s. brown and yellow-olive (26.7)	85	1·75
126		9d. on 2s. 6d. maroon and bright pink	5·50	8·50

(Typo J. Ash)

1932. *W 15 of Australia (Mult "C of A"). P 11.*

127	5	9d. lilac and violet		4·50	28·00
128		1s. 3d. lilac and pale greenish blue	7·50	32·00
127/8 Optd "Specimen"			*Set of 2.* £450	

15 Motuan Girl

18 Raggiana Bird of Paradise

20 Native Mother and Child

22 Papuan Motherhood

(Des F. E. Williams (2s., £1 and frames of other values), E. Whitehouse (2d., 4d., 6d., 1s., and 10s.); remaining centres from photos by Messrs F. E. Williams and Gibson. Recess J. Ash (all values) and W. C. G. McCracken (½d., 1d., 2d., 4d.))

1932 (14 Nov). *T 15, 18, 20, 22 and similar designs. No wmk. P 11.*

130		½d. black and orange		1·25	3·25
		a. Black and buff (McCracken)		13·00	21·00
131		1d. black and green		1·50	60
132		1½d. black and lake		90	7·00
133		2d. red		9·00	30
134		3d. black and blue		3·00	6·50
135		4d. olive-green		5·00	8·50
136		5d. black and slate-green		2·50	3·00
137		6d. bistre-brown		6·50	5·50
138		9d. black and violet		9·00	19·00
139		1s. dull blue-green		3·75	8·50
140		1s. 3d. black and dull purple		14·00	24·00
141		2s. black and slate-green		14·00	23·00
142		2s. 6d. black and rose-mauve		25·00	38·00
143		5s. black and olive-brown		55·00	50·00
144		10s. violet		80·00	80·00
145		£1 black and olive-grey		£180	£140
130/145			*Set of 16*	£350	£350

Designs: Vert (as *T 15*)—1d. A Chieftain's son; 1½d. Treehouses; 3d. Papuan dandy; 5d. Masked dancer; 9d. Papuan shooting fish; 1s. 3d. Lakatoi; 2s. Papuan art; 2s. 6d. Pottery making; 5s. Native policeman; £1 Delta house. (As *T 18*)—1s. Dubu—or ceremonial platform. Horiz (as *T 20*)—10s. Lighting a fire.

31 Hoisting the Union Jack

32 Scene on H.M.S. *Nelson*

(Recess J. Ash)

1934 (6 Nov). *50th Anniv of Declaration of British Protectorate. P 11.*

146	31	1d. green		1·00	3·00
147	32	2d. scarlet		1·75	3·00
148	31	3d. blue		1·75	3·00
149	32	5d. purple		11·00	12·00
146/9			*Set of 4*	14·00	19·00

HIS MAJESTY'S JUBILEE.

HIS MAJESTY'S JUBILEE.

1910   1935

(33)

1910 — 1935

(34)

MAJESTY'S   MAJESTY'S

Normal   "Accent" flaw
(R. 5/4)

1935 (9 July). *Silver Jubilee. Nos. 131, 133/4 and 136 optd with T 33 or 34 (2d.).*

150		1d. black and green		75	2·00
		a. "Accent" flaw		27·00	48·00
151		2d. scarlet		2·00	2·00
152		3d. black and blue		1·75	2·50
		a. "Accent" flaw		45·00	70·00
153		5d. black and slate-green		2·50	3·00
		a. "Accent" flaw		60·00	80·00
150/3			*Set of 4*	6·25	8·50

35

36 Port Moresby

(Recess J. Ash)

1937 (14 May). *Coronation. P 11.*

154	35	1d. green		55	15
155		2d. scarlet		55	50
156		3d. blue		55	70
157		5d. purple		55	1·25
154/7			*Set of 4*	2·00	2·40

Some covers franked with these stamps and posted on 2 June 1937 were postmarked 2 April 1937 in error.

(Recess J. Ash)

1938 (6 Sept). *Air. 50th Anniv of Declaration of British Possession. P 11.*

158	36	2d. rose-red		3·75	2·25
159		3d. bright blue		3·75	2·25
160		5d. green		3·75	3·25
161		8d. brown-lake		11·00	14·00
162		1s. mauve		30·00	15·00
158/62			*Set of 5*	48·00	32·00

37 Natives poling Rafts

(Recess J. Ash)

1939 (6 Sept). *Air. P 11.*

163	37	2d. rose-red		3·50	3·75
164		3d. bright blue		3·50	6·50
165		5d. green		3·75	1·50
166		8d. brown-lake		10·00	2·50
167		1s. mauve		13·00	6·00

(Recess W. C. G. McCracken)

1941 (2 Jan). *Air. P 11½.*

168	37	1s. 6d. olive-green		35·00	32·00
163/168			*Set of 6*	60·00	45·00

OFFICIAL STAMPS

1908 (Oct). *Punctured "OS".*

O1	1	2s. 6d. black and brown (No. 37)		£600	35·00
O2		2s. 6d. black and brown (No. 45)		£2500	£2250
		a. Thin paper (No. 45a)		£700	£550

1908 (Dec)–**10.** *Nos. 49/71 punctured "OS". I. Wmk upright.*

(a) P 11

O 4	6	1d. black and rose		14·00	5·00
O 5		2d. black and purple		16·00	4·50
O 6		2½d. black and bright ultramarine		28·00	23·00
		a. Black and pale ultramarine		12·00	4·25
O 7		4d. black and sepia		15·00	4·50
		a. Deformed "d" at left		75·00	23·00
O 8		6d. black and myrtle-green		32·00	16·00
O 9		1s. black and orange		32·00	16·00
O4/9			*Set of 6*	£110	45·00

(b) P 12½

O10	6	2d. black and purple		26·00	7·00
O11		2½d. black and bright ultramarine		£100	80·00
		b. Black and pale ultramarine		65·00	55·00
O12		4d. black and sepia		27·00	9·00
		a. Deformed "d" at left		£120	50·00
O13		1s. black and orange		95·00	50·00
O10/13			*Set of 4*	£190	£110

II. Wmk sideways. (a) P 11

O14	6	½d. black and yellow-green		13·00	4·50
		a. Black and deep green		50·00	30·00
O15		1d. black and carmine		28·00	8·00
O16		2d. black and purple		14·00	2·00
O17		2½d. black and dull blue		18·00	5·00
O18		4d. black and sepia		16·00	8·00
		a. Deformed "d" at left		80·00	35·00
O19		6d. black and myrtle-green		30·00	5·00
O20		1s. black and orange		90·00	28·00
O14/20			*Set of 7*	£190	50·00

(b) P 12½

O21	6	½d. black and yellow-green		9·00	1·50
		a. Black and deep green		50·00	30·00
O22		1d. black and carmine		24·00	4·00
O23		2d. black and purple		16·00	3·00
O24		2½d. black and dull blue		35·00	14·00
O25		6d. black and myrtle-green		—£1100	
O26		1s. black and orange		38·00	14·00

1910. *Nos. 47/8 punctured "OS".*

O27	5	½d. black & yellow-green (wmk upright)		13·00	13·00
O28		2s. 6d. black & chocolate (wmk sideways)	£110	85·00

1910–11. *Nos. 75/83 punctured "OS".*

O29	5	½d. black and green		13·00	5·50
O30		1d. black and carmine		27·00	5·50
O31		2d. black and dull purple		13·00	5·50
		a. "C" for "O" in "POSTAGE"		£130	65·00
O32		2½d. black and blue-violet		20·00	6·50
O33		4d. black and sepia		20·00	4·00
		a. Deformed "d" at left		90·00	32·00
O34		6d. black and myrtle-green		20·00	6·00
O35		1s. black and deep orange		29·00	9·00
O36		2s. 6d. black and brown (B)		80·00	30·00
O37		2s. 6d. black and brown (C)		95·00	65·00
O29/36			*Set of 8*	£200	65·00

1911–12. *Nos. 84/91 punctured "OS".*

O38	6	½d. yellow-green		6·50	2·00
O39		1d. rose-pink		8·00	1·25
O40		2d. bright mauve		8·00	1·25
		w. Wmk Crown to right of A		—	20·00
O41		2½d. bright ultramarine		15·00	7·50
O42		4d. pale olive-green		17·00	15·00
O43		6d. orange-brown		15·00	6·00
O44		1s. yellow		22·00	11·00
O45		2s. rose-carmine		60·00	65·00
O38/45			*Set of 8*	£130	95·00

1930. *Nos. 93/6a and 98c/103 punctured "OS".*

O46	6	½d. myrtle and apple green		4·25	7·50
O47		1d. intense black and red		9·50	3·25
O48		1½d. bright blue and bright brown		6·50	8·00
		a. "POSTACE" at right		65·00	80·00
O49		2d. deep brown-purple and lake		20·00	26·00
O50		3d. black and blue-green		35·00	48·00
O51		4d. light brown and orange		20·00	24·00
O52		6d. dull purple and pale purple		12·00	22·00
		a. "POSTACE" at left		£120	£150
O53		1s. brown and yellow-olive		21·00	35·00
O54		2s. 6d. maroon and pale pink		65·00	85·00
O46/54			*Set of 9*	£170	£225

O S

(O 1)

(Typo T. S. Harrison (1d. and 2s. 6d.) and J. Ash)

1931 (29 July)–**32.** *Optd with Type O 1. W 8 or W 15 of Australia (9d., 1s. 3d.). P 14 or 11 (9d., 1s. 3d.).*

O55	6	½d. myrtle and apple-green		1·25	4·75
O56		1d. grey-black and red			
		a. Intense black and red		3·75	7·50
O57		1½d. bright blue and bright brown		1·40	12·00
		a. "POSTACE" at right		45·00	£120
O58		2d. brown-purple and claret		2·75	9·00
O59		3d. black and blue-green		2·50	20·00
O60		4d. light brown and orange (No. 99aw)		2·50	17·00
O61		5d. bluish slate and pale brown		6·00	38·00
O62		6d. dull purple and red-purple		4·00	8·50
		a. "POSTACE" at left		85·00	£170
O63		9d. lilac and violet (1932)		40·00	55·00
O64		1s. brown and yellow-olive		9·00	28·00
O65		1s. 3d. lilac & pale greenish blue (1932)		40·00	55·00
O66		2s. 6d. maroon and pale pink (Harrison)		40·00	85·00
		a. Maroon and bright pink (Ash)		40·00	85·00
O55/66			*Set of 12*	£130	£300

Civil Administration, in Papua, was suspended in 1942; on resumption, after the Japanese defeat in 1945, Australian stamps were used until the appearance of the issue of the combined territories of Papua & New Guinea.

PAPUA NEW GUINEA

AUSTRALIAN TRUST TERRITORY

The name of the combined territory was changed from "Papua and New Guinea" to "Papua New Guinea" at the beginning of 1972.

SPECIMEN OVERPRINTS. These come from specimen sets in which the lower values were cancelled-to-order, but stamps above the value of 10s. were overprinted "Specimen". These overprints are listed as they could be purchased from the Post Office.

1 Matschie's Tree Kangaroo

2 Buka Head-dresses

3 Native Youth

14 Map of Papua and New Guinea   15 Papuan shooting Fish

(Recess Note Printing Branch, Commonwealth Bank, Melbourne)

1952 (30 Oct)–58.   *T* 1/3, 14/15 *and similar designs. P* 14.

1	½d. emerald		30	10
2	1d. deep brown		20	10
3	2d. blue		35	10
4	2½d. orange		2·25	40
5	3d. deep green		60	10
6	3½d. carmine-red		60	10
6a	3½d. black (2.6.58)		7·00	90
7	6½d. dull purple		2·00	10
	a. Maroon (1956)		6·50	15
8	7½d. blue		3·00	1·00
9	9d. brown		3·50	40
10	1s. yellow-green		2·25	10
11	1s. 6d. deep green		6·00	60
12	2s. indigo		5·00	10
13	2s. 6d. brown-purple		4·75	40
14	10s. blue-black		38·00	13·00
15	£1 deep brown		38·00	13·00
1/15		*Set of* 16	£100	27·00
14/15 Optd "Specimen"		*Set of* 2	£120	

Designs: *Vert* (as *T* 1/3)—2½d. Greater Bird of Paradise; 3d. Native policeman; 3½d. Papuan head-dress. (As *T* 15)—6½d. Kiriwina Chief House; 7½d. Kiriwina yam house; 1s. 6d. Rubber tapping; 2s. Sepik dancing masks. *Horiz* (as *T* 14)—9d. Copra making; 1s. Lakatoi; 2s. 6d. Native shepherd and flock.

(16)   (17)

1957 (29 Jan).   *Nos.* 4 *and* 10 *surch with T* **16** *or T* **17**.

16	4d. on 2½d. orange		70	10
17	7d. on 1s. yellow-green		40	10

18 Cacao Plant   19 Klinki Plymill

20 Cattle   21 Coffee Beans

(Recess Note Ptg Branch, Commonwealth Bank, Melbourne)

1958 (2 June)–60.   *New values. P* 14.

18	18	4d. vermilion		75	10
19		5d. green (10.11.60)		75	10
20	19	7d. bronze-green		6·50	10
21		8d. deep ultramarine (10.11.60)		75	1·50
22	20	1s. 7d. red-brown		15·00	10·00
23		2s. 5d. vermilion (10.11.60)		4·75	2·25
24	21	5s. crimson and olive-green		12·00	1·50
18/24			*Set of* 7	35·00	14·00

(22)   23 Council Chamber, Port Moresby

1959 (1 Dec).   *No.* 1 *surch with T* **22**.

25	1	5d. on ½d. emerald		75	10

(Photo Harrison)

1961 (10 Apr).   *Reconstitution of Legislative Council. P* 15 × 14.

26	23	5d. deep green and yellow		1·50	25
27		2s. 3d. deep green and light salmon		4·50	1·50

24 Female, Goroka,   26 Female Dancer
New Guinea

28 Traffic Policeman

(Des Pamela M. Prescott, Recess Note Ptg Branch, Reserve Bank of Australia, Melbourne)

1961 (26 July)–62.   *T* 24, 26, 28 *and similar designs. P* 14½ × 14 (1d., 3d., 3s.) *or* 14 × 14½ (*others*).

28	1d. lake		90	10
29	3d. indigo		30	10
30	1s. bronze-green		3·00	15
31	2s. maroon		45	15
32	3s. deep bluish green (5.9.62)		2·25	1·25
28/32		*Set of* 5	6·25	1·50

Designs: *Vert* (as *T* 24)—3d. Tribal elder, Tari, Papua. (As *T* 26)—2s. Male dancer.

 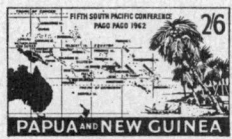

29 Campaign Emblem   30 Map of South Pacific

(Recess Note Ptg Branch, Reserve Bank of Australia, Melbourne)

1962 (7 Apr).   *Malaria Eradication. P* 14.

33	29	5d. carmine-red and light blue		40	15
34		1s. red and sepia		60	25
35		2s. black and yellow-green		80	70
33/5			*Set of* 3	1·60	1·00

(Des Pamela M. Prescott. Recess Note Ptg Branch, Reserve Bank of Australia, Melbourne)

1962 (9 July).   *Fifth South Pacific Conference, Pago Pago. P* 14½ × 14.

36	30	5d. scarlet and light green		50	15
37		1s. 6d. deep violet and light yellow		1·40	70
38		2s. 6d. deep green and light blue		1·40	1·40
36/8			*Set of* 3	3·00	2·00

31 Throwing the Javelin   33 Runners

(Des G. Hamori. Photo Courvoisier)

1962 (24 Oct).   *Seventh British Empire and Commonwealth Games, Perth. T* **31**, **33** *and similar design. P* 11½.

39	5d. brown and light blue		20	10
	a. Pair. Nos. 39/40		40	50
40	5d. brown and orange		20	10
41	2s. 3d. brown and light green		1·00	75
39/41		*Set of* 3	1·25	85

Design: (As *T* **31**)—5d. High jump.
Nos. 39/40 are arranged together *se-tenant* in sheets of 100.

34 Raggiana   35 Common Phalanger
Bird of Paradise

36 Rabaul   37 Queen Elizabeth II

(Des S. T. Cham (10s.), A. Buckley (photo) (£1). Photo Harrison (£1), Courvoisier (others)).

1963.   *P* 14½ (£1) *or* 11½ (*others*).

42	34	5d. yellow, chestnut and sepia (27 Mar)	1·50	10
43	35	6d. red, yellow-brown and grey (27 Mar)	75	1·25
44	36	10s. multicoloured (13 Feb)	15·00	8·50
45	37	£1 sepia, gold and blue-green (3 July)	4·00	2·50
		a. Gold ptd double		
42/5			*Set of* 4	19·00	11·00
44/5 Optd "Specimen"			*Set of* 2	90·00	

38 Centenary   39 Waterfront, Port Moresby
Emblem

(Des G. Hamori. Photo Note Ptg Branch, Reserve Bank of Australia, Melbourne)

1963 (1 May).   *Red Cross Centenary. P* 13½ × 13.

46	38	5d. red, grey-brown and bluish green		60	10

(Des J. McMahon (8d.), Pamela M. Prescott (2s. 3d.). Recess Note Ptg Branch, Reserve Bank of Australia, Melbourne)

1963 (8 May).   *T* **39** *and similar horiz design. P* 14 × 13½.

47	39	8d. green		30	15
48		– 2s. 3d. ultramarine		30	30

Design:—2s. 3d. Piaggio P-166B Portofino aircraft landing at Tapini.

40 Games Emblem   41 Watam Head

(Des Pamela M. Prescott. Recess Note Ptg Branch, Reserve Bank of Australia, Melbourne)

1963 (14 Aug).   *First South Pacific Games, Suva. P* 13½ × 14½.

49	40	5d. bistre		10	10
50		1s. deep green		30	20

(Des Pamela M. Prescott. Photo Courvoisier)

1964 (5 Feb).   *Native Artefacts. T* **41** *and similar vert designs. Multicoloured. P* 11½.

51	41	1½d. Type **41**		35	10
52		2s. 5d. Watam Head (*different*)		40	90
53		2s. 6d. Bosmun Head		40	10
54		5s. Medina Head		50	15
51/4			*Set of* 4	1·50	1·00

(Recess Note Ptg Branch, Reserve Bank of Australia, Melbourne)

45 Casting Vote   46 "Health Centres"

(Photo Courvoisier)

1964 (4 Mar).   *Common Roll Elections. P* 11½.

55	45	5d. brown and drab		10	10
56		2s. 3d. brown and pale blue		20	25

(Recess Note Ptg Branch, Reserve Bank of Australia, Melbourne)

1964 (5 Aug).   *Health Services. T* **46** *and similar vert designs. P* 14.

57	5d. violet		10	10
58	8d. bronze-green		15	10
59	1s. blue		15	10
60	2s. 2d. brown-red		35	35
57/60		*Set of* 4	65	50

Designs:—8d. "School health"; 1s. "Infant, child and maternal health"; 1s. 2d. "Medical training".

50 Striped Gardener   51 Emperor of Germany
Bowerbird   Bird of Paradise

(Photo Courvoisier)

1964 (28 Oct)–65. *Vert designs as T* **50** (*1d. to 8d.*) *or* **51** (*others*). *Multicoloured; background colours given. P* 11½ (*1d. to 8d.*) *or* 12 × 11½ (*1s. to 10s.*).

61	1d. pale olive-yellow (20.1.65)			40	10
62	3d. light grey (20.1.65)			50	10
63	5d. pale red (20.1.65)			55	10
64	6d. pale green			75	10
65	8d. lilac			1·50	10
66	1s. salmon			1·50	10
67	2s. light blue (20.1.65)			75	30
68	2s. 3d. light green (20.1.65)			75	85
69	3s. pale yellow (20.1.65)			75	1·25
70	5s. cobalt (20.1.65)			12·00	2·50
71	10s. pale drab (Optd S. £120)			6·00	10·00
61/71			*Set of 11*	23·00	14·00

Designs:—3d. Adelbert Bowerbird; 5d. Blue Bird of Paradise; 6d. Lawes's Parotia; 8d. Black-billed Sicklebill; 2s. Brown Sicklebill; 2s. 3d. Lesser Bird of Paradise; 3s. Magnificent Bird of Paradise; 5s. Twelve-wired Bird of Paradise; 10s. Magnificent Riflebird.

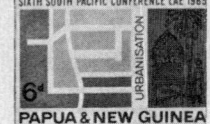

61 Canoe Prow

(Des Pamela M. Prescott. Photo Courvoisier)

1965 (24 Mar). *Sepik Canoe Prows in Port Moresby Museum. T* **61** *and similar horiz designs showing carved prows. P* 11½.

72	4d. multicoloured			50	10
73	1s. 2d. multicoloured			2·50	1·50
74	1s. 6d. multicoloured			50	10
75	4s. multicoloured			75	30
72/5			*Set of 4*	3·75	1·75

1965 (14 Apr). *50th Anniv of Gallipoli Landing. As T* **22** *of Nauru. P* 13½.

76	2s. 3d. sepia, black and emerald			20	10

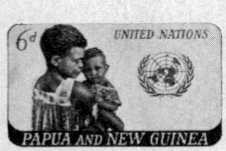

65 Urban Plan and Native House

(Des G. Hamori. Photo Courvoisier)

1965 (7 July). *Sixth South Pacific Conference, Lae. T* **65** *and similar horiz design. P* 11½.

77	6d. multicoloured			10	10
78	1s. multicoloured			10	10

No. 78 is similar to T **65** but with the plan on the right and the house on the left. Also "URBANISATION" reads downwards.

66 Mother and Child   67 Globe and U.N. Emblem

(Photo Courvoisier)

1965 (13 Oct). *20th Anniv of U.N.O. T* **66/7** *and similar vert design. P* 11½.

79	6d. sepia, blue and pale turquoise-blue			10	10
80	1s. orange-brown, blue & dp reddish violet			10	10
81	2s. blue, blue-green and light yellow-olive			15	10
79/81			*Set of 3*	30	20

Design:—2s. U.N. Emblem and globes.

(New Currency. 100 cents = 1 Australian dollar)

69 Papilio ulysses   71 Ornithoptera priamus

(Photo Courvoisier)

1966 (14 Feb–12 Oct). *Decimal Currency. Butterflies. Vert designs as T* **69** (1 to 5 c.), *or horiz as T* **71** (*others*). *Multicoloured. P* 11½.

82	1 c. Type 69			40	70
83	3 c. Cyrestis acilia			40	40
84	4 c. Graphium weiskei			40	70
85	5 c. Terinos alurgis			40	10
86	10 c. Type 71			50	30
86a	12 c. Euploea callithoe (12.10)			2·25	2·25

87	15 c. Papilio euchenor			1·50	80
88	20 c. Parthenos sylvia			75	25
89	25 c. Delias aruna			1·00	1·00
90	50 c. Apaturina erminea			10·00	1·25
91	$1 Doleschallia dasclyus			4·00	1·50
92	$2 Ornithoptera paradisea			6·00	8·50
82/92			*Set of 12*	25·00	16·00

80 "Molala Harai"   84 Throwing the Discus

(Des Rev. H. A. Brown. Photo Courvoisier)

1966 (8 June). *Folklore. Elema Art (1st series). T* **80** *and similar vert designs. P* 11½.

93	2 c. black and carmine			10	10
94	7 c. black, light yellow and light blue			10	30
95	30 c. black, carmine and apple-green			15	15
96	60 c. black, carmine and yellow			40	50
93/6			*Set of 4*	65	80

Designs:—7 c. "Marai"; 30 c. "Meavea Kivovia"; 60 c. "Toivita Tapaivita".

Nos. 93/6 were supplementary values to the decimal currency definitive issue.

See also Nos. 152/5 and 342/5.

(Photo Courvoisier)

1966 (31 Aug). *South Pacific Games, Nouméa. T* **84** *and similar vert designs. Multicoloured. P* 11½.

97	5 c. Type 84			10	10
98	10 c. Football			15	10
99	20 c. Tennis			20	40
97/9			*Set of 3*	40	50

87 Mucuna novoguineensis   91 "Fine Arts"

(Des Mrs. D. Pearce. Photo Courvoisier)

1966 (7 Dec). *Flowers. T* **87** *and similar vert designs. Multicoloured. P* 11½.

100	5 c. Type 87			15	10
101	10 c. Tecomanthe dendrophila			15	10
102	20 c. Rhododendron macgregoriae			35	10
103	60 c. Rhododendron konori			1·00	2·25
100/3			*Set of 4*	1·50	2·25

(Des G. Hamori. Photo Courvoisier)

1967 (8 Feb). *Higher Education. T* **91** *and similar horiz designs. Multicoloured. P* 12½ × 12.

104	1 c. Type 91			10	10
105	3 c. "Surveying"			10	10
106	4 c. "Civil Engineering"			10	10
107	5 c. "Science"			10	10
108	20 c. "Law"			10	10
104/8			*Set of 5*	30	30

96 Sagra speciosa   100 Laloki River

(Des Pamela M. Prescott. Photo Courvoisier)

1967 (12 Apr). *Fauna Conservation (Beetles). T* **96** *and similar vert designs. Multicoloured. P* 11½.

109	5 c. Type 96			20	10
110	10 c. Eupholus schoenherri			20	10
111	20 c. Sphingnotus albertisi			40	10
112	40 c. Cyphogastra albertisi			40	10
109/12			*Set of 4*	1·10	30

(Des G. Wade. Photo Courvoisier)

1967 (28 June). *Laloki River Hydro-Electric Scheme, and "New Industries". T* **100** *and similar vert designs. Multicoloured. P* 12½.

113	5 c. Type 100			10	10
114	10 c. Pyrethrum			10	10
115	20 c. Tea Plant			15	10
116	25 c. Type 100			15	10
113/16			*Set of 4*	40	30

---

103 Air Attack at Milne Bay   107 Papuan Lory

(Des R. Hodgkinson (2 c.), F. Hodgkinson (5 c.), G. Wade (20 c., 50 c.). Photo Courvoisier)

1967 (30 Aug). *25th Anniv of the Pacific War. T* **103** *and similar multicoloured designs. P* 11½.

117	2 c. Type 103			10	50
118	5 c. Kokoda Trail (vert)			10	10
119	20 c. The Coast Watchers			25	15
120	50 c. Battle of the Coral Sea			80	70
117/20			*Set of 4*	1·00	1·25

(Des T. Walcot. Photo Courvoisier)

1967 (29 Nov). *Christmas. Territory Parrots. T* **107** *and similar vert designs. Multicoloured. P* 12½.

121	5 c. Type 107			25	10
122	7 c. Pesquet's Parrot			30	90
123	20 c. Dusky Lory			50	10
124	25 c. Edward's Fig Parrot			50	10
121/4			*Set of 4*	1·40	1·10

111   Chimbu Head-dresses   112

(Des P. Jones. Photo Courvoisier)

1968 (21 Feb). *"National Heritage". T* **111/12** *and similar multicoloured designs. P* 12 × 12½ (5, 60 c.) *or* 12½ × 12 (10, 20 c.).

125	5 c. Type 111			10	10
126	10 c. Southern Highlands Head-dress (horiz)			15	10
127	20 c. Western Highlands Head-dress (horiz)			20	10
128	60 c. Type 112			70	45
125/8			*Set of 4*	1·00	65

115 Hyla thesaurensis   119 Human Rights Emblem and Papuan Head-dress (abstract)

(Des and photo Courvoisier)

1968 (24 Apr). *Fauna Conservation (Frogs). T* **115** *and similar horiz designs. Multicoloured. P* 11½.

129	5 c. Type 115			15	50
130	10 c. Hyla iris			15	10
131	15 c. Ceratobatrachus guentheri			15	10
132	20 c. Nyctimystes narinosa			20	50
129/32			*Set of 4*	60	1·00

(Des G. Hamori. Litho Enschedé)

1968 (26 June). *Human Rights Year. T* **119** *and similar horiz design. Multicoloured. P* 13½ × 12½.

133	5 c. Type 119			10	20
134	10 c. Human Rights in the World (abstract)			10	10

121 Leadership (abstract)   123 Common Egg Cowrie (Ovula ovum)

(Des G. Hamori. Litho Enschedé)

1968 (26 June). *Universal Suffrage. T* **121** *and similar horiz design. Multicoloured. P* 13½ × 12½.

135	20 c. Type 121			15	20
136	25 c. Leadership of the Community (abstract)			15	10

(Des P. Jones. Photo Courvoisier)

1968–69. *Sea Shells. Multicoloured designs as T* **123**. *P* 12 × 12½ ($2), 12½ × 12 (1 c. to 20 c.) *or* 11½ (*others*).

137	1 c. Type 125 (29.1.69)			10	10
138	3 c. Laciniate Conch (Strombus sinuatus) (30.10.68)			30	70
139	4 c. Lithograph Cone (Conus litoglyphus) (29.1.69)			20	10
140	5 c. Marbled Cone (Conus marmoreus marmoreus) (28.8.68)			25	10
141	7 c. Episcopal Mitre (Mitra mitra) (29.1.69)			35	10
142	10 c. Cymbiola rutila ruckeri (30.10.68)			45	10

143 12 c. Checkerboard Bonnet (*Phalium areola*) (29.1.69) 1·25 1·75
144 15 c. Scorpion Conch (*Lambis scorpius*) (30.10.68) 60 80
145 20 c. Fluted Giant Clam or Scale Tridacna (*Tridacna sqamosa*) (28.8.68) 70 10
146 25 c. Camp Pitar Venus (*Lioconcha castrensis*) (28.8.68) 70 50
147 30 c. Ramose Murex (*Murex ramosus*) (28.8.68) 70 1·00
148 40 c. Chambered or Pearly Nautilus (*Nautilus pompilius*) (30.10.68) 75 1·00
149 60 c. Trumpet Triton (*Charonia tritonis*) (28.8.68) 70 55
150 $1 Manus Green Papuina (*Papuina pulcherrima*) (30.10.68) 1·40 1·25
151 $2 Glory of the Sea Cone (*Conus gloriamaris*) (vert) (29.1.69) 16·00 7·00
137/51 Set of 15 21·00 14·00

The 1, 5, 7, 15, 40, 60 c. and $1 exist with PVA gum as well as gum arabic.

138 Tito Myth

140 Luvuapo Myth

139 Iko Myth

141 Miro Myth

(Des from native motifs by Revd. H. A. Brown. Litho Enschedé)
1969 (9 Apr). *Folklore. Elema Art (2nd series)*. P 12½ × 13½ × Roul 9 between se-tenant pairs.
152 138 5 c. black, yellow and red 10 50
　　a. Pair. Nos. 152/3 20 1·00
153 139 5 c. black, yellow and red 10 50
154 140 10 c. black, grey and red 15 50
　　a. Pair. Nos. 154/5 30 1·00
155 141 10 c. black, grey and red 15 50
152/5 Set of 4 50 1·75
Nos. 152/3 and 154/5 were issued in vertical *se-tenant* pairs, separated by a line of roulette.

142 "Fireball" Class Dinghy

145 *Dendrobium ostrinoglossum*

(Des J. Fallas. Recess Note Ptg Branch, Reserve Bank of Australia)
1969 (25 June). *Third South Pacific Games, Port Moresby*. T 142 and similar designs. P 14 × 14½ (5 c.) or 14½ × 14 (others).
156 5 c. black 10 15
157 10 c. deep bluish violet 10 10
158 20 c. myrtle-green 15 20
156/8 Set of 3 30 40
Designs: *Horiz*—10 c. Swimming pool, Boroko; 20 c. Games arena, Konedobu.

(Des P. Jones. Photo Courvoisier)
1969 (27 Aug). *Flora Conservation (Orchids)*. T 145 and similar vert designs. Multicoloured. P 11½.
159 5 c. Type 145 25 10
160 10 c. Dendrobium lawesii 35 70
161 20 c. Dendrobium pseudofrigidum 45 90
162 30 c. Dendrobium conanthum 55 70
159/62 Set of 4 1·40 2·25

149 Bird of Paradise

150 Native Potter

(Des G. Hamori. Photo Note Ptg Branch, Reserve Bank of Australia)
1969 (24 Sept)–**71**. *Coil stamps*. P 15 × imperf.
162a 149 2 c. blue, black and red (1.4.71) 10 15
163 5 c. bright green, brown and red-orange 10 10

(Des G. Hamori. Photo Courvoisier)
1969 (24 Sept). *50th Anniv of International Labour Organization*. P 11½.
164 150 5 c. multicoloured 10 10

151 Tareko

155 Prehistoric Ambun Stone

(Des G. Hamori. Photo Courvoisier)
1969 (29 Oct). *Musical Instruments*. T 151 and similar horiz designs. P 12½ × 12.
165 5 c. multicoloured 10 10
166 10 c. black, olive-green and pale yellow 10 10
167 25 c. black, yellow and brown 15 15
168 30 c. multicoloured 25 15
165/8 Set of 4 55 45
Designs:—10 c. Garamut; 25 c. Iviliko; 30 c. Kundu.

(Des R. Bates. Photo Courvoisier)
1970 (11 Feb). *"National Heritage"*. T 155 and similar horiz designs. Multicoloured. P 12½ × 12.
169 5 c. Type 155 10 10
170 10 c. Masawa canoe of Kula Circuit 10 10
171 25 c. Torres' Map, 1606 40 15
172 30 c. H.M.S. *Basilisk* (paddle-sloop), 1873 65 25
169/72 Set of 4 1·10 50

159 King of Saxony Bird of Paradise

(Des T. Walcot. Photo Courvoisier)
1970 (13 May). *Fauna Conservation (Birds of Paradise)*. T 159 and similar vert designs. Multicoloured. P 12.
173 5 c. Type 159 80 15
174 10 c. King Bird of Paradise 80 60
175 15 c. Raggiana Bird of Paradise 1·25 1·00
176 25 c. Sickle-crested Bird of Paradise 1·50 70
173/6 Set of 4 4·00 2·25

163 Douglas DC-6B and Mt Wilhelm

164 Lockheed L.188 Electra and Mt Yule

165 Boeing 727-100 and Mt Giluwe

166 Fokker F.27 Friendship and Manam Island

(Des D. Gentleman. Photo Harrison)
1970 (8 July). *Australian and New Guinea Air Services*. T 163/6 and similar horiz designs. Multicoloured. P 14½ × 14.
177 5 c. Type 163 30 10
　　a. Block of 4. Nos. 177/80 1·10
178 5 c. Type 164 30 10
179 5 c. Type 165 30 10
180 5 c. Type 166 30 10
181 25 c. Douglas DC-3 and Matupi Volcano 45 40
182 30 c. Boeing 707 and Hombrom's Bluff 45 60
177/82 Set of 6 1·90 1·25
Nos. 177/80 were issued together, *se-tenant*, in blocks of 4 throughout the sheet.

ALTERED CATALOGUE NUMBERS

Any Catalogue numbers altered from the last edition are shown as a list in the introductory pages.

169 N. Miklouho-Maclay (scientist) and Effigy

170 Wogeo Island Food Bowl

(Des D. Gentleman. Photo Courvoisier)
1970 (19 Aug). *42nd ANZAAS (Australian-New Zealand Association for the Advancement of Science) Congress, Port Moresby*. T 169 and similar horiz designs. P 11½.
183 5 c. multicoloured 10 10
184 10 c. multicoloured 20 10
185 15 c. multicoloured 90 25
186 20 c. multicoloured 60 25
183/6 Set of 4 1·60 55
Designs:—10 c. B. Malinowski (anthropologist) and native hut; 15 c. T. Salvadori (ornithologist) and Double-wattled Cassowary; 20 c. F.R.R. Schlechter (botanist) and flower.

(Des P. Jones. Photo Courvoisier)
1970 (28 Oct). *Native Artefacts*. T 170 and similar multicoloured designs. P 12½ × 12 (30 c.) or 12 × 12½ (others).
187 5 c. Type 170 10 10
188 10 c. Lime Pot 20 10
189 15 c. Aibom Sago Storage Pot 20 10
190 30 c. Manus Island Bowl (horiz) 25 30
187/90 Set of 4 70 50

171 Eastern Highlands Dwelling

172 Spotted Phalanger

(Des G. Wade. Photo Courvoisier)
1971 (27 Jan). *Native Dwellings*. T 171 and similar vert designs showing dwellings from the places given. Multicoloured. P 11½.
191 5 c. Type 171 15 10
192 7 c. Milne Bay 15 75
193 10 c. Purari Delta 15 10
194 40 c. Sepik 35 80
191/4 Set of 4 70 1·50

(Des R. Bates. Photo Courvoisier)
1971 (31 Mar). *Fauna Conservation*. T 172 and similar multicoloured designs. P 11½.
195 5 c. Type 172 30 10
196 10 c. Long-fingered Possum 45 10
197 15 c. Feather-tailed Possum 80 80
198 25 c. Long-nosed Echidna (horiz) 1·25 80
199 30 c. Ornate Tree Kangaroo (horiz) 1·25 50
195/9 Set of 5 3·50 2·00

173 "Basketball"

174 Bartering Fish for Vegetables

(Des G. Hamori, Litho D.L.R.)
1971 (9 June). *Fourth South Pacific Games, Papeete, Tahiti*. T 173 and similar horiz designs. Multicoloured. P 13½ × 14.
200 7 c. Type 173 10 10
201 14 c. "Sailing" 15 20
202 21 c. "Boxing" 15 30
203 28 c. "Athletics" 15 40
200/3 Set of 4 50 85

(Des G. Wade. Photo Courvoisier)
1971 (18 Aug). *Primary Industries*. T 174 and similar vert designs. Multicoloured. P 11½.
204 7 c. Type 174 10 10
205 9 c. Man stacking yams 15 30
206 14 c. Vegetable market 25 10
207 30 c. Highlanders cultivating garden 45 65
204/7 Set of 4 85 1·00

175 Sia Dancer　**176** Papuan Flag over Australian Flag

(Des Bette Hays. Photo Courvoisier)

1971 (27 Oct). *Native Dancers. T* **175** *and similar multicoloured designs.* P 11½.
208	7 c. Type 175		20	10
209	9 c. Urasena dancer		25	20
210	20 c. Siassi Tubuan dancers (*horiz*)		60	75
211	28 c. Sia dancers (*horiz*)		80	90
208/11		*Set of 4*	1·60	1·75

(Des R. Bates. Photo Courvoisier)

1972 (26 Jan). *Constitutional Development.* T **176** *and similar horiz design.* P 12½ × 12.
212	176	7 c. multicoloured	30	10
	a. Pair. Nos. 212/13		60	90
213	—	7 c. multicoloured	30	10

Design:—No. 213, Crest of Papua New Guinea and Australian coat of arms.
Nos. 212/13 were printed vertically *se-tenant* within the sheet.

177 Map of Papua New Guinea and Flag of South Pacific Commission　**178** Turtle

(Des R. Bates. Photo Courvoisier)

1972 (26 Jan). *25th Anniv of South Pacific Commission.* T **177** *and similar horiz design.* P 12½ × 12.
214	177	15 c. multicoloured	45	55
	a. Pair. Nos. 214/15		90	1·75
215	—	15 c. multicoloured	45	55

Design:—No. 215, Man's face and flag of the Commission.
Nos. 214/15 were printed vertically *se-tenant* within the sheet.

(Des R. Bates. Photo Courvoisier)

1972 (17 Mar). *Fauna Conservation (Reptiles).* T **178** *and similar horiz designs. Multicoloured.* P 11½.
216	7 c. Type 178		40	10
217	14 c. Rainforest Dragon		80	1·25
218	21 c. Green Python		80	1·25
219	30 c. Salvador's Monitor		1·00	1·25
216/19		*Set of 4*	2·75	3·50

179 Curtiss MF-6 Seagull Aircraft and *Eureka* (schooner)　**180** New National Flag

(Des Major L. G. Halls. Photo Courvoisier)

1972 (7 June). *50th Anniv of Aviation.* T **179** *and similar horiz designs. Multicoloured.* P 11½.
220	7 c. Type 179		50	10
221	14 c. De Havilland D.H.37 and native porters		1·00	1·25
222	20 c. Junkers G.31 and gold dredger		1·25	1·25
223	25 c. Junkers F-13 and mission church		1·25	1·25
220/3		*Set of 4*	3·50	3·50

(Des R. Bates. Photo Courvoisier)

1972 (16 Aug). *National Day.* T **180** *and similar vert designs. Multicoloured.* P 11½.
224	7 c. Type 180		20	10
225	10 c. Native drum		25	25
226	30 c. Trumpet Triton		45	50
224/6		*Set of 3*	80	70

181 Rev. Copland King　**182** Mt Tomavatur Station

(Des G. Wade. Photo Courvoisier)

1972 (25 Oct). *Christmas (Missionaries).* T **181** *and similar horiz designs. Multicoloured.* P 11½.
227	7 c. Type 181		25	40
228	7 c. Rev. Dr. Flierl		25	40
229	7 c. Bishop Verjus		25	40
230	7 c. Pastor Ruatoka		25	40
227/30		*Set of 4*	90	1·40

(Des R. Bates. Photo Courvoisier)

1973 (24 Jan). *Completion of Telecommunications Project, 1968–72.* T **182** *and similar horiz designs. Multicoloured.* P 12½ (Nos. 231/4) or 11½ (others).
231	7 c. Type 182		20	20
	a. Block of 4. Nos. 231/4		70	
232	7 c. Mt Kerigomma Station		20	20
233	7 c. Sattelburg Station		20	20
234	7 c. Wideru Station		20	20
235	9 c. Teleprinter (36 × 26 mm)		20	25
236	30 c. Network Map (36 × 26 mm)		70	75
231/6		*Set of 6*	1·50	1·60

Nos. 231/4 were printed in *se-tenant* blocks of four within the sheet.

183 Queen Carola's Parotia　**184** Wood Carver

(Des W. Cooper. Photo Courvoisier)

1973 (30 Mar). *Birds of Paradise.* T **183** *and similar vert designs. Multicoloured.* P 11½.
237	7 c. Type 183		1·00	35
238	14 c. Goldie's Bird of Paradise		2·25	1·00
239	21 c. Ribbon-tailed Bird of Paradise (18 × 49 mm)		2·50	1·50
240	28 c. Princess Stephanie's Bird of Paradise (18 × 49 mm)		3·00	2·00
237/40		*Set of 4*	8·00	4·25

(Des R. Bates. Photo Courvoisier)

1973 (13 June)–74. T **184** *and similar horiz designs. Multicoloured.* P 11½.
241	1 c. Type 184		10	10
242	3 c. Wig-makers (23.1.74)		40	10
243	5 c. Mt Bagana (22.8.73)		55	10
244	6 c. Pig Exchange (7.8.74)		70	90
245	7 c. Coastal village		30	10
246	8 c. Arawe mother (23.1.74)		35	30
247	9 c. Fire dancers		30	20
248	10 c. Tifalmin hunter (23.1.74)		55	10
249	14 c. Crocodile hunters (22.8.73)		45	70
250	15 c. Mt Elimbari		50	30
251	20 c. Canoe-racing, Manus (23.1.74)		1·00	40
252	21 c. Making sago (22.8.73)		50	80
253	25 c. Council House		50	45
254	28 c. Menyamya bowmen (22.8.73)		50	75
255	30 c. Shark-snaring (22.8.73)		50	50
256	40 c. Fishing canoes, Madang		50	40
257	60 c. Tapa cloth-making (23.1.74)		55	50
258	$1 Asaro Mudmen (23.1.74)		75	1·10
259	$2 Enga "Sing Sing" (7.8.74)		2·75	6·00
241/59		*Set of 19*	10·50	12·00

185 Stamps of German New Guinea, 1897

(Des R. Bates. Photo (1 c.), litho and recess (6 c.) or litho (7 c.) State Printing Works, Berlin. Photo and recess D.L.R. (9 c.). Recess and typo Reserve Bank of Australia (25 and 30 c.))

1973 (24 Oct). *75th Anniv of Papua New Guinea Stamps.* T **185** *and similar horiz designs. Chalky paper (25, 30 c.).* P 13½ (1, 6, 7 c.), 14 × 13½ (9 c.) or 14 × 14½ (25, 30 c.).
260	1 c. multicoloured		10	15
261	6 c. indigo, new blue and silver		20	30
262	7 c. multicoloured		20	20
263	9 c. multicoloured		20	30
264	25 c. orange and gold		40	80
265	30 c. plum and silver		40	90
260/65		*Set of 6*	1·25	2·40

Designs: *As T* **185**—6 c. 2 mark stamp of German New Guinea, 1900; 7 c. Surcharged registration label of New Guinea, 1914. 46 × 35 mm.—9 c. Papua 1s. stamp, 1901. 45 × 38 mm—25 c. ½d. stamp of New Guinea, 1925; 30 c. Papua 10s. stamp, 1932.

NEW INFORMATION

The editor is always interested to correspond with people who have new information that will improve or correct the Catalogue.

SELF-GOVERNMENT

186 Native Carved Heads　**187** Queen Elizabeth II (from photograph by Karsh)

(Des G. Wade. Photo Courvoisier)

1973 (5 Dec). *Self-Government.* P 11½.
266	186	7 c. multicoloured	30	15
267		10 c. multicoloured	50	65

(Des and photo Harrison)

1974 (22 Feb). *Royal Visit.* P 14 × 14½.
268	187	7 c. multicoloured	25	15
269		30 c. multicoloured	75	1·50

188 Blyth's Hornbill　**189** *Dendrobium bracteosum*

(Des T. Nolan. Photo Courvoisier)

1974 (12 June). *Birds' Heads.* T **188** *and similar multicoloured designs.* P 11½ (10 c.) or 12 (others).
270	7 c. Type 188		1·50	70
271	10 c. Double-wattled Cassowary (33 × 49 mm)		2·25	3·25
272	30 c. New Guinea Harpy Eagle		5·00	8·50
270/2		*Set of 3*	8·00	11·00

(Des T. Nolan. Photo Courvoisier)

1974 (20 Nov). *Flora Conservation.* T **189** *and similar vert designs. Multicoloured.* P 11½.
273	7 c. Type 189		40	10
274	10 c. *D. anosmum*		50	50
275	20 c. *D. smillieae*		60	1·25
276	30 c. *D. insigne*		75	1·50
273/6		*Set of 4*	2·00	3·00

190 Motu Lakatoi　**191** 1-toea Coin

(Des G. Wade. Photo Courvoisier)

1975 (26 Feb). *National Heritage—Canoes.* T **190** *and similar horiz designs. Multicoloured.* P 11½.
277	7 c. Type 190		30	10
278	10 c. Tami two-master morobe		40	55
279	25 c. Aramia racing canoe		75	2·50
280	30 c. Buka Island canoe		75	1·00
277/80		*Set of 4*	2·00	3·75

(New Currency. 100 toea = 1 kina)

(Des G. Wade. Photo Courvoisier)

1975 (21 Apr). *New Coinage.* T **191** *and similar multicoloured designs.* P 11½.
281	1 t. Type 191		10	10
282	7 t. New 2 t. and 5 t. coins (45 × 26 mm)		35	10
283	10 t. New 10 t. coin		35	30
284	20 t. New 20 t. coin		70	80
285	1 k. New 1 k. coin (45 × 26 mm)		2·25	4·00
281/5		*Set of 5*	3·25	4·50

192 *Ornithoptera alexandrae*　**193** Boxing

(Des R. Bates. Photo Courvoisier)

1975 (11 June). *Fauna Conservation (Birdwing Butterflies). T 192 and similar vert designs. Multicoloured. P 11½.*

286	7 t. Type 192	..	50	10
287	10 t. *O. victoriae*	..	60	65
288	30 t. *O. allottei*	..	1·00	2·00
289	40 t. *O. chimaera*	..	1·50	3·25
286/9		Set of 4	3·25	5·50

(Des R. Bates. Photo Courvoisier)

1975 (2 Aug). *Fifth South Pacific Games, Guam. T 193 and similar vert designs. Multicoloured. P 11½.*

290	7 t. Type 193	..	10	10
291	20 t. Running	..	15	30
292	25 t. Basketball	..	30	45
293	30 t. Swimming	..	30	50
290/3		Set of 4	70	1·10

INDEPENDENT

194 Map and National Flag

(Des and photo Courvoisier)

1975 (10 Sept). *Independence. T 194 and similar horiz design. Multicoloured. P 11½.*

294	7 t. Type 194	..	20	10
295	30 t. Map and National emblem	..	40	65
MS296	116 × 58 mm. Nos. 294/5	..	1·10	1·75

195 M.V. *Bulolo*   **196** Rorovana Carvings

(Des R. Bates. Photo Courvoisier)

1976 (21 Jan). *Ships of the 1930s. T 195 and similar horiz designs. Multicoloured. P 11½.*

297	7 t. Type 195	..	30	10
298	15 t. M.V. *Macdhui*	..	40	30
299	25 t. M.V. *Malaita*	..	50	65
300	60 t. S.S. *Montoro*	..	1·00	2·50
297/300		Set of 4	2·00	3·25

(Des R. Bates. Photo Courvoisier)

1976 (17 Mar). *Bougainville Art. T 196 and similar horiz designs. Multicoloured. P 11½.*

301	7 t. Type 196	..	10	10
302	20 t. Upe hats	..	20	35
303	25 t. Kapkaps	..	25	50
304	30 t. Canoe paddles	..	30	75
301/4		Set of 4	75	1·50

197 Rabaul House   **198** Landscouts

(Des G. Wade. Photo Courvoisier)

1976 (9 June). *Native Dwellings. T 197 and similar horiz designs. Multicoloured. P 11½.*

305	7 t. Type 197	..	10	10
306	15 t. Aramia house	..	20	20
307	30 t. Telefomin house	..	35	60
308	40 t. Tapini house	..	35	1·00
305/8		Set of 4	85	1·75

(Des R. Bates. Photo Courvoisier)

1976 (18 Aug). *50th Anniversaries of Survey Flight and Scouting in Papua New Guinea. T 198 and similar horiz designs. Multicoloured. P 11½.*

309	7 t. Type 198	..	20	10
310	10 t. De Havilland D.H.50A seaplane	..	20	20
311	15 t. Seascouts	..	30	40
312	60 t. De Havilland D.H.50A seaplane on water	..	80	2·50
309/12		Set of 4	1·40	2·75

199 Father Ross and New Guinea Highlands

(Des R. Bates. Photo Courvoisier)

1976 (28 Oct). *William Ross Commemoration. P 11½.*

313	**199** 7 t. multicoloured	..	40	15

200 Picture Wrasse

(Des P. Jones. Photo Courvoisier)

1976 (28 Oct). *Fauna Conservation (Tropical Fish). T 200 and similar horiz designs. Multicoloured. P 11½.*

314	5 t. Type 200	..	30	10
315	15 t. Emperor Angelfish	..	60	45
316	30 t. Six-blotched Hind	..	1·10	80
317	40 t. Thread-finned Butterflyfish	..	1·40	1·10
314/17		Set of 4	3·00	2·25

201 Man from Kundiawa   **202** Headdress, Wasara Tribe

(Des R. Bates. Litho Questa (1, 2 k.) or photo Courvoisier (others))

1977 (12 Jan)–78. *T 201/2 and similar multicoloured designs showing headdresses. P 14 (1, 2 k.) or 11½ (others).*

318	1 t. Type 201 (29.3.78)	..	10	10
319	5 t. Masked dancer, Abelam area of Maprik (29.3.78)	..	10	10
320	10 t. Headdress from Koiari (7.6.78)	..	30	15
321	15 t. Woman with face paint, Hanuabada (29.3.78)	..	30	20
322	20 t. Orokaiva dancer (7.6.78)	..	50	30
323	25 t. Haus Tambaran dancer, Abelam area of Maprik (29.3.78)	..	40	30
324	30 t. Asaro Valley headdress (29.3.78)	..	45	35
325	35 t. Singsing costume, Garaina (7.6.78)	..	50	45
326	40 t. Waghi Valley headdress (29.3.78)	..	50	35
327	50 t. Trobriand Island dancer (7.6.78)	..	75	60
328	1 k. Type 202	..	75	1·50
329	2 k. Headdress, Mekeo tribe	..	1·25	3·00
318/29		Set of 12	5·25	6·50

Sizes—1, 5, 20 t. 25×31 *mm*; 35, 40 t. 23×38 *mm*; 1 k. 28×35 *mm*; 2 k. 33×23 *mm*; others 26×26 *mm*.

203 National Flag and Queen Elizabeth II   **204** White-breasted Ground Pigeon

(Des and photo Harrison)

1977 (16 Mar). *Silver Jubilee. Horiz designs showing Queen Elizabeth as T 203. Multicoloured. P 14½ × 14.*

330	7 t. Type 203	..	20	10
	a. Silver (face value and inscr) omitted	..	£450	
331	15 t. National emblem	..	25	35
332	35 t. Map of P.N.G.	..	40	70
330/2		Set of 3	75	1·00

(Des W. Cooper. Photo Courvoisier)

1977 (8 June). *Fauna Conservation (Birds). T 204 and similar horiz designs. Multicoloured. P 11½.*

333	5 t. Type 204	..	35	10
334	7 t. Victoria Crowned Pigeon	..	35	10
335	15 t. Pheasant Pigeon	..	65	65
336	30 t. Orange-fronted Fruit Dove	..	1·00	1·10
337	50 t. Banded Imperial Pigeon	..	1·60	3·50
333/7		Set of 5	4·75	4·75

205 Guides and Gold Badge   **206** Kari Marupi Myth

(Des R. Bates. Litho Questa)

1977 (10 Aug). *50th Anniv of Guiding in Papua New Guinea. Horiz designs showing badge as T 205. Multicoloured. P 14½.*

338	7 t. Type 205	..	20	10
339	15 t. Guides mapping	..	35	20
340	30 t. Guides washing	..	55	50
341	35 t. Guides cooking	..	60	60
338/41		Set of 4	1·50	1·25

(Des Revd. H. A. Brown. Litho Enschedé)

1977 (19 Oct). *Folklore. Elema Art (3rd series). T 206 and similar vert designs. P 13½ × 13.*

342	7 t. multicoloured	..	15	10
343	20 t. multicoloured	..	35	35
344	30 t. orange-red, light blue and black	..	40	75
345	35 t. orange-red, yellow and black	..	40	75
342/5		Set of 4	1·10	1·75

Designs:—20 t. Savoripi clan myth; 30 t. Oa-Laea myth; 35 t. Oa-Iriarapo myth.

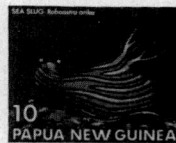

207 Blue-tailed Skink   **208** *Roboastra arika*

(Des T. Nolan. Photo Courvoisier)

1978 (25 Jan). *Fauna Conservation (Skinks). T 207 and similar horiz designs. Multicoloured. P 11½.*

346	10 t. Type 207	..	25	10
347	15 t. Green Tree Skink	..	30	25
348	35 t. Crocodile Skink	..	45	70
349	40 t. New Guinea Blue-tongued Skink	..	60	85
346/9		Set of 4	1·40	1·75

(Des B. Twigden. Photo Courvoisier)

1978 (29 Aug). *Sea Slugs. T 208 and similar horiz designs. Multicoloured. P 11½.*

350	10 t. Type 208	..	20	10
351	15 t. *Chromodoris fidelis*	..	25	30
352	35 t. *Flabellina macassarana*	..	45	85
353	40 t. *Chromodoris marginata*	..	50	1·00
350/3		Set of 4	1·25	2·00

209 Present Day Royal Papua New Guinea Constabulary   **210** Ocarina

(Des R. Bates. Photo Harrison)

1978 (26 Oct). *History of Royal Papua New Guinea Constabulary. T 209 and similar horiz designs showing uniformed police and constabulary badges. Multicoloured. P 14½.*

354	10 t. Type 209	..	20	10
355	15 t. Mandated New Guinea Constabulary, 1921–1941	..	30	15
356	20 t. British New Guinea Armed Constabulary, 1890–1906	..	35	40
357	25 t. German New Guinea Police, 1899–1914	..	35	40
358	30 t. Royal Papua and New Guinea Constabulary, 1906–1964	..	40	60
354/8		Set of 5	1·40	1·50

(Des R. Bates. Litho Questa)

1979 (24 Jan). *Musical Instruments. T 210 and similar multi-coloured designs. P 14½ × 14 (7, 28 t.) or 14 × 14½ (others).*

359	7 t. Type 210	..	10	10
360	20 t. Musical bow (*horiz*)	..	20	20
361	28 t. Launut	..	25	30
362	35 t. Nose flute (*horiz*)	..	30	45
359/62		Set of 4	75	90

211 East New Britain Canoe   **212** Katudababila (waist belt)

(Des G. Wade. Litho Questa)

1979 (28 Mar). *Traditional Canoe Prows and Paddles. T 211 and similar vert designs. Multicoloured. P 14½.*

363	14 t. Type 211	..	20	15
364	21 t. Sepik war canoe	..	30	25
365	30 t. Trobriand Island canoe	..	30	30
366	40 t. Milne Bay canoe	..	40	60
363/6		Set of 4	1·10	1·10

(Des R. Bates. Photo Courvoisier)

1979 (6 June). *Traditional Currency. T 212 and similar horiz designs. Multicoloured. P 12½ × 12.*

367	7 t. Type 212	..	10	10
368	15 t. Doga (chest ornament)	..	20	30
369	25 t. Mwali (armshell)	..	35	55
370	35 t. Soulava (necklace)	..	45	75
367/70		Set of 4	1·00	1·50

213 *Aenetus cyanochlora*

214 "The Right to Affection and Love"

(Des T. Nolan. Photo Courvoisier)

1979 (29 Aug).   *Fauna Conservation. Moths. T 213 and similar multicoloured designs.* P 11½.

371	7 t.	Type 213	..	20	10
372	15 t.	*Celerina vulgaris*	..	30	35
373	20 t.	*Alcidis aurora* (*vert*)	..	40	65
374	25 t.	*Phyllodes conspicillator*	..	45	80
375	30 t.	*Lyssa patroclus* (*vert*)	..	55	90
371/5			*Set of 5*	1·75	2·50

(Des G. Wade. Litho Enschedé)

1979 (24 Oct).   *International Year of the Child. T 214 and similar vert designs. Multicoloured.* P 13½ × 13.

376	7 t.	Type 214	..	10	10
377	15 t.	"The right to adequate nutrition and medical care"	..	15	15
378	30 t.	"The right to play"	..	20	20
379	60 t.	"The right to a free education"	..	45	60
376/9			*Set of 4*	80	90

215 "Post Office Service"

216 Detail from Betrothal Ceremony Mural, Minj District, Western Highlands Province

(Des G. Wade. Litho Enschedé)

1980 (23 Jan).   *Admission to U.P.U.* (1979). *T 215 and similar horiz designs. Multicoloured.* P 13 × 13½.

380	7 t.	Type 215	..	10	10
381	25 t.	"Wartime mail"	..	25	25
382	35 t.	U.P.U. emblem	..	35	40
383	40 t.	"Early postal services"	..	40	50
380/3			*Set of 4*	1·00	1·10

(Des W. Tubun. Photo Courvoisier)

1980 (26 Mar).   *South Pacific Festival of Arts. T 216 and similar vert designs showing different details from mural of betrothal ceremony, Minj District, Western Highlands Province.* P 11½.

384	20 t.	black, greenish yellow and pale orange	..	25	35
	a.	Strip of 5. Nos. 384/8		1·10	
385	20 t.	multicoloured (two figures—left-hand black and yellow; right-hand black, yellow and red)		25	35
386	20 t.	multicoloured (two figures—left-hand black and orange; right-hand black)		25	35
387	20 t.	multicoloured (two figures, one behind the other)		25	35
388	20 t.	multicoloured (one figure)		25	35
384/8			*Set of 5*	1·10	1·60

Nos. 384/8 were printed together, *se-tenant*, in horizontal strips of 5 throughout the sheet.

217 Family being Interviewed

(Des R. Bates. Litho Questa)

1980 (4 June).   *National Census. T 217 and similar horiz designs. Multicoloured.* P 14 × 13½.

389	7 t.	Type 217	..	10	10
390	15 t.	Population symbol	..	15	15
391	40 t.	Figures and map of Papua New Guinea		30	40
392	50 t.	Heads symbolising population growth		35	50
389/92			*Set of 4*	80	1·00

NEW INFORMATION

The editor is always interested to correspond with people who have new information that will improve or correct the Catalogue.

218 Donating Blood

219 Dugong

(Des R. Bates. Litho Questa)

1980 (27 Aug).   *Red Cross Blood Bank. T 218 and similar horiz designs. Multicoloured.* P 14½.

393	7 t.	Type 218	..	15	10
394	15 t.	Receiving transfusion	..	20	20
395	30 t.	Map of Papua New Guinea showing blood transfusion centres		25	25
396	60 t.	Blood and its components		40	60
393/6			*Set of 4*	90	1·00

(Des Dr. E. Lindgren (35 t.), T. Nolan (others). Photo Courvoisier)

1980 (29 Oct).   *Mammals. T 219 and similar multicoloured designs.* P 11½.

397	7 t.	Type 219	..	10	10
398	30 t.	New Guinea Marsupial Cat (*vert*)	..	30	45
399	35 t.	Tube-nosed Bat (*vert*)	..	30	45
400	45 t.	Rufescent Bandicoot ("Mumut")	..	40	55
397/400			*Set of 4*	1·00	1·40

220 White-headed Kingfisher

221 Native Mask

(Des W. Peckover. Photo Courvoisier)

1981 (21 Jan).   *Kingfishers. T 220 and similar multicoloured designs.* P 11½.

401	3 t.	Type 220	..	30	60
402	7 t.	Forest Kingfisher	..	30	10
403	20 t.	Sacred Kingfisher	..	70	50
404	25 t.	White-tailed Kingfisher (26 × 46 *mm*)		70	85
405	60 t.	Blue-winged Kookaburra	..	1·40	3·00
401/5			*Set of 5*	3·00	4·50

(Des R. Bates. Photo Note Ptg Branch, Reserve Bank of Australia)

1981 (21 Jan).   *Coil stamps. Vert designs as T 221.* P 15 × *imperf.*

406	2 t.	reddish violet and orange	..	10	20
407	5 t.	cerise and blue-green	..	10	20

Design:—5 t. Hibiscus flower.

222 Mortar Team

223 M.A.F. (Missionary Aviation Fellowship) Cessna 205 Super Skywagon

(Des T. Reilly (15 t.), R. Bates (others). Litho Enschedé)

1981 (25 Mar).   *Defence Force. T 222 and similar horiz designs. Multicoloured.* P 13 × 13½.

408	7 t.	Type 222	..	15	10
409	15 t.	Douglas DC-3 and aircrew	..	25	25
410	40 t.	*Aitape* (patrol boat) and seamen		45	65
411	50 t.	Medical team examining children		50	75
408/11			*Set of 4*	1·25	1·50

(Des G. Wade. Litho Questa)

1981 (17 June).   *"Mission Aviation". T 223 and similar vert designs. Multicoloured.* P 14.

412	10 t.	Type 223	..	20	10
413	15 t.	Catholic mission British Aircraft Swallow *St. Paulus*		25	15
414	20 t.	S.I.L. (Summer Institute of Linguistics) Hiller 12E helicopter		25	25
415	30 t.	Lutheran mission Junkers F-13		35	40
416	35 t.	S.D.A. (Seventh Day Adventist Church) Piper PA-23 Aztec		35	55
412/16			*Set of 5*	1·25	1·25

224 Scoop Net Fishing

225 Bühler's Papuina (*Forcartia buehleri*)

(Des G. Wade. Litho Questa)

1981 (26 Aug).   *Fishing. T 224 and similar horiz designs. Multicoloured.* P 14.

417	10 t.	Type 224	..	15	10
418	15 t.	Kite fishing	..	20	30
419	30 t.	Rod fishing	..	30	50
420	60 t.	Scissor net fishing	..	55	85
417/20			*Set of 4*	1·10	1·60

(Des P. Jones. Photo Courvoisier)

1981 (28 Oct).   *Land Snail Shells. T 225 and similar horiz designs. Multicoloured.* P 11½ × 12.

421	5 t.	Type 225	..	10	10
422	15 t.	Yellow Naninia (*Naninia citrina*)	..	20	25
423	20 t.	Adonis Papuina (*Papuina adonis*) and Hermione Papuina (*Papuina hermione*)		25	35
424	30 t.	Hinde's Papuina (*Papuina hindei*) and New Pommeranian Papuina (*Papuina novaepommeraniae*)		35	50
425	40 t.	*Papuina strabo*	..	50	80
421/5			*Set of 5*	1·25	1·75

226 Lord Baden-Powell and Flag-raising Ceremony

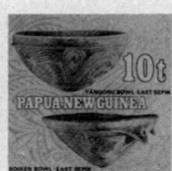
227 Yangoru and Boiken Bowls, East Sepik

(Des G. Wade. Photo Courvoisier)

1982 (20 Jan).   *75th Anniv of Boy Scout Movement. T 226 and similar horiz designs. Multicoloured.* P 11½.

426	15 t.	Type 226	..	20	15
427	25 t.	Scout leader and camp	..	25	30
428	35 t.	Scout, and hut building	..	35	45
429	50 t.	Percy Chaterton, and Scouts administering first aid		50	75
426/9			*Set of 4*	1·10	1·50

(Des R. Bates. Litho Questa)

1982 (24 Mar).   *Native Pottery. T 227 and similar multicoloured designs.* P 14 (10, 20 t.) or 14½ (*others*).

430	10 t.	Type 227	..	10	10
431	20 t.	Utu cooking pot and small Gumalu pot, Madang		20	30
432	40 t.	Wanigela pots, Northern District (37 × 23 *mm*)		40	55
433	50 t.	Ramu Valley pots, Madang (37 × 23 *mm*)		45	80
430/3			*Set of 4*	1·00	1·60

228 "Eat Healthy Foods"

229 *Stylophora sp*

(Des G. Wade, Litho J.W.)

1982 (21 May).   *Food and Nutrition. T 228 and similar horiz designs. Multicoloured.* P 14½ × 14.

434	10 t.	Type 228	..	10	10
435	15 t.	Protein foods	..	20	30
436	30 t.	Protective foods	..	40	55
437	40 t.	Energy foods	..	45	70
434/7			*Set of 4*	1·00	1·50

(Des Courvoisier or W. Peckover (5 k.). Photo Courvoisier)

1982 (21 July)—*85. Granite paper.* (a) *Corals. Multicoloured designs as T 229.* P 11½.

438	1 t.	Type 229	..	10	20
439	3 t.	*Dendrophyllia sp.* (*vert*) (12.1.83)		60	60
440	5 t.	*Acropora humilis*	..	15	10
441	10 t.	*Dendronephthya sp.* (*vert*) (12.1.83)		80	30
442	10 t.	As 10 t. (29.5.85)	..	4·00	4·75
443	15 t.	*Distichopora sp*	..	30	20
444	20 t.	*Isis sp.* (*vert*) (9.11.83)		90	25
445	25 t.	*Acropora sp.* (*vert*) (9.11.83)		40	50
446	30 t.	*Dendronephthya sp.* (*diff*) (*vert*) (12.1.83)		1·50	90
447	35 t.	*Stylaster elegans* (*vert*) (9.11.83)		1·40	
448	40 t.	*Antipathes sp.* (*vert*) (12.1.83)		1·50	75
449	45 t.	*Turbinarea sp.* (*vert*) (9.11.83)		2·50	50
450	1 k.	*Xenia sp*	..	1·25	85
451	3 k.	*Distichopora sp.* (*vert*) (12.1.83)		2·75	3·50

(b) *Bird of Paradise. Multicoloured square design, 33×33 mm*

452	5 k.	Raggiana Bird of Paradise (7.8.84)		7·00	9·00
438/52			*Set of 15*	22·00	20·00

For No. 442 surcharged "STAMP DUTY" see note below No. 631.

230 Missionaries landing on Beach

231 Athletics

(Des B. To Una. Photo Courvoisier)

1982 (15 Sept). *Centenary of Catholic Church in Papua New Guinea. Mural on wall of Nordup Catholic Church, East New Britain. T 230 and similar vert designs. Multicoloured. P 11½.*
457	10 t.	Type 230		20	35
	a.	Horiz strip of 3. Nos. 457/9		55	
458	10 t.	Missionaries talking to natives		20	35
459	10 t.	Natives with slings and spears ready to attack		20	35
457/9			*Set of 3*	55	95

Nos. 457/9 come in *se-tenant* strips of 3 horizontally throughout the sheet, each strip forming a composite design.

(Des R. Bates. Litho Questa)

1982 (6 Oct). *Commonwealth Games and "Anpex 82" Stamp Exhibition, Brisbane. T 231 and similar horiz designs. Multicoloured. P 14½.*
460	10 t.	Type 231		15	10
461	15 t.	Boxing		20	25
462	45 t.	Rifle-shooting		40	70
463	50 t.	Bowls		40	70
460/3			*Set of 4*	1·10	1·60

232 National Flag

(Des Walsall. Litho Harrison)

1983 (9 Mar). *Commonwealth Day. T 232 and similar horiz designs. Multicoloured. P 14.*
464	10 t.	Type 232		15	10
465	15 t.	Basket-weaving and cabbage-picking		20	30
466	20 t.	Crane hoisting roll of material		25	35
467	50 t.	Lorries and ships		60	75
464/7			*Set of 4*	1·10	1·40

233 Transport Communications   234 *Chelonia depressa*

(Des G. Wade. Litho J.W.)

1983 (7 Sept). *World Communications Year. T 233 and similar horiz designs. Multicoloured. P 14.*
468	10 t.	Type 233		30	10
469	25 t.	"Postal service"		50	25
470	30 t.	"Telephone service"		55	30
471	60 t.	"Transport service"		1·10	90
468/71			*Set of 4*	2·25	1·40

(Des R. Bates. Photo Courvoisier)

1984 (8 Feb). *Turtles. T 234 and similar horiz designs. Multicoloured. P 11½.*
472	5 t.	Type 234		20	10
473	10 t.	*Chelonia mydas*		30	10
474	15 t.	*Eretmochelys imbricata*		40	30
475	20 t.	*Lepidochelys olivacea*		50	35
476	25 t.	*Caretta caretta*		55	50
477	40 t.	*Dermochelys coriacea*		80	75
472/7			*Set of 6*	2·50	1·75

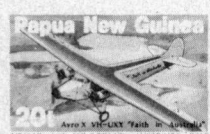

235 Avro Type 618 Ten
Faith in Australia

(Des T. Reilly. Litho Format)

1984 (9 May). *50th Anniv of First Airmail Australia-Papua New Guinea. T 235 and similar horiz designs. Multicoloured. P 14½ × 14.*
478	20 t.	Type 235		40	30
479	25 t.	De Havilland D.H.86B Dragon Express *Carmania*		40	45
480	40 t.	Westland Widgeon		65	80
481	60 t.	Consolidated PBY-5 Catalina flying boat *Guba*		1·00	1·25
478/81			*Set of 4*	2·25	2·50

236 Parliament House   237 Ceremonial Shield and Club, Central Province

(Des A. Brennan, adapted G. Vasarhelyi. Litho Harrison)

1984 (7 Aug). *Opening of New Parliament House. P 13½ × 14.*
482	236	10 t. multicoloured		30	30

(Des Revd. A. H. Brown. Photo Courvoisier)

1984 (21 Sept). *Ceremonial Shields. T 237 and similar vert designs. Multicoloured. Granite paper. P 11½.*
483	10 t.	Type 237		20	10
484	20 t.	Ceremonial shield, West New Britain		30	35
485	30 t.	Ceremonial shield, Madang Province		45	75
486	50 t.	Ceremonial shield, East Sepik		75	2·50
483/6			*Set of 4*	1·50	3·25

238 H.M.S. *Nelson* at   239 Fergusson Island
Port Moresby, 1884

(Des R. Bates, Litho Format)

1984 (6 Nov). *Centenary of Protectorate Proclamations for British New Guinea and German New Guinea. T 238 and similar horiz designs. Multicoloured. P 14½ × 14.*
487	10 t.	Type 238		35	55
	a.	Horiz pair. Nos. 487/8		70	1·10
488	10 t.	Papua New Guinea flag and Port Moresby, 1984		35	55
489	45 t.	Papua New Guinea flag and Rabaul, 1984		50	1·90
	a.	Horiz pair. Nos. 489/90		1·00	3·75
490	45 t.	German warship *Elisabeth* at Rabaul, 1884		50	1·90
487/90			*Set of 4*	1·50	4·50

Nos. 487/8 and 489/90 were each printed together, *se-tenant*, as horizontal pairs throughout the sheets, each pair forming a composite picture.

(Des R. Bates. Photo Courvoisier)

1985 (6 Feb). *Tourist Scenes. T 239 and similar multicoloured designs. Granite paper. P 11½.*
491	10 t.	Type 239		25	10
492	25 t.	Sepik River		50	60
493	40 t.	Chimbu Gorge (*horiz*)		75	1·25
494	60 t.	Dali Beach, Vanimo (*horiz*)		1·25	1·75
491/4			*Set of 4*	2·50	3·25

12t
(240)

241 Dubu Platform, Central Province

1985 (1 Apr). *No. 408 surch with T 240.*
495	12 t. on 7 t. Type 222			60	75
	a.	Surch omitted (in horiz pair with normal)		£110	
	b.	Surch inverted		†	—

At least one sheet of No. 495 exists with the surcharge completely omitted on five positions of the sheet and poorly printed on the remainder.

(Des G. Wade. Photo Heraclio Fournier)

1985 (1 May). *Ceremonial Structures. T 241 and similar vert designs. Multicoloured. P 13.*
496	15 t.	Type 241		35	15
497	20 t.	Tamuniai house, West New Britain		50	50
498	30 t.	Traditional yam tower, Trobriand Island		65	80
499	60 t.	Huli grave, Tari		1·00	1·75
496/9			*Set of 4*	2·25	3·00

Imperforate examples of Nos. 496/9 and similar designs, each 26×33 mm, perforated and with face values shown as "10", "20", "30", or "60", are reported by the Papua New Guinea Philatelic Bureau as having been removed from their archives without authority.

242 Head of New Britain   243 National Flag and
Sparrow Hawk   Parliament House

(Des P. Slater. Litho Format)

1985 (26 Aug). *Birds of Prey. T 242 and similar vert designs. Multicoloured. P 14 × 14½.*
500	12 t.	Type 242		70	1·50
	a.	Horiz pair. Nos. 500/1		1·40	3·00
501	12 t.	New Britain Sparrow Hawk in flight		70	1·50
502	30 t.	Doria's Goshawk		1·00	1·75
	a.	Horiz pair. Nos. 502/3		2·00	3·50
503	30 t.	Doria's Goshawk in flight		1·00	1·75
504	60 t.	Long-tailed Honey Buzzard		1·50	2·25
	a.	Horiz pair. Nos. 504/5		3·00	4·50
505	60 t.	Long-tailed Honey Buzzard in flight		1·50	2·25
500/5			*Set of 6*	5·75	10·00

Nos. 500/1, 502/3 and 504/5 were each printed together, *se-tenant*, in horizontal pairs throughout the sheets.

(Des R. Bates. Litho B.D.T.)

1985 (11 Sept). *10th Anniv of Independence. P 14 × 15.*
506	243	12 t. multicoloured		60	70

244 Early Postcard,   245 Figure with
Aerogramme, Inkwell   Eagle
and Spectacles

(Des R. Bates. Litho Walsall)

1985 (9 Oct). *Centenary of the Papua New Guinea Post Office. T 244 and similar horiz designs. Multicoloured. P 14½ × 14.*
507	12 t.	Type 244		45	10
508	30 t.	Queensland 1897 1d. die with proof and modern press printing stamps		1·10	1·00
509	40 t.	Newspaper of 1885 announcing shipping service and loading mail into aircraft		1·75	2·00
510	60 t.	Friedrich-Wilhelmshafen postmark of 1892 and Port Moresby F.D.C. postmark of 9 Oct 1985		2·00	3·50
507/10			*Set of 4*	4·75	6·00
MS511	90×79 mm. As Nos. 507/10, but designs continue on sheet margins			6·00	7·00

(Des R. Bates. Photo Courvoisier)

1985 (13 Nov). *Nombowai Wood Carvings. T 245 and similar vert designs. Multicoloured. Granite paper. P 11½.*
512	12 t.	Type 245		50	10
513	30 t.	Figure with clamshell		1·25	75
514	60 t.	Figure with dolphin		2·00	2·75
515	80 t.	Figure of woman with cockerel		2·50	4·75
512/15			*Set of 4*	5·75	7·50

246 Valentine or   247 Rufous Fantail
Prince Cowrie
(*Cypraea valentia*)

(Des R. Bates. Photo Courvoisier)

1986 (12 Feb). *Seashells. T 246 and similar horiz designs. Multicoloured. Granite paper. P 11½.*
516	15 t.	Type 246		75	15
517	35 t.	Bulow's Olive (*Oliva buelowi*)		1·60	1·40
518	45 t.	Parkinson's Olive (*Oliva parkinsoni*)		2·00	2·00
519	70 t.	Golden Cowrie (*Cypraea aurantium*)		2·50	5·25
516/19			*Set of 4*	6·00	8·00

(Des A. Theobald. Litho Harrison)

1986 (21 Apr). *60th Birthday of Queen Elizabeth II. Vert designs as T 230a of Jamaica. Multicoloured. P 14½×14.*
520	15 t.	Princess Elizabeth in A.T.S. uniform, 1945		15	15
521	35 t.	Silver Wedding Anniversary photograph (by Patrick Lichfield), Balmoral, 1972		25	40
522	50 t.	Queen inspecting guard of honour, Port Moresby, 1982		50	75
523	60 t.	On board Royal Yacht *Britannia*, Papua New Guinea, 1982		75	90
524	70 t.	At Crown Agents' Head Office, London, 1983		50	1·10
520/4			*Set of 5*	1·90	3·00

(Des W. Peckover. Photo Courvoisier)

1986 (22 May). *"Ameripex '86" International Stamp Exhibition, Chicago. Small Birds (1st series). T 247 and similar multicoloured designs. Granite paper. P 12½.*
525	15 t.	Type 247		90	30
526	35 t.	Streaked Berrypecker		1·75	1·25
527	45 t.	Red-breasted Pitta		1·90	1·25
528	70 t.	Olive-yellow Robin (*vert*)		2·50	5·50
525/8			*Set of 4*	6·25	7·50

The scientific name on the 15 t. value refers to the 45 t. design, and vice versa.

See also Nos. 597/601.

248 Martin Luther nailing Theses to Cathedral Door, Wittenberg, and Modern Lutheran Pastor

249 *Dendrobium vexillarius*

(Des local artist. Litho Questa)

1986 (3 July). *Centenary of Lutheran Church in Papua New Guinea. T* **248** *and similar vert design. Multicoloured. P* 14 × 15.
529	15 t. Type 248.				75	15
530	70 t. Early church, Finschhafen, and modern Martin Luther Chapel, Lae Seminary				2·25	3·25

(Des Harrison. Litho B.D.T.)

1986 (4 Aug). *Orchids. T* **249** *and similar vert designs. Multicoloured. P* 13½.
531	15 t. Type 249				95	20
532	35 t. *Dendrobium lineale*				2·00	75
533	45 t. *Dendrobium johnsoniae*				2·00	1·10
534	70 t. *Dendrobium cuthbertsonii*				2·75	5·00
531/4				*Set of* 4	7·00	6·25

250 Maprik Dancer

251 Whitebonnet Anemonefish

(Des R. Bates. Litho B.D.T.)

1986 (12 Nov). *Papua New Guinea Dancers. T* **250** *and similar vert designs. Multicoloured. P* 14.
535	15 t. Type 250				65	15
536	35 t. Kiriwina				1·40	80
537	45 t. Kundiawa				1·50	95
538	70 t. Fasu				2·40	3·25
535/8				*Set of* 4	5·50	4·75

(Des Harrison. Litho Format)

1987 (15 Apr). *Anemonefish. T* **251** *and similar horiz designs. Multicoloured. P* 15.
539	17 t. Type 251				70	25
540	30 t. Orange-finned Anemonefish				1·40	1·10
541	35 t. Fire Anemonefish ("Tomato Clown-fish")				1·50	1·40
542	70 t. Spine-cheeked Anemonefish				2·50	5·50
539/42				*Set of* 4	5·50	7·50

252 *Roebuck* (Dampier), 1700   (**253**)

(Des R. Bates. Photo Courvoisier)

1987 (15 June)–88. *Ships. T* **252** *and similar square designs. Multicoloured. Granite paper. P* 11½.
543	1 t. *La Boudeuse* (De Bougainville), 1768 (16.11.88)			50	90
544	5 t. Type 252			70	1·00
545	10 t. H.M.S. *Swallow* (Philip Carteret), 1767 (16.11.88)			1·00	1·00
546	15 t. H.M.S. *Fly* (Blackwood), 1845 (17.2.88)			1·00	80
547	17 t. As 15 t. (16.3.88)			1·00	40
548	20 t. H.M.S. *Rattlesnake* (Owen Stanley), 1849 (17.2.88)			1·10	90
549	30 t. *Vitiaz* (Maclay), 1871 (16.11.88)			1·40	2·00
550	35 t. *San Pedrico* (Torres) and zabra, 1606			70	60
551	40 t. *L'Astrolabe* (d'Urville), 1827 (17.2.88)			1·75	2·00
552	45 t. *Neva* (D'Albertis), 1876			75	1·00
553	60 t. Spanish galleon (Jorge de Meneses), 1526 (17.2.88)			2·50	3·50
554	70 t. *Eendracht* (Schouten and Le Maire), 1616			1·75	2·25
555	1 k. H.M.S. *Blanche* (Simpson), 1872 (16.3.88)			2·50	3·00
556	2 k. *Merrie England* (steamer), 1889			3·25	3·00
557	3 k. *Samoa* (German colonial steamer), 1884 (16.11.88)			4·00	6·00
543/57			*Set of* 15	21·00	25·00

A printing by lithography of a 45 t. (as issued 70 t.), 70 t. (as 45 t.), 80 t. (as 35 t.) and 2 k. was originally produced, but such stamps were not issued for postal purposes. Examples in circulation are from a small quantity sold by the U.S.A. philatelic agent in error.

For some of these designs redrawn for "Australia '99" World Stamp Exhibition see Nos. 857/61.

(Des Revd. A. H. Brown. Photo Courvoisier)

1987 (19 Aug). *War Shields. Vert designs as T* **237**. *Multi-coloured. Granite paper. P* 11½.
558	15 t. Gulf Province			20	25
559	35 t. East Sepik			45	50
560	45 t. Madang Province			55	60
561	70 t. Telefomin			85	90
558/61			*Set of* 4	1·90	2·00

1987 (23 Sept). *No.* 442 *surch with T* **253**.
562	15 t. on 12 t. *Dendronephthya sp.*			65	65

For similar 20 t. surcharge see No. 602.

254 *Protoreaster nodosus*

255 Cessna 206 Stationair 6 taking off, Rabaraba

(Des Harrison. Litho B.D.T.)

1987 (30 Sept). *Starfish. T* **254** *and similar horiz designs. Multicoloured. P* 13½.
563	17 t. Type 254			55	25
564	35 t. *Gomophia egeriae*			1·10	70
565	45 t. *Choriaster granulatus*			1·25	80
566	70 t. *Neoferdina ocellata*			1·75	3·25
563/6			*Set of* 4	4·25	4·50

(Des A. Theobald. Litho Questa)

1987 (11 Nov). *Aircraft in Papua New Guinea. T* **255** *and similar horiz designs. Multicoloured. P* 14.
567	15 t. Type 255			80	25
568	35 t. Britten-Norman Islander over Hombrum Bluff			1·50	90
569	45 t. De Havilland D.H.C.6 Twin Otter 100 over Highlands			1·50	1·00
570	70 t. Fokker F.28 Fellowship over Madang			2·50	4·25
567/70			*Set of* 4	5·75	5·75

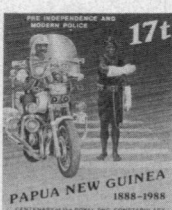

256 Pre-Independence Policeman on Traffic Duty and Present-day Motorcycle Patrol

(Des R. Bates. Litho Questa)

1988 (15 June). *Centenary of Royal Papua New Guinea Constabulary. T* **256** *and similar vert designs. Multicoloured. P* 14 × 15.
571	17 t. Type 256			45	25
572	35 t. British New Guinea Armed Constabulary, 1890, and Governor W. MacGregor			80	50
573	45 t. Police badges			90	65
574	70 t. German New Guinea Police, 1888, and Dr. A. Hahl (founder)			1·50	1·75
571/4			*Set of* 4	3·25	2·75

257 Lakatoi (canoe) and Sydney Opera House

(Des R. Bates. Litho Harrison)

1988 (30 July). *"Sydpex '88" National Stamp Exhibition, Sydney. P* 14.
575	**257** 35 t. multicoloured			80	65

258 Papua New Guinea Flag on Globe and Fireworks

259 Male and Female Butterflies in Courtship

(Des R. Bates. Litho CPE Australia Ltd, Melbourne)

1988 (30 July). *Bicentenary of Australian Settlement. T* **258** *and similar horiz design. Multicoloured. P* 13½.
576	35 t. Type 258			55	75
	a. Horiz pair. Nos. 576/7			1·10	1·50
577	35 t. Australian flag on globe and fireworks			55	75
MS578	90 × 50 mm. Nos. 576/7			1·10	1·50

Nos. 576/7 were printed together, *se-tenant*, in horizontal pairs throughout the sheet, each pair forming a composite design.

(Des M. Parsons, adapted D. Miller. Litho Walsall)

1989 (19 Sept). *Endangered Species. Ornithoptera alexandrae (Queen Alexandra's Birdwing butterfly). T* **259** *and similar multicoloured designs. P* 14½.
579	5 t. Type 259			1·00	65
580	17 t. Female laying eggs and mature larva (*vert*)			2·00	40
581	25 t. Male emerging from pupa (*vert*)			2·75	2·75
582	35 t. Male feeding			3·25	3·00
579/82			*Set of* 4	8·00	6·25

260 Athletics

(Des G. Wade. Litho CPE Australia Ltd, Melbourne)

1988 (19 Sept). *Olympic Games, Seoul. T* **260** *and similar horiz design. Multicoloured. P* 13½.
583	17 t. Type 260			20	25
584	45 t. Weightlifting			60	65

261 *Rhododendron zoelleri*

263 Writing Letter

262

(Des N. Cruttwell and I. Loe. Litho Leigh-Mardon Ltd, Melbourne)

1989 (25 Jan). *Rhododendrons. T* **261** *and similar vert designs. Multicoloured. W* **262**. *P* 14½.
585	3 t. Type 261			10	10
586	20 t. *Rhododendron cruttwellii*			50	30
587	60 t. *Rhododendron superbum*			1·25	1·50
588	70 t. *Rhododendron christianae*			1·50	1·75
585/8			*Set of* 4	3·00	3·25

(Des R. Bates. Litho Leigh-Mardon Ltd, Melbourne)

1989 (22 Mar). *International Letter Writing Week. T* **263** *and similar square designs. Multicoloured. W* **262**. *P* 14½.
589	20 t. Type 263			30	30
590	35 t. Stamping letter			55	50
591	60 t. Posting letter			90	1·10
592	70 t. Reading letter			1·10	1·40
589/92			*Set of* 4	2·50	3·00

264 Village House, Buka Island, North Solomons

265 Tit Berrypecker (female)

(Des G. Wade. Litho Leigh-Mardon Ltd, Melbourne)

1989 (17 May). *Traditional Dwellings.* T **264** *and similar horiz designs. Multicoloured.* W **262**. *P* 15.

593	20 t. Type **264**	40	35
594	35 t. Koiari tree house, Central Province	70	60
595	60 t. Longhouse, Lauan, New Ireland	1·25	1·40
596	70 t. Decorated house, Basilaki, Milne Bay	1·50	1·60
593/6	Set of 4	3·50	3·50

(Des W. Peckover. Litho Questa)

1989 (12 July). *Small Birds* (2nd issue). T **265** *and similar vert designs. Multicoloured.* P 14½.

597	20 t. Type **265**	1·00	1·00
	a. Horiz pair. Nos. 597/8	2·00	2·00
598	20 t. Tit Berrypecker (male)	1·00	1·00
599	35 t. Blue-capped Babbler	1·50	80
600	45 t. Black-throated Robin	1·50	1·00
601	70 t. Large Mountain Sericornis	2·25	2·50
597/601	Set of 5	6·50	5·75

Nos. 597/8 were printed together, *se-tenant*, in horizontal pairs throughout the sheet.

1989 (12 July). *No. 539 surch as* T **253**.

602	20 t. on 17 t. Type **251**	60	70
	a. Surch double	† £170	

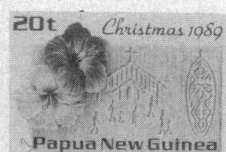

266 Motu Motu Dancer, Gulf Province	267 Hibiscus, People going to Church and Gope Board

(Des G. Wade. Litho Leigh-Mardon Ltd, Melbourne)

1989 (6 Sept). *Traditional Dancers.* T **266** *and similar vert designs. Multicoloured.* W **262**. *P* 14×14½.

603	20 t. Type **266**	65	35
604	35 t. Baining, East New Britain	1·10	90
605	60 t. Vailala River, Gulf Province	2·00	2·25
606	70 t. Timbunke, East Sepik Province	2·00	2·50
603/6	Set of 4	5·25	5·50

(Des R. Bates. Litho Leigh-Mardon Ltd, Melbourne)

1989 (8 Nov). *Christmas.* T **267** *and similar horiz designs showing flowers and carved panels. Multicoloured.* P 14×14½.

607	20 t. Type **267**	40	35
608	35 t. Rhododendron, Virgin and Child and mask	60	60
609	60 t. D'Albertis Creeper, Christmas candle and warshield	1·25	1·60
610	70 t. Pacific Frangapani, peace dove and flute mask	1·40	1·90
607/10	Set of 4	3·25	4·00

268 Guni Falls	269 Boys and Census Form

(Des A. Theobald. Litho Questa)

1990 (1 Feb). *Waterfalls.* T **268** *and similar vert designs. Multicoloured.* P 14.

611	20 t. Type **268**	60	35
612	35 t. Rouna Falls	85	75
613	60 t. Ambua Falls	1·40	1·50
614	70 t. Wawoi Falls	1·60	1·75
611/14	Set of 4	4·00	4·00

MACHINE LABELS. From 7 March 1990 gummed labels inscribed "PAPUA NEW GUINEA BOROKO" with values from 1 t. to 99 k. 99 were available from an automatic machine installed at Boroko Post Office. This machine was withdrawn on 6 March 1991. A second machine was operational at Rabaul Post Office from 8 February 1991. Labels from this machine do not carry an indication of its location.

(Des R. Bates. Litho Questa)

1990 (2 May). *National Census.* T **269** *and similar horiz design. Multicoloured.* P 14½×15.

615	20 t. Type **269**	40	30
616	70 t. Family and census form	1·50	2·00

270 Gwa Pupi Dance Mask	271 Sepik and Maori Kororu Masks

(Des G. Vasarhelyi. Litho Leigh-Mardon Ltd, Melbourne)

1990 (11 July). *Gogodala Dance Masks.* T **270** *and similar vert designs. Multicoloured.* P 13½.

617	20 t. Type **270**	80	30
618	35 t. Tauga paiyale	1·25	70
619	60 t. A:ga	2·00	3·00
620	70 t. Owala	2·00	3·25
617/20	Set of 4	5·50	6·50

(Des R. Bates. Litho Leigh-Mardon Ltd, Melbourne)

1990 (24 Aug). *"New Zealand 1990" International Stamp Exhibition, Auckland.* P 14½.

621	**271** 35 t. multicoloured	75	75

272 Dwarf Cassowary and Great Spotted Kiwi	273 Whimbrel

(Des R. Bates. Litho Leigh-Mardon Ltd, Melbourne)

1990 (24 Aug). *150th Anniv of Treaty of Waitangi.* T **272** *and similar square design. Multicoloured.* P 14½.

622	20 t. Type **272**	1·25	50
623	35 t. Double-wattled Cassowary and Brown Kiwi	1·50	1·50

(Des L. Curtis. Litho Questa)

1990 (26 Sept). *Migratory Birds.* T **273** *and similar horiz designs. Multicoloured.* P 14½×13½.

624	20 t. Type **273**	85	40
625	35 t. Sharp-tailed Sandpiper	1·25	80
626	60 t. Turnstone	2·25	3·25
627	70 t. Terek Sandpiper	2·50	3·25
624/7	Set of 4	6·25	7·00

274 Jew's Harp	275 Weigman's Papuina (*Papuina weigmani*)

(Des R. Bates. Litho Leigh-Mardon Ltd, Melbourne)

1990 (31 Oct). *Musical Instruments.* T **274** *and similar square designs. Multicoloured.* P 13.

628	20 t. Type **274**	60	30
629	35 t. Musical bow	90	50
630	60 t. Wantoat drum	1·75	2·25
631	70 t. Gogodala rattle	1·75	2·50
628/31	Set of 4	4·50	5·00

STAMP DUTY SURCHARGES. Various postage stamps exist surcharged with new value and "STAMP DUTY" for use as fiscal stamps. The Papua New Guinea post office reported Nos. 442, 631, 633, 669, 673, 677, 702 and 727 as being so surcharged. Bogus "STAMP DUTY" surcharges also exist.

(Des P. Schouter. Litho Leigh-Mardon Ltd, Melbourne)

1991 (6 Mar). *Land Shells.* T **275** *and similar horiz designs. Multicoloured.* P 14×14½.

632	21 t. Type **275**	65	30
633	40 t. *Papuina globula* and *Papuina azonata*	1·00	85
634	50 t. *Planispira deaniana*	1·40	1·60
635	80 t. Chance's Papuina (*Papuina chancei*) and Golden-mouth Papuina (*Papuina xanthochila*)	2·00	2·75
632/5	Set of 4	4·50	5·00

276 Magnificent Riflebird	277 Cricket

(Des W. Peckover (10 k.), R. Bates (others). Litho Leigh-Mardon Ltd, Melbourne)

1991 (1 May)–93. *Birds of Paradise.* T **276** *and similar multicoloured designs with imprint date at foot (except 10 k.).* P 13 (10 k.) or 14½ (others).

(a) Face values shown as "t" or "K"

636	1 t. Type **276** (20.1.93)	15	40
637	5 t. Loria's Bird of Paradise (2.9.92)	20	40
638	10 t. Sickle Crested Bird of Paradise (20.1.93)	20	40
639	20 t. Wahnes' Parotia (20.1.93)	50	30
640	21 t. Crinkle-collared Manucode (25.3.92)	70	30
641	30 t. Goldie's Bird of Paradise (20.1.93)	30	40
642	40 t. Wattle-billed Bird of Paradise (2.9.92)	40	50
643	45 t. King Bird of Paradise (25.3.92)	3·25	80
644	50 t. Short-tailed Paradigalla Bird of Paradise (2.9.92)	50	55
645	60 t. Queen Carola's Parotia (25.3.92)	5·00	2·75
646	90 t. Emperor of Germany Bird of Paradise (25.3.92)	5·50	4·00
647	1 k. Magnificent Bird of Paradise (2.9.92)	1·75	1·75
648	2 k. Superb Bird of Paradise (2.9.92)	1·90	2·00
649	5 k. Trumpet Bird (20.1.93)	6·00	9·00
650	10 k. Lesser Bird of Paradise (32×32 mm)	10·00	12·00
636/50	Set of 15	32·00	32·00

(b) Face values shown as "T" (1.7.93)

650a	21 t. Crinkle-collared Manucode	90	40
650b	45 t. King Bird of Paradise	2·00	1·00
650c	60 t. Queen Carola's Parotia	2·25	2·25
650d	90 t. Emperor of Germany Bird of Paradise	2·75	3·50
650a/d	Set of 4	7·00	6·50

It was originally intended that the 21, 45, 60 and 90 t. values should appear on 19 February 1992, but, when it was noticed that the "T" used for the currency abbreviation on Nos. 650a/d did not match the remainder of the set, the stamps were withdrawn before issue and replaced by Nos. 640, 643 and 645/6. Some examples from the original printing escaped the withdrawal notice, however, and were soon on the market at substantial prices. The postal authorities subsequently decided to release the stock of stamps showing the "T" on 1 July 1993.

Imprint dates: "1992", Nos. 637, 640, 642/8, 650a/d; "MAY 1992", Nos. 640, 643; "1993", Nos. 636, 638/41, 643, 649; "JULY 1993", Nos. 637, 647.

For 40 t., 50 t., 1 k. and 2 k. in these designs, but without "1992 BIRD OF PARADISE" at foot, see Nos. 704/7.

(Des D.D.S. Associates and T. Sipa. Litho Leigh-Mardon Ltd, Melbourne)

1991 (26 June). *9th South Pacific Games.* T **277** *and similar horiz designs. Multicoloured.* P 13.

651	21 t. Type **277**	1·75	40
652	40 t. Athletics	1·50	1·00
653	50 t. Baseball	1·75	2·25
654	80 t. Rugby Union	2·75	4·00
651/4	Set of 4	7·00	7·00

278 Cathedral of St. Peter and St. Paul, Dogura	279 Rambusto Headdress, Manus Province

(Des G. Wade. Litho Questa)

1991 (7 Aug). *Centenary of Anglican Church in Papua New Guinea.* T **278** *and similar horiz designs. Multicoloured.* P 14½.

655	21 t. Type **278**	70	30
656	40 t. Missionaries landing, 1891, and Kaieta shrine	1·40	1·40
657	80 t. First church and Modawa tree	2·25	3·50
655/7	Set of 3	4·00	5·50

(Des D.D.S. Associates and T. Sipa. Litho Leigh-Mardon Ltd, Melbourne)

1991 (16 Oct). *Tribal Headdresses.* T **279** *and similar vert designs. Multicoloured.* P 13.

658	21 t. Type **279**	60	30
659	40 t. Marawaka, Eastern Highlands	1·10	1·40
660	50 t. Tufi, Oro Province	1·25	1·60
661	80 t. Sina Sina, Simbu Province	2·00	3·25
658/61	Set of 4	4·50	6·00

280 Nina	281 Canoe Prow Shield, Bamu

(Des G. Wade. Litho Leigh-Mardon Ltd, Melbourne)

1992 (15 Apr). *500th Anniv of Discovery of America by Columbus and "EXPO '92" World's Fair, Seville. T 280 and similar horiz designs. Multicoloured. P 14.*

662	21 t. Type 280			60	30
663	45 t. *Pinta*			1·25	1·00
664	60 t. *Santa Maria*			1·75	2·00
665	90 t. Christopher Columbus and ships			2·25	3·00
662/5			Set of 4	5·25	5·75

(Des G. Wade. Litho Leigh-Mardon Ltd, Melbourne)

1992 (22 May). *"World Columbian Stamp Expo '92", Chicago. Sheet, 110×80 mm, containing Nos. 664/5. P 14.*
MS666 60 t. *Santa Maria*; 90 t. Christopher Columbus and ships (*sold at 1 k. 70*) .. 4·25 5·00

(Des I. Giles. Litho Leigh-Mardon Ltd, Melbourne)

1992 (3 June). *Papuan Gulf Artifacts. T 281 and similar vert designs. Multicoloured. P 14.*

667	21 t. Type 281			40	30
668	45 t. Skull rack, Kerewa			85	80
669	60 t. Ancestral figure, Era River			1·25	1·50
670	90 t. Gope (spirit) board, Urama			1·60	2·50
667/70			Set of 4	3·75	4·50

282 Papuan Infantryman

283 *Hibiscus tiliàceus*

(Des G. Wade. Litho Leigh-Mardon Ltd, Melbourne)

1992 (22 July). *50th Anniv of Second World War Campaigns in Papua New Guinea. T 282 and similar vert designs. Multicoloured. P 14.*

671	21 t. Type 282			60	30
672	45 t. Australian militiaman			1·25	90
673	60 t. Japanese infantryman			1·75	2·25
674	90 t. American infantryman			2·50	3·50
671/4			Set of 4	5·50	6·25

(Des T. Sipa. Litho Leigh-Mardon Ltd, Melbourne)

1992 (28 Oct). *Flowering Trees. T 283 and similar vert designs. Multicoloured. P 14.*

675	21 t. Type 283			65	30
676	45 t. *Castanospermum australe*			1·50	1·00
677	60 t. *Cordia subcordata*			2·50	2·75
678	90 t. *Acacia auriculiformis*			2·75	4·00
675/8			Set of 4	6·75	7·25

284 Three-striped Dasyure

285 Rufous Wren Warbler

(Des R. Bates. Litho Leigh-Mardon Ltd, Melbourne)

1993 (7 Apr). *Mammals. T 284 and similar horiz designs. Multicoloured. P 14.*

679	21 t. Type 284			40	30
680	45 t. Striped Bandicoot			90	80
681	60 t. Dusky Black-eared Giant Rat			1·25	1·50
682	90 t. Painted Ringtail Possum			1·75	2·50
679/82			Set of 4	3·75	4·50

(Des G. Vasarhelyi. Litho Leigh-Mardon Ltd, Melbourne)

1993 (9 June). *Small Birds. T 285 and similar vert designs. Multicoloured. P 14.*

683	21 t. Type 285			45	30
684	45 t. Superb Pitta			90	80
685	60 t. Mottled Whistler			1·25	1·50
686	90 t. Slaty-chinned Longbill			1·60	2·50
683/6			Set of 4	3·75	4·50

(286)

287 Thread-finned Rainbowfish

1993 (13 Aug). *"Taipei '93" Asian International Stamp Exhibition, Taiwan. Nos. 683/6 optd with T 286 in greenish yellow, bright green and greenish blue.*

687	21 t. Type 285			55	30
688	45 t. Superb Pitta			1·00	80
689	60 t. Mottled Whistler			1·40	2·00
690	90 t. Slaty-chinned Longbill			2·00	2·75
687/90			Set of 4	4·50	5·25

(Des I. Giles. Litho Leigh-Mardon Ltd, Melbourne)

1993 (29 Sept). *Freshwater Fishes. T 287 and similar horiz designs. Multicoloured. P 14×14½.*

691	21 t. Type 287			60	30
692	45 t. Peacock Gudgeon			1·25	80
693	60 t. Northern Rainbowfish			1·60	2·00
694	90 t. Popondetta Blue-eye			2·25	3·75
691/4			Set of 4	5·25	5·75

288 Blue Bird of Paradise

(Litho Leigh-Mardon Ltd, Melbourne)

1993 (29 Sept). *"Bangkok '93" Asian International Stamp Exhibition, Thailand. Sheet 100×65 mm. P 14.*
MS695 288 2 k. multicoloured .. .. .. 6·00 7·00

289 Douglas DC-3

290 Girl holding Matschie's Tree Kangaroo

(Des G. Vasarhelyi. Litho Leigh-Mardon Ltd, Melbourne)

1993 (27 Oct). *20th Anniv of Air Niugini. T 289 and similar horiz designs. Multicoloured. P 14.*

696	21 t. Type 289			75	25
697	45 t. Fokker F.27 Friendship			1·75	70
698	60 t. De Havilland D.H.C.7 Dash Seven			2·00	2·25
699	90 t. Airbus Industrie A310			2·75	3·75
696/9			Set of 4	6·50	6·25

(Des R. Bates. Litho Leigh-Mardon Ltd, Melbourne)

1994 (19 Jan). *Matschie's (Huon Gulf) Tree Kangaroo. T 290 and similar vert designs. Multicoloured. P 14½.*

700	21 t. Type 290			35	25
701	45 t. Adult male			90	60
702	60 t. Female with young in pouch			1·25	1·75
703	90 t. Adolescent on ground			1·90	2·75
700/3			Set of 4	4·00	4·75

(Des R. Bates. Litho Leigh-Mardon Ltd, Melbourne)

1994 (18 Feb). *"Hong Kong '94" International Stamp Exhibition. Designs as Nos. 642, 644 and 647/8, but without "1992 BIRD OF PARADISE" at foot. Multicoloured. P 14½.*

704	40 t. Yellow-breasted Bird of Paradise			85	1·25
	a. Horiz strip of 4. Nos. 704/7 plus centre label			6·50	
705	50 t. Short-tailed Paradigalla Bird of Paradise			1·25	1·50
706	1 k. Magnificent Bird of Paradise			2·00	2·50
707	2 k. Superb Bird of Paradise			3·00	3·25
704/7			Set of 4	6·50	7·50

Nos. 704/7 were printed together, *se-tenant*, in horizontal strips of 4 stamps and one centre label with each strip being sold at 4 k.

(291)

1994 (16 Mar). *Nos. 541 and 551 surch as T 291.*
708	21 t. on 35 t. Fire Anemonefish			9·00	50
709	1 k. 20 on 40 t. *L'Astrolabe* (d'Urville), 1827		2·50	1·50

COVER PRICES

Cover factors are quoted at the beginning of each country for most issues to 1945. An explanation of the system can be found on page x. The factors quoted do not, however, apply to philatelic covers.

---

292 Hagen Axe, Western Highlands

293 Ford Model "T", 1920

(Des R. Bates. Litho Leigh-Mardon Ltd, Melbourne)

1994 (23 Mar)–95. *Artifacts. T 292 and similar vert designs. Multicoloured. P 14×14½.*

710	1 t. Type 292 (29.6.94)		10	40
711	2 t. Telefomin shield, West Sepik (29.6.94)		10	10
712	20 t. Head mask, Gulf Province (29.6.94)		45	30
713	21 t. Kanganaman stool, East Sepik		10	10
714	45 t. Trobriand lime gourd, Milne Bay		20	25
715	60 t. Yuat River flute stopper, East Sepik		25	30
716	90 t. Tami Island dish, Morobe		35	40
717	1 k. Kundu (drum), Ramu River estuary (12.4.95)		2·00	1·75
723	5 k. Gogodala dance mask, Western Province (29.6.94)		2·00	2·25
724	10 k. Malanggan mask, New Ireland (12.4.95)		4·00	4·50
710/24		Set of 10	9·00	9·75

(Des G. Wade. Litho Leigh-Mardon Ltd, Melbourne)

1994 (11 May). *Historical Cars. T 293 and similar horiz designs. Multicoloured. P 14.*

725	21 t. Type 293		35	25
726	45 t. Chevrolet "490", 1915		90	60
727	60 t. Austin "7", 1931		1·25	1·75
728	90 t. Willys Jeep, 1942		1·90	2·75
725/8		Set of 4	4·00	4·75

294 Grizzled Tree Kangaroo

(Des R. Bates. Litho Leigh-Mardon Ltd, Melbourne)

1994 (10 Aug). *"Phila Korea '94" International Stamp Exhibition, Seoul. Tree Kangaroos. Sheet 106×70 mm, containing T 294 and similar vert design. Multicoloured. P 14.*
MS729 90 t. Type 294; 1 k. 20, Doria's Tree Kangaroo .. .. 4·25 5·00

(295) (296)

1994 (23 Aug–28 Nov). *Surch as T 295 or with T 296 (No. 737).*

730	—	5 t. on 35 t. mult (No. 604) (6 Oct)		1·00	75
731	—	5 t. on 35 t. mult (No. 629) (3 Oct)		18·00	13·00
		a. "5 t." omitted			
732	271	10 t. on 35 t. multicoloured (3 Oct)		25·00	8·00
733	—	10 t. on 35 t. multicoloured (No. 623)		13·00	5·00
734	—	21 t. on 80 t. mult (No. 635) (28 Aug)		45·00	1·00
735	—	50 t. on 35 t. mult (No. 612) (28 Nov)		35·00	18·00
736	—	50 t. on 35 t. mult (No. 618) (28 Nov)		90·00	25·00
		a. Surch inverted			£600
737	—	65 t. on 70 t. mult (No. 542) (28 Nov)		2·75	1·40
738	—	65 t. on 70 t. mult (No. 616) (28 Nov)		2·75	1·40
739	—	1 k. on 70 t. mult (No. 614) (28 Nov)		20·00	6·00
740	—	1 k. on 70 t. mult (No. 620) (28 Nov)		2·75	3·00
730/40			Set of 11	£225	75·00

 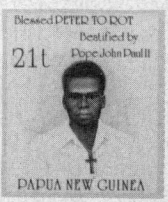

297 *Daphnis hypothous pallescens*

298 Peter To Rot

(Des G. Vasarhelyi. Litho Leigh-Mardon Ltd, Melbourne)

1994 (26 Oct). *Moths. T 297 and similar horiz designs. Multicoloured. P 14.*

741	21 t. Type 297		35	25
742	45 t. *Tanaorhinus unipuncta*		80	65
743	60 t. *Neodiphthera sciron*		1·10	1·50
744	90 t. *Parotis marginata*		1·60	2·25
741/4		Set of 4	3·50	4·25

(Des R. Bates. Litho Leigh-Mardon Ltd, Melbourne)

1995 (11 Jan). *Beatification of Peter To Rot (catechist) and Visit of Pope John Paul II. T 298 and similar vert design. P 14½×14.*

745	21 t. Type 298		1·00	1·00
	a. Horiz pair. Nos. 745/6		2·75	3·00
746	1 k. on 90 t. Pope John Paul II		1·75	2·00
	a. Surch omitted			£120

Nos. 745/6 were issued together, *se-tenant*, in sheets of 30 (6×5), showing No. 745 in vertical rows 1 and 4, No. 746 in vertical rows 3 and 6, and a stamp-size label, showing emblem, in vertical rows 2 and 5.

299 Airliner over Holiday Village

(Des G. Wade. Litho Leigh-Mardon Ltd, Melbourne)

1995 (11 Jan). *Tourism. T 299 and similar horiz designs. Multicoloured. P 14.*

747	21 t. *Melanesian Discoverer* (cruise ship) and launch		50	50
	a. Horiz pair. Nos. 747/8		1·00	1·00
748	21 t. Tourist taking photo of traditional mask		50	50
749	50 t. on 45 t. Type 299		1·25	1·25
	a. Horiz pair. Nos. 749/50		2·50	2·50
750	50 t. on 45 t. Holiday homes		1·25	1·25
751	65 t. on 60 t. Tourists and guide crossing river		1·50	1·50
	a. Horiz pair. Nos. 751/2		3·00	3·00
	b. "65 t" omitted (R. 8/3)		27·00	
752	65 t. on 60 t. White water rafting		1·50	1·50
753	1 k. on 90 t. Scuba diver and *Chertan* (launch)		2·00	2·00
	a. Horiz pair. Nos. 753/4		4·00	4·00
754	1 k. on 90 t. Divers and wreck of aircraft		2·00	2·00
747/54		Set of 8	9·50	9·50

Nos. 747/8, 749/50, 751/2 and 753/4 were printed together, *se-tenant*, in horizontal pairs throughout the sheets. Nos. 749/54 were not issued without surcharge.

(300) 300a

1995 (27 Mar–4 Aug). *Nos. 643, 646, 650b and 650d surch as T 300. (a) Original face values shown as "t"*

755	21 t. on 45 t. King Bird of Paradise (16 May)		2·00	1·00
	b. Surch as Type 300a (4 Aug)		6·00	
756	21 t. on 90 t. Emperor of Germany Bird of Paradise		2·00	1·00
	b. Surch Type 300a (4 Aug)		6·00	

(b) Original face values shown as "T"

757	21 t. on 45 t. King Bird of Paradise (16 May)		4·75	3·00
	b. Surch as Type 300a (4 Aug)		42·00	
758	21 t. on 90 t. Emperor of Germany Bird of Paradise (25 Apr)		6·00	1·00
	a. Surch double		†	£200
	b. Surch Type 300a (4 Aug)		42·00	

Nos. 755b/8b come from a second setting on which the "t" in the surcharge is the same height as the figures. On the 45 t. values these second setting surcharges show a smaller obliterating oblong than on the first setting, but for the 90 t. the oblong on the second setting is much larger.

Nos. 755b/6b occur on stamps with either "1992" or "1993" imprint dates.

MACHINE LABELS. Machines to produce counter-printed labels were introduced at eight Papua New Guinea post offices in May 1995. The initial design incorporated a stylised bird of paradise and the postal emblem, but a second design produced in September 1995 omitted the stylised bird.

21t

(301)

1995 (20 June). *Nos. 692/4 surch with T 301.*

759	21 t. on 45 t. Peacock Gudgeon		55	40
760	21 t. on 60 t. Northern Rainbowfish		2·00	2·00
	a. Surch double		†	—
761	21 t. on 90 t. Popondetta Blue-eye		55	60
759/61		Set of 3	2·75	2·50

302 *Lentinus umbrinus* 302a

(Des J. Cooter)

1995 (21 June–Sept). *Fungi. T 302 and similar vert designs. Multicoloured. (a) Litho Leigh-Mardon Ltd, Melbourne. P 14.*

762	25 t. Type 302		35	30
763	50 t. *Amanita hemibapha*		70	80
764	65 t. *Boletellus emodensis*		85	1·00
765	1 k. *Ramaria zippeli*		1·40	1·75
762/5		Set of 4	3·00	3·50

(b) Litho Southern Colour Print, Dunedin. P 12

765a	25 t. Type 302a (Sept)		35	35

On Type 302a the fungi illustration is larger, 26×32 mm instead of 27×30½ mm, face value and inscriptions are in a different type and there is no imprint date at foot.

303 Anniversary Emblem and Map of Papua New Guinea

304 *Dendrobium rigidifolium*

(Des B. Masiboda. Litho Leigh-Mardon Ltd, Melbourne)

1995 (30 Aug). *20th Anniv of Independence. T 303 and similar vert design. Multicoloured. P 14.*

766	21 t. Type 303		30	25
767	50 t. Emblem and lines on graph		70	80
768	1 k. As 50 t.		1·40	2·00
766/8		Set of 3	2·25	2·75

(Des G. Wade. Litho Leigh-Mardon Ltd, Melbourne)

1995 (30 Aug). *"Singapore '95" International Stamp Exhibition. Orchids. Sheet 150×95 mm, containing T 304 and similar horiz designs. Multicoloured. P 14.*

MS769 21 t. Type 304; 45 t. *Dendrobium convolutum*; 60 t. *Dendrobium spectabile*; 90 t. *Dendrobium tapiniense* (sold at 3 k) .. 3·75 4·50

305 Pig 306 Volcanic Eruption, Tavurvur

(Litho Leigh-Mardon Ltd, Melbourne)

1995 (14 Sept). *Chinese New Year ("Year of the Pig"). Sheet 150×95 mm. P 14½×14.*

MS770 305 3 k. multicoloured .. .. 4·50 5·00

No. MS770 is also inscribed "BEIJING '95" on the sheet margin.

(Des B. Masiboda. Litho Leigh-Mardon Ltd, Melbourne)

1995 (19 Sept). *1st Anniv of Volcanic Eruption, Rabaul. P 14.*

771 306 2 k. multicoloured .. .. 3·00 3·25

307 *Zosimus aeneus* 308 Pesquet's Parrot

(Des Jane Moore. Litho Leigh-Mardon Ltd, Melbourne)

1995 (25 Oct). *Crabs. T 307 and similar horiz designs. Multicoloured. P 14.*

772	21 t. Type 307		40	25
773	50 t. *Cardisoma carnifex*		75	60
774	65 t. *Uca tetragonon*		90	1·10
775	1 k. *Eriphia sebana*		1·25	1·75
772/5		Set of 4	3·00	3·25

(Des V. Pascoe. Litho Southern Colour Print, Dunedin)

1996 (17 Jan). *Parrots. T 308 and similar vert designs. Multicoloured. P 14.*

776	25 t. Type 308		60	30
777	50 t. Rainbow Lory		1·00	65
778	65 t. Papuan King Parrot		1·10	1·10
779	1 k. Red-winged Parrot		1·40	2·25
776/9		Set of 4	3·50	3·75

309 *Lagriomorpha indigacea*

(Des J. Cooter. Litho Southern Colour Print, Dunedin)

1996 (20 Mar). *Beetles. T 309 and similar vert designs. Multicoloured. P 12.*

780	25 t. Type 309		45	25
781	50 t. *Eupholus geoffroyi*		80	65
782	65 t. *Promechus pulcher*		95	1·00
783	1 k. *Callistola pulchra*		1·10	1·90
780/3		Set of 4	3·00	3·50

310 Guang Zhou Zhong Shang Memorial Hall

(Des Stamps World Co. Litho Southern Colour Print, Dunedin)

1996 (22 Apr). *"CHINA '96" 9th Asian International Stamp Exhibition, Peking. Sheet 105×70 mm. P 14.*

MS784 310 70 t. multicoloured .. .. 1·00 1·40

311 Rifle-shooting

(Des Danbury Studio. Litho Southern Colour Print, Dunedin)

1996 (24 July). *Olympic Games, Atlanta. T 311 and similar horiz designs. Multicoloured. P 12.*

785	25 t. Type 311		50	25
786	50 t. Athletics		1·00	70
787	65 t. Weightlifting		1·25	1·25
788	1 k. Boxing		1·50	2·25
785/8		Set of 4	3·75	4·00

312 Air Traffic Controller 313 Dr. Sun Yat-sen

(Des G. Wade. Litho Southern Colour Print, Dunedin)

1996 (11 Sept). *Centenary of Radio. T 312 and similar horiz designs. Multicoloured. P 12.*

789	25 t. Type 312		35	25
790	50 t. Radio disc-jockey		70	65
791	65 t. Dish aerials		85	1·00
792	1 k. Early radio transmitter		1·25	1·60
789/92		Set of 4	2·75	3·25

(Des B. Masiboda. Litho Southern Colour Print, Dunedin)

1996 (16 Oct). *"TAIPEI '96" 10th Asian International Stamp Exhibition, Taiwan. Sheet 105×70 mm, containing T 313 and similar vert design. Multicoloured. P 14.*

MS793 65 t. Type 313; 65 t. Dr. John Guise (former speaker of Papau New Guinea House of Assembly) .. .. 2·25 2·50

OMNIBUS ISSUES

Details, together with prices for complete sets, of the various Omnibus issues from the 1935 Silver Jubilee series to date are included in a special section following Zimbabwe at the end of Volume 2.

1t

1.50

PAPUA NEW GUINEA

314 Hibiscus rosa-sinensis   **315** Ox and National Flag

(Des B. Masiboda (1, 5, 65 t., 1 k.), J. Kipong (others). Litho Southern Colour Print, Dunedin)

1996 (27 Nov)–**97.** *Flowers. T* **314** *and similar multicoloured designs. P* 14 (1, 5, 65 t., 1 k) *or* 12 (*others*).

794	1 t. Type **314**	10	10
795	5 t. *Bougainvillea spectabilis*	10	10
796	10 t. *Thunbergia fragrans* (*vert*) (26.11.97)	10	10
797	20 t. *Caesalpinia pulcherrima* (*vert*) (26.11.97)	10	10
798	25 t. *Hoya sp.* (*vert*) (26.11.97)	10	10
799	30 t. *Heliconia spp.* (*vert*) (26.11.97)	10	15
800	50 t. *Amomun goliathensis* (*vert*) (26.11.97)	20	25
801	65 t. *Plumeria rubra*	25	30
802	1 k. *Mucuna novo-guineensis*	40	45
794/802	*Set of* 9	1·10	1·40

(Des G. Vasarhelyi. Litho Questa)

1997 (3 Feb). *"HONG KONG '97" International Stamp Exhibition. Sheet* 130×90 *mm. P* 14.
MS808 **315** 1 k. 50, multicoloured   1·50   2·00

316 Gogodala Canoe Prow

(Des T. Sipa. Litho Questa)

1997 (19 Mar). *Canoe Prows. T* **316** *and similar horiz designs. Multicoloured. P* 14½×14.

809	25 t. Type **316**	30	25
810	50 t. East New Britain	60	60
811	65 t. Trobriand Island	80	85
812	1 k. Walomo	1·10	1·60
809/12	*Set of* 4	2·50	3·00

(Des N. Shewring (No. MS819), D. Miller (others). Litho Questa (No. MS819), Enschedé (others))

1997 (25 June). *Golden Wedding of Queen Elizabeth and Prince Philip. Multicoloured designs as T* **87** *of Kiribati. P* 14×13½.

813	25 t. Prince Philip on polo pony, 1972	30	40
	a. Horiz pair. Nos. 813/14	60	80
814	25 t. Queen Elizabeth at Windsor Polo Club	30	40
815	50 t. Prince Philip carriage-driving, 1995 ..	55	65
	a. Horiz pair. Nos. 815/16	1·10	1·25
816	50 t. Queen Elizabeth and Prince Edward on horseback	55	65
817	1 k. Prince Philip waving and Peter and Zara Phillips on horseback	1·10	1·25
	a. Horiz pair. Nos. 817/18	2·10	2·50
818	1 k. Queen Elizabeth waving and Prince Harry on horseback	1·10	1·25
813/18	*Set of* 6	3·50	4·25

MS819 105×71 mm. 2 k. Queen Elizabeth and Prince Philip in landau (*horiz*). P 14×14½   2·00   2·50
Nos. 813/14, 815/16 and 818/19 were each printed together, *se-tenant,* in horizontal pairs throughout the sheets with the backgrounds forming composite designs.

317 Air Niugini Airliner over Osaka

(Des B. Masiboda. Litho Southern Colour Print, Dunedin)

1997 (19 July). *Inaugural Air Niugini Port Moresby to Osaka Flight. Sheet* 110×80 *mm. P* 12.
MS820 **317** 3 k. multicoloured ..   3·50   4·00

318 Pocillopora woodjonesi   **319** Sooty Owl

(Des Citi Studio. Litho Southern Colour Print, Dunedin)

1997 (27 Aug). *Pacific Year of the Coral Reef. Corals. T* **318** *and similar horiz designs. Multicoloured. P* 12.

821	25 t. Type **318**	25	20
822	50 t. *Subergorgia mollis*	65	55
823	65 t. *Oxypora glabra*	85	90
824	1 k. *Turbinaria reinformis*	1·50	2·25
821/4	*Set of* 4	3·00	3·50

(Des T. Nolan. Litho Southern Colour Print, Dunedin)

1998 (28 Jan). *Birds. T* **319** *and similar horiz designs. Multicoloured. P* 12.

825	25 t. Type **319**	40	20
826	50 t. Wattled Brush Turkey	60	45
827	65 t. New Guinea Grey-headed Goshawk	70	70
828	1 k. Forest Bittern	1·10	1·40
825/8	*Set of* 4	2·50	2·50

(Des D. Miller. Litho Southern Colour Print, Dunedin)

1998 (29 Mar). *Diana, Princess of Wales Commemoration. Sheet,* 145×70 *mm, containing vert designs as T* **91** *of Kiribati. Multicoloured. P* 14½.
MS829   1 k., Wearing pink jacket, 1992; 1 k., Wearing purple dress, 1988; 1 k. Wearing tartan jacket, 1990; 1 k. Carrying bouquets, 1990 (*sold at* 4 k. + 50 t. *charity premium*) ..   3·25   3·50

25t

320 Mother Teresa and   (**321**)
    Child

(Des B. Masiboda. Litho Southern Colour Print, Dunedin)

1998 (29 Apr). *Mother Teresa Commemoration. T* **320** *and similar horiz design. Multicoloured. P* 14½.

830	65 t. Type **320**	70	75
	a. Horiz pair. Nos. 830/1	1·40	1·50
831	1 k. Mother Teresa	70	75

Nos. 830/1 were printed together, *se-tenant,* in horizontal pairs throughout the sheet.

1998 (28 May). *No. 774 surch with T* **321.**
832   25 t. on 65 t. *Uca tetragonon*   40   30

322 Daphnis hypothous   **323** Coelogyne fragrans
    pallescens

(Des Citi Studio. Litho Southern Colour Print, Dunedin)

1998 (17 June). *Moths. T* **322** *and similar horiz designs. Multicoloured. P* 14.

833	25 t. Type **321**	30	20
834	50 t. *Theretra polistratus*	55	40
835	65 t. *Psilogramma casurina*	65	65
836	1 k. *Meganoton hyloicoides*	75	1·00
833/6	*Set of* 4	2·00	2·00

(Des B. Masiboda. Litho Southern Colour Print, Dunedin)

1998 (15 Sept). *Orchids. T* **323** *and similar vert designs. Multicoloured. P* 14.

837	25 t. Type **323**	30	20
838	50 t. *Den cuthbertsonii*	60	50
839	65 t. *Den vexillarius var retroflexum*	70	70
840	1 k. *Den finisterrae*	1·25	1·40
837/40	*Set of* 4	2·50	2·50

 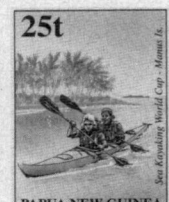

324 Weightlifting   **325** Double Kayak

(Des T. Sipa. Litho Southern Colour Print, Dunedin)

1998 (30 Sept). *16th Commonwealth Games, Kuala Lumpur, Malaysia. T* **324** *and similar vert designs. Multicoloured. P* 14.

841	25 t. Type **324**	25	20
842	50 t. Lawn bowls	45	45
843	65 t. Rugby Union	60	60
844	1 k. Squash	80	90
841/4	*Set of* 4	1·90	1·90

(Des C. Smith. Litho Southern Colour Print, Dunedin)

1998 (5 Oct). *Sea Kayaking World Cup, Manus Island. T* **325** *and similar vert designs. Multicoloured. P* 14.

845	25 t. Type **325**	25	20
846	50 t. Running	45	45
847	65 t. Traditional canoe and modern kayak	60	60
848	1 k. Single kayak and stylised Bird of Paradise	80	90
845/8	*Set of* 4	1·90	1·90

 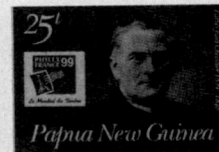

25t

326 The Holy Child   **327** Father Jules Chevalier

(Des B. Masiboda. Litho Southern Colour Print, Dunedin)

1998 (18 Nov). *Christmas. T* **326** *and similar horiz designs. Multicoloured. P* 14.

849	25 t. Type **326**	25	10
850	50 t. Mother breast-feeding baby	40	35
851	65 t. Holy Child and tribal elders	50	55
852	1 k. Map of Papua New Guinea and festive bell	70	95
849/52	*Set of* 4	1·75	1·75

(Litho Secura, Singapore)

1999 (2 Mar). *"PhilexFrance '99" International Stamp Exhibition, Paris. Famous Frenchmen. T* **327** *and similar horiz designs. Multicoloured. P* 13.

853	25 t. Type **327**	10	10
854	50 t. Bishop Alain-Marie	20	25
855	65 t. Joseph-Antoine d'Entrecasteaux (explorer)	25	30
856	1 k. Louis de Bougainville (explorer)	40	45
853/6	*Set of* 4	95	1·10

(Litho Southern Colour Print, Dunedin)

1999 (17 Mar). *"Australia '99" World Stamp Exhibition, Melbourne. Designs as Nos.* 543/5, 548/53 *and* 555/7, *showing ships, redrawn to include exhibition emblem at top right and with some face values changed. Multicoloured. P* 14½.

857	25 t. *La Boudeuse* (De Bougainville) (as No. 543)	25	20
858	50 t. *Neva* (D'Albertis) (as No. 552)	40	35
859	65 t. *Merrie England* (steamer) (as No. 556)	50	55
860	1 k. *Samoa* (German colonial steamer) (as No. 557)	70	95
857/60	*Set of* 4	1·75	1·75

MS861   165×110 mm. 5 t. H.M.S. *Rattlesnake* (Owen Stanley) (as No. 548); 10 t. H.M.S. *Swallow* (Philip Carteret) (as No. 545); 15 t. *Roebuck* (Dampier) (as No. 544); 20 t. H.M.S. *Blanche* (Simpson) (as No. 555); 30 t. *Vitiaz* (Maclay) (as No. 549); 40 t. *San Pedrico* (Torres) and zabra (as No. 550); 60 t. Spanish galleon (Jorge de Meneses) (as No. 553); 1 k. 20, *L'Astrolabe* (D'Urville) (as No. 551) ..   2·75   3·25
No. 859 is inscribed *"Merrir England"* in error. Of the designs in No. MS861 the 5 t. is inscribed *"Simpson Blanche 1872"*, 10 t. *"Carterel"*, 15 t. *"Dampien"*, 40 t. *"eabra"* and 60 t. *"Menesis"*, all in error.

K1

328 German New Guinea 1900 Yacht
    Type 2 m. Stamp

1999 (27 Apr). *"iBRA '99" International Stamp Exhibition, Nuremberg. T* **328** *and similar horiz design. Litho. Multicoloured. P* 14.

862	1 k. Type **328**	55	65
	a. Horiz pair. Nos. 862/3	1·10	1·25
863	1 k. German New Guinea 1897 3 pf and 5 pf optd on Germany	55	65

Nos. 862/3 were printed together, *se-tenant,* in horiz pairs throughout sheets of 10.

25t

329 Hiri Claypot and Traditional
    Dancer

(Litho Secura, Singapore)

1999 (8 Sept). *Hiri Moale Festival. T* **329** *and similar horiz designs. Multicoloured (except No.* MS868). *P* 13.

864	25 t. Type **329**	10	10
865	50 t. Three dancers	20	25

866	65 t. Hiri Lagatoi (trading canoe) and dancer	.. .. ..	25	30
867	1 k. Hiri Sorcerer and dancer	.. ..	40	45
864/7	.. ..	Set of 4	95	1·10

MS868 140×64 mm. 1 k. Hiri Sorcerer (dull ultramarine and dull violet-blue); 1 k. Hiri Claypot (deep reddish purple and dull violet-blue); 1 k. Hiri Lagatoi (slate-green and dull violet-blue) .. .. 1·25 1·40

STAMP BOOKLETS

POSTAGE STAMP

BOOKLET

TERRITORY OF PAPUA AND NEW GUINEA

10 5-Cent Stamps **50c**

B 1

1970 (28 Jan). *Green on olive-yellow cover as Type B* **1**, *but* "POSTAGE STAMP" *in seriffed type. Stamps attached by selvedge.*
SB1 50 c. booklet containing 5 c. (No. 140) in block of 10 £350

1970 (25 May). *Green on cream cover as Type B* **1** *with* "POSTAGE STAMP" *without serifs. Stamps attached by selvedge.*
SB2 50 c. booklet containing 5 c. (No. 140) in block of 10 15·00
No. SB2 shows "GP-P&NG/B1112" imprint on reverse.

POSTAGE STAMPS

TERRITORY OF PAPUA AND NEW GUINEA

10 × 7 CENT STAMPS

70c

B 2

1971 (1 Apr). *Red and green printed cover as Type B* **2**. *Stamps attached by selvedge.*
SB3 70 c. booklet containing 7 c. (No. 141) in block of 10 11·00

PAPUA NEW GUINEA

70c

10 × 7 Cent Stamps

POSTAGE STAMPS

B 3

1972 (14 Feb). *Orange and black printed cover as Type B* **3**. *Stamps attached by selvedge.*
SB4 70 c. booklet containing 7 c. (Nos. 212/13) in block of 10 .. .. 12·00

1973 (16 Feb). *Orange and black printed cover as Type B* **3**. *Stamps attached by selvedge.*
SB5 70 c. booklet containing 7 c. (Nos. 231/4) in block of 10 .. .. 10·00
　　a. Cover optd for "INTERPEX" Stamp Exhibition £120
An example of No. SB5 has been reported containing No. 229 in block of 10.

STAMPS

45t

10 × 45t (K4.50)

Papua New Guinea

B 4

1993 (15 Apr). *Birds of Paradise. Multicoloured covers as Type B* **4**. *Stamps attached by selvedge.*
SB6 2 k. 10, booklet containing 21 t. (No. 640) in block of 10 .. .. 7·50
　　a. With additional slotted tab at right 8·00
SB7 4 k. 50, booklet containing 45 t. (No. 643) in block of 10 .. .. 8·50
　　a. With additional slotted tab at right 9·00
Nos. SB6a and SB7a were intended for self-service sales.

1993 (9 June). *Small Birds. Multicoloured covers as Type B* **4**. *Stamps attached by selvedge.*
SB8 6 k. booklet containing 60 t.(No. 685) in block of 10 12·00
　　a. With additional slotted tab at right 12·00
SB9 9 k. booklet containing 90 t. (No. 686) in block of 10 16·00
　　a. With additional slotted tab at right 16·00
Nos. SB8a and SB9a were intended for self-service sales.

STAMPS

PAPUA NEW GUINEA

21t

10 × 21t (K2.10)

PAPUA NEW GUINEA

B 5

1994 (11 May). *Historical Cars. Multicoloured covers as Type B* **5**. *Stamps attached by selvedge.*
SB10 2 k. 10, booklet containing 21 t. (No. 725) in block of 10 7·00
SB11 4 k. 50, booklet containing 45 t. (No. 726) in block of 10 .. .. 11·00

1995 (21 June). *Fungi. Multicoloured covers as Type B* **5**. *Stamps attached by selvedge.*
SB12 2 k. 50, booklet containing 25 t. (No. 762) in block of 10 7·00
SB13 5 k. booklet containing 50 t. (No. 763) in block of 10 .. .. 11·00

POSTAGE DUE STAMPS

POSTAL CHARGES

6d.

POSTAL CHARGES

● IXIXIXIXIX **3s.**

(D 1)　　　　(D 2)

1960 (1 Mar). *Postage stamps surcharged.* (a) *No. 8 with Type* D **1**.

D1	6d. on 7½d. blue (R.)	.. ..	£800	£425
	a. Surch double		£3500	£1900

　　　　(b) *Nos. 1, 4, 6a, 7/8 as Type* D **2**.

D2	1d. on 6½d. maroon	..	5·00	6·00
D3	3d. on ½d. emerald (B.)	.. ..	6·00	4·50
	a. Surch double		£700	
D4	6d. on 7½d. blue (R.)	.. ..	27·00	12·00
	a. Surch double		£700	
D5	1s. 3d. on 3½d. black (O.)	..	7·00	5·50
D6	3s. on 2½d. orange ..	..	22·00	10·00
D2/6	.. .. ..	Set of 5	60·00	35·00

TERRITORY OF PAPUA & NEW GUINEA

1d.

POSTAL CHARGE

D 3

(Typo Note Ptg Branch, Reserve Bank of Australia, Melbourne)

1960 (2 June). *W* **15** *of Australia. P* 14.

D 7	D **3**	1d. orange	.. ..	65	75
D 8		3d. yellow-brown	.. ..	70	75
D 9		6d. blue	.. ..	75	40
D10		9d. deep red	.. ..	75	1·75
D11		1s. light emerald	.. ..	75	50
D12		1s. 3d. violet	.. ..	1·00	2·00
D13		1s. 6d. pale blue	.. ..	4·50	6·00
D14		3s. yellow	.. ..	3·50	1·25
D7/14		.. ..	Set of 8	11·00	12·00

The use of Postal Charge stamps was discontinued on 12 February 1966, but they remained on sale at the Philatelic Bureau until 31 August 1966.

Pitcairn Islands

CROWN COLONY

The settlement of Pitcairn Island by the *Bounty* mutineers in 1790 was not discovered until the American whaler *Topaz*, Capt. Mayhew Folger, called there in 1808. A visit by two Royal Navy frigates followed in 1814 and reports from their captains resulted in considerable interest being taken in the inhabitants' welfare by religious and philanthrophic circles in Great Britain.

Due to overcrowding the population was resettled on Tahiti in 1831, but many soon returned to Pitcairn which was taken under British protection in 1838. The island was again evacuated in 1856, when the inhabitants were moved to Norfolk Island, but a number of families sailed back to their original home in 1859 and 1864.

The earliest surviving letter from the island is dated 1849. Before 1921 the mail service was irregular, as it depended on passing ships, and mail for the island was often sent via Tahiti. Some covers, purportedly sent from Pitcairn between 1883 and 1890 are known handstamped "Pitcairn Island" or "PITCAIRN ISLAND", but these are now believed to be forgeries.

In 1921 a regular mail service was introduced. As there were no stamps available letters were allowed free postage as long as they carried a cachet, or manuscript endorsement, indicating their origin. Illustrations of Cachets I/VI, VIII, X, XIII and XIV are taken from *Pitcairn Islands Postal Markings 1883–1991*, published by the Pitcairn Islands Study Group, and are reproduced by permission of the author, Mr. Cy Kitching. Cachets I to XIV are shown three-quarter size.

POSTED IN PITCAIRN
NO STAMPS AVAILABLE

Cachet I

Cat No.			Value on cover
C1	1921–25	Cachet I (62×8 mm) (violet)	£3000

POSTED AT PITCAIRN ISLAND
NO STAMPS AVAILABLE.

Cachet II

| C2 | 1921–25. | Cachet II (violet or red) | £2500 |

POSTED AT PITCAIRN ISLAND
NO STAMPS AVAILABLE.

Cachet III

| C3 | 1922–28. | Cachet III (49×8½mm) (vio, pur or blk) | £1800 |

POSTED IN PITCAIRN ISLAND
1923 NO STAMPS AVAILABLE

Cachet IV

| C4 | 1923. | Cachet IV (black) | £2500 |

Posted at Pitcairn Island no Stamps Available

Cachet IVa

| C4a | 1923 | Cachet IVa (73½×22 mm) (red) | £2500 |

POSTED AT PITCAIRN ISLAND
NO STAMPS AVAILABLE

Cachet V

| C5 | 1923–28 (Aug). | Cachet V (47×9 mm) (red, violet or black) | £1700 |
| C5a | 1925–26. | As Cachet V, but second line shown as "No Stamps Available" (black) | |

Cachet VI

| C6 | 1923. | Cachet VI (blue-green) | |
| C7 | 1923. | As Cachet V, but in three lines (red) | |

POSTED AT PITCAIRN ISLAND
NO STAMPS AVAILABLE.

Cachet VII

| C8 | 1923–27. | Cachet VII (violet) | £1700 |
| C9 | 1924. | As Cachet IV, but dated "1924" (black) | £2250 |

POSTED AT PITCAIRN ISLAND.
NO STAMPS AVAILABLE.

Cachet VIII

| C10 | 1924. | Cachet VIII (36×8 mm) (violet) | £2250 |

POSTED AT PITCAIRN
NO STAMPS AVAILABLE

Cachet VIIIA

| C10A | 1924–26. | Cachet VIIIA (36×8¾ mm) | £1800 |

POSTED AT PITCAIRN ISLAND
NO STAMPS AVAILABLE

Cachet IX

| C11 | 1924 (Feb)–25. | Cachet IX (63×7 mm) (vio or blk) | £2500 |

POSTED IN PITCAIRN
NO STAMPS AVAILABLE

Cachet IXa

| C11a | 1924–28. | Cachet IXa (58×8½ mm) (vio or blk) | |
| C12 | 1925 (Sept). | As Cachet IV, but dated "1925" (blk) | £2250 |

POSTED IN PITCAIRN
NO STAMPS AVAILABLE.

Cachet X

| C13 | 1925. | Cachet X (48×5 mm) | £1900 |

POSTED AT PITCAIRN ISLAND,
NO STAMPS AVAILABLE.

Cachet XI

| C14 | 1925–26. | Cachet XI (50×10 mm) (violet or blk) | £2250 |

Posted at PITCAIRN ISLAND
No Stamps Available

Cachet XII

| C15 | 1925 | Cachet XII (55×7½ mm) (violet) | |

POSTED IN PITCAIRN
NO STAMPS AVAILABLE

Cachet XIII

| C16 | 1926 (Jan). | Cachet XIII (64×8 mm) (pur or blk) | |

The New Zealand Government withdrew the free postage concession on 12 May 1926, but after representations from the islanders opened a postal agency on Pitcairn using New Zealand stamps cancelled with Type Z 1. Some impressions of this postmark appear to show a double ring, but this is the result of heavy or uneven use of the handstamp. The postal agency operated from 7 June 1927 until 14 October 1940.

PRICES. Those quoted for Nos. Z1/72 and ZF1 are for examples showing a virtually complete strike of Type Z 1. Due to the size of the cancellation such examples will usually be on piece.

Z 1

Stamps of New Zealand cancelled with Type Z 1.

1915–29. *King George V (Nos. 419, 422/6, 428/31 and 446/9).*

Z 1	½d. green	23·00
Z 2	1½d. grey-slate	48·00
Z 3	1½d. orange-brown	40·00
Z 4	2d. yellow	35·00
Z 5	2½d. blue	65·00
Z 6	3d. chocolate	70·00
Z 7	4d. bright violet	65·00
Z 8	4½d. deep green	80·00
Z 9	5d. light blue	65·00
Z10	6d. carmine	80·00
Z11	7½d. red-brown	85·00
Z12	8d. red-brown	£110
Z13	9d. yellowish olive	£110
Z14	1s. vermilion	£110

1926–27. *King George V in Admiral's uniform (Nos. 468/9).*

Z15	1d. rose-carmine	23·00
Z16	2s. light blue	£160

1931. *Air (No. 548).*

Z18	3d. chocolate	£180

1932. *Health (No. 552)*

Z21	1d. carmine	£100

1935. *Pictorials (Nos. 556/8 and 560/9). W 43.*

Z22	½d. bright green	50·00
Z23	1d. scarlet	32·00
Z24	1½d. red-brown	75·00
Z26	2½d. chocolate and slate	65·00
Z27	3d. brown	75·00
Z28	4d. black and sepia	85·00
Z29	5d. ultramarine	90·00
Z30	6d. scarlet	85·00
Z31	8d. chocolate	90·00
Z32	9d. scarlet and black	90·00
Z33	1s. deep green	80·00
Z34	2s. olive-green	£150
Z35	3s. chocolate and yellow-brown	£180

1935. *Silver Jubilee (Nos. 573/5).*

Z36	½d. green	35·00
Z37	1d. carmine	35·00
Z38	6d. red-orange	65·00

1935. *Health (No. 576).*

Z39	1d. + 1d. scarlet	55·00

1936. *Pictorials (Nos. 577/82). W 98.*

Z40	½d. bright green	40·00
Z41	1d. scarlet	14·00
Z42	1½d. red-brown	65·00
Z43	2d. orange	50·00
Z44	2½d. chocolate and slate	55·00
Z45	3d. brown	60·00

1936. *21st Anniv of "Anzac" Landing at Gallipoli (Nos. 591/2).*

Z46	½d. + ½d. green	38·00
Z47	1d. + 1d. scarlet	38·00

1936. *Congress of British Empire Chambers of Commerce (Nos. 593/7).*

Z48	½d. emerald-green	35·00
Z49	1d. scarlet	35·00
Z50	2½d. blue	40·00
Z51	4d. violet	60·00
Z52	6d. red-brown	60·00

1936. *Health (No. 598).*

Z53	1d. + 1d. scarlet	55·00

1937. *Coronation (Nos. 599/601).*

Z54	1d. carmine	27·00
Z55	2½d. Prussian blue	29·00
Z56	6d. red-orange	29·00

1937. *Health (No. 602).*

Z57	1d. + 1d. scarlet	55·00

1938. *King George VI (Nos. 603, 605, 607).*

Z58	½d. green	55·00
Z59	1d. scarlet	55·00
Z60	1½d. purple-brown	65·00

1940. *Centenary of British Sovereignty (Nos. 613/22, 624/5).*

Z61	½d. blue-green	28·00
Z62	1d. chocolate and scarlet	32·00
Z63	1½d. light blue and mauve	35·00
Z64	2d. blue-green and chocolate	35·00
Z65	2½d. blue-green and blue	38·00
Z66	3d. purple and carmine	38·00
Z67	4d. chocolate and lake	55·00
Z68	5d. pale blue and brown	60·00
Z69	6d. emerald-green and violet	60·00
Z70	7d. black and red	80·00
Z71	9d. olive-green and orange	80·00
Z72	1s. sage-green and deep green	80·00

POSTAL FISCAL STAMPS

1932. *Arms (No. F147).*

ZF1	2s. 6d. deep brown	£180

PRICES FOR STAMPS ON COVER TO 1945
Nos. 1/8   *from* × 10

1 Cluster of Oranges   **2** Christian on *Bounty* and Pitcairn Island

(Recess B.W. (1d., 3d., 4d., 8d. and 2s. 6d.), and Waterlow (others))

1940 (15 Oct)–**51.** *T* **1/2** *and similar horiz designs. Wmk Mult Script CA. P* 11½×11 (1d., 3d., 4d., 8d. and 2s. 6d.) *or* 12½ (others).

1	½d. orange and green		40	60
2	1d. mauve and magenta		55	70
3	1½d. grey and carmine		55	50
4	2d. green and brown		1·75	1·40
5	3d. yellow-green and blue		1·25	1·40
	aw. Wmk inverted		£3250	
5b	4d. black and emerald-green (1.9.51)		15·00	10·00
6	6d. brown and grey-blue		5·00	1·50
6a	8d. olive-green and magenta (1.9.51)		16·00	7·00
7	1s. violet and grey		3·00	1·50
8	2s. 6d. green and brown		7·50	3·75
1/8		Set of 10	45·00	25·00
1/5, 6, 7/8 Perf "Specimen"		Set of 8	£800	

Designs:—1½d. John Adams and his house; 2d. Lt. Bligh and H.M.S. *Bounty*; 3d. Pitcairn Islands and Pacific Ocean; 4d. *Bounty* Bible; 6d. H.M.S. *Bounty*; 8d. School, 1949; 1s. Fletcher Christian and Pitcairn Island; 2s. 6d. Christian on H.M.S. *Bounty* and Pitcairn Coast.

Flagstaff flaw
(R. 8/2)

1946 (2 Dec). *Victory. As Nos. 141/2 of Jamaica.*

9	2d. brown		60	15
10	3d. blue		60	15
	a. Flagstaff flaw		27·00	
9/10 Perf "Specimen"		Set of 2	£140	

1949 (1 Aug). *Royal Silver Wedding. As Nos. 143/4 of Jamaica.*

11	1½d. scarlet		2·00	1·00
12	10s. mauve		48·00	50·00

1949 (10 Oct). *75th Anniv of U.P.U. As Nos. 145/8 of Jamaica.*

13	2½d. red-brown		1·00	3·50
14	3d. deep blue		11·00	4·00
15	6d. deep blue-green		7·00	5·00
16	1s. purple		7·00	5·00
13/16		Set of 4	23·00	16·00

1953 (2 June). *Coronation. As No. 153 of Jamaica, but ptd by B.W.*

17	4d. black and deep bluish green		2·00	3·25

9 *Cordyline terminalis*   **10** Pitcairn Island Map

(Recess D.L.R.)

1957 (2 July)–**63.** *T* **9/10** *and similar designs. Wmk Mult Script CA. P* 13×12½ (*horiz*) *or* 12½×13 (*vert*).

18	½d. green and reddish lilac		80	1·50
	a. Green and reddish purple (9.3.63)		1·25	1·25
19	1d. black and olive-green		3·00	1·25
	a. Black and yellow-olive (19.2.59)		11·00	16·00
	b. Black and light olive-green (24.2.60)		24·00	15·00
20	2d. brown and greenish blue		75	60
21	2½d. deep brown and red-orange		50	40
22	3d. emerald and deep ultramarine		80	40
23	4d. scarlet and deep ultramarine (I)		90	40
23a	4d. carmine-red & dp ultram (II) (5.11.58)		5·00	1·50
24	6d. pale buff and indigo		1·25	55
25	8d. deep olive-green and carmine-lake		60	40
26	1s. black and yellowish brown		1·50	40
27	2s. green and red-orange		16·00	10·00
28	2s. ultramarine and deep lake		22·00	9·00
	a. Blue and deep lake (10.2.59)		38·00	11·00
18/28		Set of 12	48·00	24·00

Designs: *Vert*—2d. John Adams and *Bounty* Bible; 2s. Island wheelbarrow. *Horiz*—2½d. Handicrafts: Bird model; 3d. Bounty Bay; 4d. Pitcairn School; 6d. Pacific Ocean map; 8d. Inland scene; 1s. Handicrafts: Ship model; 2s. 6d. Launching new whaleboat.

Nos. 23/a. Type I is inscribed "PITCAIRN SCHOOL"; Type II "SCHOOLTEACHER'S HOUSE".

See also No. 33

20 Pitcairn Island and Simon Young

(Des H. E. Maud. Photo Harrison)

1961 (15 Nov). *Centenary of Return of Pitcairn Islanders from Norfolk Island. T* **20** *and similar horiz designs. W w* **12.** *P* 14½ × 13½.

29	3d. black and yellow		50	55
30	6d. red-brown and blue		1·00	1·25
31	1s. red-orange and blue-green		1·00	1·25
29/31		Set of 3	2·25	2·75

Designs:—6d. Norfolk Island and Pitcairn Islands; 1s. Migrant brigantine *Mary Ann*.

1963 (4 June). *Freedom from Hunger. As No. 80 of Lesotho.*

32	2s. 6d. ultramarine		14·00	3·00

1963 (4 Dec). *As No. 18a, but wmk w* **12.**

33	**9**	½d. green and reddish purple	65	60

1963 (9 Dec). *Red Cross Centenary. As Nos. 203/4 of Jamaica.*

34	2d. red and black		2·50	1·00
35	2s. 6d. red and blue		9·50	5·50

23 Pitcairn Is Longboat   **24** Queen Elizabeth II (after Anthony Buckley)

(Des M. Farrar Bell. Photo Harrison)

1964 (5 Aug)–**65.** *T* **23/4** *and similar horiz designs. Multi-coloured. W w* **12.** *P* 14 × 14½.

36	½d. Type **23**		10	30
37	1d. H.M.S. *Bounty*		30	30
38	2d. "Out from Bounty Bay"		30	30
39	3d. Great Frigate Bird		75	30
40	4d. White Tern		75	30
41	6d. Pitcairn Warbler		75	30
42	8d. Red-footed Booby		75	30
	a. Pale blue (beak) omitted		£300	
43	10d. Red-tailed Tropic Birds		60	30
44	1s. Henderson Island Crake		60	30
45	1s. 6d. Stephen's Lory		5·50	1·25
46	2s. Murphy's Petrel		5·00	1·50
47	4s. Henderson Island Fruit Dove		7·00	1·75
48	8s. Type **24** (5.4.65)		2·75	1·75
36/48		Set of 13	22·00	8·00

1965 (17 May). *I.T.U. Centenary. As Nos. 98/9 of Lesotho.*

49	1d. mauve and orange-brown		1·00	40
50	2s. 6d. turquoise-green and bright blue		14·00	3·50
	w. Wmk inverted		£100	

1965 (25 Oct). *International Co-operation Year. As Nos. 100/1 of Lesotho.*

51	1d. reddish purple and turquoise-green		1·00	40
	a. "TRISTAN DA CUNHA" offset on back in reddish purple		£350	
52	1s. 6d. deep bluish green and lavender		12·00	4·50

No. 51a was caused by the back of one sheet of stamps coming into contact with the blanket plate used for applying the Tristan da Cunha inscription to the same basic design.

1966 (24 Jan). *Churchill Commemoration. As Nos. 102/5 of Lesotho.*

53	2d. new blue		1·25	85
54	3d. deep green		3·75	1·25
55	6d. brown		4·00	2·25
56	1s. bluish violet		5·50	3·50
53/6		Set of 4	13·00	7·00

25 Footballer's Legs, Ball and Jules Rimet Cup

(Des V. Whiteley. Litho Harrison)

1966 (1 Aug). *World Cup Football Championships. W w* **12** (*sideways*). *P* 14.

57	**25** 4d. violet, yellow-green, lake & yellow-brn	1·75	1·00
58	2s. 6d. chocolate, blue-grn, lake & yell-brn	4·75	1·75

1966 (20 Sept). *Inauguration of W.H.O. Headquarters, Geneva. As Nos. 185/6 of Montserrat.*

59	8d. black, yellow-green and light blue		5·00	3·25
60	1s. 6d. black, light purple and yellow-brown		9·00	3·75

1966 (1 Dec). *20th Anniv of U.N.E.S.C.O. As Nos. 342/4 of Mauritius.*

61	½d. slate-violet, red, yellow and orange		20	50
62	10d. orange-yellow, violet and deep olive		4·50	2·50
63	2s. black, bright purple and orange		9·00	4·25
61/3		Set of 3	12·50	6·50

36 Mangarevan Canoe, *circa* 1325

(Des V. Whiteley. Photo Harrison)

1967 (1 Mar). *Bicentenary of Discovery of Pitcairn Islands. T* **36** *and similar horiz designs. Multicoloured. W w* **12.** *P* 14½.

64	½d. Type **36**		10	20
65	1d. P. F. de Quiros and *San Pedro y San Pablo*, 1606		20	20
66	8d. *San Pedro y San Pablo* and *Los Tres Reyes*, 1606		40	20
67	1s. Carteret and H.M.S. *Swallow*, 1767		40	25
68	1s. 6d. *Hercules*, 1819		40	25
64/8		Set of 5	1·25	1·00

(New Currency. 100 cents = 1 New Zealand dollar)

½**c**

(41 *Bounty* Anchor)

1967 (10 July). *Decimal currency. Nos. 36/48 surch in decimal currency by die-stamping in gold as T* **41.**

69	½c. on ½d. multicoloured		10	10
	a. Deep brown omitted		£650	
	b. Surch double, one albino		£120	
70	1c. on 1d. multicoloured		30	60
71	2c. on 2d. multicoloured		25	60
72	2½c. on 3d. multicoloured		25	60
73	3c. on 4d. multicoloured		25	20
74	5c. on 6d. multicoloured		30	60
75	10c. on 8d. multicoloured		30	30
	a. "10 c." omitted		£750	
	b. Pale blue (beak) omitted		£350	
76	15c. on 10d. multicoloured		1·25	40
77	20c. on 1s. multicoloured		1·25	55
78	25c. on 1s. 6d. multicoloured		2·75	1·25
79	30c. on 2s. multicoloured		3·25	1·25
80	40c. on 4s. multicoloured		4·50	1·25
81	45c. on 8s. multicoloured		4·25	1·50
69/81		Set of 13	17·00	8·50

On No. 75a the anchor emblem is still present. Several examples of this variety have been identified as coming from R. 9/1.

The ½c. and 1 c. exist with PVA gum as well as gum arabic.

42 Bligh and *Bounty*'s Launch

(Des Jennifer Toombs. Litho D.L.R.)

1967 (7 Dec). *150th Death Anniv of Admiral Bligh. T* **42** *and similar horiz designs. P* 13½ × 13.

82	1c. turq-blue, black and royal blue (*shades*)	10	10
83	8c. black, yellow and magenta		40	65
84	20c. black, brown and pale buff		40	25
82/4		Set of 3	75	1·25

Designs:—8c. Bligh and followers cast adrift; 20 c. Bligh's tomb.

45 Human Rights Emblem

(Des G. Hamori. Litho D.L.R.)

1968 (4 Mar). *Human Rights Year. P* 13½ × 13.

85	45	1c. multicoloured		10	10
86	2c. multicoloured		10	10
87	25c. multicoloured		35	35
85/7		Set of 3	45	45

46 Miro Wood and Flower

(Des Jennifer Toombs. Photo Harrison)

1968 (19 Aug). *Handicrafts (1st series). T* **46** *and similar designs. W w* **12** (*sideways* on *vert designs*). *P* 14×13½ (5, 10 c.) *or* 13½×14 (*others*).

88	5c. multicoloured		25	30
89	10c. bronze-green, brown and orange		30	40
90	15c. deep bluish violet, chocolate and salmon		35	40
91	20c. multicoloured		40	45
	w. Wmk Crown to right of CA		£140	
88/91		Set of 4	1·10	1·50

Designs: *Horiz*—10 c. Flying Fish model. *Vert*—15 c. "Hand" vases; 20 c. Woven baskets.

*The normal sideways watermark shows Crown to left of CA, as seen from the back of the stamp.

See also Nos. 207/10.

50 Microscope and Slides

(Des Jennifer Toombs. Litho D.L.R.)

1968 (25 Nov). *20th Anniv of World Health Organisation. T* **50** *and similar horiz design.* W w **12** (*sideways*). *P* 14.
92	2 c. black, turquoise-blue and ultramarine		10	20
93	20 c. black, orange and bright purple		40	50

Design:—20 c. Hypodermic syringe and jars of tablets.

52 Pitcairn Island | **62** "Flying Fox" Cable System

(Des Jennifer Toombs. Litho Questa (50 c., $1), D.L.R. (others))

1969 (17 Sept)–**75**. *T* **52**, **62** *and similar designs. Chalk-surfaced paper.* W w **12** (*upright on 3 c., 25 c., sideways* on* $1 *and horiz designs*). *P* 14½×14 (50 c.), 14 ($1) or 13 (*others*).
94	1 c. multicoloured		1·00	30
	a. Glazed, ordinary paper (9.8.71)		1·25	1·00
	aw. Wmk Crown to right of CA		2·25	
95	2 c. multicoloured		25	15
96	3 c. multicoloured		25	15
97	4 c. multicoloured		80	15
98	5 c. multicoloured		30	15
99	6 c. multicoloured		30	20
100	8 c. multicoloured		50	20
101	10 c. multicoloured		2·50	85
	a. Glazed, ordinary paper (9.8.71)		2·00	2·75
	aw. Wmk Crown to right of CA		6·00	
102	15 c. multicoloured		1·00	50
	a. Queen's head omitted		£700	
103	20 c. multicoloured		60	40
104	25 c. multicoloured		70	40
105	30 c. multicoloured		55	45
106	40 c. multicoloured		75	60
106a	50 c. multicoloured (*glazed, ordinary paper*) (2.1.73)		4·50	11·00
106b	$1 multicoloured (*glazed, ordinary paper*) (21.4.75)		10·00	17·00
94/106b		Set of 15	21·00	29·00

Designs: *Horiz*—2 c. Captain Bligh and *Bounty* chronometer; 4 c. Plans and drawing of *Bounty*; 5 c. Breadfruit containers and plant; 6 c. Bounty Bay; 8 c. Pitcairn longboat; 10 c. Ship landing point; 15 c. Fletcher Christian's Cave; 20 c. Thursday October Christian's House; 30 c. Radio Station, Taro Ground; 40 c. *Bounty* Bible; 50 c. Pitcairn Coat of Arms. *Vert*—3 c. *Bounty* anchor; $1 Queen Elizabeth II.

*The normal sideways watermark shows Crown to left of CA, as seen from the back of the stamp.

See also No. 133.

65 Lantana | **69** Band-tailed Hind

(Des Jennifer Toombs. Litho D.L.R.)

1970 (23 Mar). *Flowers. T* **65** *and similar vert designs. Multicoloured.* W w **12**. *P* 14.
107	1 c. Type **65**		20	50
108	2 c. "Indian Shot"		35	65
109	5 c. Pulau		60	75
110	25 c. Wild Gladiolus		1·25	2·00
107/10		Set of 4	2·25	3·50

(Des Jennifer Toombs. Photo Harrison)

1970 (12 Oct). *Fishes. T* **69** *and similar horiz designs. Multicoloured.* W w **12**. *P* 14.
111	5 c. Type **69**		2·75	70
	w. Wmk inverted		7·00	3·00
112	10 c. High-finned Rudderfish		2·75	85
	w. Wmk inverted		8·00	3·50
113	15 c. Elwyn's Wrasse		3·25	1·00
	w. Wmk inverted		8·00	3·50
114	20 c. Yellow Wrasse ("Whistling Daughter")		3·50	1·25
	w. Wmk inverted		16·00	8·00
111/14		Set of 4	11·00	3·50

71 Polynesian Rock Carvings

ROYAL VISIT 1971
(70)

1971 (22 Feb). *Royal Visit. No. 101 optd with T* **70**, *in silver.*
115	10 c. multicoloured	1·25	2·00

(Des Jennifer Toombs. Litho A & M)

1971 (3 May). *Polynesian Pitcairn. T* **71** *and similar multicoloured designs.* W w **12** (*sideways* on* 10 *and* 15 *c.*). *P* 13½.
116	5 c. Type **71**		1·50	75
	w. Wmk inverted		3·00	
117	10 c. Polynesian artefacts (*horiz*)		1·75	1·00
	w. Wmk Crown to right of CA		3·50	
118	15 c. Polynesian stone fish-hook (*horiz*)		2·00	1·00
	w. Wmk Crown to right of CA		3·75	
119	20 c. Polynesian stone deity		2·25	1·25
	w. Wmk inverted		4·00	
116/19		Set of 4	6·75	3·50

*The normal sideways watermark shows Crown to left of CA, as seen from the back of the stamp.

72 Commission Flag | **73** Red-tailed Tropic Birds and Longboat

(Des Jennifer Toombs. Litho Questa)

1972 (4 Apr). *25th Anniv of South Pacific Commission. T* **72** *and similar horiz designs. Multicoloured* (*except* 4 *c.*). W w **12** (*sideways on* 4 *c.*). *P* 14.
120	4 c. Type **72** (dp blue, blue-violet & brt yell)		65	75
121	8 c. Young and elderly (Health)		65	75
122	18 c. Junior School (Education)		70	1·10
	w. Wmk inverted		3·00	
123	20 c. Goods store (Economy)		1·10	1·75
	w. Wmk inverted			
120/3		Set of 4	2·75	4·00

(Des (from photographs by D. Groves) and photo Harrison)

1972 (20 Nov). *Royal Silver Wedding. Multicoloured; background colour given.* W w **12**. *P* 14 × 14½.
124	**73** 4 c. slate-green		30	60
	w. Wmk inverted		85·00	40·00
125	20 c. bright blue		45	90
	w. Wmk inverted		16·00	

74 Rose-apple | **75** Obelisk Vertagus (*Rhinoclavis sinensis*) and Episcopal Mitre (*Mitra mitra*) Shells

(Des Jennifer Toombs. Litho J.W.)

1973 (25 June). *Flowers. T* **74** *and similar vert designs. Multicoloured.* W w **12** (*sideways*). *P* 14.
126	4 c. Type **74**		1·00	55
127	8 c. Mountain-apple		1·25	75
128	15 c. "Lata"		1·75	1·00
129	20 c. "Dorcas-flower"		1·75	1·25
130	35 c. Guava		2·25	1·75
126/30		Set of 5	7·00	4·75

1973 (14 Nov). *Royal Wedding. As Nos. 322/3 of Montserrat. Centre multicoloured.* W w **12** (*sideways*). *P* 13½.
131	10 c. bright mauve		20	15
132	25 c. emerald		25	30

1974 (4 Feb). *As No. 94a, but wmk upright. Glazed, ordinary paper.*
133	**52** 1 c. multicoloured	2·50	5·00

134/46 Catalogue numbers vacant.

(Des Jennifer Toombs. Litho Questa)

1974 (15 Apr). *Shells. T* **75** *and similar horiz designs. Multicoloured.* W w **12**. *P* 14.
147	4 c. Type **75**		1·50	80
148	10 c. Turtle Dove shell (*Pyrene testudinaria tylerae*)		1·75	1·00
149	18 c. Indo-Pacific Limpet (*Cellana radiata*), Fringed False Limpet (*Siphonaria laciniosa*) and *Siphonaria normalis*		2·00	1·40
150	50 c. *Ctena divergens*		2·75	2·00
147/50		Set of 4	7·00	4·75
MS151	130×121 mm. Nos. 147/50		7·00	14·00

76 Island Post Office

(Des Jennifer Toombs. Litho Questa)

1974 (22 July). *Centenary of Universal Postal Union. T* **76** *and similar horiz designs.* W w **12** (*sideways*). *P* 14.
152	4 c. multicoloured		25	35
153	20 c. bright purple, light cinnamon and black		40	60
154	35 c. multicoloured		50	70
152/4		Set of 3	1·00	1·50

Designs:—20 c. Pre-stamp letter, 1922; 35 c. Mailship and Pitcairn longboat.

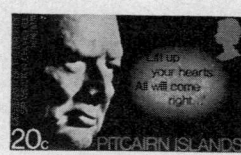

77 Churchill and Text "Lift up your Hearts . . ."

(Des Jennifer Toombs. Litho Questa)

1974 (30 Nov). *Birth Centenary of Sir Winston Churchill. T* **77** *and similar horiz design.* W w **14** (*sideways*). *P* 14½.
155	20 c. blackish olive, apple-green & dp slate		30	65
156	35 c. sepia, greenish yellow and deep slate		40	75

Design:—35 c. Text "Give us the tools . . .".

78 H.M.S. *Seringapatam* (frigate), 1830

(Des Jennifer Toombs. Litho Walsall)

1975 (22 July). *Mailboats. T* **78** *and similar horiz designs. Multicoloured.* W w **14** (*sideways**). *P* 14.
157	4 c. Type **78**		40	60
158	10 c. *Pitcairn* (missionary schooner), 1890		50	85
159	18 c. *Athenic* (liner), 1904		60	1·40
160	50 c. *Gothic* (liner), 1948		1·25	2·25
157/60		Set of 4	2·50	4·50
MS161	145×110 mm. Nos. 157/60		10·00	15·00
	w. Wmk Crown to right of CA		42·00	

*The normal watermark shows Crown to left of CA, as seen from the back of the stamp.

79 *Polistes jadwigae* (wasp) | **80** Fletcher Christian

(Des Jennifer Toombs. Litho Questa)

1975 (9 Nov). *Pitcairn Insects. T* **79** *and similar horiz designs. Multicoloured.* W w **12** (*sideways*). *P* 14.
162	4 c. Type **79**		40	45
163	6 c. *Euconocephalus sp* (grasshopper)		40	55
164	10 c. *Anomis flavia* and *Chasmina tibialis* (moths)		50	70
165	15 c. *Pantala flavescens* (skimmer)		70	1·25
166	20 c. *Gnathothlibus erotus* (Banana moth)		80	1·50
162/6		Set of 5	2·50	4·00

(Des Jennifer Toombs. Litho J.W.)

1976 (4 July). *Bicentenary of American Revolution. T* **80** *and similar vert designs. Multicoloured.* W w **14**. *P* 13½.
167	5 c. Type **80**		30	65
	a. Horiz pair. Nos. 167 and 169		80	1·60
168	10 c. H.M.S. *Bounty*		40	80
	a. Horiz pair. Nos. 168 and 170		1·10	2·25

169 30 c. George Washington 50 95
170 50 c. *Mayflower,* 1620 .. .. 70 1·50
167/70 .. .. *Set of 4* 1·75 3·50
The 5 and 30 c. and 10 and 50 c. values were each printed
together, *se-tenant*, in horizontal pairs throughout the sheets.

81 Chair of Homage **82** The Island's Bell

(Des Jennifer Toombs. Litho J.W.)
1977 (6 Feb). *Silver Jubilee. T 81 and similar vert designs. Multicoloured. W w 14. P 13.*
171 8 c. Prince Philip's visit, 1971 .. .. 10 15
172 20 c. Type 81 .. .. .. 20 25
173 50 c. Enthronement 40 50
171/3 .. .. *Set of 3* 60 80

(Des Jennifer Toombs. Litho Walsall)
1977 (12 Sept)–**81**. *Various multicoloured designs as T 82.
W w 14 (sideways* on horiz designs). P 14.*
174 1 c. Type 82 .. .. .. 30 50
175 2 c. Building a longboat *(horiz)* 30 50
176 5 c. Landing cargo *(horiz)* 35 50
177 6 c. Sorting supplies *(horiz)* 30 50
178 9 c. Cleaning wahoo (fish) 30 50
  w. Wmk inverted .. .. .. 85·00 25·00
179 10 c. Cultivation *(horiz)* 30 50
179a 15 c. Sugar Mill *(horiz)* (1.10.81) .. 1·00 1·00
180 20 c. Grating coconut and bananas *(horiz)* 30 50
181 35 c. The Island church *(horiz)* .. 35 70
  w. Wmk Crown to right of CA .. 70
182 50 c. Fetching miro logs, Henderson Is
  (horiz) 35 80
  aw. Wmk Crown to right of CA .. 2·00
182b 70 c. Burning obsolete stamp issues (1.10.81) 1·00 1·25
183 $1 Prince Philip, Bounty Bay and Royal
  Yacht *Britannia (horiz)* .. 40 1·10
184 $2 Queen Elizabeth II (photograph by
  Reginald Davis) .. .. 50 1·75
174/84 .. .. .. *Set of 13* 5·00 9·00
*The normal sideways watermark shows Crown to left of CA,
as seen from the back of the stamp.*

83 Building a *Bounty* Model **84** Coronation Ceremony

(Des E. W. Roberts. Litho Questa)
1978 (9 Jan). *"Bounty Day". T 83 and similar horiz designs.
Multicoloured. W w 14 (sideways*). P 14½.*
185 6 c. Type 83 .. .. .. 30 30
186 20 c. The model at sea 35 35
187 35 c. Burning the model 40 40
185/7 .. .. .. *Set of 3* 95 95
MS188 166×122 mm. Nos. 185/7 .. .. 6·00 9·50
  w. Wmk Crown to right of CA
*The normal sideways watermark shows Crown to left of CA,
as seen from the back of the stamp.*

(Des Jennifer Toombs. Litho Cartor)
1978 (9 Oct). *25th Anniv of Coronation. Sheet 94×78 mm.
W w 14. P 12.*
MS189 **84** $1.20, multicoloured .. .. 80 1·75
  w. Wmk inverted .. .. 4·75

85 Harbour before Development

(Des J.W. Litho Bruder Rosenbaum, Vienna)
1978 (18 Dec). *"Operation Pallium" (Harbour Development
Project). T 85 and similar horiz designs. Multicoloured.
W w 14 (sideways*). P 13½.*
190 15 c. Type 85 .. .. .. 30 50
  w. Wmk Crown to left of CA .. 75
191 20 c. Unloading R.F.A. *Sir Geraint* .. 40 60
  w. Wmk Crown to left of CA .. 85
192 30 c. Work on the jetty 45 70
  w. Wmk Crown to left of CA .. 95
193 35 c. Harbour after development .. 50 80
  w. Wmk Crown to left of CA .. 1·00
190/3 .. .. .. *Set of 4* 1·50 2·40
*The normal sideways watermark shows Crown to right of
CA, as seen from the back of the stamp.*

86 John Adams and Diary Extract

(Des Jennifer Toombs. Litho Questa)
1979 (5 Apr*). *150th Death Anniv of John Adams (mutineer
from the "Bounty"). T 86 and similar horiz design. Multicoloured. W w 14 (sideways). P 14.*
194 35 c. Type 86 .. .. .. 30 70
195 70 c. John Adams' grave and diary extract 45 90
*This is the local date of issue. The Crown Agent's released
the stamp in London on 5 March.*

87 Pitcairn's Island sketched
from H.M.S. *Amphitrite*

(Des Jennifer Toombs. Litho Questa)
1979 (12 Sept). *19th-century Engravings. T 87 and similar horiz
designs. W w 14 (sideways). P 14.*
196 6 c. black, brown-ochre and stone .. 15 20
197 9 c. black, violet and pale violet .. 15 25
198 20 c. black, brt green & pale yellowish green 15 40
199 70 c. black, scarlet and pale rose .. 50 1·00
196/9 .. .. .. *Set of 4* 85 1·75
Designs:—9 c. Bounty Bay and Village of Pitcairn; 20 c. Lookout
Ridge; 70 c. Church and School House.

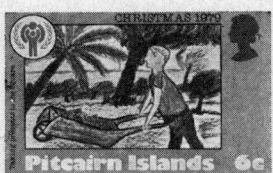
88 Taking Presents to the Square

(Des and litho J.W.)
1979 (28 Nov). *Christmas and International Year of the Child.
T 88 and similar horiz designs. Multicoloured. W w 14 (sideways). P 13.*
200 6 c. Type 88 .. .. .. 10 20
201 9 c. Decorating trees with the presents 10 25
202 20 c. Chosen men distribute the gifts.. 20 40
203 35 c. Carrying presents home 25 50
200/3 .. .. .. *Set of 4* 55 1·25
MS204 198×73 mm. Nos. 200/3. P 13½×14 .. 75 1·40

89 Loading Mail from Supply
Ship to Longboats

(Des Jennifer Toombs. Litho Format)
1980 (6 May). *"London 1980" International Stamp Exhibition.
Sheet 120×135 mm containing T 89 and similar horiz
designs. Multicoloured. W w 14 (sideways*). P 14½.*
MS205 35 c. Type 89; 35 c. Mail being conveyed
by "Flying Fox" (hoisting mechanism) to the
Edge; 35 c. Tractor transporting mail from the
Edge to Adamstown; 35 c. Mail being off-loaded
at Post Office .. .. .. 75 1·50
  w. Wmk Crown to right of CA
*The normal sideways watermark shows Crown to left of CA,
as seen from the back of the miniature sheet.*

90 Queen Elizabeth the
Queen Mother at Henley
Regatta

(Des Harrison. Litho Questa)
1980 (4 Aug). *80th Birthday of Queen Elizabeth the Queen Mother.
W w 14 (sideways). P 14.*
206 **90** 50 c. multicoloured 40 70

(Des Jennifer Toombs. Litho Questa)
1980 (29 Sept). *Handicrafts (2nd series). Multicoloured
designs as T 46. W w 14 (sideways* on 9 and 20 c.). P 14.*
207 9 c. Turtles (wood carvings) .. 10 10
208 20 c. Pitcairn wheelbarrow (wood carving) 10 15
  w. Wmk Crown to right of CA .. 95·00
209 35 c. Gannet (wood carving) *(vert)* 15 25
210 40 c. Woven bonnet and fan *(vert)* 15 25
  w. Wmk inverted £110
207/10 .. .. .. *Set of 4* 40 65
*The normal sideways watermark shows Crown to left of CA,
as seen from the back of the stamp.*

91 Part of Adamstown

(Des BG Studio. Litho Rosenbaum Bros, Vienna)
1981 (22 Jan). *Landscapes. T 91 and similar horiz designs.
Multicoloured. W w 14 (sideways*). P 13½.*
211 6 c. Type 91 .. .. .. 10 10
  w. Wmk Crown to right of CA .. 10·00
212 9 c. Big George 10 15
  w. Wmk Crown to right of CA .. 12·00
213 20 c. Christian's Cave, Gannets Ridge 15 20
  w. Wmk Crown to right of CA .. 7·00
214 35 c. Radio Station from Pawala Valley
  Ridge 20 30
  w. Wmk Crown to right of CA .. 3·50
215 70 c. Tatrimoa 30 45
211/15 .. .. .. *Set of 5* 75 1·10
*The normal sideways watermark shows Crown to left of CA,
as seen from the back of the stamp.*

92 Islanders preparing for **93** Prince Charles as
Departure Colonel-in-Chief,
  Cheshire Regiment

(Des Jennifer Toombs. Litho Heraclio Fournier)
1981 (3 May). *125th Anniv of Pitcairn Islanders' Migration to
Norfolk Island. T 92 and similar horiz designs. Multicoloured.
P 13×14.*
216 9 c. Type 92 .. .. .. 30 35
217 35 c. View of Pitcairn Island from *Morayshire* 50 60
218 70 c. *Morayshire* .. .. .. 80 1·00
216/18 .. .. .. *Set of 3* 1·40 1·75

(Des J.W. Litho Format)
1981 (22 July). *Royal Wedding. T 93 and similar vert designs.
Multicoloured. W w 14. P 14.*
219 20 c. Wedding bouquet from Pitcairn Islands 20 20
220 35 c. Type 93 .. .. .. 25 20
221 $1.20, Prince Charles and Lady Diana
  Spencer 75 60
  w. Wmk inverted .. .. 60·00
219/21 .. .. .. *Set of 3* 1·10 90

94 Lemon **95** Pitcairn Islands
  Coat of Arms

(Des Daphne Padden. Litho Harrison)

1982 (23 Feb). *Fruit. T **94** and similar horiz designs. Multi-coloured. W w 14 (sideways). P 14½.*

222	9 c. Type **94**		10	10
223	20 c. Pomegranate		15	20
224	35 c. Avocado		25	30
225	70 c. Pawpaw		50	65
222/5		Set of 4	90	1·10

(Des Jennifer Toombs. Litho Harrison)

1982 (1 July). *21st Birthday of Princess of Wales. T **95** and similar vert designs. Multicoloured. W w 14. P 14½ × 14.*

226	6 c. Type **95**		10	20
227	9 c. Princess at Royal Opera House, Covent Garden, December 1981		30	20
228	70 c. Balcony Kiss		70	60
229	$1.20, Formal portrait		1·25	80
226/9		Set of 4	2·10	1·60

96 Raphael's Angels

(Des Leslie McCombie. Litho Walsall)

1982 (19 Oct). *Christmas. T **96** and similar designs showing Raphael's Angels. W w 14 (sideways* on 15 c. and 20 c.). P 13½×14 (15 c., 20 c.) or 14×13½ (others).*

230	15 c. black, silver and pink		15	15
	w. Wmk Crown to right of CA		25·00	
231	20 c. black, silver and pale lemon		15	15
232	50 c. yellow-brown, silver and stone		30	30
233	$1 black, silver and cobalt		40	40
230/3		Set of 4	90	90

The 50 c. and $1 are vertical designs.
*The normal sideways watermark shows Crown to left of CA, as seen from the back of the stamp.

97 Radio Operator

(Des Jennifer Toombs. Litho Harrison)

1983 (14 Mar). *Commonwealth Day. T **97** and similar horiz designs. Multicoloured. W w 14 (sideways*). P 13½.*

234	6 c. Type **97**		10	10
235	9 c. Postal clerk		10	10
236	70 c. Fisherman		35	65
	w. Wmk Crown to right of CA		18·00	
237	$1.20, Artist		60	1·10
	w. Wmk Crown to right of CA		60·00	
234/7		Set of 4	1·00	1·60

*The normal sideways watermark shows Crown to left of CA, as seen from the back of the stamp.

98 Topaz sights Smoke on Pitcairn

(Des Jennifer Toombs. Litho B.D.T.)

1983 (14 June). *175th Anniv of Folger's Discovery of the Settlers. T **98** and similar horiz designs. Multicoloured. W w 14 (sideways). P 14.*

238	6 c. Type **98**		30	20
239	20 c. Three islanders approach the Topaz		45	30
240	70 c. Capt. Mayhew Folger welcomed by John Adams		85	75
241	$1.20, Folger presented with Bounty chronometer		1·25	1·10
238/41		Set of 4	2·50	2·10

99 Hattie-Tree

(Des Jennifer Toombs. Litho B.D.T.)

1983 (6 Oct). *Trees of Pitcairn Islands (1st series). T **99** and similar horiz designs. Multicoloured. W w 14 (sideways). P 13½.*

242	35 c. Type **99**		30	55
	a. Pair. Nos. 242/3		60	1·10
243	35 c. Leaves from Hattie-Tree		30	55
244	70 c. Pandanus		50	90
	a. Pair. Nos. 244/5		1·00	1·75
245	70 c. Pandanus and basket weaving		50	90
242/5		Set of 4	1·40	2·50

The two designs of each value were printed together, *se-tenant*, in horizontal and vertical pairs throughout the sheet.
See also Nos. 304/7.

100 Atava Wrasse

(Des C. Abbott. Litho Format)

1984 (11 Jan). *Fishes (1st series). T **100** and similar horiz designs. Multicoloured. W w 14 (sideways*). P 14½.*

246	1 c. Type **100**		20	30
247	4 c. Black-eared Wrasse		30	35
248	6 c. Long-finned Parrotfish		30	35
249	9 c. Yellow-edged Lyretail		30	35
250	10 c. Black-eared Angelfish		30	40
	w. Wmk Crown to right of CA		75·00	
251	15 c. Emery's Damselfish		30	40
252	20 c. Smith's Butterflyfish		40	50
253	35 c. Crosshatched Triggerfish		50	60
254	50 c. Yellow Damselfish		50	75
255	70 c. Pitcairn Angelfish		70	95
256	$1 Easter Island Soldierfish		90	1·25
257	$1.20, Long-finned Anthias		1·00	2·00
	w. Wmk Crown to right of CA		5·50	
258	$2 White Trevally		1·50	2·50
246/58		Set of 13	6·50	9·50

*The normal sideways watermark shows Crown to left of CA, as seen from the back of the stamp.
For 90 c. and $3 values see Nos. 312/13.

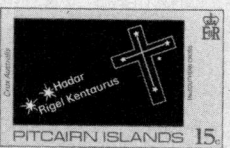

101 "Southern Cross"

(Des J. Cooter. Litho Walsall)

1984 (14 May). *Night Sky. T **101** and similar horiz designs. W w 14 (sideways). P 14.*

259	15 c. deep violet-blue, pale rose-lilac and gold	20	20
260	20 c. deep violet-blue, bright yell-grn & gold	30	30
261	70 c. deep violet-blue, yellow-ochre and gold	75	75
262	$1 deep violet-blue, pale blue and gold	1·00	1·00
259/62		Set of 4	2·00	2·00

Constellations:—20 c. "Southern Fish"; 70 c. "Lesser Dog"; $1 "The Virgin".

102 Aluminium Longboat   **103** "H.M.S. *Portland* standing off Bounty Bay" (J. Linton Palmer)

(Des C. Abbott. Litho Enschedé)

1984 (21 Sept). *"Ausipex" International Stamp Exhibition, Melbourne. Sheet 134 × 86 mm containing T **102** and similar horiz design. Multicoloured. W w 14 (sideways). P 13½ × 14.*

MS263	50 c. Type **102**; $2 Traditional-style wooden longboat		1·50	2·00

(Des Jennifer Toombs. Litho Questa)

1985 (16 Jan). *19th-Century Paintings (1st series). T **103** and similar horiz designs. Multicoloured. W w 14 (sideways). P 13½ × 14 ($2) or 14 (others).*

264	6 c. Type **103**		30	20
265	9 c. "Christian's Look Out" (J. Linton Palmer)		30	20
266	35 c. "The Golden Age" (J. Linton Palmer)		65	50
267	$2 "A View of the Village, 1825" (William Smyth) (48 × 31 mm)		1·75	1·60
264/7		Set of 4	2·75	2·25

The original printing of No. 267 was incorrectly dated "1835". The mistake was, however, spotted before issue and a replacement printing, correctly dated "1825", was provided. Those stamps dated "1835" were never issued for postal purposes, although examples exist which may have been supplied by various philatelic agents in error.
See also Nos. 308/11.

104 The Queen Mother with the Queen and Princess Margaret, 1980   **105** *Act 6* (container ship)

(Des A. Theobald ($2), C. Abbott (others). Litho Questa)

1985 (7 June). *Life and Times of Queen Elizabeth the Queen Mother. T **104** and similar vert designs. Multicoloured. W w 16. P 14½×14.*

268	6 c. Receiving the Freedom of Dundee, 1964		10	20
	w. Wmk inverted		2·00	
269	35 c. Type **104**		30	55
	w. Wmk inverted		4·00	
270	70 c. The Queen Mother in 1983		50	80
271	$1.20, With Prince Henry at his christening (from photo by Lord Snowdon)		70	1·00
	w. Wmk inverted		10·00	
268/71		Set of 4	1·40	2·25
MS272	91×73 mm. $2 In coach at Ascot Races. Wmk sideways*		1·75	2·00
	w. Wmk Crown to right of CA		14·00	

*The normal sideways watermark shows Crown to left of CA, as seen from the back of the stamp.

(Des E. Nisbet. Litho Format)

1985 (28 Aug). *Ships (1st series). T **105** and similar multicoloured designs. W w 14 (sideways*). P 14 (Nos. 273/4) or 14×13½ (others).*

273	50 c. Type **105**		95	1·75
	w. Wmk Crown to right of CA		24·00	
274	50 c. *Columbus Louisiana* (container ship)		95	1·75
	w. Wmk Crown to right of CA		32·00	
275	50 c. *Essi Gina* (tanker) (48×35 mm)		95	1·75
276	50 c. *Stolt Spirit* (tanker) (48×35 mm)		95	1·75
273/6		Set of 4	3·50	6·25

*The normal sideways watermark shows Crown to left of CA, as seen from the back of the stamp.
See also Nos. 296/9.

106 "Madonna and Child" (Raphael)   **107** Green Turtle

(Des Jennifer Toombs. Litho Walsall)

1985 (26 Nov). *Christmas. T **106** and similar vert designs showing "Madonna and Child" paintings. Multicoloured. W w 16. P 14×13½.*

277	6 c. Type **106**		60	50
278	9 c. Krause (after Raphael)		60	50
279	35 c. Andreas Mayer		1·00	70
280	$2 Unknown Austrian master		2·75	3·50
277/80		Set of 4	4·50	4·75

(Des Jane Thatcher. Litho Questa)

1986 (12 Feb). *Turtles. T **107** and similar horiz designs. Multicoloured. W w 16 (sideways). P 14½.*

281	9 c. Type **107**		1·00	90
282	20 c. Green Turtle and Pitcairn Island		1·60	1·25
283	70 c. Hawksbill Turtle		3·00	3·75
284	$1.20, Hawksbill Turtle and Pitcairn Island		3·50	4·25
281/4		Set of 4	8·25	9·00

(Des A. Theobald. Litho Questa)

1986 (21 Apr). *60th Birthday of Queen Elizabeth II. Vert designs as T **230a** of Jamaica. Multicoloured. W w 16. P 14½×14.*

285	6 c. Princess Elizabeth at Royal Lodge, Windsor, 1946		15	15
286	9 c. Wedding of Princess Anne, 1973		15	15
287	20 c. At Order of St. Michael and St. George service, St. Paul's Cathedral, 1961		25	30
288	$1.20, At Electrical Engineering Concert, Royal Festival Hall, 1971		60	1·25
289	$2 At Crown Agents Head Office, London, 1983		75	1·75
285/9		Set of 5	1·75	3·25

(Des D. Miller. Litho Questa)

1986 (23 July). *Royal Wedding. Square designs as T **231a** of Jamaica. Multicoloured. W w 16. P 14.*

290	20 c. Prince Andrew and Miss Sarah Ferguson		35	50
291	$1.20, Prince Andrew aboard *Bluenose II* off Halifax, Canada, 1985		1·40	2·00

MACHINE LABEL. A 70 c. label inscribed "PITCAIRN IS. STAMPEX 86" was available between 4 and 10 August 1986 at this Adelaide stamp exhibition.

108 John I. Tay (pioneer **109** Pitcairn Island Home missionary) and First Church

(Des A. Theobald. Litho Walsall)

1986 (18 Oct). *Centenary of Seventh-Day Adventist Church on Pitcairn. T* **108** *and similar vert designs. Multicoloured. W* w **16**. *P* 14.

292	6 c. Type **108**		50	50
293	20 c. *Pitcairn* (missionary schooner) and second church (1907)		1·25	1·00
294	35 c. Baptism at Down Isaac and third church (1945)		1·75	1·50
295	$2 Islanders singing farewell hymn and present church (1954)		3·75	4·25
292/5		*Set of 4*	6·50	6·50

(Des E. Nisbet. Litho Format)

1987 (20 Jan). *Ships (2nd series). Multicoloured designs as T* **105**. *W* w **16** *(sideways on Nos.* 298/9). *P* 14 *(Nos.* 296/7) *or* 14×13½ *(others).*

296	50 c. *Samoan Reefer* (freighter)		1·25	2·25
297	50 c. *Brussel* (container ship)		1·25	2·25
298	50 c. *Australian Exporter* (container ship) (48×35 mm)		1·25	2·25
299	50 c. *Taupo* (cargo liner) (48×35 mm)		1·25	2·25
296/9		*Set of 4*	4·50	8·00

(Des E. Roberts and D. Robertson. Litho Format)

1987 (21 Apr). *Pitcairn Island Homes. T* **109** *and similar horiz designs showing different houses. W* w **14** *(sideways). P* 13½×14.

300	**109** 70 c. black, brt reddish violet & brt violet		50	60
301	— 70 c. black, pale orange-yell & brn-ochre		50	60
302	— 70 c. black, dull blue and ultramarine		50	60
303	— 70 c. black, blue-green & deep blue-green		50	60
300/3		*Set of 4*	1·75	2·25

(Des Jennifer Toombs. Litho Format)

1987 (10 Aug). *Trees of Pitcairn Islands (2nd series). Horiz designs as T* **99**. *Multicoloured. W* w **16** *(sideways*). P* 14½.

304	40 c. Leaves and flowers from *Erythrina variegata*		80	1·10
	a. Pair. Nos. 304/5		1·60	2·10
	aw. Wmk Crown to right of CA			
305	40 c. *Erythrina variegata* tree		80	1·10
306	$1·80, Leaves from *Aleurites moluccana* and nut tree		1·75	2·75
	a. Pair. Nos. 306/7		3·50	5·50
	aw. Wmk Crown to right of CA		85·00	
307	$1·80, *Aleurites moluccana* tree		1·75	2·75
304/7		*Set of 4*	4·50	7·00

*The normal sideways watermark shows Crown to left of CA, as seen from the back of the stamp.

The two designs of each value were printed together, *se-tenant*, in horizontal and vertical pairs throughout the sheet.

(Des Jennifer Toombs. Litho Questa)

1987 (7 Dec). *19th-century Paintings (2nd series). Horiz designs as T* **103** *showing paintings by Lt. Conway Shipley in* 1848. *Multicoloured. W* w **16** *(sideways). P* 13½×14 ($1·80) *or* 14 *(others).*

308	20 c. "House and Tomb of John Adams"		45	50
309	40 c. "Bounty Bay"		70	70
310	90 c. "School House and Chapel"		1·25	1·50
311	$1·80, "Pitcairn Island" (48×31 mm)		2·00	3·25
308/11		*Set of 4*	4·00	5·50

(Des C. Abbott. Litho Format)

1988 (14 Jan). *Fishes (2nd series). Horiz designs as T* **100**. *Multicoloured. W* w **16** *(sideways*). P* 14½.

312	90 c. As No. 249		2·25	2·50
	w. Wmk Crown to right of CA		15·00	
313	$3 Wakanoui Moray		4·25	5·50
	w. Wmk Crown to right of CA		15·00	

*The normal sideways watermark shows Crown to left of CA, as seen from the back of the stamp.

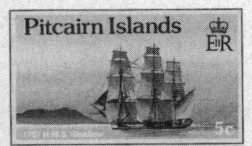

110 *Bounty* (replica)　**111** H.M.S. *Swallow* (survey ship), 1767

(Des M. Bradbery. Litho Questa)

1988 (9 May). *Bicentenary of Australian Settlement. Sheet* 112 × 76 *mm. W* w **16**. *P* 14 × 13½.

MS314	110 $3 multicoloured		3·00	2·50
	w. Wmk inverted		28·00	

(Des E. Nisbet. Litho B.D.T.)

1988 (14 Aug). *Ships. T* **111** *and similar horiz designs. Multicoloured. W* w **14** *(sideways).* "1988" *imprint date. P* 13½.

315	5 c. Type **111**		50	70
316	10 c. H.M.S. *Pandora* (frigate), 1791		50	70
317	15 c. H.M.S. *Briton* and H.M.S. *Tagus* (frigates), 1814		55	80
318	20 c. H.M.S. *Blossom* (survey ship), 1825		60	85
319	30 c. *Lucy Anne* (barque), 1831		70	90
320	35 c. *Charles Doggett* (whaling brig), 1831		70	90
321	40 c. H.M.S. *Fly* (sloop), 1838		75	95
322	60 c. *Camden* (missionary brig), 1840		1·00	1·40
323	90 c. H.M.S. *Virago* (paddle-sloop), 1853		1·25	1·50
324	$1·20, *Rakaia* (screw-steamer), 1867		1·50	1·75
325	$1·80, H.M.S. *Sappho* (screw-sloop), 1882		1·75	2·25
326	$5 H.M.S. *Champion* (corvette), 1893		4·50	5·00
315/26		*Set of 12*	12·50	16·00

For 20 c. and 90 c. values as above, but watermarked w **16** (sideways), see Nos. 369 and 374.

112 Raising the　**113** Angel
Union Jack, 1838

(Des Jennifer Toombs. Litho Walsall)

1988 (30 Nov). *150th Anniv of Pitcairn Island Constitution. T* **112** *and similar vert designs, each showing different extract from original Constitution. Multicoloured. W* w **14**. *P* 14.

327	20 c. Type **112**		15	20
328	40 c. Signing Constitution on board H.M.S. *Fly*, 1838		30	35
329	$1·05, Voters at modern polling station		75	80
330	$1·80, Modern classroom		1·25	1·40
327/30		*Set of 4*	2·25	2·50

(Des M. Grimsdale. Litho Questa)

1988 (30 Nov). *Christmas. T* **113** *and similar vert designs. Multicoloured. W* w **16**. *P* 14 × 13½.

331	90 c. Type **113**		65	70
	a. Horiz strip of 4. Nos. 331/4		2·40	
332	90 c. Holy Family		65	70
333	90 c. Two Polynesian Wise Men		65	70
334	90 c. Polynesian Wise Man and shepherd		65	70
331/4		*Set of 4*	2·40	2·50

Nos. 331/4 were printed together, *se-tenant*, in horizontal strips of four throughout the sheet.

114 Loading Stores, Deptford　**115** R.N.Z.A.F. Lockheed P-3 Orion making Mail Drop, 1985

(Des C. Abbott. Litho Questa)

1989 (22 Feb). *Bicentary of Pitcairn Island Settlement (1st issue). T* **114** *and similar horiz designs. Multicoloured. W* w **14** *(sideways). P* 14.

335	20 c. Type **114**		80	80
	a. Sheetlet. Nos. 335/40		4·25	
336	20 c. H.M.S. *Bounty* leaving Spithead		80	80
337	20 c. H.M.S. *Bounty* at Cape Horn		80	80
338	20 c. Anchored in Adventure Bay, Tasmania		80	80
339	20 c. Crew collecting breadfruit		80	80
340	20 c. Breadfruit in cabin		80	80
335/40		*Set of 6*	4·25	4·25

Nos. 335/40 were printed together, *se-tenant* in sheetlets of six, as two horizontal rows of three separated by a central gutter.

See also Nos. 341/7, 356/61 and 389/94.

(Des C. Abbott. Litho Questa (Nos. 341/6), B.D.T. (No. **MS**347))

1989 (28 Apr). *Bicentenary of Pitcairn Island Settlement (2nd issue). Horiz designs as T* **114**. *Multicoloured. W* w **14** *(sideways). P* 14.

341	90 c. H.M.S. *Bounty* leaving Tahiti		2·00	2·25
	a. Sheetlet. Nos. 341/6		11·00	
342	90 c. Bligh awoken by mutineers		2·00	2·25
343	90 c. Bligh before Fletcher Christian		2·00	2·25
344	90 c. Provisioning Bounty's launch		2·00	2·25
345	90 c. "Mutineers casting Bligh adrift" (Robert Dodd)		2·00	2·25
346	90 c. Mutineers discarding breadfruit plants		2·00	2·25
341/6		*Set of 6*	11·00	12·00
MS347	110 × 85 mm. 90 c. No. 345; 90 c. Isle of Man 1989 35p. Mutiny stamp; 90 c. Norfolk Island 39 c. Mutiny stamp. W w **16** (sideways)		3·50	4·00

Nos. 341/6 were printed in the same sheet format as Nos. 335/40.

(Des A. Theobald. Litho Questa)

1989 (25 July). *Aircraft. T* **115** *and similar horiz designs. Multicoloured. W* w **16** *(sideways). P* 14×14½.

348	20 c. Type **115**		1·00	40
349	80 c. Beech 80 Queen Air on photo-mission, 1983		2·00	1·10
350	$1·05, Boeing-Vertol CH-47 Chinook helicopter landing diesel fuel from U.S.S. Breton, 1969		2·25	1·40
351	$1·30, R.N.Z.A.F. Lockheed C-130 Hercules dropping bulldozer, 1983		2·25	1·50
348/51		*Set of 4*	6·75	4·00

116 Ducie Island

(Des A. Theobald. Litho Walsall)

1989 (23 Oct). *Islands of Pitcairn Group. T* **116** *and similar horiz designs. Multicoloured. W* w **14** *(sideways). P* 14.

352	15 c. Type **116**		30	35
353	90 c. Henderson Island		1·40	1·25
354	$1·05, Oeno Island		1·50	1·50
355	$1·30, Pitcairn Island		1·50	1·60
352/5		*Set of 4*	4·25	4·25

(Des C. Abbott. Litho Questa)

1990 (15 Jan). *Bicentenary of Pitcairn Island Settlement (3rd issue). Horiz designs as T* **114**. *Multicoloured. W* w **16** *(sideways). P* 14.

356	40 c. Mutineers sighting Pitcairn Island		1·00	85
	a. Sheetlet. Nos. 356/61		5·50	
357	40 c. Ship's boat approaching landing		1·00	85
358	40 c. Exploring island		1·00	85
359	40 c. Ferrying goods ashore		1·00	85
360	40 c. Burning of H.M.S. *Bounty*		1·00	85
361	40 c. Pitcairn Island village		1·00	85
356/61		*Set of 6*	5·50	4·50

Nos. 356/61 were printed in the same sheet format as Nos. 335/40.

117 Ennerdale, Cumbria, and Peter Heywood

(Des D. Ashby. Litho Questa)

1990 (3 May). "*Stamp World London 90*" *International Stamp Exhibition, London. T* **117** *and similar horiz designs showing English landmarks and Bounty crew members. Multicoloured. W* w **14** *(sideways). P* 14.

362	80 c. Type **117**		75	80
363	90 c. St. Augustine's Tower, Hackney, and John Adams		85	90
364	$1·05, Citadel Gateway, Plymouth, and William Bligh		1·00	1·25
365	$1·30, Moorland Close, Cockermouth, and Fletcher Christian		1·25	1·40
362/5		*Set of 4*	3·50	4·00

(Des E. Nisbet. Litho B.D.T.)

1990 (3 May). *As Nos.* 318 *and* 323, *but W* w **16** *(sideways).* "1990" *imprint date. P* 13½.

369	20 c. H.M.S. *Blossom* (survey ship), 1825		1·25	1·75
	a. Booklet pane. No. 369×4 with margins all round		4·50	
374	90 c. H.M.S. *Virago* (paddle-sloop), 1853		1·25	1·75
	a. Booklet pane. No. 374×4 with margins all round		4·50	

Nos. 369 and 374 only exist from $4·40 stamp booklets.

(Des D. Miller. Litho Questa)

1990 (4 Aug). *90th Birthday of Queen Elizabeth the Queen Mother. Vert designs as T* **107** (40 c.) *or* **108** ($3) *of Kenya. Multicoloured. W* w **16**. *P* 14×15 (40 c.) *or* 14½ ($3).

378	40 c. multicoloured		75	75
379	$3 black and dull scarlet		3·00	3·50

Designs:—40 c. Queen Elizabeth, 1937; $3 King George VI and Queen Elizabeth on way to Silver Wedding Service, 1948.

118 *Bounty* Chronometer and 1940 1d. Definitive　**119** Stephen's Lory ("Redbreast")

(Des D. Miller. Litho Walsall)

1990 (15 Oct). *50th Anniv of Pitcairn Islands Stamps. T 118 and similar horiz designs. Multicoloured.* W w **14** *(sideways).* P 13½×14.

380	20 c. Type **118**	..	80	70
381	80 c. *Bounty* Bible and 1958 4d. definitive		1·60	1·60
382	90 c. *Bounty* Bell and 1969 30 c. definitive		1·75	1·75
383	$1.05, Mutiny on the *Bounty* and 1977 $1 definitive		2·00	2·25
384	$1.30, Penny Black and 1988 15 c. ship definitive		2·25	2·50
380/4		*Set of 5*	7·50	8·00

(Des N. Harvey from paintings by Byatt. Litho Questa)

1990 (6 Dec). *"Birdpex '90" Stamp Exhibition, Christchurch, New Zealand. T 119 and similar vert designs. Multicoloured.* W w **14**. P 14.

385	20 c. Type **119**		75	65
386	90 c. Henderson Island Fruit Dove ("Wood Pigeon")		1·50	1·60
387	$1.30, Pitcairn Warbler ("Sparrow")		1·75	2·50
388	$1.80, Henderson Island Crake ("Chicken Bird")		2·00	2·75
385/8		*Set of 4*	5·50	6·75

Nos. 385/8 carry the "Birdpex '90" logo and inscription in the gutter between the two panes.

(Des N. Shewring. Litho Leigh-Mardon Ltd, Melbourne)

1991 (24 Mar). *Bicentenary of Pitcairn Islands Settlement (4th issue). Celebrations. Horiz designs as T 114. Multicoloured.* W w **16**. P 14½.

389	80 c. Re-enacting landing of mutineers		1·90	2·25
	a. Sheetlet. Nos. 389/94..		10·00	
390	80 c. Commemorative plaque		1·90	2·25
391	80 c. Memorial church service		1·90	2·25
392	80 c. Cricket match		1·90	2·25
393	80 c. Burning model of *Bounty*		1·90	2·25
394	80 c. Firework display		1·90	2·25
389/94		*Set of 6*	10·00	12·00

Nos. 389/94 were printed in the same sheet format as Nos. 335/40.

120 *Europa*

121 *Bulldozer*

(Des E. Nisbet. Litho Leigh-Mardon Ltd, Melbourne)

1991 (17 June). *Cruise Liners. T 120 and similar horiz designs. Multicoloured.* W w **16**. P 14½

395	15 c. Type **120**		1·00	60
396	80 c. *Royal Viking Star*		2·00	1·75
397	$1.30, *World Discoverer* ..		2·50	2·75
398	$1.80, *Sagafjord*		3·00	3·50
395/8		*Set of 4*	7·75	7·75

(Des D. Miller. Litho Questa)

1991 (12 July). *65th Birthday of Queen Elizabeth II and 70th Birthday of Prince Philip. Vert designs as T 58 of Kiribati. Multicoloured.* W w **16** *(sideways).* P 14½×14.

399	20 c. Prince Philip		40	30
	a. Horiz pair. Nos. 399/400 separated by label		2·00	1·50
400	$1.30, Queen in robes of Order of St. Michael and St. George		1·60	1·25

Nos. 399/400 were printed in a similar sheet format to Nos. 366/7 of Kiribati.

(Des O. Bell. Litho Questa)

1991 (25 Sept). *Island Transport. T 121 and similar diamond-shaped designs. Multicoloured.* W w **14**. P 14.

401	20 c. Type **121**		40	30
402	80 c. Two-wheeled motorcycle		1·25	1·00
403	$1.30, Tractor		1·25	1·40
404	$1.80, Three-wheeled motorcycle		2·00	2·25
401/4		*Set of 4*	4·50	4·50

122 The Annunciation

123 Insular Shark

(Des Jennifer Toombs. Litho Questa)

1991 (18 Nov). *Christmas. T 122 and similar vert designs. Multicoloured.* W w **14**. P 14.

405	20 c. Type **122**		30	30
406	80 c. Shepherds and lamb		90	90
407	$1.30, Holy Family		1·25	1·25
408	$1.80, Three Wise Men		1·75	1·75
405/8		*Set of 4*	3·75	3·75

(Des D. Miller. Litho Questa ($1.80), Leigh-Mardon Ltd, Melbourne (others))

1992 (6 Feb). *40th Anniv of Queen Elizabeth II's Accession. Horiz designs as T 113 of Kenya. Multicoloured.* W w **14** *(sideways)* ($1.80) *or* w **16** *(sideways)* *(others).* P 14.

409	20 c. *Bounty* Bay		25	25
410	60 c. Sunset over Pitcairn		70	70
411	90 c. Pitcairn coastline		90	90
412	$1 Three portraits of Queen Elizabeth		95	95
413	$1.80, Queen Elizabeth II		1·60	1·60
409/13		*Set of 5*	4·00	4·00

(Des Jane Thatcher. Litho Leigh-Mardon Ltd, Melbourne)

1992 (30 June). *Sharks. T 123 and similar horiz designs.* W w **14** *(sideways).* P 15×14½.

414	20 c. Type **123**		80	50
415	$1 Sand Tiger		2·00	1·50
416	$1.50, Black-finned Reef Shark ..		2·25	2·00
417	$1.80, Grey Reef Shark		2·50	2·00
414/17		*Set of 4*	6·75	5·50

124 *Montastrea* sp. and *Acropora* spp. (corals)

(Des I. Loe. Litho Enschedé)

1992 (11 Sept). *The Sir Peter Scott Memorial Expedition to Henderson Island. T 124 and similar horiz designs.* W w **14** *(sideways).* P 14×14½.

418	20 c. Type **124**		80	60
419	$1 Henderson Sandalwood		1·75	1·50
420	$1.50, Murphy's Petrel		3·00	2·75
421	$1.80, Henderson Hawkmoth		3·00	3·00
418/21		*Set of 4*	7·75	7·00

125 Bligh's Birthplace at St. Tudy, Cornwall

(Des Jennifer Toombs. Litho Leigh-Mardon Ltd, Melbourne)

1992 (7 Dec). *175th Death Anniv of William Bligh. T 125 and similar horiz design. Multicoloured.* W w **14**. P 14½.

422	20 c. Type **125**		50	50
423	$1 Bligh on *Bounty*		1·50	1·50
424	$1.50, Voyage in *Bounty's* launch		2·00	2·50
425	$1.80, "William Bligh" (R. Combe) and epitaph		2·25	2·75
422/5		*Set of 4*	5·50	6·50

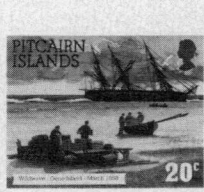

126 H.M.S. *Chichester* (frigate)		**127** Queen Elizabeth II in Coronation Robes

(Des A. Theobald. Litho Questa)

1993 (10 Mar). *Modern Royal Navy Vessels. T 126 and similar horiz designs. Multicoloured.* W w **16** *(sideways).* P 14.

426	15 c. Type **126**		75	50
427	20 c. H.M.S. *Jaguar* (frigate)		75	50
428	$1.80, H.M.S. *Andrew* (submarine)		3·25	3·25
429	$3 H.M.S. *Warrior* (aircraft carrier) and Westland Dragonfly helicopter		5·75	5·50
426/9		*Set of 4*	9·50	8·75

(Des D. Miller from photograph by Cecil Beaton. Litho Cartor)

1993 (17 June). *40th Anniv of Coronation.* W w **14**. P 13.

430	**127** $5 multicoloured		6·00	6·50

ALTERED CATALOGUE NUMBERS

Any Catalogue numbers altered from the last edition are shown as a list in the introductory pages.

---

128 Pawala Valley Ridge

(Des E. Nisbet. Litho Questa)

1993 (8 Sept). *Island Views. T 128 and similar horiz designs. Multicoloured.* W w **14** *(sideways).* P 13½×14.

431	10 c. Type **128**		20	20
432	90 c. St. Pauls		90	90
433	$1.20, Matt's Rocks from Water Valley		1·25	1·50
434	$1.50, Ridge Rope to St. Paul's Pool		1·50	1·75
435	$1.80, Ship Landing Point		1·75	2·25
431/5		*Set of 5*	5·00	6·00

129 Indo-Pacific Tree Gecko		**130** Friday October Christian

(Des G. Drummond. Litho Walsall)

1993 (14 Dec). *Lizards. T 129 and similar horiz designs. Multicoloured.* W w **14** *(sideways).* P 13×13½.

436	20 c. Type **129**		80	50
437	45 c. Stump-toed Gecko		1·00	1·25
	a. Horiz pair. Nos. 437/8		2·00	2·50
438	45 c. Mourning Gecko		1·00	1·25
439	$1 Moth Skink		2·00	1·50
440	$1.50, Snake-eyed Skink		2·50	2·75
	a. Horiz pair. Nos. 440/1		5·00	5·50
441	$1.50, White-bellied Skink		2·50	2·75
436/41		*Set of 6*	9·00	9·00

Nos. 437/8 and 440/1 were each printed together, *se-tenant*, in horizontal pairs throughout the sheet.

1994 (18 Feb). *"Hong Kong '94" International Stamp Exhibition. As Nos. 437/8 and 440/1, but* W w **16** *(sideways), optd as T 272 of Jamaica.*

442	45 c. Stump-toed Gecko		80	90
	a. Horiz pair. Nos. 442/3		1·60	1·75
443	45 c. Mourning Gecko		80	90
444	$1.50, Snake-eyed Skink		2·25	2·75
	a. Horiz pair. Nos. 444/5		4·50	5·50
445	$1.50, White-bellied Skink		2·25	2·75
442/5		*Set of 4*	5·50	6·50

(Des Jennifer Toombs. Litho Questa)

1994 (7 Mar). *Early Pitcairners. T 130 and similar vert designs. Multicoloured.* W w **14**. P 14.

446	5 c. Type **130**		20	30
447	20 c. Moses Young		50	40
448	$1.80, James Russell McCoy		2·25	2·75
449	$3 Rosalind Amelia Young		3·75	5·00
446/9		*Set of 4*	6·00	7·50

131 Landing Stores from Wreck of *Wildwave*, Oeno Island, 1858		**132** Fire Coral

(Des C. Abbott. Litho Walsall)

1994 (22 June). *Shipwrecks. T 131 and similar horiz designs. Multicoloured.* W w **14** *(sideways).* P 14×14½.

450	20 c. Type **131**		65	60
451	90 c. Longboat trying to reach *Cornwallis*, Pitcairn Island, 1875 ..		1·75	1·75
452	$1.80, *Acadia* aground, Ducie Island, 1881		3·00	3·50
453	$3 Rescuing survivors from *Oregon*, Oeno Island, 1883		4·25	4·50
450/3		*Set of 4*	8·75	9·25

(Des G. Drummond. Litho Walsall)

1994 (15 Sept). *Corals. T 132 and similar multicoloured designs.* W w **14** *(sideways on 90 c).* P 14.

454	20 c. Type **132**		80	70
455	90 c. Cauliflower Coral and Arc-eyed Hawkfish (*horiz*)		2·00	2·00
456	$1 Lobe Coral and High-finned Rudderfish		2·00	2·00
454/6		*Set of 3*	4·25	4·25
MS457	100×70 mm. $3 Coral garden and Mailed Butterflyfish (*horiz*). Wmk sideways ..		3·75	5·00

133 Angel and *Ipomoea acuminata*

(Des Jennifer Toombs. Litho Walsall)

1994 (24 Nov). *Christmas. Flowers. T* **133** *and similar multicoloured designs.* W w **14** (*sideways on horiz designs*). *P* 14×14½ (*horiz*) or 14½×14 (*vert*).

458	20 c. Type **133**		35	25
459	90 c. Shepherds and *Hibiscus rosa-sinensis* (*vert*)		1·25	1·40
460	$1 Star and *Plumeria rubra*		1·25	1·40
461	$3 Holy Family and *Alpinia speciosa* (*vert*)		3·00	3·25
458/61		*Set of 4*	5·25	5·75

134 White Tern ("Fairy Tern") on Egg

(Des D. Miller. Litho Enschedé)

1995 (8 Mar). *Birds. T* **134** *and similar multicoloured designs.* W w **14** (*sideways on horiz designs*). *P* 13½×14 (*horiz*) or 14×13½ (*vert*).

462	5 c. Type **134**		10	10
463	10 c. Red-tailed Tropic Bird chick (*vert*)		10	10
464	15 c. Henderson Island Crake with chick		15	20
465	20 c. Red-footed Booby feeding chick (*vert*)		15	20
466	45 c. Blue-grey Noddy		30	35
467	50 c. Pitcairn Warbler ("Henderson Reed Warbler") in nest		30	35
468	90 c. Common Noddy		55	60
469	$1 Blue-faced Booby ("Masked Booby") and chick (*vert*)		65	70
470	$1.80, Henderson Island Fruit Dove		1·10	1·25
471	$2 Murphy's Petrel		1·25	1·40
472	$3 Christmas Island Shearwater		1·90	2·00
473	$5 Red-tailed Tropic Bird juvenile		3·25	3·50
462/73		*Set of 12*	9·75	10·50

135 Islanders in Longboats   136 Queen Elizabeth the Queen Mother

(Des G. Vasarhelyi. Litho B.D.T.)

1995 (26 June). *Oeno Island Holiday. T* **135** *and similar horiz designs. Multicoloured.* W w **14** (*sideways*). *P* 14×15.

474	20 c. Type **135**		40	40
475	90 c. Playing volleyball on beach		1·25	1·25
476	$1.80, Preparing picnic		2·25	2·50
477	$3 Singsong		3·50	4·25
474/7		*Set of 4*	6·75	7·50

(Des Jennifer Toombs. Litho Questa)

1995 (4 Aug). *95th Birthday of Queen Elizabeth the Queen Mother. Sheet* 75×90 *mm.* W w **16**. *P* 14½×14.

MS478 **136** $5 multicoloured .. .. 5·00 5·00

137 Guglielmo Marconi and Early Wireless, 1901

(Des N. Shewring. Litho Cartor)

1995 (5 Sept). *Centenary of First Radio Transmission. T* **137** *and similar horiz designs. Multicoloured.* W w **14** (*sideways*). *P* 13.

479	20 c. Type **137**		25	35
480	$1 Pitcairn radio transmitter, c. 1938		1·10	1·25
481	$1.50, Satellite Earth Station equipment, 1994		1·75	2·25
482	$3 Communications satellite in orbit, 1992		3·25	3·75
479/82		*Set of 4*	5·75	7·00

(Des A. Theobald. Litho Walsall)

1995 (24 Oct). *50th Anniv of United Nations. Horiz designs as T* **284** *of Jamaica. Multicoloured.* W w **16** (*sideways*). *P* 14.

483	20 c. United Nations float, Lord Mayor's Show		30	30
484	$1 R.F.A. *Brambleleaf* (tanker)		1·40	1·25
485	$1.50, U.N. ambulance		2·00	2·25
486	$3 R.A.F. Lockheed L-1011 TriStar		3·50	3·75
483/6		*Set of 4*	6·50	6·75

138 Early Morning at the Jetty   139 Chinese Junk

(Des L. Harraway. Litho Enschedé)

1996 (30 Jan). *Supply Ship Day. T* **138** *and similar horiz designs. Multicoloured.* W w **14** (*sideways*). *P* 14×15.

487	20 c. Type **138**		25	30
488	40 c. Longboat meeting *America Star* (freighter)		45	55
489	90 c. Loading supplies into longboats		1·00	1·10
490	$1 Landing supplies on jetty		1·10	1·25
491	$1.50, Sorting supplies at the Co-op		1·75	2·25
492	$1.80, Tractor towing supplies		1·90	2·25
487/92		*Set of 6*	5·75	7·00

(Des D. Miller. Litho Cartor)

1996 (21 Apr). *70th Birthday of Queen Elizabeth II. Vert designs as T* **55** *of New Zealand (Tokelau), each incorporating a different photograph of the Queen. Multicoloured.* W w **14**. *P* 13½.

493	20 c. Bounty Bay		45	45
494	90 c. Jetty and landing point, Bounty Bay		1·40	1·40
495	$1.80, Matt's Rocks		2·25	2·50
496	$3 St. Pauls		4·00	4·50
493/6		*Set of 4*	7·25	8·00

(Des C. Abbott. Litho Questa)

1996 (17 May). *"CHINA '96" 9th Asian International Stamp Exhibition, Peking. T* **139** *and similar vert designs. Multicoloured.* W w **14**. *P* 14.

497	$1.80, Type **139**		2·25	2·50
498	$1.80, H.M.S. *Bounty*		2·25	2·50
MS499	80×79 mm. 90 c. China 1984 8 f. Year of the Rat stamp; 90 c. Polynesian rat eating banana. Wmk sideways		2·00	2·00

140 Island Profile and Radio Call Signs

(Des Jennifer Toombs. Litho Walsall)

1996 (4 Sept). *Amateur Radio Operations from Pitcairn Islands. T* **140** *and similar horiz designs. Multicoloured.* W w **16** (*sideways*). *P* 13½×14.

500	20 c. Type **140**		45	45
501	$1.50, Radio operator calling for medical assistance		2·00	2·25
	a. Horiz pair. Nos. 501/2		4·00	4·50
502	$1.50, Doctors giving medical advice by radio		2·00	2·25
503	$2.50, Andrew Young (first radio operator), 1938		2·75	3·00
500/3		*Set of 4*	6·50	7·25

Nos. 501/2 were printed together, *se-tenant*, in horizontal pairs throughout the sheet.

141 Henderson Island Reed Warbler   142 Coat of Arms

(Des N. Arlott ($2), A. Robinson (others). Litho Walsall)

1996 (20 Nov). *Endangered Species. Local Birds. T* **141** *and similar multicoloured designs.* W w **14** (*sideways on* $2). *P* 13½×14 ($2) *or* 14×13½ (*others*).

504	5 c. Type **141**		30	30
505	10 c. Stephen's Lory		30	30
506	20 c. Henderson Island Crake		50	50
507	90 c. Henderson Island Fruit Dove		1·25	1·25
508	$2 White Tern (*horiz*)		2·00	2·25
509	$2 Blue-faced Booby (inscr "Masked Booby") (*horiz*)		2·00	2·25
504/9		*Set of 6*	5·75	6·25

Nos. 504/9 were available from philatelic counters in Australia from 1 October 1996

(Des N. Shewring. Litho Questa)

1997 (12 Feb). *"HONG KONG '97" International Stamp Exhibition. Chinese New Year ("Year of the Ox"). Sheet* 82×87 *mm.* W w **14** (*sideways*). *P* 14½.

MS510 **142** $5 multicoloured .. .. 5·00 5·50

143 David Barker (supply ship)

(Des G. Vasarhelyi. Litho Questa)

1997 (26 May). *50th Anniv of South Pacific Commission. Sheet* 115×56 *mm, containing T* **143** *and similar horiz design. Multicoloured.* W w **14** (*sideways*). *P* 13½×14.

MS511 $2.50, Type **143**; $2.50, *McLachlan* (fishing boat) .. .. .. 5·50 5·50

144 Health Centre

(Des G. Vasarhelyi. Litho Questa)

1997 (12 Sept). *Island Health Care. T* **144** *and similar horiz designs. Multicoloured.* W w **14** (*sideways*). *P* 13½×14.

512	20 c. Type **144**		30	25
513	$1 Nurse treating patient		1·00	1·00
514	$1.70, Dentist treating woman		1·75	1·90
515	$3 Evacuating patient by ship		3·00	3·25
512/15		*Set of 4*	5·50	5·75

(Des D. Miller. Litho Cartor)

1997 (20 Nov). *Golden Wedding of Queen Elizabeth and Prince Philip. Multicoloured designs as T* **87** *of Kiribati.* W w **14**. *P* 13.

516	20 c. Prince Philip driving carriage		30	40
	a. Horiz pair. Nos. 516/17		60	80
517	20 c. Queen Elizabeth, 1994		30	40
518	$1 Prince Philip at Royal Windsor Horse Show, 1996		1·00	1·25
	a. Horiz pair. Nos. 518/19		2·00	2·50
519	$1 Queen Elizabeth with horse		1·00	1·25
520	$1.70, Queen Elizabeth and Prince Philip at the Derby, 1991		1·50	1·75
	a. Horiz pair. Nos. 520/1		3·00	3·50
521	$1.70, Prince Charles hunting, 1995		1·50	1·75
516/21		*Set of 6*	5·00	6·00

Nos. 516/17, 518/19 and 520/1 were each printed together, *se-tenant*, in horizontal pairs with the backgrounds forming composite designs.

145 Island and Star

(Des Jennifer Toombs. Litho Cartor)

1997 (1 Dec). *Christmas. T* **145** *and similar horiz designs. Multicoloured.* W w **14** (*sideways*). *P* 13½.

522	20 c. Type **145**		35	25
523	80 c. Hand ringing bell		1·00	80
524	$1.20, Presents in baskets		1·40	1·50
525	$3 Families outside church		2·75	3·00
522/5		*Set of 4*	5·00	5·00

COVER PRICES

Cover factors are quoted at the beginning of each country for most issues to 1945. An explanation of the system can be found on page x. The factors quoted do not, however, apply to philatelic covers.

146 Christian's Cave

(Des L. Harraway. Litho Walsall)

1997 (9 Dec). *Christian's Cave. T* **146** *and similar multicoloured designs showing different views.* W w **16** *(sideways on 5 c., 20 c.).* P 13½×14 *(horiz) or* 14×13½ *(vert).*

526	5 c. Type **146**			15	20
527	20 c. View from the beach			35	35
528	35 c. Cave entrance (*vert*)			50	50
529	$5 Pathway through forest (*vert*)			3·75	5·00
526/9			*Set of 4*	4·25	5·50

147 H.M.S. *Bounty* (Bligh), 1790

(Des E. Nisbet. Litho Southern Colour Print, Dunedin)

1998 (28 May). *Millennium Commemoration (1st issue). Sailing Ships. T* **147** *and similar horiz designs. Multicoloured.* W w **14**. P 14½.

530	20 c. Type **147**			40	40
531	90 c. H.M.S. *Swallow* (Carteret), 1767		1·00	1·00
532	$1.80, H.M.S. *Briton* and H.M.S. *Tagus* (frigates), 1814		1·50	1·60
533	$3 H.M.S. *Fly* (sloop), 1838			2·50	2·75
530/3			*Set of 4*	4·75	5·25

See also Nos. 549/52.

(Des D. Miller. Litho Questa)

1998 (31 Aug). *Diana, Princess of Wales Commemoration. Sheet,* 145×70 *mm, containing vert designs as T* **91** *of Kiribati. Multicoloured.* W w **14** *(sideways).* P 14½×14.

MS534 90 c. Wearing pearl choker and red evening dress; 90 c. Wearing white hat and pearl necklace; 90 c. Carrying bouquet; 90 c. Wearing white dress and hat (*sold at* $3.60 + 40 c. *charity premium*) .. .. .. 3·50 3·75

148 *Bidens mathewsii*

(Des Sue Wickison. Litho Southern Colour Print, Dunedin)

1998 (20 Oct). *Flowers. T* **148** *and similar triangular designs. Multicoloured.* P 14×13½.

535	20 c. Type **148**			40	40
	a. Tête-bêche (pair)			80	80
536	90 c. *Hibiscus* sp			1·00	1·00
	a. Tête-bêche (pair)			2·00	2·00
537	$1.80, *Osteomeles anthyllidifolia*		1·75	1·75
	a. Tête-bêche (pair)			3·50	3·50
538	$3 *Ipomoea littoralis*			2·50	2·75
	a. Tête-bêche (pair)			5·00	5·50
535/8			*Set of 4*	5·00	5·50

Nos. 535/8 were each issued in sheets of 50 on which the stamps were arranged both horizontally and vertically tête-bêche.

149 Fishing

(Des P. Martinson. Litho Southern Colour Print, Dunedin)

1998 (16 Dec). *International Year of the Ocean. T* **149** *and similar multicoloured designs.* P 14.

539	20 c. Type **149**			40	40
540	90 c. Diver at wreck of *Cornwallis* (*vert*)		1·00	1·00
541	$1.80, Reef fish			1·75	1·75
542	$3 Murphy's Petrel (*vert*)			2·50	2·50
539/42			*Set of 4*	5·00	5·00
MS543	86×86 mm. Nos. 539/42			5·00	5·50

150 George Nobbs and Class, 1838

(Des L. Harraway. Litho Questa)

1999 (15 Feb). *Development of Local Education. T* **150** *and similar horiz designs. Multicoloured.* P 14.

544	20 c. Type **150**			30	30
545	90 c. Children outside thatched school, 1893		75	75
546	$1.80, Boy in wheelbarrow outside wooden school, 1932		1·40	1·40
547	$3 Modern classroom with computer		2·25	2·25
544/7			*Set of 4*	4·25	4·25

151 H.M.S. *Bounty* and Anchor

(Des C. Abbott. Litho Southern Colour Print, Dunedin)

1999 (19 Mar). *"Australia '99" World Stamp Exhibition, Melbourne. Pitcairn Archaeology Project. Sheet,* 190×80 *mm, containing T* **151** *and similar diamond-shaped designs. Multicoloured.* P 14.

MS548 50 c. Type **151**; $1 *Bounty* approaching Pitcairn and cannon; $1.50, *Bounty* on fire and chronometer; $2 *Bounty* sinking and metal bucket .. .. 3·50 3·75

152 John Adams (survivor of *Bounty* crew) and Bounty Bay

153 Prince Edward and Miss Sophie Rhys-Jones

(Des G. Vasarhelyi. Litho Southern Colour Print, Dunedin)

1999 (25 May). *Millennium Commemoration (2nd issue). T* **152** *and similar horiz designs. Multicoloured.* W w **14**. P 14½.

549	20 c. Type **152**			30	30
550	90 c. *Topaz* (sealer), 1808			75	75
551	$1.80, George Hunn Nobbs and Norfolk Island		1·40	1·40
552	$3 H.M.S. *Champion* (corvette), 1893		2·25	2·25
549/52			*Set of 4*	4·25	4·25

(Des D. Miller. Litho Walsall)

1999 (18 June). *Royal Wedding. T* **153** *and similar vert design. Multicoloured.* W w **16**. P 14.

553	$2.50, Type **153**			1·90	2·00
554	$2.50, Engagement photograph		1·90	2·00

154 Bee-keepers at Work

155 Arrival of *Yankee* (schooner), 1937

(Des Sue Williams. Litho Southern Colour Print, Dunedin)

1999 (20 Aug–12 Sept). *Bee-keeping. T* **154** *and similar hexagonal designs. Multicoloured. Self-adhesive.* P 9.

555	20 c. Type **154** (12 Sept)			30	30
556	$1 Bee on Passion Flower (12 Sept)		80	80
557	$1.80, Bees in honeycomb (12 Sept)		1·40	1·40
558	$3 Bee on flower and jar of "Mutineer's Dream" honey (12 Sept)		2·25	2·25
555/8			*Set of 4*	4·25	4·25
MS559	74×100 mm. No. 556			80	80

No. MS559 includes the "China '99" International Stamp Exhibition emblem on the sheet margin.

(Des D. Gunson. Litho Southern Colour Print, Dunedin)

2000 (14 Jan). *Protection of "Mr. Turpen" (Galapagos Tortoise on Pitcairn). T* **155** *and similar vert designs. Multicoloured.* P 14½.

560	5 c. Type **155**			10	10
	a. Horiz strip of 4 and centre label. Nos. 560/3			3·50	
561	20 c. Off-loading Mr. Turpen at Bounty Bay		15	20
562	35 c. Mr. Turpen			20	25
563	$5 Head of Mr. Turpen			3·25	3·50
560/3			*Set of 4*	3·50	4·00

Nos. 560/3 were printed together, *se-tenant*, in horizontal strips of 4 with a central label, showing extracts from the Protection Ordinance, and with the backgrounds forming a composite design.

STAMP BOOKLETS

1940 (15 Oct). *Black on deep green cover. Stapled.*

SB1 4s. 8d. booklet containing one each ½d., 1d., 1½d., 2d.. 3d.. 6d.. 1s. and 2s. 6d. (Nos. 1/5. 6, 7/8) £2750

Genuine examples of No. SB1 are interleaved with ordinary kitchen wax-paper, which frequently tones the stamps, and are secured with staples 17 mm long.

The status of other booklets using different size staples or paper fasteners is uncertain although it is believed that some empty booklet covers were available on the island.

An unofficial booklet was released in 1986 containing Nos. 281/2, each in block of four, with "HELP PRESERVE PITCAIRN" slogan and showing the Flightless Chicken Bird and contents on the cover.

1990 (3 May). *Black on white cover. Stapled.*

SB2 $4.40, booklet containing 20 c. and 90 c., each in pane of 4 (Nos. 369a, 374a) .. .. 9·00

No. SB2 was overprinted on the cover with "New Zealand 1990" International Stamp Exhibition, Auckland, logo.

An unofficial version of No. SB2 was released in 1990 overprinted for "Birdpex '90" Stamp Exhibition, Christchurch.

1990 (3 May). *"Stamp World London 90" International Stamp Exhibition. As No.* SB2, *but with exhibition logo.*

SB3 $4.40, booklet containing 20 c. and 90 c. each in pane of 4 (Nos. 369a, 374a) .. .. 9·00

Prince Edward Island
see Canada

Qatar

An independent Arab Shaikhdom, with a British postal administration until 23 May 1963.

There was no postal service from Qatar until 18 May 1950. Prior to this date the few foreign residents made their own arrangements for their mail to be carried to Bahrain for onward transmission through the postal services.

The first organised post from the capital, Doha, was an extension of the work in the state by the British Political Officer. From 18 May 1950 British residents were able to send mail via his office. The first three sendings had the Bahrain or British Postal Agencies in Eastern Arabia stamps cancelled by a circular office stamp, but later batches, up to the introduction of the first Doha postmark in July 1950, had the stamps cancelled on arrival at Bahrain.

July 1950 Cancellation   1956 Cancellation

The Post Office became a separate entity in August 1950 when its services were made available to the general public. After initially using the Bahrain surcharges on Great Britain the supply of stamps for the Qatar office was switched to the British Postal Agencies in Eastern Arabia surcharges.

The circular cancellation, dating from July 1950, continued to be used until replaced by a slightly smaller version in early 1956.

A further post office was opened on 1 February 1956 at the Umm Said oil terminal, using its own cancellation.

Both offices were issued with standard oval Registered handstamps, Doha in 1950 and Umm Said in 1956.

1956 Umm Said Cancellation

(Currency. 100 naye paise = 1 rupee)

All stamps to 1960 surcharged on Queen Elizabeth II issues of Great Britain

QATAR	QATAR	QATAR	
NP **1** NP	NP **3** NP	**75** NP	
(1)	(2)	(3)	

1957 (1 Apr)–**59.** (a) *Nos. 540/2, 543b/8, 551 and 555/6 (St. Edwards's Crown wmk), surch as T 1 to 3.*

1	1	1 n.p. on 5d. brown			10	10
2	2	3 n.p. on ½d. orange-red			15	10
3		6 n.p. on 1d. ultramarine			15	15
4		9 n.p. on 1½d. green			15	10
5		12 n.p. on 2d. light red-brown			20	80
6	1	15 n.p. on 2½d. carmine-red (I)			15	10
7	2	20 n.p. on 3d. deep lilac (B.)			15	10
8	1	25 n.p. on 4d. ultramarine			40	60
9		40 n.p. on 6d. reddish purple			15	10
		a. Deep claret (21.7.59)			30	10
10		50 n.p. on 9d. bronze-green			40	15
11	3	75 n.p. on 1s. 3d. green			50	80
12		1 r. on 1s. 6d. grey-blue			6·00	10
1/12				Set of 12	7·50	2·75

QATAR 2 RUPEES ═ I

QATAR 2 RUPEES ═ II

(4)

QATAR **5** RUPEES ═ I

QATAR **5** RUPEES ═ II

(5)

QATAR **10** RUPEES ═ I

QATAR **10** RUPEES ═ II

(6)

Type I (**4/6**). Type-set overprints. Bold thick letters with sharp corners and straight edges. Bars close together and usually slightly longer than in Type II.

Type II (**4/6**). Plate-printed overprints by Harrison. Thinner letters, rounded corners and rough edges. Bars wider apart.

(b) *Nos.* 536/8 (*St. Edward's Crown wmk) surcharged with T* **4/6**

13	2 r. on 2s. 6d. black-brown (I) (1.4.57)		3·50	2·50
	a. Type II (18.9.57)		9·00	6·50
14	5 r. on 5s. rose-red (I) (1.4.57)		4·50	2·75
	a. Type II (18.9.57)		9·00	17·00
15	10 r. on 10s. ultramarine (I) (1.4.57)		5·50	12·00
	a. Type II (18.9.57)		45·00	£120
13/15		Set of 3	12·00	15·00
13a/15a		Set of 3	55·00	£130

QATAR
15 NP

(7)

1957 (1 Aug). *World Scout Jubilee Jamboree. Nos. 557/9 surch in two lines as T* **7** *(15 n.p.) or in three lines (others).*

16	15 n.p. on 2½d. carmine-red			25	35
17	25 n.p. on 4d. ultramarine			25	35
18	75 n.p. on 1s. 3d. green			30	35
16/18			Set of 3	70	95

1960 (26 Apr–28 Sept). *Nos. 570/5 and 579 (Mult Crown wmk) surcharged as T* **1** *or* **2.**

20	2	3 n.p. on ½d. orange-red (28.9)		70	1·75
21		6 n.p. on 1d. ultramarine (21.6)		1·25	2·75
22		9 n.p. on 1½d. green (28.9)		75	1·50
23		12 n.p. on 2d. light red-brown (28.9)		3·75	6·50
24	1	15 n.p. on 2½d. carmine-red (II)		35	10
25	2	20 n.p. on 3d. deep lilac (B.) (28.9)		35	10
26	1	40 n.p. on 6d. deep claret (21.6)		60	30
20/6			Set of 7	7·00	11·50

8 Shaikh Ahmad bin   9 Peregrine   10 Dhow
Ali al Thani   Falcon

11 Oil Derrick   12 Mosque

(Des O. C. Meronti (T **8**), M. Goaman (T **9**), M. Farrar Bell (T **10**), J. Constable and O. C. Meronti (T **11/12**). Photo Harrison, (T **8/10**). Recess D.L.R. (T **11/12**).)

1961 (2 Sept). *P* 14½ *(5 n.p. to 75 n.p.) or* 13 *(1 r. to 10 r.).*

27	8	5 n.p. carmine			10	10
28		15 n.p. black			10	10
29		20 n.p. reddish purple			10	10
30		30 n.p. deep green			10	10
31	9	40 n.p. red			85	10
32		50 n.p. sepia			1·25	10
33	10	75 n.p. ultramarine			60	1·50
34	11	1 r. scarlet			70	10
35		2 r. ultramarine			2·00	60
36	12	5 r. bronze-green			13·00	2·00
37		10 r. black			35·00	4·00
27/37			Set of 11		48·00	7·50

The Qatar Post Department took over the postal services on 23 May 1963. Later stamp issues will be found listed in Part 19 (*Middle East*) of this catalogue.

Queensland
see Australia

Rhodesia

Stamps of BECHUANALAND (see BOTSWANA) were used in Matabeleland on the runner post between Gubulawayo and Mafeking (Bechuanaland) from 9 August 1888 until 5 May 1894. Such stamps were cancelled "GUBULAWAYO" or by the barred oval "678" obliteration.

Between 27 June 1890 and 13 May 1892 external mail from Mashonaland sent via Bechuanaland was franked with that territory's stamps. A similar arrangement, using the stamps of MOZAMBIQUE existed for the route via Beira inaugurated on 29 August 1891. In both instances the stamps were cancelled by the post offices receiving the mail from Mashonaland. From 14 May until 31 July 1892 letters via Bechuanaland were franked with a combination of B.S.A Company and Bechuanaland issues.

Rhodesia joined the South African Postal Union on 1 August 1892 when its stamps became valid for international mail. Combination frankings with Mozambique stamps continued to be required until April 1894.

For the use of British Central Africa overprints in North-eastern Rhodesia from 1893 to 1899 see MALAWI (NYASALAND).

PRICES FOR STAMPS ON COVER TO 1945

Nos. 1/7	from × 5
Nos. 8/13	—
Nos. 14/17	from × 2
Nos. 18/24	from × 10
Nos. 25/6	—
Nos. 27/8	from × 7
Nos. 29/35	from × 10
Nos. 36/7	—
Nos. 41/6	from × 6
Nos. 47/50	—
Nos. 51/3	from × 2
Nos. 58/64	from × 3
Nos. 66/72	from × 8
Nos. 73/4	—
Nos. 75/87	from × 6
Nos. 88/93a	—
Nos. 94/9	from × 3
Nos. 100/10	from × 5
Nos. 111/13e	—
Nos. 114/18	from × 7
Nos. 119/60a	from × 8
Nos. 160b/6b	—
Nos. 167/78	from × 5
Nos. 179/81a	—
Nos. 182/5a	from × 4
Nos. 186/208	from × 6
Nos. 209/41	from × 5
Nos. 242/54a	—
Nos. 255/77	from × 5
Nos. 278/9c	—
Nos. 280/1	from × 10
Nos. 282/310	from × 5
Nos. 311/22	—

A. ISSUES FOR THE BRITISH SOUTH AFRICA COMPANY TERRITORY

½**d.**

1   2   (3)

(Recess B.W.)

1892 (2 Jan)*–**93.** *Thin wove paper. P* 14, 14½.

1	1	1d. black			9·00	2·50
2		6d. ultramarine			48·00	20·00
3		6d. deep blue (1893)			22·00	3·50
4		1s. grey-brown			32·00	7·50
5		2s. vermilion			40·00	25·00
6		2s. 6d. grey-purple			28·00	29·00
7		2s. 6d. lilac (1893)			40·00	32·00
8		5s. orange-yellow			60·00	50·00
9		10s. deep green			75·00	95·00
10	2	£1 deep blue			£170	£130
11		£2 rose-red**			£400	£150
12		£5 sage-green			£1600	£450
13		£10 brown			£2750	£700
1/10				Set of 10	£350	£350

Great caution is needed in buying the high values in either used or unused condition, many stamps offered being revenue stamps cleaned and re-gummed with forged postmarks.

*Printing of stamps in Types 1, 2 and 4 commenced in 1890, although none were used for postal purposes before 2 January 1892 when the route to the East Coast was inaugurated.

**For later printings of the £2 see No. 74.

The following sheet watermarks are known on Nos. 1/26: (1) William Collins, Sons & Co's paper watermarked with the firm's monogram, and "PURE LINEN WOVE BANK" in double-lined capitals (1890 and 1891 ptgs). (2) As (1) with "EXTRA STRONG" and "139" added (1892 ptgs). (3) Paper by Wiggins, Teape & Co, watermarked "W T & Co" in script letters in double-lined wavy border (1893 ptgs). (4) The same firm's paper, watermarked "1011" in double-lined figures (1894 ptgs except ½d.). (5) "WIGGINS TEAPE & CO LONDON" in double-lined block capitals (1894 ptg of No. 18). Many values can also be found on a slightly thicker paper without wmk, but single specimens are not easily distinguishable.

1892 (2 Jan). *Nos. 2 and 4 surch as T 3.*

14	1	1½d. on 6d. ultramarine				85·00	£225
15		2d. on 6d. ultramarine				85·00	£325
16		4d. on 6d. ultramarine				£110	£400
17		8d. on 1s. grey-brown				£110	£425

Caution is needed in buying these surcharges as both forged surcharges and forged postmarks exist.

4   **5** (ends of scrolls behind legs of springboks)

(T 4. Centre recess; value B.W.)

1892 (2 Jan)–**94**. *Thin wove paper (wmks as note after No. 13). P 14, 14½.*

18	4	½d. dull blue and vermilion				2·50	2·00
19		½d. deep blue and vermilion (1893)				2·75	3·75
20		2d. deep dull green and vermilion				17·00	1·75
21		3d. grey-black and green (8.92)				8·50	3·00
22		4d. chestnut and black				17·00	2·00
23		8d. rose-lake and ultramarine				10·00	7·50
24		8d. red and ultramarine (1892)				10·00	7·50
25		3s. brown and green (1894)				£120	70·00
26		4s. grey-black and vermilion (1893)				30·00	45·00
18/26					Set of 7	£180	£120

(Recess P.B. from the Bradbury, Wilkinson plates)

1895. *Thick soft wove paper. P 12½.*

27	4	2d. green and red				20·00	8·00
28		4d. yellow-brown and black				22·00	12·00
		a. Imperf (pair)				£1800	

(Centre recess; value typo P.B.)

1896–97. *Wove paper. P 14.*

(a) Die I. Plates 1 and 2.

Small dot to the right of the tail of the right-hand supporter in the coat of arms. Body of lion only partly shaded.

29	5	1d. scarlet and emerald				10·00	4·25
		a. Carmine-red and emerald					
30		2d. brown and mauve				16·00	2·00
31		3d. chocolate and ultramarine				3·50	1·50
32		4d. ultramarine and mauve				48·00	
		a. Imperf between (pair)					
		b. Blue and mauve				20·00	13·00
33		6d. mauve and pink				75·00	13·00
34		8d. green and mauve/buff				4·50	60
		a. Imperf between (pair)					
		b. Imperf (pair)				£2000	
35		1s. green and blue				15·00	2·50
36		3s. green and mauve/blue				60·00	32·00
		a. Imperf (pair)				£5000	
37		4s. orange-red and blue/green				45·00	2·75
29/37					Set of 9	£200	60·00

(b) Die II. Plates 3 and 4

No dot. Body of lion heavily shaded all over.

41	5	½d. slate and violet				2·25	3·00
42		1d. scarlet and emerald				2·75	3·25
43		2d. brown and mauve				6·00	4·25
44		4d. ultramarine and mauve				70·00	12·00
		a. Blue and mauve				8·00	50
45		6d. mauve and rose				6·00	50
46		2s. indigo and green/buff				20·00	8·50
47		2s. 6d. brown and purple/yellow				65·00	42·00
48		5s. chestnut and emerald				38·00	9·00
49		10s. slate and vermilion/rose				85·00	60·00
50					Set of 9	£200	£120
41/50							

One Penny   **THREE PENCE.**

(6)   **(7)**

(Surchd by *Bulawayo Chronicle*)

1896 (April). *Matabele Rebellion provisionals. Surch with T 6 and 7.*

51	6	1d. on 3d. (No. 21)			£425	£425
		a. "P" in "Penny" inverted			£20000	
		b. "y" in "Penny" inverted				
		c. Surch double				
52		1d. on 4s. (No. 26)			£250	£275
		a. "P" in "Penny" inverted			£17000	
		b. "y" in "Penny" inverted			£17000	
		c. Single bar through original value			£950	£1100
53	7	3d. on 5s. (No. 8)			£170	£225
		a. "R" in "THREE" inverted			£18000	
		b. "T" in "THREE" inverted			£21000	

Nos. 51 and 52 occur in two settings, one with 9¾ mm between value and upper bar, the other with 11 mm between value and upper bar.

BRITISH SOUTH AFRICA COMPANY.

(8)   **9** (Ends of scrolls between legs of springboks)

1896 (22 May–Aug). *Cape of Good Hope stamps optd by Argus Printing Co, Cape Town, with T 8. Wmk Anchor (3d. wmk Crown CA). P 14.*

58	6	½d. grey-black (No. 48a)			9·00	15·00
59	17	1d. rose-red (No. 58)			9·50	15·00
60	6	2d. deep bistre (No. 50a)			11·00	9·00
61		3d. pale claret (No. 40)			48·00	70·00
62		4d. blue (No. 51)			13·00	13·00
		a. "COMPANY," omitted			£8000	
63	4	6d. deep purple (No. 52a)			48·00	65·00
64	6	1s. yellow-ochre (No. 65) (Aug)			£120	£140
58/64				Set of 7	£225	£300

No. 62 also exists with "COMPANY" partially omitted. Examples with the word completely omitted, as No. 62a, occur on positions 1 to 6 of the setting.

Forgeries of this overprint show a narrow final "A" in "AFRICA" and have a rectangular full stop. On the genuine overprint both "As" are the same and the stop is oval.

(Eng J. A. C. Harrison (vignette), Bain or Rapkin (£1) (frames). Recess Waterlow)

1897. *P 13½ to 16.*

66	9	½d. grey-black and purple			1·60	3·75
67		1d. scarlet and emerald			3·00	4·00
68		2d. brown and mauve			4·25	1·00
69		3d. brown-red and slate-blue			2·50	30
		a. Imperf between (vert pair)			£2000	
70		4d. ultramarine and claret			7·00	1·50
		a. Imperf between (horiz pair)			£7000	£7000
71		6d. dull purple and pink			6·50	3·50
72		8d. green and mauve/buff			11·00	40
		a. Imperf between (vert pair)			—	£2250
73		£1 black and red-brown/green			£350	£225

(Recess Waterlow, from the Bradbury plate)

1897 (Jan). *P 15.*

74	2	£2 rosy red			£1700	£400

10   **11**   **12**

(Recess Waterlow)

1898–1908. *P 13½ to 15½.*

75	10	½d. dull bluish green			2·50	50
		a. Yellow-green (1904)			1·50	50
		aa. Imperf vert (horiz pair)			£650	
		ab. Imperf (pair)			£700	
76		½d. deep green (shades) (1908)			23·00	80
77		1d. rose (shades)			2·00	40
		a. Imperf (pair)			£600	£600
		b. Imperf between (vert pair)			£500	
78		1d. red (shades) (1905)			3·50	40
		a. Imperf vert (horiz pair)			£350	£375
		ab. Imperf horiz (vert pair)			£650	
		b. Imperf (pair)			£500	£500
		c. Imperf between (horiz pair)			†	£400
79		2d. brown			1·75	40
80		2½d. dull blue (shades)			3·75	70
		a. Imperf vert (horiz pair)			£800	£850
		b. Grey-blue (shades) (1903)			11·00	90
81		3d. claret			3·75	80
		a. Imperf between (vert pair)			£700	
82		4d. olive			4·25	30
		a. Imperf between (vert pair)			£700	
83		6d. reddish purple			8·50	1·75
		a. Reddish mauve (1902)			13·00	5·00
84	11	1s. bistre			11·00	1·75
		a. Imperf between (vert pair)			£2500	
		ab. Imperf between (horiz pair)			£2750	
		b. Deep olive-bistre (1907)			£275	
		bc. Imperf (pair)			£2500	
		bd. Imperf between (horiz pair)			£3250	
		c. Bistre-brown (1908)			50·00	12·00
		d. Brownish yellow (1908)			14·00	5·00
85		2s. 6d. bluish grey (11.06)			40·00	75
		a. Imperf between (vert pair)			£1000	£500
		b. Imperf (vert pair)			—	£5000
86		3s. deep violet (1902)			11·00	1·25
		a. Deep bluish violet (1908)			55·00	9·50
87		5s. brown-orange			30·00	9·00
88		7s. 6d. black (11.01)			60·00	14·00
89		10s. grey-green			18·00	1·00
90	12	£1 greyish red-purple (p 15½) (7.01)			£180	70·00
		a. Perf 14. Blackish purple (1902)			£325	65·00
91		£2 brown (5.08)			70·00	6·50
92		£5 deep blue (7.01)			£3000	£2250
93		£10 lilac (7.01)			£3250	£2250
93a		£20 yellow-bistre (1901?)			£14000	
75/90				Set of 14	£300	80·00

80/1, 85/6, 88/93 Perf "Specimen" ... £900

A £100 cherry-red, perf 13½, was ordered in June 1901, a number of mint, together with several examples showing fiscal cancellations being known.

---

13 Victoria Falls   **(14)**   **RHODESIA.**

(Recess Waterlow)

1905 (13 July). *Visit of British Association and Opening of Victoria Falls Bridge. P 13½ to 15.*

94	13	1d. red			2·75	4·25
95		2½d. deep blue			7·50	5·50
96		5d. claret (Optd S. £150)			22·00	48·00
97		1s. blue-green			22·00	35·00
		a. Imperf (pair)			£16000	
		b. Imperf between (horiz pair)			£21000	
		c. Imperf between (vert pair)			£21000	
		d. Imperf vert (horiz pair)			£17000	
98		2s. 6d. black			£100	£150
99		5s. violet			85·00	40·00
94/9				Set of 6	£200	£250
94/9 Perf (5d.) or Optd (others) "Specimen"				Set of 6	£350	

1909 (15 Apr)–**12.** *Optd as T 14. P 13½ to 15.*

100	10	½d. green to deep green			1·50	70
		a. No stop			45·00	28·00
		b. Yellow-green (1911)			35·00	27·00
101		1d. carmine-rose			1·75	60
		a. No stop			60·00	25·00
		b. Imperf between (horiz pair)			£400	
		c. Deep carmine-rose			1·75	50
		cd. Imperf between (horiz pair)			£400	
102		2d. brown			1·60	3·25
		a. No stop			80·00	55·00
103		2½d. pale dull blue			1·00	70
		a. No stop			35·00	24·00
104		3d. claret			1·60	30
		a. No stop			£100	55·00
		b. Opt inverted			†	15·00
105		4d. olive			2·75	85
		a. No stop			60·00	55·00
		b. Opt inverted			†	15·00
106		6d. reddish purple			5·00	3·00
		a. No stop				
		b. Reddish mauve				
		c. Dull purple			15·00	3·75
		ca. No stop			80·00	45·00
107	11	1s. bistre			18·00	
		a. No stop			£150	
		b. Bistre-brown				
		ba. No stop				
		c. Deep brownish bistre			8·50	2·50
		ca. No stop			80·00	38·00
108		2s. 6d. bluish grey			16·00	7·50
		a. No stop			80·00	55·00
		b. Opt inverted			†	20·00
109		3s. deep violet			15·00	7·50
110		5s. orange			25·00	25·00
		a. No stop			90·00	70·00
111		7s. 6d. black			75·00	12·00
112		10s. dull green			28·00	9·50
		a. No stop			£225	£180
113	12	£1 grey-purple			£110	65·00
		a. Vert pair, lower stamp without opt			£24000	
		b. Opt in violet			£350	£180
113c		£2 brown			£3750	£300
113d		£2 rosy brown (bluish paper) (p 14½×15) (1912)			£3250	£275
113e		£5 deep blue (bluish paper)			£6500	£3000
100/13				Set of 14	£225	£110
100/13 Perf "Specimen"				Set of 14	£325	

In some values the no stop variety occurs on every stamp in a vertical row of a sheet, in other values only once in a sheet. Other varieties, such as no serif to the right of apex of "A", no serif to top of "E", etc., exist in some values.

No. 113a comes from a sheet with the overprint omitted from the bottom row.

RHODESIA.   **RHODESIA.**

5d   **TWO SHILLINGS.**

(15)   **(16)**

1909 (April)–**11.** *Surch as T 15 and 16 (2s.), in black.*

114	10	5d. on 6d. reddish purple			6·50	10·00
		a. Surcharge in violet			90·00	
		b. Reddish mauve				
		c. Dull purple			14·00	10·00
116	11	7½d. on 2s. 6d. bluish grey			3·50	3·00
		a. Surcharge in violet			17·00	8·50
		ab. Surch double			†	£6500
117		10d. on 3s. deep violet			13·00	16·00
		a. Surcharge in violet			4·00	3·75
118		2s. on 5s. orange			12·00	7·50
114/18 Perf "Specimen"				Set of 4	£180	

In the 7½d. and 10d. surcharges the bars are spaced as in T 16.

17   **18**

(Recess Waterlow)

1910 (11 Nov)-13. (a) P 14.
119 17 ½d. yellow-green .. .. 8·00 1·25
    a. Imperf between (horiz pair) .. £18000
120   ½d. bluish green .. .. 17·00 1·75
    a. Imperf (pair) £8500 £4000
121   ½d. olive-green .. .. 24·00 2·00
122   ½d. dull green .. .. 60·00 50·00
123   1d. bright carmine .. .. 13·00 1·25
    a. Imperf between (vert pair) .. £15000 £10000
124   1d. carmine-lake .. .. 35·00 1·50
125   1d. rose-red .. .. 15·00 1·25
126   2d. black and grey .. .. 40·00 7·50
127   2d. black-purple and slate-grey £160
128   2d. black and slate-grey .. 42·00 5·00
129   2d. black and slate .. .. 50·00 6·00
130   2d. black and grey-black .. 60·00 9·50
131   2½d. ultramarine .. .. 18·00 5·50
131a   2½d. bright ultramarine .. 17·00 5·50
132   2½d. dull blue .. .. 21·00 6·00
133   2½d. chalky blue .. .. 15·00 9·50
134   3d. purple and ochre .. 23·00 25·00
135   3d. purple and yellow-ochre .. 27·00 11·00
136   3d. magenta and yellow-ochre £110 11·00
137   3d. violet and ochre .. .. 90·00 75·00
138   4d. greenish black and orange 80·00 85·00
139   4d. brown-purple and orange 60·00 50·00
140   4d. black and orange .. 27·00 11·00
141   5d. purple-brown and olive-green 21·00 38·00
141a   5d. purple-brown and olive-yellow 21·00 48·00
    ab. Error. Purple-brown and ochre £550 £150
143   5d. lake-brown and olive .. £225 60·00
143a   5d. lake-brown and green .. £19000 £1600
144   6d. red-brown and mauve .. 25·00 25·00
145   6d. brown and purple .. 25·00 10·00
145a   6d. bright chestnut and mauve £750 60·00
146   8d. black and purple .. £4250
147   8d. dull purple and purple .. £130 85·00
148   8d. greenish black and purple £120 80·00
149   10d. scarlet and reddish mauve 27·00 48·00
150   10d. carmine and deep purple .. £600 60·00
151   1s. grey-black and deep blue-green 28·00 16·00
151a   1s. black and deep blue-green .. £110 24·00
152   1s. black and pale blue-green 35·00 10·00
152a   1s. purple-black and blue-green £225 40·00
153   2s. black and ultramarine .. 70·00 50·00
154   2s. black and dull blue .. £950 55·00
154a   2s. purple-black and ultramarine £2750 £225
155   2s. 6d. black and lake .. £300 £275
155a   2s. 6d. black and crimson .. £300 £275
156   2s. 6d. sepia and deep crimson £400 £325
156a   2s. 6d. bistre-brown and crimson £1000 £500
157   2s. 6d. black and rose-carmine £275 £275
158   3s. green and violet (shades) £140 £140
158a   3s. bright green and magenta £1100 £600
159   5s. vermilion and deep green £250 £300
160   5s. scarlet and pale yellow-green £275 £180
160a   5s. crimson and yellow-green £225 £180
160b   7s. 6d. carmine and pale blue £600 £425
161   7s. 6d. carmine and light blue £650 £650
162   7s. 6d. carmine and bright blue £1900 £850
163   10s. deep myrtle and orange .. £550 £250
164   10s. blue-green and orange .. £375 £300
165   £1 carmine-red and bluish black £1000 £400
166   £1 rose-scarlet and bluish black £1000 £350
166a   £1 crimson and slate-black £1200 £750
    b. Error. Scarlet and reddish mauve £8500

(b) P 15
167 17 ½d. blue-green .. .. £250 13·00
168   ½d. yellow-green .. .. £325 11·00
169   ½d. apple-green .. .. £550 27·00
170   1d. carmine .. .. £250 8·50
170a   1d. carmine-lake .. .. £400 14·00
170b   1d. rose-carmine .. .. £275 11·00
171   2d. black and grey-black .. £750 30·00
171a   2d. black and grey .. .. £750 30·00
171b   2d. black and slate .. .. £800 30·00
172   2½d. ultramarine (shades) .. 70·00 35·00
173   3d. purple and yellow-ochre .. £4250 50·00
173a   3d. claret and pale yellow-ochre £2250 50·00
174   4d. black and orange (shades) 38·00 60·00
175   5d. lake-brown and olive .. £750 75·00
176   6d. brown and mauve .. £800 60·00
177   1s. black and blue-green (shades) £900 55·00
178   2s. black and dull blue .. £1800 £325
179   £1 red and black .. £14000 £3000

(c) P 14×15 (½d., 3d., 1s.) or 15×14 (1d., 4d.)
179a 17 ½d. yellow-green .. .. † £2750
179b   1d. carmine .. .. † £4750
180   3d. purple and ochre .. £4750 £225
181   4d. black and orange .. £425
181a   1s. black and blue-green .. £20000 £2500

(d) P 13½
182 17 ½d. yellow-green .. .. £250 40·00
182a   ½d. green .. .. £325 40·00
183   1d. bright carmine .. .. £1800 48·00
184   2½d. ultramarine (shades) .. 35·00 55·00
185   8d. black and purple (shades) 60·00 £250
185a   8d. grey-purple and dull purple £375 £425
119/185 Optd "Specimen" perf 14 except 2½d. and
    8d. perf 13½ .. .. Set of 18 £3000
Plate varieties in T 17 are:—½d., double dot below "D" in
right-hand value tablet (R. 3/9) (from £500 un. £350 used); 2d. to
£1 excluding 2½d., straight stroke in Queen's right ear known
as the "gash in ear" variety (R. 1/2) (from 3 to 5 times normal).
    Stamps from the above and the next issue are known
compound perf with 14 or 15 on one side only or on adjoining
sides but we no longer list them.
    Examples of some values are known with a forged registered
Bulawayo postmark dated "JA 10 11".

(Recess Waterlow)

1913 (1 Sept)-22. No wmk. (i) From single working plates.
(a) P 14.
186 18 ½d. blue-green .. .. 4·75 90
187   ½d. deep green .. .. 4·00 90
    a. Imperf horiz (vert pair) .. £700
188   ½d. yellow-green .. .. 8·50 90
188b   ½d. dull green .. .. 6·00 90
    ba. Imperf vert (horiz pair) .. £750 £750

189 18 ½d. bright green .. .. 13·00 90
    a. Imperf between (vert pair) .. £1200
190   1d. rose-carmine .. .. 4·00 75
    a. Imperf between (horiz pair) .. £700 £600
191   1d. carmine-red (shades) .. 8·50 75
    a. Imperf between (pair) .. £1000
192   1d. brown-red .. .. 3·00 75
193   1d. red .. .. 4·25 75
    a. Imperf between (horiz pair) .. £700
194   1d. scarlet .. .. 13·00 1·00
    a. Imperf between (horiz pair) .. £850
195   1d. rose-red .. .. 7·00 75
    a. Imperf between (horiz pair) .. £550
    b. Imperf between (vert pair) .. £1600
196   1d. rosine .. .. £500 19·00
197   1½d. brown-ochre (1919) .. 2·50 60
    a. Imperf between (horiz pair) .. £600 £600
198   1½d. bistre-brown (1917) .. 2·50 60
    a. Imperf between (horiz pair) .. £650 £650
199   1½d. drab-brown (1917) .. 3·00 60
    a. Imperf between (horiz pair) .. £550
    b. Imperf between (vert pair) .. £1500
200   2½d. deep blue .. .. 3·50 19·00
201   2½d. bright blue .. .. 3·50 19·00

(b) P 15
202 18 ½d. blue-green .. .. 8·50 11·00
203   ½d. green .. .. 13·00 9·00
204   1d. rose-red .. .. £550 22·00
    a. Imperf between (horiz pair) .. £10000
205   1d. brown-red .. .. 2·25 4·00
206   1½d. bistre-brown (1919) .. 22·00 7·00
    a. Imperf between (horiz pair) .. £12000
206b   1½d. brown-ochre (1917) .. 30·00 9·50
207   2½d. deep blue .. .. 18·00 32·00
208   2½d. bright blue .. .. 16·00 30·00

(c) P 14 × 15
208a 18 ½d. green £4500 £170

(d) P 15×14
208b 18 ½d. green £4500 £300
208c   1½d. drab-brown ..

(e) P 13½
208d 18 1d. red (1914) .. .. † £450

Die I   Die II   Die III

The remaining values were printed from double, i.e. head and
duty, plates. There are at least four different head plates made from
three different dies, which may be distinguished as follows:—
Die I. The King's left ear is neither shaded nor outlined; no
outline to top of cap. Shank of anchor in cap badge is complete.
Die II. The ear is shaded all over, but has no outline. The top of
the cap has a faint outline. Anchor as Die I.
Die III. The ear is shaded and outlined; a heavy continuous
outline round the cap. Shank of anchor is broken just below the
lowest line which crosses it.

(ii) *Printed from double plates. Head Die* I (a) P 14
209 18 2d. black and grey .. .. 8·00 6·00
210   3d. black and yellow .. .. 70·00 6·00
211   4d. black and orange-red .. 5·00 23·00
212   5d. black and green .. .. 3·50 8·50
213   6d. black and mauve .. .. £180 23·00
213a   8d. violet and green £4500
214   2s. black and brown .. .. 85·00 75·00

(b) P 15
215 18 3d. black and yellow .. .. 4·00 13·00
216   4d. black and orange-red .. £130 13·00
217   6d. black and mauve .. .. 4·00 4·50
217a   8d. violet and green .. £15000 £15000
218   2s. black and brown .. .. 10·00 24·00

(iii) *Head Die* II. (a) P 14
219 18 2d. black and grey .. .. 12·00 2·00
220   2d. black and brownish grey .. 32·00 4·00
221   3d. black and deep yellow .. 24·00 4·00
222   3d. black and yellow .. .. 60·00 4·00
223   3d. black and buff .. .. 6·50 4·00
224   4d. black and orange-red .. 17·00 5·50
225   4d. black and deep orange-red 8·00 5·50
226   5d. black and grey-green .. 13·00 26·00
227   5d. black and bright green .. 11·00 26·00
228   6d. black and mauve .. .. 23·00 2·25
229   6d. black and purple .. .. 60·00 3·50
230   8d. violet and green .. .. 9·50 42·00
231   10d. blue and carmine-red .. 15·00 32·00
232   1s. black and greenish blue 38·00 32·00
233   1s. black and turquoise-blue .. 7·00 8·00
234   2s. black and brown .. .. 65·00 7·50
235   2s. black and yellow-brown .. £250 24·00
236   2s. 6d. indigo and grey-brown 42·00 23·00
236a   2s. 6d. pale blue and brown .. £250 40·00
236b   3s. brown and blue .. .. 70·00 85·00
237   3s. chestnut and bright blue .. 65·00 90·00
238   5s. blue and yellow-green .. £110 55·00
239   5s. blue and deep green .. 42·00 48·00
240   7s. 6d. blackish purple and slate-black £225 £225
241   10s. crimson and yellow-green .. £170 £200
242   £1 black and purple £350 £450
243   £1 black and violet £350 £500

(b) P 15
244 18 2d. black and grey .. .. 4·00 4·00
245   4d. black and deep orange-vermilion £1100 £250
246   8d. violet and green £170 £140
247   10d. blue and red .. .. 4·75 24·00
248   1s. black and greenish blue .. 35·00 7·50
249   2s. 6d. indigo and grey-brown 32·00 65·00
250   3s. chocolate and blue .. £600 £250

251 18 5s. blue and yellow-green .. £100 £110
251a   5s. blue and blue-green .. £1500
252   7s. 6d. blackish purple and slate-black 95·00 £140
253   10s. red and green £150 £250
254   £1 black and purple £1200 £1200
254a   £1 black and deep purple .. £2750 £2500
186, 190, 198, 200, 209, 211/12, 215, 217/18, 230,
    232, 237/8, 240/2, 249 Optd "Specimen"
       .. .. Set of 18 £2000

(iv) *Head Die* III. *Toned paper, yellowish gum.* (a) P 14
255 18 2d. black and brownish grey .. 7·50 4·00
256   2d. black and grey-black .. 5·00 2·00
    a. Imperf between (horiz pair) .. £4250
    b. Imperf between (horiz strip of 3) £7500
    c. Imperf vert (horiz pair) .. £3750 £3750
257   2d. black and grey .. .. 6·00 2·50
258   2d. black and sepia .. .. 28·00 5·00
259   3d. black and yellow .. .. 5·50 1·40
260   3d. black and ochre .. .. 5·50 1·40
261   4d. black and orange-red .. 9·50 4·25
262   4d. black and dull red .. .. 8·00 5·00
263   5d. black and pale green .. 6·00 23·00
    a. Imperf between (horiz strip of 3) £13000
264   5d. black and green .. .. 6·00 23·00
265   6d. black and reddish mauve 4·25 3·50
    a. Imperf between (horiz pair) .. £10000
266   6d. black and dull mauve .. 4·25 3·50
267   8d. mauve and dull blue-green 18·00 50·00
268   8d. mauve and greenish blue 17·00 48·00
    a. Imperf vert (horiz pair) .. £9000
269   10d. indigo and carmine .. 12·00 45·00
270   10d. blue and red .. .. 11·00 45·00
271   1s. black and greenish blue .. 7·50 4·50
272   1s. black and pale blue-green 5·50 4·00
272a   1s. black and light blue .. 9·50 9·00
272b   1s. black and green .. .. 65·00 24·00
273   2s. black and brown .. .. 12·00 15·00
    aa. Imperf between (vert pair) .. † £20000
273a   2s. black and yellow-brown .. £1900 £100
274   2s. 6d. dp ultramarine & grey-brn 28·00 45·00
274a   2s. 6d. pale blue and pale bistre-brown
       (shades) .. .. 70·00 50·00
274b   3s. chestnut and light blue .. £170 £100
275   5s. deep blue and blue-green (shades) 65·00 50·00
276   5s. blue & pale yell-grn (shades) 85·00 50·00
276a   7s. 6d. maroon and slate-black £750 £1100
277   10s. carmine-lake and yellow-green £300 £170
278   £1 black and bright purple .. £375 £500
279   £1 black and deep purple .. £400 £500
279a   £1 black and violet-indigo .. £475 £550
279b   £1 black and deep violet .. £500 £550

(b) P 15
279c 18 2d. black and brownish grey .. £5500 £500

Half
Penny
(19)

Half-
Penny.
(20)

1917 (15 Aug). No. 190 *surch at the Northern Rhodesian Administrative Press, Livingstone, with* T 19, *in violet or violet-black.*
280 18 ½d. on 1d. rose-carmine (shades) 2·50 7·00
    a. Surch inverted .. £1400 £1400
    b. Letters "n n" spaced wider .. 11·00 25·00
    c. Letters "n y" spaced wider. .. 7·50 20·00
The setting was in two rows of 10 repeated three times in the
sheet.
The two colours of the surcharge occur on the same sheet.

1917 (22 Sept). No. 190 *surch as* T 20 (*new setting with hyphen,
    and full stop after "Penny"*), *in deep violet.*
281 18 ½d. on 1d. rose-carmine (shades) .. 1·75 5·50

1922-24. *New printings on white paper with clear white gum.*
(i) *Single working plates.* (a) P 14
282 18 ½d. dull green (1922) .. 5·50 3·50
    a. Imperf between (vert pair) .. £1800 £1300
283   ½d. deep blue-green (1922) .. 5·50 3·75
284   1d. bright rose (1922) .. 6·50 4·00
285   1d. bright rose-scarlet (1923) .. 6·50 3·75
    a. Imperf between (horiz pair) .. £1500
286   1d. aniline red (8.24) .. 20·00 4·50
287   1½d. brown-ochre (1923) .. 6·50 4·50
    a. Imperf between (vert pair) .. £1900 £1300

(b) P 15
288 18 ½d. dull green (1923) .. 40·00
289   1d. bright rose-scarlet (1923) .. 45·00
290   1½d. brown-ochre (1923) .. 48·00

(ii) *Double plates. Head Die* III. (a) P 14
291 18 2d. black and grey-purple (1922) 3·75 2·00
292   2d. black and slate-purple (1923) 4·25 2·75
293   3d. black and yellow (1922) .. 10·00 18·00
294   4d. black & orange-vermilion (1922-3) 8·50 22·00
295   6d. jet-black and lilac (1922-3) 4·75 3·75
296   8d. mauve and pale blue-green (1922) 30·00 70·00
297   8d. violet and grey-green (1923) 32·00 70·00
298   10d. bright ultramarine and red (1922) 10·00 50·00
299   10d. brt ultramarine & carm-red (1923) 14·00 50·00
300   1s. black and dull blue (1922-3) 6·00
    a. Imperf between (horiz pair) .. £8500
    b. Imperf between (vert pair) .. £10000
301   2s. black and brown (1922-3).. 19·00 32·00
302   2s. 6d. ultramarine and sepia (1922) 38·00 70·00
303   2s. 6d. violet-blue & grey-brown (1923) 45·00 65·00
304   3s. red-brown & turquoise-bl (1922) 70·00 85·00
305   3s. red-brown and grey-blue (1923) 90·00 £110
306   5s. brt ultramarine and emerald (1922) 85·00 95·00
307   5s. deep blue and bright green (1923) 85·00 95·00
308   7s. 6d. brown-purple and slate (1922) £170 £225
309   10s. crimson and brt yellow-green (1922) £160 £190
310   10s. carmine and yellow-green (1923) £160 £225
311   £1 black and deep magenta (1922) £550 £700
311a   £1 black and magenta (1923).. £500 £700

(b) P 15 (1923)

312	18	2d. black and slate-purple	..	38·00
313		4d. black and orange-vermilion	..	40·00
314		6d. jet-black and lilac	..	50·00
315		8d. violet and grey-green	..	50·00
316		10d. bright ultramarine & carmine-red		55·00
317		1s. black and dull blue	..	60·00
318		2s. black and brown	..	90·00
319		2s. 6d. violet-blue and grey-brown	..	£100
320		3s. red-brown and grey-blue	..	£130
321		5s. deep blue and bright green	..	£170
322		£1 black and magenta	..	£700

The 1922 printing shows the mesh of the paper very clearly through the gum. In the 1923 printing the gum is very smooth and the mesh of the paper is not so clearly seen. Where date is given as "(1922–23)" two printings were made, which do not differ sufficiently in colour to be listed separately.

Nos. 288/90 and 312/22 were never sent out to Rhodesia, but only issued in London. Any used copies could, therefore, only have been obtained by favour.

Southern Rhodesia, that part of the Company's territory south of the River Zambesi, became a self-governing colony on 1 October 1923. British South Africa Company rule continued in Northern Rhodesia until the administration was transferred to the Colonial Office on 1 April 1924.

The current stamps of Rhodesia, the Admiral series first issued in 1913, continued to be used in Southern Rhodesia until 1 April 1924 (invalidated 1 May 1924) and in Northern Rhodesia until 1 April 1925 (invalidated 30 September 1925).

For issues of NORTHERN and SOUTHERN RHODESIA see ZAMBIA and ZIMBABWE. Between 1954 and 1964 they were merged in the Central African Federation (see RHODESIA AND NYASALAND). In 1964 there were again separate issues for Northern and Southern Rhodesia, but after the former became independent as Zambia, Southern Rhodesia was renamed Rhodesia in October 1964. For issues inscribed "RHODESIA" between 1965 and 1978 see ZIMBABWE.

Rhodesia & Nyasaland

Stamps for the Central African Federation of Northern and Southern Rhodesia and Nyasaland Protectorate.

1   2

3 Queen Elizabeth II

(Recess Waterlow)

1954 (1 July)–56. P 13½×14 (T 1), 13½×13 (T 2) or 14½×13½ (T 3).

1	1	½d. red-orange	..	15	10
		a. Coil stamp. Perf 12½×14 (6.2.56)		30	1·50
2		1d. ultramarine	..	15	10
		a. Coil stamp. Perf 12½×14. Deep blue (9.55)		1·50	14·00
		ab. Ultramarine (1.10.55)	..	3·50	13·00
3		2d. bright green	..	15	10
3a		2½d. ochre (15.2.56)	..	3·00	10
4		3d. carmine-red	..	20	10
5		4d. red-brown	..	60	15
6		4½d. blue-green	..	15	30
7		6d. bright reddish purple	..	1·75	10
		a. Bright purple (5.5.56)	..	3·50	10
8		9d. violet	..	65	70
9		1s. grey-black	..	1·50	10
10	2	1s. 3d. red-orange and ultramarine		2·75	10
11		2s. deep blue and yellow-brown		7·00	1·25
12		2s. 6d. black and rose-red	..	5·50	1·00
13		5s. violet and olive-green	..	15·00	4·00
14	3	10s. dull blue-green and orange		17·00	7·00
15		£1 olive-green and lake	..	27·00	24·00
1/15			Set of 16	70·00	32·00

Nos. 1a and 2a printed on rotary machines by subsidiary company, Imprimerie Belge de Sécurité, in Belgium.

4 De Havilland D.H.106 Comet 1 over Victoria Falls   5 Livingstone and Victoria Falls

(Des J. E. Hughes (3d.), V. E. Horne (1s.). Recess Waterlow)

1955 (15 June). Centenary of Discovery of Victoria Falls. P 13½ (3d.) or 13 (1s.).

16	4	3d. ultramarine & dp turquoise-grn		55	30
17	5	1s. purple and deep blue	..	55	70

6 Tea Picking   10 Rhodes's Grave   11 Lake Bangweulu

12a Rhodesian Railway Trains   19 Federal Coat of Arms

(Des M. Kinsella (9d.). Recess Waterlow (½d., 1d., 2d., 1s.) until 1962, then D.L.R., D.L.R. (2½d., 4d., 6d., 9d., 2s., 2s. 6d.) and B.W. (others))

1959 (12 Aug)–62. T 6, 10/11, 12a, 19 and similar designs. P 13½×14 (½d., 1d., 2d.), 14½ (2½d., 4d., 6d., 9d., 2s., 2s. 6d.), 14×13½ (3d.), 13½×13 (1s.), 14 (1s. 3d.) or 11 (others).

18	½d. black and light emerald	..	60	30
	a. Coil stamp. Perf 12½×14	..	3·25	5·50
19	1d. carmine-red and black	..	15	10
	a. Coil stamp. Perf 12½×14	..	3·25	8·00
	ab. Carmine-red and grey-black	..	4·25	8·50
	ac. Carmine-red (centre) omitted		£375	
20	2d. violet and yellow-brown	..	1·00	50
21	2½d. purple and grey-blue	..	40	40
22	3d. black and blue	..	20	10
	a. Black (centre) omitted	..	£11000	
	b. Printed on the gummed side	..	£300	
23	4d. maroon and olive	..	1·25	10
24	6d. ultramarine and deep myrtle-green	..	70	10
24a	9d. orge-brown & reddish violet (15.5.62)		8·00	2·50
25	1s. light green and ultramarine	..	80	10
26	1s. 3d. emerald and deep chocolate		3·00	10
27	2s. grey-green and carmine	..	3·25	60
28	2s. 6d. light blue and yellow-brown		4·25	30
29	5s. deep chocolate and yellow-green		8·50	2·25
30	10s. olive-brown and rose-red	..	25·00	13·00
31	£1 black and deep violet	..	45·00	40·00
18/31		Set of 15	90·00	55·00

Designs: Vert (as T 6)—1d. V.H.F. mast; 2d. Copper mining; 2½d. Fairbridge Memorial. (As T 11)—6d. Eastern Cataract, Victoria Falls. Horiz (as T 12a)—1s. Tobacco; 1s. 3d. Lake Nyasa; 2s. Chirundu Bridge; 2s. 6d. Salisbury Airport. (As T 19)—5s. Rhodes Statue; 10s. Mlanje.

Only three examples from two different sheets, all unused, are believed to exist of No. 22a although further stamps from the same sheets can be found with the centre partially omitted.

20 Kariba Gorge, 1955

(Photo Harrison (3d., 6d.), D.L.R. (others))

1960 (17 May). Opening of Kariba Hydro-Electric Scheme. T 20 and similar horiz designs. P 14½×14 (3d., 6d.) or 13 (others).

32	3d. blackish green and red-orange		70	10
	a. Red-orange omitted	..	£3250	
33	6d. brown and yellow-brown	..	70	20
34	1s. slate-blue and green	..	2·50	2·75
35	1s. 3d. light blue and orange-brown		2·50	1·75
	a. Blue and deep orange-brown		8·00	5·50
36	2s. 6d. deep slate-purple and orange-red		3·50	7·50
37	5s. reddish violet and turquoise-blue		8·00	11·00
32/7		Set of 6	16·00	21·00

Designs:—6d. 330 kV power lines; 1s. Barrage wall; 1s. 3d. Barrage and lake; 2s. Interior of power station; 5s. Barrage wall and Queen Mother (top left).

26 Miner Drilling

(Des V. Whiteley. Photo Harrison)

1961 (8 May). Seventh Commonwealth Mining and Metallurgical Congress. T 26 and similar horiz design. P 15 × 14.

38	6d. olive-green and orange-brown		50	20
39	1s. 3d. black and light blue	..	50	80

Design:—1s. 3d. Surface installations, Nchanga Mine.
Imperforate examples of the 6d. are believed to be printer's waste.

28 De Havilland D.H.66 Hercules *City of Basra* on Rhodesian Airstrip   31 Tobacco Plant

1962 (6 Feb). 30th Anniv of First London-Rhodesia Airmail Service. T 28 and similar horiz designs. P 14½ × 14.

40	6d. bronze-green and vermilion		35	25
41	1s. light blue, black and yellow	..	1·50	50
42	2s. 6d. rose-red and deep violet	..	6·50	4·50
40/2		Set of 3	7·50	4·75

Designs:—1s. 3d. Short S.23 flying boat *Canopus* taking off from Zambesi; 2s. 6d. Hawker Siddeley Comet 4 at Salisbury airport.

(Des V. Whiteley. Photo Harrison)

1963 (18 Feb). World Tobacco Congress, Salisbury. T 31 and similar vert designs. P 14 × 14½.

43	3d. green and olive-brown	..	30	10
44	6d. green, brown and blue	..	40	35
45	1s. 3d. chestnut and indigo	..	60	45
46	2s. 6d. yellow and brown	..	1·00	2·75
43/6		Set of 4	2·00	3·25

Designs:—6d. Tobacco field; 1s. 3d. Auction floor; 2s. 6d. Cured tobacco.

35 Red Cross Emblem

(Photo Harrison)

1963 (6 Aug). Red Cross Centenary. P 14½ × 14.

47	35	3d. red	..	85 10

36 African "Round Table" Emblem

(Des V. Whiteley. Photo Harrison)

1963 (11 Sept). World Council of Young Men's Service Clubs, Salisbury. P 14½ × 14.

48	36	6d. black, gold and yellow-green	50	1·50
49		1s. 3d. black, gold, yell-grn & lilac	50	1·00

STAMP BOOKLETS

1955 (1 Jan). Black on yellow cover. Stitched.

SB1	5s. booklet containing twelve 1d. and eighteen 1d. and 2d. (Nos. 1/3) in blocks of 6 ..	40·00

1963 (4 Apr). Black on yellow cover. Stitched.

SB2	1s. booklet containing 3d. (No. 22) in block of 4	1·50

POSTAGE DUE STAMPS

After Federation in 1954 existing stocks of postage due stamps from Northern Rhodesia, Nyasaland and Southern Rhodesia continued to be used and were sometimes distributed throughout the federation.

Increased postal rates in July 1956 and in 1959 led to the exhaustion of certain values, in particular the 1d., and various offices then used Rhodesia and Nyasaland postage issues for postage due purposes. There were isolated instances of such stamps being cancelled "POSTAGE DUE" from December 1956 onwards.

Some of these handstamps may have been applied at Bulawayo while others, in violet or black, originate from the Salisbury Delivery Room at Kingsway Post Office. Only the 1d. and 2d. (Nos. 2/3) are known with such handstamps. After mint examples began to appear the Postmaster General suppressed the use of the handstamps in August 1959.

D 1

(Typo Federal Printing and Stationery Dept, Salisbury)

1961 (19 Apr). P 12½.

D1	D 1	1d. vermilion	..	3·00	5·00
		a. Imperf between (horiz pair)	..	£400	£450
D2		2d. deep violet-blue	..	2·25	3·00
D3		4d. green	..	2·25	9·00
D4		6d. purple	..	4·50	7·50
		a. Imperf between (horiz pair)		£1100	
D1/4			Set of 4	11·00	22·00

The 2d. has a stop below the "D".

The stamps of the Federation were withdrawn on 19 February 1964 when all three constituent territories had resumed issuing their own stamps.

Sabah
see Malaysia

St. Helena

CROWN COLONY

PRICES FOR STAMPS ON COVER TO 1945	
Nos. 1/5	*from* × 12
Nos. 6/30	*from* × 10
Nos. 34/45	*from* × 15
Nos. 46/52	*from* × 6
Nos. 53/67	*from* × 5
No. 71	—
Nos. 72/86	*from* × 5
Nos. 87/8	*from* × 12
Nos. 89/95	*from* × 5
No. 96	—
Nos. 97/110	*from* × 5
Nos. 111/13	—
Nos. 114/40	*from* × 4

PERKINS BACON "CANCELLED". For notes on these handstamps, showing "CANCELLED" between horizontal bars forming an oval, see Catalogue Introduction.

ONE PENNY   **FOUR PENCE**

1   (2)   (3)

(Recess P.B.)

1856 (1 Jan). *Wmk Large Star, W w* 1. *Imperf.*
1   1   6d. bl (H/S "CANCELLED" in oval £5000)   £500   £180

1861 (April (?)). *Wmk Large Star, W w* 1. (*a*) *Clean-cut perf* 14 to 16
2   1   6d. blue £1700   £275

(*b*) *Rough perf* 14 *to* 16
2*a*   1   6d. blue £400   £130

NOTE: The issues which follow consist of 6d. stamps, T 1, printed in various colours and (except in the case of the 6d. values) surcharged with a new value, as T 2 to 10, *e.g.* stamps described as "1d.", are, in fact, 1d. on 6d stamps, and so on.
The numbers in the Type column below refer to the *types of the lettering of the surcharged value.*

(Printed by D.L.R. from P.B. plate)

Two Types of Bar on 1d. value:
A. Bar 16–17 mm long.
B. Bar 18½–19 mm long.

1863 (July). *Wmk Crown CC. Surch as T* 2/3 *with thin bar approximately the same length as the words. Imperf.*
3   2   1d. lake (Type A)   ..   £110   £160
    a. Surch double   ..   £4500 £2750
    b. Surch omitted   ..   £14000
    w. Wmk inverted   ..   £200
4   1d. lake (Type B)   ..   £120 £170
    a. Vert pair. Nos. 3/4 ..   £7500
5   3   4d. carmine (*bar* 15½–16½ *mm*)   £500 £250
    a. Surch double   ..   £11000 £9000

ONE PENNY   **ONE PENNY**   **ONE PENNY**

(4 (A))   (4 (B))   (4 (C))

TWO PENCE   **THREE PENCE**   **FOUR PENCE**

(5)   (6)   (7)

ONE SHILLING   **FIVE SHILLINGS**

(8)   (9)

Three Types of Bar:
A. Thin bar (16½ to 17 mm) nearly the same length as the words.
B. Thick bar (14 to 14½ mm) much shorter than the words, except on the 2d. (Nos. 9, 22, 28) where it is nearly the same length.
C. Long bar (17 to 18 mm) same length as the words.

1864–80. *Wmk Crown CC. 6d. as T* 1, *without surcharge.*
(*a*) *P* 12½ (1864–73)
6   4   1d. lake (Type A) (1864)   ..   35·00 24·00
    a. Surch double   ..   £6000
7   1d. lake (Type B) (1868)   ..   £140 50·00
    a. Surch double
    b. Imperf   ..   £2000

---

8   4   1d. lake (Type C) (1871)   ..   70·00 17·00
    a. Surch in blue-black   ..   £1000 £550
    x. Wmk reversed   ..   £100
9   5   2d. yellow (Type B) (1868)   ..   £160 60·00
    a. Imperf   ..   £9000
    x. Wmk reversed   ..   £180
10   2d. yellow (Type C) (1873)   ..   80·00 38·00
    a. Surch in blue-black   ..   £4000 £2250
    b. Surch double, one albino
    x. Wmk reversed   ..   £100
11   6   3d. deep dull purple (Type B) (1868)   75·00 50·00
    a. Surch double   ..   — £6000
    b. Imperf   ..   £750
    c. Light purple   ..   £2750 £750
    x. Wmk reversed   ..   £100
12   3d. deep dull purple (Type A) (1873)   80·00 50·00
13   7   4d. carmine (Type A) (*words* 17 *mm long*) (1864)   ..   £120 48·00
    a. Surch double   ..   † £5500
14   4d. carmine (Type B) (*words* 18 *mm long*) (1868)   90·00 48·00
    a. Surch double   ..   † £4500
    b. Surch double (18 + 19 *mm widths*) £17000 £9000
    c. Imperf   ..   £9000
    x. Wmk reversed   ..   £110
15   4d. carmine-rose (Type B) (*words* 19 *mm long*) (1868)   ..   £200 £120
    a. Surch omitted   ..   †
16   —   6d. dull blue (1871)   ..   £600 £100
    a. Ultramarine (1873)   ..   £350 80·00
17   8   1s. deep yellow-green (Type A) (1864)   £200 26·00
    a. Surch double   ..   †£18000
    w. Wmk inverted   ..   — 40·00
18   1s. deep yellow-green (Type B) (1868)   £475 £130
    a. Surch double   ..   £13000
    b. Imperf   ..   £13000
    c. Surch omitted*   ..   £13000
19   1s. deep green (Type C) (1871)   ..   £350 16·00
    a. Surch in blue-black
20   9   5s. orange (Type B) (1868)   ..   40·00 60·00
    a. Yellow   ..   £425 £375
    x. Wmk reversed   ..   £100

(*b*) *P* 14×12½ (1876)
21   4   1d. lake (Type B)   ..   65·00 15·00
    w. Wmk inverted   ..   £100
22   5   2d. yellow (Type B)   ..   85·00 50·00
23   3d. purple (Type B)   ..   £190 70·00
24   4d. carmine (Type B) (*words* 16½ *mm long*)   ..   90·00 60·00
    y. Wmk inverted and reversed   90·00
25   —   6d. milky blue   ..   ..   £325 45·00
26   8   1s. deep green (Type C)   ..   £425 20·00

(*c*) *P* 14 (1880)
27   4   1d. lake (Type B)   ..   80·00 16·00
28   5   2d. yellow (Type B)   ..   90·00 23·00
29   —   6d. milky blue   ..   ..   £350 48·00
30   8   1s. yellow-green (Type B)   ..   20·00 12·00
    y. Wmk inverted and reversed
The only known copy of No. 15a is in the Royal Collection, although a second badly damaged example may exist.
*No. 18c is from a sheet of the 1s. with surcharge misplaced, the fifth row of 12 stamps being thus doubly surcharged and the tenth row without surcharge.

2½d

(10)   11   12

1884–94. *Wmk Crown CA. T* 1 *surch. Bars similar to Type B above (except* 2½d., *T* 10, *and the* 1s., *in which the bar is nearly the same length as the words). The* 6d. *as before without surcharge. P* 14.
34   —   ½d. emerald (*words* 17 *mm*) (1884)   ..   7·00 9·00
    a. "N" and "Y" spaced   ..   £750
    b. Surch double   ..   £1100 £1200
    ba. Ditto. "N" and "Y" spaced ..   £10000
35   —   ½d. green (*words* 17 *mm*) (1885)   ..   4·50 9·50
    a. "N" and "Y" spaced   ..   £350 £475
    x. Wmk reversed   ..   5·50 11·00
36   —   ½d. green (*words* 14½ *mm*) (1893)   ..   1·25 1·50
    a. "N" and "Y" spaced   ..   £1500
37   4   1d. red (1887)   ..   ..   2·75 2·50
    x. Wmk reversed   ..   3·25 3·00
38   1d. pale red (1890)   ..   3·50 2·00
    x. Wmk reversed   ..   4·50 2·75
39   5   2d. yellow (1894)   ..   1·25 3·50
40   10   2½d. ultramarine (1893)   ..   2·00 5·00
    a. Surch double   ..   £15000
    b. Stamp doubly printed   ..   £6500
    w. Wmk inverted   ..   15·00
41   6   3d. deep mauve (1887)   ..   4·75 7·50
    a. Surch double   ..   — £9000
42   3d. deep reddish lilac (1887)   ..   2·75 3·25
    a. Surch double   ..   £8500 £6000
    w. Wmk reversed   ..   3·50 2·75
43   7   4d. pale brn (*words* 16½ *mm*) (1890)   14·00 20·00
    a. Additional thin bar in surch (R. 7/4)   ..   £500
    by. Wmk inverted and reversed   21·00
43*c*   4d. sepia (*words* 17 *mm*) (1894)   ..   18·00 9·50
    cx. Wmk reversed   ..   21·00
44   —   6d. grey (1887)   ..   ..   12·00 4·00
    x. Wmk reversed   ..   15·00 3·50
45   8   1s. yellow-green (1894)   ..   35·00 21·00
    a. Surch double   ..   £4250
40/1, 43, 44 Optd "Specimen"   *Set of* 4 £180
Examples of the above are sometimes found showing no watermark; these are from the bottom row of the sheet, which had escaped the watermark, the paper being intended for stamps of a different size to Type 1.
Some are found without bar and others with bar at top of stamp, due to careless overprinting.
Nos. 34a and 35a occur on R. 18/12 and show a minimum space between the letters of 0.8 mm. Normal examples are spaced 0.5 mm, but some stamps show intermediate

---

measurements due to loose type, On No. 34ba only one impression of the surcharge shows "N" and "Y" spaced. On the reset surcharge, No. 36, a similar variety occurs on R. 5/9.
Of the 2½d. with double surcharge only six copies exist, and of the 2½d. double printed, one row of 12 stamps existed on one sheet only.

CANCELLATIONS. Nos. 40/5 and No. 20 were sold as remainders in 1904 cancelled with a violet diamond-shaped grill with four interior bars extending over two stamps. These cannot be considered as *used* stamps, and they are consequently not priced in the list.
This violet obliteration is easily removed and many of these remainders have been cleaned and offered as unused; some are repostmarked with a date and name in thin type rather larger than the original, a usual date being "Ap.4.01."

(Typo D.L.R.)

1890–97. *Wmk Crown CA. Plate I for the* 1½d. *Plate II for the other values (for differences see Seychelles). P* 14.
46   11   ½d. green (1897)   ..   2·75 4·50
47   1d. carmine (1896)   ..   11·00 1·00
48   1½d. red-brown and green (1890)   4·50 7·00
49   2d. orange-yellow (1896)   ..   5·00 12·00
50   2½d. ultramarine (1896)..   8·50 12·00
51   5d. mauve (1896)   ..   11·00 27·00
52   10d. brown (1896)   ..   19·00 48·00
46/52   ..   *Set of* 7 55·00 £100
46/52 Optd "Specimen"   *Set of* 7 £275
The note below No. 45a *re* violet diamond-shaped grill cancellation also applies to Nos. 48/52.

1902. *Wmk Crown CA. P* 14.
53   12   ½d. green (Mar)..   ..   1·50 1·50
54   1d. carmine (24 Feb)   ..   4·75 70
53/4 Optd "Specimen"   ..   *Set of* 2 70·00

13 Government House   14 The Wharf

(Typo D.L.R.)

1903 (May). *Wmk Crown CC. P* 14.
55   13   ½d. brown and grey-green   ..   2·00 3·25
    w. Wmk inverted   ..   90·00 £100
56   14   1d. black and carmine ..   1·50 35
57   13   2d. black and sage-green   ..   6·00 1·25
58   14   8d. black and brown   ..   22·00 32·00
59   13   1s. brown and brown-orange   22·00 40·00
60   14   2s. black and violet   ..   48·00 85·00
55/60   ..   *Set of* 6 90·00 £150
55/60 Optd "Specimen"   *Set of* 6 £200
A printing of the 1d. value in Type 14 in red only on Mult Crown CA paper was made in 1911, but not sold to the public. Examples are known overprinted "SPECIMEN" (*Price* £300).

15

(Typo D.L.R.)

1908 (May)–11. *P* 14. (*a*) *Wmk Mult Crown CA. Ordinary paper* (2½d.) *or chalk-surfaced paper* (4d., 6d.).
64   15   2½d. blue   ..   ..   1·25 1·40
66   4d. black and red/*yellow*   ..   5·50 14·00
    a. Ordinary paper (1911)   ..   1·50 10·00
67   6d. dull and deep purple   ..   9·00 22·00
    a. Ordinary paper (1911)   ..   3·00 13·00

(*b*) *Wmk Crown CA. Chalk-surfaced paper.*
71   15   10s. green and red/*green*   ..   £170 £250
64/71   ..   *Set of* 4 £170 £250
64/71 Optd "Specimen"   *Set of* 4 £225

16   17

(Typo D.L.R.)

1912–16. *Wmk Mult Crown CA. P* 14.
72   16   ½d. black and green   ..   2·00 9·50
73   17   1d. black and carmine-red   ..   2·75 1·75
    a. Black and scarlet (1916)   ..   20·00 27·00
74   1½d. black and dull orange (1913)   3·00 5·50
75   16   2d. black and greyish slate   ..   3·00 1·75
76   17   2½d. black and bright blue   ..   3·00 5·50
77   16   3d. black and purple/*yellow* (1913)   2·50 5·00
78   17   8d. black and dull purple   ..   6·00 50·00
79   16   1s. black/*green*   ..   8·00 35·00
80   17   2s. black and blue/*blue*   ..   38·00 80·00
81   3s. black and violet (1913)   ..   48·00 £130
72/81   ..   *Set of* 10 £100 £275
72/81 Optd "Specimen"   *Set of* 10 £250
No. 73a is on thicker paper than 73.

| 18 | 19 |

Split "A" (R. 8/3 of left pane) (ptgs to 1918)

(Typo D.L.R.)

1912. *Wmk Mult Crown CA. Chalk-surfaced paper. P* 14.
83	18	4d. black and red/*yellow*			9·00	22·00
84		6d. dull and deep purple			3·50	5·00
83/4		Optd "Specimen"		*Set of* 2	70·00	

1913. *Wmk Mult Crown CA. P* 14.
85	19	4d. black and red/*yellow*			7·50	2·75
		a. Split "A"			£190	
86		6d. dull and deep purple			13·00	24·00
		a. Split "A"			£325	
85/6		Optd "Specimen"		*Set of* 2	75·00	

WAR TAX

WAR TAX

ONE PENNY **1d.**

(20) (21)

1916 (Sept). *As No. 73a, on thin paper, surch with T* 20.
| 87 | 17 | 1d. + 1d. black and scarlet (Optd S. £50) | 1·25 | 2·75 |
| | | a. Surch double | | † £6000 | |

1919. *No. 73 on thicker paper, surch with T* 21.
| 88 | 17 | 1d. + 1d. black and carmine-red (*shades*) | | 70 | 3·50 |
| | | (Optd S. £50) | | | |

1922 (Jan). *Printed in one colour. Wmk Mult Script CA. P* 14.
89	17	1d. green			1·25	25·00
		w. Wmk inverted			£110	
		y. Wmk inverted and reversed		£120	
90		1½d. rose-scarlet			8·50	26·00
91	16	3d. bright blue			18·00	50·00
		y. Wmk inverted and reversed		£120	
89/91				*Set of* 3	25·00	90·00
89/91		Optd "Specimen"		*Set of* 3	80·00	

22 Badge of St. Helena

PLATE FLAWS ON THE 1922–37 ISSUE. Many constant plate varieties exist on both the vignette and duty plates of this issue.

The three major varieties are illustrated and listed below with prices for mint examples. Fine used stamps showing these flaws are worth a considerable premium over the mint prices quoted.

a. Broken mainmast. Occurs on R.2/1 of all sheets from the second printing onwards. It does not appear on Nos. 93/6 and 112/13 as these stamps only exist from the initial printing invoiced in May 1922.

b. Torn flag. Occurs on R.4/6 of all sheets from printings up to and including that invoiced in December 1922. The flaw was retouched for the printing invoiced in December 1926 and so does not occur on Nos. 99e, 103 and 107/10.

c. Cleft rock. Occurs on R.5/1 of all sheets from the second printing onwards. It does not appear on Nos. 93/6 and 112/13 as these stamps only exist from the initial printing invoiced in May 1922.

(Des T. Bruce. Typo D.L.R.)

1922 (June)–**37.** *P* 14 (a) *Wmk Mult Crown CA. Chalk-surfaced paper.*
92	22	4d. grey and black/*yellow* (2.23)		9·00	6·00
		a. Broken mainmast		£120	
		b. Torn flag		£120	
		c. Cleft rock		£100	
93		1s. 6d. grey and green/*blue-green*	22·00	50·00
		b. Torn flag		£350	
94		2s. 6d. grey and red/*yellow*	25·00	50·00
		b. Torn flag		£400	
95		5s. grey and green/*yellow*	38·00	80·00
		b. Torn flag		£475	
96		£1 grey and purple/*red*	£350	£450
		b. Torn flag		£1600	
92/6		Optd "Specimen"		*Set of* 5	£500

The paper of No. 93 is bluish on the surface with a full green back.

(b) *Wmk Mult Script CA. Ordinary paper* (1s. 6d., 2s. 6d., 5s.) *or chalk-surfaced paper (others)*
97	22	½d. grey and black (2.23)		1·25	1·75
		a. Broken mainmast		38·00	
		b. Torn flag		£110	
		c. Cleft rock		32·00	
		w. Wmk inverted		£200	£225
98		1d. grey and green		1·75	1·40
		a. Broken mainmast		42·00	
		b. Torn flag		90·00	
		c. Cleft rock		38·00	
99		1½d. rose-red (*shades*) (2.23)	2·75	12·00
		a. Broken mainmast		75·00	
		b. Torn flag		75·00	
		c. Cleft rock		70·00	
		dw. Wmk inverted		£550	
		e. Deep carmine-red (1937)	80·00	£100
		ea. Broken mainmast		£600	
		ec. Cleft rock		£600	
100		2d. grey and slate (2.23)		3·00	2·00
		a. Broken mainmast		75·00	
		b. Torn flag		£130	
		c. Cleft rock		70·00	
101		3d. bright blue (2.23)		2·00	4·00
		a. Broken mainmast		75·00	
		b. Torn flag		85·00	
		c. Cleft rock		65·00	
		x. Wmk reversed		£275	
103		5d. green and carmine/*green* (1927)	3·00	5·50
		a. Broken mainmast		£130	
		c. Cleft rock		£120	
104		6d. grey and bright purple	3·75	8·00
		a. Broken mainmast		£150	
		b. Torn flag		£150	
		c. Cleft rock		£130	
105		8d. grey and bright violet (2.23)	3·25	6·50
		a. Broken mainmast		£140	
		b. Torn flag		£140	
		c. Cleft rock		£120	
106		1s. grey and brown		6·00	9·00
		a. Broken mainmast		£180	
		b. Torn flag		£200	
		c. Cleft rock		£160	
107		1s. 6d. grey and green/*green* (1927)	14·00	45·00
		a. Broken mainmast		£225	
		c. Cleft rock		£200	
108		2s. purple and blue/*blue* (1927)	16·00	38·00
		a. Broken mainmast		£225	
		c. Cleft rock		£200	
109		2s. 6d. grey and red/*yellow* (1927)	13·00	50·00
		a. Broken mainmast		£225	
		c. Cleft rock		£200	
110		5s. grey and green/*yellow* (1927)	38·00	75·00
		a. Broken mainmast		£375	
		c. Cleft rock		£350	
111		7s. 6d. grey and yellow-orange	75·00	£120
		a. Broken mainmast		£2250	
		b. Torn flag		£600	
		c. Cleft rock		£2250	
112		10s. grey and olive-green	£110	£160
		b. Torn flag		£900	
113		15s. grey and purple/*blue*	£800	£1400
		b. Torn flag		£3000	
97/112				*Set of* 15	£250	£350
97/113		Optd "Specimen"	*Set of* 16	£1000

Examples of all values are known showing a forged St. Helena postmark dated "DE 18 27".

23 Lot and Lot's Wife 24 The "Plantation"

30 St. Helena 32 Badge of St. Helena

(Recess B.W.)

1934 (23 April). *Centenary of British Colonisation. T* 23/4, **30**, **32** *and similar horiz designs. Wmk Mult Script CA. P* 12.
114		½d. black and purple			85	80
115		1d. black and green			65	85
116		1½d. black and scarlet			2·50	3·25
117		2d. black and orange			2·25	1·25
118		3d. black and blue			1·40	4·50
119		6d. black and light blue			3·25	3·00
120		1s. black and chocolate			6·00	18·00
121		2s. black and lake			35·00	48·00
122		5s. black and chocolate			75·00	85·00
123		10s. black and purple			£200	£250
114/123				*Set of* 10	£300	£375
114/23		Perf "Specimen"		*Set of* 10	£350	

Design:—1½d. Map of St. Helena; 2d. Quay at Jamestown; 3d. James Valley; 6d. Jamestown; 1s. Munden's Promontory; 5s. High Knoll.

Examples of all values are known showing a forged St. Helena postmark dated "MY 12 34".

1935 (6 May). *Silver Jubilee. As Nos. 114/17 of Jamaica, but ptd by D.L.R. P* 13½×14.
124		1½d. deep blue and carmine			75	5·00
		f. Diagonal line by turret			55·00	
125		2d. ultramarine and grey			1·25	90
		f. Diagonal line by turret			75·00	
		g. Dot to left of chapel			95·00	
126		6d. green and indigo			6·50	3·00
		a. Frame printed double, one albino	£1500	
		f. Diagonal line by turret		£140	
		h. Dot by flagstaff		£190	
127		1s. slate and purple			9·00	12·00
		h. Dot by flagstaff			£250	
		i. Dash by turret			£250	
124/7				*Set of* 4	16·00	19·00
124/7		Perf "Specimen"		*Set of* 4	95·00	

For illustrations of plate varieties see Omnibus section following Zimbabwe.

1937 (19 May). *Coronation. As Nos. 118/20 of Jamaica.*
128		1d. green			40	30
129		2d. orange			55	30
130		3d. bright blue			80	30
128/30				*Set of* 3	1·60	80
128/30		Perf "Specimen"		*Set of* 3	60·00	

33 Badge of St. Helena

(Recess Waterlow)

1938 (12 May)–**44.** *Wmk Mult Script CA. P* 12½.
131	33	½d. violet			10	40
132		1d. green			12·00	2·25
132a		1d. yellow-orange (8.7.40)		20	30
133		1½d. scarlet			20	40
134		2d. red-orange			20	15
135		3d. ultramarine			90·00	18·00
135a		3d. grey (8.7.40)			30	30
135b		4d. ultramarine (8.7.40)		2·00	45
136		6d. light blue			2·00	30
136a		8d. sage-green (8.7.40)		3·25	90
		b. Olive-green (24.5.44)		4·50	4·00
137		1s. sepia			90	30
138		2s. 6d. maroon			17·00	4·50
139		5s. chocolate			18·00	11·00
140		10s. purple			18·00	18·00
131/140				*Set of* 14	£150	50·00
131/40		Perf "Specimen"		*Set of* 14	£300	

See also Nos. 149/51.

1946 (21 Oct). *Victory. As Nos. 141/2 of Jamaica.*
141		2d. red-orange			15	10
142		4d. blue			15	10
141/2		Perf "Specimen"		*Set of* 2	60·00	

1948 (20 Oct). *Royal Silver Wedding. As Nos. 143/4 of Jamaica.*
| 143 | | 3d. black | | | 30 | 20 |
| 144 | | 10s. violet-blue | | | 23·00 | 28·00 |

1949 (10 Oct). *75th Anniv of U.P.U. As Nos. 145/8 of Jamaica.*
145		3d. carmine			50	30
146		4d. deep blue			3·25	90
147		6d. olive			90	90
148		1s. blue-black			65	1·10
145/8				*Set of* 4	4·75	3·00

1949 (1 Nov). *Wmk Mult Script CA. P* 12½.
149	33	1d. black and green			60	80
150		1½d. black and carmine			60	80
151		2d. black and scarlet			60	80
149/51				*Set of* 3	1·60	2·25

1953 (2 June). *Coronation. As No. 153 of Jamaica.*
| 152 | | 3d. black and deep reddish violet | | 1·00 | 80 |

34 Badge of St. Helena

35 Heart-shaped Waterfall

(Recess D.L.R.)

1953 (4 Aug)–59. *Horiz designs as T 34, and T 35. Wmk Mult Script CA. P 14.*

153	½d. black and bright green		30	30
154	1d. black and deep green		15	20
155	1½d. black and reddish purple		2·00	85
	a. Black & deep reddish purple (14.1.59)		9·00	4·25
156	2d. black and claret		50	30
157	2½d. black and red		40	30
158	3d. black and brown		3·25	30
159	4d. black and deep blue		40	40
160	6d. black and deep lilac		40	30
161	7d. black and grey-black		65	1·25
162	1s. black and carmine		40	40
163	2s. 6d. black and violet		13·00	7·00
164	5s. black and deep brown		18·00	11·00
165	10s. black and yellow-orange		40·00	22·00
153/65		*Set of 13*	70·00	40·00

Designs:—1d. Flax plantation; 2d. Lace-making; 2½d. Drying flax; 3d. St. Helena Sand Plover; 4d. Flagstaff and The Barn; 6d. Donkeys carrying flax; 7d. Island map; 1s. The Castle; 2s. 6d. Cutting flax; 5s. Jamestown; 10s. Longwood House.

45 Stamp of 1856

(Recess D.L.R.)

1956 (3 Jan). *St. Helena Stamp Centenary. Wmk Mult Script CA. P 11½.*

166	**45**	3d. Prussian blue and carmine	10	10
167		4d. Prussian blue and reddish brown	10	20
168		6d. Prussian blue & dp reddish purple	15	25
166/8		*Set of 3*	30	50

46 Arms of East India Company

(Recess Waterlow)

1959 (5 May). *Tercentenary of Settlement. T 46 and similar horiz designs. W w 12. P 12½ × 13.*

169	3d. black and scarlet		10	15
170	6d. light emerald and slate-blue		40	75
171	1s. black and orange		40	75
169/71		*Set of 3*	75	1·50

Designs:—6d. East Indiaman *London* off James Bay; 1s. Commemoration Stone.

ST. HELENA
Tristan Relief
9d +
(49)

1961 (12 Oct). *Tristan Relief Fund. Nos. 46 and 49/51 of Tristan da Cunha surch as T 49 by Govt Printer, Jamestown.*

172	2½ c. + 3d. black and brown-red		—	£400
173	5 c. + 6d. black and blue		—	£425
174	7½ c. + 9d. black and rose-carmine		—	£475
175	10 c. + 1s. black and light brown		—	£550
172/5		*Set of 4*	£4250	£1700

The above stamps were withdrawn from sale on 19 October, 434 complete sets having been sold.

50 St. Helena Butterflyfish

51 Yellow Canary

---

53 Queen Elizabeth II

63 Queen Elizabeth II with Prince Andrew (after Cecil Beaton)

(Des V. Whiteley. Photo Harrison)

1961 (12 Dec)–65. *T 50/1, 53, 63 and similar designs. W w 12. P 11½ × 12 (horiz), 12 × 11½ (vert) or 14½ × 14 (£1).*

176	1d. brt blue, dull violet, yellow & carmine		40	20
	a. Chalk-surfaced paper (4.5.65)		2·50	30
177	1½d. yellow, green, black and light drab		50	20
178	2d. scarlet and grey		15	20
179	3d. light blue, black, pink and deep blue		70	20
	a. Chalk-surfaced paper (30.11.65)		1·50	50
180	4½d. yellow-green, green, brown and grey		60	60
181	6d. red, sepia and light yellow-olive		5·50	70
	a. Chalk-surfaced paper (30.11.65)		7·00	70
182	7d. red-brown, black and violet		35	70
183	10d. brown-purple and light blue		35	70
184	1s. greenish yellow, bluish green & brown		55	70
185	1s. grey, black and slate-blue		13·00	4·75
186	2s. 6d. red, pale yellow and turquoise (chalk-surfaced paper)		2·50	2·50
187	5s. yellow, brown and green		14·00	4·75
188	10s. orange-red, black and blue		17·00	12·00
189	£1 chocolate and light blue		17·00	17·00
	a. Chalk-surfaced paper (30.11.65)		40·00	42·00
176/89 (cheapest)		*Set of 14*	65·00	40·00

Designs: *Horiz (as T 50)*—2d. Brittle Starfish; 7d. Trumpetfish; 10d. Feather Starfish; 2s. 6d. Orange Starfish; 10s. Deep-water Bullseye. *Vert (as T 51)*—4½d. Red-wood Flower; 6d. Madagascar Red Fody; 1s. Gum-wood Flower; 1s. 6d. White Tern; 5s. Night-blooming Cereus.

1963 (4 June). *Freedom from Hunger. As No. 80 of Lesotho.*

190	1s. 6d. ultramarine		1·25	40

1963 (2 Sept). *Red Cross Centenary. As Nos. 203/4 of Jamaica.*

191	3d. red and black		75	25
192	1s. 6d. red and blue		2·50	1·50

FIRST LOCAL POST
4th JANUARY 1965
(64)

65 Badge of St. Helena

1965 (4 Jan). *First Local Post. Nos. 176, 179, 181 and 185 optd with T 64.*

193	1d. bright blue, dull violet, yellow & carmine		10	20
194	3d. light blue, black, pink and deep blue		10	20
195	6d. red, sepia and light yellow-olive		40	20
196	1s. 6d. grey, black and slate-blue		60	20
193/6		*Set of 4*	1·00	70

1965 (17 May). *I.T.U. Centenary. As Nos. 98/9 of Lesotho.*

197	3d. blue and grey-brown		35	25
198	6d. bright purple and bluish green		55	25

1965 (15 Oct). *International Co-operation Year. As Nos. 100/1 of Lesotho.*

199	1d. reddish purple and turquoise-green		30	15
200	6d. deep bluish green and lavender		30	15
	w. Wmk inverted			

1966 (24 Jan). *Churchill Commemoration. As Nos. 102/5 of Lesotho.*

201	1d. new blue		15	20
202	3d. deep green		35	20
203	6d. brown		50	25
204	1s. 6d. bluish violet		70	75
201/4		*Set of 4*	1·50	1·25

1966 (1 July). *World Cup Football Championships. As Nos. 57/8 of Pitcairn Islands.*

205	3d. violet, yellow-green, lake & yellow-brn		50	35
206	6d. chocolate, blue-green, lake & yellow-brn		75	35

1966 (20 Sept). *Inauguration of W.H.O. Headquarters, Geneva. As Nos. 185/6 of Montserrat.*

207	3d. black, yellow-green and light blue		75	20
208	1s. 6d. black, light purple and yellow-brown		2·75	1·00

1966 (1 Dec). *20th Anniversary of U.N.E.S.C.O. As Nos. 342/4 of Mauritius.*

209	3d. slate-violet, red, yellow and orange		75	20
210	6d. orange-yellow, violet and deep olive		1·25	50
211	1s. 6d. black, bright purple and orange		2·00	1·75
209/11		*Set of 3*	3·50	2·25

(Des W. H. Brown. Photo Harrison)

1967 (5 May). *New Constitution. W w 12 (sideways). P 14½ × 14.*

212	65	1s. multicoloured	10	10
213		2s. 6d. multicoloured	20	20
		a. Red (ribbon, etc.) omitted	£500	

66 Fire of London

(Des M. Goaman. Recess D.L.R.)

1967 (4 Sept). *300th Anniv of Arrival of Settlers after Great Fire of London. T 66 and similar horiz designs. W w 12. P 13.*

214	1d. carmine-red and black		15	10
	a. Carmine and black		90	70
215	3d. ultramarine and black		20	10
216	6d. slate-violet and black		20	10
217	1s 6d. olive-green and black		20	10
214/17		*Set of 4*	65	30

Designs:—3d. East Indiaman *Charles*; 6d. Settlers landing at Jamestown; 1s. 6d. Settlers clearing scrub.

70 Interlocking Maps of Tristan and St. Helena

(Des Jennifer Toombs. Photo Harrison)

1968 (4 June). *30th Anniv of Tristan da Cunha as a Dependency of St. Helena. T 70 and similar horiz design. W w 12. P 14 × 14½.*

218	70	4d. purple and chocolate	10	10
219	—	8d. olive and brown	10	30
220	70	1s. 9d. ultramarine and chocolate	10	40
221	—	2s. 3d. greenish blue and brown	15	40
218/21		*Set of 4*	35	1·10

Design:—8d., 2s. 3d. Interlocking maps of St. Helena and Tristan.

72 Queen Elizabeth and Sir Hudson Lowe

(Des M. Farrar Bell. Litho D.L.R.)

1968 (4 Sept). *150th Anniv of the Abolition of Slavery in St. Helena. T 72 and similar horiz design. Multicoloured. W w 12 (sideways). P 13 × 12½.*

222	3d. Type **72**		10	10
223	9d. Type **72**		10	15
224	1s. 6d. Queen Elizabeth and Sir George Bingham		15	25
225	2s. 6d. As 1s. 6d.		25	30
222/5		*Set of 4*	55	65

74 Blue Gum Eucalyptus and Road Construction

(Des Sylvia Goaman. Litho P.B.)

1968 (4 Nov). *Horiz designs as T 74. Multicoloured. W w 12 (sideways*). P 13½.*

226	½d. Type **74**		10	10
227	1d. Cabbage-tree and electricity development		10	10
	w. Wmk Crown to right of CA		4·00	
228	1½d. St. Helena Redwood and dental unit		15	10
229	2d. Scrubweed and pest control		15	10
230	3d. Tree-fern and flats in Jamestown		30	10
231	4d. Blue gum Eucalyptus, pasture and livestock improvement		20	10
232	6d. Cabbage-tree and schools broadcasting		50	10
233	8d. St. Helena Redwood and country cottages		30	10
234	10d. Scrubweed and new school buildings		30	10
235	1s. Tree-fern and reafforestation		30	10
236	1s. 6d. Blue gum Eucalyptus and heavy lift crane		70	2·50
237	2s. 6d. Cabbage-tree and Lady Field Children's Home		80	3·00
238	5s. St. Helena Redwood and agricultural training		90	3·50
239	10s. Scrubweed and New General Hospital		11·00	15·00
240	£1 Tree-fern and lifeboat *John Dutton*		11·00	15·00
226/40		*Set of 15*	16·00	26·00

*The normal sideways watermark shows Crown to left of CA, as seen from the back of the stamp.

See also No. 274 for distinct shade of £1 value.

89 Brig *Perseverance*

93 W.O. and Drummer of
the 53rd Foot, 1815

(Des J.W. Litho P.B.)

1969 (19 Apr). *Mail Communications. T* **89** *and similar horiz designs. Multicoloured.* W w 12 *(sideways).* P 13½.

241	4d. Type **89**			20	20
242	8d. *Phoebe* (screw steamer)			30	40
243	1s. 9d. *Llandovery Castle* (liner)			40	60
244	2s. 3d. *Good Hope Castle* (cargo liner)			45	75
241/4			Set of 4	1·25	1·75

No. 242 is inscribed "DANE" in error.

(Des R. North. Litho Format)

1969 (3 Sept). *Military Uniforms. T* **93** *and similar vert designs. Multicoloured.* W w 12. *P* 14.

245	6d. Type **93**			20	20
	w. Wmk inverted			60·00	
246	8d. Officer and Surgeon, 20th Foot, 1816			25	20
247	1s. 8d. Drum Major, 66th Foot, 1816, and Royal Artillery Officer, 1820			25	35
248	2s. 6d. Private, 91st Foot, and 2nd Corporal, Royal Sappers and Miners, 1832			25	40
245/8			Set of 4	85	1·00

97 Dickens, Mr. Pickwick and Job Trotter
(*Pickwick Papers*)

(Des Jennifer Toombs. Litho P.B.)

1970 (9 June). *Death Centenary of Charles Dickens. T* **97** *and similar horiz designs each incorporating a portrait of Dickens. Multicoloured. Chalk-surfaced paper.* W w 12 *(sideways*).* P 13½×13.

249	4d. Type **97**			60	15
	a. Shiny unsurfaced paper			30	1·40
	b. Yellow omitted			£325	
	w. Wmk Crown to right of CA			23·00	
250	8d. Mr. Bumble and Oliver (*Oliver Twist*)			70	20
	a. Shiny unsurfaced paper			30	1·60
251	1s. 6d. Sairey Gamp and Mark Tapley (*Martin Chuzzlewit*)			85	25
	a. Shiny unsurfaced paper			40	2·25
252	2s. 6d. Jo and Mr. Turveydrop (*Bleak House*)			1·00	35
	a. Shiny unsurfaced paper			50	2·50
249/52			Set of 4	2·75	85
249a/52a			Set of 4	1·40	7·00

*The normal sideways watermark shows Crown to left of CA, as seen from the back of the stamp.

Supplies sent to St. Helena were on paper with a dull surface which reacts to the chalky test and with PVA gum. Crown Agents supplies were from a later printing on shiny paper which does not respond to the chalky test and with gum arabic.

98 "Kiss of Life"

99 Officer's Shako Plate
(20th Foot)

(Des Jennifer Toombs. Litho J.W.)

1970 (15 Sept). *Centenary of British Red Cross. T* **98** *and similar horiz designs. Multicoloured.* W w 12 *(sideways).* P 14.

253	6d. bistre, vermilion and black			15	15
254	9d. turquoise-green, vermilion and black			20	15
255	1s. 9d. pale grey, vermilion and black			30	20
256	2s. 3d. pale lavender, vermilion and black			30	30
253/6			Set of 4	85	70

Designs:—9d. Nurse with girl in wheelchair; 1s. 9d. Nurse bandaging child's knee; 2s. 3d. Red Cross emblem.

(Des J.W. Litho Questa)

1970 (2 Nov). *Military Equipment (1st issue). T* **99** *and similar vert designs. Multicoloured.* W w 12. P 12.

257	4d. Type **99**			30	20
258	9d. Officer's Breast-plate (66th Foot)			35	30
259	1s. 3d. Officer's Full Dress Shako (91st Foot)			40	40
260	2s. 11d. Ensign's Shako (53rd Foot)			50	60
257/60			Set of 4	1·40	1·40

See also Nos. 281/4, 285/8 and 291/4.

---

100 Electricity Development

101 St. Helena holding
the "True Cross"

(Litho P.B.)

1971 (15 Feb). *Decimal Currency. Designs as Nos.* 227/40, *but with values inscr in decimal currency as in T* **100**. W w 12 *(sideways*).* P 13½.

261	½p. multicoloured			10	10
262	1p. multicoloured (as 1½d.)			10	10
	w. Wmk Crown to right of CA			50	
263	1½p. multicoloured (as 2d.)			10	10
264	2p. multicoloured (as 3d.)			1·75	90
265	2½p. multicoloured (as 4d.)			10	10
266	3½p. multicoloured (as 6d.)			30	10
267	4½p. multicoloured (as 8d.)			10	10
268	5p. multicoloured (as 10d.)			10	10
269	7½p. multicoloured (as 1s.)			40	35
270	10p. multicoloured (as 1s. 6d.)			30	35
271	12½p. multicoloured (as 2s. 6d.)			30	50
272	25p. multicoloured (as 5s.)			60	1·25
273	50p. multicoloured (as 10s.)			1·25	2·00
274	£1 multicoloured†			24·00	18·00
261/74			Set of 14	26·00	22·00

*The normal sideways watermark shows Crown to left of CA as seen from the back of the stamp.

†Although the design of No. 274 in no way differs from that of No. 240, it was reprinted specially for decimalisation, and differs considerably in shade from No. 240, as do others from their counterparts in the 1968 set.

The main differences in No. 274 are in the mountain which is blue rather than pinkish blue and in the sea which is light blue instead of greenish blue.

See also No. 309.

(Des R. Granger Barrett. Litho Questa)

1971 (5 Apr). *Easter.* W w 12. P 14 × 14½.

275	**101**	2p. multicoloured			10	10
276		5p. multicoloured			15	15
277		7½p. multicoloured			25	25
278		12½p. multicoloured			30	25
275/8				Set of 4	70	60

102 Napoleon (after painting by J.-L. David)
and Tomb on St. Helena

(Des J.W. Litho Questa)

1971 (5 May). *150th Death Anniv of Napoleon, T* **102** *and similar vert design. Multicoloured.* W w 12. P 13½.

279	2p. Type **102**			30	50
280	34p. "Napoleon at St. Helena" (H. Delaroche)			60	1·00

(Des J.W. Litho Questa)

1971 (10 Nov). *Military Equipment (2nd issue). Multicoloured designs as T* **99**. W w 12. P 14.

281	1½p. Artillery Private's hanger			35	30
282	4p. Baker rifle and socket bayonet			40	60
283	6p. Infantry Officer's sword			40	80
284	22½p. Baker rifle and sword bayonet			70	1·25
281/4			Set of 4	1·75	2·75

(Des and litho J.W.)

1972 (19 June). *Military Equipment (3rd issue). Multicoloured designs as T* **99**. W w 12. P 14.

285	2p. multicoloured			25	20
286	5p. reddish lilac, new blue and black			30	40
287	7½p. multicoloured			40	50
288	12½p. pale olive-sepia, brown and black			40	60
285/8			Set of 4	1·25	1·50

Designs:—2p. Royal Sappers and Miners breast-plate, post 1823; 5p. Infantry sergeant's spontoon, *circa* 1830; 7½p. Royal Artillery officer's breast-plate, *circa* 1830; 12½p. English military pistol, *circa* 1800.

103 St. Helena Sand Plover and White Tern

(Des (from photograph by D. Groves) and photo Harrison)

1972 (20 Nov). *Royal Silver Wedding. Multicoloured; background colour given.* W w 12. P 14 × 14½.

289	**103**	2p. slate-green			25	40
		w. Wmk inverted			23·00	
290		16p. lake-brown			50	85
		w. Wmk inverted			55·00	

(Des J.W. Litho Questa)

1973 (20 Sept). *Military Equipment (4th issue). Multicoloured designs as T* **99**. W w 12 *(sideways).* P 14.

291	2p. Other Rank's shako, 53rd Foot, 1815			40	55
292	5p. Band and Drums sword, 1830			45	1·00
293	7½p. Royal Sappers and Miners Officer's hat, 1830			60	1·25
294	12½p. General's sword, 1831			75	1·50
291/4			Set of 4	2·00	4·00

1973 (14 Nov). *Royal Wedding. As Nos.* 322/3 *of Montserrat.*

295	2p. violet-blue			15	10
296	18p. light emerald			25	20

104 *Westminster* and *Claudine* beached, 1849

(Des J.W. Litho Questa)

1973 (17 Dec). *Tercentenary of East India Company Charter. T* **104** *and similar horiz designs. Multicoloured.* W w 12. P 14.

297	1½p. Type **104**			40	45
298	4p. *True Briton*, 1790			50	70
299	6p. *General Goddard* in action, 1795			50	70
300	22½p. *Kent* burning in the Bay of Biscay, 1825			1·10	2·25
297/300			Set of 4	2·25	3·75

105 U.P.U. Emblem and Ships

(Des J.W. Litho Questa)

1974 (15 Oct). *Centenary of Universal Postal Union. T* **105** *and similar horiz design. Multicoloured.* W w 12 *(sideways on* **MS303**). P 14.

301	5p. Type **105**			20	25
302	25p. U.P.U. emblem and letters			40	55
MS303	89 × 84 mm. Nos. 301/2			75	1·50

106 Churchill in Sailor Suit, and
Blenheim Palace

107 Capt. Cook and
H.M.S. *Resolution*

(Des Jennifer Toombs. Litho Questa)

1974 (30 Nov). *Birth Centenary of Sir Winston Churchill. T* **106** *and similar horiz design.* W w 14 *(sideways).* P 14.

304	5p. multicoloured			20	20
305	25p. black, flesh and reddish purple			40	60
MS306	108×93 mm. Nos. 304/5. W w 12 *(sideways*)*			75	2·00
	w. Wmk Crown to right of CA			£300	

Design:—25p. Churchill and River Thames
*The normal sideways watermark shows Crown to left of CA, as seen from the back of the stamp.

(Des J. Cooter. Litho Questa)

1975 (14 July). *Bicentenary of Capt. Cook's Return to St. Helena. T* **107** *and similar horiz design. Multicoloured.* W w 14 *(sideways on* 25p.). P 13½.

307	5p. Type **107**			40	40
308	25p. Capt. Cook and Jamestown			70	1·00

(Litho Questa)

1975 (13 Aug). *As No.* 264 *but whiter paper.* P 14.

309	2p. multicoloured			90	5·00

NEW INFORMATION

The editor is always interested to correspond with people who have new information that will improve or correct the Catalogue.

108 *Mellissia begonifolia*
(tree)

109 £1 Note

(Des Jennifer Toombs. Litho J.W.)

1975 (20 Oct). *Centenary of Publication of "St. Helena" by J. C. Melliss. T **108** and similar multicoloured designs. W w **14** (sideways on 12 and 25p). P **13**.*
310	2p. Type **108**			20	30
311	5p. *Melissius adumbratus* (beetle)			25	45
312	12p. St. Helena Sand Plover (*horiz*)			60	1·00
313	25p. Melliss's Scorpionfish (*horiz*)			75	1·40
310/13			*Set of 4*	1·60	2·75

(Des V. Whiteley Studio. Litho J.W.)

1976 (15 Mar). *First Issue of Currency Notes. T **109** and similar horiz design. Multicoloured. W w **12** (sideways*). P **13½**.*
314	8p. Type **109**			30	30
	w. Wmk Crown to left of CA			1·10	
315	33p. £5 Note			60	80

*The normal sideways watermark shows Crown to right of CA, *as seen from the back of the stamp.*

110 1d. Stamp of 1863

(Des C. Abbott. Litho J.W.)

1976 (4 May). *Festival of Stamps, London. T **110** and similar designs. W w **14** (sideways on 5 and 25p). P **13½**.*
316	5p. light red-brown, black and light flesh		15	15
317	8p. black, green and pale dull green		20	30
318	25p. multicoloured			35	45
316/18			*Set of 3*	65	80

Designs: *Vert*—8p. 1d. stamp of 1922. *Horiz*—25p. Mail carrier Good Hope Castle.
For miniature sheet containing No. 318 see Ascension No. MS218.

111 "High Knoll, 1806"
(Capt. Barnett)

(Des C. Abbott. Litho Questa)

1976 (14 Sept)–82. *Aquatints and Lithographs of St. Helena. T **111** and similar horiz designs. Multicoloured. W w **14** (sideways*). P **13½** (£1, £2) or **14** (others).*

A. *On white paper. Without imprint date.*
319A	1p. Type **111**			40	90
	a. Cream paper (13.6.80)			60	90
	aw. Wmk Crown to right of CA		55·00	
320A	3p. "The Friar Rock, 1815" (G. Bellasis)		40	90
	a. Cream paper (13.6.80)			60	90
321A	5p. "The Column Lot, 1815" (G. Bellasis)		30	90
322A	6p. "Sandy Bay Valley, 1809" (H. Salt) (23.11.76)			30	90
323A	8p. "Scene from Castle Terrace, 1815" (G. Bellasis)			40	90
324A	9p. "The Briars, 1815" (23.11.76)		40	90
	w. Wmk Crown to right of CA		4·25	
325A	10p. "Plantation House, 1821" (J. Wathen)		50	60
326A	15p. "Longwood House, 1821" (J. Wathen) (23.11.76)			45	55
327A	18p. "St. Paul's Church" (V. Brooks)		45	1·25
328A	26p. "St. James's Valley, 1815" (Capt. Hastings)			45	1·00
329A	40p. "St. Matthew's Church, 1860" (V. Brooks)			70	1·75
330A	£1 "St. Helena, 1815" (G. Bellasis) (47×34 *mm*)			2·00	3·75
	a. Gold omitted			£750	
331A	£2 "Sugar Loaf Hill, 1821" (J. Wathen) (47×34 *mm*) (23.11.76)			3·00	6·00
319A/31A			*Set of 13*	8·75	18·00

B. *On cream paper with imprint date ("1982") (10.5.82)*
319B	1p. Type **111**			30	60
325B	10p. "Plantation House, 1821" (J. Wathen)		50	1·50
331B	£2 "Sugar Loaf Hill, 1821" (J. Wathen) (47×34 *mm*)			3·00	6·00
319B/31B			*Set of 3*	3·50	6·50

*The normal sideways watermark shows Crown to left of CA, *as seen from the back of the stamp.* No. 319Aaw occurs in stamp booklets.

112 Duke of Edinburgh paying Homage

(Des M. Shamir. Litho J.W.)

1977 (7 Feb). *Silver Jubilee. T **112** and similar horiz designs. Multicoloured. W w **14** (sideways). P **13**.*
332	8p. Royal visit, 1947			10	25
333	15p. Queen's sceptre with dove		20	35
334	26p. Type **112**			30	40
332/4			*Set of 3*	55	90

113 Halley's Comet (from Bayeux Tapestry)

114 Sea Lion

(Des C. Abbott. Litho Questa)

1977 (23 Aug). *Tercentenary of Halley's Visit. T **113** and similar horiz designs. Multicoloured. W w **14** (sideways). P **14**.*
335	5p. Type **113**			35	20
336	8p. Late 17th-century sextant		50	20
337	27p. Halley and Halley's Mount, St. Helena	1·00	60
335/7			*Set of 3*	1·75	90

(Des Jennifer Toombs. Litho Questa)

1978 (2 June). *25th Anniv of Coronation. T **114** and similar vert designs. P **15**.*
338	25p. agate, cerise and silver		30	50
	a. Sheetlet. Nos. 338/40 × 2		1·50	
339	25p. multicoloured			30	50
340	25p. agate, cerise and silver		30	50
338/40			*Set of 3*	80	1·40

Designs:—No. 338, Black Dragon of Ulster; No. 339, Queen Elizabeth II; No. 340, Type **114**.
Nos. 338/40 were printed together in small sheets of 6, containing two *se-tenant* strips of 3, with horizontal gutter margin between.

115 Period Engraving of St. Helena

(Des J.W. Litho Questa)

1978 (14 Aug). *Wreck of the "Witte Leeuw". T **115** and similar horiz designs. Multicoloured. W w **14** (sideways). P **14½**.*
341	3p. Type **115**			15	15
342	5p. Chinese porcelain			15	20
343	8p. Bronze cannon			20	30
344	9p. Chinese porcelain (*different*)		20	35
345	15p. Pewter mug and ceramic flasks		30	55
346	20p. Dutch East Indiaman			40	70
341/6			*Set of 6*	1·25	2·00

116 H.M.S. *Discovery*

117 Sir Rowland Hill

(Des and litho (25p. also embossed) Walsall)

1979 (19 Feb). *Bicentenary of Captain Cook's Voyages, 1768–79. T **116** and similar vert designs. Multicoloured. P **11**.*
347	3p. Type **116**			20	15
348	8p. Cook's portable observatory		20	25
349	12p. *Pharnaceum acidum* (based on sketch by Joseph Banks)			25	35
350	25p. Flaxman/Wedgwood medallion of Captain Cook			35	90
347/50			*Set of 4*	90	1·50

(Des J.W. Litho Questa)

1979 (10 Dec). *Death Centenary of Sir Rowland Hill. T **117** and similar designs. W w **14** (sideways* on 8 to 32p). P **14**.*
351	5p. multicoloured			10	15
	w. Wmk inverted			90·00	
352	8p. multicoloured			15	20
353	20p. multicoloured			30	40
	w. Wmk Crown to right of CA		16·00	
354	32p. black, magenta and deep mauve		40	55
	w. Wmk Crown to right of CA		18·00	
351/4			*Set of 4*	80	1·10

Designs: *Horiz*—8p, 1965 1d. 1st Local Post stamp; 20p. 1863 1d. on 6d. stamps; 32p. 1902 1d. stamp.
*The normal sideways watermark shows Crown to left of CA, *as seen from the back of the stamp.*

118 R. F. Seal's Chart of 1823 showing the Elevation of the Coastline

(Des G. Vasarhelyi. Litho Questa)

1979 (10 Dec). *150th Anniv of the Inclined Plane. T **118** and similar designs. W w **14** (sideways on 5 and 8p). P **14**.*
355	5p. black, brownish grey and stone		15	15
356	8p. black, brownish grey and stone		15	20
357	50p. multicoloured			60	75
355/7			*Set of 3*	80	1·00

Designs: *Horiz*—8p. The Inclined Plane in 1829. *Vert*—50p. The Inclined Plane in 1979.

119 Napoleon's Tomb, 1848

120 East Indiaman

(Des J.W. Litho Questa)

1980 (23 Feb). *Centenary of Empress Eugenie's Visit. T **119** and similar horiz designs. W w **14** (sideways). P **14**.*
358	5p. gold, reddish brown and pale red-brown		10	20
359	8p. gold, reddish brown and pale bistre		15	25
360	62p. gold, reddish brown & pale orange-brn		65	80
358/60			*Set of 3*	80	1·10
MS361	180 × 110 mm. Nos. 358/60		80	1·10

Designs:—8p. Landing at St. Helena; 62p. At the tomb of Napoleon.

(Des C. Abbott. Litho Format)

1980 (6 May). *"London 1980" International Stamp Exhibition. T **120** and similar vert designs. Multicoloured. W w **14**. P **14½**.*
362	5p. Type **120**			10	15
363	8p. *Dolphin* postal stone			10	15
364	47p. Postal stone outside Castle entrance, Jamestown			50	60
362/4			*Set of 3*	60	80
MS365	111 × 120 mm. Nos. 362/4		60	80

121 Queen Elizabeth the Queen Mother in 1974

(Des and litho Harrison)

1980 (18 Aug*). *80th Birthday of Queen Elizabeth the Queen Mother. W w **14** (sideways). P **14**.*
366	121	24p. multicoloured		35	50

*This is the local date of issue; the Crown Agents released the stamp on 4 August.

122 The Briars, 1815

(Des C. Abbott. Litho Questa)

1980 (17 Nov). *75th Anniv of Wellington's Visit. T **122** and similar multicoloured design. W w **14** (sideways* on 9p.). P **14**.*
367	9p. Type **122**			15	15
	w. Wmk Crown to right of CA		6·50	
368	30p. "Wellington" (Goya) (*vert*)		45	45

*The normal sideways watermark shows Crown to left of CA, *as seen from the back of the stamp.*
Nos. 367/8 were each printed in small sheets of 10 stamps.

123 Redwood

124 Detail from Reinel Portolan Chart, circa 1530

(Des Daphne Padden. Litho Enschede)

1981 (5 Jan). *Endemic Plants. T* **123** *and similar horiz designs. Multicoloured. W w* **14** (*sideways**). P* 13½.

369	5p. Type 123		15	15
	w. Wmk Crown to left of CA		3·75	
370	8p. Old Father Live Forever		15	20
371	15p. Gumwood		20	25
372	27p. Black Cabbage		35	45
369/72		Set of 4	75	95

*The normal sideways watermark shows Crown to right of CA on the 5p. and 8p., but Crown to left of CA on the 15p. and 27p., all as seen from the back of the stamp.

(Des Harrison. Litho Walsall)

1981 (22 May). *Early Maps. T* **124** *and similar horiz designs. W w* **14** (*sideways*). *P* 14 × 14½.

373	5p. multicoloured		15	15
374	8p. black, brown-lake and grey		15	20
375	20p. multicoloured		30	35
376	30p. multicoloured		35	50
373/6		Set of 4	85	1·10
MS377	114 × 83 mm. 24p. black and grey		40	65

Designs:—8p. John Thornton's Map of St. Helena, circa 1700; 20p. Map of St. Helena, 1815; 30p. Map of St. Helena, 1817; miniature sheet, Part of Gastaldi's map of Africa, 16th-century.

125 Prince Charles as Royal Navy Commander

126 Atlantic Trumpet Triton (*Charonia variegata*)

(Des J.W. Litho Questa)

1981 (22 July). *Royal Wedding. T* **125** *and similar vert designs. Multicoloured. W w* **14**. *P* 14.

378	14p. Wedding bouquet from St. Helena		15	20
379	29p. Type 125		25	30
	w. Wmk inverted		3·00	
380	32p. Prince Charles and Lady Diana Spencer		30	35
378/80		Set of 3	60	75

(Des J.W. Litho Walsall)

1981 (10 Sept). *Sea Shells. T* **126** *and similar vert designs. Multicoloured. W w* **14**. *P* 14.

381	7p. Type 126		30	20
382	10p. St. Helena Cowrie (*Cypraea spurca sanctaehelenae*)		35	25
383	25p. Common Purple Janthina (*Janthina janthina*)		60	60
384	53p. Rude Pen Shell (*Pinna rudis*)		1·00	1·25
381/4		Set of 4	2·00	2·10

127 Traffic Duty

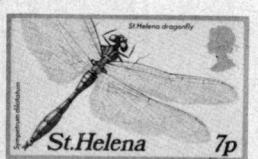
128 *Sympetrum dilatatum* (dragonfly)

(Des BG Studio. Litho Questa)

1981 (5 Nov). *25th Anniv of Duke of Edinburgh Award Scheme. T* **127** *and similar vert designs. Multicoloured. W w* **14**. *P* 14.

385	7p. Type 127		10	10
386	11p. Signposting		15	15
387	25p. Animal care		30	30
388	50p. Duke of Edinburgh, in Guards' uniform, on horse-back		60	60
385/8		Set of 4	1·00	1·00

(Des C. Abbott. Litho Questa)

1982 (4 Jan). *Insects (1st series). T* **128** *and similar horiz designs. Multicoloured. W w* **14** (*sideways on* 7, 10 *and* 25p., *inverted on* 32p.). *P* 14½.

389	7p. Type 128		20	20
390	10p. Aplothorax burchelli (beetle)		20	20
391	25p. Ampulex compressa (wasp)		35	35
392	32p. Labidura herculeana (earwig)		35	35
389/92		Set of 4	1·00	1·00

The 32p. is larger, 45×27 mm.
See also Nos. 411/14.

129 Charles Darwin

130 Prince and Princess of Wales at Balmoral, Autumn 1981

(Des L. Curtis. Litho Questa)

1982 (19 Apr). *150th Anniv of Charles Darwin's Voyage. T* **129** *and similar horiz designs. Multicoloured. W w* **14** (*sideways*). *P* 14.

393	7p. Type 129		20	20
394	14p. Flagstaff Hill and Darwin's hammer		25	35
395	25p. Ring-necked Pheasant and Chukar Partridge		50	70
396	29p. H.M.S. *Beagle* off St. Helena		60	80
393/6		Set of 4	1·40	1·90

(Des C. Abbott. Litho Format)

1982 (1 July). *21st Birthday of Princess of Wales. T* **130** *and similar vert designs. Multicoloured. W w* **14**. *P* 13½ × 14 (7, 55p.) *or* 13½ (*others*).

397	7p. St. Helena coat of arms		15	20
398	11p. Type 130		30	20
399	29p. Bride on Palace Balcony		50	50
	a. Perf 13½ × 14		15·00	17·00
	b. Imperf (pair)		£550	
400	55p. Formal portrait		1·25	80
397/400		Set of 4	2·00	1·50

1st PARTICIPATION COMMONWEALTH GAMES 1982
(131)

132 Lord Baden-Powell

1982 (25 Oct). *Commonwealth Games, Brisbane. Nos.* 326A *and* 328A *optd with T* **131**.

401	15p. "Longwood House, 1821" (J. Wathen)		25	25
402	26p. "St. James's Valley, 1815" (Capt. Hastings)		45	45

(Des L. McCombie. Litho Walsall)

1982 (29 Nov). *75th Anniv of Boy Scout Movement. T* **132** *and similar designs. W w* **14** (*inverted on* 3p., 29p.; *sideways on* 11p., 59p.). *P* 14.

403	3p. lake-brown, grey and orange-yellow		15	15
404	11p. lake-brown, grey & bright yellow-green		30	25
405	29p. lake-brown, grey and reddish orange		45	60
406	59p. lake-brown, grey & bright yellow-green		70	1·25
403/6		Set of 4	1·40	2·00

Designs: *Horiz*—11p. Boy Scout (drawing by Lord Baden-Powell); 59p. Camping at Thompsons Wood. *Vert*—29p. Canon Walcott.

133 King and Queen Rocks

134 *Trametes versicolor* ("*Coriolus versicolor*")

(Des C. Abbott. Litho B.D.T.)

1983 (14 Jan). *Views of St. Helena by Roland Svensson. T* **133** *and similar multicoloured designs. W w* **14** (*sideways on* 29p., 59p.). *P* 14.

407	7p. Type 133		20	20
408	11p. Turk's Cap		25	25
409	29p. Coastline from Jamestown (*horiz*)		50	65
410	59p. Mundens Point (*horiz*)		1·00	1·40
407/10		Set of 4	1·75	2·25

(Des C. Abbott. Litho Questa)

1983 (22 Apr). *Insects (2nd series). Horiz designs as T* **128**. *Multicoloured. W w* **14** (*sideways*). *P* 14½.

411	11p. Acherontia atropos (hawk moth)		20	30
412	15p. Helenasaldula aberrans (shore-bug)		20	35
413	29p. Anchastus compositarum (click beetle)		35	55
414	59p. Lamprochrus cossonoides (weevil)		65	1·25
411/14		Set of 4	1·25	2·25

(Des Garden Studio. Litho Format)

1983 (16 June). *Fungi. T* **134** *and similar multicoloured designs. W w* **14** (*sideways on* 29p.). *P* 14.

415	11p. Type 134		25	25
416	15p. Pluteus brunneisucus		35	40
417	29p. Polyporus induratus (horiz)		55	60
418	59p. Coprinus angulatus		80	1·25
415/18		Set of 4	1·75	2·25

135 Java Sparrow

136 Birth of St. Helena

(Des J.W. Litho Questa)

1983 (12 Sept). *Birds. T* **135** *and similar vert designs. Multicoloured. W w* **14**. *P* 14.

419	7p. Type 135		30	20
420	15p. Madagascar Red Fody		45	35
421	33p. Common Waxbill		80	70
422	59p. Yellow Canary		1·50	1·40
419/22		Set of 4	2·75	2·50

(Des Jennifer Toombs. Litho Questa)

1983 (17 Oct). *Christmas. Life of St. Helena (1st series). T* **136** *and similar vert design. Multicoloured. W w* **14**. *P* 14 × 13½.

423	10p. Type 136		20	35
	a. Sheetlet Nos. 423/4, each ×5		2·00	
424	15p. St. Helena being taken to convent		20	35

Nos. 423/4 were printed together in small sheets of 10, containing horizontal strips of 5 for each value separated by a horizontal gutter margin.
See also Nos. 450/3 and 468/71.

137 1934 ½d. Stamp

138 Prince Andrew and H.M.S. *Invincible* (aircraft carrier)

(Des C. Abbott. Litho Questa)

1984 (3 Jan). *150th Anniv of St. Helena as a British Colony. T* **137** *and similar square designs showing values of the 1934 Centenary of British Colonisation issue or Colony Arms. Multicoloured. W w* **14** (*sideways*). *P* 13½.

425	1p. Type 137		10	20
426	3p. 1934 1d. stamp		10	20
427	6p. 1934 1½d. stamp		10	30
428	7p. 1934 2d. stamp		15	30
429	11p. 1934 3d. stamp		20	40
430	15p. 1934 6d. stamp		25	45
431	29p. 1934 1s. stamp		50	95
432	33p. 1934 5s. stamp		55	1·25
433	59p. 1934 10s. stamp		80	2·00
434	£1 1934 2s. 6d. stamp		1·50	3·25
435	£2 St. Helena Coat of Arms		2·75	5·00
425/35		Set of 11	6·00	13·00

(Des D. Bowen. Litho Format)

1984 (4 Apr). *Visit of Prince Andrew. T* **138** *and similar horiz design. Multicoloured. W w* **14** (*sideways**). *P* 14.

436	11p. Type 138		25	25
	w. Wmk Crown to right of CA		70·00	
437	60p. Prince Andrew and H.M.S. *Herald* (survey ship)		75	1·40

*The normal sideways watermark shows Crown to left of CA, as seen from the back of the stamp.

139 *St. Helena* (schooner)

140 Twopenny Coin and Donkey

(Des A. Theobald. Litho Questa)

1984 (14 May). *250th Anniv of "Lloyd's List" (newspaper). T* **139** *and similar vert designs. Multicoloured. W w* **14**. *P* 14½ × 14.

438	10p. Type 139		20	20
439	18p. Solomons Facade (local agent)		35	35
440	25p. Lloyd's Coffee House, London		50	55
441	50p. Papanui (freighter)		1·00	1·00
438/41		Set of 4	1·90	1·90

(Des G. Drummond. Litho Format)

1984 (23 July). *New Coinage. T 140 and similar horiz designs. Multicoloured. W w 14 (sideways). P 14.*

442	10p. Type 140	30	35
443	15p. Five pence coin and St. Helena Sand Plover	35	45
444	29p. Penny coin and Yellow-finned Tuna	50	75
445	50p. Ten pence coin and Arum Lily	65	1·25
442/5	*Set of 4*	1·60	2·50

141 Mrs. Rebecca Fuller (former Corps Secretary)

142 Queen Elizabeth the Queen Mother aged Two

(Des L. Curtis. Litho Walsall)

1984 (12 Oct). *Centenary of Salvation Army on St. Helena. T 141 and similar multicoloured designs. W w 14 (sideways on 11p., 25p.). P 14.*

446	7p. Type 141	25	35
447	11p. Meals-on-wheels service (*horiz*)	30	45
448	25p. Salvation Army Citadel, Jamestown (*horiz*)	45	80
449	60p. Salvation Army band at Jamestown Clock Tower	75	2·00
446/9	*Set of 4*	1·60	3·25

(Des Jennifer Toombs. Litho Questa)

1984 (9 Nov). *Christmas. Life of St. Helena (2nd series). Vert designs as T 136. Multicoloured. W w 14. P 14.*

450	6p. St. Helena visits prisoners	15	20
451	10p. Betrothal of St. Helena	20	30
452	15p. Marriage of St. Helena to Constantius	25	40
453	33p. Birth of Constantine	50	70
450/3	*Set of 4*	1·00	1·40

(Des A. Theobald (70p.), C. Abbott (others). Litho Questa)

1985 (7 June). *Life and Times of Queen Elizabeth the Queen Mother. T 142 and similar vert designs. Multicoloured. W w 16. P 14½×14.*

454	11p. Type 142	20	25
455	15p. At Ascot with the Queen	20	35
	w. Wmk inverted	42·00	
456	29p. Attending Gala Ballet at Covent Garden	40	65
457	55p. With Prince Henry at his christening	60	1·00
454/7	*Set of 4*	1·25	2·00
MS458	91×73 mm. 70p. The Queen Mother with Ford "V8 Pilot". Wmk sideways	1·40	1·60

143 Axillary Cardinalfish

144 John J. Audubon

(Des L. Curtis. Litho Walsall)

1985 (12 July). *Marine Life. T 143 and similar horiz designs. Multicoloured. W w 14 (sideways*). P 13×13½.*

459	7p. Type 143	25	25
460	11p. Chub Mackerel	30	30
461	15p. Skipjack Tuna	40	40
462	33p. Yellow-finned Tuna	75	75
463	50p. Stump	1·25	1·25
	w. Wmk Crown to right of CA	30·00	
459/63	*Set of 5*	2·75	2·75

*The normal sideways watermark shows Crown to left of CA, as seen from the back of the stamp.

(Des Josephine Martin (11p.). Litho Format)

1985 (2 Sept). *Birth Bicentenary of John J. Audubon (ornithologist). T 144 and similar designs. W w 14 (inverted on 11p., sideways on others). P 14.*

464	11p. black and blackish brown	45	25
465	15p. multicoloured	55	35
466	25p. multicoloured	75	55
467	60p. multicoloured	1·40	1·40
464/7	*Set of 4*	2·75	2·25

Designs: *Horiz* (from original Audubon paintings)—15p. Moorhen ("Common Gallinule"); 25p. White-tailed Tropic Bird; 60p. Common Noddy.

(Des Jennifer Toombs. Litho Questa)

1985 (14 Oct). *Christmas. Life of St. Helena (3rd series). Vert designs as T 136. Multicoloured. W w 14. P 14×13½.*

468	7p. St. Helena journeys to the Holy Land	25	25
469	10p. Zambres slays the bull	30	30
470	15p. The bull restored to life: conversion of St. Helena	40	40
471	60p. Resurrection of the corpse: the true Cross identified	1·00	1·50
468/71	*Set of 4*	1·75	2·25

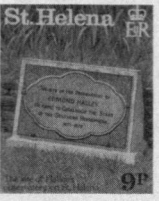

145 Church Provident Society for Women Banner

146 Plaque at Site of Halley's Observatory on St. Helena

(Des A. Theobald. Litho J.W.)

1986 (7 Jan). *Friendly Societies' Banners. T 145 and similar horiz designs. Multicoloured. W w 16 (sideways*). P 13×13½.*

472	10p. Type 145	20	25
473	11p. Working Men's Christian Association	20	25
474	25p. Church Benefit Society for Children	40	55
475	29p. Mechanics and Friendly Benefit Society	45	65
476	33p. Ancient Order of Foresters	50	70
	w. Wmk Crown to left of CA	10·00	
472/6	*Set of 5*	1·60	2·10

*The normal sideways watermark shows Crown to right of CA, as seen from the back of the stamp.

(Des A. Theobald. Litho Questa)

1986 (21 Apr). *60th Birthday of Queen Elizabeth II. Vert designs as T 230a of Jamaica. Multicoloured. W w 16. P 14½×14.*

477	10p. Princess Elizabeth making 21st birthday broadcast, South Africa, 1947	15	20
478	15p. Silver Jubilee photograph, 1977	25	30
479	20p. Princess Elizabeth on board H.M.S. *Vanguard*, 1947	30	35
480	50p. In the U.S.A., 1976	65	75
481	65p. At Crown Agents Head Office, London, 1983	80	90
477/81	*Set of 5*	1·90	2·25

(Des L. Curtis. Litho Walsall)

1986 (15 May). *Appearance of Halley's Comet. T 146 and similar vert designs. Multicoloured. W w 14. P 14½×14.*

482	9p. Type 146	25	35
483	12p. Edmond Halley	30	35
484	20p. Halley's planisphere of the southern stars	55	70
485	65p. *Unity* on passage to St. Helena, 1676	1·75	2·25
482/5	*Set of 4*	2·50	3·25

(Des D. Miller. Litho Questa)

1986 (23 July). *Royal Wedding. Square designs as T 231a of Jamaica. Multicoloured. W w 16. P 14.*

486	10p. Prince Andrew and Miss Sarah Ferguson	20	25
	w. Wmk inverted	20·00	
487	40p. Prince Andrew with Governor J. Massingham on St. Helena	80	85
	w. Wmk inverted	20·00	

147 James Ross and H.M.S. *Erebus*

(Des C. Abbott. Litho Questa)

1986 (22 Sept). *Explorers. T 147 and similar horiz designs. W w 16 (sideways). P 14½.*

488	1p. deep brown and pink	30	1·25
489	3p. royal blue and grey-blue	30	1·25
490	5p. bronze-green and deep yellow-green	30	1·25
491	9p. purple-brown and claret	40	1·25
492	10p. deep brown and light brown	40	1·25
493	12p. myrtle-green and light green	50	1·25
494	15p. red-brown and brown-rose	60	1·25
495	20p. deep dull blue and light blue	70	1·25
496	25p. sepia and salmon-pink	70	1·25
497	40p. bottle-green and dull blue-green	1·00	1·75
498	60p. reddish brown and pale orange-brown	1·25	2·00
499	£1 deep turquoise-blue and turquoise-blue	2·00	3·00
500	£2 deep lilac and reddish lilac	4·00	5·00
488/500	*Set of 13*	11·00	21·00

Designs:—3p. Robert FitzRoy and H.M.S. *Beagle*; 5p. Adam Johann von Krusenstern and *Nadezhda*; 9p. William Bligh and H.M.S. *Resolution*; 10p. Otto von Kotzebue and *Rurik*; 12p. Philip Carteret and H.M.S. *Swallow*; 15p. Thomas Cavendish and *Desire*; 20p. Louis-Antoine de Bougainville and *La Boudeuse*; 25p. Fyedor Petrovich Litke and *Senyavin*; 40p. Louis Isidore Duperrey and *La Coquille*; 60p. John Byron and H.M.S. *Dolphin*; £1 James Cook and H.M.S. *Endeavour*; £2 Jules Dumont d'Urville and *L'Astrolabe*.

The new-issue supplement to this Catalogue appears each month in

GIBBONS STAMP MONTHLY

—from your newsagent or by postal subscription— sample copy and details on request.

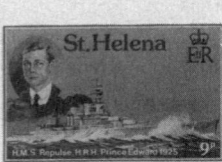

148 Prince Edward and H.M.S. *Repulse* (battle cruiser), 1925

149 St. Helena Tea Plant

(Des E. Nisbet. Litho Questa)

1987 (16 Feb). *Royal Visits to St. Helena. T 148 and similar horiz designs. Multicoloured. W w 16 (sideways). P 14.*

501	9p. Type 148	70	70
502	13p. King George VI and H.M.S. *Vanguard* (battleship), 1947	95	1·00
503	38p. Prince Philip and Royal Yacht *Britannia*, 1957	2·00	2·75
504	45p. Prince Andrew and H.M.S. *Herald* (survey ship), 1984	2·25	3·00
501/4	*Set of 4*	5·50	6·75

(Des Annette Robinson. Litho Questa)

1987 (3 Aug). *Rare Plants (1st series). T 149 and similar vert designs. Multicoloured. W w 16. P 14½×14.*

505	9p. Type 149	65	55
506	13p. Baby's Toes	80	75
507	38p. Salad Plant	1·50	2·00
508	45p. Scrubwood	1·75	2·25
505/8	*Set of 4*	4·25	5·00

See also Nos. 531/4.

150 Lesser Rorqual

151 *Defence* and Dampier's Signature, 1691

(Des A. Riley. Litho Questa)

1987 (24 Oct). *Marine Mammals. T 150 and similar horiz designs. Multicoloured. W w 16 (sideways). P 14.*

509	9p. Type 150	1·25	75
510	13p. Risso's Dolphin	1·25	1·00
511	45p. Sperm Whale	3·00	3·25
512	60p. Euphrosyne Dolphin	3·25	3·75
509/12	*Set of 4*	8·00	8·00
MS513	102×72 mm. 75p. Humpback Whale (48×31 mm). P 13½×14	5·50	6·00

1987 (9 Dec). *Royal Ruby Wedding. Nos. 477/81 optd with T 45a of Kiribati in silver.*

514	10p. Princess Elizabeth making 21st birthday broadcast, South Africa, 1947	15	30
515	15p. Silver Jubilee photograph, 1977	20	35
	a. Opt omitted (vert pair with normal)	£160	
516	20p. Princess Elizabeth on board H.M.S. *Vanguard*, 1947	35	45
517	50p. In the U.S.A., 1976	60	1·00
518	65p. At Crown Agents Head Office, London, 1983	70	1·40
514/18	*Set of 5*	1·75	3·25

No. 515a occurred on the top row of several sheets.

(Des A. Theobald. Litho Walsall)

1988 (1 Mar). *Bicentenary of Australian Settlement. T 151 and similar horiz designs showing ships and signatures. Multicoloured. W w 14 (sideways). P 14×14½.*

519	9p. Type 151	1·50	90
520	13p. H.M.S. *Resolution* (Cook), 1775	2·00	2·00
521	45p. H.M.S. *Providence* (Bligh), 1792	3·25	4·00
522	60p. H.M.S. *Beagle* (Darwin), 1836	4·25	5·50
519/22	*Set of 4*	10·00	11·00

152 "The Holy Virgin with the Child"

153 Ebony

(Des N. Harvey. Litho Questa)

1988 (11 Oct). *Christmas. T 152 and similar vert designs showing religious paintings. Multicoloured. W w 14. P 14.*

523	5p. Type 152	10	30
524	20p. "Madonna"	40	50
525	38p. "The Holy Family with St. John"	75	1·50
526	60p. "The Holy Virgin with the Child"	1·25	2·00
523/6	*Set of 4*	2·25	3·75

(Des D. Miller (8p.), E. Nisbet and D. Miller (others). Litho Questa)

1988 (1 Nov). *300th Anniv of Lloyd's of London. Designs as* T 167a *of Malawi.* W w **16** *(sideways on* 20, 45p.). P 14.

527	9p.	agate and brown	..	25	30
528	20p.	multicoloured	..	80	60
529	45p.	multicoloured	..	1·40	1·40
530	60p.	multicoloured	..	1·60	1·60
527/30		*Set of* 4		3·50	3·50

Designs: *Vert*—9p. Lloyd's Underwriting Room, 1886; 60p. *Spangereid* (full-rigged ship) on fire, St. Helena, 1920. *Horiz*—20p. *Edinburgh Castle* (liner); 45p. *Bosun Bird* (freighter).

(Des L. Ninnes. Litho Questa)

1989 (6 Jan). *Rare Plants (2nd series).* T 153 *and similar vert designs. Multicoloured.* W w **16**. P 14.

531	9p.	Type 153	..	40	40
532	20p.	St. Helena Lobelia	..	70	70
533	45p.	Large Bellflower	..	1·40	2·00
534	60p.	She Cabbage Tree	..	1·60	2·50
531/4		*Set of* 4		3·75	5·00

154 Private, 53rd Foot

(155)

(Des C. Collins. Litho Format)

1989 (5 June). *Military Uniforms of 1815.* T 154 *and similar vert designs. Multicoloured.* W w **16**. P 14.

535	9p.	Type 154	..	65	80
		a. Horiz strip of 5. Nos. 535/9		4·75	
536	13p.	Officer, 53rd Foot	..	75	90
537	20p.	Royal Marine	..	85	1·00
538	45p.	Officer, 66th Foot	..	1·40	1·75
539	60p.	Private, 66th Foot	..	1·60	2·00
535/9		*Set of* 5		4·75	5·75

Nos. 535/9 were printed together, *se-tenant*, in horizontal strips of five throughout the sheet.

1989 (7 July). *"Philexfrance 89" International Stamp Exhibition, Paris.* Nos. 535/9 optd with T 155.

540	9p.	Type 154	..	80	1·00
		a. Horiz strip of 5. Nos. 540/4		5·50	
541	13p.	Officer, 53rd Foot	..	90	1·10
542	20p.	Royal Marine	..	1·10	1·25
543	45p.	Officer, 66th Foot	..	1·50	1·90
544	60p.	Private, 66th Foot	..	1·60	2·00
540/4		*Set of* 5		5·50	6·50

156 Agricultural Studies

157 "The Madonna with the Pear" (Dürer)

(Des A. Edmonston. Litho Questa)

1989 (24 Aug). *New Prince Andrew Central School.* T 156 *and similar horiz designs. Multicoloured.* W w **16** *(sideways).* P 14×14½.

545	13p.	Type 156	..	60	55
546	20p.	Geography lesson	..	1·00	1·00
547	45p.	Walkway and classroom block	..	1·10	1·10
548	60p.	Aerial view of School	..	2·50	3·25
545/8		*Set of* 4		4·75	5·50

(Des D. Miller. Litho Questa)

1989 (23 Oct). *Christmas. Religious Paintings.* T 157 *and similar vert designs. Multicoloured.* W w **14**. P 14.

549	10p.	Type 157	..	60	40
550	20p.	"The Holy Family under the Appletree" (Rubens)	..	85	80
551	45p.	"The Virgin in the Meadow" (Raphael)	..	2·00	2·25
552	60p.	"The Holy Family with St. John" (Raphael)	..	2·50	3·00
549/52		*Set of* 4		5·50	5·75

COVER PRICES

Cover factors are quoted at the beginning of each country for most issues to 1945. An explanation of the system can be found on page x. The factors quoted do not, however, apply to philatelic covers.

158 Chevrolet "6" 30 cwt Lorry, 1930

159 Sheep

(Des E. Nesbit. Litho Questa)

1989 (1 Dec). *Early Vehicles.* T 158 *and similar horiz designs. Multicoloured.* W w **16** *(sideways).* P 14½.

553	9p.	Type 158	..	85	60
554	20p.	Austin "Seven", 1929	..	1·50	1·00
555	45p.	Morris "Cowley" 11.9 h.p., 1929	..	2·25	2·50
556	60p.	Sunbeam 25 h.p., 1932	..	2·75	3·25
553/6		*Set of* 4		6·50	6·50
MS557	93×74 mm. £1 Ford "Model A Fordor"			5·50	6·00

(Des Doreen McGuiness. Litho Questa)

1990 (1 Feb). *Farm Animals.* T 159 *and similar vert designs. Multicoloured.* W w **16**. P 14.

558	9p.	Type 159	..	50	50
559	13p.	Pigs	..	60	60
560	45p.	Cow and calf	..	1·50	2·00
561	60p.	Geese	..	2·00	2·50
558/61		*Set of* 4		4·25	5·00

160 1840 Twopence Blue

161 Satellite Dish

(Des D. Miller. Litho Walsall)

1990 (3 May). *"Stamp World London 90" International Stamp Exhibition, London.* T 160 *and similar horiz designs.* W w **14** *(sideways).* P 14.

562	13p.	black and cobalt	..	50	50
563	20p.	multicoloured	..	75	85
564	38p.	multicoloured	..	1·25	2·00
565	45p.	multicoloured	..	1·60	2·25
562/5		*Set of* 4		3·75	5·00

Designs:—20p. 1840 Penny Black and 19th-century St. Helena postmark; 38p. Delivering mail to sub-post office; 45p. Mail van and Post Office, Jamestown.

(Des N. Shewring. Litho B.D.T.)

1990 (28 July). *Modern Telecommunications Links.* T 161 *and similar vert designs. Multicoloured.* W w **14**. P 13½.

566	20p.	Type 161	..	75	1·00
		a. Block of 4. Nos. 566/9		2·75	
567	20p.	Digital telephone exchange	..	75	1·00
568	20p.	Public card phone	..	75	1·00
569	20p.	Facsimile machine	..	75	1·00
566/9		*Set of* 4		2·75	3·50

Nos. 566/9 were printed together, *se-tenant*, in blocks of 4 throughout the sheet of 16.

(Des D. Miller. Litho Questa)

1990 (4 Aug). *90th Birthday of Queen Elizabeth the Queen Mother. Vert designs as* T 107 (25p.) *or* 108 (£1) *of Kenya.* W w **16**. P 14×15 (25p.) *or* 14½ (£1).

570	25p.	multicoloured	..	1·00	75
571	£1	black and purple-brown	..	2·75	3·75

Designs:—25p. Lady Elizabeth Bowes-Lyon, April 1923; £1 Queen Elizabeth visiting communal kitchen, 1940.

162 *Dane* (mail ship), 1857

163 Baptist Chapel, Sandy Bay

(Des L. Curtis. Litho Walsall)

1990 (13 Sept). *Maiden Voyage of St. Helena II.* T 162 *and similar horiz designs. Multicoloured.* W w **14** *(sideways).* P 14×14½.

572	13p.	Type 162	..	1·25	75
573	20p.	*St. Helena I* offloading at St. Helena	..	1·60	1·25
574	38p.	Launch of *St. Helena II*	..	2·25	2·50
575	45p.	The Duke of York launching *St. Helena II*	..	2·75	3·25
572/5		*Set of* 4		7·00	7·00
MS576	100×100 mm. £1 *St. Helena II* and outline map of St. Helena			6·50	7·00

No. MS576 also contains two imperforate designs of similar stamps from Ascension and Tristan da Cunha without face values.

(Des G. Vasarhelyi. Litho Questa)

1990 (18 Oct). *Christmas. Local Churches.* T 163 *and similar horiz designs. Multicoloured.* W w **14** *(sideways).* P 14.

577	10p.	Type 163	..	30	30
578	13p.	St. Martin in the Hills Church	..	35	35
579	20p.	St. Helena and the Cross Church	..	55	65
580	38p.	St. James Church	..	1·00	90
581	45p.	St. Paul's Cathedral	..	1·25	2·00
577/81		*Set of* 5		3·25	4·75

164 "Funeral Cortège, Jamestown Wharf" (detail, V. Adam)

165 Officer, Leicestershire Regiment

(Des N. Harvey. Litho Questa)

1990 (15 Dec). *150th Anniv of Removal of Napoleon's Body.* T 164 *and similar horiz designs.* W w **14** *(sideways).* P 13½×14.

582	13p.	black, sepia and blue-green	..	1·00	70
583	20p.	black, sepia and ultramarine	..	1·50	1·25
584	38p.	black, sepia and deep magenta	..	2·25	2·50
585	45p.	multicoloured	..	2·50	3·00
582/5		*Set of* 4		6·50	6·75

Designs:—20p. "Coffin being conveyed to the *Belle Poule*" (detail, V. Adam); 38p. "Transfer of the Coffin to the *Normandie*, Cherbourg" (detail, V. Adam); 45p. "Napoleon's Tomb, St. Helena" (T. Sutherland).

(Des C. Collins. Litho Questa)

1991 (2 May). *Military Uniforms of 1897.* T 165 *and similar vert designs. Multicoloured.* W w **14**. P 14.

586	13p.	Type 165	..	1·00	1·00
587	15p.	Officer, York & Lancaster Regiment	..	1·10	1·10
588	20p.	Colour-sergeant, Leicestershire Regt	..	1·40	1·40
589	38p.	Bandsman, York & Lancaster Regt	..	2·25	2·50
590	45p.	Lance-corporal, York & Lancaster Regt	..	2·75	3·25
586/90		*Set of* 5		7·75	8·50

(Des D. Miller. Litho Questa)

1991 (1 July). *65th Birthday of Queen Elizabeth II and 70th Birthday of Prince Philip. Vert designs as* T 58 *of Kiribati. Multicoloured.* W w **16** *(sideways).* P 14½×14.

591	25p.	Queen Elizabeth II	..	80	1·25
		a. Horiz pair. Nos. 591/2 separated by label		1·60	2·50
592	25p.	Prince Philip in naval uniform	..	80	1·25

Nos. 591/2 were printed in similar sheet format to Nos. 366/7 of Kiribati.

166 "Madonna and Child" (T. Vecellio)

167 Matchless (346cc) Motorcycle, 1947

(Des G. Vasarhelyi. Litho Walsall)

1991 (2 Nov). *Christmas. Religious Paintings.* T 166 *and similar vert designs. Multicoloured.* W w **14**. P 14.

593	10p.	Type 166	..	70	55
594	13p.	"The Holy Family" (A. Mengs)	..	80	65
595	20p.	"Madonna and Child" (W. Dyce)	..	1·25	1·00
596	38p.	"The Two Trinities" (B. Murillo)	..	2·00	2·50
597	45p.	"The Virgin and Child" (G. Bellini)	..	2·25	3·00
593/7		*Set of* 5		6·25	7·00

(Des N. Shewring. Litho Questa)

1991 (16 Nov). *"Phila Nippon '91" International Stamp Exhibition, Tokyo. Motorcycles.* T 167 *and similar horiz designs.* W w **16** *(sideways).* P 14×14½.

598	13p.	Type 167	..	1·00	80
599	20p.	Triumph "Tiger 100" (500cc), 1950	..	1·50	1·10
600	38p.	Honda "CD" (175cc), 1967	..	2·25	2·75
601	45p.	Yamaha "DTE 400", 1976	..	2·50	3·00
598/601		*Set of* 4		6·50	7·00
MS602	72×49 mm. 65p. Suzuki "RM" (250cc), 1984			6·50	7·00

168 *Eye of the Wind* (cadet brig)
and Compass Rose

(Des. R. Watton. Litho Walsall)

1992 (24 Jan). *500th Anniv of Discovery of America by Columbus and Re-enactment Voyages. T* **168** *and similar horiz designs. Multicoloured. W w* 14 (*sideways*). *P* 13½×14.

603	15p. Type **168**	1·25	90
604	25p. *Soren Larsen* (cadet brigantine) and map of Re-enactment Voyages	1·75	1·75
605	35p. *Santa Maria, Nina* and *Pinta*	2·25	2·75
606	50p. Columbus and *Santa Maria*	2·50	3·50
603/6	*Set of* 4	7·00	8·00

(Des D. Miller. Litho Questa (50p.), Walsall (others))

1992 (6 Feb). *40th Anniv of Queen Elizabeth II's Accession. Horiz designs as T* **113** *of Kenya. Multicoloured. W w* 14 (*sideways*). *P* 14.

607	11p. Prince Andrew Central School	40	40
608	15p. Plantation House	55	55
609	25p. Jamestown	85	95
610	35p. Three portraits of Queen Elizabeth	1·10	1·50
611	50p. Queen Elizabeth II	1·40	1·90
607/11	*Set of* 5	3·75	4·75

169 H.M.S. *Ledbury* (minesweeper) **170** Shepherds and Angel Gabriel

(Des N. Shewring. Litho Questa)

1992 (12 June). *10th Anniv of Liberation of Falkland Islands. Ships. T* **169** *and similar square designs. Multicoloured. W w* 14 (*sideways*). *P* 14.

612	13p. Type **169**	80	70
613	20p. H.M.S. *Brecon* (minesweeper)	1·10	90
614	38p. *St. Helena I* (mail ship) off South Georgia	1·75	2·25
615	45p. Launch collecting first mail drop, 1982	2·25	2·75
612/15		5·50	6·00
MS616	116×116 mm. 13p.+3p. Type **169**; 20p.+4p. As No. 613; 38p.+8p. As No. 614; 45p.+9p. As No. 615	4·25	4·25

The premium on No. **MS**616 were for the S.S.A.F.A.

(Des G. Vasarhelyi. Litho Questa)

1992 (12 Oct). *Christmas. Children's Nativity Plays. T* **170** *and similar horiz designs. W w* 16 (*sideways*). *P* 13½×14.

617	13p. Type **170**	1·00	75
618	15p. Shepherds and Three Kings	1·10	85
619	20p. Mary and Joseph	1·25	1·00
620	45p. Nativity scene	2·50	3·50
617/20	*Set of* 4	5·25	5·50

171 Disc Jockey, Radio St. Helena (25th anniv) **172** Moses in the Bulrush

(Des D. Miller. Litho Questa)

1992 (4 Dec). *Local Anniversaries. T* **171** *and similar horiz designs. Multicoloured. W w* 14 (*sideways*). *P* 14×14½.

621	13p. Type **171**	75	70
622	20p. Scout parade (75th anniv of Scouting on St. Helena)	1·25	1·10
623	38p. H.M.S. *Providence* (sloop) and bread-fruit (bicent of Capt. Bligh's visit)	2·25	2·75
624	45p. Governor Brooke and Plantation House (bicent)	2·25	2·75
621/4	*Set of* 4	6·00	6·50

(Des M. Martineau. Litho Questa)

1993 (19 Mar). *Flowers (1st series). T* **172** *and similar vert designs. Multicoloured. W w* 16 (*sideways*). *P* 14½.

625	9p. Type **172**	75	75
626	13p. Periwinkle	90	90
627	20p. Everlasting Flower	1·25	1·25
628	38p. Cigar Plant	2·00	2·25
629	45p. *Lobelia erinus*	2·25	2·75
625/9	*Set of* 5	6·50	7·00

See also Nos. 676/80.

 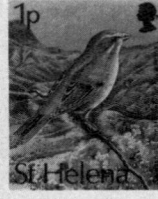

173 Adult St. Helena Sand Plover and Eggs **174** Yellow Canary ("Swainson's Canary")

(Des N. Arlott. Litho B.D.T.)

1993 (16 Aug). *Endangered Species. St. Helena Sand Plover ("Wirebird"). T* **173** *and similar horiz designs. Multicoloured. W w* 14 (*sideways*). *P* 13½.

630	3p. Type **173**	60	60
631	5p. Male attending brooding female	60	60
632	12p. Adult with downy young	1·25	1·25
633	25p. Two birds in immature plumage	1·40	1·40
634	40p. Adult in flight	1·50	1·75
635	60p. Young bird on rocks	1·75	2·50
630/5	*Set of* 6	6·25	7·25

Nos. 634/5 are without the W.W.F. emblem.

(Des A. Robinson. Litho Questa)

1993 (26 Aug). *Birds. T* **174** *and similar multicoloured designs. W w* 14 (*sideways on* 25p., 35p., £1, £2). *P* 14½×14 (*vert*) *or* 14×14½ (*horiz*).

636	1p. Type **174**	30	50
637	3p. Rock Partridge	40	50
638	11p. Rock Dove	55	55
639	12p. Common Waxbill	55	55
640	15p. Common Mynah	60	60
641	18p. Java Sparrow	65	65
642	25p. Red-billed Tropic Bird (*horiz*)	80	80
643	35p. Madeiran Storm Petrel (*horiz*)	1·10	1·10
644	75p. Madagascar Red Fody	2·00	2·25
645	£1 White Tern ("Common Fairy Tern") (*horiz*)	2·25	2·75
646	£2 Giant Petrel (*horiz*)	4·25	5·50
647	£5 St. Helena Sand Plover ("Wirebird")	10·00	12·00
636/47	*Set of* 12	21·00	25·00

For miniature sheets containing the 75p or the design of the £5 reissued as a 75p. see Nos. **MS**740 and **MS**745.

175 Football and Teddy Bear **176** Arum Lily

(Des O. Ball and R. Moss. Litho Questa)

1993 (1 Oct). *Christmas. Toys. T* **175** *and similar horiz designs. Multicoloured. W w* 14 (*sideways*). *P* 14.

648	12p. Type **175**	75	65
649	15p. Yacht and doll	80	70
650	18p. Palette and rocking horse	85	75
651	25p. Model airplane and kite	1·25	1·40
652	60p. Guitar and roller skates	2·25	3·00
648/52	*Set of* 5	5·50	6·00

(Litho Questa)

1994 (6 Jan). *Flowers and Children's Art. T* **176** *and similar vert designs. Multicoloured. W w* 16. *P* 14.

653	12p. Type **176**	40	65
	a. Horiz pair. Nos. 653/4	80	1·25
654	12p. "Arum Lily" (Delphia Mittens)	40	65
655	25p. Ebony	75	1·00
	a. Horiz pair. Nos. 655/6	1·50	2·00
656	25p. "Ebony" (Jason Rogers)	75	1·00
657	35p. Shell Ginger	95	1·10
	a. Horiz pair. Nos. 657/8	1·90	2·10
658	35p. "Shell Ginger" (Jeremy Moyce)	95	1·10
653/8	*Set of* 6	3·75	4·75

The two designs for each value, one showing an actual photograph (face value in yellow) and the other a child's painting (face value in black), were printed together, *se-tenant*, in horizontal pairs throughout the sheets.

177 Abyssinian Guinea Pig **178** Springer's Blenny

(Des Sharon Beeden. Litho Questa)

1994 (18 Feb). *"Hong Kong '94" International Stamp Exhibition. Pets. T* **177** *and similar horiz designs. Multicoloured. W w* 14 (*sideways*). *P* 14×14½.

659	12p. Type **177**	70	70
660	25p. Common tabby cat	1·40	1·40
661	53p. Plain white and black rabbits	2·25	2·75
662	60p. Golden Labrador	2·50	3·00
659/62	*Set of* 4	6·25	7·00

(Des R. Watton. Litho Walsall)

1994 (6 June). *Fishes. T* **178** *and similar horiz designs. Multicoloured. W w* 16 (*sideways*). *P* 14×14½.

663	12p. Type **178**	75	75
664	25p. St. Helena Damselfish	1·50	1·50
665	53p. Melliss's Scorpionfish	2·25	2·75
666	60p. St. Helena Wrasse	2·75	3·25
663/6	*Set of* 4	6·50	7·50

179 *Lampides boeticus*

(Des I. Loe. Litho Walsall)

1994 (9 Aug). *Butterflies. T* **179** *and similar horiz designs. Multicoloured. W w* 14 (*sideways*). *P* 14.

667	12p. Type **179**	75	75
668	25p. *Cynthia cardui*	1·50	1·50
669	53p. *Hypolimnas bolina*	2·25	2·75
670	60p. *Danaus chrysippus*	2·75	3·25
667/70	*Set of* 4	6·50	7·50

180 "Silent Night!"

(Des Jennifer Toombs. Litho Questa)

1994 (6 Oct). *Christmas. Carols. T* **180** *and similar horiz designs. Multicoloured. W w* 16 (*sideways*). *P* 14½.

671	12p. Type **180**	55	45
672	15p. "While Shepherds watched their Flocks by Night"	60	50
673	25p. "Away in a Manger"	1·00	90
674	38p. "We Three Kings"	1·50	2·00
675	60p. "Angels from the Realms of Glory"	2·25	3·00
671/5	*Set of* 5	5·50	6·25

(Des M. Martineau, adapted D. Miller. Litho Walsall)

1994 (15 Dec). *Flowers (2nd series). Vert designs as T* **172**. *Multicoloured. W w* 16. *P* 14½×14.

676	12p. Honeysuckle	35	35
677	15p. Gobblegheer	40	40
678	25p. African Lily	70	80
679	38p. Prince of Wales Feathers	1·00	1·60
680	60p. St. Johns Lily	1·75	2·75
676/80	*Set of* 5	3·75	5·50

181 Fire Engine **182** Site Clearance

(Des B. Dove. Litho Walsall)

1995 (2 Feb). *Emergency Services. T* **181** *and similar horiz designs. Multicoloured. W w* 16 (*sideways*). *P* 14.

681	12p. Type **181**	90	75
682	25p. Lifeboat	1·10	90
683	53p. Police car	2·50	2·75
684	60p. Ambulance	2·75	3·25
681/4	*Set of* 4	6·50	7·00

(Des N. Shewring. Litho Walsall)

1995 (6 Apr). *Construction of Harpers Valley Earth Dam. T* **182** *and similar horiz designs. Multicoloured. W w* 16 (*sideways*). *P* 14×14½.

685	25p. Type **182**	80	1·00
	a. Horiz strip of 5. Nos. 685/9	3·50	
686	25p. Earthworks in progress	80	1·00
687	25p. Laying outlet pipes	80	1·00
688	25p. Revetment block protection	80	1·00
689	25p. Completed dam	80	1·00
685/9	*Set of* 5	3·50	4·50

Nos. 685/9 were printed together, *se-tenant*, in horizontal strips of 5 throughout the sheet, forming a composite design.

(Des R. Watton. Litho Questa)

1995 (8 May). *50th Anniv of End of Second World War. Multicoloured designs as T 75 of Kiribati.* W w 14. P 14.

690	5p. *Lady Denison Pender* (cable ship)	..	50	65
	a. Horiz pair. Nos. 690/1		1·00	1·25
691	5p. H.M.S. *Dragon* (cruiser)	..	50	65
692	12p. R.F.A. *Darkdale* (tanker)		75	90
	a. Horiz pair. Nos. 692/3		1·50	1·75
693	12p. H.M.S. *Hermes* (aircraft carrier, launched 1919)	..	75	90
694	25p. Men of St. Helena Rifles	..	1·25	1·50
	a. Horiz pair. Nos. 694/5		2·50	3·00
695	25p. Governor Major W. J. Bain Gray taking salute	..	1·25	1·50
696	53p. 6-inch coastal gun, Ladder Hill		2·00	2·25
	a. Horiz pair. Nos. 696/7		4·00	4·50
697	53p. Flags signalling "VICTORY"		2·00	2·25
690/7		*Set of 8*	8·00	9·50
MS698	75×85 mm. £1 Reverse of 1939–45 War Medal (*vert*)	..	2·50	2·75

The two designs for each value were printed together, *se-tenant*, as horizontal pairs, forming composite designs, in sheets of 8 with decorated margins.

183 Blushing Snail

184 *Epidendrum ibaguense*

(Des I. Loe. Litho B.D.T.)

1995 (29 Aug). *Endemic Invertebrates.* T 183 *and similar horiz designs. Multicoloured.* W w 14 (*sideways*). P 14.

699	12p. Type 183	..	80	80
700	25p. Golden Sail Spider	..	1·50	1·50
701	53p. Spiky Yellow Woodlouse	..	2·25	2·75
702	60p. St. Helena Shore Crab		2·50	3·00
699/702		*Set of 4*	6·25	7·25
MS703	85×83 mm. £1 Giant Earwig	..	4·00	5·00

(Des N. Shewring. Litho Questa)

1995 (1 Sept). *"Singapore '95" International Stamp Exhibition. Orchids. Sheet, 122×74 mm, containing* T 184 *and similar vert design. Multicoloured.* W w 16 (*sideways*). P 14¹/₂×14.

MS704	50p. Type 184; 50p. "Vanda Miss Joaquim"	..	3·75	4·25

185 "Santa Claus outside Market" (Jason Alex Rogers)

186 *Walmer Castle*, 1915

(Des B. Dare. Litho Walsall)

1995 (17 Oct). *Christmas. Children's Paintings.* T 185 *and similar horiz designs. Multicoloured.* W w 14 (*sideways*). P 14¹/₂.

705	12p. Type 185	..	35	35
706	15p. "Santa Claus and band" (Ché David Yon)	..	45	45
707	25p. "Santa Claus outside Community Centre" (Leon Williams)	..	70	75
708	38p. "Santa Claus in decorated street" (Stacey McDaniel)	..	1·00	1·25
709	60p. "Make a better World" (Kissha Karla Kacy Thomas)	..	1·75	2·50
705/9		*Set of 5*	3·75	4·75

(Des J. Batchelor. Litho Walsall)

1996 (8 Jan). *Union Castle Mail Ships (1st series).* T 186 *and similar horiz designs. Multicoloured.* W w 16 (*sideways*). P 14.

710	12p. Type 186	..	45	35
711	25p. *Llangibby Castle*, 1934	..	75	65
712	53p. *Stirling Castle*, 1940	..	1·40	2·00
713	60p. *Pendennis Castle*, 1965	..	1·60	2·00
710/13		*Set of 4*	3·75	4·50

See also Nos. 757/60.

187 Early Telecommunications Equipment

(Des N. Shewring. Litho Walsall)

1996 (28 Mar). *Centenary of Radio.* T 187 *and similar horiz design. Multicoloured.* W w 14 (*sideways*). P 13¹/₂×14.

714	60p. Type 187		1·50	1·75
715	£1 Guglielmo Marconi and *Elettra* (yacht)	2·25	2·75

(Des D. Miller. Litho Walsall)

1996 (22 Apr). *70th Birthday of Queen Elizabeth II. Vert designs as* T 55 *of New Zealand (Tokelau), each incorporating a different photograph of the Queen. Multicoloured.* W w 16. P 14¹/₂.

716	15p. Jamestown	..	40	40
717	25p. Prince Andrew School		65	65
718	53p. Castle entrance	..	1·25	2·00
719	60p. Plantation House	..	1·50	2·00
716/19		*Set of 4*	3·50	4·50
MS720	64×66 mm. £1.50, Queen Elizabeth II		3·25	4·00

188 Helicopter Mail to H.M.S. *Protector* (ice patrol ship), 1964

189 "Mr. Porteous's House"

(Des A. Theobald. Litho B.D.T.)

1996 (8 June). *"CAPEX '96" International Stamp Exhibition, Toronto. Mail Transport.* T 188 *and similar horiz designs. Multicoloured.* W w 16 (*sideways*). P 14.

721	12p. Type 188	..	50	45
722	25p. Postman on motor scooter, 1965		75	65
723	53p. Loading mail plane, Wideawake Airfield, Ascension Island	..	1·40	2·00
724	60p. St. *Helena II* (mail ship) unloading at St. Helena		1·50	2·00
721/4		*Set of 4*	3·75	4·50
MS725	98×73 mm. £1 L.M.S. No. 5624 *St. Helena* locomotive (43×27 mm). P 13¹/₂		2·40	3·00

(Adapted (from contemporary paintings) D. Miller. Litho Walsall)

1996 (12 Aug). *Napoleonic Sites.* T 189 *and similar horiz designs. Multicoloured.* W w 14 (*sideways*). P 14×14¹/₂.

726	12p. Type 189	..	35	35
727	25p. "The Briars' Pavilion"		65	65
728	53p. "Longwood House"	..	1·40	2·00
729	60p. "Napoleon's Tomb"	..	1·50	2·00
726/9		*Set of 4*	3·50	4·50

190 Frangipani and Sandy Bay from Diana's Peak

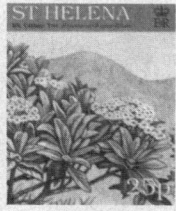

191 Black Cabbage Tree

(Des N. Shewring. Litho Questa)

1996 (1 Oct). *Christmas. Flowers and Views.* T 190 *and similar vert designs. Multicoloured.* W w 14. P 14¹/₂×14.

730	12p. Type 190	..	40	40
731	15p. Bougainvillaea and Upper Jamestown from Sampson's Battery		50	50
732	25p. Jacaranda and Jacob's Ladder		75	75
733	£1 Pink Periwinkle and Lot's Wife Ponds		2·75	4·00
730/3		*Set of 4*	4·00	5·00

(Des N. Shewring. Litho Questa)

1997 (17 Jan). *Endemic Plants from Diana's Peak National Park.* T 191 *and similar vert designs. Multicoloured.* W w 14 (*sideways*). P 14¹/₂×14.

734	25p. Type 191	..	80	90
	a. Sheetlet. Nos. 734/9	..	4·25	
735	25p. Whitewood	..	80	90
736	25p. Tree Fern	..	80	90
737	25p. Dwarf Jellico	..	80	90
738	25p. Lobelia	..	80	90
739	25p. Dogwood	..	80	90
734/9		*Set of 6*	4·25	4·75

Nos. 734/9 were printed together, *se-tenant*, in sheetlets of 6 with the backgrounds forming a composite design.

(Des D. Miller. Litho Questa)

1997 (3 Feb). *"HONG KONG '97" International Stamp Exhibition. Sheet 130×90 mm, containing design as No. 644.* W w 14 (*sideways*). P 14¹/₂×14.

MS740	75p. Madagascar Red Fody	..	1·75	2·25

192 João da Nova's Lookout sighting St. Helena, 1502

(Des R. Watton. Litho Questa)

1997 (29 May). *500th Anniv of the Discovery of St. Helena (1st issue).* T 192 *and similar vert designs. Multicoloured.* W w 14. P 14×13¹/₂.

741	20p. Type 192	..	80	65
742	25p. Don Fernando Lopez (first inhabitant) and cockerel, 1515		90	75
743	30p. Thomas Cavendish and *Desire*, 1588		1·00	1·00
744	80p. *Royal Merchant* (English galleon), 1591	2·50	3·00
741/4		*Set of 4*	4·75	4·75

See also Nos. 762/5 and 786/9.

(Des D. Miller. Litho Walsall)

1997 (20 June). *Return of Hong Kong to China. Sheet 130×90 mm, containing design as No. 647, but changed face value and imprint date.* W w 14 (*sideways*). P 14¹/₂×14.

MS745	75p. St. Helena Sand Plover ("Wirebird")	1·75	2·25

(Des N. Shewring (No. MS752), D. Miller (others). Litho Questa (No. MS752), B.D.T. (others))

1997 (10 July). *Golden Wedding of Queen Elizabeth and Prince Philip. Multicoloured designs as* T 87 *of Kiribati.* W w 16. P 13¹/₂.

746	10p. Royal Family's Visit, 1947	..	35	40
	a. Horiz pair. Nos. 746/7		70	80
747	10p. Wedding photograph of Princess Elizabeth and Prince Philip		35	40
748	15p. Princess Elizabeth and Prince Philip, 1947	..	50	65
	a. Horiz pair. Nos. 748/9		1·00	1·25
749	15p. Presenting bouquets, Royal Visit, 1947		50	65
750	50p. Prince Philip on Royal Visit, 1957	..	1·40	1·75
	a. Horiz pair. Nos. 750/1		2·75	3·50
751	50p. Wedding party on balcony, 1947		1·40	1·75
746/51		*Set of 6*	4·00	5·00
MS752	111×70 mm. £1.50, Queen Elizabeth and Prince Philip in landau (*horiz*). W w 14 (*sideways*). P 14×14¹/₂		4·00	4·50

Nos. 746/7, 748/9 and 750/1 were each printed together, *se-tenant*, in horizontal pairs throughout the sheets.

193 Flower Arrangement

(Des Jennifer Toombs. Litho Walsall)

1997 (29 Sept). *Christmas. 25th Anniv of the Duke of Edinburgh's Award in St. Helena.* T 193 *and similar horiz designs. Multicoloured.* W w 16 (*sideways*). P 13¹/₂×14.

753	15p. Type 193	..	40	35
754	20p. Calligraphy	..	50	45
755	40p. Camping	..	1·00	1·25
756	75p. Table laid for Christmas dinner		2·00	2·50
753/6		*Set of 4*	3·50	4·00

(Des J. Batchelor. Litho Questa)

1998 (2 Jan). *Union Castle Mail Ships (2nd series). Horiz designs as* T 186. *Multicoloured.* W w 16 (*sideways*). P 14.

757	20p. *Avondale Castle*, 1900	..	65	55
758	25p. *Dunnottar Castle*, 1936	..	75	65
759	30p. *Llandovery Castle*, 1943	..	85	85
760	80p. *Good Hope Castle*, 1977	..	2·25	2·75
757/60		*Set of 4*	4·00	4·25

(Des D. Miller. Litho Questa)

1998 (4 Apr). *Diana, Princess of Wales Commemoration. Sheet 145×70 mm containing vert designs as* T 91 *of Kiribati.* W w 14 (*sideways*). P 14¹/₂×14.

MS761 30p. Wearing green and white hat, 1983; 30p. Wearing white jacket; 30p. Wearing green jacket, 1996; 30p. In evening dress, 1991 (*sold at £1.20 + 20p. charity premium*) .. .. 2·75 3·00

(Des R. Watton. Litho Walsall)

1998 (2 July). *500th Anniv of the Discovery of St. Helena (2nd issue). Multicoloured designs as T 192, but horiz. W w 16 (sideways). P 14.*

762	20p. Settlers planting crops, 1659	60	55
763	25p. Dutch invasion, 1672	70	60
764	30p. Recapture by the English, 1673	80	80
765	80p. Royal Charter of 1673	2·00	2·50
762/5	Set of 4	3·50	4·00

195 *Desire* (Cavendish), 1588

196 Metal Lanterns

(Des J. Batchelor. Litho Walsall)

1998 (25 Aug). *Maritime Heritage. T 195 and similar horiz designs. Multicoloured. W w 14 (sideways). P 13½×14.*

766	10p. Type **195**	20	25
767	15p. *Witte Leeuw* (Dutch East Indiaman), 1602	30	35
768	20p. H.M.S. *Swallow* and H.M.S. *Dolphin* (Carteret), 1751	40	45
769	25p. H.M.S. *Endeavour* (Cook), 1771	50	55
770	30p. H.M.S. *Providence* (sloop), 1792	60	65
771	35p. *St. Helena* (East India Company schooner), 1815	70	75
772	40p. H.M.S. *Northumberland* (ship of the line), 1815	80	85
773	50p. *Rurik* (Von Kotzebue), 1815	1·00	1·10
774	75p. H.M.S. *Erebus* (Ross), 1826	1·50	1·60
775	80p. *Keying* (junk), 1847	1·60	1·75
776	£2 *La Belle Poule* (French frigate), 1840	4·00	4·25
777	£5 H.M.S. *Rattlesnake* (screw corvette), 1861	10·00	10·50
766/77	Set of 12	22·00	23·00

No. 771 is inscribed "H.M.S." in error.

(Des Jennifer Toombs. Litho Questa)

1998 (28 Sept). *Christmas. Island Crafts. T 196 and similar square designs. W w 16 (sideways). P 14.*

778	15p. Type **196**	40	40
779	20p. Wood-turned bowls	50	50
780	30p. Inlaid woodwork on jewellery box	70	80
781	85p. Hessian and seedwork bag and hat	2·00	2·50
778/81	Set of 4	3·25	3·75

197 H.M.S. *Endeavour* (Cook), 1771

(Des J. Batchelor. Litho Questa)

1999 (5 Mar). *"Australia '99" World Stamp Exhibition, Melbourne. Sheet 120×80 mm. W w 14 (sideways). P 13½×14.*
MS782 **197** £1·50, multicoloured .. .. 3·50 3·75

(Des D. Miller. Litho Walsall)

1999 (19 June). *Royal Wedding. Vert designs as T 153 of Pitcairn Islands. Multicoloured. W w 16. P 14.*

783	30p. Photographs of Prince Edward and Miss Sophie Rhys-Jones	60	65
784	£1·30, Engagement photograph	2·50	2·75

198 1971 Napoleon 2p. Stamp

(Des D. Miller. Litho B.D.T.)

1999 (2 July). *"PhilexFrance '99" International Stamp Exhibition, Paris. Sheet 100×70 mm. W w 16 (sideways). P 14.*
MS785 **198** £1·50, multicoloured .. .. 3·00 3·25

(Des R. Watton. Litho Walsall)

1999 (12 July). *500th Anniv of the Discovery of St. Helena (3rd issue). Multicoloured designs as T 192, but horiz. W w 14 (sideways). P 14.*

786	20p. Jamestown fortifications	45	45
787	25p. Roadway up Ladder Hill, 1718	55	55
788	30p. Governor Skottowe with Captain Cook at St. James Church, 1775	75	75
789	80p. Presentation of sword of honour to Governor Brooke, 1799	1·75	1·90
786/9	Set of 4	3·25	3·25

199 King and Queen visiting Jamestown

(Des D. Miller. Litho Cartor)

1999 (3 Sept). *"Queen Elizabeth the Queen Mother's Century". T 199 and similar horiz designs. Multicoloured. W w 16 (sideways). P 13½.*

790	15p. Type **199**	40	40
791	25p. Viewing bomb damage, Buckingham Palace, 1940	55	55
792	30p. With Prince Andrew, 1997	70	70
793	80p. Presenting colour to R.A.F. Central Flying School, and with Red Arrows	1·75	1·90
790/3	Set of 4	3·00	3·25
MS794	145×70 mm. £1·50, Queen Elizabeth, 1937, and Royal Family on balcony after Coronation	3·00	3·25

200 Modern Communications Equipment and Section of 1899 Cable

(Litho Questa)

1999 (26 Nov). *Centenary of Cable & Wireless Communications plc on St. Helena. T 200 and similar horiz designs. W w 14 (sideways). Multicoloured. P 14.*

795	20p. multicoloured	40	45
796	25p. black, reddish brown and bistre-brown	50	55
797	30p. black, reddish brown and bistre-brown	60	65
798	80p. multicoloured	1·60	1·75
795/8	Set of 4	3·00	3·25

Designs—25p. *Seine* (cable ship); 30p. *Anglia* (cable ship); 80p. Cable & Wireless Headquarters, The Briars.

201 *Victoria* (cruise liner) at St. Helena

(Litho Questa)

1999 (23 Dec). *Union Castle Line Centenary Voyage. Sheet 88×72 mm. W w 14 (sideways). P 13×13½.*
MS799 **201** £2 multicoloured .. .. 4·00 4·25

202 King Edward VI

203 Distillation Plant at Ruperts

(Des Crown Agents. Litho Walsall)

2000 (29 Feb). *"Stamp Show 2000" International Stamp Exhibition, London. Kings and Queens of England. T 202 and similar vert designs. Multicoloured. W w 14. P 14.*

800	30p. Type **202**	60	65
	a. Sheetlet. Nos. 800/5	3·50	
801	30p. King James I	60	65
802	30p. King William III and Queen Mary II	60	65
803	30p. King George II	60	65
804	30p. Queen Victoria	60	65
805	30p. King George VI	60	65
800/5	Set of 6	3·50	3·75

Nos. 800/5 were printed together, *se-tenant*, in sheetlets of 6 with an enlarged illustrated right-hand margin.

(Des A. Theobald. Litho Questa)

2000 (10 Apr). *Centenary of Second Boer War (1st issue). T 203 and similar horiz designs. Multicoloured. W w 14 (sideways). P 14.*

806	15p. Type **203**	30	35
807	25p. Camp at Broadbottom	50	55
808	30p. Committee of Boer prisoners	60	65
809	80p. General Cronje and family at Kent Cottage	1·60	1·75
806/9	Set of 4	3·00	3·25

STAMP BOOKLETS

1962 (2 Mar). *Black on green cover. Stitched.*
SB1 4s. 6d. booklet containing 1d., 1½d., 2d., 3d. and 6d. (Nos. 176/9, 181), each in block of 4 .. 50·00

1969. *Black on grey-green cover. Stapled.*
SB2 5s. 4d. booklet containing 1d., 2d., 3d., 4d. and 6d. (Nos. 227, 229/32), each in block of 4 .. 28·00

1971 (24 June). *Black on green cover. Stapled.*
SB3 44p. booklet containing ½p., 1p., 1½p., 2p., 2½p. and 3½p. (Nos. 261/6), each in block of 4 .. 15·00

1981 (June). *Black printed cover showing St. Helena Arms. Stapled.*
SB4 £1 booklet containing 1p., 3p., 5p., 6p. and 10p. (Nos. 319/22A, 325A), each in block of 4 .. 11·00

1984 (1 June). *Black on blue cover showing St. Helena Arms. Stapled.*
SB5 £1·04, booklet containing 1p., 3p., 7p. and 15p. (Nos. 425/6, 428, 430), each in block of 4 .. 5·50

1991 (17 June). *65th Birthday of Queen Elizabeth II and 70th Birthday of Prince Philip. Black on blue cover, 116×106 mm, showing St. Helena Arms. Stapled.*
SB6 £1 booklet containing 25p. (Nos. 591/2) in block of 4 stamps and 2 labels .. 2·50

POSTAGE DUE STAMPS

D 1 Outline Map of St. Helena

(Des L. Curtis. Litho Questa)

1986 (9 June). *W w 16. P 14½×14.*

D1	D 1	1p. deep brown and cinnamon	10	10
D2		2p. deep brown and bright orange	10	10
D3		5p. deep brown and orange-vermilion	10	15
D4		7p. black and bright reddish violet	10	10
D5		10p. black and violet-blue	20	25
D6		25p. black and pale emerald	50	55
D1/6		Set of 6	95	1·10

St. Kitts-Nevis

ST. CHRISTOPHER

From 1760 the postal service for St. Christopher was organised by the Deputy Postmaster General on Antigua. It was not until May 1779 that the first postmaster was appointed to the island and the use of postmarks on outgoing mail commenced.

Stamps of Great Britain were used from May 1858 and the end of March 1860 when control of the postal services passed to the local authorities. In the years which followed, prior to the introduction of St. Christopher stamps in April 1870, a circular "PAID" handstamp was used on overseas mail.

BASSETERRE

Stamps of GREAT BRITAIN *cancelled* "A 12" *as Type* Z 1 *of Jamaica.*

1858 *to* **1860.**

Z1	1d. rose-red (1857), *perf* 14	..	..	£600
Z2	2d. blue (1858) (Plate No. 7)	..	..	£900
Z3	4d. rose (1857)	..	..	£300
Z4	6d. lilac (1856)	..	..	£180
Z5	1s. green (1856)	..	..	£1200

PRICES FOR STAMPS ON COVER

Nos. 1/9	*from* × 25
Nos. 11/21	*from* × 30
Nos. 22/6	*from* × 25
No. 27	—
No. 28	*from* × 30
Nos. R1/6	—

1   Distorted "E" (R. 2/1)

1870 (1 Apr)–**79.** *Wmk Crown CC.* (a) *P* 12½.

1	1	1d. dull rose	..	65·00	42·00
		a. Wmk sideways	..	£250	£180
		w. Wmk inverted	..		
2		1d. magenta (*shades*) (1871)	..	50·00	28·00
		a. Wmk sideways	..		† £425
		w. Wmk inverted	..	75·00	
		x. Wmk reversed	..		
4		6d. yellow-green	..	95·00	18·00
		w. Wmk inverted	..		
5		6d. green (1871)	..	90·00	7·50

(b) *P* 14

6	1	1d. magenta (*shades*) (1875)	..	60·00	7·00
		a. Bisected diag or vert (½d.) (on cover) (3.82)			† £1300
		w. Wmk inverted	..		
7		2½d. red-brown (11.79)	..	£170	£225
8		4d. blue (11.79)	..	£150	15·00
		a. Wmk sideways	..	£600	£100
		w. Wmk inverted	..	£275	40·00
9		6d. green (1876)	..	55·00	5·00
		a. Imperf between (pair)	..		
		b. Wmk sideways	..	£400	90·00

The magenta used for the 1d. was a fugitive colour which reacts to both light and water.

No. 6a was authorised for use between March and June 1882 to make up the 2½d. letter rate and for ½d. book post.

1882 (June)–**90.** *Wmk Crown CA. P* 14.

11	1	½d. dull green	..	90	1·25
		a. Wmk sideways	..	£250	
		x. Wmk reversed	..		
12		1d. dull magenta	..	£475	65·00
		a. Bisected diagonally (½d.) (on cover)			
13		1d. carmine-rose (2.84)	..	1·00	2·00
		a. Bisected (½d.) (on cover)	..		
		b. Distorted "E"	..	15·00	
		w. Wmk reversed	..		
14		2½d. pale red-brown	..	£170	55·00
15		2½d. deep red-brown	..	£180	60·00
16		2½d. ultramarine (2.84)	..	1·50	1·50
17		4d. blue	..	£400	20·00
		w. Wmk inverted	..		
18		4d. grey (10.84)	..	1·25	80
19		6d. olive-brown (3.90)	..	80·00	£300
		w. Wmk inverted	..		
20		1s. mauve (6.86)	..	90·00	65·00
		w. Wmk inverted	..	—	£110
21		1s. bright mauve (1890)	..	80·00	£130
	19/20 Optd "Specimen" ..		*Set of* 2	£120	

FOUR PENCE   Halfpenny

(2)   (3)

1884 (Dec). *No.* 9 *surch with T* 2 *by The Advertiser Press.*

22	1	4d. on 6d. green	..	55·00	48·00
		a. Full stop after "PENCE"	..	55·00	48·00
		b. Surch double	..		— £1700

No. 22a occurred on alternate stamps.

1885 (March). *No.* 13 *bisected and each half diagonally surch with T* 3.

23	1	½d. on half of 1d. carmine-rose	..	24·00	38·00
		a. Unsevered pair	..	£100	£110
		ab. Ditto, one surch inverted	..	£350	£250
		b. Surch inverted	..	£200	£100
		c. Surch double ..			

ONE PENNY.   4d.

(4)   (5)

1886 (June). *No.* 9 *surch with T* 4 *or* 5 *each showing a manuscript line through the original value.*

24	1	1d. on 6d. green	..	16·00	28·00
		a. Surch inverted	..	.£5000	
		b. Surch double	..	—	£1300
25		4d. on 6d. green..	..	48·00	90·00
		a. No stop after "d"	..	£180	£250
		b. Surch double	..	£1600	£1700

No. 24b is only known penmarked with dates between 21 July and 3 August 1886, or with violet handstamp.

1887 (May). *No.* 11 *surch with T* 4 *showing a manuscript line through the original value.*

26	1	1d. on ½d. dull green	..	28·00	38·00

ONE PENNY.

(7)

1888 (May). *No.* 16 *surch.*

(a) *With T* 4. *Original value unobliterated*

27	1	1d. on 2½d. ultramarine	..	£10000	£8500

(b) *With T* 7 *showing a manuscript line through the original value*

28	1	1d. on 2½d. ultramarine	..	55·00	55·00
		a. Surch inverted	..	£8000	£5500

The 1d. of Antigua was used provisionally in St. Christopher between February and March 1890 during a shortage of 1d. stamps. Such use can be distinguished by the postmark, which is "A 12" in place of "A02" (*price from* £120 *used*).

REVENUE STAMPS USED FOR POSTAGE

Saint Christopher   SAINT KITTS NEVIS

REVENUE

(R 1)   (R 2)

1883. *Nos.* F6 *and* F8 *of Nevis optd with Type* R 1, *in violet. Wmk Crown CA. P* 14.

R1	1d. lilac-mauve	..	..	£225	
R2	6d. green	..	..	65·00	£110

1885. *Optd with Type* R 2. *Wmk Crown CA. P* 14.

R3	1d. rose	..	..	1·50	9·50
R4	3d. mauve	..	..	12·00	60·00
R5	6d. orange-brown	..	..	7·00	48·00
R6	1s. olive	..	..	1·50	38·00

Other fiscal stamps with overprints as above also exist, but none of these was ever available for postal purposes.

The stamps for St. Christopher was superseded by the general issue for Leeward Islands on 31 October 1890.

Stamps for St. Kitts, issued from 1980 onwards will be found listed after those for the combined colony.

NEVIS

Little is known concerning the early postal affairs of Nevis, but it is recorded that the British G.P.O. was to establish a branch office on the island under an Act of Parliament, passed in 1710, although arrangements may not have been finalised for a number of years afterwards. Nevis appears as "a new office" in the P.O. Accounts of 1787. Stamps of Great Britain were used on the island from May 1858 until the colonial authorities assumed control of the postal service on 1 May 1860. Between this date and the introduction of Nevis stamps in 1861 No. CC1 was again used on overseas mail.

CHARLESTOWN
CROWNED-CIRCLE HANDSTAMPS

CC 1

CC1	CC 1	NEVIS (R.) (9.1852)	..	*Price on cover* £3250

No. CC1, but struck in black, was later used on several occasions up to 1886 where there were shortages of adhesive stamps.

Stamps of GREAT BRITAIN *cancelled* "A 09" *as Type* Z 1 *of Jamaica.*

1858 *to* **1860.**

Z1	1d. rose-red (1857), *perf* 14	..	..	£375
Z2	2d. blue (1858) (Plate Nos. 7, 8)	..	..	£1600
Z3	4d. rose (1857)	..	..	£300
Z4	6d. lilac (1856)	..	..	£275
Z5	1s. green (1856)	..	..	

PRICES FOR STAMPS ON COVER

Nos. 5/22	*from* × 20
Nos. 23/4	*from* × 10
Nos. 25/34	*from* × 20
Nos. 35/6	*from* × 10
Nos. F1/8	*from* × 30

1   2

3   4

The designs on the stamps refer to a medicinal spring on the island

(Recess Nissen & Parker, London)

1861. *Greyish paper. P* 13.

5	1	1d. dull lake	..	55·00	38·00
		a. On blued paper	..	£200	£100
6	2	4d. rose	..	80·00	55·00
		a. On blued paper	..	£650	£150
7	3	6d. grey-lilac	..	80·00	42·00
		a. On blued paper	..	£500	£190
8	4	1s. green	..	£180	55·00
		a. On blued paper	..	£750	£170

1866–76. *White paper. P* 15.

9	1	1d. pale red	..	35·00	32·00
10		1d. deep red	..	35·00	32·00
11	2	4d. orange	..	95·00	19·00
12		4d. deep orange	..	95·00	19·00
13	4	1s. blue-green	..	£180	26·00
14		1s. yellow-green (1876)	..	£800	£100
		a. Vertically laid paper	..	£11000	£3500
		b. No. 9 on sheet with crossed lines on hill	£3500	£500	
		c. Ditto. On laid paper	..		† £8500

Examples of the 4d. exist showing part of a papermakers watermark reading "A. COWAN & SONS EXTRA SUPERFINE".

(Lithographed by transfer from the engraved plates Nissen and Parker, London)

1876–78. *P* 15.

15	1	1d. pale rose-red	..	16·00	13·00
		a. Imperf (pair)	..	£425	
16		1d. deep rose-red	..	26·00	20·00
17		1d. vermilion-red (1878)	..	22·00	20·00
		a. Bisected (½d.) (on cover)	..		† £1600
18	2	4d. orange-yellow	..	£140	28·00
		a. Imperf between (vert pair)	..	£3250	
19	3	6d. grey (1878)	..	£190	£170
20	4	1s. pale green (1878)	..	70·00	90·00
		a. Imperf..	..		
		b. Imperf between (horiz strip of three)	£4250		
		c. No. 9 on sheet with crossed lines on hill	£225		
21		1s. green	..	75·00	£110
		c. No. 9 on sheet with crossed lines on hill			

No. 21c occurs on a small part of the deep green printing only.

RETOUCHES. 1d. Lithograph.

i.	No. 1 on sheet. Top of hill over kneeling figure redrawn by five thick lines and eight small slanting lines	£140 £150
ii.	No. 1 on sheet. Another retouch. Three series of short vertical strokes behind the kneeling figure..	£140 £150
iii.	No. 3 on sheet. Right upper corner star and border below star retouched	£140 £150
iv.	No. 9 on sheet. Retouch in same position as on No. 3 but differing in detail	£160 £170
v.	No. 12 on sheet. Dress of standing figure retouched by a number of horizontal and vertical lines	£140 £150

1878. *Litho. P* 11½.

22	1	1d. vermilion-red	..	38·00	48·00
		a. Bisected (½d.) (on cover)	..		† £1600
		b. Imperf (pair)..	..	£300	
		c. Imperf between (horiz pair)	..		

5 (Die I)   (6)

(Typo D.L.R.)

1879–80. *Wmk Crown CC. P 14.*
23	5	1d. lilac-mauve (1880)		55·00	28·00
		a. Bisected (½d.) (on cover)		†	£900
		w. Wmk inverted			
24		2½d. red-brown		95·00	85·00

1882–90. *Wmk Crown CA. P 14.*
25	5	½d. dull green (11.83)		3·25	9·00
		a. Top left triangle detached		85·00	
26		1d. lilac-mauve		80·00	25·00
		a. Bisected (½d.) on cover (1883)		†	£700
27		1d. dull rose (11.83)		19·00	12·00
		a. *Carmine* (1884)		5·00	5·50
		ab. Top left triangle detached		£140	
28		2½d. red-brown		£100	45·00
29		2½d. ultramarine (11.83)		13·00	11·00
		a. Top left triangle detached		£275	
30		4d. blue		£275	45·00
31		4d. grey (1884)		6·50	2·75
		a. Top left triangle detached		£225	£250
32		6d. green (11.83)		£350	£350
33		6d. chestnut (10.88)		17·00	48·00
		a. Top left triangle detached		£300	
34		1s. pale violet (3.90)		85·00	£160
		a. Top left triangle detached		£700	
33/4		Optd "Specimen"		*Set of 2*	£110

For illustration of the "top left triangle detached" variety, which occurs on Plate 2 R. 3/3 of the right pane, see below Montserrat No. 5.

1883. *No. 26 bisected vertically and surch with T 6, reading upwards or downwards.*
35		½d. on half 1d. lilac-mauve (V.)		£750	35·00
		a. Surch double		—	£300
		b. Surch on half "REVENUE" stamp No. F6		—	£500
36		½d. on half 1d. lilac-mauve		£900	32·00
		a. Surch double		—	£300
		b. Unsevered pair		£2750	£400
		c. Surch on half "REVENUE" stamp No. F6		—	£500

FISCALS USED FOR POSTAGE

Revenue   REVENUE
(F 1)   (F 2)

1882. *(a) Stamps of 1876–78 optd with Type F 1.*
F1	1	1d. bright red		42·00	
F2	2	1d. rose		42·00	16·00
F3		4d. orange		75·00	
F4	3	6d. grey		£120	
F5	4	1s. green		£140	
		a. No. 9 on sheet with crossed lines on hill			

(b) Nos. 26, 30 and 32 optd with Type F 2.
F6	5	1d. lilac-mauve		45·00	45·00
		a. Bisected (½d.) (on cover)			
F7		4d. blue		23·00	50·00
F8		6d. green		15·00	55·00

Nos. F1/5 were produced from fresh transfers. Similar "REVENUE" handstamps, both with and without stop, were also applied to postage issues.

The stamps of Nevis were superseded by the general issue for Leeward Islands on 31 October 1890. Stamps for Nevis were again issued in 1980 and will be found listed after those for the combined colony.

ST. KITTS-NEVIS

CROWN COLONY

Stamps for the combined colony were introduced in 1903, and were used concurrently with the general issues of Leeward Islands until the latter were withdrawn on 1 July 1956.

PRICES FOR STAMPS ON COVER TO 1945	
Nos. 1/9	*from* × 3
No. 10	
Nos. 11/20	*from* × 3
No. 21	
Nos. 22/3	*from* × 15
Nos. 24/34	*from* × 3
Nos. 35/6	
Nos. 37/47	*from* × 2
Nos. 47a/b	
Nos. 48/57	*from* × 2
Nos. 58/60	
Nos. 61/4	*from* × 2
Nos. 65/7	*from* × 5
Nos. 68/77	*from* × 2

1 Christopher Columbus   2 Medicinal Spring

(Typo D.L.R.)

1903. *Wmk Crown CA. P 14.*
1	1	½d. dull purple and deep green		1·50	70
2	2	1d. grey-black and carmine		4·00	20
3	1	2d. dull purple and brown		2·25	11·00
4		2½d. grey-black and blue		16·00	4·25
5	2	3d. deep green and orange		9·00	25·00
6	1	6d. grey-black and bright purple		3·50	32·00
7		1s. grey-green and orange		6·00	11·00
8	2	2s. deep green and grey-black		12·00	20·00
9	1	2s. 6d. grey-black and violet		18·00	40·00
10	2	5s. dull purple and sage-green		48·00	55·00
1/10				*Set of 10*	£110 £180
1/10		Optd "Specimen"		*Set of 10*	£130

1905–18. *Wmk Mult Crown CA. Chalk-surfaced paper (1d. (No. 13), 5s.) or ordinary paper (others). P 14.*
11	1	½d. dull purple and deep green		4·50	5·50
12		½d. grey-green (1907)		75	35
		a. *Dull blue-green* (1916)		30	1·50
13	2	1d. grey-black and carmine (1906)		1·00	25
14		1d. carmine (1907)		1·60	15
		a. Scarlet (1916)		35	20
15	1	2d. dull purple and brown		6·00	6·50
		a. Chalk-surfaced paper (1906)		5·00	7·00
16		2½d. grey-black and blue (1907)		14·00	3·25
17		2½d. bright blue (1907)		1·75	40
18	2	3d. deep green and orange		3·75	6·50
		a. Chalk-surfaced paper (1906)		2·00	2·50
19	1	6d. grey-black and deep violet		18·00	35·00
		a. Chalk-surfaced paper. Grey-black and deep purple (1908)		11·00	25·00
		ab. Grey-black and bright purple (1916)		4·50	25·00
20		1s. grey-green and orange (1909)		16·00	26·00
		a. Chalk-surfaced paper		2·75	26·00
21	2	5s. dull purple and sage-green (11.18)		30·00	75·00
11/21				*Set of 11*	55·00 £130
12, 14, 17		Optd "Specimen"		*Set of 3*	60·00

WAR TAX   WAR STAMP
(3)   (3a)

1916 (Oct). *Optd with T 3. Wmk Mult Crown CA. P 14.*
22	1	½d. dull blue-green (No. 12a) (Optd S. £40)		40	40
		a. *Deep green*		40	40
		x. Wmk reversed		35·00	

No. 22a was a special printing produced for this overprint.

1918 (Aug). *Optd with T 3a. Wmk Mult Crown CA. P 14.*
23	1	½d. orange (Optd S. £45)		30	40
		a. Short opt (right pane R. 10/1)		15·00	

No. 23 was a special printing produced for this overprint.
No. 23a shows the overprint 2 mm high instead of 2½ mm.

4   5

(Typo D.L.R.)

1920–22. *Wmk Mult Crown CA (sideways*). Ordinary paper (½d. to 2½d.) or chalk-surfaced paper (others). P 14.*
24	4	½d. blue-green		3·75	5·50
25	5	1d. scarlet		2·25	5·00
26	4	1½d. orange-yellow		1·25	1·75
		x. Wmk sideways reversed		55·00	
		y. Wmk sideways inverted and reversed			
27	5	2d. slate-grey		3·00	3·50
28	4	2½d. ultramarine		1·50	8·00
		a. "A" of "CA" missing from wmk		£250	
29	5	3d. purple/yellow		1·50	11·00
30	4	6d. dull purple and bright mauve		3·50	11·00
31	5	1s. grey and black/green		3·50	3·75
32	4	2s. dull purple and blue/blue		14·00	19·00
		x. Wmk sideways reversed		£120	
33	5	2s. 6d. grey and red/blue		5·00	28·00
		y. Wmk sideways inverted and reversed		£120	
34	4	5s. green and red/pale yellow		5·00	40·00
		x. Wmk sideways reversed		80·00	
35	5	10s. green and red/green		12·00	48·00
36	4	£1 purple and black/red (1922)		£225	£300
24/36				*Set of 13*	£250 £400
24/36		Optd "Specimen"		*Set of 13*	£275

*The normal sideways watermark shows Crown to left of CA, as seen from the back of the stamp.

1921–9. *Wmk Mult Script CA (sideways*). Chalk-surfaced paper (2½d. (No. 44), 3d. (No. 45a) and 6d. to 5s.) or ordinary paper (others). P 14.*
37	4	½d. blue-green		2·00	1·50
		a. Yellow-green (1922)		1·25	80
38	5	1d. rose-carmine		50	15
39		1d. deep violet (1922)		3·50	70
		a. Pale violet (1929)		5·50	1·50
40	4	1½d. red (1925)		2·50	2·50
40a		1½d. red-brown (1929)		65	30
41	5	2d. slate-grey (1922)		40	60
42	4	2½d. pale bright blue (1922)		3·00	2·25
43		2½d. brown (1922)		1·75	8·50
44		2½d. ultramarine (1927)		1·50	3·50
45	5	3d. dull ultramarine (1922)		70	3·75
45a		3d. purple/yellow (1927)		60	3·75
46	4	6d. dull and bright purple (1924)		4·25	5·50
		aw. Wmk Crown to right of CA		3·50	5·00
46b	5	1s. black/green (1929)		3·75	6·00
47	4	2s. purple and blue (1929)		8·00	22·00
47a	5	2s. 6d. black and red/blue (1927)		13·00	29·00
47b	4	5s. green and red/yellow (1929)		38·00	60·00
37/47b				*Set of 16*	70·00 £130
37/47b		Optd/Perf "Specimen"		*Set of 16*	£325

*The normal watermark shows Crown to left of CA, as seen from the back of the stamp.

In the Specimen set listed above No. 38 is overprinted. A later printing exists perforated "Specimen" (Price £70).

6 Old Road Bay and Mount Misery

(Typo D.L.R.)

1923. *Tercentenary of Colony. Chalk-surfaced paper. P 14.*
(a) Wmk Mult Script CA (sideways)
48	6	½d. black and green		2·25	7·00
49		1d. black and bright violet		4·00	1·50
50		1½d. black and scarlet		4·50	10·00
51		2d. black and slate-grey		3·00	1·50
52		2½d. black and brown		5·00	30·00
53		3d. black and ultramarine		3·75	14·00
54		6d. black and bright purple		9·00	32·00
55		1s. black and sage-green		13·00	32·00
56		2s. black and blue/blue		38·00	50·00
57		2s. 6d. black and red/blue		48·00	70·00
58		10s. black and red/emerald		£250	£375

(b) Wmk Mult Crown CA (sideways)
59	6	5s. black and red/pale yellow		65·00	£160
60		£1 black and purple/red		£700	£1300
48/60				*Set of 13*	£1000 £1800
48/60		Optd "Specimen"		*Set of 13*	£650

Examples of all values are known showing a forged St. Kitts postmark dated "8 DE 23."

1935 (6 May). *Silver Jubilee. As Nos. 114/17 of Jamaica, but ptd by Waterlow. P 11×12.*
61		1d. deep blue and scarlet		1·00	70
		k. Kite and vertical log		48·00	
		l. Kite and horizontal log		80·00	
62		1½d. ultramarine and grey		75	75
		k. Kite and vertical log		45·00	
63		2½d. brown and deep blue		1·00	80
64		1s. slate and purple		5·50	15·00
		k. Kite and vertical log		£150	
		l. Kite and horizontal log		£170	
61/4				*Set of 4*	7·50 15·00
61/4		Perf "Specimen"		*Set of 4*	75·00

For illustrations of plate varieties see Omnibus section following Zimbabwe.

1937 (12 May). *Coronation. As Nos. 118/20 of Jamaica.*
65		1d. scarlet		30	20
66		1½d. buff		40	10
67		2½d. bright blue		60	45
65/7				*Set of 3*	1·10 65
65/7		Perf "Specimen"		*Set of 3*	55·00

Nos. 61/7 are inscribed "ST. CHRISTOPHER AND NEVIS".

7 King George VI   8 King George VI and Medicinal Spring

9 King George VI and Christopher Columbus   10 King George VI and Anguilla Island

Break in value tablet (R. 12/5) (1947 ptg only)   Break in oval (R. 12/1) (1938 ptg only)

Break in value tablet frame (R.3/2)   Break in value tablet frame (R. 12/3) (ptgs between 1941 and 1945)

Break in frame above ornament (R. 2/4) (ptgs between 1941 and 1950)

Break in oval at foot (R. 12/5)
(ptgs between 1941 and 1945
only). Sometimes touched-in by
hand painting)

Break in oval at left
(R. 7/1) (ptgs between
1941 and 1945 only)

(Typo; centre litho (T 10). D.L.R.)

1938 (15 Aug)–50. *Wmk Mult Script CA (sideways on T 8 and
9). Chalk-surfaced paper* (10s., £1). P 14 (T 7 and 10) or 13×12
(T 8/9).

68	7	½d. green	3·00	20
		a. Blue-green (5.4.43)	10	10
69		1d. scarlet	4·50	70
		a. Carmine (5.43)	80	50
		b. Carmine-pink (4.47)	60·00	16·00
		c. Rose-red (7.47)	80	80
70		1½d. orange	20	30
71	8	2d. scarlet and grey	17·00	2·50
		a. Chalk-surfaced paper. *Carmine and deep grey* (5.41*)	55·00	10·00
		b. Perf 14. *Scarlet & pale grey* (6.43*)	70	1·25
		ba. *Scarlet and deep grey* (6.42*)	20·00	5·00
		c. Perf 14. Chalk-surfaced paper. *Scarlet and pale grey* (2.50*)	1·50	2·50
72	7	2½d. ultramarine	3·50	30
		a. *Bright ultramarine* (5.4.43)	30	30
73	8	3d. dull reddish purple and scarlet	14·00	3·75
		a. Chalk-surfaced paper. *Brown-purple and carmine-red* (1940)	18·00	4·50
		b. Perf 14. Chalk-surfaced paper. *Dull reddish purple & carm-red* (6.43*)	30·00	3·75
		c. Perf 14. Ordinary paper. *Reddish lilac and scarlet* (8.46*)	2·50	12·00
		d. Perf 14. Ordinary paper. *Purple and bright scarlet* (1.46*)	6·50	6·50
		da. Break in value tablet	70·00	
		e. Perf 14. Chalk-surfaced paper. *Deep purple and scarlet* (12.47*)	75·00	18·00
		f. Perf 14. Ordinary paper. *Rose-lilac and bright scarlet* (1.49*)	6·50	7·00
		g. Perf 14. Chalk-surfaced paper. *Deep reddish purple & brt scarlet* (8.50*)	3·75	4·50
74	9	6d. green and bright purple	6·50	2·25
		a. Break in oval	85·00	
		b. Perf 14. Chalk-surfaced paper. *Green and deep claret* (6.43*)	55·00	11·00
		c. Perf 14. Ordinary paper. *Green and purple* (10.44*)	4·75	1·50
		d. Perf 14. Chalk-surfaced paper. *Green and purple* (11.48*)	4·25	3·00
75	8	1s. black and green	12·00	1·25
		a. Break in value tablet frame	£120	
		b. Perf 14 (8.43*)	3·75	85
		ba. Break in value tablet frame	70·00	
		c. Perf 14. Chalk-surfaced paper (7.50*)	3·25	3·50
		ca. Break in value tablet frame	60·00	
76		2s. 6d. black and scarlet	32·00	5·00
		a. Perf 14. Chalk-surfaced paper (12.43*)	13·00	6·00
		ab. Ordinary paper (5.45*)	12·00	3·75
77	9	5s. grey-green and scarlet	65·00	18·00
		a. Perf 14. Chalk-surfaced paper (12.43*)	£130	28·00
		ab. Break in value tablet frame	£375	
		ac. Break in frame above ornament	£375	
		ad. Break in oval at foot	£375	
		ae. Break in oval at left	£375	
		b. Perf 14. Ordinary paper. *Bluish green and scarlet* (7.11.45*)	24·00	12·00
		ba. Break in value tablet frame	£170	
		bb. Break in frame above ornament	£180	
		bc. Break in oval at foot	£160	
		bd. Break in oval at left	£170	
		c. Perf 14. Chalk-surfaced paper. *Green & scarlet-vermilion* (10.50*)	32·00	30·00
		cb. Break in frame above ornament	£190	
77d	10	10s. black and ultramarine (1.9.48)	10·00	19·00
77e		£1 black and brown (1.9.48)	10·00	23·00
68/77e			*Set of 12* 60·00	55·00
68/77 Perf "Specimen"			*Set of 10* £180	

*Earliest postmark date. Many printings were supplied to St.
Kitts-Nevis considerably earlier. Details of earliest dates are
taken, with permission, from *A Study of the King George VI
Stamps of St. Kitts-Nevis* by P. L. Baldwin (2nd edition 1997).

1946 (1 Nov). *Victory. As Nos. 141/2 of Jamaica.*

78		1½d. red-orange	10	10
79		3d. carmine	10	10
78/9 Perf "Specimen"		*Set of 2* 60·00	

1949 (3 Jan). *Royal Silver Wedding. As Nos. 143/4 of Jamaica.*

80		2½d. ultramarine	10	10
81		5s. carmine	6·00	2·50

1949 (10 Oct). *75th Anniv of U.P.U. As Nos. 145/8 of Jamaica.*

82		2½d. ultramarine	35	20
83		3d. carmine-red	1·00	60
84		6d. magenta	40	30
85		1s. blue-green	40	30
82/5			*Set of 4* 1·90	1·25

MINIMUM PRICE

The minimum price quote is 10p which represents
a handling charge rather than a basis for valuing
common stamps. For further notes about prices
see introductory pages.

ANGUILLA

ANGUILLA

ANGUILLA

TERCENTENARY
1650-1950

TERCENTENARY
1650—1950

(11)   (12)

1950 (10 Nov). *Tercentenary of British Settlement in Anguilla.
Nos. 69c, 70 and 72a (perf 14) optd as T 11 and new ptgs of
T 8/9 on chalk-surfaced paper perf 13×12½ optd as T 12.*

86	7	1d. rose-red	10	20
87		1½d. orange	10	20
		a. Error. Crown missing, W 9a	£1500	
		b. Error. St. Edward's Crown, W 9b	£850	
88		2½d. bright ultramarine	10	20
89	8	3d. dull purple and scarlet	10	40
90	9	6d. green and bright purple	10	20
91	8	1s. black and green (R.)	30	20
		a. Break in value tablet frame	9·50	
86/91			*Set of 6* 60	1·25

Nos. 87a/b occur on a row in the watermark, in which the crowns
and letters "CA" alternate.

**(New Currency. 100 cents = 1 West Indian, later East
Caribbean, dollar)**

1951 (16 Feb). *Inauguration of B.W.I. University College. As
Nos. 149/50 of Jamaica.*

92		3c. black and yellow-orange	30	15
93		12c. turquoise-green and magenta	30	85

ST. CHRISTOPHER, NEVIS AND ANGUILLA
LEGISLATIVE COUNCIL

13 Bath House and
Spa, Nevis

14 Map of the Islands

(Recess Waterlow)

1952 (14 June). *Vert designs as T 14 (3, 12 c.) or horiz as 13
(others). Wmk Mult Script CA. P 12½.*

94		1 c. deep green and ochre	15	90
95		2 c. green	75	90
96		3 c. carmine-red and violet	30	80
97		4 c. scarlet	20	20
98		5 c. bright blue and grey	30	10
99		6 c. ultramarine	30	15
100		12 c. deep blue and reddish brown	50	10
101		24 c. black and carmine-red	30	10
102		48 c. olive and chocolate	1·75	1·75
103		60 c. ochre and deep green	1·50	2·00
104		$1.20, deep green and ultramarine	5·50	2·25
105		$4.80, green and carmine	13·00	18·00
94/105			*Set of 12* 22·00	24·00

Designs:—2 c. Warner Park; 4 c. Brimstone Hill; 5 c. Nevis
from the sea, North; 6 c. Pinney's Beach, Nevis; 12 c. Sir Thomas
Warner's Tomb; 24 c. Old Road Bay; 48 c. Sea Island cotton,
Nevis; 60 c. The Treasury; $1.20, Salt pond, Anguilla; $4.80,
Sugar factory.

1953 (2 June). *Coronation. As No. 153 of Jamaica.*

106		2 c. black and bright green	30	15

25 Sombrero Lighthouse

26 Map of Anguilla and
Dependencies

(Recess Waterlow (until 1961), then D.L.R.)

1954 (1 Mar)–63. *Designs previously used for King George VI
issue, but with portrait of Queen Elizabeth II as in T 25/6 or
new values and designs (½ c., 8 c., $2.40). Wmk Mult Script
CA. P 12½.*

106a		½ c. deep olive (3.7.56)	30	10
107		1 c. deep green and ochre	20	10
		a. Deep green and orange-ochre (13.2.62)	1·25	2·50
		b. Imperf vert (horiz strip of three)	† £5000	
108		2 c. green	45	10
		a. Yellow-green (31.7.63)	4·50	6·00
109		3 c. carmine-red and violet	65	10
		a. Carmine and deep violet (31.7.63)	4·50	6·50
110		4 c. scarlet	15	10
111		5 c. bright blue and grey	15	10
112		6 c. ultramarine	50	10
		a. Blue (19.2.63)	1·25	30
112b		8 c. grey-black (1.2.57)	3·00	10
113		12 c. deep blue and red-brown	15	10
114		24 c. black and carmine-red (1.12.54)	15	10
115		48 c. olive-bistre and chocolate (1.12.54)	60	50
116		60 c. ochre and deep green (1.12.54)	15	30
117		$1.20, dp green & ultramarine (1.12.54)	18·00	1·75
		a. Deep green and violet-blue (19.2.63)	38·00	8·50
117b		$2.40, black and red-orange (1.2.57)	10·00	11·00
118		$4.80, green and carmine (1.12.54)	13·00	11·00
106a/18			*Set of 15* 48·00	24·00

Design: *Horiz*—½ c., $1.20 Salt Pond; 1 c. Bath House and Spa;
2 c. Warner Park; 4 c. Brimstone Hill; 5 c. Nevis from the sea,
North; 6 c. Pinney's Beach; 24 c. Old Road Bay; 48 c. Sea Island
cotton; 60 c. The Treasury; $4.80, Sugar factory. *Vert*—3 c. Map of
the islands; 12 c. Sir Thomas Warner's Tomb.

Stamps of St. Christopher, Nevis and Anguilla were in concurrent use with the stamps inscribed "LEEWARD ISLANDS" until
1 July 1956, when the general Leeward Islands stamps were
withdrawn.

27 Alexander Hamilton and View of Nevis

(Des Eva Wilkin. Recess Waterlow)

1957 (11 Jan). *Birth Bicentenary of Alexander Hamilton. Wmk
Mult Script CA. P 12½.*

119	27	24 c. green and deep blue	30	15

1958 (22 Apr). *Inauguration of British Caribbean Federation.
As Nos. 175/7 of Jamaica.*

120		3 c. deep green	60	15
121		6 c. blue	1·00	2·25
122		12 c. scarlet	1·50	35
120/2			*Set of 3* 2·75	2·50

MINISTERIAL GOVERNMENT

28 One Penny Stamp of 1861

(Recess Waterlow)

1961 (15 July). *Nevis Stamp Centenary. T 28 and similar horiz
designs. W w 12. P 14.*

123		2 c. red-brown and green	15	20
124		8 c. red-brown and deep blue.	20	10
125		12 c. black and carmine-red	30	15
126		24 c. deep bluish green and red-orange	35	15
123/6			*Set of 4* 90	50

Designs:—8 c. Fourpence stamp of 1861; 12 c. Sixpence stamp of
1861; 24 c. One shilling stamp of 1861.

1963 (2 Sept). *Red Cross Centenary. As Nos. 203/4 of Jamaica.*

127		3 c. red and black	10	10
128		12 c. red and blue	20	40

32 New Lighthouse,
Sombrero

33 Loading Sugar Cane, St. Kitts

(Des V. Whiteley. Photo Harrison)

1963 (20 Nov)–69. *Vert designs as T 32 (2, 3, 15, 25, 60 c., $1,
$5) or horiz as T 33 (others) in sepia and light blue (½ c.),
greenish yellow and buff ($1) or multicoloured (others).
W w 12 (upright). P 14.*

129		½ c. Type 32	10	10
		w. Wmk inverted		
130		1 c. Type 33	10	10
131		2 c. Pall Mall Square, Basseterre	10	10
		a. White fountain and church	£110	
		w. Wmk inverted		
132		3 c. Gateway, Brimstone Hill Fort, St. Kitts	10	10
		w. Wmk inverted		
133		4 c. Nelson's Spring, Nevis	10	10
		w. Wmk inverted		
134		5 c. Grammar School, St. Kitts	2·25	10
135		6 c. Crater, Mt Misery, St. Kitts	10	10
		w. Wmk inverted (19.12.69)	30	30
136		10 c. Hibiscus	15	10
137		15 c. Sea Island cotton, Nevis	55	10
		w. Wmk inverted		
138		20 c. Boat building, Anguilla	20	10
139		25 c. White-crowned Pigeon (turquoise-blue background)	1·25	10
		a. Turquoise-green background (13.4.65)	4·25	1·25
		w. Wmk inverted		65·00
140		50 c. St. George's Church Tower, Basseterre	40	25
141		60 c. Alexander Hamilton	1·00	30
142		$1 Map of St. Kitts-Nevis	2·50	40
143		$2.50, Map of Anguilla	2·50	2·50
144		$5 Arms of St. Christopher, Nevis and Anguilla	5·50	4·00
129/44			*Set of 16* 15·00	7·00

The 1, 4, 5, 6, 10 and 20 c. values exist with PVA gum as well
as gum arabic.
See also Nos. 166/71.

**ARTS
FESTIVAL
ST KITTS
1964**
(48)

49 Festival Emblem

1964 (14 Sept). *Arts Festival. Nos. 132 and 139 optd as T 48.*
145	3 c. Gateway, Brimstone Hill Fort, St. Kitts		10	15
	a. Opt double		£225	
146	25 c. White-crowned Pigeon	..	20	15
	a. "FESTIVAI" (R. 1/10)		65·00	
	w. Wmk inverted	..	—	8·00

1965 (17 May). *I.T.U. Centenary. As Nos. 98/9 of Lesotho.*
147	2 c. bistre-yellow and rose-carmine	..	10	10
148	50 c. turquoise-blue and yellow-olive	..	40	50

1965 (15 Oct). *International Co-operation Year. As Nos. 100/1 of Lesotho.*
149	2 c. reddish purple and turquoise-green		10	20
150	25 c. deep bluish green and lavender	..	20	10

1966 (24 Jan). *Churchill Commemoration. As Nos. 102/5 of Lesotho.*
151	½ c. new blue	..	10	40
	a. Value omitted		£180	
	b. Value at left instead of right	..	65·00	
152	3 c. deep green	..	20	10
153	15 c. brown	..	40	20
154	25 c. bluish violet	..	45	20
151/4		Set of 4	1·00	75

1966 (4 Feb). *Royal Visit. As Nos. 183/4 of Montserrat.*
155	3 c. black and ultramarine	..	25	15
156	25 c. black and magenta	..	55	15

1966 (1 July). *World Cup Football Championships. As Nos. 57/8 of Pitcairn Islands.*
157	6 c. violet, yellow-green, lake & yell-brn	..	40	20
158	25 c. chocolate, blue-green, lake & yell-brn		60	10

(Photo Harrison)

1966 (15 Aug). *Arts Festival. P 14 × 14½.*
159	**49**	3 c. black, buff, emerald-green and gold		10	10
160		25 c. black, buff, emerald-green and silver		20	10

1966 (20 Sept). *Inauguration of W.H.O. Headquarters, Geneva. As Nos. 185/6 of Montserrat.*
161	3 c. black, yellow-green, and light blue		10	10
162	40 c. black, light purple, and yellow-brown		30	20

1966 (1 Dec). *20th Anniv of U.N.E.S.C.O. As Nos. 342/4 of Mauritius.*
163	3 c. slate-violet, red, yellow and orange	..	10	10
164	6 c. orange-yellow, violet and deep olive	..	10	10
165	40 c. black, bright purple and orange	..	30	35
163/5	..	Set of 3	40	45

ASSOCIATED STATEHOOD

1967–69. *As Nos. 129, 131/2, 137, 139 and 142 but wmk sideways.*
166	**20**	½ c. sepia and light blue (9.1.69)	..	20	2·50
167	—	2 c. multicoloured (27.6.67)	..	1·75	10
168	—	3 c. multicoloured (16.7.68)	..	20	10
169	—	15 c. multicoloured (16.7.68)	..	70	30
170	—	25 c. multicoloured (16.7.68)	..	2·50	20
171	—	$1 greenish yellow and blue (16.7.68)	..	5·00	4·00
		a. Greenish yellow & ultramarine-blue (19.12.69)	..	11·00	6·00
166/71			Set of 6	9·25	6·50

The 2 c. and $1 values exist with PVA gum as well as gum arabic. Nos. 172/81 vacant.

50 Government Headquarters, Basseterre

53 John Wesley and Cross

(Des V. Whiteley. Photo Harrison)

1967 (1 July). *Statehood. T 50 and similar horiz designs. Multicoloured. W w 12. P 14½ × 14.*
182	3 c. Type 50	..	10	10
183	10 c. National flag	..	10	10
	w. Wmk inverted	..	18·00	
184	25 c. Coat of arms	..	15	15
182/4		Set of 3	30	30

(Litho D.L.R.)

1967 (1 Dec). *West Indies Methodist Conference. T 53 and similar vert designs. P 13 × 13½.*
185	3 c. black, cerise and reddish violet	..	10	10
186	25 c. black, light greenish blue and blue		15	15
187	40 c. black, yellow and orange	..	15	15
185/7	..	Set of 3	30	30

Designs:—25 c. Charles Wesley and Cross; 40 c. Thomas Coke and Cross.

56 Handley Page H.P.R.7 Dart Herald Aircraft over *Jamaica Producer* (freighter)

57 Dr. Martin Luther King

(Des and litho D.L.R.)

1968 (30 July). *Caribbean Free Trade Area. W w 12 (sideways). P 13.*
188	**56**	25 c. multicoloured	..	40	10
189		50 c. multicoloured	..	40	20

(Des G. Vasarhelyi. Litho Enschedé)

1968 (30 Sept). *Martin Luther King Commemoration. W w 12. P 12 × 12½.*
190	**57**	50 c. multicoloured	..	15	10

58 "Mystic Nativity" (Botticelli)

60 Tarpon Snook

(Des and photo Harrison)

1968 (27 Nov). *Christmas. Paintings. T 58 and similar vert design. Multicoloured. W w 12 (sideways). P 14½ × 14.*
191	12 c. Type 58	..	10	10
192	25 c. "The Adoration of the Magi" (Rubens)	..	10	10
193	40 c. Type 58	..	15	10
194	50 c. As 25 c.	..	15	10
191/4		Set of 4	40	30

(Des G. Drummond. Photo Harrison)

1969 (25 Feb). *Fishes. T 60 and similar horiz designs. W w 12. P 14 × 14½.*
195	6 c. multicoloured	..	10	10
196	12 c. black, turquoise-green & greenish blue		15	10
197	40 c. multicoloured	..	25	10
198	50 c. multicoloured	..	30	15
195/8		Set of 4	70	30

Designs:—12 c. Needlefish; 40 c. Horse-eyed Jack; 50 c. Black-finned Snapper.

64 The Warner Badge and Islands

67 "The Adoration of the Kings" (Mostaert)

(Des V. Whiteley. Litho Format)

1969 (1 Sept). *Sir Thomas Warner Commemoration. T 64 and similar horiz designs. Multicoloured. W w 12 (sideways). P 13½ × 14.*
199	20 c. Type 64	..	10	10
200	25 c. Sir Thomas Warner's tomb	..	10	10
201	40 c. Charles I's commission	..	15	15
199/201		Set of 3	30	30

(Des Enschedé. Litho B.W.)

1969 (17 Nov). *Christmas. Paintings. T 67 and similar vert design. Multicoloured. W w 12 (sideways). P 13½.*
202	10 c. Type 67	..	10	10
203	25 c. Type 67	..	10	10
204	40 c. "The Adoration of the Kings" (Geertgen)		10	10
205	50 c. As 40 c.	..	10	10
202/5		Set of 4	30	30

---

73 Portuguese Caravels (16th-cent)

(Des and litho J.W.)

1970 (2 Feb)–**74.** *Designs as T 73 in black, pale orange and emerald (½ c.) or multicoloured (others). W w 12 (upright on vert designs, sideways* on horiz designs). P 14.*
206	½ c. Pirates and treasure at Frigate Bay (vert)		10	10
	w. Wmk inverted (15.3.71)		20	20
207	1 c. English two-decker warship, 1650 (vert)		30	10
208	2 c. Naval flags of colonising nations (vert)		15	10
209	3 c. Rapier hilt (17th-century) (vert)		15	10
210	4 c. Type 73		20	10
	w. Wmk Crown to right of CA (24.7.74)		40	15
211	5 c. Sir Henry Morgan and fireships, 1669		30	10
	w. Wmk Crown to right of CA (24.7.74)		40	10
212	6 c. L'Ollonois and pirate carrack (16th century)		30	10
	w. Wmk Crown to right of CA (24.7.74)		40	40
213	10 c. 17th-century smugglers' ship		30	10
	w. Wmk Crown to right of CA (24.7.74)		40	15
214	15 c. "Piece-of-eight" (vert) (I)		2·00	40
214a	15 c. "Piece-of-eight" (vert) (II) (8.9.70)		70	10
215	20 c. Cannon (17th-century)		35	10
	w. Crown to right of CA (24.7.74)		50	20
216	25 c. Humphrey Cole's Astrolabe, 1574 (vert)		40	10
217	50 c. Flintlock pistol (17th-century)		85	80
	w. Wmk Crown to right of CA (24.7.74)		1·25	80
218	60 c. Dutch flute (17th-century) (vert)		2·00	70
219	$1 Captain Bartholomew Roberts and his crew's death warrant (vert)	..	2·00	75
220	$2.50, Railing piece (16th-century)		1·50	3·25
	w. Wmk Crown to right of CA (24.7.74)		2·00	3·25
221	$5 Drake, Hawkins and sea battle		2·00	4·50
	w. Wmk Crown to right of CA (24.7.74)		3·25	5·00
206/21		Set of 17	12·00	9·50

Nos. 214/a. Type I, coin inscribed "HISPANIANUM"; Type II corrected to "HISPANIARUM". No. 214a also differs considerably in shade from No. 214.
The normal sideways watermark shows Crown to left of CA, as seen from the back of the stamp.
See also Nos. 269/80 and 322/31.

85 Graveyard Scene (*Great Expectations*)

(Des Jennifer Toombs. Litho B.W.)

1970 (1 May). *Death Centenary of Charles Dickens. T 85 and similar designs. W w 12 (sideways on horiz designs). P 13.*
222	4 c. bistre-brown, gold and deep blue-green		10	15
223	20 c. bistre-brown, gold and reddish purple		10	15
224	25 c. bistre-brown, gold and olive-green		10	15
225	40 c. bistre-brown, gold and ultramarine		15	35
222/5		Set of 4	40	70

Designs: *Horiz*—20 c. Miss Havisham and Pip (*Great Expectations*). *Vert*—25 c. Dickens's Birthplace; 40 c. Charles Dickens.

86 Local Steel Band

(Des V. Whiteley. Litho Enschedé)

1970 (1 Aug). *Festival of Arts. T 86 and similar horiz designs. Multicoloured. W w 12 (sideways). P 13½.*
226	20 c. Type 86		10	10
227	25 c. Local String Band		10	10
228	40 c. Scene from *A Midsummer Night's Dream*		15	15
226/8		Set of 3	30	30

87 1d. Stamp of 1870 and Post Office, 1970

88 "Adoration of the Shepherds" (detail) (Frans van Floris)

(Des J. Cooter. Litho J.W.)

1970 (14 Sept). *Stamp Centenary. T* **87** *and similar horiz designs. W w* **12** (*sideways*). *P* 14½.
229	½ c. green and rose	10	10
230	20 c. deep blue, green and rose	10	10
231	25 c. brown-purple, green and rose	10	10
232	50 c. scarlet, green and black	30	45
229/32	*Set of 4*	50	50

Designs:—20 c., 25 c. 1d. and 6d. Stamps of 1870; 50 c. 6d. Stamp of 1870 and early postmark.

(Des Enschedé. Litho Format)

1970 (16 Nov). *Christmas. T* **88** *and similar vert design. Multi-coloured. W w* **12**. *P* 14.
233	3 c. Type **88**	10	10
234	20 c. "The Holy Family" (Van Dyck)	10	10
235	25 c. As 20 c.	10	10
236	40 c. Type **88**	15	50
233/6	*Set of 4*	30	70

89 Monkey Fiddle

(Des Sylvia Goaman. Litho Format)

1971 (1 Mar). *Flowers. T* **89** *and similar horiz designs. Multicoloured. W w* **12** (*sideways**). *P* 14½.
237	½ c. Type **89**	10	20
	w. Wmk Crown to right of CA	75	
238	20 c. Tropical Mountain Violet	15	10
239	30 c. Trailing Morning Glory	15	15
240	50 c. Fringed Epidendrum	30	1·00
237/40	*Set of 4*	55	1·25

*The normal sideways watermark shows Crown to left of CA, as seen from the back of the stamp.

90 Royal Poinciana

(Des Enschedé. Litho J.W.)

1971 (1 June). *Phillipe de Poincy Commemoration. T* **90** *and similar multicoloured designs. W w* **12** (*sideways on 20 and 30 c.*). *P* 13½.
241	20 c. Type **90**	10	10
242	30 c. Château de Poincy	10	10
243	50 c. De Poincy's badge (*vert*)	20	15
241/3	*Set of 3*	35	30

91 The East Yorks   **92** "Crucifixion" (Massys)

(Des V. Whiteley. Litho Walsall)

1971 (1 Sept). *Siege of Brimstone Hill, 1782. T* **91** *and similar horiz designs. Multicoloured. W w* **12** (*sideways**). *P* 14½.
244	½ c. Type **91**	10	10
	w. Wmk Crown to right of CA	75	
245	20 c. Royal Artillery	35	10
246	30 c. French infantry	45	10
247	50 c. The Royal Scots	60	20
244/7	*Set of 4*	1·25	35

*The normal sideways watermark shows Crown to left of CA, as seen from the back of the stamp.

(Des J. Cooter. Litho J.W.)

1972 (1 Apr). *Easter. W w* **12**. *P* 14 × 13½.
248	**92**	4 c. multicoloured	10	10
249		20 c. multicoloured	10	10
250		30 c. multicoloured	10	10
251		40 c. multicoloured	10	10
248/51		*Set of 4*	30	30

COVER PRICES

Cover factors are quoted at the beginning of each country for most issues to 1945. An explanation of the system can be found on page x. The factors quoted do not, however, apply to philatelic covers.

93 "Virgin and Child"   **94** Brown Pelicans
(Borgognone)

(Des J. Cooter. Litho J.W.)

1972 (2 Oct). *Christmas. T* **93** *and similar multicoloured designs. W w* **12** (*sideways on vert designs*). *P* 14.
252	3 c. Type **93**	10	10
253	20 c. "Adoration of the Kings" (J. Bassano) (*horiz*)	15	10
254	25 c. "Adoration of the Shepherds" (Domenichino)	15	10
255	40 c. "Virgin and Child" (Fiorenzo di Lorenzo)	20	10
252/5	*Set of 4*	45	30

(Des (from photograph by D. Groves) and photo Harrison)

1972 (20 Nov). *Royal Silver Wedding. Multicoloured; background colour given. W w* **12**. *P* 14 × 14½.
256	**94** 20 c. carmine	20	15
	w. Wmk inverted	—	35·00
257	25 c. bright blue	20	15

95 Landing on St. Christopher, 1623   **96** "The Last Supper" (Titian)

(Des J.W. Litho Questa)

1973 (28 Jan). *350th Anniv of Sir Thomas Warner's landing on St. Christopher. T* **95** *and similar horiz designs. Multicoloured. W w* **12**. *P* 13½.
258	4 c. Type **95**	15	10
259	25 c. Growing tobacco	15	10
	w. Wmk inverted	1·00	
260	40 c. Building fort at Old Road	20	10
261	$2.50, Concepcion	80	1·10
258/61	*Set of 4*	1·10	1·25

(Des J. Cooter. Litho Walsall)

1973 (16 Apr). *Easter. T* **96** *and similar multicoloured designs showing paintings of "The Last Supper" by the artists listed. W w* **12** (*sideways on $2.50*). *P* 13½ × 14 ($2.50) *or* 14 × 13½ (*others*).
262	4 c. Type **96**	10	10
263	25 c. Ascr to Roberti	10	10
264	$2.50, Juan de Juanes (*horiz*)	70	60
262/4	*Set of 3*	75	60

VISIT OF
H. R. H. THE PRINCE OF WALES 1973
(**97**)

1973 (31 May). *Royal Visit. Nos.* 258/61 *optd with T* **97** *by Questa.*
265	4 c. Type **95**	10	15
266	25 c. Growing tobacco	10	15
267	40 c. Building fort at Old Road	15	15
268	$2.50 Concepcion	45	50
265/8	*Set of 4*	65	85

(Des J.W. Litho Harrison ($10), J.W. (others))

1973 (12 Sept)–74. *As Nos.* 206, 208/9, 211/13, 214a/17, 219 *and new horiz design ($10), but W w* **12** (*sideways on vert designs, upright on horiz designs*).
269	½ c. Pirates and treasure at Frigate Bay	10	1·25
270	2 c. Naval flags of colonizing nations		1·25
271	3 c. Rapier hilt	20	1·25
272	5 c. Sir Henry Morgan and fireships, 1669	35	1·25
273	6 c. L'Ollonois and pirate carrack (16th-century)	35	80
274	10 c. 17th-century smugglers' ship	40	80
275	15 c. "Piece-of-eight" (II)	65	85
276	20 c. Cannon (17th-century)	75	1·10
277	25 c. Humphrey Cole's Astrolabe, 1574	80	1·75
278	50 c. Flintlock pistol (17th-century)	1·10	1·50
279	$1 Captain Bartholomew Roberts and his crew's death warrant	2·75	3·50
280	$10 "The Apprehension of Blackbeard" (Edward Teach) (16.11.74)	20·00	13·00
269/80	*Set of 12*	25·00	25·00

Nos. 281/4 vacant.

99 Harbour Scene and 2d. Stamp of 1903

(Des V. Whiteley Studio. Litho Enschedé)

1973 (1 Oct). *70th Anniv of First St. Kitts-Nevis Stamps. T* **99** *and similar horiz designs. Multicoloured. W w* **12** (*sideways*). *P* 13 × 13½.
285	4 c. Type **99**	10	10
286	25 c. Sugar-mill and 1d. stamp of 1903	15	10
287	40 c. Unloading boat and ½d. stamp of 1903	35	10
288	$2.50, Rock-carvings and 3d. stamp of 1903	1·50	1·00
285/8	*Set of 4*	1·75	1·10
MS289	144 × 95 mm. Nos. 285/8	1·75	4·50

1973 (14 Nov). *Royal Wedding. As Nos.* 322/3 *of Montserrat.*
290	25 c. light emerald	15	10
291	40 c. brown-ochre	15	10

100 "Madonna and Child"   **101** "Christ carrying the
(Murillo)   Cross" (S. del Piombo)

(Des J. Cooter. Litho Format)

1973 (1 Dec). *Christmas. T* **100** *and similar multicoloured designs showing "The Holy Family" by the artists listed. W w* **12** (*sideways on $1*). *P* 13½.
292	4 c. Type **100**	10	10
293	40 c. Mengs	15	10
294	60 c. Sassoferrato	20	15
295	$1 Filippino Lippi (*horiz*)	25	30
292/5	*Set of 4*	55	50

(Des J. Cooter. Litho D.L.R.)

1974 (8 Apr). *Easter. T* **101** *and similar multicoloured designs. W w* **12** (*sideways on $2.50*). *P* 13½.
296	4 c. Type **101**	10	10
297	25 c. "The Crucifixion" (Goya)	15	10
298	40 c. "The Trinity" (Ribera)	15	10
299	$2.50, "The Deposition" (Fra Bartolomeo) (*horiz*)	1·00	75
296/9	*Set of 4*	1·25	75

102 University Centre, St. Kitts   **103** Hands reaching for Globe

(Des G. Drummond. Litho Questa)

1974 (1 June). *25th Anniv of University of West Indies. T* **102** *and similar horiz design. Multicoloured. W w* **12** (*sideways**). *P* 13½.
300	10 c. Type **102**	10	10
301	$1 As Type **102** but showing different buildings	20	25
MS302	99×95 mm. Nos. 300/1	35	65
	w. Wmk Crown to right of CA	29·00	

*The normal sideways watermark shows Crown to left of CA, as seen from the back of the stamp.

(Des Jennifer Toombs. Litho Questa)

1974 (5 Aug). *Family Planning. T* **103** *and similar designs. W w* **12** (*sideways on 25 c. and $2.50*). *P* 14.
303	4 c. orange-brown, new blue and black	10	10
304	25 c. multicoloured	10	10
305	40 c. multicoloured	10	10
306	$2.50, multicoloured	35	55
303/6	*Set of 4*	50	65

Designs: *Horiz*—25 c. Instruction by nurse; $2.50, Emblem and globe on scales. *Vert*—40 c. Family group.

104 Churchill as Army Lieutenant

105 Aeroplane and Map

(Des PAD Studio. Litho Questa)

1974 (30 Nov). *Birth Centenary of Sir Winston Churchill. T 104 and similar vert designs. Multicoloured. W w 12. P 13½.*
307	4 c. Type 104	10	10
308	25 c. Churchill as Prime Minister	15	10
309	40 c. Churchill as Knight of the Garter	15	10
310	60 c. Churchill's statue, London	25	15
307/10	Set of 4	50	30
MS311	99 × 148 mm. Nos. 307/10	75	1·25

(Des J.W. Litho Questa)

1974 (16 Dec). *Opening of Golden Rock Airport, St. Kitts. Sheets 98 × 148 mm. W w 12. P 13½.*
MS312	**105**	40 c.multicoloured	20	40
MS313		45 c.multicoloured	20	40

106 "The Last Supper" (Doré)

107 E.C.C.A. H.Q. Buildings, Basseterre

(Des PAD Studio. Litho Questa)

1975 (24 Mar). *Easter. T 106 and similar vert designs showing paintings by Doré. Multicoloured. W w 12. P 14½.*
314	4 c. Type 106	10	10
315	25 c. "Christ Mocked"	10	10
316	40 c. "Jesus falling beneath the Cross"	10	10
317	$1 "The Erection of the Cross"	25	30
314/17	Set of 4	40	40

(Des J. Cooter. Litho Enschedé)

1975 (2 June*). *Opening of East Caribbean Currency Authority's Headquarters. T 107 and similar horiz designs. W w 14 (sideways). P 13 × 13½.*
318	12 c. multicoloured	10	10
319	25 c. multicoloured	10	10
320	40 c. light vermilion, silver and grey-black	15	10
321	45 c. multicoloured	15	15
	a. Silver omitted†	85·00	
318/21	Set of 4	30	30

Designs:—25 c. Specimen one-dollar banknote; 40 c. Half-dollar of 1801 and current 4-dollar coin; 45 c. Coins of 1801 and 1960.
*This is the local date of issue; the Crown Agents released the stamps on 28 April.
†This affects the dull silver coin on the left which on No. 321a appears in tones of the black plate.

1975 (11 June)–77. *As Nos. 207, 209/13, 214a/15 and 218/19 but W w 14 (sideways* on 4, 5, 6, 10, 20 and 60 c.). Cream, chalk-surfaced paper (1 c., $1) or white, ordinary paper (others). P 14.*
322	1 c. English two-decker warship, 1650 (17.5.77)	30	30
323	3 c. Rapier hilt (17th-century) (11.6.76)	20	10
	a. Cream, chalk-surfaced paper (17.5.77)	2·50	3·00
324	4 c. Type 73 (11.6.76)	20	10
	a. Cream, chalk-surfaced paper (17.5.77)	2·50	3·00
325	5 c. Sir Henry Morgan and fireships, 1669	30	50
	a. Cream, chalk-surfaced paper (16.8.77)	11·00	11·00
326	6 c. L'Ollonois and pirate carrack (16th century)	1·25	10
	a. Cream, chalk-surfaced paper (17.5.77)	1·00	2·25
	aw. Wmk Crown to right of CA	5·00	5·00
327	10 c. 17th-century smugglers' ship (11.6.76)	45	15
	a. Cream, chalk-surfaced paper (17.5.77)	1·25	2·50
328	15 c. "Piece-of-eight" (II) (11.6.76)	55	15
	a. Cream, chalk-surfaced paper (16.8.77)	11·00	9·50
329	20 c. Cannon (17th-century)	2·75	6·50
	a. Cream, chalk-surfaced paper (17.5.77)	2·00	8·50
330	60 c. Dutch flute (17th-century) (11.6.76)	9·00	2·00
331	$1 Captain Bartholomew Roberts and his crew's death warrant (16.8.77)	9·00	3·00
322/31	Set of 10	21·00	11·00

*The normal sideways watermark shows Crown to left of CA on No. 326a and to right of CA on the others, *as seen from the back of the stamp.*
Nos. 332/7 vacant.

NEW INFORMATION

The editor is always interested to correspond with people who have new information that will improve or correct the Catalogue.

---

108 Evangeline Booth (Salvation Army General)

109 Golfer

(Des Jennifer Toombs. Litho Questa)

1975 (15 Sept). *International Women's Year. T 108 and similar vert designs. Multicoloured. W w 12. P 14.*
338	4 c. Type 108	30	10
339	25 c. Sylvia Pankhurst	35	10
340	40 c. Marie Curie	2·00	80
341	$2.50, Lady Annie Allen (teacher and guider)	1·50	4·25
338/41	Set of 4	3·75	4·75

(Des Sue Lawes. Litho Questa)

1975 (1 Nov). *Opening of Frigate Bay Golf Course. W w 14 (sideways). P 13½.*
342	**109**	4 c. black and rose-red	70	10
343		25 c. black and greenish yellow	1·00	10
344		40 c. black and light emerald	1·25	20
345		$1 black and new blue	1·75	2·25
342/5		Set of 4	4·25	2·40

110 "St. Paul" (Pier Francesco Sacchi)

111 "Crucifixion" (detail)

(Des J.W. Litho Questa)

1975 (1 Dec). *Christmas. T 110 and similar vert designs showing details from paintings in the National Gallery, London. Multicoloured. W w 13½.*
346	25 c. Type 110	25	10
347	40 c. "St. James" (Bonifazio di Pitati)	30	10
348	45 c. "St. John the Baptist" (Mola)	30	10
349	$1 "St. Mary" (Raphael)	80	1·40
346/9	Set of 4	1·50	1·50

(Des J. Cooter. Litho Questa)

1976 (14 Apr). *Easter. Stained-glass Windows. T 111 and similar vert designs. Multicoloured. W w 14. P 14 × 13½ (4 c.) or 14 (others).*
350	4 c. Type 111	10	20
	a. Strip of 3. Nos. 350/2		
351	4 c. ⎱ "Crucifixion"	10	20
352	4 c. ⎰	10	20
353	25 c. "Last Supper"	35	10
354	40 c. "Last Supper" (different)	40	10
355	$1 "Baptism of Christ"	70	70
350/5	Set of 6	1·50	1·25

Nos. 350/2 were printed horizontally se-tenant, together forming a composite design, No. 350 being the left-hand stamp.
Nos. 353/5 are smaller, 27 × 35 mm.

1976 (8 July). *West Indian Victory in World Cricket Cup. As Nos. 419/20 of Jamaica.*
356	12 c. Map of the Caribbean	60	20
357	40 c. Prudential Cup	1·40	50
MS358	95 × 80 mm. Nos. 356/7	3·75	3·75

112 Crispus Attucks and the Boston Massacre

113 "The Nativity" (Sforza Book of Hours)

(Des J.W. Litho Questa)

1976 (26 July). *Bicentenary of American Revolution. T 112 and similar horiz designs. Multicoloured. W w 14 (sideways). P 13½.*
359	20 c. Type 112	20	10
360	40 c. Alexander Hamilton and Battle of Yorktown	35	10
361	45 c. Jefferson and Declaration of Independence	35	10
362	$1 Washington and the Crossing of the Delaware	70	80
359/62	Set of 4	1·40	95

(Des Jennifer Toombs. Litho Questa)

1976 (1 Nov). *Christmas. T 113 and similar vert designs. Multicoloured. W w 14. P 14.*
363	20 c. Type 113	10	10
364	40 c. "Virgin and Child with St. John" (Pintoricchio)	15	10
365	45 c. "Our Lady of Good Children" (Ford Maddox-Brown)	15	10
366	$1 "Little Hands Outstretched to Bless" (Margaret Tarrant)	35	50
363/6	Set of 4	65	60

114 Royal Visit, 1966

115 "Christ on the Cross" (Niccolo di Liberatore)

(Des J.W. Litho Questa)

1977 (7 Feb). *Silver Jubilee. T 114 and similar vert designs. Multicoloured. W w 14. P 13½.*
367	50 c. Type 114	10	10
368	55 c. The Sceptre	10	10
369	$1.50, Bishops paying homage	25	50
367/9	Set of 3	35	50

(Des G. Hutchins. Litho Questa)

1977 (14 Apr*). *Easter. T 115 and similar designs showing paintings from the National Gallery, London. Multicoloured. W w 14 (sideways on 50 c.). P 14.*
370	25 c. Type 115	10	10
371	30 c. "The Resurrection" (imitator of Mantegna)	10	10
372	50 c. "The Resurrection" (Ugolino da Siena) (horiz)	15	10
373	$1 "Christ Rising from the Tomb" (Gaudenzio Ferrari)	25	30
370/3	Set of 4	55	45

*This is the local release date; the Crown Agents released the stamps ten days earlier.

116 Estridge Mission

117 Laboratory Instruments

(Des Jennifer Toombs. Litho Cartor)

1977 (27 June). *Bicentenary of Moravian Mission. T 116 and similar horiz designs. W w 14 (sideways*). P 12½.*
374	4 c. black, greenish blue and new blue	10	10
	w. Wmk Crown to left of CA	30	
375	20 c. black, brt mauve & brt reddish violet	10	10
	w. Wmk Crown to left of CA	40	
376	40 c. black, yellow and yellow-orange	15	15
	w. Wmk Crown to left of CA	60	
374/6	Set of 3	30	30

Designs:—20 c. Mission symbol; 40 c. Basseterre Mission.
*The normal sideways watermark shows Crown to right of CA, *as seen from the back of the stamp.*

(Des G. Hutchins. Litho Questa)

1977 (11 Oct). *75th Anniv of Pan-American Health Organization. T 117 and similar vert designs. W w 14. P 14.*
377	3 c. multicoloured	20	10
378	12 c. multicoloured	25	10
379	20 c. multicoloured	30	10
380	$1 red-brown, bright orange and black	70	1·25
377/80	Set of 4	1·25	1·25

Designs:—12 c. Fat cells, blood cells and nerve cells; 20 c. "Community participation in health"; $1 Inoculation.

4c

ST. CHRISTOPHER
NEVIS·ANGUILLA

ST CHRISTOPHER
NEVIS-ANGUILLA

4c

118 "Nativity"
(West Window)

119 Savanna Monkey
with Vervet

(Des Jennifer Toombs. Litho Rosenbaum Bros, Vienna)

1977 (15 Nov).   *Christmas. Vert designs as T* **118** *showing stained-glass windows from Chartres Cathedral. Multicoloured. W w* **14** *(inverted). P* 13½.

381	4 c. Type **118**		10	10
	w. Wmk upright		30	
382	6 c. "Three Magi" (West window)		10	10
383	40 c. "La Belle Verriere"		35	10
	w. Wmk upright		55	
384	$1 "Virgin and Child" (Rose window)		75	45
	w. Wmk upright		2·50	
381/4		*Set of 4*	1·10	55

(Des BG Studio. Litho Questa)

1978 (15 Apr).   *The Savanna ("Green") Monkey. T* **119** *and similar vert design. W w* **14**. *P* 14½.

385	**119**	4 c. yellow-brown, rosine and black	10	10
386	–	5 c. multicoloured	10	10
387	**119**	55 c. yellow-brown, apple-green & black	30	10
388	–	$1.50, multicoloured	75	60
385/8		*Set of 4*	1·10	65

Design:—5 c., $1.50 Savanna Monkeys on branch.

ST.CHRISTOPHER
NEVIS ANGUILLA

Falcon of Edward III

$1

St.Christopher
Nevis Anguilla

TOMATOES

120 Falcon of
Edward III

121 Tomatoes

(Des C. Abbott. Litho Questa)

1978 (2 June).   *25th Anniv of Coronation. T* **120** *and similar vert designs. P* 15.

389	$1 olive-brown and vermilion		15	20
	a. Sheetlet. Nos. 389/91 × 2		75	
390	$1 multicoloured		15	20
391	$1 olive-brown and vermilion		15	20
389/91		*Set of 3*	40	55

Designs:—No. 389, Type **120**; No. 390, Queen Elizabeth II; No. 391, Brown Pelican.

(Des BG Studio. Litho D.L.R.)

1978 (8 Sept).   *Horiz designs as T* **121**. *Multicoloured. W w* **14** *(sideways*). P* 14½×14.

392	1 c. Type **121**		10	20
393	2 c. Defence Force band		10	20
394	5 c. Radio and T.V. station		10	10
395	10 c. Technical college		10	10
396	12 c. T.V. assembly plant		10	20
	w. Wmk Crown to left of CA		3·50	
397	15 c. Sugar cane harvesting		15	10
398	25 c. Crafthouse (craft centre)		15	10
399	30 c. *Europa* (liner)		90	80
400	40 c. Lobster and sea crab		30	10
401	45 c. Royal St. Kitts Hotel and golf course		2·75	85
	w. Wmk Crown to left of CA		8·00	
402	50 c. Pinney's Beach, Nevis		30	10
403	55 c. New runway at Golden Rock		60	10
404	$1 Cotton picking		35	30
405	$5 Brewery		75	1·25
406	$10 Pineapples and peanuts		1·50	2·50
	w. Wmk Crown to left of CA		50·00	
392/406		*Set of 15*	7·00	6·00

*The normal sideways watermark shows Crown to right of CA, as seen from the back of the stamp.

St Christopher
Nevis·Anguilla

5c

Investiture

122 Investiture

ST CHRISTOPHER NEVIS ANGUILLA

CHRISTMAS 1978

5c

123 Wise Man with Gift
of Gold

(Des L. Curtis. Litho Rosenbaum Bros, Vienna)

1978 (9 Oct).   *50th Anniv of Boy Scout Movement on St. Kitts and Nevis. T* **122** *and similar vert designs. Multicoloured. W w* **14**. *P* 13½.

407	5 c. Type **122**		10	10
408	10 c. Map reading		10	10
409	25 c. Pitching tent		20	15
410	40 c. Cooking		35	30
	w. Wmk inverted		14·00	
411	50 c. First aid		40	45
	w. Wmk inverted		14·00	
412	55 c. Rev. W.A. Beckett (founder of scouting in St. Kitts)		45	55
	w. Wmk inverted		12·00	
407/12		*Set of 6*	1·40	1·40

(Des Jennifer Toombs. Litho Walsall)

1978 (1 Dec).   *Christmas. T* **123** *and similar vert designs. Multicoloured. W w* **14**. *P* 13½.

413	5 c. Type **123**		10	10
414	15 c. Wise Man with gift of Frankincense		10	10
415	30 c. Wise Man with gift of Myrrh		10	10
416	$2.25, Wise Men paying homage to the infant Jesus		35	50
413/16		*Set of 4*	50	55

CANNA COCCINEA

St Christopher·Nevis·Anguilla

Sir Rowland Hill 1795 1879

ONE PENNY

5c

St.Christopher·Nevis·Anguilla

124 *Canna coccinea*

125 St. Christopher 1870–76 1d.
Stamp and Sir Rowland Hill

(Des Daphne Padden. Litho Questa)

1979 (19 Mar).   *Flowers (1st series). T* **124** *and similar vert designs. Multicoloured. W w* **14**. *P* 14.

417	5 c. Type **124**		10	10
418	30 c. *Heliconia bihai*		30	20
419	55 c. *Ruellia tuberosa*		35	30
420	$1.50, *Gesneria ventricosa*		70	1·60
417/20		*Set of 4*	1·25	2·00

See also Nos. 430/3.

(Des J.W. Litho Walsall)

1979 (2 July).   *Death Centenary of Sir Rowland Hill. T* **125** *and similar horiz designs showing stamps and portrait. Multicoloured. W w* **14** *(sideways). P* 14½ × 14.

421	5 c. Type **125**		10	10
422	15 c. 1970 Stamp Centenary 50 c. commemorative		10	10
423	50 c. Great Britain 1841 2d.		30	35
424	$2.50, St. Kitts-Nevis 1923 300th Anniversary of Colony £1 commemorative		70	1·10
421/4		*Set of 4*	1·00	1·40

St Christopher Nevis Anguilla

5c

126 "The Woodman's
Daughter"

Nevis Lagoon

127 Nevis Lagoon

(Des BG Studio. Litho Format)

1979 (12 Nov).   *Christmas and International Year of the Child. Paintings by Sir John Millais. T* **126** *and similar vert designs. Multicoloured. W w* **14**. *P* 13½.

425	5 c. Type **126**		10	10
426	25 c. "Cherry Ripe"		25	25
427	30 c. "The Rescue"		25	25
428	55 c. "Bubbles"		30	30
425/8		*Set of 4*	75	80
MS429	100 × 68 mm. $1 "Christ in the House of His Parents"		70	55

(Des J. Cooter. Litho Questa)

1980 (4 Feb).   *Flowers (2nd series). Vert designs as T* **124**. *Multicoloured. W w* **14** *(inverted). P* 14.

430	4 c. *Clerodendrum aculeatum*		30	10
431	55 c. *Inga laurina*		40	20
432	$1.50, *Epidendrum difforme*		1·25	1·40
433	$2 *Salvia serotina*		1·10	2·00
430/3		*Set of 4*	2·75	3·25

(Des and litho Secura, Singapore)

1980 (6 May).   *"London 1980" International Stamp Exhibition. T* **127** *and similar multicoloured designs. W w* **14** *(sideways* on 5 and 55 c., inverted on 30 c.). P* 13.

434	5 c. Type **127**		15	10
	w. Wmk Crown to right of CA		1·50	
435	30 c. Fig Tree Church (*vert*)		25	10

436	55 c. Nisbet Plantation		45	25
	w. Wmk Crown to right of CA		3·50	
437	$3 "Nelson" (Fuger) (*vert*)		1·25	1·60
	w. Wmk inverted		4·50	
434/7		*Set of 4*	1·90	1·75
MS438	107×77 mm. 75 c. Detail of "Nelson Falling" (D. Dighton). P 13½×13		1·00	70
	a. Wmk sideways		42·00	

*The normal sideways watermark shows Crown to left of CA, as seen from the back of the stamp.

OFFICIAL STAMPS

OFFICIAL

(O 1)

1980 (3 Mar).   *Nos. 396, 398 and 400/6 optd with Type O* **1**.

O1	12 c. T.V. assembly plant		80	1·00
	w. Wmk Crown to right of CA		7·00	
O2	25 c. Crafthouse (craft centre)		15	20
O3	40 c. Lobster and sea crab		40	50
O4	45 c. Royal St. Kitts Hotel and golf course		1·50	45
	w. Wmk Crown to left of CA		10·00	
O5	50 c. Pinney's Beach, Nevis		30	40
O6	55 c. New runway at Golden Rock		30	40
O7	$1 Cotton picking		70	2·25
O8	$5 Brewery		80	2·50
O9	$10 Pineapples and peanuts		1·50	3·50
O1/9		*Set of 9*	5·75	10·00

From 23 June 1980 St. Kitts and Nevis had separate postal authorities, each with their own issues.

ST. KITTS

St.Kitts

(8)

1980 (23 June).   *As Nos. 394/406 of St. Christopher, Nevis and Anguilla optd with T* **8**. *A. W w* **14** *(sideways*)*.

29A	5 c. Radio and T.V. station		10	15
30A	10 c. Technical college		10	15
	w. Wmk Crown to left of CA		45·00	
31A	12 c. T.V. assembly plant		60	80
32A	15 c. Sugar cane harvesting		10	15
33A	25 c. Crafthouse (craft centre)		10	15
34A	30 c. *Europa* (liner)		15	15
35A	40 c. Lobster and sea crab		20	20
36A	45 c. Royal St. Kitts Hotel and golf course		50	15
37A	50 c. Pinney's Beach, Nevis		15	15
38A	55 c. New runway at Golden Rock		15	15
39A	$1 Cotton picking		15	25
40A	$5 Brewery		45	1·00
41A	$10 Pineapples and peanuts		55	1·75
29A/41A		*Set of 13*	2·75	4·75

B. *No wmk*

29B	5 c. Radio and T.V. station		10	10
30B	10 c. Technical college		10	10
32B	15 c. Sugar cane harvesting		10	10
33B	25 c. Crafthouse (craft centre)		10	10
34B	30 c. *Europa* (liner)		10	10
35B	40 c. Lobster and sea crab		10	15
38B	55 c. New runway at Golden Rock		15	15
39B	$1 Cotton picking		25	25
40B	$5 Brewery		45	1·50
41B	$10 Pineapples and peanuts		70	2·50
29B/41B		*Set of 10*	1·75	4·50

*The normal sideways watermark shows Crown to right of CA, as seen from the back of the stamp.

St.KITTS

$2

H.M.S. VANGUARD 1762

4d

ST.KITTS

80th Birthday
Her Majesty Queen Elizabeth
The Queen Mother

9 H.M.S. *Vanguard*, 1762

10 Queen Elizabeth
the Queen Mother at
Royal Variety
Performance, 1978

(Litho Secura, Singapore)

1980 (8 Aug).   *Ships. T* **9** *and similar horiz designs. Multicoloured. W w* **14** *(sideways*). P* 13×13½.

42	4 c. Type **9**		10	10
	a. Opt omitted		18·00	
	c. No stop after "ST"		75	
	w. Wmk Crown to right of CA		10	
43	10 c. H.M.S. *Boreas*, 1787		10	10
	a. Opt omitted		40·00	
	c. No stop after "ST"		75	
	w. Wmk Crown to right of CA		10	
44	30 c. H.M.S. *Druid*, 1827		15	10
	a. Opt omitted		40·00	
	c. No stop after "ST"		1·00	
	w. Wmk Crown to right of CA		25	
45	55 c. H.M.S. *Winchester*, 1831		20	15
	a. Opt inverted		75·00	
	b. Opt omitted		40·00	
	c. No stop after "ST"		1·25	
	w. Wmk Crown to right of CA		50	

46	$1.50, Harrison Line *Philosopher*, 1857		40	30
	a. Opt omitted		40·00	
	c. No stop after "ST"		1·50	
	w. Wmk Crown to right of CA		80	
47	$2 Harrison Line *Contractor*, 1930		50	40
	a. Opt double		60·00	
	b. Opt omitted		90·00	
	c. No stop after "ST"		1·50	
	w. Wmk Crown to right of CA		1·00	
42/7		*Set of 6*	1·25	90

Nos. 42/7 are overprinted "ST. KITTS" and have the previous combined inscription obliterated.

*The normal sideways watermark shows Crown to left of CA, as seen from the back of the stamp.

The "no stop" variety occurs on R. 3/4 of the lower pane.

(Des and litho Format)

1980 (4 Sept). *80th Birthday of Queen Elizabeth the Queen Mother.* W w 14. P 13½.

48	10	$2 multicoloured	25	60

No. 48 was printed in sheets containing two *se-tenant* stamp-size labels.

11 The Three Wise Men

(Des Walsall. Litho Questa)

1980 (10 Nov). *Christmas.* T 11 and similar horiz designs. Multicoloured. W w 14 (sideways). P 14½ × 14.

49	5 c. Type 11		10	10
50	15 c. The Shepherds		10	10
51	30 c. Bethlehem		10	10
52	$4 Nativity scene		50	60
49/52		*Set of 4*	55	65

12 Purple-throated Carib 13 Bananaquit

(Des Jennifer Toombs. Litho Questa)

1981 (5 Feb)–**82**. *Birds.* Vert designs as T 12 (1 to 10 c.) or horiz as T 13 (15 c. to $10). Multicoloured. W w 14 (sideways on 1 to 10 c.) P 13½×14 (1 to 10 c.) or 14 (15 c. to $10).

A. Without imprint date

53A	1 c. Magnificent Frigate Bird (30.5.81)		15	20
54A	4 c. Wied's Crested Flycatcher (30.5.81)		25	20
55A	5 c. Type 12		25	20
56A	6 c. Burrowing Owl (30.5.81)		35	30
57A	8 c. Caribbean Martin (30.5.81)		30	30
58A	10 c. Yellow-crowned Night Heron		25	20
59A	15 c. Type 13		30	20
60A	20 c. Scaly-breasted Thrasher		30	20
61A	25 c. Grey Kingbird		30	20
62A	30 c. Green-throated Carib		30	20
63A	40 c. Turnstone		35	30
64A	45 c. Black-faced Grassquit		35	30
65A	50 c. Cattle Egret		40	30
66A	55 c. Brown Pelican		40	30
67A	$1 Lesser Antillean Bullfinch		60	60
68A	$2.50, Zenaida Dove		1·25	2·25
69A	$5 American Kestrel		2·25	3·50
70A	$10 Antillean Crested Hummingbird		4·50	6·00
53A/70A		*Set of 18*	11·50	14·00

B. With imprint date at foot of design (8.6.82)

53B	1 c. Magnificent Frigate Bird		45	35
54B	4 c. Wied's Crested Flycatcher		45	30
55B	5 c. Type 12		55	30
56B	6 c. Burrowing Owl		65	40
57B	8 c. Caribbean Martin		70	30
58B	10 c. Yellow-crowned Night Heron		70	30
59B	15 c. Type 13		75	30
60B	20 c. Scaly-breasted Thrasher		80	30
61B	25 c. Grey Kingbird		80	30
62B	30 c. Green-throated Carib		80	35
63B	40 c. Turnstone		90	40
64B	45 c. Black-faced Grassquit		1·00	45
65B	50 c. Cattle Egret		1·10	50
66B	55 c. Brown Pelican		1·25	50
67B	$1 Lesser Antillean Bullfinch		2·00	80
68B	$2.50, Zenaida Dove		3·25	3·00
69B	$5 American Kestrel		5·00	5·50
70B	$10 Antillean Crested Hummingbird		8·00	9·00
53B/70B		*Set of 18*	26·00	21·00

Imprint dates: "1982", Nos. 53B/70B; "1983", Nos. 59B/64B, 67B/8B.

---

14 Battalion Company Sergeant, 3rd Regt of Foot ("The Buffs"), *circa* 1801

15 Miriam Pickard (first Guide Commissioner)

(Des G. Vasarhelyi. Litho Format)

1981 (5 Mar). *Military Uniforms* (1st series). T 14 and similar vert designs. Multicoloured. W w 14. P 14½.

71	5 c. Type 14		10	10
72	30 c. Battalion Company Officer, 45th Regt of Foot, 1796–97		15	10
73	55 c. Battalion Company Officer, 9th Regt of Foot, 1790		15	10
74	$2.50, Grenadier, 38th Regt of Foot, 1751		45	35
71/4		*Set of 4*	70	45

See also Nos. 110/13 and 220/6.

(Des D. Shults. Litho Questa)

1981 (23 June–14 Dec). *Royal Wedding.* Horiz designs as T 26/27 of Kiribati. Multicoloured. (a) W w 14. P 14.

75	55 c. Saudadoes		10	10
	aw. Wmk inverted		18·00	
	b. Sheetlet. No. 75×6 and No. 76		1·10	
	bw. Wmk inverted		£130	
76	55 c. Prince Charles and Lady Diana Spencer		40	40
	aw. Wmk inverted		65·00	
77	$2.50, *Royal George*		25	30
	aw. Wmk inverted		18·00	
	b. Sheetlet No. 77×6 and No. 78		2·00	
	bw. Wmk inverted		£130	
78	$2.50, As No. 76		70	70
	aw. Wmk inverted		65·00	
79	$4 *Britannia*		35	50
	a. Sheetlet. No. 79×6 and No. 80		2·50	
80	$4 As No. 76		75	1·00
75/80		*Set of 6*	2·25	2·75
MS81	120×109 mm. $5 As No. 76. Wmk sideways. P 12 (14 Dec)		1·00	1·00

(b) Booklet stamps. No wmk. P 12 (19 Nov)

82	55 c. As No. 76		15	30
	a. Booklet pane. No. 82×4 with margins all round		55	
83	$2.50, As No. 78		65	1·25
	a. Booklet pane. No. 83×2 with margins all round		1·25	

Nos. 75/80 were printed in sheetlets of seven stamps of the same face value, each containing six of the "Royal Yacht" design and one of the larger design showing Prince Charles and Lady Diana.

Nos. 82/3 come from $9.40 stamp booklets.

(Des Jennifer Toombs. Litho Walsall)

1981 (21 Sept). *50th Anniv of St. Kitts Girl Guide Movement.* T 15 and similar vert designs. Multicoloured. W w 14. P 14.

84	5 c. Type 15		10	10
85	30 c. Lady Baden-Powell's visit, 1964		15	10
86	55 c. Visit of Princess Alice, 1960		25	10
87	$2 Thinking-Day parade, 1980's		45	35
84/7		*Set of 4*	80	45

16 Stained-glass Windows 17 Admiral Samuel Hood

(Des Jennifer Toombs. Litho Format)

1981 (30 Nov). *Christmas.* T 16 and similar vert designs showing stained-glass windows. Multicoloured. W w 14. P 13 × 14.

88	5 c. multicoloured		10	10
89	30 c. multicoloured		10	10
90	55 c. multicoloured		15	10
	w. Wmk inverted		20·00	
91	$3 multicoloured		50	50
88/91		*Set of 4*	75	60

(Des D. Shults. Litho Format)

1982 (15 Mar). *Bicentenary of Brimstone Hill Siege.* T 17 and similar horiz designs. W w 14 (sideways). P 14.

92	55 c. multicoloured		10	10
93	55 c. multicoloured		20	10
MS94	96 × 71 mm. $5 black, red-orange & yell-brn		1·10	1·10

Designs:—55 c. Marquis De Bouillé; $5 Battle scene.

---

18 Alexandra, Princess of Wales, 1863

ROYAL BABY
(19)

(Des D. Shults and J. Cooter. Litho Format)

1982 (22 June). *21st Birthday of Princess of Wales.* T 18 and similar vert designs. Multicoloured. W w 14. P 13½ × 14.

95	15 c. Type 18		10	10
	w. Wmk inverted		7·00	
96	55 c. Coat of arms of Alexandra of Denmark		15	15
97	$6 Diana, Princess of Wales		55	80
	w. Wmk inverted		5·00	
95/7		*Set of 3*	70	85

1982 (12 July). *Birth of Prince William of Wales.* Nos. 95/7 optd with T 19.

98	15 c. Type 18		10	10
	a. Opt inverted		7·00	
	w. Wmk inverted		15·00	
99	55 c. Coat of arms of Alexandra of Denmark		15	15
100	$6 Diana, Princess of Wales		55	80
	w. Wmk inverted		8·00	
98/100		*Set of 3*	70	85

20 Naturalist Badge 21 Santa with Christmas Tree and Gifts

(Des Philatelists (1980) Ltd. Litho Questa)

1982 (18 Aug). *75th Anniv of Boy Scout Movement.* T 20 and similar vert designs. Multicoloured. W w 14. P 14 × 13½.

101	5 c. Type 20		10	10
102	55 c. Rescuer badge		30	15
103	$2 First Aid badge		80	80
101/3		*Set of 3*	1·10	90

(Des Marcel Frazer (5 c.), Sinclair Herbert (55 c.), Marijka Grey ($1.10), Gary Bowrin ($3). Litho Format)

1982 (20 Oct). *Christmas. Children's Paintings.* T 21 and similar horiz designs. Multicoloured. W w 14 (sideways). P 14 × 13½.

104	5 c. Type 21		10	10
105	55 c. The Inn		15	10
106	$1.10, Three Kings		20	15
107	$3 Annunciation		40	40
104/7		*Set of 4*	65	60

22 Cruise Ship *Stella Oceanis* at Basseterre

23 Sir William Smith (founder)

(Des G. Drummond. Litho Format)

1983 (14 Mar). *Commonwealth Day.* T 22 and similar horiz design. Multicoloured. W w 14 (sideways). P 14.

108	55 c. Type 22		15	10
109	$2 Queen Elizabeth 2 at Basseterre		35	40

(Des G. Vasarhelyi. Litho Format)

1983 (25 May). *Military Uniforms* (2nd series). Vert designs as T 14. Multicoloured. W w 14. P 14½.

110	15 c. Light Company Private, 15th Regt of Foot, *circa* 1814		20	10
111	30 c. Battalion Company Officer, 15th Regt of Foot, *circa* 1780		30	10
112	55 c. Light Company Officer, 5th Regt of Foot, *circa* 1822		30	10
113	$2.50, Battalion Company Officer, 11th Regt of Foot, *circa* 1804		60	1·60
110/13		*Set of 4*	1·25	1·75

(Des J. Cooter. Litho Format)

1983 (27 July). *Centenary of the Boys' Brigade. T* **23** *and similar vert designs. Multicoloured.* W w **14**. P 13½.

114	10 c. Type **23**	25	10
115	45 c. B.B. members on steps of Sandy Point Methodist Church	30	10
116	50 c. Brigade drummers	30	10
117	$3 Boys' Brigade badge	70	2·25
114/17	*Set of 4*	1·40	2·25

(24)   (24a)   25 Montgolfier Balloon, 1783

1983 (19 Sept). *Nos.* 55, 59/63 *and* 66/70 *optd as T* **24** (*horiz* 20 *mm long on Nos.* 119/28). A. *Without imprint date*

118A	5 c. Type **12**	15	10
	c. Optd with T **24**a (local opt)	7·00	9·00
	ca. Opt inverted (reading upwards)	25·00	
119A	15 c. Type **13**	1·00	1·00
122A	30 c. Green-throated Carib	20·00	20·00
124A	55 c. Brown Pelican	50	50
125A	$1 Lesser Antillean Bullfinch	7·50	7·50
126A	$2.50, Zenaida Dove	2·00	2·00
127A	$5 American Kestrel	2·75	2·75
128A	$10 Antillean Crested Hummingbird	2·75	2·75
118A/28A	*Set of 8*	35·00	35·00

B. *With imprint date at foot of design*

118B	5 c. Type **12**	15	10
	a. Opt inverted	32·00	
	b. Pair, one without opt	80·00	
	c. Optd with T **24**a (local opt)	1·50	2·00
	ca. Opt inverted (reading upwards)	6·00	
119B	15 c. Type **13**	30	10
	a. Opt double	7·00	
120B	20 c. Scaly-breasted Thrasher	35	10
121B	25 c. Grey Kingbird	40	10
	a. Opt inverted	12·00	
122B	30 c. Green-throated Carib	45	15
123B	40 c. Turnstone	50	20
124B	55 c. Brown Pelican	55	30
	a. Opt inverted	8·50	
125B	$1 Lesser Antillean Bullfinch	1·00	50
126B	$2.50, Zenaida Dove	1·75	1·75
127B	$5 American Kestrel	2·75	3·00
128B	$10 Antillean Crested Hummingbird	5·00	5·50
118B/28B	*Set of 11*	12·00	10·50

Imprint dates: "1982", Nos. 118B/19B, 121B/2B, 127B; "1983", Nos. 119B/28B.

(Des A. Theobald. Litho Format)

1983 (28 Sept). *Bicentenary of Manned Flight. T* **25** *and similar multicoloured designs.* W w **15** (*sideways on Nos.* 130/3). P 14.

129	10 c. Type **25**	10	10
130	45 c. Sikorsky *Russky Vityaz* biplane (*horiz*)	15	10
131	50 c. Lockheed L-1011 TriStar 500 Flamingo (*horiz*)	15	10
132	$2.50, Bell XS-1 (*horiz*)	50	90
129/32	*Set of 4*	75	1·10
MS133	108×145 mm. Nos. 129/32	75	1·25

26 Star over West Indian Town   27 Parrot in Tree

(Des Jennifer Toombs. Litho Format)

1983 (7 Nov). *Christmas. T* **26** *and similar horiz designs. Multicoloured.* W w **15** (*sideways**). P 14.

134	15 c. Type **26**	10	10
135	30 c. Shepherds watching Star	10	10
	w. Wmk POST OFFICE reading upwards	22·00	
136	55 c. Mary and Joseph	10	10
137	$2.50, The Nativity	30	40
134/7	*Set of 4*	45	55
MS138	130×130 mm. Nos. 134/7. Wmk upright	50	1·10
	w. Wmk inverted	75·00	

*The normal sideways watermark shows "POST OFFICE" reading downwards.

(Des Court House Studio. Litho Format)

1984 (30 Jan). *Batik Designs (1st series). T* **27** *and similar vert designs.* W w **15**. P 14×13½.

139	45 c. multicoloured	10	10
	w. Wmk inverted	14·00	
140	50 c. multicoloured	10	10
	w. Wmk inverted	15·00	
141	$1.50, new blue, bistre-yellow & brt mag	35	60
142	$3 multicoloured	55	1·50
	w. Wmk inverted	28·00	
139/42	*Set of 4*	1·00	2·00

Designs:—50 c. Man under coconut tree; $1.50, Women with fruit; $3 Butterflies.
See also Nos. 169/72.

28 Cushion Star

(Des G. Drummond. Litho J.W.)

1984 (4 July). *Marine Wildlife. T* **28** *and similar multicoloured designs.* W w **15** (*sideways* on 5 c. to* 75 *c.*). P 14.

143	5 c. Type **28**	30	30
	w. Wmk POST OFFICE reading downwards		
144	10 c. Rough File shell (*Lima scabra*)	35	30
	w. Wmk POST OFFICE reading downwards		
145	15 c. Red-lined Cleaning Shrimp	35	15
146	20 c. Bristleworm	35	15
147	25 c. Flamingo Tongue (*Cyphoma gibbosus*)	40	15
148	30 c. Christmas Tree Worm	40	20
149	40 c. Pink-tipped Anemone	55	25
150	50 c. Smallmouth Grunt	55	30
151	60 c. Glass-eyed Snapper	1·25	75
152	75 c. Reef Squirrelfish	90	70
153	$1 Sea Fans and Flamefish (*vert*)	1·00	60
154	$2.50, Reef Butterflyfish (*vert*)	2·25	3·50
155	$5 Black-barred Soldierfish (*vert*)	5·50	14·00
	w. Wmk inverted	15·00	
156	$10 Cocoa Damselfish (*vert*)	9·00	14·00
	w. Wmk inverted	15·00	
143/56	*Set of 14*	21·00	27·00

*The normal sideways watermark shows "POST OFFICE" reading upwards.

For 10 c., 60 c., $5 and $10 with watermark w **16** and imprint dates see Nos. 194/206.

29 Agriculture

(Des G. Vasarhelyi. Litho Questa)

1984 (15 Aug). *25th Anniv of 4-H Organisation. T* **29** *and similar horiz designs. Multicoloured.* W w **15** (*sideways*). P 14.

157	30 c. Type **29**	20	10
158	55 c. Animal husbandry	30	15
159	$1.10, The 4-H Pledge	55	60
160	$3 On parade	90	1·25
157/60	*Set of 4*	1·75	1·90

IMPERFORATES. Issues between Nos. 161 and 184 exist imperforate. Such items are not listed as there is no evidence that they fulfil the criteria outlined on page xi of this catalogue.

30 Construction of Royal St. Kitts Hotel

(Des K. Tatem (15 c.), Tessa Wattley (30 c.), Myrna Elcock and L. Freeman ($1.10), A. Williams ($3), adapted Jennifer Toombs. Litho Format)

1984 (18 Sept). *First Anniv of Independence of St. Kitts-Nevis. T* **30** *and similar multicoloured designs.* W w **15** (*sideways on* 15, 30 *c.*). P 14.

161	15 c. Type **30**	15	10
162	30 c. Independence celebrations	20	15
163	$1.10, National Anthem and aerial view (*vert*)	40	60
164	$3 "Dawn of a New Day" (*vert*)	1·00	1·40
161/4	*Set of 4*	1·60	2·00

31 Opening Presents

(Des Jennifer Toombs. Litho Questa)

1984 (1 Nov). *Christmas. T* **31** *and similar horiz designs. Multicoloured.* W w **15** (*sideways*). P 14.

165	15 c. Type **31**	15	10
166	60 c. Singing carols	45	35
167	$1 Nativity play	75	60
168	$2 Leaving church on Christmas Day	1·40	1·10
165/8	*Set of 4*	2·50	1·90

(Des Court House Studio. Litho Format)

1985 (6 Feb). *Batik Designs (2nd series). Horiz designs as T* **27**. W w **15** (*sideways*). P 13½ × 14.

169	15 c. black, bright green and light green	15	10
170	40 c. black, bright greenish blue and bright new blue	30	15
171	60 c. black, orange-vermilion and vermilion	45	25
172	$3 black, lake-brown and orange-brown	1·25	2·25
169/72	*Set of 4*	1·90	2·50

Designs:—15 c. Country bus; 40 c. Donkey cart; 60 c. Rum shop and man on bicycle; $3 *Polynesia* (cruise schooner).

32 Container Ship *Tropic Jade*   33 James Derrick Cardin (leading Freemason)

(Des J. Cooter. Litho Format)

1985 (27 Mar). *Ships. T* **32** *and similar horiz designs. Multicoloured.* W w **15** (*sideways*). P 13½ × 14.

173	40 c. Type **32**	1·00	30
174	$1.20, *Atlantic Clipper* (schooner)	2·00	1·50
175	$2 *Mandalay* (schooner)	2·25	2·50
176	$2 *Cunard Countess* (liner)	2·25	2·50
173/6	*Set of 4*	6·75	6·25

(Des G. Vasarhelyi. Litho Format)

1985 (9 Nov). *150th Anniv of Mount Olive S.C. Masonic Lodge. T* **33** *and similar multicoloured designs.* W w **15** (*sideways on* 15, 75 *c., and* $3). P 15.

177	15 c. Type **33**	40	20
178	75 c. Banner of Mount Olive Lodge	1·00	1·10
179	$1.20, Masonic symbols (*horiz*)	1·25	2·50
180	$3 Lodge Charter (1835)	1·75	4·50
177/80	*Set of 4*	4·00	7·50

34 Map of St. Kitts   35 Queen Elizabeth and Prince Philip on St. Kitts

(Des J. Cooter. Litho Format)

1985 (27 Nov). *Christmas. 400th Anniv of Sir Francis Drake's Visit. T* **34** *and similar vert designs. Multicoloured.* P 15.

181	10 c. Type **34**	25	15
182	40 c. *Golden Hind*	50	35
183	60 c. Sir Francis Drake	50	50
184	$3 Drake's heraldic shield	75	3·00
181/4	*Set of 4*	1·75	3·50

(Des D. Miller. Litho B.D.T.)

1986 (9 July). *60th Birthday of Queen Elizabeth II. T* **35** *and similar vert designs. Multicoloured.* P 13½.

185	10 c. Type **35**	15	10
186	20 c. Queen Elizabeth on St. Kitts	25	15
187	40 c. At Trooping the Colour	50	30
188	$3 In Sweden	2·00	3·00
185/8	*Set of 4*	2·50	3·00

(Des D. Miller. Litho Walsall)

1986 (23 July). *Royal Wedding. Square designs as T* **231**a *of Jamaica. Multicoloured.* W w **16**. P 14½×14.

189	15 c. Prince Andrew and Miss Sarah Ferguson	15	10
190	$2.50, Prince Andrew	1·00	2·00

36 Family on Smallholding   (37)

(Des K. Tatem (15 c.), A. Williams ($1.20), adapted G. Vasarhelyi. Litho Questa)

1986 (18 Sept). *Agriculture Exhibition. T* **36** *and similar horiz design. Multicoloured.* W w **16** (*sideways*). P 13½×14.

191	15 c. Type **36**	20	10
192	$1.20, Hands holding people, computers and crops	1·25	1·60

(Litho Questa)

1986 (5 Nov)–**88.** *As Nos. 144, 151 and 155/6 but W w* **16** *(sideways on* 10, 60 *c.). With imprint date.* P 14.

194	10 c. Rough File Shell	1·25	85
201	60 c. Glass-eyed Snapper (17.8.88)	2·50	1·60
205	$5 Black-barred Soldierfish (*vert*) (17.8.88)	7·50	10·00
206	$10 Cocoa Damselfish (*vert*) (17.8.88)	11·00	15·00
194/206		*Set of 4* 20·00	25·00

Imprint dates: "1986", No. 194; "1988", Nos. 194, 201, 205/6.

1986 (12 Nov). *40th Anniv of United Nations Week. Nos.* 185/8 *optd with T* **37** *in gold.*

207	10 c. Type **35**	15	15
208	20 c. Queen Elizabeth on St. Kitts	25	20
209	40 c. At Trooping the Colour	30	30
210	$3 In Sweden	1·00	3·25
	a. Opt triple	75·00	
207/10		*Set of 4* 1·50	3·50

38 Adult Green Monkey with Young   **39** Frederic Bartholdi (sculptor)

(Des Doreen McGuinness. Litho Walsall)

1986 (1 Dec). *Endangered Species. Green Monkeys on St. Kitts. T* **38** *and similar vert designs. Multicoloured. W w* **16**. P 14×13½.

211	15 c. Type **38**	2·00	40
212	20 c. Adult on ground	2·25	40
213	60 c. Young monkey in tree	5·00	2·25
214	$1 Adult grooming young monkey	5·50	4·50
211/14		*Set of 4* 13·00	6·75

(Des D. Miller. Litho Format)

1986 (17 Dec). *Centenary of Statue of Liberty. T* **39** *and similar multicoloured designs. W w* **16** *(sideways on* 60 *c.,* $1.50*).* P 14.

215	40 c. Type **39**	30	30
216	60 c. Torch (1876) and head (1878) on exhibition (*horiz*)	40	60
217	$1.50, Isere (French warship) carrying Statue (*horiz*)	1·00	1·75
218	$3 Statue of Liberty, Paris, 1884	1·25	2·75
215/18		*Set of 4* 2·75	4·75
MS219	70×85 mm. $3.50, Head of Statue of Liberty	2·25	3·25

40 Officer, 9th Regt (East Norfolk), 1792   **41** Sugar Cane Warehouse

(Des C. Collins. Litho Format)

1987 (25 Feb). *Military Uniforms (3rd series). T* **40** *and similar vert designs. Multicoloured. W w* **16**. P 14½.

220	15 c. Type **40**	40	30
221	15 c. Officer, Regt de Neustrie, 1779	40	30
222	40 c. Sergeant, 3rd Regt ("The Buffs"), 1801	65	45
223	40 c. Officer, French Artillery, 1812	65	45
224	$2 Light Company Private, 5th Regt, 1778	1·25	3·00
225	$2 Grenadier of the Line, 1796	1·25	3·00
220/5		*Set of 6* 4·25	6·75
MS226	121×145 mm. Nos. 220/5	6·75	8·00

The two designs for each value were printed in sheets of 50 containing two panes 5×5 with the British uniform depicted on the left-hand pane and the French on the right.

(Des G. Vasarhelyi. Litho Format)

1987 (15 Apr). *Sugar Cane Industry. T* **41** *and similar vert designs. Multicoloured (colour of panel behind "ST. KITTS" given). W w* **16**. P 14.

227	15 c. greenish yellow (Type 41)	20	30
	a. Horiz strip of 5. Nos. 227/31	90	
228	15 c. cinnamon	20	30
229	15 c. lilac	20	30
230	15 c. azure	20	30
231	15 c. pale greenish blue	20	30
232	75 c. bright green	35	85
	a. Horiz strip of 5. Nos. 232/6	1·75	
233	75 c. lilac	35	85
234	75 c. dull green	35	85

235	75 c. orange-yellow	35	85
236	75 c. greenish blue	35	85
227/36		*Set of 10* 2·50	5·25

Designs:—Nos. 227/31, Sugar cane factory; Nos. 232/6, Loading sugar train.

Nos. 227/31 and 232/6 were each printed together, *se-tenant*, in horizontal strips of five throughout the sheets, each strip forming a composite design.

42 B.W.I.A. L-1011 TriStar 500   **43** *Hygrocybe occidentalis*

(Des T. Hadler. Litho Format)

1987 (24 June). *Aircraft visiting St. Kitts. T* **42** *and similar horiz designs. Multicoloured. W w* 14 *(sideways).* P 14.

237	40 c. Type **42**	75	30
238	60 c. L.I.A.T. Hawker Siddeley Super 748	95	60
239	$1.20, W.I.A. De Havilland D.H.C.6 Twin Otter 300	1·50	2·50
240	$3 American Eagle Aerospatiale/Aeritalia ATR 42	2·75	4·25
237/40		*Set of 4* 5·50	7·00

(Des I. Loe. Litho Questa)

1987 (26 Aug). *Fungi. T* **43** *and similar vert designs. Multicoloured. W w* **16**. P 14.

241	15 c. Type **43**	80	20
242	10 c. Marasmius haematocephalus	1·25	40
243	$1.20, Psilocybe cubensis	2·75	2·75
	w. Wmk inverted	12·00	
244	$2 Hygrocybe acutoconica	3·50	3·50
245	$3 Boletellus cubensis	4·00	4·50
241/5		*Set of 5* 11·00	10·00

44 Carnival Clown   **45** Ixora

(Des Rose Cameron-Smith. Litho Format)

1987 (28 Oct). *Christmas. T* **44** *and similar square designs showing different clowns. Multicoloured. W w* **16** *(sideways).* P 14½.

246	15 c. multicoloured	25	15
247	40 c. multicoloured	55	30
248	$1 multicoloured	1·25	1·40
249	$3 multicoloured	2·50	4·00
246/9		*Set of 4* 4·00	5·25

See also Nos. 266/9.

(Des Josephine Martin. Litho Questa)

1988 (20 Jan). *Flowers. T* **45** *and similar vert designs. Multicoloured. W w* **16**. P 14½×14.

250	15 c. Type **45**	30	15
251	40 c. Shrimp Plant	55	30
252	$1 Poinsettia	1·00	1·40
253	$3 Honolulu Rose	2·50	4·00
250/3		*Set of 4* 4·00	5·25

46 Fort Thomas Hotel   **47** Ball, Wicket and Leeward Islands Cricket Association Emblem

(Des L. Curtis. Litho Walsall)

1988 (20 Apr). *Tourism (1st series). Hotels. T* **46** *and similar horiz designs. Multicoloured. W w* 14 *(sideways).* P 14×14½.

254	60 c. Type **46**	70	70
255	60 c. Fairview Inn	70	70
256	60 c. Frigate Bay Beach Hotel	70	70
257	60 c. Ocean Terrace Inn	70	70
258	$3 The Golden Lemon	2·25	2·75
259	$3 Royal St. Kitts Casino and Jack Tar Village	2·25	2·75
260	$3 Rawlins Plantation Hotel and Restaurant	2·25	2·75
254/60		*Set of 7* 8·50	10·00

See also Nos. 270/5.

(Des Joan Thompson. Litho Walsall)

1988 (13 July). *75th Anniv of Leeward Islands Cricket Tournament. T* **47** *and similar vert design. Multicoloured. W w* 14. P 13 × 13½.

261	40 c. Type **47**	1·50	30
262	$3 Cricket match at Warner Park	3·75	4·50

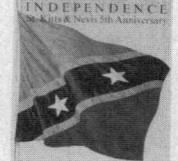

48 Flag of St. Kitts-Nevis   **49** Red Cross Nurse with Hospital Patient

(Des L. Curtis. Litho Questa)

1988 (19 Sept). *5th Anniv of Independence. T* **48** *and similar vert designs. Multicoloured. W w* **16**. P 14½ × 14.

263	15 c. Type **48**	25	10
264	60 c. Arms of St. Kitts	75	60
MS265	61 × 53 mm. $5 Princess Margaret presenting Constitutional Instrument to Prime Minister Kennedy Simmonds, 1983. W w 14	3·00	3·50

(Des Rose Cameron-Smith. Litho Format)

1988 (2 Nov). *Christmas. Square designs as T* **44** *showing carnival masqueraders. W w* 14 *(sideways).* P 14½.

266	15 c. multicoloured	10	10
267	40 c. multicoloured	20	25
268	80 c. multicoloured	40	55
269	$3 multicoloured	1·25	2·25
266/9		*Set of 4* 1·75	2·75

(Des L. Curtis. Litho Format)

1989 (25 Jan). *Tourism (2nd series). Colonial Architecture. Horiz designs as T* **46**. *Multicoloured. W w* **16** *(sideways).* P 14.

270	20 c. Georgian house	20	15
271	20 c. Colonial-style house	20	15
272	$1 Romney Manor	50	80
273	$1 Lavington Great House	50	80
274	$2 Government House	70	1·60
275	$2 Treasury Building	70	1·60
270/5		*Set of 6* 2·50	4·50

For a redrawn version of No. 275 in a miniature sheet, see No. MS400.

(Des C. Collins. Litho Format)

1989 (8 May). *125th Anniv of International Red Cross. T* **49** *and similar vert designs. Multicoloured. W w* **16**. P 14×14½.

276	40 c. multicoloured	30	30
277	$1 multicoloured	65	75
278	$3 orange-vermilion and black	1·75	2·50
276/8		*Set of 3* 2·40	3·25

Designs:—$1 Loading patient into ambulance; $3 125th anniversary logo.

50 Battle on the Champ-de-Mars   **51** Outline Map of St. Kitts

(Des D. Miller. Litho B.D.T.)

1989 (7 July). *"Philexfrance 89" International Stamp Exhibition, Paris. Sheet* 115×99 *mm. W w* **16**. P 14.

MS279	**50** $5 multicoloured	3·25	3·75

(Des A. Theobald ($5), D. Miller (others). Litho Questa)

1989 (20 July). *20th Anniv of First Manned Landing on Moon. Multicoloured designs as T* **51**a *of Kiribati. W w* **16** *(sideways on* 20 *c.,* $1*).* P 14×13½ (10 c., $2) or 14 (others).

280	10 c. Lunar rover on Moon	10	10
281	20 c. Crew of "Apollo 13" (30×30 mm)	10	10
282	$1 "Apollo 13" emblem (30×30 mm)	45	60
283	$2 "Apollo 13" splashdown, South Pacific	95	1·25
280/3		*Set of 4* 1·40	1·75
MS284	100×83 mm. $5 Aldrin leaving "Apollo 11" lunar module. Wmk inverted. P 14×13½	3·50	4·00

(Des D. Miller. Litho B.D.T.)

1989 (25 Oct). *W w* **16**. P 15×14.

285	**51** 10 c. deep mauve and black	20	20
286	15 c. bright carmine and black	25	10
287	20 c. yellow-orange and black	25	10
288	40 c. yellow and black	40	20
289	60 c. bright blue and black	60	50
290	$1 yellow-green and black	90	1·25
285/90		*Set of 6* 2·40	2·00

52 *Santa Mariagallante* passing St. Kitts, 1493

(Des L. Curtis. Litho Questa)

1989 (8 Nov). *500th Anniv of Discovery of America (1992) by Columbus (1st issue). T 52 and similar horiz designs. Multicoloured. W w 16 (sideways). P 14.*

291	15 c. Type 52		1·25	30
292	80 c. Arms of Columbus and map of fourth voyage, 1502-04		2·50	1·75
293	$1 Navigation instruments, c. 1500		2·50	1·75
294	$5 Columbus and map of second voyage, 1493-96		7·00	10·00
291/4		*Set of 4*	12·00	12·00

See also Nos. 359/60.

53 Poinciana Tree

54 *Junonia evarete*

(Des G. Vasarhelyi. Litho Walsall)

1989 (17 Nov). *"World Stamp Expo '89" International Stamp Exhibition, Washington. T 53 and similar horiz designs. Multicoloured. W w 14 (sideways). P 14.*

295	15 c. Type 53		30	10
296	40 c. Fort George Citadel, Brimstone Hill		65	30
297	$1 Private, Light Company, 5th Foot, 1778		1·40	1·25
298	$3 St. George's Anglican Church		3·00	4·50
295/8		*Set of 4*	4·75	5·50

(Des I. Loe. Litho B.D.T.)

1990 (6 June). *Butterflies. T 54 and similar horiz designs. Multicoloured. W w 14 (sideways). P 13½×14.*

299	15 c. Type 54		1·00	40
300	40 c. *Anartia jatrophae*		1·75	40
301	60 c. *Heliconius charitonia*		1·75	80
302	$3 *Biblis hyperia*		3·75	5·50
299/302		*Set of 4*	7·50	6·25

(55)　　**56** Brimstone Hill

1990 (6 June). *"EXPO 90" International Garden and Greenery Exhibition, Osaka. Nos. 299/302 optd with T 55.*

303	15 c. Type 54		1·00	40
304	40 c. *Anartia jatrophae*		1·75	40
305	60 c. *Heliconius charitonia*		1·75	80
306	$3 *Biblis hyperia*		3·75	5·50
303/6		*Set of 4*	7·50	6·25

(Des D. Miller. Litho Questa)

1990 (30 June). *300th Anniv of English Bombardment of Brimstone Hill. T 56 and similar horiz designs. Multicoloured. W w 16 (sideways). P 14.*

307	15 c. Type 56		30	20
308	40 c. Restored Brimstone Hill fortifications		50	30
309	60 c. 17th-century English marine and Fort Charles under attack		70	1·10
	a. Horiz pair. Nos. 309/10		3·25	4·00
310	$3 English sailors firing cannon		2·50	3·50
307/10		*Set of 4*	3·50	4·50

Nos. 307/9 were printed in complete sheets, each containing one value. No. 309 also exists *se-tenant*, as a horizontal pair, with No. 310. Each pair shows a composite design across the two stamps with no margin at the left of the 60 c. or at the right of the $3.

57 Supermarine Spitfire Mk Vb *St. Kitts Nevis I*, 71 Squadron

(Des A. Theobald. Litho B.D.T.)

1990 (15 Sept). *50th Anniv of Battle of Britain. Sheet 103×76 mm. containing T 57 and similar horiz design. Multicoloured. W w 16 (sideways). P 14.*

MS311　$3 Type 57; $3 Supermarine Spitfire Mk Vb *St. Kitts Nevis II*, 345 Squadron　..　9·50　9·50

58 *Romney* (freighter)

(Des S. Williams. Litho B.D.T.)

1990 (10 Oct). *Ships. T 58 and similar horiz designs. Multicoloured. W w 14 (sideways). P 14.*

312	10 c. Type 58		30	20
313	15 c. *Baralt* (freighter)		30	20
314	20 c. *Wear* (mail steamer)		40	20
315	25 c. *Sunmount* (freighter)		40	20
316	40 c. *Inanda* (cargo liner)		60	25
317	50 c. *Alcoa Partner* (freighter)		60	30
318	60 c. *Dominica* (freighter)		65	30
319	80 c. *C.G.M Provence* (container ship)		70	40
320	$1 *Director* (freighter)		80	50
321	$1.20, *Barque*		1·00	1·00
322	$2 *Chignecto* (packet steamer)		1·75	1·75
323	$3 *Berbice* (mail steamer)		2·50	2·75
324	$5 *Vamos* (freighter)		3·25	4·00
325	$10 *Federal Maple* (freighter)		5·50	7·00
312/25		*Set of 14*	17·00	17·00

For 10 c. watermarked w 16 (sideways) see No. 413.
For miniature sheet containing the $3 see No. MS472.

59 Single Fork Game

(Des G. Vasarhelyi. Litho Questa)

1990 (14 Nov). *Christmas. Traditional Games. T 59 and similar horiz designs. Multicoloured. W w 16 (sideways). P 14.*

326	10 c. Type 59		15	10
327	15 c. Boulder breaking		15	10
328	40 c. Double fork		30	30
329	$3 The run up		1·75	3·00
326/9		*Set of 4*	2·10	3·00

60 White Periwinkle

61 Census Logo

(Des Annette Robinson. Litho Cartor)

1991 (8 May). *Flowers. T 60 and similar multicoloured designs. W w 14 (sideways on 10, 40 c.). P 14×13½ (10, 40 c.) or 13½×14 (others).*

330	10 c. Type 60		50	20
331	40 c. Pink Oleander		90	30
332	60 c. Pink Periwinkle (*vert*)		1·25	70
333	$2 White Oleander (*vert*)		2·50	3·50
330/3		*Set of 4*	4·75	4·25

(Des G. Vasarhelyi, Litho B.D.T)

1991 (13 May). *National Census. W w 16. P 14.*

334	**61** 15 c. multicoloured		30	15
335	$2.40, multicoloured		2·50	3·00

The $2.40 differs from Type 61 by showing "ST. KITTS" in a curved panel.

(Des D. Miller. Litho Questa)

1991 (17 June). *65th Birthday of Queen Elizabeth II and 70th Birthday of Prince Philip. Vert designs as T 58 of Kiribati. W w 16 (sideways). P 14½×14.*

336	$1.20, Prince Philip		75	1·00
	a. Horiz pair. Nos. 336/7 separated by label		1·75	2·10
337	$1.80, Queen holding bouquet of flowers	1·00	1·10

Nos. 336/7 were printed together in a similar sheet format to Nos. 366/7 of Kiribati.

62 Nassau Grouper

(Des G. Drummond. Litho Questa)

1991 (28 Aug). *Fishes. T 62 and similar horiz designs. Multicoloured. W w 14 (sideways). P 14.*

338	10 c. Type 62		50	20
339	60 c. Hogfish		1·25	50
340	$1 Red Hind		2·00	1·50
341	$3 Porkfish		3·50	4·50
338/41		*Set of 4*	6·50	6·00

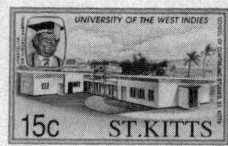

63 School of Continuing Studies, St. Kitts, and Chancellor Sir Shridath Ramphal

(Des G. Vasarhelyi. Litho Questa)

1991 (28 Sept). *40th Anniv of University of West Indies. T 63 and similar horiz designs. Multicoloured. W w 16 (sideways). P 14.*

342	15 c. Type 63		40	15
343	50 c. Administration Building, Barbados		70	40
344	$1 Engineering Building, Trinidad and Tobago		1·25	1·25
345	$3 Mona Campus, Jamaica, and Sir Shridath Ramphal		3·00	4·50
342/5		*Set of 4*	4·75	5·75

64 Whipping The Bull

(Des Marijka Grey and G. Vasarhelyi. Litho Walsall)

1991 (6 Nov). *Christmas. "The Bull" (Carnival play). T 64 and similar horiz designs. Multicoloured. W w 14 (sideways). P 14.*

346	10 c. Type 64		35	10
347	15 c. Death of The Bull		35	10
348	60 c. Cast of characters and musicians		1·00	60
349	$3 The Bull in procession		2·75	4·00
346/9		*Set of 4*	4·00	4·25

(Des D. Miller. Litho Questa ($3), Leigh-Mardon Ltd, Melbourne (others))

1992 (6 Feb). *40th Anniv of Queen Elizabeth II's Accession. Horiz designs as T 113 of Kenya. Multicoloured. W w 14 (sideways) ($3) or w 16 (sideways) (others). P 14.*

350	10 c. St. Kitts coastline		30	10
351	40 c. Warner Park Pavilion		60	25
352	60 c. Brimstone Hill		70	40
353	$1 Three portraits of Queen Elizabeth		80	85
354	$3 Queen Elizabeth II		1·90	2·50
350/4		*Set of 5*	3·75	3·75

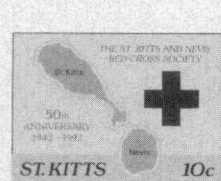

65 Map of St. Kitts–Nevis

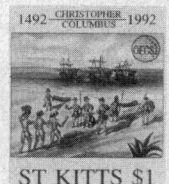

66 Columbus meeting Amerindians

(Des L. Curtis. Litho Enschedé)

1992 (8 May). *50th Anniv of St. Kitts-Nevis Red Cross Society. T 65 and similar horiz designs. Multicoloured. W w 14 (sideways). P 13½×14.*

355	10 c. Type 65		65	25
356	20 c. St. Kitts–Nevis flag		85	25
357	50 c. Red Cross House, St. Kitts		1·00	80
358	$2.40, Henri Dunant		3·00	4·25
355/8		*Set of 4*	5·00	5·00

(Adapted G. Vasarhelyi. Litho Cartor)

1992 (6 July). *Organization of East Caribbean States. 500th Anniv of Discovery of America by Columbus (2nd issue). T 66 and similar vert design. Multicoloured. W w 14. P 13.*

359	$1 Type 66		1·50	1·00
360	$2 Ships approaching island		2·25	3·00

NEW INFORMATION

The editor is always interested to correspond with people who have new information that will improve or correct the Catalogue.

67 Fountain, Independence Square

68 Joseph and Mary travelling to Bethlehem

(Des D. Miller. Litho Enschedé)

1992 (19 Aug). *Local Monuments. T* **67** *and similar vert designs. Multicoloured.* W w 14. P 12½×13.

361	25 c. Type **67**		25	20
362	50 c. Berkeley Memorial drinking fountain		35	35
363	80 c. Sir Thomas Warner's tomb		55	65
364	$2 War memorial		1·10	1·75
361/4		*Set of 4*	2·00	2·75

(Des L. Curtis. Litho Questa)

1992 (28 Oct). *Christmas. T* **68** *and similar vert designs. Multicoloured.* W w 16. P 14½.

365	20 c. Type **68**		30	20
366	25 c. Shepherds and star		30	20
367	80 c. Wise Men with gifts		65	55
368	$3 Mary, Joseph and Holy Child		1·75	3·25
365/8		*Set of 4*	2·75	3·75

(Des A. Theobald. Litho Questa)

1993 (1 Apr). *75th Anniv of Royal Air Force. Aircraft. Horiz designs as T* **166** *of Montserrat. Multicoloured.* W w 14 (*sideways*). P 14.

369	25 c. Short Singapore III		65	20
370	50 c. Bristol Type 152 Beaufort Mk II		1·00	30
371	80 c. Westland Whirlwind Series 3 H.A.R.10 helicopter		2·00	1·50
372	$1.60, English Electric Canberra T.11		2·25	3·25
369/72		*Set of 4*	5·50	4·75
MS373	110×78 mm. $2 Handley Page 0/400; $2 Fairey Long Range monoplane; $2 Vickers Wellesley; $2 Sepecat Jaguar G.R.1		8·50	9·50

69 Members of Diocesan Conference, Basseterre, 1992

70 1953 Coronation 2 c. Stamp and Ampulla

(Des G. Vasarhelyi. Litho Walsall)

1993 (21 May). *150th Anniv of Anglican Diocese of North-eastern Caribbean and Aruba. T* **69** *and similar multicoloured designs.* W w 16 (*sideways on 25 c., 80 c.*). P 13½×14 (*horiz*) or 14×13½ (*vert*).

374	25 c. Type **69**		15	10
375	50 c. Cathedral of St. John the Divine (*vert*)		40	35
376	80 c. Coat of arms and motto		70	85
377	$2 The Right Revd. Daniel Davis (first bishop) (*vert*)		1·50	2·50
374/7		*Set of 4*	2·50	3·50

(Des D. Miller. Litho Walsall)

1993 (2 June). *40th Anniv of Coronation. T* **70** *and similar vert designs. Multicoloured.* W w 16. P 14½×14.

378	10 c. Type **70**		40	20
379	25 c. 1977 Silver Jubilee $1.50 stamp and anointing spoon		50	20
380	80 c. 1977 Silver Jubilee 55 c. stamp and tassels		1·00	1·25
381	$2 1978 25th Anniv of Coronation stamps and sceptre		2·00	3·50
378/81		*Set of 4*	3·50	4·75

71 Flags of Girls Brigade and St. Kitts-Nevis

(Des G. Vasarhelyi. Litho Walsall)

1993 (1 July). *Centenary of Girls Brigade. T* **71** *and similar horiz design. Multicoloured.* W w 16 (*sideways*). P 13½×14.

382	80 c. Type **71**		1·50	1·00
383	$3 Girls Brigade badge and coat of arms		3·00	4·00

72 Aspects of St. Kitts on Flag

73 *Hibiscus sabdariffa*

(Des Ruth Vaughan (20 c.), S. Richards (80 c.), P. Maynard ($3), adapted D. Miller. Litho B.D.T.)

1993 (10 Sept). *10th Anniv of Independence. T* **72** *and similar horiz designs. Multicoloured.* W w 14 (*sideways*). P 14.

384	20 c. Type **72**		40	10
385	80 c. Coat of arms and Independence anniversary logo		1·00	80
386	$3 Coat of arms and map		3·00	4·00
384/6		*Set of 3*	4·00	4·50

(Des Jennifer Toombs. Litho Cartor)

1993 (16 Nov). *Christmas. Flowers. T* **73** *and similar vert designs. Multicoloured.* W w 14. P 13½×14.

387	25 c. Type **73**		25	10
388	50 c. *Euphorbia pulcherrima*		60	45
389	$1.60, *Euphorbia leucocephala*		1·75	2·25
387/9		*Set of 3*	2·40	2·50

74 Mesosaurus

75 Sir Shridath Ramphal

(Des N. Shewring. Litho B.D.T.)

1994 (18 Feb). *Prehistoric Aquatic Reptiles. T* **74** *and similar vert designs. Multicoloured.* W w 16. P 14.

390	$1.20, Type **74**		1·10	1·25
	a. Horiz strip of 5. Nos. 390/4		5·00	
391	$1.20, Placodus		1·10	1·25
392	$1.20, Liopleurodon		1·10	1·25
393	$1.20, Hydrotherosaurus		1·10	1·25
394	$1.20, Caretta		1·10	1·25
390/4		*Set of 5*	5·00	5·50

Nos. 390/4 were printed together, *se-tenant*, in horizontal strips of 5 throughout the sheet with the background forming a composite design.

1994 (18 Feb). *"Hong Kong '94" International Stamp Exhibition. Nos.* 390/4 *optd as T* **272** *of Jamaica.*

395	$1.20, Type **74**		1·25	1·40
	a. Horiz strip of 5. Nos. 395/9		5·50	
396	$1.20, Placodus		1·25	1·40
397	$1.20, Liopleurodon		1·25	1·40
398	$1.20, Hydrotherosaurus		1·25	1·40
399	$1.20, Caretta		1·25	1·40
395/9		*Set of 5*	5·50	6·00

(Des L. Curtis and G. Vasarhelyi. Litho B.D.T.)

1994 (21 Mar). *Centenary of Treasury Building. Sheet* 73×58 *mm. containing horiz design as No.* 275, *but with redrawn frame and inscriptions.* W w 14 (*sideways*). P 13½.

MS400	$10 multicoloured		7·50	8·50

(Des D. Miller. Litho Questa)

1994 (13 July). *First Recipients of Order of the Caribbean Community. T* **75** *and similar vert designs. Multicoloured.* W w 14. P 14½×14.

401	10 c. Type **75**		30	30
	a. Horiz strip of 5. Nos. 401, 402×2, 403/4		1·10	
402	10 c. Star of Order		20	20
403	10 c. Derek Walcott		30	30
404	10 c. William Demas		30	30
405	$1 Type **75**		1·25	1·25
	a. Horiz strip of 5. Nos. 405, 406×2, 407/8		5·00	
406	$1 As No. 402		1·00	1·00
407	$1 As No. 403		1·25	1·25
408	$1 As No. 404		1·25	1·25
401/8		*Set of 8*	5·25	5·25

Nos. 401/4 and 405/8 were printed together, *se-tenant*, in horizontal strips of 5 throughout the sheets with examples of Nos. 402 or 406 in the second and fourth positions in each strip.

76 Family singing Carols

(Des Jennifer Toombs. Litho B.D.T.)

1994 (31 Oct). *Christmas. International Year of the Family. T* **76** *and similar horiz designs. Multicoloured.* W w 16 (*sideways*). P 13½.

409	25 c. Type **76**		15	10
410	25 c. Family unwrapping Christmas presents		15	10
411	80 c. Preparing for Christmas carnival		60	60
412	$2.50, Nativity		1·90	2·75
409/12		*Set of 4*	2·50	3·25

1995 (13 Jan). *As No.* 312, *but* W w 16 (*sideways*). P 14.

413	10 c. Type **58**		30	30

77 Green Turtle swimming

(Des A. Robinson. Litho B.D.T.)

1995 (27 Feb). *Endangered Species. Green Turtle. T* **77** *and similar horiz designs. Multicoloured.* W w 14 (*sideways*). P 14.

427	10 c. Type **77**		40	50
	a. Strip of 4. Nos. 427/30		2·10	
428	40 c. Turtle crawling up beach		55	60
429	50 c. Burying eggs		60	65
430	$1 Young heading for sea		75	1·00
427/30		*Set of 4*	2·10	2·40

In addition to separate sheets of 50 Nos. 427/30 were also available in small sheets of 16 containing four strips, *se-tenant* both vertically and horizontally.

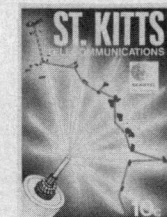

78 St. Christopher 1d. Stamps of 1870

79 Telecommunication Links between Islands

(Des D. Miller. Litho Cartor)

1995 (10 Apr). *125th Anniv of St. Kitts Postage Stamps. T* **78** *and similar horiz designs, each including the St. Christopher 1870 1d.* W w 14 (*sideways*). P 13½.

431	25 c. Type **78**		15	10
432	80 c. St. Kitts–Nevis 1935 Silver Jubilee 1d.		45	25
433	$2.50, St. Kitts–Nevis 1946 Victory 1½d.		1·75	2·25
434	$3 St. Christopher Nevis Anguilla 1953 Coronation 2 c.		2·00	2·50
431/4		*Set of 4*	4·00	4·75

(Des R. Watton. Litho Cartor (Nos. 435/8) or Questa (Nos. MS439))

1995 (8 May). *50th Anniv of End of Second World War. Multicoloured designs as T* **75** *of Kiribati.* W w 14 (*sideways*). P 13½.

435	20 c. Caribbean Regiment patrol, North Africa		15	10
436	50 c. Grumman TBF Avengers (bombers)		35	30
437	$2 Supermarine Spitfire Mk Vb (fighter)		1·25	1·50
438	$8 U.S. Navy destroyer escort		5·00	6·00
435/8		*Set of 4*	6·00	7·25
MS439	75×85 mm. $3 Reverse of 1939–45 War Medal (*vert*). Wmk upright. P 14		1·75	2·00

(Des D. Miller. Litho Enschedé)

1995 (27 Sept). *10th Anniv of SKANTEL (telecommunication company). T* **79** *and similar vert designs. Multicoloured.* W w 14. P 13×14½.

440	10 c. Type **79**		25	10
441	25 c. Payphone and computer link		30	15
442	$2 Telecommunications tower and dish aerial		2·25	2·50
443	$3 Silhouette of dish aerial at sunset		2·50	3·00
440/3		*Set of 4*	4·75	5·25

80 Water Treatment Works

81 F.A.O. Emblem and Vegetables

(Des D. Miller. Litho Cartor)

1995 (24 Oct). *50th Anniv of United Nations. T* **80** *and similar horiz designs. Multicoloured. W* w **14** (*sideways*). *P* 13½×13.
444	40 c. Type **80**	..	30	25
445	50 c. Beach	..	35	30
446	$1.60, Dust cart ..	..	1·10	1·60
447	$2.50, Forest	..	1·90	2·75
444/7	.. .. ..	*Set of* 4	3·25	4·50

(Des G. Vasarhelyi. Litho Cartor)

1995 (13 Nov). *50th Anniv of Food and Agriculture Organization. T* **81** *and similar horiz designs. Multicoloured. W* w **14** (*sideways*). *P* 13½.
448	25 c. Type **81**		20	10
449	50 c. Glazed carrots and West Indian peas with rice		35	30
450	80 c. Tania and Cassava plants		50	60
451	$1.50, Waterfall, Green Hill Mountain		90	1·40
448/51		*Set of* 4	1·75	2·25

82 Flame Helmet

83 L.M.S. No. 45614 *Leeward Islands* Steam Locomotive in Green Livery

(Des G. Drummond. Litho Cartor)

1996 (10 Jan). *Sea Shells. T* **82** *and similar vert designs. Multicoloured. W* w **14**. *P* 13.
452	$1.50, Type **82**	..	95	1·00
	a. Horiz strip of 5. Nos. 452/6	..	4·25	
453	$1.50, Triton's Trumpet	..	95	1·00
454	$1.50, King Helmet	..	95	1·00
455	$1.50, True Tulip	..	95	1·00
456	$1.50, Queen Conch	..	95	1·00
452/6		*Set of* 5	4·25	4·50

Nos. 452/6 were printed together, *se-tenant*, in horizontal strips of 5 throughout the sheet.

(Des A. Theobald. Litho Enschedé)

1996 (1 May). *"CAPEX '96" International Stamp Exhibition, Toronto. T* **83** *and similar horiz design. Multicoloured. W* w **14** (*sideways*). *P* 13½×14.
457	10 c. Type **83**		40	30
MS458	110×80 mm. $10 L.M.S. No. 5614 *Leeward Islands* steam locomotive in red livery (48×31½ mm). *P* 14×14½	..	5·75	6·50

84 Athlete and National Flag

85 Volunteer Rifleman, 1896

(Des R. Watton. Litho Walsall)

1996 (30 June). *Centennial Olympic Games, Atlanta. T* **84** *and similar vert designs. Multicoloured. W* w **16**. *P* 14.
459	10 c. Type **84**		15	15
460	25 c. High jumper and U.S.A. flag		20	20
461	80 c. Athlete and Olympic flag	..	50	55
462	$3 Poster for 1896 Olympic Games, Athens		1·75	2·50
459/62		*Set of* 4	2·40	3·00
MS463	70×64 mm. $6 Olympic torch	..	3·25	3·50

(Des W. Cribbs. Litho Cot Printery Ltd, Barbados)

1996 (1 Nov). *Centenary of Defence Force. T* **85** *and similar vert designs. Multicoloured. W* w **14**. *P* 14.
464	10 c. Type **85**	..	15	15
465	50 c. Mounted infantryman, 1911	..	35	35
466	$2 Drummer, 1940–60 ..		1·25	1·75
467	$2.50, Ceremonial uniform, 1996		1·40	2·00
464/7		*Set of* 4	2·75	3·75

The new-issue supplement to this Catalogue appears each month in

GIBBONS STAMP MONTHLY

—from your newsagent or by postal subscription— sample copy and details on request.

86 "Holy Virgin and Child" (A. Colin)

87 Princess Parrotfish

(Des D. Miller. Litho Questa)

1996 (29 Nov). *Christmas. Religious Paintings. T* **86** *and similar vert designs. Multicoloured. W* w **14**. *P* 14½.
468	15 c. Type **86**	..	20	10
469	25 c. "Holy Family" (after Rubens)		25	10
470	50 c. "Madonna with the Goldfinch" (Krause after Raphael)		45	35
471	80 c. "Madonna on Throne with Angels" (17th-cent Spanish)		75	1·00
468/71		*Set of* 4	1·50	1·40

(Des D. Miller. Litho Questa)

1997 (3 Feb). *"HONG KONG '97" International Stamp Exhibition. Sheet* 130×90 *mm, containing No.* 323. *W* w **14** (*sideways*). *P* 14.
MS472	$3 *Berbice* (mail steamer)	..	1·60	2·00

(Des G. Vasarhelyi. Litho Cartor)

1997 (24 Apr). *Fishes. T* **87** *and similar horiz designs. Multicoloured. P* 13½.
473	$1 Type **87**		70	70
	a. Sheetlet. Nos. 473/84		7·50	
474	$1 Yellow-bellied Hamlet ..		70	70
475	$1 Coney ..		70	70
476	$1 Fin-spot Wrasse		70	70
477	$1 Doctor Fish		70	70
478	$1 Squirrelfish		70	70
479	$1 Queen Angelfish		70	70
480	$1 Spanish Hogfish		70	70
481	$1 Red Hind		70	70
482	$1 Red Grouper		70	70
483	$1 Yellow-tailed Snapper ..		70	70
484	$1 Mutton Hamlet		70	70
473/84		*Set of* 12	7·50	7·50

Nos. 473/84 were printed together, *se-tenant*, in sheetlets of 12.

(Des N. Shewring (No. **MS491**), D. Miller (others). Litho Questa (No. **MS491**), B.D.T. (others))

1997 (10 July). *Golden Wedding of Queen Elizabeth and Prince Philip. Multicoloured designs as T* **87** *of Kiribati. W* w **14**. *P* 13½.
485	10 c. Queen Elizabeth in evening dress	..	20	30
	a. Horiz pair. Nos. 485/6	..	40	60
486	10 c. Prince Philip and Duke of Kent at Trooping the Colour ..	..	20	30
487	25 c. Queen Elizabeth in phaeton at Trooping the Colour ..	..	35	40
	a. Horiz pair. Nos. 487/8	..	70	80
488	25 c. Prince Philip in naval uniform	..	35	40
489	$3 Queen Elizabeth and Prince Philip ..		1·75	2·00
	a. Horiz pair. Nos. 489/90		3·50	4·00
490	$3 Peter Phillips on horseback ..		1·75	2·00
485/90		*Set of* 6	4·25	4·75
MS491	110×70 mm. $6 Queen Elizabeth and Prince Philip in landau (*horiz*). Wmk sideways. *P* 14×14½		3·75	4·50

Nos. 485/6, 487/8 and 489/90 were each printed together, *se-tenant*, in horizontal pairs throughout the sheets with the backgrounds forming composite designs.

88 C. A. Paul Southwell (first Chief Minister)

89 Wesley Methodist Church

(Des G. Vasarhelyi. Litho Cartor)

1997 (16 Sept). *National Heroes Day. T* **88** *and similar multicoloured designs. W* w **14** (*sideways on* $3). *P* 13½.
492	25 c. Type **88**		15	20
493	25 c. Sir Joseph France (trade union leader)		15	20
494	25 c. Robert Bradshaw (first Prime Minister)		15	20
495	$3 Sir Joseph France, Robert Bradshaw and C. A. Paul Southwell (*horiz*)		1·75	2·25
492/5		*Set of* 4	2·00	2·50

(Des D. Miller. Litho Walsall)

1997 (31 Oct). *Christmas. Churches. T* **89** *and similar multicoloured designs. W* w **16** (*sideways on horiz designs*). *P* 13½×14 (*horiz*) *or* 14×13½ (*vert*).
496	10 c. Type **89**	..	10	10
497	10 c. Zion Moravian Church	..	10	10
498	$1.50, St. George's Anglican Church (*vert*)	1·00	1·00	
499	$15 Co-Cathedral of the Immaculate Conception (*vert*)		8·50	10·00
496/9		*Set of* 4	8·75	10·00

90 Common Long-tail Skipper

(Des I. Loe. Litho Cot Printery Ltd, Barbados)

1997 (29 Dec). *Butterflies. T* **90** *and similar horiz designs. Multicoloured. W* w **14** (*sideways*). *P* 14×14½.
500	10 c. Type **90**	..	10	10
501	15 c. White Peacock	..	10	10
502	25 c. Caribbean Buckeye	..	10	15
503	30 c. The Red Rim ..		15	20
504	40 c. Cassius Blue	..	15	20
505	50 c. The Flambeau	..	20	25
506	60 c. Lucas's Blue ..	..	25	30
507	90 c. Cloudless Sulphur	..	40	45
508	$1 The Monarch	..	45	50
509	$1.20, Fiery Skipper	..	50	55
510	$1.60, The Zebra	..	70	75
511	$3 Southern Dagger Tail	..	1·25	1·40
512	$5 Polydamus Swallowtail	..	2·10	2·25
513	$10 Tropical Chequered Skipper ..		4·25	4·50
500/13		*Set of* 14	10·50	11·50

(Des D. Miller. Litho Questa)

1998 (31 Mar). *Diana, Princess of Wales Commemoration. Vert designs as T* **91** *of Kiribati. Multicoloured. W* w **16** (30 c.). *P* 13½×14.
514	30 c. Wearing hat ..	..	20	30
MS515	145×70 mm. $1.60, As 30 c.; $1.60, Wearing red jacket; $1.60, Wearing white jacket; $1.60, Carrying bouquets. W w **14** (*sideways*) (*sold at* $6.40 + 90 c. *charity premium*)		3·00	3·50

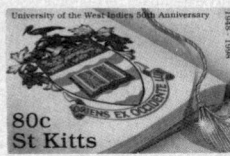

91 University Arms on Book

(Des D. Miller. Litho Cartor)

1998 (20 July). *50th Anniv of University of West Indies. T* **91** *and similar horiz design. Multicoloured. W* w **14** (*sideways*). *P* 13½×13.
516	80 c. Type **91**	..	45	40
517	$2 University arms and mortar-board	..	95	1·10

92 Santa at Carnival

93 Launching Rowing Boat

(Des R. Watton. Litho Cot Printery Ltd, Barbados)

1998 (30 Oct). *Christmas. T* **92** *and similar horiz design. Multicoloured. W* w **14** (*sideways*). *P* 14.
518	80 c. Type **92**	..	45	40
519	$1.20, Santa with two carnival dancers		65	70

(Des adapted D. Miller. Litho B.D.T.)

1999 (5 Mar). *125th Anniv of Universal Postal Union. T* **93** *and similar vert design. Multicoloured. W* w **16**. *P* 13½.
520	30 c. Type **93**	..	25	20
521	90 c. Pictorial map of St. Kitts	..	50	60

94 Caribbean Martin

(Des I. Loe. Litho B.D.T.)

1999 (27 Apr). *Birds of the Eastern Caribbean. T* **94** *and similar horiz designs. Multicoloured. W w* 14 (*sideways*). *P* 13½×14.

522	80 c. Type **94**		50	55
	a. Sheetlet. Nos. 522/37		7·00	
523	80 c. Spotted Sandpiper		50	55
524	80 c. Sooty Tern		50	55
525	80 c. Red-tailed Hawk		50	55
526	80 c. Brown Trembler		50	55
527	80 c. Belted Kingfisher		50	55
528	80 c. Black-billed Whistling Duck		50	55
529	80 c. Yellow Warbler		50	55
530	80 c. Blue-headed Hummingbird		50	55
531	80 c. Blue-headed Euphonia ("Antillean Euphonia")		50	55
532	80 c. Fulvous Whistling Duck		50	55
533	80 c. Mangrove Cuckoo		50	55
534	80 c. Carib Grackle		50	55
535	80 c. Caribbean Elaenia		50	55
536	80 c. Scaly-breasted Ground Dove ("Common Ground Dove")		50	55
537	80 c. Forest Thrush		50	55
522/37		Set of 16	7·00	8·00

Nos. 522/37 were printed together, *se-tenant*, in sheetlets of 16 which show the "iBRA '99" International Stamp Exhibition, Nuremberg, emblem on the sheet margins.

(Des N. Shewring. Litho Walsall)

1999 (20 July). *30th Anniv of First Manned Landing on Moon. Multicoloured designs as T* **296** *of Jamaica. W w* **16**. *P* 14×13½.

538	80 c. Lift-off		45	40
539	90 c. In Moon orbit		55	50
540	$1 Buzz Aldrin on Moon's surface		60	60
541	$1.20, Heat shields burning during re-entry		70	80
538/41		Set of 4	2·10	2·10
MS542	90×80 mm. $10 Earth as seen from Moon (circular, 40 mm diam). Wmk sideways. P 14		4·75	5·00

95 Local Quartet

(Des Jennifer Toombs. Litho Questa)

1999 (29 Oct). *Christmas. Musicians. T* **95** *and similar horiz designs. W w* 14 (*sideways*). *Multicoloured. P* 13½×14.

543	10 c. Type **95**		15	10
544	30 c. Trio		25	20
545	80 c. Sextet		50	40
546	$2 Quartet in green jerseys		1·10	1·25
543/6		Set of 4	1·75	1·75

96 "Rockets, Saturn and Earth" (A. Taylor)

(Adapted D. Miller. Litho Questa)

1999 (29 Dec). *New Millennium. Children's Paintings. T* **96** *and similar horiz designs. Multicoloured. W w* 14 (*sideways*). *P* 14.

547	10 c. Type **96**		10	10
548	30 c. "Y2K, computer and Earth weeping" (T. Liburd)		15	20
549	50 c. "Alien destroying computer" (D. Moses)		20	25
550	$1 "Technology past, present and future" (P. Liburd)		45	50
547/50		Set of 4	90	1·00

STAMP BOOKLET

1981 (19 Nov). *Royal Wedding. Multicoloured cover,* 105×65 *mm, showing* The Saudadoes. *Stitched.*

SB1	$9.40, booklet containing eight 55 c. in panes of 4 (No. 82a) and $2.50 in pane of 2 (No. 83a)		2·10

OFFICIAL STAMPS

1980 (23 June). *Nos. 32/41 additionally optd with Type* O 1 *of St. Christopher, Nevis and Anguilla. A. W w* 14 (*sideways*)

O 1A	15 c. Sugar cane harvesting		10	10
O 2A	25 c. Crafthouse (craft centre)		10	10
O 3A	30 c. *Europa* (liner)		10	10
O 4A	40 c. Lobster and sea crab		10	10
O 5A	45 c. Royal St. Kitts Hotel and golf course		15	15
O 6A	50 c. Pinney's Beach, Nevis		15	15
O 7A	55 c. New runway at Golden Rock		15	15
	a. Opt inverted		22·00	
O 8A	$1 Cotton picking		25	25
O 9A	$5 Brewery		80	1·50
O10A	$10 Pineapples and peanuts		1·00	2·50
	a. Opt inverted		£100	
O1A/10A		Set of 10	2·50	4·50

               B. *No wmk*

O 2B	25 c. Crafthouse (craft centre)		25	15
O 3B	30 c. *Europa* (liner)		50	30
O 4B	40 c. Lobster and sea crab		9·00	12·00
O 7B	55 c. New runway at Golden Rock		60	60
O 8B	$1 Cotton picking		1·00	1·00
O 9B	$5 Brewery		3·00	4·50
O10B	$10 Pineapples and peanuts		3·50	6·50
O2B/10B		Set of 7	16·00	23·00

OFFICIAL

(O 1)

1981 (5 Feb). *Nos. 59A/70A optd with Type* O 1.

O11	15 c. Type **13**		20	10
O12	20 c. Scaly-breasted Thrasher		20	10
O13	25 c. Grey Kingbird		25	10
O14	30 c. Green-throated Carib		25	10
O15	40 c. Turnstone		35	15
O16	45 c. Black-faced Grassquit		40	20
O17	50 c. Cattle Egret		40	20
O18	55 c. Brown Pelican		50	25
O19	$1 Lesser Antillean Bullfinch		75	45
O20	$2.50, Zenaida Dove		1·60	1·00
O21	$5 American Kestrel		2·75	2·00
O22	$10 Antillean Crested Hummingbird		5·00	4·25
O11/22		Set of 12	11·50	8·00

1983 (2 Feb). *Nos. 75/80 optd with Type* O 1 (55 c.) *or surch also* (*others*).

O23	45 c. on $2.50, *Royal George* (New Blue)		15	15
	a. Sheetlet. No. O23×6 and No. O24		1·00	
	b. Surch double		16·00	
	c. Albino surch		7·00	
	f. Deep ultramarine surch		50	
	fd. Surch inverted		3·00	
	fe. Surch inverted (horiz pair)		12·00	
	g. Black opt			
O24	45 c. on $2.50, Prince Charles and Lady Diana Spencer (New Blue)		25	25
	b. Surch double		60·00	
	c. Albino surch		25·00	
	f. Deep ultramarine surch		75	
	fd. Surch inverted		20·00	
	g. Black opt			
O25	55 c. *Saudadoes* (New Blue)		15	15
	a. Sheetlet. No. O25×6 and No. O26		1·10	
	b. Opt double		18·00	
	c. Albino opt		7·00	
	d. Opt inverted		6·00	
	e. Opt inverted (horiz pair)		18·00	
	f. Block of 3 containing No. O25×2 without opt and No. O26 with two opts		60	
	g. Deep ultramarine opt		60	
	gd. Opt inverted		4·00	
	ge. Opt inverted (horiz pair)		15·00	
O26	55 c. Prince Charles and Lady Diana Spencer (New Blue)		30	30
	b. Opt double		60·00	
	c. Albino opt		27·00	
	d. Opt inverted		23·00	
	f. Deep ultramarine opt		90	
	fd. Opt inverted		19·00	
O27	$1.10 on $4 *Britannia* (Blk.)		30	40
	a. Sheetlet. No. O27×6 and No. O28		2·25	
	b. Surch double		15·00	
	f. Deep ultramarine surch		2·25	
	fd. Surch inverted			
	fe. Surch inverted (horiz pair)			
O28	$1.10 on $4 Prince Charles and Lady Diana Spencer (Blk.)		60	70
	b. Surch double		45·00	
	f. Deep ultramarine surch		25·00	
	fd. Surch inverted			
O23/8		Set of 6	1·60	1·75

Nos. O23fe, O25e, O25ge and O27fe show the surcharge or overprint intended for the large design, inverted and struck across a horizontal pair of the smaller. Nos. O24fd, O26d, O26fd and O28fd each show two inverted surcharges or overprints intended for a horizontal pair of the smaller design.

1984 (4 July). *Nos. 145/56 optd with Type* O 1.

O29	15 c. Red-lined Cleaning Shrimp		70	1·25
O30	20 c. Bristleworm		80	1·50
O31	25 c. Flamingo Tongue (*Cyphoma gibbosus*)		80	1·50
O32	30 c. Christmas Tree Worm		90	1·50
O33	40 c. Pink-tipped Anemone		1·00	1·50
O34	50 c. Small-mouthed Grunt		1·00	1·50
O35	60 c. Glass-eyed Snapper		1·25	2·00
O36	75 c. Reef Squirrelfish		1·50	2·50
O37	$1 Sea Fans and Flamefish (*vert*)		2·00	2·50
O38	$2.50, Reef Butterflyfish (*vert*)		3·50	3·00
O39	$5 Black-barred Soldierfish (*vert*)		5·50	3·00
O40	$10 Cocoa Damselfish (*vert*)		8·50	6·00
O29/40		Set of 12	25·00	27·00

NEVIS

(7) 8 Nevis Lighter

1980 (23 June). *Nos. 394/406 of St. Christopher, Nevis and Anguilla optd with T* **7**.

37	5 c. Radio and T.V. station	.. ..	10	10
38	10 c. Technical college	.. ..	10	10
	w. Wmk Crown to left of CA	..	30·00	
39	12 c. T.V. assembly plant	.. ..	10	30
40	15 c. Sugar cane harvesting	.. ..	10	10
41	25 c. Crafthouse (craft centre)..	..	10	10
	a. No wmk	.. ..	1·00	1·75
42	30 c. *Europa* (liner)	.. ..	20	15
43	40 c. Lobster and sea crab	.. ..	20	40
44	45 c. Royal St. Kitts Hotel and golf course		80	70
45	50 c. Pinney's Beach, Nevis	.. ..	20	30
46	55 c. New runway at Golden Rock	..	40	15
47	$1 Picking cotton	.. ..	15	30
	a. No wmk	.. ..	2·50	5·00
48	$5 Brewery	.. ..	30	75
49	$10 Pineapples and peanuts ..	..	40	1·00
37/49		*Set of 13*	2·50	3·75

1980 (4 Sept). *80th Birthday of Queen Elizabeth the Queen Mother. As T* **10** *of St. Kitts, but inscr* "NEVIS".

50	$2 multicoloured	.. ..	20	30

No. 50 was printed in sheets including two *se-tenant* stamp-size labels.

(Des Jennifer Toombs. Litho Questa)

1980 (8 Oct). *Boats. T* **8** *and similar multicoloured designs. W w* **14** (*sideways on 5, 30 and 55 c.*). *P* 14.

51	5 c. Type **8**..	.. ..	10	10
52	30 c. Local fishing boat	.. ..	15	10
53	55 c. *Caona* (catamaran)	.. ..	15	10
54	$3 *Polynesia* (cruise schooner) (39×53 *mm*)		40	40
	a. Perf 12 (booklets)	.. ..	30	60
	ab. Booklet pane of 3	.. ..	80	
	aw. Wmk inverted	.. ..	30	
	awb. Booklet pane of 3	..	80	
51/4		*Set of 4*	65	60

No. 54a comes from $12.30 stamp booklets containing No. 53 × 6 and one pane as No. 54ab. In this pane each stamp is surrounded by white margins, the pane being divided in three by vertical roulettes.

9 Virgin and Child

(Des Jennifer Toombs. Litho Format)

1980 (20 Nov). *Christmas. T* **9** *and similar vert designs. Multicoloured. W w* **14**. *P* 14.

55	5 c. Type **9**	.. ..	10	10
56	30 c. Angel	.. ..	10	10
57	$2.50, The Three Wise Men..	..	20	30
55/7		*Set of 3*	20	35

Nos. 55/7 were each printed in sheets of 8 stamps and 1 label.

10 Charlestown Pier **11** New River Mill

(Des Jennifer Toombs. Litho Questa)

1981 (5 Feb)–82. *Horiz designs as T* **10** (5, 10 *c.*) *or T* **11** (15 *c. to* $10). *Multicoloured. W w* **14**. *P* 14×13½ (5, 10 *c.*) *or* 14 (*others*). A. *Without imprint date*

58A	5 c. Type **10**	.. ..	10	10
59A	10 c. Court House and Library	..	10	10
60A	15 c. Type **11**	.. ..	10	10
61A	20 c. Nelson Museum	.. ..	10	10
62A	25 c. St. James' Parish Church	..	15	15
63A	30 c. Nevis Lane	.. ..	20	20
64A	40 c. Zetland Plantation	.. ..	20	20
65A	45 c. Nisbet Plantation	.. ..	20	25
66A	50 c. Pinney's Beach	.. ..	25	25
67A	55 c. Eva Wilkin's Studio	.. ..	25	30
68A	$1 Nevis at dawn	.. ..	30	45
69A	$2.50, Ruins of Fort Charles	..	35	80
70A	$5 Old Bath House	.. ..	40	1·00
71A	$10 Beach at Nisbet's	.. ..	50	1·50
58A/71A		*Set of 14*	2·50	4·50

B. *With imprint date at foot* (9.6.82).

58B	5 c. Type **10** (*wmk inverted*)	..	30	30
59B	10 c. Court House and Library (*wmk inverted*)		30	30
60B	15 c. Type **11**	.. ..	10	10
61B	20 c. Nelson Museum	.. ..	10	10
62B	25 c. St James' Parish Church	..	15	15
63B	30 c. Nevis Lane	.. ..	15	15
64B	40 c. Zetland Plantation	.. ..	20	20
65B	45 c. Nisbet Plantation	.. ..	20	25
66B	50 c. Pinney's Beach	.. ..	25	25
67B	55 c. Eva Wilkin's Studio	.. ..	25	30
68B	$1 Nevis at dawn	.. ..	30	45
69B	$2.50, Ruins of Fort Charles	..	55	80
70B	$5 Old Bath House	.. ..	65	1·00
71B	$10 Beach at Nisbet's	.. ..	80	2·00
58B/71B		*Set of 14*	3·50	5·00

Imprint dates: "1982", Nos. 58/71B; "1983", Nos. 61B/7B, 69B.

(Des D. Shults. Litho Questa)

1981 (23 June–14 Dec). *Royal Wedding. Horiz designs as T* **26/27** *of Kiribati. Multicoloured.* (a) *W w* **14**. *P* 14.

72	55 c. *Royal Caroline*	.. ..	15	15
	a. Sheetlet. No. 72 × 6 and No. 73..		1·10	
73	55 c. Prince Charles and Lady Diana Spencer		40	40
74	$2 *Royal Sovereign*	.. ..	30	30
	aw. Wmk inverted	.. ..	8·00	
	b. Sheetlet. No. 74×6 and No. 75		2·40	
	bw. Wmk inverted	.. ..	70·00	
75	$2 As No. 73	.. ..	80	1·25
	aw. Wmk inverted	.. ..	35·00	
76	$5 *Britannia*	.. ..	45	80
	aw. Wmk inverted	.. ..	4·00	
	b. Sheetlet. No. 76×6 and No. 77		3·25	
	bw. Wmk inverted	.. ..	35·00	
77	$5 As No. 73	.. ..	1·00	2·00
	aw. Wmk inverted	.. ..	17·00	
72/7		*Set of 6*	2·75	4·50
MS78	120×109 mm. $4.50, As No. 73, Wmk sideways. P 12 (14 Dec)		1·10	1·25

(b) *Booklet stamps. No wmk. P* 12 (19 Nov)

79	55 c. As No. 72	.. ..	15	30
	a. Booklet pane. No. 79×4 with margins all round		55	
80	$2 As No. 75	.. ..	60	1·25
	a. Booklet pane. No. 80×2 with margins all round		1·10	

Nos. 72/7 were printed in sheetlets of seven stamps of the same face value, each containing six of the "Royal Yacht" design and one of the larger design showing Prince Charles and Lady Diana.
Nos. 79/80 come from $8.40 stamp booklets.

12 *Heliconius charithonia* **13** Caroline of Brunswick, Princess of Wales, 1793

(Des Jennifer Toombs. Litho Questa)

1982 (16 Feb). *Butterflies (1st series). T* **12** *and similar horiz designs. Multicoloured. W w* **14** (*sideways*). *P* 14.

81	5 c. Type **12**	.. ..	10	10
82	30 c. *Siproeta stelenes*	.. ..	15	10
83	55 c. *Marpesia petreus*	.. ..	20	15
84	$2 *Phoebis agarithe*	.. ..	60	70
81/4		*Set of 4*	90	90

See also Nos. 105/8.

(Des D. Shults and J. Cooter. Litho Format)

1982 (22 June). *21st Birthday of Princess of Wales. T* **13** *and similar vert designs. Multicoloured. W w* **14**. *P* 13½ × 14.

85	30 c. Type **13**	.. ..	10	10
86	55 c. Coat of arms of Caroline of Brunswick		15	15
87	$5 Diana, Princess of Wales	..	60	1·00
85/7		*Set of 3*	75	1·10

1982 (12 July). *Birth of Prince William of Wales. Nos. 85/7 optd with T* **19** *of St. Kitts.*

88	30 c. Type **13**	.. ..	10	10
89	55 c. Coat of arms of Caroline of Brunswick ..		15	15
	a. Opt triple..	.. ..	25·00	
90	$5 Diana, Princess of Wales	..	60	1·00
88/90		*Set of 3*	75	1·10

14 Cyclist

(Des Philatelists (1980) Ltd. Litho Questa)

1982 (18 Aug). *75th Anniv of Boy Scout Movement. T* **14** *and similar horiz designs. Multicoloured. W w* **14** (*sideways*). *P* 13½×14.

91	5 c. Type **14**	.. ..	20	10
92	30 c. Athlete	.. ..	25	10
93	$2.50, Camp cook	.. ..	50	65
91/3		*Set of 3*	85	70

15 Santa Claus **16** Tube Sponge

(Des Eugene Seabrookes (15 c.), Kharenzabeth Glasgow (30 c.), Davia Grant ($1.50), Leonard Huggins ($2.50); adapted Jennifer Toombs. Litho Questa)

1982 (20 Oct). *Christmas. Children's Paintings. T* **15** *and similar multicoloured designs. W w* **14** (*sideways on* $1.50 *and* $2.50). *P* 13½×14 (15 *c.*, 30 *c.*) *or* 14×13½ (*others*).

94	15 c. Type **15**	.. ..	10	10
95	30 c. Carollers	.. ..	10	10
96	$1.50, Decorated house and local band (*horiz*)		15	25
97	$2.50, Adoration of the Shepherds (*horiz*)	..	25	40
94/7		*Set of 4*	45	65

(Des G. Drummond. Litho Format)

1983 (12 Jan). *Corals (1st series). T* **16** *and similar vert designs. Multicoloured. W w* **14**. *P* 14.

98	15 c. Type **16**	.. ..	10	10
99	30 c. Stinging coral	.. ..	15	10
100	55 c. Flower coral	.. ..	15	10
101	$3 Sea Rod and Red Fire Sponge	..	50	80
98/101		*Set of 4*	75	90
MS102	82 × 115 mm. Nos. 98/101	..	1·40	2·50

See also Nos. 423/6.

17 H.M.S. *Boreas* off Nevis

(Des G. Drummond. Litho Format)

1983 (14 Mar). *Commonwealth Day. T* **17** *and similar horiz design. Multicoloured. W w* **14** (*sideways*). *P* 14.

103	55 c. Type **17**	.. ..	15	10
104	$2 Capt. Horatio Nelson and H.M.S. *Boreas* at anchor..		45	60

(Des Jennifer Toombs. Litho Format)

1983 (8 June). *Butterflies (2nd series). Multicoloured designs as T* **12**. *W w* **14** (*sideways* on* 30 *c. and* $2). *P* 14.

105	30 c. *Pyrgus oileus*	.. ..	15	10
	w. Wmk Crown to right of CA	..	16·00	
106	55 c. *Junonia evarete* (*vert*)	..	20	10
107	$1.10, *Urbanus proteus* (*vert*)	..	30	40
108	$2 *Hypolimnas misippus*	.. ..	40	75
	w. Wmk Crown to right of CA	..	17·00	
105/8		*Set of 4*	95	1·25

*The normal sideways watermark shows Crown to left of CA, *as seen from the back of the stamp.*

INDEPENDENCE 1983 INDEPENDENCE 1983

(18) (18a) **19** Montgolfier Balloon, 1783

1983 (19 Sept). *Nos. 58 and 60/71 optd as T* **18** (20 *mm long on Nos. 110/21*). A. *Without imprint date*

109Ab	5 c. Type **10** (optd locally with T **18**a)		13·00	11·00
110A	15 c. Type **11**	.. ..	35·00	35·00
111A	20 c. Nelson Museum	.. ..	5·00	5·00
112A	25 c. St. James' Parish Church	..	5·00	5·00
113A	30 c. Nevis Lane	.. ..	90	90
114A	40 c. Zetland Plantation	.. ..	75	75
117A	55 c. Eva Wilkin's Studio	.. ..	75	75
118A	$1 Nevis at dawn	.. ..	75	75
119A	$2.50, Ruins of Fort Charles	..	1·10	1·10
120A	$5 Old Bath House	.. ..	1·90	2·25
121A	$10 Beach at Nisbet's	.. ..	3·50	4·25
	a. Opt inverted	.. ..	60·00	
109Ab/21A		*Set of 11*	60·00	60·00

B. *With imprint date at foot*

109B	5 c. Type **10**	.. ..	10	10
	a. Vert pair, lower stamp without opt		65·00	
	b. Optd with T **18**a (local opt)	..	1·00	2·00
	ba. Opt T **18**a inverted	..	32·00	
110B	15 c. Type **11**	.. ..	10	10
111B	20 c. Nelson Museum	.. ..	10	10
112B	25 c. St. James' Parish Church	..	10	15

113B	30 c. Nevis Lane	..	..	15	15
	a. Opt inverted	..	..	11·00	
114B	40 c. Zetland Plantation	..	..	15	20
115B	45 c. Nisbet Plantation	..	..	20	25
116B	50 c. Pinney's Beach	..	..	20	25
117B	55 c. Eva Wilkin's Studio	..	..	25	30
	a. Opt double	..	..	12·00	
118B	$1 Nevis at dawn	..	..	30	30
119B	$2.50, Ruins of Fort Charles	..	..	30	45
120B	$5 Old Bath House	..	..	40	55
121B	$10 Beach at Nisbet's	..	..	50	70
109B/21B		*Set of 13*	2·40	3·00

Imprint dates: "1982", Nos. 109B/10B; "1983", Nos. 110B/21B.

(Des A. Theobald. Litho Format)

1983 (28 Sept). *Bicentenary of Manned Flight. T* **19** *and similar multicoloured designs. W w* **15** (*sideways* on* 45 c. *to* $2.50). *P* 14.

122	10 c. Type **19**	..	..	10	10
123	45 c. Sikorsky S-38 flying boat (*horiz*)			15	10
124	50 c. Beech 50 Twin Bonanza (*horiz*)			15	10
125	$2.50, Hawker Siddeley Sea Harrier (*horiz*)			30	60
122/5		*Set of 4*		55	70
MS126	118×145 mm. Nos. 122/5. Wmk sideways			75	1·00
	w. Wmk POST OFFICE reading downwards			55·00	

*The normal sideways watermark shows "POST OFFICE" reading downwards on Nos. 122/5 and upwards on No. **MS**126.

20 Mary praying over Holy Child

(Des Jennifer Toombs. Litho Format)

1983 (7 Nov). *Christmas. T* **20** *and similar horiz designs. Multicoloured. W w* **15** (*sideways*). *P* 14.

127	5 c. Type **20**	..	..	10	10
128	30 c. Shepherds with flock	..	..	10	10
129	55 c. Three Angels	..	..	10	10
130	$3 Boy with two girls	..	..	30	60
127/30		*Set of 4*		45	70
MS131	135 × 149 mm. Nos. 127/30	..	..	85	1·75

IMPERFORATES AND MISSING COLOURS. Various issues between Nos. 134 and 422 exist either imperforate or with colours omitted. Such items are not listed as there is no evidence that they fulfil the criteria outlined on page xi of this catalogue.

21 *County of Oxford* (1945)   **22** Boer War

(Des J. W. Litho Format)

1983 (10 Nov). *Leaders of the World. Railway Locomotives* (1st *series). T* **21** *and similar horiz designs, the first in each pair showing technical drawings and the second the locomotive at work. P* 12½.

132	55 c. multicoloured	..	..	10	20
	a. Vert pair. Nos. 132/3	..	..	20	40
133	55 c. multicoloured	..	..	10	20
134	$1 bright crimson, new blue and black	..	10	20
	a. Vert pair. Nos. 134/5	..	..	20	40
135	$1 multicoloured	..	..	10	20
136	$1 magenta, new blue and black	..	10	20
	a. Vert pair. Nos. 136/7	..	..	20	40
137	$1 multicoloured	..	..	10	20
138	$1 bright crimson, black and greenish yellow		10	20
	a. Vert pair. Nos. 138/9	..	..	20	40
139	$1 multicoloured	..	..	10	20
140	$1 multicoloured	..	..	10	20
	a. Vert pair. Nos. 140/1	..	..	20	40
141	$1 multicoloured	..	..	10	20
142	$1 greenish yellow, black and new blue	..	10	20
	a. Vert pair. Nos. 142/3	..	..	20	40
143	$1 multicoloured	..	..	10	20
144	$1 greenish yellow, black & brt magenta	..	10	20
	a. Vert pair. Nos. 144/5	..	..	20	40
145	$1 multicoloured	..	..	10	20
146	$1 multicoloured	..	..	10	20
	a. Vert pair. Nos. 146/7	..	..	20	40
147	$1 multicoloured	..	..	10	20
132/47		*Set of 16*		1·40	3·00

Designs:—Nos. 132/3, *County of Oxford*, Great Britain (1945); 134/5, *Evening Star*, Great Britain (1960); 136/7, Stanier Class 5 No. 44806, Great Britain (1934); 138/9, *Pendennis Castle*, Great Britain (1924); 140/1, *Winston Churchill*, Great Britain (1946); 142/3, *Mallard*, Great Britain (1938) (inscr "1935" in error); 144/5, *Britannia*, Great Britain (1951); 146/7, *King George V*, Great Britain (1927).

Nos. 132/3, 134/5, 136/7, 138/9, 140/1, 142/3, 144/5 and 146/7 were printed together, *se-tenant*, in vertical pairs throughout the sheets.

See also Nos. 219/26, 277/84, 297/308, 352/9 and 427/42.

(Des Court House Studio. Litho Format)

1984 (11 Apr). *Leaders of the World. British Monarchs* (1st *series*). *T* **22** *and similar vert designs. Multicoloured. P* 12½.

148	5 c. Type **22**	..	..	10	10
	a. Horiz pair. Nos. 148/9	..	..	10	10
149	5 c. Queen Victoria	..	..	10	10
150	50 c. Queen Victoria at Osborne House	..	10	30
	a. Horiz pair. Nos. 150/1	..	..	20	60
151	50 c. Osborne House	..	..	10	30
152	60 c. Battle of Dettingen	..	..	10	30
	a. Horiz pair. Nos. 152/3	..	..	20	60
153	60 c. George II	..	..	10	30
154	75 c. George II at the Bank of England	..	10	30
	a. Horiz pair. Nos. 154/5	..	..	20	60
155	75 c. Bank of England	..	..	10	30
156	$1 Coat of Arms of George II	..	..	10	30
	a. Horiz pair. Nos. 156/7	..	..	20	60
157	$1 George II (*different*)	..	..	10	30
158	$3 Coat of Arms of Queen Victoria	..	20	50
	a. Horiz pair. Nos. 158/9	..	..	40	1·00
159	$3 Queen Victoria (*different*)	..	..	20	50
148/59		*Set of 12*		1·10	3·00

Nos. 148/9, 150/1, 152/3, 154/5, 156/7 and 158/9 were printed together, *se-tenant* in horizontal pairs throughout the sheet.

See also Nos. 231/6.

23 Golden Rock Inn

(Des Jennifer Toombs. Litho J.W.)

1984 (16 May). *Tourism.* (1st *series*). *T* **23** *and similar horiz designs. Multicoloured. W w* **15** (*sideways*). *P* 14.

160	55 c. Type **23**	..	..	25	20
161	55 c. Rest Haven Inn	..	..	25	20
162	55 c. Cliffdwellers Hotel	..	..	25	20
163	55 c. Pinney's Beach Hotel	..	..	25	20
160/3		*Set of 4*		90	70

See also Nos. 245/8.

24 Early Seal of Colony

(Des G. Drummond. Litho Format)

1984 (8 June). *W w* **15** (*sideways*). *P* 14.

164	**24** $15 dull scarlet	..	..	1·40	4·00

25 Cadillac

(Des J. W. Litho Format)

1984 (25 July). *Leaders of the World. Automobiles* (1st *series*). *T* **25** *and similar horiz designs, the first in each pair showing technical drawings and the second the paintings. P* 12½.

165	1 c. greenish yellow, black and magenta	..	10	10
	a. Vert pair. Nos. 165/6	..	..	10	10
166	1 c. multicoloured	..	..	10	10
167	5 c. new blue, magenta and black	..	10	10
	a. Vert pair. Nos. 167/8	..	..	10	10
168	5 c. multicoloured	..	..	10	15
169	15 c. multicoloured	..	..	10	10
	a. Vert pair. Nos. 169/70	..	..	10	30
170	15 c. multicoloured	..	..	10	15
171	35 c. magenta, greenish yellow and black	..	10	25
	a. Vert pair. Nos. 171/2	..	..	10	50
172	35 c. multicoloured	..	..	10	25
173	45 c. new blue, magenta and black	..	10	25
	a. Vert pair. Nos. 173/4	..	..	15	50
174	45 c. multicoloured	..	..	10	25
175	55 c. multicoloured	..	..	10	25
	a. Vert pair. Nos. 175/6	..	..	15	50
176	55 c. multicoloured	..	..	10	25
177	$2.50, magenta, black and greenish yellow	..	25	60
	a. Vert pair. Nos. 177/8	..	..	50	1·10
178	$2.50, multicoloured	..	..	25	60
179	$3 new blue, greenish yellow and black	..	25	70
	a. Vert pair. Nos. 179/80	..	..	50	1·40
180	$3 multicoloured	..	..	25	70
165/80		*Set of 16*		1·40	4·00

Designs:—Nos. 165/6, Cadillac "V16 Fleetwood Convertible" (1932); 167/8, Packard "Twin Six Touring Car" (1916); 169/70, Daimler, "2 Cylinder" (1886); 171/2, Porsche "911 S Targa" (1970); 173/4, Benz "Three Wheeler" (1885); 175/6, M.G. "TC" (1947); 177/8, Cobra "Roadster 289" (1966), 179/80, Aston Martin "DB6 Hardtop" (1966).

Nos. 165/6, 167/8, 169/70, 171/2, 173/4, 175/6, 177/8 and 179/80 were printed together, *se-tenant* in vertical pairs throughout the sheet.

See also Nos. 203/10, 249/64, 326/37, 360/71 and 411/22.

---

26 Carpentry   **27** Yellow Bell

(Des Jennifer Toombs. Litho Questa)

1984 (1 Aug). *10th Anniv of Culturama Celebrations. T* **26** *and similar horiz designs. Multicoloured. W w* **15** (*sideways**). *P* 14.

181	30 c. Type **26**	..	..	10	10
182	55 c. Grass mat and basket-making	..	10	10
	w. Wmk POST OFFICE reading upwards		3·50	
183	$1 Pottery-firing	..	..	15	25
184	$3 Culturama Queen and dancers	..	40	55
181/4		*Set of 4*		65	85

*The normal sideways watermark shows "POST OFFICE" reading downwards.

(Des Jennifer Toombs. Litho Format)

1984 (8 Aug)–86. *Flowers. T* **27** *and similar vert designs. Multicoloured. W w* **15**. *P* 14. A. *Without imprint date*

185A	5 c. Type **27**	..	..	10	10
186A	10 c. Plumbago	..	..	10	10
187A	15 c. Flamboyant	..	..	10	10
188A	20 c. Eyelash Orchid	..	..	60	15
189A	30 c. Bougainvillea	..	..	10	10
190A	40 c. Hibiscus *sp.*	..	..	70	25
191A	50 c. Night-blooming Cereus	..	15	20
192A	55 c. Yellow Mahoe	..	..	20	25
193A	60 c. Spider-lily	..	..	20	25
194A	75 c. Scarlet Cordia	..	..	25	30
195A	$1 Shell-ginger	..	..	25	40
196A	$3 Blue Petrea	..	..	40	1·10
197A	$5 Coral Hibiscus	..	..	60	2·00
198A	$10 Passion Flower	..	..	90	3·50
185A/98A		*Set of 14*		4·00	7·75

B. *With imprint date* ("1986") *at foot of design* (23.7.86)

188B	20 c. Eyelash Orchid	..	..	60	30
190B	40 c. Hibiscus *sp.*	..	..	30	30

28 Cotton-picking and Map   **29** C.P. Mead

(Des A. Grant (15 c.), Tracy Watkins (55 c.), C. Manners ($1.10), D. Grant ($3), adapted Court House Advertising. Litho Format)

1984 (18 Sept). *First Anniv of Independence of St. Kitts-Nevis. T* **28** *and similar horiz designs. Multicoloured. W w* **15** (*sideways*). *P* 14.

199	15 c. Type **28**	..	..	10	10
200	55 c. Alexander Hamilton's birthplace	..	10	10
201	$1.10, Local agricultural produce	..	20	40
202	$3 Nevis Peak and Pinneys Beach	..	50	1·00
199/202		*Set of 4*		75	1·40

(Des J. W. Litho Format)

1984 (23 Oct). *Leaders of the World. Automobiles* (2nd *series*). *Horiz designs as T* **25**, *the first in each pair showing technical drawings and the second the paintings. P* 12½.

203	5 c. black, pale new blue and yellow-brown	10	10
	a. Vert pair. Nos. 203/4	..	..	10	10
204	5 c. multicoloured	..	..	10	10
205	30 c. black, pale turquoise-green & lake-brn	15	15
	a. Vert pair. Nos. 205/6	..	..	30	30
206	30 c. multicoloured	..	..	15	15
207	50 c. black, pale drab and red-brown	..	15	15
	a. Vert pair. Nos. 207/8	..	..	30	30
208	50 c. multicoloured	..	..	15	15
209	$3 black, grey-brown and dull green	..	30	45
	a. Vert pair. Nos. 209/10	..	..	60	90
210	$3 multicoloured	..	..	30	45
203/10		*Set of 8*		1·10	1·40

Designs:—Nos. 203/4, Lagonda "Speed Model" touring car (1929); 205/6, Jaguar "E-Type" 4.2 litre (1967); 207/8, Volkswagen "Beetle" (1947); 209/10, Pierce Arrow "V12" (1932). Nos. 203/10 were issued in a similar sheet format to Nos. 165/80.

(Des Court House Studio. Litho Format)

1984 (23 Oct). *Leaders of the World. Cricketers* (1st *series*). *T* **29** *and similar vert designs, the first in each pair showing a head portrait and the second the cricketer in action. P* 12½.

211	5 c. multicoloured	..	..	10	10
	a. Horiz pair. Nos. 211/12	..	..	15	15
212	5 c. multicoloured	..	..	10	10
213	25 c. multicoloured	..	..	20	30
	a. Horiz pair. Nos. 213/14	..	..	40	60
214	25 c. multicoloured	..	..	20	30
215	55 c. multicoloured	..	..	30	40
	a. Horiz pair. Nos. 215/16	..	..	60	80
216	55 c. multicoloured	..	..	30	40

217	$2.50, multicoloured	50	1·25
	a. Horiz pair. Nos. 217/18	1·00	2·50
218	$2.50, multicoloured	50	1·25
211/18	*Set of 8*	2·00	3·50

Designs:—Nos. 211/12, C. P. Mead; 213/14, J. B. Statham; 215/16, Sir Learie Constantine; 217/18, Sir Leonard Hutton.
Nos. 211/12, 213/14, 215/16 and 217/18 were printed together, *se-tenant*, in horizontal pairs throughout the sheets.
See also Nos. 237/44.

(Des J. W. Litho Format)

1984 (29 Oct). *Leaders of the World. Railway Locomotives (2nd series). Horiz designs as T* **21** *the first in each pair showing technical drawings and the second the locomotive at work.* P 12½.

219	5 c. multicoloured	10	10
	a. Vert pair. Nos. 219/20	10	10
220	5 c. multicoloured	10	10
221	10 c. multicoloured	10	10
	a. Vert pair. Nos. 221/2	10	15
222	10 c. multicoloured	10	10
223	60 c. multicoloured	15	25
	a. Vert pair. Nos. 223/4	30	50
224	60 c. multicoloured	15	25
225	$2.50, multicoloured	50	70
	a. Vert pair. Nos. 225/6	1·00	1·40
226	$2.50, multicoloured	50	70
219/26	*Set of 8*	1·25	1·75

Designs:—Nos. 219/20, Class EF81 electric locomotive, Japan (1968); 221/2, Class 5500 electric locomotive, France (1927); 223/4, Class 240P, France (1940); 225/6, "Hikari" express train, Japan (1964).
Nos. 219/26 were issued in a similar sheet format to Nos. 132/47.

30 Fifer and Drummer from Honeybees Band

(Des Jennifer Toombs. Litho Questa)

1984 (2 Nov). *Christmas. Local Music. T* **30** *and similar horiz designs. Multicoloured. W w* **15** *(sideways).* P 14.

227	15 c. Type **30**	15	10
228	40 c. Guitar and "barhow" players from Canary Birds Band	25	10
229	60 c. Shell All Stars steel band	30	10
230	$3 Organ and choir, St. John's Church, Fig Tree	1·25	1·00
227/30	*Set of 4*	1·75	1·10

(Des Court House Studio. Litho Format)

1984 (20 Nov). *Leaders of the World. British Monarchs (2nd series). Vert designs as T* **22.** *Multicoloured.* P 12½.

231	5 c. King John and Magna Carta	10	10
	a. Horiz pair. Nos. 231/2	10	10
232	5 c. Barons and King John	10	10
233	55 c. King John	10	15
	a. Horiz pair Nos. 233/4	20	30
234	55 c. Newark Castle	10	15
235	$2 Coat of arms	25	40
	a. Horiz pair. Nos. 235/6	50	80
236	$2 King John (*different*)	25	40
231/6	*Set of 6*	65	1·00

Nos. 231/6 were issued in a similar sheet format to Nos. 148/59.

(Des Court House Studio. Litho Format)

1984 (20 Nov). *Leaders of the World. Cricketers (2nd series). Vert designs as T* **29,** *the first in each pair listed showing a head portrait and the second the cricketer in action.* P 12½.

237	5 c. multicoloured	10	10
	a. Horiz pair. Nos. 237/8	10	15
238	5 c. multicoloured	10	10
239	15 c. multicoloured	10	15
	a. Horiz pair. Nos. 239/40	15	30
240	15 c. multicoloured	10	15
241	55 c. multicoloured	15	20
	a. Horiz pair. Nos. 241/2	30	40
242	55 c. multicoloured	15	20
243	$2.50, multicoloured	40	60
	a. Horiz pair. Nos. 243/4	80	1·10
244	$2.50, multicoloured	40	60
237/44	*Set of 8*	1·25	1·75

Designs:—Nos. 237/8, J. D. Love; 239/40, S. J. Dennis; 241/2, B. W. Luckhurst; 243/4, B. L. D'Oliveira.
Nos. 237/44 were issued in a similar sheet format to Nos. 211/18.

(Des Jennifer Toombs. Litho Format)

1985 (12 Feb). *Tourism (2nd series). Horiz designs as T* **23.** *Multicoloured. W w* **15** *(sideways).* P 14.

245	$1.20 Croney's Old Manor Hotel	15	25
246	$1.20, Montpelier Plantation Inn	15	25
247	$1.20, Nisbet's Plantation Inn	15	25
248	$1.20, Zetland Plantation Inn	15	25
245/8	*Set of 4*	55	90

(Des G. Turner (10 c.), J.W. (others). Litho Format)

1985 (20 Feb). *Leaders of the World. Automobiles (3rd series). Horiz designs as T* **25,** *the first in each pair showing technical drawings and the second paintings.* P 12½.

249	1 c. black, light green and pale green	10	10
	a. Vert pair. Nos. 249/50	10	10
250	1 c. multicoloured	10	10
251	5 c. black, cobalt and pale violet-blue	10	10
	a. Vert pair. Nos. 251/2	10	10
252	5 c. multicoloured	10	10
253	10 c. black, grey-olive and pale green	10	10
	a. Vert pair. Nos. 253/4	10	10
254	10 c. multicoloured	10	10

255	50 c. black, sage-green and pale cinnamon	10	10
	a. Vert pair. Nos. 255/6	10	20
256	50 c. multicoloured	10	10
257	60 c. black, dull yellowish green and pale blue	10	10
	a. Vert pair. Nos. 257/8	10	20
258	60 c. multicoloured	10	10
259	75 c. black, dull vermilion and pale orange	10	10
	a. Vert pair. Nos. 259/60	15	20
260	75 c. multicoloured	10	10
261	$2.50, black, light green and azure	20	30
	a. Vert pair. Nos. 261/2	40	60
262	$2.50, multicoloured	20	30
263	$3 black, bright yellow-green and pale green	20	30
	a. Vert pair. Nos. 263/4	40	60
264	$3 multicoloured	20	30
249/64	*Set of 16*	1·00	1·75

Designs:—Nos. 249/50, Delahaye "Type 35 Cabriolet" (1935); 251/2, Ferrari "Testa Rossa" (1958); 253/4, Voisin "Aerodyne" (1934); 255/6, Buick "Riviera" (1963); 257/8, Cooper "Climax" (1960); 259/60, Ford "999" (1904); 261/2, MG "M-Type Midget" (1930); 263/4, Rolls-Royce "Corniche" (1971).
Nos. 249/64 were issued in a similar sheet format to Nos. 165/80.

31 Broad-winged Hawk   32 Eastern Bluebird

(Des Jennifer Toombs. Litho Format)

1985 (19 Mar). *Local Hawks and Herons. T* **31** *and similar horiz designs. Multicoloured. W w* **15** *(sideways).* P 14.

265	20 c. Type **31**	1·00	20
266	40 c. Red-tailed Hawk	1·25	30
267	60 c. Little Blue Heron	1·25	40
268	$3 Great Blue Heron (white phase)	1·90	
265/8	*Set of 4*	5·50	2·50

No. 268 was re-issued on 24 May 1990 overprinted "40th Anniversary C.S.S." to mark the fortieth anniversary of Charlestown Secondary School. This overprint was only available on First Day Covers.

(Des R. Vigurs. Litho Format)

1985 (25 Mar). *Leaders of the World. Birth Bicentenary of John J. Audubon (ornithologist) (1st issue). T* **32** *and similar vert designs. Multicoloured.* P 12½.

269	5 c. Type **32**	10	10
	a. Horiz pair. Nos. 269/70.	20	20
270	5 c. Common Cardinal	10	10
271	55 c. Belted Kingfisher	20	55
	a. Horiz pair. Nos. 271/2	40	1·10
272	55 c. Mangrove Cuckoo	20	55
273	60 c. Yellow Warbler	20	55
	a. Horiz pair. Nos. 273/4	40	1·10
274	60 c. Cerulean Warbler	20	55
275	$2 Burrowing Owl	60	1·25
	a. Horiz pair. Nos. 275/6	1·10	2·50
276	$2 Long-eared Owl	60	1·25
269/76	*Set of 8*	2·00	4·50

Nos. 269/70, 271/2, 273/4 and 275/6 were printed together, *se-tenant*, in horizontal pairs throughout the sheets.
See also Nos. 285/92.

(Des J.W. Litho Format)

1985 (26 Apr). *Leaders of the World. Railway Locomotives (3rd series). Horiz designs as T* **21,** *the first in each pair showing technical drawings and the second the locomotive at work.* P 12½.

277	1 c. multicoloured	10	10
	a. Vert pair. Nos. 277/8	10	10
278	1 c. multicoloured	10	10
279	60 c. multicoloured	20	20
	a. Vert pair. Nos. 279/80	40	40
280	60 c. multicoloured	20	20
281	90 c. multicoloured	25	25
	a. Vert pair. Nos. 281/2	50	50
282	90 c. multicoloured	25	25
283	$2 multicoloured	40	60
	a. Vert pair. Nos. 283/4	80	1·10
284	$2 multicoloured	40	60
277/84	*Set of 8*	1·50	1·75

Designs:—Nos. 277/8, Class "Wee Bogie", Great Britain (1882); 279/80, *Comet*, Great Britain (1851); 281/2, Class 8H No. 6173, Great Britain (1908); 283/4, Class A No. 23, Great Britain (1866).
Nos. 277/84 were issued in a similar sheet format to Nos. 132/47.

(Des R. Vigurs. Litho Format)

1985 (3 June). *Leaders of the World. Birth Bicentenary of John J. Audubon (ornithologist) (2nd issue). Vert designs as T* **32** *showing original paintings. Multicoloured.* P 12½.

285	1 c. Painted Bunting	10	10
	a. Horiz pair. Nos. 285/6	10	10
286	1 c. Golden-crowned Kinglet	10	10
287	40 c. Common Flicker	25	40
	a. Horiz pair. Nos. 287/8	50	80
288	40 c. Western Tanager	25	40
289	60 c. Varied Thrush ("Sage Thrasher")	25	45
	a. Horiz pair. Nos. 289/90.	50	90
290	60 c. Evening Grosbeak	25	45
291	$2.50, Blackburnian Warbler	50	80
	a. Horiz pair. Nos. 291/2	1·00	1·60
292	$2.50, Northern Oriole	50	80
285/92	*Set of 8*	1·75	3·00

Nos. 285/92 were issued in a similar sheet format to Nos. 269/76.
Nos. 285/92 exist with yellow omitted from stock dispersed by the liquidator of Format International Security Printers Ltd.

33 Guides and Guide Headquarters   34 The Queen Mother at Garter Ceremony

(Des G. Vasarhelyi. Litho Format)

1985 (17 June). *75th Anniv of Girl Guide Movement. T* **33** *and similar multicoloured designs. W w* **15** *(inverted on 60 c., sideways on 15 c.).* P 14.

293	15 c. Type **33**	10	10
294	60 c. Girl Guide uniforms of 1910 and 1985 (*vert*)	15	25
295	$1 Lord and Lady Baden-Powell (*vert*)	20	40
296	$3 Princess Margaret in Guide uniform (*vert*)	50	1·25
293/6	*Set of 4*	75	1·75

(Des T. Hadler (75 c., $1, $2.50), J.W. (others). Litho Format)

1985 (26 July). *Leaders of the World. Railway Locomotives (4th series). Horiz designs as T* **21,** *the first in each pair showing technical drawings and the second the locomotive at work.* P 12½.

297	5 c. multicoloured	10	10
	a. Vert pair. Nos. 297/8	10	10
298	5 c. multicoloured	10	10
299	30 c. multicoloured	10	15
	a. Vert pair. Nos. 299/300	10	30
300	30 c. multicoloured	10	15
301	60 c. multicoloured	10	20
	a. Vert pair. Nos. 301/2	20	40
302	60 c. multicoloured	10	20
303	75 c. multicoloured	10	25
	a. Vert pair. Nos. 303/4	20	50
304	75 c. multicoloured	10	25
305	$1 multicoloured	10	25
	a. Vert pair. Nos. 305/6	20	50
306	$1 multicoloured	10	25
307	$2.50, multicoloured	20	60
	a. Vert pair. Nos. 307/8	40	1·10
308	$2.50, multicoloured	20	60
297/308	*Set of 12*	1·10	2·50

Designs:—Nos. 297/8, Snowdon Ranger, Great Britain (1878); 299/300, Large Belpaire locomotive, Great Britain (1904); 301/2, Class "County" No. 3821, Great Britain (1904); 303/4, *L'Outrance*, France (1877); 305/6, Class PB-15, Australia (1899); 307/8, Class 64, Germany (1928).
Nos. 297/308 were issued in a similar sheet format to Nos. 132/47.

(Des Court House Studio. Litho Format)

1985 (31 July). *Leaders of the World. Life and Times of Queen Elizabeth the Queen Mother. Various vertical portraits as T* **34.** P 12½.

309	45 c. multicoloured	10	15
	a. Horiz pair. Nos. 309/10.	20	30
310	45 c. multicoloured	10	15
311	75 c. multicoloured	10	20
	a. Horiz pair. Nos. 311/12.	20	40
312	75 c. multicoloured	10	20
313	$1.20, multicoloured	15	35
	a. Horiz pair. Nos. 313/14..	30	70
314	$1.20, multicoloured	15	35
315	$1.50, multicoloured	15	40
	a. Horiz pair. Nos. 315/16..	30	80
316	$1.50, multicoloured	15	40
309/16	*Set of 8*	90	2·00
MS317	85×114 mm. $2 multicoloured; $2 multicoloured	50	1·40

The two designs of each value were issued, *se-tenant*, in horizontal pairs within the sheets.
Each *se-tenant* pair shows a floral pattern across the bottom of the portraits which stops short of the left-hand edge on the left-hand stamp and of the right-hand edge on the right-hand stamp.
Nos. 309/16 exist in unissued miniature sheets, one for each value, from stock dispersed by the liquidator of Format International Security Printers Ltd.
Designs as Nos. 309/10 and 315/16, but with face values of $3.50 × 2 and $6 × 2, also exist in additional miniature sheets from a restricted printing issued 27 December 1985.

35 Isambard Kingdom Brunel   36 St. Pauls Anglican Church, Charlestown

(Des Tudor Art Agency. Litho Format)

1985 (31 Aug). *150th Anniv of the Great Western Railway. T* **35** *and similar vert designs showing railway engineers and their achievements. Multicoloured.* P 12½.

318	25 c. Type **35**	15	35
	a. Horiz pair. Nos. 318/19.	30	70
319	25 c. Royal Albert Bridge, 1859	15	35

320	50 c. William Dean			20	45
	a. Horiz pair. Nos. 320/1			40	90
321	50 c. Locomotive *Lord of the Isles*, 1895		20	45
322	$1 Locomotive *Lode Star*, 1907		25	65
	a. Horiz pair. Nos. 322/3			50	1·25
323	$1 G. J. Churchward			25	65
324	$2.50, Locomotive *Pendennis Castle*, 1924	35	80
	a. Horiz pair. Nos. 324/5			70	1·60
325	$2.50, C. B. Collett			35	80
318/25			*Set of 8*	1·75	4·00

Nos. 318/19, 320/1, 322/3 and 324/5 were printed together, *se-tenant*, in horizontal pairs throughout the sheets, each pair forming a composite design.

(Des J.W. Litho Format)

1985 (4 Oct). *Leaders of the World. Automobiles (4th series). Horiz designs as T 25, the first in each pair showing technical drawings and the second paintings.* P 12½.

326	10 c. black, azure and brown-red		10	10
	a. Vert pair. Nos. 326/7			10	15
327	10 c. multicoloured			10	10
328	35 c. black, pale turquoise-grn & greenish bl	10	25
	a. Vert pair. Nos. 328/9			10	50
329	35 c. multicoloured			10	25
330	75 c. black, bright green & lt purple-brown	10	40
	a. Vert pair. Nos. 330/1			15	80
331	75 c. multicoloured			10	40
332	$1.15, black, pale cinnamon & olive-green	15	45
	a. Vert pair. Nos. 332/3			30	90
333	$1.15, multicoloured			15	45
334	$1.50, black, pale blue and carmine		15	50
	a. Vert pair. Nos. 334/5			30	1·00
335	$1.50, multicoloured			15	50
336	$2 black, rose-lilac and reddish violet	20	60
	a. Vert pair. Nos. 336/7			40	1·10
337	$2 multicoloured			20	60
326/37			*Set of 12*	1·10	4·00

Designs:—Nos. 326/7, Sunbeam "Coupe de l'Auto" (1912); 328/9, Cisitalia "Pininfarina Coupe" (1948); 330/1, Porsche "928 S" (1980); 332/3, MG "K3 Magnette" (1933); 334/5, Lincoln "Zephyr" (1937); 336/7, Pontiac 2 Door (1926).

Nos. 326/37 were issued in a similar sheet format to Nos. 165/80.

1985 (23 Oct). *Royal Visit. Nos. 76/7, 83, 86, 92/3, 98/9 and 309/10 optd as T 114 of Montserrat or surch also.*

338	**16** 15 c. multicoloured			75	1·25
339	— 30 c. multicoloured (No. 92)		1·75	1·75
340	— 30 c. multicoloured (No. 99)		75	1·25
341	— 4c on 55 c. multicoloured (No. 86)	1·75	2·00
342	**34** 45 c. multicoloured			1·50	2·75
	a. Horiz pair. Nos. 342/3			3·00	5·50
343	— 45 c. multicoloured (No. 310)		1·50	2·75
344	— 55 c. multicoloured (No. 83)		1·25	1·25
345	— $1.50 on $5 multicoloured (No. 76)	2·00	2·50
	aw. Wmk inverted				
	b. Sheetlet. No. 345×6 and No. 346	19·00	
	bw. Wmk inverted				
	c. Error. Surch $1.60		1·40	2·25
	ca. Sheetlet. No. 345c×6 and No. 346c	13·00	
346	— $1.50 on $5 multicoloured (No. 77)	10·00	13·00
	aw. Wmk inverted				
	c. Error. Surch $1.60		6·50	11·00
347	— $2.50, multicoloured (No. 93)		2·25	3·00
338/47			*Set of 10*	21·00	28·00

Nos. 345c/ca and 346c had the surcharge intended for similar St. Vincent sheetlets applied by mistake.

(Des G. Drummond. Litho Format)

1985 (5 Nov). *Christmas. Churches of Nevis (1st series). T 36 and similar horiz designs. Multicoloured.* W w 15. P 15.

348	10 c. Type **36**			15	10
349	40 c. St. Theresa Catholic Church, Charlestown		35	30
350	60 c. Methodist Church, Gingerland		50	50
351	$3 St. Thomas Anglican Church, Lowland	1·25	2·75
348/51			*Set of 4*	2·00	3·25

See also Nos. 462/5.

(Des T. Hadler. Litho Format)

1986 (30 Jan). *Leaders of the World. Railway Locomotives (5th series). Horiz designs as T 21, the first in each pair showing technical drawings and the second the locomotive at work.* P 12½.

352	30 c. multicoloured			15	25
	a. Vert pair. Nos. 352/3			30	50
353	30 c. multicoloured			15	25
354	75 c. multicoloured			25	50
	a. Vert pair. Nos. 354/5			50	1·00
355	75 c. multicoloured			25	50
356	$1.50, multicoloured			40	70
	a. Vert pair. Nos. 356/7			80	1·40
357	$1.50, multicoloured			40	70
358	$2 multicoloured			50	80
	a. Vert pair. Nos. 358/9			1·00	1·60
359	$2 multicoloured			50	80
352/9			*Set of 8*	2·40	4·00

Designs:—Nos. 352/3, Stourbridge Lion, U.S.A. (1829); 354/5, EP-2 Bi-Polar electric locomotive, U.S.A. (1919); 356/7, Gas turbine, No. 59, U.S.A. (1953); 358/9, Class FL9 diesel locomotive No. 2039, U.S.A. (1955).

Nos. 352/9 were issued in a similar sheet format to Nos. 132/47.

(Des G. Turner (60 c.), J.W. (others). Litho Format)

1986 (30 Jan). *Leaders of the World. Automobiles (5th series). Horiz designs as T 25, the first in each pair showing technical drawings and the second paintings.* P 12½.

360	10 c. pale cinnamon and yellow-olive	10	10
	a. Vert pair. Nos. 360/1			20	20
361	10 c. multicoloured			10	10
362	60 c. black, salmon and bright scarlet	15	25
	a. Vert pair. Nos. 362/3			30	50
363	60 c. multicoloured			15	25
364	75 c. black, pale cinnamon and cinnamon	15	25
	a. Vert pair. Nos. 364/5			30	50
365	75 c. multicoloured			15	25

366	$1 black, lavender-grey and violet-grey	15	30
	a. Vert pair. Nos. 366/7			30	60
367	$1 multicoloured			15	30
368	$1.50, black, pale olive-yellow & olive-grn	20	35
	a. Vert pair. Nos. 368/9			40	70
369	$1.50, multicoloured			20	35
370	$3 black, azure and cobalt			30	65
	a. Vert pair. Nos. 370/1			60	1·25
371	$3 multicoloured			30	65
360/71			*Set of 12*	1·75	3·25

Designs:—No. 360/1, Adler "Trumpf" (1936); 362/3, Maserati "Tipo 250F" (1957); 364/5, Oldsmobile "Limited" (1910); 366/7, Jaguar "C-Type" (1951); 368/9, ERA "1.5L B Type" (1937); 370/1 Chevrolet "Corvette" (1953).

Nos. 360/71 were issued in a similar sheet format to Nos. 165/80.

37 Supermarine Spitfire Prototype, 1936

(Des J. Batchelor. Litho Format)

1986 (5 Mar). *50th Anniv of the Spitfire (fighter aircraft). T 37 and similar horiz designs. Multicoloured.* P 12½.

372	$1 Type **37**			20	50
373	$2.50, Supermarine Spitfire Mk 1A in Battle of Britain, 1940		30	75
374	$3 Supermarine Spitfire Mk XII over convoy, 1944		30	75
375	$4 Supermarine Spitfire Mk XXIV, 1948	30	1·25
372/5			*Set of 4*	1·00	3·00
MS376	114×86 mm. $6 Supermarine Seafire Mk III on escort carrier H.M.S. *Hunter*	1·10	3·75

38 Head of Amerindian   **39** Brazilian Player

(Litho Format)

1986 (11 Apr). *500th Anniv of Discovery of America (1992) (1st issue). T 38 and similar vert designs. Multicoloured.* P 12½.

377	75 c. Type **38**			55	55
	a. Horiz pair. Nos. 377/8			1·10	1·10
378	75 c. Exchanging gifts for food from Amerindians		55	55
379	$1.75, Columbus's coat of arms		1·25	1·75
	a. Horiz pair. Nos. 379/80			2·50	3·50
380	$1.75, Breadfruit plant			1·25	1·75
381	$2.50, Columbus's fleet			1·25	2·00
	a. Horiz pair. Nos. 381/2			2·50	4·00
382	$2.50, Christopher Columbus		1·25	2·00
377/82			*Set of 6*	5·50	7·75
MS383	95×84 mm. $6 Christopher Columbus (*different*)		5·50	8·50

The two designs of each value were printed together, *se-tenant*, in horizontal pairs throughout the sheets. Each pair forms a composite design showing charts of Columbus's route in the background.

Miniature sheets, each containing $2×2 stamps in the above designs, also exist from a restricted printing and from stock dispersed by the liquidator of Format International Security Printers Ltd.

See also Nos. 546/54, 592/600, 678/84 and 685/6.

(Des Court House Studio. Litho Format)

1986 (21 Apr). *60th Birthday of Queen Elizabeth II. Multicoloured designs as T 117a of Montserrat.* P 12½.

384	5 c. Queen Elizabeth in 1976		10	10
385	75 c. Queen Elizabeth in 1953		15	25
386	$2 In Australia			20	60
387	$8 In Canberra, 1982 (*vert*)		75	2·00
384/7			*Set of 4*	1·00	2·50
MS388	85×115 mm. $10 Queen Elizabeth II		4·00	6·50

The 5 c., 75 c. and $2 values exist with PVA gum as well as gum arabic.

No. 387 also exists watermarked w 15 (inverted), but no examples have been reported used from Nevis.

Nos. 384/7 exist in separate miniature sheets from unissued stock dispersed by the liquidator of Format International Security Printers Ltd.

(Des Court House Studio. Litho Format)

1986 (16 May). *World Cup Football Championship, Mexico. T 39 and similar multicoloured designs.* P 12½ (75 c., $1, $1.75, $6) or 15 (others).

389	1 c. Official World Cup mascot (*horiz*)	10	10
390	2 c. Type **39**			10	10
391	5 c. Danish player			10	10
392	10 c. Brazilian player (*different*)		10	10
393	20 c. Denmark v Spain			20	20
394	30 c. Paraguay v Chile			30	30
395	60 c. Italy v West Germany		45	55

396	75 c. Danish team (56×36 *mm*)		50	65
397	$1 Paraguayan team (56×36 *mm*)		55	70
398	$1.75, Brazilian team (56×36 *mm*)		75	1·25
399	$3 Italy v England			1·10	1·90
400	$6 Italian team (56×36 *mm*)		1·10	1·90
389/400			*Set of 12*	5·00	8·00
MS401	Five sheets, each 85×115 mm. (a) $1.50, As No. 398. (b) $2 As No. 393. (c) $2 As No. 400. (d) $2.50, As No, 395. (e) $4 As No. 394		*Set of 5 sheets*	10·00	13·00

40 Clothing Machinist   **41** Gorgonia

(Des G. Vasarhelyi. Litho Questa)

1986 (18 July). *Local Industries. T 40 and similar horiz designs. Multicoloured.* W w 15. P 14.

402	15 c. Type **40**			20	15
403	40 c. Carpentry/joinery workshop		45	35
404	$1.20, Agricultural produce market		1·25	1·50
405	$3 Fishing boats landing catch		2·50	3·25
402/5			*Set of 4*	4·00	4·75

(Des Court House Studio. Litho Format)

1986 (23 July–15 Oct). *Royal Wedding (1st issue). Multicoloured designs as T 118a of Montserrat.* P 12½.

406	60 c. Prince Andrew in midshipman's uniform		15	25
	a. Pair. Nos. 406/7			30	50
407	60 c. Miss Sarah Ferguson			15	25
408	$2 Prince Andrew on safari in Africa (*horiz*)		40	60
	a. Pair. Nos. 408/9			80	1·10
409	$2 Prince Andrew at the races (*horiz*)	40	60
406/9			*Set of 4*	1·00	1·90
MS410	115×85 mm. $10 Duke and Duchess of York on Palace balcony after wedding (*horiz*) (15.10.86)		2·50	5·00

Nos. 406/7 and 408/9 were each printed together, *se-tenant*, in horizontal and vertical pairs throughout the sheets.

Nos. 406/9 imperforate come from souvenir stamp booklets.

Nos. 408/9 exist in *tête-bêche* pairs from unissued stock dispersed by the liquidator of Format International Security Printers Ltd.

See also Nos. 454/7.

(Litho Format)

1986 (15 Aug). *Automobiles (6th series). Horiz designs as T 25, the first in each pair showing technical drawings and the second paintings.* P 12½.

411	15 c. multicoloured			10	15
	a. Vert pair. Nos. 411/12			20	25
412	15 c. multicoloured			10	15
413	45 c. black, light blue and grey-blue	20	25
	a. Vert pair. Nos. 413/14			40	50
414	45 c. multicoloured			20	25
415	60 c. multicoloured			20	30
	a. Vert pair. Nos. 415/16			40	60
416	60 c. multicoloured			20	30
417	$1 black, yellow-green and dull green	25	40
	a. Vert pair. Nos. 417/18			50	80
418	$1 multicoloured			25	40
419	$1.75, black, pale reddish lilac & deep lilac	30	50
	a. Vert pair. Nos. 419/20			60	1·00
420	$1.75, multicoloured			30	50
421	$3 multicoloured			50	90
	a. Vert pair. Nos. 421/2			1·00	1·80
422	$3 multicoloured			50	90
411/22			*Set of 12*	2·75	4·25

Designs:—Nos. 411/12, Riley "Brooklands Nine" (1930); 413/14, Alfa Romeo "GTA" (1966); 415/16, Pierce Arrow "Type 66" (1913); 417/18, Willys-Knight "66 A" (1928); 419/20, Studebaker "Starliner" (1953); 421/2, Cunningham "V-8" (1919).

Nos. 411/22 were issued in a similar sheet format to Nos. 165/80.

(Des G. Drummond. Litho Format)

1986 (8 Sept). *Corals (2nd series). T 41 and similar vert designs. Multicoloured.* W w 15 (*sideways*). P 15.

423	15 c. Type **41**			25	15
424	60 c. Fire Coral			55	50
425	$2 Elkhorn Coral			90	2·00
426	$3 Vase Sponge and Feather Star		1·10	2·50
423/6			*Set of 4*	2·50	4·75

(Des Court House Studio. Litho Format)

1986 (1 Oct). *Railway Locomotives (6th series). Horiz designs as T 21, the first in each pair showing technical drawings and the second the locomotive at work.* P 12½.

427	15 c. multicoloured			10	10
	a. Vert pair. Nos. 427/8			20	20
428	15 c. multicoloured			10	10
429	45 c. multicoloured			15	20
	a. Vert pair. Nos. 429/30			30	50
430	45 c. multicoloured			15	20
431	60 c. multicoloured			20	30
	a. Vert pair. Nos. 431/2			40	60
432	60 c. multicoloured			20	30
433	75 c. multicoloured			20	40
	a. Vert pair. Nos. 433/4			40	80
434	75 c. multicoloured			20	40
435	$1 multicoloured			20	50
	a. Vert pair. Nos. 435/6			40	1·00

436	$1 multicoloured	..	..	20	50
437	$1.50, multicoloured	..	..	25	60
	a. Vert pair. Nos. 437/8	..	..	50	1·10
438	$1.50, multicoloured	..	..	25	60
439	$2 multicoloured	..	..	30	65
	a. Vert pair. Nos. 439/40 ..		..	60	1·25
440	$2 multicoloured	..	..	30	65
441	$3 multicoloured	..	..	35	80
	a. Vert pair. Nos. 441/2 ..		..	70	1·60
442	$3 multicoloured	..	..	35	80
427/42			*Set of 16*	3·00	6·25

Designs:—Nos. 427/8, Connor Single Class, Great Britain (1859); 429/30, Class P2 *Cock o' the North*, Great Britain (1934); 431/2, Class 7000 electric locomotive, Japan (1926); 433/4, Class P3, Germany (1897); 435/6, *Dorchester*, Canada (1836); 437/8, Class "Centennial" diesel locomotive, U.S.A. (1969); 439/40, *Lafayette*, U.S.A. (1837); 441/2, Class C-16 No. 222, U.S.A., (1882).
Nos. 427/42 were issued in a similar sheet format to Nos. 132/47.

(Des Court House Studio. Litho Format)

1986 (28 Oct). *Centenary of Statue of Liberty.* Multicoloured designs as T 121a of Montserrat. P 13½×14 ($1, $2) or 14×13½ (*others*).
443	15 c. Statue of Liberty and World Trade Centre, Manhattan	20	15
444	25 c. Sailing ship passing Statue	30	20
445	40 c. Statue in scaffolding	30	25
446	60 c. Statue (side view) and scaffolding	30	30
447	75 c. Statue and regatta	40	40
448	$1 Tall Ships parade passing Statue (*horiz*)	40	45
449	$1.50, Head and arm of Statue above scaffolding	40	60
450	$2 Ships with souvenir flags (*horiz*)	55	80
451	$2.50, Statue and New York waterfront ..	60	90
452	$3 Restoring Statue	80	1·25
443/52	.. .. .. *Set of 10*	3·75	4·75
MS453	Four sheets, each 85×115 mm. (a) $3.50, Statue at dusk. (b) $4 Head of Statue. (c) $4.50, Statue and lightning. (d) $5 Head and torch at sunset .. .. .. *Set of 4 sheets*	4·00	11·00

1986 (17 Nov). *Royal Wedding* (2nd issue). Nos. 406/9 optd as T 121 of Montserrat in silver.
454	60 c. Prince Andrew in midshipman's uniform	15	40
	a. Pair. Nos. 454/5..	30	80
455	60 c. Miss Sarah Ferguson	15	40
456	$2 Prince Andrew on safari in Africa (*horiz*)	40	1·00
	a. Pair. Nos. 456/7..	80	2·00
457	$2 Prince Andrew at the races (*horiz*) ..	40	1·00
454/7	.. .. .. *Set of 4*	1·00	2·50

42 Dinghy sailing

(Des G. Vasarhelyi. Litho Questa)

1986 (21 Nov). *Sports.* T 42 and similar horiz designs. Multicoloured. P 14.
458	10 c. Type 42	15	10
459	25 c. Netball ..	30	15
460	$2 Cricket ..	2·50	2·50
461	$3 Basketball ..	3·00	3·00
458/61	*Set of 4*	5·50	5·00

43 St. George's Anglican Church, Gingerland

44 Constitution Document, Quill and Inkwell

(Des J. Cooter. Litho Questa)

1986 (8 Dec). *Christmas. Churches of Nevis* (2nd series). T 43 and similar horiz designs. Multicoloured. P 14.
462	10 c. Type 43	15	10
463	40 c. Trinity Methodist Church, Fountain ..	30	25
464	$1 Charlestown Methodist Church	60	65
465	$5 Wesleyan Holiness Church, Brown Hill	2·75	3·75
462/5	*Set of 4*	3·50	4·25

(Des Maxine Marsh. Litho Questa)

1987 (11 Jan). *Bicentenary of U.S. Constitution and 230th Birth Anniv of Alexander Hamilton* (U.S. statesman). T 44 and similar vert designs. Multicoloured. P 14.
466	15 c. Type 44 ..	10	10
467	40 c. Alexander Hamilton and Hamilton House	20	25
468	60 c. Alexander Hamilton ..	25	35
469	$2 Washington and his Cabinet ..	90	1·25
466/9	.. .. .. *Set of 4*	1·25	1·75
MS470	70×82 mm. $5 Model ship *Hamilton* on float, 1788..	6·50	7·50

America's Cup 1987 Winners 'Stars & Stripes'

(45)

1987 (20 Feb). *Victory of Stars and Stripes in America's Cup Yachting Championship.* No. 54 optd with T 45.
471	$3 Windjammer's S.V. *Polynesia* ..	1·10	1·60

46 Fig Tree Church

(Des Maxine Marsh. Litho Questa)

1987 (11 Mar). *Bicentenary of Marriage of Horatio Nelson and Frances Nisbet.* T 46 and similar horiz designs. Multicoloured. W w 15. P 14.
472	15 c. Type 46	15	10
473	60 c. Frances Nisbet ..	40	30
474	$1 H.M.S. *Boreas* (frigate) ..	1·25	1·00
475	$3 Captain Horatio Nelson ..	2·50	3·25
472/5	*Set of 4*	3·75	4·25
MS476	102×82 mm. $3 As No. 473; $3 No. 475	5·00	6·50

47 Queen Angelfish

(Des C. Abbott. Litho Format)

1987 (6 July). *Coral Reef Fishes.* T 47 and similar triangular designs. Multicoloured. P 14½.
477	60 c. Type 47	35	60
	a. Vert pair. Nos. 477/8	70	1·10
478	60 c. Blue Angelfish ..	35	60
479	$1 Stoplight Parrotfish (male) ..	40	80
	a. Vert pair. Nos. 479/80 ..	80	1·60
480	$1 Stoplight Parrotfish (female) ..	40	80
481	$1.50, Red Hind ..	45	90
	a. Vert pair. Nos. 481/2 ..	90	1·75
482	$1.50, Rock Hind ..	45	90
483	$2.50, Coney (bicoloured phase) ..	50	1·50
	a. Vert pair. Nos. 483/4 ..	1·00	3·00
484	$2.50, Coney (red-brown phase) ..	50	1·50
477/84	*Set of 8*	3·00	6·75

Nos. 477/8, 479/80, 481/2 and 483/4 were each printed together, *se-tenant*, in pairs throughout the sheets. The second design for each value is in the form of an inverted triangle.
Nos. 477/84 exist imperforate from stock dispersed by the liquidator of Format International Security Printers Ltd.

48 *Panaeolus antillarum*

49 Rag Doll

(Des J. Cooter. Litho Format)

1987 (16 Oct). *Fungi* (1st series). T 48 and similar vert designs. Multicoloured. W w 16. P 14.
485	15 c. Type 48 ..	85	30
486	50 c. *Pycnoporus sanguineus*	1·50	80
487	$2 *Gymnopilus chrysopellus*	3·00	3·25
488	$3 *Cantharellus cinnabarinus*	3·25	4·25
485/8	*Set of 4*	7·75	7·75

See also Nos. 646/54.

(Des J.W. Litho Walsall)

1987 (4 Dec). *Christmas. Toys.* T 49 and similar horiz designs. Multicoloured. W w 16 (*sideways*). P 14½.
489	10 c. Type 49 ..	10	10
490	40 c. Coconut boat ..	20	25
491	$1.20, Sandbox cart ..	55	60
492	$5 Two-wheeled cart ..	2·25	3·75
489/92	*Set of 4*	2·75	4·25

NEW INFORMATION

The editor is always interested to correspond with people who have new information that will improve or correct the Catalogue.

50 Hawk-wing Conch

51 Visiting Pensioners at Christmas

(Des Josephine Martin. Litho Questa)

1988 (15 Feb). *Seashells and Pearls.* T 50 and similar vert designs. Multicoloured. W w 16. P 14½×14.
493	15 c. Type 50	20	15
494	40 c. Rooster-tail Conch	30	20
495	60 c. Emperor Helmet	50	40
496	$2 Queen or Pink Conch	1·60	2·00
497	$3 King Helmet ..	1·75	2·25
493/7	*Set of 5*	4·00	4·50

(Des L. Curtis. Litho Walsall)

1988 (20 June). *125th Anniv of International Red Cross.* T 51 and similar horiz designs. Multicoloured. W w 16 (*sideways*). P 14 × 14½.
498	15 c. Type 51	10	10
499	40 c. Teaching children first aid	15	20
500	60 c. Providing wheelchairs for the disabled	25	35
501	$5 Helping cyclone victim ..	2·10	3·25
498/501	.. .. .. *Set of 4*	2·25	3·50

52 Athlete on Starting Blocks

53 Outline Map and Arms of St. Kitts– Nevis

(Des G. Vasarhelyi. Litho Format)

1988 (26 Aug). *Olympic Games, Seoul.* T 52 and similar vert designs. Multicoloured. W w 16. P 14.
502	10 c. Type 52	10	35
	a. Horiz strip of 4. Nos. 502/5	2·40	
503	$1.20, At start ..	50	85
504	$2 During race ..	85	1·25
505	$3 At finish ..	1·25	1·50
502/5	*Set of 4*	2·40	3·50
MS506	137 × 80 mm. As Nos. 502/5, but each size 24 × 36 mm. Wmk sideways ..	2·75	3·75

Nos. 502/5 were printed together, *se-tenant*, in horizontal strips of 4 throughout the sheet, each strip forming a composite design showing an athlete from start to finish of race.

(Des L. Curtis. Litho Questa)

1988 (19 Sept). *5th Anniv of Independence.* W w 14. P 14½ × 14.
507	53 $5 multicoloured..	2·10	2·75

(Des D. Miller (15 c., $2.50), E. Nisbet and D. Miller (60 c., $3). Litho Questa)

1988 (31 Oct). *300th Anniversary of Lloyd's of London.* Multicoloured designs as T 167a of Malawi. W w 16 (*sideways on 60 c.*, $2.50). P 14.
508	15 c. House of Commons passing Lloyd's Bill, 1871	20	10
509	60 c. *Cunard Countess* (liner) (*horiz*)	1·10	65
510	$2.50, Space shuttle deploying satellite (*horiz*)	2·25	3·00
511	$3 *Viking Princess* (cargo liner) on fire, 1966	2·25	3·00
508/11	.. .. .. *Set of 4*	5·25	6·00

54 Poinsettia

55 British Fleet off St. Kitts

(Des I. Loe. Litho Questa)

1988 (7 Nov). *Christmas. Flowers.* T 54 and similar vert designs. Multicoloured. W w 16. P 14½ × 14.
512	15 c. Type 54	10	10
513	40 c. Tiger Claws	15	20
514	60 c. Sorrel Flower .	25	30
515	$1 Christmas Candle	40	60
516	$5 Snow Bush ..	1·60	3·50
512/16	*Set of 5*	2·25	4·25

(Des Jane Hartley. Litho Format)

1989 (17 Apr). *"Philexfrance 89" International Stamp Exhibition, Paris. Battle of Frigate Bay, 1782. T* **55** *and similar vert designs. Multicoloured. W w* **16**. *P* 13½×14 ($3) *or* 14 (*others*).

517	50 c. Type **55**		75	1·00
	a. Horiz strip of 3. Nos. 517/19		2·75	
518	$1.20, Battle off Nevis		1·00	1·40
519	$2 British and French fleets exchanging broadsides		1·25	1·60
520	$3 French map of Nevis, 1764		1·60	2·00
517/20		*Set of 4*	4·25	5·50

Nos. 517/19 were printed together, *se-tenant*, in horizontal strips of 3 throughout the sheet, each strip forming a composite design.

56 Cicada

57 Queen or Pink Conch feeding

(Des I. Loe. Litho Questa)

1989 (15 May). *"Sounds of the Night". T* **56** *and similar vert designs. Multicoloured. W w* **16**. *P* 14.

521	10 c. Type **56**		20	15
522	40 c. Grasshopper		40	35
523	60 c. Cricket		55	50
524	$5 Tree frog		3·75	5·50
521/4		*Set of 4*	4·50	6·00
MS525	135×81 mm. Nos. 521/4		5·50	7·00

(Des A. Theobald ($6), D. Miller (others). Litho Questa)

1989 (20 July). *20th Anniv of First Manned Landing on Moon. Multicoloured designs as T* **51a** *of Kiribati. W w* **16** (*sideways on* 40 c., $2). *P* 14×13½ (15 c., $3) *or* 14 (*others*).

526	15 c. Vehicle Assembly Building, Kennedy Space Centre		15	10
527	40 c. Crew of "Apollo 12" (30×30 *mm*)		20	25
528	$2 "Apollo 12" emblem (30×30 *mm*)		1·00	1·60
529	$3 "Apollo 12" astronaut on Moon		1·40	1·90
	w. Wmk inverted		32·00	
526/9		*Set of 4*	2·50	3·50
MS530	100×83 mm. $6 Aldrin undertaking lunar seismic experiment. P 14×13½		2·50	3·50

(Des Deborah Dudley Max. Litho Questa)

1990 (31 Jan). *Queen or Pink Conch. T* **57** *and similar horiz designs. Multicoloured. P* 14.

531	10 c. Type **57**		60	30
532	40 c. Queen or Pink Conch from front		90	40
533	60 c. Side view of shell		1·25	90
534	$1 Back and flare		1·40	90
531/4		*Set of 4*	4·00	3·25
MS535	72×103 mm. $5 Underwater habitat		3·50	4·50

58 Wyon Medal Portrait

59

(Des M. Pollard. Litho B.D.T.)

1990 (3 May). *150th Anniv of the Penny Black. T* **58** *and similar vert designs. P* 14×15.

536	15 c. black and brown		15	10
537	40 c. black and deep blue-green		30	25
538	60 c. black		45	55
539	$4 black and ultramarine		2·00	3·25
536/9		*Set of 4*	3·00	3·75
MS540	114×84 mm. $5 blk, brn-lake & pale buff		4·00	5·00

Designs:—40 c. Engine-turned background; 60 c. Heath's engraving of portrait; $4 Essay with inscriptions; $5 Penny Black.

No. MS540 also commemorates "Stamp World London 90" International Stamp Exhibition.

(Des S. Pollard. Litho B.D.T.)

1990 (3 May). *500th Anniv of Regular European Postal Services. T* **59** *and similar square designs with different corner emblems. P* 13½.

541	15 c. brown		20	15
542	40 c. deep dull green		35	25
543	60 c. bright reddish violet		55	65
544	$4 ultramarine		2·75	3·50
541/4		*Set of 4*	3·50	4·00
MS545	110×82 mm. $5 brown-lake, pale buff and pale grey		4·00	5·00

Nos. 541/5 commemorate the Thurn and Taxis postal service and the designs are loosely based on those of the initial 1852–58 series.

60 Sand Fiddler Crab

(Des Mary Walters. Litho Questa)

1990 (25 June). *500th Anniv of Discovery of America by Columbus* (1992) (*2nd issue*). *New World Natural History – Crabs. T* **60** *and similar horiz designs. Multicoloured. P* 14.

546	5 c. Type **60**		10	10
547	15 c. Great Land Crab		15	15
548	20 c. Blue Crab		15	15
549	40 c. Stone Crab		30	30
550	60 c. Mountain Crab		45	45
551	$2 Sargassum Crab		1·40	1·60
552	$3 Yellow Box Crab		1·75	2·00
553	$4 Spiny Spider Crab		2·25	2·50
546/53		*Set of 8*	6·00	6·50
MS554	Two sheets, each 101×70 mm. (a) $5 Sally Lightfoot. (b) $5 Wharf Crab *Set of 2 sheets*		7·50	8·50

(Des Young Phillips Studio. Litho Questa)

1990 (5 July). *90th Birthday of Queen Elizabeth the Queen Mother. Vert designs as T* **198a** *of Lesotho showing portraits, 1930–39. P* 14.

555	$2 brownish black, magenta and pale buff		1·40	1·60
	a. Strip of 3. Nos. 555/7		3·75	
556	$2 brownish black, magenta and pale buff		1·40	1·60
557	$2 brownish black, magenta and pale buff		1·40	1·60
555/7		*Set of 3*	3·75	4·25
MS558	90×75 mm. $6 chestnut, magenta & blk		3·50	4·25

Designs:—No. 555, Duchess of York with corgi; No. 556, Queen Elizabeth in Coronation robes, 1937; No. 557, Duchess of York in garden; No. MS558, Queen Elizabeth in Coronation robes, 1937 (*different*).

Nos. 555/7 were printed together, horizontally and vertically *se-tenant*, in sheetlets of 9 (3×3).

61 MaKanaky, Cameroons

62 *Cattleya deckeri*

(Des Young Phillips Studio. Litho Questa)

1990 (1 Oct). *World Cup Football Championship, Italy. Star Players. T* **61** *and similar vert designs. Multicoloured. P* 14.

559	10 c. Type **61**		40	10
560	25 c. Chovanec, Czechoslovakia		45	15
561	$2.50, Robson, England		2·75	3·25
562	$5 Voller, West Germany		3·75	5·00
559/62		*Set of 4*	6·50	7·50
MS563	Two sheets, each 90×75 mm. (a) $5 Maradona, Argentina (b) $5 Gordillo, Spain *Set of 2 sheets*		6·75	8·00

(Des Mary Walters. Litho B.D.T.)

1990 (19 Nov). *Christmas. Native Orchids. T* **62** *and similar vert designs. Multicoloured. P* 14.

564	10 c. Type **62**		55	20
565	15 c. *Epidendrum ciliare*		55	20
566	20 c. *Epidendrum fragrans*		65	20
567	40 c. *Epidendrum ibaguense*		85	25
568	60 c. *Epidendrum latifolium*		1·10	50
569	$1.20, *Maxillaria conferta*		1·40	1·75
570	$2 *Epidendrum strobiliferum*		1·75	2·75
571	$3 *Brassavola cucullata*		2·00	3·00
564/71		*Set of 8*	8·00	8·00
MS572	102×71 mm. $5 *Rodriguezia lanceolata*		7·00	8·00

(Des T. Agans. Litho Questa)

1991 (14 Jan). *350th Death Anniv of Rubens. Multicoloured designs as T* **250** *of Maldive Islands, showing details from "The Feast of Achelous". P* 13½×14.

573	10 c. Two jugs (*vert*)		25	15
574	40 c. Woman at table (*vert*)		50	30
575	60 c. Two servants with fruit (*vert*)		65	45
576	$4 Achelous (*vert*)		2·75	3·50
573/6		*Set of 4*	3·50	4·00
MS577	101×71 mm. $5 "The Feast of Achelous". P 14×13½		3·50	4·00

63 *Agraulis vanillae*

(Des L. Nelson. Litho Questa)

1991 (1 Mar)–92. *Butterflies. T* **63** *and similar horiz designs. Multicoloured. P* 14. A. *Without imprint date*

578A	5 c. Type **63**		40	60
579A	10 c. *Historis odius*		40	40
580A	15 c. *Marpesia corinna*		50	30
581A	20 c. *Anartia amathea*		60	30
582A	25 c. *Junonia evarete*		60	30
583A	40 c. *Heliconius charithonia*		70	40
584A	50 c. *Marpesia petreus*		70	50
585A	60 c. *Dione juno*		75	50
586A	75 c. *Heliconius doris*		85	80
587A	$1 *Hypolimnas misippus*		90	80
588A	$3 *Danaus plexippus*		2·00	2·75
589A	$5 *Heliconius sara*		2·75	4·00
590A	$10 *Tithorea harmonia*		5·00	8·00
591A	$20 *Dryas julia*		9·50	13·00
578A/91A		*Set of 14*	23·00	29·00

B. *With imprint date* (1.3.92)

578B	5 c. Type **63**		20	30
579B	10 c. *Historis odius*		20	20
580B	15 c. *Marpesia corinna*		20	20
581B	20 c. *Anartia amathea*		30	30
582B	25 c. *Junonia evarete*		30	30
583B	40 c. *Heliconius charithonia*		40	30
584B	50 c. *Marpesia petreus*		45	35
585B	75 c. *Heliconius doris*		60	60
586cB	80 c. As 60 c.		60	60
587B	$1 *Hypolimnas misippus*		70	70
588B	$3 *Danaus plexippus*		2·00	2·75
589B	$5 *Heliconius sara*		2·75	4·00
590B	$10 *Tithorea harmonia*		5·00	8·00
591B	$20 *Dryas julia*		10·00	13·00
578B/91B		*Set of 14*	21·00	29·00

Nos. 579A/B are inscribed "Historis osius", Nos. 581A/B "Anatria amathea", Nos. 583A/B "Heliconius charitonius", Nos. 587A/B "Hypolimanas misippus" and Nos. 591A/B "Dryas iulia" all in error.

Imprint dates: "1992", Nos. 578B/84B, 586B/91B; "1994", Nos. 578B/9B, 582B, 584B, 586cB.

64 "Viking Mars Lander", 1976

(Des T. Agans. Litho Questa)

1991 (23 Apr). *500th Anniv of Discovery of America by Columbus* (1992) (*3rd issue*). *History of Exploration. T* **64** *and similar multicoloured designs. P* 14.

592	15 c. Type **64**		20	15
593	40 c. "Apollo 11", 1969		30	25
594	60 c. "Skylab", 1973		45	45
595	75 c. "Salyut 6", 1977		55	55
596	$1 "Voyager 1", 1977		65	65
597	$2 "Venera 7", 1970		1·25	1·40
598	$4 "Gemini 4", 1965		2·50	2·75
599	$5 "Luna 3", 1959		2·75	3·00
592/9		*Set of 8*	7·75	8·50
MS600	Two sheets each 105×76 mm. (a) $6 Bow of *Santa Maria* (*vert*). (b) $6 Christopher Columbus (*vert*) *Set of 2 sheets*		8·00	9·00

65 Magnificent Frigate Bird

66 *Marasmius haemtocephalus*

(Des Jennifer Toombs. Litho Questa)

1991 (28 May). *Island Birds. T* **65** *and similar horiz designs. Multicoloured. P* 14.

601	40 c. Type **65**		55	55
	a. Sheetlet. Nos. 601/20		10·00	
602	40 c. Roseate Tern		55	55
603	40 c. Red-tailed Hawk		55	55
604	40 c. Zenaida Dove		55	55
605	40 c. Bananaquit		55	55
606	40 c. American Kestrel		55	55
607	40 c. Grey Kingbird		55	55
608	40 c. Prothonotary Warbler		55	55
609	40 c. Blue-hooded Euphonia		55	55
610	40 c. Antillean Crested Hummingbird		55	55
611	40 c. White-tailed Tropic Bird		55	55
612	40 c. Yellow-bellied Sapsucker		55	55
613	40 c. Green-throated Carib		55	55
614	40 c. Purple-throated Carib		55	55
615	40 c. Red-billed Whistling Duck ("Black-bellied Tree-duck")		55	55
616	40 c. Ringed Kingfisher		55	55
617	40 c. Burrowing Owl		55	55
618	40 c. Turnstone		55	55
619	40 c. Great Blue Heron		55	55
620	40 c. Yellow-crowned Night-heron		55	55
601/20		*Set of 20*	10·00	10·00
MS621	76×59 mm. $6 Great Egret		8·00	9·00

Nos. 601/20 were printed together, *se-tenant*, in sheetlets of 20, forming a composite design.

(Des D. Miller. Litho Walsall)

1991 (5 July). *65th Birthday of Queen Elizabeth II. Horiz designs as T 210 of Lesotho. Multicoloured. P 14.*

622	15 c. Queen Elizabeth at polo match with Prince Charles	30	20
623	40 c. Queen and Prince Philip on Buckingham Palace balcony	45	35
624	$2 In carriage at Ascot, 1986	1·40	1·75
625	$4 Queen Elizabeth II at Windsor polo match, 1989	2·75	3·75
622/5	*Set of 4*	4·50	5·50

MS626 68×90 mm. $5 Queen Elizabeth and Prince Philip .. .. .. 4·00 5·00

(Des D. Miller. Litho Walsall)

1991 (5 July). *10th Wedding Anniv of Prince and Princess of Wales. Horiz designs as T 210 of Lesotho. Multicoloured. P 14.*

627	10 c. Prince Charles and Princess Diana	20	20
628	50 c. Prince of Wales and family	50	30
629	$1 Prince William and Prince Harry	85	90
630	$5 Prince and Princess of Wales	3·00	3·50
627/30	*Set of 4*	4·00	4·50

MS631 68×90 mm. $5 Prince and Princess of Wales in Hungary, and young princes at Christmas .. .. 4·50 5·00

(Litho Questa)

1991 (12 Aug). *"Phila Nippon '91" International Stamp Exhibition, Tokyo. Japanese Railway Locomotives. Multicoloured designs as T 257 of Maldive Islands. P 14.*

632	10 c. Class C62 steam locomotive	50	30
633	15 c. Class C56 steam locomotive (*horiz*)	55	30
634	40 c. Class C55 streamlined steam locomotive (*horiz*)	80	50
635	60 c. Class 1400 steam locomotive (*horiz*)	95	80
636	$1 Class 485 diesel train	1·25	1·00
637	$2 Class C61 steam locomotive	2·00	2·00
638	$3 Class 485 diesel train (*horiz*)	2·25	2·25
639	$4 Class 7000 electric train (*horiz*)	2·75	2·75
632/9	*Set of 8*	10·00	9·00

MS640 Two sheets, each 108×72 mm. (a) $5 Class D51 steam locomotive (*horiz*). (b) $5 "Hikari" express train (*horiz*) .. *Set of 2 sheets* 8·00 8·50

(Litho B.D.T.)

1991 (20 Dec). *Christmas. Drawings by Albrecht Dürer. Vert designs as T 211 of Lesotho. P 13.*

641	10 c. black and apple-green	10	10
642	40 c. black and yellow-orange	20	25
643	60 c. black and new blue	25	30
644	$3 black and bright mauve	1·40	2·40
641/4	*Set of 4*	1·90	2·75

MS645 Two sheets, each 96×124 mm. (a) $6 black. (b) $6 black .. *Set of 2 sheets* 5·50 6·25
Designs:—10 c. "Mary being Crowned by an Angel"; 40 c. "Mary with the Pear"; 60 c. "Mary in a Halo"; $3 "Mary with Crown of Stars and Sceptre"; $6 (No. **MS**645a) "The Holy Family" (detail); $6 (No. **MS**645b) "Mary at the Yard Gate" (detail).

(Des D. Miller. Litho B.D.T.)

1991 (20 Dec). *Fungi (2nd series). T 66 and similar multicoloured designs. P 14.*

646	15 c. Type 66	30	20
647	40 c. *Psilocybe cubensis*	40	30
648	60 c. *Hygrocybe acutoconica*	50	40
649	75 c. *Hygrocybe occidentalis*	60	60
650	$1 *Boletellus cubensis*	70	70
651	$2 *Gymnopilus chrysopellus*	1·25	1·50
652	$4 *Cantharellus cinnabarinus*	2·25	2·50
653	$5 *Chlorophyllum molybdites*	2·25	2·50
646/53	*Set of 8*	7·50	8·00

MS654 Two sheets, each 70×58 mm. (a) $6 *Psilocybe cubensis, Hygrocybe acutoconica* and *Boletellus cubensis* (*horiz*). (b) $6 *Hygrocybe occidentalis, Marasmius haematocephalus* and *Gymnopilus chrysopellus* (*horiz*) *Set of 2 sheets* 7·50 8·00

(Des D. Miller. Litho Questa)

1992 (26 Feb). *40th Anniv of Queen Elizabeth II's Accession. Horiz designs as T 214 of Lesotho. Multicoloured. P 14.*

655	10 c. Charlestown from the sea	25	10
656	40 c. Charlestown square	40	25
657	$1 Mountain scenery	70	60
658	$5 Early cottage	2·75	3·50
655/8	*Set of 4*	3·50	4·00

MS659 Two sheets, each 74×97 mm. (a) $6 Queen or Pink Conch on beach. (b) $6 Nevis sunset .. .. .. *Set of 2 sheets* 7·00 8·00

NEVIS **20¢**

67 Monique Knol (cycling), Netherlands

68 "Landscape" (Mariano Fortuny i Marsal)

(Des R. Sauber. Litho B.D.T.)

1992 (7 May). *Olympic Games, Barcelona. Gold Medal Winners of 1988. T 67 and similar vert designs. Multicoloured. P 14.*

660	20 c. Type 67	30	30
661	25 c. Roger Kingdom (hurdles), U.S.A.	30	30
662	50 c. Yugoslavia (men's waterpolo)	50	50
663	80 c. Anja Fichtel (foil), West Germany	70	70
664	$1 Said Aouita, (mid-distance running), Morocco	80	80
665	$1.50, Yuri Sedykh (hammer throw), U.S.S.R.	1·10	1·10
666	$3 Shushunova (women's gymnastics), U.S.S.R.	2·00	2·50
667	$5 Valimir Artemov (men's gymnastics), U.S.S.R.	2·50	3·00
660/7	*Set of 8*	7·25	8·25

MS668 Two sheets, each 103×73 mm. (a) $6 Niam Suleymanoglu (weightlifting), Turkey. (b) $6 Florence Griffith-Joyner (women's 100 metres), U.S.A. .. .. *Set of 2 sheets* 5·50 6·25
No. 660 is inscribed "FRANCE" in error.

(Litho B.D.T.)

1992 (1 June). *"Granada '92" International Stamp Exhibition, Spain. Spanish Paintings. T 68 and similar multicoloured designs. P 13×13½ (vert) or 13½×13 (horiz).*

669	20 c. Type 68	30	30
670	25 c. "Dona Juana la Loca" (Francisco Pradilla Ortiz) (*horiz*)	30	30
671	50 c. "Idyll" (Fortuny i Marsal)	50	50
672	80 c. "Old Man Naked in the Sun" (Fortuny i Marsal)	70	70
673	$1 "The Painter's Children in the Japanese Salon" (detail) (Fortuny i Marsal)	80	80
674	$2 "The Painter's Children in the Japanese Salon" (different detail) (Fortuny i Marsal)	1·25	1·25
675	$3 "Still Life: Sea Bream and Oranges" (Luis Eugenio Meléndez) (*horiz*)	2·00	2·50
676	$5 "Still Life: Box of Sweets, Pastry and Other Objects" (Meléndez)	2·50	3·00
669/76	*Set of 8*	7·50	8·50

MS677 Two sheets, each 121×95 mm. (a) $6 "Bullfight" (Fortuny i Marsal) (111×86 mm). (b) $6 "Moroccans" (Fortuny i Marsal) (111×86 mm). Imperf .. .. .. *Set of 2 sheets* 5·50 5·75

69 Early Compass and Ship

70 Minnie Mouse

(Des L. Fried. Litho Questa)

1992 (6 July). *500th Anniv of Discovery of America by Columbus (4th issue) and "World Columbian Stamp Expo '92", Chicago. T 69 and similar multicoloured designs. P 14.*

678	20 c. Type 69	40	25
679	50 c. Manatee and fleet	75	50
680	80 c. Green Turtle and *Santa Maria*	1·00	80
681	$1.50, *Santa Maria* and arms	1·50	1·75
682	$3 Queen Isabella of Spain and commission	2·25	2·75
683	$5 Pineapple and colonists	3·00	4·00
678/83	*Set of 6*	8·00	9·00

MS684 Two sheets, each 101×70 mm. (a) $6 British Storm Petrel and town (*horiz*). (b) $6 Peppers and Carib canoe (*horiz*) *Set of 2 sheets* 8·50 10·00

(Des F. Paul ($1), J. Esquino ($2). Litho Questa)

1992 (24 Aug). *500th Anniv of Discovery of America by Columbus (5th issue). Organization of East Caribbean States. Vert designs as Nos. 911/12 of Montserrat. Multicoloured. P 14½.*

685	$1 Columbus meeting Amerindians	50	50
686	$2 Ships approaching island	1·25	1·40

(Des Kerri Schiff. Litho Questa)

1992 (28 Oct). *Postage Stamp Mega Event, New York. Sheet 100×70 mm containing multicoloured design as T 219 of Lesotho. P 14.*

MS687 $6 Empire State Building .. .. 3·25 3·75

(Des Walt Disney Co. Litho Questa)

1992 (9 Nov). *Mickey's Portrait Gallery. T 70 and similar multicoloured designs. P 13½×14.*

688	10 c. Type 70	40	20
689	15 c. Mickey Mouse	40	20
690	40 c. Donald Duck	60	30
691	80 c. Mickey Mouse, 1930	80	70
692	$1 Daisy Duck	90	80
693	$2 Pluto	1·50	1·50
694	$4 Goofy	2·50	2·75
695	$5 Goofy, 1932	2·50	2·75
688/95	*Set of 8*	8·50	8·25

MS696 Two sheets. (a) 102×128 mm. $6 Mickey in armchair (*horiz*). (b) 128×102 mm. $6 Mickey and Minnie in airplane (*horiz*). P 13½ .. .. *Set of 2 sheets* 9·00 10·00

(Litho Questa)

1992 (16 Nov). *Christmas. Religious Paintings. Vert designs as T 218 of Lesotho. Multicoloured. P 13½.*

697	20 c. "The Virgin and Child between Two Saints" (Giovanni Bellini)	30	15
698	40 c. "Virgin and Child surrounded by Four Angels" (Master of the Castello Nativity)	45	25
699	50 c. "Virgin and Child surrounded by Angels with St. Frediano and St. Augustine" (detail) (Filippo Lippi)	50	30
700	80 c. "The Virgin and Child between St. Peter and St. Sebastian" (Bellini)	70	70
701	$1 "The Virgin and Child with St. Julian and St. Nicholas of Myra" (Lorenzo di Credi)	80	80
702	$2 "St. Bernadino and a Female Saint presenting a Donor to Virgin and Child" (Francesco Bissolo)	1·50	1·50
703	$4 "Madonna and Child with Four Cherubs" (ascr Barthel Bruyn)	2·50	3·00
704	$5 "The Virgin and Child" (Quentin Metsys)	2·75	3·25
697/704	*Set of 8*	8·50	9·50

MS705 Two sheets, each 76×102 mm. (a) $6 "Virgin and Child surrounded by Two Angels" (detail) (Perugino). (b) $6 "Madonna and Child with the Infant, St. John and Archangel Gabriel" (Sandro Botticelli). P 13½×14 .. *Set of 2 sheets* 7·00 8·00
No. 699 is inscribed "Fillipo Lippi" in error.

71 Care Bear and Butterfly

72 Japanese Launch Vehicle H-11

(Des T.C.F.C. Inc. Litho Questa)

1993 (14 Jan). *Ecology. T 71 and similar vert design showing Care Bear cartoon characters. Multicoloured. P 14.*

706 80 c. Type 71 .. .. 60 60
MS707 71×101 mm. $2 Care Bear on beach .. 1·50 2·00

(Litho Walsall)

1993 (14 Jan). *Bicentenary of the Louvre, Paris. Vert designs as T 221 of Lesotho. Multicoloured. P 12.*

708	$1 "The Card Cheat" (left detail) (La Tour)	85	85
	a. Sheetlet. Nos. 708/15	6·00	
709	$1 "The Card Cheat" (centre detail) (La Tour)	85	85
710	$1 "The Card Cheat" (right detail) (La Tour)	85	85
711	$1 "St. Joseph, the Carpenter" (La Tour)	85	85
712	$1 "St. Thomas" (La Tour)	85	85
713	$1 "Adoration of the Shepherds" (left detail) (La Tour)	85	85
714	$1 "Adoration of the Shepherds" (right detail) (La Tour)	85	85
715	$1 "Mary Magdalene with a Candle" (La Tour)	85	85
708/15	*Set of 8*	6·00	6·00

MS716 70×100 mm. $6 "Archangel Raphael leaving the Family of Tobius" (Rembrandt) (52×85 mm). P 14½×2 .. .. 4·25 4·75
Nos. 708/15 were printed together, *se-tenant*, in sheetlets of 8 stamps and one centre label.

(Des A. Nahigian. Litho Questa)

1993 (14 Jan). *15th Death Anniv of Elvis Presley (singer). Vert designs as Nos. 1772/4 of Maldive Islands. Multicoloured. P 14.*

717	$1 Elvis Presley	85	85
	a. Strip of 3. Nos. 717/19	2·25	
718	$1 Elvis with guitar	85	85
719	$1 Elvis with microphone	85	85
717/19	*Set of 3*	2·25	2·25

Nos. 717/19 were printed together, horizontally and vertically *se-tenant*, in sheetlets of 9 (3×3).

(Des W. Wright and L. Fried (Nos. 720, 731, **MS**734a), W. Wright and W. Hanson (Nos. 721, 732, **MS**734b), J. Genzo (Nos. 728, **MS**734e), W. Wright (others). Litho B.D.T.)

1993 (14 Jan). *Anniversaries and Events. T 72 and similar multicoloured designs. P 14.*

720	15 c. Type 72	40	20
721	50 c. Airship LZ-129 *Hindenburg* on fire, 1937 (*horiz*)	65	65
722	75 c. Konrad Adenauer and Charles de Gaulle (*horiz*)	65	65
723	80 c. Red Cross emblem and map of Nevis (*horiz*)	70	70
724	80 c. *Resolute* (yacht), 1920	70	70
725	80 c. Nelson Museum and map of Nevis (*horiz*)	70	70
726	80 c. St. Thomas's Church (*horiz*)	70	70
727	$1 Blue Whale (*horiz*)	1·25	80
728	$3 Mozart	1·75	1·75
729	$3 Graph and U.N. emblems (*horiz*)	1·60	1·60
730	$3 Lions Club emblem	1·60	1·60
731	$5 Soviet "Energia" launch vehicle SL-17	3·00	3·50
732	$5 Lebaudy-Juillot airship No. 1 *La Jaune*, 1903 (*horiz*)	3·00	3·50

733	$5 Adenauer and Pres. Kennedy (*horiz*)	3·00	3·50
720/33	*Set of 14*	17·00	18·00

MS734 Five sheets. (a) 104×71 mm. $6 Astronaut. (b) 104×71 mm. $6 Zeppelin LZ-5, 1909 (*horiz*). (c) 100×70 mm. $6 Konrad Adenauer (*horiz*). (d) 75×103 mm. $6 *America 3* (yacht), 1992 (*horiz*). (e) 98×66 mm. $6 Masked reveller from *Don Giovanni* (*horiz*)

	Set of 5 sheets 18·00 19·00

Anniversaries and Events:—Nos. 720, 731, **MS734a**, International Space Year; Nos. 721, 732, **MS734b**, 75th death anniv of Count Ferdinand von Zeppelin (airship pioneer); Nos. 722, 733, **MS734c**, 25th death anniv of Konrad Adenauer (German statesman); No. 723, 50th anniv of St. Kitts–Nevis Red Cross; Nos. 724, **MS734d**, Americas Cup Yachting Championship; No. 725, Opening of Nelson Museum; No. 726, 150th anniv of Anglican Diocese of North-eastern Caribbean and Aruba; No. 727, Earth Summit '92, Rio; Nos. 728, **MS734e**, Death bicent of Mozart; No. 729, International Conference on Nutrition, Rome; No. 730, 75th anniv of International Association of Lions Clubs.

73 *Plumeria rubra*   74 Antillean Blue (*male*)

(Des Mary Walters, Litho Questa)

1993 (26 Mar). *West Indian Flowers.* T **73** *and similar vert designs. Multicoloured.* P 14.

735	10 c. Type **73**	40	30
736	25 c. *Bougainvillea*	50	30
737	50 c. *Allamanda cathartica*	65	50
738	80 c. *Anthurium andraeanum*	85	70
739	$1 *Ixora coccinea*	95	75
740	$2 *Hibiscus rosa-sinensis*	1·75	1·75
741	$4 *Justicia brandegeeana*	3·00	3·50
742	$5 *Antigonon leptopus*	3·00	3·50
735/42	*Set of 8*	10·00	10·00

MS743 Two sheets, each 100×70 mm. (a) $6 *Lantana camara.* (b) $6 *Petrea volubilis*

	Set of 2 sheets 7·50 8·50

(Des T. Muse. Litho Questa)

1993 (17 May). *Butterflies.* T **74** *and similar horiz designs. Multicoloured.* P 14.

744	10 c. Type **74**	60	40
745	25 c. Cuban Crescentspot (*female*)	75	40
746	50 c. Ruddy Daggerwing	1·00	50
747	80 c. Little Yellow (*male*)	1·25	75
748	$1 Atala	1·25	90
749	$1.50, Orange-barred Giant Sulphur	2·00	2·00
750	$4 Tropic Queen (*male*)	3·25	4·25
751	$5 Malachite	3·25	4·25
744/51	*Set of 8*	12·00	12·00

MS752 Two sheets, each 76×105 mm. (a) $6 Polydamus Swallowtail (*male*). (b) $6 West Indian Buckeye .. .. *Set of 2 sheets* 10·00 11·00

(Des Kerri Schiff. Litho Questa)

1993 (2 June). *40th Anniv of Coronation. Vert designs as* T **224** *of Lesotho.* P 13½×14.

753	10 c. multicoloured	10	10
	a. Sheetlet. Nos. 753/6×2	6·50	
754	80 c. deep chocolate and black	35	40
755	$2 multicoloured	90	95
756	$4 multicoloured	1·90	2·00
753/6	*Set of 4*	3·25	3·25

MS757 71×101 mm. $6 multicoloured. P 14 .. 2·75 3·00

Designs: (38×47 *mm*)—10 c. Queen Elizabeth II at Coronation (photograph by Cecil Beaton); 80 c. Queen wearing Imperial State Crown; $2 Crowning of Queen Elizabeth II; $4 Queen and Prince Charles at polo match. (28½×42½ *mm*)—$6 "Queen Elizabeth II, 1977" (detail) (Susan Crawford).

Nos. 753/6 were printed together in sheetlets of 8 containing two *se-tenant* blocks of 4.

75 Flag and National Anthem   76 "Annunciation of Mary" (Dürer)

(Des Jennifer Toombs. Litho B.D.T.)

1993 (19 Sept). *10th Anniv of Independence of St. Kitts-Nevis.* T **75** *and similar vert design. Multicoloured.* P 13½.

758	25 c. Type **75**	40	20
759	80 c. Brown Pelican and map of St. Kitts-Nevis	1·00	90

(Des Rosemary DeFiglio. Litho Cartor)

1993 (9 Nov). *World Cup Football Championship 1994, U.S.A. Multicoloured designs as* T **278** *of Maldive Islands.* P 14×13½.

760	10 c. Imre Garaba (Hungary) and Michel Platini (France) (*horiz*)	40	20
761	25 c. Diego Maradona (Argentina) and Giuseppe Bergomi (Italy) (*horiz*)	55	20
762	50 c. Luis Fernandez (France) and Vasily Rats (Russia) (*horiz*)	75	45
763	80 c. Victor Munez (Spain) (*horiz*)	1·00	55
764	$1 Preben Elkjaer (Denmark) and Andoni Goicoechea (Spain) (*horiz*)	1·10	70
765	$2 Elzo Coelho (Brazil) and Jean Tigana (France) (*horiz*)	2·00	2·00
766	$3 Pedro Troglio (Argentina) and Sergei Alejnikov (Russia) (*horiz*)	2·25	2·50
767	$5 Jan Karas (Poland) and Antonio Luiz Costa (Brazil) (*horiz*)	2·75	3·50
760/7	*Set of 8*	9·75	9·00

MS768 Two sheets. (a) 100×70 mm. $5 Belloumi (Algeria). (b) 70×100 mm. $5 Trevor Steven (England). P 13 .. *Set of 2 sheets* 9·00 9·50

(Litho Cartor)

1993 (30 Nov). *Christmas. Religious Paintings.* T **76** *and similar designs. Black, pale lemon and red (Nos. 769/73, 776, MS777a) or multicoloured (others).* P 13.

769	20 c. Type **76**	40	10
770	40 c. "The Nativity" (drawing) (Dürer)	60	25
771	50 c. "Holy Family on a Grassy Bank" (Dürer)	70	30
772	80 c. "The Presentation of Christ in the Temple" (Dürer)	90	55
773	$1 "Virgin in Glory on the Crescent" (Dürer)	1·00	70
774	$1.60, "The Nativity" (painting) (Dürer)	1·50	40
775	$3 "Madonna and Child" (Dürer)	2·25	2·75
776	$5 "The Presentation of Christ in the Temple" (detail) (Dürer)	2·75	4·00
769/76	*Set of 8*	9·00	9·50

MS777 Two sheets, each 105×130 mm. (a) $6 "Mary, Child and the Long-tailed Monkey" (detail) (Dürer). (b) $6 "The Rest on the Flight into Egypt" (detail) (Jean-Honore Fragonard) (*horiz*) .. .. *Set of 2 sheets* 7·50 8·50

77 Mickey Mouse playing Basketball

(Litho Questa)

1994 (15 Feb). *Sports and Pastimes.* T **77** *and similar multicoloured designs showing Walt Disney cartoon characters.* P 14×13½ (*horiz*) or 13½×14 (*vert*).

778	10 c. Type **77**	40	30
779	25 c. Minnie Mouse sunbathing (*vert*)	50	20
780	50 c. Mickey playing volleyball	70	40
781	80 c. Minnie dancing (*vert*)	80	60
782	$1 Mickey playing football	1·00	70
783	$1.50, Minnie hula hooping (*vert*)	1·75	1·75
784	$4 Minnie skipping (*vert*)	2·75	3·25
785	$5 Mickey wrestling Big Pete	2·75	3·25
778/85	*Set of 8*	9·50	9·50

MS786 Two sheets. (a) 127×102 mm. $6 Mickey, Donald Duck and Goofy in tug of war (black, bright rosine and blue-green). (b) 102×127 mm. $6 Mickey using Test your Strength machine

	Set of 2 sheets 9·00 10·00

(Litho Questa)

1994 (18 Feb). *"Hong Kong '94" International Stamp Exhibition. No.* **MS752** *optd with "HONG KONG '94" logo on sheet margins.*

MS787 Two sheets, each 76×105 mm. (a) $6 Polydamas Swallowtail (*male*). (b) $6 West Indian Buckeye .. .. *Set of 2 sheets* 7·50 8·00

(Litho Questa)

1994 (6 Apr). *Hummel Figurines. Vert designs as* T **256** *of Maldive Islands. Multicoloured.* P 14.

788	5 c. Girl with umbrella	15	40
789	25 c. Boy holding beer mug and parsnips ..	45	15
790	50 c. Girl sitting in tree	65	35
791	80 c. Boy in hat and scarf	85	60
792	$1 Boy with umbrella	1·00	70
793	$1.60, Girl with bird	1·75	1·75
794	$2 Boy on sledge	2·00	2·00
795	$5 Boy sitting in apple tree	2·75	3·75
788/95	*Set of 8*	8·50	8·75

MS796 Two sheets, each 94×125 mm. (a) Nos. 788 and 792/4. (b) Nos. 789/91 and 795

	Set of 2 sheets 6·50 7·50

79 Beekeeper collecting Wild Nest

(Des R. Vigurs. Litho Questa)

1994 (13 June). *Beekeeping.* T **79** *and similar horiz designs. Multicoloured.* P 14.

797	50 c. Type **79**	55	30
798	80 c. Beekeeping club	80	40
799	$1.60, Extracting honey from frames	1·60	1·75
800	$3 Keepers placing queen in hive	2·50	3·25
797/800	*Set of 4*	4·75	5·00

MS801 100×70 mm. $6 Queen and workers in hive and mechanical honey extractor .. .. 4·50 5·00

80 Blue Point Himalayan   81 Black Coral

(Des R. Sauber. Litho Questa)

1994 (20 July). *Persian Cats.* T **80** *and similar horiz designs. Multicoloured.* P 14.

802	80 c. Type **80**	60	60
	a. Sheetlet. Nos. 802/9	4·25	
803	80 c. Black and White Persian	60	60
804	80 c. Cream Persian	60	60
805	80 c. Red Persian	60	60
806	80 c. Persian	60	60
807	80 c. Persian Black Smoke	60	60
808	80 c. Chocolate Smoke Persian	60	60
809	80 c. Black Persian	60	60
802/9	*Set of 8*	4·25	4·25

MS810 Two sheets, each 100×70 mm. (a) $6 Silver Tabby Persian. (b) $6 Brown Tabby Persian .. .. *Set of 2 sheets* 8·50 9·00

Nos. 802/9 were printed together, *se-tenant*, in sheetlets of 8.

(Des P. Chinelli. Litho Questa)

1994 (25 July). *Endangered Species. Black Coral.* T **81** *and similar vert designs showing forms of coral.* P 14.

811	25 c. multicoloured	50	60
	a. Horiz strip of 4. Nos. 811/14	2·25	
812	40 c. multicoloured	60	75
813	50 c. multicoloured	60	75
814	70 c. multicoloured	70	85
811/14	*Set of 4*	2·25	2·25

Nos. 811/14 were printed in small sheets of 12 containing three horizontal *se-tenant* strips of 4 with each horizontal row starting with a different value.

82 Striped Burrfish   83 Symbol 1. Turtles and Cloud

(Des P. Chinelli. Litho Questa)

1994 (25 July). *Fishes.* T **82** *and similar multicoloured designs.* P 14.

815	10 c. Type **82**	20	20
816	50 c. Flame-backed Angelfish	35	35
	a. Sheetlet. Nos. 816/23	2·50	
817	50 c. Reef Bass	35	35
818	50 c. Long-finned Damselfish ("Honey Gregory")	35	35
819	50 c. Saddle Squirrelfish	35	35
820	50 c. Cobalt Chromis	35	35
821	50 c. Genie's Neon Goby	35	35
822	50 c. Slender-tailed Cardinalfish	35	35
823	50 c. Royal Gramma	35	35
824	$1 Blue-striped Grunt	60	60
825	$1.60, Blue Angelfish	1·00	1·25
826	$3 Cocoa Damselfish	2·50	3·00
815/26	*Set of 12*	5·50	6·00

MS827 Two sheets, each 100×70 mm. (a) $6 Blue Marlin. (b) $6 Sailfish (*vert*) *Set of 2 sheets* 8·00 8·50

Nos. 816/23 were printed together, *se-tenant*, in sheetlets of 8 with the backgrounds forming a composite design.

No. 824 is inscribed "BLUESRIPED GRUNT" in error.

Nos. 816a was re-issued on 16 August 1994 showing the "Philakorea '94" International Stamp Exhibition logo on each corner of the sheetlet margins. The stamps show no listable differences.

OMNIBUS ISSUES

Details, together with prices for complete sets of the various Omnibus issues from the 1935 Silver Jubilee series to date are included in a special section following Zimbabwe at the end of Volume 2.

(Litho Questa)

1994 (16 Aug). *"Philakorea '94" International Stamp Exhibition, Seoul. T **83** and similar vert designs showing longevity symbols. Multicoloured. P 13½×14.*

828	50 c. Type **83**	35	40
	a. Sheetlet. Nos. 828/35	2·50	
829	50 c. Symbol 2. Cranes and bamboo	35	40
830	50 c. Symbol 3. Deer and bamboo	35	40
831	50 c. Symbol 4. Turtles and Sun	35	40
832	50 c. Symbol 5. Cranes under tree	35	40
833	50 c. Symbol 6. Deer and tree	35	40
834	50 c. Symbol 7. Turtles and rock	35	40
835	50 c. Symbol 8. Cranes above tree	35	40
828/35	*Set of 8*	2·50	2·75

Nos. 828/35 were printed together, *se-tenant*, in sheetlets of 8.

84 Twin-roofed House with Veranda

(Des R. Vigurs. Litho Questa)

1994 (22 Aug). *Island Architecture. T **84** and similar horiz designs. Multicoloured. P 14.*

836	25 c. Type **84**	40	10
837	50 c. Two-storey house with outside staircase	65	30
838	$1 Government Treasury	90	80
839	$5 Two-storey house with red roof	3·25	4·25
836/9	*Set of 4*	4·75	4·75
MS840	102×72 mm. $6 Raised bungalow with veranda	3·50	4·50

85 William Demas

86 "The Virgin Mary as Queen of Heaven" (detail) (Jan Provost)

(Litho Questa)

1994 (1 Sept). *First Recipients of Order of Caribbean Community. T **85** and similar horiz designs. Multicoloured. P 14.*

841	25 c. Type **85**	30	10
842	50 c. Sir Shridath Ramphal	50	45
843	$1 Derek Walcott	10	80
841/3	*Set of 3*	1·60	1·25

(Litho Questa)

1994 (1 Dec). *Christmas. Religious Paintings. T **86** and similar vert designs. Multicoloured. P 14.*

844	20 c. Type **86**	20	10
845	40 c. "The Virgin Mary as Queen of Heaven" (different detail) (Provost)	35	25
846	50 c. "The Virgin Mary as Queen of Heaven" (different detail) (Provost)	40	30
847	80 c. "Adoration of the Magi" (detail) (Circle of Van der Goes)	60	40
848	$1 "Adoration of the Magi" (different detail) (Circle of Van der Goes)	70	50
849	$1.60, "Adoration of the Magi" (different detail) (Circle of Van der Goes)	1·25	1·25
850	$3 "Adoration of the Magi" (different detail) (Circle of Van der Goes)	2·00	2·25
851	$5 "The Virgin Mary as Queen of Heaven" (different detail) (Provost)	3·00	3·50
844/51	*Set of 8*	7·75	7·75
MS852	Two sheets, each 96×117 mm. (a) $5 "The Virgin Mary as Queen of Heaven" (different detail) (Provost). (b) $6 "Adoration of the Magi" (different detail) (Circle of Van der Goes)		
	Set of 2 sheets	8·00	8·50

87 Mickey and Minnie Mouse

(Des Alvin White Studio. Litho Questa)

1995 (14 Feb). *Disney Sweethearts (1st series). T **87** and similar multicoloured designs showing Walt Disney cartoon characters. P 14×13½.*

853	10 c. Type **87**	20	20
854	25 c. Donald and Daisy Duck	35	20
855	50 c. Pluto and Fifi	50	35
856	80 c. Clarabelle Cow and Horace Horsecollar	70	50
857	$1 Pluto and Figaro	85	65
858	$1.50, Polly and Peter Penguin	1·25	1·50
859	$4 Prunella Pullet and Hick Rooster	2·50	3·00
860	$5 Jenny Wren and Cock Robin	2·50	3·00
853/60	*Set of 8*	8·00	8·50
MS861	Two sheets, each 133×107 mm. (a) $6 Daisy Duck (*vert*). (b) $6 Minnie Mouse (*vert*). P 13½×14		
	Set of 2 sheets	7·00	7·50

See also Nos. 998/1007.

88 Rufous-breasted Hermit

89 Pointer

(Des Mary Walters (Nos. 862/73), Marilyn Abramowitz (others). Litho Questa).

1995 (30 Mar). *Birds. T **88** and similar vert designs. Multicoloured. P 14.*

862	50 c. Type **88**	40	40
	a. Sheetlet. Nos. 862/73	4·25	
863	50 c. Purple-throated Carib	40	40
864	50 c. Green Mango	40	40
865	50 c. Bahama Woodstar	40	40
866	50 c. Hispaniolan Emerald	40	40
867	50 c. Antillean Crested Hummingbird	40	40
868	50 c. Green-throated Carib	40	40
869	50 c. Antillean Mango	40	40
870	50 c. Vervain Hummingbird	40	40
871	50 c. Jamaican Mango	40	40
872	50 c. Cuban Emerald	40	40
873	50 c. Blue-headed Hummingbird	40	40
874	50 c. Hooded Merganser	40	40
875	80 c. Green-backed Heron	65	50
876	$2 Double-crested Cormorant	1·25	1·40
877	$3 Ruddy Duck	1·50	1·75
862/77	*Set of 16*	7·75	8·00
MS878	Two sheets, each 100×70 mm. (a) $6 Black Skimmer. (b) $6 Snowy Plover		
	Set of 2 sheets	7·50	8·00

Nos. 862/73 were printed together, *se-tenant*, in sheetlets of 12.

No. 870 is inscribed "VERVIAN" in error.

(Des D. Miller. Litho B.D.T.)

1995 (23 May). *Dogs. T **89** and similar horiz designs. Multicoloured. P 14.*

879	25 c. Type **89**	30	20
880	50 c. Old Danish Pointer	50	50
881	80 c. Irish Setter	65	65
	a. Sheetlet. Nos. 881/9	5·00	
882	80 c. Weimaraner	65	65
883	80 c. Gordon Setter	65	65
884	80 c. Brittany Spaniel	65	65
885	80 c. American Cocker Spaniel	65	65
886	80 c. English Cocker Spaniel	65	65
887	80 c. Labrador Retriever	65	65
888	80 c. Golden Retriever	65	65
889	80 c. Flat-coated Retriever	65	65
890	$1 German Short-haired Pointer	75	75
891	$2 English Setter	1·40	1·40
879/91	*Set of 13*	7·75	7·75
MS892	Two sheets, each 72×58 mm. (a) $6 German Shepherds. (b) $6 Bloodhounds		
	Set of 2 sheets	7·50	8·00

Nos. 881/9 were printed together, *se-tenant*, in sheetlets of 9. "POINTER" is omitted from the inscription on No. 890. No. MS892a is incorrectly inscribed "SHEPHARD".

90 Schulumbergera truncata

91 Scouts backpacking

(Des Mary Walters. Litho Questa)

1995 (20 June). *Cacti. T **90** and similar vert designs. Multicoloured. P 14.*

893	40 c. Type **90**	30	20
894	50 c. *Echinocereus pectinatus*	40	25
895	80 c. *Mammillaria zeilmanniana alba*	65	40
896	$1.60, *Lobivia hertriehiana*	1·10	1·25
897	$2 *Hammatocactus setispinus*	1·40	1·50
898	$3 *Astrophytum myriostigma*	1·60	2·00
893/8	*Set of 6*	4·75	5·00
MS899	Two sheets, each 106×76 mm. (a) $6 *Opuntia robusta*. (b) $6 *Rhipsalidopsis gaertneri*		
	Set of 2 sheets	7·00	7·50

(Des B. Hargreaves. Litho Questa)

1995 (20 July). *18th World Scout Jamboree, Netherlands. T **91** and similar multicoloured designs. P 14.*

900	$1 Type **91**	75	90
	a. Horiz strip. Nos. 900/2	3·50	
901	$2 Scouts building aerial rope way	1·25	1·50
902	$4 Scout map reading	2·00	2·25
900/2	*Set of 3*	3·50	4·25
MS903	101×71 mm. $6 Scout in canoe (*vert*)	3·50	4·00

Nos. 900/2 were printed together in sheets of 9 containing three *se-tenant* horizontal strips of 3, each forming a composite design.

(Des J. Iskowitz. Litho Questa)

1995 (20 July). *50th Anniv of End of Second World War in Europe. Multicoloured designs as T **317** of Maldive Islands. P 14.*

904	$1.25. Clark Gable and aircraft	90	90
	a. Sheetlet. Nos. 904/11	6·50	
905	$1.25, Audie Murphy and machine-gunner	90	90
906	$1.25, Glenn Miller playing trombone	90	90
907	$1.25, Joe Louis and infantry	90	90
908	$1.25, Jimmy Doolittle and U.S.S. *Hornet* (aircraft carrier)	90	90
909	$1.25, John Hersey and jungle patrol	90	90
910	$1.25, John F. Kennedy in patrol boat	90	90
911	$1.25, James Stewart and bombers	90	90
904/11	*Set of 8*	6·50	6·50
MS912	101×71 mm. $6 Jimmy Doolittle (*vert*)	2·75	3·00

Nos. 904/11 were printed together, *se-tenant*, in sheetlets of 8 with the stamps arranged in two horizontal strips of 4 separated by a gutter showing ticker-tape parade and U.S. sailor kissing nurse in New York.

92 Oriental and African People

93 Rotary Emblem on Nevis Flag

(Des J. Iskowitz. Litho Questa)

1995 (20 July). *50th Anniv of United Nations. T **92** and similar vert designs, each pale lilac and black or multicoloured (No. MS916). P 14.*

913	$1.25, Type **92**	55	60
	a. Horiz strip of 3. Nos. 913/15	2·50	
914	$1.60, Asian people	75	80
915	$3 American and European people	1·40	1·50
913/15	*Set of 3*	2·50	2·75
MS916	105×75 mm. $6 Pres. Nelson Mandela of South Africa	2·50	3·00

Nos. 913/15 were printed together in sheets of 9 containing three *se-tenant* horizontal strips of 3, each forming a composite design.

(Des J. Iskowitz. Litho Questa)

1995 (20 July). *50th Anniv of Food and Agriculture Organization. Vert designs as T **92**. Multicoloured. P 14.*

917	40 c. Woman wearing yellow headdress	15	20
	a. Horiz strip of 3. Nos. 917/19	2·25	
918	$2 Babies and emblem	85	90
919	$3 Woman wearing blue headdress	1·25	1·40
917/19	*Set of 3*	2·25	2·50
MS920	105×80 mm. $6 Man carrying hoe	2·50	3·00

Nos. 917/19 were printed together in sheets of 9 containing three *se-tenant* horizontal strips of 3, each forming a composite design.

No. MS920 is inscribed "1945–1955" in error.

(Des G. Bibby. Litho Questa)

1995 (20 July). *90th Anniv of Rotary International. T **93** and similar horiz design. Multicoloured. P 14.*

921	$5 Type **93**	2·50	3·00
MS922	95×66 mm. $6 Rotary emblem and beach	3·00	3·50

(Litho Questa)

1995 (20 July). *95th Birthday of Queen Elizabeth the Queen Mother. Vert designs as T **321** of Maldive Islands. P 13½×14.*

923	$1.50, orange-brown, pale brown and black	1·00	1·10
	a. Sheetlet. Nos. 923/6×2	7·00	
924	$1.50, multicoloured	1·00	1·10
925	$1.50, multicoloured	1·00	1·10
926	$1.50, multicoloured	1·00	1·10
923/6	*Set of 4*	3·50	4·00
MS927	102×127 mm. $6 multicoloured	3·50	4·00

Designs:—No. 923, Queen Elizabeth the Queen Mother (pastel drawing); No. 924, Wearing pink hat; No. 925, At desk (oil painting); No. 926, Wearing blue hat; No. MS927, Wearing tiara.

Nos. 923/6 were printed together in sheetlets of 8, containing two *se-tenant* horizontal strips of 4.

(Des J. Batchelor. Litho Questa)

1995 (20 July). *50th Anniv of End of Second World War in the Pacific. United States Aircraft. Horiz designs as T **317** of Maldive Islands. Multicoloured. P 14.*

928	$2 Grumman F4F Wildcat	1·40	1·40
	a. Sheetlet. Nos. 928/33	7·50	
929	$2 Chance Vought F4U-1A Corsair	1·40	1·40
930	$2 Vought SB2U Vindicator	1·40	1·40
931	$2 Grumman F6F Hellcat	1·40	1·40

932	$2 Douglas SDB Dauntless	.. ..	1·40	1·40
933	$2 Grumman TBF-1 Avenger	.. ..	1·40	1·40
928/33		*Set of 6*	7·50	7·50

MS934 108×76 mm. $6 Chance Vought F4U-1A
Corsair on carrier flight deck .. .. .. 4·25 4·75

Nos. 928/33 were printed together, *se-tenant*, in sheetlets of 6
with the stamps arranged in two horizontal strips of 3 separated
by a gutter showing U.S.S. *Saratoga* (aircraft carrier).

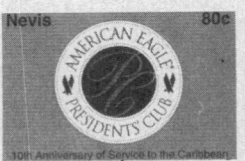

94 Emil von Behring
(1901 Medicine)

95 American Eagle Presidents'
Club Logo

(Des R. Sauber. Litho Questa)

1995 (20 July). *Centenary of Nobel Trust Fund. Past Prize
Winners.* T **94** *and similar vert designs. Multicoloured.* P 14.

935	$1.25, Type **94**	.. ..	75	85
	a. Sheetlet. Nos. 935/43	..	6·00	
936	$1.25, Wilhelm Röntgen (1901 Physics)		75	85
937	$1.25, Paul Heyse (1910 Literature)	..	75	85
938	$1.25, Le Duc Tho (1973 Peace)	..	75	85
939	$1.25, Yasunari Kawabata (1968 Literature)		75	85
940	$1.25, Tsung-dao Lee (1957 Physics)		75	85
941	$1.25, Werner Heisenberg (1932 Physics)		75	85
942	$1.25, Johannes Stark (1919 Physics)		75	85
943	$1.25, Wilhelm Wien (1911 Physics)		75	85
935/43		*Set of 9*	6·00	7·00

MS944 101×71 mm. $6 Kenzaburo Oe (1994
Literature) .. .. 3·25 3·75

Nos. 935/43 were printed together, *se-tenant*, in sheetlets of 9.

(Des Y. Lee. Litho Questa)

1995 (28 Aug). *10th Anniv of American Eagle Air Services to
the Caribbean. Sheet, 70×100 mm, containing* T **95** *and
similar horiz design. Multicoloured.* P 14.

MS945 80 c. Type **95**; $3 Aircraft over Nevis
beach .. .. 2·40 2·50

96 Great Egrets

97 SKANTEL
Engineer

(Des Grace De Vito. Litho Questa)

1995 (1 Sept). *Marine Life.* T **96** *and similar multicoloured
designs.* P 14.

946	50 c. Type **96**	.. ..	35	35
	a. Sheetlet. Nos. 946/61	..	5·00	
947	50 c. 17th-century galleon	..	35	35
948	50 c. Galleon and Marlin	..	35	35
949	50 c. Herring Gulls	..	35	35
950	50 c. Nassau Groupers	..	35	35
951	50 c. Spotted Eagleray	..	35	35
952	50 c. Leopard Shark and Hammerhead		35	35
953	50 c. Hourglass Dolphins	..	35	35
954	50 c. Spanish Hogfish	..	35	35
955	50 c. Jellyfish and Seahorses	..	35	35
956	50 c. Angelfish and buried treasure		35	35
957	50 c. Hawksbill Turtle	..	35	35
958	50 c. Common Octopus	..	35	35
959	50 c. Moray Eel	..	35	35
960	50 c. Queen Angelfish and Butterflyfish		35	35
961	50 c. Ghost Crab and Sea Star	..	35	35
946/61		*Set of 16*	5·00	5·00

MS962 Two sheets. (a) 106×76 mm. $5 Nassau
Grouper. (b) 76×106 mm. $5 Queen Angelfish
(*vert*) .. .. .. *Set of 2 sheets* 7·00 7·00

Nos. 946/61 were printed together, *se-tenant*, in sheetlets of
16, forming a composite design.

No. MS962 also commemorates the "Singapore '95"
International Stamp Exhibition.

(Des M. Friedman. Litho Questa)

1995 (23 Oct). *10th Anniv of SKANTEL* (telecommunications
company). T **97** *and similar multicoloured designs.* P 14.

963	$1 Type **97**	.. ..	60	50
964	$1.50, SKANTEL sign outside Nevis office		80	1·00

MS965 76×106 mm. $5 St. Kitts SKANTEL
office (*horiz*) .. .. 3·00 3·25

NEW INFORMATION

The editor is always interested to correspond with
people who have new information that will
improve or correct the Catalogue.

98 "Rucellai Madonna
and Child" (detail)
(Duccio)

99 View of Nevis Four
Seasons Resort

(Litho Questa)

1995 (1 Dec). *Christmas. Religious Paintings by Duccio di
Buoninsegna.* T **98** *and similar vert designs. Multicoloured.*
P 13½×14.

966	20 c. Type **98**	..	15	10
967	50 c. "Angel from the Rucellai Madonna" (detail)		30	25
968	80 c. "Madonna and Child" (*different*)		50	40
969	$1 "Angel from the Annunciation" (detail)		65	50
970	$1.60, "Madonna and Child" (*different*) ..		1·00	1·00
971	$3 "Angel from the Rucellai Madonna" (*different*)		1·60	2·00
966/71		*Set of 6*	3·75	3·75

MS972 Two sheets, each 102×127 mm. (a) $5
"Nativity with the Prophets Isaiah and Ezekiel"
(detail). (b) $6 "The Crevole Madonna" (detail)
Set of 2 sheets 6·50 7·00

(Des M. Friedman. Litho Questa)

1996 (14 Feb). *5th Anniv of Four Seasons Resort, Nevis.* T **99**
and similar horiz designs. Multicoloured. P 14.

973	25 c. Type **99**	..	10	15
974	50 c. Catamarans, Pinney's Beach		20	25
975	80 c. Robert Trent Jones II Golf Course		35	40
976	$2 Prime Minister Simeon Daniel laying foundation stone		85	90
973/6		*Set of 4*	1·50	1·60

MS977 76×106 mm. $6 Sunset over resort .. 2·50 2·75

100 Rat, Plant and
Butterfly

101 Ancient Greek Boxers

(Des Y. Lee. Litho Questa)

1996 (28 Feb). *Chinese New Year ("Year of the Rat").* T **100**
and similar vert designs. Multicoloured. P 14.

978	$1 Type **100**	..	45	50
	a. Block of 4. Nos. 978/81	..	1·75	
979	$1 Rat with prickly plant ..	..	45	50
980	$1 Rat and bee	..	45	50
981	$1 Rat and dragonfly	..	45	50
978/81		*Set of 4*	1·75	2·00

MS982 74×104 mm. Nos. 978/81 .. 1·90 2·00
MS983 74×104 mm. $3 Rat eating .. 1·25 1·40

Nos. 978/81 were printed together, *se-tenant*, in blocks of 4
throughout sheets of 16.

(Des B. Durand. Litho B.D.T.)

1996 (28 May). *Olympic Games, Atlanta. Previous Medal
Winners.* T **101** *and similar multicoloured designs.* P 14.

984	25 c. Type **101**	..	10	10
985	50 c. Mark Spitz (U.S.A.) (Gold – swimming, 1972)		20	25
986	80 c. Siegbert Horn (East Germany) (Gold – single kayak slalom, 1972)		35	40
987	$1 Jim Thorpe on medal (U.S.A.), 1912 (*vert*)		45	50
	a. Sheetlet. Nos. 987/95	..	4·00	
988	$1 Glenn Morris on medal (U.S.A.), 1936 (*vert*)		45	50
989	$1 Bob Mathias on medal (U.S.A.), 1948 and 1952 (*vert*)		45	50
990	$1 Rafer Johnson on medal (U.S.A.), 1960 (*vert*)		45	50
991	$1 Bill Toomey (U.S.A.), 1968 (*vert*)		45	50
992	$1 Nikolay Avilov (Russia), 1972 (*vert*)		45	50
993	$1 Bruce Jenner (U.S.A.), 1976 (*vert*)		45	50
994	$1 Daley Thompson (Great Britain), 1980 and 1984 (*vert*)		45	50
995	$1 Christian Schenk (East Germany), 1988 (*vert*)		45	50
996	$3 Olympic Stadium and Siegestor Arch, Munich (*vert*)		1·25	1·40
984/96		*Set of 13*	5·50	6·00

MS997 Two sheets, each 105×75 mm. (a) $5
Willi Holdorf (West Germany) (Gold – decathlon,
1964) (*vert*). (b) $5 Hans-Joachim Walde (West
Germany) (Silver – decathlon, 1968) (*vert*)
Set of 2 sheets 4·25 4·50

Nos. 987/95 were printed together, *se-tenant*, in sheetlets of 9
and depict decathlon gold medal winners.

(Des Alvin White Studios. Litho Questa)

1996 (17 June). *Disney Sweethearts (2nd series). Horiz designs
as* T **87** *showing Walt Disney cartoon characters.
Multicoloured.* P 14×13½.

998	$2 Pocahontas and John Smith		1·50	1·50
	a. Sheetlet. Nos. 998/1006		12·00	
999	$2 Mowgli and the Girl	..	1·50	1·50
1000	$2 Belle and the Beast	..	1·50	1·50
1001	$2 Cinderella and Prince Charming		1·50	1·50
1002	$2 Pinocchio and the Dutch Girl		1·50	1·50
1003	$2 Grace Martin and Henry Coy		1·50	1·50
1004	$2 Snow White and the Prince		1·50	1·50
1005	$2 Aladdin and Jasmine	..	1·50	1·50
1006	$2 Pecos Bill and Slue Foot Sue		1·50	1·50
998/1006		*Set of 9*	12·00	12·00

MS1007 Two sheets, each 110×130 mm. (a) $6
Sleeping Beauty and Prince Phillip (*vert*).
P 13½×14. (b) $6 Ariel and Eric. *Set of 2 sheets* 8·00 8·50

Nos. 998/1006 were printed together, *se-tenant*, in sheetlets of
9.

102 Qian Qing Gong, Peking

(Des Y. Lee. Litho Questa)

1996 (1 July). *"CHINA '96" 9th Asian International Stamp
Exhibition, Peking. Peking Pagodas.* T **102** *and similar
multicoloured designs.* P 14.

1008	$1 Type **102**	..	45	50
	a. Sheetlet. Nos. 1008/16		4·00	
1009	$1 Temple of Heaven	..	45	50
1010	$1 Zhongnanhai	..	45	50
1011	$1 Da Zing Hall, Shehyang Palace		45	50
1012	$1 Temple of the Sleeping Buddha		45	50
1013	$1 Huang Qiong Yu, Altar of Heaven		45	50
1014	$1 The Grand Bell Temple		45	50
1015	$1 Imperial Palace	..	45	50
1016	$1 Pu Tuo Temple	..	45	50
1008/16		*Set of 9*	4·00	4·50

MS1017 104×74 mm. $6 Summer Palace of
Emperor Wan Yan-liang (*vert*) .. 2·50 2·75

Nos. 1008/16 were printed together, *se-tenant*, in sheetlets of
9.

(Litho Questa)

1996 (1 July). *70th Birthday of Queen Elizabeth II. Vert
designs as* T **334** *of Maldive Islands. Multicoloured.*
P 13½×14.

1018	$2 As Type **334** of Maldive Islands		85	90
	a. Strip of 3. Nos. 1018/20	..	2·40	
1019	$2 Wearing evening dress	..	85	90
1020	$2 In purple hat and coat	..	85	90
1018/20		*Set of 3*	2·40	2·50

MS1021 125×103 mm. $6 Taking the salute at
Trooping the Colour .. .. 2·75 3·00

Nos. 1018/20 were printed together, *se-tenant*, in horizontal
and vertical strips of 3 throughout sheets of 9.

103 Children reading Book

(Des R. Sauber. Litho Questa)

1996 (1 July). *50th Anniv of U.N.I.C.E.F.* T **103** *and similar
multicoloured designs.* P 14.

1022	25 c. Type **103**	..	10	10
1023	50 c. Doctor and child	..	20	30
1024	$4 Children	..	1·75	1·90
1022/4		*Set of 3*	2·00	2·25

MS1025 75×105 mm. $6 Young girl (*vert*) .. 2·50 2·75

104 Cave Paintings, Tassili n'Ajjer,
Algeria

(Des M. Friedman. Litho Questa)

1996 (1 July). *50th Anniv of U.N.E.S.C.O.* T **104** *and similar
multicoloured designs.* P 13½×14 ($2) *or* 14×13½ (*others*).

1026	25 c. Type **104**	..	10	10
1027	$2 Temple, Tikal National Park, Guatemala (*vert*)		85	90
1028	$3 Temple of Hera, Samos, Greece		1·25	1·40
1026/8		*Set of 3*	2·10	2·25

MS1029 106×76 mm. $6 Pueblo, Taos, U.S.A 2·50 2·75

105 American Academy of
Ophthalmology Logo

106 *Rothmannia
longiflora*

(Des M. Friedman. Litho Questa)

1996 (1 July). *Centenary of American Academy of Ophthalmology. P* 14.
1030 **105** $5 multicoloured .. .. .. 2·10 2·25

(Des T. Wood. Litho Questa)

1996 (24 Sept). *Flowers.* T **106** *and similar vert designs. Multicoloured. P* 14.
1031 25 c. Type **106** 10 10
1032 50 c. *Gloriosa simplex* 20 25
1033 $1 *Monodora myristica* 45 50
   a. Sheetlet. Nos. 1033/41 .. .. 4·00
1034 $1 Giraffe 45 50
1035 $1 *Adansonia digitata* 45 50
1036 $1 *Ansellia gigantea* 45 50
1037 $1 *Geissorhiza rochensis* 45 50
1038 $1 *Arctotis venusta* 45 50
1039 $1 *Gladiotus cardinalis* 45 50
1040 $1 *Eucomis bicolor* 45 50
1041 $1 *Protea obtusifolia* 45 50
1042 $2 *Catharanthus roseus* 85 90
1043 $3 *Plumbago auriculata* .. .. 1·25 1·40
1031/43 .. .. *Set of* 13 6·25 6·75
MS1044 75×105 mm. $5 *Strelitzia reginae* .. 2·10 2·75
Nos. 1033/41 were printed together, *se-tenant*, in sheetlets of 9.

107 Western
Meadowlark on
Decoration

108 Ox (from "Five Oxen" by Han
Huang)

(Des R. Rundo. Litho B.D.T.)

1996 (2 Dec). *Christmas. Birds.* T **107** *and similar multicoloured designs. P* 14.
1045 25 c. Type **107** 10 10
1046 50 c. Bird (incorrectly inscr as "American
   Goldfinch") with decorations (*horiz*) 20 25
1047 80 c. Santa Claus, sleigh and reindeer
   (*horiz*) 35 40
1048 $1 American Goldfinch on stocking .. 45 50
1049 $1.60, Mockingbird with snowman
   decoration 70 75
1050 $5 Yellow-rumped Cacique and bauble .. 2·10 2·25
1045/50 .. .. *Set of* 6 3·75 4·25
MS1051 Two sheets. (a) 106×76 mm. $6 Macaw
(*horiz*). (b) 76×106 mm. $6 Vermilion Flycatcher
(*horiz*) .. .. *Set of 2 sheets* 5·25 5·50
No. 1048 is inscribed "WESTERN MEADOWLARK" and No.
1050 "YELLOW-RUMPED CAIEQUE", both in error.

(Des Y. Lee. Litho Questa)

1997 (16 Jan). *Chinese New Year* ("*Year of the Ox*"). T **108** *and similar oxen from the painting by Han Huang. Sheet* 230×93 *mm. P* 14×15.
MS1052 50 c., 80 c., $1.60, $2 multicoloured .. 2·10 2·25
The fifth ox appears on a small central label

109 Giant Panda eating
Bamboo Shoots

110 Elquemedo
Willett

(Des L. Fried. Litho Questa)

1997 (12 Feb). "*HONG KONG '97*" *International Stamp Exhibition. Giant Pandas.* T **109** *and similar vert designs. Multicoloured. P* 14.
1053 $1.60, Type **109** 70 75
   a. Sheetlet. Nos. 1053/8 .. .. 4·00
1054 $1.60, Head of Panda 70 75

1055 $1.60, Panda with new-born cub .. 70 75
1056 $1.60, Panda hanging from branch .. 70 75
1057 $1.60, Panda asleep on tree .. 70 75
1058 $1.60, Panda climbing trunk .. 70 75
1053/8 .. .. *Set of* 6 4·00 4·50
MS1059 73×103 mm. $5 Panda with cub .. 2·10 2·25
Nos. 1053/8 were printed together, *se-tenant*, in sheetlets of 6, with enlarged right-hand margin.

(Des M. Friedman. Litho B.D.T.)

1997 (1 May). *Nevis Cricketers.* T **110** *and similar multicoloured designs. P* 14.
1060 25 c. Type **110** 10 15
1061 80 c. Stuart Williams 35 40
1062 $2 Keith Arthurton 85 90
1060/2 .. .. *Set of* 3 1·25 1·40
MS1063 Two sheets, each 106×76 mm. (a) $5
Willett, Arthurton and Williams as part of the
1990 Nevis team (*horiz*); (b) $5 Williams and
Arthurton as part of the 1994 West Indies team
.. .. .. *Set of 2 sheets* 4·25 4·50

111 Crimson-speckled Moth

(Des Rinah Lyamph. Litho B.D.T.)

1997 (12 May). *Butterflies and Moths.* T **111** *and similar horiz designs. Multicoloured. P* 14.
1064 10 c. Type **111** 10 10
1065 25 c. Purple Emperor 10 15
1066 50 c. Regent Skipper 20 25
1067 80 c. Provence Burnet Moth .. 35 40
1068 $1 Common Wall Butterfly .. 45 50
1069 $1 Red-lined Geometrid 45 50
   a. Sheetlet. Nos. 1069/77 .. 4·00
1070 $1 Boisduval's Autumnal Moth .. 45 50
1071 $1 Blue Pansy 45 50
1072 $1 Common Clubtail 45 50
1073 $1 Tufted Jungle King 45 50
1074 $1 Lesser Marbled Fritillary .. 45 50
1075 $1 Peacock Royal 45 50
1076 $1 Emperor Gum Moth 45 50
1077 $1 Orange Swallow-tailed Moth .. 45 50
1078 $4 Cruiser Butterfly .. .. 1·75 1·90
1064/78 .. .. *Set of* 15 6·75 7·75
MS1079 Two sheets. (a) 103×73 mm. $5 Great
Purple ("*Saskiai charondal*"). (b) 73×103 mm. $5
Jersey Tiger Moth .. .. *Set of 2 sheets* 4·25 4·50
Nos. 1069/77 were printed together, *se-tenant*, in sheetlets of 9.
No. 1073 is inscribed "TUFTED JUNGLE QUEEN" in error

112 Boy with Two Pigeons
("Two Pigeons")

(Des R. Rundo. Litho Questa)

1997 (29 May). *300th Anniv of Mother Goose Nursery Rhymes. Sheet* 72×102 *mm. P* 14.
MS1080 **112** $5 multicoloured .. .. 2·10 2·25

113 Paul Harris and Literacy
Class

(Des J. Iskowitz. Litho Questa)

1997 (29 May). *50th Death Anniv of Paul Harris* (*founder of Rotary International*). T **113** *and similar horiz design. Multicoloured. P* 14.
1081 $2 Type **113** 85 90
MS1082 78×108 mm. $5 Football coaching
session, Chile .. .. 2·10 2·25

(Litho Questa)

1997 (29 May). *Golden Wedding of Queen Elizabeth and Prince Philip. Horiz designs as* T **350** *of Maldive Islands. Multicoloured. P* 14.
1083 $1 Queen Elizabeth II 45 50
   a. Sheetlet. Nos. 1083/8 .. 2·75
1084 $1 Royal coat of arms 45 50
1085 $1 Queen Elizabeth wearing red hat and
   coat with Prince Philip .. 45 50
1086 $1 Queen Elizabeth in blue coat and Prince
   Philip 45 50
1087 $1 Caernarvon Castle 45 50
1088 $1 Prince Philip in R.A.F. uniform .. 45 50
1083/8 .. .. *Set of* 6 2·75 3·00
MS1089 100×70 mm. $5 Queen Elizabeth at
Coronation .. .. 2·10 2·25
Nos. 1083/8 were printed together, *se-tenant*, in sheetlets of 6.

(Des J. Iskowitz. Litho Questa)

1997 (29 May). "*Pacific '97*" *International Stamp Exhibition, San Francisco. Death Centenary of Heinrich von Stephan. Horiz designs as* T **351** *of Maldive Islands. P* 14.
1090 $1.60, turquoise-green .. 70 75
   a. Sheetlet. Nos. 1090/2 .. 2·10
1091 $1.60, chestnut 70 75
1092 $1.60, deep blue 70 75
1090/2 .. .. *Set of* 3 2·10 2·25
MS1093 82×118 mm. $5 sepia .. 2·10 2·25
   Designs:—No. 1090, Russian reindeer post, 1859; No. 1091,
Von Stephan and Mercury; No. 1092, *City of Cairo* (paddle-
steamer), Mississippi, 1800s; No. MS1093, Von Stephan and
Bavarian postal messenger, 1640.
Nos. 1090/2 were printed together, *se-tenant*, in sheets of 3
with enlarged right-hand margin.

(Litho Questa)

1997 (29 May). *Birth Bicentenary of Hiroshige* (*Japanese painter*). "*One Hundred Famous Views of Edo*". *Vert designs as* T **352** *of Maldive Islands. Multicoloured. P* 13½×14.
1094 $1.60, "Scattered Pines, Tone River" 70 75
   a. Sheetlet. Nos. 1094/9 .. 4·00
1095 $1.60, "Mouth of Nakagawa River" .. 70 75
1096 $1.60, "Niijuku Ferry" 70 75
1097 $1.60, "Horie and Nekozane" .. 70 75
1098 $1.60, "Konodai and the Tone River" .. 70 75
1099 $1.60, "Maple Trees, Tekona Shrine and
   Bridge, Mama" 70 75
1094/9 .. .. *Set of* 6 4·00 4·50
MS1100 Two sheets, each 102×127 mm. (a) $6
"Mitsumata Wakarenofuchi". (b) $6 "Moto-
Hachiman Shrine, Sunamura" .. *Set of 2 sheets* 5·25 5·50
Nos. 1094/9 were printed together, *se-tenant*, in sheetlets of 6.

114 Augusta National Course,
U.S.A.

115 *Cantharellus
cibarius*

(Des M. Friedman. Litho B.D.T.)

1997 (15 July). *Golf Courses of the World.* T **114** *and similar horiz designs. Multicoloured. P* 14.
1101 $1 Type **114** 45 50
   a. Sheetlet. Nos. 1101/9 .. 4·00
1102 $1 Cabo del Sol, Mexico .. 45 50
1103 $1 Cypress Point, U.S.A. .. 45 50
1104 $1 Lost City, South Africa .. 45 50
1105 $1 Moscow Country Club, Russia .. 45 50
1106 $1 New South Wales, Australia .. 45 50
1107 $1 Royal Montreal, Canada .. 45 50
1108 $1 St. Andrews, Scotland .. 45 50
1109 $1 Four Seasons Resort, Nevis .. 45 50
1101/9 .. .. *Set of* 9 4·00 4·50
Nos. 1101/9 were printed together, *se-tenant*, in sheetlets of 9.

(Des D. Miller. Litho Enschedé)

1997 (12 Aug). *Fungi.* T **115** *and similar vert designs. Multicoloured. P* 13.
1110 25 c. Type **115** 10 10
1111 50 c. *Stropharia aeruginosa* .. 20 25
1112 80 c. *Suillus hiteus* 35 40
   a. Sheetlet. Nos. 1112/17 .. 2·10
1113 80 c. *Amanita muscaria* .. 35 40
1114 80 c. *Lactarius rufus* 35 40
1115 80 c. *Amanita rubescens* .. 35 40
1116 80 c. *Armillaria mellea* .. 35 40
1117 80 c. *Russula sardonia* .. 35 40
1118 $1 *Boletus edulis* 45 50
   a. Sheetlet. Nos. 1118/23 .. 2·75
1119 $1 *Pholiota lenta* 45 50
1120 $1 *Cortinarius bolaris* 45 50
1121 $1 *Coprinus picaceus* 45 50
1122 $1 *Amanita phalloides* 45 50
1123 $1 *Cystolepiota aspera* 45 50
1124 $3 *Lactarius turpis* .. .. 1·25 1·40
1125 $4 *Entoloma clypeatum* .. .. 1·75 1·90
1110/25 .. .. *Set of* 16 8·50 9·00
MS1126 Two sheets, each 98×68 mm. (a) $5
Galerina mutabilis. (b) $5 *Gymnopilus junonius*
.. .. .. *Set of 2 sheets* 4·25 4·50
Nos. 1112/17 and 1118/23 were each printed together,
se-tenant, in sheetlets of 6 with the backgrounds forming
composite designs.

116 Diana, Princess
of Wales

117 Victoria Govt Class S
Pacific Locomotive, Australia

(Des Y. Lee. Litho Questa)

1997 (19 Sept). *Diana, Princess of Wales Commemoration. T* **116** *and similar vert portraits. Multicoloured.* P 14.

1127	$1 Type **116**		60	70
	a. Sheetlet. Nos. 1127/35		4·75	
1128	$1 Wearing white blouse		60	70
1129	$1 In wedding dress, 1981		60	70
1130	$1 Wearing turquoise blouse		60	70
1131	$1 Wearing tiara		60	70
1132	$1 Wearing blue blouse		60	70
1133	$1 Wearing pearl necklace		60	70
1134	$1 Wearing diamond drop earrings		60	70
1135	$1 Wearing sapphire necklace and earrings		60	70
1127/35		*Set of 9*	4·75	5·50

Nos. 1127/35 were printed together, *se-tenant*, in sheetlets of 9 with an illustrated right-hand margin.

(Des D. Miller. Litho Questa)

1997 (29 Sept). *Trains of the World. T* **117** *and similar horiz designs. Multicoloured.* P 14.

1136	10 c. Type **117**		10	10
1137	50 c. Express steam locomotive, Japan		20	30
1138	80 c. L.M.S. steam-turbine locomotive, Great Britain		35	40
1139	$1 Electric locomotive, Switzerland		45	50
1140	$1.50, "Mikado" steam locomotive, Sudan		65	70
	a. Sheetlet. Nos. 1140/5		4·00	
1141	$1.50, *Mohammed Ali el Kebir* steam locomotive, Egypt		65	70
1142	$1.50, Southern Region steam locomotive *Leatherhead*		65	70
1143	$1.50, Great Southern Railway Drumm battery-powered railcar, Ireland		65	70
1144	$1.50, Pacific locomotive, Germany		65	70
1145	$1.50, Canton–Hankow Railway Pacific locomotive, China		65	70
1146	$2 L.M.S. high-pressure locomotive, Great Britain		85	90
1147	$3 Great Northern Railway *Kestrel*, Ireland		1·25	1·40
1136/47		*Set of 12*	7·00	7·75

MS1148 Two sheets, each 71×48 mm. (a) $5 L.M.S. high-pressure locomotive. (b) $5 G.W.R. *King George V* .. *Set of 2 sheets* 4·25 4·50

Nos. 1140/5 were printed together, *se-tenant*, in sheetlets of 6.

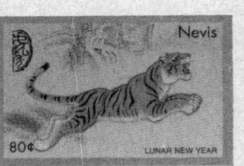

118 "Selection of Angels" (detail) (Dürer)

119 Tiger (semi-circular character at top left)

(Litho Questa)

1997 (26 Nov). *Christmas. Paintings. T* **118** *and similar multicoloured designs.* P 14.

1149	20 c. Type **118**		10	10
1150	25 c. "Selection of Angels" (different detail) (Dürer)		10	15
1151	50 c. "Andromeda and Perseus" (Rubens)		20	25
1152	80 c. "Harmony" (detail) (Raphael)		35	40
1153	$1.60, "Harmony" (different detail) (Raphael)		70	75
1154	$5 "Holy Trinity" (Raphael)		2·10	2·25
1149/54		*Set of 6*	3·50	3·75

MS1155 Two sheets, each 114×104 mm. (a) $5 "Study Muse" (Raphael) (*horiz*). (b) $5 "Ezekiel's Vision" (Raphael) (*horiz*) .. *Set of 2 sheets* 4·25 4·50

(Des Kan-chen Wang. Litho B.D.T.)

1998 (19 Jan). *Chinese New Year ("Year of the Tiger"). T* **119** *and similar multicoloured designs showing symbolic tigers.* P 14.

1156	80 c. Type **119**		35	40
	a. Sheetlet. Nos. 1156/9		1·40	
1157	80 c. Oblong character at bottom right		35	40
1158	80 c. Circular character at top left		35	40
1159	80 c. Square character at bottom right		35	40
1156/9		*Set of 4*	1·40	1·60

MS1160 67×97 mm. $2 Tiger (*vert*) .. 85 90

Nos. 1156/9 were printed together, *se-tenant*, in sheetlets of 4.

120 Social Security Board Emblem

121 Soursop

(Des M. Friedman. Litho Cartor)

1998 (2 Feb). *20th Anniv of Social Security Board. T* **120** *and similar multicoloured designs.* P 13.

1161	30 c. Type **120**		15	20
1162	$1.20, Opening of Social Security Building, Charlestown (*horiz*)		50	55

MS1163 100×70 mm. $6 Social Security staff (59×39 *mm*). P 13½×13 .. 2·50 2·75

(Des Zina Saunders. Litho Questa)

1998 (9 Mar). *Fruits. T* **121** *and similar vert designs. Multicoloured.* P 14.

1164	5 c. Type **121**		10	10
1165	10 c. Carambola		10	10
1166	25 c. Guava		10	15
1167	30 c. Papaya		15	20
1168	50 c. Mango		20	25
1169	60 c. Golden Apple		25	30
1170	80 c. Pineapple		35	40
1171	90 c. Watermelon		40	45
1172	$1 Bananas		45	50
1173	$1.80, Orange		80	85
1174	$3 Honeydew		1·25	1·40
1175	$5 Cantelope		2·10	2·25
1176	$10 Pomegranate		4·25	4·50
1177	$20 Cashew		8·75	9·00
1164/77		*Set of 14*	19·00	20·00

122 African Fish Eagle

123 Chaim Topol (Israeli actor)

(Des Zina Saunders. Litho Questa)

1998 (31 Mar). *Endangered Species. T* **122** *and similar horiz designs. Multicoloured.* P 14.

1178	30 c. Type **122**		15	20
1179	80 c. Summer Tanager at nest		35	40
1180	90 c. Orang-utan and young		40	45
1181	$1 Young chimpanzee		45	50
	a. Sheetlet. Nos. 1181/9		4·00	
1182	$1 Keel-billed Toucan		45	50
1183	$1 Chaco Peccary		45	50
1184	$1 Spadefoot Toad and insect		45	50
1185	$1 Howler Monkey		45	50
1186	$1 Alaskan Brown Bear		45	50
1187	$1 Koala bears		45	50
1188	$1 Brown Pelican		45	50
1189	$1 Iguana		45	50
1190	$1.20, Tiger cub		50	55
1191	$2 Cape Pangolin		85	90
1192	$3 Hoatzin		1·25	1·40
1178/92		*Set of 15*	7·50	8·25

MS1193 Two sheets, each 69×99 mm. (a) $5 Young Mandrill. (b) $5 Polar Bear cub *Set of 2 sheets* 4·25 4·50

Nos. 1181/9 were printed together, *se-tenant*, in sheetlets of 9. No. 1185 is inscribed "MOWLER MONKEY" and No. 1192 "MOATZIN", both in error.

(Des G. Eichorn. Litho Cartor)

1998 (17 May). *"Israel 98" International Stamp Exhibition, Tel-Aviv.* P 13½.

1194 **123** $1.60, multicoloured .. 70 75

No. 1194 was printed in sheets of 6 with enlarged illustrated right-hand margin.

124 Boeing 747 200B (U.S.A.)

125 Anniversary Logo

(Des M. Servin. Litho Questa)

1998 (19 May). *Aircraft. T* **124** *and similar horiz designs. Multicoloured.* P 14.

1195	10 c. Type **124**		10	10
1196	90 c. Cessna 185 Skywagon (U.S.A.)		40	45
1197	$1 Northrop B-2 A (U.S.A.)		45	50
	a. Sheetlet. Nos. 1197/204		3·50	
1198	$1 Lockheed SR-71A (U.S.A.)		45	50
1199	$1 Beechcraft T-44A (U.S.A.)		45	50
1200	$1 Sukhoi Su-27UB (U.S.S.R.)		45	50
1201	$1 Hawker Siddeley Harrier GR. Mk1 (Great Britain)		45	50
1202	$1 Boeing E-3A Sentry (U.S.A.)		45	50
1203	$1 Convair B-36H (U.S.A.)		45	50
1204	$1 IAI KFIR C2 (Israel)		45	50

1205	$1.80, McDonnell Douglas DC-9 SO (U.S.A.)		75	80
1206	$5 Airbus A-300 B4 (U.S.A.)		2·10	2·25
1195/206		*Set of 12*	6·75	7·50

MS1207 Two sheets, each 76×106 mm. (a) $5 Lockheed F-117A (U.S.A.) (56×42 *mm*). (b) $5 Concorde (Great Britain) (56×42 *mm*) .. *Set of 2 sheets* 4·25 4·50

Nos. 1197/204 were printed together, *se-tenant*, in sheetlets of 8 with enlarged left-hand margin.

126 Butterflyfish

127 Prime Minister Kennedy Simmonds receiving Constitutional Instruments from Princess Margaret, 1983

(Des M. Friedman. Litho Questa)

1998 (18 June). *10th Anniv of "Voice of Nevis" Radio. T* **125** *and similar designs.* P 14.

1208	20 c. violet, bright reddish violet and black		10	10
1209	30 c. multicoloured		15	20
1210	$1.20, multicoloured		50	55
1208/10		*Set of 3*	75	85

MS1211 110×85 mm. $5 multicoloured .. 2·10 2·25

Designs: *Horiz*—30 c. Evered Herbert (Station Manager); $1.20, V.O.N. studio; $5 Merritt Herbert (Managing Director)

(Litho Questa)

1998 (18 Aug). *International Year of the Ocean. T* **126** *and similar multicoloured designs.* P 14.

1212	30 c. Type **126**		15	20
1213	80 c. Bicolor Cherub		35	40
1214	90 c. Copperbanded Butterflyfish (*vert*)		40	45
	a. Sheetlet. Nos. 1214/22		3·50	
1215	90 c. Forcepsfish (*vert*)		40	45
1216	90 c. Double-saddled Butterflyfish (*vert*)		40	45
1217	90 c. Blue Surgeonfish (*vert*)		40	45
1218	90 c. Orbiculate Batfish (*vert*)		40	45
1219	90 c. Undulated Triggerfish (*vert*)		40	45
1220	90 c. Rock Beauty (*vert*)		40	45
1221	90 c. Flamefish (*vert*)		40	45
1222	90 c. Queen Angelfish (*vert*)		40	45
1223	$1 Pyjama Cardinal Fish		45	50
	a. Sheetlet. Nos. 1223/31		4·00	
1224	$1 Wimplefish		45	50
1225	$1 Long-nosed Filefish		45	50
1226	$1 Oriental Sweetlips		45	50
1227	$1 Blue-spotted Boxfish		45	50
1228	$1 Blue-stripe Angelfish		45	50
1229	$1 Goldrim Tang		45	50
1230	$1 Blue Chromis		45	50
1231	$1 Common Clownfish		45	50
1232	$1.20, Silver Badgerfish		50	55
1233	$2 Asfur Angelfish		85	90
1212/33		*Set of 22*	9·25	10·50

MS1234 Two sheets. (a) 76×106 mm. $5 Red-faced Batfish (*vert*). (b) 106×76 mm. $5 Longhorned Cowfish (*vert*) 4·25 4·50

Nos. 1214/22 and 1223/31 were each printed together, *se-tenant*, in sheetlets of 9 with the backgrounds forming composite designs.

No. 1223 is inscribed "Pygama" in error.

(Des M. Friedman. Litho Questa)

1998 (19 Sept). *15th Anniv of Independence.* P 14.

1235 **127** $1 multicoloured .. 45 50

128 Stylised "50"

(Des M. Friedman. Litho Questa)

1998 (15 Oct). *50th Anniv of Organization of American States.* P 13½×14.

1236 **128** $1 chalky blue, light new blue and black 45 50

129 365 "California"

(Des F. Rivera. Litho Questa)

1998 (15 Oct). *Birth Centenary of Enzo Ferrari (car manu-facturer). T* **129** *and similar horiz designs. Multicoloured. P* 14.
1237	$2 Type **129**			85	90
	a. Sheetlet. Nos. 1237/9			2·50	
1238	$2 Pininfarina's P6			85	90
1239	$2 250 LM			85	90
1237/9			*Set of 3*	2·50	2·75

MS1240 104×70 mm. $5 212 "Export Spyder"
(91×34 *mm*). P 14×14½ .. .. 2·10 2·25
Nos. 1237/9 were printed together, *se-tenant*, in sheetlets of 3.

130 Scouts of Different Nationalities

131 Gandhi in South Africa, 1914

(Des J. Iskowitz. Litho Questa)

1998 (15 Oct). *19th World Scout Jamboree, Chile. T* **130** *and similar horiz designs. Multicoloured. P* 14.
1241	$3 Type **130**			1·25	1·40
	a. Sheetlet. Nos. 1241/3			3·75	
1242	$3 Scout and Gettysburg veterans, 1913			1·25	1·40
1243	$3 First black scout troop, Virginia, 1928			1·25	1·40
1241/3			*Set of 3*	3·75	4·00

Nos. 1241/3 were printed together, *se-tenant*, in sheetlets of 3 with enlarged illustrated top and right margins.

(Des M. Leboeuf. Litho Questa)

1998 (15 Oct). *50th Death Anniv of Mahatma Gandhi. T* **131** *and similar vert design. Multicoloured. P* 14.
1244	$1 Type **131**			45	50
	a. Sheetlet of 6			2·50	
1245	$1 Gandhi in Downing Street, London			45	50
	a. Sheetlet of 6			2·50	

Nos. 1244 and 1245 were each printed together, *se-tenant*, in sheetlets of 6.

132 Panavia Tornado F3

133 Princess Diana

(Des D. Miller. Litho Questa)

1998 (15 Oct). *80th Anniv of Royal Air Force. T* **132** *and similar horiz designs. Multicoloured. P* 14.
1246	$2 Type **132**			85	90
	a. Sheetlet. Nos. 1246/9			3·25	
1247	$2 Panavia Tornado F3 firing Skyflash missile			85	90
1248	$2 Tristar Mk1 Tanker refuelling Tornado GR1			85	90
1249	$2 Panavia Tornado GR1 firing AIM-9L missile			85	90
1246/9			*Set of 4*	3·25	3·50

MS1250 Two sheets, each 91×68 mm. (a) $5 Bristol F2B Fighter and two falcons (birds). (b) $5 Wessex helicopter and EF-2000 Eurofighter
Set of 2 sheets 4·25 4·50
Nos. 1246/9 were printed together, *se-tenant*, in sheetlets of 4 with enlarged illustrated margins.

(Des G. Eichorn. Litho Questa)

1998 (15 Oct). *1st Death Anniv of Diana, Princess of Wales. P* 14½ .
1251	**133**	$1 multicoloured		45	50
		a. Sheetlet of 6		2·50	

No. 1251 was printed in sheetlets of 6 with enlarged illustrated margins.

134 Kitten and Santa Claus Decoration

(Des E. Moreiro. Litho B.D.T.)

1998 (24 Nov). *Christmas. T* **134** *and similar multicoloured designs. P* 14.
1252	25 c. Type **134**			10	15
1253	60 c. Kitten playing with bauble			25	30
1254	80 c. Kitten in Christmas stocking (*vert*)			35	40
1255	90 c. Fox Terrier puppy and presents			40	45
1256	$1 Angel with swallows			45	50
1257	$3 Boy wearing Santa hat (*vert*)			1·25	1·40
1252/7			*Set of 6*	2·75	3·00

MS1258 Two sheets. (a) 71×102 mm. $5 Two dogs. (b) 102×71 mm. $5 Family with dog (*vert*)
Set of 2 sheets 4·25 4·50

135 Mickey Mouse

(Des Rosemary De Figlio. Litho Questa)

1998 (24 Dec). *70th Birthday of Mickey Mouse. T* **135** *and similar multicoloured designs showing Walt Disney cartoon characters playing basketball. P* 13½×14.
1259	$1 Type **135**			70	70
	a. Sheetlet. Nos. 1259/66			5·00	
1260	$1 Donald Duck bouncing ball			70	70
1261	$1 Minnie Mouse in green kit			70	70
1262	$1 Goofy wearing purple			70	70
1263	$1 Huey in green baseball cap			70	70
1264	$1 Goofy and Mickey			70	70
1265	$1 Mickey bouncing ball			70	70
1266	$1 Huey, Dewey and Louie			70	70
1267	$1 Mickey, in purple, shooting ball			70	70
	a. Sheetlet. Nos. 1267/74			5·00	
1268	$1 Goofy in yellow shorts and vest			70	70
1269	$1 Minnie in purple			70	70
1270	$1 Mickey in yellow vest and blue shorts			70	70
1271	$1 Minnie in yellow			70	70
1272	$1 Donald spinning ball on finger			70	70
1273	$1 Donald and Mickey			70	70
1274	$1 Dewey shooting for goal			70	70
1259/74			*Set of 16*	10·00	10·00

MS1775 Four sheets. (a) 127×105 mm. $5 Minnie wearing purple bow (*horiz*). (b) 105×127 mm. $5 Minnie wearing green bow (*horiz*). (c) 105×127 mm. $6 Mickey in yellow vest (*horiz*). (d) 105×127 mm. $6 Mickey in purple vest (*horiz*). P 14×13½ .. *Set of 4 sheets* 12·00 13·00
Nos. 1259/66 and 1267/74 were each printed together, *se-tenant*, in sheetlets of 8.

136 Black Silver Fox Rabbits

(Des Y. Lee. Litho Questa)

1999 (4 Jan). *Chinese New Year ("Year of the Rabbit"). T* **136** *and similar horiz designs. Multicoloured. P* 14.
1276	$1.60, Type **136**			70	75
	a. Sheetlet. Nos. 1276/9			2·75	
1277	$1.60, Dutch rabbits (brown with white "collar")			70	75
1278	$1.60, Dwarf rabbits (brown)			70	75
1279	$1.60, Netherlands Dwarf rabbits (white with brown markings)			70	75
1276/9			*Set of 4*	2·75	3·00

MS1280 106×76 mm. $5 Dwarf Albino Rabbit and young (57×46 *mm*) .. .. 2·10 2·25
Nos. 1276/9 were printed together, *se-tenant*, in sheetlets of 4.

137 Laurent Blanc (France)

(Des Joanna Singh. Litho B.D.T.)

1999 (18 Jan). *Leading Players of 1998 World Cup Football Championship, France. T* **137** *and similar horiz designs. Multicoloured. P* 13½ .
1281	$1 Type **137**			45	50
	a. Sheetlet. Nos. 1281/8			3·50	
1282	$1 Dennis Bergkamp (Holland)			45	50
1283	$1 Davor Sukor (Croatia)			45	50
1284	$1 Ronaldo (Brazil)			45	50
1285	$1 Didier Deschamps (France)			45	50
1286	$1 Patrick Kluivert (Holland)			45	50
1287	$1 Rivaldo (Brazil)			45	50
1288	$1 Zinedine Zidane (France)			45	50
1281/8			*Set of 8*	3·50	4·00

MS1289 121×96 mm. $5 Zinedine Zidane (France) .. .. 2·10 2·25
Nos. 1281/8 were printed together, *se-tenant*, in sheetlets of 8 with the backgrounds forming a composite design.

138 Kritosaurus

139 Emperor Haile Selassie of Ethiopia

(Des R. Company. Litho Questa)

1999 (22 Feb). *"Australia '99" World Stamp Exhibition, Melbourne. Prehistoric Animals. T* **138** *and similar horiz designs. Multicoloured. P* 14.
1290	30 c. Type **138**			15	20
1291	60 c. Oviraptor			25	30
1292	80 c. Eustreptospondylus			35	40
1293	$1.20, Tenontosaurus			50	55
1294	$1.20, Edmontosaurus			50	55
	a. Sheetlet. Nos. 1294/9			3·00	
1295	$1.20, Avimimus			50	55
1296	$1.20, Minmi			50	55
1297	$1.20, Segnosaurus			50	55
1298	$1.20, Kentrosaurus			50	55
1299	$1.20, Deinonychus			50	55
1300	$1.20, Saltasaurus			50	55
	a. Sheetlet. Nos. 1300/5			3·00	
1301	$1.20, Compsognathus			50	55
1302	$1.20, Hadrosaurus			50	55
1303	$1.20, Tuojiangosaurus			50	55
1304	$1.20, Euoplocephalus			50	55
1305	$1.20, Anchisaurus			50	55
1306	$2 Ouranosaurus			85	90
1307	$3 Muttaburrasaurus			1·25	1·40
1290/1307			*Set of 18*	9·25	10·00

MS1308 Two sheets, each 110×85 mm. (a) $5 Triceratops. (b) $5 Stegosaurus. *Set of 2 sheets* 4·25 4·50
Nos. 1294/9 and 1300/5 were each printed together, *se-tenant*, in sheetlets of 6 with the backgrounds forming composite designs.

(Des S. Stirnweis. Litho Questa)

1999 (8 Mar). *Millennium Series. Famous People of the Twentieth Century. World Leaders. T* **139** *and similar multicoloured designs. P* 14.
1309	90 c. Type **139**			40	45
	a. Sheetlet. Nos. 1309/16			3·00	
1310	90 c. Haile Selassie and Ethiopian warriors (56×41 *mm*)			40	45
1311	90 c. David Ben-Gurion, woman soldier and ancient Jewish prophet (56×41 *mm*)			40	45
1312	90 c. David Ben-Gurion (Prime Minister of Israel)			40	45
1313	90 c. President Franklin D. Roosevelt of U.S.A. and Mrs. Roosevelt			40	45
1314	90 c. Franklin and Eleanor Roosevelt campaigning (56×41 *mm*)			40	45
1315	90 c. Mao Tse-tung and the Long March, 1934 (56×41 *mm*)			40	45
1316	90 c. Poster of Mao Tse-tung (founder of People's Republic of China)			40	45
1309/16			*Set of 8*	3·00	3·50

MS1317 Two sheets. (a) 76×105 mm. $5 President Nelson Mandela of South Africa. (b) 105×76 mm. $5 Mahatma Gandhi (leader of Indian Independence movement) *Set of 2 sheets* 4·25 4·50
Nos. 1309/16 were printed together, *se-tenant*, in sheetlets of 8 with enlarged illustrated margins.

140 Malachite Kingfisher

141 *Phaius* hybrid

(Des R. Sauber. Litho B.D.T.)

1999 (10 May). *Birds. T* **140** *and similar multicoloured designs. P* 14.
1318	$1.60, Type **140**			70	75
	a. Sheetlet. Nos. 1318/23			4·00	
1319	$1.60, Lilac-breasted Roller			70	75
1320	$1.60, Swallow-tailed Bee Eater			70	75
1321	$1.60, Jay			70	75
1322	$1.60, Black-collared Apalis			70	75
1323	$1.60, Grey-backed Camaroptera			70	75
1324	$1.60, Yellow Warbler			70	75
	a. Sheetlet. Nos. 1324/9			4·00	
1325	$1.60, Common Yellowthroat			70	75
1326	$1.60, Painted Bunting			70	75

1327	$1.60, Belted Kingfisher	.. ..	70	75
1328	$1.60, American Kestrel	.. ..	70	75
1329	$1.60, Northern Oriole	.. ..	70	75
1318/29		*Set of 12*	8·00	9·00

MS1330 Two sheets, each 76×106 mm. (a) $5 Bananaquit. (b) $5 Groundscraper Thrush (*vert*)

	Set of 2 sheets	4·25	4·50

Nos. 1318/23 and 1324/9 were each printed together, *se-tenant*, in sheetlets of 6 stamps with enlarged illustrated margins.

(Des E. Moreino. Litho B.D.T.)

1999 (15 June). *Orchids. T* **141** *and similar multicoloured designs.* P 14.

1331	20 c. Type **141**	.. ..	10	10
1332	25 c. *Cuitlauzina pendula*	.. ..	10	15
1333	50 c. *Bletilla striata*	.. ..	20	25
1334	80 c. *Cymbidium* "Showgirl"	..	35	40
1335	$1 *Cattleya intermedia*	..	45	50
	a. Sheetlet. Nos. 1335/42		3·50	
1336	$1 *Cattleya* "Sophia Martin"	..	45	50
1337	$1 *Phalaenopsis* "Little Hal"	..	45	50
1338	$1 *Laeliocattleya alisal* "Rodeo"		45	50
1339	$1 *Laelia lucasiana fournieri*	..	45	50
1340	$1 *Cymbidium* "Red Beauty"	..	45	50
1341	$1 *Sobralia* sp.	.. ..	45	50
1342	$1 *Promenaea xanthina*	..	45	50
1343	$1 *Cattleya pumpernickel*	..	45	50
	a. Sheetlet. Nos. 1343/50		3·50	
1344	$1 *Odontocidium artur elle*	..	45	50
1345	$1 *Neostylis lou sneary*	..	45	50
1346	$1 *Phalaenopsis aphrodite*	..	45	50
1347	$1 *Arkundina graminieolia*	..	45	50
1348	$1 *Cymbidium* "Hunter's Point"		45	50
1349	$1 *Rhynchostylis coelestis*	..	45	50
1350	$1 *Cymbidium* "Elf's Castle"	..	45	50
1351	$1.60, *Zygopetalum crinitium* (*horiz*)		70	75
1352	$3 *Dendrobium nobile* (*horiz*)	..	1·25	1·40
1331/52		*Set of 22*	9·50	11·00

MS1353 Two sheets, each 106×81 mm. (a) $5 *Spathoglottis plicata* (*horiz*). (b) $5 *Arethusa bulbosa* .. .. .. *Set of 2 sheets* 4·25 4·50

Nos. 1335/42 and 1343/50 were each printed together, *se-tenant*, in sheetlets of 8.

142 Miss Sophie Rhys-Jones and Prince Edward

143 Steelband

(Des J. Iskowitz. Litho Questa)

1999 (19 June). *Royal Wedding. T* **142** *and similar multicoloured designs.* P 14½×14.

1354	$2 Type **142**	.. ..	85	90
	a. Sheetlet. Nos. 1354/7	..	3·25	
1355	$2 Miss Sophie Rhys-Jones at Ascot	..	85	90
1356	$2 Miss Sophie Rhys-Jones smiling	..	85	90
1357	$2 Prince Edward smiling	..	85	90
1358	$2 Miss Sophie Rhys-Jones wearing black and white checked jacket	..	85	90
	a. Sheetlet. Nos. 1358/61	..	3·25	
1359	$2 Prince Edward and Miss Sophie Rhys-Jones wearing sunglasses		85	90
1360	$2 Miss Sophie Rhys-Jones wearing black hat and jacket	..	85	90
1361	$2 Prince Edward wearing red-striped tie		85	90
1354/61		*Set of 8*	6·50	7·00

MS1362 Two sheets, each 83×66 mm. (a) $5 Prince Edward and Miss Sophie Rhys-Jones smiling (*horiz*). (b) $5 Prince Edward kissing Miss Sophie Rhys-Jones (*horiz*). P 14×14½

	Set of 2 sheets	4·25	4·50

Nos. 1354/7 and 1358/61 were each printed together, *se-tenant*, in sheetlets of 4.

(Des R. Sauber. Litho Questa)

1999 (1 July). *"iBRA '99" International Stamp Exhibition, Nuremberg. Horiz designs as T* **262** *of Lesotho. Multicoloured.* P 14.

1363	30 c. *Beuth* (railway locomotive) and Baden 1851 1 k. stamp		15	20
1364	80 c. *Beuth* and Brunswick 1852 1 sgr. stamp		35	40
1365	90 c. *Kruzenshstern* (cadet barque) and Bergedorf 1861 ½ s. and 1 s. stamps		40	45
1366	$1 *Kruzenshstern* and Bremen 1855 3 gr. stamp	..	45	50
1363/6		*Set of 4*	1·25	1·50

MS1367 134×90 mm. $5 1912 First Bavarian air flight label. P 14×14½ .. .. .. 2·10 2·25

(Des R. Sauber. Litho Questa)

1999 (1 July). *150th Death Anniv of Katsushika Hokusai (Japanese artist). Multicoloured designs as T* **263** *of Lesotho, but vert.* P 13½×14.

1368	$1 "Women returning Home at Sunset" (women by lake)		45	50
	a. Sheetlet. Nos. 1368/73		2·50	
1369	$1 "Blind Man" (without beard)	..	45	50
1370	$1 "Women returning Home at Sunset" (women descending hill)		45	50
1371	$1 "Young Man on a White Horse"	..	45	50
1372	$1 "Blind Man" (with beard)	..	45	50
1373	$1 "Peasant crossing a Bridge"	..	45	50

1374	$1.60, "Poppies" (one flower)	..	70	75
	a. Sheetlet. Nos. 1374/9	..	4·00	
1375	$1.60, "Blind Man" (with beard)	..	70	75
1376	$1.60, "Poppies" (two flowers)	..	70	75
1377	$1.60, "Abe No Nakamaro gazing at the Moon from a Terrace"		70	75
1378	$1.60, "Blind Man" (without beard)	..	70	75
1379	$1.60, "Cranes on a Snowy Pine"	..	70	75
1368/79		*Set of 12*	6·50	7·50

MS1380 Two sheets, each 74×103 mm. (a) $5 "Carp in a Waterfall". (b) $5 "Rider in the Snow"

	Set of 2 sheets	4·25	4·50

Nos. 1368/73 and 1374/9 were each printed together, *se-tenant*, in sheetlets of 6.

(Des B. Pevsner. Litho Questa)

1999 (1 July). *"PhilexFrance '99" International Stamp Exhibition, Paris. Two sheets, each* 106×81 *mm, containing horiz designs as T* **372** *of Maldive Islands. Multicoloured.* P 14×13½.

MS1381 (a) $5 First Class carriage, 1837. (b) $5 "141.R" Mixed Traffic steam locomotive

	Set of 2 sheets	4·25	4·50

(Litho B.D.T.)

1999 (1 July). *25th Culturama Festival. T* **143** *and similar horiz designs. Multicoloured.* P 14.

1382	30 c. Type **143**	.. ..	15	20
1383	80 c. Clowns	.. ..	35	40
1384	$1.80, Masqueraders with band	..	80	85
1385	$5 Local string band	..	2·10	2·25
1382/5		*Set of 4*	3·25	3·50

(Litho Questa)

1999 (4 Aug). *"Queen Elizabeth the Queen Mother's Century". Vert designs as T* **267** *of Lesotho.* P 14.

1386	$2 black and gold	..	85	90
	a. Sheetlet. Nos. 1386/9	..	3·25	
1387	$2 multicoloured	..	85	90
1388	$2 black and gold	..	85	90
1389	$2 multicoloured	..	85	90
1386/9		*Set of 4*	3·25	3·50

MS1390 153×157 mm. $6 multicoloured .. 2·50 2·75

Designs: (As *Type* **267** *of Lesotho*)—No. 1386, Lady Elizabeth Bowes-Lyon on Wedding Day, 1923; No. 1387, Duchess of York with Princess Elizabeth, 1926; No. 1388, King George VI and Queen Elizabeth during Second World War; No. 1389, Queen Mother in 1983. (37×49 *mm*)—No. **MS**1390, Queen Mother in 1957.

Nos. 1386/9 were printed together, *se-tenant*, as a sheetlet of 4 stamps and central label with inscribed and embossed margins. No. **MS**1390 also shows the Royal Arms embossed in gold.

144 "Adoration of the Magi" (Dürer)

145 Flowers forming Top of Head

(Litho Questa)

1999 (12 Nov). *Christmas. Religious Paintings. T* **144** *and similar multicoloured designs.* P 14.

1391	30 c. Type **144**	..	15	20
1392	90 c. "Canigiani Holy Family" (Raphael)		40	45
1393	$1.20, "The Nativity" (Dürer)	..	50	55
1394	$1.80, "Madonna and Child surrounded by Angels" (Rubens)		80	85
1395	$3 "Madonna and Child surrounded by Saints" (Rubens)	..	1·25	1·40
1391/5		*Set of 5*	3·00	3·25

MS1396 76×106 mm. $5 "Madonna and Child by a Window" (Dürer) (*horiz*) .. .. 2·10 2·25

(Des R. Silvers. Litho Questa)

1999 (31 Dec). *Faces of the Millennium: Diana, Princess of Wales. T* **145** *and similar vert designs showing collage of miniature flower photographs. Multicoloured.* P 13½×14.

1397	$1 Type **145** (face value at left)	..	45	50
	a. Sheetlet. Nos. 1397/1404	..	3·50	
1398	$1 Top of head (face value at right)	..	45	50
1399	$1 Ear (face value at left)	..	45	50
1400	$1 Eye and temple (face value at right)	..	45	50
1401	$1 Cheek (face value at left)	..	45	50
1402	$1 Cheek (face value at right)	..	45	50
1403	$1 Blue background (face value at left)	..	45	50
1404	$1 Chin (face value at right)	..	45	50
1397/1404		*Set of 8*	3·50	4·00

Nos. 1397/1404 were printed together, *se-tenant*, in sheetlets of 8 with the stamps arranged in two vertical columns separated by a gutter also containing miniature photographs. When viewed as a whole, the sheetlet forms a portrait of Diana, Princess of Wales.

(Des Spotlight Designs. Litho Cartor)

2000 (4 Jan). *New Millennium. People and Events of Eighteenth Century* (1700–49). *Multicoloured designs as T* **268** *of Lesotho.* P 12½.

1405	30 c. Jonathan Swift (*Gulliver's Travels*, 1726)		15	20
	a. Sheetlet. Nos. 1405/21		2·50	
1406	30 c. Emperor Kangxi of China		15	20
1407	30 c. Bartolommeo Cristofori (invention of piano, 1709)		15	20
1408	30 c. Captain William Kidd hanging on gibbet, 1701		15	20
1409	30 c. William Herschel (astronomer)		15	20
1410	30 c. King George I of Great Britain, 1714		15	20
1411	30 c. Peter the Great of Russia (trade treaty with China, 1722)		15	20
1412	30 c. "Death" (bubonic plague in Austria and Germany, 1711)		15	20
1413	30 c. "Standing Woman" (Kaigetsudo Dohan (Japanese artist)		15	20
1414	30 c. Queen Anne of England, 1707		15	20
1415	30 c. Anders Celcius (invention of centigrade thermometer, 1742)		15	20
1416	30 c. Vitus Bering (discovery of Alaska and Aleutian Islands, 1741)		15	20
1417	30 c. Edmund Halley (calculation of Halley's Comet, 1705)		15	20
1418	30 c. John Wesley (founder of Methodist Church, 1729)		15	20
1419	30 c. Sir Isaac Newton (publication of *Optick Treatise*, 1704)		15	20
1420	30 c. Queen Anne (Act of Union between England and Scotland, 1707) (59×39 *mm*)		15	20
1421	30 c. Johann Sebastian Bach (composition of "klavier", 1722)		15	20
1405/21		*Set of 17*	2·50	3·25

Nos. 1405/21 were printed together, *se-tenant*, in sheetlets of 17 including a central label (59×39 mm) and inscribed left margin.

No. 1417 is inscribed "cometis" in error.

146 Boris Yeltsin (President of Russian Federation, 1991)

147 Dragon

(Des Spotlight Designs. Litho Cartor)

2000 (4 Jan). *New Millennium. People and Events of Twentieth Century* (1990–99). *T* **146** *and similar multicoloured designs.* P 12½.

1422	50 c. Type **146**	.. ..	20	25
	a. Sheetlet. Nos. 1422/38		3·25	
1423	50 c. American soldiers and burning oil wells (Gulf War, 1991)		20	25
1424	50 c. Soldiers (Bosnian Civil War, 1992) ..		20	25
1425	50 c. Pres. Clinton, Yitzchak Rabin and Yasser Arafat, (Oslo Accords, 1993)		20	25
1426	50 c. Prime Ministers John Major and Albert Reynolds (Joint Declaration on Northern Ireland, 1993)		20	25
1427	50 c. Frederik de Klerk and Nelson Mandela (end of Apartheid, South Africa, 1994)		20	25
1428	50 c. Cal Ripkin (record number of consecutive baseball games, 1995)		20	25
1429	50 c. Kobe from air (earthquake, 1995)		20	25
1430	50 c. Mummified Inca girl preserved in ice, 1995		20	25
1431	50 c. NASA's *Sojourner* on Mars, 1997 ..		20	25
1432	50 c. Dr. Ian Wilmat and cloned sheep, 1997..		20	25
1433	50 c. Death of Princess Diana, 1997		20	25
1434	50 c. Fireworks over Hong Kong on its return to China, 1997		20	25
1435	50 c. Mother with septuplets, 1998		20	25
1436	50 c. Guggenheim Museum, Bilbao, 1998		20	25
1437	50 c. "2000" and solar eclipse, 1999 (59×39 *mm*)		20	25
1438	50 c. Pres. Clinton (impeachment in 1999)		20	25
1422/38		*Set of 17*	3·25	4·25

Nos. 1422/38 were printed together, *se-tenant*, in sheetlets of 17 including a central label (59×39 mm) and inscribed left margin.

No. 1422 incorrectly identifies his office as "Prime Minister".

(Des Y. Lee. Litho Questa)

2000 (5 Feb). *Chinese New Year ("Year of the Dragon"). T* **147** *and similar multicoloured designs.* P 14.

1439	$1.60, Type **147**	..	70	75
	a. Sheetlet. Nos. 1439/42		2·75	
1440	$1.60, Dragon with open claws (face value bottom left)		70	75
1441	$1.60, Dragon holding sphere (face value bottom right)		70	75
1442	$1.60, Dragon looking up (face value bottom left)		70	75
1439/42		*Set of 4*	2·75	3·00

MS1443 76×106 mm. $5 Dragon (37×50 *mm*). P 13½×14 .. .. 2·10 2·25

Nos. 1439/42 were printed together, *se-tenant*, in sheetlets of 4.

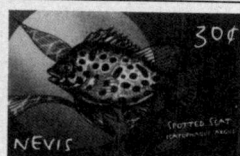

148 Spotted Scat

(Des D. Burkhart. Litho Walsall)

2000 (27 Mar). *Tropical Fish. T* **148** *and similar horiz designs showing fish in spotlight. Multicoloured. P* 14.

1444	30 c. Type **148**		15	20
1445	80 c. Delta Topsail Platy ("Platy Variatus")		35	40
1446	90 c. Emerald Betta		40	45
1447	$1 Sail-finned Tang		45	50
	a. Sheetlet. Nos. 1447/54		3·50	
1448	$1 Black-capped Basslet ("Black-capped Gramma")		45	50
1449	$1 Sail-finned Snapper ("Majestic Snapper")		45	50
1450	$1 Purple Fire Goby		45	50
1451	$1 Clown Triggerfish		45	50
1452	$1 Forceps Butterflyfish ("Yellow Long-nose")		45	50
1453	$1 Clown Wrasse		45	50
1454	$1 Yellow-headed Jawfish		45	50
1455	$1 Oriental Sweetlips		45	50
	a. Sheetlet. Nos. 1455/62		3·50	
1456	$1 Royal Gramma		45	50
1457	$1 Thread-finned Butterflyfish		45	50
1458	$1 Yellow Tang		45	50
1459	$1 Bicoloured Angelfish		45	50
1460	$1 Catalina Goby		45	50
1461	$1 Striped Mimic Blenny ("False Cleanerfish")		45	50
1462	$1 Powder-blue Surgeonfish		45	50
1463	$4 Long-horned Cowfish		1·75	1·90
1444/63		*Set of* 20	9·50	10·50

MS1464 Two sheets, each 97×68 mm. (a) $5 Clown Killifish; (b) $5 Twin-spotted Wrasse ("Clown Coris") .. *Set of* 2 *sheets* 4·25 4·50
Nos. 1447/54 and 1455/62 were each printed together, *se-tenant*, in sheetlets of 8 with the backgrounds forming composite designs.

STAMP BOOKLETS

1980 (8 Oct). *Boats. Multicoloured cover,* 175×95 *mm. Stitched.*
SB1 $12.30, booklet containing 55 c. (No. 53) in block of 6 and $3 in pane of 3 (No. 54ab) .. 1·60

1981 (19 Nov). *Royal Wedding. Multicoloured cover,* 105×65 *mm, showing The Royal Charlotte. Stitched.*
SB2 $8.40, booklet containing eight 55 c. in panes of 4 (No. 79a) and $2 in pane of 2 (No. 80a) .. 2·00

1986 (23 July). *Royal Wedding. Gold* (No. SB3) *or silver* (No. SB4) *on orange-red covers,* 152×80 *mm. Stapled.*
SB3 $7.20, booklet (Westminster Abbey) containing twelve 60 c. (Nos. 406/7) in blocks of 4 .. 3·00
SB4 $10.40, booklet (State Coach) containing 60 c. and $2 (Nos. 406/9, but imperforate) in blocks of 4 3·50

OFFICIAL STAMPS

1980 (4 July*). *Nos.* 40/9 *additionally optd with Type* O **1** *of St. Christopher, Nevis and Anguilla.*

O 1	15 c. Sugar cane harvesting		10	10
O 2	25 c. Crafthouse (craft centre)		10	10
	a. "OFFICIAL" opt double		35·00	
	b. "OFFICIAL" opt omitted (in horiz pair with normal)		75·00	
	c. Optd on No. 41a		3·50	7·00
O 3	30 c. *Europa* (liner)		10	10
O 4	40 c. Lobster and sea crab		15	15
O 5	45 c. Royal St. Kitts Hotel and golf course		20	20
	a. Opt inverted		13·00	
O 6	50 c. Pinney's Beach, Nevis		15	20
	a. Opt inverted		55·00	
O 7	55 c. New runway at Golden Rock		15	20
	a. Opt double		12·00	
O 8	$1 Picking cotton		15	25
O 9	$5 Brewery		45	55
	a. Opt inverted		70·00	
O10	$10 Pineapples and peanuts		70	90
O1/10		*Set of* 10	2·00	2·50

*Earliest known date of use.

1981 (Mar). *Nos.* 60A/71A *optd with Type* O **1** *of St. Kitts.*

O11	15 c. New River Mill		10	10
O12	20 c. Nelson Museum		10	10
O13	25 c. St. James' Parish Church		10	15
O14	30 c. Nevis Lane		15	15
O15	40 c. Zetland Plantation		15	20
O16	45 c. Nisbet Plantation		20	25
O17	50 c. Pinney's Beach		20	25
O18	55 c. Eva Wilkin's Studio		25	30
O19	$1 Nevis at dawn		30	30
O20	$2.50, Ruins of Fort Charles		40	50
O21	$5 Old Bath House		50	65
O22	$10 Beach at Nisbet's		80	1·00
O11/22		*Set of* 12	2·75	3·50

1983 (2 Feb). *Nos.* 72/7 *optd with Type* O **1** *of St. Kitts* (55 c.) *or surch also* (*others*).

O23	45 c. on $2 *Royal Sovereign* (New Blue)		10	15
	aw. Wmk inverted		10·00	
	b. Sheetlet. No. O23×6 and No. O24		70	
	bw. Wmk inverted		80·00	
	c. Surch inverted		6·00	
	d. Surch inverted (horiz pair)		30·00	
	e. Albino surch		6·50	
	ea. Albino surch inverted			
	f. Horiz pair, one without surch			
	g. Deep ultramarine surch		40	50
	gc. Surch inverted		5·00	
	gd. Surch inverted (horiz pair)		12·00	
	h. Black surch		40·00	
O24	45 c. on $2 Prince Charles and Lady Diana Spencer (New Blue)		20	25
	aw. Wmk inverted		35·00	
	c. Surch inverted		20·00	
	e. Albino surch		15·00	
	g. Deep ultramarine surch		40	50
	gc. Surch inverted		12·00	
	h. Black surch		£110	
O25	55 c. *Royal Caroline* (New Blue)		10	15
	b. Sheetlet. No. O25×6 and No. O26		75	
	e. Albino opt		7·00	
	ea. Albino opt inverted		10·00	
	eb. Albino opt inverted (horiz pair)		12·00	
	g. Deep ultramarine opt		75	
	gc. Opt inverted		5·00	
	gd. Opt inverted (horiz pair)		15·00	
	ge. Opt double		14·00	
	h. Black opt		40·00	
O26	55 c. Prince Charles and Lady Diana Spencer (New Blue)		25	25
	e. Albino opt		15·00	
	ea. Albino opt inverted		20·00	
	g. Deep ultramarine opt		1·00	
	gc. Opt inverted		15·00	
	gd. Opt double		27·00	
	h. Black opt		£110	
O27	$1.10 on $5 *Britannia* (Blk.)		20	25
	aw. Wmk inverted		10·00	
	b. Sheetlet. No. O27×6 and No. O28		1·60	
	bw. Wmk inverted		80·00	
	e. Albino surch		7·50	
	f. Decimal point omitted from surch (R. 3/2)		2·50	
	g. Deep ultramarine surch		6·00	
	gc. Surch inverted		6·50	
	gd. Surch inverted (horiz pair)		32·00	
	gf. Decimal point omitted from surch (R. 3/2)		3·00	

O28	$1.10 on $5 Prince Charles and Lady Diana Spencer (Blk.)		55	60
	aw. Wmk inverted		35·00	
	e. Albino surch		22·00	
	g. Deep ultramarine surch		35·00	
	gc. Surch inverted		38·00	
O23/8		*Set of* 6	1·25	1·40

Nos. O23d, O23gd, O25eb, O25gd and O27gd show the surcharge or overprint intended for the large design inverted and struck across a horizontal pair of the smaller. Nos. O24c, O24gc, O26ea, O26gc and O28gc each show two inverted surcharges intended for a horizontal pair of the smaller design.

1985 (2 Jan). *Nos.* 187/98 *optd with Type* O **1** *of St. Kitts.*

O29	15 c. Flamboyant		20	20
O30	20 c. Eyelash Orchid		30	30
O31	30 c. Bougainvillea		30	40
O32	40 c. Hibiscus sp.		30	40
O33	50 c. Night-blooming Cereus		35	40
O34	55 c. Yellow Mahoe		35	45
O35	60 c. Spider-lily		40	50
O36	75 c. Scarlet Cordia		45	55
O37	$1 Shell-ginger		60	60
O38	$3 Blue Petrea		1·25	1·75
O39	$5 Coral Hibiscus		2·00	2·25
O40	$10 Passion Flower		2·00	2·25
O29/40		*Set of* 12	8·50	9·00

1993 (1 Mar). *Nos.* 578B/91B *optd with Type* O **1** *of St. Kitts.*

O41	5 c. Type **63**		30	40
O42	10 c. *Historis odius*		30	40
O43	15 c. *Marpesia corinna*		30	30
O44	20 c. *Anartia amathea*		30	30
O45	25 c. *Junonia evarete*		30	20
O46	40 c. *Heliconius charithonia*		40	30
O47	50 c. *Marpesia petreus*		50	30
O48	75 c. *Heliconius doris*		65	40
O49	80 c. *Dione juno*		65	40
O50	$1 *Hypolimnas misippus*		75	60
O51	$3 *Danaus plexippus*		1·75	2·00
O52	$5 *Heliconius sara*		2·25	3·00
O53	$10 *Tithorea harmonia*		4·50	5·50
O54	$20 *Dryas julia*		9·25	10·00
O41/54		*Set of* 14	20·00	21·00

Imprint date: "1992", Nos. O41/54.

OFFICIAL

(O **1**)

1999 (22 Feb). *Nos.* 1166/77 *optd with Type* O **1**.

O55	25 c. Guava		10	15
O56	30 c. Papaya		15	20
O57	50 c. Mango		20	25
O58	60 c. Golden Apple		25	30
O59	80 c. Pineapple		35	40
O60	90 c. Watermelon		40	45
O61	$1 Bananas		45	50
O62	$1.80, Orange		80	85
O63	$3 Honeydew		1·25	1·40
O64	$5 Cantaloupe		2·10	2·25
O65	$10 Pomegranate		4·25	4·50
O66	$20 Cashew		8·75	9·00
O55/66		*Set of* 12	19·00	20·00

St. Lucia

Although a branch office of the British G.P.O. was not opened at Castries, the island capital, until 1844 some form of postal arrangements for overseas mails existed from at least 1841 when the issue of a Ship Letter handstamp is recorded.

The stamps of Great Britain were used on the island from May 1858 until the end of April 1860 when the local authorities assumed responsibility for the postal service. No. CC1 was again used on overseas mail between 1 May and the introduction of St. Lucia stamps in December 1860.

CASTRIES
CROWN-CIRCLE HANDSTAMPS

CC1

CC1 CC1 ST. LUCIA (R.) (1.5.1844)   *Price on cover* £750
No. CC1 was utilised, struck in black, during a shortage of 1d. stamps in late April and early May 1904. *Price on cover* £325.

Stamps of GREAT BRITAIN *cancelled* "A 11" *as Type Z* **1** *of Jamaica.*

1858 *to* **1860**
Z1	1d. rose-red (1857), *perf* 14			£1000
Z2	2d. blue (1855)			
Z3	4d. rose (1857)			£375
Z4	6d. lilac (1856)			£200
Z5	1s. green (1856)			£1000

PRICES FOR STAMPS ON COVER TO 1945
Nos. 1/3	*from* × 60
Nos. 5/8	*from* × 30
Nos. 9/10	†
Nos. 11/24	*from* × 15
Nos. 25/30	*from* × 10
Nos. 31/6	*from* × 6
Nos. 39/42	*from* × 10
Nos. 43/50	*from* × 15
Nos. 51/2	—
Nos. 53/62	*from* × 6
No. 63	*from* × 15
Nos. 64/75	*from* × 4
Nos. 76/7	*from* × 3
Nos. 78/88	*from* × 3
No. 89	*from* × 4
No. 90	*from* × 20
Nos. 91/112	*from* × 3
Nos. 113/24	*from* × 2
Nos. 125/7	*from* × 10
Nos. 128/41	*from* × 2
Nos. D1/6	*from* × 10
Nos. F1/28	—

CROWN COLONY

PERKINS BACON "CANCELLED". For notes on these handstamps, showing "CANCELLED" between horizontal bars forming an oval, see Catalogue Introduction.

Half penny

1 (1)   **(2)**

(Recess P.B.)

1860 (18 Dec). *Wmk Small Star, W w* **2**. *P* 14 *to* 16.
1	1	(1d.) rose-red (H/S "CANCELLED" in oval £4000)	80·00	60·00
		a. Imperf vert (horiz pair)		£1800
		b. Double impression		£1800
2		(4d.) blue (H/S "CANCELLED" in oval £5000)	£200	£150
		a. Deep blue		
		b. Imperf vert (horiz pair)		
3		(6d.) green (H/S "CANCELLED" in oval £5000)	£250	£200
		a. Imperf vert (horiz pair)		
		b. Deep green	£300	£225

(Recess D.L.R.)

1863. *Wmk Crown CC. P* 12½.
5	1	(1d.) lake	55·00	80·00
		ax. Wmk reversed	—	80·00
		b. Brownish lake	75·00	75·00
		bx. Wmk reversed		
7		(4d.) indigo	90·00	£100
		x. Wmk reversed		
8		(6d.) emerald-green	£150	£150
		w. Wmk inverted		
		x. Wmk reversed	—	£150

Prepared for use, but not issued. Surch as T **2**
9	1	½d. on (6d.) emerald-green		55·00
		x. Wmk reversed		
10		6d. on (4d.) indigo		£900

All three values exist imperforate from proof sheets.

1864 (19 Nov)–**76.** *Wmk Crown CC.* (*a*) *P* 12½.
11	1	(1d.) black	17·00	12·00
		a. Intense black	16·00	11·00
		ax. Wmk reversed		15·00
12		(4d.) yellow	£140	30·00
		b. Lemon-yellow	£1500	
		c. Chrome-yellow	£150	30·00
		d. Olive-yellow	£300	70·00
		w. Wmk inverted		
		x. Wmk reversed	£200	
		y. Wmk inverted and reversed		
13		(6d.) violet	90·00	28·00
		a. Mauve	£150	28·00
		b. Deep lilac	£100	32·00
		x. Wmk reversed	£100	
14		(1s.) brown-orange	£300	25·00
		b. Orange	£225	25·00
		c. Pale orange	£160	25·00
		ca. Imperf between (horiz pair)		
		x. Wmk reversed		

(*b*) *P* 14
15	1	(1d.) black (6.76)	19·00	15·00
		a. Imperf between (horiz pair)		
		x. Wmk reversed	—	15·00
16		(4d.) yellow (6.76)	75·00	18·00
		a. Olive-yellow	£200	80·00
		w. Wmk inverted		
		x. Wmk reversed		
17		(6d.) mauve (6.76)	75·00	30·00
		a. Pale lilac	75·00	18·00
		b. Violet	£190	60·00
		x. Wmk reversed		
18		(1s.) orange (10.76)	£200	22·00
		a. Deep orange	£130	16·00
		w. Wmk inverted		
		x. Wmk reversed	—	22·00

All four values exist imperforate from proof sheets.

HALFPENNY   **2½ PENCE**   5
(3)   **(4)**

1881 (Sept). *Surch with T* **3** *or* **4**. *Wmk Crown CC. P* 14.
23	1	½d. green	55·00	75·00
		x. Wmk reversed		
24		2½d. brown-red	26·00	19·00

The 1d. black is known surcharged "1d." in violet ink by hand, but there is no evidence that this was done officially.

1882–84. *Surch as T* **3**. *Wmk Crown CA.* (*a*) *P* 14
25	1	½d. green (1882)	15·00	23·00
26		1d. black (C.)	21·00	8·50
		a. Bisected (on cover)	†	
27		4d. yellow	£190	17·00
28		6d. violet	24·00	26·00
29		1s. orange	£250	£160

(*b*) *P* 12
30	1	4d. yellow	£250	28·00

Deep blue stamps, wmk Crown CA, perf 14 or 12, are fiscals from which the overprint "THREE PENCE—REVENUE", or "REVENUE", has been fraudulently removed.

(Typo D.L.R.)

1883 (6 July)–**86.** *Wmk Crown CA. Die* I. *P* 14.
31	5	½d. dull green	6·00	3·75
		a. Top left triangle detached		
32		1d. carmine-rose	32·00	8·50
33		2½d. blue	28·00	2·00
		a. Top left triangle detached	£325	75·00
34		4d. brown (1885)	25·00	80
		a. Top left triangle detached	£325	60·00
35		6d. lilac (1886)	£250	£200
36		1s. orange-brown (1885)	£350	£140

The 4d. and 6d. exist imperforate from proof sheets.

For illustration of "top left triangle detached" variety on this and the following issue see above No. 6 of Montserrat.

1886–87. *Wmk Crown CA. Die* I. *P* 14.
39	5	1d. dull mauve	4·00	6·00
		a. Top left triangle detached	85·00	
40		3d. dull mauve and green	85·00	16·00
41		6d. dull mauve and blue (1887)	3·50	8·00
		a. Top left triangle detached	95·00	
42		1s. dull mauve and red (1887)	90·00	19·00
		a. Top left triangle detached		
39/42			Set of 4	£160	45·00
39/42		Optd "Specimen"	Set of 4	£180	

The 1d. exists imperforate from proof sheets.

1891–98. *Wmk Crown CA. Die* II. *P* 14.
43	5	½d. dull green	1·75	90
44		1d. dull mauve	2·00	20
45		2d. ultramarine and orange (1898)	1·25	1·00
46		2½d. ultramarine	2·00	90
47		3d. dull mauve and green	3·50	5·50
48		4d. brown	1·75	2·25
49		6d. dull mauve and blue	20·00	18·00
50		1s. dull mauve and red	3·50	5·00
51		5s. dull mauve and orange	40·00	£120
52		10s. dull mauve and black	75·00	£120
43/52			Set of 10	£130	£250
45, 51, 52	Optd "Specimen"		Set of 3	£120	

For description and illustration of differences between Die I and Die II see Introduction.

ONE HALF PENNY $\frac{1}{2}d$ **ONE PENNY**
(6)   **(7)**   **(8)**

N   N
Normal "N"   Thick "N"

Three types of T **8**
I. All letters "N" normal.
II. Thick diagonal stroke in first "N".
III. Thick diagonal stroke in second "N".

1891–92. (*a*) *Stamps of Die* I *surch.*
53	6	½d. on 3d. dull mauve and green	£100	65·00
		a. Small "A" in "HALF"	£250	£140
		b. Small "O" in "ONE"	£250	£140
		c. Top left triangle detached	£500	
54	7	½d. on half 6d. dull mauve and blue	16·00	3·25
		a. No fraction bar	£180	£120
		b. Surch sideways	£750	
		c. Surch double	£500	£500
		d. "2" in fraction omitted	£400	£450
		e. Thick "1" with sloping serif	£180	£110
		f. Surch triple	£850	
		g. Figure "1" used as fraction bar	£425	£250
55	8	1d. on 4d. brown (I) (12.91)	3·00	3·50
		a. Surch double	£180	
		b. Surch inverted	£700	£600
		c. Type II	23·00	20·00
		ca. Surch double	£325	
		cb. Surch inverted	—	£700
		d. Type III	22·00	20·00
		e. Top left triangle detached	£100	£100

(*b*) *Stamp of Die* II *surch*
56	6	½d. on 3d. dull mauve and green	55·00	21·00
		a. Surch double	£700	£600
		b. Surch inverted	£1700	£600
		c. Surch both sides	—	£650
		d. Small "O" in "ONE"	£140	90·00
		e. Small "A" in "HALF"	£140	90·00
		f. "ONE" misplaced ("O" over "H")	£140	90·00

9   10

(Typo D.L.R.)

1902–3. *Wmk Crown CA. P* 14.
58	9	½d. dull purple and green	2·25	1·50
59		1d. dull purple and carmine	4·00	45
60		2½d. dull purple and ultramarine	15·00	5·50
61	10	3d. dull purple and yellow	4·00	8·50
62		1s. green and black	10·00	21·00
58/62			Set of 5	32·00	32·00
58/62	Optd "Specimen"		Set of 5	£100	

11 The Pitons

(Recess D.L.R.)

1902 (15 Dec). *400th Anniv of Discovery by Columbus. Wmk Crown CC, sideways. P* 14
63	11	2d. green and brown	8·50	1·75
63	Optd "Specimen"			60·00	

This stamp was formerly thought to have been issued on 16 December but it has been seen on a postcard clearly postmarked 15 December.

1904–10. *Wmk Mult Crown CA. Chalk-surfaced paper* (*Nos.* 71, 73/5 *and* 77) *or ordinary paper* (*others*). *P* 14.
64	9	½d. dull purple and green	4·00	30
		a. Chalk-surfaced paper	2·50	95
65		½d. green (1907)	1·75	1·00
66		1d. dull purple and carmine	5·50	1·00
		a. Chalk-surfaced paper	2·00	1·00
67		1d. carmine (1907)	4·00	30
68		2½d. dull purple and ultramarine	9·50	1·25
		a. Chalk-surfaced paper	7·00	4·50
69		2½d. blue (1907)	3·75	1·75
70	10	3d. dull purple and yellow	3·75	3·00
71		3d. purple/yellow (1909)	2·25	12·00
72		6d. dull purple and violet (1905)	12·00	15·00
		a. Chalk-surfaced paper	17·00	20·00
		ab. Dull purple and bright purple (1907)	5·50	20·00
73		6d. dull purple (1910)	28·00	50·00
74		1s. green and black (1905)	27·00	20·00
75		1s. black/green (1909)	4·00	8·00
76		5s. green and carmine (1905)	55·00	£120
77		5s. green and red/yellow (1907)	55·00	70·00
64/77			Set of 14	£180	£300
65, 67, 69, 71/2, 72ab and 75/7 Optd "Specimen"			Set of 9	£180	

Examples of Nos. 71/7 are known with a forged Castries postmark dated "JA 21 09".

12   13   14

15   16

(Typo D.L.R.)

1912–21. *Die I. Wmk Mult Crown CA. Chalk-surfaced paper (3d. to 5s.). P 14.*

78	12	½d. deep green	..	70	40
		a. Yellow-green (1916)	..	65	30
79		1d. carmine-red	..	1·90	10
		a. Scarlet (1916)	..	3·00	10
		b. Rose-red	..	6·00	75
80	13	2d. grey	..	1·50	4·00
		a. Slate-grey (1916)	..	14·00	12·00
81	12	2½d. ultramarine	..	3·25	2·75
		a. Bright blue	..	1·75	2·75
		b. Deep bright blue (1916)	..	10·00	10·00
82	15	3d. purple/yellow	..	1·25	2·00
		b. Die II. On pale yellow (1921)	..	7·50	28·00
		bw. Wmk inverted			
83	14	4d. black and red/yellow	..	90	1·75
		a. White back (Optd S. £25)	..	70	1·50
84	15	6d. dull and bright purple	..	2·00	8·50
		a. Grey-purple and purple (1918)	..	16·00	16·00
85		1s. black/green	..	2·75	4·75
		a. On blue-green (olive back) (1918)	..	5·50	6·00
86		1s. orange-brown (1920)	..	8·00	45·00
87	16	2s. 6d. black and red/blue	..	22·00	29·00
88	15	5s. green and red/yellow	..	22·00	75·00
78/88			Set of 11	55·00	£150
78/88 Optd "Specimen"			Set of 11	£190	

WAR TAX   WAR TAX

(17)   (18)

1916 (June). *No. 79a optd locally with T 17.*

89	12	1d. scarlet	..	7·00	7·50
		a. Opt double	..	£375	£375
		b. Carmine-red	..	48·00	30·00

For the overprinting with Type 17 the top margin of the sheet was folded beneath the top row of stamps so that marginal examples from this row show an inverted albino impression of the overprint in the top margin.

1916 (Sept). *No. 79a optd in London with T 18.*

90	12	1d. scarlet (Optd S. £40)	..	30	30

1921–30. *Die II. Wmk Mult Script CA. Chalk-surfaced paper (3d. (No. 100) to 5s.). P 14.*

91	12	½d. green	..	30	30
92		1d. rose-carmine	..	7·50	12·00
93		1d. deep brown (1922)	..	90	15
94	14	1½d. dull carmine (1922)	..	50	2·00
95	13	2d. slate-grey	..	40	15
96	12	2½d. bright blue	..	3·25	2·75
97		2½d. orange (1925)	..	10·00	48·00
98		2½d. dull blue (1926)	..	3·25	2·50
99	15	3d. bright blue (1922)	..	4·50	15·00
		a. Dull blue (1924)	..	2·00	11·00
100		3d. purple/pale yellow (1926)	..	80	12·00
		a. Deep purple/pale yellow (1930)	..	10·00	12·00
101	14	4d. black and red/yellow (1924)	..	1·00	4·00
102	15	6d. grey-purple and purple	..	1·75	4·75
103		1s. orange-brown	..	1·75	3·25
104	16	2s. 6d. black and red/blue (1924)	..	17·00	26·00
105	15	5s. green and red/pale yellow (1923)	..	40·00	75·00
91/105			Set of 15	75·00	£180
91/105 Optd "Specimen"			Set of 15	£250	

1935 (6 May). *Silver Jubilee. As Nos. 114/17 of Jamaica, but ptd by D.L.R. P 13½×14.*

109		½d. black and green	..	15	40
		f. Diagonal line by turret	..	22·00	
110		2d. ultramarine and grey	..	45	55
		f. Diagonal line by turret	..	32·00	
111		2½d. brown and deep blue	..	90	85
		f. Diagonal line by turret	..	45·00	
		g. Dot to left of chapel	..	75·00	
112		1s. slate and purple	..	4·00	7·50
		h. Dot by flagstaff	..	£170	
109/12			Set of 4	5·00	8·50
109/12 Perf "Specimen"			Set of 4	55·00	

For illustrations of plate varieties see Omnibus section following Zimbabwe.

OMNIBUS ISSUES

Details, together with prices for complete sets, of the various Omnibus issues from the 1935 Silver Jubilee series to date are included in a special section following Zimbabwe at the end of Volume 2.

---

19 Port Castries   20 Columbus Square, Castries (inscr "COLOMBUS SQUARE" in error)

21 Ventine Falls   25 The Badge of the Colony

(Recess D.L.R.)

1936 (1 Mar–Apr). *T 19/21, 25 and similar designs. Wmk Mult Script CA. P 14 or 13 × 12 (1s. and 10s.).*

113	19	½d. black and bright green		30	45
		a. Perf 13 × 12 (8.4.36)		1·60	8·00
114	20	1d. black and brown		40	10
		a. Perf 13 × 12 (8.4.36)		2·25	2·50
115	21	1½d. black and scarlet		55	30
		a. Perf 12 × 13		5·50	1·75
116	19	2d. black and grey		40	15
117	20	2½d. black and blue		40	15
118	21	3d. black and dull green		1·25	70
119	19	4d. black and red-brown		30	1·00
120	20	6d. black and orange		85	1·00
121	—	1s. black and blue		1·25	2·00
122	—	2s. 6d. black and ultramarine		8·00	14·00
123	—	5s. black and violet		8·00	20·00
124	25	10s. black and carmine		42·00	65·00
113/124			Set of 12	55·00	95·00
113/24 Perf "Specimen"			Set of 12	£180	

Designs: *Vert (as T 21)*—2s. 6d. Inniskilling monument. *Horiz (as T 19)*—1s. Fort Rodney, Pigeon Island; 5s. Government House.

Examples of most values are known with a forged Castries postmark dated "1 MR 36".

1937 (12 May). *Coronation. As Nos. 118/20 of Jamaica, but ptd by B.W. P 11×11½.*

125		1d. violet	..	30	30
126		1½d. carmine	..	55	20
127		2½d. blue	..	55	50
125/7			Set of 3	1·25	90
125/7 Perf "Specimen"			Set of 3	55·00	

26 King George VI   27 Columbus Square

28 Government House   31 Device of St. Lucia

(Des E. Crafer (T 26), H. Fleury (5s.). Recess Waterlow (½d. to 3½d., 8d., 3s., 5s., £1), D.L.R. (6d., 1s.) and B.W. (2s., 10s.))

1938 (22 Sept)–48. *T 26/8, 31 and similar designs. Wmk Mult Script CA (sideways on 2s.).*

128	26	½d. green (p 14½ × 14)	..	75	10
		a. Perf 12½ (1943)		10	10
129		1d. violet (p 14½ × 14)		90	75
		a. Perf 12½ (1938)		10	15
129b		1d. scarlet (p 12½) (1947)		10	10
		c. Perf 14½×14 (1948)		10	10
130		1½d. scarlet (p 14½ × 14)		1·25	40
		a. Perf 12½ (1943)		30	70
131		2d. grey (p 14½ × 14)		90	1·25
		a. Perf 12½ (1943)		10	10
132		2½d. ultramarine (p 14½ × 14)		1·75	15
		a. Perf 12½ (1943)		10	10
132b		2½d. violet (p 12½) (1947)		30	10
133		3d. orange (p 14½ × 14)		15	10
		a. Perf 12½ (1943)		10	10
133b		3½d. ultramarine (p 12½) (1947)		30	15
134	27	6d. claret (p 13½)		3·00	50
		a. Carmine-lake (p 13½) (1945)		1·75	30
		b. Perf 12. Claret (1948)		1·00	70
134c	26	8d. brown (p 12½) (1946)		2·75	30
135	28	1s. brown (p 13½)		55	30
		a. Perf 12 (1948)		40	20
136	—	2s. blue and purple (p 12)		3·50	1·25
136a	26	3s. bright purple (p 12½) (1946)		8·00	2·25
137	—	5s. black and mauve (p 12½)		14·00	6·00

138	31	10s. black/yellow (p 12)	..	4·50	9·00
141	26	£1 sepia (p 12½) (1946)	..	11·00	8·00
128a/141			Set of 17	40·00	26·00
128/41 Perf "Specimen"			Set of 17	£300	

Designs: *Horiz (as T 28)*—2s. The Pitons; 5s. Lady Hawkins loading bananas.

1946 (8 Oct). *Victory. As Nos. 141/2 of Jamaica.*

142		1d. lilac	..	10	10
143		3½d. blue	..	10	10
142/3 Perf "Specimen"			Set of 2	50·00	

1948 (26 Nov). *Royal Silver Wedding. As Nos. 143/4 of Jamaica.*

144		1d. scarlet	..	15	10
145		£1 purple-brown	..	13·00	35·00

(New Currency. 100 cents = 1 West Indian, later Eastern Caribbean dollar)

32 King George VI   33 Device of St. Lucia

(Recess Waterlow (32), B.W. (33))

1949 (1 Oct)–50. *Value in cents or dollars. Wmk Mult Script CA. P 12½ (1 c. to 16 c.), 11 × 11½ (others).*

146	32	1 c. green	..	10	10
		a. Perf 14 (1949)		1·50	40
147		2 c. magenta		10	10
		a. Perf 14½ × 14 (1949)		1·50	1·00
148		3 c. scarlet		10	90
149		4 c. grey		10	10
		a. Perf 14½ × 14		† £5500	
150		5 c. violet		10	10
151		6 c. orange		15	90
152		7 c. ultramarine		1·50	1·75
153		12 c. claret		4·50	1·25
		a. Perf 14½ × 14 (1950)		£475	£350
154		16 c. brown		2·00	20
155	33	24 c. light blue		30	10
156		48 c. olive-green		1·50	95
157		$1.20, purple		2·25	7·00
158		$2.40, blue-green		3·00	17·00
159		$4.80, rose-carmine		6·00	18·00
146/159			Set of 14	19·00	42·00

Most examples of Nos. 146a and 147a were produced as coils, but a few sheets in these perforations were distributed and blocks of four are scarce.

1949 (10 Oct). *75th Anniv of U.P.U. As Nos. 145/8 of Jamaica.*

160		5 c. violet	..	20	20
161		6 c. orange		1·40	95
162		12 c. magenta		30	20
163		24 c. blue-green		65	20
160/3			Set of 4	2·25	1·40

1951 (16 Feb). *Inauguration of B.W.I. University College. As Nos. 149/50 of Jamaica.*

164		3 c. black and scarlet	..	45	50
165		12 c. black and deep carmine	..	55	50

34 Phoenix rising from Burning Buildings   NEW 1951 CONSTITUTION (35)

(Flames typo, rest recess B.W.)

1951 (19 June). *Reconstruction of Castries. Wmk Mult Script CA. P 13½ × 13.*

166	34	12 c. red and blue	..	15	70

1951 (25 Sept). *New Constitution. Nos. 147, 149/50 and 153 optd with T 35 by Waterlow. P 12½.*

167	32	2 c. magenta	..	15	50
168		4 c. grey	..	15	50
169		5 c. violet	..	15	30
170		12 c. claret	..	15	50
167/70			Set of 4	55	1·60

1953 (2 June). *Coronation. As No. 153 of Jamaica.*

171		3 c. black and scarlet	..	50	10

36 Queen Elizabeth II   37 Device of St. Lucia

(Recess Waterlow (T **36**), until 1960, then D.L.R. B.W. (T **37**))

1953 (28 Oct)–**63**. *Wmk Mult Script CA. P* 14½×14 (*T* **36**) or 11×11½ (*T* **37**))

172	**36**	1 c. green (1.4.54)	10	10
173		2 c. magenta	10	10
174		3 c. red (2.9.54)	10	10
175		4 c. slate (7.1.54)	10	10
176		5 c. violet (1.4.54)	10	10
		a. *Slate-violet* (19.2.63)	10·00	1·75
177		6 c. orange (2.9.54)	15	30
		a. *Brown-orange* (26.9.61)	9·00	50
178		8 c. lake (2.9.54)	30	10
179		10 c. ultramarine (2.9.54)	30	10
		a. *Blue* (14.8.62)	30	10
180		15 c. red-brown (2.9.54)	30	10
		a. *Brown* (30.10.57)	30	10
181	**37**	25 c. deep turquoise-blue (2.9.54)	30	10
182		50 c. deep olive-green (2.9.54)	4·50	50
183		$1 bluish green (2.9.54)	4·00	2·25
184		$2.50, carmine (2.9.54)	5·00	4·25
172/84		Set of 13	13·00	7·00

1958 (22 Apr). *Inauguration of British Caribbean Federation. As Nos. 175/7 of Jamaica.*

185	3 c. deep green		40	20
186	6 c. blue		65	1·75
187	12 c. scarlet		90	80
185/7		Set of 3	1·75	2·50

MINISTERIAL GOVERNMENT

38 Columbus's *Santa Maria* off the Pitons

39 Stamp of 1860

(Recess Waterlow)

1960 (1 Jan). *New Constitution for the Windward and Leeward Islands. W* **12**. *P* 13.

188	**38**	8 c. carmine-red	40	45
189		10 c. red-orange	40	45
190		25 c. deep blue	60	50
188/90		Set of 3	1·25	1·25

(Eng H. Bard. Recess Waterlow)

1960 (18 Dec). *Stamp Centenary. W* **12**. *P* 13½.

191	**39**	5 c. rose-red and ultramarine	15	10
192		16 c. deep blue and yellow-green	40	70
193		25 c. green and carmine-red	40	20
191/3		Set of 3	85	90

1963 (4 June). *Freedom from Hunger. As No. 80 of Lesotho.*

194	25 c. bluish green	30	10

1963 (2 Sept). *Red Cross Centenary. As Nos. 203/4 of Jamaica.*

195	4 c. red and black	20	35
196	25 c. red and blue	65	1·40

40 Queen Elizabeth II **41**
(after A. C. Davidson-Houston)

42 Fishing Boats **43** Castries Harbour

44 Vigie Beach **45** Queen Elizabeth II

(Des V. Whiteley. Photo Harrison)

1964 (1 Mar)–**69**. *Designs as T* **40/5**, *W w* **12**. *P* 14½ (*T* **40**), *others* 14½×14 (*vert*) *or* 14×14½ (*horiz*).

197	**40**	1 c. crimson	10	10
		w. Wmk inverted	75	
198		2 c. bluish violet	30	30
		w. Wmk inverted	—	5·00
199		4 c. turquoise-green	35	30
		a. *Deep turquoise* (5.8.69)	1·75	1·25
		w. Wmk inverted	—	5·00
200		5 c. Prussian blue	30	10
		w. Wmk inverted	2·00	
201		6 c. yellow-brown	45	65
202	**41**	8 c. multicoloured	10	10
203		10 c. multicoloured	50	10
204	**42**	12 c. multicoloured	40	90
205	—	15 c. multicoloured	20	10
206	—	25 c. multicoloured	20	10
207	**43**	35 c. blue and buff	2·75	10
208	—	50 c. multicoloured	2·25	10
209	**44**	$1 multicoloured	1·25	75
210	**45**	$2.50 multicoloured	2·00	2·25
197/210		Set of 14	10·00	4·50

Designs: *Horiz as T* **42/3**—15 c. Pigeon Island; 25 c. Reduit Beach; 50 c. The Pitons.
See also No. 249.

1964 (23 Apr). *400th Birth Anniv of William Shakespeare. As No. 156 of Montserrat.*

211	10 c. blue-green	30	10

1965 (17 May). *I.T.U. Centenary. As Nos. 98/9 of Lesotho.*

212	4 c. mauve and magenta	10	10
213	50 c. lilac and light olive-green	70	90

1965 (25 Oct). *International Co-operation Year. As Nos. 100/1 of Lesotho.*

214	1 c. reddish purple and turquoise-green	10	10
215	25 c. deep bluish green and lavender	20	20

1966 (24 Jan). *Churchill Commemoration. As Nos. 102/5 of Lesotho.*

216	4 c. new blue	10	10
217	6 c. deep green	25	90
218	25 c. brown	35	15
219	35 c. bluish violet	40	20
216/19	Set of 4	1·00	1·25

1966 (4 Feb). *Royal Visit. As Nos. 183/4 of Montserrat.*

220	4 c. black and ultramarine	25	25
221	25 c. black and magenta	75	75

1966 (1 July). *World Cup Football Championship, England. As Nos. 57/8 of Pitcairn Islands.*

222	4 c. violet, yellow-green, lake & yellow-brn	25	10
223	25 c. chocolate, blue-green, lake & yellow-brn	65	30

1966 (20 Sept). *Inauguration of W.H.O. Headquarters, Geneva. As Nos. 185/6 of Montserrat.*

224	4 c. black, yellow-green and light blue	15	10
225	25 c. black, light purple and yellow-brown	45	20

1966 (1 Dec). *20th Anniv of U.N.E.S.C.O. As Nos. 342/4 of Mauritius.*

226	4 c. slate-violet, red, yellow and orange	15	10
227	12 c. orange-yellow, violet and deep olive	25	30
228	25 c. black, bright purple and orange	50	35
226/8	Set of 3	80	65

ASSOCIATED STATEHOOD

STATEHOOD 1st MARCH 1967	**STATEHOOD 1st MARCH 1967**
(49)	(50)

51 Map of St. Lucia

(Optd by Art Printery, Castries from dies supplied by Harrison. Photo Harrison (No. 240))

1967 (7 Mar). *Statehood.* (a) *Postage. Nos.* 198 *and* 200/9 *optd with T* **49** (2, 5, 6 c.) *or T* **50** (*others*) *in red.*

229	2 c. bluish violet		20	15
	a. Horiz pair, one without opt			
230	5 c. Prussian blue		10	10
	a. Opt inverted		45·00	
231	6 c. yellow-brown		10	10
232	8 c. multicoloured		20	10
	a. Opt double		£1500	
233	10 c. multicoloured		25	10
234	12 c. multicoloured		20	10
235	15 c. multicoloured		50	30
236	25 c. multicoloured		30	30

237	35 c. blue and buff	50	35
238	50 c. multicoloured	50	55
239	$1 multicoloured	50	55
229/39	Set of 11	2·75	2·25

(b) *Air. P* 14½ × 14.

240	**51**	15 c. new blue	10	10

Overprinted 1 c. and $2.50 stamps were prepared for issue but were not put on sale over the post office counter. Later, however, they were accepted for franking (*Price for set of 2* £2·75 *mint,* £8 *used*).

The 1 c., 6 c. and $2.50 also exist with overprint in black, instead of red, and the 25 c. U.N.E.S.C.O. value is also known with a similar overprint in blue or black.

52 "Madonna and Child with the Infant Baptist" (Raphael)

53 Batsman and Sir Frederick Clarke (Governor)

(Des and photo Harrison)

1967 (16 Oct). *Christmas. W w* **12** (*sideways*). *P* 14½.

241	**52**	4 c. multicoloured	10	10
242		25 c. multicoloured	30	10

(Des V. Whiteley. Photo Harrison)

1968 (8 Mar). *M.C.C.'s West Indies Tour. W w* **12** (*sideways*). *P* 14½ × 14.

243	**53**	10 c. multicoloured	20	30
244		35 c. multicoloured	45	55

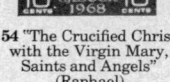

54 "The Crucified Christ with the Virgin Mary, Saints and Angels" (Raphael)

55 "Noli me tangere" (detail by Titian)

(Des and photo Harrison)

1968 (25 Mar). *Easter. W w* **12** (*sideways*). *P* 14 × 14½.

245	**54**	10 c. multicoloured	10	10
246	**54**	15 c. multicoloured	10	10
247	**54**	25 c. multicoloured	15	10
248	**55**	35 c. multicoloured	15	10
		a. Yellow (sunset) omitted	£140	
245/8		Set of 4	40	30

1968 (14 May)*. *As No.* 205 *but W w* **12** (*sideways*).

249	15 c. multicoloured	30	30

*This is the London release date. Stamps from this printing were available some months earlier on St. Lucia.

56 Dr. Martin Luther King

57 "Virgin and Child in Glory" (Murillo)

(Des V. Whiteley. Litho D.L.R.)

1968 (4 July). *Martin Luther King Commemoration. W w* **12**. *P* 13½ × 14.

250	**56**	25 c. blue, black and flesh	15	15
251		35 c. violet-black, black and flesh	15	15

(Des and photo Harrison)

1968 (17 Oct). *Christmas. Paintings. T* **57** *and similar vert design. Multicoloured. W w* **12** (*sideways*). *P* 14½ × 14.

252		5 c. Type **57**	10	10
253		10 c. "Madonna with Child" (Murillo)	10	10
254		25 c. Type **57**	15	10
255		35 c. As 10 c.	15	10
252/5		Set of 4	40	30

59 Purple-throated Carib

(Des V. Whiteley. Litho Format)

1969 (10 Jan). *Birds. T* **59** *and similar horiz design. Multicoloured. W* w **12** *(sideways). P* 14.

256	10 c. Type 59	..	55	35
257	15 c. St. Lucia Amazon	..	70	40
258	25 c. Type 59	..	90	45
259	35 c. As 15 c.	..	1·25	50
256/9		*Set of* 4	3·00	1·50

61 "Head of Christ Crowned with Thorns" (Reni)

62 "Resurrection of Christ" (Sodoma)

(Des and photo Harrison)

1969 (20 Mar). *Easter. W* w **12** *(sideways). P* 14½ × 14.

260	61	10 c. multicoloured	10	10
261	62	15 c. multicoloured	10	10
262	61	25 c. multicoloured	15	15
263	62	35 c. multicoloured	15	15
260/3		*Set of* 4	40	40

63 Map showing "CARIFTA" Countries

(Des J. Cooter. Photo Harrison)

1969 (29 May). *First Anniv of CARIFTA (Caribbean Free Trade Area). T* **63** *and similar horiz designs. Multicoloured. W* w **12**. P 14.

264	5 c. Type 63	..	10	10
265	10 c. Type 63	..	10	10
266	25 c. Handclasp and names of CARIFTA countries		15	15
267	35 c. As 25 c.	..	15	15
264/7		*Set of* 4	40	40

65 Emperor Napoleon and Empress Josephine

66 "Virgin and Child" (P. Delaroche)

(Des and litho Enschedé)

1969 (22 Sept). *Birth Bicentenary of Napoleon Bonaparte. P* 14 × 13.

268	65	15 c. multicoloured	10	10
269		25 c. multicoloured	10	10
270		35 c. multicoloured	10	10
271		50 c. multicoloured	15	55
268/71		*Set of* 4	30	75

(Des J. W. Photo Harrison)

1969 (27 Oct). *Christmas. Paintings. T* **66** *and similar vert design. Multicoloured. W* w **12** *(sideways). P* 14½ × 14.

272	5 c. Type 66	..	10	10
273	10 c. "Holy Family" (Rubens)		10	10
274	25 c. Type 66	..	20	10
275	35 c. As 10 c.	..	20	10
272/5		*Set of* 4	50	30

ALTERED CATALOGUE NUMBERS

Any Catalogue numbers altered from the last edition are shown as a list in the introductory pages.

68 House of Assembly

69 "The Sealing of the Tomb" (Hogarth)

(Des J. Cooter ($10), Sylvia and M. Goaman (others). Litho Questa ($10), Format (others))

1970 (2 Feb)–73. *T* **68** *and similar designs. Multicoloured. W* w **12** *(sideways* on 1 c. to 35 c. and $10). P* 14.

276	1 c. Type 68	..	10	10
277	2 c. Roman Catholic Cathedral		15	10
278	4 c. The Boulevard, Castries		1·00	10
	w. Wmk Crown to right of CA		5·00	
279	5 c. Castries Harbour		1·25	10
280	6 c. Sulphur springs		15	10
281	10 c. Vigie Airport		80	10
282	12 c. Reduit Beach		20	10
283	15 c. Pigeon Island		30	10
284	25 c. The Pitons and yacht		80	10
	w. Wmk Crown to right of CA		12·00	
285	35 c. Marigot Bay		40	10
	w. Wmk Crown to right of CA		9·50	
286	50 c. Diamond Waterfall (*vert*)		70	80
287	$1 Flag of St. Lucia (*vert*)		40	70
288	$2.50, St. Lucia Coat of Arms (*vert*)		55	1·75
289	$5 Queen Elizabeth II (*vert*)		1·50	4·00
289a	$10 Map of St. Lucia (*vert*) (3.12.73)		5·00	9·00
276/89a		*Set of* 15	12·00	15·00

*The normal sideways watermark shows Crown to left of CA, as seen from the back of the stamp.
See also Nos. 367/8 and 395/8.

(Des V. Whiteley. Litho Enschedé)

1970 (7 Mar). *Easter. Triptych by Hogarth. T* **69** *and similar multicoloured designs. W* w **12** *(sideways). Roul.* 9 × *P* 12½.

290	25 c. Type 69	..	15	20
	a. Strip of 3. Nos. 290/2		55	
291	35 c. "The Three Marys at the Tomb"		15	20
292	$1 "The Ascension" (39 × 55 *mm*)		30	40
290/2		*Set of* 3	55	70

Nos. 290/2 were issued in sheets of 30 (6 × 5) containing the Hogarth Triptych spread over all three values of the set. This necessitated a peculiar arrangement with the $1 value (which depicts the centre portion of the triptych) 10 mm higher than the other values in the *se-tenant* strip.

72 Charles Dickens and Dickensian Characters

(Des V. Whiteley. Litho B.W.)

1970 (8 June). *Death Centenary of Charles Dickens. W* w **12** *(sideways). P* 14.

293	72	1 c. multicoloured	10	10
294		25 c. multicoloured	20	10
295		35 c. multicoloured	25	10
296		50 c. multicoloured	35	1·25
293/6		*Set of* 4	70	1·25

73 Nurse and Emblem

(Des R. Granger Barrett. Litho J.W.)

1970 (18 Aug). *Centenary of British Red Cross. T* **73** *and similar horiz designs. Multicoloured. W* w **12** *(sideways*). P* 14.

297	10 c. Type 73		15	15
298	15 c. Flags of Great Britain, Red Cross and St. Lucia		25	25
299	25 c. Type 73		35	40
300	35 c. As 15 c.		40	40
	w. Wmk Crown to right of CA		17·00	
297/300		*Set of* 4	1·00	1·10

*The normal sideways watermark shows Crown to left of CA, as seen from the back of the stamp.

74 "Madonna with the Lilies" (Luca della Robbia)

75 "Christ on the Cross" (Rubens)

(Des P. B. Litho and embossed Walsall)

1970 (16 Nov). *Christmas. P* 11.

301	74	5 c. multicoloured	10	10
302		10 c. multicoloured	15	10
303		35 c. multicoloured	30	10
304		40 c. multicoloured	30	30
301/4		*Set of* 4	75	50

(Des and litho Enschedé)

1971 (29 Mar). *Easter. T* **75** *and similar vert design. Multicoloured. W* w **12**. P 13½ × 13.

305	10 c. Type 75		10	10
	w. Wmk inverted		30	
306	15 c. "Descent from the Cross" (Rubens)		15	10
	w. Wmk inverted		30	
307	35 c. Type 75		30	10
308	40 c. As 15 c.		30	40
	w. Wmk inverted		80	
305/8		*Set of* 4	75	60

76 Moule à Chique Lighthouse

(Des J. W. Litho Questa)

1971 (1 May). *Opening of Beane Field Airport. T* **76** *and similar horiz design. Multicoloured. W* w **12** *(sideways). P* 14½ × 14.

309	5 c. Type 76		30	15
310	25 c. Boeing 727-200 aircraft landing at Beane Field		45	15

77 Morne Fortune

78 Morne Fortune, Modern View

(Des V. Whiteley. Litho Questa)

1971 (10 Aug). *Old and New Views of St. Lucia. T* **77/8** *and similar horiz designs. Multicoloured. W* w **12** *(sideways*). P* 13½×13.

311	5 c. Type 77		10	20
	a. Pair. Nos. 311/12		15	40
312	5 c. Type 78		10	20
313	10 c. Old view of Castries city		10	20
	a. Pair. Nos. 313/14		15	40
314	10 c. Modern view of Castries city		10	20
315	25 c. Old view of Pigeon Island		15	30
	a. Pair. Nos. 315/16		30	60
316	25 c. Modern view of Pigeon Island		15	30
317	50 c. Old view from Government House		25	75
	a. Pair. Nos. 317/18		50	1·50
	w. Wmk Crown to right of CA		50	
	wa. Pair. Nos. 317w/18w		1·00	
318	50 c. Modern view of Government House		25	75
	w. Wmk Crown to right of CA		50	
311/18		*Set of* 8	1·00	2·50

*The normal sideways watermark shows Crown to left of CA, as seen from the back of the stamp.

Each value of this issue was printed horizontally and vertically *se-tenant* in two designs showing respectively old and new views of St. Lucia.

The old views are taken from paintings by J. H. Caddy.

79 "Virgin and Child with Two Angels" (Verrocchio)

80 "St. Lucia" (Dolci School) and Coat of Arms

(Des J. Cooter. Litho J.W.)

1971 (15 Oct). *Christmas. T* **79** *and similar vert designs. Multicoloured. W* w **12**. *P* 14.

319		5 c. Type **79**			10	10
320		10 c. "Virgin and Child, St. John the Baptist and an Angel" (Morando)			10	10
321		35 c. "Madonna and Child" (Battista)			15	10
322		40 c. Type **79**			20	25
319/22				Set of 4	40	40

(Des and litho Harrison)

1971 (13 Dec). *National Day. W* w **12**. *P* 14×14½.

323	**80**	5 c. multicoloured			10	10
324		10 c. multicoloured			15	10
325		25 c. multicoloured			25	10
		w. Wmk inverted			19·00	
326		50 c. multicoloured			45	40
323/6				Set of 4	85	50

81 "The Dead Christ Mourned" (Carracci)

(Des G. Drummond. Litho Questa)

1972 (15 Feb). *Easter. T* **81** *and similar horiz design. Multicoloured. W* w **12**. *P* 14.

327		10 c. Type **81**			10	10
328		25 c. "Angels weeping over the dead Christ" (Guercino)			20	10
329		35 c. Type **81**			30	10
330		50 c. As 25 c.			40	40
327/30				Set of 4	85	45

82 Science Block and Teachers' College

(Des P. Powell. Litho Questa)

1972 (18 Apr). *Morne Educational Complex. T* **82** *and similar horiz designs. Multicoloured. W* w **12**. *P* 14.

331		5 c. Type **82**			10	10
		w. Wmk inverted			1·40	
332		15 c. University Centre			10	10
333		25 c. Secondary School			10	10
334		35 c. Technical College			15	10
331/4				Set of 4	30	30

83 Steamship Stamp and Map

(Des J. Cooter. Litho Questa)

1972 (22 June). *Centenary of First Postal Service by St. Lucia Steam Conveyance Co Ltd. T* **83** *and similar horiz designs. W* w **12**. *P* 14.

335		5 c. multicoloured			15	10
		w. Wmk inverted				
336		10 c. ultramarine, mauve and black			20	10
337		35 c. lt rose-carmine, pale greenish bl & blk			60	10
338		50 c. multicoloured			1·00	1·00
335/8				Set of 4	1·75	1·00

Designs:—10 c. Steamship stamp and Castries Harbour; 35 c. Steamship stamp and Soufrière; 50 c. Steamship stamps.

84 "The Holy Family" (Sebastiano Ricci)

(Des J. Cooter. Litho J.W.)

1972 (18 Oct). *Christmas. W* w **12** *(sideways). P* 14½.

339	**84**	5 c. multicoloured			10	10
340		10 c. multicoloured			10	10
341		35 c. multicoloured			20	10
342		40 c. multicoloured			25	15
339/42				Set of 4	50	30

85 Arms and St. Lucia Amazon

86 Week-day Headdress

(Des (from photograph by D. Groves) and photo Harrison)

1972 (20 Nov). *Royal Silver Wedding. Multicoloured; background colour given. W* w **12**. *P* 14 × 14½.

343	**85**	15 c. carmine			20	20
		w. Wmk inverted			12·00	
344		35 c. yellow-olive			20	20
		w. Wmk inverted			35·00	

(Des Sylvia Goaman. Litho A. & M.)

1973 (1 Feb). *Local Headdresses. T* **86** *and similar vert designs. Multicoloured. W* w **12**. *P* 13.

345		5 c. Type **86**			10	10
346		10 c. Formal style			10	10
347		25 c. Unmarried girl's style			15	10
348		50 c. Ceremonial style			25	50
345/8				Set of 4	45	60

87 Coat of Arms

88 H.M.S. *St. Lucia*, 1803

(Des and litho Harrison)

1973 (19 Apr)–**76**. *Coil Stamps. P* 14½×14. A. *W* w **12** *upright*

349A	**87**	5 c. olive-green			10	75
350A		10 c. new blue			15	75
351A		25 c. lake-brown			15	75
349A/51A				Set of 3	35	2·00

B. *W* w **12** *(sideways)* (1976)

349B	**87**	5 c. olive-green			50	2·00
350B		10 c. new blue			50	2·00
351B		25 c. lake-brown			13·00	

For 10 c. value watermarked w **16** see No. 953.

(Des R. Granger Barrett. Litho Questa)

1973 (24 May). *Historic Ships. T* **88** *and similar horiz designs. Multicoloured. W* w **12**. *P* 13½ × 14.

352		15 c. Type **88**			20	20
353		35 c. H.M.S. *Prince of Wales*, 1765			25	10
354		50 c. *Oliph Blossom*, 1605			40	20
355		$1 H.M.S. *Rose*, 1757			55	65
352/5				Set of 4	1·25	90
MS356		122×74 mm. Nos. 352/5			1·25	2·75

89 Plantation and Flower

90 "The Virgin with Child" (Maratta)

(Des PAD Studio. Litho Walsall)

1973 (26 July). *Banana Industry. T* **89** *and similar horiz designs. Multicoloured. W* w **12**. *P* 14.

357		5 c. Type **89**			10	10
358		15 c. Aerial spraying			15	10
359		35 c. Boxing plant			20	10
		w. Wmk inverted			4·00	
360		50 c. Loading a boat			50	40
357/60				Set of 4	85	45

(Des J. Cooter. Litho Walsall)

1973 (17 Oct). *Christmas. T* **90** *and similar vert designs. Multicoloured. W* w **12** *(sideways*). P* 13½.

361		5 c. Type **90**			10	10
362		15 c. "Madonna in the Meadow" (Raphael)			10	10
363		35 c. "The Holy Family" (Bronzino)			20	10
364		50 c. "Madonna of the Pear" (Dürer)			30	35
		w. Wmk Crown to right of CA			2·00	
361/4				Set of 4	60	40

*The normal sideways watermark shows Crown to left of CA, as seen from the back of the stamp.

1973 (14 Nov). *Royal Wedding. As Nos.* 322/3 *of Montserrat.*

365		40 c. grey-green			10	10
366		50 c. rosy lilac			10	10

1974 (15 Mar). *As Nos.* 277/8 *but wmk upright.*

367		2 c. Roman Catholic Cathedral			60	70
368		4 c. The Boulevard, Castries			80	90

91 "The Betrayal"

92 3-Escalins Coins, 1798

(Des J. Cooter. Litho D.L.R.)

1974 (1 Apr). *Easter. T* **91** *and similar horiz designs showing paintings by Ugolino da Siena. Multicoloured. W* w **12** *(sideways on Nos.* 369/72, *upright on MS373). P* 13.

369		5 c. Type **91**			10	10
370		35 c. "The Way to Calvary"			15	10
371		80 c. "The Deposition"			15	15
372		$1 "The Resurrection"			20	25
369/72				Set of 4	50	40
MS373		180 × 140 mm. Nos. 369/72			1·00	2·00

(Des J. Cooter. Litho Format)

1974 (20 May). *Coins of Old St. Lucie. T* **92** *and similar vert designs. Multicoloured. W* w **12** *(sideways). P* 14 × 13½.

374		15 c. Type **92**			15	10
375		35 c. 6-escalins coins, 1798			15	10
376		40 c. 2-livres 5-sols coins, 1813			20	10
377		$1 6-livres 15-sols coins, 1813			35	65
374/7				Set of 4	75	75
MS378		151 × 115 mm. Nos. 374/7			1·25	2·75

93 Baron de Laborie

94 "Virgin and Child" (Andrea del Verrocchio)

(Des J. W. Litho Questa)

1974 (29 Aug). *Past Governors of St. Lucia. T* **93** *and similar vert designs. Multicoloured. W* w **12** *(sideways*). P* 14.

379		5 c. Type **93**			10	10
380		10 c. Sir John Moore			10	10
381		80 c. Sir Dudley Hill			15	10
		w. Wmk Crown to right of CA			40·00	
382		$1 Sir Frederick Clarke			25	35
379/82				Set of 4	50	50
MS383		153×117 mm. Nos. 379/82. Wmk upright			50	2·00
		w. Wmk inverted			50·00	

*The normal sideways watermark shows Crown to left of CA, as seen from the back of the stamp.

(Des PAD Studio. Litho D.L.R.)

1974 (18 Nov). *Christmas. T* **94** *and similar vert designs. Multicoloured. W* w **12**. *P* 13 × 13½.

384		5 c. Type **94**			10	10
385		35 c. "Virgin and Child" (Andrea della Robbia)			10	10
386		80 c. "Madonna and Child" (Luca della Robbia)			15	15
387		$1 "Virgin and Child" (Rossellino)			20	25
384/7				Set of 4	40	40
MS388		92 × 140 mm. Nos. 384/7			90	2·00

95 Churchill and Montgomery

96 "Christ on the Cross" (School of Van der Weyden)

(Des PAD Studio. Litho Format)

1974 (30 Nov). *Birth Centenary of Sir Winston Churchill. T* **95** *and similar horiz design. Multicoloured. W w* **12** *(sideways). P* 14.
389   5 c. Type **95** 10   10
390   $1 Churchill and Truman 30   35

(Des J. Cooter. Litho Questa)

1975 (27 Mar). *Easter. T* **96** *and similar vert designs. Multicoloured. W w* **12**. *P* 13½.
391   5 c. Type **96** 10   10
392   35 c. "Noli me tangere" (Romano) .. 10   10
393   80 c. "Calvary" (Gallego) 20   20
394   $1 "Noli me tangere" (Correggio) .. 30   35
391/4 .. .. *Set of 4* 55   60

1975 (28 July). *As Nos. 278 etc. but W w* **14** *(sideways).*
395   4 c. The Boulevard, Castries 70   2·00
396   5 c. Castries Harbour 80   1·10
397   10 c. Vigie Airport .. .. 1·00   1·40
398   15 c. Pigeon Island .. .. 1·75   2·00
395/8 .. .. *Set of 4* 3·75   6·00

97 "Nativity"   98 American Schooner *Hanna*
(French Book of Hours)

(Des J. Cooter. Litho Questa)

1975 (12 Dec). *Christmas. T* **97** *and similar vert designs. Multicoloured. W w* **12**. *P* 14½.
399   5 c. Type **97** 10   10
400   10 c. "King" (stained glass window) 10   15
    a. Horiz strip of 3. Nos. 400/2 .. 30
401   10 c. "Virgin and Child" (stained glass
    window) 10   15
402   10 c. "King and Cattle" (stained glass
    window) 10   15
403   40 c. "Nativity" (Hastings Book of Hours) 30   20
404   $1 "Virgin and Child with Saints"
    (Borgognone) 70   60
399/404 .. .. .. *Set of 6* 1·25   1·25
MS405   105×109 mm. Nos. 399 and 403/4 .. 75   1·00
    Nos. 400/2 were printed horizontally *se-tenant* within the sheet to form a composite design of the Epiphany.

(Des J. W. Litho Format)

1976 (26 Jan). *Bicentenary of American Revolution. T* **98** *and similar horiz designs showing ships. Multicoloured. P* 14½.
406   ½ c. Type **98** 10   10
407   1 c. *Prince of Orange* (British sailing
    packet) 10   10
408   2 c. H.M.S. *Edward* (sloop) .. 10   10
409   5 c. *Millern* (British merchantman) .. 30   10
410   15 c. *Surprise* (American lugger) .. 45   10
411   35 c. H.M.S. *Serapis* (frigate) .. 60   20
412   50 c. *Randolph* (American frigate) .. 65   1·00
413   $1 *Alliance* (American frigate) .. 80   2·50
406/13 .. .. *Set of 8* 2·50   3·50
MS414   142×116 mm. Nos. 410/13. *P* 13 .. 3·00   4·50

99 Laughing Gull   100 H.M.S. *Ceres*

(Des J.W. Litho Questa)

1976 (17 May)–79. *Birds. T* **99** *and similar vert designs. Multicoloured. Ordinary paper. W w* **12** (1 c.) *or w* **14** (others). *P* 14.
415   1 c. Type **99** 30   90
416   2 c. Little Blue Heron 30   90
417   4 c. Belted Kingfisher 35   90
418   5 c. St. Lucia Amazon .. .. 1·75   90
419   6 c. St. Lucia Oriole .. .. 1·25   90
420   8 c. Brown Trembler .. .. 1·50   1·50
421   10 c. American Kestrel .. .. 1·25   35
422   12 c. Red-billed Tropic Bird .. 2·00   2·50
423   15 c. Moorhen .. .. .. 1·25   10
424   25 c. Common Noddy .. .. 1·75   1·75
    a. Chalk-surfaced paper (7.79) .. 1·00
425   35 c. Sooty Tern .. .. .. 3·25   1·25
    a. Chalk-surfaced paper (1979) .. 3·25   3·25
426   50 c. Osprey .. .. .. 6·50   3·50
427   $1 White-breasted Trembler .. 4·00   3·50
428   $2.50, St. Lucia Black Finch .. 7·00   6·00
429   $5 Red-necked Pigeon .. .. 7·50   4·50
430   $10 Caribbean Elaenia .. .. 7·00   8·00
    a. Chalk-surfaced paper (7.79) .. 3·00   7·50
415/30a .. .. .. *Set of 16* 38·00   32·00

1976 (19 July). *West Indian Victory in World Cricket Cup. As Nos. 419/20 of Jamaica.*
431   50 c. Caribbean map .. .. 1·00   1·00
432   $1 Prudential Cup .. .. 1·50   2·50
MS433   92 × 79 mm. Nos. 431/2 .. 3·50   4·50

(Des J. Cooter. Litho Walsall)

1976 (4 Sept). *Royal Navy Crests. T* **100** *and similar vert designs. Multicoloured. W w* **14** *(inverted). P* 14.
434   10 c. Type **100** 35   10
435   20 c. H.M.S. Pelican 60   10
436   40 c. H.M.S. *Ganges* 85   10
437   $2 H.M.S. *Ariadne* .. .. 2·00   2·00
434/7 .. .. *Set of 4* 3·50   2·00

101 "Madonna and Child"   102 Queen Elizabeth II
(Murillo)

(Des J. Cooter. Litho Questa)

1976 (15 Nov). *Christmas. T* **101** *and similar vert designs. Multicoloured. W w* **14**. *P* 13½.
438   10 c. Type **101** 10   10
439   20 c. "Madonna and Child with Angels" (Costa) 10   10
440   50 c. "Madonna and Child Enthroned"
    (Isenbrandt) 15   10
441   $2 "Madonna and Child with St. John"
    (Murillo) 50   65
438/41 .. .. *Set of 4* 70   75
MS442   105 × 93 mm. $2.50, As Type **101** .. 1·00   1·25

(Des Daphne Padden. Litho Questa)

1977 (7 Feb). *Silver Jubilee. W w* **14** *(sideways*). P* 14.
443   **102** 10 c. multicoloured 10   10
444   20 c. multicoloured 10   10
    w. Wmk Crown to right of CA .. £110
445   40 c. multicoloured 10   15
446   $2 multicoloured 40   90
443/6 .. .. *Set of 4* 50   1·00
MS447   128×95 mm. **102** $2.50, multicoloured .. 45   1·00
    *The normal sideways watermark shows Crown to left of CA, as seen from the back of the stamp.
    Nos. 443/6 were each issued in sheets of five stamps and one label.

103 Scouts from Tapion   104 "Nativity" (Giotto)
School

(Des J. W. Litho Format)

1977 (17 Oct). *Caribbean Boy Scout Jamboree. T* **103** *and similar vert designs. Multicoloured. P* 14½.
448   ½ c. Type **103** 10   10
449   1 c. Sea scouts 10   10
450   2 c. Scout from Micoud 10   10
451   10 c. Two scouts from Tapion School .. 15   10
452   20 c. Venture scouts 15   10
453   50 c. Scout from Gros Islet .. 30   45
454   $1 Sea scouts in motor boat .. 50   1·00
448/54 .. .. *Set of 7* 1·00   1·60
MS455   75 × 85 mm. $2.50, As $1. .. 1·10   3·00

(Des J. W. Litho Questa)

1977 (31 Oct). *Christmas. T* **104** *and similar vert designs. Multicoloured. P* 14.
456   ½ c. Type **104** 10   10
457   1 c. "Perugia triptych" (Fra Angelico) 10   10
458   2 c. "Virgin and Child" (El Greco) .. 10   10
459   20 c. "Madonna of the Rosary" (Caravaggio) 15   10
460   50 c. "Adoration of the Magi" (Velazquez) 20   10
461   $1 "Madonna of Carmel" (Tiepolo) 30   35
462   $2.50, "Adoration of the Magi" (Tiepolo) 45   80
456/62 .. .. *Set of 7* 1·00   1·25

105 "Susan Lunden"   106 Yeoman of the Guard and
    Life Guard

PETER PAUL RUBENS 1577-1640

(Des C. Abbott. Litho Harrison)

1977 (28 Nov). *400th Birth Anniv of Rubens. T* **105** *and similar vert designs. Multicoloured. W w* **14** *(sideways). P* 14 × 15.
463   10 c. Type **105** 10   10
464   35 c. "The Rape of the Sabine Women" (detail) 15   10
465   50 c. "Ludovicus Nonnius" .. 30   10
466   $2.50, "Minerva protects Pax from Mars"
    (detail) 85   80
463/6 .. .. *Set of 4* 1·25   90
MS467   145 × 120 mm. Nos. 463/6 .. 1·25   2·25

(Des J. W. Litho Questa)

1978 (2 June). *25th Anniv of Coronation. T* **106** *and similar horiz designs. Multicoloured. P* 14.
468   15 c. Type **106** 10   10
469   20 c. Groom and postillion .. 10   10
470   50 c. Footman and coachman .. 10   10
471   $3 State trumpeter and herald .. 35   80
468/71 .. .. *Set of 4* 50   90
MS472   114 × 88 mm. $5 Master of the Horse and
    Gentleman-at-Arms 60   90
    Nos. 468/71 also exist perf 12 (*Price for set of 4 60p. mint or used*) from additional sheetlets of 3 stamps and one label. Stamps perforated 14 are from normal sheets of 50.

107 Queen Angelfish

(Des G. Vasarhelyi. Litho Format)

1978 (19 June). *Fishes. T* **107** *and similar horiz designs. Multicoloured. P* 15.
473   10 c. Type **107** 30   10
474   20 c. Four-eyed Butterflyfish .. 50   10
475   50 c. French Angelfish 80   30
476   $2 Yellow-tailed Damselfish .. 1·10   1·75
473/6 .. .. *Set of 4* 2·40   2·00
MS477   155×89 mm. $2.50, Rock Beauty .. 1·75   1·90
    Nos. 473/6 exist imperforate from stock dispersed by the liquidator of Format International Security Printers Ltd.

108 French Grenadier and Map of   109 The Annunciation
    the Battle

(Des J. W. Litho Questa)

1978 (29 Nov). *Bicentenary of Battle of Cul-de-Sac. T* **108** *and similar horiz designs. Multicoloured. P* 14
478   10 c. Type **108** 40   10
479   30 c. British Grenadier officer and map of St.
    Lucia (Bellin), 1762 65   10
480   50 c. Coastline from Gros Islet to Cul-de-Sac
    and British fleet opposing French
    landings 85   15
481   $2.50, General James Grant, 1798, and Light
    Infantrymen of 46th Regiment .. 1·75   1·50
478/81 .. .. *Set of 4* 3·25   1·60

(Des Jennifer Toombs. Litho Questa)

1978 (4 Dec). *Christmas. T* **109** *and similar horiz design. Multicoloured. W w* **14**. *P* 14.
482   30 c. Type **109** 10   10
483   50 c. Type **109** 15   10
484   55 c. The Nativity 15   10
485   80 c. As 55 c. 20   20
482/5 .. .. *Set of 4* 55   40

INDEPENDENT

INDEPENDENCE 1979
SAINT LUCIA 10c

110 Hewanorra International Air Terminal

(Des J. W. Litho Questa)

1979 (22 Feb). *Independence. T* **110** *and similar horiz designs. Multicoloured. W w* **14** *(sideways). P* 14.
486   10 c. Type **110** 10   10
487   30 c. New coat of arms 10   10
488   50 c. Government House and Sir Allen Lewis
    (first Governor-General) .. 15   10
489   $2 French, St. Lucia and Union flags on map
    of St. Lucia 30   45
486/9 .. .. *Set of 4* 50   55
MS490   127 × 80 mm. Nos. 486/9 .. 50   1·00

111 Popes Paul VI and John Paul I

(Des J.W. Litho Harrison)

1979 (28 May). *Pope Paul VI Commemoration. T* **111** *and similar horiz designs. Multicoloured.* W w 14 (sideways). *P* 14½ × 14.
491	10 c. Type 111			10	10
492	30 c. President Sadat of Egypt with Pope Paul			20	10
493	50 c. Pope Paul with Secretary-General U Thant			35	10
494	55 c. Pope Paul and Prime Minister Golda Meir of Israel			40	25
495	$2 Martin Luther King received in audience by Pope Paul			1·00	70
491/5			Set of 5	1·75	1·00

112 Dairy Farming

(Des G. Drummond. Litho Format)

1979 (2 July). *Agriculture Diversification. T* **112** *and similar horiz designs. Multicoloured.* W w 14 (sideways). *P* 14.
496	10 c. Type 112			10	10
497	35 c. Fruit and vegetables			10	10
498	50 c. Water conservation			10	10
499	$3 Copra industry			35	70
496/9			Set of 4	50	85

113 Lindbergh and Sikorsky S-38A Flying Boat

114 "A Prince of Saxony" (Cranach the Elder)

(Des L. Curtis. Litho Walsall)

1979 (2 Oct). *50th Anniv of Lindbergh's Inaugural Airmail Flight via St. Lucia. T* **113** *and similar horiz designs.* W w 14 (sideways). *P* 14.
500	10 c. black, Indian red and pale orange			30	10
501	30 c. multicoloured			40	10
502	50 c. multicoloured			40	10
503	$2 multicoloured			60	75
500/3			Set of 4	1·50	90

Designs:—30 c. Sikorsky S-38A flying boat and route map; 50 c. Arrival at La Toc, September, 1929; $2 Letters on first flight.

(Litho Questa)

1979 (6 Dec). *International Year of the Child. Paintings. T* **114** *and similar vert designs. Multicoloured. P.* 14.
504	10 c. Type 114			10	10
505	50 c. "The Infanta Margarita" (Velazquez)			15	10
506	$2 "Girl playing Badminton" (Chardin)			40	40
507	$2.50, "Mary and Francis Wilcox" (Stock)			45	45
504/7			Set of 4	95	80
MS508	113 × 94 mm. $5 "Two Children" (Picasso)			1·10	1·25

115 Notice of Introduction of Penny Post

116 "Madonna and Child" (Bernardino Fungai)

(Des J.W. Litho Questa)

1979 (10 Dec). *Death Centenary of Sir Rowland Hill. T* **115** *and similar vert designs. Multicoloured. P.* 14.
509	10 c. Type 115			10	10
510	50 c. Original stamp sketch			15	10
511	$2 1860 1d. stamp			35	50
512	$2.50, Penny Black stamp			45	60
509/12			Set of 4	85	1·10
MS513	111 × 85 mm. $5 Sir Rowland Hill			70	90

Nos. 509/12 also exist perf 12 (*Price for set of 4* 85p. *mint or used*) from additional sheetlets of 5 stamps and one label. Stamps perforated 14 are from normal sheets of 40.

(Des R. Vigurs. Litho Walsall)

1980 (14 Jan). *Christmas* (1979) *and International Year of the Child. T* **116** *and similar vert designs showing "Madonna and Child" paintings by various artists. Multicoloured.* W w 14. *P* 14.
514	10 c. Type 116			10	10
	w. Wmk inverted			20·00	
515	50 c. Carlo Dolci			20	10
516	$2 Titian			50	40
517	$2.50, Giovanni Bellini			60	60
514/17			Set of 4	1·25	95
MS518	94×120 mm. Nos. 514/17			1·25	1·60

117 St. Lucia Steam Conveyance Company Cover, 1873

118 Mickey Mouse astride Rocket

(Des G. Drummond. Litho Questa)

1980 (6 May). *"London 1980" International Stamp Exhibition. T* **117** *and similar horiz designs. Multicoloured.* W w 14 (sideways). *P* 14.
519	10 c. Type 117			10	10
520	30 c. S.S. *Assistance* 1d. postmark of 1879			10	10
521	50 c. Postage due handstamp of 1893			15	10
522	$2 Crowned-circle paid stamp of 1844			40	55
519/22			Set of 4	60	65
MS523	85 × 76 mm. Nos. 519/22			65	90

(Litho Format)

1980 (29 May). *10th Anniv of Moon Landing* (1979). *Walt Disney Cartoon Characters. T* **118** *and similar multicoloured designs showing characters in space scenes. P.* 11.
524	½ c. Type 118			10	10
525	1 c. Donald Duck being towed by rocket (*horiz*)			10	10
526	2 c. Minnie Mouse on Moon			10	10
527	3 c. Goofy hitching lift to Mars			10	10
528	4 c. Goofy and moondog (*horiz*)			10	10
529	5 c. Pluto burying bone on Moon (*horiz*)			10	10
530	10 c. Donald Duck and love-sick martian (*horiz*)			10	10
531	$2 Donald Duck paddling spaceship (*horiz*)			1·60	1·00
532	$2.50, Mickey Mouse driving moonbuggy (*horiz*)			1·60	1·10
524/32			Set of 9	3·25	2·00
MS533	102 × 127 mm. $5 Goofy leaping from space-ship on to Moon. P 13½			3·25	2·75

119 Queen Elizabeth the Queen Mother

(Litho Questa)

1980 (4 Aug). *80th Birthday of Queen Elizabeth the Queen Mother. P* 14.
534	119	10 c. multicoloured		15	10
535		$2.50, multicoloured		35	1·00
MS536	85 × 65 mm. 119 $3 multicoloured			60	1·50

120 Hawker Siddeley H.S.748

(Des A. Theobald. Litho Harrison)

1980 (11 Aug). *Transport. Horiz designs as T* **120**. *Multicoloured.* W w 14 (sideways on 5 c. to $1). *P* 14½ × 14.
537	5 c. Type 120			30	30
538	10 c. Douglas DC-10-30 airliner			65	20
539	15 c. Local bus			35	30
540	20 c. *Geestcrest* (freighter)			35	30
541	25 c. Britten Norman Islander aircraft			65	20
542	30 c. *Charles* (pilot boat)			40	40
543	50 c. Boeing 727-200 airliner			1·00	60
544	75 c. *Cunard Countess* (liner)			65	1·00
545	$1 Lockheed L-1011 Tristar 500 airliner			85	1·10
546	$2 *Booker Vulcan* (cargo liner)			1·25	2·00
547	$5 Boeing 707-420 airliner			4·50	6·00
548	$10 *Queen Elizabeth 2* (liner)			5·00	8·00
537/48			Set of 12	14·00	18·00

For stamps with watermark W w 15 see Nos. 690/8.

121 Shot-putting

122 Coastal Landscape within Cogwheel

(Des M. Diamond. Litho Questa)

1980 (22 Sept). *Olympic Games, Moscow. T* **121** *and similar horiz designs. Multicoloured. P* 14.
549	10 c. Type 121			10	10
550	50 c. Swimming			20	10
551	$2 Gymnastics			70	50
552	$2.50, Weightlifting			80	60
549/52			Set of 4	1·60	1·10
MS553	108×83 mm. $5 Athletes with Olympic Torch			1·25	1·40

(Des BG Studio. Litho Questa)

1980 (30 Sept). *75th Anniv of Rotary International. T* **122** *and similar vert designs showing different coastal landscapes within cogwheels. P* 14.
554	10 c. multicoloured			10	10
555	50 c. multicoloured			15	10
556	$2 greenish black, carmine & greenish yell			40	40
557	$2.50, multicoloured			50	55
554/7			Set of 4	1·00	1·00
MS558	103 × 106 mm. $5 multicoloured			1·25	1·75

123 Sir Arthur Lewis

(Des J. W. Litho Questa)

1980 (23 Oct). *Nobel Prize Winners. T* **123** *and similar vert designs. Multicoloured. P* 14.
559	10 c. Type 123			10	10
560	50 c. Martin Luther King Jnr.			20	15
561	$2 Ralph Bunche			50	60
562	$2.50, Albert Schweitzer			70	80
559/62			Set of 4	1·25	1·40
MS563	115 × 91 mm. $5 Albert Einstein			1·75	2·00

1980
HURRICANE

$1.50 RELIEF

(124)

1980 (3 Nov). *Hurricane Relief. Nos.* 539/40 *and* 543 *surch with T* 124.
564	$1.50 on 15 c. Local bus			30	40
565	$1.50 on 20 c. Refrigerated freighter			30	40
566	$1.50 on 50 c. Boeing 727-200 airliner			30	40
564/6			Set of 3	80	1·10

125 "The Nativity" (Giovanni Battista)

126 Brazilian Agouti

(Des J. Cooter. Litho Questa)

1980 (1 Dec). *Christmas. Paintings. T* **125** *and similar vert designs. Multicoloured.* W w 14. *P* 14 × 13½.
567	10 c. Type 125			10	10
	w. Wmk inverted			18·00	
568	30 c. "Adoration of the Kings" (Pieter the Elder)			10	10
569	$2 "Adoration of the Shepherds" (ascribed to Murillo)			40	60
567/9			Set of 3	50	60
MS570	102×88 mm. $1×3, Angel with people of St. Lucia (*composite design*) (*each* 30×75 *mm*). P 14½×14			80	90

(Des G. Drummond. Litho Questa)

1981 (19 Jan). *Wildlife. T* **126** *and similar vert designs. Multicoloured. P* 14.

571	10 c. Type **126**	..	15	10
572	50 c. St. Lucia Amazon	..	1·00	20
573	$2 Purple-throated Carib	..	1·75	80
574	$2.50, Fiddler Crab	..	1·25	1·00
571/4		*Set of 4*	3·75	1·75
MS575	103×87 mm. $5 *Danaus plexippus* (butterfly)		2·40	2·50

127 Prince Charles at Balmoral

128 Lady Diana Spencer

(Des J. W. Litho Questa)

1981 (23 June). *Royal Wedding. T* **127** *and similar vert designs. Multicoloured. P* 14.

576	25 c. Prince Charles and Lady Diana Spencer	10	10
577	50 c. Clarence House	10	10
578	$4 Type **127**	40	55
576/8	*Set of 3*	50	60
MS579	96 × 82 mm. $5 Glass Coach and coachman	50	50

Nos. 576/8 also exist perforated 12 (*price for set of 3 50p mint or used*) from additional sheetlets of five stamps and one label. These stamps have changed background colours.

(Manufactured by Walsall)

1981 (23 June). *Royal Wedding. Booklet stamps. T* **128** *and similar vert designs. Multicoloured. Roul 5 × imperf* Self-adhesive.*

580	50 c. Type **128**		25	45
	a. Booklet pane. Nos. 580/1 each × 3		1·50	
581	$2 Prince Charles		30	60
582	$5 Prince Charles and Lady Diana Spencer		1·50	1·75
	a. Booklet pane of 1		1·50	
580/2		*Set of 3*	1·90	2·40

*The 50 c. and $2 values were each separated by various combinations of rotary knife (giving a straight edge) and roulette. The $5 value exists only with straight edges.

129 "The Cock"

130 "Industry"

(Des J.W. Litho Questa)

1981 (20 July). *Birth Centenary of Picasso. T* **129** *and similar vert designs. Multicoloured. P* 13½ × 14.

583	30 c. Type **129**	25	10
584	50 c. "Man with an Ice-Cream"	35	10
585	55 c. "Woman dressing her Hair"	35	10
586	$3 "Seated Woman"	95	85
583/6	*Set of 4*	1·75	1·00
MS587	128 × 102 mm. $5 "Night Fishing at Antibes"	2·50	2·50

(Des Walsall. Litho Format)

1981 (28 Sept). *25th Anniv of Duke of Edinburgh Award Scheme. T* **130** *and similar vert designs. Multicoloured. W w* 14. *P* 14½.

588	10 c. Type **130**	10	10
589	35 c. "Community service"	15	10
590	50 c. "Physical recreation"	15	10
591	$2.50, Duke of Edinburgh speaking at Caribbean Conference, 1975	45	70
588/91	*Set of 4*	70	75

131 Louis Braille

132 "Portrait of Fanny Travis Cochran" (Cecilia Beaux)

(Des J.W. Litho Questa)

1981 (10 Nov). *International Year for Disabled Persons. Famous Disabled People. T* **131** *and similar horiz designs. Multicoloured. P* 14.

592	10 c. Type **131**	10	10
593	50 c. Sarah Bernhardt	20	10
594	$2 Joseph Pulitzer	60	70
595	$2.50, Henri de Toulouse-Lautrec	65	85
592/5	*Set of 4*	1·40	1·60
MS596	115 × 90 mm. $5 Franklin Delano Roosevelt	1·00	1·25

(Des BG Studio. Litho Questa)

1981 (1 Dec). *Decade for Women. Paintings. T* **132** *and similar vert designs. Multicoloured. P* 14.

597	10 c. Type **132**	10	10
598	50 c. "Women with Dove" (Marie Laurencin)	20	10
599	$2 "Portrait of a Young Pupil of David" (Aimee Duvivier)	60	70
600	$2.50, "Self-portrait" (Rosalba Carriera)	65	85
597/600	*Set of 4*	1·40	1·60
MS601	104 × 78 mm. $5 "Self-portrait" (Elizabeth Vigee-le-Brun)	1·00	1·25

133 "The Adoration of the Magi" (Sfoza)

134 1860 1d. Stamp

(Des BG Studio. Litho Format)

1981 (15 Dec). *Christmas Paintings. T* **133** *and similar vert designs. Multicoloured. W w* 14. *P* 14.

602	10 c. Type **133**	10	10
603	30 c. "The Adoration of the Kings" (Orcanga)	20	10
604	$1.50, "The Adoration of the Kings" (Gerard)	45	50
605	$2.50, "The Adoration of the Kings" (Foppa)	75	85
602/5	*Set of 4*	1·25	1·25

(Des J.W. Litho Questa)

1981 (29 Dec). *First Anniv of U.P.U. Membership. T* **134** *and similar horiz designs. Multicoloured. P* 14.

606	10 c. Type **134**	20	10
607	30 c. 1969 First anniversary of Caribbean Free Trade Area 25 c. commemorative	40	10
608	50 c. 1979 Independence $2 commemorative	45	50
609	$2 U.P.U. emblem with U.P.U. and St. Lucia flags	95	2·25
606/9	*Set of 4*	1·75	2·50
MS610	128 × 109 mm. $5 U.P.U. Headquarters, Berne, and G.P.O. Building, Castries	1·00	1·50

135 Scene from Football Match

(Des Clover Mill. Litho Format)

1982 (15 Feb). *World Cup Football Championship, Spain. T* **135** *and similar horiz designs showing scenes from different matches. P* 15.

611	10 c. multicoloured	35	10
612	50 c. multicoloured	90	15
613	$2 multicoloured	1·50	90
614	$2.50, multicoloured	1·75	1·00
611/14	*Set of 4*	4·00	1·90
MS615	104 × 84 mm. $5 multicoloured	2·50	2·25

136 Pigeon Island National Park

137 Map-reading

(Des J. Cooter. Litho Format)

1982 (13 Apr). *Bicentenary of Battle of the Saints. T* **136** *and similar horiz designs. Multicoloured. W w* 14. *P* 14.

616	10 c. Type **136**	25	15
617	35 c. Battle scene	80	15
618	50 c. Rodney (English admiral) and De Grasse (French admiral)	1·10	65
619	$2.50, Map of the Saints, Martinique and St. Lucia	3·25	4·50
616/19	*Set of 4*	5·00	5·00
MS620	125 × 75 mm. Nos. 616/19	5·50	7·00

(Litho Questa)

1982 (4 Aug). *75th Anniv of Boy Scout Movement. T* **137** *and similar vert designs. Multicoloured. W w* 14. *P* 14.

621	10 c. Type **137**	10	10
622	50 c. First Aid practice	30	15
623	$1.50, Camping	75	80
624	$2.50, Campfire singsong	1·25	1·50
621/4	*Set of 4*	2·25	2·25

138 Leeds Castle

139 "Adoration of the Kings" (detail, Jan Brueghel)

(Des PAD Studio. Litho Questa)

1982 (1 Sept). *21st Birthday of Princess of Wales. T* **138** *and similar vert designs. Multicoloured. P* 14½ × 14.

625	50 c. Type **138**	30	20
626	$2 Princess Diana boarding aircraft	1·75	75
627	$4 Wedding	2·00	1·40
625/7	*Set of 3*	3·50	2·10
MS628	102 × 75 mm. $5 Princess of Wales	3·25	2·00

(Des PAD Studio. Litho Harrison)

1982 (10 Nov). *Christmas. T* **139** *and similar vert designs depicting details from paintings. Multicoloured. W w* 14. *P* 14.

629	10 c. Type **139**	10	10
630	30 c. "Nativity" (Lorenzo Costa)	15	10
631	50 c. "Virgin and Child" (Fra Filippo Lippi)	25	15
632	80 c. "Adoration of the Shepherds" (Nicolas Poussin)	40	55
629/32	*Set of 4*	75	75

140 The Pitons

141 Crown Agents Headquarters, Millbank, London

(Des D. Bowen. Litho Questa)

1983 (14 Mar). *Commonwealth Day. T* **140** *and similar horiz designs. Multicoloured. W w* 14 (*sideways*). *P* 14.

633	10 c. Type **140**	10	10
634	30 c. Tourist beach	15	10
635	50 c. Banana harvesting	20	15
636	$2 Flag of St. Lucia	75	1·00
633/6	*Set of 4*	1·00	1·10

(Des L. Curtis. Litho Questa)

1983 (1 Apr). *150th Anniv of Crown Agents. T* **141** *and similar vert designs. Multicoloured. W w* 14. *P* 14.

637	10 c. Type **141**	10	10
638	15 c. Road construction	10	10
639	50 c. Road network map	20	25
640	$2 First St. Lucia stamp	60	1·25
637/40	*Set of 4*	80	1·50

IMPERFORATES AND MISSING COLOURS. Various issues between Nos. 641 and 947 exist either imperforate or with colours omitted. Such items are not listed as there is no evidence that they fulfil the criteria outlined on page xi of this catalogue.

142 Communications at Sea

(Des J.W. Litho Format)

1983 (12 July). *World Communications Year. T* **142** *and similar horiz designs. Multicoloured. P* 14½.

641	10 c. Type **142**	15	10
642	50 c. Communications in the air	40	15
643	$1.50, T.V. transmission via satellite	90	75
644	$2.50, Computer communications	1·40	1·25
641/4	*Set of 4*	2·50	2·00
MS645	107 × 88 mm. $5 Weather satellite	1·50	2·75

143 Long-jawed Squirrelfish

(Des G. Drummond. Litho Format)

1983 (23 Aug). *Coral Reef Fishes. T* **143** *and similar horiz designs. Multicoloured.* P 14½.

646	10 c. Type **143**	10	10
647	50 c. Banded Butterflyfish	20	15
648	$1.50, Black-barred Soldierfish	60	85
649	$2.50 Yellow-tailed Snapper	80	1·40
646/9	*Set of 4*	1·50	2·25
MS650	122×97 mm. $5 Red Hind	2·50	3·25

144 *Duke of Sutherland (1930)*   145 *"The Niccolini-Cowper Madonna"*

(Des J.W. Litho Format)

1983 (14 Oct). *Leaders of the World. Railway Locomotives (1st series). T* **144** *and similar horiz designs, the first in each pair showing technical drawings and the second the locomotive at work.* P 12½.

651	35 c. multicoloured	15	20
	a. Vert pair. Nos. 651/2	30	40
652	35 c. multicoloured	15	20
653	35 c. multicoloured	15	20
	a. Vert pair. Nos. 653/4	30	40
654	35 c. multicoloured	15	20
655	50 c. multicoloured	20	30
	a. Vert pair. Nos. 655/6	40	60
656	50 c. multicoloured	20	30
657	50 c. multicoloured	20	30
	a. Vert pair. Nos. 657/8	40	60
658	50 c. multicoloured	20	30
659	$1 multicoloured	30	50
	a. Vert pair. Nos. 659/60	60	1·00
660	$1 multicoloured	30	50
661	$1 multicoloured	30	50
	a. Vert pair. Nos. 661/2	60	1·00
662	$1 multicoloured	30	50
663	$2 multicoloured	40	70
	a. Vert pair. Nos. 663/4	80	1·40
664	$2 multicoloured	40	70
665	$2 multicoloured	40	70
	a. Vert pair. Nos. 665/6	80	1·40
666	$2 multicoloured	40	70
651/66	*Set of 16*	3·50	6·50

Designs:—Nos. 651/2, *Duke of Sutherland*, Great Britain (1930); 653/4, *City of Glasgow*, Great Britain (1940); 655/6, *Lord Nelson*, Great Britain (1926); 657/8, *Leeds United*, Great Britain (1928); 659/60, *Bodmin*, Great Britain (1945); 661/2, *Eton*, Great Britain (1930); 663/4, *Flying Scotsman*, Great Britain (1923); 665/6, *Rocket*, Great Britain (1829).

Nos. 651/2, 653/4, 655/6, 657/8, 659/60, 661/2, 663/4 and 665/6 were printed together, *se-tenant*, in vertical pairs throughout the sheets.

See also Nos. 715/26, 761/76, 824/31 and 858/73.

(Litho Format)

1983 (21 Nov). *Christmas. 500th Birth Anniv of Raphael. T* **145** *and similar vert designs showing details of Raphael paintings. Multicoloured.* W w **14.** P 14.

667	10 c. Type **145**	10	10
668	30 c. "The Holy Family with a Palm Tree"	15	10
669	50 c. "The Sistine Madonna"	20	30
670	$5 "The Alba Madonna"	1·00	3·25
667/70	*Set of 4*	1·25	3·25

146 *George III*   147 *Clarke & Co's Drug Store*

(Des Court House Studio. Litho Format)

1984 (13 Mar). *Leaders of the World. British Monarchs. T* **146** *and similar vert designs. Multicoloured.* P 12½.

671	5 c. Battle of Waterloo	10	10
	a. Horiz pair. Nos. 671/2	10	10
672	5 c. Type **146**	10	10
673	10 c. George III at Kew	10	10
	a. Horiz pair. Nos. 673/4	10	15
674	10 c. Kew Palace	10	10
675	35 c. Coat of Arms of Elizabeth I	10	20
	a. Horiz pair. Nos. 675/6	20	40
676	35 c. Elizabeth I	10	20
677	60 c. Coat of Arms of George III	20	30
	a. Horiz pair. Nos. 677/8	40	60
678	60 c. George III *(different)*	20	30
679	$1 Elizabeth I at Hatfield	20	35
	a. Horiz pair. Nos. 679/80	40	70

680	$1 Hatfield Palace	20	35
681	$2.50, Spanish Armada	30	60
	a. Horiz pair. Nos. 681/2	60	1·10
682	$2.50, Elizabeth I *(different)*	30	60
671/82	*Set of 12*	1·50	2·75

Nos. 671/2, 673/4, 675/6, 677/8, 679/80 and 681/2 were printed together in *se-tenant* horizontal pairs throughout the sheets.

Unissued 30, 50 c., $1, $2.50 and $5 values, showing Alfred the Great or Richard I, exist from stock dispersed by the liquidator of Format International Security Printers Ltd.

(Des J. Cooter. Litho Questa)

1984 (6 Apr). *Historic Buildings. T* **147** *and similar multicoloured designs.* W w **15** *(sideways on 45 c. to $2.50).* P 14 × 13½ (10 c.) *or* 13½ × 14 *(others).*

683	10 c. Type **147**	10	10
684	45 c. Colonial architecture *(horiz)*	30	25
685	65 c. Colonial "chattel" house *(horiz)*	45	35
686	$2.50, Treasury after 1906 earthquake *(horiz)*	1·75	1·60
683/6	*Set of 4*	2·40	2·00

1984 (15 May). *As Nos. 540/42, 545/6 and 548, but* W w **15** *(sideways on 20 c. to $1).* P 14½ × 14.

690	20 c. Geestcrest (freighter)	1·50	30
691	25 c. Britten Norman Islander aircraft	2·00	35
692	30 c. Charles (pilot boat)	1·75	45
695	$1 Lockheed L-1011 Tristar 500 airliner	4·25	90
696	$2 Booker Vulcan (cargo liner)	5·00	3·00
698	$10 Queen Elizabeth 2 (liner)	10·00	14·00
690/8	*Set of 6*	22·00	17·00

148 *Logwood*

(Des J. Cooter. Litho Format)

1984 (12 June). *Forestry Resources. T* **148** *and similar multicoloured designs.* W w **15** *(inverted on 65 c., sideways on others).* P 14 × 13½ (65 c.) *or* 13½ × 14 *(others).*

699	10 c. Type **148**	10	10
700	45 c. Calabash	30	30
701	65 c. Gommier *(vert)*	35	45
702	$2.50, Raintree	60	2·75
699/702	*Set of 4*	1·10	3·25

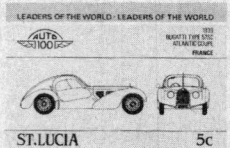

149 *Bugatti Type "57SC Atlantic Coupe"*

(Des J.W. Litho Format)

1984 (25 June). *Leaders of the World. Automobiles (1st series). T* **149** *and similar horiz designs, the first in each pair showing technical drawings and the second the paintings.* P 12½.

703	5 c. black, reddish lavender and lemon	10	10
	a. Vert pair. Nos. 703/4	10	10
704	5 c. multicoloured	10	10
705	10 c. black, azure and rose-carmine	10	10
	a. Vert pair. Nos. 705/6	10	10
706	10 c. multicoloured	10	10
707	$1 black, pale green and orange-brown	15	25
	a. Vert pair. Nos. 707/8	30	50
708	$1 multicoloured	15	25
709	$2.50, black, pale flesh and slate-blue	30	40
	a. Vert pair. Nos. 709/10	60	80
710	$2.50, multicoloured	30	40
703/10	*Set of 8*	80	1·25

Designs:—Nos. 703/4, Bugatti Type "57SC Atlantic Coupe"; 705/6, Chevrolet "Bel Air Convertible"; 707/8, Alfa Romeo "1750 GS (Zagato)"; 709/10, Duesenberg "S J Roadster".

Nos. 703/4, 705/6, 707/8 and 709/10 were printed together, *se-tenant*, in vertical pairs throughout the sheets.

See also Nos. 745/60, 789/96 and 902/13.

150 *Pygmy Gecko*   151 *Men's Volleyball*

(Des Jennifer Toombs. Litho Format)

1984 (8 Aug). *Endangered Wildlife. T* **150** *and similar horiz designs. Multicoloured.* W w **15** *(sideways).* P 14.

711	10 c. Type **150**	30	10
712	45 c. Maria Island Ground Lizard	70	50
713	65 c. Green Iguana	75	85
714	$2.50 Couresse Snake	1·00	3·50
711/14	*Set of 4*	2·50	4·50

(Des J.W. Litho Format)

1984 (21 Sept). *Leaders of the World. Railway Locomotives (2nd series). Horiz designs as T* **144**, *the first in each pair showing technical drawings and the second the locomotive at work.* P 12½.

715	1 c. multicoloured	10	10
	a. Vert pair. Nos. 715/16	10	10
716	1 c. multicoloured	10	10
717	15 c. multicoloured	10	15
	a. Vert pair. Nos. 717/18	15	30
718	15 c. multicoloured	10	15
719	50 c. multicoloured	15	15
	a. Vert pair. Nos. 719/20	30	30
720	50 c. multicoloured	15	15
721	75 c. multicoloured	15	20
	a. Vert pair. Nos. 721/2	30	40
722	75 c. multicoloured	15	20
723	$1 multicoloured	20	25
	a. Vert pair. Nos. 723/4	40	50
724	$1 multicoloured	20	25
725	$2 multicoloured	25	35
	a. Vert pair. Nos. 725/6	50	50
726	$2 multicoloured	25	35
715/26	*Set of 12*	1·50	2·00

Designs:—Nos. 715/16, *Taw*, Great Britain (1897); 717/18, Class Be 6/8 "Crocodile" electric locomotive, Switzerland (1920); 719/20, *The Countess*, Great Britain (1903); 721/2, Class GE6/6 electric locomotive, Switzerland (1921); 723/4, Class P8, Germany (1906); 725/6, *Adler*, Germany (1835).

Nos. 715/26 were issued in a similar sheet format to Nos. 651/66.

Nos. 715/26 exist imperforate from stock dispersed by the liquidator of Format International Security Printers Ltd.

(Des Court House Studio. Litho Format)

1984 (21 Sept). *Leaders of the World. Olympic Games, Los Angeles. T* **151** *and similar vert designs. Multicoloured.* P 12½.

727	5 c. Type **151**	10	10
	a. Horiz pair. Nos. 727/8	10	10
728	5 c. Women's volleyball	10	10
729	10 c. Women's hurdles	10	10
	a. Horiz pair. Nos. 729/30	10	10
730	10 c. Men's hurdles	10	10
731	65 c. Show jumping	15	20
	a. Horiz pair. Nos. 731/2	30	40
732	65 c. Dressage	15	20
733	$2.50, Women's gymnastics	40	50
	a. Horiz pair. Nos. 733/4	80	1·00
734	$2.50, Men's gymnastics	40	50
727/34	*Set of 8*	1·10	1·40

Nos. 727/8, 729/30, 731/2, 733/4 were printed together, *se-tenant*, in horizontal pairs throughout the sheets.

Examples of No. 537 exist overprinted "RUMBRIDGE PACK R.F.C./1984 TOUR". This was a private souvenir, connected with a tour to St. Lucia by an English rugby club in October 1984. It was not sold by the St. Lucia Post Office or Philatelic Bureau.

152 *Glass of Wine and Flowers*   153 *Slaves preparing Manioc*

(Des G. Vasarhelyi. Litho Format)

1984 (31 Oct). *Christmas. T* **152** *and similar vert designs. Multicoloured.* W w **15.** P 14.

735	10 c. Type **152**	10	10
736	35 c. Priest and decorated altar	10	10
737	65 c. Nativity scene	15	25
738	$3 Holy Family	50	1·50
	w. Wmk inverted	5·00	
735/8	*Set of 4*	60	1·75
MS739	147×77 mm. Nos. 735/8	1·60	4·50

(Des J. Cooter. Litho Format)

1984 (12 Dec). *150th Anniv of Abolition of Slavery. T* **153** *and similar vert designs. Each black and yellow-ochre.* W w **15.** P 14 × 13½.

740	10 c. Type **153**	10	10
741	35 c. Sifting and cooking cassava flour	10	10
742	55 c. Cooking pot, and preparing tobacco	10	20
743	$5 Stripping tobacco leaves for twist tobacco	70	1·50
740/3	*Set of 4*	80	1·60
MS744	154 × 110 mm. As Nos. 740/3, but without dates and side inscription and with the face values in different positions	1·50	4·50

(Des Artists International (65 c.), J.W. (others). Litho Format)

1984 (19 Dec). *Leaders of the World. Automobiles (2nd series). Horiz designs as T* **149**, *the first in each pair showing technical drawings and the second paintings.* P 12½.

745	10 c. black, pale green and lake-brown	10	10
	a. Vert pair. Nos. 745/6	10	15
746	10 c. multicoloured	10	10
747	30 c. black, azure and bright yellow-green	15	15
	a. Vert pair. Nos. 747/8	30	30
748	30 c. multicoloured	15	15
749	55 c. black, greenish yellow and orange-brown	20	30
	a. Vert pair. Nos. 749/50	40	60
750	55 c. multicoloured	20	30
751	65 c. black, grey and brown-lilac	20	35
	a. Vert pair. Nos. 751/2	40	70
752	65 c. multicoloured	20	35
753	75 c. black, pale cinnamon, & orange-verm	20	35
	a. Vert pair. Nos. 753/4	40	70
754	75 c. multicoloured	20	35
755	$1 black, pale cinnamon and dull violet-blue	20	40
	a. Vert pair. Nos. 755/6	40	80

756	$1 multicoloured	..	..	20	40
757	$2 black, pale green and orange-red	..	25	50
	a. Vert pair. Nos. 757/8	..	..	50	1·00
758	$2 multicoloured	..	..	25	50
759	$3 black, pale cinnamon & orange-verm	30	60
	a. Vert pair. Nos. 759/60	..	..	60	1·10
760	$3 multicoloured	..	..	30	60
745/60		*Set of 16*	2·75	4·75

Designs:—Nos. 745/6, Panhard and Levassor; 747/8, N.S.U. "RO-80" Saloon; 749/50, Abarth "Bialbero"; 751/2, TVR "Vixen 2500M"; 753/4, Ford "Mustang" Convertible; 755/6, Ford "Model T"; 757/8, Aston Martin" DB3S"; 759/60, Chrysler "Imperial CG Dual Cowl" Phaeton.

Nos. 745/60 were issued in a similar sheet format to Nos. 703/10.

(Des T. Hadler (5, 15, 35 c.), J.W. (others). Litho Format)

1985 (4 Feb). *Leaders of the World. Railway Locomotives* (3rd series). *Horiz designs as T* **144,** *the first in each pair showing technical drawings and the second the locomotive at work.* P 12½.

761	5 c. multicoloured	..	..	10	10
	a. Vert pair. Nos. 761/2	..	10	10
762	5 c. multicoloured	..	..	10	10
763	15 c. multicoloured	..	..	10	15
	a. Vert pair. Nos. 763/4	..	20	30
764	15 c. multicoloured	..	..	10	15
765	35 c. multicoloured	..	..	15	15
	a. Vert pair. Nos. 765/6	..	30	30
766	35 c. multicoloured	..	..	15	15
767	60 c. multicoloured	..	..	15	15
	a. Vert pair. Nos. 767/8	..	30	30
768	60 c. multicoloured	..	..	15	15
769	75 c. multicoloured	..	..	15	20
	a. Vert pair. Nos. 769/70	..	20	40
770	75 c. multicoloured	..	..	15	20
771	$1 multicoloured	..	..	15	20
	a. Vert pair. Nos. 771/2	..	30	40
772	$1 multicoloured	..	..	15	20
773	$2 multicoloured	..	..	25	40
	a. Vert pair. Nos. 773/4	..	50	80
774	$2 multicoloured	..	..	25	40
775	$2.50, multicoloured	..	..	30	55
	a. Vert pair. Nos. 775/6	..	60	1·10
776	$2.50, multicoloured	..	..	30	55
761/76		*Set of 16*	2·25	3·25

Designs:—Nos. 761/2, Class C53, Japan (1928); 763/4, Class L No. 39, India (1885); 765/6, Class B18¼, Australia (1926); 767/8, Owain Glyndwr, Great Britain (1923); 769/70, Lion, Great Britain (1838); 771/2, LNWR locomotive, Great Britain (1873); 773/4, Class Q6 No. 2238, Great Britain (1921); 775/6, Class H No. 106, Great Britain (1920).

Nos. 761/76 were issued in a similar sheet format to Nos. 651/66.

154 Girl Guide Badge in Shield and Crest of St. Lucia **155** *Clossiana selene*

(Des Court House Studio. Litho Questa)

1985 (21 Feb). *75th Anniv of Girl Guide Movement and 60th Anniv of Guiding in St. Lucia.* W w **15.** P 14.

777	**154**	10 c. multicoloured	..	30	10
778		35 c. multicoloured	..	1·00	10
779		65 c. multicoloured	..	1·50	75
780		$3 multicoloured	..	3·75	5·00
777/80			*Set of 4*	6·00	5·50

(Des Jennifer Toombs. Litho Format)

1985 (28 Feb). *Leaders of the World. Butterflies. T* **155** *and similar vert designs. Multicoloured.* P 12½.

781	15 c. Type **155**	..	..	10	10
	a. Horiz pair. Nos. 781/2	..	15	15
782	15 c. *Inachis io*	..	..	10	10
783	40 c. *Philaethria dido* (s sp *werneckei*)	10	15
	a. Horiz pair. Nos. 783/4	..	20	30
784	40 c. *Callicore sorana*	..	10	15
785	60 c. *Kallima inachus*	..	15	15
	a. Horiz pair. Nos. 785/6	..	30	30
786	60 c. *Hypanartia paullus*	..	15	15
787	$2.25, *Morpho helena*	..	25	50
	a. Horiz pair. Nos. 787/8	..	50	1·00
788	$2.25, *Ornithoptera meridionalis*	25	50
781/8			*Set of 8*	1·00	1·60

Nos. 781/2, 783/4, 785/6 and 787/8 were printed together, se-tenant, in horizontal pairs throughout the sheets.

(Des J.W. Litho Format)

1985 (29 Mar). *Leaders of the World. Automobiles* (3rd series). *Horiz designs as T* **149,** *the first in each pair showing technical drawings and the second the paintings.* P 12½.

789	15 c. black, cobalt and Indian red	..	10	10
	a. Vert pair. Nos. 789/90	..	15	20
790	15 c. multicoloured	..	..	10	10
791	50 c. black, pale orange and deep rose-red	15	20
	a. Vert pair. Nos. 791/2	..	30	40
792	50 c. multicoloured	..	..	15	20
793	$1 black, pale green and reddish orange	..	15	20
	a. Vert pair. Nos. 793/4	..	30	40
794	$1 multicoloured	..	..	15	20
795	$1.50, black, pale green & pale red-brown	20	35
	a. Vert pair. Nos. 795/6	..	40	70
796	$1.50, multicoloured	..	..	20	35
789/96			*Set of 8*	1·00	1·60

Designs:—Nos. 789/90, Hudson "Eight" (1940); 791/2, KdF (1937); 793/4, Kissel "Goldbug" (1925); 795/6, Ferrari "246 GTS" (1973).

Nos. 789/96 were issued in a similar sheet format to Nos. 703/10.

156 Grenadier, 70th **157** Messerschmitt Bf 109E
Regiment, c 1775

(Des J. Cooter. Litho Format)

1985 (7 May). *Military Uniforms. T* **156** *and similar vert designs. Multicoloured.* W w **15** *(sideways). With imprint date.* P 15.

797	5 c. Type **156**..	..	..	25	40
798	10 c. Officer, Grenadier Company, 14th Regiment, 1780..	..	25	15
799	20 c. Officer, Battalion Company, 46th Regiment, 1781	40	30
800	25 c. Officer, Royal Artillery, c. 1782	40	15
801	30 c. Officer, Royal Engineers, 1782	60	30
802	35 c. Officer, Battalion Company, 54th Regiment, 1782	50	20
803	45 c. Private, Grenadier Company, 14th Regiment, 1782..	80	40
804	50 c. Gunner, Royal Artillery, 1796..	80	40
805	65 c. Private, Battalion Company, 85th Regiment, c. 1796	70	55
806	75 c. Private, Battalion Company, 76th Regiment, 1796	75	80
807	90 c. Private, Battalion Company, 81st Regiment, c. 1796	85	90
808	$1 Sergeant, 74th (Highland) Regiment, 1796	90	90
809	$2.50, Private, Light Company, 93rd Regiment, 1803	3·50	6·50
810	$5 Private, Battalion Company, 1st West India Regiment, 1803	6·00	12·00
811	$15 Officer, Royal Artillery, 1850 ..	8·00	18·00
797/811		*Set of 15*	22·00	38·00

Imprint dates: "1984", Nos. 797/811; "1986", Nos. 799/800.
Examples of the 5, 10, 15, 45, 50 c. and $20 with "1986" imprint date, and in some cases imperforate, come from stock dispersed by the liquidator of Format International Security Printers Ltd.

For 5, 10, 30, 45, 50 c., $2.50, $5, and additional values, all without watermark see Nos. 928/46.

For 5, 10, 20, 25 c. and additional values, all watermarked w **16** (sideways) see Nos. 993/1003.

(Des J.W. Litho Format)

1985 (30 May). *Leaders of the World. Military Aircraft. T* **157** *and similar horiz designs, the first in each pair showing paintings and the second technical drawings.* P 12½.

812	5 c. multicoloured	..	..	10	15
	a. Vert pair. Nos. 812/13 ..	..	10	25
813	5 c. black, pale new blue and pale yellow ..	10	15
814	55 c. multicoloured	..	..	25	40
	a. Vert pair. Nos. 814/15 ..	..	50	80
815	55 c. black, pale new blue and pale yellow ..	25	40
816	60 c. multicoloured	..	..	25	40
	a. Vert pair. Nos. 816/17 ..	..	50	80
817	60 c. black, pale new blue and pale yellow ..	25	40
818	$2 multicoloured	..	..	40	75
	a. Vert pair. Nos. 818/19 ..	..	80	1·50
819	$2 black, pale new blue and pale yellow ..	40	75
812/19		*Set of 8*	1·75	3·00

Designs:—Nos. 812/13, Messerschmitt Bf 109E; 814/15, Avro Type 683 Lancaster Mk 1; 816/17, North American P-51D Mustang; 818/19, Supermarine Spitfire Mk II.
Nos. 812/13, 814/15, 816/17 and 818/19 were printed together, se-tenant, in vertical pairs throughout the sheets.

158 Magnificent Frigate **159** Queen Elizabeth the
Birds, Frigate Island Queen Mother
Bird Sanctuary

(Des G. Drummond. Litho Format)

1985 (20 June). *Nature Reserves. T* **158** *and similar horiz designs. Multicoloured.* W w **15.** P 15.

820	10 c. Type **158**..	..	..	35	20
821	35 c. Mangrove Cuckoo, Scorpion Island, Savannes Bay	65	45
822	65 c. Lesser Yellowlegs, Maria Island Reserve ..	..	75	85
823	$3 Audubon's Shearwaters, Lapins Island Reserve ..	1·00	5·00
820/3		*Set of 4*	2·50	6·00

(Des Tudor Art Agency ($2.50), J.W. (others). Litho Format)

1985 (26 June). *Leaders of the World. Railway Locomotives* (4th series). *Horiz designs as T* **144,** *the first in each pair showing technical drawings and second the locomotive at work.* P 12½.

824	10 c. multicoloured	..	..	10	10
	a. Vert pair. Nos. 824/5 ..	..	20	20
825	10 c. multicoloured	..	..	10	10
826	30 c. multicoloured	..	..	15	15
	a. Vert pair. Nos. 826/7 ..	..	30	30
827	30 c. multicoloured	..	..	15	15

828	75 c. multicoloured	..	..	20	25
	a. Vert pair. Nos. 828/9 ..	..	40	50
829	75 c. multicoloured	..	..	20	25
830	$2.50, multicoloured	..	..	40	70
	a. Vert pair. Nos. 830/1 ..	..	80	1·40
831	$2.50, multicoloured	..	..	40	70
824/31		*Set of 8*	1·50	2·25

Designs:—Nos. 824/5, Tank locomotive No. 28, Great Britain (1897); 826/7, Class M No. 1621, Great Britain (1893); 828/9, Class "Dunalastair", Great Britain (1896); 830/1, "Big Bertha" type No. 2290, Great Britain (1919).

Nos. 824/31 were issued in a similar sheet format to Nos. 651/66.

(Des Court House Studio. Litho Format)

1985 (16 Aug). *Leaders of the World. Life and Times of Queen Elizabeth the Queen Mother. Various vertical portraits as T* **159.** P 12.

832	40 c. multicoloured	..	..	10	20
	a. Horiz pair. Nos. 832/3 ..	..	15	40
833	40 c. multicoloured	..	..	10	20
834	75 c. multicoloured	..	..	10	25
	a. Horiz pair. Nos. 834/5 ..	..	20	50
835	75 c. multicoloured	..	..	10	25
836	$1.10, multicoloured	..	..	15	35
	a. Horiz pair. Nos. 836/7 ..	..	30	70
837	$1.10, multicoloured	..	..	15	35
838	$1.75, multicoloured	..	..	20	55
	a. Horiz pair. Nos. 838/9 ..	..	35	1·10
839	$1.75, multicoloured	..	..	20	55
832/9		*Set of 8*	90	2·50
MS840	84×114 mm. $2 mult; $2 mult		60	1·40

The two designs of each value were issued, *se-tenant,* in horizontal pairs within the sheets.

Each *se-tenant* pair shows a floral pattern across the bottom of the portraits which stops short of the left-hand edge on the left-hand stamp and of the right-hand edge on the right-hand stamp.

Nos. 832/9, together with two unissued 25 c. designs, exist in miniature sheets, one for each value, from stock dispersed by the liquidator of Format International Security Printers Ltd.

Designs as Nos. 832/3 and 836/7, but with face values of $3 × 2 and $6 × 2, also exist in additional miniature sheets from a restricted printing issued 31 December 1985.

160 "Youth playing Banjo" **161** "Papa Jab"
(Wayne Whitfield)

(Litho Format)

1985 (5 Sept). *International Youth Year. Paintings by Young St. Lucians. T* **160** *and similar designs.* W w **15** *(sideways).* P 15.

841	10 c. black, new blue and bright magenta ..	10	10
842	45 c. multicoloured	..	..	30	25
843	75 c. multicoloured	..	..	50	50
844	$3.50, multicoloured	..	..	1·40	3·00
841/4		*Set of 4*	2·00	3·50
MS845	123×86 mm. $5 multicoloured ..	1·25	3·50

Designs: Vert (as T **160**)—45 c. "Motorcyclist" (Mark Maragh); 75 c. "Boy and Girl at Pitons" (Bartholomew Eugene); $3.50, "Abstract" (Lyndon Samuel). Horiz (80 × 55 *mm*)—$5 Young people and St. Lucia landscapes.

1985 (26 Oct). *Royal Visit. Nos.* 649, 685/6, 702, 713, 778 *and* 836/7 *optd as T* **114** *of Montserrat.*

846	**154**	35 c. multicoloured	..	4·50	2·75
847	–	65 c. multicoloured (No. 685)	..	1·00	2·50
848	–	65 c. multicoloured (No. 713)	..	4·00	3·50
849	–	$1.10, multicoloured (No. 836)	4·75	7·00
		a. Horiz pair. Nos. 849/50 ..	9·50	14·00
850	–	$1.10, multicoloured (No. 837)	4·75	7·00
851	–	$2.50, multicoloured (No. 649)	5·50	7·00
852	–	$2.50, multicoloured (No. 686)	1·00	2·75
853	–	$2.50, multicoloured (No. 702)	1·00	2·75
846/53			*Set of 8*	24·00	32·00

(Litho Format)

1985 (24 Dec). *Christmas. Masqueraders. T* **161** *and similar vert designs. Multicoloured.* P 15.

854	10 c. Type **161**..	..	..	15	10
855	45 c. "Paille Bananne"	..	..	25	25
856	65 c. "Cheval Bois"	..	..	30	75
854/6		*Set of 3*	60	1·00
MS857	70×83 mm. $4 "Madonna and Child" (Dunstan St. Omer) ..	90	1·90

(Des T. Hadler. Litho Format)

1986 (27 Jan). *Leaders of the World. Railway Locomotives* (5th series). *Horiz designs as T* **144,** *the first in each pair showing technical drawings and the second the locomotive at work.* P 12½.

858	5 c. multicoloured	..	..	10	15
	a. Vert pair. Nos. 858/9	..	10	30
859	5 c. multicoloured	..	..	10	15
860	15 c. multicoloured	..	..	15	15
	a. Vert pair. Nos. 860/1	..	30	30
861	15 c. multicoloured	..	..	15	15
862	30 c. multicoloured	..	..	20	30
	a. Vert pair. Nos. 862/3	..	40	60

863	30 c. multicoloured	..	..	..	20	30
864	60 c. multicoloured	..	..	..	25	40
	a. Vert pair. Nos. 864/5	..	..		50	80
865	60 c. multicoloured	..	..	..	25	40
866	75 c. multicoloured	..	..	..	30	50
	a. Vert pair. Nos. 866/7	..	..		60	1·00
867	75 c. multicoloured	..	..	..	30	50
868	$1 multicoloured	..	..	..	35	60
	a. Vert pair. Nos. 868/9	..	..		70	1·10
869	$1 multicoloured	..	..	..	35	60
870	$2.25, multicoloured	..	..	..	45	80
	a. Vert pair. Nos. 870/1	..	..		90	1·60
871	$2.25, multicoloured	..	..	..	45	80
872	$3 multicoloured	..	..	..	45	80
	a. Vert pair. Nos. 872/3	..	..		90	1·60
873	$3 multicoloured	..	..	..	45	80
858/73				Set of 16	4·00	6·50

Designs:—Nos. 858/9, Cog locomotive *Tip Top*, U.S.A. (1983); 860/1, Electric locomotive *Stephenson*, Great Britain (1975); 862/3, Class D No. 737, Great Britain (1901); 864/5, No. 13 electric locomotive, Great Britain (1922); 866/7, Electric locomotive *Electra*, Great Britain (1954); 868/9, *City of Newcastle*, Great Britain (1922); 870/1, Von Kruckenburg propeller-driven rail car, Germany (1930); 872/3, No. 860, Japan (1893).

Nos. 858/73 were issued in a similar sheet format to Nos. 651/66.

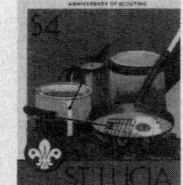

162 Campfire Cooking Utensils

(Des Court House Studio. Litho Format)

1986 (3 Mar). *75th Anniv of Girl Guide Movement and Boy Scouts of America*. Two sheets, each 85 × 113 mm, containing vert designs as T **162**. Multicoloured. P 12½.

MS874	$4 Type **162**: $4 Scout salute	..	1·75	3·25
MS875	$6 Wickerwork: $6 Lady Baden-Powell	..	2·75	4·25

The two stamps in each sheet were printed together, *se-tenant*, in horizontal pairs, each forming a composite design.

Nos. **MS874/5** exist with plain or decorative margins.

Overprints on these miniature sheets commemorating "Capex '87" International Stamp Exhibition, Toronto, were not authorised by the St. Lucia administration.

(Des Court House Studio. Litho Format)

1986 (21 Apr). *60th Birthday of Queen Elizabeth II (1st issue)*. Multicoloured designs as T **117a** of Montserrat. P 12½.

876	5 c. Queen Elizabeth II				10	10
877	$1 Princess Elizabeth				15	30
878	$3.50, Queen Elizabeth II (*different*)			40	90
879	$6 In Canberra, 1982 (*vert*)		..	55	1·40
876/9				Set of 4	1·00	2·40
MS880	85 × 115 mm. $8 Queen Elizabeth II (*different*)				3·25	6·00

Nos. 876/9 exist in separate miniature sheets from stock dispersed by the liquidator of Format International Security Printers Ltd.

163 Queen Elizabeth and Marian Home

(Des Court House Studio. Litho Questa)

1986 (14 June). *60th Birthday of Queen Elizabeth II (2nd issue)*. T **163** and similar horiz designs. Multicoloured. W w **15** (*sideways*). P 14 × 15.

881	10 c. Type **163**.	..	..	25	15
882	45 c. Queen addressing rally, Mindoo Phillip Park, 1985		55	35
883	50 c. Queen opening Leon Hess Comprehensive School, 1985		65	50
884	$5 Queen Elizabeth and Government House, Castries	..	2·50	4·00
881/4	..	..		Set of 4	3·50	4·50
MS885	121 × 85 mm. $7 Queen Elizabeth and Royal Yacht *Britannia*, Castries..		4·50	7·00

164 Pope John Paul II kissing Ground, Castries Airport

(Des Court House Studio. Litho Questa)

1986 (7 July). *Visit of Pope John Paul II*. T **164** *and similar multicoloured designs*. W w **15** (*sideways on* 55, 60 c.). P 14½ × 14 (80 c.) or 14 × 14½ (*others*).

886	55 c. Type **164**.			70	70
887	60 c. Pope and St. Joseph's Convent		70	80
888	80 c. Pope and Castries Catholic Cathedral (*vert*)		1·10	1·60
886/8			Set of 3	2·25	2·75
MS889	85 × 123 mm. $6 Pope John Paul II (*vert*). P 14½ × 14		6·50	7·50

(Litho Format)

1986 (12 Aug). *Royal Wedding (1st issue)*. Multicoloured designs as T **118a** of Montserrat. P 12½.

890	80 c. Miss Sarah Ferguson			40	65
	a. Pair. Nos. 890/1			80	1·25
891	80 c. Prince Andrew			40	65
892	$2 Prince Andrew and Miss Sarah Ferguson (*horiz*)		70	1·60
	a. Pair. Nos. 892/3..			1·40	3·00
893	$2 Prince Andrew with Mrs Nancy Reagan (*horiz*)		70	1·60
890/3	..	..	Set of 4	2·00	4·00

Nos. 890/1 and 892/3 were each printed together, *se-tenant*, in horizontal and vertical pairs throughout the sheets. Nos. 890/3 imperforate come from souvenir stamp booklets. See also Nos. 897/901.

165 Peace Corps Teacher with Students   **166** Prince Andrew in Carriage

(Des J. Cooter. Litho Questa)

1986 (25 Sept). *25th Anniv of United States Peace Corps*. T **165** *and similar multicoloured designs*. W w **15** (*sideways on* $2). P 14.

894	80 c. Type **165**.		35	40
895	$2 President John Kennedy (*vert*)		1·10	1·60
896	$3.50, Peace Corps emblem between arms of St. Lucia and U.S.A...		1·60	2·50
894/6	..	Set of 3	2·75	4·00

(Des Court House Studio. Litho Format)

1986 (15 Oct). *Royal Wedding (2nd issue)*. T **166** *and similar vert designs*. Multicoloured. P 15.

897	50 c. Type **166**.			40	30
898	80 c. Miss Sarah Ferguson in coach.		50	50
899	$1 Duke and Duchess of York at altar		55	60
900	$3 Duke and Duchess of York in carriage		1·00	2·25
897/900		Set of 4	2·25	3·25
MS901	115 × 85 mm. $7 Duke and Duchess of York on Palace balcony after wedding (*horiz*)		3·50	5·50

Examples of an unissued $10 miniature sheet exist from stock dispersed by the liquidator of Format International Security Printers Ltd.

(Des Court House Studio. Litho Format)

1986 (23 Oct). *Automobiles (4th series)*. Horiz designs as T **149**, the first in each pair showing technical drawings and the second paintings. P 12½.

902	20 c. multicoloured	..	..	..	15	15
	a. Vert pair. Nos. 902/3			30	30
903	20 c. multicoloured	..	..	..	15	15
904	50 c. multicoloured	..	..	..	15	20
	a. Vert pair. Nos. 904/5			30	40
905	50 c. multicoloured	..	..	..	15	20
906	60 c. multicoloured	..	..	..	15	20
	a. Vert pair. Nos. 906/7			30	40
907	60 c. multicoloured	..	..	..	15	20
908	$1 multicoloured	..	..	..	15	20
	a. Vert pair. Nos. 908/9			30	40
909	$1 multicoloured	..	..	..	15	20
910	$1.50, multicoloured	..	..		20	20
	a. Vert pair. Nos. 910/11			40	40
911	$1.50, multicoloured	..	..		20	20
912	$3 multicoloured	..	..	..	30	45
	a. Vert pair. Nos. 912/13			60	90
913	$3 multicoloured	..	..	..	30	45
902/13			Set of 12	2·00	2·50

Designs:—Nos. 902/3, AMC "AMX" (1969); 904/5, Russo-Baltique (1912); 906/7, Lincoln "K.B." (1932); 908/9, Rolls Royce "Phantom II Continental" (1933); 910/11, Buick "Century" (1939); 912/13, Chrysler "300 C" (1957).

Nos. 902/13 were issued in a similar sheet format to Nos. 703/10.

167 Chak-Chak Band

(Des Jennifer Toombs. Litho Format)

1986 (7 Nov). *Tourism (1st series)*. T **167** *and similar horiz designs*. Multicoloured. W w **15**. P 15.

914	15 c. Type **167**.	..	..	10	10
915	45 c. Folk dancing	..		15	15
916	80 c. Steel band	..	..	30	50
917	$5 Limbo dancing	..	..	75	2·25
914/17			Set of 4	1·10	2·75
MS918	157 × 109 mm. $10 Fire-eating. Wmk sideways		3·50	7·00

See also Nos. 988/92.

168 St. Ann Catholic Church, Mon Repos   **169** Outline Map of St. Lucia

(Litho Format)

1986 (3 Dec). *Christmas*. T **168** *and similar multicoloured designs*. P 15.

919	10 c. Type **168**.	..	..	10	10
920	40 c. St. Joseph the Worker Catholic Church, Gros Islet		25	15
921	80 c. Holy Trinity Anglican Church, Castries		35	60
922	$4 Our Lady of the Assumption Catholic Church, Soufriere (*vert*)		85	2·50
919/22			Set of 4	1·40	3·00
MS923	120 × 101 mm $7 St. Lucy Catholic Church, Micoud		2·25	5·00

(Des L. Curtis. Litho Walsall)

1987 (24 Feb)–**89**. W w **14** (*sideways*). P 14. A. *No imprint at foot*

924A	**169**	5 c. black and cinnamon		20	40
925A		10 c. black and pale emerald		20	20
926A		45 c. black and bright orange		50	50
927A		50 c. black and violet-blue		60	60
927cA		$1 black and bright rose (17.3.89)		75	75
924A/7cA			Set of 5	2·00	2·25

B. *With imprint date*

924B	**169**	5 c. black and cinnamon (9.88)		20	20
925B		10 c. black and pale emerald (9.88)		20	20
927B		50 c. black and violet-blue (17.3.89)		60	60

Imprint dates: "1988", Nos. 924B/5B; "1989", No. 927B. For 5 c. and 10 c. watermarked w **16** (*sideways*) see Nos. 1018/19.

(Des J. Cooter. Litho Format)

1987 (16 Mar). *As Nos. 797/8, 801, 803/4, 809/10 and new values (15, 60, 80 c. and* $20*), all without wmk*. "1986" imprint date. P 15.

928	5 c. Type **156**.			20	30
929	10 c. Officer, Grenadier Company, 14th Regiment, 1780		25	25
930	15 c. Private, Battalion Company, 2nd West India Regiment, 1803		35	35
933	30 c. Officer, Royal Engineers, 1782		45	45
935	45 c. Private, Grenadier Company, 14th Regiment, 1782..		50	50
936	50 c. Gunner, Royal Artillery, 1796..		60	60
937	60 c. Officer, Battalion Company, 5th Regiment, 1778		70	70
940	80 c. Officer, Battalion Company, 27th Regiment, c. 1780		90	90
943	$2.50, Private, Light Company, 93rd Regiment, 1803		3·00	4·50
944	$5 Private, Battalion Company, 1st West India Regiment, 1803 ..		3·75	9·00
946	$20 Private, Grenadier Company, 46th Regiment, 1778 ..		17·00	24·00
928/46		Set of 11	25·00	38·00

Imprint dates: "1986", Nos. 928/46; "1987", No. 944. For various values watermarked w **16** (*sideways*) see Nos. 993/1003.

170 Statue of Liberty and Flags of France and U.S.A.   **171** First Cadastral Survey Map and Surveying Instruments, 1775

(Des A. Theobald. Litho Format)

1987 (29 Apr). *Centenary of Statue of Liberty (1986)*. T **170** *and similar vert designs*. Multicoloured. W w **16**. P 14½.

947	15 c. Type **170**.			15	10
948	80 c. Statue and *Mauretania I* (liner)		75	65
949	$1 Statue and Concorde		1·75	1·00
950	$5 Statue and flying boat at sunset		2·25	4·25
947/50		Set of 4	4·50	5·50
MS951	107 × 88 mm. $6 Statue and Manhattan at night. Wmk sideways		3·00	4·25

Unissued $3.50, $4 and $5 miniature sheets exist from stock dispersed by the liquidator of Format International Security Printers Ltd.

1987 (July). *Coil stamp. As No. 350, but W w* **16**. P 14½ × 14.

953	**87**	10 c. turquoise-green	..	50	50

(Des N. Shewring. Litho Walsall)

1987 (31 Aug). *New Cadastral Survey of St. Lucia. T 171 and similar vert designs. Multicoloured. W w 16. P 14.*

955	15 c. Type 171	60	15
956	60 c. Map and surveying instruments, 1814	1·25	85
957	$1 Map and surveying instruments, 1888	1·50	1·50
958	$2.50, Cadastral survey map and surveying instruments, 1987	2·75	4·00
955/8	..	5·50	6·00

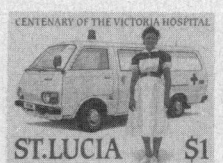

172 Ambulance and Nurse, 1987

173 "The Holy Family"

(Des C. Abbott. Litho Questa)

1987 (4 Nov). *Centenary of Victoria Hospital, Castries. T 172 and similar horiz designs. Multicoloured. W w 16 (sideways). P 14 × 14½.*

959	172 $1 multicoloured	2·00	2·25
	a. Pair. Nos. 959/60	4·00	4·50
960	– $1 indigo	2·00	2·25
961	– $2 multicoloured	2·50	2·75
	a. Pair. Nos. 961/2	5·00	5·50
962	– $2 indigo	2·50	2·75
959/62	*Set of 4*	8·00	9·00
MS963	86 × 68 mm. $4.50, multicoloured	6·50	8·00

Designs:—No. 960, Nurse and carrying hammock, 1913; No. 961, $2 Victoria Hospital, 1987; No. 962, Victoria Hospital, 1887; No. **MS**963, Hospital gates, 1987.

Nos. 959/60 and 961/2 were each printed together, *se-tenant*, in horizontal and vertical pairs throughout the sheets.

(Des D. Miller. Litho Format)

1987 (30 Nov). *Christmas. T 173 and similar square designs showing paintings. Multicoloured. W w 16 (sideways). P 14½.*

964	15 c. Type 173	30	10
965	50 c. "Adoration of the Shepherds"	60	30
966	60 c. "Adoration of the Magi"	60	80
967	90 c. "Madonna and Child"	85	2·00
964/7	*Set of 4*	2·10	2·75
MS968	82 × 67 mm. $6 Type 173	3·00	5·00

174 St Lucia Amazon perched on Branch

175 Carib Clay Zemi

(Des W. Oliver. Litho Walsall)

1987 (18 Dec). *St. Lucia Amazon. T 174 and similar vert designs. Multicoloured. W w 16. P 14.*

969	15 c. Type 174	2·00	40
970	35 c. Pair in flight	3·00	55
971	50 c. Perched on branch (rear view)	4·00	2·25
972	$1 Emerging from tree	5·50	5·00
969/72	*Set of 4*	13·00	7·00

(Des C. Collins. Litho Walsall)

1988 (24 Feb). *Amerindian Artifacts. T 175 and similar vert designs. Multicoloured. W w 16. P 14½×14.*

973	15 c. Type 175	15	10
974	30 c. Troumassee cylinder	20	15
975	80 c. Three pointer stone	45	45
976	$3.50, Dauphine petroglyph	1·75	3·50
973/6	*Set of 4*	2·25	3·75

176 East Caribbean Currency

177 Rural Telephone Exchange

(Des D. Miller (10 c.), S. Conlin (others). Litho B.D.T.)

1988 (29 Apr). *50th Anniv of St. Lucia Co-operative Bank. T 176 and similar horiz designs. Multicoloured. W w 14 (sideways). P 15 × 14.*

977	10 c. Type 176	20	10
978	45 c. Castries branch	55	35
979	60 c. As 45 c.	75	95
980	80 c. Vieux Fort branch	1·25	1·60
977/80	*Set of 4*	2·50	2·75

(Des A. Theobald. Litho Walsall)

1988 (10 June). *50th Anniv of Cable and Wireless (West Indies) Ltd. T 177 and similar horiz designs. Multicoloured. W w 16 (sideways). P 14.*

981	15 c. Type 177	15	10
982	25 c. Early and modern telephones	15	15
983	80 c. St. Lucia Teleport dish aerial	40	45
984	$2.50, Map showing Eastern Caribbean Microwave System	1·40	2·25
981/4	*Set of 4*	1·90	2·75

178 Stained Glass Window

179 Garnished Lobsters

(Des O. Bell. Litho Format)

1988 (15 Aug). *Centenary of Methodist Church in St. Lucia. T 178 and similar diamond-shaped designs. Multicoloured. W w 16 (sideways). P 14½.*

985	15 c. Type 178	10	10
986	80 c. Church interior	40	45
987	$3.50, Methodist Church, Castries	1·50	2·25
985/7	*Set of 3*	1·75	2·50

(Des D. Miller. Litho Harrison)

1988 (15 Sept). *Tourism (2nd series). T 179 and similar vert designs showing local delicacies. Multicoloured. W w 16. P 14 × 13½.*

988	10 c. Type 179	55	65
	a. Horiz strip of 4. Nos. 988/91	4·00	
989	30 c. Cocktail and tourists at buffet	65	75
990	80 c. Fresh fruits and roasted breadfruit	1·10	1·25
991	$2.50, Barbecued Red Snappers (fish)	3·00	4·50
988/91	*Set of 4*	4·00	4·50
MS992	88 × 104 mm. $5.50, Fruit stall, Castries market. P 14½ × 14	2·25	3·00

Nos. 988/91 were printed together, *se-tenant*, in horizontal strips of four throughout the sheet, forming a composite design of tourists at beach barbecue.

(Des J. Cooter. Litho Format)

1988 (Sept)–**89**. *As Nos. 797/800, 930, 937, 940 and 946, but W w 16 (sideways). With imprint date. P 15.*

993	5 c. Type 156 (6.89)	60	90
994	10 c. Officer, Grenadier Company, 14th Regiment, 1780 (6.89)	75	50
995	15 c. Private, Battalion Company, 2nd West India Regiment, 1803	90	75
996	20 c. Officer, Battalion Company, 46th Regiment, 1781 (6.89)	1·00	1·00
997	25 c. Officer, Royal Artillery, c. 1782	1·00	1·00
999	60 c. Officer, Battalion Company, 5th Regiment, 1778	1·75	1·75
1000	80 c. Officer, Battalion Company, 27th Regiment, c. 1780	2·00	2·00
1003	$20 Private, Grenadier Company, 46th Regiment, 1778 (6.89)	21·00	30·00
993/1003	*Set of 8*	26·00	35·00

Imprint dates: "1988", Nos. 995, 997, 999/1000; "1989", Nos. 993/7, 1003.

(Des D. Miller (10 c.), L. Curtis and D. Miller (60 c.), E. Nisbet and D. Miller (80 c.), S. Noon and D. Miller ($2.50). Litho Questa)

1988 (17 Oct). *300th Anniv of Lloyd's of London. Designs as T 167a of Malawi. W w 14 (sideways on 60, 80 c.) P 14.*

1004	10 c. black, grey-lilac and brown	45	15
1005	60 c. multicoloured	1·25	75
1006	80 c. multicoloured	1·60	1·25
1007	$2.50, multicoloured	3·00	4·50
1004/7	*Set of 4*	5·75	6·00

Designs: *Vert*—10 c. San Francisco earthquake, 1906; $2.50, Castries fire, 1948. *Horiz*—60 c. Castries Harbour; 80 c. *Lady Nelson* (hospital ship) 1942.

180 Snow on the Mountain

181 Princess Alexandra presenting Constitution

(Des R. Gorringe. Litho Format)

1988 (22 Nov). *Christmas. Flowers. T 180 and similar vert designs. Multicoloured. W w 16. P 14.*

1008	15 c. Type 180	30	10
1009	45 c. Christmas Candle	55	50
1010	60 c. Balisier	70	90
	w. Wmk inverted	2·00	
1011	80 c. Poinsettia	1·00	1·60
	w. Wmk inverted	2·00	
1008/11	*Set of 4*	2·25	2·75
MS1012	79×75 mm. $5.50, Christmas flower arrangement. Wmk sideways	2·00	3·50

(Des S. Noon. Litho Walsall)

1989 (22 Feb). *10th Anniv of Independence. T 181 and similar vert designs. Multicoloured. W w 14. P 13½ × 13.*

1013	15 c. Type 181	30	10
1014	80 c. Geothermal well	1·00	60
1015	$1 Sir Arthur Lewis Community College	70	60
1016	$2.50, Pointe Seraphine shopping centre	1·10	2·00
1013/16	*Set of 4*	2·75	3·00
MS1017	47 × 62 mm. $5 Man with national flag. W w 16.	2·25	3·00

1989 (12 Apr). *As Nos. 924B/5B, but W w 16 (sideways). With "1989" imprint date. P 14.*

1018	169	5 c. black and cinnamon	80	80
1019		10 c. black and pale emerald	80	80

182 Gerronema citrinum

183 Local Revolutionary Declaration, 1789 and View of St. Lucia

(Des Josephine Martin. Litho Questa)

1989 (31 May). *Fungi. T 182 and similar vert designs. Multicoloured. W w 16. P 14½×14.*

1022	15 c. Type 182	1·25	30
1023	25 c. Lepiota spiculata	1·50	30
1024	50 c. Calocybe cyanocephala	2·50	1·10
1025	$5 Russula puiggarii	7·00	9·50
1022/5	*Set of 4*	11·00	10·00

(Litho Questa)

1989 (14 July). *Bicentenary of the French Revolution. T 183 and similar multicoloured designs each including the "Philexfrance" International Stamp Exhibition logo. W w 14 (sideways on 60 c., $3.50). P 14.*

1026	10 c. Type 183	30	15
1027	60 c. Hoisting Revolutionary flag, Morne Fortune, 1791 (horiz)	1·75	80
1028	$1 Declaration of Rights of Man and view of St. Lucia	2·00	1·50
1029	$3.50, Arrival of Capt. La Crosse, Gros Islet, 1792 (horiz)	6·00	7·50
1026/9	*Set of 4*	9·00	9·00

184 Red Cross Headquarters, St. Lucia

185 Christmas Lantern

(Des A. Theobald. Litho Questa)

1989 (10 Oct). *125th Anniv of International Red Cross. T 184 and similar horiz designs. Multicoloured. W w 16 (sideways). P 14×14½.*

1030	50 c. Type 184	1·25	1·25
1031	80 c. Red Cross seminar, Castries, 1987	1·75	2·00
1032	$1 Red Cross ambulance	2·00	2·25
1030/2	*Set of 3*	4·50	5·00

(Des Jennifer Toombs. Litho Questa)

1989 (17 Nov). *Christmas. T 185 and similar horiz designs showing decorative "building" lanterns. W w 16 (sideways). P 14×14½.*

1033	10 c. multicoloured	25	10
1034	50 c. multicoloured	65	40
1035	90 c. multicoloured	1·00	1·25
1036	$1 multicoloured	1·25	1·25
1033/6	*Set of 4*	2·75	2·75

MINIMUM PRICE

The minimum price quote is 10p which represents a handling charge rather than a basis for valuing common stamps. For further notes about prices see introductory pages.

186 Gwi Gwi

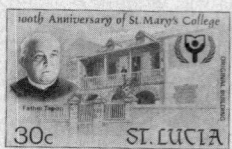

187 Father Tapon and Original College Building

(Des R. Gorringe. Litho B.D.T.)

1990 (21 Feb–25 June). *Endangered Trees. T* **186** *and similar vert designs. Multicoloured.* W w **16**. "1990" *imprint date.* P 14.

1037	10 c. Chinna (12 Apr)	50	50
1038	15 c. Latanier (12 Apr)	70	70
1039	20 c. Type **186**	70	70
1040	25 c. L'Encens	70	70
1041	50 c. Bois Lélé	1·00	1·00
1042	80 c. Bois D'Amande (12 Apr)	70	40
1043	95 c. Mahot Piman Grand Bois (25 June)	75	65
1044	$1 Balata (25 June)	75	65
1045	$1.50 Pencil Cedar (12 Apr)	1·50	1·75
1046	$2.50, Bois Cendre (25 June)	2·50	2·75
1047	$5 Lowye Cannelle (25 June)	3·50	4·00
1048	$25 Chalantier Grand Bois	13·00	17·00
1037/48	*Set of* 12	24·00	27·00

For these designs, but watermark w **14**, see Nos. 1081/5.

(Des G. Vasarhelyi. Litho Questa)

1990 (6 June). *International Literacy Year. Centenary of St. Mary's College, Castries. T* **187** *and similar horiz designs. Multicoloured.* W w **14** (*sideways*). P 14.

1049	30 c. Type **187**	15	15
1050	45 c. Brother M. C. Collins and St. Mary's College	25	25
1051	75 c. Literacy class	45	55
1052	$2 Children approaching "door to knowledge"	1·50	2·00
1049/52	*Set of* 4	2·10	2·75

(Des D. Miller. Litho Questa)

1990 (3 Aug). *90th Birthday of Queen Elizabeth the Queen Mother. Vert designs as T* **107** (50 *c.*) *or* **108** ($5) *of Kenya.* W w **16**. P 14×15 (50 *c.*) *or* 14½ ($5).

1053	50 c. multicoloured	50	35
1054	$5 brownish black and deep violet-blue	3·00	4·00

Designs:—50 c. Crowning of Queen Consort, 1937; $5 Queen Elizabeth arriving at New Theatre, London, 1949.

(188)

189 "Adoration of the Magi" (Rubens)

1990 (13 Aug). *"EXPO 90" International Garden and Greenery Exhibition, Osaka. No.* 1047 *optd with T* **188**.

1055	$5 Lowye Cannelle	2·75	3·50

(Des D. Miller. Litho Questa)

1990 (3 Dec). *Christmas. Religious Paintings. T* **189** *and similar vert designs. Multicoloured.* W w **16**. P 14.

1056	10 c. Type **189**	30	10
1057	30 c. "Adoration of the Shepherds" (Murillo)	80	15
1058	80 c. "Adoration of the Magi" (Rubens) (*different*)	1·75	75
1059	$5 "Adoration of the Shepherds" (Philippe de Champaigne)	6·00	7·50
1056/9	*Set of* 4	8·00	7·75

190 *Vistafjord* (liner)

191 *Battus polydamas*

(Des E. Nisbet. Litho Walsall)

1991 (27 Mar). *Cruise Ships. T* **190** *and similar horiz designs. Multicoloured.* W w **14** (*sideways*). P 14½.

1060	50 c. Type **190**	1·50	40
1061	80 c. *Windstar* (schooner)	2·00	1·10
1062	$1 *Unicorn* (brig)	2·25	1·50
1063	$2.50, Game-fishing launch	4·75	7·50
1060/3	*Set of* 4	9·50	9·50
MS1064	82×65 mm. $5 Ships in Castries Harbour	7·50	8·00

(Des I. Loe. Litho Walsall)

1991 (15 Aug). *Butterflies. T* **191** *and similar vert designs. Multicoloured.* W w **16**. P 14.

1065	60 c. Type **191**	2·00	65
1066	80 c. *Strymon simaethis*	2·25	1·10
1067	$1 *Mestra cana*	2·75	1·25
1068	$2.50, *Allosmaitia piplea*	5·50	7·50
1065/8	*Set of* 4	11·00	9·50

192 Mural, Jacmel Church

193 Yacht and Map

(Des D. Miller. Litho Questa)

1991 (20 Nov). *Christmas. Paintings by Duncan St. Omer. T* **192** *and similar multicoloured designs.* W w **16** (*sideways on* 10, 80 *c.*). P 14½.

1069	10 c. Type **192**	30	10
1070	15 c. "Red Madonna" (*vert*)	40	10
1071	80 c. Mural, Monchy Church	1·50	70
1072	$5 "Blue Madonna" (*vert*)	4·50	6·50
1069/72	*Set of* 4	6·00	6·75

(Des P. Devarreaux. Litho Questa)

1991 (10 Dec). *Atlantic Rally for Cruising Yachts. T* **193** *and similar horiz design. Multicoloured.* W w **16** (*sideways*). P 14.

1073	60 c. Type **193**	1·50	1·50
1074	80 c. Yachts off St. Lucia	1·75	1·75

(Adapted G. Vasarhelyi. Litho Cartor)

1992 (6 July). *Organization of East Caribbean States. 500th Anniv of Discovery of America by Columbus. Vert designs as T* **66** *of St. Kitts. Multicoloured.* W w **14**. P 13.

1075	$1 Columbus meeting Amerindians	2·00	1·75
1076	$2 Ships approaching island	2·75	3·25

194 Amerindian Village

195 "Virgin and Child" (Delaroche)

(Des D. Miller. Litho Cartor)

1992 (7 Aug). *Discovery of St. Lucia. T* **194** *and similar horiz designs. Multicoloured.* W w **14** (*sideways*). P 13½.

1077	15 c. Type **194**	40	20
1078	40 c. Ships of Juan de la Cosa and islands, 1499	1·50	50
1079	50 c. Columbus sailing between Martinique and St. Lucia, 1502	1·60	70
1080	$5 Legendary shipwreck of Gimie	6·00	8·00
1077/80	*Set of* 4	8·50	8·50

1992 (Aug)–95. *As Nos.* 1037/41, *but* W w **14**. *With imprint date.* P 14.

1081	10 c. Chinna (11.12.92)	10	10
1082	15 c. Latanier (11.12.92)	15	15
1083	20 c. Type **186** (4.95)	90	1·00
1084	25 c. L'Encens (5.94)	20	20
1085	50 c. Bois Lélé	30	30
1081/5	*Set of* 5	1·50	1·50

Imprint dates: "1992", Nos. 1081/2, 1085; "1993", Nos. 1081, 1085; "1994", Nos. 1081/2, 1084/5; "1995", No. 1083.

(Des D. Miller. Litho Walsall)

1992 (9 Nov). *Christmas. Religious Paintings. T* **195** *and similar vert designs. Multicoloured.* W w **14**. P 14½.

1092	10 c. Type **195**	40	20
1093	15 c. "The Holy Family" (Rubens)	40	20
1094	60 c. "Virgin and Child" (Luini)	1·75	1·75
1095	80 c. "Virgin and Child" (Sassoferrato)	2·00	2·00
1092/5	*Set of* 4	4·00	3·75

OMNIBUS ISSUES

Details, together with prices for complete sets, of the various Omnibus issues from the 1935 Silver Jubilee series to date are included in a special section following Zimbabwe at the end of Volume 2.

196 "Death" and Gravestone

197 "Gros Piton from Delcer, Choiseul" (Dunstan St. Omer)

(Adapted D. Miller. Litho Cartor)

1993 (1 Feb). *Anti-drugs Campaign.* W w **14**. P 13½.

1096	**196** $5 multicoloured	6·00	6·50

(Des G. Vasarhelyi. Litho Cartor)

1993 (1 Nov). *Carib Art. T* **197** *and similar horiz designs. Multicoloured.* W w **14** (*sideways*). P 13.

1097	20 c. Type **197**	20	10
1098	75 c. "Reduit Bay" (Derek Walcott)	75	75
1099	$5 "Woman and Child at River" (Nancy Cole Auguste)	4·25	5·75
1097/9	*Set of* 3	4·75	6·00

198 "The Madonna of the Rosary" (Murillo)

199 The Pitons

(Des D. Miller. Litho B.D.T.)

1993 (6 Dec). *Christmas. Religious Paintings. T* **198** *and similar horiz designs. Multicoloured.* W w **14** (*sideways*). P 14.

1100	15 c. Type **198**	20	10
1101	60 c. "The Madonna and Child" (Van Dyck)	65	60
1102	95 c. "The Annunciation" (Champaigne)	1·10	1·50
1100/2	*Set of* 2	1·75	2·00

(Des G. Vasarhelyi. Litho Cartor)

1994 (25 July). *Bicentenary of the Abolition of Slavery in St. Lucia.* W w **14**. P 13½.

1103	**199** 20 c. multicoloured	65	45
MS1104	115×75 mm. **199** $5 multicoloured	4·50	5·50

200 *Euphorbia pulcherrima*

201 18th-century Map of St. Lucia

(Adapted D. Miller from local designs. Litho Enschedé)

1994 (9 Dec). *Christmas. Flowers. T* **200** *and similar vert designs. Multicoloured.* W w **14**. P 12½×13.

1105	20 c. Type **200**	15	10
1106	75 c. *Heliconia rostrata*	55	50
1107	95 c. *Alpinia purpurata*	75	75
1108	$5.50, *Anthurium andreanum*	3·75	6·00
1105/8	*Set of* 4	4·75	6·50

See also Nos. 1122/5 and 1156/9.

(Litho Cartor)

1995 (28 Apr). *Bicentenary of Battle of Rabot. T* **201** *and similar horiz designs. Multicoloured.* W w **14** (*sideways*). P 13½.

1109	20 c. Type **201**	25	15
1110	75 c. Insurgent slaves	60	55
1111	95 c. 9th Foot (Royal Norfolk Regiment) attacking	1·10	1·40
1109/11	*Set of* 3	1·75	1·90
MS1112	150×100 mm. $5.50, Plan of battle. P 13	3·25	3·75

(Des R. Watton. Litho Cartor (Nos. 1113/16) or Questa (No. **MS**1117))

1995 (8 May). *50th Anniv of End of Second World War. Multicoloured designs as T* **75** *of Kiribati.* W w **14** (*sideways*). P 13½.

1113	20 c. St. Lucian members of the A.T.S.	40	15
1114	75 c. German U-boat off St. Lucia	1·25	80

1115 95 c. Bren gun-carriers of the Caribbean
      Regiment, North Africa .. .. 1·50 1·25
1116 $1.10, Supermarine Spitfire Mk V *St.
      Lucia* .. .. 1·75 2·00
1113/16 .. .. *Set of 4* 4·50 3·75
MS1117 75×85 mm. $5.50, Reverse of 1939–45
      War Medal (*vert*). Wmk upright. P 14 .. 3·25 3·50

(Des A. Theobald. Litho B.D.T.)

1995 (24 Oct). *50th Anniv of United Nations. Horiz designs as
T 284 of Jamaica. Multicoloured. W w 14 (sideways). P 14.*
1118 10 c. Sud Aviation SE 330 Puma helicopter,
      Cambodia, 1991–93 .. .. 15 10
1119 65 c. Renault lorry, Bosnia, 1995 .. 50 50
1120 $1.35, Transall C-160 aircraft, Cam-
      bodia, 1991–93 .. .. 95 1·40
1121 $5 Douglas DC-3 aircraft, Korea,
      1950–54 .. .. .. 3·75 5·00
1118/21 .. .. *Set of 4* 4·75 6·25

(Adapted D. Miller. Litho Cartor)

1995 (20 Nov). *Christmas. Flowers. Vert designs as T 200,
each including Madonna and Child. Multicoloured. W w 14.
P 13×13½.*
1122 15 c. *Eranthemum nervosum* 15 10
1123 70 c. *Bougainvillea* 45 45
1124 $1.10, *Allamanda cathartica* 70 90
1125 $3 *Rosa sinensis* .. .. 1·75 2·75
1122/5 .. .. *Set of 4* 2·75 3·75

202 Calypso King   203 Dry River Bed

(Des G. Vasarhelyi. Litho B.D.T.)

1996 (19 Feb). *Carnival. T 202 and similar vert designs.
Multicoloured. W w 16. P 14.*
1126 20 c. Type **202** 30 10
1127 65 c. Carnival dancers 75 55
1128 95 c. King of the Band float .. .. 1·00 85
1129 $3 Carnival Queen .. .. 2·75 4·00
1126/9 .. .. *Set of 4* 4·25 5·00

(Des A. St. Omer and G. Vasarhelyi (20, 55 c.), G. Vasarhelyi
($5). Litho Cot Printery Ltd, Barbados)

1996 (5 Mar). *Inauguration of New Irrigation Project. T 203
and similar vert designs. Multicoloured. W w 14. P 14.*
1130 20 c. Type **203** 10 10
1131 65 c. People bathing in stream .. 40 45
1132 $5 New dam .. .. .. 3·00 4·00
1130/2 .. .. *Set of 3* 3·25 4·00

204 Produce Market

(Des D. Miller. Litho Cot Printery Ltd, Barbados)

1996 (11 May). *Tourism. T 204 and similar horiz designs.
Multicoloured. W w 14 (sideways). P 14.*
1133 65 c. Type **204** 45 45
1134 75 c. Horse-riding on beach 55 55
1135 95 c. Bride and groom 70 75
1136 $5 Jazz band .. .. .. 2·75 4·00
1133/6 .. .. *Set of 4* 4·00 5·25

205 Athlete of 1896

(Des S. Noon (15 c.), R. Watton (75 c.). Litho Cot Printery Ltd,
Barbados)

1996 (19 July). *Centenary of Modern Olympic Games. T 205
and similar horiz designs. Multicoloured. W w 14 (sideways).
P 14.*
1137 15 c. Type **205** 25 35
      a. Horiz pair. Nos. 1137/8 .. .. 50 70
1138 15 c. Athlete of 1996 .. .. 25 35
1139 75 c. Catamaran and dinghy .. .. 1·00 1·25
      a. Horiz pair. Nos. 1139/40 .. 2·00 2·50
1140 75 c. Sailing dinghies .. .. 1·00 1·25
1137/40 .. .. *Set of 4* 2·25 2·75
      Nos. 1137/8 and 1139/40 were each printed together,
se-tenant, in horizontal pairs forming composite designs,
throughout the sheets.

206 Spanish Royal Standard, 1502,
and Caravel

(Des J. Batchelor. Litho B.D.T.)

1996 (16 Sept)–**97**. *Flags and Ships. T 206 and similar horiz
designs. Multicoloured. W w 16 (sideways). P 14×15.*
1141 10 c. Type **206** 30 30
1142 15 c. Skull and crossbones, 1550, and pirate
      carrack 40 40
1143 20 c. Dutch royal standard, 1650, and
      galleon 40 40
1144 25 c. Union Jack, 1739, and ship of the line 10 15
1145 40 c. French royal standard, 1750, and ship
      of the line 15 20
1146 50 c. Martinique and St. Lucia flag, 1766,
      and French brig (18.11.96) .. 50 50
1147 55 c. White Ensign, 1782, and frigate
      squadron (18.11.96) 25 30
1148 65 c. Red Ensign, 1782, and frigates in
      action (18.11.96) 30 35
1149 75 c. Blue Ensign, 1782, and brig (18.11.96) 35 40
1150 95 c. The Tricolour, 1792, and French
      frigate (18.11.96) 40 45
1151 $1 Union Jack, 1801, and West Indies
      Grand Fleet (8.1.97) 45 50
1152 $2.50, Confederate States of America
      flag, 1861, and cruiser (8.1.97) .. 1·10 1·25
1153 $5 Canadian flag, 1915–19, and "V & W"
      class destroyer (8.1.97) .. .. 2·10 2·25
1154 $10 United States flag, 1942–48, and
      "Fletcher" class destroyer (8.1.97) .. 4·25 4·50
1155 $25 Flag of St. Lucia and *Royal Princess*
      (cruise liner) (8.1.97) .. .. 10·50 11·00
1141/55 .. .. *Set of 15* 20·00 22·00
      For these designs with W w 14 (sideways) see Nos. 1182/7.

(Des Jennifer Toombs. Litho Questa)

1996 (27 Nov). *Christmas. Flowers. Vert designs as T 200,
each including Madonna and Child. Multicoloured. W w 16.
P 14.*
1156 20 c. *Cordia sebestena* 15 10
1157 75 c. *Cryptosegia grandiflora* 50 50
1158 95 c. *Hibiscus elatus* 65 65
1159 $5 *Caularthron bicornutum* .. .. 3·50 4·25
1156/9 .. .. *Set of 4* 4·25 5·00

(Des N. Shewring (No. MS1166), D. Miller (others). Litho
Questa (No. MS1166), Cot Printery Ltd, Barbados (others))

1997 (10 July). *Golden Wedding of Queen Elizabeth and Prince
Philip. Multicoloured designs as T 87 of Kiribati. W w 14.
P 14½×14.*
1160 75 c. Queen Elizabeth at Warwick, 1996 55 65
      a. Horiz pair. Nos. 1160/1 .. .. 1·10 1·25
1161 75 c. Prince Philip with carriage horses .. 55 65
1162 95 c. Prince Philip 70 75
      a. Horiz pair. Nos. 1162/3 .. .. 1·40 1·50
1163 95 c. Queen in phaeton at Trooping the
      Colour 70 75
1164 $1 Queen Elizabeth and Prince Philip at
      Sandringham, 1982 .. .. 70 75
      a. Horiz pair. Nos. 1164/5 .. .. 1·40 1·50
1165 $1 Princess Anne show jumping .. 70 75
1160/5 .. .. *Set of 6* 3·50 3·75
MS1166 110×70 mm. $5 Queen Elizabeth and
      Prince Philip in landau (*horiz*). Wmk sideways.
      P 14×14½ .. .. .. 3·00 3·50
      Nos. 1160/1, 1162/3 and 1164/5 were each printed together,
se-tenant, in horizontal pairs throughout the sheets with the
backgrounds forming composite designs.

207 *St. George* capsized, 1935

(Des E. Nisbet. Litho B.D.T.)

1997 (14 July). *Marine Disasters. T 207 and similar horiz
designs. Multicoloured. W w 16 (sideways). P 14×15.*
1167 20 c. Type **207** 40 10
1168 55 c. Wreck of *Belle of Bath* (freighter) .. 60 30
1169 $1 *Ethelgonda* (freighter) aground on
      rocks, 1897 .. .. .. 1·00 85
1170 $2.50, Hurricane, 1817 .. .. 2·00 2·75
1167/70 .. .. *Set of 4* 3·50 3·50

208 Attack on Praslin

(Des R. Watton. Litho Questa)

1997 (15 Aug). *Bicentenary of the Brigands' War. T 208 and
similar horiz designs. Multicoloured. W w 14 (sideways).
P 13½×14.*
1171 20 c. Type **208** 40 10
1172 55 c. British troops at Battle of Dennery .. 50 30
1173 70 c. Discussing peace agreement .. 65 60
1174 $3 Members of 1st West India Regiment 2·25 2·75
1171/4 .. .. *Set of 4* 3·50 3·50

209 "Roseau Church" (detail,   210 Diana, Princess
Dunstan St. Omer)   of Wales

(Des D. Miller. Litho B.D.T.)

1997 (1 Dec). *Christmas. Paintings by Dunstan St. Omer.
T 209 and similar horiz designs. Multicoloured. W w 16
(sideways). P 14×15.*
1175 20 c. Type **209** 20 10
1176 60 c. Altarpiece, Regional Seminary,
      Trinidad 45 35
1177 95 c. "Our Lady of the Presentation",
      Trinidad 60 60
1178 $5 "The Four Days of Creation" .. 2·75 4·00
1175/8 .. .. *Set of 4* 3·50 4·00

1998 (19 Jan). *Diana, Princess of Wales Commemoration.
Litho. P 14.*
1179 **210** $1 multicoloured 60 65
      No. 1179 was printed in sheets of 9 with decorative margins.

211 Signatories to CARICOM   212 St. Lucia Oriole
Treaty, 1973

(Des G. Vasarhelyi. Litho Cartor)

1998 (1 July). *25th Anniv of CARICOM. T 211 and similar
horiz design. Multicoloured. W w 14 (sideways). P 13½.*
1180 20 c. Type **211** 15 10
1181 75 c. Flags of CARICOM and St. Lucia .. 45 50

1998 (12 July). *As Nos. 1141/3 and 1146, but W w 14
(sideways) and with imprint date ("1998"). P 14×15.*
1182 10 c. Spanish royal standard, 1502, and
      caravel 10 10
1183 15 c. Skull and crossbones, 1550, and pirate
      carrack 10 10
1184 20 c. Dutch royal standard, 1650, and
      galleon 10 10
1187 50 c. Martinique and St. Lucia flag, 1766,
      and French brig 20 25
1182/7 .. .. *Set of 4* 45 50

(Des I. Loe. Litho Questa)

1998 (23 Oct). *Wildlife (1st series). Birds. T 212 and similar
vert designs. Multicoloured. W w 16. P 14.*
1197 70 c. Type **212** 50 40
1198 75 c. Lesser Antillean Pewee 50 45
1199 95 c. Bridled Quail Dove 60 55
1200 $1.10, Semper's Warbler 75 80
1197/200 .. .. *Set of 4* 2·10 2·00
      See also Nos. 1212/15.

213 *Siproeta stelenes* and   214 *Tabebuia
Chain   serratifolia*

(Des D. Miller. Litho Questa)

1998 (28 Oct). *50th Anniv of Universal Declaration of Human
Rights. Butterflies. T 213 and similar horiz designs.
Multicoloured. W w 16 (sideways). P 14.*
1201 20 c. Type **213** 35 10
1202 65 c. *Pseudolycaena marsyas* and chain .. 70 50
1203 70 c. *Heliconius melpomene* and rope .. 70 50
1204 $5 *Phoebis philea* and chain .. 3·25 4·00
1201/4 .. .. *Set of 4* 4·50 4·50

(Des Jennifer Toombs. Litho Cot Printery Ltd, Barbados)

1998 (25 Nov). *Christmas. Flowers. T* **214** *and similar vert designs. Multicoloured. W w* **14**. *P* 14.

1205	20 c. Type **214**		15	10
1206	50 c. *Hibiscus sabdariffa*		35	30
1207	95 c. *Euphorbia leucocephala*		55	45
1208	$2.50, *Calliandra slaneae*		1·40	2·00
1205/8		Set of 4	2·10	2·50

215 "The Black Prometheus"
(wall painting)

(Des D. Miller. Litho Cot Printery Ltd, Barbados)

1998 (30 Nov). *50th Anniv of University of West Indies. T* **215** *and similar horiz designs. Multicoloured. W w* **14** (*sideways*). *P* 14.

1209	15 c. Type **215**		15	10
1210	75 c. Sir Arthur Lewis College, St. Lucia		50	40
1211	$5 University arms and the Pitons, St. Lucia		2·75	3·25
1209/11		Set of 3	3·00	3·25

216 St. Lucia Tree Lizard

(Des I. Loe. Litho Cartor)

1999 (15 July). *Wildlife* (*2nd series*). *Reptiles. T* **216** *and similar horiz designs. Multicoloured. W w* **14** (*sideways*). *P* 13½.

1212	20 c. Type **216**		15	10
1213	75 c. Boa Constrictor		50	40
1214	95 c. Leatherback Turtle		55	45
1215	$5 St. Lucia Whiptail		2·50	2·75
1212/15		Set of 4	3·25	3·25

217 *Tees* (mail steamer), 1893

(Des J. Batchelor (Nos 1216/19), D. Miller (No. **MS**1220). Litho Questa)

1999 (8 Oct). *125th Anniv of Universal Postal Union. T* **217** *and similar multicoloured designs. W w* **14** (*sideways*). *P* 14.

1216	20 c. Type **217**		15	10
1217	65 c. Sikorsky S.38 (flying boat), 1929		40	35
1218	95 c. *Lady Drake* (cargo liner), 1930		55	45
1219	$3 DC10 airliner, 1999		1·60	1·75
1216/19		Set of 4	2·40	2·40
MS1220	100×84 mm. $5 Heinrich von Stephan (founder of U.P.U.) (30×37 *mm*). P 14½		2·50	2·75

218 The Nativity

(Des D. Miller. Litho Questa)

1999 (14 Dec). *Christmas and New Millennium. T* **218** *and similar horiz design. Multicoloured. W w* **14** (*sideways*). *P* 13½×14.

1221	20 c. Type **218**		10	10
1222	$1 Cathedral of the Immaculate Conception		45	50

Nos. 1221/2 were each printed in sheets of 12 (2×6) with the vertical rows of stamps separated by a row of inscribed labels.

219 Original Badge of the Colony

(Des D. Miller. Litho Cartor)

2000 (29 Feb). *21st Anniv of Independence. T* **219** *and similar horiz designs. Multicoloured. W w* **14** (*sideways*). *P* 13½.

1223	20 c. Type **219**		10	10
1224	75 c. Colonial badge, 1939		35	40
1225	95 c. Coat of Arms as Associated State, 1967		40	45
1226	$1 Coat of Arms on Independence, 1979		45	50
1223/6		Set of 4	1·25	1·40

STAMP BOOKLETS

1981 (23 June). *Royal Wedding. Multicoloured cover,* 165×90 *mm. Stitched.*

SB1 $12.50, booklet containing *se-tenant* pane of 6 and
    pane of 1 (Nos. 580a, 582a)   ..   ..   2·75

1986 (12 Aug). *Royal Wedding. Gold* (No. SB2) *or silver* (No. SB3) *on deep carmine-red covers,* 152×80 *mm. Stapled.*

SB2 $9.60, booklet (Westminster Abbey) containing
    twelve 80 c. (Nos. 890/1) in blocks of 4   4·75

SB3 $11.20, booklet (State Coach) containing 80 c. and
    $2 (Nos. 890/3, but imperf) in blocks of 4   5·50

POSTAGE DUE STAMPS

D 1

No. No.

Normal   Wide fount

(Type-set Government Printing Office)

1930. *Each stamp individually handstamped with different number. No wmk. No gum. Rough perf 12.* (a) *Horizontally laid paper.*

D1	D 1	1d. black/*blue* ..	..	4·00 15·00
		b. Wide, wrong fount "No."	..	13·00 38·00
		c. Missing stop after "ST"	..	65·00 £110
		d. Missing stop after "LUCIA"	..	65·00 £110
		e. Handstamped number double	..	£300
		f. Handstamped number triple	..	
		g. Incorrect number with correction above	..	
		h. Two different numbers on same stamp	..	£375

(b) *Wove paper*

D2	D 1	2d. black/*yellow* ..	..	12·00 40·00
		a. Imperf between (vert pair)	..	£4000
		b. Wide, wrong fount "No."	..	30·00 95·00
		c. Missing stop after "ST"	..	£140 £275
		d. Missing stop after "LUCIA"	..	
		g. Incorrect number with correction above	..	£475
		h. Two different numbers on same stamp	..	£550

Nos. D1/2 were produced in sheets of 60 (6×10) usually with imperforate outer edges at the top, at right and at foot. It would appear that the sheets were bound into books from which they could be detached using the line of perforations along the left-hand side.

There were three printings of each value, utilising the same basic type. The paper for the first two printings of the 1d. and the first printing of the 2d. showed papermaker's watermarks, that for the 1d. being "KINGSCLERE" in double-lined capitals below a crown with parts occurring on between ten and fourteen stamps in each sheet.

Details of the printings are as follows:

1d.

First printing. On paper with sheet watermark. Shows wide fount "No." on R. 10/3–6 and missing stop after "ST" on R. 5/3

Second printing. On paper with sheet watermark. Shows wide fount "No." on R. 10/2–6 and missing stop after "ST" on R. 5/3. The first two printings of the 1d. were numbered together as 1 to 12000.

Third printing. On paper without watermark. Shows wide fount "No." on all stamps in Row 10. Missing stop after "ST" on R. 5/3 corrected, but missing stop after "LUCIA" occurs on R. 9/2. Numbered 12001 to 24000.

2d.

First printing. On paper with sheet watermark. Shows wide fount "No." on R. 10/2–6 and missing stop after "ST" on R. 5/3 (as 1d. second printing). Numbered 1 to 4800.

Second printing. On paper without watermark. Shows wide fount "No." on all stamps in Row 10. Missing stop after "ST" corrected (printed *before* 1d. third printing). Numbered 4801 to 14820.

Third printing. On paper without watermark. Shows wide fount "No." on all stamps in Row 10. Missing stop after "ST" corrected, but missing stop after "LUCIA" occurs on R. 4/4 and 9/2 (printed *after* 1d. third printing). Numbered 14821 to 16800.

The handstamped numbers were applied at the Post Office using a numbering machine. Mistakes in the numbering on the 1d. were sometimes partially erased and then corrected by a second strike, either of the complete number or of incorrect digits, using a machine with a smaller font.

D 2

D 3

D 4 St. Lucia
Coat of Arms

(Typo D.L.R.)

1933–47. *Wmk Mult Script CA. P* 14.

D3	D 2	1d. black	..		4·50 6·00
D4		2d. black	..		16·00 8·00
D5		4d. black (28.6.47)	..		5·50 32·00
D6		8d. black (28.6.47)	..		5·50 42·00
D3/6				Set of 4	28·00 80·00
D3/6 Perf "Specimen"			..	Set of 4	£130

1949 (1 Oct)–**52.** *Value in cents. Wmk Mult Script CA. Typo. P* 14.

D 7	D 3	2 c. black	..		1·75 24·00
		a. Chalk-surfaced paper (27.11.52)			10 7·50
		ab. Error. Crown missing, W 9a			95·00
		ac. Error. St. Edward's Crown, W 9b			30·00
D 8		4 c. black			3·50 17·00
		a. Chalk-surfaced paper (27.11.52) ..			40 9·00
		ab. Error. Crown missing, W 9a			£130
		ac. Error. St. Edward's Crown, W 9b			42·00
D 9		8 c. black			3·25 21·00
		a. Chalk-surfaced paper (27.11.52) ..			3·00 28·00
		ac. Error. St. Edward's Crown, W 9b			£225
D10		16 c. black			15·00 65·00
		a. Chalk-surfaced paper (27.11.52) ..			4·00 48·00
		ac. Error. St. Edward's Crown, W 9b			£325
D7/10				Set of 4	21·00 £110
D7a/10a				Set of 4	6·75 85·00

1965 (9 Mar). *As Nos. D7/8, but wmk w* **12.** *Ordinary paper. P* 14.

D11	D 3	2 c. black	..	..	35 9·00
D12		4 c. black	..	..	45 9·00

Nos D9a, D10a and D11/12 exist with a similar overprint to Type **49** in red (*Price for set of 4 £150 mint*).

(Des L. Curtis. Litho Format)

1981 (4 Aug). *W w* **14.** *P* 14.

D13	D 4	5 c. brown-purple	..		10 45
D14		15 c. emerald	..		15 50
D15		25 c. red-orange	..		15 50
D16		$1 deep ultramarine	..		30 1·25
D13/16				Set of 4	60 2·40

(Des L. Curtis. Litho Questa)

1991 (14 Feb). *W w* **16.** *P* 15×14.

D17	D 4	5 c. deep carmine	..		10 10
D18		15 c. emerald	..		10 10
D19		25 c. red-orange	..		10 10
D20		$1 ultramarine	..		45 50
D17/20				Set of 4	75 80

OFFICIAL STAMPS

OFFICIAL   OFFICIAL

(O 1)   (O 2)

1983 (13 Oct). *Nos. 537/48 optd with Type O* 1.

O 1	5 c. Type **120**	20	20
O 2	10 c. Douglas DC-10-30 airliner	30	20
O 3	15 c. Local bus	40	30
O 4	20 c. *Geestcrest* (freighter)	50	30
O 5	25 c. Britten Norman Islander aircraft	60	30
O 6	30 c. *Charles* (pilot boat) ..	70	30
O 7	50 c. Boeing 727-200 airliner	90	40
O 8	75 c. *Cunard Countess* (liner)	1·10	60
O 9	$1 Lockheed L-1011 TriStar 500 airliner	1·50	85
O10	$2 *Booker Vulcan* (cargo liner)	2·00	2·00
O11	$5 Boeing 707-420 airliner	3·50	3·75
O12	$10 *Queen Elizabeth 2* (liner)	6·50	7·50
O1/12		Set of 12	16·00 15·00

1985 (7 May). *Nos. 797/811 optd with Type O* 2.

O13	5 c. Type **156**	50	80
O14	10 c. Officer, Grenadier Company, 14th Regiment, 1780 ..	50	80
O15	20 c. Officer, Battalion Company, 46th Regiment, 1781	60	70
O16	25 c. Officer, Royal Artillery, c 1782	60	70
O17	30 c. Officer, Royal Engineers, 1782	70	80
O18	35 c. Officer, Battalion Company, 54th Regiment, 1782	70	80
O19	45 c. Private, Grenadier Company, 14th Regiment, 1782..	80	85
O20	50 c. Gunner, Royal Artillery, 1796	80	85
O21	65 c. Private, Battalion Company, 85th Regiment, c 1796	1·10	1·40
O22	75 c. Private, Battalion Company, 76th Regiment, 1796..	1·10	1·75
O23	90 c. Private, Battalion Company, 81st Regiment, c 1796	1·25	1·75
O24	$1 Sergeant, 74th (Highland) Regiment, 1796	1·40	1·75
O25	$2.50, Private, Light Company, 93rd Regiment, 1803	2·50	3·75
O26	$5 Private, Battalion Company, 1st West India Regiment, 1803	4·00	4·00
O27	$15 Officer, Royal Artillery, 1850 ..	9·00	9·00
O13/27		Set of 15	23·00 27·00

OFFICIAL

(O 3)

1990 (21 Feb–25 June). *Nos. 1037/48 optd with Type O* 3.

O28	10 c. Chinna (12 Apr) ..	15	10
O29	15 c. Latanier (12 Apr) ..	15	10
O30	20 c. Type **186**	15	10
O31	25 c. L'Encens	15	10
O32	50 c. Bois Lélé	25	30
O33	80 c. Bois D'Amande (12 Apr)	35	40
O34	95 c. Mahot Piman Grand Bois (25 June)	45	50
O35	$1 Balata (25 June)	45	50
O36	$1.50, Pencil Cedar (12 Apr)	85	90
O37	$2.50, Bois Cendre (25 June) ..	1·40	1·50
O38	$5 Lowye Cannelle (25 June) ..	2·50	2·75
O39	$25 Chalantier Grand Bois	12·00	13·00
O28/39		Set of 12	17·00 18·00

POSTAL FISCAL STAMPS

Nos. F1/28 were authorised for postal use from 14 April 1885.

CANCELLATIONS. Many used examples of the Postal Fiscal stamps have had previous pen cancellations removed before being used postally.

SHILLING STAMP	One Penny Stamp	HALFPENNY Stamp
(F 1)	(F 2)	(F 3)

1881. *Wmk Crown CC. P* 14. (a) *Surch as Type F* 1.

F1	1	ONE PENNY STAMP, black (C.)	..	45·00 48·00
		a. Surch inverted	..	£700 £700
		b. Surch double	..	£650 £700
F2		FOUR PENNY STAMP, yellow..		75·00 70·00
		a. Bisected (2d.) (on cover)		
F3		SIX PENCE STAMP, mauve	..	£130 £130
F4		SHILLING STAMP, orange	..	70·00 65·00
		a. "SHILEING"	..	£650
		b. "SHILDING"	..	£650 £600

(b) *Surch as Type F* 2

F 7	1	One Penny Stamp, black (R.)	..	45·00 48·00
		a. Surch double	..	£700
		w. Wmk inverted		
F 8		Four Pence Stamp, yellow	..	75·00 65·00
		x. Wmk reversed		
F 9		Six Pence Stamp, mauve	..	75·00 65·00
F10		Shilling Stamp, orange	..	80·00 85·00

(c) *Surch as Type F* 3

F11	1	Halfpenny Stamp, green..	..	50·00 55·00
		a. "Stamp" double	..	£450 £450
F12		One Shilling Stamp, orange (wmk Crown CA)	..	85·00 75·00
		a. "Stamp" double	..	£450 £500

A fiscally used example of No. F1b is known showing one red and one black surcharge.

FOUR PENCE

REVENUE   Revenue   REVENUE

(F 4)   (F 5)   (F 6)

1882. *Wmk Crown CA. Surch as Type F* 4. (a) *P* 14.

F13	1	1d. black (C.)	..	30·00 22·00
F14		2d. pale blue	..	20·00 9·50
F15		3d. deep blue (C.)	..	65·00 45·00
F16		4d. yellow	..	24·00 4·00
F17		6d. mauve	..	40·00 25·00

(b) *P* 12

F18	1	1d. black (C.)	..	30·00 23·00
F19		3d. deep blue (C.)	..	45·00 20·00
F20		1s. orange	..	48·00 13·00

For imperforate examples of the 1d., 2d. and 1d. see note below No.36

1883. *Nos. 25, 26, 30 and 32 optd locally as Type F* 5.

(a) *Word 11 mm long*

F21		1d. black (C.)	..	27·00 40·00
		a. Opt inverted	..	
		b. Opt double	..	£275 £350

(b) *Word 13 mm*

F22		1d. black (C.)	..	— 65·00

(c) *Word 15½ mm*

F23		½d. green	..	— 55·00
		a. "Revenue" double	..	— £250
F24		1d. black (C.)	..	25·00 10·00
		a. "Revenue" double	..	£140
		b. "Revenue" triple	..	£275
		c. "Revenue" double, one inverted	..	£250 £300
F25		1d. rose (No. 32)	..	— 60·00
F26		4d. yellow	..	— 65·00

1884–85. *Optd with Type F* 6. *Wmk Crown CA. P* 14.

F27	5	1d. slate (C.)	..	18·00 12·00
F28		1d. dull mauve (Die I) (1885)	..	18·00 7·50

St. Vincent

Although postal markings for St. Vincent are recorded as early as 1793 it was not until 1852 that the British G.P.O. opened a branch office at Kingstown, the island's capital.

The stamps of Great Britain were used between May 1858 and the end of April 1860. From 1 May in that year the local authorities assumed responsibility for the postal services and fell back on the use of No. CC1 until the introduction of St. Vincent stamps in 1861.

KINGSTOWN

CROWNED-CIRCLE HANDSTAMPS

CC 1

CC1 CC 1 ST. VINCENT (R.) (30.1.1852) Price on cover £800

Stamps of GREAT BRITAIN cancelled "A 10" as Type Z 1 of Jamaica.

1858 to 1860.

Z1	1d. rose-red (1857), perf 14	£550
Z2	2d. blue (1855)	
Z3	4d. rose (1857)	£350
Z4	6d. lilac (1856)	£250
Z5	1s. green (1856)	£1000

PRICES FOR STAMPS ON COVER TO 1945

Nos. 1/7	from × 15
No. 8	—
No. 9	from × 15
No. 10	—
Nos. 11/19	from × 10
Nos. 20/1	from × 6
Nos. 22/5	from × 10
Nos. 26/8	—
Nos. 29/31	from × 12
No. 32	—
Nos. 33/4	from × 10
No. 35	—
Nos. 36/8	from × 8
Nos. 39/41	from × 15
Nos. 42/5	from × 8
No. 46	from × 15
Nos. 47/54	from × 4
Nos. 55/8	from × 8
No. 59	from × 10
No. 60	from × 6
Nos. 61/3	from × 8
Nos. 67/75	from × 3
Nos. 76/84	from × 2
Nos. 85/92	from × 3
No. 93	—
Nos. 94/8	from × 3
Nos. 99/107	from × 2
Nos. 108/19	from × 3
No. 120	—
No. 121	from × 3
No. 122	from × 5
No. 123	—
No. 124	from × 5
Nos. 126/9	from × 10
Nos. 131/45	from × 3
Nos. 146/8	from × 6
Nos. 149/59	from × 2

CROWN COLONY

1

d.
1
(2)

3

(T 1, 3 and 7 recess P.B.)

1861 (8 May). No wmk. Rough to intermediate perf 14 to 16.

1	1	1d. rose-red	42·00 14·00
		a. Imperf vert (horiz pair)	£300
		b. Imperf (pair)	£250
2		6d. deep yellow-green	£6500 £200

The perforations on the 1d. are usually rough, but individual examples can be found on which some, or all, of the holes have the appearance of the intermediate perforations. All examples of the 6d. show intermediate perforations.

Imperforate examples, possibly proofs, exist of the 1d. rose-red and 6d. deep green handstamped "CANCELLED" in oval of bars (see note on Perkins Bacon "CANCELLED" in Catalogue Introduction). (Price 1d. £4000 6d. £5000).

1862 (Sept). No wmk. Rough perf 14 to 16.

4	1	6d. deep green	55·00 18·00
		a. Imperf between (horiz pair)	£3000 £4000
		b. Imperf (pair)	£850

1863–68. No wmk. (a) P 11 to 12½.

5	1	1d. rose-red (3.63)	35·00 15·00
6		4d. deep blue (shades) (1866)	£275 £110
		a. Imperf between (horiz pair)	
7		6d. deep green (7.68)	£200 70·00
8		1s. slate-grey (8.66)	£1800 £900

(b) P 14 to 16

9	1	1s. slate-grey (8.66)	£300 £130

(c) P 11 to 12½×14 to 16

10	1	1d. rose-red (1866)	£3250 £1100
11		1s. slate-grey (shades) (8.66)	£225 £120

1869 (Apr–Sep). Colours changed. No wmk. P 11 to 12½.

12	1	4d. yellow (9.69)	£350 £150
13		1s. indigo	£325 90·00
14		1s. brown (9.69)	£450 £160

1871 (Apr). Wmk Small Star, W w 2. Rough perf 14 to 16.

15	1	1d. black	45·00 10·00
		a. Imperf between (vert pair)	£5500
16		6d. deep green	£250 70·00
		a. Wmk sideways	— 85·00

1872 (June). Colour changed. W w 2 (sideways). P 11 to 12½.

17	1	1s. deep rose-red	£750 £140

1872–75. W w 2 (sideways). (a) Perf about 15.

18	1	1d. black (shades) (11.72)	40·00 7·50
		a. Wmk upright	45·00 8·50
19		6d. dull blue-green (shades) (1873)	£850 45·00
		b. Deep blue-green (1875)	£600 42·00
		c. Wmk upright	

(b) P 11 to 12½×15

20	1	1s. lilac-rose (1873)	£5000 £350

1875. Colour changed. W w 2 (sideways). P 11 to 12½.

21	1	1s. claret	£600 £250

1875–78. W w 2 (sideways). (a) P 11 to 12½×15.

22	1	1d. black (shades) (4.75)	65·00 9·00
		a. Imperf between (horiz pair)	† £5000
		b. Wmk upright	— 50·00
23		6d. pale green (1877)	£500 50·00
24		1s. vermilion (2.77)	£850 85·00
		a. Imperf vert (horiz pair)	

(b) P 11 to 12½

25	1	4d. deep blue (7.77)	£450 90·00

(c) Perf about 15

26	1	6d. pale green (3.77)	£1500 £450
		a. Wmk upright. Lt yellow-green (1878)	£650 25·00
27		1s. vermilion (1878?)	† £10000
		a. Imperf	† £6500

1880 (May). No. 19a divided vertically by a line of perforation gauging 12, and surch locally with T 2 in red.

28	1	1d. on half 6d. deep blue-green	£425 £325
		a. Unsevered pair	£1500 £1100

1880 (June). W w 2. P 11 to 12½.

29	1	1d. olive-green	£130 3·75
		a. Wmk sideways	
30		6d. bright green	£350 65·00
31		1s. bright vermilion	£650 50·00
		a. Imperf between (horiz pair)	£7000
32	3	5s. rose-red	£1000 £1200
		a. Imperf	£3750

d
1
2
(4)

ONE PENNY
(5)

4d
(6)

1881. Nos. 30/31 surch locally. No. 33 is divided vertically like No. 28.

33	4	½d. on half 6d. bright green (R.) (1.9)	£160 £160
		a. Unsevered pair	£400 £400
		b. Fraction bar omitted (pair with and without bar)	£3750 £4250
34	5	1d. on 6d. bright green (30.11)	£425 £325
35	6	4d. on 1s. bright vermilion (28.11)	£1400 £750

No. 33 exists showing the "1" of "¹⁄₂" with a straight serif. Some examples come from a constant variety on R. 6/20, but others are the result of faulty type.

It is believed that Type 4 was applied as a setting of 36 (6×6) surcharges repeated three times on each sheet across rows 1 to 9. The missing fraction bar occurs on R. 6/3 of the setting.

The tenth vertical row of stamps appears to have been surcharged from a separate setting of 12 (2×6) on which the constant "straight serif" flaw occurs on the bottom right half-stamp.

Three unused single copies of No. 33 are known with the surcharge omitted.

It is believed that Nos. 34 and 35 were surcharged in settings of 30 (10×3).

No. 34 was only on sale between the 30 November and 3 December when supplies of No. 37 became available.

2½ PENCE
(8)

1d
~~2½ PENCE~~
(9)

7

1881 (Dec). W w 2. P 11 to 12½.

36	7	½d. orange (shades)	7·00 8
37		1d. drab (shades)	£500 8
38		4d. bright blue	£1200 £1
		a. Imperf between (horiz pair)	

(Recess D.L.R. from Perkins, Bacon plates)

1882 (Nov)–83. No. 40 is surch with T 8. Wmk Crown C P 14.

39	1	1d. drab	42·00 8
40		2½d. on 1d. lake (1883)	12·00
		w. Wmk inverted	
		x. Wmk reversed	80·00 10·
		y. Wmk inverted and reversed	
41		4d. ultramarine	£400 32·
		a. Dull ultramarine	£950 £3
		w. Wmk inverted	
		x. Wmk reversed	— 32·
		y. Wmk inverted and reversed	

1883–84. Wmk Crown CA. P 12.

42	7	½d. green (1884)	75·00 26·
		x. Wmk reversed	
43	1	4d. ultramarine-blue	£400 22·
		a. Grey-blue	£1000 £3
		w. Wmk inverted	
		x. Wmk reversed	— 20·
		y. Wmk inverted and reversed	
44		6d. bright green	£150 £3
		x. Wmk reversed	
45		1s. orange-vermilion	£120 55·
		x. Wmk reversed	

The ½d. orange, 1d. rose-red, 1d. milky blue (without surcharge) and 5s. carmine-lake which were formerly listed an now considered to be colour trials. They are, however, of grea interest (Prices un. ½d. £900, 1d. £900, 1d. blue £1200 5s. £1600).

1885 (Mar). No. 40 further surch locally as in T 9.

46	1	1d. on 2½d. on 1d. lake	22·00 16·
		w. Wmk inverted	
		x. Wmk reversed	22·00 16·

Stamps with three cancelling bars instead of two are considered to be proofs.

1885–93. No. 49 is surch with T 8. Wmk Crown CA. P 14.

47	7	½d. green	1·00
		a. Deep green	2·50
		w. Wmk inverted	
		x. Wmk reversed	
48	1	1d. rose-red	3·00 1·0
		a. Rose (1886)	4·50 1·7
		b. Red (1887)	1·60 8
		c. Carmine-red (1889)	24·00 3·7
		w. Wmk inverted	
		x. Wmk reversed	5·00 1·5
49		2½d. on 1d. milky blue (1889)	23·00 5·5
		x. Wmk reversed	
50		4d. red-brown	£850 22·0
		x. Wmk reversed	
51		4d. purple-brown (1886)	48·00 7
		a. Chocolate (1887)	48·00 1·2
		w. Wmk inverted	
		x. Wmk reversed	
		y. Wmk inverted and reversed	
52		6d. violet (1888)	£130 £15
		w. Wmk inverted	£140 £17
		x. Wmk reversed	
53	3	5s. lake (1888)	27·00 50·0
		a. Printed both sides	£4000
		b. Brown-lake (1893)	30·00 50·0
		w. Wmk inverted	
49, 51, 52 Optd "Specimen"			Set of 3 £180

2½d.
(10)

5
PENCE
(11)

1890 (Aug). No. 51a surch locally with T 10.

54	1	2½d. on 4d. chocolate	65·00 90·00
		a. No fraction bar (R. 1/7, 2/4)	£300 £350

1890–93. No. 55 is surch with T 8. Colours changed. Wmk Crown CA. P 14.

55	1	2½d. on 1d. grey-blue (1890)	18·00 55
		a. Blue (1893)	1·25 35
		w. Wmk inverted	
56		4d. yellow (1893) (Optd S. 30)	1·60 60
57		6d. dull purple (1891)	2·25 9·00
58		1s. orange (1891)	5·50 11·00
		a. Red-orange (1892)	11·00 17·00

1892 (Nov). No. 51a surch locally with T 11, in purple.

59	1	5d. on 4d. chocolate (Optd S. 30)	15·00 26·00

Some letters are known double due to loose type, the best known being the first "E", but they are not constant.

FIVE PENCE

(12) 13 14

1893–94. *Surch with T 12. Wmk Crown CA. P 14.*
60	1	5d. on 6d. carmine-lake (Optd S. £45)		20·00	30·00
		a. *Deep lake* (1893)		1·00	1·75
		b. *Lake* (1894)		1·75	4·25
		c. *Surch double*		£4000	£2500

(Recess D.L.R.)

1897 (13 July). *New values. Wmk Crown CA. P 14.*
61	1	2½d. blue		3·00	1·75
62		5d. sepia		5·50	18·00
61/2 Optd "Specimen"			Set of 2	60·00	

1897 (6 Oct). *Surch as T 12. Wmk Crown CA. P 14.*
63	1	3d. on 1d. mauve (Optd S. £40)		6·00	17·00
		a. *Red-mauve*		10·00	27·00

(Typo D.L.R.)

1899 (1 Jan). *Wmk Crown CA. P 14.*
67	13	½d. dull mauve and green		2·75	2·00
68		1d. dull mauve and carmine		4·00	1·00
		w. Wmk inverted			
69		2½d. dull mauve and blue		4·00	2·00
70		3d. dull mauve and olive		4·00	11·00
71		4d. dull mauve and orange		4·00	15·00
72		6d. dull mauve and black		7·00	13·00
73		6d. dull mauve and brown		13·00	30·00
74	14	1s. green and carmine		13·00	48·00
75		5s. green and blue		75·00	£130
67/75			Set of 9	£110	£225
67/75 Optd "Specimen"			Set of 9	£170	

15 16

(Typo D.L.R.)

1902. *Wmk Crown CA. P 14.*
76	15	½d. dull purple and green		2·00	60
77		1d. dull purple and carmine		3·25	30
78	16	2d. dull purple and black		2·00	2·25
79	15	2½d. dull purple and blue		4·50	3·25
80		3d. dull purple and olive		3·75	2·50
81		6d. dull purple and brown		11·00	30·00
82	16	1s. green and carmine		20·00	50·00
83	15	2s. green and violet		25·00	55·00
84	16	5s. green and blue		70·00	£120
76/84			Set of 9	£120	£225
76/84 Optd "Specimen"			Set of 9	£120	

1904–11. *Wmk Mult Crown CA. Ordinary paper* (½d., 1d., 1s.) *or chalk-surfaced paper* (others). *P 14.*
85	15	½d. dull purple and green (1905)		6·00	2·00
		a. Chalk-surfaced paper		1·25	90
86		1d. dull purple and carmine		20·00	75
		a. Chalk-surfaced paper		18·00	90
88		2½d. dull purple and blue (1906)		15·00	38·00
89		6d. dull purple and brown (1905)		15·00	38·00
90	16	1s. green and carmine (1906)		16·00	45·00
		a. Chalk-surfaced paper		15·00	40·00
91	15	2s. purple and bright blue/*blue* (3.09?)		22·00	42·00
92	16	5s. green and red/*yellow* (3.09?)		17·00	50·00
93		£1 purple and black/*red* (22.7.11)		£250	£325
85/93			Set of 8	£300	£450
91/3 Optd "Specimen"			Set of 3	£180	

Examples of most values are known showing a forged Kingstown postmark, code letter "O", dated "JA 7 10". This has also been seen on some values of the 1899 and 1902 issues.

17 18

(Recess D.L.R.)

1907–08. *Wmk Mult Crown CA. P 14.*
94	17	½d. green (2.7.07)		2·75	2·25
95		1d. carmine (26.4.07)		3·25	15
96		2d. orange (5.08)		1·50	6·50
97		2½d. blue (8.07)		26·00	8·50
98		3d. violet (1.6.07)		7·50	15·00
94/8			Set of 5	38·00	29·00
94/8 Optd "Specimen"			Set of 5	£100	

1909. *No dot below "d". Wmk Mult Crown CA. P 14.*
99	18	1d. carmine (3.09)		1·25	30
100		6d. dull purple (16.1.09)		5·50	30·00
101		1s. black/*green* (16.1.09)		3·75	8·50
99/101			Set of 3	9·50	35·00
99/101 Optd "Specimen"			Set of 3	65·00	

1909 (Nov)—11. *T 18, redrawn (dot below "d", as in T 17). Wmk Mult Crown CA. P 14.*
102		½d. green (31.10.10)		1·50	50
		w. Wmk inverted			
103		1d. carmine		1·50	15
104		2d. grey (3.8.11)		4·00	8·50
105		2½d. ultramarine (25.7.10)		8·00	3·50
106		3d. purple/*yellow*		2·50	5·00
107		6d. dull purple		8·00	5·00
102/7			Set of 6	23·00	21·00
102 and 104/6 Optd "Specimen"			Set of 4	85·00	

ONE PENNY.

19 (20)

(Recess D.L.R.)

1913 (1 Jan)—17. *Wmk Mult Crown CA. P 14.*
108	19	½d. green		45	20
109		1d. red		60	25
		a. *Rose-red*		1·00	65
		b. *Scarlet* (1.17)		14·00	5·00
		w. Wmk inverted			
		y. Wmk inverted and reversed		75·00	
110		2d. grey		7·00	27·00
		a. *Slate*		2·50	27·00
111		2½d. ultramarine		35	50
112		3d. purple/*yellow*		80	5·00
		a. *On lemon*		2·75	12·00
		aw. Wmk inverted			
		ax. Wmk reversed			
		b. *On pale yellow*		2·50	9·00
113		4d. red/*yellow*		80	2·00
114		5d. olive-green (7.11.13)		2·25	13·00
		x. Wmk reversed			
115		6d. claret		2·00	4·50
116		1s. black/*green*		1·50	3·75
117		1s. bistre (1.5.14)		3·75	20·00
118	18	2s. blue and purple		4·75	25·00
119		5s. carmine and myrtle		13·00	48·00
		x. Wmk reversed		£150	
120		£1 mauve and black		80·00	£150
108/20			Set of 13	£100	£250
108/20 Optd "Specimen"			Set of 13	£250	

Nos. 118/20 are from new centre and frame dies, the motto "PAX ET JUSTITIA" being slightly over 7 mm long, as against just over 8 mm in Nos. 99 to 107. Nos. 139/41 are also from the new dies.

1915. *No. 116 surch with T 20.*
121	19	1d. on 1s. black/*green* (R.)		7·50	25·00
		a. "ONE" omitted		£900	£800
		b. "ONE" double		£650	
		c. "PENNY" and bar double		£650	£650

The spacing between the two words varies from 7¾ mm to 10 mm.

WAR STAMP. **WAR STAMP.** **WAR STAMP**

(21) (22) (24)

1916 (June). *No. 109 optd locally with T 21.* (a) *First and second settings; words 2 to 2½ mm apart.*
122	19	1d. red		3·25	6·00
		a. Opt double		£150	£150
		b. Comma for stop		8·00	14·00
		w. Wmk inverted			

In the first printing every second stamp has the comma for stop. The second printing of this setting has full stops only. These two printings can therefore only be distinguished in blocks or pairs.

(b) *Third setting; words only 1½ mm apart.*
123	19	1d. red			80·00
		a. Opt double			£1100

Stamps of the first setting are offered as this rare one. Care must be taken to see that the distance between the lines is not over 1½ mm.

(c) *Fourth setting; optd with T 22. Words 3½ mm apart.*
124	19	1d. carmine-red		3·00	10·00
		a. Opt double			£200
		w. Wmk inverted			
		y. Wmk inverted and reversed			

1916 (Aug)—18. *T 19, from new printings, optd with T 24.*
126		1d. carmine-red (Optd S. £60)		30	80
		w. Wmk inverted			
		x. Wmk reversed			
127		1d. pale rose-red		80	80
		w. Wmk inverted		60·00	
128		1d. deep rose-red		50	80
129		1d. pale scarlet (1918)		30	80

1921–32. *Wmk Mult Script CA. P 14.*
131	19	½d. green (3.21)		1·75	30
132		1d. carmine (6.21)		1·00	80
		a. *Red*		2·25	15
132b		1½d. brown (1.12.32)		2·25	80
133		2d. grey (3.22)		2·25	80
133a		2½d. bright blue (12.25)		1·00	60
134		3d. bright blue (3.22)		90	6·00
135		3d. purple/*yellow* (1.12.26)		75	1·50
135a		4d. red/*yellow* (9.30)		1·75	6·00
136		5d. sage-green (8.3.24)		80	6·00
137		6d. claret (1.11.27)		90	3·50
138		1s. bistre-brown (9.21)		5·50	22·00
		a. *Ochre* (1927)		3·00	16·00
139	18	2s. blue and purple (8.3.24)		7·50	13·00
140		5s. carmine and myrtle (8.3.24)		18·00	32·00
141		£1 mauve and black (9.28)		80·00	£120
131/41			Set of 14	£100	£180
131/41 Optd/Perf "Specimen"			Set of 14	£250	

1935 (6 May). *Silver Jubilee. As Nos. 114/17 of Jamaica, but ptd by Waterlow. P 11×12.*
142		1d. deep blue and scarlet		40	1·25
143		1½d. ultramarine and grey		1·00	3·00
144		2½d. brown and deep blue		1·90	3·50
145		1s. slate and purple		2·00	3·50
		l. Kite and horizontal log		£225	
142/5			Set of 4	4·75	10·00
142/5 Perf "Specimen"			Set of 4	75·00	

For illustration of plate variety see Omnibus section following Zimbabwe.

1937 (12 May). *Coronation. As Nos. 118/20 of Jamaica, but ptd by B.W. P 11×11½.*
146		1d. violet		35	40
147		1½d. carmine		40	30
148		2½d. blue		45	1·50
146/8			Set of 3	1·10	2·00
146/8 Perf "Specimen"			Set of 3	50·00	

25 26 Young's Island and Fort Duvernette

27 Kingstown and Fort Charlotte 28 Bathing Beach at Villa

29 Victoria Park, Kingstown

NEW CONSTITUTION 1951

(29a)

(Recess B.W.)

1938 (11 Mar)—47. *Wmk Mult Script CA. P 12.*
149	25	½d. blue and green		10	10
150	26	1d. blue and lake-brown		10	10
151	27	1½d. green and scarlet		20	10
152	25	2d. green and black		40	35
153	28	2½d. blue-black and blue-green		20	40
153a	29	2½d. green and purple-brown (1947)		40	20
154	25	3d. orange and purple		20	10
154a	28	3½d. blue-black and blue-green (1947)		40	1·75
155	25	6d. black and lake		1·00	40
156	29	1s. purple and green		1·00	80
157	25	2s. blue and purple		6·00	75
157a		2s. 6d. red-brown and blue (1947)		1·25	3·50
158		5s. scarlet and deep green		10·00	2·50
158a		10s. violet and brown (1947)		3·75	8·50
		aw. Wmk inverted		—£1300	
159		£1 purple and black		16·00	15·00
149/59			Set of 15	35·00	30·00
149/59 Perf "Specimen"			Set of 15	£250	

1946 (15 Oct). *Victory. As Nos. 141/2 of Jamaica.*
160		1½d. carmine		10	10
161		3½d. blue		10	10
160/1 Perf "Specimen"			Set of 2	50·00	

1948 (30 Nov). *Royal Silver Wedding. As Nos. 143/4 of Jamaica.*
162		1½d. scarlet		10	10
163		£1 bright purple		15·00	17·00

No. 163 was originally printed in black, but the supply of these was stolen in transit. A few archive examples exist, some perforated "Specimen".

(New Currency. 100 cents = 1 West Indian, later East Caribbean dollar)

1949 (26 Mar)—52. *Value in cents and dollars. Wmk Mult Script CA. P 12.*
164	25	1 c. blue and green		20	1·00
164a		1 c. green and black (10.6.52)		30	2·00
165	26	2 c. blue and lake-brown		15	40
166	27	3 c. green and scarlet		40	50
166a	25	3 c. orange and purple (10.6.52)		30	2·00
167		4 c. green and black		35	20
167a		4 c. blue and green (10.6.52)		30	15
168	29	5 c. green and purple-brown		15	10
169	25	6 c. orange and purple		40	75
169a	27	6 c. green and scarlet (10.6.52)		30	2·00
170	28	7 c. blue-black and blue-green		3·50	80
170a	25	10 c. blue-black and blue-green (10.6.52)		50	20
171	25	12 c. black and lake		35	15
172	29	24 c. purple and green		35	45
173	25	48 c. blue and purple		2·00	2·00
174		60 c. red-brown and blue		1·75	3·00
175		$1.20, scarlet and deep green		4·25	4·00
176		$2.40, violet and brown		6·00	9·00
177		$4.80, purple and black		11·00	19·00
164/77			Set of 19	29·00	40·00

1949 (10 Oct). *75th Anniv of U.P.U. As Nos. 145/8 of Jamaica.*

178	5 c. blue	25	15
179	6 c. purple	55	1·40
180	12 c. magenta	30	1·40
181	24 c. blue-green	50	25
178/81	*Set of 4*	1·40	2·75

1951 (16 Feb). *Inauguration of B.W.I. University College. As Nos. 149/50 of Jamaica.*

182	3 c. deep green and scarlet	30	30
183	12 c. black and purple	30	50

1951 (21 Sept). *New Constitution. Optd with T 29a by B.W.*

184	27	3 c. green and scarlet	15	90
185	25	4 c. green and black	15	30
186	29	5 c. green and purple-brown	15	30
187	25	12 c. black and lake	60	30
184/7		*Set of 4*	95	1·60

1953 (2 June). *Coronation. As No. 153 of Jamaica.*

188	4 c. black and green	30	20

30 **31**

(Recess Waterlow (until 1961), then D.L.R.)

1955 (16 Sept)–**63**. *Wmk Mult Script CA. P 13½×14 (T 30) or 14 (T 31).*

189	30	1 c. orange	10	10
		a. *Deep orange* (11.12.62)	4·50	4·75
190		2 c. ultramarine	1·40	60
		a. *Blue* (26.9.61)	1·40	60
191		3 c. slate	30	10
192		4 c. brown	20	10
193		5 c. scarlet	40	10
194		10 c. reddish violet	20	10
		a. *Deep lilac* (12.2.58)	50	10
195		15 c. deep blue	65	30
196		20 c. green	60	10
197		25 c. black-brown	50	10
198	31	50 c. red-brown	4·50	1·75
		a. *Chocolate* (11.6.58)	5·00	1·25
199		$1 myrtle-green	8·00	1·00
		a. *Deep myrtle-green* (11.6.58)	15·00	4·00
		b. *Deep yellowish green* (15.1.63)	25·00	11·00
200		$2.50, deep blue	14·00	8·00
		a. *Indigo-blue* (30.7.62)	32·00	14·00
189/200		*Set of 12*	26·00	9·50

See also Nos. 207/20 and **MS633**.

1958 (22 Apr). *Inauguration of British Caribbean Federation. As Nos. 175/7 of Jamaica.*

201	3 c. deep green	30	20
202	6 c. blue	35	1·25
203	12 c. scarlet	45	50
201/3	*Set of 3*	1·00	1·75

MINISTERIAL GOVERNMENT

1963 (4 June). *Freedom from Hunger. As No. 80 of Lesotho.*

204	8 c. reddish violet	60	50

1963 (2 Sept). *Red Cross Centenary. As Nos. 203/4 of Jamaica.*

205	4 c. red and black	15	20
206	8 c. red and blue	35	50

(Recess D.L.R.)

1964–65. *As 1955 but wmk w 12. (a) P 12½ (14 Jan–Feb 1964).*

207	30	10 c. deep lilac	30	30
208		15 c. deep blue	30	50
209		20 c. green (24.2.64*)	2·25	55
210		25 c. black-brown	30	30
211	31	50 c. chocolate	9·00	9·00
207/11		*Set of 5*	7·25	9·50

(b) P 13×14 (T 30) or 14 (T 31)

212	30	1 c. orange (15.12.64)	15	10
213		2 c. blue (15.12.64)	15	10
214		3 c. slate (15.12.64)	50	10
215		5 c. scarlet (15.12.64)	15	10
216		10 c. deep lilac (15.12.64)	15	10
217		15 c. deep blue (9.11.64)	80	30
218		20 c. green (1964)	45	10
		w. Wmk inverted		
219		25 c. black-brown (20.10.64)	85	15
220	31	50 c. chocolate (18.1.65)	3·75	7·00
212/20		*Set of 9*	6·25	7·00

*This is the earliest known date recorded in St. Vincent although it may have been put on sale on 14.1.64.

PRICES OF SETS

Set prices are given for many issues, generally those containing three stamps or more. Definitive sets include one of each value or major colour change, but do not cover different perforations, die types or minor shades. Where a choice is possible the set prices are based on the cheapest versions of the stamps included in the listings.

32 Scout Badge and Proficiency Badges

33 Tropical Fruits

(Des V. Whiteley. Litho Harrison)

1964 (23 Nov). *50th Anniv of St. Vincent Boy Scouts Association. W w 12. P 14½.*

221	32	1 c. yellow-green and chocolate	10	10
222		4 c. blue and brown-purple	10	10
223		20 c. yellow and black-violet	30	10
224		50 c. red and bronze-green	45	70
221/4		*Set of 4*	80	80

(Des V. Whiteley. Photo Harrison)

1965 (23 Mar). *Botanic Gardens Bicentenary. T 33 and similar multicoloured designs. W w 12. P 14½ × 13½ (horiz) or 13½ × 14½ (vert).*

225	1 c. Type 33	10	10
226	4 c. Breadfruit and H.M.S. *Providence* (sloop), 1793	10	10
227	25 c. Doric Temple and pond (*vert*)	15	10
228	40 c. Talipot Palm and Doric Temple (*vert*)	30	1·25
225/8	*Set of 4*	50	1·25

1965 (17 May). *I.T.U. Centenary. As Nos. 98/9 of Lesotho.*

229	4 c. light blue and light olive-green	20	10
230	48 c. ochre-yellow and orange	55	45

37 Boat-building, Bequia (inscr "BEQUIA")

(Des M. Goaman. Photo Harrison)

1965 (16 Aug)–**67**. *T 37 and similar multicoloured designs. W w 12. P 14½ × 13½ (horiz designs) or 13½ × 14½ (vert).*

231	1 c. Type 37 ("BEQUIA")	10	85
231a	1 c. Type 37 ("BEQUIA") (27.6.67)	65	30
232	2 c. Friendship Beach, Bequia	10	10
233	3 c. Terminal Building, Arnos Vale Airport	30	10
	w. Wmk inverted	6·00	
234	4 c. Woman with bananas (*vert*)	1·00	30
	w. Wmk inverted		
235	5 c. Crater Lake	15	10
236	6 c. Carib Stone (*vert*)	15	40
237	8 c. Arrowroot (*vert*)	30	10
238	10 c. Owia Salt Pond	30	10
239	12 c. Deep water wharf	70	10
	w. Wmk inverted	†	—
240	20 c. Sea Island cotton (*vert*)	30	10
	w. Wmk inverted	—	30·00
241	25 c. Map of St. Vincent and islands (*vert*)	35	10
	w. Wmk inverted	26·00	
242	50 c. Breadfruit (*vert*)	50	30
243	$1 Baleine Falls (*vert*)	4·00	30
244	$2.50, St. Vincent Amazon (*vert*)	18·00	6·50
245	$5 Arms of St. Vincent (*vert*)	5·00	9·50
231/45	*Set of 16*	27·00	17·00

The 1 c. (No. 231a), 2 c., 3 c., 5 c. and 10 c. exist with PVA gum as well as gum arabic.
See also No. 261.

1966 (24 June). *Churchill Commemoration. As Nos. 102/5 of Lesotho.*

246	1 c. new blue	10	10
247	4 c. deep green	20	10
248	20 c. brown	35	30
249	40 c. bluish violet	55	1·00
246/9	*Set of 4*	1·00	1·25

1966 (4 Feb). *Royal Visit. As Nos. 183/4 of Montserrat.*

250	4 c. black and ultramarine	75	20
251	25 c. black and magenta	2·00	80

1966 (20 Sept). *Inauguration of W.H.O. Headquarters, Geneva. As Nos. 185/6 of Montserrat.*

252	4 c. black, yellow-green and light blue	30	10
253	25 c. black, light purple and yellow-brown	70	80

1966 (1 Dec). *20th Anniv of U.N.E.S.C.O. As Nos. 342/4 of Mauritius.*

254	4 c. slate-violet, red, yellow and orange	30	10
255	8 c. orange-yellow, violet and deep olive	55	10
256	25 c. black, bright purple and orange	1·25	60
254/6	*Set of 3*	1·90	70

38 Coastal View of Mount Coke Area

(Des and photo Harrison)

1967 (1 Dec). *Autonomous Methodist Church. T 38 and similar horiz designs. Multicoloured. W w 12. P 14 × 14½.*

257	2 c. Type 38	10	10
258	8 c. Kingstown Methodist Church	10	10
259	25 c. First Licence to perform marriages	25	10
260	35 c. Conference Arms	25	10
257/60	*Set of 4*	55	30

1968 (20 Feb). *As No. 234, but W w 12 sideways.*

261	4 c. Woman with bananas	30	30

The above exists with PVA gum as well as gum arabic.

39 Meteorological Institute

(Des G. Vasarhelyi. Photo Harrison)

1968 (28 May). *World Meteorological Day. W w 12. P 14 × 14½.*

262	39	4 c. multicoloured	10	10
263		25 c. multicoloured	10	10
264		35 c. multicoloured	15	15
262/4		*Set of 3*	30	30

40 Dr. Martin Luther King and Cotton Pickers

(Des V. Whiteley. Litho D.L.R.)

1968 (28 Aug). *Martin Luther King Commemoration. W w 12 (sideways). P 13.*

265	40	5 c. multicoloured	10	10
266		25 c. multicoloured	10	10
267		35 c. multicoloured	15	15
265/7		*Set of 3*	30	30

41 Speaker addressing Demonstrators **42** Scales of Justice and Human Rights Emblem

(Des V. Whiteley. Photo Enschedé)

1968 (1 Nov). *Human Rights Year. P 13 × 14 (3 c.) or 14 × 13 (35 c.).*

268	41	3 c. multicoloured	10	10
269	42	35 c. royal blue and turquoise-blue	20	10

43 Male Masquerader **44** Steel Bandsman

(Des V. Whiteley. Litho Format)

1969 (17 Feb). *St. Vincent Carnival. T 43/4 and similar designs. P 14.*

270	1 c. multicoloured	10	10
271	5 c. red and deep chocolate	10	10
272	8 c. multicoloured	10	10
273	25 c. multicoloured	15	20
270/3	*Set of 4*	30	40

Designs: Horiz—8 c. Carnival Revellers. Vert—25 c. Queen of Bands.

METHODIST CONFERENCE MAY 1969

(47)

1969 (14 May). *Methodist Conference. Nos. 257/8, 241 and 260 optd with T 47.*

274	2 c. multicoloured	10	15
275	8 c. multicoloured	15	25
276	25 c. multicoloured	15	25
277	35 c. multicoloured	1·00	2·75
274/7	*Set of 4*	1·25	3·00

48 "Strength in Unity" 49 Map of "CARIFTA" Countries

(Des J. Cooter. Litho D.L.R.)

1969 (1 July). *First Anniv of CARIFTA (Caribbean Free Trade Area).* W w **12** (sideways on T **48**). P 13.
278 48 2 c. black, pale buff and red .. 10 10
279 49 5 c. multicoloured .. 10 10
280 48 8 c. black, pale buff and pale green .. 10 10
281 49 25 c. multicoloured .. 35 15
278/81 *Set of 4* 50 30

ASSOCIATED STATEHOOD

50 Flag of St. Vincent

(Des V. Whiteley, based on local designs. Photo Harrison)

1969 (27 Oct). *Statehood.* T **50** and similar horiz designs. W w **12**. P 14 × 14½.
282 4 c. multicoloured .. 10 10
283 10 c. multicoloured .. 10 10
284 50 c. grey, black and orange .. 35 20
282/4 *Set of 3* 50 30
Designs:—10 c. Battle scene with insets of Petroglyph and Carib chief Chatoyer; 50 c. Carib House with maces and scales.

51 Green Heron

(Des J.W. Photo Harrison)

1970 (12 Jan)–**71.** T **51** and similar multicoloured designs. Chalk-surfaced paper. W w **12** (sideways* on 1, 2, 3, 6, 8, 20, 25 c., $1, $2.50 and upright on others). P 14.
285 ½ c. House Wren (vert) .. 10 85
286 1 c. Type 51 .. 35 2·50
  a. Glazed, ordinary paper (9.8.71) 30 1·50
  aw. Wmk Crown to right of CA 1·25 1·75
287 2 c. Lesser Antillean Bullfinches .. 15 40
  w. Wmk Crown to right of CA 16·00
288 3 c. St. Vincent Amazons .. 15 30
289 4 c. Rufous-throated Solitaire (vert) 20 30
290 5 c. Red-necked Pigeon (vert) 3·75 30
  a. Glazed, ordinary paper (9.8.71) 1·50 30
291 6 c. Bananaquits .. 30 30
292 8 c. Purple-throated Carib .. 40 20
  w. Wmk Crown to right of CA 28·00
293 10 c. Mangrove Cuckoo (vert) .. 30 10
294 12 c. Common Black Hawk (vert) 40 10
295 20 c. Bare-eyed Thrush .. 60 15
296 25 c. Hooded Tanager .. 70 20
297 50 c. Blue Hooded Euphonia .. 2·00 75
  w. Wmk inverted 50·00
298 $1 Barn Owl (vert) .. 7·50 4·00
299 $2.50, Yellow-bellied Elaenia (vert) 6·00 4·75
300 $5 Ruddy Quail Dove .. 8·00 6·50
285/300 *Set of 16* 25·00 18·00
*The normal sideways watermark shows Crown to left of CA, as seen from the back of the stamp.
See also Nos. 361/8 and 396/8.

52 De Havilland D.H.C.6 Twin Otter 100

(Des R. Granger Barrett. Litho Enschedé)

1970 (13 Mar). *20th Anniv of Regular Air Services.* T **52** and similar horiz designs. Multicoloured. W w **12** (sideways). P 14 × 13.
301 5 c. Type 52 .. 10 10
302 8 c. Grumman G.21 Goose .. 15 10
303 10 c. Hawker Siddeley H.S.748 .. 20 10
304 25 c. Douglas DC-3 .. 65 30
301/4 *Set of 4* 1·00 40

53 "Children's Nursery" 54 "Angel and the Two Marys at the Tomb" (stained-glass window)

(Des R. Granger Barrett. Photo Harrison)

1970 (1 June). *Centenary of British Red Cross.* T **53** and similar horiz designs. Multicoloured. W w **12.** P 14.
305 3 c. Type 53 .. 10 10
306 5 c. "First Aid" .. 15 10
  w. Wmk inverted 50·00
307 12 c. "Voluntary Aid Detachment" .. 35 1·00
  w. Wmk inverted 2·25
308 25 c. "Blood Transfusion" .. 55 50
305/8 *Set of 4* 1·00 1·50

(Des L. Curtis. Litho J.W.)

1970 (7 Sept). *150th Anniv of St. George's Cathedral, Kingstown.* T **54** and similar multicoloured designs. W w **12** (sideways* on horiz designs). P 14.
309 ½ c. Type 54 .. 10 10
310 5 c. St. George's Cathedral (horiz) 10 10
  w. Wmk Crown to right of CA
311 25 c. Tower, St. George's Cathedral 10 10
312 35 c. Interior, St. George's Cathedral (horiz) 15 10
313 50 c. Type 54 .. 20 30
309/13 *Set of 5* 45 35
*The normal sideways watermark shows Crown to left of CA, as seen from the back of the stamp.

55 "The Adoration of the Shepherds" (Le Nain)

(Des J. Cooter. Litho Questa)

1970 (23 Nov). *Christmas.* T **55** and similar vert design. Multicoloured. W w **12** (sideways* on 25 c., 50 c.). P 14.
314 8 c. "The Virgin and Child" (Bellini) 10 10
315 25 c. Type 55 .. 10 10
  w. Wmk Crown to right of CA 90
316 35 c. As 8 c. .. 10 10
317 50 c. Type 55 .. 15 20
  w. Wmk Crown to right of CA 1·50
314/17 *Set of 4* 35 30
*The normal sideways watermark shows Crown to left of CA, as seen from the back of the stamp.

56 New Post Office and 6d. Stamp of 1861

(Des J. Cooter. Litho Questa)

1971 (29 Mar). *110th Anniv of First St. Vincent Stamps.* T **56** and similar horiz design. Multicoloured. W w **12** (sideways). P 14.
318 2 c. Type 56 .. 10 10
319 4 c. 1d. Stamp of 1861 and New Post Office .. 10 10
320 25 c. Type 56 .. 10 10
321 $1 As 4 c. .. 35 45
318/21 *Set of 4* 45 50

57 Trust Seal and Wildlife 58 "Madonna appearing to St. Anthony" (Tiepolo)

(Des G. Drummond. Litho J.W.)

1971 (4 Aug). *St. Vincent's National Trust.* T **57** and similar horiz design. Multicoloured. W w **12** (sideways). P 13½ × 14.
322 12 c. Type 57 .. 55 55
323 30 c. Old Cannon, Fort Charlotte .. 35 25
324 40 c. Type 57 .. 65 40
325 45 c. As 30 c. .. 40 90
322/5 *Set of 4* 1·75 1·90

(Des J. Cooter. Litho Questa)

1971 (6 Oct). *Christmas.* T **58** and similar horiz design. Multicoloured. W w **12** (sideways* on 10 c. and $1). P 14½×14 (10 c., $1) or 14×14½ (5 c., 25 c.).
326 5 c. Type 58 .. 10 10
327 10 c. "The Holy Family on the Flight into Egypt" (detail, Pietro da Cortona) 10 10
  w. Wmk Crown to right of CA 2·25
328 25 c. Type 58 .. 10 10
329 $1 As 10 c. .. 40 35
  w. Wmk Crown to right of CA 2·25 2·50
326/9 *Set of 4* 50 40
*The normal sideways watermark shows Crown to left of CA, as seen from the back of the stamp.

59 Careening 60 Private, Grenadier Company, 32nd Foot (1764)

(Des J. Cooter. Litho J.W.)

1971 (25 Nov). *The Grenadines of St. Vincent.* T **59** and similar vert designs. Multicoloured. W w **12.** P 13½.
330 1 c. Type 59 .. 10 10
331 5 c. Seine fishermen .. 10 10
332 6 c. Map of the Grenadines .. 10 10
333 15 c. Type 59 .. 20 10
334 20 c. As 5 c. .. 20 10
335 50 c. As 6 c. .. 65 1·00
330/5 *Set of 6* 1·00 1·25
MS336 177 × 140 mm. Nos. 330/5 .. 6·00 9·50

(Des and litho J.W.)

1972 (14 Feb). *Military Uniforms.* T **60** and similar vert designs. Multicoloured. W w **12.** P 14 × 13½.
337 12 c. Type 60 .. 75 15
338 30 c. Officer, Battalion Company, 31st Foot (1772) 1·00 65
339 50 c. Private, Grenadier Company, 6th Foot (1772) 1·10 1·25
337/9 .. *Set of 3* 2·50 1·90

61 Breadnut Fruit 62 Candlestick Cassia

(Des P. Powell. Litho Questa)

1972 (16 May). *Fruit.* T **61** and similar vert designs. Multicoloured. W w **12** (sideways). P 13½.
340 3 c. Type 61 .. 10 10
341 5 c. Pawpaw .. 10 10
342 12 c. Plumrose or Roseapple .. 15 30
343 25 c. Mango .. 35 70
340/3 .. *Set of 4* 60 1·00

(Des Sylvia Goaman. Litho B.W.)

1972 (31 July). *Flowers.* T **62** and similar vert designs. Multicoloured. P 13 ($1) or 13½ × 14 (others).
344 1 c. Type 62 .. 10 10
345 30 c. Lobster Claw .. 15 10
346 40 c. White Trumpet .. 15 15
347 $1 Soufriere tree .. 50 1·25
344/7 .. *Set of 4* 75 1·40

63 Sir Charles Brisbane and Coat of Arms

(Des Jennifer Toombs. Litho J.W.)

1972 (29 Sept). *Birth Bicentenary of Sir Charles Brisbane.* T **63** and similar horiz designs. W w **12** (sideways). P 13½.
348 20 c. yellow-ochre, gold and red-brown 15 10
349 30 c. light yellow, light mauve and black 35 10
350 $1 multicoloured .. 90 70
348/50 *Set of 3* 1·25 75
MS351 171 × 111 mm. Nos. 348/50 (sold at $2) .. 4·50 6·50
Designs:—30 c. H.M.S. Arethusa, 1807; $1 H.M.S. Blake, 1808.

64 Arrowroot and Breadfruit

(Des (from photograph by D. Groves) and photo Harrison)

1972 (20 Nov). *Royal Silver Wedding. Multicoloured; background colour given.* W w 12. P 14 × 14½.

352	64	30 c. red-brown	..	10	10
353		$1 myrtle-green	..	20	10
		w. Wmk inverted	..	£275	

65 Sighting St. Vincent

66 "The Last Supper" (French Stained-glass Window)

(Des J. Cooter. Litho Enschedé)

1973 (31 Jan). *475th Anniv of Columbus's Third Voyage to the West Indies.* T **65** *and similar triangular designs. Multicoloured.* W w 12. P 13½.

354	5 c. Type **65**	..		25	30
355	12 c. Caribs watching Columbus's fleet			35	30
356	30 c. Christopher Columbus	..		55	90
357	50 c. *Santa Maria*	..	..	80	2·25
354/7 ..	..	..	*Set of 4*	1·75	3·25

(Des J. Cooter. Litho Questa)

1973 (19 Apr). *Easter.* T **66** *and similar vert designs. Multicoloured.* W w 12 (*sideways*). P 14 × 13½.

358	66	15 c. multicoloured	..	10	10
		a. Horiz strip of 3. Nos. 358/60		45	
359	—	60 c. multicoloured	..	20	20
360	—	$1 multicoloured	..	20	20
358/60		..	*Set of 3*	45	45

Nos. 358, 360 and 359 were printed, in that order, horizontally *se-tenant* throughout a sheet of 45 stamps, and form a composite design of "The Last Supper".

1973 (13 June–23 Nov). *As Nos. 285 etc., but* W w 12 *upright on* 2, 3, 6, 20 *c. and sideways* on others. Glazed paper.*

361	2 c. Lesser Antillean Bullfinches (23.11) ..	30	45
362	3 c. St. Vincent Amazons (23.11)	30	45
363	4 c. Rufous-throated Solitaire (*vert*) (23.11)	30	30
364	5 c. Red-necked Pigeon (*vert*)	30	20
	w. Wmk Crown to left of CA (23.11)	90	80
365	6 c. Bananaquits (23.11)	40	60
366	10 c. Mangrove Cuckoo (*vert*) (23.11)	40	15
367	12 c. Common Black Hawk (*vert*) (23.11)	60	75
368	20 c. Bare-eyed Thrush (23.11)	70	40
361/8	..	*Set of 8*	3·00	3·00

*The normal sideways watermark shows Crown to right of CA on No. 364 and to left of CA on the others, *as seen from the back of the stamp*.

For the 1 c. value with watermark upright see Grenadines of St. Vincent No. 3a.

67 William Wilberforce and Poster

68 P.P.F. Symbol

(Des Jennifer Toombs. Litho D.L.R.)

1973 (11 July). *140th Death Anniv of William Wilberforce.* T **67** *and similar horiz designs. Multicoloured.* W w 12. P 14 × 13½.

369	30 c. Type **67**	..	15	10
	w. Wmk inverted	..	45·00	
370	40 c. Slaves cutting cane	..	20	15
371	50 c. Wilberforce and medallion	..	20	15
369/71	..	*Set of 3*	50	35

1973 (3 Oct). *21st Anniv of International Planned Parenthood Federation.* T **68** *and similar vert design. Multicoloured.* W w 12 (*sideways*). P 14.

372	12 c. Type **68**	..	10	10
373	40 c. "IPPF" and symbol	..	20	20

1973 (14 Nov). *Royal Wedding. As Nos.* 322/3 *of Montserrat.*

374	50 c. deep blue	..	15	10
375	70 c. grey-green	..	15	10

69 Administrative Block, Mona

(Des PAD Studio. Litho Questa)

1973 (13 Dec). *25th Anniv of West Indies University.* T **69** *and similar multicoloured designs.* W w 12 (*sideways on* $1). P 14.

376	5 c. Type **69**	..	10	10
377	10 c. University Centre, Kingstown	..	10	10
378	30 c. Aerial view, Mona University	..	15	10
379	$1 University coat of arms (*vert*)	..	35	60
376/9	..	*Set of 4*	50	65

(70)

1973 (15 Dec). *Nos.* 297, 292 *and* 298 *surch in half sheets with* T **70**, *by the Govt Printer, St. Vincent.*

380	30 c. on 50 c. multicoloured	..	2·00	1·00
	a. Surch double	..	22·00	
	b. Surch double (on front) and single inverted (on reverse)	..	65·00	
	c. Surch double, one inverted	..	50·00	
	d. Surch inverted			
381	40 c. on 8 c. multicoloured	..	2·00	1·00
	a. Surch double	..	28·00	
	b. Surch inverted	..	£130	
382	$10 on $1 multicoloured	..	8·00	8·00
	a. Surch double	..	95·00	
	b. Surch inverted	..	£110	
	c. Surch double, one inverted	..	£110	
380/2	..	*Set of 3*	11·00	9·00

SPECIMEN STAMPS. From No. 383 onwards the stamps of St. Vincent exist overprinted "SPECIMEN", these being produced for publicity purposes.

(Des PAD Studio. Litho Enschedé)

1974 (10 Apr). *Easter.* T **71** *and similar vert designs showing sculptures. Multicoloured.* W w 12 (*sideways*). P 14 × 13½.

383	5 c. Type **71**	..	10	10
384	30 c. "The Deposition" (English, 14th-century)	10	10
385	40 c. "Pieta" (Fernandez)	..	10	10
386	$1 "The Resurrection" (French, 16th-century)	20	25
383/6	..	*Set of 4*	30	30

72 Istra

(Des J.W. Litho Questa)

1974 (28 June). *Cruise Ships.* T **72** *and similar horiz designs. Multicoloured.* W w 12 (*sideways**). P 14.

387	15 c. Type **72**	..	20	10
	w. Wmk Crown to right of CA	..	27·00	
388	20 c. *Oceanic*	..	25	10
389	30 c. *Aleksandr Pushkin*	..	25	10
390	$1 *Europa*	..	50	30
387/90	..	*Set of 4*	1·10	40
MS391	134×83 mm. Nos. 387/90	..	1·00	2·75

*The normal sideways watermark shows Crown to left of CA, *as seen from the back of the stamp.*

COVER PRICES

Cover factors are quoted at the beginning of each country for most issues to 1945. An explanation of the system can be found on page x. The factors quoted do not, however, apply to philatelic covers.

73 U.P.U. Emblem

(Des J.W. Litho Questa)

1974 (25 July). *Centenary of Universal Postal Union.* T **73** *and similar horiz designs. Multicoloured.* W w 12. P 14.

392	5 c. Type **73**	..	10	10
	w. Wmk inverted	..	27·00	
393	12 c. Globe within posthorn	..	10	10
394	60 c. Map of St. Vincent and hand-cancelling	20	10
395	90 c. Map of the World	..	25	30
392/5	..	*Set of 4*	50	40

74 Royal Tern

75 Scout Badge and Emblems

(Des J.W. Litho Questa)

1974 (29 Aug). T **74** *and similar vert designs. Multicoloured. Glazed paper.* W w 12 (*sideways on* 40 *c. and* $10). P 14.

396	30 c. Type **74**	..	2·00	90
397	40 c. Brown Pelican	..	2·00	90
398	$10 Magnificent Frigate Bird	..	13·00	11·00
396/8	..	*Set of 3*	15·00	11·50

(Des Sylvia Goaman. Litho Enschedé)

1974 (9 Oct). *Diamond Jubilee of Scout Movement in St. Vincent.* W w 12. P 13 × 13½.

399	75	10 c. multicoloured	..	10	10
400		25 c. multicoloured	..	20	10
401		45 c. multicoloured	..	20	15
402		$1 multicoloured	..	35	90
399/402	..	*Set of 4*	70	1·10

76 Sir Winston Churchill

77 The Shepherds

(Des C. Abbott. Litho Questa)

1974 (28 Nov). *Birth Centenary of Sir Winston Churchill.* T **76** *and similar vert designs. Multicoloured.* W w 12. P 14.

403	25 c. Type **76**	..	10	10
404	35 c. Churchill in military uniform	..	15	10
405	45 c. Churchill in naval uniform	..	15	10
406	$1 Churchill in air-force uniform	..	20	50
403/6	..	*Set of 4*	50	60

(Des Jennifer Toombs. Litho Enschedé)

1974 (5 Dec). *Christmas.* T **77** *and similar vert designs.* W w 12. P 12 × 12½.

407	77	3 c. violet-blue and black	..	10	10
		a. Horiz strip of 4. Nos. 407/10	15	
408	—	3 c. violet-blue and black	..	10	10
409	—	3 c. violet-blue and black	..	10	10
410	—	3 c. violet-blue and black	..	10	10
411	77	8 c. apple-green and black	..	10	10
412	—	35 c. rose and deep maroon	..	10	10
413	—	45 c. olive-bistre and brown-black	..	10	10
414	—	$1 lavender and slate-black	..	20	50
407/14	..	*Set of 8*	55	85

Designs:—Nos. 408, 412 Mary and crib; Nos. 409, 413 Joseph, ox and ass; Nos. 410, 414 The Magi.

Nos. 407/10 were issued horizontally *se-tenant* within the sheet, together forming a composite design of the Nativity.

78 Faces

(Des G. Drummond. Litho D.L.R.)

1975 (7–27 Feb). *Kingstown Carnival. T **78** and similar horiz designs. Multicoloured. W w **12**. P 14 × 13½.*

415	1 c. Type **78**		10	10
	a. Booklet pane. No. 415 × 2 plus printed label (27.2)		35	
	b. Booklet pane. Nos. 415, 417 and 419 (27.2)		40	
416	15 c. Pineapple women		15	15
	a. Booklet pane. Nos. 416, 418 and 420 (27.2)		50	
417	25 c. King of the Bands		15	15
418	35 c. Carnival dancers		15	15
419	45 c. Queen of the Bands		15	20
420	$1.25, "African Splendour"		25	55
415/20		Set of 6	75	1·10
MS421	146 × 128 mm. Nos. 415/20		1·00	3·00

79 French Angelfish

Two types of $2.50:

I

II

Type I. Fishing-line attached to fish's mouth. Imprint "1975".
Type II. Fishing-line omitted. Imprint "1976".

(Des G. Drummond. Litho Questa)

1975 (10 Apr)–**76**. *Marine Life. T **79** and similar horiz designs. Multicoloured. W w **14** (sideways*). With imprint date. P 14½.*

422	1 c. Type **79**		15	80
	w. Wmk Crown to right of CA		18·00	
423	2 c. Spot-finned Butterflyfish		15	95
424	3 c. Yellow Jack		15	55
425	4 c. Spanish Mackerel		20	10
426	5 c. French Grunt		20	45
	w. Wmk Crown to right of CA		27·00	
427	6 c. Spotted Goatfish		20	90
428	8 c. Ballyhoo		20	2·00
429	10 c. Sperm Whale		30	10
430	12 c. Humpback Whale		40	1·60
431	15 c. Scribbled Cowfish		1·25	1·60
	w. Wmk Crown to right of CA		14·00	
432	15 c. Skipjack Tuna (14.10.76)		3·50	1·50
433	20 c. Queen Angelfish		40	10
434	25 c. Princess Parrotfish		45	20
435	35 c. Red Hind		65	1·75
436	45 c. Atlantic Flyingfish		80	90
437	50 c. Porkfish		65	1·75
438	70 c. Yellow-finned Tuna (14.10.76)		6·50	1·50
439	90 c. Pompano (14.10.76)		6·50	70
440	$1 Queen Triggerfish		65	20
441	$2.50, Sailfish (I)		2·50	6·50
	a. Type II (7.1.76)		1·25	1·25
442	$5 Dolphin (fish)		3·75	2·50
443	$10 Blue Marlin		2·50	7·50
422/43		Set of 22	27·00	26·00

*The normal sideways watermark shows Crown to left of CA, as seen from the back of the stamp.
Imprint dates: "1975", Nos. 422/31, 433/7, 440/1, 442/3; "1976", Nos. 425, 429, 432/3, 438/40, 441a; "1977", Nos. 422/4, 426/8, 430, 432, 437, 443; "1978", No. 429.

80 Cutting Bananas

(Des G. Drummond. Litho Questa)

1975 (26 June). *Banana Industry. T **80** and similar horiz designs. Multicoloured. W w **12** (sideways). P 13½.*

447	25 c. Type **80**		15	10
448	35 c. Packaging Station, La Croix		15	10
449	45 c. Cleaning and boxing		20	10
450	70 c. Shipping bananas aboard *Geestide* (freighter)		40	30
447/50		Set of 4	80	50

81 Snorkel Diving

(Des G. Drummond. Litho Questa)

1975 (31 July). *Tourism. T **81** and similar horiz designs. Multicoloured. W w **14** (sideways). P 13½.*

451	15 c. Type **81**		40	15
452	20 c. Aquaduct Golf Course		1·50	1·00
453	35 c. Steel Band at Mariner's Inn		45	15
454	45 c. Sunbathing at Young Island		45	15
455	$1.25, Yachting marina		1·40	2·75
451/5		Set of 5	3·75	3·75

82 George Washington, John Adams, Thomas Jefferson and James Madison

(Des G. Drummond. Litho Questa)

1975 (11 Sept). *Bicentenary of American Revolution. T **82** and similar horiz designs. P 14.*

456	½ c. black and lavender		10	10
457	1 c. black and light emerald		10	10
458	1½ c. black and light magenta		10	10
459	5 c. black and bright yellow-green		10	10
460	10 c. black and light violet-blue		10	10
461	25 c. black and dull orange-yellow		10	10
462	35 c. black and light greenish blue		15	10
463	45 c. black and bright rose		15	10
464	$1 black and light orange		30	40
465	$2 black and light yellow-olive		40	85
456/65		Set of 10	1·10	1·50
MS466	179 × 156 mm. Nos. 456/65		1·25	1·50

Presidents:—1 c. Monroe, Quincy Adams, Jackson, van Buren; 1½ c. W. Harrison, Tyler, Polk, Taylor; 5 c. Fillmore, Pierce, Buchanan, Lincoln; 10 c. Andrew Johnson, Grant, Hayes, Garfield; 25 c. Arthur, Cleveland, B. Harrison, McKinley; 35 c. Theodore Roosevelt, Taft, Wilson, Harding; 45 c. Coolidge, Hoover, Franklin Roosevelt, Truman; $1 Eisenhower, Kennedy, Lyndon Johnson, Nixon; $2 Pres. Ford and White House.
Nos. 456/65 were each issued in sheets of ten stamps and two se-tenant labels.

83/4 "Shepherds"

(Des Jennifer Toombs. Litho Harrison)

1975 (4 Dec). *Christmas. T **83/4** and similar triangular designs. P 13½×14. A. W w **12** (upright or inverted)*

467A	3 c. black and magenta		10	10
	c. Block of 4. Nos. 467A/70A		20	30
468A	3 c. black and magenta		10	10
469A	3 c. black and magenta		10	10
470A	3 c. black and magenta		10	10
471A	8 c. black and light greenish blue		10	10
	c. Pair. Nos. 471A/2A		10	15
472A	8 c. black and light greenish blue		10	10
473A	35 c. black and yellow		15	20
	c. Pair. Nos. 473A/4A		30	40
474A	35 c. black and yellow		15	20
475A	45 c. black and yellow-green		15	30
	c. Pair. Nos. 475A/6A		30	60
476A	45 c. black and yellow-green		15	30
477A	$1 black and bright lilac		30	80
	c. Pair. Nos. 477A/8A		60	1·60
478A	$1 black and bright lilac		30	80
467A/78A		Set of 12	1·25	2·75

B. W w 12 (sideways to left or right)

467B	3 c. black and magenta		10	10
	c. Block of 4. Nos. 467B/70B		20	30
468B	3 c. black and magenta		10	10
469B	3 c. black and magenta		10	10
470B	3 c. black and magenta		10	10
471B	8 c. black and light greenish blue		10	10
	c. Pair. Nos. 471B/2B		10	15
472B	8 c. black and light greenish blue		10	10
473B	35 c. black and yellow		15	20
	c. Pair. Nos. 473B/4B		30	40
474B	35 c. black and yellow		15	20
475B	45 c. black and yellow-green		15	30
	c. Pair. Nos. 475B/6B		30	60
476B	45 c. black and yellow-green		15	30

477B	$1 black and bright lilac		30	80
	c. Pair. Nos. 477B/8B		60	1·60
478B	$1 black and bright lilac		30	80
467B/78B		Set of 12	1·25	1·75

Designs:—No. 467, "Star of Bethlehem"; 468, "Holy Trinity"; 469, As T **83**; 470, "Three Kings"; 471/2, As 467; 473/4, As 468; 475/6, T **83/4**; 477/8 As 470. The two designs of each denomination (Nos. 471/8) differ in that the longest side is at the foot or at the top as shown in T **83/4**.

Each denomination was printed in sheets of 16, the designs being se-tenant and so arranged that the watermark comes upright, inverted, sideways right and sideways left.

85 Carnival Dancers

(Des G. Drummond. Litho Questa)

1976 (19 Feb). *Kingstown Carnival. T **85** and similar horiz designs. Multicoloured. W w **14** (sideways*). P 13½.*

479	1 c. Type **85**		10	10
	a. Booklet pane. Nos. 479 and 480 plus printed label		20	
	w. Wmk Crown to right of CA		60	
480	2 c. Humpty-Dumpty people		10	10
	a. Booklet pane. Nos. 480/2		30	
	w. Wmk Crown to right of CA		90	
481	5 c. Smiling faces		10	10
	w. Wmk Crown to right of CA		90	
482	35 c. Dragon worshippers		15	10
	a. Booklet pane. Nos. 482/4		60	
	w. Wmk Crown to right of CA		2·00	
483	45 c. Carnival tableaux		20	10
	w. Wmk Crown to right of CA		1·00	
484	$1.25, Bumble-Bee dancers		30	50
	w. Wmk Crown to right of CA		1·50	
479/84		Set of 6	70	80

*The normal sideways watermark shows Crown to left of CA, as seen from the back of the stamp.

70¢

(86)

87 Blue-headed Hummingbird and Yellow Hibiscus

1976 (8 Apr). *Nos. 424 and 437 surch as T **86**. "1975" imprint date.*

485	70 c. on 3 c. Horse-eyed Jack		55	1·00
	a. Surch inverted		25·00	
486	90 c. on 50 c. Porkfish		55	1·25
	a. Surch inverted		25·00	

(Des G. Drummond. Litho Walsall)

1976 (20 May). *Hummingbirds and Hibiscuses. T **87** and similar vert designs. Multicoloured. W w **14** (inverted). P 13½.*

487	5 c. Type **87**		35	10
488	10 c. Antillean Crested Hummingbird and Pink Hibiscus		60	15
489	35 c. Purple-throated Carib and White Hibiscus		1·00	30
	a. No wmk		20·00	
490	45 c. Blue-headed Hummingbird and Red Hibiscus		1·00	35
	w. Wmk upright		1·00	90
491	$1.25 Green-throated Carib and Peach Hibiscus		5·00	5·00
487/91		Set of 5	7·00	5·50

1976 (16 Sept). *West Indian Victory in World Cricket Cup. As Nos. 419/20 of Jamaica.*

492	15 c. Map of the Caribbean		75	25
493	45 c. Prudential Cup		1·25	1·00

88 St Mary's Church, Kingstown

(Des G. Drummond. Litho Questa)

1976 (18 Nov). *Christmas. T **88** and similar horiz designs. Multicoloured. W w **14** (sideways). P 14.*

494	35 c. Type **88**		15	10
495	45 c. Anglican Church, Georgetown		15	10
496	50 c. Methodist Church, Georgetown		20	10
497	$1.25, St. George's Cathedral, Kingstown		40	60
494/7		Set of 4	80	70

89 Barrancoid Pot-stand

(Des G. Vasarhelyi. Litho J.W.)

1976 (16 Dec). *National Trust. T 89 and similar horiz designs. Multicoloured. W w 14 (sideways). P 13½.*

498	5 c. Type 89			10	10
499	45 c. National Museum			15	10
500	70 c. Carib sculpture			20	20
501	$1 Ciboney petroglyph			30	50
498/501			Set of 4	60	75

90 William I, William II, Henry I and Stephen

(Des G. Vasarhelyi. Litho J.W.)

1977 (7 Feb). *Silver Jubilee. T 90 and similar horiz designs. Multicoloured. P 13½. (a) W w 14 (sideways*). From sheets.*

502	½ c. Type 90			10	10
503	1 c. Henry II, Richard I, John, Henry III			10	10
504	1½ c. Edward I, Edward II, Edward III, Richard II			10	10
	w. Wmk Crown to left of CA			27·00	
505	2 c. Henry IV, Henry V, Henry VI, Edward IV			10	10
506	5 c. Edward V, Richard III, Henry VII, Henry VIII			10	10
507	10 c. Edward VI, Lady Jane Grey, Mary I, Elizabeth I			10	10
	w. Wmk Crown to left of CA			65·00	
508	25 c. James I, Charles I, Charles II, James II			10	10
509	35 c. William III, Mary II, Anne, George I			10	10
510	45 c. George II, George III, George IV			10	10
	w. Wmk Crown to right of CA			40	35
511	75 c. William IV, Victoria, Edward VII			15	25
	w. Wmk Crown to left of CA			60	60
512	$1 George V, Edward VIII, George VI			20	40
	w. Wmk Crown to left of CA			75	75
513	$2 Elizabeth II leaving Westminster Abbey			30	60
	w. Wmk Crown to left of CA			10	
502/13			Set of 12	1·00	1·60
MS514	170×146 mm. Nos. 502/13. P 14½×14			1·00	2·00

(b) No wmk. From booklets

515	½ c. Type 90			40	1·25
	a. Booklet pane. Nos. 515/18 se-tenant			1·40	
516	1 c. As No. 503			40	1·25
517	1½ c. As No. 504			40	1·25
518	2 c. As No. 505			40	1·25
519	5 c. As No. 506			40	1·25
	a. Booklet pane. Nos. 519/22 se-tenant			1·40	
520	10 c. As No. 507			40	1·25
521	25 c. As No. 508			40	1·25
522	35 c. As No. 509			40	1·25
523	45 c. As No. 510			40	1·25
	a. Booklet pane. Nos. 523/6 se-tenant			1·40	
524	75 c. As No. 511			40	1·25
525	$1 As No. 512			40	1·25
526	$2 As No. 513			40	1·25
515/26			Set of 12	4·00	13·00

The normal sideways watermark shows Crown to left of CA on the 45 c., and to the right of CA on others, as seen from the back of the stamp.

Nos. 502/13 were each issued in sheets of ten stamps and two se-tenant labels.

91 Grant of Arms

(Des G. Drummond. Litho Questa)

1977 (12 May). *Centenary of Windward Is Diocese. T 91 and similar horiz designs. Multicoloured. W w 14 (sideways). P 13½.*

527	15 c. Type 91			10	10
528	35 c. Bishop Berkeley and mitres			10	10
529	45 c. Map and arms of diocese.			10	10
530	$1.25, St. George's Cathedral and Bishop Woodroffe			30	55
527/30			Set of 4	45	60

CARNIVAL 1977
JUNE 25TH–JULY 5TH
(92)

1977 (2 June). *Kingstown Carnival. Nos. 426, 429, 432/3 and 440 optd with T 92.*

531	5 c. French Grunt			10	10
	a. Red opt			25·00	
	b. Hyphen omitted			1·40	
	w. Wmk Crown to right of CA			30·00	

532	10 c. Sperm Whale (R.)			10	10
	a. Opt double (R. and Blk.)			50·00	
	b. Hyphen omitted			1·60	
533	15 c. Skipjack Tuna (R.)			10	10
	a. Black opt			25·00	
	b. Hyphen omitted			2·00	
534	20 c. Queen Angelfish (R.)			10	10
	a. Opt inverted			17·00	
	b. Black opt			40·00	
	c. Hyphen omitted			2·25	
535	$1 Queen Triggerfish			40	70
	a. Red opt			50·00	
	b. Hyphen omitted			3·50	
531/5			Set of 5	70	95

The variety showing the hyphen omitted from the second line of the overprint occurred on R. 4/4 of the lower pane.

Imprint dates: "1975", Nos. 531/2, 534/5; "1976", Nos. 532/5; "1977", Nos. 531, 533.

93 Guide and Emblem

CARIBBEAN VISIT 1977

(94)

(Des PAD Studio. Litho J.W.)

1977 (1 Sept). *50th Anniv of St. Vincent Girl Guides. T 93 and similar vert designs. The $2 value is additionally optd. "1930–1977". Multicoloured. W w 14. P 13½.*

536	5 c. Type 93			10	10
537	15 c. Early uniform, ranger, guide and brownie			10	10
	w. Wmk inverted			10·00	
538	20 c. Early uniform and guide			10	10
539	$2 Lady Baden-Powell			40	75
	a. Optd dates omitted			15·00	
	b. Optd dates double			50·00	
536/9			Set of 4	55	80

1977 (27 Oct). *Royal Visit. No. 513 optd with T 94.*

540	$2 Queen Elizabeth leaving Westminster Abbey			30	30
	a. Opt inverted			35·00	
	w. Wmk Crown to left of CA			23·00	

95 Map of St. Vincent **96** Opening Verse and Scene

(Des G. Drummond. Litho Questa)

1977–78. *Provisionals. W w 12. P 14½ × 14.*

541	95 20 c. blk, dull violet-bl & pale bl (31.1.78)			15	15
542	40 c. black, dull orange & flesh (30.11.77)			25	20
	a. Black (value) omitted			10·00	
543	40 c. black, magenta and salmon (31.1.78)			20	15
541/3			Set of 3	55	45

Nos. 541/3 were printed in 1974, without value, for provisional use; they were locally surcharged before going on sale.

(Des Jennifer Toombs. Litho Enschedé)

1977 (1 Dec). *Christmas. Scenes and Verses from the carol "While Shepherds Watched their Flocks by Night". T 96 and similar vert designs. Multicoloured. W w 14. P 13 × 11.*

544	5 c. Type 96			10	10
545	10 c. Angel consoling shepherds			10	10
546	15 c. View of Bethlehem			10	10
547	25 c. Nativity scene			10	10
548	50 c. Throng of Angels.			10	10
549	$1.25, Praising God			30	65
544/9			Set of 6	50	85
MS550	150 × 170 mm. Nos. 544/9. P 13½			90	1·75

97 *Cynthia cardui* and *Bougainvillea glabra var. alba*

(Des Daphne Padden. Litho Walsall)

1978 (6 Apr). *Butterflies and Bougainvilleas. T 97 and similar horiz designs. Multicoloured. W w 14 (sideways). P 14.*

551	5 c. Type 97			15	10
552	25 c. *Dione juno* and "Golden Glow"			20	10
553	40 c. *Anartia amathea* and "Mrs McLean"			30	10
554	50 c. *Hypolimnas misippus* and "Cyphen"			35	10
555	$1.25, *Pseudolycaena marsyas* and "Thomasii"			70	70
551/5			Set of 5	1·60	90

(Des G. Drummond. Litho J.W.)

1978 (2 June). *25th Anniv of Coronation. Horiz designs as Nos. 422/5 of Montserrat. Multicoloured. W w 14 (sideways). P 13.*

556	40 c. Westminster Abbey			10	10
557	50 c. Gloucester Cathedral			10	10
558	$1.25, Durham Cathedral			15	15
559	$2.50, Exeter Cathedral			15	25
556/9			Set of 4	30	45
MS560	130 × 102 mm. Nos. 556/9. P 13½ × 14			40	1·00

Nos. 556/9 were each printed in sheets of ten stamps and two se-tenant labels.

98 Rotary International Emblem and Motto

99 "Co-operation in Education Leads to Mutual Understanding and Respect"

(Des G. Hutchins. Litho Questa)

1978 (13 July). *International Service Clubs. T 98 and similar horiz designs showing club emblems and mottoes. Multicoloured. W w 14 (sideways). P 14½.*

561	40 c. Type 98			15	10
562	50 c. Lions International			15	10
563	$1 Jaycees			35	50
561/3			Set of 3	60	55

(Des G. Hutchins. Litho Questa)

1978 (7 Sept). *10th Anniv of Project School to School (St. Vincent-Canada school twinning project). T 99 and similar multicoloured design showing flags and blackboard. W w 14 (sideways on $2). P 14.*

564	40 c. Type 99			10	10
565	$2 "Co-operation in Education Leads to the Elimination of Racial Intolerance" (horiz)			40	50

100 Arnos Vale Airport **101** Young Child

(Des G. Drummond. Litho Questa)

1978 (19 Oct). *75th Anniv of Powered Flight. T 100 and similar horiz designs. Multicoloured. W w 14 (sideways). P 14½ × 14.*

566	10 c. Type 100			10	10
567	40 c. Wilbur Wright landing Wright Flyer I			15	10
568	50 c. Orville Wright in Wright Flyer III			15	10
569	$1.25, Orville Wright and Wright Flyer I airborne			45	35
566/9			Set of 4	70	45

(Des A. Paish. Litho Questa)

1979 (14 Feb). *International Year of the Child. T 101 and similar vert designs showing portraits of young children. W w 14. P 14 × 13½.*

570	8 c. black, gold and pale yellow-green			10	10
571	20 c. black, gold and pale rose-lilac			10	10
572	50 c. black, gold and pale violet-blue			15	10
573	$2 black, gold and flesh			50	50
570/3			Set of 4	75	55

10c+5c

SOUFRIERE RELIEF FUND 1979

(102)

103 Sir Rowland Hill

(Des G. Drummond. Litho Questa)

1979 (17 Apr). *Soufrière Eruption Relief Fund. Designs as T 95 but surchd as T 102 by Reliance Printery, Kingstown. W w 12. P 14½ × 14.*

574	10 c. + 5 c. violet-blue and pale rose-lilac		10	15
575	50 c. + 25 c. yellow-brown and buff		20	20
576	$1 + 50 c. reddish brown and brownish grey		25	30
577	$2 + $1 deep green and apple-green		40	50
574/7		*Set of 4*	75	1·00

(Des J.W. Litho Harrison)

1979 (31 May). *Death Centenary of Sir Rowland Hill. T 103 and similar horiz designs. Multicoloured. W w 14 (sideways*). P 14.*

578	40 c. Type 103		15	10
579	50 c. Penny Black and Twopenny Blue stamps		15	15
580	$3 1861 1d. and 6d. stamps		40	1·10
578/80		*Set of 3*	60	1·25
MS581	170×123 mm. Nos. 578/80, 594/5 and 599 (see footnote after No. 601)		1·40	2·50
	w. Wmk Crown to right of CA		35·00	

*The normal sideways watermark shows Crown to left of CA, as seen from the back of the stamp.

Nos. 578/80 were each printed in sheets including two se-tenant stamp-size labels.

104 First and Latest Buccament Postmarks and Map of St. Vincent (105)

(Des J.W. Litho Harrison)

1979 (31 May–1 Sept). *St. Vincent Post Offices. Horiz designs as T 104 showing first and latest postmarks and map of St. Vincent. Multicoloured. W w 14 (sideways*). With imprint date. P 14.*

582	1 c. Type 104		10	10
583	2 c. Sion Hill		10	10
584	3 c. Cumberland		10	10
585	4 c. Questelles		10	10
586	5 c. Layou		10	10
	w. Wmk Crown to right of CA		35·00	
587	6 c. New Ground		10	10
588	8 c. Mesopotamia		10	10
589	10 c. Troumaca		10	10
590	12 c. Arnos Vale		15	10
591	15 c. Stubbs		15	10
592	20 c. Orange Hill		15	10
593	25 c. Calliaqua		15	10
594	40 c. Edinboro		25	20
595	40 c. Colonarie		30	25
596	80 c. Biabou		40	30
597	$1 Chateaubelair		40	50
598	$2 Head P.O., Kingstown		45	80
599	$3 Barrouallie		45	1·25
600	$5 Georgetown		60	2·00
601	$10 Kingstown		1·25	4·00
582/601		*Set of 20*	4·50	9·00

*The normal sideways watermark shows Crown to left of CA, as seen from the back of the stamp.

Dates of issue:—40, 50 c., $3 (from No. MS581 and booklets only) 31.5.79; others, 40, 50 c., $3 from sheets, 1.9.79.

Imprint dates: "1979", Nos. 582/601; "1981", No. 597; "1982", Nos. 586, 589, 593.

See also Nos. MS581 and MS637.

1979 (6 Aug). *Opening of St. Vincent and the Grenadines Air Service. No. 566 optd with T 105, in red, by Reliance Printery, Kingstown.*

602	10 c. Type 100		10	10
	w. Wmk Crown to right of CA		40·00	10·00

*The normal sideways watermark shows Crown to left of CA, as seen from the back of the stamp.

INDEPENDENT

106 National Flag and *Ixora coccinea* (flower)

(Des J.W. Litho Enschedé)

1979 (27 Oct). *Independence. T 106 and similar horiz designs. Multicoloured. W w 14 (sideways*). P 12½×12.*

603	20 c. Type 106		15	10
604	50 c. House of Assembly and *Ixora stricta* (flower)		20	10
	w. Wmk Crown to right of CA		5·50	
605	80 c. Prime Minister R. Milton Cato and *Ixora williamsii* (flower)		25	20
603/5		*Set of 3*	55	30

*The normal sideways watermark shows Crown to left of CA, as seen from the back of the stamp.

INDEPENDENCE 1979
(107)

1979 (27 Oct). *Independence. Nos. 422, 425/30, 432, 434, 437/40, 441a and 443 optd with T 107, by Letchworth Press, Barbados.*

606	1 c. Type 79		10	10
607	4 c. Spanish Mackerel		10	10
608	5 c. French Grunt		10	10
609	6 c. Spotted Goatfish		10	10
610	8 c. Ballyhoo		10	10
611	10 c. Sperm Whale		15	15
612	12 c. Humpback Whale		15	15
613	15 c. Skipjack Tuna		15	15
614	25 c. Princess Parrotfish		20	20
615	50 c. Porkfish		35	35
616	70 c. Yellow-finned Tuna		45	45
617	90 c. Pompano		45	50
618	$1 Queen Triggerfish		45	50
619	$2.50, Sailfish (II)		70	1·00
	a. Opt inverted		£100	
	b. Optd on Type I (No. 441)		9·00	9·00
620	$10 Blue Marlin		1·40	4·25
606/20		*Set of 15*	4·25	7·00

Imprint dates: "1975", Nos. 606/10, 612, 614/15, 619b, 620; "1976", Nos. 607, 616/19; "1977", Nos. 606, 608/10, 612/13, 615, 620; "1978", No. 611; "1979", Nos. 607/8, 610, 614, 618, 620.

108 Virgin and Child | 109 *Polistes cinctus* (wasp) and Oleander

(Des Jennifer Toombs. Litho Questa)

1979 (1 Nov). *Christmas. Scenes and Verses from the carol "Silent Night". T 108 and similar horiz designs. Multicoloured. W w 14 (sideways). P 13½.*

621	10 c. Type 108		10	10
622	20 c. Jesus in manger		10	10
623	25 c. Shepherds		10	10
624	40 c. Angel		10	10
625	50 c. Angels with infant Jesus		10	10
626	$2 Nativity scene		40	45
621/6		*Set of 6*	55	60
MS627	151 × 170 mm. Nos. 621/6		70	1·25

(Des J.W. Litho Walsall)

1979 (13 Dec). *Flowers and Insects. T 109 and similar vert designs showing insects and different varieties of Oleander flower. Multicoloured. W w 14. P 14.*

628	5 c. Type 109		10	10
629	10 c. *Pyrophorus noctiluca* (click beetle)		10	10
630	25 c. *Stagmomantis limbata* (mantid)		10	10
631	50 c. *Psiloptera lampetis* (beetle)		10	10
632	$2 *Diaprepies abbreviatus* (weevil)		30	30
628/32		*Set of 5*	50	40

(Des and litho D.L.R.)

1980 (28 Feb). *Centenary of St. Vincent "Arms" Stamps. Sheet 116×72 mm containing designs as T 31. W w 14 (sideways*). P 14×13½.*

MS633	116×72 mm. 50 c. reddish brown; $1 deep grey-green; $2.50 deep blue		50	75
	w. Wmk Crown to left of CA		1·00	

*The normal sideways watermark shows Crown to right of CA, as seen from the back of the stamp.

110 Queen Elizabeth II

(Des J.W. Litho Harrison)

1980 (24 Apr). *"London 1980" International Stamp Exhibition. T 110 and similar horiz designs. Multicoloured. W w 14 (sideways). P 14.*

634	80 c. Type 110		15	20
635	$1 Great Britain 1954 3d. and St. Vincent 1954 5 c. definitive stamps		20	30
636	$2 Unadopted postage stamp design of 1971		35	60
634/6		*Set of 3*	60	1·00
MS637	165 × 115 mm. Nos. 596/8 and 634/6		75	1·50

Nos. 634/6 were each printed in sheets containing 2 se-tenant stamp-size labels.

MINIMUM PRICE

The minimum price quote is 10p which represents a handling charge rather than a basis for valuing common stamps. For further notes about prices see introductory pages.

---

111 Steel Band | 112 Football

(Des G. Drummond. Litho Questa)

1980 (12 June). *Kingstown Carnival. T 111 and similar horiz design. Multicoloured. W w 14 (sideways). P 13½ × 14.*

638	20 c. Type 111		15	40
	a. Pair. Nos. 638/9		30	80
639	20 c. Steel band (*different*)		15	40

Nos. 638/9 were printed together, se-tenant, in horizontal and vertical pairs throughout the sheet.

(Des Polygraphic. Litho Rosenbaum Bros, Vienna)

1980 (7 Aug). *"Sport for All". T 112 and similar vert designs. Multicoloured. W w 14 (inverted). P 13½.*

640	10 c. Type 112		10	10
	w. Wmk upright		22·00	
641	60 c. Cycling		30	15
642	80 c. Basketball		40	40
643	$2.50, Boxing		40	1·25
640/3		*Set of 4*	1·10	1·60

HURRICANE RELIEF 50¢
(113)

114 Brazilian Agouti

1980 (7 Aug). *Hurricane Relief. As Nos. 640/3, but W w 14 (upright), surch with T 113.*

644	10 c. + 50 c. Type 112		15	15
645	60 c. + 50 c. Cycling		20	25
646	80 c. + 50 c. Basketball		35	40
	w. Wmk inverted		22·00	
647	$2.50 + 50 c. Boxing		40	85
	w. Wmk inverted		22·00	
644/7		*Set of 4*	1·00	1·50

(Des L. Curtis. Litho Questa)

1980 (2 Oct). *Wildlife. T 114 and similar horiz designs. Multicoloured. W w 14 (sideways). P 14 × 14½.*

648	25 c. Type 114		10	10
649	50 c. Giant Toad		15	10
650	$2 Small Indian Mongoose		40	55
648/50		*Set of 3*	60	60

115 Map of World showing St. Vincent | 116 *Ville de Paris* (French ship of the line), 1782

(Des G. Drummond. Litho Questa)

1980 (4 Dec). *St. Vincent "On the Map". T 115 and similar designs depicting maps showing St. Vincent. Multicoloured. W w 14 (sideways). P 13½ × 14.*

651	10 c. Type 115		10	10
652	50 c. Western hemisphere		25	10
653	$1 Central America		40	15
654	$2 St. Vincent		60	30
651/4		*Set of 4*	1·25	50
MS655	143 × 95 mm. No. 654. P 12		50	75

(Des J.W. Litho Rosenbaum Bros, Vienna)

1981 (19 Feb). *Sailing Ships. T 116 and similar vert designs. Multicoloured. W w 14. P 13½.*

656	50 c. Type 116		55	20
657	60 c. H.M.S. *Ramillies* (ship of the line), 1782		60	40
658	$1.50, H.M.S. *Providence* (sloop), 1793		1·00	1·25
659	$2 *Dee* (paddle-steamer packet)		1·25	1·50
656/9		*Set of 4*	3·00	3·00

117 Arrowroot Cultivation

(Des G. Drummond. Litho Format)

1981 (21 May). *Agriculture. T 117 and similar horiz designs. Multicoloured. W w 14 (sideways). P 14.*

660	25 c. Type 117		10	15
	a. Pair. Nos. 660/1		15	30
661	25 c. Arrowroot processing		10	15
662	50 c. Banana cultivation		10	25
	a. Pair. Nos. 662/3		20	50
663	50 c. Banana export packaging station		10	25
664	60 c. Coconut plantation		15	30
	a. Pair. Nos. 664/5		30	60
665	60 c. Copra drying frames		15	30
666	$1 Cocoa cultivation		15	45
	a. Pair. Nos. 666/7		30	90
667	$1 Cocoa beans and sun drying frames		15	45
660/7		*Set of 8*	85	2·00

The two designs of each value were printed together, *se-tenant*, in horizontal and vertical pairs throughout the sheet.

(Des D. Shults. Litho Questa)

1981 (17 July–26 Nov). *Royal Wedding. Horiz designs as T 26/7 of Kiribati. Multicoloured. (a) W w 15. P 14.*

668	60 c. Isabella		15	15
	b. Sheetlet. No. 668×6 and No. 669		1·10	
669	60 c. Prince Charles and Lady Diana Spencer		30	30
670	$2.50, Alberta (tender)		30	30
	aw. Wmk inverted		8·50	
	b. Sheetlet. No. 670×6 and No. 671		1·75	
	bw. Wmk inverted		70·00	
671	$2.50, As No. 669		70	70
	aw. Wmk inverted		30·00	
672	$4 Britannia		35	40
	aw. Wmk inverted		8·50	
	b. Sheetlet. No. 672×6 and No. 673		2·00	
	bw. Wmk inverted		70·00	
673	$4 As No. 669		1·00	1·25
	aw. Wmk inverted		30·00	
668/73		*Set of 6*	2·50	2·75
MS674	120×109 mm. $5 As No. 669. Wmk sideways. P 12 (26 Nov)		75	75

(b) Booklet stamps. No wmk. P 12 (26 Nov)

675	60 c. As No. 668		15	25
	a. Booklet pane. No. 675×4 with margins all round		50	
676	$2.50, As No. 671		40	1·25
	a. Booklet pane. No. 676×2 with margins all round		80	

Nos. 668/73 were printed in sheetlets of seven stamps of the same face value, each containing six of the "Royal Yacht" design and one of the larger design showing Prince Charles and Lady Diana.

Nos. 675/6 come from $9.80 stamp booklets.

118 Kingstown General Post Office 119

(Des G. Drummond. Litho Questa)

1981 (1 Sept). *U.P.U. Membership. W w 14 (sideways). P 14.*

677	118	$2 multicoloured	40	90
		a. Horiz pair. Nos. 677/8	80	1·75
678	119	$2 multicoloured	40	90

Nos. 677/8 were printed together, *se-tenant*, in horizontal pairs throughout the sheet, forming a composite design.

120 St. Vincent Flag with Flags of other U.N. Member Nations

(Des L. Curtis. Litho Format)

1981 (11 Sept). *First Anniv of U.N. Membership. T 120 and similar horiz design. Multicoloured. W w 14 (sideways). P 13½ × 14.*

679	$1.50, Type 120		25	25
680	$2.50, Prime Minister Robert Milton Cato		35	50

Nos. 679/80 are inscribed "ST. VINCENT and the GRENA-DINES" and were each printed in small sheets of 6 including one *se-tenant* stamp-size label.

121 Silhouettes of Figures at Old Testament Reading, and Bible Extract

(Des Jennifer Toombs. Litho Security Printers (M), Malaysia)

1981 (19 Nov). *Christmas. T 121 and similar horiz designs showing silhouettes of figures. Multicoloured. W w 14 (sideways*). P 12.*

681	50 c. Type 121		15	10
682	60 c. Madonna, and angel		15	10
	w. Wmk Crown to left of CA		80	

683	$1 Madonna, and Bible extract		25	25
	w. Wmk Crown to left of CA		1·40	
684	$2 Joseph and Mary travelling to Bethlehem		50	50
	w. Wmk Crown to left of CA		2·25	
681/4		*Set of 4*	95	85
MS685	129×127 mm. Nos. 681/4. P 13½		95	1·40
	w. Wmk Crown to right of CA		4·50	

The normal sideways watermark shows Crown to left of CA, as seen from the back of the stamp, on the 50 c. and the miniature sheet but to right on the other values.

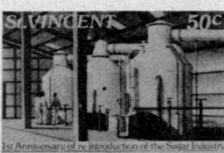

122 Sugar Boilers

(Des L. Curtis. Litho Format)

1982 (5 Apr). *First Anniv of Re-introduction of Sugar Industry. T 122 and similar horiz designs. Multicoloured. W w 14 (sideways). P 14.*

686	50 c. Type 122		20	15
687	60 c. Sugar drying plant		20	20
688	$1.50, Sugar mill machinery		40	75
689	$2 Crane loading sugar cane		50	1·00
686/9		*Set of 4*	1·10	1·90

123 Butterfly Float   124 Augusta of Saxe-Gotha, Princess of Wales, 1736

(Des G. Vasarhelyi. Photo Heraclio Fournier)

1982 (10 June). *Carnival 1982. T 123 and similar multicoloured designs. P 13½.*

690	50 c. Type 123		20	15
691	60 c. Angel dancer (vert)		20	15
692	$1.50, Winged dancer (vert)		50	80
693	$2 Eagle float		70	1·50
690/3		*Set of 4*	1·50	2·40

(Des D. Shults and J. Cooter. Litho Format)

1982 (1 July). *21st Birthday of Princess of Wales. T 124 and similar vert designs. Multicoloured. W w 15. P 13½ × 14.*

694	50 c. Type 124		15	20
	w. Wmk inverted		50	
695	60 c. Coat of arms of Augusta of Saxe-Gotha		15	25
	w. Wmk inverted		75	
696	$6 Diana, Princess of Wales		70	1·25
	w. Wmk inverted		3·50	
694/6		*Set of 3*	90	1·50

125 Scout Emblem   126 De Havilland D.H.60G Gipsy Moth

(Des L. Curtis. Litho Questa)

1982 (15 July). *75th Anniv of Boy Scout Movement. T 125 and similar vert design. Multicoloured. W w 14. P 14.*

697	$1.50, Type 125		70	1·00
698	$2.50, 75th anniv emblem		90	1·50

1982 (19 July). *Birth of Prince William of Wales. Nos. 694/6 optd with T 19 of St. Kitts.*

699	50 c. Type 124		15	20
700	60 c. Coat of arms of Augusta of Saxe-Gotha		15	25
	a. Opt inverted		30·00	
	w. Wmk inverted		5·50	
701	$6 Diana, Princess of Wales		70	1·50
	a. Opt double		8·50	
	w. Wmk inverted		5·50	
699/701		*Set of 3*	90	1·75

(Des A. Theobald. Litho Questa)

1982 (29 July). *50th Anniv of Airmail Service. T 126 and similar horiz designs. Multicoloured. W w 14 (sideways). P 14.*

702	50 c. Type 126		55	30
703	60 c. Grumman G.21 Goose, 1952		65	40
704	$1.50, Hawker Siddeley H.S.748, 1968		1·25	1·50
705	$2 Britten Norman "long nose" Trislander, 1982		1·40	2·00
702/5		*Set of 4*	3·50	3·75

127 Geestport (freighter)

(Des G. Drummond. Litho Format)

1982 (27 Dec). *Ships. T 127 and similar horiz designs. Multicoloured. W w 14 (sideways). P 14.*

706	45 c. Type 127		40	25
707	60 c. Stella Oceanis (liner)		50	40
708	$1.50, Victoria (liner)		95	1·50
709	$2 Queen Elizabeth 2 (liner)		1·25	2·00
706/9		*Set of 4*	2·75	3·75

128 Pseudocorynactis caribbeorum

(Des McCombie-De Bay. Litho Security Printers (M), Malaysia)

1983 (10 Feb). *Marine Life. T 128 and similar multicoloured designs. W w 14 (sideways* on 60 c., $1.50, $2). P 12.*

710	50 c. Type 128		65	25
711	60 c. Actinoporus elegans (vert)		75	40
712	$1.50, Arachnanthus nocturnus (vert)		1·40	2·00
	w. Wmk Crown to left of CA		4·00	
713	$2 Reid's Seahorse (vert)		1·60	2·25
710/13		*Set of 4*	4·00	4·50

The normal sideways watermark shows Crown to right of CA, as seen from the back of the stamp.

129 Satellite View of St. Vincent   (130)

(Des R. Vigurs. Litho Questa)

1983 (14 Mar). *Commonwealth Day. T 129 and similar horiz designs. Multicoloured. W w 14 (sideways). P 14.*

714	45 c. Type 129		15	20
715	60 c. Flag of St. Vincent		20	25
716	$1.50, Prime Minister R. Milton Cato		30	65
717	$2 Harvesting bananas		45	90
714/17		*Set of 4*	1·00	1·75

Nos. 714/17 are inscribed "St. Vincent & The Grenadines".

1983 (26 Apr). *No. 681 surch with T 130 by Reliance Printery, Kingstown.*

718	45 c. on 50 c. Type 121		40	30

131 Symbolic Handshake   132 Sir William Smith (founder)

(Des J.W. Litho Security Printers (M), Malaysia)

1983 (6 July). *10th Anniv of Treaty of Chaguaramas. T 131 and similar vert designs. Multicoloured. W w 14 (sideways). P 11½ × 12.*

719	45 c. Type 131		25	20
	w. Wmk Crown to left of CA		3·00	
720	60 c. Commerce emblem		30	30
	w. Wmk Crown to left of CA		3·00	
721	$1.50 Caribbean map		60	1·00
722	$2 Flags of member countries and map of St. Vincent		85	1·25
719/22		*Set of 4*	1·75	2·50

The normal sideways watermark shows Crown to right of CA, as seen from the back of the stamp.

(Des L. Curtis. Litho Security Printers (M), Malaysia)

1983 (6 Oct). *Centenary of Boys' Brigade. T 132 and similar vert designs. Multicoloured.* W w **14.** P 12 × 11½.
723	45 c. Type 132		25	25
724	60 c. On parade		30	35
725	$1.50, Craftwork		70	1·10
726	$2 Community service		95	1·60
723/6		Set of 4	2·00	3·00

133 Ford "Model T" (1908)

(Des J.W. Litho Format)

1983 (25 Oct). *Leaders of the World. Automobiles (1st series). T 133 and similar horiz designs, the first in each pair showing technical drawings and the second paintings.* P 12½.
727	10 c. multicoloured		10	10
	a. Vert pair. Nos. 727/8		10	10
728	10 c. multicoloured		10	10
729	60 c. multicoloured		10	15
	a. Vert pair. Nos. 729/30		15	30
730	60 c. multicoloured		10	15
731	$1.50, multicoloured		15	20
	a. Vert pair. Nos. 731/2		30	40
732	$1.50, multicoloured		15	20
733	$1.50, multicoloured		15	20
	a. Vert pair. Nos. 733/4		30	40
734	$1.50, multicoloured		15	20
735	$2 multicoloured		15	20
	a. Vert pair. Nos. 735/6		30	40
736	$2 multicoloured		15	20
737	$2 multicoloured		15	20
	a. Vert pair. Nos. 737/8		30	40
738	$2 multicoloured		15	20
727/38		Set of 12	1·25	1·75

Designs:—Nos. 727/8, Ford "Model T" (1908); 729/30, Supercharged Cord "812" (1937); 731/2, Citroen "Open Tourer" (1937); 733/4, Mercedes Benz "300SL Gull-Wing" (1954); 735/6, Rolls-Royce "Phantom I" (1925); 737/8, Ferrari "Boxer 512BB" (1976).
Nos. 727/8, 729/30, 731/2, 733/4, 735/6 and 737/8 were printed together, *se-tenant*, in vertical pairs throughout the sheets.
See also Nos. 820/9, 862/7, 884/92 and 959/70.

134 Appearance of the Nativity Star

(Des Jennifer Toombs. Litho Security Printers (M), Malaysia)

1983 (15 Nov). *Christmas. T 134 and similar horiz designs showing the Shepherds.* W w **14.** P 12.
739	10 c. Type 134		10	10
740	50 c. Message of the Angel		20	10
741	$1.50, The Heavenly Host		50	75
742	$2.40, Worshipping Jesus		75	1·25
739/42		Set of 4	1·40	2·00
MS743	130×130 mm. Nos. 739/42. Wmk sideways		1·25	1·75

135 *King Henry VIII*

(Des J.W. Litho Format)

1983 (8 Dec). *Leaders of the World. Railway Locomotives (1st series). T 135 and similar horiz designs, the first in each pair showing technical drawings and the second the locomotive at work.* P 12½.
744	10 c. multicoloured		10	10
	a. Vert pair. Nos. 744/5		10	10
745	10 c. multicoloured		10	10
746	10 c. multicoloured		10	10
	a. Vert pair. Nos. 746/7		10	10
747	10 c. multicoloured		10	10
748	25 c. multicoloured		15	20
	a. Vert pair. Nos. 748/9		30	40
749	25 c. multicoloured		10	10
750	50 c. multicoloured		15	20
	a. Vert pair. Nos. 750/1		30	40
751	50 c. multicoloured		15	20
752	60 c. multicoloured		15	20
	a. Vert pair Nos. 752/3		30	40
753	60 c. multicoloured		15	20
754	75 c. multicoloured		15	25
	a. Vert pair. Nos. 754/5		30	50
755	75 c. multicoloured		15	25
756	$2.50, multicoloured		20	35
	a. Vert pair. Nos. 756/7		40	70
757	$2.50, multicoloured		20	35
758	$3 multicoloured		25	50
	a. Vert pair. Nos. 758/9		50	1·00
759	$3 multicoloured		25	50
744/59		Set of 16	1·75	3·00

Designs:—Nos. 744/5, *King Henry VIII*, Great Britain (1927); 746/7, Diesel locomotive *Royal Scots Greys*, Great Britain (1961); 748/9, *Hagley Hall*, Great Britain (1928); 750/1, *Sir Lancelot*, Great Britain (1925) (dated "1926" in error); 752/3 Class B12, Great Britain (1912); 754/5, Deeley "Compound type", Great Britain (1902); 755/7, *Cheshire*, Great Britain (1927); 758/9, Bulleid "Austerity" Class Q1, Great Britain (1942).
Nos. 744/59 were issued in a similar sheet format to No. 727/38.
See also Nos. 792/807, 834/41, 872/83, 893/904 and 1001/8.

136 Fort Duvernette

(Des Walsall. Litho Questa)

1984 (13 Feb). *Fort Duvernette. T 136 and similar horiz designs. Multicoloured.* W w **15** (sideways). P 14 × 14½.
760	35 c. Type 136		20	30
761	45 c. Soldiers on fortifications		25	30
762	$1 Cannon facing bay		40	60
763	$3 Map of St. Vincent and mortar		1·25	1·75
760/3		Set of 4	1·90	2·75

137 White Frangipani

(Des J. Cooter. Litho Harrison)

1984 (2 Apr). *Flowering Trees and Shrubs. T 137 and similar horiz designs. Multicoloured.* W w **14** (sideways*). P 13½×14.
764	5 c. Type 137		20	10
765	10 c. Genip		25	10
766	15 c. Immortelle		30	10
767	20 c. Pink Poui		40	10
768	25 c. Buttercup		50	10
769	35 c. Sandbox		65	20
770	45 c. Locust		70	25
771	60 c. Colville's Glory		75	60
772	75 c. Lignum Vitae		75	75
773	$1 Golden Shower		75	1·00
	w. Wmk Crown to right of CA		22·00	
774	$5 Angelin		2·25	8·00
775	$10 Roucou		3·00	13·00
764/75		Set of 12	9·50	22·00

*The normal sideways watermark shows Crown to left of CA, as seen from the back of the stamp.

138 Trench Warfare,
First World War

139 Musical Fantasy Costume

(Des Court House Studio. Litho Format)

1984 (25 Apr). *Leaders of the World. British Monarchs. T 138 and similar vert designs. Multicoloured.* P 12½.
776	1 c. Type 138		10	10
	a. Horiz pair. Nos. 776/7		10	10
777	1 c. George V and trenches		10	10
778	5 c. Battle of Bannockburn		10	10
	a. Horiz pair. Nos. 778/9		10	10
779	5 c. Edward II and battle		10	10
780	60 c. George V		15	20
	a. Horiz pair. Nos. 780/1		30	40
781	60 c. York Cottage, Sandringham		15	20
782	75 c. Edward II		15	20
	a. Horiz pair. Nos. 782/3		30	40
783	75 c. Berkeley Castle		15	20
784	$1 Coat of arms of Edward II		15	25
	a. Horiz pair. Nos. 784/5		30	50
785	$1 Edward II (*different*)		15	25
786	$4 Coat of arms of George V		35	60
	a. Horiz pair. Nos. 786/7		70	1·10
787	$4 George V and Battle of Jutland		35	60
776/87		Set of 12	1·50	2·25

Nos. 776/7, 778/9, 780/1, 782/3, 784/5 and 786/7 were printed together, *se-tenant*, in horizontal pairs throughout the sheets, each pair forming a composite design.

(Des G. Vasarhelyi. Litho Questa)

1984 (25 June). *Carnival 1984. T 139 and similar horiz designs showing Carnival costumes. Multicoloured.* W w **15** (sideways). P 14.
788	35 c. Type 139		15	15
789	45 c. African princess		20	20

790	$1 Market woman		40	40
791	$3 Carib hieroglyph		1·25	1·75
788/91		Set of 4	1·75	2·25

IMPERFORATES AND MISSING COLOURS. Various issues between Nos. 792 and 1143 exist either imperforate or with colours omitted. Such items are not listed as there is no evidence that they fulfil the criteria outlined on page xi of this catalogue.

(Des J.W. Litho Format)

1984 (27 July). *Leaders of the World. Railway Locomotives (2nd series). Horiz designs as T 135, the first in each pair showing technical drawings and the second the locomotive at work.* P 12½.
792	1 c. multicoloured		10	10
	a. Vert pair. Nos. 792/3		10	10
793	1 c. multicoloured		10	10
794	2 c. multicoloured		10	10
	a. Vert pair. Nos. 794/5		10	10
795	2 c. multicoloured		10	10
796	3 c. multicoloured		10	10
	a. Vert pair. Nos. 796/7		10	10
797	3 c. multicoloured		10	10
798	50 c. multicoloured		20	30
	a. Vert pair. Nos. 798/9		40	60
799	50 c. multicoloured		20	30
800	75 c. multicoloured		20	35
	a. Vert pair. Nos. 800/1		40	70
801	75 c. multicoloured		20	35
802	$1 multicoloured		20	35
	a. Vert pair. Nos. 802/3		40	70
803	$1 multicoloured		20	35
804	$2 multicoloured		25	40
	a. Vert pair. Nos. 804/5		50	80
805	$2 multicoloured		25	40
806	$3 multicoloured		25	50
	a. Vert pair. Nos. 806/7		50	1·00
807	$3 multicoloured		25	50
792/807		Set of 16	2·00	3·50

Designs:—Nos. 792/3, Class 141-R Liberation, France (1945); 794/5, Diesel locomotive *Dreadnought*, Great Britain (1967); 796/7, No. 242A1, France (1946); 798/9, Class "Dean Goods", Great Britain (1883); 800/1, Hetton Colliery No. 1, Great Britain (1822); 802/3, *Pen-y-Darren*, Great Britain (1804); 804/5, *Novelty*, Great Britain (1829); 806/7, Class 44, Germany (1925).
Nos. 792/807 were issued in a similar sheet format to Nos. 727/38.

140 Slaves tilling Field **141** Weightlifting

(Des G. Vasarhelyi. Litho Questa)

1984 (1 Aug). *150th Anniv of Emancipation of Slaves on St. Vincent. T 140 and similar horiz designs. Multicoloured.* W w **15** (sideways). P 14.
808	35 c. Type 140		20	20
809	45 c. Sugar-cane harvesting		25	25
810	$1 Cutting sugar-cane		45	60
811	$3 William Wilberforce and African slave caravan		1·25	2·50
808/11		Set of 4	2·00	3·25

(Des Court House Studio. Litho Format)

1984 (30 Aug). *Leaders of the World. Olympic Games, Los Angeles. T 141 and similar vert designs. Multicoloured.* P 12½.
812	1 c. Judo		10	10
	a. Horiz pair. Nos. 812/13		10	10
813	1 c. Type 141		10	10
814	3 c. Pursuit cycling		10	10
	a. Horiz pair. Nos. 814/15		10	10
815	3 c. Cycle road-racing		10	10
816	60 c. Women's backstroke swimming		15	15
	a. Horiz pair. Nos. 816/17		30	30
817	60 c. Men's butterfly swimming		15	15
818	$3 Sprint start		40	55
	a. Horiz pair. Nos. 818/19		80	1·10
819	$3 Finish of long distance race		40	55
812/19		Set of 8	1·10	1·40

Nos. 812/13, 814/15, 816/17 and 818/19 were printed together, *se-tenant*, in horizontal pairs throughout the sheets.

(Des J.W. Litho Format)

1984 (22 Oct). *Leaders of the World. Automobiles (2nd series). Horiz designs as T 133, the first in each pair showing technical drawings and the second paintings.* P 12½.
820	5 c. black, drab and bright green		10	10
	a. Vert pair. Nos. 820/1		10	10
821	5 c. multicoloured		10	10
822	20 c. black, pink and pale new blue		10	10
	a. Vert pair. Nos. 822/3		20	20
823	20 c. multicoloured		10	10
824	55 c. black, pale green and lake-brown		20	20
	a. Vert pair. Nos. 824/5		40	40
825	55 c. multicoloured		20	20
826	$1.50, black, pale turq-grn & turq-grn		25	30
	a. Vert pair. Nos. 826/7		50	60
827	$1.50, multicoloured		25	30
828	$2.50, black, turquoise-green and lilac		30	35
	a. Vert pair. Nos. 828/9		60	70
829	$2.50, multicoloured		30	35
820/9		Set of 10	1·50	1·75

Designs:—Nos. 820/1, Austin-Healey "Sprite" (1958); 822/3, Maserati "Ghibli Coupe" (1971); 824/5, Pontiac "GTO" (1964); 826/7, Jaguar "D-Type" (1957); 828/9, Ferrari "365 GTB4 Daytona" (1970).
Nos. 820/9 were issued in a similar sheet format to Nos. 727/38.

142 Grenadier, 70th Regt
of Foot, 1773

143 N. S. Taylor

(Des J. Cooter. Litho Questa)

1984 (12 Nov). *Military Uniforms.* T **142** *and similar vert designs.*
Multicoloured. W w **15**. *P* 14.
830	45 c. Type **142**			50	30
831	60 c. Grenadier, 6th Regt of Foot, 1775			60	35
832	$1.50, Grenadier, 3rd Regt of Foot, 1768			1·00	1·10
833	$2 Battalion Company officer, 14th Regt of Foot, 1780			1·25	1·60
830/3			*Set of 4*	3·00	3·00

(Des J.W. Litho Format)

1984 (21 Nov). *Leaders of the World. Railway Locomotives (3rd series). Horiz designs as* T **135**, *the first in each pair showing technical drawings and the second the locomotive at work. Multicoloured. P* 12½.
834	5 c. multicoloured			10	10
	a. Vert pair. Nos. 834/5			10	15
835	5 c. multicoloured			10	10
836	40 c. multicoloured			15	15
	a. Vert pair. Nos. 836/7			30	30
837	40 c. multicoloured			15	15
838	75 c. multicoloured			15	20
	a. Vert pair. Nos. 838/9			30	40
839	75 c. multicoloured			15	20
840	$2.50, multicoloured			50	65
	a. Vert pair. Nos. 840/1			1·00	1·25
841	$2.50, multicoloured			50	65
834/41			*Set of 8*	1·40	1·90

Designs:—Nos. 834/5, 20th Class, Rhodesia (1954); 836/7, *Southern Maid*, Great Britain (1928); 838/9, *Prince of Wales*, Great Britain (1911); 840/1, Class 05, Germany (1935).
Nos. 834/41 were issued in a similar sheet format to Nos. 727/38.

(Des Court House Studio. Litho Format)

1985 (7 Jan). *Leaders of the World. Cricketers.* T **143** *and similar vert designs, the first in each pair showing a head portrait and the second the cricketer in action. P* 12½.
842	5 c. multicoloured			10	10
	a. Horiz pair. Nos. 842/3			10	10
843	5 c. multicoloured			10	10
844	35 c. multicoloured			30	20
	a. Horiz pair. Nos. 844/5			60	40
845	35 c. multicoloured			30	20
846	50 c. multicoloured			30	30
	a. Horiz pair. Nos. 846/7			60	60
847	50 c. multicoloured			30	30
848	$3 multicoloured			50	1·25
	a. Horiz pair. Nos. 848/9			1·00	2·50
849	$3 multicoloured			50	1·25
842/9			*Set of 8*	2·00	3·25

Designs:—Nos. 842/3, N. S. Taylor; 844/5. T. W. Graveney; 846/7, R. G. D. Willis; 848/9, S. D. Fletcher.
Nos. 842/3, 844/5, 846/7, and 848/9 were printed together, *se-tenant,* in vertical pairs throughout the sheets.

144 Eye Lash Orchid

145 Brown Pelican

(Des G. Drummond. Litho Format)

1985 (31 Jan). *Orchids.* T **144** *and similar vert designs. Multicoloured.* W w **15**. *P* 14.
850	35 c. Type **144**			20	30
851	45 c. *Ionopsis utricularioides*			20	30
852	$1 *Epidendrum secundum*			30	65
853	$3 *Oncidium altissimum*			40	2·00
850/3			*Set of 4*	1·00	3·00

(Des R. Vigurs. Litho Format)

1985 (7 Feb). *Leaders of the World. Birth Bicentenary of John J. Audubon (ornithologist).* T **145** *and similar vert designs. Multicoloured. P* 12½.
854	15 c. Type **145**			10	10
	a. Horiz pair. Nos. 854/5			20	20
855	15 c. Green Heron			10	10
856	40 c. Pileated Woodpecker			15	20
	a. Horiz pair. Nos. 856/7			30	40
857	40 c. Common Flicker			15	20
858	60 c. Painted Bunting			15	30
	a. Horiz pair. Nos. 858/9			30	60
859	60 c. White-winged Crossbill			15	30
860	$2.25, Red-shouldered Hawk			30	90
	a. Horiz pair. Nos. 860/1			60	1·75
861	$2.25, Common Caracara			30	90
854/61			*Set of 8*	1·25	2·75

Nos. 854/5, 856/7, 858/9 and 860/1 were printed together, *se-tenant,* in horizontal pairs throughout the sheets.

(Des Artists International. Litho Format)

1985 (11 Mar). *Leaders of the World. Automobiles (3rd series). Horiz designs as* T **133**, *the first in each pair showing technical drawings and the second paintings. P* 12½.
862	1 c. black, pale lemon and blue-green			10	10
	a. Vert pair. Nos. 862/3			10	10
863	1 c. multicoloured			10	10
864	55 c. black, pale new blue and violet-grey			15	25
	a. Vert pair. Nos. 864/5			30	50
865	55 c. multicoloured			15	25
866	$2 black, pale lemon & dull reddish purple			40	70
	a. Vert pair. Nos. 866/7			80	1·40
867	$2 multicoloured			40	70
862/7			*Set of 6*	1·00	1·60

Designs:—Nos. 862/3, Lancia "Aprilia" (1937); 864/5, Pontiac "Firebird Trans Am" (1973); 866/7, Cunningham "C-5R" (1953).
Nos. 862/7 were issued in a similar sheet format to Nos. 727/38.

146 Pepper

147 Bamboo Flute

(Des G. Drummond. Litho Format)

1985 (22 Apr). *Herbs and Spices.* T **146** *and similar vert designs. Multicoloured.* W w **15**. *P* 14.
868	25 c. Type **146**.			10	10
869	35 c. Sweet Marjoram			10	15
870	$1 Nutmeg			20	50
871	$3 Ginger			55	2·25
868/71			*Set of 4*	75	2·75

The scientific name on the 35 c. is incorrectly spelt "Marjorana hortensis".

(Des. T. Hadler ($2.50), J.W. (others). Litho Format)

1985 (26 Apr). *Leaders of the World. Railway Locomotives (4th series). Horiz designs as* T **135**, *the first in each pair showing technical drawings and the second the locomotive at work. P* 12½.
872	1 c. multicoloured			10	10
	a. Vert pair. Nos. 872/3			10	10
873	1 c. multicoloured			10	10
874	10 c. multicoloured			10	10c
	a. Vert pair. Nos. 874/5			10	15
875	10 c. multicoloured			10	10
876	40 c. multicoloured			15	30
	a. Vert pair. Nos. 876/7			30	60
877	40 c. multicoloured			15	30
878	60 c. multicoloured			15	30
	a. Vert pair. Nos. 878/9			30	60
879	60 c. multicoloured			15	30
880	$1 multicoloured			25	40
	a. Vert pair. Nos. 880/1			50	80
881	$1 multicoloured			25	40
882	$2.50, multicoloured			40	60
	a. Vert pair. Nos. 882/3			80	1·10
883	$2.50, multicoloured			40	60
872/83			*Set of 12*	1·75	3·00

Designs:—Nos. 872/3, *Glen Douglas*, Great Britain (1913); 874/5, *Fenchurch*, Great Britain (1872); 876/7, No. 1 Stirling "single", Great Britain (1870); 878/9, No. 158A, Great Britain (1866); 880/1, Jones Goods locomotive No. 103, Great Britain (1893); 882/3, *The Great Bear*, Great Britain (1908).
Nos. 872/83 were issued in a similar sheet format to Nos. 727/38.

(Des J.W. (25 c.), G. Turner ($1), Artists International (others). Litho Format)

1985 (7 June). *Leaders of the World. Automobiles (4th series). Horiz designs as* T **133**, *the first in each pair showing drawings and the second paintings. P* 12½.
884	25 c. black, greenish grey and brown-red			10	10
	a. Vert pair. Nos. 884/5			15	20
885	25 c. multicoloured			10	10
886	60 c. black, pale flesh and red-orange			15	20
	a. Vert pair. Nos. 886/7			30	40
887	60 c. multicoloured			15	20
888	$1 black, azure and dull lavender			15	25
	a. Vert pair. Nos. 888/9			30	50
889	$1 multicoloured			15	25
890	$1.50, black, pale blue and scarlet			20	30
	a. Vert pair. Nos. 890/1			40	60
891	$1.50, multicoloured			20	30
884/91			*Set of 8*	1·00	1·50
MS892	180×121 mm. $4×2 As Nos. 890/1; $5×2 As Nos. 888/9. P 14			1·75	4·50

Designs:—Nos. 884/5, Essex "Coach" (1922); 886/7, Nash "Rambler" (1950); 888/9, Ferrari "Tipo 156" (1961); 890/1, Eagle-Weslake "Type 58" (1967).
Nos. 884/91 were issued in a similar sheet format to Nos. 727/38.

(Des J.W. (5 c., 30 c., $1), T. Hadler (others). Litho Format)

1985 (27 June). *Leaders of the World. Railway Locomotives (5th series). Horiz designs as* T **135**, *the first in each pair showing technical drawings and the second the locomotive at work. P* 12½.
893	5 c. multicoloured			10	10
	a. Vert pair. Nos. 893/4			10	10
894	5 c. multicoloured			10	10
895	30 c. multicoloured			15	20
	a. Vert pair. Nos. 895/6			30	40

896	30 c. multicoloured			15	20
897	60 c. multicoloured			20	30
	a. Vert pair. Nos. 897/8			40	60
898	60 c. multicoloured			20	30
899	75 c. multicoloured			20	30
	a. Vert pair. Nos. 899/900			40	60
900	75 c. multicoloured			20	30
901	$1 multicoloured			25	40
	a. Vert pair. Nos. 901/2			50	80
902	$1 multicoloured			25	40
903	$2.50, multicoloured			30	60
	a. Vert pair. Nos. 903/4			60	1·10
904	$2.50, multicoloured			30	60
893/904			*Set of 12*	2·00	3·25

Designs:—Nos. 893/4, *Loch*, Isle of Man (1874); 895/6, Class 47XX, Great Britain (1919); 897/8, Class 121, France (1876); 899/900, Class 24, Germany (1927); 901/2, Tank locomotive No. 1008, Great Britain (1889); 903/4, Class PS-4, U.S.A. (1926).
Nos. 893/904 were issued in a similar sheet format to Nos. 727/38.

(Des Jennifer Toombs. Litho Format)

1985 (10 July). *Traditional Musical Instruments.* T **147** *and similar multicoloured designs.* W w **15** *(sideways on* $1, $2). P 15.
905	25 c. Type **147**.			10	15
906	35 c. Quatro (four-stringed guitar)			10	25
907	$1 Ba-ha (bamboo pipe) (*vert*)			25	55
908	$2 Goat-skin drum (*vert*)			35	1·10
905/8			*Set of 4*	70	1·90
MS909	141×100 mm. Nos. 905/8			1·60	4·50

148 Queen Elizabeth the
Queen Mother

149 Elvis Presley

(Des Court House Studio. Litho Format)

1985 (9 Aug). *Leaders of the World. Life and Times of Queen Elizabeth the Queen Mother. Various vertical portraits as* T **148**. *P* 12½.
910	35 c. multicoloured			10	20
	a. Horiz pair. Nos. 910/11.			10	40
911	35 c. multicoloured			10	20
912	85 c. multicoloured			10	25
	a. Horiz pair. Nos. 912/13.			10	50
913	85 c. multicoloured			10	25
914	$1.20, multicoloured			15	30
	a. Horiz pair. Nos. 914/15.			25	60
915	$1.20, multicoloured			15	30
916	$1.60, multicoloured			15	35
	a. Horiz pair. Nos. 916/17.			25	70
917	$1.60, multicoloured			15	35
910/17			*Set of 8*	60	2·00
MS918	85×114 mm. $2.10, multicoloured; $2.10, multicoloured			1·50	1·50

The two designs of each value were issued, *se-tenant,* in horizontal pairs within the sheets.
Each *se-tenant* pair shows a floral pattern across the bottom of the portraits which stops short of the left-hand edge on the left-hand stamp and of the right-hand edge on the right-hand stamp.
Designs as Nos. 910/11 and 912/13, but with face values of $6×2 and $3.50×2, also exist in additional miniature sheets from a restricted printing issued 19 December 1985.

(Des Court House Studio. Litho Format)

1985 (16 Aug). *Leaders of the World. Elvis Presley (entertainer). Various vertical portraits as* T **149**. *Multicoloured, background colours given. P* 12½.
919	10 c. multicoloured (T **149**)			20	15
	a. Horiz pair. Nos. 919/20.			40	30
920	10 c. multicoloured (bright blue)			20	15
921	60 c. multicoloured (brown)			30	35
	a. Horiz pair. Nos. 921/2			60	70
922	60 c. multicoloured (pale grey)			30	35
923	$1 multicoloured (brown)			30	55
	a. Horiz pair. Nos. 923/4			60	1·10
924	$1 multicoloured (bright blue)			30	55
925	$5 multicoloured (azure)			60	1·75
	a. Horiz pair. Nos. 925/6			1·10	3·50
926	$5 multicoloured (bright blue)			60	1·75
919/26			*Set of 8*	2·40	5·00
MS927	Four sheets each 145 × 107 mm. (a) 30 c. As Nos. 919/20 each × 2; (b) 50 c. As Nos. 921/2 each × 2; (c) $1.50 As Nos. 923/4 each × 2; (d) $4.50 As Nos. 925/6 each × 2 *Set of 4 sheets*			20·00	20·00

The two designs of each value were printed together, *se-tenant,* in horizontal pairs throughout the sheets.
Two similar designs, each with a face value of $4, were prepared, but not issued.
St. Vincent Philatelic Services Ltd. report that unauthorised reprints of Nos. 919/27 exist, poorly printed on whiter paper.

150 Silos and Conveyor Belt

151 Michael Jackson

(Des G. Vasarhelyi. Litho Format)

1985 (17 Oct). *St. Vincent Flour Milling Industry. T 150 and similar horiz designs. Multicoloured. W w 15. P 15.*

928	20 c. Type 150		10	15
929	30 c. Roller mills		10	20
930	75 c. Administration building		20	35
931	$3 Bran finishers		50	1·40
928/31		Set of 4	70	1·90

1985 (27 Oct). *Royal Visit. Nos. 672/3, 697/8, 711, 724 and 912/13 optd as T 114 of Montserrat or surch also.*

932	– 60 c. multicoloured (No. 711)	1·00	2·00
933	– 60 c. multicoloured (No. 724)	1·25	2·25
934	– 85 c. multicoloured (No. 912)	3·50	4·00
	a. Horiz pair. Nos. 934/5	7·00	8·00
935	– 85 c. multicoloured (No. 913)	3·50	4·00
936	125 $1.50, multicoloured	1·25	2·75
937	– $1.60 on $4 multicoloured (No. 672)	70	2·25
	a. Sheetlet. No. 937×6 and No. 938	11·00	
	ab. Sheetlet. No. 937×6 and No. 938a	11·00	
938	– $1.60 on $4 multicoloured (No. 673)		
	(surch $1.60 only)	8·00	15·00
	a. Additionally optd "CARIBBEAN ROYAL VISIT—1985"	8·00	
939	– $2.50, multicoloured (No. 698)	1·50	3·50
932/9	Set of 8	19·00	32·00

No. 938 shows a new face value only. "CARIBBEAN ROYAL VISIT—1985" being omitted from the surcharge. No. 938a is the corrected version issued subsequently.

(Des Court House Studio. Litho Format)

1985 (2 Dec). *Leaders of the World. Michael Jackson (entertainer). Various vertical portraits as T 151. Multicoloured. P 12½.*

940	60 c. multicoloured	25	30
	a. Horiz pair. Nos. 940/1	50	60
941	60 c. multicoloured	25	30
942	$1 multicoloured	30	45
	a. Horiz pair. Nos. 942/3	60	90
943	$1 multicoloured	30	45
944	$2 multicoloured	35	80
	a. Horiz pair. Nos. 944/5	70	1·60
945	$2 multicoloured	35	80
946	$5 multicoloured	50	1·75
	a. Horiz pair. Nos. 946/7	1·00	3·50
947	$5 multicoloured	50	1·75
940/7	Set of 8	2·50	6·00
MS948	Four sheets, each 144 × 109 mm. (a) 45 c. As Nos. 940/1 each × 2; (b) 90 c. As Nos. 942/3 each × 2; (c) $1.50 As Nos. 944/5 each × 2; (d) $4 As Nos. 946/7 each × 2. Set of 4 sheets	3·25	7·50

The two designs for each value were printed together, *se-tenant*, in horizontal pairs throughout the sheets. The left-hand design shows the face value at top left (as on Type 151) and the right-hand design at top right.

St. Vincent Philatelic Services Ltd. report that unauthorised reprints of Nos. 940/7 exist, poorly printed on whiter paper.

152 "The Serenaders" (Kim de Freitas) **153** Santa Maria

(Litho Format)

1985 (9 Dec). *Christmas. Children's Paintings. T 152 and similar vert designs. Multicoloured. W w 15. P 13½ × 14.*

949	25 c. Type 152	10	15
950	75 c. "Poinsettia" (Jackie Douglas)	20	40
951	$2.50, "Jesus our Master" (Bernadette Payne)	55	2·00
949/51	Set of 3	75	2·25

(Litho Format)

1986 (23 Jan). *500th Anniv of Discovery of America (1992) by Columbus (1st issue). T 153 and similar vert designs. Multicoloured. P 12½.*

952	60 c. Type 153	50	55
	a. Horiz pair. Nos. 952/3	1·00	1·10
953	60 c. Christopher Columbus	50	55
954	$1.50, Columbus at Spanish Court	70	1·25
955	$1.50, King Ferdinand and Queen Isabella of Spain	70	1·25
956	$2.75, *Santa Maria* and fruits	1·00	2·00
	a. Horiz pair. Nos. 956/7	2·00	4·00
957	$2.75, Maize and fruits	1·00	2·00
952/7	Set of 6	4·00	7·00
MS958	95×85 mm. $6 Christopher Columbus (different)	2·25	5·00

The two designs of each value were printed together, *se-tenant*, in horizontal pairs within the sheets.
See also Nos. 1125/31, 1305/24, 1639/57, 1677/85, 1895/1901 and 1981/4.

(Des Artists International. Litho Format)

1986 (27 Jan). *Leaders of the World. Automobiles (5th series). Horiz designs as T 133, the first in each pair showing technical drawings and the second paintings. P 12½.*

959	30 c. black, cobalt and dull orange	10	15
	a. Vert pair. Nos. 959/60	15	30
960	30 c. multicoloured	10	15
961	45 c. black, lavender-grey and blue	10	15
	a. Vert pair. Nos. 961/2	15	30
962	45 c. multicoloured	10	15
963	60 c. black, bright blue and vermilion	15	20
	a. Vert pair. Nos. 963/4	30	40

964	60 c. multicoloured	15	20
965	90 c. black, greenish yellow and bright blue	15	50
	a. Vert pair. Nos. 965/6	30	50
966	90 c. multicoloured	15	20
967	$1.50, black, pale rose-lilac & brt magenta	20	40
	a. Vert pair. Nos. 967/8	40	80
968	$1.50, multicoloured	20	40
969	$2.50, black, blue and bright blue	20	50
	a. Vert pair. Nos. 969/70	40	1·00
970	$2.50, multicoloured	20	50
959/70	Set of 12	1·50	3·00

Designs:—Nos. 959/60, Cadillac "Type 53" (1916); 961/2, Triumph "Dolomite" (1939); 963/4, Panther "J-72" (1972); 965/6, Ferrari "275 GTB/4" (1967); 967/8, Packard "Caribbean" (1953); 969/70, Bugatti "Type 41 Royale" (1931).
Nos. 959/70 were issued in a similar sheet format to Nos. 727/38.

154 Guide Salute and Handclasp **155** Halley's Comet

(Des Court House Studio. Litho Format)

1986 (25 Feb). *75th Anniv of Girl Guide Movement and Boy Scouts of America. Two sheets, each 85 × 113 mm, containing vert designs as T 154. Multicoloured. P 12½.*

MS971	$5 Type 154: $5 Palette and paintbrushes	2·00	5·00
MS972	$6 Cross-tied logs: $6 Lord Baden-Powell	2·00	6·00

The two stamps in each sheet were printed together, *se-tenant*, in horizontal pairs, each forming a composite design.
Nos. MS971/2 exist with plain or decorative margins.
Overprints on these miniature sheets commemorating "Capex '87" International Stamp Exhibition, Toronto, were not authorised by the St. Vincent administration.

(Des G. Vasarhelyi. Litho Format)

1986 (14 Apr). *Appearance of Halley's Comet. T 155 and similar horiz designs. Multicoloured. W w 15. P 15.*

973	45 c. Type 155	35	20
974	60 c. Edmond Halley	35	30
975	75 c. Newton's telescope and astronomers	40	55
976	$3 Amateur astronomer on St. Vincent	60	2·25
973/6	Set of 4	1·50	3·00
MS977	155 × 104 mm. Nos. 973/6	2·00	4·50

(Des Court House Studio. Litho Format)

1986 (21 Apr). *60th Birthday of Queen Elizabeth II (1st issue). Multicoloured designs as T 117a of Montserrat. P 12½.*

978	10 c. Queen Elizabeth II	10	10
979	90 c. Princess Elizabeth	20	30
980	$2.50, Queen gathering bouquets from crowd	35	75
981	$8 In Canberra, 1982 (vert)	1·00	2·25
978/81	Set of 4	1·40	3·00
MS982	85×115 mm. $10 Queen Elizabeth II (different)	3·00	6·00

See also Nos. 996/1000

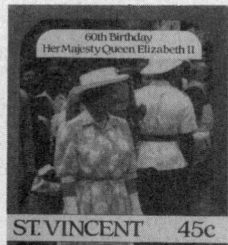

156 Mexican Player **157** Queen Elizabeth at Victoria Park, Kingstown

(Des Court House Studio. Litho Format)

1986 (7 May–3 July). *World Cup Football Championship, Mexico. T 156 and similar multicoloured designs. P 12½ (75 c., $2, $4, $5) or 15 (others).*

983	1 c. Football and world map (horiz)	10	10
984	2 c. Type 156	10	10
985	5 c. Mexican player (different)	10	10
986	5 c. Hungary v Scotland	10	10
987	10 c. Spain v Scotland	10	10
988	30 c. England v U.S.S.R. (horiz)	20	20
989	45 c. Spain v France	30	30
990	75 c. Mexican team (56×36 mm)	45	45
991	$1 England v Italy	75	65
992	$2 Scottish team (56×36 mm)	1·10	1·50
993	$4 Spanish team (56×36 mm)	2·10	2·75
994	$5 English team (56×36 mm)	2·25	3·25
983/94	Set of 12	6·50	8·50
MS995	Six sheets, each 84×114 mm. (a) $1.50, As Type 156 (5 July); (b) $1.50, As No. 993. P 12½; (c) $2.25, As No. 992. P 12½; (d) $2.50, As No. 990. P 12½; (e) $3 As No. 989. P 15 (3 July); (f) $5.50, As No. 994. P 12½ Set of 6 sheets	7·00	10·00

(Des Court House Studio. Litho Questa)

1986 (14 June). *60th Birthday of Queen Elizabeth II (2nd issue). T 157 and similar vert designs showing scenes from 1985 Royal Visit. Multicoloured. W w 15. P 15 × 14.*

996	45 c. Type 157	50	30
997	60 c. Queen and Prime Minister James Mitchell, Bequia	65	55
998	75 c. Queen, Prince Phillip and Mr. Mitchell, Port Elizabeth, Bequia	75	65
999	$2.50, Queen, Prince Phillip and Mr. Mitchell watching Independence Day parade, Victoria Park	1·50	2·50
996/9	Set of 4	3·00	3·50
MS1000	121×85 mm. $3 Queen at Victoria Park	3·50	4·25

(Des T. Hadler. Litho Format)

1986 (15 July). *Leaders of the World. Railway Locomotives (6th series). Horiz designs as T 135. Multicoloured. P 12½.*

1001	30 c. multicoloured	10	10
	a. Vert pair. Nos. 1001/2	20	20
1002	30 c. multicoloured	10	10
1003	50 c. multicoloured	15	20
	a. Vert pair. Nos. 1003/4	30	40
1004	50 c. multicoloured	15	20
1005	$1 multicoloured	20	30
	a. Vert pair. Nos. 1005/6	40	60
1006	$1 multicoloured	20	30
1007	$3 multicoloured	35	70
	a. Vert pair. Nos. 1007/8	70	1·40
1008	$3 multicoloured	35	70
1001/8	Set of 8	1·40	2·25

Designs:—Nos. 1001/2, Class ED41 BZZB electric rack and adhesion locomotive, Japan (1926); 1003/4, *The Judge*, Chicago Railroad Exposition, U.S.A. (1883); 1005/6, Class E60C electric locomotive, U.S.A. (1973); 1007/8, Class SD40-2 diesel locomotive, U.S.A. (1972).
Nos. 1001/8 were issued in a similar sheet format to Nos. 727/38.
Nos. 1007/8 exist with the green omitted from stock dispersed by the liquidator of Format International Security Printers Ltd.

(Des Court House Studio. Litho Format)

1986 (18 July–15 Oct). *Royal Wedding (1st issue). Multicoloured designs as T 118a of Montserrat. P 12½.*

1009	60 c. Profile of Prince Andrew	20	25
	a. Pair. Nos. 1009/10	40	50
1010	60 c. Miss Sarah Ferguson	20	25
1011	$2 Prince Andrew with Mrs. Nancy Reagan (horiz)	45	75
	a. Pair. Nos. 1011/12	90	1·50
1012	$2 Prince Andrew in naval uniform (horiz)	45	75
1009/12	Set of 4	1·10	1·75
MS1013	115×85 mm. $10 Duke and Duchess of York in carriage after wedding (horiz) (15.10)	2·50	4·50

Nos. 1009/10 and 1011/12 were printed together, *se-tenant*, in horizontal and vertical pairs throughout the sheets.
Nos. 1009/12 imperforate come from souvenir stamp booklets.

158 Acrocomia aculeata **159** Cadet Force Emblem and Cadets of 1936 and 1986

(Des J. Cooter. Litho Questa)

1986 (30 Sept). *Timber Resources of St. Vincent. T 158 and similar vert designs. Multicoloured. W w 15 (sideways). P 14.*

1014	10 c. Type 158	40	20
1015	60 c. Pithecellobium saman	1·25	80
1016	75 c. White Cedar	1·60	95
1017	$3 Andira inermis	3·50	4·50
1014/17	Set of 4	6·00	5·75

(Des G. Vasarhelyi. Litho Questa)

1986 (30 Sept). *50th Anniv of St. Vincent Cadet Force (45 c., $2) and 75th Anniv of St. Vincent Girls' High School (others). T 159 and similar multicoloured designs. W w 15 (sideways on 45 c.). P 14.*

1018	45 c. Type 159	40	30
1019	60 c. Grimble Building, Girls' High School (horiz)	45	40
1020	$1.50, High School pupils (horiz)	1·00	1·75
1021	$2 Cadets on parade (horiz)	1·50	2·25
1018/21	Set of 4	3·00	4·25

1986 (15 Oct). *Royal Wedding (2nd issue). Nos. 1009/12 optd as T 121 of Montserrat.*

1022	60 c. Profile of Prince Andrew	40	65
	a. Pair. Nos. 1022/3	80	1·25
1023	60 c. Miss Sarah Ferguson	40	65
1024	$2 Prince Andrew with Mrs. Nancy Reagan (horiz)	1·25	2·00
	a. Pair. Nos. 1024/5	2·50	4·00
1025	$2 Prince Andrew in naval uniform (horiz)	1·25	2·00
1022/5	Set of 4	3·00	4·75

160 King Arthur

(Des G. Vasarhelyi. Litho Format)

1986 (3 Nov). *The Legend of King Arthur. T* **160** *and similar horiz designs. Multicoloured. P* 14 × 13½.

1026	30 c. Type **160**		40	40
1027	45 c. Merlin taking baby Arthur		50	50
1028	60 c. Arthur pulling sword from stone		60	60
1029	75 c. Camelot		70	70
1030	$1 Arthur receiving Excalibur from the Lady of the Lake		80	80
1031	$1.50, Knights at the Round Table		1·00	1·25
1032	$2 The Holy Grail		1·25	1·50
1033	$5 Sir Lancelot jousting		2·00	2·75
1026/33		Set of 8	6·50	7·75

Nos. 1026/9 cancelled-to-order exist imperforate from stock dispersed by the liquidator of Format International Security Printers Ltd.

161 Statue of Liberty Floodlit

162 Fishing for Tri Tri

(Des Court House Studio. Litho Format)

1986 (26 Nov). *Centenary of Statue of Liberty. T* **161** *and similar vert designs showing aspects of the Statue. P* 14 × 13½.

1034	15 c. multicoloured			10	10
1035	25 c. multicoloured			15	15
1036	40 c. multicoloured			20	25
1037	55 c. multicoloured			25	30
1038	75 c. multicoloured			35	45
1039	90 c. multicoloured			35	60
1040	$1.75, multicoloured			50	1·10
1041	$2 multicoloured			55	1·25
1042	$2.50, multicoloured			60	1·60
1043	$3 multicoloured			70	1·75
1034/43			Set of 10	3·25	6·75
MS1044	Three sheets, each 85 × 115 mm. $3.50; $4; $5		Set of 3 sheets	3·50	7·50

(Des T. Hadler. Litho Format)

1986 (10 Dec). *Freshwater Fishing. T* **162** *and similar horiz designs. Multicoloured. P* 15.

1045	75 c. Type **162**		25	40
	a. Pair. Nos. 1045/6		50	80
1046	75 c. Plumier's Goby ("Tri Tri")		25	40
1047	$1.50, Crayfishing		35	80
	a. Pair. Nos. 1047/8		70	1·60
1048	$1.50, Crayfish		35	80
1045/8		Set of 4	1·10	2·10

Nos. 1045/6 and 1047/8 were each printed together, *se-tenant*, in horizontal and vertical pairs throughout the sheets.

163 Baby on Scales

WORLD POPULATION
5 BILLION
11TH JULY 1987

(164)

(Des C. Abbott. Litho Format)

1987 (10 June). *Child Health Campaign. T* **163** *and similar vert designs. Multicoloured. P* 14.

1049	10 c. Type **163**		10	10
1050	50 c. Oral rehydration therapy		45	55
1051	75 c. Breast feeding		55	90
1052	$1 Nurse giving injection		60	1·25
1049/52		Set of 4	1·50	2·50

1987 (10 June). *World Population Control. Nos.* 1049/52 *optd with T* **164**.

1053	10 c. Type **163**		10	10
1054	50 c. Oral rehydration therapy		40	55
1055	75 c. Breast feeding		50	90
1056	$1 Nurse giving injection		55	1·25
1053/6		Set of 4	1·40	2·50

165 Hanna Mandlikova   **166 Miss Prima Donna, Queen of the Bands, 1986**

(Litho Format)

1987 (22 June). *International Lawn Tennis Players. T* **165** *and similar vert designs. Multicoloured. P* 12½.

1057	40 c. Type **165**		20	25
1058	60 c. Yannick Noah		20	35
1059	80 c. Ivan Lendl		20	40
1060	$1 Chris Evert		20	40
1061	$1.25, Steffi Graf		20	50
1062	$1.50, John McEnroe		20	55
1063	$1.75, Martina Navratilova with Wimbledon trophy		20	65
1064	$2 Boris Becker with Wimbledon trophy		30	75
1057/64		Set of 8	1·50	3·50
MS1065	115 × 85 mm. $2.25 As No. 1063; $2.25 As No. 1064		1·40	3·50

Designs as Nos. 1063/4, but each with a face value of $10, also exist embossed on gold foil from a restricted printing.

(Des Young Phillips. Litho Format)

1987 (29 June). *10th Anniv of Carnival. T* **166** *and similar vert designs. Multicoloured. P* 12½.

1066	20 c. Type **166**		10	15
1067	45 c. Donna Young, Miss Carnival, 1985		15	15
1068	55 c. Miss St. Vincent and the Grenadines, 1986		15	15
1069	$3.70, "Spirit of Hope" costume, 1986		50	1·40
1066/9		Set of 4	75	1·75

The 45 c. value is inscribed "Miss Carival" in error.

THE KING OF ROCK AND ROLL LIVES FOREVER · AUGUST 16TH

1977–1987

(167)   **168 Queen Victoria, 1841**

1987 (26 Aug). *10th Death Anniv of Elvis Presley* (entertainer). *Nos.* 919/27 *optd with T* **167** *in silver*.

1070	10 c. multicoloured (T **149**)		10	10
	a. Horiz pair. Nos. 1070/1		20	20
1071	10 c. multicoloured (bright blue)		10	10
1072	60 c. multicoloured (brown)		25	30
	a. Horiz pair. Nos. 1072/3		50	60
1073	60 c. multicoloured (pale grey)		25	30
1074	$1 multicoloured (brown)		25	45
	a. Horiz pair. Nos. 1074/5		50	90
1075	$1 multicoloured (bright blue)		25	45
1076	$5 multicoloured (azure)		80	2·25
	a. Horiz pair. Nos. 1076/7		1·60	4·50
1077	$5 multicoloured (bright blue)		80	2·25
1070/7		Set of 8	2·50	5·50
MS1078	Four sheets, each 145 × 107 mm. (a) 30 c. As Nos. 1070/1 each × 2; (b) 50 c. As Nos. 1072/3 each × 2; (c) $1.50, As Nos. 1074/5 each × 2; (d) $4.50, As Nos. 1076/7 each × 2		7·50	10·00

(Des Young Phillips. Litho Format)

1987 (15 Oct). *Royal Ruby Wedding and 150th Anniv of Queen Victoria's Accession. T* **168** *and similar vert designs. Multicoloured. P* 12½.

1079	15 c. Type **168**		10	10
1080	75 c. Queen Elizabeth and Prince Andrew, 1960		20	35
1081	$1 Coronation, 1953		20	40
1082	$2.50, Duke of Edinburgh, 1948		50	1·40
1083	$5 Queen Elizabeth II, c. 1980		80	1·90
1079/83		Set of 5	1·50	3·75
MS1084	85 × 115 mm. $6 Princess Elizabeth with Prince Charles at his Christening, 1948		1·75	4·50

ALTERED CATALOGUE NUMBERS

Any Catalogue numbers altered from the last edition are shown as a list in the introductory pages.

169 Karl Benz and Benz Three-wheeler (1886)

(Litho Format)

1987 (4 Dec). *Century of Motoring. T* **169** *and similar horiz designs. Multicoloured. P* 12½.

1085	$1 Type **169**		40	60
1086	$2 Enzo Ferrari and Ferrari "Dino 206SP" (1966)		50	1·10
1087	$4 Charles Rolls and Sir Henry Royce and Rolls-Royce "Silver Ghost" (1907)		65	1·50
1088	$5 Henry Ford and Ford "Model T" (1908)		65	1·75
1085/8		Set of 4	2·00	4·50
MS1089	Four sheets, each 144 × 75 mm. (a) $3 As Type **169**. (b) $5 As No. 1086. (c) $6 As No. 1087. (d) $8 As No. 1088		Set of 4 sheets	7·50	15·00

Nos. 1085/8 with the gold omitted and Nos. 1088 and MS1089d with Henry Ford facing right all exist from stock dispersed by the liquidator of Format International Security Printers Ltd.

170 Everton Football Team

(Litho Format)

1987 (4 Dec). *English Football Teams. T* **170** *and similar horiz designs. Multicoloured. P* 12½.

1090	$2 Type **170**		1·25	1·25
1091	$2 Manchester United		1·25	1·25
1092	$2 Tottenham Hotspur		1·25	1·25
1093	$2 Arsenal		1·25	1·25
1094	$2 Liverpool		1·25	1·25
1095	$2 Derby County		1·25	1·25
1096	$2 Portsmouth		1·25	1·25
1097	$2 Leeds United		1·25	1·25
1090/7		Set of 8	9·00	9·00

171 Five Cent Coins   **172 Charles Dickens**

(Des Questa ($20), Young Phillips Studio (others))

1987 (11 Dec)–**91**. *East Caribbean Currency. T* **171** *and similar multicoloured designs. (a) Litho Format. P* 15

1098	5 c. Type **171**		20	10
1099	6 c. Two cent coins		20	10
1100	10 c. Ten cent coins		20	10
1101	12 c. Two and ten cent coins		30	10
1102	15 c. Five cent coins		30	10
1103	20 c. Ten cent coins		35	10
1104	25 c. Twenty-five cent coins		40	15
1105	30 c. Five and twenty-five cent coins		40	15
1106	35 c. Twenty-five and ten cent coins		40	20
1107	45 c. Twenty-five and two ten cent coins		50	30
1108	50 c. Fifty cent coins		50	30
1109	65 c. Fifty, ten and five cent coins		60	45
1110	75 c. Fifty and twenty-five cent coins		60	50
1111	$1 One dollar note (horiz)		75	65
1112	$2 Two one dollar notes (horiz)		1·25	1·75
1113	$3 Three one dollar notes (horiz)		1·50	2·50
1114	$5 Five dollar note (horiz)		3·25	5·00
1115	$10 Ten dollar note (horiz)		3·50	6·00
1098/1115		Set of 18	14·50	18·00

(b) Litho Questa. P 14 (1989–91)

1115a	5 c. Type **171**		45	30
1115c	10 c. Ten cent coins		45	30
1115e	15 c. Five cent coins		60	30
1115f	20 c. Ten cent coins		60	30
1115g	25 c. Twenty-five cent coins		60	30
1115j	45 c. Twenty-five and two ten cent coins		80	30
1115k	50 c. Fifty cent coins		90	35
1115l	65 c. Fifty, ten and five cent coins		1·00	65
1115m	75 c. Fifty and twenty-five cent coins		1·25	75
1115n	$1 One dollar note (horiz)		1·40	85
1115o	$2 Two one dollar notes (horiz)		2·50	2·75
1115q	$5 Five dollar note (horiz)		5·00	6·00
1115s	$20 Twenty-dollar note (horiz) (7.11.89)		10·00	14·00
1115a/s		Set of 13	23·00	24·00

No. 1100 overprinted "SPECIMEN" and with the blue omitted exists from stock dispersed by the liquidator of Format International Security Printers Ltd.

(Des Jennifer Toombs. Litho Format)

1987 (17 Dec). *Christmas. 175th Birth Anniv of Charles Dickens.* T **172** *and similar vert designs. Multicoloured.* P 14 × 14½.

1116	6 c. Type **172**		25	25
	a. Horiz pair. Nos. 1116/17		50	50
1117	6 c. "Mr. Fezziwig's Ball"		25	25
1118	25 c. Type **172**		30	30
	a. Horiz pair. Nos. 1118/19		60	60
1119	25 c. "Scrooge's Third Visitor"		30	30
1120	50 c. Type **172**		35	55
	a. Horiz pair. Nos. 1120/1		70	1·10
1121	50 c. "The Cratchits' Christmas"		35	55
1122	75 c. Type **172**		35	75
	a. Horiz pair. Nos. 1122/3		70	1·50
1123	75 c. "A Christmas Carol"		35	75
1116/23		*Set of 8*	2·25	3·25
MS1124	141 × 101 mm. $5 Teacher reading to class		1·75	4·50

Nos. 1116/17, 1118/19, 1120/1 and 1122/3 were printed together, *se-tenant*, in horizontal pairs throughout the sheets, each pair forming a composite design showing an open book. The first design in each pair shows Type **172** and the second a scene from *A Christmas Carol*.

173 *Santa Maria*

174 Brown Pelican

(Des M. Pollard. Litho Format)

1988 (11 Jan). *500th Anniv of Discovery of America* (1992) *by Columbus* (2nd issue). T **173** *and similar square designs. Multicoloured.* P 14.

1125	15 c. Type **173**		20	20
1126	75 c. *Nina* and *Pinta*		30	60
1127	$1 Compass and hourglass		30	60
1128	$1.50, Claiming the New World for Spain		40	1·00
1129	$3 Arawak village		60	1·10
1130	$4 Blue and Yellow Macaw, Cuban Tody, pineapple and maize		70	2·00
1125/30		*Set of 6*	2·25	5·50
MS1131	114×86 mm. $5 Columbus, Arms and *Santa Maria*. P 13½×14		2·25	5·50

Further unissued $2 and $6 miniature sheets exist from stock dispersed by the liquidator of Format International Security Printers Ltd.

(Des Maxine Marsh. Litho Format)

1988 (15 Feb). P 14.

1132	**174** 45 c. multicoloured	30	30

For similar 55 c. value see No. 1304.

175 Windsurfing

(Litho Format)

1988 (26 Feb). *Tourism.* T **175** *and similar multicoloured designs.* P 15.

1133	10 c. Type **175**		10	10
1134	45 c. Scuba diving		20	25
1135	65 c. Aerial view of Young Island (*horiz*)		30	60
1136	$5 Cruising yacht (*horiz*)		2·10	3·50
1133/6		*Set of 4*	2·40	4·00
MS1136a	115×85 mm. $10 Two windsurfers off St. Vincent (60×40 mm). P 12½		2·50	5·50

176 *Nuestra Senora del Rosario* (Spanish galleon) and Spanish Knight's Cross

(Litho Format)

1988 (29 July). *400th Anniv of Spanish Armada.* T **176** *and similar horiz designs. Multicoloured.* P 12½.

1137	15 c. Type **176**		15	10
1138	75 c. *Ark Royal* (galleon) and English Armada medal		30	35

1139	$1.50, English fleet and Drake's dial		50	75
1140	$2 Dismasted Spanish galleon and 16th-century shot		55	85
1141	$3.50, Attack of English fireships at Calais and 16th-century grenade		70	1·75
1142	$5 *Revenge* (English galleon) and Drake's Drum		90	2·00
1137/42		*Set of 6*	2·75	5·25
MS1143	123×92 mm. $8 Sighting the Armada		2·00	4·50

177 D. K. Lillee

178 Athletics

(Litho Format)

1988 (29 July). *Cricketers of 1988 International Season.* T **177** *and similar square designs. Multicoloured.* P 14.

1144	15 c. Type **177**		30	30
1145	50 c. G. A. Gooch		50	50
1146	75 c. R. N. Kapil Dev		70	70
1147	$1 S. M. Gavaskar		85	85
1148	$1.50, M. W. Gatting		1·25	1·50
1149	$2.50, Imran Khan		1·25	2·00
1150	$3 I. T. Botham		1·25	2·25
1151	$4 I. V. A. Richards		1·25	2·50
1144/51		*Set of 8*	6·50	9·50
MS1152	130 × 80 mm. $2 As $4; $3.50, As $3		2·25	5·00

Examples of No. **MS**1152 imperforate or part perforate exist from stock dispersed by the liquidator of Format International Security Printers Ltd.

(Des S. Angela. Litho Questa)

1988 (7 Dec). *Olympic Games, Seoul.* T **178** *and similar multicoloured designs.* P 14.

1153	10 c. Type **178**		10	10
1154	50 c. Long jumping (*vert*)		20	25
1155	$1 Triple jumping		40	50
1156	$5 Boxing (*vert*)		2·10	2·75
1153/6		*Set of 4*	2·50	3·25
MS1157	85 × 63 mm. $10 Olympic flame		4·75	6·50

A different set of six values and a miniature sheet for this event was not issued, but exists from stock dispersed by the liquidator of Format International Security Printers Ltd.

179 Babe Ruth

180 Los Angeles Dodgers (National League Champions)

(Litho Questa)

1988 (7 Dec). *Famous Baseball Players* (1st series). P 14.

1158	**179** $2 multicoloured	1·40	1·40

No. 1158 also exists embossed on gold foil from a restricted printing.

See also Nos. 1264/75, 1407, 1408/88, 2152/4, 2155/6, 2426 and 3004/12.

(Des W. Storozuk. Litho Questa)

1988 (7 Dec). *1988 Baseball World Series. Sheet* 115×85 *mm containing* T **180** *and similar horiz design. Multicoloured.* P 14½×13½.

MS1159	$2 Type **180**; $2 Team logos of Dodgers and Oakland Athletics		2·00	2·25

(Des Walt Disney Co. Litho Questa)

1988 (23 Dec). *Christmas. "Mickey's Christmas Train". Multicoloured designs as* T **171a** *of Lesotho.* P 14×13½.

1160	1 c. Minnie Mouse in parcels van (*horiz*)		10	10
1161	2 c. Mordie and Ferdie on low-loader wagon (*horiz*)		10	10
1162	3 c. Chip n'Dale in wagon with Christmas trees (*horiz*)		10	10
1163	4 c. Donald Duck's nephews riding with reindeer (*horiz*)		10	10
1164	5 c. Donald and Daisy Duck in restaurant car (*horiz*)		10	10
1165	10 c. Grandma Duck, Uncle Scrooge McDuck, Goofy and Clarabelle carol singing in carriage (*horiz*)		10	10
1166	$5 Mickey Mouse driving locomotive (*horiz*)		3·25	3·50
1167	$6 Father Christmas in guard's van (*horiz*)		4·00	4·50
1160/7		*Set of 8*	6·75	7·50
MS1168	Two sheets, each 127 × 102 mm, (a) $5 Mickey Mouse and nephews at railway station. (b) $5 Mickey and Minnie Mouse on carousel. P 13½×14	*Set of 2 sheets*	7·00	8·00

MICKEY & MINNIE WITH A COBRA

181 Mickey Mouse as Snake Charmer

(Des Walt Disney Co. Litho Questa)

1989 (8 Feb). *"India-89" International Stamp Exhibition, New Delhi.* T **181** *and similar multicoloured designs showing Walt Disney cartoon characters in India.* P 14×13½.

1169	1 c. Type **181**		10	10
1170	2 c. Goofy with Chowsingha Antelope		10	10
1171	3 c. Mickey and Minnie Mouse with Common Peafowl		10	10
1172	5 c. Goofy with Briolette Diamond and Mickey Mouse pushing mine truck		10	10
1173	10 c. Clarabelle with Orloff Diamond		10	10
1174	25 c. Mickey Mouse as tourist and Regent Diamond, Louvre, Paris		20	15
1175	$4 Minnie and Mickey Mouse with Kohinoor Diamond		3·50	4·00
1176	$5 Mickey Mouse and Goofy with Indian Rhinoceros		3·50	4·00
1169/76		*Set of 8*	6·75	7·50
MS1177	Two sheets, each 127 × 102 mm. (a) $6 Mickey Mouse riding Indian elephant. P 14×13½. (b) $6 Mickey Mouse as postman delivering Hope Diamond to Smithsonian Museum, U.S.A. (*vert*). P 13½×14.	*Set of 2 sheets*	8·50	10·00

182 Harry James

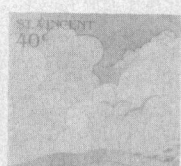

183 Birds in Flight

(Des A. Nahigian. Litho Questa)

1989 (3 Apr). *Jazz Musicians.* T **182** *and similar horiz designs. Multicoloured.* P 14.

1178	10 c. Type **182**		30	20
1179	15 c. Sidney Bechet		40	20
1180	25 c. Benny Goodman		50	20
1181	35 c. Django Reinhardt		55	20
1182	50 c. Lester Young		70	35
1183	90 c. Gene Krupa		85	85
1184	$3 Louis Armstrong		2·00	2·75
1185	$4 Duke Ellington		2·50	3·00
1178/85		*Set of 8*	7·00	7·00
MS1186	Two sheets, each 107×92 mm. (a) $5 Charlie Parker. (b) $5 Billie Holliday	*Set of 2 sheets*	7·50	8·00

(Des N. Waldman. Litho B.D.T.)

1989 (10 Apr). *Wildlife Conservation. Noah's Ark.* T **183** *and similar square designs. Multicoloured.* P 14.

1187	40 c. Type **183**		30	30
	a. Sheetlet. Nos. 1187/211		6·50	
1188	40 c. Rainbow (left side)		30	30
1189	40 c. Noah's Ark on mountain		30	30
1190	40 c. Rainbow (right side)		30	30
1191	40 c. Birds in flight (*different*)		30	30
1192	40 c. Cow elephant		30	30
1193	40 c. Bull elephant		30	30
1194	40 c. Top of eucalyptus tree		30	30
1195	40 c. Kangaroos		30	30
1196	40 c. Hummingbird		30	30
1197	40 c. Lions		30	30
1198	40 c. White-tailed Deer		30	30
1199	40 c. Koala in fork of tree		30	30
1200	40 c. Koala on branch		30	30
1201	40 c. Hummingbird approaching flower		30	30
1202	40 c. Keel-billed Toucan and flower		30	30
1203	40 c. Keel-billed Toucan facing right		30	30
1204	40 c. Camels		30	30
1205	40 c. Giraffes		30	30
1206	40 c. Mountain Sheep		30	30
1207	40 c. Ladybirds on leaf		30	30
1208	40 c. Swallowtail butterfly		30	30
1209	40 c. Swallowtail butterfly behind leaves		30	30
1210	40 c. Pythons		30	30
1211	40 c. Dragonflies		30	30
1187/211		*Set of 25*	6·50	6·50

Nos. 1187/211 were printed together, *se-tenant*, in a sheetlet of 25, forming a composite design showing Noah's Ark and animals released after the Flood.

(Litho Questa)

1989 (17 Apr). *Easter. 500th Birth Anniv of Titian* (artist). *Vert designs as* T **186a** *of Lesotho. Multicoloured.* P 13½×14.

1212	5 c. "Baptism of Christ" (detail)		10	10
1213	30 c. "Temptation of Christ"		25	15
1214	45 c. "Ecce Homo"		40	25
1215	65 c. "Noli Me Tangere" (fragment)		55	55
1216	75 c. "Christ carrying the Cross" (detail)		60	65
1217	$1 "Christ crowned with Thorns" (detail)		70	75
1218	$4 "Lamentation over Christ" (detail)		2·75	3·25
1219	$5 "The Entombment" (detail)		3·25	3·75
1212/19		*Set of 8*	7·75	8·50
MS1220	(a) 98×111 mm. $6 "Pietà" (detail). (b) 114×95 mm. $6 "The Deposition" (detail)	*Set of 2 sheets*	7·00	8·00

184 *Ile de France*

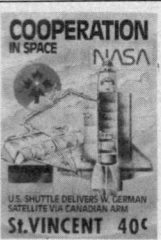

185 Space Shuttle
deploying West
German Satellite,
1983

(Des W. Wright. Litho Questa)

1989 (21 Apr). *Ocean Liners.* T **184** *and similar horiz designs. Multicoloured.* P 14.

1221	10 c. Type **184**			55	20
1222	40 c. *Liberté*			90	30
1223	50 c. *Mauretania I* (launched 1906)			1·00	40
1224	75 c. *France*			1·50	1·00
1225	$1 *Aquitania*			1·75	1·10
1226	$2 *United States*			2·25	2·50
1227	$3 *Olympic*			3·00	3·25
1228	$4 *Queen Elizabeth*			3·00	3·50
1221/8			*Set of 8*	12·50	11·00
MS1229	Two sheets, each 141×108 mm. (a) $6 *Queen Mary* (85×28 mm). (b) $6 *Queen Elizabeth 2* (85×28 mm)		*Set of 2 sheets*	9·00	11·00

(Des M. Dorfman. Litho Questa)

1989 (26 Apr). *International Co-operation in Space.* T **185** *and similar vert designs. Multicoloured.* P 14.

1230	40 c. Type **185**			70	20
1231	60 c. Vladimir Remek (Czech cosmonaut) and "Soyuz 28", 1978			90	50
1232	$1 Projected "Hermes" space plane and "Columbus" Space Station			1·25	1·00
1233	$4 Ulf Merbold (West German astronaut), 1983, and proposed European Spacelab			3·25	4·75
1230/3			*Set of 4*	5·50	5·75
MS1234	93×67 mm. $5 Meeting in space of "Apollo/Soyuz" mission crews, 1975			3·00	4·00

186 "Mercury 9"
Capsule and
Astronaut Cooper

187 Head of St. Vincent
Amazon

(Des M. Dorfman. Litho Questa)

1989 (26 Apr). *25th Anniv of Launching of "Telstar II" Communications Satellite* (1988). T **186** *and similar vert designs, each showing satellite and T.V. screen. Multicoloured.* P 14.

1235	15 c. Type **186**			20	15
1236	35 c. Martin Luther King addressing crowd, 1963			30	20
1237	50 c. Speedskater. Winter Olympic Games, Innsbruck, 1964			45	50
1238	$3 Pope John XXIII blessing crowd			1·75	2·75
1235/8			*Set of 4*	2·40	3·25
MS1239	107×77 mm. $5 Launch of "Telstar II", 1963			2·75	3·50

(Des L. McQueen. Litho Questa)

1989 (3 May). *Wildlife Conservation. St. Vincent Amazon* ("St. Vincent Parrot"). T **187** *and similar multicoloured designs.* P 14.

1240	10 c. Type **187**			70	30
1241	20 c. St. Vincent Amazon in flight			1·25	45
1242	40 c. Feeding			2·00	50
1243	70 c. At entrance to nest (*vert*)			2·75	3·25
1240/3			*Set of 4*	6·00	4·25

188 Blue-hooded Euphonia
("Mistletoe Bird")

(Des Tracy Pedersen. Litho Questa)

1989 (3 May). *Birds of St. Vincent.* T **188** *and similar multicoloured designs.* P 14.

1244	25 c. Type **188**			45	20
1245	75 c. Common Black Hawk ("Crab Hawk")			1·00	65
1246	$2 Mangrove Cuckoo ("Coucou")			1·75	2·00

1247	$3 Hooded Tanager ("Prince Bird")			2·00	2·50
1244/7			*Set of 4*	4·75	4·75
MS1248	Two sheets. (a) 75×105 mm. $5 Rufous-throated Solitaire ("Soufriere Bird") (*vert*). (b) 105×75 mm. $5 Purple-throated Carib ("Doctor Bird")		*Set of 2 sheets*	5·50	7·00

(Litho Questa)

1989 (6 July). *Japanese Art. Multicoloured designs as* T **187**a *of Lesotho.* P 14×13½.

1249	10 c. "Autumn Flowers in Front of the Full Moon" (Hiroshige)			10	10
1250	40 c. "Hibiscus" (Hiroshige)			25	25
1251	50 c. "Iris" (Hiroshige)			30	30
1252	75 c. "Morning Glories" (Hiroshige)			50	50
1253	$1 "Dancing Swallows" (Hiroshige)			1·00	75
1254	$2 "Sparrow and Bamboo" (Hiroshige)			2·00	2·00
1255	$3 "Yellow Bird and Cotton Rose" (Hiroshige)			2·25	2·25
1256	$4 "Judos Chrysanthemums in a Deep Ravine in China" (Hiroshige)			2·25	2·50
1249/56			*Set of 8*	7·75	7·75
MS1257	Two sheets, each 102×76 mm. (a) $6 "Rural Cottages in Spring" (Sotatsu). (b) $6 "The Six Immortal Poets portrayed as Cats" (Kuniyoshi) (*vert*). P 13½×14		*Set of 2 sheets*	7·00	8·50

Nos. 1249/56 were each printed in sheetlets of 10 containing two horizontal strips of 5 stamps separated by printed labels commemorating Emperor Hirohito.

189 Schooner

190 Johnny Bench

(Des J. Batchelor. Litho Questa)

1989 (7 July). *"Philexfrance 89" International Stamp Exhibition, Paris, and Bicentenary of French Revolution.* T **189** *and similar multicoloured designs, showing 18th-century French naval vessels.* P 13½×14.

1258	30 c. Type **189**			70	30
1259	55 c. Corvette			90	50
1260	75 c. Frigate			1·25	1·10
1261	$1 Ship of the line			1·50	1·40
1262	$3 *Ville de Paris* (ship of the line)			4·00	5·50
1258/62			*Set of 5*	7·50	8·00
MS1263	76×108 mm. $6 Map of St. Vincent in 18th century (*vert*). P 14×13½			3·50	4·50

(Des Rosemary De Figlio and W. Storozuk. Litho Questa)

1989 (23 July). *Famous Baseball Players* (2nd series). T **190** *and similar vert designs. Multicoloured.* P 14.

1264	$2 Type **190**			1·10	1·00
1265	$2 Red Schoendienst			1·10	1·00
1266	$2 Carl Yastrzemski			1·10	1·00
1267	$2 Ty Cobb			1·10	1·00
1268	$2 Willie Mays			1·10	1·00
1269	$2 Stan Musial			1·10	1·00
1270	$2 Ernie Banks			1·10	1·00
1271	$2 Lou Gehrig			1·10	1·00
1272	$2 Jackie Robinson			1·10	1·00
1273	$2 Bob Feller			1·10	1·00
1274	$2 Ted Williams			1·10	1·00
1275	$2 Al Kaline			1·10	1·00
1264/75			*Set of 12*	12·00	11·00

Nos. 1264/75 also exist embossed on gold foil from a restricted printing.

191 Dante Bichette, 1989

192 Chris Sabo

(Des Rosemary De Figlio. Litho Questa)

1989 (23 July). *Major League Baseball Rookies.* T **191** *and similar vert designs. Multicoloured.* P 13½×14.

1276	60 c. Type **191**			50	50
	a. Sheetlet. Nos. 1276/84			4·00	
1277	60 c. Carl Yastrzemski, 1961			50	50
1278	60 c. Randy Johnson, 1989			50	50
1279	60 c. Jerome Walton, 1989			50	50
1280	60 c. Ramon Martinez, 1989			50	50
1281	60 c. Ken Hill, 1989			50	50
1282	60 c. Tom McCarthy, 1989			50	50
1283	60 c. Gaylord Perry, 1963			50	50
1284	60 c. John Smoltz, 1989			50	50
1285	60 c. Bob Milacki, 1989			50	50
	a. Sheetlet. Nos. 1285/93			4·00	
1286	60 c. Babe Ruth, 1915			50	50
1287	60 c. Jim Abbott, 1989			50	50
1288	60 c. Gary Sheffield, 1989			50	50
1289	60 c. Gregg Jeffries, 1989			50	50
1290	60 c. Kevin Brown, 1989			50	50

1291	60 c. Cris Carpenter, 1989			50	50
1292	60 c. Johnny Bench, 1968			50	50
1293	60 c. Ken Griffey Jr, 1989			50	50
1276/93			*Set of 18*	8·00	8·00

Nos. 1276/84 and 1285/93 were each printed together, *se-tenant*, in sheetlets of 9.

(Des Rosemary De Figlio. Litho Questa)

1989 (23 July). *Major League Baseball Award Winners.* T **192** *and similar vert designs. Multicoloured.* P 13½×14.

1294	60 c. Type **192**			50	50
	a. Sheetlet. Nos. 1294/302			4·00	
1295	60 c. Walt Weiss			50	50
1296	60 c. Willie Mays			50	50
1297	60 c. Kirk Gibson			50	50
1298	60 c. Ted Williams			50	50
1299	60 c. Jose Canseco			50	50
1300	60 c. Gaylord Perry			50	50
1301	60 c. Orel Hershiser			50	50
1302	60 c. Frank Viola			50	50
1294/1302			*Set of 9*	4·00	4·00

Nos. 1294/302 were printed together, *se-tenant*, in a sheetlet of 9.

193 All-Star Game Line-up
(*Illustration reduced. Actual size 115 × 80 mm*)

(Des Rosemary De Figlio. Litho Questa)

1989 (23 July). *American League v National League All-Star Game, 1989. Sheet 115×81 mm. Imperf.*

MS1303	**193** $5 multicoloured			2·40	2·75

194 St. Vincent
Amazon

195 Queen or Pink Conch and
Wide-mouthed Purpura Shells

(Des Maxine North. Litho Questa)

1989 (31 July). P 15×14.

1304	**194** 55 c. multicoloured			45	35

(Des I. MacLaury. Litho B.D.T.)

1989 (31 Aug). *500th Anniv of Discovery of America by Columbus* (1992) (3rd issue). T **195** *and similar horiz designs.* P 14.

1305	50 c. multicoloured			45	50
	a. Sheetlet. Nos. 1305/24			8·00	
1306	50 c. multicoloured			45	50
1307	50 c. dull ultramarine, black & brt new blue			45	50
1308	50 c. dull ultramarine, black & brt new blue			45	50
1309	50 c. multicoloured			45	50
1310	50 c. multicoloured			45	50
1311	50 c. multicoloured			45	50
1312	50 c. black and bright new blue			45	50
1313	50 c. multicoloured			45	50
1314	50 c. multicoloured			45	50
1315	50 c. multicoloured			45	50
1316	50 c. multicoloured			45	50
1317	50 c. multicoloured			45	50
1318	50 c. multicoloured			45	50
1319	50 c. multicoloured			45	50
1320	50 c. multicoloured			45	50
1321	50 c. multicoloured			45	50
1322	50 c. multicoloured			45	50
1323	50 c. multicoloured			45	50
1324	50 c. multicoloured			45	50
1305/24			*Set of 20*	8·00	9·00

Designs:—No. 1305, Type **195**; 1306, Caribbean reef fishes; 1307, Sperm Whale; 1308, Fleet of Columbus; 1309, Sharksucker (fish); 1310, Columbus planting flag; 1311, Navigational instruments; 1312, Sea monster; 1313, Kemp's Ridley Turtle; 1314, Magnificent Frigate Bird; 1315, Caribbean Manatee; 1316, Caribbean Monk Seal; 1317, Mayan chief, dugout canoe and caravel; 1318, Blue-footed Boobies; 1319, Venezuelan pile village; 1320, Atlantic Wing Oyster and Lion's-paw Scallop; 1321, Great Hammerhead and Short-finned Mako; 1322, Brown Pelican and Hyacinth Macaw; 1323, Venezuelan bowmen; 1324, Capuchin and Squirrel Monkeys.

Nos. 1305/24 were printed together, *se-tenant*, in a sheetlet of 20 (4×5), forming a composite design of a Caribbean map showing the voyages of Columbus.

196 Command Module
Columbia returning to Earth

(Des W. Wright. Litho Questa)

1989 (11 Sept). *20th Anniv of First Manned Landing on Moon.* T **196** *and similar multicoloured designs.* P 14.

1325	35 c. Type **196**		60	25
1326	75 c. Lunar module *Eagle* landing		1·00	80
1327	$1 "Apollo 11" launch		1·00	80
1328	$2 Buzz Aldrin on Moon		1·50	1·75
	a. Horiz strip of 4. Nos. 1328/31		5·50	
1329	$2 Lunar module *Eagle*		1·50	1·75
1330	$2 Earthrise from the Moon		1·50	1·75
1331	$2 Neil Armstrong		1·50	1·75
1332	$3 *Eagle* and *Columbia* in Moon Orbit		1·75	2·00
1325/32	*Set of 8*		9·25	9·75

MS1333 Two sheets, each 108×79 mm. (a) $3 Command Module *Columbia*, $3 Lunar Module *Eagle*. (b) $6 Neil Armstrong stepping on to Moon (*vert*) .. *Set of 2 sheets* .. 7·50 10·00

Nos. 1328/31 were printed together, *se-tenant*, in horizontal strips of four throughout the sheet.

197 Jay Howell and Alejandro Pena

1989 (23 Sept). *Centenary of the Los Angeles Dodgers* (1st issue). *Baseball Players.* T **197** *and similar horiz designs. Multicoloured. Litho.* P 12½.

1334	60 c. Type **197**		45	45
	a. Sheetlet. Nos. 1334/41		3·50	
1335	60 c. Mike Davis and Kirk Gibson		45	45
1336	60 c. Fernando Valenzuela and John Shelby		45	45
1337	60 c. Jeff Hamilton and Franklin Stubbs		45	45
1338	60 c. Aerial view of Dodger stadium		45	45
1339	60 c. Ray Searage and John Tudor		45	45
1340	60 c. Mike Sharperson and Mickey Hatcher		45	45
1341	60 c. Coaching staff		45	45
1342	60 c. John Wetteland and Ramon Martinez		45	45
1343	60 c. Tim Belcher and Tim Crews		45	45
	a. Sheetlet. Nos. 1343/51		3·50	
1344	60 c. Orel Hershiser and Mike Morgan		45	45
1345	60 c. Mike Scioscia and Rick Dempsey		45	45
1346	60 c. Dave Anderson and Alfredo Griffin		45	45
1347	60 c. Dodgers emblem		45	45
1348	60 c. Kal Daniels and Mike Marshall		45	45
1349	60 c. Eddie Murray and Willie Randolph		45	45
1350	60 c. Tom Lasorda and Jose Gonzalez		45	45
1351	60 c. Lenny Harris, Chris Gwynn and Billy Bean		45	45
1334/51	*Set of 18*		7·00	7·00

Nos. 1334/42 and 1343/51 were each printed together, *se-tenant*, in sheetlets of 9.

For similar stamps, but rouletted 7, see Nos. 1541/58.

198 *Eurema venusta*

199 Young Footballers

(Des D. Bruckner. Litho Questa)

1989 (16 Oct). *Butterflies.* T **198** *and similar multicoloured designs.* P 14×14½.

1352	6 c. Type **198**		25	15
1353	10 c. *Historis odius*		30	15
1354	15 c. *Cynthia virginiensis*		40	15
1355	75 c. *Leptotes cassius*		80	65
1356	$1 *Battus polydamas*		90	75
1357	$2 *Astraptes talus*		2·00	2·25
1358	$3 *Danaus gilippus*		2·50	2·75
1359	$5 *Myscelia antholia*		3·50	4·00
1352/9	*Set of 8*		9·50	9·75

MS1360 Two sheets, each 76×103 mm. (a) $6 *Danaus plexippus* (*vert*). (b) $6 *Eurema daira* (*vert*). P 14½×14 .. .. *Set of 2 sheets* 8·00 9·00

(Des R. Vigurs. Litho B.D.T.)

1989 (16 Oct). *World Cup Football Championship, Italy* (1st issue) (1990). T **199** *and similar horiz designs. Multicoloured.* P 14.

1361	10 c. Type **199**		35	20
1362	55 c. Youth football teams		70	30
1363	$1 St. Vincent team in training		1·25	90
1364	$5 National team with trophies		4·00	4·50
1361/4	*Set of 4*		4·75	5·50

MS1365 Two sheets, each 103×73 mm. (a) $6 Youth team. (b) $6 National team *Set of 2 sheets* 11·00 11·00

See also Nos. 1559/63.

The new-issue supplement to this Catalogue appears each month in

GIBBONS
STAMP MONTHLY

—from your newsagent or by postal subscription— sample copy and details on request.

---

200 St. Vincent Amazon

+ 10c

CALIF. EARTHQUAKE RELIEF

(201)

(Des Tracy Pedersen. Litho Questa)

1989 (1 Nov). *Wildlife.* T **200** *and similar multicoloured designs.* P 14.

1366	65 c. Type **200**		75	65
1367	75 c. Whistling Warbler		90	75
1368	$5 Black Snake		4·00	5·50
1366/8	*Set of 3*		5·00	6·25

MS1369 97×70 mm. $6 Volcano Plant (*vert*) .. 4·00 6·00

1989 (17 Nov). *California Earthquake Relief Fund.* Nos. 1276/1302 *surch as* T **201**.

1370	60 c. + 10 c. Type **191**		40	40
	a. Sheetlet. Nos. 1370/8		3·25	
1371	60 c. + 10 c. Carl Yastrzemski		40	40
1372	60 c. + 10 c. Randy Johnson		40	40
1373	60 c. + 10 c. Jerome Walton		40	40
1374	60 c. + 10 c. Ramon Martinez		40	40
1375	60 c. + 10 c. Ken Hill		40	40
1376	60 c. + 10 c. Tom McCarthy		40	40
1377	60 c. + 10 c. Gaylord Perry		40	40
1378	60 c. + 10 c. John Smoltz		40	40
1379	60 c. + 10 c. Bob Milacki		40	40
	a. Sheetlet. Nos. 1379/87		3·25	
1380	60 c. + 10 c. Babe Ruth		40	40
1381	60 c. + 10 c. Jim Abbott		40	40
1382	60 c. + 10 c. Gary Sheffield		40	40
1383	60 c. + 10 c. Gregg Jeffries		40	40
1384	60 c. + 10 c. Kevin Brown		40	40
1385	60 c. + 10 c. Cris Carpenter		40	40
1386	60 c. + 10 c. Johnny Bench		40	40
1387	60 c. + 10 c. Ken Griffey Jr		40	40
1388	60 c. + 10 c. Type **192**		40	40
	a. Sheetlet. Nos. 1388/96		3·25	
1389	60 c. + 10 c. Walt Weiss		40	40
1390	60 c. + 10 c. Willie Mays		40	40
1391	60 c. + 10 c. Kirk Gibson		40	40
1392	60 c. + 10 c. Ted Williams		40	40
1393	60 c. + 10 c. Jose Canseco		40	40
1394	60 c. + 10 c. Gaylord Perry		40	40
1395	60 c. + 10 c. Orel Hershiser		40	40
1396	60 c. + 10 c. Frank Viola		40	40
1370/96	*Set of 27*		9·50	9·50

(Des Walt Disney Co. Litho Questa)

1989 (17 Nov). *"World Stamp Expo '89" International Stamp Exhibition, Washington* (1st issue). *Multicoloured designs as* T **234** *of Maldive Islands showing Walt Disney cartoon characters and U.S. monuments.* P 13½×14.

1397	1 c. Mickey and Minnie Mouse by Seagull Monument, Utah (*vert*)		10	10
1398	2 c. Mickey Mouse and Goofy at Lincoln Memorial (*vert*)		10	10
1399	3 c. Mickey and Minnie Mouse at Crazy Horse Memorial, South Dakota (*vert*)		10	10
1400	4 c. Mickey Mouse saluting "Uncle Sam" Wilson statue, New York (*vert*)		10	10
1401	5 c. Goofy and Mickey Mouse at Benjamin Franklin Memorial, Philadelphia (*vert*)		10	10
1402	10 c. Goofy and Mickey Mouse at George Washington statue, New York (*vert*)		10	10
1403	$3 Mickey Mouse at John F. Kennedy's birthplace, Massachusetts (*vert*)		3·50	4·00
1404	$6 Mickey and Minnie Mouse at Mount Vernon, Virginia (*vert*)		5·50	6·00
1397/1404	*Set of 8*		8·00	9·00

MS1405 Two sheets, each 127×100 mm. (a) $5 Mickey and Minnie Mouse over Mount Rushmore, South Dakota. (b) $5 Mickey Mouse and Donald Duck at Stone Mountain, Georgia. P 14×13½ .. .. *Set of 2 sheets* 9·00 10·00

(Des Design Element. Litho Questa)

1989 (17 Nov). *"World Stamp Expo '89" International Stamp Exhibition, Washington* (2nd issue). *Sheet* 61×78 *mm containing multicoloured designs as* T **193**a *of Lesotho.* P 14.

MS1406 $5 Washington Monument (*vert*) .. 2·10 2·50

St. Vincent

383 LEAGUE LEADING STRIKEOUTS, 1973

Nolan Ryan $2

202 Nolan Ryan

---

203 Early Wynn

204 Arms and 1979 Independence 50 c. Stamp

(Des W. Storozuk. Litho)

1989 (30 Nov). *Famous Baseball Players* (3rd series). P 12½.

1407	**202** $2 multicoloured		85	1·00
	a. Sheetlet of 9		7·75	

No. 1407 was printed in sheetlets of 9, with each stamp showing a different commemorative inscription.

(Des Susan Gansbourg. Litho)

1989 (30 Nov). *Famous Baseball Players* (4th series). T **203** *and similar horiz designs.* P 12½.

1408/88 30 c. × 81 multicoloured .. *Set of 81* 16·00 18·00

Nos. 1408/88 were issued as nine sheetlets, each of 9 different designs. No. 1456 (Mike Greenwell) was also available in sheetlets containing nine examples of the one design.

(Des and litho Questa)

1989 (20 Dec). *10th Anniv of Independence.* P 14.

1489	**204** 65 c. multicoloured		50	50
MS1490	57×77 mm. **204** $10 multicoloured		5·00	6·50

(Litho Questa)

1989 (20 Dec). *Christmas. Paintings by Botticelli and Da Vinci. Vert designs as* T **193**b *of Lesotho. Multicoloured.* P 14.

1491	10 c. Holy Family (detail, "The Adoration of the Magi") (Botticelli)		15	10
1492	25 c. Crowd (detail, "The Adoration of the Magi") (Botticelli)		25	15
1493	30 c. "The Madonna of the Magnificat" (detail) (Botticelli)		25	15
1494	40 c. "The Virgin and Child with St. Anne and St. John the Baptist" (detail) (Da Vinci)		30	20
1495	55 c. Angel (detail, "The Annunciation") (Da Vinci)		40	30
1496	75 c. Virgin Mary (detail, "The Annunciation") (Da Vinci)		50	50
1497	$5 "Madonna of the Carnation" (detail) (Da Vinci)		3·00	3·50
1498	$6 "The Annunciation" (detail) (Botticelli)		3·50	4·00
1491/8	*Set of 8*		7·50	8·00

MS1499 Two sheets, each 70×94 mm. (a) $5 "The Virgin of the Rocks" (detail) (Da Vinci). (b) $5 Holy Family (detail, "The Adoration of the Magi") (Botticelli) .. *Set of 2 sheets* 5·50 6·50

205 Boy Scout, 1989

206 Man and Blind Girl

(Des A. Fagbohun. Litho Questa)

1989 (20 Dec). *75th Anniv of Boy Scout and 60th Anniv of Girl Guide Movements in St. Vincent.* T **205** *and similar multicoloured designs, each showing portrait of Lord or Lady Baden-Powell.* P 14.

1500	35 c. Type **205**		55	40
1501	35 c. Guide, ranger and brownie		55	40
1502	55 c. Boy scout in original uniform		75	40
1503	55 c. Mrs. Jackson (founder of St. Vincent Girl Guides)		75	40
1504	$2 Scouts' 75th Anniv logo		2·00	3·25
1505	$2 Mrs. Russell (Girl Guide leader, 1989)		2·00	3·25
1500/5	*Set of 6*		6·00	7·25

MS1506 Two sheets, each 105×75 mm. (a) $5 Scout in canoe. (b) $5 Scout and Guide with flagpoles (*horiz*) .. *Set of 2 sheets* 9·00 10·00

(Des W. Hanson Studio. Litho Questa)

1990 (5 Mar). *25th Anniv of Lions Club of St. Vincent* (1989). T **206** *and similar multicoloured designs.* P 14.

1507	10 c. Type **206**		40	20
1508	65 c. Handing out school books (*horiz*)		70	50
1509	75 c. Teacher explaining diabetes (*horiz*)		80	60
1510	$2 Blood sugar testing machine (*horiz*)		1·75	2·00
1511	$4 Distributing book on drugs (*horiz*)		2·75	3·50
1507/11	*Set of 5*		5·75	6·00

(Des W. Wright. Litho Questa)

1990 (2 Apr). *50th Anniv of Second World War. Horiz designs as* T **242** *of Maldive Islands. Multicoloured.* P 14.

1512	5 c. Scuttling of *Admiral Graf Spee* (German pocket battleship), 1939		35	35
1513	10 c. General De Gaulle and French resistance, 1940		35	30
1514	15 c. British tank, North Africa, 1940		40	30
1515	25 c. U.S.S. *Reuben James* (destroyer) in periscope sight, 1941		50	30
1516	30 c. General MacArthur and map of S.W. Pacific, 1942		55	35

1517	40 c.	American parachute drop on Corregidor, 1945	60	40
1518	55 c.	H.M.S. *King George V* (battleship) engaging *Bismarck* (German battle-ship), 1941	70	55
1519	75 c.	American battleships entering Tokyo Bay, 1945	80	70
1520	$5	Hoisting the Soviet flag on the Reichstag, Berlin, 1945	3·25	3·75
1521	$6	American aircraft carriers, Battle of Philippines Sea, 1944	3·75	4·00
1512/21		*Set of 10*	10·00	10·00
MS1522		100×70 mm. $6 Japanese Mitsubishi A6M Zero-Sen fighter, Battle of Java Sea, 1942	3·75	4·25

Sixth No-Hitter
11 June 90
Oakland Athletics

207 Two Pence Blue   (208)

(Des M. Pollard. Litho B.D.T.)

1990 (3 May). *150th Anniv of the Penny Black. T* **207** *and similar vert designs. P* 14×15.

1523	$2	black, blue-green and bright magenta	1·25	1·50
1524	$4	black and bright magenta	2·50	3·25
MS1525		130×99 mm. $6 black, scarlet & yellow	4·00	4·75

Designs:—$4, $6 Penny Black.

(Des Walt Disney Co. Litho Questa)

1990 (3 May). *"Stamp World London 90" International Stamp Exhibition. British Uniforms. Multicoloured designs as T* 239a *of Maldive Islands showing Walt Disney cartoon characters. P* 13½×14.

1526	5 c.	Scrooge McDuck as 18th-century admiral (*vert*)	20	15
1527	10 c.	Huey as Light Infantry bugler, 1854 (*vert*)	25	15
1528	15 c.	Minnie Mouse as Irish Guards drummer, 1900 (*vert*)	35	20
1529	25 c.	Goofy as Seaforth Highlanders lance-corporal, 1944 (*vert*)	45	30
1530	$1	Mickey Mouse as 58th Regiment ensign, 1879 (*vert*)	1·25	1·00
1531	$2	Donald Duck as Royal Engineers officer, 1813 (*vert*)	1·90	2·00
1532	$4	Mickey Mouse as Duke of Edinburgh's Royal Regiment drum major (*vert*)	3·00	3·50
1533	$5	Goofy as Cameronians sergeant piper, 1918 (*vert*)	3·00	3·50
1526/33		*Set of 8*	9·25	9·75
MS1534		Two sheets, each 120x100 mm. (a) $6 Goofy as officer in King's Lifeguard of Foot, 1643. P 13½×14. (b) $6 Mickey Mouse as Grenadier Guards drummer (*vert*). P 14×13½		
		Set of 2 sheets	7·00	8·00

1990 (23 June). *Nolan Ryan–Sixth No-hitter. No.* 1407 *optd with T* **208**.

1535	**202**	$2 multicoloured	95	1·00
		a. Sheetlet of 9	7·75	

(Des Young Phillips Studio. Litho Questa)

1990 (5 July). *90th Birthday of Queen Elizabeth the Queen Mother. Vert designs as T* 198a *of Lesotho showing portraits,* 1950–59. *P* 14.

1536	$2	black, bright sage-green and magenta	1·50	1·75
		a. Strip of 3. Nos. 1536/8	4·00	
1537	$2	black, bright sage-green and magenta	1·50	1·75
1538	$2	black, bright sage-green and magenta	1·50	1·75
1536/8		*Set of 3*	4·00	4·75
MS1539		90×75 mm. $6 multicoloured	3·50	4·50

Designs:—No. 1536, Queen Elizabeth signing visitors' book; Nos. 1537, MS1539, Queen Elizabeth in evening dress; No. 1538, Queen Elizabeth the Queen Mother in Coronation robes, 1953.

Nos. 1536/8 were printed together, horizontally and vertically *se-tenant,* in sheetlets of 9 (3×3).

300th Win
Milwaukee Brewers
July 31, 1990

(209)

210 Maradona, Argentina

1990 (3 Aug). *Nolan Ryan–300th Win. No.* 1407 *optd with T* **209**.

1540	**202**	$2 multicoloured	95	1·00
		a. Sheetlet of 9	7·75	

1990 (21 Sept). *Centenary of Los Angeles Dodgers (2nd issue). Baseball Players. Multicoloured designs as T* **197**. *Litho. Rouletted* 7.

1541	60 c.	Mickey Hatcher and Jay Howell	45	45
		a. Sheetlet. Nos. 1541/9	3·50	
1542	60 c.	Juan Samuel and Mike Scioscia	45	45

1543	60 c.	Lenny Harris and Mike Hartley	45	45
1544	60 c.	Ramon Martinez and Mike Morgan	45	45
1545	60 c.	Aerial view of Dodger stadium	45	45
1546	60 c.	Stan Javier and Don Aase	45	45
1547	60 c.	Ray Searage and Mike Sharperson	45	45
1548	60 c.	Tim Belcher and Pat Perry	45	45
1549	60 c.	Dave Walsh, Jose Vizcaino, Jim Neidlinger, Jose Offerman and Carlos Hernandez	45	45
1550	60 c.	Hubie Brooks and Orel Hershiser	45	45
		a. Sheetlet. Nos. 1550/8	3·50	
1551	60 c.	Tom Lasorda and Tim Crews	45	45
1552	60 c.	Fernando Valenzuela and Eddie Murray	45	45
1553	60 c.	Kal Daniels and Jose Gonzalez	45	45
1554	60 c.	Dodgers emblem	45	45
1555	60 c.	Chris Gwynn and Jeff Hamilton	45	45
1556	60 c.	Kirk Gibson and Rick Dempsey	45	45
1557	60 c.	Jim Gott and Alfredo Griffin	45	45
1558	60 c.	Ron Perranoski, Bill Russell, Joe Ferguson, Joe Amalfitano, Mark Cresse, Ben Hines and Manny Mota	45	45
1541/58		*Set of 18*	7·00	7·00

Nos. 1541/9 and 1550/8 were each printed together, *se-tenant,* in sheetlets of nine.

(Des Young Phillips Studio. Litho Questa)

1990 (24 Sept). *World Cup Football Championship, Italy (2nd issue). T* **210** *and similar vert designs. Multicoloured. P* 14.

1559	10 c.	Type **210**	40	15
1560	75 c.	Valderrama, Colombia	85	75
1561	$1	Francescoli, Uruguay	1·10	95
1562	$5	Beulemans, Belgium	4·25	6·50
1559/62		*Set of 4*	6·00	6·50
MS1563		Two sheets, each 101×85 mm. (a) $6 Klinsmann, West Germany. (b) $6 Careca, Brazil		
		Set of 2 sheets	7·50	8·50

	JOE DELOACH U.S.A.	STEVE LEWIS U.S.A.	PAUL ERANG KENYA

(211)   (212)

1990 (18 Oct). *95th Anniv of Rotary International. Nos.* 1230/8 *optd with T* **211**.

1564	10 c.	Type **186**	30	20
1565	40 c.	*Liberté*	50	40
1566	50 c.	*Mauretania I* (launched 1906)	55	45
1567	75 c.	*France*	80	60
1568	$1	*Aquitania*	90	80
1569	$2	*United States*	1·60	1·75
1570	$3	*Olympic*	2·00	2·50
1571	$4	*Queen Elizabeth*	2·25	2·75
1564/71		*Set of 8*	8·00	8·50
MS1572		Two sheets, each 141×108 mm. (a) $6 *Queen Mary* (85×28 mm). (b) $6 *Queen Elizabeth 2* (85×28 mm) . . *Set of 2 sheets*	8·00	10·00

1990 (18 Oct). *Olympic Medal Winners, Seoul. Nos.* 1153/7 *optd as T* **212**.

1573	10 c.	Type **178**	20	20
1574	50 c.	Long jumping (optd "CARL LEWIS U.S.A.")	60	60
		a. Opt inverted	†	
1575	$1	Triple jumping (optd "HRISTO MARKOV BULGARIA")	90	90
1576	$5	Boxing (optd "HENRY MASKE E. GERMANY")	3·25	3·75
		a. Opt inverted	†	
1573/6		*Set of 4*	4·50	5·00
MS1577		85×63 mm. $10 Olympic flame*	6·50	7·50

*No. MS1577 is overprinted "FINAL MEDAL STANDINGS" and medal totals for either South Korea and Spain or U.S.S.R. and U.S.A. on the margin (*same price for either opt*).

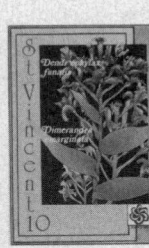

213 *Dendrophylax funalis* and *Dimerandra emarginata*

214 "Miraculous Draught of Fishes" (detail, Rubens)

(Litho B.D.T.)

1990 (23 Nov). *"EXPO 90" International Garden and Greenery Exposition, Osaka. Orchids. T* **213** *and similar vert designs. Multicoloured. P* 14.

1578	10 c.	Type **213**	35	20
1579	15 c.	*Epidendrum elongatum*	40	25
1580	45 c.	*Comparettia falcata*	60	30
1581	60 c.	*Brassia maculata*	75	60
1582	$1	*Encyclia cochleata* and *Encyclia cordigera*	90	80
1583	$2	*Cyrtopodium punctatum*	1·50	1·75
1584	$4	*Cattleya labiata*	2·50	2·50
1585	$5	*Bletia purpurea*	2·75	3·25
1578/85		*Set of 8*	8·75	9·00
MS1586		Two sheets, each 108×78 mm. (a) $6 *Vanilla planifolia* Jackson. (b) $6 *Ionopsis utricularioides* . . *Set of 2 sheets*	7·50	8·50

(Litho Questa)

1990 (3 Dec). *Christmas. 350th Death Anniv of Rubens. T* **214** *and similar vert designs. Multicoloured. P* 13½×14.

1587	10 c.	Type **214**	25	20
1588	45 c.	"Crowning of Holy Katherine" (detail)	45	25
1589	50 c.	"St. Ives of Treguier" (detail)	50	30
1590	65 c.	"Allegory of Eternity" (detail)	65	40
1591	$1	"St. Bavo receives Monastic Habit of Ghent" (detail)	90	80
1592	$2	"Crowning of Holy Katherine" (different detail)	1·50	1·50
1593	$4	"St. Bavo receives Monastic Habit of Ghent" (different detail)	2·75	3·25
1594	$5	"Communion of St. Francis" (detail)	3·00	3·25
1587/94		*Set of 8*	9·00	9·00
MS1595		Four sheets. (a) 70×100 mm. $6 "Allegory of Eternity" (different detail). (b) 70×100 mm. $6 As 50 c. P 13½×14. (c) 100×70 mm. $6 As Type **214** (*horiz*). P 14×13½. (d) 100×70 mm. $6 "St. Bavo receives Monastic Habit of Ghent" (different detail) (*horiz*). P 14×13½ . . *Set of 4 sheets*	12·50	13·00

215 Geoffrey Chaucer   **216** American Football Game

(Des N. Waldman. Litho Cartor)

1990 (12 Dec). *International Literacy Year* (1st issue). *Chaucer's Canterbury Tales. T* **215** *and similar square designs. Multicoloured. P* 13½.

1596	40 c.	Type **215**	40	40
		a. Sheetlet. Nos. 1596/1619	8·50	
1597	40 c.	"When April with his showers…"	40	40
1598	40 c.	"When Zephyr also has…"	40	40
1599	40 c.	"And many little birds…"	40	40
1600	40 c.	"And palmers to go seeking out…"	40	40
1601	40 c.	Quill in ink well and open book	40	40
1602	40 c.	Green bird in tree	40	40
1603	40 c.	Brown bird in tree and franklin's head	40	40
1604	40 c.	Purple bird in tree and banner	40	40
1605	40 c.	Canterbury	40	40
1606	40 c.	Knight's head	40	40
1607	40 c.	Black bird in tree and squire's head	40	40
1608	40 c.	Friar	40	40
1609	40 c.	Franklin	40	40
1610	40 c.	Prioress and monk holding banner	40	40
1611	40 c.	Summoner, Oxford clerk and parson	40	40
1612	40 c.	Serjeant-at-Law and knight on horse-back	40	40
1613	40 c.	Squire	40	40
1614	40 c.	"In fellowship…"	40	40
1615	40 c.	Cockerel and horse's legs	40	40
1616	40 c.	Hens	40	40
1617	40 c.	Hen and rabbit	40	40
1618	40 c.	Horses' legs and butterfly	40	40
1619	40 c.	"And briefly, when the sun…"	40	40
1596/1619		*Set of 24*	8·50	8·50

Nos. 1596/1619 were printed together, *se-tenant,* as a sheetlet of 24, forming a composite design.
See also Nos. 1777/1802.

(Litho Cartor)

1990 (17 Dec). *Death Centenary of Van Gogh (painter). Vert designs as T* 255 *of Maldive Islands. Multicoloured. P* 13.

1620	1 c.	Self-portrait, 1889	45	45
		a. Vert strip of 4. Nos. 1620/3	1·60	
1621	5 c.	Self-portrait, 1886	45	45
1622	10 c.	Self-portrait with hat and pipe, 1888	45	45
1623	15 c.	Self-portrait at easel, 1888	45	45
1624	20 c.	Self-portrait, 1887	1·00	1·00
		a. Vert strip of 4. Nos. 1624/7	7·50	
1625	45 c.	Self-portrait, 1889 (different)	1·25	1·25
1626	$5	Self-portrait with pipe, 1889	3·00	3·50
1627	$6	Self-portrait wearing straw hat, 1887	3·00	3·50
1620/7		*Set of 8*	8·00	9·25

Nos. 1620/3 and 1624/7 were each printed in sheets of 16 (4×4) with the four values vertically *se-tenant.*

(Litho Questa)

1990 (30 Dec). *Hummel Figurines. Vert designs as T* 256 *of Maldive Islands. Multicoloured. P* 14.

1628	10 c.	"The Photographer"	30	15
1629	15 c.	"Ladder and Rope"	40	15
1630	40 c.	"Druggist"	60	30
1631	60 c.	"Hello"	75	45
1632	$1	"Boots"	1·00	80
1633	$2	"The Artist"	1·40	1·60
1634	$4	"Waiter"	2·50	3·00
1635	$5	"The Postman"	2·75	3·25
1628/35		*Set of 8*	8·75	8·75
MS1636		Two sheets, each 94×121 mm. (a) Nos. 1628, 1631/2 and 1635. (b) Nos. 1629/30 and 1633/4 . . *Set of 2 sheets*	9·00	10·00

1991 (15 Jan). *25th Anniv of Super Bowl American Football Championship* (1st issue). *T* **216** *and similar vert designs. Multicoloured. Litho. P* 13½×14.

MS1637		Twenty-five sheets, each 127×101 mm, containing 50 c. × 2 as horiz pairs forming composite designs of game scenes or 50 c. × 3 (final sheet) showing Vince Lombardi Trophy and helmets of participating teams		
		Set of 25 sheets	15·00	

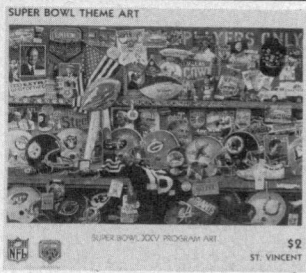

SUPER BOWL THEME ART

$2

217 Programme Cover of XXV Super Bowl
(*Illustration reduced. Actual size* 105×95 *mm*)

1991 (15 Jan). *25th Anniv of Super Bowl American Football Championships* (2nd issue). T **217** *and similar multicoloured designs, each showing a different programme cover illustration. Litho. Imperf.*
MS1638 Twenty-five sheets, 125×99 mm or 99×125 mm, each with a face value of $2
Set of 25 sheets 28·00

218 U.S.A. 1893 1 c.
Columbus Stamp

1991 (18 Mar). *500th Anniv of Discovery of America* (1992) *by Columbus* (4th issue). T **218** *and similar horiz designs showing U.S.A. 1893 Columbian Exposition, Chicago, stamps* (*Nos.* 1639/54) *or ships* (*others*). *Multicoloured. Litho.* P 13½×14.
1639	1 c. Type **218**		10	10
	a. Sheetlet. Nos. 1639/46 and 1655		5·00	
1640	2 c. U.S.A. Columbus 2 c.		10	10
1641	3 c. U.S.A. Columbus 3 c.		10	10
1642	4 c. U.S.A. Columbus 4 c.		10	10
1643	5 c. U.S.A. Columbus 5 c.		10	10
1644	6 c. U.S.A. Columbus 6 c.		10	10
1645	8 c. U.S.A. Columbus 8 c.		10	10
1646	10 c. U.S.A. Columbus 10 c.		10	10
1647	15 c. U.S.A. Columbus 15 c.		10	10
	a. Sheetlet. Nos. 1647/54 and 1656		11·50	
1648	30 c. U.S.A. Columbus 30 c.		15	20
1649	50 c. U.S.A. Columbus 50 c.		25	30
1650	$1 U.S.A. Columbus $1		50	55
1651	$2 U.S.A. Columbus $2		95	1·00
1652	$3 U.S.A. Columbus $3		1·40	1·50
1653	$4 U.S.A. Columbus $4		2·00	2·10
1654	$5 U.S.A. Columbus $5		2·40	2·50
1655	$10 *Santa Maria*, Scarlet Macaw and tropical flower		5·00	5·25
1656	$10 Logo, *Santa Maria* and Amerindian hut		5·00	5·25
1639/56		*Set of 18*	16·00	17·00

MS1657 Two sheets, each 98×72 mm. (a) $6 Sailors on ship's fo'c'sle. (b) $6 Ship's figurehead
Set of 2 sheets 8·00 9·00
Nos. 1639/46 and 1655 and Nos. 1647/54 and 1656 were each printed together, *se-tenant*, in sheetlets of 9.

10c
St.Vincent

219 Pebbles and Hoppy boxing

(Des Hanna-Barbera Productions. Litho Questa)

1991 (25 Mar). *Sports.* T **219** *and similar horiz designs showing characters from the Flintstones cartoons. Multicoloured.* P 14×13½.
1658	10 c. Type **219**		30	10
1659	15 c. Fred Flintstone and Dino playing football		45	15
1660	45 c. Fred losing rowing race to Barney Rubble		65	30
1661	55 c. Betty Rubble, Wilma Flintstone and Pebbles in dressage competition		80	50
1662	$1 Fred playing basketball		1·25	1·00
1663	$2 Bamm Bamm wrestling Barney with Fred as referee		1·75	1·50
1664	$4 Fred and Barney playing tennis		2·75	2·75
1665	$5 Fred, Barney and Dino cycling		2·75	2·75
1658/65		*Set of 8*	9·50	8·75

MS1666 Two sheets, each 117×95 mm. (a) $6 Fred at the plate in baseball game. (b) $6 Fred running to homeplate
Set of 2 sheets 7·50 8·00

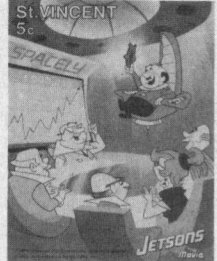

St. VINCENT
5c

JETSONS

220 Board Meeting

(Des Hanna-Barbera Productions. Litho Questa)

1991 (25 March). *The Jetsons* (cartoon film). T **220** *and similar multicoloured designs.* P 14×13½ (60 c., $1, $2) or 13½×14 (*others*).
1667	5 c. Type **220**		15	10
1668	20 c. Jetsons with Dog		30	15
1669	45 c. Judy and Apollo Blue		50	25
1670	50 c. Cosmo Spacely and George Jetson		50	35
1671	60 c. George and Elroy catching cogs (*horiz*)		70	50
1672	$1 Judy, Apollo, Elroy and Teddy in cavern (*horiz*)		1·00	1·00
1673	$2 Drill destroying the cavern (*horiz*)		1·50	1·50
1674	$4 Jetsons celebrating with the Grungees		2·75	2·75
1675	$5 The Jetsons returning home		2·75	2·75
1667/75		*Set of 9*	9·00	8·50

MS1676 Two sheets, each 114×76 mm. (a) $6 The Jetsons in spacecraft (*horiz*). (b) $6 The Jetsons in control room (*horiz*). P 14×13½
Set of 2 sheets 7·00 8·00

(Des T. Agans. Litho Questa)

1991 (13 May). *500th Anniv of Discovery of America by Columbus*, (1992) (5th issue). *History of Exploration. Multicoloured designs as* T **64** *of St. Kitts-Nevis* (*Nevis*). P 14.
1677	5 c. "Sänger 2" (projected space shuttle)		15	15
1678	10 c. "Magellan" satellite, 1990		15	15
1679	25 c. "Buran" space shuttle		25	25
1680	75 c. Projected "Freedom" space station		65	65
1681	$1 Projected Mars mission space craft		80	80
1682	$2 "Hubble" telescope, 1990		1·60	1·60
1683	$4 Projected Mars mission "sailship"		2·50	2·50
1684	$5 Projected "Craf" satellite		2·50	2·50
1677/84		*Set of 8*	7·75	7·75

MS1685 Two sheets, each 105×71 mm. (a) $6 Bow of caravel (*vert*). (b) $6 Caravel under full sail
Set of 2 sheets 7·00 8·00

(Des D. Miller. Litho Walsall)

1991 (5 July). *65th Birthday of Queen Elizabeth II. Horiz designs as* T **210** *of Lesotho. Multicoloured.* P 14.
1686	5 c. Queen and Prince Philip during visit to Spain, 1988		15	15
1687	60 c. Queen and Prince Philip in landau		60	45
1688	$2 Queen at Caen Hill Waterway, 1990		1·75	1·75
1689	$4 Queen at Badminton, 1983		3·00	3·25
1686/9		*Set of 4*	5·00	5·00

MS1690 68×91 mm. $5 Queen Elizabeth II in 1988 and Prince Philip in 1989
3·50 4·00

(Des D. Miller. Litho Walsall)

1991 (5 July). *10th Wedding Anniv of the Prince and Princess of Wales. Horiz designs as* T **210** *of Lesotho. Multicoloured.* P 14.
1691	20 c. Prince and Princess in hard hats, 1987		40	20
1692	25 c. Portraits of Prince and Princess and sons		40	20
1693	$1 Prince Henry and Prince William, both in 1988		90	90
1694	$5 Princess Diana in France and Prince Charles in 1987		4·75	4·75
1691/4		*Set of 4*	5·75	5·50

MS1695 68×90 mm. $5 Princes Henry and William in Majorca, and Princess Diana presenting polo trophy to Prince Charles
4·00 4·00

75c
St. Vincent

221 Class D51 Steam Locomotive

(Des K. Gromell. Litho Cartor)

1991 (12 Aug). *"Phila Nippon '91" International Stamp Exhibition, Tokyo. Japanese Trains.* T **221** *and similar multicoloured designs.* P 13½.
1696	75 c. Type **221**		65	65
	a. Sheetlet. Nos. 1696/1704		5·25	
1697	75 c. Class 9600 steam locomotive		65	65
1698	75 c. Goods wagons and chrysanthemum emblem		65	65
1699	75 c. Passenger coach		65	65
1700	75 c. Decorated Class C57 steam locomotive		65	65
1701	75 c. Oil tanker wagon		65	65
1702	75 c. Class C53 steam locomotive		65	65
1703	75 c. First Japanese steam locomotive		65	65
1704	75 c. Class C11 steam locomotive		65	65
1705	$1 Class 181 electric unit		65	65
	a. Sheetlet. Nos. 1705/13		5·25	

1706	$1 Class EH10 electric locomotive		65	65
1707	$1 Passenger coaches and Special Express symbol		65	65
1708	$1 Class 1 electric tramcar, Sendai City		65	65
1709	$1 Class 485 electric unit		65	65
1710	$1 Street-cleaning tram, Sendai City		65	65
1711	$1 "Hikari" express train		65	65
1712	$1 Class ED11 electric locomotive		65	65
1713	$1 Class EF66 electric locomotive		65	65
1696/1713		*Set of 18*	10·50	10·50

MS1714 Four sheets, each 108×77 mm. (a) $6 Class C55 steam locomotive (*vert*). P 13×13½. (b) $6 Series 400 electric train. P 13½×13. (c) $6 Class C62 steam locomotive (*vert*). P 13×13½. (d) $6 "Super Hitachi" electric train. P 13×13½
Set of 4 sheets 15·00 16·00
Nos. 1696/1704 and 1705/13 were each printed together, *se-tenant*, in sheetlets of 9.

ST. VINCENT
$1

MARCELLO MASTROIANNI

222 Marcello Mastroianni
(actor)

(Des J. Iskowitz. Litho Cartor)

1991 (22 Aug). *Italian Entertainers.* T **222** *and similar multicoloured designs.* P 13.
1715	$1 Type **222**		70	70
	a. Sheetlet. Nos. 1715/23		5·75	
1716	$1 Sophia Loren (actress)		70	70
1717	$1 Mario Lanza (singer)		70	70
1718	$1 Federico Fellini (director)		70	70
1719	$1 Arturo Toscanini (conductor)		70	70
1720	$1 Anna Magnani (actress)		70	70
1721	$1 Giancarlo Giannini (actor)		70	70
1722	$1 Gina Lollobrigida (actress)		70	70
1723	$1 Enrico Caruso (operatic tenor)		70	70
1715/23		*Set of 9*	5·75	5·75

MS1724 117×80 mm. $6 Luciano Pavarotti (operatic tenor) (*horiz*)
5·50 6·00
Nos. 1715/23 were printed together, *se-tenant*, in sheetlets of 9.

ST. VINCENT
$1

MADONNA

223 Madonna

(Des J. Iskowitz. Litho Cartor)

1991 (22 Aug). *Madonna* (American singer). T **223** *and similar vert portraits. Multicoloured.* P 13.
1725	$1 Type **223**		95	95
	a. Sheetlet. Nos. 1725/33		7·50	
1726	$1 In strapless dress		95	95
1727	$1 Wearing necklaces, looking right		95	95
1728	$1 In green dress		95	95
1729	$1 Wearing necklaces, looking to front		95	95
1730	$1 With wrist bangles		95	95
1731	$1 With hand to face		95	95
1732	$1 In purple dress		95	95
1733	$1 With microphone		95	95
1725/33		*Set of 9*	7·50	7·50

MS1734 79×118 mm. $6 Madonna (25×40 *mm*). P 12×13
6·50 7·00
Nos. 1725/33 were printed together, *se-tenant*, in sheetlets of 9.

ST. VINCENT
$1
+ 2c

JOHN LENNON 1940-1980

224 John Lennon

(Des J. Iskowitz. Litho Cartor)

1991 (22 Aug). *John Lennon (British musician). T **224** and similar vert portraits. Multicoloured. P 13.*

1735	$1 + 2 c. Type **224**		90	90
	a. Sheetlet. Nos. 1735/43		7·00	
1736	$1 + 2 c. With Beatle hair cut		90	90
1737	$1 + 2 c. In cap		90	90
1738	$1 + 2 c. In red polka-dot shirt		90	90
1739	$1 + 2 c. In green polo-neck jumper and jacket		90	90
1740	$1 + 2 c. In glasses and magenta jacket		90	90
1741	$1 + 2 c. With long hair and glasses		90	90
1742	$1 + 2 c. In black jumper		90	90
1743	$1 + 2 c. In polo-neck jumper		90	90
1735/43		*Set of 9*	7·00	7·00

Nos. 1735/43 were printed together, *se-tenant,* in sheetlets of 9.

225 Free French Resistance Fighters, 1944

226 Myrvyn Bennion

(Des L. Fried (Nos. 1746, 1749/51, **MS**1761a), W. Hanson (Nos. 1747, 1753, 1760, **MS**1761d), J. Iskowitz (Nos. 1752, 1759, **MS**1761b), W. Wright (Nos. 1754/8). Litho Questa)

1991 (18 Nov). *Anniversaries and Events. T **225** and similar multicoloured designs. P 14.*

1744	10 c. Type **225**		20	15
1745	45 c. De Gaulle with Churchill, 1944		60	40
1746	50 c. Protestor with banner		45	45
1747	65 c. Tales around the camp fire (vert)		70	50
1748	75 c. Liberation of Paris, 1944		70	60
1749	75 c. Building Berlin Wall		70	60
1750	90 c. German flag and protestors' shadows		70	70
1751	$1 Presidents Bush and Gorbachev shaking hands		80	80
1752	$1 *Marriage of Figaro*		1·25	1·00
1753	$1.50, British trenches and Mafeking Siege 3d. stamp		1·50	1·50
1754	$1.50, Class P-36 steam locomotive, Trans-Siberian Railway		1·50	1·50
1755	$1.50, Map of Switzerland and woman in traditional costume		1·50	1·50
1756	$1.65, Lilienthal's signature and *Flugzeug Nr. 13 Doppeldecker*		1·75	1·75
1757	$2 Street fighting, Kiev		2·25	2·25
1758	$2 Gottfried Leibniz (mathematician)		2·25	2·25
1759	$3 *The Clemency of Titus*		2·50	2·50
1760	$3.50, Angelfish and scout diver		2·50	2·50
1744/60		*Set of 17*	19·00	19·00

MS1761 Four sheets. (a) 101×72 mm. $4 Arms of Berlin. (b) 77×116 mm. $4 Mozart and signature (vert). (c) 77×116 mm. $5 President De Gaulle (vert). (d) 117×89 mm. $5 Scout badge and Jamboree emblem *Set of 4 sheets* 13·00 15·00

Anniversaries and Events:—Nos. 1744/5, 1748, **MS**1761c, Birth centenary of Charles de Gaulle (French statesman); Nos. 1746, 1749/51, **MS**1761a, Bicentenary of Brandenburg Gate, Berlin; Nos. 1747, 1753, 1760, **MS**1761d, 50th death anniv of Lord Baden-Powell and World Scout Jamboree, Korea; Nos. 1752, 1759, **MS**1761b, Death bicentenary of Mozart; No. 1754 Centenary of Trans-Siberian Railway; No. 1755, 700th anniv of Swiss Confederation; No. 1756, Centenary of Otto Lilienthal's gliding experiments; No. 1757, 50th anniv of capture of Kiev; No. 1758, 750th anniv of Hanover.

(Des D. Ben-Ami. Litho Questa)

1991 (18 Nov). *50th Anniv of Japanese Attack on Pearl Harbor. T **226** and similar horiz designs showing recipients of Congressional Medal of Honor. Multicoloured. P 14¹/₂×15.*

1762	$1 Type **226**		70	70
	a. Sheetlet. Nos. 1762/76		9·50	
1763	$1 George Cannon		70	70
1764	$1 John Finn		70	70
1765	$1 Francis Flaherty		70	70
1766	$1 Samuel Fuqua		70	70
1767	$1 Edwin Hill		70	70
1768	$1 Herbert Jones		70	70
1769	$1 Isaac Kidd		70	70
1770	$1 Jackson Pharris		70	70
1771	$1 Thomas Reeves		70	70
1772	$1 Donald Ross		70	70
1773	$1 Robert Scott		70	70
1774	$1 Franklin Van Valkenburgh		70	70
1775	$1 James Ward		70	70
1776	$1 Cassin Young		70	70
1762/76		*Set of 15*	9·50	9·50

Nos. 1762/76 were printed together, *se-tenant,* in sheetlets of 15.

(Des Walt Disney Co. Litho Questa)

1991 (18 Nov). *International Literacy Year (1990) (2nd issue). Multicoloured designs as T **246** of Maldive Islands, but horiz, showing scenes from Disney cartoon films. P 14×13¹/₂.*

(a) The Prince and the Pauper

1777	5 c. Mickey Mouse, Goofy and Pluto as pauper pals		15	15
1778	10 c. Mickey as the bored prince		15	15
1779	15 c. Donald Duck as the valet		20	20
1780	25 c. Mickey as the prince and the pauper		25	25
1781	60 c. Exchanging clothes		55	55
1782	65 c. Prince and pauper with suit of armour		65	65
1783	80 c. Throwing food from the battlements		70	70
1784	$1 Pete as Captain of the Guard		85	85
1785	$2 Mickey and Donald in the dungeon		1·50	1·50
1786	$3 Mickey and Donald at dungeon window		1·75	1·75

1787	$4 Goofy rescuing Mickey and Donald		2·50	2·50
1788	$5 Crowning the real prince		2·50	2·50
1777/88		*Set of 12*	10·50	10·50

MS1789 Four sheets, each 127×101 mm. (a) $6 Crowning the wrong prince. (b) $6 Pete holding Mickey. (c) $6 The pauper on the throne. (d) $6 Mickey telling troops to seize the guard
Set of 4 sheets 14·00 15·00

(b) The Rescuers Down Under

1790	5 c. Miss Bianca		15	15
1791	10 c. Bernard		15	15
1792	15 c. Matre d'Francoise		20	20
1793	25 c. Wilbur the Albatross		25	25
1794	60 c. Jake the Kangaroo mouse		55	55
1795	75 c. Bernard, Bianca and Jake in the outback		65	65
1796	80 c. Bianca and Bernard to the rescue		70	70
1797	$1 Marahute the Eagle		85	85
1798	$2 Cody and Marahute with eggs		1·50	1·50
1799	$3 McLeach and his pet, Joanna the Goanna		1·75	1·75
1800	$4 Frank the Frill-necked Lizard		2·50	2·50
1801	$5 Red Kangaroo, Krebbs Koala and Polly Platypus		2·50	2·75
1790/1801		*Set of 12*	10·50	10·50

MS1802 Four sheets, each 127×102 mm. (a) $6 The Rescuers. (b) $6 Ethiopian and Japanese mice delegates. (c) $6 Wilbur carrying Bianca and Bernard. (d) $6 Wilbur in pain *Set of 4 sheets* 14·00 15·00

227 Hans-Dietrich Genscher and "Winged Victory" Statue

228 Walt Disney Characters decorating Christmas Tree, 1982

(Des J. Puvilland. Litho Questa)

1991 (25 Nov). *European History. T **227** and similar vert designs. Multicoloured. P 14¹/₂×14.*

1803	$1 Type **227**		1·25	1·25
	a. Sheetlet. Nos. 1803/10		9·00	
1804	$1 Destruction of Berlin Wall		1·25	1·25
1805	$1 Churchill, De Gaulle and Appeal to the French, 1940		1·25	1·25
1806	$1 Eisenhower, De Gaulle and D-Day, 1944		1·25	1·25
1807	$1 Brandenburg Gate, Berlin (bicent)		1·25	1·25
1808	$1 Chancellor Helmut Kohl and meeting of Berlin Mayors, 1989		1·25	1·25
1809	$1 De Gaulle with Chancellor Adenauer		1·25	1·25
1810	$1 Pres. Kennedy's visit to Europe, 1961, Washington and Lafayette		1·25	1·25
1803/10		*Set of 8*	9·00	9·00

MS1811 106×88 mm. $6 Casablanca Conference, 1942, and demolition of Berlin Wall (24¹/₂×39 *mm*). P 14 4·25 5·50

Nos. 1803/10 were printed together, *se-tenant,* in sheetlets of 8.

(Des J. Puvilland. Litho Questa)

1991 (25 Nov). *Famous Golfers. Vert designs as T **227**. Multicoloured. P 14¹/₂×14.*

1812	$1 Gary Player		1·25	1·25
	a. Sheetlet. Nos. 1812/19		9·00	
1813	$1 Nick Faldo		1·25	1·25
1814	$1 Severiano Ballesteros		1·25	1·25
1815	$1 Ben Hogan		1·25	1·25
1816	$1 Jack Nicklaus		1·25	1·25
1817	$1 Greg Norman		1·25	1·25
1818	$1 José-Maria Olazabal		1·25	1·25
1819	$1 Bobby Jones		1·25	1·25
1812/19		*Set of 8*	9·00	9·00

Nos. 1812/19 were printed together, *se-tenant,* in sheetlets of 8.

(Des J. Puvilland. Litho Questa)

1991 (25 Nov). *Famous Entertainers. Vert designs as T **227**. Multicoloured. P 14¹/₂.*

1820	$2 Michael Jackson		1·75	1·75
	a. Sheetlet. Nos. 1820/7		12·00	
1821	$2 Madonna		1·75	1·75
1822	$2 Elvis Presley		1·75	1·75
1823	$2 David Bowie		1·75	1·75
1824	$2 Prince		1·75	1·75
1825	$2 Frank Sinatra		1·75	1·75
1826	$2 George Michael		1·75	1·75
1827	$2 Mick Jagger		1·75	1·75
1820/7		*Set of 8*	12·00	12·00

MS1828 Two sheets, each 110×82 mm. (a) $6 Madonna (29×43 *mm*). (b) $6 Elvis Presley (29×43 *mm*). P 14 *Set of 2 sheets* 9·50 10·00

Nos. 1820/7 were printed together, *se-tenant,* in sheetlets of 8.

(Des J. Puvilland. Litho Questa)

1991 (25 Nov). *Famous Chess Masters. Vert designs as T **227**. Multicoloured. P 14¹/₂.*

1829	$1 Francoise Philidor		1·00	1·00
	a. Sheetlet. Nos. 1829/36		7·00	
1830	$1 Karl Anderssen		1·00	1·00
1831	$1 Wilhelm Steinitz		1·00	1·00
1832	$1 Alexandrovich Alekhine		1·00	1·00

1833	$1 Boris Spassky		1·00	1·00
1834	$1 Robert Fischer		1·00	1·00
1835	$1 Anatoly Karpov		1·00	1·00
1836	$1 Garry Kasparov		1·00	1·00
1829/36		*Set of 8*	7·00	7·00

Nos. 1829/36 were printed together, *se-tenant,* in sheetlets of 8.

(Des J. Puvilland. Litho Questa)

1991 (25 Nov). *Nobel Prizewinners. Vert designs as T **227**. Multicoloured. P 14¹/₂.*

1837	$1 Albert Einstein (mathematical physicist)		85	85
	a. Sheetlet. Nos. 1837/44		6·00	
1838	$1 Wilhelm Rontgen (physicist)		85	85
1839	$1 William Shockley (chemist)		85	85
1840	$1 Charles Townes (physicist)		85	85
1841	$1 Lev Landau (physicist)		85	85
1842	$1 Guglielmo Marconi (applied physicist)		85	85
1843	$1 Willard Libby (chemist)		85	85
1844	$1 Ernest Lawrence (nuclear physicist)		85	85
1837/44		*Set of 8*	6·00	6·00

Nos. 1837/44 were printed together, *se-tenant,* in sheetlets of 8.

(Des Walt Disney Co. Litho Questa)

1991 (23 Dec). *Christmas. Walt Disney Christmas Cards. T **228** and similar vert designs. Multicoloured. P 13¹/₂×14.*

1845	10 c. Type **228**		15	15
1846	45 c. Mickey and Moose, 1980		40	30
1847	55 c. Mickey, Pluto and Donald carrying bauble, 1970		50	40
1848	75 c. Duckling and egg shell, 1943		70	70
1849	$1.50, Walt Disney characters decorating globe, 1941		1·25	1·25
1850	$2 The Lady and the Tramp by Christmas tree, 1986		1·50	1·50
1851	$4 Walt Disney characters carol singing, 1977		2·75	2·75
1852	$5 Mickey in fairy-tale castle, 1965		2·75	3·00
1845/52		*Set of 8*	9·00	9·00

MS1853 Two sheets. (a) 102×128 mm. $6 Characters in balloon basket, 1966. (b) 128×102 mm. $6 Characters in national costumes, 1966 *Set of 2 sheets* 9·00 9·50

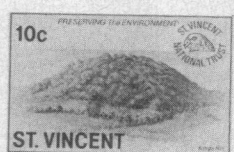

229 Kings Hill

(Litho Questa)

1992 (17 Feb). *Preserving the Environment. T **229** and similar horiz designs. Multicoloured. P 14.*

1854	10 c. Type **229**		20	20
1855	55 c. Planting sapling		50	45
1856	75 c. Doric Temple, Botanic Gardens		60	65
1857	$2 18th-century map of Kings Hill		1·40	2·00
1854/7		*Set of 4*	2·40	3·00

(Des D. Miller. Litho Questa)

1992 (2 Mar). *40th Anniv of Queen Elizabeth II's Accession. Horiz designs as T **214** of Lesotho. Multicoloured. P 14.*

1858	10 c. Kingstown from the cliffs		20	15
1859	20 c. Deep water wharf, Kingstown		35	15
1860	$1 Residential suburb, Kingstown		60	60
1861	$5 Kingstown from the interior		2·75	3·25
1858/61		*Set of 4*	3·50	3·75

MS1862 Two sheets, each 75×92 mm. (a) $6 Deep water wharf (different). (b) $6 Beach *Set of 2 sheets* 7·50 8·00

Two different $5 designs and two $10 miniature sheets, all embossed on gold foil, also exist from a limited printing.

230 Women's Luge

(Litho Questa)

1992 (21 Apr). *Winter Olympic Games, Albertville (1st issue). T **230** and similar multicoloured designs. P 14.*

1863	10 c. Type **230**		15	15
1864	15 c. Women's figure skating (vert)		20	20
1865	25 c. Two-man bobsleigh		25	25
1866	30 c. Mogul skiing (vert)		30	30
1867	45 c. Nordic combination		40	40
1868	55 c. Ski jump		55	55
1869	75 c. Men's giant slalom		65	65
1870	$1.50, Women's slalom (vert)		1·10	1·10
1871	$5 Ice hockey		3·25	3·50
1872	$8 Biathlon (vert)		4·25	4·50
1863/72		*Set of 10*	10·00	10·50

MS1873 Two sheets, each 100×70 mm. (a) $6 Women's speed skating (vert). (b) $6 Men's downhill skiing (vert). *Set of 2 sheets* 9·50 11·00

See also Nos. 1966/80.

231 Women's Synchronized
Swimming

(Litho Questa)

1992 (21 Apr). *Olympic Games, Barcelona. T **231** and similar multicoloured designs.* P 14.

1874	10 c. Type **231**	..	..	20	20
1875	15 c. Men's high jump (*vert*)		..	20	20
1876	25 c. Men's small-bore rifle shooting			30	20
1877	30 c. Men's 200 metres (*vert*)			30	20
1878	45 c. Men's judo (*vert*)		..	35	25
1879	55 c. Men's 200 metres freestyle swimming			40	30
1880	75 c. Men's javelin (*vert*)		..	50	50
1881	$1.50, Men's 4000 metre pursuit cycling (*vert*)			2·00	1·50
1882	$5 Boxing (*vert*)		..	2·50	3·25
1883	$8 Women's basketball (*vert*)			7·00	7·50
1874/83			*Set of 10*	12·00	12·50

MS1884 Two sheets, each 100×70 mm. (a) $15 Sailboarding (*vert*). (b) $15 Men's singles tennis (*vert*) .. .. .. *Set of 2 sheets* 17·00 17·00

(Des Walt Disney Co. Litho Questa)

1992 (28 Apr). *International Stamp Exhibitions. Multicoloured designs as T **215** of Lesotho showing Walt Disney cartoon characters.*

(a) *"Granada '92" Spain. The Three Pigs in Spanish Uniforms.* P 13½×14

1885	15 c. The Wolf as General of Spanish Moors		20	10
1886	40 c. Pig as Captain of Infantry	..	40	25
1887	$2 Pig as Halberdier	..	1·25	1·50
1888	$4 Pig as Nobleman	..	2·25	2·75
1885/8		*Set of 4*	3·50	4·00

MS1889 128×102 mm. $6 Nobleman at castle window .. .. 3·00 3·75

(b) *"World Columbian Stamp Expo '92". Chicago Landmarks.* P 14½×13½

1890	10 c. Mickey Mouse and Goofy looking at Picasso sculpture (*horiz*)	20	15
1891	50 c. Mickey and Donald Duck admiring Robie House (*horiz*)	45	35
1892	$1 Calder sculpture in Sears Tower (*horiz*)	80	60
1893	$5 Goofy in Buckingham Memorial Fountain (*horiz*)	2·50	2·75
1890/3	*Set of 4*	3·50	3·50

MS1894 128×102 mm. $6 Mickey painting Minnie. P 13½×14 .. .. 3·00 3·75

232 Nina

(Des W. Wright. Litho Questa)

1992 (22 May). *500th Anniv of Discovery of America by Columbus (6th issue). "World Columbian Stamp Expo '92", Chicago. T **232** and similar multicoloured designs.* P 14.

1895	5 c. Type **232**	..	..	40	40
1896	10 c. *Pinta*		..	40	30
1897	45 c. *Santa Maria*		..	75	50
1898	55 c. Fleet leaving Palos, 1492			75	55
1899	$4 Christopher Columbus (*vert*)			3·00	3·50
1900	$5 Arms of Columbus (*vert*)			3·00	3·50
1895/1900			*Set of 6*	7·50	8·00

MS1901 Two sheets, each 115×86 mm. (a) $6 *Santa Maria* sighting land (42½×57 *mm*). (b) $6 Route of voyage (42½×57 *mm*) .. *Set of 2 sheets* 8·50 9·50

 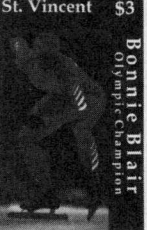

233 Elvis looking Pensive   **234** Bonnie Blair

(Des J. Iskowitz. Litho Questa)

1992 (25 May). *15th Death Anniv of Elvis Presley (1st issue). T **233** and similar vert designs. Multicoloured.* P 13½×14.

1902	$1 Type **233**	..	..	1·00	1·00
	a. Sheetlet. Nos. 1902/10			8·00	
1903	$1 Wearing black and yellow striped shirt			1·00	1·00
1904	$1 Singing into microphone			1·00	1·00
1905	$1 Wearing wide-brimmed hat			1·00	1·00
1906	$1 With microphone in right hand			1·00	1·00
1907	$1 In Army uniform			1·00	1·00
1908	$1 Wearing pink shirt			1·00	1·00

1909	$1 In yellow shirt			1·00	1·00
1910	$1 In jacket and bow tie			1·00	1·00
1902/10			*Set of 9*	8·00	8·00

MS1911 76×107 mm. $6 In blue shirt (28½×42½ *mm*). P 14 .. .. 6·50 7·00
Nos. 1902/10 were printed together, *se-tenant*, in sheetlets of 9.
See also Nos. 2029/37, 2038/46 and 2047/9.

(Des and litho Stamp Venturers, Virginia)

1992 (25 May). *Bonnie Blair's Victories in 500 Metres Speed Skating at Calgary and Albertville Olympic Games. T **234** and similar multicoloured designs.* P 13½.

1912	$3 Type **234**			2·25	2·50

MS1913 185×127 mm. $2 Turning corner (*horiz*); $2 With skates in arms (43×51 *mm*); $2 On straight (*horiz*) .. .. 4·50 4·75

235 *Astraptes anaphus*   **236** *Collybia subpruinosa*

(Des Wendy Smith-Griswold. Litho Questa)

1992 (15 June). *"Genova '92" International Thematic Stamp Exhibition (1st issue). Butterflies. T **235** and similar multicoloured designs.* P 14.

1914	5 c. Type **235**	..	..	30	40
1915	10 c. *Anartia jatrophae* (*horiz*)			30	20
1916	35 c. *Danaus eresimus*	..	..	55	40
1917	45 c. *Battus polydamus*	..	..	60	45
1918	55 c. *Junonia evarete* (*horiz*)			70	50
1919	65 c. *Urbanus proteus*	..	..	80	60
1920	75 c. *Pyrgus oileus* (*horiz*)			90	65
1921	$1 *Biblis hyperia*	..	..	1·00	75
1922	$2 *Eurema daira*	..	..	1·50	1·50
1923	$3 *Leptotes cassius* (*horiz*)			1·75	2·00
1924	$4 *Ephyriades brunnea* (*horiz*)			2·25	2·50
1925	$5 *Victorina stelenes*	..	..	3·00	2·50
1914/25			*Set of 12*	12·00	11·50

MS1926 Three sheets, each 98×72 mm. (a) $6 *Phoebis sennae*. (b) $6 *Heliconius charitonius* (*horiz*). (c) $6 *Dryas julia* (*horiz*) *Set of 3 sheets* 12·00 13·00
See also Nos. 1940/52.

(Des R. Sauber. Litho Questa)

1992 (2 July). *Fungi. T **236** and similar vert designs. Multicoloured.* P 14.

1927	10 c. Type **236**	..	..	30	20
1928	15 c. *Gerronema citrinum*		..	40	20
1929	20 c. *Amanita antillana*		..	45	30
1930	45 c. *Dermoloma atrobrunneum*			60	35
1931	50 c. *Inopilus maculosus*		..	70	40
1932	65 c. *Pulveroboletus brachyspermus*			80	55
1933	75 c. *Mycena violacella*		..	90	60
1934	$1 *Xerocomus brasiliensis*			1·00	70
1935	$2 *Amanita ingrata*			1·50	1·75
1936	$3 *Leptonia caeruleocapitata*			1·75	2·25
1937	$4 *Limacella myochroa*			2·25	2·75
1938	$5 *Inopilus magnificus*			2·50	2·75
1927/38			*Set of 12*	12·00	11·50

MS1939 Three sheets, each 101×68 mm. (a) $6 *Limacella guttata*. (b) $6 *Amanita agglutinata*. (c) $6 *Trogia buccinalis* .. .. *Set of 3 sheets* 11·00 12·00
No. 1936 is inscribed "*Leptonia caeruleocaptata*" in error.

237 Rufous-breasted Hermit   **238** Coral Vine

(Des Mary Walters. Litho Questa)

1992 (2 July). *"Genova '92" International Thematic Stamp Exhibition (2nd issue). Hummingbirds. T **237** and similar vert designs. Multicoloured.* P 14.

1940	5 c. Type **237**	..	..	30	40
1941	15 c. Hispaniolan Emerald		..	35	20
1942	45 c. Green-throated Carib		..	60	35
1943	55 c. Jamaican Mango		..	70	45
1944	65 c. Vervain Hummingbird			80	60
1945	75 c. Purple-throated Carib			90	70
1946	90 c. Green Mango		..	90	75
1947	$1 Bee Hummingbird		..	1·00	80
1948	$2 Cuban Emerald		..	1·75	1·75
1949	$3 Puerto Rican Emerald			1·90	2·00
1950	$4 Antillean Mango		..	2·40	2·75
1951	$5 Streamertail		..	3·00	2·75
1940/51			*Set of 12*	13·00	12·00

MS1952 Three sheets, each 98×67 mm. (a) $6 Bahama Woodstar. (b) $6 Antillean Crested Hummingbird. (c) $6 Blue-headed Hummingbird .. .. *Set of 3 sheets* 13·00 14·00

(Des Dot Barlowe. Litho B.D.T.)

1992 (22 July). *Medicinal Plants. T **238** and similar vert designs. Multicoloured.* P 14.

1953	75 c. Type **238**	..	..	70	70
	a. Sheetlet. Nos. 1953/64			7·50	
1954	75 c. Cocoplum		..	70	70
1955	75 c. Angel's Trumpet		..	70	70
1956	75 c. Lime		..	70	70
1957	75 c. White Ginger		..	70	70
1958	75 c. Pussley		..	70	70
1959	75 c. Sea Grape		..	70	70
1960	75 c. Indian Mulberry		..	70	70
1961	75 c. Plantain		..	70	70
1962	75 c. Lignum Vitae		..	70	70
1963	75 c. Periwinkle		..	70	70
1964	75 c. Guava		..	70	70
1953/64			*Set of 12*	7·50	7·50

MS1965 Three sheets, each 98×69 mm. (a) $6 Wild Sage. (b) $6 Clove Tree. (c) $6 Aloe .. .. *Set of 3 sheets* 10·50 11·00
Nos. 1953/64 were printed together, *se-tenant*, in sheetlets of 12.

239 Kristi Yamaguchi
(U.S.A.) (figure skating)

(Des J. Puvilland. Litho Questa)

1992 (10 Aug). *Winter Olympic Games, Albertville (2nd issue). Gold Medal Winners. T **239** and similar vert designs. Multicoloured.* P 14.

1966	$1 Type **239**	..	..	80	80
	a. Sheetlet. Nos. 1966/72			5·00	
1967	$1 Pernilla Wiberg (Sweden) (giant slalom skiing)			80	80
1968	$1 Lyubov Yegorova (C.I.S.) (10 kms cross-country skiing)			80	80
1969	$1 Josef Polig (Italy) (combined alpine skiing)			80	80
1970	$1 Fin Christian-Jagge (Norway) (slalom skiing)			80	80
1971	$1 Kerrin Lee-Gartner (Canada) (downhill skiing)			80	80
1972	$1 Steffania Belmondo (Italy) (30 kms cross-country skiing)			80	80
1973	$1 Alberto Tomba (Italy) (giant slalom skiing)			80	80
	a. Sheetlet. Nos. 1973/9			5·00	
1974	$1 Fabrice Guy (France) (nordic combined skiing)			80	80
1975	$1 Patrick Ortlieb (Austria) (downhill skiing)			80	80
1976	$1 Vegard Ulvang (Norway) (nordic cross-country skiing)			80	80
1977	$1 Edgar Grospiron (France) (freestyle mogul skiing)			80	80
1978	$1 Andre Aamodt (Norway) (super giant slalom skiing)			80	80
1979	$1 Viktor Petrenko (C.I.S.) (figure skating)			80	80
1966/79			*Set of 14*	10·00	10·00

MS1980 Two sheets. (a) 108×78 mm. $6 Kristi Yamaguchi (U.S.A.) (figure skating) (*different*). (b) 111×81 mm. $6 Alberto Tomba (Italy) (giant slalom skiing) (*different*) .. *Set of 2 sheets* 8·50 9·50
Nos. 1966/72 and 1973/9 were each printed together, *se-tenant*, in sheetlets of 7 stamps and 1 stamp-size label.
No. 1968 is inscribed "LYUBOV EGOROVA" in error.

(Des F. Paul ($1), J. Esquino ($2). Litho Questa)

1992 (24 Aug). *500th Anniv of Discovery of America by Columbus (7th issue). Organization of East Caribbean States. Vert designs as Nos. 911/12 of Montserrat. Multicoloured.* P 14½.

1981	$1 Columbus meeting Amerindians		..	1·00	75
1982	$2 Ships approaching island		..	1·75	2·00

240 Pinocchio

(Des Euro-Disney, Paris. Litho Cartor.)

1992 (11 Sept). *Opening of Euro-Disney Resort, Paris. T **240** and similar multicoloured designs.* P 13.

1983	$1 Type **240**	..	..	1·00	1·00
	a. Sheetlet. Nos. 1983/8	..		5·50	
1984	$1 Alice in Wonderland	..	..	1·00	1·00

1985	$1 *Bambi*	1·00	1·00
1986	$1 *Cinderella*	1·00	1·00
1987	$1 *Snow White and the Seven Dwarfs*	1·00	1·00
1988	$1 *Peter Pan*	1·00	1·00
1983/8		Set of 6 5·50	5·50

MS1989 187×101 mm. $5 Mickey Mouse (56×76 mm). P 12½ .. .. 4·50 5·00
Nos. 1983/8 were printed together, *se-tenant*, in sheetlets of 6.

(Des Kerri Schiff. Litho Questa)

1992 (28 Oct). *Postage Stamp Mega Event, New York.*
Multicoloured design as T 219 *of Lesotho. Sheet* 100×70 mm.
P 14.
MS1990 $6 Jacob K. Javits Convention Centre
(*horiz*) .. .. 4·25 5·00
No. MS1990 is inscribed "Jaritts" in error.

241 Spanish Galleon and
Paddle-steamer

(Litho Questa)

1992 (28 Oct). *First use of Adhesive Stamps on Trans-Atlantic
Mail, 1840, Commemoration. Sheet* 100×70 mm. P 14.
MS1991 **241** $6 multicoloured .. .. 5·50 6·00

(Litho Questa)

1992 (16 Nov). *Christmas. Religious Paintings. Vert designs
as* T 218 *of Lesotho. Multicoloured.* P 13½×14.

1992	10 c.	"Hospitality refused to the Virgin Mary and Joseph" (detail) (Metsys)	20	20
1993	40 c.	"The Nativity" (detail) (Dürer)	40	30
1994	45 c.	"The Nativity" (Geertgen Tot Sint Jans)	40	30
1995	50 c.	"The Nativity" (Jacopo Tintoretto)	50	35
1996	55 c.	"The Nativity" (detail) (Follower of Calcar)	50	35
1997	65 c.	"The Nativity" (Workshop of Fra Angelico)	60	50
1998	75 c.	"The Nativity" (Master of the Louvre Nativity)	65	50
1999	$1	"The Nativity" (detail) (Lippi)	80	75
2000	$2	"The Nativity" (Petrus Christus)	1·50	1·50
2001	$3	"The Nativity" (detail) (Edward Burne-Jones)	2·00	2·25
2002	$4	"The Nativity" (detail) (Giotto)	2·50	2·75
2003	$5	"Birth of Christ" (detail) (Domenico Ghirlandaio)	2·75	3·00
1992/2003		Set of 12	11·50	11·50

MS2004 Three sheets, each 72×99 mm. (a) $6
"Birth of Christ" (detail) (Gerard Horenbout). (b)
$6 "The Nativity" (detail) (Botticelli). (c) $6 "The
Nativity" (detail) (Jean Fouquet) *Set of 3 sheets* 12·00 13·00

242 Gaston

(Des Rosemary DeFiglio and Walt Disney Co. Litho Questa)

1992 (15 Dec). *Walt Disney's Beauty and the Beast* (*cartoon
film*). T 242 *and similar multicoloured designs.* P 14×13½
(*horiz*) *or* 13½×14 (*vert*).

2005	2 c.	Type 242	20	20
2006	3 c.	Belle and her father, Maurice	20	20
2007	5 c.	Lumiere, Mrs. Potts and Cogsworth	25	25
2008	10 c.	Philippe	25	25
2009	15 c.	Beast and Lumiere	25	25
2010	20 c.	Lumiere and Feather Duster	25	25
2011	60 c.	Belle and Gaston	50	50
		a. Sheetlet. Nos. 2011/19	4·00	
2012	60 c.	Maurice	50	50
2013	60 c.	The Beast	50	50
2014	60 c.	Mrs. Potts	50	50
2015	60 c.	Belle and enchanted vase	50	50
2016	60 c.	Belle discovers enchanted rose	50	50
2017	60 c.	Belle with wounded Beast	50	50
2018	60 c.	Belle	50	50
2019	60 c.	Household objects alarmed	50	50
2020	60 c.	Belle and Chip (*vert*)	50	50
		a. Sheetlet. Nos. 2020/7	3·50	
2021	60 c.	Lumiere (*vert*)	50	50
2022	60 c.	Cogsworth (*vert*)	50	50
2023	60 c.	Armoire (*vert*)	50	50
2024	60 c.	Belle and Beast (*vert*)	50	50
2025	60 c.	Feather Duster (*vert*)	50	50
2026	60 c.	Footstool (*vert*)	50	50
2027	60 c.	Belle sitting on stone (*vert*)	50	50
2005/27		Set of 23	9·00	9·00

MS2028 Five sheets, each 127×103 mm. (a) $6
Lumiere (*vert*). (b) 127×103 mm. $6 Belle
reading book (*vert*). (c) 127×103 mm. $6 The
Beast (*vert*). (d) 127×103 mm. $6 Belle dancing
(*vert*). (e) 103×127 mm. $6 Lumiere, Chip and
Mrs. Potts .. .. *Set of 5 sheets* 18·00 19·00
Nos. 2011/19 and 2020/7 were each printed together, *se-tenant*,
in sheetlets of 9 (Nos. 2011/19) or 8 (Nos. 2020/7).

	15th Anniversary	15th Anniversary Elvis Presley's Death August 16, 1977
	(243)	(244)

1992 (15 Dec). *15th Death Anniv of Elvis Presley* (2nd issue).
Nos. 1902/10 *optd with* T 243.

2029	$1	Type 233	1·00	1·00
		a. Sheetlet. Nos. 2029/37	8·00	
2030	$1	Wearing black and yellow striped shirt	1·00	1·00
2031	$1	Singing into microphone	1·00	1·00
2032	$1	Wearing wide-brimmed hat	1·00	1·00
2033	$1	With microphone in right hand	1·00	1·00
2034	$1	In Army uniform	1·00	1·00
2035	$1	Wearing pink shirt	1·00	1·00
2036	$1	In yellow shirt	1·00	1·00
2037	$1	In jacket and bow tie	1·00	1·00
2029/37		Set of 9	8·00	8·00

1992 (15 Dec). *15th Death Anniv of Elvis Presley* (3rd issue).
Nos. 1820/7 *and* MS1828b *optd as* T 244.

2038	$2	Michael Jackson	1·90	1·90
		a. Sheetlet. Nos. 2038/45	13·50	
2039	$2	Madonna	1·90	1·90
2040	$2	Elvis Presley	1·90	1·90
2041	$2	David Bowie	1·90	1·90
2042	$2	Prince	1·90	1·90
2043	$2	Frank Sinatra	1·90	1·90
2044	$2	George Michael	1·90	1·90
2045	$2	Mick Jagger	1·90	1·90
2038/45		Set of 8	13·50	13·50

MS2046 110×82 mm. $6 Elvis Presley (29×43
mm) .. .. 8·00 8·00
No. MS2046 is overprinted on the sheet margin.

(Des A. Nahigian. Litho Walsall)

1992 (15 Dec). *15th Death Anniv of Elvis Presley* (4th issue).
Vert designs as Nos. 1768/70 *of Maldive Islands.
Multicoloured.* P 14.

2047	$1	Elvis Presley	1·75	1·75
		a. Strip of 3. Nos. 2047/9	4·75	
2048	$1	Elvis with guitar	1·75	1·75
2049	$1	Elvis with microphone	1·75	1·75
2047/9		Set of 3	4·75	4·75

Nos. 2047/9 were printed together, *se-tenant*, horizontally and vertically
se-tenant, in sheetlets of 9 (3×3).

245 Fifer Pig building House of
Straw

(Des Rosemary DeFiglio and Walt Disney Co. Litho Questa)

1992 (15 Dec). *Walt Disney Cartoon Films.* T 245 *and similar
multicoloured designs.* P 14×13½ (*horiz*) *or* 13½×14 (*vert*).
2050/2138 60 c. × 89 multicoloured .. *Set of 89* 27·00 30·00
MS2139 Twenty sheets, each 128×103 mm or
103×128 mm. $6×20 multicoloured
Set of 20 sheets 60·00 70·00
Nos. 2050/2138 were printed as ten *se-tenant* sheetlets, each
of nine different designs except for that for *Darkwing Duck*
which contains eight vertical designs (Nos. 2131/8). The other
nine sheetlets depict scenes from *The Three Little Pigs, Thru the
Mirror, Clock Cleaners, Orphans Benefit, The Art of Skiing,
Symphony Hour, How to Play Football, The Small One and Chip
N'Dale Rescue Rangers.*
No. MS2139 contains two sheets for each film, one sheet for
The Three Little Pigs being in a vertical format. The stamp
designs for *The Three Little Pigs* (horizontal sheet), *How to
Play Football* (one), *Chip N'Dale Rescue Rangers* (both) and
Darkwing Duck (both) are vertical.
For Nos. 2050/8 and MS2139a/b (*The Three Little Pigs*) with
different face values see Nos. 2852/61.

ST. VINCENT
AND THE GRENADINES

$2

246 Scottie Pippen

247 Tom Seaver

(Des J. Genzo. Litho Questa)

1992 (15 Dec). *Olympic Gold Medal Winners, Barcelona.* T 246
*and similar horiz designs showing members of U.S.A.
basketball team. Multicoloured.* P 14.

2140	$2	Type 246	1·25	1·25
		a. Sheetlet. Nos. 2140/5	6·50	
2141	$2	Earvin "Magic" Johnson	1·25	1·25
2142	$2	Larry Bird	1·25	1·25
2143	$2	Christian Laettner	1·25	1·25
2144	$2	Karl Malone	1·25	1·25
2145	$2	David Robinson	1·25	1·25
2146	$2	Michael Jordan	1·25	1·25
		a. Sheetlet. Nos. 2146/51	6·50	

2147	$2	Charles Barkley	1·25	1·25
2148	$2	John Stockton	1·25	1·25
2149	$2	Chris Mullin	1·25	1·25
2150	$2	Clyde Drexler	1·25	1·25
2151	$2	Patrick Ewing	1·25	1·25
2140/51		Set of 12	13·00	13·00

Nos. 2140/5 and 2146/51 were each printed together,
se-tenant, in sheetlets of 6.

(Des W. Storozuk. Litho Questa)

1992 (21 Dec). *Famous Baseball Players* (5th issue). T 247 *and
similar vert designs. Multicoloured.* P 14.

2152	$2	Type 247	1·40	1·40
2153	$2	Roberto Clemente	1·40	1·40
2154	$2	Hank Aaron	1·40	1·40
2152/4		Set of 3	3·50	3·50

248 Don Mattingly   **249** Earth and U.N. Emblem

(Des J. Iskowitz. Litho Questa)

1992 (21 Dec). *Famous Baseball Players* (6th issue). T 248 *and
similar vert design. Multicoloured.* P 14.

2155	$5	Type 248	3·00	3·50
2156	$5	Howard Johnson	3·00	3·50

(Des W. Wright and L. Fried (Nos. 2157, 2167), W. Wright and
W. Hanson (Nos. 2158, 2170, MS2171a), W. Wright (others).
Litho Questa)

1992 (22 Dec). *Anniversaries and Events.* T 249 *and similar
multicoloured designs.* P 14.

2157	10 c.	Type 249	30	20
2158	45 c.	Airship LZ-11 *Viktoria Luise* over Kiel Regatta, 1912 (*vert*)	60	25
2159	75 c.	Adenauer and German flag	60	50
2160	75 c.	Trophy and Bill Koch (skipper) of *America III*, 1992	60	50
2161	$1	Konrad Adenauer	60	50
2162	$1	Snow Leopard and emblem	1·00	50
2163	$1.50,	Caribbean Manatee	1·25	1·25
2164	$2	Humpback Whale	2·50	2·25
2165	$3	Adenauer and Pres. Kennedy, 1962	1·60	1·60
2166	$3	Doctor checking patient's eye	2·25	2·25
2167	$4	*Discovery* space shuttle (*vert*)	3·00	3·00
2168	$4	Adenauer and Pope John XXIII, 1960	3·00	3·00
2169	$5	Schumacher and racing car	3·50	3·75
2170	$6	Zeppelin LZ-1 over Lake Constance, 1900	3·75	4·00
2157/70		Set of 14	21·00	21·00

MS2171 Five sheets. (a) 70×100 mm. $6 Cabin of
airship LZ-127 *Graf Zeppelin*. (b) 70×100 mm.
$6 Douglas DC-6 airplane from Berlin Airlift. (c)
100×70 mm. $6 Konrad Adenauer making
speech. (d) 70×100 mm. $6 Woolly Spider
Monkey. (e) 119×89 mm. $6 Schumacher
winning race .. .. *Set of 5 sheets* 18·00 19·00
Anniversaries and Events:—Nos. 2157, 2167, International
Space Year; Nos. 2158, 2170, MS2171a, 75th death anniv of
Count Ferdinand von Zeppelin; Nos. 2159, 2161, 2165, 2168,
MS2171b/c, 25th death anniv of Konrad Adenauer (German
statesman); No. 2160, Americas Cup Yachting Championship;
Nos. 2162/4, MS2171d, Earth Summit '92, Rio; No. 2166, 75th
anniv of International Association of Lions Clubs; No. 2169,
MS2171e, Michael Schumacher's Victory in 1992 Belgium
Grand Prix.

(Des T.C.F.C. Inc. Litho Questa)

1992 (28 Dec). *Ecology. Multicoloured designs as* T 71 *of St.
Kitts-Nevis* (Nevis). P 14.
2172 75 c. Care Bear and American White
Pelican 70 55
MS2173 101×72 mm. $2 Care Bear in hot air
balloon (*horiz*) .. .. 1·40 1·75

250 Farmer, Fisherman and
Emblem

(Litho Questa)

1993 (4 Feb). *International Conference on Nutrition, Rome.*
P 14.
2174 **250** 65 c. multicoloured 80 70

ALTERED CATALOGUE NUMBERS

Any Catalogue numbers altered from the last
edition are shown as a list in the introductory
pages.

251 Coastal Village

(Litho Questa)

1993 (4 Feb). *"Uniting the Windward Islands". T* **251** *and similar horiz designs. Multicoloured. P* 14.

2175	10 c.	Type **251**	40	20
2176	40 c.	Children from different islands	80	60
2177	45 c.	Children and palm tree	80	60
2175/7		*Set of 3*	1·75	1·25

252 Fisherman holding Catch   **253** Brown Pelican

(Litho Questa)

1993 (4 Feb). *Fishing. T* **252** *and similar horiz designs. Multicoloured. P* 14.

2178	5 c.	Type **252**	15	15
2179	10 c.	Fish market	15	15
2180	50 c.	Fishermen landing catch	60	60
2181	$5	Fishing with nets	3·00	3·50
2178/81		*Set of 4*	3·50	4·00

(Des J. Genzo. Litho Questa)

1993 (1 Apr). *Migratory Birds. T* **253** *and similar multicoloured designs. P* 14.

2182	10 c.	Type **253**	40	20
2183	25 c.	Red-necked Grebe (*horiz*)	50	20
2184	45 c.	Belted Kingfisher (*horiz*)	65	30
2185	55 c.	Yellow-bellied Sapsucker	70	30
2186	$1	Great Blue Heron	90	60
2187	$2	Common Black Hawk ("Crab Hawk") (*horiz*)	1·60	1·60
2188	$4	Yellow Warbler	2·50	3·00
2189	$5	Northern Oriole (*horiz*)	2·50	3·00
2182/9		*Set of 8*	8·75	8·25

MS2190 Two sheets, each 100×70 mm. (a) $6 Blue-winged Teal (*horiz*). (b) $6 White Ibis (*horiz*) .. .. .. *Set of 2 sheets* 9·00 10·00

254 Sergeant Major   **255** Hexagonal Muricop (*Muricopsis oxytatus*)

(Des W. Storozuk. Litho Questa)

1993 (13 Apr). *Fishes. T* **254** *and similar multicoloured designs. P* 14.

2191	5 c.	Type **254**	40	30
2192	10 c.	Rainbow Parrotfish	40	20
2193	55 c.	Hogfish	65	30
2194	75 c.	Porkfish	75	40
2195	$1	Spot-finned Butterflyfish	90	60
2196	$2	Buffalo Trunkfish	1·60	1·60
2197	$4	Queen Triggerfish	2·50	3·00
2198	$5	Queen Angelfish	2·50	3·00
2191/8		*Set of 8*	8·75	8·50

MS2199 Two sheets, each 100×70 mm. (a) $6 Bigeye (*vert*). (b) $6 Small-mouthed Grunt (*vert*) .. .. .. *Set of 2 sheets* 7·00 7·50

(Litho Walsall)

1993 (19 Apr). *Bicentenary of the Louvre, Paris. Paintings by various artists. Designs as T* **221** *of Lesotho. P* 12.

2200/39	$1×40 multicoloured	40 21·00	23·00

MS2240 Three sheets, either 70×100 mm or 100×70 mm. $6×3 multicoloured. P 14½ .. .. .. *Set of 3 sheets* 12·00 14·00

Nos. 2200/39 were printed as *se-tenant* sheetlets, each of eight different designs and one centre label. The five sheetlets show paintings by Géricault, Ingres, Le Sueur and Poussin, Poussin, and Boucher, Brueghel, Dumont, Gainsborough, Goya and Van Eyck.

The three sheets of No. **MS**2240 depict paintings by Chassériau (52×85 *mm*), Delacroix and Ingres (both 85×52 *mm*).

(Litho B.D.T.)

1993 (24 May). *Shells. T* **255** *and similar multicoloured designs. P* 14.

2241	10 c.	Type **255**	30	20
2242	15 c.	Caribbean Vase (*Vasum muricatum*)	30	20
2243	30 c.	Measled Cowrie (*Cypraea zebra*)	40	20
2244	45 c.	Dyson's Keyhole Limpet (*Diodora dysoni*)	50	25
2245	50 c.	Atlantic Hairy Triton (*Cymatium pileare martinianum*)	50	40
2246	65 c.	Orange-banded Marginella (*Marginella avena*)	60	45
2247	75 c.	Bleeding Tooth (*Nerita peloronta*)	70	50
2248	$1	Queen or Pink Conch (*Strombus gigas*)	80	65
2249	$2	Hawk-wing Conch (*Strombus raninus*)	1·25	1·40
2250	$3	Music Volute (*Voluta musica*)	1·75	2·00
2251	$4	Alphabet Cone (*Conus spurius*)	2·25	2·75
2252	$5	Antillean or Incomparable Cone (*Conus cedonulli*)	2·25	2·75
2241/52		*Set of 12*	10·50	10·50

MS2253 Three sheets, each 103×76 mm. (a) $6 Wide-mouthed Purpura (*Purpura patula*) (*horiz*). (b) $6 Netted Olive (*Oliva reticularis*) (*horiz*). (c) $6 Flame Auger (*Terebra taurina*) (*horiz*) .. .. .. *Set of 3 sheets* 13·00 14·00

256 Ishihara holding Tennis Racket   **257** *Erynnyis ello*

1993 (24 May). *7th Death Anniv of Yujiro Ihishara (Japanese actor). T* **256** *and similar designs. Litho. P* 13½×14.

2254	55 c.	black, light grey and dull ultramarine	80	80
		a. Sheetlet. Nos. 2254/62	6·50	
2255	55 c.	black, light grey and dull ultramarine	80	80
2256	55 c.	black, light grey and dull ultramarine	80	80
2257	55 c.	multicoloured	80	80
2258	55 c.	multicoloured	80	80
2259	$1	multicoloured	80	80
2260	$1	multicoloured	80	80
2261	$1	multicoloured	80	80
2262	$1	multicoloured	80	80
2254/62		*Set of 9*	6·50	6·50

MS2263 Four sheets, each 180×140 mm. (a) 55 c., $1, $2 × 2 multicoloured. P 14½×14. (b) 55 c. black, light grey and gold; $1 multicoloured; $2 black, light grey and gold; $2 multicoloured. P 13½×14. (c) 55 c., $2, $4, multicoloured. P 14×14½. (d) 55 c., $4 × 2 multicoloured. P 14×14½ .. *Set of 4 sheets* 17·00 19·00

Designs: *Vert* (*as T* **256**)—No. 2255, Ishihara holding camera; No. 2256, In striped shirt; No. 2257, Holding drink and cigarette; No. 2258, On board yacht; No. 2259, In naval uniform; No. 2260, In jacket and tie; No. 2261, Wearing sunglasses; No. 2262, Wearing pink shirt; No. **MS**2263b, 55 c. As No. 2255, $1 In formal suit, $2 In white jacket, $2 With guitar. (28×37 *mm*)—No. **MS**2263a, 55 c. As No. 2259, $1 Laughing, $2 In striped shirt, $2 As No. 2258. *Horiz* (56×37 *mm*)—No. **MS**2263c, 55 c. In yellow shirt with actress, $2 In checked jacket with actress, $4 In bar with actress; No. **MS**2263d, 55 c. With cigarette, $4 As No. 2262, $4 As 2261.

Nos. 2254/62 were printed together, *se-tenant*, in sheetlets of 9.

(Des Kerri Schiff. Litho Questa)

1993 (7 June). *40th Anniv of Coronation. Vert designs as T* **224** *of Lesotho. P* 13½×14.

2264	45 c.	multicoloured	65	75
		a. Sheetlet. Nos. 2264/7×2	8·50	
2265	65 c.	multicoloured	75	85
2266	$2	blackish olive and black	1·40	1·60
2267	$4	multicoloured	1·90	2·00
2264/7		*Set of 4*	4·25	4·75

MS2268 70×100 mm. $6 multicoloured. P 14 4·00 4·25

Designs:—45 c. Queen Elizabeth II at Coronation (photograph by Cecil Beaton); 65 c. Queen Elizabeth opening Parliament; $2 Queen Elizabeth during Coronation; $4 Queen Elizabeth with corgi. (28½×42½ *mm*)—$6 "Queen Elizabeth as a Young Girl" (detail)

Nos. 2264/7 were printed together in sheetlets of 8, containing two *se-tenant* blocks of 4.

(Litho Questa)

1993 (14 June). *Moths. T* **257** *and similar vert designs. Multicoloured. P* 14.

2269	10 c.	Type **257**	20	20
2270	50 c.	*Aellopos tantalus*	55	30
2271	65 c.	*Erynnyis alope*	60	40
2272	75 c.	*Manduca rustica*	70	50
2273	$1	*Xylophanes pluto*	80	65
2274	$2	*Hyles lineata*	1·50	1·75
2275	$4	*Pseudosphinx tetrio*	2·50	2·75
2276	$5	*Protambulyx strigilis*	2·50	2·75
2269/76		*Set of 8*	8·50	8·50

MS2277 Two sheets, each 100×70 mm. (a) $6 *Utetheisa ornatrix*. (b) $6 *Xylophanes tersa* .. .. .. *Set of 2 sheets* 7·50 8·50

---

258 Early Astronomical Quadrant   **259** Supermarine Spitfire

(Des Kerri Schiff (Nos. 2280, 2284, 2292, 2294, **MS**2297c, e). Litho Questa)

1993 (30 June). *Anniversaries and Events. T* **258** *and similar designs. Venetian red and black (Nos. 2281, 2293,* **MS**2297d) *or multicoloured (others). P* 14.

2278	45 c.	Type **258**	40	25
2279	45 c.	"Massacre in Korea" (Picasso) (*horiz*)	40	25
2280	45 c.	Marc Girardelli (Luxembourg) (giant slalom) (*horiz*)	40	25
2281	45 c.	Willy Brandt and Pres. Nixon, 1971 (*horiz*)	40	25
2282	45 c.	Count Johannes and Countess Gloria of Thurn and Taxis	40	25
2283	65 c.	Count and Countess of Thurn and Taxis with children (*horiz*)	60	40
2284	65 c.	Masako Owada and engagement photographs (*horiz*)	60	40
2285	$1	"Family of Saltimbanques" (Picasso) (*horiz*)	60	50
2286	$1	Princess Stephanie of Monaco	60	60
2287	$1	"Deux Tetes" (left detail) (S. Witkiewicz)	80	80
		a. Horiz pair. Nos. 2287 and 2289	2·10	2·10
2288	$2	Countess Gloria of Thurn & Taxis	1·25	1·25
2289	$3	"Deux Tetes" (right detail) (S. Witkiewicz)	1·50	1·50
2290	$4	Launch of American space shuttle	2·25	2·25
2291	$4	"La Joie de Vivre" (Picasso) (*horiz*)	2·25	2·25
2292	$5	Paul Accola (Switzerland) (downhill skiing) (*horiz*)	2·75	2·75
2293	$5	Willy Brandt and Robert F. Kennedy, 1967 (*horiz*)	2·75	2·75
2294	$5	Prince Naruhito in traditional dress and engagement photographs (*horiz*)	2·75	2·75
2295	$5	Pres. Clinton with school children (*horiz*)	2·75	2·75
2296	$6	Bogusz Church, Gozlin (*horiz*)	3·00	3·00
2278/96		*Set of 19*	24·00	23·00

MS2297 Seven sheets. (a) 110×76 mm. $5 Copernicus. (b) 110×76 mm. $6 "Woman eating a Melon and Boy writing" (detail) (Picasso). (c) 110×76 mm. $6 Thommy Moe (U.S.A.) (downhill skiing). (d) 110×76 mm. $6 Willy Brandt at signing of Common Declaration, 1973 (*horiz*). (e) 110×76 mm. $6 Masako Owada. (f 76×110 mm. $6 "Dancing" (detail) (Wladyslaw Roguski). (g) 76×110 mm. $6 Pres. Clinton wearing stetson .. .. .. *Set of 7 sheets* 24·00 25·00

Anniversaries and Events:—Nos. 2278, 2290, **MS**2297a, 450th death anniv of Copernicus (astronomer); Nos. 2279, 2285, 2291, **MS**2297b, 20th death anniv of Picasso (artist); Nos. 2280, 2292, **MS**2297c, Winter Olympic Games '94, Lillehammer; Nos. 2281, 2293, **MS**2297d, 80th birth anniv of Willy Brandt (German politician); Nos. 2282/3, 2288, 500th anniv of Thurn and Taxis postal service (1990); Nos. 2284, 2294, **MS**2297e, Marriage of Crown Prince Naruhito of Japan; No. 2286, Marriage of Princess Stephanie of Monaco; Nos. 2287, 2289, 2296, **MS**2297f, "Polska '93" International Stamp Exhibition, Poznań; Nos. 2295, **MS**2297g, Inauguration of U.S. President William Clinton.

Nos. 2287 and 2289 were printed together, *se-tenant*, in horizontal pairs throughout the sheet.

(Litho Questa)

1993 (30 June). *Aviation Anniversaries. T* **259** *and similar multicoloured designs. P* 14.

2298	50 c.	Type **259**	45	30
2299	$1	Eckener, and airship LZ-127 *Graf Zeppelin* over Egypt, 1931	80	65
2300	$1	Blanchard and Pres. Washington with balloon, 1793	80	65
2301	$2	De Havilland D.H.98 Mosquito Mk VI	1·40	1·50
2302	$2	Eckener and airship LZ-127 *Graf Zeppelin* over New York, 1928	1·40	1·50
2303	$3	Eckener and airship LZ-127 *Graf Zeppelin* over Tokyo, 1929	2·25	2·50
2304	$4	Blanchard's balloon ascending from Walnut St Prison, Philadelphia	2·25	2·50
2298/304		*Set of 7*	8·50	8·75

MS2305 Three sheets, each 100×70 mm. (a) $6 Hawker Hurricane Mk I. (b) $6 Dr. Hugo Eckener (*vert*). (c) $6 Blanchard's balloon (*vert*) .. .. .. *Set of 3 sheets* 10·50 11·00

Anniversaries:—Nos. 2298, 2301, **MS**2305a, 75th anniv of Royal Air Force; Nos. 2299, 2302/3, **MS**2305b, 125th birth anniv of Hugo Eckener (airship commander); Nos. 2300, 2304, **MS**2305c, Bicent of first airmail flight.

No. 2303 is inscribed "Toyko" in error.

PRICES OF SETS

Set prices are given for many issues, generally those containing three stamps or more. Definitive sets include one of each value or major colour change, but do not cover different perforations, die types or minor shades. Where a choice is possible the set prices are based on the cheapest versions of the stamps included in the listings.

260 First Ford Car, Model "T" and "V8"

261 Pope John Paul II and Denver Skyline

(Litho Questa)

1993 (29 July). *Centenaries of Henry Ford's First Petrol Engine (Nos. 2306, 2309, MS2310a) and Karl Benz's First Four-wheeled Car (others). T 260 and similar vert designs. Multicoloured. P 14.*

2306	$1 Type **260**	..	90	60
2307	$2 Benz racing car, 1908, "Stuttgart" and "540K"		1·75	1·60
2308	$3 Benz car, 1894, "Tourenwagen" and "Blitzen Benz"		2·25	2·50
2309	$4 Ford "Runabout", 1903, Model "T" Tourer and saloon, 1935		2·50	2·75
2306/9		*Set of 4*	6·75	6·75
MS2310	Two sheets, each 100×70 mm. (a) $6 Henry Ford. (b) $6 Karl Benz .. *Set of 2 sheets*		8·50	9·00

(Des and litho Questa)

1993 (13 Aug). *Papal Visit to Denver, Colorado, U.S.A. T 261 and similar horiz design. Multicoloured. P 14.*

2311	$1 Type **261**	..	80	60
MS2312	100×70 mm. $6 Pope and clock tower		4·25	4·75

No. 2311 was issued in small sheets of 9 with commemorative inscriptions on the margins.

262 Corvette of 1953

(Des J. Gordon. Litho Questa)

1993 (13 Aug). *40th Anniv of Corvette Range of Cars. T 262 and similar horiz designs. Multicoloured. P 14×13½.*

2313	$1 Type **262**	..	80	80
	a. Sheetlet. Nos. 2313/24		8·50	
2314	$1 1993 model	..	80	80
2315	$1 1958 model	..	80	80
2316	$1 1960 model	..	80	80
2317	$1 "40" and symbolic chequered flag emblem	..	80	80
2318	$1 1961 model	..	80	80
2319	$1 1963 model	..	80	80
2320	$1 1968 model	..	80	80
2321	$1 1973 model	..	80	80
2322	$1 1975 model	..	80	80
2323	$1 1982 model	..	80	80
2324	$1 1984 model	..	80	80
2313/24		*Set of 12*	8·50	8·50

Nos. 2313/24 were printed together, *se-tenant*, in sheetlets of 12.

263 Gedung Shrine, 1920

(Des Kerri Schiff. Litho Questa)

1993 (16 Aug). *Asian International Stamp Exhibitions. T 263 and similar multicoloured designs.*

(a) *"Indopex '93", Surabaya, Indonesia. P 14×13½*

2325/54	5, 10, 20, 45, 55, 75 c., $1×2, $1.50×18, $2, $4, $5×2 ..	*Set of 30*	23·00 24·00
MS2355	Three sheets. (a) 105×135 mm. $6 Relief of Sudamala epic, Mt Lawu. P 14×13½. (b) 105×135 mm. $6 Plaque from Banyumas, Java. P 14×13½. (c) 135×105 mm. $6 Panel from Ramayana reliefs (*vert*). P 13½×14		
		Set of 3 sheets	11·00 12·00

Nos. 2325/32 and 2351/4 show Indonesian scenes. Nos. 2333/50 were printed in three *se-tenant* sheetlets of 6 showing masks (Nos. 2333/8) or paintings (Nos. 2339/50).

(b) *"Taipei '93", Taiwan. P 14×13½*

2356/85	5, 10, 20, 45, 55, 75 c., $1×2, $1.50×18, $2, $4, $5×2 ..	*Set of 30*	23·00 24·00

MS2386 Three sheets, each 135×105 mm. (a) $6 Two Stone Guardians, Longmen Caves, Henan. P 14×13½. (b) $6 Stone Guardian, Longmen Caves, Henan (*vert*). P 13½×14. (c) $6 Giant Buddha, Yungang Caves (*vert*). P 13½×14

Set of 3 sheets 11·00 12·00

Nos. 2356/63 and 2382/5 show Chinese scenes. Nos. 2364/81 were printed in three *se-tenant* sheetlets of 6 showing kites (Nos. 2364/9) or paintings (Nos. 2370/81).

The "St" of "St. Vincent" is omitted from the bottom left stamp, inscribed "Nezha Stirs Up the Sea", on all examples of one of the sheetlets of six.

(c) *"Bangkok '93", Thailand. P 13½×14 (5, 55 c., $2, $4) or 14×13½ (others)*

2387/416	5, 10, 20, 45, 55, 75 c., $1×2, $1.50×18, $2, $4, $5×2 ..	*Set of 30*	22·00 23·00
MS2417	Three sheets, each 105×135 mm. (a) $6 Masked dancer. P 14×13½. (b) $6 Standing Buddha, Hua Hin (*vert*). P 13½×14. (c) $6 Carved roof boss, Dusit Mahaprasad (*vert*). P 13½×14		
		Set of 3 sheets	11·00 12·00

Nos. 2387/94 and 2413/16 show Thai scenes with the 5, 55 c., $2 and $4 being vertical. Nos. 2395/412 were printed in three *se-tenant* sheetlets of 6 showing murals from Buddhaisawan Chapel (Nos. 2395/400), paintings (Nos. 2401/6) or sculptures (Nos. 2407/12).

264 Players from St. Vincent and Mexico

(Litho Questa)

1993 (2 Sept). *Qualifying Rounds for World Cup Football Championship, U.S.A. T 264 and similar horiz designs showing different matches. Multicoloured. P 14.*

2418	5 c. Type **264**	..	15	20
2419	10 c. Honduras	..	15	15
2420	65 c. Costa Rica	..	55	35
2421	$5 St. Vincent goalkeeper	..	3·25	4·00
2418/21		*Set of 4*	3·50	4·25

265 Fish Delivery Van

(Litho Questa)

1993 (2 Sept). *Japanese Aid for Fishing Industry. T 265 and similar multicoloured designs. P 14.*

2422	10 c. Type **265**	..	20	10
2423	50 c. Fish aggregation device (*vert*)	..	45	30
2424	75 c. Game fishing launch	..	60	50
2425	$5 Fish market	..	3·25	4·00
2422/5		*Set of 4*	4·00	4·50

(Des W. Storozuk. Litho Questa)

1993 (4 Oct). *Famous Baseball Players (7th issue). Multicoloured design as T 247. P 14.*

2426	$2 Reggie Jackson	..	1·10	1·10

(Litho Questa)

1993 (18 Nov). *Christmas. Religious Paintings. Designs as T 76 of Nevis (St. Kitts-Nevis). Black, pale lemon and red (Nos. 2427/9, 2434, MS2435a) or multicoloured (others). P 13½×14.*

2427	10 c. "Adoration of the Magi" (detail) (Dürer)		20	10
2428	35 c. "Adoration of the Magi" (different detail) (Dürer)		40	20
2429	40 c. "Adoration of the Magi" (different detail) (Dürer)		45	25
2430	50 c. "Holy Family with Saint Francis" (detail) (Rubens)		55	30
2431	55 c. "Adoration of the Shepherds" (detail) (Rubens)		55	30
2432	65 c. "Adoration of the Shepherds" (different detail) (Rubens)		65	40
2433	$1 "Holy Family" (Rubens)		90	75
2434	$5 "Adoration of the Magi" (different detail) (Dürer)		2·50	3·75
2427/34		*Set of 8*	5·50	5·50
MS2435	Two sheets, each 103×127 mm. (a) $6 "Adoration of the Magi" (different detail) (Dürer) (*horiz*). P 14×13½. (b) $6 "Holy Family with Sts. Elizabeth and John" (detail) (Rubens). P 13½×14			
		Set of 2 sheets	7·50	8·00

267 Barbra Streisand

268 Roy Acuff

(Litho Questa)

1993 (31 Dec). *Barbra Streisand's Grand Garden Concert. P 14.*

2436	**267** $2 multicoloured	..	1·10	1·10

(Des K. Tanner. Litho Questa)

1994 (17 Jan). *Legends of Country Music. T 268 and similar vert designs. Multicoloured. P 14.*

2437	$1 Type **268**	..	65	65
	a. Sheetlet. Nos. 2437/48	..	7·00	
2438	$1 Patsy Cline in pink shirt	..	65	65
2439	$1 Jim Reeves in dinner jacket	..	65	65
2440	$1 Hank Williams in brown jacket	..	65	65
2441	$1 Hank Williams in purple jacket	..	65	65
2442	$1 Roy Acuff with microphone	..	65	65
2443	$1 Patsy Cline wearing white scarf	..	65	65
2444	$1 Jim Reeves with microphone	..	65	65
2445	$1 Jim Reeves in orange jacket	..	65	65
2446	$1 Patsy Cline with microphone	..	65	65
2447	$1 Hank Williams in grey jacket	..	65	65
2448	$1 Roy Acuff in grey jacket	..	65	65
2437/48		*Set of 12*	7·00	7·00

Nos. 2437/48 were printed together, *se-tenant*, in sheetlets of 12.

269 Mobile Library

270 Woman planting Breadfruit

(Litho Cartor)

1994 (24 Jan). *Centenary of Library Service. T 269 and similar horiz designs. Multicoloured. P 14×13½.*

2449	5 c. Type **269**	..	10	20
2450	10 c. Old Public Library building	..	10	10
2451	$1 Family reading	..	65	60
2452	$1 Line of books joining youth and old man	..	65	70
2449/52		*Set of 4*	1·25	1·50

(Litho Cartor)

1994 (24 Jan). *Bicentenary of Introduction of Breadfruit. T 270 and similar vert designs. Multicoloured. P 13½×14.*

2453	10 c. Type **270**	..	15	10
2454	45 c. Captain Bligh with breadfruit plant	..	75	30
2455	65 c. Slice of breadfruit	..	50	40
2456	$5 Breadfruit growing on branch	..	3·25	4·50
2453/6		*Set of 4*	4·25	4·75

271 Family Picnic

(Litho Cartor)

1994 (14 Feb). *International Year of the Family (1st issue). T 271 and similar multicoloured designs. P 13½×14 ($1) or 14×13½ (others).*

2457	10 c. Type **271**	..	15	10
2458	50 c. Family in church	..	40	30
2459	65 c. Working in the garden	..	50	35
2460	75 c. Jogging	..	55	55
2461	$1 Family group (*vert*)	..	70	70
2462	$2 On the beach	..	1·40	1·75
2457/62		*Set of 6*	3·25	3·25

See also No. 2836.

(Des W. Hanson. Litho Questa)

1994 (18 Feb). *"Hong Kong '94" International Stamp Exhibition (1st issue). Horiz designs as T 293 of Maldive Islands. Multicoloured. P 14.*

2463	40 c. Hong Kong 1992 $2.30 Olympic Games stamp and "Hong Kong Harbour in 19th Century" (left detail)		25	30
	a. Horiz pair. Nos. 2463/4	..	50	60

2464 40 c. St. Vincent 1991 $3.50 Scouts Jamboree stamp and "Hong Kong Harbour in 19th Century" (right detail) 25 30
Nos. 2463/4 were printed together, *se-tenant*, in horizontal pairs throughout the sheet with the centre part of each pair forming the complete painting.

(Des Kerri Schiff. Litho Questa)

1994 (18 Feb). *"Hong Kong '94" International Stamp Exhibition (2nd issue). Multicoloured designs as T **294** of Maldive Islands.* P 14.
2465/94 40 c. × 12, 45 c. × 12, 50 c. × 6 *Set of 30* 7·50 8·50
Nos. 2465/94 were printed as five *se-tenant* sheetlets, each of six different designs, depicting Ching porcelain (40 c.), dragon boat races (40 c.), seed-stitch purses (45 c.), junks (45 c.) and Qing ceramic figures (vert designs) (50 c.).

272 Bird on a Flowering Spray Plate, Qianlong   **273** Blue Flasher

(Litho Questa)

1994 (18 Feb). *"Hong Kong '94" International Stamp Exhibition (3rd issue). T **272** and similar vert designs. Multicoloured.* P 13½×14.
2495 50 c. Type **272** 40 40
    a. Sheetlet. Nos. 2495/500 .. 2·25
2496 50 c. Large decorated dish, Kangxi 40 40
2497 50 c. Cocks on rocky ground plate, Yongzheng 40 40
2498 50 c. Green decorated dish, Yuan 40 40
2499 50 c. Porcelain pug dog 40 40
2500 50 c. Dish decorated with Dutch ship, Qianlong 40 40
2495/500 .. .. .. *Set of 6* 2·25 2·25
MS2501 Two sheets, each 126×95 mm. (a) $2 Dr. Sun Yat-sen. (b) $2 Chiang Kai-shek
    Set of 2 sheets 2·75 3·00
Nos. 2495/500 were printed together, *se-tenant*, in sheetlets of 6.
No. 2497 is incorrectly inscribed "Cocks on a Rocky Ground".

(Des M. Malamud. Litho Questa)

1994 (18 Feb). *Butterflies. T **273** and similar horiz designs. Multicoloured.* P 14½.
2502 50 c. Type **273** 35 35
    a. Sheetlet. Nos. 2502/17 .. 5·00
2503 50 c. Tiger Swallowtail 35 35
2504 50 c. Lustrous Copper 35 35
2505 50 c. Tailed Copper 35 35
2506 50 c. Blue Copper 35 35
2507 50 c. Ruddy Copper 35 35
2508 50 c. Viceroy 35 35
2509 50 c. California Sister 35 35
2510 50 c. Mourning Cloak 35 35
2511 50 c. Red Passion-flower .. 35 35
2512 50 c. Small Flambeau 35 35
2513 50 c. Blue Wave 35 35
2514 50 c. Chiricahua Metalmark .. 35 35
2515 50 c. Monarch 35 35
2516 50 c. Anise Swallowtail 35 35
2517 50 c. Buckeye 35 35
2502/17 .. .. .. *Set of 16* 5·00 5·00
Nos. 2502/17 were printed together, *se-tenant*, in sheetlets of 16.

274 Antonio Cabrini   **275** *Epidendrum ibaguense*

(Des Kerri Schiff. Litho Questa)

1994 (22 Mar). *Juventus Football Club (Italy) Commemoration. T **274** and similar multicoloured designs showing past and present players.* P 14.
2518 $1 Type **274** 65 65
2519 $1 Michel Platini and Roberto Baggio 65 65
2520 $1 Roberto Bettega 65 65
2521 $1 Gaetano Scirea 65 65
2522 $1 Jurgen Kohler 65 65
2523 $1 Marco Tardelli 65 65
2524 $1 Paolo Rossi 65 65
2525 $1 Giuseppe Furino 65 65
2526 $1 Dino Zoff 65 65

2527 $1 Franco Causio 65 65
2528 $1 Claudio Gentile 65 65
2518/28 .. .. .. *Set of 11* 6·50 6·50
MS2529 100×70 mm. $6 U.E.F.A. Cup, Cup Winners Cup and European Cup trophies (all won by Juventus) (horiz) .. .. 3·75 4·25

(Des R. Brickman. Litho Questa)

1994 (6 Apr). *Orchids. T **275** and similar vert designs. Multicoloured.* P 14.
2530 10 c. Type **275** 40 30
2531 25 c. Ionopsis utricularioides .. 50 30
2532 50 c. Brassavola cucullata .. 60 50
2533 65 c. Encyclia cochleata 70 60
2534 $1 Liparis nervosa 85 75
2535 $2 Vanilla phaeantha .. .. 1·40 1·60
2536 $4 Elleanthus cephalotus .. 2·50 2·75
2537 $5 Isochilus linearis .. .. 2·50 2·75
2530/7 .. .. .. *Set of 8* 8·50 8·50
MS2538 Two sheets, each 100×70 mm. (a) $6 Rodriguezia lanceolata. (b) $6 Eulophia alta
    Set of 2 sheets 7·50 8·00

276 Dimorphodon

(Des Yemi. Litho B.D.T.)

1994 (20 Apr). *Prehistoric Animals (1st series). T **276** and similar horiz designs. Multicoloured.* P 14.
2539 75 c. Type **276** 60 60
    a. Sheetlet. Nos. 2539/46 .. 4·25
2540 75 c. Camarasaurus 60 60
2541 75 c. Spinosaurus 60 60
2542 75 c. Allosaurus 60 60
2543 75 c. Rhamphorhynchus 60 60
2544 75 c. Pteranodon and body of Allosaurus 60 60
2545 75 c. Eudimorphodon 60 60
2546 75 c. Ornithomimus 60 60
2547 75 c. Protoavis 60 60
    a. Sheetlet. Nos. 2547/54 .. 4·25
2548 75 c. Pteranodon 60 60
2549 75 c. Quetzalcoatlus 60 60
2550 75 c. Lesothosaurus 60 60
2551 75 c. Heterodontosaurus .. 60 60
2552 75 c. Archaeopteryx 60 60
2553 75 c. Cearadactylus 60 60
2554 75 c. Anchisaurus 60 60
2539/54 .. .. .. *Set of 16* 8·00 8·00
Nos. 2539/46 and 2547/54 were each printed together, *se-tenant*, in sheetlets of 8 forming composite designs.

277 Triceratops

(Litho and thermography Cartor)

1994 (20 Apr). *"Hong Kong '94" International Stamp Exhibition (4th issue). Prehistoric Animals. Sheet 206×121 mm, containing T **277** and similar multicoloured designs.* P 13.
MS2555 $1.50, Type **277**; $1.50, Tyrannosaurus rex (vert); $1.50, Diplodocus; $1.50, Stegosaurus (vert) .. .. 4·00 4·50

278 Albertosaurus

(Des W. Wright. Litho B.D.T.)

1994 (20 Apr). *Prehistoric Animals (2nd series). T **278** and similar multicoloured designs.* P 14.
2556/603 75 c. × 48 .. .. *Set of 48* 20·00 22·00
MS2604 Four sheets, each 115×86 mm. (a) $6 Tyrannosaurus rex. (b) $6 Triceratops. (c) $6 Pteranodon and Diplodocus carnegii. (d) $6 Styracosaurus (vert) .. *Set of 4 sheets* 14·00 15·00
Nos. 2556/603 were printed together, *se-tenant*, as four sheetlets of 12 with Nos. 2556/79 being horizontal and Nos. 2580/603 vertical. The species depicted are Albertosaurus, Chasmosaurus, Brachiosaurus, Coelophysis, Deinonychus, Anatosaurus, Iguanodon, Baryonyx, Stenosaurus, Nanotyrannus, Camptosaurus, Camarasaurus, Hesperonis, Mesosaurus, Plesiosaurus Dolichorhynchops, Squalicorax, Tylosaurus, Plesiosoar, Stenopterygius Ichthyosaurus, Steneosaurus, Eurhinosaurus Longirostris, Cryptocleidus

Oxoniensis, Caturus, Protostega, Dimorphodon, Pterodactylus, Rhamphorhynchus, Pteranodon, Gallimimus, Stegosaurus, Acanthopolis, Trachodon, Thecodonts, Ankylosaurus, Compsognathus, Protoceratops, Quetzalcoatlus, Diplodocus, Spinosaurus, Apatosaurus, Ornitholestes, Lesothosaurus, Trachodon, Protoavis, Oviraptor, Coelophysis, Ornitholestes and Archaeopteryx.

279 Mickey Mouse as Pilot

(Litho Questa)

1994 (5 May). *65th Anniv of Mickey Mouse (1993). T **279** and similar multicoloured designs showing Walt Disney cartoon characters.* P 13½×14.
2605 5 c. Type **279** 30 30
2606 10 c. Mickey in Foreign Legion .. 30 30
2607 15 c. Mickey as frontiersman .. 40 40
2608 20 c. Mickey, Goofy and Donald Duck 40 40
2609 35 c. Horace Horsecollar and Clarabelle Cow 50 50
2610 50 c. Minnie Mouse, Frankie and Figuro 60 60
2611 75 c. Donald and Pluto 70 70
2612 80 c. Mickey holding balloons .. 75 75
2613 85 c. Daisy Duck and Minnie .. 75 75
2614 95 c. Minnie 80 80
2615 $1 Mickey in red trousers .. 80 80
2616 $1.50, Mickey raising hat .. 1·40 1·40
2617 $2 Mickey with hands in pockets .. 1·60 1·60
2618 $3 Mickey and Minnie .. .. 2·50 2·50
2619 $4 Mickey with birthday cake .. 2·75 2·75
2620 $5 Mickey as Uncle Sam .. 2·75 2·75
2605/20 .. .. .. *Set of 16* 15·00 15·00
MS2621 Four sheets. (a) 102×127 mm. $6 Pluto looking at portrait of Mickey. P 13½×14. (b) 127×102 mm. $6 Mickey and camera (horiz). P 14×13½. (c) 127×102 mm. $6 Minnie disco dancing (horiz). P 14×13½. (d) 127×102 mm. $6 Donald with Mickey's baby photo (horiz). P 14×13½ .. *Set of 4 sheets* 18·00 18·00

280 Argentine Team

(Litho Questa)

1994 (12 May). *World Cup Football Championship, U.S.A. T **280** and similar horiz designs showing competing teams. Multicoloured.* P 13½.
2622 50 c. Type **280** 40 40
2623 50 c. Belgium 40 40
2624 50 c. Bolivia 40 40
2625 50 c. Brazil 40 40
2626 50 c. Bulgaria 40 40
2627 50 c. Cameroun 40 40
2628 50 c. Colombia 40 40
2629 50 c. Germany 40 40
2630 50 c. Greece 40 40
2631 50 c. Netherlands 40 40
2632 50 c. Republic of Ireland .. 40 40
2633 50 c. Italy 40 40
2634 50 c. Mexico 40 40
2635 50 c. Morocco 40 40
2636 50 c. Nigeria 40 40
2637 50 c. Norway 40 40
2638 50 c. Rumania 40 40
2639 50 c. Russia 40 40
2640 50 c. Saudi Arabia 40 40
2641 50 c. South Korea 40 40
2642 50 c. Spain 40 40
2643 50 c. Sweden 40 40
2644 50 c. Switzerland 40 40
2645 50 c. U.S.A. 40 40
2622/45 .. .. .. *Set of 24* 8·50 8·50
Nos. 2622/45 were each printed, *se-tenant*, in sheetlets of 8 stamps and one centre label.

STANLEY GIBBONS STAMP COLLECTING SERIES

Introductory booklets on *How to Start*, *How to Identify Stamps* and *Collecting by Theme*. A series of well illustrated guides at a low price.
Write for details.

281 Marilyn Monroe

(Litho Questa)

1994 (16 May). *Marilyn Monroe (American film star) Commemoration.* T **281** *and similar vert designs showing different portraits. Multicoloured.* P 13½×14.

2646	$1	Type **281**		75	75
	a. Sheetlet. Nos. 2646/54			6·00	
2647	$1	Asleep		75	75
2648	$1	With long hair style and pendulum earrings		75	75
2649	$1	Wearing striped sweater		75	75
2650	$1	With gloved hand to face		75	75
2651	$1	With bare hand to face		75	75
2652	$1	In black and white dress		75	75
2653	$1	In sequined evening dress		75	75
2654	$1	With short hair and no earrings		75	75
2646/54			*Set of* 9	6·00	6·00

Nos. 2646/54 were printed together, *se-tenant*, in sheetlets of 9.

282 Capt. Jean-Luc Picard

(Litho Questa)

1994 (27 June). *Star Trek – The Next Generation (T.V. series).* T **282** *and similar multicoloured designs.* P 13½.

2655	$2	Type **282**		1·25	1·25
	a. Sheetlet. Nos. 2656/63			10·00	
2656	$2	Commander William Riker		1·25	1·25
2657	$2	Lt-Commander Data		1·25	1·25
2658	$2	Lt. Worf		1·25	1·25
2659	$2	Crew members		1·25	1·25
2660	$2	Dr. Beverley Crusher		1·25	1·25
2661	$2	Lt. Worf and female crew member		1·25	1·25
2662	$2	Q wearing hat		1·25	1·25
2663	$2	Counsellor Deanna Troi		1·25	1·25
2655/63			*Set of* 9	10·00	10·00

MS2664 83×101 mm. $10 As No. 2659 (59×40 mm). P 14×14½ .. .. .. 6·50 7·00

Nos. 2655/63 were printed together, *se-tenant*, in sheetlets of 9 with No. 2659 also issued as separate sheetlets of 9.

A $50 value embossed on gold foil also exists from a limited printing.

283 Shigetatsu Matsunaga (Yokohama Marinos)

284 Jef United Team

(Litho Questa)

1994 (1 July). *Japanese Professional Football League. Multicoloured.* P 14.

(a) *Vert designs as* T **283** *showing individual players and league emblem*

2665/76 55 c. × 8, $1.50 × 4 .. *Set of* 12 6·00 6·00
Designs:—55 c. Masami Ihara (Yokohama Marinos); Shunzoh Ohno (Kashima Antlers); Luiz Carlos Pereira (Verdy Kawasaki); Tetsuji Hashiratani (Verdy Kawasaki); Carlos Alberto Souza dos Santos (Kashima Antlers); Yasuto Honda (Kashima Antlers); Kazuyoshi Miura (Verdy Kawasaki); $1.50, League emblem; Takumi Horiike (Shimizu S-Pulse); Rui Ramos (Verdy Kawasaki); Ramon Angel Diaz (Yokohama Marinos).
Nos. 2665/76 were printed together, *se-tenant*, in sheetlets of 12.

(b) *Horiz designs as* T **284** *showing teams*

2677/88 55 c. × 8, $1.50 × 4 .. *Set of* 12 6·00 6·00
Designs:—55 c. Verdy Yomiuri; Yokohama Marinos; A. S. Flügels; Bellmare; Shimizu S-Pulse; Jubilo Iwata; Panasonic Gamba Osaka; $1.50, Kashima Antlers; Red Diamonds; Nagoya Grampus Eight; Sanfrecce Hiroshima.
Nos. 2677/88 were printed together, *se-tenant*, in sheetlets of 12.

(c) *Horiz designs as* T **284** *showing players and teams arranged as individual sheetlets of* 6 *containing two horizontal strips of* 3 *either side of a central team photograph*

2689/94	55 c. × 3, $1.50 × 2, $3 A. S. Flügels		3·50	3·75
2695/700	55 c. × 3, $1.50 × 2, $3 Bellmare		3·50	3·75
2701/6	55 c. × 3, $1.50 × 2, $3 Panasonic Gamba Osaka		3·50	3·75
2707/12	55 c. × 3, $1.50 × 2, $3 Jef United		3·50	3·75
2713/18	55 c. × 3, $1.50 × 2, $3 Jubilo Iwata		3·50	3·75
2719/24	55 c. × 3, $1.50 × 2, $3 Kashima Antlers		3·50	3·75
2725/30	55 c. × 3, $1.50 × 2, $3 Nagoya Grampus Eight		3·50	3·75
2731/6	55 c. × 3, $1.50 × 2, $3 Sanfrecce Hiroshima		3·50	3·75
2737/42	55 c. × 3, $1.50 × 2, $3 Shimizu S-Pulse		3·50	3·75
2743/8	55 c. × 3, $1.50 × 2, $3 Red Diamonds		3·50	3·75
2749/54	55 c. × 3, $1.50 × 2, $3 Verdy Kawasaki		3·50	3·75
2755/60	55 c. × 3, $1.50 × 2, $3 Yokohama Marinos		3·50	3·75
2689/760		*Set of* 12 *sheetlets*	42·00	45·00

(Des W. Hanson. Litho Questa)

1994 (12 July). *25th Anniv of First Moon Landing. Horiz designs as* T **302** *of Maldive Islands. Multicoloured.* P 14.

2761	$1	Fred Whipple and Halley's Comet		75	75
	a. Sheetlet. Nos. 2761/9			6·00	
2762	$1	Robert Gilruth and "Gemini 12"		75	75
2763	$1	George Mueller and space walk from "Gemini IV"		75	75
2764	$1	Charles Berry and Johnsville Centrifuge		75	75
2765	$1	Christopher Kraft and "Apollo 4"		75	75
2766	$1	James van Allen and "Explorer I"		75	75
2767	$1	Robert Goddard and Goddard-liquid fuel rocket		75	75
2768	$1	James Webb and "Spirit of 76" flight		75	75
2769	$1	Rocco Patrone and "Apollo 8"		75	75
2770	$1	Walter Dornberger and German rocket		75	75
	a. Sheetlet. Nos. 2770/8			6·00	
2771	$1	Alexander Lippisch and Messerschmitt ME 163B Komet (airplane)		75	75
2772	$1	Kurt Debus and "A4b" rocket		75	75
2773	$1	Hermann Oberth and projected spaceship		75	75
2774	$1	Hanna Reitsch and "Reichenberg" flying bomb		75	75
2775	$1	Ernst Stuhlinger and "Explorer I"		75	75
2776	$1	Werner von Braun and rocket-powered Heinkel He 112		75	75
2777	$1	Arthur Rudolph and rocket motor		75	75
2778	$1	Willy Ley and rocket airplane		75	75
2761/78			*Set of* 18	12·00	12·00

MS2779 Two sheets, each 131×109 mm. (a) $6 Eberhardt Rees and German rocket (50×37 mm). (b) $6 Hogler Toftoy (50×37 mm). P 14×13½ .. .. .. 7·50 8·00
Nos. 2761/9 and 2770/8 were each printed together, *se-tenant*, in sheetlets of 9.

(Des J. Batchelor. Litho Questa)

1994 (19 July). *50th Anniv of D-Day. Horiz designs as* T **304** *of Maldive Islands. Multicoloured.* P 14.

2780	40 c. Supply convoy		60	25
2781	$5 Unloading beached supply ship		2·75	3·00

MS2782 106×76 mm. $6 Liberty ship .. 3·25 3·75

285 Yorkshire Terrier Bitch

286 Mark Ramprakash (England) and Wisden Trophy

(Des D. Miller. Litho Questa)

1994 (21 July). *Chinese New Year ("Year of the Dog").* T **285** *and similar vert designs. Multicoloured.* P 14.

2783	10 c. Type **285**		30	20
2784	25 c. Yorkshire Terrier dog		35	20
2785	50 c. Golden Retriever		45	45
2786	50 c. Pomeranian		45	45
	a. Sheetlet. Nos. 2786/97		4·75	
2787	50 c. English Springer Spaniel		45	45
2788	50 c. Bearded Collie		45	45
2789	50 c. Irish Wolfhound		45	45
2790	50 c. Pekingese		45	45
2791	50 c. Irish Setter		45	45
2792	50 c. Old English Sheepdog		45	45
2793	50 c. Basset Hound		45	45
2794	50 c. Cavalier King Charles Spaniel		45	45
2795	50 c. Kleiner Münsterlander		45	45
2796	50 c. Shetland Sheepdog		45	45
2797	50 c. Dachshund		45	45
2798	65 c. Bernese Mountain Dog		55	55
2799	$1 Vorstehhund		70	70
2800	$2 Tibetan Terrier		1·40	1·40
2801	$4 West Highland Terrier		2·50	2·50
2802	$5 Shih Tzu		2·75	2·75
2783/802		*Set of* 20	13·00	13·00

MS2803 Two sheets, each 100×100 mm. (a) $6 Afghan Hound with puppy. (b) $6 German Shepherd .. .. .. *Set of* 2 *sheets* 6·50 7·00
Nos. 2786/97 were printed together, *se-tenant*, in sheetlets of 12.

(Des Kerri Schiff. Litho Questa)

1994 (25 July). *Centenary of International Olympic Committee. Gold Medal Winners. Multicoloured designs as* T **303** *of Maldive Islands.* P 14.

2804	45 c. Peter Frennel (Germany) (20 km walk), 1972		40	25
2805	50 c. Kijung Son (Japan) (marathon), 1936		45	30
2806	75 c. Jesse Owens (U.S.A.) (100 and 200 metres), 1936		65	50
2807	$1 Greg Louganis (U.S.A.) (diving), 1984 and 1988		70	75
2804/7		*Set of* 4	2·00	1·60

MS2808 106×76 mm. $6 Katja Seizinger (Germany) (women's downhill skiing), 1994 (*horiz*) .. .. 3·50 4·00

(Des A. Melville-Brown. Litho Questa)

1994 (25 July). *Centenary of First English Cricket Tour to the West Indies* (1995). T **286** *and similar multicoloured designs.* P 14.

2809	10 c. Type **286**		30	20
2810	30 c. Phil Simmonds (West Indies) and Wisden Trophy		40	25
2811	$2 Garfield Sobers (West Indies) (*vert*)		1·40	1·75
2809/11		*Set of* 3	1·90	2·00

MS2812 76×96 mm. $3 First English touring team, 1895 (black and grey-brown) .. 2·25 2·75

(Des Kerri Schiff. Litho Questa (Nos. 2813/14, 2831/5) or B.D.T. (Nos. 2815/30))

1994 (25 July). *"Philakorea '94" International Stamp Exhibition, Seoul. Multicoloured designs as* T **305** *of Maldive Islands.* P 13½ (Nos. 2815/30) or 14 (*others*).

2813	10 c. Oryon Waterfall (*vert*)		30	20
2814	45 c. Indoor sports stadium, Pyongyang		40	25
2815	50 c. Illuminated character with house at bottom right		40	40
	a. Sheetlet. Nos. 2815/22		2·75	
2816	50 c. Illuminated character with red dots in centre		40	40
2817	50 c. Illuminated character with animal at right		40	40
2818	50 c. Illuminated character with flowers at bottom right		40	40
2819	50 c. Illuminated character with dragon at left		40	40
2820	50 c. Illuminated character with house at top		40	40
2821	50 c. Illuminated character with dragon at top		40	40
2822	50 c. Illuminated character with sun at top		40	40
2823	50 c. Fish and character		40	40
	a. Sheetlet. Nos. 2823/30		2·75	
2824	50 c. Two pheasants and character		40	40
2825	50 c. Plant and cabinet		40	40
2826	50 c. Vases and cabinet		40	40
2827	50 c. Books on decorated cabinet		40	40
2828	50 c. Pheasant, decorated cabinet and vase		40	40
2829	50 c. Pheasant and lamp on table		40	40
2830	50 c. Cabinet, vase and table		40	40
2831	65 c. Pombong, Chonhwadae (*vert*)		50	50
2832	75 c. Uisangdae, Naksansa (*vert*)		55	55
2833	$1 Buddha of the Sokkuram Grotto, Kyangju		60	60
2834	$2 Moksogwon		1·10	1·10
2813/34		*Set of* 22	9·00	8·75

MS2835 Two sheets. (a) 70×100 mm. $4 Chongdong Mirukbul (*vert*). (b) 100×70 mm. $4 Tiger hunting scene (embroidery) *Set of* 2 *sheets* 4·25 4·50
Nos. 2815/22 and 2823/30, each 24×47 mm, were printed together, *se-tenant*, in sheetlets of 8.
Nos. 2825/6 and 2830 are inscr "Bookshlef" in error.

287 St. Vincent Family

288 Sir Shridath Ramphal and Map of Guyana

(Litho Questa)

1994 (1 Sept). *International Year of the Family (2nd issue).* P 14.

2836 **287** 75 c. multicoloured 50 50

(Litho Questa)

1994 (1 Sept). *First Recipients of Order of the Caribbean Community. T* **288** *and similar multicoloured designs.* P 14.

2837	$1 Type **288**	70	50
2838	$2 Derek Walcott and map of St. Lucia	1·75	1·75
2839	$5 William Demas and map of Trinidad (*horiz*)	3·00	4·00
2837/9	*Set of 3*	5·00	5·75

No. 2838 is inscribed "Wilcott" in error.

289 Twin-engined Airliner, Bequia Airport

(Litho Questa)

1994 (1 Dec). *50th Anniv of International Civil Aviation Organization. T* **289** *and similar horiz designs. Multicoloured.* P 14.

2840	10 c. Type **289**	20	20
2841	65 c. Union Island Airport	50	40
2842	75 c. L.I.A.T. 8-100 at E. T. Joshua Airport	55	50
2843	$1 Aircraft and logo	65	75
2844	$1 Britten Norman Islander at J. F. Mitchell Airport, Bequia	65	75
2840/4	*Set of 5*	2·25	2·40

290 "The Annunciation"   **291** Mealy Amazon Parrot

(Litho Questa)

1994 (15 Dec). *Christmas. Religious Paintings from Jean de Berry's Book of Hours. T* **290** *and similar vert designs. Multicoloured.* P 13½×14.

2845	10 c. Type **290**	15	10
2846	45 c. "The Visitation"	40	25
2847	50 c. "The Nativity"	45	30
2848	65 c. "The Purification of the Virgin" (detail)	60	40
2849	75 c. "Presentation of Jesus in the Temple"	70	45
2850	$5 "Flight into Egypt"	3·25	4·25
2845/50	*Set of 6*	5·00	5·25
MS2851	110×126 mm. $6 "Adoration of the Magi" (detail)	4·00	4·50

No. 2847 is inscribed "The Annunciation" in error.

1995 (24 Jan). *Chinese New Year ("Year of the Pig") (1st issue). Designs as Nos.* 2050/8 *and* **MS**2139a/b, *but with different face values and with Year of the Pig logo.* P 14×13½.

2852	30 c. Type **245**	40	40
	a. Sheetlet. Nos. 2852/60	3·25	
2853	30 c. Fiddler Pig building house of sticks	40	40
2854	30 c. Practical Pig building house of bricks	40	40
2855	30 c. The Big Bad Wolf	40	40
2856	30 c. Wolf scaring Fiddler and Fifer Pig	40	40
2857	30 c. Wolf blowing down straw house	40	40
2858	30 c. Wolf in sheep costume	40	40
2859	30 c. Wolf blowing down stick house	40	40
2860	30 c. Wolf attempting to blow down brick house	40	40
2852/60	*Set of 9*	3·25	3·25

MS2861 Two sheets. (a) 103×128 mm. $3 Original sketch of Practical Pig building house of brick. P 14×13½. (b) 128×103 mm. $3 Practical Pig playing piano (*vert*). P 13½×14
Set of 2 sheets 4·25 4·50

Nos. 2852/60 were printed together, *se-tenant*, in sheetlets of 9.

See also Nos. 2900/3.

(Des D. Burkhart. Litho Questa)

1995 (25 Apr). *Parrots. T* **291** *and similar multicoloured designs.* P 14.

2862	$1 Type **291**	75	75
	a. Sheetlet. Nos. 2862/70	6·00	
2863	$1 Nanday Conure	75	75
2864	$1 Black-headed Caique	75	75
2865	$1 Scarlet Macaw	75	75
2866	$1 Red-masked Conure	75	75
2867	$1 Blue-headed Parrot	75	75
2868	$1 Hyacinth Macaw	75	75
2869	$1 Sun Conure	75	75
2870	$1 Blue and Yellow Macaw	75	75
2862/70	*Set of 9*	6·00	6·00

MS2871 104×76 mm. $5 White-eared Conure (*vert*) 3·50 4·00

Nos. 2862/70 were printed together, *se-tenant*, in sheetlets of 9, the backgrounds forming a composite design.

292 Snowshoe

(Des D. Burkhart. Litho Questa)

1995 (25 Apr). *Cats. T* **292** *and similar multicoloured designs.* P 14.

2872	$1 Type **292**	75	75
	a. Sheetlet. Nos. 2872/80	6·00	
2873	$1 Abyssinian	75	75
2874	$1 Ocicat	75	75
2875	$1 Tiffany	75	75
2876	$1 Russian Blue	75	75
2877	$1 Siamese	75	75
2878	$1 Bi-colour	75	75
2879	$1 Malayan	75	75
2880	$1 Manx	75	75
2872/80	*Set of 9*	6·00	6·00

MS2881 104×76 mm. $6 Birman (*vert*) 4·75 5·00

Nos. 2872/80 were printed together, *se-tenant*, in sheetlets of 9, the background forming a composite design.

293 Blue-faced Booby ("Masked Booby")

(Des D. Burkhart. Litho Questa)

1995 (2 May). *Birds. T* **293** *and similar multicoloured designs.* P 14.

2882	75 c. Type **293**	55	55
	a. Vert strip of 4. Nos. 2882/5	2·00	
2883	75 c. Pair of Blue-faced Boobies	55	55
2884	75 c. Blue-faced Booby preening	55	55
2885	75 c. Blue-faced Booby stretching	55	55
2886	75 c. Great Egrets	55	55
	a. Sheetlet. Nos. 2886/97	6·00	
2887	75 c. Roseate Spoonbills	55	55
2888	75 c. Ring-billed Gull	55	55
2889	75 c. Ruddy Quail Dove	55	55
2890	75 c. Royal Terns	55	55
2891	75 c. Killdeers	55	55
2892	75 c. Osprey	55	55
2893	75 c. Magnificent Frigate Bird	55	55
2894	75 c. Blue-faced Boobies ("Masked Booby")	55	55
2895	75 c. Green Heron	55	55
2896	75 c. Double-crested Cormorants	55	55
2897	75 c. Brown Pelican	55	55
2882/97	*Set of 16*	8·00	8·00

MS2898 Two sheets, each 100×69 mm. (a) $5 Greater Flamingo (*vert*). (b) $6 Purple Gallinule (*vert*) *Set of 2 sheets* 7·50 8·00

Nos. 2882/5, which show the W.W.F emblem, were printed together, *se-tenant*, in sheets of 12 (3×4) each vertical row containing one of each design.

Nos. 2886/97 were printed together, *se-tenant*, in sheetlets of 12, the background forming a composite design.

294 Churchill, Roosevelt   **295** Pig
and Stalin at Yalta
Conference

(Des J. Gordon. Litho Questa)

1995 (8 May). *50th Anniv of V.E. Day.* P 13½.

2899 **294** $1 multicoloured 1·00 90

No. 2899 was printed in sheets of 9.

A $50 value in the same design, but embossed on gold foil, exists from a limited printing.

(Des Y. Lee. Litho Questa)

1995 (8 May). *Chinese New Year ("Year of the Pig") (2nd issue). T* **295** *and similar multicoloured designs showing central panel in colours indicated.* P 14.

2900	75 c. Type **295** (myrtle-green)	45	55
	a. Horiz strip of 3. Nos. 2900/2	1·25	
2901	75 c. Pig (orange-brown)	45	55
2902	75 c. Pig (rosine)	45	55
2900/2	*Set of 3*	1·50	1·50

MS2903 71×101 mm. $2 Two pigs (*horiz*) 1·25 1·50

Nos. 2900/2 were printed together, *se-tenant*, in horizontal strips of 3 throughout the sheet of 9.

296 National Flag   **297** Globe and Peace
and Globe   Dove

(Litho Questa)

1995 (8 May). *18th World Scout Jamboree, Netherlands. T* **296** *and similar vert designs. Multicoloured.* P 14.

2904	$1 Type **296**	70	50
2905	$4 Lord Baden-Powell	2·25	2·50
2906	$5 Handshake	2·50	2·75
2904/6	*Set of 3*	4·75	5·25

MS2907 Two sheets, each 81×112 mm. (a) $6 Scout greeting. (b) $6 Scout salute *Set of 2 sheets* 7·00 8·00

(Des W. Wright. Litho Questa)

1995 (8 May). *50th Anniv of End of Second World War in Europe. Horiz designs as T* **317** *of Maldive Islands. Multicoloured.* P 14.

2908	$2 Tank of U.S. First Army	1·25	1·25
	a. Sheetlet. Nos. 2908/15	9·00	
2909	$2 V2 rocket	1·25	1·25
2910	$2 Consolidated B-24 Liberator bombers	1·25	1·25
2911	$2 French troops advancing to Strasbourg	1·25	1·25
2912	$2 Gloster G.41 Meteor fighter	1·25	1·25
2913	$2 Berlin on fire	1·25	1·25
2914	$2 Soviet tanks in Berlin	1·25	1·25
2915	$2 *Chicago Daily Tribune* headline	1·25	1·25
2908/15	*Set of 8*	9·00	9·00

MS2916 107×77 mm. $6 Sortie markings on aircraft (57×42½ mm) 3·50 4·00

Nos. 2908/15 were printed together, *se-tenant*, in sheetlets of 8 with the stamps arranged in two horizontal strips of 4 separated by a gutter showing Auschwitz Concentration Camp. No. 2909 is inscribed "Y2" in error.

(Des R. Martin. Litho Questa)

1995 (8 May). *50th Anniv of United Nations. T* **297** *and similar vert designs. Multicoloured.* P 14.

2917	$2 Type **297**	1·00	1·10
	a. Horiz strip of 3. Nos. 2917/19	2·75	
2918	$2 Liberty	1·00	1·10
2919	$2 U.N. Building, New York, and peace dove	1·00	1·10
2917/19	*Set of 3*	2·75	3·00

MS2920 71×107 mm. $6 Asian child 2·75 3·25

Nos. 2917/19 were printed together in sheets of 9 containing three *se-tenant* horizontal strips of 3 forming a composite design. No. **MS**2920 is inscribed "1945–1955" in error.

298 Women preparing   **299** Paul Harris (founder) and
Food   Logo

(Des R. Martin. Litho Questa)

1995 (8 May). *50th Anniv of Food and Agriculture Organization. T* **298** *and similar vert designs. Multicoloured.* P 14.

2921	$2 Type **298**	1·00	1·10
	a. Horiz strip of 3. Nos. 2921/3	2·75	
2922	$2 Woman mixing food	1·00	1·10
2923	$2 Harvesting grain	1·00	1·10
2921/3	*Set of 3*	2·75	3·00

MS2924 76×106 mm. $6 Baby and logo 2·75 3·25

Nos. 2921/3 were printed together in sheets of 9 containing three *se-tenant* horizontal strips of 3 forming a composite design. No. **MS**2924 is inscribed "1945–1955" in error.

(Litho Questa)

1995 (8 May). *90th Anniv of Rotary International. T* **299** *and similar horiz design. Multicoloured.* P 14.

2925	$5 Type **299**	2·50	3·00

MS2926 113×79 mm. $6 National flag and logo 2·75 3·25

(Litho Questa)

1995 (8 May). *95th Birthday of Queen Elizabeth the Queen Mother. Vert designs as T* **321** *of Maldive Islands.* P 13½×14.

2927	$1.50, orange-brown, pale brown and black	1·00	1·10
	a. Sheetlet. Nos. 2927/30×2	7·00	
2928	$1.50, multicoloured	1·00	1·10
2929	$1.50, multicoloured	1·00	1·10
2930	$1.50, multicoloured	1·00	1·10
2927/30	*Set of 4*	3·50	4·50

MS2931 102×127 mm. $6 multicoloured 3·50 4·00

Designs:—No. 2927, Queen Elizabeth the Queen Mother (pastel drawing); No. 2928, Wearing blue hat; No. 2929, At desk (oil painting); No. 2930, Wearing mauve dress; No. **MS2931**, Wearing yellow dress.

Nos. 2927/30 were printed together in sheetlets of 8, containing two *se-tenant* horizontal strips of 4.

(Des J. Batchelor. Litho Questa)

1995 (8 May). *50th Anniv of End of Second World War in the Pacific. Horiz designs as T* **317** *of Maldive Islands. Multicoloured. P* 14.

2932	$2	Douglas Devastator torpedo bomber	1·25	1·25
		a. Sheetlet. Nos. 2932/7	6·50	
2933	$2	Doolittle's North American B-25 Mitchell *Ruptured Duck*	1·25	1·25
2934	$2	Curtiss SB2C Helldiver bomber	1·25	1·25
2935	$2	U.S.S. *Yorktown* (aircraft carrier)	1·25	1·25
2936	$2	U.S.S. *Wasp* (aircraft carrier)	1·25	1·25
2937	$2	U.S.S. *Lexington* (aircraft carrier) sinking	1·25	1·25
2932/7		*Set of 6*	6·50	6·50
MS2938		107×77 mm. $6 American aircraft carriers	3·50	4·00

Nos. 2932/7 were printed together, *se-tenant*, in sheetlets of 6 with the stamps arranged in two horizontal strips of 3 separated by a gutter showing U.S.S. *Hornet* (aircraft carrier) launching B-25's.

 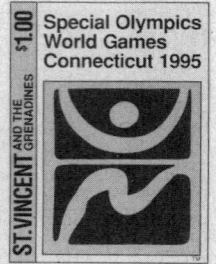

300 Head of Humpback Whales   **301** Symbolic Disabled Athlete

(Des D. Miller. Litho B.D.T.)

1995 (23 May). *Marine Life. T* **300** *and similar multicoloured designs. P* 14.

2939	90 c.	Type **300**	60	60
		a. Sheetlet. Nos. 2939/47	4·75	
2940	90 c.	Green Turtles	60	60
2941	90 c.	Bottlenose Dolphin	60	60
2942	90 c.	Monk Seals	60	60
2943	90 c.	Krill	60	60
2944	90 c.	Blue Sharks	60	60
2945	90 c.	Porkfish	60	60
2946	90 c.	Reef Butterflyfish	60	60
2947	90 c.	Shipwreck	60	60
2948	$1	Beaugregory (fish) (*horiz*)	60	60
		a. Sheetlet. Nos. 2948/51	2·25	
2949	$1	Grey Angelfish (*horiz*)	60	60
2950	$1	Yellow-tailed Damselfish (*horiz*)	60	60
2951	$1	Four-eyed Butterflyfish (*horiz*)	60	60
2939/51		*Set of 13*	7·00	7·00
MS2952		Two sheets, each 100×70 mm. (a) $6 Sea Anemones. (b) $6 *Physalia physalis* (jelly fish) *Set of 2 sheets*	7·00	7·50

Nos. 2939/47 were printed together, *se-tenant*, in sheetlets of 9 forming a composite design. Nos. 2948/51 were printed together, *se-tenant*, in sheetlets of 4.

(Des J. Gordon. Litho Questa)

1995 (6 July). *Paralympic Games '95, Connecticut. P* 13½×14.

2953	**301**	$1 chrome-yellow, royal blue and black	65	65

302 Ingrid Kristiansen   **303** Nolan Ryan in Blue Jersey

(Des K. Sandven. Litho Questa)

1995 (31 July). *World Athletic Championships, Gothenburg. Norwegian Athletes. T* **302** *similar multicoloured designs. P* 14×14½ (*No.* 2959) *or* 14½×14 (*others*).

2954	$1	Type **302**	60	60
		a. Sheetlet. Nos. 2954/9	3·25	
2955	$1	Trine Hattestad	60	60
2956	$1	Grete Waitz	60	60
2957	$1	Vebjörn Rodal	60	60
2958	$1	Geir Moen	60	60
2959	$1	Steinar Hoen (*horiz*)	60	60
2954/9		*Set of 6*	3·25	3·25

Nos. 2954/9 were printed together, *se-tenant*, in sheetlets of 6.

(Des J. Gordon. Litho Questa)

1995 (1 Aug). *Retirement of Nolan Ryan (baseball player)* (1993). *T* **303** *and similar vert designs. Multicoloured. P* 13½.

2960	$1	Type **303**	60	60
		a. Sheetlet. Nos. 2960/8	4·75	
2961	$1	With glove	60	60
2962	$1	In white jersey	60	60
2963	$1	Making pitch from left	60	60
2964	$1	Texas Rangers "All Star Game" emblem	60	60
		a. Sheetlet. Nos. 2964×4 and 2973×5	4·75	
2965	$1	Making pitch from right	60	60
2966	$1	Bleeding from blow to mouth	60	60
2967	$1	Preparing to pitch	60	60
2968	$1	Waving cap	60	60
2969	$1	Wearing "NY" cap	60	60
		a. Sheetlet. Nos. 2969/77	4·75	
2970	$1	Wearing stetson with dog	60	60
2971	$1	Wearing "T" cap	60	60
2972	$1	Throwing American football	60	60
2973	$1	Nolan Ryan Foundation emblem	60	60
2974	$1	With son	60	60
2975	$1	Laughing	60	60
2976	$1	With family	60	60
2977	$1	Wearing "H" cap	60	60
2960/77		*Set of 18*	9·50	9·50
MS2978		146×101 mm. $6 After final game for Texas Rangers	3·00	3·50

Nos. 2960/68, 2964 and 2973, and 2969/77 were printed together, *se-tenant*, in sheetlets of 9.

A $30 value embossed on gold foil also exists from a limited printing.

304 Breast and Bowl of Baby Food

(Des Y. Lee. Litho Questa)

1995 (4 Aug). *"Baby Friendly" Campaign. T* **304** *and similar multicoloured designs. P* 14.

2979	15 c.	Type **304**	20	10
2980	20 c.	Hands squeezing milk into bowl (*vert*)	20	10
2981	90 c.	Breast feeding (*vert*)	60	45
2982	$5	Breast feeding emblem (*vert*)	2·75	3·25
2979/82		*Set of 4*	3·25	3·50

305 Aerial View of Leeward Coastal Road   **306** "The God of Fire" (woodcut) (Shunichi Kadowaki)

(Des Y. Lee. Litho Questa)

1995 (8 Aug). *25th Anniv of Caribbean Development Bank. T* **305** *and similar multicoloured designs. P* 14.

2983	10 c.	Type **305**	15	15
2984	15 c.	Feeder roads project	20	15
2985	25 c.	*Anthurium andraeanum* (flower)	20	15
2986	50 c.	Coconut Palm tree (*vert*)	30	30
2987	65 c.	Fairhall Housing Scheme	40	35
2983/7		*Set of 5*	1·10	1·00

(Litho Questa)

1995 (8 Aug). *Japanese Art. P* 14.

2988	**306**	$1.40, multicoloured	85	85

307 Jean Shiley (U.S.A.) (high jump)   **308** Frank Thomas

(Des J. Iskowitz. Litho Questa)

1995 (24 Aug). *Olympic Games, Atlanta (1996) (1st issue). T* **307** *and similar vert designs. Multicoloured. P* 14.

2989	$1	Type **307**	60	60
		a. Sheetlet. Nos. 2989/96	4·25	
2990	$1	Ruth Fuchs (Germany) (javelin)	60	60
2991	$1	Alessandro Andrei (Italy) (shot put)	60	60
2992	$1	Dorando Pietri (Italy) (marathon)	60	60

2993	$1	Heide Rosendahl (Germany) (long jump)	60	60
2994	$1	Mitsuoki Watanabe (Japan) (gymnastics)	60	60
2995	$1	Yasuhiro Yamashita (Japan) (judo)	60	60
2996	$1	Dick Fosbury (U.S.A.) (high jump)	60	60
2997	$2	Long jumper and dove	1·10	1·10
		a. Sheetlet. Nos. 2997/3002	6·00	
2998	$2	Hurdler and deer	1·10	1·10
2999	$2	Sprinter and cheetah	1·10	1·10
3000	$2	Marathon runner and tiger	1·10	1·10
3001	$2	Gymnast and dove	1·10	1·10
3002	$2	Rower and duck	1·10	1·10
2989/3002		*Set of 14*	10·00	10·00
MS3003		Two sheets (a) 70×100 mm. $5 Magic Johnson (U.S.A.) (basketball). (b) 106×76 mm. $5 Swimmers hand (*horiz*) *Set of 2 sheets*	6·50	6·50

Nos. 2989/96 and 2997/3002 were each printed together, *se-tenant*, in sheetlets of 8 (Nos. 2989/96) or 6 (Nos. 2997/3002). See also Nos. 3357/3401.

(Des J. Gordon. Litho Questa)

1995 (6 Sept). *Famous Baseball Players (8th series). T* **308** *and similar vert designs. Multicoloured. P* 13½×14.

3004	$1	Type **308**	60	60
		a. Sheetlet. Nos. 3004/12	4·75	
3005	$1	Cal Ripken Jnr wearing "8" jersey and helmet	60	60
3006	$1	Ken Griffey Jnr wearing "S" cap	60	60
3007	$1	Ken Griffey Jnr wearing turquoise-blue jersey	60	60
3008	$1	Frank Thomas in "Sox" cap with bat on shoulder	60	60
3009	$1	Cal Ripken Jnr with ball and glove	60	60
3010	$1	Cal Ripkin Jnr wearing Orioles cap	60	60
3011	$1	Ken Griffey Jnr wearing "Seattle" jersey and helmet	60	60
3012	$1	Frank Thomas wearing "Chicago 35" jersey	60	60
3004/12		*Set of 9*	4·75	4·75

Nos. 3004/12 were printed together, *se-tenant*, in sheetlets of 9.

A $30 value embossed on gold foil also exists from a limited printing.

309 John Lennon

(Des R. Martin (Nos. 3013/21, **MS**3064a), S. Stevens (Nos. 3022/30, **MS**3064b), M. Leboff (Nos. 3031/6), J. Iskowitz (Nos. 3037/45), M. Chatrik (Nos. 3046/63, **MS**3064c/d). Litho Questa)

1995 (18 Sept). *Centenary of Cinema. Entertainers. T* **309** *and similar vert designs. Multicoloured. P* 13½×14.

3013/21	$1 × 9, John Lennon (as T **309**)			
	a. Sheetlet. Nos. 3013/21		6·00	
3022/30	$1 × 9, Elvis Presley			
	a. Sheetlet. Nos. 3022/30		6·00	
3031/6	$1 × 6, Elvis Presley			
	a. Sheetlet. Nos. 3031/6		4·50	
3037/45	$1 × 9, Marilyn Monroe (with stairway in centre of sheetlet)			
	a. Sheetlet. Nos. 3037/45		5·00	
3046/54	$1 × 9, Marilyn Monroe (with superimposed full length portrait)			
	a. Sheetlet. Nos. 3046/54		5·00	
3055/63	$1 × 9, Marilyn Monroe (design with hand raised in centre of top row)			
	a. Sheetlet. Nos. 3055/63		5·00	
3013/63		*Set of 51*	28·00	30·00
MS3064	Four sheets. (a) 110×80 mm. $6 John Lennon. (b) 80×110 mm. $6 Elvis Presley. (c) 80×110 mm. $6 Marilyn Monroe wearing red jacket. (d) 70×100 mm. $6 Marilyn Monroe in black slip *Set of 4 sheets*		14·00	14·00

Nos. 3013/21, 3022/30, 3031/6, 3037/45, 3046/54 and 3055/63 were each printed together, *se-tenant*, in sheetlets of 6 (Nos. 3031/6) or 9 (others).

$20 (Elvis Presley) and £30 (Marilyn Monroe) values embossed on gold foil also exist from limited printings.

310 Heinrich Boll (1972 Literature)

(Des R. Sauber. Litho Questa)

1995 (2 Oct). *Centenary of Nobel Prize Trust Fund. T* **310** *and similar horiz designs. Multicoloured. P* 14.

3065/3112	$1×48	*Set of 48*	25·00	26·00
MS3113	Four sheets, each 74×104 mm. (a) $6 Adolf Windaus (1928 Chemistry). (b) $6 Hideki Yukawa (1949 Physics). (c) $6 Bertha von Suttner (1905 Peace). (d) $6 Karl Landsteiner (1930 Medicine) *Set of 4 sheets*		14·00	14·00

Designs:—No. 3065, Type **310**; No. 3066, Walther Bothe (1954 Physics); No. 3067, Richard Kuhn (1938 Chemistry); No. 3068, Hermann Hesse (1946 Literature); No. 3069, Knut Hamsun (1920 Literature); No. 3070, Konrad Lorenz (1973 Medicine); No. 3071, Thomas Mann (1929 Literature); No. 3072, Fridtjof Nansen (1922 Peace); Nos. 3073, Fritz Pregl (1923 Chemistry); No. 3074, Christian Lange (1921 Peace); No. 3075, Otto Loewi (1936 Medicine); No. 3076, Erwin Schrodinger (1933 Physics); No. 3077, Giosue Carducci (1906 Literature); No. 3078, Wladislaw Reymont (1924 Literature); No. 3079, Ivan Bunin (1933 Literature); No. 3080, Pavel Cherenkov (1958 Physics); No. 3081, Ivan Pavlov (1904 Medicine); No. 3082, Pyotr Kapitza (1978 Physics); No. 3083, Lev Landau (1962 Physics); No. 3084, Daniel Bovet (1957 Medicine); No. 3085, Henryk Sienkiewicz (1905 Literature); No. 3086, Aleksandr Prokhorov (1964 Physics); No. 3087, Julius von Jauregg (1927 Medicine); No. 3088, Grazia Deledda (1926 Literature); No. 3089, Bjornstjerne Bjornson (1903 Literature); No. 3090, Frank Kellogg (1929 Peace); No. 3091, Gustav Hertz (1925 Physics); No. 3092, Har Khorana (1968 Medicine); No. 3093, Kenichi Fukui (1981 Chemistry); No. 3094, Henry Kissinger (1973 Peace); No. 3095, Martin Luther King Jr. (1964 Peace); No. 3096, Odd Hassel (1969 Chemistry); No. 3097, Polykarp Kusch (1955 Physics); No. 3098, Ragnar Frisch (1969 Economics); No. 3099, Willis Lamb Jr. (1955 Physics); No. 3100, Sigrid Undset (1928 Literature); No. 3101, Robert Barany (1914 Medicine); No. 3102, Ernest Walton (1951 Physics); No. 3103, Alfred Fried (1911 Peace); No. 3104, James Franck (1925 Physics); No. 3105, Werner Forssmann (1956 Medicine); No. 3106, Yasunari Kawabata (1968 Literature); No. 3107, Wolfgang Pauli (1945 Physics); No. 3108, Jean-Paul Sartre (1964 Literature); No. 3109, Aleksandr Solzhenitsyn (1970 Literature); No. 3110, Hermann Staudinger (1953 Chemistry); No. 3111, Igor Tamm (1958 Physics); No. 3112, Samuel Beckett (1969 Literature).

Nos. 3065/76, 3077/88, 3089/100 and 3101/12 were each printed together, *se-tenant*, in sheetlets of 12.

311 ET4-03 Electric Train, Germany 312 Grey Wolf

(Des W. Wright. Litho Questa)

1995 (3 Oct). *History of Transport.* T **311** and similar horiz designs showing modern passenger trains (Nos. 3114/19) or classic cars (Nos. 3120/5). Multicoloured. P 14.
3114	$1.50, Type 311	85 85
	a. Sheetlet. Nos. 3114/19	4·50
3115	$1.50 TGV express train, France	85 85
3116	$1.50, Class 87 electric locomotive, Great Britain	85 85
3117	$1.50, Class "Beijing" diesel locomotive, China	85 85
3118	$1.50, Amtrak turbotrain, U.S.A.	85 85
3119	$1.50, Class RC4 electric train, Sweden	85 85
3120	$1.50, Duesenberg Model "J", 1931	85 85
	a. Sheetlet. Nos. 3120/5	4·50
3121	$1.50, Sleeve-valve Minerva, 1913	85 85
3122	$1.50, Delage "D.8.SS", 1933	85 85
3123	$1.50, Bugatti "Royale Coupe' De Ville", 1931–32	85 85
3124	$1.50, Rolls Royce "Phantom I Landau-ette", 1926	85 85
3125	$1.50, Mercedes Benz "S236/120/180PS", 1927	85 85
3114/25	*Set of 12*	9·00 9·00

MS3126 Two sheets, each 105×75 mm. (a) $5 Hispano-Suiza Type "H6B" sports car, 1924 (85×28¹/₂ mm). (b) $6 Eurostar train, Great Britain and France (85×28¹/₂ mm)
Set of 2 sheets 7·00 7·50

Nos. 3114/19 and 3120/5 were printed together, *se-tenant*, in sheetlets of 6.
Nos. 3120/5 also include the "Singapore '95" International Stamp Exhibition logo.

(Des M. Friedman. Litho Questa)

1995 (1 Dec). *Centenary of Sierra Club (environmental protection society)* (1992). T **312** and similar multicoloured designs. P 14.
3127	$1 Type 312	60 60
	a. Sheetlet. Nos. 3127/35	4·75
3128	$1 Grey Wolf cub	60 60
3129	$1 Head of Grey Wolf	60 60
3130	$1 Hawaiian Goose	60 60
3131	$1 Pair of Hawaiian Geese	60 60
3132	$1 Head of Jaguar	60 60
3133	$1 Liontail Macaque	60 60
3134	$1 Sand Cat kitten	60 60
3135	$1 Three Sand Cat kittens	60 60
3136	$1 Orang-Utan in tree (horiz)	60 60
	a. Sheetlet. Nos. 3136/44	4·75
3137	$1 Orang-Utan on ground (horiz)	60 60
3138	$1 Young Orang-Utan (horiz)	60 60
3139	$1 Jaguar lying down (horiz)	60 60
3140	$1 Head of Jaguar (horiz)	60 60
3141	$1 Pair of Sand Cats (horiz)	60 60
3142	$1 Hawaiian Goose (horiz)	60 60
3143	$1 Three Liontail Macaque (horiz)	60 60
3144	$1 Head of Liontail Macaque (horiz)	60 60
3127/44	*Set of 18*	9·50 9·50

Nos. 3127/35 and 3136/44 were printed together, *se-tenant*, in sheetlets of 9.
Nos. 3136/8 are inscribed "Orangutang" in error.

313 River Nile, Egypt

(Des R. Sauber. Litho Questa)

1995 (1 Dec). *Natural Landmarks.* T **313** and similar horiz designs. Multicoloured. P 14.
3145	$1.10, Type 313	70 70
	a. Sheetlet. Nos. 3145/52	5·00
3146	$1.10, River Yangtze, China	70 70
3147	$1.10, Niagara Falls, U.S.A.–Canada border	70 70
3148	$1.10, Victoria Falls, Zambia–Zimbabwe border	70 70
3149	$1.10, Grand Canyon, U.S.A.	70 70
3150	$1.10, Sahara Desert, Algeria	70 70
3151	$1.10, Mt Kilimanjaro, Tanzania	70 70
3152	$1.10, River Amazon, Brazil	70 70
3145/52	*Set of 8*	5·00 5·00

MS3153 106×76 mm. $6 Haleakala Crater, Hawaii 3·50 3·75
Nos. 3145/52 were printed together, *se-tenant*, in sheetlets of 8.

314 Lionel Santa Handcar

(Des Rosemary DeFiglio. Litho Questa)

1995 (7 Dec). *Christmas. Antique Disney Toys.* T **314** and similar horiz designs. Multicoloured. P 14×13¹/₂.
3154	1 c. Type 314	10 10
3155	2 c. Mickey Mouse "choo-choo"	10 10
3156	3 c. Minnie Mouse pram	10 10
3157	5 c. Mickey Mouse acrobats pull-toy	10 10
3158	10 c. Mickey and Pluto clockwork cart	15 10
3159	25 c. Mickey Mouse motorcycle	45 10
3160	$3 Lionel Mickey Mouse handcar	3·00 3·00
3161	$5 Casey Jr. Disneyland train	4·50 5·00
3154/61	*Set of 8*	7·50 7·50

MS3162 Two sheets. (a) 127×100 mm. $6 Lionel streamlined locomotive and Mickey Mouse wagon. (b) 100×127 mm. $6 "Silver Link" locomotive and Mickey the Stoker tender
Set of 2 sheets 8·00 9·00

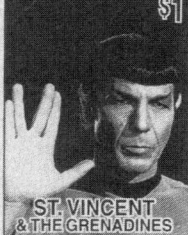

315 Symbolic Rat 316 Spock giving Vulcan Salute

(Des Y. Lee. Litho Questa)

1996 (2 Jan). *Chinese New Year ("Year of the Rat").* T **315** and similar vert designs showing different rats. P 14¹/₂.
3163	**315** 75 c. black, mauve and yellow-olive	35 40
	a. Horiz strip of 3. Nos. 3163/5	1·00
3164	— 75 c. black, orange-red and yellow-olive	35 40
3165	— 75 c. black, claret & dp turquoise-green	35 40
3163/5	*Set of 3*	1·00 1·25

MS3166 100×50 mm. $1 Type 315; $1 As No. 3164; $1 As No. 3165 1·40 1·50
MS3167 71×102 mm. $2 black, orge-red & yell-ol 85 90
Nos. 3163/5 were printed together, *se-tenant*, as horizontal strips of 3 in sheets of 9.

(Des J. Gordon. Litho Questa)

1996 (4 Jan). *30th Anniv of Star Trek Television Series.* T **316** and similar vert designs. Multicoloured. P 13¹/₂×14.
3168	$1 Type 316	45 50
	a. Sheetlet. Nos. 3168/76	4·00
3169	$1 Capt. Kirk and Spock dressed as gangsters	45 50
3170	$1 Kirk in front of computer	45 50
3171	$1 Kirk with Tribbles	45 50
3172	$1 Kirk, Spock and Lt. Uhura in front of Time Portal	45 50
3173	$1 Uhura and Lt. Sulu	45 50
3174	$1 Romulan commander and crew	45 50
3175	$1 City and planet	45 50
3176	$1 Khan	45 50
3177	$1 Spock with phaser	45 50
	a. Sheetlet. Nos. 3177/85	4·00
3178	$1 Capt. Kirk	45 50
3179	$1 Lt. Uhura	45 50
3180	$1 Lt. Sulu	45 50
3181	$1 Starship U.S.S. Enterprise	45 50
3182	$1 Dr. McCoy	45 50
3183	$1 Chief Engineer Scott	45 50
3184	$1 Kirk, Spock and McCoy	45 50
3185	$1 Chekov	45 50
3168/85	*Set of 18*	8·00 9·00

MS3186 152×107 mm. $6 Spock and Uhura 2·50 2·75
Nos. 3168/76 and 3177/85 were printed together, *se-tenant*, in sheetlets of 9.
A $30 value embossed on gold foil also exists from a limited printing.

317 Goofy the Stamp Dealer

(Des Alvin White Studio. Litho Questa)

1996 (8 Jan). *Occupations (1st series).* T **317** and similar multicoloured designs showing Walt Disney cartoon characters at work. P 14×13¹/₂ (horiz) or 13¹/₂×14 (vert).
3187/95	10 c. × 9 (Type **317**; Supermarket assistant; Car salesman; Florist; Fast food assistant; Street vendor; Gift shop assistant; Hobby shop assistant; Baker)	
	a. Sheetlet. Nos. 3187/95	1·00
3196/204	50 c. × 9 (Delivery man; Truck driver; Aircraft flight crew; Train crew; Bus driver; Tour guide; Cycle messenger; Tram conductor; Air traffic controller)	
	a. Sheetlet. Nos. 3196/204	3·00
3205/13	75 c. × 9 (Postal inspector; Traffic policeman; Private detectives; Highway Patrolman; Justice of the Peace; Security guard; Judge and lawyer; Sheriff; Court stenographer)	
	a. Sheetlet. Nos. 3205/13	4·00
3214/22	90 c. × 9 (Basketball player; Referee; Athletic coach; Ice skater; Golfer and caddy; Sports commentator; Tennis players; Football coach; Racing car driver)	
	a. Sheetlet. Nos. 3214/22	5·50
3223/31	95 c. × 9 (Paleontologist; Archaeologist; Inventor; Astronaut; Chemist; Engineer; Computer expert; Astronomer; Zoologist)	
	a. Sheetlet. Nos. 3223/31	5·50
3232/9	$1.10 × 8 (Classroom teacher; Nursery school teacher; Music teacher; Electronic teacher; School psychologist; School principal; Professor; Graduate (all vert))	
	a. Sheetlet. Nos. 3232/9	5·50
3240/8	$1.20 ×9 (Ship builders; Fisherman; Pearl diver; Underwater photographer; Bait and tackle shop owner; Swim suit models; Marine life painter; Life guard; Lighthouse keeper)	
	a. Sheetlet. Nos. 3240/8	6·00
3187/3248	*Set of 62*	27·00 29·00

MS3249 Seven sheets, each 127×102 mm. (a) $6 Ice cream seller. (b) $6 Tug boat captain (vert). (c) $6 Members of Jury (vert). (d) $6 Cheerleaders (vert). (e) $6 Oceanographer. (f) $6 Librarian (vert). (g) $6 Deep sea diver (vert)
Set of 7 sheets 23·00 24·00

Nos. 3187/95, 3196/3204, 3205/13, 3214/22, 3223/31, 3232/9, and 3240/8 were each printed together, *se-tenant*, in sheetlets of 8 (Nos. 3232/9) or 9 (others).
See also Nos. 3510/56.

(Litho Questa)

1996 (1 Feb). *125th Anniv of Metropolitan Museum of Art, New York.* Multicoloured designs as T **331** of Maldive Islands. P 13¹/₂×14.
3250/7	75 c. × 8 ("Moses striking Rock" (Abraham Bloemaert); "The Last Communion" (Botticelli); "The Musicians" (Caravaggio); "Francesco Sassetti and Son" (Ghirlandaio); "Pepito Costa y Bunells" (Goya); "Saint Andrew" (Martini); "The Nativity" (The Dutch School); "Christ Blessing" (Solario))	
	a. Sheetlet. Nos. 3250/7 plus centre label	2·75
3258/66	90 c. × 9 ("Madame Cézanne"; "Still Life with Apples and Pears"; "Man in a Straw Hat"; "Still Life with a Ginger Jar"; "Madame Cézanne in a Red Dress"; "Still Life with Crockery"; "Dominique Aubert"; "Still Life with Flowers"; "The Card Players" (all by Cézanne))	
	a. Sheetlet. Nos. 3258/66	3·75

3267/75	$1 × 9 ("Bullfight" (Goya); "Portrait of a Man" (Hals); "Mother and Son" (Sully); "Portrait of a Young Man" (Memling); "Matilde Stoughton de Jaudenes" (Stuart); "Josef de Jaudenes y Nebot" (Stuart); "Mont Sainte-Victoire" (Cézanne); "Gardanne" (Cézanne); "Empress Eugenie" (Winterhalter)			
	a. Sheetlet. Nos. 3267/75		4·25	
3276/84	$1.10 × 9 ("The Dissolute Household" (Steen); "Gerard de Lairesse" (Rembrandt); "Juan de Pareja" (Velázquez); "Curiosity" (Ter Borch); "The Companions of Rinaldo" (Poussin); "Don Gaspar de Guzman" (Velázquez); "Merry Company on a Terrace" (Steen); "Pilate washing Hands" (Rembrandt); "Portrait of a Man" (Van Dyck))			
	a. Sheetlet. Nos. 3276/84		4·50	
3250/84		Set of 35	15·00	16·00

MS3285 Four sheets, each 95×70 mm. (a) $6 "Hagar in the Wilderness" (Corot) (81×53 mm). P 14. (b) $6 "Two Young Peasant Women" (Pissarro) (81×53 mm). P 14. (c) $6 "Young Ladies from the Village" (Courbet) (81×53 mm). P 14. (d) $6 "Allegory of the Planets and Continents" (Tiepolo) (81×53 mm). P 14

Set of 4 sheets 10·00 10·50

Nos. 3250/7, 3258/66, 3267/75 and 3276/84 were each printed together, se-tenant, in sheetlets of 8 stamps and one centre label (Nos. 3250/7) or 9 (others).

318 Alien Band   319 Yoda

(Des J. Gordon. Litho Walsall (Nos. 3292/5))

1996 (19 Mar). *Star Wars (film trilogy). (a) T 318 and similar horiz designs. Multicoloured. P 14.*

3286	35 c. Type 318		70	70
	a. Sheetlet. Nos. 3286/91		3·75	
3287	35 c. Darth Vader in battle		70	70
3288	35 c. Fighter ship		70	70
3289	35 c. Space craft orbiting planet		70	70
3290	35 c. Space craft and shuttle		70	70
3291	35 c. Luke Skywalker on space bike		70	70

(b) Self-adhesive. T 319 and similar multicoloured designs. P 7

3292	$1 Darth Vader		1·25	1·25
	a. Strip of 3. Nos. 3292/4		3·25	3·25
3293	$1 Type 319		1·25	1·25
3294	$1 Storm Trooper		1·25	1·25
3286/94		Set of 9	7·00	7·00

MS3295 148×71 mm. $2×3 Designs as Nos. 3292/4 but triangular, 65×36½ mm. P 9   4·00 4·25

Nos. 3286/91 were printed together, se-tenant, in sheetlets of 6.

Nos. 3292/4 were printed in horizontal and vertical strips of 3 throughout the sheet of 9, with each stamp being separate on the backing paper with die-cut perforations.

Three $2 values embossed on gold foil also exist from a limited printing.

320 Anteos menippe   321 Michael Jordan (basketball player)

(Des T. Woods. Litho Questa)

1996 (15 Apr). *Butterflies. T 320 and similar vert designs. Multicoloured. P 14.*

3296	70 c. Type 320		30	35
3297	90 c. Papilio lycophron		40	45
	a. Sheetlet. Nos. 3297/3305		3·50	
3298	90 c. Prepona buckleyana		40	45
3299	90 c. Parides agavus		40	45
3300	90 c. Papilio cacicus		40	45
3301	90 c. Euryades duponchelli		40	45
3302	90 c. Diaethria dymena		40	45
3303	90 c. Orimba jansoni		40	45
3304	90 c. Polystichtis siaka		40	45
3305	90 c. Papilio machaonides		40	45

3306	$1 Eunica alcmena		45	50
3307	$1.10, Doxocopa lavinia		50	55
3308	$2 Tithorea tarricina		85	90
3296/3308		Set of 13	5·50	6·25

MS3309 Two sheets, each 75×104 mm. (a) $5 Adelpha albia. (b) $6 Themone pais

Set of 2 sheets 4·75 5·00

Nos. 3297/3305 were printed together, se-tenant, in sheetlets of 9, the backgrounds forming a composite design.

(Des J. Gordon. Litho Questa)

1996 (17 Apr). *Sports Legends. (a) Vert designs as T 321. P 14.*

3310	$2 Type 321		90	1·00
	a. Sheetlet. Nos. 3310×16 and 3312		17·00	
3311	$2 Joe Montana (American footballer)		90	1·00
	a. Sheetlet. Nos. 3311×16 and 3313		18·00	

(b) Size 69×103 mm. Imperf

3312	$6 Michael Jordan		4·50	5·50
3313	$10 Joe Montana		6·50	7·50
3310/13		Set of 4	11·50	13·50

Nos. 3310 with 3312 and 3311 with 3313 were each printed in sheetlets of 16 of the $2 with an example of the larger imperforate stamp included in the enlarged right-hand margin.

322 The Monkey King

(Des Y. Lee. Litho Walsall)

1996 (10 May). *"CHINA '96" 9th Asian International Stamp Exhibition (1st issue). Chinese Animated Films – Uproar in Heaven (Nos. 3314/18) and Nezha conquers the Dragon King (Nos. 3319/23). T 322 and similar multicoloured designs. P 12.*

3314	15 c. Type 322		10	10
	a. Sheetlet. Nos. 3314/23×2		1·40	
3315	15 c. Monkey King flying towards illuminated pole		10	10
3316	15 c. Monkey King and flying horses		10	10
3317	15 c. Monkey King picking fruit		10	10
3318	15 c. Monkey King drinking from flask		10	10
3319	15 c. Nezha waking up		10	10
3320	15 c. Nezha swimming with fish		10	10
3321	15 c. Nezha on back of sea serpent		10	10
3322	15 c. Nezha with sword		10	10
3323	15 c. Nezha in battle		10	10
3314/23		Set of 10	70	75

MS3324 Two sheets, each 85×105 mm. (a) 75 c. Monkey King (vert). (b) 75 c. Nezha (vert)

Set of 2 sheets 70 75

Nos. 3314/23 were printed together, se-tenant, in sheetlets of 20 containing two of each design.

323 Chongqing Dazu Buddha

(Des Y. Lee. Litho Walsall)

1996 (10 May). *"CHINA '96" 9th Asian International Stamp Exhibition (2nd issue). Sheet 115×80 mm. P 12.*

MS3325 323 $2 multicoloured   85 90

(Litho Questa)

1996 (12 June). *70th Birthday of Queen Elizabeth II. Multicoloured designs as T 334 of Maldive Islands showing different photographs. P 13½×14.*

3326	$2 As Type 334 of Maldive Islands		85	90
	a. Strip of 3. Nos. 3326/8		2·50	
3327	$2 Wearing Garter robes		85	90
3328	$2 Wearing pink hat and coat		85	90
3326/8		Set of 3	2·50	2·75

MS3329 125×103 mm. $6 On Buckingham Palace balcony (horiz). P 14×13½   2·50 2·75

Nos. 3326/8 were printed together, se-tenant, in horizontal and vertical strips of 3 throughout sheets of 9.

324 West Indian Boy

(Litho Questa)

1996 (11 July). *50th Anniv of U.N.I.C.E.F. T 324 and similar horiz designs. Multicoloured. P 14.*

3330	$1 Type 324		45	50
3331	$1.10, European girls		50	55
3332	$2 South-east Asian girl		85	90
3330/2		Set of 3	1·75	1·90

MS3333 104×74 mm. $5 Arab boy   2·10 2·25

325 Menorah and The Knesset

(Des Rachel Deitch. Litho Questa)

1996 (11 July). *3000th Anniv of Jerusalem. T 325 and similar horiz designs. Multicoloured. P 14.*

3334	$1 Type 325		45	50
3335	$1.10, The Montefiore Windmill		50	55
3336	$2 Shrine of the Book		85	90
3334/6		Set of 3	1·75	1·90

MS3337 104×74 mm. $5 Old City, Jerusalem   2·10 2·25

The captions on Nos. 3334 and 3336 were transposed in error.

326 Walter Winchell   327 Bananaquit

(Des J. Iskowitz. Litho Questa)

1996 (11 July). *Centenary of Radio. Entertainers. T 326 and similar vert designs. Multicoloured. P 13½×14.*

3338	90 c. Type 326		40	45
3339	$1 Fred Allen		45	50
3340	$1.10, Hedda Hopper		50	55
3341	$2 Eve Arden		85	90
3338/41		Set of 4	2·10	2·40

MS3342 72×102 mm. $6 Major Bowes   2·75 3·00

(Des Jennifer Toombs. Litho B.D.T.)

1996 (11 July). *Birds. T 327 and similar multicoloured designs. P 14.*

3343	60 c. Type 327		25	30
3344	$1 Rufous-throated Solitaire		45	50
3345	$1 Purple Martin (horiz)		45	50
	a. Sheetlet. Nos. 3345/53		4·00	
3346	$1 Broad-winged Hawk (horiz)		45	50
3347	$1 White-tailed Tropic Bird (horiz)		45	50
3348	$1 Black-winged Stilt (horiz)		45	50
3349	$1 Bridled Tern (horiz)		45	50
3350	$1 Blue-hooded Euphonia (horiz)		45	50
3351	$1 Turnstone (horiz)		45	50
3352	$1 Green-throated Carib (horiz)		45	50
3353	$1 Yellow-crowned Night Heron (horiz)		45	50
3354	$1.10, Hooded Tanager		50	55
3355	$2 Purple-throated Carib		90	95
3343/55		Set of 13	6·00	6·75

MS3356 Two sheets, each 89×92 mm. (a) $5 Red-billed Whistling Duck. (b) $6 St. Vincent Amazon   Set of 2 sheets 4·75 5·00

Nos. 3345/53 were printed together, se-tenant, in sheetlets of 9 with the backgrounds forming a composite design.

328 Maurice King (St. Vincent) (weightlifting), Pan American Games, 1959   329 Notre Dame Cathedral, Paris

(Des M. Friedman and S. Stines. Litho Questa)

1996 (19 July). *Olympic Games, Atlanta (2nd issue). T 328 and similar multicoloured designs. P 14.*

3357	20 c. Type 328		10	10

3358	70 c. Eswort Coombs (St. Vincent) (400m sprint, World University Student Games)		30	35
3359	90 c. Pamenos Ballantyne (St. Vincent) (O.E.C.S. road-running) and Benedict Ballantyne (St. Vincent) (Guinness Half-marathon, 1994)		40	45
3360	90 c. Ancient Greek runners, Olympia (horiz)		40	45
3361	$1 London landmarks (horiz)		45	50
3362	$1 Women's archery (Korea), 1988, 1992		45	50
	a. Sheetlet. Nos. 3362/70		4·00	
3363	$1 Gymnastics (Japan), 1960–76		45	50
3364	$1 Basketball (U.S.A.), 1936, 1948–68, 1976, 1984 and 1992		45	50
3365	$1 Soccer (Spain), 1992		45	50
3366	$1 Water polo (Hungary), 1956		45	50
3367	$1 Baseball (Cuba), 1992		45	50
3368	$1 Kayak (Germany), 1980		45	50
3369	$1 Fencing (France), 1980		45	50
3370	$1 Cycling (Germany), 1908, 1964, 1972–76 and 1992		45	50
3371	$1 Vitaly Shcherbo (Russia) (gymastics), 1992		45	50
	a. Sheetlet. Nos. 3371/9		4·00	
3372	$1 Fu Mingxia (China) (diving), 1992		45	50
3373	$1 Wilma Rudolph (U.S.A.) (track and field), 1960		45	50
3374	$1 Rafer Johnson (U.S.A.) (decathlon), 1960		45	50
3375	$1 Teofilo Stevenson (Cuba) (boxing), 1972–80		45	50
3376	$1 Babe Didrikson (U.S.A.) (track and field), 1932		45	50
3377	$1 Kyoko Iwasaki (Japan) (swimming), 1992		45	50
3378	$1 Yoo Namkyu (Korea) (table tennis), 1988		45	50
3379	$1 Michael Gross (Germany) (swimming), 1984–88		45	50
3380	$1 Yasuhiro Yamashita (Japan) (judo), 1984 (horiz)		45	50
	a. Sheetlet. Nos. 3380/8		4·00	
3381	$1 Peter Rono (Kenya) (1500m race), 1988 (horiz)		45	50
3382	$1 Aleksandr Kourlovitch (Russia) (weight-lifting), 1988 (horiz)		45	50
3383	$1 Juha Tiainen (Finland) (hammer throw), 1984 (horiz)		45	50
3384	$1 Sergei Bubka (Russia) (pole vault), 1988 (horiz)		45	50
3385	$1 Q.F. Newall (Great Britain) (archery), 1908 (horiz)		45	50
3386	$1 Nadia Comaneci (Rumania) (gymnastics), 1976 (horiz)		45	50
3387	$1 Carl Lewis (U.S.A.) (long jump), 1988 (horiz)		45	50
3388	$1 Bob Mathias (U.S.A.) (decathlon), 1948 (horiz)		45	50
3389	$1 Chuhei Nambu (Japan) (triple jump), 1932 (horiz)		45	50
	a. Sheetlet. Nos. 3389/97		4·00	
3390	$1 Duncan McNaughton (Canada) (high jump), 1932 (horiz)		45	50
3391	$1 Jack Kelly (U.S.A.) (single sculls), 1920 (horiz)		45	50
3392	$1 Jackie Joyner-Kersee (U.S.A.) (heptathlon), 1988 (horiz)		45	50
3393	$1 Tyrell Biggs (U.S.A.) (super heavy-weight boxing), 1984 (horiz)		45	50
3394	$1 Larisa Latynina (Russia) (gymnastics), 1964 (horiz)		45	50
3395	$1 Bob Garrett (U.S.A.) (discus), 1896 (horiz)		45	50
3396	$1 Paavo Nurmi (Finland) (5000 m), 1924 (horiz)		45	50
3397	$1 Eric Lemming (Sweden) (javelin), 1908 (horiz)		45	50
3398	$1.10, Rodney Jack (St. Vincent) (1995 Caribbean Nations Football Cup)		50	55
3399	$1.10, Dorando Pietri (Italy) (marathon), 1908		50	55
3400	$2 Yachting (horiz)		85	90
3357/400		Set of 44	20·00	22·00

MS3401 Four sheets. (a) 74×104 mm. $5 Olympic flag (horiz). (b) 74×104 mm. $5 Carl Lewis (U.S.A.) (relay). (c) 104×74 mm. $5 Hannes Kolehmainen (Finland) (marathon), 1920 (horiz). (d) 104×74 mm. $5 Alexander Ditiatin (Russia) (gymnastics), 1980 (horiz)

Set of 4 sheets 8·25 8·50

Nos. 3362/70, 3371/9, 3380/8 and 3389/97, which show Olympic gold medal winners, were each printed, se-tenant, in sheetlets of 9.

No. 3371 is inscribed "GYMNASTIECS" in error.

(Des Alvin White Studios. Litho Questa)

1996 (25 July). *The Hunchback of Notre Dame. T* **329** *and similar multicoloured designs showing scenes from the Disney cartoon film. Multicoloured. P 13¹/₂×14 (vert) or 14×13¹/₂ (horiz).*

3402/7	10 c. × 6 (Type **329**; People watching puppet show; Judge Frollo on black horse; Quasimodo and his parents captured; Gargoyles; Quasimodo)			
	a. Sheetlet. Nos. 3402/7		1·00	
3408/16	30 c. × 9 (Captain Phoebus meets Esmeralda; Captain Phoebus and Judge Frollo; Esmeralda dancing; Esmeralda and candidates for King of Fools; Quasimodo wearing crown; Quasimodo pelted; Quasimodo carrying Esmeralda; Phoebus on black horse; Quasimodo, Esmeralda and a wounded Phoebus (all horiz))			
	a. Sheetlet. Nos. 3408/16		2·25	

3417/25	$1 × 9 (Quasimodo chained to bell tower; Three gargoyles and Quasimodo; Quasimodo pulling down pillars; Quasimodo rescuing Esmeralda; Phoebus leading citizens; Quasimodo throwing wood; Quasimodo weeping over Esmeralda; Quasimodo and Frollo fighting; Quasimodo and Esmeralda on ledge (all horiz))			
	a. Sheetlet. Nos. 3417/25		6·00	
3426/33	$1 × 8 (Quasimodo; Phoebus; Laverne and Hugo; Clopin; Frollo; Esmeralda; Victor; Djali)			
	a. Sheetlet. Nos. 3426/33		5·50	
3402/33		Set of 31	13·00	14·00

MS3434 Five sheets. (a) 124×102 mm. $6 Quasimodo, Phoebus and Esmeralda (horiz). (b) 124×102 mm. $6 Esmeralda. (c) 124×102 mm. $6 Quasimodo cheering. (d) 104×126 mm. $6 Esmeralda and Quasimodo (horiz). (e) 104×126 mm. $6 Esmeralda and Phoebus (horiz)

Set of 5 sheets 20·00 22·00

Nos. 33402/7, 3408/16, 3417/25 and 3426/33 were each printed together, se-tenant, in sheetlets of 6 (Nos. 3402/7), 8 (Nos. 3426/33) or 9 (Nos. 3408/16).

No. 3416 is inscribed "wonded phoebus" in error.

330 French Angelfish   331 *Beloperone guttata*

(Des D. Burkhardt. Litho Questa)

1996 (10 Aug). *Fishes. T* **330** *and similar horiz designs. Multicoloured. P 14.*

3435	70 c. Type **330**		30	35
3436	90 c. Red-spotted Hawkfish		40	45
3437	$1 Barred Hamlet		45	50
	a. Sheetlet. Nos. 3437/45		4·00	
3438	$1 Flamefish		45	50
3439	$1 Caribbean Long-nosed Butterflyfish		45	50
3440	$1 Royal Gramma ("Fairy Basslet")		45	50
3441	$1 Red-tailed Parrotfish		45	50
3442	$1 Black-barred Soldierfish		45	50
3443	$1 Three-spotted Damselfish		45	50
3444	$1 Candy Basslet		45	50
3445	$1 Spot-finned Hogfish		45	50
3446	$1 Jackknife Fish		45	50
	a. Sheetlet. Nos. 3446/54		4·00	
3447	$1 Surgeon Fish		45	50
3448	$1 Muttonfish		45	50
3449	$1 Seahorse		45	50
3450	$1 Comber Fish		45	50
3451	$1 Angel Shark		45	50
3452	$1 Moray Eel		45	50
3453	$1 Bicolour Parrotfish		45	50
3454	$1 Tritonium nodiferum (sea snail)		45	50
3455	$1.10, Balloonfish ("Spiny Puffer")		50	55
3456	$2 Grey Triggerfish		85	90
3435/56		Set of 22	10·00	11·00

MS3457 Two sheets, each 106×76 mm. (a) $5 Queen Triggerfish. (b) $6 Blue Marlin

Set of 2 sheets 4·75 5·00

Nos. 3437/45 and 3446/54 were each printed together, se-tenant, in sheetlets of 9 with the backgrounds of Nos. 3446/54 forming a composite design.

No. 3445 is inscribed "HOFGFISH" in error.

(Des Jennifer Toombs. Litho B.D.T.)

1996 (15 Aug). *Flowers. T* **331** *and similar horiz designs. Multicoloured. P 13¹/₂×14.*

3458	70 c. Type **331**		30	35
3459	90 c. *Datura candida*		40	45
	a. Sheetlet. Nos. 3459/67		3·50	
3460	90 c. *Amherstia nobilis*		40	45
3461	90 c. *Ipomoea acuminata*		40	45
3462	90 c. *Bougainvillea glabra*		40	45
3463	90 c. *Cassia alata*		40	45
3464	90 c. *Cordia sebestena*		40	45
3465	90 c. *Opuntia dilenii*		40	45
3466	90 c. *Cryptostegia grandiflora*		40	45
3467	90 c. *Rodriguezia lanceolata*		40	45
3468	$1 *Epidendrum elongatum*		45	50
3469	$1.10, *Petrea volubilis*		50	55
3470	$2 *Oncidium altissimum*		85	90
3458/70		Set of 13	5·50	6·25

MS3471 Two sheets, each 78×64 mm. (a) $5 Hibiscus rosa-sinensis. (b) $5 Acalypha hispida

Set of 2 sheets 4·25 4·50

Nos. 3459/67 were printed together, se-tenant, in sheetlets of 9 with the backgrounds forming a composite design.

1996 (5 Sept). *Passenger Ships. T* **332** *and similar horiz designs. Multicoloured. Litho. P 14.*

3472	$1.10, Type **332**		50	55
	a. Sheetlet. Nos. 3472/7		3·00	
3473	$1.10, *Nerissa*, 1926		50	55
3474	$1.10, *Howick Hall*, 1910		50	55
3475	$1.10, *Jervis Bay*, 1922		50	55
3476	$1.10, *Vauban*, 1912		50	55
3477	$1.10, *Orinoco*, 1928		50	55
3478	$1.10, *Lady Rodney*, 1929		50	55
	a. Sheetlet. Nos. 3478/83		3·00	
3479	$1.10, *Empress of Russia*, 1913		50	55
3480	$1.10, *Providence*, 1914*		50	55
3481	$1.10, *Reina Victori-Eugenia*, 1913		50	55
3482	$1.10, *Balmoral Castle*, 1910		50	55
3483	$1.10, *Tivives*, 1911		50	55
3472/83		Set of 12	6·00	6·50

MS3484 Two sheets, each 106×76 mm. (a) $6 *Aquitania*, 1914. (b) $6 *Imperator*, 1913

Set of 2 sheets 5·25 5·50

*Although the design of No. 3480 is inscribed "1914" the *Providence* was not built until 1915.

Nos. 3472/7 and 3478/83 were each printed together, se-tenant, in sheetlets of 6.

(Des Y. Lee. Litho Questa)

1996 (8 Sept). *Elvis Presley (singer) Commemoration. T* **333** *and similar vert designs showing different portraits. Multicoloured. P 13¹/₂×14.*

3485	$2 Type **333**		85	90
	a. Sheetlet. Nos. 3485/90		5·00	
3486	$2 Wearing checked shirt with guitar		85	90
3487	$2 Playing piano		85	90
3488	$2 Wearing black jacket and playing guitar		85	90
3489	$2 Wearing white shirt and black tie		85	90
3490	$2 Singing into studio microphone		85	90
3485/90		Set of 6	5·00	5·25

Nos. 3485/90 were printed together, se-tenant, in sheetlets of 6 with an enlarged illustrated margin.

334 Sandy Koufax (baseball player)   335 Richard Petty's 1990 Pontiac

(Des J. Gordon. Litho Questa)

1996 (26 Sept). *Sports Legends. Sandy Koufax. T* **334** *and similar vert designs. Multicoloured. P 14 or imperf (No. 3494).*

3491	$2 Type **334**		85	90
	a. Sheetlet. Nos. 3491×6, 3492/3 each × 5 and 3494		16·00	
3492	$2 Pitching ball		85	90
3493	$2 Preparing to pitch with arm raised		85	90
3494	$6 Sandy Koufax (69×103 mm)		2·50	2·75
3491/4		Set of 4	5·00	5·75

Nos. 3491/4 were printed in sheetlets containing 16 $2 stamps and one example of the imperforate $6 included in the enlarged right-hand margin.

A $30 value embossed on gold foil also exists from a limited printing.

(Des W. Wright. Litho Questa)

1996 (26 Sept). *Richard Petty (stock car driver) Commemoration. T* **335** *and similar horiz designs. Multicoloured. P 14.*

3495	$2 Type **335**		85	90
	a. Sheetlet. Nos. 3495/8		3·25	
3496	$2 Richard Petty		85	90
3497	$2 1972 Plymouth		85	90
3498	$2 1974 Dodge		85	90
3495/8		Set of 4	3·25	3·50

MS3499 Two sheets. (a) 104×74 mm. $5 1970 Plymouth "Superbird" (84×28 mm). (b) 64×48 mm. $6 1996 25th Anniversary STP Pontiac

Set of 2 sheets 4·75 5·00

Nos. 3495/8 were printed together, se-tenant, in sheetlets of 4 with an enlarged illustrated margin.

332 *Doric*, 1923   333 Elvis Presley

336 D. S. Cozier (founder) and Cadet Force Emblem

(Litho Questa)

1996 (23 Oct). *60th Anniv of St. Vincent Army Cadet Force. T* **336** *and similar horiz design. Multicoloured. P* 14×13½.
3500 70 c. Type **336** 30 35
3501 90 c. Emblem and first cadets with Cozier 40 45

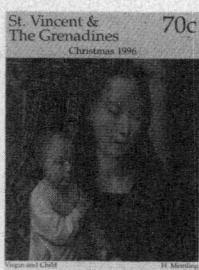
337 "Virgin and Child" (detail, Memling)

338 Sylvester Stallone in *Rocky IV*

(Litho Questa)

1996 (14 Nov). *Christmas. Religious Paintings. T* **337** *and similar vert designs. Multicoloured. P* 13½×14.
3502 70 c. Type **337** 30 35
3503 90 c. "St. Anthony" (detail, Memling) 40 45
3504 $1 "Madonna and Child" (detail, D. Bouts) 45 50
3505 $1.10, "Virgin and Child" (detail, Lorenzo Lotto) 50 55
3506 $2 "St. Roch" (detail, Lotto) .. 85 90
3507 $5 "St. Sebastian" (detail, Lotto) 2·10 2·25
3502/7 .. .. .. *Set of 6* 4·50 5·00
MS3508 Two sheets, each 106×76 mm. (a) $5 "Virgin and Child with St. Roch and St. Sebastian" (Lotto). (b) $5 "Virgin and Child with St. Anthony and Donor" (Memling).
.. .. .. *Set of 2 sheets* 4·25 4·50

(Des Shannon. Litho Questa)

1996 (21 Nov). *20th Anniv of Rocky (film). Sheet* 143×182 *mm. P* 14×13½.
MS3509 **338** $2×3 multicoloured .. 2·50 2·75
No. **MS**3509 was printed with an enlarged illustrated left-hand margin.

(Des Alvin White Studios. Litho Questa)

1996 (3 Dec). *Occupations (2nd series). Multicoloured designs as Nos.* 3196/3248, *but all with face value of* 10 c. *P* 14×13½ (*horiz*) *or* 13½×14 (*vert*).
3510/17 10 c. × 8 As Nos. 3196/9 and 3201/4
  a. Sheetlet. Nos. 3510/17 and central label .. .. .. 1·00
3518/25 10 c. × 8 As Nos. 3205/8 and 3210/13
  a. Sheetlet. Nos. 3518/25 and central label .. .. .. 1·00
3526/33 10 c. × 8 As Nos. 3214/17 and 3519/22
  a. Sheetlet. Nos. 3526/33 and central label .. .. .. 1·00
3534/41 10 c. × 8 As Nos. 3523/6 and 3528/31
  a. Sheetlet. Nos. 3534/41 and central label .. .. .. 1·00
3542/8 10 c. × 7 As Nos. 3232/4 and 3236/9 (all vert)
  a. Sheetlet. Nos. 3542/8 and top right-hand corner label .. .. 1·00
3549/56 10 c. × 8 As Nos. 3240/3 and 3245/8
  a. Sheetlet. Nos. 3549/56 and central label .. .. .. 1·00
3510/56 .. .. .. *Set of 47* 5·50 6·50
Nos. 3510/17, 3518/25, 3526/33, 3534/41, 3542/8 and 3549/56 were printed together, *se-tenant*, in sheetlets of 7 (Nos. 3542/8) or 8 (others). In each case one stamp shown on the original sheetlet has been replaced with a stamp-sized label as indicated.

339 Symbolic Ox

340 Lieut. Tuvok

(Des Y. Lee. Litho Questa)

1997 (2 Jan). *Chinese New Year ("Year of the Ox"). T* **339** *and similar vert designs showing different oxen. P* 14½×15.
3557 75 c. black, salmon and brown-rose 30 35
  a. Horiz strip of 3. Nos. 3557/9 90
3558 75 c. black, emerald and lilac .. 30 35
3559 75 c. black, bright rose and rose-carmine 30 35
3557/9 .. .. .. *Set of 3* 90 1·00
MS3560 97×48 mm. Nos. 3557/9 .. 90 1·00
MS3561 71×101 mm. $2 black, dull orange and orange-yellow 85 90
Nos. 3557/9 were printed together, *se-tenant*, as horizontal strips of 3 in sheets of 9.

1997 (23 Jan). Star Trek Voyager (*television series*). *T* **340** *and similar vert designs. Multicoloured. Litho. P* 13½×14.
3562 $2 Type **340** 85 90
  a. Sheetlet. Nos. 3562/70 .. 7·50
3563 $2 Kes 85 90
3564 $2 Tom Paris 85 90
3565 $2 The Doctor 85 90
3566 $2 Captain Katherine Janeway .. 85 90
3567 $2 B'Elanna Torres 85 90
3568 $2 Neelix 85 90
3569 $2 Harry Kim 85 90
3570 $2 First Officer Chakotay .. 85 90
3562/70 .. .. .. *Set of 9* 7·50 8·00
MS3571 88×120 mm. $6 Crew of the *Star Trek Voyager* (28×45 *mm*) .. .. 2·75 3·00
Nos. 3562/70 were printed together, *se-tenant*, in sheetlets of 9.
A $30 value embossed on gold foil also exists from a limited printing.

341 Mickey Mantle

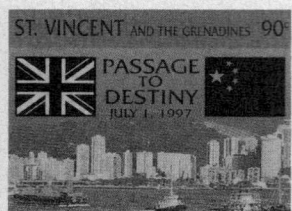
342 Hong Kong Waterfront

(Des J. Gordon. Litho Questa)

1997 (10 Feb). *Sports Legends. Mickey Mantle (baseball player). T* **341** *and similar vert design. Multicoloured. P* 14 (*No.* 3572) *or imperf* (*No.* 3573).
3572 $2 Type **341** 85 90
  a. Sheetlet. Nos. 3572×16 and 3573 16·00
3573 $6 Mickey Mantle (67×100 *mm*) .. 2·50 2·75
Nos. 3572/3 were printed together, *se-tenant*, in sheetlets containing 16 $2 stamps and one example of the imperforate $6 included in the enlarged illustrated right-hand margin.

(Des S. Nicodemus (No. **MS**3584). Litho B.D.T.)

1997 (12 Feb). *"Hong Kong '97" International Stamp Exhibition. T* **342** *and similar horiz designs showing the Hong Kong waterfront by day* (*Nos.* 3574/8) *or night* (*Nos.* 3579/83). *Multicoloured. P* 14.
3574 90 c. Type **342** 40 45
  a. Sheetlet. Nos. 3574/83 .. 4·00
3575 90 c. Two ferries in foreground .. 40 45
3576 90 c. Construction site on waterfront 40 45
3577 90 c. One launch 40 45
3578 90 c. Hong Kong Bank and yellow building in centre 40 45
3579 90 c. Large building with spire on right .. 40 45
3580 90 c. Electronic billboards including HITACHI 40 45
3581 90 c. Mansions on hillside at right .. 40 45
3582 90 c. Toshiba and NEC billboards in centre 40 45
3583 90 c. Hong Kong bank building under Union Jack 40 45
3574/83 .. .. .. *Set of 10* 4·00 4·50
MS3584 Three sheets, each 127×85 mm. (a) $2 Boy and girl at Full Moon Festival; $2 Couple on bridge; $2 Two girls with lanterns. (b) $2 Incense candles; $2 Buddhist monk at Polin Monastery; $2 Orchids. (c) $2 Wanchai Market; $2 Chinese couple in street; $2 Man choosing fruit. (*all designs* 34×25 *mm*). P 13½ .. *Set of 3 sheets* 7·50 8·00
Nos. 3574/83 were printed together, *se-tenant* in two horizontal strips of five forming two composite designs.
A $30 value embossed on gold foil also exists from a limited printing.

(Des M. Freedman and Dena Rubin. Litho Questa)

1997 (24 Mar). *50th Anniv of U.N.E.S.C.O. Multicoloured designs as T* **348** *of Maldive Islands. P* 13½×14 (*vert*) *or* 14×13½ (*horiz*).
3585 70 c. Lord Howe Island, Australia 30 35
3586 90 c. Uluru-kata Tjuta National Park, Australia 40 45
3587 $1 Cave paintings, Kakadu National Park, Australia 45 50
3588 $1.10, Te Wahipounamu National Park, New Zealand 50 55
3589 $1.10, Castle, Himeji-jo, Japan 50 55
  a. Sheetlet. Nos. 3589/96 and central label .. .. .. 4·00
3590 $1.10, Temple, lake and gardens, Kyoto, Japan 50 55
3591 $1.10, Walkway, Kyoto, Japan .. 50 55
3592 $1.10, Buddha, Temple of Ninna, Japan 50 55
3593 $1.10, View from castle, Himeji-jo, Japan 50 55
3594 $1.10, Forest, Shirakami-sanchi, Japan 50 55
3595 $1.10, Forest and mountains, Yaku-shima, Japan 50 55
3596 $1.10, Forest, Yakushima, Japan 50 55
3597 $1.10, City of San Gimignano, Italy 50 55
  a. Sheetlet. Nos. 3597/3604 and central label .. .. .. 4·00
3598 $1.10, Cathedral of Santa Maria Asunta, Pisa, Italy 50 55
3599 $1.10, Cathedral of Santa Maria Fiore, Florence, Italy 50 55
3600 $1.10, Archaeological site, Valley of the Boyne, Ireland 50 55
3601 $1.10, Church of St Savin-sur-Gartempe, France 50 55

3602 $1.10, Regency mansion, Bath, England 50 55
3603 $1.10, Rooftop view of Bath, England 50 55
3604 $1.10, Street in Bath, England 50 55
3605 $1.10, Monastery of Rossanou, Meteora, Greece 50 55
  a. Sheetlet. Nos. 3605/12 and central label .. .. .. 4·00
3606 $1.10, Ceiling painting, Mount Athos, Greece 50 55
3607 $1.10, Monastery Osios Varlaam, Meteora, Greece 50 55
3608 $1.10, Ruins, Athens, Greece .. 50 55
3609 $1.10, Carvings, Acropolis Museum, Athens, Greece 50 55
3610 $1.10, Painted cloisters, Mount Athos, Greece 50 55
3611 $1.10, Lake, Mount Athos, Greece 50 55
3612 $1.10, Painting above door, Mount Athos, Greece 50 55
3613 $1.50, Palace, Wudang Mountains, China (*horiz*) 65 70
  a. Sheetlet. Nos. 3613/17 and label 3·25
3614 $1.50, Caves, Mogao, China (*horiz*) 65 70
3615 $1.50, House, Taklamakan Desert, China (*horiz*) 65 70
3616 $1.50, Section going through forest, Great Wall, China (*horiz*) 65 70
3617 $1.50, Section going through desert, Great Wall, China (*horiz*) 65 70
3618 $1.50, House and church, Quedlinburg, Germany (*horiz*) .. 65 70
  a. Sheetlet. Nos. 3618/22 and label 3·25
3619 $1.50, Decorated house fronts, Quedlinburg (*horiz*) .. 65 70
3620 $1.50, Decorative house windows, Quedlinburg, Germany (*horiz*) 65 70
3621 $1.50, House front, Quedlinburg, Germany (*horiz*) .. 65 70
3622 $1.50, Church spires, Quedlinburg (*horiz*) 65 70
3623 $1.50, Valley of the Ingenios, Cuba (*horiz*) 65 70
  a. Sheetlet. Nos. 3623/7 and label 3·25
3624 $1.50, City of Zacatecas, Mexico (*horiz*) 65 70
3625 $1.50, Lima, Peru (*horiz*) .. 65 70
3626 $1.50, Monastic ruins, Paraguay (*horiz*) 65 70
3627 $1.50, Mayan ruins, Copan, Honduras (*horiz*) 65 70
3628 $2 Tongariro National Park, New Zealand (*horiz*) 85 90
3629 $5 Tongariro National Park, New Zealand (*horiz*) .. .. 2·10 2·25
3585/629 .. .. *Set of 45* 26·00 29·00
MS3630 Seven sheets, each 127×102 mm. (a) $5 Great Wall, China (*horiz*). (b) $5 Venice, Italy (*horiz*). (c) $5 Dunbuang Oasis, China (*horiz*). (d) $5 Wall, Quedlinburg, Germany (*horiz*). (e) $5 Meteora Monastery, Greece (*horiz*). (f) $5 Himeji-jo, Japan (*horiz*). (g) $5 Dome of the Rock, Jerusalem (*horiz*) .. *Set of 7 sheets* 14·00 15·00
Nos. 3589/96, 3597/604 and 3605/12 were each printed together, *se-tenant*, in sheetlets of 8 stamps with a central label and Nos. 3613/17, 3618/22 and 3623/7 in sheetlets of 5 stamps with a top left-hand corner label.

343 Microwave Radio Relay Tower, Dorsetshire Hill

344 Smooth-billed Ani

(Des M. Freedman. Litho Questa)

1997 (3 Apr). *125th Anniv of Telecommunications in St. Vincent. T* **343** *and similar multicoloured designs (except* 70 c.). *P* 14½.
3631 5 c. Type **343** 10 10
3632 10 c. Cable and Wireless headquarters, Kingstown 10 10
3633 20 c. Microwave relay tower (*vert*) .. 10 10
3634 35 c. Cable and Wireless complex, Arnos Vale 15 20
3635 50 c. Cable and Wireless tower, Mount St. Andrew 25 30
3636 70 c. *Dacia* (cable ship), 1872 (black and bluish violet) 30 35
3637 90 c. Eastern telecommunications network map, 1872 .. .. 40 45
3638 $1.10, World telegraph map, 1876 .. 50 55
3631/8 .. .. .. *Set of 8* 1·75 2·00

(Litho Questa)

1997 (7 Apr). *Birds of the World. T* **344** *and similar vert designs. Multicoloured. P* 14.
3639 60 c. Type **344** 25 30
3640 70 c. Belted Kingfisher 30 35
3641 90 c. Blackburnian Warbler .. 40 45
3642 $1 Blue Grosbeak 45 50
  a. Sheetlet. Nos. 3642/7 .. 2·75
3643 $1 Bananaquit 45 50
3644 $1 Cedar Waxwing 45 50
3645 $1 Ovenbird 45 50
3646 $1 Hooded Warbler 45 50
3647 $1 Flicker 45 50
3648 $1.10, Blue Tit 50 55
3649 $2 Chaffinch 85 90
3650 $2 Song Thrush 85 90
  a. Sheetlet. Nos. 3650/5 .. 5·00
3651 $2 Robin 85 90
3652 $2 Blackbird 85 90
3653 $2 Great Spotted Woodpecker .. 85 90

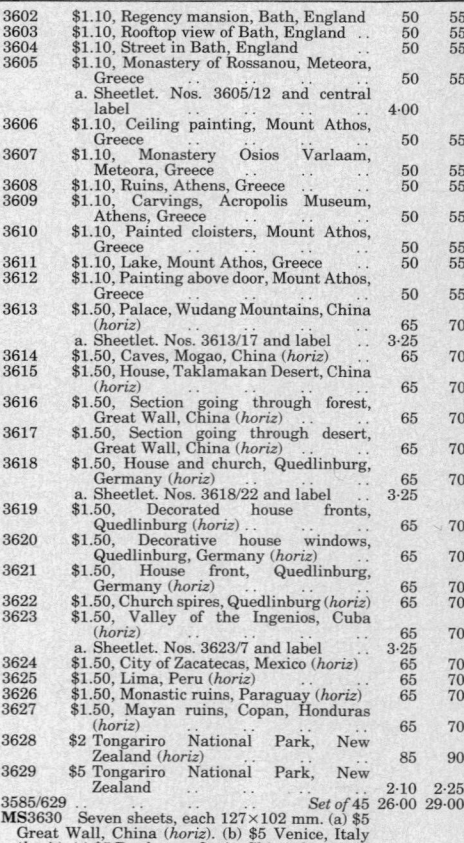
PASSAGE TO DESTINY JULY 1, 1997

3654	$2 Wren	85	90
3655	$2 Kingfisher	85	90
3656	$5 Ruddy Turnstone	2·10	2·25
3639/56	*Set of 18*	12·00	13·00

MS3657 Two sheets, each 101×75 mm. (a) $5 St. Vincent Parrot. (b) $5 Tawny Owl *Set of 2 sheets* 4·25 4·50
Nos. 3642/7 and 3650/5 were each printed together, *se-tenant*, in sheetlets of 6 with the backgrounds forming composite designs.

345 Mandarin Duck   346 Frank Robinson

(Des R. Rundo. Litho Questa)

1997 (7 Apr). *Sea Birds. T 345 and similar multicoloured designs. P 15×14½ (horiz) or 14½×15 (vert).*

3658	70 c. Type 345	30	35
3659	90 c. Green Heron	40	45
3660	$1 Ringed Teal drake	45	50
3661	$1.10 Blue-footed Booby and chick	50	55
3662	$1.10, Crested Auklet (*vert*)	50	55
	a. Sheetlet. Nos. 3662/7	3·00	
3663	$1.10, Whiskered Auklet (*vert*)	50	55
3664	$1.10, Pigeon Guillemot (*vert*)	50	55
3665	$1.10, Adelie Penguins (*vert*)	50	55
3666	$1.10, Rockhopper Penguin (*vert*)	50	55
3667	$1.10, Emperor Penguin and chick (*vert*)	50	55
3668	$2 Australian Jacana (*vert*)	85	90
3669	$5 Reddish Egret (*vert*)	2·10	2·25
3658/69	*Set of 12*	7·50	8·25

MS3670 Two sheets, each 101×75 mm. (a) $5 Flamingos. (b) $5 Snowy Egrets *Set of 2 sheets* 4·25 4·50
Nos. 3662/7 were printed together, *se-tenant*, in sheetlets of 6 with the backgrounds forming a composite design.

1997 (15 Apr). *Baseball Legends. T 346 and similar vert designs. (a) P 14×15 (Nos. 3671/86) or imperf (No. 3687).*

3671	$1 Type 345	45	50
	a. Sheetlet. Nos. 3671/87	10·00	
3672	$1 Satchel Paige	45	50
3673	$1 Billy Williams	45	50
3674	$1 Reggie Jackson	45	50
3675	$1 Roberto Clemente	45	50
3676	$1 Ernie Banks	45	50
3677	$1 Hank Aaron	45	50
3678	$1 Roy Campanella	45	50
3679	$1 Willie McCovey	45	50
3680	$1 Monte Irvin	45	50
3681	$1 Willie Stargell	45	50
3682	$1 Rod Carew	45	50
3683	$1 Ferguson Jenkins	45	50
3684	$1 Bob Gibson	45	50
3685	$1 Lou Brock	45	50
3686	$1 Joe Morgan	45	50
3687	$6 Jackie Robinson (67×101 mm)	2·50	2·75
3671/87	*Set of 17*	9·75	10·50

(b) Self-adhesive. P 7

MS3688 133×67 mm. $1×3 Jackie Robinson (32×46 mm) 1·40 1·50
Nos. 3671/87 were printed together, *se-tenant*, in sheetlets containing 16 $2 stamps and one example of the imperforate $6 included in the enlarged illustrated right-hand margin.

(Des R. Rundo. Litho Questa)

1997 (3 June). *300th Anniv of Mother Goose Nursery Rhymes. Sheet, 102×72 mm containing horiz design as T 112 of St. Kitts–Nevis (Nevis). Multicoloured. P 14.*

MS3689 $5 Girl sewing ("Curly-Locks") 2·10 2·25

347 Child's Face and   348 Couple with Dog
U.N.E.S.C.O. Emblem

(Litho Questa)

1997 (3 June). *10th Anniv of Chernobyl Nuclear Disaster. T 347 and similar vert design. Multicoloured. P 13½×14.*

3690	$2 Type 347	85	90
3691	$2 As Type 347 but inscribed "CHABAD'S CHILDREN OF CHERNOBYL" at foot	85	90

(Des J. Iskowitz. Litho Questa)

1997 (3 June). *50th Death Anniv of Paul Harris (founder of Rotary International). Horiz designs as T 113 of St. Kitts–Nevis (Nevis). Multicoloured. P 14.*

3692 $2 Paul Harris and Thai children receiving blankets 85 90
MS3693 78×108 mm. $5 Luis Vincente Giay (International President) with President Carter of the United States 2·10 2·25

(Litho Questa)

1997 (3 June). *Golden Wedding of Queen Elizabeth and Prince Philip. Horiz designs as T 350 of Maldive Islands. Multicoloured. P 14.*

3694	$1.10, Queen Elizabeth II	50	55
	a. Sheetlet. Nos. 3694/9	3·00	
3695	$1.10, Royal coat of arms	50	55
3696	$1.10, Queen Elizabeth and Prince Philip	50	55
3697	$1.10, Queen Elizabeth and Prince Philip on royal visit	50	55
3698	$1.10, Buckingham Palace	50	55
3699	$1.10, Prince Philip in naval uniform	50	55
3694/9	*Set of 6*	3·00	3·25

MS3700 100×70 mm. $5 Queen Elizabeth on Coronation day 2·10 2·25
Nos. 3694/9 were printed together, *se-tenant*, in sheetlets of 6.
A $20 value embossed on gold foil also exists from a limited printing.

(Des J. Iskowitz. Litho Questa)

1997 (3 June). *"Pacific '97" International Stamp Exhibition, San Francisco. Death Centenary of Heinrich von Stephan (founder of the U.P.U). Horiz designs as T 351 of Maldive Islands. P 14.*

3701	$2 violet and black	85	90
	a. Sheetlet. Nos. 3701/3	2·50	
3702	$2 chestnut and black	85	90
3703	$2 dull blue and black	85	90
3701/3	*Set of 3*	2·50	2·75

MS3704 82×118 mm. $5 sepia 2·10 2·25
Designs:—No. 3701, Bicycle postman, India, 1800s; No. 3702, Von Stephan and Mercury; No. 3703, Ox-drawn postal cart, Indochina; No. MS3704, Von Stephan and post rider, Indochina.
Nos. 3701/3 were printed together, *se-tenant*, in sheetlets of 3 with enlarged right-hand margin.

(Litho Questa)

1997 (3 June). *Birth Bicentenary of Hiroshige (Japanese painter). "One Hundred Views of Edo". Vert designs as T 352 of Maldive Islands. Multicoloured. P 13½×14.*

3705	$1.50, "Furukawa River, Hiroo"	65	70
	a. Sheetlet. Nos. 3705/10	3·75	
3706	$1.50, "Chiyogaike Pond, Meguro"	65	70
3707	$1.50, "New Fuji, Meguro"	65	70
3708	$1.50, "Moon-viewing Point"	65	70
3709	$1.50, "Ushimachi, Takanawa"	65	70
3710	$1.50, "Original Fuji, Meguro"	65	70
3705/10	*Set of 6*	3·75	4·00

MS3711 Two sheets, each 102×127 mm. (a) $5 "Gotenyama, Shinagawa". (b) $5 "Shinagawa Susaki" *Set of 2 sheets* 4·25 4·50
Nos. 3705/10 were printed together, *se-tenant*, in sheetlets of 6.

(Des R. Sauber. Litho Questa)

1997 (3 June). *175th Anniv of Brothers Grimm's Third Collection of Fairy Tales. T 348 and similar vert designs showing "Old Sultan" (Nos. 3712/14) and "The Cobbler and the Elves" (Nos. 3715/17). Multicoloured. P 13½×14.*

3712	$2 Type 348	85	90
	a. Sheetlet. Nos. 3712/14	2·50	
3713	$2 Sheepdog on hillside	85	90
3714	$2 Wolf and sheepdog	85	90
3715	$2 The cobbler	85	90
	a. Sheetlet. Nos. 3715/17	2·50	
3716	$2 The elves	85	90
3717	$2 Cobbler with elf	85	90
3712/17	*Set of 6*	5·00	5·25

MS3718 Two sheets (a) 124×96 mm. $5 Couple and baby with Old Sultan. (b) 96×124 mm. $5 Elf *Set of 2 sheets* 4·25 4·50
Nos. 3712/14 and 3715/17 were each printed together, *se-tenant*, in sheetlets of 3 with illustrated margins.

349 Deng Xiaoping   350 Alphonso Theodore Roberts

1997 (3 June). *Deng Xiaoping (Chinese statesman) Commemoration. T 349 and similar designs. Litho. P 14.*

3719	$2 agate	85	90
	a. Sheetlet. Nos. 3719/22	3·25	
3720	$2 agate	85	90
3721	$2 agate	85	90
3722	$2 agate	85	90
3723	$2 blue and slate-blue	85	90
	a. Sheetlet. Nos. 3723/6	3·25	
3724	$2 blue and slate-blue	85	90

3725	$2 blue and slate-blue	85	90
3726	$2 blue and slate-blue	85	90
3727	$2 black	85	90
	a. Sheetlet. Nos. 3727/30	3·25	
3728	$2 black	85	90
3729	$2 black	85	90
3730	$2 black	85	90
3719/30	*Set of 12*	9·75	10·00

MS3731 76×106 mm. $5 multicoloured 2·10 2·25
Designs: *Vert*—3719, Type 349; No. 3720, Looking left; No. 3721, In military uniform; No. 3722, Full face; No. 3723, Looking right; No. 3724, Smiling; No. 3725, With head tilted to right; No. 3726, Looking down; No. 3727, Looking right; No. 3728, Looking left; No. 3729, Full face; No. 3730, Facing left and smiling. *Horiz*—No. MS3731 Deng Xiaoping and Zhuo Lin.
Nos. 3719/22, 3723/6 and 3727/30 were each printed together, *se-tenant*, in sheetlets of 4 with enlarged illustrated right-hand margins.

(Litho Questa)

1997 (20 June). *Inaugural Cricket Test Match at Arnos Vale. T 350 and similar multicoloured design. P 13½×14 (90 c.) or 14×13½ ($5).*

3732	90 c. Type 350	40	45
3733	$5 Arnos Vale cricket ground (*horiz*)	2·10	2·25

351 "Cinemax" Mardi   352 Hand above Globe
Gras Band   of Flowers

(Litho B.D.T.)

1997 (24 July). *20th Anniv of Vincy Mas Carnival. T 351 and similar multicoloured designs. P 15×14 (horiz) or 14×15 (vert).*

3734	10 c. Type 351	10	10
3735	20 c. Queen of the Bands "Jacintha Ballantyne"	10	10
3736	50 c. Queen of the Bands "Out of the Frying Pan and into the Fire" (*vert*)	25	30
3737	70 c. King of the Bands "Conquistodore"	30	35
3738	90 c. Starlift Steel Orchestra	40	45
3739	$2 Frankie McIntosh (musical arranger) (*vert*)	85	90
3734/9	*Set of 6*	1·90	2·00

(Litho Questa)

1997 (28 Aug). *World Cup Football Championship, France (1998). Designs as T 246 of Lesotho. P 14×13½ (horiz) or 13½×14 (vert).*

3740	70 c. multicoloured	30	35
3741	90 c. agate	40	45
3742	$1 multicoloured	45	50
3743/50	$1 × 8 (grey-black; multicoloured; grey-black; multicoloured; grey-black; multicoloured; grey-black; multicoloured; grey-black)		
	a. Sheetlet. Nos. 3743/50 and central label	3·75	
3751/8	$1 × 8 (each multicoloured)		
	a. Sheetlet. Nos. 3751/8 and central label	3·75	
3759/66	$1 × 8 (multicoloured; grey-black; multicoloured; grey-black; grey-black; multicoloured; grey-black; multicoloured)		
	a. Sheetlet. Nos. 3759/66 and central label	3·75	
3767/74	$1 × 8 (slate-blue; multicoloured; slate-blue; multicoloured; multicoloured; slate-blue; multicoloured; slate-blue)		
	a. Sheetlet. Nos. 3767/74 and central label	3·75	
3775	$1.10, sepia	50	55
3776	$2 multicoloured	85	90
3777	$10 grey-black	4·25	4·50
3740/77	*Set of 38*	22·00	23·00

MS3778 Four sheets, each 102×127 mm. (a) $5 multicoloured. (b) $5 multicoloured. (c) $5 grey-black. (d) $5 grey-black.. *Set of 4 sheets* 8·25 8·50
Designs: *Horiz*—No. 3740, Beckenbauer, West Germany; No. 3741, Moore, England; No. 3742, Lato, Poland; No. 3759, Argentine and West German players, 1986; Nos. 3760 and 3769, English and West German players, 1966; No. 3761, Goal mouth melee, 1986; No. 3762, Italian and West German players, 1982; Nos. 3763 and 3770, English player heading ball, 1966; No. 3764, Argentine player with ball, 1978; No. 3765, Argentine player chasing ball, 1978; No. 3766, Dutch player with ball; No. 3767, Wembley Stadium, England 1966; No. 3768, West German player with ball; No. 3771, English player in air heading ball; No. 3772, German player tackling English player; No. 3773, Celebrating English team; No. 3774, Celebrating German player; No. 3775, Pele, Brazil; No. 3776, Maier, West Germany; No. 3777, Eusebio, Portugal; No. MS3778d, Paulao, Angola. *Vert*—No. 3743 Argentine player kicking ball; No. 3744, Argentine player holding trophy; No. 3745, Goal mouth melee; No. 3746, Dutch player; No. 3747, Celebrating Argentine player; No. 3748, Argentine tackling Dutch player; No. 3749, Argentine and two Dutch players; No. 3750, Players attempting to head ball; No. 3751, Bergkamp, Netherlands; No. 3752, Seaman, England; No. 3753, Schmeichel, Denmark; No. 3754, Ince, England; No. 3755, Futre, Portugal; No. 3756, Ravanelli, Italy; No. 3757, Keane, Republic of Ireland; No. 3758, Gascoigne, England; No. MS3778a, Salvatori Schillaci, Italy; No. MS3778b, Ally McCoist, Scotland; No. MS3778c, Mario Kempes, Argentina.
Nos. 3743/50, 3751/8, 3759/66 and 3767/74 were each printed together, *se-tenant*, in sheetlets of 8 stamps and 1 central label.

(Des M. Friedman. Litho B.D.T.)

1997 (16 Sept). *10th Anniv of the Signing of the Montreal Protocol on Substances that Deplete the Ozone Layer.* P 14.
3779 **352** 90 c. multicoloured 40 45

353 *Rhyncholaelia digbyana*   **354** Snow Leopard

(Des W. Wright. Litho Questa)

1997 (18 Sept). *Orchids of the World.* T **353** *and similar multicoloured designs.* P 14.
3780	90 c. Type **353**		40	45
3781	$1 *Laeliocattleya* "Chitchat Tangerine"		45	50
3782	$1 *Eulophia speciosa*		45	50
	a. Sheetlet. Nos. 3782/90		4·00	
3783	$1 *Aerangis rhodosticta*		45	50
3784	$1 *Angraecum infundibularea*		45	50
3785	$1 *Calanthe sylvatica*		45	50
3786	$1 *Phalaenopsis mariae*		45	50
3787	$1 *Paphiopedilum insigne*		45	50
3788	$1 *Dendrobium nobile*		45	50
3789	$1 *Aerangis kotschyana*		45	50
3790	$1 *Cyrtorchis chailluana*		45	50
3791	$1.10, *Doritis pulcherrima*		50	55
3792	$2 *Phalaenopsis* "Barbara Moler"		85	90
3780/92		*Set of 13*	6·00	6·75

MS3793 Two sheets, each 106×81 mm. (a) $5 *Sanguine broughtonia* (50×37 mm). P 14×13½.
(b) $5 *Brassavola nodosa* "Lady of the Night" (50×37 mm). P 14×13½ .. *Set of 2 sheets* 4·25 4·50
Nos. 3782/90 were printed together, *se-tenant*, in sheetlets of 9.

(Litho Questa)

1997 (18 Sept). *Sierra Club Conservation.* T **354** *and similar multicoloured designs.* P 14.
3794/802 20 c. × 9 (Type **354**; Polar Bear; Plants, Isle Royale National Park; Waterway, Isle Royale National Park; Denali National Park at night; Denali National Park; Plants, Joshua Tree National Park; Mountains, Joshua Tree National Park; Rock, Joshua Tree National Park)
    a. Sheetlet. Nos. 3794/802 80

3803/11 40 c. × 9 (Mountain Gorilla showing teeth; Mountain Gorilla; Young Mountain Gorilla; Snow Leopard; Young Snow Leopard; Polar Bear; Polar Bear cub; Denali National Park; Isle Royale National Park (*all vert*))
    a. Sheetlet. Nos. 3803/11 .. 1·75

3812/20 50 c. × 9 (Sifaka with young; Sifaka on branch; Head of Sifaka; Peregrine Falcon; Peregrine Falcon with stretched wings; Galapagos Tortoise; Waterfall, African rainforest; Tree, African rainforest; China's Yellow Mountains (*all vert*))
    a. Sheetlet. Nos. 3812/20 .. 2·25

3821/9 60 c. × 9 (Head of Red Panda; Red Panda on branch; Red Panda on ground; Peregrine Falcon with chicks; Head of Galapagos Tortoise; Galapagos Tortoise on grass; African rainforest; Tops of trees, China's Yellow Mountains; Gorge, China's Yellow Mountains)
    a. Sheetlet. Nos. 3821/9 .. 2·50

3830/8 70 c. × 9 (Mountain Lion; Siberian Tiger; Head of Siberian Tiger; Red Wolf; Black Bear; Lake, Wolong National Reserve; Belize rainforest; Base of tree, Belize rainforest; Mountains, Wolong National Reserve)
    a. Sheetlet. Nos. 3830/8 .. 2·75

3839/47 90 c. × 9 (Siberian Tiger; Head of Mountain Lion; Mountain Lion cubs; Black Bear on branch; Head of Black Bear; Red Wolf; Head of Red Wolf; Belize rainforest; Wolong National Reserve (*all vert*))
    a. Sheetlet. Nos. 3839/47 .. 3·50

3848/56 $1 × 9 (Indri hanging from tree; Indri face on; Indri holding onto tree; Gopher Tortoise inside shell; Gopher Tortoise on ground; Black-footed Ferret facing forward; Head of Black-footed Ferret; Haleakala National Park; Grand Teton National Park (*all vert*))
    a. Sheetlet. Nos. 3848/56 .. .. 4·00

3857/65 $1.10 × 9 (Black-footed Ferret; Gopher Tortoise; River, Grand Teton National Park; Hillside, Grand Teton National Park; River, Haleakala National Park; Plants, Haleakala National Park; Misty view of Madagascar rainforest; Trees, Madagascar rainforest; Cleared forest, Madagascar rainforest)
    a. Sheetlet. Nos. 3857/65 4·50
3794/865 .. *Set of 72* 22·00 23·00

MS3866 Three sheets, each 110×80 mm. (a) $5 Lake, Olympic National Park. (b) $5 Hillside, Olympic National Park (*vert*). (c) $5 Snow-covered Mountains, Olympic National Park (*vert*) .. *Set of 3 sheets* 6·25 6·50
Nos. 3794/802, 3803/11, 3812/20, 3821/9, 3830/8, 3839/47, 3848/56 and 3857/65 were each printed together, *se-tenant*, in sheetlets of 9.

355 Raised Stern   **356** "Morrison Hotel"
of *Titanic*   Album Cover,
February 1970

(Litho Questa)

1997 (5 Nov). *85th Anniv of the Sinking of the* Titanic (*liner*). T **355** *and similar vert designs. Multicoloured.* P 14.
3867	$1 Type **355**		90	90
	a. Sheetlet. Nos. 3867/71		4·00	
3868	$1 Lifeboat rowing away		90	90
3869	$1 One funnel and lifeboat being lowered into water		90	90
3870	$1 Two funnels		90	90
3871	$1 One funnel in water and lifeboat rowing away		90	90
3867/71		*Set of 5*	4·00	4·00

Nos. 3867/71 were printed together, *se-tenant*, in sheetlets of 5 forming a composite design.
A $20 value embossed in gold foil also exists from a limited printing.

(Litho Questa)

1997 (5 Nov). *30th Anniv of The Doors (rock group) and Rock and Roll Hall of Fame, Cleveland.* T **356** *and similar square designs. Multicoloured.* P 14.
3872	90 c. Type **356**		40	45
	a. Sheetlet. No. 3872×8		3·25	
3873	95 c. "Waiting for the Sun" album cover, April 1968		40	45
	a. Sheetlet. No. 3874×8		3·50	
3874	$1 Rock and Roll Hall of Fame and Museum, Cleveland, Ohio		45	50
	a. Sheetlet. No. 3874×8		3·50	
3875	$1 "L.A. Women" album cover, April 1971		45	50
	a. Sheetlet. No. 3875×8		3·50	
3876	$1.10, "The Soft Parade" album cover, July 1969		50	55
	a. Sheetlet. No. 3876×8		4·00	
3877	$1.20, "Strange Days" album cover, October 1967		50	55
	a. Sheetlet. No. 3877×8		4·00	
3878	$1.50, Rock and Roll Hall of Fame guitar logo		65	70
	a. Sheetlet. No. 3878×8		5·00	
3879	$1.50, "The Doors" album cover, January 1967		65	70
	a. Sheetlet. No. 3879×8		5·00	
3872/9		*Set of 8*	4·00	4·25

Nos. 3872/9 were each printed, *se-tenant*, in sheetlets of 8 containing two vertical strips of four separated by a larger representation of the design.

357 Joe "King" Oliver   **358** Diana, Princess
of Wales

(Des Andrea Mistretta. Litho Questa)

1997 (5 Nov). *New Orleans School of Jazz Commemoration.* T **357** *and similar horiz designs. Multicoloured.* P 14×13½.
3880	$1 Type **357**		60	60
	a. Sheetlet. Nos. 3880/5		3·25	
3881	$1 Louis Armstrong		60	60
3882	$1 Sidney Bechet		60	60
3883	$1 Nick Larocca		60	60
3884	$1 Louis Prima		60	60
3885	$1 "Buddy" Charles Bolden		60	60
3880/5		*Set of 6*	3·25	3·25

Nos. 3880/5 were printed together, *se-tenant*, in sheetlets of 6.

(Des Zina Saunders (portraits), R. Sauber (others). Litho Questa)

1997 (5 Nov). *Millennium Series. Famous People of the Twentieth Century. Multicoloured designs as* T **139** *of St. Kitts-Nevis (Nevis).* P 14. (*a*) *Sculptors*
3886	$1.10, Constantin Brancusi		50	55
	a. Sheetlet. Nos. 3886/93		4·00	
3887	$1.10, "The New Born" (Brancusi) (56×42 mm)		50	55
3888	$1.10, "Four Elements" (Calder) (56×42 mm)		50	55
3889	$1.10, Alexander Calder		50	55
3890	$1.10, Isamu Noguchi		50	55
3891	$1.10, "Dodge Fountain" (Noguchi) (56×42 mm)		50	55
3892	$1.10, "The Shuttlecock" (Oldenburg) (56×42 mm)		50	55
3893	$1.10, Claes Oldenburg		50	55

(*b*) *Opera Singers*
3894	$1.10, Lily Pons		50	55
	a. Sheetlet. Nos. 3894/3901		4·00	
3895	$1.10, Lily Pons in Donizetti's *Lucia di Lammermoor* (56×42 mm)		50	55
3896	$1.10, Maria Callas in Bellini's *I Puritani* (56×42 mm)		50	55
3897	$1.10, Maria Callas		50	55
3898	$1.10, Beverly Sills		50	55
3899	$1.10, Beverly Sills in Donizetti's *La Fille du Regiment* (56×42 mm)		50	55
3900	$1.10, Jessye Norman in Schoenberg's *Erwartung* (56×42 mm)		50	55
3901	$1.10, Jessye Norman		50	55
3902	$1.10, Enrico Caruso		50	55
	a. Sheetlet. Nos. 3902/9		4·00	
3903	$1.10, Enrico Caruso in Verdi's *Rigoletto* (56×42 mm)		50	55
3904	$1.10, Mario Lanza in *The Seven Hills of Rome* (56×42 mm)		50	55
3905	$1.10, Mario Lanza		50	55
3906	$1.10, Luciano Pavarotti		50	55
3907	$1.10, Luciano Pavarotti in Donizetti's *L'Elisir d'Amore* (56×42 mm)		50	55
3908	$1.10, Placido Domingo in Puccini's *Tosca* (56×42 mm)		50	55
3909	$1.10, Placido Domingo		50	55
3886/909		*Set of 24*	12·00	13·00

Nos. 3886/93, 3894/3901 and 3902/9 were each printed together, *se-tenant*, in sheetlets of 8 with illustrated margins.

(Des J. Iskowitz. Litho Questa)

1997 (20 Nov). *Diana, Princess of Wales Commemoration.* T **358** *and similar vert designs. Multicoloured.* P 14.
3910	$2 Type **358**		85	90
	a. Sheetlet. Nos. 3910/13		3·25	
3911	$2 Wearing pearl-drop earrings		85	90
3912	$2 Wearing black jacket		85	90
3913	$2 Wearing blue jacket and pearl earrings		85	90
3914	$2 Wearing tiara		85	90
	a. Sheetlet. Nos. 3914/17		3·25	
3915	$2 In black evening dress		85	90
3916	$2 Wearing blue jacket		85	90
3917	$2 Wearing beige blouse		85	90
3910/17		*Set of 8*	6·75	7·00

MS3918 Two sheets, each 100×70 mm. (a) $6 Wearing light blue jacket. (b) $6 Wearing white blouse .. *Set of 2 sheets* 5·50 5·75
Nos. 3910/13 and 3914/17 were each printed together, *se-tenant*, in sheetlets of 4 with illustrated margins.
Two $20 values embossed on gold foil and a $8 on silver showing a hologram also exist from limited printings.

359 "The Sistine Madonna"   **360** Symbolic Tiger
(detail, Raphael)

(Litho B.D.T.)

1997 (26 Nov). *Christmas. Paintings and Sculptures.* T **359** *and similar multicoloured designs.* P 14.
3919	60 c. Type **359**		25	30
3920	70 c. "Angel" (Edward Burne-Jones)		30	35
3921	90 c. "Cupid" (sculpture, Etienne-Maurice Flaconet)		40	45
3922	$1 "Saint Michael" (sculpture, Hubert Gerhard)		45	5
3923	$1.10, "Apollo and the Hoare" (Giambattista Tiepolo)		50	
3924	$2 "Madonna in a Garland of Flowers" (detail, Rubens and Brueghel the Elder)		85	9
3919/24		*Set of 6*	2·50	2·7

MS3925 Two sheets, each 106×95 mm. (a) $5 "Madonna in a Garland of Flowers" (different detail, Rubens and Brueghel the Elder). (b) $5 "The Sacrifice of Isaac" (Giambattista Tiepolo) (detail) (*horiz*) .. *Set of 2 sheets* 4·25 4·50

(Des Y. Lee. Litho Questa)

1998 (5 Jan). *Chinese New Year ("Year of the Tiger"). T* **360** *and similar vert designs showing different tigers.* P 14½.

3926	**360**	$1 black, olive-grey and grey-brown		45	50
		a. Sheetlet. Nos. 3926/8		1·25	
3927	–	$1 black, silver and ochre		45	50
3928	–	$1 black, lilac and brown-rose		45	50
3926/8			*Set of 3*	1·25	1·50
MS3929		71×101 mm. $2 black, brown-lilac and dull orange		85	90

Nos. 3926/8 were printed together, *se-tenant*, as a sheetlet containing a horizontal strip of 3.

361 Children and School
Savings Bank

(Des M. Serviro. Litho B.D.T.)

1998 (5 Jan). *Economic Development. T* **361** *and similar multicoloured designs.* P 13½.

3930	20 c. Type **361**			10	10
3931	90 c. Agricultural workers and Credit Union Office (*vert*)			40	45
3932	$1.10, Freighter at quay			50	55
3930/2			*Set of 3*	1·00	1·10

362 Ice Hockey

(Des R. Company, R. Sauber and D. Keren. Litho Questa)

1998 (2 Feb). *Winter Olympic Games, Nagano. T* **362** *and similar multicoloured designs.* P 14.

3933	70 c. Type **362**			30	35
3934	$1.10, Bobsleigh			50	55
3935	$1.10, Bjorn Daehlie (Norway) (Gold medal, Nordic skiing, 1994)			50	55
	a. Sheetlet. Nos. 3935/42			4·00	
3936	$1.10, Gillis Grafstrom (Sweden) (Gold medal, figure skating, 1924, 1928)			50	55
3937	$1.10, Sonja Henie (Norway) (Gold medal, figure skating, 1928, 1932)			50	55
3938	$1.10, Ingemar Stenmark (Sweden) (Gold medal, slalom and giant slalom, 1980)			50	55
3939	$1.10, Christan Jagge (Norway) (Gold medal, slalom, 1992)			50	55
3940	$1.10, Tomas Gustafson (Sweden) (Gold medal, 5000m speed skating, 1992)			50	55
3941	$1.10, Johann Olav Koss (Norway) (Gold medal, 1500m speed skating, 1992, 1994)			50	55
3942	$1.10, Thomas Wassberg (Sweden) (Gold medal, 50km cross country skiing, 1984)			50	55
3943	$1.50, Downhill (red suit) (*vert*)			65	70
	a. Sheetlet. Nos. 3943/8			3·75	
3944	$1.50, Two-man bobsleigh (*vert*)			65	70
3945	$1.50, Ski jump (red suit) (*vert*)			65	70
3946	$1.50, Downhill (red and white suit) (*vert*)			65	70
3947	$1.50, Luge (*vert*)			65	70
3948	$1.50, Biathlon (*vert*)			65	70
3949	$1.50, Downhill (yellow and red suit) (*vert*)			65	70
	a. Sheetlet. Nos. 3949/54			3·75	
3950	$1.50, Figure skating (*vert*)			65	70
3951	$1.50, Ski jump (green suit) (*vert*)			65	70
3952	$1.50, Speed skating (*vert*)			65	70
3953	$1.50, Four-man bobsleigh (*vert*)			65	70
3954	$1.50, Cross-country skiing (*vert*)			65	70
3955	$2 Pairs figure skating (*vert*)			85	90
3956	$2 Ski jump (*vert*)			85	90
3933/56			*Set of 24*	14·00	15·00
MS3957	Two sheets. (a) 110×80 mm. $5 Ice Hockey. (b) 80×100 mm. $5 Downhill				
			Set of 2 sheets	4·25	4·50

Nos. 3935/42, 3943/8 and 3949/54 were each printed together, *se-tenant*, in sheetlets of 8 (Nos. 3935/42) or 6 with the backgrounds forming composite designs (Nos. 3943/8 and 3949/54).

363 Rock-iguana (Anegada)

364 *Gymnopilus spectabilis* and *Atildes halesus* (butterfly)

(Des Jennifer Toombs. Litho Cartor)

1998 (23 Feb). *Endangered Species of the Caribbean. T* **363** *and similar horiz designs.* Multicoloured. P 13.

3958	50 c. Type **363**			20	25
3959	70 c. *Papilio homerus* (butterfly) (Jamaica)			30	35
3960	90 c. Blossom-bat (Cuba)			40	45
3961	$1 Haitian Solenodon (Dominican Republic)			45	50
3962	$1.10, Hawksbill Turtle (Grenada)			50	55
3963	$1.10, Roseate Spoonbill			50	55
	a. Sheetlet. Nos. 3963/8			3·00	
3964	$1.10, Golden Swallow			50	55
3965	$1.10, Short-snouted Spinner Dolphin			50	55
3966	$1.10, Queen or Pink Conch (*Strombus gigas*)			50	55
3967	$1.10, American Manatee			50	55
3968	$1.10, Loggerhead Turtle			50	55
3969	$1.10, Magnificent Frigate Bird			50	55
	a. Sheetlet. Nos. 3969/74			3·00	
3970	$1.10, Humpback Whale			50	55
3971	$1.10, *Marpesia petreus* (butterfly)			50	55
3972	$1.10, St. Lucia Whiptail			50	55
3973	$1.10, St. Lucia Oriole			50	55
3974	$1.10, Green Turtle			50	55
3975	$2 Black-billed Whistling Duck (Barbuda)			85	90
3958/75			*Set of 18*	8·50	9·50
MS3976	Two sheets, each 102×90 mm. (a) $5 St. Vincent Amazon. (b) $5 Antiguan Racer (snake)				
			Set of 2 sheets	4·25	4·50

Nos. 3963/8 and 3964/74 were each printed together, *se-tenant* in sheetlets of 6, forming composite background designs.

(Des T. Wood. Litho Cartor)

1998 (23 Feb). *Fungi. T* **364** *and similar vert designs.* Multicoloured. P 13½.

3977	10 c. Type **364**			10	10
3978	20 c. *Entoloma lividium*			10	10
3979	70 c. *Pholiota flammans*			30	35
3980	90 c. *Panaeolus semiovatus*			40	45
3981	$1 *Stropharia rugosoannulata*			45	50
3982	$1 *Amanita caesarea*			45	50
	a. Sheetlet. Nos. 3982/90			4·00	
3983	$1 *Amanita muscaria*			45	50
3984	$1 *Aminita ovoidea*			45	50
3985	$1 *Amanita phalloides*			45	50
3986	$1 *Amanitopsis inaurata*			45	50
3987	$1 *Amanitopsis vaginata*			45	50
3988	$1 *Psalliota campestris*			45	50
3989	$1 *Psalliota arvensis*			45	50
3990	$1 *Coprinus comatus*			45	50
3991	$1.10, *Tricholoma sulphureum*			50	55
3992	$1.10, *Coprinus picaceus*			50	55
	a. Sheetlet. Nos. 3992/4000			4·50	
3993	$1.10, *Stropharia umbonatescens*			50	55
3994	$1.10, *Hebeloma crustuliniforme*			50	55
3995	$1.10, *Cortinarius collinitus*			50	55
3996	$1.10, *Cortinarius violaceus*			50	55
3997	$1.10, *Cortinarius armillatus*			50	55
3998	$1.10, *Tricholoma aurantium*			50	55
3999	$1.10, *Russula virescens*			50	55
4000	$1.10, *Clitocybe infundibuliformis*			50	55
3977/4000			*Set of 24*	10·00	11·00
MS4001	Two sheets. (a) 70×100 mm. $6 *Hygrocybe conica*. (b) 100×70 mm. $6 *Amanita caesarea*				
			Set of 2 sheets	4·75	5·00

Nos. 3982/90 and 3992/4000 were printed together, *se-tenant*, in sheetlets of 9.

365 *Amarynthis meneria meneria*

(Des S. Thurston. Litho Cartor)

1998 (23 Feb). *Butterflies. T* **365** *and similar multicoloured designs.* P 13½.

4002	20 c. Type **365**			10	10
4003	50 c. *Papilio polyxenes*			20	25
4004	70 c. *Emesis fatima fatima* (*vert*)			30	35
4005	$1 *Anartia amathea*			45	50
4006	$1 *Heliconius erato* (*vert*)			45	50
	a. Sheetlet. Nos. 4006/14			4·00	
4007	$1 *Danaus plexippus* (*vert*)			45	50
4008	$1 *Papilio phorcas* (*vert*)			45	50
4009	$1 *Morpho peleides* (*vert*)			45	50
4010	$1 *Pandoriana pandora* (*vert*)			45	50
4011	$1 *Basilarchia astyanax* (*vert*)			45	50
4012	$1 *Vanessa cardui* (*vert*)			45	50
4013	$1 *Colobura dirce* (*vert*)			45	50
4014	$1 *Heraclides cresphontes* (*vert*)			45	50
4002/14			*Set of 13*	5·00	5·50
MS4015	Two sheets, each 100×70 mm. (a) $6 *Colias eurytheme*. (b) $6 *Everes comyntas*				
			Set of 2 sheets	4·75	5·00

Nos. 4006/14 were printed together, *se-tenant*, in sheetlets of 9 with the backgrounds forming a composite design.

St.Vincent AND THE Grenadines   2c

366 Pluto waking Mickey

(Des Walt Disney Co. Litho Questa)

1998 (23 Mar). *70th Birthday of Disney's Mickey Mouse (1st issue). T* **366** *and similar multicoloured designs.* P 14×13½ (*horiz*) or 13½×14 (*vert*).

4016	2 c. Type **366**			10	10
4017	3 c. Mickey and Pluto on morning run			10	10
4018	4 c. Singing in the bath			10	10
4019	5 c. Breakfast time			10	10
4020	10 c. Mickey going to school			15	10
4021	65 c. Mickey playing basketball			50	50
4022	$1.10, Mickey as drum major (*vert*)			70	70
	a. Sheetlet. Nos. 4022/7			3·75	
4023	$1.10, Mickey with hat and cane (*vert*)			70	70
4024	$1.10, Mickey in bow tie and tails (*vert*)			70	70
4025	$1.10, Mickey the magician (*vert*)			70	70
4026	$1.10, Mickey as circus musician (*vert*)			70	70
4027	$1.10, Mickey as cowboy (*vert*)			70	70
4028	$3 Mickey in soup kitchen			1·60	1·60
4029	$4 Mickey and Minnie in restaurant			2·00	2·00
4030	$5 Mickey and Pluto praying			2·25	2·25
4016/30			*Set of 15*	10·00	10·00
MS4031	Four sheets, each 127×104 mm. (a) $5 Mickey reading paper (*vert*). (b) $6 Using computer (*vert*). (c) $6 Dancing at piano (*vert*). (d) $6 Blowing trumpet				
			Set of 4 sheets	9·75	10·00

Nos. 4022/7 were printed together, *se-tenant*, in sheetlets of 6. See also Nos. 4179/97.

367 Winnie the Pooh in Window   368 Australian Terrier

(Des Walt Disney Co. Litho)

1998 (23 Mar). *Stories of Winnie the Pooh. T* **367** *and similar horiz designs.* Multicoloured. P 14×13½.

4032	$1 Type **367**			60	60
	a. Sheetlet. Nos. 4032/40			4·75	
4033	$1 Eeyore, Kanga and Roo			60	60
4034	$1 Winnie the Pooh with balloon			60	60
4035	$1 Pooh stuck in Rabbit's burrow			60	60
4036	$1 Christopher Robin pulling Pooh			60	60
4037	$1 Piglet sweeping leaves			60	60
4038	$1 Pooh asleep			60	60
4039	$1 Eeyore			60	60
4040	$1 Pooh and Tigger			60	60
4032/40			*Set of 9*	4·75	4·75
MS4041	127×102 mm. $6 Tigger, Pooh and Piglet			3·50	3·75

Nos. 4032/40 were printed together, *se-tenant*, in sheetlets of 9.

(Des R. Martin. Litho Questa)

1998 (21 Apr). *Dogs of the World. T* **368** *and similar multicoloured designs.* P 14.

4042	70 c. Type **368**			30	35
4043	90 c. Bullmastiff			40	45
4044	$1.10, Pomeranian			50	55
4045	$1.10, Beagle (*horiz*)			50	55
	a. Sheetlet. Nos. 4045/50			3·00	
4046	$1.10, German Shepherd and cockerel (*horiz*)			50	55
4047	$1.10, Pointer (*horiz*)			50	55
4048	$1.10, Vizsla (*horiz*)			50	55
4049	$1.10, Bulldog (*horiz*)			50	55
4050	$1.10, Shetland Sheepdogs (*horiz*)			50	55
4051	$1.10, Tyrolean Hunting Dog (*horiz*)			50	55
	a. Sheetlet. Nos. 4051/6			3·00	
4052	$1.10, King Charles Spaniel (*horiz*)			50	55
4053	$1.10, Fox Terriers (*horiz*)			50	55
4054	$1.10, Bernese Mountain Dog (*horiz*)			50	55
4055	$1.10, Papillon (*horiz*)			50	55
4056	$1.10, German Shepherd (*horiz*)			50	55
4057	$2 Dandie Dinmont Terrier			85	90
4042/57			*Set of 16*	8·00	8·75
MS4058	Two sheets, each 106×76 mm. (a) $6 Scottish Terrier and bush. (b) $6 Scottish Terrier lying down				
			Set of 2 sheets	5·25	5·50

Nos. 4045/50 and 4051/6 were each printed together, *se-tenant*, in sheetlets of 6 with the backgrounds forming composite designs.

The captions on Nos. 4052 and 4055 are transposed in error.

(369)   370 L.M.S. No. 5596 *Bahamas*

1998 (19 May). *"Israel 98" International Stamp Exhibition, Tel-Aviv.* Nos. 3334/7 optd with T **369**, and No. MS4062 *further optd* "ISRAEL 98 – WORLD STAMP EXHIBITION TEL-AVIV 13–21 MAY 1998" *on margin.*

4059	$1 Type **325**			45	50
4060	$1.10, The Montefiore Windmill			50	55
4061	$2 Shrine of the Book			85	90
4059/61			*Set of 3*	1·75	1·90
MS4062	104×74 mm. $5 Old City, Jerusalem			2·10	2·25

(Des S. Gardner. Litho Questa)

1998 (2 June). *Railway Steam Locomotives of the World. T* **370** *and similar horiz designs. Multicoloured. P* 14.

4063	10 c. Type **370**		10	10
4064	20 c. Ex.Mza 1400		10	10
4065	50 c. *Mallard*		20	25
4066	70 c. Tank locomotive *Monarch*		30	35
4067	90 c. *Big Chief*		40	45
4068	$1.10, L.M.S. No. 6228 *Duchess of Rutland*		50	55
4069	$1.10, Holmes J36		50	55
	a. Sheetlet. Nos. 4069/76		4·00	
4070	$1.10, *Patentee*		50	55
4071	$1.10, *Kingfisher*		50	55
4072	$1.10, No. 23 *St Pierre*		50	55
4073	$1.10, South African Railways Class 19c		50	55
4074	$1.10, South African Railways Class 6J		50	55
4075	$1.10, No. 92220 *Evening Star*		50	55
4076	$1.10, No. 1		50	55
4077	$1.10, "The Hadrian Flyer"		50	55
	a. Sheetlet. Nos. 4077/84		4·00	
4078	$1.10, Class "Highland Jones Goods" No. 103		50	55
4079	$1.10, No. 34023 *Blackmore Vale*		50	55
4080	$1.10, S.E.C.R. No. 27		50	55
4081	$1.10, Class "Brighton Terrier" *Stepney*		50	55
4082	$1.10, R.E.N.F.E. No. 2184		50	55
4083	$1.10, Southern Railway No. 24 *Calbourne*		50	55
4084	$1.10, "*Clun Castle*"		50	55
4063/84		*Set of 22*	9·50	10·50

MS4085 Two sheets, each 101×70 mm. (a) $5 *Caledonia*. (b) $5 No. 6000 *King George V*
Set of 2 sheets 4·25 4·50

Nos. 4069/76 and 4077/84 were each printed together, *se-tenant*, in sheetlets of 8 with enlarged illustrated top margins. The identification of the locomotive on No. 4084 has been reported as incorrect.

371 Cock-of-the Rock   372 White Whale

(Des L. Schwinger. Litho Questa)

1998 (16 June). *Birds of the World. T* **371** *and similar multicoloured designs. P* 14.

4086	50 c. Type **371**		20	25
4087	60 c. Resplendant Quetzal		25	30
4088	70 c. American Wood Stork		30	35
4089	90 c. St. Vincent Amazon (species inscr at right)		40	45
4090	90 c. Toucan (*horiz*)		40	45
4091	90 c. Racquet-tailed Motmot		40	45
	a. Sheetlet. Nos. 4091/102		4·75	
4092	90 c. Red-billed Quelea		40	45
4093	90 c. Leadbeater's Cockatoo		40	45
4094	90 c. Scarlet Macaw		40	45
4095	90 c. Bare-throated Bellbird		40	45
4096	90 c. Tucaman Amazon		40	45
4097	90 c. Black-lored Red Tanager		40	45
4098	90 c. Fig Parrot		40	45
4099	90 c. St. Vincent Amazon (species inscr at top)		40	45
4100	90 c. Peach-faced Love Birds		40	45
4101	90 c. Blue-fronted Amazon		40	45
4102	90 c. Yellow-billed Amazon		40	45
4103	$1 Greater Bird of Paradise (*horiz*)		45	50
4104	$1.10, Sun-bittern (*horiz*)		50	55
4105	$2 Green Honeycreeper (*horiz*)		85	90
4086/105		*Set of 20*	8·00	9·00

MS4106 Two sheets, each 98×62 mm. (a) $5 Hyacinth Macaw. (b) $5 Blue-headed Hummingbird
Set of 2 sheets 4·25 4·50

Nos. 4091/102 were printed together, *se-tenant*, in sheetlets of 12 with the background forming a composite design.

(Des B. Durand. Litho Questa)

1998 (1 July). *International Year of the Ocean. T* **372** *and similar multicoloured designs. P* 14.

4107	70 c. Type **372**		30	35
4108	90 c. Atlantic Manta		40	45
4109	$1 Harlequin Wrasse and Pelican (*vert*)		45	50
	a. Sheetlet. Nos. 4109/17		4·00	
4110	$1 Blue Surgeonfish (*vert*)		45	50
4111	$1 Spotted Trunkfish and sailing ship (*vert*)		45	50
4112	$1 Regal Angelfish (*vert*)		45	50
4113	$1 Porcupine Fish (*vert*)		45	50
4114	$1 Clownfish (*vert*)		45	50
4115	$1 Lion Fish (*vert*)		45	50
4116	$1 Moray Eel (*vert*)		45	50
4117	$1 French Angelfish (*vert*)		45	50
4118	$1 Lemonpeel Angelfish, Flying Fish and gulls (*vert*)		45	50
	a. Sheetlet. Nos. 4118/26		4·00	
4119	$1 Narwhal (*vert*)		45	50
4120	$1 Panther Grouper, Puffin and house (*vert*)		45	50
4121	$1 Fur Seal and jellyfish (*vert*)		45	50
4122	$1 Spiny Boxfish (*vert*)		45	50
4123	$1 Loggerhead Turtle (*vert*)		45	50
4124	$1 Opah (*vert*)		45	50
4125	$1 Clown Triggerfish (*vert*)		45	50
4126	$1 Bighead Searobin (*vert*)		45	50
4127	$1.10, Forceps Butterflyfish, Moorish Idol and Copperband Butterflyfish		50	55
4128	$2 Octopus		85	90
4107/28		*Set of 22*	10·00	11·00

MS4129 Two sheets, each 98×73 mm. (a) $5 Seahorse (*vert*). (b) $5 Australian Seadragon (*vert*)
Set of 2 sheets 4·25 4·50

Nos. 4109/17 and 4118/26 were each printed together, *se-tenant*, in sheetlets of 9 with the backgrounds forming composite designs.

No. 4108 is inscribed "Harlequin Warasse" in error.

(Des R. Sauber. Litho Cartor)

1998 (4 July). *25th Anniv of Caribbean Community. Horiz design as T* **293** *of Jamaica showing flags of St. Vincent and CARICOM. P* 13½.

4130	$1 multicoloured		45	50

(Des M. Friedman. Litho Questa)

1998 (15 Sept). *50th Anniv of Organization of American States. Vert design as T* **128** *of St. Kitts-Nevis* (*Nevis*). *P* 13½×14.

4131	$1 bluish violet, light green and black		45	50

373 "Landscape"   374 H. Daisley (64 years of service)

(Des Diana Catherines. Litho Questa)

1998 (15 Sept). *25th Death Anniv of Pablo Picasso* (*painter*). *T* **373** *and similar multicoloured designs. P* 14½.

4132	$1.10, Type **373**		50	55
4133	$2 "The Death of the Female Torero"		85	90
4134	$2 "The Kiss"		85	90
4132/4		*Set of 3*	2·10	2·25

MS4135 102×127 mm. $5 "Flute Player" (*vert*) 2·10 2·25

(Des F. Rivera. Litho Questa)

1998 (15 Sept). *Birth Centenary of Enzo Ferrari* (*car manufacturer*). *Horiz designs as T* **129** *of St. Kitts-Nevis* (*Nevis*). *Multicoloured. P* 14.

4136	$2 365 GTS		85	90
	a. Sheetlet. Nos. 4136/8		2·50	
4137	$2 Testarossa		85	90
4138	$2 365 GT4 B B		85	90
4136/8		*Set of 3*	2·50	2·75

MS4139 104×70 mm. $6 Dino 206 GT (91×34 mm). P 14×14½ 2·50 2·75

Nos. 4136/8 were printed together, *se-tenant*, in sheetlets of 3.

(Des J. Iskowitz. Litho Questa)

1998 (15 Sept). *19th World Scout Jamboree, Chile. Designs as T* **130** *of St. Kitts-Nevis* (*Nevis*). *P* 14.

4140	$2 dp reddish lilac, reddish violet & black		85	90
	a. Sheetlet. Nos. 4140/2		2·50	
4141	$2 deep brown, reddish violet and black		85	90
4142	$2 orange-brown, reddish violet and black		85	90
4140/2		*Set of 3*	2·50	2·75

MS4143 70×100 mm. $5 slate-blue, deep brown and brownish black 2·10 2·25

Designs: *Horiz*—No. 4140, Presentation of Silver Buffalo award to John Glenn (U.S. astronaut); No. 4141, Herb Shriner learning knot-tying, 1960; No. 4142, Breaking camp, 1940s. *Vert*—No. **MS**4143, Lord Baden-Powell in court dress.

Nos. 4140/2 were printed together, *se-tenant*, in sheetlets of 3 with enlarged illustrated margins at top and right.

(Des J. Iskowitz. Litho Questa)

1998 (15 Sept). *50th Death Anniv of Mahatma Gandhi. Designs as T* **131** *of St. Kitts-Nevis* (*Nevis*). *P* 14.

4144	$1 multicoloured		45	50
	a. Sheetlet. No. 4144×4		1·75	

MS4145 107×76 mm. $5 yellow-brown, deep dull purple and black 3·00 3·25

Designs: *Vert*—$1 Mahatma Gandhi. *Horiz*—$5 Gandhi at conference table.

No. 4144 was printed in sheetlets of 4 with enlarged illustrated margins at top and left.

(Des D. Miller. Litho Questa)

1998 (15 Sept). *80th Anniv of Royal Air Force. Horiz designs as T* **132** *of St. Kitts-Nevis* (*Nevis*). *Multicoloured. P* 14.

4146	$2 AEW 1 (Airborne Early Warning)		85	90
	a. Sheetlet. Nos. 4146/9		3·25	
4147	$2 Eurofighter EF-2000		85	90
4148	$2 Sepecat Jaguar GR1A		85	90
4149	$2 BAe Hawk T1A trainer		85	90
4150	$2 Two Sepecat Jaguar GR1s		85	90
	a. Sheetlet. Nos. 4150/3		3·25	
4151	$2 Panavia Tornado F3		85	90
4152	$2 Three BAe Harrier GR7s		85	90
4153	$2 Panavia Tornado F3 IDV		85	90
4146/53		*Set of 8*	6·50	7·00

MS4154 Four sheets, each 90×70 mm. (a) $6 Bristol F2B fighter and Falcon (bird). (b) $6 Bristol F2B fighter and Golden Eagle (bird). (c) $6 Mosquito and Eurofighter EF-2000. (d) $6 Vulcan B2 and Eurofighter EF-2000
Set of 4 sheets 10·00 10·50

Nos. 4146/9 and 4150/3 were each printed together, *se-tenant*, in sheetlets of 4 with enlarged illustrated margins.

(Des R. Sauber. Litho Cartor)

1998 (15 Sept). *1st Death Anniv of Diana, Princess of Wales. Vert design as T* **365** *of Maldive Islands. Multicoloured. Litho. P* 14½×14.

4155	$1.10, Diana, Princess of Wales		50	55
	a. Sheetlet of 6		3·00	

No. 4155 was printed in sheetlets of 6 with an enlarged illustrated right margin.

(Des R. Sauber. Litho Cartor)

1998 (29 Oct). *150th Anniv of Local Court of Ancient Order of Foresters. T* **374** *and similar vert designs. Multicoloured* (*except 70 c.*). *P* 13½.

4156	10 c. Type **374**		10	10
4157	20 c. R. Jack (71 years of service)		10	10
4158	50 c. Ancient Order of Foresters' arms		20	25
4159	70 c. Bow and arrow symbol (yellow-green and black)		30	35
4160	90 c. Court's headquarters		40	45
4156/60		*Set of 5*	1·10	1·25

375 Bi-colour Longhair   376 Flautist

(Des Jennifer Toombs. Litho B.D.T.)

1998 (1 Dec). *Christmas. Cats. T* **375** *and similar horiz designs. Multicoloured. P* 13½×14.

4161	20 c. Type **375**		10	10
4162	50 c. Korat		20	25
4163	60 c. Seal-point Siamese		25	30
4164	70 c. Red Self Longhair		30	35
4165	90 c. Black Longhair		40	45
4166	$1.10, Red Tabby Exotic Shorthair		50	55
4161/6		*Set of 6*	1·75	2·00

MS4167 Two sheets, each 75×66 mm. (a) $5 Seal-point Colourpoint. (b) $5 Tortoiseshell Shorthair *Set of 2 sheets* 4·00 4·50

(Des Zina Saunders. Litho Questa)

1998 (15 Dec). *900th Birth Anniv of St. Hildegard von Bingen* (*German mystic*). *T* **376** *and similar vert designs. Multicoloured. P* 14.

4168	$1.10, Type **376**		50	55
	a. Sheetlet. Nos. 4168/73		3·00	
4169	$1.10, St. Hildegard and abbey		50	55
4170	$1.10, Viola player		50	55
4171	$1.10, Pope Eugenius		50	55
4172	$1.10, Town of Bingen		50	55
4173	$1.10, St. Hildegard		50	55
4168/73		*Set of 6*	3·00	3·25

MS4174 85×110 mm. $5 St. Hildegard 2·10 2·25

Nos. 4168/73 were printed together, *se-tenant*, in sheetlets of 6 with enlarged illustrated margins.

377 Rabbit facing Right   378 Mickey Mouse

(Des Y. Lee. Litho Questa)

1999 (4 Jan). *Chinese New Year* ("*Year of the Rabbit*"). *T* **377** *and similar vert designs showing stylised rabbits. Multicoloured* (*except No.* **MS**4178). *P* 14½.

4175	$1 Type **377**		45	50
	a. Sheetlet. Nos. 4175/7		1·25	
4176	$1 Rabbit facing front		45	50
4177	$1 Rabbit facing left		45	50
4175/7		*Set of 3*	1·25	1·50

MS4178 70×100 mm. $2 As No. 4176 (black, bright lilac and rose-pink) 85 90

Nos. 4175/7 were printed together, *se-tenant*, as a sheetlet of 3.

(Des Rosemary De Figlio. Litho Questa)

1999 (21 Jan). *70th Birthday of Mickey Mouse* (*2nd issue*). *T* **378** *and similar multicoloured designs showing Walt Disney characters playing winter sports. P* 13½×14.

4179	$1.10, Type **378**		70	70
	a. Sheetlet. Nos. 4179/84		3·25	
4180	$1.10, Goofy on skis wearing goggles		70	70
4181	$1.10, Donald Duck skiing in yellow sweatshirt		70	70
4182	$1.10, Goofy and Mickey in red bobsleigh		70	70
4183	$1.10, Goofy on skis in yellow		70	70
4184	$1.10, Minnie on skis with yellow bow		70	70

4185	$1.10, Daisy Duck on skis wearing purple bow	70	70
	a. Sheetlet. Nos. 4185/90	3·75	
4186	$1.10, Mickey on skis wearing goggles	70	70
4187	$1.10, Goofy and Mickey in green bobsleigh	70	70
4188	$1.10, Goofy on skis in blue	70	70
4189	$1.10, Minnie snowboarding	70	70
4190	$1.10, Donald on skis in blue sweatshirt	70	70
4191	$1.10, Minnie skiing with blue and purple bow	70	70
	a. Sheetlet. Nos. 4191/6	3·75	
4192	$1.10, Mickey snowboarding	70	70
4193	$1.10, Goofy on skis in blue and purple vest	70	70
4194	$1.10, Donald skiing in blue and purple sweatshirt	70	70
4195	$1.10, Mickey snowboarding in yellow hat and goggles	70	70
4196	$1.10, Daisy skiing in blue and purple	70	70
4179/96	*Set of 18*	10·00	10·00

MS4197 Three sheets. (a) 102×127 mm. $5 Mickey Mouse. P 13½×14. (b) 127×102 mm. $5 Minnie Mouse. P 13½×14. (c) 127×102 mm. $5 Goofy (*horiz*). P 14×13½ ... *Set of 3 sheets* 8·00 8·50
Nos. 4179/84, 4185/90 and 4191/6 were each printed together, *se-tenant*, in sheetlets of 6.

379 Hollywood Hogan   **380** Plateosaurus

(Des Spotline Design. Litho Questa)

1999 (25 Jan). *World Championship Wrestling.* T **379** and similar vert designs. Multicoloured. P 13.

4198	70 c. Type **379**	30	35
	a. Sheetlet. Nos. 4198/205	2·40	
4199	70 c. Sting	30	35
4200	70 c. Bret Hart	30	35
4201	70 c. Giant	30	35
4202	70 c. Kevin Nash	30	35
4203	70 c. Randy Savage	30	35
4204	70 c. Diamond Dallas	30	35
4205	70 c. Goldberg	30	35
4198/205	*Set of 8*	2·40	2·75

Nos. 4198/205 were printed together, *se-tenant*, in sheetlets of 8 arranged as 2 vertical strips separated by wrestling scenes.

(Des E. Nisbet. Litho Questa)

1999 (1 Mar). *"Australia '99" World Stamp Exhibition, Melbourne. Prehistoric Animals.* T **380** and similar multicoloured designs. P 14.

4206	70 c. Type **380**	30	35
4207	70 c. Struthiomimus	30	35
	a. Sheetlet. Nos. 4207/18	3·50	
4208	70 c. Indricotherium	30	35
4209	70 c. Giant Moa	30	35
4210	70 c. Deinonychus	30	35
4211	70 c. Sabre Tooth Tiger	30	35
4212	70 c. Dawn Horse	30	35
4213	70 c. Peittacosaurus	30	35
4214	70 c. Giant Ground Sloth	30	35
4215	70 c. Woolly Rhinoceros	30	35
4216	70 c. Mosasaur	30	35
4217	70 c. Mastodon	30	35
4218	70 c. Syndyoceras	30	35
4219	90 c. Euoplacephalus	40	45
4220	90 c. Rhamphorhynchus	40	45
	a. Sheetlet. Nos. 4220/31	4·75	
4221	90 c. Pteranodon	40	45
4222	90 c. Archaeopterix	40	45
4223	90 c. Dimetrodon	40	45
4224	90 c. Stegasaurus	40	45
4225	90 c. Parasaurolophus	40	45
4226	90 c. Iguanodon	40	45
4227	90 c. Triceratops	40	45
4228	90 c. Tyrannosaurus	40	45
4229	90 c. Ichthyosaurus	40	45
4230	90 c. Plesiosaurus	40	45
4231	90 c. Hesperonis	40	45
4232	$1.10, Pachycephalosaurus	50	55
4233	$1.40, Dilophosaurus	60	65
4206/33	*Set of 28*	9·75	11·50

MS4234 Two sheets, each 107×77 mm. (a) $5 Diplodocus. (b) $5 Woolly Mammoth (*vert*).
.. *Set of 2 sheets* 4·25 4·50
Nos. 4207/18 and 4220/31 were each printed together, *se-tenant*, in sheetlets of 12 with enlarged inscribed bottom margins.

(Litho B.D.T.)

1999 (12 Apr). *Fauna and Flora.* T **381** and similar multicoloured designs. P 14.

4235	10 c. Type **381**	10	10
4236	20 c. Green Turtle and Coconut Palm seedling	10	10
4237	25 c. White Ibis and Mangrove tree	10	15
4238	50 c. Tiger Swallowtail and Ironweed	20	25
4239	70 c. Eastern Box Turtle and Jack-in-the-Pulpit (plant) (*vert*)	30	35
4240	70 c. Basilisk Lizard and Strangler Fig (*vert*)	30	35
	a. Sheetlet. Nos. 4240/51	3·50	
4241	70 c. Scarlet Macaw and Kapok trees (*vert*)	30	35
4242	70 c. Howler Monkey and Cecropia tree (*vert*)	30	35
4243	70 c. Toucan and Cecropia tree (*vert*)	30	35
4244	70 c. Poison-arrow Frog and Bromiliad (*vert*)	30	35
4245	70 c. *Heliconius phyllis* (butterfly) and Rattlesnake Orchid (*vert*)	30	35
4246	70 c. Bat-eating Hawk and Tree Fern (*vert*)	30	35
4247	70 c. Jaguar and Tillandsia (*vert*)	30	35
4248	70 c. Margay and Sierra Palm (*vert*)	30	35
4249	70 c. Lesser Bird of Paradise and Aristolchia (*vert*)	30	35
4250	70 c. *Parides* (butterfly) and Erythrina (*vert*)	30	35
4251	70 c. Fer-de-Lance (snake) and Zebra plant (*vert*)	30	35
4252	70 c. Red-tailed Hawk and Ocitillo (*vert*)	30	35
	a. Sheetlet. Nos. 4252/63	3·50	
4253	70 c. Mourning Dove and Organ Pipe Cactus (*vert*)	30	35
4254	70 c. Burrowing Owl and Paloverde tree (*vert*)	30	35
4255	70 c. Cactus Wren and Saguaro Cactus (*vert*)	30	35
4256	70 c. Puma and Ocitillo (*vert*)	30	35
4257	70 c. Grey Fox and Organ Pipe Cactus (*vert*)	30	35
4258	70 c. Coyote and Prickly Pear Cactus (*vert*)	30	35
4259	70 c. Gila Woodpecker and Saguaro Cactus (*vert*)	30	35
4260	70 c. Collared Lizard and Barrel Cactus (*vert*)	30	35
4261	70 c. Gila Monster (lizard) and Cowblinder Cactus (*vert*)	30	35
4262	70 c. Roadrunner and Hedgehog Cactus (*vert*)	30	35
4263	70 c. Jack Rabbit and Saguaro Cactus (*vert*)	30	35
4264	90 c. Praying Mantis and Milkweed (*vert*)	40	45
4265	$1.10, Spotted-sided Finch and Bottle Brush (*vert*)	50	55
4266	$1.40, Koala and Gum tree (*vert*)	60	65
4235/66	*Set of 32*	9·00	10·50

MS4267 Two sheets, each 110×85 mm. (a) $5 Alligator and Water Lilies. (b) $5 Rivoli's Hummingbird .. *Set of 2 sheets* 4·25 4·50
Nos. 4240/51 and 4252/63 were each printed together, *se-tenant*, in sheetlets of 12 stamps, the backgrounds forming composite designs. Nos. 4235/9 and 4264/6 were printed in sheets of 6.
No. 4253 is inscribed "MORNING DOVE", No. 4265 "ZEBRA FINCH" and No. **MS**4267(b) "RIUOLIS HUMMINGBIRD", all in error.

(Des R. Company. Litho Questa)

1999 (26 Apr). *Aircraft.* T **382** and similar multicoloured designs. P 14.

4268	60 c. Montgolfier Balloon, 1783 (*vert*)	25	30
4269	70 c. Type **382**	30	35
4270	90 c. Zeppelin (airship)	40	45
4271	$1 Wilbur Wright and *Flyer*, 1903	45	50
4272	$1.10, M-130 Clipper	50	55
	a. Sheetlet. Nos. 4272/9	4·00	
4273	$1.10, DC-3, 1937	50	55
4274	$1.10, Staggerwing Beech CVR FT C-17L	50	55
4275	$1.10, Hughes H-1 Racer	50	55
4276	$1.10, Gee Bee Model R-1, 1932	50	55
4277	$1.10, Lockheed 8 Sirius *Tingmissartoq* seaplane	50	55
4278	$1.10, Fokker T-2, 1923	50	55
4279	$1.10, Curtiss CW-16E seaplane	50	55
4280	$1.10, Dayton Wright DH-4 Bomber	50	55
	a. Sheetlet. Nos. 4280/7	4·00	
4281	$1.10, Sopwith Camel	50	55
4282	$1.10, Sopwith Dove	50	55
4283	$1.10, Jeannin Stahl Taube	50	55
4284	$1.10, Fokker DR-1 triplane	50	55
4285	$1.10, Albatross Diva	50	55
4286	$1.10, Sopwith Pup	50	55
4287	$1.10, SPAD XIII Smith IV	50	55
4268/87	*Set of 20*	9·25	10·25

MS4288 Two sheets, each 110×85 mm. (a) $5 Lebauldy-Juillot airship No. 1 *La Jaune*, 1903. (b) $5 Bleriot XI crossing Channel, 1914
.. *Set of 2 sheets* 4·25 4·50
Nos. 4272/9 and 4280/7 were each issued, *se-tenant*, in sheetlets of 8 stamps, with the backgrounds forming composite designs.
No. **MS**4288a is inscribed "LE BANDY AIRSHIP" in error.

(Litho B.D.T.)

1999 (6 May). *Space Exploration.* T **383** and similar multicoloured designs. P 14.

4289	20 c. Type **383**	10	10
4290	50 c. Konstantin Tsiolkovsky (aeronautical engineer), 1903	20	25
4291	70 c. Robert Goddard (rocket scientist), 1926	30	35
4292	90 c. Sir Isaac Newton (physicist), 1668 (*vert*)	40	45
4293/301	$1 × 9 ("Explorer" rocket, 1958; "Lunokhod Explorer", 1970; "Viking Lander", 1975; A-1 (SL-3) rocket, 1959; Edward White (astronaut), 1965; "Salyut 1" space station, 1971; Ancient observatory; "Freedom 7" rocket, 1961; "Ariane" rocket, 1980s) (*all vert*)		
	a. Sheetlet. Nos. 4293/301	4·00	
4302/10	$1 × 9 ("Luna 3", 1959; "Soyuz 11", 1971; "MIR" space station, 1986; "Sputnik 1", 1957; "Apollo 4", 1967; Bruce McCandles (astronaut), 1984; Sir William Herschel's telescope, 1781; John Glenn (astronaut), 1962; Space shuttle *Columbia*, 1981)		
	a. Sheetlet. Nos. 4302/10	4·00	
4311/19	$1 × 9 (Yuri Gagarin (cosmonaut), 1961; "Lunar Rover", 1971; "Mariner 10", 1974–5; Laika (first dog in space), 1957; Edwin Aldrin on Moon, 1969; "Skylab" space station, 1973; German "V-2" rocket, 1942; "Gemini 4" rocket, 1965; Hubble telescope, 1990) (*all vert*)		
	a. Sheetlet. Nos. 4311/19	4·00	
4289/319	*Set of 31*	13·00	14·50

MS4320 Two sheets, each 85×110 mm. (a) $5 Space shuttle *Atlantis* docking with "MIR". (b) $5 Saturn 5 rocket, 1969 (*vert*) . *Set of 2 sheets* 4·25 4·50
Nos. 4293/301, 4302/10 and 4311/19 were each printed together, *se-tenant*, in sheetlets of 9 with the backgrounds forming composite designs.
No. 4296 is inscribed "1957 - R7 ROCKET", No. 4302 "LUNA 9", No. 4311 "1962" and No. 4315 "NEIL ARMSTRONG", all in error.

(Litho B.D.T.)

1999 (19 June). *Royal Wedding.* T **384** and similar multicoloured designs. Litho. P 13½.

4321	$3 Type **384**	1·25	1·40
	a. Sheetlet. Nos. 4321/3	3·75	
4322	$3 Miss Sophie Rhys-Jones and Prince Edward	1·25	1·40
4323	$3 Miss Sophie Rhys-Jones	1·25	1·40
4321/3	*Set of 3*	3·75	4·00

MS4324 78×108 mm. $6 Prince Edward and Miss Sophie Rhys-Jones (*horiz*) 2·50 2·75
Nos. 4321/3 were printed together, as a *se-tenant* horizontal strip of 3, in sheetlets with illustrated margins.

(Litho Questa)

1999 (25 June). *"iBRA '99" International Stamp Exhibition, Nuremberg. Horiz design as* T **262** *of Lesotho.* Multicoloured. P 14×14½.

4325 $1 Steam locomotive and power station 45 50
No. 4325 is inscribed "THE KRAUSS-MAFFEI V-200 DIESEL LOCOMOTIVE: GERMANY 1852" in error.

(Des R. Sauber. Litho Questa)

1999 (25 June). *150th Death Anniv of Katsushika Hokusai (Japanese artist).* Multicoloured designs as T **263** of Lesotho, but vert. P 13½×14.

4326	$1.10, "Admiring the Irises at Yatsuhashi" (pine tree in foreground)	50	55
	a. Sheetlet. Nos. 4326/31	3·00	
4327	$1.10, "Sea Life" (turtle facing top left)	50	55
4328	$1.10, "Admiring the Irises at Yatsuhashi" (Japanese inscr at top right)	50	55
4329	$1.10, "Pilgrims bathing in Roben Waterfall"	50	55
4330	$1.10, "Sea Life" (turtle facing top right)	50	55
4331	$1.10, "Farmers crossing a Suspension Bridge"	50	55
4332	$1.10, "Landscape with a Hundred Bridges" (mountains)	50	55
	a. Sheetlet. Nos. 4332/7	3·00	
4333	$1.10, "Sea Life" (turtle facing bottom left)	50	55
4334	$1.10, "Landscape with a Hundred Bridges" (Japanese inscr at top)	50	55
4335	$1.10, "A View of Aoigaoka Waterfall in Edo"	50	55
4336	$1.10, "Sea Life" (crab)	50	55
4337	$1.10, "Women on the Beach at Enoshima"	50	55
4326/37	*Set of 12*	6·00	6·50

MS4338 Two sheets, each 71×102 mm. (a) $5 "In the Horse-washing Waterfall". (b) $5 "Fisherman at Kajikazawa". .. *Set of 2 sheets* 4·25 4·50
Nos. 4326/31 and 4332/7 were each printed together, *se-tenant*, in sheetlets of 6.

1999 (25 June). *10th Anniv of United Nations Rights of the Child Convention. Vert designs as* T **264** *of Lesotho.* Multicoloured. Litho. P 14.

4339	90 c. Tyreek Isaacs	40	45
	a. Sheetlet. Nos. 4339/42	1·60	
4340	90 c. Fredique Isaacs	40	45
4341	90 c. Jerome Burke III	40	45
4342	90 c. Kellisha Roberts	40	45
4343	$3 Girl with ribbons in hair	1·25	1·40
	a. Sheetlet. Nos. 4343/5	3·75	

Bottom images

381 African Elephant and Acacia Tree

382 Lilenthal's Glider, 1894

383 Galileo Galilei (astronomer), 1609

384 Prince Edward

4344	$3 Girl in straw hat	1·25	1·40
4345	$3 Girl with kitten	1·25	1·40
4339/45	*Set of* 7	5·25	6·00
MS4346	110×80 mm. $5 Japanese child	2·10	2·25

Nos. 4339/42 and 4343/5 were each printed together, *se-tenant*, in sheetlets of 4 or 3 with enlarged, illustrated margins.

1999 (25 June). *"PhilexFrance '99" International Stamp Exhibition, Paris. Railway Locomotives. Two sheets, each 106×81 mm containing horiz designs as T 372 of Maldive Islands. Multicoloured. Litho.* P 14×13¹/₂.

MS4347	(a) $6 Pacific steam locomotive for "Fleche d'Or". (b) $6 Quadrt electric high-speed locomotive, 1940		
	Set of 2 *sheets*	5·25	5·50

1999 (25 June). *250th Birth Anniv of Johann von Goethe (German writer). Designs as T 265 of Lesotho. Litho.* P 14.

4348	$3 grey and black	1·25	1·40
	a. Sheetlet. Nos. 4348/50	3·75	
4349	$3 dull ultramarine, purple and black	1·25	1·40
	a. Sheetlet. Nos. 4349 and 4351/2	3·75	
4350	$3 grey-blue and black	1·25	1·40
4351	$3 bright mauve and black	1·25	1·40
4352	$3 cinnamon and black	1·25	1·40
4348/52	*Set of* 5	6·25	7·00
MS4353	Two sheets, each 78×108 mm. (a) $5 olive-sepia and black. (b) $5 orange-brown, red-brown and black		
	Set of 2 *sheets*	4·25	4·50

Designs: *Horiz*—No. 4348, Faust, Helena and Euphonon; No. 4349, Von Goethe and Von Schiller; No. 4350, Mephistopheles leading the Lemures to Faust; No. 4351, Faust dying; No. 4352, Faust's spirit being carried by angels. *Vert*—No. MS4353a, Von Goethe; No. MS4353b, Immortal soul of Faust.

Nos. 4348/50 and 4349 with 4351/2 were each printed together, *se-tenant*, in sheetlets of three with enlarged illustrated margins.

385	I. M. Pei	386 Henry Alphaeus Robertson

1999 (25 June). *Year of the Elder Person. T 385 and similar vert designs. Multicoloured. Litho.* P 14.

4354	70 c. Type 385	30	35
	a. Sheetlet. Nos. 4354/65	3·50	
4355	70 c. Billy Graham	30	35
4356	70 c. Barbara Cartland	30	35
4357	70 c. Mike Wallace	30	35
4358	70 c. Jeanne Moreau	30	35
4359	70 c. B. B. King	30	35
4360	70 c. Elie Wiesel	30	35
4361	70 c. Arthur Miller	30	35
4362	70 c. Colin Powell	30	35
4363	70 c. Jack Palance	30	35
4364	70 c. Neil Simon	30	35
4365	70 c. Eartha Kitt	30	35
4354/65	*Set of* 12	3·50	4·00
MS4366	115×134 mm. $1.10, Thomas Saunders; $1.10, Mother Sarah Baptiste; $1.10, Sir Sydney Gun-Munro; $1.10, Dr. Earle Kirby	2·00	2·10

Nos. 4354/65 were printed together, *se-tenant*, in sheetlets of 12 with enlarged, illustrated left and top margins.

(Litho Questa)

1999 (25 June). *World Teachers' Day. T 386 and similar vert designs. Multicoloured.* P 14¹/₂.

4367	$2 Type 386	85	90
	a. Sheetlet. Nos. 4367/70	3·25	
4368	$2 Yvonne Francis-Gibson	85	90
4369	$2 Edna Peters	85	90
4370	$2 Christopher Wilberforce Prescod	85	90
4367/70	*Set of* 4	3·25	3·50

Nos. 4367/70 were printed together, *se-tenant*, in sheetlets of 4 with an enlarged illustrated right margin.

(Litho Questa)

1999 (18 Oct). *"Queen Elizabeth the Queen Mother's Century". Vert designs as T 267 of Lesotho.* P 14.

4371	$2 black and gold	85	90
	a. Sheetlet. Nos. 4371/4	3·25	
4372	$2 black and gold	85	90
4373	$2 multicoloured	85	90
4374	$2 multicoloured	85	90
4371/4	*Set of* 4	3·25	3·50
MS4375	153×156 mm. $6 multicoloured. P 13¹/₂×14	2·50	2·75

Designs: (*As Type 267 of Lesotho*)—No. 4371, Lady Elizabeth Bowes-Lyon, 1909; No. 4372, King George VI and Queen Elizabeth with Princess Elizabeth, 1930; No. 4373, Queen Mother at Badminton, 1977; No. 4374, Queen Mother waving, 1983. (37×50 mm)—No. MS4375, Queen Mother wearing yellow dress, 1987.

Nos. 4371/4 were printed together, *se-tenant*, as a sheetlet of 4 stamps and a central label with inscribed and embossed margins.

No. MS4375 also shows the Royal Arms embossed in gold. A $20 value embossed in gold foil also exists from a limited printing.

387	"The Resurrection" (Dürer)	388 Mail Coach, 1800

(Litho Questa)

1999 (22 Nov). *Christmas. Religious Paintings. T 387 and similar vert designs. Multicoloured.* P 13¹/₂×14.

4376	20 c. Type 387	10	10
4377	50 c. "Christ in Limbo" (Dürer)	20	25
4378	70 c. "Christ falling on the Way to Calvary" (Raphael)	30	35
4379	90 c. "St. Ildefonso with the Madonna and Child" (Rubens)	40	45
4380	$5 "The Crucifixion" (Raphael)	2·10	2·25
4376/80	*Set of* 5	3·00	3·25
MS4381	76×106 mm. $6 "The Sistine Madonna" (Raphael)	2·50	2·75

No. 4377 is inscribed "Christ in Llmbo" in error.

(Litho Questa)

1999 (7 Dec). *125th Anniv of Universal Postal Union. T 388 and similar horiz designs. Multicoloured.* P 14.

4382	$3 Type 388	1·25	1·40
	a. Sheetlet. Nos. 4382/4	3·75	
4383	$3 Seaplane leaving liner	1·25	1·40
4384	$3 Concorde	1·25	1·40
4382/4	*Set of* 3	3·75	4·00

Nos. 4382/4 were printed together, *se-tenant*, in sheetlets of 3 with an enlarged illustrated and inscribed left margin.

STAMP BOOKLETS

1974 (5 Sept). *Blue and green printed covers. Size 98×58 mm (No. SB1), or 150×48 mm (No. SB2). Stapled. Back cover in six different designs:*
(a) Kingstown Harbour
(b) Indian Bay
(c) St. Mary's R.C. Church, Kingstown
(d) St. George's Cathedral, Kingstown
(e) View of the interior
(f) Sunset over Young Island

SB1	60 c. booklet (*any cover*) containing 1 c., 2 c., 3 c., 4 c. and 5 c. (Nos. 286a, 361/4) in blocks of 4	1·25	
	Set of 6 *different cover designs*	7·00	
SB2	75 c. booklet (*any cover*) containing 1 c., 2 c., 3 c., 4 c. and 5 c. (Nos. 286a, 361/4) in strips of 5	1·25	
	Set of 6 *different cover designs*	7·00	

1975 (27 Feb). *Kingstown "Carnival'75". Multicoloured cover. Stapled.*

SB3	$2.50, booklet containing two panes of two 1 c. plus label (No. 415a) and two different *se-tenant* panes of 3 (Nos. 415b, 416a)	1·25

1976 (19 Feb). *Kingstown "Carnival'76". Multicoloured cover. Stapled.*

SB4	$2.50 booklet containing two *se-tenant* panes of 2 stamps and 1 label (No. 479a) and two different *se-tenant* panes of 3 (Nos. 480a, 482a)	1·25

1977 (7 Feb). *Silver Jubilee. Black and red printed cover, 105×71 mm. Stapled.*

SB5	$5 booklet containing three different *se-tenant* panes of 4 (Nos. 515a, 519a, 523a)	4·00

1978 (20 July). *25th Anniv of Coronation. Multicoloured cover as No. SB3 of Montserrat. Stapled.*

SB6	$9.30, booklet containing 40 c., 50 c., $1.25 and $2.50 (Nos. 556/9) in pairs	1·10

1979 (31 May). *Death Centenary of Sir Rowland Hill. Silver, black and blue printed cover, 108×32 mm. Stapled.*

SB7	$7.80, booklet containing two 40 c. (Nos. 578, 594), two 50 c. (Nos. 579, 595) and two $3 (Nos. 580, 599), each in *se-tenant* pairs taken from No. MS581	1·25

1979 (1 Sept). *Brown and cream (No. SB8) or deep blue and pale blue (No. SB9) covers, 100×60 mm. Stapled.*

SB8	$3 booklet containing 5 c., 20 c. and 50 c. (Nos. 586, 592, 595) in blocks of 4	1·75
SB9	$5 booklet containing 10 c., 25 c., 40 c. and 50 c. (Nos. 589, 593/5) in blocks of 4	2·50

1980 (24 Apr). *"London 1980" International Stamp Exhibition. Black printed cover, 108×60 mm, showing exhibition emblem and St. Vincent arms. Stapled.*

SB10	$15.20, booklet containing 80 c., $1 and $2 (Nos. 634/6) in blocks of 4	2·00

1981 (26 Nov). *Royal Wedding. Multicoloured cover, 105×65 mm, showing The Isabella. Stitched.*

SB11	$9.80, booklet containing eight 60 c. in panes of 4 (No. 675a) and two $2.50 in pane of 2 (No. 676a)	1·75

1986 (18 July). *Royal Wedding. Gold (No. SB12) or silver (No. SB13) on ultramarine covers, 152×80 mm. Stapled.*

SB12	$7.20, booklet (Westminster Abbey) containing twelve 60 c. (Nos. 1009/10) in blocks of 4	2·50
SB13	$10.40, booklet (State Coach) containing 60 c. and $2 (Nos. 1009/12, but imperf) in blocks of 4	3·50

OFFICIAL STAMPS

OFFICIAL

(O 1)

1982 (11 Oct). *Nos. 668/73 optd with Type O 1.*

O1	60 c. *Isabella*	15	15
	a. Sheetlet. No. O1 × 6 and No. O2	1·10	
	b. Opt double		
	c. Albino opt	8·00	
O2	60 c. Prince Charles and Lady Diana Spencer	40	50
	b. Opt double		
	c. Albino opt	23·00	
O3	$2.50, *Alberta* (tender)	15	25
	a. Sheetlet. No. O3 × 6 and No. O4	1·25	
	b. Opt inverted	22·00	
	c. Opt inverted (horiz pair)	70·00	
	d. Albino opt	15·00	
O4	$2.50, Prince Charles and Lady Diana Spencer	55	70
	b. Opt inverted	70·00	
	c. Albino opt	45·00	
O5	$4 *Britannia*	25	30
	a. Sheetlet. No. O5 × 6 and No. O6	2·00	
	b. Opt double		
	c. Albino opt	11·00	
	d. Opt inverted		
	e. Opt inverted (horiz pair)		

O6	$4 Prince Charles and Lady Diana Spencer		80	90
	b. Opt double	..		
	c. Albino opt	.. .. ..		45·00
	d. Opt inverted	.. ..		
O1/6		.. .. *Set of 6*	2·00	2·50

Nos. O3c and O5e show the long overprint, intended for Nos. O4 or O6, inverted and struck across a horizontal pair of Nos. O3 or O5. Nos. O4b and O6d show two examples of Type O **1** inverted on the same stamp.

POSTAL FISCAL STAMPS

The following were primarily intended for the payment of passport fees, but were also valid for postal purposes and are frequently found used on parcels.

$5

STAMP DUTY

(F **1**)   F **2** St. Vincent Coat of Arms

1980 (Feb). *Stamps as T* **95**, *without value, surch as Type* F **1**. *W* w **12**. *P* 14½ × 14.

F1	$5 deep lavender and azure..	..	..	1·75	2·00
F2	$10 light green and apple green	..		3·00	4·50
F3	$20 reddish purple and pale rose-lilac	..		4·75	10·00
F1/3	.. ..	..	*Set of 3*	8·50	15·00

(Des Harrison. Recess D.L.R.)

1980 (19 May). *W* w **14**. *P* 14 × 13.

F4	F **2**	$5 chalky blue ..	..	..	1·75	2·25
F5		$10 deep green ..	..	..	3·00	3·75
F6		$20 brown-red ..	..	..	5·00	8·50
F4/6	..	.. .. ..	..	*Set of 3*	8·75	13·00

1984 (22 May). *As No.* F6, *but W* w **15**. *P* 12.

F9	F **2**	$20 brown-red ..	..	..	6·00	8·00

A 10 c. in a design similar to Type F **2**, but inscribed "REVENUE", was issued in April 1988. Examples can be found used on commercial mail, but such use was unauthorised.

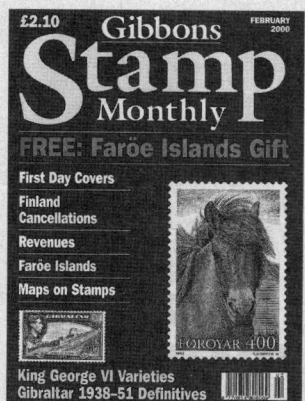

GRENADINES OF ST. VINCENT

A group of islands south of St. Vincent which includes Bequia, Mustique, Canouan and Union.

For stamps inscribed "The Grenadines of St. VINCENT" issued by St. Vincent in 1971, see under St. Vincent Nos. 330/6.

Stamps of the Grenadines of St. Vincent exist overprinted "SPECIMEN", these being produced for publicity purposes.

1973 (14 Nov). *Royal Wedding. As Nos. 322/3 of Montserrat.*

1	25 c. light green	.. ..	10	10
2	$1 ochre	.. ..	15	15

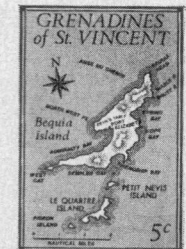

GRENADINES
OF

(1)

2 Map of Bequia

1974 (24 Apr). *Stamps of St. Vincent. T 51 etc. optd in litho with T 1 by Harrison & Sons. Glazed paper. W w 12 (sideways on 4, 5, 10, 12, 50 c. and $5).*

3	1 c. Green Heron	.. ..	10	10
	a. Opt omitted	..	50·00	
	b. Albino opt	..	45·00	
4	2 c. Lesser Antillean Bullfinches	..	15	15
	w. Wmk inverted	..	3·25	
5	3 c. St. Vincent Amazons	..	75	75
6	4 c. Rufous-throated Solitaire	..	10	10
7	5 c. Red-necked Pigeon	..	10	10
8	6 c. Bananaquits	..	15	10
	w. Wmk inverted	..	22·00	
9	8 c. Purple-throated Carib	..	15	10
10	10 c. Mangrove Cuckoo	..	15	10
11	12 c. Common Black Hawk	..	20	15
	a. Opt double	..	£130	
12	20 c. Bare-eyed Thrush	..	30	20
13	25 c. Hooded Tanager	..	30	20
14	50 c. Blue-hooded Euphonia	..	60	40
	a. Albino opt	..	80·00	
15	$1 Barn Owl	..	1·00	75
16	$2.50, Yellow-bellied Elaenia	..	1·00	1·00
17	$5 Ruddy Quail Dove	..	1·25	1·75
3/17		Set of 15	5·50	5·00

(Des G. Drummond. Litho Enschedé)

1974 (9 May). *Maps (1st series). T 2 and similar vert designs. W w 12 (sideways*). P 13×12½.*

18	5 c. black, light dull green & deep dull green	10	10
	w. Wmk Crown to right of CA	..	5·50	
19	15 c. multicoloured ..	..	10	10
20	20 c. multicoloured ..	..	10	10
21	30 c. black, light rose-lilac and lake	10	10
22	40 c. black, lavender and deep ultramarine	10	10
23	$1 black, cobalt and bright ultramarine	20	20
18/23		Set of 6	45	35

Maps:—15 c. The Grenadines and Prune Island (inset); 20 c. Mayreau Island and Tobago Cays; 30 c. Mustique Island; 40 c. Union Island; $1 Canouan Island.

*The normal sideways watermark shows Crown to left of CA, as seen from the back of the stamp.

Nos. 18/23 were each issued in sheets of ten stamps and two se-tenant labels.

See also Nos. 85/8.

**GRENADINES
OF**

(3)

4 Boat-building

1974 (7 June). *Nos. 361/2 of St. Vincent optd in typo with T 3 by Govt Printer, St. Vincent. Glazed paper. W w 12.*

24	2 c. Lesser Antillean Bullfinches	..	25	30
25	3 c. St. Vincent Amazons	..	25	30
	a. Opt double	..	38·00	
	b. Albino opt	..	7·00	
	c. Chalky paper. Wmk sideways (No. 288)	5·00	12·00

1974 (25 July). *Centenary of Universal Postal Union. As Nos. 392/5 of St. Vincent but colours and face-values changed and inscr "Grenadines of St. Vincent".*

26	2 c. U.P.U. emblem	..	10	10
	a. Red (U.P.U. emblem) omitted	..	£650	
	w. Wmk inverted	..	29·00	
27	15 c. Globe within posthorn	..	10	10
28	40 c. Map of St. Vincent and hand-cancelling	10	10
29	$1 Map of the World	..	25	15
26/9		Set of 4	40	30

No. 26a was caused by a paper fold.

(Des G. Drummond. Litho Questa)

1974. *Bequia Island (1st series). T 4 and similar horiz designs. Multicoloured. P 14 (a) W w 12 (sideways*) (26.9.74).*

30	5 c. Type 4	..	35	1·50
	w. Wmk Crown to right of CA	..	£120	
31	30 c. Careening at Port Elizabeth	..	10	10
32	35 c. Admiralty Bay	..	10	10
33	$1 Fishing boat race	..	15	25

(b) W w 14 (sideways) (12.74)

34	5 c. Type 4	..	10	15
30/4		Set of 5	65	1·75

*The normal sideways watermark shows Crown to left of CA, as seen from the back of the stamp.

No. 34 differs in shade from No. 30, notably in the shirt of the man at right, which is red on No. 34 instead of purple.

Nos. 30/4 were each issued in sheets of ten stamps and two se-tenant labels.

See also Nos. 185/8.

5 Music Volute (*Voluta musica*)

(Des R. Granger Barrett. Litho Questa)

1974 (27 Nov)–77. *Shells and Molluscs. Horiz designs as T 5. Multicoloured. W w 14 (sideways*). P 14. A. No imprint.*

35A	1 c. American Thorny Oyster (*Spondylas americanus*)	..	10	10
	w. Wmk Crown to right of CA	9·00	
36A	2 c. Zigzag Scallop (*Pecten ziczac*)	..	10	10
37A	3 c. Reticulated Cowrie-helmet (*Cypraecassis testiculus*)	..	10	10
38A	4 c. Type 5	..	10	10
39A	5 c. Amber Pen Shell (*Pinna carnea*)	10	10
40A	6 c. Angular Triton (*Cymatium femorale*)	10	10
41A	8 c. Flame Helmet (*Cassis flammea*)	10	10
42A	10 c. Caribbean Olive (*Oliva caribaeensis*)	10	10
43A	12 c. American or Common Sundial (*Architectonica nobilis*)	..	10	10
44A	15 c. Glory of the Atlantic Cone (*Conus granulatus*)	..	25	20
45A	20 c. Flame Auger (*Terebra taurina*)	30	35
46A	25 c. King Venus (*Chione paphia*)	50	20
47A	35 c. Long-spined Star Shell (*Astraea phoebia*)	..	35	30
48A	45 c. Speckled Tellin (*Tellina listeri*)	35	30
49A	50 c. Rooster-tail Conch (*Strombus gallus*)	40	20
50A	$1 Green Star Shell (*Astraea tuber*)	50	75
51A	$2.50, Antillean or Incomparable Cone (*Conus cedonulli*)	..	60	75
52A	$5 Rough File Shell (*Lima scabra*)	75	80
52cA	$10 Measled Cowrie (*Cypraea zebra*) (12.7.76)	..	3·50	1·00
35A/52cA		Set of 19	7·00	4·50

B. With imprint at foot

38B	4 c. Type 5 (12.7.76)	..	10	10
39B	5 c. Amber Pen Shell (*Pinna carnea*) (12.7.76)	..	10	10
40B	6 c. Angular Triton (*Cymatium femorale*) (12.7.76)	..	10	10
41B	8 c. Flame Helmet (*Cassis flammea*) (12.7.76)	..	10	10
42B	10 c. Caribbean Olive (*Oliva caribaeensis*) (12.7.76)	..	10	10
	c. Corrected imprint (2.6.77)	70	10
44B	15 c. Glory of the Atlantic Cone (*Conus granulatus*) (2.6.77)	..	80	15
45B	20 c. Flame Auger (*Terebra taurina*) (12.7.76)	..	30	20
	c. Corrected imprint (2.6.77)	1·25	15
46B	25 c. King Venus (*Chione paphia*) (2.6.77)	80	15
47B	35 c. Long-spined Star Shell (*Astraea phoebia*) (12.7.76)	..	35	25
	c. Corrected imprint (2.6.77)	1·25	15
49B	50 c. Rooster-tail Conch (*Strombus gallus*) (12.7.76)	..	45	30
50B	$1 Green Star Shell (*Astraea tuber*) (12.7.76)	..	60	60
51B	$2.50, Antillean or Incomparable Cone (*Conus cedonulli*) (2.6.77)	..	2·50	80
52B	$5 Rough File Shell (*Lima scabra*) (2.6.77)	3·50	1·25
38B/52B		Set of 13	8·50	3·50

*The normal sideways watermark shows Crown to left of CA, as seen from the back of the stamp.

Imprint dates: "1976", Nos. 38B/42B, 45B, 47B, 49B/50B; "1977", Nos. 42Bc, 44B, 45Bc, 46B, 47Bc, 51B/2B.

On Nos. 42Bc, 44B, 45Bc, 46B, 47Bc, 51B and 52B, the designer's name is correctly spelt as "R. Granger Barrett". Previously the last name had been spelt "Barratt".

1974 (28 Nov). *Birth Centenary of Sir Winston Churchill. As Nos. 403/6 of St. Vincent but colours and face-values changed and inscr "GRENADINES OF ST. VINCENT".*

53	5 c. Type 75	..	10	10
54	40 c. As 35 c.	..	10	15
55	50 c. As 45 c.	..	10	15
56	$1 As $1	..	20	30
53/6		Set of 4	35	60

6 Cotton House, Mustique

(Des G. Drummond. Litho Questa)

1975 (27 Feb). *Mustique Island. T 6 and similar horiz design. Multicoloured. W w 14 (sideways). P 14.*

57	5 c. Type 6	..	10	
58	35 c. "Blue Waters", Endeavour Bay	10	
59	45 c. Endeavour Bay	10	
60	$1 "Les Jolies Eaux", Gelliceaux Bay	25	2
57/60		Set of 4	40	3

Nos. 57/60 were each issued in sheets of ten stamps and two se-tenant labels.

7 *Danaus plexippus*

(Des G. Drummond. Litho Questa)

1975 (15 May). *Butterflies. T 7 and similar horiz designs. Multi-coloured. W w 14 (sideways). P 14.*

61	3 c. Type 7	..	20	1
62	5 c. *Agraulis vanillae*	..	25	1
63	35 c. *Battus polydamas*	..	50	1
64	45 c. *Evenus dindymus* and *Junonia evarete*	60	1
65	$1 *Anartia jatrophae*	..	90	4
61/5		Set of 5	2·25	7

8 Resort Pavilion

(Des G. Drummond. Litho Harrison)

1975 (24 July). *Petit St. Vincent. T 8 and similar horiz design. Multicoloured. W w 14 (sideways*). P 14.*

66	5 c. Type 8 ..	..	10	1
67	35 c. The Harbour	..	10	1
68	45 c. The Jetty	..	15	1
	w. Wmk Crown to right of CA	..	30·00	
69	$1 Sailing in coral lagoon	..	50	8
	w. Wmk Crown to right of CA	..	30·00	
66/9		Set of 4	70	1·0

*The normal sideways watermark shows Crown to left of CA, as seen from the back of the stamp.

Nos. 66/9 were each issued in sheets of ten stamps and two se-tenant labels.

9 Ecumenical Church, Mustique

(Des G. Drummond. Litho Questa)

1975 (20 Nov). *Christmas. T 9 and similar horiz designs. Multi-coloured. W w 12 (sideways). P 14.*

70	5 c. Type 9	..	10	1
71	25 c. Catholic Church, Union Island	10	1
72	50 c. Catholic Church, Bequia	15	1
73	$1 Anglican Church, Bequia	25	1
70/3		Set of 4	40	3

10 Sunset Scene

(Des G. Drummond. Litho J.W.)

1976 (26 Feb). *Union Island (1st series). T 10 and similar horiz designs. W w 12 (sideways) (5 c.) or w 14 (sideways) (others). P 13½.*

74	5 c. Type 10	..	10	1
	w. Wmk Crown to left of CA	..	20·00	
75	35 c. Customs and Post Office, Clifton	10	1
76	45 c. Anglican Church, Ashton	10	1
77	$1 Mail schooner, Clifton Harbour	25	2
74/7		Set of 4	45	3

*The normal sideways watermark on the 5 c. shows Crown to right of CA, as seen from the back of the stamp.

Nos. 74/7 were each issued in sheets of ten stamps and two se-tenant labels.

See also Nos. 242/5.

11 Staghorn Coral

(Des G. Drummond. Litho Questa)

1976 (13 May). *Corals. T* **11** *and similar horiz designs. Multi-coloured. W w* **14** *(sideways).P* 14.

78	5 c. Type **11**	..	..	10	10
79	35 c. Elkhorn coral	..	..	20	10
80	45 c. Pillar coral	..	..	20	10
81	$1 Brain coral	..	..	40	20
78/81	..	..	*Set of 4*	75	30

12 25 c. Bicentennial Coin

(Des J. Cooter. Litho Questa)

1976 (15 July). *Bicentenary of American Revolution. T* **12** *and similar horiz designs. W w* **14** *(sideways). P* 13½.

82	25 c. silver, black and light violet-blue	..	10	10
83	50 c. silver, black and light rose-red	..	20	10
84	$1 silver, black and mauve	..	25	20
82/4	..	*Set of 3*	50	30

Designs:—50 c. Half-dollar coin; $1 One dollar coin.
Nos. 82/4 were each issued in sheets of ten stamps and two *se-tenant* labels.

(Des G. Drummond. Litho Questa)

1976 (23 Sept). *Maps* (2nd series). *Vert designs as T* **2**, *showing various islands as detailed below. W w* **14**. *P* 13½.

A. Bequia   D. Mustique   F. Prune
B. Canouan   E. Petit St. Vincent   G. Union
C. Mayreau

To indicate individual islands, use the above letters as a suffix to the following catalogue numbers.

85	5 c. black, myrtle-green and pale emerald	..	10	10
	a. Booklet pane. Nos. 85/6 and 88 plus printed label		45	
	b. Booklet pane. Nos. 85 × 2 and 86 plus printed label		30	
86	10 c. black, ultramarine and greenish blue	..	10	10
	a. Booklet pane. Nos. 86 × 2 and 87 plus printed label		40	
87	35 c. black, red-brown and bright rose	..	20	20
	a. Booklet pane. Nos. 87 × 2 and 88 plus printed label		65	
88	45 c. black, scarlet and yellow-orange	..	25	25
85/8		*Set of 4 (one island)*	60	60
85/8		*Set of 28 (seven islands)*	4·00	4·00

Nos. 85/8 were only issued in $2.50 stamp booklets.

13 Station Hill School and Post Office

(Des G. Drummond. Litho Questa)

1976 (2 Dec). *Mayreau Island. T* **13** *and similar horiz designs. Multicoloured. W w* **14** *(sideways).P* 14.

89	5 c. Type **13**	..	10	10
90	35 c. Church at Old Wall	..	10	10
91	45 c. La Sourciere Anchorage	..	10	10
92	$1 Saline Bay	..	25	15
89/92	..	*Set of 4*	40	30

Nos. 89/92 were each issued in sheets of ten stamps and two *se-tenant* labels.

14 Coronation Crown Coin

(Des G. Vasarhelyi. Litho Questa)

1977 (3 Mar). *Silver Jubilee. T* **14** *and similar horiz designs. Multicoloured. W w* **14** *(sideways).P* 14.

93	25 c. Type **14**	..	15	10
94	50 c. Silver Wedding Crown	..	20	10
95	$1 Silver Jubilee Crown	..	20	15
93/5	..	*Set of 3*	50	30

Nos. 93/5 were each issued in sheets of ten stamps and two *se-tenant* labels.

15 Fiddler Crab

(Des BG Studio. Litho Questa)

1977 (19 May). *Crustaceans. T* **15** *and similar horiz designs. Multicoloured. W w* **14** *(sideways).P* 14.

96	5 c. Type **15**	..	10	10
	w. Wmk Crown to right of CA	..	7·00	
97	35 c. Ghost crab	..	20	10
	w. Wmk Crown to right of CA	..	25·00	
98	50 c. Blue crab	..	25	10
	w. Wmk Crown to right of CA	..	4·50	
99	$1.25, Spiny lobster	..	55	40
	w. Wmk Crown to right of CA	..	25·00	
96/9		*Set of 4*	95	55

*The normal sideways watermark shows Crown to left of CA, as seen from the back of the stamp.

16 Snorkel Diving

(Des G. Drummond. Litho Questa)

1977 (25 Aug). *Prune Island. T* **16** *and similar horiz designs. Multicoloured. W w* **14** *(sideways).P* 14½.

100	5 c. Type **16**	..	10	10
101	35 c. Palm Island Resort	..	10	10
102	45 c. Casuarina Beach	..	10	15
103	$1 Palm Island Beach Club	..	30	95
	w. Wmk Crown to right of CA	..	20·00	
100/3		*Set of 4*	50	1·10

*The normal sideways watermark shows Crown to left of CA, as seen from the back of the stamp.
Nos. 100/3 were each issued in sheets of ten stamps and two *se-tenant* labels.

17 Mustique Island

(Des G. Drummond. Litho Questa)

1977 (31 Oct). *Royal Visit. Previously unissued stamps without face values, locally surch with new inscription. W w* **12**. *P* 14½ × 14.

104	**17** 40 c. turquoise-green and blue-green (Blk. (value) and R.)	..	15	10
105	$2 yellow-ochre and yellow-brown (R. (value) and B.)	..	40	25

18 The Clinic, Charlestown

(Des G. Drummond. Litho Harrison)

1977 (8 Dec). *Canouan Island* (1st series). *T* **18** *and similar horiz designs. Multicoloured. W w* **14**. *P* 14½.

106	5 c. Type **18**	..	10	10
107	35 c. Town jetty, Charlestown	..	15	10
108	45 c. Mail schooner arriving at Charlestown	15	10
109	$1 Grand Bay	..	35	90
106/9		*Set of 4*	65	1·10

Nos. 106/9 were each issued in sheets of ten stamps and two *se-tenant* labels.
See also Nos. 307/10.

19 Tropical Mockingbird

(Des J.W. Litho Enschedé)

1978 (11 May). *Birds and their Eggs. Horiz designs as T* **19**. *Multicoloured. W w* **14** *(sideways). With imprint date. P* 12½×12.

110	1 c. Type **19**	..	10	50
111	2 c. Mangrove Cuckoo	..	15	50
112	3 c. Osprey	..	20	50
	w. Wmk Crown to right of CA	7·00	
113	4 c. Smooth-billed Ani	..	20	50
114	5 c. House Wren	..	20	40
	w. Wmk Crown to right of CA	6·00	
115	6 c. Bananaquit	..	20	40
116	8 c. Carib Grackle	..	20	45
	w. Wmk Crown to right of CA		
117	10 c. Yellow-bellied Elaenia	..	20	45
	w. Wmk Crown to right of CA	10·00	
118	12 c. Collared Plover	..	30	1·00
119	15 c. Cattle Egret	..	30	45
120	20 c. Red-footed Booby	..	30	45
	w. Wmk Crown to right of CA	4·00	
121	25 c. Red-billed Tropic Bird	..	30	45
	w. Wmk Crown to right of CA		
122	40 c. Royal Tern	..	45	90
	w. Wmk Crown to right of CA	10·00	
123	50 c. Grenada Flycatcher	..	45	90
124	80 c. Purple Gallinule	..	70	90
125	$1 Broad-winged Hawk	..	75	90
	w. Wmk Crown to right of CA	12·00	
126	$2 Scaly-breasted Ground Dove	90	1·60
127	$3 Laughing Gull	..	1·25	1·75
128	$5 Common Noddy	..	1·75	2·00
129	$10 Grey Kingbird	..	3·00	3·00
110/29		*Set of 20*	11·00	15·00

*The normal sideways watermark shows Crown to right of CA, as seen from the back of the stamp.
Imprint dates: "1978", Nos. 110/29; "1979", Nos. 116, 120, 124/6; "1980", Nos. 114/15, 117, 119, 121.
See also Nos. **MS**155 and **MS**170.

(Des G. Drummond. Litho J.W.)

1978 (2 June). *25th Anniv of Coronation. Horiz designs as Nos. 422/5 of Montserrat. Multicoloured. W w* **14** *(sideways). P* 13.

130	5 c. Worcester Cathedral	..	10	10
131	40 c. Coventry Cathedral	..	10	10
132	$1 Winchester Cathedral	..	15	20
133	$3 Chester Cathedral	..	25	45
130/3	..	*Set of 4*	45	70
MS134	130 × 102 mm. Nos. 130/3. P 13½ × 14		45	80
	a. Top horiz pair imperf three sides		£350	

Nos. 130/3 were each issued in sheets of ten stamps and two *se-tenant* labels.
No. **MS**134a shows the 5 c. and 40 c. stamps in the sheet perforated along the top, but imperforate on the other three sides.

20 Green Turtle **21** Three Kings following Star

(Des R. Granger Barrett. Litho Walsall)

1978 (20 July). *Turtles. T* **20** *and similar horiz designs. Multicoloured. W w* **14** *(sideways). P* 14.

135	5 c. Type **20**	..	10	10
136	40 c. Hawksbill turtle	..	15	10
137	50 c. Leatherback turtle	..	15	10
138	$1.25, Loggerhead turtle	..	40	40
135/8	..	*Set of 4*	65	60

(Des Jennifer Toombs. Litho Questa)

1978 (2 Nov). *Christmas. Scenes and Verses from the Carol "We Three Kings of Orient Are". T* **21** *and similar vert designs. Multicoloured. W w* **14**. *P* 14 × 13½.

139	5 c. Type **21**	..	10	10
140	10 c. King with gift of Gold	..	10	10
141	25 c. King with gift of Frankincense	10	10
142	50 c. King with gift of Myrrh	..	10	10
143	$2 Three Kings paying homage to infant Jesus	..	30	20
139/43		*Set of 5*	45	30
MS144	154 × 175 mm. Nos. 139/43		70	1·25

PRICES OF SETS

Set prices are given for many issues, generally those containing three stamps or more. Definitive sets include one of each value or major colour change, but do not cover different perforations, die types or minor shades. Where a choice is possible the set prices are based on the cheapest versions of the stamps included in the listings.

22 Sailing Yachts

23 False Killer Whale

(Des G. Drummond. Litho Questa)

1979 (25 Jan). *National Regatta. T 22 and similar vert designs showing sailing yachts. W w 14. P 14.*

145	5 c. multicoloured		10	10
146	40 c. multicoloured		20	10
147	50 c. multicoloured		25	10
148	$2 multicoloured		75	60
145/8		Set of 4	1·10	75

(Des L. Curtis. Litho Questa)

1979 (8 Mar). *Wildlife. Horiz designs as T 114 of St. Vincent. Multicoloured. W w 14 (sideways). P 14 × 14½.*

149	20 c. Green Iguana		10	10
150	40 c. Common Opossum ("Manicou")		15	10
151	$2 Red-legged Tortoise		60	65
149/51		Set of 3	75	75

Nos. 149/51 were each printed in four panes of 12 throughout the sheet, each pane including two *se-tenant* labels.

(Des J.W. Litho. Enschedé)

1979 (21 May). *Death Centenary of Sir Rowland Hill. Horiz designs as T 103 of St. Vincent. Multicoloured. W w 14 (sideways*). P 12½×12.*

152	80 c. Sir Rowland Hill		15	15
153	$1 Great Britain 1d. and 4d. stamps of 1858 with "A10" (Kingstown, St. Vincent) postmark		15	25
154	$2 St. Vincent ½d. and 1d. stamps of 1894 with Bequia postmark		25	40
152/4		Set of 3	50	70
MS155	165×115 mm. No. 124/6 ("1979" imprint date) and 152/4		1·40	2·50
	w. Crown to right of CA		32·00	

*The normal sideways watermark shows Crown to left of CA, as seen from the back of the stamp.

Nos. 152/4 were printed in sheets including two *se-tenant* stamp-size labels.

1979 (24 Oct). *International Year of the Child. As Nos. 570/3 of St. Vincent.*

156	6 c. black, silver and pale blue		10	10
157	40 c. black, silver and salmon		10	10
158	$1 black, silver and buff		20	10
159	$3 black, silver and lilac		45	30
156/9		Set of 4	65	45

(Des J.W. Litho Enschedé)

1979 (27 Oct). *Independence. Horiz designs as T 106 of St. Vincent. Multicoloured. W w 14 (sideways*). P 12½×12.*

160	5 c. National flag and *Ixora salicifolia* (flower)		10	10
	w. Wmk Crown to right of CA		9·00	
161	40 c. House of Assembly and *Ixora odorata* (flower)		10	10
162	$1 Prime Minister R. Milton Cato and *Ixora javanica* (flower)		20	20
160/2		Set of 3	30	30

*The normal sideways watermark shows Crown to left of CA, as seen from the back of the stamp.

(Des R. Granger Barrett. Litho Walsall)

1980 (31 Jan). *Whales and Dolphins. T 23 and similar horiz designs. Multicoloured. W w 14 (sideways*). P 14.*

163	10 c. Type 23		60	10
	w. Wmk Crown to right of CA		2·50	
164	50 c. Spinner Dolphin		60	35
	w. Wmk Crown to right of CA		25·00	
165	90 c. Bottle-nosed Dolphin		70	80
	w. Wmk Crown to right of CA		4·00	
166	$2 Short-finned Pilot Whale ("Blackfish")		2·00	1·50
163/6		Set of 4	3·50	2·50

*The normal sideways watermark shows Crown to left of CA, as seen from the back of the stamp.

(Des J.W. Litho Enschedé)

1980 (24 Apr). *"London 1980" International Stamp Exhibition. Horiz designs as T 110 of St. Vincent. Multicoloured. W w 14 (sideways). P 12½ × 12.*

167	40 c. Queen Elizabeth II		10	10
168	50 c. St Vincent 1965 2 c. definitive		15	10
169	$3 1973 Royal Wedding commemoratives		40	1·00
167/9		Set of 3	60	1·10
MS170	165×115 mm. Nos. 122/3, 127 ("1980" imprint date) and 167/9		2·00	2·50

Nos. 167/9 were printed in sheets including two *se-tenant* stamp-size labels.

(Des Polygraphic. Litho Rosenbaum Bros, Vienna)

1980 (7 Aug). *"Sport for All". Vert designs as T 112 of St. Vincent. Multicoloured. W w 14. P 13½.*

171	25 c. Running		10	10
172	50 c. Sailing		10	10
	w. Wmk inverted		9·00	
173	$1 Long jumping		20	20
174	$2 Swimming		30	30
171/4		Set of 4	60	60

1980 (7 Aug). *Hurricane Relief. Nos. 171/4 surch with T 113 of St. Vincent.*

175	25 c.+50 c. Running		10	30
176	50 c.+50 c. Sailing		15	40
177	$1+50 c. Long jumping		20	50
178	$2+50 c. Swimming		30	70
175/8		Set of 4	65	1·75

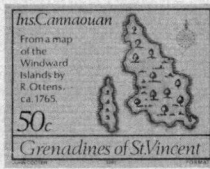

24 Scene and Verse from the Carol "De Borning Day"

25 Post Office, Port Elizabeth

(Des Jennifer Toombs. Litho Questa)

1980 (13 Nov). *Christmas. T 24 and similar vert designs showing scenes and verses from the carol "De Borning Day". W w 14. P 14 × 13½.*

179	5 c. multicoloured		10	10
180	50 c. multicoloured		10	10
181	60 c. multicoloured		10	10
182	$1 multicoloured		15	15
183	$2 multicoloured		25	25
179/83		Set of 5	50	50
MS184	159 × 178 mm. Nos. 179/83		50	1·40

(Des G. Drummond. Litho Questa)

1981 (19 Feb). *Bequia Island (2nd series). T 25 and similar horiz designs. Multicoloured. W w 14 (sideways). P 14½ × 14.*

185	50 c. Type 25		15	15
186	60 c. Moonhole		15	20
187	$1.50, Fishing boats, Admiralty Bay		30	40
188	$2 Friendship Rose (yacht) at jetty		40	55
185/8		Set of 4	90	1·10

The $2 value was originally printed with the country name in black and the face value in white. A quantity of these were stolen in transit before issue and the remainder were not placed on sale, the stamp being reprinted with the inscriptions in red.

Nos. 185/8 were each printed in sheets including two *se-tenant* stamp-size labels.

26 Ins. Cannaouan (map of Windward Islands by R. Ottens, *circa* 1765)

27 Bar Jack

(Des J. Cooter. Litho Format)

1981 (2 Apr). *Details from Early Maps. T 26 and similar horiz designs. Multicoloured. W w 14 (sideways). P 13½.*

189	50 c. Type 26		30	30
	a. Pair. Nos. 189/90		60	60
190	50 c. Cannouan Is. (chart by J. Parsons, 1861)		30	30
191	60 c. Ins. Moustiques (map of Windward Islands by R. Ottens, *circa* 1765)		30	35
	a. Pair. Nos. 191/2		60	70
192	60 c. Mustique Is. (chart by J. Parsons, 1861)		30	35
193	$2 Ins. Bequia (map of Windward Islands by R. Ottens, *circa* 1765)		50	75
	a. Pair. Nos. 193/4		1·00	1·50
194	$2 Bequia Is. (map surveyed in 1763 by T. Jefferys)		50	75
189/94		Set of 6	2·00	2·50

The two designs of each value were printed together, *se-tenant*, in horizontal and vertical pairs throughout the sheet.

(Des D. Shults. Litho Questa)

1981 (17 July–26 Nov). *Royal Wedding. Horiz designs as T 26/27 of Kiribati. Multicoloured.* (a) W w 15. P 14.

195	50 c. *Mary*		10	15
	b. Sheetlet. No. 195×6 and No. 196		85	
196	50 c. Prince Charles and Lady Diana Spencer		35	40
197	$3 *Alexandra*		20	30
	aw. Wmk inverted		8·00	
	b. Sheetlet. No. 197×6 and No. 198		1·60	
	bw. Wmk inverted		75·00	
198	$3 As No. 196		60	90
	aw. Wmk inverted		35·00	

199	$3.50, *Britannia*		25	35
	aw. Wmk inverted		8·00	
	b. Sheetlet. No. 199×6 and No. 200		1·90	
	bw. Wmk inverted		75·00	
200	$3.50, As No. 196		65	90
	aw. Wmk inverted		35·00	
195/200		Set of 6	1·90	2·75
MS201	120×109 mm. $5 As No. 196. Wmk sideways. P 12 (26 Nov)		75	75

(b) *Booklet stamps. No wmk. P 12 (26 Nov)*

202	50 c. As No. 195		15	30
	a. Booklet pane. No. 202×4 with margins all round		55	
203	$3 As No. 198		65	1·25
	a. Booklet pane. No. 203×2 with margins all round		1·25	

Nos. 195/200 were printed in sheetlets of seven stamps of the same face value, each containing six of the "Royal Yacht" design and one of the larger design showing Prince Charles and Lady Diana.

Nos. 202/3 come from $10 stamp booklets.

(Des N. Weaver. Litho Questa)

1981 (9 Oct). *Game Fish. T 27 and similar horiz designs. Multicoloured. W w 14 (sideways). P 14.*

204	10 c. Type 27		15	10
205	50 c. Tarpon		30	10
206	60 c. Cobia		35	10
207	$2 Blue Marlin		1·00	70
204/7		Set of 4	1·60	85

28 H.M.S. *Experiment* (frigate)

29 Prickly Pear Fruit

(Des J. Cooter. Litho Security Printers (M), Malaysia)

1982 (28 Jan). *Ships. Horiz designs as T 28. Multicoloured. W w 14. P 13½ × 13.*

208	1 c. Type 28		10	20
209	3 c. *Lady Nelson* (cargo liner)		15	20
210	5 c. *Daisy* (brig)		20	20
211	6 c. Carib canoe		20	20
212	10 c. *Hairoun Star* (freighter)		30	10
213	15 c. *Jupiter* (liner)		40	10
214	20 c. *Christina* (steam yacht)		40	10
215	25 c. *Orinoco* (mail paddle-steamer)		55	15
216	30 c. H.M.S. *Lively* (frigate)		55	15
217	50 c. *Alabama* (Confederate warship)		70	30
218	60 c. *Denmark* (freighter)		80	30
	w. Wmk inverted		4·00	
219	75 c. *Santa Maria*		1·10	50
220	$1 *Baffin* (research vessel)		1·10	55
221	$2 *Queen Elizabeth 2* (liner)		1·50	1·25
	w. Wmk inverted		11·00	
222	$3 R.Y. *Britannia*		1·50	1·75
	w. Wmk inverted		12·00	
223	$5 *Geeststar* (freighter)		1·50	2·00
224	$10 *Grenadines Star* (ferry)		2·50	5·00
208/24		Set of 17	12·00	11·50

(Des G. Drummond. Litho Harrison)

1982 (5 Apr). *Prickly Pear Cactus. T 29 and similar vert designs. Multicoloured. W w 14. P 14.*

225	10 c. Type 29		15	15
226	50 c. Prickly Pear flower buds		35	35
227	$1 Flower of Prickly Pear Cactus		60	60
228	$2 Prickly Pear Cactus		1·25	1·25
225/8		Set of 4	2·10	2·10

30 Anne Neville, Princess of Wales, 1470

31 Old and New Uniforms

(Des D. Shults and J. Cooter. Litho Format)

1982 (1 July). *21st Birthday of Princess of Wales. T 30 and similar vert designs. Multicoloured. W w 15. P 13½ × 14.*

229	50 c. Type 30		10	15
	w. Wmk inverted		7·00	
230	60 c. Coat of arms of Anne Neville		10	15
231	$6 Diana, Princess of Wales		60	80
	w. Wmk inverted		9·00	
229/31		Set of 3	70	1·00

(Des L. Curtis. Litho W.S. Cowell Ltd)

1982 (15 July). *75th Anniv of Boy Scout Movement. T 31 and similar vert design. Multicoloured. W w 14 (inverted). P 14½.*
232 $1.50, Type 31 .. .. .. 60 75
233 $2.50, Lord Baden-Powell .. 90 1·00

(32)

33 Silhouette Figures of Mary and Joseph

1982 (19 July). *Birth of Prince William of Wales. Nos. 229/31 optd with various island names as T 32.*
A. Bequia   B. Canouan   C. Mayreau
     D. Mustique   E. Union Island
To indicate individual islands, use the above letters as a suffix to the following catalogue numbers.
234 50 c. Type 30 .. .. .. 10 15
 a. Opt A (Bequia) double .. .. 30·00
 b. Opt C (Mayreau) inverted .. 17·00
 c. Opt D (Mustique) inverted .. 17·00
 wA. Wmk inverted .. .. 6·00
 wB. Wmk inverted .. .. 6·00
 wC. Wmk inverted .. .. 6·00
 wD. Wmk inverted .. .. 6·00
 wE. Wmk inverted .. .. 6·00
235 60 c. Coat of arms of Anne Neville .. 10 15
 a. Opt D (Mustique) inverted .. 30·00
 b. Opt E (Union Island) inverted .. 45·00
 c. Opt E (Union Island) double .. £110
236 $6 Diana, Princess of Wales .. 60 80
 wA. Wmk inverted .. .. 7·50
 wB. Wmk inverted .. .. 8·50
 wC. Wmk inverted .. .. 10·00
 wD. Wmk inverted .. .. 10·00
 wE. Wmk inverted .. .. 8·50
234/6 .. .. .. Set of 3 70 1·00

(Des Jennifer Toombs. Litho Security Printers (M), Malaysia)

1982 (18 Nov). *Christmas. T 33 and similar horiz designs showing silhouettes of figures. Multicoloured. W w 14. P 13½.*
237 10 c. Type 33 .. .. .. 10 10
238 $1.50, Animals in stable .. 45 45
239 $2.50, Mary and Joseph with baby Jesus .. 60 60
237/9 .. .. .. Set of 3 1·00 1·00
MS240 168 × 99 mm. Nos. 237/9 .. 1·00 2·00

(34)

35 Power Station, Clifton

1983 (26 Apr). *No. 123 surch with T 34 by Reliance Printery, Kingstown.*
241 45 c. on 50 c. Grenada Flycatcher .. 30 30

(Des G. Drummond. Litho Security Printers (M), Malaysia)

1983 (12 May). *Union Island (2nd series). T 35 and similar horiz designs. Multicoloured. W w 14. P 13½.*
242 50 c. Type 35 .. .. .. 25 15
243 60 c. Sunrise, Clifton harbour .. 25 15
 w. Wmk inverted .. .. 30·00
244 $1.50, Junior Secondary School, Ashton 60 40
245 $2 Frigate Rock and Conch Shell Beach 85 55
 w. Wmk inverted .. .. 30·00
242/5 .. .. .. Set of 4 1·75 1·10
Nos. 242/5 were each printed in sheets including two *se-tenant* stamp-size labels.

36 British Man-of-war   **37** Montgolfier Balloon, 1783

(Des J.W. Litho Questa)

1983 (4 Aug). *Bicentenary of Treaty of Versailles. T 36 and similar vert designs. Multicoloured. W w 14. P 14½.*
246 45 c. Type 36 .. .. .. 35 15
247 60 c. American man-of-war .. 35 15
248 $1.50, Soldiers carrying U.S. flags .. 75 45
249 $2 British troops in battle .. 80 55
246/9 .. .. .. Set of 4 2·00 1·10

(Des A. Theobald. Litho Format)

1983 (15 Sept). *Bicentenary of Manned Flight. T 37 and similar multicoloured designs. W w 14 (sideways on Nos. 251/53). P 14.*
250 45 c. Type 37 .. .. .. 10 15
251 60 c. Ayres Turbo Thrush Commander (horiz) 15 15
252 $1.50, Lebaudy-Juillot airship No. 1 *La Jaune* (horiz) 35 45
253 $2 Space shuttle *Columbia* (horiz) .. 40 55
250/3 .. .. .. Set of 4 90 1·10
MS254 110×145 mm. Nos. 250/3. Wmk sideways 90 1·50

38 Coat of Arms of Henry VIII   **39** Quarter Dollar and Half Dollar, 1797

(Des Court House Studio. Litho Format)

1983 (25 Oct). *Leaders of the World. British Monarchs. T 38 and similar vert designs. Multicoloured. P 12½.*
255 60 c. Type 38 .. .. .. 15 25
 a. Horiz pair. Nos. 255/6 .. 30 50
256 60 c. Henry VIII 15 25
257 60 c. Coat of arms of James I .. 15 25
 a. Horiz pair. Nos. 257/8 .. 30 50
258 60 c. James I 15 25
259 75 c. Henry VIII 15 25
 a. Horiz pair. Nos. 259/60 .. 30 50
260 75 c. Hampton Court 15 25
261 75 c. James I 15 25
 a. Horiz pair. Nos. 261/2 .. 30 50
262 75 c. Edinburgh Castle 15 25
263 $2.50, The *Mary Rose* 25 35
 a. Horiz pair. Nos. 263/4 .. 50 70
264 $2.50, Henry VIII and Portsmouth harbour 25 35
265 $2.50, Gunpowder Plot 25 35
 a. Horiz pair. Nos. 265/6 .. 50 70
266 $2.50, James I and the Gunpowder Plot .. 25 35
255/66 .. .. .. Set of 12 2·00 3·00
Nos. 255/6, 257/8, 259/60, 261/2, 263/4 and 265/6 were printed together, *se-tenant*, in horizontal pairs throughout the sheets.

(Des J. Cooter. Litho Walsall)

1983 (1 Dec). *Old Coinage. T 39 and similar vert designs. Multicoloured. W w 14. P 14.*
267 20 c. Type 39 .. .. .. 10 10
268 45 c. Nine Bitts, 1811–14 .. 15 15
269 75 c. Twelve Bitts and Six Bitts, 1811–14 25 25
270 $3 Sixty-six Shillings, 1798 .. 80 80
267/70 .. .. .. Set of 4 1·10 1·10

40 Class D13

(Des J.W. Litho Format)

1984 (15 Mar). *Leaders of the World. Railway Locomotives (1st series). T 40 and similar horiz designs, the first in each pair showing technical drawings and the second the locomotive at work. P 12½.*
271 5 c. multicoloured 10 10
 a. Vert pair. Nos. 271/2 .. 10 10
272 5 c. multicoloured 10 10
273 10 c. multicoloured 10 10
 a. Vert pair. Nos. 273/4 .. 10 15
274 10 c. multicoloured 10 10
275 15 c. multicoloured 10 15
 a. Vert pair. Nos. 275/6 .. 20 30
276 15 c. multicoloured 10 15
277 35 c. multicoloured 15 20
 a. Vert pair. Nos. 277/8 .. 30 40
278 35 c. multicoloured 15 20
279 45 c. multicoloured 15 20
 a. Vert pair. Nos. 279/80 .. 30 40
280 45 c. multicoloured 15 20
281 60 c. multicoloured 15 20
 a. Vert pair. Nos. 281/2 .. 30 40
282 60 c. multicoloured 15 20
283 $1 multicoloured 20 25
 a. Vert pair. Nos. 283/4 .. 40 50
284 $1 multicoloured 20 25
285 $2.50, multicoloured 25 35
 a. Vert pair. Nos. 285/6 .. 50 70
286 $2.50, multicoloured 25 35
271/86 .. .. .. Set of 16 1·75 2·50
Designs:—Nos. 271/2, Class D13, U.S.A. (1892), 273/4, High Speed Train 125, Great Britain (1980); 275/6, Class T9, Great Britain (1899); 277/8, *Claud Hamilton*, Great Britain (1900); 279/80, Class J, U.S.A. (1941); 281/2, Class D16, U.S.A. (1895); 283/4, *Lode Star*, Great Britain (1907); 285/6, *Blue Peter*, Great Britain (1948).
Nos. 271/2, 273/4, 275/6, 277/8, 279/80, 281/2, 283/4 and 285/6 were printed together, *se-tenant* in vertical pairs throughout the sheet.
See also Nos. 311/26, 351/9, 390/7, 412/19, 443/58, 504/19 and 520/35.

GRENADINES of St.VINCENT

41 Spotted Eagle Ray

(Des G. Drummond. Litho Format)

1984 (26 Apr). *Reef Fishes. T 41 and similar horiz designs. Multicoloured. W w 15 (sideways*). P 14.*
287 45 c. Type 41 .. .. .. 25 20
 w. Wmk POST OFFICE reading upwards 6·00
288 60 c. Queen Triggerfish 25 35
289 $1.50, White-spotted Filefish .. 40 1·25
290 $2 Schoolmaster .. .. 40 1·50
287/90 .. .. .. Set of 4 1·10 3·25
*The normal sideways watermark shows "POST OFFICE" reading downwards.

42 R. A. Woolmer   **43** Junior Secondary School

(Des Court House Studio. Litho Format)

1984 (16 Aug). *Leaders of the World. Cricketers (1st series). T 42 and similar vert designs, the first in each pair showing a portrait and the second the cricketer in action. P 12½.*
291 1 c. multicoloured 10 10
 a. Horiz pair. Nos. 291/2 .. 10 10
292 1 c. multicoloured 10 10
293 3 c. multicoloured 10 10
 a. Horiz pair. Nos. 293/4 .. 10 10
294 3 c. multicoloured 10 10
295 5 c. multicoloured 10 10
 a. Horiz pair. Nos. 295/6 .. 10 10
296 5 c. multicoloured 10 10
297 30 c. multicoloured 30 30
 a. Horiz pair. Nos. 297/8 .. 60 60
298 30 c. multicoloured 30 30
299 60 c. multicoloured 40 40
 a. Horiz pair. Nos. 299/300 .. 80 80
300 60 c. multicoloured 40 40
301 $1 multicoloured 40 40
 a. Horiz pair. Nos. 301/2 .. 80 80
302 $1 multicoloured 40 40
303 $2 multicoloured 45 70
 a. Horiz pair. Nos. 303/4 .. 90 1·40
304 $2 multicoloured 45 70
305 $3 multicoloured 55 80
 a. Horiz pair. Nos. 305/6 .. 1·10 1·60
306 $3 multicoloured 55 80
291/306 .. .. .. Set of 16 3·75 4·75
Designs:—Nos. 293/4, K. S. Ranjitsinhji; 295/6, W. R. Hammond; 297/8, D. L. Underwood; 299/300, W. G. Grace; 301/2, E. A. E. Baptiste; 303/4, A. P. E. Knott; 305/6, L. E. G. Ames.
See also Nos. 331/8 and 364/9.

(Des G. Drummond. Litho Questa)

1984 (3 Sept). *Canouan Island (2nd series). T 43 and similar horiz designs. Multicoloured. W w 15 (sideways). P 14.*
307 35 c. Type 43 .. .. .. 20 20
308 45 c. Police Station 25 25
309 $1 Post Office 50 50
310 $3 Anglican Church .. .. 1·25 1·50
307/10 .. .. .. Set of 4 2·00 2·25

IMPERFORATES AND MISSING COLOURS. Various issues between Nos. 311 and 572 exist either imperforate or with colours omitted. Such items are not listed as there is no evidence that they fulfil the criteria outlined on page xi of this catalogue.

(Des J.W. Litho Format)

1984 (9 Oct). *Leaders of the World. Railway Locomotives (2nd series). Horiz designs as T 40, the first in each pair showing technical drawings and the second the locomotive at work. P 12½.*
311 1 c. multicoloured 10 10
 a. Vert pair. Nos. 311/12 .. 10 10
312 1 c. multicoloured 10 10
313 5 c. multicoloured 10 10
 a. Vert pair. Nos. 313/14 .. 10 10
314 5 c. multicoloured 10 10
315 20 c. multicoloured 15 15
 a. Vert pair. Nos. 315/16 .. 30 30
316 20 c. multicoloured 15 15
317 35 c. multicoloured 15 15
 a. Vert pair. Nos. 317/18 .. 30 30
318 35 c. multicoloured 15 15
319 60 c. multicoloured 20 20
 a. Vert pair. Nos. 319/20 .. 40 40
320 60 c. multicoloured 20 20
321 $1 multicoloured 20 25
 a. Vert pair. Nos. 321/2 .. 40 50
322 $1 multicoloured 20 25
323 $1.50, multicoloured 25 30
 a. Vert pair. Nos. 323/4 .. 50 60
324 $1.50, multicoloured 25 30

325	$3 multicoloured	..	35	55
	a. Vert pair. Nos. 325/6		70	1·10
326	$3 multicoloured	..	35	55
311/26		*Set of 16*	2·40	3·00

Designs:—Nos. 311/12, Class C62, Japan (1948); 313/14, Class V, Great Britain (1903); 315/16, Richard Trevithick's *Catch-Me-Who-Can*, Great Britain (1808); 317/18, Class E10, Japan (1948); 319/20, *J. B. Earle*, Great Britain (1904); 321/2, No. 762 *Lyn*, Great Britain (1898); 323/4, *Talyllyn*, Great Britain (1865); 325/6, *Cardean*, Great Britain (1906).

Nos. 311/26 were issued in a similar sheet format to Nos. 271/86.

44 Lady of the Night

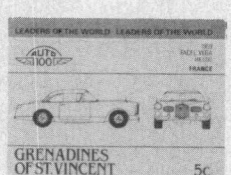
45 Facel "Vega HK500"

(Des Jennifer Toombs. Litho Questa)

1984 (15 Oct). *Night-blooming Flowers.* T **44** and similar vert designs. Multicoloured. W w **15**. P 14.

327	35 c. Type 44	..	35	30
328	45 c. Four o'clock		40	35
329	75 c. Mother-in-Law's Tongue	..	60	60
330	$3 Queen of the Night	..	1·50	2·75
327/30		*Set of 4*	2·50	3·50

(Des Court House Studio. Litho Format)

1984 (28 Nov). *Leaders of the World. Cricketers (2nd series).* Vert designs as T **42**, the first in each pair listed showing a head portrait and the second the cricketer in action. P 12½.

331	5 c. multicoloured	..	10	10
	a. Horiz pair. Nos. 331/2		10	10
332	5 c. multicoloured	..	10	10
333	30 c. multicoloured	..	25	25
	a. Horiz pair. Nos. 333/4		50	40
334	30 c. multicoloured	..	25	20
335	$1 multicoloured	..	30	40
	a. Horiz pair. Nos. 335/6		60	80
336	$1 multicoloured	..	30	40
337	$2.50, multicoloured	..	45	80
	a. Horiz pair. Nos. 337/8		90	1·60
338	$2.50 multicoloured	..	45	80
331/8		*Set of 8*	1·75	2·50

Designs:—Nos. 331/2, S. F. Barnes; 333/4, R. Peel; 335/6, H. Larwood; 337/8, Sir John Hobbs.

Nos. 331/8 were issued in a similar sheet format to Nos. 291/306.

(Des J.W. Litho Format)

1984 (28 Nov). *Leaders of the World. Automobiles (1st series).* T **45** and similar horiz designs, the first in each pair showing technical drawings and the second the paintings. P 12½.

339	5 c. black, azure and dull yellow-green		10	10
	a. Vert pair. Nos. 339/40		10	10
340	5 c. multicoloured	..	10	10
341	25 c. black, pale lilac and pink	..	10	10
	a. Vert pair. Nos. 341/2		20	20
342	25 c. multicoloured	..	10	10
343	50 c. black, pale blue and pale orange		15	15
	a. Vert pair. Nos. 343/4		30	30
344	50 c. multicoloured	..	15	15
345	$3 black, stone and brown lake	..	30	45
	a. Vert pair. Nos. 345/6		60	90
346	$3 multicoloured	..	30	45
339/46		*Set of 8*	1·00	1·25

Designs:—Nos. 339/40, Facel "Vega HK500"; 341/2, B.M.W. "328"; 343/4, Frazer-Nash "TT Replica 1.5L"; 345/6, Buick "Roadmaster Riviera".

Nos. 339/40, 341/2, 343/4 and 345/6 were printed together, se-tenant, in vertical pairs throughout the sheets.

See also Nos. 378/85 and 431/42.

46 The Three Wise Men and Star

(Des Jennifer Toombs. Litho Format)

1984 (3 Dec). *Christmas.* T **46** and similar horiz designs. Multicoloured. W w **15** (sideways). P 14½.

347	20 c. Type 46	..	10	10
348	45 c. Journeying to Bethlehem		15	25
349	$3 Presenting gifts	..	70	1·40
347/9		*Set of 3*	75	1·60
MS350	177 × 107 mm. Nos. 347/9. Wmk inverted		90	2·00

(Des J.W. Litho Format)

1985 (31 Jan). *Leaders of the World. Railway Locomotives (3rd series).* Horiz designs as T **40**, the first in each pair showing technical drawings and the second the locomotive at work. P 12½.

351	1 c. multicoloured	..	10	10
	a. Vert pair. Nos. 351/2		10	10
352	1 c. multicoloured	..	10	10
353	15 c. multicoloured	..	15	15
	a. Vert pair Nos. 353/4		15	15
354	15 c. multicoloured	..	10	10

355	75 c. multicoloured	..	20	25
	a. Vert pair. Nos. 355/6		40	50
356	75 c. multicoloured	..	20	25
357	$3 multicoloured	..	50	70
	a. Vert pair. Nos. 357/8		1·00	1·40
358	$3 multicoloured	..	50	70
351/8		*Set of 8*	1·40	1·90
MS359	142 × 122 mm. Nos. 355/8. W w 15.		1·75	6·50

Designs:—Nos. 351/2, "Grosse C", France (1898); 353/4, Class C12, Japan (1932); 355/6, Class D50, Japan (1923); 357/8, *Fire Fly*, Great Britain (1840).

Nos. 351/8 were issued in a similar sheet format to Nos. 271/86.

47 Caribbean King Crab

48 *Cypripedium calceolus*

(Des G. Drummond. Litho Format)

1985 (11 Feb). *Shell Fish.* T **47** and similar horiz designs. Multicoloured. W w **15** (sideways). P 14.

360	25 c. Type 47	..	20	15
361	60 c. Queen or Pink Conch (*Strombus gigas*)		30	35
362	$1 White Sea Urchin	..	35	55
363	$3 West Indian Top Shell or Wilk (*Cittarium pica*)		75	1·75
360/3		*Set of 4*	1·40	2·50

(Des Court House Studio. Litho Format)

1985 (22 Feb). *Leaders of the World. Cricketers (3rd series).* Vert designs as T **42** (55 c., 60 c.), the first in each pair showing a head portrait and the second the cricketer in action, or horiz designs showing teams ($2). P 12½.

364	55 c. multicoloured	..	25	35
	a. Horiz pair. Nos. 364/5		50	70
365	55 c. multicoloured	..	25	35
366	60 c. multicoloured	..	25	40
	a. Horiz pair. Nos. 366/7		50	80
367	60 c. multicoloured	..	25	40
368	$2 multicoloured	..	40	85
369	$2 multicoloured	..	40	85
364/9		*Set of 6*	1·60	2·75

Designs:—Vert (as T **42**)—Nos. 364/5, M. D. Moxon; 366/7, L. Potter. Horiz (59 × 42 *mm*)—No. 368, Kent team; 369, Yorkshire team.

Nos. 364/5 and 366/7 were issued in a similar sheet format to Nos. 291/306.

(Des Jennifer Toombs. Litho Format)

1985 (13 Mar). *Leaders of the World. Flowers.* T **48** and similar vert designs. Multicoloured. P 12½.

370	5 c. Type 48	..	10	10
	a. Horiz pair. Nos. 370/1		10	10
371	5 c. *Gentiana asclepiadea*		10	10
372	55 c. *Clianthus formosus*		15	20
	a. Horiz pair. Nos. 372/3		30	40
373	55 c. *Clemisia coriacea*		15	20
374	60 c. *Erythronium americanum*		15	20
	a. Horiz pair. Nos. 374/5		30	40
375	60 c. *Laelia anceps*		15	20
376	$2 *Leucadendron discolor*		35	50
	a. Horiz pair. Nos. 376/7		70	1·00
377	$2 *Meconopsis horridula*		35	50
370/7		*Set of 8*	1·10	1·60

Nos. 370/1, 372/3, 374/5 and 376/7 were printed together, se-tenant, in horizontal pairs throughout the sheets.

(Des J.W. (5 c.), G. Turner (others). Litho Format)

1985 (9 Apr). *Leaders of the World. Automobiles (2nd series).* Horiz designs as T **45**, the first in each pair showing technical drawings and the second paintings. P 12½.

378	5 c. black, pale lemon and turquoise-blue	..	10	10
	a. Vert pair. Nos. 378/9		10	10
379	5 c. multicoloured	..	10	10
380	60 c. black, pale yellow and pale orange		15	15
	a. Vert pair. Nos. 380/1		30	30
381	60 c. multicoloured	..	15	15
382	$1 black, pale green and azure		15	20
	a. Vert pair. Nos. 382/3		30	40
383	$1 multicoloured	..	15	20
384	$1.50, black, pale cobalt and light green	..	15	25
	a. Vert pair. Nos. 384/5		30	50
385	$1.50 multicoloured	..	15	25
378/85		*Set of 8*	80	1·25

Designs:—Nos. 378/9, Winton (1903); 380/1, Invicta 4½ litre (1931); 382/3, Daimler "SP250 Dart" (1959); 384/5, Brabham "Repco BT19" (1966).

Nos. 378/85 were issued in a similar sheet format to Nos. 339/46.

49 Windsurfing

(Des G. Vasarhelyi. Litho Format)

1985 (9 May). *Tourism. Watersports.* T **49** and similar horiz designs. Multicoloured. W w **15** (sideways). P 14.

386	35 c. Type 49	..	20	15
387	45 c. Water-skiing		20	15
388	75 c. Scuba-diving		20	25
389	$3 Deep-sea game fishing	..	40	1·40
386/9		*Set of 4*	90	1·75

(Des J.W. (50 c.), T. Hadler (others). Litho Format)

1985 (17 May). *Leaders of the World. Railway Locomotives (4th series).* Horiz designs as T **40**, the first in each pair showing technical drawings and the second the locomotive at work. P 12½.

390	10 c. multicoloured	..	10	10
	a. Vert pair. Nos. 390/1		10	10
391	10 c. multicoloured	..	10	10
392	40 c. multicoloured	..	20	20
	a. Vert pair. Nos. 392/3		40	40
393	40 c. multicoloured	..	20	20
394	50 c. multicoloured	..	20	20
	a. Vert pair. Nos. 394/5		40	40
395	50 c. multicoloured	..	20	20
396	$2.50, multicoloured	..	70	80
	a. Vert pair. Nos. 396/7		1·40	1·60
397	$2.50 multicoloured	..	70	80
390/7		*Set of 8*	2·00	2·25

Designs:—Nos. 390/1, Class 581 electric train, Japan (1968); 392/3, Class 231-132BT, Algeria (1936); 394/5, *Slieve Gullion*, Ireland (1913); 396/7, Class "Beattie" well tank, Great Britain (1874).

Nos. 390/7 were issued in a similar sheet format to Nos. 271/86.

50 Passion Fruits and Blossom

51 Queen Elizabeth the Queen Mother

(Des G. Drummond. Litho Format)

1985 (24 June). *Fruits and Blossoms.* T **50** and similar horiz designs. Multicoloured. W w **15**. P 15.

398	30 c. Type 50	..	15	20
399	75 c. Guava		25	40
400	$1 Sapodilla	..	35	55
401	$2 Mango	..	50	1·10
398/401		*Set of 4*	1·10	2·00
MS402	145×120 mm. Nos. 398/401. Wmk sideways. P 14½×15		2·00	2·25

(Des Court House Studio. Litho Format)

1985 (31 July). *Leaders of the World. Life and Times of Queen Elizabeth the Queen Mother. Various vertical portraits as T **51**. P 12½.

403	40 c. multicoloured	..	10	20
	a. Horiz pair. Nos. 403/4		10	40
404	40 c. multicoloured	..	10	20
405	75 c. multicoloured	..	10	20
	a. Horiz pair. Nos. 405/6		15	40
406	75 c. multicoloured	..	10	20
407	$1.10, multicoloured	..	15	20
	a. Horiz pair. Nos. 407/8		25	40
408	$1.10, multicoloured	..	15	20
409	$1.75, multicoloured	..	15	30
	a. Horiz pair. Nos. 409/10.		25	40
410	$1.75, multicoloured	..	15	30
403/10		*Set of 8*	65	1·60
MS411	85 × 114 mm. $2 multicoloured; $2 multi-coloured		50	1·50

The two designs of each value were issued, se-tenant, in horizontal pairs within the sheets.

Each se-tenant pair shows a floral pattern across the bottom of the portraits which stops short of the left-hand edge on the left-hand stamp and of the right-hand edge on the right-hand stamp.

Designs as Nos. 403/4 and 407/8, but with face values of $4×2 and $5×2, also exist in additional miniature sheets from a restricted printing issued 19 December 1985.

(Des J.W. (35 c.), T. Hadler (others). Litho Format)

1985 (16 Sept). *Leaders of the World. Railway Locomotives (5th series).* Horiz designs as T **40**, the first in each pair showing technical drawings and the second the locomotive at work. P 12½.

412	35 c. multicoloured	..	15	20
	a. Vert pair. Nos. 412/13		30	40
413	35 c. multicoloured	..	15	20
414	70 c. multicoloured	..	20	30
	a. Vert pair. Nos. 414/15		40	60
415	70 c. multicoloured	..	20	30
416	$1.20 multicoloured	..	30	40
	a. Vert pair. Nos. 416/17		60	80
417	$1.20, multicoloured	..	30	40
418	$2 multicoloured	..	40	65
	a. Vert pair. Nos. 418/19		80	1·25
419	$2 multicoloured	..	40	65
412/19		*Set of 8*	1·90	2·75

Designs:—Nos. 412/13, *Coronation*, Great Britain (1937); 414/15, Class E18 electric locomotive, Germany (1935); 416/17, "Hayes" type No. 198, U.S.A. (1854); 418/19, Class 2120, Japan (1890).

Nos. 412/19 were issued in a similar sheet format to Nos. 271/86.

1985 (27 Oct). *Royal Visit. Nos. 199/200, 222, 287, 398 and 407/8 optd as T 114 of Montserrat or surch also.*

420	50	30 c. multicoloured	..	80	1·25
421	41	45 c. multicoloured	..	1·00	1·75
422		$1.10, multicoloured (No. 407)		1·75	3·75
		a. Horiz pair. Nos. 422/3	..	3·50	7·50
423		$1.10, multicoloured (No. 408)		1·75	3·75
424		$1.50 on $3.50, mult (No. 199)		2·00	2·25
		a. Sheetlet. No. 424×6 and No. 425..	21·00	
425		$1.50 on $3.50, mult (No. 200)		15·00	17·00
426		$3 multicoloured (No. 222)		2·25	3·25
420/6			*Set of 7*	22·00	30·00

52 Donkey Man

(Des Jennifer Toombs. Litho Format)

1985 (16 Dec). *Traditional Dances. T 52 and similar multicoloured designs. P 15.*

427	45 c. Type 52	..	..	15	30
428	75 c. Cake Dance (*vert*)		20	40
429	$1 Bois-Bois Man (*vert*)		25	55
430	$2 Maypole Dance ..		45	1·10
427/30			*Set of 4*	95	2·10

(Des Artists International (15 c.), J.W. ($3), G. Turner (others). Litho Format)

1986 (20 Feb). *Leaders of the World. Automobiles (3rd series). Horiz designs as T 45, the first in each pair showing technical drawings and the second paintings. P 12½.*

431	15 c. black, pale rose-lilac and dull mauve ..	10	10
	a. Vert pair. Nos. 431/2		10	20
432	15 c. multicoloured		10	10
433	45 c. black, pale yellow and light brown	10	20
	a. Vert pair. Nos. 433/4		20	40
434	45 c. multicoloured		10	20
435	60 c. black, pale green and turquoise-blue ..	10	25
	a. Vert pair. Nos. 435/6		20	50
436	60 c. multicoloured		10	25
437	$1 black, pale cinnamon and sage-green ..	15	25
	a. Vert pair. Nos. 437/8		30	50
438	$1 multicoloured		15	25
439	$1.75, black, pale yellow and pale orange ..	15	35
	a. Vert pair. Nos. 439/40		30	70
440	$1.75, multicoloured		15	35
441	$3 multicoloured		25	45
	a. Vert pair. Nos. 441/2		50	90
442	$3 multicoloured		25	45
431/42		*Set of 12*	1·40	3·00

Designs:—Nos. 431/2, Mercedes-Benz 4.5 litre (1914); 433/4, Rolls Royce "Silver Wraith" (1954); 435/6, Lamborghini "Countach" (1974); 437/8, Marmon "V-16" (1932): 439/40, Lotus-Ford "49 B" (1968); 441/2, Delage 1.5 litre (1927).
Nos. 431/42 were issued in a similar sheet format to Nos. 339/46.

(Des T. Hadler (15 c., $3), J.W. (others). Litho Format)

1986 (14 Mar). *Leaders of the World. Railway Locomotives (6th series). Horiz designs as T 40, the first in each pair showing technical drawings and the second the locomotive at work. P 12½.*

443	15 c. multicoloured	..	..	15	10
	a. Vert pair. Nos. 443/4		30	20
444	15 c. multicoloured		15	10
445	45 c. multicoloured		20	20
	a. Vert pair. Nos. 445/6		40	40
446	45 c. multicoloured		20	20
447	60 c. multicoloured		20	30
	a. Vert pair. Nos. 447/8		40	60
448	60 c. multicoloured		20	30
449	75 c. multicoloured		20	35
	a. Vert pair. Nos. 449/50		40	70
450	75 c. multicoloured		20	35
451	$1 multicoloured		25	40
	a. Vert pair. Nos. 451/2		50	80
452	$1 multicoloured		25	40
453	$1.50, multicoloured		25	50
	a. Vert pair. Nos. 453/4		50	1·00
454	$1.50, multicoloured		25	50
455	$2 multicoloured		30	65
	a. Vert pair. Nos. 455/6		60	1·25
456	$2 multicoloured		30	65
457	$3 multicoloured		30	80
	a. Vert pair. Nos. 457/8		60	1·40
458	$3 multicoloured		30	80
443/58		*Set of 16*	3·25	5·50

Designs:—Nos. 443/4, Class T15, Germany (1897); 445/6, Class 13, Great Britain (1900); 447/8, Halesworth, Great Britain (1879); 449/50, Class "Problem", Great Britain (1859); 451/2, Class "Western" diesel locomotive, Great Britain (1961); 453/4, Drummond's "Bug", Great Britain (1899); 455/6, Class "Clan", Great Britain (1951); 457/8, Class 1800, Japan (1884).
Nos. 443/58 were issued in a similar sheet format to Nos. 271/86.

(Des Court House Studio. Litho Format)

1986 (21 Apr). *60th Birthday of Queen Elizabeth II. Multicoloured designs as T 117a of Montserrat. P 12½.*

459	5 c. Queen Elizabeth II		15	15
460	$1 At Princess Anne's christening, 1950 ..	30	35
461	$4 Princess Elizabeth		60	90
462	$6 In Canberra, 1982 (*vert*)		75	1·50
459/62		*Set of 4*	1·60	2·50
MS463	85×115 mm. $8 Queen Elizabeth II (*different*)		1·50	4·25

53 Handmade Dolls

(Des G. Drummond. Litho Format)

1986 (22 Apr). *Handicrafts. T 53 and similar horiz designs. Multicoloured. W w 15. P 15.*

464	10 c. Type 53		10	10
465	60 c. Basketwork	..	20	35
466	$1 Scrimshaw work		30	50
467	$3 Model sailing dinghy		80	1·90
464/7		*Set of 4*	1·25	2·50

54 Uruguayan Team

(Des Court House Studio. Litho Format)

1986 (7 May). *World Cup Football Championship, Mexico. T 54 and similar multicoloured designs. P 12½ (1 c., 10 c., $4, $5) or 15 (others).*

468	1 c. Type 54	..	..	10	10
469	10 c. Polish team		10	10
470	45 c. Bulgarian player (28×42 mm)	25	30
471	75 c. Iraqi player (28×42 mm)	35	40
472	$1.50, South Korean player (28×42 mm)..	75	90
473	$2 Northern Irish player (28×42 mm)	80	1·10
474	$4 Portuguese team		1·25	1·50
475	$5 Canadian team ..		1·25	1·50
468/75		*Set of 8*	4·25	5·25
MS476	Two sheets, 85×114 mm. (a) $1 As No. 474; (b) $3 Type 54. P 12½ .. *Set of 2 sheets*	1·50	2·50

A further $3 miniature sheet, showing the South Korean team, was prepared, but not issued.

55 *Marasmius pallescens*   56 *Brachymesia furcata*

(Des G. Drummond. Litho Questa)

1986 (23 May). *Fungi. T 55 and similar vert designs. Multicoloured. W w 15 (sideways). P 14.*

477	45 c. Type 55		2·25	75
478	60 c. *Leucocoprinus fragilissimus*	2·50	1·10
479	75 c. *Hygrocybe occidentalis*	2·75	1·60
480	$3 *Xerocomus hypoxanthus*	8·00	7·00
477/80		*Set of 4*	14·00	9·50

(Des Court House Studio. Litho Format)

1986 (18 July–15 Oct). *Royal Wedding (1st issue). Multicoloured designs as T 118a of Montserrat. P 12½.*

481	60 c. Miss Sarah Ferguson and Princess Diana applauding		15	25
	a. Pair. Nos. 481/2..		30	50
482	60 c. Prince Andrew at shooting match	15	25
483	$2 Prince Andrew and Miss Sarah Ferguson (*horiz*)		50	80
	a. Pair. Nos. 483/4..		1·00	1·60
484	$2 Prince Charles, Prince Andrew, Princess Anne and Princess Margaret on balcony (*horiz*)		50	80
481/4		*Set of 4*	1·10	1·90
MS485	115×85 mm. $8 Duke and Duchess of York in carriage after wedding (*horiz*) (15.10.86)	2·75	4·00

Nos. 481/2 and 483/4 were printed together, se-tenant, in horizontal and vertical pairs throughout the sheets.
Nos. 481/4 imperforate come from souvenir stamp booklets.

1986 (15 Oct). *Royal Wedding (2nd issue). Nos. 481/4 optd as T 121 of Montserrat in silver.*

486	60 c. Miss Sarah Ferguson and Princess Diana applauding		30	50
	a. Pair. Nos. 486/7..		60	1·00
487	60 c. Prince Andrew at shooting match	30	50
488	$2 Prince Andrew and Miss Sarah Ferguson (*horiz*)		1·00	1·25
	a. Pair. Nos. 488/9..		2·00	2·50
489	$2 Prince Charles, Prince Andrew, Princess Anne and Princess Margaret on balcony (*horiz*)		1·00	1·25
486/9 ..		*Set of 4*	2·40	3·25

(Des M. Hillier. Litho Format)

1986 (19 Nov). *Dragonflies. T 56 and similar multicoloured designs. P 15.*

490	45 c. Type 56		25	20
491	60 c. *Lepthemis vesiculosa*	30	40
492	75 c. *Perithemis domitta*	30	45
493	$2.50, *Tramea abdominalis* (*vert*)..	45	1·40
490/3		*Set of 4*	1·10	2·25

(Des Court House Studio. Litho Format)

1986 (26 Nov). *Centenary of Statue of Liberty. Vert views of Statue as T 121a of Montserrat in separate miniature sheets. Multicoloured. P 14×13½.*

MS494 Nine sheets, each 85×115 mm. $1.50; $1.75; $2; $2.50; $3; $3.50; $5; $6; $8
     Set of 9 sheets   7·00   14·00

57 American Kestrel   58 Santa playing Steel Band Drums

(Des Toni Lance. Litho Questa)

1986 (26 Nov). *Birds of Prey. T 57 and similar vert designs. Multicoloured. P 14.*

495	10 c. Type 57		75	45
496	45 c. Common Black Hawk ..	1·90	50
497	60 c. Peregrine Falcon		2·25	1·25
498	$4 Osprey ..		5·00	6·50
495/8		*Set of 4*	9·00	8·00

(Des Court House Studio. Litho Questa)

1986 (26 Nov). *Christmas. T 58 and similar vert designs. Multicoloured. P 14.*

499	45 c. Type 58		30	30
500	60 c. Santa windsurfing		35	35
501	$1.25, Santa skiing		60	85
502	$2 Santa limbo dancing		1·10	1·60
499/502		*Set of 4*	2·10	2·75
MS503	166×128 mm. Nos. 499/502 ..	7·00	8·00

(Litho Format)

1987 (5 May). *Railway Locomotives (7th series). Horiz designs as T 40, the first in each pair showing technical drawings and the second the locomotive at work. Multicoloured. P 12½.*

504	10 c. multicoloured		15	10
	a. Vert pair. Nos. 504/5		30	10
505	10 c. multicoloured		15	10
506	40 c. multicoloured		25	25
	a. Vert pair. Nos. 506/7		50	50
507	40 c. multicoloured		25	25
508	50 c. multicoloured		30	30
	a. Vert pair. Nos. 508/9		60	60
509	50 c. multicoloured		30	30
510	60 c. multicoloured		30	30
	a. Vert pair. Nos. 510/11		60	60
511	60 c. multicoloured		30	30
512	75 c. multicoloured		30	40
	a. Vert pair. Nos. 512/13		60	80
513	75 c. multicoloured		30	40
514	$1 multicoloured		30	50
	a. Vert pair. Nos. 514/15		60	1·00
515	$1 multicoloured		30	50
516	$1.25, multicoloured		30	60
	a. Vert pair. Nos. 516/17		60	1·25
517	$1.25, multicoloured		30	60
518	$1.50, multicoloured		40	75
	a. Vert pair. Nos. 518/19		80	1·50
519	$1.50, multicoloured		40	75
504/19		*Set of 16*	4·25	5·75

Designs:—Nos. 504/5, Class 1001 No. 1275, Great Britain (1874); 506/7, Class 4P Garratt, Great Britain (1927); 508/9, Papyrus, Great Britain (1929); 510/11, Class V1, Great Britain (1930); 512/13, Class 40 diesel locomotive No. D200, Great Britain (1958); 514/15, Class "42 Warship" diesel locomotive, Great Britain (1958); 516/17, Class P-69, U.S.A. (1902); 518/19, Class 60-3 Shay, No. 15, U.S.A. (1913).
Nos. 504/19 were issued in a similar sheet format to Nos. 271/86.

(Litho Format)

1987 (26 Aug). *Railway Locomotives (8th series). Horiz designs as T 40, the first in each pair showing technical drawings and the second the locomotive at work. P 12½.*

520	10 c. multicoloured	..	..	15	15
	a. Vert pair. Nos. 520/1		30	30
521	10 c. multicoloured		15	15
522	40 c. multicoloured		25	30
	a. Vert pair. Nos. 522/3		50	60
523	40 c. multicoloured		25	30
524	50 c. multicoloured		30	35
	a. Vert pair. Nos. 524/5		60	70
525	50 c. multicoloured		30	35
526	60 c. multicoloured		30	40
	a. Vert pair. Nos. 526/7		60	80
527	60 c. multicoloured		30	40
528	75 c. multicoloured		30	45
	a. Vert pair. Nos. 528/9		60	90
529	75 c. multicoloured		30	45
530	$1 multicoloured		30	45
	a. Vert pair. Nos. 530/1		60	90

531	$1 multicoloured	30	45
532	$1.50, multicoloured	40	55
	a. Vert pair. Nos. 532/3	80	1·10
533	$1.50, multicoloured	40	55
534	$2 multicoloured	45	70
	a. Vert pair. Nos. 534/5	90	1·40
535	$2 multicoloured	45	70
520/35	*Set of 16*	4·50	6·00

Designs:—Nos. 520/1, Class 142 diesel locomotive, East Germany (1977); 522/3, Class 120 electric locomotive, West Germany (1979); 524/5, Class X diesel locomotive, Australia (1954); 526/7, Class 59 diesel locomotive, Great Britain (1986); 528/9, *Spuyten Duyvel*, U.S.A. (1875); 530/1, *Stevens* (later *John Bull*), U.S.A. (1831); 532/3, Class H1-d, No. 2850, Canada (1938), 534/5, "Pioneer Zephyr" 3-car diesel set, U.S.A. (1934).

Nos. 520/35 were issued in a similar sheet format to Nos. 271/86.

59 Queen Elizabeth with Prince Andrew	**60** Banded Coral Shrimp

(Des Young Phillips. Litho Format)

1987 (15 Oct). *Royal Ruby Wedding and 150th Anniv of Queen Victoria's Accession.* T **59** *and similar vert designs.* P 12½.

536	15 c. multicoloured	20	15
537	45 c. deep chocolate, black & greenish yellow	25	20
538	$1.50 multicoloured	30	50
539	$3 multicoloured	45	80
540	$4 multicoloured	50	1·10
536/40	*Set of 5*	1·50	2·50
MS541	85×115 mm. $6 multicoloured ..	1·25	2·50

Designs:—45 c. Queen Victoria and Prince Albert, *c* 1855; $1.50, Queen and Prince Philip after Trooping the Colour, 1977; $3 Queen and Duke of Edinburgh, 1953; $4 Queen in her study, *c* 1980; $6 Princess Elizabeth, 1947.

(Litho Format)

1987 (17 Dec). *Marine Life.* T **60** *and similar horiz designs. Multicoloured.* P 15.

542	45 c. Type **60**	55	35
543	50 c. Arrow Crab and Flamingo Tongue	60	50
544	65 c. Cardinalfish	70	90
545	$5 Spotted Moray	2·00	3·75
542/5	*Set of 4*	3·50	5·00
MS546	85×115 mm. $5 Porcupinefish ("Puffer Fish")	2·25	4·50

61 *Australia IV*	**62** Seine-fishing Boats racing

(Litho Format)

1988 (31 Mar). *Ocean Racing Yachts.* T **61** *and similar vert designs. Multicoloured.* P 12½.

547	50 c. Type **61**	30	35
548	65 c. *Crusader II*	35	50
549	75 c. *New Zealand II*	40	60
550	$2 *Italia*	60	1·25
551	$4 *White Crusader*	70	2·00
552	$5 *Stars and Stripes*	70	2·25
547/52	*Set of 6*	2·75	6·25
MS553	100×140 mm. $1 *Champosa V* ..	85	1·50

(Litho Format)

1988 (31 Mar). *Bequia Regatta.* T **62** *and similar horiz designs. Multicoloured.* P 15.

554	5 c. Type **62**	10	15
555	50 c. *Friendship Rose* (cruising yacht) ..	15	30
556	75 c. Fishing boats racing ..	20	45
557	$3.50, Yachts racing	75	2·25
554/7	*Set of 4*	1·00	2·75
MS558	115×85 mm. $8 Port Elizabeth, Bequia (60×40 *mm*). P 12½	3·00	5·50

COVER PRICES

Cover factors are quoted at the beginning of each country for most issues to 1945. An explanation of the system can be found on page x. The factors quoted do not, however, apply to philatelic covers.

---

63 Britten Norman Islander making Night Approach

(Litho Format)

1988 (26 May). *Mustique Airways.* T **63** *and similar multicoloured designs.* P 14 × 13½.

559	15 c. Type **63**	10	15
560	65 c. Beech 58 Baron aircraft in flight	15	35
561	75 c. Britten Norman Islander over forest	15	35
562	$5 Beech 58 Baron on airstrip ..	1·00	2·25
559/62	*Set of 4*	1·25	2·75
MS563	115×85 mm. $10 Baleine Falls (36×56 *mm*). P 12½	2·50	5·50

64 *Sv. Pyotr* in Arctic (Bering)	**65** Asif Iqbal Razvi

(Litho Format)

1988 (29 July). *Explorers.* T **64** *and similar square designs. Multicoloured.* P 14 × 13½.

564	15 c. Type **64**	35	20
565	75 c. Bering's ships in pack ice	40	30
566	$1 Livingstone's steam launch *Ma-Robert* on Zambesi	40	40
567	$2 Meeting of Livingstone and H. M. Stanley at Ujiji	50	75
568	$3 Speke and Burton at Tabori ..	50	90
569	$3.50, Speke and Burton in canoe on Lake Victoria	50	1·10
570	$4 Sighting the New World, 1492 ..	60	1·25
571	$4.50, Columbus trading with Indians	60	1·40
563/71	*Set of 8*	3·50	5·50
MS572	Two sheets, each 115 × 85 mm. (a) $5 Sextant and coastal scene. (b) $5 *Santa Maria* at anchor. P 13½ × 14 .. *Set of 2 sheets*	2·25	5·00

An unissued $6 miniature sheet, showing the *Santa Maria*, exists from stock dispersed by the liquidator of Format International Security Printers Ltd.

(Litho Format)

1988 (29 July). *Cricketers of 1988 International Season.* T **65** *and similar multicoloured designs.* P 15.

573	20 c. Type **65**	30	30
574	45 c. R. J. Hadlee	50	50
575	75 c. M. D. Crowe	70	80
576	$1.25, C. H. Lloyd	80	1·25
577	$1.50, A. R. Boarder	90	1·50
578	$2 M. D. Marshall	1·10	2·00
579	$2.50, G. A. Hick	1·10	2·25
580	$3.50, C. G. Greenidge (*horiz*) ..	1·25	2·75
573/80	*Set of 8*	6·00	10·00
MS581	115 × 85 mm. $3 As $2	2·50	5·00

66 Pam Shriver

(Litho Format)

1988 (29 July). *International Tennis Players.* T **66** *and similar multicoloured designs.* P 12½.

582	15 c. Type **66**	20	20
583	50 c. Kevin Curran (*vert*) ..	20	30
584	75 c. Wendy Turnbull (*vert*) ..	25	35
585	$1 Evonne Cawley (*vert*) ..	30	50
586	$1.50, Ilie Nastase	35	65
587	$2 Billie Jean King (*vert*) ..	40	75
588	$3 Bjorn Borg (*vert*)	45	1·25
589	$3.50, Virginia Wade with Wimbledon trophy (*vert*)	50	1·50
582/9	*Set of 8*	2·40	5·00
MS590	115 × 85 mm. $2.25, Stefan Edberg with Wimbledon cup; $2.25, Steffi Graf with Wimbledon trophy	1·50	3·25

No. 584 is inscribed "WENDY TURNBALL" in error.

Examples of an unissued set of six values and a miniature sheet for the 1988 Olympic Games at Seoul exist from stock dispersed by the liquidator of Format International Security Printers Ltd.

---

67 Mickey and Minnie Mouse visiting Fatehpur Sikri

(Des Walt Disney Co. Litho Questa)

1989 (8 Feb). *"India-89" International Stamp Exhibition, New Delhi.* T **67** *and similar multicoloured designs showing Walt Disney cartoon characters in India.* P 14×13½.

591	1 c. Type **67**	10	10
592	2 c. Mickey and Minnie Mouse aboard "Palace on Wheels" train ..	10	10
593	3 c. Mickey and Minnie Mouse passing Old Fort, Delhi	10	10
594	5 c. Mickey and Minnie Mouse on camel, Pinjore Gardens, Haryana ..	10	10
595	10 c. Mickey and Minnie Mouse at Taj Mahal, Agra	15	10
596	25 c. Mickey and Minnie Mouse in Chandni Chowk, Old Delhi	20	10
597	$4 Goofy on elephant with Mickey and Minnie Mouse at Agra Fort, Jaipur ..	3·00	3·50
598	$5 Goofy, Mickey and Minnie Mouse at Gandhi Memorial, Cape Comorin	3·00	3·50
591/8	*Set of 8*	6·00	6·75
MS599	Two sheets, each 127 × 102 mm. (a) $6 Mickey and Minnie Mouse in vegetable cart, Jaipur. P 14 × 13½. (b) $6 Mickey and Minnie Mouse leaving carriage, Qutab Minar, New Delhi (*vert*). P 13½ × 14 .. *Set of 2 sheets*	8·00	9·00

(Litho Questa)

1989 (6 July). *Japanese Art. Horiz designs as* T **187**a *of Lesotho. Multicoloured.* P 14×13½.

600	5 c. "The View at Yotsuya" (Hokusai)	20	20
601	30 c. "Landscape at Ochanomizu" (Hokuju)	50	50
602	45 c. "Itabashi" (Eisen)	60	60
603	65 c. "Early Summer Rain" (Kunisada)	75	75
604	75 c. "High Noon at Kasumigaseki" (Kuniyoshi)	80	80
605	$1 "The Yoshiwara Embankment by Moonlight" (Kuniyoshi) ..	1·00	1·00
606	$4 "The Bridge of Boats at Sano" (Hokusai)	2·75	3·00
607	$5 "Lingering Snow on Mount Hira" (Kunitora)	2·75	3·00
600/7	*Set of 8*	8·50	9·00
MS608	Two sheets, each 103×76 mm. (a) $6 "Colossus of Rhodes" (Kunitora). (b) $6 "Shinobazu Pond" (Kokan) .. *Set of 2 sheets*	7·00	8·00

Nos. 600/7 were each printed in sheetlets of 10 containing two horizontal strips of 5 stamps separated by printed labels commemorating Emperor Hirohito.

68 Player with Ball and Mt Vesuvius	**69** Arawak smoking Tobacco

(Des J. Genzo. Litho B.D.T.)

1989 (10 July). *World Cup Football Championship, Italy (1st issue).* T **68** *and similar vert designs each showing players and Italian landmarks. Multicoloured.* P 14.

609	$1.50, Type **68**	1·40	1·40
	a. Sheetlet. Nos. 609/16 ..	10·00	
610	$1.50, Fallen player, opponent kicking ball and Coliseum	1·40	1·40
611	$1.50, Player blocking ball and Venice	1·40	1·40
612	$1.50, Player tackling and Forum, Rome	1·40	1·40
613	$1.50, Two players competing for ball and Leaning Tower, Pisa	1·40	1·40
614	$1.50, Goalkeeper and Florence ..	1·40	1·40
615	$1.50, Two players competing for ball and St. Peter's, Vatican	1·40	1·40
616	$1.50, Player kicking ball and Pantheon	1·40	1·40
609/16	*Set of 8*	10·00	10·00

Nos. 609/16 were printed together, *se-tenant*, in a sheetlet of 8.

See also Nos. 680/4.

(Des D. Miller. Litho B.D.T.)

1989 (2 Oct). *500th Anniv of Discovery of America (1992) by Columbus (1st issue). Pre-Columbian Arawak Society.* T C**9** *and similar vert designs. Multicoloured.* P 14.

617	25 c. Type **69**	35	25
618	75 c. Arawak rolling cigar	65	65
619	$1 Applying body paint	80	80
620	$1.50, Making fire	1·10	1·40
	a. Horiz strip of 4. Nos. 620/3 ..	4·00	
621	$1.50, Cassava production	1·10	1·40

622	$1.50, Woman baking bread		1·10	1·40
623	$1.50, Using stone implement		1·10	1·40
624	$4 Arawak priest		2·50	2·75
617/24		*Set of 8*	8·00	9·00

MS625 Two sheets, each 70×84 mm. (a) $6 Arawak chief. (b) $6 Men returning from fishing expedition .. .. *Set of 2 sheets* 9·00 10·00

Nos. 620/4 were printed together, *se-tenant*, in horizontal strips of 4 throughout the sheet of 20, each strip forming a composite design.

See also Nos. 818/24 and 864/5.

70 Command Module *Columbia*   **71** *Marpesia petreus*

(Des W. Wright. Litho B.D.T.)

1989 (2 Oct). *20th Anniv of First Manned Landing on Moon. T 70 and similar multicoloured designs. P 14.*

626	5 c. Type 70		30	30
627	40 c. Astronaut Neil Armstrong saluting U.S. flag		1·00	85
628	55 c. *Columbia* above lunar surface		1·25	90
629	65 c. Lunar module *Eagle* leaving Moon		1·25	1·10
630	70 c. *Eagle* on Moon		1·25	1·10
631	$1 *Columbia* re-entering Earth's atmosphere		1·40	1·40
632	$3 "Apollo 11" emblem		2·75	3·00
633	$5 Armstrong and Aldrin on Moon		3·00	3·50
626/33		*Set of 8*	11·00	11·00

MS634 Two sheets, each 110×82 mm. (a) $6 Launch of "Apollo 11" (*vert*). (b) $6 "Apollo 11" splashdown .. .. .. *Set of 2 sheets* 8·00 10·00

(Des D. Bruckner. Litho Questa)

1989 (16 Oct). *Butterflies. T 71 and similar horiz designs. Multicoloured. P 14½.*

635	5 c. Type 71		40	40
636	30 c. *Papilio androgeus*		1·00	60
637	45 c. *Strymon maesites*		1·25	65
638	65 c. *Junonia coenia*		1·60	1·40
639	75 c. *Eurema gratiosa*		1·75	1·50
640	$1 *Hypolimnas misippus*		2·00	1·75
641	$4 *Urbanus proteus*		3·75	4·00
642	$5 *Junonia evarete*		3·75	4·00
635/42		*Set of 8*	14·00	13·00

MS643 Two sheets. (a) 76×104 mm. $6 *Phoebis agarithe*. (b) 104×76 mm. $6 *Dryas julia* .. .. *Set of 2 sheets* 14·00 13·00

72 *Solanum urens*   **73** Goofy and Mickey Mouse in Rolls-Royce "Silver Ghost", 1907

(Des Mary Walters. Litho Questa)

1989 (1 Nov). *Flowers from St. Vincent Botanical Gardens. T 72 and similar vert designs. Multicoloured. P 14.*

644	80 c. Type 72		1·25	1·25
645	$1.25, *Passiflora andersonii*		1·60	1·60
646	$1.65, *Miconia andersonii*		2·00	2·00
647	$1.85, *Pitcairnia sulphurea*		2·25	2·25
644/7		*Set of 4*	6·25	6·25

(Des Walt Disney Co. Litho Questa)

1989 (20 Dec). *Christmas. T 73 and similar horiz designs showing Walt Disney cartoon characters and cars. Multicoloured. P 14×13½.*

648	5 c. Type 73		20	15
649	10 c. Daisy Duck driving first Stanley Steamer, 1897		20	15
650	15 c. Horace Horsecollar and Clarabelle Cow in Darracq "Genevieve", 1904		25	20
651	45 c. Donald Duck driving Detroit electric coupe, 1914		50	35
652	55 c. Mickey and Minnie Mouse in first Ford, 1896		55	40
653	$2 Mickey Mouse driving Reo "Runabout", 1904		2·00	2·00
654	$3 Goofy driving Winton mail truck, 1899		2·75	2·75
655	$5 Mickey and Minnie Mouse in Duryea car, 1893		3·50	4·00
648/55		*Set of 8*	9·00	9·00

MS656 Two sheets, each 127×102 mm. (a) $6 Mickey and Minnie Mouse in Pope-Hartford, 1912. (b) $6 Mickey and Minnie Mouse in Buick "Model 10", 1908. P 13½×14 .. *Set of 2 sheets* 10·00 12·00

(Des W. Wright. Litho Questa)

1990 (2 Apr). *50th Anniv of Second World War. Horiz designs as T 242 of Maldive Islands. Multicoloured. P 14.*

657	10 c. Destroyers in action, First Battle of Narvik, 1940		25	25
658	15 c. Allied tank at Anzio, 1944		35	35

659	20 c. U.S. carrier under attack, Battle of Midway, 1942		40	40
660	45 c. U.S. North American B-25 Mitchell bombers over Gustav Line, 1944		70	70
661	55 c. Map showing Allied zones of Berlin, 1945		75	75
662	65 c. German U-boat pursuing convoy, Battle of the Atlantic, 1943		80	80
663	90 c. Allied tank, North Africa, 1943		1·00	1·00
664	$3 U.S. forces landing on Guam, 1944		2·50	2·50
665	$5 Crossing the Rhine, 1945		3·50	3·50
666	$6 Japanese battleships under attack, Leyte Gulf, 1944		4·00	4·00
657/66		*Set of 10*	13·00	13·00

MS667 100×70 mm. $6 Avro Type 683 Lancaster Mk III on "Dambusters" raid, 1943 5·00 5·50

(Des Walt Disney Co. Litho Questa)

1990 (3 May). *"Stamp World London 90" International Stamp Exhibition (1st issue). Mickey's Shakespeare Company. Multicoloured designs as T 239a of Maldive Islands showing Walt Disney cartoon characters. P 14×13½.*

668	20 c. Goofy as Mark Anthony (*Julius Caesar*)		30	20
669	30 c. Clarabelle Cow as the Nurse (*Romeo and Juliet*)		35	25
670	45 c. Pete as Falstaff (*Henry IV*)		50	40
671	50 c. Minnie Mouse as Portia (*The Merchant of Venice*)		55	40
672	$1 Donald Duck as Hamlet (*Hamlet*)		1·00	85
673	$2 Daisy Duck as Ophelia (*Hamlet*)		1·75	2·00
674	$4 Donald and Daisy Duck as Benedick and Beatrice (*Much Ado About Nothing*)		3·00	3·25
675	$5 Minnie Mouse and Donald Duck as Katherine and Petruchio (*The Taming of the Shrew*)		3·00	3·25
668/75		*Set of 8*	9·50	9·50

MS676 Two sheets, each 127×101 mm. (a) $6 Clarabelle as Titania (*A Midsummer Night's Dream*) (*vert*). (b) $6 Mickey Mouse as Romeo (*Romeo and Juliet*) (*vert*). P 13½×14 .. .. *Set of 2 sheets* 11·00 12·00

74 Exhibition Emblem   **75** Scaly-breasted Ground Dove

(Des M. Pollard. Litho B.D.T.)

1990 (3 May). *"Stamp World London 90" International Stamp Exhibition (2nd issue). 150th Anniv of Penny Black. T 74 and similar vert designs. P 14×15.*

677	$1 black, brown-rose and magenta		1·50	1·25
678	$5 black, grey-lilac and ultramarine		3·75	4·25

MS679 130×100 mm. $6 black and pale blue 5·00 6·00

Designs:—$5 Negative image of Penny Black; $6 Penny Black.

(Des Young Phillips Studio. Litho Questa)

1990 (24 Sept). *World Cup Football Championship, Italy (2nd issue). Multicoloured designs as T 210 of St. Vincent, but horiz. P 14.*

680	25 c. McCleish, Scotland		80	40
681	50 c. Rasul, Egypt		1·10	80
682	$2 Lindenberger, Austria		2·75	2·75
683	$4 Murray, U.S.A.		3·75	4·25
680/3		*Set of 4*	7·50	7·50

MS684 Two sheets, each 102×77 mm. (a) $6 Robson, England. (b) $6 Gullit, Netherlands .. .. *Set of 2 sheets* 12·00 11·00

(Des Dorothy Novick. Litho B.D.T.)

1990 (23 Nov). *"EXPO 90" International Garden and Greenery Exposition, Osaka. Orchids. Vert designs as T 213 of St. Vincent. Multicoloured. P 14.*

685	5 c. *Paphiopedilum*		50	40
686	25 c. *Dendrobium phalaenopsis* and *Cymbidium* hybrid		1·00	90
687	30 c. *Miltonia candida* hybrid		1·00	90
688	50 c. *Epidendrum ibaguense* and *Cymbidium* Elliot Rogers		1·50	1·25
689	$1 *Rossioglossum grande*		2·00	1·75
690	$2 *Phalaenopsis* Elisa Chang Lou and *Masdevallia coccinea*		2·50	2·25
691	$4 *Cypripedium acaule* and *Cypripedium calceolus*		3·00	3·50
692	$5 *Orchis spectabilis*		3·00	3·50
685/92		*Set of 8*	13·00	13·00

MS693 Two sheets, each 108×78 mm. (a) $6 *Dendrobium anosmum*. (b) $6 *Epidendrum ibaguense* and *Phalaenopsis* .. *Set of 2 sheets* 13·00 13·00

(Des W. Wright. Litho B.D.T.)

1990 (26 Nov). *Birds of the Caribbean. T 75 and similar horiz designs. Multicoloured. P 14.*

694	5 c. Type 75		20	20
695	25 c. Purple Martin		40	40
696	45 c. Painted Bunting		70	70
697	55 c. Blue-hooded Euphonia		80	80
698	75 c. Blue-grey Tanager		1·00	1·00
699	$1 Red-eyed Vireo		1·25	1·25

700	$2 Palm Chat		2·00	2·00
701	$3 Northern Jacana		2·50	2·50
702	$4 Green-throated Carib		2·75	2·75
703	$5 St. Vincent Amazon		3·00	3·00
694/703		*Set of 10*	13·00	13·00

MS704 Two sheets, each 117×87 mm. (a) $3 Magnificent Frigate Bird; $3 Bananaquit. (b) $6 Red-legged Honeycreeper .. *Set of 2 sheets* 7·50 8·50

(Des Young Phillips Studio. Litho B.D.T.)

1991 (14 Feb). *90th Birthday of Queen Elizabeth the Queen Mother. Vert designs as T 198a of Lesotho. P 14.*

705	$2 multicoloured		1·40	1·25
	a. Sheetlet. Nos. 705/13		11·00	
706	$2 multicoloured		1·40	1·25
707	$2 multicoloured		1·40	1·25
708	$2 multicoloured		1·40	1·25
709	$2 multicoloured		1·40	1·25
710	$2 multicoloured		1·40	1·25
711	$2 multicoloured		1·40	1·25
712	$2 multicoloured		1·40	1·25
713	$2 multicoloured		1·40	1·25
714	$2 multicoloured		1·40	1·25
	a. Sheetlet. Nos. 714/22		11·00	
715	$2 multicoloured		1·40	1·25
716	$2 multicoloured		1·40	1·25
717	$2 black and rose-lilac		1·40	1·25
718	$2 black and rose-lilac		1·40	1·25
719	$2 black, pale yellow-olive and rose-lilac		1·40	1·25
720	$2 multicoloured		1·40	1·25
721	$2 black and rose-lilac		1·40	1·25
722	$2 multicoloured		1·40	1·25
723	$2 multicoloured		1·40	1·25
	a. Sheetlet. Nos. 723/31		11·00	
724	$2 multicoloured		1·40	1·25
725	$2 multicoloured		1·40	1·25
726	$2 multicoloured		1·40	1·25
727	$2 multicoloured		1·40	1·25
728	$2 multicoloured		1·40	1·25
729	$2 multicoloured		1·40	1·25
730	$2 multicoloured		1·40	1·25
731	$2 multicoloured		1·40	1·25
705/31		*Set of 27*	30·00	27·00

MS732 Nine sheets containing details of designs indicated. (a) 120×115 mm. $5 As No. 705. (b) 115×120 mm. $5 As No. 710. (c) 115×120 mm. $5 As No. 712. (d) 115×120 mm. $5 As No. 715. (e) 120×115 mm. $5 As No. 719. (f) 120×115 mm. $5 As No. 720. (g) 120×115 mm. $5 As No. 724. (h) 120×115 mm. $5 As No. 726. (i) 120×115 mm. $5 As No. 730 .. *Set of 9 sheets* 26·00 27·00

Designs:—No. 705, Lady Elizabeth Bowes-Lyon with brother; No. 706, Young Lady Elizabeth in long dress; No. 707, Young Lady Elizabeth wearing a hat; No. 708, Lady Elizabeth leaning on wall; No. 709, Lady Elizabeth on pony; No. 710, Studio Portrait; No. 711, Lady Elizabeth in evening dress; No. 712, Duchess of York in fur-lined cloak; No. 713, Duchess of York holding rose; No. 714, Coronation, 1937; No. 715, King and Queen with Princess Elizabeth at Royal Lodge, Windsor; No. 716, Queen Elizabeth in blue hat; No. 717, King George VI and Queen Elizabeth; No. 718, Queen Elizabeth with Princess Elizabeth; No. 719, Queen Elizabeth watching sporting fixture; No. 720, Queen Elizabeth in white evening dress; No. 721, Princess Anne's christening, 1950; No. 722, Queen Mother with yellow bouquet; No. 723, Queen Mother and policewoman; No. 724, Queen Mother at ceremonial function; No. 725, Queen Mother in pink coat; No. 726, Queen Mother in academic robes; No. 727, Queen Mother in carriage with Princess Margaret; No. 728, Queen Mother in blue coat and hat; No. 729, Queen Mother with bouquet; No. 730, Queen Mother outside Clarence House on her birthday; No. 731, Queen Mother in turquoise coat and hat.

Nos. 705/13, 714/22 and 723/31 were printed, *se-tenant*, in sheetlets of nine.

(Litho Walsall)

1991 (11 June). *Death Centenary of Vincent van Gogh (artist) (1990). Multicoloured designs as T 255 of Maldive Islands. P 13½.*

733	5 c. "View of Arles with Irises" (*horiz*)		20	20
734	10 c. "Saintes-Maries"		20	20
735	15 c. "Old Woman of Arles"		25	25
736	20 c. "Orchard in Blossom, bordered by Cypresses" (*horiz*)		30	30
737	25 c. "Three White Cottages in Saintes-Maries" (*horiz*)		30	30
738	35 c. "Boats at Saintes-Maries" (*horiz*)		40	40
739	40 c. "Interior of a Restaurant in Arles" (*horiz*)		45	45
740	45 c. "Peasant Women"		50	50
741	55 c. "Self-portrait"		60	60
742	60 c. "Pork Butcher's Shop from a Window"		70	70
743	75 c. "The Night Cafe in Arles" (*horiz*)		80	80
744	$1 "2nd Lieut. Millet of the Zouaves" (*horiz*)		95	95
745	$2 "The Café Terrace, Place du Forum, Arles at Night"		1·50	1·50
746	$3 "The Zouave"		2·00	2·00
747	$4 "The Two Lovers" (detail)		2·75	2·75
748	$5 "Still Life" (*horiz*)		3·00	3·00
733/48		*Set of 16*	13·50	13·50

MS749 Four sheets, each 112×76 mm. (a) $5 "Street in Saintes-Maries" (*horiz*). (b) $5 "Lane near Arles" (*horiz*). (c) $6 "Harvest at La Crau, with Montmajour in the Background" (*horiz*). (d) $6 "The Sower". Imperf. .. *Set of 4 sheets* 15·00 16·00

(Des D. Miller. Litho Walsall)

1991 (5 July). *65th Birthday of Queen Elizabeth II. Horiz designs as T 210 of Lesotho. Multicoloured. P 14.*

750	15 c. Inspecting the Yeomen of the Guard		30	20
751	40 c. Queen Elizabeth II with the Queen Mother at the Derby, 1988		55	30
752	$2 The Queen and Prince Philip leaving Euston, 1986		2·00	2·00
753	$4 The Queen at the Commonwealth Institute, 1987		2·75	3·00
750/3		*Set of 4*	5·00	5·00

MS754 68×90 mm. $5 Queen Elizabeth and Prince Philip with Prince Andrew in naval uniform .. .. 3·25 3·75

(Des D. Miller. Litho Walsall)

1991 (5 July). *10th Wedding Anniv of Prince and Princess of Wales. Horiz designs as T 210 of Lesotho. Multicoloured.* P 14.

755	10 c. Prince and Princess at polo match, 1987	50	20
756	50 c. Separate family portraits	90	40
757	$1 Prince William and Prince Henry at Kensington Palace, 1991	1·00	1·00
758	$5 Portraits of Prince Charles and Princess Diana	3·75	4·00
755/8	*Set of 4*	5·50	5·00
MS759	68×90 mm. $5 Separate portraits of Prince and Princess and sons	4·75	4·25

76 Class 150 Steam Locomotive (1871) and Map

(Des K. Gromell. Litho Cartor)

1991 (12 Aug). *"Phila Nippon '91" International Stamp Exhibition, Tokyo. Japanese Railway Locomotives.* T **76** *and similar designs, each in black, scarlet-vermilion and dull blue-green.* P 14×13½.

760	10 c. Type **76**	60	50
761	25 c. Class 7100 *Benkei* steam locomotive (1880)	90	80
762	35 c. Class 8620 steam locomotive (1914)	1·00	90
763	50 c. Class C53 stream-lined steam locomotive (1928)	1·50	1·25
764	$1 Class DD-51 diesel-hydraulic locomotive (1962)	2·00	1·75
765	$2 Class KTR001 "Tango Explorer" electric rail car (inscr "RF22327")	2·50	2·50
766	$4 Class EF55 electric locomotive (1936)	3·00	3·50
767	$5 Class EF58 electric locomotive (1946)	3·00	3·50
760/7	*Set of 8*	13·00	13·00
MS768	Four sheets, each 114×73 mm showing frontal views. (a) $6 Class 9600 steam locomotive (1913) (*vert*). (b) $6 Class C57 steam locomotive (1937) (*vert*). (c) $6 Class C62 steam locomotive (1948) (*vert*). (d) $6 Class 4100 tank locomotive (1912) (*vert*) ... *Set of 4 sheets*	15·00	16·00

 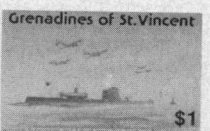

77 President Gorbachev and Brandenburg Gate

78 Japanese Aircraft and Submarines leaving Truk

(Des L. Fried (Nos. 769, 771/2, MS783a/b), J. Iskowitz (Nos. 773, 781, MS783e/f), W. Hanson (Nos. 777, 782, MS783h/i), W. Wright (Nos. 774/6, 778/80, MS783g, j/k). Litho Questa)

1991 (18 Nov). *Anniversaries and Events.* T **77** *and similar designs. Rose-lilac, yellow-green and black (No. MS781k) or multicoloured (others).* P 14.

769	45 c. Type **77**	40	40
770	60 c. General De Gaulle in Djibouti, 1959	90	55
771	65 c. "DIE MAUER MUSS WEG!" slogan	65	65
772	80 c. East German border guard escaping to West	80	80
773	$1 *Abduction from the Seraglio*	1·75	1·50
774	$1.50, Lilienthal and glider	1·75	1·75
775	$1.75, Trans-Siberian identity plate	2·25	2·00
776	$1.75, Trans-Siberian steam locomotive (*vert*)	2·25	2·00
777	$2 Czechoslovakia 1918 20 h. stamp and scout delivering mail	2·25	2·25
778	$2 Zurich couple maypole dancing	2·25	2·25
779	$2 Man and woman in Vaud traditional costumes	2·25	2·25
780	$2 Georg Laves (architect) and Hoftheater	2·25	2·25
781	$3 Dresden, 1749	3·00	2·50
782	$4 Scouts and cog train on Snowdon (*vert*)	3·00	2·75
769/82	*Set of 14*	22·00	21·00
MS783	Eleven sheets. (a) 100×71 mm. $5 Arms of Berlin. (b) 100×71 mm. $5 Berlin police badge. (c) 77×112 mm. $5 De Gaulle in civilian dress. (d) 69×101 mm. $5 General Charles de Gaulle (*vert*). (e) 75×101 mm. $5 Portrait of Mozart (*vert*). (f) 75×101 mm. $5 Bust of Mozart (*vert*). (g) 115×85 mm. $5 Trans-Siberian Class P36 No. 0250 steam locomotive leaving Moscow at night (43×56 *mm*). (h) 118×89 mm. $5 Jamboree emblem (buff background) (*vert*). (i) 118×89 mm. $5 Jamboree emblem (bluish violet background) (*vert*). (j) 101×72 mm. $5 Arms of Appenzell and Thurgau. (k) 101×72 mm. $5 Old Hanover ... *Set of 11 sheets*	29·00	30·00

Anniversaries and Events:—Nos. 769, 771/2, MS783a/b, Bicentenary of Brandenburg Gate; Nos. 770, MS783c/d, Birth centenary of Charles de Gaulle (French statesman); Nos. 773, 781, MS783e/f, Death bicentenary of Mozart; No. 774 Centenary of Otto Lilienthal's gliding experiments; Nos. 775/6, MS783g, Centenary of Trans-Siberian Railway; Nos. 777, 782, MS783h/i, 50th death anniv of Lord Baden-Powell and World Scout Jamboree, Korea; Nos. 778/9, MS783j, 700th anniv of Swiss Confederation; Nos. 780, MS783k, 750th anniv of Hanover.

(Des J. Batchelor. Litho Questa)

1991 (18 Nov). *50th Anniv of Japanese Attack on Pearl Harbor.* T **78** *and similar horiz designs. Multicoloured.* P 14½×15.

784	$1 Type **78**	1·60	1·60
	a. Sheetlet. Nos. 784/93	14·00	
785	$1 *Akagi* (Japanese aircraft carrier)	1·60	1·60
786	$1 Nakajima B5N2 "Kate" aircraft	1·60	1·60
787	$1 Nakajima B5N2 "Kate" bombers attacking Battleship Row	1·60	1·60
788	$1 Burning aircraft, Ford Island airfield	1·60	1·60
789	$1 Doris Miller winning Navy Cross	1·60	1·60
790	$1 U.S.S. *West Virginia* and *Tennessee* (battleships) ablaze	1·60	1·60
791	$1 U.S.S. *Arizona* (battleship) sinking	1·60	1·60
792	$1 U.S.S. *New Orleans* (cruiser)	1·60	1·60
793	$1 President Roosevelt declaring war	1·60	1·60
784/93	*Set of 10*	14·00	14·00

Nos. 784/93 were printed together, *se-tenant*, in sheetlets of 10 with the stamps arranged in two horizontal rows of 5 separated by a map of Pearl Harbor.

(Des Walt Disney Co. Litho Questa)

1991 (23 Dec). *Christmas. Walt Disney Company Christmas Cards. Multicoloured designs as* T **228** *of St. Vincent.* P 14×13½.

794	10 c. Pluto pulling Mickey Mouse in sledge, 1974 (*horiz*)	35	30
795	55 c. Mickey, Pluto and Donald Duck watching toy band, 1961 (*horiz*)	80	70
796	65 c. "The Same Old Wish", 1942 (*horiz*)	85	85
797	75 c. Mickey, Peter Pan, Donald Duck and Nephews with Merlin the magician, 1963 (*horiz*)	95	95
798	$1.50, Mickey, Donald and leprechauns, 1958 (*horiz*)	1·75	2·00
799	$2 Mickey and friends with book *Old Yeller*, 1957 (*horiz*)	2·00	2·25
800	$4 Mickey controlling Pinocchio, 1953 (*horiz*)	3·25	3·50
801	$5 Cinderella and Prince dancing, 1987 (*horiz*)	3·25	3·50
794/801	*Set of 8*	12·00	12·50
MS802	Two sheets, each 128×102 mm. (a) $6 Santa Claus and American bomber, 1942. (b) $6 Snow White, 1957. P 13½×14 ... *Set of 2 sheets*	13·00	14·00

(Des D. Miller. Litho Questa)

1992 (2 Mar). *40th Anniv of Queen Elizabeth II's Accession. Horiz designs as* T **214** *of Lesotho. Multicoloured.* P 14.

803	15 c. View across bay	40	20
804	45 c. Schooner at anchor, Mayreau	75	25
805	$2 Hotel on hillside	1·50	1·75
806	$4 Tourist craft at anchor	3·00	3·25
803/6	*Set of 4*	5·00	5·00
MS807	Two sheets, each 74×97 mm. (a) $6 Beach and palms. (b) $6 Aerial view of hotel by beach ... *Set of 2 sheets*	7·00	7·50

(Des Walt Disney Co. Litho Questa)

1992 (28 Apr). *International Stamp Exhibitions. Multicoloured designs as* T **215** *of Lesotho, showing Walt Disney cartoon characters.* P 14×13½.

(a) *"Granada '92", Spain. Spanish Explorers*

808	15 c. Big Pete as Hernando Cortes in Mexico (*horiz*)	30	15
809	40 c. Mickey Mouse as Hernando de Soto at Mississippi River (*horiz*)	50	30
810	$2 Goofy as Vasco Nunez de Balboa sights Pacific (*horiz*)	1·75	1·75
811	$4 Donald Duck as Francisco Coronado on Rio Grande (*horiz*)	2·75	3·00
808/11	*Set of 4*	4·75	4·75
MS812	127×102 mm. $6 Mickey as Ponce de Leon. P 13½×14	4·25	4·75

(b) *"World Columbian Stamp Expo '92", Chicago, Local Personalities*

813	10 c. Mickey Mouse and Pluto outside Walt Disney's birthplace (*horiz*)	30	20
814	50 c. Donald Duck and nephews in George Pullman's railway sleeping car (*horiz*)	70	55
815	$1 Daisy Duck as Jane Addams (social reformer) and Hull House (*horiz*)	1·00	85
816	$5 Mickey as Carl Sandburg (novelist, poet and historian) (*horiz*)	3·25	3·75
813/16	*Set of 4*	4·75	4·75
MS817	127×102 mm. $6 Daisy as Mrs O'Leary with her cow (source of Chicago fire of 1871). P 13½×14	4·25	4·75

79 King Ferdinand and Queen Isabella of Spain

(Des W. Wright. Litho Questa)

1992 (22 May). *500th Anniv of Discovery of America by Columbus (2nd issue).* T **79** *and similar multicoloured designs.* P 14.

818	10 c. Type **79**	25	25
819	45 c. *Santa Maria* and *Nina* in Acul Bay, Haiti	50	50
820	55 c. *Santa Maria* (*vert*)	55	55
821	$2 Ships of Columbus (*vert*)	1·40	1·40
822	$4 Wreck of *Santa Maria*	2·50	2·50
823	$5 *Pinta* and *Nina*	2·75	2·75
818/23	*Set of 6*	7·25	7·25
MS824	Two sheets, each 114×85 mm. (a) $6 Columbus landing on San Salvador. (b) $6 *Santa Maria* in storm ... *Set of 2 sheets*	7·00	8·00

(Des J. Barberis. Litho Questa)

1992 (15 June). *"Genova '92" International Thematic Stamp Exhibition (1st issue). Butterflies. Multicoloured designs as* T **235** *of St. Vincent.* P 14.

825	15 c. *Paulogramma sp* (*horiz*)	65	65
826	20 c. *Heliconius cydno* (*horiz*)	70	70
827	30 c. *Eutresis hypereia* (*horiz*)	75	75
828	45 c. *Eurytides columbus*	90	90
829	55 c. *Papilio ascolius* (*horiz*)	1·00	1·00
830	75 c. *Anaea pasibula* (*horiz*)	1·25	1·25
831	80 c. *Heliconius doris* (*horiz*)	1·25	1·25
832	$1 *Perisama pitheas* (*horiz*)	1·25	1·25
833	$2 *Batesia hypochlora* (*horiz*)	1·75	1·75
834	$3 *Heliconius erato* (*horiz*)	2·25	2·25
835	$4 *Elzunia cassandrina* (*horiz*)	2·50	2·50
836	$5 *Sais ivcidice* (*horiz*)	2·50	2·50
825/36	*Set of 12*	15·00	15·00
MS837	Three sheets, each 109×79 mm. (a) $6 *Oleria tigilla* (*horiz*). (b) $6 *Dismorphia orise* (*horiz*). (c) $6 *Podotricha telesiphe* (*horiz*) ... *Set of 3 sheets*	11·00	12·00

See also Nos. 851/63.

(Des R. Sauber. Litho Questa)

1992 (2 July). *Fungi. Vert designs as* T **236** *of St. Vincent. Multicoloured.* P 14.

838	10 c. *Entoloma bakeri*	50	50
839	15 c. *Hydropus paraensis*	55	55
840	20 c. *Leucopaxillus gracillimus*	60	60
841	45 c. *Hygrotrama dennisianum*	80	80
842	50 c. *Leucoagaricus hortensis*	80	80
843	65 c. *Pyrrhoglossum pyrrhum*	1·00	1·00
844	75 c. *Amanita craeoderma*	1·00	1·00
845	$1 *Lentinus bertieri*	1·25	1·25
846	$2 *Dennisiomyces griseus*	2·00	2·00
847	$3 *Xerulina asprata*	2·50	2·50
848	$4 *Hygrocybe acutoconica*	3·00	3·00
849	$5 *Lepiota spiculata*	3·00	3·00
838/49	*Set of 12*	15·00	15·00
MS850	Three sheets, each 101×68 mm. (a) $6 *Pluteus crysophlebius*. (b) $6 *Amanita lilloi*. (c) $6 *Lepiota volvatua* ... *Set of 3 sheets*	12·00	13·00

(Des Susan Carlson. Litho Questa)

1992 (2 July). *"Genova '92" International Thematic Stamp Exhibition (2nd issue). Hummingbirds. Multicoloured designs as* T **237** *of St. Vincent.* P 14.

851	5 c. Antillean Crested Hummingbird (female) (*horiz*)	30	30
852	10 c. Blue-tailed Emerald (female) (*horiz*)	30	30
853	35 c. Antillean Mango (male) (*horiz*)	45	45
854	45 c. Antillean Mango (female) (*horiz*)	45	45
855	55 c. Green-throated Carib (*horiz*)	55	55
856	65 c. Green Violetear (male)	70	70
857	75 c. Blue-tailed Emerald (male) (*horiz*)	80	80
858	$1 Purple-throated Carib	1·00	1·00
859	$2 Copper-rumped Hummingbird (*horiz*)	2·00	2·00
860	$3 Rufous-breasted Hermit	2·75	2·75
861	$4 Antillean Crested Hummingbird (male)	3·50	3·50
862	$5 Green-breasted Mango (male)	3·75	3·75
851/62	*Set of 12*	15·00	15·00
MS863	Three sheets, each 105×74 mm. (a) $6 Blue-tailed Emerald. (b) $6 Antillean Mango. (c) $6 Antillean Crested Hummingbird ... *Set of 3 sheets*	13·00	14·00

(Des F. Paul ($1), J. Esquino ($2). Litho Questa)

1992 (24 Aug). *500th Anniv of Discovery of America by Columbus (3rd issue). Organization of East Caribbean States. Vert designs as Nos. 911/12 of Montserrat. Multicoloured.* P 14½.

864	$1 Columbus meeting Amerindians	75	75
865	$2 Ships approaching island	1·75	2·25

(Litho Questa)

1992 (14 Sept). *Olympic Games, Albertville and Barcelona. Multicoloured designs as* T **216** *of Lesotho.* P 14.

866	10 c. Men's volleyball	40	40
867	15 c. Men's gymnastics (*horiz*)	50	50
868	25 c. Men's cross-country skiing	60	60
869	30 c. Men's 110 metres hurdles (*horiz*)	60	60
870	45 c. Men's 120 metre ski-jump (*horiz*)	70	70
871	55 c. Women's 4×100 metre relay	80	80
872	75 c. Men's triple jump	1·00	1·00
873	80 c. Men's mogul skiing	1·00	1·00
874	$1 Men's 110 metre butterfly swimming (*horiz*)	1·25	1·25
875	$2 "Tornado" Class yachting (*horiz*)	1·75	1·75
876	$3 Men's decathlon (*horiz*)	1·90	1·90
877	$5 Show jumping (*horiz*)	2·75	2·75
866/77	*Set of 12*	12·00	12·00
MS878	Three sheets, each 101×70 mm. (a) $6 Ice hockey (*horiz*). (b) $6 Men's single luge (*horiz*). (c) $6 Football ... *Set of 3 sheets*	14·00	14·00

(Litho Questa)

1992 (16 Nov). *Christmas. Religious Paintings. Vert designs as* T **218** *of Lesotho. Multicoloured.* P 13½×14.

879	10 c. "Our Lady with St. Roch and St. Anthony of Padua" (Giorgione)	30	30
880	40 c. "Anthony of Padua" (Master of the Embroidered Leaf)	55	55
881	45 c. "Madonna and Child" (detail) (Orazio Gentileschi)	60	60
882	50 c. "Madonna and Child with St. Anne" (detail) (Da Vinci)	65	65
883	55 c. "The Holy Family" (Crespi)	70	70
884	65 c. "Madonna and Child" (Del Sarto)	80	80
885	75 c. "Madonna and Child with Sts. Lawrence and Julian" (Gentile da Fabriano)	90	90
886	$1 "Virgin and Child" (detail) (School of Parma)	1·10	1·10
887	$2 "Madonna with the Iris" (detail) (style of Dürer)	1·75	1·75

888	$3 "Virgin and Child with St. Jerome and St. Dominic" (Lippi)		2·25	2·25
889	$4 "Rapolano Madonna" (Ambrogio Lorenzetti)		2·75	2·75
890	$5 "The Virgin and Child with Angels in a Garden with a Rose Hedge" (Stefano da Verona)		2·75	2·75
879/90		*Set of 12*	13·50	13·50

MS891 Three sheets, each 73×98 mm. (a) $6 "Madonna and Child with Grapes" (detail) (Cranach the Elder). (b) $6 "Virgin and Child with St. John the Baptist" (detail) (Botticelli). (c) $6 "Madonna and Child with St. Anne" (different detail) (Da Vinci) .. .. *Set of 3 sheets* 14·00 14·00

80 *Nina in Baracoa Harbour*

(Des W. Wright (Nos. 892/3, 896, 902, **MS**906a/c), W. Wright and L. Fried (Nos. 900, **MS**906f), J. Genzo (Nos. 904, **MS**906g). Litho Questa)

1992 (15 Dec). *Anniversaries and Events. T* 80 *and similar multicoloured designs. P* 14.

892	10 c. Type 80		70	70
893	75 c. Zeppelin LZ-3		1·75	1·75
894	75 c. Blind man with guide dog (*vert*)		1·75	1·75
895	75 c. Training guide dog		1·75	1·75
896	$1 Ships of Columbus		1·75	1·75
897	$1 Adenauer, state arms and German flag		1·75	1·75
898	$1 *America III* and *Il Moro* (yachts) with trophy		1·50	1·50
899	$1 Hands breaking bread and emblem (*vert*)		1·50	1·50
900	$2 "Voyager 2" and planet		1·50	1·50
901	$3 Adenauer and children watching Berlin Airlift		2·75	2·50
902	$4 Airship LZ-37 in flames		2·50	3·00
903	$4 Adenauer and ruins in Cologne		2·75	3·00
904	$4 Mozart with his wife Constanze (*vert*)		3·00	3·00
905	$5 Adenauer and modern office blocks		2·75	3·00
892/905		*Set of 14*	26·00	26·00

MS906 Seven sheets. (a) 100×70 mm. $6 Columbus sighting land. (b) 100×70 mm. $6 Count von Zeppelin facing left. (c) 110×70 mm. $6 Count von Zeppelin facing right. (d) 100×70 mm. $6 Konrad Adenauer (*vert*). (e) 100×70 mm. $6 Konrad Adenauer. (f) 100×70 mm. $6 "Mars Observer" spacecraft. (g) 100×70 mm. $6 Costume for "Don Giovanni" by Cassandre .. .. *Set of 7 sheets* 28·00 30·00

Anniversaries and Events:—Nos. 892, 896, **MS**906a, 500th anniv of discovery of America by Columbus; Nos. 893, 902, **MS**906b/c, 75th death anniv of Count Ferdinand von Zeppelin (airship pioneer); Nos. 894/5, 75th anniv of International Association of Lions Clubs; Nos. 897, 901, 903, 905, **MS**906d/e, 25th death anniv of Konrad Adenauer (German statesman); No. 898, Americas Cup yachting championship; No. 899, International Conference on Nutrition, Rome; Nos. 900, **MS**906f, International Space Year; Nos. 904, **MS**906g, Death bicentenary of Mozart.

81 *Olivia and Flaversham*

(Des Walt Disney Co. Litho Questa)

1992 (15 Dec). *Walt Disney Cartoon Films. T* 81 *and similar designs. P* 14×13½ (*horiz*) or 13½×14 (*vert*).

907/50	60 c.×44 multicoloured	*Set of 44*	19·00	21·00
MS951	Ten sheets, each 127×103 mm. $6×10 multicoloured. P 14×13½ (*horiz*) or 13½×14 (*vert*)	*Set of 10 sheets*	35·00	38·00

Nos. 907/50 were printed as five *se-tenant* sheetlets, each of nine different designs except for that for *Darkwing Duck* which contains eight vertical designs (Nos. 943/50). The other four sheetlets depict scenes from *The Great Mouse Detective, Oliver and Company, The Legend of Sleepy Hollow* and *Ducktales the Movie.*

No. **MS**951 contains two sheets for each film. On one sheet in the pairs for *The Legend of Sleepy Hollow, Ducktales the Movie* and *Darkwing Duck* the stamp design is vertical.

(Des A. Nahigian. Litho Walsall)

1992 (15 Dec). *15th Death Anniv of Elvis Presley (singer). Vert designs as Nos. 1768/70 of Maldive Islands. Multicoloured. P* 14.

952	$1 Elvis Presley		2·50	2·25
	a. Strip of 3. Nos. 952/4		6·75	
953	$1 Elvis with guitar		2·50	2·25
954	$1 Elvis with microphone		2·50	2·25
952/4		*Set of 3*	6·75	6·00

Nos. 952/4 were printed together, horizontally and vertically *se-tenant*, in sheetlets of 9 (3×3).

82 *Prince Mickey searching for Bride*

83 *Oleander*

(Des Walt Disney Co. Litho Questa)

1992 (15 Dec). *Tales of Uncle Scrooge (fairy stories). T* 82 *and similar designs showing Walt Disney cartoon characters. P* 14×13½.

955/1008	60 c.×54 multicoloured	*Set of 54*	21·00	22·00
MS1009	Twelve sheets, each 128×102 mm or 102×128 mm. $6×12 multicoloured. P 14×13½ (*horiz*) or 13½×14 (*vert*)	*Set of 12 sheets*	40·00	45·00

Nos. 955/1008 (issued as six sheetlets, each of nine different designs) depict scenes from "The Princess and the Pea", "Little Red Riding Hood", "Goldilocks and the Three Bears", "The Pied Piper of Hamelin", "Hop O'-My-Thumb" and "Puss in Boots".

No. **MS**1009 contains two sheets for each story, all being horizontal with the exception of the second sheet for "Puss in Boots". Of the stamp designs in these miniature sheets the two for "Little Red Riding Hood" and one of each for "Goldilocks and the Three Bears", "The Pied Piper of Hamelin" and "Puss in Boots" are vertical.

(Litho China Security Ptg Ltd, Hong Kong)

1994 (20 May). *Medicinal Plants. T* 83 *and similar vert designs. Multicoloured. P* 13½×13.

1010	5 c. Type 83		20	30
1011	10 c. Beach Morning Glory		30	30
1012	30 c. Calabash		40	30
1013	45 c. Portia Tree		50	30
1014	55 c. Cashew		60	40
1015	75 c. Prickly Pear		70	70
1016	$1 Shell Ginger		80	80
1017	$1.50, Avocado Pear		1·40	1·60
1018	$2 Mango		1·75	2·00
1019	$3 Blood Flower		2·25	2·50
1020	$4 Sugar Apple		2·50	2·75
1021	$5 Barbados Lily		2·50	2·75
1010/21		*Set of 12*	12·50	13·00

STAMP BOOKLETS

1976 (26 Sept). *Tourism. Multicoloured covers, 152×75 mm, showing maps of seven different islands. Stapled.*
SB1	$2.50, booklet containing four different *se-tenant* panes of 3 stamps and 1 label (Nos. 85a/b, 86a, 87a)		1·75
	Set of 7 booklets showing different islands		12·00

1978 (20 July). *25th Anniv of Coronation. Multicoloured cover as No. SB3 of Montserrat. Stapled.*
SB2	$8.90, booklet containing 5 c., 40 c., $1 and $3 (Nos. 130/3) in pairs		1·25

1979 (31 May). *Death Centenary of Sir Rowland Hill. Black, gold and red printed cover, 108×32 mm. Stapled.*
SB3	$7.60, booklet containing two 80 c. (Nos. 124, 152), two $1 (Nos. 125, 153) and two $2 (Nos. 126, 154), each value as a *se-tenant* pair taken from No. **MS**155		1·50

1980 (24 Apr). *"London 1980" International Stamp Exhibition. Black printed cover, 110×60 mm. Stapled.*
SB4	$15.60, booklet containing 40 c., 50 c. and $3 (Nos. 167/9), each in block of 4		2·25

1981 (26 Nov). *Royal Wedding. Multicoloured cover, 105×65 mm, showing* The Mary. *Stitched.*
SB5	$10 booklet containing eight 50 c. in panes of 4 (No. 202a) and two $3 in pane of 2 (No. 203a)		1·75

1986 (18 July). *Royal Wedding. Gold (No. SB6) or silver (No. SB7) on emerald covers, 152×80 mm. Stapled.*
SB6	$7.20, booklet (Westminster Abbey) containing twelve 60 c. (Nos. 481/2) in blocks of 4		2·50
SB7	$10.40, booklet (State Coach) containing 60 c. and $2 (Nos. 481/4, but imperforate) in blocks of 4		3·50

OFFICIAL STAMPS

1982 (11 Oct). *Nos. 195/200 optd with Type O 1 of St. Vincent.*

O1	50 c. *Mary*		10	15
	a. Sheetlet. No. O1 × 6 and No. O2		65	
	b. Opt double			
	c. Albino opt		3·00	
	d. Horiz pair, one without opt			
O2	50 c. Prince Charles and Lady Diana Spencer		30	35
	b. Opt double			
	c. Albino opt		7·50	
O3	$3 *Alexandra*		20	20
	a. Sheetlet. No. O3 × 6 and No. O4		1·75	
	b. Opt double		32·00	
	c. Albino opt		5·00	
O4	$3 Prince Charles and Lady Diana Spencer		65	70
	b. Opt double		£130	
	c. Albino opt		18·00	
O5	$3.50, *Britannia*		20	20
	a. Sheetlet. No. O5 × 6 and No. O6		1·75	
	c. Albino opt		6·00	
O6	$3.50, Prince Charles and Lady Diana Spencer		65	70
	c. Albino opt		20·00	
O1/6		*Set of 6*	1·75	2·00

Appendix

The following issues for individual islands in the Grenadines group fall outside the criteria for full listing as detailed on page xi of the General Catalogue Information in this edition.

BEQUIA

1984

Leaders of the World. Railway Locomotives (1st series). *Two designs for each value, the first showing technical drawings and the second the locomotive at work.* 1, 5, 10, 25, 35, 45 c., $1.50, $2, *each × 2*

Grenadines of St. Vincent 1982 *Ships definitives (Nos. 208/24) optd* "BEQUIA". 1, 3, 5, 6, 10, 15, 20, 25, 30, 50, 60, 75 c., $1, $2, $3, $5, $10

Leaders of the World. Automobiles (1st series). *Two designs for each value, the first showing technical drawings and the second the car in action.* 5, 40 c., $1, $1.50, *each × 2*

Leaders of the World. Olympic Games, Los Angeles. 1, 10, 60 c., $3, *each × 2*

Leaders of the World. Railway Locomotives (2nd series). *Two designs for each value, the first showing technical drawings and the second the locomotive at work.* 1, 5, 10, 35, 75 c., $1, $2.50, $3, *each × 2*

Leaders of the World. Automobiles (2nd series). *Two designs for each value, the first showing technical drawings and the second the car in action.* 5, 10, 20, 25, 75 c., $1, $2.50, $3, *each × 2*

1985

Leaders of the World. Railway Locomotives (3rd series). *Two designs for each value, the first showing technical drawings and the second the locomotive at work.* 25, 55, 60 c., $2, *each × 2*

Leaders of the World. Dogs. 25, 35, 55 c., $2, *each × 2*

Leaders of the World. Warships of the Second World War. Two designs for each value, the first showing technical drawings and the second the ship at sea. 15, 50 c., $1, $1.50, *each × 2*

Leaders of the World. Flowers. 10, 20, 70 c., $2.50, *each × 2*

Leaders of the World. Automobiles (3rd series). *Two designs for each value, the first showing technical drawings and the second the car in action.* 5, 25, 50 c., $1, $1.25, $2, *each × 2*

Leaders of the World. Railway Locomotives (4th series). *Two designs for each value, the first showing technical drawings and the second the locomotive at work.* 25, 55, 60, 75 c., $1, $2.50, *each × 2*

Leaders of the World. Life and Times of Queen Elizabeth the Queen Mother. Two designs for each value, showing different portraits. 20, 65 c., $1.35, $1.80, *each* × 2
Leaders of the World. Automobiles (4th series). Two designs for each value, the first showing technical drawings and the second the car in action. 20, 45 c., $1.50, $2, *each* × 2

1986

Leaders of the World. Automobiles (5th series). Two designs for each value, the first showing technical drawings and the second the car in action. 25, 50, 65, 75 c., $1, $3, *each* × 2
60th Birthday of Queen Elizabeth II. 5, 75 c., $2, $8
World Cup Football Championship, Mexico. 1, 2, 5, 10, 45, 60, 75 c., $1, $1.50, $2, $3.50, $6
Royal Wedding (1st issue). 60 c., $2, *each* × 2
Railway Engineers and Locomotives. $1, $2.50, $3, $4
Royal Wedding (2nd issue). Previous issue optd "Congratulations T.R.H. The Duke & Duchess of York". 60 c., $2, *each* × 2.
Automobiles (6th series). Two designs for each value, the first showing technical drawings and the second the car in action. 20, 60, 75, 90 c., $1, $3, *each* × 2

1987

Automobiles (7th series). Two designs for each value, the first showing technical drawings and the second the car in action. 5, 20, 35, 60, 75, 80 c., $1.25, $1.75, *each* × 2
Royal Ruby Wedding. 15, 75 c., $1, $2.50, $5
Railway Locomotives (5th series). Two designs for each value, the first showing technical drawings and the second the locomotive at work. 15, 25, 40, 50, 60, 75 c., $1, $2, *each* × 2

1988

Explorers. 15, 50 c., $1.75, $2, $2.50, $3, $3.50, $4
International Lawn Tennis Players. 15, 45, 80 c., $1.25, $1.75, $2, $2.50, $3

1989

"Philexfrance 89" International Stamp Exhibition, Paris. Walt Disney Cartoon Characters. 1, 2, 3, 4, 5, 10 c., $5, $6

1991

Centenary of Otto Lilienthal's Gliding Experiments. $5
50th Anniv of Japanese Attack on Pearl Harbor. 50 c., $1
Death Bicent of Mozart 10, 75 c., $4
50th Death Anniv of Lord Baden-Powell and World Scout Jamboree, Korea. 50 c, $1, $2, $3

1997

Diana, Princess of Wales Commemoration. $1

CANOUAN

1997

Diana, Princess of Wales Commemoration. $1

MUSTIQUE

1997

Diana, Princess of Wales Commemoration. $1

UNION ISLAND

1984

Leaders of the World. British Monarchs. Two designs for each value, forming a composite picture. 1, 5, 10, 20, 60 c., $3, *each* × 2
Leaders of the World. Railway Locomotives (1st series). Two designs for each value, the first showing technical drawings and the second the locomotive at work. 5, 60 c., $1, $2
Grenadines of St. Vincent 1982 Ships definitives (Nos. 208/24) optd "UNION ISLAND". 1, 3, 5, 6, 10, 15, 20, 25, 30, 50, 60, 75 c., $1, $2, $3, $5, $10
Leaders of the World. Cricketers. Two designs for each value, the first showing a portrait and the second the cricketer in action. 1, 10, 15, 55, 60, 75 c., $1.50, $3, *each* × 2
Leaders of the World. Railway Locomotives (2nd series). Two designs for each value, the first showing technical drawings and the second the locomotive at work. 5, 10, 20, 25, 75 c., $1, $2.50, $3, *each* × 2

1985

Leaders of the World. Automobiles (1st series). Two designs for each value, the first showing technical drawings and the second the car in action. 1, 50, 75 c., $2.50, *each* × 2
Leaders of the World. Birth Bicent of John J. Audubon (ornithologist). Birds. 15, 50 c., $1, $1.50, *each* × 2
Leaders of the World. Railway Locomotives (3rd series). Two designs for each value, the first showing technical drawings and the second the locomotive at work. 5, 50, 60 c., $2, *each* × 2
Leaders of the World. Butterflies. 15, 25, 75 c., $2, *each* × 2
Leaders of the World. Automobiles (2nd series). Two designs for each value, the first showing technical drawings and the second the car in action. 5, 60 c., $1, $1.50, *each* × 2
Leaders of the World. Automobiles (3rd series). Two designs for each value, the first showing technical drawings and the second the car in action. 10, 55, 60, 75, 90 c., $1, $1.50, $2, *each* × 2
Leaders of the World. Life and Times of Queen Elizabeth the Queen Mother. Two designs for each value, showing different portraits. 55, 70 c., $1.05, $1.70, *each* × 2

1986

Leaders of the World. Railway Locomotives (4th series). Two designs for each value, the first showing technical drawings and the second the locomotive at work. 15, 30, 45, 60, 75 c., $1.50, $2.50, $3, *each* × 2
60th Birthday of Queen Elizabeth II. 10, 60 c., $2, $8
World Cup Football Championship, Mexico. 1, 10, 30, 75 c., $1, $2.50, $3, $6
Royal Wedding (1st issue). 60 c., $2, *each* × 2
Automobiles (4th series). Two designs for each value, the first showing technical drawings and the second the car in action. 10, 60, 75 c., $1, $1.50, $3, *each* × 2
Royal Wedding (2nd issue). Previous issue optd as Bequia. 60 c., $2, *each* × 2

Railway Locomotives (5th series). Two designs for each value, the first showing technical drawings and the second the locomotive at work. 15, 45, 60, 75 c., $1, $1.50, $2, $3, *each* × 2

1987

Railway Locomotives (6th series). Two designs for each value, the first showing technical drawings and the second the locomotive at work. 15, 25, 40, 50, 60, 75 c., $1, $2, *each* × 2
Royal Ruby Wedding. 15, 45 c., $1.50, $3, $4
Railway Locomotives (7th series). Two designs for each value, the first showing technical drawings and the second the locomotive at work. 15, 20, 30, 45, 50, 75 c., $1, $1.50, *each* × 2

1989

"Philexfrance 89" International Stamp Exhibition, Paris. Walt Disney Cartoon Characters. 1, 2, 3, 4, 5, 10 c., $5, $6

1997

Diana, Princess of Wales Commemoration. $1

Samoa

INDEPENDENT KINGDOM OF SAMOA

The first postal service in Samoa was organised by C. L. Griffiths, who had earlier run the *Fiji Times* Express post in Suva. In both instances the principal purpose of the service was the distribution of newspapers of which Griffiths was the proprietor. The first issue of the *Samoa Times* (later the *Samoa Times and South Sea Gazette*) appeared on 6 October 1877 and the newspaper continued in weekly publication until 27 August 1881.

Mail from the Samoa Express post to addresses overseas was routed via New South Wales, New Zealand or U.S.A. and received additional franking with stamps of the receiving country on landing.

Cancellations, inscribed "APIA SAMOA", did not arrive until March 1878 so that examples of Nos. 1/9 used before that date were cancelled in manuscript.

1

A
2nd State (Nos. 4/9)

B
3rd State (Nos. 10/19)

(Des H. H. Glover. Litho S. T. Leigh & Co, Sydney, N.S.W.)

1877 (1 Oct)–80.

A. 1st state: *white line above "X" in "EXPRESS" not broken.*
P 12½

1	1	1d. ultramarine	..	£250	£120
2		3d. deep scarlet	..	£300	£130
3		6d. bright violet	..	£300	£110
		a. Pale lilac	..	£325	£110

B. 2nd state: *white line above "X" broken by a spot of colour, and dot between top of "M" and "O" of "SAMOA". P 12½ (1878–79)*

4	1	1d. ultramarine	..	90·00	95·00
5		3d. bright scarlet	..	£325	£130
6		6d. bright violet	..	£190	90·00
7		1s. dull yellow	..	£150	90·00
		a. Line above "X" not broken	£180	£120
		b. Perf 12 (1879)	80·00	95·00
		c. Orange-yellow	95·00	£100
8		2s. red-brown	..	£275	£200
		a. Chocolate	..	£300	£350
9		5s. green	..	£800	£1000
		a. Line above "X" not broken	£1000	£1200

C. 3rd state: *line above "X" repaired, dot merged with upper right serif of "M" (1879). (a) P 12½*

10	1	1d. ultramarine	..	90·00	90·00
11		3d. vermilion	..	£120	£120
12		6d. lilac	..	£120	85·00
13		2s. brown	..	£250	£250
		a. Chocolate	..	£250	£250
14		5s. green	..	£500	£500
		a. Line above "X" not repaired (R.2/3)	£650	

(b) P 12

15	1	1d. blue	..	24·00	40·00
		a. Deep blue	..	32·00	70·00
		b. Ultramarine	..	28·00	40·00
16		3d. vermilion	..	48·00	75·00
		a. Carmine-vermilion	48·00	85·00
17		6d. bright violet	..	40·00	48·00
		a. Deep violet	..	40·00	80·00
18		2s. deep brown	..	£150	£250
19		5s. yellow-green	..	£400	£600
		a. Deep green	..	£375	£550
		b. Line above "X" not repaired (R.2/3)	£500	

D. 4th state: *spot of colour under middle stroke of "M". P 12 (1880)*

20	1	9d. orange-brown	..	60·00	£120

Originals exist imperf, but are not known used in this state.

On sheets of the 1d., 1st state, at least eight stamps have a stop after "PENNY". In the 2nd state, three stamps have the stop, and in the 3rd state, only one.

In the 1st state, all the stamps, 1d., 3d. and 6d., were in sheets of 20 (5×4) and also the 1d. in the 3rd state.

All values in the 2nd state, all values except the 1d. in the 3rd state and No. 20 were in sheets of 10 (5×2).

As all sheets of all printings of the originals were imperf at the outer edges, the only stamps which can have perforations on all four sides are Nos. 1 to 3a, 10 and 15 to 15b, all other originals being imperf on one or two sides.

The perf 12 stamps, which gauge 11.8, are generally very rough but later the machine was repaired and the 1d., 3d. and 6d. are known with clean-cut perforations.

Remainders of the 1d., unissued 2d. rose, 6d. (in sheets of 21 (7×3), 3d., 9d., 1s. (in sheets of 12 (4×3)) and of the 2s. and 5s. (sheet format unknown) were found in the Samoan post office when the service closed down in 1881. The remainders are rare in complete sheets, but of very little value as singles, compared with the originals.

Reprints of all values, in sheets of 40 (8×5), were made after the originals had been withdrawn from sale. These are practically worthless.

The majority of both reprints and remainders are in the 4th state as the 9d. with the spot of colour under the middle stroke of the "M", but a few stamps (both remainders and reprints) do not show this, while on some it is very faint.

There are three known types of forgery, one of which is rather dangerous, the others being crude.

The last mail despatch organised by the proprietors of the Samoa Express took place on 31 August 1881, although one cover is recorded postmarked 24 September 1881.

After the withdrawal of the Samoa Express service it would appear that the Apia municipality appointed a postmaster to continue the overseas post. Covers are known franked with U.S.A. or New Zealand stamps in Samoa, or routed via Fiji.

In December 1886 the municipal postmaster, John Davis, was appointed Postmaster of the Kingdom of Samoa by King Malietoa. Overseas mail sent via New Zealand was subsequently accepted without the addition of New Zealand stamps, although letters to the U.S.A. continued to require such franking until August 1891.

2 Palm Trees

3 King Malietoa Laupepa

4a 6 mm

4b 7 mm

4c 4 mm

Description of Watermarks

(These are the same as W 12a/c of New Zealand)

W 4a. 6 mm between "N Z" and star; broad irregular star; comparatively wide "N"; "N Z" 11½ mm wide.

W 4b. 7 mm between "N Z" and star; narrower star; narrow "N"; "N Z" 10 mm wide.

W 4c. 4 mm between "N Z" and star; narrow star; wide "N"; "N Z" 11 mm wide.

(Des A. E. Cousins (T 3). Dies eng W. R. Bock and A. E. Cousins (T 2) or A. E. Cousins (T 3). Typo Govt Ptg Office, Wellington)

1886–1900. (i) W 4a. (a) P 12½ (Oct–Nov 1886).

21	2	½d. purple-brown	..	19·00	48·00
22		1d. yellow-green	..	7·50	12·00
23		2d. dull orange	..	22·00	9·50
24		4d. blue	..	38·00	9·50
25		1s. rose-carmine	..	65·00	9·00
		*a. Bisected (2½d.) (on cover)**	†	£325
26		2s. 6d. reddish lilac	..	55·00	70·00

(b) P 12×11½ (July–Nov 1887)

27	2	½d. purple-brown	..	70·00	80·00
28		1d. yellow-green	..	£100	23·00
29		2d. yellow	..	95·00	£140
30		4d. blue	..	£250	£200
31		6d. brown-lake	..	24·00	10·00
32		1s. rose-carmine	..	—	£190
33		2s. 6d. reddish lilac	..	£350	

(ii) W 4c. P 12×11½ (May 1890)

34	2	½d. purple-brown	..	75·00	26·00
35		1d. green	..	55·00	32·00
36		2d. brown-orange	..	80·00	38·00
37		4d. blue	..	£140	5·00
38		6d. brown-lake	..	£300	11·00
39		1s. rose-carmine	..	£350	13·00
		x. Wmk reversed	†	30·00
40		2s. 6d. reddish lilac	..	£400	8·50

(iii) W 4b. (a) P 12 × 11½ (1890–92)

41	2	½d. pale purple-brown	..	3·75	3·75
		a. Blackish purple	..	3·75	3·75
42		1d. myrtle-green (5.90)	..	22·00	1·40
		a. Green	..	22·00	1·40
		b. Yellow-green	22·00	1·40
43		2d. dull orange (5.90)	..	27·00	1·75
44	3	2½d. rose (11.92)	..	75·00	3·50
		a. Pale rose	..	75·00	3·50
45	2	4d. blue	..	£225	17·00
46		6d. brown-lake	..	£110	8·50
47		1s. rose-carmine	..	£225	5·00
48		2s. 6d. slate-lilac	..	—	7·50

(b) P 12½ (Mar 1891–92)

49	2	½d. purple-brown			
50		1d. green			
51		2d. orange-yellow	..	—	£160
52	3	2½d. rose (1.92)	..	22·00	4·50
53	2	4d. blue	..	—	£450
54		6d. brown-purple	..	£2500	£1100
55		1s. rose-carmine	..	—	£450
56		2s. 6d. slate-lilac			

(c) P 11 (May 1895–1900)

57	2	½d. purple-brown	..	2·00	1·75
		a. Deep purple-brown	..	1·50	1·75
		b. Blackish purple (1900)	1·75	35·00
58		1d. green	..	4·50	1·75
		a. Bluish green (1897)	..	4·50	1·75
		b. Deep green (1900)	2·00	22·00
59		2d. pale yellow	..	40·00	40·00
		a. Orange (1896)	..	40·00	40·00
		b. Bright yellow (1.97).	9·50	4·50
		c. Pale ochre (10.97)	4·50	1·25
		d. Dull orange (1900)	6·50	
60	3	2½d. rose	..	2·00	4·50
		a. Deep rose-carmine (1900)	1·75	42·00
61	2	4d. blue	..	8·00	5·00
		a. Deep blue (1900)	1·25	50·00
62		6d. brown-lake	..	8·00	3·00
		a. Brown-purple (1900)	1·75	60·00
63		1s. rose	..	8·00	3·75
		a. Dull rose-carmine/toned (5.98)	2·50	35·00
		b. Carmine (1900)	1·25	
64		2s. 6d. purple	..	55·00	10·00
		a. Reddish lilac (wmk inverted) (1897)	11·00	7·50
		b. Deep purple/toned (wmk reversed) (5.98)	4·75	9·50
		ba. Imperf between (vert pair)..	£350	
		c. Slate-violet	..	£120	

*Following a fire on 1 April 1895 which destroyed stocks of all stamps except the 1s. value perf 12½, this was bisected diagonally and used as a 2½d. stamp for overseas letters between 24 April and May 1895, and was cancelled in blue. Fresh supplies of the 2½d. did not arrive until July 1895, although other values were available from 23 May.

Examples of the 1s. rose perforated 11, No. 63, were subsequently bisected and supplied cancelled-to-order by the post office to collectors, often with backdated cancellations. Most of these examples were bisected vertically and all were cancelled in black (*Price £7*).

The dates given relate to the earliest dates of printing in the various watermarks and perforations and not to issue dates.

The perf 11 issues (including those later surcharged or overprinted), are very unevenly perforated owing to the large size of the pins. Evenly perforated copies are extremely hard to find.

For the 2½d. black, see Nos. 81/2 and for the ½d. green and 1d. red-brown, see Nos. 88/9.

FIVE PENCE	FIVE PENCE	**5d**
(5)	(6)	(7)

1893 (Nov–Dec). *Handstamped singly, at Apia.*

(a) In two operations

65	5	5d. on 4d. blue (37)	..	50·00	45·00
		a. Bars omitted	..	£500	£400
66		5d. on 4d. blue (45)	..	65·00	£100
67	6	5d. on 4d. blue (37)	..	95·00	£110
68		5d. on 4d. blue (45)	..	95·00	

(b) In three operations (Dec)

69	7	5d. on 4d. blue (37) (R.)	..	23·00	29·00
		a. Stop after "d"	..	£250	60·00
		b. Bars omitted	..	—	£400
70		5d. on 4d. blue (45) (R.)	..	26·00	50·00

In Types 5 and 6 the bars obliterating the original value vary in length from 13½ to 16½ mm and can occur with either the thick bar over the thin one or vice versa.

Double handstamps exist but we do not list them.
No. 69a came from a separate handstamp which applied the "5d."
at one operation. Where the "d" was applied separately its position
in relation to the "5" naturally varies.

Surcharged 1½d.   R 3d.

	(9)	(10)
8		

The "R" in Type **10** indicates use for registration fee.

(Des and die eng A. E. Cousins. Typo New Zealand Govt Ptg Office)

1894–1900. W **4**b (*sideways*). (a) P 11½ × 12.
| 71 | 8 | 5d. dull vermilion (3.94) | | | 28·00 | 2·75 |
| | | a. Dull red | | | 28·00 | 3·75 |

(b) P 11
| 72 | 8 | 5d. dull red (1895) | | | 17·00 | 7·00 |
| | | a. Deep red (1900) | | | 2·25 | 15·00 |

1895–1900. W **4**b.
(i) *Handstamped with* T **9** *or* **10**. (a) P 12 × 11½ (26.1.95)
| 73 | 2 | 1½d. on 2d. dull orange (B.) | | | 12·00 | 6·50 |
| 74 | | 3d. on 2d. dull orange | | | 38·00 | 9·50 |

(b) P 11 (6.95)
75	2	1½d. on 2d. orange (B.)			2·50	6·00
		a. Pair, one without handstamp				
		b. On 2d. yellow			75·00	60·00
76		3d. on 2d. orange			7·50	9·50
		a. On 2d. yellow			75·00	60·00

(ii) *Surch printed*. P* 11
| 77 | 2 | 1½d. on 2d. orange-yellow (B.) | | | £100 | |

(iii) *Handstamped as* T **9** *or* **10**.† *P* 11 (1896)
78	2	1½d. on 2d. orange-yellow (B.)			2·50	22·00
79		3d. on 2d. orange-yellow			3·75	45·00
		a. Imperf between (vert pair)			£400	
		b. Pair, one without handstamp				

(iv) *Surch typo as* T **10**. *P* 11 (Feb 1900)
| 80 | 2 | 3d. on 2d deep red-orange (G.) | | | 1·50 | £130 |

*It is believed that this was type-set from which clichés were
made and set up in a forme and then printed on a hand press. This
would account for the clear indentation on the back of the stamp
and the variation in the position on the stamps which probably
resulted from the clichés becoming loose in the forme.
†In No. 78 the "2" has a serif and the handstamp is in pale
greenish blue instead of deep blue. In No. 79 the "R" is slightly
narrower. In both instances the stamp is in a different shade.
A special printing in a distinctly different colour was made for
No. 80 and the surcharge is in green.
Most of the handstamps exist double.

1896 (Aug). *Printed in the wrong colour.* W **4**b. (a) P 10 × 11.
| 81 | 3 | 2½d. black | | | 1·50 | 3·00 |

(b) P 11
| 82 | 3 | 2½d. black | | | 50·00 | 65·00 |
| | | a. Mixed perfs 10 and 11 | | | £350 | |

Surcharged 2½d.   PROVISIONAL GOVT.

	(11)	(12)

1898–99. W **4**b. P 11. (a) *Handstamped as* T **11** (10.98).
| 83 | 2 | 2½d. on 1s. dull rose-carmine/toned | | | 40·00 | 48·00 |

(b) *Surch as* T **11** (1899)
84	2	2½d. on 1d. bluish green (R.)			75	2·75
		a. Surch inverted			—	£350
85		2½d. on 1s. dull rose-carmine/toned (R.)		6·50	13·00
		a. Surch double			£350	
86		2½d. on 1s. dull rose-carmine/toned (Blk.)		6·50	13·00
		a. Surch double			£450	
87		2½d. on 2s. deep purple/toned			7·00	15·00

The typographed surcharge was applied in a setting of nine,
giving seven types differing in the angle and length of the frac-
tional line, the type of stop, etc.

1899. *Colours changed.* W **4**b. P 11.
88	2	½d. dull blue-green			1·60	2·00
		a. Deep green			1·60	2·00
89		1d. deep red-brown			1·60	2·00

1899–1900. *Provisional Government. New printings optd with*
T **12** (*longer words and shorter letters on* 5d.). W **4**b. P 11.
90	2	½d. dull blue-green (R.)			1·00	2·75
		a. Yellowish green (1900)			1·25	3·75
91		1d. chestnut (B.)			2·25	5·50
92		2d. dull orange (R.)			2·00	6·00
		a. Orange-yellow (1900)			1·75	6·00
93		4d. deep dull blue (R.)			70	7·50
94	8	5d. dull vermilion (B.)			2·25	7·00
		a. Red (1900)			2·25	7·00
95	2	6d. brown-lake (B.)			1·25	6·50
96		1s. rose-carmine (B.)			1·50	20·00
97		2s. 6d. reddish purple (R.)			4·75	21·00
90/7				Set of 8	14·00	65·00

The Samoan group of islands was partitioned on 1 March 1900:
Western Samoa (Upolu, Savaii, Apolima and Manono) to
Germany and Eastern Samoa (Tutuila, the Manu'a Is and Rose
Is) to the United States. German issues of 1900–14 will be found
listed in Part 7 (*Germany*) of this catalogue, there were no U.S.
issues.
The Samoan Kingdom post office run by John Davis was
suspended in March 1900.

WESTERN SAMOA
NEW ZEALAND OCCUPATION

The German Islands of Samoa surrendered to the New Zealand
Expeditionary Force on 30 August 1914 and were administered by
New Zealand until 1962.

G.R.I.   G.R.I.   1d.   1 Shillings.

	(13)	(14)

SETTINGS. Nos. 101/9 were surcharged by a vertical setting of
ten, repeated ten times across the sheet. Nos. 110/14 were from a
horizontal setting of four repeated five times in the sheet.
Nos. 101b, 102a and 104a occurred on position 6. The error was
corrected during the printing of No. 102.
Nos. 101c, 102c, 104d and 105b are from position 10.
Nos. 101d, 102e and 104b are from position 1.
No. 108b is from position 9.

(Surch by *Samoanische Zeitung*, Apia)

1914 (3 Sept). *German Colonial issue* (*ship*) (*no wmk*) *inscr*
"SAMOA" *surch as* T **13** *or* **14** (*mark values*).
101		½d. on 3 pf. brown			26·00	9·00
		a. Surch double			£650	£500
		b. No fraction bar			55·00	30·00
		c. Comma after "I"			£600	£400
		d. "1" to left of "2" in "½"			55·00	30·00
102		½d. on 5 pf. green			48·00	9·00
		a. No fraction bar			£120	55·00
		c. Comma after "I"			£350	£170
		d. Surch double			£650	£500
		e. "1" to left of "2" in "½"			£100	40·00
103		1d. on 10 pf. carmine			95·00	40·00
		a. Surch double			£650	£500
104		2½d. on 20 pf. ultramarine			35·00	10·00
		b. "1" to left of "2" in "½"			75·00	38·00
		c. Surch inverted			£800	£750
		d. Comma after "I"			£450	£325
		e. Surch double			£650	£550
105		3d. on 25 pf. black and red/yellow			55·00	40·00
		a. Surch double			£750	£600
		b. Comma after "I"			£4750	£1000
106		4d. on 30 pf. black and orange/buff			£110	60·00
107		5d. on 40 pf. black and carmine.			£110	70·00
108		6d. on 50 pf. black and purple/buff			60·00	35·00
		a. Surch double			£850	£800
		b. Inverted "9" for "6"			£170	£100
109		9d. on 80 pf. black and carmine/rose			£200	£100
110		"1 shillings" on 1 m. carmine			£3250	£3500
111		"1 shilling" on 1 m. carmine			£9500	£7000
112		2s. on 2 m. blue			£3000	£2750
113		3s. on 3 m. violet-black			£1400	£1200
		a. Surch double			£8000	£9000
114		5s. on 5 m. carmine and black			£1100	£1000
		a. Surch double			£11000	£11000

No. 108b is distinguishable from 108, as the "d" and the "9" are
not in a line, and the upper loop of the "9" turns downwards to the
left.

UNAUTHORISED SURCHARGES. Examples of the 2d. on
20 pf., 3d. on 30 pf., 3d. on 40 pf., 4d. on 40 pf., 6d. on 80 pf., 2s. on
3 m. and 2s. on Marshall Islands 2 m., together with a number of
errors not listed above, were produced by the printer on stamps
supplied by local collectors. These were not authorised by the New
Zealand Military Administration.

SAMOA.

(15)

1914 (29 Sept)–**15**. *Stamps of New Zealand.* T **50**, **51**, **52** *and*
27, *optd as* T **15**, *but opt only* 14 *mm long on all except* 2½d.
Wmk "N Z" *and Star,* W **43** *of New Zealand.*
115		½d. yellow-green (R.) (p 14×15)			60	30
116		1d. carmine (B.) (p 14×15)			60	10
117		2d. mauve (R.) (p 14×14½) (10.14)			75	95
118		2½d. deep blue (R.) (p 14) (10.14)			1·50	1·75
		w. Wmk inverted				
119		6d. carmine (B.) (p 14×14½) (10.14)			1·50	1·75
		a. Perf 14×13½			17·00	21·00
		b. Vert pair. Nos. 119/a (1915)			45·00	50·00
120		6d. pale carmine (B.) (p 14×14½) (10.14)		10·00	10·00
121		1s. vermilion (B.) (p 14×14½) (10.14)		4·50	16·00
115/21				Set of 6	8·50	19·00

1914–24. *Postal Fiscal stamps as Type* F **4** *of New Zealand optd*
with T **15**. W **43** *of New Zealand* (*sideways*). *Chalk-surfaced*
"De La Rue" *paper.*
(a) P 14 (Nov 1914–17)
122		2s. blue (R.) (9.17)			85·00	£100
123		2s. 6d. grey-brown (B.) (9.17)			5·50	8·50
124		5s. yellow-green (R.)			12·00	11·00
125		10s. maroon (B.)			22·00	28·00
126		£1 rose-carmine (R.)			60·00	45·00

(b) P 14½×14, comb (1917–24)
127		2s. deep blue (R.) (3.18)			5·50	5·50
128		2s. 6d. grey-brown (B.) (10.24)			£200	£140
129		3s. purple (R.) (6.23)			15·00	42·00
130		5s. yellow-green (R.) (9.17)			15·00	15·00
131		10s. maroon (B.) (11.17)			50·00	45·00
132		£1 rose-carmine (B.) (3.18)			60·00	70·00

We no longer list the £2 value as it is doubtful if this was used for
postal purposes.
See also Nos. 165/6e.

1916–19. *King George V stamps of New Zealand optd as* T **15**,
but 14 *mm long.* (a) *Typo.* P 14×15.
134	61	½d. yellow-green (R.)			50	90
135		1½d. slate (1917)			40	25
136		1½d. orange-brown (R.) (1919)			30	40
137		2d. yellow (R.) (14.2.18)			1·25	20
138		3d. chocolate (B.) (1919)			1·25	14·00

(b) Recess. P 14×13½
139	60	2½d. blue (R.)			55	35
		a. Perf 14×14½			1·00	60
		b. Vert pair. Nos. 139/a			15·00	23·00
140		3d. chocolate (B.) (1917)			50	50
		a. Perf 14×14½			50	90
		b. Vert pair. Nos. 140/a			15·00	26·00
141		6d. carmine (B.) (5.5.17)			1·50	3·25
		a. Perf 14×14½			1·50	90
		b. Vert pair. Nos. 141/a			17·00	30·00
142		1s. vermilion (B.)			1·75	1·50
		a. Perf 14×14½			4·50	9·00
		b. Vert pair. Nos. 142/a			22·00	42·00
134/42				Set of 9	7·25	17·00

LEAGUE OF NATIONS MANDATE

Administered by New Zealand.

1920 (July). *Victory. Nos.* 453/8 *of New Zealand optd as* T **15**,
but 14 *mm long.*
143		½d. green (R.)			3·00	6·00
144		1d. carmine (B.)			2·50	6·00
145		1½d. brown-orange (R.)			1·50	7·00
146		3d. chocolate (B.)			7·50	9·00
147		6d. violet (R.)			4·00	6·50
148		1s. orange-red (B.)			13·00	11·00
143/8				Set of 6	28·00	40·00

SILVER JUBILEE OF KING GEORGE V 1910–1935.

16 Native Hut	(17)

(Eng B.W. Recess-printed at Wellington, N.Z.)

1921 (23 Dec). W **43** *of New Zealand.* (a) P 14×14½.
149	16	½d. green			1·60	5·50
150		1d. lake			2·75	30
151		1½d. chestnut			70	9·00
152		2d. yellow			2·25	2·00
149/52				Set of 4	6·50	15·00

(b) P 14 × 13½
153	16	½d. green			4·00	1·75
154		1d. lake			4·50	20
155		1½d. chestnut			9·00	8·50
156		2d. yellow			10·00	70
157		2½d. grey-blue			1·75	7·00
158		3d. sepia			1·75	4·00
159		4d. violet			1·75	3·00
160		5d. light blue			1·75	6·00
161		6d. bright carmine			1·75	5·00
162		8d. red-brown			1·75	9·00
163		9d. olive-green			2·00	22·00
164		1s. vermilion			1·75	22·00
153/64				Set of 12	38·00	80·00

1925–28. *Postal Fiscal stamps as Type* F **4** *of New Zealand*
optd with T **15**. W **43** *of New Zealand* (*sideways*). P 14½×14.
(a) *Thick, opaque, white chalk-surfaced* "Cowan" *paper.*
165		2s. blue (R.) (12.25)			£130	£150
166		2s. 6d. deep grey-brown (B.) (10.28)		70·00	90·00
166a		3s. mauve (9.25)			55·00	65·00
166b		5s. yellow-green (R.) (11.26)			15·00	35·00
		ba. Opt at top of stamp			£1100	
166c		10s. brown-red (B.) (12.25)			£120	85·00
166d		£1 rose-pink (B.) (11.26)			60·00	75·00
165/6d				Set of 6	£400	£450

(b) *Thin, hard, chalk-surfaced* "Wiggins Teape" *paper.*
| 166e | | £1 rose-pink (B.) (1928) | | | — | £850 |

1926–27. T **72** *of New Zealand, optd with* T **15**, *in red.*
(a) "Jones" *paper*
167		2s. deep blue (11.26)			4·50	16·00
168		3s. mauve (10.26)			11·00	40·00
		w. Wmk inverted			11·00	40·00

(b) "Cowan" *paper*
| 169 | | 2s. light blue (10.11.27) | | | 6·00 | 45·00 |
| 170 | | 3s. pale mauve (10.11.27) | | | 48·00 | 95·00 |

1932 (Aug). *Postal Fiscal stamps as Type* F **6** *of New Zealand optd*
with T **15**. W **43** *of New Zealand. Thick, opaque, white*
chalk-surfaced "Cowan" *paper.* P 14.
171		2s. 6d. deep brown (B.)			16·00	40·00
172		5s. green (R.)			25·00	42·00
173		10s. carmine-lake (B.)			45·00	90·00
174		£1 pink (B.)			60·00	£120
175		£2 bright purple (R.)			£650	
176		£5 indigo-blue (R.)			£1700	

The £2 and £5 values were primarily for fiscal use.

1935 (7 May). *Silver Jubilee. Optd with* T **17**. P 14×13½.
177	16	1d. lake			30	30
		a. Perf 14 × 14½			85·00	£150
178		2½d. grey-blue			60	65
179		6d. bright carmine			2·75	2·50
177/9				Set of 3	3·25	3·00

18 Samoan Girl

19 Apia

21 Chief and Wife

25 Lake Lanuto'o

(Recess D.L.R.)

1935 (7 Aug). *T* 18/19, 21, 25 *and similar designs. W* 43 *of New Zealand ("N Z" and Star). P* 14×13½ (½d., 2½d., 2s., 3s.), 14 (2d.) *or* 13½×14 (*others*).

180	½d. green	..	..	..	10	35
181	1d. black and carmine	..	..	10	10
182	2d. black and orange	..	..	3·50	3·25
	aw. Wmk inverted	..	..		
	b. Perf 13½×14	..	..	4·00	4·25
183	2½d. black and blue	..	..	10	10
184	4d. slate and sepia	..	..	60	15
185	6d. bright magenta	..	..	40	10
186	1s. violet and brown	..	..	30	10
187	2s. green and purple-brown	..	80	50
188	3s. blue and brown-orange	..	1·50	3·50
180/8	..	..	..	*Set of* 9	6·50	7·00

Designs: *Horiz*—2d. River scene; 4d. Canoe and house; 6d. R. L. Stevenson's home "Vailima"; 1s. Stevenson's Tomb. *Vert (as T* 25)—3s. Falefa Falls.
See also Nos. 200/3.

WESTERN SAMOA.
(27)

1935–42. *Postal Fiscal stamps as Type* F 6 *of New Zealand optd with T* 27. *W* 43 *of New Zealand. P* 14.

(*a*) *Thick, opaque chalk-surfaced "Cowan" paper* (7.8.35)

189	2s. 6d. deep brown (B.)	..	..	6·00	16·00
190	5s. green (B.)	..	..	11·00	20·00
191	10s. carmine-lake (B.)	..	..	45·00	60·00
192	£1 pink (B.)	..	..	60·00	95·00
193	£2 bright purple (R.)	..	..	£140	£300
194	£5 indigo-blue (R.)	..	..	£250	£550

(*b*) *Thin, hard chalk-surfaced "Wiggins, Teape" paper* (1941–42)

194a	5s. green (B.) (6.42)	..	80·00	90·00
194b	10s. pale carmine-lake (B.) (6.41)	..	£130	£130
194c	£2 bright purple (R.) (2.42)	..	£500	£700
194d	£5 indigo-blue (R.) (2.42)	..	£850	£1000

The £2 and £5 values were primarily for fiscal use.
See also Nos. 207/14.

28 Coastal Scene

31 Robert Louis Stevenson

(Des J. Berry (1d. and 1½d.). L. C. Mitchell (2½d. and 7d.). Recess B.W.)

1939 (29 Aug). 25*th Anniv of New Zealand Control. T* 28, 31 *and similar horiz designs. W* 98 *of New Zealand. P* 13½ × 14 *or* 14 × 13½ (7d.).

195	1d. olive-green and scarlet ..	..	30	10
196	1½d. light blue and red-brown	..	45	30
197	2½d. red-brown and blue	..	90	65
198	7d. violet and slate-green	..	6·50	2·75
195/8	..	..	*Set of* 4	7·50	3·25

Designs:—1½d. Map of Western Samoa; 2½d. Samoan dancing party.

32 Samoan Chief

33 Apia Post Office

(Recess B.W.)

1940 (2 Sept). *W* 98 *of New Zealand (Mult "N Z" and Star). P* 14 × 13½.

199	**32**	3d. on 1½d. brown	..	20	10

T 32 was not issued without surcharge.

(T 33. Des L. C. Mitchell. Recess B.W.)

1944–49. *As Nos.* 180, 182/3 *and T* 33. *W* 98 *of New Zealand (Mult "N Z" and Star) (sideways on* 2½d.). *P* 14 *or* 13½ × 14 (5d.).

200	½d. green	..	..	30	14·00
202	2d. black and orange	..	2·50	5·50
203	2½d. black and blue (1948)	..	4·25	24·00
205	5d. sepia and blue (8.6.49)	..	1·00	50
200/5	..	..	*Set of* 4	7·25	40·00

1945–53. *Postal Fiscal stamps as Type* F 6 *of New Zealand optd with T* 27. *W* 98 *of New Zealand. Thin hard, chalk-surfaced "Wiggins Teape" paper. P* 14.

207	2s. 6d. deep brown (B.) (6.45)	..	5·00	13·00
	w. Wmk inverted	..		6·50	10·00
208	5s. green (B.) (5.45)	..	12·00	12·00
	w. Wmk inverted	..		13·00	13·00
209	10s. carmine-lake (B.) (4.46)	..	20·00	17·00
	w. Wmk inverted	..		26·00	27·00
210	£1 pink (B.) (6.48)	..	90·00	£160
211	30s. brown (8.48)	..	£150	£300
	w. Wmk inverted	..		£275	£400
212	£2 bright purple (R.) (11.47)	..	£150	£275
	w. Wmk inverted	..		£200	£300
213	£3 green (8.48)	..	£180	£375
	w. Wmk inverted	..		£300	£475
214	£5 indigo-blue (R.) (1946)	..	£325	£450
	w. Wmk inverted (5.53)	..		£325	£450
207/10	..	..	*Set of* 4	£110	£180

The £2 to £5 values were mainly used for fiscal purposes. See also Nos. 232/5.

WESTERN SAMOA
(34)

1946 (4 June). *Peace Issue. Nos.* 668, 670 *and* 674/5 *of New Zealand optd with T* 34 (*reading up and down at sides on* 2d.).

215	1d. green (B.)	..	10	10
	w. Wmk inverted	..		£130
216	2d. purple (B.)	..	10	10
217	6d. chocolate and vermilion	..	20	10
218	8d. black and carmine (B.)	..	20	10
215/18	..	*Set of* 4	50	30

UNITED NATIONS TRUST TERRITORY
Administered by New Zealand.

35 Making Siapo Cloth

42 Thatching a Native Hut

43 Preparing Copra

44 Samoan Chieftainess

(Recess B.W.)

1952 (10 Mar). *T* 35, 42/4 *and similar designs. W* 98 *of New Zealand (sideways on* 1s. *and* 3s.). *P* 13 (½d., 2d., 5d. *and* 1s.) *or* 13½ (*others*).

219	½d. claret and orange-brown..	..	10	1·75
220	1d. olive-green and green	..	10	20
221	2d. carmine-red	..	10	10
222	3d. pale ultramarine and indigo	..	40	10
223	5d. brown and deep green	..	5·50	70
224	6d. pale ultramarine and rose-magenta	75	10
225	8d. carmine	..	30	30
226	1s. sepia and blue	..	15	10
227	2s. yellow-brown	..	1·00	40
228	3s. chocolate and brown-olive	..	3·00	3·00
219/28	..	*Set of* 10	9·50	6·00

Designs: *Horiz (as T* 43)—1d. Native houses and flags; 3d. Malifa Falls (wrongly inscribed "Aleisa Falls"); 6d. Bonito fishing canoe; 8d. Cacao harvesting. *Vert (as T* 35)—2d. Seal of Samoa; 5d. Tooth-billed Pigeon.

1953 (25 May). *Coronation. Designs as Nos.* 715 *and* 717 *of New Zealand, but inscr* "WESTERN SAMOA".

229	2d. brown	..	..	1·00	15
230	6d. slate-grey	..	..	1·00	35

WESTERN
SAMOA
(45)

1955 (14 Nov). *Postal Fiscal stamps as Type* F 6 *of New Zealand optd with T* 45. *W* 98. *Chalk-surfaced "Wiggins, Teape" paper. P* 14.

232	5s. green (B.)..	..	9·00	21·00
233	10s. carmine-lake (B.)	..	9·00	28·00
234	£1 pink (B.)	..	16·00	38·00
235	£2 bright purple (R.)	..	85·00	£150
232/5	..	*Set of* 4	£110	£200

The £2 value was mainly used for fiscal purposes.

46 Native Houses and Flags

47 Seal of Samoa

(Recess B.W.)

1958 (21 Mar). *Inauguration of Samoan Parliament. T* 46/7 *and similar horiz design. W* 98 *of New Zealand (sideways). P* 13½ × 13 (6d.) *or* 13½ (*others*).

236	4d. cerise	..	15	20
237	6d. deep reddish violet	..	15	20
238	1s. deep ultramarine	..	90	40
236/8	..	*Set of* 3	1·10	70

Design:—1s. Map of Samoa, and the Mace.

INDEPENDENT

Samoa became independent on 1 January 1962.

49 Samoan Fine Mat

50 Samoa College

(Litho B.W.)

1962 (2 July). *Independence. T* 49/50 *and similar designs. W* 98 *of New Zealand (sideways on horiz stamps). P* 13½.

239	1d. brown and rose-carmine	..	10	10
240	2d. brown, green, yellow and red	..	10	10
241	3d. brown, blue-green and blue	..	10	10
242	4d. magenta, yellow, blue and black	..	15	20
243	6d. yellow and blue	..	80	20
244	8d. bluish green, yellow-green and blue	..	80	10
245	1s. brown and bluish green	..	20	10
246	1s. 3d. yellow-green and blue	..	1·25	45
247	2s. 6d. red and ultramarine	..	2·75	2·25
248	5s. ultramarine, yellow, red and drab	..	3·50	3·75
239/48	..	*Set of* 10	8·50	6·50

Designs: *Horiz*—3d. Public library; 4d. Fono House; 6d. Map of Samoa; 8d. Airport; 1s. 3d. "Vailima"; 2s. 6d. Samoan flag; 5s. Samoan seal. *Vert*—1s. Samoan orator.
See Nos. 257/62.

59 Seal and Joint Heads of State

60 Signing the Treaty

(Des L. C. Mitchell. Photo Harrison)

1963 (1 Oct). *First Anniv of Independence. W* 98 *of New Zealand. P* 14.

249	**59**	1d. deep sepia and green	..	10	10
250		4d. deep sepia and blue..	..	10	10
251		8d. deep sepia and rose-pink	..	10	10
252		2s. deep sepia and orange	..	20	15
249/52		..	*Set of* 4	35	30

(Des L. C. Mitchell. Photo Enschedé)

1964 (1 Sept). 2*nd Anniv of New Zealand–Samoa Treaty of Friendship. P* 13½.

253	**60**	1d. multicoloured	..	10	10
254		8d. multicoloured	..	10	10
255		2s. multicoloured	..	20	10
256		3s. multicoloured	..	20	30
253/6		..	*Set of* 4	40	45

61 Kava Bowl

1965 (4 Oct)–**66**? *As Nos. 239, 241/5, but* W **61** (*sideways on horiz designs*).
257	1d. brown and rose-carmine ..	..	20	60
258	3d. brown, blue-green and blue (1966?)	..	27·00	3·75
259	4d. magenta, yellow, blue and black	..	25	60
260	6d. yellow and blue	..	75	50
261	8d. bluish green, yellow-green and blue	..	30	10
262	1s. brown and bluish green	..	25	60
257/62	.. ..	Set of 6	27·00	5·50

62 Red-tailed Tropic Bird

63 Flyingfish

(Des L. C. Mitchell. Photo Harrison.)

1965 (29 Dec). *Air.* W **61** (*sideways*). *P* 14½.
263	62	8d. black, red-orange and blue	..	50	10
264	63	2s. black and blue	..	75	20

64 Aerial View of Deep Sea Wharf

(Des Tecon Co (U.S.A.). Photo Enschedé.)

1966 (3 Mar). *Opening of First Deep Sea Wharf, Apia. T* **64** *and similar horiz design. Multicoloured.* W **61** (*sideways*). *P* 13½.
265	1d. Type 64	..	10	10
266	8d. Aerial view of wharf and bay	..	15	10
267	2s. As 8d.	..	25	25
268	3s. Type 64	..	30	35
265/8	.. .. ..	Set of 4	70	65

66 W.H.O. Building

(Des M. Goaman. Photo D.L.R.)

1966 (4 July). *Inauguration of W.H.O. Headquarters, Geneva. T* **66** *and similar horiz design.* W **61** (*sideways**). *P* 14.
269	3d. yellow-ochre, blue and light slate-lilac		35	10
270	4d. blue, yellow, green & light orange-brown		40	15
271	6d. reddish lilac, emerald and yellow-olive		45	20
	w. Wmk legs to left		1·75	
272	1s. blue, yellow, green and turquoise-green		80	25
269/72	.. .. ..	Set of 4	1·75	60

Designs:—3d., 6d. Type 66; 4d., 1s. W.H.O. Building on flag.
*The normal sideways watermark has the legs of the bowl pointing to the right, *as seen from the back of the stamp.*

HURRICANE RELIEF

6^d

(68)

1966 (1 Sept). *Hurricane Relief Fund. No. 261 surch with T* **68** *by Bradbury, Wilkinson.*
273	8d. + 6d. bluish green, yellow-green and blue		10	10

69 Hon. Tuatagaloa L. S. (Minister of Justice)

(Des and photo Harrison)

1967 (16 Jan). *Fifth Anniv of Independence. T* **69** *and similar horiz designs.* W **61** (*sideways*). *P* 14½ × 14.
274	3d. sepia and bluish violet	..	10	10
275	8d. sepia and light new blue..	..	10	10
276	2s. sepia and olive	..	10	10
277	3s. sepia and magenta	..	15	15
274/7	..	Set of 4	30	30

Designs:—8d. Hon. F. C. F. Nelson (minister of Works, Marine and Civil Aviation); 2s. Hon. To'omata T. L. (minister of Lands); Hon. Fa'alava'au G. (minister of Post Office, Radio and Broadcasting).

73 Samoan Fales (houses), 1890

(Des V. Whiteley. Photo Harrison)

1967 (16 May). *Centenary of Mulinu'u as Seat of Government. T* **73** *and similar horiz design. Multicoloured.* W **61**. *P* 14½ × 14.
278	8d. Type 73	..	15	10
279	1s. Fono (Parliament) House, 1967 ..		15	10

(New Currency. 100 sene or cents=1 tala or dollar)

75 Carunculated Honeyeater

76 Black-breasted Honeyeater

(Des V. Whiteley. Litho Format ($2, $4). Photo Harrison (others))

1967 (10 July)–**69**. *Decimal currency. Multicoloured designs as T* **75** (1 s. to $1) *or* **76** ($2, $4). W **61** (*sideways*). *P* 13½ ($2, $4) or 14 × 14½ (others).
280	1 s. Type 75	..	10	10
281	2 s. Pacific Pigeon	..	10	10
282	3 s. Samoan Starling	..	10	10
283	5 s. White-vented Flycatcher	..	10	10
284	7 s. Red-headed Parrot Finch	..	10	10
285	10 s. Purple Swamphen	..	15	10
286	20 s. Barn Owl	..	1·60	40
287	25 s. Tooth-billed Pigeon	..	50	15
288	50 s. Island Thrush	..	50	30
289	$1 Samoan Fantail	..	75	1·75
289a	$2 Type 76 (14.7.69)	..	3·50	7·00
289b	$4 Savaii White Eye (6.10.69)	..	45·00	45·00
280/9b	..	Set of 12	48·00	48·00

85 Nurse and Child

(Des G. Vasarhelyi. Photo D.L.R.)

1967 (1 Dec). *South Pacific Health Service. T* **85** *and similar horiz designs. Multicoloured. P* 14.
290	3 s. Type 85	..	15	15
291	7 s. Leprosarium	..	20	15
292	20 s. Mobile X-ray Unit	..	35	30
293	25 s. Apia Hospital	..	40	35
290/3	.. ..	Set of 4	1·00	85

PRICES OF SETS

Set prices are given for many issues, generally those containing three stamps or more. Definitive sets include one of each value or major colour change, but do not cover different perforations, die types or minor shades. Where a choice is possible the set prices are based on the cheapest versions of the stamps included in the listings.

---

89 Thomas Trood

93 Cocoa

(Des M. Farrar-Bell. Litho B.W.)

1968 (15 Jan). *6th Anniv of Independence. T* **89** *and similar horiz designs. Multicoloured. P* 13½.
294	2 s. Type 89	..	10	10
295	7 s. Dr. Wilhelm Solf	..	10	10
296	20 s. J. C. Williams	..	10	10
297	25 s. Fritz Marquardt	..	15	15
294/7	..	Set of 4	30	30

(Des Jennifer Toombs. Photo Enschedé)

1968 (15 Feb). *Agricultural Development. T* **93** *and similar vert designs.* W **61**. *P* 13 × 12½.
298	3 s. deep red-brown, yellow-green and black		10	10
299	5 s. myrtle-green, greenish yellow & lt brn	..	10	10
300	10 s. scarlet, blackish brown and olive-yellow		10	10
301	20 s. yellow-bistre, yellow and blackish olive..		15	15
298/301		Set of 4	50	30

Designs:—5 s. Breadfruit; 10 s. Copra; 20 s. Bananas.

97 Women weaving Mats

(Des G. Vasarhelyi. Photo Harrison)

1968 (22 Apr). *21st Anniv of the South Pacific Commission. T* **97** *and similar horiz designs. Multicoloured.* W **61**. *P* 14½ × 14.
302	7 s. Type 97	..	10	10
303	20 s. Palm trees and bay	..	15	10
304	25 s. Sheltered cove	..	15	15
302/4	..	Set of 3	30	30

1928-1968
KINGSFORD-SMITH
TRANSPACIFIC FLIGHT

20 SENE ≡

(100)

1968 (13 June). *40th Anniv of Kingsford Smith's Trans-Pacific Flight. No. 285 surch with T* **100**.
305	20 s. on 10 s. Purple Swamphen	..	10	10

101 Bougainville's Route

(Des Jennifer Toombs. Litho B.W.)

1968 (17 June). *Bicentenary of Bougainville's Visit to Samoa. T* **101** *and similar horiz designs.* W **61** (*sideways*). *P* 14.
306	3 s. new blue and black	..	10	15
307	7 s. light ochre and black	..	15	15
308	20 s. multicoloured	..	45	25
309	25 s. multicoloured	..	60	35
306/9	..	Set of 4	1·10	80

Designs:—7 s. Louis de Bougainville; 20 s. Bougainvillea flower; 25 s. Ships *La Boudeuse* and *L'Etoile*.

105 Globe and Human Rights Emblem

106 Dr. Martin Luther King

(Des G. Vasarhelyi. Photo Harrison)

1968 (26 Aug). *Human Rights Year.* W **61**. P 14.

310	**105**	7 s. greenish blue, brown and gold			10	10
311		20 s. orange, green and gold			10	15
312		25 s. violet, green and gold	..	..	15	15
310/12		..	..	*Set of 3*	30	30

(Des and litho D.L.R.)

1968 (23 Sept). *Martin Luther King Commemoration.* W **61**. P 14½ × 14.

313	**106**	7 s. black and olive-green	..	..	15	10
314		20 s. black and bright purple		..	15	10

107 Polynesian Version of Madonna and Child **108** Frangipani—*Plumeria acuminata*

(Des and litho D.L.R.)

1968 (14 Oct). *Christmas.* W **61**. P 14.

315	**107**	1 s. multicoloured		..	..	10	10
316		3 s. multicoloured		..	..	10	10
317		20 s. multicoloured		..	..	10	10
318		30 s. multicoloured		..	..	15	15
315/18					*Set of 4*	30	30

(Des J.W. Litho Format)

1969 (20 Jan). *Seventh Anniv of Independence.* T **108** *and similar multicoloured designs.* P 14½.

319	**108**	2 s. Type **108**			10	10
320		7 s. Hibiscus (*vert*)			15	10
321		20 s. Red-Ginger (*vert*)	..		25	10
322		30 s. "Moso'oi"	..	..	35	80
319/22				*Set of 4*	70	1·00

109 R. L. Stevenson and *Treasure Island* **110** Weightlifting

(Des Jennifer Toombs. Litho D.L.R.)

1969 (21 Apr). *75th Death Anniv of Robert Louis Stevenson. Horiz designs, each showing portrait as in T **109**. Multicoloured.* W **61** (*sideways*). P 14.

323		3 s. Type **109**	..		15	10
324		7 s. *Kidnapped*			15	10
325		20 s. *Dr. Jekyll and Mr. Hyde*	..	..	25	50
326		22 s. *Weir of Hermiston*	..	..	25	50
323/6				*Set of 4*	70	1·00

(Des J. Mason. Photo Note Ptg Branch, Reserve Bank of Australia)

1969 (21 July). *Third South Pacific Games, Port Moresby.* T **110** *and similar vert designs.* P 13½.

327		3 s. black and sage-green			10	10
328		20 s. black and light blue	..		10	10
329		22 s. black and dull orange	..	..	15	15
327/9				*Set of 3*	30	30

Designs:—20 s. Yachting; 22 s. Boxing.

113 U.S. Astronaut on the Moon and the Splashdown near Samoan Islands

(Des J. Mason. Photo Note Ptg Branch, Reserve Bank of Australia)

1969 (24 July). *First Man on the Moon.* P 13½.

330	**113**	7 s. multicoloured			15	15
331		20 s. multicoloured			15	15

114 "Virgin with Child" (Murillo)

(Des and photo Heraclio Fournier)

1969 (13 Oct). *Christmas.* T **114** *and similar vert designs. Multicoloured.* P 14.

332		1 s. Type **114**			10	10
333		3 s. "The Holy Family" (El Greco)	..		10	10
334		20 s. "The Nativity" (El Greco)			35	10
335		30 s. "The Adoration of the Magi" (detail, Velazquez)			40	15
332/5				*Set of 4*	70	30
MS336		116 × 126 mm. Nos. 332/5		..	75	1·25

115 Seventh Day Adventists' Sanatorium, Apia

(Des V. Whiteley. Litho Format)

1970 (19 Jan). *Eighth Anniv of Independence.* T **115** *and similar designs.* W **61** (*sideways on 2, 7 and 22 s.*). P 14.

337		2 s. yellow-brown, pale slate and black		10	10
338		7 s. violet, buff and black	..	10	10
339		20 s. rose, lilac and black	..	15	10
340		22 s. olive-green, cinnamon and black		15	15
337/40			*Set of 4*	30	30

Designs: *Horiz*—7 s. Rev. Father Violette and Roman Catholic Cathedral, Apia; 22 s. John Williams, 1797–1839, and London Missionary Society Church, Sapapali'l. *Vert*—20 s. Mormon Church of Latter Day Saints, Tuasivi-on-Safotulafai.

119 Wreck of *Adler* (German steam gunboat)

(Des J.W. Litho Questa)

1970 (27 Apr). *Great Apia Hurricane of 1889.* T **119** *and similar horiz designs. Multicoloured.* W **61** (*sideways*). P 13½.

341		5 s. Type **119**			30	10
342		7 s. U.S.S. *Nipsic* (steam sloop)			30	10
343		10 s. H.M.S. *Calliope* (screw corvette)			40	25
344		20 s. Apia after the hurricane			70	75
341/4				*Set of 4*	1·50	1·10

120 Sir Gordon Taylor's Short S.25 Sandringham 7 Flying Boat *Frigate Bird III*

(Des R. Honisett. Photo Note Ptg Branch, Reserve Bank of Australia)

1970 (27 July). *Air. Aircraft.* T **120** *and similar horiz designs. Multicoloured.* P 13½ × 13.

345		3 s. Type **120**		..	45	10
346		7 s. Polynesian Airlines Douglas DC-3			70	10
347		20 s. Pan-American Sikorsky S-42A flying boat *Samoan Clipper*			1·50	60
348		30 s. Air Samoa Britten Norman Islander			1·50	1·75
		a. Pale purple omitted			£250	
345/8				*Set of 4*	3·75	2·25

ALTERED CATALOGUE NUMBERS

Any Catalogue numbers altered from the last edition are shown as a list in the introductory pages.

121 Kendal's Chronometer and Cook's Sextant **122** "Peace for the World" (F. B. Eccles)

(Des J. Berry, adapted J. Cooter. Litho Questa)

1970 (14 Sept). *Cook's Exploration of the Pacific.* T **121** *and similar designs.* W **61** (*sideways on 30 s.*). P 14.

349		1 s. carmine, silver and black			15	15
350		2 s. multicoloured			30	15
351		20 s. black, bright blue and gold			75	25
352		30 s. multicoloured	..	..	1·50	80
349/52				*Set of 4*	2·50	1·25

Designs: *Vert*—2 s. Cook's statue, Whitby; 20 s. Cook's head. *Horiz* (83 × 25 *mm*)—30 s. Cook, H.M.S. *Endeavour* and island.

(Des from paintings. Photo Heraclio Fournier)

1970 (26 Oct). *Christmas.* T **122** *and similar vert designs. Multicoloured.* P 13.

353		2 s. Type **122**			10	10
354		3 s. "The Holy Family" (W. E. Jahnke)			10	10
355		20 s. "Mother and Child" (F. B. Eccles)			15	10
356		30 s. "Prince of Peace" (Meleane Fe'ao)			20	15
353/6				*Set of 4*	35	30
MS357		111 × 158 mm. Nos. 353/6	..		60	1·25

123 Pope Paul VI **124** Native and Tree

(Des J. Cooter. Litho Format)

1970 (20 Nov). *Visit of Pope Paul to Samoa.* W **61**. P 14 × 14½.

358	**123**	8 s. black and grey-blue	..	..	15	15
359		20 s. black and plum	..	..	35	15

(Des G. Drummond from sketches by the American Timber Co. Litho Questa)

1971 (1 Feb). *Timber Industry.* T **124** *and similar multicoloured designs.* P 13½.

360		3 s. Type **124**			10	10
361		8 s. Bulldozer in clearing (*horiz*)	..	..	15	10
362		20 s. Log in sawmill (*horiz*)			30	10
363		22 s. Floating logs and harbour			30	15
360/3		..		*Set of 4*	70	30

125 Fautasi (large canoe) in Apia Harbour and first stamps of Samoa and U.S.A.

(*Half-sized illustration. Actual size 84 × 26 mm*)

(Des E. Roberts. Photo Courvoisier)

1971 (12 Mar). *"Interpex" Stamp Exhibition, New York. Sheet 138 × 80 mm.* P 11½.

MS364	**125**	70 s. multicoloured	..		85	1·40

126 Siva Dance **127** "Queen Salamasina"

(Des and litho J.W.)

1971 (9 Aug). *Tourism.* T **126** *and similar horiz designs. Multicoloured.* W **61** *(sideways).* P 14.

365	5 s. Type **126**	..	..	40	10
366	7 s. Samoan cricket	..	..	1·00	60
367	8 s. Hideaway Hotel	..	..	1·00	35
368	10 s. Aggie Grey and her hotel	..	1·00	60
365/8	..	..	..	*Set of 4* 3·00	1·40

(Des Jennifer Toombs. Litho J.W.)

1971 (20 Sept). *Myths and Legends of Old Samoa (1st series).* T **127** *and similar vert designs from carvings by S. Ortquist. Multicoloured.* W **61** *(sideways).* P 14 × 13½.

369	2 s. Type **127**	..	..	10	10
370	8 s. "Lu and his Sacred Hens"	..	15	10
371	10 s. "God Tagaloa fishes Samoa from the sea"	20	10
372	22 s. "Mount Vaea and the Pool of Tears"	35	40
369/72	..	..	..	*Set of 4* 70	50

See also Nos. 426/9.

128 "The Virgin and Child" (Bellini)

129 Map and Scales of Justice

(Des J. Cooter. Litho J.W.)

1971 (4 Oct). *Christmas.* T **128** *and similar design.* W **61**. P 14 × 13½.

373	**128**	2 s. multicoloured	..	10	10
374		3 s. multicoloured	..	10	10
375	–	20 s. multicoloured	..	30	10
376	–	30 s. multicoloured	..	40	20
373/6		..	..	*Set of 4* 75	35

Design: *Vert*—20 s., 30 s. "The Virgin and Child with St. Anne and John the Baptist" (Leonardo da Vinci).

(Des E. Roberts. Photo Courvoisier)

1972 (10 Jan). *First South Pacific Judicial Conference.* P 11½ × 11.

377	**129**	10 s. multicoloured	..	15	15

Issued on matt, almost invisible gum.

130 Asau Wharf, Savaii

131 Flags of Member Countries

(Des V. Whiteley. Litho A. & M.)

1972 (10 Jan). *Tenth Anniv of Independence.* T **130** *and similar horiz designs. Multicoloured.* W **61** *(sideways).* P 13.

378	1 s. Type **130**	..	..	10	10
379	8 s. Parliament Building	..	10	10
380	10 s. Mothers' Centre	..	10	10
381	22 s. "Vailima" Residence and rulers	20	25
378/81	..	..	..	*Set of 4* 40	30

(Des V. Whiteley. Litho Questa)

1972 (17 Mar). *25th Anniv of South Pacific Commission.* T **131** *and similar multicoloured designs.* W **61** *(sideways on 8 s. and 10 s.).* P 14 × 13½ (3 *and* 7 s.) *or* 13½ × 14 (*others*).

382	3 s. Type **131**	..	..	10	15
383	7 s. Flag and Afoafouvale Misimoa (Secretary-General)	10	15
384	8 s. H.Q. building, Nouméa (*horiz*)	15	15
385	10 s. Flags and area map (*horiz*)	15	15
382/5	..	..	..	*Set of 4* 40	55

132 Expedition Ships

133 Bull Conch (*Strombus taurus*)

(Des J. Berry; adapted J. Cooter. Litho Questa)

1972 (14 June). *250th Anniv of sighting of Western Samoa by Jacob Roggeveen.* T **132** *and similar horiz designs. Multicoloured.* W **61** *(sideways, except 2 s.).* P 14½.

386	2 s. Type **132**	..	..	15	10
387	8 s. Ships in storm	..	45	10
388	10 s. Ships passing island	..	50	10
389	30 s. Route of Voyage (85 × 25 *mm*)	1·75	1·50
386/9	..	..	..	*Set of 4* 2·50	1·60

(Des Format ($5) or J.W. (others). Litho Format ($5), Questa (others))

1972 (18 Oct)–76. T **133** *and similar multicoloured designs.* W **61** *(sideways, on 1 s. to 50 s.). White, ordinary paper.* P 13½ ($1 *to* $5) *or* 14½ (*others*).

390	1 s. Type **133**	..	..	30	30
	a. Cream, chalk-surfaced paper (30.11.76)	1·75	2·00
391	2 s. *Oryctes rhinoceros* (beetle)	30	30
	a. Cream, chalk-surfaced paper (30.11.76)	1·75	2·00
392	3 s. Skipjack Tuna	..	30	65
393	4 s. Painted Crab	..	30	30
	a. Cream, chalk-surfaced paper (30.11.76)	1·75	2·00
394	5 c. Melon Butterflyfish	..	35	40
	a. Cream, chalk-surfaced paper (30.11.76)	1·75	2·00
395	7 s. *Danaus hamata* (butterfly)	2·00	70
396	10 s. Trumpet Triton (*Charonia tritonis*)	2·50	70
397	20 s. *Chrysochroa abdominalis* (beetle)	1·25	30
398	50 s. Spiny Lobster	..	2·00	2·75
399	$1 *Gnathothlibus erotus* (moth) (29×45 *mm*)	8·00	4·50
399a	$2 Green Turtle (29×45 *mm*) (18.6.73)	5·50	3·50
399b	$4 Black Marlin (29×45 *mm*) (27.3.74)	3·00	7·00
399c	$5 Green Tree Lizard (29×45 *mm*) (30.6.75)	3·00	9·00
390/9c	..	..	*Set of 13* 26·00	27·00

134 "The Ascension"

135 Erecting a Tent

(Des PAD Studio. Litho Harrison)

1972 (1 Nov). *Christmas. Stained-glass Windows in Apia.* T **134** *and similar vert designs. Multicoloured.* W **61**. P 14 × 14½.

400	1 s. Type **134**	..	..	10	10
401	4 s. "The Blessed Virgin and Infant Christ"	10	10
402	10 s. "St. Andrew blessing Samoan canoe"	10	10
403	30 s. "The Good Shepherd"	..	40	30
400/3	..	..	..	*Set of 4* 50	40
MS404	70 × 159 mm. Nos. 400/3	..	90	1·25

(Des G. Drummond. Litho Format)

1973 (29 Jan). *Boy Scout Movement.* T **135** *and similar horiz designs. Multicoloured.* W **61** *(sideways).* P 14.

405	2 s. Saluting the flag	..	10	10
406	3 s. First-aid	..	..	10	10
407	8 s. Type **135**	..	..	25	10
408	20 s. Samoan action-song	..	60	85
405/8	..	..	..	*Set of 4* 80	95

136 Hawker Siddeley H.S.748

(Des E. Roberts. Photo Courvoisier)

1973 (9 Mar). *Air.* T **136** *and similar horiz designs showing aircraft at Faleolo Airport. Multicoloured.* P 11½.

409	8 s. Type **136**	..	..	55	15
410	10 s. Hawker Siddeley H.S.748 in flight	65	15
411	12 s. Hawker Siddeley H.S.748 on runway	75	35
412	22 s. B.A.C. One Eleven	..	1·10	60
409/12	..	..	..	*Set of 4* 2·75	1·10

Issued on matt, almost invisible gum.

PRICES OF SETS

Set prices are given for many issues, generally those containing three stamps or more. Definitive sets include one of each value or major colour change, but do not cover different perforations, die types or minor shades. Where a choice is possible the set prices are based on the cheapest versions of the stamps included in the listings.

---

137 Apia General Hospital

138 Mother and Child, and Map

(Des C. Abbott. Litho Questa)

1973 (20 Aug). *25th Anniv of W.H.O.* T **137** *and similar vert designs. Multicoloured.* W **61**. P 14.

413	3 s. Type **137**	..	..	10	10
414	8 s. Baby clinic	..	..	15	10
415	20 s. Filariasis research	..	30	20
416	22 s. Family welfare	..	30	30
413/16	..	..	..	*Set of 4* 75	55

(Des W. E. Jahnke (3 s.), Fiasili Keil (4 s.), E. Cooter (others); adapted Jennifer Toombs. Litho J.W.)

1973 (15 Oct). *Christmas.* T **138** *and similar vert designs. Multicoloured.* W **61**. P 14.

417	3 s. Type **138**	..	..	10	10
418	4 s. Mother and child, and village	10	10
419	10 s. Mother and child, and beach	10	10
420	30 s. Samoan stable	..	55	50
417/20	..	..	..	*Set of 4* 65	55
MS421	144×103 mm. Nos. 417/20	..	65	75
	w. Wmk inverted	..	..	32·00	

139 Boxing

(Des G. Drummond. Litho Questa)

1974 (24 Jan). *Commonwealth Games, Christchurch.* T **139** *and similar horiz designs. Multicoloured.* W **61** *(sideways).* P 14.

422	8 s. Type **139**	..	..	10	10
423	10 s. Weightlifting	..	10	10
424	20 s. Bowls	..	..	20	10
425	30 s. Athletics stadium	..	35	45
422/5	..	..	..	*Set of 4* 70	60

(Des Jennifer Toombs. Litho Questa)

1974 (13 Aug). *Myths and Legends of Old Samoa (2nd series). Vert designs as* T **127** *from carvings by S. Ortquist. Multicoloured.* W **61**. P 14 × 13½.

426	2 s. Tigilau and sacred dove	..	10	10
427	8 s. Pili, his sons and fishing net	10	10
428	20 s. Sina and the origin of the coconut	30	10
429	30 s. The warrior, Nafanua	..	45	55
426/9	..	..	..	*Set of 4* 80	65

140 Mail-van at Faleolo Airport

(Des E. Roberts. Photo Heraclio Fournier)

1974 (4 Sept). *Centenary of Universal Postal Union.* T **140** *and similar horiz designs. Multicoloured.* P 13 × 12½ (50 s.) *or* 13 (*others*).

430	8 s. Type **140**	..	..	35	10
431	20 s. *Mariposa* (cargo liner) at Apia Wharf	50	15
432	22 s. Early Post Office, Apia, and letter	50	25
433	50 s. William Willis and *Age Unlimited* (raft) (87×29 *mm*)	95	1·25
430/3	..	..	..	*Set of 4* 2·10	1·60
MS434	140×82 mm. No. 433	..	90	1·75

141 "Holy Family" (Sebastiano)

(Des PAD Studio. Litho Enschedé)

1974 (25 Nov). *Christmas.* T **141** *and similar horiz designs. Multicoloured.* W **61** *(sideways).* P 13×13½.

435	3 s. Type **141**	..	..	10	10
436	4 s. "Virgin and Child with Saints" (Lotto)	10	10
437	10 s. "Madonna and Child with St. John" (Titian)	20	10
438	30 s. "Adoration of the Shepherds" (Rubens)	55	45
435/8	..	..	..	*Set of 4* 75	50
MS439	128 × 87 mm. Nos. 435/8	..	80	1·40

142 Winged Passion Flower

(Des J.W. Litho Questa)

1975 (15 Jan). *Tropical Flowers. T **142** and similar multicoloured designs. W **61** (sideways on 8 and 30 s.). P 14.*

440	8 s. Type **142**	..	15	10
441	20 s. Gardenia (*vert*)	..	30	25
442	22 s. *Barringtonia samoensis* (*vert*)	..	30	30
443	30 s. Malay apple	..	35	75
440/3		*Set of 4*	1·00	1·25

143 *Joyita* (inter-island coaster) loading at Apia

144 "Pate" Drum

(Des E. Roberts. Photo Heraclio Fournier)

1975 (14 Mar). *"Interpex 1975" Stamp Exhibition, New York, and "Joyita Mystery". T **143** and similar horiz designs. Multicoloured. P 13½.*

444	1 s. Type **143**	..	10	10
445	8 s. *Joyita* sails for Tokelau Islands	..	15	10
446	20 s. Taking to rafts	..	20	25
447	22 s. *Joyita* abandoned	..	25	30
448	50 s. Discovery of *Joyita* north of Fiji	..	50	1·25
444/8		*Set of 5*	1·00	1·75
MS449	150 × 100 mm. Nos. 444/8. Imperf	..	1·50	3·50

(Des Iosua To'afa; adapted L. Curtis. Litho Harrison)

1975 (30 Sept). *Musical Instruments. T **144** and similar vert designs. Multicoloured. W **61** (sideways). P 14.*

450	8 s. Type **144**	..	10	10
451	20 s. "Lali" drum	..	20	10
452	22 s. "Logo" drum	..	20	10
453	30 s. "Pu" shell horn	..	35	30
450/3		*Set of 4*	75	50

145 "Mother and Child" (Meleane Fe'ao)

146 "The Boston Massacre, 1770" (Paul Revere)

(Des local artists; adapted G. Vasarhelyi. Litho Walsall)

1975 (25 Nov). *Christmas. T **145** and similar vert designs. Multicoloured. W **61** (inverted). P 14.*

454	3 s. Type **145**	..	10	10
455	4 s. "The Saviour" (Polataia Tuigamala)	..	10	10
456	10 s. "A Star is Born" (Iosua To'afa)	..	10	10
457	30 s. "Madonna and Child" (Ernesto Coter)	..	30	45
454/7		*Set of 4*	45	50
MS458	101 × 134 mm. Nos. 454/7	..	60	1·25

(Des J. Cooter. Litho Walsall)

1976 (20 Jan). *Bicentenary of American Revolution. T **146** and similar horiz designs. Multicoloured. W **61** (sideways*). P 13½.*

459	7 s. Type **146**	..	20	10
	w. Wmk legs to left	..	1·40	
460	8 s. "The Declaration of Independence" (Trumbull)	..	20	10
	w. Wmk legs to left	..	2·00	
461	20 s. "The Ship that Sank in Victory, 1779" (Ferris)	..	40	10
462	22 s. "Pitt addressing the Commons, 1782" (R. A. Hickel)	..	40	10
463	50 s. "The Battle of Princeton" (Mercer)	..	80	1·25
459/63		*Set of 5*	1·75	1·50
MS464	160×125 mm. Nos. 459/63	..	4·50	8·00
	w. Wmk legs to left	..	35·00	

*The normal sideways watermark has the legs of the bowl pointing to the right, *as seen from the back of the stamp.*

147 Mullet Fishing

(Des V. Whiteley Studio. Litho Harrison)

1976 (27 Apr). *Fishing. T **147** and similar horiz designs. Multicoloured. W **61**. P 14.*

465	10 s. Type **147**	..	10	10
466	12 s. Fish traps	..	10	10
467	22 s. Samoan fishermen	..	30	10
468	50 s. Net fishing	..	85	70
465/8		*Set of 4*	1·25	90

148 Paul Revere's Ride

(Des J. Berry. Photo Heraclio Fournier)

1976 (29 May). *"Interphil" Stamp Exhibition. Sheet 120 × 80 mm. P 13.*

MS469	**148** $1 gold, black and emerald	..	1·50	1·50

149 Boxing

150 Mary and Joseph going to Bethlehem

(Des C. Abbott. Litho Questa)

1976 (21 June). *Olympic Games, Montreal. T **149** and similar horiz designs. Multicoloured. W **61** (sideways*). P 14.*

470	10 s. Type **149**	..	10	10
471	12 s. Wrestling	..	10	10
	w. Wmk legs to left	..	40·00	
472	22 s. Javelin	..	15	10
473	50 s. Weightlifting	..	45	50
470/3		*Set of 4*	70	60

*The normal sideways watermark has the legs of the bowl pointing to the right, *as seen from back of the stamp.*

(Des C. Abbott. Litho Questa)

1976 (18 Oct). *Christmas. T **150** and similar vert designs. Multicoloured. W **61**. P 13½.*

474	3 s. Type **150**	..	10	10
475	5 s. The Shepherds	..	10	10
476	22 s. The Holy Family	..	10	10
477	50 s. The Magi	..	55	65
474/7		*Set of 4*	70	75
MS478	124×115 mm. Nos. 474/7	..	80	1·75

151 Queen Elizabeth and View of Apia

(Des BG Studio. Litho Questa)

1977 (11 Feb). *Silver Jubilee and Royal Visit. T **151** and similar horiz designs. Multicoloured. W **61** (sideways*). P 13½.*

479	12 s. Type **151**	..	10	10
	w. Wmk legs to left	..	4·75	
480	26 s. Presentation of Spurs of Chivalry	..	15	20
481	32 s. Queen and Royal Yacht *Britannia*	..	20	25
	w. Wmk legs to left	..	30·00	
482	50 s. Queen leaving Abbey	..	20	60
479/82		*Set of 4*	60	1·00

*The normal sideways watermark has the legs of the bowl pointing to the right, *as seen from the back of the stamp.*

MINIMUM PRICE

The minimum price quote is 10p which represents a handling charge rather than a basis for valuing common stamps. For further notes about prices see introductory pages.

152 Map of Flight Route

(Des C. Abbott. Litho Walsall)

1977 (20 May). *50th Anniv of Lindbergh's Translantic Flight. Horiz designs showing the Spirit of St. Louis. Multicoloured. W **61** (sideways*). P 14.*

483	22 s. Type **152**	..	25	10
484	24 s. In flight	..	35	15
485	26 s. Landing	..	35	15
	w. Wmk legs to left	..	3·00	
486	50 s. Col. Lindbergh	..	80	75
483/6		*Set of 4*	1·60	1·00
MS487	194×93 mm. Nos. 483/6	..	2·40	2·75
	w. Wmk legs to left	..	40·00	

*The normal sideways watermark has the legs of the bowl pointing to the right, *as seen from the back of the stamp.*

153 3d. Express Stamp and First Mail Notice

(Des J. Cooter. Litho Questa)

1977 (29 Aug). *Stamp Centenary. T **153** and similar horiz designs. W **61** (sideways). P 13½.*

488	12 s. lemon, red and sepia	..	20	10
489	13 s. multicoloured	..	20	15
490	26 s. multicoloured	..	45	30
491	50 s. multicoloured	..	80	1·50
488/91		*Set of 4*	1·50	1·75

Designs:—13 s. Early cover and 6d. Express; 26 s. Apia Post Office and 1d. Express; 50 s. Schooner *Energy*, 1877, and 6d. Express.

154 Apia Automatic Telephone Exchange

155 "Samoan Nativity" (P. Feata)

(Des J.W. Litho Questa)

1977 (28 Oct*). *Telecommunications Project. T **154** and similar horiz designs. Multicoloured. W **61** (sideways). P 14.*

492	12 s. Type **154**	..	15	10
493	13 s. Mulinuu Radio Terminal	..	15	10
494	26 s. Old and new telephones	..	30	20
495	50 s. "Global communication"	..	50	70
492/5		*Set of 4*	1·00	1·00

*The above were originally scheduled for release on 11 July and were put on sale by the Crown Agents in England on that date.

(Designs adapted by J.W. Litho Questa)

1977 (31 Oct). *Christmas. T **155** and similar vert designs. Multicoloured. W **61**. P 14.*

496	4 s. Type **155**	..	10	10
497	6 s. "The Offering" (E. Saofaiga)	..	10	10
498	26 s. "Madonna and Child" (F. Tupou)	..	20	10
499	50 s. "Emmanuel" (M. Sapa'u)	..	35	40
496/9		*Set of 4*	55	50
MS500	117×159 mm. Nos. 496/9	..	55	85

156 Polynesian Airlines Boeing 737

(Des E. Roberts. Litho Heraclio Fournier)

1978 (21 Mar). *Aviation Progress. T **156** and similar horiz designs. Multicoloured. P 14.*

501	12 s. Type **156**	..	20	10
502	24 s. Wright brothers Flyer I	..	40	20
503	26 s. Kingsford Smith's Fokker F.VIIa/3m *Southern Cross*	..	40	20
504	50 s. Concorde	..	50	70
501/4		*Set of 4*	1·90	1·25
MS505	150×120 mm. Nos. 501/4	..	2·25	2·75

157 Hatchery, Aleipata

158 Pacific Pigeon

(Des J.W. Litho Questa)

1978 (14 Apr). *Hawksbill Turtle Conservation Project. T* **157** *and similar horiz design. Multicoloured. W* **61** *(sideways). P* 14½ × 14.
506 24 s. Type **157** .. .. 1·00 30
507 $1 Turtle .. .. 3·75 1·60

(Des Jennifer Toombs. Litho Questa)

1978 (21 Apr). *25th Anniv of Coronation. T* **158** *and similar vert designs. P* 15.
508 26 s. black, brown and deep magenta.. 20 30
  a. Sheetlet. Nos. 508/10 × 2 1·00
509 26 s. multicoloured .. 20 30
510 26 s. black, brown and deep magenta.. 20 30
508/10 .. .. .. *Set of 3* 50 80
Designs:—No. 508, King's Lion; No. 509, Queen Elizabeth II; No. 510, Type **158**.
Nos. 508/10 were printed together in small sheets of 6, containing two *se-tenant* strips of 3, with horizontal gutter margin between.

159 Flags of Western Samoa and Canada with Canadian National Tower

160 Captain Cook

(Des BG Studio. Litho Walsall)

1978 (9 June). *"Capex '78" International Stamp Exhibition, Toronto. Sheet* 119 × 79 *mm. W* **61.** *P* 14½.
MS511 **159** $1 blue, red and black.. .. 75 1·40

(Des J. Berry. Litho Harrison)

1978 (28 Aug). *250th Birth Anniv of Captain Cook. T* **160** *and similar vert designs. Multicoloured. W* **61.** *P* 14½ × 14.
512 12 s. Type **160** 30 15
513 24 s. Cook's cottage, Gt Ayton, Yorkshire 35 35
514 26 s. Old drawbridge over the river Esk, Whitby 35 35
515 50 s. H.M.S. *Resolution* .. 1·00 1·50
512/15 .. .. .. *Set of 4* 1·75 2·10

161 Thick-edged Cowrie (*Cypraea caurica*)

162 "Madonna on the Crescent"

(Photo Courvoisier)

1978 (15 Sept)–**80.** *Shells. Horiz designs as T* **161.** *Multicoloured. P* 12½.
516 1 s. Type **161** 15 10
517 2 s. Controversial Isabelle Cowrie (*Cypraea isabella controversa*) .. 15 10
518 3 s. Money Cowrie (*Cypraea moneta*) .. 25 10
519 4 s. Eroded Cowrie (*Cypraea erosa*) 30 10
520 6 s. Honey Cowrie (*Cypraea helvola*) 30 10
521 7 s. Asellus or Banded Cowrie (*Cypraea asellus*) .. 35 10
522 10 s. Globular or Globe Cowrie (*Cypraea globulus*) .. 40 10
523 11 s. Mole Cowrie (*Cypraea talpa*) 40 10
524 12 s. Children's Cowrie (*Cypraea childreni*) 40 10
525 13 s. Flag Cone (*Conus vexillum vexillum*) (20.11.78) .. 40 10
526 14 s. Soldier Cone (*Conus miles*) (20.11.78) 40 10
527 24 s. Textile or Cloth of Gold Cone (*Conus textile*) (20.11.78) .. 40 10
528 26 s. Lettered Cone (*Conus litteratus*) (20.11.78) .. 45 10
529 50 s. Tesselate or Tiled Cone (*Conus tessalatus*) (20.11.78) .. 50 15
530 $1 Black Marble Cone (*Conus marmoreus nigrescens*) (20.11.78) .. 80 60
530a $2 Marlin-spike Auger (*Terebra maculata*) (18.7.79) .. 85 70

530b $3 Scorpion Conch (*Lambis scorpius*) (18.7.79) .. 1·00 1·25
530c $5 Common or Major Harp (*Harpa major*) (26.8.80) .. 1·75 2·25
516/30c .. .. .. *Set of 18* 8·25 4·75
Nos. 530a/c are larger, size 36×26 mm. Issued on matt, almost invisible gum.

(Des C. Abbott. Litho Questa)

1978 (6 Nov). *Christmas. Woodcuts by Dürer. T* **162** *and similar vert designs. W* **61.** *P* 14.
531 4 s. black and yellow-brown .. 10 10
  w. Wmk inverted £225
532 6 s. black and turquoise-blue .. 10 10
533 26 s. black and bright blue .. 15 10
534 50 s. black and bright violet .. 35 50
531/4 .. .. .. *Set of 4* 50 55
MS535 103×154 mm. Nos. 531/4 .. 70 1·00
Designs:—6 s. Nativity"; 26 s. "Adoration of the Magi"; 50 s. "Annunciation".

163 Boy with Coconuts

164 *Charles W. Morgan*

(Des G. Drummond. Litho Questa)

1979 (10 Apr). *International Year of the Child. T* **163** *and similar horiz designs. Multicoloured. W* **61** *(sideways). P* 14.
536 12 s. Type **163** 15 10
537 24 s. White Sunday 20 15
538 26 s. Children at pump .. 20 15
539 50 s. Young girl with ukulele .. 60 80
536/9 .. .. .. *Set of 4* 1·00 1·10

(Des J. Cooter. Litho Format)

1979 (29 May). *Sailing Ships (1st series). Whaling Ships. T* **164** *and similar horiz designs. Multicoloured. W* **61** *(sideways). P* 13½.
540 12 s. Type **164** 30 10
541 14 s. *Lagoda* 30 10
542 24 s. *James T. Arnold* .. 40 20
543 50 s. *Splendid* 70 85
540/3 .. .. .. *Set of 4* 1·50 1·10
See also Nos. 561/4 and 584/7.

165 Launch of "Apollo 11"

166 Sir Rowland Hill (statue) and Penny Black

(Des J.W. Litho Questa)

1979 (20 June). *10th Anniv of Moon Landing. T* **165** *and similar designs in chocolate and dull vermilion* (12 s.) *or multicoloured (others). W* **61** *(sideways on* 14, 26 s. *and* $1). *P* 14½ × 14 (12, 24, 50 s.) *or* 14 × 14½ *(others).*
544 12 s. Type **165** 20 10
545 14 s. Lunar module and astronaut on Moon (horiz) .. 20 10
546 24 s. View of Earth from Moon .. 20 15
547 26 s. Astronaut on Moon (horiz) .. 20 15
548 50 s. Lunar and Command modules in Space 35 55
549 $1 Command module after splash-down (horiz) .. .. 70 1·50
544/9 .. .. .. *Set of 6* 1·75 2·25
MS550 90 × 130 mm. No. 549 .. 75 1·75
No. MS550 is inscribed "Spashdown" in error.

(Des and litho J.W.)

1979 (27 Aug). *Death Centenary of Sir Rowland Hill. T* **166** *and similar vert designs. Multicoloured. W* **61.** *P* 14.
551 12 s. Type **166** 15 10
552 24 s. Two-penny Blue with "Maltese Cross" postmark 15 15
553 26 s. Sir Rowland Hill and Penny Black 15 15
554 $1 Two-penny Blue and Sir Rowland Hill (statue) 45 75
551/4 .. .. .. *Set of 4* 80 1·00
MS555 128×95 mm. Nos. 551/4 .. 80 1·60
  w. Wmk inverted .. .. 38·00

167 Anglican Church, Apia

(Des A. Peake. Photo Courvoisier)

1979 (22 Oct). *Christmas. Churches. T* **167** *and similar horiz designs. P* 11½.
556 4 s. black and pale blue .. 10 10
557 6 s. black and bright yellow-green .. 10 10
558 26 s. black and yellow-ochre .. 15 10
559 50 s. black and reddish lilac .. 30 30
556/9 .. .. .. *Set of 4* 45 35
MS560 150 × 124 mm. Nos. 556/9 .. 75 1·25
Designs:—6 s. Congregational Christian, Leulumoega; 26 s. Methodist, Piula; 50 s. Protestant, Apia.
Issued on matt, almost invisible gum.

(Des J. Cooter. Litho Format)

1980 (22 Jan). *Sailing Ships (2nd series). Whaling Ships. Horiz designs as T* **164.** *Multicoloured. W* **61** *(sideways) P* 13½.
561 12 s. *William Hamilton* .. 35 10
562 14 s. *California* 35 15
563 24 s. *Liverpool II* 40 25
564 50 s. *Two Brothers* .. .. 60 1·10
561/4 .. .. .. *Set of 4* 1·50 1·40

168 "Equipment for a Hospital"

(Des M. Goaman (12, 50 s.), E. Roberts (others). Photo Heraclio Fournier)

1980 (26 Mar). *Anniversaries. T* **168** *and similar horiz designs. Multicoloured. P* 13½ × 14.
565 12 s. Type **168** 45 10
566 13 s. John Williams, dove with olive twig and commemorative inscription .. 45 50
567 14 s. Dr. Wilhelm Solf (instigator), flag and commemorative inscription .. 50 15
568 24 s. Cairn Monument .. 65 25
569 26 s. Williams Memorial, Savai'i .. 70 25
570 50 s. Paul P. Harris (founder) .. 1·25 2·50
565/70 .. .. .. *Set of 6* 3·50 3·25
Commemorations—12, 50 s. 75th anniversary of Rotary International; 13, 26 s. 150th anniversary of John Williams' (missionary) arrival in Samoa; 14, 24 s. 80th anniversary of raising of German flag.

169 Samoan Village Scene

(Des J.W. Litho Walsall)

1980 (6 May). *"London 1980" International Stamp Exhibition. Sheet* 140 × 81 *mm. W* **61** *(sideways). P* 14.
MS571 **169** $1 multicoloured 60 90

170 Queen Elizabeth the Queen Mother in 1970

(Des Harrison. Litho Questa)

1980 (4 Aug). *80th Birthday of Queen Elizabeth the Queen Mother. P* 14.
572 **170** 50 s. multicoloured 30 30

171 1964 2nd Anniversary of New Zealand–Samoa Treaty of Friendship 2 s. Commemorative and "Zeapex '80" Emblem

(Des E. Roberts. Photo Heraclio Fournier)

1980 (23 Aug). *"Zeapex '80" International Stamp Exhibition, Auckland. Sheet* 130 × 80 *mm. P* 14.
MS573 **171** $1 multicoloured 60 90

172 Afiamalu Satellite Earth Station

(Des and photo Courvoisier)

1980 (20 Sept). *Afiamalu Satellite Earth Station. T 172 and similar horiz designs. Multicoloured. P 11½.*
574	12 s.	Type 172		15	10
575	14 s.	Satellite station (different)		20	10
576	24 s.	Satellite station and map of Savai'i and Upolu		30	15
577	50 s.	Satellite and globe		60	60
574/7			Set of 4	1·10	85

173 Afiamalu Satellite Earth Station 24 s. Commemorative Stamp and "Sydpex 80" Emblem

(Des E. Roberts. Litho Sprintpak, Mayne Nickless Ltd, Australia)

1980 (29 Sept). *"Sydpex 80" International Stamp Exhibition, Sydney. Sheet 130 × 80 mm. Imperf.*
MS578	173	$2 multicoloured	1·00	1·00

174 "The Saviour" (J. Poynton) **175** President Franklin D. Roosevelt and Hyde Park (family home)

(Des G. Vasarhelyi. Litho Format)

1980 (28 Oct). *Christmas. Paintings. T 174 and similar vert designs. Multicoloured. W 61. P 13½.*
579	8 s.	Type 174		10	10
580	14 s.	"Madonna and Child" (Lealofi F. Siaopo)		10	10
581	27 s.	"Nativity" (Pasila Feata)		15	10
582	50 s.	"Yuletide" (R. P. Aiono)		25	40
			Set of 4	55	55
MS583		90×105 mm. Nos. 579/82		1·00	1·50
		w. Wmk inverted		16·00	

(Des J. Cooter. Litho Format)

1981 (26 Jan). *Sailing Ships (3rd series). Horiz designs as T 164. Multicoloured.*
584	12 s.	Ocean (whaling ship)		30	10
585	18 s.	Horatio (whaling ship)		40	15
586	27 s.	H.M.S. Calliope (screw corvette)		55	55
587	32 s.	H.M.S. Calypso (screw corvette)		60	50
584/7			Set of 4	1·60	90

(Des J.W. Litho Format)

1981 (29 Apr). *International Year for Disabled Persons. President Franklin D. Roosevelt Commemoration. T 175 and similar horiz designs. Multicoloured. P 14.*
588	12 s.	Type 175		15	10
589	18 s.	Roosevelt's inauguration, 4 March 1933		15	10
590	27 s.	Franklin and Eleanor Roosevelt		20	15
591	32 s.	Roosevelt's Lend-lease Bill (Atlantic convoy, 1941)		25	20
592	38 s.	Roosevelt the philatelist		25	25
593	$1	Campobello House (summer home)		50	90
588/93			Set of 6	1·40	1·50

176 Hotel Tusitala **177** Wedding Bouquet from Samoa

(Des and litho Walsall)

1981 (29 June). *Tourism. T 176 and similar horiz designs. Multicoloured. W 61 (sideways). P 14½ × 14.*
594	12 s.	Type 176		15	10
595	18 s.	Apia Harbour		25	15
596	27 s.	Aggie Grey's Hotel		25	20
597	32 s.	Preparation for Ceremonial Kava		30	30
598	54 s.	Piula water pool		55	55
594/8			Set of 5	1·40	1·10

(Des J.W. Litho Walsall)

1981 (22 July). *Royal Wedding. T 177 and similar vert designs. Multicoloured. W 61. P 14.*
599	18 s.	Type 177		15	10
600	32 s.	Prince Charles as Colonel-in-Chief, Gordon Highlanders		20	10
601	$1	Prince Charles and Lady Diana Spencer		30	50
599/601			Set of 3	60	60

178 Tattooing Instruments **179** Black Marlin

(Des E. Roberts. Litho Cambec Press, Melbourne)

1981 (29 Sept). *Tattooing. T 178 and similar horiz designs. Multicoloured. P 13½.*
602	12 s.	Type 178		15	20
		a. Horiz strip of 4. Nos. 602/5		1·00	
603	18 s.	First stage of tattooing		20	25
604	27 s.	Progressive stage		25	30
605	$1	Completed tattoo		50	70
602/5			Set of 4	1·00	1·25

Nos. 602/5 were printed together, *se-tenant*, in horizontal strips of 4 throughout the sheet.

(Des E. Roberts. Litho Cambec Press, Melbourne)

1981 (9 Oct). *"Philatokyo '81" International Stamp Exhibition, Tokyo. Sheet 130 × 80 mm. P 14 × 13½.*
MS606	179	$2 multicoloured	1·00	1·00

180 Thespesia populnea **181** George Washington's Pistol

(Des and litho J.W.)

1981 (30 Nov). *Christmas. Flowers. T 180 and similar vert designs. Multicoloured. W 61. P 13½.*
607	11 s.	Type 180		15	10
		w. Wmk inverted		3·50	
608	15 s.	Copper Leaf		15	15
609	23 s.	Allamanda cathartica		20	25
610	$1	Mango		60	1·00
607/10			Set of 4	1·00	1·40
MS611		86×120 mm. Nos. 607/10		1·40	2·25

(Des J.W. Litho Format)

1982 (26 Feb). *250th Birth Anniv of George Washington. T 181 and similar horiz designs, each in black, ochre and stone. P 13½.*
612	23 s.	Type 181		25	30
613	25 s.	Mount Vernon (Washington's house)		25	30
614	34 s.	George Washington		30	40
612/14			Set of 3	70	90
MS615		104 × 103 mm. $1 Washington taking Oath of Office as President		70	1·00

182 Forum Samoa (container ship)

(Des E. Roberts. Litho Cambec Press, Melbourne)

1982 (24 May). *20th Anniv of Independence. T 182 and similar horiz designs. Multicoloured. P 13½ × 14.*
616	18 s.	Type 182		40	20
617	23 s.	"Air services"		50	30
618	25 s.	N.P.F. (National Provident Fund) Building, Apia		40	30
619	$1	"Telecommunications"		1·10	1·00
616/19			Set of 4	2·25	1·60

MINIMUM PRICE

The minimum price quote is 10p which represents a handling charge rather than a basis for valuing common stamps. For further notes about prices see introductory pages.

---

183 Scouts map-reading and "75" **184** Boxing

(Des J.W. Litho Walsall)

1982 (20 July). *75th Anniv of Boy Scout Movement. T 183 and similar horiz designs. Multicoloured. W 61 (sideways). P 14½.*
620	5 s.	Type 183		10	10
621	38 s.	Scout salute and "75"		40	40
622	44 s.	Scout crossing river by rope, and "75"		50	50
623	$1	"Tower" of Scouts and "75"		1·00	1·00
620/23			Set of 4	1·75	1·75
MS624		93 × 81 mm. $1 As No. 623 but with portrait of Lord Baden-Powell replacing emblem (47 × 35 mm). P 11		1·25	1·25

(Des Garden Studio. Litho Walsall)

1982 (20 Sept). *Commonwealth Games, Brisbane. T 184 and similar vert designs. Multicoloured. W w 14. P 14½.*
625	23 s.	Type 184		20	20
626	25 s.	Hurdling		20	20
627	34 s.	Weightlifting		25	30
628	$1	Bowling		75	1·50
625/8			Set of 4	1·25	2·00

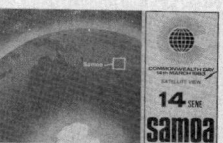

185 "Mary and Joseph" (Emma Dunlop) **186** Satellite View of Australasia

(Des J.W. Litho Questa)

1982 (15 Nov). *Christmas. Children's Pictures. T 185 and similar horiz designs. Multicoloured. W 61 (sideways). P 14 × 14½.*
629	11 s.	Type 185		15	10
630	15 s.	"Mary, Joseph and baby Jesus" (Marie Tofaeono)		15	15
631	38 s.	"Madonna and Child" (Ralph Laban and Fetalaiga Fareni)		40	30
632	$1	"Mother and Child" (Panapa Pouesi)		90	2·00
629/32			Set of 4	1·40	2·25
MS633		130 × 119 mm. Nos. 629/32		1·60	2·75

(Des Walsall. Litho Enschedé)

1983 (23 Feb). *Commonwealth Day. T 186 and similar horiz designs. Multicoloured. W w 14 (sideways). P 13 × 13½.*
634	14 s.	Type 186		10	10
635	29 s.	Flag of Samoa		15	20
636	43 s.	Harvesting copra		25	25
637	$1	Head of State Malietoa Tanumafili II		50	80
634/7			Set of 4	90	1·25

187 Douglas DC-1

(Des J.W. Litho Questa)

1983 (7 June). *Bicentenary of Manned Flight and 50th Anniv of Douglas Commercial Aircraft. Sheet, 215 × 113 mm, containing horiz designs as T 187. Multicoloured. W w 14 (sideways). P 14.*
MS638		32 s. × 10, each design showing a different Douglas aircraft from the DC-1 to the DC-10	4·00	3·25

188 Pole-vaulting **189** Lime

(Des McCombie Skinner Studio. Litho Format)

1983 (31 Aug). *South Pacific Games. T* **188** *and similar vert designs. Multicoloured. W w* **14.** *P* 14 × 14½.

639	8 s. Type 188			35	10
640	15 s. Netball			45	20
641	25 s. Tennis			70	50
642	32 s. Weight-lifting			70	70
643	35 s. Boxing			75	1·00
644	46 s. Football			90	1·40
645	48 s. Golf			1·40	1·50
646	56 s. Rugby			1·40	1·75
639/46			*Set of 8*	6·00	6·50

(Des E. Roberts. Litho Enschedé)

1983 (28 Sept)–**84.** *Fruit. T* **189** *and similar vert designs. Multicoloured. W w* **14** *(inverted on 1 s.). P* 13½ *($2 to $5) or* 14 × 13½ *(others).*

647	1 s. Type 189			10	60
648	2 s. Star fruit			10	70
649	3 s. Mangosteen			10	70
650	4 s. Lychee			10	70
651	7 s. Passion fruit			15	70
652	8 s. Mango			15	70
653	11 s. Pawpaw			20	70
654	13 s. Pineapple			20	70
655	14 s. Breadfruit			20	70
656	15 s. Banana			30	70
657	21 s. Cashew Nut (30.11.83)			1·75	1·50
658	25 s. Guava (30.11.83)			1·75	80
659	32 s. Water Melon (30.11.83)			1·75	1·50
660	48 s. Sasalapa (30.11.83)			2·00	2·25
661	56 s. Avocado (30.11.83)			2·00	2·25
662	$1 Coconut (30.11.83)			2·00	2·00
663	$2 Vi Apple (11.4.84)			1·75	3·00
664	$4 Grapefruit (11.4.84)			2·50	4·50
665	$5 Orange (11.4.84)			3·00	4·75
647/65			*Set of 19*	18·00	26·00

Nos. 663/5 are larger, size 25 × 35½ mm.

190 On Parade   191 Togitogiga Falls, Upolu

(Des Brian Melton Studio. Litho Format)

1983 (10 Oct). *Centenary of Boys' Brigade. Sheet* 120 × 83 *mm. W w* **14.** *P* 14.

MS668	190 $1 multicoloured			2·50	2·00

(Litho Format)

1984 (15 Feb). *Scenic Views. T* **191** *and similar horiz designs. Multicoloured. W w* **14** *(sideways). P* 14.

669	25 s. Type 191			30	15
670	32 s. Lano Beach, Savai'i			40	60
671	48 s. Mulinu'u Point, Upolu			55	1·10
672	56 s. Nu'utele Island			55	1·75
669/72			*Set of 4*	1·60	3·25

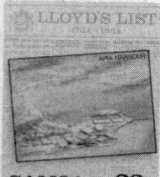

192 Apia Harbour   (193)

(Des Jennifer Toombs. Litho Questa)

1984 (24 May). *250th Anniv of "Lloyd's List" (newspaper). T* **192** *and similar vert designs. Multicoloured. W w* **14.** *P* 14 × 14½.

673	32 s. Type 192			25	20
674	48 s. Apia hurricane, 1889			40	45
675	60 s. *Forum Samoa* (container ship)			45	50
676	$1 *Matua* (inter-island freighter)			75	80
673/6			*Set of 4*	1·75	1·75

1984 (7 June). *Universal Postal Union Congress, Hamburg. No.* 662 *optd with T* **193.**

677	$1 Coconut			1·40	80

194 Olympic Stadium

(Des Garden Studio. Litho Format)

1984 (26 June). *Olympic Games, Los Angeles. T* **194** *and similar horiz designs. Multicoloured. W w* **14** *(sideways). P* 14½.

678	25 s. Type 194			20	20
679	32 s. Weightlifting			20	25
680	48 s. Boxing			30	45
681	$1 Running			60	80
678/81			*Set of 4*	1·10	1·50
MS682	170 × 120 mm. Nos. 678/81			1·40	1·60

195 Government Aircraft Factory N24A Nomad

(Des E. Roberts. Litho Walsall)

1984 (21 Sept). *"Ausipex" International Stamp Exhibition, Melbourne. Sheet* 131 × 80 *mm. W w* **14** *(sideways). P* 14.

MS683	195 $2.50, multicoloured			4·00	5·00

196 "Faith"

(Litho Walsall)

1984 (7 Nov). *Christmas. "The Three Virtues" (Raphael). T* **196** *and similar horiz designs. Multicoloured. W w* **14** *(sideways). P* 14.

684	25 s. Type 196			30	15
685	35 s. "Hope"			40	40
686	$1 "Charity"			1·60	2·75
684/6			*Set of 3*	2·10	3·00
MS687	63 × 76 mm. Nos. 684/6			2·50	3·50

197 *Dendrobium biflorum*   198 Ford "Model A", 1903

(Des Jennifer Toombs. Litho Format)

1985 (23 Jan). *Orchids (1st series). T* **197** *and similar vert designs. Multicoloured. P* 14.

688	48 s. Type 197			55	35
689	56 s. *Dendrobium vaupelianum* Kraenzl			65	45
690	67 s. *Glomera montana*			80	60
691	$1 *Spathoglottis plicata*			1·10	1·10
688/91			*Set of 4*	2·75	2·25

See also Nos. 818/21.

(Des A. Theobald. Litho Walsall)

1985 (26 Mar). *Veteran and Vintage Cars. T* **198** *and similar horiz designs. Multicoloured. P* 14.

692	48 s. Type 198			1·50	60
693	56 s. Chevrolet "Tourer", 1912			1·60	85
694	67 s. Morris "Oxford", 1913			1·75	1·75
695	$1 Austin "Seven", 1923			2·25	3·25
692/5			*Set of 4*	6·25	5·75

199 *Dictyophora indusiata*   200 The Queen Mother at Liverpool Street Station

(Des Doreen McGuinness. Litho Walsall)

1985 (17 Apr). *Fungi. T* **199** *and similar vert designs. Multicoloured. P* 14½.

696	48 s. Type 199			1·10	55
697	56 s. *Ganoderma tornatum*			1·25	85
698	67 s. *Mycena chlorophos*			1·60	1·75
699	$1 *Mycobonia flava*			2·25	3·25
696/9			*Set of 4*	5·50	5·75

(Des A. Theobald ($2), C. Abbott (others). Litho Questa)

1985 (7 June). *Life and Times of Queen Elizabeth the Queen Mother. T* **200** *and similar vert designs. Multicoloured. W w* **16.** *P* 14½ × 14.

700	32 s. At Glamis Castle, aged 9			35	25
701	48 s. At Prince Henry's Christening with other members of the Royal family			45	35
702	56 s. Type 200			65	65
703	$1 With Prince Henry at his christening (from photo by Lord Snowdon)			75	1·40
700/3			*Set of 4*	2·00	2·40
MS704	91 × 73 mm. $2 Arriving at Tattenham Corner Station with the Queen. Wmk sideways			2·75	1·75

201 Map of Pacific and Exhibition Logo   202 I.Y.Y. Emblem and Map (Alaska—Arabian Gulf)

(Des D. Hartley. Litho Enschedé)

1985 (26 Aug). *"Expo '85" World Fair, Japan. Sheet* 70 × 45 *mm. P* 14.

MS705	201 $2 multicoloured			1·50	2·00

(Des Garden Studio. Litho B.D.T.)

1985 (18 Sept). *International Youth Year. T* **202** *and similar vert designs, showing background map and emblem (Nos.* 706 *and* 710) *or raised arms (others). Multicoloured. P* 14.

706	60 s. Type 202			40	45
	a. Horiz strip of 5. Nos. 706/10			1·75	
707	60 s. Raised arms (Pakistan–Mexico)			40	45
708	60 s. Raised arms (Central America–China)			40	45
709	60 s. Raised arms (Japan–Greenland)			40	45
710	60 s. As Type 202 (Iceland–Siberia)			40	45
706/10			*Set of 5*	1·75	2·00

Nos. 706/10 were printed together, *se-tenant*, in horizontal strips of 5, throughout the sheet, the background forming a composite design of three continuous world maps.

203 "System"   204 *Hypolimnas bolina*

(Des L. Curtis. Litho Format)

1985 (5 Nov). *Christmas. T* **203** *and similar vert designs showing illustrations by Millicent Sowerby for R. L. Stevenson's "A Child's Garden of Verses". Multicoloured. P* 14 × 14½.

711	32 s. Type 203			20	25
712	48 s. "Time to Rise"			30	35
713	56 s. "Auntie's Skirts"			35	40
714	$1 "Good Children"			65	1·50
711/14			*Set of 4*	1·40	2·25
MS715	87 × 109 mm. Nos. 711/14			1·75	3·25

(Des Annette Robinson. Litho Walsall)

1986 (13 Feb). *Butterflies. T* **204** *and similar vert designs. Multicoloured. W w* **16.** *P* 14½ × 14.

716	25 s. Type 204			35	30
717	32 s. *Belenois java*			40	30
718	48 s. *Deudorix epijarbas*			60	45
719	56 s. *Badamia exclamationis*			65	85
720	60 s. *Danaus hamata*			65	85
721	$1 *Catochrysops taitensis*			1·00	1·75
716/21			*Set of 6*	3·25	4·00

205 Halley's Comet over Apia   206 U.S.S. *Vincennes* (frigate)

(Des N. Shewring. Litho Walsall)

1986 (24 Mar). *Appearance of Halley's Comet.* T **205** *and similar horiz designs. Multicoloured.* W w **16** *(sideways).* P 14 × 14½.

722	32 s. Type **205**	..	40	20
723	48 s. Edmond Halley	..	50	35
724	60 s. Comet passing Earth	..	60	50
725	$2 Preparing *Giotto* spacecraft	..	1·25	1·75
722/5	..	*Set of 4*	2·50	2·50

(Des A. Theobald. Litho Questa)

1986 (21 Apr). *60th Birthday of Queen Elizabeth II. Vert designs as* T **230a** *of Jamaica. Multicoloured.* W w **16**. P 14½ × 14.

726	32 s. Engagement photograph, 1947	..	15	20
727	48 s. Queen with Liberty Bell, U.S.A., 1976.		15	35
728	56 s. At Apia, 1977	..	20	40
729	67 s. At Badminton Horse Trials, 1978	..	30	45
730	$2 At Crown Agents Head Office, London, 1983		60	1·25
726/30	..	*Set of 5*	1·25	2·40

(Des E. Nisbet. Litho Questa)

1986 (22 May). *"Ameripex '86" International Stamp Exhibition, Chicago.* T **206** *and similar horiz designs. Multicoloured.* P 14 × 14½.

731	48 s. Type **206**	..	50	35
732	56 s. Sikorsky S-42A flying boat	..	55	40
733	60 s. U.S.S. *Swan* (patrol boat)	..	55	40
734	$2 "Apollo 10" descending	..	1·25	2·00
731/4	..	*Set of 4*	2·50	2·75

207 Vailima

(Des E. Roberts. Litho Cambec Press, Melbourne)

1986 (4 Aug). *"Stampex '86" Stamp Exhibition, Adelaide. Sheet* 158 × 97 *mm. P* 13½.

MS735	**207** $3 multicoloured	..	3·50	3·50

208 High-finned Grouper

(Des P. Rymers. Litho Walsall)

1986 (13 Aug). *Fishes.* T **208** *and similar horiz designs. Multicoloured.* P 14.

736	32 s. Type **208**	..	60	40
737	48 s. Scarlet-finned Squirrelfish	..	90	45
738	60 s. Yellow-edged Lyretail ("Lunartail Grouper")		1·00	90
739	67 s. Yellow-striped Snapper	..	1·10	1·50
740	$1 Big-scaled Soldierfish	..	1·50	2·25
736/40	..	*Set of 5*	4·50	5·00

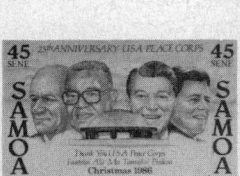

209 Samoan Prime Ministers, American Presidents and Parliament House

210 *Hibiscus rosa-sinensis* and Map of Samoa

(Des N. Shewring. Litho Format)

1986 (1 Dec). *Christmas. 25th Anniv of United States Peace Corps.* T **209** *and similar horiz design. Multicoloured.* P 14½.

741	45 s. Type **209**	..	25	30
742	60 s. French and American Presidents, Samoan Prime Minister and Statue of Liberty		35	40
MS743	131 × 72 mm. Nos. 741/2	..	3·00	4·50

No. **MS**743 also commemorates the Centenary of the Statue of Liberty.

(Des local artist, adapted G. Vasarhelyi. Litho Format)

1987 (16 Feb). *25th Anniv of Independence.* T **210** *and similar multicoloured designs.* P 14½ × 14 ($2) *or* 14 × 14½ *(others).*

744	15 s. Type **210**	..	25	10
745	45 s. Parliament Building, Apia	..	40	30
746	60 s. Longboat race at Independence celebration		45	40
747	70 s. Peace dove and laurel wreath	..	50	60
748	$2 Head of State Malietoa Tanumafili II and national flag *(horiz)*		1·25	2·00
744/8	..	*Set of 5*	2·50	3·00

211 Gulper (*Eurypharynx*)

(Des J. Walker. Litho Format)

1987 (31 Mar). *Deep Ocean Fishes.* T **211** *and similar horiz designs. Multicoloured.* P 14.

749	45 s. Type **211**	..	45	30
750	60 s. Hatchetfish	..	60	60
751	70 s. Bearded Angelfish	..	70	1·00
752	$2 Swallower (*Saccopharynx*)	..	1·40	3·00
749/52	..	*Set of 4*	2·75	4·50

212 Workmen trimming Logs and building Fale (traditional house)

(Des Jennifer Toombs. Litho Questa)

1987 (13 June). *"Capex 87" International Stamp Exhibition, Toronto. Sheet* 122 × 66 *mm. P* 14½.

MS753	**212** $3 multicoloured	..	1·90	1·90

213 Lefaga Beach, Upolu

214 Abel Tasman

(Des D. Miller. Litho Questa)

1987 (29 July). *Coastal Scenery.* T **213** *and similar horiz designs. Multicoloured.* P 14.

754	45 s. Type **213**	..	70	30
755	60 s. Vaisala Beach, Savaii	..	90	40
756	70 s. Solosolo Beach, Upolu	..	95	75
757	$2 Neiafu Beach, Savaii	..	1·75	3·00
754/7	..	*Set of 4*	3·75	4·00

(Des M. Bradbery. Litho Questa)

1987 (30 Sept). *Bicentenary of Australian Settlement (1988) (1st issue). Explorers of the Pacific.* T **214** *and similar horiz designs. Multicoloured.* P 14 × 14½.

758	40 s. Type **214**	..	50	25
759	45 s. Capt. James Cook	..	65	40
760	80 s. Comte Louis-Antoine de Bougainville		80	80
761	$2 Comte Jean de la Perouse	..	1·40	2·25
758/61	..	*Set of 4*	3·00	3·25
MS762	90 × 73 mm. No. 761	..	1·40	1·75

See also Nos. 768/72.

(215)

216 Christmas Tree

1987 (16 Oct). *"Hafnia" International Stamp Exhibition, Copenhagen. No.* **MS**762 *optd with* T **215** *in red.*

MS763	90 × 73 mm. $2 Comte Jean de la Perouse	..	2·00	2·00

(Des Josephine Martin. Litho Questa)

1987 (30 Nov). *Christmas.* T **216** *and similar square designs. Multicoloured.* P 14.

764	40 s. Type **216**	..	30	25
765	45 s. Family going to church	..	40	30
766	50 s. Bamboo fire-gun	..	45	35
767	80 s. Inter-island transport	..	1·10	1·00
764/7	..	*Set of 4*	2·00	1·75

OMNIBUS ISSUES

Details, together with prices for complete sets, of the various Omnibus issues from the 1935 Silver Jubilee series to date are included in a special section following Zimbabwe at the end of Volume 2.

217 Samoa Coat of Arms and Australia Post Logo

218 Airport Terminal and Douglas DC-9 Airliner taking off

(Des A. Theobald. Litho Questa)

1988 (27 Jan). *Bicentenary of Australian Settlement (2nd issue). Postal Services.* T **217** *and similar vert designs. Multicoloured.* P 14½ × 14.

768	45 s. Type **217**	..	80	80
	a. Horiz strip of 5. Nos. 768/72	..	3·50	
769	45 s. Samoan mail van and Boeing 727 airplane		80	80
770	45 s. Loading Boeing 727 mail plane	..	80	80
771	45 s. Australian mail van and Boeing 727	..	80	80
772	45 s. "Congratulations Australia" message on airmail letter		80	80
768/72	..	*Set of 5*	3·50	3·50

Nos. 768/72 were printed together, *se-tenant*, in horizontal strips of 5 throughout the sheet, Nos. 769/71 forming a composite design.

(Des E. Nisbet. Litho Walsall)

1988 (24 Mar). *Opening of Faleolo Airport.* T **218** *and similar horiz designs. Multicoloured.* P 13 × 13½.

773	40 s. Type **218**	..	60	35
774	45 s. Boeing 727	..	65	35
775	60 s. De Havilland D.H.C.6 Twin Otter	..	80	65
776	70 s. Boeing 737	..	90	1·25
777	80 s. Boeing 727 and control tower	..	1·00	1·40
778	$1 Douglas DC-9 over "fale" (house)	..	1·10	1·60
773/8	..	*Set of 6*	4·50	5·00

219 "Expo '88" Pacific Islands Village

220 Mormon Temple, Apia

(Des C. Abbott. Litho Walsall)

1988 (30 Apr). *"Expo '88" World Fair, Brisbane.* T **219** *and similar horiz designs. Multicoloured.* P 14 × 14½.

779	45 s. Type **219**	..	30	30
780	70 s. Expo Complex and monorail	..	1·25	1·25
781	$2 Map of Australia showing Brisbane	..	2·00	2·75
779/81	..	*Set of 3*	3·25	3·75

(Des Jennifer Toombs. Litho CPE Australia Ltd, Melbourne)

1988 (9 June). *Centenary of Arrival of the Latter-Day Saints in Samoa. Sheet* 86 × 77 *mm. P* 13½.

MS782	**220** $3 multicoloured	..	1·50	2·00

221 Athletics

222 Spotted Triller

(Des D. Miller. Litho Format)

1988 (10 Aug). *Olympic Games, Seoul.* T **221** *and similar vert designs. Multicoloured.* P 14.

783	15 s. Type **221**	..	10	10
784	60 s. Weightlifting	..	30	35
785	80 s. Boxing	..	40	45
786	$2 Olympic stadium	..	1·10	1·25
783/6	..	*Set of 4*	1·75	1·90
MS787	85 × 100 mm. Nos. 783/6	..	1·90	2·40

(Des N. Arlott (No. 797a), D. Johnston (others). Litho CPE Australia Ltd, Melbourne (Nos. 788/97) or Questa (Nos. 797a/803))

1988 (17 Aug)–**98**. *Birds.*

(a) Vert designs as T **222**. *Multicoloured.* P 13½.

788	10 s. Type **222**	..	60	30
789	15 s. Samoan Wood Rail	..	70	35
790	20 s. Flat-billed Kingfisher	..	90	45
791	25 s. Samoan Fantail	..	90	45
792	35 s. Scarlet Robin	..	1·00	55
793	40 s. Black-breasted Honeyeater ("Mao")	..	1·00	45
794	50 s. Cardinal Honeyeater	..	1·00	40
795	65 s. Yellow-fronted Whistler	..	1·50	50
796	75 s. Many-coloured Fruit Dove	..	1·75	60
797	85 s. White-throated Pigeon	..	1·75	70

(b) Multicoloured designs, 25×40 mm (25 s.) or 45×28 mm (others). P 14 (25 s.) or 13½×14 (others)

797a	25 s.	Many-coloured Fruit Dove (24.8.98)	10	10
798	75 s.	Silver Gull (28.2.89)	1·75	80
799	85 s.	Great Frigate Bird (28.2.89)	1·75	90
800	90 s.	Eastern Reef Heron (28.2.89)	3·50	1·25
801	$3	Short-tailed Albatross (28.2.89)	1·50	1·40
802	$10	White Tern (31.7.89)	4·00	4·25
803	$20	Shy Albatross (31.7.89)	8·25	8·50
788/803		Set of 17	28·00	20·00

For No. 797a in miniature sheet commemorating "Hong Kong '97" see No. MS1004.

223 Forest

224 Congregational Church of Jesus, Apia

(Des G. Vasarhelyi. Litho Questa)

1988 (25 Oct). *National Conservation Campaign.* T **223** and similar multicoloured designs. P 14 × 13½ (15, 40, 45 s.) or 13½ × 14 (others).

807	15 s.	Type 223	50	15
808	40 s.	Samoan handicrafts	55	30
809	45 s.	Forest wildlife	90	35
810	50 s.	Careful use of water (horiz)	80	40
811	60 s.	Fishing (horiz)	1·10	60
812	$1	Coconut plantation (horiz)	1·25	1·00
807/12		Set of 6	4·50	2·50

(Des N. Shewring. Litho Format)

1988 (14 Nov). *Christmas. Samoan Churches.* T **224** and similar vert designs. Multicoloured. P 14.

813	15 s.	Type 224	15	10
814	40 s.	Roman Catholic Church, Leauva'a	35	25
815	45 s.	Congregational Christian Church, Moataa	40	30
816	$2	Baha'i Temple, Vailima	1·25	2·50
813/16		Set of 4	2·25	2·75
MS817	143 × 64 mm. Nos. 813/16		2·75	2·75

225 Phaius flavus

226 Eber (German gunboat)

(Des H. Bevan. Litho Questa)

1989 (31 Jan). *Orchids (2nd series).* T **225** and similar vert designs. Multicoloured. P 14 × 13½.

818	15 s.	Type 225	15	10
819	45 s.	Calanthe triplicata	35	30
820	60 s.	Luisia teretifolia	40	35
821	$3	Dendrobium mohlianum	1·75	2·00
818/21		Set of 4	2·40	2·50

(Des E. Nisbet. Litho Walsall)

1989 (16 Mar). *Centenary of Great Apia Hurricane.* T **226** and similar horiz designs. Multicoloured. P 14.

822	50 s.	Type 226	1·10	55
		a. Horiz strip of 4. Nos. 822/5	4·75	
823	65 s.	Olga (German corvette)	1·25	65
824	85 s.	H.M.S. Calliope (screw corvette)	1·40	75
825	$2	U.S.S. Vandalia (corvette)	1·60	1·40
822/5		Set of 4	4·75	3·00

Nos. 822/5 were printed together, *se-tenant*, in horizontal strips of 4 throughout the sheet.
See also No. MS839.

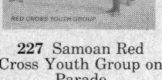

227 Samoan Red Cross Youth Group on Parade

228 Virgin Mary and Joseph

(Des L. Curtis. Litho Questa)

1989 (15 May). *125th Anniv of International Red Cross.* T **227** and similar vert designs. Multicoloured. P 14½×14.

826	50 s.	Type 227	30	30
827	65 s.	Blood donors	40	45

828	75 s.	Practising first aid	45	55
829	$3	Red Cross volunteers carrying patient	1·60	2·25
826/9		Set of 4	2·50	3·25

(Des A. Theobald ($3), D. Miller (others). Litho Questa)

1989 (20 July). *20th Anniv of First Manned Landing on Moon.* Multicoloured designs as T **126** of Ascension. W w **16** (sideways on 50, 65 c.). P 14×13½ (18 s., $2) or 14 (others).

830	18 s.	Saturn rocket on mobile launcher	40	15
831	50 s.	Crew of "Apollo 14" (30×30 mm)	60	35
832	65 s.	"Apollo 14" emblem (30×30 mm)	75	45
833	$2	Tracks of lunar transporter	1·60	1·75
830/3		Set of 4	3·00	2·40
MS834	100×83 mm. $3 Aldrin with U.S. flag on Moon. P 14×13½		2·75	3·50

(Des T. Chance. Litho Cartor)

1989 (1 Nov). *Christmas.* T **228** and similar horiz designs. Multicoloured. P 13½.

835	18 s.	Type 228	30	10
836	50 s.	Shepherds	75	30
837	55 s.	Donkey and ox	80	35
838	$2	Three Wise Men	2·50	4·00
S35/8		Set of 4	3·75	4·25

(Litho Walsall)

1989 (17 Nov). *"World Stamp Expo '89" International Stamp Exhibition, Washington.* Sheet 91×105 mm containing designs as Nos. 824/5. Multicoloured. W **61**. Imperf.

MS839	85 s. H.M.S. Calliope; $2 U.S.S. Vandalia		3·75	4·25

229 Pao Pao Outrigger

(Des R. Roberts. Litho Note Ptg Branch, Reserve Bank of Australia)

1990 (31 Jan). *Local Transport.* T **229** and similar horiz designs. Multicoloured. P 14×15.

840	18 s.	Type 229	35	20
841	55 s.	Fautasi (large canoe)	85	65
842	60 s.	Polynesian Airlines De Havilland D.H.C.6 Twin Otter aircraft	1·75	1·40
843	$3	Lady Samoa (ferry)	3·75	5·00
840/3		Set of 4	6·00	6·50

230 Bismarck and Brandenburg Gate, Berlin

(Des G. Vasarhelyi. Litho Cartor)

1990 (19 Apr). *Treaty of Berlin, 1889, and Opening of Berlin Wall, 1989.* T **230** and similar horiz designs. Multicoloured. P 14×13½.

844	75 s.	Type 230	1·75	2·25
		a. Horiz pair. Nos. 844/5	5·25	6·00
845	$3	Adler (German steam gunboat)	3·50	3·75

Nos. 844/5 were printed together, *se-tenant*, in horizontal pairs throughout the sheet, each pair forming a composite design showing Berliners on the Wall near the Brandenburg Gate.

231 Penny Black and Alexandra Palace, London

(Des G. Vasarhelyi. Litho Cartor)

1990 (3 May). *"Stamp World London 90" International Stamp Exhibition.* P 14×13½.

846	231	$3 multicoloured	2·50	3·00

232 Visitors' Bureau

(Des D. Miller. Litho B.D.T.)

1990 (30 July). *Tourism.* T **232** and similar horiz designs. Multicoloured. P 14.

847	18 s.	Type 232	30	10
848	50 s.	Village resort	55	30
849	65 s.	Aggie's Hotel	70	60
850	$3	Swimming pool, Tusitala Hotel	2·50	4·00
847/50		Set of 4	3·50	4·50

233 1964 2nd Anniv of Treaty of Friendship 3 s. Commemorative and "NZ 1990" Logo

(Des N. Eustis. Litho Leigh-Mardon Ltd, Melbourne)

1990 (24 Aug). *"New Zealand 1990" International Stamp Exhibition, Auckland.* Sheet 130×85 mm. P 13.

MS851	233	$3 multicoloured	2·75	3·75

234 "Virgin and Child" (Bellini)

235 William Draper III (administrator) and 40th Anniv Logo

(Des G. Vasarhelyi. Litho Security Printers (M), Malaysia)

1990 (31 Oct). *Christmas. Paintings.* T **234** and similar vert designs. Multicoloured. P 12½.

852	18 s.	Type 234	30	10
853	50 s.	"Virgin and Child with St. Peter and St. Paul" (Bouts)	70	30
854	55 s.	"School of Love" (Correggio)	75	35
855	$3	"Virgin and Child" (Cima)	3·25	4·25
852/5		Set of 4	4·50	4·50

The 55 s. value should have shown "The Madonna of the Basket" by the same artist and is so inscribed.

(Des D. Miller. Litho Cartor)

1990 (26 Nov). *40th Anniv of U.N. Development Programme.* P 13½.

856	235	$3 multicoloured	2·50	3·25

236 Black-capped Lory

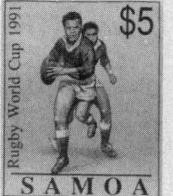

237 Peter Fatialofa (Samoan captain)

(Des R. Roberts. Litho B.D.T.)

1991 (8 Apr). *Parrots.* T **236** and similar vert designs. Multicoloured. P 13½.

857	18 s.	Type 236	75	40
858	50 s.	Eclectus Parrot	1·25	60
859	65 s.	Scarlet Macaw	1·25	85
860	$3	Palm Cockatoo	2·75	4·50
857/60		Set of 4	5·50	5·75

(Des D. Miller. Litho Questa)

1991 (17 June). *65th Birthday of Queen Elizabeth II and 70th Birthday of Prince Philip.* Vert designs as T **58** of Kiribati. Multicoloured. W w **16** (sideways). P 14½×14.

861	75 s.	Prince Philip in the countryside	90	1·25
		a. Horiz pair. Nos. 861/2 separated by label	2·40	3·00
862	$2	Queen wearing yellow lei	1·50	1·75

Nos. 861/2 were printed together in a similar sheet format to Nos. 366/7 of Kiribati.

(Des G. Vasarhelyi. Litho Questa)
1991 (21 Oct). *World Cup Rugby Championships. Sheet 121×75 mm. P 14½×14.*
MS863 237 $5 multicoloured .. .. 7·00 7·50

238 "O Come All Ye Faithful"   239 *Herse convolvuli*

(Des Jennifer Toombs. Litho Questa)
1991 (31 Oct). *Christmas. Carols (1st series). T* **238** *and similar horiz designs. Multicoloured. P 14×14½.*
864 20 s. Type 238 .. .. 45 10
865 60 s. "Joy to the World" 85 40
866 75 s. "Hark the Herald Angels sing" .. 1·10 70
867 $4 "We wish you a Merry Christmas" .. 4·00 6·00
864/7 .. .. Set of 4 5·75 6·50
See also Nos. 886/9 and 907/11.

(Des I. Loe. Litho Questa)
1991 (16 Nov). *"Phila Nippon '91" International Stamp Exhibition, Tokyo. Samoan Hawkmoths. T* **239** *and similar horiz designs. P 13½×14.*
868 60 s. Type 239 .. .. 1·00 70
869 75 s. *Gnathothlibus erotus* .. .. 1·10 80
870 85 s. *Deilephila celerio* .. .. 1·25 1·00
871 $3 *Cephonodes armatus* .. .. 4·00 5·25
868/71 .. .. Set of 4 6·50 7·00

240 Head of State inspecting Guard of Honour   241 Samoa Express 1d. Stamp, 1877

(Des G. Vasarhelyi and D. Miller. Litho Walsall)
1992 (8 Jan). *30th Anniv of Independence. T* **240** *and similar horiz designs. Multicoloured. P 14.*
872 50 s. Type 240 .. .. 70 30
873 65 s. Siva ceremony 75 50
874 $1 Commemorative float .. .. 1·25 1·50
875 $3 Raising Samoan flag .. .. 3·00 4·50
872/5 .. .. Set of 4 5·25 6·00

(Des D. Miller. Litho Questa ($3), Leigh-Mardon Ltd, Melbourne (others))
1992 (6 Feb). *40th Anniv of Queen Elizabeth II's Accession. Horiz designs as T* **113** *of Kenya. Multicoloured. W w 14 (sideways) ($3) or w 16 (sideways) (others). P 14.*
876 20 s. Queen and Prince Philip with umbrellas 45 10
877 60 s. Queen and Prince Philip on Royal Yacht .. .. 1·25 70
878 75 s. Queen in multicoloured hat .. 85 75
879 85 s. Three portraits of Queen Elizabeth .. 95 85
880 $3 Queen Elizabeth II .. .. 2·25 3·25
876/80 .. .. Set of 5 5·25 5·00

(Des L. Curtis. Litho Questa)
1992 (17 Apr). *500th Anniv of Discovery of America by Columbus. Sheet 91×70 mm. P 14½×14.*
MS881 241 $4 multicoloured .. .. 3·00 3·75

242 Weightlifting   243 Narrow-banded Batfish

(Des D. Miller. Litho Questa)
1992 (28 July). *Olympic Games, Barcelona. T* **242** *and similar vert designs. Multicoloured. P 14.*
882 60 s. Type 242 .. .. 80 70
883 75 s. Boxing 90 80
884 85 s. Running .. .. 1·00 1·00
885 $3 Montjuic Olympic Stadium, Barcelona 3·00 4·00
882/5 .. .. Set of 4 5·25 6·00

(Des Jennifer Toombs. Litho Walsall)
1992 (28 Oct). *Christmas. Carols (2nd series). Horiz designs as T* **238**. *Multicoloured. P 14×14½.*
886 50 s. "God rest you Merry Gentle-men" .. 55 30
887 60 s. "While Shepherds watched their Flocks by Night" .. 65 55
888 75 s. "Away in a Manger, no Crib for a Bed" 75 70
889 $4 "O little Town of Bethlehem" .. 3·25 5·00
886/9 .. .. Set of 4 4·75 6·00

(Des G. Drummond. Litho Walsall)
1993 (17 Mar). *Fishes. T* **243** *and similar horiz designs. Multicoloured. P 14.*
890 60 s. Type 243 .. .. 70 60
891 75 s. Clown Surgeonfish 85 85
892 $1 Black-tailed Snapper .. .. 1·25 1·75
893 $3 Long-nosed Emperor .. .. 2·75 4·00
890/3 .. .. Set of 4 5·00 6·50

244 Samoan Players performing Traditional War Dance

(Des G. Vasarhelyi. Litho Questa)
1993 (12 May). *Rugby World Cup Seven-a-Side Championship, Edinburgh. T* **244** *and similar multicoloured designs. P 13½×14.*
894 60 s. Type 244 .. .. 1·00 65
895 75 s. Two players (*vert*) .. .. 1·10 75
896 85 s. Player running with ball and badge (*vert*) .. .. 1·25 1·10
897 $3 Edinburgh Castle .. .. 4·25 5·50
894/7 .. .. Set of 4 7·00 7·25

245 Flying Foxes hanging from Branch   246 Exhibition Emblem

(Des Jennifer Toombs. Litho Questa)
1993 (10 June). *Endangered Species. Flying Foxes. T* **245** *and similar horiz designs. Multicoloured. P 14×14½.*
898 20 s. Type 245 .. .. 90 30
899 50 s. Flying Fox with young .. .. 1·40 70
900 60 s. Flying Foxes hunting for food .. 1·60 1·00
901 75 s. Flying Fox feeding from plant .. 1·75 1·60
898/901 .. .. Set of 4 5·00 3·25

(Des and litho Walsall)
1993 (16 Aug). *"Taipei '93" Asian International Stamp Exhibition, Taiwan. Sheet 137×64 mm. P 14.*
MS902 246 $5 lemon, light greenish blue & black 6·50 7·50

247 Globe, Letter and Flowers

(Des G. Vasarhelyi. Litho Walsall)
1993 (8 Oct). *World Post Day. T* **247** *and similar horiz designs. Multicoloured. P 14.*
903 60 s. Type 247 .. .. 55 45
904 75 s. Post Office counter 70 80
905 85 s. Hands exchanging letter .. 80 90
906 $4 Globe, national flags and letter .. 3·50 5·00
903/6 .. .. Set of 4 5·00 6·50

(Des Jennifer Toombs. Litho Walsall)
1993 (1 Nov). *Christmas. Carols (3rd series). Horiz designs as T* **238**. *Multicoloured. P 14×14½.*
907 20 s. "Silent Night" 25 10
908 60 s. "As with Gladness Men of Old" .. 65 45
909 75 s. "Mary had a Baby - yes, Lord!" .. 80 55
910 $1.50 "Once in Royal David's City" .. 1·40 2·25
911 $3 "Angels from the Realms of Glory" .. 3·50 4·50
907/11 .. .. Set of 5 6·00 7·00

248 *Alveopora allingi*

(Des I. Loe. Litho B.D.T.)
1994 (18 Feb). *Corals. T* **248** *and simlar horiz designs. Multicoloured. P 14.*
912 20 s. Type 248 .. .. 30 10
913 60 s. *Acropora polystoma* 65 45
914 90 s. *Acropora listeri* 90 90
915 $4 *Acropora grandis* .. .. 2·75 3·75
912/15 .. .. Set of 4 4·25 4·75

1994 (18 Feb). *"Hong Kong '94" International Stamp Exhibition. Nos. 912/15 optd as T* **272** *of Jamaica.*
916 20 s. Type 248 .. .. 30 10
917 60 s. *Acropora polystoma* 65 45
918 90 s. *Acropora listeri* 90 90
919 $4 *Acropora grandis* .. .. 2·75 3·75
916/19 .. .. Set of 4 4·25 4·75

249 Samoan Rugby Management Team   250 *Anaphaeis java* and *Acraea andromacha* (butterflies)

(Des G. Vasarhelyi. Litho Walsall)
1994 (11 Apr). *Samoan National Rugby Team. T* **249** *and similar horiz designs. Multicoloured. P 14.*
920 70 s. Type 249 .. .. 70 60
921 90 s. Test match against Wales .. 80 80
922 95 s. Test match against New Zealand .. 80 80
923 $4 Apia Park Stadium .. .. 3·50 5·00
920/3 .. .. Set of 4 5·25 6·50

(Des R. Watton. Litho Cartor)
1994 (16 Aug). *"Philakorea '94" International Stamp Exhibition, Seoul. Sheet 99×82 mm. P 13×13½.*
MS924 250 $5 multicoloured .. .. 3·75 4·50

251 Solo Singer and Choir   252 *Equator* (schooner)

(Des Patricia Altman. Litho Southern Colour Print, Dunedin, New Zealand)
1994 (22 Sept). *Teuila Tourism Festival. T* **251** *and similar horiz designs. Multicoloured. P 13½.*
925 70 s. Type 251 .. .. 65 45
926 90 s. Fire dancer 75 65
927 95 s. Festival float 75 65
928 $4 Band outside hotel .. .. 3·75 5·00
925/8 .. .. Set of 4 5·50 6·00

(Des C. Abbott. Litho Walsall)
1994 (21 Nov). *Death Centenary of Robert Louis Stevenson (author). T* **252** *and similar multicoloured designs. P 14.*
929 70 s. Type 252 .. .. 60 50
930 90 s. Robert Louis Stevenson 70 80
931 $1.20 Stevenson's tomb, Mt Vaea .. 95 1·25
932 $4 Vailima House (*horiz*) .. .. 3·25 4·50
929/32 .. .. Set of 4 5·00 6·50

PRICES OF SETS

Set prices are given for many issues, generally those containing three stamps or more. Definitive sets include one of each value or major colour change, but do not cover different perforations, die types or minor shades. Where a choice is possible the set prices are based on the cheapest versions of the stamps included in the listings.

253 Santa Claus   254 Lotofaga Beach, Aleipata
on House

(Des D. Miller. Litho Questa)

1994 (30 Nov). *Christmas. Children's Paintings. T 253 and similar vert designs. Multicoloured. P 14.*
933	70 s. Type 253			60	50
934	95 s. Star over house and palm trees			70	70
935	$1.20, Family outing			95	1·25
936	$4 "Merry Christmas"			3·25	5·00
933/6			Set of 4	5·00	6·75

(Des D. Miller. Litho Enschedé)

1995 (29 Mar). *Scenic Views. T 254 and similar horiz designs. Multicoloured. P 14½×13½.*
937	5 s. Type 254			10	10
938	10 s. Nuutele Island			10	10
939	30 s. Satuiatua, Savaii			10	15
940	50 s. Sinalele, Aleipata			20	25
941	60 s. Paradise Beach, Lefaga			25	30
942	70 s. Houses at Piula Cave			30	35
943	80 s. Taga blowholes			35	40
944	90 s. View from East Coast road			35	40
945	95 s. Outrigger canoes, Leulumoega			40	45
946	$1 Parliament Building			40	45
937/46			Set of 10	2·25	2·75

255 Under-12s' Rugby Players   256 Leatherback
Turtle

(Des G. Vasarhelyi. Litho Enshedé)

1995 (25 May). *World Cup Rugby Championship, South Africa. T 255 and similar horiz designs. Multicoloured. P 14½×13.*
957	70 s. Type 255			55	55
958	90 s. Secondary school players			70	70
959	$1 Samoan and New Zealand test match			75	75
960	$4 Ellis Park Stadium, Johannesburg			2·75	4·00
957/60			Set of 4	4·25	5·50

(Des R. Watton. Litho Cartor (Nos. 961/4) or Questa (Nos. MS965))

1995 (31 May). *50th Anniv of End of Second World War. Multicoloured designs as T 75 of Kiribati. P 13½.*
961	70 s. Vought Sikorsky OS2U Kingfisher (seaplane)			65	55
962	90 s. Chance Vought F4U Corsair (fighter)			80	70
963	95 s. American transport ship and landing craft			85	75
964	$3 American marines landing on Samoa			4·00	4·00
961/4			Set of 4	4·75	5·50
MS965	75×85 mm. $4 Reverse of 1939-45 War Medal (vert). P 14			2·40	2·75

(Des D. Miller. Litho Cartor)

1995 (24 Aug). *Year of the Sea Turtle. T 256 and similar vert designs. Multicoloured. P 13×13½.*
966	70 s. Type 256			55	55
967	90 s. Loggerhead Turtle			70	70
968	$1 Green Turtle			75	75
969	$4 Pacific Ridley Turtle			2·75	3·50
966/9			Set of 4	4·25	5·00

257 *Phaius tankervilleae*   258 Madonna and Child

(Des Jennifer Toombs. Litho B.D.T.)

1995 (1 Sept). *"Singapore '95" International Stamp Exhibition. Orchids. Sheet 76×100 mm. P 13½.*
MS970	257 $5 multicoloured			3·25	3·75

For further miniature sheet using this design as a $2.50 value see No. MS1006.

(Des A. Theobald. Litho Walsall)

1995 (24 Oct). *50th Anniv of United Nations. Horiz designs as T 284 of Jamaica. Multicoloured. P 14.*
971	70 s. Hospital lorry, Bosnia, 1995			85	55
972	90 s. Bell Sioux helicopter and ambulance, Korea, 1952			1·40	85
973	$1 Bell 212 helicopter, Bosnia, 1995			1·60	95
974	$4 R.N.Z.A.F. Hawker Siddeley Andover, Somalia, 1995			3·50	4·00
971/4			Set of 4	6·50	5·75

(Des D. Miller. Litho Walsall)

1995 (15 Nov). *Christmas. T 258 and similar vert designs. Multicoloured. P 14½×14.*
975	25 s. Type 258			20	10
976	70 s. Wise Man wearing green turban			60	50
977	90 s. Wise Man with Child in manger			75	65
978	$5 Wise Man wearing red turban			3·50	5·50
975/8			Set of 4	4·75	6·00

259 Hands cupped   260 Moon Hare
under Waterfall   preparing Elixir of
and Bird   Life

(Des G. Vasarhelyi. Litho Walsall)

1996 (26 Jan). *Environment. Water Resources. T 259 and similar vert designs. Multicoloured. P 14.*
979	70 s. Type 259			50	50
980	90 s. Young girl and "WATER FOR LIFE" slogan			65	65
981	$2 Village and waterfall			1·40	2·00
982	$4 Irrigation system			2·75	3·75
979/82			Set of 4	4·75	6·25

(Des D. Miller. Litho Walsall)

1996 (22 Apr). *70th Birthday of Queen Elizabeth II. Vert designs as T 55 of New Zealand (Tokelau), each incorporating a different photograph of the Queen. Multicoloured. P 14½.*
983	70 s. Main Street, Apia			50	40
984	90 s. Beach scene, Neiafu			65	50
985	$1 Vailima House (Head of State's residence)			75	60
986	$3 Parliament Building			2·00	3·25
983/6			Set of 4	3·50	4·25
MS987	64×66 mm. $5 Queen Elizabeth II			3·00	3·50

(Des N. Shewring. Litho B.D.T.)

1996 (18 May). *Moon Festival. Sheet 103×83 mm. P 14.*
MS988	260 $2.50, multicoloured			1·60	2·00

No. MS988 also includes the "CHINA '96" International Stamp Exhibition logo on the sheet margin.

261 Meeting Venue   262 Boxing

(Des N. Shewring. Litho Enschedé)

1996 (19 June). *63rd Session of the EU-ACP Council of Ministers. Sheet 135×71 mm. P 13½.*
MS989	261 $5 multicoloured			3·25	3·75

(Des D. Miller. Litho Enschedé)

1996 (15 July). *Centenary of Modern Olympic Games. T 262 and similar vert designs. Multicoloured. P 13½.*
990	70 s. Type 262			60	40
991	90 s. Running			70	55
992	$1 Weightlifting			80	60
993	$4 Throwing the javelin			2·75	4·50
990/3			Set of 4	4·25	5·50

ALTERED CATALOGUE NUMBERS

Any Catalogue numbers altered from the last edition are shown as a list in the introductory pages.

---

263 Festival Logo   264 Young Children

(Des D. Miller. Litho Questa)

1996 (13 Sept). *7th Pacific Festival of Arts, Apia. T 263 and similar vert designs. Multicoloured. P 14.*
994	60 s. Type 263			40	35
995	70 s. Decorated pottery			50	40
996	80 s. Textile pattern			55	55
997	90 s. Traditional dancing			60	60
998	$1 Carved poles			70	70
999	$4 Man wearing traditional headdress and necklace			2·00	3·00
994/9			Set of 6	4·25	5·00

(Des G. Vasarhelyi. Litho Questa)

1996 (24 Oct). *50th Anniv of U.N.I.C.E.F. T 264 and similar horiz designs. Multicoloured. P 14.*
1000	70 s. Type 264			45	40
1001	90 s. Children in hospital			60	60
1002	$1 Child receiving injection			70	70
1003	$4 Mothers and children			2·00	2·75
1000/3			Set of 4	3·25	4·00

(Des N. Arlott. Litho Questa)

1997 (3 Feb). *"HONG KONG '97" International Stamp Exhibition. Sheet, 130×90 mm, containing No. 797a. P 14.*
MS1004	$3 Many-coloured Fruit Dove			1·75	2·00

266 First U.S.A. and Samoa Postage Stamps

(Des G. Vasarhelyi. Litho Questa)

1997 (29 May). *"Pacific '97" International Stamp Exhibition, San Francisco. Sheet 96×70 mm. P 14½×15.*
MS1005	266 $5 multicoloured			2·75	3·25

(Des Jennifer Toombs. Litho Walsall)

1997 (20 June). *Return of Hong Kong to China. Sheet 130×90 mm, containing design as T 257, but with new value and imprint date. W w 14. P 14½×14.*
MS1006	257 $2.50, multicoloured			1·50	1·75

(Des N. Shewring (No. MS1013), D. Miller (others). Litho Questa (No. MS1013), Cartor (others))

1997 (10 July). *Golden Wedding of Queen Elizabeth and Prince Philip. Multicoloured designs as T 87 of Kiribati. W w 14. P 13.*
1007	70 s. Queen Elizabeth			65	65
	a. Horiz pair. Nos. 1007/8			1·25	1·25
1008	70 s. Prince Philip carriage-driving at Royal Windsor Horse Show, 1996			65	65
1009	90 s. Queen Elizabeth and horse			80	90
	a. Horiz pair. Nos. 1009/10			1·60	1·75
1010	90 s. Prince Philip laughing			80	90
1011	$1 Prince Philip and Prince Edward with Zara Phillips on horseback, 1993			80	90
	a. Horiz pair. Nos. 1011/12			1·60	1·75
1012	$1 Queen Elizabeth and Prince William			80	90
1007/12			Set of 6	4·00	4·50
MS1013	111×70 mm. $5 Queen Elizabeth and Prince Philip in landau (horiz). No wmk. P 14×14½			3·00	3·50

Nos. 1007/8, 1009/10 and 1011/12 were each printed together, se-tenant, in horizontal pairs throughout the sheets with the backgrounds forming composite designs.

267 Dolphin on Surface

(Des D. Miller. Litho Questa)

1997 (17 Sept). *26th Anniv of Greenpeace (environmental organisation). T 267 and similar horiz designs. Multicoloured. P 13½×14.*
1014	50 s. Type 267			45	25
1015	60 s. Two dolphins swimming underwater			55	35
1016	70 s. Heads of two dolphins underwater			60	55
1017	$1 Dolphin "laughing"			75	90
1014/17			Set of 4	2·10	1·90
MS1018	113×91 mm. $1.25×4 As Nos. 1014/17			2·75	3·25

268 Christmas Bells   **269** Mangrove Fruit

(Des D. Miller. Litho Questa)

1997 (19 Nov). *Christmas. T* **268** *and similar horiz designs. Multicoloured. P* 14.

1019	70 s.	Type 268		45	35
1020	80 s.	Christmas bauble		50	40
1021	$2	Candle		1·40	1·75
1022	$3	Christmas star		1·60	2·00
1019/22			*Set of* 4	3·50	4·00

(Des Doreen McGuiness. Litho Cartor)

1998 (26 Feb). *Mangroves. T* **269** *and similar vert designs. Multicoloured. P* 13½.

1023	70 s.	Type 269		30	35
1024	80 s.	Mangrove seedlings		35	40
1025	$2	Mangrove roots		1·00	1·25
1026	$4	Mangrove tree on seashore		2·00	2·50
1023/6			*Set of* 4	3·25	4·00

(Des D. Miller. Litho Questa)

1998 (31 Mar–17 Apr). *Diana, Princess of Wales Commemoration. Vert designs as T* **91** *of Kiribati. Multicoloured. P* 14½×14.

1027	50 s.	Wearing red jacket, 1990 (17 Apr)		20	25

MS1028 145×70 mm. $1.40, As 50 s.; $1.40 Wearing tweed jacket, 1981; $1.40, Wearing red dress, 1988; $1.40, Carrying bouquets, 1993 (*sold at* $5.60 + 75 s. *charity premium*) .. 2·75 3·25

270 Westland Wallace

(Des A. Theobald. Litho Cartor)

1998 (1 Apr). *80th Anniv of the Royal Air Force. T* **270** *and similar horiz designs. Multicoloured. P* 13½.

1029	70 s.	Type 270		60	35
1030	80 s.	Hawker Fury Mk I		60	40
1031	$2	Vickers Varsity		1·50	1·75
1032	$5	BAC Jet Provost		3·00	3·50
1029/32			*Set of* 4	5·25	5·50

MS1033 110×77 mm. $2 Norman Thompson N.T.2b; $2 Nieuport 27 Scout; $2 Miles Magister; $2 Bristol Bomber .. 4·25 4·50

271 Christmas Star

(Des D. Miller. Litho B.D.T.)

1998 (16 Nov). *Christmas. T* **271** *and similar horiz designs, each showing palm branch and festive decoration. Multicoloured. P* 14.

1034	70 s.	Type 271		50	35
1035	$1.05,	Bell		70	50
1036	$1.40,	Bauble		85	70
1037	$5	Cross		3·25	3·75
1034/7			*Set of* 4	4·75	4·75

272 Outrigger Canoe   **273** Hibiscus and Star

(Des J. Batchelor. Litho Walsall)

1999 (19 Mar). *"Australia '99" World Stamp Exhibition, Melbourne. Maritime Heritage. T* **272** *and similar horiz designs. Multicoloured. P* 14.

1038	70 s.	Type 272		40	35
1039	90 s.	*Heemskerk* and *Zeehan* (Tasman), 1642		50	40
1040	$1.05,	H.M.S. *Resolution* and H.M.S. *Adventure* (Cook), 1773		65	55
1041	$6	New Zealand scow schooner, 1880		3·25	3·50
1038/41			*Set of* 4	4·25	4·25

(Des D. Miller. Litho Walsall)

1999 (19 June). *Royal Wedding. Vert designs as T* **153** *of Pitcairn Islands. Multicoloured. P* 14.

1042	$1.50,	Photographs of Prince Edward and Miss Sophie Rhys-Jones		75	75
1043	$6	Engagement photograph		3·00	3·25

(Des N. Shewring. Litho Walsall)

1999 (20 July). *30th Anniv of First Manned Landing on Moon. Multicoloured designs as T* **296** *of Jamaica. P* 14×13½.

1044	70 s.	Lift-off		40	35
1045	90 s.	Lunar lander separating from service module		45	40
1046	$3	Buzz Aldrin on Moon's surface		1·50	1·60
1047	$5	Command module descending on parachutes		2·50	2·75
1044/7			*Set of* 4	4·25	4·50

MS1048 90×80 mm. $5 Earth as seen from Moon (*circular,* 40 *mm diam*). P 14 .. 2·40 2·75

(Des D. Miller. Litho Cartor)

1999 (24 Aug). *"Queen Elizabeth the Queen Mother's Century". Horiz designs as T* **199** *of St. Helena. Multicoloured. P* 13½.

1049	70 s.	Talking to air-raid victims, 1940		30	35
1050	90 s.	King, Queen and Princess Elizabeth at garden party, South Africa, 1947		35	40
1051	$2	Reviewing scouts at Windsor, 1991		80	85
1052	$6	With Princess Eugenie, 1998		2·50	2·75
1049/52			*Set of* 4	3·75	4·25

MS1053 145×70 mm. $5 Lady Elizabeth Bowes-Lyon, 1923, and Charlie Chaplin film .. 2·40 2·75

(Litho Cartor)

1999 (30 Nov). *Christmas and Millennium. T* **273** *and similar vert designs. Multicoloured. P* 13½.

1054	70 s.	Type 273		30	35
1055	90 s.	Poinsettia and star		35	40
1056	$2	Christmas Cactus and star		80	85
1057	$6	Southern Cross constellation and Samoan flag		2·50	2·75
1054/7			*Set of* 4	3·75	4·25

274 Sunrise

(Litho Questa)

2000 (1 Jan). *New Millennium. T* **274** *and similar horiz design. Multicoloured. P* 14.

1058	70 s.	Type 274		30	35
	a.	Horiz pair. Nos. 1058/9		60	70
1059	70 s.	Sunset		30	35

Nos. 1058/9 were printed together, *se-tenant*, in horizontal pairs throughout the sheets.

(Des Children's Television Workshop. Litho Questa)

2000 (22 Mar). *Sesame Street (children's T.V. programme). Vert designs as T* **101** *of Kiribati. Multicoloured. P* 14½×15.

1060	90 s.	The Count on ladder		35	40
	a.	Sheetlet. Nos. 1060/8		3·00	
1061	90 s.	Ernie on trapeze		35	40
1062	90 s.	Grover swinging on rope		35	40
1063	90 s.	Cookie Monster singing and Prairie Dawn playing piano		35	40
1064	90 s.	Bert with bucket on his head, Elmo and Zoe		35	40
1065	90 s.	Big Bird dressed as tree		35	40
1066	90 s.	Little Bear writing and Telly		35	40
1067	90 s.	Mumiford coming through trap door		35	40
1068	90 s.	Oscar the Grouch and Slimey		35	40
1060/8			*Set of* 9	3·00	3·50

MS1069 139×86 mm. $3 Cookie Monster eating popcorn .. 1·25 1·40

Nos. 1060/8 were printed together, *se-tenant*, in sheetlets of 9 with the backgrounds forming a composite design.

STAMP BOOKLETS

1958. *Blue on yellow (No. SB1) and blue (No. SB3) or black on pink (No. SB2). Stapled.*

SB1 2s. 7d. booklet containing ½d. and 2d. (Nos. 219, 221), each in block of 6, 1d. and 3d. (Nos. 220, 222), each in block of 4

SB2 6s. booklet containing 1d., 3d., 6d. and 8d. (Nos. 220, 222, 224/5), each in block of 4

SB3 9s. 9d. booklet containing ½d., 2d., 5d. and 1s. (Nos. 219, 221, 223, 226), each in block of 6

Set of 3 £400

1960 (Apr). *Contents as Nos. SB1/3, but arms and inscription in black, and colour of covers changed. Stapled.*

SB4 2s. 7d. Green cover
    a. Buff cover
SB5 6s. Grey cover
    a. Blue cover
SB6 9s. 9d. Yellow cover
    a. White cover

Set of 3 (*Nos.* SB4, SB5, SB6) £160
Set of 3 (*Nos.* SB4a, SB5a, SB6a) £160

1962 (Sept). *Black on buff (No. SB7) or green (No. SB8) covers. Inscr* "POSTAGE STAMP BOOKLET NO. 1" (11s. 9d.) *or* "NO. 2" (6s. 9d.). *Stapled.*

SB7 6s. 9d. booklet containing one each of 1d., 2d., 3d., 4d., 6d., 8d., 1s., 1s. 3d. and 2s. 6d. (Nos. 239/47) (loose in cellophane bag) .. 48·00

SB8 11s. 9d. booklet containing one each of 1d., 2d., 3d., 4d., 6d., 8d., 1s., 1s. 3d., 2s. 6d. and 5s. (Nos. 239/48) (loose in cellophane bag) .. 48·00

1962 (Sept)–**64.** *Black on pink (No. SB9) or blue (No. SB10) covers. Inscr* "POSTAGE STAMP BOOKLET NO. 3" (12s.) *or* "NO. 4" (6s.). *Stapled.*

SB9 6s. booklet containing 1d., 3d., 6d. and 8d. (Nos. 239, 241, 243/4), each in block of 4 .. 42·00

SB10 12s. booklet containing 1d., 2d., 3d., 4d., 6d., 8d. and 1s. (Nos. 239/45), each in block of 4 .. 42·00

1964 (Sept)–**67.** *As Nos. SB9/10 but containing stamps with mixed wmks (W* **98** *of New Zealand or W* **61** *of Samoa). Stapled.*

SB11	6s. As No. SB9		*From* 42·00
SB12	12s. As No. SB10		*From* 48·00

1965 (Feb)–**67.** *As Nos. SB7/8, but containing stamps with mixed wmks (W* **98** *of New Zealand or W* **61** *of Samoa). Stapled.*

SB13	6s. 9d. As No. SB7		*From* 42·00
SB14	11s. 9d. As No. SB8		*From* 50·00

The composition of Nos. SB11/14 can vary as to the watermark and as it is possible to substitute stamps of one watermark for those of another, both in the cellophane bags and the blocks, we do not attempt to list them in greater detail. Prices will vary according to the contents.

Sarawak
see Malaysia

Seychelles

Seychelles was administered as a dependency of Mauritius from 1810 until 1903, although separate stamp issues were provided from April 1890 onwards.

The first post office was opened, at Victoria on Mahé, on 11 December 1861 and the stamps of Mauritius were used there until 1890. No further post offices were opened until 1901.

Z 1

Stamps of MAURITIUS *cancelled with Type* Z **1**.

1848–59.
Z1	2d. blue (intermediate impression) (No. 14)		£9000

1859–61.
Z2	6d. blue (No. 32)		£800
Z3	6d. dull purple-slate (No. 33)		£1600
Z4	1s. vermilion (No. 34)		£1300

1860–63. (*Nos. 45/53*).
Z 5	1d. purple-brown		£150
Z 6	2d. blue		£190
Z 7	4d. rose		£160
Z 8	6d. green		£600
Z 9	6d. slate		£450
Z10	9d. dull purple		90·00
Z11	1s. buff		£275
Z12	1s. green		£475

1862.
Z13	6d. slate (No. 54)		£800

1863–72. (*Nos. 56/72*).
Z14	1d. purple-brown		£100
Z14*a*	1d. brown		85·00
Z15	1d. bistre		90·00
Z16	2d. pale blue		95·00
Z17	2d. bright blue		95·00
Z18	3d. deep red		£140
Z19	3d. dull red		85·00
Z20	4d. rose		48·00
Z21	6d. dull violet		£200
Z22	6d. yellow-green		£100
Z23	6d. blue-green		70·00
Z24	9d. yellow-green		£1000
Z25	10d. maroon		£300
Z26	1s. yellow		95·00
Z27	1s. blue		£275
Z28	1s. orange		95·00
Z29	5s. rosy mauve		£650
Z30	5s. bright mauve		£650

1876. (*Nos. 76/7*).
Z31	½d. on 9d. dull purple		£250
Z32	½d. on 10d. maroon		£250

1877. (*Nos. 79/82*).
Z33	½d. on 10d. rose		£425
Z34	1d. on 4d. rose-carmine		
Z35	1s. on 5s. rosy mauve		
Z36	1s. on 5s. bright mauve		

1878. (*Nos. 83/91*).
Z37	2 c. dull rose (lower label blank)		75·00
Z38	4 c. on 1d. bistre		£325
Z39	8 c. on 2d. blue		40·00
Z40	13 c. on 3d. orange-red		£100
Z41	17 c. on 4d. rose		40·00
Z42	25 c. on 6d. slate-blue		90·00
Z43	38 c. on 9d. pale violet		£400
Z44	50 c. on 1s. green		£100
Z45	2 r. 50 on 5s. bright mauve		£400

1879–80. (*Nos. 92/100*).
Z46	2 c. Venetian red		£120
Z47	4 c. orange		£120
Z48	8 c. blue		40·00
Z49	13 c. slate		£900
Z50	17 c. rose		85·00
Z51	25 c. olive-yellow		£170
Z52	38 c. bright purple		£1300
Z53	50 c. green		£800
Z54	2 r. 50, brown-purple		£750

1883–90.
Z55	2 c. Venetian red (No. 102)		85·00
Z56	2 c. green (No. 103)		£150
Z57	4 c. orange (No. 104)		65·00
Z58	4 c. carmine (No. 105)		85·00
Z59	16 c. chestnut (No. 109)		50·00
Z60	25 c. olive-yellow (No. 110)		£100
Z61	50 c. orange (No. 111)		£900

1883.
Z62	16 c. on 17 c. rose (No. 112)		£120

1883.
Z63	16 c. on 17 c. rose (No. 115)		40·00

1885.
Z64	2 c. on 38 c. bright purple (No. 116)		

1887.
Z65	2 c. on 13 c. slate (No. 117)		

POSTAL FISCAL

1889.
ZR1	4 c. lilac (No. R2)		£650

Mauritius stamps are occasionally found cancelled with the "SEYCHELLES" cds. Examples are known dated between 25 and 29 February 1884 when it seems that Type Z **1** may have been mislaid (*Price from* £250).

We no longer list the G.B. 1862 6d. lilac with this obliteration as there is no evidence that the stamps of Great Britain were sold by the Victoria post office.

PRICES FOR STAMPS ON COVER TO 1945

Nos. 1/8	*from* × 20
Nos. 9/24	*from* × 30
No. 25	*from* × 10
No. 26	*from* × 20
No. 27	*from* × 10
Nos. 28/32	*from* × 20
No. 33	*from* × 5
No. 34	*from* × 30
Nos. 35/6	—
Nos. 37/40	*from* × 40
Nos. 41/2	*from* × 25
Nos. 43/5	*from* × 10
Nos. 46/50	*from* × 30
Nos. 51/4	*from* × 10
Nos. 55/6	—
Nos. 57/9	*from* × 10
No. 60/7	*from* × 20
Nos. 68/70	—
Nos. 71/81	*from* × 10
Nos. 82/131	*from* × 5
Nos. 132/4	*from* × 10
Nos. 135/49	*from* × 3

(Currency: 100 cents = 1 Mauritius, later Seychelles rupee)

DEPENDENCY OF MAURITIUS

PRINTERS. Nos. 1 to 123 were typographed by De La Rue & Co.

1

Die I   Die II

In Die I there are lines of shading in the middle compartment of the diadem which are absent from Die II.

Normal   Malformed "S"   Repaired "S"

The malformed "S" occurs on R. 7/3 of the left pane from Key Plate 2. It is believed that the repair to it took place in mid-1898. Both states may occur on other stamps in Types 1 and 4. Stamps subsequently printed from Key Plate 3 showed the "S" normal.

1890 (5 April)–**92.** *Wmk Crown CA. P* 14. (i) *Die I.*
1	1	2 c. green and carmine	2·50	9·00
2		4 c. carmine and green	21·00	11·00
3		8 c. brown-purple and blue	6·50	3·50
4		10 c. ultramarine and brown	6·00	14·00
5		13 c. grey and black	6·00	11·00
6		16 c. chestnut and blue	4·00	4·00

7	1	48 c. ochre and green	20·00	16·00
8		96 c. mauve and carmine	50·00	48·00
1/8			*Set of 8* £100	£100
1/8	Optd "Specimen"		*Set of 8* £190	

(ii) *Die II* (1892)
9	1	2 c. green and rosine	2·25	90
10		4 c. carmine and green	2·25	1·00
11		8 c. brown-purple and ultramarine	5·50	1·75
12		10 c. bright ultramarine and brown	7·00	3·25
13		13 c. grey and black	2·75	1·75
14		16 c. chestnut and ultramarine	42·00	17·00
		a. Malformed "S"		
9/14			*Set of 6* 55·00	17·00

The 10 c. Die I also exists in ultramarine and chestnut, but has so far only been found with "SPECIMEN" overprint (*Price* £375)

(SEYCHELLES POSTAGE 1R. stamp image)

3 cents   **18 CENTS**   4
(2)   (3)

1893 (1 Jan). *Surch locally as T* **2**.
15		3 c. on 4 c. (No. 10)	1·10	1·50
		a. Surch inverted	£300	£375
		b. Surch double	£475	
		c. Surch omitted (in pair with normal)	£5500	
16		12 c. on 16 c. (No. 6)	1·50	3·75
		a. Surch inverted	£450	
		b. Surch double	—	£4500
17		12 c. on 16 c. (No. 14)	7·50	27·00
		a. Surch double	£3750	£3750
		b. Surch omitted (in pair with normal)		
18		15 c. on 16 c. (No. 6)	8·50	13·00
		a. Surch inverted	£300	£350
		b. Surch double	£1100	£1100
19		15 c. on 16 c. (No. 14)	9·00	2·75
		a. Surch inverted	£850	£900
		b. Surch double	£650	£700
		c. Surch triple	£4250	
20		45 c. on 48 c. (No. 7)	18·00	5·50
21		90 c. on 96 c. (No. 8)	40·00	32·00
		a. Wide "O" (3½ mm wide instead of 3 mm)		
		(R. 1/1, 2/1)	£180	
15/21			*Set of 7* 75·00	55·00

Nos. 15, 16, 18, 19 and 20 exist with "cents" omitted and with "cents" above value due to misplacement of the surcharge.

Most examples of the inverted surcharge error No. 16a were officially defaced with a red vertical ink line (*Price* £200, *unused*). Similarly examples of No. 19a exist defaced with a horizontal ink line (*Price* £400, *unused*).

1893 (Nov). *New values. Die II. Wmk Crown CA. P* 14.
22	1	3 c. dull purple and orange	1·50	90
23		12 c. sepia and green	2·50	60
24		15 c. sage-green and lilac	4·50	2·00
25		45 c. brown and carmine	23·00	32·00
22/5			*Set of 4* 28·00	32·00
22/5	Optd "Specimen"		*Set of 4* 95·00	

1896 (1 Aug). *No. 25 surch as T* **3**.
26	1	18 c. on 45 c. brown and carmine	7·00	2·75
		a. Surch double	£1300	£1300
		b. Surch triple	£1700	
27		36 c. on 45 c. brown and carmine	8·00	45·00
		a. Surch double	£1400	
26/7	Optd "Specimen"		*Set of 2* 70·00	

1897–1900. *Colours changed and new values. Die II. Wmk Crown CA. P* 14.
28	1	2 c. orange-brown and green (1900)	2·00	80
		a. Repaired "S"	£130	
29		6 c. carmine (1900)	3·50	40
		a. Repaired "S"	£190	
30		15 c. ultramarine (1900)	3·75	3·25
		a. Repaired "S"	£190	
31		18 c. ultramarine	4·00	90
32		36 c. brown and carmine	20·00	90
33	4	75 c. yellow and violet (1900)	50·00	70·00
		a. Repaired "S"	£325	
34		1 r. bright mauve and deep red	13·00	4·25
35		1 r. 50, grey and carmine (1900)	60·00	85·00
		a. Repaired "S"	£350	
36		2 r. 25, bright mauve and green (1900)	90·00	85·00
		a. Repaired "S"	£425	
28/36			*Set of 9* £225	£225
28/36	Optd "Specimen"		*Set of 9* £225	

3 cents

==========

6 cents

(5)   (5*a*)

1901 (21 June–Oct). *Surch locally with T* **5** *or* **5***a*.
37		3 c. on 10 c. bright ultramarine and brown (No. 12) (10.01)	1·00	60
		a. Surch double	£600	
		b. Surch triple		
		c. Malformed "S"	£120	
38		3 c. on 16 c. chestnut and ultramarine (No. 14) (8.01)	1·75	3·00
		a. Surch inverted	£600	£600
		b. Surch double	£500	
		c. "3 cents" omitted	£500	£550
		d. Malformed "S"	£140	
39		3 c. on 36 c. brown and carmine (No. 32)	50	75
		a. Surch double	£700	£800
		b. "3 cents" omitted	£650	£700
40		6 c. on 8 c. brn-pur & ultram (No. 11) (8.01)	1·00	2·75
		a. Surch inverted	£650	£750
37/40			*Set of 4* 3·75	6·25
37/40	H/S "Specimen"		*Set of 4* £100	

1902 (June). *Surch locally as T 5.*

41	1	2 c. on 4 c. carmine and green (No. 10)		1·60	2·75
42	4	30 c. on 75 c. yellow and violet (No. 33)		1·50	4·00
		a. Narrow "0" in "30" (R. 3/6, 5/2-4)		10·00	42·00
		b. Repaired "S"			£170
43		30 c. on 1 r. bright mauve & dp red (No. 34)		4·50	24·00
		a. Narrow "0" in "30" (R. 3/6, 5/2-4)		22·00	85·00
		b. Surch double			£1400
44		45 c. on 1 r. bright mauve & dp red (No. 34)		3·50	24·00
45		45 c. on 2 r. 25, brt mauve & grn (No. 36)		38·00	70·00
		a. Narrow "5" in "45" (R. 4/1)		£160	£300
		b. Repaired "S"			£325
41/5			*Set of 5*	45·00	£110
41/5 Optd "Specimen"			*Set of 5*	£120	

3 cents

6	7	(8)

Dented frame (R. 1/6 of left pane)

1903 (26 May). *Wmk Crown CA. P 14.*

46	6	2 c. chestnut and green		1·75	1·50
		a. Dented frame		60·00	
47		3 c. dull green		1·00	1·25
		a. Dented frame		50·00	
48		6 c. carmine		2·25	1·00
		a. Dented frame		70·00	
49		12 c. olive-sepia and dull green		2·25	2·25
		a. Dented frame		75·00	
50		15 c. ultramarine		4·00	2·25
		a. Dented frame		£110	
51		18 c. sage-green and carmine		4·00	6·50
		a. Dented frame		£110	
52		30 c. violet and dull green		6·50	11·00
		a. Dented frame		£130	
53		45 c. brown and carmine		7·00	11·00
		a. Dented frame		£180	
		w. Wmk inverted		£200	
54	7	75 c. yellow and violet		10·00	27·00
		a. Dented frame		£180	
55		1 r. 50, black and carmine		42·00	70·00
		a. Dented frame		£325	
56		2 r. 25, purple and green		28·00	85·00
		a. Dented frame		£275	
46/56			*Set of 11*	95·00	£190
46/56 Optd "Specimen"			*Set of 11*	£190	

1903. *Surch locally with T 8.*

57	6	3 c. on 15 c. ultramarine (3.7)		85	3·00
		a. Dented frame		£100	
58		3 c. on 18 c. sage-green and carmine (2.9)		2·50	30·00
		a. Dented frame		£150	
59		3 c. on 45 c. brown and carmine (21.7)		2·75	3·00
		a. Dented frame		£150	
57/9			*Set of 3*	5·50	32·00
57/9 H/S "Specimen"			*Set of 3*	80·00	

CROWN COLONY

The Seychelles became a Separate Crown Colony by Letters Patent dated 31 August 1903.

1906. *Wmk Mult Crown CA. P 14.*

60	6	2 c. chestnut and green		1·50	4·25
		a. Dented frame		50·00	
61		3 c. dull green		1·50	1·50
		a. Dented frame		60·00	
62		6 c. carmine		1·75	80
		a. Dented frame		65·00	
63		12 c. olive-sepia and dull green		3·00	2·75
		a. Dented frame		95·00	
64		15 c. ultramarine		3·00	2·00
		a. Dented frame		90·00	
65		18 c. sage-green and carmine		3·00	6·50
		a. Dented frame		90·00	
66		30 c. violet and dull green		6·00	8·00
		a. Dented frame		£160	
67		45 c. brown and carmine		3·00	6·50
		a. Dented frame		£140	
68	7	75 c. yellow and violet		8·50	55·00
		a. Dented frame		£190	
69		1 r. 50, black and carmine		50·00	60·00
		a. Dented frame		£350	
70		2 r. 25, purple and green		32·00	60·00
		a. Dented frame		£300	
60/70			*Set of 11*	£100	£180

9	10

1912 (Apr)–13. *Wmk Mult Crown CA. P 14.*

71	9	2 c. chestnut and green		60	4·50
		a. Split "A"		42·00	
72		3 c. green		1·50	60
		a. Split "A"		60·00	

73	9	6 c. aniline carmine (6.13)		10·00	4·50
		a. Carmine-red		4·00	55
		b. Split "A"		95·00	48·00
74		12 c. olive-sepia and dull green (1.13)		1·25	3·75
		a. Split "A"		70·00	
75		15 c. ultramarine		3·00	50
		a. Split "A"		90·00	48·00
76		18 c. sage-green and carmine (1.13)		2·75	4·00
		a. Split "A"		90·00	
77		30 c. violet and green (1.13)		5·00	1·25
		a. Split "A"		£130	80·00
78		45 c. brown and carmine (1.13)		2·75	32·00
		a. Split "A"		£110	
79	10	75 c. yellow and violet (1.13)		2·75	5·50
		a. Split "A"		£110	
80		1 r. 50, black and carmine (1.13)		6·50	85
		a. Split "A"		£190	80·00
81		2 r. 25, dp magenta & grn (*shades*) (1.13)		42·00	2·50
		a. Split "A"		£350	£120
71/81			*Set of 11*	65·00	50·00
71/81 Optd "Specimen"			*Set of 11*	£200	

For illustration of "Split A" flaw see above St. Helena No. 83.

11	12	13

1917–22. *Die I. Wmk Mult Crown CA. Chalk-surfaced paper* (18 c. to 5 r.). *P 14.*

82	11	2 c. chestnut and green		30	2·50
83		3 c. green		1·75	1·25
84	12	5 c. deep brown (1920)		2·00	6·00
85	11	6 c. carmine		1·00	1·50
		a. Rose (1919)		4·50	2·50
86	12	12 c. grey (1919)		75	1·00
87		15 c. ultramarine		1·50	1·50
88		18 c. purple/*yellow* (1919)		3·25	20·00
		a. On orange-buff (1920)		14·00	50·00
		b. On buff (1920)			
		c. Die II. On pale yellow (1922)		1·00	16·00
89	13	25 c. black and red/*buff* (1920)		1·50	28·00
		a. On orange buff (1920)		40·00	70·00
		b. Die II. On pale yellow (1922)		1·50	9·00
90	11	30 c. dull purple and olive (1918)		1·50	8·00
91		45 c. dull purple and orange (1919)		3·00	35·00
92	13	50 c. dull purple and black (1920)		5·00	22·00
93		75 c. black/*blue-green* (*olive back*) (1918)		1·60	14·00
		a. Die II. On emerald back (1922)		1·40	19·00
94		1 r. dull purple and red (1920)		10·00	42·00
95		1 r. 50, reddish purple & blue/*blue* (1918)		9·00	50·00
		a. Die II. Blue-pur & blue/*blue* (1922)		11·00	32·00
96		2 r. 25, yellow-green and violet (1918)		42·00	£120
97		5 r. green and blue (1920)		70·00	£200
82/97			*Set of 16*	£130	£450
82/97 Optd "Specimen"			*Set of 16*	£300	

1921–32. *Die II. Wmk Mult Script CA. Chalk-surfaced paper* (18 c. and 25 c. to 5 r.). *P 14.*

98	11	2 c. chestnut and green		15	15
99		3 c. green		1·50	15
100		3 c. black (1922)		1·00	30
101		4 c. green (1922)		80	2·50
102		4 c. sage-green and carmine (1928)		5·50	15·00
103	12	5 c. deep brown		75	5·50
104	11	6 c. carmine		2·50	8·50
		w. Wmk inverted		95·00	
105		6 c. deep mauve (1922)		50	10
106	13	9 c. red (1927)		3·00	4·00
107	11	12 c. grey		2·50	20
		a. Die I (1932)		8·00	65
108		12 c. carmine-red (1922)		50	30
110		15 c. bright blue		2·00	55·00
111		15 c. yellow (1922)		75	2·50
112		18 c. purple/*pale yellow* (1925)		2·50	11·00
113	13	20 c. bright blue (1922)		1·25	35
		a. Dull blue (1924)		7·00	55
114		25 c. black and red/*pale yellow* (1925)		2·50	10·00
115	11	30 c. dull purple and olive		1·00	14·00
		w. Wmk inverted			
116		45 c. dull purple and orange (1926)		1·00	5·00
117	13	50 c. dull purple and black		2·25	2·25
118		75 c. black/*emerald* (1924)		8·00	21·00
119		1 r. dull purple and red		12·00	18·00
		a. Die I (1932)		12·00	35·00
121		1 r. 50, purple and blue/*blue* (1924)		13·00	21·00
122		2 r. 25, yellow-green and violet		9·00	14·00
123		5 r. yellow-green and blue		55·00	£130
98/123			*Set of 24*	£110	£300
98/123 Optd "Specimen"			*Set of 24*	£400	

The 3 c. green and 12 c. grey (Die II) were reissued in 1927. "Specimen" overprints on these printings are 15·5×1·75 mm instead of the 14·5×2·5 mm of the original issue. (*Price, £110 each*).

1935 (6 May). *Silver Jubilee. As Nos. 114/17 of Jamaica. P 11×12.*

128		6 c. ultramarine and grey-black		80	1·75
		a. Extra flagstaff		£190	£225
		b. Short extra flagstaff		£160	£170
		c. Lightning conductor		£200	
		d. Flagstaff on right-hand turret		£200	
		e. Double flagstaff		£225	£170
129		12 c. green and indigo		2·25	1·00
		a. Extra flagstaff		£2750	£2500
		b. Short extra flagstaff		£250	£160
		c. Lightning conductor		£1200	
		d. Flagstaff on right-hand turret		£325	
		e. Double flagstaff		£325	
130		20 c. brown and deep blue		2·00	1·00
		a. Extra flagstaff		£275	£300
		b. Short extra flagstaff		£180	
		c. Lightning conductor		£275	
		d. Flagstaff on right-hand turret		£275	
		e. Double flagstaff		£275	

131		1 r. slate and purple		5·00	11·00
		a. Extra flagstaff		£160	£190
		b. Short extra flagstaff		£250	
		c. Lightning conductor		£160	
		d. Flagstaff on right-hand turret		£325	
128/31			*Set of 4*	9·00	13·00
128/31 Perf "Specimen"			*Set of 4*	95·00	

For illustrations of plate varieties see Omnibus section following Zimbabwe.

1937 (12 May). *Coronation. As Nos. 118/20 of Jamaica, but ptd by B.W. P 11×11½.*

132		6 c. sage-green		35	15
133		12 c. orange		50	30
134		20 c. blue		70	65
132/4			*Set of 3*	1·40	1·00
132/4 Perf "Specimen"			*Set of 3*	55·00	

14 Coco-de-mer Palm 15 Giant Tortoise

16 Fishing Pirogue

"Handkerchief" on oar flaw (R. 6/2)

(Photo Harrison)

1938 (1 Jan)–49. *Wmk Mult Script CA. Chalk-surfaced paper. P 14½×13½ (vert) or 13½×14½ (horiz).*

135	14	2 c. purple-brown (10.2.38)		1·00	40
		a. Ordinary paper (18.11.42)		30	90
136	15	3 c. green		7·00	1·25
136a		3 c. orange (8.8.41)		1·25	50
		ab. Ordinary paper (18.11.42)		55	1·50
137	16	6 c. orange		7·00	2·50
137a		6 c. greyish green (8.8.41)		3·50	70
		aw. Wmk inverted		£450	
		b. Ordinary paper. *Green* (18.11.42)		55	1·25
		c. *Green* (5.4.49)		2·75	75
138	14	9 c. scarlet (10.2.38)		10·00	2·00
138a		9 c. grey-blue (8.8.41)		5·00	40
		ab. Ordinary paper (18.11.42)		6·50	1·25
		ac. Ordinary paper. *Dull bl* (19.11.45)		4·00	1·75
		ad. *Dull blue* (5.4.49)		10·00	6·00
		aw. Wmk inverted			
139	15	12 c. reddish violet		38·00	1·25
139a		15 c. brown-carmine (8.8.41)		6·00	30
		ab. Ordinary paper. *Brn-red* (18.11.42)		3·75	1·75
139c	14	18 c. carmine-lake (8.8.41)		6·00	60
		ca. Ordinary paper (18.11.42)		3·25	1·50
		cb. *Rose-carmine* (5.4.49)		10·00	9·00
140	16	20 c. blue		42·00	5·00
140a		20 c. brown-ochre (8.8.41)		4·75	45
		ab. Ordinary paper (18.11.42)		2·50	1·75
		ac. "Handkerchief" flaw		£100	
141	14	25 c. brown-ochre		85·00	14·00
142	15	30 c. carmine (10.2.38)		60·00	9·00
142a		30 c. blue (8.8.41)		4·75	50
		ab. Ordinary paper (18.11.42)		1·75	2·50
143	16	45 c. chocolate (10.2.38)		10·00	1·25
		a. Ordinary paper. *Pur-brn* (18.11.42)		1·75	1·75
		b. *Purple-brown* (5.4.49)		11·00	9·50
144	14	50 c. deep reddish violet (10.2.38)		4·25	60
		a. Ordinary paper (18.11.42)		1·00	2·25
144b		50 c. bright lilac (13.6.49)		80	1·50
145	15	75 c. slate-blue (10.2.38)		85·00	38·00
145a		75 c. deep slate-lilac (8.8.41)		6·50	1·50
		ab. Ordinary paper (18.11.42)		1·25	2·25
146	16	1 r. yellow-green (10.2.38)		£100	48·00
146a		1 r. grey-black (8.8.41)		8·00	85
		ab. Ordinary paper (18.11.42)		1·25	2·25
147	14	1 r. 50, ultramarine (10.2.38)		15·00	1·50
		a. Ordinary paper (18.11.42)		4·50	5·00
		aw. Wmk inverted		£1200	
148	15	2 r. 25, olive (10.2.38)		19·00	4·00
		a. Ordinary paper (18.11.42)		10·00	12·00
149	16	5 r. red (10.2.38)		8·00	3·25
		a. Ordinary paper (18.11.42)		12·00	16·00
135/49			*Set of 25*	£400	£120
135/49 (*excl No. 144b*) Perf "Specimen"			*Set of 24*	£375	

Lamp on mast flaw (R. 1/5)

1946 (23 Sept). *Victory. As Nos. 141/2 of Jamaica.*
150	9 c. light blue	10	10
151	30 c. deep blue	10	10
	a. Lamp on mast flaw	18·00	
150/1 Perf "Specimen"		Set of 2 50·00	

Line by crown (R. 1/3)

1948 (5 Nov). *Royal Silver Wedding. As Nos. 143/4 of Jamaica.*
152	9 c. ultramarine	15	25
	a. Line by crown	18·00	
153	5 r. carmine	11·00	22·00

1949 (10 Oct). *75th Anniv of U.P.U. As Nos. 145/8 of Jamaica, but inscribed "SEYCHELLES" in recess.*
154	18 c. bright reddish purple	30	15
155	50 c. purple	1·50	50
156	1 r. grey	40	15
157	2 r. 25, olive	50	60
154/7		Set of 4 2·50	1·25

17 Sailfish   18 Map of Indian Ocean

(Photo Harrison)

1952 (3 Mar). *Various designs as T 14/16 but with new portrait and crown as in T 17/18. Chalk-surfaced paper. Wmk Mult Script CA. P 14½ × 13½ (vert) or 13½ × 14½ (horiz).*
158	**17**	2 c. lilac	50	70
		a. Error. Crown missing, W 9a	£400	
		b. Error. St. Edward's Crown, W 9b	£110	
159	**15**	3 c. orange	50	30
		a. Error. Crown missing, W 9a	£350	
		b. Error. St. Edward's Crown, W 9b	£110	
160	**14**	9 c. chalky blue	50	1·25
		a. Error. Crown missing, W 9a	£550	
		b. Error. St. Edward's Crown, W 9b	£190	
161	**16**	15 c. deep yellow-green	40	75
		a. Error. Crown missing, W 9a	£450	
		b. Error. St. Edward's Crown, W 9b	£190	
162	**18**	18 c. carmine-lake	85	20
		a. Error. Crown missing, W 9a	£550	
		b. Error. St. Edward's Crown, W 9b	£275	
163	**16**	20 c. orange-yellow	90	60
		a. Error. Crown missing, W 9a	£600	
		b. Error. St. Edward's Crown, W 9b	£325	
164	**15**	25 c. vermilion	70	80
		a. Error. Crown missing, W 9a	£700	
		b. Error. St. Edward's Crown, W 9b	£300	
165	**17**	40 c. ultramarine	70	90
		a. Error. Crown missing, W 9a	£700	
		b. Error. St. Edward's Crown, W 9b	£375	
166	**16**	45 c. purple-brown	70	30
		a. Error. Crown missing, W 9a	£800	
		b. Error. St. Edward's Crown, W 9b	£400	
167	**14**	50 c. reddish violet	1·25	60
		a. Error. Crown missing, W 9a	£850	
		b. Error. St. Edward's Crown, W 9b	£400	
168	**18**	1 r. grey-black	2·50	2·00
		b. Error. St. Edward's Crown, W 9b	£700	
169	**14**	1 r. 50, blue	5·50	10·00
		b. Error. St. Edward's Crown, W 9b	£950	
170	**15**	2 r. 25, brown-olive	8·00	10·00
		b. Error. St. Edward's Crown, W 9b	£800	
171	**18**	5 r. red	8·50	12·00
		b. Error. St. Edward's Crown, W 9b	£700	
172	**17**	10 r. green	16·00	26·00
158/72		Set of 15 42·00	60·00	

See *Introduction* re the watermark errors.

1953 (2 June). *Coronation. As No. 153 of Jamaica.*
173	9 c. black and deep bright blue	60	70

19 Sailfish   20 Seychelles Flying Fox

(Photo Harrison)

1954 (1 Feb)–**61**. *Designs previously used for King George VI issue, but with portrait of Queen Elizabeth II, as in T 19 and T 20. Chalk-surfaced paper. Wmk Mult Script CA. P 14½ × 13½ (vert) or 13½ × 14½ (horiz).*
174	**19**	2 c. lilac	10	10
175	–	3 c. orange	10	10
175a	**20**	5 c. violet (25.10.57)	30	30
176	–	9 c. chalky blue	10	10
176a	–	10 c. chalky blue (15.9.56)	50	80
		ab. *Blue* (11.7.61)	7·00	3·75
177	–	15 c. deep yellow-green	30	15
178	–	18 c. crimson	10	10
179	–	20 c. orange-yellow	50	20
180	–	25 c. vermilion	60	85
180a	–	35 c. crimson (15.9.56)	2·75	90
181	**19**	40 c. ultramarine	30	25
182	–	45 c. purple-brown	20	15
183	–	50 c. reddish violet	30	20
183a	–	70 c. purple-brown (15.9.56)	4·75	1·25
184	–	1 r. grey-black	50	40
185	–	1 r. 50, blue	3·50	3·75
186	–	2 r. 25, brown-olive	3·50	7·50
187	–	5 r. red	18·00	8·50
188	**19**	10 r. green	28·00	18·00
174/88		Set of 19 55·00	38·00	

Designs: *Horiz*—15 c., 20 c., 45 c., 70 c. Fishing pirogue; 18 c., 35 c., 1 r., 5 r. Map of Indian Ocean. *Vert*—3 c., 25 c., 2 r. 25, Giant Tortoise; 9 c., 50 c., 1 r. 50, Coco de Mer Palm.

21 "La Pierre de Possession"   (22)

(Photo Harrison)

1956 (15 Nov). *Bicentenary of "La Pierre de Possession". Wmk Mult Script CA. P 14½ × 13½.*
189	**21**	40 c. ultramarine	15	15
190		1 r. black	15	15

| 191 | 191a | 191 | 191b | 191 | 191c |

1957 (16 Sept). *No. 182 surch with T 22.*
191	5 c. on 45 c. purple-brown	15	10
	a. Italic "e"	4·50	
	b. Italic "s"	4·25	
	c. Italic "c"	3·75	
	d. Thick bars omitted	£750	
	e. Surch double	£375	

There were two settings of this surcharge. The first setting contained No. 191a on R. 3/1, No. 191b on R. 5/3, No. 191c on R. 6/1 and 9/2, and No. 191d on R. 5/2. Nos. 191a and 191d did not occur on the second setting which shows No. 191b on R. 1/4, and No. 191c on R. 5/1 and R. 10/4.

23 Mauritius 6d. Stamp with Seychelles "B 64" Cancellation

(Recess: cancellation typo B.W.)

1961 (11 Dec). *Centenary of First Seychelles Post Office. W w 12. P 11½.*
193	**23**	10 c. blue, black and purple	30	10
194		35 c. blue, black and myrtle-green	60	10
195		2 r. 25, blue, black and orange-brown	1·10	45
193/5		Set of 3 1·75	50	

24 Black Parrot   29 Anse Royale Bay

40 Colony's Badge

(Des V. Whiteley. Photo Harrison)

1962 (21 Feb)–**68**. *T 24, 29, 40 and similar designs. W w 12 (upright). P 13½ × 14½ (horiz designs and 10 r.) or 14½ × 13½ (others).*
196	5 c. multicoloured	2·75	10
197	10 c. multicoloured	1·50	10
198	15 c. multicoloured	30	10
199	20 c. multicoloured	30	10
200	25 c. multicoloured	30	10
200a	30 c. multicoloured (15.7.68)	4·00	4·00
201	35 c. multicoloured	1·75	2·00
202	40 c. multicoloured	20	1·00
203	45 c. multicoloured (1.8.66)	3·50	4·00
204	50 c. multicoloured	40	25
205	70 c. ultramarine and light blue	6·00	3·00
206	75 c. multicoloured (1.8.66)	2·25	3·75
207	1 r. multicoloured	30	10
208	1 r. 50, multicoloured	5·50	6·00
209	2 r. 25, multicoloured	5·50	5·00
210	3 r. 50, multicoloured	2·25	6·00
211	5 r. multicoloured	3·50	2·50
212	10 r. multicoloured	12·00	4·50
196/212		Set of 18 42·00	38·00

Designs: *Vert (as T 24)*—10 c. Vanilla vine; 15 c. Fisherman; 20 c. Denis Island lighthouse; 25 c. Clock Tower, Victoria; 50 c. Cascade Church; 70 c. Sailfish; 75 c. Coco-de-Mer palm. *Horiz (as T 29)*—30 c., 35 c. Anse Royale Bay; 40 c. Government House; 45 c. Fishing pirogue; 1 r. Cinnamon; 1 r. 50, Copra; 2 r. 25, Map; 3 r. 50, Land settlement; 5 r. Regina Mundi Convent.

The 1 r. exists with PVA gum as well as gum arabic, but the 30 c. exists with PVA gum only.
See also Nos. 233/7.
For stamps of the above issue overprinted "B.I.O.T." see under British Indian Ocean Territory.

1963 (4 June). *Freedom from Hunger. As No. 80 of Lesotho.*
213	70 c. reddish violet	60	25

1963 (16 Sept). *Red Cross Centenary. As Nos. 203/4 of Jamaica.*
214	10 c. red and black	25	10
215	75 c. red and blue	75	60

45 CENTS (41)   42 Seychelles Flying Fox

1965 (15 Apr). *Nos. 201 and 205 surch as T 41.*
216	45 c. on 35 c. multicoloured	10	15
217	75 c. on 70 c. ultramarine and light blue	20	15

1965 (1 June). *I.T.U. Centenary. As Nos. 98/9 of Lesotho.*
218	5 c. orange and ultramarine	10	10
219	1 r. 50, mauve and apple-green	50	25

1965 (25 Oct). *International Co-operation Year. As Nos. 100/1 of Lesotho.*
220	5 c. reddish purple and turquoise-green	15	10
221	40 c. deep bluish green and lavender	35	20

1966 (24 Jan). *Churchill Commemoration. As Nos. 102/5 of Lesotho.*
222	5 c. new blue	15	10
223	15 c. deep green	35	10
224	75 c. brown	60	10
225	1 r. 50, bluish violet	90	60
222/5		Set of 4 1·75	80

1966 (1 July). *World Cup Football Championships. As Nos. 57/8 of Pitcairn Islands.*
226	15 c. violet, yellow-green, lake & yellow-brn	20	10
	a. "50 c GRENADA" on front of stamp		
227	1 r. chocolate, blue-green, lake & yell-brn	35	30

No. 226a shows a positive offset of the Grenada duty plate from the blanket on the front and a negative offset on the reverse.

1966 (20 Sept). *Inauguration of W.H.O. Headquarters, Geneva. As Nos. 185/6 of Montserrat.*
228	20 c. black, yellow-green and light blue	20	10
229	50 c. black, light purple and yellow-brown	40	20

1966 (1 Dec). *20th Anniv of U.N.E.S.C.O. As Nos. 342/4 of Mauritius.*
230	15 c. slate-violet, red, yellow and orange	20	10
231	1 r. orange-yellow, violet and deep olive	35	10
232	5 r. black, bright purple and orange	80	1·00
230/2		Set of 3 1·25	1·00

1967–**69**. *As Nos. 196/7, 204 and new values as T 42 but wmk w 12 (sideways).*
233	5 c. multicoloured (7.2.67)	35	2·25
234	10 c. multicoloured (4.6.68)	30	15
235	50 c. multicoloured (13.5.69)	1·75	3·75
236	60 c. red, blue and blackish brown (15.7.68)	1·75	45
237	85 c. ultramarine and light blue (as No. 205) (15.7.68)	90	40
233/7		Set of 5 4·50	6·50

The 10 c. exists with PVA gum as well as gum arabic, but the 50 c. to 85 c. exist with PVA gum only.

UNIVERSAL ADULT SUFFRAGE 1967

(43)

44 Money Cowrie, Mole Cowrie and Tiger Cowrie

1967 (18 Sept). *Universal Adult Suffrage. As Nos. 198 and 206, but W w 12 (sideways), and Nos. 203 and 210 (wmk upright), optd with T 43.*
238	15 c. multicoloured	..	10	10
	a. Opt double			
239	45 c. multicoloured	..	10	10
240	75 c. multicoloured	..	10	10
241	3 r. 50, multicoloured	..	20	30
238/41	.. .. ..	*Set of 4*	30	50

(Des V. Whiteley. Photo Harrison)

1967 (4 Dec). *International Tourist Year. T 44 and similar horiz designs. Multicoloured. W w 12. P 14 × 13.*
242	15 c. Type 44		20	10
243	40 c. Beech Cone, Textile or Cloth of Gold Cone and Virgin Cone	..	25	10
244	1 r. Arthritic Spider Conch	..	35	10
245	2 r. 25, Subulate Auger and Trumpet Triton Shells ..		60	1·25
242/5	.. ..	*Set of 4*	1·25	1·25

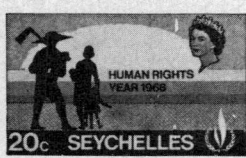

= 30

(48)

49 Farmer with Wife and Children at Sunset

1968 (16 Apr). *Nos. 202/3 and as No. 206 surch as T 48 (30 c.) or with "CENTS" added, and three bars (others). W w 12 (sideways on No. 248).*
246	30 c. on 40 c. multicoloured	..	10	10
247	60 c. on 45 c. multicoloured	..	15	10
248	85 c. on 75 c. multicoloured	..	20	15
246/8 ..	.. ..	*Set of 3*	40	30

(Des Mary Hayward. Litho Harrison)

1968 (2 Sept). *Human Rights Year. W w 12. P 14½ × 13½.*
249	49 20 c. multicoloured	..	10	10
250	50 c. multicoloured	..	10	10
251	85 c. multicoloured	..	10	10
252	2 r. 25, multicoloured	..	20	1·00
249/52	.. ..	*Set of 4*	30	1·10

50 Expedition landing at Anse Possession

54 Apollo Launch

(Des Mary Hayward. Litho and die-stamped Harrison)

1968 (30 Dec). *Bicentenary of First Landing on Praslin. T 50 and similar multicoloured designs. W w 12 (sideways on 50 c., 85 c.). P 14.*
253	20 c. Type 50	..	30	10
254	50 c. French warships at anchor (*vert*)	..	35	15
255	85 c. Coco-de-Mer and Black Parrot (*vert*)	..	80	20
256	2 r. 25, French warships under sail	..	80	1·75
253/6 ..	..	*Set of 4*	2·00	2·00

(Des V. Whiteley. Litho Format)

1969 (9 Sept). *First Man on the Moon. T 54 and similar horiz designs. Multicoloured. W w 12 (sideways on horiz designs). P 13½.*
257	5 c. Type 54	..	10	50
258	20 c. Module leaving Mother-ship for Moon	..	15	10
259	50 c. Astronauts and Space Module on Moon	..	20	15
260	85 c. Tracking station ..	..	25	15
261	2 r. 25, Moon craters with Earth on the "Horizon" ..		45	1·60
257/61	..	*Set of 5*	1·00	2·25

59 Picault's Landing, 1742

60 Badge of Seychelles

(Des Mary Hayward. Litho Enschedé)

1969 (3 Nov)–**75**. *Horiz designs as T 59/60. Multicoloured. W w 12 (sideways*). Slightly toned paper. P 13×12½.*
262	5 c. Type 59	..	10	10
	w. Wmk Crown to right of CA	..	1·25	
263	10 c. U.S. satellite-tracking station	..	10	10
	a. Whiter paper (8.3.73)	..	70	60
264	15 c. *Königsberg I* (German cruiser) at Aldabra, 1914†	..	2·25	2·00
	a. Whiter paper (8.3.73)	..	5·50	4·50
265	20 c. Fleet re-fuelling off St. Anne, 1939–45		1·00	10
	a. Whiter paper (13.6.74)	..	1·25	1·75
266	25 c. Exiled Ashanti King Prempeh	..	20	10
	a. Whiter paper (8.3.73)	..	65	2·00
267	30 c. Laying Stone of Possession, 1756	..	1·00	3·25
268	40 c. As 30 c. (11.12.72)	..	1·75	1·25
	a. Whiter paper (13.6.74)	..	1·60	1·60
269	50 c. Pirates and treasure	..	30	15
	a. Whiter paper (13.6.74)	..	1·50	1·75
270	60 c. Corsairs attacking merchantman	..	1·00	1·50
271	65 c. As 60 c. (11.12.72)	..	6·00	6·00
	aw. Wmk Crown to left of CA	..	6·00	
	b. Whiter paper (8.3.75)	..	6·50	9·50
272	85 c. Impression of proposed airport	..	2·00	1·75
273	95 c. As 85 c. (11.12.72)	..	6·50	4·25
	a. Whiter paper (13.6.74)	..	4·50	3·25
274	1 r. French Governor capitulating to British naval officer, 1794		35	15
	a. Whiter paper (8.3.73)	..	1·00	1·00
275	1 r. 50, H.M.S. *Sybille* (frigate) and *Chiffone* (French frigate) in battle, 1801		1·75	2·00
	a. Whiter paper (8.3.73)	..	3·50	9·00
276	3 r. 50, Visit of the Duke of Edinburgh, 1956		1·00	2·00
	a. Whiter paper (13.8.75)	..	2·50	14·00
277	5 r. Chevalier Queau de Quincy	..	1·00	2·75
278	10 r. Indian Ocean chart, 1574	..	2·75	6·00
279	15 r. Type 60	..	4·00	11·00
262/79	..	*Set of 18*	28·00	38·00
263a/76a ..	..	*Set of 11*	25·00	40·00

*The normal sideways watermark shows Crown to right of CA on the 40, 65 and 95 c. and to left of CA on the others, *as seen from the back of the stamp.*

†The design is incorrect in that it shows *Königsberg II* and the wrong date ("1915").

The stamps on the whiter paper are highly glazed, producing shade variations and are easily distinguishable from the original printings on toned paper.

74 White Terns, French Warship and Island

(Des A. Smith; adapted V. Whiteley. Litho D.L.R.)

1970 (27 Apr). *Bicentenary of First Settlement, St. Anne Island. T 74 and similar horiz designs. Multicoloured. W w 12 (sideways). P 14.*
280	20 c. Type 74	..	60	10
281	50 c. Spot-finned Flyingfish, ship and island	..	40	10
282	85 c. Compass and chart	..	40	10
283	3 r. 50, Anchor on sea-bed	..	60	1·25
280/3	.. ..	*Set of 4*	1·75	1·40

78 Girl and Optician's Chart

79 Pitcher Plant

(Des A. Smith. Litho Questa)

1970 (4 Aug). *Centenary of British Red Cross. T 78 and similar multicoloured designs. W w 12 (sideways on horiz designs). P 14.*
284	20 c. Type 78	..	40	10
285	50 c. Baby, scales and milk bottles	..	40	10
286	85 c. Woman with child and umbrella (*vert*)	..	40	10
287	3 r. 50, Red Cross local H.Q. building	..	1·50	2·75
284/7 ..	..	*Set of 4*	2·40	2·75

(Des G. Drummond. Litho J.W.)

1970 (29 Dec). *Flowers. T 79 and similar vert designs. Multicoloured. W w 12. P 14.*
288	20 c. Type 79	..	35	15
289	50 c. Wild Vanilla	..	45	15
290	85 c. Tropic-Bird Orchid	..	1·40	30
291	3 r. 50, Vare Hibiscus	..	2·00	2·25
288/91	..	*Set of 4*	3·75	2·50
MS292	81 × 133 mm. Nos. 288/91. Wmk inverted		4·50	13·00

80 Seychelles "On the Map"

81 Piper PA-31 Navajo

(Des and litho J.W.)

1971 (18 May). *"Putting Seychelles on the Map". Sheet 152 × 101 mm. W w 12 (sideways). P 13½.*
MS293	**80** 5 r. multicoloured	..	2·50	9·00

(Des and litho J.W.)

1971 (28 June). *Airport Completion. T 81 and similar multicoloured designs showing aircraft. W w 12 (sideways on horiz designs). P 14 × 14½ (5, 20 and 60 c.) or 14½ (others).*
294	5 c. Type 81	..	30	40
295	20 c. Westland Wessex HAS-1 helicopter	..	65	10
296	50 c. Consolidated PBY-5A Catalina amphibian (*horiz*)		70	10
297	60 c. Grumman SA-16 Albatross	..	75	10
298	85 c. Short S.26 "G" Class flying boat *Golden Hind* (*horiz*)		90	10
299	3 r. 50, Supermarine Walrus Mk 1 amphibian (*horiz*)		4·50	3·25
294/9	..	*Set of 6*	7·00	3·50

82 Santa Claus delivering Gifts (Jean-Claude Waye Hive)

(83)

(Des Jennifer Toombs. Litho A. & M.)

1971 (12 Oct). *Christmas. Drawings by local children. T 82 and similar horiz designs. Multicoloured. W w 12 (sideways*). P 13½.*
300	10 c. Type 82	..	10	10
	w. Wmk Crown to left of CA	..	50	
301	15 c. Santa Claus seated on turtle (Edison Thérésine)		10	10
	w. Wmk Crown to left of CA	..	50	
302	3 r. 50, Santa Claus landing on island (Isabelle Tirant)		40	90
300/2	..	*Set of 3*	50	90

*The normal sideways watermark shows Crown to right of CA, *as seen from the back of the stamp.*

1971 (21 Dec). *Nos. 267, 270 and 272 surch in grey as T 83.*
303	40 c. on 30 c. Laying Stone of Possession, 1756		30	55
304	65 c. on 60 c. Corsairs attacking merchantman		40	75
305	95 c. on 85 c. Impression of proposed airport		45	1·00
303/5 ..	..	*Set of 3*	1·00	2·10

ROYAL VISIT 1972

(84)

85 Seychelles Brush Warbler

1972 (20 Mar). *Royal Visit. Nos. 265 and 277 optd with T 84.*
306	20 c. Fleet re-fuelling off St. Anne, 1939–45		15	20
307	5 r. Chevalier Queau de Quincy (Gold)		1·00	2·50

(Des R. Gillmor. Litho Questa)

1972 (24 July). *Rare Seychelles Birds. T 85 and similar vert designs. Multicoloured. W w 12 (sideways*). P 13½.*
308	5 c. Type 85	..	50	50
309	20 c. Bare-legged Scops Owl	..	1·75	50
310	50 c. Seychelles Blue Pigeon	..	1·75	65
	w. Wmk Crown to right of CA	..	18·00	
311	65 c. Seychelles Magpie Robin	..	2·25	75
312	95 c. Seychelles Paradise Flycatcher	..	2·50	2·50
313	3 r. 50, Seychelles Kestrel	..	7·00	11·00
308/13	..	*Set of 6*	14·00	14·00
MS314	144×162 mm. Nos. 308/13	..	20·00	27·00
	w. Wmk Crown to right of CA	..	£170	

*The normal sideways watermark shows Crown to left of CA, *as seen from the back of the stamp.*

86 Fireworks Display

87 Giant Tortoise and Sailfish

(Des V. Whiteley. Litho Questa)

1972 (18 Sept.). *"Festival '72". T **86** and similar multicoloured designs. W w **12** (sideways* on 10 and 25 c.). P 14.*

315	10 c. Type **86**	10	10
	w. Wmk Crown to right of CA	8·50	
316	15 c. Pirogue race (horiz)	10	10
317	25 c. Floats and costumes	10	10
318	5 r. Water skiing (horiz)	60	80
315/18	*Set of 4*	65	80

*The normal sideways watermark shows Crown to left of CA, as seen from the back of the stamp.

(Des (from photograph by D. Groves) and photo Harrison)

1972 (20 Nov.). *Royal Silver Wedding. Multicoloured; background colour given. W w **12** × 14½. P 14 × 14½.*

319	**87** 95 c. turquoise-blue	15	10
320	1 r. 50, red-brown	15	10
	w. Wmk inverted	2·75	

1973 (14 Nov.). *Royal Wedding. As Nos. 322/3 of Montserrat.*

321	95 c. ochre	10	10
322	1 r. 50, dull deep blue	10	10

88 Seychelles Squirrelfish

(Des G. Drummond. Litho Questa)

1974 (5 Mar.). *Fishes. T **88** and similar horiz designs. Multicoloured. W w **12**. P 14½ × 14.*

323	20 c. Type **88**	25	15
324	50 c. Harlequin Filefish	35	15
325	95 c. Pennant Coralfish ("Papillon")	40	40
326	1 r. 50, Oriental Sweetlips ("Peau d'ane canal")	85	1·75
323/6	*Set of 4*	1·60	2·25

89 Globe and Letter

(Des Sylvia Goaman. Litho Enschedé)

1974 (9 Oct.). *Centenary of Universal Postal Union. T **89** and similar horiz designs. Multicoloured. W w **12** (sideways*). P 12½×12.*

327	20 c. Type **89**	10	10
	w. Wmk Crown to right of CA	25·00	
328	50 c. Globe and radio beacon	20	10
329	95 c. Globe and postmark	35	40
330	1 r. 50, Emblems within "UPU"	50	70
327/30	*Set of 4*	1·00	1·10

*The normal sideways watermark shows Crown to left of CA, as seen from the back of the stamp.

90 Sir Winston Churchill

VISIT OF Q.E. II
(91)

(Des G. Vasarhelyi. Litho Questa)

1974 (30 Nov.). *Birth Centenary of Sir Winston Churchill. T **90** and similar horiz design. Multicoloured. W w **12**. P 14.*

331	95 c. Type **90**	20	15
332	1 r. 50, Profile portrait	35	40
MS333	81×109 mm. Nos. 331/2	60	1·75
	w. Wmk inverted	£170	

1975 (8 Feb.). *Visit of R.M.S. "Queen Elizabeth II". Nos. 265a, 269a, 273a and 275a optd with T **91**.*

334	20 c. Fleet re-fuelling off St. Anne, 1939–45	15	15
335	50 c. Pirates and treasure	20	20
336	95 c. Impression of proposed airport (Sil)	25	40
337	1 r. 50, H.M.S. Sybille (frigate) and Chiffone (French frigate) in battle, 1801	35	1·00
334/7	*Set of 4*	85	1·60

INTERNAL SELF-GOVERNMENT OCTOBER 1975
(92)

93 Queen Elizabeth I

1975 (1 Oct.). *Internal Self-Government. Nos. 265a, 271b, 274a, and 276a optd with T **92** in gold, by Enschedé.*

338	20 c. Fleet re-fuelling off St. Anne, 1939–45	15	15
339	65 c. Corsairs attacking merchantman	25	30
340	1 r. French Governor capitulating to British naval officer, 1794	30	35
341	3 r. 50, Visit of Duke of Edinburgh, 1956	75	1·50
338/41	*Set of 4*	1·25	2·00

(Des C. Abbott. Litho Walsall)

1975 (15 Dec.). *International Women's Year. T **93** and similar vert designs. Multicoloured. W w **14** (inverted). P 13½.*

342	10 c. Type **93**	10	10
343	15 c. Gladys Aylward	10	10
344	20 c. Elizabeth Fry	10	10
345	25 c. Emmeline Pankhurst	10	10
346	65 c. Florence Nightingale	25	20
347	1 r. Amy Johnson	40	35
348	1 r. 50, Joan of Arc	50	80
349	3 r. 50, Eleanor Roosevelt	1·50	2·75
342/9	*Set of 8*	2·50	4·00

94 Map of Praslin and Postmark

95 First Landing, 1609 (inset portrait of Premier James Mancham)

(Des J.W. Litho Questa)

1976 (30 Mar.). *Rural Posts. T **94** and similar vert designs showing maps and postmarks. Multicoloured. W w **14**. P 14.*

350	20 c. Type **94**	20	10
351	65 c. La Digue	30	20
352	1 r. Mahé with Victoria postmark	35	25
353	1 r. 50, Mahé with Anse Royale postmark	55	1·25
350/3	*Set of 4*	1·25	1·50
MS354	166 × 127 mm. Nos. 350/3	1·50	3·00

INDEPENDENT

(Des G. Drummond. Litho J.W.)

1976 (29 June). *Independence. T **95** and similar vert designs. Multicoloured. W w **12** (sideways). P 13½.*

355	20 c. Type **95**	15	10
356	25 c. The Possession Stone	15	10
357	40 c. First settlers, 1770	20	15
358	75 c. Chevalier Queau de Quincy	25	20
359	1 r. Sir Bickham Sweet-Escott	25	20
360	1 r. 25, Legislative Building	30	50
361	1 r. 50, Seychelles badge	30	60
362	3 r. 50, Seychelles flag	60	1·60
355/62	*Set of 8*	2·00	3·00

96 Flags of Seychelles and U.S.A.

(Des and litho J.W.)

1976 (12 July). *Seychelles Independence and American Independence Bicentenary. T **96** and similar horiz design. Multicoloured. W w **12** (sideways). P 13½.*

363	1 r. Type **96**	25	15
364	10 r. Statehouses of Seychelles and Philadelphia	1·25	2·50

97 Swimming

98 Seychelles Paradise Flycatcher

(Des J.W. Litho Questa)

1976 (26 July). *Olympic Games, Montreal. T **97** and similar horiz designs. W w **14** (sideways). P 14.*

365	20 c. ultramarine, cobalt and sepia	10	10
366	65 c. bottle-green, apple-green and grey-black	35	10
367	1 r. chestnut, blue-green and grey-black	35	10
368	3 r. 50, crimson, rose and grey-black	50	2·25
365/8	*Set of 4*	1·10	2·25

Designs:—65 c. Hockey; 1 r. Basketball; 3 r. 50, Football.

(Des Mrs. R. Fennessy. Litho Questa)

1976 (8 Nov.)–**77**. *Fourth Pan-African Ornithological Congress, Seychelles. T **98** and similar multicoloured designs. W w **14** (sideways on Nos. 370/1). Ordinary paper. P 14.*

369	20 c. Type **98**	40	20
	a. Chalk-surfaced paper (7.3.77)	40	20
370	1 r. 25, Seychelles Sunbird (horiz)	1·10	1·00
	a. Chalk-surfaced paper (7.3.77)	1·10	1·00
371	1 r. 50, Seychelles Brown White Eye (horiz)	1·50	1·25
	a. Chalk-surfaced paper (7.3.77)	1·50	1·25
372	5 r. Black Parrot	2·50	4·00
	a. Chalk-surfaced paper (7.3.77)	2·50	4·00
369/72	*Set of 4*	5·00	5·75
369a/72a	*Set of 4*	5·00	5·75
MS373	161×109 mm. Nos. 369/72	6·50	9·00
	a. 5 r. value in miniature sheet imperf	£850	

Independence 1976
(99)

100 Inauguration of George Washington

1976 (22 Nov.). *Independence. Nos. 265a, 269, 271b, 273a, 274a, 276a and 277/9 optd with T **99** (No. 271 additionally surch). W w **12** (sideways*).*

374	20 c. Fleet re-fuelling off St. Anne, 1939–45	70	1·50
375	50 c. Pirates and treasure	60	1·75
376	95 c. Impression of proposed airport	1·75	1·75
	a. Opt inverted	85·00	
	w. Wmk Crown to right of CA	3·00	
377	1 r. French Governor capitulating to British naval officer, 1794	55	1·75
378	3 r. 50, Visit of Duke of Edinburgh, 1956	2·75	3·50
	a. Opt inverted	75·00	
	b. On No. 276	3·50	3·50
	ba. Opt inverted	£100	
379	5 r. Chevalier Queau de Quincy	2·25	5·00
380	10 r. Indian Ocean chart, 1574	3·50	10·00
381	15 r. Type **60**	4·50	10·00
382	25 r. on 65 c. Corsairs attacking merchantman	5·50	16·00
374/82	*Set of 9*	20·00	45·00

*The normal sideways watermark shows Crown to left of CA, as seen from the back of the stamp.

(Des Jennifer Toombs. Litho Questa)

1976 (21 Dec.). *Bicentenary of American Revolution. T **100** and similar horiz designs. P 14 × 13½.*

383	1 c. crimson and light rose	10	10
384	2 c. violet and light lilac	10	10
385	3 c. bright blue and azure	10	10
386	4 c. chestnut and light yellow	10	10
387	5 c. emerald and light yellow-green	10	10
388	1 r. 50, sepia and cinnamon	50	35
389	3 r. 50, dp turquoise-blue & pale blue-green	60	70
390	5 r. chestnut and light yellow	70	80
391	10 r. chalky blue and azure	1·00	1·50
383/91	*Set of 9*	2·75	3·25
MS392	141 × 141 mm. 25 r. plum and magenta	3·50	6·50

Designs:—2 c. Jefferson and Louisiana Purchase; 3 c. William Seward and Alaska Purchase; 4 c. Pony Express, 1860; 5 c. Lincoln's Emancipation Proclamation; 1 r. 50 Transcontinental Railroad, 1869; 3 r. 50 Wright Brothers flight, 1903; 5 r. Henry Ford's assembly-line, 1913; 10 r. J. F. Kennedy and 1969 Moon-landing; 25 r. Signing Independence Declaration, 1776.

101 Silhouette of the Islands

102 Cruiser *Aurora* and Flag

(Des G. Hutchins (Nos. 395/8), J.W. (others). Litho Questa)

1977 (5 Sept). *Silver Jubilee. T* **101** *and similar multicoloured designs.* W w **14** *(sideways* on* 20 *and* 40 *c.,* 5 *and* 10 *r.).* P 14.

393	20 c. Type **101**	..	10	10
	w. Wmk Crown to right of CA	..	£100	
394	40 c. Silhouette (*different*)	..	10	10
395	50 c. The Orb (*vert*)	..	10	10
396	1 r. St. Edward's Crown (*vert*)	..	10	15
397	1 r. 25, Ampulla and Spoon (*vert*)	..	10	15
398	1 r. 50, Sceptre with Cross (*vert*)	..	10	15
399	5 r. Silhouette (*different*)	..	25	30
400	10 r. Silhouette (*different*)	..	45	60
393/400		*Set of* 8	1·00	1·25
MS401	133×135 mm. 20 c., 50 c., 1 r., 10 r. all wmk sideways		55	1·40
	w. Wmk Crown to right of CA		£170	

**The normal sideways watermark shows Crown to left of CA, as seen from the back of the stamp.*

(Litho State Printing Works, Moscow)

1977 (7 Nov). *60th Anniv of Russian October Revolution.* P 12 × 12½.

402	**102**	1 r. 50, multicoloured	55	30
MS403	101 × 129 mm. No. 402		80	1·10

103 Coral Scene

(Des G. Drummond. Litho Walsall (40 c., 1 r., 1 r. 25, 1 r. 50), J.W. or Questa (25 c. (No. 408B)), J.W. (others))

1977 (10 Nov)–84. *Multicoloured designs as T* **103.** *Rupee values show* "Re" *or* "Rs". W w **14** *(sideways on* 10, 20, 50 *and* 75 *c.*). P 14½×14 (40 *c.,* 1 *r.,* 1 *r.* 25, 1 *r.* 50), 13 (5, 10, 15, 20 *r.*) *or* 14 *(others).* **A.** *No imprint*

404A	5 c. Reef fish (10.4.78)	..	30	1·25
405A	10 c. Hawksbill Turtle (6.2.78)	..	50	10
406A	15 c. Coco-de-Mer (10.4.78)	..	30	1·50
407A	20 c. Wild Vanilla Orchid (6.2.78)	..	1·50	20
408A	25 c. *Hypolimnas misippus* (butterfly) (10.4.78)	..	1·50	85
409A	40 c. Type **103**	..	40	10
410A	50 c. Giant Tortoise (6.2.78)	..	30	10
411A	75 c. Crayfish (6.2.78)	..	40	10
412A	1 r. Madagascar Red Fody	..	1·25	10
413A	1 r. 25, White Tern	..	1·25	20
414A	1 r. 50, Seychelles Flying Fox	..	1·50	20
415A	3 r. 50, Green Gecko (10.4.78)	..	75	2·50
416A	5 r. Octopus (6.2.78)	..	2·00	40
417A	10 r. Tiger Cowrie (*Cypraea tigris*) (10.4.78)	..	2·25	2·50
418A	15 r. Pitcher Plant (10.4.78)	..	2·25	2·50
419A	20 r. Coat of arms (6.2.78)	..	2·25	2·50
404A/19A		*Set of* 16	16·00	13·50

B. *With imprint date at foot*

405B	10 c. Hawksbill Turtle (14.3.80)	..	20	10
406B	15 c. Coco-de-Mer (14.3.80)	..	20	15
407B	20 c. Wild Vanilla Orchid (5.84)	..	2·25	2·00
408B	25 c. *Hypolimnas misippus* (butterfly) (14.3.80)	..	2·25	2·25
409B	40 c. Type **103** (14.3.80)	..	20	10
410B	50 c. Giant Tortoise (14.3.80)	..	40	10
411B	75 c. Crayfish (14.3.80)	..	50	30
412B	1 r. Madagascar Red Fody (14.3.80)	..	7·50	75
	w. Wmk inverted		8·50	
414B	1 r. 50, Seychelles Flying Fox (14.3.80)	..	2·00	50
405B/14B		*Set of* 9	14·00	5·50

The 40 c., 1 r., 1 r. 25 and 1 r. 50 values are horizontal designs, 31 × 27 mm; the 5, 10, 15 and 20 r. are vertical, 28 × 36 mm; the others are horizontal, 29 × 25 mm.

Imprint dates: "1979", Nos. 405B/6B, 408B/14B; "1981", No. 409B; "1982", Nos. 405B/9B; "1988", No. 408B (Questa).

For rupee values showing face value as "R" see Nos. 487/94.

For 10 c. and 50 c. with watermark w **14** (upright) and printed by Questa see Nos. 718 and 722. A printing of the 25 c. by Questa on the same date has the same perforation and watermark as J.W. printings of No. 408B.

For 50 c. and 3 r. (inscr "Rs") with watermark w **16** and printed by Questa see Nos. 732/8.

104 St. Roch Roman Catholic Church, Bel Ombre

(Des G. Drummond. Litho Walsall)

1977 (5 Dec). *Christmas. T* **104** *and similar horiz designs. Multi-coloured.* W w **14** *(sideways).* P 13½ × 14.

420	20 c. Type **104**	..	10	10
421	1 r. Anglican cathedral, Victoria	..	10	10
422	1 r. 50, Roman Catholic cathedral, Victoria	..	15	10
423	5 r. St. Mark's Anglican church, Praslin	..	30	45
420/3		*Set of* 4	50	55

105 Liberation Day ringed on Calendar

106 Stamp Portraits of Edward VII, George V and George VI

(Des local artists; adapted L. Curtis. Litho Questa)

1978 (5 June). *Liberation Day. T* **105** *and similar vert designs. Multicoloured.* W w **14.** P 14 × 13½.

424	40 c. Type **105**	..	10	10
425	1 r. 25, Hands holding bayonet, torch and flag		15	10
426	1 r. 50, Fisherman and farmer		15	15
427	5 r. Soldiers and rejoicing people		35	40
424/7		*Set of* 4	60	60

(Des G. Drummond. Litho Questa)

1978 (21 Aug). *25th Anniv of Coronation. T* **106** *and similar vert designs. Multicoloured.* W w **14.** P 14.

428	40 c. Type **106**	..	10	10
429	1 r. 50, Victoria and Elizabeth II		15	10
430	3 r. Queen Victoria Monument		25	25
431	5 r. Queen's Building, Victoria		35	35
428/31		*Set of* 4	75	65
MS432	87 × 129 mm. Nos. 428/31		75	85

107 Gardenia

(Des G. Hutchins. Litho Questa)

1978 (16 Oct). *Wildlife. T* **107** *and similar horiz designs. Multi-coloured.* W w **14** *(sideways).* P 13½ × 14.

433	40 c. Type **107**	..	15	10
434	1 r. 25, Seychelles Magpie Robin		1·25	60
435	1 r. 50, Seychelles Paradise Flycatcher		1·25	60
436	5 r. Green Turtle		1·25	1·50
433/6		*Set of* 4	3·50	2·50

108 Possession Stone   **109** Seychelles Fody

(Des G. Hutchins. Litho Questa)

1978 (15 Dec). *Bicentenary of Victoria. T* **108** *and similar horiz designs. Multicoloured.* W w **14** *(sideways).* P 13½ × 14.

437	20 c. Type **108**	..	10	10
438	1 r. 25, Plan of 1782 "L'Etablissement"		15	15
439	1 r. 50, Clock Tower		15	15
440	5 r. Bust of Pierre Poivre		40	60
437/40		*Set of* 4	65	85

(Des G. Drummond. Litho Questa)

1979 (27 Feb). *Birds (1st series). T* **109** *and similar vert designs. Multicoloured.* W w **14.** P 14.

441	2 r. Type **109**	..	55	50
	a. Horiz strip of 5. Nos. 441/5		2·50	
442	2 r. Green Heron	..	55	50
443	2 r. Thick-billed Bulbul	..	55	50
444	2 r. Seychelles Cave Swiftlet	..	55	50
445	2 r. Grey-headed Lovebird	..	55	50
441/5		*Set of* 5	2·50	2·25

Nos. 441/5 were printed together, *se-tenant,* in horizontal strips of 5 throughout the sheet.

See also Nos. 463/7, 500/4 and 523/7.

OMNIBUS ISSUES

Details, together with prices for complete sets, of the various Omnibus issues from the 1935 Silver Jubilee series to date are included in a special section following Zimbabwe at the end of Volume 2.

110 Patrice Lumumba

111 1978 5 r. Liberation Day Commemorative and Sir Rowland Hill

(Des G. Vasarhelyi. Litho Questa)

1979 (5 June). *African Liberation Heroes. T* **110** *and similar vert designs.* W w **14.** P 14 × 14½.

446	40 c. black, deep violet and lilac	..	10	10
447	2 r. black, blue and pale blue	..	20	25
448	2 r. 25, black, reddish brown & orange-brn	..	20	30
449	5 r. black, bronze-green and dull green	..	45	1·00
446/9		*Set of* 4	80	1·50

Designs:—2 r. Kwame Nkrumah; 2 r. 25, Dr. Eduardo Mondlane; 5 r. Hamilcar Cabral.

(Des J.W. Litho Questa)

1979 (27 Aug). *Death Centenary of Sir Rowland Hill. T* **111** *and similar vert designs showing stamps and Sir Rowland Hill. Multicoloured.* W w **14.** P 14.

450	40 c. Type **111**	..	10	10
451	2 r. 25, 1972 50 c. Rare Birds commemorative		35	40
452	3 r. 1962 50 c. definitive	..	45	55
450/2		*Set of* 3	75	95
MS453	112 × 88 mm. 5 r. 1892 4 c. definitive. Wmk inverted		40	55

112 Child with Book   **113** The Herald Angel

(Des BG Studio. Litho Questa)

1979 (26 Oct). *International Year of the Child. T* **112** *and similar multicoloured designs.* W w **14** *(sideways on* 40 *c. and* 2 *r.* 25). P 14½.

454	40 c. Type **112**	..	10	10
455	2 r. 25, Children of different races		15	30
456	3 r. Young child with ball (*vert*)		20	45
457	5 r. Girl with glove-puppet (*vert*)		35	65
454/7		*Set of* 4	70	1·25

Nos. 454/7 were each printed in sheets including two *se-tenant* stamp-size labels.

(Des J. Cooter. Litho Walsall)

1979 (3 Dec). *Christmas. T* **113** *and similar multicoloured designs.* W w **14** *(sideways on* 3 *r.*). P 14½ × 14 (3 *r.*) *or* 14 × 14½ *(others).*

458	20 c. Type **113**	..	10	10
459	2 r. 25, The Virgin and Child		30	40
460	3 r. The Three Kings (*horiz*)		40	55
458/60		*Set of* 3	65	90
MS461	87 × 75 mm. 5 r. The Flight into Egypt (*horiz*) (wmk sideways). P 14½ × 14		50	70

(114)   **115** Seychelles Kestrel

1979 (7 Dec). *As Nos.* 415 *but with* "1979" *imprint date, surch with T* **114.**

462	1 r. 10 on 3 r. 50, Green Gecko		30	50

(Des G. Drummond. Litho Questa)

1980 (29 Feb). *Birds (2nd series). Seychelles Kestrel. T* **115** *and similar vert designs. Multicoloured.* W w **14** *(inverted).* P 14.

463	2 r. Type **115**	..	70	60
	a. Horiz strip of 5. Nos. 463/7		3·25	
	aw. Wmk upright		65·00	
464	2 r. Pair of Seychelles Kestrels		70	60
465	2 r. Seychelles Kestrel with eggs		70	60
466	2 r. Seychelles Kestrel on nest with chick		70	60
467	2 r. Seychelles Kestrel chicks in nest		70	60
463/7		*Set of* 5	3·25	2·75

Nos. 463/7 were printed together, *se-tenant,* in horizontal strips of 5 throughout the sheet.

116 10 Rupees Banknote

117 Sprinting

(Des B. Grout. Litho Questa)

1980 (18 Apr). *"London 1980" International Stamp Exhibition. New Currency.* T **116** *and similar multicoloured designs showing banknotes.* W w 14 *(sideways on* 40 c. *and* 1 r. 50). P 14.

468	40 c. Type **116**	..	15	10
469	1 r. 50, 25 rupees	..	30	15
470	2 r. 25, 50 rupees (*vert*)	..	40	25
471	5 r. 100 rupees (*vert*) ..	..	80	75
468/71		*Set of 4*	1·50	1·10
MS472	119 × 102 mm. Nos. 468/71 (wmk sideways)		1·50	1·60

(Des J.W. Litho Questa)

1980 (13 June). *Olympic Games, Moscow.* T **117** *and similar vert designs. Multicoloured.* W w 14. P 14 × 14½.

473	40 c. Type **117**	..	10	10
474	2 r. 25, Weightlifting	..	20	20
475	3 r. Boxing	..	30	30
476	5 r. Sailing	..	60	40
473/6		*Set of 4*	1·10	80
MS477	90×121 mm. Nos. 473/6	..	1·40	2·25

118 Boeing 747-200

119 Female Palm

(Des A. Theobald. Litho Questa)

1980 (22 Aug). *International Tourism Conference, Manila.* T **118** *and similar horiz designs. Multicoloured.* W w 14 *(sideways).* P 14.

478	40 c. Type **118** ..	..	10	10
479	2 r. 25, Bus	..	25	30
480	3 r. Cruise liner	..	35	40
481	5 r. *La Belle Coralline* (tourist launch)	..	55	65
478/81		*Set of 4*	1·10	1·25

(Des L. Curtis. Litho Harrison)

1980 (14 Nov). *Coco-de-Mer (palms).* T **119** *and similar vert designs. Multicoloured.* W w 14. P 14.

482	40 c. Type **119**	..	10	10
483	2 r. 25, Male Palm	..	25	20
484	3 r. Artefacts	..	40	35
485	5 r. Fisherman's gourd	..	55	55
482/5		*Set of 4*	1·10	1·00
MS486	82×140 mm. Nos. 482/5	..	1·60	1·60
	w. Wmk inverted	..		£150

1981 (9 Jan)–**91**. *As Nos. 412/14, 415 (but new value), and 416/19 all with face values redrawn to show "R" instead of "Re" or "Rs" and imprint date at foot. Chalk-surfaced paper.*

487	1 r. Madagascar Red Fody	..	1·00	50
	a. Ordinary paper (11.86)	..	1·00	80
488	1 r. 10, Green Gecko	..	70	80
489	1 r. 25, White Tern	..	2·75	1·25
490	1 r. 50, Seychelles Flying Fox	..	50	75
	a. Ordinary paper (11.91)	..	2·25	2·50
491	5 r. Octopus	..	1·25	1·40
492	10 r. Tiger Cowrie (*Cypraea tigris*)	..	3·25	3·50
493	15 r. Pitcher Plant	..	4·00	4·50
494	20 r. Coat of arms	..	5·00	6·00
487/94		*Set of 8*	16·00	17·00

Imprint dates: "1980", Nos. 487/94; "1981", No. 490; "1982", Nos. 487, 490; "1985", No. 491; "1986", No. 487a; "1988", No. 487; "1990", No. 487a; "1991", Nos. 487a, 490a.

For 1 r. 25, 3 r. and 5 r. watermarked w **16** see Nos. 735/8.

120 Vasco da Gama's *Sao Gabriel, 1497*

121 Male White Tern

(Des J.W. Litho Format)

1981 (27 Feb). *Ships.* T **120** *and similar horiz designs. Multicoloured.* W w 14 *(sideways).* P 14½ × 14.

495	40 c. Type **120**	..	15	10
496	2 r. 25, Mascarenhas' caravel, 1505	..	50	55
497	3 r. 50, Darwin's H.M.S. *Beagle*, 1831	..	55	1·00
498	5 r. *Queen Elizabeth 2* (liner), 1968	..	60	1·40
495/8		*Set of 4*	1·60	2·75
MS499	141 × 91 mm. Nos. 495/98	..	2·00	3·50

(Des G. Drummond. Litho Questa)

1981 (10 Apr). *Birds (3rd series). White Tern.* T **121** *and similar vert designs. Multicoloured.* W w 14. P 14.

500	2 r. Type **121**	..	1·00	65
	a. Horiz strip of 5. Nos. 500/4	..	4·50	
501	2 r. Pair of White Terns	..	1·00	65
502	2 r. Female White Tern	..	1·00	65
503	2 r. Female White Tern on nest, and egg	..	1·00	65
504	2 r. White Tern and chick	..	1·00	65
500/4		*Set of 5*	4·50	3·00

Nos. 500/4 were printed together, *se-tenant*, in horizontal strips of 5 throughout the sheet.

(Des D. Shults. Litho Questa)

1981 (23 June–16 Nov). *Royal Wedding. Horiz designs as* T **26/27** *of Kiribati. Multicoloured.* (a) W w 14. P 14.

505	1 r. 50, *Victoria and Albert I*	..	15	25
	a. Sheetlet. No. 505×6 and No. 506	..	1·25	
506	1 r. 50, Prince Charles and Lady Diana Spencer	..	50	75
507	5 r. *Cleveland*	..	35	60
	a. Sheetlet. No. 507×6 and No. 508	..	3·00	
508	5 r. As No. 506	..	1·25	2·50
509	10 r. *Britannia*	..	60	1·50
	aw. Wmk inverted	..	14·00	
	b. Sheetlet. No. 509×6 and No. 510	..	4·50	
	bw. Wmk inverted	..	£110	
510	10 r. As No. 506	..	1·50	2·75
	aw. Wmk inverted	..	48·00	
505/10		*Set of 6*	4·00	7·50
MS511	120×109 mm. 7 r. 50, As No. 506. Wmk sideways. P 12 (16 Nov)		1·00	1·00

(*b*) *Booklet stamps. No wmk.* P 12 (16 Nov)

512	1 r. 50, As No. 505	..	20	50
	a. Booklet pane. No. 512×4 with margins all round	..	80	
513	5 r. As No. 508	..	80	1·75
	a. Booklet pane. No. 513×2 with margins all round	..	1·60	

Nos. 505/10 were printed in sheetlets of seven stamps of the same face value, each containing six of the "Royal Yacht" design and one of the larger design showing Prince Charles and Lady Diana.

Nos. 512/13 come from 22 r. stamp booklets.

122 Britten Norman Islander

123 Seychelles Flying Foxes in Flight

(Litho Harrison)

1981 (27 July). *10th Anniv of Opening of Seychelles International Airport. Aircraft.* T **122** *and similar horiz designs. Multicoloured.* W w 14 *(sideways*).* P 14½.

514	40 c. Type **122**	..	15	10
515	2 r. 25, Britten Norman "long nose" Trislander	..	55	45
	w. Wmk Crown to right of CA	..	11·00	
516	3 r. 50, Vickers Super VC-10 airliner	..	80	70
517	5 r. Boeing 747-100 airliner	..	1·00	1·00
514/17		*Set of 4*	2·25	2·00

*The normal sideways watermark shows Crown to left of CA, as seen from the back of the stamp.

(Litho Format)

1981 (9 Oct). *Seychelles Flying Fox (Roussette).* T **123** *and similar vert designs. Multicoloured.* W w 14. P 14.

518	40 c. Type **123**	..	10	10
519	2 r. 25, Flying Fox eating	..	30	45
520	3 r. Flying Fox climbing across tree branch	..	45	70
521	5 r. Flying Fox hanging from tree branch	..	55	1·00
518/21		*Set of 4*	1·25	2·00
MS522	95 ×130 mm. Nos. 518/21	..	1·75	3·75

124 Chinese Little Bittern (male)

125 Silhouette Island and La Digue

(Des G. Drummond. Litho Questa)

1982 (4 Feb). *Birds (4th series). Chinese Little Bittern.* T **124** *and similar vert designs. Multicoloured.* W w 14. P 14.

523	3 r. Type **124**	..	2·00	1·00
	a. Horiz strip of 5. Nos. 523/7	..	9·00	
524	3 r. Chinese Little Bittern (female)	..	2·00	1·00
525	3 r. Hen on nest	..	2·00	1·00
526	3 r. Nest and eggs	..	2·00	1·00
527	3 r. Hen with chicks	..	2·00	1·00
523/7		*Set of 5*	9·00	4·50

Nos. 523/7 were printed together, *se-tenant*, in horizontal strips of 5 throughout the sheet.

(Des J. Cooter. Litho Format)

1982 (22 Apr). *Modern Maps.* T **125** *and similar vert designs. Multicoloured.* W w 14. P 14½.

528	40 c. Type **125**	..	15	10
529	1 r. 50, Denis and Bird Islands	..	30	25
530	2 r. 75, Praslin	..	55	65
531	7 r. Mahé	..	1·00	2·00
528/31		*Set of 4*	1·75	2·75
MS532	92 × 128 mm. Nos. 528/31	..	2·50	5·00

126 "Education"

(Des PAD Studio. Litho Harrison)

1982 (5 June). *5th Anniv of Liberation.* T **126** *and similar horiz designs. Multicoloured.* W w 14 *(sideways).* P 14.

533	40 c. Type **126**	..	10	10
534	1 r. 75, "Health"	..	25	25
535	2 r. 75, "Agriculture"	..	30	45
536	7 r. "Construction"	..	80	1·40
533/6		*Set of 4*	1·25	2·00
MS537	128 × 120 mm. Nos. 533/6. P 14½		2·75	6·50

127 Tourist Board Emblem

128 Tata Bus

(Des and litho Harrison)

1982 (1 Sept). *Tourism.* T **127** *and similar horiz designs. Multicoloured.* W w 14 *(sideways).* P 14.

538	1 r. 75, Type **127**	..	25	35
539	1 r. 75, Northolme Hotel	..	25	35
540	1 r. 75, Reef Hotel	..	25	35
541	1 r. 75, Barbarous Beach Hotel	..	25	35
542	1 r. 75, Coral Strand Hotel	..	25	35
543	1 r. 75, Beau Vallon Bay Hotel	..	25	35
544	1 r. 75, Fisherman's Cove Hotel	..	25	35
545	1 r. 75, Mahé Beach Hotel	..	25	35
538/45		*Set of 8*	1·75	2·50

(Des C. Abbott. Litho Harrison)

1982 (18 Nov). *Land Transport.* T **128** *and similar horiz designs. Multicoloured.* W w 14 *(sideways).* P 14.

546	20 c. Type **128**	..	10	10
547	1 r. 75, Mini-moke	..	25	25
548	2 r. 75, Ox-cart	..	40	55
549	7 r. Truck	..	1·10	2·25
546/9		*Set of 4*	1·60	2·75

129 Radio Seychelles Control Room

(Des A. Theobald. Litho Questa)

1983 (25 Feb). *World Communications Year.* T **129** *and similar horiz designs. Multicoloured.* W w 14 *(sideways).* P 14.

550	40 c. Type **129**	..	10	10
551	2 r. 75, Satellite Earth Station	..	35	50
552	3 r. 50, Radio Seychelles Television control room	..	60	70
553	5 r. Postal services sorting office	..	80	1·25
550/3		*Set of 4*	1·60	2·25

NEW INFORMATION

The editor is always interested to correspond with people who have new information that will improve or correct the Catalogue.

130 Agricultural Experimental Station

(Des L. Curtis. Litho Questa)

1983 (14 Mar). *Commonwealth Day. T* **130** *and similar horiz designs. Multicoloured.* W w 14 *(sideways).* P 14.
554	40 c. Type 130	..	10	10
555	2 r. 75, Food processing plant	..	25	40
556	3 r. 50, Unloading fish catch ..	..	40	60
557	7 r. Seychelles flag	..	65	1·40
554/7	..	Set of 4	1·25	2·25

131 Denis Island Lighthouse

(Des Harrison. Litho Format)

1983 (14 July). *Famous Landmarks. T* **131** *and similar horiz designs. Multicoloured.* W w 14 *(sideways).* P 14 × 13½.
558	40 c. Type 131	..	10	10
559	2 r. 75, Victoria Hospital	..	30	45
560	3 r. 50, Supreme Court	..	35	65
561	7 r. State House	..	55	1·40
558/61	..	Set of 4	1·10	2·25
MS562	110 × 98 mm. Nos. 558/61	..	2·75	6·50

132 *Royal Vauxhall Balloon, 1836*

(Des A. Theobald. Litho Harrison)

1983 (15 Sept). *Bicentenary of Manned Flight. T* **132** *and similar horiz designs. Multicoloured.* W w 14 *(sideways).* P 14.
563	40 c. Type 132	..	15	10
564	1 r. 75, De Havilland D.H.50J	..	50	30
565	2 r. 75, Grumman SA-16 Albatross flying boat		60	55
566	7 r. Swearingen Merlin IIIA	..	1·25	1·75
563/6	..	Set of 4	2·25	2·25

133 Douglas DC-10-30 Aircraft   134 Swamp Plant and Moorhen

(Des Park Advertising. Litho Walsall)

1983 (26 Oct). *1st International Flight of Air Seychelles.* W w 14 *(sideways).* P 14.
567	133	2 r. multicoloured	..	1·75	2·00

(Des L. Curtis. Litho Questa)

1983 (17 Nov). *Centenary of Visit to Seychelles by Marianne North (botanic artist). T* **134** *and similar vert designs. Multicoloured.* W w 14. P 14.
568	40 c. Type 134	..	15	10
569	1 r. 75, Wormia flagellaria	..	50	30
570	2 r. 75, Asiatic Pancratium	..	65	60
571	7 r. Pitcher Plant	..	1·25	2·00
568/71	..	Set of 4	2·25	2·75
MS572	90 × 121 mm. Nos. 568/71	..	3·50	6·50

50c

(135)

1983 (28 Dec). *Nos. 505/10 surch as T* **135**.
573	50 c. on 1 r. 50, Victoria and Albert I	..	15	20
	a. Sheetlet. No. 573 × 6 and No. 574		1·10	
	b. Albino surch		32·00	
	c. Surch double, one albino.		35·00	
	d. Surch double, one inverted		55·00	
	e. Surch double, one in 2 r. 25 value		45·00	

574	50 c. on 1 r. 50, Prince Charles and Lady Diana Spencer	..	40	70
	b. Albino surch		75·00	
	c. Surch double, one albino.		85·00	
	d. Surch double, one inverted		£130	
	e. Surch double, one in 2 r. 25 value		£110	
575	2 r. 25 on 5 r. Cleveland	..	45	50
	a. Sheetlet. No. 575 × 6 and No. 576		3·25	
576	2 r. 25 on 5 r. As No. 574	..	1·25	2·25
577	3 r. 75 on 10 r. Britannia	..	75	80
	a. Sheetlet. No. 577 × 6 and No. 578		5·50	
	b. Albino surch		30·00	
	c. Surch double		75·00	
578	3 r. 75 on 10 r. As No. 574	..	1·60	2·75
	b. Albino surch		65·00	
	c. Surch double		£225	
573/8	..	Set of 6	4·25	6·50

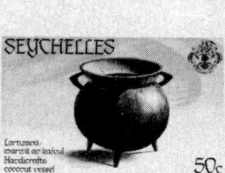

136 Coconut Vessel   137 Victoria Port

(Des Jennifer Toombs. Litho Format)

1984 (29 Feb). *Traditional Handicrafts. T* **136** *and similar horiz designs. Multicoloured.* W w 14 *(sideways).* P 14.
579	50 c. Type 136	..	15	10
580	2 r. Scarf and doll	..	40	70
581	3 r. Coconut-fibre roses	..	45	1·00
582	10 r. Carved fishing boat and doll	..	1·25	4·00
579/82	..	Set of 4	2·00	5·25

(Des C. Collins. Litho Questa)

1984 (21 May). *250th Anniv of "Lloyd's List" (newspaper). T* **137** *and similar vert designs. Multicoloured.* W w 14. P 14½×14.
583	50 c. Type 137	..	25	10
584	2 r. Boissevain (cargo liner)	..	65	55
585	3 r. Sun Viking (liner)	..	90	80
586	10 r. Loss of R.F.A. Ennerdale II (tanker)	..	2·40	3·00
583/6	..	Set of 4	3·75	4·00

138 Old S.P.U.P. Office

(Des D. Miller. Litho B.D.T.)

1984 (2 June). *20th Anniv of Seychelles People's United Party. T* **138** *and similar multicoloured designs.* W w 14 *(sideways on 50 c., 3 r.).* P 14.
587	50 c. Type 138	..	10	10
588	2 r. Liberation statue (vert)	..	30	50
589	3 r. New S.P.U.P. office	..	40	85
590	10 r. President René (vert)	..	1·25	3·50
587/90	..	Set of 4	1·75	4·50

139 1949 U.P.U. 2 r. 25 Stamp

(Des M. Joyce. Litho Harrison)

1984 (18 June). *Universal Postal Union Congress, Hamburg. Sheet* 70 × 85 mm. W w 14 *(sideways).* P 14½.
MS591	139 5 r. yellow-olive, flesh and black	..	1·40	2·25

140 Long Jumping

(Des L. Curtis. Litho Questa)

1984 (28 July). *Olympic Games, Los Angeles. T* **140** *and similar horiz designs. Multicoloured.* W w 14 *(sideways).* P 14.
592	50 c. Type 140	..	10	10
593	2 r. Boxing	..	40	45
594	3 r. Swimming	..	60	75
595	10 r. Weightlifting	..	1·75	2·00
592/5	..	Set of 4	2·50	3·50
MS596	100 × 100 mm. Nos. 592/5		2·50	4·25

141 Sub-aqua Diving

(Des A. Theobald. Litho Questa)

1984 (24 Sept). *Water Sports. T* **141** *and similar horiz designs. Multicoloured.* W w 14 *(sideways).* P 14.
597	50 c. Type 141	..	30	10
598	2 r. Paraskiing	..	90	45
599	3 r. Sailing	..	1·00	75
600	10 r. Water-skiing	..	2·40	2·50
597/600	..	Set of 4	4·25	3·50

142 Humpback Whale   143 Two Bare-legged Scops Owls in Tree

(Des A. Jardine. Litho Questa)

1984 (19 Nov). *Whale Conservation. T* **142** *and similar horiz designs. Multicoloured.* W w 14 *(sideways).* P 14.
601	50 c. Type 142	..	1·50	20
602	2 r. Sperm Whale	..	2·75	1·75
603	3 r. Black Right Whale	..	3·00	2·50
604	10 r. Blue Whale	..	6·00	9·00
601/4	..	Set of 4	12·00	12·00

(Des I. Lewington. Litho Walsall)

1985 (11 Mar). *Birth Bicentenary of John J. Audubon (ornithologist). Bare-legged Scops Owl. T* **143** *and similar vert designs. Multicoloured.* W w 14. P 14.
605	50 c. Type 143	..	1·75	50
606	2 r. Owl on branch	..	2·50	2·25
	w. Wmk inverted		†	—
607	3 r. Owl in flight	..	2·75	2·75
608	10 r. Owl on ground	..	5·50	8·50
605/8	..	Set of 4	11·00	12·50

144 Giant Tortoises   145 The Queen Mother with Princess Anne and Prince Andrew, 1970

(Des D. Miller. Litho Format)

1985 (15 Mar). *"Expo '85" World Fair, Japan. T* **144** *and similar vert designs. Multicoloured.* W w 14. P 14.
609	50 c. Type 144	..	70	30
610	2 r. White Terns	..	1·75	1·75
611	3 r. Windsurfing	..	1·75	2·25
612	5 r. Coco-de-Mer	..	1·75	3·50
609/12	..	Set of 4	5·50	7·00
MS613	130 × 80 mm. Nos. 609/12		6·00	8·00

For these designs without "Expo '85" inscription see No. MS650.

(Des A. Theobald (10 r.), C. Abbott (others). Litho Questa)

1985 (7 June). *Life and Times of Queen Elizabeth the Queen Mother. T* **145** *and similar vert designs. Multicoloured.* W w 16. P 14½ × 14.
614	50 c. The Queen Mother in 1930	..	10	10
615	2 r. Type 145	..	35	50
616	3 r. On her 75th Birthday	..	50	70
617	5 r. With Prince Henry at his christening (from photo by Lord Snowdon)		80	1·25
614/17	..	Set of 4	1·60	2·40
MS618	91×73 mm. 10 r. Arriving at Blenheim Palace by Westland Wessex helicopter. Wmk sideways		2·50	2·25

MINIMUM PRICE

The minimum price quote is 10p which represents a handling charge rather than a basis for valuing common stamps. For further notes about prices see introductory pages.

146 Boxing

147 Agriculture Students

(Des O. Bell. Litho Questa)

1985 (24 Aug). *2nd Indian Ocean Islands Games. T **146** and similar horiz designs. Multicoloured. W w **14** (sideways). P 14.*
619	50 c. Type **146**. .	. .	. .	15	10
620	2 r. Football . .	. .	. .	55	50
621	3 r. Swimming	. .	. .	75	75
622	10 r. Windsurfing	. .	. .	2·40	2·75
619/22			*Set of 4*	3·50	3·50

1985 (1 Nov). *Acquisition of 1st Air Seychelles "Airbus". As No. 735, but additionally inscribed "AIR SEYCHELLES FIRST AIRBUS". "1985" imprint date.*
623	1 r. 25, White Tern	. .	1·75	1·75

(Des Joan Thompson. Litho Questa)

1985 (28 Nov). *International Youth Year. T **147** and similar vert designs. Multicoloured. W w **16**. P 14.*
624	50 c. Type **147**. .	. .	. .	10	10
625	2 r. Construction students building wall	. .	55	50
626	3 r. Carpentry students	. .	. .	70	85
627	10 r. Science students	. .	. .	2·25	3·50
624/7	. .	. .	*Set of 4*	3·25	4·50

148 Ford "Model T" (1919)

149 Five Foot Transit Instrument

(Des J.W. Litho Questa)

1985 (18 Dec). *Vintage Cars. T **148** and similar horiz designs. Multicoloured. W w **16** (sideways). P 14.*
628	50 c. Type **148**. .	. .	. .	50	20
629	2 r. Austin "Seven" (1922) . .	. .	1·50	1·00
630	3 r. Morris "Oxford" (1924). .	. .	1·60	1·50
631	10 r. Humber "Coupé" (1929)	. .	3·00	5·00
628/31			*Set of 4*	6·00	7·00

(Des Harrison. Litho Format)

1986 (28 Feb). *Appearance of Halley's Comet. T **149** and similar vert designs. Multicoloured. W w **16**. P 14.*
632	50 c. Type **149**. .	. .	. .	30	10
633	2 r. Eight foot quadrant	. .	. .	1·00	50
634	3 r. Comet's orbit	. .	. .	1·00	75
635	10 r. Edmond Halley . .	. .	. .	1·75	2·40
632/5	. .	. .	*Set of 4*	3·50	3·50

150 Ballerina

151 Ferry to La Digue

(Des C. Abbott. Litho Format)

1986 (4 Apr). *Visit of Ballet du Louvre Company. "Giselle". T **150** and similar vert designs. Multicoloured. W w **16**. P 13½.*
636	2 r. Type **150** . .	. .	. .	50	60
637	3 r. Male dancer	. .	. .	60	90
MS638	80×90 mm. 10 r. Pas de deux	. .	1·40	2·40

(Des A. Theobald. Litho Questa)

1986 (21 Apr). *60th Birthday of Queen Elizabeth II. Vert designs as T **230**a of Jamaica. Multicoloured. W w **16**. P 14½×14.*
639	50 c. Wedding photograph, 1947 . .	. .	10	10
640	1 r. 25, At State Opening of Parliament, 1982	. .	25	35
641	2 r. Queen accepting bouquet, Seychelles, 1972	. .	30	50
642	3 r. On board Royal Yacht *Britannia*, Qatar, 1979	. .	40	75
643	5 r. At Crown Agents Head Office, London, 1983	. .	60	1·25
639/43	. .	. .	*Set of 5*	1·40	2·75

(Des G. Drummond. Litho Questa)

1986 (22 May). *"Ameripex '86" International Stamp Exhibition, Chicago. Inter-island Communications. T **151** and similar multicoloured designs. W w **16** (sideways on 50 c., 7r.). P 14.*
644	50 c. Type **151**	. .	. .	60	10
645	2 r. Telephone kiosk (vert)	. .	. .	1·25	60
646	3 r. Post Office counter, Victoria (vert)	. .	1·40	85
647	7 r. Air Seychelles Britten Norman "short nose" Trislander aircraft	. .	4·00	2·00
644/7	. .	. .	*Set of 4*	6·50	3·25

LAZOURNEN ENTERNASYONAL KREOL

152 Crests of Seychelles and Knights of Malta

(153)

(Des Jennifer Toombs. Litho Format)

1986 (7 June). *Seychelles Knights of Malta Day. W w **16** (sideways). P 14.*
648	**152** 5 r. multicoloured	. .	1·10	1·60
MS649	101×81 mm. No. 648	. .	2·25	3·50

1986 (12 July). *Seychelles Philatelic Exhibition, Tokyo. Miniature sheet, 130×80 mm, containing stamps as Nos. 609/12, but without "Expo '85" inscription and emblem. W w **16**. P 14.*
MS650	As Nos. 609/12 . .	. .	1·75	3·00

(Des D. Miller. Litho Questa)

1986 (23 July). *Royal Wedding. Vert designs as T **231**a of Jamaica. Multicoloured. W w **16**. P 14.*
651	2 r. Prince Andrew and Miss Sarah Ferguson	. .	35	50
652	10 r. Prince Andrew boarding Wessex helicopter, 1983	. .	1·25	2·40

1986 (28 Oct). *International Creole Day. No. 487a optd with T **153**. "1986" imprint date.*
653	1 r. Madagascar Red Fody	. .	1·75	1·25

154 Pope John Paul at Seychelles Airport

155 *Melanitis leda*

(Des L. Curtis. Litho Questa)

1986 (1 Dec). *Visit of Pope John Paul II. T **154** and similar vert designs, each showing Pope and Seychelles scene. Multicoloured. W w **16**. P 14½×14.*
654	50 c. Type **154**. .	. .	. .	75	30
655	2 r. Catholic Cathedral, Victoria . .	. .	2·00	1·25
656	3 r. Baie Lazare Parish Church	. .	2·50	2·00
657	10 r. Aerial view of People's Stadium	. .	4·25	6·00
654/7	. .	. .	*Set of 4*	8·50	8·50
MS658	95×106 mm. Nos. 654/7. Wmk inverted	11·00	13·00

(Des R. Lewington. Litho Questa)

1987 (18 Feb). *Butterflies. T **155** and similar horiz designs. Multicoloured. W w **16** (sideways). P 14½.*
659	1 r. Type **155**. .	. .	. .	1·00	30
660	2 r. *Phalanta philiberti*	. .	. .	1·60	85
661	3 r. *Danaus chrysippus*	. .	. .	1·90	1·60
662	10 r. *Euploea mitra* . .	. .	. .	2·25	2·40
659/62			*Set of 4*	8·50	8·00

156 Royal Oak Scallop (*Cryptopecten pallium*)

157 Statue of Liberation

(Des Josephine Martin. Litho Walsall)

1987 (7 May). *Seashells. T **156** and similar vert designs. Multicoloured. W w **14**. P 14½×14.*
663	1 r. Type **156** . .	. .	. .	1·25	30
664	2 r. Golden Thorny Oyster (*Spondylus versicolor*)	. .	2·00	85
665	3 r. Ventral or Single Harp (*Harpa ventricosa*) and Ornate Pitar Venus (*Lioconcha ornata*)	. .	2·25	1·60
666	10 r. Silver Conch (*Strombus lentiginosus*)	5·50	6·00
663/6	. .	. .	*Set of 4*	10·00	8·00

(Des Harrison. Litho Format)

1987 (5 June). *10th Anniv of Liberation. T **157** and similar multicoloured designs. W w **16** (sideways). P 14.*
667	1 r. Type **157**. .	. .	. .	20	25
668	2 r. Seychelles Hospital (horiz)	. .	35	50
669	3 r. Orphanage Village (horiz)	. .	45	75
670	10 r. Proposed Sail-fish Monument . .	. .	1·00	2·50
667/70			*Set of 4*	1·75	3·50

158 Seychelles Savings Bank, Praslin

(Des A. Theobald. Litho Format)

1987 (25 June). *Centenary of Banking in Seychelles. T **158** and similar horiz designs. W w **16** (sideways). P 14.*
671	1 r. bronze-green and sage-green	. .	20	25
672	2 r. bistre-brown and salmon	. .	. .	35	50
673	10 r. royal blue and cobalt	. .	. .	1·40	2·50
671/3	. .	. .	*Set of 3*	1·75	3·00
Designs:—2 r. Development Bank; 10 r. Central Bank.

1987 (9 Dec). *Royal Ruby Wedding. Nos. 639/43 optd with T **45**a of Kiribati in silver.*
674	50 c. Wedding photograph, 1947 . .	. .	15	15
	a. Opt inverted	. .	. .	75·00	
675	1 r. 25, At State Opening of Parliament, 1982	. .	25	40
676	2 r. Queen accepting bouquet, Seychelles, 1972	. .	30	60
677	3 r. On board Royal Yacht *Britannia*, Qatar, 1979	. .	40	85
678	5 r. At Crown Agents Head Office, London, 1983	. .	60	1·40
674/8	. .	. .	*Set of 5*	1·50	3·00

159 Tuna-canning Factory

(Des O. Bell. Litho B.D.T.)

1987 (11 Dec). *Seychelles Fishing Industry. T **159** and similar diamond-shaped designs. Multicoloured. W w **16**. P 14.*
679	50 c. Type **159** . .	. .	. .	15	15
680	2 r. Trawler	. .	. .	45	50
681	3 r. Weighing catch	. .	. .	70	75
682	10 r. Unloading net	. .	. .	2·25	2·40
	w. Wmk inverted	. .	. .	32·00	
679/82	. .	. .	*Set of 4*	3·25	3·50

160 Water Sports

161 Young Turtles making for Sea

(Des Jennifer Toombs. Litho Questa)

1988 (9 Feb). *Tourism. T **160** and similar horiz designs, each showing beach hotel. Multicoloured. W w **16** (sideways). P 14½.*
683	1 r. Type **160**. .	. .	. .	40	25
684	2 r. Speedboat and yachts	. .	. .	75	65
685	3 r. Yacht at anchor . .	. .	. .	1·10	1·25
686	10 r. Hotel at night . .	. .	. .	3·00	4·50
683/6	. .	. .	*Set of 4*	4·75	6·00

(Des Doreen McGuinness. Litho Questa)

1988 (22 Apr). *The Green Turtle. T **161** and similar vert designs. Multicoloured. W w **14**. P 14½ × 14.*
687	2 r. Type **161**	. .	. .	1·50	2·00
	a. Vert pair. Nos. 687/8	. .	. .	3·00	4·00
688	2 r. Young turtles hatching	. .	. .	1·50	2·00
689	3 r. Female turtle leaving sea	. .	1·75	2·25
	a. Vert pair. Nos. 689/90	. .	. .	3·50	4·50
690	3 r. Female laying eggs	. .	. .	1·75	2·25
687/90	. .	. .	*Set of 4*	6·00	7·75
Nos. 687/8 and 689/90 were each printed together, se-tenant, in vertical pairs throughout the sheets, each pair forming a composite design.

162 Shot Put   **163** Police Motorcyclists

(Des O. Bell. Litho Walsall)

1988 (29 July). *Olympic Games, Seoul.* T **162** *and similar vert designs. Multicoloured.* W w **16**. P 14½.

691	1 r. Type **162**		30	25
692	2 r. Type **162**		55	70
	a. Horiz strip of 5. Nos. 692/6		2·50	
693	2 r. High jump		55	70
694	2 r. Gold medal winner on podium		55	70
695	2 r. Athletics		55	70
696	2 r. Javelin		55	70
697	3 r. As No. 694		60	70
698	4 r. As No. 695		80	85
699	5 r. As No. 696		1·00	1·10
691/9		*Set of 9*	4·75	5·75
MS700	121×52 mm. 10 r. Tennis. W w **14** (sideways)*		4·00	5·50
	w. Wmk Crown to right of CA		50·00	

*The normal sideways watermark shows Crown to left of CA, as seen from the back of the stamp.

Nos. 691, 693 and 697/9 were each printed in sheets of 50 of one design. No. 693 also exists from sheets containing Nos. 692/6 printed together, *se-tenant*, in horizontal strips of five.

(Des D. Miller (1 r.), L. Curtis and D. Miller (2 r.), E. Nisbet and D. Miller (3 r.), S. Noon and D. Miller (10 r.). Litho Questa)

1988 (30 Sept). *300th Anniv of Lloyd's of London. Multicoloured designs as T* **167a** *of Malawi.* W w **16** (sideways on 2, 3 r.). P 14.

701	1 r. Leadenhall Street, 1928		60	25
702	2 r. *Cinq Juin* (travelling post office) (*horiz*)		1·25	65
703	3 r. *Queen Elizabeth 2* (liner) (*horiz*)		1·75	1·10
704	10 r. Loss of LZ-129 *Hindenburg* (airship), 1937		4·50	4·00
701/4		*Set of 4*	7·25	5·50

(Des A. Theobald. Litho Questa)

1988 (25 Nov). *1st Anniv of Defence Forces Day.* T **163** *and similar horiz designs. Multicoloured.* W w **14** (sideways). P 14.

705	1 r. Type **163**		1·75	1·75
706	2 r. Hindustan Aircraft Chetak helicopter		3·00	2·25
707	3 r. *Andromanche* (patrol boat)		3·00	2·75
708	10 r. BRDM armoured car		6·75	8·50
705/8		*Set of 4*	13·00	12·50

164 Father Christmas with Basket of Presents   **165** *Dendrobium sp.*

(Des S. Hoareau (50 c.), R. Leste (2 r.), F. Anacoura (3 r.), A. McGaw (10 r.), adapted N. Harvey. Litho B.D.T.)

1988 (1 Dec). *Christmas.* T **164** *and similar vert designs. Multicoloured.* W w **14**. P 13½.

709	50 c. Type **164**		15	10
710	2 r. Bird and gourd filled with presents		70	70
711	3 r. Father Christmas basket weaving		90	90
712	10 r. Christmas bauble and palm tree		2·50	3·25
709/12		*Set of 4*	3·75	4·50

(Des Annette Robinson. Litho Questa)

1988 (21 Dec). *Orchids (1st series).* T **165** *and similar multicoloured designs.* W w **16** (sideways on 2, 10 r.). P 14.

713	1 r. Type **165**		55	25
714	2 r. *Arachnis hybrid* (*horiz*)		85	65
715	3 r. *Vanda caerulea*		1·10	95
716	10 r. *Dendrobium phalaenopsis* (*horiz*)		2·75	4·75
713/16		*Set of 4*	4·75	6·00

See also Nos. 767/70 and 795/8.

(Litho Questa)

1988 (30 Dec). *As Nos.* 405B *and* 410B, *but* W w **14** (upright). "1988" *imprint date.* P 14.

718	10 c. Hawksbill Turtle		1·00	1·25
722	50 c. Giant Tortoise		1·50	1·50

A Questa new printing of the 25 c. was issued on the same date. It has the same watermark and perforation as No. 408B.

166 India 1976 25 p. Nehru Stamp   **167** Pres. Rene addressing Rally at Old Party Office

(Des O. Bell. Litho B.D.T.)

1989 (30 Mar). *Birth Centenary of Jawaharlal Nehru (Indian statesman).* T **166** *and similar horiz design, each showing flags of Seychelles and India. Multicoloured.* W w **16** (sideways). P 13½.

724	2 r. Type **166**		75	50
725	10 r. Jawaharlal Nehru		2·75	3·50

(Litho Walsall (1 r. 25), Questa (others))

1989 (May)–**91**. *As Nos.* 410, 415 (*but new value*), 489 *and* 491, *but* W w **16**. *Chalk-surfaced paper* (1 r. 25). *Imprint date at foot.* P 14½×14 (1 r. 25), 14×14½ (5 r.) *or* 14 (*others*).

732	50 c. Giant Tortoise (11.91)		1·75	1·50
735	1 r. 25, White Tern		2·75	2·50
736	3 r. Green Gecko (as No. 415) (11.91)		2·75	3·25
738	5 r. Octopus (1.91)		3·50	5·00
732/8		*Set of 4*	9·75	11·00

Imprint dates: "1989", No. 735; "1990", No. 738; "1991", Nos. 732, 736.

(Des D. Miller. Litho Walsall)

1989 (5 June). *25th Anniv of Seychelles People's United Party.* T **167** *and similar vert designs. Multicoloured.* W w **16**. P 14.

742	1 r. Type **167**		20	25
743	2 r. Women with Party flags and Maison du Peuple		40	45
744	3 r. President Rene making speech and Torch of Freedom		60	75
745	10 r. President Rene, Party flag and Torch of Freedom		2·00	2·75
742/5		*Set of 4*	2·75	3·75

(Des A. Theobald (10 r.), D. Miller (others). Litho Questa)

1989 (20 July). *20th Anniv of First Manned Landing on Moon. Multicoloured designs as T* **51a** *of Kiribati.* W w **16** (sideways on 2, 3 r.). P 14×13½ (1, 5 r.) *or* 14 (*others*).

746	1 r. Lift off of "Saturn 5" rocket		45	25
747	2 r. Crew of "Apollo 15" (30×30 mm)		75	65
748	3 r. "Apollo 15" emblem (30×30 mm)		90	90
749	5 r. James Irwin saluting U.S. flag on Moon		1·50	1·75
746/9		*Set of 4*	3·25	3·25
MS750	100×83 mm. 10 r. Aldrin alighting from "Apollo 11" on Moon. P 14×13½		5·00	6·50

168 British Red Cross Ambulance, Franco-Prussian War, 1870   **169** Black Parrot and Map of Praslin

(Des A. Theobald. Litho Questa)

1989 (12 Sept). *125th Anniv of International Red Cross.* T **168** *and similar horiz designs.* W w **16** (sideways). P 14½×14.

751	1 r. black and orange-vermilion		1·50	35
752	2 r. black, light green and orange-vermilion		2·00	1·50
753	3 r. black and orange-vermilion		2·50	2·50
754	10 r. black and orange-vermilion		7·50	9·00
751/4		*Set of 4*	12·00	12·00

Designs:—2 r. *Liberty* (hospital ship), 1914–18; 3 r. Sunbeam "Standard" army ambulance, 1914–18; 10 r. "White Train" (hospital train), South Africa, 1899–1902.

(Des I. Loe. Litho Questa)

1989 (16 Oct). *Island Birds.* T **169** *and similar vert designs. Multicoloured.* W w **16**. P 14½×14.

755	50 c. Type **169**		1·00	35
756	2 r. Sooty Tern and Ile aux Vaches		2·00	1·75
757	3 r. Seychelles Magpie Robin and Frégate		2·25	2·25
758	5 r. Roseate Tern and Aride		2·75	4·25
755/8		*Set of 4*	7·25	7·75
MS759	83×109 mm. Nos. 755/8		9·00	11·00

MINIMUM PRICE

The minimum price quote is 10p which represents a handling charge rather than a basis for valuing common stamps. For further notes about prices see introductory pages.

170 Flags of Seychelles and France

(Adapted D. Miller from local artwork. Litho B.D.T.)

1989 (17 Nov). *Bicentenary of French Revolution and "World Stamp Expo '89", International Stamp Exhibition, Washington.* T **170** *and similar horiz designs.* W w **16** (sideways). P 14.

760	2 r. multicoloured		2·00	1·50
761	5 r. black, new blue and scarlet		3·25	4·25
MS762	78×100 mm. 10 r. multicoloured		4·50	6·00

Designs:—5 r. Storming the Bastille, Paris, 1789; 10 r. Reading Revolutionary proclamation, Seychelles, 1791.

171 Beau Vallon School   **172** *Disperis tripetaloides*

(Des L. Curtis. Litho B.D.T.)

1989 (29 Dec). *25th Anniv of African Development Bank.* T **171** *and similar multicoloured designs.* W w **16** (sideways on 1, 2 r.). P 14.

763	1 r. Type **171**		45	25
764	2 r. Seychelles Fishing Authority Headquarters		80	90
765	3 r. *Variola* (fishing boat) (*vert*)		2·25	2·25
766	10 r. *Deneb* (fishing boat) (*vert*)		6·00	8·00
763/6		*Set of 4*	8·50	10·00

(Des N. Shewring. Litho Questa)

1990 (26 Jan). *Orchids (2nd series).* T **172** *and similar vert designs. Multicoloured.* W w **16**. P 14.

767	1 r. Type **172**		1·75	40
768	2 r. *Vanilla phalaenopsis*		2·25	1·50
769	3 r. *Angraecum eburneum* subsp *superbum*		2·50	2·50
770	10 r. *Polystachya concreta*		6·00	8·00
767/70		*Set of 4*	11·00	11·00

See also Nos. 795/8.

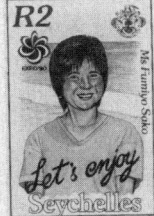

173 Seychelles 1903 2 c. and Great Britain 1880 1½d. Stamps   **174** Fumiyo Sako

(Des D. Miller. Litho Security Printers (M), Malaysia)

1990 (3 May). *"Stamp World London 90" International Stamp Exhibition.* T **173** *and similar horiz designs, each showing stamps. Multicoloured.* W w **14** (sideways). P 12½.

771	1 r. Type **173**		75	25
772	2 r. Seychelles 1917 25 c. and G.B. 1873 1s.		1·25	1·25
773	3 r. Seychelles 1917 2 c. and G.B. 1874 6d.		1·75	2·25
774	5 r. Seychelles 1890 2 c. and G.B. 1841 1d. red-brown		2·50	3·50
771/4		*Set of 4*	5·75	6·50
MS775	88×60 mm. 10 r. Seychelles 1961 Post Office Centenary 2 r. 25 and G.B. 1840 Penny Black. Wmk upright		7·00	7·50

(Des D. Miller. Litho B.D.T.)

1990 (8 June). *"EXPO 90" International Garden and Greenery Exhibition, Osaka.* T **174** *and similar vert designs. Multicoloured.* W w **14**. P 14.

776	2 r. Type **174**		1·00	1·00
777	3 r. Male and female Coco-de-Mer palms		1·25	1·25
778	5 r. Pitcher Plant and Aldabra Lily		1·75	2·25
779	7 r. Arms of Seychelles and Gardenia		2·50	3·00
776/9		*Set of 4*	6·00	6·75
MS780	130×85 mm. Nos. 776/9. Wmk inverted		6·50	8·00

175 Air Seychelles Boeing 767-200ER over Island

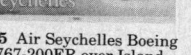

176 Adult Class

(Des D. Miller. Litho Questa)

1990 (27 July). *Air Seychelles "Boeing 767-200ER" World Record-breaking Flight* (1989). W w **16**. P 14×14½.
781 **175** 3 r. multicoloured . . . . 2·25 2·50
  No. 781 was printed in sheetlets of 10, containing two horizontal strips of 5, separated by a central gutter showing a map of the flight route from Grand Rapids, U.S.A. to the Seychelles.

(Des D. Miller. Litho Questa)

1990 (4 Aug). *90th Birthday of Queen Elizabeth the Queen Mother. Vert designs as* T **107** (2 r.) *or* **108** *of Kenya.* W w **16**. P 14×15 (2 r.) or 14½ (10 r.).
782 2 r. multicoloured . . . . 1·25 75
783 10 r. brownish black and violet . . 1·25 75
  Designs:—2 r. Queen Elizabeth in Coronation robes, 1937; 10 r. Queen Elizabeth visiting Lord Roberts Workshops, 1947.

(Des G. Vasarhelyi. Litho Questa)

1990 (8 Sept). *International Literacy Year.* T **176** *and similar vert designs. Multicoloured.* W w **14**. P 14.
784 1 r. Type **176** 75 25
785 2 r. Reading a letter . . . . 1·50 1·25
786 3 r. Following written instructions . . 2·00 2·00
787 10 r. Typewriter, calculator and crossword 4·50 7·00
784/7 . . . . *Set of 4* 8·00 9·50

177 Sega Dancers

178 Beach

(Des Jennifer Toombs. Litho Cartor)

1990 (27 Oct). *Kreol Festival. Sega Dancing.* T **177** *and similar vert designs. Multicoloured.* W w **14**. P 13½×14.
788 2 r. Type **177** . . . . 1·50 1·60
  a. Horiz strip of 5. Nos. 788/92 . . 6·50
789 2 r. Dancing couple (girl in yellow dress) 1·50 1·60
790 2 r. Female Sega dancer . . 1·50 1·60
791 2 r. Dancing couple (girl in floral pattern skirt) . . . . 1·50 1·60
792 2 r. Dancing couple (girl in red patterned skirt) . . . . 1·50 1·60
788/92 . . . . *Set of 5* 6·50 7·00
  Nos. 788/92 were printed together, *se-tenant*, in horizontal strips of 5 throughout the sheet.

(Des D. Miller. Litho Questa)

1990 (10 Dec). *First Indian Ocean Regional Seminar on Petroleum Exploration.* T **178** *and similar horiz design. Multicoloured.* W w **16** (*sideways*). P 14½.
793 3 r. Type **178** . . . . 1·75 1·50
794 10 r. Geological map . . . . 5·25 6·50

(Des N. Shewring. Litho Questa)

1991 (1 Feb). *Orchids* (3rd series). *Vert designs as* T **172**. *Multicoloured.* W w **16**. P 14.
795 1 r. Bulbophyllum intertextum . . 1·75 45
796 2 r. Agrostophyllum occidentale . . 2·25 1·75
797 3 r. Vanilla planifolia . . . . 2·50 2·50
798 10 r. Malaxis seychellarum . . 6·00 7·50
795/8 . . . . *Set of 4* 11·00 11·00

(Des D. Miller. Litho Questa)

1991 (17 June). *65th Birthday of Queen Elizabeth II and 70th Birthday of Prince Philip. Vert designs as* T **58** *of Kiribati. Multicoloured.* W w **16** (*sideways*). P 14½×14.
799 4 r. Queen in evening dress . . 1·60 2·00
  a. Horiz pair. Nos. 799/800 separated by label . . . . 3·00 4·00
800 4 r. Prince Philip in academic robes . . 3·00 4·00
  Nos. 799/800 were printed in a similar sheet format to Nos. 366/7 of Kiribati.

---

179 *Precis rhadama*

180 "The Holy Virgin, Joseph, The Holy Child and St. John" (S. Vouillemont after Raphael)

(Des I. Loe. Litho Walsall)

1991 (15 Nov). *"Phila Nippon '91" International Stamp Exhibition, Tokyo. Butterflies.* T **179** *and similar horiz designs.* W w **14** (*sideways*). P 14×14½.
801 1 r. 50, Type **179** . . . . 2·00 85
802 3 r. Lampides boeticus . . . . 2·00 85
803 3 r. 50, Zizeeria knysna . . . . 2·50 2·25
804 10 r. Phalanta phalantha . . . . 2·75 2·50
801/4 . . . . 7·25 7·50
  . . . . *Set of 4* 13·00 12·00
MS805 78×81 mm. 10 r. Eagris sabadius 6·50 6·50

(Des D. Miller. Litho B.D.T.)

1991 (2 Dec). *Christmas. Woodcuts.* T **180** *and similar vert designs.* W w **16**. P 13½×14.
806 50 c. black, brown-ochre and bright crimson 50 15
807 1 r. black, brown-ochre and myrtle-green 90 25
808 2 r. black, brown-ochre and blue . . 1·75 1·10
809 7 r. black, brown-ochre & deep violet-blue 4·50 6·50
806/9 . . . . *Set of 4* 7·00 7·25
  Designs:—1 r. "The Holy Virgin, the Child and Angel" (A. Blooting after Van Dyck); 2 r. "The Holy Family, St. John and St. Anna" (L. Vorsterman after Rubens); 7 r. "The Holy Family, Angel and St. Cathrin" (C. Bloemaert).

(Des D. Miller. Litho Questa (5 r.), Walsall (others))

1992 (6 Feb). *40th Anniv of Queen Elizabeth II's Accession. Horiz designs as* T **113** *of Kenya. Multicoloured.* W w **14** (*sideways*). P 14.
810 1 r. Seychelles coastline 65 25
811 1 r. 50, Clock Tower, Victoria . . 80 40
812 3 r. Victoria harbour . . . . 1·50 1·50
813 3 r. 50, Three portraits of Queen Elizabeth 1·60 1·75
814 5 r. Queen Elizabeth II . . . . 1·75 2·75
810/14 . . . . *Set of 5* 5·75 6·00

181 Seychelles Brush Warbler

(Des I. Loe. Litho B.D.T.)

1993 (1 Mar)–**96**. *Flora and Fauna.* T **181** *and similar multicoloured designs.* W w **14** (*sideway..* * *on horiz designs*). *With imprint date.* P 13½.
815 10 c. Type **181** 10 10
  w. Wmk Crown to left of CA (1.7.96) 10 10
816 25 c. Bronze Gecko (*vert*) . . 10 10
817 50 c. Seychelles Tree Frog . . 10 15
  w. Wmk Crown to left of CA (1.7.96) 10 15
818 1 r. Seychelles Splendid Palm (*vert*) 25 30
819 1 r. 50, Seychelles Skink (*vert*) . . 35 40
820 2 r. Giant Tenebrionid Beetle . . 50 55
  w. Wmk Crown to left of CA (1.7.96) 50 55
821 3 r. Seychelles Sunbird 70 75
822 3 r. 50, Seychelles Killifish . . 85 90
823 4 r. Seychelles Magpie Robin . . 95 1·00
824 5 r. Seychelles Vanilla (plant) (*vert*) 1·25 1·40
825 10 r. Tiger Chameleon . . . . 2·40 2·50
826 15 c. Coco-de-mer (*vert*) . . 3·50 3·75
827 25 r. Seychelles Paradise Flycatcher (*vert*) 6·00 6·25
828 50 r. Giant Tortoise . . . . 12·00 12·50
815/28 . . . . *Set of 14* 29·00 30·00
  *The normal sideways watermark shows Crown to right of CA, as seen from the back of the stamp.
  Imprint dates: "1993", Nos. 815/28; "1994", Nos. 818, 824/5, 827/8; "1996", Nos. 815w, 816, 817w, 820w, 826; "1998", No. 821.

182 Archbishop George Carey and Anglican Cathedral, Victoria

183 Athletics

(Des G. Vasarhelyi. Litho Cartor)

1993 (8 June). *First Visit of an Archbishop of Canterbury to Seychelles.* T **182** *and similar horiz design. Multicoloured.* W w **14** (*sideways*). P 13½.
834 3 r. Type **182** . . . . 2·00 1·50
835 10 r. Archbishop Carey with Air France Boeing 747-400 and Air Seychelles Boeing 737-200 airliners . . 4·50 6·00

(Des S. Noon. Litho Walsall)

1993 (21 Aug). *4th Indian Ocean Island Games.* T **183** *and similar vert designs. Multicoloured.* W w **14**. P 14½×14.
836 1 r. 50, Type **183** 55 55
837 3 r. Football . . . . 1·00 1·00
838 3 r. 50, Cycling . . . . 1·75 1·50
839 10 r. Sailing . . . . 3·25 4·50
836/9 . . . . *Set of 4* 6·00 7·00

184 Scotia (cable ship) off Victoria, 1893

(Des C. Abbott. Litho Cartor)

1993 (12 Nov). *Centenary of Telecommunications.* T **184** *and similar horiz designs. Multicoloured.* W w **14** (*sideways*). P 13.
840 1 r. Type **184** . . . . 1·25 50
841 3 r. Eastern Telegraph Co office, Victoria, 1904 . . . . 2·00 1·75
842 4 r. HF Transmitting Station, 1971 . . 2·25 2·25
843 10 r. New Telecoms House, Victoria, 1993 4·50 6·00
840/3 . . . . *Set of 4* 9·00 9·50

R1

(185)

1994 (18 Feb). *"Hong Kong '94" International Stamp Exhibition. Nos. 62, 64 and 66/7 of Zil Elwannyen Sesel surch as* T **185**.
844 1 r. on 2 r. 10, Souimanga Sunbird . . 40 30
845 1 r. 50, on 2 r. 75, Sacred Ibis . . 55 60
846 3 r. 50, on 7 r. Seychelles Kestrel (*vert*) 1·40 1·60
847 10 r. on 15 r. Comoro Blue Pigeon (*vert*) 3·00 3·75
844/7 . . . . *Set of 4* 4·75 5·75

186 *Eurema floricola*

187 Lady Elizabeth Bowes-Lyon

(Des I. Loe. Litho Walsall)

1994 (16 Aug). *Butterflies.* T **186** *and similar horiz designs. Multicoloured.* W w **16** (*sideways*). P 14×14½.
848 1 r. 50, Type **186** . . . . 1·75 75
849 3 r. Coeliades forestan . . . . 2·50 2·00
850 3 r. 50, Borbo borbonica . . 2·75 2·75
851 10 r. Zizula hylax . . . . 5·50 7·00
848/51 . . . . *Set of 4* 11·00 11·00

(Des Jennifer Toombs. Litho B.D.T.)

1995 (26 Sept). *95th Birthday of Queen Elizabeth the Queen Mother.* T **187** *and similar vert designs. Multicoloured.* W w **14**. P 14.
852 1 r. 50, Type **187** 65 40
853 3 r. Duchess of York on wedding day, 1923 1·25 1·00
854 3 r. 50, Queen Elizabeth . . . . 1·40 1·40
855 10 r. Queen Elizabeth the Queen Mother 3·25 5·00
852/5 . . . . *Set of 4* 6·00 7·00

NEW INFORMATION

The editor is always interested to correspond with people who have new information that will improve or correct the Catalogue.

188 Female Seychelles Paradise Flycatcher feeding Chick

189 Swimming

(Des N. Shewring. Litho B.D.T.)

1996 (12 July). *Endangered Species. Seychelles Paradise Flycatcher. T* **188** *and similar vert designs. Multicoloured. W* w **16**. *P* 14.

856	1 r. Type 188			55	65
	a. Strip of 4. Nos. 856/9			2·00	
857	1 r. Male bird in flight			55	65
858	1 r. Female bird on branch			55	65
859	1 r. Male bird on branch			55	65
856/9			Set of 4	2·00	2·40

MS860 60×53 mm. 10 r. Pair on branch .. 4·00 4·25
In addition to normal sheets of each value Nos. 856/9 were also available in sheets of 16 with the stamps horizontally and vertically *se-tenant*.

(Des R. Watton. Litho Walsall)

1996 (15 July). *Centenary of Modern Olympic Games. T* **189** *and similar vert designs. Multicoloured. W* w **16**. *P* 14.

861	50 c. Type 189			40	20
862	1 r. 50, Running			60	45
863	3 r. Sailing			1·25	1·50
864	5 r. Boxing			1·90	2·75
861/4			Set of 4	3·75	4·50

190 Archbishop Makarios at Table

191 Comoro Blue Pigeon

(Litho Walsall)

1996 (19 Aug). *40th Anniv of Exile of Archbishop Makarios of Cyprus to Seychelles. T* **190** *and similar vert design. Multi-coloured. W* w **14**. *P* 14.

865	3 r. Type 190			1·50	1·00
866	10 r. Archbishop Makarios in priest's robes			3·25	4·25

(Des N. Arlott. Litho Questa)

1996 (11 Nov). *Birds. T* **191** *and similar vert designs. Multicoloured. W* w **14**. *P* 14½.

867	3 r. Type 191			1·25	1·25
	a. Horiz pair. Nos. 867/8			2·50	2·50
868	3 r. Seychelles Blue Pigeon			1·25	1·25
869	3 r. Souimanga Sunbird			1·25	1·25
	a. Horiz pair. Nos. 869/70			2·50	2·50
870	3 r. Seychelles Sunbird			1·25	1·25
871	3 r. Red-headed Fody			1·25	1·25
	a. Horiz pair. Nos. 871/2			2·50	2·50
872	3 r. Seychelles Fody			1·25	1·25
873	3 r. Madagascar White Eye			1·25	1·25
	a. Horiz pair. Nos. 873/4			2·50	2·50
874	3 r. Seychelles White Eye			1·25	1·25
867/74			Set of 8	9·00	9·00

Nos. 867/8, 869/70, 871/2 and 873/4 were each printed together, *se-tenant*, in horizontal pairs throughout the sheets with the background of each pair forming a composite design showing a regional map.

R 1.50

(192)

1997 (12 Feb). *"HONG KONG '97" International Stamp Exhibition. No. 226 of Zil Elwannyen Sesel surch with T* **192**.
875 1 r. 50 on 2 r. Western Reef Heron ("Dimorphic Little Egret") .. 60 60

(Des N. Shewring (No. **MS**882), D. Miller (others). Litho Questa (No. **MS**882), Cartor (others))

1997 (20 Nov). *Golden Wedding of Queen Elizabeth and Prince Philip. Multicoloured designs as T* **87** *of Kiribati. W* w **14**. *P* 13.

876	1 r. Queen Elizabeth wearing red and white suit			35	45
	a. Horiz pair. Nos. 876/7			70	90
877	1 r. Prince Philip driving carriage			35	45
878	1 r. 50, Prince Philip			45	65
	a. Horiz pair. Nos. 878/9			90	1·25
879	1 r. 50, Queen Elizabeth with horse			45	65
880	3 r. Prince Charles and Princess Anne on horseback			90	1·00
	a. Horiz pair. Nos. 880/1			1·75	2·00
881	3 r. Prince Philip and Queen Elizabeth			90	1·00
876/81			Set of 6	3·00	3·75

MS882 110×70 mm. 10 r. Queen Elizabeth and Prince Philip in landau (*horiz*). Wmk sideways.
P 14½ .. .. 3·00 3·25
Nos. 876/7, 878/9 and 880/1 were each printed together, *se-tenant*, in horizontal pairs throughout the sheets with the backgrounds forming composite designs.

193 Powderblue Surgeonfish

194 *Vierge du Cap* (galleon), 1721

(Des D. Miller. Litho Questa)

1998 (31 Mar). *Diana, Princess of Wales Commemoration. Sheet, 145×70 mm, containing vert designs as T* **91** *of Kiribati. Multicoloured. W* w **14** (*sideways*). *P* 14½×14.
MS883 3 r. Wearing red jacket, 1992; 3 r. Wearing floral dress, 1981; 3 r. Wearing blue and black jacket, 1993; 3 r. Wearing white dress, Nepal 1993 (*sold at* 12 r. + 2 r. *charity premium*) 3·50 4·00

(Litho Walsall)

1998 (30 Nov). *International Year of the Ocean. T* **193** *and similar horiz designs. Multicoloured. W* w **14** (*sideways*). *P* 14.

884	3 r. Type 193			70	75
	a. Horiz strip of 6. Nos. 884/9			4·00	
885	3 r. Shoal of Soldierfish			70	75
886	3 r. Lionfish			70	75
887	3 r. School of fish			70	75
888	3 r. Coral			70	75
889	3 r. Turtle			70	75
884/9			Set of 6	4·00	4·50

Nos. 884/9 were printed together, *se-tenant*, as horizontal strips of 6 throughout the sheet.

(Des J. Batchelor. Litho Questa)

1999 (19 Mar). *18th-century Ships. T* **194** *and similar multi-coloured designs. W* w **16** (*sideways*). *P* 14.

890	1 r. 50, Type 194			25	30
891	3 r. *L'Elizabeth* (corvette), 1741			70	75
892	3 r. 50, *Curieuse* (sloop), 1768			85	1·00
893	10 r. *La Flèche* (frigate), 1801			2·40	2·75
890/3			Set of 4	4·00	4·50

MS894 105×70 mm. 20 r. *Le Cheval Marin* (French merchantman), 1774 (*vert*) .. 5·50 6·00
No. **MS**894 also includes the "Australia '99" World Stamp Exhibition, Melbourne, emblem on the sheet margin.

195 Royal Couple on steps of Chapel Royal, Windsor

196 Cathedral of the Immaculate Conception

(Des D. Miller. Litho Cartor)

1999 (1 Sept). *Royal Wedding. T* **195** *and similar vert design. Multicoloured. W* w **14**. *P* 13½.

895	3 r. Type 195			70	75
896	15 r. In landau			3·50	3·75

(Litho Questa)

1999 (14 Dec). *New Millennium. T* **196** *and similar horiz designs. Multicoloured. W* w **14** (*sideways*). *P* 14½.

897	1 r. Type 196			25	30
898	1 r. 50, Fairy Tern at sunrise			35	40
899	2 r. 50, Dolphin and island			50	55
900	10 r. Comet over beach			2·40	2·50
897/900			Set of 4	3·50	3·75

STAMP BOOKLETS

1979 (25 Apr). *Deep green on green (No. SB1), deep blue on blue (No. SB2) or black printed (No. SB3) covers, 120×75 mm, showing Seychelles arms. Stapled.*

SB1	5 r. booklet containing four 20 c. and 25 c. and eight 40 c. (Nos. 407/9) in blocks of 4		8·00
SB2	10 r. booklet containing four 50 c., 75 c. and 1 r. 25 (Nos. 410/11, 413) in pairs		8·00
SB3	20 r. booklet containing four 1 r. 50 and 3 r. 50 (Nos. 402, 415) in pairs		11·00

1979 (26 Oct). *Red (No. SB4) or blue (No. SB5) printed covers, 118×78 mm, showing Seychelles arms. Stamps attached by selvedge.*

SB4	15 r. booklet containing 10 c., 15 c., 1 r. 50 and 2 r. (Nos. 405/6, 414, 447), each in block of 4		8·00
SB5	20 r. booklet containing four 25 c., 1 r. 25 and 2 r. (Nos. 408, 413, 441/2 or 444/5) in blocks of 4, and two 3 r. (No. 452) in pair		12·00

1980 (29 Feb). *75th Anniv of Rotary International (No. SB6) and Centenary of Visit of General Gordon (No. SB7). Orange (No. SB6) or black (No. SB7) printed covers, 120×79 mm. Stamps attached by selvedge.*

SB6	15 r. booklet containing four 15 c., 1 r. and 1 r. 10 on 3 r. 50, and two 3 r. (Nos. 406, 412, 460, 462) in pairs		9·00
SB7	20 r. booklet containing 75 c., 2 r. and 2 r. 25 (Nos. 411, 441/2 or 444/5, 459), each in block of 4		9·00

1980 (28 Nov). *Black on orange (No. SB8) or black printed (No. SB9) covers, 123×80 mm, showing Clock Tower, Central Victoria. Stamps attached by selvedge.*

SB8	15 r. booklet containing four 40 c., 1 r. and 1 r. 25 (Nos. 409B, 412B, 413) in blocks of 4 and four 1 r. 10 on 3 r. 50 (No. 462) in pairs		15·00
SB9	20 r. booklet containing 1 r. 25, 1 r. 50 and 2 r. 25 (Nos. 413, 414B, 474), each in block of 4		11·00

1981 (27 Feb). *Ships. Multicoloured cover, 160×93 mm. Stapled.*

SB10	35 r. 15, booklet containing 40 c. (No. 495) in block of 10, 5 r. (No. 498) in strip of 4 and No. MS499		7·50

1981 (16 Nov). *Royal Wedding. Multicoloured cover, 105×65 mm, showing The Victoria and Albert I.*

SB11	22 r. booklet containing eight 1 r. 50 in panes of four (No. 512a) and 5 r. in pane of two (No. 513a)		2·75

1998 (30 Nov). *International Year of the Ocean. Folded multicoloured card cover, 91×70 mm, showing marine life. Stamps attached by selvedge.*

SB12	36 r. booklet containing Nos. 884/9, each × 2		8·50

POSTAGE DUE STAMPS

D 1

(Frame recess, value typo B.W.)

1951 (1 Mar). *Wmk Mult Script CA. P 11½.*

D1	D 1	2 c. scarlet and carmine		80	1·50
D2		3 c. scarlet and green		2·00	1·50
D3		6 c. scarlet and bistre		2·00	1·25
D4		9 c. scarlet and orange		2·00	1·25
D5		15 c. scarlet and violet		1·75	11·00
D6		18 c. scarlet and blue		1·75	11·00
D7		20 c. scarlet and brown		1·75	11·00
D8		30 c. scarlet and claret		1·75	7·50
D1/8			Set of 8	12·50	42·00

1964 (7 July)**–65.** *As 1951 but W w 12.*

D 9	D 1	2 c. scarlet and carmine		2·50	12·00
D10		3 c. scarlet and green (14.9.65)		1·25	14·00

(Litho Walsall)

1980 (29 Feb). *Design as Type D 1 but redrawn, size 18 × 22 mm. W w 14 (sideways). P 14.*

D11	5 c. rosine and magenta		15	80
D12	10 c. rosine and deep blue-green		15	80
D13	15 c. rosine and bistre		20	80
D14	20 c. rosine and orange-brown		20	80
D15	25 c. rosine and bright violet		20	80
D16	75 c. rosine and maroon		30	80
D17	80 c. rosine and deep grey-blue		30	90
D18	1 r. rosine and deep reddish purple		30	90
D11/18		Set of 8	1·60	6·00

MINIMUM PRICE

The minimum price quote is 10p which represents a handling charge rather than a basis for valuing common stamps. For further notes about prices see introductory pages.

ZIL ELWANNYEN SESEL

(SEYCHELLES OUTER ISLANDS)

For use from Aldabra, Coetivy, Farquhar and the Amirante Islands, served by the M.V. *Cinq-Juin* travelling post office.

I Inscr "ZIL ELOIGNE SESEL"

1 Reef Fish **2 Cinq Juin**

1980 (20 June)–**81.** *Designs as Nos. 404/11 (with imprint) and 487/94 of Seychelles but inscr. "ZIL ELOIGNE SESEL" as in T 1. W w 14 (sideways on 10, 20, 50, 75 c.). P 14½ × 14 (40 c., 1 r., 1 r. 25, 1r. 50), 13½ (5, 10, 15, 20 r.) or 14 (others).*

1	5 c. Type 1		15	60
2	10 c. Hawksbill Turtle		15	60
3	15 c. Coco-de-Mer		15	60
4	20 c. Wild Vanilla		20	60
5	25 c. *Hypolimnas misippus* (butterfly)		80	60
6	40 c. Coral scene		30	60
7	50 c. Giant Tortoise		30	60
8	75 c. Crayfish		35	60
9	1 r. Madagascar Red Fody		1·00	70
10	1 r. 10, Green Gecko		40	70
11	1 r. 25, White Tern		1·25	70
12	1 r. 50, Seychelles Flying Fox		45	70
	w. Wmk inverted		1·75	
13	5 r. Octopus		70	1·00
	a. Perf 13 (1981)		65	1·50
14	10 r. Tiger Cowrie (*Cypraea tigris*)		80	1·50
	a. Perf 13 (1981)		80	2·50
15	15 r. Pitcher Plant		1·00	2·50
	a. Perf 13 (1981)		1·10	2·50
16	20 r. Seychelles coat of arms		1·00	3·25
	a. Perf 13 (1981)		1·40	3·75
1/16		Set of 16	7·50	14·00

Imprint dates: "1980", Nos. 1/16; "1981", Nos. 1/12, 13a/16a.

(Des L. Curtis. Litho Walsall)

1980 (24 Oct). *Establishment of Travelling Post Office. T 2 and similar horiz designs. Multicoloured. W w 14 (sideways). P 14.*

17	1 r. 50, Type 2		20	15
18	2 r. 10, Hand-stamping covers		25	20
19	5 r. Map of Zil Eloigne Sesel		40	40
17/19		Set of 3	75	65

Nos. 17/19 were printed in sheets including two *se-tenant* stamp-size labels.

The original version of No. 19 incorrectly showed the Agalega Islands as Seychelles territory. A corrected version was prepared prior to issue and stamps in the first type were intended for destruction. Mint examples and some used on first day covers are known, originating from supplies sent to some philatelic bureau standing order customers in error. Such stamps are not listed as they were not available from Seychelles post offices or valid for postage.

3 Yellow-finned Tuna

(Des G. Drummond. Litho Rosenbaum Bros, Vienna)

1980 (28 Nov). *Marine Life. T 3 and similar horiz designs. Multicoloured. W w 14. P 14.*

20	1 r. 50, Type 3		20	20
	w. Wmk inverted		23·00	
21	2 r. 10, Blue Marlin		35	35
	w. Wmk inverted		28·00	
22	5 r. Sperm Whale		70	70
	w. Wmk inverted		23·00	
20/2		Set of 13	1·10	1·10

Nos. 20/2 were printed in sheets including two *se-tenant* stamp-size labels.

(Des D. Shults. Litho Questa)

1981 (23 June–16 Nov). *Royal Wedding. Horiz designs as T 26/27 of Kiribati. Multicoloured. (a) W w 15. P 14.*

23	40 c. Royal Escape		10	10
	aw. Wmk inverted		15·00	
	b. Sheetlet. No. 23×6 and No. 24		90	
	bw. Wmk inverted		£110	
24	40 c. Prince Charles and Lady Diana Spencer		40	55
	aw. Wmk inverted		48·00	
25	5 r. *Victoria and Albert II*		35	40
	a. Sheetlet. No. 25×6 and No. 26		3·00	
26	5 r. As No. 24		1·25	1·75
27	10 r. *Britannia*		60	85
	a. Sheetlet. No. 27×6 and No. 28		4·50	
28	10 r. As No. 24		1·50	3·25
23/8		Set of 6	3·75	6·25
MS29	120×109 mm. 7 r. 50, As No. 24. Wmk sideways. P 12 (16 Nov)		1·40	1·75

	(b) Booklet stamps. No wmk. P 12 (16 Nov)			
30	40 c. As No. 23		35	75
	a. Booklet pane. No. 30×4 with margins all round		1·25	
31	5 r. As No. 26		1·00	1·75
	a. Booklet pane. No. 31×2 with margins all round		2·00	

Nos. 23/8 were printed in sheetlets of seven stamps of the same face value, each containing six of the "Royal Yacht" design and one of the larger design showing Prince Charles and Lady Diana. Nos. 30/1 come from 13 r. 20 stamp booklets.

4 Wright's Skink

(Des and litho Walsall)

1981 (11 Dec). *Wildlife (1st series). T 4 and similar horiz designs. Multicoloured. W w 14 (sideways). P 14.*

32	1 r. 40, Type 4		15	15
33	2 r. 25, Tree Frog		20	20
34	5 r. Robber Crab		40	40
32/4		Set of 3	65	65

See also Nos. 45/7.

5 Cinq Juin ("Communications")

(Des L. Curtis. Litho Harrison)

1982 (11 Mar). *Island Development. Ships. T 5 and similar horiz designs. W w 14. P 14 × 14½.*

35	1 r. 75, black and orange		50	20
	w. Wmk inverted		30·00	
36	2 r. 10, black and turquoise-blue		60	30
	w. Wmk inverted		3·50	
37	5 r. black and bright scarlet		70	50
35/7		Set of 3	1·60	90

Designs:—2 r. 10, *Junon* ("fisheries protection"); 5 r. *Diamond M. Dragon* (drilling ship).

II Inscr "ZIL ELWAGNE SESEL"

6 Paulette

(Des L. Curtis. Litho Harrison)

1982 (22 July). *Local Mail Vessels. T 6 and similar horiz designs. Multicoloured. W w 14 (sideways). P 14.*

38	40 c. Type 6		45	45
39	1 r. 75, *Janette*		60	80
40	2 r. 75, *Lady Esme*		70	95
41	3 r. 50, *Cinq Juin*		70	1·00
38/41		Set of 4	2·25	2·75

7 Birds flying over Island **8 Red Land Crab**

(Des Harrison. Litho Format)

1982 (19 Nov). *Aldabra, World Heritage Site. T 7 and similar horiz designs. Multicoloured. W w 14 (sideways). P 14.*

42	40 c. Type 7		30	15
43	2 r. 75, Map of the atoll		45	35
44	7 r. Giant Tortoises		50	75
42/4		Set of 3	1·10	1·10

(Des G. Drummond. Litho Questa)

1983 (25 Feb). *Wildlife (2nd series). T 8 and similar horiz designs. Multicoloured. W w 14 (sideways). P 14 × 14½.*

45	1 r. 75, Type 8		35	35
46	2 r. 75, Black Terrapin		45	45
47	7 r. Madagascar Green Gecko		90	90
45/7		Set of 3	1·50	1·50

9 Map of Poivre Island and Île du Sud   **10** Aldabra Warbler

(Des J. Cooter. Litho Format)

1983 (27 Apr). *Island Maps. T* **9** *and similar vert designs. Multicoloured. W* w **14.** *P* 14.

48	40 c. Type 9	..	25	30
49	1 r. 50, Île des Roches	..	40	45
50	2 r. 75, Astove Island..	..	50	60
51	7 r. Coëtivy Island	..	80	1·25
48/51		*Set of* 4	1·75	2·40
MS52	93 × 129 mm. Nos. 48/51	..	1·75	3·00

(Des G. Drummond. Litho Harrison)

1983 (13 July). *Birds. T* **10** *and similar multicoloured designs. W* w **14** (*sideways on 5 c. to 2 r. 75*). "1983" *imprint date. P* 14½.

53	5 c. Type 10	..	40	60
54	10 c. Zebra Dove ("Barred Ground Dove")	..	90	60
55	15 c. Madagascar Nightjar	..	30	40
56	20 c. Madagascar Cisticola ("Malagasy Grass Warbler")	..	30	40
57	25 c. Madagascar White Eye	..	60	60
58	40 c. Mascarene Fody	..	30	40
59	50 c. White-throated Rail	..	2·50	60
60	75 c. Black Bulbul	..	40	60
61	2 r. Western Reef Heron ("Dimorphic Little Egret")	..	2·00	1·25
62	2 r. 10, Souimanga Sunbird	..	50	90
63	2 r. 50, Madagascar Turtle Dove	..	1·00	65
64	2 r. 75, Sacred Ibis	..	70	75
65	3 r. 50, Black Coucal (*vert*)	..	90	95
66	7 r. Seychelles Kestrel (*vert*)	..	2·75	1·90
67	15 r. Comoro Blue Pigeon (*vert*)	..	4·00	5·00
68	20 r. Greater Flamingo (*vert*)	..	5·25	5·50
53/68		*Set of* 16	20·00	19·00

For 5 c., 10 c., 25 c., 50 c. and 2 r. values in these designs, but inscribed "Zil Elwannyen Sesel", see Nos. 100/7, 165/73 and 226.

11 Windsurfing

(Des G. Wilby. Litho Questa)

1983 (27 Sept). *Tourism. T* **11** *and similar horiz designs. Multicoloured. W* w **14** (*sideways*). *P* 14.

69	50 c. Type 11	..	10	10
70	2 r. Hotel	..	25	25
71	3 r. View of beach	..	35	35
72	10 r. Islands at sunset ..	..	1·40	1·75
69/72	..	*Set of* 4	1·75	2·10

1983 (16–28 Dec). *Nos. 23/8 surch as T* **135** *of Seychelles.*

73	30 c. on 40 c. *Royal Escape*	..	25	25
	a. Sheetlet. No. 73 × 6 and No. 74.		1·75	
	b. Surch double		50·00	
	c. Error. Surch 50 c. (as Seychelles No. 573)		60·00	
74	30 c. on 40 c. Prince Charles and Lady Diana Spencer	..	50	60
	b. Surch double		£130	
	c. Error. Surch 50 c. (as Seychelles No. 574)		£140	
75	2 r. on 5 r. *Victoria and Albert II* (28.12.83)		70	70
	a. Sheetlet. No. 75 × 6 and No. 76.		5·00	
	b. Albino surch		40·00	
	c. Surch double		75·00	
76	2 r. on 5 r. As No. 74 (28.12.83)		1·25	1·75
	b. Albino surch		65·00	
	c. Surch double		£200	
77	3 r. on 10 r. *Britannia* (28.12.83)		85	85
	a. Sheetlet. No. 77 × 6 and No. 78.		6·00	
78	3 r. on 10 r. As No. 74 (28.12.83)		1·60	2·50
73/8	..	*Set of* 6	4·75	6·00

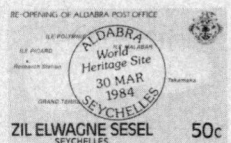

12 Map of Aldabra and Commemorative Postmark

(Des L. Curtis. Litho Questa)

1984 (30 Mar). *Re-opening of Aldabra Post Office. T* **12** *and similar horiz designs. Multicoloured. W* w **14** (*sideways*). *P* 14.

79	50 c. Type 12	..	15	25
80	2 r. 75, White-throated Rail.	..	60	95
81	3 r. Giant Tortoise	..	60	1·10
82	10 r. Red-footed Booby	..	2·25	3·25
79/82	..	*Set of* 4	3·25	5·00

13 Fishing from Launch

(Des L. Curtis. Litho Walsall)

1984 (31 May). *Game Fishing. T* **13** *and similar multicoloured designs. W* w **14** (*sideways on 50 c., 10 r.*). *P* 14.

83	50 c. Type 13	..	15	20
84	2 r. Hooked fish (*vert*)	..	45	65
85	3 r. Weighing catch (*vert*)	..	60	65
86	10 r. Fishing from boat (*different*)	..	2·00	2·75
83/6		*Set of* 4	2·75	4·00

14 Giant Hermit Crab   **15** Constellation of "Orion"

(Des G. Drummond. Litho Format)

1984 (24 Aug). *Crabs. T* **14** *and similar horiz designs. Multicoloured. W* w **14** (*sideways*). *P* 14½.

87	50 c. Type 14	..	25	40
88	2 r. Fiddler Crabs	..	55	1·10
89	3 r. Sand Crab	..	65	1·50
90	10 r. Spotted Pebble Crab	..	1·40	4·25
87/90	..	*Set of* 4	2·50	6·50

(Des A. Theobald. Litho Format)

1984 (16 Oct). *The Night Sky. T* **15** *and similar vert designs. Multicoloured. W* w **14.** *P* 14.

91	50 c. Type 15	..	25	15
92	2 r. "Cygnus"	..	50	55
93	3 r. "Virgo"	..	60	80
94	10 r. "Scorpio"	..	1·40	2·25
91/4	..	*Set of* 4	2·50	3·25

III Inscr "ZIL ELWANNYEN SESEL"

16 Lenzites elegans   **17** The Queen Mother attending Royal Opera House, Covent Garden

(Des G. Drummond. Litho Walsall)

1985 (31 Jan). *Fungi. T* **16** *and similar vert designs. Multicoloured. W* w **14.** *P* 14.

95	50 c. Type 16	..	85	85
96	2 r. *Xylaria telfairei*	..	2·00	2·00
	w. Wmk inverted			
97	3 r. *Lentinus sajor-caju*	..	2·00	2·00
98	10 r. *Hexagonia tenuis*	..	3·50	3·50
95/8	..	*Set of* 4	7·50	7·50

(Litho Harrison)

1985 (May)–**87.** *As Nos.* 54, 57, 59 *and* 61 *but inscr* "Zil Elwannyen Sesel". *W* w **14** (*sideways*). *P* 14½.

100	10 c. Zebra Dove ("Barred Ground Dove")	..	1·75	2·00
103	25 c. Madagascar White Eye	..	1·75	1·25
105	50 c. White-throated Rail (1.7.87)	..	2·75	1·60
107	2 r. Western Reef Heron ("Dimorphic Little Egret")	..	5·50	5·50
100/7	..	*Set of* 4	10·50	9·25

Imprint dates: "1985", Nos. 100, 103, 107; "1987", Nos. 100, 105.

For 10 c., 50 c. and 2 r. values watermarked w **16** (*sideways*) see Nos. 165/73 and 226.

(Des A. Theobald (10 r.), C. Abbott (others). Litho Questa)

1985 (7 June). *Life and Times of Queen Elizabeth the Queen Mother. T* **17** *and similar vert designs. Multicoloured. W* w **16.** *P* 14½ × 14.

115	1 r. The Queen Mother, 1936 (from photo by Dorothy Wilding)	..	20	25
	w. Wmk inverted		3·00	
116	2 r. With Princess Anne at Ascot, 1974	..	35	50
	w. Wmk inverted		65	
117	3 r. Type 17	..	45	70
	w. Wmk inverted		14·00	
118	5 r. With Prince Henry at his christening (from photo by Lord Snowdon)	..	60	1·25
115/18		*Set of* 4	1·40	2·40
MS119	91×73 mm. 10 r. In a launch, Venice, 1985. Wmk sideways		1·50	2·75

18 Giant Tortoise

(Des. G. Vasarhelyi. Litho J.W.)

1985 (27 Sept. *Giant Tortoises of Aldabra* (1st series). *T* **18** *and similar horiz designs. Multicoloured. W* w **16** (*sideways*). *P* 14.

120	50 c. Type 18	..	2·50	90
121	75 c. Giant Tortoises at stream	..	2·75	1·00
122	1 r. Giant Tortoises on grassland	..	3·00	1·10
123	2 r. Giant Tortoise (side view)	..	4·00	2·00
120/3		*Set of* 4	11·00	4·50
MS124	70×60 mm. 10 r. Two Giant Tortoises. P 13×13½		12·00	12·00

For stamps as Nos. 120/3, but without circular inscription around W.W.F. emblem, see Nos. 153/6.

19 Phoenician Trading Ship (600 B.C.)   **20** *Acropora palifera* and *Tubastraea coccinea*

(Des N. Shewring. Litho Format)

1985 (25 Oct). *Famous Visitors. T* **19** *and similar horiz designs. Multicoloured. W* w **14** (*sideways*). *P* 14.

125	50 c. Type 19	..	80	80
126	2 r. Sir Hugh Scott and H.M.S. *Sealark*, 1908	..	1·75	2·00
127	10 r. Vasco da Gama and *Sao Gabriel*, 1502	..	3·50	4·50
125/7		*Set of* 3	5·50	6·50

(Des A. Theobald. Litho Questa)

1986 (21 Apr). *60th Birthday of Queen Elizabeth II. Vert designs as T* **230**a *of Jamaica. Multicoloured. W* w **16.** *P* 14½×14.

128	75 c. Princess Elizabeth at Chester, 1951	..	15	25
129	1 r. Queen and Duke of Edinburgh at Falklands Service, St. Paul's Cathedral, 1985		15	25
130	1 r. 50, At Order of St. Michael and St. George service, St. Paul's Cathedral, 1968		25	40
131	3 r. 75, In Mexico, 1975	..	40	90
132	5 r. At Crown Agents Head Office, London, 1983	..	45	1·25
128/32		*Set of* 5	1·25	2·75

(Des D. Miller. Litho Questa)

1986 (23 July). *Royal Wedding. Square designs as T* **231**a *of Jamaica. Multicoloured. W* w **16.** *P* 14.

133	3 r. Prince Andrew and Miss Sarah Ferguson on Buckingham Palace balcony..	..	45	75
134	7 r. Prince Andrew in naval uniform	..	65	1·75

(Des I. Loe. Litho Harrison)

1986 (17 Sept). *Coral Formations. T* **20** *and similar vert designs. Multicoloured. W* w **16.** *P* 14.

135	2 r. Type 20	..	1·75	1·75
	a. Horiz strip of 5. Nos. 135/9		8·00	
136	2 r. *Echinopora lamellosa* and *Favia pallida*	..	1·75	1·75
137	2 r. *Sarcophyton sp.* and *Porites lutea*	..	1·75	1·75
138	2 r. *Goniopora sp.* and *Goniastrea retiformis*	..	1·75	1·75
139	2 r. *Tubipora musica* and *Fungia fungites*	..	1·75	1·75
135/9		*Set of* 5	8·00	8·00

Nos. 135/9 were printed together, *se-tenant*, in horizontal strips of 5 throughout the sheet, forming a composite design.

21 *Hibiscus tiliaceus*   **22** Teardrop Butterflyfish and Lined Butterflyfish

(Des Annette Robinson. Litho Walsall)

1986 (12 Nov). *Flora. T* **21** *and similar vert designs. Multicoloured. W* w **16.** *P* 14.

140	50 c. Type 21	..	35	30
141	2 r. *Crinum angustum*	..	1·60	1·50
142	3 r. *Phaius tetragonus*	..	2·25	2·00
143	10 r. *Rothmannia annae*	..	3·75	4·00
140/3	..	*Set of* 4	7·00	7·00

(Des G. Drummond. Litho Questa)

1987 (26 Mar). *Coral Reef Fishes. T 22 and similar vert designs. Multicoloured. W w 16. P 14.*

144	2 r. Type 22	.. ..	1·10	1·40
	a. Horiz strip of 5. Nos. 144/8	..	5·00	
145	2 r. Knifejaw	..	1·10	1·40
146	2 r. Narrow-banded Batfish	..	1·10	1·40
147	2 r. Ringed Sergeant	..	1·10	1·40
148	2 r. Lined Butterflyfish and Meyer's Butterflyfish		1·10	1·40
144/8		*Set of 5*	5·00	6·00

Nos. 144/8 were printed together, *se-tenant*, in horizontal strips of 5 throughout the sheet, forming a composite design.

23 Coconut
24 "Vallee de Mai" (Christine Harter)

(Des R. Gorringe. Litho Walsall)

1987 (26 Aug). *Trees. T 23 and similar vert designs. Multicoloured. W w 16. P 14½.*

149	1 r. Type 23	.. ..	80	80
150	2 r. Mangrove	.. ..	1·40	1·75
151	3 r. Pandanus Palm	..	2·00	2·50
152	5 r. Indian Almond	..	3·00	3·25
149/52		*Set of 4*	6·50	7·50

(Des G. Vasarhelyi. Litho Questa)

1987 (9 Sept). *Giant Tortoises of Aldabra (2nd series). Designs as Nos. 120/3, but without circular inscr around W.W.F. emblem. Multicoloured. W w 16 (sideways). P 14.*

153	50 c. As Type 18	..	1·75	1·75
154	75 c. Giant Tortoises at stream	..	2·50	2·50
155	1 r. Giant Tortoises on grassland	..	3·50	3·50
156	2 r. Giant Tortoise (side view)	..	4·50	4·50
153/6	..	*Set of 4*	11·00	11·00

1987 (9 Dec). *Royal Ruby Wedding. Nos. 128/32 optd with T 45a of Kiribati in silver.*

157	75 c. Princess Elizabeth at Chester, 1951		20	20
158	1 r. Queen and Duke of Edinburgh at Falklands Service, St. Paul's Cathedral, 1985		25	25
159	1 r. 50, At Order of St. Michael and St. George service, St. Paul's Cathedral, 1968		35	40
160	3 r. 75, In Mexico, 1975		50	90
161	5 r. At Crown Agents Head Office, London, 1983		60	1·25
157/61		*Set of 5*	1·75	2·75

(Des D. Miller. Litho Questa)

1987 (16 Dec). *Tourism. T 24 and similar vert designs. Multicoloured. W w 16. P 14.*

162	3 r. Type 24	..	2·00	1·60
	a. Horiz strip of 3. Nos. 162/4	..	5·50	
163	3 r. Ferns	..	2·00	1·60
164	3 r. Bamboo	..	2·00	1·60
162/4		*Set of 3*	5·50	4·25

Nos. 162/4 were printed together, *se-tenant*, in horizontal strips of 3 throughout the sheet, forming the complete picture.

(Litho Harrison)

1988 (July–24 Nov). *As No. 53, but inscr "Zil Elwannyen Sesel", and Nos. 100, 105 and 107, all W w 16 (sideways). "1988" imprint date. P 14½.*

165	5 c. Type 10 (24.11)	..	1·75	1·75
166	10 c. Zebra Dove ("Barred Ground Dove") (24.11)		1·75	1·75
171	50 c. White-throated Rail (24.11)	..	2·75	2·75
173	2 r. Western Reef Heron ("Dimorphic Little Egret")		5·50	6·00
165/73		*Set of 4*	10·50	11·00

For 2 r. printed by Walsall and perforated 14×14½ see No. 226.

25 *Yanga seychellensis* (beetle)

(Des I. Loe. Litho Walsall)

1988 (28 July). *Insects. T 25 and similar horiz designs. Multicoloured. W w 14 (sideways). P 14.*

180	1 r. Type 25	..	1·00	80
181	2 r. *Belenois aldabrensis* (butterfly)	..	1·75	1·40
182	3 r. *Polyspilota seychelliana* (mantid)	..	2·00	2·00
183	5 r. *Polposipus herculeanus* (beetle)	..	2·50	2·75
180/3		*Set of 4*	6·50	6·25

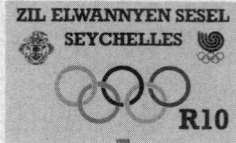

26 Olympic Rings

(Des Joan Thompson. Litho Format)

1988 (31 Aug). *Olympic Games, Seoul. Sheet 99 × 73 mm. W w 16 (sideways). P 14.*

MS184	**26** 10 r. multicoloured	..	2·40	2·40

(Des D. Miller (1 r.), E. Nisbet and D. Miller (2 r.), O. Bell and D. Miller (3 r.), A. Theobald and D. Miller (5 r.). Litho Walsall)

1988 (28 Oct). *300th Anniv of Lloyd's of London. Multicoloured designs as T 167a of Malawi. W w 14 (sideways on 2, 3 r.). P 14.*

185	1 r. Modern Lloyd's Building, London		70	55
186	2 r. *Retriever* (cable ship) (*horiz*)		1·00	90
187	3 r. *Chantel* (fishing boat) (*horiz*)		1·75	1·40
188	5 r. Wreck of *Torrey Canyon* (tanker), Cornwall, 1967		2·25	1·75
185/8		*Set of 4*	5·25	4·25

27 "Father Christmas landing with Presents" (Jean-Claude Boniface)

(Adapted G. Vasarhelyi. Litho Questa)

1988 (18 Nov). *Christmas. Children's Paintings. T 27 and similar multicoloured designs. W w 16 (sideways on 1, 5 r.). P 13½ × 14 (horiz) or 14 × 13½ (vert).*

189	1 r. Type 27	..	35	35
190	2 r. "Church" (Francois Barra) (*vert*)		60	70
191	3 r. "Father Christmas flying on Bird" (Wizy Ernesta) (*vert*)		85	1·00
192	5 r. "Father Christmas in Sleigh over Island" (Federic Lang)		1·40	1·60
189/92		*Set of 4*	2·75	3·25

(Des A. Theobald (10 r.), D. Miller (others). Litho Questa)

1989 (20 July). *20th Anniv of First Manned Landing on Moon. Multicoloured designs as T 51a of Kiribati. W w 16 (sideways on 2, 3 r.). P 14×13½ (1, 5 r.) or 14 (others).*

193	1 r. Firing Room, Launch Control Centre	..	1·00	1·00
194	2 r. Crews of "Apollo-Soyuz" mission (30×30 mm)		1·50	1·50
195	3 r. "Apollo-Soyuz" emblem (30×30 mm)		1·75	1·90
196	5 r. "Apollo" and "Soyuz" docking in space		2·50	2·75
193/6		*Set of 4*	6·00	6·50
MS197	82×100 mm. 10 r. Recovery of "Apollo 11." P 14×13½		8·00	9·00

28 Dumb Cane
29 Tec-Tec Broth

(Des Lynn Chadwick. Litho Questa)

1989 (9 Oct). *Poisonous Plants (1st series). T 28 and similar horiz designs. Multicoloured. W w 16 (sideways). P 14.*

198	1 r. Type 28	..	1·75	1·75
199	2 r. Star of Bethlehem	..	2·25	2·25
200	3 r. Indian Liquorice	..	2·50	2·50
201	5 r. Black Nightshade	..	3·50	3·50
198/201		*Set of 4*	9·00	9·00

See also Nos. 214/17.

(Des O. Bell. Litho B.D.T.)

1989 (18 Dec). *Creole Cooking. T 29 and similar vert designs. Multicoloured. W w 16. P 14.*

202	1 r. Type 29	..	1·50	1·50
203	2 r. Pilaff à la Seychelloise	..	2·00	2·00
204	3 r. Mullet grilled in banana leaves	..	2·25	2·50
205	5 r. Daube	..	3·25	3·50
202/5		*Set of 4*	8·00	8·50
MS206	125×80 mm. Nos. 202/5		8·50	9·50

Stamps from No. MS206 have the white margin omitted on one or both vertical sides.

30 1980 Marine Life 5 r. Stamp

(Des D. Miller. Litho Security Printers (M), Malaysia)

1990 (3 May). *"Stamp World London 90" International Stamp Exhibition. T 30 and similar horiz designs showing stamps. Multicoloured. W w 14 (sideways). P 12½.*

207	1 r. Type 30	..	1·75	1·75
208	2 r. 1980 5 r. definitive	..	2·25	2·25
209	3 r. 1983 2 r. 75 definitive	..	2·50	2·50
210	5 r. 1981 Wildlife 5 r.	..	3·50	3·50
207/10		*Set of 4*	9·00	9·00
MS211	124×84 mm. Nos. 207/10. Wmk upright		9·50	10·00

(Des D. Miller. Litho Questa)

1990 (4 Aug). *90th Birthday of Queen Elizabeth the Queen Mother. Vert designs as T 107 (2 r.) or 108 (10 r.) of Kenya. W w 16. P 14×15 (2 r.) or 14½ (10 r.).*

212	2 r. multicoloured	..	2·00	2·00
213	10 r. black and orange-brown	..	3·75	4·50

Designs:—2 r. Duchess of York with baby Princess Elizabeth, 1926; 10 r. King George VI and Queen Elizabeth visiting bombed district, London, 1940.

(Des Lynn Chadwick. Litho Security Printers (M), Malaysia)

1990 (5 Nov). *Poisonous Plants (2nd series). Horiz designs as T 28. Multicoloured. W w 14 (sideways). P 12½.*

214	1 r. Ordeal Plant	..	1·75	1·75
215	2 r. Thorn Apple	..	2·25	2·25
216	3 r. Strychnine Tree	..	2·50	2·50
217	5 r. Bwa Zasmen	..	3·50	3·50
214/17		*Set of 4*	9·00	9·00

(Litho Walsall)

1991 (Jan). *As No. 173, but different printer. W w 16 (sideways). "1990" imprint date. P 14×14½.*

226	2 r. Western Reef Heron ("Dimorphic Little Egret")		3·00	3·25

(Des D. Miller. Litho Questa)

1991 (17 June). *65th Birthday of Queen Elizabeth II and 70th Birthday of Prince Philip. Vert designs as T 58 of Kiribati. Multicoloured. W w 16 (sideways). P 14½×14.*

234	4 r. Queen Elizabeth II	..	1·60	1·75
	a. Horiz pair. Nos. 234/5 separated by label		3·00	3·50
235	4 r. Prince Philip	..	1·60	1·75

Nos. 234/5 were printed in a similar sheet format to Nos. 366/7 of Kiribati.

31 *St. Abbs* (full-rigged ship), 1860
32 *Lomatophyllum aldabrense* (plant)

(Des J. Batchelor. Litho Walsall)

1991 (28 Oct). *Shipwrecks. T 31 and similar horiz designs. Multicoloured. W w 14 (sideways). P 14.*

236	1 r. 50, Type 31	..	2·00	2·00
237	3 r. *Norden* (barque), 1862	..	2·50	2·50
238	3 r. 50, *Clan Mackay* (freighter), 1894	..	2·75	2·75
239	10 r. *Glenlyon* (freighter), 1905	..	6·00	7·50
236/9	..	*Set of 4*	12·00	13·00

(Des D. Miller. Litho Questa (5 r.), Walsall (others))

1992 (6 Feb). *40th Anniv of Queen Elizabeth II's Accession. Horiz designs as T 113 of Kenya. Multicoloured. W w 14 (sideways). P 14.*

240	1 r. Beach	..	75	75
241	1 r. 50, Aerial view of Desroches	..	1·10	1·25
242	3 r. Tree-covered coastline	..	1·50	1·75
243	3 r. 50, Three portraits of Queen Elizabeth II	1·60	1·90
244	5 r. Queen Elizabeth II	..	1·75	2·25
240/4	..	*Set of 5*	6·00	6·00

(Des D. Miller. Litho Questa)

1992 (19 Nov). *10th Anniv of Aldabra as a World Heritage Site. T 32 and similar vert designs. Multicoloured. W w 14. P 14½×14.*

245	1 r. 50, Type 32	..	1·25	1·25
246	3 r. White-throated Rail	..	3·25	3·00
247	3 r. 50, Robber Crab	..	2·50	3·00
248	10 r. Aldabra Drongo	..	7·50	8·50
245/8		*Set of 4*	13·00	14·00

STAMP BOOKLETS

1980 (28 Nov). *Black on yellow cover, 126×80 mm, showing map of Zil Elwannyen Sesel. Stamps attached by selvedge.*
SB1   25 r. booklet containing 40 c., 1 r. and 1 r. 10 (Nos. 6, 9/10), each in block of 4, and three 5 r. (No. 13) in pair and single .. .. .. 14·00

1981 (16 Nov). *Royal Wedding. Multicoloured cover, 105×65 mm, showing the Royal Escape. Stitched.*
SB2   13 r. 20, booklet containing eight 40 c. in panes of 4 (No. 30a) and two 5 r. in pane of 2 (No. 31a)   4·00

Sierra Leone

PRICES FOR STAMPS ON COVER TO 1945	
Nos. 1/15	*from* × 10
Nos. 16/26	*from* × 15
Nos. 27/34	*from* × 20
Nos. 35/7	*from* × 10
No. 38	
No. 39	*from* × 15
Nos. 41/52	*from* × 8
No. 53	—
No. 54	*from* × 40
Nos. 55/63	*from* × 5
Nos. 64/71	—
Nos. 73/84	*from* × 4
No. 85	—
Nos. 86/97	*from* × 4
No. 98	—
Nos. 99/110	*from* × 4
No. 111	—
Nos. 112/26	*from* × 2
Nos. 127/30	—
Nos. 131/45	*from* × 2
Nos. 146/8	—
Nos. 155/66	*from* × 2
No. 167	—
Nos. 168/78	*from* × 2
Nos. 179/80	—
Nos. 181/4	*from* × 6
Nos. 185/7	*from* × 5
Nos. 188/200	*from* × 2

CROWN COLONY AND PROTECTORATE

The first settlement in Sierra Leone intended as a home for repatriated Africans, and subsequently those released by the Royal Navy from slave ships, was established in 1787. The Sierra Leone Company was created by Act of Parliment in 1791, but its charter was surrendered in 1808 and the coastal settlements then became a Crown Colony. The inland region was proclaimed a British protectorate on 21 August 1896.

A post office was established in 1843 but, until the inclusion of Freetown in the British Post Office packet system in 1850, overseas mail was carried at irregular intervals by passing merchant or naval vessels.

The stamps of GREAT BRITAIN were not sold at Sierra Leone post offices, although examples from ships of the West African Squadron do exist with local cancellations.

PRINTERS. All issues of Sierra Leone until 1932 were typographed by De La Rue & Co. Ltd, London.

HALF PENNY

| 1 | 2 | (3) |

Dot after "SIX" and break in octagonal frame (R. 19/11)

1859 (21 Sept)–**74**. *No wmk. P 14.*
1 1 6d. dull purple .. .. £200 50·00
2   6d. grey-lilac (1865) .. .. £250 40·00
    a. Dot after "SIX" .. .. — £275
3   6d. reddish violet (*p* 12½) (1872) .. £375 60·00
    a. Dot after "SIX" .. .. — £375
4   6d. reddish lilac (1874) .. .. 45·00 27·00
    a. Dot after "SIX" £250 £150
Imperforate proofs exist.
The paper used for the 6d. value often shows varying degrees of blueing, caused by a chemical reaction.
The 6d. plate contained 240 stamps arranged in panes of 20 (4×5) with the sheets containing 12 such panes in four horizontal rows of three.

1872–73. *Wmk Crown CC. P 12½. (a) Wmk sideways* (April 1872).
7 2 1d. rose-red .. .. .. 70·00 29·00
8   3d. buff .. .. .. £110 35·00
9   4d. blue .. .. .. £150 38·00
10   1s. green .. .. .. £350 50·00

(b) Wmk upright (Sept 1873)
11 2 1d. rose-red .. .. .. 90·00 30·00
    w. Wmk inverted .. £140 75·00
12   2d. magenta .. .. £110 48·00
13   3d. saffron-yellow .. £500 85·00
14   4d. blue .. .. .. £250 50·00
15   1s. green .. .. .. £400 90·00

1876. *Wmk Crown CC. P 14.*
16 2 ½d. brown .. .. .. 2·00 6·50
    w. Wmk inverted .. 90·00
17   1d. rose-red .. .. 45·00 12·00
18   1½d. lilac (Nov) .. 48·00 7·50
19   2d. magenta .. .. 60·00 4·00
20   3d. buff .. .. .. 50·00 4·25
    w. Wmk inverted
21   4d. blue .. .. .. £130 6·50
    w. Wmk inverted
22   1s. green .. .. .. 55·00 6·50
16/22 .. .. *Set of 7* £325 42·00

1883 (June–26 Sept). *Wmk Crown CA. P 14.*
23 2 ½d. brown .. .. .. 20·00 48·00
24   1d. rose-red (26.9.83) .. £200 35·00
25   2d. magenta .. .. 48·00 8·50
26   4d. blue .. .. .. £850 28·00

1884 SIERRA 5s. LEONE SURCHARGE. From 2 June 1884 the administration decided that, as a temporary measure, revenue and fiscal duties were to be paid with ordinary postage stamps. At that time there was no postage value higher than 1s., so a local surcharge, reading "SIERRA 5s. LEONE", was applied to No. 22 (Price £200 *unused*). Until withdrawal on 1 March 1885 this surcharge was valid for both fiscal and postal purposes, although no genuine postal cover or piece has yet been found. One mint example is known with overprint inverted (*Price* £700).
Remainders of the surcharge were cancelled by a horizontal red brush stroke (*Price* £32 *with upright surcharge,* £160 *with inverted surcharge*).

1884 (July)–**91.** *Wmk Crown CA. P 14.*
27 2 ½d. dull green 80 90
    w. Wmk inverted .. † 90·00
28   1d. carmine .. .. .. 2·25 90
    a. Rose-carmine (1885?) .. 28·00 8·50
    aw. Wmk inverted .. † 90·00
29   1½d. pale violet (1889) .. 2·50 6·50
30   2d. grey .. .. .. 26·00 2·50
31   2½d. ultramarine (1891) .. 7·00 1·00
32   3d. yellow (1889) .. .. 2·50 8·50
33   4d. brown .. .. .. 1·50 1·50
34   1s. red-brown (1888) .. 17·00 11·00
27/34 .. .. *Set of 8* 55·00 29·00
27/8, 30/1, 33/4 (*perf 14*) Optd "Specimen" *Set of 6* £500
27/8, 30, 33 (*perf 12*) Optd "Specimen" *Set of 4* £750

1885–96. *Wmk Crown CC. P 14.*
35 1 6d. dull violet (1885) .. 60·00 23·00
    a. Bisected (3d.) (on cover) .. † £2500
    b. Dot after "SIX" .. — £130
36   6d. brown-purple (1890) (Optd S. £60) 14·00 14·00
    a. Dot after "SIX" .. 85·00 85·00
    w. Wmk inverted
37   6d. purple-lake (1896) .. 2·00 6·50
    a. Dot after "SIX" .. 35·00 60·00
Proofs of the 6d. brown-purple exist from 1889 on Crown CA watermark and perforated 12 (*Price* £1500, *unused*).

1893 (18 Jan). *Surch with T 3. (a) On No. 18. Wmk Crown CC.*
38 2 ½d. on 1½d. lilac £475 £600
    a. "PFNNY" (R. 3/1) .. £2250 £3000

(b) On No. 29. Wmk Crown CA
39 2 ½d. on 1½d. pale violet .. 2·75 3·00
    a. Surch inverted .. £100 £100
    b. "PFNNY" (R. 3/1) .. 70·00 £100
    ba. Ditto. Surch inverted .. £1800
On Nos. 38/9 the surcharge and the cancelling bars were applied separately so that No. 39a exists with the bars either normal or inverted with the rest of the surcharge.
Forged surcharges exist with "HALF PENNY" shown on one line.
The 6d. fiscal, inscribed "STAMP DUTY" as Type 6, surcharged "ONE-PENNY" is known used for postage between June and August 1894, but no official sanction for such usage has been found.

SIERRA LEONE (1d.) **SIERRA LEONE** (3d.)

| 4 | 5 |

1896–97. *Wmk Crown CA. P 14.*
41 4 ½d. dull mauve and green (1897) .. 1·25 2·50
42   1d. dull mauve and carmine .. 1·50 1·75
43   1½d. dull mauve and black (1897) .. 3·50 14·00
44   2d. dull mauve and orange .. 2·25 5·00
45   2½d. dull mauve and ultramarine .. 1·40 1·25
46 5 3d. dull mauve and slate .. 7·00 7·00
47   4d. dull mauve and carmine (1897) .. 8·50 13·00
48   5d. dull mauve and black (1897) .. 9·00 12·00
49   6d. dull mauve (1897) .. 7·00 18·00
50   1s. green and black .. 6·00 18·00
51   2s. green and ultramarine .. 24·00 45·00
52   5s. green and carmine .. 55·00 £140
53   £1 purple/*red* £140 £375
41/53 .. .. *Set of 13* £225 £600
41/53 Optd "Specimen" .. *Set of 13* £200
Examples of most values are known showing forged oval registered postmarks dated "16 JUL 11" or "4 SP 11".

SIERRA LEONE STAMP DUTY ONE PENNY

| 6 | |

POSTAGE AND REVENUE
| | (7) |

$2\tfrac{1}{2}$d. $2\tfrac{1}{2}$d. $2\tfrac{1}{2}$d.
(8)   (9)   (10)

$2\tfrac{1}{2}$d. $2\tfrac{1}{2}$d. $2\tfrac{1}{2}$d.
(11)   (12)   (13)

POSTAGE AND REVENUE   REVENUE
   (14)   Italic "N" (R. 3/4 of the setting)

1897. *Fiscal stamps as T 6. Wmk CA over Crown, w 7. P 14.*
    (a) Optd with T 7 (26 Feb*)
54   1d. dull purple and green .. 2·00 2·25
    a. Opt double £1400 £1400

(b) Optd with T 7 and surch T 8, 10, 11 (with square stop) or 12 with six thin bars across the original face value (1 Mar)
55 8 2½d. on 3d. dull purple and green .. 11·00 13·00
    a. Surch double £16000
    b. Surch double (Types 8 + 10) .. £13000
    c. Surch double (Types 8 + 11) .. £22000
56 10 2½d. on 3d. dull purple and green .. 50·00 65·00
57 11 2½d. on 3d. dull purple and green .. £140 £170
58 12 2½d. on 3d. dull purple and green .. £300 £375
59 8 2½d. on 6d. dull purple and green .. 8·50 13·00
60 10 2½d. on 6d. dull purple and green .. 40·00 50·00
61 11 2½d. on 6d. dull purple and green .. £100 £110
62 12 2½d. on 6d. dull purple and green .. £225 £250
Nos. 55/8 and 59/62 were surcharged from a setting of 30 (10×3) which contained twenty-two examples of Type 8 (including three with square stops), five of Type 10, two of Type 11 and one of Type 12.
Two examples are known of No. 55a, one of No. 55b (of which two are in the Royal Collection) and two of No. 55c (one in the Royal Collection). A unique example of a double surcharge on No. 55 showing Types 8 + 12 is also in the Royal Collection.

(c) Optd with T 14 and surch T 8, 9, 10, 11 (with round stop) or 13 with five thin bars across the original face value (1 Mar)
63 8 2½d. on 1s. dull lilac .. 85·00 65·00
64 9 2½d. on 1s. dull lilac .. £1200 £1200
65 10 2½d. on 1s. dull lilac .. £700 £700
66 11 2½d. on 1s. dull lilac .. £400 £400
    a. Italic "N" £1000 £1000
66b 13 2½d. on 1s. dull lilac .. £1200 £1200
67 8 2½d. on 2s. dull lilac .. £1600 £1700
68 9 2½d. on 2s. dull lilac .. £32000 £35000
69 10 2½d. on 2s. dull lilac .. £14000
70 11 2½d. on 2s. dull lilac .. £7500 £8500
    a. Italic "N" £15000 £15000
71 13 2½d. on 2s. dull lilac .. £32000 £35000
*Earliest known postmark date.
The setting of 30 (10×3) used for both Nos. 63/6b and 67/71 contained twenty-two examples of Type 8 (including one with square stop), one of Type 9, two of Type 10, four of Type 11 (including one with italic "N") and one of Type 13.
Most examples of Nos. 63/6b are water-stained. Stamps in this condition are worth about 30% of the price quoted.

SIERRA LEONE (½d.)   **SIERRA LEONE** (3d.)

| 15 | 16 |

1903. *Wmk Crown CA. P 14.*
73 15 ½d. dull purple and green .. 3·00 4·50
74   1d. dull purple and rosine .. 1·75 1·00
75   1½d. dull purple and black .. 1·25 10·00
76   2d. dull purple and brown-orange .. 3·75 16·00
77   2½d. dull purple and ultramarine .. 4·50 8·00
78 16 3d. dull purple and grey .. 9·00 13·00
79   4d. dull purple and rosine .. 7·00 14·00
80   5d. dull purple and black .. 8·00 32·00
81   6d. dull purple .. .. 11·00 15·00
82   1s. green and black .. 14·00 45·00
83   2s. green and ultramarine .. 40·00 50·00
84   5s. green and carmine .. 65·00 90·00
85   £1 purple/*red* £200 £225
73/85 .. .. *Set of 13* £325 £475
73/85 Optd "Specimen" .. *Set of 13* £180

1904–5. *Wmk Mult Crown CA. Ordinary paper* (1d.) *or chalk-surfaced paper* (others). *P 14.*
86 15 ½d. dull purple and green (1905) .. 5·00 4·50
87   1d. dull purple and rosine .. 1·00 1·00
    a. Chalk-surfaced paper (1905) .. 4·00 1·25
88   1½d. dull purple and black (1905) .. 2·75 13·00
89   2d. dull purple and brown-orange (1905) .. 4·25 4·00
90   2½d. dull purple and ultramarine (1905) .. 4·50 2·00
91 16 3d. dull purple and grey (1905) .. 30·00 3·50
    w. Wmk inverted .. 45·00
92   4d. dull purple and rosine (1905) .. 7·00 7·00
    w. Wmk inverted .. 80·00

93	16	5d. dull purple and black (1905)	..	12.00	24.00
94		6d. dull purple (1905)	..	4.00	3.25
95		1s. green and black (1905)	..	7.50	9.00
96		2s. green and ultramarine (1905)		18.00	27.00
97		5s. green and carmine (1905)	..	30.00	50.00
98		£1 purple/red (1905)	..	£200	£225
86/98			Set of 13	£275	£325

1907–12. *Wmk Mult Crown CA. Ordinary paper (¹/₂d. to 2¹/₂d.)
or chalk-surfaced paper (others). P 14.*

99	15	¹/₂d. green	..	55	50
100		1d. carmine	..	11.00	75
		a. Red	..	4.00	60
101		1¹/₂d. orange (1910)		60	2.00
102		2d. greyish slate (1909)		80	1.50
103		2¹/₂d. blue	..	2.75	3.00
104	16	3d. purple/yellow (1909)	..	7.50	2.75
		a. Ordinary paper (1912)		8.00	10.00
105		4d. black and red/yellow (1908)		2.25	1.40
106		5d. purple and olive-green (1908)		5.50	5.00
107		6d. dull and bright purple (1908)		6.00	8.00
108		1s. black (1908)	..	5.50	5.00
109		2s. purple and bright blue/blue (1908)		15.00	19.00
110		5s. green and red/yellow (1908)		38.00	55.00
111		£1 purple and black/red (1911)		£200	£190
99/111			Set of 13	£250	£250
99/111		Optd "Specimen"	Set of 13	£300	

Most values from the 1903, 1904–05 and 1907–12 issues are known with forged postmarks. These include oval registered examples dated "16 JUL 11" or "4 SP 11".

USED HIGH VALUES. The £2 and £5 values of the King George V series were intended for fiscal use only. Before the introduction of the airmail service at the end of 1926 there was no postal rate for which they could be used. Under the airmail rates used between 1926 and 1932 it is just possible that a very heavy letter may have required a £2 value. Postmarks on the £5 and on the £2 before December 1926 can only have been applied "by favour" or, in the case of the cds type, are on stamps removed from telegraph forms. Used prices quoted for Nos. 129/30 and 147/8 are for "by favour" cancellations.

17   18

19   20

1912–21. *Die I. Wmk Mult Crown CA. Chalk-surfaced paper
(3d. and 6d. to £5). P 14.*

112	17	¹/₂d. blue-green	..	2.75	2.50
		a. Yellow-green (1914)	..	2.75	2.50
		b. Deep green (1919)	..	4.50	2.75
113		1d. carmine-red	..	1.50	20
		a. Scarlet (1916)	..	2.75	1.00
		b. Rose-red (1918)	..	3.50	80
		bx. Wmk reversed	..		
114		1¹/₂d. orange (1913)	..	2.00	2.00
		a. Orange-yellow (1919)	..	4.50	95
115		2d. greyish slate	..	1.25	20
		w. Wmk inverted	..	35.00	35.00
116		2¹/₂d. deep blue	..	9.50	2.50
		a. Ultramarine (1917)	..	1.00	80
116b	20	3d. purple/yellow	..	3.00	3.25
		ba. On pale yellow (1921)		3.25	3.25
117	18	4d. black and red/yellow		2.75	8.50
		a. On lemon (1915)	..	4.00	6.50
		b. Die II. On pale yellow (1921)		4.25	5.50
118		5d. purple and olive-green		1.00	5.00
119		6d. dull and bright purple		3.25	5.00
120	19	7d. purple and orange		3.00	8.50
121		9d. purple and black	..	5.00	11.00
122	18	10d. purple and red	..	3.00	18.00
124	20	1s. black/green	..	4.25	4.50
		a. On blue-green, green back		4.50	3.25
		w. Wmk inverted	..	48.00	48.00
125		2s. blue and purple/blue	..	13.00	5.50
126		5s. green and red/yellow	..	13.00	25.00
127		10s. red and green/green	..	65.00	£110
		a. Carmine and blue-green/green		85.00	£130
		b. Carmine and yellow-green/green		85.00	£130
128		£1 black and purple/red		£140	£180
129		£2 blue and dull purple (S. £100)		£475	£650
130		£5 orange and green (S. £225)		£1200	£1600
112/28			Set of 17	£225	£350
112/28		Optd "Specimen"	Set of 17	£275	

1921–27. *Die II. Wmk Mult Script CA. Chalk-surfaced paper
(6d. to £5). P 14.*

131	17	¹/₂d. dull green	..	1.25	50
		a. Bright green	..	3.50	1.25
132		1d. bright violet (Die I) (1924)		1.25	2.00
		a. Die II (1925)	..	3.00	20
133		1¹/₂d. scarlet (1925)	..	1.25	1.25
134		2d. grey (1922)	..	90	20
135		2¹/₂d. ultramarine	..	1.00	5.00
136	18	3d. bright blue (1922)	..	1.00	90
137		4d. black and red/pale yellow (1925)		1.75	3.25
138		5d. purple and olive-green		90	90
139		6d. grey-purple and bright purple		1.25	2.50
		y. Wmk inverted and reversed			

140	19	7d. purple and orange (1927)		2.75	17.00
141		9d. purple and black (1922)		2.75	12.00
142	18	10d. purple and red (1925)		3.00	22.00
143	20	1s. black/emerald (1925)		6.50	7.00
144		2s. blue and dull purple/blue		9.50	10.00
		w. Wmk inverted		90.00	95.00
145		5s. red and green/yellow (1927)		9.50	45.00
146		10s. red and green/green (1927)		75.00	£160
147		£2 bl & dull pur (1923) (Optd S. £100)		£425	£650
148		£5 orange & brn (1923) (Optd S. £225)		£1100	£1500
131/46			Set of 16	£110	£250
131/46		Optd "Specimen"	Set of 16	£250	

21 Rice Field   **22** Palms and
                        Cola Tree

(Eng J.A.C. Harrison (T 21))

1932 (1 Mar). *Wmk Mult Script CA. (a) Recess Waterlow. P 12¹/₂.*

155	21	¹/₂d. green	..	20	30
156		1d. violet	..	30	30
157		1¹/₂d. carmine	..	30	1.25
		a. Imperf between (horiz pair)			
158		2d. brown	..	30	30
159		3d. blue	..	60	1.75
160		4d. orange	..	60	5.00
161		5d. bronze-green	..	75	2.50
162		6d. light blue	..	50	2.50
163		1s. lake	..	1.75	4.50

(b) Recess B.W. P 12.

164	22	2s. chocolate	..	5.00	5.00
165		5s. deep blue	..	12.00	18.00
166		10s. green	..	55.00	£110
167		£1 purple	..	85.00	£170
155/67			Set of 13	£140	£275
155/67		Perf "Specimen"	Set of 13	£180	

23 Arms of   **24** Old Slave
Sierra Leone   Market, Freetown

27 African Elephant   **28** King George V

(Des Father F. Welsh. Recess B.W.)

1933 (2 Oct). *Centenary of Abolition of Slavery and of Death of
William Wilberforce. T 23/4, 27/8 and similar designs. Wmk
Mult Script CA (sideways on horiz designs). P 12.*

168		¹/₂d. green	..	45	1.25
169		1d. black and brown	..	40	10
170		1¹/₂d. chestnut	..	4.50	4.50
171		2d. purple	..	2.75	20
172		3d. blue	..	2.75	1.75
173		4d. brown	..	6.50	10.00
174		5d. green and chestnut	..	7.00	16.00
175		6d. black and brown-orange	..	7.00	8.00
176		1s. violet	..	4.75	17.00
177		2s. brown and light blue	..	22.00	40.00
178		5s. black and purple	..	£140	£160
179		10s. black and sage-green	..	£170	£250
180		£1 violet and orange	..	£300	£400
168/180			Set of 13	£600	£800
168/80		Perf "Specimen"	Set of 13	£500	

Designs: *Vert*—1d. "Freedom"; 1¹/₂d. Map of Sierra Leone; 4d. Government sanatorium. *Horiz*—3d. Native fruit seller; 5d. Bullom canoe; 6d. Punting near Banana; 1s. Government buildings; 2s. Bunce Island; £1 Freetown harbour.

1935 (6 May). *Silver Jubilee. As Nos. 114/17 of Jamaica.
P 11×12.*

181		1d. ultramarine and grey-black	..	1.00	2.25
		a. Extra flagstaff	..	45.00	65.00
		b. Short extra flagstaff	..	95.00	
		c. Lightning conductor	..	35.00	
182		3d. brown and deep blue	..	1.00	8.50
		a. Extra flagstaff	..	60.00	80.00
		b. Short extra flagstaff	..	£200	
		c. Lightning conductor	..	65.00	
183		5d. green and indigo	..	1.40	8.50
		a. Extra flagstaff	..	90.00	£130
		b. Short extra flagstaff	..	£275	
		c. Lightning conductor	..	95.00	
184		1s. slate and purple	..	6.00	4.75
		a. Extra flagstaff	..	£275	£190
		b. Short extra flagstaff	..	£275	
		c. Lightning conductor	..	£275	£190
181/4			Set of 4	8.50	22.00
181/4		Perf "Specimen"	Set of 4	80.00	

For illustrations of plate varieties see Omnibus section following Zimbabwe.

1937 (12 May). *Coronation. As Nos. 118/20 of Jamaica, but ptd
by B.W.*

185		1d. orange	..	70	50
186		2d. purple	..	90	50
187		3d. blue	..	1.50	3.25
185/7			Set of 3	2.75	3.75
185/7		Perf "Specimen"	Set of 3	55.00	

30 Freetown from the Harbour

31 Rice Harvesting

(Recess Waterlow)

1938 (1 May)**–44.** *Wmk Mult Script CA (sideways). P 12¹/₂.*

188	30	¹/₂d. black and blue-green	..	15	30
189		1d. black and lake	..	40	40
		a. Imperf between (vert pair)		†	—
190	31	1¹/₂d. scarlet	..	20.00	70
190a		1¹/₂d. mauve (1.2.41)	..	30	60
191		2d. mauve	..	40.00	1.75
191a		2d. scarlet (1.2.41)	..	30	1.00
192	30	3d. black and ultramarine	..	40	40
193		4d. black and red-brown (20.6.38)		80	2.75
194	31	5d. olive-green (20.6.38)	..	5.00	3.50
195		6d. grey (20.6.38)	..	75	40
196	30	1s. black and olive-green (20.6.38)		1.50	50
196a	31	1s. 3d. yellow-orange (1.7.44)		40	40
197	30	2s. black and sepia (20.6.38)		4.50	2.00
198	31	5s. red-brown (20.6.38)	..	10.00	5.00
199		10s. emerald-green (20.6.38)		16.00	7.50
200	30	£1 deep blue (20.6.38)	..	17.00	18.00
188/200			Set of 16	£100	38.00
188/200		Perf "Specimen"	Set of 16	£250	

1946 (1 Oct). *Victory. As Nos. 141/2 of Jamaica.*

201		1¹/₂d. lilac	..	20	10
202		3d. ultramarine	..	20	10
201/2		Perf "Specimen"	Set of 2	55.00	

1948 (1 Dec). *Royal Silver Wedding. As Nos. 143/4 of Jamaica.*

203		1¹/₂d. bright purple	..	15	15
204		£1 indigo	..	16.00	16.00

1949 (10 Oct). *75th Anniv of U.P.U. As Nos. 145/8 of Jamaica.*

205		1¹/₂d. purple	..	20	50
206		3d. deep blue	..	1.25	2.50
207		6d. grey	..	35	2.75
208		1s. olive	..	35	1.00
205/8			Set of 4	1.90	6.00

1953 (2 June). *Coronation. As No. 153 of Jamaica, but ptd by
B.W.*

209		1¹/₂d. black and purple	..	30	30

32 Cape Lighthouse   **33** Cotton Tree,
                            Freetown

(Recess Waterlow)

1956 (2 Jan)**–61.** *Designs as T 32/3. Wmk Mult Script CA.
P 13¹/₂ × 13 (horiz) or 14 (vert).*

210		¹/₂d. black and deep lilac	..	90	1.75
211		1d. black and olive	..	90	30
212		1¹/₂d. black and ultramarine	..	1.60	3.75
213		2d. black and brown	..	70	10
214		3d. black and bright blue	..	1.25	10
		a. Perf 13 × 13¹/₂	..	1.75	8.50
215		4d. black and slate-blue	..	2.50	1.25
216		6d. black and violet	..	1.00	30
217		1s. black and scarlet	..	1.25	30
218		1s. 3d. black and sepia	..	11.00	20
219		2s. 6d. black and chestnut	..	14.00	6.50
220		5s. black and deep green	..	2.50	2.00
221		10s. black and bright reddish purple		3.50	2.50
		a. Black and purple (19.4.61)		10.00	25.00
222		£1 black and orange	..	17.00	17.00
210/22			Set of 13	45.00	32.00

Designs: *Horiz*—1d. Queen Elizabeth II Quay; 1¹/₂d. Piassava workers; 4d. Iron ore production, Marampa; 6d. Whale Bay, York Village; 1s. 3d. Bristol 170 Freighter Mk 31 airplane and map; 10s. Law Courts, Freetown; £1, Government House. *Vert*—3d. Rice harvesting; 1s. Bullom canoe; 2s. 6d. Orugu Railway Bridge; 5s. Kuranko Chief.

Nos. 210/11 and 214 exist in coils, constructed from normal sheets.

INDEPENDENT

45 Palm Fruit Gathering   46 Licensed Diamond Miner

52

(Des K. Penny (½d., 1s.), Messrs Thoma, Turrell and Larkins (1d., 3d., 6d., 2s. 6d.), W. G. Rumley (1½d., 5s.), J. H. Vandi (2d., 10s.), R. A. Sweet (4d., 1s 3d.), J. White (£1). Recess B.W.)

1961 (27 Apr). *Independence. T 45/6 and similar designs. W 52. P 13½.*

223	½d. chocolate and deep bluish green	..	20	10
224	1d. orange-brown and myrtle-green	..	1·25	10
225	1½d. black and emerald	..	20	10
226	2d. black and ultramarine	..	20	10
227	3d. orange-brown and blue	..	20	10
228	4d. turquoise-blue and scarlet	..	20	10
229	6d. black and purple	..	20	10
230	1s. chocolate and yellow-orange	..	20	10
231	1s. 3d. turquoise-blue and violet	..	20	10
232	2s. 6d. deep green and black	..	2·75	20
233	5s. black and red	..	1·00	1·25
234	10s. black and green	..	1·00	1·25
235	£1 carmine-red and yellow	..	8·00	5·00
223/235		*Set of 13*	14·00	7·50

Designs: Vert—1½d., 5s. Bundu mask; 2d., 10s. Bishop Crowther and Old Fourah Bay College; 1s. Palm fruit gathering; £1, Forces Bugler. Horiz—3d., 6d. Sir Milton Margai; 4d., 1s. 3d. Lumley Beach, Freetown; 2s. 6d. Licensed diamond miner.

53 Royal Charter, 1799   55 Old House of Representatives, Freetown, 1924

(Des C. P. Rang (3d., 4d.), F. H. Burgess (1s. 3d.). Recess B.W.)

1961 (25 Nov). *Royal Visit. T 53, 55 and similar designs. W 52. P 13½.*

236	3d. black and rose-red	..	15	10
237	4d. black and violet	..	15	90
238	6d. black and yellow-orange	..	20	10
239	1s. 3d. black and blue	..	2·50	90
236/9		*Set of 4*	2·75	1·75

Designs: Vert—4d. King's Yard Gate, Freetown, 1817. Horiz—1s. 3d. Royal Yacht *Britannia* at Freetown.

57 Campaign Emblem

(Recess B.W.)

1962 (7 Apr). *Malaria Eradication. W 52. P 11 × 11½.*

240	57	3d. carmine-red	..	10	10
241		1s. 3d. deep green	..	20	10

58 Fireball Lily   59 Jina-gbo

(Des M. Goaman. Photo Harrison)

1963 (1 Jan). *Flowers. Vert designs as T 58 (½d., 1½d., 3d., 4d., 1s., 2s. 6d., 5s., 10s.) or horiz as T 59 (others). Multicoloured. N 52 (sideways on vert designs). P 14.*

242	½d. Type 58	..	10	10
243	1d. Type 59	..	10	10
244	1½d. Stereospermum	..	20	10
245	2d. Black-eyed Susan	..	20	10
246	3d. Beniseed	..	20	10
247	4d. Blushing Hibiscus	..	20	10
248	6d. Climbing Lily	..	30	10
249	1s. Beautiful Crinum	..	40	10
250	1s. 3d. Blue Bells	..	1·50	20
251	2s. 6d. Broken Hearts	..	1·25	30
252	5s. Ra-ponthi	..	1·25	80
253	10s. Blue Plumbago	..	2·50	1·50
254	£1 African Tulip Tree	..	8·00	7·00
242/254		*Set of 13*	14·50	9·00

71 Threshing Machine and Corn Bins

(Des V. Whiteley. Recess B.W.)

1963 (21 Mar). *Freedom from Hunger. T 71 and similar horiz design. W 52. P 11½ × 11.*

255	3d. black and yellow-ochre	..	20	10
256	1s. 3d. sepia and emerald-green	..	35	40

Design:—1s. 3d. Girl with onion crop.

2ND YEAR OF INDEPENDENCE 19 PROGRESS 63 DEVELOPMENT **3d.**	2nd Year Independence Progress Development 1963 **10d.**
(73)	(74)

(Optd by Govt Printer, Freetown)

1963 (27 Apr). *Second Anniv of Independence. Surch or optd as T 73/4. (a) Postage.*

257	3d. on ½d. black & deep lilac (No. 210) (R.)		40	10
	a. Small "c" in "INDEPENDENCE"	..	4·00	5·50
258	4d. on 1½d. black & ultram (No. 212) (Br.)	..	15	10
259	6d. on ½d. black & deep lilac (No. 210) (O.)		30	10
	a. Small "c" in "INDEPENDENCE"	..	4·50	6·00
260	10d. on 3d. black & bright blue (No. 214) (R.)		50	10
261	1s. 6d. on 3d. black & brt bl (No. 214) (V.)		30	20
262	3s. on 3d. black & brt bl (No. 214) (Ult.)		40	20

(b) Air. Additionally optd "AIR MAIL"

263	7d. on 1½d. black & ultram (No. 212) (C.)	..	20	10
264	1s. 3d. on 1½d. blk & ultram (No. 212) (R.)		20	10
265	2s. 6d. black and chestnut (No. 219) (V.)	..	1·00	40
266	3s. on 3d. black & bright blue (No. 214) (B.)		40	20
267	6s. on 3d. black & bright blue (No. 214) (V.)		1·00	20
268	11s. on 10s. black and bright reddish purple (No. 221) (C.)		1·40	85
269	11s. on £1 black and orange (No. 222) (C.)		£500	£180
257/268		*Set of 12*	5·50	2·50

75 Centenary Emblem

(Des M. Goaman. Recess B.W.)

1963 (1 Nov). *Centenary of Red Cross. T 75 and similar vert designs. W 52. P 11 × 11½.*

270	3d. red and violet	..	50	10
271	6d. red and black	..	50	15
272	1s. 3d. red and deep bluish green	..	65	20
270/2		*Set of 3*	1·50	40

Designs:—6d. Red Cross emblem; 1s. 3d. Centenary emblem.

1853–1859–1963 **Oldest Postal Service Newest G.P.O. in West Africa** **1s.**	1853–1859–1963 Oldest Postage Stamp Newest G.P.O. in West Africa AIRMAIL
(78)	(79)

1963 (4 Nov). *Postal Commemorations. Optd or surch by Govt Printer, Freetown. (a) Postage. As T 78.*

273	3d. black and bright blue (No. 214)		10	10
	a. "1895" for "1859" (R. 3/3)	..	2·50	
	b. "1853/1859/1963" (R. 2/3)		2·50	
	ba. As No. 273b, but showing "S vice" also (R. 2/3)			
274	4d. on 1½d. black & ultram (No. 212) (C.)	..	10	10
	a. "1895" for "1859" (R. 1/2)	..	3·50	
	b. "1853*1859*1963" (R. 3/2, 11/4)	..	2·75	
	c. "1853 1859*1963" (R. 11/4)	..	3·75	
	d. No stop after "O", but stop after "Africa" (R. 10/1)		2·75	

275	9d. on 1½d. black & ultram (No. 212) (V.)		10	10
	a. "1853*1859*1963" (R. 3/2, 11/4)	..	2·40	
	b. No stop after "O" (R. 7/5)			
	c. No stop after "O", but stop after "Africa" (R. 10/1)		2·75	
276	1s. on 1s. 3d. turq-blue & vio (No. 231) (C.)		10	10
	a. "1853*1859*1963" (R. 3/4, 10/2)	..	3·00	
277	1s. 6d. on ½d. black and deep lilac (No. 210) (Mag.)		15	10
	a. "1853*1859*1963" (R. 11/1)	..	4·50	
	b. "1853 1859 1963" (R. 4/5)	..	7·50	
278	2s. on 3d. black & brt blue (No. 214) (Br.)		15	10
	a. "1895" for "1859" (R. 4/10)	..	8·00	
	b. "1853/1859/1963" (R. 2/3)	..	6·00	

(b) Air. As T 79

279	7d. on 3d. black & rose-red (No. 236) (Br.)		20	50
	a. "1895" for "1859" (R.3/6, 4/4)	..	3·25	
	b. "1853·1859·1963" (R.2/3, 4/10)	..	2·50	
	c. No stop after "O" (R.1/2)		3·50	
280	1s. 3d. black and blue (No. 239) (C.)	..	2·00	1·25
	a. "1895" for "1859" (R.7/3)	..	20·00	
	b. "1853*1859*1963" (R.3/2, 10/4)	..	9·00	
	c. No stop after "O" (R.8/3)		10·00	
281	2s. 6d. on 4d. turq-blue & scarlet (No. 228)		1·25	20
	a. "1895" for "1859" (R.7/3)	..	48·00	
	b. "1853*1859*1963" (R.3/2, 10/4)	..	6·00	
	c. No stop after "O" (R.8/3)		10·00	
282	3s. on 3d. black and rose-red (No. 236) (V.)		2·50	1·75
	a. "1895" for "1859" (R.3/3)	..	£325	
	b. "1853-1859-1963" (R.2/3, 4/10)	..	10·00	
	c. No stop after "O" (R.1/2)		13·00	
283	6s. on 6d. blk & yell-orge (No. 238) (Ult.)		1·00	70
	a. "1895" for "1859" (R.1/1)	..	48·00	
	b. "1853*1859*1963" (R.3/2, 10/4)	..	7·50	
	c. No stop after "O" (R.8/3)		11·00	
284	£1 black and orange (No. 222) (R.)	..	17·00	15·00
	a. "1895" for "1859" (R.11/4)	..	£250	
	b. "1853*1859*1963" (R.4/5, 11/1)	..	40·00	
273/84		*Set of 12*	22·00	17·00

The events commemorated are: 1853, "First Post Office"; 1859, "First Postage Stamps"; and 1963 "Newest G.P.O." in West Africa. Nos. 273, 278 have the overprint in five lines; Nos. 279, 282 in six lines (incl "AIRMAIL").

Some of the overprint varieties were corrected during printing.

80 Lion Emblem and Map   81 Globe and Map

Extended "A" in "SIERRA" (R. 3/3, later corrected on the 4d. value)

(Recess and litho Walsall Lithographic Co. Ltd)

1964 (10 Feb). *World's Fair, New York. Imperf. Self-adhesive.*

(a) Postage.

285	80	1d. multicoloured	..	10	10
286		3d. multicoloured	..	10	10
		a. Lion omitted			
287		4d. multicoloured	..	10	10
		b. Extended "A"	..	2·00	
288		6d. multicoloured	..	10	10
		b. Extended "A"	..	2·00	
289		1s. multicoloured	..	10	10
		a. "POSTAGE 1/-" omitted	..	38·00	
		b. Extended "A"	..	2·00	
290		2s. multicoloured	..	30	20
		b. Extended "A"	..	3·00	
291		5s. multicoloured	..	50	50
		a. "POSTAGE 5/-" omitted	..	40·00	
		b. Extended "A"	..	5·00	

(b) Air.

292	81	7d. multicoloured	..	10	10
293		9d. multicoloured	..	10	10
		a. "AIR MAIL 9d." omitted			
294		1s. 3d. multicoloured	..	20	10
		a. "AIR MAIL 1/3" omitted	..	40·00	
295		2s. 6d. multicoloured	..	30	15
296		3s. 6d. multicoloured	..	30	20
		a. "AIR MAIL 3/6" omitted			
297		6s. multicoloured	..	55	60
		a. "AIR MAIL 6/-" omitted	..	42·00	
298		11s. multicoloured	..	70	1·00
		a. "AIR MAIL 11/-" omitted	..	45·00	
285/98			*Set of 14*	2·75	2·75

Nos. 285/98 were issued in sheets of 30 (6 × 5) on green (postage) or yellow (airmail) backing paper with the emblems of Samuel Jones & Co. Ltd, self-adhesive paper-makers, on the back.

WARNING. These and later self-adhesive stamps should be kept on their backing paper except commercially used, which should be retained on cover or piece.

82 Inscription and Map   83 Pres. Kennedy and Map

(Recess and litho Walsall)

1964 (11 May). *President Kennedy Memorial Issue. Imperf. Self-adhesive. (a) Postage. Green backing paper.*

299	82	1d. multicoloured	.. ..	10	10
300		3d. multicoloured	.. ..	10	10
301		4d. multicoloured	.. ..	10	10
302		6d. multicoloured	.. ..	10	10
		b. Extended "A"	.. ..	2·00	
303		1s. multicoloured	..	10	10
		b. Extended "A"	.. ..	2·00	
304		2s. multicoloured	.. ..	30	20
		b. Extended "A"	.. ..	3·00	
305		5s. multicoloured	.. ..	50	50
		b. Extended "A"	.. ..	5·00	

(b) Air. Yellow backing paper.

306	83	7d. multicoloured	.. ..	10	10
307		9d. multicoloured	.. ..	10	10
308		1s. 3d. multicoloured	..	15	10
309		2s. 6d. multicoloured	..	30	20
310		3s. 6d. multicoloured	..	30	20
311		6s. multicoloured	.. ..	55	60
312		11s. multicoloured	.. ..	70	1·00
299/312	..		*Set of 14*	2·75	2·75

(New Currency. 100 cents = 1 leone)

3c   **AIRMAIL**   **7c**   **Le 1·00**

(84)   (85)   (86)

1964–66. *Decimal currency. Various stamps surch locally.*

*(i) First issue (4.8.64). (a) Postage. Surch as T **84***

313	–	1 c. on 6d. multicoloured (No. 248) (R.)		10	10
314	53	2 c. on 3d. black and rose-red	..	10	10
315	–	3 c. on 3d. multicoloured (No. 246)	..	10	10
		a. Surch inverted	.. ..	£120	
316	45	5 c. on ½d. chocolate & dp bluish grn (B.)		10	10
317	71	8 c. on 3d. black & yellow-ochre (R.)	..	10	10
318	–	10 c. on 1s. 3d. mult (No. 250) (R.)	..	10	10
319	–	15 c. on 1s. multicoloured (No. 249)	..	15	10
320	55	25 c. on 6d. black & yellow-orange (V.)		30	25
321	–	50 c. on 2s. 6d. dp grn & blk (No. 232) (O.)		1·50	65

*(b) Air. As T **85** or **86** (Nos. 326/7)*

322	–	7 c. on 1s. 3d. sepia and emerald-green (No. 256) (B.)		10	10
		a. Surch omitted (in horiz pair with normal)			
		b. Surch double	.. ..	60·00	
323	–	20 c. on 4d. turq-blue & scarlet (No. 228)		25	15
324	–	30 c. on 10s. black & green (No. 234) (R.)		40	30
325	–	40 c. on 5s. black and red (No. 233) (B.)		50	40
326	83	1 l. on 1s. 3d. multicoloured (R.)	..	75	90
327	–	2 l. on 11s. multicoloured	..	1·25	1·90
313/27			*Set of 15*	4·75	4·25

TWO LEONES

1c   **Le 2·00**

(87)   (88)

*(ii) Second issue (20.1.65). Surch as T **87** or **88** (Nos. 332/3)*

(a) Postage

328	–	1 c. on 3d. orge-brown & blue (No. 227)		10	10
329	82	2 c. on 3d. multicoloured	..	10	10
330		4 c. on 3d. multicoloured	..	10	10
		a. Error. 4 c. on 1d.	.. ..	£120	£225
		b. Stamp omitted (in pair with normal)			
331	–	5 c. on 2d. multicoloured (No. 245)	..	10	10
332	–	1 l. on 5s. multicoloured (No. 252) (Gold)		1·25	1·25
333	–	2 l. on £1 carm-red & yell (No. 235) (B.)		2·25	2·25
		a. Surch double (B. + Blk.)	..	—	65·00

(b) Air

334	83	7 c. on 7d. multicoloured (R.)	..	10	10
335		60 c. on 9d. multicoloured	..	50	45
328/35			*Set of 8*	3·75	3·75

On No. 330b the stamp became detached before the surcharge was applied so that "4c" appears on the backing paper.

1c   **1c**

Normal   Small "c" (R. 3/3).

(iii) Third issue (4.65). Surch in figures (various sizes).

(a) Postage

336	–	1 c. on 1½d. black & emer (No. 225) (R.)	10	10
		a. Small "c"	.. ..	4·00	
337	82	2 c. on 3d. multicoloured	..	10	10
338	80	2 c. on 4d. multicoloured	..	10	10
		b. Extended "A"	.. ..	2·00	
339	59	3 c. on 1d. multicoloured	..	10	10
340	–	3 c. on 2d. black & ultram (No. 226) (R.)		10	10
341	–	5 c. on 1s. 3d. turq-bl & vio (No. 231) (R.)		10	10
		a. Surch inverted			
342	82	15 c. on 6d. multicoloured	..	80	50
		b. Extended "A"	.. ..	7·00	
343		15 c. on 1s. multicoloured (R.)	..	1·25	90
		b. Extended "A"	.. ..	10·00	
344	–	20 c. on 6d. black & purple (No. 229) (R.)	30	15
345	–	25 c. on 6d. multicoloured (No. 248) (R.)	35	20
346	–	50 c. on 3d. orge-brown & bl (No. 227) (R.)	80	55
347	80	60 c. on 5s. multicoloured (V.)	..	3·25	2·00
		b. Extended "A"	.. ..	25·00	
348	82	1 l. on 6d. multicoloured (R.)	..	3·75	3·50
349	–	2 l. on £1 carm-red & yell (No. 235) (B.)	7·00	6·00

(b) Air

350	81	7 c. on 9d. multicoloured	..	15	10
336/50			*Set of 15*	16·00	13·00

TWO   **2c Leones**

(89)   (90)

*(iv) Fourth issue (9.11.65). Surch as T **89**. (a) Postage*

351	80	1 c. on 6d. multicoloured (V.)	..	2·25	7·00
		b. Extended "A"	.. ..	20·00	
352		1 c. on 2s. multicoloured (V.)	..	2·25	7·00
		b. Extended "A"	.. ..	20·00	
353	82	1 c. on 2s. multicoloured (V.)	..	2·25	7·00
		b. Extended "A"	.. ..	20·00	
354		1 c. on 5s. multicoloured (V.)	..	2·25	7·00
		b. Extended "A"	.. ..	20·00	

(b) Air

355	81	2 c. on 1s. 3d. multicoloured	..	2·25	7·00
356	83	2 c. on 1s. 3d. multicoloured	..	2·25	7·00
357		2 c. on 3s. 6d. multicoloured	..	2·25	7·00
358	81	3 c. on 7d. multicoloured	..	2·25	7·00
359	83	3 c. on 9d. multicoloured	..	2·25	7·00
360	81	5 c. on 2s. 6d. multicoloured	..	2·25	7·00
361	83	5 c. on 2s. 6d. multicoloured	..	2·25	7·00
362	81	5 c. on 3s. 6d. multicoloured	..	2·25	7·00
363		5 c. on 6s. multicoloured	..	2·25	7·00
364	83	5 c. on 6s. multicoloured	..	2·25	7·00
351/64			*Set of 14*	28·00	90·00

*(v) Fifth issue (28.1.66). Air. No. 374 further surch with T **90***

365	–	2 l. on 30 c. on 6d. multicoloured		1·50	1·50

IN MEMORIAM   **2c**
TWO GREAT LEADERS

SIR MILTON MARGAI   SIR WINSTON CHURCHILL
1895-1964   1874-1965

(91 Margai and Churchill)

1965 (19 May). *Sir Milton Margai and Sir Winston Churchill Commemoration. Nos. 242/3, 245/50 and 252/4 surch as T **91** on horiz designs or with individual portraits on vert designs as indicated.*

(a) Postage

366		2 c. on 1d. Type **59**	10	10
		a. Horiz pair, one with "2 c" omitted		
		b. Surch and portraits omitted (in horiz pair with normal)	..	£400
367		3 c. on 3d. Beniseed (Margai)	10	10
		a. Portrait and "3 c" double	£100	
		b. Portrait and "3 c" double, one inverted	£120	
		c. "3 c" omitted	..	£400
368		10 c. on 1s. Beautiful Crinum (Churchill)	20	10
		a. "10 c" omitted	..	£275
369		20 c. on 1s. 3d. Blue Bells	40	10
		a. Portraits and "20 c" double, one inverted	£110	
		b. "20 c" omitted	..	£400
		c. "20 c" double, one inverted	£110	
370		50 c. on 4d. Blushing Hibiscus (Margai)	90	35
		a. Portrait inverted	£110	
		ab. Portrait inverted and "50 c" omitted	£130	
371		75 c. on 5s. Ra-ponthi (Churchill)	2·25	90
		a. Surch value inverted	..	£200

(b) Air. Additionally optd "AIRMAIL"

372		7 c. on 2d. Black-eyed Susan	20	10
		a. "AIRMAIL" and "7 c." omitted	£130	
		b. "AIRMAIL" and "7 c" double, one inverted	£130	
373		15 c. on ½d. Type **58** (Margai)	35	10
		a. "AIRMAIL" and "15 c" double, one inverted	£130	
		b. Portrait double, one inverted	£110	
374		30 c. on 6d. Climbing Lily (O. and W.)	1·25	25
		a. "AIRMAIL" and "30 c" double, one inverted	£110	
		b. "AIRMAIL" and "30 c" omitted	£110	

375		1 l. on £1 African Tulip Tree		4·00	1·00
		a. "AIRMAIL" and "1 l" double, one inverted		£110	
		b. "AIRMAIL" and "1 l" omitted		£400	
376		2 l. on 10s. Blue Plumbago (Churchill)		11·00	5·00
		a. Surch value omitted		£150	
366/76	..		*Set of 11*	18·00	7·00

On Nos. 366/76 the portraits and commemorative inscription were applied in a separate operation from the surcharge and, on Nos. 372/6, the word "AIRMAIL".

92 Cola Plant and Nut

93 Arms of Sierra Leone

94 Inscription and Necklace

(Des M. Meers. Manufactured by Walsall Lithographic Co, Ltd)

1965 (Nov). *Imperf. Self-adhesive.*

A. *Embossed on silver foil, backed with paper bearing advertisements. Emerald, olive-yellow and carmine; denominations in colours given. Postage.*

377	92	1 c. emerald	.. ..	25	10
378		2 c. carmine	.. ..	25	10
379		3 c. olive-yellow	..	25	10
380		4 c. silver/*emerald*	..	30	10
381		5 c. silver/*carmine*	..	30	10

B. *Typo and embossed on cream paper backed with advertisements*

(a) Postage

382	93	20 c. multicoloured	..	1·75	50
383		50 c. multicoloured	..	3·50	3·50

(b) Air

384	93	40 c. multicoloured	..	3·25	3·50

C. *Die-stamped and litho, with advertisements on white paper backing (see footnote). Air.*

385	94	7 c. multicoloured	..	70	15
		a. Bright green and gold (inscr and face value) omitted		95·00	
386		15 c. multicoloured	..	1·00	70
377/86			*Set of 10*	10·50	8·00

The above stamps were issued in single form with attached tabs to remove the backing paper, with the exception of No. 385 which was in sheets of 25 bearing a single large advertisement on the back.

No. 385a shows the die-stamping omitted.

For other stamps in Type **92** see Nos. 421/31 and 435/42a. For 10 c. stamps in Type **93** see Nos. 433/b.

2c   **15c**

AIRMAIL

FIVE YEARS	FIVE YEARS
INDEPENDENCE	INDEPENDENCE
1961-1966	1961-1966
(95)	(96)

1966 (27 Apr). *Fifth Anniv of Independence. Various stamps surch.*

(a) Postage. As T 95

387		1 c. on 6d. multicoloured (No. 248)	..	10	10
388		2 c. on 4d. multicoloured (No. 247)	..	10	10
389		3 c. on 1½d. black & ultram (No. 212) (B.)		10	10
390		8 c. on 1s. multicoloured (No. 249) (B.)		15	10
391		10 c. on 2s. 6d. multicoloured (No. 251) (B.)		15	10
392		20 c. on 2d. black and brown (No. 213) (B.)		20	10

(b) Air. As T 96

393		7 c. on 3d. red and violet (No. 270)	..	10	10
394		15 c. on 1s. multicoloured (No. 249)	..	20	10
395		25 c. on 2s. 6d. multicoloured (No. 251)		65	60
396		50 c. on 1½d. multicoloured (No. 244)	..	1·00	80
397		1 l. on 4d. multicoloured (No. 247)	..	1·60	1·60
387/397			*Set of 11*	3·75	3·00

The inscription on No. 387 is in larger type.

97 Lion's Head

98 Map of Sierra Leone

(Des and embossed Walsall)

1966 (12 Nov). *First Sierra Leone Gold Coinage Commemoration. Circular designs, embossed on gold foil, backed with paper bearing advertisements. Imperf. (a) Postage.*

(i) ¼ golde coin. Diameter 1½ in.

398	97	2 c. magenta and yellow-orange		10	10
399	98	3 c. emerald and bright purple	..	10	10

(ii) ½ golde coin. Diameter 2⅛ in.

400	97	5 c. vermilion and ultramarine		10	10
401	98	8 c. turquoise-blue and black	..	15	15

(iii) 1 golde coin. Diameter 3¼ in.

402	97	25 c. violet and emerald	..	35	35
403	98	1 l. orange and cerise		2·50	2·75

(b) Air. (i) ¼ golde coin. Diameter 1½ in.

404	98	7 c. red-orange and cerise	..	10	10
405	97	10 c. cerise and greenish blue	..	15	15

(ii) ½ golde coin. Diameter 2⅛ in.

406	98	15 c. orange and cerise		25	25
407	97	30 c. bright purple and black	..	40	45

(iii) 1 golde coin. Diameter 3¼ in.

408	98	50 c. bright green and purple		75	75
409	97	2 l. black and emerald	..	3·75	4·00
398/409			*Set of 12*	7·50	8·00

$12\frac{1}{2}$ $17\frac{1}{2}$ $=17\frac{1}{2}$

(99)   (100)   (101)

1967 (2 Dec). *Decimal Currency Provisionals. Surch as T 99 (Nos. 410/13), T 100 (Nos. 415/17) or T 101 (others). (a) Postage.*

410	–	6½ c. on 75 c. on 5s. mult (No. 371) (R.)		15	15
411	–	7½ c. on 75 c. on 5s. mult (No. 371) (S.)		15	15
412	–	9½ c. on 50 c. on 4d. mult (No. 370) (G.)		20	20
413	–	12½ c. on 20 c. on 1s. 3d. multicoloured (No. 369) (V.)		25	25
414	93	17½ c. on 50 c. multicoloured	..	1·40	1·40
415	82	17½ c. on 1 l. on 4d. mult (No. 348) (B.)		1·40	1·40
416		18½ c. on 1 l. on 4d. mult (No. 348)		1·40	1·40
417	80	18½ c. on 60 c. on 5s. mult (No. 347)		4·00	4·50
		b. Extended "A"	..	40·00	
418	93	25 c. on 50 c. multicoloured	..	60	70

(b) Air

419	93	11½ c. on 40 c. multicoloured	..	20	20
420		25 c. on 40 c. multicoloured	..	60	70
410/20			*Set of 11*	9·25	10·00

102 Eagle

(Manufactured by Walsall)

1967 (2 Dec)–**69**. *Decimal Currency. Imperf. Self-adhesive.*

(a) Postage. As T 92, but embossed on white paper, backed with paper bearing advertisements. Background colours given first, and value tablet colours in brackets.

421	92	½ c. carmine-red (carmine/*white*)	..	10	10
422		1 c. carmine (carmine/*white*)	..	15	10
423		1½ c. orange-yellow (green/*white*)	..	20	15
424		2 c. carmine-red (green/*white*)	..	35	10
425		2½ c. apple-green (yellow/*white*)	..	50	40
426		3 c. carmine-red (white/*carmine*)	..	30	10
427		3½ c. reddish purple (white/*green*)	..	50	40
428		4 c. carmine-red (white/*green*)	..	50	15
429		4½ c. dull green (green/*white*)	..	50	40
430		5 c. carmine (yellow/*white*)	..	50	15
431		5½ c. brown-red (green/*white*)	..	50	50

(b) Air. T 102 embossed on black paper, backed with paper bearing advertisements; or, (No. 433), as T 93, typo and embossed on cream paper, also with advertisements

432	102	9½ c. red and gold/*black*	..	60	60
432a		9½ c. blue and gold/*black* (10.9.69)	..	5·00	5·00
433	93	10 c. multicoloured (red frame)	..	65	65
		a. Face value omitted	..	..	
433b		10 c. mult (black frame) (10.9.69)	..	5·50	5·50
434	102	15 c. green and gold/*black*	..	85	85
434a		15 c. red and gold/*black* (10.9.69)	..	6·00	6·00
421/34a			*Set of 17*	20·00	19·00

The ½, 1½, 2, 2½, 3, 3½ and 5 c. also exist without advertisements.

The footnote below Nos. 377/86 also applies here.

Although only released for collectors on 2 December, the 5 c. was known to be in use locally in February and the 3 c. in March. The 1 c. and 2 c. were also released locally some months earlier.

See also Nos. 538/44.

1968. *No advertisements on back, and colours in value tablet reversed. Background colours given first, and value tablet colours in brackets.*

435	92	½ c. carmine (white/*green*)	..	10	10
436		1 c. carmine (white/*carmine*)	..	15	10
437		2 c. carmine (white/*green*)	..	4·25	4·50
438		2½ c. apple-green (white/*yellow*)	..	4·75	5·00
439		3 c. carmine-red (carmine/*white*)	..	1·75	65

On Nos. 435 and 438, the figure "½" is larger than in Nos. 421 and 425.

It is believed that the ½ c. was released in February, the 2½ c. in April and the others in March.

The 1 c. also exists with advertisements on the backing paper.

The footnote below Nos. 377/86 also applies here.

1968–69. *No advertisements on back, colours changed and new value (7 c.). Background colours given first, and value tablet colours in brackets. (a) Postage.*

440	92	2 c. pink (white/*brown-lake*)	..	1·75	1·50
441		2½ c. deep bluish green (white/*orange*)	..	1·75	1·50
442		3½ c. olive-yellow (blue/*white*)	..	2·25	1·60

(b) Air

442a	92	7 c. yellow (carmine/*white*) (10.9.69)	..	6·50	3·50
435/42a			*Set of 9*	21·00	17·00

On Nos. 441/2 the fraction "½" is larger than in Nos. 425 and 427.

It is believed that the 3½ c. was released in March 1968 and the 2 and 2½ c. in May 1968.

The 2 c. also exists with advertisements on the backing paper.

The footnote below Nos. 377/86 also applies here.

103 Outline Map of Africa

(Litho Walsall)

1968 (25 Sept). *Human Rights Year. Each value comes in six types, showing different territories in yellow, as below. Imperf. Self-adhesive.*

A. Portuguese Guinea.   D. Rhodesia.
B. South Africa.   E. South West Africa.
C. Mozambique.   F. Angola.

To indicate yellow territory use above letters as suffix to the following catalogue numbers.

(a) Postage

					Each Territory	
443	103	½ c. multicoloured	..	..	10	10
444		2 c. multicoloured	..	..	10	10
445		2½ c. multicoloured	..	..	10	10
446		3½ c. multicoloured	..	..	10	10
447		5 c. multicoloured	..	..	15	15
448	103	11½ c. multicoloured		20	20	
449		15 c. multicoloured		25	25	

(b) Air

450	103	7½ c. multicoloured		15	15
451		9½ c. multicoloured		20	20
452		14½ c. multicoloured		25	25
453		18½ c. multicoloured		30	30
454		25 c. multicoloured		40	40
455		1 l. multicoloured		4·00	5·50
456		2 l. multicoloured		10·00	12·00
443/56		Each territory	*Set of 14*	14·00	18·00
443/56		Six territories	*Set of 84*	75·00	£100

Nos. 443/56 were issued in sheets of 30 (6 × 5) on backing paper depicting diamonds or the coat of arms on the reverse. The six types occur once in each horizontal row.

MEXICO 1968   OLYMPIC PARTICIPATION

POSTAGE   *6½

(104)

1968 (30 Nov). *Mexico Olympics Participation.*

(a) Postage. No. 383 surch or optd (No. 461) as T 104

457	93	6½ c. on 50 c. multicoloured	..	20	15
458		17½ c. on 50 c. multicoloured	..	25	20
459		22½ c. on 50 c. multicoloured	..	40	35
		a. Surch double	..	£170	
460		28½ c. on 50 c. multicoloured	..	50	60
461		50 c. multicoloured	..	80	90

(b) Air. No. 384 surch or optd (No. 466) as T 104 in red

462	93	6½ c. on 40 c. multicoloured	..	20	15
		a. Surch double	..	£190	
463		17½ c. on 40 c. multicoloured	..	25	20
464		22½ c. on 40 c. multicoloured	..	40	35
465		28½ c. on 40 c. multicoloured	..	50	60
466		40 c. multicoloured	..	80	90
457/66		..	*Set of 10*	3·75	3·75

105 1859 6d.

111 1965 15 c. Self-adhesive

(Litho Walsall)

1969 (1 Mar). *Fifth Anniv of World's First Self-adhesive Postage Stamps. Reproductions of earlier issues. Multicoloured. Imperf. Self-adhesive.*

(a) Postage. Vert designs.

467	1 c. Type 105	..	10	10
468	2 c. 1965 2 c. self-adhesive	..	10	10
469	3½ c. 1961 Independence £1	..	10	10
470	5 c. 1965 20 c. self-adhesive	..	10	10
471	12½ c. 1948 Royal Silver Wedding £1	..	30	15
472	1 l. 1923 £2	..	2·50	1·50

(b) Air. Horiz designs.

473	7½ c. Type 111	..	20	10
474	9½ c. 1967 9½ c. self-adhesive	..	20	10
475	20 c. 1964 1s. 3d. self-adhesive	..	40	25
476	30 c. 1964 President Kennedy Memorial 6s. commemorative self-adhesive	..	55	35
477	50 c. 1933 Centenary of Abolition of Slavery £1 commemorative	..	1·50	75
478	2 l. 1963 2nd Anniversary of Independence 11s. commemorative	..	9·00	8·00
467/478		*Set of 12*	13·00	10·00

Nos. 467 and 473 were issued with tabs as note under Nos. 377/86 and No. 474 exists with tabs and also in the normal version on backing paper.

All values are on white backing paper with advertisements printed on the reverse.

117 Ore Carrier, Globe and Flags of Sierra Leone and Japan

118 Ore Carrier, Map of Europe and Africa and Flags of Sierra Leone and Netherlands

The 3½ c., 9½ c., 2 l. and 10 c., 50 c., 1 l. are as T 118 but show respectively the flags of Great Britain and West Germany instead of the Netherlands.

(Litho Walsall)

1969 (10 July). *Pepel Port Improvements. Imperf. Self-adhesive, backed with paper bearing advertisements. (a) Postage.*

479	117	1 c. multicoloured	..	10	10
480	118	2 c. multicoloured	..	10	10
481	—	3½ c. multicoloured	..	10	10
482	—	10 c. multicoloured	..	10	10
483	118	18½ c. multicoloured	..	20	25
484	—	50 c. multicoloured	..	80	85

(b) Air

485	117	7½ c. multicoloured	..	10	10
486	—	9½ c. multicoloured	..	15	10
487	117	15 c. multicoloured	..	20	25
488	118	25 c. multicoloured	..	30	35
489	—	1 l. multicoloured	..	1·50	1·75
490	—	2 l. multicoloured	..	2·00	4·00
479/80			Set of 12	5·00	7·00

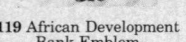

119 African Development Bank Emblem 　　　120 Boy Scouts Emblem in "Diamond"

(Litho and embossed Walsall)

1969 (10 Sept). *Fifth Anniv of African Development Bank. Self-adhesive, backed with paper bearing advertisements. Imperf.*

(a) Postage

491	119	3½ c. deep green, gold and blue		..	25	40

(b) Air

492	119	9½ c. bluish violet, gold and apple-green	..	35	70

(Litho Walsall)

1969 (6 Dec). *Boy Scouts Diamond Jubilee. T 120 and similar design. Imperf. Self-adhesive, backed with paper bearing advertisements.*

(a) Postage

493	120	1 c. multicoloured	..	..	10	10
494		2 c. multicoloured	..	..	10	10
495		3½ c. multicoloured	..	..	15	10
496		4½ c. multicoloured	..	..	15	15
497		5 c. multicoloured	..	..	15	15
498		75 c. multicoloured	..	..	5·50	2·75

(b) Air

499	—	7½ c. multicoloured	..	35	20
500	—	9½ c. multicoloured	..	45	25
501	—	15 c. multicoloured	..	70	50
502	—	22 c. multicoloured	..	90	70
503	—	55 c. multicoloured	..	4·00	2·00
504	—	3 l. multicoloured	..	50·00	35·00
493/504			Set of 12	55·00	38·00

Design: *Octagonal Shape* (65×51 *mm*)—Nos. 499/504 Scout saluting, Baden-Powell and badge.

MINIMUM PRICE

The minimum price quote is 10p which represents a handling charge rather than a basis for valuing common stamps. For further notes about prices see introductory pages.

---

(121)

1970 (28 Mar). *Air. No. 443 surch as T 121.*

Each Territory

505	103	7½ c. on ½ c. multicoloured (G.)	..	20	10
506		9½ c. on ½ c. multicoloured (P.)	..	20	10
507		15 c. on ½ c. multicoloured (B.)	..	40	25
508		28 c. on ½ c. multicoloured (G.)	..	70	55
509		40 c. on ½ c. multicoloured (B.)	..	1·25	1·40
510		2 l. on ½ c. multicoloured (Sil.)	..	5·00	9·00
505/10	Each Territory		Set of 6	7·00	10·00
505/10	Six Territories		Set of 36	38·00	55·00

122 Expo Symbol and Maps of Sierra Leone and Japan

(Litho Walsall)

1970 (22 June). *World Fair, Osaka. T 122 and similar design. Imperf. Self-adhesive, backed with paper bearing advertisements.*

(a) Postage

511	122	2 c. multicoloured	..	10	10
512		3½ c. multicoloured	..	10	10
513		10 c. multicoloured	..	15	10
514		12½ c. multicoloured	..	15	10
515		20 c. multicoloured	..	20	10
516		45 c. multicoloured	..	45	45

(b) Air

517	—	7½ c. multicoloured	..	10	10
518	—	9½ c. multicoloured	..	15	10
519	—	15 c. multicoloured	..	20	10
520	—	25 c. multicoloured	..	40	20
521	—	50 c. multicoloured	..	55	50
522	—	3 l. multicoloured	..	1·75	5·50
511/22			Set of 12	3·50	6·50

Design: *Chrysanthemum shape* (43 × 42 *mm*)—Nos. 517/22 Maps of Sierra Leone and Japan.

123 Diamond

124 Palm Nut

(Litho and embossed Walsall)

1970 (3 Oct). *Imperf. Self-adhesive, backed with paper bearing advertisements.*

523	123	1 c. multicoloured	..	..	10	10
524		1½ c. multicoloured	..	..	10	10
525		2 c. multicoloured	..	..	10	10
526		2½ c. multicoloured	..	..	10	10
527		3 c. multicoloured	..	..	15	10
528		3½ c. multicoloured	..	..	15	10
529		4 c. multicoloured	..	..	15	10
530		5 c. multicoloured	..	..	20	10
531	124	6 c. multicoloured	..	..	25	10
532		7 c. multicoloured	..	..	30	15
533		8½ c. multicoloured	..	..	40	15
534		9 c. multicoloured	..	..	40	15
535		10 c. multicoloured	..	..	45	15
536		11½ c. multicoloured	..	..	55	20
537		18½ c. multicoloured	..	..	85	45

1970 (3 Oct). *Air. As T 102, but embossed on white paper. Backed with paper bearing advertisements.*

538	102	7½ c. gold and red	..	35	10
539		9½ c. rose and bright green	..	40	10
540		15 c. pink and greenish blue	..	70	20
541		25 c. gold and purple	..	1·25	50
542		50 c. bright green and orange	..	2·50	1·75
543		1 l. royal blue and silver	..	6·00	8·00
544		2 l. ultramarine and gold	..	11·00	17·00
523/44			Set of 22	23·00	26·00

---

126 "Jewellery Box" and Sewa Diadem

(Litho and embossed Walsall)

1970 (30 Dec). *Diamond Industry. T 126 and similar design. Imperf (backing paper roll 20). Self-adhesive, backed with paper bearing advertisements. (a) Postage.*

545	126	2 c. multicoloured	..	30	10
546		3½ c. multicoloured	..	30	10
547		10 c. multicoloured	..	55	15
548		12½ c. multicoloured	..	75	25
549		40 c. multicoloured	..	1·75	1·00
550		1 l. multicoloured	..	10·00	8·50

(b) Air

551	—	7½ c. multicoloured	..	50	10
552	—	9½ c. multicoloured	..	60	10
553	—	15 c. multicoloured	..	95	30
554	—	25 c. multicoloured	..	1·40	60
555	—	75 c. multicoloured	..	5·50	4·50
556	—	2 l. multicoloured	..	24·00	20·00
545/556			Set of 12	42·00	32·00

Design: *Horiz* (63 × 61 *mm*)—Nos. 551/6, Diamond and curtain.

127 "Traffic Changeover" 　　　(128)

(Manufactured by Walsall)

1971 (1 Mar). *Changeover to Driving on the Right of the Road. Imperf (backing paper roll 20). Self-adhesive, backed with paper bearing advertisements. (a) Postage.*

557	127	3½ c. yellow-orange, ultram & blk	1·50	1·00

(b) Air

558	127	9½ c. ultramarine, yell-orge & blk	2·00	2·50

1971 (1 Mar). *Air. Surch as T 128, in red (No. 559), blue (Nos. 560 and 562) or black (others).*

559		10 c. on 2d. black and ultramarine (No. 226)	..	40	20
560		20 c. on 1s. chocolate & yell-orge (No. 230)	..	2·50	1·75
561		50 c. on 1d. multicoloured (No. 243)	..	1·25	1·25
562		70 c. on 30 c. multicoloured (No. 476)	..	2·00	3·50
563		1 l. on 30 c. multicoloured (No. 476)	..	3·00	4·50
559/63			Set of 5	6·50	9·00

REPUBLIC

129 Flag and Lion's Head 　　　130 Pres. Siaka Stevens

(Manufactured by Walsall)

1971 (27 Apr). *Tenth Anniv of Independence. T 129 and similar design. Imperf. Self-adhesive, backed with paper bearing advertisements. (a) Postage.*

564	129	2 c. multicoloured	..	10	10
565		3½ c. multicoloured	..	10	10
566		10 c. multicoloured	..	15	10
567		12½ c. multicoloured	..	20	10
568		40 c. multicoloured	..	70	40
569		1 l. multicoloured	..	1·50	2·50

		(b) Air			
570	–	7½ c. multicoloured	.. .. ..	15	10
571	–	9½ c. multicoloured	.. .. ..	15	10
572	–	15 c. multicoloured	.. .. ..	25	10
573	–	25 c. multicoloured	.. .. ..	35	35
574	–	75 c. multicoloured	.. .. ..	1·10	1·50
575	–	2 l. multicoloured	.. .. ..	3·00	6·50
564/75			Set of 12	7·00	10·50

Design: "Map" shaped as T 129—Nos. 570/5, Bugles and lion's head.

(Litho D.L.R.)

1972 (5 Dec)–78. *Multicoloured; colour of background given. Glazed ordinary paper.* P 13.

576	130	1 c. light rose-lilac	.. ..	10	10
		a. Chalk-surfaced paper	..	40	40
577		2 c. lavender (shades)	.. ..	10	10
		a. Chalk-surfaced paper	..	30	30
578		4 c. cobalt	.. ..	10	10
		a. Chalk-surfaced paper	..	65	40
579		5 c. light cinnamon	.. ..	10	10
		a. Chalk-surfaced paper	..	65	30
580		7 c. light rose	.. ..	15	15
		a. Chalk-surfaced paper	..	90	30
581		10 c. olive-bistre	.. ..	15	10
		a. Chalk-surfaced paper	..	90	30
582		15 c. pale yellow-green	..	25	15
		a. Chalk-surfaced paper	..	1·50	75
583		18 c. yellow-ochre	.. ..	25	15
		a. Chalk-surfaced paper	..	1·50	1·00
584		20 c. pale greenish blue	..	30	15
		a. Chalk-surfaced paper	..	1·50	1·25
585		25 c. orange-ochre	.. ..	35	15
		a. Chalk-surfaced paper	..	1·50	1·25
586		50 c. light turquoise-green	..	1·00	55
		a. Chalk-surfaced paper	..	4·00	3·25
587		1 l. bright reddish mauve (shades)		1·50	1·00
		a. Chalk-surfaced paper	..	4·50	3·75
588		2 l. orange-salmon	..	2·75	3·50
		a. Chalk-surfaced paper	..	11·00	17·00
589		5 l. light stone	.. ..	4·50	8·50
		a. Chalk-surfaced paper	..	18·00	32·00
576/89			Set of 14	10·00	13·00
576a/89a			Set of 14	42·00	55·00

The chalk-surfaced paper printings appeared in 1975–78.

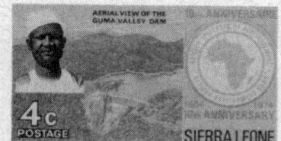

131 Guma Valley Dam and Bank Emblem

(Litho D.L.R.)

1975 (14 Jan). *Tenth Anniv of African Development Bank (1974).* P 13½ × 13. (a) Postage.

590	131	4 c. multicoloured	.. ..	45·00	28·00
		(b) Air			
591	131	15 c. multicoloured	.. ..	1·00	80

132 Opening Ceremony

(Litho D.L.R.)

1975 (25 Aug). *Opening of New Congo Bridge and President Stevens' 70th Birthday.* P 12½ × 13. (a) Postage.

592	132	5 c. multicoloured	.. ..	2·00	85
		(b) Air			
593	132	20 c. multicoloured	.. ..	50	25

133 Presidents Tolbert and Stevens, and Handclasp

(Litho D.L.R.)

1975 (3 Oct). *1st Anniv of Mano River Union.* P 12½ × 13. (a) Postage.

594	133	4 c. multicoloured	.. ..	30	40
		(b) Air			
595	133	15 c. multicoloured	.. ..	20	20

The new-issue supplement to this Catalogue appears each month in

GIBBONS STAMP MONTHLY

—from your newsagent or by postal subscription— sample copy and details on request.

134 "Quaid-i-Azam" (Mohammed Ali Jinnah)	135 Queen Elizabeth II

(Litho Pakistan Security Printing Corporation)

1977 (28 Jan). *Birth Centenary of Mohammed Ali Jinnah (Quaid-i-Azam).* P 13.

596	134	30 c. multicoloured	.. ..	75	30

(Des A. Larkins. Litho De La Rue, Colombia)

1977 (28 Nov). *Silver Jubilee.* P 12½ × 12.

597	135	5 c. multicoloured	.. ..	10	10
598		1 l. multicoloured	.. ..	65	80

136 College Buildings	137 St. Edward's Crown and Sceptres

(Des A. Larkins. Litho De La Rue, Colombia)

1977 (19 Dec). *150th Anniv of Fourah Bay College. T 136 and similar vert design. Multicoloured.* P 12 × 12½ (5 c.) or 12½ × 12 (20 c.).

599		5 c. Type 136	.. ..	10	10
600		20 c. The old college	.. ..	35	30

(Des L. Curtis. Litho Harrison)

1978 (14 Sept). *25th Anniv of Coronation. T 137 and similar vert designs. Multicoloured.* P 14½ × 14.

601		5 c. Type 137	.. ..	10	10
602		50 c. Queen Elizabeth II in Coronation Coach		20	40
603		1 l. Queen Elizabeth II and Prince Philip		35	60
601/3		.. .. ..	Set of 3	50	1·00

138 Myrina silenus	139 Young Child's Face

(Des J. Cooter. Litho Questa)

1979 (9 Apr). *Butterflies (1st series). T 138 and similar horiz designs. Multicoloured.* P 14½ × 14.

604		5 c. Type 138	.. ..	10	10
605		15 c. Papilio nireus	..	25	15
606		25 c. Catacroptera cloanthe		40	15
607		1 l. Druryia antimachus	..	1·00	1·50
604/7			Set of 4	1·50	1·60

See also Nos. 646/9.

(Des BG Studio. Litho Walsall)

1979 (13 Aug). *International Year of the Child and 30th Anniv of S.O.S. International (child distress organisation). T 139 and similar vert designs. Multicoloured.* W w 14. P 14 × 13½.

608		5 c. Type 139	.. ..	10	10
609		27 c. Young child with baby	..	20	25
610		1 l. Mother with young child	..	50	1·10
608/10			Set of 3	65	1·25
MS611		114 × 84 mm. No. 610. Wmk sideways		75	1·75

140 Presidents Stevens (Sierra Leone) and Tolbert (Liberia), Dove with Letter and Bridge

(Des L. Curtis. Litho Questa)

1979 (3 Oct). *5th Anniv of Mano River Union and 1st Anniv of Postal Union.* W w 14 (sideways). P 13½ × 14.

612	140	5 c. sepia, orange and greenish yellow	..	10	10
613		22 c. sepia, orge-yell & brt reddish violet		10	15
614		27 c. sepia, light blue and orange		10	15
615		35 c. sepia, blue-green and orange-red		15	20
616		1 l. sepia, brt reddish violet & lt blue		50	1·00
612/16			Set of 5	75	1·40
MS617		144 × 73 mm. No. 616	..	55	1·00

141 Great Britain 1848 10d. Stamp	142 Knysna Turaco

(Des J.W. Litho Walsall)

1979 (19 Dec). *Death Centenary of Sir Rowland Hill. T 141 and similar vert designs showing stamps.* W w 14. P 14 × 14½.

618		10 c. black, orange-brown and new blue		15	10
		w. Wmk inverted		1·50	
619		15 c. black, brown-ochre and greenish blue		20	15
		w. Wmk inverted		1·25	
620		50 c. black, carmine and greenish yellow		40	70
		w. Wmk inverted		1·00	
618/20			Set of 3	65	85
MS621		90×99 mm. 1 l. black, carm-red & flesh		60	80

Designs:—15 c. 1872 4d.; 50 c. 1961 £1 Independence commemorative; 1 l. 1912 £1.

(Des J.W. Litho Format)

1980 (29 Jan)–82. *Birds. Multicoloured designs as T 142.* W w 14 (sideways* on 1, 2, 3, 5, 7 c., 1, 2 and 5 l.). P 14.

A. No imprint

622A		1 c. Type 142	.. ..	50	1·25
		w. Wmk Crown to right of CA	38·00	
623A		2 c. Olive-bellied Sunbird	..	50	1·25
624A		3 c. Western Black-headed Oriole		80	1·25
		w. Wmk Crown to right of CA	10·00	
625A		5 c. Spur-winged Goose	..	80	60
626A		7 c. Didric Cuckoo	..	80	60
627A		10 c. Grey Parrot (vert)	..	80	70
628A		15 c. Blue Quail (vert)	..	1·50	2·00
629A		20 c. African Wood Owl (vert)	..	1·75	2·50
630A		30 c. Great Blue Turaco (vert)	..	1·75	2·50
		w. Wmk inverted		2·00	
631A		40 c. Blue-breasted Kingfisher (vert)		1·40	3·00
632A		50 c. Black Crake (vert)	..	1·40	2·50
633A		1 l. Hartlaub's Duck	..	1·40	2·50
634A		2 l. Black Bee Eater	..	2·00	4·00
635A		5 l. Barrow's Bustard	..	3·50	9·00
622A/35A			Set of 14	17·00	30·00

B. With imprint date at foot

622B		1 c. Type 142 (15.3.82)	..	30	1·25
623B		2 c. Olive-bellied Sunbird (15.3.82)		40	1·25
624B		3 c. Western Black-headed Oriole (15.3.82)		40	1·25
625B		5 c. Spur-winged Goose (21.12.81)		40	65
626B		7 c. Didric Cuckoo (11.10.82)		13·00	4·50
627B		10 c. Grey Parrot (vert) (21.12.81)		40	70
628B		15 c. Blue Quail (vert) (21.12.81)		50	1·75
629B		20 c. African Wood Owl (vert) (15.3.82)		50	2·00
630B		30 c. Great Blue Turaco (vert) (21.12.81)		50	2·25
631B		40 c. Blue-breasted Kingfisher (vert) (21.12.81)		60	2·25
632B		50 c. Black Crake (vert) (21.12.81)		60	2·25
633B		1 l. Hartlaub's Duck (21.12.81)		60	3·50
634B		2 l. Black Bee Eater (21.12.81)		70	6·50
635B		5 l. Barrow's Bustard (21.12.81)		1·00	11·00
622B/35B			Set of 14	18·00	38·00

*The normal sideways watermark shows Crown to left of CA, as seen from the back of the stamp.

Imprint dates: "1981", Nos. 622B/5B, 627B/35B; "1982", Nos. 622B/35B.

Nos. 622A/35A and 629A/B exist imperforate from stock dispersed by the liquidator of Format International Security Printers Ltd.

For similar stamps, but without watermark, see Nos. 760/73.

143 Paul P. Harris (founder), President Stevens of Sierra Leone and Rotary Emblem

(Des BG Studio. Litho Walsall)

1980 (23 Feb). *75th Anniv of Rotary International.* W w 14 (sideways). P 13½.

636	143	5 c. multicoloured	.. ..	10	10
637		27 c. multicoloured	.. ..	10	10
638		50 c. multicoloured	.. ..	20	25
639		1 l. multicoloured	.. ..	40	55
636/9			Set of 4	65	85

144 *Maria*, 1884

145 Organisation for African Unity Emblem

(Des L. Dunn. Litho Walsall)

1980 (6 May). *"London 1980" International Stamp Exhibition. Mail Ships. T* **144** *and similar horiz designs. Multicoloured. W w* **14** (sideways). *P* 14.

640	6 c. Type **144**	..	..	30	10
641	31 c. *Tarquah*, 1902			40	35
642	50 c. *Aureol*, 1951			50	70
643	1 l. *Africa Palm*, 1974			60	1·60
640/3	.. ..		*Set of 4*	1·60	2·50

(Des L. Curtis. Litho Questa)

1980 (1 July). *African Summit Conference, Freetown. W w* **14**. *P* 14 × 14½.

644	**145** 20 c. black, light blue and bright purple			10	10
645	1 l. black, bright purple and light blue			45	45

146 *Graphium policenes*

147 Arrival at Freetown Airport

(Des I. Loe. Litho Questa)

1980 (6 Oct). *Butterflies (2nd series). T* **146** *and similar vert designs. Multicoloured. W w* **14**. *P* 13½.

646	5 c. Type **146**	..	..	10	10
647	27 c. *Charaxes varanes*	..		30	15
648	35 c. *Charaxes brutus*	..		35	25
649	1 l. *Euphaedra zaddachi*	..		1·10	1·40
646/9			*Set of 4*	1·75	1·75

(Des L. Curtis. Litho Format)

1980 (5 Dec). *Tourism. T* **147** *and similar vert designs. Multicoloured. W w* **14**. *P* 13½.

650	6 c. Type **147**	..		10	10
651	26 c. Welcome to tourists	..		10	20
652	31 c. Freetown cotton tree	..		10	25
653	40 c. Beinkongo Falls	..		20	30
654	50 c. Sports facilities	..		20	40
655	1 l. African Elephant	..		1·00	95
650/5	.. ..		*Set of 6*	1·40	2·00

148 Servals

149 Soldiers (Defence)

(Des P. Oxenham. Litho Questa)

1981 (28 Feb). *Wild Cats. T* **148** *and similar horiz designs. Multicoloured. W w* **14** (sideways). *P* 13½ × 14.

656	6 c. Type **148**	..		20	10
	a. Horiz pair. Nos. 656/7	..		40	20
657	6 c. Serval cubs	..		20	10
658	31 c. African Golden Cats	..		50	30
	a. Horiz pair. Nos. 658/9	..		1·00	60
659	31 c. African Golden Cat cubs	..		50	30
660	50 c. Leopards	..		70	45
	a. Horiz pair. Nos. 660/1	..		1·40	90
661	50 c. Leopard cubs	..		70	45
662	1 l. Lions	..		1·00	80
	a. Horiz pair. Nos. 662/3	..		2·00	1·60
663	1 l. Lion cubs	..		1·00	80
656/63			*Set of 8*	4·25	2·75

The two designs of each value were printed together, *se-tenant*, in horizontal pairs throughout the sheet, forming composite designs.

(Des G. Hutchins. Litho Walsall)

1981 (18 Apr). *20th Anniv of Independence and 10th Anniv of Republic. National Services. T* **149** *and similar multicoloured designs. W w* **14** (sideways on 31 c. and 1 l.). *P* 14½.

664	6 c. Type **149**			40	10
665	31 c. Nurses administering first aid, and ambulance (Health) (*horiz*)			1·25	20
666	40 c. Controlling traffic (Police Force)			2·25	60
667	1 l. Patrol boat (Coastguard) (*horiz*)			2·75	2·50
664/7			*Set of 4*	6·00	3·00

150 Wedding Bouquet from Sierra Leone

151 Sandringham

(Des J.W. Litho Harrison)

1981 (22 July). *Royal Wedding (1st issue). T* **150** *and similar vert designs. Multicoloured. W w* **14**. *P* 14.

668	31 c. Type **150**			10	10
669	45 c. Prince Charles as helicopter pilot	..		15	20
670	1 l. Prince Charles and Lady Diana Spencer			20	90
	w. Wmk inverted	..		20·00	
668/70	.. ..		*Set of 3*	40	1·10

(Des J.W. Litho Format)

1981 (9 Sept–30 Nov). *Royal Wedding (2nd issue). T* **151** *and similar vert designs. Multicoloured.* (a) *Sheet stamps. P* 12.

671	35 c. Type **151**	..		10	15
672	60 c. Prince Charles in outdoor clothes	..		15	25
673	1 l. 50, Prince Charles and Lady Diana Spencer			25	90
671/3	..		*Set of 3*	45	1·10
MS674	96 × 83 mm. 3 l. Royal Landau. P 14			65	65

(b) *Booklet stamps. P* 14 (30 Nov)

675	70 c. Type **151**			75	90
	a. Booklet pane. Nos. 675/6 × 2 plus two printed labels			2·75	
676	1 l. 30, As 60 c.			75	90
677	2 l. As 1 l. 50			1·50	2·00
	a. Booklet pane of 1			1·50	
675/7			*Set of 3*	2·75	3·50

Nos. 671/3 were each printed in small sheets of 6 including one *se-tenant* stamp-size label.

152 "Physical Recreation"

153 Pineapples

(Des BG Studio. Litho Questa)

1981 (30 Sept). *25th Anniv of Duke of Edinburgh Award Scheme and President's Award Scheme Publicity. T* **152** *and similar vert designs. Multicoloured. W w* **14**. *P* 14.

678	6 c. Type **152**	..	..	10	10
679	31 c. "Community service"	..		15	10
680	1 l. Duke of Edinburgh	..		30	40
681	1 l. President Siaka Stevens	..		30	40
678/81			*Set of 4*	70	85

(Des BG Studio. Litho Questa)

1981 (16 Oct). *World Food Day (1st issue). T* **153** *and similar vert designs. Multicoloured. W w* **14**. *P* 14.

682	6 c. Type **153**	..		10	10
683	31 c. Groundnuts	..		15	10
684	50 c. Cassava fruits	..		20	15
685	1 l. Rice plants	..		50	50
682/5	..		*Set of 4*	75	70

154 Groundnuts

(Litho Format)

1981 (2 Nov). *World Food Day (2nd issue). Agricultural Industry. T* **154** *and similar horiz designs. Multicoloured. P* 14½.

686	6 c. Type **154**			10	10
687	31 c. Cassava	..		25	10
688	50 c. Rice	..		40	25
689	1 l. Pineapples			65	70
686/9			*Set of 4*	1·25	1·00

Examples of Nos. 686/9 *se-tenant* come from unissued sheetlets dispersed by the liquidator of Format International Security Printers Ltd.

155 Scouts with Cattle

(156)

(Des M. Diamond. Litho Questa)

1982 (23 Aug). *75th Anniv of Boy Scout Movement. T* **155** *and similar horiz designs. Multicoloured. P* 14.

690	20 c. Type **155**			25	10
691	50 c. Scouts picking flowers			50	40
692	1 l. Lord Baden-Powell			90	1·00
693	2 l. Scouts fishing			1·90	2·00
690/3			*Set of 4*	3·25	3·00
MS694	101 × 70 mm. 3 l. Scouts raising flag			2·75	3·25

1982 (30 Aug)–85. *Nos. 668/74 surch as T* **156**.

695	50 c. on 31 c. Type **150**			40	40
696	50 c. on 35 c. Type **151**			40	40
697	50 c. on 45 c. Prince Charles as helicopter pilot			40	40
698	50 c. on 60 c. Prince Charles in outdoor clothes			40	40
699	90 c. on 1 l. Prince Charles and Lady Diana Spencer			75	75
699a	1 l. 30 on 60 c. Prince Charles in outdoor clothes (1985)			1·75	2·00
699b	2 l. on 35 c. Type **151** (1985)			2·75	3·00
	ba. Surch double			20·00	
700	2 l. on 11.50, Prince Charles and Lady Diana Spencer			1·50	1·75
700a	8 l. on 11.50, Prince Charles and Lady Diana Spencer (1985)			8·75	11·00
695/700a			*Set of 9*	15·00	18·00
MS701	95 × 83 mm. 3 l. 50 on 3 l. Royal Landau			1·00	1·00

Nos. 699a/b and 700a also exist surcharged in blue from a limited printing (*Price for set of 3 £50 mint*).

157 Heading

158 Prince and Princess of Wales

(Des PAD Studio. Litho Questa)

1982 (7 Sept). *World Cup Football Championship, Spain. T* **157** *and similar vert designs. Multicoloured. P* 14.

702	20 c. Type **157**			45	15
703	30 c. Dribbling	..		70	20
704	1 l. Tackling	..		2·25	2·25
705	2 l. Goalkeeping	..		3·50	3·75
702/5			*Set of 4*	6·25	5·75
MS706	92 × 75 mm. 3 l. Shooting			4·75	3·00

Nos. 702/5 were each printed in small sheets of 6 including one, *se-tenant*, stamp-sized label.

(Des PAD Studio. Litho Questa)

1982 (15 Sept). *21st Birthday of Princess of Wales. T* **158** *and similar vert designs. Multicoloured. P* 14½ × 14.

707	31 c. Caernarvon Castle	..		20	15
708	50 c. Type **158**	..		40	15
709	2 l. Princess of Wales	..		1·75	75
707/9			*Set of 3*	2·10	95
MS710	103 × 75 mm. 3 l. Princess of Wales (*different*)			1·40	1·00

Nos. 707/9 also exist in sheetlets of 5 stamps and 1 label.

1982 (15 Oct). *Birth of Prince William of Wales. Nos. 707/10 optd with T* **212a** *of Jamaica.*

711	31 c. Caernarvon Castle	..		15	15
712	50 c. Type **158**	..		30	15
713	2 l. Princess of Wales			1·00	95
711/13			*Set of 3*	1·25	95
MS714	103 × 75 mm. 3 l. Princess of Wales (*different*)			1·25	1·00

Nos. 711/13 also exist in sheetlets of 5 stamps and 1 label.

MINIMUM PRICE

The minimum price quote is 10p which represents a handling charge rather than a basis for valuing common stamps. For further notes about prices see introductory pages.

159 Washington with Troops   **160** Temptation of Christ

(Des C. Mill. Litho Questa)

1982 (30 Oct). *250th Birth Anniv of George Washington. T* **159** *and similar multicoloured designs.* P 14.

715	6 c. Type **159**	..	10	10
716	31 c. Portrait of Washington (*vert*)	..	20	20
717	50 c. Washington with horse	..	35	35
718	1 l. Washington standing on battlefield (*vert*)	..	65	80
715/18		*Set of 4*	1·10	1·25
MS719	103 × 71 mm. 2 l. Washington at home		75	1·25

(Des N. Waldman Studio. Litho Questa)

1982 (18 Nov). *Christmas. Stained-glass Windows. T* **160** *and similar vert designs. Multicoloured.* P 13½ × 14.

720	6 c. Type **160**	..	10	10
721	31 c. Baptism of Christ	..	15	20
722	50 c. Annunciation	..	20	40
723	1 l. Nativity	..	55	90
720/3		*Set of 4*	85	1·40
MS724	74 × 104 mm. 2 l. Mary and Joseph		70	1·10

WORLD CUP WINNERS	
ITALY (3)	
vs.	**162** Long Snouted Crocodile
W. GERMANY (1)	
(**161**)	

1982 (2 Dec). *World Cup Football Championship Winners. Nos. 702/6 optd with T* **161**.

725	20 c. Type **157**	..	..	30	20
726	30 c. Dribbling	..	..	30	30
727	1 l. Tackling	..	..	80	75
728	2 l. Goalkeeping	..	..	1·25	1·75
725/8			*Set of 4*	2·40	2·75
MS729	91 × 75 mm. 3 l. Shooting	..	..	1·00	2·00

(Des G. Drummond. Litho Questa)

1982 (10 Dec). *Death Centenary of Charles Darwin. T* **162** *and similar horiz designs. Multicoloured.* P 14.

730	6 c. Type **162**	..	80	20
731	31 c. Rainbow Lizard	..	1·75	75
732	50 c. River Turtle	..	2·00	2·00
733	1 l. Chameleon	..	3·25	4·75
730/3		*Set of 4*	7·00	7·00
MS734	90 × 70 mm. 2 l. Royal Python (*vert*)	..	2·25	3·00

163 Diogenes

(Des Design Images. Litho Questa)

1983 (28 Jan). *500th Birth Anniv of Raphael. Details from painting "The School of Athens". T* **163** *and similar multicoloured designs.* P 13½.

735	6 c. Type **163**	..	15	10
736	31 c. Euclid, Ptolemy, Zoroaster, Raphael and Sodoma	..	30	30
737	50 c. Euclid and his pupils	..	45	45
738	2 l. Pythagoras, Francesco Maria della Rovere and Heraclitus	..	1·40	1·40
735/8		*Set of 4*	2·00	2·00
MS739	101 × 126 mm. 3 l. Plato and Aristotle (*vert*)		1·50	2·00

STANLEY GIBBONS STAMP COLLECTING SERIES

164 Agricultural Training   **165** Map of Africa and Flag of Sierra Leone

(Litho Questa)

1983 (14 Mar). *Commonwealth Day. T* **164** *and similar horiz designs. Multicoloured.* P 14.

740	6 c. Type **164**	..	10	10
741	10 c. Tourism development	..	10	10
742	50 c. Broadcasting training	..	45	45
743	1 l. Airport services	..	1·50	1·25
740/3		*Set of 4*	1·75	1·60

(Des M. Diamond. Litho J.W.)

1983 (29 Apr). *25th Anniv of Economic Commission for Africa.* P 13.

744	**165**	1 l. multicoloured	80	1·10

166 Chimpanzees in Tree

(Des J. Iskowitz. Litho Questa)

1983 (19 May). *Endangered Species. T* **166** *and similar multicoloured designs.* P 14.

745	6 c. Type **166**	..	1·50	20
746	10 c. Three Chimpanzees (*vert*)	..	1·75	30
747	31 c. Chimpanzees swinging in tree (*vert*)	..	3·25	90
748	60 c. Group of Chimpanzees	..	5·50	7·50
745/8		*Set of 4*	11·00	8·00
MS749	115 × 80 mm. 3 l. African Elephant	..	2·75	2·25

167 Traditional Communications   **168** Montgolfier Balloon, Paris, 1783

(Des R. Sauber. Litho Questa)

1983 (14 July). *World Communications Year. T* **167** *and similar horiz designs. Multicoloured.* P 14.

750	6 c. Type **167**	..	10	10
751	10 c. Mail via Mano River	..	15	10
752	20 c. Satellite ground station	..	15	10
753	1 l. British packet, *circa* 1805	..	90	65
750/3		*Set of 4*	1·10	80
MS754	115 × 85 mm. 2 l. Telecommunications		80	1·25

(Des Artists International. Litho Questa)

1983 (31 Aug). *Bicentenary of Manned Flight. T* **168** *and similar multicoloured designs.* P 14.

755	6 c. Type **168**	..	30	10
756	20 c. Wolfert's *Deutschland* airship, Berlin, 1879 (*horiz*)	..	70	20
757	50 c. Amundsen's airship N.1 *Norge*, North Pole, 1926 (*horiz*)	..	1·75	1·75
758	1 l. *Cap Sierra* sport balloon, Freetown, 1983	..	1·75	2·50
755/8		*Set of 4*	4·00	4·00
MS759	115×85 mm. 2 l. Airship of 21st century		1·00	1·75

1983 (Oct). *Birds. As Nos. 622B/35B but without wmk. "1983" imprint date.*

760	1 c. Type **142**	..	1·25	2·00
761	2 c. Olive-bellied Sunbird	..	1·25	2·00
763	5 c. Spur-winged Goose	..	1·40	80
765	10 c. Grey Parrot (*vert*)	..	1·40	80
766	15 c. Blue Quail (*vert*)	..	1·50	1·75
767	20 c. African Wood Owl (*vert*)	..	3·00	2·25
768	30 c. Great Blue Turaco (*vert*)	..	1·75	2·50
769	40 c. Blue-breasted Kingfisher (*vert*)	..	2·75	3·50
770	50 c. Black Crake (*vert*)	..	3·25	3·50
772	2 l. Black Bee Eater	..	5·00	12·00
773	5 l. Barrow's Bustard	..	10·00	18·00
760/73		*Set of 11*	29·00	45·00

Nos. 760/73 exist imperforate from stock dispersed by the liquidator of Format International Security Printers Ltd.

Examples of the 1, 2, 3 c. and 2 l. with 1981 imprint date come from the liquidator's stock.

169 Mickey Mouse

(Litho Format)

1983 (18 Nov). *Space Ark Fantasy. T* **169** *and similar horiz designs featuring Disney cartoon characters. Multicoloured.* P 13½.

774	1 c. Type **169**	..	10	10
775	1 c. Huey, Dewey and Louie	..	10	10
776	3 c. Goofy in spaceship	..	10	10
777	3 c. Donald Duck	..	10	10
778	10 c. Ludwig von Drake	..	10	10
779	10 c. Goofy	..	10	10
780	2 l. Mickey Mouse and Giraffe in spaceship		1·25	1·60
781	3 l. Donald Duck floating in space	..	1·75	2·00
774/81		*Set of 8*	3·00	3·50
MS782	140 × 116 mm. 5 l. Mickey Mouse leaving spaceship		3·00	3·50

170 Graduates from Union Training Programme

(Des G. Vasarhelyi. Litho Format)

1984 (8 Feb). *10th Anniv of the Mano River Union. T* **170** *and similar horiz designs. Multicoloured.* P 15.

783	6 c. Type **170**	..	10	10
784	25 c. Intra-Union trade	..	10	10
785	31 c. Member Presidents on map	..	10	10
786	41 c. Signing ceremony marking Guinea's accession		15	15
783/6		*Set of 4*	30	30
MS787	75 × 113 mm. No. 786	..	35	90

Nos. 783/7 exist imperforate from stock dispersed by the liquidator of Format International Security Printers Ltd.

171 Gymnastics   **172** "Apollo 11" Lift-off

(Des J. Iskowitz. Litho Questa)

1984 (27 Mar). *Olympic Games, Los Angeles. T* **171** *and similar horiz designs. Multicoloured.* P 14.

788	90 c. Type **171**	..	30	40
789	1 l. Hurdling	..	30	40
790	3 l. Javelin-throwing	..	75	1·25
788/90		*Set of 3*	1·25	1·90
MS791	104 × 71 mm. 7 l. Boxing	..	1·10	2·00

(Des J. Iskowitz. Litho Questa)

1984 (14 May). *15th Anniv of First Moonwalk. T* **172** *and similar multicoloured designs.* P 14.

792	50 c. Type **172**	..	20	20
793	75 c. Lunar module	..	30	30
794	1 l. 25, First Moonwalk	..	45	45
795	2 l. 50, Lunar exploration	..	85	85
792/5		*Set of 4*	1·60	1·60
MS796	99 × 69 mm. 5 l. Family watching Moonwalk on television (*horiz*)	..	1·60	2·25

173 Concorde

(Des Susan David. Litho Walsall)

1984 (19 June). *Universal Postal Union Congress, Hamburg. T* **173** *and similar horiz design. Multicoloured.* P 14.

797	4 l. Type **173**	..	2·75	1·75
MS798	100 × 70 mm. 4 l. Heinrich von Stephan (founder of U.P.U.)	..	1·50	2·25

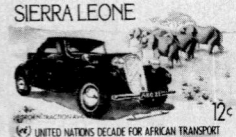

174 Citroen "Traction Avante" (175)

25c

(Des Susan David. Litho Format)

1984 (16 July). *United Nations Decade for African Transport. T 174 and similar horiz designs. Multicoloured. P 14½ × 15.*

799	12 c. Type **174**		30	10
800	60 c. Locomobile		50	35
801	90 c. A.C. "Ace"		65	45
802	1 l. Vauxhall "Prince Henry"		65	45
803	1 l. Delahaye "135"		80	70
804	2 l. Mazda "1105"		90	90
799/804		Set of 6	3·50	2·50
MS805	107 × 75 mm. 6 l. Volkswagen "Beetle". P 15		3·75	4·50

1984 (3 Aug). *Surch as T 175. Imprint date at foot.* (a) Nos. 625, 627 and 634. W w 14 (*sideways on horiz designs*)

806	25 c. on 10 c. Grey Parrot (*vert*) (No. 627B)		6·50	6·50
	a. Without imprint date (No. 627A)		6·50	6·50
807	40 c. on 10 c. Grey Parrot (*vert*) (No. 627B)		6·50	6·50
	a. Without imprint date (No. 627A)		6·50	6·50
808	50 c. on 2 l. Black Bee Eater (No. 634B)		6·50	6·50
	a. Without imprint date (No. 634A)		6·50	6·50
809	70 c. on 5 c. Spur-winged Goose (No. 625B)		6·50	6·50
	a. Without imprint date (No. 625A)		6·50	6·50
810	10 l. on 5 c. Spur-winged Goose (No. 625B)		13·00	13·00
	a. Without imprint date (No. 625A)		13·00	13·00
806/10		Set of 5	35·00	35·00

(b) On Nos. 763, 765 and 772. No wmk

811	25 c. on 10 c. Grey Parrot (*vert*) (No. 765)		75	85
812	40 c. on 10 c. Grey Parrot (*vert*) (No. 765)		50	70
813	50 c. on 2 l. Black Bee Eater (No. 772)		50	70
814	70 c. on 5 c. Spur-winged Goose (No. 763)		50	70
815	10 l. on 5 c. Spur-winged Goose (No. 763)		3·00	3·50
811/15		Set of 5	4·75	5·75

Imprint dates: "1981", Nos. 806/10; "1982", Nos. 806/10; "1983", Nos. 811/15.

AUSIPEX 84

(176)   177 Portuguese Caravel

1984 (22 Aug). *"Ausipex" International Stamp Exhibition, Melbourne. Optd with T 176. Imprint date at foot.* (a) On Nos. 632 and 635. W w 14 (*sideways on horiz designs*)

816	50 c. Black Crake (No. 632B)		5·00	5·00
	a. Without imprint date (No. 632A)		5·00	5·00
817	5 l. Barrow's Bustard (No. 635B)		15·00	15·00
	a. Without imprint date (No. 635A)		15·00	15·00

(b) On Nos. 770 and 773. No wmk

818	50 c. Black Crake		1·00	75
819	5 l. Barrow's Bustard		2·75	2·00

Imprint dates: "1981", Nos. 816/17; "1982", Nos. 816/17; "1983", Nos. 818/19.

(Des G. Drummond. Litho Questa)

1984 (5 Sept)–85. *History of Shipping. T 177 and similar horiz designs. Multicoloured.* A. P 12 (15, 25 l.) or 14 (*others*). *Without imprint date below design.*

820A	2 c. Type **177**		65	1·50
821A	5 c. Merlin of Bristol		1·00	85
822A	10 c. Golden Hind		1·50	85
823A	15 c. Mordaunt		1·75	90
824A	20 c. Atlantic (transport)		1·75	1·00
825A	25 c. H.M.S. Lapwing		1·75	1·00
826A	30 c. Traveller (brig)		2·00	1·00
827A	40 c. Amistad (schooner)		2·00	1·00
828A	50 c. H.M.S. Teazer		2·00	1·00
829A	70 c. Scotia (cable ship)		2·50	2·00
830A	1 l. H.M.S. Alecto		3·00	2·00
831A	2 l. H.M.S. Blonde (9.10.84)		8·00	7·00
832A	5 l. H.M.S. Fox (9.10.84)		8·00	11·00
833A	10 l. Accra (liner) (7.11.84)		8·00	14·00
833cA	15 l. H.M.S. Favourite (15.11.85)		3·00	4·00
833dA	25 l. H.M.S. Euryalus (15.11.85)		3·00	4·50
820A/33dA		Set of 16	45·00	48·00

B. With imprint date ("1985") below design. P 12

820B	2 c. Type **177** (7.85)		55	1·50
821B	5 c. Merlin of Bristol (7.85)		55	80
822B	10 c. Golden Hind (7.85)		75	70
824B	20 c. Atlantic (transport) (7.85)		80	60
825B	25 c. H.M.S. Lapwing (7.85)		80	60
826B	30 c. Traveller (brig) (7.85)		80	60
827B	40 c. Amistad (schooner) (7.85)		90	60
828B	50 c. H.M.S. Teazer (7.85)		1·00	60
829B	70 c. Scotia (cable ship) (7.85)		1·75	2·00
830B	1 l. H.M.S. Alecto (7.85)		1·75	2·00
831B	2 l. H.M.S. Blonde (7.85)		2·00	3·00
832B	5 l. H.M.S. Fox (7.85)		2·75	4·50
833B	10 l. Accra (liner) (7.85)		3·25	5·50
833cB	15 l. H.M.S. Favourite (1985?)			
833dB	25 l. H.M.S. Euryalus (1985?)			
820B/33B		Set of 13	16·00	21·00

NEW INFORMATION

The editor is always interested to correspond with people who have new information that will improve or correct the Catalogue.

---

178 Mail Runner approaching   179 "Madonna and Child"
Mano River Depot, c 1843   (Pisanello)

(Des Susan David. Litho Walsall)

1984 (9 Oct). *125th Anniv of First Postage Stamps. T 178 and similar horiz designs. Multicoloured. P 14.*

834	50 c. Type **178**		35	15
835	2 l. Isaac Fitzjohn, First Postmaster, receiving letters, 1855		1·25	85
836	3 l. 1859 packet franked with four 6d. stamps		1·75	1·50
834/6		Set of 3	3·00	2·25
MS837	100 × 70 mm. 5 l. Sierra Leone 1859 6d. purple and Great Britain 1840 Penny Black stamps		1·50	1·60

(Litho Walsall)

1984 (15 Nov). *Christmas. Madonna and Child paintings by artists named. T 179 and similar vert designs. Multicoloured. P 14.*

838	20 c. Type **179**		10	10
839	1 l. Memling		40	40
840	2 l. Raphael		75	90
841	3 l. Van der Werff		1·10	1·40
838/41		Set of 4	2·00	2·50
MS842	100 × 69 mm. 6 l. Picasso		2·75	2·75

180 Donald Duck in the "The Wise Little Hen"

(Litho Questa)

1984 (26 Nov). *50th Birthday of Donald Duck. Walt Disney Cartoon Characters. T 180 and similar horiz designs. Multicoloured. P 12 (2 l.) or 14 × 13½ (others).*

843	1 c. Type **180**		10	10
844	2 c. Mickey Mouse and Donald Duck in "Boat Builders"		10	10
845	3 c. Panchito, Donald Duck and Jose Carioca in "The Three Caballeros"		10	10
846	4 c. Donald Duck meeting Pythagoras in "Mathmagic Land"		10	10
847	5 c. Donald Duck and nephew in "The Mickey Mouse Club"		10	10
848	10 c. Mickey Mouse, Goofy and Donald Duck in "Donald on Parade"		10	10
849	1 l. Donald Duck riding donkey in "Don Donald"		1·00	1·00
850	2 l. Donald Duck in "Donald Gets Drafted"		2·00	2·00
851	4 l. Donald Duck meeting children in Tokyo Disneyland		3·25	3·25
843/51		Set of 9	6·00	6·00
MS852	126 × 102 mm. 5 l. Style sheet for Donald Duck		4·25	2·50

No. 850 was printed in sheetlets of 8.

181 Fischer's Whydah

(Des Susan David. Litho Walsall)

1985 (31 Jan). *Birth Bicentenary of John J. Audubon (ornithologist). Songbirds of Sierra Leone. T 181 and similar horiz designs. Multicoloured. P 14.*

853	40 c. Type **181**		1·75	55
854	90 c. Spotted Flycatcher		3·00	1·75
855	1 l. 30, Garden Warbler		3·25	3·50
856	3 l. Speke's Weaver		5·50	7·50
853/6		Set of 4	12·00	12·00
MS857	100 × 70 mm. 5 l. Great Grey Shrike		3·00	3·00

182 Fishing

(Des M. Zacharow. Litho Walsall)

1985 (14 Feb). *International Youth Year. T 182 and similar horiz designs. Multicoloured. P 14.*

858	1 l. 15, Type **182**		45	55
859	1 l. 50, Sawing timber		60	75
860	2 l. 15, Rice farming		75	95
858/60		Set of 3	1·60	2·00
MS861	100 × 70 mm. 5 l. Polishing diamonds		1·75	1·50

183 Eddie Rickenbacker and Spad "XIII", 1918

(Des K. Gromol. Litho Walsall)

1985 (28 Feb). *40th Anniv of International Civil Aviation Organization. T 183 and similar horiz designs. Multicoloured. P 14.*

862	70 c. Type **183**		1·50	75
863	1 l. 25, Samuel P. Langley and *Aerodrome A*, 1903		2·00	1·75
864	1 l. 30, Orville and Wilbur Wright with Wright Flyer I, 1903		2·00	1·75
865	2 l. Charles Lindbergh and Ryan NYP Special *Spirit of St. Louis*, 1927		2·25	2·75
862/5		Set of 4	7·00	6·25
MS866	100 × 69 mm. 5 l. Sierra Leone Airlines Boeing 707-384C		2·00	1·75

184 "Temptation of Christ"   185 The Queen
(Botticelli)   Mother at St. Paul's
                                  Cathedral

(Des C. Walters. Litho Questa)

1985 (29 Apr). *Easter. Religious Paintings. T 184 and similar multicoloured designs. P 14.*

867	45 c. Type **184**		30	15
868	70 c. "Christ at the Column" (Velasquez)		55	35
869	1 l. 55, "Pietà" (Botticelli) (*vert*)		90	75
870	10 l. "Christ on the Cross" (Velasquez) (*vert*)		4·75	5·00
867/70		Set of 4	6·00	5·75
MS871	106 × 76 mm. 12 l. "Man of Sorrows" (Botticelli)		4·00	4·00

(Des J.W. Litho Questa)

1985 (8 July). *Life and Times of Queen Elizabeth the Queen Mother. T 185 and similar multicoloured designs. P 14.*

872	1 l. Type **185**		20	25
873	1 l. 70, With her racehorse, "Double Star", at Sandown (*horiz*)		30	40
874	10 l. At Covent Garden, 1971		1·75	2·50
872/4		Set of 3	2·00	2·75
MS875	56 × 85 mm. 12 l. With Princess Anne at Ascot		1·75	2·25

**75th ANNIVERSARY
OF GIRL GUIDES**

70c

(186)

1985 (25 July). *75th Anniv of Girl Guide Movement. Nos. 690/4 surch as T 186.*

876	70 c. on 20 c. Type **155**		30	30
877	1 l. 30 on 50 c. Scouts picking flowers		55	55
878	5 l. on 1 l. Lord Baden-Powell		1·60	1·60
879	7 l. on 2 l. Scouts fishing		2·25	2·25
876/9		Set of 4	4·25	4·25
MS880	101 × 70 mm. 15 l. on 3 l. Scouts raising flag		3·75	4·00

**MA YANHONJG
CHINA
GOLD MEDAL**

Le2

(187)

1985 (25 July). *Olympic Gold Medal Winners, Los Angeles. Nos. 788/91 surch as T 187.*

881	2 l. on 90 c. Type **171** (surch T 187)		50	55
882	4 l. on 1 l. Hurdling (surch "E. MOSES U.S.A. GOLD MEDAL")		1·00	1·25
883	8 l. on 3 l. Javelin-throwing (surch "A. HAERKOENEN FINLAND GOLD MEDAL")		2·00	2·10
881/3		Set of 3	3·25	3·50
MS884	104 × 71 mm. 15 l. on 7 l. Boxing (surch "M. TAYLOR U.S.A. GOLD MEDAL")		3·25	3·75

70c

188 Chater-Lea (1905) at Hill   **(189)**
Station House

(Des A. DiLorenzo. Litho Questa)

1985 (15 Aug). *Centenary of the Motor Cycle and Decade for African Transport. T* **188** *and similar horiz designs. Multicoloured. P* 14.
885	1 l. 40, Type **188**		1·00	1·00
886	2 l. Honda "XR 350 R" at Queen Elizabeth II Quay, Freetown		1·40	1·40
887	4 l. Kawasaki "Vulcan" at Bo Clock Tower		2·50	2·50
888	5 l. Harley-Davidson "Electra-Glide" in Makeni village		2·75	2·75
885/8		*Set of* 4	7·00	7·00
MS889	104×71 mm. 12 l. Millet (1893)..		4·50	4·25

(Des Susan David. Litho Questa)

1985 (3 Sept). *300th Birth Anniv of Johann Sebastian Bach (composer). Vert designs as T* **204a** *of Maldive Islands. P* 14.
890	70 c. multicoloured		85	25
891	3 l. multicoloured		2·00	80
892	4 l. multicoloured		2·10	1·10
893	5 l. multicoloured		2·25	1·40
890/3		*Set of* 4	6·50	3·25
MS894	103×77 mm. 12 l. black		5·00	3·50

Designs:—70 c. Viola pomposa; 3 l. Spinet; 4 l. Lute; 5 l. Oboe; 12 l. "Johann Sebastian Bach" (Toby E. Rosenthal).

1985 (30 Sept). *Surch as T* **189**. (*a*) *On Nos.* 707/10
895	70 c. on 31 c. Caernarvon Castle		30	30
896	4 l. on 50 c. Type **158**		2·00	2·50
897	5 l. on 2 l. Princess of Wales		2·50	3·00
MS898	103×75 mm. 15 l. on 3 l. Princess of Wales (*different*)		6·50	6·00

(*b*) *On Nos.* 711/14
899	1 l. 30 on 31 c. Caernarvon Castle		1·25	1·25
900	5 l. on 50 c. Type **158**		3·00	3·50
901	7 l. on 2 l. Princess of Wales		4·00	4·50
895/7, 899/901		*Set of* 6	11·50	13·50
MS902	103×75 mm. 15 l. on 3 l. Princess of Wales (*different*)		6·50	6·00

190 "Madonna and Child"   **191** Player kicking Ball
(Crivelli)

(Litho Questa)

1985 (18 Oct). *Christmas. "Madonna and Child" Paintings by artists named. T* **190** *and similar vert designs. Multicoloured. P* 14.
903	70 c. Type **190**		25	10
904	3 l. Bouts		80	40
905	4 l. Da Messina		95	55
906	5 l. Lochner		1·10	65
903/6		*Set of* 4	2·75	1·50
MS907	113×85 mm. 12 l. Miniature from Book of Kells		1·50	1·60

(Des Walt Disney Productions. Litho Questa)

1985 (30 Oct). *150th Birth Anniv of Mark Twain (author). Vert designs as T* **160a** *of Lesotho showing Walt Disney cartoon characters illustrating Mark Twain quotations. Multicoloured. P* 13½×14.
908	1 l. 50, Snow White and Bashful		40	40
909	3 l. Three Little Pigs		60	90
910	4 l. Donald Duck and nephew		70	1·10
911	5 l. Pinocchio and Figaro the cat		85	1·25
908/11		*Set of* 4	2·25	3·25
MS912	126×101 mm. 15 l. Winnie the Pooh		4·00	2·50

(Des Walt Disney Productions. Litho Questa)

1985 (3 Oct). *Birth Bicentenaries of Grimm Brothers (folklorists). Designs as T* **160b** *of Lesotho, but horiz, showing Walt Disney cartoon characters from "Rumpelstiltskin". Multicoloured. P* 14×13½.
913	70 c. The Miller (Donald Duck) and his daughter (Daisy Duck) meet the King (Uncle Scrooge)		20	25
914	1 l. 30, The King puts the Miller's daughter to work		35	40
915	2 l. Rumpelstiltskin demands payment		50	55
916	10 l. The King with gold spun from straw		2·75	3·50
913/16		*Set of* 4	3·50	4·25
MS917	126×100 mm. 15 l. The King and Queen with baby		5·50	4·50

(Litho Format)

1985 (28 Nov). *40th Anniv of United Nations Organization. Multicoloured designs as T* **159** *of Lesotho showing United Nations (New York) stamps. P* 14½.
918	2 l. John Kennedy and 1954 Human Rights 8 c..		50	70
919	4 l. Albert Einstein (scientist) and 1958 Atomic Energy 3 c.		1·00	1·60
920	7 l. Maimonides (physician) and 1956 W.H.O. 8 c.		3·50	4·25
918/20		*Set of* 3	4·50	6·00
MS921	110×85 mm. 12 l. Martin Luther King (civil rights leader) (*vert*)..		1·25	1·75

(Des M. Lemel. Litho Questa)

1986 (3 Mar). *World Cup Football Championship, Mexico. T* **191** *and similar vert designs. Multicoloured. P* 14.
922	70 c. Type **191**..		55	10
923	3 l. Player controlling ball		1·00	50
924	4 l. Player chasing ball		1·25	70
925	5 l. Player kicking ball (*different*)		1·50	80
922/5		*Set of* 4	3·75	1·90
MS926	105×74 mm. 12 l. Player kicking ball (*different*) ..		1·50	1·75

191a Times   **192** Chicago-Milwaukee
Square, 1905   "Hiawatha Express'

(Des J. Iskowitz. Litho Questa)

1986 (11 Mar). *Centenary of Statue of Liberty (1st issue). T* **191a** *and similar multicoloured designs. P* 14.
927	40 c. Type **191a**		10	10
928	70 c. Times Square, 1986		15	10
929	1 l. "Tally Ho" coach, c 1880 (*horiz*)		35	15
930	10 l. Express bus, 1986 (*horiz*)		2·00	1·90
927/30		*Set of* 4	2·25	2·00
MS931	105×75 mm. 12 l. Statue of Liberty		2·25	2·25

See also Nos. 1001/9.

(Des W. Hanson. Litho Questa)

1986 (1 Apr). *Appearance of Halley's Comet (1st issue). Horiz designs as T* **162a** *of Lesotho. Multicoloured. P* 14.
932	15 c. Johannes Kepler (astronomer) and Paris Observatory		30	10
933	50 c. N.A.S.A. Space Shuttle landing, 1985..		40	10
934	70 c. Halley's Comet (from Bayeux Tapestry)		40	15
935	10 l. Comet of 530 A.D. and Merlin predicting coming of King Arthur		2·25	1·60
932/5		*Set of* 4	3·00	1·75
MS936	101×70 mm. 12 l. Halley's Comet		1·50	1·60

See also Nos. 988/92.

(Des and litho Questa)

1986 (23 Apr). *60th Birthday of Queen Elizabeth II. Vert designs as T* **163a** *of Lesotho. P* 14.
937	10 c. black and yellow		20	10
938	1 l. 70, multicoloured		45	35
939	10 l. multicoloured		2·00	2·50
937/9		*Set of* 3	2·40	2·50
MS940	120×85 mm. 12 l. black and grey-brown		1·75	1·75

Designs:—10 c. Princess Elizabeth inspecting guard of honour, Cranwell, 1951; 1 l. 70, In Garter robes; 10 l. At Braemar Games, 1970; 12 l. Princess Elizabeth, Windsor Castle, 1943.

(Des P. Rhymer. Litho Questa)

1986 (22 May). *"Ameripex" International Stamp Exhibition, Chicago. American Trains. T* **192** *and similar horiz designs. Multicoloured. P* 14.
941	50 c. Type **192**..		90	40
942	2 l. Rock Island Line "The Rocket"		1·75	1·75
943	4 l. Rio Grande "Prospector"		2·75	3·25
944	7 l. Southern Pacific "Daylight Express" ..		3·50	5·00
941/4		*Set of* 4	8·00	9·25
MS945	105×85 mm. 12 l. Pennsylvania "Broadway Limited"		3·00	2·25

(Litho Questa)

1986 (1 July). *Royal Wedding. Vert designs as T* **170a** *of Lesotho. Multicoloured. P* 14.
946	10 c. Prince Andrew and Miss Sarah Ferguson		10	10
947	1 l. 70, Prince Andrew at clay pigeon shoot		30	35
948	10 l. Prince Andrew in naval uniform		1·40	1·75
946/8		*Set of* 3	1·60	2·00
MS949	88×88 mm. 12 l. Prince Andrew and Miss Sarah Ferguson (*different*)		2·25	1·60

OMNIBUS ISSUES

Details, together with prices for complete sets, of the various Omnibus issues from the 1935 Silver Jubilee series to date are included in a special section following Zimbabwe at the end of Volume 2.

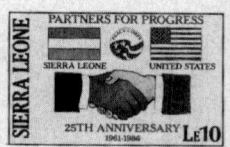

193 Monodora myristica   **194** Handshake and Flags of
Sierra Leone and U.S.A.

(Des G. Drummond. Litho Format)

1986 (25 Aug). *Flowers of Sierra Leone. T* **193** *and similar vert designs. Multicoloured. P* 15.
950	70 c. Type **193**..		15	10
951	1 l. 50, Gloriosa simplex		20	15
952	4 l. Mussaenda erythrophylla		35	25
953	6 l. Crinum ornatum		50	40
954	8 l. Bauhinia purpurea		60	60
955	10 l. Bombax costatum		70	70
956	20 l. Hibiscus rosasinensis		1·25	1·50
957	30 l. Cassia fistula		1·75	2·00
950/7		*Set of* 8	5·00	5·00
MS958	Two sheets, each 101×92 mm. (a) 40 l. Clitoria ternatea. (b) 40 l. Plumbago auriculata			
		Set of 2 sheets	5·00	5·00

(Litho Questa)

1986 (26 Aug). *25th Anniv of United States Peace Corps. P* 14.
959	**194** 10 l. multicoloured		70	70

Le30

70ᵉ

195 Transporting Goods by Canoe   **(196)**   **(197)**

(Des T. O'Toole. Litho Questa)

1986 (1 Sept). *International Peace Year. T* **195** *and similar horiz designs. Multicoloured. P* 14.
960	1 l. Type **195**..		30	15
961	2 l. Teacher and class		40	25
962	5 l. Rural post office.		80	50
963	10 l. Fishermen in longboat ..		1·60	1·25
960/3		*Set of* 4	2·75	1·90

1986 (15 Sept). *Various stamps surch.*
(*a*) *As T* **196** *on Nos.* 820A, 826/7A *and* 829A
964	30 l. on 2 c. Type **177**..		2·00	2·75
965	40 l. on 30 c. Traveller (brig)		2·50	3·25
966	45 l. on 40 c. Amistad (schooner)		2·75	3·50
967	50 l. on 70 c. Scotia (cable ship)		3·00	3·50

(*b*) *As T* **197** *on Nos.* 937 *and* 939/40 (*in silver or on Nos.* 968/9)
968	70 c. on 10 c. black and yellow		60	10
969	45 l. on 10 l. multicoloured		4·50	2·50
MS970	120×85 mm. 50 l. on 12 l. black and grey-brown		2·50	3·00

(*c*) *As T* **197** *on Nos.* 946 *and* 948/9, *in silver*
971	70 c. on 10 c. Prince Andrew and Miss Sarah Ferguson..		10	10
972	45 l. on 10 l. Prince Andrew in naval uniform		2·50	2·50
964/9, 971/2		*Set of* 8	16·00	16·00
MS973	88×88 mm. 50 l. on 12 l. Prince Andrew and Miss Sarah Ferguson (*different*) ..		2·50	3·00

1986 (15 Sept). *World Cup Football Championship Winners, Mexico. Nos.* 922/6 *optd with T* **213a** *of Maldive Islands or surch also, all in gold.*
974	70 c. Type **191**		35	10
975	3 l. Player controlling ball		75	30
976	4 l. Player chasing ball		80	40
977	40 l. on 5 l. Player kicking ball (*different*) ..		6·50	4·50
974/7		*Set of* 4	7·50	4·75
MS978	105×74 mm. 40 l. on 12 l. Player kicking ball (*different*) ..		2·75	2·50

198 Mickey and Minnie Mouse as Jack and Jill

(Des Walt Disney Co. Litho Format)

1986 (22 Sept). *"Stockholmia '86" International Stamp Exhibition, Sweden. T* **198** *and similar horiz designs showing Walt Disney cartoon characters in scenes from nursery rhymes. Multicoloured. P* 11.
979	70 c. Type **198**..		10	10
980	1 l. Donald Duck as Wee Willie Winkie		15	15
981	2 l. Minnie Mouse as Little Miss Muffet		20	20
982	4 l. Goofy as Old King Cole		40	40
983	5 l. Clarabelle as Mary Quite Contrary		50	50

984	10 l. Daisy Duck as Little Bo Peep		90	1·00
985	25 l. Daisy Duck and Minnie Mouse in "Polly put the Kettle on"		2·00	2·75
986	35 l. Goofy, Mickey Mouse and Donald Duck as the Three Men in a Tub		2·50	3·25
979/86		Set of 8	6·00	7·50
MS987	Two sheets, each 127×102 mm. P 14×13½. (a) 40 l. Aunt Matilda as the Old Woman in the Shoe. (b) 40 l. Goofy as Simple Simon	Set of 2 sheets	6·50	6·50

1986 (15 Oct). *Appearance of Halley's Comet (2nd issue). Nos. 932/6 optd as T 213b of Maldive Islands (in silver on 50 l.) or surch also.*

988	50 c. N.A.S.A. Space Shuttle landing, 1985 ..		20	10
989	70 c. Halley's Comet (from Bayeux Tapestry)		20	10
990	1 l. 50 on 15 c. Johannes Kepler (astronomer) and Paris Observatory ..		20	10
991	45 l. on 10 l. Comet of 530 A.D. and Merlin predicting coming of King Arthur		4·00	3·75
988/91		Set of 4	4·25	3·75
MS992	101×70 mm. 50 l. on 12 l. Halley's Comet		3·25	3·75

199 "Virgin and Child with St. Dorothy"   200 Nomoli (soapstone figure)

(Litho Questa)

1986 (17 Nov). *Christmas. Paintings by Titian. T 199 and similar multicoloured designs. P 14.*

993	70 c. Type 199		10	10
994	1 l. 50, "The Gypsy Madonna" (vert)		15	10
995	20 l. "The Holy Family"		2·25	2·50
996	30 l. "Virgin and Child in an Evening Landscape" (vert)		2·75	3·25
993/6		Set of 4	4·75	5·50
MS997	76×102 mm. 40 l. "Madonna with the Pesaro Family" (vert)		7·00	7·00

(Des A. DiLorenzo. Litho Format)

1987 (2 Jan). *Bicentenary of Sierra Leone. T 200 and similar vert designs. Multicoloured. P 15.*

998	2 l. Type 200		15	15
999	5 l. King's Yard Gate, Royal Hospital, 1817..		30	40
MS1000	100×70 mm. 60 l. Early 19th-century British warship at Freetown		2·75	3·75

Nos. 998/1000 exist imperforate from stock dispersed by the liquidator of Format International Security Printers Ltd.

201 Removing Top of Statue's Torch   202 Emblem, Mother with Child and Syringe

(Litho Questa)

1987 (2 Jan). *Centenary of Statue of Liberty (1986) (2nd issue). T 201 and similar multicoloured designs. P 14.*

1001	70 c. Type 201		10	10
1002	1 l. 50, View of Statue's torch and New York Harbour (horiz) ..		10	10
1003	2 l. Crane lifting torch		10	10
1004	3 l. Workman steadying torch		10	15
1005	4 l. Statue's crown (horiz)..		15	20
1006	5 l. Statue of Liberty (side view) and fireworks		20	25
1007	10 l. Statue of Liberty and fireworks		40	45
1008	25 l. Bedloe Island, Statue and fireworks (horiz)		1·00	1·40
1009	30 l. Statue's face		1·25	1·75
1001/9		Set of 9	3·00	4·00

(Litho Questa)

1987 (18 Mar). *40th Anniv of U.N.I.C.E.F. P 14.*

1010	**202** 10 l. multicoloured		40	55

203 U.S.A., 1987   204 Mickey Mouse as Mountie and Parliament Building, Ottawa

---

(Des S. Heinmann. Litho Questa)

1987 (15 June). *America's Cup Yachting Championship. T 203 and similar multicoloured designs. P 14.*

1011	1 l. Type 203		15	10
1012	1 l. 50, New Zealand II, 1987 (horiz)		15	10
1013	2 l. 50, French Kiss, 1987		15	10
1014	10 l. Stars and Stripes, 1987 (horiz)		75	45
1015	15 l. Australia II, 1983		1·00	75
1016	25 l. Freedom, 1980		1·75	1·40
1017	30 l. Kookaburra, 1987 (horiz)		1·75	1·60
1011/17		Set of 7	5·00	4·00
MS1018	100×70 mm. 50 l. Constellation, 1964		2·25	2·50

(Des Walt Disney Co. Litho Format)

1987 (15 June). *"Capex '87" International Stamp Exhibition, Toronto. T 204 and similar horiz designs showing Walt Disney cartoon characters in Canada. Multicoloured. P 11.*

1019	2 l. Type 204		20	20
1020	5 l. Goofy dressed as Mountie and totem poles		35	35
1021	10 l. Goofy windsurfing and Donald Duck fishing off Perce Rock ..		60	45
1022	20 l. Goofy with mountain goat in Rocky Mountains		1·00	1·25
1023	25 l. Donald Duck and Mickey Mouse in Old Quebec ..		1·25	1·40
1024	45 l. Goofy emerging from igloo and Aurora Borealis..		1·75	2·50
1025	50 l. Goofy as gold prospector and post office, Yukon		2·00	3·00
1026	75 l. Dumbo flying over Niagara Falls		3·25	4·50
1019/26		Set of 8	9·25	12·00
MS1027	Two sheets, each 127×101 mm. (a) 100 l. Mickey Mouse driving chuckwagon in Calgary Stampede. (b) 100 l. Mickey Mouse and Goofy as Vikings in Newfoundland. P 14×13½	Set of 2 sheets	8·00	12·00

205 Salamis temora   206 Cycling

(Des S. Heinmann. Litho Questa)

1987 (4 Aug)–**89**. *Butterflies. T 205 and similar vert designs. Multicoloured. "Sierra Leone" in black. A. Without imprint date. P 14*

1028A	10 c. Type 205		1·25	40
	c. Perf 12 (6.88)		75	40
1029A	20 c. Stugeta marmorea ("Iolaus marmorea")		1·25	40
	c. Perf 12 (6.88)		1·00	40
1030A	40 c. Graphium ridleyanus		1·25	40
	c. Perf 12 (6.88)		1·00	40
1031A	1 l. Papilio bromius		1·25	40
	c. Perf 12 (6.88)		1·00	40
1032A	2 l. Iterus zalmoxis ("Papilio zalmoxis")		1·25	60
	c. Perf 12 (6.88)		1·25	60
1033A	3 l. Cymothoe sangaris		1·50	60
	c. Perf 12 (6.88)		1·25	60
1034A	5 l. Graphium tynderaeus		1·50	40
	c. Perf 12 (6.88)		1·25	30
1035A	10 l. Graphium policenes		2·50	70
	c. Perf 12 (6.88)		1·25	30
1036A	20 l. Tanuetheira timon ("Iolaus timon")		4·50	2·50
	c. Perf 12 (6.88)		1·50	60
1037A	25 l. Danaus limniace		4·75	2·75
	c. Perf 12 (6.88)		1·50	30
1038A	30 l. Papilio hesperus		4·75	3·50
	c. Perf 12 (8.88)		1·75	65
1039A	45 l. Charaxes smaragdalis		8·00	4·50
	c. Perf 12 (8.88)		1·75	30
1040A	60 l. Charaxes lucretius		2·00	4·25
	c. Perf 12 (10.88)		2·00	2·25
1041A	75 l. Antanartia delius		2·50	4·25
	c. Perf 12 (10.88)		2·25	2·75
1042A	100 l Abisara talantus		3·25	6·00
	c. Perf 12 (3.89)		7·00	7·50
1028A/42A		Set of 15	38·00	28·00
1028Ac/42Ac		Set of 15	24·00	16·00

B. With "1989" imprint date. P 14 (1989)

1028B	10 c. Type 205		60	60
	c. Perf 12½×11½		1·25	
	d. Perf 12		2·00	
1029B	20 c. Stugeta marmorea ("Iolaus marmorea")		60	60
	c. Perf 12½×11½		1·25	
	d. Perf 12		2·00	
1030B	40 c. Graphium ridleyanus		60	50
	c. Perf 12½×11½		1·25	
	d. Perf 12		2·00	
1031B	1 l. Papilio bromius		80	70
	c. Perf 12½×11½		1·75	
	d. Perf 12		2·00	
1032B	2 l. Iterus zalmoxis ("Papilio zalmoxis")		1·00	1·00
	c. Perf 12½×11½		3·00	
	d. Perf 12		2·00	
1033B	3 l. Cymothoe sangaris		1·40	1·40
	c. Perf 12½×11½		3·00	
1033Bd	3 l. As 40 c.		3·50	2·25
	da. Perf 12½×11½			
	db. Perf 12			
1034Bc	9 l. As 3 l. (No. 1033)		4·50	3·00
	ca. Perf 12½×11½			
	cd. Perf 12		2·00	

1035Bc	12 l. Type 205		5·00	3·25
	ca. Perf 12½×11½			
1035Bd	16 l. As 20 c.		5·00	3·25
	da. Perf 12½×11½			

Stamps perforated 12½×11½ show a larger perforation hole on every sixth perforation, both vertically and horizontally.
For similar stamps, but with "Sierra Leone" in blue, see Nos. 1658/72.

(Des BG Studio. Litho Questa)

1987 (10 Aug). *Olympic Games, Seoul (1988) (1st issue). T 206 and similar vert designs. Multicoloured. P 14.*

1043	5 l. Type 206		20	25
1044	10 l. Three Day Eventing		40	50
1045	45 l. Athletics		1·75	2·00
1046	50 l. Tennis		2·00	2·40
1043/6		Set of 4	4·00	4·75
MS1047	73×84 mm. 100 l. Olympic gold medal		4·00	4·50

See also Nos. 1137/41.

206a "The Quarrel" (Chagall)   206b "Apollo 8" Spacecraft (first manned Moon orbit), 1968

(Litho Questa)

1987 (17 Aug). *Birth Centenary of Marc Chagall (artist). T 206a and similar multicoloured designs. P 13½×14.*

1048	3 l. Type 206a		15	15
1049	5 l. "Rebecca giving Abraham's Servant a Drink" ..		20	25
1050	10 l. "The Village" ..		40	45
1051	20 l. "Ida at the Window" ..		60	65
1052	25 l. "Promenade" ..		1·00	1·10
1053	45 l. "Peasants" ..		2·00	2·25
1054	50 l. "Turquoise Plate" (ceramic) ..		3·25	2·25
1055	75 l. "Cemetery Gate" ..		3·25	3·75
1048/55		Set of 8	9·00	9·75
MS1056	Two sheets, each 110×95 mm. (a) 100 l. "Wedding Feast" (stage design) (104×78 mm). (b) 100 l. "The Falling Angel" (104×78 mm). Imperf ..	Set of 2 sheets	9·00	10·00

(Des W. Wright. Litho Format)

1987 (28 Aug). *Milestones of Transportation. T 206b and similar multicoloured designs. P 15.*

1057	3 l. Type 206b		15	15
1058	5 l. Blanchard's balloon (first U.S. balloon flight), 1793 (horiz) ..		20	20
1059	10 l. Amelia Earhart's Lockheed Vega 5B (first solo transatlantic flight by woman), 1932 (horiz) ..		40	40
1060	15 l. Vicker's FB-27 Vimy (first non-stop transatlantic flight), 1919 (horiz) ..		60	70
1061	20 l. British "Mk 1" tank (first combat tank), 1916 (horiz) ..		80	90
1062	25 l. Vought-Sikorsky VS-300 (first U.S. helicopter flight), 1939 (horiz) ..		90	1·00
1063	30 l. Wright brothers' Flyer I (first powered flight), 1903 (horiz) ..		1·10	1·25
1064	35 l. Bleriot XI (first cross Channel flight), 1909 (horiz) ..		1·25	1·40
1065	40 l. Paraplane (first flexible-wing ultralight), .1983 ..		1·50	1·75
1066	50 l. Daimler's first motorcycle, 1885 ..		1·75	2·00
1057/66		Set of 10	7·75	8·75
MS1067	114×83 mm. 100 l "Rhinegold Express" (first electric express service) (horiz) ..		3·75	6·00

207 Evonne Goolagong

(Des W. Storozuk. Litho Questa)

1987 (4 Sept). *Wimbledon Tennis Champions. T 207 and similar horiz designs. Multicoloured. P 14.*

1068	2 l. Type 207		35	35
1069	5 l. Martina Navratilova ..		55	55
1070	10 l. Jimmy Connors ..		85	85
1071	15 l. Bjorn Borg ..		1·25	1·25
1072	30 l. Boris Becker ..		2·25	2·25
1073	40 l. John McEnroe ..		2·50	2·50
1074	50 l. Chris Evert Lloyd ..		2·75	2·75
1075	75 l. Virginia Wade ..		3·50	3·50
1068/75		Set of 8	12·50	12·50
MS1076	Two sheets, each 105×75 mm. (a) 100 l. Boris Becker (different). (b) 100 l. Steffi Graf	Set of 2 sheets	13·00	13·00

208 Ducats, *Santa Maria* and Issac Abravanel (financier)

209 Cotton Tree

(Litho Questa)

1987 (11 Sept). *500th Anniv of Discovery of America by Columbus (1992). T 208 and similar horiz designs. Multicoloured. P 14.*

1077	5 l.	Type **208**	70	20
1078	10 l.	Astrolabe, *Pinta* and Abraham Zacuto (astronomer)	80	35
1079	45 l.	Maravedis (coins), *Nina* and Luis de Santangel (financier)	2·50	3·00
1080	50 l.	Carib and Spaniard with tobacco plant and Luis de Torres (translator)	2·75	3·25
1077/80		*Set of 4*	6·00	6·00
MS1081		101 × 70 mm. 100 l. Christopher Columbus and map	3·00	3·50

(Des Mary Walters. Litho Questa)

1987 (15 Sept). *Flora and Fauna. T 209 and similar horiz designs. Multicoloured. P 14.*

1082	3 l.	Type **209**	15	15
1083	5 l.	Dwarf Crocodile	35	25
1084	10 l.	Kudu	40	35
1085	20 l.	Yellowbells	65	65
1086	25 l.	Hippopotamus and calf	1·75	1·25
1087	45 l.	Comet Orchid	3·25	2·50
1088	50 l.	Baobab Tree	2·25	2·50
1089	75 l.	Elephant and calf	4·25	5·00
1082/9		*Set of 8*	11·50	11·50
MS1090		Two sheets, each 100 × 70 mm. (a) 100 l. Bananas, Coconut Palm, Papayas and Pineapple. (b) 100 l. Leopard		
		Set of 2 sheets	5·75	7·00

210 Scouts at Ayers Rock

210a White House

(Des R. Vigurs. Litho Format)

1987 (5 Oct). *World Scout Jamboree, Australia. T 210 and similar horiz designs. Multicoloured. P 15.*

1091	5 l.	Type **210**	30	20
1092	15 l.	Scouts sailing yacht	65	65
1093	40 l.	Scouts and Sydney skyline	1·50	2·50
1094	50 l.	Scout, Sydney Harbour Bridge and Opera House	2·50	2·75
1091/4		*Set of 4*	4·50	5·50
MS1095		114 × 78 mm. 100 l. Flags of Sierra Leone, Australia and Boy Scouts	3·00	3·50

Stamps in the design of the 50 l., but with a face value of 1 l. 50, exist from stock dispersed by the liquidator of Format International Security Printers Ltd.

(Des and litho Questa)

1987 (9 Nov). *Bicentenary of U.S. Constitution. T 210a and similar multicoloured designs. P 14.*

1096	5 l.	Type **210a**	15	20
1097	10 l.	George Washington (Virginia delegate) (*vert*)	30	35
1098	30 l.	Patrick Henry (statesman) (*vert*)	90	95
1099	65 l.	State Seal, New Hampshire	1·90	2·40
1096/9		*Set of 4*	3·00	3·50
MS1100		105 × 75 mm. 100 l. John Jay (jurist) (*vert*)	2·00	3·00

210b Mickey and Minnie Mouse on Space Mountain

(Des Walt Disney Company. Litho Questa)

1987 (9 Dec). *60th Anniv of Mickey Mouse (Walt Disney cartoon character). T 210b and similar horiz designs showing cartoon characters at Tokyo Disneyland. Multicoloured. P 14×13½.*

1101	20 c.	Type **210b**	10	10
1102	40 c.	Mickey Mouse at Country Bear Jamboree	10	10
1103	80 c.	Mickey Mouse as bandleader and Minnie Mouse, Goofy and Pluto as musicians	10	10
1104	1 l.	Goofy, Mickey Mouse and children in canoe and Mark Twain's river boat	10	10
1105	2 l.	Mickey Mouse, Goofy and Chip n'Dale on Western River Railroad	10	10

1106	3 l.	Goofy and Mickey Mouse as Pirates of the Caribbean	15	15
1107	10 l.	Mickey Mouse, Goofy and children aboard Big Thunder Mountain train	55	55
1108	20 l.	Mickey Mouse, Morty and Ferdie in boat and Goofy on flying carpet	1·25	1·50
1109	30 l.	Mickey and Minnie Mouse in kimonos at Disneyland entrance	1·75	2·00
1101/9		*Set of 9*	3·50	4·00
MS1110		127 × 102 mm. 65 l. Mickey and Minnie Mouse in kimonos at Cinderella's Castle	5·50	4·50

211 "The Annunciation" (detail) (Titian)

211a Wedding of Princess Elizabeth and Duke of Edinburgh, 1947

(Litho Questa)

1987 (21 Dec). *Christmas. Religious Paintings by Titian. T 211 and similar multicoloured designs. P 14.*

1111	2 l.	Type **211**	20	10
1112	10 l.	"Madonna and Child with Saints"	60	35
1113	20 l.	"Madonna and Child with Saints Ulfus and Brigid"	1·10	1·25
1114	35 l.	"The Madonna of the Cherries"	1·90	2·75
1111/14		*Set of 4*	3·50	4·00
MS1115		70 × 100 mm. 65 l. "The Pesaro Altarpiece" (*vert*)	3·50	4·00

(Des and litho Questa)

1988 (15 Feb). *Royal Ruby Wedding. T 211a and similar vert designs. P 14.*

1116	2 l.	deep brown, black and grey	20	10
1117	3 l.	multicoloured	20	10
1118	10 l.	deep brown, black and orange	40	35
1119	50 l.	multicoloured	2·00	2·50
1116/19		*Set of 4*	2·25	2·75
MS1120		76 × 100 mm. 65 l. multicoloured	2·25	2·50

Designs:—3 l. Prince Charles' christening photograph, 1949; 10 l. Queen Elizabeth II with Prince Charles and Princess Anne, c. 1951; 50 l. Queen Elizabeth, c. 1960; 65 l. Wedding photograph, 1947.

212 *Russula cyanoxantha*

213 Golden Pheasant Panchax

(Des L. Nelson. Litho Questa)

1988 (29 Feb). *Fungi. T 212 and similar vert designs. Multicoloured. P 14.*

1121	3 l.	Type **212**	45	30
1122	10 l.	*Lycoperdon perlatum*	1·10	70
1123	20 l.	*Lactarius deliciosus*	1·90	2·00
1124	30 l.	*Boletus edulis*	2·25	2·75
1121/4		*Set of 4*	5·25	5·25
MS1125		100 × 70 mm. 65 l. *Amanita muscaria*	4·75	4·75

(Des Mary Walters. Litho Format)

1988 (13 Apr). *Fishes of Sierra Leone. T 213 and similar horiz designs. Multicoloured. P 15.*

1126	3 l.	Type **213**	15	15
1127	10 l.	Banded Panchax	30	30
1128	20 l.	Jewel Cichlid	50	75
1129	35 l.	Freshwater Butterflyfish	75	1·40
1126/9		*Set of 4*	1·50	2·40
MS1130		99×69 mm. 65 l. Long-finned Tetra	2·50	4·00

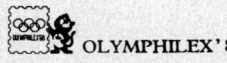

OLYMPHILEX '88

(213a)

1988 (19 Apr). *Stamp Exhibitions. Nos. 1016, 1072 and 1079 optd as T 213a with various emblems.*

1131	25 l.	*Freedom*, 1980 (optd "INDEPEND-ENCE 40, Israel")	1·10	1·40
1132	30 l.	Boris Becker (optd Type 213a)	1·25	1·75
1133	45 l.	Maravedis (coins), *Nina* and Luis de Santangel (financier) (optd "PRAGA 88", Prague)	1·75	2·25
1131/3		*Set of 3*	3·75	4·75

214 Hands holding Coffee Beans and Woman with Cocoa

215 Basketball

(Des L. Lamm. Litho Questa)

1988 (3 May). *International Fund for Agricultural Development. T 214 and similar horiz designs. Multicoloured. P 14.*

1134	3 l.	Type **214**	20	20
1135	15 l.	Tropical fruits and man climbing palm tree	70	80
1136	25 l.	Sheaf of rice and harvesters	1·25	1·50
1134/6		*Set of 3*	1·90	2·25

(Des L. Fried. Litho Questa)

1988 (15 June). *Olympic Games, Seoul (2nd issue). T 215 and similar vert designs. Multicoloured. P 14.*

1137	3 l.	Type **215**	10	10
1138	10 l.	Judo	30	35
1139	15 l.	Gymnastics	45	55
1140	40 l.	Synchronized swimming	1·25	1·75
1137/40		*Set of 4*	2·00	2·50
MS1141		73 × 101 mm. 65 l. Sierra Leone athlete	1·90	2·50

216 Swallow-tailed Bee Eater

217 *Aureol* (liner)

(Des L. Nelson. Litho Questa)

1988 (25 June). *Birds. T 216 and similar vert designs. Multicoloured. P 14.*

1142	3 l.	Type **216**	85	75
1143	5 l.	Double-toothed Barbet	1·10	1·00
1144	8 l.	African Golden Oriole	1·40	1·25
1145	10 l.	Red Bishop	1·40	1·25
1146	12 l.	Red-billed Shrike	1·40	1·25
1147	20 l.	European Bee Eater	1·60	1·40
1148	35 l.	Common Gonolek ("Barbary Shrike")	2·25	2·00
1149	40 l.	Western Black-headed Oriole	2·25	2·25
1142/9		*Set of 8*	11·00	10·00
MS1150		Two sheets, each 111 × 82 mm. (a) 65 l. Purple Heron. (b) 65 l. Saddle-bill Stork		
		Set of 2 sheets	3·75	4·50

(Des D. Miller. Litho Questa)

1988 (1 July). *Ships. T 217 and similar horiz designs. Multicoloured. P 14.*

1151	3 l.	Type **217**	60	30
1152	10 l.	*Dunkwa* (freighter)	1·50	80
1153	15 l.	*Melampus* (container ship)	2·00	1·60
1154	30 l.	*Dumbaia* (freighter)	2·75	3·00
1151/4		*Set of 4*	6·25	5·00
MS1155		95 × 95 mm. 65 l. Loading container ship, Freetown	2·25	2·50

(Litho Questa)

1988 (22 Aug). *500th Birth Anniv of Titian (artist). Vert designs as T 186a of Lesotho showing paintings. Multicoloured. P 13½×14.*

1156	1 l.	"The Concert" (detail)	10	10
1157	2 l.	"Philip II of Spain"	15	15
1158	3 l.	"Saint Sebastian" (detail)	20	20
1159	5 l.	"Martyrdom of St. Peter Martyr"	30	30
1160	15 l.	"St. Jerome"	75	85
1161	20 l.	"St. Mark enthroned with Saints"	90	1·10
1162	25 l.	"Portrait of a Young Man"	1·10	1·40
1163	30 l.	"St. Jerome in Penitence"	1·25	1·50
1156/63		*Set of 8*	4·25	5·00
MS1164		Two sheets, each 110 × 95 mm. (a) 50 l. "Self Portrait". (b) 50 l. "Orpheus and Eurydice"		
		Set of 2 sheets	4·00	4·50

218 Sikorsky S-58 Helicopter lowering "Mercury" Capsule to Flight Deck

219 Famine Relief Convoy crossing Desert

(Des W. Hanson. Litho B.D.T.)

1988 (26 Sept). *25th Death Anniv of John F. Kennedy (American statesman). U.S. Space Achievements. T* **218** *and similar horiz designs. Multicoloured. P* 14.

1165	3 l.	Type **218**	65	15
1166	5 l.	*Liberty Bell 7* capsule descending (*vert*)	65	20
1167	15 l.	Launch of first manned American capsule (*vert*)	80	70
1168	40 l.	*Freedom 7* orbiting Earth	1·50	2·00
1165/8		*Set of 4*	3·25	2·75
MS1169		98 × 69 *mm*. 65 l. President Kennedy and quotation	1·90	2·25

(Des J. Genzo. Litho B.D.T.)

1988 (1 Nov). *125th Anniv of International Red Cross. T* **219** *and similar multicoloured designs. P* 14.

1170	3 l.	Type **219**	60	40
1171	10 l.	Rifle and map of Battle of Solferino, 1859	2·00	90
1172	20 l.	World War II hospital ship in Pacific	2·50	2·00
1173	40 l.	Red Cross tent and World War I German biplanes	3·25	3·25
1170/3		*Set of 4*	7·50	6·00
MS1174		100 × 70 *mm*. 65 l. Henri Dunant (founder), Alfred Nobel and Peace Prize scroll (*horiz*)	2·40	3·00

(Des Walt Disney Company. Litho Questa)

1988 (1 Dec). *Christmas.* "*Mickey's Christmas Dance*". *Vert designs as T* **171***a of Lesotho showing Walt Disney cartoon characters. Multicoloured. P* 13½×14.

1175	10 l.	Donald Duck's nephews playing as band	70	80
		a. Sheetlet. Nos. 1175/82	5·00	
1176	10 l.	Clarabelle	70	80
1177	10 l.	Goofy	70	80
1178	10 l.	Scrooge McDuck and Grandma Duck	70	80
1179	10 l.	Donald Duck	70	80
1180	10 l.	Daisy Duck	70	80
1181	10 l.	Minnie Mouse	70	80
1182	10 l.	Mickey Mouse	70	80
1175/82		*Set of 8*	5·00	5·50
MS1183		Two sheets, each 127 × 102 *mm*. (a) 70 l. Mickey Mouse dancing the Charleston. (b) 70 l. Mickey Mouse jiving		
		Set of 2 sheets	6·50	6·50

Nos. 1175/82 were printed together, *se-tenant* as a composite design, in sheetlets of eight.

GRAND SLAM WINNER

220 "Adoration of the Magi" (detail)   (**221**)

(Litho Questa)

1988 (15 Dec). *Christmas. Religious Paintings by Rubens. T* **220** *and similar vert designs. Multicoloured. P* 13½ × 14.

1184	3 l.	Type **220**	15	15
1185	3 l.	60, "Adoration of the Shepherds" (detail)	15	15
1186	5 l.	"Adoration of the Magi" (detail)	25	25
1187	10 l.	"Adoration of the Shepherds" (different detail)	40	40
1188	20 l.	"Virgin and Child surrounded by Flowers"	75	75
1189	40 l.	"St. Gregory the Great and Other Saints" (detail)	1·60	1·75
1190	60 l.	"Adoration of the Magi" (detail)	2·25	2·75
1191	80 l.	"Madonna and Child with Saints" (detail)	2·75	3·25
1184/91		*Set of 8*	7·50	8·50
MS1192		Two sheets, each 76 × 113 *mm*. (a) 100 l. "Virgin and Child enthroned with Saints". (b) 100 l. "St. Gregory the Great and Other Saints"		
		Set of 2 sheets	7·00	9·00

1989 (16 Jan). *Steffi Graf's "Grand Slam" Tennis Victories. No. MS*1076*b optd* "GOLD MEDALIST" (*No. MS*1193*e*) *or with T* **221** (*others*), *each with different inscription on sheet margin, all in gold.*

MS1193	105×75 *mm*. 100 l. Steffi Graf. (a) Optd "AUSTRALIAN OPEN JANUARY 11–24, 1988 GRAF v EVERET". (b) Optd "FRENCH OPEN MAY 23–JUNE 5, 1988 GRAF v ZVEREVA". (c) Optd "WIMBLEDON JUNE 20–JULY 4, 1988 GRAF v NAVRATILOVA". (d) Optd "U.S. OPEN AUGUST 29–SEPTEMBER 11, 1988 GRAF v SABATINI". (e) Optd "SEOUL OLYMPICS 1988 GRAF v SABATINI"	
	Set of 5 sheets	16·00 15·00

Each marginal overprint includes score of match involved. No. **MS**1193a is overprinted "EVERET" in error for "EVERT".

222 Brazil v. Sweden, 1958

223 Decathlon (Gold, C. Schenk, East Germany)

(Des J. McDaniel. Litho B.D.T.)

1989 (28 Apr). *World Cup Football Championship, Italy* (1st issue). *T* **222** *and similar vert designs, each showing action from previous World Cup finals. Multicoloured. P* 14.

1194	3 l.	Type **222**	40	30
1195	6 l.	West Germany v. Hungary, 1954	50	40
1196	8 l.	England v. West Germany, 1966	60	45
1197	10 l.	Argentina v. Netherlands, 1978	70	50
1198	12 l.	Brazil v. Czechoslovakia, 1962	75	75
1199	20 l.	West Germany v. Netherlands, 1974	1·00	1·00
1200	30 l.	Italy v. West Germany, 1982	1·40	1·60
1201	40 l.	Brazil v. Italy, 1970	1·75	1·90
1194/201		*Set of 8*	6·25	6·25
MS1202		Two sheets, each 73×104 *mm*. (a) 100 l. Argentina v. West Germany, 1986. (b) 100 l. Uruguay v. Brazil, 1950		
		Set of 2 sheets	6·75	6·75

See also Nos. 1455/74.

(Des L. Fried. Litho B.D.T.)

1989 (28 Apr). *Olympic Medal Winners, Seoul* (1988). *T* **223** *and similar multicoloured designs. Multicoloured. P* 14.

1203	3 l.	Type **223**	60	30
1204	6 l.	Men's heavyweight judo (Gold, H. Saito, Japan)	70	40
1205	10 l.	Women's cycle road race (Silver, J. Niehaus, West Germany)	1·25	50
1206	15 l.	Men's single sculls (Gold, T. Lange, East Germany)	1·25	80
1207	20 l.	Men's 50 metres freestyle swimming (Gold, M. Biondi, U.S.A.)	1·25	1·00
1208	30 l.	Men's 100 metres (Gold, C. Lewis, U.S.A.)	1·50	1·50
1209	40 l.	Dressage (Gold, West Germany)	1·75	1·75
1210	50 l.	Greco-Roman wrestling (57 kg) (Gold, A. Sike, Hungary)	1·75	1·90
1203/10		*Set of 8*	9·00	7·50
MS1211		Two sheets, each 70×100 *mm*. (a) 100 l. Olympic gold medal. (b) 100 l. Olympic torch and rings		
		Set of 2 sheets	6·75	6·75

224 Map of Union States, Mail Lorry and Post Office

(Des J. Genzo. Litho B.D.T.)

1989 (19 May). *15th Anniv of Mano River Union. T* **224** *and similar horiz designs. Multicoloured. P* 14.

1212	1 l.	Type **224**	50	30
12..3	3 l.	Map of West Africa and Presidents Momoh, Conte and Doe	90	30
1214	10 l.	Construction of Freetown–Monrovia Highway	1·40	80
1212/14		*Set of 3*	2·50	1·25
MS1215		96×68 *mm*. 15 l. Presidents signing anniversary meeting communique	1·00	1·00

225 *Richard III*

226 Centenary Logo

(Des G. Vasarhelyi. Litho B.D.T.)

1989 (30 May). *425th Birth Anniv of Shakespeare. T* **225** *and similar horiz designs. Multicoloured. P* 13.

1216	15 l.	Type **225**	60	60
		a. Sheetlet. Nos. 1216/23	4·25	
1217	15 l.	*Othello* (Iago)	60	60
1218	15 l.	*Two Gentlemen of Verona*	60	60
1219	15 l.	*Macbeth* (Lady Macbeth)	60	60
1220	15 l.	*Hamlet*	60	60
1221	15 l.	*The Taming of the Shrew*	60	60
1222	15 l.	*The Merry Wives of Windsor*	60	60
1223	15 l.	*Henry IV* (Sir John Falstaff)	60	60
1224	15 l.	*Macbeth* (The Witches)	60	60
		a. Sheetlet. Nos. 1224/31	4·25	

1225	15 l.	*Romeo and Juliet*	60	60
1226	15 l.	*Merchant of Venice*	60	60
1227	15 l.	*As You Like It*	60	60
1228	15 l.	*The Taming of the Shrew* (banquet scene)	60	60
1229	15 l.	*King Lear*	60	60
1230	15 l.	*Othello* (Othello and Desdemona)	60	60
1231	15 l.	*Henry IV* (Justice Shallow)	60	60
1216/31		*Set of 16*	8·50	8·50
MS1232		Two sheets, each 117×82 *mm*. (a) 100 l. Shakespeare and arms (49×36 *mm*). (b) 100 l. Shakespeare (49×36 *mm*)		
		Set of 2 sheets	8·00	8·50

Nos. 1216/23 and 1224/31 were each printed together, *se-tenant*, in sheetlets of eight stamps and one central stamp-size label.

(Litho Questa)

1989 (8 June). *Centenary of Ahmadiyya Muslim Society. P* 14.

1233	**226**	3 l. brownish black and new blue	30	30

(Litho Questa)

1989 (3 July). *Japanese Art* (1st series). *Paintings by Seiho. Multicoloured designs as T* **187***a of Lesotho. P* 14×13½ (3, 10, 12, 40 l.) *or* 13½×14 (*others*).

1234	3 l.	"Lapping Waves"	35	35
1235	6 l.	"Hazy Moon" (*vert*)	45	45
1236	8 l.	"Passing Spring" (*vert*)	45	45
1237	10 l.	"Mackerels"	45	45
1238	12 l.	"Calico Cat"	45	45
1239	30 l.	"The First Time to be a Model" (*vert*)	1·00	80
1240	40 l.	"Kingly Lion"	1·25	1·10
1241	75 l.	"After a Shower" (*vert*)	2·00	1·75
1234/41		*Set of 8*	5·75	5·25
MS1242		Two sheets, each 102×77 *mm*. (a) 150 l. "Dozing in the midst of all the Chirping" (detail) (*vert*). P 13½×14. (b) 150 l. "Domesticated Monkeys and Rabbits" (detail). P 14×13½		
		Set of 2 sheets	8·50	8·50

Nos. 1234/41 were each printed in sheetlets of 10 containing two horizontal or vertical strips of 5 stamps separated by printed labels commemorating Emperor Hirohito.

See also Nos. 1321/51.

227 Robespierre and Bastille

(Des Design Element. Litho B.D.T.)

1989 (13 July). "*Philexfrance 89*" *International Stamp Exhibition, Paris, and Bicentenary of French Revolution. T* **227** *and similar multicoloured designs. P* 14.

1243	6 l.	Type **227**	45	35
1244	20 l.	Danton and Louvre	90	80
1245	45 l.	Queen Marie Antoinette and Notre Dame	1·40	1·25
1246	80 l.	Louis XVI and Palace of Versailles	2·00	2·75
1243/6		*Set of 4*	4·25	4·75
MS1247		77×107 *mm*. 150 l. Celebrating crowd, Paris (*vert*)	3·25	4·00

228 "Sputnik" Satellite in Orbit, 1957   **229** *Bulbophyllum barbigerum*

(Des G. Vasarhelyi. Litho B.D.T.)

1989 (20 July). *History of Space Exploration. T* **228** *and similar horiz designs. P* 14.

1248/301	10 l.×27, 15 l.×27 multicoloured		
		Set of 54	22·00 23·00
MS1302	Three sheets, each 112×90 *mm*. 100 l. ×3 multicoloured		
		Set of 3 sheets	12·00 13·00

Nos. 1248/301 were issued as six sheetlets, each of nine different designs.

(Des W. Hanson Studio. Litho B.D.T.)

1989 (8 Sept). *Orchids of Sierra Leone. T* **229** *and similar vert designs. Multicoloured. P* 14.

1303	3 l.	Type **229**	55	40
1304	6 l.	*Bulbophyllum falcatum*	85	60
1305	12 l.	*Habenaria macrara*	1·25	90
1306	20 l.	*Eurychone rothchildiana*	1·60	1·40
1307	50 l.	*Calyptrochilum christyanum*	2·25	2·25
1308	60 l.	*Bulbophyllum distans*	2·50	2·75
1309	70 l.	*Eulophia guineensis*	2·50	2·75
1310	80 l.	*Diaphananthe pellucida*	2·75	3·25
1303/10		*Set of 8*	13·00	13·00
MS1311		Two sheets, each 112×80 *mm*. (a) 100 l. *Cyrtorchis arcuata* and Pagoda, Kew Gardens. (b) 100 l. *Eulophia cucullata*		
		Set of 2 sheets	15·00	14·00

230 Salamis temora

(Des Mary Walters. Litho B.D.T.)

1989 (11 Sept). *Butterflies.* T **230** *and similar multicoloured designs.* P 14.

1312	6 l.	Type 230		85	75
1313	12 l.	*Pseudacraea lucretia*		1·25	1·10
1314	18 l.	*Charaxes boueti* (vert)		1·60	1·40
1315	30 l.	*Graphium antheus* (vert)		2·25	2·00
1316	40 l.	*Colotis protomedia*		2·50	2·25
1317	60 l.	*Asterope pechueli* (vert)		3·00	2·75
1318	72 l.	*Coenyra aurantiaca*		3·25	3·00
1319	80 l.	*Precis octavia* (vert)		3·25	3·00
1312/19			*Set of 8*	16·00	14·50

MS1320 Two sheets, each 100×70 mm. (a) 100 l. *Charaxes cithaeron* (vert). (b) 100 l. *Euphaedra themis* .. .. .. *Set of 2 sheets* 14·00 14·00

(Litho Questa)

1989 (13 Nov). *Japanese Art (2nd series). Paintings by Hiroshige of "The Fifty-three Stations on the Tokaido Road". Horiz designs as* T **187a** *of Lesotho. Multicoloured.* P 14×13½.

1321	25 l.	"Ferry-boat to Kawasaki"		80	80
1322	25 l.	"The Hilly Town of Hodogaya"		80	80
1323	25 l.	"Lute Players at Fujisawa"		80	80
1324	25 l.	"Mild Rainstorm at Oiso"		80	80
1325	25 l.	"Lake Ashi and Mountains of Hakone"		80	80
1326	25 l.	"Twilight at Numazu"		80	80
1327	25 l.	"Mount Fuji from Hara"		80	80
1328	25 l.	"Samurai Children riding through Yoshiwara"		80	80
1329	25 l.	"Mountain Pass at Yui"		80	80
1330	25 l.	"Harbour at Ejiri"		80	80
1331	25 l.	"Halt at Fujieda"		80	80
1332	25 l.	"Misty Kanaya on the Oi River"		80	80
1333	25 l.	"The Bridge to Kakegawa"		80	80
1334	25 l.	"Teahouse at Fukuroi"		80	80
1335	25 l.	"The Ford at Mistuke"		80	80
1336	25 l.	"Coolies warming themselves at Hamamatsu"		80	80
1337	25 l.	"Imakiri Ford at Maisaka"		80	80
1338	25 l.	"Pacific Ocean from Shirasuka"		80	80
1339	25 l.	"Futakawa Street-singers"		80	80
1340	25 l.	"Repairing Yoshida Castle"		80	80
1341	25 l.	"The Inn at Akasaka"		80	80
1342	25 l.	"The Bridge to Okazaki"		80	80
1343	25 l.	"Samurai's Wife entering Narumi"		80	80
1344	25 l.	"Harbour at Kuwana"		80	80
1345	25 l.	"Autumn in Ishiyakushi"		80	80
1346	25 l.	"Snowfall at Kameyama"		80	80
1347	25 l.	"The Frontier-station of Seki"		80	80
1348	25 l.	"Teahouse at Sakanoshita"		80	80
1349	25 l.	"Kansai Houses at Minakushi"		80	80
1350	25 l.	"Kusatsu Station"		80	80
1321/50			*Set of 30*	22·00	22·00

MS1351 Two sheets, each 102×75 mm. (a) 120 l. "Nihom Bridge, Edo". (b) 120 l. "Sanjo Bridge, Kyoto" .. .. *Set of 2 sheets* 8·00 8·50

The English captions of the two miniature sheets of No. **MS**1351 are transposed. The sheet showing the Nihom Bridge, Edo, has a group of fishmongers in the left foreground.

(Des Design Element. Litho Questa)

1989 (17 Nov). *"World Stamp Expo '89" International Stamp Exhibition, Washington (1st issue). Landmarks of Washington. Sheet 78×61 mm containing horiz design as* T **193a** *of Lesotho. Multicoloured.* P 14.

MS1352 100 l. Jefferson Memorial .. .. 1·00 1·50

231 Formosan Sika Deer

(Des J. Genzo. Litho B.D.T.)

1989 (29 Nov). *"World Stamp Expo '89" International Stamp Exhibition, Washington (2nd issue). Endangered Fauna.* T **231** *and similar multicoloured designs.* P 14.

1353	6 l.	Humpback Whale		50	40
1354	9 l.	Type 231		40	40
1355	16 l.	Spanish Lynx		65	60
1356	20 l.	Goitred Gazelle		60	60
1357	30 l.	Japanese Sea Lion		65	65
1358	50 l.	Long-eared Owl		1·50	1·25
1359	70 l.	Lady Amherst's ("Chinese Copper") Pheasant		1·50	1·50
1360	100 l.	Siberian Tiger		2·25	2·50
1353/60			*Set of 8*	7·25	7·25

MS1361 Two sheets, each 103×75 mm. (a) 150 l. Mauritius Kestrel (vert). (b) 150 l. Japanese Crested Ibis .. .. *Set of 2 sheets* 9·00 10·00

(Des Walt Disney Co. Litho Questa)

1989 (18 Dec). *Christmas. Horiz designs as* T **73** *of St. Vincent Grenadines showing Walt Disney cartoon characters with cars. Multicoloured.* P 14×13½.

1362	3 l.	Mickey Mouse and Goofy in Rolls-Royce "Phantom II Roadstar", 1934		55	30
1363	6 l.	Mickey and Minnie Mouse in Mercedes-Benz "500K", 1935		70	40
1364	10 l.	Mickey and Minnie Mouse with Jaguar "SS-100", 1938		80	45

1365	12 l.	Mickey Mouse and Goofy with U.S. army jeep, 1941		90	55
1366	20 l.	Mickey and Minnie Mouse with Buick Roadmaster Sedan "Model 91", 1937		1·25	90
1367	30 l.	Mickey Mouse driving 1948 Tucker		1·50	1·25
1368	40 l.	Mickey and Minnie Mouse in Alfa Romeo, 1933		1·60	1·40
1369	50 l.	Mickey and Minnie Mouse with 1937 Cord		1·75	1·60
1362/9			*Set of 8*	8·25	6·00

MS1370 Two sheets, each 127×101 mm. (a) 100 l. Mickey in Fiat Topolino, 1938. (b) 100 l. Mickey Mouse with gifts and Pontiac "Model 401", 1931 .. .. *Set of 2 sheets* 6·50 7·00

(Litho Questa)

1989 (22 Dec). *Christmas. Paintings by Rembrandt. Vert designs as* T **193b** *of Lesotho. Multicoloured.* P 14.

1371	3 l.	"The Adoration of the Magi"		40	30
1372	6 l.	"The Holy Family with a Cat"		50	40
1373	10 l.	"The Holy Family with Angels"		60	45
1374	15 l.	"Simeon in the Temple"		75	55
1375	30 l.	"The Circumcision"		1·25	1·10
1376	90 l.	"The Holy Family"		2·25	2·50
1377	100 l.	"The Visitation"		2·25	2·50
1378	120 l.	"The Flight into Egypt"		2·25	2·75
1371/8			*Set of 8*	9·50	9·50

MS1379 Two sheets, each 70×95 mm. (a) 150 l. "The Adoration of the Shepherds" (detail). (b) 150 l. "The Presentation of Jesus in the Temple" (detail) .. .. *Set of 2 sheets* 5·00 6·00

232 Johann Kepler (astronomer)   **232a** Dolittle's North American B-25 Mitchell *Ruptured Duck,* 1942

(Des G. Vasarhelyi. Litho Questa)

1990 (15 Jan). *Exploration of Mars.* T **232** *and similar horiz designs showing astronomers, spacecraft and Martian landscapes.* P 14.

1380/1415 175 l. × 36 multicoloured .. *Set of 36* 60·00 70·00

MS1416 Two sheets, each 105×85 mm. (a) 150 l. The "Face" on Mars. (b) 150 l. Section of space station .. .. .. *Set of 2 sheets* 8·00 8·50

Nos. 1380/1415 were issued as four sheetlets each of nine different designs.

(Des J. Batchelor. Litho Questa)

1990 (5 Feb). *50th Anniv of Second World War. American Aircraft.* T **232a** *and similar horiz designs. Multicoloured.* P 14.

1417	1 l.	Type 232a		30	10
1418	2 l.	Consolidated B-24 Liberator		40	10
1419	3 l.	Douglas A20J Boston attacking Japanese convoy, Bismark Sea, 1943		40	10
1420	9 l.	Lockheed P-38 Lightning		60	35
1421	15 l.	Martin B-26 Marauder		75	40
1422	16 l.	Two Boeing B-17F Flying Fortress bombers		85	55
1423	50 l.	North American B-25D Mitchell bomber		2·00	1·75
1424	80 l.	Boeing B-29 Superfortress		2·25	2·50
1425	90 l.	Boeing B-17G Flying Fortress bomber		2·25	2·50
1426	100 l.	Boeing B-29 Superfortress *Enola Gay*		2·50	2·75
1417/26			*Set of 10*	11·00	10·00

MS1427 Two sheets, each 106×77 mm. (a) 150 l. North American B-25 Mitchell *Ruptured Duck* taking off from U.S.S. *Hornet,* 1942. (b) 150 l. Boeing B-17G Flying Fortress of 447th Bomber Group .. .. *Set of 2 sheets* 6·50 7·00

233 Mickey Mouse at Bauxite Mine   **234** Olivier as Antony in *Antony and Cleopatra,* 1951

(Des Walt Disney Co. Litho Questa)

1990 (23 Apr). *Sierra Leone Sites and Scenes.* T **233** *and similar multicoloured designs, each showing Walt Disney cartoon characters.* P 14×13½.

1428	3 l.	Type 233		20	15
1429	6 l.	Scrooge McDuck panning for gold		20	15
1430	10 l.	Minnie Mouse at Lungi Airport		25	20
1431	12 l.	Mickey Mouse at Old Fourah Bay College		35	20
1432	16 l.	Mickey Mouse mining bauxite		45	25
1433	20 l.	Huey, Dewey and Louie harvesting rice		50	30
1434	30 l.	Mickey and Minnie Mouse admire the Freetown Cotton Tree		60	40
1435	100 l.	Mickey Mouse flying over Rutile Mine		2·25	2·25

1436	200 l.	Mickey Mouse fishing at Goderich		3·00	3·75
1437	225 l.	Mickey and Minnie Mouse at Bintumani Hotel		3·00	3·75
1428/37			*Set of 10*	9·75	10·00

MS1438 Two sheets, each 130×100 mm. (a) 250 l. Dwarfs with diamonds. P 14×13½. (b) 250 l. Mickey and Minnie Mouse at King Jimmy Market (vert). P 13½×14 .. *Set of 2 sheets* 7·00 7·50

(Des J. Iskowitz. Litho Questa)

1990 (27 Apr). *Sir Laurence Olivier (actor) Commemoration.* T **234** *and similar vert designs. Multicoloured.* P 14.

1439	3 l.	Type 234		30	20
1440	9 l.	As King Henry V in *Henry V,* 1943		40	30
1441	16 l.	As Oedipus in *Oedipus,* 1945		55	35
1442	20 l.	As Heathcliffe in *Wuthering Heights,* 1939		60	40
1443	30 l.	As Szell in *Marathon Man,* 1976		70	55
1444	70 l.	As Othello in *Othello,* 1964		1·25	1·40
1445	175 l.	As Michael in *Beau Geste,* 1929		2·25	2·50
1446	200 l.	As King Richard III in *Richard III,* 1956		2·50	2·75
1439/46			*Set of 8*	7·75	7·75

MS1447 Two sheets, each 98×68 mm. (a) 250 l. As Hamlet in *Hamlet,* 1947. (b) 250 l. As Sir Hugh Dowding in *The Battle of Britain,* 1969 .. .. .. *Set of 2 sheets* 7·50 8·00

235 Penny Black   **236** Cameroons World Cup Team

(Des M. Pollard. Litho Questa)

1990 (3 May). *150th Anniv of the Penny Black.* P 14×13½.

1448	235	50 l. deep ultramarine		1·75	1·50
1449		100 l. purple-brown		2·50	2·75
MS1450		145×96 mm. 235 250 l. black		4·00	4·50

(Des Young Phillips Studio. Litho Questa)

1990 (11 May). *World Cup Football Championship, Italy (2nd issue). Finalists.* T **236** *and similar horiz designs. Multicoloured.* P 14×13½.

1451/74 15 l. × 8 (Type 236, Colombia, Costa Rica, Egypt, Rumania, South Korea, U.A.E., Yugoslavia), 30 l. × 8 (Austria, Belgium, Czechoslovakia, Netherlands, Scotland, Sweden, Uruguay, U.S.S.R.), 45 l. × 8 (Argentina, Brazil, England, Ireland, Italy, Spain, U.S.A., West Germany) .. .. *Set of 24* 14·00 15·00

No. 1452 is inscribed "COLUMBIA" in error, as are the margins of each sheetlet.

Each design of Nos. 1451/74 was issued in separate sheetlets of 8 stamps with a central label showing the World Cup and Championship logo.

237 Great Crested Grebe

(Des Mary Walters. Litho Questa)

1990 (4 June). *Birds.* T **237** *and similar horiz designs. Multicoloured.* P 14.

1475	3 l.	Type 237		20	20
1476	6 l.	Green Wood Hoopoe		25	25
1477	10 l.	African Jacana		30	30
1478	12 l.	Avocet		35	35
1479	20 l.	Peters's Finfoot		40	40
1480	80 l.	Glossy Ibis		1·25	1·50
1481	150 l.	Hammerkop		1·75	2·00
1482	200 l.	Black-throated Honeyguide		2·00	2·50
1475/82			*Set of 8*	6·00	6·75

MS1483 Two sheets, each 100×70 mm. (a) 250 l. African Palm Swift. (b) 250 l. Painted Snipe .. .. .. *Set of 2 sheets* 7·00 8·00

(Des Walt Disney Co. Litho Questa)

1990 (6 June). *"Stamp World London 90" International Stamp Exhibition. British Costumes. Multicoloured designs as* T **239a** *of Maldive Islands showing Walt Disney cartoon characters.* P 13½×14.

1484	3 l.	Mickey Mouse as a Yeoman Warder (vert)		15	15
1485	6 l.	Scrooge McDuck as a lamplighter (vert)		15	15
1486	12 l.	Goofy as a medieval knight (vert)		20	20
1487	15 l.	Clarabelle as Anne Boleyn (vert)		20	20
1488	75 l.	Minnie Mouse as Queen Elizabeth I (vert)		2·00	2·00
1489	100 l.	Donald Duck as a chimney sweep (vert)		2·25	2·25
1490	125 l.	Pete as King Henry VIII (vert)		2·50	2·50
1491	150 l.	Clarabelle, Minnie Mouse and Daisy Duck as May dancers (vert)		2·50	2·50
1484/91			*Set of 8*	9·00	9·00

MS1492 Two sheets, each 127×102 mm. (a) 250 l. Donald Duck as a lawyer (vert). P 13½×14. (b) 250 l. Minnie Mouse as Queen Boadicea. P 14×13½ .. *Set of 2 sheets* 7·50 8·50

(Des Young Phillips Studio. Litho Questa)

1990 (5 July). *90th Birthday of Queen Elizabeth the Queen Mother. Vert designs as T 198a of Lesotho showing portraits, 1980–89. Multicoloured. P 14.*
1493	75 l.	Queen Mother on Remembrance Sunday	85 1·00
	a. Strip of 3. Nos. 1493/5		2·25
1494	75 l.	Queen Mother in yellow hat	85 1·00
1495	75 l.	Waving to crowds on 85th birthday	85 1·00
1493/5		*Set of 3*	2·25 2·75

MS1496 90×75 mm. 250 l. As No. 1495 .. 2·50 2·75
Nos. 1493/5 were printed together, horizontally and vertically *se-tenant*, in sheetlets of 9 (3×3).
Nos. 1493/6 exist imperforate from a limited printing.

238 Golden Cat   239 Rabbit

(Des S. Barlowe. Litho Questa)

1990 (24 Sept). *Wildlife. T 238 and similar multicoloured designs. P 14.*
1497	25 l.	Type 238	65 65
	a. Sheetlet. Nos. 1497/1514		10·00
1498	25 l.	White-backed Night Heron	65 65
1499	25 l.	Bateleur	65 65
1500	25 l.	Marabou Stork	65 65
1501	25 l.	White-faced Whistling Duck	65 65
1502	25 l.	Aardvark	65 65
1503	25 l.	Royal Antelope	65 65
1504	25 l.	Pygmy Hippopotamus	65 65
1505	25 l.	Leopard	65 65
1506	25 l.	Sacred Ibis	65 65
1507	25 l.	Mona Monkey	65 65
1508	25 l.	African Darter	65 65
1509	25 l.	Chimpanzee	65 65
1510	25 l.	African Elephant	65 65
1511	25 l.	Potto	65 65
1512	25 l.	African Manatee	65 65
1513	25 l.	African Fish Eagle	65 65
1514	25 l.	African Spoonbill	65 65
1497/1514		*Set of 18*	10·00 10·00

MS1515 106×76 mm. 150 l. Crowned Eagle (*vert*) .. .. .. 6·00 6·50
Nos. 1497/1514 were printed together, *se-tenant*, in sheetlets of 18 with the background forming a map of Sierra Leone.
Nos. 1497/1515 exist imperforate from a limited printing.

(Litho Questa)

1990 (22 Oct). *Fairground Carousel Animals. T 239 and similar vert designs. Multicoloured. P 14.*
1516	5 l.	Type 239	15 15
1517	10 l.	Horse with panther saddle	20 20
1518	20 l.	Ostrich	30 30
1519	30 l.	Zebra	40 40
1520	50 l.	Horse	55 55
1521	80 l.	Sea monster	80 80
1522	100 l.	Giraffe	1·00 1·00
1523	150 l.	Armoured horse	1·40 1·40
1524	200 l.	Camel	1·75 1·75
1516/24		*Set of 9*	6·00 6·00

MS1525 Two sheets (a) 98×68 mm. 300 l. Masked horse. (b) 68×98 mm. 300 l. Baden-Powell as Centaur .. *Set of 2 sheets* 7·50 8·50
Nos. 1516/25 exist imperforate from a limited printing.

(Des B. Grout. Litho B.D.T.)

1990 (12 Nov). *Olympic Games, Barcelona (1992). Multicoloured designs as T 202 of Lesotho. P 14.*
1526	5 l.	Start of Men's 100 metres	20 15
1527	10 l.	Men's 4×400 metres relay	25 20
1528	20 l.	Men's 100 metres in progress	40 30
1529	30 l.	Weightlifting	50 40
1530	40 l.	Freestyle wrestling	55 45
1531	80 l.	Water polo	80 90
1532	150 l.	Women's gymnastics	1·40 1·50
1533	200 l.	Cycling	2·75 2·25
1526/33		*Set of 8*	6·25 5·50

MS1534 Two sheets, each 103×75 mm. (a) 400 l. Boxing (*horiz*). (b) 400 l. Olympic flag (*horiz*)
.. .. .. *Set of 2 sheets* 7·50 8·50
Nos. 1526/34 exist imperforate from a limited printing.

240 Morty assembling Bicycle by Christmas Tree

241 "Holy Family with St. Elizabeth" (Mantegna)

(Des Walt Disney Co. Litho B.D.T.)

1990 (17 Dec). *Christmas. "The Night before Christmas". T 240 and similar designs showing Walt Disney cartoon characters in scenes from Clement Moore's poem. P 13.*
1535/58 50 l. × 8, 75 l. × 8, 100 l. × 8 *Set of 24* 16·00 18·00
MS1559 Six sheets, each 129×107 mm. 400 l. × 6 multicoloured .. *Set of 6 sheets* 16·00 18·00
Nos. 1535/58 were issued as three sheetlets of eight, each containing stamps of the same face value *se-tenant*.
Of the stamps in No. **MS**1559 four horizontal and two vertical.

(Litho Cartor)

1990 (17 Dec). *Christmas. Paintings. T 241 and similar vert designs. Multicoloured. P 13.*
1560	10 l.	"Holy Family resting" (Rembrandt)	25 15
1561	20 l.	Type 241	35 20
1562	30 l.	"Virgin and Child with an Angel" (Correggio)	45 30
1563	50 l.	"Annunciation" (Bernardo Strozzi)	70 45
1564	100 l.	"Madonna and Child appearing to St. Anthony" (Lippi)	1·25 80
1565	175 l.	"Virgin and Child" (Giovanni Boltraffio)	2·25 2·50
1566	200 l.	"Esterhazy Madonna" (Raphael)	2·50 2·50
1567	300 l.	"Coronation of Mary" (Andrea Orcagna)	3·00 3·25
1560/7		*Set of 8*	9·50 9·00

MS1568 Two sheets, each 75×114 mm. (a) 400 l. "Adoration of the Shepherds" (Bronzino). (b) 400 l. "Adoration of the Shepherds" (Gerard David) .. .. *Set of 2 sheets* 9·00 9·50

(Litho Questa)

1990 (24 Dec). *350th Death Anniv of Rubens (1st issue). Multicoloured designs as T 250 of Maldive Islands, but vert. P 13½×14.*
1569	5 l.	"Helena Fourment as Hagar in the Wilderness" (detail)	15 10
1570	10 l.	"Isabella Brant"	20 15
1571	20 l.	"Countess of Arundel and her Party" (detail)	30 20
1572	60 l.	"Countess of Arundel and her Party" (different detail)	70 70
1573	80 l.	"Nicolaas Rockox"	90 90
1574	100 l.	"Adriana Perez"	1·00 1·00
1575	150 l.	"George Villiers, Duke of Buckingham" (detail)	1·75 2·00
1576	300 l.	"Countess of Buckingham"	2·50 2·75
1569/76		*Set of 8*	6·75 7·00

MS1577 Two sheets, each 71×100 mm. (a) 350 l. "Giovanni Carlo Dorio" (detail). (b) 350 l. "Veronica Spinola Dorio" (detail) *Set of 2 sheets* 8·00 8·50
See also Nos. 1595/603.

242 *Chlorophyllum molybdites*

243 "The Flight of St. Barbara" (detail) (Rubens)

(Des Mary Walters. Litho Questa)

1990 (31 Dec). *Fungi. T 242 and similar vert designs. Multicoloured. P 14.*
1578	3 l.	Type 242	30 15
1579	5 l.	*Lepista nuda*	30 15
1580	10 l.	*Clitocybe nebularis*	40 20
1581	15 l.	*Cyathus striatus*	50 30
1582	20 l.	*Bolbitius vitellinus*	55 35
1583	25 l.	*Leucoagaricus naucinus*	55 40
1584	30 l.	*Suillus luteus*	60 45
1585	40 l.	*Podaxis pistillaris*	70 55
1586	50 l.	*Oudemansiella radicata*	80 60
1587	60 l.	*Phallus indusiatus*	90 70
1588	80 l.	*Macrolepiota rhacodes*	1·00 1·10
1589	100 l.	*Mycena pura*	1·25 1·25
1590	150 l.	*Volvariella volvacea*	1·60 1·75
1591	175 l.	*Omphalotus olearius*	1·90 2·25
1592	200 l.	*Sphaerobolus stellatus*	2·00 2·50
1593	250 l.	*Schizophyllum commune*	2·25 2·75
1578/93		*Set of 16*	14·00 14·00

MS1594 Four sheets, each 101×70 mm. (a) 350 l. *Hypholoma fasciculare*. (b) 350 l. *Psilocybe coprophila*. (c) 350 l. *Agaricus campestris*. (d) 350 l. *Suillus granulatus* .. *Set of 4 sheets* 15·00 15·00

(Litho Questa)

1991 (8 Apr). *Easter. 350th Death Anniv of Rubens (1990) (2nd issue). T 243 and similar vert designs. Multicoloured. P 13½×14.*
1595	10 l.	Type 243	30 15
1596	20 l.	"The Last Judgement" (detail)	40 20
1597	30 l.	"St. Gregory of Nazianzus"	50 30
1598	50 l.	"Doubting Thomas"	65 45
1599	80 l.	"The Way to Calvary" (detail)	1·10 1·10
1600	100 l.	"St. Gregory with Sts. Domitilla, Maurus and Papianus"	1·25 1·25
1601	175 l.	"Sts. Gregory, Maurus and Papianus"	2·00 2·25
1602	300 l.	"Christ and the Penitent Sinners"	3·25 4·00
1595/1602		*Set of 8*	8·50 8·75

MS1603 Two sheets, each 70×101 mm. (a) 400 l. "The Last Judgement" (different detail). (b) 400 l. "The Way to Calvary" (different detail)
.. .. .. *Set of 2 sheets* 8·50 9·00

244 Krauss Class 1400 Steam Locomotive, 1895

(Des K. Gromell. Litho Questa)

1991 (13 May). *"Phila Nippon '91" International Stamp Exhibition, Tokyo. Japanese Trains. T 244 and similar horiz designs. Each multicoloured (Nos. 1604/11) or black and rosine (No. MS1612). P 14.*
1604	10 l.	Type 244	35 20
1605	20 l.	Class C55 streamline steam locomotive, 1935	50 25
1606	30 l.	Class ED17 electric locomotive, 1931	70 40
1607	60 l.	Class EF13 electric locomotive, 1944	1·00 85
1608	100 l.	Baldwin Mikado steam locomotive, 1897	1·25 1·25
1609	150 l.	Class C62 steam locomotive, 1948	1·75 2·00
1610	200 l.	Class Kiha 81 diesel multiple unit, 1960	2·00 2·25
1611	300 l.	Schenectady Class 8550 steam locomotive, 1899	2·25 2·75
1604/11		*Set of 8*	9·00 9·00

MS1612 Four sheets, each 106×76 mm. (a) 400 l. Class 9600 steam locomotive, 1913. (b) 400 l. Class D51 steam locomotive, 1936. (c) 400 l. Class 7000 electric multiple unit. (d) 400 l. "Hikari" express train
.. .. .. *Set of 4 sheets* 15·00 15·00

245 Turquoise Killifish

(Des W. Hanson Studio. Litho Questa)

1991 (3 June). *Fishes. T 245 and similar horiz designs. Multicoloured. P 14.*
1613	10 l.	Type 245	45 20
1614	20 l.	Red-chinned Panchax	65 25
1615	30 l.	Peters' Killifish	80 40
1616	60 l.	Micro-walkeri Killifish	1·40 90
1617	100 l.	Freshwater Butterflyfish	1·60 1·25
1618	150 l.	Green Panchax	2·00 2·25
1619	200 l.	Six-banded Lyretail	2·25 2·50
1620	300 l.	Nile Pufferfish	2·25 2·50
1613/20		*Set of 8*	10·00 9·00

MS1621 Two sheets, each 96×70 mm. (a) 400 l. Spot-finned Squeaker. (b) 400 l. Two-striped Panchax .. *Set of 2 sheets* 8·50 8·50
Nos. 1613/21 exist imperforate from a limited printing.

(Litho Walsall)

1991 (28 June). *Death Centenary of Vincent van Gogh (artist). Multicoloured designs as T 255 of Maldive Islands. P 13½.*
1622	10 c.	"The Langlois Bridge at Arles" (*horiz*)	10 10
1623	50 c.	"Tree in Garden at Saint-Paul Hospital"	10 10
1624	1 l.	"Wild Flowers and Thistles in a Vase"	10 10
1625	2 l.	"Still Life: Vase with Oleanders and Books" (*horiz*)	10 10
1626	5 l.	"Farmhouses in a Wheatfield near Arles" (*horiz*)	15 10
1627	10 l.	"Self-portrait, September 1889"	25 15
1628	20 l.	"Patience Escalier"	35 20
1629	30 l.	"Doctor Félix Rey"	45 30
1630	50 l.	"The Iris"	70 45
1631	60 l.	"The Shepherdess"	80 65
1632	80 l.	"Vincent's House in Arles" (*horiz*)	1·00 1·00
1633	100 l.	"The Road Menders" (*horiz*)	1·10 1·10
1634	150 l.	"The Garden of Saint-Paul Hospital"	1·75 2·00
1635	200 l.	"View of the Church, Saint-Paul-de-Mausole" (*horiz*)	2·00 2·25
1636	250 l.	"Seascape at Saintes-Maries" (*horiz*)	2·25 2·50
1637	300 l.	"Pietà"	2·25 2·50
1622/37		*Set of 16*	12·00 12·00

MS1638 Six sheets. (a) 102×76 mm. 400 l. "Haystacks in Provence" (96×70 *mm*). (b) 102×76 mm. 400 l. "The Trinquetaille Bridge" (96×70 *mm*). (c) 102×76 mm. 400 l. "Vineyards with a View of Auvers" (96×70 *mm*). (d) 102×76 mm. 400 l. "The Garden of Saint-Paul Hospital" (96×107 *mm*). (e) 76×102 mm. 400 l. "Church at Auvers-sur-Dise" (70×96 *mm*). (f) 76×102 mm. 400 l. "Two Poplars on a Road through the Hills" (70×96 *mm*). Imperf .. *Set of 6 sheets* 16·00 16·00
Nos. 1622/38 exist imperforate from a limited printing.

(Des D. Miller. Litho Walsall)

1991 (5 July). *65th Birthday of Queen Elizabeth II. Horiz designs as T 210 of Lesotho. Multicoloured. P 14.*
1639	10 l.	The Queen and Prince Charles at polo match	10 10
1640	30 l.	The Queen at Windsor, 1989	20 20
1641	200 l.	The Queen and Princess Diana in Nigeria, 1989	1·75 2·00
1642	250 l.	The Queen and Prince Philip	2·00 2·25
1639/42		*Set of 4*	3·75 4·00

MS1643 68×90 mm. 400 l. Separate photographs of the Queen and Prince Philip in 1987 and 1988 3·50 3·75
Nos. 1639/43 exist imperforate from a limited printing.

(Des D. Miller. Litho Walsall)

1991 (5 July). *10th Wedding Anniv of Prince and Princess of Wales. Horiz designs as T **210** of Lesotho. Multicoloured. P 14.*
1644	20 l.	Prince and Princess of Wales in August 1987	40	15
1645	80 l.	Separate photographs of Prince, Princess and sons	1·00	85
1646	100 l.	Prince Henry in Majorca and Prince William on his first day at school	1·00	95
1647	300 l.	Prince Charles at Caister, April 1988, and Princess Diana in Hyde Park, May 1989	3·00	3·25
1644/7		*Set of 4*	4·75	4·75

MS1648 68×90 mm. 400 l. Prince, Princess and Prince Henry in Majorca and Prince William going to school .. .. 4·25 4·50

Nos. 1644/8 exist imperforate from a limited printing.

246 *Graphium latreillianus and Ancistrochilus rothschildianus*

(Des I. Maclaury. Litho Cartor)

1991 (5 Aug). *Butterflies and Flowers. T **246** and similar horiz designs. Multicoloured. P 14×13½.*
1649	10 l.	Type **246**	65	30
1650	30 l.	*Euphraedra eleus* and *Clitoria ternatea*	1·00	45
1651	50 l.	*Graphium antheus* and *Gloriosa simplex*	1·25	60
1652	60 l.	*Salamis cacta* and *Stenandriopsis guineensis*	1·40	85
1653	80 l.	*Kallima rumia* and *Cassia fistula* ..	1·75	1·25
1654	100 l.	*Hypolimnas salmacis* and *Amorphophallus abyssinicus*	2·00	1·50
1655	200 l.	*Danaus formosa* and *Nephthytis afzelii*	3·00	3·25
1656	300 l.	*Graphium leonidas* and *Clappertonia ficifolia*	3·50	4·00
1649/56		*Set of 8*	13·00	11·00

MS1657 Four sheets, each 102×74 mm. (a) 400 l. *Charaxes cynthia* and *Plumbago auriculata.* (b) 400 l. *Colias electo* and *Combretum grandiflorum.* (c) 400 l. *Cynandra opis* and *Bombax costatum.* (d) 400 l. *Eurema brigitta* and *Monodora myristica.* P 13×12 .. *Set of 4 sheets* 14·00 14·00

1991 (Oct). *Butterflies. Designs as Nos. 1028/42, but "Sierra Leone" in blue. Multicoloured. With "1990" imprint date at foot. P 14.*
1658	10 c.	*Danaus limniace*	7·50	40
1660	50 c.	*Graphium ridleyanus*	7·50	30
		a. Perf 12½×11½	1·00	
		b. Perf 12	1·00	
1661	1 l.	*Papilio bromius*	7·50	30
1662	2 l.	*Iterus zalmoxis* ("Papilio zalmoxis")	7·50	30
1663	5 l.	*Graphium tyndereaus*	—	30
1665	10 l.	*Graphium policenes*	7·50	30
1666	20 l.	*Tanuetheira timon* ("Iolaus timon")	—	40
1667	30 l.	*Cymothoe sangaris*	—	50
1668	50 l.	Type **205**	7·50	55
		a. Perf 12½×11½	1·50	
		b. Perf 12	1·75	
1669	60 l.	*Charaxes lucretius* ..	7·50	70
1670	80 l.	*Stugeta marmorea* ("Iolaus marmorea")	14·00	1·00
		a. Perf 12½×11½	1·50	
		b. Perf 12	2·25	
1671	100 l.	*Abisara talantus*	—	1·00
1672	300 l.	*Papilio hesperus*	14·00	2·50
		a. Perf 12½×11½	3·00	
		b. Perf 12	3·00	

Stamps perforated 12½×11½ show a larger hole on every sixth perforation, both vertically and horizontally.

247 Audie Murphy in *To Hell and Back*

248 Meissen China Parrot Ornament, Munich Botanic Garden

(Des R. Jung. Litho Questa)

1991 (14 Oct). *Films of Second World War. T **247** and similar horiz designs. Multicoloured. P 14.*
1675	2 l.	Type **247**	10	10
1676	5 l.	Jack Palance in *Attack*	15	15
1677	10 l.	Greer Garson and Walter Pidgeon in *Mrs. Miniver*	20	20
1678	20 l.	Heavy artillery from *The Guns of Navarone*	30	30
1679	30 l.	Charlie Chaplin and Paulette Goddard in *The Great Dictator*	40	40
1680	50 l.	Steam locomotive from *The Train*	60	60
1681	60 l.	Diary and fountain pen from *The Diary of Anne Frank*	70	70
1682	80 l.	William Holden in *The Bridge on the River Kwai*	90	90

1683	100 l.	Tallulah Bankhead in *Lifeboat* and Alfred Hitchcock (director)	1·00	1·00
1684	200 l.	John Wayne in *Sands of Iwo Jima*	1·90	1·90
1685	300 l.	Van Johnson and Spencer Tracy in *Thirty Seconds over Tokyo*	2·75	2·75
1686	350 l.	Humphrey Bogart and Ingrid Bergman in *Casablanca*	3·00	3·00
1675/86		*Set of 12*	11·00	11·00

MS1687 Three sheets, each 116×76 mm. (a) 450 l. George C. Scott in *Patton.* (b) 450 l. Gregory Peck in *Twelve O'Clock High.* (c) 450 l. Burning American cruiser from *Tora! Tora! Tora!* .. .. .. *Set of 3 sheets* 11·00 11·00

Nos. 1675/87 exist imperforate from a limited printing.

(Des Dot Barlowe. Litho Questa)

1991 (28 Oct). *Botanical Gardens of the World. T **248** and similar multicoloured designs. P 14.*
1688/1735 60 l.×48 .. .. *Set of 48* 18·00 19·00
MS1736 Three sheets, each 97×69 mm. (a) 600 l. Munich Botanic Garden. (b) 600 l. Kyoto Botanic Garden. (c) 600 l. Brooklyn Botanic Garden
.. .. .. *Set of 3 sheets* 12·00 13·00

Nos. 1688/1735 were issued as se-tenant sheetlets, each of 16 (4×4), depicting features and plants from Munich (Nos. 1688/1703), Kyoto (Nos. 1704/19) and Brooklyn (Nos. 1720/35). The single designs in the three miniature sheets of No. **MS**1736 are horizontal.

(Litho Walsall)

1991 (9 Dec). *Christmas. Drawings and Paintings by Albrecht Dürer. Vert designs as T **211** of Lesotho. P 12.*
1737	6 l.	black and bright magenta	15	10
1738	60 l.	black and new blue	35	30
1739	80 l.	multicoloured	45	40
1740	100 l.	multicoloured	65	65
1741	200 l.	multicoloured	1·60	1·60
1742	300 l.	multicoloured	2·00	2·00
1743	700 l.	multicoloured	4·75	5·00
1737/43		*Set of 7*	9·00	9·00

MS1744 Two sheets, each 102×127 mm. (a) 600 l. multicoloured. (b) 600 l. multicoloured. P 14 .. .. .. *Set of 2 sheets* 7·50 7·50
Designs:—6 l. "Mary being Crowned by Two Angels"; 60 l. "St. Christopher"; 80 l. "Virgin and Child with St. Anne" (detail); 100 l. "Virgin with the Pear" (detail); 200 l. "Madonna and Child" (detail); 300 l. "The Virgin in Half-Length" (detail); 700 l. "The Madonna with the Siskin" (detail); 600 l. (No. **MS**1744a) "Virgin and Child with St. Anne", 600 l. (No. **MS**1744b) "The Feast of the Rose Garlands" (detail).

Nos. 1737/44 exist imperforate from a limited printing.

249 National Theatre, Prague

(Des J. Iskowitz (Nos. 1745/6, 1750, **MS**1751a), W. Hanson Studio (Nos. 1747/9, **MS**1751b). Litho Questa)

1991 (20 Dec). *Anniversaries and Events. T **249** and similar multicoloured designs. P 14.*
1745	50 l.	Type **249**	30	20
1746	100 l.	St. Peter's Abbey, Salzburg	45	35
1747	250 l.	Sea Scouts learning sailing	1·00	1·00
1748	300 l.	Sierra Leone scouts emblem and Lord Baden-Powell	1·00	1·00
1749	400 l.	Scouts playing baseball at Mt. Sorak Jamboree	1·40	1·40
1750	500 l.	Scene from *Idomeneo*	2·50	3·00
1745/50		*Set of 6*	6·00	6·25

MS1751 Two sheets. (a) 75×105 mm. 600 l. Bust of Mozart (vert). (b) 89×117 mm. 750 l. 17th World Scout Jamboree emblem (vert)
.. .. .. *Set of 2 sheets* 10·00 10·00
Anniversaries and Events:—Nos. 1745/6, 1750, **MS**1751a, Death bicentenary of Mozart; Nos. 1747/9, **MS**1751b, 50th death anniv of Lord Baden-Powell and World Scout Jamboree, Korea.

250 Aichi D3A "Val" Dive Bomber

251 Greater Flamingo

(Des J. Batchelor. Litho Questa)

1991 (20 Dec). *50th Anniv of Japanese Attack on Pearl Harbor. T **250** and similar horiz designs. Multicoloured. P 14½×15.*
1752	75 l.	Type **250**	55	55
		a. Sheetlet. Nos. 1752/66	7·50	
1753	75 l.	Japanese Aichi D3A "Val" dive bomber and smoke	55	55
1754	75 l.	Battleship Row burning	55	55
1755	75 l.	Planes and burning dockyard	55	55
1756	75 l.	Burning installations	55	55
1757	75 l.	Two Japanese Aichi D3A "Val" dive bombers	55	55
1758	75 l.	Burning ships and hangars	55	55

1759	75 l.	Airfield under attack	55	55
1760	75 l.	American Curtiss P-40C fighter	55	55
1761	75 l.	Japanese Mitsubishi A6M Zero-Sen fighter-bombers	55	55
1762	75 l.	Japanese Mitsubishi A6M Zero-Sen fighter-bombers over suburb	55	55
1763	75 l.	Japanese Nakajima B5N "Kate" bombers attacking ships	55	55
1764	75 l.	Japanese Nakajima B5N "Kate" aircraft on fire	55	55
1765	75 l.	Japanese Nakajima B5N "Kate" bombers over jungle	55	55
1766	75 l.	Mitsubishi A6M Zero-Sen fighters	55	55
1752/66		*Set of 15*	7·50	7·50

Nos. 1752/66 were printed together, se-tenant, in sheetlets of 15 forming a composite design showing an aerial view.

(Des Walt Disney Co. Litho Questa)

1991 (24 Dec). *Christmas. Walt Disney Christmas Cards. Multicoloured designs as T **228** of St. Vincent. P 14×13½.*
1767	12 l.	Mickey Mouse, Donald Duck and characters from *Peter Pan*, 1952 (horiz)	20	10
1768	30 l.	Disney characters reading *Alice in Wonderland*, 1950 (horiz)	30	10
1769	60 l.	Sleepy and animals, 1938 (horiz)	45	25
1770	75 l.	Mickey, Minnie, Donald and Pluto posting card, 1936 (horiz)	55	30
1771	100 l.	Disney cartoon characters, 1984 (horiz)	70	45
1772	125 l.	Mickey and Donald singing carols with Donald's nephews and Pluto reading, 1954 (horiz)	90	90
1773	150 l.	*101 Dalmatians*, 1960 (horiz)	1·10	1·10
1774	200 l.	Mickey and Donald opening presents, 1948 (horiz)	1·40	1·40
1775	300 l.	Mickey, Minnie, Morte and Ferde decorating tree, 1983 (horiz)	1·75	2·00
1776	400 l.	Donald decorating tree and nephews watching television, 1956 (horiz)	2·00	2·25
1777	500 l.	Characters from Disney films, 1972 (horiz)	2·00	2·25
1778	600 l.	Mickey, Donald, Pluto and friends singing, 1964 (horiz)	2·00	2·50
1767/78		*Set of 12*	12·00	12·00

MS1779 Three sheets, each 128×102 mm. (a) 900 l. Mad Hatter's tea party, 1950; (b) 900 l. Disneyland, 1955. (c) 900 l. Seven Dwarfs in toboggan, 1959. P 13½×14 .. *Set of 3 sheets* 12·00 13·00

(Des Walt Disney Co. Litho B.D.T.)

1992 (9 Mar). *Mickey's World Tour. Multicoloured designs as T **270** of Maldive Islands showing Walt Disney cartoon characters in different countries. P 13.*
1780	6 l.	Minnie Mouse as Chiquita with Pluto, Cuba	20	10
1781	10 l.	Goofy as Olympic discus champion, Greece	20	10
1782	20 l.	Donald and Daisy Duck as flamenco dancers, Spain	30	15
1783	30 l.	Goofy and Donald as guardsman, England	40	15
1784	50 l.	Mickey and Minnie at Paris fashion show, France	50	25
1785	100 l.	Goofy in the Alps, Switzerland	80	50
1786	200 l.	Daisy and Minnie in grass skirts, Hawaii	1·50	1·75
1787	350 l.	Mickey, Donald and Goofy as ancient Egyptians (horiz)	2·00	2·25
1788	500 l.	Daisy and Minnie as cancan dancers, France (horiz)	2·25	2·50
1780/8		*Set of 9*	7·25	7·00

MS1789 Three sheets, each 83×105 mm. (a) 700 l. Mickey playing bagpipes, Scotland. (b) 700 l. Donald the gondolier, Italy. (c) 700 l. Mickey and Goofy smashing plates, Greece
.. .. .. *Set of 3 sheets* 12·00 13·00

(Des D. Miller. Litho Questa)

1992 (9 Mar). *40th Anniv of Queen Elizabeth II's Accession. Horiz designs as T **214** of Lesotho. Multicoloured. P 14.*
1790	60 l.	State House	55	20
1791	100 l.	Beach	80	40
1792	300 l.	Parliament Building	2·25	2·50
1793	400 l.	Canoe on beach	2·50	3·00
1790/3		*Set of 4*	5·50	5·50

MS1794 Two sheets, each 75×97 mm. (a) 700 l. Jungle hillside. (b) 700 l. Freetown
.. .. .. *Set of 2 sheets* 9·00 9·50

(Litho B.D.T.)

1992 (25 May). *"Granada '92" International Stamp Exhibition, Spain. Paintings by Francisco Zurbarán. Vert designs as T **68** of St. Kitts-Nevis (Nevis). Multicoloured. P 13.*
1795	1 l.	"Visit of St. Thomas Aquinas to St. Bonaventure"	10	10
1796	10 l.	"St. Gregory"	10	10
1797	30 l.	"St. Andrew"	20	20
1798	50 l.	"St. Gabriel the Archangel"	30	30
1799	60 l.	"The Blessed Henry Suso"	30	30
1800	100 l.	"St. Lucy"	40	40
1801	300 l.	"St. Casilda"	95	95
1802	400 l.	"St. Margaret of Antioch"	1·40	1·40
1803	500 l.	"St. Apollonia"	1·60	1·60
1804	600 l.	"St. Bonaventure at Council of Lyons"	1·75	1·75
1805	700 l.	"St. Bonaventure on his Bier"	2·00	2·00
1806	800 l.	"The Martyrdom of St. James" (detail)	2·25	2·25
1795/1806		*Set of 12*	10·00	10·00

MS1807 Three sheets. (a) 95×112 mm. 900 l. "The Martyrdom of St. James". (b) 900 l. "The Young Virgin". (c) 112×95 mm. 900 l. "St. Hugh in the Refectory". Imperf
.. .. .. *Set of 3 sheets* 8·50 9·00

Nos. 1795/1806 exist imperforate from a limited printing.

(Des D. Burkhart, Litho B.D.T.)

1992 (8 June). *Prehistoric Animals. Multicoloured designs as T 217 of Lesotho, but vert. P 14.*

1808	50 l.	Rhamphorhynchus	55	55
	a. Sheetlet. Nos. 1808/27		10·00	
1809	50 l.	Pteranodon	55	55
1810	50 l.	Dimorphodon	55	55
1811	50 l.	Pterodactyl	55	55
1812	50 l.	Archaeopteryx	55	55
1813	50 l.	Iguanodon	55	55
1814	50 l.	Hypsilophodon	55	55
1815	50 l.	Nothosaurus	55	55
1816	50 l.	Brachiosaurus	55	55
1817	50 l.	Kentrosaurus	55	55
1818	50 l.	Plesiosaurus	55	55
1819	50 l.	Trachodon	55	55
1820	50 l.	Hesperornis	55	55
1821	50 l.	Henodus	55	55
1822	50 l.	Stenosaurus	55	55
1823	50 l.	Stenopterygius	55	55
1824	50 l.	Eurhinosaurus	55	55
1825	50 l.	Placodus	55	55
1826	50 l.	Mosasaurus	55	55
1827	50 l.	Mixosaurus	55	55
1808/27		*Set of 20*	10·00	10·00
MS1828	106×76 mm. No. 1820		1·25	1·50

Nos. 1808/27 were printed together, *se-tenant*, in sheetlets of 20 forming a composite design.

No. 1811 is inscribed "Pteradactyl" and No. 1826 "Mosasaurs", both in error.

(Des P. Chinelli. Litho B.D.T.)

1992 (20 July). *Birds. T 251 and similar vert designs. Multicoloured. P 14.*

1829	30 l.	Type **251**	30	30
1830	50 l.	African White-crested Hornbill	35	35
1831	100 l.	Crested Touraco	55	55
1832	170 l.	Yellow-spotted Barbet	95	95
1833	200 l.	African Spoonbill	1·10	1·10
1834	250 l.	Saddle-bill Stork	1·25	1·25
1835	300 l.	Red-faced Lovebird ("Red Headed Lovebird")	1·50	1·50
1836	600 l.	Yellow-billed Barbet	3·75	3·75
1829/36		*Set of 8*	8·75	8·75
MS1837	Two sheets, each 72×101 mm. (a) 1000 l. Fire-bellied Woodpecker. (b) 1000 l. Swallow-tailed Bee Eater			
		Set of 2 sheets	10·00	10·00

(Litho Questa)

1992 (8 Sept). *Olympic Games, Albertville and Barcelona. Multicoloured designs as T 216 of Lesotho. P 14.*

1838	10 l.	Marathon	20	20
1839	20 l.	Men's parallel bars	25	25
1840	30 l.	Men's discus	25	25
1841	50 l.	Men's 110 metres hurdles (*horiz*)	30	30
1842	60 l.	Women's longjump	30	30
1843	100 l.	Men's floor exercise (*horiz*)	45	45
1844	200 l.	Windsurfing	80	80
1845	250 l.	Women's biathlon	1·00	1·00
1846	300 l.	Cycle road race	2·25	2·25
1847	400 l.	Weightlifting	2·25	2·25
1848	500 l.	Men's speed skating	2·75	2·75
1849	600 l.	Men's downhill skiing (*horiz*)	3·75	3·75
1838/49		*Set of 12*	13·00	13·00
MS1850	Three sheets, each 102×71 mm. (a) 900 l. Football (*horiz*). (b) 900 l. Men's single luge (*horiz*). (c) 900 l. Pairs ice dancing	*Set of 3 sheets*	11·00	12·00

Nos. 1838/50 exist imperforate from a limited printing.

252 Minnie Mouse and Chip
decorating Christmas Tree

(Des Walt Disney Co. Litho Questa)

1992 (16 Nov). *Christmas. T 252 and similar multicoloured designs, each showing Walt Disney cartoon characters. P 13½×14.*

1851	10 l.	Type **252**	20	10
1852	20 l.	Goofy as Father Christmas	30	10
1853	30 l.	Daisy Duck and Minnie decorating Christmas Tree	30	10
1854	50 l.	Mickey Mouse, and Goofy lighting candle	45	20
1855	80 l.	Big Pete as Father Christmas	60	40
1856	100 l.	Donald Duck as Father Christmas	60	40
1857	150 l.	Morty and Ferdie decorating cake	1·25	1·25
1858	200 l.	Mickey and bauble	1·40	1·40
1859	300 l.	Goofy and toy Father Christmas	1·60	1·75
1860	500 l.	Chip and Dale with sledge	2·25	2·50
1861	600 l.	Donald and Dale with musical instruments	2·25	2·50
1862	800 l.	Huey, Dewy and Louie making patterns in snow	2·75	3·25
1851/62		*Set of 12*	12·50	12·50
MS1863	Three sheets, each 128×102 mm. (a) 900 l. Mickey as Father Christmas. P 13½×14. (b) 900 l. Chip and Christmas tree fairy (*horiz*). P 14×13½. (c) 900 l. Mickey and Minnie (*horiz*). P 14×13½	*Set of 3 sheets*	13·00	14·00

253 Toy Pennsylvania
Railroad GG-1 Electric
Locomotive No. 6-18306, 1992

254 African
Pygmy Goose

(Des W. Hanson. Litho B.D.T.)

1992 (23 Nov). *"Genova '92" International Thematic Stamp Exhibition. Toy Trains. T 253 and similar horiz designs showing electric locomotives and rolling stock manufactured by Lionel. Multicoloured. P 14.*

1864	150 l.	Type **253**	1·00	1·00
	a. Sheetlet. Nos. 1864/72		8·00	
1865	150 l.	Wabash Railroad Hudson locomotive No. 8610, 1985	1·00	1·00
1866	150 l.	Locomotive No. 1911, 1911	1·00	1·00
1867	150 l.	Chesapeake & Ohio locomotive No. 6-18627, 1992	1·00	1·00
1868	150 l.	Gang car No. 50, 1954	1·00	1·00
1869	150 l.	Rock Island & Peoria locomotive No. 8004, 1980	1·00	1·00
1870	150 l.	Western Maryland Railroad Shay locomotive No. 6-18023, 1992	1·00	1·00
1871	150 l.	Boston & Albany Railroad Hudson locomotive No. 784, 1986	1·00	1·00
1872	150 l.	Locomotive No. 6, 1906	1·00	1·00
1873	170 l.	Special F-3 diesel locomotive, 1947	1·00	1·00
	a. Sheetlet. Nos. 1873/81		8·00	
1874	170 l.	Pennsylvania Railroad diesel switcher locomotive No. 6-18905, 1992	1·00	1·00
1875	170 l.	No. 1 Trolley, 1913	1·00	1·00
1876	170 l.	Seaboard Railroad diesel freight locomotive, No. 602, 1958	1·00	1·00
1877	170 l.	Pennsylvania Railroad S-2 turbine locomotive, 1991	1·00	1·00
1878	170 l.	Western Pacific GP-9 diesel loco-motive No. 6-18822, 1992	1·00	1·00
1879	170 l.	Locomotive No. 10, 1929	1·00	1·00
1880	170 l.	Locomotive No. 400E, 1931	1·00	1·00
1881	170 l.	Locomotive No. 384E, 1928	1·00	1·00
1882	170 l.	Pennsylvania Railroad "Torpedo" streamlined locomotive No. 238EW, 1936	1·00	1·00
	a. Sheetlet. Nos. 1882/90		8·00	
1883	170 l.	Denver & Rio Grande Western Type PA diesel locomotive, 1992	1·00	1·00
1884	170 l.	Locomotive No. 480E, 1930	1·00	1·00
1885	170 l.	Mickey Mouse 60th Birthday boxcar No. 19241, 1991	1·00	1·00
1886	170 l.	Polished brass locomotive No. 54, 1913	1·00	1·00
1887	170 l.	Pennsylvania Railroad "Broadway Limited" locomotive No. 392E, 1936	1·00	1·00
1888	170 l.	Great Northern Railroad EP-5 electric locomotive No. 18302, 1988	1·00	1·00
1889	170 l.	Locomotive No. 6, 1918	1·00	1·00
1890	170 l.	Locomotive No. 400E, 1933	1·00	1·00
1864/90		*Set of 27*	24·00	24·00
MS1891	Three sheets, each 119×90 mm. (a) 1000 l. Joshua Lionel Cowen commemorative locomotive (50×37 *mm*). (b) 1000 l. Trolley No. 300 (50×37 *mm*). (c) 1000 l. Locomotive No. 381E, 1928 (50×37 *mm*). P 13	*Set of 3 sheets*	13·00	13·00

Nos. 1864/72, 1873/81 and 1882/90 were each printed together, *se-tenant*, in sheetlets of 9.

Nos. 1874 and 1877 are inscribed "Pennsylvannia" in error.

(Litho Questa)

1992 (1 Dec)–**99**. *Birds. T 254 and similar horiz designs. Multicoloured. P 14×15.* A. *Without imprint date*

1892A	50 c.	Type **254**	10	10
1893A	1 l.	Spotted Eagle Owl	10	10
1894A	2 l.	Crested Touraco	10	10
1895A	5 l.	Saddle-bill Stork	10	10
1896A	10 l.	African Golden Oriole	10	10
1897A	20 l.	Malachite Kingfisher	10	10
1898A	30 l.	Red-crowned Bishop ("Fire-crowned Bishop")	10	10
1899A	40 l.	Fire-bellied Woodpecker	10	10
1900A	50 l.	Red-billed Fire Finch	1·00	75
1901A	80 l.	Blue Flycatcher	10	10
1902A	100 l.	Crested Malimbe	2·00	1·75
1903A	150 l.	Vitelline Masked Weaver	2·50	2·25
1904A	170 l.	Great Blue Turaco ("Blue Plantain-eater")	10	10
1905A	200 l.	Superb Sunbird	3·00	2·50
1906A	250 l.	Swallow-tailed Bee Eater	2·75	2·25
1907A	300 l.	Cabanis's Yellow Bunting	3·25	3·00
1908A	500 l.	Egyptian Plover ("Crocodile Bird")	3·50	3·50
1909A	750 l.	White-faced Scops Owl	45	50
1910A	1000 l.	African Blue Cuckoo Shrike	3·50	3·50
1911A	2000 l.	White-necked Bald Crow ("Bare-headed Rock Fowl")	1·25	1·40
1912A	3000 l.	African Red-tailed Buzzard	11·00	12·00
1913A	4000 l.	Grey-headed Bush Shrike (18.2.99)	2·50	2·50
1914A	5000 l.	Black-backed Puffback (18.2.99)	3·25	3·50
1915A	6000 l.	Burchell's Gonolek ("Crimson-breasted Shrike") (18.2.99)	3·75	4·00
1915Ac	10000 l.	Northern Shrike (18.5.99)	6·25	6·50
1892A/1915Ac		*Set of 25*	45·00	45·00

B. *With imprint date*

1900B	50 l.	Red-billed Fire Finch (1994)	10	10
1902B	100 l.	Crested Malimbe (1994)	10	10
1903B	150 l.	Vitelline Masked Weaver (1994)	10	10
1905B	200 l.	Superb Sunbird (1994)	15	15
1906B	250 l.	Swallow-tailed Bee Eater (1997)	15	20
1907B	300 l.	Cabanis's Yellow Bunting (1994)	20	25
1908B	500 l.	Egyptian Plover ("Crocodile Bird") (1996)	30	35
1910B	1000 l.	African Blue Cuckoo Shrike (1996)	60	65
1911B	2000 l.	White-necked Bald Crow ("Bare-headed Rock Fowl") (1999)	1·25	1·40
1912B	3000 l.	African Red-tailed Buzzard (1996)	1·90	2·00
1900B/12B		*Set of 10*	4·75	5·25

Imprint dates: "1994", Nos. 1900B, 1902B/3B, 1905B, 1907B; "1996", Nos. 1902B, 1905B, 1907B/8B, 1910B, 1912B; "1997", Nos. 1900B, 1902B, 1905B/8B; "1999", Nos. 1902B, 1905B, 1907B, 1910B/11B.

(Litho Questa)

1992 (7 Dec). *Christmas. Religious Paintings. Vert designs as T 218 of Lesotho. Multicoloured. P 13½×14.*

1916	1 l.	"Virgin and Child" (Fiorenzo di Lorenzo)	10	10
1917	10 l.	"Madonna and Child on a Wall" (School of Bouts)	15	15
1918	20 l.	"Virgin and Child with the Flight into Egypt" (Master of Hoog-straeten)	20	20
1919	30 l.	"Madonna and Child before Firescreen" (Robert Campin)	25	25
1920	50 l.	"Mary in a Rosegarden" (detail) (Hans Memling)	30	25
1921	100 l.	"Virgin Mary and Child" (Lucas Cranach the Elder)	55	45
1922	170 l.	"Virgin and Child" (Rogier van der Weyden)	1·00	1·00
1923	200 l.	"Madonna and Saints" (detail) (Perugino)	1·10	1·10
1924	250 l.	"Madonna Enthroned with Sts Catherine and Barbara" (Master of Hoogstraeten)	1·25	1·25
1925	300 l.	"The Virgin in a Rose Arbour" (Stefan Lochner)	1·50	1·50
1926	500 l.	"Madonna with Child and Angels" (Botticelli)	2·50	2·50
1927	1000 l.	"Madonna and Child with young St. John the Baptist (Fra Bartolo-mmeo)	4·50	5·00
1916/27		*Set of 12*	12·00	12·50
MS1928	Three sheets, each 76×102 mm. (a) 900 l. "Virgin and Child" (detail) (Jan Gossaert). (b) 900 l. "Virgin and Child" (detail) (Lucas Cranach the Younger). (c) 900 l. "The Virgin with the Green Cushion" (detail) (Andrea Solario)	*Set of 3 sheets*	11·50	11·50

255 Mickey Mouse and
Sousaphone (magazine
cover, 1936)

256 Emblems

(Des Walt Disney Co. Litho Questa)

1992 (17 Dec). *Mickey Mouse in Literature. T 255 and similar multicoloured designs each showing Walt Disney cartoon characters on magazine or book covers. P 13½×14.*

1929	10 l.	Type **255**	15	10
1930	20 l.	Mickey and Minnie Mouse, 1936	20	10
1931	30 l.	Mickey and Donald Duck, 1936	20	10
1932	40 l.	Mickey, Minnie and Goofy in car, 1937	20	15
1933	50 l.	Mickey as Ringmaster, 1937	20	15
1934	60 l.	Mickey as Father Christmas, 1937	25	25
1935	70 l.	Donald and Goofy representing 1937 and 1938	25	25
1936	150 l.	Mickey and Minnie steering ship, 1935	80	80
1937	170 l.	Mickey and Tanglefoot the horse, 1936	85	85
1938	200 l.	Mickey tied up	95	95
1939	300 l.	Mickey and Goofy in jungle	1·25	1·40
1940	400 l.	Mickey and Goofy on submarine	1·60	1·75
1941	500 l.	Mickey and Minnie singing and dancing, 1931	1·75	2·00
1929/41		*Set of 13*	7·75	7·75
MS1942	Three sheets. (a) 127×102 mm. 900 l. Mickey reading to Morty and Ferdie, 1933 (*horiz*). P 14×13½. (b) 102×127 mm. 900 l. Mickey with book, 1935 (*horiz*). (c) 102×127 mm. 900 l. Mickey the hunter, 1948. P 13½×14	*Set of 3 sheets*	12·00	13·00

(Des W. Wright and L. Fried (Nos. 1952, **MS**1954c). Litho B.D.T.)

1993 (14 Jan). *Anniversaries and Events. T 256 and similar multicoloured designs. P 14.*

1943	150 l.	Type **256**	70	70
1944	170 l.	Cow and cereal with emblems	80	80
1945	170 l.	Airship LZ-127 *Graf Zeppelin*	80	80
1946	200 l.	Starving child and W.H.O. emblem	95	95
1947	250 l.	Summit emblem and cottonwood tree	1·25	1·25
1948	250 l.	Lions Club emblem and World map	1·25	1·25
1949	300 l.	Emblem and African Elephant	1·40	1·40
1950	300 l.	Columbus, King Ferdinand and Queen Isabella	1·40	1·40
1951	500 l.	Landing in the New World	2·25	2·25
1952	600 l.	American space shuttle	2·40	2·40
1953	700 l.	Construction drawings of LZ-127 *Graf Zeppelin*	2·75	2·75
1943/53		*Set of 11*	14·50	14·50

MS1954 Three sheets. (a) 100×70 mm. 900 l. Count Ferdinand von Zeppelin (*vert*). (b) 97×67 mm. 900 l. Christopher Columbus (*vert*). (c) 100×70 mm. 900 l. American astronaut on space walk .. .. *Set of 3 sheets* 10·50 11·50

Anniversaries and Events:—Nos. 1943/4 International Conference on Nutrition, Rome; Nos. 1945, 1953, 75th death anniv of Count Ferdinand von Zeppelin (airship pioneer); No. 1946, United Nations World Health Organization Projects; Nos. 1947, 1949, Earth Summit '92, Rio; No. 1948, 75th anniv of International Association of Lions Clubs; Nos. 1950/1, **MS1954b** 500th anniv of discovery of America by Columbus; Nos. 1952, **MS1954c**, International Space Year.

257 Joe Louis

258 *Amanita flammeola*

(Des P. Wolff. Litho Questa)

1993 (8 Feb). *Centenary of Modern Boxing (1st issue) World Champions*. T **257** *and similar vert designs. Multicoloured.* P 13½×14.

1955	200 l.	Type **257**	1·00	1·00
		a. Sheetlet. Nos. 1955/62	7·00	
1956	200 l.	Archie Moore	1·00	1·00
1957	200 l.	Muhammad Ali	1·00	1·00
1958	200 l.	George Foreman	1·00	1·00
1959	200 l.	Joe Frazier	1·00	1·00
1960	200 l.	Marvin Hagler	1·00	1·00
1961	200 l.	Sugar Ray Leonard	1·00	1·00
1962	200 l.	Evander Holyfield	1·00	1·00
1955/62		*Set of 8*	7·00	7·00

MS1963 128×102 mm. 1000 l. Muhammad Ali (*different*) .. .. 4·00 4·25

Nos. 1955/62 were printed together, *se-tenant*, in sheetlets of 8.

(Des P. Wolff. Litho Questa)

1993 (8 Feb). *Centenary of Modern Boxing (2nd issue). Boxing Films. Vert designs as* T **257**. *Multicoloured.* P 13½×14.

1964	200 l.	Wallace Beery (*The Champ*)	80	80
		a. Sheetlet. Nos. 1964/71	5·50	
1965	200 l.	William Holden (*Golden Boy*)	80	80
1966	200 l.	John Garfield (*Body and Soul*)	80	80
1967	200 l.	Kirk Douglas (*Champion*)	80	80
1968	200 l.	Robert Ryan (*The Set-Up*)	80	80
1969	200 l.	Anthony Quinn (*Requiem for a Heavyweight*)	80	80
1970	200 l.	Elvis Presley (*Kid Galahad*)	80	80
1971	200 l.	Jeff Bridges (*Fat City*)	80	80
1964/71		*Set of 8*	5·50	5·50

MS1972 Two sheets, each 128×102 mm. (a) 1000 l. Errol Flynn (*Gentleman Jim*). (b) 1000 l. Sylvester Stallone (*Rocky III*) .. *Set of 2 sheets* 7·00 7·50

Nos. 1964/71 were printed together, *se-tenant*, in sheetlets of 8.

(Litho Walsall)

1993 (8 Mar). *Bicentenary of the Louvre, Paris. Multicoloured designs as* T **221** *of Lesotho.* P 12.

1973	70 l.	"Young Orphan at a Cemetery" (Delacroix)	45	45
		a. Sheetlet. Nos. 1973/80	3·25	
1974	70 l.	"Algerian Women in their Apartment" (left detail) (Delacroix)	45	45
1975	70 l.	"Algerian Women in their Apartment" (right detail) (Delacroix)	45	45
1976	70 l.	"Dante and Virgil" (Delacroix)	45	45
1977	70 l.	"Self-portrait" (Delacroix)	45	45
1978	70 l.	"Massacre of Chios" (left detail) (Delacroix)	45	45
1979	70 l.	"Massacre of Chios" (right detail) (Delacroix)	45	45
1980	70 l.	"Frédéric Chopin" (Delacroix)	45	45
1981	70 l.	"Entry of the Crusaders into Constantinople" (left detail) (Delacroix)	45	45
		a. Sheetlet. Nos. 1981/8	3·25	
1982	70 l.	"Entry of the Crusaders into Constantinople" (right detail) (Delacroix)	45	45
1983	70 l.	"Jewish Wedding, Morocco" (left detail) (Delacroix)	45	45
1984	70 l.	"Jewish Wedding, Morocco" (right detail) (Delacroix)	45	45
1985	70 l.	"Death of Sardanopoulous" (left detail) (Delacroix)	45	45
1986	70 l.	"Death of Sardanopoulous" (right detail) (Delacroix)	45	45
1987	70 l.	"Liberty leading the People" (left detail) (Delacroix)	45	45
1988	70 l.	"Liberty leading the People" (right detail) (Delacroix)	45	45
1973/88		*Set of 16*	6·50	6·50

MS1989 100×70 mm. 900 l. "The Sabine Women" (Louis David) (85×53 mm). P 14½ .. 4·00 4·50

Nos. 1973/80 and 1981/8 were printed together, *se-tenant*, in sheetlets of 8 stamps and one centre label.

(Des I. MacLaury. Litho Questa)

1993 (5 May). *Mushrooms.* T **258** *and similar vert designs. Multicoloured.* P 14.

1990	30 l.	Type **258**	40	20
1991	50 l.	*Cantharellus pseudocibarius*	50	20
1992	100 l.	*Volvariella volvacea*	70	40

1993	200 l.	*Termitomyces microcarpus*	1·10	90
1994	300 l.	*Auricularia auricula-judae*	1·60	1·40
1995	400 l.	*Lentinus tuber-regium* ("*Pleurotus tuberregium*")	1·75	1·75
1996	500 l.	*Schizophyllum commune*	1·90	1·90
1997	600 l.	*Termitomyces robustus*	2·00	2·00
1990/7		*Set of 8*	9·00	8·00

MS1998 Two sheets, each 106×76 mm. (a) 1000 l. *Daldinia concentrica*. (b) 1000 l. *Phallus rubicundus* .. .. *Set of 2 sheets* 8·00 8·50

Nos. 1990/8 exist imperforate from a limited printing.

259 *Pseudacraea boisduvali*

Black Persian

260 Black Persian

(Des L. Nelson. Litho Questa)

1993 (5 May). *Butterflies.* T **259** *and similar vert designs. Multicoloured.* P 14.

1999	20 l.	Type **259**	45	20
2000	30 l.	*Salamis temora*	50	25
2001	50 l.	*Charaxes jasius*	55	30
2002	100 l.	*Amblypodia anita*	65	40
2003	150 l.	*Papilio nireus*	80	70
2004	170 l.	*Danaus chrysippus*	85	85
2005	200 l.	*Meneris tulbaghia*	90	90
2006	250 l.	*Precis octavia*	1·00	1·00
2007	300 l.	*Palla ussheri*	1·25	1·25
2008	500 l.	*Catacroptera cloanthe*	1·40	1·50
2009	600 l.	*Cynthia cardui*	1·60	2·00
2010	700 l.	*Euphaedra neophron*	1·75	2·00
1999/2010		*Set of 12*	10·50	10·00

MS2011 Three sheets, each 100×70 mm. (a) 1000 l. *Papilio zalmoxis*. (b) 1000 l. *Hypolimnas salmacis*. (c) 1000 l. *Kallimoides rumia* .. .. *Set of 3 sheets* 11·00 11·00

Nos. 1999/2011 exist imperforate from a limited printing.

(Des Jennifer Toombs. Litho Questa)

1993 (17 May). *Cats.* T **260** *and similar multicoloured designs.* P 14.

2012	150 l.	Type **260**	75	75
		a. Sheetlet. Nos. 2012/23	8·00	
2013	150 l.	Blue-point Siamese	75	75
2014	150 l.	American Wirehair	75	75
2015	150 l.	Birman	75	75
2016	150 l.	Scottish Fold	75	75
2017	150 l.	American Shorthair Red Tabby	75	75
2018	150 l.	Blue and White Persian Bicolour	75	75
2019	150 l.	Havana Brown	75	75
2020	150 l.	Norwegian Forest Cat	75	75
2021	150 l.	Brown Tortie Burmese	75	75
2022	150 l.	Angora	75	75
2023	150 l.	Exotic Shorthair	75	75
2024	150 l.	Somali	75	75
		a. Sheetlet. Nos. 2024/35	8·00	
2025	150 l.	Egyptian Mau Smoke	75	75
2026	150 l.	Chocolate-point Siamese	75	75
2027	150 l.	Mi-Ke Japanese Bobtail	75	75
2028	150 l.	Chinchilla	75	75
2029	150 l.	Red Burmese	75	75
2030	150 l.	British Shorthair Brown Tabby	75	75
2031	150 l.	Blue Persian	75	75
2032	150 l.	British Silver Classic Tabby	75	75
2033	150 l.	Oriental Ebony	75	75
2034	150 l.	Red Persian	75	75
2035	150 l.	British Calico Shorthair	75	75
2012/35		*Set of 24*	16·00	16·00

MS2036 Two sheets, each 108×65 mm. (a) 1000 l. American Shorthair Blue Tabby. (b) 1000 l. Seal-point Colourpoint .. *Set of 2 sheets* 8·00 8·50

Nos. 2012/23 and 2024/35 were printed together, *se-tenant*, in sheetlets of 12.

Nos. 2012/36 exist imperforate from a limited printing.

261 Gorilla

(Des T. Wood. Litho Questa)

1993 (17 June). *Wildlife.* T **261** *and similar horiz designs. Multicoloured.* P 14.

2037	30 l.	Type **261**	50	30
2038	100 l.	Bongo	60	35
2039	150 l.	Potto	70	60
2040	170 l.	Chimpanzee	90	90
2041	200 l.	Dwarf Galago	1·00	1·00
2042	300 l.	African Linsang	1·25	1·25
2043	500 l.	Banded Duiker	1·75	2·00
2044	750 l.	Diana Monkey	2·25	3·00
2037/44		*Set of 8*	8·00	8·50

MS2045 Two sheets, each 106×77 mm. (a) 1200 l. African Elephant. (b) 1200 l. Leopard .. .. *Set of 2 sheets* 11·00 11·00

Nos. 2037/45 exist imperforate from a limited printing.

262 *Clerodendrum thomsonae*　　263 Royal Family

(Litho Questa)

1993 (5 July). *Flowers.* T **262** *and similar horiz designs. Multicoloured.* P 14.

2046	30 l.	Type **262**	30	20
2047	40 l.	*Passiflora quadrangularis*	35	25
2048	50 l.	*Hydrangea macrophylla*	35	25
2049	60 l.	*Begonia semperflorens*	40	30
2050	100 l.	*Hibiscus rosa-sinensis*	50	40
2051	150 l.	*Lagerstroemia indica*	75	75
2052	170 l.	*Bougainvillea glabra*	85	85
2053	200 l.	*Plumbago capensis*	1·00	1·00
2054	250 l.	*Gerbera jamesonae*	1·25	1·25
2055	300 l.	*Thunbergia alata*	1·40	1·50
2056	500 l.	*Gloriosa superba*	1·75	2·00
2057	900 l.	*Viola odorata*	2·75	3·25
2046/57		*Set of 12*	10·50	11·00

MS2058 Three sheets, each 72×102 mm. (a) 1200 l. *Hibiscus rosa-sinensis* (*different*). (b) 1200 l. *Passiflora quadrangularis* (*different*). (c) 1200 l. *Gloriosa superba* (*different*) .. *Set of 3 sheets* 12·00 13·00

Nos. 2046/58 exist imperforate from a limited printing.

(Litho B.D.T.)

1993 (8 Nov). *Anniversaries and Events.* T **263** *and similar vert designs. Black (No. 2061) or multicoloured (others).* P 14.

2059	100 l.	Type **263**	50	40
2060	170 l.	"Woman with Hat" (Picasso)	75	75
2061	200 l.	Coronation procession	1·00	1·00
2062	200 l.	"Buste de Femme" (Picasso)	1·00	1·00
2063	250 l.	Early telescope	1·25	1·25
2064	600 l.	Queen Elizabeth II in Coronation robes (from photograph by Cecil Beaton)	2·00	2·00
2065	800 l.	"Maya with a Doll" (Picasso)	2·50	3·00
2066	800 l.	Craters on Moon	2·50	3·00
2059/66		*Set of 8*	10·50	11·00

MS2067 Two sheets. (a) 100×70 mm. 1500 l. "Woman of Algiers" (detail) (Picasso). (b) 73×103 mm. 1500 l. "Queen Elizabeth II" (detail) (Pietro Annigoni) .. .. *Set of 2 sheets* 10·00 11·00

Anniversaries and Events:—Nos. 2059, 2061, 2064, **MS2067b**, 40th anniv of Coronation; Nos. 2060, 2062, 2065, **MS2067a**, 20th death anniv of Picasso (artist); Nos. 2063, 2066, 450th death anniv of Copernicus (astronomer).

(Litho Questa)

1993 (2 Dec). *Christmas. Religious Paintings. Vert designs as* T **76** *of Nevis (St. Kitts-Nevis). Black, pale lemon and red (Nos. 2071/4,* **MS2076b**) *or multicoloured (others).* P 13½×14.

2068	50 l.	"Madonna of the Fish" (detail) (Raphael)	30	10
2069	100 l.	"Madonna of the Fish" (different detail) (Raphael)	45	20
2070	150 l.	"Madonna and Child enthroned with Five Saints" (detail) (Raphael)	70	30
2071	200 l.	"The Circumcision" (detail) (Dürer)	80	55
2072	250 l.	"The Circumcision" (different detail) (Dürer)	90	75
2073	300 l.	"The Circumcision" (different detail) (Dürer)	95	95
2074	500 l.	"Holy Family with Saints and Two Angels playing Music" (detail) (Dürer)	1·75	2·00
2075	800 l.	"The Holy Family with the Lamb" (detail) (Raphael)	2·25	3·25
2068/75		*Set of 8*	7·25	7·25

MS2076 Two sheets. (a) 102×127 mm. 1200 l. "Madonna of the Fish" (different detail) (Raphael). (b) 127×102 mm. 1200 l. "Holy Family with Saints and Two Angels playing Music" (different detail) (Dürer) *Set of 2 sheets* 8·50 9·00

265 Donald Duck and Toy Train

(Des Alvin White Studios (Nos. 2079/81, 2083, **MS2085d**), Rosemary DeFiglio (others). Litho Questa)

1993 (13–17 Dec). *Christmas.* T **265** *and similar multicoloured designs showing Walt Disney cartoon characters in Christmas scenes.* P 13½×14.

2077	50 l.	Type **265**	40	10
2078	100 l.	Disney carol singers	55	20
2079	170 l.	Mickey drinking punch (17 Dec)	90	70
2080	200 l.	Pluto with cream-covered bones (17 Dec)	1·10	85

2081	250 l. Goofy eating angel cakes (17 Dec)		1·40	1·25
2082	500 l. Donald's nephews decorating Christmas tree		2·25	2·50
2083	600 l. Donald dropping Christmas cake on foot (17 Dec)		2·50	3·00
2084	800 l. Uncle Scrooge and Daisy under mistletoe		2·75	3·50
2077/84		*Set of* 8	10·50	11·00

MS2085 Four sheets. (a) 127×102 mm. 1200 l. Father Christmas in sleigh. P 13½×14. (b) 102×127 mm. 1200 l. Disney carol singers in wood (*horiz*). P 14×13½. (c) 127×102 mm. 1200 l. Father Christmas (*horiz*). P 14×13½. (d) 127×102 mm. 1200 l. Mickey and Minnie with turkey (*horiz*). P 14×13½ (17 Dec)
Set of 4 sheets 15·00 16·00

(Litho Questa)

1993 (22 Dec). *World Cup Football Championship, U.S.A. (1994) (1st issue). Vert designs as T **278** of Maldive Islands. Multicoloured. P 13½×14.*

2086	30 l. José Brown with goalkeeper (Argentina)		40	20
2087	50 l. Gary Lineker (England)		60	30
2088	100 l. Carlos Valderrama (Colombia)		70	35
2089	250 l. Tomas Skuhravy (Czechoslovakia) and Hector Marchena (Costa Rica)		1·40	1·25
2090	300 l. Butragueno (Spain)		1·60	1·60
2091	400 l. Roger Milla (Cameroun)		2·00	2·25
2092	500 l. Roberto Donadoni (Italy)		2·25	2·50
2093	700 l. Enzo Scifo (Belgium)		2·50	3·00
2086/93		*Set of* 8	10·50	10·50

MS2094 Two sheets, each 70×100 mm. 1200 l. Mark Wright (England) and Stephane Demol (Belgium). (b) 100×70 mm. 1200 l. Socrates (Brazil). P 13 ... ... *Set of 2 sheets* 10·00 10·50
See also Nos. 2130/6.

(Des W. Hanson. Litho Questa)

1994 (18 Feb). *"Hong Kong '94" International Stamp Exhibition (1st issue). Horiz designs as T **293** of Maldive Islands. Multicoloured. P 14.*

2095	200 l. Hong Kong 1985 $1.70 Bauhinia stamp and Pagoda, Tiger Baum Garden		40	50
	a. Horiz pair. Nos. 2095/6		80	1·00
2096	200 l. Sierra Leone 1989 70 l. Orchid stamp and Aw Par Gardens		40	50

Nos. 2095/6 were printed together, *se-tenant*, in horizontal pairs throughout the sheet.

(Des Kerri Schiff. Litho Questa)

1994 (18 Feb). *"Hong Kong '94" International Stamp Exhibition (2nd issue). Ching Dynasty Carved Lacquerware. Multicoloured designs as T **294** of Maldive Islands, but horiz. P 14.*

2097	100 l. Bowl		30	30
	a. Sheetlet. Nos. 2097/102		1·60	
2098	100 l. Four-wheeled box		30	30
2099	100 l. Flower container		30	30
2100	100 l. Box with human figure design		30	30
2101	100 l. Shishi dog		30	30
2102	100 l. Box with persimmon design		30	30
2097/102		*Set of* 6	1·60	1·60

Nos. 2097/102 were printed together, *se-tenant*, in sheetlets of 6.

(266)   **267** Pekingese

1994 (18 Feb). *"Hong Kong '94" International Stamp Exhibition (3rd issue). Nos. 2013, 2025 and MS2036 optd with T **266**.*

2103	150 l. Blue-point Siamese		40	40
	a. Sheetlet. Nos. 2012, 2014/23 and 2103		4·25	
2104	150 l. Egyptian Mau Smoke		40	40
	a. Sheetlet. Nos. 2024, 2026/35 and 2104		4·25	

MS2105 Two sheets, each 108×65 mm. (a) 1000 l. American Shorthair Blue Tabby. (b) 1000 l. Seal-point Colourpoint ... *Set of 2 sheets* 6·50 7·00
Nos. 2103a and 2104a only show overprint Type **266** on Nos. 2103 and 2104, and on the sheetlet margins. On No. MS2105 Type **266** appears on the margins of the miniature sheets.

(Des R. Sauber. Litho Questa)

1994 (20 June). *Chinese New Year ("Year of the Dog"). T **267** and similar horiz designs. Multicoloured. P 14.*

2106	100 l. Type **267**		65	75
	a. Sheetlet. Nos. 2106/13		7·75	
2107	150 l. Dobermann Pinscher		80	90
2108	200 l. Tibetan Terrier		90	1·00
2109	300 l. Weimaraner		90	1·00
2110	400 l. Rottweiler		1·10	1·25
2111	500 l. Akita		1·25	1·40
2112	600 l. Schnauzer		1·40	1·60
2113	1000 l. Tibetan Spaniel		1·60	1·75
2106/13		*Set of* 8	7·75	8·75

MS2114 Two sheets, each 116×88 mm. (a) 1200 l. Wire-haired Pointing Griffon. (b) 1200 l. Shih Tzu ... *Set of 2 sheets* 6·00 6·50
Nos. 2106/13 were printed together, *se-tenant*, in sheetlets of 8.

(Des J. Batchelor. Litho B.D.T.)

1994 (11 July). *50th Anniv of D-Day. Horiz designs as T **304** of Maldive Islands. Multicoloured. P 14.*

2115	500 l. British paratroop drop		1·25	1·25
2116	750 l. U.S. paratrooper jumping from aircraft		1·75	1·75

MS2117 106×76 mm. 1000 l. U.S. paratrooper preparing to jump from Douglas C-47 Dakota 2·75 3·00

(Des Kerri Schiff. Litho Questa (Nos. 2119/26), B.D.T. (others))

1994 (11 July). *"Philakorea '94" International Stamp Exhibition, Seoul. Multicoloured designs as T **305** of Maldive Islands. P 14 (Nos. 2118, 2127/8) or 13 (others).*

2118	100 l. Traditional wedding		40	25
2119	200 l. Tiger and cubs		60	60
	a. Sheetlet. Nos. 2119/26		4·25	
2120	200 l. Munsa-pasal		60	60
2121	200 l. Extinct Korean tiger		60	60
2122	200 l. Tiger and bamboo		60	60
2123	200 l. Tiger, three cubs and magpies		60	60
2124	200 l. Tiger, two cubs and magpies		60	60
2125	200 l. Mountain spirit		60	60
2126	200 l. Tiger and magpie		60	60
2127	400 l. Royal tombs, Kaesong		1·00	1·00
2128	600 l. Terraced fields, Chungmu		1·50	1·75
2118/28		*Set of* 11	7·00	7·00

MS2129 100×70 mm. 1200 l. Tiger hunt. P 14 4·00 4·50
Nos. 2119/26, each 23×48 mm, were printed together, *se-tenant*, in sheetlets of 8 and show paintings of tigers.
No. MS2129 is inscribed "Sierre Leone" in error.

268 Kim Ho (South Korea)

(Litho Questa)

1994 (15 July). *World Cup Football Championship, U.S.A. (2nd issue). T **268** and similar horiz designs. Multicoloured. P 14.*

2130	250 l. Type **268**		75	75
	a. Sheetlet. Nos. 2130/5		4·00	
2131	250 l. Cobi Jones (U.S.A.) ("No. 13")		75	75
2132	250 l. Claudio Suarez (Mexico) ("No. 2")		75	75
2133	250 l. Tomas Brolin (Sweden) ("No. 11")		75	75
2134	250 l. Ruud Gullit (Holland) (red shirt without number)		75	75
2135	250 l. Andreas Herzog (Austria) (white shirt without number)		75	75
2130/5		*Set of* 6	4·00	4·00

MS2136 Two sheets. (a) 70×100 mm. 1500 l. Player and Giant Stadium, New Jersey. (b) 100×70 mm. 1500 l. Sierra Leone national team ... *Set of 2 sheets* 8·00 9·00
Nos. 2130/5 were printed together, *se-tenant*, in sheetlets of 6.

(Des W. Hanson. Litho Questa)

1994 (20 July). *25th Anniv of First Moon Landing. Multicoloured designs as T **302** of Maldive Islands. P 14.*

2137	200 l. Buzz Aldrin gathering Moon samples		55	55
	a. Sheetlet. Nos. 2137/42		3·00	
2138	200 l. Lunar Module *Eagle* on Moon's surface		55	55
2139	200 l. Tranquility Base		55	55
2140	200 l. Aldrin with U.S. flag		55	55
2141	200 l. Plaque		55	55
2142	200 l. "Apollo 11" crew with stamps		55	55
2143	200 l. Edwin Aldrin		55	55
	a. Sheetlet. Nos. 2143/8		3·00	
2144	200 l. Michael Collins		55	55
2145	200 l. Neil Armstrong		55	55
2146	200 l. "Apollo 11" lift off		55	55
2147	200 l. Aldrin descending to Moon's surface		55	55
2148	200 l. Reflection in Aldrin's face shield		55	55
2137/48		*Set of* 12	6·00	6·00

MS2149 103×73 mm. 1000 l. First lunar footprint (*vert*) | | | 2·25 | 2·75
Nos. 2137/42 and 2143/8 were each printed together, *se-tenant*, in sheetlets of 6.

269 White-necked Bald Crow ("White-necked Picathartes") feeding Chicks

270 Aerangis kotschyana

(Litho Questa)

1994 (10 Aug). *Birds. T **269** and similar multicoloured designs. P 14.*

2150	50 l. Type **269**		65	65
	a. Vert strip of 4. Nos. 2150/3		2·75	
2151	100 l. Adult White-necked Bald Crow		75	75
2152	150 l. Pair of White-necked Bald Crows		85	85
2153	200 l. Young White-necked Bald Crow		90	90
2154	250 l. Black Kite		1·00	1·00
2155	300 l. Superb Sunbird		1·10	1·10

2156	500 l. Martial Eagle		1·60	2·00
2157	800 l. Red Bishop		2·00	2·50
2150/7		*Set of* 8	8·00	8·75

MS2158 Two sheets, each 90×65 mm. (a) 1200 l. Greater Flamingo (*vert*). (b) 1200 l. White-necked Bald Crow (*vert*) ... *Set of 2 sheets* 8·00 9·00
Nos. 2150/3, which carry the W.W.F. Panda emblem, were printed together, *se-tenant*, as vertical strips of four in sheetlets of 12.
Nos. 2150/7 exist imperforate from a limited printing.

(Des D. Burkhart. Litho Questa)

1994 (1 Sept). *Orchids. T **270** and similar vert designs. Multicoloured. P 14.*

2159	50 l. Type **270**		40	20
2160	100 l. *Brachycorythis kalbreyeri*		50	30
2161	150 l. *Diaphananthe pellucida*		65	55
2162	200 l. *Eulophia guineensis*		75	65
2163	300 l. *Eurychone rothschildiana*		1·00	85
2164	500 l. *Tridactyle tridactylites*		1·60	1·60
2165	750 l. *Cyrtorchis arcuata*		2·25	2·75
2166	900 l. *Ancistrochilus rothschildianus*		2·50	3·25
2159/66		*Set of* 8	8·75	9·00

MS2167 Two sheets, each 117×78 mm. (a) 1500 l. *Plectrelminthus caudatus*. (b) 1500 l. *Polystachya affinis* ... *Set of 2 sheets* 8·00 9·00

271 Family working in Field

(Litho Questa)

1994 (19 Dec). *Christmas. Religious Paintings. Vert designs as T **290** of St. Vincent. Multicoloured. P 13½×14.*

2168	50 l. "The Birth of the Virgin" (Murillo)		35	10
2169	100 l. "Education of the Virgin" (Murillo)		45	20
2170	150 l. "Annunciation" (detail) (Filippino Lippi)		75	55
2171	200 l. "Marriage of the Virgin" (Bernard van Orley)		85	70
2172	250 l. "The Visitation" (Nicolas Vleughels)		1·00	90
2173	300 l. "Castelfranco Altarpiece" (detail) (Giorgione)		1·25	1·25
2174	400 l. "Adoration of the Magi" (workshop of Bartholome Zeitblom)		1·60	1·75
2175	600 l. "Presentation of Infant Jesus in the Temple" (Master of the Prado)		2·00	2·75
2168/75		*Set of* 8	7·50	7·50

MS2176 Two sheets, each 115×95 mm. (a) 1500 l. "Nativity Altarpiece" (detail) (Lorenzo Monaco). (b) 1500 l. "Allendale Nativity" (detail) (Giorgione) ... *Set of 2 sheets* 8·00 9·00

272 Mickey Mouse stroking Cat

(Des Alvin White Studios. Litho Questa)

1995 (23 Jan). *Christmas. T **272** and similar multicoloured designs showing Walt Disney cartoon characters. P 14×13½ (horiz) or 13½×14 (vert).*

2179	50 l. Type **272**		35	10
2180	100 l. Goofy with Christmas tree and axe (vert)		45	20
2181	150 l. Donald Duck giving Daisy Duck a plant		70	45
2182	200 l. Donald finding Chipmunk in stocking (vert)		80	60
2183	250 l. Minnie Mouse in airplane		95	85
2184	300 l. Goofy in snowball (vert)		1·25	1·00
2185	400 l. Goofy with Chip N' Dale at mail box		1·40	1·50
2186	500 l. Mickey and Donald on sledge (vert)		1·60	1·75
2187	600 l. Mickey and Minnie making snowmouse		1·90	2·50
2188	800 l. Mickey and Pluto with cake (vert)		2·25	3·00
2179/88		*Set of* 10	10·50	10·50

MS2189 Two sheets. (a) 108×133 mm. 1500 l. Goofy caught up in Christmas lights. (b) 130×108 mm. 1500 l. Mickey asleep in armchair (vert) ... *Set of 2 sheets* 8·00 9·00

OMNIBUS ISSUES

Details, together with prices for complete sets, of the various Omnibus issues from the 1935 Silver Jubilee series to date are included in a special section following Zimbabwe at the end of Volume 2.

273 "Madonna Duck" (after Da Vinci)

274 Ragnar Lundberg (Sweden) (1952 pole vault bronze medal)

(Des Alvin White Studios. Litho Questa)

1995 (23 Jan). *Donald's Gallery of Old Masters.* T **273** *and similar multicoloured designs showing Donald and Daisy Duck in portraits inspired by famous paintings.* P 13½×14.

2190	50 l.	Type **273**	25	15
2191	100 l.	"Portrait of a Venetian Duck" (after Tintoretto)	35	25
2192	150 l.	"Duck with a Glove" (after Frans Hals)	50	50
2193	200 l.	"Donald with a Pink" (after Massys)	60	60
2194	250 l.	"Pinkie Daisy" (after Lawrence)	70	70
2195	300 l.	"Donald's Whistling Mother" (after Whistler)	80	80
2196	400 l.	"El Quacko" (after El Greco)	90	90
2197	500 l.	"The Noble Snob" (after Rembrandt)	1·00	1·00
2198	600 l.	"The Blue Duck" (after Gainsborough)	1·25	1·50
2199	800 l.	"Modern Quack" (after Picasso)	1·40	1·60
2190/9		*Set of 10*	7·00	7·25

MS2200 Two sheets, each 133×108 mm. (a) 1500 l. "Soup's On" (detail) (after Brueghel). P 13½×14. (b) 1500 l. "Two Duck Dancers" (detail) (after Degas) (*horiz*). P 14×13½
Set of 2 sheets 7·75 8·50

(Litho Questa)

1995 (6 Feb). *Centenary of International Olympic Committee. Medal Winners.* T **274** *and similar multicoloured designs.* P 14.

2201	75 l.	Type **274**	25	25
	a.	Sheetlet. Nos. 2201/12	2·75	
2202	75 l.	Karin Janz (Germany) (1972 gymnastics silver)	25	25
2203	75 l.	Matthias Volz (Germany) (1936 gymnastics bronze)	25	25
2204	75 l.	Carl Lewis (U.S.A.) (1988 long jump gold)	25	25
2205	75 l.	Sara Simeoni (Italy) (1976 high jump silver)	25	25
2206	75 l.	Daley Thompson (Great Britain) (1980 decathlon gold)	25	25
2207	75 l.	Japan and Britain (1964 football)	25	25
2208	75 l.	Gabriella Dorio (Italy) (1984 1500 metres gold)	25	25
2209	75 l.	Daniela Hunger (Germany) (1988 swimming gold)	25	25
2210	75 l.	Kyoko Iwasaki (Japan) (1992 swimming bronze)	25	25
2211	75 l.	Italian team (1960 water polo gold)	25	25
2212	75 l.	David Wilkie (Great Britain) (1976 swimming gold)	25	25
2213	200 l.	Katja Seizinger (Germany) (1994 alpine skiing gold)	40	40
	a.	Sheetlet. Nos. 2213/24	4·25	
2214	200 l.	Hot air balloon showing Olympic Rings	40	40
2215	200 l.	Elvis Stojko (Canada) (1994 figure skating silver)	40	40
2216	200 l.	Jans Weissflog (Germany) (1994 ski jumping gold)	40	40
2217	200 l.	Bjorn Daehlie (Norway) (1994 cross-country skiing gold)	40	40
2218	200 l.	German team (1994 four-man bobsled gold)	40	40
2219	200 l.	Markus Wasmeier (Germany) (1994 alpine skiing gold)	40	40
2220	200 l.	Georg Hacki (Germany) (1994 luge gold)	40	40
2221	200 l.	Jayne Torvill and Christopher Dean (Great Britain) (1994 ice dancing, bronze)	40	40
2222	200 l.	Bonnie Blair (U.S.A.) (1994 speed skating gold)	40	40
2223	200 l.	Nancy Kerrigan (U.S.A.) (1994 figure skating silver)	40	40
2224	200 l.	Sweden team (1994 ice hockey gold)	40	40
2201/24		*Set of 24*	7·00	7·00

MS2225 Two sheets, each 100×70 mm. (a) 1000 l. Medal winners (1994 women's figure skating) (*horiz*). (b) 1000 l. Athlete holding Olympic Torch (*horiz*) .. *Set of 2 sheets* 4·50 5·00
Nos. 2201/12 and 2213/24 were printed together, *se-tenant*, in sheetlets of 12 forming composite designs.

275 Ceratosaurus

(Des D. Burkhart. Litho Questa)

1995 (4 May). *Prehistoric Animals.* T **275** *and similar multicoloured designs.* P 14.

2226	200 l.	Type **275**	40	40
	a.	Sheetlet. Nos. 2226/37	4·25	
2227	200 l.	Brachiosaurus	40	40
2228	200 l.	Pteranodon	40	40
2229	200 l.	Stegoceras	40	40
2230	200 l.	Saurolophus	40	40
2231	200 l.	Ornithomumus	40	40
2232	200 l.	Compsognathus	40	40
2233	200 l.	Deinonychus	40	40
2234	200 l.	Ornitholestes	40	40
2235	200 l.	Archaeopteryx	40	40
2236	200 l.	Heterodontosaurus	40	40
2237	200 l.	Lesothosaurus	40	40
2226/37		*Set of 12*	4·25	4·25

MS2238 130×58 mm. 100 l. Triceratops (*vert*); 250 l. Protoceratops (*vert*); 400 l. Monoclonius (*vert*); 800 l. Styracosaurus (*vert*) .. 3·00 3·25
MS2239 Two sheets, each 99×79 mm. (a) 2500 l. Rhamphorynchus (*vert*). (b) 2500 l. Deinonychus (*vert*) .. .. .. *Set of 2 sheets* 5·00 5·50
Nos. 2226/37 were printed together, *se-tenant*, in sheetlets of 12 forming a composite design.

276 Pig (on red panel)

(Des Y. Lee. Litho Questa)

1995 (8 May). *Chinese New Year ("Year of the Pig").* T **276** *and similar multicoloured designs.* P 14.

2240	100 l.	Type **276**	50	50
	a.	Block of 4. Nos. 2240/3	1·75	
	ab.	Error. Stamp shows face value as "75 c."	15·00	
2241	100 l.	Pig facing right (on green panel)	50	50
2242	100 l.	Pig facing left (on green panel)	50	50
2243	100 l.	Pig facing right (on red panel)	50	50
2240/3		*Set of 4*	1·75	1·75

MS2244 77×105 mm. 500 l. Two pigs (*vert*) .. 2·00 2·75
Nos. 2240/3 were printed together, *se-tenant*, as blocks of 4 in sheets of 16.
No. 2240ab comes from the initial supplies sent to Freetown and withdrawn on day of issue when the incorrect face values were noticed.

(Litho Questa)

1995 (10 May). *Centenary of Sierra Club (environmental protection society) (1992). Endangered Species. Multicoloured designs as* T **296** *of Maldive Islands.* P 14.

2245	150 l.	Black-faced Impalas (*horiz*)	40	40
	a.	Sheetlet. Nos. 2245/53	3·25	
2246	150 l.	Herd of Black-faced Impalas (*horiz*)	40	40
2247	150 l.	Black-faced Impalas drinking (*horiz*)	40	40
2248	150 l.	Bonobo with young (*horiz*)	40	40
2249	150 l.	Black-footed Cat in foliage (*horiz*)	40	40
2250	150 l.	Close-up of Black-footed Cat (*horiz*)	40	40
2251	150 l.	L'Hoest's Monkey on all fours (*horiz*)	40	40
2252	150 l.	L'Hoest's Monkey squatting (*horiz*)	40	40
2253	150 l.	Pair of Mandrills (*horiz*)	40	40
2254	150 l.	L'Hoest's Monkey	40	40
	a.	Sheetlet. Nos. 2254/62	3·25	
2255	150 l.	Black-footed Cat	40	40
2256	150 l.	Head of Colobus Monkey	40	40
2257	150 l.	Colobus Monkey in tree fork	40	40
2258	150 l.	Head of Mandrill	40	40
2259	150 l.	Bonobo with young	40	40
2260	150 l.	Bonobo asleep on log	40	40
2261	150 l.	Mandrill facing right	40	40
2262	150 l.	Colobus Monkey on log	40	40
2245/62		*Set of 18*	6·50	6·50

Nos. 2245/53 and 2254/62 were each printed together, *se-tenant*, in sheetlets of 9.

277 Denver and Rio Grande Western Railroad

(Des W. Wright. Litho China Security Ptg Ltd)

1995 (23 May). *Railways of the World.* T **277** *and similar horiz designs. Multicoloured.* P 14.

2263/74 200 l. × 12 (Type **277**; Central of Georgia; Seaboard Air Line; Missouri Pacific Lines; Atchison, Topeka and Sante Fe; Chicago, Milwaukee, St. Paul and Pacific; Texas and Pacific; Minneapolis, St. Paul and Sault Ste. Marie; Western Pacific; Great Northern; Baltimore and Ohio; Chicago, Rock Island and Pacific)
a. Sheetlet. Nos. 2263/74 .. 4·50 4·75
2275/86 200 l. × 12 (Southern Pacific; Belgian National; Indian; Southern Australian; Union Pacific; British Railways; German Federal;

Japanese National; Pennsylvania; East African; Milwaukee; Paris–Orleans)
a. Sheetlet. Nos. 2275/86 .. 4·50 4·75
2287/98 250 l. × 12 (Eurostar; E.T.R. 401 Pendolino express; British Rail Intercity 125; Talgo "Virgen" express, Spain; French National TGV; Amtrak "Southwest Chief" express; French National TGV "Atlantique" express; Greek "Peloponnese Express"; Japanese "Hikari" express train; Canadian National Turbotrain; Australian XPT high-speed train; Chinese SS1 electric locomotive)
a. Sheetlet. Nos. 2287/98 .. 5·50 6·00
2299/310 300 l. × 12 (Canadian National U1-f locomotive; Union Pacific steam locomotive, No. 119; LNER Class A4, No. 4468 *Mallard*; New York Central Class J3a steam locomotive; Canadian National Class U4 locomotive; Australian Class 38 locomotive; Canadian Pacific Class G3c locomotive; Southern Railway Class "West Country" locomotive; Norfolk & Western Class J locomotive; China Class RM locomotive; Russia Class F-36 locomotive; GWR Class "King" locomotive)
a. Sheetlet. Nos. 2298/310 6·50 7·00
2263/310 .. *Set of 48* 19·00 20·00
MS2311 Five sheets, each 107×79 mm. containing larger designs. (a) 1500 l. British Railways No. 45627 *Sierra Leone* locomotive. (b) 1500 l. China Railways Class QJ locomotive. (c) 1500 l. Denver and Rio Grande Western Railroad "California Zephyr" express. (d) 1500 l. China Railways Beijing–Shanghai express. (e) 1500 l. China Railways first train across Yangtze Bridge, 1968 .. *Set of 5 sheets* 13·00 14·00
Nos. 2263/74, 2275/86, 2287/98 and 2299/310 were each printed together, *se-tenant*, in sheetlets of 12.
No. 2290 is inscribed "VIRGIN"; No. 2300 "CENTRAL PACIFIC RAILWAY" and No. 2302 "J-32", all in error.

278 National Flag and Scout Emblems

1995 (10 July). *18th World Scout Jamboree, Netherlands.* T **278** *and similar horiz designs. Multicoloured.* Litho. P 14.

2312	400 l.	Type **278**	70	80
	a.	Horiz strip of 3. Nos. 2312/14	2·25	
2313	500 l.	Lord Baden-Powell	80	90
2314	600 l.	Scout sign	90	1·00
2312/14		*Set of 3*	2·25	2·40

MS2315 80×111 mm. 1500 l. Scout saluting .. 2·25 2·40
Nos. 2312/14 were printed in sheets of 9 containing three *se-tenant* horizontal strips.

(Des W. Wright. Litho)

1995 (10 July). *50th Anniv of End of Second World War in Europe. Horiz designs as* T **317** *of Maldive Islands showing warships. Multicoloured.* P 14.

2316	250 l.	U.S.S. *Idaho* (battleship)	60	60
	a.	Sheetlet. Nos. 2316/23	4·25	
2317	250 l.	H.M.S. *Ark Royal* (aircraft carrier)	60	60
2318	250 l.	*Admiral Graf Spee* (German pocket battleship)	60	60
2319	250 l.	American destroyer	60	60
2320	250 l.	H.M.S. *Nelson* (battleship)	60	60
2321	250 l.	U.S.S. *PT 109* (motor torpedo boat)	60	60
2322	250 l.	U.S.S. *Iowa* (battleship)	60	60
2323	250 l.	*Bismarck* (German battleship)	60	60
2316/23		*Set of 8*	4·25	4·25

MS2324 105×74 mm. 1500 l. H.M.S. *Indomitable* (aircraft carrier) (57×42½ mm) .. 2·00 2·50
Nos. 2316/23 were printed together, *se-tenant*, in sheetlets of 8 with the stamps arranged in two horizontal strips of 4 separated by a gutter showing German U-boat pursuing Allied convoy.

(Des R. Rundo. Litho)

1995 (10 July). *50th Anniv of the United Nations. Multicoloured designs as* T **319** *of Maldive Islands, but vert.* P 14.

2325	300 l.	U.N. emblem above podium	60	70
	a.	Horiz strip of 3. Nos. 2325/7	1·90	
2326	400 l.	U Thant (Secretary-General, 1961–71)	70	80
2327	500 l.	Peace dove and U.N. Building, New York	80	90
2325/7		*Set of 3*	1·90	2·25

MS2328 105×74 mm. 1500 l. Dag Hammarskjold (Secretary-General, 1953–61) .. 2·00 2·50
Nos. 2325/7 were printed together in sheets of 9 containing three *se-tenant* horizontal strips of 3 forming a composite design.

(Des R. Rundo. Litho)

1995 (10 July–Sept). *50th Anniv of Food and Agriculture Organization. Multicoloured designs as T 298 of St. Vincent. P* 14.

2329	300 l.	Fisherman in boat (*horiz*)	60	70
	a.	Horiz strip of 3. Nos. 2329/31	1·90	
2330	400 l.	Boy carrying wood (*horiz*)	70	80
2331	500 l.	Woman with fruit (*horiz*)	80	90
2329/31		*Set of 3*	1·90	2·25
MS2332	76×106 mm.	1500 l. Mother and child		

(without date below emblem on woman's shoulder) (Sept) .. .. 2·00 2·50

a. Inscr "1945–55" below emblem on woman's shoulder .. .. 2·75 3·00

Nos. 2329/31 were printed together in sheets of 9 containing three se-tenant horizontal strips.

No. MS2332a comes from the initial supplies sent to Freetown and withdrawn on day of issue when the wrong date was noticed.

(Litho Questa)

1995 (10 July). *90th Anniv of Rotary International. Horiz designs as T 299 of St. Vincent. Multicoloured. P* 14.

2333	500 l.	National flag and Rotary logo	80	90
MS2334	105×75 mm.	1000 l. Paul Harris		

(founder) and logo .. .. 1·60 1·75

(Litho Questa)

1995 (10 July). *95th Birthday of Queen Elizabeth the Queen Mother. Vert designs as T 321 of Maldive Islands. P* 13½×14.

2335	400 l.	orange-brown, pale brown and black	70	75
	a.	Sheetlet. Nos. 2335/8×2	5·00	
2336	400 l.	multicoloured	70	75
2337	400 l.	multicoloured	70	75
2338	400 l.	multicoloured	70	75
2335/8		*Set of 4*	2·50	2·75
MS2339	102×127 mm.	1500 l. multicoloured	2·75	3·00

Designs:—No. 2335, Queen Elizabeth the Queen Mother (pastel drawing); No. 2336, Holding bouquet of flowers; Nos. 2337, At desk (oil painting); No. 2338, Wearing pink evening dress; No. MS2339, Wearing blue hat.

Nos. 2335/8 were printed together in sheetlets of 8, containing two se-tenant horizontal strips of 4.

(Des J. Batchelor. Litho Questa)

1995 (10 July). *50th Anniv of End of Second World War in the Pacific. Horiz designs as T 317 of Maldive Islands. Multicoloured. P* 14.

2340	300 l.	American B-17 bomber	70	70
	a.	Sheetlet. Nos. 2340/5	3·75	
2341	300 l.	American B-25 bomber	70	70
2342	300 l.	American Consolidated B-24 Liberator bomber	70	70
2343	300 l.	U.S.S. *Missouri* (battleship)	70	70
2344	300 l.	American Douglas A-20 Boston bomber	70	70
2345	300 l.	American battle fleet in Lingayen Gulf	70	70
2340/5		*Set of 6*	3·75	3·75
MS2346	108×76 mm.	1500 l. Nose of B-29 Superfortress	2·75	3·00

Nos. 2340/5 were printed together, se-tenant, in sheetlets of 6 with the stamps arranged in two horizontal strips of 3 separated by a gutter showing sinking U.S.S. *Arizona* (battleship). No. 2340 is inscribed "B-179" in error.

279 Black-spotted Pufferfish

280 Flame Lily

(Des Y. Lee. Litho Questa)

1995 (4 Sept). *"Singapore '95" International Stamp Exhibition (1st issue). Marine Life. T 279 and similar multicoloured designs. P* 14.

2347	300 l.	Type 279	60	60
	a.	Sheetlet. Nos. 2347/55	4·75	
2348	300 l.	Coral Hind	60	60
2349	300 l.	Hawksbill Turtle	60	60
2350	300 l.	Hogfish	60	60
2351	300 l.	Emperor Angelfish	60	60
2352	300 l.	Red-tailed Butterflyfish	60	60
2353	300 l.	Lemon Butterflyfish	60	60
2354	300 l.	Green-beaked Parrot Fish	60	60
2355	300 l.	Spotted Reef Moray	60	60
2356	300 l.	Cape Pigeons	60	60
	a.	Sheetlet. Nos. 2356/64	4·75	
2357	300 l.	Pelican	60	60
2358	300 l.	Puffin	60	60
2359	300 l.	Humpback Whale	60	60
2360	300 l.	Greater Shearwater	60	60
2361	300 l.	Bottlenose Dolphin	60	60
2362	300 l.	Gurnards	60	60
2363	300 l.	Atlantic Salmon	60	60
2364	300 l.	John Dory	60	60
2347/64		*Set of 18*	9·50	9·50
MS2365	Two sheets. (a) 71×101 mm. 1500 l.			

Ocean Surgeonfish. (b) 101×71 mm. 1500 l. Pennant Coralfish ("Angelfish") (*vert*)

Set of 2 sheets 6·00 6·50

Nos. 2347/55 and 2356/64 were printed together, se-tenant, in sheetlets of 9 forming composite designs.

(Des T. Pedersen. Litho Questa)

1995 (5 Sept). *"Singapore '95" International Stamp Exhibition (2nd issue). African Flora and Fauna. T 280 and similar vert designs. Multicoloured. P* 14.

2366	300 l.	Type 280	90	90
	a.	Sheetlet. Nos. 2366/73	6·50	
2367	300 l.	Grant's Gazelle	90	90
2368	300 l.	Dogbane	90	90
2369	300 l.	Gold-banded Forester	90	90
2370	300 l.	Horned Chameleon	90	90
2371	300 l.	Malachite Kingfisher	90	90
2372	300 l.	Leaf Beetle	90	90
2373	300 l.	Acanthus	90	90
2374	300 l.	African Tulip Tree	90	90
	a.	Sheetlet. Nos. 2374/81	6·50	
2375	300 l.	Senegal Bush Locust	90	90
2376	300 l.	Killfish	90	90
2377	300 l.	Bird of Paradise (flower)	90	90
2378	300 l.	Mandrill	90	90
2379	300 l.	Painted Reed Frog	90	90
2380	300 l.	Large Spotted Acraea	90	90
2381	300 l.	Carmine Bee Eater	90	90
2366/81		*Set of 16*	13·00	13·00
MS2382	Two sheets, each 103×73 mm. (a)			

1500 l. Elephant. (b) 1500 l. Lion *Set of 2 sheets* 6·00 6·50

Nos. 2366/73 and 2374/81 were printed together, se-tenant, in sheetlets of 8.

281 School Building and Emblem

(Litho Questa)

1995 (27 Sept). *150th Anniv of Sierra Leone Grammar School. P* 14.

2383	**281** 300 l.	sepia, deep magenta and black	50	50

(Litho Questa)

1995 (1 Dec). *Christmas. Religious Paintings. Vert designs as T 98 of St. Kitts-Nevis (Nevis). Multicoloured. P* 13½×14.

2384	50 l.	"Holy Family" (detail) (Beccafumi)	15	10
2385	100 l.	"The Rest on the Flight into Egypt" (detail) (Federico Barocci)	20	10
2386	150 l.	"The Virgin" (Jacopo Bellini)	30	15
2387	200 l.	"The Flight" (Cavaliere d'Arpino)	35	20
2388	600 l.	"Adoration of the Magi" (detail) (Francken)	1·10	1·40
2389	800 l.	"The Annunciation" (Cima de Conegliano)	1·40	1·60
2384/9		*Set of 6*	3·25	3·25
MS2390	Two sheets, each 102×127 mm. (a)			

1500 l. "Virgin and Child" (detail) (Cranach). (b) 1500 l. "Madonna and Child" (detail) (Berlinghiero) .. .. *Set of 2 sheets* 6·00 6·50

282 Mickey Mouse Doll

283 Andrew Huxley (1963 Medicine)

(Des Rosemary DeFiglio. Litho Questa)

1995 (4 Dec). *Christmas. Disney Toys. T 282 and similar vert designs. Multicoloured. P* 13½×14.

2391	5 l.	Type 282	10	10
2392	10 l.	Donald Duck drum-major doll	10	10
2393	15 l.	Donald Duck wind-up toy	10	10
2394	20 l.	Donald Duck toothbrush holder	10	10
2395	25 l.	Mickey Mouse telephone	10	10
2396	30 l.	Mickey Mouse walking toy	10	10
2397	800 l.	Toy film projector	2·25	2·25
2398	1000 l.	Goofy tricycle toy	2·50	2·50
2391/8		*Set of 8*	4·75	4·75
MS2399	Two sheets, each 133×107 mm. (a)			

1500 l. Black Mickey Mouse doll. (b) 1500 l. First Mickey Mouse book .. *Set of 2 sheets* 6·00 6·50

(Des R. Martin (Nos. 2400/8), Shyna Magid (others). Litho Questa)

1995 (29 Dec). *Centenary of Nobel Prize Trust Fund. T 283 and similar multicoloured designs. Multicoloured. P* 14.

2400/8	250 l. × 9	(Type **283**; Nelson Mandela (1993 Peace); Gabriela Mistral (1945 Literature); Otto Diels (1950 Chemistry); Hannes Alfven (1970 Physics); Wole Soyinka (1986 Literature); Hans Dehmelt (1989 Physics); Desmond Tutu (1984 Peace); Leo Esaki (1973 Physics))		
	a.	Sheetlet. Nos. 2400/8	5·00	5·50

2409/17	250 l. × 9	(Tobias Asser (1911 Peace); Andrei Sakharov (1975 Peace); Frédéric Passy (1901 Peace); Dag Hammarskjöld (1961 Peace); Aung San Suu Kyi (1991 Peace); Ludwig Quidde (1927 Peace); Elie Wiesel (1986 Peace); Bertha von Suttner (1905 Peace); The Dalai Lama (1989 Peace))		
	a.	Sheetlet. Nos. 2409/17	5·00	5·50
2418/26	250 l. × 9	(Richard Zsigmondy (1925 Chemistry); Robert Huber (1988 Chemistry); Wilhelm Ostwald (1909 Chemistry); Johann Deisenhofer (1988 Chemistry); Heinrich Wieland (1922 Chemistry); Gerhard Herzberg (1971 Chemistry); Hans von Euler-Chelpin (1929 Chemistry); Richard Willsätter (1915 Chemistry); Fritz Haber (1918 Chemustry))		
	a.	Sheetlet. Nos. 2418/26	5·00	5·50
2427/35	250 l. × 9	(Maria Goeppert Mayer (1963 Physics); Iréne Joliot-Curie (1935 Chemistry); Mother Teresa (1979 Peace); Selma Lagerlöf (1909 Literature); Rosalyn Yalow (1977 Medicine); Dorothy Hodgkin (1964 Chemistry); Rita Levi-Montalcini (1986 Medicine); Mairead Corrigan (1976 Peace); Betty Williams (1976 Peace))		
	a.	Sheetlet. Nos. 2427/35	5·00	5·50
2400/35		*Set of 36*	18·00	20·00
MS2436	Three sheets, each 80×110 mm. (a)			

1500 l. Albert Einstein (1921 Physics). (b) 1500 l. Wilhelm Röntgen (1901 Physics). (c) 1500 l. Sin-Itiro Tomonaga (1965 Physics) .. *Set of 3 sheets* 8·00 9·00

Nos. 2400/8, 2409/17, 2418/26 and 2427/35 were each printed together, se-tenant, in sheetlets of 9.

284 Rat

(Des Y. Lee. Litho Questa)

1996 (2 Jan). *Chinese New Year ("Year of the Rat"). T 284 and similar designs with background colour given. P* 14.

2437	**284** 200 l.	mult (yellow-brown background)	10	15
	a.	Block of 4. Nos. 2437/40	40	
2438	— 200 l.	mult (rose-red background)	10	15
2439	— 200 l.	mult (orange-verm background)	10	15
2440	— 200 l.	mult (turquoise-bl background)	10	15
2437/40		*Set of 4*	40	60
MS2441	110×84 mm.	1500 l. multicoloured. Nos. 2437/40	40	60
MS2442	76×106 mm.	500 l. multicoloured (orange-red background) (*vert*)	30	35

Nos. 2437/40 were printed together, se-tenant, as blocks of 4 in sheets of 16.

285 Mickey Mouse as Magician

286 Lumiére Brothers (cine camera inventors) and Train

(Litho Questa)

1996 (29 Jan). *Disney Circus Performers. T 285 and similar multicoloured designs showing cartoon characters. P* 13½×14.

2443	100 l.	Type 285	40	20
2444	200 l.	Clarabelle Cow walking tightrope	60	50
2445	250 l.	Donald Duck and nephews as clowns	70	60
2446	300 l.	Donald as lion tamer	85	75
2447	800 l.	Minnie Mouse riding bareback	2·25	2·50
2448	1000 l.	Goofy on trapeze	2·50	2·75
2443/8		*Set of 6*	6·50	6·50
MS2449	Two sheets, each 104×125 mm. (a)			

1500 l. Mickey with dinosaur (*horiz*). (b) 1500 l. Pluto balancing ball on nose (*horiz*). P 14×13½

Set of 2 sheets 6·50 7·00

1996 (26 Feb). *Centenary of Cinema. T 286 and similar vert designs. Multicoloured. Litho. P* 13½×14.

2450	250 l.	Type 286	15	20
	a.	Sheetlet. Nos. 2450/8	1·25	
2451	250 l.	Georges Méliès (director)	15	20
2452	250 l.	Toshiro Méfune (director)	15	20
2453	250 l.	David O. Selznick (director)	15	20

2454 250 l. Character from *Metropolis* .. 15 20
2455 250 l. Akira Kurosawa (director) .. 15 20
2456 250 l. Charlie Chaplin (actor) .. 15 20
2457 250 l. Marlène Dietrich (actress) .. 15 20
2458 250 l. Steven Spielberg (director) .. 15 20
2459 250 l. Film camera .. 15 20
   a. Sheetlet. Nos. 2459/67 .. 1·25
2460 250 l. Pete (dog) .. 15 20
2461 250 l. Silver (horse) .. 15 20
2462 250 l. Rin-Tin-Tin (dog) .. 15 20
2463 250 l. King Kong (gorilla) .. 15 20
2464 250 l. Flipper (dolphin) .. 15 20
2465 250 l. Great White Shark from *Jaws* .. 15 20
2466 250 l. Elsa (lioness) .. 15 20
2467 250 l. Whale from *Moby Dick* .. 15 20
2450/67   Set of 18 2·50 3·50
MS2468 Two sheets, each 109×80 mm. (a) 1500 l. Cecil B. De Mille (producer). (b) 1500 l. Lassie (dog) .. Set of 2 sheets 1·90 2·00
Nos. 2450/8 and 2459/67 were printed together, *se-tenant*, in sheetlets of 9 forming composite designs.

(Litho Questa)

1996 (29 Apr). *125th Anniv of Metropolitan Museum of Art, New York. Multicoloured designs as T 331 of Maldive Islands.* P 13½×14.
2469/76 200 l. × 8 ("Honfleur" (detail) (Jongkind); "A Boat on the Shore" (detail) (Courbet); "Barges at Pontoise" (detail) (Pissarro); "The Dead Christ with Angels" (Manet); "Salisbury Cathedral" (detail) (Constable); "Lady with a Setter Dog" (detail) (Eakins); "Tahitian Women Bathing" (detail) (Gauguin); "Majas on a Balcony" (detail) (Goya))
   a. Sheetlet. Nos. 2469/76 plus centre label .. 1·10 1·25
2477/84 200 l. × 8 ("In the Meadow"; "By the Seashore" (detail); "Still Life with Peaches and Grapes" (detail); "Marguerite Bérard"; "Young Girl in Pink and Black Hat"; "Waitress at Duval's Restaurant" (detail); "A Road in Louveciennes" (detail); "Two Young Girls at the Piano" (detail) (all by Renoir))
   a. Sheetlet. Nos. 2477/84 plus centre label .. 1·10 1·25
2485/92 200 l. × 8 ("Morning, An Overcast Day, Rouen" (detail) (Pissarro); "The Horse Fair" (detail) (Bonheur); "High Tide: The Bathers" (detail) (Homer); "The Dance Class" (Degas); "The Brioche" (detail) (Manet); "The Grand Canal, Venice" (detail) (Turner); "St. Tecia interceding for plague-stricken Este" (detail) (Tiepolo); "Bridge at Villeneuve" (detail) (Sisley))
   a. Sheetlet. Nos. 2485/92 plus centre label .. 1·10 1·25
2493/2500 200 l. × 8 ("Madame Charpentier" (detail) (Renoir); "Head of Christ" (detail) (Rembrandt); "The Standard-bearer" (detail) (Rembrandt); "Girl Asleep" (Vermeer); "Lady with a Lute" (Vermeer); "Portrait of a Woman" (detail) (Rembrandt); "La Grenouillére" (detail) (Monet); "Woman with Chrysanthemums" (detail) (Degas))
   a. Sheetlet. Nos. 2493/2500 plus centre label .. 1·10 1·25
2469/2500   Set of 32 4·25 5·00
MS2501 Four sheets, each 95×70 mm. (a) 1500 l. "The Death of Socrates" (J. L. David) (85×56 mm). P 14. (b) 1500 l. "Battle of Constantine and Licinius" (detail) (Rubens) (85×56 mm). P 14. (c) 1500 l. "Samson and Delilah" (detail) (Rubens) (85×56 mm). P 14. (d) 1500 l. "The Emblem of Christ appearing to Constantine" (detail) (Rubens) (85×56 mm). P 14 .. Set of 4 sheets 3·75 4·00
Nos. 2469/76, 2477/84, 2485/92 and 2493/500 were each printed together, *se-tenant*, in sheetlets of 8 stamps and one centre label.

287 Olympic Stadium, Los Angeles, 1932
288 *Cantharellus cinnabarinus*

(Litho Questa)

1996 (11 June). *Olympic Games, Atlanta. T 287 and similar multicoloured designs.* P 14.
2502 100 l. Type 287 .. 10 10
2503 150 l. Archery .. 10 10
2504 300 l. Hockey .. 20 25
   a. Sheetlet. Nos. 2504/9 .. 1·10
2505 300 l. Swimming .. 20 25
2506 300 l. Equestrian .. 20 25
2507 300 l. Boxing .. 20 25

2508 300 l. Pommel horse exercises .. 20 25
2509 300 l. 100m running .. 20 25
2510 500 l. Rings exercises .. 30 35
2511 600 l. Pole vault .. 35 40
2502/11   Set of 10 1·90 2·40
MS2512 104×75 mm. 1500 l. Running (*vert*) .. 95 1·00
Nos. 2504/9 were printed together, *se-tenant*, in sheetlets of 6.

(Litho Questa)

1996 (17 June). *Fungi. T 288 and similar multicoloured designs.* P 14.
2513 50 l. Type 288 .. 10 10
2514 250 l. *Poronidulus conchifer* and *Aphyllophorales polyporaceae* .. 15 20
   a. Sheetlet. Nos. 2514/21 .. 1·10
2515 250 l. *Ceratiomyxa fruticulosa* .. 15 20
2516 250 l. *Cortinarius semisanguineus* and *Cortinariaceae agaricales* .. 15 20
2517 250 l. *Volvamella surrecta* and *Pluteaceae agricales* .. 15 20
2518 250 l. *Lepiota cepaestipes* .. 15 20
2519 250 l. *Amanita rubescens* .. 15 20
2520 250 l. *Phyllotopsis nidulans* and *Tricholomataceas agaricales* .. 15 20
2521 250 l. *Lysyrus gardneri* and *Clathraceae phallales* .. 15 20
2522 250 l. *Lactarius indigo* .. 15 20
   a. Sheetlet. Nos. 2522/9 .. 1·10
2523 250 l. *Coprinus quadrifidus* .. 15 20
2524 250 l. *Geopyxis carbonaria* .. 15 20
2525 250 l. *Astraeus hygrometricus* .. 15 20
2526 250 l. *Agaicaceae agaricales* .. 15 20
2527 250 l. *Mycena maculata* .. 15 20
2528 250 l. *Lactarius delciosus* .. 15 20
2529 250 l. *Amanita fulva* .. 15 20
2530 300 l. *Suillus grevillci* .. 20 25
2531 400 l. *Morchella esculenta* .. 25 30
2532 500 l. *Cortinamaceae agaricales* .. 30 35
2513/32   Set of 20 3·00 4·00
MS2533 Two sheets, each 110×80 mm. (a) 1500 l. *Psathyrella epimyces* (*horiz*). (b) 1500 l. *Rhodotus parmatus* (*horiz*) .. Set of 2 sheets 1·90 2·00
Nos. 2514/21 and 2522/9 were each printed together, *se-tenant*, in sheetlets of 8.

289 Abyssinian Cat
290 Three Asian Girls reading

1996 (17 June). *Cats. T 289 and similar vert designs. Multicoloured. Litho.* P 14.
2534 200 l. Type 289 .. 10 15
   a. Sheetlet. Nos. 2534/45 .. 1·10
2535 200 l. British Tabby .. 10 15
2536 200 l. Norwegian Forest Cat .. 10 15
2537 200 l. Maine Coon .. 10 15
2538 200 l. Bengal .. 10 15
2539 200 l. Asian .. 10 15
2540 200 l. American Curl .. 10 15
2541 200 l. Devon Rex .. 10 15
2542 200 l. Tonkinese .. 10 15
2543 200 l. Egyptian Mau .. 10 15
2544 200 l. Burmese .. 10 15
2545 200 l. Siamese .. 10 15
2546 200 l. British Shorthair .. 10 15
   a. Sheetlet. Nos. 2546/57 .. 1·10
2547 200 l. Tiffany .. 10 15
2548 200 l. Birman .. 10 15
2549 200 l. Somali .. 10 15
2550 200 l. Malayan .. 10 15
2551 200 l. Japanese Bobtail .. 10 15
2552 200 l. Himalayan .. 10 15
2553 200 l. Tortoiseshell .. 10 15
2554 200 l. Oriental .. 10 15
2555 200 l. Ocicat .. 10 15
2556 200 l. Chartreux .. 10 15
2557 200 l. Ragdoll .. 10 15
2534/57   Set of 24 2·00 3·50
MS2558 Two sheets, each 110×80 mm. (a) 2000 l. Persian. (b) 2000 l. Burmilla .. Set of 2 sheets 2·50 2·75
Nos. 2534/45 and 2546/57 were each printed together, *se-tenant*, in sheetlets of 12.

(Litho Questa)

1996 (15 July). *70th Birthday of Queen Elizabeth II. Vert designs as T 334 of Maldive Islands showing different photographs. Multicoloured.* P 13½×14.
2559 600 l. As Type 334 of Maldive Islands .. 35 40
   a. Strip of 3. Nos. 2559/61 .. 1·00
2560 600 l. Receiving posy .. 35 40
2561 600 l. Carrying bouquets .. 35 40
2559/61   Set of 3 1·00 1·10
MS2562 125×103 mm. 1500 l. Waving from balcony .. 95 1·00
Nos. 2559/61 were printed together, *se-tenant*, in horizontal and vertical strips of 3 throughout sheets of 9.

(Litho Questa)

1996 (15 July). *50th Anniv of U.N.I.C.E.F. T 290 and similar horiz designs. Multicoloured.* P 14.
2563 300 l. Type 290 .. 20 25
2564 400 l. African children reading .. 25 30
2565 500 l. Children in class .. 30 35
2563/5   Set of 3 75 90
MS2566 104×74 mm. 1500 l. Children's faces .. 95 1·00

291 "Pioneer" Spacecraft in Venus Orbit, 1986–1992

1996 (15 July). *Space Exploration. T 291 and similar horiz designs. Multicoloured. Litho.* P 14.
2567 300 l. Type 291 .. 20 25
   a. Sheetlet. Nos. 2567/72 .. 1·10
2568 300 l. Hubble Space Telescope .. 20 25
2569 300 l. "Voyager" Space Probe .. 20 25
2570 300 l. Space Shuttle *Challenger* .. 20 25
2571 300 l. "Pioneer II" Space Probe .. 20 25
2572 300 l. "Viking I" Mars Lander .. 20 25
2567/72   Set of 6 1·10 1·50
MS2573 104×74 mm. 1500 l. Space Shuttle *Challenger* landing .. 95 1·00
Nos. 2567/72 were printed together, *se-tenant*, in sheetlets of 6, the background forming a composite design.

292 Rat

1996 (15 July). *Chinese Lunar Calendar. T 292 and similar vert designs. Multicoloured. Litho.* P 13½.
2574 150 l. Type 292 .. 10 10
   a. Sheetlet. Nos. 2574/85 .. 1·10
2575 150 l. Ox .. 10 10
2576 150 l. Tiger .. 10 10
2577 150 l. Hare .. 10 10
2578 150 l. Dragon .. 10 10
2579 150 l. Snake .. 10 10
2580 150 l. Horse .. 10 10
2581 150 l. Sheep .. 10 10
2582 150 l. Monkey .. 10 10
2583 150 l. Cockerel .. 10 10
2584 150 l. Dog .. 10 10
2585 150 l. Pig .. 10 10
2574/85   Set of 12 1·10 1·10
Nos. 2574/85 were printed together, *se-tenant*, in sheetlets of 12.

293 *Charaxes pleione*
294 *Begonia multiflora* "Rambouillet"

(Litho Questa)

1996 (15 Aug). *Butterflies. T 293 and similar horiz designs. Multicoloured.* P 14.
2586 150 l. Type 293 .. 10 10
2587 200 l. *Eurema brigitta* .. 10 15
2588 250 l. *Precis orithya* .. 15 20
   a. Sheetlet. Nos. 2588/96 .. 1·25
2589 250 l. *Palla ussheri* .. 15 20
2590 250 l. *Junonia orithya* .. 15 20
2591 250 l. *Cymothoe sangaris* .. 15 20
2592 250 l. *Cyrestis camillus* .. 15 20
2593 250 l. *Precis rhadama* .. 15 20
2594 250 l. *Precis cebrene* .. 15 20
2595 250 l. *Hypolimnas misippus* .. 15 20
2596 250 l. *Colotis danae* .. 15 20
2597 300 l. *Charaxes ameliae* .. 20 25
2598 500 l. *Kallimoides rumia* .. 30 35
2586/98   Set of 13 2·00 2·50
MS2599 Two sheets, each 100×70 mm. (a) 1500 l. *Papilio antimachus*. (b) 1500 l. *Charaxes bohemani* .. Set of 2 sheets 1·90 2·00
Nos. 2588/96 were printed together, *se-tenant*, in sheetlets of 9.

(Litho Questa)

1996 (19 Aug). *Flowers. T 294 and similar vert designs. Multicoloured.* P 14.
2600 150 l. *Tulipa* "Georgette" .. 10 10
2601 200 l. *Helichrysum bracteatum* "Monstrosum" .. 10 15
2602 200 l. Fountain .. 10 15
   a. Sheetlet. Nos. 2602/10 .. 90

2603	200 l.	Type **294**	10	15
2604	200 l.	*Narcissus* "Trumpet Daffodil"	10	15
2605	200 l.	*Crocus speciosus*	10	15
2606	200 l.	*Chrysanthemum frutescens* "Marguerite"	10	15
2607	200 l.	*Petunia* "Polaris" and *Danaus gilippus* (butterfly)	10	15
2608	200 l.	*Cosmos pipinnatus* "Sensation" and *Papilio calguanabus* (butterfly)	10	15
2609	200 l.	*Anemone coronaris*	10	15
2610	200 l.	*Convolvulus minor*	10	15
2611	300 l.	*Paphiopedilum* "Claire de Lune"	20	25
		a. Sheetlet. Nos. 2611/19	1·75	
2612	300 l.	*Cymbidium* "Peach Bloom"	20	25
2613	300 l.	Yacht	20	25
2614	300 l.	*Miltonia* "Peach Blossom"	20	25
2615	300 l.	*Parides gundalachianus* (butterfly)	20	25
2616	300 l.	*Laeliocattleya* "Grand Gate"	20	25
2617	300 l.	*Lycaste aromatica*	20	25
2618	300 l.	*Brassolaeliocattleya* "Golden Land"	20	25
2619	300 l.	*Cymbidium* "Southern Lace" and *Catastica teutila* (butterfly)	20	25
2620	400 l.	*Viola* "Pansy"	25	30
2621	500 l.	*Phalaenopsis* "Pink Beauty"	30	35
2600/21		*Set of 22*	3·25	4·25

MS2622 Two sheets, each 80×110 mm. (a) 1500 l. *Helianthus annuus*. (b) 1500 l. *Cymbidium* "Lucifer" .. *Set of 2 sheets* 1·90 2·00

Nos. 2602/10 and 2611/19 were each printed together, *se-tenant*, in sheetlets of 9, with the backgrounds forming composite designs.

295 Greek War Galley (4th-century B.C.)

296 "The Sea Dragon's Daughter"

1996 (29 Oct). *History of Ships.* T **295** and similar horiz designs. Multicoloured. Litho. P 14.

2623	300 l.	Type **295**	20	25
		a. Sheetlet. Nos. 2623/31	1·75	
2624	300 l.	Roman war galley (A.D. 50)	20	25
2625	300 l.	Viking longship (9th-century)	20	25
2626	300 l.	Flemish carrack (15th-century)	20	25
2627	300 l.	Merchantman (16th-century)	20	25
2628	300 l.	Tudor galleon (16th-century)	20	25
2629	300 l.	Elizabethan galleon (17th-century)	20	25
2630	300 l.	Dutch warship (17th-century)	20	25
2631	300 l.	*Maestrale* (18th-century Maltese galley)	20	25
2632	300 l.	*Cutty Sark* (19th-century clipper)	20	25
		a. Sheetlet. Nos. 2632/40	1·75	
2633	300 l.	*Great Britain*, 1846 (steam/sail liner)	20	25
2634	300 l.	H.M.S. *Dreadnought*, 1906 (battleship)	20	25
2635	300 l.	*Queen Elizabeth*, 1940 (liner)	20	25
2636	300 l.	Ocean-going yacht, 1962	20	25
2637	300 l.	*United States*, 1952 (liner)	20	25
2638	300 l.	Nuclear-powered submarine, 1950s	20	25
2639	300 l.	Super tanker, 1960s	20	25
2640	300 l.	U.S.S. *Enterprise*, 1961 (aircraft carrier)	20	25
2623/40		*Set of 18*	3·50	4·50

MS2641 Two sheets, each 96×66 mm. (a) 1500 l. Egyptian ship (1480 B.C.) (56×42 *mm*). (b) 1500 l. *Legend of the Seas*, 1996 (cruise ship) (56×42 *mm*) .. .. *Set of 2 sheets* 1·90 2·00

Nos. 2623/31 and 2632/40 were each printed together, *se-tenant*, in sheetlets of 9.

No. 2634 is inscribed "Dreadnaught" in error.

(Litho Questa)

1996 (12 Dec). *Christmas. Religious Paintings.* Vert designs as T **337** of St. Vincent. Multicoloured. P 13½×14.

2642	200 l.	"Madonna of Humility" (Filippo Lippi)	10	15
2643	250 l.	"Coronation of the Virgin" (Lippi)	15	20
2644	400 l.	"The Annunciation" (Lippi)	25	30
2645	500 l.	"Annunciation" (*different*) (Lippi)	30	35
2646	600 l.	"Barbadori Altarpiece" (Lippi)	35	40
2647	800 l.	"Coronation of the Virgin" (*different*) (Lippi)	50	55
2642/7		*Set of 6*	1·60	1·90

MS2648 Two sheets, each 76×106 mm. (a) 2000 l. "Adoration of the Magi" (Rubens). (b) 2000 l. "Holy Family with St. Anne" (Rubens) .. *Set of 2 sheets* 2·50 2·75

No. 2646 is inscribed "Alterpiece" in error.

(Des L. Birmingham. Litho Questa)

1996 (19 Dec). *Legends of the Seas.* Forty sheets, each 105×75 mm, containing T **296** and similar multicoloured designs. P 14.

MS2649 (a) 1500 l. Type **296**; (b) 1500 l. *Homo aquaticus*; (c) 1500 l. Chinese sea fairy; (d) 1500 l. Sea totem pole; (e) 1500 l. *The Turtle* (fantasy submarine); (f) 1500 l. Mermaid (*horiz*); (g) 1500 l. "How the Whale Got its Throat" (*horiz*); (h) 1500 l. Killer Whale crest; (i) 1500 l. Odysseus and siren (*horiz*); (j) 1500 l. "The Little Mermaid" (Hans Christian Andersen) (*horiz*); (k) 1500 l. Squamish Indians (*horiz*); (l) 1500 l. Boy on Dolphin (*horiz*); (m) 1500 l. Atlantis airship (*horiz*);

(n) 1500 l. Sea Bishop (*horiz*); (o) 1500 l. "Twenty Thousand Leagues Under the Sea" (Jules Verne); (p) 1500 l. "Whale Song" (*horiz*); (q) 1500 l. Arion (*horiz*); (r) 1500 l. Dragonrider of Pern (*horiz*); (s) 1500 l. Kelpie (*horiz*); (t) 1500 l. Natsihlane on Sea Lion (*horiz*); (u) 1500 l. Triton; (v) 1500 l. Lang (dragon) (*horiz*); (w) 1500 l. *The Flying Dutchman* (*horiz*); (x) 1500 l. Lilith; (y) 1500 l. "Queen of the Orkney Islands"; (z) 1500 l. Merman; (za) 1500 l. Sea Centaur (*horiz*); (zb) 1500 l. Albatross (*horiz*); (zc) 1500 l. *The Rime of the Ancient Mariner* (Samuel Coleridge); (zd) 1500 l. Haida Eagle (*horiz*); (ze) 1500 l. Poseidon; (zf) 1500 l. Captain Ahab (*Moby Dick*); (zg) 1500 l. Underwater City; (zh) 1500 l. Jonah and the Whale; (zi) 1500 l. Waskos (*horiz*); (zj) 1500 l. Tom Swift (*horiz*); (zk) 1500 l. Arthropod sea monsters; (zl) 1500 l. Sea Serpent; (zm) 1500 l. Ship's figurehead Aphrodite (*horiz*); (zn) 1500 l. Ship's figurehead .. .. *Set of 40 sheets* 38·00 40·00

297 Ox

(Des Y. Lee. Litho Questa)

1997 (8 Jan). *Chinese New Year* ("*Year of the Ox*"). T **297** and similar multicoloured designs. P 14.

2650	250 l.	Type **297** (on purple panel)	15	20
		a. Block of 4. Nos. 2650/3	60	
2651	250 l.	Ox (on green panel)	15	20
2652	250 l.	Ox (on blue panel)	15	20
2653	250 l.	Ox (on brown panel)	15	20
2650/3		*Set of 4*	60	80

MS2654 106×76 mm. Nos. 2650/3 60 80
MS2655 106×76 mm. 800 l. Ox (*vert*) 50 55

Nos. 2650/3 were printed together, *se-tenant*, as blocks of 4 in sheets of 16.

298 Aladdin and Jasmine

299 Hong Kong Skyline by Day

(Litho Questa)

1997 (27 Jan). *Christmas. Aladdin.* T **298** and similar multicoloured designs showing Disney cartoon characters. P 13½×14.

2656	10 l.	Type **298**	10	10
2657	15 l.	Genie and Santa Claus	10	10
2658	20 l.	Aladdin and Jasmine on magic carpet	15	10
2659	25 l.	Genie as a Christmas tree	15	10
2660	30 l.	Genie as Santa Claus and Aladdin	15	10
2661	100 l.	Aladdin, Jasmine and Genie on magic carpet	40	20
2662	800 l.	Genie writing letter to Santa Claus	2·25	2·50
2663	1000 l.	Genie with four heads	2·50	2·75
2656/63		*Set of 8*	5·00	5·00

MS2664 Two sheets, each 127×101 mm. (a) 2000 l. Aladdin under a pile of gold; (b) 2000 l. Aladdin and Jasmine on magic carpet (*horiz*). P 14×13½ .. .. *Set of 2 sheets* 6·50 7·00

(Des M. Friedman. Litho B.D.T.)

1997 (12 Feb). *"Hong Kong '97" International Stamp Exhibition.* Two sheets, each 125×68 mm, containing T **299** and similar vert designs. Multicoloured. P 14.

MS2665 (a) 500 l. ×4 forming panorama of central Hong Kong by day. (b) 500 l. ×4 forming panorama of central Hong Kong by night .. .. *Set of 2 sheets* 2·40 2·50

(Des M. Freedman and Dena Rubin. Litho Questa)

1997 (24 Mar). *50th Anniv of U.N.E.S.C.O.* Multicoloured designs as T **348** of Maldive Islands. P 13½×14 (*vert*) or 14×13½ (*horiz*).

2666	60 l.	Church, Kizhi Pogost, Russia	10	10
2667	200 l.	Durmitor National Park, Yugoslavia	10	15
2668	250 l.	Nessebar, Bulgaria	15	20
2669	300 l.	Roros, Norway	20	25
		a. Sheetlet. Nos. 2669/76 and central label	1·60	
2670	300 l.	Varsovia city gate, Poland	20	25
2671	300 l.	Nuestra Senora Cathedral, Luxembourg	20	25
2672	300 l.	Tower, Vilnius, Lithuania	20	25
2673	300 l.	Jelling, Denmark	20	25
2674	300 l.	Petajavesi Church, Finland	20	25
2675	300 l.	Round house, Sweden	20	25

2676	300 l.	Berne Cathedral, Switzerland	20	25
2677	300 l.	Slopes of Mount Kilimanjaro, Tanzania	20	25
		a. Sheetlet. Nos. 2677/84 and central label	1·60	
2678	300 l.	Tombs, Fasil Ghebbi, Ethiopia	20	25
2679	300 l.	Mount Ruwenzori National Park, Uganda	20	25
2680	300 l.	Nubia Monument, Abu Simbel, Egypt	20	25
2681	300 l.	Tsingy of Bemaraha Nature Reserve, Madagascar	20	25
2682	300 l.	House, Djenné, Mali	20	25
2683	300 l.	Traditional house, Ghana	20	25
2684	300 l.	House, Abomey, Benin	20	25
2685	400 l.	Gateway, Bukhara, Uzbekistan	25	30
2686	300 l.	Monastery, Petchersk, Ukraine	30	35
2687	500 l.	Tower, Himeji-jo, Japan (*horiz*)	30	35
		a. Sheetlet. Nos. 2687/91 and label	1·50	
2688	500 l.	Gateway, Himeji-jo, Japan (*horiz*)	30	35
2689	500 l.	Outer wall and turrets, Himeji-jo, Japan (*horiz*)	30	35
2690	500 l.	Village, Himeji-jo, Japan (*horiz*)	30	35
2691	500 l.	Ornate gables, Himeji-jo, Japan (*horiz*)	30	35
2692	800 l.	Mountains, Slovakia	50	55
2666/92		*Set of 27*	6·00	7·00

MS2693 Two sheets, each 127×102 mm. (a) 2000 l. Djudj National Bird Sanctuary, Senegal (*horiz*). (b) 2000 l. The Acropolis, Athens, Greece (*horiz*) .. .. *Set of 2 sheets* 2·50 2·75

Nos. 2669/76 and 2677/84 were each printed together, *se-tenant* in sheetlets of 8 stamps with a central label and Nos. 2687/91 in sheetlets of 5 stamps with a top left-hand corner label.

No. 2676 is inscribed "BERNA", No. 2677 "KILIMANDJARO" and No. 2686 "MONESTRY", all in error.

(Des R. Rundo. Litho Questa)

1997 (23 June). *300th Anniv of Mother Goose Nursery Rhymes.* Two sheets, each 72×102 mm, containing horiz designs as T **112** of St. Kitts-Nevis (Nevis). Multicoloured. P 14.

MS2694 (a) 1500 l. "Three Blind Mice". (b) 1500 l. Woman in pink dress ("Myself") .. *Set of 2 sheets* 1·90 2·00

(Litho Questa)

1997 (23 June). *10th Anniv of Chernobyl Nuclear Disaster.* Vert designs as T **347** of St. Vincent. Multicoloured. P 13½×14.

2695	1000 l.	Child's face and U.N.E.S.C.O. emblem	60	65
2696	1500 l.	As 1000 l., but inscribed "CHABAD'S CHILDREN OF CHERNOBYL" at foot	95	1·00

(Litho Questa)

1997 (23 June). *Golden Wedding of Queen Elizabeth and Prince Philip.* Horiz designs as T **350** of Maldive Islands. Multicoloured (except Nos. 2699/2700). P 14.

2697	400 l.	Queen Elizabeth II	25	30
		a. Sheetlet. Nos. 2697/702	1·50	
2698	400 l.	Royal coat of arms	25	30
2699	400 l.	Queen Elizabeth with Prince Philip in military uniform (grey-black)	25	30
2700	400 l.	Queen Elizabeth with Prince Philip in naval mess dress (grey-black)	25	30
2701	400 l.	St. James's Palace	25	30
2702	400 l.	Prince Philip	25	30
2697/702		*Set of 6*	1·50	1·75

MS2703 100×70 mm. 1500 l. Queen Elizabeth with Prince Philip in naval uniform 95 1·00

Nos. 2697/702 were printed together, *se-tenant*, in sheetlets of 6.

(Litho Questa)

1997 (23 June). *Birth Bicentenary of Hiroshige (Japanese painter). "One Hundred Famous Views of Edo".* Vert designs as T **352** of Maldive Islands. Multicoloured. P 13½×14.

2704	400 l.	"Hatsune Riding Grounds, Bakuro-cho"	25	30
		a. Sheetlet. Nos. 2704/9	1·50	
2705	400 l.	"Mannen Bridge, Fukagawa"	25	30
2706	400 l.	"Ryogoku Bridge and the Great Riverbank"	25	30
2707	400 l.	"Asakusa River, Great Riverbank, Miyato River"	25	30
2708	400 l.	"Silk-goods Lane, Odenma-cho"	25	30
2709	400 l.	"Mokuboji Temple, Uchigawa Inlet, Gozensaihata"	25	30
2704/9		*Set of 6*	1·50	1·75

MS2710 Two sheets, each 102×127 mm. (a) 1500 l. "Nihonbashi Bridge and Edobashi Bridge". (b) 1500 l. "Tsukudajima from Eitai Bridge" .. .. *Set of 2 sheets* 1·90 2·00

Nos. 2704/9 were printed together, *se-tenant*, in sheetlets of 6.

300 Hong Kong Skyline

(Litho Questa)

1997 (23 June). *Return of Hong Kong to China. T 300 and similar horiz designs showing modern Hong Kong or Deng Xiaoping* (800 l.). P 14.

2711	400 l. multicoloured		25	30
	a. Sheetlet of 3		75	
2712	500 l. multicoloured		30	35
	a. Sheetlet of 3		90	
2713	550 l. multicoloured		35	40
	a. Sheetlet of 3		1·00	
2714	600 l. multicoloured		35	40
	a. Sheetlet of 3		1·00	
2715	650 l. multicoloured		45	50
	a. Sheetlet of 3		1·25	
2716	800 l. multicoloured		50	55
	a. Sheetlet of 3		1·50	
2711/16		*Set of 6*	2·00	2·50

Nos. 2711/16 were each printed *se-tenant*, in sheetlets of 3 with an illustrated left or right-hand margin.

301 Calgary Stadium, 1988

302 *Vindula erota*

(Litho Questa)

1997 (16 July). *Winter Olympic Games, Nagano, Japan* (1998). *T 301 and similar multicoloured designs.* P 14.

2717	250 l. Type **301**		15	20
2718	300 l. Freestyle Skiing Aerials, 1994 (*vert*)		20	25
2719	300 l. Peggy Fleming (U.S.A.) (figure skating, 1968) (*vert*)		20	25
	a. Sheetlet. Nos. 2719/22 each × 2		3·25	
2720	300 l. Japanese competitor (Nordic combined–ski jump, 1992/4) (*vert*)		20	25
2721	300 l. German team (two-man luge, 1968 to 1992) (*vert*)		20	25
2722	300 l. Frank-Peter Roetsch (East Germany) (biathlon, 1988) (*vert*)		20	25
2723	300 l. Ice Hockey (*vert*)		30	35
2724	800 l. Dan Jansen (U.S.A.) (speed skating, 1994) (*vert*)		50	55
2717/24		*Set of 8*	1·90	2·25

MS2725 Two sheets. (a) 106×76 mm. 1500 l. Jamaican bobsleigh team (*vert*). (b) 76×106 mm. 1500 l. Johann Olav Koss (Norway) (speed skating, 1992/4) (*vert*) .. *Set of 2 sheets* 1·90 2·00

Nos. 2719/22 were printed together, *se-tenant*, in sheetlets of 8 containing two of each design.

(Litho Questa)

1997 (23 July). *World Cup Football Championship, France* (1998). *Designs as T 246 of Lesotho.* P 13¹⁄₂×14 (*vert*) or 14×13¹⁄₂ (*horiz*).

2726	100 l. black		10	10
2727	150 l. black		10	10
2728	200 l. black		10	15
2729	250 l. black		15	20
2730	300 l. multicoloured		20	25
	a. Sheetlet. Nos. 2730/7 and two labels		1·60	
2731	300 l. multicoloured		20	25
2732	300 l. multicoloured		20	25
2733	300 l. multicoloured		20	25
2734	300 l. multicoloured		20	25
2735	300 l. multicoloured		20	25
2736	300 l. multicoloured		20	25
2737	300 l. multicoloured		20	25
2738	500 l. black		30	35
2739	600 l. black		30	35
2726/39		*Set of 14*	2·50	3·25

MS2740 Two sheets, each 127×102 mm. (a) 1500 l. agate. (b) 1500 l. multicoloured .. *Set of 2 sheets* 1·90 2·00

Designs: *Vert*—No. 2726, Stabile, Uruguay; No. 2727, Schavio, Italy; No. 2728, Kocsis, Hungary; No. 2729, Nejedly, Czechoslovakia; No. 2730, Dwight Yorke, Trinidad and Tobago; No. 2731, Dennis Bergkamp, Netherlands; No. 2732, Steve McManaman, England; No. 2733, Ryan Giggs, Wales; No. 2734, Romario, Brazil; No. 2735, Faustino Asprilla, Colombia; No. 2736, Roy Keane, Republic of Ireland; No. 2737, Peter Schmeichel, Denmark; No. 2738, Leonidas, Brazil; No. 2739, Ademir, Brazil. *Horiz*—No. **MS**2740a, Pele, Brazil; No. **MS**2740b, Lato, Poland.

Nos. 2730/7 were printed together, *se-tenant*, in sheetlets of 8 stamps and 2 labels, one at each end of the bottom row.

(Litho Questa)

1997 (1 Aug). *Butterflies of the World. T 302 and similar multicoloured designs.* P 14.

2741	150 l. Type **302**		10	10
2742	200 l. *Pereute leucodrosime*		10	15
2743	250 l. *Dynastor napolean*		15	20
2744	300 l. *Thauria aliris*		20	25
2745	500 l. *Lycaena dispar*		30	35
	a. Sheetlet. Nos. 2745/50		1·75	
2746	500 l. *Graphium sarpedon*		30	35
2747	500 l. *Euploe core*		30	35
2748	500 l. *Papilio cresphontes*		30	35
2749	500 l. *Colotis danae*		30	35
2750	500 l. *Battus philenor*		30	35
2751	600 l. *Papilio aegeus*		35	40
2752	600 l. *Mylothris chloris*		35	40
	a. Sheetlet. Nos. 2752/7		2·10	
2753	600 l. *Argynnis lathonia*		35	40
2754	600 l. *Elymnias agondas*		35	40
2755	600 l. *Palla ussheri*		35	40

2756	600 l. *Papilio glaucus*		35	40
2757	600 l. *Cercyonis pegala*		35	40
2758	800 l. *Amblyopidia anita*		50	55
2759	1500 l. *Kallimoides rumia*		95	1·00
2760	2000 l. *Papilio dardanus*		1·25	1·40
2741/60		*Set of 20*	7·25	8·50

MS2761 Two sheets, each 74×103 mm. (a) 3000 l. *Hebomoia glaucippe* (*horiz*). (b) 3000 l. *Colias eurytheme* (*horiz*) .. *Set of 2 sheets* 3·75 4·00

Nos. 2745/50 and 2752/7 were each printed together, *se-tenant*, in sheetlets of 6 with the backgrounds forming composite designs.

303 Lon Chaney in *Phantom of the Opera*, 1925

304 Shetland Sheepdog

(Des Zina Saunders (Nos. 2762/70, **MS**2780b), Michelle Amatrula (Nos. 2771/9, **MS**2780a). Litho B.D.T.)

1997 (15 Aug). *Famous Films. T 303 and similar vert designs showing Horror classics* (Nos. 2762/70) *or the films of Alfred Hitchcock* (Nos. 2771/9). *Multicoloured.* P 14.

2762	300 l. Type **303**		20	25
	a. Sheetlet. Nos. 2762/70		1·75	
2763	300 l. Boris Karloff in *The Mummy*, 1932		20	25
2764	300 l. Fredric March in *Dr. Jekyll and Mr Hyde*, 1932		20	25
2765	300 l. Lon Chaney Jr. in *The Wolf Man*, 1941		20	25
2766	300 l. Charles Laughton in *Island of Lost Souls*, 1933		20	25
2767	300 l. Lionel Atwill in *Mystery of the Wax Museum*, 1933		20	25
2768	300 l. Bela Lugosi in *Dracula*, 1931		20	25
2769	300 l. Vincent Price in *The Haunted Palace*, 1963		20	25
2770	300 l. Elsa Lanchester in *Bride of Frankenstein*, 1935		20	25
2771	350 l. Ray Milland in *Dial M for Murder*, 1954		20	25
	a. Sheetlet. Nos. 2771/9		1·75	
2772	350 l. James Stewart and Kim Novak in *Vertigo*, 1958		20	25
2773	350 l. Cary Grant, Ingrid Bergman and Claude Rains in *Notorious*, 1946		20	25
2774	350 l. Farley Granger and John Dall in *Rope*, 1948		20	25
2775	350 l. Cary Grant in *North by Northwest*, 1959		20	25
2776	350 l. James Stewart and Grace Kelly in *Rear Window*, 1954		20	25
2777	350 l. Joan Fontaine and Laurence Olivier in *Rebecca*, 1940		20	25
2778	350 l. Tippi Hedren in *The Birds*, 1963		20	25
2779	350 l. Janet Leigh in *Psycho*, 1960		20	25
2762/79		*Set of 18*	3·50	4·50

MS2780 Two sheets. (a) 72×102 mm. 1500 l. Alfred Hitchcock. (b) 82×82 mm. 3000 l. Boris Karloff in *Son of Frankenstein*, 1939 .. *Set of 2 sheets* 2·75 3·00

Nos. 2762/70 and 2771/9 were each printed together, *se-tenant*, in sheetlets of 9 with the backgrounds forming composite designs.

(Des R. Martin. Litho Questa)

1997 (29 Aug). *Dogs and Cats. T 304 and similar multicoloured designs.* P 14.

2781	100 l. Type **304**		10	10
2782	150 l. American Shorthair Tabby cat		10	10
2783	200 l. British Shorthair cat		10	15
2784	250 l. Alaskan Husky		15	20
2785	400 l. Basset Hound		25	30
	a. Sheetlet. Nos. 2785/90		1·50	
2786	400 l. Irish Setter		25	30
2787	400 l. St. Bernard		25	30
2788	400 l. German Shepherd		25	30
2789	400 l. Dalmatian		25	30
2790	400 l. Cocker Spaniel		25	30
2791	400 l. Chartreux cat		25	30
	a. Sheetlet. Nos. 2791/6		1·50	
2792	400 l. Abyssinian cat		25	30
2793	400 l. Burmese cat		25	30
2794	400 l. White Angora cat		25	30
2795	400 l. Japanese Bobtail cat		25	30
2796	400 l. Cymric cat		25	30
2797	500 l. Turkish Angora cat		30	35
2798	600 l. Jack Russell Terrier		35	40
2781/98		*Set of 18*	4·00	4·75

MS2799 Two sheets, each 106×75 mm. (a) 1500 l. Boxer (31×63 *mm*). (b) 1500 l. Egyptian Mau cat (63×31 *mm*) .. *Set of 2 sheets* 1·90 2·00

Nos. 2785/90 and 2791/6 were each printed together, *se-tenant*, in sheetlets of 6 with enlarged illustrated right-hand margins.

NEW INFORMATION

The editor is always interested to correspond with people who have new information that will improve or correct the Catalogue.

305 *Ansellia africana*

306 Daisy Duck

(Litho Questa)

1997 (1 Sept). *Orchids of the World. T 305 and similar vert designs. Multicoloured.* P 14.

2800	150 l. Type **305**		10	10
2801	200 l. *Maxillaria praestans*		10	15
2802	250 l. *Cymbidium mimi*		15	20
2803	300 l. *Dendrobium bigibbum*		20	25
2804	400 l. *Laelia anceps*		25	30
	a. Sheetlet. Nos. 2804/9		1·50	
2805	400 l. *Paphiopedilum fairrieanum*		25	30
2806	400 l. *Restrepia lansbergii*		25	30
2807	400 l. *Yamadara cattleya*		25	30
2808	400 l. *Cleistes divaricata*		25	30
2809	400 l. *Calypso bulbosa*		25	30
2810	500 l. *Encyclia vitellina*		30	35
2811	800 l. *Epidendrum prismatocarpum*		50	55
2800/11		*Set of 12*	2·75	3·50

MS2812 Two sheets, each 76×106 mm. (a) 1500 l. *Paphiopedilum tonsum*. (b) 1500 l. *Odontoglossum schlieperianum* Set of 2 sheets 1·90 2·00

Nos. 2804/9 were printed together, *se-tenant*, in sheetlets of 6.

(Litho Questa)

1997 (1 Oct). *Christmas. Disney Holidays. T 306 and similar multicoloured designs.* P 13¹⁄₂×14.

2813	50 l. Type **306**		20	20
	a. Sheetlet. Nos. 2813/18		1·10	
2814	50 l. Huey, Dewey and Louie		20	20
2815	50 l. Donald Duck		20	20
2816	50 l. Minnie Mouse		20	20
2817	50 l. Morty and Ferdie		20	20
2818	50 l. Mickey Mouse		20	20
2819	150 l. As No. 2814		60	60
2820	200 l. As No. 2817		75	75
2821	250 l. Type **306**		90	90
2822	300 l. As No. 2816		1·10	1·10
2823	400 l. As No. 2818		1·25	1·40
2824	500 l. As No. 2815		1·50	1·60
2825	600 l. Pluto		1·75	2·00
2826	800 l. Goofy		2·25	2·50
2813/26		*Set of 14*	10·00	11·00

MS2827 Two sheets. (a) 114×140 mm. 2000 l. Mickey Mouse in sleigh. P 13¹⁄₂×14. (b) 140×114 mm. 2000 l. Mickey, Donald and Daisy (*horiz*). P 14×13¹⁄₂ .. *Set of 2 sheets* 11·00 12·00

Nos. 2813/18 were printed together, *se-tenant*, in sheetlets of 6.

307 Benoist Type XIV

308 "The Annunciation" (Titian)

(Des W. Wright. Litho Questa)

1997 (6 Oct). *Development of the Civil Airliner. T 307 and similar horiz designs. Multicoloured.* P 14¹⁄₂×14.

2828	600 l. Type **307**		35	40
	a. Sheetlet. Nos. 2828/31		1·40	
2829	600 l. Douglas DC-3		35	40
2830	600 l. Junkers JU52/3m sea plane		35	40
2831	600 l. Sikorsky S-42 flying boat		35	40
2832	600 l. Sud Caravelle 6		35	40
	a. Sheetlet. Nos. 2832/5		1·40	
2833	600 l. Boeing 707		35	40
2834	600 l. De Havilland Comet		35	40
2835	600 l. Airbus Industrie A300		35	40
2828/35		*Set of 8*	2·75	3·00

MS2836 Two sheets, each 121×96 mm. (a) 2000 l. Lockheed L.1649A Starliner (91×34 *mm*). (b) 2000 l. Concorde (91×34 *mm*). P 13¹⁄₂×14 .. *Set of 2 sheets* 2·50 2·75

Nos. 2828/31 and 2832/5 were each printed together in sheetlets of 4 containing two vertical pairs separated by a large aircraft illustration.

(Litho B.D.T.)

1997 (24 Dec). *Christmas. Religious Paintings. T* **308** *and similar multicoloured designs. P* 14.

2837	100 l.	Type **308**	10	10
2838	150 l.	"The Annunciation" (Titian) (*different*)	10	10
2839	200 l.	"Madonna of Foligno" (Raphael)	10	15
2840	250 l.	"The Annunciation" (Michelino)	15	20
2841	500 l.	"The Prophet Isaiah" (Michelangelo)	30	35
2842	600 l.	"Three Angels" (Master of the Rhenish Housebook)	35	40
2837/42		*Set of* 6	1·10	1·25

MS2843 Two sheets, each 105×95 mm. (a) 2000 l. "The Fall of the Rebel Angels" (Bruegel the Elder) (*horiz*). (b) 2000 l. Angel and Monk (Anon) (*horiz*) .. .. *Set of 2 sheets* 2·50 2·75

(Litho Questa)

1998 (12 Jan). *Diana, Princess of Wales Commemoration. Vert designs as T* **249** *of Lesotho. Multicoloured (except Nos.* 2844, 2849, 2854 *and* 2856). *P* 14.

2844	400 l.	With daffodils (violet and black)	25	30
		a. Sheetlet. Nos. 2844/9	1·50	
2845	400 l.	Carrying bouquet	25	30
2846	400 l.	With Mother Teresa	25	30
2847	400 l.	Wearing green and black jacket	25	30
2848	400 l.	With shawl over head	25	30
2849	400 l.	In evening dress (brt carmine & blk)	25	30
2850	400 l.	Wearing choker and earrings	25	30
		a. Sheetlet. Nos. 2850/5	1·50	
2851	400 l.	With Prince William	25	30
2852	400 l.	Wearing grey-blue jacket and hat	25	30
2853	400 l.	Wearing white jacket	25	30
2854	400 l.	Wearing hat (chestnut and black)	25	30
2855	400 l.	Wearing black evening dress	25	30
2856	400 l.	Laughing (slate-blue and black)	25	30
		a. Sheetlet. Nos. 2856/61	1·50	
2857	400 l.	Wearing blue and white jacket and hat	25	30
2858	400 l.	Wearing green jacket with arms folded	25	30
2859	400 l.	Wearing black and white hat	25	30
2860	400 l.	Wearing open white shirt	25	30
2861	400 l.	Getting out of car	25	30
2844/61		*Set of* 18	4·50	5·25

MS2862 Three sheets. (a) 100×70 mm. 1500 l. Spooning food into bowl. (b) 100×70 mm. 1500 l. Wearing grey-blue hat and jacket. (c) 70×100 mm. 1500 l. Inspecting guard of honour
.. .. *Set of 3 sheets* 2·75 3·00

Nos. 2844/9, 2850/5 and 2856/61 were each printed together, *se-tenant*, in sheetlets of 6.

309 Tiger

310 *Metagyrphus nitens*

1998 (26 Jan). *Chinese New Year ("Year of the Tiger"). T* **309** *and similar designs with the tiger in the colour given. Litho. P* 14.

2863	**309**	250 l. multicoloured (deep mauve)	15	20
		a. Sheetlet. Nos. 2863/6	60	
2864	—	250 l. multicoloured (carmine-lake)	15	20
2865	—	250 l. multicoloured (bright purple)	15	20
2866	—	250 l. multicoloured (dull vermilion)	15	20
2863/6		*Set of* 4	60	80

MS2867 76×106 mm. 800 l. multicoloured (*vert*) 50 55

Nos. 2863/6 were printed together, *se-tenant*, in sheetlets of 4.

(Des R. Rundo. Litho Questa)

1998 (4 Aug). *Fauna and Flora. T* **310** *and similar multi-coloured designs. P* 14.

2868	200 l.	Type **310**	10	15
2869	250 l.	Lord Derby's Parakeet	15	20
2870	300 l.	Narcissus	20	25
2871	400 l.	*Barbus tetrazona* (fish) (*horiz*)	25	30
2872	450 l.	Japanese White-eyes (bird) (*horiz*)	30	35
		a. Sheetlet. Nos. 2872/7	1·75	
2873	450 l.	Rhododendron (*horiz*)	30	35
2874	450 l.	Slow Loris (*horiz*)	30	35
2875	450 l.	Gentiana (flower) (*horiz*)	30	35
2876	450 l.	*Orthetrum albistylum* (dragonfly) (*horiz*)	30	35
2877	450 l.	*Coluber jugularis* (snake) (*horiz*)	30	35
2878	450 l.	Cheetah (*horiz*)	30	35
		a. Sheetlet. Nos. 2878/83	1·75	
2879	450 l.	*Ornithogalum thyrsoides* (plant) (*horiz*)	30	35
2880	450 l.	Ostrich (*horiz*)	30	35
2881	450 l.	Common Chameleon (*horiz*)	30	35
2882	450 l.	Fennec Fox (*horiz*)	30	35
2883	450 l.	*Junonia hierta cebrene* (butterfly) (*horiz*)	30	35
2884	500 l.	*Agalychnis callidryas* (frog) (*horiz*)	30	35
2885	600 l.	Wolverine (*horiz*)	35	40
2868/85		*Set of* 18	4·75	5·75

MS2886 Two sheets. (a) 70×100 mm. 2000 l. Tricoloured Heron. (b) 100×70 mm. 2000 l. *Atheris squamiger* (snake) (*horiz*) *Set of 2 sheets* 2·50 2·75

Nos. 2872/7 and 2878/83 were each printed together, *se-tenant*, in sheetlets of 6, depicting the wildlife of either China or Africa, with the backgrounds forming composite designs.

311 Hypsilophodon

312 Phoenician Galley

(Des G. Bibby and B. Pevsner. Litho Questa)

1998 (18 Aug). *Prehistoric Animals. T* **311** *and similar multicoloured designs. P* 14.

2887	200 l.	Type **311**	10	15
2888	400 l.	Lambeosaurus	25	30
2889	500 l.	Corythosaurus	30	35
2890	500 l.	Tyrannosaurus (*horiz*)	30	35
		a. Sheetlet. Nos. 2890/5	1·75	
2891	500 l.	Tenontosaurus (*horiz*)	30	35
2892	500 l.	Deinonychus (*horiz*)	30	35
2893	500 l.	Triceratops (*horiz*)	30	35
2894	500 l.	Maiasaura with eggs (*horiz*)	30	35
2895	500 l.	Struthiomimus (*horiz*)	30	35
2896	500 l.	Plateosaurus	30	35
		a. Sheetlet. Nos. 2896/901	1·75	
2897	500 l.	Tyrannosaurus	30	35
2898	500 l.	Brachiosaurus	30	35
2899	500 l.	Iguanodon	30	35
2900	500 l.	Styracosaurus	30	35
2901	500 l.	Hadrosaurus	30	35
2902	600 l.	Stegosaurus	35	40
2903	800 l.	Antrodemus (*horiz*)	50	55
2887/903		*Set of* 17	5·00	5·75

MS2904 Two sheets. (a) 73×103 mm. 2000 l. Triceratops (*horiz*). (b) 83×108 mm. 2000 l. Tyrannosaurus (*horiz*) .. *Set of 2 sheets* 2·50 2·75

Nos. 2890/5 and 2896/901 were each printed together, *se-tenant*, in sheetlets of 6 with the backgrounds forming composite designs.

1998 (25 Aug). *Ships of the World. T* **312** *and similar horiz designs. Multicoloured. Litho. P* 14.

2905	300 l.	Type **312**	20	25
		a. Sheetlet. Nos. 2905/10	1·10	
2906	300 l.	Viking longship	20	25
2907	300 l.	Carrack	20	25
2908	300 l.	Venetian galley	20	25
2909	300 l.	Galeasse	20	25
2910	300 l.	Chebeck	20	25
2911	300 l.	Junk	20	25
		a. Sheetlet. Nos. 2911/16	1·10	
2912	300 l.	H.M.S. *Victory* (ship of the line, 1765)	20	25
2913	300 l.	*Savannah* (paddle-steamer)	20	25
2914	300 l.	*Gaissa* (sailing canoe)	20	25
2915	300 l.	H.M.S. *Warrior* (ironclad)	20	25
2916	300 l.	*Preussen* (full-rigged ship)	20	25
2905/16		*Set of* 12	2·10	3·00

MS2917 Two sheets, each 108×83 mm. (a) 2000 l. *Santa Maria* (Columbus) (56×41 mm). (b) 2000 l. *Titanic* (liner) (56×41 mm)
.. .. .. *Set of 2 sheets* 2·50 2·75

Nos. 2905/10 and 2911/16 were each printed together, *se-tenant*, in sheetlets of 6.

(313)

314 Kiara and Butterfly

1998 (31 Aug). *70th Birthday of Mickey Mouse. Nos.* 2813/18 *and* MS2827 *optd with T* **313**.

2918	50 l.	Type **306**	20	20
		a. Sheetlet. Nos. 2918/23	1·10	
2919	50 l.	Huey, Duey and Louie	20	20
2920	50 l.	Donald Duck	20	20
2921	50 l.	Minnie Mouse	20	20
2922	50 l.	Morty and Ferdie	20	20
2923	50 l.	Mickey Mouse	20	20
2918/23		*Set of* 6	1·10	1·10

MS2924 Two sheets. (a) 114×140 mm. 2000 l. Mickey Mouse in sleigh. (b) 140×114 mm. 2000 l. Mickey, Donald and Daisy .. *Set of 2 sheets* 9·00 10·00

No. MS2924 shows Type 313 on the sheet margins which are also overprinted "MICKEY & MINNIE — 70th ANNIVERSARY".

(Des Walt Disney Co. Litho)

1998 (15 Sept). *Disney's Lion King (cartoon film). T* **314** *and similar multicoloured designs. P* 13½×14.

2925	500 l.	Type **314**	1·00	1·00
		a. Sheetlet. Nos. 2925/30	5·50	
2926	500 l.	Timon and Pumbaa	1·00	1·00
2927	500 l.	Kiara	1·00	1·00
2928	500 l.	Kiara and Kovu lying down	1·00	1·00
2929	500 l.	Kovu with bird	1·00	1·00

2930	500 l.	Kiara sitting with Kovu	1·00	1·00
2931	500 l.	Kiara and bird	1·00	1·00
		a. Sheetlet. Nos. 2931/6	5·50	
2932	500 l.	Pumbaa	1·00	1·00
2933	500 l.	Kiara and Kovu side by side	1·00	1·00
2934	500 l.	Kovu	1·00	1·00
2935	500 l.	Kiara and Kovu back to back	1·00	1·00
2936	500 l.	Timon	1·00	1·00
2925/36		*Set of* 12	11·00	11·00

MS2937 Two sheets, each 130×104 mm. (a) 2500 l. Pumbaa and Timon. P 13½×14. (b) 2500 l. Kiara, Kovu and butterflies (*horiz*). P 14×13½ .. .. 9·50 11·00

Nos. 2925/30 and 2931/6 were each printed together, *se-tenant*, in sheetlets of 6.

315 "Mary Magdalen Penitent" (Titian)

316 "Rocks and a Small Valley" (Delacroix)

(Litho B.D.T.)

1998 (14 Dec). *Christmas. Religious Paintings. T* **315** *and similar vert designs. Multicoloured. P* 14.

2938	200 l.	Type **315**	10	15
2939	500 l.	"Lamentation of Christ" (Veronese)	30	35
2940	1500 l.	"Building Noah's Ark" (Guido Reni)	95	1·00
2941	2000 l.	"Abraham and Isaac" (Rembrandt)	1·25	1·40
2938/41		*Set of* 4	2·50	2·75

MS2942 Two sheets, each 70×100 mm. (a) 3000 l. "The Assumption of the Virgin" (Murillo). (b) 3000 l. "Adoration of the Shepherds" (Murillo) .. .. *Set of 2 sheets* 3·75 4·00

(Des Diana Catherines. Litho Questa)

1998 (15 Dec). *25th Death Anniv of Pablo Picasso (painter). Multicoloured designs as T* **373** *of St. Vincent. P* 14½.

2943	400 l.	"Man with Straw Hat and Ice Cream Cone" (*vert*)	25	30
2944	600 l.	"Woman in a Red Armchair" (*vert*)	35	40
2945	800 l.	"Nude in a Garden" (*vert*)	50	55
2943/5		*Set of* 3	1·10	1·25

MS2946 101×127 mm. 2000 l. "Girl holding a Dove" (*vert*) .. .. .. 1·25 1·40

(Des J. Iskowitz. Litho Questa)

1998 (15 Dec). *19th World Scout Jamboree, Chile. Multi-coloured designs (except No.* 2950) *as T* **364** *of Maldive Islands. P* 14.

2947	1500 l.	Dan Beard and Lord Baden-Powell, 1937	95	1·00
		a. Sheetlet. Nos. 2947/9	2·75	
2948	1500 l.	Kuwaiti Scouts	95	1·00
2949	1500 l.	Scout leader feeding bear cub	95	1·00
2950	1500 l.	William D. Boyce (founder of Lone Scouts) (brown-purple, yellow-brown and black) (*vert*)	95	1·00
		a. Sheetlet. Nos. 2950/2	2·75	
2951	1500 l.	Guion S. Bluford (astronaut and former Eagle scout) (*vert*)	95	1·00
2952	1500 l.	Ellison S. Onizuka (astronaut and former Eagle scout) (*vert*)	95	1·00
2947/52		*Set of* 6	5·50	6·00

MS2953 Two sheets, each 70×100 mm. (a) 3000 l. Lord and Lady Baden-Powell, 1932. (b) 3000 l. Feeding bear cub from bottle
.. .. .. *Set of 2 sheets* 3·75 4·00

Nos. 2947/9 and 2950/2 were each printed together, *se-tenant*, in sheetlets of 3 with enlarged illustrated margins.

(Des J. Iskowitz. Litho Questa)

1998 (15 Dec). *50th Death Anniv of Mahatma Gandhi. Designs as T* **131** *of St. Kitts-Nevis (Nevis) showing Gandhi as a young man. P* 14.

2954	600 l.	multicoloured	35	40
		a. Sheetlet of 4	1·40	

MS2955 98×59 mm. 2000 l. bistre and black (*horiz*) 35 40

No. 2954 was printed in sheetlets of 4 with enlarged illustrated margins at top and left.

(Des D. Miller. Litho Questa)

1998 (15 Dec). *80th Anniv of Royal Air Force. Horiz designs as T* **132** *of St. Kitts-Nevis (Nevis). Multicoloured. P* 14.

2956	800 l.	McDonnell Douglas FRG2 Phantom	50	55
		a. Sheetlet. Nos. 2956/9	2·00	
2957	800 l.	Pair of Panavia Tornado GR1's	50	55
2958	800 l.	Sepecat Jaguar GR1A	50	55
2959	800 l.	Lockheed C-130 Hercules	50	55
2956/9		*Set of* 4	2·00	2·10

MS2960 Two sheets, each 92×70 mm. 2000 l. Lysander (reconnaissance) and Eurofighter EF-2000; 2000 l. Bird of prey and Bristol F2B fighter .. .. *Set of 2 sheets* 2·50 2·75

Nos. 2956/9 were printed together, *se-tenant*, in sheetlets of 4 with enlarged illustrated margins.

1998 (15 Dec). *Birth Bicentenary of Eugéne Delacroix (painter).* T **316** *and similar multicoloured designs. Litho.* P 14.

2961	400 l. Type **316**	..	..	25	30
	a. Sheetlet. Nos. 2961/8		..	2·00	
2962	400 l. "Jewish Musicians from Magador"		25	30
2963	400 l. "Moroccans travelling"		..	25	30
2964	400 l. "Women of Algiers in their Apartment"			25	30
2965	400 l. "Moroccan Military Training"		25	30
2966	400 l. "Arabs skirmishing in the Mountains"			25	30
2967	400 l. "Arab Chieftain reclining on a Carpet"			25	30
2968	400 l. "Procession in Tangier"		..	25	30
2961/8			*Set of 8*	2·00	2·25
MS2969	85×100 mm. 400 l. "Self-portrait" (*vert*)		25	30

Nos. 2961/8 were printed together in sheetlets of 8, containing two *se-tenant* horizontal strips of 4 separated by a gutter showing the paintings depicted on Nos. 2963 and 2966.

1998 (15 Dec). *1st Death Anniv of Diana, Princess of Wales. Vert design as* T **365** *of Maldive Islands. Multicoloured. Litho.* P 14½×14.

2970	600 l. Diana, Princess of Wales		..	35	40
	a. Sheetlet of 6		..	2·10	

No. 2970 was printed in sheetlets of 6 with an enlarged illustrated margin at left.

317 Rabbit

1998 (24 Dec). *Chinese New Year ("Year of the Rabbit").* T **317** *and similar designs with the rabbit in the colour given. Litho.* P 14.

2971	700 l. multicoloured (scarlet)	..	..	45	50
	a. Sheetlet. Nos. 2971/4		..	1·75	
2972	700 l. multicoloured (deep magenta)		45	50
2973	700 l. multicoloured (deep turquoise-blue)		45	50
2974	700 l. multicoloured (light reddish violet)		45	50
2971/4			*Set of 4*	1·75	2·00
MS2975	76×106 mm. 1500 l. mult (*vert*)		95	1·00

Nos. 2971/4 were printed together, *se-tenant*, in sheetlets of 4.

318 Powder-blue Surgeonfish

(Des D. Burkhart and R. Martin. Litho Questa)

1999 (22 Feb). *International Year of the Ocean.* T **318** *and similar horiz designs. Multicoloured.* P 14.

2976	150 l. Type **318**	..	..	10	10
2977	250 l. Frilled Anemone		..	15	20
2978	400 l. Eastern Reef Heron		..	25	30
	a. Sheetlet. Nos. 2978/89		..	3·00	
2979	400 l. Dolphins		..	25	30
2980	400 l. Humpback Whale and ship		25	30
2981	400 l. Green-winged Macaw ("Red and Green Macaw")			25	30
2982	400 l. Blue Tangs		..	25	30
2983	400 l. Guitarfish and Blue-striped Pipefish		25	30
2984	400 l. Manatees		..	25	30
2985	400 l. Hammerhead Shark		25	30
2986	400 l. Blue Shark		..	25	30
2987	400 l. Lemon Goby and Moorish Idol		25	30
2988	400 l. Ribbon Moray ("Ribbon Eels")		25	30
2989	400 l. Loggerhead Turtle		25	30
2990	500 l. Blue Shark		..	30	35
	a. Sheetlet. Nos. 2990/8		2·50	
2991	500 l. Tiger Shark		..	30	35
2992	500 l. Bull Shark		..	30	35
2993	500 l. Great White Shark		30	35
2994	500 l. Scalloped Hammerhead Shark		30	35
2995	500 l. Oceanic White-tipped Shark		30	35
2996	500 l. Zebra Shark		..	30	35
2997	500 l. Leopard Shark		30	35
2998	500 l. Horn Shark		..	30	35
2999	500 l. Hector's Dolphin		30	35
	a. Sheetlet. Nos. 2999/3007		2·50	
3000	500 l. Tucuxi		..	30	35
3001	500 l. Hourglass Dolphin		30	35
3002	500 l. Bottlenose Dolphin		30	35
3003	500 l. Gray's Beaked Whale		30	35
3004	500 l. Bowhead Whale		30	35
3005	500 l. Fin Whale		..	30	35
3006	500 l. Gray Whale		..	30	35
3007	500 l. Blue Whale		..	30	35
3008	600 l. Red Beard Sponge		35	40
3009	1500 l. Dusky Batfish ("Red-finned Batfish")		50	55
2976/3009			*Set of 34*	9·00	11·00

MS3010 Three sheets, each 110×85 mm. (a) 3000 l. Purple Fire Goby ("Purple Fire-fish"). (b) 3000 l. Spotted Eagle Ray. (c) 3000 l. Leatherback Turtle .. .. *Set of 3 sheets* 5·50 5·75

Nos. 2978/89, 2990/8 and 2999/3007 were each printed together, *se-tenant*, in sheetlets of 12 (Nos. 2978/89) or 9 (others), with the backgrounds forming composite designs.

---

319 Grumman X-29

(Des F. Rivera. Litho Questa)

1999 (22 Mar). *Aircraft.* T **319** *and similar horiz designs. Multicoloured.* P 14.

3011	200 l. Type **319**	..	..	10	15
3012	300 l. Bell XS-1 rocket aircraft		20	25
3013	400 l. Mikoyan Gurevich MiG-21		25	30
3014	600 l. Bleriot XI	..	..	35	40
3015	600 l. Niueport 11 "Bébé"		..	35	40
	a. Sheetlet. Nos. 3015/22		2·75	
3016	600 l. D.H.100 Vampire		..	35	40
3017	600 l. Aerospatiale/Aeritalia ATR 72		35	40
3018	600 l. Fiat CR-32		..	35	40
3019	600 l. Curtiss P-6E Hawk		35	40
3020	600 l. SAAB JA 37 Viggen		35	40
3021	600 l. Piper PA-46 Malibu		35	40
3022	600 l. Grumman F-14 Tomcat		35	40
3023	600 l. Grumman F3F-1		..	35	40
	a. Sheetlet. Nos. 3023/30		2·75	
3024	600 l. North American F-86A Sabre		35	40
3025	600 l. Cessna 377 Super Skymaster		35	40
3026	600 l. General Dynamics F-16 Fighting Falcon			35	40
3027	600 l. *Voyager* experimental aircraft		35	40
3028	600 l. Fairchild A10A Thunderbolt II		35	40
3029	600 l. Wiley Post's Lockheed Vega, 1933		35	40
3030	600 l. Amelia Earhart's Lockheed Vega, 1930			35	40
3031	600 l. Sopwith Tabloid		..	35	40
	a. Sheetlet. Nos. 3031/8		2·75	
3032	600 l. Vickers F.B.5 "Gun Bus"		35	40
3033	600 l. Savoia-Marchetti S.M. 79-II Sparviero			35	40
3034	600 l. Mitsubishi A6M3 "Zero Sen"		35	40
3035	600 l. Morane-Saulnier L		35	40
3036	600 l. Shorts 360	..	..	35	40
3037	600 l. Tupolev TU-160		35	40
3038	600 l. Mikoyan-Gurevich MiG-15		35	40
3039	800 l. Fokker F.VIIa/3m *Southern Cross*		50	55
3040	1500 l. Supermarine S6B (seaplane)		95	1·00
3011/40			*Set of 30*	10·50	13·00

MS3041 Two sheets, each 98×68 mm. (a) 3000 l. Ryan NYP Special *Spirit of St. Louis* (56×42 mm). (b) 3000 l. Canadair CL-215 (fire-fighting amphibian) (56×42 mm) .. *Set of 2 sheets* 3·75 4·00

Nos. 3015/22, 3023/30 and 3031/8 were each printed together, *se-tenant*, in sheetlets of 8 with enlarged illustrated right or top margins.

No. 3023 is inscribed "GUMMAN F3F-1" and No. 3030 "Amella Earhart", both in error.

320 *Geranium wallichianum*

321 Red-headed Malimbe

(Des R. Rundo. Litho Questa)

1999 (14 Apr). *"Australia '99" World Stamp Exhibition, Melbourne. Flowers.* T **320** *and similar multicoloured designs.* P 14.

3042	150 l. Type **320**	..	..	10	10
3043	200 l. Osmanthus × burkwoodii		10	15
3044	250 l. Iris pallida dalmatica (*vert*)		15	20
3045	500 l. Rhododendron (*vert*)		30	35
3046	600 l. Rose (*vert*)		..	35	40
3047	600 l. Clematis hybrida (*vert*)		35	40
	a. Sheetlet. Nos. 3047/52		2·10	
3048	600 l. Cardiospermum halicacabum (*vert*)		35	40
3049	600 l. Fritillaria imperialis (*vert*)		35	40
3050	600 l. Iris foetidiissima (*vert*)		35	40
3051	600 l. Pyracantha (*vert*)		35	40
3052	600 l. Hepatica transsilvanica (*vert*)		35	40
3053	600 l. Aquilegia olympica (*vert*)		35	40
	a. Sheetlet. Nos. 3053/8		2·10	
3054	600 l. Lilium (orange)		35	40
3055	600 l. Magnolia grandiflora		35	40
3056	600 l. Polygonatum × hybridum		35	40
3057	600 l. Clematis montana		35	40
3058	600 l. Vinca minor		..	35	40
3059	600 l. Narcissus "Jack Snipe"		35	40
	a. Sheetlet. Nos. 3059/64		2·10	
3060	600 l. Alstroemeria ligtu		35	40
3061	600 l. Lilium (yellow)		35	40
3062	600 l. Rose "Marjorie Fair"		35	40
3063	600 l. Anemone coronaria		35	40
3064	600 l. Clematis ranncu lanaceae		35	40
3065	600 l. Colchicum speciosum		35	40
	a. Sheetlet. Nos. 3065/70		2·10	
3066	600 l. Scandere		..	35	40
3067	600 l. Helianthus annuus		35	40
3068	600 l. Dahlia "Lady Kerkrade"		35	40
3069	600 l. Clematis × durandii		35	40
3070	600 l. Lilium regale		35	40
3071	800 l. Fuchsia "Papoose" (*vert*)		50	55

3072	1500 l. Viola labradorica (*vert*)		95	1·00
3073	2000 l. Rosa banksiae lutea (*vert*)		1·25	1·40
3042/73		*Set of 32*	12·00	13·50

MS3074 Four sheets. (a) 100×75 mm. 4000 l. *Clerodendrum trichotomum fargesii.* (b) 75×100 mm. 4000 l. *Rubus fruitcosus* (*vert*). (c) 75×100 mm. 4000 l. *Crocus angustifolius* (*vert*). (d) 75×100 mm. 4000 l. *Holboellia* .. *Set of 4 sheets* 10·00 10·50

Nos. 3047/52, 3053/8, 3059/64 and 3065/70 were printed together, *se-tenant*, in sheetlets of 6 with the backgrounds forming composite designs.

Only Nos. 3042/6 and 3071/3 show the "Australia '99" emblem actually printed on the designs.

No. 3043 is inscribed "Osmanthus burkwoodu" and No. 3069 "Clematix x durandii", both in error.

(Litho Questa)

1999 (18 May). *Birds of Africa.* T **321** *and similar multicoloured designs.* P 14.

3075	400 l. Type **321**	..	..	25	30
3076	500 l. Common Kestrel		30	35
3077	600 l. Little Owl		..	35	40
3078	600 l. Eastern White Pelican		35	40
	a. Sheetlet. Nos. 3078/85		2·75	
3079	600 l. Superb Starling		35	40
3080	600 l. Red-throated Bee Eater		35	40
3081	600 l. Woodland Kingfisher		35	40
3082	600 l. Purple Swamphen		35	40
3083	600 l. Lesser Pied Kingfisher		35	40
3084	600 l. African Spoonbill		35	40
3085	600 l. Egyptian Plover ("Crocodilebird")		35	40
3086	600 l. Cattle Egret		35	40
	a. Sheetlet. Nos. 3086/93		2·75	
3087	600 l. White-fronted Bee Eater		35	40
3088	600 l. Gray Parrot		35	40
3089	600 l. Cinnamon-chested Bee Eater		35	40
3090	600 l. Malachite Kingfisher		35	40
3091	600 l. White-throated Bee Eater		35	40
3092	600 l. Yellow-billed Stork		35	40
3093	600 l. Hildebrandt's Starling		35	40
3094	600 l. White-faced Whistling Duck (*horiz*)		35	40
	a. Sheetlet. Nos. 3094/102		3·00	
3095	600 l. Black-headed Heron (*horiz*)		35	40
3096	600 l. Black-headed Gonolek (*horiz*)		35	40
3097	600 l. Malachite Kingfisher (*horiz*)		35	40
3098	600 l. African Fish Eagle (*horiz*)		35	40
3099	600 l. African Spoonbill (*horiz*)		35	40
3100	600 l. African Skimmer (*horiz*)		35	40
3101	600 l. Black Heron (*horiz*)		35	40
3102	600 l. Allen's Gallinule (*horiz*)		35	40
3103	600 l. Montagu's Harrier (*horiz*)		35	40
	a. Sheetlet. Nos. 3103/11		3·00	
3104	600 l. Booted Eagle (*horiz*)		35	40
3105	600 l. Yellow-crested Helmet Shrike (*horiz*)		35	40
3106	600 l. Red-tufted Malachite Sunbird (*horiz*)		35	40
3107	600 l. Pin-tailed Whydah (*horiz*)		35	40
3108	600 l. Red-headed Malimbe (*horiz*)		35	40
3109	600 l. Violet-backed Sunbird (*horiz*)		35	40
3110	600 l. Yellow White Eye (*horiz*)		35	40
3111	600 l. Brubru Shrike (*horiz*)		35	40
3112	600 l. African Paradise Flycatcher ("Monarch") (*horiz*)			35	40
	a. Sheetlet. Nos. 3112/20		3·00	
3113	600 l. Lilac-breasted Roller (*horiz*)		35	40
3114	600 l. Scops Owl (*horiz*)		35	40
3115	600 l. African Emerald Cuckoo (*horiz*)		35	40
3116	600 l. Blue Flycatcher ("Monarch") (*horiz*)		35	40
3117	600 l. African Golden Oriole (*horiz*)		35	40
3118	600 l. White-throated Bee Eater (*horiz*)		35	40
3119	600 l. Black-bellied Seedcracker (*horiz*)		35	40
3120	600 l. Hoopoe (*horiz*)		35	40
3121	600 l. Scimitar-bill (*horiz*)		35	40
	a. Sheetlet. Nos. 3121/9		3·00	
3122	600 l. Bateleur (*horiz*)		35	40
3123	600 l. Village Weaver (*horiz*)		35	40
3124	600 l. Variable Sunbird (*horiz*)		35	40
3125	600 l. Blue Swallow (*horiz*)		35	40
3126	600 l. Red-crowned Bishop (*horiz*)		35	40
3127	600 l. Namaqua Dove (*horiz*)		35	40
3128	600 l. Golden-breasted Bunting (*horiz*)		35	40
3129	600 l. Hartlaub's Bustard (*horiz*)		35	40
3075/129		*Set of 55*	18·00	21·00

MS3130 Six sheets, each 85×110 mm (3000 l.) or 73×98 mm (4000 l.). (a) 3000 l. African Fish Eagle. (b) 3000 l. Baglafecht Weaver ("Richenow's Weaver"). (c) 4000 l. African Pygmy Kingfisher. (d) 4000 l. Ruwenzori Turaco. (e) 4000 l. South African ("Grey") Crowned Crane. (f) 4000 l. Whale-headed Stork ("Shoebill") .. *Set of 6 sheets* 13·50 14·00

Nos. 3078/85, 3086/93, 3094/102, 3103/11, 3112/20 and 3121/9 were each printed together, *se-tenant*, in sheetlets of 8 (Nos. 3078/85 and 3086/93) or 9 (others) with the backgrounds forming composite designs.

No. 3077 is inscribed "LITTLE OWL", No. 3087 "BMerops bullockoides", No. 3112 "Terpsiphonevirdis", No. 3121 "Scimitarbill", No. 3124 "Nectarina", No. 3126 "hordeaceus" and No. MS3130 (d) "Rwenzori", all in error.

322 Diana Monkey

323 Steam Locomotive, Benguela Railway, Angola

(Litho Questa)

1999 (31 May). *Wildlife. T* **322** *and similar vert designs. Multicoloured.* P 14.

3131	300 l.	Type **322**	20	25
3132	800 l.	Bush Pig	50	55
3133	900 l.	Flap-necked Chameleon	55	60
		a. Sheetlet. Nos. 3133/8	3·25	
3134	900 l.	Golden Oriole	55	60
3135	900 l.	European Bee Eater	55	60
3136	900 l.	Leopard	55	60
3137	900 l.	Lion	55	60
3138	900 l.	Chimpanzee	55	60
3139	900 l.	Senegal Galago	55	60
		a. Sheetlet. Nos. 3139/44	3·25	
3140	900 l.	Hoopoe	55	60
3141	900 l.	Long-tailed Pangolin	55	60
3142	900 l.	Hippopotamus	55	60
3143	900 l.	African Elephant	55	60
3144	900 l.	Red-billed Hornbill	55	60
3145	1500 l.	Lioness	95	1·00
3131/45		*Set of 15*	8·00	9·00

MS3146 Two sheets, each 85×110 mm. (a) 3000 l. Grey Parrot. (b) 3000 l. West African Linsang .. .. *Set of 2 sheets* 3·75 4·00
Nos. 3133/8 and 3139/44 were each printed together, *se-tenant*, in sheetlets of 6 forming composite designs.

(Litho Questa)

1999 (4 Aug). *Famous Trains. T* **323** *and similar multicoloured designs.* P 14.

3147	100 l.	The *Rocket* (*vert*)	10	10
3148	150 l.	Type **323**	10	10
3149	200 l.	Class 310 steam locomotive, Sudan	10	15
3150	250 l.	Steam locomotive, Chicago, Burlington and Quincy Railway, U.S.A.	15	20
3151	300 l.	Class "Terrier" tank locomotive, Great Britain	20	25
3152	400 l.	Dublin to Cork express train, Ireland	25	30
3153	500 l.	Steam locomotive *George Stephenson*, Scotland	30	35
3154	600 l.	Shay steam locomotive	35	40
3155	800 l.	Class 19D, Africa	50	55
		a. Sheetlet. Nos. 3155/60	3·00	
3156	800 l.	Double-headed train on viaduct over Kaaiman River, Africa	50	55
3157	800 l.	Bo-Bo electric locomotive, Egypt	50	55
3158	800 l.	Gmam Garratt steam locomotive, South Africa	50	55
3159	800 l.	Passenger train at Rabat, Morocco	50	55
3160	800 l.	Class 14A Garratt, Rhodesia	50	55
3161	800 l.	Western type steam locomotive, U.S.A.	50	55
		a. Sheetlet. Nos. 3161/6	3·00	
3162	800 l.	"The Flying Scotsman" express, Scotland	50	55
3163	800 l.	Steam locomotive *Lord Nelson*	50	55
3164	800 l.	Steam locomotive *Mallard*	50	55
3165	800 l.	Steam locomotive *Evening Star*	50	55
3166	800 l.	Indian Railways Class WP steam locomotive No. 7418	50	55
3167	1500 l.	"South Wind" express, U.S.A. (*horiz*)	95	1·00
3147/67		*Set of 21*	8·50	9·25

MS3168 Two sheets. (a) 76×106 mm. 3000 l. Railcar on an Alpine rack railway (*vert*). (b) 106×76 mm. 3000 l. Royal train, Rhodesia .. .. *Set of 2 sheets* 3·75 4·00
Nos. 3155/60 and 3161/6 were each printed together, *se-tenant*, in sheetlets of 6 with enlarged illustrated right margins.
No. 3166 is inscribed "THE BRITIANIA" and No. MS3168a "MOUNTAIN CLASS GARRATT/AFRICA", both in error.

(Litho Questa)

1999 (4 Aug). *"iBRA '99" International Stamp Exhibition, Nuremburg. Horiz designs as T* **262** *of Lesotho. Multicoloured.* P 14×14½.

3169	1500 l.	*Claud Hamilton* steam locomotive, Germany	95	1·00
3170	2000 l.	*Borsig* steam locomotive, 1835, Germany	1·25	1·40

(Litho Questa)

1999 (4 Aug). *150th Death Anniv of Katsushika Hokusai (Japanese artist). Multicoloured designs as T* **263** *of Lesotho.* P 14×13½.

3171	1000 l.	"People admiring Mount Fuji from a Tea House"	60	65
		a. Sheetlet. Nos. 3171/6	3·50	
3172	1000 l.	"People on a Temple Balcony"	60	65
3173	1000 l.	"Sea Life" (shrimp)	60	65
3174	1000 l.	"Sea Life" (shells)	60	65
3175	1000 l.	"The Pontoon Bridge at Sano in Winter"	60	65
3176	1000 l.	"A Shower below the Summit"	60	65
3177	1000 l.	"The Hanging Cloud Bridge"	60	65
		a. Sheetlet. Nos. 3177/82	3·50	
3178	1000 l.	"The Timber Yard by the Tate River"	60	65
3179	1000 l.	"Bird Drawings" (owl)	60	65
3180	1000 l.	"Bird Drawings" (ducks)	60	65
3181	1000 l.	"Travellers crossing the Oi River"	60	65
3182	1000 l.	"Travellers on the Tokaido Road at Hodogaya"	60	65
3171/82		*Set of 12*	7·00	7·75

MS3183 Two sheets, each 100×70 mm. (a) 3000 l. "A View of Mount Fuji and Travellers by a Bridge" (*vert*). (b) 3000 l. "A Sudden Gust of Wind at Ejiri" (*vert*). P 13½×14 .. *Set of 2 sheets* 3·75 4·00
Nos. 3171/6 and 3177/82 were each printed together, *se-tenant*, in sheetlets of 6.

(Litho Questa)

1999 (4 Aug). *10th Anniv of United Nations Rights of the Child Convention. Multicoloured designs as T* **264** *of Lesotho.* P 14.

3184	1600 l.	Japanese girl holding candle	1·00	1·10
		a. Sheetlet. Nos. 3184/6	3·00	
3185	1600 l.	Two Japanese children	1·00	1·10
3186	1600 l.	Japanese girl in kimono	1·00	1·10
3184/6		*Set of 3*	3·00	3·25

MS3187 110×85 mm. 3000 l. Baby boy (*horiz*) 1·90 2·00
Nos. 3184/6 were printed together, *se-tenant*, in sheetlets of 3.

(Litho Questa)

1999 (4 Aug). *"PhilexFrance '99" International Stamp Exhibition, Paris. Railway Locomotives. Two sheets, each 106×76 mm containing horiz designs as T* **372** *of Maldive Islands. Multicoloured.* P 14×13½.
MS3188 (a) 3000 l. Crampton locomotive, French Eastern Railway. (b) 3000 l. De Glehn Compound locomotive, French Northern Railway .. .. *Set of 2 sheets* 3·75 4·00

(Litho Questa)

1999 (4 Aug). *250th Birth Anniv of Johann von Goethe (German writer). Designs as T* **265** *of Lesotho.* P 14.

3189	1600 l.	multicoloured	1·00	1·10
		a. Sheetlet. Nos. 3189/91	3·00	
3190	1600 l.	dp ultramarine, slate-lilac & black	1·00	1·10
		a. Sheetlet. Nos. 3190 and 3192/3	3·00	
3191	1600 l.	multicoloured	1·00	1·10
3192	1600 l.	dp turquoise-blue, black & slate-grn	1·00	1·10
3193	1600 l.	bright new blue, deep blue & black	1·00	1·10
3189/93		*Set of 5*	5·00	5·50

MS3194 Two sheets. (a) 106×76 mm. 3000 l. orange-brown and black. (b) 76×106 mm. 3000 l. orange-brown and black .. *Set of 2 sheets* 3·75 4·00
Designs: *Horiz*—No. 3189, Helena with her Chorus; No. 3190, Von Goethe and Von Schiller; No. 3191, Faust seated beside Helena; No. 3192, The Witch beseeching Faust to drink her fiery brew; No. 3193, Margaret placing flowers before the niche of Mater Dolorosa; No. MS3194a, Angelic spirit. *Vert*—No. MS3194b, Ariel.
Nos. 3189/91 and 3190 with 3192/3 were each printed together, *se-tenant*, in sheetlets of 3 with enlarged illustrated margins.
No. 3192 is inscribed "BESEIGES" in error.

(Litho Questa)

1999 (4 Aug). *"Queen Elizabeth the Queen Mother's Century". Vert designs as T* **267** *of Lesotho.* P 14.

3195	1300 l.	black and gold	80	85
		a. Sheetlet. Nos. 3195/8	3·00	
3196	1300 l.	multicoloured	80	85
3197	1300 l.	black and gold	80	85
3198	1300 l.	multicoloured	80	85
3195/8		*Set of 4*	3·00	3·25

MS3199 153×157 mm. 4000 l. multicoloured. P 13½×14 .. .. .. 2·50 2·75
Designs: (As T **267** of Lesotho)—No. 3195, Duke and Duchess of York and Princess Elizabeth, 1926; No. 3196, Queen Mother, 1979; No. 3197, Queen Mother visiting Nairobi, 1959; No. 3198, Queen Mother holding bouquet, 1991. (37×50 *mm*)—No. MS3199, Queen Elizabeth in Coronation robes, 1937.
Nos. 3195/8 were printed together, *se-tenant*, as a sheetlet of 4 stamps and a central label with inscribed and embossed margins.
No. MS3199 also shows the Royal Arms embossed in gold.

324 "Interpretation of a Poem of Shi-Tao" (Fu Baoshi)

(Litho Questa)

1999 (4 Aug). *"China '99" International Stamp Exhibition, Beijing. Paintings of Fu Baoshi (Chinese artist). T* **324** *and similar multicoloured designs.* P 12½.

3200	400 l.	Type **324**	25	30
		a. Sheetlet. Nos. 3200/9	2·50	
3201	400 l.	"Autumn of Ho-Pao"	25	30
3202	400 l.	"Landscape in Rain" (bridge at bottom right)	25	30
3203	400 l.	"Landscape in Rain" (mountain peaks)	25	30
3204	400 l.	"Landscape in Rain" (mountain rest house)	25	30
3205	400 l.	"Portrait of To-Fu"	25	30
3206	400 l.	"Classic Lady" (amongst green trees)	25	30
3207	400 l.	"Portrait of Li-Pai"	25	30
3208	400 l.	"Sprite of the Mountain"	25	30
3209	400 l.	"Classic Lady" (amongst bare trees)	25	30
3200/9		*Set of 10*	2·50	3·00

MS3210 138×105 mm. 800 l. "Four Seasons–Winter" (51×39 *mm*) (*vert*); 1500 l. "Four Seasons–Summer" (51×39 *mm*) (*vert*). P 13 1·40 1·50
Nos. 3200/9 were printed together, *se-tenant*, in sheetlets of 10.

325 Macao Skyline inside "MACAU"

(Litho Questa)

1999 (4 Aug). *Return of Macao to China.* P 14.
3211 **325** 1200 l. multicoloured .. 75 80
  a. Sheetlet of 3 .. .. 2·25
No. 3211 was printed in sheetlets of 3 with an enlarged illustrated right margin.

326 Sophie Rhys-Jones

(Des R. Sauber. Litho Questa)

1999 (4 Aug). *Royal Wedding. T* **326** *and similar multicoloured designs.* P 13½.

3212	2000 l.	Type **326**	1·25	1·40
		a. Sheetlet. Nos. 3212/15	5·00	
3213	2000 l.	Prince Edward (wearing striped shirt and black jacket)	1·25	1·40
3214	2000 l.	Sophie Rhys-Jones (*different*)	1·25	1·40
3215	2000 l.	Prince Edward	1·25	1·40
3212/15		*Set of 4*	5·00	5·50

MS3216 117×115 mm. 4000 l. Sophie Rhys-Jones and Prince Edward (*horiz*) 2·50 2·75
Nos. 3212/5 were printed together, *se-tenant*, in sheetlets of 4 with enlarged illustrated margins.

STAMP BOOKLETS

1929.
SB1 1s. booklet containing twelve 1d. (No. 132a)
SB2 2s. booklet containing twelve 2d. (No. 134)

1981 (30 Nov). *Royal Wedding. Multicoloured cover, 164×92 mm, showing Prince Charles and Lady Diana. Stapled.*
SB3 6 l. booklet containing *se-tenant* pane of 4 stamps and 1 label and pane of 1 2 l. (Nos. 675a, 677a) 4·00

Singapore

A Crown Colony until the end of 1957. From 1 August 1958, an internally self-governing territory designated the State of Singapore. From 16 September 1963, part of the Malaysian Federation until 9 August 1965, when it became an independent republic within the Commonwealth.

Stamps in the Crown Colony Victory design with face values of 8 c. and 15 c. were prepared for Singapore in 1946, but were not issued.

(Currency. 100 cents = 1 Malayan, later Singapore dollar)

CROWN COLONY

(Typo D.L.R.)

1948 (1 Sept)–52. *As T 58 of Malaysia (Straits Settlements), but inscribed "SINGAPORE" at foot. Wmk Mult Script CA. Chalk-surfaced paper.* (a) P 14.

1	1 c. black	..	..	15	60
2	2 c. orange			15	30
3	3 c. green	..	..	50	50
4	4 c. brown	..	..	20	75
6	6 c. grey			40	50
5	8 c. scarlet (1.10.48)	..		30	50
7	10 c. purple			20	10
8	15 c. ultramarine (1.10.48)	..	8·50	15
9	20 c. black and green (1.10.48)	..	3·50	20
10	25 c. purple and orange (1.10.48)	..	4·25	15
11	40 c. red and purple (1.10.48)	..	8·00	5·00
12	50 c. black and blue (1.10.48)	..	3·25	10
13	$1 blue and purple (1.10.48)	..	10·00	2·00
14	$2 green and scarlet (25.10.48)	..	48·00	3·25
15	$5 green and brown (1.10.48)	..	£120	4·50
1/15			*Set of 15*	£180	16·00

(b) P 17½×18

16	1 c. black (21.5.52)	..	..	60	2·75
17	2 c. orange (31.10.49)	..	70	80
19	4 c. brown (1.7.49)	..	..	80	10
19a	5 c. bright purple (1.9.52)	..	2·50	90
20	6 c. grey (10.12.52)	..	1·25	75
21	8 c. green ..9.52)	..	4·00	3·00
21a	10 c. purple (9.2.50)	..	50	10
22	12 c. scarlet (1.9.52)	..	4·50	6·50
23	15 c. ultramarine (9.2.50)	..	12·00	10
24	20 c. black and green (31.10.49)	..	3·25	2·50
24a	20 c. bright blue (1.9.52)	..	4·00	10
25	25 c. purple and orange (9.2.50)	..	80	10
25a	35 c. scarlet and purple (1.9.52)	..	4·00	90
26	40 c. red and purple (4.5.51*)	..	30·00	11·00
27	50 c. black and blue (9.2.50)	..	7·50	10
28	$1 blue and purple (31.10.49)	..	13·00	20
	a. Error. St. Edward's Crown, W 9b	..	£4750	
29	$2 green and scarlet (24.5.51)	..	90·00	1·75
	a. Error. St. Edward's Crown, W 9b	..	£4750	
	w. Wmk inverted			
30	$5 green and brown (19.12.51)	..	£180	1·75
	w. Wmk inverted			
16/30		*Set of 18*	£325	29·00

*Earliest known postmark date.

Single-colour values were from single plate printings (Die II) and all bi-colour, except the 25 c., from separate plate and duty plates (Die I). For differences between the Dies see after Nos. 278/98 of Malaysia (Straits Settlements). The 25 c. is unique in this series in that it combines a Die II frame with a separate head plate.

Nos. 28a and 29a occur on rows in the watermark in which the crowns and letters "CA" alternate.

Postal forgeries of the 50 c., $1 and $2 exist on unwatermarked paper and perforated 14×14½.

1948 (25 Oct). *Royal Silver Wedding. As Nos. 143/4 of Jamaica.*

31	10 c. violet	..	..	75	50
32	$5 brown	..	..	£110	30·00

1949 (10 Oct). *75th Anniv of U.P.U. As Nos. 145/8 of Jamaica.*

33	10 c. purple	..	..	75	30
34	15 c. deep blue	..	6·00	2·25
35	25 c. orange	..	6·00	2·25
36	50 c. blue-black	..	6·00	3·00
33/6		*Set of 4*	17·00	7·00

1953 (2 June). *Coronation. As No. 153 of Jamaica.*

37	10 c. black and reddish purple	..	1·75	30

1 Chinese Sampan

2 Raffles Statue

3 Singapore River **4** Arms of Singapore

(Des Dr. C. A. Gibson-Hill, except 25 c., 30 c., 50 c. and $5 (from photographs, etc.). Photo Harrison (1 c. to 50 c.). Recess (centre typo on $5) B.W. (others))

1955 (4 Sept)–59. *Designs as T 1/4. Wmk Mult Script CA. P* 13½×14½ (1 c. to 50 c.) or 14 (others).

38	1 c. black	..	..	10	50
39	2 c. yellow-orange	..	1·75	1·00
40	4 c. brown	..	..	90	15
	w. Wmk inverted			£160	
41	5 c. bright purple	..	65	15
42	6 c. deep grey-blue	..	65	40
43	8 c. turquoise-blue	..	1·25	70
44	10 c. deep lilac	..	3·00	10
45	12 c. rose-carmine	..	3·00	2·75
46	20 c. ultramarine	..	2·25	10
	a. Blue (13.3.58)	..	3·25	20
47	25 c. orange-red and bluish violet	..	3·50	1·00
	a. Orange-red and purple (21.1.59)	..	16·00	3·00
48	30 c. violet and brown-purple	..	3·75	10
49	50 c. blue and black	..	2·25	10
50	$1 blue and deep purple	..	30·00	30
	a. Deep purple (Queen's head) omitted	£9000	
51	$2 blue-green and scarlet	..	42·00	1·75
52	$5 yellow, red, brown and slate-black	..	42·00	5·00
38/52		*Set of 15*	£120	12·00

Designs: *Horiz as T 1*—2 c. Malay kolek; 4 c. Twa-kow lighter; 5 c. Lombok sloop; 6 c. Trengganu pinas; 8 c. Palari schooner; 10 c. Timber tongkong; 12 c. Hainan junk; 20 c. Cocos-Keeling schooner; 25 c. Douglas DC-4M2 "Argonaut" aircraft; 30 c. Oil tanker; 50 c. *Chusan III* (liner).

Plate 2A and 2B of the 10 c. (12 April 1960) and the blue "3A" and "3B" plates of the 50 c. "3A–2A", "3B–2B" (part of the 24 January 1961 issue and later printings) were printed with a finer screen (250 dots per inch, instead of the normal 200) (*Price* 10 c. .3·50 *un,* 20p *us.* 50 c. .3·50 *un,* 10p *us*).

No. 50a was caused by a paper fold.

INTERNAL SELF-GOVERNMENT

16 The Singapore Lion **17** State Flag

(Photo Harrison)

1959 (1 June). *New Constitution. W w* 12. *P* 11½ × 12.

53	16	4 c. yellow, sepia and rose-red	..	65	75
54		10 c. yellow, sepia and reddish purple	1·00	40
55		20 c. yellow, sepia and bright blue	..	2·25	3·00
56		25 c. yellow, sepia and green	..	2·50	2·25
57		30 c. yellow, sepia and violet	..	2·50	3·25
58		50 c. yellow, sepia and deep slate	..	3·25	3·25
53/8			*Set of 6*	11·00	11·50

(Litho Enschedé)

1960 (3 June). *National Day. W w* 12 (*sideways**). *P* 13½.

59	17	4 c. red, yellow and blue	..	75	90
		w. Wmk Crown to right of CA	..	60·00	
60		10 c. red, yellow and grey	..	2·25	30
		w. Wmk Crown to right of CA	..	60·00	

*The normal sideways watermark shows Crown to left of CA, as seen from the back of the stamp.

18 Clasped Hands

(Photo Enschedé)

1961 (3 June). *National Day. W w* 12. *P* 13½.

61	18	4 c. black, brown and pale yellow	..	1·00	85
62		10 c. black, deep green and pale yellow	..	1·25	10

19 Arachnis "Maggie Oei" (orchid)

20 Yellow Seahorse

21 Tiger Barb

24 Vanda "Tan Chay Yan" (orchid)

26a Black-naped Tern

30 White-rumped Shama

(Photo Harrison (orchids, fish and 15 c. bird) D.L.R. (birds, except 15 c.))

1962 (31 Mar)–66. *T* 19/21, 24, 26a, 30 *and similar designs. W w* 12. *P* 12½ (i), 14½×12½ (ii), 13½×14½ (iii), 13½×13 (iv) or 13×13½ (v).

63	1 c. multicoloured (i) (10.3.63)	..	30	90
64	2 c. brown and green (ii)	..	30	1·75
65	4 c. black and orange-red (iii)	..	30	60
	a. Black omitted	..	£450	
66	5 c. red and black (iii)	..	20	10
	a. Red omitted	..	£450	
67	6 c. black and greenish yellow (ii)	..	55	80
68	8 c. multicoloured (i) (10.3.63)	..	1·25	3·50
69	10 c. red-orange and black (iii)	..	40	10
	a. Red-orange omitted	..	£300	
70	12 c. multicoloured (i) (10.3.63)	..	1·25	3·50
70a	15 c. multicoloured (i) (9.11.66)	..	2·00	10
	ab. Orange (eye) omitted	..	35·00	
	aw. Wmk inverted	..	7·00	
71	20 c. orange and blue (ii)	..	40	10
	a. Orange omitted	..	£475	
72	25 c. black and orange (iii)	..	75	10
73	30 c. multicoloured (i) (10.3.63)	..	1·25	10
	a. Yellow (flowers) omitted	..	90·00	
74	50 c. multicoloured (iv) (10.3.63)	..	1·25	10
75	$1 multicoloured (iv) (10.3.63)	..	20·00	60
76	$2 multicoloured (iv) (10.3.63)	..	14·00	85
77	$5 multicoloured (v) (10.3.63)	..	27·00	4·25
	w. Wmk inverted	..	£110	
63/77		*Set of 16*	60·00	15·00

Designs: *Horiz* (as *T* 21)—5 c. Orange Clownfish; 10 c. Harlequinfish; 25 c. Three-spotted Goramy. (As *T* 30)—$1 White-breasted Kingfisher. *Vert* (as *T* 20)—6 c. Archerfish; 20 c. Copper-banded Butterflyfish. (As *T* 24)—12 c. *Grammatophyllum speciosum* (orchid); 30 c. *Vanda* "Miss Joaquim" (orchid). (As *T* 26a)—$2 Yellow-bellied Sunbird; $5 White-bellied Sea Eagle.

The 10 c. exists in coils, constructed from normal sheets.

The 15 c., 30 c., $2 and $5 exist with PVA gum as well as gum arabic.

See also Nos. 83/8.

34 "The Role of Labour in Nation-Building"

35 Blocks of Flats, Singapore

(Photo Courvoisier)

1962 (3 June). *National Day. P* 11½ × 12.

78	34	4 c. yellow, rose-carmine and black	..	90	1·75
79		10 c. yellow, blue and black	..	1·00	60

(Photo Harrison)

1963 (3 June). *National Day. W w* 12. *P* 12½.

80	35	4 c. orange-red, black, blue & turq-blue	40	65
81		10 c. orange-red, blk, yell-olive & turq-bl	85	15
		w. Wmk inverted	..	35·00	

36 Dancers in National Costume

37 Workers

(Photo Harrison)

1963 (8 Aug). *South East Asia Cultural Festival. W w* 12. *P* 14 × 14½.

82	36	5 c. multicoloured	..	..	50	50

INDEPENDENT REPUBLIC

1966 (1 Mar)–67. *As Nos.* 63, 66, 69, 72, 74/5, *but W w* 12 (*sideways**).

83	1 c. multicoloured (22.6.67)	..	10	2·00
84	5 c. red and black (30.5.67)	..	2·75	2·50
85	10 c. red-orange and black (19.5.67†)	..	1·25	10
86	25 c. black and orange (9.66†)	..	70	1·50
	w. Wmk Crown to right of CA	..	3·00	
87	50 c. multicoloured (11.1.66†)	..	4·50	3·00
	a. Imperf (pair)	..	£475	
88	$1 multicoloured (18.5.67)	..	16·00	9·00
83/8		*Set of 6*	23·00	17·00

*The normal sideways watermark show Crown to left of CA, as seen from the back of the stamp.

†The 25 and 50 c. values were not released in London until 30.5.67 and 9.6.66. The 25 c. value, however, is known used in September 1966 and the 50 c. on 11.1.66. The 10 c., released in London on 30 May 1967, is known used locally on 19 May.

The 1 c. and 25 c. exist with PVA gum as well as gum arabic.

(Photo D.L.R.)

1966 (9 Aug). *First Anniv of Republic.* W w **12** (30 c.) *or no wmk (others).* P 12½ × 13.

89	37	15 c. multicoloured			75	30
90		20 c. multicoloured			1·00	1·25
91		30 c. multicoloured			1·25	2·00
89/91				*Set of 3*	2·75	3·25

38 Flag Procession

(Photo D.L.R.)

1967 (9 Aug). *National Day.* P 14 × 14½.

92	38	6 c. rosine, brown and slate			50	75
93		15 c. reddish purple, brown and slate			80	10
94		50 c. bright blue, brown and slate			1·50	1·60
92/4				*Set of 3*	2·50	2·25

Nos. 92/4 are respectively inscribed "Build a Vigorous Singapore" in Chinese, Malay and Tamil in addition to the English inscription.

39 Skyscrapers and Afro-Asian Map

40 Symbolical Figure wielding Hammer, and Industrial Outline of Singapore

(Photo D.L.R.)

1967 (7 Oct). *2nd Afro-Asian Housing Congress.* P 14 × 13.

95	39	10 c. multicoloured			30	10
		a. Opt omitted			£650	£650
96		25 c. multicoloured			75	1·00
97		50 c. multicoloured			1·40	1·60
95/7				*Set of 3*	2·25	2·40

The above were originally scheduled for release in 1966, and when finally issued were overprinted with the new date and a black oblong obliterating the old date.

(Photo Harrison)

1968 (9 Aug). *National Day.* Inscription at top in Chinese (6 c.), Malay (15 c.) or Tamil (50 c.). P 13½ × 14.

98	40	6 c. orange-red, black and gold			35	65
99		15 c. apple-green, black and gold			45	15
100		50 c. greenish blue, black and gold			1·00	1·25
98/100				*Set of 3*	1·60	1·90

41 Half check Pattern

42 Scrolled "S" multiple

43 Mirudhangam

44 Pi Pa

45 Sword Dance

51 Dragon Dance

(Photo D.L.R. (5 c. to $1), Japanese Govt Printing Bureau, Tokyo (others))

1968 (1 Dec)–**73**. T **43/5**, **51** *and similar designs.* W **41** (5 c. to $1) *or* W **42** (*upright on 1 c., $5; sideways on 4 c., $2, $10*). *Chalk-surfaced paper* (5 c. to $1). P 14 (5 c. to $1) *or* 13½ (*others*).

101		1 c. multicoloured (10.11.69)			15	2·25
102		4 c. multicoloured (10.11.69)			60	2·75
103		5 c. multicoloured (29.12.68)			60	80
		a. Glazed unsurfaced paper (16.12.70)			10·00	8·50
		b. Perf 13 (27.6.73)			7·50	9·00
104		6 c. black, lemon and orange			1·25	2·00
105		10 c. multicoloured (29.12.68)			20	10
		a. Glazed unsurfaced paper (16.12.70)			12·00	8·00
		b. Perf 13 (14.7.73*)			7·50	7·50
106		15 c. multicoloured (29.12.68)			60	10
107		20 c. multicoloured			70	95
		a. Perf 13 (12.9.73)			9·00	13·00
108		25 c. multicoloured (29.12.68)			1·00	70
		a. Perf 13 (27.6.73)			6·50	11·00
109		30 c. multicoloured			40	70
		a. Perf 13 (12.9.73)			11·00	15·00
110		50 c. black, orange-red & light yellow-brown			50	50
		a. Perf 13 (12.9.73)			12·00	24·00
111		75 c. multicoloured			3·00	2·50
112		$1 multicoloured (29.12.68)			4·00	80
		a. Perf 13 (12.9.73)			17·00	19·00
113		$2 multicoloured (10.11.69)			3·50	1·00
114		$5 multicoloured (10.11.69)			10·00	1·50
115		$10 multicoloured (6.12.69)			38·00	15·00
101/15				*Set of 15*	60·00	27·00
103b/12a				*Set of 7*	65·00	85·00

Designs: *Vert* (as T **45**)—6 c. Lion dance; 10 c. Bharatha Natyam; 15 c. Tari Payong; 20 c. Kathak Kali; 25 c. Lu Chih Shen and Lin Chung; 50 c. Tari Lilin; 75 c. Tarian Kuda Kepang; $1 Yao Chi. (As T **44**)—$2, Rebab; $10 Ta Ku. *Horiz* (as T **43**)—$5 Vina.
*Earliest known date of use.

 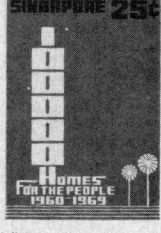

58 E.C.A.F.E. Emblem

59 "100000" and Slogan as Block of Flats

(Des Eng Siak Loy. Photo Japanese Govt Ptg Bureau, Tokyo)

1969 (15 Apr). *25th Plenary Session of the U.N. Economic Commission for Asia and the Far East.* P 13.

116	58	15 c. black, silver and pale blue			40	20
117		30 c. black, silver and red			85	1·25
118		75 c. black, silver and violet-blue			1·40	2·50
116/18				*Set of 3*	2·40	3·50

(Des Tay Siew Chiah. Litho B.W.)

1969 (20 July). *Completion of "100,000 Homes for the People" Project.* P 13½.

119	59	25 c. black and emerald			1·00	50
120		50 c. black and deep blue			1·25	1·25

60 Aircraft over Silhouette of Singapore Docks

61 Sea Shells

(Des Eng Siak Loy and Han Kuan Cheng. Litho B.W.)

1969 (9 Aug). *150th Anniv of Founding of Singapore.* T **60** *and similar vert designs.* P 14 × 14½.

121		15 c. black, vermilion and yellow			2·50	70
122		30 c. black, blue and new blue			2·50	1·75
123		75 c. multicoloured			4·50	2·00
124		$1 black and vermilion			10·00	10·00
125		$5 vermilion and black			35·00	55·00
126		$10 black and bright green			48·00	55·00
121/6				*Set of 6*	90·00	£110
MS127		120 × 120 mm. Nos. 121/6. P 13½			£450	£475

Designs:—30 c. U.N. emblem and outline of Singapore; 75 c. Flags and outline of Malaysian Federation; $1 Uplifted hands holding crescent and stars; $5 Tail of Japanese aircraft and searchlight beams; $10 Bust from statue of Sir Stamford Raffles.

(Des Tay Siew Chiah (15 c.), Eng Siak Loy (others). Litho Rosenbaum Bros, Vienna)

1970 (15 Mar). *World Fair, Osaka.* T **61** *and similar vert designs. Multicoloured.* P 13½.

128		15 c. Type **61**			1·50	1
129		30 c. Veil-tailed Guppys			2·75	1
130		75 c. Greater Flamingo and Helmeted Hornbill			7·50	3·7
131		$1 Orchid			7·50	6·0
128/31				*Set of 4*	17·00	9·7
MS132		94×154 mm. Nos. 128/31			24·00	22·0

62 "Kindergarten"

63 Soldier charging

(Des Choy Weng Yang. Litho B.W.)

1970 (1 July). *Tenth Anniv of People's Association.* T **62** *and similar square designs.* P 13½.

133		15 c. agate and bright orange			85	2
134		50 c. ultramarine and yellow-orange			2·25	2·7
135		75 c. bright purple and black			3·50	4·5
133/5				*Set of 3*	6·00	6·5

Designs:—50 c. "Sport"; 75 c. "Culture".

(Des Choy Weng Yang. Litho Rosenbaum Bros, Vienna)

1970 (9 Aug). *National Day.* T **63** *and similar vert designs. Multicoloured.* P 13½.

136		15 c. Type **63**			1·25	2
137		50 c. Soldier on assault course			3·75	3·5
138		$1 Soldier jumping			5·00	8·5
136/8				*Set of 3*	9·00	11·0

64 Sprinters

(Des Choy Weng Yang. Photo Japanese Govt Ptg Bureau, Tokyo

1970 (23 Aug). *Festival of Sports.* T **64** *and similar horiz designs.* P 13 × 13½.

139		10 c. magenta, black and ultramarine			2·00	3·0
		a. Horiz strip of 4. Nos. 139/42			9·00	
140		15 c. black, ultramarine and red-orange			2·50	3·2
141		25 c. black, red-orange and bright green			2·75	3·5
142		50 c. black, bright green and magenta			3·00	3·5
139/42				*Set of 4*	9·00	12·0

Designs:—15 c. Swimmers; 25 c. Tennis-players; 50 c. Racing cars.

Nos. 139/42 were issued together *se-tenant* in horizontal strips four within the sheet.

65 *Neptune Aquamarine* (freighter)

(Des W. Lee. Litho Rosenbaum Bros, Vienna)

1970 (1 Nov). *Singapore Shipping.* T **65** *and similar horiz designs.* P 12.

143		15 c. multicoloured			2·75	6
144		30 c. yellow-ochre and ultramarine			6·00	5·5
145		75 c. yellow-ochre and vermilion			10·00	8·5
143/5				*Set of 3*	17·00	13·0

Designs:—30 c. Container berth; 75 c. Ship-building.

66 Country Names forming Circle

(Des W. Lee. Litho D.L.R.)

1971 (1 Jan). *Commonwealth Heads of Government Meeting, Singapore. T* **66** *and similar horiz designs. Multicoloured.* P 14 ($1) *or* 15 × 14½ (*others*).

146	15 c. Type 66		90	20
147	30 c. Flags in circle		1·75	80
148	75 c. Commonwealth flags		3·25	3·75
149	$1 Commonwealth flags linked to Singapore (63 × 61 mm)		4·25	6·50
146/9		Set of 4	9·00	10·00

Imperforate examples of Nos. 146/7 overprinted "Specimen" are from printer's sample sheets.

67 Bicycle Rickshaws   **68** Chinese New Year

(Des Eng Siak Loy (15, 20 and 30 c.), W. Lee (others). Litho B.W.)

1971 (4 Apr). *Visit A.S.E.A.N. Year (A.S.E.A.N. = Association of South East Asian Nations). T* **67** *and similar designs.* P 13 × 13½ (50, 75 c.) *or* 11½ (*others*).

150	15 c. black, deep bluish violet and orange		80	25
151	20 c. indigo, orange and turquoise-blue		1·10	1·00
152	30 c. vermilion and deep maroon		1·40	1·75
153	50 c. multicoloured		4·75	7·50
154	75 c. multicoloured		6·50	9·50
150/4		Set of 5	13·00	18·00

Designs: *As T* **67**—20 c. Houseboat "village" and sampans; 30 c. Bazaar. *Horiz* (68×18 *mm*)—50 c. Modern harbour skyline; 75 c. Religious buildings.

(Des W. Lee. Litho Rosenbaum Bros, Vienna)

1971 (9 Aug). *Singapore Festivals. T* **68** *and similar vert designs. Multicoloured.* P 14.

155	15 c. Type 68		1·25	15
156	30 c. Hari Raya		3·00	2·50
157	50 c. Deepavali		4·00	6·50
158	75 c. Christmas		5·00	7·50
155/8		Set of 4	12·00	15·00
MS159	150 × 125 mm. Nos. 155/8		70·00	48·00

69 "Dish" Aerial

(Des W. Lee. Litho B.W.)

1971 (23 Oct). *Opening of Satellite Earth Station.* P 13½.

160	69	15 c. multicoloured	3·00	1·50
161	—	30 c. multicoloured	13·00	12·00
		a. Block of 4. Nos. 161/4	50·00	
162	—	30 c. multicoloured	13·00	12·00
163	—	30 c. multicoloured	13·00	12·00
164	—	30 c. multicoloured	13·00	12·00
160/4		Set of 5	50·00	45·00

Designs:—Nos. 161/4 were printed in *se-tenant* blocks of four throughout the sheet, the four stamps forming a composite design similar to T **69**. They can be identified by the colour of the face value which is: yellow (No. 161), green (No. 162), magenta (No. 163) or orange (No. 164).

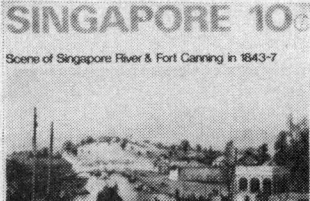

70 "Singapore River and Fort Canning, 1843–7" (Lieut. E. A. Porcher)

(Des W. Lee. Litho B.W.)

1971 (5 Dec). *Art. T* **70** *and similar horiz designs. Multicoloured.* P 12½ × 13 (50 c. and $1) or 13 (*others*).

165	10 c. Type 70		2·50	2·50
166	15 c. "The Padang, 1851" (J. T. Thomson)		3·50	4·00
167	20 c. "Singapore Waterfront, 1848–9" (J. T. Thomson)		4·50	4·50
168	35 c. "View from Fort Canning, 1846" (J. T. Thomson)		9·00	9·00
169	50 c. "View from Mt Wallich, 1857" (P. Carpenter) (69 × 47 mm)		13·00	14·00
170	$1 "Singapore Waterfront, 1861" (W. Gray) (69 × 47 mm)		16·00	19·00
165/70		Set of 6	45·00	48·00

71 One Dollar of 1969

(Des W. Lee. Litho B.W.)

1972 (4 June). *Coins. T* **71** *and similar horiz designs.* P 13½.

171	15 c. orange, black and deep green		1·25	35
172	35 c. black and vermilion		2·75	3·00
173	$1 yellow, black and bright blue		5·00	8·00
171/3		Set of 3	8·00	10·00

Designs:—15 c. One-cent coin of George V; $1 One hundred and fifty dollar gold coin of 1969.

72 "Moon Festival" (Seah Kim Joo)   **73** Lanterns and Fish

(Des W. Lee. Litho State Bank Note Printing Works, Helsinki)

1972 (9 July). *Contemporary Art. T* **72** *and similar multicoloured designs.* P 12½.

174	15 c. Type 72		80	30
175	35 c. "Complimentary Forces" (Thomas Yeo) (36 × 54 mm)		2·00	3·00
176	50 c. "Rhythm in Blue" (Yusman Aman) (36 × 54 mm)		3·00	4·50
177	$1 "Gibbons" (Chen Wen Hsi)		5·50	7·50
174/7		Set of 4	10·00	14·00

(Des Eng Siak Loy. Litho State Bank Note Printing Works, Helsinki)

1972 (9 Aug). *National Day. T* **73** *and similar vert designs symbolising Festivals. Multicoloured.* P 12½.

178	15 c. Type 73		75	20
179	35 c. Altar and candles		1·40	2·75
180	50 c. Jug, bowl and gifts		2·00	4·00
181	75 c. Candle		3·00	5·50
178/81		Set of 4	6·50	11·00

74 Student Welding   **75** *Maria Rickmers* (barque)

(Des Eng Siak Loy. Photo Kultura, Budapest)

1972 (1 Oct). *Youth. T* **74** *and similar horiz designs.* P 12.

182	15 c. multicoloured		80	30
183	35 c. multicoloured		2·50	3·50
184	$1 red-orange, blue-violet & yellowish grn		4·50	8·00
182/4		Set of 3	7·00	10·50

Designs:—35 c. Sport; $1 Dancing.

(Des Choy Weng Yang (Nos. 185/7), Eng Siak Loy (**MS**188). Litho Harrison)

1972 (17 Dec). *Shipping. T* **75** *and similar multicoloured designs.* P 14 × 14½.

185	15 c. *Neptune Ruby* (container ship) (42×29 mm)		2·25	80
186	75 c. Type 75		7·50	8·00
187	$1 Chinese junk		8·00	9·00
185/7		Set of 3	16·00	16·00
MS188	152×84 mm. Nos. 185/7		42·00	42·00

76 P.Q.R. Slogan   **77** Jurong Bird Park

(Des W. Lee. Litho B.W.)

1973 (25 Feb). *"Prosperity through Quality and Reliability" Campaign. T* **76** *and similar vert designs.* P 14.

189	76	15 c. multicoloured	60	15
190	—	35 c. multicoloured	2·00	3·25
191	—	75 c. multicoloured	2·25	3·75
192	—	$1 multicoloured	2·25	5·00
189/92		Set of 4	6·50	11·00

Nos. 190/2 show various P.Q.R. emblems.

(Des Han Kuan Cheng. Litho Harrison)

1973 (29 Apr). *Singapore Landmarks. T* **77** *and similar vert designs.* P 12½.

193	15 c. black and red-orange		1·00	15
194	35 c. black and myrtle-green		2·50	3·25
195	50 c. black and red-brown		3·25	4·25
196	$1 black and purple		5·00	6·50
193/6		Set of 4	10·50	13·00

Designs:—35 c. National Theatre; 50 c. City Hall; $1 Fullerton Building and Singapore River.

78 Aircraft Tail-fins   **79** "Culture"

(Des W. Lee. Litho B.W.)

1973 (24 June). *Aviation. T* **78** *and similar horiz designs. Multicoloured.* P 13½ × 13.

197	10 c. Type 78		50	10
198	35 c. Emblem of Singapore Airlines and destinations		1·75	2·00
199	75 c. Emblem on tail-fin		2·25	2·50
200	$1 Emblems encircling the globe		2·75	3·50
197/200		Set of 4	6·50	7·25

(Des Eng Siak Loy. Litho Harrison)

1973 (9 Aug). *National Day. T* **79** *and similar vert designs.* P 13½.

201	79	10 c. orange and black	2·00	2·25
		a. Block of 4. Nos. 201/4	8·50	
202	—	35 c. orange and black	2·25	2·75
203	—	50 c. orange and black	2·50	3·00
204	—	75 c. orange and black	2·75	3·50
201/4		Set of 4	8·50	10·50

Nos. 201/4 were printed in *se-tenant* blocks of four within the sheet, and form a composite design representing Singapore's culture.

80 Athletics, Judo and Boxing   **81** Agave   **82** Mangosteen

(Des C. Lim. Photo Heraclio Fournier)

1973 (1 Sept). *Seventh S.E.A.P.* Games. T* **80** *and similar designs.* P 14 (10 *to* 35 c.) *or* 13 × 14 (*others*).

205	10 c. gold, silver and indigo		55	20
206	15 c. gold and grey-black		1·75	1·50
207	25 c. gold, silver and black		1·50	1·75
208	35 c. gold, silver and deep blue		3·00	3·25
209	50 c. multicoloured		2·00	4·00
210	$1 silver, royal blue and yellow-green		3·25	7·00
205/10		Set of 6	11·00	16·00
MS211	130 × 111 mm. Nos. 205/10. P 13 × 14		32·00	35·00

Designs: *As T* **80**—15 c. Cycling, weight-lifting, pistol-shooting and sailing; 25 c. Footballs; 35 c. Table-tennis bat, shuttlecock, tennis ball and hockey stick. *Horiz* (41 × 25 *mm*):—50 c. Swimmers; $1 Stadium.

*S.E.A.P. = South East Asian Peninsula.

(Des W. Lee (1 c. to 75 c.), Eng Siak Loy (others). Photo Heraclio Fournier)

1973 (30 Sept–1 Nov). *Various multicoloured designs as T* **81**/2. *With fluorescent security markings.*

(a) *Stylized flowers and plants, size as T* **81**. P 13.

212	1 c. Type 81		90	65
213	5 c. *Coleus blumei*		10	45
	a. Booklet pane. Nos. 213×4, 214×4, 216×2		7·00	
214	10 c. *Vinca rosea*		15	10
215	15 c. *Helianthus angustifolius*		1·25	10
	a. Green printed double		†	—
216	20 c. *Licuala grandis*		45	60
217	25 c. *Wedelia trilobata*		3·00	55
218	35 c. *Chrysanthemum frutescens*		90	90
219	50 c. *Costus malorticanus*		1·00	55
220	75 c. *Gerbera jamesonii*		2·50	90

(b) *Fruits, size as T* **82**. P 12½ × 13 (1.11.73)

221	$1 Type 82		1·50	40
222	$2 Jackfruit		3·25	1·25
223	$5 Coconut		5·00	7·00
224	$10 Pineapple		9·00	13·00
212/24		Set of 13	26·00	23·00

Booklet pane No. 213a has the upper and lower edges imperforate and there are margins at left and right.

83 Tiger and Orang-Utans   84 Delta Guppy

(Des Eng Siak Loy. Litho B.W.)

1973 (16 Dec). *Singapore Zoo. T* **83** *and similar vert designs. Multicoloured. P* 13.

225	5 c. Type **83**	..	..	85	85
226	10 c. Leopard and Waterbuck	..	..	1·00	45
227	35 c. Leopard and Thamin	..	..	4·50	5·50
228	75 c. Horse and Lion	..	..	6·00	8·50
225/8	..	..	*Set of 4*	11·00	14·00

(Des Eng Siak Loy. Photo Heraclio Fournier)

1974 (21 Apr). *Tropical Fish. T* **84** *and similar vert designs. Multicoloured. P* 14.

229	5 c. Type **84**	..	..	60	60
230	10 c. Half-black Delta Guppy	..	..	60	15
231	35 c. Delta Guppy (*different*)	..	..	2·50	3·50
232	$1 Black Delta Guppy	..	..	4·50	8·00
229/32	..	..	*Set of 4*	7·50	11·00

85 Scout Badge within "9"   86 U.P.U. Emblem and Multiple "Centenary"

(Des W. Lee. Litho Harrison)

1974 (9 June). *Ninth Asia-Pacific Scout Conference. P* 13½ × 14½.

233	85	10 c. multicoloured	..	40	10
234		75 c. multicoloured	..	1·60	2·00

(Des W. Lee. Litho Harrison)

1974 (7 July). *Centenary of Universal Postal Union. T* **86** *and similar vert designs. P* 14 × 13½.

235	10 c. orange-brown, purple-brown and gold	..	20	10
	a. Gold (U.P.U. symbol) omitted	..	£400	
236	35 c. new blue, deep blue and gold	..	55	1·60
237	75 c. multicoloured	..	1·25	2·75
235/7	..	..	*Set of 3*	1·75	4·00

Designs:—35 c. U.P.U. emblem and multiple U.N. symbols; 75 c. U.P.U. emblem and multiple peace doves.

87 Family Emblem   88 "Tree and Sun" (Chia Keng San)

(Des Eng Siak Loy. Litho B.W.)

1974 (9 Aug). *World Population Year. T* **87** *and similar horiz designs. Multicoloured. P* 12½ × 13½.

238	10 c. Type **87**	..	..	30	10
239	35 c. Male and female symbols	..	..	80	1·60
	a. Emerald (male symbol) omitted	..	£550	
240	75 c. World population map	..	..	1·75	3·25
238/40	..	..	*Set of 3*	2·50	4·50

(Des Eng Siak Loy. Photo Heraclio Fournier)

1974 (1 Oct). *Universal Children's Day. T* **88** *and similar vert designs showing children's paintings. Multicoloured. P* 13½.

241	5 c. Type **88**	..	..	40	50
242	10 c. "My Daddy and Mummy" (Angeline Ang)	..	40	20
243	35 c. "A Dump Truck" (Si-Hoe Yeen Joong)	2·50	3·50
244	50 c. "My Aunt" (Raymond Teo)	..	2·75	4·25
241/4	..	..	*Set of 4*	5·50	7·75
MS245	138×100 mm. Nos. 241/4. P 13		22·00	24·00

89 Street Scene

(Des Loy Chin. Litho Secura, Singapore)

1975 (26 Jan). *Singapore Views. T* **89** *and similar horiz designs. Multicoloured. P* 14.

246	15 c. Type **89**	..	..	80	20
247	20 c. Singapore River	..	..	1·50	1·50
248	$1 "Kelong" (fish-trap)	..	..	5·00	7·50
246/8	..	..	*Set of 3*	6·50	8·25

90 Emblem and Lighters' Prows   91 Satellite Earth Station, Sentosa

(Des Choy Weng Yang. Litho Secura, Singapore)

1975 (10 Mar). *Ninth Biennial Conference of International Association of Ports and Harbours, Singapore. T* **90** *and similar horiz designs. Multicoloured. P* 14.

249	5 c. Type **90**	..	..	30	15
250	25 c. Freighter and ship's wheel	..	1·75	1·50
251	50 c. Oil-tanker and flags	..	2·25	3·00
252	$1 Container-ship and propellers	..	3·50	6·00
249/52	..	..	*Set of 4*	7·00	9·50

(Des Sim Tong Khern. Photo Heraclio Fournier)

1975 (29 June). *"Science and Industry". T* **91** *and similar multicoloured designs. P* 13½.

253	10 c. Type **91**	..	..	35	10
254	35 c. Oil refineries (*vert*)	..	2·50	2·75
255	75 c. "Medical Sciences"	..	2·75	4·00
253/5	..	..	*Set of 3*	5·00	6·00

92 "Homes and Gardens"   93 South African Crowned Cranes

(Des Tay Siew Chiah. Litho Secura, Singapore)

1975 (9 Aug). *Tenth National Day. T* **92** *and similar square designs. Multicoloured. P* 13½.

256	10 c. Type **92**	..	..	20	10
257	35 c. "Shipping and Ship-building"	..	1·75	2·00
258	75 c. "Communications and Technology"	2·25	3·50
259	$1 "Trade, Commerce and Industry"	2·50	4·00
256/9	..	..	*Set of 4*	6·00	8·50

(Des Eng Siak Loy. Litho Harrison)

1975 (5 Oct). *Birds. T* **93** *and similar vert designs. Multicoloured. P* 14½ × 13½.

260	5 c. Type **93**	..	..	1·75	80
261	10 c. Great Indian Hornbill	..	1·75	30
262	35 c. White-breasted Kingfisher and White-collared Kingfisher	9·50	9·50
263	$1 Sulphur-crested Cockatoo and Blue and Yellow Macaw	14·00	16·00
260/3	..	..	*Set of 4*	24·00	24·00

94 "Equality"   95 Yellow Flame

(Des Tay Siew Chiah. Litho Secura, Singapore)

1975 (7 Dec). *International Women's Year. T* **94** *and similar square designs. Multicoloured. P* 13½.

264	10 c. Type **94**	..	..	25	10
265	35 c. "Development"	..	1·75	3·00
266	75 c. "Peace"	..	2·25	6·00
264/6	..	..	*Set of 3*	3·75	8·00
MS267	128 × 100 mm. Nos. 264/6		15·00	19·00

(Des Tay Siew Chiah. Litho Secura, Singapore)

1976 (18 Apr). *Wayside Trees. T* **95** *and similar vert designs. Multicoloured. P* 14.

268	10 c. Type **95**	..	..	60	10
269	35 c. Cabbage Tree	..	2·50	3·50
270	50 c. Rose of India	..	2·75	3·50
271	75 c. Variegated Coral Tree	..	3·25	6·25
268/71	..	..	*Set of 4*	8·00	12·00

96 *Arachnis hookeriana* × *Vanda* Hilo Blue   97 Festival Symbol and Band

(Des Eng Siak Loy. Litho Secura, Singapore)

1976 (20 June). *Singapore Orchids. T* **96** *and similar vert designs. Multicoloured. P* 14.

272	10 c. Type **96**	..	..	1·50	10
273	35 c. *Arachnis Maggie Oei* × *Vanda insignis*	4·00	4·00
274	50 c. *Arachnis Maggie Oei* × *Vandu Rodman*	4·75	4·50
275	75 c. *Arachnis hookeriana* × *Vanda* Dawn Nishimura	6·00	8·00
272/5	..	..	*Set of 4*	14·50	15·00

(Des Han Kuan Cheng. Litho Harrison)

1976 (9 Aug). *Tenth Anniv of Singapore Youth Festival. Horiz designs showing festival symbol as T* **97**. *Multicoloured. P* 12½.

276	10 c. Type **97**	..	..	20	10
277	35 c. Athletes	..	..	1·25	1·25
278	75 c. Dancers	..	..	1·40	2·00
276/8	..	..	*Set of 3*	2·50	3·00

98 "Queen Elizabeth Walk"

(Des H. Weepaul. Litho Secura, Singapore)

1976 (14 Nov). *Paintings of Old Singapore, circa* 1905–10, *by A. L. Watson. T* **98** *and similar horiz designs. Multicoloured. With fluorescent security markings. P* 14.

279	10 c. Type **98**	..	..	50	20
280	50 c. "The Padang"	..	..	3·75	4·00
281	$1 "Raffles Place"	..	..	4·50	5·50
279/81	..	..	*Set of 3*	8·00	8·75
MS282	164 × 91 mm. Nos. 279/81. P 13½		18·00	22·00

99 Chinese Costume   100 Radar, Missile and Soldiers

(Des Margaret Heng. Litho Harrison)

1976 (19 Dec). *Bridal Costumes. T* **99** *and similar vert designs. Multicoloured. P* 14½.

283	10 c. Type **99**	..	..	65	10
284	35 c. Indian costume	..	..	2·25	2·50
285	75 c. Malay costume	..	..	3·75	5·75
283/5	..	..	*Set of 3*	6·00	7·50

(Des Eng Siak Loy. Litho Harrison)

1977 (12 Mar). *Tenth Anniv of National Service. T* **100** *and similar vert designs. Multicoloured. P* 14½.

286	10 c. Type **100**	..	..	65	10
287	50 c. Tank and soldiers	..	..	2·50	2·50
288	75 c. Soldiers, wireless operators, pilot and Douglas A-4 Skyhawk aircraft	3·50	3·50
286/8	..	..	*Set of 3*	6·00	5·50

101 Lyrate Cockle (*Lyrocardium lyratum*)   102 Spotted Hermit Crab

(Des Tay Siew Chiah, Litho Secura, Singapore)

1977 (9 Apr–4 June). *Multicoloured designs as T* **101/2**. *With fluorescent security markings. P* 13 × 13½. (*a*) *Shells as T* **101**

289	1 c. Type **101**	..	..	50	1·50
290	5 c. Folded or Plicate Scallop (*Decatopecten plicus*)	..	20	10
	a. Booklet pane. Nos. 290×4 and 291×8 se-tenant	..	3·75	

291 10 c. Marble Cone (*Conus marmoreus marmoreus*) 20 10
  a. Imperf (pair) £450
292 15 c. Scorpion Conch (*Lambis scorpius*) 1·00 40
293 20 c. Amplustre or Royal Paper Bubble (*Aplustrum amplustre*) 90 10
294 25 c. Spiral Babylon (*Babylonia spirata*) 1·25 1·50
295 35 c. Royal Thorny or Spiny Oyster (*Spondylus regius*) .. .. 1·50 1·50
296 50 c. Maple-leaf Triton or Winged Frog Shell (*Biplex perca*) .. .. 2·00 10
297 75 c. Troschel's Murex (*Murex troscheli*) 3·00 20

(*b*) Fish and Crustaceans as T 102 (4.6.77)
298 $1 Type 102 .. .. 2·25 15
299 $2 Zuge's Stingray .. .. .. 2·25 75
300 $5 Cuttlefish .. .. 4·00 2·25
301 $10 Lionfish .. .. 7·50 5·50
289/301 .. .. .. *Set of 13* 24·00 12·00
  Booklet pane No. 290a has the upper and lower edges imperforate and there are margins at left and right.

103 Shipbuilding

104 Keyhole and Banknotes

(Des W. Lee. Litho Secura, Singapore)
1977 (1 May). *Labour Day. T 103 and similar horiz designs. Multicoloured. P 13 × 12½.*
302 10 c. Type 103 .. .. 30 10
303 50 c. Building construction .. .. 1·25 1·00
304 75 c. Road construction .. .. 1·75 1·25
302/4 .. .. .. *Set of 3* 3·00 2·00

(Des Tay Siew Chiah. Litho Secura, Singapore)
1977 (16 July). *Centenary of Post Office Savings Bank. T 104 and similar vert designs. Multicoloured. P 13.*
305 10 c. Type 104 .. .. 30 10
  a. Perf 14
306 35 c. On-line banking service 75 50
  a. Perf 14
307 75 c. GIRO service .. .. .. 1·75 1·50
  a. Perf 14
305/7 .. .. .. *Set of 3* 2·50 1·90

105 Flags of Member Nations

106 "Chingay Procession" (Liang Yik Yin)

(Des Eng Siak Loy. Litho Secura, Singapore)
1977 (8 Aug). *Tenth Anniv of A.S.E.A.N. (Association of South-East Asian Nations). T 105 and similar vert designs. Multicoloured. P 14.*
308 10 c. Type 105 .. .. 30 10
309 35 c. "Agriculture" 75 50
310 75 c. "Industry" .. .. 1·75 1·10
308/10 .. .. .. *Set of 3* 2·50 1·50

(Des H. Weepaul. Litho Secura, Singapore)
1977 (1 Oct). *Children's Art. T 106 and similar horiz designs. Multicoloured. P 12½.*
311 10 c. Type 106 .. .. 30 10
312 35 c. "At the Bus Stop" (Chong Khing Ann) 1·00 50
313 75 c. "Playground" (Yap Li Hwa) .. 2·25 2·75
311/13 .. .. .. *Set of 3* 3·25 3·00
MS314 160 × 97 mm. Nos. 311/13 .. .. 13·00 15·00

107 "Life Sciences"

108 Botanical Gardens and Esplanade, Jurong Bird Park

(Des Tay Siew Chiah. Litho Format)
1977 (10 Dec). *Singapore Science Centre. T 107 and similar vert designs. Multicoloured. P 14½×14.*
315 10 c. Type 107. .. .. 10 10
316 35 c. "Physical sciences" 45 30
  a. Deep green and brown omitted .. £425
317 75 c. "Science and technology" .. 1·25 1·75
318 $1 Singapore Science Centre .. 1·50 1·75
315/18 .. .. .. *Set of 4* 3·00 3·50

(Des C. Kiat. Litho Harrison)
1978 (22 Apr). *Parks and Gardens. T 108 and similar multi-coloured designs. P 14½.*
319 10 c. Type 108 .. .. 20 10
320 35 c. Lagoon, East Coast Park (*vert*) .. 80 70
321 75 c. Botanical Gardens (*vert*) .. 1·50 2·00
319/21 .. .. .. *Set of 3* 2·25 2·50

109 Red-whiskered Bulbul

111 Map of South East Asia showing Cable Network

110 Thian Hock Keng Temple

(Des Eng Siak Loy. Litho Secura, Singapore)
1978 (1 July). *Singing Birds. T 109 and similar vert designs. Multicoloured. P 13½×14.*
322 10 c. Type 109 .. .. 60 20
323 35 c. Oriental White Eye .. .. 1·75 1·25
324 50 c. White-rumped Shama .. .. 2·00 2·00
325 75 c. White-crested Laughing Thrush and Hwamei .. .. .. 2·25 3·25
322/5 .. .. .. *Set of 4* 6·00 6·00

(Des Eng Siak Loy. Litho Secura, Singapore)
1978 (9 Aug). *National Monuments. T 110 and similar horiz designs. Multicoloured. P 13½.*
326 10 c. Type 110 .. .. 45 55
327 10 c. Hajjah Fatimah Mosque 45 55
328 10 c. Armenian Church 45 55
329 10 c. Sri Mariamman Temple 45 55
326/9 .. .. .. *Set of 4* 1·60 2·00
MS330 173 × 86 mm. 35 c. × 4, as Nos. 326/9 4·25 3·75
  Stamps from No. **MS**330 are similar in design to Nos. 326/9 but have no borders and the inscriptions are slightly larger.

(Des J. Heng. Litho Secura, Singapore)
1978 (3 Oct). *A.S.E.A.N. (Association of South East Asian Nations) Submarine Cable Network (1st issue). Completion of Philippines–Singapore section. P 14 (around design as well as stamp).*
331 111 10 c. multicoloured 15 10
332 35 c. multicoloured 60 55
333 50 c. multicoloured 80 85
334 75 c. multicoloured .. .. 90 1·25
331/4 .. .. .. *Set of 4* 2·25 2·50
  See also Nos. 385/8 and 458/62.

112 Neptune Spinel (bulk carrier)

(Des P. Wee Hui Hong. Litho Secura, Singapore)
1978 (18 Nov). *10th Anniv of Neptune Orient Shipping Lines. T 112 and similar horiz designs. Multicoloured. P 13½×14.*
335 10 c. Type 112 .. .. 70 15
336 35 c. Neptune Aries (tanker) .. .. 1·75 1·00
337 50 c. Anro Temasek (container ship) .. 2·00 2·00
338 75 c. Neptune Pearl (container ship) .. 2·50 3·00
335/8 .. .. .. *Set of 4* 6·25 5·50

113 Concorde

114 10 Kilometre Marker

(Des P. Wee Hui Hong. Litho Secura, Singapore)
1978 (16 Dec). *Aviation. T 113 and similar horiz designs. Multicoloured. P 13½.*
339 10 c. Type 113 .. .. 1·00 30
340 35 c. Boeing 747-200 .. .. .. 1·25 1·00
341 50 c. Vickers Vimy .. .. .. 1·50 1·75
342 75 c. Wright Brothers' Wright Flyer I .. 1·75 3·00
339/42 .. .. .. *Set of 4* 5·00 5·50

115 Vanda Hybrid

116 Envelope with new Singapore Postcode

(Des W. Lee. Litho Secura, Singapore)
1979 (24 Feb). *Metrication. T 114 and similar vert designs. Multi-coloured. P 13½.*
343 10 c. Type 114 .. .. 15 10
344 35 c. Tape measure 30 50
345 75 c. Weighing scales .. .. .. 60 1·25
343/5 .. .. .. *Set of 3* 95 1·75

(Des P. Wee Hui Hong. Litho Harrison)
1979 (14 Apr). *Orchids. T 115 and similar designs showing different varieties of Vanda Hybrid. P 15×14 (10, 35 c.) or 14×15 (others).*
346 10 c. multicoloured 30 10
347 35 c. multicoloured 75 75
348 50 c. multicoloured (*vert*) .. .. 90 1·00
349 75 c. multicoloured (*vert*) .. .. 1·25 1·40
346/9 .. .. .. *Set of 4* 2·75 2·75

(Des P. Wee Hui Hong. Litho Secura, Sinapore)
1979 (1 July). *Postal Code Publicity. P 13.*
350 116 10 c. multicoloured 10 10
351 — 50 c. multicoloured 60 80
  The 50 c. design is as Type 116, but the envelope is addressed to the Philatelic Bureau, General Post Office and has the postcode "Singapore 0104".

117 Early Telephone and Overhead Cables

118 "Lantern Festival" (Eng Chun-Ngan)

(Des Eng Siak Loy. Litho J.W.)
1979 (5 Oct). *Centenary of Telephone Service. T 117 and similar horiz designs. P 13½×13.*
352 10 c. yellow-brown and new blue .. 15 10
353 35 c. bright orange, blue and reddish violet .. 30 40
354 50 c. blue, dp turquoise-grn & yellowish grn .. 45 70
355 75 c. yellowish green and bright orange .. 65 1·25
352/5 .. .. .. *Set of 4* 1·40 2·25
  Designs:—35 c. Telephone dial and world map; 50 c. Modern telephone and city scene; 75 c. Latest computerised telephone and circuit diagram.

(Des Han Kuan Cheng. Litho Secura, Singapore)
1979 (10 Nov). *International Year of the Child. Children's Drawings. T 118 and similar horiz designs. Multicoloured. P 13.*
356 10 c. Type 118 .. .. 10 10
357 35 c. "Singapore Harbour" (Wong Chien Chien) 30 40
358 50 c. "Use Your Hands" (Leong Choy Yeen) 40 70
359 75 c. "Soccer" (Tan Cheong Hin) .. 65 1·25
356/9 .. .. .. *Set of 4* 1·25 2·25
MS360 154 × 98 mm. Nos. 356/9 .. .. 4·75 4·25

119 View of Gardens

120 Hainan Junk

(Des Eng Siak Loy. Litho Secura, Singapore)
1979 (15 Dec). *120th Anniv of Botanic Gardens. T 119 and similar horiz designs showing different views of the gardens. P 13½.*
361 10 c. multicoloured 30 10
  a. Imperf (pair) £700
362 50 c. multicoloured .. .. .. 1·00 1·50
363 $1 multicoloured .. .. .. 1·50 2·50
361/3 .. .. .. *Set of 3* 2·50 3·50

(Des Eng Siak Loy. Litho J.W.)
1980 (5 Apr)–84. *Ships. Multicoloured designs as T 120. Ordinary paper (1 c., 10 c.), phosphorised paper ($1 to $10) and ordinary or phosphorised paper (others). P 14 (1 to 75 c.) or 13½ ($1 to $10).*
364 1 c. Type 120 (26.4.80) .. .. 60 1·25
365 5 c. Full-rigged clipper (26.4.80) .. 30 55
366 10 c. Fujian junk (26.4.80) 30 10
  p. One narrow (4 mm) phosphor band (12.81) 45 30
  pa. One wide (10 mm) phosphor band (2.84) .. .. .. 1·50 2·25
367 15 c. Golekkan (sailing craft) (26.4.80) 40 15
368 20 c. Palari (sailing craft) (26.4.80) .. 70 40
369 25 c. East Indiaman (26.4.80) 80 50

370	35 c. Galleon (26.4.80)			90	50
371	50 c. Caravel (26.4.80)			60	70
372	75 c. Jiangsu trading junk (26.4.80)		1·25	1·50
373	$1 Kedah (coaster) (42×25 mm)		70	55
	a. Imperf (pair)				£275
374	$2 Murex (tanker) (42×25 mm)		1·25	90
375	$5 Chusan (screw steamer) (42×25 mm)		3·00	3·00
376	$10 Braganza (paddle-steamer) (42×25 mm)		6·00	6·00
364/76			Set of 13	15·00	14·00

 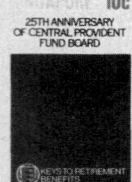

121 Straits Settlements 1867 1½ c. Stamp and Map of Singapore, 1843

122 C.P.F. Emblem and "Keys to Retirement Benefits"

(Des P. Wee Hui Hong. Litho Secura, Singapore)

1980 (6 May). "London 1980" International Stamp Exhibition. T **121** and similar vert designs. Multicoloured. P 13.

377	10 c. Type **121**			20	10
378	35 c. Straits Settlements 1906 $500 stamp and treaty between Johore and British Colony of Singapore		35	25
379	$1 1948 $2 stamp and map of Malaysia		70	1·10
380	$2 1969 150th Anniversary of Singapore $10 commemorative and letter to Col. Addenbrooke from Sir Stamford Raffles		1·25	2·25
377/80			Set of 4	2·25	3·25
MS381	148 × 104 mm. Nos. 377/80		2·50	4·50

(Des P. Wee Hui Hong. Litho Secura, Singapore)

1980 (1 July). 25th Anniv of Central Provident Fund Board. T **122** and similar vert designs showing C.P.F. emblem. Multicoloured. P 13.

382	10 c. Type **122**			10	10
383	50 c. "C.P.F. savings for home ownership"		40	40
384	$1 "C.P.F. savings for old-age"		75	1·25
382/4			Set of 3	1·10	1·60

 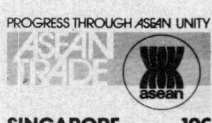

123 Map of South East Asia showing Cable Network

124 A.S.E.A.N. Trade Fair Emblem

(Des J. Heng. Litho Secura, Singapore)

1980 (8 Aug). A.S.E.A.N. (Association of South East Asian Nations) Submarine Cable Network (2nd issue). Completion of Indonesia–Singapore Section. P 14 (around design as well as stamp).

385	**123**	10 c. multicoloured		10	10
386		35 c. multicoloured		50	30
387		50 c. multicoloured		60	75
388		75 c. multicoloured		75	1·25
385/8			Set of 4	1·75	2·25

(Des P. Wee Hui Hong. Litho Secura, Singapore)

1980 (3 Oct). A.S.E.A.N. (Association of South East Asian Nations) Trade Fair. P 13.

389	**124**	10 c. multicoloured		10	10
		a. Perf 13½×14			30·00
390		35 c. multicoloured		30	30
		a. Perf 13½×14			10·00
391		75 c. multicoloured		60	1·00
		a. Perf 13½×14			15·00
389/91			Set of 3	85	1·25

125 Ixora

126 International Currency Symbols

(Des S. Tan and Chua Ban Har. Litho J.W.)

1980 (8 Nov). National Tree Planting Day. Flowers. T **125** and similar horiz designs. Multicoloured. P 13½ × 13.

392	10 c. Type **125**			10	10
393	35 c. Allamanda			40	45
394	50 c. Sky Vine			50	70
395	75 c. Bougainvillea			60	1·10
392/5			Set of 4	1·40	2·00

(Des P. Wee Hui Hong. Litho Secura, Singapore)

1981 (24 Jan). 10th Anniv of Monetary Authority of Singapore. P 14.

396	**126**	10 c. black, vermilion & greenish yellow	10	10
397		35 c. multicoloured		30	30
398		75 c. multicoloured		55	1·25
396/8			Set of 3	80	1·50

(127)

128 Woodwork

1981 (4 Mar). No. 65 surch with T **127**.

399	**21**	10 c. on 4 c. black and orange-red		30	40

(Des Sng Tong Beng. Litho J.W.)

1981 (11 Apr). Technical Training. T **128** and similar vert designs. Multicoloured. P 13 × 13½.

400	10 c. Type **128**			10	10
401	35 c. Building construction		25	25
402	50 c. Electronics			40	60
403	75 c. Precision machining		50	1·10
400/3			Set of 4	1·10	1·75

129 Figures representing various Sports

130 "The Rights to Environmental Aids"

(Des Lim Ching San. Litho J.W.)

1981 (25 Aug). "Sports for All". T **129** and similar vert designs showing figures representing various sports. P 14.

404	10 c. multicoloured			30	10
405	75 c. multicoloured			2·00	2·25
406	$1 multicoloured			2·50	3·00
404/6			Set of 3	4·25	4·75

(Des Chua Ban Har. Litho Harrison)

1981 (24 Nov). International Year for Disabled Persons. T **130** and similar vert designs. Multicoloured. One centre phosphor band (10 c.) or phosphorised paper (others). P 14½.

407	10 c. Type **130**			10	10
408	35 c. "The right to social integration".		40	25
409	50 c. "The right to education"		60	50
410	75 c. "The right to work"		80	90
407/10			Set of 4	1·75	1·60

Nos. 407/10 were printed with phosphor bands or on phosphorised paper similar to that used on contemporary Great Britain issues.

131 Control Tower and Passenger Terminal Building, Changi Airport

132 Parthenos sylvia

(Des J. Heng. Litho Secura, Singapore Ltd)

1981 (29 Dec). Opening of Changi Airport. P 14 × 13½.

411	**131**	10 c. multicoloured		10	10
412		35 c. multicoloured		30	20
413		50 c. multicoloured		40	60
414		75 c. multicoloured		50	1·10
415		$1 multicoloured		55	1·40
411/15			Set of 5	1·60	3·00
MS416	154 × 105 mm. Nos. 411/15		2·25	4·00

The five values show different background emblems representing the Parks and Recreation Dept, Public Works Dept, Telecommunications Authority, Port of Singapore and Dept of Civil Aviation.

(Des Eng Siak Loy. Litho J.W.)

1982 (3 Mar). Butterflies. T **132** and similar horiz designs. Multicoloured. One centre phosphor band (10 c.) or phosphorised paper (others). P 14.

417	10 c. Type **132**			40	15
418	50 c. Danaus vulgaris		1·25	1·75
419	$1 Trogonoptera brookiana		1·75	1·75
417/19			Set of 3	3·00	2·40

133 A.S.E.A.N. Emblem

134 Football and Stylised Player

(Des P. Wee Hui Hong. Litho Secura, Singapore)

1982 (14 June). 15th Anniv of A.S.E.A.N. (Association of South East Asian Nations). One centre phosphor band (10 c.) or phosphorised paper (others). P 14½×14.

420	**133**	10 c. multicoloured		10	10
421		35 c. multicoloured		30	35
422	–	50 c. multicoloured		40	65
423	–	75 c. multicoloured		60	1·00
420/3			Set of 4	1·25	1·90

The 50 and 75 c. values are as Type **133**, but are inscribed "15th ASEAN Ministerial Meeting".

(Des P. Wee Hui Hong. Litho Secura, Singapore)

1982 (9 July). World Cup Football Championship, Spain. T **134** and similar vert designs. One centre phosphor band (10 c.) or phosphorised paper (others). P 14.

424	10 c. black, bright blue and greenish blue		20	10
425	75 c. multicoloured			75	1·50
426	$1 multicoloured			95	1·50
424/6			Set of 3	1·75	2·75

Designs:—75 c. Football and World Cup, Asian Zone Four emblem; $1 Football and globe.

135 Sultan Shoal Lighthouse, 1896

136 Yard Gantry Cranes

(Des Eng Siak Loy. Litho Secura, Singapore)

1982 (7 Aug). Lighthouses of Singapore. T **135** and similar horiz designs. Multicoloured. One centre phosphor band (10 c.) or phosphorised paper (others). P 12.

427	10 c. Type **135**			50	15
428	75 c. Horsburgh Lighthouse, 1855		1·40	1·75
429	$1 Raffles Lighthouse, 1855		1·50	2·00
427/9			Set of 3	3·00	3·50
MS430	148 × 104 mm. Nos. 427/9		3·25	4·25

No. **MS**430 was printed on plain paper without phosphor.

(Des Goh Seng Lim. Litho Secura, Singapore)

1982 (15 Sept). 10th Anniv of Container Terminal. T **136** and similar horiz designs. Multicoloured. One centre phosphor band (10 c.) or phosphorised paper (others). P 13½.

431	10 c. Type **136**			10	10
432	35 c. Computer			25	30
433	50 c. Freightlifter			35	50
434	75 c. Straddle carrier			65	70
431/4			Set of 4	1·25	1·40

137 Scouts on Parade

138 Productivity Movement Slogans

(Des Poh Siew Wah. Litho Secura, Singapore)

1982 (15 Oct). 75th Anniv of Boy Scout Movement. T **137** and similar vert designs. Multicoloured. One centre phosphor band (10 c.) or phosphorised paper (others). P 14×13½.

435	10 c. Type **137**			15	10
436	35 c. Scouts hiking			45	25
437	50 c. Scouts building tower		65	35
438	75 c. Scouts canoeing			95	80
435/8			Set of 4	2·00	1·25

(Des M. Gan. Litho Secura, Singapore)

1982 (17 Nov). *Productivity Movement. T* **138** *and similar diamond-shaped designs. One centre phosphor band* (10 c.) *or phosphorised paper* (*others*). *P* 13½.

439	10 c. orange and emerald	10	10
440	35 c. yellow-ochre and deep dull blue	35	40
441	50 c. maroon, bistre-yellow and brownish grey	55	80
442	75 c. maroon and lemon	75	1·10
439/42	*Set of* 4	1·60	2·25

Designs:—35 c. Family and housing ("Benefits of Productivity"); 50 c. Works meeting ("Quality Control Circles"); 75 c. Aspects of Singapore business ("Everybody's Business").

139 Commonwealth Logo and Country Names

140 Soccer

(Des Eng Siak Loy. Litho Secura, Singapore)

1983 (14 Mar). *Commonwealth Day. One centre phosphor band* (10 c.) *or phosphorised paper* (*others*). *P* 13 × 13½.

443 **139**	10 c. multicoloured	10	10
444	35 c. multicoloured	20	25
445	75 c. multicoloured	45	85
446	$1 multicoloured	65	1·00
443/6	*Set of* 4	1·25	2·00

(Des Lim Ching San. Litho Secura, Singapore)

1983 (28 May). *12th South-East Asia Games. T* **140** *and similar vert designs. Multicoloured. One centre phosphor band* (10 c.) *or phosphorised paper* (*others*). *P* 13½ × 13.

447	10 c. Type **140**	10	10
448	35 c. Racket games	20	25
449	75 c. Athletics	45	50
450	$1 Swimming	65	70
447/50	*Set of* 4	1·25	1·40

141 Policeman and Family

142 1977 ASEAN Stamps and Statue of King Chulalongkorn

(Des Lim Ching San. Litho J.W.)

1983 (24 June). *Neighbourhood Watch Scheme. T* **141** *and similar horiz designs. Multicoloured. One wide centre phosphor band* (10 c.) *or phosphorised paper* (*others*). *P* 14.

451	10 c. Type **141**	15	10
452	35 c. Policeman and children	55	35
453	75 c. Policeman and inhabitants with linked arms	1·00	1·25
451/3	*Set of* 3	1·50	1·50

(Des Sylvia Tan and Ko Hui-Huy. Litho J.W.)

1983 (4 Aug). *Bangkok International Stamp Exhibition. T* **142** *and similar vert designs. Multicoloured. One wide centre phosphor band* (10 c.), *phosphorised paper* (35 c., $1) *or ordinary paper* (*miniature sheet*). *P* 14.

454	10 c. Type **142**	20	10
455	35 c. 1980 ASEAN stamps and map of South-East Asia	55	50
456	$1 1982 ASEAN stamps and signatures of Heads of State	1·25	1·60
454/6	*Set of* 3	1·75	2·00
MS457	147 × 104 mm. Nos. 454/6	2·75	4·00

143 Map of South-East Asia showing Cable Network

(Des J. Heng. Litho Secura, Singapore)

1983 (27 Sept). *A.S.E.A.N.* (*Association of South-East Asian Nations*) *Submarine Cable Network* (3*rd issue*). *Completion of Malaysia-Singapore-Thailand section. One centre phosphor band* (10 c.), *phosphorised paper* (35 c. *to* 75 c.) *or ordinary paper* (*miniature sheet*). *P* 13½ (*around design as well as stamp*).

458 **143**	10 c. multicoloured	15	10
459	35 c. multicoloured	55	75
460	50 c. multicoloured	80	1·25
461	75 c. multicoloured	1·25	1·75
458/61	*Set of* 4	2·50	3·50
MS462	146 × 100 mm. Nos. 331, 388, 458/61	3·50	4·25

144 Teletex Service

(Des Sylvia Tan and Ko Hui-Huy. Litho Enschedé)

1983 (10 Nov). *World Communications Year. T* **144** *and similar horiz designs. Phosphorised paper. P* 12½ × 13.

463	10 c. greenish yellow, light emerald and black	20	15
464	35 c. greenish yellow, brt rose-red & chocolate	55	65
465	75 c. bright yellow-green, greenish blue and deep violet-blue	1·00	1·40
466	$1 greenish yell, olive-brn & brownish blk	1·25	2·00
463/6	*Set of* 4	2·75	3·75

Designs:—35 c. World telephone numbering plan; 75 c. Satellite transmission; $1 Sea communications.

145 Blue-breasted Banded Rail

146 House of Tan Yeok Nee

(Des Poh Siew Wah. Litho Harrison)

1984 (15 Mar). *Coastal Birds. T* **145** *and similar horiz designs. Multicoloured. One wide centre phosphor band* (10 c.) *or phosphorised paper* (*others*). *P* 14½ × 13½.

467	10 c. Type **145**	60	15
468	35 c. Black Bittern	1·50	1·40
469	50 c. Brahminy Kite	1·75	1·90
470	75 c. Moorhen	2·00	2·75
467/70	*Set of* 4	5·25	5·50

(Des Poh Siew Wah. Litho Secura, Singapore)

1984 (7 June). *National Monuments. T* **146** *and similar vert designs. Multicoloured. One centre phosphor band* (10 c.) *or phosphorised paper* (*others*). *P* 12.

471	10 c. Type **146**	15	10
472	35 c. Thong Chai building	55	60
473	50 c. Telok Ayer market	75	90
474	$1 Nagore Durgha shrine	1·25	2·00
471/4	*Set of* 4	2·40	3·25

147 1970 $1 National Day Stamp

148 Schoolchildren

(Des P. Hong. Litho Secura, Singapore)

1984 (9 Aug–23 Nov). *"25 Years of Nation Building." T* **147** *and similar vert designs showing various Singapore stamps. Multicoloured. One centre phosphor band* (10 c.) *or phosphorised paper* (*others*). *P* 14 × 14½.

475	10 c. Type **147**	15	10
476	35 c. 1981 $1 "Sports for All" stamp	60	60
477	50 c. 1969 25 c. "100,000 Homes for the People" stamp	75	90
478	75 c. 1976 10 c. Wayside Trees stamp	90	1·25
479	$1 1981 $1 Opening of Changi Airport stamp	1·00	1·75
480	$2 1981 10 c. Monetary Authority stamp	1·90	3·50
475/80	*Set of* 6	4·75	7·25
MS481	132 × 106 mm. Nos. 475/80. P 12½ (23 Nov)	7·00	7·00

No. **MS**481 is on ordinary paper without a phosphor band on the 10 c. stamp.

(Des Lim Ching San. Litho Secura, Singapore)

1984 (26 Oct). *"Total Defence". T* **148** *and similar vert designs. One centre phosphor band. P* 12.

482	10 c. brown and orange-vermilion	15	20
	a. Horiz strip of 5. Nos. 482/6	65	
483	10 c. brown, yellow-olive and new blue	15	20
484	10 c. brown, bright violet and pale salmon	15	20
485	10 c. brown, orange-brown and mauve	15	20
486	10 c. brown, yellow and yellow-olive	15	20
482/6	*Set of* 5	65	90

Designs:—No. 482, Type **148**; 483, People of Singapore; 484, Industrial workers; 485, Civil Defence first aid worker; 486, Anti-aircraft gun crew.

Nos. 482/6 were printed together, *se-tenant*, in horizontal strips of five throughout the sheet.

149 Coleman Bridge

150 *Ceriagrion cerinorubellum* (damselfly)

(Des Eng Siak Loy. Recess Harrison)

1985 (15 Mar). *Bridges of Singapore. T* **149** *and similar horiz designs. One phosphor band* (10 c.) *or phosphorised paper* (*others*). *P* 14½ × 14.

487	10 c. black (Type **149**)	15	10
488	35 c. black (Cavenagh Bridge)	30	30
489	75 c. black (Elgin Bridge)	55	55
490	$1 black (Benjamin Sheares Bridge)	70	70
487/90	*Set of* 4	1·50	1·50

(Des Eng Siak Loy. Litho Japanese Govt Ptg Bureau, Tokyo, to 1986, thereafter Leigh-Mardon Ltd, Melbourne (5 c. to 75 c.). Recess and photo Japanese Govt Ptg Bureau, Tokyo ($1 to $10))

1985 (24 Apr)–**89.** *Insects. T* **150** *and similar horiz designs. Multicoloured. One narrow* (5 *mm*) *phosphor band* (10 c.) *or phosphorised paper* (*others*). *P* 13×13½.

491	5 c. Type **150**	1·25	40
	a. Leigh-Mardon ptg (9.12.86)	1·50	80
492	10 c. *Apis javana* (bee)	1·25	40
	a. Leigh-Mardon ptg (on phosphorised paper) (15.10.88)	1·50	55
493	15 c. *Delta arcuata* (wasp)	1·50	70
	a. Leigh-Mardon ptg (4.4.87)	9·50	1·00
494	20 c. *Xylocopa caerulea* (bee)	1·00	90
	a. Leigh-Mardon ptg (15.12.86)	12·00	1·25
495	25 c. *Donacia javana* (water beetle)	1·00	1·00
	a. Leigh-Mardon ptg (22.9.86)	12·00	1·50
496	35 c. *Heteroneda reticulata* (ladybird)	1·25	30
	a. Leigh-Mardon ptg (25.5.88)	13·00	1·50
497	50 c. *Catacanthus nigripes* (bug)	1·50	55
	a. Leigh-Mardon ptg (20.1.89)	35·00	2·25
498	75 c. *Chremistica pontianaka* (cicada)	1·50	1·75
	a. Leigh-Mardon ptg (3.7.89)	42·00	4·00
499	$1 *Homoexipha lycoides* (cricket) (5.6.85)	2·75	60
500	$2 *Traulia azureipennis* (grasshopper) (5.6.85)	2·00	1·25
501	$5 *Trithemis aurora* (dragonfly) (5.6.85)	2·75	3·50
502	$10 *Scambophyllum sanguinolentum* (grasshopper) (5.6.85)	5·75	7·50
491/502	*Set of* 12	21·00	17·00
491a/8a	*Set of* 8	£110	11·50

Nos. 499/502 are larger, 35×30 mm.

Although the work of the two printers is very similar as far as shade, paper and perforation are concerned Leigh-Mardon used new printing plates taken from the original colour separations and, in consequence, each value does differ from its predecessor printed by the Japanese Government Printing Bureau.

It can be misleading to sort stamps by the paper thickness. Although most Tokyo printings were on paper noticeably thinner than that used by Leigh-Mardon there were Japanese printings of the 5, 15, 20 and 25 c., released in the first half of 1987, which were on thick paper.

J.G.P.B.

L.-M.

5 c. On the J.G.P.B. printing the tail of the insect is ½ mm from the bottom edge of the vignette. On the L.-M. printing the distance is 1 mm.

J.G.P.B.

L.-M.

10 c. The J.G.P.B. printing shows the petals at bottom right cut by the edge of the design. On the L.-M. printing all three petals are complete.

J.G.P.B.   L.-M.

15 c. The J.G.P.B. printing shows the rock at bottom right 1½ mm from the right-hand edge. On the L.-M. stamp this distance is 2 mm.

J.G.P.B.   L.-M.

20 c. On the J.G.P.B. stamp the pink flowers above "SINGAPORE" touch the edge of the vignette. For the L.-M. printing the right-hand petal is clear of the edge.

J.G.P.B.   L.-M.

25 c. The J.G.P.B. printing shows the uppermost feeler of the water beetle touching the top of the design. On the L.-M. stamp the feeler does not reach the edge of the design.

J.G.P.B.   L.-M.

35 c. On the J.G.P.B. printing the vein on the leaf at bottom left stops just short of the corner of the design. The L.-M. stamp shows this vein reaching the left-hand edge of the design above the corner.

J.G.P.B.   L.-M.

50 c. The J.G.P.B. stamp has the uppermost leaf cut by the top edge of the design. On the L.-M. printing the leaf is complete.

J.G.P.B.   L.-M.

75 c. On the J.G.P.B. printing the shadow of the wings is 1½mm above the bottom edge of the vignette. For the L.-M. stamp the shadow touches the bottom edge.

151 Tennis, Canoeing, Judo and Children Playing

(Des M. Chiew. Litho Secura, Singapore)

1985 (1 July). *25th Anniv of the People's Association. T* **151** *and similar horiz designs. Multicoloured. One phosphor band* (10 c.) *or phosphorised paper* (others). *P* 13½ × 14.

503	10 c. Type **151**..	25	10
504	35 c. Lion dance, martial arts and athletes with flags	30	30
505	50 c. Tae-kwon-do, Indian dance and Dragon dance	40	40
506	75 c. Boxing, table tennis, basketball and dancing ..	75	75
503/6	.. *Set of 4*	1.50	1.40

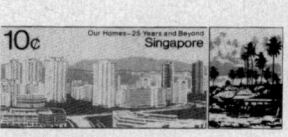

152 Modern Housing Estate and Squatter Settlement   153 Brownies

(Des Eng Siak Loy. Litho Secura, Singapore)

1985 (9 Aug). *25th Anniv of Housing and Development Board. Horiz designs as T* **152** *with different aspects of housing shown at left. Multicoloured. One phosphor band* (10 c.) *or phosphorised paper* (others). *P* 13½×14.

507	10 c. Type **152**..	15	10
508	35 c. Singapore family (Home-ownership) ..	30	30
509	50 c. Group of residents (Community development) ..	40	40
510	75 c. Construction workers (Building technology) ..	55	55
507/10	*Set of 4*	1.25	1.25
MS511	126 × 105 mm. Nos. 507/10	3.25	3.50

(Des Foo Lye Lin. Litho J.W.)

1985 (6 Nov). *75th Anniv of Girl Guide Movement. T* **153** *and similar vert designs. One phosphor band* (10 c.) *or phosphorised paper* (others). *Multicoloured. P* 14.

512	10 c. Type **153**..	15	10
513	35 c. Guides practising first aid ..	35	30
514	50 c. Senior Branch ..	45	45
515	75 c. Adult leaders and guides ..	65	75
512/15	*Set of 4*	1.40	1.40

154 Badges and Emblems of Singapore Youth Organizations   155 Guava

(Des Eng Siak Loy. Litho Secura, Singapore)

1985 (18 Dec). *International Youth Year. T* **154** *and similar horiz designs. Multicoloured. One phosphor band* (10 c.) *or phosphorised paper* (others). *P* 12.

516	10 c. Type **154**..	10	10
517	75 c. Hand protecting sapling ..	70	55
518	$1 Stylised figures and dove ..	90	70
516/18	*Set of 3*	1.50	1.25

(Des Poh Siew Wah. Litho J.W.)

1986 (26 Feb). *Singapore Fruits. T* **155** *and similar vert designs. Multicoloured. One centre phosphor band* (10 c.) *or phosphorised paper* (others). *P* 14.

519	10 c. Type **155**..	30	10
520	35 c. Jambu Air ..	85	45
521	50 c. Rambutan ..	1.10	90
522	75 c. Ciku ..	1.40	1.10
519/22	*Set of 4*	3.25	2.00

156 Laboratory Technician and Salesmen with Bar Graph   157 Calligraphy

(Des W. Lee. Litho Secura, Singapore)

1986 (1 May). *25th Anniv of National Trades Union Congress. T* **156** *and similar vert designs. Multicoloured. One phosphor band. P* 13½.

523	10 c. Type **156**..	25	40
	a. Horiz strip of 4. Nos. 523/6	90	
524	10 c. Computer operator and welder	25	40
525	10 c. Draughtsmen and surveyors ..	25	40
526	10 c. Group of workers	25	40
523/6	*Set of 4*	90	1.40
MS527	148 × 100 mm. As Nos. 523/6, but each stamp with a face value of 35 c. Phosphorised paper	3.50	4.25

Nos. 523/6 were printed together, *se-tenant*, in horizontal strips of 4 throughout the sheet, forming a composite design.

(Des Chua Ban Har. Litho (50 c. also die-stamped) Leigh-Mardon Ltd, Melbourne)

1986 (2 May). *"Expo '86" World Fair, Vancouver. T* **157** *and similar horiz designs. Multicoloured. "All-over" phosphor. P* 14×14½.

528	50 c. Type **157**..	45	75
	a. Horiz strip of 3. Nos. 528/30	1.60	
529	75 c. Garland maker ..	60	95
530	$1 Batik printer ..	75	1.25
528/30	*Set of 3*	1.60	2.75

Nos. 528/30 were printed together, *se-tenant*, in horizontal strips of 3 throughout the sheet.

158 Industrial Automation   159 Map showing Route of Cable and Vercors (cable ship)

(Des Eng Siak Loy. Litho J.W.)

1986 (1 Aug). *25th Anniv of Economic Development Board. T* **158** *and similar vert designs. Multicoloured. Phosphorised paper. P* 15×14½.

531	10 c. Type **158**..	10	10
532	35 c. Manufacture of aircraft components ..	25	30
533	50 c. Electronics industry ..	30	50
534	75 c. Biotechnology industry ..	50	90
531/4	.. *Set of 4*	1.00	1.60

(Des J. Heng. Litho Secura, Singapore)

1986 (8 Sept). *SEA–ME–WE Submarine Cable Project. Phosphorised paper. P* 13½.

535	**159** 10 c. multicoloured ..	40	10
536	35 c. multicoloured ..	85	45
537	50 c. multicoloured ..	1.10	80
538	75 c. multicoloured ..	1.40	1.40
535/8	.. *Set of 4*	3.25	2.50

160 Stylized Citizens   161 Peace Doves and People of Different Races

(Des W. Lee. Litho Secura, Singapore)

1986 (15 Oct). *21st Anniv of Citizens' Consultative Committees. T* **160** *and similar vert designs showing citizens. Phosphorised paper. P* 12.

539	10 c. multicoloured ..	30	35
	a. Block of 4. Nos. 539/42 ..	1.90	
540	35 c. multicoloured ..	45	50
541	50 c. multicoloured ..	55	60
542	75 c. multicoloured ..	75	80
539/42	*Set of 4*	1.90	2.00

Nos. 539/42 were printed together, *se-tenant*, in blocks of 4 throughout the sheet, each block forming a composite design.

(Des Eng Siak Loy. Litho Secura, Singapore)

1986 (17 Dec). *International Peace Year. T* **161** *and similar horiz designs. Multicoloured. Phosphorised paper. P* 14 × 13½.

543	10 c. Type **161**..	15	10
544	35 c. Doves and map of ASEAN countries ..	40	45
545	$1 Doves and globe ..	95	1.75
543/5	*Set of 3*	1.40	2.00

162 Orchard Road   163 Flags of Member Nations and Logo

(Des Chua Ban Har. Litho Secura, Singapore)

1987 (25 Feb). *Singapore Skyline. T* **162** *and similar horiz designs. Multicoloured. Phosphorised paper. P* 12.

546	10 c. Type **162**..	15	10
547	50 c. Central Business District ..	50	65
548	75 c. Marina Centre and Raffles City ..	75	1.25
546/8	*Set of 3*	1.25	1.75

(Des Chua Ban Har. Litho Secura, Singapore)

1987 (15 June). *20th Anniv of Association of South-east Asian Nations. Phosphorised paper. P* 12.

549	**163** 10 c. multicoloured ..	10	10
550	35 c. multicoloured ..	30	30
551	50 c. multicoloured ..	45	45
552	75 c. multicoloured ..	55	55
549/52	.. *Set of 4*	1.25	1.25

164 Soldier with Rocket
Launcher and Tank

165 Singapore River
and Dragon Boats

(Des M. Ng Puay Chiew. Litho Questa)

1987 (1 July). *20th Anniv of National Service. T 164 and similar vert designs. Multicoloured. Phosphorised paper. P 15×14.*

553	10 c. Type 164		55	70
	a. Horiz strip of 4. Nos. 553/6		2·00	
554	10 c. Radar operator and patrol boat		55	70
555	10 c. Fighter pilot, General Dynamics F-16 Fighting Falcon and Douglas A-4 Skyhawk aircraft		55	70
556	10 c. Servicemen pledging allegiance		55	70
553/6		*Set of 4*	2·00	2·50
MS557	148×100 mm. 35 c. × 5. As Nos. 553/6 and Singapore lion symbol (scarlet and black)		4·00	4·50

Nos. 553/6 were printed together, *se-tenant*, in horizontal strips of 4 throughout the sheet.

(Des Ng Keng Seng. Litho Secura, Singapore)

1987 (2 Sept). *River Conservation. T 165 and similar square designs. Multicoloured. Phosphorised paper. P 13½.*

558	10 c. Type 165		30	10
559	50 c. Kallang Basin, canoe and fishing punt		80	90
560	$1 Kranji Reservoir, athletes and cyclist		2·00	2·50
558/60		*Set of 3*	2·75	3·25

166 Majapahit Gold Bracelet and Museum

(Des M. Ng Puay Chiew. Litho Secura, Singapore)

1987 (12 Oct). *Centenary of National Museum. T 166 and similar horiz designs, each showing different drawings of Museum. Multicoloured. Phosphorised paper. P 13½×14.*

561	10 c. Type 166		30	10
562	75 c. Ming fluted kendi (water vessel)		1·25	1·50
563	$1 Patani hulu pekakak keris (sword)		1·40	2·00
561/3		*Set of 3*	2·75	3·25

167 Omni-theatre

(Des Eng Siak Loy. Litho Leigh-Mardon Ltd, Melbourne)

1987 (10 Dec). *10th Anniv of Singapore Science Centre. T 167 and similar horiz designs. Multicoloured. Phosphorised paper. P 14½.*

564	10 c. Type 167		15	10
565	35 c. Omni-planetarium		1·25	75
566	75 c. Model of body cell		1·50	1·75
567	$1 Physical sciences exhibits		1·50	2·25
564/7		*Set of 4*	4·00	4·25

168 Modern Anti-aircraft Gun

169 Route Map

(Des L. Teck Chong. Litho Secura, Singapore)

1988 (22 Feb). *Centenary of Singapore Artillery. T 168 and similar horiz designs. Multicoloured. Phosphorised paper. P 13½×14.*

568	10 c. Type 168		55	15
569	35 c. 25-pounder field gun firing salute		1·25	1·90
570	50 c. Gunner and 12-pounder gun, c. 1920		1·50	1·75
571	$1 Gunner and Maxim gun, 1889		2·25	3·50
568/71		*Set of 4*	5·00	5·50

(Des Ng Keng Seng. Litho Secura, Singapore)

1988 (12 Mar). *Singapore Mass Rapid Transit System. T 169 and similar horiz designs. Multicoloured. Phosphorised paper. P 13½ × 14.*

572	10 c. Type 169		50	15
573	50 c. Train on elevated section		1·75	1·90
574	$1 Train in tunnel		2·75	3·50
572/4		*Set of 3*	4·50	5·00

170 Camera, Film and
Outside Broadcast Van

(Des E. Soriano. Litho CPE Australia Ltd, Melbourne)

1988 (4 Apr). *25th Anniv of Television in Singapore. T 170 and similar horiz designs. Multicoloured. Phosphorised paper. P 13½ × 14.*

575	10 c. Type 170		40	10
576	35 c. Camera, studio lights and microphone		80	60
577	75 c. Television set and transmitter		1·25	1·50
578	$1 Globe on TV screen and dish aerial		1·50	1·75
575/8		*Set of 4*	3·50	3·50

MACHINE LABELS. From 19 April 1988 self-adhesive labels in the above design, with the background printed in orange and grey, were available from machines situated outside a number of Singapore post offices. Face values between 5 c. and $2 could be selected and the location of individual machines is indicated by the code number, from 0001 to 0050, at bottom left.

The designs was changed to three lions' heads in red on 5 June 1989, to the Fullerton Building G.P.O. in brown on 8 September 1990, to Haw Par Villa in red on 2 October 1991, to trishaws in brown on 1 December 1992, to the Singapore skyline in turquoise-green on 5 April 1994 and to orchids in red on 1 April 1995.

A new series, showing a family in a park, was introduced on 19 May 1997. These carry code numbers S001 to S094.

Vertical labels inscribed "SINGAPORE POSTAGE" with face values and, in some instances a weight, also exist. These were introduced in January 1983 and come from machines used by P. O. counter clerks to process parcels and registered mail. For a time, 1986–87, these labels were on self-adhesive paper.

A new series of encrypted postage labels was introduced from August 1998 onwards. These come from Pitney Bowes Meter Label Printers which produce white self-adhesive labels 57×40 mm showing a stamp outline enclosing the encrypted information.

171 Water Droplet
and Blocks of Flats

172 Greeting Neighbours

(Des Ng Keng Seng. Litho CPE Australia Ltd, Melbourne)

1988 (4 May). *25th Anniv of Public Utilities Board. T 171 and similar vert designs, each showing a different skyline. Multicoloured. Phosphorised paper. P 13½.*

579	10 c. Type 171		20	10
580	50 c. Electric light bulb and city centre		1·00	1·00
581	$1 Gas flame and factories		1·50	1·50
579/81		*Set of 3*	2·75	3·25
MS582	116 × 75 mm. Nos. 579/81		3·25	4·25

(Des M. Ng Puay Chiew. Litho Leigh-Mardon Ltd, Melbourne)

1988 (6 July). *10th Anniv of National Courtesy Campaign. T 172 and similar horiz designs, each showing campaign mascot "Singa". Multicoloured. Phosphorised paper. P 14½.*

583	10 c. Type 172		20	10
584	30 c. Queueing at checkout		50	45
585	$1 Helping the elderly		1·50	2·25
583/5		*Set of 3*	2·00	2·50

173 Modern 30 Metre
Turntable Fire Appliance

174 Container Ships
and Warehouses

(Des Eng Siak Loy. Litho Secura, Singapore)

1988 (1 Nov). *Centenary of Fire Service. T 173 and similar horiz design. Multicoloured. Phosphorised paper. P 13½.*

586	10 c. Type 173		75	25
587	$1 Steam fire engine, c. 1890		2·75	2·25

(Des Ng Keng Seng. Litho Secura, Singapore)

1989 (3 Apr). *25th Anniv of Singapore Port Authority. T 174 and similar vert designs. Multicoloured. Phosphorised paper. P 14×13½.*

588	10 c. Type 174		40	10
589	30 c. Shipping and oil storage depot		75	40
590	75 c. Container ships and Singapore skyline		1·40	1·25
591	$1 Container port at night		1·50	1·50
588/91		*Set of 4*	3·50	2·75

175 "Sago Street"

176 North-west Singapore
City, 1920

(Litho Questa)

1989 (17 May). *Paintings of Chinatown by Choo Keng Kwang. T 175 and similar square designs. Multicoloured. Phosphorised paper. P 14½.*

592	10 c. Type 175		40	15
593	35 c. "Pagoda Street"		1·25	70
594	75 c. "Trengganu Street"		2·00	2·00
595	$1 "Temple Street"		2·25	2·25
592/5		*Set of 4*	5·50	4·50

(Des L. Teck Chong. Litho Harrison)

1989 (26 July). *Maps of Singapore. T 176 and similar multicoloured designs. Phosphorised paper. P 14×14½ (15 c.) or 12½×13 (others).*

596	15 c. Type 176 (top left)		90	90
	a. Block of 4. Nos. 596/9		3·25	
597	15 c. North-east Singapore (top right)		90	90
598	15 c. South-west Singapore (bottom left)		90	90
599	15 c. South-east Singapore (bottom right)		90	90
600	50 c. Singapore Island and Dependencies, 1860s		2·00	2·00
601	$1 British Settlement of Singapore, 1820s		2·75	2·75
596/601		*Set of 6*	7·50	7·50

Nos. 596/9 were printed together, *se-tenant*, in blocks of 4 throughout the sheet, each block forming a composite design. Individual stamps can be identified by the position of the lion emblem which is quoted in brackets.

177 Clown Triggerfish

178 "Hari Raya
Puasa" (Loke Yoke
Yun)

(Des Eng Siak Loy. Litho Harrison)

1989 (6 Sept). *Fishes. T 177 and similar horiz designs. Multicoloured. Phosphorised paper. P 13½.*

602	15 c. Type 177		85	20
603	30 c. Blue-girdled Angelfish		1·50	90
604	75 c. Emperor Angelfish		2·75	3·00
605	$1 Regal Angelfish		3·00	3·75
602/5		*Set of 4*	7·25	7·00

(Adapted S. Ang Woon Beng. Litho Harrison)

1989 (25 Oct). *Festivals of Singapore. Children's Drawings. T 178 and similar vert designs. Multicoloured. Phosphorised paper. P 14½.*

606	15 c. Type 178		40	10
607	35 c. "Chinese New Year" (Simon Koh)		70	55
608	75 c. "Thaipusam" (Henry Setiono)		1·40	1·00
609	$1 "Christmas" (Wendy Ang Lin Min)		1·75	1·50
606/9		*Set of 4*	3·75	2·75
MS610	126×75 mm. Nos. 606/9. P 14		4·00	4·00

179 North Entrance of Stadium

180 "Singapore River,
1839" (Louis le Breton)

(Des Lim Ching San. Litho Harrison)

1989 (27 Dec). *Opening of Singapore Indoor Stadium. T 179 and similar horiz designs. Multicoloured. Phosphorised paper. P 14.*

611	30 c. Type 179		85	30
612	75 c. Arena		1·75	1·50
613	$1 East entrance		2·00	1·75
611/13		*Set of 3*	4·25	3·25
MS614	104×104 mm. Nos. 611/13		4·50	4·50

(Des Choy Weng Yang. Litho Leigh-Mardon Ltd, Melbourne)

1990 (21 Mar). *Lithographs of 19th-century Singapore. T* **180** *and similar horiz designs. Multicoloured. Phosphorised paper. P* 13.

615	15 c. Type **180**			40	15
	a. Booklet pane. No. 615×10			8·00	
616	30 c. "Chinatown, 1837" (Barthelemy Lauvergne)			80	55
617	75 c. "Singapore Harbour, 1837" (Barthelemy Lauvergne)			1·50	1·50
618	$1 "View from the French Resident's House, 1824" (Deroy)			1·75	1·75
615/18			*Set of 4*	4·00	3·50

The upper and lower edges of booklet pane No. 615a are imperforate.

181 1969 150th Anniv of Singapore Stamp Issue

(Des Sylvia Tan. Litho Leigh-Mardon Pty Ltd, Melbourne)

1990 (3 May). *150th Anniv of the Penny Black. T* **181** *and similar horiz designs, each showing a different map in the background. Multicoloured. Phosphorised paper. P* 13½.

619	50 c. Type **181**			1·00	60
620	75 c. Indian stamps, including bisect, used from Singapore in 1859			1·25	1·25
621	$1 Indian stamps used from Singapore in 1854			1·90	1·75
622	$2 Penny Black and Two Pence Blue			3·00	4·75
619/22			*Set of 4*	6·50	7·50
MS623	134×90 mm. Nos. 619/22			8·50	7·50

No. MS623 also commemorates the "Stamp World London 90" international stamp exhibition.

182 Zoological Gardens

183 Chinese Opera Singer and Siong Lim Temple

(Des Ng Keng Seng (5 to 75 c.), Lim Ching San ($1 to $10). Photo (5 to 75 c.) or recess and photo ($1 to $10) Harrison)

1990 (4 July)–**91**. *Tourism. Multicoloured. Phosphorised paper. (a) T* **182** *and similar square designs. P* 14½.

624	5 c. Type **182**			30	40
625	15 c. Sentosa Island			30	10
	a. Booklet pane. No. 625×10			11·00	
626	20 c. Singapore River			30	20
	a. Booklet pane. No. 626×10 (6.3.91)			4·50	
627	25 c. Dragon Boat Festival			55	25
628	30 c. Raffles Hotel			70	30
629	35 c. Coffee shop bird singing contest			1·25	35
630	40 c. Jurong Bird Park			1·50	40
631	50 c. Chinese New Year boat float			1·25	45
632	75 c. Peranakan Place			1·75	70

(b) T **183** *and similar horiz designs. P* 15×14 (9.10.90)

633	$1 Type **183**			2·50	90
634	$2 Malay dancer and Sultan Mosque			3·25	1·75
635	$5 Indian dancer and Sri Mariamman Temple			6·00	5·50
636	$10 Ballet dancer and Victoria Memorial Hall			10·00	10·00
624/36			*Set of 13*	26·00	19·00

The upper and lower edges of booklet panes Nos. 625a and 626a are imperforate.

184 Armed Forces Personnel

185 Stag's Horn Fern

(Des Chua Ban Har. Litho Harrison)

1990 (16 Aug). *25th Anniv of Independence. T* **184** *and similar horiz designs. Multicoloured. Phosphorised paper. P* 14×15.

637	15 c. Type **184**			40	40
	a. Perf 14			85	1·00
	ab. Booklet pane. No. 637a×10			9·50	
638	35 c. Inhabitants of Singapore			90	75
639	75 c. Workers and technological achievements			1·60	1·75
640	$1 Cultural activities			1·75	2·50
637/40			*Set of 4*	4·25	4·75

No. 637a only comes from $1.50 stamp booklets in which the pane, No. 637ab, has margins at left and right.

(Des Poh Siew Wah. Litho Questa)

1990 (14 Nov). *Ferns. T* **185** *and similar horiz designs. Multicoloured. Phosphorised paper. P* 14.

641	15 c. Type **185**			25	10
642	35 c. Maiden Hair Fern			60	55
643	75 c. Bird's Nest Fern			1·25	1·25
644	$1 Rabbit's Foot Fern			1·60	2·00
641/4			*Set of 4*	3·25	3·50

186 Carved Dragon Pillar, Hong San See Temple

187 *Vanda* "Miss Joaquim"

(Des L. Teck Chong. Litho Leigh-Mardon Ltd, Melbourne)

1991 (23 Jan). *National Monuments. T* **186** *and similar multicoloured designs. Phosphorised paper. P* 14½.

645	20 c. Type **186**			30	50
	a. Vert pair. Nos. 645/6			60	1·00
646	20 c. Hong San See Temple (40×25 mm)			30	50
647	50 c. Interior of dome, Abdul Gaffoor Mosque			55	75
	a. Vert pair. Nos. 647/8			1·10	1·50
648	50 c. Abdul Gaffoor Mosque (40×25 mm)			55	75
649	75 c. Statue of Vishnu, Sri Perumal Hindu Temple			80	1·00
	a. Vert pair. Nos. 649/50			1·60	2·00
650	75 c. Sri Perumal Temple (40×25 mm)			80	1·00
651	$1 Stained glass window, St Andrew's Cathedral			90	1·40
	a. Vert pair. Nos. 651/2			1·75	2·75
652	$1 St Andrew's Cathedral (40×25 mm)			90	1·40
645/52			*Set of 8*	4·50	6·50

The two designs for each value were printed together, *se-tenant*, in vertical pairs throughout the sheets.

(Des Chua Ban Har. Litho Leigh-Mardon Ltd, Melbourne)

1991 (24 Apr). *"Singapore '95" International Stamp Exhibition. Orchids (1st issue). T* **187** *and similar horiz design. Multicoloured. Phosphorised paper. P* 14.

653	$2 Type **187**			3·50	4·00
	a. Horiz pair. Nos. 653/4			7·00	8·00
654	$2 *Dendrobium* "Anocha"			3·50	4·00
MS655	123×80 mm. Nos. 653/4			7·00	8·00

Nos. 653/4 were issued together, *se-tenant*, in sheets of 30 (6×5), showing No. 653 in vertical rows 1 and 4, Nos. 654 in vertical rows 3 and 6, and stamp-size labels with exhibition emblem in vertical rows 2 and 5.

See also Nos. 674/6, 725/7, 755/7, 795/7 and **MS**818.

188 Changi Airport Terminal II, 1991, and Boeing 747-400

189 *Arachnopsis* "Eric Holttum"

(Des L. Teck Chong. Recess and litho Harrison)

1991 (1 June). *Singapore Civil Aviation. T* **188** *and similar horiz designs. Multicoloured. Phosphorised paper. P* 13½×14½.

656	20 c. Type **188**			85	20
657	75 c. Changi Airport Terminal I, 1981, and Boeing 747-200			2·00	1·50
658	$1 Paya Lebar Airport, 1955–1981, and Concorde			2·25	1·75
659	$2 Kallang Airport, 1937–1955, and Douglas DC-2			3·50	5·00
656/9			*Set of 4*	7·75	7·50

(Des Chua Ban Har. Litho Questa)

1991 (7 Aug). *Orchid Dress Motifs. T* **189** *and similar horiz designs. Multicoloured. Phosphorised paper. P* 14½×14.

660	20 c. Type **189**			1·00	20
661	30 c. *Cattleya meadii*			1·25	1·10
662	$1 *Calanthe vestita*			3·00	4·25
660/2			*Set of 3*	4·75	4·50

190 Long-tailed Tailor Bird

191 Productivity Discussion

(Des M. Ng Puay Chiew. Litho Leigh-Mardon Ltd, Melbourne)

1991 (19 Sept). *Garden Birds. T* **190** *and similar horiz designs. Multicoloured. Phosphorised paper. P* 14.

663	20 c. Type **190**			45	20
	a. Booklet pane. No. 663×10			13·00	
664	35 c. Scarlet-backed Flowerpecker			1·50	1·00
665	75 c. Black-naped Oriole			2·25	2·50
666	$1 Common Iora			2·50	3·25
663/6			*Set of 4*	6·00	6·25

Booklet pane No. 663a has the upper and lower edges imperforate and there are margins at left and right.

(Des Foo Lye Lin. Litho Questa)

1991 (1 Nov). *10th Anniv of Productivity Movement. T* **191** *and similar vert design. Multicoloured. Phosphorised paper. P* 14×14½.

667	20 c. Type **191**			30	30
668	$1 Construction workers			95	1·60

192 Railway Creeper

193 "Singapore Waterfront" (Georgette Chen Liying)

(Des Eng Siak Loy. Litho Leigh-Mardon Ltd, Melbourne)

1991 (16 Nov). *"Phila Nippon '91" International Stamp Exhibition, Tokyo. Wild Flowers. T* **192** *and similar vert designs. Multicoloured. Phosphorised paper. P* 14½×14.

669	30 c. Type **192**			75	25
670	75 c. Asystasia			1·25	85
671	$1 Singapore Rhododendron			1·50	1·50
672	$2 Coat Buttons			2·50	4·00
669/72			*Set of 4*	5·50	6·00
MS673	132×90 mm. Nos. 669/72			6·00	7·00

(Des Chua Ban Har. Litho Leigh-Mardon Ltd, Melbourne)

1992 (22 Jan). *"Singapore '95" International Stamp Exhibition. Orchids (2nd issue). Horiz designs as T* **187**. *Multicoloured. Phosphorised paper. P* 14.

674	$2 *Dendrobium* "Sharifah Fatimah"			2·75	3·50
	a. Horiz pair. Nos. 674/5			5·50	7·00
675	$2 *Phalaenopsis* "Shim Beauty"			2·75	3·50
MS676	123×80 mm. Nos. 674/5			6·50	7·50

Nos. 674/5 were printed in the same sheet format as Nos. 653/4.

(Des Lim Ching San. Litho Secura, Singapore)

1992 (11 Mar). *Local Artists (1st series). T* **193** *and similar square designs. Multicoloured. Phosphorised paper. P* 14.

677	20 c. Type **193**			40	20
678	75 c. "Kampung Hut" (Lim Cheng Hoe)			85	1·00
679	$1 "The Bridge" (Poh Siew Wah)			1·10	1·25
680	$2 "Singapore River" (Lee Boon Wang)			2·25	3·25
677/80			*Set of 4*	4·25	5·00

See also Nos. 818/21.

194 Football

195 Chinese Family and Samfu Pattern

(Des L. Teck Chong. Litho Leigh-Mardon Ltd, Melbourne)

1992 (24 Apr). *Olympic Games, Barcelona. T* **194** *and similar horiz designs. Multicoloured. Phosphorised paper. P* 14.

681	20 c. Type **194**			25	20
682	35 c. Athletics			35	30
683	50 c. Swimming			55	65
684	75 c. Basketball			1·25	1·25
685	$1 Tennis			1·50	1·50
686	$2 Yachting			2·00	2·75
681/6			*Set of 6*	5·50	6·00
MS687	132×90 mm. Nos. 681/6			7·00	7·50

(Des Chua Ban Har. Litho Leigh-Mardon Ltd, Melbourne)

1992 (22 May). *Singapore Costumes of 1910. T* **195** *and similar vert designs. Multicoloured. Phosphorised paper. P* 14½.

688	20 c. Type **195**			40	20
689	35 c. Malay family and sarong pattern			50	45
690	75 c. Indian family and sari pattern			1·00	1·25
691	$2 Straits Chinese family and belt pattern			2·00	3·00
688/91			*Set of 4*	3·50	4·50

NEW INFORMATION

The editor is always interested to correspond with people who have new information that will improve or correct the Catalogue.

196 Infantryman, Air Force Pilot and Navy Gunner

197 Crafts from A.S.E.A.N. Countries

(Des T. Koh. Litho Leigh-Mardon Ltd, Melbourne)

1992 (1 July). *25th Anniv of National Service. T 196 and similar horiz designs. Multicoloured. Phosphorised paper. P 14½.*

692	20 c. Type 196		60	30
693	35 c. Navy diver, General Dynamics F-16 Fighting Falcon and FH-88 155 mm howitzer		85	75
694	$1 General Dynamics F-16 Fighting Falcon in flight, corvette and AMX-13SM1 tank		2·50	3·75
692/4		Set of 3	3·50	4·25

(Des Chua Ban Har. Litho Questa)

1992 (8 Aug). *25th Anniv of A.S.E.A.N (Association of South East Asian Nations). T 197 and similar horiz designs. Multicoloured. Phosphorised paper. P 14×14½.*

695	20 c. Type 197		40	20
696	35 c. National dances		90	70
697	$1 National landmarks		2·00	3·25
695/7		Set of 3	3·00	3·75

198 Mosaic Crab

199 Coins

(Des Chua Ban Har. Litho Leigh-Mardon Ltd, Melbourne)

1992 (21 Aug). *Crabs. T 198 and similar horiz designs. Multicoloured. Phosphorised paper. P 14½.*

698	20 c. Type 198		35	25
	a. Booklet pane. No. 698×10		5·50	
699	50 c. Johnson's Freshwater Crab		1·00	1·25
700	75 c. Singapore Freshwater Crab		1·50	1·75
701	$1 Swamp Forest Crab		1·75	2·50
698/701		Set of 4	4·25	5·25

The upper and lower edges of booklet pane No. 698a are imperforate.

(Des Lim Ching San. Litho Leigh-Mardon Ltd, Melbourne)

1992 (2 Oct). *25th Anniv of Singapore Currency. T 199 and similar square designs. Multicoloured. Phosphorised paper. P 14½.*

702	20 c. Type 199		75	1·00
	a. Block of 4. Nos. 702/5		5·50	
703	75 c. Currency note from "orchid" series		1·50	2·00
704	$1 Currency note from "ship" series		1·75	2·25
705	$2 Currency note from "bird" series		2·25	2·50
702/5		Set of 4	5·50	7·00

Nos. 702/5 were printed together, *se-tenant*, as blocks of four throughout the sheet of 20, each block forming a composite design.

200 Sun Bear

201 "Thank You"

(Des Eng Siak Loy. Litho Leigh-Mardon Ltd, Melbourne)

1993 (13 Jan). *South-East Asian Mammals. T 200 and similar horiz designs. Multicoloured. Phosphorised paper. P 14½.*

706	20 c. Type 200		30	20
707	30 c. Orang-utan		60	55
708	75 c. Slow Loris		1·10	1·25
709	$2 Greater Malay Chevrotain ("Large Mouse Deer")		2·25	3·25
706/9		Set of 4	3·75	4·75

(Des N. Loh Fook Chee. Litho Printset Cambec Pty Ltd, Australia)

1993 (10 Feb). *Greetings Stamps. T 201 and similar square designs. Multicoloured. Phosphorised paper. P 14½×14.*

710	20 c. Type 201		55	80
	a. Booklet pane. Nos. 710/14 × 2		4·50	
711	20 c. "Congratulations"		55	80
712	20 c. "Best Wishes"		55	80
713	20 c. "Happy Birthday"		55	80
714	20 c. "Get Well Soon"		55	80
710/14		Set of 5	2·50	3·50

Nos. 710/14 were only available from $2 booklets. The upper and lower edges of booklet pane No. 710a are imperforate and there are margins at both left and right.

202 Shophouses

203 "Cranes" (painting) (Chen Wen Hsi)

(Des Ng Keng Seng ($2), W. Kee (others). Litho Leigh-Mardon Ltd, Melbourne)

1993 (10 Mar). *Conservation of Tanjong Pagar District. T 202 and similar horiz designs. Multicoloured. Phosphorised paper. P 14.*

715	20 c. Type 202		35	20
716	30 c. Jinrikisha Station		75	60
717	$2 View of Tanjong Pagar		3·25	4·00
715/17		Set of 3	4·00	4·25

(Des L. Teck Chong. Photo Courvoisier)

1993 (28 May). *"Indopex '93" International Philatelic Exhibition, Surabaya. Phosphorised granite paper. P 12.*

718	203 $2 multicoloured		2·00	3·00

204 Football

205 *Danaus chrysippus*

(Des L. Teck Chong. Litho Questa)

1993 (12 June). *17th South-East Asia Games, Singapore. T 204 and similar vert designs. Multicoloured. Phosphorised paper. P 14.*

719	20 c. Type 204		30	20
720	35 c. Basketball		70	60
721	50 c. Badminton		90	1·00
722	75 c. Athletics		1·00	1·25
723	$1 Waterpolo		1·40	1·75
724	$2 Yachting		2·25	3·50
719/24		Set of 6	6·00	7·50

(Des Chua Ban Har. Litho Leigh-Mardon Ltd, Melbourne)

1993 (13 Aug). *"Singapore '95" International Stamp Exhibition. Orchids (3rd issue). Multicoloured designs as T 187, but each 25×35 mm. Phosphorised paper. P 14½.*

725	$2 Phalaenopsis amabilis		3·00	3·50
	a. Horiz pair. Nos. 725/6		6·00	7·00
726	$2 Vanda sumatrana		3·00	3·50
MS727	123×80 mm. Nos. 725/6		6·50	7·50

Nos. 725/6 were printed in the same sheet format as Nos. 653/4.

No. MS727 also commemorates "Taipei '93" Asian International Stamp Exhibition, Taiwan.

(Des Eng Siak Loy. Litho Leigh-Mardon Ltd, Melbourne)

1993 (21 Aug). *Butterflies. T 205 and similar horiz designs. Multicoloured. Phosphorised paper. P 14½.*

728	20 c. Type 205		30	30
	a. Booklet pane. No. 728×10		6·50	
729	50 c. Cethosia hypsea		65	60
730	75 c. Amathusia phidippus		90	1·10
731	$1 Papilio demolion		1·25	1·60
728/31		Set of 4	2·75	3·25

The upper and lower edges of booklet pane No. 728a are imperforate.

206 Papaya

207 Egrets drinking

(Des Poh Siew Wah. Litho Leigh-Mardon Ltd, Melbourne)

1993 (1 Oct). *"Bangkok '93" International Stamp Exhibition. Local Fruits. T 206 and similar vert designs. Multicoloured. Phosphorised paper. P 14½×14.*

732	20 c. Type 206		40	20
733	35 c. Pomegranate		60	50
734	75 c. Starfruit		1·25	1·25
735	$2 Durian		2·25	3·25
732/5		Set of 4	4·00	4·75
MS736	120×89 mm. Nos. 732/5		4·00	4·75

(Des Eng Siak Loy. Litho Enschedé)

1993 (10 Nov). *Endangered Species. Swinhoe's Egret ("Chinese Egret"). T 207 and similar square designs. Multicoloured. Phosphorised paper. P 13½.*

737	20 c. Type 207		40	60
	a. Horiz strip of 4. Nos. 737/40		1·75	
738	25 c. Egrets eating		45	65
739	30 c. Egrets searching for fish		55	75
740	35 c. Egrets in flight		55	75
737/40		Set of 4	1·75	2·50

Nos. 737/40 were printed together, *se-tenant*, in horizontal strips of 4 throughout the sheet, with the background forming a composite design.

208 Palm Tree

209 Tiger Cowrie

(Des Eng Siak Loy. Photo Avery Dennison, Pasadena)

1993 (24 Nov). *Self-adhesive Automatic Cash Machine Stamps. Phosphorised polyester film. Die-cut.*

741	208 (20 c.) multicoloured		30	30

No. 741 was issued, in sheets of 15 (5×3), from bank automatic cash machines and philatelic centres. It was only valid for use on mail to local addresses and was initially sold at 20 c. Advertising on the backing paper originally featured Speedpost, but this was subsequently changed to details of "Singapore '95" on 20 January 1995.

(Des Sylvia Tan)

1994 (12 Jan)–*97. Reef Life (1st series). T 209 and similar horiz designs. Multicoloured. Phosphorised paper. P 13×13½ (5 c. to 75 c.) or 14* ($1 to $10).*

(a) Litho (5 c. to 75 c.) or recess and litho ($1 to $10) Leigh-Mardon Ltd. Melbourne

742	5 c. Type 209		30	30
743	20 c. Sea-fan		30	20
	a. Booklet pane. No. 743×10		5·50	
744	25 c. Tunicate		40	25
745	30 c. Clown Anemonefish		40	30
746	35 c. Ruppell's Nudibranch		50	40
747	40 c. Sea-urchin		60	50
748	50 c. Soft coral		70	50
749	75 c. Pin Cushion Star		1·00	70
750	$1 Knob coral (31×27 mm) (23.3.94)		1·60	90
751	$2 Mushroom coral (31×27 mm) (23.3.94)		2·75	2·25
752	$5 Bubble coral (31×27 mm) (23.3.94)		6·00	5·50
753	$10 Octopus coral (31×27 mm) (23.3.94)		10·00	10·00
742/53		Set of 12	22·00	20·00

(b) Photo Enschedé (5 c. to 50 c.) or litho and embossed Questa ($1 to $10)

753a	5 c. Type 209 (27.1.97)		3·75	1·00
753b	25 c. Tunicate (4.4.96)		20·00	50
753c	30 c. Clown Anemonefish (22.3.96)		2·50	60
753d	35 c. Ruppell's Nudibranch (13.1.97)		2·75	75
753e	40 c. Sea-urchin (9.9.96)		3·00	1·00
753f	50 c. Soft coral (23.2.96)		3·25	1·00
753g	$1 Knob coral (31×27 mm) (4.11.96)		7·50	2·25
753h	$2 Mushroom coral (31×27 mm) (2.12.97)		8·00	8·50
753i	$5 Bubble coral (31×27 mm) (5.5.97)		25·00	11·00
753j	$10 Octopus coral (31×27 mm) (13.1.97)		35·00	17·00
753a/j		Set of 10	£100	40·00

The upper and lower edges of booklet pane No. 743a are imperforate and there are margins at left and right.

*Nos. 753/3 and 753g/j include a large elliptical hole in both the top and bottom perforations. On the Questa printings this is more elongated than on those produced by Leigh-Mardon.

Nos. 750/3 show a large central lion emblem printed in yellow fluorescence as a security marking. On Nos. 753g/j this is replaced by lines of smaller images, also in yellow fluorescence, and by a larger lion emblem in colourless embossing.

On the Leigh-Mardon printings of the $1 to $10 "SINGAPORE" and the face value are shaded. On the Questa printings of these values they are white.

For similar design inscribed "FOR LOCAL ADDRESSES ONLY" see Nos. 784/5c.

A used example of the 50 c., No. 753f, has been seen with the red colour omitted.

(Des Chua Ban Har. Litho Leigh-Mardon Ltd, Melbourne)

1994 (18 Feb). *"Singapore '95" International Stamp Exhibition. Orchids (4th issue). Multicoloured designs as T 187, but each 25×35 mm. Phosphorised paper. P 14½.*

755	$2 Paphiopedilum victoriaregina		3·50	3·75
	a. Horiz pair. Nos. 755/6		7·00	7·50
756	$2 Dendrobium smillieae		3·50	3·75
MS757	123×80 mm. Nos. 755/6		7·00	7·50

Nos. 755/6 were printed in the same sheet format as Nos. 653/4.

No. MS757 also commemorates "Hong Kong '94" International Stamp Exhibition.

210 Dancers

(Des Elsie Koh. Litho Questa)

1994 (18 May). *Singapore Festival of Arts. T 210 and similar horiz designs. Multicoloured. Phosphorised paper. P 13½×14.*

758	20 c. Type 210		35	20
759	30 c. Actors and puppet		55	55

760	50 c. Musicians			75	1·00
761	$1 Artists			1·40	2·25
758/61			Set of 4	2·75	3·50

211 Civilian taking Pledge, National Day Parade and Soldier with Anti-tank Missile

212 Black-crowned Night Heron

(Des D. Kuah. Litho Enschedé)

1994 (1 July). *25th Anniv of Operationally-ready National Servicemen. T 211 and similar horiz designs. Multicoloured. Phosphorised paper. P 13½.*

762	20 c. Type **211**			60	30
763	30 c. Serviceman on beach with family and on jungle patrol			70	70
764	35 c. Serviceman relaxing at home and with machine gun			85	90
765	75 c. National Service officer at work and commanding patrol			1·75	2·50
762/5			Set of 4	3·50	4·00

(Des Eng Siak Loy. Litho Leigh-Mardon Ltd, Melbourne)

1994 (16 Aug). *Herons. T 212 and similar square designs. Multicoloured. Phosphorised paper. P 14.*

766	20 c. Type **212**			50	60
	a. Block of 4. Nos. 766/9			2·75	
	b. Booklet pane. No. 766×10			6·50	
767	50 c. Green Heron ("Little Heron")			70	85
768	75 c. Purple Heron			85	1·00
769	$1 Grey Heron			95	1·25
766/9			Set of 4	2·75	3·25

Nos. 766/9 were printed together, *se-tenant*, in blocks of 4 throughout the sheet, each block forming a composite design.

The upper and lower edges of booklet pane No. 766b are imperforate and there are margins at left and right.

213 Traditional and Modern Education

214 Balloons

(Des Lim Ching San. Litho Enschedé)

1994 (31 Aug). *175th Anniv of Modern Singapore. T 213 and similar horiz designs. Multicoloured. Phosphorised paper. P 13½×14.*

770	20 c. Type **213**			25	25
771	50 c. Rickshaws and Mass Rapid Transit train			70	70
772	75 c. Sampans and modern container port			1·00	1·40
773	$1 Victorian buildings and modern skyline			1·25	2·00
770/3			Set of 4	2·75	4·00
MS774	135×95 mm. Nos. 770/3			3·00	4·00

No. **MS**774 also exists with the "Singpex '94" logo added in gold for sale at this philatelic exhibition.

(Des Chua Ban Har. Litho Printset-Cambec Pty Ltd, Australia)

1994 (14 Sept). *Self-adhesive Greetings Stamps. T 214 and similar vert designs. Multicoloured. Phosphorised paper. P 11½.*

775	(20 c.) Type **214**			40	55
	a. Booklet pane. Nos. 775/9, each × 2			3·50	
776	(20 c.) Fireworks			40	55
777	(20 c.) Gift-wrapped parcel			40	55
778	(20 c.) Bouquet of flowers			40	55
779	(20 c.) Birthday cake			40	55
775/9			Set of 5	1·75	2·50

Nos. 775/9 are inscribed "For Local Addresses Only" and were available from booklets of 10 sold for $2.

215 Logo and Globe

(Des N. Loh Fook Chee. Litho Questa)

1994 (5 Oct). *50th Anniv of International Civil Aviation Organization. T 215 and similar horiz designs. Phosphorised paper. P 14.*

780	20 c. Type **215**			20	20
781	35 c. Boeing 747 and Changi Airport control tower			60	50
782	75 c. Projected hypersonic aircraft over airport			85	1·00
783	$2 Control tower, satellite and Boeing 747			2·00	3·00
780/3			Set of 4	3·25	4·00

(Des Sylvia Tan)

1994 (16 Nov)–**97**. *Reef Life (2nd series). Multicoloured design as T 209, but inscr "FOR LOCAL ADDRESSES ONLY".*

(a) Litho Leigh-Mardon Ltd, Melbourne. Phosphorised paper. P 13×13½

784	(20 c.) Blue-spotted Stingray			20	25

(b) Litho Leigh-Mardon Ltd, Melbourne. Self-adhesive. Phosphor frame. P 9.

785	(20 c.) As No. 784			20	25
	a. Booklet pane. No. 785×10			2·00	
	b. Broad phosphor band (12.4.95)			40	40
	ba. Booklet pane. No. 785b×10			4·50	

(c) Photo Enschedé. Phosphorised paper. P 13×13½

785c	(22 c.) As No. 784 (2.12.97)			3·00	2·50

Booklet panes Nos. 785a and 785ba are arranged as two blocks of four and a pair with backing card forming the booklet cover.

Nos. 784/5 were initially sold at 20 c., but this was increased to 22 c. on 1 April 1995.

The inscriptions on No. 785c are redrawn so that the "SINGAPORE" is 26 mm long instead of 26½ and the others are also smaller. On No. 784 the "y" of "stingray" is to the right of the "A" in "SINGAPORE"; on No. 785c it is under the left leg of the "A".

216 Singapore International Convention and Exhibition Centre, Suntec City

217 "Love, LOVE, Love"

(Des M. Ng Puay Chiew. Litho Enschedé)

1995 (11 Jan). *Opening of Singapore International Convention and Exhibition Centre. T 216 and similar horiz designs. Multicoloured. Phosphorised paper. P 13½.*

786	(20 c.) Type **216**			20	20
787	75 c. Suntec City skyline			85	85
788	$1 Temasek Boulevard			1·10	1·25
789	$2 Fountain Terrace			1·75	2·50
786/9			Set of 4	3·50	4·25

No. 786 is inscribed "FOR LOCAL ADDRESSES ONLY".

Nos. 786 and 789 also exist in miniature sheets issued at the "Singapore '95" exhibition. A different marginal illustration was used for each of the ten days of the exhibition.

(Des Design Objectives. Litho Printset-Cambec Pty Ltd, Australia)

1995 (8 Feb). *Self-adhesive Greeting Stamps. T 217 and similar vert designs. Phosphor frame. P 11½.*

790	**217** (20 c.) multicoloured			40	50
	a. Booklet pane. Nos. 790/4, each × 2			3·50	
791	— (20 c.) vermilion and black			40	50
792	— (20 c.) multicoloured			40	50
793	— (20 c.) multicoloured			40	50
794	— (20 c.) multicoloured			40	50
790/4			Set of 5	1·75	2·25

Designs:—No. 791, "LOVE" forming spiral around heart; No. 792, "LOVE, LOVE"; No. 793, "Love" in four different languages; No. 794, Geometric symbols.

Nos. 709/4 are inscribed "For Local Addresses Only" and were available from booklets of 10 initially sold for $2, but increased to $2.20 from 1 April 1995.

(Des Chua Ban Har. Litho Leigh-Mardon Ltd, Melbourne)

1995 (15 Mar). *"Singapore '95" International Stamp Exhibition. Orchids (5th issue). Horiz designs as T 187. Multicoloured. Phosphorised paper. P 14.*

795	$2 *Vanda* "Marlie Dolera"			2·00	2·75
	a. Horiz pair. Nos. 795/6			4·00	5·50
796	$2 *Vanda limbata*			2·00	2·75
MS797	123×80 mm. Nos. 795/6 with sheet margins showing animals from Singapore Zoo			4·50	6·00

Nos. 795/6 were printed in the same sheet format as Nos. 653/4.

No. **MS**797 also exists imperforate from the "Singapore '95" exhibition catalogue.

For further miniature sheet containing these stamps see No. **MS**817.

218 Ribbons and "My Singapore, My Country, Happy Birthday"

219 Rejoicing Crowd and 1945 B.M.A. $5 Stamp

(Des L. Teck Chong. Litho Enschedé)

1995 (19 Apr). *30th Anniv of Independence. T 218 and similar multicoloured designs. Phosphorised paper. P 13½.*

798	(22 c.) Type **218**			20	20
799	50 c. Chinese inscr and 1985 Housing and Development 50 c. stamp (horiz)			65	70
800	75 c. National anthem, Civil Aviation 20 c. and inscr in Malay (horiz)			90	1·00

801	$1 National flag, 1986 Economic Development Board $1 and inscr in Tamil			1·25	1·75
798/801			Set of 4	2·75	3·25
MS802	120×78 mm. Nos. 798/801			3·00	3·75

No. 798 is inscribed "For Local Addresses Only".

(Des Chua Ban Har. Litho Enschedé)

1995 (21 June). *50th Anniv of End of Second World War. T 219 and similar multicoloured designs. Phosphorised paper. P 14×13½ (vert) or 13½×14 (horiz).*

803	(22 c.) Type **219**			30	20
804	60 c. Lord Mountbatten accepting Japanese surrender at Singapore and 1945 B.M.A. 15 c. stamp			1·00	80
805	70 c. Emergency food kitchen (horiz)			80	1·00
806	$2 Police road block during State of Emergency (horiz)			2·75	3·50
803/6			Set of 4	4·25	5·00

No. 803 is inscribed "For Local Addresses Only".

220 Yellow-faced Angelfish

221 Envelope, Stamps and Museum

(Des Sylvia Tan. Litho Enschedé)

1995 (19 July). *Marine Fishes. T 220 and similar horiz designs. Multicoloured. Phosphorised paper. P 13½×14.*

807	(22 c.) Type **220**			35	25
808	60 c. Harlequin Sweetlips			80	80
809	70 c. Lionfish			90	1·00
810	$1 Pennant Coralfish ("Longfin Bannerfish")			1·25	1·75
807/10			Set of 4	3·00	3·50

No. 807 is inscribed "For Local Addresses Only".

(Des Poh Siew Wah. Litho Japanese Govt Ptg Bureau, Tokyo)

1995 (19 Aug). *Opening of Singapore Philatelic Museum. T 221 and similar vert designs, each showing Museum. Multicoloured. Phosphorised paper. P 13×13½.*

811	(22 c.) Type **221**			30	25
812	50 c. Stamps and stamp booklet			70	55
813	60 c. Stamps and philatelic equipment			80	80
814	$2 Museum displays			2·25	3·00
811/14			Set of 4	3·75	4·25

No. 811 is inscribed "FOR LOCAL ADDRESSES ONLY".

222 Two, Four and Six Digit Post Codes

(Des L. Huei Hoon. Litho Printset-Cambec Pty Ltd, Australia)

1995 (1 Sept). *Introduction of Six Digit Postal Codes. T 222 and similar horiz design. Multicoloured. Phosphorised paper. P 14×13½.*

815	(22 c.) Type **222**			30	25
816	$2 Six empty post code boxes			2·25	2·75

No. 815 is inscribed "For local addresses only".

(Des Chua Ban Har. Litho Leigh-Mardon Ltd, Melbourne)

1995 (1 Sept). *"Singapore '95" International Stamp Exhibition. Orchids (6th issue). Sheet 123×80 mm, containing Nos. 795/6 with sheet margins showing Sentosa Gardens. Phosphorised paper. P 14.*

MS817	$2×2 multicoloured			4·50	6·00

No. **MS**817 also exists either with the marginal illustration in a single colour or with the stamps imperforate, both showing an additional gold embossed inscription. Such miniature sheets were distributed to individual collectors contributing to exhibition funds.

223 "Tropical Fruits" (Georgette Chen Liying)

(Des Poh Siew Wah. Litho Japanese Govt Ptg Bureau, Tokyo)

1995 (20 Oct). *Local Artists (2nd series). T 223 and similar multicoloured designs. Phosphorised paper. P 13½×13 ($2) or 12½ (others).*

818	(22 c.) Type **223**			30	25
819	30 c. "Bali Beach" (Cheong Soo Pieng)			40	40
820	70 c. "Gibbons" (Chen Wen Hsi)			80	90
821	$2 "Shi (Lion)" (Pan Shou) (22½×38½ mm)			2·25	3·00
818/21			Set of 4	3·25	4·00

No. 818 is inscribed "FOR LOCAL ADDRESSES ONLY".

224 Bukit Pasoh, Chinatown   **225** Pair of Rats

(Des Poh Siew Wah. Litho Enschedé)

1996 (17 Jan). *Architectural Conservation. T* **224** *and similar horiz designs. Multicoloured. Phosphorised paper. P* 13½×14.

822	(22 c.) Type **224**		35	25
823	35 c. Jalan Sultan, Kampong Glam		50	45
824	70 c. Dalhousie Lane, Little India		80	1·00
825	$1 Supreme Court, Civic District		1·10	1·60
822/5		*Set of 4*	2·50	3·00

No. 822 is inscribed "FOR LOCAL ADDRESSES ONLY".

Two Types of No. 826:

Type I (sheets of 50) – Top left emblem cut by curved "FOR LOCAL ADDRESSES ONLY" label. Bottom right emblem clear of right edge of design.

Type II (*se-tenant* sheetlets of 18) – Top left emblem clear of curved label. Bottom right emblem cut by right edge of design.

(Des N. Loh Fook Chee. Litho, Southern Colour Print, Dunedin)

1996 (9 Feb). *Chinese New Year* ("*Year of the Rat*"). *T* **225** *and similar vert design. Multicoloured. Phosphorised paper. P* 12.

826	(22 c.) Type **225** (I)		30	25
	b. Type II		50	50
	ba. Pair. Nos. 826b/7		2·75	3·25
827	$2 Rat holding orange		2·25	2·75

No. 826 is inscribed "FOR LOCAL ADDRESSES ONLY".

In addition to separate sheets of 50, the stamps were also issued in sheetlets of 18 horizontally and vertically *se-tenant*.

For these stamps in miniature sheets see Nos. MS832/3 and MS838.

226 The Straits of Singapore,   **227** 17th-century Chinese
1794 (Thomas Jefferys)   Calligraphy by Zhang
              Ruitu and Museum
              Building

(Des D. Kuah. Litho Southern Colour Print, Dunedin, New Zealand)

1996 (13 Mar). *Old Maps. T* **226** *and similar horiz designs. Multicoloured. Phosphorised paper. P* 12.

828	(22 c.) Type **226**		35	25
829	60 c. Singapore (19th-century)		65	75
830	$1 Singapore by James Duncan, 1835		1·00	1·25
831	$2 Singapore by J. B. Tassin, 1839		2·00	2·75
828/31		*Set of 4*	3·50	4·50

No. 828 is inscribed "FOR LOCAL ADDRESSES ONLY" and was sold for 22 c.

(Litho Southern Colour Print, Dunedin)

1996 (21 Mar). "*Indonesia 96*" *International Youth Stamp Exhibition, Bandung. Sheet* 123×80 *mm. Phosphorised paper. P* 12.

MS832   22 c. As Type **225**; $2 No. 827   3·00   3·75

(Litho Southern Colour Print, Dunedin)

1996 (18 May). "*CHINA '96*" 9*th Asian International Stamp Exhibition, Peking. Sheet* 123×80 *mm. Phosphorised paper. P* 12.

MS833   22 c. As Type **225**; $2 No. 827   3·00   3·75

(Des M. Ng Puay Chiew. Litho Enschedé)

1996 (5 June). *Inauguration of Asian Civilizations Museum. T* **227** *and similar horiz designs, each including museum building. Multicoloured. Phosphorised paper. P* 13½.

834	(22 c.) Type **227**		35	25
835	60 c. Javanese divination manuscript, 1842		70	70
836	70 c. 19th-century temple hanging, South India		80	80
837	$2 17th to 19th-century calligraphic implements, Iran and Turkey		2·00	3·00
834/7		*Set of 4*	2·75	4·25

No. 834 is inscribed "FOR LOCAL ADDRESSES ONLY" and was sold for 22 c.

(Litho Southern Colour Print, Dunedin)

1996 (8 June). "*CAPEX '96*" *International Stamp Exhibition, Toronto. Sheet* 123×80 *mm. Phosphorised paper. P* 12.

MS838   22 c. As Type **225**; $2 No. 827   3·00   3·75

---

228 "Children in   **229** Wind Surfing
Library" (Ivan Chang)   and Dinghy
               Sailing

(Adapted Design Business Ltd. Litho SNP Cambec, Australia)

1996 (10 July). *Self-adhesive Greetings Stamps.* "*Courtesy*". *Children's Drawings. T* **228** *and similar horiz designs. Multicoloured. Phosphorised paper. P* 11½.

839	(22 c.) Type **228**		20	25
	a. Booklet pane. No. 839×10		2·50	
	b. Booklet pane. No. 839×5, No. 840×2 and Nos. 841/3		4·25	
840	35 c. "Children crossing Road" (Cheong Kah Yin)		40	45
841	50 c. "Waiting for Bus" (Jeannie Fong)		55	65
842	60 c. "In the Rain" (Liew Cai Yun)		60	70
843	$1 "On the Train" (Yong Wan Quan)		1·00	1·25
839/43		*Set of 5*	2·50	3·00
MS844	200×130 mm. 22 c. As Type **228** and Nos. 840/3. Phosphor frame		4·25	4·50

No. 839 is inscribed "For Local Addresses Only".

Nos. 839/43 were only issued in $2.20 and $3.90 stamp booklets or as No. MS844.

(Des N. Loh Fook Chee. Litho Southern Colour Print, Dunedin)

1996 (19 July). *Olympic Games, Atlanta. T* **229** *and similar vert designs. Multicoloured. Phosphorised paper. P* 14½.

845	(22 c.) Type **229**		35	25
846	60 c. Tennis and football		90	80
847	70 c. Pole vaulting and hurdling		90	90
848	$2 Diving and swimming		2·25	2·75
845/8		*Set of 4*	4·00	4·25
MS849	120×70 mm. 22 c. As Type **229** and Nos. 846/8		2·75	4·50

No. 845 is inscribed "For Local Addresses Only".

230 *Cinnamomum*   **231** Panmen Gate, Suzhou, China
iners

(Des Poh Siew Wah. Litho Southern Colour Print, Dunedin)

1996 (11 Sept). *Singapore Trees. T* **230** *and similar vert designs. Multicoloured. Phosphorised paper. P* 13½.

850	(22 c.) Type **230**		30	25
851	60 c. *Hibiscus tiliaceus*		70	80
852	70 c. *Parkia speciosa*		80	90
853	$1 *Terminalia catappa*		1·25	1·50
850/3		*Set of 4*	2·75	3·00

No. 850 is inscribed "FOR LOCAL ADDRESSES ONLY".

(Des Jiang Zhi Nan, adapted Sylvia Tan. Litho Enschedé)

1996 (9 Oct). *Singapore–China Joint Issue. T* **231** *and similar horiz design. Multicoloured. Phosphorised paper. P* 13×13½.

854	(22 c.) Type **231**		30	25
855	60 c. Singapore waterfront		80	1·00
MS856	120×78 mm. 22 c. As Type **231** and No. 855	1·10	1·25

No. 854 is inscribed "FOR LOCAL ADDRESSES ONLY".

No. MS856 also exists overprinted "SINGAPORE–CHINA STAMP EXHIBITION 9–13 OCT '96" for sale at this exhibition.

232 Conference Logo

(Des Design Objectives. Litho Harrison)

1996 (20 Nov). *Inaugural Ministerial Conference of World Trade Organization. Phosphorised paper. P* 13½.

857	**232** (22 c.) multicoloured		30	25
858	60 c. multicoloured		70	80
859	$1 multicoloured		1·25	1·50
860	$2 multicoloured		2·25	3·00
857/60		*Set of 4*	4·00	5·00

No. 857 is inscribed "For local Addresses Only".

---

233 Ox   **234** Shuttlecock

(Des N. Loh Fook Chee. Litho Enschedé)

1997 (10 Jan). *Chinese New Year* ("*Year of the Ox*"). *T* **233** *and similar vert design showing stylised ox. Phosphorised paper. P* 13½×14.

861	(22 c.) multicoloured		15	20
	a. Pair. Nos. 861/2		1·50	1·60
862	$2 multicoloured		1·40	1·50

No. 861 is inscribed "FOR LOCAL ADDRESSES ONLY" and was sold for 22 c.

In addition to separate sheets of 50 Nos. 861/2 were also issued in sheetlets of 18 with the stamps horizontally and vertically *se-tenant*.

(Litho Enschedé)

1997 (12 Feb). "*HONG KONG '97*" *International Stamp Exhibition. Chinese New Year* ("*Year of the Ox*"). *Sheet* 123×80 *mm. Phosphorised paper. P* 13½×14.

MS863   22 c. As Type **233**; $2 No. 862   3·00   3·50

(Des Chua Ban Har. Litho Southern Colour Print, Dunedin)

1997 (21 Feb). "*SINGPEX '97*" *International Stamp Exhibition. Traditional Games. T* **234** *and similar vert designs. Multicoloured. Phosphorised paper. P* 14½×15.

864	(22 c.) Type **234**		15	20
865	35 c. Marbles		25	30
866	60 c. Tops		45	50
867	$1 Fivestones		70	75
864/7		*Set of 4*	1·50	1·75
MS868	140×75 mm. 22 c. As Type **234** and Nos. 865/7		1·50	1·75

No. 864 is inscribed "For Local Addresses Only" and was sold for 22 c.

235 Bullock Cart   **236** Taxi

(Des Design Business Ltd. Eng C. Slania ($1 to $10))

1997 (19 Mar–23 Apr). *Transportation. Multicoloured. Phosphorised paper.* (a) *Litho Ashton-Potter Canada. T* **235** *and similar designs. P* 13½.

869	5 c. Type **235**		10	10
870	20 c. Bicycle (*vert*)		15	20
871	(22 c.) Jinrickshaw (*vert*)		15	20
872	30 c. Electric tram		20	25
873	35 c. Trolley bus		25	30
874	40 c. Trishaw (*vert*)		30	35
875	50 c. Vintage car (*vert*)		35	40
876	60 c. Horse-drawn carriage		40	45
877	70 c. Fire engine		50	55
MS878	132×76 mm. 22 c. As No. 871 and Nos. 869/70, 872/7		2·40	2·50

(b) *Recess and litho Enschedé. T* **236** *and similar designs. P* 13 (23 Apr)

879	$1 Type **236**		70	75
880	$2 Bus (43×24 mm)		1·40	1·50
881	$5 Mass Rapid Transit train		3·50	3·75
882	$10 Light Rapid Transit carriages (43×24 mm)		7·00	7·25
869/77, 879/82		*Set of 13*	14·50	15·50
MS883	119×71 mm. Nos. 879/82		12·50	13·00

(c) *Litho Ashton-Potter Canada. Self-adhesive. P* 12.

884	(22 c.) As No. 871		15	20
	a. Booklet pane. No. 884×10		1·50	

Nos. 871 and 884 are inscribed "For Local Addresses Only". In addition to booklets containing No. 884a the self-adhesive version was also available in sheets of 20 (2 panes 5×2).

The original printing of booklet pane No. 884a showed the phosphor printed over the designs rather than included in the paper coating. Later printings were on phosphorised paper; although some printings of the self-adhesive sheet stamps subsequently appeared with the "all-over" printed phosphor. These differences cannot be distinguished without a U.V. lamp.

NEW INFORMATION

The editor is always interested to correspond with people who have new information that will improve or correct the Catalogue.

237 Man's Head

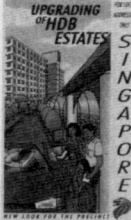
238 Family with Car

(Des L. Teck Chong. Litho Enschedé)

1997 (14 May). *Self-adhesive Greeting Stamps. "Friends". T 237 and similar vert designs. Multicoloured. Phosphorised paper. P 15.*

885	(22 c.) Type 237	30	35
	a. Booklet pane. Nos. 885/9, each × 2	2·75	
886	(22 c.) Hands holding umbrella	30	35
887	(22 c.) Two penguins	30	35
888	(22 c.) Two butterflies	30	35
889	(22 c.) Cup and saucer	30	35
890	(22 c.) Large flower	30	35
	a. Booklet pane. Nos. 890/4, each × 2	2·75	
891	(22 c.) Candle	30	35
892	(22 c.) Tree	30	35
893	(22 c.) Jar with stars	30	35
894	(22 c.) Simple telephone	30	35
885/94	*Set of 10*	2·75	3·25

Nos. 885/94 are inscribed "FOR LOCAL ADDRESSES ONLY" and were available from two different booklets of 10, each sold for $2.20.

(Litho Enschedé)

1997 (29 May). *"Pacific '97" International Stamp Exhibition, San Francisco. Sheet 123×80 mm, containing designs as Nos. 861/2. Phosphorised paper. P 13¹/₂×14.*

MS895	22 c. As Type 233; $2 No. 862	4·00	4·50

(Des D. Kuah. Litho Southern Colour Print, Dunedin)

1997 (16 July). *Renovation of Housing and Development Board Estates. T 238 and similar vert designs. Multicoloured. Phosphorised paper. P 14.*

896	(22 c.) Type 238	15	20
897	30 c. Family at playground	20	25
898	70 c. Couple walking through garden	50	55
899	$1 Family on balcony	70	75
896/9	*Set of 4*	1·50	1·75

No. 896 is inscribed "FOR LOCAL ADDRESSES ONLY" and was sold for 22 c.

239 Globe and Hand Clasp

240 Flower and Tree ("Clean Environment")

(Des M. Chiew. Litho Southern Colour Print, Dunedin)

1997 (8 Aug). *30th Anniv of A.S.E.A.N. (Association of Southeast Asian Nations). T 239 and similar semi-circular designs. Multicoloured. Phosphorised paper. P 15 (and 14 around design).*

900	(22 c.) Type 239	15	20
901	35 c. Dancers, kite flying and decorated truck	25	30
902	60 c. Dish aerial and map	45	50
903	$1 National landmarks	70	75
900/3	*Set of 4*	1·50	1·75

No. 900 is inscribed "FOR LOCAL ADDRESSES ONLY" and was sold for 22 c.

(Des Design Objectives. Litho Enschedé)

1997 (13 Sept). *25th Anniv of the Ministry of the Environment. T 240 and similar vert designs. Multicoloured. Phosphorised paper. P 13¹/₂.*

904	(22 c.) Type 240	15	20
	a. Booklet pane. No. 904×10 with margins all round	1·50	
905	60 c. Fish and river ("Clean Waters")	45	50
906	70 c. Bird and sky ("Clean Air")	50	55
907	$1 Dustbin and block of flats ("Clean Homes")	70	75
904/7	*Set of 4*	1·75	2·00

No. 904 is inscribed "FOR LOCAL ADDRESSES ONLY" and was sold for 22 c.

NEW INFORMATION

The editor is always interested to correspond with people who have new information that will improve or correct the Catalogue.

---

241 Drupa morum

242 Tiger

(Des R., Saichumdee. Adapted Elsie Koh. Litho Enschedé)

1997 (9 Oct). *Singapore–Thailand Joint Issue. Sea Shells. T 241 and similar horiz designs. Multicoloured. Phosphorised paper. P 13¹/₂×14.*

908		15	20
909	35 c. Nerita chamaeleon	25	30
910	60 c. Littoraria melanostoma	45	50
911	$1 Cryptospira elegans	70	75
908/11	*Set of 4*	1·50	1·75
MS912	125×80 mm. 22 c. As Type 241 and Nos. 909/11	1·50	1·75

No. 908 is inscribed "FOR LOCAL ADDRESSES ONLY" and was sold for 22 c.

1997 (19 Nov). *"Shanghai '97" International Stamp and Coin Exhibition. Sheet 123×80 mm. Phosphorised paper. P 13¹/₂×14.*

MS913	22 c. As Type 233; $2 No. 862	2·00	2·50

(Des N. Loh Fook Chee. Litho Enschedé)

1998 (9 Jan). *Chinese New Year ("Year of the Tiger"). T 242 and similar horiz design showing stylised tigers. Phosphorised paper. P 13¹/₂×14.*

914	(22 c.) multicoloured	15	20
	a. Pair. Nos. 914/15	1·50	1·60
915	$2 multicoloured	1·40	1·50

No. 914 is inscribed "FOR LOCAL ADDRESSES ONLY" and was sold for 22 c.

In addition to separate sheets of 50 Nos. 914/15 were also issued in sheetlets of 18 (3×6) with the stamps horizontally and vertically se-tenant.

243 Pentaceratops

244 Lesser Green Leafbird

(Des N. Loh Fook Chee and Elsie Koh. Litho Avery Dennison, U.S.A.)

1998 (22 Apr). *Self-adhesive Automatic Cash Machine Stamps. Dinosaurs. T 243 and similar vert designs. Multicoloured. Phosphorised paper. Die-cut.*

916	(22 c.) Type 243	15	20
	a. Horiz strip of 3. Nos. 916/18	45	
917	(22 c.) Apatosaurus	15	20
918	(22 c.) Albertosaurus	15	20
916/18	*Set of 3*	45	60

Nos. 916/18 are inscribed "For Local Addresses Only" and were sold at 22 c. They were printed together, se-tenant, in sheetlets of 15 (3×5) available from bank automatic cash machines and philatelic centres.

(Des Sylvia Tan. Photo Courvoisier)

1998 (6 May). *Songbirds. T 244 and similar horiz designs. Multicoloured. P 11¹/₂.*

919	(22 c.) Type 244	15	20
920	60 c. Magpie Robin	45	50
921	70 c. Straw-crowned Bulbul	50	55
922	$2 Yellow-bellied Prinia	1·40	1·50
919/22	*Set of 4*	2·50	2·75

No. 919 is inscribed "For Local Addresses Only" and was sold for 22 c.

1998 (13 May). *"Israel 98" International Stamp Exhibition. Sheet 122×80 mm. Phosphorised paper. P 13¹/₂×14.*

MS923	22 c. As Type 242; $2 No. 915	2·00	2·50

245 "Hello" in Yellow and Orange Bubble

246 Rhino Beetle

(Des Design Objectives. Litho SNP Cambec, Melbourne)

1998 (20 May). *Self-adhesive Greetings Stamps. T 245 and similar vert designs, each showing different coloured bubbles. Multicoloured. Phosphorised paper. P 11¹/₂.*

924	(22 c.) Type 245	20	25
	a. Booklet pane. Nos. 924/8, each × 2	2·00	
925	(22 c.) "hello" in red and yellow bubble	20	25
926	(22 c.) "hello" in yellow and green bubble	20	25
927	(22 c.) "Hello" in bluish violet and blue bubble	20	25
928	(22 c.) "Hello" in black, red and yellow bubble	20	25
924/8	*Set of 5*	1·00	1·10

Nos. 924/8 are inscribed "FOR LOCAL ADDRESSES ONLY" and were only available in booklets of 10 stamps sold for $2.20.

(Des Design Business Ltd. Photo Enschedé)

1998 (5 June). *25th Anniv of Singapore Zoological Gardens and Launch of New "Fragile Forest" Display. T 246 and similar horiz designs. Multicoloured. Phosphorised paper. Self-adhesive. P 12×11.*

929	(22 c.) Type 246	20	25
	a. Booklet pane. Nos. 929/33, each × 2	2·00	
	ab. Imperf (booklet pane)		
930	(22 c.) Surinam Horned Frog	20	25
931	(22 c.) Green Iguana	20	25
932	(22 c.) Atlas Moth	20	25
933	(22 c.) Giant Scorpion	20	25
934	(22 c.) Hissing Cockroach	20	25
	a. Booklet pane. Nos. 934/8, each × 2	2·00	
935	(22 c.) Two-toed Sloth	20	25
936	(22 c.) Cobalt Blue Tarantula	20	25
937	(22 c.) Archer Fish	20	25
938	(22 c.) Greater Mousedeer	20	25
929/38	*Set of 10*	2·00	2·25

Nos. 929/38 are inscribed "FOR LOCAL ADDRESSES ONLY" and were available from two different booklets of 10, each sold for $2.20.

247 Students and Workers Demonstrating, 1955–59

248 Phalaenopsis rosenstromii

(Des Chua Ban Har. Litho Enschedé)

1998 (7 July). *"The Singapore Story" Exhibition. T 247 and similar horiz designs. Multicoloured. Phosphorised paper. P 13×13¹/₂.*

939	(22 c.) Type 247	15	20
940	60 c. Self-government, 1959–63	45	50
941	$1 Creation of Malaysian Federation, 1961–65	70	75
942	$2 Celebrating Independence, 1965	1·40	1·50
939/42	*Set of 4*	2·50	2·75
MS943	214×105 mm. 22 c. As Type 247 and Nos. 940/2 (sold at $7)	6·00	6·50

No. 939 is inscribed "FOR LOCAL ADDRESSES ONLY" and was sold for 22 c.

The stamps in No. MS943 show the main features of each design printed in varnish ink. No. MS943, which also commemorates "SINGPEX '98" National Stamp Exhibition, was only available in a special folder.

(Des Clare Kaegi and C. Willie. Photo Courvoisier)

1998 (6 Aug). *Singapore–Australia Joint Issue. Orchids. T 248 and similar vert designs. Multicoloured. Phosphorised granite paper. P 11¹/₂.*

944	(22 c.) Type 248	15	20
945	70 c. Arundina graminifolia	50	55
946	$1 Grammatophyllum speciosum	70	75
947	$2 Dendrobium phalaenopsis	1·40	1·50
944/7	*Set of 4*	2·75	3·00
MS948	134×73 mm. 22 c. As Type 248 and Nos. 945/7	3·50	3·75

No. 944 is inscribed "For Local Addresses Only" and was sold for 22 c.

249 Canna Hybrid

250 Hari Raya Aidilfitri (Muslim)

(Des Elsie Koh. Litho Ashton Potter Canada)

1998 (9 Sept). *Flowers of Singapore. T 249 and similar horiz designs. Phosphorised paper. P 14¹/₂×14.*

949	(22 c.) Type 249	15	20
	a. Horiz strip of 4. Nos. 949/52	60	
	b. Booklet pane. Nos. 949/50×3 and 951/2×2	1·25	
950	(22 c.) Caesalpinia pulcherrima	15	20
951	(22 c.) Wedilia trilobata	15	20
952	(22 c.) Dillenia suffruticosa	15	20
953	35 c. Zephyranthes rosea	25	30
	a. Horiz strip of 4. Nos. 953/6	1·25	
954	35 c. Cassia alata	25	30
955	60 c. Heliconia rostrata	40	45
956	60 c. Allamanda cathartica	40	45
949/56	*Set of 8*	1·75	2·25
MS957	206×82 mm. Nos. 949/56	1·75	2·25

Nos. 949/52 are inscribed "FOR LOCAL ADDRESSES ONLY" and were sold at 22 c.

Nos. 949/52 and 953/6 were each printed together, se-tenant, in horizontal strips of 4 throughout the sheets.

The upper and lower edges of booklet pane No. 949b are imperforate and there are margins at left and right.

Nos. 949/57 and the stamp booklet No. SB36 were impregnated with a flowery scent.

(Des See Pin Pin. Litho Enschedé)

1998 (7 Oct). *Festivals. T 250 and similar multicoloured designs. Phosphorised paper. (a) P 13¹/₂×14 (Nos. 958/61) or 13¹/₂×13 (others).*

958	(22 c.) Type 250	15	20
	a. Block of 4. Nos. 958/61	60	
959	(22 c.) Christmas	15	20

960	(22 c.) Chinese New Year	15	20
961	(22 c.) Deepavali (Hindu)	15	20
962	30 c. Boy and decorations (Hari Raya Aidilfitri) (20×39 mm)	20	25
963	30 c. Girl with holly (Christmas) (20×39 mm)	20	25
964	30 c. Boy with lanterns (Chinese New Year) (20×39 mm)	20	25
965	30 c. Girl with oil lamps (Deepavali) (20×39 mm)	20	25
958/65	Set of 8	1·40	1·75

(b) Self-adhesive. P 8

966	(22 c.) Type 250	15	20
967	(22 c.) As No. 959	15	20
968	(22 c.) As No. 960	15	20
969	(22 c.) As No. 961	15	20
966/9	Set of 4	60	80

Nos. 958/61 and 966/9 are inscribed "For Local Addresses Only" and were sold at 22 c.

Nos. 958/61 were printed together, se-tenant, in blocks of four throughout the sheet of 16, each block forming a composite design. Nos. 962/5 and 966/9 were printed in separate sheets of 20.

(Litho Enschedé)

1998 (23 Oct). *"Italia 98". International Stamp Exhibition, Milan. Sheet 123×80 mm. Phosphorised paper. P 13½×14.*

MS970 22 c. As Type 242; $2 No. 915 .. .. 2·00 2·50

251 Parliament House, 1827

(Des Equinox Art and Design Ltd. Litho Enschedé)

1998 (4 Nov). *Historical Buildings. T 251 and similar horiz designs. Multicoloured. Phosphorised paper. P 13½×14.*

971	(22 c.) Type 251	15	20
972	70 c. Chapel of former Convent of the Holy Infant Jesus, 1903	50	55
973	$1 Hill Street Building, 1934	70	75
974	$2 Sun Yat Sen Nanyang Memorial Hall, 1900	1·40	1·50
971/4	Set of 4	2·75	3·00

No. 971 is inscribed "For Local Addresses Only" and was sold for 22 c.

252 Anniversary Logo and List of Religions

(Des L. Chua. Litho Enschedé)

1999 (15 Jan). *50th Anniv of Inter-Religious Organization. Phosphorised paper. P 13×13½.*

975	**252** (22 c.) multicoloured	15	20
976	60 c. multicoloured	40	45
977	$1 multicoloured	70	75
975/7	Set of 3	1·25	1·40

No. 975 is inscribed "For Local Addresses Only" and was sold for 22 c.

253 Rabbit   **254** Clipper, Tank Locomotive and Tongkang Junk

(Des N. Loh Fook Chee. Litho Southern Colour Print, Dunedin)

1999 (15 Jan). *Chinese New Year ("Year of the Rabbit"). T 253 and similar horiz design showing stylised rabbits. Phosphorised paper. P 14.*

978	(22 c.) multicoloured	15	20
	a. Pair. Nos. 978/9	1·50	1·60
979	$2 multicoloured	1·40	1·50

No. 978 is inscribed "FOR LOCAL ADDRESSES ONLY" and was sold for 22 c.

In addition to separate sheets of 50 Nos. 978/9 were also issued in sheetlets of 18 (3×6) with the stamps horizontally and vertically se-tenant.

(Des G. Hwee Kheng. Litho Southern Colour Print, Dunedin)

1999 (19 Mar). *Maritime Heritage. T 254 and similar multicoloured designs. Phosphorised paper. P 14½.*

980	(22 c.) Type 254	15	20
981	70 c. Twakow (barge) and Sampan Kotek (vert)	50	55
982	$1 Fujian junk (vert)	70	75
983	$2 Maduran Golekkan (sailing vessel)	1·40	1·50
980/3	Set of 4	2·75	3·00

MS984 200×67 mm. 22 c. As Type 254 and Nos. 981/3 .. .. 2·75 3·00

No. 980 is inscribed "For Local Addresses Only" and was sold for 22 c.

No. MS984 also includes the "Australia '99" World Stamp Exhibition, Melbourne, emblem on the sheet margin.

1999 (27 Apr). *"iBRA '99" International Stamp Exhibition, Nuremberg. Sheet 123×80 mm. Phosphorised paper. P 14.*

MS985 22 c. As Type 253; $2 No. 979 .. .. 2·00 2·25

255 Washing Lines ("Think of others")   **256** Hong Kong Harbour

(Des Lee Chee Chew. Litho Southern Colour Print, Dunedin)

1999 (12 May). *Self-adhesive Greeting Stamps. "Try a Little Kindness". T 255 and similar vert designs. Multicoloured. Fluorescent frame. P 10.*

986	(22 c.) Type 255	15	20
	a. Booklet pane. Nos. 986/90, each × 2	1·50	
987	(22 c.) Man throwing litter ("Do not litter")	15	20
988	(22 c.) Girl feeding cat and dog ("Be kind to animals")	15	20
989	(22 c.) Man watching television ("Be considerate")	15	20
990	(22 c.) Boy putting money in collection tin ("Be generous")	15	20
986/90	Set of 5	1·00	

Nos. 986/90 are inscribed "FOR LOCAL ADDRESSES ONLY" and were only issued in $2.20 stamp booklets.

(Des C. Willie and A. Lam. Litho Enschedé)

1999 (1 July). *Singapore–Hong Kong, China Joint Issue. T 256 and similar square designs. Multicoloured. Phosphorised paper. P 14×13½.*

991	(22 c.) Type 256	15	20
992	35 c. Singapore skyline	25	30
993	50 c. Giant Buddha, Lantau Island, Hong Kong	35	40
994	60 c. Merlion statue, Sentosa Island, Singapore	45	50
995	70 c. Street scene, Hong Kong ..	50	55
996	$1 Bugis Junction, Singapore ..	70	75
991/6	Set of 6	2·40	2·40

MS997 125×93 mm. 22 c. As Type 256 and Nos. 992/6 .. .. 2·40 2·50

No. 991 is inscribed "FOR LOCAL ADDRESSES ONLY".

1999 (2 July). *"PhilexFrance '99" International Stamp Exhibition, Paris. Sheet 123×80 mm. Phosphorised paper. P 14.*

MS998 22 c. As Type 253; $2 No. 979 .. .. 2·00 2·25

257 Peacock Butterfly   **258** Pres. Yusof bin Ishak

(Des Olàf Baldursdottir. Eng C. Slania. Recess and litho Stamp Ptg Office, Stockholm)

1999 (12 Aug). *Singapore–Sweden Joint Issue. Butterflies. T 257 and similar horiz designs. Multicoloured. Phosphorised paper. P 12½×13.*

999	(22 c.) Type 257	15	20
1000	70 c. Blue Pansy	50	55
1001	$1 Great Egg-fly	70	75
1002	$2 Red Admiral	1·40	1·50
999/1002	Set of 4	2·75	3·00

MS1003 129×75 mm. 22 c. As Type 257 and Nos. 1000/2 .. .. 2·75 3·00

No. 999 is inscribed "FOR LOCAL ADDRESSES ONLY".

(Litho Southern Colour Print, Dunedin)

1999 (21 Aug). *"China '99" International Stamp Exhibition, Peking. Sheet 123×80 mm. Phosphorised paper. P 14.*

MS1004 22 c. As Type 253; $2 As No. 979 .. 2·00 2·25

(Des Sylvia Tan. Eng C. Slania. Recess and litho Enschedé)

1999 (9 Sept). *Yusof bin Ishak (first President of Singapore) Commemoration. Phosphorised paper. P 13½×14.*

1005 **258** $2 multicoloured .. .. 1·40 1·50

No. 1005 was printed in sheets of 32 containing eight blocks of 4, each surrounded by margins. Examples were available either as blocks of 4 or as uncut sheets.

---

259 Green Turtle

(Des L. Teck Chong. Litho Southern Colour Print, Dunedin)

1999 (13 Oct). *Amphibians and Reptiles. T 259 and similar horiz designs. Multicoloured. Phosphor bands. P 14.*

1006	(22 c.) Type 259	15	20
1007	60 c. Green Crested Lizard	45	50
1008	70 c. Copper-cheeked Frog	50	55
1009	$1 Water Monitor	70	75
1006/9	Set of 4	1·75	2·00

No. 1006 is inscribed "For Local Addresses Only". Nos. 1006/9 each show two vertical phosphor bands.

260 New Parliament House from North

(Des Design Objectives. Litho Enschedé)

1999 (17 Nov). *Opening of New Parliament House. T 260 and similar horiz designs. Phosphorised paper. Multicoloured. P 13½×14.*

1010	(22 c.) Type 260	15	20
1011	60 c. North-east view	45	50
1012	$1 South-east view	70	75
1013	$2 West view	1·40	1·50
1010/13	Set of 4	2·50	2·75

No. 1010 is inscribed "For Local Addresses Only" and was sold for 22 c.

The lion's head emblem on these stamps is printed in optically variable ink which changes colour when viewed from different angles.

261 Sir Stamford Raffles and Sir Frank Swettenham (British Governors) and Raffles Museum   **262** Dragon

(Des Elsie Koh. Litho Ashton-Potter Canada)

1999 (31 Dec). *New Millennium (1st issue). 20th Century Singapore. T 261 and similar horiz designs. Phosphorised paper. Multicoloured. P 13×12½.*

1014	(22 c.) Type 261	15	20
	a. Sheetlet. Nos. 1014/23 ..	4·00	
1015	(22 c.) Past and present schooling ..	15	20
1016	35 c. Street scene, 1900, and Samsui woman	25	30
1017	35 c. Parliament	25	30
1018	60 c. British surrender, 1942, and Lord Mountbatten celebrating Japanese surrender, 1945	45	50
1019	60 c. Soldiers firing missile and fighter aircraft	45	50
1020	70 c. Singapore River, 1902, and modern forms of transportation	50	55
1021	70 c. Festival scenes	50	55
1022	$1 Housing, past and present ..	70	75
1023	$1 Skyscrapers	70	75
1014/23	Set of 10	4·00	4·50

Nos. 1014/15 are inscribed "for Local addresses only" and were sold for 22 c.

Nos. 1014/23 were printed together, se-tenant, in sheetlets of 10 as two horizontal strips separated by a gutter margin.

See also Nos. 1027/31.

(Des N. Loh. Litho (No. MS1026 also embossed in gold) Cartor)

2000 (1 Jan). *Chinese New Year ("Year of the Dragon"). T 262 and similar horiz design. Multicoloured. Phosphorised paper. P 13×13½.*

1024	(22 c.) Type 262	15	20
1025	$2 Dragon curled around spheres ..	1·40	1·50
MS1026	105×65 mm. $10 As No. 1025. P 13	7·50	7·50

No. 1024 is inscribed "FOR LOCAL ADDRESSES ONLY" and was sold for 22 c.

No. MS1026 was only sold in a decorative hongbao (envelope).

STANLEY GIBBONS STAMP COLLECTING SERIES

Introductory booklets on *How to Start, How to Identify Stamps* and *Collecting by Theme.* A series of well illustrated guides at a low price.

Write for details.

263 Information
Technology
Equipment

264 Post Office from across
Singapore River, 1854

(Des Sylvia Tan. Photo Courvoisier)

2000 (1 Jan). *New Millennium (2nd issue). Singapore in 2000.
T 263 and similar vert designs. Multicoloured. "All-over"
phosphor. Granite paper. P 14×15.*

1027	(22 c.) Type **263**	..	15	20
	a. Horiz strip of 4. Nos. 1027/30	..	2·50	
1028	60 c. Symbols of Arts and Culture	..	45	50
1029	$1 Heritage artifacts ..	..	70	75
1030	$2 Modern global communications	..	1·40	1·50
1027/30	..	*Set of* 4	2·50	2·75
MS1031	140×75 mm. 22 c. As Type **263** and Nos.			
1028/30	.. ..	..	2·50	2·75

No. 1027 is inscribed "For local addresses only" and was sold
for 22 c.

Nos. 1027/30 were printed together, *se-tenant*, as horizontal
strips of 4 in sheetlets 20 (4×5) with "2000" shown in the
phosphor across each strip.

(Des Chua Ban Har. Litho Enschedé)

2000 (8 Mar). *Opening of Singapore Post Centre. Postal
Landmarks. T 264 and similar horiz designs. Multicoloured.
Phosphorised paper. P 13½.*

1032	(22 c.) Type **264** ..	..	15	20
	a. Booklet pane. Nos. 1032×4 and			
	1033×2 with margins all round	..	1·50	
1033	60 c. General Post Office, c. 1873	..	45	50
1034	$1 G.P.O. Fullerton Building, 1928	..	70	75
	a. Booklet pane. Nos. 1034×4 and			
	1035×2 with margins all round	..	5·50	
1035	$2 Singapore Post Centre, 2000	..	1·40	1·50
1032/5	..	*Set of* 4	2·50	2·75
MS1036	110×94 mm. 22 c. As Type **264** and Nos.			
1033/5	..	..	2·50	2·75

No. 1032 is inscribed "FOR LOCAL ADDRESSES ONLY" and
was sold for 22 c.

(Des N. Loh. Litho Cartor)

2000 (25 Mar). *"Bangkok 2000" International Stamp
Exhibition. Sheet 123×75 mm. Multicoloured. Phosphorised
paper. P 13×13½.*

MS1037	22 c. As Type **262**; $2 No. 1025	.. 1·50	1·60

STAMP BOOKLETS

1969 (1 Nov). *Black on green cover. Stapled.*
SB1 $1.80, booklet containing twelve 15 c. (No. 106) in blocks of 4 .. .. 42·00

1973 (30 Sept)–74. *Grey and black printed cover. Opening hours of Philatelic Counter quoted on back cover as "8 A.M. to 9 P.M. daily". Pane attached by selvedge.*
SB2 $1 booklet containing *se-tenant* pane of 10 (No. 213a) .. .. 7·00
   a. Opening hours of Philatelic Counter quoted as "daily except Sundays and Public Holidays" (1974)

1977 (9 Apr). *Blue printed cover. Pane attached by selvedge.*
SB3 $1 booklet containing *se-tenant* pane of 12 (No. 290a) .. .. 3·75

1980 (26 Apr). *Green printed cover. Stamps attached by selvedge.*
SB4 $1 booklet containing 10 c. (No. 366) in block of 10 3·50

ART SERIES:
LITHOGRAPHS OF
19TH CENTURY
SINGAPORE

$1.50

B 1 Full-rigged Sailing Ship

1990 (21 Mar). *Lithographs of 19th-century Singapore. Black printed cover as Type B 1. Pane attached by selvedge.*
SB5 $1.50, booklet containing pane of ten 15 c. (No. 615a) .. .. 8·00

Singapore Definitive Stamps (Tourism Series)
Stamp Booklet $1.50

B 2 Mouth of Singapore River

1990 (4 July). *Tourism. Deep ultramarine, light greenish blue and light emerald printed cover as Type B 2. Pane attached by selvedge.*
SB6 $1.50, booklet containing pane of ten 15 c. (No. 625a) .. .. 11·00

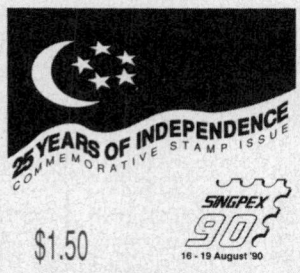

B 3 National Flag and "Singpex 90" National Stamp Exhibition Emblem

1990 (16 Aug). *25th Anniv of Independence. Red. black and grey printed cover as Type B 3. Pane attached by selvedge.*
SB7 $1.50, booklet containing pane of ten 15 c. (No. 637ab) .. .. 9·50

1991 (6 Mar–30 Aug). *Tourism. Deep ultramarine, light greenish blue and light emerald printed cover as Type B 2. "PRODUCED BY SINGAPORE PHILATELIC BUREAU" on outside back cover. Pane attached by selvedge.*
SB8 $2 booklet containing pane of ten 20 c. (No. 626a) 9·50
   a. "PRODUCED BY SINGAPORE PHILATELIC BUREAU" on inside back cover (30 Aug) ..

NEW INFORMATION
The editor is always interested to correspond with people who have new information that will improve or correct the Catalogue.

Singapore Definitive Stamps. Tourism Series
Stamp Booklet $2.00

B 4 "Mobil 1" Oil Can

1991 (15 May). *Tourism. Multicoloured cover as Type B 4. Pane attached by selvedge.*
SB9 $2 booklet containing pane of ten 20 c. (No. 626a) 9·00

B 5 Kingfisher

1991 (19 Sept). *Garden Birds. Multicoloured cover as Type B 5. Pane attached by selvedge.*
SB10 $2 booklet containing pane of ten 20 c. (No. 663a) 13·00

SINGAPORE DEFINITIVE STAMPS (TOURISM SERIES)
STAMP BOOKLET $2.00

Minted with purity.
Given with love.
Now, wrapped with velvet.

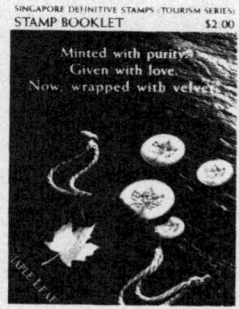

B 6 Maple Leaf Gold Coins

1991 (11 Nov). *Tourism. Multicoloured cover as Type B 6. Pane attached by selvedge.*
SB11 $2 booklet containing pane of ten 20 c. (No. 626a) 11·00

MARINE LIFE SERIES
CRABS

B 7 Swamp Forest Crab

1992 (21 Aug). *Crabs. Multicoloured cover as Type B 7. Pane attached by selvedge.*
SB12 $2 booklet containing pane of ten 20 c. (No. 698a) 5·50

KUALA LUMPUR '92 - 5TH ASIAN
INTERNATIONAL PHILATELIC
EXHIBITION 1992

Singapore Definitive Stamps (Tourism Series)
Stamp Booklet $2.00

B 8 Aspects of Singapore

1992 (1 Sept). *"Kuala Lumpur '92" International Stamp Exhibition. Multicoloured cover as Type B 8. Pane attached by selvedge.*
SB13 $2 booklet containing pane of ten 20 c. (No. 626a) 4·50

Greetings Stamp Booklet $2.00

B 9 Children and Party Streamers

1993 (10 Feb). *Greetings Stamps. Multicoloured cover as Type B 9. Pane attached by selvedge.*
SB14 $2 booklet containing pane of ten 20 c. in five different designs (No. 710a) .. .. 4·50

B 10 Butterflies and Flowers

1993 (21 Aug). *Butterflies. Multicoloured cover as Type B 10. Pane attached by selvedge.*
SB15 $2 containing pane of ten 20 c. (No. 728a) .. 6·50

CORALS AND REEF LIFE DEFINITIVES
STAMP BOOKLET $2.00

B 11 Sea-fan

1994 (12 Jan–20 May). *Reef Life (1st series). Multicoloured cover as Type B 11 with black bands at top and bottom. Pane attached by selvedge.*
SB16 $2 booklet containing pane of ten 20 c. (No. 743a) 5·50
   a. Blue bands at top and bottom of cover (31 Mar) 6·50
   ab. Revised cover showing silver inscr in three lines with the second and third lines aligned at right (20 May) .. .. 6·50

BIRD SERIES *Herons*

B 12 Grey Heron

1994 (16 Aug). *Herons. Multicoloured cover as Type B 12. Pane attached by selvedge.*
SB17 $2 booklet containing pane of ten 20 c. (No. 766b) 6·50

CONGRATULATIONS
CELEBRATIONS
Greetings
BEST WISHES

GREETINGS STAMP BOOKLET

B 13 Greetings Messages

1994 (14 Sept). *Greetings Stamps. Multicoloured cover as Type B 13. Self-adhesive.*
SB18 ($2) booklet containing pane of ten self-adhesive stamps (No. 775a) .. .. 3·50
The booklet cover, which forms the backing card for the stamps also incorporates 10 self-adhesive labels.

1994 (16 Nov). *Reef Life (2nd series). Multicoloured cover as Type B 11 showing Blue-spotted Stingray. Self-adhesive.*
SB19 ($2) booklet containing pane of ten self-adhesive stamps (No. 785a) .. .. .. 2·00

GREETINGS STAMP BOOKLET
Stickers can be peeled off for use with stamps

B 14 Symbols of Love

1995 (8 Feb). *Greetings Stamps. Multicoloured cover as Type B 14. Self-adhesive.*
SB20 ($2.20) booklet containing pane of ten self-adhesive stamps (No. 790a) .. 3·50
The booklet cover, which forms the backing card for the stamps also incorporates 10 self-adhesive labels.

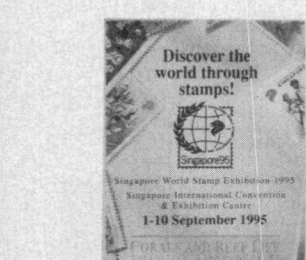

B 15 Exhibition Logo and Stamps (inscr "Discover the World through Stamps")

1995 (12 Apr–5 July). *"Singapore '95" International Stamp Exhibition. Multicoloured covers as Type B 15. Self-adhesive.*
SB21 ($2.20) booklet containing pane of ten self-adhesive stamps (No. 785ba) (Type B 15) .. 4·50
SB22 ($2.20) booklet containing pane of ten self-adhesive stamps (No. 785ba) (vert design for "POSTECH 1995" Postal Equipment and Machinery Exhibition) (7 June) .. 4·50
SB23 ($2.20) booklet containing pane of ten self-adhesive stamps (No. 785ba) (horiz cover showing map and inscr "We've Got The Route to Real Excitement!" (5 July) .. .. 4·50

B 16 Yellow-faced Angelfish

1995 (19 July). *Marine Fishes. Multicoloured cover as Type B 16. Pane attached by selvedge.*
SB24 ($2.20) booklet containing ten 22 c. stamps (No. 807) .. .. 3·75

B 17 "6 DIGIT POSTAL CODE"

1995 (1 Sept). *Introduction of Six Digit Postal Codes. Multicoloured cover as Type B 17. Self-adhesive.*
SB25 ($2.20) booklet containing pane of ten self-adhesive stamps (No. 785ba) .. .. 4·50

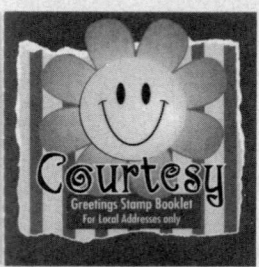

B 18 Smiling Flower

1996 (10 July). *Greetings Stamps. "Courtesy". Children's Drawings. Multicoloured covers as Type B 18. Self-adhesive.*
SB26 ($2.20) booklet containing pane of ten self-adhesive stamps (No. 839a) (Type B 18) .. 2·50
SB27 $3.90 booklet containing pane of ten self-adhesive stamps (No. 839b) (cover showing smiling flowers) .. .. .. 4·25
The booklet covers, which forms the backing card for the stamps also incorporate 10 self-adhesive labels.

B 19 *Cinnamomum iners*

1996 (11 Sept). *Singapore Trees. Multicoloured cover as Type B 19. Pane attached by selvedge.*
SB28 ($2.20) booklet containing ten 22 c. stamps (No. 850) .. .. 3·50

B 20 Jinrickshaw

1997 (19 Mar). *Transportation. Multicoloured cover as Type B 20. Self-adhesive.*
SB29 ($2.20) booklet containing pane of ten self-adhesive stamps (No. 884a) .. .. 1·50

B 21 Apple

1997 (14 May). *Greetings stamps. "Friends". Multicoloured covers as Type B 21. Self-adhesive.*
SB30 ($2.20) booklet containing pane of ten self-adhesive stamps (No. 885a) (Type B 21, "friendship" in vermilion) .. .. 2·75

SB31 ($2.20) booklet containing pane of ten self-adhesive stamps (No. 890a) (as Type B 21, but "friendship" in ultramarine) .. 2·75
The booklet covers, which form the backing cards for the stamps each incorporate 10 self-adhesive labels.

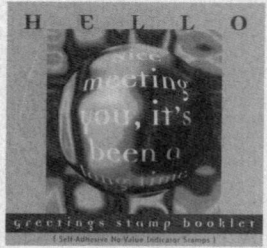

B 22 Flowers

1997 (13 Sept). *25th Anniv of the Ministry of the Environment. Multicoloured cover as Type B 22. Pane attached by selvedge.*
SB32 ($2.20) booklet containing pane of ten (22 c.) (No. 904a) .. .. 1·50

B 23 "Nice meeting you, it's been a long time" in Bubble

1998 (20 May). *Greetings Stamps. Multicoloured cover as Type B 23. Self-adhesive.*
SB33 ($2.20) booklet containing pane of ten self-adhesive stamps (No. 924a) .. .. 2·00
The booklet cover forms the backing card for the stamps and also incorporates 10 self-adhesive labels.

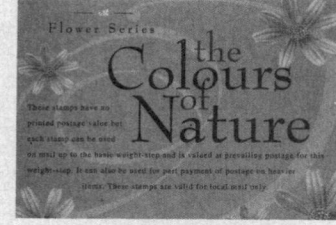

B 24 "Fragile Forest", Twig and Animal Tracks

1998 (5 June). *25th Anniv of Singapore Zoological Gardens and Launch of New "Fragile Forest" Display. Multicoloured covers as Type B 24. Self-adhesive.*
SB34 ($2.20) booklet containing pane of ten self-adhesive stamps (No. 929a) .. 2·00
SB35 ($2.20) booklet containing pane of ten self-adhesive stamps (No. 934a) (cover as Type B 24 but showing single leaf) .. 2·00
The covers form the backing for the stamps and also incorporate a scratch card inside each booklet.

B 25 "The Colours of Nature"

1998 (9 Sept). *Flowers of Singapore. Multicoloured cover as Type B 25. Pane attached by selvedge.*
SB36 ($2.20) booklet containing pane of ten (22 c.) stamps (No. 949b) .. .. .. 1·50

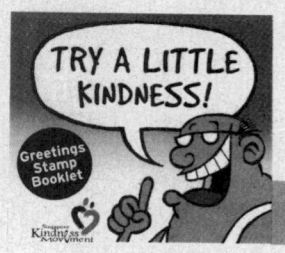

B 26

1999 (12 May). *Greetings Stamps. "Try a Little Kindness".*
Multicoloured cover as Type B 26. Self-adhesive.
SB37 ($2.20) booklet containing pane of ten (22 c.) (No.
986a) .. .. 1·50

B 27 Green Turtle

1999 (13 Oct). *Amphibians and Reptiles. Multicoloured cover*
as Type B 27. Stamps attached by selvedge.
SB38 $2.20, booklet containing block of ten (22 c.) (No.
1006) .. .. 1·50

B 28 Singapore Post Centre
(Illustration further reduced. Actual size 155×105 mm)

2000 (8 Mar). *Opening of Singapore Post Centre. Postal*
Landmarks. Multicoloured cover as Type B 28. Stitched.
SB39 $10.50, booklet containing two different
se-tenant panes of 6 (Nos. 1032a and 1034a) 7·75

POSTAGE DUE STAMPS

The postage due stamps of Malayan Postal Union were in use in
Singapore until replaced by the following issues.

D 1   D 2   D 3

(Litho B.W.)

1968 (1 Feb)–**69**. *Toned paper. W w* **12**. *P* 9.
D1	D 1	1 c. green	..	..	..	60	2·00
D2		2 c. red		..	..	60	2·50
D3		4 c. yellow-orange	..	..	..	1·25	5·50
D4		8 c. chocolate	..	..	..	50	1·50
D5		10 c. magenta	..	..	..	50	90
		a. White paper (16.12.69)	..	..	1·50	4·25
D6		12 c. slate-violet	..	..	..	1·50	2·25
		a. White paper (16.12.69)	..	..	6·50	9·00
D7		20 c. new blue	..	..	..	2·00	3·25
		a. White paper (16.12.69)	..	..	8·50	11·00
D8		50 c. drab	..	..	..	8·50	5·00
D1/8		..	..	Set of 8	13·50	21·00

1973. *White paper. W w* **12**. *P* 13 × 13½.
D 9	D 1	10 c. bright magenta (27.4)	..	..	75	4·50
D10		50 c. sage-green (24.8)	..	..	8·50	12·00

1977–78. *White paper. No wmk. P* 13 × 13½.
D11	D 1	1 c. green	..	..	..	42·00	35·00
D12		4 c. yellow-orange	..	..	42·00	65·00
D13		10 c. bright magenta	..	..	45·00	32·00
D14		20 c. new blue	..	..	50·00	42·00
D15		50 c. sage-green	..	..	60·00	48·00
D11/15		..	..	Set of 5	£225	£200

(Litho Secura, Singapore)
1978 (25 Sept)–**81**. *No wmk. P* 13 × 13½.
D16	D 2	1 c. blue-green	..	..	65	3·50
		a. Perf 12 × 11½ (1981)	..	15	2·50
D17		4 c. pale orange	..	..	75	6·00
		a. Perf 12 × 11½ (1981)	..	20	4·25
D18		10 c. cerise	..	..	85	2·25
		a. Perf 12 × 11½ (1981)	..	50	1·50
D19		20 c. light blue	..	..	95	2·50
		a. Perf 12 × 11½ (1981)	..	65	2·00
D20		50 c. yellow-green	..	..	1·60	2·75
		a. Perf 12 × 11½ (1981)	..	90	2·50
D16/20		..	..	Set of 5	4·25	15·00
D16a/20a	..	..	..	Set of 5	2·25	11·50

(Litho Secura, Singapore)
1989 (12 July)–**97**. *P* 13 × 13½.
D21	D 3	1 c. bright emerald (7.11.97)	..		
D22		4 c. orange-brown (7.11.97)	..		
D23		5 c. bright mauve	..	..	20	50
D24		10 c. carmine	..	..	20	40
D25		20 c. bright greenish blue	..	30	60
D26		50 c. yellow-green	..	..	60	1·00
D27		$1 blackish brown (30.4.93)	..	2·25	2·50

Postage Due stamps were withdrawn on 31 December 1997
and replaced by labels from electronic machines.

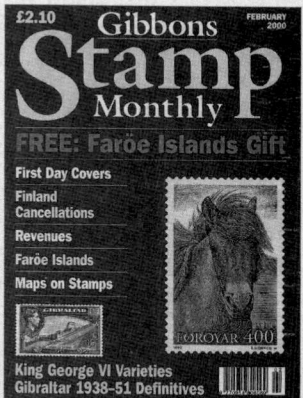

Solomon Islands
(formerly British Solomon Islands)

The first British Resident Commissioner, Charles Woodford, was appointed in 1896 and a administrative centre established at Tulagi.

Mail was initially sent unstamped by sealed bag to Sydney where New South Wales stamps were applied and cancelled. Later the Resident Commissioner kept a stock of New South Wales stamps which were still not cancelled until arrival at Sydney. From April 1906 Mr. Woodford used a vertical oblong "BRITISH SOLOMON ISLANDS PAID" handstamp in place of New South Wales stamps which were then added to many of the covers by the postal authorities in Sydney.

PRICES FOR STAMPS ON COVER TO 1945	
Nos. 1/7	from × 12
Nos. 8/17	from × 25
Nos. 18/36	from × 6
Nos. 37/8	
Nos. 39/51	from × 6
No. 52	
Nos. 53/6	from × 2
Nos. 57/9	from × 6
Nos. 60/72	from × 2
Nos. D1/8	from × 5

BRITISH PROTECTORATE

1   **2**

(Des C. M. Woodford. Litho W. E. Smith & Co, Sydney)

1907 (14 Feb). *No wmk. P 11.*

1	1	½d. ultramarine	..	8·50	14·00
2		1d. rose-carmine	..	22·00	25·00
3		2d. indigo	..	26·00	30·00
4		2½d. orange-yellow	..	32·00	38·00
		a. Imperf between (vert pair)..		£4000	
		b. Imperf between (horiz pair)		£5500	£4250
5		5d. emerald-green	..	50·00	65·00
6		6d. chocolate	..	55·00	60·00
		a. Imperf between (vert pair)..		£3750	
7		1s. bright purple	..	75·00	75·00
1/7			*Set of 7*	£225	£275

Three types exist of the ½d. and 2½d., and six each of the other values, differing in minor details.

Forgeries of Nos. 1/7 show different perforations and have the boat paddle touching the shore. Genuine stamps show a gap between the paddle and the shore.

(Recess D.L.R.)

1908 (1 Nov)–**11.** *Wmk Mult Crown CA (sideways). P 14.*

8	2	½d. green	..	1·50	80
9		1d. red	..	1·25	70
10		2d. greyish slate	..	1·25	1·00
11		2½d. ultramarine	..	3·75	2·00
11a		4d. red/yellow (6.3.11)	..	3·25	11·00
12		5d. olive	..	8·50	7·00
13		6d. claret	..	10·00	6·50
14		1s. black/green	..	8·50	8·00
15		2s. purple/blue (7.3.10)	..	40·00	55·00
16		2s. 6d. red/blue (7.3.10)	..	48·00	70·00
17		5s. green/yellow (7.3.10)	..	75·00	£100
8/17			*Set of 11*	£170	£225
8/17 Optd "Specimen"			*Set of 11*	£250	

The ½d. and 1d. were issued in 1913 on rather thinner paper and with brownish gum.

3   **4**

(T **3** and **4**. Typo D.L.R.)

1913. *Inscribed "POSTAGE POSTAGE". Wmk Mult Crown CA. P 14.*

18	3	½d. green (1.4)	..	80	3·50
19		1d. red (1.4)	..	80	14·00
20		3d. purple/yellow (27.2)	..	80	4·00
		a. On orange-buff		7·00	24·00
21		11d. dull purple and scarlet (27.2)		3·00	12·00
18/21			*Set of 4*	4·75	30·00
18/21 Optd "Specimen"			*Set of 4*	70·00	

1914 (Mar)–**23.** *Inscribed "POSTAGE REVENUE". Wmk Mult Crown CA. Chalk-surfaced paper (3d. to £1). P 14.*

22	4	½d. green	..	80	11·00
23		½d. yellow-green (1917)	..	4·00	17·00
24		1d. carmine-red	..	1·50	1·00
25		1d. scarlet (1917)	..	4·50	6·50
26		2d. grey (7.14)	..	3·00	9·00
27		2½d. ultramarine (7.14)	..	2·00	5·00
28		3d. purple/pale yellow (3.23)		20·00	80·00
29		4d. black and red/yellow (7.14)		2·00	2·50
30		5d. dull purple and olive-green (7.14)		20·00	30·00

31	4	5d. brown-purple and olive-green (7.14)		20·00	30·00
32		6d. dull and bright purple (7.14)		6·00	14·00
33		1d. black/green (7.14)	..	4·75	7·00
		a. On blue-green, olive back (1923)		7·50	23·00
34		2s. purple and blue/blue (7.14)		7·00	10·00
35		2s. 6d. black and red/blue (7.14)		9·00	20·00
36		5s. green and red/yellow (7.14)		27·00	45·00
		a. On orange-buff (1920)		45·00	70·00
37		10s. green and red/green (7.14)		75·00	80·00
38		£1 purple and black/red (7.14)		£200	£120
22/38			*Set of 14*	£325	£400
22/38 Optd "Specimen"			*Set of 14*	£400	

Variations in the coloured papers are mostly due to climate and do not indicate separate printings.

1922–31. *Wmk Mult Script CA. Chalk-surfaced paper (4d. and 5d. to 10s.). P 14.*

39	4	½d. green (10.22)	..	30	3·25
40		1d. scarlet (4.23)	..	11·00	10·00
41		1d. dull violet (2.27)	..	1·00	7·00
42	3	1½d. bright scarlet (7.24)	..	2·25	50
43	4	3d. slate-grey (4.23)	..	3·00	14·00
44		3d. pale ultramarine (11.23)		70	4·00
45		4d. black and red/yellow (7.27)		3·50	22·00
45a		4½d. red-brown (1931)	..	3·00	19·00
46		5d. dull purple and olive-green (12.27)		3·00	25·00
47		6d. dull and bright purple (12.27)		3·75	25·00
48		1s. black/emerald (12.27)		2·75	12·00
49		2s. purple and blue/blue (2.27)		8·00	32·00
50		2s. 6d. black and red/blue (12.27)		7·50	32·00
51		5s. green and red/pale yellow (12.27)		25·00	50·00
52		10s. green and red/emerald (1.25)		90·00	95·00
39/52			*Set of 15*	£140	£300
39/52 Optd/Perf "Specimen"			*Set of 15*	£300	

1935 (6 May). *Silver Jubilee. As Nos. 114/17 of Jamaica, but ptd by D.L.R. P 13½×14.*

53		1½d. deep blue and carmine	..	1·00	85
		f. Diagonal line by turret		50·00	
		h. Dot by flagstaff		85·00	
54		3d. brown and deep blue	..	3·00	6·00
		f. Diagonal line by turret		90·00	
		h. Dot by flagstaff		£160	
55		6d. light blue and olive-green		8·50	12·00
		a. Frame printed double, one albino			
		b. Frame printed triple, two albino		£1200	
		h. Dot by flagstaff		£225	
		i. Dash by turret		£225	
56		1s. slate and purple		7·50	10·00
		a. Frame printed double, one albino		£1500	
		f. Diagonal line by turret		£180	
		h. Dot by flagstaff		£225	
		i. Dash by turret		£225	
53/6			*Set of 4*	18·00	26·00
53/6 Perf "Specimen"			*Set of 4*	90·00	

The second albino impression on No. 55b is sometimes almost co-incidental with the inked impression of the frame.

For illustrations of plate varieties see Omnibus section following Zimbabwe.

1937 (13 May). *Coronation. As Nos. 118/20 of Jamaica, but ptd by B.W. P 11×11½.*

57		1d. violet	..	30	70
58		1½d. carmine	..	30	60
59		3d. blue	..	50	50
57/9			*Set of 3*	1·00	1·60
57/9 Perf "Specimen"			*Set of 3*	60·00	

5 Spears and Shield   **6** Native Constable and Chief

7 Canoe House   **8** Roviana Canoe

(Recess D.L.R. (2d., 3d., 2s. and 2s. 6d.), Waterlow (others))

1939 (1 Feb)–**1951.** *T 5/8 and similar designs. Wmk Mult Script CA. P 13½ (2d., 3d., 2s. and 2s. 6d.) or 12½ (others).*

60		½d. blue and blue-green	..	15	1·00
61		1d. brown and deep violet	..	30	1·00
62		1½d. blue-green and carmine		70	1·25
63		2d. orange-brown and black		80	1·50
		a. Perf 12 (7.11.51)		30	1·50
64		2½d. magenta and sage-green		1·50	1·50
		a. Imperf horiz (vert pair)		£8500	
65		3d. black and ultramarine		1·00	1·25
		a. Perf 12 (29.11.51)		1·50	2·50
66		4½d. green and chocolate		4·00	13·00
67		6d. deep violet and reddish purple		75	1·00
68		1s. green and black		1·25	90
69		2s. black and orange		6·00	50
70		2s. black and violet		26·00	4·50
71		5s. emerald-green and scarlet		32·00	9·50
72		10s. sage-green and magenta (27.4.42)		5·50	8·50
60/72			*Set of 13*	70·00	45·00
60/72 Perf "Specimen"			*Set of 13*	£275	

Designs: *Horiz (as T **8**)*—1½d. Artificial Island, Malaita; 1s. Breadfruit; 5s. Malaita canoe. *(As T **7**)*—3d. Roviana canoes; 2s. Tinakula volcano; 2s. 6d. Common Scrub Hen. *Vert (as T **6**)*—4½d., 10s. Native house, Reef Islands; 6d. Coconut plantation.

1946 (15 Oct). *Victory. As Nos. 141/2 of Jamaica.*

73		1½d. carmine	..	15	80
74		3d. blue	..	15	10
73/4 Perf "Specimen"			*Set of 2*	55·00	

Pocket handkerchief flaw (R. 1/6)

1949 (14 Mar). *Royal Silver Wedding. As Nos. 143/4 of Jamaica.*

75		2d. black	..	50	50
		a. Pocket handkerchief flaw		22·00	
76		10s. magenta	..	13·00	11·00

1949 (10 Oct). *75th Anniv of U.P.U. As Nos. 145/8 of Jamaica.*

77		2d. red-brown	..	75	1·00
78		3d. deep blue	..	2·25	1·00
79		5d. deep blue-green	..	75	1·40
80		1s. blue-black	..	75	1·00
77/80			*Set of 4*	4·00	4·00

1953 (2 June). *Coronation. As No. 153 of Jamaica.*

81		2d. black and grey-black	..	50	1·25

17 Ysabel Canoe   **18** Roviana Canoe

24 Native Constable and Chief   **25** Arms of the Protectorate

(Des Miss I. R. Stinson (½d.), R. Bailey (2½d.), R. A. Sweet (5d., 1s., 1s. 3d.), Capt. J. Brett Hilder (6d., 8d., 9d., 5s.). Recess B.W. (½d., 2½d., 5d., 6d., 8d., 9d., 1s., 1s. 3d., 5s.), D.L.R. (1d., 2d., 2s.), Waterlow (1½d., 3d., 2s. 6d., 10s., £1), until 1962, then D.L.R.)

1956 (1 Mar)–**63.** *T 17/18, 24/5 and similar horiz designs. Wmk Mult Script CA. P 12 (1d., 2d., 2s.). 13 (1½d., 3d., 2s 6d., 10s., £1) or 11½ (others).*

82		½d. orange and purple		15	50
83		1d. yellow-green and red-brown		15	15
84		1½d. slate-green and carmine-red		15	70
		a. Slate-green and brown-red (31.7.63)		60	40
85		2d. deep brown and dull green		30	30
86		2½d. black and blue		60	10
87		3d. blue-green and red		60	15
88		5d. black and blue		30	55
89		6d. black and turquoise-green		50	25
90		8d. bright blue and black		25	15
90a		9d. emerald and black (28.1.60)		3·25	80
91		1s. slate and yellow-brown		50	50
		a. Slate and orange-brown (13.6.61)		3·50	3·00
91b		1s. black and blue (28.1.60)		6·00	1·75
		ba. Black and pale ultramarine (11.12.62)		10·00	3·25
92		2s. black and carmine		13·00	1·75
93		2s. 6d. emerald and bright purple		7·50	45
		a. Emerald and reddish purple (19.2.63)		11·00	1·75
94		5d. red-brown		15·00	3·75
95		10s. sepia		20·00	4·75
96		£1 black and blue (5.11.58)		42·00	35·00
82/96			*Set of 17*	90·00	45·00

Designs: (As T **17**)—5d., 1s. 3d. Map; 6d. Miena (schooner); 1s. Voyage of H.M.S. Swallow, 1767; 2s. 6d. Native house, Reef Islands; 5s. Mendaña and Todos los Santos. (As T **25**)—1d. Roviana canoe; 1½d. Artificial Island, Malaita; 2d. Canoe house; 3d. Malaita Canoe; 8d., 9d. Henderson airfield, Guadalcanal; 2s. Tinakula volcano.

LEGISLATIVE COUNCIL

32 Great Frigate Bird

(Litho Enschedé)

1 (19 Jan). *New Constitution, 1960.* W w 12 *(sideways*).*
P 13×12½.

32	2d. black and turquoise-green	..	10	30
	w. Wmk Crown to right of CA		10	30
	3d. black and rose-carmine		10	10
	w. Wmk Crown to right of CA		10	10
	9d. black and reddish purple		15	30
	w. Wmk Crown to right of CA		15	30
		Set of 3	30	60

This issue with watermark sideways exists in almost equal
\ntities with the watermark showing Crown to left or right of

3 (4 June). *Freedom from Hunger. As No. 80 of Lesotho.*

	1s. 3d. ultramarine		1·50	35

3 (2 Sept). *Red Cross Centenary. As Nos. 203/4 of Lesotho.*

2d. red and black		50	20
9d. red and blue		1·00	1·25

3–64. *As Nos. 83/5, 87, 89, 90a and 91a/3, but wmk w 12.*

	1d. yellow-green and red-brown (9.7.64)		25	30
	1½d. slate-green and red		40	50
	2d. deep brown and dull green (9.7.64)		20	20
	3d. light blue-green and scarlet (16.11.63)		55	15
	a. Yellowish green and red (9.7.64)		1·25	1·75
	6d. black and turquoise (7.7.64)		60	40
	9d. emerald and black (7.7.64)		40	35
	1s. 3d. black and blue (7.7.64)		60	70
	2s. black and carmine (9.7.64)		1·00	5·50
	2s. 6d. emerald & reddish purple (9.7.64)		15·00	11·00
\/11		*Set of 9*	17·00	17·00

33 Makira Food Bowl (48)

(Des M. Farrar-Bell. Litho D.L.R.)

65 (24 May). *Horiz designs as T 33.* W w 12. *P 13 × 12½.*

2	½d. black, deep slate-blue and light blue	..	10	80
3	1d. black, orange and yellow	..	70	90
4	1½d. black, blue and yellow-green	..	35	50
5	2d. black, ultramarine and light blue		60	60
6	2½d. black, light brown & pale yellow-brown		10	45
7	3d. black, green and light green	..	10	10
8	6d. black, magenta and yellow-orange		35	80
9	9d. brownish blk, dp bluish grn & pale yell		40	15
0	1s. black, chocolate and magenta		90	15
2	1s. 3d. black and rose-red		4·00	3·25
2	2s. black, bright purple and lilac ..		8·00	3·25
3	2s. 6d. black, olive-brown and light brown		1·00	70
4	5s. black, ultramarine and violet ..		12·00	5·00
5	10s. black, olive-green and yellow ..		14·00	4·00
6	£1 black, deep reddish violet and pink		12·00	5·00
2/126		*Set of 15*	45·00	22·00

Designs:—1d. *Dendrobium veratrifolium* (orchid); 1½d.
\niragra Spider Conch; 2d. Blyth's Hornbill; 2½d. Ysabel
\neld; 3d. Rennellese club; 6d. Moorish Idol; 9d. Lesser Frigate
\nrd; 1s. *Dendrobium macrophyllum* (orchid); 1s. 3d.
\nndrobium spectabilis (orchid); 2s. Sanford's Sea Eagle; 2s. 6d.
\nalaita belt; 5s. *Ornithoptera victoreae* (butterfly); 10s. Ducorp's
\nckatoo; £1, Western canoe figurehead.

065 (28 June). *I.T.U. Centenary. As Nos. 98/9 of Lesotho.*

7	2d. orange-red and turquoise-blue ..		20	15
\8	3d. turquoise-blue and olive-brown ..		20	15

065 (25 Oct). *International Co-operation Year. As Nos. 100/1
of Lesotho.*

29	1d. reddish purple and turquoise-green		10	10
30	2s. 6d. deep bluish green and lavender		45	20

066 (24 Jan). *Churchill Commemoration. As Nos. 102/5 of
Lesotho.*

31	2d. new blue	..	15	10
32	9d. deep green	..	25	10
33	1s. 3d. brown	..	35	10
34	2s. 6d. bluish violet	..	40	25
31/4		*Set of 4*	1·00	40

**New Currency. 100 cents = 1 Australian, later Solomon
Islands dollar)**

8 c. 8 c.

Normal "8"	Inverted "8" (No. 142a) (R. 9/2. Later corrected)

066 (14 Feb)–67. *Decimal Currency. Nos. 112/26 variously
surch as T 48 by De La Rue. A. Wmk upright.*

35A	1 c. on ½d. black, dp slate-blue & lt blue		10	10
36A	2 c. on 1d. black, orange and yellow ..		10	10
37A	3 c. on 1½d. black, blue and yellow-green		10	10
38A	4 c. on 2d. black, ultramarine & light blue		15	10
39A	5 c. on 6d. black, magenta & yellow-orge		15	10
40A	6 c. on 2½d. black, lt brn & pale yell-brn		15	10
41A	7 c. on 3d. black, green and light green		15	10
42A	8 c. on 9d. brownish black, deep bluish green and pale yellow	..	25	10
	a. Inverted "8"	..	27·00	17·00
	b. Surch omitted (vert pair)	..	£2500	
43A	10 c. on 1s. black, chocolate and magenta		30	10
45A	13 c. on 1s. 3d. black and rose-red		1·50	15
47A	20 c. on 2s. black, bright purple and lilac		2·50	25
48A	25 c. on 2s. 6d. black, olive-brn & lt brn		60	10
50A	50 c. on 5s. black, ultramarine & violet (R.)		5·50	2·75
51A	$1 on 10s. black, olive-green and yellow		3·00	3·00
52A	$2 on £1 black, dp reddish violet & pink		2·75	6·50
35A/52A		*Set of 15*	15·00	12·00

B. *Wmk sideways*

135B	1 c. on ½d. black, dp slate-bl & lt bl (6.66)		10	10
136B	2 c. on 1d. black, orange and yellow (6.66)		10	10
137B	3 c. on 1½d. black, bl & yellow-grn (6.66)		15	10
138B	4 c. on 2d. black, ultram & lt blue (6.66)		15	10
139B	5 c. on 6d. black, mag & yell-orge (6.66)		15	10
140B	6 c. on 2½d. black, light brown and pale yellow-brown (6.66)		10	10
141B	7 c. on 3d. black, green & lt green (6.66)		10	10
142B	8 c. on 9d. brownish black, deep bluish green and pale yellow (6.66)		15	10
143B	10 c. on 1s. black, chocolate & mag (6.66)		40	10
144B	12 c. on 1s. 3d. black and rose-red (1.3.67)		65	10
145B	13 c. on 1s. 3d. black and rose-red (6.66)		4·50	1·75
146B	14 c. on 3d. black, green & lt green (1.3.67)		40	10
147B	20 c. on 2s. black, brt purple & lilac (6.66)		3·25	30
148B	25 c. on 2s. 6d. blk, olive-brn & lt brn (6.66)		2·50	35
149B	35 c. on 2s. black, ultram & lt blue (1.3.67)		2·00	25
	a. Surch omitted (horiz pair with normal)		£2500	
	b. Surch value only omitted			
150B	50 c. on 5s. black, ultram & vio (R.) (6.66)		10·00	5·50
151B	$1 on 10s. black, olive-green & yell (6.66)		7·00	1·25
152B	$2 on £1 black, dp reddish vio & pk (6.66)		5·00	3·00
135B/52B		*Set of 18*	30·00	11·50

The positions of the bars in the surcharge vary considerably from
stamp to stamp within the sheets.

The stamps with sideways watermark are all from new printings
and in some instances there are marked shade variations from Nos.
112/26 which were used for making Nos. 135A/152A.

No. 142Ab comes from the bottom left-hand corner of the
sheet and was and was covered by a paper fold. The bottom stamp in the
pair is completely without surcharge and the upper has the
surcharge value and one bar missing.

1966 (1 July). *World Cup Football Championships. As Nos.
57/8 of Pitcairn Islands.*

153	8 c. violet, yellow-green, lake & yellow-brn ..		15	15
154	35 c. chocolate, blue-green, lake & yellow-brn		30	15

1966 (20 Sept). *Inauguration of W.H.O. Headquarters, Geneva.
As Nos. 185/6 of Montserrat.*

155	3 c. black, yellow-green and light blue	..	20	10
156	50 c. black, light purple and yellow-brown		60	20

1966 (1 Dec). *20th Anniv of U.N.E.S.C.O. As Nos. 342/4 of
Mauritius.*

157	3 c. slate-violet, red, yellow and orange		15	10
158	25 c. orange-yellow, violet and deep olive		30	15
159	$1 black, bright purple and orange		75	70
157/9 ..		*Set of 3*	1·10	85

49 Henderson Field

(Des V. Whiteley. Photo Harrison)

1967 (28 Aug). *25th Anniv of Guadalcanal Campaign (Pacific
War). T 49 and similar horiz design. Multicoloured.* W w 12.
P 14 × 14½.

160	8 c. Type 49	..	15	15
161	35 c. Red Beach landings	..	15	15

51 Mendaña's *Todos los Santos* off Point Cruz

(Des V. Whiteley. Photo Harrison)

1968 (7 Feb). *Quatercentenary of the Discovery of Solomon Is. T 51
and similar horiz designs. Multicoloured.* W w 12. *P 14.*

162	3 c. Type 51	..	20	10
163	8 c. Arrival of missionaries	..	20	10
164	30 c. Pacific Campaign, World War II		40	10
165	$1 Proclamation of the Protectorate		60	1·50
.162/5 ..		*Set of 4*	1·25	1·60

55 Vine Fishing

(Des R. Granger Barrett. Photo Harrison)

1968 (20 May)–71. *Horiz designs as T 55. Chalk-surfaced
paper.* W w 12. *P 14½.*

166	1 c. turquoise-blue, black and brown		10	10
	a. Glazed, ordinary paper (9.8.71)		90	90
	aw. Wmk inverted		1·25	
167	2 c. apple-green, black and brown		10	10
	aw. Wmk inverted. Glazed, ordinary paper (9.8.71)		90	90
168	3 c. green, myrtle-green and black		10	10
	a. Glazed, ordinary paper (9.8.71)		90	90
169	4 c. bright purple, black and brown		15	10
	a. Glazed, ordinary paper (9.8.71)		90	90
170	6 c. multicoloured		30	10
171	8 c. multicoloured		25	10
	a. Glazed, ordinary paper (9.8.71)		1·50	1·60

172	12 c. yellow-ochre, brown-red and black		65	40
	a. Glazed, ordinary paper (9.8.71)		2·25	2·50
	aw. Wmk inverted		4·00	
173	14 c. orange-red, chocolate and black		2·00	2·50
174	15 c. multicoloured		80	80
	a. Glazed, ordinary paper (9.8.71)		2·50	3·75
175	20 c. bright blue, red and black		4·00	3·00
	a. Glazed, ordinary paper (9.8.71)		4·25	7·00
176	24 c. rose-red, black and yellow		2·00	2·75
177	35 c. multicoloured		2·00	50
178	45 c. multicoloured		1·50	50
179	$1 violet-blue light green and black		2·50	2·00
180	$2 multicoloured		6·00	5·00
	w. Wmk inverted		8·00	
166/80		*Set of 15*	18·00	16·00
166a/75a ..		*Set of 18*	13·00	17·00

Designs:—2 c. Kite fishing; 3 c. Platform fishing; 4 c. Net fishing;
6 c. Gold Lip shell diving; 8 c. Night fishing; 12 c. Boat building;
14 c. Cocoa; 15 c. Road building; 20 c. Geological survey; 24 c.
Hauling timber; 35 c. Copra; 45 c. Harvesting rice; $1, Honiara
Port; $2, Internal air service.

The stamps on glazed, ordinary paper exist with PVA gum only.
The 1 c. to 12 c. and 20 c. on chalk-surfaced paper exist with PVA
gum as well as gum arabic, but the others exist with gum arabic
only.

70 Map of Australasia and Diagram 71 Basketball Player

(Des R. Gates. Litho Enschedé)

1969 (10 Feb). *Inaugural Year of the South Pacific University.
P 12½ × 12.*

181	70	3 c. multicoloured	..	10	10
182		12 c. multicoloured	..	10	10
183		35 c. multicoloured	..	15	10
181/3 ..			*Set of 3*	30	20

(Des J. Cooter. Photo Harrison)

1969 (13 Aug). *Third South Pacific Games, Port Moresby. T 71
and similar vert designs. Multicoloured.* W w 12 *(sideways*).*
P 14½×14.

184	3 c. Type 71	..	10	10
	w. Wmk Crown to right of CA ..		65	80
185	8 c. Footballer	..	10	10
186	14 c. Sprinter	..	10	10
187	45 c. Rugby player	..	20	15
184/7		*Set of 4*	40	30
MS188	126×120 mm. Nos. 184/7 ..		3·50	8·00

*The normal sideways watermark shows Crown to left of CA,
as seen from the back of the stamp.*

Stamps from the miniature sheets differ slightly from those in
the ordinary sheets, particularly the 14 c. value, which has a
shadow below the feet on the runner. The footballer and rugby
player on the 8 c. and 45 c. values also have shadows below their
feet, but these are more pronounced than on the stamps from the
ordinary sheets.

75 South Sea Island with 76 Southern Cross, "PAX"
Star of Bethlehem and Frigatebird
(stained glass window)

(Des L. Curtis. Photo Harrison)

1969 (21 Nov). *Christmas.* W w 12 *(sideways). P 14½ × 14.*

189	75	8 c. black, violet and turquoise-green ..		10	10
190	76	35 c. multicoloured	..	20	20

77 "Paid" Stamp, New South Wales 1896–1906 2d. Stamp and
1906–07 Tulagi Postmark

(Des G. Drummond. Litho B.W.)

1970 (15 Apr). *Inauguration of New G.P.O. Honiara. T 77 and
similar horiz designs.* W w 12 *(sideways). P 13.*

191	7 c. light magenta, deep blue and black		20	15
192	14 c. sage-green, deep blue and black ..		25	15
193	18 c. multicoloured		25	15
194	23 c. multicoloured		30	20
191/4 ..		*Set of 4*	90	60

Designs:—14 c. 1906–07 2d. stamp and C. M. Woodford; 18 c.
1910–14 5s. stamp and Tulagi postmark, 1913; 23 c. New G.P.O.,
Honiara.

81 Coat of Arms   **83** British Red Cross H.Q., Honiara

(Des V. Whiteley. Photo Harrison)

1970 (15 June). *New Constitution. T 81 and similar design. W w 12 (sideways on 18 c.). P 14½ × 14 (18 c.) or 14 × 14½ (35 c.).*

195	18 c. multicoloured	..	15	10
196	35 c. pale apple-green, deep blue and ochre	..	35	20

Design: *Horiz*—35 c. Map.

(Des L. Curtis. Litho Questa)

1970 (17 Aug). *Centenary of British Red Cross. T 83 and similar horiz design. W w 12 (sideways). P 14 × 14½.*

197	3 c. multicoloured	..	10	10
198	35 c. blue, vermilion and black	..	25	20

Design:—35 c. Wheelchair and map.

86 Reredos (Altar Screen)

(Des L. Curtis. Litho J.W.)

1970 (19 Oct). *Christmas. T 86 and similar design. W w 12 (sideways on 45 c.). P 14 × 13½ (8 c.) or 13½ × 14 (45 c.).*

199	8 c. ochre and bluish violet	..	10	10
200	45 c. chestnut, yellow-orange & blackish brn		25	20

Design: *Vert*—8 c. Carved angel.

87 La Perouse and *La Boussole*

(Des J.W. Litho Questa)

1971 (28 Jan). *Ships and Navigators (1st series). T 87 and similar horiz designs. Multicoloured. W w 12 (sideways). P 14.*

201	3 c. Type 87	..	45	20
202	4 c. Astrolabe and Polynesian Reed Map	..	45	20
203	12 c. Abel Tasman and *Heemskerk*	..	60	30
204	35 c. Te Puki canoe, Santa Cruz	..	70	50
201/4		*Set of 4*	2·00	1·10

See also Nos. 215/18, 236/9, 254/7 and 272/5.

88 J. Atkin, Bishop Patteson and S. Taroaniara

(Des J.W. Litho Questa)

1971 (5 April). *Death Centenary of Bishop Patteson. T 88 and similar multicoloured designs. W w 12 (sideways on 2 c., 4 c.). P 14½ × 14 (2 c., 4 c.) or 14 × 14½ (others).*

205	2 c. Type 88	..	10	10
206	4 c. Last Landing at Nukapu	..	10	10
207	14 c. Memorial Cross and Nukapu (*vert*)	..	10	10
208	45 c. Knotted Leaf and canoe (*vert*)	..	20	10
205/8		*Set of 4*	30	30

89 Torch Emblem and Boxers   **90** Melanesian Lectern

(Des C. Debenham. Litho Questa)

1971 (9 Aug). *Fourth South Pacific Games, Tahiti. T 89 and similar horiz designs. Multicoloured. W w 12 (sideways*). P 14.*

209	3 c. Type 89	..	10	10
210	8 c. Emblem and footballers	..	10	10
	w. Wmk Crown to right of CA	..	40·00	
211	12 c. Emblem and runner	..	10	10
212	35 c. Emblem and skin-diver	..	15	15
209/12		*Set of 4*	30	30

*The normal sideways watermark shows Crown to left of CA, as seen from the back of the stamp.

(Des C. Abbott. Litho A. & M.)

1971 (15 Nov). *Christmas. T 90 and similar vert design. Multicoloured. W w 12. P 13½.*

213	9 c. Type 90	..	10	10
	w. Wmk inverted	..	40	
214	45 c. "United we Stand" (Margarita Bara)	20	20
	w. Wmk inverted	..	90	

(Des J.W. Litho Questa)

1972 (1 Feb). *Ships and Navigators (2nd series). Horiz designs as T 87. Multicoloured. W w 12 (sideways). P 14.*

215	4 c. Bougainville and *La Boudeuse*	..	30	10
216	9 c. Horizontal planisphere and ivory backstaff	..	50	10
217	15 c. Philip Carteret and H.M.S. *Swallow*	60	15
218	45 c. Malaita canoe	..	1·75	90
215/18		*Set of 4*	2·75	1·10

91 *Cupha woodfordi*

(Des R. Granger Barrett. Litho Questa)

1972 (3 July)–**73**. *T 91 and similar horiz designs. Multicoloured. Cream paper. W w 12 (upright on $5, sideways* on others). P 14.*

219	1 c. Type 91	..	15	50
220	2 c. *Ornithoptera priamus*	..	25	50
221	3 c. *Vindula sapor*	..	25	60
222	4 c. *Papilio ulysses*	..	25	60
223	5 c. Big-eyed Trevally	..	25	30
	w. Wmk Crown to right of CA	..	1·75	1·75
224	8 c. Australian Bonito	..	40	50
225	9 c. Blue Demoiselle	..	50	65
226	12 c. *Costus speciosus*	..	1·25	90
227	15 c. Clown Clownfish ("Orange Anenome Fish")	..	1·25	1·00
	w. Wmk Crown to right of CA	..	32·00	
228	20 c. *Spathoglottis plicata*	..	3·00	1·75
229	25 c. *Ephemerantha comata*	..	3·00	1·50
230	35 c. *Dendrobium cuthbertsonii*	..	3·00	2·25
231	45 c. *Heliconia salomonica*	..	2·50	3·00
232	$1 Dotty Triggerfish	..	3·00	4·50
233	$2 *Ornithoptera alottei*	..	9·00	15·00
233a	$5 Great Frigate Bird (2.7.73)	..	14·00	16·00
219/33a		*Set of 16*	38·00	45·00

*The normal sideways watermark shows Crown to left of CA, as seen from the back of the stamp.

The 1 to 4 c. and $2 are butterflies; the 5 to 9 c., 15 c. and $1 are fishes; the 12 c. and 20 to 45 c. are flowers and the $5 a bird.

92 Greetings and Message Drum

(Des (from photograph by D. Groves) and photo Harrison)

1972 (20 Nov). *Royal Silver Wedding. Multicoloured; background colour given. W w 12. P 14 × 14½.*

234	**92** 8 c. rose-carmine	..	10	10
	w. Wmk inverted	..	4·50	
235	45 c. deep yellow-olive	..	20	20
	w. Wmk inverted	..	35·00	

(Des J.W. Litho Questa)

1973 (9 Mar). *Ships and Navigators (3rd series). Horiz designs as T 87. Multicoloured. W w 12. P 14.*

236	4 c. D'Entrecasteaux and *La Recherche*	..	30	20
237	9 c. Ship's hour-glass and chronometer	..	60	20
	w. Wmk inverted	..	2·00	
238	15 c. Lt. Shortland and H.M.S. *Alexander*	75	30
239	35 c. Tomoko (war canoe)	..	1·50	1·10
236/9		*Set of 4*	2·75	1·60

COVER PRICES

Cover factors are quoted at the beginning of each country for most issues to 1945. An explanation of the system can be found on page x. The factors quoted do not, however, apply to philatelic covers.

93 Pan Pipes

(Des and litho J.W.)

1973 (1 Oct). *Musical Instruments. T 93 and similar horiz designs. Multicoloured. W w 12. P 13½.*

240	4 c. Type 93	..	10	10
241	9 c. Castanets	..	10	10
242	15 c. Bamboo flute	..	15	10
243	35 c. Bauro gongs	..	35	25
244	45 c. Bamboo band	..	35	30
240/4		*Set of 5*	90	65

(Des PAD Studio. Litho Questa)

1973 (14 Nov). *Royal Wedding. As Nos. 322/3 of Montserrat.*

245	4 c. deep grey-blue	..	10	10
246	35 c. bright blue	..	15	10
	w. Wmk Crown to right of CA	..	70·00	

*The normal sideways watermark shows CA to left of CA, as seen from the back of the stamp.

94 "Adoration of the Kings" (Jan Brueghel)

(Des PAD Studio. Litho Questa)

1973 (26 Nov). *Christmas. T 94 and similar designs showing "Adoration of the Kings" by the artists listed. Multicoloured. W w 12 (sideways on 22 c.). P 13½ (45 c.) or 14 (others).*

247	8 c. Type 94	..	10	10
248	22 c. Pieter Brueghel (*vert*)	..	30	25
249	45 c. Botticelli (48 × 35 mm)	..	60	50
247/9		*Set of 3*	90	70

95 Queen Elizabeth II and Map   **96** "Postman"

(Des G. Drummond. Litho Questa)

1974 (18 Feb). *Royal Visit. W w 12. P 13½.*

250	**95** 4 c. multicoloured	..	25	10
	w. Wmk inverted	..	1·25	
251	9 c. multicoloured	..	25	10
252	15 c. multicoloured	..	30	20
253	35 c. multicoloured	..	50	1·25
	w. Wmk inverted	..	9·00	
250/3		*Set of 4*	1·10	1·40

(Des and litho J.W.)

1974 (15 May). *Ships and Navigators (4th series). Horiz designs as T 87. Multicoloured. W w 12 (sideways). P 14.*

254	4 c. Commissioner landing from S.S. *Titus*	..	20	10
255	9 c. Radar scanner	..	20	10
256	15 c. Natives being transported to a "Blackbirder" brig	..	35	15
257	45 c. Lieut. John F. Kennedy's *P.T. 109*	1·50	90
254/7		*Set of 4*	2·00	1·10

(Des Jennifer Toombs. Litho Questa)

1974 (29 Aug). *Centenary of Universal Postal Union. T 96 and similar designs showing Origami figures. W w 12 (sideways on 9 and 45 c.). P 14.*

258	4 c. light yellow-green, deep green and black	10	10
259	9 c. light olive-bistre, lake-brown and black	10	10
260	15 c. mauve, purple and black	..	15	10
261	45 c. cobalt, dull ultramarine and black	..	35	80
258/61		*Set of 4*	65	90

Designs: *Horiz*—9 c. Carrier-pigeon; 45 c. Pegasus. *Vert*—15 c. St. Gabriel.

97 "New Constitution" Stamp of 1970

(Des R. Granger Barrett. Litho Questa)

1974 (16 Dec). *New Constitution. T* **97** *and similar horiz design.* W w 14 *(sideways). P* 14.

262	**97**	4 c. multicoloured		10	10
263	—	9 c. dull rose-red, black & lt yell-ochre		15	10
264	—	15 c. dull rose-red, blk & lt greenish yell		20	10
265	**97**	35 c. multicoloured		45	50
262/5			*Set of 4*	80	60
MS266	134 × 84 mm. Nos. 262/5			1·75	3·50

Design:—9 c., 15 c. "New Constitution" stamp of 1961 (inscr "1960").

98 Golden Whistler

(Des G. Drummond. Litho Questa)

1975 (7 Apr). *Birds. T* **98** *and similar horiz designs.* Multi-coloured. W w 12. *P* 14.

267	1 c. Type **98**			45	65
268	2 c. Common Kingfisher			50	80
269	3 c. Red-bibbed Fruit Dove			55	85
270	4 c. Little Button Quail			55	85
271	$2 Duchess Lorikeet			9·50	10·50
267/71			*Set of 5*	10·50	12·00

See also Nos. 305/20.

(Des and litho J.W.)

1975 (29 May). *Ships and Navigators (5th series). Horiz designs as T* **87**. *Multicoloured.* W w 12. *P* 13½.

272	4 c. Walande (coaster)			45	10
273	9 c. Melanesian (coaster)			60	10
274	15 c. Marsina (container ship)			80	15
275	45 c. Himalaya (liner)			1·50	1·50
272/5			*Set of 4*	3·00	1·60

99 800-Metres Race

(Des PAD Studio, Litho Walsall)

1975 (4 Aug). *Fifth South Pacific Games, Guam. T* **99** *and similar horiz designs. Multicoloured.* W w 14 *(sideways*). P* 13½.

276	4 c. Type **99**			10	10
	w. Wmk Crown to right of CA			6·00	
277	9 c. Long-jump			10	10
278	15 c. Javelin-throwing			15	10
279	45 c. Football			45	45
276/9			*Set of 4*	70	55
MS280	130×95 mm. Nos. 276/9			4·00	4·00

*The normal sideways watermark shows Crown to left of CA, as seen from the back of the stamp.

100 Christmas Scene and Candles   (**101**)

(Des G. Vasarhelyi. Litho Questa)

1975 (13 Oct). *Christmas. T* **100** *and similar horiz designs. Multicoloured.* W w 12 *(sideways). P* 14.

281	15 c. Type **100**			15	10
282	35 c. Shepherds, angels and candles			30	15
283	45 c. The Magi and candles			40	40
281/3			*Set of 3*	75	60
MS284	140 × 130 mm. Nos. 281/3			4·00	5·00

1975 (12 Nov). *Nos. 267/70, 223/32, 271 and 233a with obliterating bar as T* **101** *over* "BRITISH".

285	1 c. Type **98**			60	55
286	2 c. Common Kingfisher			90	55
287	3 c. Red-bibbed Fruit Dove			70	55
288	4 c. Little Button Quail			95	55
289	5 c. Big-eyed Trevally			50	55
290	8 c. Australian Bonito			50	60
291	9 c. Blue Demoiselle			50	60
292	12 c. Costus speciosus			1·50	1·00
293	15 c. Clown Clownfish ("Orange Anemone Fish")			1·75	1·25
294	20 c. Spathoglottis plicata			2·75	1·50
295	25 c. Ephemerantha comata			2·75	1·75
296	35 c. Dendrobium cuthbertsonii			3·00	1·75
297	45 c. Heliconia salomonica			2·50	3·00
298	$1 Dotty Triggerfish (cream paper)			2·00	2·00
	a. White paper			4·75	4·50
299	$2 Duchess Lorikeet			8·00	10·00
300	$5 Great Frigate Bird (white paper)			6·00	13·00
	a. Cream paper			23·00	23·00
285/300			*Set of 16*	26·00	35·00

SELF-GOVERNMENT

102 Ceremonial Food-bowl

(Des J. Cooter. Litho Questa)

1976 (12 Jan). *Artefacts (1st series). T* **102** *and similar multi-coloured designs.* W w 12 *(upright on 35 c.; sideways on others). P* 14.

301	4 c. Type **102**			10	10
302	15 c. Chieftains' money			10	10
303	35 c. Nguzu-nguzu (canoe protector spirit) (vert)			25	20
304	45 c. Nguzu-nguzu canoe prow			30	25
301/4			*Set of 4*	65	55

See also Nos. 337/40, 353/6 and 376/9.

103 Golden Whistler

(Des G. Drummond. Litho Questa)

1976 (8 Mar–6 Dec). *Nos. 267/71 with new country inscr (omitting* "BRITISH") *as T* **103**, *and new values. Multi-coloured.* W w 14 *(sideways*). P* 14.

305	1 c. Type **103**			30	50
306	2 c. Common Kingfisher			70	80
307	3 c. Red-bibbed Fruit Dove			50	50
	w. Wmk Crown to right of CA			14·00	
308	4 c. Little Button Quail			50	60
309	5 c. Willie Wagtail			70	80
310	6 c. Golden Cowrie			60	50
311	10 c. Glory of the Sea Cone			60	60
312	12 c. Rainbow Lory			60	80
313	15 c. Chambered or Pearly Nautilus			65	40
314	20 c. Venus Comb Murex			1·25	45
315	25 c. Commercial Trochus			85	50
316	35 c. Blood-red Volute			1·00	70
317	45 c. Orange Spider Conch			1·00	1·25
318	$1 Trumpet Triton			2·25	3·00
319	$2 Duchess Lorikeet			5·50	4·75
320	$5 Great Frigate Bird (6 Dec)			4·50	6·00
305/20			*Set of 16*	18·00	19·00

*The normal sideways watermark shows Crown to left of CA, as seen from the back of the stamp.

104 Coastwatchers, 1942   105 Alexander Graham Bell

(Des J. Cooter. Litho Walsall)

1976 (24 May). *Bicentenary of American Revolution. T* **104** *and similar horiz designs. Multicoloured.* W w 14 *(sideways*). P* 14.

321	6 c. Type **104**			25	10
322	20 c. Amagiri (Japanese destroyer) ramming U.S.S. PT109 and Lt. J. F. Kennedy			75	30
	w. Wmk Crown to right of CA			20·00	
323	35 c. Henderson Airfield			1·00	40
324	45 c. Map of Guadalcanal			1·00	60
	w. Wmk Crown to right of CA			12·00	
321/4			*Set of 4*	2·75	1·40
MS325	95×115 mm. Nos. 321/4			5·50	8·00

*The normal sideways watermark shows Crown to left of CA, as seen from the back of the stamp.

(Des P. Powell. Litho Harrison)

1976 (26 July). *Telephone Centenary. T* **105** *and similar vert designs.* W w 14 *(sideways*). P* 14½×14.

326	6 c. multicoloured			10	10
327	20 c. multicoloured			15	10
328	35 c. brown-orange, lt orange & lt vermilion			30	15
	w. Wmk Crown to right of CA			30·00	
329	45 c. multicoloured			40	35
326/9			*Set of 4*	85	55

Designs:—20 c. Radio telephone via satellite; 35 c. Ericson's magneto telephone; 45 c. Stick telephone and first telephone.

*The normal sideways watermark shows Crown to left of CA, as seen from the back of the stamp.

106 B.A.C. One Eleven 200/400   107 The Communion Plate

(Des and litho Walsall)

1976 (13 Sept). *50th Anniv of First Flight to Solomon Islands. T* **106** *and similar horiz designs. Multicoloured.* W w 14 *(sideways). P* 14.

330	6 c. Type **106**			35	10
331	20 c. Britten Norman Islander			65	15
332	35 c. Douglas DC-3			90	20
333	45 c. De Havilland D.H.50A seaplane A8-1			95	55
330/3			*Set of 4*	2·50	85

(Des Jennifer Toombs. Litho Questa)

1977 (7 Feb). *Silver Jubilee. T* **107** *and similar vert designs. Multicoloured.* W w 14. *P* 13½.

334	6 c. Queen's visit, 1974			10	10
	w. Wmk inverted			90·00	
335	35 c. Type **107**			15	20
336	45 c. The Communion			25	45
334/6			*Set of 3*	45	65

108 Carving from New Georgia   109 Spraying Roof and Mosquito

(Des J. Cooter. Litho Questa)

1977 (9 May). *Artefacts (2nd series). T* **108** *and similar vert designs showing carvings.* W w 14. *P* 14.

337	6 c. multicoloured			10	10
338	20 c. multicoloured			10	10
339	35 c. slate-black, grey and rose-red			20	15
340	45 c. multicoloured			25	30
337/40			*Set of 4*	55	50

Designs:—20 c. Sea adaro (spirit); 35 c. Shark-headed man; 45 c. Man from Ulawa or Malaita.

(Des G. Vasarhelyi. Litho Questa)

1977 (27 July). *Malaria Eradication. T* **109** *and similar horiz designs. Multicoloured.* W w 14 *(sideways*). P* 14.

341	6 c. Type **109**			10	10
342	20 c. Taking blood samples			15	10
343	35 c. Microscope and map			20	15
344	45 c. Delivering drugs			30	40
	w. Wmk Crown to right of CA			35·00	
341/4			*Set of 4*	65	60

*The normal sideways watermark shows Crown to left of CA, as seen from the back of the stamp.

110 The Shepherds   111 Feather Money

(Des M. and G. Shamir. Litho Questa)

1977 (12 Sept). *Christmas. T* **110** *and similar vert designs. Multi-coloured.* W w 14. *P* 14.

345	6 c. Type **110**			10	10
346	20 c. Mary and Jesus in stable			10	10
347	35 c. The Three Kings			20	15
348	45 c. "The Flight into Egypt"			25	25
345/8			*Set of 4*	50	45

(Des D.L.R. Litho Harrison)

1977 (24 Oct). *Introduction of Solomon Islands Coins and Banknotes. T 111 and similar horiz designs. Multicoloured. W w 14. P 14 × 14½.*

349	6 c. Type 111 ..	10	10
	a. Horiz pair. Nos. 349/50	20	20
350	6 c. New currency coins	10	10
351	45 c. New currency notes	25	25
	a. Horiz pair. Nos. 351/2	50	50
352	45 c. Shell money	25	25
349/52	*Set of 4*	60	60

The two designs of each value were printed in horizontal se-tenant pairs throughout their sheets.

112 Figure from Shortland Island

113 Sanford's Sea Eagle

(Des J. Cooter. Litho Questa)

1978 (11 Jan). *Artefacts (3rd series). T 112 and similar vert designs. W w 14. P 14.*

353	6 c. multicoloured	10	10
354	20 c. multicoloured ..	10	10
355	35 c. deep brown, black and orange ..	20	15
356	45 c. multicoloured	25	30
353/6	*Set of 4*	55	50

Designs:—20 c. Ceremonial shield; 35 c. Santa Cruz ritual figure; 45 c. Decorative combs.

(Des Jennifer Toombs. Litho Questa)

1978 (21 Apr). *25th Anniv of Coronation. T 113 and similar vert designs. Multicoloured. P 15.*

357	45 c. black, vermilion and silver ..	15	25
	a. Sheetlet. Nos. 357/9 × 2 ..	75	
358	45 c. multicoloured	15	25
359	45 c. black, vermilion and silver	15	25
357/9	*Set of 3*	40	65

Designs:—No. 357, King's Dragon; No. 358, Queen Elizabeth II; No. 359, Type 113.

Nos. 357/9 were printed together in small sheets of 6, containing two se-tenant strips of 3, with horizontal gutter margin between.

INDEPENDENT

114 National Flag

115 John

(Des L. Curtis. Litho Questa)

1978 (7 July). *Independence. T 114 and similar vert designs. Multicoloured. W w 14. P 14.*

360	6 c. Type 114	10	10
361	15 c. Governor-General's flag	20	10
362	35 c. The Cenotaph, Honiara	35	30
363	45 c. National coat of arms	40	50
360/3	*Set of 4*	95	85

(Des J.W. Litho Questa)

1978 (4 Oct). *450th Death Anniv of Dürer. Details from his Painting "Four Apostles". T 115 and similar vert designs. Multicoloured. W w 14. P 14.*

364	6 c. Type 115 ..	10	10
365	20 c. Peter	15	10
366	35 c. Paul	20	15
367	45 c. Mark	30	30
364/7	*Set of 4*	60	50

116 Firelighting

117 H.M.S. *Discovery*

(Des K. G. Watkinson; adapted J.W. Litho Questa)

1978 (15 Nov). *50th Anniv of Scouting in Solomon Islands. T 116 and similar horiz designs. Multicoloured. W w 14 (sideways). P 14.*

368	6 c. Type 116 ..	15	10
369	20 c. Camping	20	20
370	35 c. Solomon Islands Scouts	40	40
371	45 c. Canoeing ..	50	70
368/71	*Set of 4*	1·10	1·25

(Des and litho (45 c. also embossed) Walsall)

1979 (16 Jan). *Bicentenary of Captain Cook's Voyages, 1768–79. T 117 and similar vert designs. P 11.*

372	8 c. multicoloured	30	10
373	18 c. multicoloured	30	15
374	35 c. black, yellowish green and silver	40	25
375	45 c. multicoloured	40	40
372/5	*Set of 4*	1·25	80

Designs:—18 c. "Captain Cook" (Nathaniel Dance); 35 c. Sextant; 45 c. Flaxman/Wedgwood medallion of Captain Cook.

118 Fish Net Float

119 Running

(Des J. Cooter. Litho Questa)

1979 (21 Mar). *Artefacts (4th series). T 118 and similar designs. W w 14 (sideways on 8 and 35 c.). P 14.*

376	8 c. multicoloured	10	10
377	20 c. multicoloured	10	10
378	35 c. black, grey and rose	15	15
379	45 c. black, chestnut and apple-green.	20	30
376/9	*Set of 4*	45	50

Designs: *Vert*—20 c. Armband of shell money; 45 c. Forehead ornament. *Horiz*—35 c. Ceremonial food bowl.

(Des L. Curtis. Litho Format)

1979 (4 June). *South Pacific Games, Fiji. T 109 and similar horiz designs. Multicoloured. W w 14 (sideways). P 13½.*

380	8 c. Type 119 ..	10	10
381	20 c. Hurdling ..	10	10
382	35 c. Football	15	15
383	45 c. Swimming	25	35
380/3	*Set of 4*	55	50

120 1908 6d. Stamp

121 Sea Snake

(Des J.W. Litho Format)

1979 (16 Aug). *Death Centenary of Sir Rowland Hill. T 120 and similar vert designs showing stamps. W w 14. P 14.*

384	8 c. carmine and pale rose	10	10
385	20 c. deep mauve and pale mauve	15	30
386	35 c. multicoloured	25	45
384/6	*Set of 3*	45	75
MS387	121 × 121 mm. 45 c. rosine, deep dull green and pink	45	65

Designs:—20 c. Great Britain 1856 6d.; 35 c. 1978 45 c. Independence commemorative; 45 c. 1922 10s.

(Des L. Curtis. Litho Enschedé)

1979 (18 Sept)–83. *Reptiles. Vert designs as T 121. Multi-coloured. W w 14. P 13½×13. A. Without imprint date*

388A	1 c. Type 121	10	60
389A	3 c. Red-banded Tree Snake	10	60
390A	4 c. Whip Snake	10	60
391A	6 c. Pacific Boa ..	10	60
392A	8 c. Skink	10	50
393A	10 c. Gecko (*Lepidodactylus lugubris*)	10	50
394A	12 c. Monitor	50	70
	w. Wmk inverted	2·50	
395A	15 c. Anglehead	30	60
396A	20 c. Giant Toad ..	30	60
397A	25 c. Marsh Frog	60	80
398A	30 c. Horned Frog	1·50	1·00
399A	35 c. Tree Frog	30	80
400A	45 c. Guppy's Snake	30	1·25
401A	$1 Large Skink	75	75
402A	$2 Guppy's Frog	75	2·75
403A	$5 Estuarine Crocodile	3·00	3·00
388A/403A	*Set of 16*	6·25	18·00

B. With imprint date at foot

394Bw	12 c. Monitor (*wmk inverted*) (27.8.82)	30	80
397Bw	25 c. Marsh Frog (*wmk inverted*) (27.8.82)	30	90
398B	30 c. Horned Frog (31.8.83)	1·00	1·75
	w. Wmk inverted	1·25	1·75
399cB	40 c. Burrowing Snake (24.1.83)	45	1·75
400cB	50 c. Tree Gecko (24.1.83)	50	75

401B	$1 Large Skink (25.1.82) ..	1·50	90
403B	$5 Estuarine Crocodile (25.1.82)	3·00	3·00
	aw. Wmk inverted	12·00	
403cB	$10 Hawksbill Turtle (20.9.82)	5·00	5·50
394Bw/403cB	*Set of 8*	11·00	14·00

Imprint dates: "1982", Nos. 394Bw, 397Bw, 401B, 403B, 403cB; "1983", Nos. 398B, 399cB, 400cB.

122 "Madonna and Child" (Morando)

123 H.M.S. *Curacoa* (frigate), 1839

(Des BG Studio. Litho Questa)

1979 (15 Nov). *Christmas. International Year of the Child. T 122 and similar vert designs showing "Madonna and Child" paintings by various artists. Multicoloured. W w 14. P 14 × 14½.*

404	4 c. Type 122 ..	10	10
405	20 c. Luini	15	15
406	35 c. Bellini	20	15
407	50 c. Raphael	30	70
404/7	*Set of 4*	65	1·00
MS408	92 × 133 mm. Nos. 404/7	1·25	2·00

(Des L. Curtis. Litho Questa)

1980 (23 Jan). *Ships and Crests (1st series). T 123 and similar horiz designs. Multicoloured. W w 14 (sideways*). P 14.*

409	8 c. Type 123	30	20
	w. Wmk Crown to right of CA	15·00	
410	20 c. H.M.S. *Herald* (survey ship), 1854	45	40
411	35 c. H.M.S. *Royalist* (screw corvette), 1889	65	80
412	45 c. H.M.S. *Beagle* (survey schooner), 1878	70	1·40
	w. Wmk Crown to right of CA	50·00	
409/12	*Set of 4*	1·75	2·50

*The normal sideways watermark shows Crown to left of CA, as seen from the back of the stamp.
See also Nos. 430/3.

124 *Solomon Fisher* (fishery training vessel)

(Des G. Hutchins. Litho Secura, Singapore)

1980 (27 Mar). *Fishing. Ancillary Craft. T 124 and similar horiz designs. Multicoloured. W w 14 (sideways). P 13½.*

413	8 c. Type 124..	15	10
414	20 c. *Solomon Hunter* (fishery training vessel)	20	20
415	45 c. *Ufi Na Tasi* (refrigerated fish transport)	35	40
416	80 c. Research Vessel..	60	1·75
413/16	*Set of 4*	1·10	2·25

125 *Comliebank* (cargo-liner) and 1935 Tulagi Registered Letter Postmark

(Des A. Theobald. Litho Questa)

1980 (6 May). *"London 1980" International Stamp Exhibition. Mail-carrying Transport. T 125 and similar horiz designs. Multi-coloured. W w 14 (sideways). P 14½ × 14.*

417	45 c. Type 125	30	45
	a. Sheetlet. Nos. 417/20	1·10	
418	45 c. Douglas C-47 Skytrain (U.S. Army Postal Service, 1943)	30	45
419	45 c. B.A.C. One Eleven airliner and 1979 Honiara postmark	30	45
420	45 c. *Corabank* (container ship) and 1979 Auki postmark	30	45
417/20	*Set of 4*	1·10	1·60

Nos. 417/20 were printed together as a sheetlet containing a se-tenant block of 4.

MINIMUM PRICE

The minimum price quote is 10p which represents a handling charge rather than a basis for valuing common stamps. For further notes about prices see introductory pages.

126 Queen Elizabeth the Queen Mother   **127** Angel with Trumpet

(Des Harrison. Litho Questa)

1980 (4 Aug). *80th Birthday of Queen Elizabeth the Queen Mother.* W w 14 (*sideways*). P 14.

421 **126** 45 c. multicoloured	..	..	30	35

(Des C. Abbott. Litho Walsall)

1980 (2 Sept). *Christmas. T* **127** *and similar vert designs. Multicoloured. W* w 14. *P* 14½ × 14.

422	8 c. Type **127** ..	..	10	10
423	20 c. Angel with fiddle..	..	10	10
424	45 c. Angel with trumpet (*different*) ..	..	25	25
425	80 c. Angel with lute	..	40	45
422/5	.. .. ..	*Set of 4*	70	75

128 *Parthenos sylvia*   **129** Francisco Antonio Maurelle

(Des J. Cooter. Litho Secura, Singapore)

1980 (12 Nov). *Butterflies* (1st series). *T* **128** *and similar horiz designs. Multicoloured. W* w 14 (*sideways**). *P* 13½.

426	8 c. Type **128** ..	..	40	10
	w. Wmk Crown to right of CA	..	38·00	
427	20 c. *Delias schoenbergi*	..	55	20
	w. Wmk Crown to right of CA	..	80	
428	45 c. *Jamides cephion*	..	90	40
	w. Wmk Crown to right of CA	..	48·00	
429	80 c. *Ornithoptera victoriae*	..	1·50	1·40
	w. Wmk Crown to right of CA	..	7·00	
426/9	.. ..	*Set of 4*	3·00	1·90

*The normal sideways watermark shows Crown to left of CA, as seen from the back of the stamp.
See also Nos. 456/9 and 610/13.

(Des L. Curtis. Litho Questa)

1981 (14 Jan). *Ships and Crests* (2nd series). *Horiz designs as T* **123**. *Multicoloured. W* w 14 (*sideways**). *P* 14.

430	8 c. H.M.S. *Mounts Bay* (frigate), 1959 ..		15	10
	w. Wmk Crown to right of CA	..	12·00	
431	20 c. H.M.S. *Charybdis* (frigate), 1970	..	25	20
432	45 c. H.M.S. *Hydra* (survey ship), 1972	..	40	40
433	$1 Royal Yacht *Britannia*, 1974	..	1·00	1·75
430/3	.. ..	*Set of 4*	1·60	2·25

*The normal sideways watermark shows Crown to left of CA, as seen from the back of the stamp.

(Des J. Cooter. Litho Questa)

1981 (23 Mar). *Bicentenary of Maurelle's Visit and Production of Bauche's Chart, 1791* (No. **MS438**). *T* **129** *and similar designs. Wmk CA Diagonal* (*sideways on 8 c. and* $1). *P* 13½ × 14 (8 c., $1) *or* 14 × 13½ (*others*).

434	8 c. black, deep brown and greenish yellow ..		15	10
435	10 c. black, vermilion and stone	..	20	10
436	45 c. multicoloured	..	60	65
437	$1 multicoloured	..	1·00	1·10
434/7	.. ..	*Set of 4*	1·75	1·75

MS438 126 × 91 mm. 25 c. × 4, each black, vermilion and stone (wmk sideways). P 14½ .. 90 1·10

Designs: *Horiz*—10 c. Bellin's map of 1742 showing route of *La Princesa*; 45 c. *La Princesa. Vert*—$1 Spanish compass cards, 1745 and 1757. No. **MS438**, "Chart of a part of the South Sea" (*each stamp* 44 × 28 *mm*).
Stamps in No. **MS438** were printed to form a composite design.

130 Netball   **131** Prince Charles as Colonel-in-Chief, Royal Regiment of Wales

---

(Des R. Granger Barrett. Litho Security Printers (M), Malaysia)

1981 (7 July). *Mini South Pacific Games. T* **130** *and similar vert designs. Multicoloured. W* w 14. *P* 12.

439	8 c. Type **130**	..	10	10
440	10 c. Tennis	..	15	15
	w. Wmk inverted	..		
441	25 c. Running	..	25	25
442	30 c. Football	..	25	25
443	45 c. Boxing	..	40	40
439/43	.. ..	*Set of 5*	1·00	1·00

MS444 102×67 mm $1 Stylised athletes (wmk sideways) 70 75

(Des and litho J.W.)

1981 (22 July). *Royal Wedding. T* **131** *and similar vert designs. Multicoloured. W* w 14. *P* 13½ × 14.

445	8 c. Wedding bouquet from Solomon Islands	10	10
446	45 c. Type **131**		15	15
447	$1 Prince Charles and Lady Diana Spencer	45	70
445/7	.. ..	*Set of 3*	60	85

132 "Music"   **133** Primitive Church

(Des BG Studio. Litho Questa)

1981 (28 Sept). *25th Anniv of Duke of Edinburgh Award Scheme. T* **132** *and similar vert designs. Multicoloured. W* w 14. *P* 14.

448	8 c. Type **132**	..	10	10
449	25 c. "Handicrafts"	..	10	10
450	45 c. "Canoeing"	..	15	10
451	$1 Duke of Edinburgh	..	35	60
448/51	.. ..	*Set of 4*	60	75

(Des BG Studio. Litho Format)

1981 (12 Oct). *Christmas. Churches. T* **133** *and similar horiz designs. W* w 14 (*sideways*). *P* 14.

452	8 c. black, buff and cobalt	..	10	10
453	10 c. multicoloured	..	10	10
454	25 c. black, buff and dull green	..	15	10
455	$2 multicoloured	..	70	1·25
452/5	.. ..	*Set of 4*	90	1·25

Designs:—10 c. St. Barnabas Anglican Cathedral, Honiara; 25 c. Early church; $2 Holy Cross Cathedral, Honiara.

(Des J. Cooter. Litho Secura, Singapore)

1982 (5 Jan). *Butterflies* (2nd series). *Horiz designs as T* **128**. *Multicoloured. W* w 14 (*sideways**). *P* 13½×13.

456	10 c. *Doleschallia bisaltide*	..	25	10
	w. Wmk Crown to right of CA	..	2·75	
457	25 c. *Papilio bridgei*	..	45	25
	w. Wmk Crown to right of CA	..	9·00	
458	35 c. *Taenaris phorcas*	..	50	30
	aw. Wmk Crown to right of CA	..	3·25	
	b. Wmk inverted	..	60·00	
459	$1 *Graphium sarpedon*	..	1·60	1·50
456/9	.. ..	*Set of 4*	2·50	1·90

*The normal sideways watermark shows Crown to left of CA, as seen from the back of the stamp.
No. 458b shows a change of watermark position from sideways to inverted.

(134)

135 Pair of Sanford's Sea Eagles constructing Nest

5 CENTS SURCHARGE CYCLONE RELIEF FUND 1982

"0" of "50" omitted from surcharge (R. 4/5)

1982 (3 May). *Cyclone Relief Fund. No. 447 surch with T* **134** *in red.*

460	$1 + 50 c. Prince Charles and Lady Diana Spencer		75	2·00
	a. "0" omitted	.. ..	10·00	

(Des N. Arlott. Litho Walsall)

1982 (15 May). *Sanford's Sea Eagle. T* **135** *and similar vert designs. Multicoloured. W* w 14. *P* 14.

461	12 c. Type **135**	..	35	50
	a. Horiz strip of 5. Nos. 461/5		1·75	
462	12 c. Egg and chick	..	35	50
463	12 c. Hen feeding chicks	..	35	50
464	12 c. Fledgelings	..	35	50
465	12 c. Young bird in flight	..	35	50
466	12 c. Pair of birds and village dwellings	35	50
461/6	.. ..	*Set of 6*	1·90	2·75

Nos. 461/6 were printed together, *se-tenant*, in various combinations throughout sheets also including one stamp-size label.

136 Wedding Portrait   **137** Flags of Solomon Islands and United Kingdom

(Des Jennifer Toombs. Litho Walsall)

1982 (1 July). *21st Birthday of Princess of Wales. T* **136** *and similar vert designs. Multicoloured. W* w 14. *P* 14½ × 14.

467	12 c. Solomon Islands coat of arms		10	10
468	40 c. Lady Diana Spencer at Broadlands, May 1981		50	40
469	50 c. Type **136**	..	70	50
470	$1 Formal portrait	..	1·50	1·50
467/70	.. ..	*Set of 4*	2·50	2·25

(Des Studio 53. Litho Questa)

1982 (11 Oct). *Royal Visit* (Nos. 471/2, **MS475**) *and Commonwealth Games, Brisbane* (Nos. 473/4, **MS476**). *T* **137** *and similar square designs. Multicoloured. W* w 14 (*sideways*). *P* 14.

471	12 c. Type **137**	..	15	20
	a. Pair. Nos. 471/2	..	30	40
472	12 c. Queen and Prince Philip..		15	20
473	25 c. Running ..	..	30	45
	a. Pair. Nos. 473/4	..	60	90
474	25 c. Boxing	..	30	45
471/4	.. ..	*Set of 4*	80	1·25

MS475 123 × 123 mm. Nos. 471/2 and $1 Royal Yacht *Britannia* .. .. 1·75 2·50
MS476 123 × 123 mm. Nos. 473/4 and $1 Royal Yacht *Britannia* .. .. 1·75 2·50

Nos. 471/2 and 473/4 were each printed in small sheets of 10, including 2 *se-tenant*, stamp-size, labels, the two stamp designs appearing *se-tenant*, both horizontally and vertically.

138 Boy Scouts

(Des McCombie Skinner. Litho Format)

1982 (4 Nov). *75th Anniv of Boy Scout Movement* (Nos. 477, 479, 481, 483) *and Centenary of Boys' Brigade* (others). *T* **138** *and similar horiz designs. Multicoloured. W* w 14 (*sideways*). *P* 14.

477	12 c. Type **138**	..	15	15
478	12 c. Boys' Brigade cadets	..	15	15
479	25 c. Lord Baden-Powell	..	20	40
480	25 c. Sir William Smith	..	20	40
481	35 c. Type **138** ..	..	20	50
482	35 c. As No. 478	..	20	50
483	50 c. As No. 479	..	30	1·10
484	50 c. As No. 480	..	30	1·10
477/84	.. ..	*Set of 8*	1·50	3·75

139 Leatherback Turtle

(Des L. Curtis. Litho Format)

1983 (5 Jan). *Turtles. T* **139** *and similar horiz designs. Multicoloured. W* w 14 (*sideways*). *P* 14½.

485	18 c. Type **139**	..	35	25
486	35 c. Loggerhead turtle	..	55	45
487	45 c. Pacific Ridley turtle	..	65	60
488	50 c. Green turtle	..	65	65
485/8	.. ..	*Set of 4*	2·00	1·75

140 Black Olive (*Oliva vidula*),
General Cone (*Conus generalis*) and
Troschel's Murex (*Murex troscheli*)

(Des W. Fenton. Litho Questa)

1983 (14 Mar). *Commonwealth Day. Shells. T* **140** *and similar horiz designs. Multicoloured. W w* 14 *(sideways). P* 14.

489	12 c.	Type **140**		15	15
490	35 c.	Romu, Kurila, Kakadu and money belt		35	40
491	45 c.	Shells from "Bride-price" necklaces		50	60
492	50 c.	Commercial Trochus (*Trochus niloticus*) polished and in its natural state		55	65
489/92			*Set of* 4	1·40	1·60

141 Montgolfier Balloon

(Des A. Theobald. Litho Format)

1983 (30 June). *Bicentenary of Manned Flight. T* **141** *and similar horiz designs. Multicoloured. W w* 14 *(sideways*). P* 14.

493	30 c.	Type **141**		40	40
494	35 c.	R.A.A.F. Lockheed C-130 Hercules		45	45
495	40 c.	Wright brothers' Type A		55	55
	w.	Wmk Crown to right of CA		40·00	
496	45 c.	Space shuttle *Columbia*		60	60
497	50 c.	Beech C55 Baron		65	65
493/7			*Set of* 5	2·40	2·40

*The normal sideways watermark shows Crown to left of CA, as seen from the back of the stamp.

142 Weto Dancers

(Des J.W. Litho Format)

1983 (25 Aug). *Christmas. T* **142** *and similar horiz designs. Multicoloured. W w* 14 *(sideways). P* 14.

498	12 c.	Type **142**		10	10
499	15 c.	Custom wrestling		10	20
500	18 c.	Girl dancers		15	20
501	20 c.	Devil dancers		15	20
502	25 c.	Bamboo band		20	35
503	35 c.	Gilbertese dancers		25	45
504	40 c.	Pan pipers		25	55
505	45 c.	Girl dancers		30	65
506	50 c.	Cross surrounded by flowers		30	70
498/506			*Set of* 9	1·60	3·00
MS507	153 × 112 mm. Nos. 498/506			1·25	3·00

Stamps from No. **MS507** are without the inscription, "Christmas 1983", shown on Nos. 498/506.

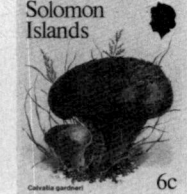

143 Earth Satellite Station   **144** *Calvatia gardneri*

(Des Jennifer Toombs. Litho Format)

1983 (19 Dec). *World Communications Year. T* **143** *and similar horiz designs. Multicoloured. W w* 14 *(sideways). P* 14.

508	12 c.	Type **143**		20	15
509	18 c.	Ham radio operator		20	20
510	25 c.	1908 2½d. Canoe stamp		25	30
511	$1	1908 6d. Canoe stamp		60	2·75
508/11			*Set of* 4	1·10	3·00
MS512	131 × 103 mm. No. 511			1·40	2·25

(Des Gillian Tomblin. Litho Enschedé)

1984 (30 Jan). *Fungi. T* **144** *and similar vert designs. Multicoloured. W w* 14. *P* 13½.

513	6 c.	Type **144**		10	10
514	18 c.	*Marasmiellus inoderma*		20	25
	a.	Booklet pane of 6		4·50	
	w.	Wmk inverted		55·00	

515	35 c.	*Pycnoporus sanguineus*		35	45
	a.	Booklet pane of 6		4·50	
	w.	Wmk inverted		45·00	
516	$2	*Filoboletus manipularis*		2·25	3·00
513/16			*Set of* 4	2·50	3·50

Booklet panes Nos. 514a and 515a were from special sheets providing blocks of 6 (3×2) with vertical margins at both the left and right of each pane.

145 Cross surrounded by Flowers   **146** *Olivebank* (barque), 1892

(Des J.W. Litho Format)

1984 (16 Apr). *Visit of Pope John Paul II. W w* 14 *(sideways). P* 14.

517	**145**	12 c. multicoloured		20	15
518		50 c. multicoloured		65	1·10

(Des Studio 53. Litho Questa)

1984 (21 Apr). *250th Anniv of "Lloyd's List" (newspaper). T* **146** *and similar vert designs. Multicoloured. W w* 14. *P* 14.

519	12 c.	Type **146**		70	15
520	15 c.	*Tinhow* (freighter), 1906		75	40
521	18 c.	*Oriana* (liner) at Point Cruz, Honiara		85	60
522	$1	*Silwyn Range* (container ship), Point Cruz, Honiara		1·40	3·25
519/22			*Set of* 4	3·25	4·00

(Des Jennifer Toombs. Litho Format)

1984 (18 June). *Universal Postal Union Congress, Hamburg. As No.* **MS512** *but with changed sheet inscriptions and U.P.U. logo in margin. Multicoloured. W w* 14 *(sideways). P* 14.

MS523	$1 1908 6d. Canoe stamp		1·40	1·40

147 Village Drums   **148** Solomon Islands Flag and Torch-bearer

(Des McCombie Skinner Studio. Litho Questa)

1984 (2 July). *20th Anniv of Asia-Pacific Broadcasting Union. T* **147** *and similar horiz designs. Multicoloured. W w* 14 *(sideways). P* 13½ × 14.

524	12 c.	Type **147**		15	15
525	45 c.	Radio City, Guadalcanal		35	60
526	60 c.	S.I.B.C. studios, Honiara		50	80
527	$1	S.I.B.C. Broadcasting House		60	1·40
524/7			*Set of* 4	1·40	2·75

(Des McCombie Skinner Studio. Litho Format)

1984 (4 Aug–22 Sept). *Olympic Games, Los Angeles. T* **148** *and similar multicoloured designs. W w* 14 *(sideways on 25 c. to* $1). *P* 14 × 13½ (12 c.) *or* 13½ × 14 (*others*).

528	12 c.	Type **148**		15	10
529	25 c.	Lawson Tama Stadium, Honiara (*horiz*)		30	25
	a.	Booklet pane Nos. 529/30, each × 2 (22.9.84)		2·00	
530	50 c.	Honiara Community Centre (*horiz*)		40	50
531	95 c.	Alick Wickham inventing crawl stroke, Bronte Baths, New South Wales, 1898 (*horiz*) (22.9.84)		6·00	8·00
	a.	Booklet pane of 1		6·00	
532	$1	Olympic Stadium, Los Angeles (*horiz*)		50	1·10
528/32			*Set of* 5	6·50	9·00

No. 531 only exists from $3·95 stamp booklets.

149 Little Pied Cormorant   **150** The Queen Mother with Princess Margaret at Badminton Horse Trials

(Des I. Loe. Litho Questa)

1984 (21 Sept). *"Ausipex" International Stamp Exhibition, Melbourne. Birds. T* **149** *and similar vert designs. Multicoloured. W* 14. *P* 14½.

533	12 c.	Type **149**		40	40
534	18 c.	Spotbill Duck		55	40
535	35 c.	Rufous Night Heron		80	50
536	$1	Eastern Broad-billed Roller ("Dollar-bird")		1·60	3·25
533/6			*Set of* 4	3·00	4·00
MS537	130 × 96 mm. Nos. 533/6			3·00	4·00

(Des A. Theobald ($1·50), C. Abbott (others). Litho Questa)

1985 (7 June). *Life and Times of Queen Elizabeth the Queen Mother. T* **150** *and similar vert designs. Multicoloured. W w* 16. *P* 14½ × 14.

538	12 c.	With Winston Churchill at Buckingham Palace, VE Day, 1945		10	10
539	25 c.	Type **150**		20	30
	w.	Wmk inverted		1·50	
540	35 c.	At a St. Patrick's Day parade		25	35
541	$1	With Prince Henry at his christening (from photo by Lord Snowdon)		75	95
	w.	Wmk inverted		45·00	
538/41			*Set of* 4	1·10	1·50
MS542	91 × 73 mm. $1.50, In a gondola, Venice, 1985. Wmk sideways			1·10	1·50

151 Japanese Memorial Shrine,
Mount Austen, Guadalcanal

(Des D. Slater. Litho Questa)

1985 (28 June). *"Expo '85" World Fair, Japan. T* **151** *and similar horiz designs. Multicoloured. W w* 14 *(sideways). P* 14.

543	12 c.	Type **151**		10	10
544	25 c.	Digital telephone exchange equipment		25	30
545	45 c.	Fishing vessel *Soltai No.* 7		50	55
546	85 c.	Coastal village scene		90	1·40
543/6			*Set of* 4	1·60	2·10

152 Titiana Village   **153** Girl Guide Activities

(Des O. Bell. Litho Walsall)

1985 (30 Aug). *Christmas. "Going Home for the Holiday". T* **152** *and similar horiz designs. Multicoloured. W w* 14 *(sideways). P* 14½.

547	12 c.	Type **152**		10	10
548	25 c.	Sigana, Santa Isabel		25	30
549	35 c.	Artificial Island and Langa Lagoon		30	35
547/9			*Set of* 3	60	70

(Des D. Slater. Litho Walsall)

1985 (30 Sept). *75th Anniv of Girl Guide Movement* (12, 45 c. *and International Youth Year* (others). *T* **153** *and similar vert designs. Multicoloured. W w* 16. *P* 14.

550	12 c.	Type **153**		60	10
551	15 c.	Boys playing and child in wheelchair (Stop Polio)		65	40
552	25 c.	Runners and Solomon Island scenes		90	70
553	35 c.	Runners and Australian scenes ("Run Round Australia")		1·25	80
554	45 c.	Guide colour party and badges		1·25	90
550/4			*Set of* 5	4·00	2·50
MS555	100 × 75 mm. Nos. 552/3			1·00	1·00

154 Osprey   **155** Water-powered Generator, Iriri

(Des Annette Robinson and C. Abbott. Litho Format)

1985 (25 Nov). *Birth Bicentenary of John J. Audubon* (ornithologist). *Sheet* 121×107 *mm containing T* **154** *and similar vert design.* W w **16**. *P* 14.

MS556   45 c. black, gold and deep blue; 50 c. (×2) multicoloured   ..   ..   3·25   3·75
Design:—45 c. John J. Audubon.

(Des B. Drake. Litho Walsall)

1986 (24 Jan). *Village Hydro-electric Schemes. Sheet* 109×135 *mm. containing T* **155** *and similar vert design. Multicoloured.* W w **16**. *P* 14.

MS557   30 c. Type **155**; 60 c. Domestic lighting   75   80
w. Wmk inverted   ..   ..   ..   75·00

156 Building Red Cross Centre, Gizo

157 U.S. Memorial Obelisks, Henderson Airfield, Guadalcanal

(Des N. Shewring. Litho Walsall)

1986 (27 Mar). *Operation Raleigh* (volunteer project). *T* **156** *and similar diamond-shaped designs. Multicoloured.* W w 14. *P* 14½×14.

558   18 c. Type **156**   80   20
559   30 c. Exploring rainforest   ..   ..   1·50   45
560   60 c. Observing Halley's Comet   ..   2·25   1·40
561   $1 Sir Walter Raleigh (support ship) and Zebu (brigantine)   ..   ..   2·75   2·00
558/61   ..   ..   ..   *Set of* 4   6·50   3·50
Details of watermark and perforation for the stamps are given with the designs oriented so that the royal cypher appears in the top left corner.

(Des A. Theobald. Litho Questa)

1986 (21 Apr). *60th Birthday of Queen Elizabeth II. Vert designs as T* **230a** *of Jamaica. Multicoloured.* W w **16**. *P* 14½×14.

562   5 c. Princess Elizabeth and Duke of Edinburgh at Clydebank Town Hall, 1947 ..   10   10
563   18 c. At St. Paul's Cathedral for Queen Mother's 80th birthday service, 1980 ..   15   20
564   22 c. With children, Solomon Islands, 1982 ..   20   25
565   55 c. At Windsor Castle on her 50th birthday, 1976   40   45
566   $2 At Crown Agents Head Office, London, 1983   ..   ..   ..   1·40   1·50
562/6   ..   ..   ..   *Set of* 5   2·00   2·25

(Des D. Miller. Litho Cambec Press, Melbourne)

1986 (22 May). *"Ameripex '86" International Stamp Exhibition, Chicago. International Peace Year. Sheet* 100×75 *mm containing T* **157** *and similar horiz design. Multicoloured. P* 13½.

MS567   55 c. Type **157**; $1.65 Peace Corps emblem, President Kennedy and Statue of Liberty (25th anniv of Peace Corps)   ..   ..   1·50   1·60

(Des D. Miller. Litho Questa)

1986 (23 July). *Royal Wedding. Square designs as T* **231a** *of Jamaica. Multicoloured.* W w **16**. *P* 14.

568   55 c. Prince Andrew and Miss Sarah Ferguson   40   55
569   60 c. Prince Andrew at helm of Yacht *Bluenose II* off Nova Scotia, 1985 ..   45   70

158 *Freedom* (winner 1980)   **(159)**

(Des J. Dixon. Litho Leigh-Mardon Ltd, Melbourne)

1986 (22 Aug). *America's Cup Yachting Championship* (1987) (1st issue). *T* **158** *and similar vert designs. P* 14½.

570   18 c. multicoloured   20   35
a. Sheet of 50   ..   ..   18·00
571   30 c. multicoloured   75   1·50
572   $1 multicoloured   50   1·00
570/2   ..   ..   *Set of* 3   1·25   2·50
Nos. 570/2 were issued as a sheet of 50, each horizontal strip of 5 being separated by gutter margins. The sheet contains 20 different designs at 18 c., 10 at 30 c. and 20 at $1. Individual stamps depict yachts, charts, the America's Cup or the emblem of the Royal Perth Yacht Club.
See also No. MS575.

1986 (23 Sept). *Cyclone Relief Fund. Nos.* 541 *and* MS567 *surch as T* **159** *in red.*

573   $1+50 c. Queen Mother with Prince Henry at his christening (from photo by Lord Snowdon)   75   1·25
MS574   100×75 mm. 55 c.+25 c. Type **157**; $1.65+75 c. Peace Corps emblem, President Kennedy and Statue of Liberty (25th anniv of Peace Corps)   ..   ..   3·00   3·00
The surcharges on No. MS574 are vertical, in smaller type (length 16½ mm) and do not include "1986".

(Des J. Dixon. Litho Leigh-Mardon Ltd, Melbourne)

1987 (4 Feb). *America's Cup Yachting Championship* (2nd issue). *Sheet* 111×75 *mm, containing vert design as T* **158**. *Multicoloured. P* 14½.

MS575 $5 Stars and Stripes (1987 winner)   ..   3·50   4·25
Similar miniature sheets showing the yacht *Kookaburra III* were prepared, but destroyed once the result of the Cup races was known. It is believed that at least one example of this unissued miniature sheet has survived.
No. MS575 was also issued printed on gold foil and sold at a premium of $20 over the face value of the stamp.

160 *Dendrophyllia gracilis*   **161** *Cassia fistula*

(Des D. Miller. Litho Format)

1987 (11 Feb). *Corals. T* **160** *and similar horiz designs. Multicoloured.* W w **16** (sideways). *P* 14.

576   18 c. Type **160**..   20   15
577   45 c. *Dendronephthya sp*   60   50
578   60 c. *Clavularia sp*   80   1·40
579   $1.50, *Melithaea squamata* ..   1·60   3·50
576/9   ..   ..   *Set of* 4   3·00   5·00

(Des Gill Tomblin. Litho Walsall)

1987 (12 May)–88. *Flowers. T* **161** *and similar vert designs. Multicoloured.* W w **16**. *P* 14½×14.

580   1 c. Type **161**   10   50
581   5 c. *Allamanda cathartica*   ..   20   60
582   10 c. *Catharanthus roseus* ..   30   60
w. Wmk inverted
583   18 c. *Mimosa pudica*   50   15
584   20 c. *Hibiscus rosa-sinensis* ..   50   15
585   22 c. *Clerodendrum thomsonae* ..   50   15
586   25 c. *Bauhinia variegata*   ..   50   30
587   28 c. *Gloriosa rothschildiana* ..   55   30
588   30 c. *Heliconia solomonensis* ..   60   30
589   40 c. *Episcia hybrid*   70   30
590   45 c. *Bougainvillea hybrid* ..   70   30
591   50 c. *Alpinia purpurata*   ..   70   30
592   55 c. *Plumeria rubra*   75   35
w. Wmk inverted   ..   ..   24·00
593   60 c. *Acacia farnesiana*   ..   85   60
594   $1 *Ipomea purpurea*   ..   2·00   80
595   $2 *Dianella ensifolia*   ..   3·00   4·50
596   $5 *Passiflora foetida*   ..   4·50   8·00
597   $10 *Hemigraphis sp* (1.3.88)   ..   7·00   12·00
580/97   ..   ..   *Set of* 8   22·00   27·00

162 Mangrove Kingfisher on Branch   **163** *Dendrobium conanthum*

(Des Josephine Martin. Litho Format)

1987 (15 July). *Mangrove Kingfisher. T* **162** *and similar vert designs. Multicoloured.* W w **16**. *P* 14.

598   60 c. Type **162**..   ..   ..   2·40   3·00
a. Horiz strip of 4. Nos. 598/601 ..   8·50
599   60 c. Kingfisher diving   ..   2·40   3·00
600   60 c. Entering water ..   ..   2·40   3·00
601   60 c. Kingfisher with prey   ..   2·40   3·00
598/601   ..   ..   *Set of* 4   8·50   11·00
Nos. 598/601 were printed together, *se-tenant*, in horizontal strips of 4 throughout the sheet, forming a composite design.

(Des Sue Wickison. Litho Walsall)

1987 (23 Sept). *Christmas. Orchids* (1st series). *T* **163** *and similar vert designs. Multicoloured.* W w **16**. *P* 13½×13.

602   18 c. Type **163**.   85   10
603   30 c. *Spathoglottis plicata* ..   1·50   20
604   55 c. *Dendrobium gouldii* ..   1·75   50
605   $1.50, *Dendrobium goldfinchii* ..   3·75   3·00
602/5   ..   ..   *Set of* 4   7·00   3·50
See also Nos. 640/3 and 748/51.

---

164 Telecommunications Control Room and Satellite   **165** Pupa of *Ornithoptera victoriae*

(Des D. Hartley. Litho CPE Australia Ltd, Melbourne)

1987 (16 Nov). *Asia-Pacific Transport and Communications Decade. T* **164** *and similar horiz designs. Multicoloured. P* 13½.

606   18 c. Type **164**   20   15
607   30 c. De Havilland D.H.C.6 Twin Otter 300 mail plane   45   20
608   60 c. Guadalcanal road improvement project   50   60
609   $2 Beech 80 Queen Air and Henderson Control Tower   ..   ..   2·00   2·50
606/9   ..   ..   *Set of* 4   2·75   3·00

(Des R. Lewington. Litho Questa)

1987 (25 Nov). *Butterflies* (3rd series). Ornithoptera victoriae (*Queen Victoria's Birdwing*). *T* **165** *and similar vert designs. Multicoloured.* W w **16** (sideways). *P* 14½×14.

610   45 c. Type **165**.   ..   ..   3·50   3·50
a. Strip of 4. Nos. 610/13 ..   12·00
611   45 c. Larva   ..   ..   ..   3·50   3·50
612   45 c. Female butterfly   ..   3·50   3·50
613   45 c. Male butterfly ..   ..   3·50   3·50
610/13   ..   ..   *Set of* 4   12·00   12·00
Nos. 610/13 were printed together, *se-tenant*, in horizontal and vertical strips of 4 throughout the sheet of 16.

166 Student and National Agriculture Training Institute   **167** Building Fishing Boat

(Des D. Miller. Litho Format)

1988 (12 Feb). *10th Anniv of International Fund for Agricultural Development. T* **166** *and similar square designs. Multicoloured.* W w **16**. *P* 14½.

614   50 c. Type **166**   40   55
aw. Wmk inverted   ..   5·00
b. Horiz pair. Nos. 614/15   ..   80   1·10
bw. Wmk inverted   ..   10·00
615   50 c. Students working in fields   ..   40   55
aw. Wmk inverted   ..   5·00
616   $1 Transport by lorry   ..   50   1·00
aw. Wmk inverted   ..   11·00
b. Horiz pair. Nos. 616/17   ..   1·00   2·00
bw. Wmk inverted   ..   22·00
617   $1 Canoe transport   ..   50   1·00
aw. Wmk inverted   ..   11·00
614/17   ..   ..   *Set of* 14   1·60   2·75
Nos. 614/15 and 616/17 were printed together, *se-tenant*, in horizontal pairs throughout the sheets, each pair forming a composite design.

(Des N. Shewring. Litho CPE Australia Ltd, Melbourne)

1988 (28 Apr). *"Expo '88" World Fair, Brisbane. T* **167** *and similar horiz designs. Multicoloured. P* 13½×14.

618   22 c. Type **167**   20   15
619   80 c. War canoe   50   45
620   $1.50, Traditional village   ..   95   85
618/20   ..   ..   *Set of* 3   1·50   1·25
MS621   130×53 mm. Nos. 618/20   ..   1·50   1·40
No. MS621 also exists, as a restricted issue, surcharged $3.50 for "New Zealand 1990" International Stamp Exhibition, Auckland.

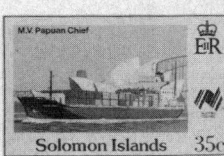

168 *Todos los Santos* in Estrella Bay, 1568   **169** *Papuan Chief* (container ship)

(Des M. Bradbury and J. Sayer. Litho Walsall)

1988 (6 July). *10th Anniv of Independence. T* **168** *and similar horiz designs. Multicoloured.* W w 14 (sideways*). *P* 13×13½.

622   22 c. Type **168**   80   15
w. Wmk Crown to right of CA   ..   8·00
623   55 c. Raising the Union Jack, 1893   ..   1·00   45
624   80 c. High Court Building   ..   1·25   1·10
625   $1 Dancers at traditional celebration   1·40   1·40
622/5   ..   ..   *Set of* 4   4·00   2·75
*The normal sideways watermark shows Crown to left of CA, as seen from the back of the stamp.

(Des E. Nisbet. Litho Walsall)

1988 (30 July). *Bicentenary of Australian Settlement and "Sydpex '88" National Stamp Exhibition, Sydney.* T **169** *and similar horiz designs. Multicoloured.* W w **16** *(sideways).* P 14.

626	35 c. Type **169**	80	25
627	60 c. *Nimos* (container ship)	1·10	40
628	70 c. *Malaita* (liner)	1·25	65
629	$1.30, *Makambo* (inter-island freighter)	1·40	1·50
626/9	*Set of* 4	4·00	2·50
MS630	140×76 mm. Nos. 626/9. W w **14** (sideways)	2·00	2·00

170 Archery   **171** *Bulbo-phyllum dennisii*

(Des Joan Thompson. Litho Walsall)

1988 (5 Aug). *Olympic Games, Seoul.* T **170** *and similar multicoloured designs.* W w **16**. P 14½.

631	22 c. Type **170**	50	20
632	55 c. Weightlifting	70	45
633	70 c. Athletics	80	65
634	80 c. Boxing	95	70
631/4	*Set of* 4	2·75	1·75
MS635	100 × 80 mm. $2 Olympic Stadium (*horiz*). W w **14** (sideways)	1·25	1·25

(Des D. Miller (22, 65 c.), O. Bell and D. Miller (50 c.), E. Nisbet and D. Miller ($2). Litho Questa)

1988 (31 Oct). *300th Anniv of Lloyd's of London. Designs as* T **167***a of Malawi.* W w **16** (sideways on 50, 65 c.). P 14.

636	22 c. brownish black and brown	30	15
637	50 c. multicoloured	1·10	30
638	65 c. multicoloured	1·25	55
639	$2 multicoloured	2·75	1·75
636/9	*Set of* 4	4·75	2·50

Designs: *Vert*—22 c. King George V and Queen Mary laying foundation stone of Leadenhall Street Building, 1925; $2 *Empress of China* (liner), 1911. *Horiz*—50 c. *Forthbank* (container ship); 65 c. Soltel satellite communications station.

(Des Sue Wickison. Litho Walsall)

1989 (20 Jan). *Orchids (2nd series).* T **171** *and similar vert designs. Multicoloured.* W w **14**. P 13½ × 13.

640	22 c. Type **171**	65	15
641	35 c. *Calanthe langei*	80	30
642	55 c. *Bulbophyllum blumei*	1·00	
643	$2 *Grammatophyllum speciosum*	2·00	2·00
640/3	*Set of* 4	4·00	2·75

172 Red Cross Workers with Handicapped Children   **173** Varicose Nudibranch (*Phyllidia varicosa*)

(Des A. Theobald. Litho Questa)

1989 (16 May). *125th Anniv of International Red Cross.* T **172** *and similar horiz designs. Multicoloured.* W w **16** (sideways). P 14½.

644	35 c. Type **172**	35	35
	a. Horiz pair. Nos. 644/5	70	70
645	35 c. Handicapped Children Centre minibus	35	35
646	$1.50, Blood donor	1·25	1·25
	a. Horiz pair. Nos. 646/7	2·50	2·50
647	$1.50, Balance test	1·25	1·25
644/7	*Set of* 4	3·00	3·00

Nos. 644/5 and 646/7 were each printed together, *se-tenant*, in horizontal pairs throughout the sheets, each pair forming a composite design.

(Des Sue Wickison. Litho Questa)

1989 (30 June). *Nudibranchs (Sea Slugs).* T **173** *and similar horiz designs. Multicoloured.* W w **14** (sideways). P 14 × 14½.

648	22 c. Type **173**	80	20
649	70 c. Bullock's Nudibranch (*Chromodoris bullocki*)	2·00	1·50
650	80 c. *Chromodoris leopardus*	2·00	1·60
651	$1.50, *Phidiana indica*	2·50	4·00
648/51	*Set of* 4	6·50	6·50

(Des A. Theobald ($4), D. Miller (others). Litho Questa)

1989 (20 July). *20th Anniv of First Manned Landing on Moon. Multicoloured designs as* T **51***a of Kiribati.* W w **16** (sideways on 35, 70 c.). P 14×13½ (22, 80 c.) or 14 (others).

652	22 c. "Apollo 16" descending by parachute	45	20
653	35 c. Launch of "Apollo 16" (30×30 *mm*)	70	45
654	70 c. "Apollo 16" emblem (30×30 *mm*)	1·25	1·60
655	80 c. Ultra-violet colour photograph of Earth	1·40	1·75
652/5	*Set of* 4	3·50	3·50
MS656	100×83 mm. $4 Moon's surface seen from Space. Wmk inverted. P 14×13½	3·00	3·00

174 Five Stones Catch   **175** Fishermen and Butterfly

(Des D. Miller ($3), R. Stewart (others). Litho B.D.T. ($3) or Walsall (others))

1989 (19 Nov). *"World Stamp Expo '89", International Stamp Exhibition, Washington. Children's Games.* T **174** *and similar multicoloured designs.* W w **16** (sideways on 67, 73 c.). P 14.

657	5 c. Type **174**	15	40
658	67 c. Blowing soap bubbles (*horiz*)	1·25	1·40
659	73 c. Coconut shell game (*horiz*)	1·25	1·40
660	$1 Seed wind sound	1·75	2·00
657/60	*Set of* 4	4·00	4·75
MS661	72×72 mm. $3 Softball. W w **14**	5·50	5·50

(Des N. Kohia and C. Vendi, adapted G. Vasarhelyi. Litho Questa)

1989 (30 Nov). *Christmas.* T **175** *and similar horiz designs. Multicoloured.* W w **16** (sideways). P 14.

662	18 c. Type **175**	40	10
663	25 c. The Nativity	55	20
664	45 c. Hospital ward at Christmas	1·00	30
665	$1.50, Village tug-of-war	2·50	4·00
662/5	*Set of* 4	4·00	4·25

176 Man wearing Headband, Necklace and Sash   **177** Spindle Cowrie or Tokio's Volva (*Phenacovolva tokioi*)

(Des Sue Wickison. Litho Questa)

1990 (14 Mar). *Personal Ornaments.* T **176** *and similar vert designs. Multicoloured.* W w **14**. P 14.

666	5 c. Type **176**	30	50
667	12 c. Pendant	40	30
668	18 c. Man wearing medallion, nose ring and earrings	40	30
669	$2 Forehead ornament	4·00	5·00
666/9	*Set of* 4	4·50	5·50

First day covers of Nos. 666/9 were postmarked 26 February 1990, which was the originally intended date of issue, but the stamps were not placed on sale until 14 March.

(Des Lynn Chadwick. Litho Questa)

1990 (23 July). *Cowrie Shells.* T **177** *and similar horiz designs. Multicoloured.* W w **14** (sideways). P 14.

670	4 c. Type **177**	30	50
671	20 c. All-red Map Cowrie (*Cypraea mappa panerythra*)	75	30
672	35 c. Sieve Cowrie (*Cypraea cribaria*)	1·00	35
673	50 c. Umbilical Ovula or Little Egg Cowrie (*Calpurnus verrucosus*)	1·40	1·60
674	$1 Valentine or Prince Cowrie (*Cypraea valentia*)	2·25	3·00
670/4	*Set of* 5	5·25	5·25

(Des D. Miller. Litho Questa)

1990 (4 Aug). *90th Birthday of Queen Elizabeth the Queen Mother. Vert designs as* T **107** (25 c.) *or* **108** ($5) *of Kenya.* P 14×15 (25 c.) or 14½ ($5).

675	25 c. multicoloured	75	25
676	$5 black and deep claret	3·75	4·75

Designs:—25 c. Queen Mother, 1987; $5 King George VI and Queen Elizabeth inspecting bomb damage to Buckingham Palace, 1940.

178 Postman with Mail Van

(Des N. Shewring. Litho Questa)

1990 (15 Oct). *150th Anniv of the Penny Black.* T **178** *and similar horiz designs. Multicoloured.* W w **14** (sideways). P 14.

677	35 c. Type **178**	90	35
678	45 c. General Post Office	95	40
679	50 c. 1907 ½d. stamp	1·10	1·10
680	55 c. Child collecting stamps	1·40	1·50
681	60 c. Penny Black and Solomon Islands 1913 1d. stamp	1·50	2·25
677/81	*Set of* 5	5·25	5·00

179 Purple Swamphen   **180** *Cylas formicarius* (weevil)

(Des N. Arlott. Litho Questa)

1990 (5 Dec). *"Birdpex '90" Stamp Exhibition, Christchurch, New Zealand.* T **179** *and similar horiz designs showing birds. Multicoloured.* W w **14** (sideways). P 14.

682	10 c. Type **179**	65	55
683	25 c. Mackinlay's Cuckoo Dove ("Rufous Brown Pheasant Dove")	1·00	50
684	30 c. Superb Fruit Dove	1·25	55
685	45 c. Cardinal Honeyeater	1·40	60
686	$2 Finsch's Pygmy Parrot	2·25	3·75
682/6	*Set of* 5	6·00	5·50

(Des Josephine Martin. Litho B.D.T.)

1991 (16 Jan). *Crop Pests.* T **180** *and similar vert designs. Multicoloured.* W w **14**. P 14.

687	7 c. Type **180**	55	40
688	25 c. *Dacus cucurbitae* (fruit-fly)	85	30
689	40 c. *Papuana uninodis* (beetle)	1·25	45
690	90 c. *Pantorhytes biplagiastus* (weevil)	2·00	2·25
691	$1.50, *Scapanes australis* (beetle)	2·25	3·50
687/91	*Set of* 5	6·25	6·25

(Des D. Miller. Litho Questa)

1991 (17 June). *65th Birthday of Queen Elizabeth II and 70th Birthday of Prince Philip. Vert designs as* T **58** *of Kiribati. Multicoloured.* W w **16** (sideways). P 14½×14.

692	90 c. Prince Philip in evening dress	1·00	1·25
	a. Horiz pair. Nos. 692/3 separated by label	2·40	3·00
693	$2 Queen Elizabeth II	1·40	1·75

Nos. 692/3 were printed in a similar sheet format to Nos. 366/7 of Kiribati.

181 Child drinking from Coconut   **182** Volleyball

(Des G. Vasarhelyi. Litho Walsall)

1991 (24 June). *Health Campaign.* T **181** *and similar horiz designs. Multicoloured.* W w **14** (sideways). P 14.

694	5 c. Type **181**	15	40
695	75 c. Mother feeding child	1·10	1·10
696	80 c. Breast feeding	1·25	1·40
697	90 c. Local produce	1·40	1·60
694/7	*Set of* 4	3·50	4·00

A 65 c. value, showing healthy and less healthy foods, was prepared, but not issued.

(Des N. Shewring. Litho Questa)

1991 (8 Aug). *9th South Pacific Games.* T **182** *and similar vert designs. Multicoloured.* W w **16**. P 14.

698	25 c. Type **182**	90	25
699	40 c. Judo	1·25	55
700	65 c. Squash	1·75	2·00
701	90 c. Bowling	2·25	3·00
698/701	*Set of* 4	5·50	5·25
MS702	92×112 mm. $2 Games emblem. Wmk sideways	4·50	5·50

 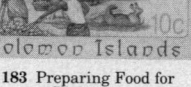

183 Preparing Food for Christmas   **184** Yellow-finned Tuna

(Des G. Vasarhelyi. Litho B.D.T.)

1991 (28 Oct). *Christmas.* T **183** *and similar horiz designs. Multicoloured.* W w **14** (sideways). P 14.

703	10 c. Type **183**	30	10
704	25 c. Christmas Day church service	60	15
705	65 c. Christmas Day feast	1·50	85
706	$2 Cricket match	3·75	5·00
703/6	*Set of* 4	5·50	5·50
MS707	138×110 mm. Nos. 703/6	5·50	6·00

(Des O. Bell. Litho Leigh-Mardon Ltd, Melbourne)

1991 (16 Nov). *"Phila Nippon '91" International Stamp Exhibition, Tokyo. Tuna Fishing.* T **184** *and similar multicoloured designs.* W w **16** (*sideways*). P 14.

708	5 c. Type **184**	..	10	20
709	30 c. Pole and line tuna fishing boat	..	60	25
710	80 c. Pole and line fishing	..	1·50	1·75
711	$2 Processing "arabushi" (smoked tuna)		2·75	4·00
708/11		Set of 4	4·50	5·50
MS712	101×80 mm. 80 c. Plate of "tori nanban" (25×42 mm); 80 c. Bowl of "aka miso" (25×42 mm). P 14½		1·75	2·00

(Des D. Miller. Litho Questa ($5), Leigh-Mardon Ltd, Melbourne (others))

1992 (6 Feb). *40th Anniv of Queen Elizabeth II's Accession. Horiz designs as* T **113** *or* T **113**. *Multicoloured.* W w **14** (*sideways*) (20 c., 40 c., $5) *or* w **16** (5 c., 60 c.). P 14.

713	5 c. Aerial view of Honiara	..	25	50
714	20 c. Sunset across lagoon	..	50	20
715	40 c. Honiara harbour	..	75	40
716	60 c. Three portraits of Queen Elizabeth		80	1·00
717	$5 Queen Elizabeth II	..	3·25	4·50
713/17		Set of 5	5·00	6·00

185 Mendana's Fleet in Thousand Ships Bay, 1568

186 Sgt-major Jacob Vouza

(Des J. Batchelor. Litho Leigh-Mardon Ltd, Melbourne)

1992 (24 Apr). *"Granada '92" International Stamp Exhibition, Spain. Mendana's Discovery of Solomon Islands.* T **185** *and similar horiz designs.* W w **14** (*sideways*). P 15×14½.

718	10 c. Type **185**	..	35	15
719	65 c. Map of voyage	..	80	60
720	80 c. Alvaro Mendana de Niera	..	1·10	1·25
721	$1 Settlement at Graciosa Bay	..	1·40	1·75
722	$5 Mendana's fleet at sea	..	3·50	4·75
718/22		Set of 5	6·50	7·50

(Des T. Rider, adapted G. Vasarhelyi. Litho Enschedé)

1992 (3 May). *Birth Centenary of Sgt-major Jacob Vouza (war hero).* T **186** *and similar vert designs. Multicoloured.* W w **14**. P 14×13½.

723	25 c. Type **186**	..	50	30
	a. Booklet pane. Nos. 723 and 725, each ×2, with margins all round	..	2·75	
724	70 c. Vouza in U.S. Marine corps battle dress		1·00	1·25
	a. Booklet pane. Nos. 724 and 726, each ×2, with margins all round	..	4·00	
725	90 c. Vouza in U.S. Marine corps uniform		1·00	1·40
726	$2 Statue of Vouza	..	1·25	2·25
723/6		Set of 4	3·25	4·75
MS727	113×76 mm. $4 Sgt-major Vouza in ceremonial uniform		5·00	5·00

187 Solomon Airlines Domestic Routes

188 Japanese Troops landing at Esperance

(Des D. Miller. Litho Enschedé)

1992 (22 May). *500th Anniv of Discovery of America by Columbus and "World Columbian Stamp Expo '92" Exhibition, Chicago.* T **187** *and similar vert designs. Multicoloured.* W w **14**. P 14×13½.

728	25 c. Type **187**	..	60	20
729	80 c. Solomon Airlines Boeing 737-400 Guadalcanal		1·40	1·25
730	$1.50, Solomon Airlines international routes		2·00	2·25
731	$5 Columbus and *Santa Maria*	..	4·75	6·00
728/31		Set of 4	8·00	8·75
MS732	120×94 mm. Nos. 728/31	..	8·00	9·00

(Des J. Batchelor. Litho Questa)

1992 (7 Aug)–**99**. *50th Anniv of Battle of Guadalcanal.* T **188** *and similar horiz designs. Multicoloured.* P 14.

733	30 c. Type **188**	..	80	80
	a. Sheetlet. Nos. 733/7		3·50	
	b. Sheetlet. Nos. 733/7 and 956/60 (1.12.99)		4·00	
734	30 c. American troops in landing-craft		80	80
735	30 c. H.M.A.S. *Hobart* (cruiser)		80	80
736	30 c. U.S. Navy post office		80	80
737	30 c. R.N.Z.A.F. Consolidated PBY-5A Catalina flying boat		80	80
738	80 c. U.S. Marine Corps Grumman F4F Wildcat fighters		1·00	1·00
	a. Sheetlet. Nos. 738/47		9·00	

739	80 c. Henderson Field	..	1·00	1·00
740	80 c. U.S.S. *Quincy* (heavy cruiser)		1·00	1·00
741	80 c. H.M.A.S. *Canberra* (heavy cruiser)		1·00	1·00
742	80 c. U.S. Marine Corps landing craft		1·00	1·00
743	80 c. *Ryujo* (Japanese aircraft carrier)		1·00	1·00
744	80 c. Japanese Mitsubishi A6M Zero-Sen fighters		1·00	1·00
745	80 c. Japanese Mitsubishi G4M "Betty" bombers		1·00	1·00
746	80 c. Japanese destroyer	..	1·00	1·00
747	80 c. *Chokai* (Japanese heavy cruiser)		1·00	1·00
733/47		Set of 15	12·50	12·50

Nos. 733/7 and 738/47 were each printed together, *se-tenant*, in sheetlets with the 30 c. designs as a horizontal strip of 5 below a label showing Henderson Field and the 80 c. designs in two horizontal strips of 5 separated by a gutter showing night naval action off Savo Island.

It was originally intended that the 30 c. sheetlet should also contain ten stamps, but in 1992 the top row of five was removed before the sheetlets were issued. The missing five 30 c. designs were released, as a separate commemorative issue, in 1999 when the complete sheetlet became available.

189 *Dendrobium* hybrid

190 Stalk-eyed Ghost Crab

(Des Annette Robinson. Litho Leigh-Mardon Ltd, Melbourne)

1992 (14 Dec). *Orchids (3rd series).* T **189** *and similar horiz designs. Multicoloured.* W w **14** (*sideways*). P 14½.

748	15 c. Type **189**	..	50	20
749	70 c. *Vanda* "Amy Laycock"	..	1·00	90
750	95 c. *Dendrobium mirbelianum*	..	1·25	1·25
751	$2.50, *Dendrobium macrophyllum*		2·00	3·50
748/51		Set of 4	4·25	5·25

For stamps in these designs, but with different face values and inscribed "World Orchid Conference" or "Indopex '93" see Nos. 771/2 and 773/4.

(Des G. Drummond. Litho Cartor)

1993 (15 Jan). *Crabs.* T **190** *and similar horiz designs. Multicoloured.* W w **14** (*sideways*). P 13.

752	5 c. Type **190**	..	10	10
753	10 c. Red-spotted Crab	..	10	10
754	25 c. Flat Crab	..	10	10
755	30 c. Land Hermit Crab	..	10	10
756	40 c. Grapsid Crab	..	10	10
757	45 c. Red and White Painted Crab		10	15
758	55 c. Swift-footed Crab	..	15	20
759	60 c. Spanner Crab	..	15	20
760	70 c. Red Hermit Crab	..	15	20
761	80 c. Red-eyed Crab	..	20	25
762	90 c. Rathbun Red Crab	..	20	25
763	$1 Coconut Crab	..	25	30
764	$1.10, Red-spotted White Crab		30	35
765	$4 Ghost Crab	..	1·10	1·25
766	$10 Mangrove Fiddler Crab		2·50	2·75
752/66		Set of 15	5·25	5·75

For miniature sheet containing the $4 see No. **MS**874.

191 U.S. War Memorial, Skyline Ridge

192 U.S.S. *PT 109* being rammed by *Amagiri* (Japanese destoyer)

(Des G. Vasarhelyi. Litho Walsall)

1993 (19 Apr). *50th Anniv of Second World War.* T **191** *and similar horiz designs. Multicoloured.* W w **14** (*sideways*). P 14.

767	30 c. Type **191**	..	35	20
768	80 c. National flags at half mast		1·00	1·10
769	95 c. Major-general Alexander Vandegrift and map		1·10	1·25
770	$4 Aerial dogfight, U.S. carrier and Solomon Islands scouts		4·00	5·00
767/70		Set of 4	5·75	6·75

(Des Annette Robinson. Litho Leigh-Mardon Ltd, Melbourne)

1993 (24 Apr). *14th World Orchid Conference, Glasgow. Designs as Nos. 748 and 751, but different face values, additionally inscr "World Orchid Conference".* W w **14** (*sideways*). P 14½.

771	20 c. Type **189**	..	40	25
772	$3 *Dendrobium macrophyllum*	..	2·00	2·75

(Des Annette Robinson. Litho Leigh-Mardon Ltd, Melbourne)

1993 (29 May). *"Indopex '93" International Philatelic Exhibition, Surabaya. Designs as Nos. 749/50, but different face values, additionally inscr "Indopex '93 Exhibition".* W w **14** (*sideways*). P 14½.

773	85 c. *Vanda* "Amy Laycock"	..	90	1·00
774	$1.15, *Dendrobium mirbelianum*		1·00	1·25

(Des J. Batchelor and G. Vasarhelyi. Litho Walsall)

1993 (30 July). *50th Anniv of Sinking of U.S.S. PT 109 (motor torpedo-boat commanded by John F. Kennedy).* T **192** *and similar horiz designs. Multicoloured.* W w **14** (*sideways*). P 13×13½.

775	30 c. Type **192**	..	30	20
776	50 c. Kennedy thanking islander		45	45
777	95 c. Message in coconut shell and islanders in canoe		75	1·00
778	$1.10, Pres. Kennedy and medal		1·00	1·40
775/8		Set of 4	2·25	2·75
MS779	77×43 mm. $5 U.S.S. *PT 109*		4·75	5·50

1993 (14 Aug). *"Taipei '93" Asian International Stamp Exhibition, Taiwan. No.* **MS**732 *optd "TAIPEI '93" and emblem on sheet margin.*

MS780	120×94 mm. Nos. 728/31		4·50	5·50

193 Nicobar Pigeon

194 Pair of Dachshunds

(Des A. Robinson. Litho B.D.T.)

1993 (21 Sept). *Endangered Species. Nicobar Pigeon.* T **193** *and similar square designs. Multicoloured.* W w **14** (*sideways*). P 14.

781	30 c. Type **193**	..	35	20
782	50 c. Pigeon on ground	..	50	35
783	65 c. Pair of Pigeons perched on branches		60	50
784	70 c. Pigeon on branch looking left		65	60
785	$1.10, Pigeon on branch looking right		1·00	1·25
786	$3 Pigeons in flight	..	2·25	3·25
781/6		Set of 6	4·75	5·50

(Des Doreen McGuiness. Litho Walsall)

1994 (18 Feb). *"Hong Kong '94" International Stamp Exhibition. Chinese New Year ("Year of the Dog").* T **194** *and similar horiz designs. Multicoloured.* W w **14** (*sideways*). P 14½.

787	30 c. Type **194**	..	35	25
788	80 c. German Shepherd Dog		70	85
789	95 c. Pair of Dobermann Pinschers		80	1·00
790	$1.10, Australian Cattle Dog		95	1·40
787/90		Set of 4	2·50	3·25
MS791	70×55 mm. $4 Boxer	..	5·50	6·00

No. **MS**791 surcharged "19–25 Aug. Jakarta '95 Surcharge $2.00" was only available at this philatelic exhibition in Indonesia.

195 Striped Dolphin

(Des N. Shewring. Litho Walsall)

1994 (9 May). *Dolphins.* T **195** *and similar horiz designs. Multicoloured.* W w **16** (*sideways*). P 14.

792	75 c. Type **195**	..	75	65
793	85 c. Risso's Dolphin	..	80	80
794	$1.15, Common Dolphin		1·10	1·25
795	$2.50, Spinner Dolphin		2·25	2·50
796	$3 Bottlenose Dolphin	..	2·50	3·00
792/6		Set of 5	6·75	7·50

196 *Vindula sapor*

197 Girl in Brisbane writing letter to Family in Santa Isabel

(Des K. McGee. Litho Enschedé)

1994 (16 Aug). *"Philakorea '94" International Stamp Exhibition, Seoul. Butterflies.* T **196** *and similar horiz designs. Multicoloured.* W w **14** (*sideways*). P 13½×14.

797	70 c. Type **196**	..	50	65
	a. Sheetlet. Nos. 797/805		4·00	
798	70 c. *Papilio aegeus*	..	50	65
799	70 c. *Graphium hicetaon*	..	50	65
800	70 c. *Graphium mendana*	..	50	65
801	70 c. Exhibition logo	..	50	65
802	70 c. *Graphium meeki*	..	50	65
803	70 c. *Danaus schenkii*	..	50	65

804	70 c. *Papilio ptolychus*	..	50	65
805	70 c. *Phaedyma fissizonata vella*	..	50	65
797/805		*Set of 9*	4·00	5·00

Nos. 797/805 were printed together, *se-tenant*, in sheetlets of 9.

(Des S. Noon. Litho Cartor)

1994 (18 Aug). *International Year of the Family. T* **197** *and similar vert designs. Multicoloured.* W w **14**. P 13.

806	$1.10, Type **197**	..	80	1·00
	a. Horiz strip of 5. Nos. 806/10		3·50	
807	$1.10, Boeing 737-400 leaving Brisbane	..	80	1·00
808	$1.10, Boeing 737-400 at Henderson Airfield and De Havilland D.H.C.6 Twin Otter leaving for Santa Isabel		80	1·00
809	$1.10, De Havilland D.H.C.6 Twin Otter at Fera Airfield, Santa Isabel		80	1·00
810	$1.10, Family reunited	..	80	1·00
806/10		*Set of 5*	3·50	4·50
MS811	160×75 mm. Nos. 806/10		3·50	4·50

Nos. 806/10 were printed together, *se-tenant*, in horizontal strips of 5 throughout the sheet.

198 Cook Island Volcano, 1967

199 La Perouse with King Louis XVI and Map

(Des N. Shewring. Litho Questa)

1994 (24 Oct). *Volcanoes. T* **198** *and similar horiz designs. Multicoloured.* W w **14** (*sideways*). P 14×14½.

812	30 c. Type **198**	..	30	20
813	70 c. Kavachi underwater eruption, 1977	..	50	70
814	80 c. Kavachi volcano forming temporary island, 1978		60	80
815	90 c. Tinakula volcanic island	..	80	1·10
812/15		*Set of 4*	2·00	2·50
MS816	130×60 mm. $2 Map of Solomon Islands volcanoes; $2 Diagram showing formation of volcanic islands. Wmk upright	..	2·50	3·00

(Des R. Watton. Litho Walsall)

1994 (16 Dec). *Loss of the La Perouse Expedition, Santa Cruz Islands, 1788. T* **199** *and similar horiz designs. Multicoloured.* W w **16** (*sideways*). P 14×14½.

817	30 c. Type **199**	..	40	20
818	80 c. Map of Ile de La Perouse	..	80	80
819	95 c. *L'Astrolabe*	..	85	90
820	$1.10, *La Boussole*	..	1·00	1·25
821	$3 *L'Astrolabe* foundering on reef	..	2·00	3·50
817/21		*Set of 5*	4·50	6·00

200 Hermit Crab, Shells and Dancers

(Des B. Dare. Litho Leigh-Mardon Ltd, Melbourne)

1995 (17 Feb). *Visit South Pacific Year. T* **200** *and similar horiz designs. Multicoloured.* W w **14** (*sideways*). P 15×14½.

822	30 c. Type **200**	..	20	20
823	50 c. *Dendrobium rennellii* (orchid) and *Danaus plexippus* (butterfly)		50	40
824	95 c. Scuba diver and fish	..	60	90
825	$1.15, Grapsid Crab, canoes, rusty Second World War gun and catamaran		65	1·00
822/5		*Set of 4*	1·75	2·25
MS826	98×81 mm. $4 Yellow-bibbed Lory		3·75	4·00

201 Emblem and Bananas

202 *Calanthe triplicata*

(Des Sue Wickison. Litho Southern Colour Print, Dunedin, New Zealand)

1995 (5 Apr). *50th Anniv of Food and Agriculture Organization. Fruits. T* **201** *and similar horiz designs. Multicoloured.* W w **14**. P 12.

827	70 c. Type **201**	..	70	70
828	75 c. Paw paws	..	70	70
829	95 c. Pomelos	..	85	90
830	$2 Star fruits	..	2·00	2·75
827/30		*Set of 4*	3·75	4·50
MS831	90×75 mm. $3 Mangos		1·60	2·00

(Des R. Watton. Litho Cartor (Nos. 832/5) or Questa (No. MS836))

1995 (8 May). *50th Anniv of End of Second World War. Multicoloured designs as T* **75** *of Kiribati.* W w **14** (*sideways*). P 13½.

832	95 c. Vice-Admiral Nagumo and *Akagi* (Japanese aircraft carrier)	..	1·00	1·00
833	$1 Rear-Admiral Fletcher and U.S.S. *Yorktown* (aircraft carrier)	..	1·00	1·00
834	$2 Vice-Admiral Ghormley and U.S.S. *Wasp* (aircraft carrier)	..	1·75	2·00
835	$3 Vice-Admiral Halsey and U.S.S. *Enterprise* (aircraft carrier)	..	2·50	2·75
832/5		*Set of 4*	5·50	6·00
MS836	75×85 mm. $5 Reverse of 1939–45 War Medal (*vert*). Wmk upright. P 14		2·25	2·40

(Des Sue Wickison. Litho Questa)

1995 (1 Sept). *Orchids. T* **202** *and similar vert designs. Multicoloured.* W w **14**. P 14.

837	45 c. Type **202**	..	65	30
838	75 c. *Dendrobium mohlianum*	..	90	80
839	85 c. *Flickingeria comata*	..	1·00	1·00
840	$1.15, *Dendrobium spectabile*	..	1·50	2·00
837/40		*Set of 4*	3·50	3·50
MS841	75×90 mm. $4 *Coelogyne asperata*		2·50	3·25

No. MS841 includes the "Singapore '95" International Stamp Exhibition emblem on the sheet margin.

203 Start of Canoe Race

(Des G. Vasarhelyi. Litho Cartor)

1995 (6 Nov). *Christmas. Local Festivities. T* **203** *and similar horiz designs. Multicoloured.* W w **14** (*sideways*). P 13½.

842	90 c. Type **203**	..	70	60
843	$1.05, Pan-pipe players and Christmas Tree	..	70	80
844	$1.25, Picnic on the beach	..	80	85
845	$1.45, Church service and infant Jesus	1·00	1·25
842/5		*Set of 4*	2·75	3·25

204 Marconi demonstrating Radio Transmitter, Salisbury Plain, 1896

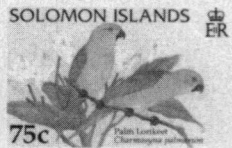

205 Palm Lorikeet

(Des N. Shewring. Litho Walsall)

1996 (28 Feb). *Centenary of Radio. T* **204** *and similar square designs. Multicoloured.* W w **14** (*sideways*). P 14½×14.

846	$1.05, Type **204**	..	70	70
847	$1.20, Ship's radio room, 1900	..	80	80
848	$1.35, Wireless transmitter, Croydon Aerodrome, 1920		90	1·10
849	$1.45, Marconi in Japan, 1933	..	1·00	1·40
846/9		*Set of 4*	3·00	3·50

(Des R. Parks. Litho Questa)

1996 (10 Apr). *Birds. T* **205** *and similar horiz designs. Multicoloured.* W w **14** (*sideways*). P 14.

850	75 c. Type **205**	..	70	55
851	$1.05, Duchess Lorikeet	..	85	75
852	$1.20, Yellow-bibbed Lory	..	90	85
853	$1.35, Cardinal Lory	..	1·25	1·50
854	$1.45, Meek's Lorikeet	..	1·25	1·50
850/4		*Set of 5*	4·50	4·75
MS855	94×69 mm. $3 Rainbow Lory ("Lorikeet")	1·90	2·25

ALTERED CATALOGUE NUMBERS

Any Catalogue numbers altered from the last edition are shown as a list in the introductory pages.

---

206 Dug-out Canoe on Beach and Canoe with Outboard Motor

207 Tokyo 1964 Poster

(Des R. Watton. Litho Cartor)

1996 (8 June). *"CAPEX '96" International Stamp Exhibition, Toronto. Mail Transport. T* **206** *and similar horiz designs.* W w **14** (*sideways*). P 13.

856	40 c. Type **206**	..	35	20
857	90 c. Postman with bicycle	..	1·00	70
858	$1.20, Post van	..	1·00	90
859	$1.45, *Tulagi Express* (cruise launch)	..	1·50	2·00
856/9		*Set of 4*	3·50	3·50
MS860	88×73 mm. $4 "Tepuke" (traditional canoe)		1·90	2·40

(Des D. Miller. Litho Walsall)

1996 (30 June). *Centenary of Modern Olympic Games. T* **207** *and similar vert designs showing promotional posters from previous games.* W w **16**. P 14×13½.

861	90 c. Type **207**	..	50	40
862	$1.20, Los Angeles, 1932	..	60	70
863	$1.35, Paris, 1924	..	65	80
864	$2.50, London, 1908	..	1·10	1·50
861/4		*Set of 4*	2·50	3·00

208 Suiesi and Map of Makira Bay

209 Sanford's Sea Eagle

(Des G. Vasarhelyi. Litho Questa)

1996 (12 Sept). *150th Anniv of First Christian Mission. T* **208** *and similar horiz designs. Multicoloured.* W w **14** (*sideways*). P 13½×14.

865	40 c. Type **208**	..	30	20
866	65 c. Surimahe and sketches of artefacts by Revd. L. Verguet		45	35
867	$1.35, Bishop Espalle and grave, Isabel	60	90
868	$1.45, John Claude Colin and Makira Mission	..	65	1·00
865/8		*Set of 4*	1·75	2·25

(Des N. Arlott. Litho Questa)

1996 (21 Oct). *"Taipei '96" 10th Asian International Stamp Exhibition, Taiwan. Sheet* 100×80 mm. W w **14** (*inverted*). P 14×13½.

MS869	**209** $1.50, multicoloured	..	75	1·00

210 Children eating Fruit

(Des Jennifer Toombs. Litho Questa)

1996 (21 Nov). *50th Anniv of U.N.I.C.E.F. T* **210** *and similar horiz designs. Multicoloured.* W w **14** (*sideways*). P 14½.

870	40 c. Type **210**	..	25	20
871	$1.05, Children in canoes	..	50	50
872	$1.35, Doctor and child	..	60	40
873	$2.50, Teacher and child	..	1·00	1·75
870/3		*Set of 4*	2·10	2·75

(Des D. Miller. Litho Questa)

1997 (3 Feb). *"HONG KONG '97" International Stamp Exhibition. Sheet* 130×90 mm, containing design as No. 765. *Multicoloured.* W w **14** (*sideways*). P 14×14½.

MS874	$4 Ghost Crab	..	1·50	2·00

1997 (21 Feb). *"Singpex '97" International Stamp Exhibition. No. 797a optd* "SINGPEX '97 FEBRUARY 21-25 SINGAPORE" *and logo within "perforation" frame in red across the entire sheetlet.*

875	70 c. Type **196**	..	40	50
	a. Sheetlet. Nos. 875/83	..	3·25	
876	70 c. *Papilio aegeus*	..	40	50
877	70 c. *Graphium hicetaon*	..	40	50
878	70 c. *Graphium mendana*	..	40	50
879	70 c. Exhibition logo	..	40	50
880	70 c. *Graphium meeki*	..	40	50
881	70 c. *Danaus schenkii*	..	40	50
882	70 c. *Papilio ptolychus*	..	40	50
883	70 c. *Phaedyma fissizonata vella*	..	40	50
875/83		*Set of 9*	3·25	4·00

Individual stamps show parts of the overprint only.
Nos. 875/83 also exist with the overprint in black from a limited printing.

211 Common Phalanger

212 Whale and Calf

(Des Sue Wickison. Litho Southern Colour Print, Dunedin)

1997 (21 Apr). *Common Phalanger ("Northern Common Cuscus"). T* **211** *and similar horiz designs. Multicoloured. W w 14 (sideways). P 12.*

884	15 c. Type **211**	..	20	15
885	60 c. Common Phalanger eating fruit	..	30	30
886	$2.50, Common Phalanger hanging on branch	..	85	1·25
887	$3 Two Common Phalangers	..	95	1·40
884/7		*Set of 4*	2·10	2·75

(Des Mary Butterfield. Litho Questa)

1997 (29 May). *"Pacific '97" International Stamp Exhibition, San Francisco. Sheet 96×74 mm, containing T* **212** *and similar multicoloured design. W w 14. P 15×14½ (vert) or 14½×15 (horiz).*

MS888	$2 Type **212**; $2 Whale breaking surface (*horiz*)	..	2·00	2·50

(Des N. Shewring (No. MS893), D. Miller (others). Litho Questa (No. MS893), Cartor (others))

1997 (10 July). *Golden Wedding of Queen Elizabeth and Prince Philip. Multicoloured designs as T* **87** *of Kiribati. W w 14. P 13.*

889	$3 Prince Philip playing polo	..	1·75	2·00
	a. Horiz pair. Nos. 889/90	..	3·50	4·00
890	$3 Queen Elizabeth	..	1·75	2·00
891	$3 Queen Elizabeth leading two horses	..	1·75	2·00
	a. Horiz pair. Nos. 891/2	..	3·50	4·00
892	$3 Prince Philip	..	1·75	2·00
889/92		*Set of 4*	7·00	8·00
MS893	110×70 mm. $3 Queen Elizabeth and Prince Philip in landau (*horiz*). Wmk sideways. P 14×14½		1·25	1·60

Nos. 889/90 and 891/2 were each printed together, *se-tenant*, in horizontal pairs throughout the sheets with the backgrounds forming composite designs.

213 Turtle laying Eggs

(Des Doreen McGuiness. Litho Walsall)

1997 (29 Sept). *50th Anniv of the South Pacific Commission. Common Green Turtle. T* **213** *and similar horiz designs. W w 16 (sideways). Multicoloured. P 14.*

894	50 c. Type **213**	..	30	20
895	90 c. Young turtles heading towards sea	..	50	40
896	$1.50, Four turtles swimming under water	..	70	1·10
897	$2 Pair of turtles swimming	..	85	1·40
894/7		*Set of 4*	2·10	2·75

214 Oni Mako Player

215 Golden Whistler

(Des G. Vasarhelyi. Litho Cartor)

1997 (24 Nov). *Christmas. T* **214** *and similar horiz designs. Multicoloured. W w 14 (sideways). P 13½.*

898	$1.10, Type **214**	..	50	35
899	$1.40, Ysabel dancing women	..	60	60
900	$1.50, Pan pipers from Small Malaita	..	60	70
901	$1.70, Western bamboo band	..	75	1·00
898/901		*Set of 4*	2·25	2·40

(Des G. Vasarhelyi. Litho Questa)

1997 (5 Dec). *"Bangkok '97" China Stamp Exhibition, Thailand. Christmas. Sheet 135×87 mm, containing T* **215** *and similar vert design. Multicoloured. W w 14 (sideways). P 14.*

MS902	$1.50, Type **215**; $1.50, *Papilio aegeus* and *Graphium meeki* (butterflies)		1·75	2·25

216 Black Marlin

217 Water Melon Cultivation

(Des Sue Wickison. Litho Southern Colour Print, Dunedin)

1998 (27 Feb). *Billfishes. T* **216** *and similar vert designs. Multicoloured. P 14½.*

903	50 c. Type **216**	..	30	20
904	$1.20, Shortbill Swordfish	..	65	60
905	$1.40, Swordfish	..	70	75
906	$2 Indo-Pacific Sailfish	..	1·00	1·10
903/6		*Set of 4*	2·40	2·40

For No. 906 in miniature sheet see No. **MS922**.

(Des D. Miller. Litho Questa)

1998 (31 Mar–17 Apr). *Diana, Princess of Wales Commemoration. Vert designs as T* **91** *of Kiribati. Multicoloured. W w 16 (No. 907). P 14½×14.*

907	$2 Wearing pearl earrings (17 Apr)	..	50	55
MS908	145×70 mm. $2.50, As No. 907; $2.50, Wearing white hat; $2.50, In evening dress; $2.50, Accepting flowers from children. W w 14 (sideways) (*sold at $10 + 50 c. charity premium*)		3·25	3·50

(Des Sue Wickison. Litho Cartor)

1998 (29 May). *Technical Co-operation between Solomon Islands and Republic of China (Taiwan). T* **217** *and similar horiz designs. Multicoloured. W w 14 (sideways). P 13.*

909	50 c. Type **217**	..	20	20
910	$1.50, Harvesting rice	..	55	55
MS911	105×60 mm. 80 c. Growing cucumbers; $1.20, Inspecting tomato plants		75	1·00

218 War Dance

(Des G. Vasarhelyi. Litho Cartor)

1998 (3 July). *Melanesian Trade and Culture Show. T* **218** *and similar horiz designs. W w 14 (sideways). P 13½.*

912	50 c. Type **218**	..	30	40
	a. Sheetlet. Nos. 912/20	..	2·75	
913	50 c. Islanders with bows and arrows	..	30	40
914	50 c. Man on beach	..	30	40
915	$1.20, War dance (*different*)	..	35	45
916	$1.20, Warrior in mask	..	35	45
917	$1.20, Woman wearing shell necklace and headband	..	35	45
918	$1.50, Dance with poles	..	40	45
919	$1.50, Hunter with spear, shield and axe	..	40	45
920	$1.50, Man with nose and ear ornaments	..	40	45
912/20		*Set of 9*	2·75	3·50

Nos. 912/20 were printed together, *se-tenant*, in sheetlets of 9.

219 New National Parliament Building

(Des D. Miller. Litho Cartor)

1998 (7 July). *20th Anniv of Independence. Sheet 110×79 mm. W w 14 (sideways). P 13½.*

MS921	**219** $4 multicoloured	..	1·50	2·00

(Des Sue Wickison. Litho Southern Colour Print, Dunedin, New Zealand)

1998 (23 July). *"Singpex 98" International Stamp Exhibition and International Year of the Ocean. Sheet, 90×60 mm, containing No. 906. Multicoloured. W* **156** *of Niue. P 14½.*

MS922	$2 Indo-Pacific Sailfish	..	1·00	1·40

220 H.M.S. *Endeavour* (Cook), 1770

(Des J. Batchelor. Litho Cartor)

1999 (19 Mar). *"Australia '99" World Stamp Exhibition, Melbourne. Maritime History. Sheet, 96×55 mm, containing T* **220** *and similar horiz design. Multicoloured. W w 14 (sideways). P 13½.*

MS923	$10 Type **220**; $10 *Los Reyes* (Alvare Mendana) careened at Guadalcanal, 1568		5·50	6·50

221 Beach

(222)

(Des A. Robinson. Litho Cartor)

1999 (2 July). *"PhilexFrance '99" International Stamp Exhibition, Paris. Marine Life. T* **221** *and similar horiz designs. Multicoloured. W w 14 (sideways). P 13.*

924	$1 Type **221**	..	35	40
	a. Sheetlet. Nos. 924/35	..	3·75	
925	$1 Great Frigate Bird	..	35	40
926	$1 Coconut Crab	..	35	40
927	$1 Green Turtle	..	35	40
928	$1 Royal Spanish Dancer Nudibranch	..	35	40
929	$1 Sun Moon and Stars Butterflyfish	..	35	40
930	$1 Striped Sweetlips	..	35	40
931	$1 Saddle-back Butterflyfish	..	35	40
932	$1 Cuttlefish	..	35	40
933	$1 Giant Clam	..	35	40
934	$1 Lionfish	..	35	40
935	$1 Spiny Lobster	..	35	40
924/35		*Set of 12*	3·75	4·25

Nos. 924/35 were printed together, *se-tenant*, in sheetlets of 12, with the backgrounds forming a composite design.

(Des N. Shewring. Litho Walsall)

1999 (20 July). *30th Anniv of First Manned Landing on Moon. Multicoloured designs as T* **296** *of Jamaica. W w 16. P 14×13½.*

936	50 c. Lift-off	..	15	15
937	$1.50, Lunar module above Moon's surface	..	45	50
938	$2.50, Buzz Aldrin with American flag on Moon	..	70	80
939	$3.40, Command module splashdown	..	95	1·10
936/9		*Set of 4*	2·00	2·25
MS940	90×80 mm. $4 Earth as seen from Moon (*circular, 40 mm diam*). Wmk sideways. P 14		1·10	1·25

(Des D. Miller. Litho Cartor)

1999 (16 Aug). *"Queen Elizabeth the Queen Mother's Century". Horiz design as T* **199** *of St. Helena. Multicoloured (except $5). W w 16 (sideways). P 13½.*

941	$1 Inspecting bomb damage at Portsmouth, 1941	..	35	30
942	$1.50, At the Derby, 1983	..	50	45
943	$2.30, Receiving birthday bouquets from children	..	70	70
944	$4.90, Inspecting Royal Army Medical Corps parade	..	1·40	1·60
941/4		*Set of 4*	2·75	2·75
MS945	145×70 mm. $5 Duchess of York, 1920s, and with King George VI and Prime Minister Winston Churchill, VE Day, 1945 (black)		1·50	1·75

1999 (21 Aug). *"China '99" International Stamp Exhibition, Beijing. No. 687 optd with T* **222** *in red.*

946	70 c. Type **180**	..	15	10

ALTERED CATALOGUE NUMBERS

Any Catalogue numbers altered from the last edition are shown as a list in the introductory pages.

223 Ferrari 212 E

224 Bishop George
Augustus Selwyn

(Litho Questa)

1999 (27 Sept). *Birth Centenary of Enzo Ferrari (car designer) (1998). Racing Cars.* T **223** *and similar horiz designs. Multicoloured.* W w **14** *(sideways).* P 14.

947	$1 Type **223**	..	..	25	30
948	$1.50, 250 TR	..	..	35	40
949	$3.30, 250 LM	..	..	75	80
950	$4.20, 612 CAN-AM	..	..	90	95
947/50			Set of 4	2·25	2·40

(Des Tracey Yager. Litho B.D.T.)

1999 (12 Nov). *Christmas. 150th Anniv of Melanesian Mission.* T **224** *and similar vert designs. Multicoloured (except $3.30).* P 14.

951	$1 Type **224**	..	..	25	30
	a. Horiz strip of 5. Nos. 951/5			1·90	
952	$1 Bishop John Coleridge Patteson			25	30
953	$1.50, Stained glass windows			35	40
954	$1.50, *Southern Cross* (missionary ship) and religious symbols			35	40
955	$3.30, "150 YEARS MELANESIAN MISSION" (black)	..		75	80
951/5			Set of 5	1·90	2·10

Nos. 951/5 were printed together, *se-tenant*, in horizontal strips of 5, with the $3.30 in the centre, throughout the sheet with the backgrounds forming a composite design.

225 National Flags at Half
Mast

(Des J. Batchelor. Litho Questa)

1999 (1 Dec). *Second World War Veterans' Millennium Visit.* T **225** *and similar horiz designs. Multicoloured.* W w **16** *(sideways).* P 14.

956	30 c. Type **225**	..	..	10	15
	a. Sheetlet. Nos. 956/60	..	..	50	
957	30 c. The Cenotaph, Honiara	..		10	15
958	30 c. Solomon Peace Memorial Park			10	15
959	30 c. U.S. War Memorial, Skyline Ridge			10	15
960	30 c. *Ocean Pearl* (cruise ship)			10	15
956/60			Set of 5	50	75

Nos. 956/60 were originally intended for issue with Nos. 733/7 in 1992 and formed the top horizontal row of a sheetlet of 10 which had the two rows separated by a large gutter margin showing Henderson Field.

Nos. 956/60 were available either as a complete sheetlet, see No. 733b, or with the bottom row of stamps, containing Nos. 733/7, removed.

STAMP BOOKLETS

1959 (1 Apr). *Black on buff (No. SB1) or grey (No. SB2) covers. Stapled.*

SB1	4s. booklet containing eight 1d., 2d. and 3d. (Nos. 83, 85, 87) in blocks of 4	..	32·00
SB2	11s. booklet containing eight 1d. and 8d., and four 3d. and 1s. (Nos. 83, 87, 90/1) in blocks of 4		42·00

1960 (May)–**64**. *Black on green (No. SB3) or orange (No. SB4) covers. Stapled.*

SB3	5s. booklet containing eight 1d., 1½d., 2d. and 3d. (Nos. 83/5, 87) in blocks of 4		50·00
SB4	£1 booklet containing eight 1d., 2d., 3d., 9d. and 1s. 3d. (Nos. 83, 85, 87, 90a, 91a) in blocks of 4		80·00
	a. Contents as No. SB4, but Nos. 103, 85, 106a, 108/9 (1964)		

1982 (11 Oct). *Royal Visit and Commonwealth Games, Brisbane. Light green and apple-green cover, 90×108 mm, showing two-headed figure. Stamps attached by selvedge.*

SB5	$2.96, booklet containing 12 c. (Nos. 471/2) and 25 c. (Nos. 473/4), each value in block of eight and two labels		4·50

1984 (30 Jan). *Fungi. Black and greenish yellow cover, 122×92 mm. Panes attached by selvedge.*

SB6	$3.18, booklet containing 18 c. and 35 c., each in pane of 6 (Nos. 514a, 515a)		9·00

1984 (22 Sept). *Olympic Games, Los Angeles. Multicoloured cover, 125×82 mm, showing Australian, American and Solomon Islands flags. Stitched.*

SB7	$3.95, booklet containing two *se-tenant* panes of 4 and pane of one 95 c. (Nos. 529a, 531a)	..	8·00

1992 (3 May). *Birth Centenary of Sgt-Major Jacob Vouza (war hero). Black on bright green cover, size 131×92 mm, showing Guadalcanal. Panes attached by selvedge.*

SB8	$11.70, booklet containing two different *se-tenant* panes of 4 (Nos. 723a, 724a) and No. **MS727**		11·00

1998 (17 Apr). *Diana, Princess of Wales Commemoration. Black on pink cover, size 70×113 mm, showing roses. Stamps attached by selvedge.*

SB9	$22.50, booklet containing ten $2 (No. 907)	..	5·50

The price of No. SB9 includes a charity premium of $2.50.

POSTAGE DUE STAMPS

D 1

(Typo B.W.)

1940 (1 Sept). *Wmk Mult Script CA.* P 12.

D1	D **1**	1d. emerald-green	..		..	6·50	7·00
D2		2d. scarlet	..	..	..	7·00	7·00
D3		3d. brown	..	..	..	7·00	11·00
D4		4d. blue	..	..	..	11·00	11·00
D5		5d. grey-green	..	..		12·00	21·00
D6		6d. purple	..	..	..	12·00	15·00
D7		1s. violet	..	..	..	16·00	26·00
D8		1s. 6d. turquoise-green	..		..	26·00	48·00
D1/8					Set of 8	85·00	£130
D1/8		Perf "Specimen"	..	..	Set of 8		£150

Somaliland Protectorate

Egyptian post offices were opened in Somaliland during 1876 and the stamps of Egypt were used there until the garrisons were withdrawn in 1884.

Cancellations for these offices have been identified as follows (for illustrations of postmark types see SUDAN).

BARBARA (Berbera). Open 1876 to 1 November 1884. Circular datestamp as Sudan Type I.

ZEILA. Open 1876 to 1 November 1884. Circular datestamp as Sudan Types G and I, sometimes inscr ZEJLA. One example with seal type cancellation as Sudan Type B is also known.

Stamps of India were used at the two post offices from 1 January 1887 until 1903 usually cancelled with circular datestamps or the "B" obliterator used by all offices controlled from Bombay.

The Protectorate Post Office was established on 1 June 1903, when control of British Somaliland was transferred from the Indian Government to the British Foreign Office.

PRICES FOR STAMPS ON COVER TO 1945	
Nos. 1/11	from × 25
Nos. 12/13	—
Nos. 18/22	from × 12
Nos. 23/4	—
Nos. 25/30	from × 30
Nos. 32/59	from × 12
Nos. 60/92	from × 6
Nos. 93/104	from × 3
Nos. 105/16	from × 4
Nos. O1/13	from × 8
Nos. O14/15	—

(Currency. 12 pies = 1 anna; 16 annas = 1 rupee)

BRITISH SOMALILAND

(1)   2   3

SETTINGS OF TYPE 1

In all printings the ½, 1, 2, 2½, 3, 4, 8, 12 a. and 1 r. values were overprinted from a setting of 240 (2 panes 12 × 10, one above the other), covering the entire sheet at one operation.

The 6 a., which was in sheets of 320 (4 panes, each 8 × 10), had a modified setting of 160, applied twice to each sheet.

The high values were overprinted in sheets of 96 (8 panes, each 4 × 3).

The settings for the low value stamps contained two slightly different styles of overprint, identified by the position of "B" of "BRITISH". Type A shows this letter over the "M" of "SOMALI-LAND" and Type B over the "OM".

For the first printing with the overprint at the top of the design the 240 position setting showed all the stamps in the upper pane and 63 in the lower as Type A, with the remaining 57 as Type B. When the setting was used for the printing with overprint at foot it was amended slightly so that one of the Type A examples in the upper pane became a Type B.

The 6 a. value with overprint at top shows 250 examples of Type A and 70 as Type B in each sheet. This proportion altered in the printing with overprint at foot to 256 as Type A and 64 as Type B.

OVERPRINT VARIETIES

Missing second "I" in "BRITISH"—Occurs on the stamps with overprint at top from R.2/6 of the upper pane and R.5/1 of the lower, although it is believed that the example on the 2½ a. (No. 4a) only occurs from the second position. On the later printing with overprint at foot a similar error can be found on R.7/12 of the upper pane. Some examples of both these errors show traces of the letter remaining, but the prices quoted are for stamps with it completely omitted.

Figure "1" for first "I" in "BRITISH"—Occurs on R.6/4 of the upper pane for all printings of the 240 impression setting. In addition it has been reported from R.7/12 of the Queen Victoria 2½, 12 a. and 1 r. values, and both versions of the 6 a. show the variety on R.6/4 of the upper left and upper right panes.

Curved overprint—Occurs on R.3/4 of the top right-hand pane of the high values.

"SUMALILAND"—Occurs on R.2/9 of the upper pane for all low values with the overprint at foot, except the 6 a. A similar variety occurs on the high values from the same series on R.1/3 of the top left pane.

"SOMAL.LAND"—Occurs on R.7/5 of the lower pane from the 240 impression setting with the overprint at foot. In addition the Edwardian values of this series also have an example on R.6/7. The 6 a. has examples of the flaw on R.6/9 and R.7/5 of both the lower right and left panes. A similar variety occurs on the high values from the same series at R.3/4 of the third pane in the left-hand column.

1903 (1 June). *Nos. 80, 94, 96, 98, 100, 106/9, 114/16 and 118 of India* (Queen Victoria) *optd with T* **1,** *at top of stamp, in Calcutta. Wmk Elephant Head* (6 a.) *or Star* (others).

1		½ a. yellow-green			2·75	3·75
	a.	"BRIT SH"			£160	
2		1 a. carmine			2·75	3·50
	a.	"BRIT SH"			£180	£250
	b.	"BR1TISH"			£130	
3		2 a. pale violet			2·25	1·50
	a.	"BRIT SH"			£275	£350
	b.	"BR1TISH"			£225	
	c.	Opt double			£650	

4		2½ a. ultramarine			2·00	1·75
	a.	"BRIT SH"			£425	
	b.	"BR1TISH"			£275	
5		3 a. brown-orange			3·25	2·75
	a.	"BRIT SH"			£450	
	b.	"BR1TISH"			£300	
6		4 a. slate-green			3·50	2·75
	a.	"BR1TISH"			£300	
7		6 a. olive-bistre			4·75	4·50
	a.	"BR1TISH"			£200	
8		8 a. dull mauve			3·50	5·00
	a.	"BR1TISH"			£300	
9		12 a. purple/red			3·00	7·00
	a.	"BR1TISH"			£300	
10		1 r. green and aniline carmine			6·00	10·00
	a.	"BR1TISH"			£350	
11		2 r. carmine and yellow-brown			24·00	42·00
	a.	Curved opt			£225	
12		3 r. brown and green			19·00	48·00
	a.	Curved opt			£225	
13		5 r. ultramarine and violet			30·00	55·00
	a.	Curved opt			£275	
1/13				Set of 13	95·00	£170

1903 (1 Sept–2 Nov). *Stamps of India optd with T* **1,** *at bottom of stamp, in Calcutta.* (a) *On Nos. 80, 100, 106/9 and 118* (Queen Victoria).

18		2½ a. ultramarine (2.11)			2·50	5·00
	a.	"BR1TISH"			£160	
	b.	"SUMALILAND"			£200	
	c.	"SOMAL.LAND"			£200	
19		6 a. olive-bistre (2.11)			5·00	5·00
	a.	"BR1TISH"			£200	
	b.	"SOMAL.LAND"			£130	
20		12 a. purple/red (2.11)			4·50	12·00
	a.	"BR1TISH"			£190	
	b.	"SUMALILAND"			£275	
	c.	"SOMAL.LAND"			£275	
21		1 r. green and aniline carmine (2.11)			2·50	11·00
	a.	"BR1TISH"			£225	
	b.	"SUMALILAND"			£350	
	c.	"SOMAL.LAND"			£350	
22		2 r. carmine and yellow-brown (2.11)			60·00	90·00
	a.	Curved opt			£375	
	b.	"SUMALILAND"			£375	
	c.	"SOMAL.LAND"			£375	
23		3 r. brown and green (2.11)			65·00	95·00
	a.	Opt double, both inverted with one albino			£550	
	b.	Curved opt			£425	
	c.	"SUMALILAND"			£425	
	d.	"SOMAL.LAND"			£425	
24		5 r. ultramarine and violet (2.11)			60·00	80·00
	a.	Curved opt			£350	
	b.	"SUMALILAND"			£350	
	c.	"SOMAL.LAND"			£350	

(b) *On Nos. 122/4, 127/8 and 133* (King Edward VII)

25		½ a. green			2·00	55
	a.	"BRIT SH"			£325	
	b.	"BR1TISH"			70·00	
	c.	"SUMALILAND"			70·00	
	d.	"SOMAL.LAND"			38·00	
26		1 a. carmine (8.10)			1·25	30
	a.	"BRIT SH"			£200	
	b.	"BR1TISH"			75·00	75·00
	c.	"SUMALILAND"			75·00	
	d.	"SOMAL.LAND"			38·00	38·00
27		2 a. violet (2.11)			1·75	2·50
	a.	"BRIT SH"			£850	
	b.	"BR1TISH"			£160	
	c.	"SUMALILAND"			£160	
	d.	"SOMAL.LAND"			65·00	
28		3 a. orange-brown (2.11)			2·50	2·50
	a.	"BR1TISH"			£160	
	b.	"SUMALILAND"			£160	
	c.	"SOMAL.LAND"			70·00	
29		4 a. olive (2.11)			1·50	4·00
	a.	"BR1TISH"			£170	
	b.	"SUMALILAND"			£170	
	c.	"SOMAL.LAND"			75·00	
30		8 a. purple (2.11)			1·75	2·25
	a.	"BR1TISH"			£190	
	b.	"SUMALILAND"			£190	
	c.	"SOMAL.LAND"			95·00	
18/30				Set of 13	£180	£275

(Typo D.L.R.)

1904 (15 Feb–3 Sept). (a) *Wmk Crown CA. P* 14.

32	**2**	½ a. dull green and green			75	4·00
33		1 a. grey-black and red (3.9)			6·00	3·00
34		2 a. dull and bright purple (3.9)			1·50	2·00
35		2½ a. bright blue (3.9)			2·00	3·50
36		3 a. chocolate and grey-green (3.9)			1·25	2·25
37		4 a. green and black (3.9)			1·50	3·50
38		6 a. green and violet (3.9)			3·50	15·00
39		8 a. grey-black and pale blue (3.9)			3·50	5·50
40		12 a. grey-black and orange-buff (3.9)			6·00	11·00

(b) *Wmk Crown CC. P* 14

41	**3**	1 r. (3.9)			12·00	40·00
42		2 r. dull and bright purple (3.9)			38·00	70·00
43		3 r. green and black (3.9)			38·00	80·00
44		5 r. grey-black and red (3.9)			38·00	80·00
32/44				Set of 13	£130	£275
32/44 Optd "Specimen"				Set of 13	£180	

1905 (July)–11. *Wmk Mult Crown CA. Ordinary paper. P* 14.

45	**2**	½ a. dull green and green			80	7·00
46		1 a. grey-black and red (10.7.05)			11·00	4·00
	a.	Chalk-surfaced paper (1906)			9·00	1·60
47		2 a. dull and bright purple			7·00	7·50
	a.	Chalk-surfaced paper (1909)			6·50	10·00
48		2½ a. bright blue			3·00	10·00
49		3 a. chocolate and grey-green			1·75	13·00
	a.	Chalk-surfaced paper (1911)			9·00	20·00
50		4 a. green and black			3·50	13·00
	a.	Chalk-surfaced paper (1911)			11·00	27·00
51		6 a. green and violet			2·75	22·00
	a.	Chalk-surfaced paper (1911)			18·00	32·00
52		8 a. grey-black and pale blue			4·75	8·00
	a.	Chalk-surfaced paper. *Black and blue* (27.1.11)			40·00	70·00

53	**2**	12 a. grey-black and orange-buff			6·50	10·00
	a.	Chalk-surfaced paper. *Black and orange-brown* (9.11.11)			17·00	55·00

1909 (30 Apr–May). *Wmk Mult Crown CA. P* 14.

58	**2**	½ a. bluish green (May)			20·00	22·00
59		1 a. red (Optd S. £25)			2·50	1·75
45/59				Set of 11	55·00	£100

4

5

(Typo D.L.R.)

1912 (Nov)–19. *Wmk Mult Crown CA. Chalk-surfaced paper* (2 a. *and* 3 a. *to* 5 r.). *P* 14.

60	**4**	½ a. green (11.13)			50	7·50
	w.	Wmk inverted			15·00	60·00
61		1 a. red			2·25	50
	a.	*Scarlet* (1917)			3·00	1·25
62		2 a. dull and bright purple (12.13)			3·50	12·00
	a.	*Dull purple and violet-purple* (4.19)			19·00	27·00
63		2½ a. bright blue (10.13)			90	8·50
64		3 a. chocolate and grey-green (10.13)			2·00	6·00
	w.	Wmk inverted			80·00	
65		4 a. green and black (12.12)			2·00	9·00
66		6 a. green and violet (4.13)			2·25	5·00
67		8 a. grey-black and pale blue (10.13)			3·00	14·00
68		12 a. grey-black and orange-buff (10.13)			2·75	18·00
69	**5**	1 r. green			9·50	14·00
70		2 r. dull purple and purple (4.19)			18·00	65·00
71		3 r. green and black (4.19)			50·00	£110
72		5 r. black and scarlet (4.19)			50·00	£150
60/72				Set of 13	£130	£350
60/72 Optd "Specimen"				Set of 13	£170	

1921. *Wmk Mult Script CA. Chalk-surfaced paper* (2 a. *and* 3 a. *to* 5 r.). *P* 14.

73	**4**	½ a. blue-green			2·75	7·50
74		1 a. carmine-red			3·50	60
75		2 a. dull and bright purple			4·00	1·00
76		2½ a. bright blue			1·00	3·50
77		3 a. chocolate and green			2·50	7·50
78		4 a. green and black			2·50	7·00
79		6 a. green and violet			1·50	13·00
80		8 a. grey-black and pale blue			2·00	5·50
81		12 a. grey-black and orange-buff			8·00	15·00
82	**5**	1 r. dull green			7·50	48·00
83		2 r. dull purple and purple			23·00	48·00
84		3 r. dull green and black			32·00	£100
85		5 r. black and scarlet			65·00	£160
73/85				Set of 13	£130	£350
73/85 Optd "Specimen"				Set of 13	£170	

Examples of most values are known showing a forged Berbera postmark dated "21 OC 1932".

1935 (6 May). *Silver Jubilee. As Nos. 114/17 of Jamaica, but ptd by Waterlow. P* 11×12.

86		1 a. deep blue and scarlet			2·25	2·25
	m.	"Bird" by turret			70·00	
87		2 a. ultramarine and grey			2·75	2·00
	k.	Kite and vertical log			55·00	
88		3 a. brown and deep blue			2·25	9·50
	k.	Kite and vertical log			85·00	
	l.	Kite and horizontal log			75·00	
89		1 r. slate and purple			7·00	9·50
	k.	Kite and vertical log			£130	
	l.	Kite and horizontal log			£110	
86/9				Set of 4	13·00	21·00
86/9 Perf "Specimen"				Set of 4	75·00	

For illustrations of plate varieties see Omnibus section following Zimbabwe.

1937 (13 May). *Coronation. As Nos. 118/20 of Jamaica.*

90		1 a. scarlet			15	20
91		2 a. grey-black			55	1·25
92		3 a. bright blue			70	55
90/2				Set of 3	1·25	1·75
90/2 Perf "Specimen"				Set of 3	55·00	

6 Berbera Blackhead Sheep   7 Lesser Kudu

8 Somaliland Protectorate

(Des H. W. Claxton. Recess Waterlow)

1938 (10 May). *Portrait to left. Wmk Mult Script CA. P* 12½.

93	**6**	½ a. green			30	4·00
94		1 a. scarlet			30	1·00
95		2 a. maroon			70	4·00
96		3 a. bright blue			7·00	8·50
97	**7**	4 a. sepia			4·00	6·00
98		6 a. violet			4·75	11·00
99		8 a. grey			1·00	11·00
100		12 a. red-orange			4·00	12·00

101	8	1 r. green	8·50	38·00
102		2 r. purple	14·00	38·00
103		3 r. bright blue	18·00	26·00
104		5 r. black	18·00	26·00
		a. Imperf between (horiz pair)	£12000	
93/104			Set of 12 70·00	£160
93/104 Perf "Specimen"			Set of 12	£150

Examples of most values are known showing a forged Berbera postmark dated "15 AU 38".

Following the Italian Occupation, from 19 August 1940 until 16 March 1941, the stamps of ADEN were used at Berbera from 1 July 1941 until 26 April 1942.

9 Berbera Blackhead Sheep

5 Cents (10)

1 Shilling (11)

(Recess Waterlow)

1942 (27 Apr). *As T 6/8 but with full-face portrait of King George VI, as in T 9. Wmk Mult Script CA. P 12½.*

105	9	½ a. green	20	30
106		1 a. scarlet	20	10
107		2 a. maroon	40	20
108		3 a. bright blue	1·25	20
109	7	4 a. sepia	2·00	20
110		6 a. violet	2·25	20
111		8 a. grey	1·75	20
112		12 a. red-orange	2·75	30
113	8	1 r. green	1·25	40
114		2 r. purple	1·25	4·00
115		3 r. bright blue	1·75	7·00
116		5 r. black	6·00	5·00
105/16			Set of 12 19·00	16·00
105/16 Perf "Specimen"			Set of 12	£150

1946 (15 Oct). *Victory. As Nos. 141/2 of Jamaica. P 13½×14.*

117		1 a. carmine	10	10
		a. Perf 13½	10·00	45·00
118		3 a. blue	10	10
117/18 Perf "Specimen"			Set of 2 48·00	

1949 (28 Jan). *Royal Silver Wedding. As Nos. 143/4 of Jamaica.*

119		1 a. scarlet	10	10
120		5 r. black	3·50	3·25

1949 (10 Oct). *75th Anniv of U.P.U. As Nos. 145/8 of Jamaica. Surch with face values in annas.*

121		1 a. on 10 c. carmine	30	15
122		3 a. on 30 c. deep blue (R.)	75	50
123		6 a. on 50 c. purple	40	50
124		12 a. on 1s. red-orange	55	50
121/4			Set of 4 1·75	1·50

(New Currency. 100 cents = 1 shilling)

1951 (1 Apr). *1942 issue surch as T 10/11.*

125		5 c. on ½ a. green	20	50
126		10 c. on 2 a. maroon	20	30
127		15 c. on 3 a. bright blue	60	30
128		20 c. on 4 a. sepia	80	20
129		30 c. on 6 a. violet	90	40
130		50 c. on 8 a. grey	90	40
131		70 c. on 12 a. red-orange	1·50	2·75
132		1 s. on 1 r. green	60	20
133		2 s. on 2 r. purple	3·50	9·00
134		2 s. on 3 r. bright blue	3·75	2·50
135		5 s. on 5 r. black (R.)	4·50	4·25
125/35			Set of 11 15·00	19·00

1953 (2 June). *Coronation. As No. 153 of Jamaica.*

136		15 c. black and green	30	20

12 Camel and Gurgi

13 Sentry, Somaliland Scouts

(Recess B.W.)

1953 (15 Sept)–**58.** *T 12/13 and similar horiz designs. Wmk Mult Script CA. P 12½.*

137	12	5 c. slate-black	15	50
138	13	10 c. red-orange	1·75	60
		a. Salmon (20.3.58)	6·50	2·00
139	12	15 c. blue-green	50	60
140		20 c. scarlet	50	40
141	13	30 c. reddish brown	2·00	40
142		35 c. blue	3·00	1·75
143		50 c. brown and rose-carmine	3·00	55
144		1 s. light blue	50	30
145		1 s. 30, ultramarine and black (1.9.58)	8·00	3·25
146		2 s. brown and bluish violet	22·00	5·00
147		5 s. red-brown and emerald	22·00	6·00
148		10 s. brown and reddish violet	15·00	14·00
137/48			Set of 12 70·00	30·00

Designs:—35 c., 2 s. Somali Stock Dove; 50 c., 5 s. Martial Eagle; 1 s. Berbera Blackhead Sheep; 1 s. 30, Sheikh Isaaq's Tomb, Mait; 10 s. Taleh Fort.

OPENING OF THE LEGISLATIVE COUNCIL 1957 (19)

LEGISLATIVE COUNCIL UNOFFICIAL MAJORITY, 1960 (20)

1957 (21 May). *Opening of Legislative Council. Nos. 140 and 144 optd with T 19.*

149		20 c. scarlet	10	15
150		1 s. light blue	30	15

1960 (5 Apr). *Legislative Council's Unofficial Majority. Nos. 140 and 145 optd as T 20.*

151		20 c. scarlet	10	15
152		1 s. 30, ultramarine and black	65	15

OFFICIAL STAMPS

SERVICE

BRITISH SOMALILAND (O 1)

BRITISH SOMALILAND (O 2)

O.H.M.S. (O 3)

SETTING OF TYPE O 1

The 240 impression setting used for the Official stamps differs considerably from that on the contemporary postage issue with overprint at foot, although the "BR1TISH" error can still be found on R.6/4 of the upper pane. The Official setting is recorded as consisting of 217 overprints as Type A and 23 as Type B.

OVERPRINT VARIETIES

Figure "1" for first "I" in "BRITISH". Occurs on R.6/4 of the upper pane as for the postage issue.
"BRITIS H"—Occurs on R8, stamps 4 and 10 of the lower pane.

1903 (1 June). *Nos. O45, O48, O49a and O50/1 of India (Queen Victoria optd "O.H.M.S.") additionally optd with Type O 1 in Calcutta.*

O1	½ a. yellow-green		6·00	48·00
	a. "BR1TISH"		£250	
	b. "BRITIS H"		£110	
O2	1 a. carmine		14·00	8·00
	a. "BR1TISH"		£275	£275
	b. "BRITIS H"		£130	
O3	2 a. pale violet		8·00	48·00
	a. "BR1TISH"		£300	
	b. "BRITIS H"		£140	
O4	8 a. dull mauve		10·00	£375
	a. "BR1TISH"		£600	
	b. "BRITIS H"		£275	
	c. Stop omitted after "M" of "O.H.M.S." (lower pane R. 12/10)		£1100	
O5	1 r. green and carmine		10·00	£550
	a. "BR1TISH"		£600	
	b. "BRITIS H"		£275	
O1/5			Set of 5 42·00	£900

No. O4c was caused by an attempt to correct a minor spacing error of the "O.H.M.S." overprint which is known on the equivalent India Official stamp.

SETTING OF TYPE O 2

This 240 impression setting of "BRITISH SOMALILAND" also differs from that used to prepare the postage issue with overprint at foot, although many of the errors from the latter still occur in the same positions for the Official stamps. The setting used for Nos. O6/9f contained 180 overprints as Type A and 60 as Type B.

OVERPRINT VARIETIES

Missing second "I" in "BRITISH"—Occurs R.7/12 of upper pane as for the postage issue.
Figure "1" for first "I" in "BRITISH"—Occurs R.6/4 of upper pane as for the postage issue.
"SUMALILAND"—Occurs R.2/9 of the upper pane as for the postage issue.
"SOMAL.LAND"—Occurs R.6/7 of the lower pane as for the postage issue.

SERVICE

(O 2a)

"SERVICE" in wrong fount (Type O 2a)—Occurs R.1/7 of lower pane.

1903. *Prepared for use but not issued. Nos. 106, 122/4 and 133 of India (1 r. Queen Victoria, rest King Edward VII), optd with Type O 2 in Calcutta.*

O6	½ a. green			40
	a. "BRIT SH"			65·00
	b. "BR1TISH"			45·00
	c. "SUMALILAND"			45·00
	d. "SOMAL.LAND"			32·00
	e. "SERVICE" as Type O 2a			40·00
O7	1 a. carmine			40
	a. "BRIT SH"			65·00
	b. "BR1TISH"			45·00
	c. "SUMALILAND"			45·00
	d. "SOMAL.LAND"			32·00
	e. "SERVICE" as Type O 2a			40·00
O8	2 a. violet			70
	a. "BRIT SH"			95·00
	b. "BR1TISH"			65·00
	c. "SUMALILAND"			65·00
	d. "SERVICE" as Type O 2a			45·00
O9	8 a. purple			4·00
	a. "BRIT SH"			£1200
	b. "BR1TISH"			£350
	c. "SUMALILAND"			£350
	d. "SERVICE" as Type O 2a			£350

O9f	1 r. green and aniline carmine		17·00	
	fa. "BRIT SH"		£1200	
	fb. "BR1TISH"		£350	
	fc. "SUMALILAND"		£350	
	fd. "SOMAL.LAND"		£350	
	fe. "SERVICE" as Type O 2a		£350	
O6/9f			Set of 5 20·00	

Used examples of Nos. O6/9f are known, but there is no evidence that such stamps did postal duty.

SETTING OF TYPE O 3

The anna values were overprinted in sheets of 120 (2 panes 6 × 10) from a setting matching the pane size. The full stop after the "M" on the fifth vertical column was either very faint or completely omitted. The prices quoted are for stamps with the stop missing; examples with a partial stop are worth much less.

The 1 r. value was overprinted from a separate setting of 60 which did not show the "missing stop" varieties.

1904 (1 Sept)–**05.** *Stamps of Somaliland Protectorate optd with Type O 3. P 14. (a) Wmk Crown CA.*

O10	2	½ a. dull green and green	3·25	48·00
		a. No stop after "M"	£275	
O11		1 a. grey-black and carmine	3·25	7·00
		a. No stop after "M"	£200	£275
O12		2 a. dull and bright purple	£140	50·00
		a. No stop after "M"	£1300	£650
O13		8 a. grey-black and pale blue	60·00	£130
		a. No stop after "M"	£450	
		(b) Wmk Mult Crown CA		
O14	2	2 a. dull and bright purple, O (7.05?)	75·00	£650
		a. No stop after "M"	£1200	
		(c) Wmk Crown CC		
O15	3	1 r. green		£160	£475
O10/13, O15			Set of 5 £250	£600
O10/13, O15 Optd "Specimen"			Set of 5 £120	

All Somaliland Protectorate stamps were withdrawn from sale on 25 June 1960 and until the unification on 1 July, issues of Italian Somalia together with Nos. 353/5 of Somalia Republic were used. Later issues will be found listed in Part 14 (*Africa since Independence N–Z*) of this catalogue.

South Africa

South Africa as a nation, rather than a geographical term, came into being with the creation of the Union of South Africa on 31 May 1910.

The development, both political and philatelic, of the area is very complex and the method adopted by the catalogue is to first list, in alphabetical order, the various colonies and republics which formed this federation, followed by stamps for the Union of South Africa and Republic of South Africa with the issues for the four Bantu "homelands" (granted independence in the 1970s but reincorporated into the Republic of South Africa in 1994) at the end.

The section is divided as follows:

  I. CAPE OF GOOD HOPE. British Kaffraria. Mafeking Siege Stamps. Vryburg
  II. GRIQUALAND WEST
  III. NATAL.
  IV. NEW REPUBLIC.
  V. ORANGE FREE STATE. Orange River Colony
  VI. TRANSVAAL. Pietersburg. Local British Occupation Issues
  VII. ZULULAND
  VIII. BRITISH ARMY FIELD OFFICES DURING SOUTH AFRICAN WAR
  IX. UNION OF SOUTH AFRICA
  X. REPUBLIC OF SOUTH AFRICA
  XI. BOPHUTHATSWANA
  XII. CISKEI
  XIII. TRANSKEI
  XIV. VENDA

I. CAPE OF GOOD HOPE

PRICES FOR STAMPS ON COVER

Nos. 1/4	from × 4
Nos. 5/14	from × 3
Nos. 18/21	from × 5
No. 22	
Nos. 23/6	from × 5
Nos. 27/31	from × 8
Nos. 32/3	from × 10
No. 34	from × 25
No. 35	from × 20
No. 36	from × 10
Nos. 37/8	from × 25
Nos. 39/45	from × 10
Nos. 46/7	from × 12
Nos. 48/54	from × 10
Nos. 55/6	from × 25
No. 57	from × 50
Nos. 58/69	from × 10
Nos. 70/8	from × 6

PRICES. Our prices for early Cape of Good Hope are for stamps in very fine condition. Exceptional copies are worth more, poorer copies considerably less.

1 Hope

2

(Des Charles Bell, Surveyor-General. Eng W. Humphrys. Recess P.B.)

1853 (1 Sept). W 2. Imperf. (a) Paper deeply blued.
1	1	1d. pale brick-red	..	..£3500	£275
		a. Deep brick-red	..	£5000	£300
		b. Wmk sideways	..	†	£375
2		4d. deep blue	..	£2000	£160
		a. Wmk sideways	..	£3000	£250

Plate proofs of the 4d. in a shade similar to the issued stamp exist on ungummed watermarked paper. The blueing on the reverse of these proofs is uneven giving a blotchy appearance.

(b) Paper slightly blued (blueing not pronounced at back)
3	1	1d. brick-red	..	..£3000	£200
		a. Brown-red	..	£3250	£225
		b. Wmk sideways	..	†	£300
4		4d. deep blue	..	£1300	£110
		a. Blue	..	£1400	£150
		b. Wmk sideways	..	†	£250

PERKINS BACON "CANCELLED". For notes on these handstamps showing "CANCELLED" between horizontal bars forming an oval, see Catalogue Introduction.

1855–63. W 2. (a) Imperf.
5	1	1d. brick-red/cream toned paper (1857)	..	£5000	£900
		a. Rose (1858) (H/S "CANCELLED" in oval £10000)	..	£450	£200
		ab. Wmk sideways	..	—	£350
		b. Deep rose-red	..	£650	£250
		ba. Wmk sideways	..	—	£350
6		4d. deep blue/white paper (1855)	..	£600	45·00
		a. Blue (H/S "CANCELLED" in oval £10000)	..	£400	45·00
		b. Bisected (on cover)	..		†£35000
		c. Wmk sideways	..	†	£150
7		6d. pale rose-lilac/white paper (18.2.58) (H/S "CANCELLED" in oval £8000)	..	£750	£200
		a. Wmk sideways	..		£600
		b. Deep rose-lilac/white paper	..	£1700	£300
		c. Slate-lilac/blued paper (1862)	..	£4250	£450
		d. Slate-purple/blued paper (1863)	..	£3500	£1000
		e. Bisected (on cover)	..	†	—
8		1s. brt yellow-green/white paper (18.2.58) (H/S "CANCELLED" in oval £10000)	£2500	£180
		a. Wmk sideways	..	†	£650
		b. Deep dark green (1859)	..	£225	£500

The method adopted for producing the plate of the 4d., 6d and 1s. stamps involved the use of two dies, so that there are two types of each of these values differing slightly in detail, but produced in equal numbers.

The 1d. value in dull rose on ungummed watermarked paper with the watermark sideways is a plate proof.

The 4d. is known bisected in 1858 and used with two other 4d. values to pay the inland registered fee. The 6d. is known bisected and used with 1d. for 4d. rate.

The paper of No. 5 is similar to that of Nos. 1/4, but is without the blueing. It is much thicker than the white paper used for later printings of the 1d. The evolution of the paper on these Cape of Good Hope stamps is similar to that on the line-engraved issues of Great Britain. Examples of the 6d. slate-lilac apparently on white paper have had the blueing washed out.

The 4d. value is known printed in black on white watermarked paper. Eleven authenticated copies have been recorded, the majority of which show cancellations or, at least, some indication that they have been used.

It was, at one time, believed that these stamps came from a small supply printed in black to mark the death of the Prince Consort, but references to examples can be found in the philatelic press before news of this event reached Cape Town.

It is now thought that these stamps represent proof sheets, possibly pressed into service during a shortage of stamps in 1861.

There is, however, no official confirmation of this theory. (Price £35000 un, £30000 with obliteration).

(b) Unofficially rouletted
9	1	1d. brick-red	..	†	£3000
10		4d. blue	..	†	£2250
11		6d. rose-lilac	..	†	£1500
12		1s. bright yellow-green	..	†	£3250
		a. Deep dark green	..	†	£3500

These rouletted stamps are best collected on cover.

3 Hope

(Local provisional (so-called "wood-block") issue. Engraved on steel by C. J. Roberts. Printed from stereotyped plates by Saul Solomon & Co, Cape Town)

1861 (Feb–April). Laid paper. Imperf.
13	3	1d. vermilion (27 February)	..	£14000	£2250
		a. Carmine (7 March)	..	£24000	£3000
		b. Brick-red (10 April)	..	£35000	£4250
		c. Error. Pale milky blue	..	—	£28000
		ca. Pale bright blue	..		—£30000
14		4d. pale milky blue (23 February)	£10000	£1600
		aa. Retouch or repair to rt-hand corner	—	£5500
		a. Pale grey-blue (March?)	..	£11000	£1600
		b. Pale bright blue (March?)	..	£11000	£1900
		ba. Retouch or repair to rt-hand corner	—	£5500
		c. Deep bright blue (12 April)	..	£95000	£4500
		d. Blue	..	£15000	£3000
		e. Error. Vermilion	..	£150000	£40000
		ea. Carmine	..	—	£95000
		f. Sideways tête-bêche (pair)		† £100000

Nos. 13/14 were each issued in tête-bêche pairs normally joined at edges bearing the same inscription ("POSTAGE" against "POSTAGE", etc). No. 14f, of which only one used example is known, comes from the first printing and shows the right-hand stamp misplaced so that "FOUR PENCE" adjoins "POSTAGE".

Nos. 13c/ca and 14e/ea were caused by the inclusion of incorrect clichés in the plates of the 1d. or 4d. values.

Both values were officially reprinted in March 1883, on wove paper. The 1d. is in deep red, and the 4d. in a deeper blue than that of the deepest shade of the issued stamp.

Specimens of the reprints have done postal duty, but their use was thus not intended. There are no reprints of the errors or of the retouched 4d.

Further reprints were made privately but with official permission, in 1940/41, in colours much deeper than those of any of the original printings, and on thick carton paper.

Examples of the 4d. are known unofficially rouletted.

Early in 1863, Perkins Bacon handed over the four plates used for printing the triangular Cape of Good Hope stamps to De La Rue & Co, Ltd, who made all the subsequent printings.

(Printed from the P.B. plates by D.L.R.)

1863–4. Imperf. (a) W 2.
18	1	1d. deep carmine-red (1864)	..	£120	£225
		a. Wmk sideways	..	£300	£300
		b. Deep brown-red	..	£375	£250
		ba. Wmk sideways	..	£500	£300
		c. Brownish red	..	£375	£225
		ca. Wmk sideways	..	£500	£275
19		4d. deep blue (1864)	..	£120	48·00
		a. Blue	..	£130	60·00
		b. Slate-blue	..	£2000	£500
		c. Steel-blue	..	£2000	£300
		d. Wmk sideways	..	£375	£150
20		6d. bright mauve (1864)	..	£160	£450
		a. Wmk sideways	..	†	£750
21		1s. bright emerald-green	..	£350	£450
		a. Pale emerald-green	..		£1000

(b) Wmk Crown CC (sideways)
22	1	1d. deep carmine-red	..		£15000

No. 22 was a trial printing, and is only known unused.

Our prices for the 4d. blue are for stamps which are blue by comparison with the other listed shades. An exceptionally pale shade is recognised by specialists and is rare.

With the exception of the 4d., these stamps may be easily distinguished from those printed by Perkins Bacon by their colours, which are quite distinct.

The De La Rue stamps of all values are less clearly printed, the figure of Hope and the lettering of the inscriptions standing out less boldly, while the fine lines of the background appear blurred and broken when examined under a glass. The background as a whole often shows irregularity in the apparent depth of colour, due to wear of the plates.

For note regarding the two dies of the 4d., 6d., and 1s. values, see after No. 8.

All the triangular stamps were demonetised as from 1 October 1900.

Four Pence.

4 "Hope" seated, with vine and ram. (With outer frame-line)

(5)

(Des Charles Bell. Die engraved on steel and stamps typo by D.L.R.)

1864–77. With outer frame-line surrounding the design. Wmk Crown CC. P 14.
23	4	1d. carmine-red (5.65)	..	85·00	18·00
		a. Rose-red	..	80·00	17·00
		w. Wmk inverted	..	—	60·00
24		4d. pale blue (8.65)	..	95·00	2·50
		a. Blue	..	£100	2·50
		b. Ultramarine	..	£250	55·00
		c. Deep blue (1872)	..	£140	3·25
		w. Wmk inverted	..	£250	50·00
25		6d. pale lilac (before 21.3.64)	..	£100	20·00
		a. Deep lilac	..	£200	6·50
		b. Violet (to bright) (1877)	..	£120	1·50
		w. Wmk inverted	..	†	£100
26		1s. deep green (1.64)	..	£500	18·00
		a. Green	..	£100	2·50
		ax. Wmk reversed	..		
		b. Blue-green	..	£110	3·75
		w. Wmk inverted	..	£500	£100

The 1d. rose-red, 4d. lilac, and 1s. blue-green are known imperf, probably from proof sheets.

The 1d. and 4d. stamps of this issue may be found with side and/or top outer frame-lines missing, due to wear of the plates. See also Nos. 44 and 52/3.

(Surch by Saul Solomon & Co, Cape Town)

1868 (17 Nov). No. 25a surch with T 5.
27	4	4d. on 6d. deep lilac (R.)	..	£190	16·00
		a. "Peuce" for "Pence"	..	£1800	£700
		b. "Fonr" for "Four"	..	—	£700
		w. Wmk inverted	..	—	£100

Specimens may also be found with bars omitted or at the top of the stamp, due to misplacement of the sheet.

The space between the words and bars varies from 12½ to 16 mm, stamps with spacing 15½ and 16 mm being rare. There were two printings, one of 120,000 in November 1868 and another of 1,000,000 in December. Stamps showing widest spacings are probably from the earlier printing.

6 (No outer frame-line)

(Die re-engraved. Typo D.L.R.)

1871–6. Outer frame-line removed. Wmk Crown CC. P 14.
28	6	½d. grey-black (shades) (12.75)	..	12·00	5·00
		w. Wmk inverted	..	—	50·00
29		1d. carmine-red (shades) (2.72)	..	28·00	60
		w. Wmk inverted	..		
30		4d. dull blue (shades) (12.76)	..	90·00	75
		b. Ultramarine	..	£200	50·00
		w. Wmk inverted	..		
31		5s. yellow-orange (25.8.71)	..	£250	14·00

The ½d., 1d. and 5s. are known imperf, probably from proof sheets.

See also Nos. 36, 39, 40/3, 48/51, 54, 61/2 and 64/8.

ONE PENNY   **THREE PENCE**

(7)   (8)

(Surch by Saul Solomon & Co, Cape Town)

1874–6. Nos. 25a and 26a surch with T 7.
32	4	1d. on 6d. deep lilac (R.) (1.9.74)	..	£400	80·00
		a. "E" of "PENNY" omitted	..	—	£900
33		1d. on 1s. green (11.76)	..	55·00	35·00

These provisionals are found with the bar only, either across the centre of the stamp or at top, with value only; or with value and bar close together, either at top or foot. Such varieties are due to misplacement of sheets during surcharging.

1879 (1 Nov). No. 30 surch with T 8.
34	6	3d. on 4d. blue (R.)	..	80·00	1·75
		a. "PENCB" for "PENCE"	..	£1500	£275
		b. "THE.EE" for "THREE"	..	£1800	£350
		c. Surch double	..	£7500	£2750
		w. Variety b. double	..		

The double surcharge must also have existed showing variety a. but only variety b. is known.

There are numerous minor varieties, including letters broken or out of alignment, due to defective printing and use of poor type.

The spacing between the bar and the words varies from 16½ to 18 mm.

THREEPENCE   **3**   **3**

(9)   (10)   (11)

(Surch by D.L.R.)

1880 (Feb). Special printing of the 4d. in new colour, surch. with T 9. Wmk Crown CC.
35	6	3d. on 4d. pale dull rose	..	55·00	1·75
		w. Wmk inverted	..	—	50·00

A minor constant variety exists with foot of "P" in "PENCE" broken off, making the letter appear shorter.

1880 (1 July). Wmk Crown CC. P 14.
36	6	3d. pale dull rose	..	£160	20·00
		w. Wmk inverted	..		

(Surch by Saul Solomon & Co, Cape Town)

1880 (Aug). No. 36 surch.
37	10	"3" on 3d. pale dull rose	..	60·00	1·00
		a. Surch inverted	..	£800	40·00
		b. Vert pair. Nos. 37/8	..	£800	£325
		w. Wmk inverted	..	—	50·00
38	11	"3" on 3d. pale dull rose	..	£150	5·00
		a. Surch inverted	..	£7000	£900
		w. Wmk inverted	..	—	£150

The "3" (T 10) is sometimes found broken. Vert pairs are known showing the two types of surcharge se-tenant, and vertical strips of three exist, the top stamp having surcharge T 10, the middle stamp being without surcharge, and the lower stamp having surcharge T 11 (Price for strip of 3 £3750 un.).

1881 (Jan). Wmk Crown CC. P 14.
39	6	3d. pale claret	..	95·00	2·25
		a. Deep claret	..	£100	2·00
		w. Wmk inverted	..		

This was a definite colour change made at the request of the Postmaster-General owing to the similarity between the colours of the 1d. stamp and the 3d. in pale dull rose. Imperf copies are probably from proof sheets.

Proofs of this value were printed in brown, on unwatermarked wove paper and imperf, but the colour was rejected as unsuitable.

1882 (July)–83. *Wmk Crown CA. P* 14.

40	6	½d. black (1.9.82)	..	..	18·00	80
		a. *Grey-black*	..	..	15·00	70
		w. *Wmk inverted*				
41		1d. rose-red	..	..	38·00	80
		a. *Deep rose-red*	..	..	45·00	80
		w. *Wmk inverted*	..	..	—	35·00
42		2d. pale bistre (1.9.82)	..	..	80·00	40
		a. *Deep bistre*	..	..	85·00	40
		w. *Wmk inverted*	..	..	—	50·00
43		3d. pale claret	..	..	6·50	90
		a. *Deep claret*	..	..	10·00	75
		aw. *Wmk inverted*				
44	4	6d. mauve (to bright) (8.82)		..	75·00	70
45	6	5s. orange (8.83)	..	..	£750	£200

Imperf pairs of the ½d., 1d. and 2d. are known, probably from proof sheets.

One
Half-penny.

(12)   13 "Cabled Anchor"

(Surch by Saul Solomon & Co, Cape Town)

1882 (July). *Nos. 39a and 43a surch with T* 12.

46	6	½d. on 3d. deep claret (Wmk CC)	..	£1700	£130
		a. *Hyphen omitted*		—	£3250
47		½d. on 3d. deep claret (Wmk CA)	..	18·00	2·50
		a. "p" in "penny" omitted	..	£2000	£700
		b. "y" in "penny" omitted	..	£1000	
		c. *Hyphen omitted*	..	£500	£350
		w. *Wmk inverted*			

Varieties also exist with broken and defective letters, and with the obliterating bar omitted or at the top of the stamp.

1884–90. *W* 13. *P* 14.

48	6	½d. black (1.86)	..		2·50	10
		a. *Grey-black*	..	..	2·50	10
		w. *Wmk inverted*				
49		1d. rose-red (12.85)	..	..	2·50	10
		a. *Carmine-red*	..	..	2·50	10
		w. *Wmk inverted*	..	..	—	40·00
50		2d. pale bistre (12.84)	..		20·00	60
		a. *Deep bistre*	..	..	6·00	10
		w. *Wmk inverted*	..	..	—	50·00
51		4d. blue (6.90)	..	..	7·00	30
		a. *Deep blue*	..	..	7·00	30
52	4	6d. reddish purple (12.84)	..	60·00	1·60
		a. *Purple (shades)*	..	..	6·00	20
		b. *Bright mauve*	..	..	9·50	40
53		1s. green (12.85)	..	..	£110	4·50
		a. *Blue-green* (1889)	..	..	55·00	
		w. *Wmk inverted*				
54	6	5s. orange (7.87)	..	..	60·00	4·00
		48/54		*Set of* 7	£120	4·50

All the above stamps are known in imperf pairs, probably from proof sheets.

For later shade and colour changes, etc., see Nos. 61, etc.

ONE PENNY.

2½d

(14)   15   (16)

(Surch by D.L.R.)

1891 (Mar). *Special printing of the* 3d. *in new colour, surch with T* 14.

55	6	2½d. on 3d. pale magenta	..	3·50	90
		a. *Deep magenta*	..	..	3·00	20
		b. "1" with horiz serif	..	..	50·00	32·00

No. 55b occurs on two stamps (Nos. 8 and 49) of the pane of 60.
Two types of "d" are found in the surcharge, one with square end to serif at top, and the other with pointed serif.

1892 (June). *W* 13. *P* 14.

56	15	2½d. sage-green	..	..	4·50	10
		a. *Olive-green*	..	..	7·50	55

See also No. 63.

(Surch by W. A. Richards & Sons, Cape Town)

1893 (Mar). *Nos.* 50/a *surch with T* 16.

57	6	1d. on 2d. pale bistre	..	..	2·75	40
		a. *Deep bistre*	..	..	1·60	40
		b. *No stop after "PENNY"*	..	45·00	11·00
		c. *Surch double*	..	..	—	£400

No. 57b occurs on stamp No. 42 of the upper left-hand pane, and on No. 6 of the lower right-hand pane.

Minor varieties exist showing broken letters and letters out of alignment or widely spaced. Also with obliterating bar omitted, due to misplacement of the sheet during surcharging.

17 "Hope" standing. Table Bay in background

18 Table Mountain and Bay with Arms of the Colony

(Des Mr. Mountford. Typo D.L.R.)

1893 (Oct)–1902. *W* 13. *P* 14.

58	17	½d. green (9.98)	..	..	1·00	10
59		1d. rose-red	..	..	1·75	50
		a. *Carmine*	..	..	65	10
60		3d. magenta (3.02)	..	..	4·00	1·00

The 1d. is known in imperf pairs, probably from proof sheets.

1893–98. *New colours, etc. W* 13. *P* 14.

61	6	½d. yellow-green (12.96)	..	1·50	20
		a. *Green*	..	..	2·75	40
62		2d. chocolate-brown (3.97)	..	2·00	15
63	15	2½d. pale ultramarine (3.96)	..	3·25	15
		a. *Ultramarine*	..	..	3·25	10
64	6	3d. bright magenta (9.98)	..	4·50	60
65		4d. sage-green (3.97)	..	..	4·00	90
66		1s. blue-green (12.93)	..	50·00	2·50
		a. *Deep blue-green*	..	..	70·00	7·50
67		1s. yellow-ochre (5.96)	..	7·00	1·00
68		5s. brown-orange (6.96)	..	60·00	3·50
		61/8		*Set of* 8	£120	8·00

(Des E. Sturman. Typo D.L.R.)

1900 (Jan). *W* 13. *P* 14.

69	18	1d. carmine	..	..	1·75	10
		w. *Wmk inverted*				

19   20   21

22   23   24

25   26   27

(Typo D.L.R.)

1902 (Dec)–04. *W* 13. *P* 14.

70	19	½d. green	..	..	1·50	10
71	20	1d. carmine	..	..	1·50	10
		w. *Wmk inverted*				
		y. *Wmk inverted and reversed*			
72	21	2d. brown (10.04)	..	..	7·00	80
		w. *Wmk inverted*				
73	22	2½d. ultramarine (3.04)	..	2·75	6·50
74	23	3d. magenta (4.03)	..	..	6·50	60
75	24	4d. olive-green (2.03)	..	6·00	65
76	25	6d. bright mauve (3.03)	..	12·00	30
77	26	1s. yellow-ochre	..	..	11·00	80
78	27	5s. brown-orange (2.03)	..	65·00	9·00
		70/8		*Set of* 9	£100	17·00

All values exist in imperf pairs, from proof sheets.

STAMP BOOKLETS

1902. *Black on red cover. Stapled.*
SB1 1s. ½d. booklet containing twelve 1d. (No. 71) in blocks of 6 .. .. £2000

1902. *Black on red cover. Stapled.*
SB2 2s. 7d. booklet containing thirty 1d. (No. 71) in blocks of 6 .. .. £2000

OFFICIAL STAMPS

The following stamps, punctured with a double triangle device, were used by the Stationery and Printed Forms Branch of the Cape of Good Hope Colonial Secretary's Department between 1904 and 1906. Later South Africa issues may have been similarly treated, but this has not been confirmed.

(O 1)

1904. *Various issues punctured as Type O* 1. (*a*) *Nos.* 50 *and* 52a.

O 1	6	2d. pale bistre	..		11·00	
O 2	4	6d. purple	..	..	11·00	

(*b*) *Nos.* 58 *and* 60

O 3	17	½d. green	..	..	14·00	
O 4		3d. magenta	..	..	11·00	

(*c*) *Nos.* 62 *and* 64/5

O 5	6	2d. chocolate-brown	..		11·00	
O 6		3d. bright magenta	..	..	14·00	
O 7		4d. sage-green	..	..	14·00	

(*d*) *No.* 69

O 8	18	1d. carmine	..	..	11·00	

(*e*) *Nos.* 70/2 *and* 74/8

O 9	19	½d. green	..	..	14·00	
O10	20	1d. carmine	..	..	8·00	
O11	21	2d. brown	..	..	11·00	
O12	23	3d. magenta	..	..	11·00	
O13	24	4d. olive-green	..	..	11·00	
O14	25	6d. bright mauve	..	..	11·00	
O15	26	1s. yellow-ochre	..	..	14·00	
O16	27	5s. brown-orange	..	..	35·00	

Nos. O1/16 are only known used.

Cape of Good Hope became a province of the Union of South Africa on 31 May 1910.

BRITISH KAFFRARIA

The history of the Cape eastern frontier was punctuated by a series of armed conflicts with the native population, known as the Kaffir Wars. After a particularly violent outbreak in 1846 the Governor, Sir Harry Smith, advanced the line of the Cape frontier to the Keikama and Tyumie Rivers. In the area between the new frontier and the Kei River a buffer state, British Kaffraria, was established on 17 December 1847. This area was not annexed to the Cape, but was administered as a separate Crown dependency by the Governor of Cape Colony in his capacity as High Commissioner for South Africa.

The territory, with its administration based on King William's Town, used the stamps of the Cape of Good Hope from 1853 onwards, the mail being sent via Port Elizabeth or overland from the Cape. Covers from British Kaffraria franked with the triangular issues are rare.

The first postal marking known from British Kaffraria is the 1849 type octagonal numeral No. 47 from Port Beaufort. Oval postmarks of the 1853 type were used at Alice, Aliwal North, Bedford, Fort Beaufort, King William's Town and Queenstown. In 1864 numeral cancellations were issued to all post offices within the Cape system and it is known that the following numbers were initially assigned to post towns in Kaffraria: 4 (King William's Town), 7 (Bedford), 11 (Queenstown), 29 (East London), 32 (Fort Beaufort), 38 (Aliwal North) and 104 (Cathcart).

It is believed that post offices may have also existed at Adelaide, Barkly East, Sterkstoom and Stutterheim, but, to date, no examples of handstamps or cancellations are known from them during the British Kaffraria period.

Following the decimation by famine of the Xhosa tribes in 1857 British Kaffraria was annexed to Cape Colony in 1865. The area eventually formed the basis of the Ciskei independent "homeland".

MAFEKING SIEGE STAMPS

PRICES FOR STAMPS ON COVER	
Nos. 1/16	*from* × 12
Nos. 17/18	*from* × 20
Nos. 19/20	*from* × 15
Nos. 21/2	*from* × 10

23 MARCH to 17 MAY 1900

There are numerous forgeries of the Mafeking overprints, many of which were brought home by soldiers returning from the Boer War.

MAFEKING,
3d.
BESIEGED.

(1)

MAFEKING
3d.
BESIEGED.

(2)

(Surcharged by Townsend & Co, Mafeking)

1900 (23 Mar–28 Apr). *Various stamps surch as T* 1 *and* 2.

(*a*) *Cape of Good Hope stamps surch as T* 1 (23 Mar)

1	6	1d. on ½d. green	..	£170	55·00
2	17	1d. on ½d. green (24.3)	..	£225	65·00
3		3d. on 1d. carmine	..	£170	50·00
4	6	6d. on 3d. magenta (24.3)	..	£25000	£250
5		1s. on 4d. sage-green (24.3)	..	£5500	£325

A variety in the setting of each value exists without comma after "MAFEKING".

(*b*) *Nos.* 59 *and* 61/3 *of Bechuanaland Protectorate (optd on Great Britain) surch as T* 1

6		1d. on ½d. vermilion (28.3)	..	£170	55·00
		a. *Surch inverted*	..	†	£4250
		b. *Vert pair, surch tête-bêche*		†	£20000
7		3d. on 1d. lilac (4.4)	..	£850	85·00
		a. *Surch double*	..	..	†	£15000
8		6d. on 2d. green and carmine (6.4)	£1600	70·00
9		6d. on 3d. purple/*yellow* (30.3)	..	£4000	£250
		a. *Surch inverted*	..	..	†	£19000
		b. *Surch double*			

(*c*) *Nos.* 12 *and* 35 *of British Bechuanaland (optd on Great Britain) surch as T* 1

10		6d. on 3d. lilac and black (27.3)	..	£350	60·00
11		1s. on 4d. green and purple-brown (29.3)	£1200	70·00
		a. *Surch double (both Type 1)*	..	†	£16000
		ab. *Surch double (Type 1 and Type 2)*	£6500	£4250
		b. *Surch treble*	..	..	†	£16000
		c. *Surch double, one inverted*	..	†	£16000

(*d*) *Nos.* 61/2 *and* 65 *of Bechuanaland Protectorate (optd on Great Britain) surch as T* 2

12		3d. on 1d. lilac (1 Apr)	..	£900	70·00
		a. *Surch double*	..	..	†	£6500
13		6d. on 2d. green and carmine (25 Apr)	£1100	70·00
14		1s. on 6d. purple/*rose-red* (12 Apr)	£3750	85·00

(*e*) *Nos.* 36/7 *of British Bechuanaland (optd on Great Britain) surch as T* 2

15		1s. on 6d. purple/*rose-red* (28 Apr)	£13000	£650
16		2s. on 1s. green (13 Apr)	..	£7000	£325

On the stamps overprinted "BECHUANALAND PROTECT-ORATE" and "BRITISH BECHUANALAND" the local surcharge is so adjusted as not to overlap the original overprint.

3 Cadet Sergt.-major
Goodyear   4 General Baden-Powell

(Des Dr. W. A. Hayes (T 3), Capt. H. Greener (T 4))

1900 (6–11 Apr). *Produced photographically by Dr. D. Taylor. Horiz laid paper with sheet wmk* "OCEANA FINE". *P* 12.

(a) 18½ *mm wide.* (b) 21 *mm wide*

17	3	1d. pale blue/*blue* (7.4)	..	£800	£275
18		1d. deep blue/*blue*	..	£800	£275
19	4	3d. pale blue/*blue* (a)	..	£1200	£400
		a. Reversed design	..	£45000	£35000
20		3d. deep blue/*blue* (a)	..	£1200	£350
		a. Imperf between (horiz pair)	..	† £48000	
		b. Double print	..	† £16000	
21		3d. pale blue/*blue* (b) (11.4)	..	£6500	£750
22		3d. deep blue/*blue* (b) (11.4)	..	£7000	£950

These stamps vary a great deal in colour from deep blue to pale grey.

No. 18 imperforate and without gum is believed to be a proof (*Price for unused pair* £15000).

No. 19a comes from a sheet of 12 printed in reverse of which nine, three mint and six used, are known to have survived.

VRYBURG

PRICES FOR STAMPS ON COVER	
Nos. 1/4	*from* × 5
Nos. 11/12	*from* × 2

BOER OCCUPATION

Vryburg was occupied by Boer forces on 15 October 1899. Unoverprinted stamps of Transvaal were used initially. Nos. 1/4 were only available from 24 to 29 November. The Boers evacuated the town on 7 May 1900.

½ PENCE

Z.A.R.

(1)

1899 (24 Nov). *Cape stamps surch as T* 1. *Surch* 12 *mm high on No.* 3 *and* 10 *mm on all other values.*

1	6	½ PENCE green	..	£200	80·00
		a. Italic "Z"	..	£1700	£700
		b. Surch 12 mm high	..	£1700	£700
2	17	1 PENCE rose	..	£225	£100
		a. Italic "Z"	..	£1900	£800
		b. Surch 12 mm high	..	£1900	£800
		c. "I" for "1"	..	£1200	£500
3	4	2 PENCE on 6d. mauve	..	£2250	£500
		a. Italic "Z"	..	£10000	£4250
4	15	2½ PENCE on 2½d. blue	..	£2000	£425
		a. Italic "Z"	..	£10000	£4250
		b. Surch 12 mm high	..	£10000	£4250

The "2 PENCE" on 6d. shows the surcharge 12 mm high. It is possible that this was the first value surcharged as the remaining three show the height reduced to 10 mm with the exception of one position in the second vertical row of the setting. The italic "Z" occurs on one position in the sixth vertical row. It is believed that the setting was of 60 (6×10).

BRITISH REOCCUPATION

(2)

1900 (16 May). *Provisionals issued by the Military Authorities. Stamps of Transvaal handstamped with T* 2.

11	30	½d. green	..	—	£1800
11a		1d. rose-red (No. 206)			
12		1d. rose-red and green (No. 217)	..	£8000	£4000
13		2d. brown and green			
14		2½d. dull blue and green	..		

No. 11 is known used with double handstamp and Nos. 11/12 with the overprint reading downwards

II. GRIQUALAND WEST

Griqualand West was situated to the North of Cape Colony, bounded on the north by what became British Bechuanaland and on the east by the Orange Free State.

The area was settled in the early nineteenth century by the Griqua tribal group, although many members of the tribe, including the paramount chief, migrated to Griqualand East (between Basutoland and the east coast of South Africa) in 1861–63. There was little European involvement in Griqualand West before 1866, but in that year the diamond fields along the Vaal River were discovered. Sovereignty was subsequently claimed by the Griqua Chief, the Orange Free State and the South African Republic (Transvaal). In 1871 the British authorities arbitrated in favour of the Griqua Chief who promptly ceded his terri-

tory to Great Britain. Griqualand West became a separate Crown Colony in January 1873.

During the initial stages of the prospecting boom mail was passed via the Orange Free State, but a post office connected to the Cape Colony postal system was opened at Klip Drift (subsequently Barkly) in late 1870. Further offices at De Beer's New Rush (subsequently Kimberley), Douglas and Du Toit's Pan (subsequently Beaconsfield) were open by September 1873.

Cape of Good Hope stamps to the 5s. value were in use from October 1871, but those originating in Griqualand West can only be identified after the introduction of Barred Oval Diamond Numeral cancellations in 1873. Numbers known to have been issued in the territory are:

  1 De Beers N.R. (New Rush) (subsequently Kimberley)
  3 Junction R. & M. (Riet and Modder Rivers)
  4 Barkly
  6 or 9 Du Toit's Pan (subsequently Beaconsfield)
  8 Langford (transferred to Douglas)
 10 Thornhill

PRICES FOR STAMPS ON COVER

The stamps of Griqualand West are worth from ×10 the price quoted for used stamps, when on cover from the territory.

FORGED OVERPRINTS. Many stamps show forged overprints. Great care should be taken when purchasing the scarcer items.

Stamps of the Cape of Good Hope, Crown CC, perf 14, *overprinted.*

1874 (Sept). *No.* 24a *of Cape of Good Hope surch* "1d." *in red manuscript by the Kimberley postmaster.*

1	1d. on 4d. blue	..	£750	£1300

G. W.

(1)

1877 (Mar). *Nos.* 29/30 *of Cape of Good Hope optd with T* 1.

2	1d. carmine-red	..	£425	75·00
	a. Opt double	..	† £1600	
3	4d. dull blue (R.)	..	£325	65·00

G	G	G	G	G	G
(1a)	(2)	(3)	(4)	(5)	(6)

G	G	G	G	G
(7)	(8)	(9)	(10)	(11)

G	G	G
(12)	(13)	(14)

1877 (Mar)–78. *Nos.* 24a, 25a, 26a *and* 28/31 *Cape of Good Hope optd with capital* "G".

(a) First printing. Optd with T 1a/6 *and* 8 *in black* (1d.) *or red (others)*

4	⅓d. grey-black				
	a. Opt Type 1a	..	..	16·00	20·00
	b. Opt Type 2	..	..	38·00	45·00
	c. Opt Type 3	..	..	22·00	26·00
	d. Opt Type 4	..	..	38·00	45·00
	e. Opt Type 5	..	..	42·00	50·00
	f. Opt Type 6	..	..	20·00	24·00
	g. Opt Type 8	..	..	£325	£350
5	1d. carmine-red				
	a. Opt Type 1a	..	..	17·00	12·00
	b. Opt Type 2	..	..	40·00	28·00
	c. Opt Type 3	..	..	22·00	18·00
	d. Opt Type 4	..	..	40·00	28·00
	e. Opt Type 5	..	..	45·00	32·00
	f. Opt Type 6	..	..	17·00	12·00
	g. Opt Type 8	..	..		*
6	4d. blue (with frame-line) (No. 24a)				
	a. Opt Type 1a	..	..	£150	26·00
	b. Opt Type 2	..	..	£375	75·00
	c. Opt Type 3	..	..	£275	38·00
	d. Opt Type 4	..	..	£375	75·00
	e. Opt Type 5	..	..	£425	85·00
	f. Opt Type 6	..	..	£200	35·00
	g. Opt Type 8	..	..		£450
7	4d. dull blue (without frame-line) (No. 30)				
	a. Opt Type 1a	..	..	£110	18·00
	b. Opt Type 2	..	..	£275	48·00
	c. Opt Type 3	..	..	£180	24·00
	d. Opt Type 4	..	..	£275	48·00
	e. Opt Type 5	..	..	£325	60·00
	f. Opt Type 6	..	..	£170	23·00
	g. Opt Type 8	..	..	£1200	£325
8	6d. deep lilac				
	a. Opt Type 1a	..	..	85·00	20·00
	b. Opt Type 2	..	..	£180	50·00
	c. Opt Type 3	..	..	£120	27·00
	d. Opt Type 4	..	..	£180	50·00
	e. Opt Type 5	..	..	£225	65·00
	f. Opt Type 6	..	..	£110	26·00
	g. Opt Type 8	..	..		£400
9	1s. green				
	a. Opt Type 1a	..	..	£100	17·00
	ab. Opt inverted	..	..	—	£350
	b. Opt Type 2	..	..	£225	38·00
	ba. Opt inverted				
	c. Opt Type 3	..	..	£160	22·00
	d. Opt Type 4	..	..	£225	38·00
	da. Opt inverted				
	e. Opt Type 5	..	..	£275	45·00
	f. Opt Type 6	..	..	£150	20·00
	fa. Opt inverted				
	g. Opt Type 8	..	..	—	£400

10	5s. yellow-orange				
	a. Opt Type 1a	..	..	£400	19·00
	b. Opt Type 2	..	..	—	42·00
	c. Opt Type 3	..	..	£550	23·00
	d. Opt Type 4	..	..	—	42·00
	e. Opt Type 5	..	..	£950	50·00
	f. Opt Type 6	..	..	£500	22·00
	g. Opt Type 8	..	..	£1900	

*The 1d. with overprint Type 8 from this setting can only be distinguished from that of the second printing when *se-tenant* with overprint Type 3.

Nos. 4/10 were overprinted by a setting of 120 covering two panes of 60 (6×10). This setting contained 41 examples of Type 1a, 10 of Type 2, 23 of Type 3, 10 of Type 4, 8 of Type 5, 27 of Type 6 and 1 of Type 8. Sub-types of Types 1a and 2 exist. The single example of Type 8 occurs on R. 7/4 of the right-hand pane.

It is believed that there may have been an additional setting used for the 5s. which was in considerable demand to cover the postage and registration on diamond consignments. It is also possible that single panes of this value and of the 1s. were overprinted using the right-hand half of the normal 120 setting.

(b) Second printing. Optd with T 6/14 *in black* (1878)

11	1d. carmine-red				
	a. Opt Type 6	..	..		*
	b. Opt Type 7	..	..	19·00	13·00
	c. Opt Type 8	..	..	38·00	24·00
	d. Opt Type 9	..	..	20·00	14·00
	e. Opt Type 10	..	..	55·00	50·00
	f. Opt Type 11	..	..	42·00	32·00
	g. Opt Type 12	..	..	50·00	45·00
	h. Opt Type 13	..	..	85·00	75·00
	i. Opt Type 14	..	..	£300	£250
12	4d. dull blue (without frame-line) (No. 30)				
	a. Opt Type 6	..	..	£225	42·00
	b. Opt Type 7	..	..	90·00	18·00
	c. Opt Type 8	..	..	£200	40·00
	d. Opt Type 9	..	..	£100	19·00
	e. Opt Type 10	..	..	£275	60·00
	f. Opt Type 11	..	..	£225	48·00
	g. Opt Type 12	..	..	£250	55·00
	h. Opt Type 13	..	..	£425	£120
	i. Opt Type 14	..	..	—	£375
13	6d. deep lilac				
	a. Opt Type 6	..	..	£350	75·00
	b. Opt Type 7	..	..	£170	40·00
	ba. Opt double				
	c. Opt Type 8	..	..	£325	70·00
	d. Opt Type 9	..	..	£190	45·00
	da. Opt double	..	..	—	£550
	e. Opt Type 10	..	..	£400	£110
	ea. Opt double	..	..	†	£700
	f. Opt Type 11	..	..	£350	80·00
	g. Opt Type 12	..	..	£350	£100
	h. Opt Type 13	..	..	£550	£180
	i. Opt Type 14	..	..	£1400	£475

*The 1d. with overprint Type 6 from this setting can only be distinguished from that of the first printing when *se-tenant* with Types 11, 12 or 13.

Nos. 11/13 were overprinted by another double-pane setting of 120 in which only Types 6 and 8 were repeated from that used for the first printing. The second printing setting contained 12 examples of Type 6, 30 of Type 7, 13 of Type 8, 27 of Type 9, 9 of Type 10, 11 of Type 11, 11 of Type 12, 6 of Type 13 and 1 of Type 14. Sub-types of Types 7 and 12 exist.

G	G	G
(15)	(16)	(17)

1878 (June). *Nos.* 24a, 25a *and* 28/30 *of Cape of Good Hope optd with small capital* "G", T 15/16.

14	15	½d. grey-black (R.)	..	5·50	7·00
		a. Opt inverted	..	7·00	7·00
		b. Opt double	..	32·00	42·00
		c. Opt double, both inverted	..	60·00	80·00
		d. Black opt	..	£140	75·00
		da. Opt inverted	..	£140	
		db. Opt double, one inverted in red	..	£275	
		dc. Opt double, one inverted (Type 16) in red	..	80·00	
15	16	½d. grey-black (R.)	..	7·00	7·00
		a. Opt inverted	..	7·00	8·50
		b. Opt double	..	55·00	55·00
		c. Opt double, both inverted			
		d. Black opt	..	32·00	32·00
		da. Opt inverted	..	32·00	32·00
		db. Opt double, one inverted (Type 15) in red	..	£110	
16	15	1d. carmine-red	..	6·50	4·50
		a. Opt inverted	..	6·50	6·50
		b. Opt double	..	£130	32·00
		c. Opt double, both inverted	..	£130	48·00
		d. Opt double, both inverted with one in red	..	26·00	28·00
		e. Opt double, both inverted with one (Type 16) in red			
17	16	1d. carmine-red	..	6·50	6·50
		a. Opt inverted	..	60·00	22·00
		b. Opt double	..	—	65·00
		c. Opt double, both inverted	..	—	80·00
		d. Opt double, both inverted with one in red	..	60·00	60·00
18	15	4d. blue (with frame-line) (No. 24a)	..	—	£100
19	16	4d. blue (with frame-line) (No. 24a)	..	—	£100
20	15	4d. dull blue (without frame-line) (No. 30)	90·00	20·00
		a. Opt inverted	..	£150	60·00
		b. Opt double	..	—	£140
		c. Opt double, both inverted	..	—	£190
		d. Red opt	..	£225	75·00
		da. Opt inverted	..	£700	55·00
21	16	4d. dull blue (without frame-line) (No. 30)	£110	8·50
		a. Opt inverted	..	£160	22·00
		b. Opt double	..	—	£150
		c. Opt double, both inverted	..	—	£190
		d. Red opt	..		
		da. Opt inverted	..	£225	60·00
22	15	6d. deep lilac	..	90·00	19·00
23	16	6d. deep lilac	..	—	19·00

Nos. 14/23 were also overprinted using a double-pane setting of 120. Based on evidence from surviving ½d. and 1d. sheets all overprints in the left-hand pane were roman, Type 15, and all those in the right-hand pane italic, Type 16, except for R. 1/6, 4/5, 6/6, 7/6, 8/6, 9/6 and 10/6 which were Type 15. There is considerable evidence to suggest that after the ½d. value had been overprinted the setting was amended to show a Type 15, instead of a Type 16, on R. 10/5 of the right-hand pane. Two strikes of the setting were required to overprint the sheets of 240 and it would appear that on many sheets the bottom two panes had the overprints inverted.

1879. *Nos. 25b, 26b and 28/31 of Cape of Good Hope optd with small capital "G", T 17.*

24	½d. grey-black	..	..		10·00	5·50
	a. Opt double	..	..		£325	£225
25	1d. carmine-red	..	..		10·00	3·50
	a. Opt inverted	..	..		—	75·00
	b. Opt double	..	..		—	£120
	c. Opt treble	..	..		—	£170
26	4d. dull blue	..	..		20·00	3·50
	a. Opt double	..	..		—	95·00
27	6d. violet	..	..		95·00	60·00
	a. Opt inverted	..	..		—	24·00
	b. Opt double	..	..		£450	£140
28	1s. green	..	..		80·00	3·50
	a. Opt double	..	..		£250	80·00
29	5s. yellow-orange	..	..		£300	6·00
	a. Opt double	..	..		£350	60·00
	b. Opt treble	..	..		—	£250

Nos. 24/9 were also overprinted using a setting of 120 which contained a number of minor type varieties.

Griqualand West was merged with Cape Colony in October 1880. The remaining stock of the overprinted stamps was returned from Kimberley to Cape Town and redistributed among various post offices in Cape Colony where they were used as ordinary Cape stamps.

III. NATAL

PRICES FOR STAMPS ON COVER		
Nos. 1/7	*from* × 2	
Nos. 9/25	*from* × 3	
Nos. 26/56	*from* × 4	
Nos. 57/8	—	
Nos. 59/73	*from* × 5	
Nos. 76/84	*from* × 4	
Nos. 85/93	*from* × 3	
Nos. 96/103	*from* × 6	
Nos. 104/5	*from* × 5	
Nos. 106/25	*from* × 6	
Nos. 127/42	*from* × 4	
Nos. 143/5*a*	—	
Nos. 146/57	*from* × 4	
No. 162	—	
Nos. 165/71	*from* × 3	
No. F1	—	
Nos. O1/6	*from* × 10	

(Embossed in plain relief on coloured wove paper)

1857 (26 May)**–61.** *Imperf.*

1	1	1d. rose (1858)	..	..	..	— £1700
2		1d. buff (1861)	..		..	— £1000
3		1d. blue (8.59)	..		..	— £1100
4	2	3d. rose	..	..	..	— £400
		a. *Tête-bêche* (pair)	..			— £32000
5	3	6d. green	..		..	— £1100
6	4	9d. blue	..		..	— £7000
7	5	1s. buff	..		..	— £5500

All the above have been reprinted more than once, and the early reprints of some values cannot always be distinguished with certainty from originals.

Stamps on surface-coloured paper, perforated 12½, are fiscals.

NOTE. The value of the above stamps depends on their dimensions, and the clearness of the embossing, but our prices are for fine used.

PERKINS BACON "CANCELLED". For notes on these handstamps showing "CANCELLED" between horizontal bars forming an oval, see Catalogue Introduction.

6 7

(Eng C. H. Jeens. Recess P.B.)

1859–60. *No wmk. P 14.*

9	6	1d. rose-red (1860) (H/S "CANCELLED" in oval £6000)			£120	70·00
10		3d. blue	..		£140	42·00
		a. Imperf between (vert pair)			† £6000

No. 10a is only known from a cover of 1867 franked with two such pairs.

The 3d. also exists with "CANCELLED" in oval, but no examples are believed to be in private hands.

1861. *No wmk. Intermediate perf 14 to 16.*

11	6	3d. blue	..	..		£200	65·00

1861–62. *No wmk. Rough perf 14 to 16.*

12	6	3d. blue	..	..	£100	32·00
		a. Imperf between (pair)			£3000
		b. Imperf (pair)			— £2500
13		6d. grey (1862)	..	..	£160	50·00

1862. *Wmk Small Star. Rough perf 14 to 16.*

15	6	1d. rose-red	..	..		£120	65·00

The 1d. without watermark and the 3d. watermark Small Star, both imperforate, are proofs.

(Recess D.L.R.)

1863. *Thick paper. No wmk. P 13.*

18	6	1d. lake	..	..		85·00	27·00
19		1d. carmine-red	..	..		85·00	27·00

1863–65. *Wmk Crown CC. P 12½.*

20	6	1d. brown-red	..	..	£120	35·00
21		1d. rose	..	..	85·00	32·00
22		1d. bright red	..	..	85·00	30·00
		x. Wmk reversed			
23		6d. lilac	..	..	55·00	17·00
24		6d. violet	..	..	42·00	27·00
		x. Wmk reversed			42·00	27·00

(Typo D.L.R.)

1867 (Apr). *Wmk Crown CC. P 14.*

25	7	1s. green	..	..		£130	28·00
		w. Wmk inverted				— £200

POSTAGE   Postage.   Postage.

(7*a*)   (7*b*)   (7*c*)

Postage.   POSTAGE.

(7*d*)   (7*e*)

1869 (23 Aug). *Optd horiz in Natal. No wmk (3d.), wmk Crown CC (others). P 14 or 14–16 (3d.), 12½ (1d., 6d) or 14 (1s.).*

(a) With T 7a (tall capitals without stop)

26	6	1d. rose	..	..	£350	75·00
27		1d. bright red	..	..	£300	65·00
28		3d. blue (No. 10)	..		£1400	£550
28*a*		3d. blue (No. 11)	..		£500	£225
28*b*		3d. blue (No. 12)	..		£425	85·00
29		6d. lilac	..		—	65·00
30		6d. violet	..		£400	75·00
31	7	1s. green	..		£5500	£1100

(b) With T 7b (12¾ mm long)

32	6	1d. rose	..	..	£325	70·00
33		1d. bright red	..	..	£275	60·00
		a. Opt double			† £1100
34		3d. blue (No. 10)	..		— £250
34*a*		3d. blue (No. 11)	..		£450	£180
34*b*		3d. blue (No. 12)	..		£400	75·00
35		6d. lilac	..		£425	60·00
36		6d. violet	..		£350	70·00
37	7	1s. green	..		£4250	£800

(c) With T 7c (13¾ mm long)

38	6	1d. rose	..	..	£550	£190
39		1d. bright red	..	..	£650	£170
40		3d. blue (No. 10)	..		
40*a*		3d. blue (No. 11)	..		— £650
40*b*		3d. blue (No. 12)	..		£1000	£300
41		6d. lilac	..		£1100	£140
42		6d. violet	..		£950	£130
		x. Wmk reversed			
43	7	1s. green	..		— £1700

(d) With T 7d (14½ to 15½ mm long)

44	6	1d. rose	..	..	£475	£160
45		1d. bright red	..	..	£475	£140
46		3d. blue (No. 10)	..		
46*a*		3d. blue (No. 11)	..		— £325
46*b*		3d. blue (No. 12)	..		— £225
47		6d. lilac	..		— 95·00
48		6d. violet	..		£850	90·00
49	7	1s. green	..		£8000	£1500

(e) With T 7e (small capitals with stop)

50	6	1d. rose	..	..	85·00	32·00
51		1d. bright red	..	..	£140	32·00
52		3d. blue (No. 10)	..		£250	65·00
53		3d. blue (No. 11)	..		£140	42·00
54		3d. blue (No. 12)	..		£170	38·00
		a. Opt double			† £850
54*b*		6d. lilac	..		£170	55·00
55		6d. violet	..		£130	45·00
56	7	1s. green	..		£190	60·00

It is believed that there were two settings of these overprints. The first setting, probably of 240, contained 60 examples of Type 7*a*, 72 of Type 7*b*, 20 of Type 7*c*, 28 of Type 7*d* and 60 of Type 7*e*. The second, probably of 60 (6×10), contained Type 7*e* only.

(8)

1870. *No. 25 optd with T 8 by De La Rue.*

57	7	1s. green (C.)	..	..	— £3250
58		1s. green (Blk.)	..		— £1200
		a. Opt double			— £2000
59		1s. green (G.)	..		70·00	10·00

For 1s. orange, see No. 108.

POSTAGE POSTAGE POSTAGE POSTAGE POSTAGE

(9)   (10)   (11)

1870–73. *Optd with T 9 by De La Rue. Wmk Crown CC. P 12½.*

60	6	1d. bright red	..	..	70·00	13·00
		x. Wmk reversed			70·00	13·00
61		3d. bright blue (R.) (1872)	..	75·00	13·00
62		6d. mauve (1873)	..		£150	25·00

1873 (July). *Fiscal stamp optd locally with T 10. Wmk Crown CC. P 14.*

63	7	1s. purple-brown	..	..		£150	18·00

1874 (July). *No 21 optd locally with T 11.*

65	6	1d. rose	..	..		£190	60·00
		a. Opt double				

12   13   14

15   16

(Typo D.L.R.)

1874 (Jan)**–99.** *Wmk Crown CC (sideways on 5s.). P 14.*

66	12	1d. dull rose (1876)	..		21·00	2·25
67		1d. bright rose	..		21·00	2·25
68	13	3d. blue	..		90·00	15·00
		a. Perf 14×12½			£1500	£850
69	14	4d. brown (1878)	..		95·00	11·00
		aw. Wmk inverted			
		b. Perf 12½			£325	65·00
70	15	6d. bright reddish violet	..	38·00	6·00
71	16	5s. maroon (1882)	..		£150	38·00
		a. Perf 15½×15 (1874)			£225	75·00
72		5s. rose	..		65·00	28·00
73		5s. carmine (H/S S. £160) (1899)	60·00	27·00
		a. Wmk upright			

POSTAGE   POSTAGE   HALF ½

(17)   (18)   (19)

1875–76. *Wmk Crown CC. P 14 (1s.) or 12½ (others). (a) Optd locally with T 17.*

76	6	1d. rose	..	..	95·00	45·00
		a. Opt double			£800	£425
77		1d. bright red	..		90·00	60·00

(b) Optd locally with T 18 (14½ mm long, without stop)

81	6	1d. rose (1876)	..		80·00	50·00
		a. Opt inverted			£950	£425
82		1d. yellow (1876)	..		70·00	70·00
		a. Opt double, one albino			£200
83		6d. violet (1876)	..		55·00	6·00
		a. Opt double			— £550
		b. Opt inverted			£650	£150
		w. Wmk inverted			
84	7	1s. green (1876)	..		80·00	5·50
		a. Opt double			— £325

TYPE 19. There are several varieties of this surcharge, of which T 19 is an example. They may be divided as follows:

(*a*) "½" 4½ mm high, "2" has straight foot.
(*b*) As last but "½" is 4 mm high.
(*c*) As last but "2" has curled foot.
(*d*) "½" 3½ mm. high, "2" has straight foot.
(*e*) As last but "2" has curled foot.
(*f*) As last but "2" smaller.

As the "½" and "HALF" were overprinted separately, they vary in relative position, and are frequently overlapping.

1877 (13 Feb). *No. 66 surch locally as T* **19**.

85	12	½d. on 1d. rose (a)	..	..	23·00 65·00
		a. "½" double	..	..	£100
86		½d. on 1d. rose (b)	..	..	£100
87		½d. on 1d. rose (c)	..	..	90·00
88		½d. on 1d. rose (d)	..	..	50·00 85·00
89		½d. on 1d. rose (e)	..	..	50·00
90		½d. on 1d. rose (f)	..	..	60·00

POSTAGE

Half-penny

ONE HALF-PENNY.

(21) 23 (24)

1877 (7 Oct)–**79**. *T* **6** (*wmk Crown CC. P* 12½) *surch locally as T* **21**.

91		½d. on 1d. yellow	..	..	8·00 12·00
		a. Surch inverted	..	..	£275 £190
		b. Surch double	..	..	£250 £180
		c. Surch omitted (lower stamp, vertical pair)	..		£1500 £1100
		d. "POSTAGE" omitted (in pair with normal)			£1500
		e. "S" of "POSTAGE" omitted (R. 8/3)			£250 £190
		f. "T" of "POSTAGE" omitted	..		£250 £250
92		1d. on 6d. violet (10.10.77)	..		50·00 8·50
		a. "S" of "POSTAGE" omitted (R. 8/3)			£375 £150
93		1d. on 6d. rose (12.2.79)	..		95·00 35·00
		a. Surch inverted	..		£550 £300
		b. Surch double	..		— £250
		c. Surch double, one inverted			£250 £200
		d. Surch four times	..		£375 £240
		e. "S" of "POSTAGE" omitted (R. 8/3)			£450 £300

No. 93c. is known with one surcharge showing variety "S" of "POSTAGE" omitted.
Other minor varieties exist in these surcharges.

(Typo D.L.R.)

1880 (13 Oct). *Wmk Crown CC. P* 14.

96	23	½d. green	..	..	9·50 14·00
		a. Imperf between (vert pair)	..		

1882 (20 Apr)–**89**. *Wmk Crown CA. P* 14.

97	23	½d. blue-green (23.4.84)	..		85·00 16·00
		a. Dull green (10.4.85)	..		1·25 90
99	12	1d. rose (shades) (1.84)	..		2·00 10
		a. Carmine	..		2·25 20
100	13	3d. blue (23.4.84)	..		£100 17·00
101		3d. grey (11.89)	..		2·75 95
102	14	4d. brown	..		3·25 75
103	15	6d. mauve	..		3·25 80
		w. Wmk inverted	..		† 75·00
97a/103				Set of 6	£100 18·00
97a, 99a, 101/3 H/S "Specimen"			Set of 5	£250	

1885 (26 Jan). *No. 99 surch locally with T* **24**.

104	12	½d. on 1d. rose	..		16·00 11·00
		a. No hyphen after "HALF"	..		60·00 42·00

TWO PENCE

TWO PENCE

TWOPENCE HALFPENNY

(25) 26 (27)

1886 (7 Jan). *No. 101 surch with T* **25** *by D.L.R.*

105	13	2d. on 3d. grey	..		18·00 5·50

(Typo D.L.R.)

1887 (Sept)–**89**. *Wmk Crown CA. P* 14.

106	26	2d. olive-green (Die I*) (Optd S. £70)	..	25·00 1·60
		a. Top left triangle detached	..		— £100
107		2d. olive-grn (Die II) (1889) (H/S S. £60)	2·25 1·40

*The differences between Dies I and II are shown in the introduction.

1888 (16 Mar). *As No. 25, but colour changed and wmk Crown CA, optd with T* **8** *by D.L.R.*

108	7	1s. orange (C.) (H/S S. £90)	..	3·50 85
		a. Opt double	..	..	— £1500

1891 (22 Apr). *Surch locally with T* **27**.

109	14	2½d. on 4d. brown (H/S S. £50)	..	11·00 8·50
		a. "TWOPENGE"	..	..	55·00
		b. "HALFPENN"	..	..	£225 £180
		c. Surch double	..	..	£250 £180
		d. Surch inverted	..	..	£350 £275

POSTAGE.

Half-penny

2½d

POSTAGE.

Varieties of long-tailed letters

28 (29) **POSTAGE.**

(Typo D.L.R.)

1891 (June). *Wmk Crown CA. P* 14.

113	28	2½d. bright blue (H/S S. £60)	..	3·75 50

1895 (12 Mar). *No. 24 surch locally with T* **29** *in carmine.*

114		½d. on 6d. violet (H/S S. £50)	..	1·25 2·75
		a. "Ealf-Penny"	..		20·00 24·00
		b. "Half-Penny" and long "P"		18·00 24·00
		ba. "Half Penny" and long "T" and "A"	18·00 24·00
		c. No stop after "POSTAGE" and long "P", "T" and "A"	18·00 24·00
		d. Long "P"	..		2·25 3·75
		e. Long "T"	..		2·25 3·75
		f. Long "A"	..		3·25 4·50
		g. Long "P" and "T"	..		2·25 3·75
		h. Long "P" and "A"	..		2·25 3·75
		i. Long "T" and "A"	..		3·00 4·25
		k. Long "P", "T" and "A"	..		3·00 4·25
		ka. Long "P", "T" and "A" with comma after "POSTAGE"		6·50 9·00
		l. Surch double	..		£250
		la. Surch double, one vertical	..	£250
		m. "POSTAGE" omitted	..		£1000
		x. Wmk reversed	..		1·25 2·75

The surcharge was applied as a setting of 60 (12×5) which contained seventeen normals, one each of Nos. 114a, 114b, 114ba, 114c, six of No. 114d, six of 114e, three of 114f, six of 114g, seven of 114h, five of No. 114i, four of 114k and two of No. 114ka.

HALF

(30) 31 32

1895 (18 Mar). *No. 99 surch locally with T* **30**.

125		HALF on 1d. rose (shades) (H/S S. £50)	1·00 75
		a. Surch double	..	..	£325 £325
		b. "H" with longer left limb	..	20·00
		c. Pair, one without surcharge	..	

No. 125b occurs on the second, fourth, sixth etc., stamps of the first vertical row of the righthand pane. It was very soon corrected.
In some printings what appears to be a broken "E" (with the top limb removed) was used instead of "L" in "HALF" on the last stamp in the sheet (*Price* £30)

(Typo D.L.R.)

1902–03. *Inscr* "POSTAGE REVENUE". *Wmk Crown CA. P* 14.

127	31	½d. blue-green	..	..	1·25 15
128		1d. carmine	..	..	3·50 15
129		1½d. green and black	..		2·00 2·00
130		2d. red and olive-green	..		1·25 25
131		2½d. bright blue	..		1·25 3·00
132		3d. purple and grey	..		1·00 90
133		4d. carmine and cinnamon	..	3·25 12·00
134		5d. black and orange	..	1·50 2·75
		w. Wmk inverted	..		— 60·00
135		6d. green and brown-purple	..	1·50 1·75
136		1s. carmine and pale blue	..	2·75 1·75
137		2s. green and bright violet	..	48·00 9·00
138		2s. 6d. purple	..		38·00 12·00
139		4s. deep rose and maize	..	60·00 70·00
		a. Imperf between (horiz pair)		
127/39				Set of 13	£150 £100
127/39 Optd "Specimen"			Set of 13	£160	

No. 139a is also imperforate between stamp and left-hand margin.

(Typo D.L.R.)

1902–3. *Wmk Crown CC. P* 14.

140	32	5s. dull blue and rose	..	..	22·00 9·00
141		10s. deep rose and chocolate	..	65·00 26·00
142		£1 black and bright blue	..	£150 50·00
143		£1 10s. green and violet (Optd S. £65)	£300 85·00
144		£5 mauve and black (Optd S. £100)	£1900 £500
145		£10 green and orange (Optd S. £200)	£6500 £2500
145a		£20 red and green (Optd S. £325)	£13000 £6000
140/2 Optd "Specimen"			Set of 3	£100	

USED HIGH VALUES. Collectors are warned against fiscally used high value Natal stamps with penmarks cleaned off and forged postmarks added.

1904–8. *Wmk Mult Crown CA. Chalk-surfaced paper* (£1 10s.). *P* 14.

146	31	½d. blue-green	..	..	3·00 15
147		1d. rose-carmine	..	..	3·50 15
		a. Booklet pane of 6, one stamp optd "NOT FOR USE"	..	£250
148		1d. deep carmine	..		6·00 20
		w. Wmk inverted	..		† 75·00
149		2d. red and olive-green	..	5·50 3·25
152		4d. carmine and cinnamon	..	2·75 1·00
153		5d. black and orange (1908)	..	3·50 4·00
155		1s. carmine and pale blue	..	65·00 7·00
156		2s. dull green and bright violet	55·00 35·00
157		2s. 6d. purple	..		45·00 35·00
162	32	£1 10s. brown-orange and deep purple (1908) (Optd S. £170)	£1000 £1800
146/57				Set of 9	£160 75·00

1908–9. *Inscr* "POSTAGE POSTAGE". *Wmk Mult Crown CA. P* 14.

165	31	6d. dull and bright purple	..	4·50 2·25
166		1s. black/green	..		o·00 2·00
167		2s. purple and bright blue/blue	15·00 3·00
168		2s. 6d. black and red/blue	..	25·00 3·00
169	32	5s. green and red/yellow	..	18·00 20·00
170		10s. green and red/green	..	55·00 60·00
171		£1 purple and black/red	..	£225 £200
165/71				Set of 7	£300 £250
165/71 Optd "Specimen"			Set of 7	£180	

STAMP BOOKLETS

1904. *Black on red cover. Stapled.*

SB1 2s. 6d. booklet containing thirty 1d. (No. 147) in blocks of 6 .. .. £1800

The first stamp of the first block in No. SB1 was cancelled "NOT FOR USE", the additional penny being used to defray the cost of production.

1905. *Black on red cover. Stapled.*

SB2 2s. 7d. booklet containing thirty 1d. (No. 147) in blocks of 6

FISCALS USED FOR POSTAGE

1869. *Embossed on coloured wove, surfaced paper. P* 12½.

F1 1 1d. yellow .. .. 50·00 80·00

NATAL REVENUE
FIVE POUNDS

Examples of 1d. yellow and 6d. rose values as Type **6**, 1s. purple-brown as Type **7** and various values between 5s. and £10 in the design illustrated above are believed to exist postally used, but, as such use was not authorised, they are not now listed.

OFFICIAL STAMPS

OFFICIAL

(O 1)

1904. *T* **31**, *wmk Mult Crown CA, optd with Type* O 1. *P* 14.

O1		½d. blue-green	..	..	3·00 35
O2		1d. carmine	..	..	2·25 70
O3		2d. red and olive-green	..	18·00 9·50
O4		3d. purple and grey	..	9·50 4·00
O5		6d. green and brown-purple ..	32·00 40·00
O6		1s. carmine and pale blue	..	95·00 £160
O1/6				Set of 6	£140 £190

The use of stamps overprinted as above was discontinued after 30 May 1907. Stamps perforated with the letters "N.G.R." were for use on Government Railways.

Natal became a province of the Union of South Africa on 31 May 1910.

IV. NEW REPUBLIC

During the unrest following the death of Cetshwayo, the Zulu king, in 1884, a group of Boers from the Transvaal offered their support to his son, Dinizulu. The price for this support was the cession of a sizeable portion of Zulu territory to an independent Boer republic. The New Republic, centred on Vryheid, was proclaimed on 16 August 1884 with the remaining Zulu territory becoming a protectorate of the new administration. The first reference to an organised postal service occurs in December 1884.

Alarmed by these developments the British authorities annexed the southernmost part of the land grant, around St. Lucia Bay, to prevent access to the Indian Ocean. The remainder of the New Republic was, however, recognised as independent on 22 October 1886. Zululand was annexed by the British on 22 May 1887.

Difficulties beset the New Republic, however, and its Volksraad voted for union with the South African Republic (Transvaal). The two republics united on 21 July 1888. In 1903 the territory of the former New Republic was transferred to Natal.

Mail from Vryheid in 1884–85 was franked with issues of Transvaal (for dispatches made via Utrecht) or Natal (for those sent via Dundee from August 1885 onwards). Issues of the New Republic were never accepted as internationally valid by these administrations so that all external mail continued to show Transvaal or Natal stamps used in combination with those of the republic.

PRICES FOR STAMPS ON COVER

No. 1	
Nos. 2/5	from × 50
Nos. 6/25	
Nos. 26/9	from × 50
Nos. 30/47	
Nos. 48/50	from × 50
No. 51	
Nos. 52/3	from × 50
Nos. 72/5	from × 50
Nos. 76/7b	
Nos. 78/80	from × 50
Nos. 81/95	

NIEUWE REPUBLIEK 1d 8 NOV 88 ZUID-AFRIKA.

1

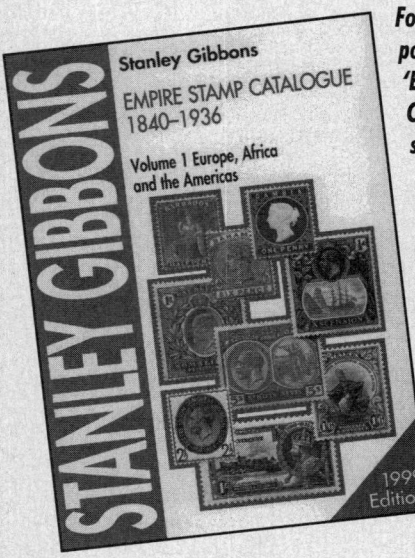

Printed with a rubber handstamp on paper bought in Europe and sent out ready gummed and perforated.

1886 (7 Jan)–**87.** *Various dates indicating date of printing.* P 11½.

A. *Without Arms.* (i) *Yellow paper*

1	1	1d. black (9.1.86)	..		† £3000
2		1d. violet (9.1.86)	..	10·00	12·00
		a. "1d." omitted (in pair with normal) (24.4.86)	..	£1500	
3		2d. violet (9.1.86)	..	10·00	15·00
		a. "d" omitted (13.10.86)	..	£3000	
4		3d. violet (13.1.86)	..	23·00	
		a. "d" omitted (13.10.86)	..	£3000	
		b. *Tête-bêche* (pair) (13.10.86)	..		
5		4d. violet (30.8.86)	..	35·00	
6		6d. violet (20.2.86)	..	30·00	
		a. "6d." omitted (in pair with normal) (2.7.86)	..		
7		9d. violet (13.1.86)	..	30·00	
8		1s. violet (30.8.86)	..	65·00	
		a. "1s." omitted (in pair with normal) (6.9.86)	..		
9		1/s. violet (13.10.86)	..	£500	
10		1/6 violet (30.8.86)	..	65·00	
11		1s. 6d. violet (13.1.86)	..	£400	
		a. *Tête-bêche* (pair) (6.9.86)	..		
		b. "d" omitted (13.10.86)	..	85·00	
12		2s. violet (30.8.86)	..	38·00	
		a. *Tête-bêche* (pair) (6.9.86)	..	£475	
13		2/6 violet (13.1.86)	..	£150	
14		2s. 6d. violet (1.86)	..	95·00	
15		4/s. violet (17.1.87)	..	£400	
16		5s. violet (1.86)	..	28·00	30·00
		a. "s" omitted (in pair with normal) (7.3.86)	..	£2000	
17		5/6 violet (20.2.86)	..	35·00	
18		5s. 6d. violet (13.1.86)	..	£160	
19		7/6 violet (13.1.86)	..	£170	
20		7s. 6d. violet (24.5.86)	..	95·00	
21		10s. violet (13.1.86)	..	95·00	
		a. *Tête-bêche* (pair) (2.7.86)	..	£170	
22		10s. 6d. violet (1.86)	..	48·00	
		a. "d" omitted (1.86)	..	48·00	
23		13s. violet (24.11.86)	..	£400	
24		£1 violet (13.1.86)	..	£120	
		a. *Tête-bêche* (pair) (13.10.86)	..	95·00	
25		30s. violet (13.1.86)	..	95·00	
		a. *Tête-bêche* (pair) (24.11.86)	..	£500	

(ii) *Blue granite paper*

26	1	1d. violet (20.1.86)	..	13·00	14·00
		a. "d" omitted (24.11.86)	..	£375	
		b. "1" omitted (in pair with normal) (24.11.86)	..		
27		2d. violet (24.1.86)	..	13·00	14·00
		a. "d" omitted (24.4.86)	..	£750	
		b. "2d." omitted (in pair with normal) (24.4.86)	..		
28		3d. violet (13.10.86)	..	16·00	18·00
		a. *Tête-bêche* (pair) (13.10.86)	..	£275	
29		4d. violet (24.5.86)	..	13·00	16·00
30		6d. violet (7.3.86)	..	25·00	21·00
		a. "6" omitted (in pair with normal) (24.5.86)	..	£1500	
31		9d. violet (6.9.86)	..	24·00	
32		1s. violet (1.86)	..	28·00	30·00
		a. *Tête-bêche* (pair) (21.5.86)	..	£300	
		b. "1s." omitted (in pair with normal) (29.4.86)	..	£1500	
33		1s. 6d. violet (2.7.86)	..	35·00	
		a. *Tête-bêche* (pair) (6.9.86)	..	£475	
34		1/6 violet (6.9.86)	..	£150	
35		2s. violet (21.5.86)	..	£120	
		a. "2s." omitted (in pair with normal) (24.5.86)	..	£1500	
36		2s. 6d. violet (19.8.86)	..	£140	
37		2/6 violet (19.8.86)	..	£180	
38		4/s. violet (17.1.87)	..	£200	
39		5/6 violet (13.1.86)	..	£200	
		a. "/" omitted (13.1.87)	..		
40		5s. 6d. violet (13.1.86)	..	£170	
41		7/6 violet (13.1.86)	..	£200	
41a		7s. 6d. violet (13.1.86)	..		
42		10s. violet (1.86)	..	£200	£200
		a. *Tête-bêche* (pair) (2.7.86)	..	£400	
		b. "s" omitted (13.1.86)	..		
43		10s. 6d. violet (1.86)	..	£200	
		a. *Tête-bêche* (pair) (13.1.86)	..		
		b. "d" omitted (1.86)	..	£450	
44		12s. violet (13.1.86)	..	£300	
45		13s. violet (17.1.87)	..	£400	
46		£1 violet (13.1.86)	..	£250	
47		30s. violet (13.1.86)	..	£250	

B. *With embossed Arms of New Republic.* (i) *Yellow paper*

48	1	1d. violet (20.1.86)	..	13·00	15·00
		a. Arms inverted (20.1.86)	..	25·00	25·00
		b. Arms *tête-bêche* (pair) (14.4.86)	..	£100	£120
		c. *Tête-bêche* (pair) (3.11.86)	..	£800	
49		2d. violet (30.8.86)	..	13·00	15·00
		a. Arms inverted (24.11.86)	..	23·00	28·00
50		4d. violet (2.12.86)	..	18·00	22·00
		a. Arms inverted (12.86)	..	95·00	60·00
		b. Arms *tête-bêche* (pair) (12.86)	..	£250	
51		6d. violet (2.12.86)	..	45·00	

(ii) *Blue granite paper*

52	1	1d. violet (20.1.86)	..	14·00	16·00
		a. Arms inverted (10.2.86)	..	35·00	40·00
		b. Arms *tête-bêche* (pair) (3.11.86)	..		
53		2d. violet (24.5.86)	..	14·00	16·00
		a. Arms inverted (30.8.86)	..	48·00	
		b. Arms *tête-bêche* (pair) (2.12.86)	..	£500	£500

Stamps as Type 1 were produced as and when stocks were required, each printing including in its design the date on which it was prepared. The dates quoted above for Nos. 1/53 are those on which the various stamps first appeared. Details of the various printing dates are given below. From these dates it can be seen that some values share common printing dates, and, it is believed, that the different values were produced *se-tenant* within the same sheet, at least in some instances. A reported proof sheet in the Pretoria Postal Museum, on yellow paper and embossed, contains 4 examples of the 6d. value and 3 each of the 3d., 4d., 9d., 1s., 1/6, 2/-, 2/6, 3s., 4s., 5s., 5/6, 7/6, 10/-, 10/6, £1 and 30/-.

The significance, if any, of the two coloured papers and the use of the embossing machine have never been satisfactorily explained. Both the different papers and the embossing machine were introduced in January 1886, and occur throughout the period that the stamps with dates were used.

PRINTINGS

Date	Paper	Face value	Cat. No.	Un.	Us.
Jan 86	Yellow	5s.	16	28·00	30·00
		10s. 6d.	22	£170	
		10s. 6d.	22a	80·00	
	Blue	1s.	32		
		10s.	42	£200	£200
		10s. 6d.	43	£200	
		10s. 6d.	43b	£450	
7 Jan 86	Yellow	10s. 6d.	22	£160	
	Blue	10s.	42		
		10s. 6d.	43	£450	
9 Jan 86	Yellow	1d. blk	1	†	£3000
		1d. vio	2	10·00	12·00
		2d.	3	10·00	15·00
13 Jan 86	Yellow	1d.	2	35·00	
		2d.	3	14·00	15·00
		3d.	4	40·00	
		9d.	7	£200	
		1s. 6d.	11	£400	
		2/6	13	£160	
		2s. 6d.	14	95·00	
		5s. 6d.	18		
		7/6	19	£170	
		10s.	21		
		£1	24	£130	
		30s.	25	95·00	
	Blue	5/6	39	£200	
		5s. 6d.	40	£170	
		7/6	41	£200	
		7s. 6d.	41a		
		10s.	42	£400	
		10s.	42b		
		10s. 6d.	43	£200	
		10s. 6d.	43a		
		12s.	44	£300	
		£1	46	£250	
		30s.	47	£250	
20 Jan 86	Yellow	1d.	2		
	Blue	1d.	26	£250	
	Yellow, embossed	1d.	48	32·00	
		1d.	48a	48·00	
	Blue, embossed	1d.	52	95·00	
Jan 20 86	Blue	1d.	26	23·00	
	Yellow, embossed	1d.	48a		
	Blue, embossed	1d.	52	£100	
24 Jan 86	Blue	1d.	26	18·00	
		2d.	27	30·00	
10 Feb 86	Yellow	1d.	2		
	Yellow, embossed	1d.	48		
		1d.	48a	48·00	
	Blue, embossed	1d.	52	£130	
		1d.	52a	35·00	
20 Feb 86	Yellow	6d.	6		
		1s. 6d.	11		
		2s. 6d.	14	£130	
		5/6	17	£120	
		5s. 6d.	18		
7 Mar 86	Yellow	1d.	2	£110	
		2/6	13		
		2s. 6d.	14	95·00	
		5s.	16	£200	85·00
		5s.	16a		
		5/6	17	35·00	
		5s. 6d.	18	£160	
	Blue	2d.	27	95·00	
		6d.	30		
		1s.	32		
17 Mar 86	Yellow	1d.	2	95·00	
	Yellow, embossed	1d.	48	48·00	
	Blue, embossed	1d.	52	95·00	
		1d.	52a	80·00	
26 Mar 86	Blue, embossed	1d.	52a	£130	
14 Apr 86	Yellow	1d.	2		
	Yellow, embossed	1d.	48	23·00	
		1d.	48a	£120	
		1d.	48b	£100	£120
	Blue, embossed	1d.	52	45·00	
		1d.	52a		
24 Apr 86	Yellow	1d.	2	£100	
		1d.	2a	£1500	
		5s.	16		
	Blue	2d.	27	28·00	
		2d.	27a	£750	
		2d.	27b		
29 Apr 86	Blue	1s.	32	£110	
		1s.	32b		
21 May 86	Yellow	6d.	6	£130	
	Blue	1d.	26	85·00	
		1s.	32	28·00	30·00
		1s.	32a	£300	
		1s.	32b	£1500	
		2s.	35	£275	
23 May 86	Blue, embossed	1d.	52a	95·00	
24 May 86	Yellow	1d.	2	95·00	
		2d.	3	£120	
		5s.	16	70·00	
		7/6	19	£170	
		7s. 6d.	20	95·00	
	Blue	1d.	26	13·00	14·00
		2d.	27	£300	£300
		4d.	29	85·00	
		6d.	30	£120	
		6d.	30a		
		1s.	32	£200	
		1s.	32b		
		2s.	35	£120	
		2s.	35a	£1500	
	Blue, embossed	2d.	53		
26 May 86	Yellow	1d.	2		
	Blue	1d.	26	£110	
	Yellow, embossed	1d.	48	£250	
		1d.	48a	95·00	
	Blue, embossed	1d.	52	48·00	50·00
		1d.	52a		
28 May 86	Yellow, embossed	1d.	48	32·00	
Jun 30 86	Blue	1d.	26	15·00	16·00
	Yellow, embossed	1d.	48	14·00	16·00

Date	Paper	Face value	Cat. No.	Un.	Us.
		1d.	48a	25·00	28·00
		1d.	48b	£200	£225
	Blue, embossed	1d.	52	45·00	40·00
2 Jul 86	Yellow	6d.	6	£200	
		6d.	6a		
		9d.	7	95·00	95·00
		10s.	21		
		10s.	21a		
	Blue	1s. 6d.	33	35·00	
		10s.	42	£200	
		10s.	42a	£400	
		10s. 6d.	43		
		10s. 6d.	43b		
3 Jul 86	Blue	10s.	42		
Jul 7 86	Yellow, embossed	1d.	48	25·00	
		1d.	48a	95·00	95·00
	Blue, embossed	1d.	52	14·00	16·00
		1d.	52a	55·00	40·00
4 Aug 86	Yellow	1d.	2		
	Yellow, embossed	1d.	48	55·00	
	Blue, embossed	1d.	52	35·00	
19 Aug 86	Yellow	2/6	13		
		2s. 6d.	14	£140	
	Blue	2s. 6d.	36	£140	
		2/6	37	£180	
30 Aug 86	Yellow	1d.	2	10·00	12·00
		2d.	3	11·00	
		3d.	4	23·00	
		4d.	5	48·00	
		6d.	6	32·00	
		9d.	7	48·00	
		1s.	8	65·00	
		1/6	10	65·00	
		2s.	12	95·00	
		2/6	13	£150	
	Blue	2d.	27	13·00	14·00
	Yellow, embossed	2d.	49		
	Blue, embossed	2d.	53	42·00	
		2d.	53a	£110	
6 Sep 86	Yellow	1d.	2	12·00	
		2d.	3	8·50	9·00
		3d.	4	38·00	
		4d.	5	40·00	
		6d.	6	30·00	
		9d.	7	30·00	
		1s.	8	95·00	
		1s.	8a		
		1/6	10	70·00	
		1s. 6d.	11	£400	
		1s. 6d.	11a		
		2s.	12	£100	
		2s.	12a	£475	
		2/6	13	£150	
		2s. 6d.	14		
		5s.	16	£140	
		7s. 6d.	20	£200	
		10s.	21	95·00	
		£1	24	£120	
	Blue	6d.	30	20·00	21·00
		9d.	31	£110	
		1s.	32	65·00	
		1s. 6d.	33	£140	
		1s. 6d.	33a	£475	
		1/6	34		
		2s. 6d.	36		
		2/6	37	£400	
		10s. 6d.	43		
13 Sep 86	Yellow	1d.	2		
	Yellow, embossed	1d.	48	48·00	
		1d.	48a	48·00	
	Blue, embossed	1d.	52	85·00	
6 Oct 86	Yellow	1d.	2		
	Blue	1d.	26	85·00	
	Yellow, embossed	1d.	48	23·00	18·00
		1d.	48a		
	Blue, embossed	1d.	52	45·00	18·00
		1d.	52a	85·00	
13 Oct 86	Yellow	1d.	2	12·00	12·00
		2d.	3	10·00	11·00
		2d.	3a	£3000	
		3d.	4	23·00	25·00
		3d.	4a	£3000	
		3d.	4b		
		4d.	5	35·00	
		6d.	6	30·00	32·00
		9d.	7	35·00	
		1s.	8	70·00	
		1/s	9	£500	
		1/6	10	£150	
		1s. 6d.	11b	85·00	
		2s.	12	38·00	
		2/6	13	£160	
		5s.	16	42·00	
		10s.	21	95·00	£100
		10s. 6d.	22a	48·00	
		£1	24	£120	
		£1	24a		
	Blue	2d.	27	13·00	14·00
		3d.	28	16·00	18·00
		3d.	28a	£275	
		4d.	29	28·00	28·00
		1s.	32	28·00	
		1/6	34	£150	
		2s.	35	£120	
3 Nov 86	Yellow	1d.	2	28·00	
	Blue	1d.	26		
	Yellow, embossed	1d.	48	13·00	15·00
		1d.	48a	25·00	28·00
		1d.	48b	£100	£120
		1d.	48c	£800	
	Blue, embossed	1d.	52	14·00	
		1d.	52a	35·00	40·00
		1d.	52b		
13 Nov 86	Yellow	1d.	2	35·00	
24 Nov 86	Yellow	1d.	2	14·00	
		2d.	3	10·00	11·00
		3d.	4	30·00	32·00
		1/6	10		
		10s.	21	£200	
		13s.	23	£400	

601

Date	Paper	Face value	Cat. No.	Un.	Us.
		30s.	25	95·00	
		30s.	25a	£500	
	Blue	1d.	26	38·00	17·00
		1d.	26a	£375	
		1d.	26b		
		2d.	27	18·00	
		2d.	27a		
		4d.	29	13·00	16·00
		6d.	30	20·00	21·00
		9d.	31	24·00	
		1s.	32	45·00	48·00
		1/6	34	£160	
		2s.	35	£140	
		2s.	35a	£3000	
	Yellow, embossed	2d.	49	£160	
		2d.	49a		
26 Nov 86	Yellow	1/6	10	£140	
2 Dec 86	Yellow	1d.	2		
		2d.	3		
	Blue	2d.	27		
	Yellow, embossed	1d.	48	13·00	15·00
		1d.	48a	£160	
		2d.	49	13·00	15·00
		2d.	49a	23·00	28·00
		4d.	50	80·00	
		6d.	51	45·00	
	Blue, embossed	1d.	52	28·00	
		1d.	52a	£160	
		2d.	53	14·00	16·00
		2d.	53a	48·00	
		2d.	53b	£500	£500
3 Dec 86	Yellow, embossed	6d.	51		
Dec 86	Yellow	6d.	6		
	Blue	4d.	29		
	Yellow, embossed	4d.	50	18·00	22·00
		4d.	50a	95·00	60·00
		4d.	50b	£250	
		6d.	51	42·00	
4 Jan 87	Yellow	1d.	2	35·00	
		2d.	3	32·00	
		13s.	23	£400	
	Blue	1d.	26	13·00	14·00
		2d.	27	16·00	14·00
	Blue, embossed	2d.	53	42·00	
13 Jan 87	Blue	5/6	39	£400	
		5/6	39a		
		7/6	41	£400	
17 Jan 87	Yellow	1d.	2	38·00	
		2d.	3	30·00	
		3d.	4	45·00	
		4/s.	15	£200	
	Blue	1d.	26	75·00	
		4/s.	38	£200	
		13s.	45	£400	
		30s.	47	£250	
20 Jan 87	Blue	2d.	27	32·00	
	Yellow, embossed	2d.	49	50·00	
		2d.	49a	£140	
	Blue, embossed	2d.	53	42·00	
		2d.	53a	95·00	
Jan 20 87	Yellow, embossed	1d.	48a	£400	

1887 (Jan–Mar). *As T 1, but without date. With embossed Arms.*

(a) Blue granite paper

72	1d. violet			14·00	14·00
	a. Imperf between (pair)				
	b. Stamps *tête-bêche* (pair)			£375	
	c. Arms *tête-bêche* (pair)				
	d. Arms inverted			23·00	23·00
	e. Arms omitted			£110	£110
	f. Arms sideways				
73	2d. violet			8·50	8·50
	a. Stamps *tête-bêche* (pair)			£275	
	b. Arms inverted			23·00	23·00
	c. Arms omitted			£110	95·00
	d. Arms *tête-bêche* (pair)				
74	3d. violet			13·00	13·00
	a. Stamps *tête-bêche* (pair)			£375	
	b. Arms *tête-bêche* (pair)				
	c. Arms inverted			48·00	48·00
75	4d. violet			13·00	13·00
	a. Stamps *tête-bêche* (pair)			£325	
	b. Arms *tête-bêche* (pair)			£275	
	c. Arms inverted			85·00	
76	6d. violet			13·00	13·00
	a. Arms inverted			85·00	
77	1/6 violet			14·00	14·00
	a. Arms inverted			80·00	
	b. Arms *tête-bêche* (pair)			£350	
77c	2/6 violet			†	£750

(b) Yellow paper (March 1887)

78	2d. violet (arms omitted)			13·00	
79	3d. violet			13·00	13·00
	a. Imperf between (pair)				
	b. Stamps *tête-bêche* (pair)			£325	£375
	c. Arms *tête-bêche* (pair)			£200	
	d. Arms inverted			23·00	23·00
	da. Double impression				
80	4d. violet			13·00	13·00
	a. Arms inverted			14·00	14·00
81	6d. violet			8·00	8·00
	a. Arms *tête-bêche* (pair)			£350	
	b. Arms inverted			42·00	42·00
	c. Arms omitted			80·00	
	ca. Double impression				
82	9d. violet			8·50	8·50
	a. Arms inverted			£200	
	b. Arms *tête-bêche* (pair)			£350	
83	1s. violet			8·50	8·50
	a. Arms inverted			70·00	
84	1/6 violet			17·00	14·0
85	2s. violet			18·00	16·00
	a. Arms inverted			55·00	50·00
	b. Arms omitted			70·00	
86	2/6 violet			23·00	23·00
	a. Arms inverted			28·00	28·00
87	3s. violet			42·00	42·00
	a. Arms inverted			45·00	45·00
	b. Stamps *tête-bêche* (pair)			£450	
88	4s. violet			11·00	11·00
	a. Arms omitted			£180	

88b	4/s violet			90·00
	ba. Arms omitted			£130
89	5s. violet			13·00 13·00
	a. Imperf between (pair)			
	b. Arms inverted			— 80·00
90	5/6 violet			12·00 12·00
91	7/6 violet			14·00 17·00
	a. Arms *tête-bêche* (pair)			
	b. Arms inverted			45·00
92	10s. violet			12·00 12·00
	a. Imperf between (pair)			
	b. Arms *tête-bêche* (pair)			£120
	c. Arms inverted			23·00
	d. Arms omitted			£110 45·00
93	10/6 violet			16·00 16·00
	a. Imperf between (pair)			
	b. Arms inverted			
94	£1 violet			45·00 45·00
	a. Stamps *tête-bêche* (pair)			£300 £350
	b. Arms inverted			55·00
95	30s. violet			£110

A £15 value as Nos. 78/95 exists, but is only known fiscally used (*Price £4000*).

New Republic united with the South African Republic (Transvaal) on 21 July 1888. In 1903 the territory of the former New Republic was transferred to Natal.

V. ORANGE FREE STATE

PRICES FOR STAMPS ON COVER	
Nos. 1/9	*from* × 20
Nos. 10/13	*from* × 25
Nos. 18/19	*from* × 20
No. 20	—
Nos. 21/42	*from* × 20
Nos. 48/51	*from* × 25
Nos. 52/138	*from* × 10
Nos. 139/51	*from* × 7
Nos. F1/17	
Nos. PF1/3	*from* × 20
No. M1	—

Supplies of Cape of Good Hope stamps were available at Bloemfontein and probably elsewhere in the Orange Free State, from mid-1856 onwards for use on mail to Cape Colony and beyond. Such arrangements continued after the introduction of Orange Free State stamps in 1868. It is not known if the dumb cancellations used on the few surviving covers were applied in the Free State or at Cape Town.

1

(Typo D.L.R.)

1868 (1 Jan)–94. *P 14.*

1	1	1d. pale brown	8·00	1·00
2		1d. red-brown	8·00	45
3		1d. deep brown	9·00	45
4		6d. pale rose (1868)	38·00	7·00
5		6d. rose (1871)	15·00	5·50
6		6d. rose-carmine (1891)	15·00	12·00
7		6d. bright carmine (1894)	9·00	2·00
8		1s. orange-buff	70·00	5·50
9		1s. orange-yellow	24·00	1·50
		a. Double print	—	£4000

4 **4** **4** **4**
(2) (a)   (b)   (c)   (d)

1877. *No. 5 surcharged T 2 (a) to (d).*

10	1	4d. on 6d. rose (a)	£325	55·00
		a. Surch inverted	—	£550
		b. Surch double (a + c)		
		c. Surch double, one inverted (a + c inverted)	—	£2750
		d. Surch double, one inverted (a inverted + c)	—	£4500
11		4d. on 6d. rose (b)	£1200	£160
		a. Surch inverted	—	£1100
		b. Surch double (b + d)		
12		4d. on 6d. rose (c)	£180	25·00
		a. Surch inverted	—	£350
		b. Surch double		
13		4d. on 6d. rose (d)	£225	35·00
		a. Surch inverted	£1100	£375

1878 (July). *P 14.*

18	1	4d. pale blue	15·00	2·50
19		4d. ultramarine	4·00	2·50
20		5s. green	9·00	11·00

1d. **1d.** **1d.** **1d.** **1d.** **1d.**
(3) (a)   (b)   (c)   (d)   (e)   (f)

Type 3: (a) Small "1" and "d". (b) Sloping serif. (c) Same size as (b), but "1" with straighter horizontal serif. (d) Taller "1" with horizontal serif and antique "d". (e) Same size as (d) but with sloping serif and thin line at foot. (f) as (d) but with Roman "d".

1881 (19 May). *No. 20 surch T 3 (a) to (f) with heavy black bar cancelling the old value.*

21	1	1d. on 5s. green (a)	80·00	14·00
22		1d. on 5s. green (b)	45·00	14·00
		a. Surch inverted	—	£750
		b. Surch double	—	£1000
23		1d. on 5s. green (c)	£160	65·00
		a. Surch inverted	—	£1100
		b. Surch double	—	£1300
24		1d. on 5s. green (d)	65·00	14·00
		a. Surch inverted	£1500	£750
		b. Surch double	—	£1000
25		1d. on 5s. green (e)	£375	£225
		a. Surch inverted	—	£2000
		b. Surch double	—	£2000
26		1d. on 5s. green (f)	65·00	14·00
		a. Surch inverted	—	£700
		b. Surch double	—	£800

No. 21 was the first printing in one type only. Nos. 22 to 25 constitute the second printing about a year later, and are all found on the same sheet; and No. 26 the third printing of which about half have the stop raised.

Owing to defective printing examples of Nos. 22 and 24/5 may be found with the obliterating bar at the top of the stamps or, from the top row, without the bar.

½d
(4)

1882 (Aug). *No. 20 surch with T 4 and with a thin black line cancelling old value.*

36	1	½d. on 5s. green	10·00	3·75
		a. Surch double	£400	£325
		b. Surch inverted	—	£800

3d **3d** **3d** **3d** **3d**
(5) (a)   (b)   (c)   (d)   (e)

1882. *No. 19 surch with T 5 (a) to (e) with thin black line cancelling value.*

38	1	3d. on 4d. ultramarine (a)	70·00	23·00
		a. Surch double	—	£750
39		3d. on 4d. ultramarine (b)	70·00	18·00
		a. Surch double	—	£700
40		3d. on 4d. ultramarine (c)	27·00	16·00
		a. Surch double	—	£700
41		3d. on 4d. ultramarine (d)	70·00	19·00
		a. Surch double	—	£700
42		3d. on 4d. ultramarine (e)	£180	60·00
		a. Surch double	—	£1400

Examples of Nos. 39 and 41/2 exist without the cancelling bar due to the misplacement of the surcharge.

1883–84. *P 14.*

48	1	½d. chestnut	1·25	50
49		2d. pale mauve	8·00	40
50		2d. bright mauve	8·00	30
51		3d. ultramarine	2·00	2·00

For 1d. purple, see No. 68.

2d **2d** **2d**
(6) (a)   (b)   (c)

1888 (Sept–Oct). *No. 51 surch with T 6(a), (b) or (c).*

(a) Wide "2". (b) Narrow "2"

52	1	2d. on 3d. ultramarine (a) (Sept)	45·00	9·00
		a. Surch inverted	—	£700
53		2d. on 3d. ultramarine (b)	23·00	2·00
		a. Surch inverted	—	£300
		b. "2" with curved foot (c)	—	£500

1d **1d** **1d**
(7) (a)   (b)   (c)

1890 (Dec)–91. *Nos. 51 and 19 surch with T 7 (a) to (c).*

54	1	1d. on 3d. ultramarine (a)	2·75	60
		a. Surch double	80·00	70·00
		c. "1" and "d" wide apart	£140	£110
55		1d. on 3d. ultramarine (b)	14·00	2·75
		a. Surch double	£225	£250
57		1d. on 4d. ultramarine (a)	20·00	3·75
		a. Surch double	£130	£110
		b. Surch double (a + b)	£375	
		c. Surch triple	—	£1500
58		1d. on 4d. ultramarine (b)	75·00	50·00
		a. Surch double	£375	£300
59		1d. on 4d. ultramarine (c)	£1300	£475
		a. Surch double		

The settings of the 1d. on 3d. and on 4d. are not identical. The variety (c) does not exist on the 3d.

2½d.
(8)

1892 (Oct). *No 51 surch with T 8.*

67	1	2½d. on 3d. ultramarine	7·50	70
		a. No stop after "d"	70·00	

1894 (Sept). *Colour changed. P 14.*

68	1	1d. purple	2·25	30

NEW INFORMATION

The editor is always interested to correspond with people who have new information that will improve or correct the Catalogue.

$\frac{1}{2}$**d** $\frac{1}{2}$**d** $\frac{1}{2}$**d**

(9) *(a)*   *(b)*   *(c)*

$\frac{1}{2}$**d** $\frac{1}{2}$**d** $\frac{1}{2}$**d** $\frac{1}{2}$**d**

(d)   *(e)*   *(f)*   *(g)*

Types (*a*) and (*e*) differ from types (*b*) and (*f*) respectively, in the serifs of the "1", but owing to faulty overprinting this distinction is not always clearly to be seen.

1896 (Sept). *No. 51 surch with T 9 (a) to (g).*

69	1	½d. on 3d. ultramarine (*a*)		2·75	8·00
70		½d. on 3d. ultramarine (*b*)		6·50	6·50
71		½d. on 3d. ultramarine (*c*)		5·50	2·50
72		½d. on 3d. ultramarine (*d*)		5·50	2·25
73		½d. on 3d. ultramarine (*e*)		5·50	2·25
74		½d. on 3d. ultramarine (*f*)		7·00	8·50
75		½d. on 3d. ultramarine (*g*)		4·00	2·75
		a. Surch double		13·00	10·00
		b. Surch triple		60·00	60·00

The double and triple surcharges are often different types, but are always type (*g*), or in combination with type (*g*).

Double surcharges in the same type, but without the "d" and bar, also exist, probably from a trial sheet prepared by the printer. Both mint and used examples are known.

Halve Penny.

2½

(10)   **(11)**

1896. *No. 51 surch with T 10.*

77	1	½d. on 3d. ultramarine		35	50

(i) Errors in setting

78	1	½d. on 3d. (no stop)		10·00	23·00
79		½d. on 3d. ("Peuny")		10·00	23·00

(ii) Surch inverted

81	1	½d. on 3d.			55·00
81*a*		½d. on 3d. (no stop)			
81*b*		½d. on 3d. ("Peuny")			£1500

(iii) Surch double, one inverted

81*c*	1	½d. on 3d. (Nos. 77 and 81)		£180	£200
81*d*		½d. on 3d. (Nos. 77 and 81*a*)		£750	£750
81*e*		½d. on 3d. (Nos. 77 and 81*b*)		£850	£850
81*f*		½d. on 3d. (Nos. 81 and 78)			£850
82		½d. on 3d. (Nos. 81 and 79)		—	£850

Examples from the top horizontal row can be found without the bar due to the surcharge being misplaced.

Nos. 69 to 75 also exist surcharged as last but they are considered not to have been issued with authority (*Prices from £30 each, unused*).

1897 (1 Jan). *No. 51 surch with T 11.* (*a*) As in illustration. (*b*) With Roman "1" and antique "2" in fraction.

83	1	2½d. on 3d. ultramarine (*a*)		3·50	80
83*a*		2½d. on 3d. ultramarine (*b*)		£140	90·00

1897. *P 14.*

84	1	½d. yellow (March)		1·75	35
85		½d. orange		1·75	35
87		1s. brown (Aug)		15·00	1·50

The 6d. blue was prepared for use in the Orange Free State, but had not been brought into use when the stamps were seized in Bloemfontein. A few have been seen without the "V.R.I." overprint, but they were not authorized or available for postage (*Price £55*).

BRITISH OCCUPATION

V. R. I.   **V. R. I.**   **V. R. I.**

4d   **½d**   **½d**

31 (Level stops)   **(32)** (Raised stops) **(33)**

       Thin "V"   Thick "V"

V. R I.

Inserted "R"

(Surch by Curling & Co, Bloemfontein)

1900. *T 1 surch as T 31/33 (2½d. on 3d. optd "V.R.I." only).*

(a) First printings surch as T 31 with stops level (March)

101		½d. on ½d. orange		2·00	2·00
		a. No stop after "V"		17·00	18·00
		b. No stop after "I"		£160	£160
		c. "½" omitted		£170	£170
		d. "I" omitted			£300
		e. "V.R.I." omitted			£160
		f. Value omitted			£100
		g. Small "½"		50·00	50·00
		h. Surch double			£160

102		1d. on 1d. purple		2·00	90
		a. Surch on 1d. deep brown (No. 3)		£600	£400
		b. No stop after "V"		10·00	10·00
		c. No stop after "R"		£150	£160
		d. No stop after "I"			
		e. "1" omitted		£170	£180
		f. "I" omitted		£300	£300
		g. "I" and stop after "R" omitted		£300	£300
		h. "V.R.I." omitted		£140	£150
		i. "d" omitted		£300	£300
		j. Value omitted		80·00	85·00
		k. Inverted stop after "R"		£200	
		l. Wider space between "1" and "d"		£100	£100
		m. "V" and "R" close		£150	
		n. Pair, one without surch		£425	
		o. "V" omitted		£800	
103		2d. on 2d. bright mauve		90	80
		a. No stop after "V"		10·00	14·00
		b. No stop after "R"		£250	
		c. No stop after "I"		£250	
		d. "V.R.I." omitted		£300	
		e. Value omitted		£300	
104		2½d. on 3d. ultramarine (*a*)		10·00	8·00
		a. No stop after "V"		70·00	70·00
105		2½d. on 3d. ultramarine (*b*)		£180	£180
106		3d. on 3d. ultramarine		1·75	95
		a. No stop after "V"		14·00	14·00
		b. Pair, one without surch		£400	
		c. "V.R.I." omitted		£250	
		d. Value omitted		£250	
107		4d. on 4d. ultramarine		4·75	8·50
		a. No stop after "V"		50·00	55·00
108		6d. on 6d. bright carmine		35·00	35·00
		a. No stop after "V"		£250	£275
		b. "6" omitted		£300	£300
109		6d. on 6d. blue		4·50	2·75
		a. No stop after "V"		30·00	32·00
		b. "6" omitted		60·00	65·00
		c. "V.R.I." omitted		—	£300
110		1s. on 1s. brown		6·00	2·75
		a. Surch on 1s. orange-yellow (No. 9)		£2750	£2250
		b. No stop after "V"		30·00	30·00
		c. "1" omitted		£100	£100
		d. "1" omitted and spaced stop after "s"		£120	£130
		e. "V.R.I." omitted		£150	£150
		f. Value omitted		£150	£150
		g. Raised stop after "s"		11·00	11·00
		h. Wider space between "1" and "s"		£150	£150
111		5s. on 5s. green		17·00	35·00
		a. No stop after "V"		£200	£225
		b. "5" omitted		£900	£900
		c. Inverted stop after "R"		£650	£650
		d. Wider space between "5" and "s"		£120	£120
		e. Value omitted		£350	

All values are found with a rectangular, instead of an oval, stop after "R". Misplaced surcharges (upwards or sideways) occur.

(b) Subsequent printings. (i) *Surch as T 32*

112		½d. on ½d. orange		30	20
		a. Raised and level stops mixed		1·75	2·00
		b. Pair, one with level stops		10·00	14·00
		c. No stop after "V"		2·50	2·75
		d. No stop after "I"		26·00	27·00
		e. "V" omitted		£550	
		f. Small "½"		14·00	16·00
		g. As a, and small "½"		14·00	16·00
		i. Space between "V" and "R"		£120	
113		1d. on 1d. purple		30	20
		a. Raised and level stops mixed		1·40	1·90
		b. Pair, one with level stops		19·00	20·00
		c. No stop after "V"		3·25	5·50
		d. No stop after "R"		15·00	16·00
		e. No stop after "I"		15·00	16·00
		f. No stops after "V" and "I"		£275	
		g. Surch inverted		£300	
		h. Surch double		£100	90·00
		i. Pair, one without surch		£200	
		j. Short figure "1"		£100	£100
		k. Space between "V" and "R"		55·00	60·00
		l. Space between "R" and "I"		£100	
		m. Space between "1" and "d"		£180	
		n. Inserted "R"		£325	
		o. Inserted "V"		£700	
114		2d. on 2d. bright mauve		60	30
		a. Raised and level stops mixed		4·50	4·50
		b. Pair, one with level stops		8·00	8·50
		c. Surch inverted		£300	£300
		d. "I" raised		75·00	
		e. Pair, one without surch		£275	
		f. No stop after "V"		£1000	
115		2½d. on 3d. ultramarine (*a*)		£200	£180
		a. Raised and level stops mixed		£550	
116		2½d. on 3d. ultramarine (*b*)		£1200	
117		3d. on 3d. ultramarine		30	30
		a. Raised and level stops mixed		6·50	6·50
		b. Pair, one with level stops		17·00	18·00
		c. No stop after "V"		£140	£140
		d. No stop after "R"		£350	£450
		e. "I" omitted		£400	
		f. Surch double		£400	
		g. Surch double, one diagonal		£375	
		h. Ditto, diagonal surch with mixed stops	£6500	
		n. Inserted "R"			
		o. Space between "3" and "d"		£140	
118		4d. on 4d. ultramarine		1·25	2·25
		a. Raised and level stops mixed		7·50	10·00
		b. Pair, one with level stops		18·00	25·00
119		6d. on 6d. bright carmine		35·00	48·00
		a. Raised and level stops mixed		£140	£140
		b. Pair, one with level stops		£200	£250
120		6d. on 6d. blue		70	40
		a. Raised and level stops mixed		7·50	7·50
		b. Pair, one with level stops		19·00	20·00
		c. No stop after "V"		£500	
		d. No stop after "R"		£300	
		e. Value omitted		£450	
121		1s. on 1s. brown		2·25	45
		a. Surch on 1s. orange-yellow (No. 9)		£1300	£1300
		b. Raised and level stops mixed		14·00	16·00
		c. Pair, one with level stops		27·00	30·00
		f. "s" omitted		£250	
		g. "V.R.I." omitted		£400	

122		5s. on 5s. green (H/S S. £50)		6·50	8·50
		a. Raised and level stops mixed		£300	£300
		b. Pair, one with level stops		£950	
		c. Short top to "5"		60·00	70·00

(ii) *Surch as T 33*

123		½d. on ½d. orange		2·25	1·25
124		1d. on 1d. purple		2·50	35
		a. Inverted "1" for "I"		17·00	18·00
		b. No stops after "R" and "I"		85·00	65·00
		c. No stop after "R"		38·00	42·00
		d. Surch double		£300	£300
		n. Inserted "R"		£400	£400
125		2d. on 2d. bright mauve		4·50	6·50
		a. Inverted "1" for "I"		24·00	27·00
126		2½d. on 3d. ultramarine (*a*)		£600	£700
127		2½d. on 3d. ultramarine (*b*)		£3500	
128		3d. on 3d. ultramarine		4·50	7·50
		a. Inverted "1" for "I"		65·00	70·00
		b. Surch double		£550	
		ba. Surch double, one diagonal		£550	
129		6d. on 6d. bright carmine		£425	
130		6d. on 6d. blue		7·50	18·00
131		1s. on 1s. brown		14·00	7·50
132		5s. on 5s. green (H/S S. £150)		40·00	48·00

Stamps with thick "V" occur in certain positions in *later* settings of the type with stops above the line (T **32**). *Earlier* settings with stops above the line have all stamps with thin "V".

Some confusion has previously been caused by the listing of certain varieties as though they occurred on stamps with thick "V", in fact they occur on stamps showing the normal thin "V", included in the settings which also contained the thick "V".

For a short period small blocks of unsurcharged Free State stamps could be handed in for surcharging so that varieties occur which are not found in the complete settings. Nos. 102a, 110a and 121a also occur from such stocks.

The inserted "R" variety occurs on positions 6 (T **32**) and 12 (T **33**) of the forme. The "R" of the original surcharge failed to print and the "R", but not the full stop, was added by the use of a handstamp. Traces of the original letter are often visible. The broken "V" flaw, also shown in the illustration, does not appear on No. 124n.

ORANGE RIVER COLONY

CROWN COLONY

E. R. I.

ORANGE RIVER COLONY.   **4d**   **6d**

(34)   **(35)**   **(36)**

1900 (10 Aug)–02. *Nos. 58a, 61a and 67 of Cape of Good Hope (wmk Cabled Anchor. P 14) optd with T 34 by W. A. Richards and Sons, Cape Town.*

133		½d. green (13.10.00)		20	10
		a. No stop		7·00	14·00
		b. Opt double		£600	£650
134		1d. carmine (May 1902)		40	10
		a. No stop		12·00	20·00
135		2½d. ultramarine		50	35
		a. No stop		55·00	65·00
133/5				Set of 3 1·00	45

In the ½d. and 2½d., the "no stop" after "COLONY" variety was the first stamp in the left lower pane. In the 1d. it is the twelfth stamp in the right lower pane on which the stop was present at the beginning of the printing but became damaged and soon failed to print.

1902 (14 Feb). *Surch with T 35 by "Bloemfontein Express".*

136		4d. on 6d. on 6d. blue (No. 120) (R.)		1·00	75
		a. No stop after "R"		32·00	38·00
		b. No stop after "I"		£1200	
		c. No stop on No. 130 (Thick "V")		2·00	5·00
		ca. Inverted "1" for "I"		6·00	13·00

1902 (Aug). *Surch with T 36.*

137	1	6d. on 6d. blue		2·50	7·00
		a. Surch double, one inverted			
		b. Wide space between "6" and "d" (R.4/2)		60·00	85·00

One Shilling

✳

(37)

38 King Edward VII, Springbok and Gnu

1902 (Sept). *Surch with T 37.*

138	1	1s. on 5s. green (O.)		7·00	9·00
		a. Thick "V"		15·00	27·00
		b. Short top to "5"		70·00	75·00
		c. Surch double			

(Typo D.L.R.)

1903 (3 Feb)–04. *Wmk Crown CA. P 14.*

139	38	½d. yellow-green (6.7.03)		7·50	1·25
		w. Wmk inverted		—	85·00
140		1d. scarlet		4·00	10
		w. Wmk inverted		—	75·00
141		2d. brown (6.7.03)		4·50	80
142		2½d. bright blue (6.7.03)		1·60	50
143		3d. mauve (6.7.03)		7·00	90
144		4d. scarlet and sage-green (6.7.03)		30·00	2·00
		a. "IOSTAGE" for "POSTAGE"		£800	£450
145		6d. scarlet and mauve (6.7.03)		6·50	90
146		1s. scarlet and bistre (6.7.03)		25·00	1·75
147		5s. blue and brown (31.10.04)		75·00	22·00
139/47				Set of 9 £140	27·00
139/47		Optd "Specimen"		Set of 9 £150	

No. 144a occurs on R.10/2 of the upper left pane.

Several of the above values are found with the overprint "C.S.A.R.", in black, for use by the Central South African Railways.

1905 (Nov)–09. *Wmk Mult Crown CA. P* 14.

148	38	½d. yellow-green (28.7.07)	..	..	9·00	50
149		1d. scarlet		..	7·50	30
150		4d. scarlet and sage-green (8.11.07)	..	4·50	1·75
		a. "IOSTAGE" for "POSTAGE"		..	£180	£150
151		1s. scarlet and bistre (2.09)	..	..	35·00	12·00
148/51		..	..	*Set of 4*	50·00	13·00

POSTCARD STAMPS

From 1889 onwards the Orange Free State Post Office sold postcards franked with adhesives as Type 1, some subsequently surcharged, over which the State Arms had been overprinted.

There are five known dies of the Arms overprint which can be identified as follows:

(a) Shield without flags. Three cows (two lying down, one standing) at left. Point of shield complete.
(b) Shield with flags. Four cows (two lying down, two standing) at left (*illustrated*).
(c) Shield with flags. Three cows (one lying down, two standing) at left.
(d) Shield without flags. Three cows (one lying down, two standing) at left.
(e) Shield without flags. Three cows (two lying down, one standing) at left. Point of shield broken.
There are also other differences between the dies.

PRICES. Those in the left-hand column are for unused examples on complete postcard; those on the right for used examples off card. Examples used on postcard are worth more.

1889 (Feb). *No.* 2 *(placed sideways on card) optd Shield Type* (a).
P1	1	1d. red-brown..	..	..	70·00	32·00
		a. Optd Shield Type (b)	..	..	24·00	5·50

1891 (Aug). *No.* 48 *optd Shield Type* (b).
P2	1	1½d. chestnut	..	..	3·50	1·25
		a. Optd Shield Type (c)	..	..	8·00	3·50
		b. Optd Shield Type (d)	..	..	4·00	1·75
		c. Optd Shield Type (e)	..	..	9·50	4·00

1892 (June). *No.* 54 *optd Shield Type* (b).
P3	1	1d. on 3d. ultramarine	..	..	70·00	38·00
		a. Optd Shield Type (c)	..	..	11·00	2·50

1½d.   1½d.   1½d.
(P 1)   (P 2)   (P 3)

1892 (Sept)–95. *Nos.* 50/1 *optd Shield Type* (b) *or* (d) (*No.* P6) *and surch with Types* P 1/3.
P4	1	1½d. on 2d. bright mauve (Type P 1) (11.92)	6·00	3·00
P5		1½d. on 2d. bright mauve (Type P 2) (9.93)	3·50	1·25
		a. Surch inverted			
P6		1½d. on 2d. brt mauve (Type P 3) (R.) (6.95)	9·00	3·50
P7		1½d. on 3d. ultramarine (Type P 1)	5·50	1·75

No. P5a shows the stamp affixed to the card upside down with the surcharge correctly positioned in relation to the card.

½d.
(P 4)

1895 (Aug). *No.* 48 *optd Shield Type* (e) *and surch with Type* P 4.
P8	1	½d. on ½d. chestnut..	..	..	9·00	2·25

1½d.   1½d.
(P 5)   (P 6)

1895 (Dec)–97. *No.* 50 *optd Shield Type* (e) *and surch with Types* P 5/6.
P 9	1	1½d. on 2d. bright mauve (Type P 5)	4·50	2·25
P10		1½d. on 2d. brt mauve (Type P 6) (12.97)	5·00	2·75
P11		1½d. on 2d. bright mauve (as Type P 6, but without stop) (12.97)	5·00	2·75

1897 (Mar). *No.* 85 *optd Shield Type* (d).
P12	1	1½d. orange	..	..	9·00	1·25
		a. Optd Shield Type (e)	..	..	10·00	2·25

V.R.I.
(P 7)

1900. *Nos.* P10/11 *optd as T* 31/2 *or with Type* P 7.
P13	1	1½d. on 2d. bright mauve (No. P10) (T 31)	20·00	4·50
P14		1½d. on 2d. bright mauve (No. P11) (T 31)	20·00	4·50
P15		1½d. on 2d. bright mauve (No. P11) (T 32)	20·00	4·50
P16		1½d. on 2d. bright mauve (No. P11) (T 32)	20·00	4·50
P17		1½d. on 2d. brt mve (No. P10) (Type P 7)	30·00	8·50
P18		1½d. on 2d. brt mve (No. P11) (Type P 7)	30·00	8·50

POLICE FRANK STAMPS

The following frank stamps were issued to members of the Orange Free State Mounted Police ("Rijdende Dienst Macht") for use on official correspondence.

PF 1 (eight ornaments at left and right)   PF 2

1896. *P* 12.
PF1	PF 1	(–) Black	..	..	..	£190

No. PF1 was printed in horizontal strips of 5 surrounded by wide margins.

1898. *As Type* PF 1, *but with nine ornaments at left and right. P* 12.
PF2		(–) Black	..	..	£130 £160

No. PF2 was printed in blocks of 4 (2×2) surrounded by wide margins.

1899. *P* 12.
PF3	PF 2	(–) Black/yellow	..	..	£120 £120

No. PF3 was printed in sheets of 24 (6×4) with the edges of the sheet imperforate. It is believed that they were produced from a setting of 8 (2×4) repeated three times.

Examples of No. PF3 are known postmarked as late as 28 April 1900. The O.F.S. Mounted Police were disbanded by the British authorities at the end of the following month.

MILITARY FRANK STAMP

M 1

(Typeset Curling & Co, Bloemfontein)

1899 (15 Oct). *P* 12.
M1	M 1	(–) Black/*bistre-yellow*	..	12·00 45·00

Supplies of No. M1 were issued to members of the Orange Free State army on active service during the Second Boer War. To pass free through the O.F.S. fieldpost system letters had to be franked with No. M1 or initialled by the appropriate unit commander. The franks were in use between October 1899 and February 1900.

No. M1 was printed in sheets of 20 (5×4) using a setting of five different types in a horizontal row. The colour in the paper runs in water.

Typeset forgeries can be identified by the appearance of 17 pearls, instead of the 16 of the originals, in the top and bottom frames. Forgeries produced by lithography omit the stops after "BRIEF" and "FRANKO".

FISCAL STAMPS USED FOR POSTAGE

The following were issued in 1878 (Nos. F1 and F3 in 1882) and were authorised for postal use between 1882 and 1886.

F 1   F 2

(Typo D.L.R.)

1882–86. *P* 14.
F 1	F1	6d. pearl-grey	..	..	6·00	10·00
F 2		6d. purple-brown	..	..	22·00	16·00
F 3	F2	1s. purple-brown	..	..	7·00	14·00
F 4		1s. pearl-grey	..	..	35·00	42·00
F 5		1s. blue	..	..	13·00	10·00
F 6		2s. magenta	..	..	13·00	10·00
F 7		3s. chestnut	..	..	16·00	42·00
F 8		4s. grey	..	..		
F 9		5s. rose	..	..	18·00	18·00
F10		6s. green	..	..	—	45·00
F11		7s. violet	..	..		
F12		10s. orange	..	..	38·00	27·00
F13		£1 purple	..	..	48·00	30·00
F14		£2 red-brown	..	..	55·00	
F14a		£4 carmine				
F15		£5 green	..	..	80·00	38·00

A fiscally used example of No. F2 exists showing "ZES PENCE" double, one inverted. The 8s. yellow was prepared but we have no evidence of its use postally without surcharge Type F 3.

ZES PENCE.
(F 3)

1886. *Surch with Type* F 3.
F16	F 2	6d. on 4s. grey	..	..	..	£190
F17		6d. on 8s. yellow	..	..	..	£160

Postage stamps overprinted for use as Telegraph stamps and used postally are omitted as it is impossible to say with certainty which stamps were genuinely used for postal purposes.

Orange Free State became a province of the Union of South Africa on 31 May 1910.

VI. TRANSVAAL
(*formerly* **South African Republic**)

From 1852 mail from the Transvaal was forwarded to the Cape of Good Hope, via the Orange Free State, by a post office at Potchefstroom. In 1859 the Volksraad voted to set up a regular postal service and arrangements were made for letters sent to the Cape and for overseas to be franked with Cape of Good Hope stamps.

The Potchefstroom postmaster placed his first order for these on 23 August 1859 and examples of all four triangular values are known postmarked there.

PRICES FOR STAMPS ON COVER

Nos. 1/6 are rare used on cover.

Nos. 7/80	*from* × 20
Nos. 86/155	*from* × 3
Nos. 156/62	*from* × 6
Nos. 163/9	*from* × 5
Nos. 170/225	*from* × 10
Nos. 226/34	*from* × 20
Nos. 235/7	—
Nos. 238/43	*from* × 12
Nos. 244/55	*from* × 4
Nos. 256/7	*from* × 6
Nos. 258/9	—
Nos. 260/76	*from* × 20
Nos. F1/5	*from* × 5
Nos. D1/7	*from* × 20

The issues for Pietersburg, Lydenburg, Rustenburg, Schweizer Renecke and Wolmaransstad are very rare when on cover.

1 (Eagle with   2   3
spread wings)

(Typo Adolph Otto, Gustrow, Mecklenburg-Schwerin)

1870 (1 May). *Thin paper, clear and distinct impressions.*
(a) Imperf
1	1	1d. brown-lake	..	..	£350	
		a. Orange-red	..	..	£350	£350
2		6d. bright ultramarine	..	£130	£130
		a. Pale ultramarine	..	..	£150	£160
3		1s. deep green	..	..	£550	£550
		a. Tête-bêche (pair)	..	..		

(b) Fine roulette, 15½ to 16
4	1	1d. brown-lake	..	..	85·00	
		a. Brick-red	..	..	65·00	
		b. Orange-red	..	..	65·00	
		c. Vermilion	..	..	65·00	
5		6d. bright ultramarine	..	60·00	60·00
		a. Pale ultramarine	..	..	70·00	
6		1s. deep green	..	..	£130	£130
		a. Yellow-green	..	..	£100	95·00
		b. Emerald-green	..	..	80·00	80·00

Examples of Nos. 1/6 may have been sold to dealers at some stage between their arrival in Transvaal during August 1869 and the sale of stamps to the public for postal purposes on 1 May 1870.

PLATES. The German printings of the 1d., 6d. and 1s. in Type 1 were printed from two pairs of plates, each pair printing sheets of 80 in two panes of five horizontal rows of eight.

One pair of plates, used for Nos. 4a, 4c, 5a and 6/a, produced stamps spaced 1¼ to 1½ mm apart with the rouletting close to the design on all four sides. The 1d. from these "narrow" plates shows a gap in the outer frame line at the bottom right-hand corner. The second pair, used for Nos. 1/3, 4, 4b, 5/a and 6b, had 2½ to 3½ mm between the stamps. These "wide" plates were sent to the Transvaal in 1869 and were used there to produce either single or double pane prinfings until 1883.

The 6d. and 1s. "wide" plates each had an inverted *cliché*. When printed these occurred on right-hand pane R. 4/1 of the 6d. and right-hand pane R.1/1 of the 1s. These were never corrected and resulted in *tête-bêche* pairs of these values as late as 1883.

REPRINTS AND IMITATIONS. A number of unauthorised printings were made of these stamps by the German printer. Many of these can be identified by differences in the central arms, unusual colours or, in the case of the 1d., by an extra frame around the numeral tablets at top.

Genuine stamps always show the "D" of "EENDRAGT" higher than the remainder of the word, have no break in the border above "DR" and depict the flagstaff at bottom right, behind "MAGT", stopping short of the central shield. They also show the eagle's eye as a clear white circle. On the forgeries the eye is often blurred.

The most difficult of the reprints to detect is the 1s. yellow-green which was once regarded as genuine, but was subsequently identified, by J. N. Luff in *The Philatelic Record* 1911–12, as coming from an unauthorised plate of four. Stamps from this plate show either a white dot between "EEN" and "SHILLING" or a white flaw below the wagon pole.

(Typo M. J. Viljoen, Pretoria)

1870 (1 May–4 July).

I. *Thin gummed paper from Germany. Impressions coarse and defective.* (a) *Imperf*

8	1	1d. dull rose-red ..	..	70·00
		a. Reddish pink ..	..	60·00
		b. Carmine-red ..	..	55·00 65·00
9		6d. dull ultramarine ..	..	£250 60·00
		a. Tête-bêche (pair)		

(b) *Fine roulette, 15½ to 16*

10	1	1d. carmine-red ..	..	£700 £250
11		6d. dull ultramarine	..	£180 90·00
		a. Imperf between (vert pair) ..		£550

(c) *Wide roulette, 6½*

12	1	1d. carmine-red ..	..	— £850

II. *Thick, hard paper with thin yellow smooth gum (No. 15) or yellow streaky gum (others).* (a) *Imperf*

13	1	1d. pale rose-red ..	..	60·00
		a. Carmine-red ..	..	60·00 70·00
14		1s. yellow-green ..	..	85·00 75·00
		a. Tête-bêche (pair)	..	£14000
		b. Bisected (6d.) (on cover)		† £1200

(b) *Fine roulette, 15½ to 16*

15	1	1d. carmine-red (24 May)	..	80·00
16		6d. ultramarine (10 May)	..	80·00 80·00
		a. Tête-bêche (pair)	..	£22000 £17000
17		1s. yellow-green	..	£550 £550

III. *Medium paper, blotchy heavy printing and whitish gum. Fine roulette 15½ to 16 (4 July)*

18	1	1d. rose-red ..	..	60·00 75·00
		a. Carmine-red ..	..	38·00 45·00
		b. Crimson. From over-inked plate		£130
19		6d. ultramarine ..	..	75·00 65·00
		a. Tête-bêche (pair)		
		b. Deep ultram. From over-inked plate		£400 £150
20		1s. deep green ..	..	£100 65·00
		a. From over-inked plate	..	£450 £150

The rouletting machine producing the wide 6½ gauge was not introduced until 1875.

Nos. 18b, 19b and 20a were printed from badly over-inked plates giving heavy blobby impressions.

(Typo J. P. Borrius, Potchefstroom)

1870 (Sept)–71. *Stout paper, but with colour often showing through, whitish gum.* (a) *Imperf*

21	1	1d. black ..	..	£120 £100

(b) *Fine roulette, 15½ to 16*

22	1	1d. black ..	..	15·00 25·00
		a. Grey-black ..	..	15·00 25·00
23		6d. blackish blue (7.71) ..	..	£120 60·00
		a. Dull blue ..	..	90·00 75·00

(Typo Adolph Otto, Gustrow, Mecklenburg-Schwerin)

1871 (July). *Thin paper, clear and distinct impressions. Fine roulette, 15½ to 16.*

24	2	3d. pale reddish lilac	..	80·00 90·00
		a. Deep lilac ..	..	85·00 95·00
		b. Vert laid paper		

No. 24 and later printings in the Transvaal were produced from a pair of plates in the same format as the 1869 issue. All genuine stamps have a small dot on the left leg of the eagle.

Imperforate examples in the issued shade, without the dot on eagle's leg, had been previously supplied by the printer, probably as essays, but were not issued for postal purposes. (*Price* £750 *unused*). They also exist tête-bêche (Price for un pair £3250).

Imperforate and rouletted stamps in other colours are reprints.

(Typo J. P. Borrius, Potchefstroom)

1872–74. *Fine roulette, 15½ to 16.* (a) *Thin transparent paper*

25	1	1d. black ..	..	£170 £550
26		1d. bright carmine ..	..	£140 50·00
27		6d. ultramarine ..	..	£100 40·00
28		1s. green ..	..	£120 50·00

(b) *Thinnish opaque paper, clear printing* (Dec 1872)

29	1	1d. reddish pink ..	..	55·00 38·00
		a. Carmine-red ..	..	55·00 38·00
30	2	3d. grey-lilac ..	..	85·00 45·00
31	1	6d. ultramarine ..	..	55·00 27·00
		a. Pale ultramarine	..	65·00 29·00
32		1s. yellow-green ..	..	70·00 38·00
		a. Green ..	..	70·00 38·00
		aa. Bisected (6d.) (on cover)		† £1400

(c) *Thickish wove paper* (1873–74)

33	1	1d. dull rose ..	..	£400 70·00
		a. Brownish rose ..	..	£475 £110
		b. Printed on both sides		
34		6d. milky blue ..	..	£140 45·00
		a. Deep dull blue ..	..	85·00 40·00
		aa. Imperf (pair) ..	..	£600
		ab. Imperf between (horiz pair) ..		£650
		ac. Wide roulette 6½ ..		

(d) *Very thick dense paper* (1873–74)

35		1d. dull rose ..	..	£500 £120
		a. Brownish rose ..	..	£375 95·00
36		6d. dull ultramarine ..	..	£170 65·00
		a. Bright ultramarine ..	..	£180 60·00
37		1s. yellow-green ..	..	£750 £550

(Typo P. Davis & Son, Pietermaritzburg)

1874 (Sept). *P 12½.* (a) *Thin transparent paper.*

38	1	1d. pale brick-red ..	..	80·00 35·00
		a. Brownish red..	..	75·00 35·00
39		6d. deep blue ..	..	£120 50·00

(b) *Thicker opaque paper*

40	1	1d. pale red ..	..	£130 65·00
41		6d. blue ..	..	£100 45·00
		a. Imperf between (pair)		
		b. Deep blue	..	£100 45·00

(Typo Adolph Otto, Gustrow, Mecklenburg-Schwerin)

1874 (Oct). *Thin smooth paper, clearly printed. Fine roulette 15½ to 16.*

42	3	6d. bright ultramarine	..	60·00 22·00
		a. Bisected (3d.) (on cover)		† £1100

Stamps in other shades of blue, brown or red, often on other types of paper, are reprints.

(Typo J. F. Celliers on behalf of Stamp Commission, Pretoria)

1875 (29 Apr)–77.

I. *Very thin, soft opaque (semi-pelure) paper.* (a) *Imperf*

43	1	1d. orange-red ..	..	£120 45·00
		a. Pin-perf ..	..	£500 £250
44	2	3d. lilac ..	..	80·00 40·00
45	1	6d. blue ..	..	75·00 38·00
		a. Milky blue ..	..	£120 40·00
		aa. Tête-bêche (pair) ..		£9500
		ab. Pin-perf ..	..	— £250

(b) *Fine roulette, 15½ to 16*

46	1	1d. orange-red ..	..	£400 £130
47	2	3d. lilac ..	..	£425 £140
48	1	6d. blue ..	..	£400 £130

(c) *Wide roulette, 6½*

49	1	1d. orange-red ..	..	— £150
50	2	3d. lilac ..	..	£550 £225
51	1	6d. blue ..	..	— £120
		a. Bright blue ..	..	— £120
		b. Milky blue ..	..	— £120

II. *Very thin, hard transparent (pelure) paper* (1875–76) (a) *Imperf*

52	1	1d. brownish red..	..	48·00 27·00
		a. Orange-red ..	..	38·00 22·00
		b. Dull red..	..	42·00 42·00
		ba. Pin-perf..	..	£425 £250
53	2	3d. lilac ..	..	45·00 38·00
		a. Pin-perf ..	..	— £225
		b. Deep lilac ..	..	55·00 38·00
54	1	6d. pale blue ..	..	45·00 45·00
		a. Blue ..	..	45·00 38·00
		ab. Tête-bêche (pair)		
		ac. Pin-perf..	..	— £200
		b. Deep blue ..	..	50·00 42·00

(b) *Fine roulette 15½ to 16*

55	1	1d. orange-red ..	..	£250 £120
		a. Brown-red ..	..	£250 £120
56	2	3d. lilac ..	..	£325 £110
57	1	6d. blue ..	..	£150 95·00
		a. Deep blue ..	..	£150 £110

(c) *Wide roulette, 6½*

58	1	1d. orange-red ..	..	£700 £160
		a. Bright red ..	..	— £140
59	2	3d. lilac ..	..	— £190
60	1	6d. deep blue ..	..	£700 90·00

III. *Stout hard-surfaced paper with smooth, nearly white, gum* (1876). (a) *Imperf*

61	1	1d. bright red ..	..	20·00 14·00
62	2	3d. lilac ..	..	£300 £100
63	1	6d. bright blue ..	..	90·00 20·00
		a. Tête-bêche (pair)		
		b. Pale blue ..	..	90·00 22·00
		c. Deep blue (deep brown gum)	..	55·00 18·00
		ca. Tête-bêche (pair)	..	—£14000

(b) *Fine roulette, 15½ to 16*

64	1	1d. bright red ..	..	£400 £150
65	2	3d. lilac ..	..	£275
66	1	6d. bright blue ..	..	— £110
		a. Deep blue (deep brown gum)	..	£250

(c) *Wide roulette, 6½*

67	1	1d. bright red ..	..	£450 £140
68		6d. pale blue ..	..	— £200
		a. Deep blue (deep brown gum)	..	£500 £250

IV. *Coarse, soft white paper* (1876–77). (a) *Imperf*

69	1	1d. brick-red ..	..	£100 50·00
70		6d. deep blue ..	..	£160 50·00
		a. Milky blue ..	..	£275 90·00
71		1s. yellow-green ..	..	£275 £100
		a. Bisected (6d.) (on cover)	..	† £1200

(b) *Fine roulette, 15½ to 16*

72	1	1d. brick-red ..	..	— £250
73		6d. deep blue ..	..	— £130
74		1s. yellow-green ..	..	£550 £275

(c) *Wide roulette, 6½*

75	1	1d. brick-red ..	..	— £300
76		6d. deep blue ..	..	— £750
77		1s. yellow-green ..	..	— £800

(d) *Fine × wide roulette*

78	1	1d. brick-red ..	..	£550 £250

V. *Hard, thick, coarse yellowish paper* (1876–77)

79	1	1d. brick-red (imperf) ..	..	— £200
80		1d. brick-red (wide roulette) ..	..	— £300

The pin-perforated stamps have various gauges and were probably produced privately by one or more post offices other than Pretoria.

On Nos. 63ca, 66a and 68a the brown gum used was so intense that it caused staining of the paper which is still visible on used examples.

See also Nos. 171/4.

FIRST BRITISH OCCUPATION

By 1876 conditions in the Transvaal had deteriorated and the country was faced by economic collapse, native wars and internal dissension. In early 1877 Sir Theophilus Shepstone, appointed Special Commissioner to the South African Republic by the British Government, arrived in Pretoria and on 12 April annexed the Transvaal with the acquiesence of at least part of the European population.

V. R.   V. R.

TRANSVAAL.   TRANSVAAL.

(4)   (5)

T 4 is the normal overprint, but Setting I No. 11 (R. 2/3) has a wider-spaced overprint as T 5.

1877 (Apr). *Optd with T 4 in red.* (a) *Imperf.*

86	2	3d. lilac (semi-pelure) (No. 44)	..	£1100 £250
		a. Opt Type 5		
87		3d. lilac (pelure) (No. 53)	..	£1100 £160
		a. Opt Type 5	..	£3500 £1400
		b. Opt on back ..	..	£3000 £3000
		c. Opt double, in red and in black	..	£4750
88	1	6d. milky blue (No. 70) ..	..	£1300 £160
		a. Opt inverted	..	— £4250
		b. Opt double	..	£3500 £750
		c. Opt Type 5	..	£4250
		d. Deep blue	..	— £225
89		1s. yellow-green (No. 71) ..	..	£475 £160
		a. Bisected (6d.) (on cover)		† £1300
		b. Opt inverted	..	— £3250
		c. Opt Type 5 ..	..	£3000 £750
		d. Tête-bêche (pair)		

(b) *Fine roulette, 15½ to 16*

90	2	3d. lilac (pelure) (No. 56)	..	—£1100
91	1	6d. deep blue (No. 73) ..	..	—£1100
92		1s. yellow-green (No. 74) ..	..	£1100 £500
		a. Opt Type 5		

(c) *Wide roulette, 6½*

93	2	3d. lilac (pelure) (No. 59)	..	—£1100
		a. Opt Type 5 ..		
94	1	6d. deep blue (No. 76) ..	..	—£1100
		a. Opt Type 5		
95		1s. yellow-green (No. 77) ..	..	£2750 £1000
		a. Opt inverted	..	— £3500

Nos. 88a, 89b and 95a occurred on the inverted *cliché* of the basic stamps.

1877 (June). *Optd with T 4 in black.*

I. *Very thin, hard transparent (pelure) paper*

96	1	1d. orange-red (imperf) (No. 52a)	..	£170 95·00
97		1d. orange-red (fine roulette) (No. 55)	..	—£1000

II. *Stout hard-surfaced paper with smooth, nearly white, gum*

98	1	1d. bright red (imperf) (No. 61) ..	..	20·00 20·00
		a. Opt inverted ..	..	£475 £400
		b. Opt Type 5 ..	..	£550 £600
99		1d. bright red (fine roulette) (No. 64)	..	£140 45·00
		a. Opt inverted		
		b. Opt double ..	..	£750
		c. Imperf between (horiz pair) ..		£650
100		1d. bright red (wide roulette) (No. 67)	..	£475 £140
100a		1d. bright red (fine×wide roulette) (No. 78)		

III. *New ptgs on coarse, soft white paper.* (a) *Imperf*

101	1	1d. brick-red (5.77) ..	..	20·00 20·00
		a. Opt double	..	— £900
		b. Opt Type 5		£600
102	2	3d. lilac ..	..	70·00 35·00
		a. Opt inverted		
		b. Deep lilac	..	£140 80·00
103	1	6d. dull blue ..	..	85·00 30·00
		a. Opt double	..	£2750
		b. Opt inverted	..	£1200 £150
		d. Opt Type 5	..	— £750
		da. Opt Type 5 inverted		
		e. Blue (bright to deep)	..	£150 27·00
		ea. Bright blue, opt inverted	..	— £475
		f. Pin-perf ..	..	— £450
104		1s. yellow-green ..	..	85·00 40·00
		a. Opt inverted	..	£900 £180
		b. Tête-bêche (pair) ..	..	£15000 £15000
		c. Opt Type 5	..	£2750 £900
		d. Bisected (6d.) (on cover)	..	† £1000

(b) *Fine roulette, 15½ to 16*

105	1	1d. brick-red ..	..	65·00 65·00
		a. Imperf horiz (vert strip of 3) ..		
		b. Imperf between (horiz pair) ..	..	† £600
106	2	3d. lilac ..	..	£140 55·00
107	1	6d. dull blue ..	..	£160 45·00
		a. Opt inverted	..	— £550
		b. Opt Type 5	..	£3500
108		1s. yellow-green ..	..	£160 80·00
		a. Opt inverted ..	..	£800 £375
		b. Opt Type 5	..	— £2500

(c) *Wide roulette, 6½*

109	1	1d. brick-red ..	..	£550 £140
		a. Opt Type 5	..	— £650
110	2	3d. lilac ..	..	— £1100
111	1	6d. dull blue ..	..	— £1100
		a. Opt inverted	..	— £3000
112		1s. yellow-green ..	..	£350 £120
		a. Opt inverted	..	£1100 £475

1877 (31 Aug). *Optd with T 4 in black.*

113	1	6d. blue/rose (imperf)	..	70·00 45·00
		a. Bisected (3d.) (on cover)		
		b. Opt inverted	..	85·00 45·00
		c. Tête-bêche (pair)		
		d. Opt omitted	..	£2750 £2000

114	1	6d. blue/*rose* (*fine roulette*)			£150	60·00
		a. Opt inverted	..	..	£425	60·00
		b. *Tête-bêche* (pair)				
		c. Opt omitted				
		d. Bisected (3d.) (on cover)				
115		6d. blue/*rose* (*wide roulette*)				
		a. Opt inverted				
		b. Opt omitted				

Nos. 113/15 were overprinted from a setting of 40 which was applied upright to one pane in each sheet and inverted on the other.

V. R.   V. R.

Transvaal   Transvaal
(6)   (7)

1877 (28 Sept)–**79.** *Optd with T* **6** *in black.* (*a*) *Imperf*

116	1	1d. red/*blue*	..	..	45·00	24·00
		a. "Transvral" (Right pane R. 2/3)	..	£4000	£2000
		b. Opt double	..	..	£3000	
		c. Opt inverted	..	..	£600	£300
		d. Opt omitted				
117		1d. red/*orange* (6.12.77)			15·00	16·00
		a. Pin-perf				
		b. Printed both sides				
		c. Opt double	..	..	£2500	
		d. Optd with Type **7** (15.4.78)		45·00	38·00
		e. Pair. Nos. 117 and 117d			£100	
118	2	3d. mauve/*buff* (24.10.77)			38·00	24·00
		a. Opt inverted	..	..	—	£550
		b. Pin-perf				
		c. Bisected (1½d.) (on cover)		†	—
		d. Optd with Type **7** (15.4.78)		50·00	32·00
		da. Pin-perf	..	..	£550	£550
		e. Pair. Nos. 118 and 118d		£130	
119		3d. mauve/*green* (18.4.79)		£140	40·00
		a. Pin-perf				
		b. Opt inverted	..	..	—	£1500
		c. Opt double				
		d. Printed both sides	..	†	—
		e. Optd with Type **7**	..	95·00	32·00
		ea. Opt inverted	..	..	—	£1500
		eb. Printed both sides				
		f. Opt omitted	..	..	£2750	
		g. Pair. Nos. 119 and 119e	..	£300	
120	1	6d. blue/*green* (27.11.77)		75·00	32·00
		a. *Deep blue/green*		90·00	35·00
		b. Broken "Y" for "V" in "V.R." (Left pane R. 3/7)		—	£550
		c. Small "v" in "Transvaal" (Left pane R. 5/2)		—	£550
		d. "V..R" (Right pane R. 3/4)		—	£550
		e. *Tête-bêche* (pair)		—	£14000
		f. Opt inverted	..	..	—	£700
		g. Pin-perf				
		h. Bisected (3d.) (on cover)	†	—
121		6d. blue/*blue* (20.3.78)		48·00	22·00
		a. *Tête-bêche* (pair)				
		b. Opt inverted	..	..	—	£700
		c. Opt omitted	..	..	—	£1600
		d. Opt double	..	..	—	£2500
		e. Pin-perf				
		f. Bisected (3d.) (on cover)		†	£700
		g. Optd with Type **7**	..	95·00	27·00
		ga. *Tête-bêche* (pair)		£11000	
		gb. Opt inverted	..	..	—	£400
		gc. Bisected (3d.) (on cover)		†	—
		h. Pair. Nos. 121 and 121g	..	£200	

(*b*) *Fine roulette*, 15½ *to* 16

122	1	1d. red/*blue*	..	..	70·00	32·00
		a. "Transvral" (Right pane R. 2/3)		—	£2250
123		1d. red/*orange* (6.12.77)	..	28·00	22·00
		a. Imperf between (pair)	..	£500	
		b. Optd with Type **7** (15.4.78)		£130	£110
		c. Pair. Nos. 123 and 123b	..	£225	
124	2	3d. mauve/*buff* (24.10.77)		85·00	22·00
		a. Imperf horiz (vert pair)	..	£600	
		b. Opt inverted	..	..	—	£2500
		c. Optd with Type **7** (15.4.78)		£130	95·00
		ca. Imperf between (pair)				
		d. Pair. Nos. 124 and 124c		£325	
125		3d. mauve/*green* (18.4.79)		£550	£150
		a. Optd with Type **7**	..	£500	£150
		b. Pair. Nos. 125 and 125a				
126	1	6d. blue/*green* (27.11.77)		70·00	32·00
		a. "V..R" (Right pane R. 3/4)		—	£1000
		b. *Tête-bêche* (pair)				
		c. Opt inverted	..	..	—	£500
		d. Opt omitted	..	..	—	£3000
		e. Bisected (3d.) (on cover)		†	£550
127		6d. blue/*blue* (20.3.78)		£180	48·00
		a. Opt inverted	..	..	—	£900
		b. Opt omitted	..	..	—	£2500
		c. Imperf between (pair)				
		d. Bisected (3d.) (on cover)		†	£600
		e. Optd with Type **7**	..	£300	£100
		ea. Opt inverted	..	..	—	£800

(*c*) *Wide roulette,* 6¼

128	1	1d. red/*orange* (15.4.78)	..	£250	£100
		a. Optd with Type **7**	..	—	£250
129	2	3d. mauve/*buff* (24.10.77)		—	£100
		a. Optd with Type **7** (15.4.78)		—	£300
130		3d. mauve/*green* (18.4.79)		£375	£275
		a. Optd with Type **7**	..	—	£300
131	1	6d. blue/*green* (27.11.77)		—	£850
132		6d. blue/*blue* (20.3.78)		—	£250
		a. Opt inverted				
		b. Optd with Type **7**	..	—	£300
		ba. Opt inverted				

Nos. 116/32 were overprinted from various settings covering sheets of 80 or panes of 40 (8×5). Initially these settings contained Type **6** only, but from March 1878 settings also contained examples of Type **7**. Details of these mixed settings are as follows:
1d. red/*orange* (sheets of 80): all Type **6** except for 16 Type **7**.
3d. mauve/*buff* (panes of 40): 16 Type **7**.

3d. mauve/*green* (panes of 40): uncertain, some panes at least contained 27 Type **7**.
6d. blue/*blue* (sheets of 80): either 24 or 27 Type **7**.

9
(Recess B.W.)

1878 (26 Aug)–**80.** *P* 14, 14½.

133	9	½d. vermilion (1880)	..	..	18·00	65·00
134		1d. pale red-brown	..	..	8·50	3·00
		a. *Brown-red*	..	..	8·00	2·50
135		3d. dull rose	..	..	10·00	3·25
		a. *Claret*	..	..	15·00	4·75
136		4d. sage-green	..	..	15·00	4·25
137		6d. olive-black	..	..	7·50	3·25
		a. *Black-brown*	..	..	9·00	2·75
138		1s. green	..	..	£100	32·00
139		2s. blue	..	..	£140	65·00

The above prices are for specimens perforated on all four sides. Stamps from margins of sheets, with perforations absent on one or two sides, can be supplied for about 30% less.

1 Penny   1 Penny   1 Penny
(10)   (11)   (12)

1 Penny   1 Penny
(13)   (14)

1 PENNY   *1 Penny*
(15)   (16)

1879 (22 Apr). *No.* 137a *surch with T* **10** *to* **16** *in black.*

140	10	1d. on 6d.	..	..	65·00	40·00
		a. Surch in red	..	..	£180	£120
141	11	1d. on 6d.	..	..	£160	75·00
		a. Surch in red	..	..	£450	£250
142	12	1d. on 6d.	..	..	£160	75·00
		a. Surch in red	..	..	£450	£250
143	13	1d. on 6d.	..	..	70·00	45·00
		a. Surch in red	..	..	£200	£140
144	14	1d. on 6d.	..	..	£425	£130
		a. Surch in red	..	..	—	£1500
145	15	1d. on 6d.	..	..	35·00	22·00
		a. Surch in red	..	..	£110	60·00
146	16	1d. on 6d.	..	..	£150	70·00
		a. Surch in red	..	..	£400	£225

Nos. 140/6 were surcharged from a setting of 60 containing eleven examples of Type **10**, four of Type **11**, four of Type **12**, nine of Type **13**, two of Type **14** (although there may have been only one in the first two ptgs), twenty-five of Type **15** and five of Type **16**.
The red surcharges may have been produced first.

V. R.   V. R.

Transvaal   Transvaal
(16a)   Small "T" (R. 2/8, 3/8, 4/8, 5/8 on right pane of 1d. and left pane of 3d.)

1879 (Aug–Sept). *Optd with T* **16a** *in black.* (*a*) *Imperf.*

147	1	1d. red/*yellow*	..	..	38·00	32·00
		a. Small "T"	..	..	£225	£150
		b. *Red/orange*	..	..	32·00	25·00
		ba. Small "T"	..	..	£160	£150
148	2	3d. mauve/*green* (Sept)	..	35·00	20·00
		a. Small "T"	..	..	£160	85·00
149		3d. mauve/*blue* (Sept)	..	40·00	25·00
		a. Small "T"	..	..	£170	85·00

(*b*) *Fine roulette* 15½ *to* 16

150	1	1d. red/*yellow*	..	..	£350	£200
		a. Small "T"	..	..	£800	£550
		b. *Red/orange*	..	..	£750	£375
		ba. Small "T"				
151	2	3d. mauve/*green*	..	..	£700	£225
		a. Small "T"				
152		3d. mauve/*blue*	..	..	—	£160
		a. Small "T"	..	..	—	£600

(*c*) *Wide roulette* 6½

153	1	1d. red/*yellow*	..	..	£600	£600
		a. Small "T"				
		b. *Red/orange*				
154	2	3d. mauve/*green*				
		a. Small "T"				
155		3d. mauve/*blue*				

(*d*) *Pin-perf about* 17

156	1	1d. red/*yellow*	..	..	—	£450
		a. Small "T"				
157	2	3d. mauve/*blue*	..	..	—	£600

SECOND REPUBLIC

Following the first Boer War the independence of the South African Republic was recognised by the Convention of Pretoria from 8 August 1881.
Nos. 156/62 remained valid and some values were available for postage until 1885.

EEN PENNY
(17)

1882 (11 Aug). *No.* 136 *surch with T* **17.**

| 170 | 9 | 1d. on 4d. sage-green | .. | 8·00 | 3·75 |
| | | a. Surch inverted | .. | £300 | £200 |

Used examples of a similar, but larger, surcharge (width 20 mm) are known. These were previously considered to be forgeries, but it is now believed that some, at least, may represent a trial printing of the "EEN PENNY" surcharge.

(Typo J. F. Celliers)

1883 (20 Feb). *Re-issue of T* **1** *and* **2.** *P* 12.

171	1	1d. grey (*to black*) (Apr)	..	3·75	1·25
		a. Imperf vert (horiz pair)	..	£250	
		b. Imperf horiz (vert pair)	..	†	£325
172	2	3d. grey-black (*to black*)/*rose*	..	19·00	3·75
		a. Bisected (1d.) (on cover)		†	£500
173		3d. pale red (Mar)	..	7·00	1·75
		a. Bisected (1d.) (on cover)		†	£500
		b. *Chestnut*	..	..	22·00	3·50
		ba. Imperf between (horiz pair)		†	—
		c. *Vermilion*	..	..	22·00	4·50
174	1	1s. green (*to deep*) (July)	..	38·00	7·75
		a. Bisected (6d.) (on cover)		†	£375
		b. *Tête-bêche* (pair)	..	£650	£120

Reprints are known of Nos. 172, 173, 173*b* and 173*c*. The paper of the first is *bright rose* in place of *dull rose*, and the impression is brownish black in place of grey-black to deep black. The reprints on white paper have the paper thinner than the originals, and the gum yellowish instead of white. The colour is a dull deep orange-red.

18

PERFORATIONS. Stamps perforated 11½×12 come from the first vertical row of sheets of the initial printing otherwise perforated 12½×12.

REPRINTS. Reprints of the general issues 1885–93, 1894–95, 1895–96 and 1896–97 exist in large quantities produced using the original plates from 1911 onwards. They cannot readily be distinguished from genuine originals except by comparison with used stamps, but the following general characteristics may be noted. The reprints are all perf 12½, large holes; the paper is whiter and thinner than that usually employed for the originals and their colours lack the lustre of those of the genuine stamps.
Forged surcharges have been made on these reprints.

(Des J. Vurtheim. Typo Enschedé)

1885 (13 Mar)–**1893.** *P* 12½.

175	18	½d. grey (30.3.85)	..	..	30	10
		a. Perf 13½	..	..	4·75	90
		b. Perf 12½×12	..	..	1·75	10
		ba. Perf 11½×12	..	20·00	6·00
176		1d. carmine	..	..	30	10
		a. Perf 12½×12	..	..	70	10
		aa. Perf 11½×12	..	12·00	2·75
		b. *Rose*	..	..	30	10
		ba. Perf 12½×12	..	..	65	10
177		2d. brown-purple (*p* 12½×12) (9.85)	1·60	1·60
178		2d. olive-bistre (14.4.87)	..	40	10
		a. Perf 12½×12	..	..	3·50	10
179		2½d. mauve (*to bright*) (8.93)	1·25	40
180		3d. mauve (*to bright*)	..	1·50	70
		a. Perf 12½×12	..	..	6·00	75
		aa. Perf 11½×12	..	27·00	17·00
181		4d. bronze-green	..	..	2·25	50
		a. Perf 13½	..	..	6·00	85
		b. Perf 12½×12	..	..	13·00	65
		ba. Perf 11½×12	..	£160	60·00
182		6d. pale dull blue	..	..	3·75	2·25
		a. Perf 13½	..	..	4·50	70
		b. Perf 12½×12	..	..	5·50	20
		ba. Perf 11½×12				
183		1s. yellow-green	..	..	2·50	35
		a. Perf 13½	..	..	20·00	5·50
		b. Perf 12½×12	..	..	7·50	45
184		2s. 6d. orange-buff (*to buff*) (2.12.85)	3·75	1·60
		a. Perf 12½×12	..	..	14·00	4·00
185		5s. slate (2.12.85)	..	..	6·00	2·75
		a. Perf 12½×12	..	..	28·00	4·50
186		10s. fawn (2.12.85)	..	..	28·00	5·50
187		£5 dp grn (3.92)* (Optd "Monster" £150)	£3250	£180

Singles of the 6d. pale dull blue imperforate have been reported used in 1893.
*Most examples of No. 187 on the market are either forgeries or reprints.

HALVE PENNY

(19)

1885 (22 May–Aug). *Surch with T 19. Reading up or down.*
188	2	¹/₂d. on 3d. (No. 173)	..	..	3·50	7·50
189	1	¹/₂d. on 1s. (No. 174) (Aug)	..	15·00	38·00
		a. *Tête-bêche* (pair)	..		£600	£300

Nos. 188/9 were surcharged by a setting of 40. After the left pane had been surcharged reading down the sheets were turned so that the right pane had the surcharges reading up.

HALVE PENNY Z.A.R	TWEE PENCE Z.A.R.	HALVE PENNY
(20)	(21)	(22)

1885 (1 Sept). *No. 137a surch with T 20/1 in red.*
190	9	¹/₂d. on 6d. black-brown	..	35·00	60·00
191		2d. on 6d. black-brown	..	3·50	7·00

1885 (28 Sept). *No. 180a surch with T 22.*
192	18	¹/₂d. on 3d. mauve	..	2·50	2·50
		a. "PRNNY" (R. 6/6)	..	30·00	45·00
		b. 2nd "N" inverted (R. 3/8)	70·00	85·00
		c. Perf 11¹/₂×12	..	9·00	8·50

2d **2d**

(23)   (24)

1887 (15 Jan). *No. 180a surch with T 23/4.*
193	18	2d. on 3d. mauve (Type 23)	..	5·00	5·00
		a. Surch double	..	—	£225
		b. Perf 11¹/₂×12	..	19·00	10·00
194		2d. on 3d. mauve (Type 24)	..	85	1·75
		a. Surch double	..	—	£160
		b. Perf 11¹/₂×12	..	4·75	6·50

Nos. 193/4 were surcharged from the same setting of 60 (10 × 6) which showed Type 24 on the top five horizontal rows and Type 23 on the sixth horizontal row.

Halve Penny	1 Penny
(25)	(26)

2¹/₂ Pence	2¹/₂ Pence
(27)	(28)

Two types of surcharge:
A. Vertical distance between bars 12¹/₂ mm.
B. Distance 13¹/₂ mm.

1893. *T 18 surch. P 12¹/₂. (a) In red.*
195	25	¹/₂d. on 2d. olive-bistre (A) (27 May)	..	80	80
		a. Surch inverted	..	1·75	1·50
		b. Surch Type B	..	1·50	1·50
		ba. Surch inverted	..	4·75	7·50

(b) In black
196	25	¹/₂d. on 2d. olive-bistre (A) (2 July)	..	85	60
		a. Surch inverted	..	4·00	4·50
		b. Extra surch on back inverted	£150	
		c. Surch Type B	..	1·10	1·10
		ca. Surch inverted	..	17·00	14·00
		cb. Extra surch on back inverted	£250	
197	26	1d. on 6d. blue (A) (26 Jan)	..	50	30
		a. Surch double	..	50·00	40·00
		b. Surch inverted	..	1·40	1·60
		c. Surch treble	..		
		d. Surch Type B	..	70	55
		da. Surch inverted	..	4·50	3·25
		db. Surch double	..	—	70·00
		e. Pair, one without surch	..	£200	

1885 (22 May–Aug). *continued*

198	27	2¹/₂d. on 1s. green (A) (2 Jan)	..	90	2·00
		a. "2¹/₂" for "2¹/₂" (R. 1/10)	..	30·00	40·00
		b. Surch inverted	..	6·50	7·50
		ba. Surch inverted and "2¹/₂" for "2¹/₂"	£325	£275
		c. Extra surch on back inverted	£400	£400
		d. Surch double, one inverted	£600	
		e. Surch Type B	..	1·50	2·25
		ea. Surch inverted	..	7·50	14·00
199	28	2¹/₂d. on 1s. green (A) (24 June)	..	3·00	3·00
		a. Surch double	..	45·00	40·00
		b. Surch inverted	..	7·00	7·00
		c. Surch Type B	..	6·50	7·00
		cb. Surch inverted	..	16·00	16·00

Surcharge Types 25/8 all show a similar setting of the horizontal bars at top and bottom. On horizontal rows 1 to 4 and 6 the bars are 12¹/₂ mm apart and on row 5 the distance is 13¹/₂ mm.

29 (Wagon with shafts)   30 (Wagon with pole)

1894 (July). *P 12¹/₂.*
200	29	¹/₂d. grey	..	50	10
201		1d. carmine	..	50	10
202		2d. olive-bistre	..	50	10
203		6d. pale dull blue	..	1·00	40
204		1s. yellow-green	..	7·00	9·00

For note *re* reprints, see below T 18.

1895 (16 Mar)–**96.** *P 12¹/₂.*
205	30	¹/₂d. pearl-grey (1895)	..	30	10
		a. *Lilac-grey*	..	30	10
206		1d. rose-red (1895)	..	30	10
207		2d. olive-bistre (1895)	..	30	10
208		3d. mauve (1895)	..	80	10
209		4d. olive-black (1895)	..	1·50	80
210		6d. pale dull blue (1895)	..	1·50	40
211		1s. yellow-green (18.3.95)	..	2·00	75
212		5s. slate (1896)	..	11·00	18·00
212a		10s. pale chestnut (1896)	..	11·00	3·75
205/8, 211 Optd "Monster"		*Set of 5*	£150

For note *re* reprints, see below T 18.

Halve Penny

(31)

1d.   **1d.**

(32—Round dot)   (32a—Square dot)

1895 (July–August). *Nos. 211 and 179 surch with T 31/2.*
213	30	¹/₂d. on 1s. green (R.)	..	30	10
		a. Surch spaced	..	85	75
		b. "Pennij" for "Penny" (R. 6/6)	42·00	50·00
		c. Surch inverted	..	3·50	4·50
		d. Surch double	..	60·00	85·00
214	18	1d. on 2¹/₂d. bright mauve (G.)	..	30	10
		a. Surch inverted	..	17·00	14·00
		b. Surch double	..	60·00	60·00
		c. Surch on back only	..	70·00	
		d. Surch Type 32a	..	1·25	1·25
		da. Surch inverted	..	60·00	
		e. Surch treble	..	£500	

The normal space between "Penny" and the bars is 3 mm. On No. 213a, which comes from the fifth horizontal row of the setting, this is increased to 4 mm. Copies may be found in which one or both of the bars have failed to print.

Type 32a with square stop occurred on R. 3/3-4, 3/6-8, 4/4-5, 4/7-8, 4/10, 6/3, 6/7-8 and 6/10 of the setting of 60.

33   34

1895 (July). *Fiscal stamp optd "POSTZEGEL". P 11¹/₂.*
215	33	6d. bright rose (G.)	..	50	1·75
		a. Imperf between (pair)	..		

(Litho The Press Printing and Publishing Works, Pretoria)

1895 (6 Sept). *Introduction of Penny Postage. P 11.*
215b	34	1d. red (pale *to* deep)	..	1·25	1·40
		ba. Imperf between (pair)	..	60·00	65·00
		bb. Imperf vert (horiz pair)		
		bc. Imperf (pair)	..		

1896–97. *P 12¹/₂.*
216	30	¹/₂d. green (1896)	..	20	10
217		1d. rose-red and green (1896)	..	20	10
218		2d. brown and green (2.97)	..	20	10
219		2¹/₂d. dull blue and green (6.96)	..	30	10
220		3d. purple and green (3.97)	..	80	80
221		4d. sage-green and green (3.97)	..	80	80
222		6d. lilac and green (11.96)	..	40	80
223		1s. ochre and green (3.96)	..	50	15
224		2s. 6d. dull violet and green (6.96)	1·25	1·25

For note *re* reprints, see below T 18.

SECOND BRITISH OCCUPATION

The Second Boer War began on 11 October 1899 and was concluded by the Peace of Vereeniging on 31 May 1902. Pretoria was occupied by the British on 5 June 1900 and a civilian postal service began operating thirteen days later.

FORGERIES. The forgeries of the "V.R.I." and "E.R.I." overprints most often met with can be recognised by the fact that the type used is perfect and the three stops are always in alignment with the bottom of the letters. In the genuine overprints, which were made from old type, it is impossible to find all three letters perfect and all three stops perfect and in exact alignment with the bottom of the letters.

V. R. I.	E. R. I.	E. R. I. Half Penny
(35)	(36)	(37)

1900 (18 June). *Optd with T 35.*
226	30	¹/₂d. green	..	15	15
		a. No stop after "V"	..	10·00	
		b. No stop after "R"	..	8·00	
		c. No stop after "I"	..	6·50	
		d. Opt inverted	..	8·00	
		e. Opt double	..		
		f. "V.I.R." (R.4/4)	..	£500	
227		1d. rose-red and green	..	15	15
		a. No stop after "V"	..	10·00	
		b. No stop after "R"	..	8·00	
		c. No stop after "I"	..	5·00	
		d. Opt inverted	..	8·00	
		e. Opt double	..	60·00	75·00
		f. No stops after "R" and "I"	65·00	65·00
		g. Opt omitted (in pair with normal)	£250	
228		2d. brown and green	..	1·75	75
		a. No stop after "V"	..	23·00	
		c. No stop after "I"	..	27·00	
		d. Opt inverted	..	13·00	
		e. Opt double	..		
		f. "V.I.R." (R.4/4)	..	£500	
229		2¹/₂d. dull blue and green	..	70	80
		a. No stop after "V"	..	17·00	
		b. No stop after "R"	..	40·00	
		c. No stop after "I"	..	13·00	
		d. Opt inverted	..	8·00	
230		3d. purple and green	..	70	75
		a. No stop after "V"	..	20·00	
		b. No stop after "R"	..	40·00	
		c. No stop after "I"	..	26·00	
		d. Opt inverted	..	60·00	
231		4d. sage-green and green	..	1·50	30
		a. No stop after "V"	..	35·00	
		b. No stop after "R"	..	45·00	
		c. No stop after "I"	..	30·00	
		d. Opt inverted	..	20·00	
		f. "V.I.R." (R.4/4)	..	£500	
232		6d. lilac and green	..	1·50	70
		a. No stop after "V"	..	15·00	
		b. No stop after "R"	..	20·00	
		c. No stop after "I"	..	20·00	
		d. Opt inverted	..	20·00	
233		1s. ochre and green	..	1·50	1·75
		a. No stop after "V"	..	15·00	
		b. No stop after "R"	..	15·00	
		c. No stop after "I"	..	27·00	
		d. Opt inverted	..	26·00	
		e. Opt double	..	60·00	
234		2s. 6d. dull violet and green	..	2·50	5·50
		a. No stop after "V"	..	27·00	
		b. No stop after "R"	..	60·00	
235		5s. slate	..	4·75	7·50
		a. No stop after "V"	..	85·00	
236		10s. pale chestnut	..	7·00	9·00
		a. No stop after "V"	..	70·00	
		c. No stop after "I"	..	70·00	
237	18	£5 deep green*	..	£1800	£750
		a. No stop after "V"	..		
234/7 Optd "Specimen"		*Set of 4*	£200

*Many examples of No. 237 on the market are forgeries and the stamps should only be purchased if accompanied by a recent expert committee certificate.

The error "V.I.R." occurred on R.4/4 in the first batch of stamps to be overprinted—a few sheets of the ¹/₂d., 2d. and 4d. The error was then corrected and stamps showing it are very rare.

A number of different settings were used to apply the overprint to Nos. 226/37. The missing stop varieties listed above developed during overprinting and occur on different positions in the various settings.

1901 (Jan)–02. *Optd with T 36.*
238	30	¹/₂d. green	..	40	30
239		1d. rose-red and green (20.3.01)	..	40	10
		a. "E" of opt omitted	..	65·00	
240		3d. purple and green (6.02)	..	2·00	2·50
241		4d. sage-green and green (6.02)	..	2·00	2·50
242		2s. 6d. dull violet and green (10.02)	6·00	10·00

1901 (July). *Surch with T 37.*
243	30	¹/₂d. on 2d. brown and green	..	50	50
		a. No stop after "E" (R.4/6)	..	45·00	

38 (POSTAGE REVENUE)   39 (POSTAGE POSTAGE)

(Typo D.L.R.)

1902 (1 Apr)–03. *Wmk Crown CA. P 14.*
244	38	½d. black and bluish green	..	1·25	20
		w. Wmk inverted	..	70·00	50·00
245		1d. black and carmine	..	1·25	15
		w. Wmk inverted	..	50·00	40·00
246		2d. black and purple	..	2·50	50
247		2½d. black and blue	..	3·50	1·25
		w. Wmk inverted	..	50·00	15·00
248		3d. black and sage-green (1903)		4·00	50
249		4d. black and brown (1903)		4·00	75
250		6d. black and orange-brown		2·50	60
251		1s. black and sage-green		9·00	5·50
252		2s. black and brown		25·00	30·00
253	39	2s. 6d. magenta and black		14·00	8·00
254		5s. black and purple/*yellow*		20·00	20·00
255		10s. black and purple/*red*		42·00	24·00
244/55			*Set of 12*	£120	80·00
244/55 (*inc* 247w) Optd "Specimen"			*Set of 12*	£130	

The colour of the "black" centres varies from brownish grey or grey to black.

1903. *Wmk Crown CA. P 14.*
256	39	1s. grey-black and red-brown	..	8·50	2·00
257		2s. grey-black and yellow	..	14·00	9·00
258		£1 green and violet	..	£150	95·00
259		£5 orange-brown and violet	..	£1200	£475
256/9 Optd "Specimen"			*Set of 4*	£180	

1904–09. *Wmk Mult Crown CA. Ordinary paper. P 14.*
260	38	½d. black and bluish green	..	4·75	2·00
		w. Wmk inverted	..	70·00	50·00
		y. Wmk inverted and reversed	..	60·00	20·00
261		1d. black and carmine	..	2·75	20
262		2d. black and purple (*chalk-surfaced paper*) (1906)		6·50	50
263		2½d. black and blue (1905)	..	7·50	4·25
		a. Chalk-surfaced paper	..	7·50	1·50
264		3d. black & sage-green (*chalk-surfaced paper*) (1906)		3·50	30
265		4d. black and brown (*chalk-surfaced paper*) (1906)		3·75	50
		w. Wmk inverted	..	65·00	50·00
266		6d. black and orange (1905)	..	5·00	50
		a. Chalk-surfaced paper. *Black and brown-orange* (1906)		2·25	50
		w. Wmk inverted	..	75·00	60·00
267	39	1s. black and red-brown (1905)	..	4·50	50
268		2s. black and yellow (1906)	..	17·00	4·50
269		2s. 6d. magenta and black (1909)		28·00	3·25
270		5s. black and purple/*yellow*		15·00	1·50
271		10s. black and purple/*red* (1907)		32·00	2·75
272		£1 green and violet (1908)	..	£140	22·00
		a. Chalk-surfaced paper	..	£150	16·00
260/72			*Set of 13*	£225	30·00

There is considerable variation in the "black" centres as in the previous issue.

1905–09. *Wmk Mult Crown CA. P 14.*
273	38	½d. yellow-green	..	1·50	10
		a. *Deep green* (1908)	..	2·25	20
		w. Wmk inverted	..	£100	60·00
274		1d. scarlet	..	1·25	10
		aw. Wmk inverted	..		
		b. Wmk Cabled Anchor, T **13** of Cape of Good Hope		†	£325
275		2d. purple (1909)	..	3·25	50
276		2½d. bright blue (1909)	..	10·00	3·00
273/6			*Set of 4*	14·50	3·25
273/6 Optd "Specimen"			*Set of 4*	50·00	

A 2d. grey, T **38**, was prepared for use but not issued. It exists overprinted "Specimen", *price* £120.

The monocoloured ½d. and 1d. are printed from new combined plates. These show a slight alteration in that the frame does not touch the crown.

Many of the King's Head stamps are found overprinted or perforated "C.S.A.R.", for use by the Central South African Railways.

STAMP BOOKLETS

1905 (July). *Black on red cover. Stapled.*
SB1	2s. 7d. booklet containing thirty 1d. (No. 261) in blocks of 6	..	£2250

1905. *Black on red cover. Stapled.*
SB2	2s. 7d. booklet containing thirty 1d. (No. 274) in blocks of 6	..	£2250

1909. *Black on red cover. Stapled.*
SB3	2s. 6d. booklet containing ten ½d. (No. 273) in block of 6 and block of 4, and twenty-four 1d. (No. 274) in blocks of 6		£2750

Stocks of No. SB3 were supplied containing twelve examples of the ½d., it being intended that the postal clerks would remove two stamps before the booklets were sold. In some instances this did not occur.

COVER PRICES

Cover factors are quoted at the beginning of each country for most issues to 1945. An explanation of the system can be found on page x. The factors quoted do not, however, apply to philatelic covers.

POSTAL FISCAL STAMPS

1900–02. *Fiscal stamps as in T **33**, but optd with T **35**. P 11½.*
F1	1d. pale blue	..	—	45·00
F2	6d. dull carmine	..	—	60·00
F3	1s. olive-bistre	..	—	75·00
F4	1s. 6d. brown	..	—	90·00
F5	2s. 6d. dull purple	..	—	£100

Nos. F1/5, previously listed as Nos. 1/5 of Volksrust, are fiscal issues which are known postally used from various Transvaal post offices between June 1900 and June 1902.

Other fiscal stamps are found apparently postally used, but these were used on telegrams not on postal matter.

POSTAGE DUE STAMPS

D 1

(Typo D.L.R.)

1907. *Wmk Mult Crown CA. P 14.*
D1	D 1	½d. black and blue-green	..	3·25	1·25
D2		1d. black and scarlet	..	4·00	85
D3		2d. brown-orange	..	4·00	1·25
D4		3d. black and blue	..	7·50	4·00
D5		5d. black and violet	..	2·00	12·00
D6		6d. black and red-brown	..	4·25	12·00
D7		1s. scarlet and black	..	8·50	7·00
D1/7 ..			*Set of 7*	30·00	35·00

Transvaal became a province of the Union of South Africa on 31 May 1910.

PIETERSBURG

After the fall of Pretoria to the British in June 1900 the Transvaal government withdrew to the north of the country. Those post offices in areas not occupied by the British continued to function, but by early the following year supplies of stamps were exhausted. The following stamps were then authorised by the State Secretary and remained in use in some towns to early May 1901. Pietersburg itself was taken by British forces on 9 April.

PRICES. Genuinely used examples are very rare. Stamps cancelled by favour exist and are worth the same as the unused prices quoted.

The issued stamps are initialled by the Controller J. T. de V. Smit. All values exist without his signature and these are believed to come from remainders abandoned when the Boers evacuated Pietersburg.

P 1   P 2

P 3

TYPES P 1/3. Each value was printed in sheets of 24 (6×4) of which the first two horizontal rows were as Type P **1**, the third row as Type P **2** and the fourth as Type P **3**. The stamps were issued to post offices in blocks of 12.

(Type-set *De Zoutpansberg Wachter* Press, Pietersburg)

1901 (20 Mar (1d.)–3 Apr (*others*)). A. *Imperf.*
(a) Controller's initials in black
1	P 1	½d. black/*green*	..	15·00
		e. Controller's initials omitted		95·00
2	P 2	½d. black/*green*	..	45·00
		d. Controller's initials omitted		95·00
3	P 3	½d. black/*green*	..	45·00
		d. Controller's initials omitted		95·00
4	P 1	1d. black/*red*	..	3·50
5	P 2	1d. black/*red*	..	5·50
6	P 3	1d. black/*red*	..	7·00
7	P 1	2d. black/*orange*	..	6·00
8	P 2	2d. black/*orange*	..	14·00
9	P 3	2d. black/*orange*	..	22·00
10	P 1	4d. black/*blue*	..	5·50
11	P 2	4d. black/*blue*	..	9·50
12	P 3	4d. black/*blue*	..	32·00
13	P 1	6d. black/*green*	..	9·50
14	P 2	6d. black/*green*	..	15·00
15	P 3	6d. black/*green*	..	40·00
16	P 1	1s. black/*yellow*	..	8·00

17	P 2	1s. black/*yellow*	..	..	14·00
18	P 3	1s. black/*yellow*	..	..	25·00

(b) Controller's initials in red
19	P 1	½d. black/*green*	..	..	15·00
20	P 2	½d. black/*green*	..	..	35·00
21	P 3	½d. black/*green*	..	..	40·00

B. *P 11½. (a) Controller's initials in red*
22	P 1	½d. black/*green*	..	..	5·50
		c. Imperf vert (horiz pair)			95·00
23	P 2	½d. black/*green*	..	..	17·00
		c. Imperf vert (horiz pair)			£120
24	P 3	½d. black/*green*	..	..	12·00
		b. Imperf vert (horiz pair)			£120

(b) Controller's initials in black
25	P 1	1d. black/*red*	..	..	2·00
		m. Imperf vert (horiz pair)			55·00
		n. Imperf between (vert pair: No. 25 + No. 26)			
		o. Imperf horiz (vert pair)			
26	P 2	1d. black/*red*	..	..	2·75
		f. Imperf vert (horiz pair)			80·00
		g. Imperf horiz (vert pair: No. 26 + No. 27)			
27	P 3	1d. black/*red*	..	..	4·00
		f. Imperf vert (horiz pair)			80·00
28	P 1	2d. black/*orange*	..	..	5·50
29	P 2	2d. black/*orange*	..	..	8·00
30	P 3	2d. black/*orange*	..	..	14·00

For the ½d. the First printing had initials in either black or red, those of the Second printing had them in black and all of the Third were in red.

CONSTANT VARIETIES

Rows 1 and 2 are as Type P **1**, Row 3 as Type P **2** and Row 4 as Type P **3**.

½d. value
First printing—Imperf
R.1/1	& 4 Top left "½"inverted, no stop after right "AFR"	..	(No. 19c)	70·00
R.1/2	Top right "½" inverted	..	(No. 19d)	90·00
R.1/3	"⅓" at lower right	..	(No. 19e)	90·00
R.1/5	"POSTZFGEL"	..	(No. 19f)	90·00
R.1/6	Left spray inverted, "AFB" at right	..	(No. 19g)	90·00
R.2/1	"REB" at left. left side of inner frame 3 mm too high	..	(No. 19h)	90·00
R.2/2	"BEP" at left	..	(No. 19i)	90·00
R.2/3	"POSTZEOEL"	..	(No. 19j)	90·00
R.2/4	"AER" at right, left side of inner frame 2 mm too high	..	(No. 19k)	90·00
R.2/5	No stop after date	..	(No. 19l)	90·00
R.2/6	No stop after "PENNY"	..	(No. 19m)	
R.3/1	"⅓" at top left, "PE" of "PENNY" spaced	..	(No. 20c)	90·00
R.3/2	Right spray inverted	..	(No. 20d)	90·00
R.3/3	Top left "½" inverted	..	(No. 20e)	90·00
R.3/4	No stop after "2" at left	..	(No. 20f)	
R.3/5	Centre figures "½" level	..	(No. 20g)	
R.3/6	"POSTZEGFL", no stop after "AFR"	..	(No. 20h)	
R.4/3	"⅓" at top right	..	(No. 21b)	90·00
R.4/4	Lower left "½" inverted	..	(No. 21c)	90·00
R.4/5	"¼" at top left	..	(No. 21d)	90·00
R.4/6	Left spray inverted, "901" for "1901"	..	(No. 21e)	

This printing was produced first and was then adapted for the higher values.

Second printing
R.1/2	No stop after left "AFR"	*Imperf*	(No. 1a)	60·00
R.1/3	"⅓" at top left, no bar over lower right "½"	*Imperf*	(No. 1b)	60·00
R.1/6	No stop after date	*Imperf*	(No. 1c)	60·00
R.2/5	"BEP" at left, no stop after date	*Imperf*	(No. 1d)	60·00
R.3/3	"AFB" at left	*Imperf*	(No. 2a)	60·00
		Perf	(No. 23a)	
R.3/4	"POSTZEGEI"	*Imperf*	(No. 2b)	60·00
		Perf	(No. 23b)	
R.3/6	No bar over lower right "½"	*Imperf*	(No. 2c)	60·00
R.4/1	No stop after right "AFR"	*Imperf*	(No. 3a)	60·00
R.4/4	No stop after left "Z", no bar under top right "½"	*Imperf*	(No. 3b)	60·00
		Perf	(No. 23c)	
R.4/5	"POSTZECEL AER" at left	*Imperf*	(No. 3c)	60·00

Third printing
R.1/4	No stop after right "AFR"	*Imperf*	(No. 19a)	70·00
		Perf	(No. 22a)	40·00
R.2/1	Left side of inner frame too high	*Imperf*	(No. 19b)	70·00
		Perf	(No. 22b)	40·00
R.3/5	Centre figures "½" level	*Imperf*	(No. 20a)	70·00
		Perf	(No. 23d)	40·00
R.3/6	No stop after right "AFR"	*Imperf*	(No. 20b)	70·00
		Perf	(No. 23e)	40·00
R.4/6	Hyphen between right "AFR" and "REP"	*Imperf*	(No. 21a)	70·00
		Perf	(No. 24a)	40·00

1d. value
First printing
R.1/2	Inverted "1" at lower left, first "1" of date dropped	*Imperf*	(No. 4a)	35·00
		Perf	(No. 25a)	22·00
R.1/3	No bar under top left "1"	*Imperf*	(No. 4b)	35·00
		Perf	(No. 25b)	22·00
R.1/4	No bar over lower right "1"	*Imperf*	(No. 4c)	35·00
		Perf	(No. 25c)	22·00
R.1/5	"POSTZFGEL"	*Imperf*	(No. 4d)	35·00
		Perf	(No. 25d)	22·00
R.1/6	"AFB" at right	*Imperf*	(No. 4e)	35·00
		Perf	(No. 25e)	22·00
R.2/1	"REB" at left	*Imperf*	(No. 4f)	35·00
		Perf	(No. 25f)	22·00
R.2/2	"BEP" at left	*Imperf*	(No. 4g)	35·00
		Perf	(No. 25g)	22·00
R.2/3	"POSTZEOEL"	*Imperf*	(No. 4h)	35·00
		Perf	(No. 25h)	22·00

R.2/4	"AER" at right	.. .. Imperf	(No. 4i)	35·00
		Perf	(No. 25i)	22·00
R.2/5	No stop after date	.. .. Imperf	(No. 4j)	35·00
		Perf	(No. 25j)	22·00
R.2/6	No stop after "PENNY"	.. Imperf	(No. 4k)	35·00
		Perf	(No. 25k)	22·00
R.3/2	Right spray inverted	.. Imperf	(No. 5a)	22·00
		Perf	(No. 26a)	22·00
R.3/3	No bar over lower left "1"	.. Imperf	(No. 5b)	22·00
		Perf	(No. 26b)	22·00
R.3/4	No stop after left "Z"	.. Imperf	(No. 5c)	22·00
		Perf	(No. 26c)	22·00
R.3/6	"POSTZEGFL", no stop after right "AFR"	.. Imperf	(No. 5d)	35·00
		Perf	(No. 26d)	22·00
R.4/1	No stop after right "AFR"	.. Imperf	(No. 6a)	35·00
		Perf	(No. 27a)	22·00
R.4/2 & 6	Left spray inverted	.. Imperf	(No. 6b)	22·00
		Perf	(No. 27b)	13·00
R.4/3	"POSTZEGEI"	.. .. Imperf	(No. 6c)	22·00
		Perf	(No. 27c)	22·00
R.4/4	No bar under top right "1"	.. Imperf	(No. 6d)	35·00
		Perf	(No. 27d)	22·00

Second printing

R.1/2	First "1" in date dropped	.. Imperf	(No. 4l)	35·00
		Perf	(No. 25l)	22·00
R.3/6	No stop after right "AFR"	.. Imperf	(No. 5e)	22·00
		Perf	(No. 26e)	22·00
R.4/5	Dropped "P" in "PENNY"	.. Imperf	(No. 6e)	22·00
		Perf	(No. 27e)	22·00

It has been suggested that there may have been a third printing.

2d. value

First printing—Imperf

R.1/1	"1" at lower right	(No. 7a)	45·00
R.1/2	No stop after left "AFR" (on small part of printing)	(No. 7b)	90·00
R.1/3	No bar over lower right "2" (on small part of printing)	(No. 7c)	90·00
R.1/3	"PENNY" for "PENCE"	(No. 7d)	45·00
R.1/5	"POSTZFGEL"	(No. 7e)	45·00
R.1/6	"AFB" at right	(No. 7f)	45·00
R.2/1	"REB" at left	(No. 7g)	45·00
R.2/2	"AFB" at left	(No. 7h)	45·00
R.2/3	"POSTZEOEL"	(No. 7i)	45·00
R.2/4	"AER" at right	(No. 7j)	45·00
R.2/5	No stop after date	(No. 7k)	45·00
R.2/6	No stop after date, vertical line after "POSTZEGEL"	(No. 7l)	45·00
R.3/2	Right spray inverted	(No. 8a)	45·00
R.3/3	No bar over lower left "2"	(No. 8b)	45·00
R.3/4	Centre "2" inverted, no stop after left "Z"	(No. 8c)	45·00
R.3/6	"POSTZEGFL", no stop after right "AFR"	(No. 8d)	45·00
R.4/1	Centre "2" wider, no stop after right "AFR" (occurs on second printing also)	(No. 9a)	38·00
R.4/2	Centre "2" wider, left spray inverted	(No. 9b)	45·00
R.4/3	"POSTZEGEI"	(No. 9c)	45·00
R.4/4	No bar under top right "2"	(No. 9d)	45·00
R.4/5	"1" at lower left, "P" in "PENCE" dropped	(No. 9e)	45·00
R.4/6	Left spray inverted	(No. 9f)	45·00

Second printing

R.1/2	First "1" in date dropped	.. Imperf	(No. 7m)	45·00
		Perf	(No. 28a)	30·00
R.2/1	No stop after left "REP"	.. Imperf	(No. 7n)	45·00
		Perf	(No. 28b)	30·00
R.3/4	No stop after left "Z"	.. Imperf	(No. 8e)	45·00
R.3/6	No stop after right "AFR"	.. Imperf	(No. 8f)	45·00
		Perf	(No. 29a)	30·00
R.4/1	Centre 2 wider, no stop after right "AFR" (occurs on first printing also)	.. Imperf	(No. 9a)	38·00
		Perf	(No. 30a)	30·00
R.4/2	Centre "2" wider	.. Imperf	(No. 9g)	45·00
		Perf	(No. 30b)	30·00
R.4/5	"P" in "PENCE" dropped	.. Imperf	(No. 9h)	45·00
		Perf	(No. 30c)	30·00

It has been suggested that there was a third printing of this value.

4d. value

First printing

R.1/2	No stop after left "AFR"	(No. 10a)	45·00
R.1/3	No bar over lower right "4"	(No. 10b)	45·00
R.1/3	"PENNY" for "PENCE" (on small part of printing)	(No. 10c)	90·00
R.1/5	"POSTZFGEL"	(No. 10d)	45·00
R.1/6	"AFB" at right	(No. 10e)	45·00
R.2/1	"REB" at left	(No. 10f)	45·00
R.2/2	"AFB" at left	(No. 10g)	45·00
R.2/3	"POSTZEOEL"	(No. 10h)	45·00
R.2/4	"AER" at right	(No. 10i)	45·00
R.2/5	No stop after date	(No. 10j)	45·00
R.3/2	Right spray inverted	(No. 11a)	45·00
R.3/3	No bar over lower left "4" (on small part of printing)	(No. 11b)	90·00
R.3/4	No stop after "Z"	(No. 11c)	45·00
R.3/6	"POSTZEGFL"	(No. 11d)	45·00
R.4/1	Centre "4" wider, no stop after right "AFR"	(No. 12a)	45·00
R.4/2	Centre "4" wider, left spray inverted	(No. 12b)	45·00
R.4/3	"POSTZEGEI"	(No. 12c)	45·00
R.4/4	No bar under top right "4"	(No. 12d)	45·00
R.4/5	"AER" at left, "P" in "PENCE" dropped	(No. 12e)	45·00
R.4/6	Left spray inverted	(No. 12f)	45·00

Second printing

R.2/1	Left inner frame too high	(No. 10k)	45·00
R.4/1–2	Centre "4" wider	(No. 12g)	35·00
R.4/5	"P" in "PENCE" dropped	(No. 12h)	45·00

6d. value

First printing

R.1/2	No stop after left "AFR"	(No. 13a)	55·00
R.1/3	No bar over lower right "6"	(No. 13b)	55·00

R.1/3	"PENNY" for "PENCE" (on small part of printing)	(No. 13c)	£100
R.1/5	"POSTZFGEL"	(No. 13d)	55·00
R.1/6	"AFB" at right	(No. 13e)	55·00
R.2/1	"REB" at left	(No. 13f)	55·00
R.2/2	"AFB" at left	(No. 13g)	55·00
R.2/3	"POSTZEOEL"	(No. 13h)	55·00
R.2/4	"AER" at right	(No. 13i)	55·00
R.2/5	No stop after date	(No. 13j)	55·00
R.3/2	Right spray inverted	(No. 14a)	55·00
R.3/4	Centre "6" inverted, no stop after "Z" (on small part of printing)	(No. 14b)	£100
R.3/4	No stop after left "Z"	(No. 14c)	55·00
R.3/6	"POSTZEGFL"	(No. 14d)	55·00
R.4/1	Centre "6" wider, no stop after right "AFR"	(No. 15a)	55·00
R.4/2	Centre "6" wider, left spray inverted	(No. 15b)	55·00
R.4/3	"POSTZEGEI"	(No. 15c)	55·00
R.4/4	No bar under top right "6"	(No. 15d)	55·00
R.4/5	"AER" at left, "P" in "PENCE" dropped	(No. 15e)	55·00
R.4/6	Left spray inverted	(No. 15f)	55·00

Second printing

R.2/1	Left inner frame too high, no stop after left "REP"	(No. 13k)	55·00
R.4/1–2	Centre "6" wider	(No. 15g)	40·00
R.4/5	"P" in "PENCE" dropped	(No. 15h)	55·00

1s. value

R.1/2	No stop after left "AFR"	(No. 16a)	40·00
R.1/3	No bar over lower right "1"	(No. 16b)	40·00
R.2/5	No stop after date	(No. 16c)	40·00
R.3/3	Centre "1" inverted (on small part of printing)	(No. 17a)	40·00
R.3/4	"POSTZEGEI", no stop after left "Z"	(No. 17b)	40·00
R.4/1	No stop after right "AFR"	(No. 18a)	40·00
R.4/4	No bar under top right "1"	(No. 18b)	40·00
R.4/5	"AER" at left	(No. 18c)	40·00

LOCAL BRITISH OCCUPATION ISSUES DURING THE SOUTH AFRICAN WAR 1900–2

Stamps of the Transvaal Republic, unless otherwise stated, variously overprinted or surcharged.

LYDENBURG

Lydenburg fell to the British on 6 September 1900.

V.R.I.
3d.
(L 1)

1900 (Sept). *Nos. 215b and 217 surch as Type L 1, others optd* "V.R.I" *only.*

1	30	½d. green	.. ..	£110	£110
2		1d. rose-red and green	..	£100	90·00
2a	34	1d. on 1d. red	..	—	—
3	30	2d. brown and green	..	£800	£600
4		2½d. blue and green	..	£1900	£800
5		3d. on 1d. rose-red and green	..	85·00	75·00
6		3d. purple and green	..	—	—
7		4d. sage-green and green	..	£2500	£650
8		6d. lilac and green	..	£1900	£550
9		1s. ochre and green	..	£3500	£2250

The above were cancelled by British Army postal service postmarks. These overprints with Transvaal cancellations are believed to be forgeries.

RUSTENBURG

The British forces in Rustenburg, west of Pretoria, were besieged by the Boers during June 1900. When relieved on the 22 June 1900 no "V.R.I" stamps were available so a local handstamp was applied.

V.R.
(R 1)

1900 (23 June). *Handstamped with Type R 1 in violet.*

1	30	½d. green	.. ..	£130	85·00
2		1d. rose-red and green	..	95·00	65·00
3		2d. brown and green	..	£275	95·00
4		2½d. blue and green	..	£160	85·00
5		3d. purple and green	..	£200	£100
6		6d. lilac and green	..	£1000	£300
7		1s. ochre and green	..	£1400	£700
8		2s. 6d. dull violet and green	..	£8500	£4250
		a. Handstamp in black	..	†	£7500

Nos. 2 and 5 exist with the handstamp inverted.

SCHWEIZER RENECKE

BESIEGED
(SR 1)

1900 (Sept). *Handstamped with Type SR 1 in black, reading vert up or down. (a) On stamps of Transvaal.*

1	30	½d. green	..	†	£225
2		1d. rose-red and green	..	†	£225
3		2d. brown and green	..	†	£300
4		6d. lilac and green	..	†	£800

(b) On stamps of Cape of Good Hope

5	17	½d. green	..	†	£400
6		1d. carmine	..	†	£400

Schweizer Renecke, near the Bechuanaland border, was under siege from 1 August 1900 to 9 January 1901. The British commander authorised the above stamps shortly after 19 August. All stamps were cancelled with the dated circular town postmark ("Schweizer Renecke, Z.A.R.") usually after having been stuck on paper before use. Unused, without the postmark, do not exist.

No. 4 exists with double handstamp.

WOLMARANSSTAD

A British column occupied this town in the south-west of the Transvaal for two weeks in June 1900. Transvaal stamps, to a face value of £5 2s. 6d., were found at the local firm of Thos. Leask and Co. and surcharged as below. The first mail left on 24 June and the last on 19 July after which the Boers re-occupied the town.

Cancelled	Cancelled
V-R-I.	**V-R-I.**
(L 3)	(L 4)

1900 (24 June). *Optd with Type L 3.*

1	30	½d. green (B.)	..	£225	£350
		a. Opt inverted		£700	
		b. Opt in black (B.)			
1c		½d. on 1s. green (B.)			
2		1d. rose-red and green (B.)		£150	£250
		a. Opt in green		£1800	
		b. Opt in black (B.)			
3		2d. brown and green (B.)	..	£1600	£1600
		a. Opt in black (B.)		£3000	
4		2½d. blue and green (R.)		£1600	
		a. Opt in blue		£2750	£2750
		b. Opt in black (B.)			
5		3d. purple and green (B.)	..	£2750	£3000
6		4d. sage-green and green (B.)		£3500	£4000
7		6d. lilac and green (B.)		£3750	£4000
8		1s. ochre and green (B.)	..	—	£7500

The two lines of the overprint were handstamped separately. The ½d. exists with two impressions of the "Cancelled" handstamp, the 2½d. with two impressions of "V-R-I", one in red and one in blue and the 3d. with "Cancelled" in green and "V.R.I." in blue.

1900 (24 June). *Optd with Type L 4.*

9	34	1d. red (B.)	..	£150	£275

The ½d., 1d. and 3d. in Type 30 are also known with this overprint.

VII. ZULULAND

Zululand remained an independent kingdom until annexed by Great Britain on 19 May 1887 when it was declared a Crown Colony.

The first European postal service was operated by a Natal postal agency at Eshowe opened in 1876 which cancelled Natal stamps with a "No. 56 P.O. Natal" postmark. The agency closed during the Zulu War of 1879 and did not re-open until 1885 when a Eshowe postmark was provided. "ZULULAND" was added to the cancellation in 1887 and stamps of Natal continued to be used until replaced by the overprinted series on 1 May 1888.

PRICES FOR STAMPS ON COVER	
Nos. 1/2	from × 100
Nos. 3/10	from × 20
No. 11	
Nos. 12/16	from × 20
Nos. 20/3	from × 30
No. 24	from × 20
Nos. 25/6	from × 12
Nos. 27/9	—
No. F1	from × 100

ZULULAND	ZULULAND.
(1)	(2)

1888 (1 May)–93. (a) *Nos. 173, 180, 197, 200/2, 205a, 207a/8, 209 and 211 of Great Britain (Queen Victoria) optd with T 1.*

1	½d. vermilion (11.88)	..	2·75	2·50
2	1d. deep purple	..	25·00	3·75
3	2d. grey-green and carmine	..	11·00	23·00
4	2½d. purple/blue (9.91)	..	18·00	20·00
5	3d. purple/yellow	..	25·00	22·00
6	4d. green and deep brown	..	40·00	55·00
7	5d. dull purple and blue (3.93)	..	90·00	£120
8	6d. purple/rose-red	..	11·00	17·00
9	9d. dull purple and blue (4.92)	..	85·00	90·00
10	1s. dull green (4.92)	..	£110	£130
11	5s. rose (4.92)	..	£500	£600
¹/11		Set of 11	£800	£950
1 and 3/11 H/S "Specimen"		Set of 10	£600	

(b) *No. 97a of Natal optd with T 2.*

12	½d. dull green (with stop) (7.88)	..	55·00	75·00
	a. Opt double		£1000	£1100
	b. Opt inverted		£1200	
	d. Opt omitted (vert pair with normal)		£5500	
13	½d. dull green (without stop)	..	23·00	38·00
	a. Opt double		£1200	£1300

1893 (29 Nov*). *T 15 of Natal (Wmk Crown CA. P 14) optd with T 1.*

16	6d. dull purple	..	55·00	55·00

*Earliest known date of use.

PRICES OF SETS

Set prices are given for many issues, generally those containing three stamps or more. Definitive sets include one of each value or major colour change, but do not cover perforations, die types or minor shades. Where a choice is possible the set prices are based on the cheapest versions of the stamps included in the listings.

3   4

(Typo D.L.R.)

1894 (18 Apr)–96. *Wmk Crown CA. P 14.*

0	3	½d. dull mauve and green	3·00 4·25
		w. Wmk inverted	£110
1		1d. dull mauve and carmine	5·00 1·75
2		2½d. dull mauve and ultramarine	14·00 8·50
3		3d. dull mauve and olive-brown	8·00 3·00
4	4	6d. dull mauve and black	20·00 20·00
5		1s. green	35·00 38·00
6		2s. 6d. green and black (2.96)	75·00 85·00
7		4s. green and carmine	£110 £150
8		£1 purple/red	£450 £475
9		£5 purple and black/red (Optd S. £400)	£4250 £1500
0/8			Set of 9 £600 £650
0/8		Optd "Specimen"	Set of 9 £350

Dangerous forgeries exist of the £1 and £5.

FISCAL STAMP USED FOR POSTAGE

1891 (5 May*). *Fiscal stamp of Natal (Wmk Crown CA. P 14) optd with T 1.*

′1	1d. dull mauve (Optd S. £60)	3·00 3·00
	a. Top left triangle detached	£100 £100

*Earliest known date of postal use. A proclamation published in the *Natal Government Gazette* on 27 June 1891 authorised the use of this stamp for postal purposes, but it is clear from the wording that such use had already commenced.

Other values, 1s. to £20 as No. F1 exist apparently with postmarks, but, as these were never authorised for postal use, they are no longer listed.

Zululand was annexed to Natal on 31 December 1897 and its stamps were withdrawn from sale on 30 June 1898.

VIII. BRITISH ARMY FIELD OFFICES DURING SOUTH AFRICAN WAR, 1899–1902

Z 1   Z 2

Stamps of GREAT BRITAIN used by British Army Field Offices in South Africa cancelled as Types Z 1, Z 2 or similar postmarks.

1881. *Stamp of Queen Victoria.*

Z1	1d. lilac (16 *dots*)	5·00

1883–84. *Stamps of Queen Victoria.*

Z1a	2s. 6d lilac	£200
Z2	5s. rose	£200
Z2a	10s. ultramarine	£375

1887–92. *Stamps of Queen Victoria.*

Z 3	½d. vermilion	6·00
Z 4	1½d. dull purple and green	20·00
Z 5	2d. grey-green and carmine	12·00
Z 6	2½d. purple/*blue*	6·00
Z 7	3d. purple/*yellow*	12·00
Z 8	4d. green and brown	16·00
Z 9	4½d. green and carmine	45·00
Z10	5d. dull purple and blue (Die II)	14·00
Z11	6d. purple/*rose-red*	10·00
Z12	9d. dull purple and blue	45·00
Z13	10d. dull purple and carmine	45·00
Z14	1s. dull green	70·00
Z15	£1 green	£750

1900. *Stamps of Queen Victoria.*

Z16	½d. blue-green	6·00
Z17	1s. green and carmine	£110

1902. *Stamps of King Edward VII.*

Z18	½d. blue-green	7·00
Z19	1d. scarlet	5·00
Z20	1½d. purple and green	
Z21	2d. yellowish green and carmine-red	
Z22	2½d. ultramarine	10·00
Z23	3d. purple/*orange-yellow*	
Z24	4d. green and grey-brown	
Z25	5d. dull purple and ultramarine	
Z26	6d. pale dull purple	15·00
Z27	9d. dull purple and ultramarine	
Z28	10d. dull purple and carmine	
Z29	1s. dull green and carmine	

ARMY OFFICIAL STAMPS

1896–1901. *Stamps of Queen Victoria optd "ARMY OFFICIAL".*

ZO1	½d. vermilion	£100
ZO2	½d. blue-green	£100
ZO3	1d. lilac (16 *dots*)	85·00
ZO4	6d. purple/*rose-red*	

IX. UNION OF SOUTH AFRICA

The province continued to use their existing issues until the introduction of Nos. 3/17. From 19 August 1910 the issues of any province were valid for use throughout the Union until they were demonetised on 31 December 1937.

PRICES FOR STAMPS ON COVER TO 1945	
Nos. 1/15	*from* × 4
Nos. 16/17	
Nos. 18/21	*from* × 6
Nos. 26/32	*from* × 2
No. 33	*from* × 4
Nos. 34/110	*from* × 1
Nos. D1/7	*from* × 4
Nos. D8/33	*from* × 6
Nos. O1/33	*from* × 4

1

(Des H. S. Wilkinson. Recess D.L.R.)

1910 (4 Nov). *Opening of Union Parliament. Inscribed bilingually. Wmk Multiple Rosettes. P 14.*

1	1	2½d. deep blue (H/S S. £325)	3·00 3·00
2		2½d. blue	1·75 1·40

The deep blue shade is generally accompanied by a blueing of the paper.

The price quoted for the "Specimen" handstamp is for the small italic type with capital and lower case letters.

2   3   4 Springbok's Head

(Typo D.L.R.)

1913 (1 Sept)–**24.** *Inscribed bilingually. W 4. (a) P 14.*

3	2	2½d. green	1·00 20
		a. Stamp doubly printed	£11000
		b. *Blue-green*	2·00 20
		c. *Yellow-green*	2·50 50
		d. Printed on the gummed side	£550
		w. Wmk inverted	2·00 50
4		1d. rose-red (*shades*)	1·00 10
		a. *Carmine-red*	2·00 10
		b. *Scarlet* (*shades*)	1·75 30
		c. Printed on the gummed side	£550
		w. Wmk inverted	2·50 50
5		1½d. chestnut (*shades*) (23.8.20)	60 10
		a. *Tête-bêche* (pair)	1·75 18·00
		b. Printed on the gummed side	£550
		w. Wmk inverted	60 10
6	3	2d. dull purple	1·75 10
		a. *Deep purple*	2·50 10
		b. Printed on the gummed side	£550
		w. Wmk inverted	3·25 1·25
7		2½d. bright blue	3·75 1·25
		a. *Deep blue*	5·50 3·00
		w. Wmk inverted	60·00 60·00
8		3d. black and orange-red	9·00 30
		a. *Black and dull orange-red*	9·50 70
		w. Wmk inverted	16·00 6·50
9		3d. ultramarine (*shades*) (4.10.22)	3·50 1·75
		w. Wmk inverted	8·50 4·75
10		4d. orange-yellow and olive-green	8·50 45
		a. *Orange-yellow and sage-green*	6·00 45
		w. Wmk inverted	8·00 50
11		6d. black and violet	5·50 60
		a. *Black and bright violet*	8·00 60
		aw Wmk inverted	16·00 8·50
12		1s. orange	16·00 80
		a. *Orange-yellow*	25·00 1·00
		w. Wmk inverted	18·00 1·25
13		1s. 3d. violet (*shades*) (1.9.20)	13·00 7·00
		w. Wmk inverted	85·00 85·00
14		2s. 6d. purple and green	55·00 1·50
15		5s. purple and blue	£110 7·50
		a. *Reddish purple and light blue*	£110 8·50
		w. Wmk inverted	— £1500
16		10s. deep blue and olive-green	£180 7·50
		w. Wmk inverted	£3500 £2000
17		£1 green and red (7.16)	£600 £350
		a. *Pale olive-green and red* (1924)	£800 £1200
3/17			Set of 15 £900 £350
3/8, 10/17		Optd or H/S "Specimen"	Set of 14 £1300

(b) Coil stamps. P 14×imperf

18	2	½d. green	6·00 1·00
		w. Wmk inverted	£450 £250
19		1d. rose-red (13.2.14)	7·00 3·75
		a. *Scarlet*	9·50 7·50
		w. Wmk inverted	£450 £250
20		1½d. chestnut (15.11.20)	9·00 15·00
		w. Wmk inverted	† —
21	3	2d. dull purple (7.10.21)	10·00 4·75
18/21			Set of 4 29·00 22·00

The 6d. exists with "Z" of "ZUID" wholly or partly missing due to wear of plate (*Price wholly missing*, £80 un, £38 us).

5 De Havilland
D.H.9 Biplane

(Eng A. J. Cooper. Litho *Cape Times* Ltd)

1925 (26 Feb). *Air. Inscr bilingually. P 12.*

26	5	1d. carmine	4·50 9·50
27		3d. ultramarine	8·50 9·50
28		6d. magenta	12·00 14·00
29		9d. green	23·00 48·00
26/9			Set of 4 42·00 70·00

Beware of forgeries of all values perforated 11, 11½ or 13.

INSCRIPTIONS. From 1926 until 1951 (also Nos. 167 and 262/5), most issues were inscribed in English and Afrikaans alternately throughout the sheets.

PRICES for Nos. 30/135 are for unused horizontal pairs, used horizontal pairs and used singles (either inscription), *unless otherwise indicated.* Vertical pairs are worth between 30% and 50% of the prices quoted for horizontal pairs.

6 Springbok   7 *Dromedaris*
(Van Riebeeck's ship)

8 Orange Tree   9

(Typo Waterlow until 1927, thereafter Govt Printer, Pretoria)

1926 (2 Jan)–**27.** *W 9. P 14½×14.*

			Un pair	Used pair	Used single
30	6	½d. black and green	3·00	4·00	10
		a. Missing "1" in "½"	£2000		
		b. Centre omitted (in pair with normal)	£1300		
		cw. Wmk inverted	3·75	4·00	
		d. Frame printed double			
		e. Perf 13½×14 (1927)	50·00	55·00	4·00
		ea. *Tête-bêche* (pair)	£850		
		ew. Wmk inverted	50·00	55·00	
31	7	1d. black and carmine	2·00	45	10
		a. Imperf (vert pair)*	£750		
		b. Imperf 3 sides (vert pair)*	£750	£800	
		cw. Wmk inverted	4·50	1·50	
		d. Perf 13½×14 (1927)	60·00	55·00	4·00
		da. *Tête-bêche* (pair)	£950		
		dw. Wmk inverted	60·00	55·00	
32	8	6d. green and orange (1.5.26)	38·00	38·00	1·50
		w. Wmk inverted	60·00	70·00	
30/2			Set of 3 38·00	38·00	1·50

No. 30a exists in Afrikaans only. Nos. 30e and 31d were only issued in booklets.

No. 30d occurred on the bottom left-hand corner of one sheet and included the bottom four stamps in the first vertical row and the bottom two in the second. As listed No. 30d shows the left-hand stamp with the frame completely double and the right-hand stamp with two-thirds of the frame double.

*Both Nos. 31a and 31b occur in blocks of four with the other vertical pair imperforate at left.

For ½d. with pale grey centre, see No. 126.

For rotogravure printing see Nos. 42, etc.

10 "Hope"

(Recess B.W.)

1926 (2 Jan). *T* **10**. *Inscribed in English or Afrikaans. W* **9** (*upright or inverted in equal quantities*).

			Single stamps	
33	4d. grey-blue (English inscr) (*shades*)		1·75	85
	a. Inscr in Afrikaans		1·75	85

In this value the English and Afrikaans inscriptions are on separate sheets.

This stamp is known with private perforations or roulettes.

11 Union Buildings, Pretoria

12 Groot Schuur

12a A Native Kraal

13 Black and Blue Wildebeest

14 Ox-wagon inspanned

15 Ox-wagon outspanned

16 Cape Town and Table Bay

(Recess B.W.)

1927 (1 Mar)–30. *W* **9**. *P* 14.

				Un pair	Used pair	Used single
34	11	2d. grey and maroon		13·00	20·00	60
		aw. Wmk inverted		£300	£350	
		b. Perf 14×13½ (2.30)		18·00	20·00	70
35	12	3d. black and red		20·00	28·00	60
		a. Perf 14×13½ (1930)		42·00	48·00	80
35b	12a	4d. brown (23.3.28)		30·00	50·00	1·00
		bw. Wmk inverted		£450	£400	
		c. Perf 14×13½ (1930)		42·00	55·00	1·25
36	13	1s. brown and deep blue		35·00	55·00	1·00
		a. Perf 14×13½ (1930)		48·00	60·00	1·25
37	14	2s. 6d. green and brown		£110	£325	16·00
		a. Perf 14×13½ (1930)		£250	£400	22·00
38	15	5s. black and green		£225	£650	35·00
		a. Perf 14×13½ (1930)		£350	£750	40·00
39	16	10s. bright blue and brown		£150	£130	10·00
		a. Centre inverted (*single stamp*)		£9500		
		b. Perf 14×13½ (1930)		£160	£140	11·00
34/9			Set of 7	£500	£1100	55·00
34/9 H/S "Specimen"			Set of 7	£850		

17 De Havilland D.H.60 Cirrus Moth

(Typo Govt Ptg Wks, Pretoria)

1929 (16 Aug). *Air. Inscribed bilingually. No wmk. P* 14 × 13½.

						Un single	Us single
40	17	4d. green				5·50	2·50
41		1s. orange				16·00	13·00

PRINTER. All the following issues, except *where stated otherwise*, are printed by rotogravure (the design having either plain lines or a dotted screen) by the Government Printer, Pretoria.

The new-issue supplement to this Catalogue appears each month in

GIBBONS STAMP MONTHLY

—from your newsagent or by postal subscription— sample copy and details on request.

I

II

The two types of the 1d. differ in the spacing of the horizontal lines in the side panels:—Type I close; Type II wide. The Afrikaans had the spacing of the words POSSEEL-INKOMSTE close in Type I and more widely spaced in Type II.

Window flaw (R. 20/4 on all ptgs before 1937)

Spear flaw (R. 9/2)

Twisted horn (Cyl 7020 R.1/5)

1930–45. *T* 6 *to* 8 *and* 11 *to* 14 *redrawn*, "SUIDAFRIKA" (*in one word*) *on Afrikaans stamps. W* **9**. *P* 15 × 14 (½d., 1d., *and* 6d.) *or* 14.

			Un pair	Used pair	Used single
42	½d. black and green (5.30)		2·50	2·50	10
	a. Two English or two Afrikaans stamps *se-tenant* (vert strip of 4)		40·00		
	b. *Tête-bêche*		£850		
	w. Wmk inverted		2·25	1·75	10
43	1d. black and carmine (I) (4.30)		3·25	2·25	10
	a. *Tête-bêche*		£1000		
	b. Frame omitted (*single stamp*)		£450		
	cw. Wmk inverted		3·25	1·50	10
43d	1d. black and carmine (II) (8.32)		30·00	2·50	10
	dw. Wmk inverted		28·00	2·50	10
44	2d. slate-grey and lilac (4.31)		18·00	8·50	20
	a. *Tête-bêche*		£3000		
	b. Frame omitted (*single stamp*)		£1500		
	cw. Wmk inverted		16·00	7·50	20
44d	2d. blue and violet (3.38)		£275	65·00	2·50
45	3d. black and red (11.31)		50·00	65·00	2·00
	aw. Wmk inverted		48·00	60·00	1·25
	b. Window flaw		£120		
45c	3d. blue (10.33)		16·00	7·00	20
	cw. Wmk inverted		8·50	4·75	10
	d. Window flaw		38·00		
	e. Centre omitted				
46	4d. brown (19.11.32)		£120	80·00	11·00
	aw. Wmk inverted		35·00	30·00	40
	b. Spear flaw		£130		
46c	4d. brown (*shades*) (*again redrawn*) (1936)		3·50	3·25	10
	cw. Wmk inverted		11·00	6·00	10

				Un pair	Used pair	Used single
47	6d. green and orange (*wmk inverted*) (13.5.31)			17·00	3·00	10
	w. Wmk upright (8.32)			26·00	5·00	10
48	1s. brown and deep blue (14.9.32)			75·00	35·00	40
	aw. Wmk inverted			48·00	25·00	25
	b. Twisted horn flaw			£160		
49	2s. 6d. grn & brn (*shades*) (24.12.32)			95·00	£100	3·25
	aw. Wmk inverted			£110	£120	3·25
49b	2s. 6d. blue and brown (1945)			23·00	9·00	20
42/9b			Set of 13	£500	£275	6·50

For similar designs with "SUID-AFRIKA" hyphenated, see Nos. 54 etc. and Nos. 114 etc.

Nos. 42/3, 43d/4 exist in coils.

No. 42a comes from the coil printing on the cylinder for which two horizontal rows were incorrectly etched so that two Afrikaans-inscribed stamps were followed by two English. This variety is normally without a coil join, although some examples do occur showing a repair join.

The 1d. (Type I) exists without watermark from a trial printing (Price £25 *un*).

Although it appears to be printed in one colour No. 45c was produced from vignette and frame cylinders in the same way as the bicoloured version. The clouds in the background, which are present on No. 45e, were printed from the frame cylinder.

Nos. 45b, 45d, 46b and 48b all occur on printings with either upright or inverted watermark. The price quoted is for the cheapest version in each instance.

The Rotogravure printings may be distinguished from the preceding Typographed and Recess printed issues by the following tests:—

ROTOGRAVURE:

½d., 1d. and 6d. Leg of "R" in "AFR" ends squarely on the bottom line.

2d. The newly built War Memorial appears to the left of the value.

3d. Two fine lines have been removed from the top part of the frame.

4d. No. 46. The scroll is in solid colour.
No. 46b. The scroll is white with a crooked line running through it. (No. 35b. The scroll is shaded by the diagonal lines.)

1s. The shading of the last "A" partly covers the flower beneath.

2s. 6d. The top line of the centre frame is thick and leaves only one white line between it and the name.

5s. (Nos. 64/a). The leg of the "R" is straight.

Rotogravure impressions are generally coarser.

18 Church of the Vow

19 "The Great Trek" (C. Michell)

20 A Voortrekker

21 Voortrekker Woman

Blurred "SOUTH AFRICA" and red "comet"
flaw (Cyls 6917/6922 R. 2/7)

(Des J. Prentice (½d., 2d., 3d.))

1933 (3 May)**—36.** *Voortrekker Memorial Fund.* W 9 (*sideways*).
P 14.

50	18	½d. + ½d. black and green (16.1.36)	4·00	4·00	50
51	19	1d. + ½d. grey-black and pink	3·25	1·50	25
		a. Blurred "SOUTH AFRICA" and red "comet" flaw	40·00		
52	20	2d. + 1d. grey-green and purple	4·25	4·00	55
53	21	3d. + 1½d. grey-green and blue	7·50	5·00	70
50/3		*Set of 4*	17·00	13·00	1·75

22 Gold Mine

22a Groot Schuur

Dies of 6d.

I

II

III

23 Groot Constantia

"Falling ladder" flaw (R. 5/10)

1933–48. "SUID-AFRIKA" (*hyphenated*) *on Afrikaans stamps.*
W 9. P 15×14 (½d., 1d. and 6d.) or 14 (*others*).

54	6	½d. grey and green (*wmk inverted*) (9.35)	3·25	1·50	10
		aw. Wmk upright (1936)	7·00	1·60	10
		b. Coil stamp. Perf 13½×14 (1935)	30·00	50·00	1·00
		bw. Wmk upright	30·00	50·00	1·00
		c. Booklet pane of 6 (with adverts on margins) (*wmk upright*)	20·00		
56	7	1d. grey & car (*shades*) (19.4.34)	50	75	10
		a. Imperf (pair)	£140		
		b. Frame omitted (*single stamp*)	£250		
		cw. Wmk inverted	40	75	10
		d. Coil stamp. Perf 13½×14 (1935)	32·00	55·00	1·40
		dw. Wmk inverted	32·00	55·00	1·40
		e. Booklet pane of 6 (with adverts on margins) (1935)	11·00		
		f. Booklet pane of 6 (with blank margins) (1937)	12·00		
		h. Booklet pane of 6 (with postal slogans on margins) (1948)	4·00		
		i. *Grey & brt rose-carm* (7.48)	55	1·00	10
57	22	1½d. green & brt gold (12.11.36)	2·50	2·00	10
		a. Shading omitted from mine dump (in pair with normal)	£160	£140	
		bw. Wmk inverted	1·50	1·50	10
		c. *Blue-grn & dull gold* (8.40)	6·50	3·00	10
58	11	2d. blue and violet (11.38)	65·00	32·00	75
58a		2d. grey and dull purple (5.41)	40·00	65·00	1·25

59	22a	3d. ultramarine (2.40)	6·00	1·75	10
61	8	6d. green & vermilion (I) (10.37)	70·00	20·00	70
		a. "Falling ladder" flaw	£180		
61b		6d. green & vermilion (II) (6.38)	30·00	1·00	10
61c		6d. grn & red-orge (III) (11.46)	14·00	75	10
62	13	1s. brown & chalky blue (2.39)	42·00	8·50	10
		a. Frame omitted (*single stamp*)	£1900		
64	15	5s. black and green (10.33)	55·00	55·00	1·75
		aw. Wmk inverted	£110	£100	3·00
		b. *Black and blue-green* (9.44)	35·00	15·00	35
64c	23	10s. blue and sepia (8.39)	65·00	14·00	70
		ca. *Blue & blackish brn* (8.39)	42·00	5·50	30
54/9, 61c/64ca		*Set of 10*	£225	£110	2·50

The ½d. and 1d. coil stamps may be found in blocks emanating
from the residue of the large rolls which were cut into sheets and
distributed to Post Offices.

Nos. 54 and 56 also exist in coils.

1d. Is printed from Type II. Frames of different sizes exist due to
reductions made from time to time for the purpose of providing
more space for the perforations.

3d. In No. 59 the frame is unscreened and composed of solid lines.
Centre is diagonally screened. Scrolls above "3d." are clear lined,
light in the middle and dark at sides.

6d. Die I. Green background lines faint. "SUID-AFRIKA"
16¼ mm long.

Die II. Green background lines heavy. "SUID-AFRIKA" 17 mm
long. "S" near end of tablet. Scroll open.

Die III. Scroll closed up and design smaller (18 × 22 mm).

Single specimens of the 1933–48 issue inscribed in English
may be distinguished from those of 1930–45 as follows:—

½d. and 1d. Centres in grey instead of varying intensities of
black.

2d. The letters of "SOUTH AFRICA" are narrower and
thinner.

3d. The trees are taller and the sky is without lines.

6d. The frame is vermilion.

1s. The frame is chalky blue.

For similar designs, but printed in screened rotogravure, see
Nos. 114 to 122a.

BOOKLET PANES. Booklets issued in 1935 contained ½d.
and 1d. stamps in panes with advertisements in the top and
bottom margins and no margin at right (Nos. 54b and 56d).
These were replaced in 1937 by editions showing blank margins
on all four sides (Nos. 56e and 75ba). Following a period when
the booklet panes were without margins, a further 3s. booklet
was issued in 1948 which had four margins on the panes and
postal slogans at top and bottom (Nos. 56h, 87b and 114a).

24

JIPEX

1936

(24a)

"Cleft skull" flaw (R. 14/2)

(Des J. Booysen)

1935 (1 May). *Silver Jubilee. Inscr bilingually.* W 9. P 15×14.

65	24	½d. black and blue-green	2·25	12·00	10
		a. "Cleft skull" flaw	6·00		
66		1d. black and carmine	2·25	4·25	10
		a. "Cleft skull" flaw	6·00		
67		3d. blue	17·00	55·00	2·25
		a. "Cleft skull" flaw	42·00		
68		6d. green and orange	30·00	70·00	3·25
		a. "Cleft skull" flaw	75·00		
65/8		*Set of 4*	45·00	£130	5·00

In stamps with English at top the ½d., 3d. and 6d. have
"SILWER JUBILEUM" to left of portrait, and "POSTAGE
REVENUE" or "POSTAGE" (3d. and 6d.) in left value tablet. In the
1d., "SILVER JUBILEE" is to the left of portrait. In alternate
stamps the positions of English and Afrikaans inscriptions are
reversed.

1936 (2 Nov). *Johannesburg International Philatelic Exhibition.*
Optd with T 24a.

			Un sheet	Us sheet
MS69	6	½d. grey and green (No. 54)	4·50	10·00
MS70	7	1d. grey and carmine (No. 56)	3·50	6·00

Issued each in miniature sheet of six stamps with marginal
advertisements.

NEW INFORMATION

The editor is always interested to correspond with
people who have new information that will
improve or correct the Catalogue.

25

25a

"Mouse" flaw (R. 4/1)

(Des J. Prentice)

1937 (12 May). *Coronation.* W 9 (*sideways**). P 14.

71	25	½d. grey-black and blue-green	50	70	10
		w. Wmk horns pointing to left	50	50	10
72		1d. grey-black and carmine	50	50	10
		w. Wmk horns pointing to left	50	50	10
73		1½d. orange and greenish blue	50	50	10
		a. "Mouse" flaw	5·00		
		w. Wmk horns pointing to left	50	50	10
74		3d. ultramarine	2·00	2·25	10
		w. Wmk horns pointing to left	2·00	2·25	10
75		1s. red-brown and turquoise-blue	3·50	4·25	15
		a. Hyphen on Afrikaans stamp omitted (R. 2/13)	45·00		
		w. Wmk horns pointing to left	3·50	4·25	15
71/5		*Set of 5*	6·00	7·50	40

*The normal sideways watermark shows the horns of the
springbok pointing to the right, *as seen from the back of the
stamp.*

No. 75a shows the hyphen completely omitted and the top of
the "K" damaged. A less distinct flaw, on which part of the
hyphen is still visible and with no damage to the "K", occurs on
R. 4/17.

"Tick" flaw on ear and spot on nose
(multipositive flaw (occurring in
1947) (R. 3/4, or 3/1 on some ptgs
of No. 114)

1937–40. W 9. P 15×14.

75b	25a	½d. grey and green	7·50	90	10
		ba. Booklet pane of 6 (with blank margins) (1937)	42·00		
		bd. *Grey and blue-green* (1940)	5·50	90	10
		be. "Tick" flaw and spot on nose	50·00		

The lines of shading in T 25a are all horizontal and thicker
than in T 6. In Nos. 75b and 75bd the design is composed of solid
lines. For stamps with designs composed of dotted lines, see No.
114. Later printings of No. 75bd have a smaller design.

26 Voortrekker Ploughing

27 Wagon crossing
Drakensberg

28 Signing of Dingaan–Retief Treaty

29 Voortrekker Monument

(Des W. Coetzer and J. Prentice)

1938 (14 Dec). *Voortrekker Centenary Memorial Fund.* W **9**. *P* 14 (*Nos.* 76/7) *or* 15 × 14 (*others*).

76	26	½d. + ½d. blue and green	..	10·00	4·00	30
77	27	1d. + 1d. blue and carmine	..	11·00	5·00	40
78	28	1½d. + 1½d. chocolate & blue-grn	15·00	9·50	80
79	29	3d. + 3d. bright blue	..	17·00	11·00	1·00
76/9		.. ..	Set of 4	48·00	27·00	2·25

30 Wagon Wheel

31 Voortrekker Family

Three bolts in wheel rim (R. 15/5)

(Des W. Coetzer and J. Prentice)

1938 (14 Dec). *Voortrekker Commemoration.* W **9**. *P* 15×14.

80	30	1d. blue and carmine	..	4·50	4·25	30
		a. Three bolts in wheel rim	27·00		
81	31	1½d. greenish blue and brown	..	6·50	4·25	30

32 Old Vicarage, Paarl, now a museum   33 Symbol of the Reformation

34 Huguenot Dwelling, Drakenstein Mountain Valley

(Des J. Prentice)

1939 (17 July). *250th Anniv of Huguenot Landing in South Africa and Huguenot Commemoration Fund.* W **9**. *P* 14 (*Nos.* 82/3) *or* 15 × 14 (*No.* 84).

82	32	½d. + ½d. brown and green	..	4·75	6·00	30
83	33	1d. + 1d. green and carmine	..	11·00	6·50	30
84	34	1½d. + 1½d. blue-green and purple	26·00	13·00	1·00
82/4		.. ..	Set of 3	38·00	23·00	1·40

34a Gold Mine

1941 (Aug)–48. W **9** (*sideways*). *P* 14 × 15.

87	34a	1½d. blue-grn and yellow-buff (shades)	..	80	40	10
		a. Yellow-buff (centre) omitted £1500			
		b. Booklet pane of 6 (with postal slogans on margins) (1948)	..	3·50		

35 Infantry   36 Nurse and Ambulance   37 Airman

38 Sailor, Destroyer and Lifebelts   39 Women's Auxiliary Services

40 Artillery   41 Electric Welding

42 Tank Corps   42a Signaller

"Stain" on uniform (R. 14/11)

"Cigarette" flaw (R. 18/2)

1941–46. *War Effort.* W **9** (*sideways on* 2d., 4d., 6d.). *P* 14 (2d., 4d., 6d.) *or* 15 × 14 (*others*). (a) *Inscr alternately.*

88	35	½d. green (19.11.41)	..	1·50	1·75	10
		a. Blue-green (7.42)	..	3·50	2·25	10
89	36	1d. carmine (3.10.41)	..	2·00	1·75	10
		a. "Stain" on uniform flaw	20·00		
90	37	1½d. myrtle-green (12.1.42)	1·50	1·25	10
91	39	3d. blue (1.8.41)	..	20·00	25·00	50
		a. "Cigarette" flaw	..	70·00		
92	40	4d. orange-brown (20.8.41)	19·00	14·00	15
		a. Red-brown (6.42)	..	35·00	32·00	1·25
93	41	6d. red-orange (3.9.41)	..	12·00	9·00	15
94	42a	1s. 3d. olive-brown (21.43)	..	12·00	6·50	20
		a. Blackish brown (5.46)	..	4·00	6·50	20

(b) *Inscr bilingually*

			Un single	Us single
95	38	2d. violet (15.9.41)	90	30
96	42	1s. brown (27.10.41) ..	3·25	50
88/96		.. .. Set of 7 pairs and 2 singles	55·00	50·00

ALTERED CATALOGUE NUMBERS

Any Catalogue numbers altered from the last edition are shown as a list in the introductory pages.

43 Infantry   44 Nurse   45 Airman   46 Sailor

47 Women's Auxiliary Services   48 Electric Welding   49 Heavy Gun in Concrete Turret

50 Tank Corps

Unit (*pair*)

Unit (*triplet*)

Apostrophe flaw (R. 19/1) (later corrected)   "Bursting Shell" (R. 11/20)

1942–44. *War Effort.* Reduced sizes. In pairs perf 14 (P) or strips of three, perf 15×14 (T), subdivided by roulette 6½. W **9** (*sideways** on 3d., 4d. and 1s.). (a) *Inscr alternately.*

				Un unit	Us unit	Us single
97	43	½d. blue-green (T) (10.42)	..	90	1·50	10
		a. Green (3.43)	..	2·75	2·00	10
		b. Greenish blue (7.44)	..	2·00	1·50	10
		b. Roulette omitted	..	£500		
98	44	1d. carmine-red (T) (5.1.43)	..	1·50	1·25	10
		a. Bright carmine (3.44)	..	1·00	1·00	10
		b. Both roulettes omitted	£425		
		ba. Left-hand roulette omitted	£550		
99	45	1½d. red-brown (P) (9.42)	..	65	1·50	10
		a. Roulette 13 (8.42)	..	1·50	4·00	15
		b. Roulette omitted	..	£225	£250	
100	46	2d. violet (P) (2.43)	..	90	1·75	10
		a. Reddish violet (6.43)	..	1·50	65	10
		b. Roulette omitted	..	£400		
		c. Apostrophe flaw	..	50·00		
101	47	3d. blue (T) (10.42)	..	7·00	15·00	10
102	48	6d. red-orange (P) (10.42)	..	2·00	1·60	10

(b) *Inscr bilingually*

103	49	4d. slate-green (T) (10.42)	..	18·00	6·50	10
104	50	1s. brown (11.42)	..	15·00	3·25	10
		a. "Bursting shell"	..	60·00		
97/104		Set of 8	40·00	27·00	65	

*The sideways watermark shows springbok horns pointing to left on the 3d. and 1s., and to right on the 4d., *all as seen from the back of the stamp.*

52   53

1943. *Coil stamps.* Redrawn. In single colours with plain background. W **9**. *P* 15 × 14.

				Un pair	Used pair	Used single
105	52	½d. blue-green (18.2.43)	..	1·25	3·75	20
106	53	1d. carmine (9.43)	..	2·25	3·00	15

Quoted prices are for *vertical* pairs.

54 Union Buildings, Pretoria

1945–46. *Redrawn.* W **9.** *P* 14.
107	54	2d. slate and violet (3.45)	..	10·00	2·50	10
		a. Slate & brt vio *(shades)* (10.46)		2·50	7·50	15

In Nos. 107 and 107a the Union Buildings are shown at a different angle from Nos. 58 and 58a. Only the centre is screened i.e., composed of very small square dots of colour arranged in straight diagonal lines. For whole design screened and colours changed, see No. 116. No. 107a also shows "2" of "2d." clear of white circle at top.

55 "Victory" **56** "Peace"

57 "Hope"

1945 (3 Dec). *Victory.* W **9.** *P* 14.
108	55	1d. brown and carmine	..	20	80	10
109	56	2d. slate-blue and violet	..	20	85	10
110	57	3d. deep blue and blue	..	20	1·25	10
108/10			*Set of* 3	55	2·75	25

58 King George VI **59** King George VI and Queen Elizabeth

60 Queen Elizabeth II as Princess, and Princess Margaret

"Bird" on "2" (Cyl 6912 R. 10/6)

(Des J. Prentice)

1947 (17 Feb). *Royal Visit.* W **9.** *P* 15 × 14.
111	58	1d. black and carmine	..	10	10	10
112	59	2d. violet	..	15	30	10
		a. "Bird" on "2" flaw	..	2·50		
113	60	3d. blue	..	15	30	10
111/13			*Set of* 3	35	60	20

"Flying saucer" flaw (Cyl 17 R. 17/2)

I
II

5s.

1947–54. "SUID-AFRIKA" *hyphenated on Afrikaans stamps. Printed from new cylinders with design in screened rotogravure.* W **9.** *P* 15×14 (½d., 1d. and 6d.) *or* 14 (*others*).
114	25a	½d. grey and green (frame only screened) (1947)	..	90	2·00	10
		a. Booklet pane of 6 (with postal slogans on margins) (1948)		3·00		
		b. "Tick" flaw and spot on nose	..	30·00		
		c. Entire design screened (2.49)	..	90	2·00	10
		ca. Booklet pane of 6 (with margin at right) (1951)		3·50		
115	7	1d. grey and carmine (1.9.50)	..	70	1·75	10
		a. Booklet pane of 6 (with margin at right) (1951)		4·00		
116	54	2d. slate-blue & purple (3.50)	..	1·00	5·00	10
117	22a	3d. dull blue (4.49)	..	2·00	4·25	10
117a		3d. blue (3.51)	..	2·50	3·50	10
		ab. "Flying saucer" flaw	..	22·00		
		b. Deep blue (1954)	..	60·00	55·00	3·50
118	12a	4d. brown (22.8.52)	..	1·50	6·00	10
119	8	6d. grn & red-orge (III) (1.50)		1·75	50	10
		a. Grn & brn-orge (III) (1951)		1·50	40	10
120	13	1s. brown & chalky blue (1.50)		10·00	6·00	10
		a. Blackish brown & ultram (4.52)		18·00	9·00	15
121	14	2s. 6d. green and brown (8.49)		10·00	26·00	85
122	15	5s. blk & pale bl-grn (I) (9.49)		45·00	55·00	1·00
122a		5s. blk & dp yell-grn (II) (1.54)		70·00	80·00	2·50
			Set of 9	65·00	95·00	1·75
114/22						

In screened rotogravure the design is composed of very small squares of colour arranged in straight diagonal lines.
½d. Size 17¾ × 21¾ mm. Early printings have only the frame screened.
1d. Size 18 × 22 mm. For smaller, redrawn design, see No. 135.
2d. For earlier issue with centre only screened, and in different colours, see Nos. 107/a.
3d. No. 117. Whole stamp screened with irregular grain. Scrolls above "3d." solid and toneless. Printed from two cylinders.
No. 117a/b. Whole stamp diagonally screened. Printed from one cylinder. Clouds more pronounced.
4d. Two groups of white leaves below name tablet and a clear white line down left and right sides of stamp.

61 Gold Mine **62** King George VI and Queen Elizabeth

1948 (1 Apr). W **9** (*sideways*). *In pair, perf* 14, *sub-divided by roulette* 6½.
				Un	Us	Used
				unit of 4	*unit single*	
124	61	1½d. blue-green and yellow-buff		1·75	3·00	10

(Des J. Booysen and J. Prentice)

1948 (26 Apr). *Silver Wedding.* W **9.** *P* 14.
				Un	Used	Used
				pair	*pair*	*single*
125	62	3d. blue and silver	..	50	50	10

(Typo Government Printer, Pretoria)

1948 (July). W **9.** *P* 14½ × 14.
126	6	½d. pale grey and blue-green		85	8·00	65

This was an economy printing made from the old plates of the 1926 issue for the purpose of using up a stock of cut paper. For the original printing in black and green, see No. 30.

63 *Wanderer* (emigrant ship) entering Durban

Extended rigging on mainmast (R. 14/2)

(Des J. Prentice)

1949 (2 May). *Centenary of Arrival of British Settlers in Natal.* W **9.** *P* 15 × 14.
127	63	1½d. claret	..	50	50	10
		a. Extended rigging	..	6·00		

---

64 Hermes **65** Wagons approaching Bingham's Berg

Serif on "C" (R. 1/1)

"Lake" in East Africa (R. 2/19)

(Des J. Booysen and J. Prentice)

1949 (1 Oct). *75th Anniv of Universal Postal Union. As T* 64 *inscr* "UNIVERSAL POSTAL UNION" *and* "WERELDPOSUNIE" *alternately.* W **9** (*sideways*). *P* 14 × 15.
128	64	½d. blue-green	..	..	60	85	10
129		1½d. brown-red	..	..	60	85	10
130		3d. bright blue	..	..	1·00	1·40	10
		a. Serif on "C"	..	22·00		
		b. "Lake" in East Africa	..	22·00		
128/30			*Set of* 3	2·00	2·75	25

(Des W. Coetzer and J. Prentice)

1949 (1 Dec). *Inauguration of Voortrekker Monument, Pretoria. T* 65 *and similar horiz designs.* W **9.** *P* 15 × 14.
				Un	Us
				single	*single*
131		1d. magenta	..	10	10
132		1½d. blue-green	..	10	10
133		3d. blue	..	15	15
131/3			*Set of* 3	30	30

Designs:—1½d. Voortrekker Monument, Pretoria; 3d. Bible, candle and Voortrekkers.

68 Union Buildings, Pretoria

1950 (Apr)–51. W **9** (*sideways*). *P* 14 × 15.
				Un	Used	Used
				pair	*pair*	*single*
134	68	2d. blue and violet	..	30	50	10
		a. Booklet panes of 6 (with margin at right) (1951)		4·00		

1951 (22 Feb). *As No.* 115, *but redrawn with the horizon clearly defined. Size reduced to* 17¼ × 21¼ *mm.*
135	7	1d. grey and carmine	..	95	1·75	10

PRICES. All later issues except Nos. 167 and 262/5 are inscribed bilingually and prices are for single copies, unused and used.

69 Seal and Monogram **70** "Maria de la Quellerie" (D. Craey)

Des Miss R. Reeves and J. Prentice (1d., 4½d.), Mrs T. Campbell and J. Prentice (others))

1952 (14 Mar). *Tercentenary of Landing of Van Riebeeck.* T **69/70** *and similar designs.* W **9** *(sideways on* 1d. *and* 4½d.*).* P 14 × 15 (1d. *and* 4½d.) *or* 14 × 15 (*others*).

136	½d. brown-purple and olive-grey	..	10	10
137	1d. deep blue-green	..	10	10
138	2d. deep violet	..	50	10
139	4½d. blue	..	10	10
140	1s. brown	..	40	10
136/40		*Set of 5*	90	30

Designs: *Horiz*—2d. Arrival of Van Riebeeck's ships; 1s. "Landing at the Cape" (C. Davidson Bell). *Vert*—4½d. "Jan van Riebeeck" (D. Craey).

SATISE SADIPU

(74)   (75)   **76** Queen Elizabeth II

1952 (26 Mar). *South African Tercentenary International Stamp Exhibition, Cape Town. No.* 137 *optd with* T **74** *and No.* 138 *with* T **75**.

141	1d. deep blue-green	..	20	1·75
142	2d. deep violet	..	50	1·25

(Des H. Kumst)

1953 (3 June). *Coronation.* W **9** *(sideways).* P 14 × 15.

143	**76**	2d. deep violet-blue	..	30	10
		a. Ultramarine ..	..	30	10

77 1d. "Cape Triangular" Stamp

(Des H. Kumst)

1953 (1 Sept). *Centenary of First Cape of Good Hope Stamp.* T **77** *and similar horiz design.* W **9**. P 15 × 14.

144	1d. sepia and vermilion	..	10	10
145	4d. deep blue and light blue ..	..	50	20

Design:—4d. Four pence "Cape Triangular" stamp.

79 Merino Ram   **80** Springbok

81 Aloes

(Des A. Hendriksz and J. Prentice (4½d.))

1953 (1 Oct). W **9**. P 14.

146	**79**	4½d. slate-purple and yellow	..	20	10
147	**80**	1s. 3d. chocolate	..	1·50	10
148	**81**	1s. 6d. vermilion and deep blue-green		80	55
146/8		.. ..	*Set of 3*	2·25	60

82 Arms of Orange Free State and Scroll

(Des H. Kumst)

1954 (23 Feb). *Centenary of Orange Free State.* W **9**. P 15 × 14.

149	**82**	2d. sepia and pale vermilion	..	10	10
150		4½d. purple and slate	..	20	50

83 Warthog   **92** Springbok   **93** Gemsbok

(Des H. Kumst)

1954 (14 Oct). T **83**, **92/3** *and similar designs.* W **9** *(sideways on large vert designs).* P 15 × 14 (½d. *to* 2d.), 14 (*others*).

151	½d. deep blue-green	..	10	10
152	1d. brown-lake	..	10	10
153	1½d. sepia ..	..	10	10
154	2d. plum ..	..	10	10
155	3d. chocolate and turquoise-blue	..	30	10
156	4d. indigo and emerald	..	50	10
157	4½d. blue-black and grey-blue	..	60	1·50
158	6d. sepia and orange	..	50	10
159	1s. deep brown and pale chocolate ..		80	10
160	1s. 3d. brown and bluish green	..	2·00	10
161	1s. 6d. brown and rose	..	1·75	60
162	2s. 6d. brown-black and apple-green	..	3·50	20
163	5s. black-brown and yellow-orange	..	10·00	1·40
164	10s. black and cobalt ..	..	17·00	4·50
151/64		*Set of 14*	32·00	7·50

Designs: *Vert* (as T **83**)—1d. Black Wildebeest; 1½d. Leopard; 2d. Mountain Zebra. (*As* T **93**)—3d. White Rhinoceros; 4d. African Elephant; 4½d. Hippopotamus; 1s. Greater Kudu; 2s. 6d. Nyala; 5s. Giraffe; 10s. Sable Antelope. *Horiz* (as T **92**)—6d. Lion.
No. 152 exists in coils.
See also Nos. 170/7 and 185/97.

97 President Kruger   **98** President M. Pretorius

(Des H. Kumst)

1955 (21 Oct). *Centenary of Pretoria.* W **9** *(sideways).* P 14 × 15.

165	**97**	3d. slate-green	..	10	10
166	**98**	6d. maroon	..	10	30

99 A. Pretorius, Church of the   **100** Settlers' Block-wagon
Vow and Flag   and House

(Des H. Kumst)

1955 (1 Dec). *Voortrekker Covenant Celebrations, Pietermaritzburg.* W **9**. P 14.

				Un pair	Us pair	Us pair single
167	**99**	2d. blue and magenta	..	45	3·25	10

(Des H. Kumst)

1958 (1 July). *Centenary of Arrival of German Settlers in South Africa.* W **9**. P 14.

168	**100**	2d. chocolate and pale purple	..	10	10

101 Arms of the Academy

(Des H. Kumst)

1959 (1 May). *50th Anniv of the South African Academy of Science and Art, Pretoria.* W **9**. P 15 × 14.

169	**101**	3d. deep blue and turquoise-blue		10	10
		a. Deep blue printing omitted	..	£1600	

102 Union Coat of Arms   I   II

1959–60. *As Nos.* 151/2, 155/6, 158/9 *and* 162/3, *but* W **102** *(sideways on Nos.* 172/3 *and* 175/7*).*

170	½d. deep greenish blue (12.60)	..	15	4·50
171	1d. brown-lake (I) (11.59)	..	10	10
	a. Redrawn. Type II (10.60)	..	20	10
172	3d. chocolate and turquoise-blue (9.59)		15	10
173	4d. indigo and emerald (1.60)	..	50	20
174	6d. sepia and orange (2.60)	..	70	1·00
175	1s. deep brown and pale chocolate (11.59)		6·00	50
176	2s. 6d. brown-black & apple-green (12.59)		2·75	4·00
177	5s. black-brown & yellow-orange (10.60)		6·50	30·00
170/7		*Set of 8*	15·00	35·00

Nos. 171/a. In Type II "1d. Posgeld Postage" is more to the left in relation to "South Africa", with "1" almost central over "S" instead of to right as in Type I.
No. 171 exists in coils.

103 Globe and Antarctic Scene

(Des H. Kumst)

1959 (16 Nov). *South African National Antarctic Expedition.* W **102**. P 14 × 15.

178	**103**	3d. blue-green and orange	..	20	10

104 Union Flag   **106** "Wheel of Progress"

(Des V. Ivanoff and H. Kumst (1s.), H. Kumst (others))

1960 (2 May). *50th Anniv of Union of South Africa.* T **104**, **106** *and similar designs.* W **102** *(sideways on* 4d. *and* 6d.*).* P 14 × 15 (4d., 6d.) *or* 15 × 14 (*others*).

179	4d. orange-red and blue	..	30	10
180	6d. red, brown and light green	..	30	10
181	1s. deep blue and light yellow	..	30	10
182	1s. 6d. black and light blue ..	..	1·10	2·25
179/82		*Set of 4*	1·75	2·25

Designs: *Vert*—6d. Union Arms. *Horiz*—1s. 6d. Union Festival emblem.
See also No. 190, 192/3.

108 Steam Locomotives *Natal* (1860) and Class 25 (1950s)

(Des V. Ivanoff)

1960 (2 May). *Centenary of South African Railways.* W **102**. P 15 × 14.

183	**108**	1s. 3d. deep blue	..	2·00	30

109 Prime Ministers Botha, Smuts, Hertzog, Malan, Strijdom and Verwoerd

1960 (31 May). *Union Day.* W **102**. P 15 × 14.

184	**109**	3d. brown and pale brown	..	15	10
		a. Pale brown omitted*	..	£2500	

*This is due to a rectangular piece of paper adhering to the background cylinder, resulting in R.2/1 missing the colour completely and six adjoining stamps having it partially omitted. The item in block of eight is probably unique.

(New Currency. 100 cents=1 rand)

1961 (14 Feb). *As previous issues but with values in cents and rand.* W **102** *(sideways on* 3½ c., 7½ c., 20 c., 50 c., 1 r.*).* P 15 × 14 (½ c., *to* 2½ c., 10 c.), 14 × 15 (3½ c., 7½ c.) *or* 14 (*others*).

185	½ c. deep bluish green (as 151)	..	10	10
186	1 c. brown-lake (as 152) ..	..	10	10
187	1½ c. sepia (as 153) ..	..	10	10
188	2 c. plum (as 154) ..	..	10	30
189	2½ c. brown (as 184) ..	..	10	10
190	3½ c. orange-red and blue (as 179) ..		15	1·25
191	5 c. sepia and orange (as 158) ..		20	10

192	7½ c. red, brown and light green (as 180)		20	1·50
193	10 c. deep blue and light yellow (as 181)		40	40
194	12½ c. brown and bluish green (as 160)		1·00	1·75
195	20 c. brown and rose (as 161)		2·25	3·25
196	50 c. black-brown & orange-yellow (as 163)		6·00	10·00
197	1 r. black and cobalt (as 164)		18·00	26·00
185/97		*Set of 13*	25·00	40·00

X. REPUBLIC OF SOUTH AFRICA
OUTSIDE THE COMMONWEALTH

110 African Pygmy Kingfisher

111 Kafferboom Flower

112 Afrikander Bull

113 Pouring Gold

114 Groot Constantia

115 Burchell's Gonolek

116 Baobab Tree

117 Maize

118 Cape Town Castle Entrance

119 Protea

120 Secretary Bird

121 Cape Town Harbour

122 Strelitzia

Two types of ½ c.:

I   II

Type I from sheets. Spurs of branch indistinct.
Type II from coils. Spurs strengthened.

Three types of 1 c.:

I   II

III

Type I. Lowest point of flower between "OS" of "POSTAGE". Right-hand petal over "E".
Type II. Flower has moved fractionally to the right so that lowest point is over "S" of "POSTAGE". Right-hand petal over "E".
Type III. Lowest point directly over "O". Right-hand petal over "G".

Two types of 2½ c.

In Type I the lines of the building are quite faint. In Type II all lines of the building have been strengthened by re-engraving.

(Des Mrs. T. Campbell (½ c., 3 c., 1 r.); Miss N. Desmond (1 c.); De La Rue (2½ c., 5 c., 12½ c.); H. L. Prager (50 c.); Govt. Ptg Dept artist (others))

1961 (31 May)–**63.** *Unsurfaced paper.* W 102 *(sideways* on ½ c., 1½ c., 2½ c., 5 c. to 20 c.).* P 14×15 *(½ c., 1½ c.), 15×14 (1 c.) or 14 (others).*

198	110	½ c. bright blue, carmine & brown (I)	10	10
		a. Perf 14 (3.63)	10	15
		b. Type II (coils) (18.5.63)	70	1·10
199	111	1 c. red and olive-grey (I)	10	10
		a. Type II (1.62)	10	10
		b. Type III (coils) (5.63)	1·00	1·50
200	112	1½ c. brown-lake and light purple (I)	10	10
201	113	2 c. ultramarine and yellow	1·25	10
202	114	2½ c. violet and green (I)	15	10
		aw. Wmk top of arms to right	30	10
		b. Type II. *Dp violet & green* (9.61)	20	10
203	115	3 c. red and deep blue	80	10
204	116	5 c. yellow and greenish blue	30	10
205	117	7½ c. yellow-brown and light green	60	10
206	118	10 c. sepia and green	75	10
207	119	12½ c. red, yellow and black-green	2·00	30
		a. Yellow omitted	£600	
		b. Red omitted	£650	
208	120	20 c. turquoise-blue, carm & brn-orge	3·00	30
209	121	50 c. black and bright blue	26·00	2·25
210	122	1 r. orange, olive-green & light blue	16·00	2·25
198/210		*Set of 13*	45·00	4·50

*The normal sideways watermark shows the top of the arms to left, *as seen from the back of the stamp.*

1961–74 *Definitives*
Key to designs, perfs, watermarks, papers and phosphors

Value	Type	Perf	W 102. Ordinary	No wmk. Ordinary	W 127. Chalky
½ c.	110 (I)	14×15	198	—	—
	(I)	14	198a	—	—
	(II)	14×15	198b	—	—
1 c.	111 (I)	15×14	199	211	—
	(II)		199a	211a	227
	(III)		199b	—	—
1½ c.	112	14×15	200	—	228
2 c.	113	14	201	212	229
2½ c.	114 (I)	14	202	—	—
	(II)		202a	213/a	230/a
3 c.	115	14	203	214	—
5 c.	116	14	204	215	231
7½ c.	117	14	205	216	232
10 c.	118	14	206	217/b	233/a
12½ c.	119	14	207	—	—
20 c.	120	14	208	218	234/a
50 c.	121	14	209	219	235
1 r.	122	14	210	—	236

Redrawn Designs

			W 127 Upright or Tête-bêche. Plain or phosphorised	W 127 Tête-bêche Phos frame	No wmk. Phosphorised Glossy Chalky
½ c.	130a	14	238	—	— —
		14×15	238b	—	— —
		14	238c/d	—	— —
1 c.	131	15×14	239	—	— —
		13½×14	239a	—	— —
1½ c.	132	14×15	240/b	284	— —
		14×13½	240c	—	— —
2 c.	133	14	241/a	285/a	315a —
		12½	—	315	315b
2½ c.	134	14	242/a	286/a	— —
3 c.	135	14	243/a	287	— —
		12½	—	—	316 316a
4 c.	134	14	243b	288	— —

			W 127 Upright or Tête-bêche. Plain or phos-phorised	W 127 Tête-bêche. Phosframe	No wmk. Phosphorised Glossy Chalky
5 c.	136	14	244/a	289	318a —
		12½	—	318	318b
6 c.	137	14	—	290	—
		12½	—	—	319
7½ c.	137	14	245	291	—
9 c.	139	14	245a	292	—
		12½	—	—	320/a
10 c.	138	14	246/a	293	—
		12½	—	—	321a 321b
					321
12½ c.	139	14	247/a	294	—
15 c.	140	14	248	295	—
20 c.	141	14	249/a	296/a	—
		12½	—	—	323 323a
50 c.	142	14	250	—	—
		12½	—	—	324 324a
1 r.	143	14	251	—	—
		12½	—	—	325 —

New Designs

			W 127 Tête-bêche. Plain or phos-phorised	W 127 Tête-bêche. Phos-frame	No wmk. Phosphorised Glossy Chalky
½ c.	168	14 × 13½	276	282	— —
		14 × 14½	276a	—	313 —
		14 × 15	—	282a	— —
1 c.	169	13½ × 14	277	283	— —
		14	—	—	314 —
4 c.	182	14	310/a	—	— —
		12½	—	—	317/b 317c
15 c.	182a	14	311	—	— —
		12½	—	—	— 322

1961 (Aug)–**63.** *As Nos.* 199, 201/6 *and* 208/9 *but without wmk.*

211	111	1 c. red and olive-grey (I)	20	30
		a. Type II (9.62)	55	55
212	113	2 c. ultramarine and yellow (8.63)	7·50	60
213	114	2½ c. deep violet and green (II)	30	10
		a. *Violet and green* (12.61)	30	10
214	115	3 c. red and deep blue (10.61)	45	10
215	116	5 c. yellow & greenish blue (12.61)	50	10
216	117	7½ c. yellow-brown & lt green (3.62)	80	30
217	118	10 c. sepia and green (11.61)	1·00	40
		a. *Sepia and emerald*	40·00	17·00
		b. *Sepia-brown & lt green* (7.63)	2·25	55
218	120	20 c. turq-bl, carm & brn-orge (4.63)	14·00	4·25
219	121	50 c. black and bright blue (8.62)	14·00	4·25
211/19		*Set of 9*	35·00	9·00

123 Blériot XI Monoplane and Boeing 707 Airliner over Table Mountain

124 Folk-dancers

1961 (1 Dec). *50th Anniv of First South African Aerial Post.* W 102 *(sideways).* P 14 × 15.

220	123	3 c. blue and red	50	10

(Des K. Esterhuysen)

1962 (1 Mar). *50th Anniv of Volkspele (folk-dancing) in South Africa.* W 102 *(sideways).* P 14 × 15.

221	124	2½ c. orange-red and brown	15	10

125 The Chapman (emigrant ship)

1962 (20 Aug). *Unveiling of Precinct Stone, British Settlers Monument, Grahamstown.* W 102. P 15 × 14.

222	125	2½ c. turquoise-green and purple	50	10
223		12½ c. blue and deep chocolate	3·00	1·75

126 Red Disa (orchid), Castle Rock and Gardens

(Des M. F. Stern)

1963 (14 Mar). *50th Anniv of Kirstenbosch Botanic Gardens, Cape Town.* P 13½ × 14.

224	126	2½ c. multicoloured	20	10
		a. Red (orchid, etc) omitted	£1500	

127 (normal version)

128 Centenary Emblem and Nurse

129 Centenary Emblem and Globe

1963 (30 Aug). *Centenary of Red Cross. Chalk-surfaced paper. Wmk 127 (sideways on 2½ c.). P 14 × 13½ (2½ c.) or 15 × 14 (12½ c.).*

225	128	2½ c. red, black and reddish purple ..	20	10
		w. Wmk reversed	3·00	1·40
226	129	12½ c. red and indigo	3·25	1·00
		a. Red cross omitted	£1300	

1963–67. *As 1961–3 but chalk-surfaced paper and W 127 (sideways on 1½ c., 2½ c., 5 c., 7½ c., 10 c., 20 c.). P 15 × 14 (1 c.), 14 × 15 (1½ c.), or 14 (others).*

227	111	1 c. red and olive-grey (II) (9.63) ..	10	10
		w. Wmk reversed	65	65
228	112	1½ c. brown-lake & light purple (1.67)	1·75	2·00
229	113	2 c. ultramarine and yellow (11.64)	15	20
230	114	2½ c. violet and green (I) (10.63)	10	10
		a. Brt reddish vio & emer (II) (3.66)	35	20
		aw. Wmk inverted	2·50	90
231	116	5 c. yellow and greenish blue (9.66)	1·25	30
232	117	7½ c. yellow-brown & brt grn (23.2.66)	7·50	5·50
233	118	10 c. sepia-brown & lt emerald (9.64)	40	10
		a. Sepia-brown and green (1.67)	45	10
234	120	20 c. turq-blue, carm & brn-orge (7.64)	1·50	70
		a. Dp turq-bl, carm & flesh (20.7.65)	1·75	70
235	121	50 c. black and ultramarine (4.66)	30·00	8·50
236	122	1 r. orange, lt green & pale bl (7.64)	55·00	38·00
227/36		*Set of 10*	90·00	48·00

In the 2½ c. (No. 230*a*), 5 c., 7½ c., 10 c. (Jan 1967 printing only) and 50 c. the watermark is indistinct but they can easily be distinguished from the stamps without watermark by their shades and the chalk-surfaced paper which is appreciably thicker and whiter.

130 Assembly Building, Umtata

1963 (11 Dec). *First Meeting of Transkei Legislative Assembly. Chalk-surfaced paper. W 127. P 15 × 14.*

237	130	2½ c. sepia and light green	10	10
		a. Light green omitted	£1300	

130a African Pygmy Kingfisher

131 Kafferboom Flower

132 Afrikander Bull

133 Pouring Gold

134 Groot Constantia

135 Burchell's Gonolek

136 Baobab Tree

---

137 Maize

138 Cape Town Castle Entrance

139 Protea

140 Industry

141 Secretary Bird

142 Cape Town Harbour

143 Strelitzia

(15 c. des C. E. F. Skotnes)

Redrawn types.

½ c. "½C" larger and "REPUBLIEK VAN REPUBLIC OF" smaller.

3 c. and 12½ c. Inscriptions and figures of value larger.

Others. "SOUTH AFRICA" and "SUID-AFRIKA" larger and bolder. The differences vary in each design but are easy to see by comparing the position of the letters of the country name with "REPUBLIC OF" and "REPUBLIEK VAN".

1964–72. *As 1961–63 but designs redrawn and new values (4 c., 9 c. and 15 c.). Chalk-surfaced paper. W 127 (sideways* on ½, 1½, 2½, 4, 5, 7½, 9, 10, 15 and 20 c.). P 14×15 (1½ c.), 15×14 (1 c.) or 14 (others).*

238	130a	½ c. brt blue, carm & brn (21.5.64)	10	10
		a. Imperf (pair) ..	£275	
		b. Perf 14×15. *Brt blue, carmine and yellow-brown (6.7.67)* ..	20	20
		c. Perf 14. *Bright blue, lake and yellow-brown (3.68)* ..	50	50
		d. Perf 14. *Bright blue, carmine-lake and yellow-brown (9.68)* ..	30	10
239	131	1 c. red and olive-grey (9.3.67)	10	10
		a. Perf 13½×14 (7.68) ..	30	10
240	132	1½ c. dull red-brn & lt pur (21.9.67)	15	10
		a. *Purple-brown & lt pur (1968)*	15	10
		b. *Brt red-brown & lt pur (5.68)*	15	10
		c. Perf 14×13½. *Red-brown and light purple (14.8.69)* ..	70	70
241	133	2 c. ultramarine & yellow (8.1.68)	20	10
		a. *Blue and yellow (10.71)* ..	40	10
242	134	2½ c. violet and green (19.4.67)	20	10
		a. *Reddish violet and green (8.67)*	20	10
		w. Wmk top of RSA to left ..	£180	65·00
243	135	3 c. red and deep blue (11.64)	30	10
		a. *Brown-red and deep blue (3.72)*	75	30
243b	134	4 c. violet and green (10.71)	75	30
244	136	5 c. yellow & greenish bl (14.2.68)	40	10
		a. *Lemon & dp greenish bl (10.71)*	8·00	90
245	137	7½ c. yellow-brn & brt grn (26.7.67)	60	10
245a	139	9 c. red, yellow & slate-green (2.72)	7·00	3·50
246	138	10 c. sepia and green (10.6.68)	1·75	10
		a. *Brown and pale green (7.68)*	4·25	3·25
247	139	12½ c. red, yellow & blk-green (3.64)	1·75	40
		a. *Red, pale yell & bl-grn (2.2.66)*	2·75	40
248	140	15 c. black, light olive-yellow and red-orange (1.3.67) ..	1·50	25
249	141	20 c. turquoise-blue, carmine and brown-orange (2.68) ..	5·00	15
		a. *Turquoise-blue, carmine and orange-buff (12.71)* ..	5·00	1·00
250	142	50 c. black and bright blue (17.6.68)	2·50	40
251	143	1 r. orange, lt green & lt bl (6.65)	2·50	1·00
		w. Wmk inverted		
238/51		.. .. *Set of 16*	22·00	5·25

*The normal sideways watermark shows the top of RSA to right *as seen from the back of the stamp.*

WATERMARK. Two forms of the watermark Type 127 exist in the above issue: the normal Type 127 (sometimes indistinct), and a very faint *tête-bêche* watermark, i.e. alternately facing up and down, which was introduced in mid-1967. As it is extremely difficult to distinguish these on single stamps we do not list it.

The ½ (both perfs), 1, 2, 2½, 3, 15 c. and 1 r. are known in both forms, the 1½, 4, 5, 7½, 9, 10, 20 and 50 c. only in the *tête-bêche* form, and the 12½ c. Type 127 only.

GUM. The 2, 3, 5, 20, 50 c. and 1 r. exist with PVA gum as well as gum arabic.

PHOSPHORISED PAPER. From October 1971 onwards phosphor bands (see Nos. 282/96) gave way to phosphorised paper which cannot be distinguished from non-phosphor stamps without the aid of a lamp. For this reason we do not distinguish these printings in the above issue, but some are slightly different shades which are listed in the *Elizabethan Catalogue* and all have PVA gum.

The 4 c. and 9 c. are on phosphorised paper only and differ from Nos. 288 and 292 by the lack of phosphor bands.

---

145 "Springbok" Badge of Rugby Board

147 Calvin

1964 (8 May). *75th Anniv of South African Rugby Board. Chalk-surfaced paper. T 145 and similar horiz design. W 127 (sideways on 2½ c.). P 14 × 15 (2½ c.) or 15 × 14 (12½ c.).*

252		2½ c. yellow-brown and deep green ..	15	10
253		12½ c. black and light yellow-green ..	4·50	4·25
		Design:—12½ c. Rugby footballer.		

1964 (10 July). *400th Death Anniv of Calvin (Protestant reformer). Chalk-surfaced paper. W 127 (sideways). P 14 × 13½.*

254	147	2½ c. cerise, violet and brown ..	10	10

148 Nurse's Lamp

149 Nurse holding Lamp

I. Screened II. Clear base
base to lamp to lamp

1964 (12 Oct). *50th Anniv of South African Nursing Association. Chalk-surfaced paper. W 127 (sideways on 2½ c.). P 14 × 15 (2½ c.) or 15 × 14 (12½ c.).*

255	148	2½ c. ultramarine and dull gold (Type I)	10	10
256		2½ c. brt blue & yellow-gold (Type II)	30	10
		a. *Ultramarine and dull gold*	15	10
257	149	12½ c. bright blue and gold ..	3·25	2·25
		a. Gold omitted	£1200	
255/7		.. .. *Set of 3*	3·25	2·25

150 I.T.U. Emblem and Satellites

1965 (17 May). *I.T.U. Centenary. T 150 and similar horiz design. Chalk-surfaced paper. W 127. P 15 × 14.*

258		2½ c. orange and blue	25	10
259		12½ c. brown-purple and green ..	3·00	1·75
		Design:—12½ c. I.T.U. emblem and symbols.		

152 Pulpit in Groote Kerk, Cape Town

153 Church Emblem

1965 (21 Oct). *Tercentenary of Nederduites Gereformeerde Kerk (Dutch Reformed Church) in South Africa. Chalk-surfaced paper. W 127 (sideways on 2½ c., inverted on 12½ c.). P 14 × 15 (2½ c.) or 15 × 14 (12½ c.).*

260	152	2½ c. brown and light yellow ..	15	10
261	153	12½ c. black, light orange and blue ..	1·75	1·25

154 Diamond

155 Bird in flight

SOUTH AFRICA — 1966

(Des C. E. F. Skotnes)

1966 (31 May). *Fifth Anniv of Republic. T 154/5 and similar designs. Chalk-surfaced paper. W 127 (sideways on 1 c., 3 c.). P 14 × 13½ (1 c.), 13½ × 14 (2½ c.), 14 × 15 (3 c.) or 15 × 14 (7½ c.).*

			Un pair	Us pair	Us single
262	1 c. black, bluish green & olive-yell		45	45	10
263	2½ c. blue, deep blue & yellow-green		1·25	1·25	10
264	3 c. red, greenish yellow & red-brn		4·75	4·75	10
265	7½ c. blue, ultramarine and yellow		5·50	6·00	20
262/5		Set of 4	11·00	11·00	40

Designs: *Vert*—3 c. Maize plants. *Horiz*—7½ c. Mountain landscape.

Nos. 262/5 exist on Swiss-made paper with *tête-bêche* watermark from a special printing made for use in presentation albums for delegates to the U.P.U. Congress in Tokyo in 1969, as supplies of the original Harrison paper were by then exhausted (*Set of 4 pairs price £140 mint*).

158 Verwoerd and Union Buildings, Pretoria

(Des from portrait by Dr. Henkel)

1966 (6 Dec). *Verwoerd Commemoration. T 158 and similar designs. Chalk-surfaced paper. W 127 (sideways on 3 c.). P 14 × 15 (3 c.) or 15 × 14 (others).*

266	2½ c. blackish brown and turquoise	..		10	10
267	3 c. blackish brown and yellow-green	..		10	10
	a. Blackish brown (portrait) omitted			£2750	
268	12½ c. blackish brown and greenish blue			80	60
266/8		Set of 3		90	60

Designs: *Vert*—3 c. "Dr. H.F. Verwoerd" (I. Henkel). *Horiz*—12½ c. Verwoerd and map of South Africa.

161 "Martin Luther" (Cranach the Elder)   **162** Wittenberg Church Door

1967 (31 Oct). *450th Anniv of Reformation. W 127 ((sideways), normal on 2½ c., tête-bêche on 12½ c.). P 14 × 15.*

269	161	2½ c. black and rose-red		10	10
270	162	12½ c. black and yellow-orange	..	1·75	2·50

163 "Profile of Pres. Fouché" (I. Henkel)   **164** Portrait of Pres. Fouché

1968 (10 Apr). *Inauguration of President Fouché. W 127 (sideways). P 14 × 15.*

271	163	2½ c. chocolate and pale chocolate		10	10
272	164	12½ c. deep blue and light blue	..	80	1·25

No. 272 also exists with the watermark *tête-bêche* (*Price un £1; used £1.50*).

165 Hertzog in 1902

1968 (21 Sept). *Inauguration of General Hertzog Monument, Bloemfontein. T 165 and similar designs. W 127 (tête-bêche on 2½ c., inverted on 3 c., sideways on 12½ c.). P 14 × 13½ (12½ c.) or 13½ × 14 (others).*

273		2½ c. black, brown and olive-yellow		10	10
274		3 c. black, red-brown, red-orange and yellow		15	10
275		12½ c. black, red and yellow-orange		2·00	1·50
273/5	..	Set of 3		2·00	1·50

Designs: *Horiz*—3 c. Hertzog in 1924. *Vert*—12½ c. Hertzog Monument.

168 African Pygmy Kingfisher   **169** Kafferboom Flower

1969. *W 127 (tête-bêche, sideways on 1 c.). P 14 × 13½ (½ c.) or 13½ × 14 (1 c.).*

276	168	½ c. new bl, carm-red & yell-ochre (1.69)		10	30
		a. Coil. Perf 14 × 14½ (5.69)	..	2·25	2·75
277	169	1 c. rose-red and olive-brown (1.69)		10	10

See also Nos. 282/3 and 313/14.

170 Springbok and Olympic Torch   **171** Professor Barnard and Groote Schuur Hospital

1969 (15 Mar). *South African Games, Bloemfontein. W 127 (tête-bêche, sideways). P 14 × 13½.*

278	170	2½ c. black, blue-black, red & sage-grn		15	10
279		12½ c. black, blue-blk, red & cinnamon	..	1·00	1·75

1969 (7 July). *World's First Heart Transplant and 47th South African Medical Association Congress. T 171 and similar horiz design. W 127 (tête-bêche). P 13½ × 14 (2½ c.) or 15 × 14 (12½ c.).*

280		2½ c. plum and rose-red		10	10
281		12½ c. carmine-red and royal blue	..	2·00	2·25

Design:—12½ c. Hands holding heart.

1969–72. *As 1964–72 issue, Nos. 276/7, and new value (6 c.), but with phosphor bands printed horizontally and vertically between the stamp designs, over the perforations, producing a frame effect. W 127 arranged tête-bêche (upright on 1, 2 and 3 c., sideways on others). P 14 × 13½ (½, 1½ c.), 13½ × 14 (1 c.), or 14 (others).*

282	168	½ c. new blue, carmine-red and yellow-ochre (1.70)	..	15	70
		a. Coil. Perf 14 × 15 (2.71)		3·25	3·75
		w. Wmk reversed		65	55
283	169	1 c. rose-red & olive-brown (12.69)		15	10
		w. Wmk reversed		55	35
284	132	1½ c. red-brown & light purple (12.69)		20	10
285	133	2 c. ultramarine and yellow (11.69)		40	10
		a. Dp ultramarine & yellow (8.70)		90	50
286	134	2½ c. violet and green (1.70)		25	10
		a. Purple and green (24.7.70)		1·00	10
		w. Wmk reversed		18·00	15·00
287	135	3 c. red and deep blue (30.9.69)		80	10
288	134	4 c. violet and green (1.3.71)		40	50
289	136	5 c. yellow & greenish bl (17.11.69)		85	10
290	137	6 c. yellow-brown & brt grn (3.5.71)		1·00	30
291		7½ c. yellow-brn & brt grn (17.11.69)		75	30
292	139	9 c. red, yellow & black-grn (17.5.71)		1·50	30
293	138	10 c. brown and pale green (1.70)		1·50	10
294	139	12½ c. red, yell & black-grn (2.5.70)		4·00	3·00
295	140	15 c. blk, lt ol-yellow & red-orge (1.70)		1·50	1·75
296	141	20 c. turquoise-blue, carmine and brown-orange (18.2.70)		8·00	1·75
		a. Turquoise-blue, carmine and orange-buff (9.72)		11·00	85
282/96		Set of 15		21·00	7·50

No. 286 exists on normal RSA wmk as well as RSA *tête-bêche* wmk.

The 1, 2, 2½, 3, 10, 15 and 20 c. exist with PVA gum as well as gum arabic, but the 4, 6 and 9 c. exist with PVA gum only.

For stamps without wmk, see Nos. 313, etc.

173 Mail Coach   **174** Transvaal Stamp of 1869

1969 (6 Oct). *Centenary of First Stamps of South African Republic (Transvaal). Phosphor bands on all four sides (2½ c.). W 127 (tête-bêche, sideways on 12½ c.). P 13½ × 14 (2½ c.) or 14 × 13½ (12½ c.).*

297	173	2½ c. yellow, indigo and yellow-brown		15	10
298	174	12½ c. emerald, gold and yellow-brown		3·25	3·25

PHOSPHOR FRAME. Nos. 299/306 have phosphor applied on all four sides as a frame.

175 "Water 70" Emblem   **177** "The Sower"

1970 (14 Feb). *Water 70 Campaign. T 175 and similar design. W 127 (tête-bêche (sideways on 2½ c.)). P 14 × 13½ (2½ c.) or 13½ × 14 (3 c.).*

299		2½ c. green, bright blue and chocolate		30	10
300		3 c. Prussian blue, royal blue and buff	..	30	10

Design: *Horiz*—3 c. Symbolic waves.

1970 (24 Aug). *150th Anniv of Bible Society of South Africa. T 177 and similar horiz design (gold die-stamped on 12½ c.). W 127 (tête-bêche, sideways on 2½ c.). P 14 × 13½ (2½ c.) or 13½ × 14 (12½ c.).*

301		2½ c. multicoloured		15	10
302		12½ c. gold, black and blue	..	2·00	2·75

Design:—12½ c. "Biblia" and open book.

178 J. G. Strijdom and Strijdom Tower   **179** Map and Antarctic Landscape

1971 (22 May). *"Interstex" Stamp Exhibition, Cape Town. P 14 × 13½. A. W 127 (sideways tête-bêche).*

303A	178	5 c. lt greenish blue, black & pale yell		20	10
		B. W 102 (sideways)			
303B	178	5 c. lt greenish blue, black & pale yell		1·75	5·00

1971 (22 May). *Tenth Anniv of Antarctic Treaty. W 127 (tête-bêche). P 13½ × 14.*

304	179	12½ c. blue-black, greenish bl & orge-red		2·50	5·00

180 "Landing of British Settlers, 1820" (T. Baines)

1971 (31 May). *Tenth Anniv of the Republic of South Africa. T 180 and similar design. W 127 (tête-bêche sideways on 4 c.). P 13½ × 14 (2 c.) or 14 × 13½ (4 c.).*

305		2 c. pale flesh and brown-red	..	15	20
		w. Wmk reversed		60	60
306		4 c. green and black	..	15	10
		w. Wmk reversed		1·40	85

Design: *Vert*—4 c. Presidents Steyn and Kruger and Treaty of Vereeniging Monument.

No. 306 exists with PVA gum as well as gum arabic.

PHOSPHORISED PAPER. All issues from here are on phosphorised paper *unless otherwise stated.*

181 View of Dam

(Des C. Bridgeford (4 c.), C. Lindsay (others))

1972 (4 Mar). *Opening of Hendrik Verwoerd Dam. T 181 and similar horiz designs. Multicoloured. W 127 (tête-bêche). P 13½ × 14.*

307		4 c. Type 181		20	10
308		5 c. Aerial view of Dam		25	10
309		10 c. Dam and surrounding country (58 × 21 mm)		1·50	2·50
307/9		Set of 3		1·75	2·50

182 Sheep   **182a** Lamb

(Des K. Esterhuysen (4 c.), H. Botha (15 c.))
1972 (15 May–Oct). W **127** (*tête-bêche*). P 14.
310	**182**	4 c. olive-brn, yell, pale bl & slate-bl	30	10
		a. Grey-olive, yellow, bright blue and slate-blue (10.72)	30	10
311	**182**a	15 c. pale stone, deep blue and dull blue	3·25	20

Other shades exist of the 4 c.
See also Nos. 317 and 322.

183 Black and Siamese Cats

184 Transport and Industry

1972 (19 Sept). *Centenary of Societies for the Prevention of Cruelty to Animals.* W **127** (*sideways tête-bêche*). P 14 × 13½.
312	**183**	5 c. multicoloured	1·75	10

1972–74. *As Nos.* 310/11 *and* 282 *etc. but no wmk.* P 14 × 14½ (½ c.), 14 (1 c.) *or* 12½ (*others*). *Phosphorised, glossy paper.*
313	**168**	½ c. bright blue, scarlet and yellow-ochre (6.73)	15·00	16·00
314	**169**	1 c. rose-red and olive-brown (1.74)	40	10
315	**133**	2 c. blue and orange-yellow (11.72)	15	10
		a. Perf 14. *Deep ultramarine and orange-yellow* (coil) (7.73)	11·00	13·00
		b. Chalky paper (17.7.74)	40	70
316	**135**	3 c. scarlet and deep blue (8.5.73)	50	20
		a. Chalky paper (18.2.74)	1·25	1·25
317	**182**	4 c. grey-blue, yellow, blue and bluish slate* (1.10.73)	30	30
		a. *Olive-sepia, yellow, azure and slate-blue* (18.2.74)	60	30
		b. *Lavender-brown, pale yellow, blue and bluish slate* (26.7.74)	30	20
		c. Chalky paper* (22.8.74)	60	45
318	**136**	5 c. orge-yell & greenish bl (4.10.73)	2·00	90
		a. Perf 14. *Yellow and light greenish blue* (coil) (7.73)	12·00	14·00
		b. Chalky paper (5.74)	2·25	1·50
319	**137**	6 c. yellow-brown and bright green (*chalky paper*) (22.7.74)	2·50	3·25
320	**139**	9 c. red, yellow-green & grn-blk (6.73)	1·75	2·00
		a. *Red, deep yellowish green and green-black* (4.74)	2·75	1·50
321	**138**	10 c. reddish brown & brt grn (8.5.73)	85	60
		a. Perf 14 (coil) (6.73)	14·00	16·00
		b. Chalky paper (17.7.74)	1·50	70
322	**182**a	15 c. pale stone, deep blue and dull blue (*chalky paper*) (4.9.74)	5·00	6·00
323	**141**	20 c. turquoise-blue, rose-carmine and orange-buff (8.5.73)	3·25	65
		a. Chalky paper (5.74)	5·00	70
324	**142**	50 c. black and bright blue (6.73)	4·50	2·00
		a. Chalky paper (5.74)	9·50	7·50
325	**143**	1 r. orange, lt green & lt blue (8.10.73)	12·00	2·50
		a. Orange omitted	£1200	
313/25		*Set of 13*	42·00	30·00

*On these stamps the colours are known to vary within the sheet.
No. 314 also differs in that the central design has been moved down about 1 mm.
Nos. 317/c also differ from No. 310 by measuring 26¼ × 21 mm instead of 27¼ × 21¾ mm.
No. 325a exists on the bottom row of one sheet.

(Des J. Hoekstra (4 c.), M. Barnett (others))
1973 (1 Feb). *50th Anniv of ESCOM (Electricity Supply Commission).* T **184** *and similar vert designs. Multicoloured.* P 12 × 12½ (4 c.) *or* 12½ (*others*).
326		4 c. Type **184**	20	10
327		5 c. Pylon (21 × 28 *mm*)	30	10
328		15 c. Cooling Towers (21 × 28 *mm*)	3·00	3·50
326/8		*Set of 3*	3·25	3·50

185 University Coat of arms

187 C. J. Langenhoven

186 Rescuing Sailors

(Des P. de Wet (15 c.), H. Meiring (others))
1973 (2 Apr). *Centenary of University of South Africa.* T **185** *and similar designs.* W **127** (*tête-bêche*) (5 c.) *or no wmk* (*others*). P 12 × 12½ (5 c.) *or* 12½ (*others*).
329		4 c. multicoloured	20	10
330		5 c. multicoloured	30	15
331		15 c. black and gold	3·00	3·50
329/31		*Set of 3*	3·25	3·50

Designs: *Horiz* (37 × 21 *mm*)—5 c. University Complex, Pretoria. *Vert* (*As* T **185**)—15 c. Old University Building, Cape Town.

WATERMARK. All issues from this date are on unwatermarked paper, *unless otherwise stated.*

(Des M. Barnett)
1973 (2 June). *Bicentenary of Rescue by Wolraad Woltemade.* T **186** *and similar horiz designs.* P 11½ × 12½.
332		4 c. lt red-brown, lt yellow-green and black	25	10
333		5 c. yellow-olive, light yellow-green & black	40	10
334		15 c. red-brown, light yellow-green and black	5·00	6·00
332/4		*Set of 3*	5·00	6·00

Designs:—5 c. *De Jonge Thomas* foundering; 15 c. *De Jonge Thomas* breaking up and sailors drowning.

(Des J. Mostert)
1973 (1 Aug). *Birth Centenary of C. J. Langenhoven (politician and composer of national anthem).* T **187** *and similar designs.* P 12½ (4 and 5 c.) *or* 11½ × 12½ (15 c.).
335	**187**	4 c. multicoloured	25	10
336	—	5 c. multicoloured	35	10
337	—	15 c. multicoloured	7·50	6·00
335/7		*Set of 3*	5·00	6·00

Nos. 336/7 are as T **187** but with motifs rearranged. The 5 c. is vert, 21 × 38 mm, and the 15 c. is horiz, 38 × 21 mm.

188 Communications Map

(Des C. Webb)
1973 (1 Oct). *World Communications Day.* P 12½.

(a) No wmk. Glossy paper
338	**188**	15 c. multicoloured	80	1·40

(b) W **127** (*tête-bêche*). *Chalky paper*
339	**188**	15 c. multicoloured	1·50	5·00

189 Restored Buildings

190 Burgerspond (obverse and reverse)

(Des W. Jordaan)
1974 (14 Mar). *Restoration of Tulbagh.* T **189** *and similar multicoloured design.* P 12½.
340		4 c. Type **189**	15	10
341		5 c. Restored Church Street (58 × 21 *mm*)	40	60

(Des P. de Wet. Litho)
1974 (6 Apr). *Centenary of the Burgerspond (coin).* P 12½ × 12.
342	**190**	9 c. brown, orange-red & pale yell-olive	60	95

191 Dr. Malan   **192** Congress Emblem

(Des I. Henkel)
1974 (22 May). *Birth Centenary of Dr. D. F. Malan (Prime Minister).* P 12½ × 12.
343	**191**	4 c. blue and light blue	20	10

(Des Ingrid Paul)
1974 (13 June). *15th World Sugar Congress, Durban.* P 12 × 12½.
344	**192**	15 c. deep ultramarine and silver	75	1·25

193 "50" and Radio Waves

(Des Ingrid Paul)
1974 (13 July). *50th Anniv of Broadcasting in South Africa.* P 12 × 12½.
345	**193**	4 c. red and black	10	10

---

194 Monument Building

(Des G. Cunningham)
1974 (13 July). *Inauguration of British Settlers' Monument, Grahamstown.* P 12 × 12½.
346	**194**	5 c. red and black	10	10

195 Stamps of the South African Provinces

(Des K. Esterhuysen)
1974 (9 Oct). *Centenary of Universal Postal Union.* P 12½.
347	**195**	15 c. multicoloured	70	80

196 Iris   **197** Bokmakierie Shrikes

(Des E. de Jong. Recess and photo)
1974 (20 Nov)–76. *Multicoloured. Glossy paper* (2, 3, 4, 6, 7, 30 c. *and* 1 r.) *or chalk-surfaced paper* (*others*). P 12½ (1 to 25 c.) *or* 12×12½ (*others*).

(a) Vert designs as T **196** *showing flowers, or horiz designs showing birds or fish*
348		1 c. Type **196**	10	10
349		2 c. Wild Heath	15	10
		a. Chalk-surfaced paper (2.75)	10	10
350		3 c. Geranium	30	10
		a. Chalk-surfaced paper (*deep claret background*) (6.75)	10	10
		ab. Imperf (pair)	£110	
		ac. *Brown-purple background* (6.76)	10	10
351		4 c. Arum Lily	30	10
		a. Chalk-surfaced paper (2.75)	10	10
		ab. Imperf (pair)	£110	
352		5 c. Cape Gannet	20	10
353		6 c. Galjoen (fish)	50	10
354		7 c. Bontrok Seabream	25	10
355		9 c. Dusky Batfish	30	10
356		10 c. Moorish Idol	30	10
357		14 c. Roman Seabream	30	10
358		15 c. Greater Double-collared Sunbird	30	10
359		20 c. Yellow-billed Hornbill	45	10
360		25 c. Barberton Daisy	45	10

(b) Horiz designs as T **197**
361		30 c. Type **197**	8·50	70
362		50 c. Stanley Cranes	2·00	35
363		1 r. Bateleurs	8·50	3·00
348/63		*Set of 16*	20·00	4·25

A used block of 4 and a single on cover of No. 351 have been seen with the yellow omitted.

1974 (20 Nov)–76. *Coil stamps. As Nos.* 348/9, 352 *and* 356 *but photo, colours changed. Glossy paper.* P 12½.
370		1 c. reddish violet and pink	75	60
		a. Perf 14. Chalk-surfaced paper (12.75)	55	60
371		2 c. bronze-green and yellow-ochre	80	60
		a. Chalk-surfaced paper (7.75)	1·10	60
		b. Perf 14. Chalk-surfaced paper (11.76?)	1·40	50
372		5 c. black and light slate-blue	2·25	80
373		10 c. deep violet-blue and light blue	6·00	8·50
		a. Perf 14. Chalk-surfaced paper (4.76)	4·75	5·25
370/3		*Set of 4*	7·50	6·50

198 Voortrekker Monument and Encampment

(Des J. Hoekstra)
1974 (6 Dec). *25th Anniv of Voortrekker Monument, Pretoria.* P 12½.
374	**198**	4 c. multicoloured	20	30

199 SASOL Complex   **200** President Diederichs

(Des C. Webb)

1975 (26 Feb). *25th Anniv of SASOL (South African Coal, Oil and Gas Corporation Ltd).* P 11½ × 12½.
375 **199** 15 c. multicoloured .. .. 75 1·50

(Des J. L. Booysen. Recess (4 c.) or photo (15 c.))

1975 (19 Apr). *Inauguration of the State President.* P 12½ × 11½.
376 **200** 4 c. agate and gold 10 10
377   15 c. royal blue and gold .. .. 50 1·25

201 Jan Smuts   **202** "Dutch East Indiaman, Table Bay"

(Des J. Hoekstra. Recess and photo)

1975 (24 May). *Jan Smuts Commemoration.* P 12½ × 11½.
378 **201** 4 c. black and olive-black 10 10

(Des J. Hoekstra. Photo (Nos. 379/82) or litho (**MS**383))

1975 (18 June). *Death Centenary of Thomas Baines (painter).* T **202** *and similar horiz designs. Multicoloured.* P 11½ × 12½.
379   5 c. Type **202** 15 10
380   9 c. "Cradock, 1848" 25 20
381   15 c. "Thirsty Flat, 1848" 40 50
382   30 c. "Pretoria, 1874" .. .. .. 60 1·75
379/82   *Set of 4* 1·25 2·25
MS383   120 × 95 mm. Nos. 379/82 . .. 1·25 3·75

203 Gideon Malherbe's House, Paarl

(Des P. de Wet. Recess and photo)

1975 (14 Aug). *Centenary of Genootskap van Regte Afrikaners (Afrikaner Language Movement).* P 12½.
384 **203** 4 c. multicoloured 10 10

204 "Automatic Sorting"   **205** Title Page of *Die Afrikaanse Patriot*

(Des J. Sampson)

1975 (11 Sept). *Postal Mechanisation.* P 12½ × 11½.
385 **204** 4 c. multicoloured 10 10

(Des K. Esterhuysen. Recess and photo (4 c.). Des P. de Wet. Litho (5 c.))

1975 (10 Oct). *Inauguration of the Language Monument, Paarl.* T **205** *and similar vert design.* P 12½ × 11½.
386   4 c. black, pale stone and bright orange .. 10 10
387   5 c. multicoloured 10 10
Design:—5 c. "Afrikaanse Taalmonument".

206 Table Mountain

(Des P. Bosman and J. Hoekstra. Litho)

1975 (13 Nov). *Tourism.* T **206** *and similar horiz designs. Multi-coloured.* P 12½.
388   15 c. Type **206** .. .. 3·50 4·25
   a. Block of 4. Nos. 388/91 .. 12·00
   ab. Yellow-orange and pale lemon ("RSA 15 c") omitted £1400 £800
389   15 c. Johannesburg .. .. 3·50 4·25
390   15 c. Cape Vineyards .. .. 3·50 4·25
391   15 c. Lions in Kruger National Park .. 3·50 4·25
388/91   *Set of 4* 12·00 15·00
Nos. 388/91 were printed together, *se-tenant*, in blocks of 4 throughout the sheet.
Nos. 388/91 were printed in six colours. At least two sheets, one of which was subsequently used to prepare official first day covers at Pretoria, had the final two colours, yellow-orange and pale lemon, omitted.

207 Globe and Satellites

(Des J. Hoekstra. Litho)

1975 (3 Dec). *Satellite Communication.* P 12½.
392 **207** 15 c. multicoloured 30 30

208 Bowls   **(209)**

(Des J. Maskew. Litho)

1976. *Sporting Commemorations.* T **208** *and similar vert designs.* P 12½ × 11½.
393   15 c. black and light sage-green (18.2) .. 30 70
394   15 c. black and bright yellow-green (15.3) .. 75 1·40
395   15 c. black and pale yellow-olive (16.8) .. 40 60
396   15 c. black and apple-green (2.12) .. 60 55
393/6   *Set of 4* 1·90 3·00
MS397   161 × 109 mm. Nos. 393/6 (2.12) .. 2·00 4·00
Designs:—No. 393, Type **208** (World Bowls Championships, Johannesburg); No. 394, Batsman (Centenary of Organised Cricket in South Africa); No. 395, Polo player; No. 396, Gary Player (golfer).

1976 (6 Apr). *South Africa's Victory in World Bowls Championships. No. 393 optd with* T **209** *in gold.*
398 **208** 15 c. black and light sage-green 30 80

210 "Picnic under a Baobab Tree"

(Des J. Hoekstra. Photo (4 c.) or litho (others and **MS**403))

1976 (20 Apr). *Birth Centenary of Erich Mayer (painter).* T **210** *and similar horiz designs. Multicoloured.* P 11½ × 12½.
399   4 c. Type **210** 15 10
   a. Imperf (pair) £950
400   10 c. "Foot of the Blaawberg" .. 35 25
401   15 c. "Harbeespoort Dam" .. 50 1·25
402   20 c. "Street scene, Doornfontein" .. 70 1·50
399/402   *Set of 4* 1·50 2·75
MS403   121 × 95 mm. Nos. 399/402 .. 1·50 4·00

211 Cheetah   **212** "Emily Hobhouse" (H. Naude)

(Des P. Bosman. Photo (3 c.) or litho (others))

1976 (5 June). *World Environmental Day.* T **211** *and similar horiz designs. Multicoloured.* P 11½ × 12½.
404   3 c. Type **211** 15 10
405   10 c. Black Rhinoceros 70 40
406   15 c. Blesbok .. .. 85 1·25
407   20 c. Mountain Zebra.. .. 1·25 2·00
404/7   *Set of 4* 2·75 3·25

(Des J. Hoekstra)

1976 (8 June). *50th Death Anniv of Emily Hobhouse (welfare worker).* P 12½ × 11½.
408 **212** 4 c. multicoloured 10 10

213 *Dunrobin Castle* (mail ship), 1876   **214** Family with Globe

(Des K. Esterhuysen. Litho)

1976 (5 Oct). *Ocean Mail Service Centenary.* P 11½ × 12½.
409 **213** 10 c. multicoloured 60 85
   a. Imperf (horiz pair) £900

(Des I. Ross)

1976 (6 Nov). *Family Planning and Child Welfare.* P 12½ × 11½.
410 **214** 4 c. chestnut and light salmon 10 10

215 Glasses of Wine   **216** Dr. Jacob du Toit

First "die" of Afrikaans inscription at left omitted (R. 1/3 on every third sheet)

(Des H. Botha. Litho)

1977 (14 Feb). *International Wine Symposium, Cape Town.* P 12½ × 11½.
411 **215** 15 c. multicoloured 40 85
   a. "die" omitted .. .. 15·00 19·00

(Des J. Hoekstra)

1977 (21 Feb). *Birth Centenary of J. D. du Toit (theologian and poet).* P 12½ × 11½.
412 **216** 4 c. multicoloured 10 10

217 Palace of Justice   **218** *Protea repens*

(Des H. Meiring)

1977 (18 May). *Centenary of Transvaal Supreme Court.* P 11½ × 12½.
413 **217** 4 c. red-brown 10 10

(Des D. Findlay. Photo (1, 2, 3 c. (No. 416), 4, 5, 8, 10 to 20 c. (Nos. 425/a) and coil stamps) or litho (others))

1977 (27 May)**–82.** *Vert designs as* T **218** *showing Proteas or other Succulents. Multicoloured.* (a) Sheet stamps. P 12½.
414   1 c. Type **218** 10 10
415   2 c. *P punctata* 15 50
416   3 c. *P neriifolia* (photo) (p 12½) .. 10 10
416a   3 c. *P neriifolia* (litho) (p 14 × 13½) (1.10.79) .. 10 50
417   4 c. *P longifolia* 10 10
   a. Imperf (pair) £100
418   5 c. *P cynaroides* 10 10
   a. Perf 14 × 13½ (4.3.81) .. 10 10
   b. Imperf (pair) £160
419   6 c. *P canaliculata* 35 60
   a. Black (face value and inscr at foot) omitted .. .. 90·00
   b. Perf 14 × 13½ (25.10.79*) .. 30 80
420   7 c. *P lorea* 25 80
   a. Emerald ("RSA") omitted £110
   b. Perf 14 × 13½ (19.9.80) .. 20 80

421	8 c. *P. mundii*	..	..	..	20	30
	a. Perf 14 × 13½ (10.7.81)	..			15	10
422	9 c. *P. roupelliae*	..	..	..	20	70
	a. Perf 14 × 13½ (22.12.78)	..			3·75	2·50
423	10 c. *P. aristata*	..	..	..	30	10
	a. Perf 14 × 13½ (12.1.82)	..			20	50
424	15 c. *P. eximia*	..	..	..	25	10
425	20 c. *P. magnifica* (photo)	..	..		30	10
	a. Perf 14 × 13½ (16.2.78)	..			60	90
425*b*	20 c. *P. magnifica* (litho) (p 14 × 13½) (24.5.82)				1·25	1·00
426	25 c. *P. grandiceps*	..	..		60	75
	a. Emerald ("RSA" and leaves) omitted				£160	
	b. Black (face value and inscr) omitted				£160	
	c. Perf 14×13½ (3.6.80)	..			40	75
427	30 c. *P. amplexicaulis*	..	..		45	10
	a. Perf 14×13½ (19.10.80)	..			40	50
428	50 c. *Leucospermum cordifolium*	..		65	15
	a. Perf 14×13½ (9.10.80)	..			45	15
429	1 r. *Paranomus reflexus*	..	..		70	95
	a. Perf 14×13½ (30.7.80)	..			60	75
430	2 r. *Orothamnus zeyheri*	..	..		1·25	2·50
	a. Perf 14×13½ (22.5.81)	..			80	1·00

(*b*) Coil stamps. *Imperf × perf* 14

431	1 c. *Leucadendron argenteum*	..	..		35	80
432	2 c. *Mimetes cucullatus*	..	..		35	80
433	5 c. *Serruria florida*	..	..		35	80
434	10 c. *Leucadendron sessile*	..	..		35	90
414/34			*Set of 21*		5·50	8·00

*Sheets dated 15 August 1979.

There were two emerald plates used for the 7 c.; one for the design and background and a second, common with other values in the issue, used to apply "RSA". No. 420a shows this second emerald plate omitted.

Later printings of the coil stamps come with every fifth stamp numbered on the back.

219 Gymnast   **220** Metrication Symbol on Globe

(Des D. Cowie. Litho)

1977 (15 Aug). *Eighth Congress of International Association of Physical Education and Sports for Girls and Women.* P 12½ × 11½.
435 **219** 15 c. black, salmon-red and yellow .. 30 30

(Des L. Wilsenach. Litho)

1977 (15 Sept). *Metrication.* P 12 × 12½.
436 **220** 15 c. multicoloured 30 30

221 Atomic Diagram

(Des R. Sargent. Litho)

1977 (8 Oct). *Uranium Development.* P 12 × 12½.
437 **221** 15 c. multicoloured 40 30

222 National Flag

(Des J. Hoekstra)

1977 (11 Nov). *50th Anniv of National Flag.* P 12 × 12½.
438 **222** 5 c. multicoloured 10 10

223 Walvis Bay, 1878

(Des A. H. Barrett. Litho)

1978 (10 Mar). *Centenary of Annexation of Walvis Bay.* P 12½.
439 **223** 15 c. multicoloured 60 60

COVER PRICES

Cover factors are quoted at the beginning of each country for most issues to 1945. An explanation of the system can be found on page x. The factors quoted do not, however, apply to philatelic covers.

224 Dr. Andrew Murray   **225** Steel Rail

(Des J. Hoekstra. Litho)

1978 (9 May). *150th Birth Anniv of Dr. Andrew Murray (church statesman).* P 12½ × 12.
440 **224** 4 c. multicoloured 10 10

(Des H. Botha. Litho)

1978 (5 June). *50th Anniv of I.S.C.O.R. (South African Iron and Steel Industrial Corporation).* P 12½.
441 **225** 15 c. multicoloured 30 30

226 Richards Bay

(Des A. H. Barrett. Litho)

1978 (31 July). *Harbours. T* **226** *and similar horiz design. Multi-coloured.* P 12½.
442 15 c. Type **226** .. .. .. 50 1·00
   a. Pair. Nos. 442/3 .. .. .. 1·00 2·00
443 15 c. Saldanhabaai .. .. .. 50 1·00
Nos. 442/3 were printed together, *se-tenant*, in horizontal and vertical pairs throughout the sheet.

227 "Shepherd's Lonely Dwelling, Riversdale"   **228** Pres. B. J. Vorster

(Des G. Mynhardt. Litho)

1978 (21 Aug). *125th Birth Anniv of J. E. A. Volschenk (painter). T* **227** *and similar horiz designs. Multicoloured.* P 12½.
444 10 c. Type **227** 20 20
445 15 c. "Clouds and Sunshine, Laneberg Range, Riversdale" .. 40 35
446 20 c. "At the Foot of the Mountain" .. 60 1·00
447 25 c. "Evening on the Veldt" .. 70 1·75
444/7 .. .. .. *Set of 4* 1·75 3·00
MS448 124 × 90 mm. Nos. 444/7 .. 1·75 4·00

(Des A. H. Barrett. Litho)

1978 (10 Oct). *Inauguration of President Vorster.* P 14 × 13½.
449 **228** 4 c. brown-purple and gold .. 70 20
   a. Perf 12½ × 12 .. 10 10
450 15 c. dull violet and gold .. 25 60

229 Golden Gate

(Des A. H. Barrett. Litho)

1978 (13 Nov). *Tourism. T* **229** *and similar horiz designs. Multi-coloured.* P 12½.
451 10 c. Type **229** 15 10
452 15 c. Blyde River Canyon 25 35
453 20 c. Amphitheatre, Drakensberg .. 40 1·00
454 25 c. Cango Caves .. .. 55 1·40
451/4 .. .. .. *Set of 4* 1·25 2·50

230 Dr. Wadley (inventor) and Tellurometer

(Des A. H. Barrett. Litho)

1979 (12 Feb). *25th Anniv of Tellurometer (radio distance measurer).* P 12½.
455 **230** 15 c. multicoloured 20 20

231 1929 4d. Airmail Stamp

(Des G. Mynhardt. Litho)

1979 (30 Mar). *50th Anniv of Stamp Production in South Africa.* P 14.
456 **231** 15 c. green, cream and slate .. 30 20

232 "Save Fuel"

(Des A. H. Barrett)

1979 (2 Apr). *Fuel Conservation.* P 12 × 12½.
457 **232** 4 c. black and vermilion .. 25 50
   a. Pair. Nos. 457/8 .. .. 50 1·00
458 4 c. black and vermilion .. 25 50
No. 458 is as T **232** but has face value and country initials in bottom left-hand corner, and Afrikaans inscription above English.
Nos. 457/8 were printed together, *se-tenant*, in horizontal and vertical pairs throughout the sheet.

233 Isandlwana   **234** "Health Care"

(Des A. H. Barrett. Litho)

1979 (25 May). *Centenary of Zulu War. T* **233** *and similar horiz designs in black and rose-red, showing drawings.* P 14.
459 4 c. Type **233** 15 10
460 15 c. Ulundi 45 45
461 20 c. Rorke's Drift 60 75
459/61 .. .. *Set of 3* 1·10 1·10
MS462 125 × 90 mm. Nos. 459/61. P 12½ .. 2·25 3·50

(Des J. Hoekstra. Litho)

1979 (19 June). *Health Year.* P 12½ × 12.
463 **234** 4 c. multicoloured 10 10
   a. Perf 14 × 13½ 30 30

235 Children looking at Candle

(Des G. Mynhardt. Litho)

1979 (13 Sept). *50th Anniv of Christmas Stamp Fund.* P 14.
464 **235** 4 c. multicoloured 10 10
   a. Gold (inscr) omitted .. ..

236 University of Cape Town   **237** "Gary Player"

(Des G. Mynhardt. Litho)

1979 (1 Oct). *50th Anniv of University of Cape Town.* P 13½ × 14.
465 **236** 4 c. multicoloured 20 30
   a. Perf 12 × 12½ 15 15

(Des H. de Klerk. Litho)

1979 (4 Oct). *"Rosafari 1979" World Rose Convention, Pretoria. T* **237** *and similar vert designs. Multicoloured.* P 14 × 13½.
466 4 c. Type **237** 15 10
467 15 c. "Prof. Chris Barnard" 40 40
468 20 c. "Southern Sun" 50 60
469 25 c. "Soaring Wings" 55 85
466/9 .. .. *Set of 4* 1·40 1·75
MS470 100 × 125 mm. Nos. 466/9 .. 1·40 2·50

238 University of Stellenbosch

239 F.A.K. Emblem

(Des A. H. Barrett. Litho)

1979 (8 Nov). *300th Anniv of Stellenbosch (oldest town in South Africa). T **238** and similar horiz design. Multicoloured. P 14.*
471   4 c. Type **238** 10   10
472   15 c. Rhenish Church on the Braak 20   40

(Des J. Hoekstra)

1979 (18 Dec). *50th Anniv of F.A.K. (Federation of Afrikaans Cultural Societies). P 12½ × 12.*
473   **239**   4 c. multicoloured 10   15

240 "Still-life with Sweet Peas"

241 "Cullinan II"

(Des G. Mynhardt. Litho)

1980 (6 May). *Paintings by Pieter Wenning. T **240** and similar multicoloured design. P 14 × 13½.*
474   5 c. Type **240** 10   10
475   25 c. "House in the Suburbs, Cape Town"
        (44½ × 37 mm) 40   60
MS476   94 × 121 mm. Nos. 474/5 .. .. 1·00   1·60

(Des A. H. Barrett. Litho)

1980 (12 May). *World Diamond Congresses, Johannesburg. T **241** and similar vert design. Multicoloured. P 14.*
477   15 c. Type **241** 60   60
478   20 c. "Cullinan I (Great Star of Africa)" .. 65   65

242 C. L. Leipoldt

243 University of Pretoria

(Des J. Hoekstra. Litho)

1980 (3 Sept). *Birth Centenary of C. L. Leipoldt (poet). P 14 × 13½.*
479   **242**   5 c. multicoloured 10   10

(Des P. de Wet. Litho)

1980 (9 Oct). *50th Anniv of University of Pretoria. P 14 × 13½.*
480   **243**   5 c. multicoloured 10   10

244 "Marine with Shipping" (Willem van de Velde)

(Des G. Mynhardt. Litho)

1980 (3 Nov). *Paintings from South African National Gallery, Cape Town. T **244** and similar multicoloured designs. P 14.*
481   5 c. Type **244** 15   10
482   10 c. "Firetail and his Trainer" (George Stubbs)   20   20
483   15 c. "Lavinia" (Thomas Gainsborough) (vert)   25   45
484   20 c. "Classical Landscape" (Pieter Post) .. 30   65
481/4 .. .. Set of 4 80   1·25
MS485   126 × 90 mm. Nos. 481/4 .. .. 1·00   1·75

245 Joubert, Kruger and M. Pretorius (Triumvirate Government)

246 Boers advancing up Amajuba Mountain

(Des A. H. Barrett. Litho)

1980 (15 Dec). *Centenary of Paardekraal Monument (cairn commemorating formation of Boer Triumvirate Government). T **245** and similar multicoloured design. P 14 × 13½ (5 c.) or 13½ × 14 (10 c.).*
486   5 c. Type **245** 10   10
487   10 c. Paardekraal Monument (vert) .. 20   40

(Des Diana Arbuthnot. Litho)

1981 (27 Feb). *Centenary of Battle of Amajuba. T **246** and similar multicoloured design. P 13½ × 14 (5 c.) or 14 × 13½ (15 c.).*
488   5 c. Type **246** 20   10
489   15 c. British troops defending hill (horiz) .. 40   65

247 Ballet *Raka*

(Des H. Botha. Litho)

1981 (23 May). *Opening of State Theatre, Pretoria. T **247** and similar horiz design. Multicoloured. P 14.*
490   20 c. Type **247** 25   30
491   25 c. Opera *Aida* 40   35
MS492   110 × 90 mm. Nos. 490/1 65   70

248 Former Presidents C. R. Swart, J. J. Fouché, N. Diederichs and B. J. Vorster

(Des A. H. Barrett. Litho)

1981 (30 May). *20th Anniv of Republic. T **248** and similar design. P 14.*
493   5 c. black, grey-olive and bistre 15   10
494   15 c. multicoloured 30   30
Design: (28 × 22 mm)—15 c. President Marais Viljoen.

249 Girl with Hearing Aid

250 Microscope

251 Calanthe natalensis

(Des Mare Mouton. Litho)

1981 (12 June). *Centenary of Institutes for Deaf and Blind, Worcester. T **249** and similar vert design. Multicoloured. P 13½ × 14.*
495   5 c. Type **249** 10   10
496   15 c. Boy reading braille 20   25

(Des N. Hanna. Litho)

1981 (10 July). *50th Anniv of National Cancer Association. P 13½ × 14.*
497   **250**   5 c. multicoloured 10   10

(Des Jeanette Stead. Litho)

1981 (11 Sept). *Tenth World Orchid Conference, Durban. T **251** and similar vert designs. Multicoloured. P 14.*
498   5 c. Type **251** 15   10
499   15 c. Eulophia speciosa 30   35
500   20 c. Disperis fanniniae 40   65
501   25 c. Disa uniflora 50   90
498/501 .. .. .. Set of 4 1·25   1·75
MS502   120 × 91 mm. Nos. 498/501 .. 2·25   2·00

252 Voortrekkers in Uniform

253 Lord Baden-Powell

254 Dr. Robert Koch

(Des J. Hoekstra. Litho)

1981 (30 Sept). *50th Anniv of Voortrekker Movement (Afrikaans cultural youth organization). P 14.*
503   **252**   5 c. multicoloured 10   10

(Des J. Meyer. Litho)

1982 (22 Feb). *75th Anniv of Boy Scout Movement. P 13½ × 14.*
504   **253**   15 c. multicoloured 30   30

(Des J. Meyer. Litho)

1982 (24 Mar). *Centenary of Discovery of Tubercle Bacillus by Dr. Robert Koch. P 13½ × 14.*
505   **254**   20 c. multicoloured 20   30

255 Maria van Riejbeck (submarine)

256 Old Provost, Grahamstown

(Des A. H. Barrett. Litho)

1982 (2 Apr). *25th Anniv of Simonstown as South African Navy Base. T **255** and similar horiz designs. Multicoloured. P 14.*
506   8 c. Type **255** 15   10
507   15 c. Missile patrol vessel 20   30
508   20 c. Durban (minesweeper) 25   50
509   25 c. Harbour patrol boats 30   70
506/9 .. .. .. Set of 4 80   1·40
MS510   125×90 mm. Nos. 506/9 .. .. 2·00   2·00

(Des A. H. Barrett. Recess (Nos. 511, 512b, 513, 514, 515a, 516a, 521, 522a, 524, 525, 526 and 527), photo (Nos. 528/31) or litho (others))

1982 (15 July)–87. *South African Architecture. Designs as T **256**. (a) Sheet stamps. P 14.*
511   1 c. reddish brown (recess) 15   20
511a   1 c. reddish brown (2.4.84) 30   30
      ab. Imperf (horiz pair) .. .. 35·00
512   2 c. yellow-olive (litho) 20   30
512a   2 c. deep green (litho) (9.5.83) .. 90   30
512b   2 c. bottle green (recess) (28.11.83) 10   20
512c   2 c. bottle green (litho) (21.11.85) 90   30
513   3 c. violet (recess) 30   30
513a   3 c. violet (litho) (28.11.85) .. 1·75   50
514   4 c. brown-olive (recess) 20   15
514a   4 c. brown-olive (litho) (25.3.85) .. 1·25   40
515   5 c. carmine (litho) 40   30
515a   5 c. brown-purple (recess) (11.11.83) 10   10
      ab. Imperf (pair) £100
516   6 c. deep blue-green (litho) .. 45   40
516a   6 c. blackish green (recess) (9.8.84) 80   50
517   7 c. dull yellowish green (litho) .. 30   50
518   8 c. greenish blue (litho) 30   30
518a   8 c. indigo (litho) (3.1.83) .. 40   10
519   9 c. deep mauve (litho) 40   20
520   10 c. Venetian red (litho) 40   40
520a   10 c. purple-brown (litho) (26.1.83) 35   10
520b   11 c. cerise (litho) (2.4.84) .. 40   20
520c   12 c. deep violet-blue (litho) (1.4.85) 70   10
520d   14 c. lake-brown (litho) (1.4.86) .. 1·50   10
521   15 c. deep violet-blue (recess) .. 30   15
521a   16 c. rosine (litho) (1.4.87) .. 1·00   60
522   20 c. vermilion (litho) 65   30
522a   20 c. brownish black (recess) (15.6.83) 80   10
522b   20 c. brownish black (litho) (14.11.85) 1·50   15
523   25 c. bistre (litho) 50   30
523a   25 c. ochre (litho) (3.6.87) .. 1·75   55
524   30 c. agate (recess) 65   30
524a   30 c. reddish brown (litho) (12.3.86) 95   30
525   50 c. deep turquoise-blue (recess) 80   30
      a. Deep slate-blue (18.3.83) .. 2·00   65
525b   50 c. turquoise-blue (litho) (13.10.86) 2·75   30
526   1 r. deep violet (recess) .. 1·00   15
526a   1 r. deep violet (litho) (17.12.86) 1·50   40

624

527	2 r. deep carmine (*recess*)			1·25	40
527a	2 r. deep carmine (*litho*) (5.12.85)			1·25	50
511/27	*Set of 21 (one of each value)*			9·50	4·25

Designs: (28 × 20 *mm*)—2 c. Tuynhuys, Cape Town; 3 c. Appèlhof, Bloemfontein; 4 c. Raadsaal, Pretoria; 5 c. Cape Town Castle; 6 c. Goewermentsgebou, Bloemfontein; 7 c. Drostdy, Graaff-Reinet; 8 c. Leeuwenhof, Cape Town; 9 c. Libertas, Pretoria; 10 c. City Hall, Pietermaritzburg; 11 c. City Hall, Kimberley; 12 c. City Hall, Port Elizabeth; 14 c. City Hall, Johannesburg; 15 c. Matjesfontein; 16 c. City Hall, Durban; 20 c. Post Office, Durban; 25 c. Melrose House, Pretoria. (45 × 28 *mm*)—30 c. Old Legislative Assembly Building, Pietermaritzburg; 50 c. Raadsaal, Bloemfontein; 1 r. Houses of Parliament, Cape Town; 2 r. Uniegebou, Pretoria.

For certain printings of Nos. 511/27a the design width of each stamp was reduced by a millimetre. Of the original set of 17 all showed "wide" designs with the exception of the 1 r. Changes in design size occurred in subsequent printings so that Nos. 512c, 513, 521 and 524 can be found in both wide and narrow versions. Of the remainder Nos. 511a, 512b, 513a, 514a, 515a, 516a, 520b/d, 521a, 522a/b, 524a, 525a/b, 526 and 527a exist as "narrow" designs only.

(b) Coil stamps. P 14 × imperf

528	1 c. brown			30	60
529	2 c. yellow-green			30	65
530	5 c. lake-brown			30	65
531	10 c. light brown			30	70
528/31			*Set of 4*	1·10	2·40

Designs: (28 × 20 *mm*)—1 c. Drostdy, Swellendam; 2 c. City Hall, East London; 5 c. Head Post Office, Johannesburg; 10 c. Morgenster, Somerset West.

257 Bradysaurus   **258** Gough Island Base

(Des Sheila Nowers. Litho)

1982 (1 Dec). *Karoo Fossils.* T **257** *and similar horiz designs.* Multicoloured. P 14.

532	8 c. Type **257**			40	10
533	15 c. Lystrosaurus			50	75
534	20 c. Euparkeria			60	85
535	25 c. Thrinaxodon			70	1·10
532/5			*Set of 4*	2·00	2·50
MS536	107 × 95 mm. Nos. 532/5			2·50	3·25

(Des D. Thorpe. Litho)

1983 (19 Jan). *Weather Stations.* T **258** *and similar horiz designs.* Multicoloured. P 13½ × 14.

537	8 c. Type **258**			20	10
538	20 c. Marion Island base			45	45
539	25 c. Taking meteorological readings			45	50
540	40 c. Launching weather balloon, Sanae			70	90
537/40			*Set of 4*	1·60	1·75

259 Class S2 Krupp Locomotive, 1952   **260** Rugby

(Des H. Botha. Litho)

1983 (27 Apr). *Steam Railway Locomotives.* T **259** *and similar horiz designs.* Multicoloured. P 14.

541	10 c. Type **259**			35	10
542	20 c. Class 16E Henschel express locomotive, 1935			70	75
543	25 c. Class 6H locomotive, 1901			80	1·00
544	40 c. Class 15F locomotive, 1939			1·25	1·75
541/4			*Set of 4*	2·75	3·25

(Des Sheila Nowers. Litho)

1983 (20 July). *Sport in South Africa.* T **260** *and similar multicoloured designs.* P 14.

545	10 c. Type **260**			15	10
546	20 c. Soccer (*horiz*)			35	40
547	25 c. Yachting			45	50
548	40 c. Horse-racing (*horiz*)			75	95
545/8			*Set of 4*	1·50	1·75

261 Plettenberg Bay   **262** Thomas Pringle

(Des A. H. Barrett. Litho)

1983 (12 Oct). *Tourism. Beaches.* T **261** *and similar horiz designs.* Multicoloured. P 14.

549	10 c. Type **261**			10	10
550	20 c. Durban			25	30
551	30 c. West coast			30	35
552	40 c. Clifton			50	65
549/52			*Set of 4*	1·10	1·25
MS553	128 × 90 mm. Nos. 549/52			1·75	2·50

(Des J. van Ellinckhuijzen. Litho)

1984 (24 Feb). *South African English Authors.* T **262** *and similar vert designs.* P 14.

554	10 c. olive-brown, yellow-brown and grey		10	10
555	20 c. olive-brown, deep bluish green and grey		25	40
556	25 c. olive-brown, deep brown-rose and grey		30	50
557	40 c. olive-brown, olive-ochre and grey		50	85
554/7			*Set of 4*	1·10	1·75

Designs:—20 c. Pauline Smith; 25 c. Olive Schreiner; 40 c. Sir Percy Fitzpatrick.

263 Manganese

(Des H. Botha. Litho)

1984 (8 June). *Strategic Minerals.* T **263** *and similar horiz designs.* Multicoloured. P 14.

558	11 c. Type **263**			40	10
559	20 c. Chromium			75	75
560	25 c. Vanadium			90	1·00
561	30 c. Titanium			1·00	1·25
558/61			*Set of 4*	2·75	2·75

264 Bloukrans River Bridge   **265** Preamble to the Constitution in Afrikaans

(Des D. Bagnall. Litho)

1984 (24 Aug). *South African Bridges.* T **264** *and similar horiz designs.* Multicoloured. P 14.

562	11 c. Type **264**			40	10
563	25 c. Durban four level interchange			80	75
564	30 c. Mfolozi Railway Bridge			85	95
565	45 c. Gouritz River bridge			1·10	1·75
562/5			*Set of 4*	2·75	3·25

(Des G. Mynhardt. Litho)

1984 (3 Sept). *New Constitution.* T **265** *and similar vert designs.* P 14.

566	11 c. stone, black and bistre			90	1·25
	a. Horiz pair. Nos. 566/7			1·75	2·50
567	11 c. stone, black and bistre			90	1·25
568	25 c. stone, deep claret and bistre			60	65
569	30 c. multicoloured			60	65
566/9			*Set of 4*	2·75	3·50

Designs:—No. 566, Preamble to the Constitution in English; 568, Last two lines of National Anthem; 569, South African coat of arms.
Nos. 566/7 were printed together, *se-tenant*, in horizontal pairs.

266 Pres. P. W. Botha   **267** Pro Patria Medal

1984 (2 Nov). *Inauguration of President Botha. Litho.* P 14.

570	**266**	11 c. multicoloured		30	10
571		25 c. multicoloured		55	40

(Des B. Jackson. Litho)

1984 (9 Nov). *Military Decorations.* T **267** *and similar vert designs.* Multicoloured. P 14.

572	11 c. Type **267**			25	10
573	25 c. De Wet Decoration			40	45
574	30 c. John Chard Decoration			45	65
575	45 c. Honoris Crux (Diamond) Decoration			55	1·10
572/5			*Set of 4*	1·50	2·10
MS576	71 × 116 mm. Nos. 572/5			1·50	3·00

268 "Reflections" (Frans Oerder)   **269** Cape Parliament Building

1985 (22 Feb). *Paintings by Frans Oerder.* T **268** *and similar horiz designs.* Multicoloured. Litho. P 14.

577	11 c. Type **268**			25	15
578	25 c. "Ladies in a Garden"			35	35
579	30 c. "Still-life with Lobster"			40	45
580	50 c. "Still-life with Marigolds"			70	70
577/80			*Set of 4*	1·50	1·50
MS581	129 × 74 mm. Nos. 577/80			2·00	3·00

(Des A. H. Barrett. Litho)

1985 (15 May). *Centenary of Cape Parliament Building.* T **269** *and similar horiz designs.* Multicoloured. P 14.

582	12 c. Type **269**			25	10
583	25 c. Speaker's Chair			40	55
584	30 c. "National Convention 1908–9" (Edward Roworth)			55	65
585	50 c. Republic Parliamentary emblem			80	1·25
	a. Black (inscr and outline) omitted			£275	
582/5			*Set of 4*	1·75	2·25

270 Freesia   **271** Sugar Bowl

(Des Sheila Nowers. Litho)

1985 (23 Aug). *Floral Emigrants.* T **270** *and similar vert designs.* Multicoloured. P 14.

586	12 c. Type **270**			30	10
587	25 c. Nerine			50	75
588	30 c. Ixia			60	85
589	50 c. Gladiolus			80	1·60
586/9			*Set of 4*	2·00	3·00

(Des H. Botha. Litho)

1985 (5 Nov). *Cape Silverware.* T **271** *and similar multicoloured designs.* P 14.

590	12 c. Type **271**			30	10
591	25 c. Teapot			50	60
592	30 c. Loving cup (*vert*)			60	80
593	50 c. Coffee pot (*vert*)			80	1·00
590/3			*Set of 4*	2·00	3·00

272 Blood Donor Session   **273** National Flag

(Des Sheila Nowers. Litho)

1986 (20 Feb). *Blood Donor Campaign.* T **272** *and similar horiz designs.* Multicoloured. P 14.

594	12 c. Type **272**			45	10
595	20 c. Baby receiving blood transfusion			75	80
596	25 c. Operation in progress			80	95
597	30 c. Ambulanceman and accident victim			95	1·60
594/7			*Set of 4*	2·75	3·00

(Des J. Hoekstra. Litho)

1986 (30 May). *25th Anniv of Republic of South Africa.* T **273** *and similar horiz design.* Multicoloured. P 14.

598	14 c. Type **273**			75	1·00
	a. Horiz pair. Nos. 598/9			1·50	2·00
599	14 c. As Type **273**, but inscr "UNITY IS STRENGTH"			75	1·00

Nos. 598/9 were printed together, *se-tenant*, in horizontal pairs throughout the sheet.

274 Drostdyhof, Graaff-Reinet

(Des A. H. Barrett. Litho)

1986 (14 Aug). *Restoration of Historic Buildings.* T **274** *and similar horiz designs.* Multicoloured. P 14.

600	14 c. Type **274**			30	10
601	20 c. Pilgrim's Rest mining village			55	70
602	25 c. Strapp's Store, Bethlehem			60	90
603	30 c. Palmdene, Pietermaritzburg			75	1·40
600/3			*Set of 4*	2·00	2·75

NEW INFORMATION

The editor is always interested to correspond with people who have new information that will improve or correct the Catalogue.

MACHINE LABELS. From 14 August 1986 gummed labels in the above design, ranging in value from 1 c. to 99 r. 99, were available from an experimental machine at Sunnyside Post Office in Pretoria. The machine was moved to the "Johannesburg 100" exhibition from 6 to 11 October 1986 and was then reinstalled at Sunnyside on 17 October 1986. Further machines were introduced subsequently and each can be identified by a code number, between P.001 and P.034, at right.

Commemorative labels were subsequently available at "PAARL 300" (1987), "PIETERMARITZBURG 150" (1988), "WANDERERS 101" (1989), "STAMPS 150" (1990), "CAPE TOWN 1991", "PRETORIA 92", eTHEKWINI (Durban 1993) and "BENONI '94" stamp exhibitions. All machines were withdrawn on 30 November 1994.

PHILATELIC FOUNDATION MINIATURE SHEETS. These miniature sheets were issued by the Philatelic Foundation of Southern Africa and not the postal administration. They could be purchased by post or from a limited number of philatelic offices at a premium in aid of various national and international stamp exhibitions.

275 Von Brandis Square, Johannesburg, c 1900

(Des J. van Niekerk. Litho)

1986 (25 Sept). *Centenary of Johannesburg.* T **275** *and similar horiz designs. Multicoloured.* P 14.

604	14 c. Type 275.		35	15
605	20 c. Gold mine (26 × 20 mm)		1·00	1·25
606	25 c. Johannesburg skyline, 1986		1·00	1·40
607	30 c. Gold bars (26 × 20 mm)..		1·50	2·25
604/7		*Set of 4*	3·50	4·50

The 30 c. value exists as a Philatelic Foundation miniature sheet.

276 Gordon's Rock, Paarlberg	277 *Cicindela regalis*

(Des A. H. Barrett. Litho)

1986 (20 Nov). *Rock Formations.* T **276** *and similar vert designs. Multicoloured.* P 14.

608	14 c. Type 276..		60	10
609	20 c. The Column, Drakensberg		85	90
610	25 c. Maltese Cross, Sederberge		95	1·25
611	30 c. Bourke's Luck Potholes, Blyde River Gorge		1·25	1·75
608/11		*Set of 4*	3·25	3·50

(Des E. Holm. Litho)

1987 (6 Mar). *South African Beetles.* T **277** *and similar vert designs. Multicoloured.* P 14.

612	14 c. Type 277		50	10
613	20 c. *Trichostetha fascicularis*		70	75
614	25 c. *Julodis viridipes*		85	1·10
615	30 c. *Ceroplesis militaris*		1·10	2·00
612/15		*Set of 4*	2·75	3·50

278 Eland, Sebaaieni Cave

(Des H. Botha. Litho)

1987 (4 June). *Rock Paintings.* T **278** *and similar horiz designs. Multicoloured.* P 14.

616	16 c. Type 278..		50	10
617	20 c. Leaping lion, Clocolan		75	75
618	25 c. Black Wildebeest, uMhlwazini Valley		90	1·10
619	30 c. Bushman dance, Floukraal		1·10	2·00
616/19		*Set of 4*	3·00	3·50

279 Oude Pastorie, Paarl

(Des A. H. Barrett. Litho)

1987 (3 Sept). *300th Anniv of Paarl.* T **279** *and similar horiz designs. Multicoloured.* P 14.

620	16 c. Type 279.		30	10
621	20 c. Grapevines		50	70
622	25 c. Wagon-building..		55	85
623	30 c. KWV Cathedral Wine Cellar		75	1·50
620/3		*Set of 4*	1·90	2·75

The 30 c. value exists as a Philatelic Foundation miniature sheet.

(280)	281 "Belshazzar's Feast" (Rembrandt)

1987 (16 Nov). *Natal Flood Relief Fund (1st issue).* No. 521a surch as T **280** *in Afrikaans or English.*

624	16 c. + 10 c. rosine (surch T 280)		45	70
	a. Pair. Nos. 624/5..		90	1·40
625	16 c. + 10 c. rosine (surch "NATAL FLOOD DISASTER")		45	70

Nos. 624/5 were surcharged together, *se-tenant*, in horizontal and vertical pairs throughout the sheet.
See also Nos. 629/30 and 635/6.

(Des Sheila Nowers. Litho)

1987 (19 Nov). *The Bible Society of South Africa.* T **281** *and similar multicoloured designs.* P 14.

626	16 c. "The Bible" in 75 languages (54 × 34 mm)		40	10
627	30 c. Type 281.		70	85
628	50 c. "St. Matthew and the Angel" (Rembrandt) (*vert*)		90	1·25
626/8		*Set of 3*	1·75	2·00

A 40 c. value, showing the inscription "The Word of God" in various languages, was prepared, but due to religious objections was recalled before issue, although examples are known to have been sold to the public at some smaller post offices (*Price £550 mint, £650 used*).

1987 (1 Dec). *Natal Flood Relief Fund (2nd issue).* No. 626 surch as T **280**, *but larger (Afrikaans version 32 mm wide).*

629	16 c. + 10 c. multicoloured (surch "NATAL FLOOD DISASTER")		45	70
	a. Pair. Nos. 629/30		90	1·40
630	16 c. + 10 c. multicoloured (surch as T 280)		45	70

Nos. 629/30 were surcharged together, *se-tenant*, in horizontal and vertical pairs throughout the sheet.
These stamps are known postmarked at Mooirivier on 25 November 1987.

282 Bartolomeu Dias and Cape of Good Hope	283 Huguenot Monument, Franschhoek

(Des Sheila Nowers. Litho)

1988 (3 Feb). *500th Anniv of Discovery of Cape of Good Hope by Bartolomeu Dias.* T **282** *and similar horiz designs. Multicoloured.* P 14.

631	16 c. Type 282..		55	10
632	30 c. Kwaaihoek Monument..		80	85
633	40 c. Caravels..		1·00	1·25
634	50 c. Martellus map, c. 1489..		1·50	2·00
631/4		*Set of 4*	3·50	3·75

The 50 c. value exists as a Philatelic Foundation miniature sheet.

1988 (1 Mar). *Natal Flood Relief Fund (3rd issue).* No. 631 surch as T **280**, *but larger (Afrikaans version 19 mm wide).*

635	16 c. + 10 c. multicoloured (surch as T 280)		45	70
	a. Pair. Nos. 635/6..		90	1·40
636	16 c. + 10 c. multicoloured (surch "NATAL FLOOD DISASTER")		45	70

Nos. 635/6 were surcharged together, *se-tenant*, in horizontal and vertical pairs throughout the sheet.

(Des H. Botha. Litho)

1988 (13 Apr). *300th Anniv of Arrival of First French Huguenots at the Cape.* T **283** *and similar vert designs. Multicoloured.* P 14.

637	16 c. Type 283..		30	10

638	30 c. Map of France showing Huguenot areas..		70	80
639	40 c. Title page of French/Dutch New Testament of 1672		80	1·25
640	50 c. St. Bartholomew's Day Massacre, Paris, 1572		1·00	1·50
637/40		*Set of 4*	2·50	3·25

(284)	285 Pelican Point Lighthouse, Walvis Bay

1988 (13 Apr). *National Flood Relief Fund.* Nos. 637/40 surch as T **284** *in English* (E) *or in Afrikaans* ("Nasionale Vloedramp") (A).

641	16 c. + 10 c. multicoloured (E)		40	65
	a. Pair. Nos. 641/2		80	1·25
642	16 c. + 10 c. multicoloured (A)		40	65
643	30 c. + 10 c. multicoloured (A)		55	75
	a. Pair. Nos. 643/4		1·10	1·50
644	30 c. + 10 c. multicoloured (E)		55	75
645	40 c. + 10 c. multicoloured (A)		70	90
	a. Pair. Nos. 645/6		1·40	1·75
646	40 c. + 10 c. multicoloured (E)		70	90
647	50 c. + 10 c. multicoloured (E)		90	1·25
	a. Pair. Nos. 647/8		1·75	2·50
648	50 c. + 10 c. multicoloured (A)		90	1·25
641/8		*Set of 8*	4·50	6·25

The two versions of each surcharge were printed together, *se-tenant*, both horizontally and vertically, throughout the sheets.

(Des Sheila Nowers. Litho)

1988 (9 June). *Lighthouses.* T **285** *and similar horiz designs. Multicoloured.* P 14.

649	16 c. Type 285		50	10
650	30 c. Green Point, Cape Town		70	70
651	40 c. Cape Agulhas		90	1·25
652	50 c. Umhlanga Rocks, Durban		1·25	1·75
649/52		*Set of 4*	3·00	3·50
MS653	132 × 112 mm. Nos. 649/52		4·00	3·75

286 *Huernia zebrina*	287 Map of Great Trek Routes

(Des H. Botha)

1988 (1 Sept)–**93**. *Succulents.* T **286** *and similar horiz designs. Multicoloured.*

(a) Sheet stamps. Litho. P 14

654	1 c. Type 286		10	10
	a. Coil strip. Nos. 654/7 and 662 (11.5.93)		50	
655	2 c. *Euphorbia symmetrica*		10	10
656	5 c. *Lithops dorotheae*		10	10
657	7 c. *Gibbaeum nebrownii*		15	10
658	10 c. *Didymaotus lapidiformis*		15	10
659	16 c. *Vanheerdea divergens*		60	10
659a	18 c. *Faucaria tigrina* (1.4.8		50	10
660	20 c. *Conophytum mundum*		60	10
660a	21 c. *Gasteria armstrongii* (2.4.90)		40	10
661	25 c. *Cheiridopsis peculiaris*		60	10
	a. Imperf (pair)		£180	
662	30 c. *Tavaresia barklyi*		60	20
663	35 c. *Dinteranthus witmotianus*		70	20
664	40 c. *Frithia pulchra*		70	25
665	50 c. *Lapidaria margaretae*		70	25
666	90 c. *Dioscorea elephantipes*		85	45
667	1 r. *Trichocaulon cactiforme*		75	50
668	2 r. *Crassula columnaris*		1·25	90
668a	5 r. *Anacampseros albissima* (1.3.90)		3·00	2·40
654/68a		*Set of 18*	10·50	5·25

(b) Coil stamps. Photo. P 14 × *imperf.*

669	1 c. *Adromischus marianiae*		1·00	1·50
670	2 c. *Titanopsis calcarea*		50	60
671	5 c. *Dactylopsis digitata*		50	60
672	10 c. *Pleiospilos bolusii*		55	70
669/72		*Set of 4*	2·25	3·00

Multi-value coil strip No. 654a was produced by the South African Post Office for use by a large direct mail marketing firm. Strips were also available from the Philatelic Service.

For similar design, but without face value and inscribed "Standardised mail" in English and Afrikaans, see No. 778.

(Des J. van Niekerk (16 c.). Litho)

1988 (21 Nov). *150th Anniv of Great Trek.* T **287** *and similar multicoloured designs.* P 14.

673	16 c. Type 287		60	10
674	30 c. "Exodus" (tapestry by W. Coetzer) (56 × 20 mm)		90	90
675	40 c. "Crossing the Drakensberg" (tapestry by W. Coetzer) (77 × 20 mm)		1·10	1·10
676	50 c. "After the Service, Church of the Vow" (J. H. Pierneef) (*horiz*)		1·40	1·75
673/6		*Set of 4*	3·50	3·50

288 Coelacanth   **289** Man-made Desert

(Des A. McBride. Litho)

1989 (9 Feb). *50th Anniv of Discovery of Coelacanth. T* **288** *and similar horiz designs. Multicoloured. P* 14.
677   16 c. Type **288** 75   15
678   30 c. Prof. J. L. B. Smith and Dr. M. Courtenay-Latimer examining Coelacanth .. .. 1·10 1·25
679   40 c. J. L. B. Smith Institute of Ichthyology, Grahamstown .. .. .. 1·40 1·60
680   50 c. Coelacanth and *GEO* midget submarine .. .. 1·50 2·25
677/80 .. .. *Set of* 4   4·25 4·75
The 50 c. value exists as a Philatelic Foundation miniature sheet and also as a corporate miniature sheet, containing two examples, sponsored by Two Oceans Environmental Trust. See note above No. 822.

(Des D. Murphy. Litho)

1989 (3 May). *National Grazing Strategy. T* **289** *and similar horiz designs. Multicoloured. P* 14.
681   18 c. Type **289** 40   15
682   30 c. Formation of erosion gully .. 65   75
683   40 c. Concrete barrage in gully .. 70 1·00
684   50 c. Reclaimed veldt .. .. 80 1·40
681/4 .. .. *Set of* 4   2·25 3·00

290 South Africa *v* France   **291** "Composition in Match, 1980   Blue"

(Des B. Jackson. Litho)

1989 (22 June). *Centenary of South African Rugby Board. T* **290** *and similar horiz designs. Multicoloured. P* 14.
685   18 c. Type **290** 60   15
686   30 c. South Africa *v* Australia, 1963 .. 95   90
687   40 c. South Africa *v* New Zealand, 1937 1·00 1·40
688   50 c. South Africa *v* British Isles, 1896 1·10 1·60
685/8 .. .. *Set of* 4   3·25 3·50

1989 (3 Aug). *Paintings by Jacob Hendrik Pierneef. T* **291** *and similar horiz designs. Litho. P* 14.
689   18 c. Type **291** 30   15
690   30 c. "Zanzibar" 50   60
691   40 c. "The Bushveld" 65   90
692   50 c. "Cape Homestead" .. .. 75 1·10
689/92 .. .. *Set of* 4   2·00 2·50
MS693   114×86 mm. Nos. 689/92 .. 2·00 2·50

292 Pres. F. W. de   **293** Gas-drilling Rig, Klerk   Mossel Bay

1989 (20 Sept). *Inauguration of President F. W. de Klerk. T* **292** *and similar vert design. Multicoloured. Litho. P* 14.
694   18 c. Type **292** 40   15
695   45 c. F. W. de Klerk (*different*) .. 70 1·10

(Des H. Botha. Litho)

1989 (19 Oct). *Energy Sources. T* **293** *and similar horiz designs. Multicoloured. P* 14×14½.
696   18 c. Type **293** 40   10
697   30 c. Coal to oil conversion plant .. 70   70
698   40 c. Nuclear power station 80   85
699   50 c. Thermal electric power station .. 90 1·25
396/9 .. .. *Set of* 4   2·50 2·50

294 Electric Goods Train and   **295** Great Britain Map of Railway Routes   1840 Penny Black

(Des A. H. Barrett. Litho)

1990 (15 Feb). *Co-operation in Southern Africa. T* **294** *and similar horiz designs. Multicoloured. P* 14½×14.
700   18 c. Cahora Bassa Hydro-electric Scheme, Mozambique, and map of transmission lines (68×26 *mm*) 50   25
701   30 c. Type **294** 70   70
702   40 c. Projected dam on upper Orange River, Lesotho and map of Highlands Water Project (68×26 *mm*) 85   90
703   50 c. Cow, syringe, and outline map of Africa 95 1·10
700/3 .. .. *Set of* 4   2·75 2·75
MS704   136×78 mm. Nos. 700/3 .. .. 2·75 2·75

1990 (12 May). *National Stamp Day. T* **295** *and similar vert designs showing stamps. Multicoloured. Litho. P* 14.
705   21 c. Type **295** 40   50
          a. Horiz strip of 5. Nos. 705/9 .. 1·75
706   21 c. Cape of Good Hope 1853 4d. triangular pair 40   50
707   21 c. Natal 1857 1s. 40   50
708   21 c. Orange Free State 1868 1s. .. 40   50
709   21 c. Transvaal 1869 1s. 40   50
705/9 .. .. *Set of* 5   1·75 2·25
Nos. 705/9 were printed together, *se-tenant*, in horizontal strips of 5 throughout the sheet.

296 Knysna   **297** Karoo Landscape Turaco   near Britstown

(Des C. Finch-Davies. Litho)

1990 (2 Aug). *Birds. T* **296** *and similar vert designs. Multicoloured. P* 14.
710   21 c. Type **296** 50   20
711   35 c. Red-capped Robin Chat .. 70   80
712   40 c. Rufous-naped Bush Lark .. 70   90
713   50 c. Bokmakierie Shrike .. .. 90 1·40
710/13 .. .. *Set of* 4   2·50 3·00
The 50 c. value exists as a Philatelic Foundation miniature sheet.

1990 (1 Nov). *Tourism. T* **297** *and similar horiz designs. Multicoloured. Litho. P* 14.
714   50 c. Type **297** .. .. 85 1·10
          a. Block of 4. Nos. 714/17 .. 3·00
715   50 c. Camps Bay, Cape of Good Hope .. 85 1·10
716   50 c. Giraffes in Kruger National Park .. 85 1·10
717   50 c. Boschendal Vineyard, Drakenstein Mts 85 1·10
714/17 .. .. *Set of* 4   3·00 4·00
Nos. 714/17 were printed together, *se-tenant*, in blocks of 4 throughout the sheet.

298 Woltemade   **299** Boer Horses Cross for Bravery

(Des J. Hoekstra. Litho)

1990 (6 Dec). *National Orders. T* **298** *and similar vert designs. Multicoloured. P* 14.
718   21 c. Type **298** 30   40
          a. Horiz strip of 5. Nos. 718/22 .. 1·40
719   21 c. Order of the Southern Cross .. 30   40
720   21 c. Order of the Star of South Africa .. 30   40
721   21 c. Order for Meritorious Service .. 30   40
722   21 c. Order of Good Hope 30   40
718/22 .. .. *Set of* 5   1·40 1·75
MS723   143×70 mm. Nos. 718/22 .. 1·40 1·75
Nos. 718/22 were printed together, *se-tenant*, in horizontal strips of 5 throughout the sheet.

(Des A. Ainslie. Litho)

1991 (12 Feb). *Animal Breeding in South Africa. T* **299** *and similar horiz designs. Multicoloured. P* 14.
724   21 c. Type **299** 50   60
          a. Horiz strip of 5. Nos. 724/8 .. 2·25
725   21 c. Bonsmara bull 50   60
726   21 c. Dorper sheep 50   60
727   21 c. Ridgeback dogs 50   60
728   21 c. Putterie racing pigeons .. 50   60
724/8 .. .. *Set of* 5   2·25 2·75
Nos. 724/8 were printed together, *se-tenant*, in horizontal strips of five throughout the sheet.

300 Diagram of   **301** State Human Heart and   Registration of Transplant   Nurses Act, 1891 Operation

(Des A. H. Barrett. Litho)

1991 (30 May). *30th Anniv of Republic. Scientific and Technological Achievements. T* **300** *and similar multicoloured designs. P* 14.
729   25 c. Type **300** 20   10
730   40 c. Matimba Power Station (*horiz*) .. 35   35
731   50 c. Dolos design breakwater (*horiz*) .. 45   45
732   60 c. Western Deep Levels gold mine .. 60   60
729/32 .. .. *Set of* 4   1·40 1·40
The 60 c. value exists as a Philatelic Foundation miniature sheet.

(Des T. Marais. Litho)

1991 (15 Aug). *Centenary of State Registration for Nurses and Midwives. P* 14.
733   **301**   60 c. multicoloured 60   60

302 South Africa   **303** Sir Arnold Theiler Post Office Ltd   (veterinarian) Emblem

(Des Liza van der Wal. Litho)

1991 (1 Oct). *Establishment of Post Office Ltd and Telekom Ltd. T* **302** *and similar horiz design. Multicoloured. P* 14×14½.
734   27 c. Type **302** 25   25
          a. Vert pair. Nos. 734/5 50   50
735   27 c. Telekom SA Ltd emblem .. 25   25
Nos. 734/5 were printed together, *se-tenant*, in vertical pairs throughout the sheet.

(Des A. H. Barrett. Litho)

1991 (9 Oct). *South African Scientists. T* **303** *and similar horiz designs. Multicoloured. P* 14.
736   27 c. Type **303** 30   15
737   45 c. Sir Basil Schonland (physicist) .. 60   60
738   65 c. Dr. Robert Broom (palaeontologist) .. 80   90
739   85 c. Dr. Alex du Toit (geologist) .. 1·00 1·75
736/9 .. .. *Set of* 4   2·40 3·00

304 *Agulhas* (Antarctic   **305** Soil Conservation research ship)

(Des Liza van der Wal (27 c.), T. Marais (65 c.). Litho)

1991 (5 Dec). *30th Anniv of Antarctic Treaty. T* **304** *and similar horiz design. Multicoloured. P* 14.
740   27 c. Type **304** 75   20
741   65 c. Chart showing South African National Antarctic Expedition base .. .. 1·25   80

(Des J. van Niekerk. Litho)

1992 (6 Feb). *Environmental Conservation. T* **305** *and similar horiz designs. Multicoloured. P* 14×14½.
742   27 c. Type **305** 35   15
743   65 c. Water pollution 85   65
744   85 c. Air pollution .. .. .. 1·10   85
742/4 .. .. *Set of* 3   2·10 1·50
The 65 c. value exists as a Philatelic Foundation miniature sheet.

306 Dutch Fleet   **307** Queen Anne approaching Table   Settee, *c* 1750 Bay

(Des J. van Niekerk. Litho)

1992 (9 May). *National Stamp Day. Cape of Good Hope Postal Stones. T 306 and similar horiz designs. Multicoloured. P 14.*
745	35 c. Type 306		45	35
	a. Horiz strip of 5. Nos. 745/9		2·00	
746	35 c. Landing for water and provisions		45	35
747	35 c. Discovering a postal stone		45	35
748	35 c. Leaving letters under a stone		45	35
749	35 c. Reading letters		45	35
745/9		*Set of 5*	2·00	1·60

Nos. 745/9 were printed together, *se-tenant*, in horizontal strips of 5 throughout the sheet

1992 (9 July). *Antique Cape Furniture. T 307 and similar multicoloured designs. Litho. P 14.*
750	35 c. Type 307		35	35
	a. Sheetlet. Nos. 750/9		3·25	
751	35 c. Stinkwood settee, c 1800		35	35
752	35 c. Canopy bed, c 1800 (vert)		35	35
753	35 c. 19th-century rocking cradle		35	35
754	35 c. Waterbutt, c 1800 (vert)		35	35
755	35 c. Flemish style cabinet, c 1700 (vert)		35	35
756	35 c. Armoire, c 1780 (vert)		35	35
757	35 c. Late 17th-century church chair (vert)		35	35
758	35 c. Tub chair, c 1770 (vert)		35	35
759	35 c. Bible desk, c 1750 (vert)		35	35
750/9		*Set of 10*	3·25	3·25

Nos. 750/9 were printed together, *se-tenant*, as a sheetlet of 10.

308 Grand Prix Motor Racing	309 "Women's Monument" (Van Wouw)

(Des Liza van der Wal (35 c. (No. 761)), C. Prinsloo (55 c.), B. Jackson (70 c., 1 r. 05). Litho)

1992 (24 July). *Sports. T 308 and similar horiz designs. Multicoloured. P 14×14½.*
760	35 c. Type 308		25	25
761	35 c. Football		25	25
762	55 c. Total Paris–Cape Motor Rally		35	35
763	70 c. Athletics		50	50
764	90 c. Rugby		65	65
765	1 r. 05, Cricket		1·00	1·00
760/5		*Set of 6*	2·75	2·75
MS766	167×69 mm. Nos. 760/5		3·25	3·00

1992 (8 Oct). *130th Birth Anniv of Anton van Wouw (sculptor). T 309 and similar vert designs. Multicoloured. Litho. P 14.*
767	35 c. Type 309		30	20
768	70 c. "Sekupu Player"		60	60
769	90 c. "The Hunter"		80	80
770	1 r. 05, "Postman Lehman"		85	100
767/70		*Set of 4*	2·25	2·40
MS771	96×149 mm. Nos. 767/70		2·25	2·40

310 Walvis Bay Harbour	311 Bristol "Boxkite", 1907

1993 (28 Jan). *South African Harbours. T 310 and similar horiz designs. Multicoloured. Litho. P 14.*
772	35 c. Type 310		30	20
773	55 c. East London		40	35
774	70 c. Port Elizabeth		60	50
775	90 c. Cape Town		80	75
776	1 r. 05, Durban		85	95
772/6		*Set of 5*	2·75	2·50
MS777	147×112 mm. Nos. 772/6		2·75	2·50

(Des H. Botha. Litho)

1993 (1 Apr). *Succulents. Design as T 286, but inscr "Standardised mail" in English and Afrikaans. P 14.*
778	(–) Stapelia grandiflora		50	25

No. 778 was sold at 45 c.

(Des D. Stahmer. Litho)

1993 (7 May). *Aviation in South Africa. T 311 and similar horiz designs. Multicoloured. P 14.*
779	45 c. Type 311		55	30
	a. Sheetlet. Nos. 779/803		12·00	
780	45 c. Voisin "Boxkite", 1909		55	30
781	45 c. Bleriot XI, 1911		55	30
782	45 c. Paterson No. 2 biplane, 1913		55	30
783	45 c. Henri Farman H.F.27, 1915		55	30
784	45 c. Royal Aircraft Factory B.E.2.E., 1918		55	30
785	45 c. Vickers Vimy Silver Queen II, 1920		55	30
786	45 c. Royal Aircraft Factory S.E.5A., 1921		55	30
787	45 c. Avro 504k, 1921		55	30
788	45 c. Armstrong Whitworth A.W.15 Atalanta, 1930		55	30
789	45 c. De Havilland D.H.66 Hercules, 1931		55	30
790	45 c. Westland Wapiti, 1931		55	30
791	45 c. Junkers F-13, 1932		55	30

792	45 c. Handley Page H.P.42, 1933		55	30
793	45 c. Junkers Ju 52/3m, 1934		55	30
794	45 c. Junkers Ju 86, 1936		55	30
795	45 c. Hawker Hartbees, 1936		55	30
796	45 c. Short S.23 Empire "C" Class flying boat Canopus, 1937		55	30
797	45 c. Miles Master II and Airspeed A.S.10 Oxford, 1940		55	30
798	45 c. North American AT-6 Harvard Mk IIa, 1942		55	30
799	45 c. Short S.25 Sunderland flying boat, 1945		55	30
800	45 c. Avro Type 685 York, 1946		55	30
801	45 c. Douglas DC-7B, 1955		55	30
802	45 c. Sikorsky S-55c helicopter, 1956		55	30
803	45 c. Boeing 707-344, 1959		55	30
779/803		*Set of 25*	12·00	6·50

Nos. 779/803 were printed together, *se-tenant*, in sheetlets of 25 (5×5).
Nos. 779 and 803 exist as a Philatelic Foundation miniature sheet.

312 Table Mountain Ghost Frog	313 Dragoons carrying Mail between Cape Town and False Bay, 1803

Two types of species inscr:
I. Species name in Latin.
II. Species name in English.

Two types of "Standardised mail" stamp (No. 821):
III. Small rhinoceros. Inscr "DICEROS BICORNIS".
IV. Redrawn with larger rhinoceros. Inscr "BLACK RHINOCEROS".

(Des D. Murphy. Litho)

1993 (3 Sept)–97. *Endangered Fauna. T 312 and similar horiz designs. Multicoloured. P 14. (a) Face values as T 312*
804	1 c. Type 312 (I)		10	10
	a. Coil strip. Nos. 804, 805×2 and 808×2 (15.4.94)		50	
	b. Coil. Imperf × p 14 (1.9.95)		20	20
	ba. Coil strip. Nos. 804b, 805b×2, 806b and 810b (50 c. stamp at right)		1·00	
	bb. Coil strip. As No. 804ba, but 50 c. stamp in centre (1.12.95)		1·00	
	c. Type II (coil. Imperf × p 14) (1.8.96)		20	20
	ca. Coil strip. Nos. 804c, 805c×2, 807c and 811c		1·10	
805	2 c. Smith's Dwarf Chameleon (I)		10	10
	b. Coil. Imperf × p 14 (1.9.95)		20	20
	c. Type II (coil. Imperf × p 14) (1.8.96)		20	20
806	5 c. Giant Girdle-tailed Lizard (I)		10	10
	a. Coil strip. Nos. 806/7, each × 2, and 808 (24.8.94)		50	
	b. Coil. Imperf × p 14 (2.95)		30	30
	ba. Coil strip. Nos. 806b×2, 807b×2 and 808b		1·40	
807	10 c. Geometric Tortoise (I)		10	10
	b. Coil. Imperf × p 14 (2.95)		30	30
	c. Type II (coil. Imperf × p 14) (1.8.96)		30	30
808	20 c. Southern African Hedgehog (I)		10	10
	b. Coil. Imperf × p 14 (2.95)		50	50
	c. Type II (25.6.97)		30	30
809	40 c. Riverine Rabbit (I)		20	10
	c. Type II (27.3.97)		10	10
810	50 c. Samango Monkey (I)		25	20
	b. Coil. Imperf × p 14 (1.9.95)		30	20
	c. Type II (1.7.97)		30	30
811	55 c. Aardwolf (I)		20	10
	c. Type II (coil. Imperf × p 14) (1.8.96)		30	30
812	60 c. Cape Hunting Dog (I)		40	20
813	70 c. Roan Antelope (I)		40	25
	c. Type II (19.5.97)		20	20
814	75 c. African Striped Weasel (I)		40	30
815	80 c. Kori Bustard (I)		40	25
815a	85 c. Lemon-breasted Seedeater (I) (2.10.95)		50	25
816	90 c. Jackass Penguin (I)		70	30
	a. Booklet pane. No. 816×10 with outer edges of pane imperf (1.12.95)		3·50	
	c. Type II (18.6.97)		40	30
817	1 r. Wattled Crane (I)		60	30
	c. Type II (8.8.96)		60	30
818	2 r. Blue Swallow (I)		80	55
	c. Type II (23.7.97)		70	55
819	5 r. Martial Eagle (I)		1·75	1·40
	c. Type II (18.6.97)		1·25	1·40
820	10 r. Bateleur (I)		2·00	2·10
804/20		*Set of 18*	6·50	5·50

(b) *Inscr "Standardised mail" in English and Afrikaans (No. 821) or "Airmail postcard rate" (others)*
821	(45 c.) Black Rhinoceros (III)		30	25
	a. Booklet pane. No. 821×10 with outer edges of pane imperf (14.2.95)		3·00	
	b. Type IV (9.4.96)		30	25
	ba. Booklet pane. No. 821b×10 with outer edges of pane imperf		3·00	
821c	(1 r.) White Rhinoceros (II) (8.5.96)		35	30
	a. Horiz strip of 5. Nos. 821c/g		1·50	
	cb. Pane. Nos. 821c/g plus 3 advertising and 2 airmail labels with margins all round		2·50	
	cc. Booklet pane. Nos. 821c/g plus 5 airmail labels with outer edges of pane imperf		2·50	
	cd. Booklet pane. Nos. 821c/g plus 5 Thulamela labels with outer edges of pane imperf (27.7.97)		2·50	
821d	(1 r.) Buffalo (II) (8.5.96)		35	30
821e	(1 r.) Lion (II) (8.5.96)		35	30

821f	(1 r.) Leopard (II) (8.5.96)		35	30
821g	(1 r.) African Elephant (II) (8.5.96)		35	30
821c/g		*Set of 6*	1·75	1·60

Multi-value coil strips Nos. 804a, 804ba/bb, 804ca, 806a and 806ba were produced by the South African Post Office for use by Reader's Digest. Strips were also available from the Philatelic Service and philatelic counters.

Nos. 804ba/bb and 804ca each include a label showing the Reader's Digest emblem at left. In each instance the righthand stamp (50 c. on No. 804ba, 5 c. on No. 804bb and 55 c. on No. 804ca) is imperforate on three sides.

No. 804ba originally had a black label, but was re-issued with a red label on 1 December 1995. No. 804bb had a blue label and No. 804ca a green one, but this was re-issued with an orange label on 11 November 1996.

No. 806ba occurs with both the left and righthand stamps (5 c. and 20 c.), or just the righthand stamp, imperforate on three sides.

No. 821 was initially sold at 45 c. and No. 821b was only issued in stamp booklets, initially sold at 6 r. The "Standardised mail" rate was increased to 50 c. in August 1994, 60 c. in April 1996, 70 c. in August 1996, 1 r. on 7 April 1997 and to 1 r. 10 on 14 April 1998.

Nos. 821c/g, which were each initially sold at 1 r., were printed together, *se-tenant*, in sheets of 10 containing two horizontal strips of 5.

No. 821b exists as a corporate miniature sheet sponsored by MILSET and commemorating the "ESI '97" Exhibition at Pretoria.

No. 821e exists as a corporate miniature sheet sponsored by Coach House.

For stamps with elliptical perforations see Nos. 913/18 and for redrawn designs without frame and inscribed "South Africa" only see Nos. 1013/44.

CORPORATE MINIATURE SHEETS. Such miniature sheets were introduced in 1996 and were produced for firms or other corporate bodies to use for advertising and publicity purposes. Each sponsor has to agree to purchase a minimun of 10,000 sheets with further supplies being placed on sale, at face value, by the South Africa Philatelic Bureau, philatelic counters and overseas agents.

(Des J. van Niekerk. Litho)

1993 (8 Oct). *National Stamp Day. Early 19th-century Postal Services. T 313 and similar horiz designs. Multicoloured. P 14.*
822	45 c. Type 313		30	25
823	65 c. Ox wagon carrying Stellenbosch to Cape Town mail, 1803		45	50
824	85 c. Khoi-Khoin mail runners from Stellenbosch, 1803		65	70
825	1 r. 05, Mounted postmen, 1804		80	90
822/5		*Set of 4*	2·00	2·10

314 Flowers from Namaqualand

1993 (12 Nov). *Tourism. T 314 and similar horiz designs. Multicoloured. Litho. P 14.*
826	85 c. Type 314 (Afrikaans inscr)		65	55
	a. Horiz strip of 5. Nos. 826/30		3·00	
827	85 c. North Beach, Durban (English inscr)		65	55
828	85 c. Lion (German inscr)		65	55
829	85 c. "Appel Express" on Van Staden's Bridge (Dutch inscr)		65	55
830	85 c. Gemsbok (antelope) (French inscr)		65	55
826/30		*Set of 5*	3·00	2·40

Nos. 826/30 were printed together, *se-tenant*, in horizontal strips of 5 throughout the sheet.

315 Grapes and Packing Bench

(Des B. Jackson. Litho)

1994 (28 Jan). *Export Fruits. T 315 and similar horiz designs. Multicoloured. P 14½×14.*
831	85 c. Type 315		55	50
832	90 c. Apple and picker		55	50
833	1 r. 05, Plum and fork-lift truck		65	60
834	1 r. 25, Orange and tractor with trailer		75	70
835	1 r. 40, Avocado and loading freighter		85	80
831/5		*Set of 5*	3·00	2·75

The 85 c. value exists as a Philatelic Foundation miniature sheet.

OMNIBUS ISSUES

Details, together with prices for complete sets, of the various Omnibus issues from the 1935 Silver Jubilee series to date are included in a special section following Zimbabwe at the end of Volume 2.

316 "Children of Different Races" **317** Pres. Mandela
(Nicole Davies)

1994 (8 Apr). *Peace Campaign. Children's Paintings. T* 316 *and similar horiz designs. Multicoloured. Litho. P* 14½×14.
836	45 c. Type **316**			25	20
837	70 c. "Dove and Tree" (Robynne Lawrie)			40	40
838	95 c. "Children and Dove" (Batami Nothmann)			55	55
839	1 r. 15, "Multi-racial Crowd" (Karen Uys)			75	80
836/9			*Set of* 4	1·75	1·75

No. 839 exists as a corporate miniature sheet sponsored by I.G.P.C. and commemorating Chernobyl's Children charities.

(Des Liza van der Wal (70 c., 95c.). Litho)

1994 (10 May). *Inauguration of President Nelson Mandela. T* 317 *and similar multicoloured designs. P* 14×14½ (45 c.) *or* 14½×14 (*others*).
840	45 c. Type **317**			45	20
841	70 c. South African national anthems			70	60
842	95 c. New national flag			90	90
843	1 r. 15, Union Buildings, Pretoria			1·25	1·40
840/3			*Set of* 4	3·00	2·75

318 Tug *T. S. McEwen* towing
Winchester Castle (liner), 1935

(Des Sheila Nowers. Litho)

1994 (13 May). *Tugboats. T* 318 *and similar horiz designs. Multicoloured. P* 14½×14.
844	45 c. Type **318**			30	20
845	70 c. *Sir William Hoy* with *Karanja* (liner), 1970			50	40
846	95 c. *Sir Charles Elliott* and wreck of *Dunedin Star* (liner), 1942			65	55
847	1 r. 15, *Eland* and freighter at wharf, 1955			85	75
848	1 r. 35, *Pioneer* (paddle tug) and sailing ships, 1870			95	90
844/8			*Set of* 5	2·75	2·50
MS849	163×84 mm. Nos. 844/8			2·75	2·50

**COMMONWEALTH MEMBER
1 JUNE 1994**

319 "Mother hands out Work" (Emile du Toit)

1994 (1 July). *International Year of the Family. Children's Paintings. T* 319 *and similar horiz designs. Multicoloured. Litho. P* 14.
850	45 c. Type **319**			35	30
	a. Vert strip of 5. Nos. 850/4			1·60	
851	45 c. "My Friends and I at Play" (Patrick Mackenzie)			35	30
852	45 c. "Family Life" (Michelle du Pisani)			35	30
853	45 c. "Sunday in Church" (Elizabeth Nel)			35	30
854	45 c. "I visit my Brother in Hospital" (Zwelinzema Sam)			35	30
850/4			*Set of* 5	1·60	1·25

Nos. 850/4 were printed together, *se-tenant*, in vertical strips of 5 throughout the sheet.

320 Hands holding Invoice and Bulk
Mail Envelope

(Des J. van Niekerk. Litho)

1994 (30 Sept). *National Stamp Day. T* 320 *and similar horiz designs. Multicoloured. P* 14.
855	50 c. Type **320**			30	25
856	70 c. Certified mail			40	40
857	95 c. Registered mail			50	55
858	1 r. 15, Express Delivery mail			60	65
855/8			*Set of* 4	1·60	1·75

321 *Erica tenuifolia*

(Des J. van Niekerk. Litho)

1994 (18 Nov). *Heathers. T* 321 *and similar vert designs. Multicoloured. P* 14.
859	95 c. Type **321**			65	65
	a. Horiz strip of 5. Nos. 859/63			3·00	
860	95 c. *Erica urna-viridis*			65	65
861	95 c. *Erica decora*			65	65
862	95 c. *Erica aristata*			65	65
863	95 c. *Erica dichrus*			65	65
859/63			*Set of* 5	3·00	3·00

Nos. 859/63 were printed together, *se-tenant*, in horizontal strips of 5 throughout the sheet.

322 Warthogs (Eastern Transvaal) and Map

(Des A. Ainslie. Litho)

1995 (18 Jan–30 June). *Tourism. T* 322 *and similar horiz designs, each including map. Multicoloured. P* 14½×14. (*a*) *Face values as T* 322
864	50 c. Type **322**			50	25
865	50 c. Lost City Resort (North-West Province) (15 Feb)			50	25

(*b*) *Inscr* "Standardised mail" *in English and Afrikaans*
866	(60 c.) White Rhinoceros and calf (Kwazulu/ Natal) (28 April)			50	25
867	(60 c.) Cape Town waterfront (Western Cape) (12 May)			50	25
868	(60 c.) Baobab tree (Northern Transvaal) (30 June)			50	50
	a. Vert strip of 5. Nos. 868/72			2·25	
869	(60 c.) Highland Route (Free State) (30 June)			50	50
870	(60 c.) Augrabies Falls (Northern Cape) (30 June)			50	50
871	(60 c.) Herd of elephants, Addo National Park (Eastern Cape) (30 June)			50	50
872	(60 c.) Union Buildings, Pretoria (Gauteng) (30 June)			50	50
864/72			*Set of* 9	4·00	3·25

Nos. 868/72 were printed together, *se-tenant*, in sheets of 10 containing two vertical *se-tenant* strips of 5.

No. 864 exists as a Philatelic Foundation miniature sheet.

No. 868 exists imperforate on three sides with a *se-tenant* stamp-size label as a corporate product sponsored by Coach House. The same value subsequently appeared as a corporate miniature sheet.

323 De Havilland D.H.9 Biplane and
Cheetah D Jet Fighter

(Des Anne de Goede (50 c.), A. H. Barrett (95 c.). Litho)

1995 (1 Feb). *Aviation Anniversaries. T* 323 *and similar horiz design. Multicoloured. P* 14.
873	50 c. Type **323** (75th anniv of South African Air Force)			55	30
874	95 c. Vickers Vimy *Silver Queen II* (75th anniv of first Trans-African flight)			70	75

---

324 Player running with **325** Rural Water
Ball and Silhouettes   Purification System

1995 (25 May). *World Cup Rugby Championship, South Africa. T* 324 *and similar multicoloured designs. Litho. P* 14.
875	(60 c.) Type **324**			30	25
	a. Perf 14×imperf (booklets)			35	35
	ab. Booklet pane. Nos. 875a/6a, each × 5			3·25	
876	(60 c.) Player running with ball and silhouettes (*vert*)			30	25
	a. Imperf × perf 14 (booklets)			35	35
	ab. Booklet pane. No. 876a×10			3·25	
877	1 r. 15, Player taking ball from scrum (68×26½ mm)			75	85
875/7			*Set of* 3	1·25	1·25
MS878	109×61 mm. No. 876			45	50

Nos. 875/6 are inscribed "STANDARD POSTAGE" in English and Afrikaans.

(Des J. van Niekerk. Litho)

1995 (15 June). *50th Anniv of C.S.I.R. (technological research organization). P* 14.
879	**325** (60 c.) multicoloured			45	45

No. 879 in inscribed "Standardised mail" in English and Afrikaans.

326 Player with Ball   **327** Dr. John Gilchrist,
South African Pilchards
and *Africana* (oceano-
graphic research ship)

1995 (28 June). *South Africa's Victory in Rugby World Cup. T* 326 *and similar multicoloured design. Litho. P* 14.
880	(60 c.) Type **326**			40	40
881	(60 c.) South African player holding trophy aloft (*vert*)			40	40

Nos. 880/1 are inscribed "STANDARD POSTAGE" in English and Afrikaans.

(Des D. Thorpe. Litho)

1995 (25 Aug). *Centenary of Marine Science in South Africa. P* 14.
882	**327** (60 c.) multicoloured			30	30

No. 882 is inscribed "Standard Postage" in English and Afrikaans.

328 Singapore Lion   **329** People building Flag
Wall

(Des A. Ainslie. Litho)

1995 (1 Sept). *"Singapore '95" International Stamp Exhibition. Sheet* 71×55 *mm. P* 14.
MS883	**328** (60 c.) multicoloured			75	90

No. MS883 is inscribed "STANDARD POSTAGE" in English and Afrikaans.

A second printing of No. MS883 included the date, "DEC 1995", on the sheet margin at bottom left.

1995 (16 Sept–1 Dec). *Masakhane Campaign. Litho. P* 14.
884	**329** (60 c.) multicoloured (34×24 *mm*)			20	20
	a. Booklet pane. No. 884×10			2·00	
884*b*	(60 c.) mult (26×20 *mm*) (1 Dec)			20	20
	ba. Booklet pane. No. 884*b*×10			2·00	

Nos. 884 and 884*b* are inscribed "STANDARD POSTAGE" in English and Afrikaans.

No. 884*b* was only issued in 6 r. stamp booklets.

Nos. 884a and 884ba show the three outer edges of the panes imperforate.

ALTERED CATALOGUE NUMBERS

Any Catalogue numbers altered from the last edition are shown as a list in the introductory pages.

330 Papal Arms   331 Gandhi wearing Suit

1995 (16 Sept). *Visit of Pope John Paul II. Litho. P 14.*
885 330 (60 c.) multicoloured 40 30
No. 885 is inscribed "STANDARD POSTAGE" in English and Afrikaans.

(Des A. Ainslie. Litho)

1995 (2 Oct). *India–South Africa Co-operation. 125th Birth Anniv of Mahatma Gandhi (1994). T* **331** *and similar vert design. P 14.*
886 (60 c.) deep violet 50 25
887 1 r. 40, bistre-brown 75 85
MS888 71×71 mm. No. 887 .. .. 1·00 1·10
Design:—1 r. 40, Gandhi wearing dhoti.
No. 886 is inscribed "STANDARD POSTAGE" in English and Afrikaans.
Stamps in similar designs were issued by India.
No. 886 exists as a corporate miniature sheet sponsored by Pradip Jain and commemorating the 50th anniversary of the Congress Alliance for a Democratic South Africa.

332 Traditional African Postman   333 "50" and U.N. Emblem

(Des C. Emslie. Litho.)

1995 (9 Oct). *World Post Day. P 14.*
889 332 (60 c.) multicoloured 30 30
No. 889 is inscribed "STANDARD POSTAGE" in English and Afrikaans.
No. 889 exists as a corporate miniature sheet sponsored by the South African Stamp Colour Catalogue.

(Des C. Emslie. Litho.)

1995 (19 Oct). *"Total Stampex '95" and "Ilsapex '98" Stamp Exhibitions. Sheet, 70×66 mm, containing T* **332** *and "ILSAPEX '98" logo. Imperf.*
MS890 5 r. multicoloured .. .. 2·00 2·25

(Des C. Emslie (No. 891), A. Ainslie and F. Frescura (No. MS892). Litho)

1995 (24 Oct). *50th Annivs of United Nations and U.N.E.S.C.O. T* **333** *and similar multicoloured design. P 14.*
891 (60 c.) Type 333 .. .. .. 30 30
MS892 101×78 mm. (60 c.) Traditional village (30×47 mm) 30 30
Nos. 891/2 are inscribed "STANDARD POSTAGE" in English and Afrikaans.

334 *Afrivoluta pringlei*   335 Map of Africa and Player   336 South African Player, Map and Trophy

(Des L. Kriedemann. Litho)

1995 (24 Nov). *Sea Shells. T* **334** *and similar vert designs. Multicoloured. P 14½×14.*
893 (60 c.) Type 334 .. .. 35 35
    a. Horiz strip of 5. Nos. 893/7 .. 1·60
894 (60 c.) *Lyria africana* 35 35
895 (60 c.) *Marginella mosaica* .. 35 35
896 (60 c.) *Conus pictus* 35 35
897 (60 c.) *Gypreaea fultoni* .. 35 35
893/7 *Set of 5* 1·60 1·60
Nos. 893/7 were printed together, *se-tenant*, as horizontal strips of 5 in sheets of 10, each stamp being inscribed "STANDARD POSTAGE" in English and Afrikaans.
No. 893 is inscribed "priglei" in error.

(Des M. de Jong (Nos. 898/902), Z. Mashinini (No. **MS903**). Litho)

1996 (10 Jan). *African Nations Football Championship, South Africa. T* **335** *and similar vert designs showing map and players. P 14½×14.*
898 335 (60 c.) multicoloured ("RSA" in deep ultramarine) 45 45
    a. Horiz strip of 5. Nos. 898/902 .. 2·00
899 – (60 c.) multicoloured ("RSA" in brown-ochre) 45 45
900 – (60 c.) multicoloured ("RSA" in brt scar) 45 45
901 – (60 c.) multicoloured ("RSA" in ol-grey) 45 45
902 – (60 c.) multicoloured ("RSA" in dp emer) 45 45
898/902 *Set of 5* 2·00 2·00
MS903 75×55 mm. (60 c.) mult (young player) 50 60
Nos. 898/902 were printed together, *se-tenant*, as horizontal strips of 5 in sheets of 10.
Nos. 898/903 are inscribed "STANDARD POSTAGE" in English and Afrikaans.

(Des M. de Jong. Litho)

1996 (8 Feb). *South Africa's Victory in African Nations Football Championship. P 14.*
904 336 (60 c.) multicoloured 40 30
    a. Football missing above date at bottom right (R. 1/2) .. 4·50
No. 904 is inscribed "STANDARD POSTAGE" in English and Afrikaans.
It is understood that No. 904a occurs on every tenth sheet.

337 Historical Buildings, Bloemfontein   338 Rat

(Des J. van Beukering. Litho)

1996 (28 Mar). *150th Anniv of City of Bloemfontein. P 14.*
905 337 (60 c.) multicoloured 40 20
No. 905 is inscribed "Standard Postage" in English and Afrikaans.

(Des D. Murphy. Litho)

1996 (18 May). *"CHINA '96" 9th Asian International Stamp Exhibition, Peking. Sheet 109×85 mm. P 14.*
MS906 338 60 c. multicoloured 50 50

339 "Man in a Donkey Cart" (Gerard Sekoto)

1996 (1 June). *Gerard Sekoto (artist) Commemoration. T* **339** *and similar multicoloured designs. Litho. P 14.*
907 1 r. Type 339 .. .. 30 30
908 2 r. "Song of the Pick" 80 80
MS909 108×70 mm. 2 r. "Yellow Houses, Sophiatown" (detail) (*vert*) .. .. 1·00 1·10

340 Parliament Building, Cape Town   341 Children playing

(Des A. Ainslie. Litho)

1996 (8 June). *"CAPEX '96" International Stamp Exhibition, Toronto. Sheet 72×49 mm. P 14.*
MS910 340 2 r. multicoloured .. .. 1·00 1·10

1996 (8 June). *Youth Day. Litho. P 14.*
911 341 (60 c.) multicoloured 30 20
No. 911 is inscribed "STANDARD POSTAGE" in English and Afrikaans.

342 Marathon Runners

(Des M. de Jong. Litho)

1996 (8 June). *75th Anniv of Comrades Marathon. P 14.*
912 342 (60 c.) multicoloured 30 20
No. 912 is inscribed "Standard postage" in English and Afrikaans.

(Des D. Murphy. Litho)

1996 (1 July)–**97**. *Endangered Fauna. As Nos. 808c, 810c, 812 (but with English inscr), 817c, 821b and new value (20 r.) but P 14½ (20 r.) or 14 (others), each with two elliptical holes on horizontal sides. (a) Face values as T* **312**
913 20 c. Southern African Hedgehog (II) (28.5.97) 10 10
914 50 c. Samango Monkey (II) (1.7.97) 10 10
915 60 c. Cape Hunting Dog (II) (12.5.97) 10 10
916 1 r. Wattled Crane (II) (11.6.97) .. 20 25
917 20 r. Fish Eagle (II) (34×24 mm) (20.3.97) 4·00 4·25
(b) Inscr. "Standardised mail" in English and Afrikaans
918 (60 c.) Black Rhinoceros (IV) .. 30 30
913/18 *Set of 6* 4·50 4·75
The "Standardised mail" rate was increased to 70 c. in August 1996, to 1 r. on 7 April 1997 and to 1 r. 10 on 14 April 1998. The printing of No. 918 issued on 1 July 1996 was shared between the Government Printer and Cape & Transvaal Printers.

343 Cycling   344 Constitutional Assembly Logo

(Des M. de Jong. Litho)

1996 (5 July). *Olympic Games, Atlanta. T* **343** *and similar vert designs. Multicoloured. P 14.*
919 (70 c.) Type 343 .. .. 30 30
    a. Horiz strip of 5. Nos. 919/23 .. 1·25
920 (70 c.) Swimming 30 30
921 (70 c.) Boxing .. .. ·30 30
922 (70 c.) Running 30 30
923 (70 c.) Pole vaulting 30 30
924 1 r. 40, South African Olympic emblem 55 55
919/24 *Set of 6* 1·90 1·90
Nos. 919/23, which are inscribed "STANDARD POSTAGE" in English and Afrikaans, were printed together in sheets of 10 containing two *se-tenant* horizontal strips of 5.

(Des M. de Jong. Litho)

1996 (1 Aug). *New Democratic Constitution. P 14.*
925 344 (70 c.) myrtle-green, orange-red & blk 30 30
    a. Horiz strip of 5. Nos. 925/9 .. 1·25
926 (70 c.) brt turquoise-blue, dp vio, & blk 30 30
927 (70 c.) dp violet, orange-yellow & black 30 30
928 (70 c.) ultramarine, scarlet and black 30 30
929 (70 c.) scarlet, orange-yellow and black 30 30
925/9 *Set of 5* 1·25 1·25
Nos. 925/9 are inscribed "Standard Postage" in English and Afrikaans and were printed together, *se-tenant*, in horizontal strips of 5 throughout the sheet.

345 Sea Pioneer (bulk carrier)   346 "Xhosa Woman" (G. Pemba)

(Des E. Wale (No. 927), P. Bilas (others). Litho)

1996 (5 Aug). *50th Anniv of South African Merchant Marine. T* **345** *and similar horiz designs. Multicoloured. P 14.*
930 (70 c.) Type 345 .. .. 40 40
    a. Horiz pair. Nos. 930/1 .. 80 80
931 (70 c.) Winterberg (container ship) .. 40 40
932 1 r. 40, Langkloof (freighter) .. 80 80
    a. Horiz pair. Nos. 932/3 .. 1·60 1·60
933 1 r. 40, Vaal (liner) 80 80
930/3 *Set of 4* 2·25 2·25
MS934 102×63 mm. 2 r. Constantia (freighter) and tug (71×30 mm) (inscr "SOUTH AFRICAN MERCHANT MARINE 1946–1996" on top margin) 95 95
Nos. 930/1 are inscribed "Standard Postage" in English and Afrikaans.
Nos. 930/1 and 932/3 were printed together, *se-tenant*, in horizontal pairs throughout the sheets.
No. 931 exists as a corporate miniature sheet sponsored by Safmarine. No. MS934 also comes with the top margin inscription replaced by "Safmarine" and logo.

1996 (9 Aug). *National Women's Day. Litho. P 14.*
935 346 70 c. multicoloured 30 25

347 Postman delivering   348 Candles
Letters   and Holly

(Des J. van Niekerk. Litho)

1996 (9 Oct). World Post Day. P 14.
.36 347   70 c. multicoloured 30   25

(Des A. Ainslie. Litho)

1996 (9 Oct). Christmas. P 14.
.37 348   70 c. multicoloured 30   25
    a. Booklet pane. No. 937×10   3·00
No. 937a has the three outer edges of the pane imperforate.
No. 937 exists as a corporate miniature sheet sponsored by
ANTA and sold at 2 r. for charitable purposes.

349 "Liner Oranje at Cape Town" (E. Wale)

1996 (9 Oct). "Bloemfontein 150" National Stamp Show. Sheet
86×56 mm. Litho. P 14.
MS938 349   2 r. multicoloured .. .. .. 1·25   1·25

350 Max Theiler   351 Early Motor Car
(Medicine, 1951)

1996 (4 Nov). South African Nobel Laureates. T 350 and
similar vert designs. Litho. P 14.
939   (70 c.) dull violet and maroon 30   30
    a. Sheetlet. Nos. 939/48 2·75
940   (70 c.) dp bluish green, maroon & dull violet 30   30
941   (70 c.) maroon and dull violet 30   30
942   (70 c.) dp bluish green, maroon & dull violet 30   30
943   (70 c.) dull violet and maroon 30   30
944   (70 c.) dull violet and maroon 30   30
945   (70 c.) dp bluish green, maroon & dull violet 30   30
946   (70 c.) maroon and dull violet 30   30
947   (70 c.) dp bluish green, maroon & dull violet 30   30
948   (70 c.) dull violet and maroon 30   30
939/48   Set of 10 2·75   2·75
Designs—No. 939, Type 350; No. 940, Albert Luthuli (Peace,
1961); No. 941, Alfred Nobel; No. 942, Allan Cormack
(Medicine, 1979); No. 943, Aaron Klug (Chemistry, 1982); No.
944, Desmond Tutu (Peace, 1984); No. 945, Nadine Gordimer
(Literature, 1991); No. 946, Nobel Prizes symbol; No. 947,
Nelson Mandela (Peace, 1993); No. 948, F. W. de Klerk (Peace,
1993).
No. 939/48, which are inscribed "Standard Postage" in
English and Afrikaans, were printed together, se-tenant, in
sheets of 10.
No. 941 exists as a corporate miniature sheet sponsored by
AECI and celebrating the centenary of Modderfontein
Industrial Complex.

(Des D. Bagnall. Litho)

1997 (4 Jan). Centenary of Motoring in South Africa. P 14.
.349 351 (70 c.) multicoloured 40   25
No. 949 is inscribed "STANDARD POSTAGE" in English and
Afrikaans.
No. 949 exists as a corporate miniature sheet sponsored by
Total.

352 Lion   353 Vegetables and
              Water Pump

(Des A. Ainslie. Litho)

1997 (12 Feb). "Hong Kong '97" International Stamp
Exhibition. Sheet 82×68 mm. P 14 (with two elliptical holes on
each vertical side).
MS950 352   3 r. ultramarine, gold and rosine .. 1·10   1·10

(Des D. Murphy. Litho)

1997 (25 Mar). National Water Conservation. T 353 and
similar horiz designs. Multicoloured. P 14 (with two elliptical
holes at top or bottom).
951   (70 c.) Type 353 40   40
    a. Booklet pane. Nos. 951/5, each × 2   3·25
    b. Perf 14 (without elliptical holes) .. 40   40
    ba. Booklet pane. Nos. 951b/5b, each × 2   3·25
952   (70 c.) Flowers and watering can .. 40   40
    b. Perf 14 (without elliptical holes) .. 40   40
953   (70 c.) Child in bath 40   40
    b. Perf 14 (without elliptical holes) .. 40   40
954   (70 c.) Building tools 40   40
    b. Perf 14 (without elliptical holes) .. 40   40
955   (70 c.) Water cart and stand pipe .. 40   40
    b. Perf 14 (without elliptical holes) .. 40   40
951/5   Set of 5 1·75   1·75
Nos. 951/5 and 951b/5b are inscribed "STANDARD
POSTAGE" and were sold in 7 r. stamp booklets containing Nos.
951a or 951ba.
Both booklet panes are imperforate on the three outer edges.
On No. 951a the elliptical holes only occur on the horizontal line
of perforations separating the two rows of stamps. Like many
other modern South African booklet panes Nos. 951a and 951ba
were available to collectors as uncut booklet sheets.

354 S.A.S. Umkomaas   355 Election Day
(minesweeper)   Poster

(Des Sheila Nowers. Litho)

1997 (1 Apr). 75th Anniv of South African Navy. T 354 and
similar horiz designs. Multicoloured. P 14 (with two elliptical
holes on each vertical side).
956   (70 c.) Type 354 40   40
    a. Block of 4. Nos. 956/9 .. 1·40
957   (70 c.) S.A.S. Emily Hobhouse (submarine)
       and S.A.S. President Steyn (frigate) 40   40
958   (70 c.) S.A.S. Kobie Coetsee (fast attack
       craft) 40   40
959   (70 c.) S.A.S. Protea (hydrographic survey
       ship) 40   40
956/9   Set of 4 1·40   1·40
Nos. 956/9, which are inscribed "Standard Postage" in English
and Afrikaans, were printed together, se-tenant, in blocks of 4
throughout the sheet.

(Des M. Maapola. Litho)

1997 (27 Apr). Freedom Day. T 355 and similar vert designs.
Each black and red. P 14 (with two elliptical holes on each
vertical side).
960   (1 r.) Type 355 40   40
    a. Horiz strip of 5. Nos. 960/4 .. 1·75
961   (1 r.) People queueing 40   40
962   (1 r.) People registering 40   40
963   (1 r.) Voting booth 40   40
964   (1 r.) Woman placing vote in ballot box 40   40
960/4   Set of 5 1·75   1·75
Nos. 960/4, which are inscribed "STANDARD POSTAGE",
were printed together, se-tenant, in horizontal strips of five
throughout the sheet forming a composite design.

356 Brahman Bull   357 Zulu Baskets

(Des Leigh Voigt. Litho)

1997 (2 May). Chinese New Year ("Year of the Ox"). "SAPDA
'97" Stamp Exhibition, Johannesburg. Sheet 107×61 mm.
P 14.
MS965 356   4 r. 50, multicoloured .. .. 1·00   1·00

(Des D. Murphy. Litho Govt Printer (Nos. 966/75) or Questa
(Nos. 966b/75b))

1997 (17 May–8 Dec). Year of Cultural Experiences. T 357 and
similar vert designs. Multicoloured. P 14.
966   (1 r.) Type 357 40   40
    a. Sheetlet. Nos. 966/75 3·50
    b. Perf 14×15 (8 Dec) .. 40   40
    ba. Booklet pane. Nos. 966b/75b 3·50
967   (1 r.) Southern Sotho figure .. 40   40
    b. Perf 14×15 (8 Dec) .. 40   40
968   (1 r.) South Ndebele figure .. 40   40
    b. Perf 14×15 (8 Dec) .. 40   40

969   (1 r.) Venda door 40   40
    b. Perf 14×15 (8 Dec) .. 40   40
970   (1 r.) Tsonga medicine gourd .. 40   40
    b. Perf 14×15 (8 Dec) .. 40   40
971   (1 r.) Wooden pot, Northern Cape .. 40   40
    b. Perf 14×15 (8 Dec) .. 40   40
972   (1 r.) Khoi walking stick 40   40
    b. Perf 14×15 (8 Dec) .. 40   40
973   (1 r.) Tswana knife handle .. 40   40
    b. Perf 14×15 (8 Dec) .. 40   40
974   (1 r.) Xhosa pipe 40   40
    b. Perf 14×15 (8 Dec) .. 40   40
975   (1 r.) Swazi vessel 40   40
966/75   Set of 10 3·50   3·50
Nos. 966/75, which are inscribed "Standard Postage", were
printed together, se-tenant, in sheetlets of 10 with illustrated
left-hand margin.
The stamps printed by Questa, Nos. 966b/75b, show some
designs redrawn and were only issued in 20 r. stamp booklets.

358 Grocott's, Muirhead   359 White-breasted
and Gowie Buildings,   Cormorant
Grahamstown

(Des A. Ainslie. Litho)

1997 (29 May). "Pacific '97" International Stamp Exhibition,
San Francisco. Sheet 94×49 mm. P 14.
MS976 358   5 r. multicoloured .. .. 1·25   1·25

(Des Julia Birkhead and D. Murphy. Litho Govt Printer (Nos.
977/86) or Questa (Nos. 977b/86b))

1997 (5 June–8 Dec). World Environment Day. Waterbirds.
T 359 and similar vert designs. Multicoloured. P 14.
977   (1 r.) Type 359 40   40
    a. Sheetlet. Nos. 977/86 3·50
    b. Perf 14×15 (8 Dec) .. 40   40
    ba. Booklet pane. Nos. 977b/86b 3·50
978   (1 r.) Hamerkop 40   40
    b. Perf 14×15 (8 Dec) .. 40   40
979   (1 r.) Pied Kingfisher .. 40   40
    b. Perf 14×15 (8 Dec) .. 40   40
980   (1 r.) Purple Heron .. 40   40
    b. Perf 14×15 (8 Dec) .. 40   40
981   (1 r.) Black-headed Heron .. 40   40
    b. Perf 14×15 (8 Dec) .. 40   40
982   (1 r.) Darter 40   40
    b. Perf 14×15 (8 Dec) .. 40   40
983   (1 r.) Green-backed Heron .. 40   40
    b. Perf 14×15 (8 Dec) .. 40   40
984   (1 r.) White-faced Duck .. 40   40
    b. Perf 14×15 (8 Dec) .. 40   40
985   (1 r.) Saddle-billed Stork .. 40   40
    b. Perf 14×15 (8 Dec) .. 40   40
986   (1 r.) Water Dikkop .. 40   40
    b. Perf 14×15 (8 Dec) .. 40   40
977/86   Set of 10 3·50   3·50
Nos. 977/86, are inscribed "STANDARD POSTAGE" and
were printed together, se-tenant, in sheetlets of 10, with
illustrated margin at left.
The stamps printed by Questa, Nos. 977b/86b, are in different
shades and were only issued in 20 r. stamp booklets.
No. 984 exists as a corporate miniature sheet sponsored by the
"Junass" exhibition in aid of junior philately.

360 Double-headed Class 6E 1 Electric
Locomotives

(Des A. Ainslie. Litho Govt Printer, Pretoria (Nos. 987/91) or
Questa (Nos. 987b/91b))

1997 (1 Aug)–98. Inauguration of Revived Blue Train Service.
T 360 and similar horiz designs. Multicoloured. P 14 (with
four elliptical holes on each horizontal side).
987   (1 r. 20) Type 360 55   55
    a. Vert strip of 5. Nos. 987/91 2·50
    b. Perf 15×14. One side phosphor band
       (11.98) 55   55
    ba. Booklet pane. Nos. 987b/91b, each × 2 4·50
988   (1 r. 20) Double-headed Class 6E 1 electric
       locomotives (different) .. 55   55
    b. Perf 15×14. One side phosphor band
       (11.98) 55   55
989   (1 r. 20) Double-headed Class 25NC steam
       locomotives 55   55
    b. Perf 15×14. One side phosphor band
       (11.98) 55   55
990   (1 r. 20) Double-headed Class 34,900 diesel
       locomotives on Modder River bridge 55   55
    b. Perf 15×14. One side phosphor band
       (11.98) 55   55
991   (1 r. 20) Double-headed Class 34 diesel
       locomotives and Baobab tree 55   55
    b. Perf 15×14. One side phosphor band
       (11.98) 55   55
987/91   Set of 5 2·50   2·50
Nos. 987/91, which are inscribed "AIRMAIL POSTCARD

RATE", were printed together, *se-tenant*, in vertical strips of 5 throughout the sheets of 10. The rate for Airmail postcards increased to 1 r. 30 on 14 April 1998.

Nos. 987b/91b were only available from 13 r. stamp booklets with the pane folded vertically down the centre. There are no elliptical holes in the perforations of these booklet stamps.

No. 989b is inscr "HUTCHINSON" instead of "HUCHINSON" (989) and No. 991b is inscr "NORTHERN PROVINCE" instead of "NORTHERN TRANSVAAL" (991).

Nos. 987 and 989 exist in separate corporate miniature sheets sponsored by Harmers of London (No. 987) or Eastgate Universal Stamps and Coins Ltd (No. 989).

361 Nguni Breed   **362** Leopard Seal

(Des D. Murphy. Litho)

1997 (10 Aug). *Cattle Breeds. T 361 and similar horiz designs. Multicoloured. P 14½ (with two elliptical holes on each horizontal side).*

992	(1 r.) Type 361	..	..	50 50
	a. Block of 4. Nos. 992/5			1·75
993	(1 r.) Bonsmara	..	..	50 50
994	(1 r.) Afrikander	..	..	50 50
995	(1 r.) Drakensberger	..	..	50 50
992/5			Set of 4	1·75 1·75

Nos. 992/5 which are inscribed "Standard Postage" in English and Afrikaans, were printed together, *se-tenant*, in blocks of four throughout the sheet.

(Des D. Murphy. Litho)

1997 (27 Aug). *Antarctic Fauna. T 362 and similar horiz designs. Multicoloured. P 14.*

996	(1 r.) Type 362	..	..	30 25
997	1 r. 20, Antarctic Skua	..	..	60 40
998	1 r. 70, King Penguin	..	..	70 70
996/8			Set of 3	1·40 1·25

No. 996 is inscribed "Standard Postage" in English and Afrikaans. The Standard Postage rate increased to 1 r. 10 on 14 April 1998.

363 Enoch Sontonga and Verse from *Nkosi Sikelel'i Afrika*

(Des Thea Swanepoel and A. Ainslie. Litho)

1997 (24 Sept). *Heritage Day. Centenary of Nkosi Sikele'i Afrika (National Anthem). T 363 and similar horiz design. Multicoloured. P 14 (with two elliptical holes on each vertical side).*

999	(1 r.) Type 363	..	..	50 50
	a. Horiz pair. Nos. 999/1000			1·00 1·00
1000	(1 r.) As Type 363 but portrait at right	..		50 50

Nos. 999/1000, which are inscribed "Standard Postage", were printed together, *se-tenant*, in horizontal pairs throughout the sheet.

364 Horse-drawn Postcart delivering Mail   **365** Modern Postbox

(Des D. Bagnall. Litho)

1997 (8 Oct). *"Cape Town '97" National Stamp Show. Sheet 85×64 mm. P 14½×14.*

MS1001 **364** 4 r. 50, multicoloured   ..   1·00 1·00

(Des Thea Swanepoel. Litho)

1997 (9 Oct). *World Post Day. Sheet, 108×69 mm. P 14 (with two elliptical hole on each vertical side).*

MS1002 **365** (1 r.) multicoloured   ..   30 30
No. MS1002 is inscribed "STANDARD POSTAGE".

COVER PRICES

Cover factors are quoted at the beginning of each country for most issues to 1945. An explanation of the system can be found on page x. The factors quoted do not, however, apply to philatelic covers.

---

366 Bethlehem   **367** Black Rhinoceros

1997 (3 Nov). *Christmas. 50th Anniv of S.A.N.T.A. (South African National Tuberculosis Association). T 366 and similar vert designs showing charity labels. Multicoloured. Litho. P 14 (with two elliptical holes on each vertical side).*

1003	(1 r.) Type 366	..	..	35 35
	a. Sheetlet. Nos. 1003/12			3·25
1004	(1 r.) Cross of Lorraine and candles		35 35
1005	(1 r.) Cross of Lorraine, angels and candles		35 35
1006	(1 r.) Angel kneeling before Cross of Lorraine		35 35
1007	(1 r.) Father Christmas carrying sack	..	35 35
1008	(1 r.) Mary and Jesus	..	..	35 35
1009	(1 r.) Christmas trees	..	..	35 35
1010	(1 r.) Wise men on camels	..	..	35 35
1011	(1 r.) Christmas bell	..	..	35 35
1012	(1 r.) Child kneeling	..	..	35 35
1003/12			Set of 10	3·25 3·25

Nos. 1003/12 which are inscribed "STANDARD POSTAGE", were printed together, *se-tenant*, in sheetlets of 10, with illustrated left-hand margin.

(Des D. Murphy. Litho Cape & Transvaal Printers (No. 1029) or Government Printer (others))

1997 (12 Dec)–**98**. *Endangered Fauna (3rd series). Redrawn values as 1993–97 issue and new designs (Nos. 1030/4), all without frame or imprint and inscr "South Africa" only as in T 367. Multicoloured.*

(a) *Designs as Nos. 807/20, and some new values, redrawn.*

(i) *P 14.*

1013	10 c. Geometric Tortoise (5.2.98)	..	10 10
1014	20 c. Southern African Hedgehog (19.3.98)	10 10
1015	30 c. Spotted Hyena (13.3.98)	..	10 10
1016	40 c. Riverine Rabbit (8.1.98)	..	10 10
1017	50 c. Samango Monkey (23.3.98)	..	10 10
1018	60 c. Cape Hunting Dog (29.8.98)	..	10 15
1019	70 c. Roan Antelope (18.12.97)	..	15 20
1020	80 c. Kori Bustard (16.3.98)	..	15 20
1021	90 c. Jackass Penguin (19.12.97)	..	20 25
1022	1 r. Wattled Crane (12.12.97)	..	20 25
1024	3 r. Giraffe (24.3.98)	..	60 65
1025	5 r. Martial Eagle (17.3.98)	..	1·00 1·10
1026	10 r. Bateleur (34×24 mm) (28.8.98)	2·00 2·25

(ii) *P 14 (2 r.) or 14½ (20 r.), both with two elliptical holes on each vertical side*

1027	2 r. Blue Swallow (18.3.98)	..	40 45
1028	20 r. Fish Eagle (34×24 mm) (26.8.98)	..	4·00 4·25

(b) *Inscr "Standard Postage" (No. 1029) or "standard postage" (others). P 14 (Nos. 1030/4 with two elliptical holes on each vertical side)*

1029	(1 r.) Black Rhinoceros (16.1.98)	..	20 25
	a. Booklet pane. No. 1029×10 with outer edges of pane imperf		2·00
1030	(1 r. 10) Eland (vert) (4.98)	..	20 25
	a. Booklet pane. Nos. 1030/4, each × 2, with outer edges of pane imperforate		2·00
	b. Perf 14 (without elliptical holes) (18.5.98)		20 25
	ba. Strip of 5. Nos. 1030b/4b		1·00
1031	(1 r. 10) Greater Kudu (vert) (4.98)	..	20 25
	b. Perf 14 (without elliptical holes) (18.5.98)		20 25
1032	(1 r. 10) Impala (vert) (4.98)	..	20 25
	b. Perf 14 (without elliptical holes) (18.5.98)		20 25
1033	(1 r. 10) Waterbuck (vert) (4.98)	..	20 25
	b. Perf 14 (without elliptical holes) (18.5.98)		20 25
1034	(1 r. 10) Blue Wildebeest (vert) (4.98)	..	20 25
	b. Perf 14 (without elliptical holes) (18.5.98)		20 25

(d) *Inscr "Airmail Postcard". P 14 (with two elliptical holes at top or bottom) (26.1.98)*

1040	(1 r. 20) White Rhinoceros	..	25 30
	a. Booklet pane. Nos. 1040/4, each × 2, with outer edges of pane imperf		2·50
1041	(1 r. 20) Buffalo	..	..	25 30
1042	(1 r. 20) Lion	..	..	25 30
1043	(1 r. 20) Leopard	..	..	25 30
1044	(1 r. 20) African Elephant	..	25 30
1029/44		Set of 11	2·25 2·75

Nos. 1029/44 were only issued in booklets. On pane No. 1040a the elliptical holes only occur on the horizontal line of perforations separating the two strips.

Nos. 1030b/4b were printed together, *se-tenant*, both horizontally and vertically, as strips of 5 in sheets of 100.

For self-adhesive versions of Nos. 1030/4 see Nos. 1075/9.

The Standard Postage and Airmail Postcard rates increased to 1 r. 10 and 1 r. 30 on 14 April 1998, to 1 r. 20 and 1 r. 70 on 1 April 1999, and to 1 r. 30 and 1 r. 90 on 1 April 2000.

368 Tiger (woodcut)   **369** *Rescue 8* (lifeboat)

(Des Thea Swanepoel. Litho Questa)

1998 (28 Jan). *Chinese New Year ("Year of the Tiger"). Sheet 67×85 mm. P 14×14½.*

MS1051 **368** 5 r. vermilion, black and deep green   1·00 1·10

(Des D. Bagnall. Litho)

1998 (11 Feb). *30th Anniv of National Sea Rescue Institute (1997). P 14 (with two elliptical holes on each horizontal side).*

1052 **369** (1 r.) multicoloured   ..   30 30

370 Leopard   **371** Football Player

(Des J. Swanepoel. Litho)

1998 (1 May). *"SAPDA '98" National Stamp Exhibition, Johannesburg. Sheet 64×84 mm. P 14×14½.*

MS1053 **370** 5 r. multicoloured ..   1·00 1·10

(Des M. de Jong. Litho)

1998 (8 June). *World Cup Football Championship, France. P 14.*

1054 **371** (1 r. 10) multicoloured   ..   30 25
No. 1054 is inscribed "STANDARD POSTAGE".

372 Stone Age Hand Axe   **373** Pale Chanting Goshawk

(Des Sue Wickison. Litho Questa)

1998 (28 June). *Early South African History. T 372 and similar vert designs. Multicoloured. Ordinary paper. Two phosphor bands. P 14×15.*

1055	(1 r. 10) Type 372	..	..	30 30
	a. Sheetlet. Nos. 1055/64			2·75
	b. Booklet pane. Nos. 1055/64			2·75
1056	(1 r. 10) Musuku (altar)	..	..	30 30
1057	(1 r. 10) San rock engravings	..	30 30
1058	(1 r. 10) Early Iron Age pot	..	30 30
1059	(1 r. 10) Khoekhoe pot	..	30 30
1060	(1 r. 10) Florisbad skull	..	30 30
1061	(1 r. 10) San rock painting	..	30 30
1062	(1 r. 10) Mapungubwe gold rhinoceros and pot		30 30
1063	(1 r. 10) Lydenburg Head (ceremonial mask)		30 30
1064	(1 r. 10) Taung skull	..	..	30 30
1055/64			Set of 10	2·75 2·75

Nos. 1055/64, which are inscribed "standard postage", were printed together, *se-tenant*, in sheetlets of 10 with illustrated left-hand margin and the top, bottom and right-hand margins perforated through. No. 1055b has these three margins imperforate.

(Des C. van Rooyen. Litho Questa)

1998 (16 Aug). *South African Raptors. T 373 and similar vert designs. Multicoloured. Ordinary paper. Two phosphor bands. P 14×15.*

1065	(1 r. 10) Type 373	..	..	30 30
	a. Sheetlet. Nos. 1065/74			2·75
	b. Booklet pane. Nos. 1065/74			2·75
1066	(1 r. 10) Augur Buzzard ("Jackal Buzzard")		30 30
1067	(1 r. 10) Lanner Falcon	..	30 30
1068	(1 r. 10) Lammergeier ("Bearded Vulture")		30 30
1069	(1 r. 10) Black Harrier	..	30 30
1070	(1 r. 10) Cape Vulture	..	30 30
1071	(1 r. 10) Bateleur	..	30 30
1072	(1 r. 10) Spotted Eagle Owl	..	30 30
1073	(1 r. 10) White-headed Vulture	..	30 30
1074	(1 r. 10) African Fish Eagle	..	30 30
1065/74			Set of 10	2·75 2·75

Nos. 1065/74, which are inscribed "standard postage", were printed together, *se-tenant*, in sheetlets of 10 with an illustrated left-hand margin and the top, bottom and right-hand margins perforated through. No. 1065b has these three margins imperforate.

(Litho Pemara (Nos. 1075/9) or SNP Cambec (Nos. 1075a/9a))

1998 (18 Aug). *Endangered Fauna. Antelopes. Designs as Nos. 1030/4, but self-adhesive. Phosphor frame. P 13×12½.*

1075	(1 r. 10) Eland (vert)	..	20 25
	a. Phosphor frame at left and foot		20 25
	ab. Booklet pane. Nos. 1075a/9a, each × 2	2·00

1076	(1 r. 10) Greater Kudu (*vert*)	..	20	25
	a. Phosphor frame at left and foot	..	20	25
1077	(1 r. 10) Impala (*vert*)	..	20	25
	a. Phosphor frame at left and foot	..	20	25
1078	(1 r. 10) Waterbuck (*vert*)	..	20	25
	a. Phosphor frame at left and foot	..	20	25
1079	(1 r. 10) Blue Wildebeest (*vert*)	..	20	25
	a. Phosphor frame at left and foot	..	20	25
1075/9		*Set of 5*	1·00	1·25
1075a/9a		*Set of 5*	1·00	1·25

The above are inscribed "standard postage" and were printed in rolls of 100 (Nos. 1075/9) with the surplus self-adhesive paper around each stamp removed or in booklets of 10 (Nos. 1075a/9a) with the surplus paper retained.

The phosphor shows yellow under U.V. light. It forms a regular frame on Nos. 1075/9, but on Nos. 1075a/9a it is present at the left, following the outline of the antelope, and bottom only.

374 Shepherd's Tree

(Des Joan van Gogh. Litho Questa)

1998 (4 Sept). *Trees. T* **374** *and similar horiz designs. Multicoloured. Ordinary paper. One side phosphor band. P* 13½×14.

1080	(1 r. 10) Type **374**	..	40	40
	a. Block of 4. Nos. 1080/3	..	1·40	
1081	(1 r. 10) Karee	..	40	40
1082	(1 r. 10) Baobab	..	40	40
1083	(1 r. 10) Umbrella Thorn	..	40	40
1080/3		*Set of 4*	1·40	1·40

Nos. 1080/3 are inscribed "Standard Postage" and were printed together, *se-tenant*, in sheets of 10, providing two blocks of 4 and a horizontal pair of Nos. 1080/1.

375 Sandstone Cliffs, Cape Point   **376** Angel

(Des A. Ainslie. Litho Questa)

1998 (28 Sept). *"Explore South Africa". T* **375** *and similar horiz designs. Multicoloured. Ordinary paper. Two horiz phosphor bands. P* 15×14. (*a*) *Western Cape.*

1084	(1 r. 30) Type **375**	..	35	35
	a. Booklet pane. Nos. 1084/8×2	..	3·25	
1085	(1 r. 30) Robben Island	..	35	35
1086	(1 r. 30) Ostrich farming, Pinehurst Homestead	..	35	35
1087	(1 r. 30) Victoria and Alfred Waterfront, Capetown	..	35	35
1088	(1 r. 30) Homestead, Boschendal Wine Estate	..	35	35

(*b*) *KwaZulu-Natal.*

1089	(1 r. 30) Drakensberg waterfall	..	35	35
	a. Booklet pane. Nos. 1089/93×2	..	3·25	
1090	(1 r. 30) Zulu women preparing food	..	35	35
1091	(1 r. 30) Pelicans and rhinoceros	..	35	35
1092	(1 r. 30) Rickshaw driver	..	35	35
1093	(1 r. 30) Indian dancers	..	35	35
1084/93		*Set of 10*	3·25	3·25

Nos. 1084/8 and 1089/93, which are inscribed "AIRMAIL POSTCARD", were only available from separate 13 r. stamp booklets, with the panes showing an illustrated margin at top, a small blank margin at foot and the vertical sides imperforate.

(Des Annamart Dednam. Litho Questa)

1998 (9 Oct). *Christmas. T* **376** *and similar vert designs. Multicoloured. Ordinary paper. One side phosphor band. P* 14×15.

1094	(1 r. 10) Type **376**	..	35	35
	a. Horiz strip of 5. Nos. 1094/8	..	1·60	
1095	(1 r. 10) Christmas bell	..	35	35
1096	(1 r. 10) Present	..	35	35
1097	(1 r. 10) Christmas tree	..	35	35
1098	(1 r. 10) Star	..	35	35
1094/8		*Set of 5*	1·60	1·60

Nos. 1094/8 are inscribed "STANDARD POSTAGE" and were printed together, *se-tenant*, as horizontal strips of 5, in sheets of 10.

The new-issue supplement to this Catalogue appears each month in

GIBBONS STAMP MONTHLY

—from your newsagent or by postal subscription—
sample copy and details on request.

---

377 African Harrier Hawk   **378** London Pictorial Essay, 1927

(Des C. van Rooyen. Litho Questa)

1998 (9 Oct). *World Post Day. Sheet* 67×85 *mm. Ordinary paper. P* 14×14½.

MS1099	**377** 5 r. multicoloured	..	1·00	1·10

(Des Thea Swanepoel. Litho Questa)

1998 (20 Oct). *"ILSAPEX '98" International Stamp Exhibition, Johannesburg. Sheet,* 108×80 *mm, containing T* **378** *and similar vert design. Ordinary paper. P* 14½.

MS1100	5 r. deep green, scarlet and cream (Type **378**); 5 r. black, deep green and cream (as Type **378**, but "SOUTH AFRICA" at top) ..	2·00	2·25

MACHINE LABELS. A new series of machine labels, with nine different designs showing province landscapes, was introduced on 20 October 1998 with operational values from 1 r. 10 upwards. Sets showing other face values were available against special order.

379 Cuvier's Beaked Whale   **380** Emblem and Buildings

(Des C. Grant (Nos. 1101/4), M. Butterfield (No. MS1105). Litho Questa)

1998 (23 Oct). *Endangered Species. Whales of the Southern Ocean. T* **379** *and similar horiz designs. Multicoloured. Ordinary paper. One side phosphor band. P* 15×14.

1101	(1 r. 30) Type **379**	..	50	50
	a. Block of 4. Nos. 1101/4	..	1·75	
1102	(1 r. 30) Minke Whale	..	50	50
1103	(1 r. 30) Bryde's Whale	..	50	50
1104	(1 r. 30) Pygmy Right Whale	..	50	50
1101/4		*Set of 4*	1·75	1·75
MS1105	103×68 mm. 5 r. Blue Whale. No phosphor band. P 14	..	1·00	1·10

Nos. 1101/4 are inscribed "airmail postcard" and were printed together, *se-tenant*, in sheets of 10 providing two blocks of 4 and a horizontal pair of Nos. 1101/2.

No. MS1105 forms part of joint issue with Namibia and Norfolk Island.

A corporate miniature sheet, sponsored by Clover SA for their centenary, showing an ice-cream van was issued on 15 November 1998.

(Des F. Frescura. Litho Questa)

1998 (9 Dec). *50th Anniv of Universal Declaration of Human Rights. Ordinary paper. One side phosphor band. P* 14½.

1106	**380** (1 r. 10) multicoloured	..	30	25

No. 1106 is inscribed "Standard Postage".

381 Dennis Mail Van, 1913

(Des D. Bagnall. Litho Questa)

1999 (15 Feb). *125th Anniv of Universal Postal Union. T* **381** *and similar horiz designs. Multicoloured. Ordinary paper. U.P.U. emblem and one side band in phosphor. P* 13½×14.

1107	(1 r. 10) Type **381**	..	35	35
	a. Block of 4. Nos. 1107/10	..	1·25	
1108	(1 r. 10) Ford V8 post van, 1935	..	35	35

1109	(1 r. 10) Mobile Post Office, 1937	..	35	35
1110	(1 r. 10) Trojan Post Office van, 1927	..	35	35
1107/10		*Set of 4*	1·25	1·25

Nos. 1107/10 are inscribed "Standard Postage", and were printed *se-tenant* in sheets of 10, providing two blocks of 4 and a horizontal pair of Nos. 1107/8.

382 Rabbit

(Des D. Murphy. Litho Questa)

1999 (16 Feb). *Chinese New Year ("Year of the Rabbit"). Sheet* 85×67 *mm. Ordinary paper. P* 14×13½.

MS1111	**382** 5 r. multicoloured	..	1·00	1·10

383 *Discovery* (Scott)

(Des D. Bagnall. Litho Questa)

1999 (19 Mar). *Famous Ships. T* **383** *and similar horiz designs. Multicoloured. Ordinary paper. One side phosphor band. P* 13½×14.

1112	(1 r. 10) Type **383**	..	35	35
	a. Block of 4. Nos. 1112/15	..	1·25	
1113	(1 r. 10) *Heemskerk* (Tasman)	..	35	35
1114	(1 r. 10) H.M.S. *Endeavour* (Cook)	..	35	35
1115	(1 r. 10) H.M.S. *Beagle* (Darwin)	..	35	35
1112/15		*Set of 4*	1·25	1·25

Nos. 1112/15 are inscribed "standard postage", and were printed *se-tenant* in sheets of 10, providing two blocks of 4 and a horizontal pair of Nos. 1112/13.

384 *Lawhill* (barque)   **385** Traditional Nguni Love Token with AIDS Ribbon

(Des D. Bagnall. Litho Questa)

1999 (19 Mar). *"Australia '99" International Stamp Exhibition, Melbourne. Sheet* 65×85 *mm. Ordinary paper. P* 13½×14.

MS1116	**384** 5 r. multicoloured	..	1·00	1·10

(Des Thea Swanepoel. Litho Questa)

1999 (1 Apr). *AIDS Awareness Campaign. One side phosphor band. P* 14½×14.

1117	**385** (1 r. 20) multicoloured (bluish violet background)	..	25	30
	a. Booklet pane. Nos. 1100/1, each × 5	..	2·50	
1118	(1 r. 20) mult (emerald background)	..	25	30

Nos. 1117/18 are inscribed "Standard Postage" and were printed *se-tenant* in 12 r. stamp booklets containing No. 1100a which has the horizontal edges of the pane imperforate.

STAMP BOOKLETS

1913. *Black on red cover. With "UNION OF SOUTH AFRICA" at top and "UNIE VAN ZUID AFRIKA" at foot. Stapled.*
SB1   2s. 6d. booklet containing twelve ½d. and twenty-four 1d. (Nos. 3/4) in blocks of 6 .. ..£3500

1913–20. *Black on red cover with "UNION OF SOUTH AFRICA" and "UNIE VAN ZUID AFRIKA" both at top. Stapled.*
SB2   2s. 6d. booklet containing twelve ½d. and twenty-four 1d. (Nos. 3/4) in blocks of 6 .. ..£3250
  a. Black on pink cover (1920) £3000

1921. *Black on salmon-pink cover with "UNION OF SOUTH AFRICA" and "UNIE VAN ZUID AFRIKA" either side of arms and telegraph rates beneath. Stapled.*
SB3   3s. booklet containing twelve ½d., 1d. and 1½d. (Nos. 3/5) in blocks of 6 .. ..£500

1922. *Black on salmon-pink cover as No. SB3 surch. Stapled.*
SB4   3s. 6d. on 3s. booklet containing twelve ½d., 1d. and 2d. (Nos. 3/4, 6) in blocks of 6 .. ..£425

1926. *Black on salmon-pink cover as No. SB3. Stitched.*
SB5   2s. 6d. booklet containing twelve ½d. and twenty-four 1d. (Nos. 30/1) £375

1927. *Black on salmon-pink cover as No. SB3, but inscr "Union of South Africa" and "Únie van Suidafrika". Stitched.*
SB6   2s. 6d. booklet containing twelve ½d. and twenty-four 1d. (Nos. 30e, 31d) £3250

1930. *Black on pink cover as No. SB6, but with advertisement at foot instead of telegraph rates. Stitched.*
SB7   2s. 6d. booklet containing twelve ½d. and twenty-four 1d. (Nos. 42/3) in blocks of 6 .. ..£250

1931. *Black on pink cover. Smaller inscr and advertisement on front cover. Stitched.*
SB8   3s. booklet containing twelve 1d. (No. 43) in blocks of 6 and twelve 2d. (No. 44) in blocks of 4 ..£300

1935. *Black on lemon cover. Advertisement on front cover. Stitched.*
SB9   2s. 6d. booklet containing two panes of six ½d. (No. 54c) and four panes of six 1d. (No. 56e), all with adverts on margins £100

1937. *Black on lemon cover. Advertisement on front cover. Stitched.*
SB10 2s. 6d. booklet containing two panes of six ½d. (No. 75ba) and four panes of six 1d. (No. 56f), all with blank margins £200

1937. *Machine vended booklets. Red cover. Stitched.*
SB11 6d. booklet containing four ½d. and 1d. (Nos. 75b, 56) in pairs .. .. ..7·00

1938. *Machine vended booklets. Blue cover. Stitched.*
SB12 3d. booklet containing ½d. and 1d. (Nos. 75b, 56), each in pair .. .. ..30·00

1938. *Black on buff cover. Union arms at top left with advertisement at foot. Stitched.*
SB13 2s. 6d. booklet containing twelve ½d. and twenty-four 1d. (Nos. 75b, 56) in blocks of 6 ..£300

1939. *Black on buff cover. Union arms centred at top with advertisement at foot. Stitched.*
SB14 2s. 6d. booklet containing twelve ½d. and twenty-four 1d. (Nos. 75b, 56) in blocks of 6 ..£150

1939–40. *Green on buff cover. Union arms centred at top with large advertisement at bottom left. Stitched.*
SB15 2s. 6d. booklet containing twelve ½d. and twenty-four 1d. (Nos. 75b, 56) in blocks of 6 ..£2500
  a. Blue on buff cover (1940) .. ..70·00

1941. *Blue on buff cover as No. SB15. Stitched.*
SB17 2s. 6d. booklet containing twelve ½d. and 1d. (Nos. 75b, 56) in blocks of 6 and 1½d. (No. 57) in block of 4 .. .. ..£110

1948. *Black on buff cover. With advertisement. Stitched.*
SB18 3s. booklet containing two panes of six ½d., 1d. and 1½d. (Nos. 114a, 56h, 87b), all with postal slogans on margins, and pane of air mail labels .. .. ..24·00

1951. *Black on buff cover. Stitched.*
SB19 3s. 6d. booklet containing two panes of six ½d., 1d. and 2d. (Nos. 114ca, 115a, 134a), each with margins at right .. ..15·00

COVER PRICES

Cover factors are quoted at the beginning of each country for most issues to 1945. An explanation of the system can be found on page x. The factors quoted do not, however, apply to philatelic covers.

B 1 City Hall, Durban

1987 (16 Nov)–**88**. *Flood Relief Fund. Multicoloured covers as Type B 1. Stamps attached by selvedge.*
SB20 2 r. 60, booklet (cover Type B 1) containing 16 c. + 10 c. (Nos. 624/5) in block of 10 .. ..6·50
SB21 2 r. 60, booklet (cover, 139×85 mm, showing Bible) containing 16 c. + 10 c. (Nos. 629/30) in block of 10 (1.12.87) .. ..6·50
SB22 2 r. 60, booklet (cover showing Bartolomeu Dias) containing 16 c. + 10 c. (Nos. 635/6) in block of 10 (1.3.88) .. ..6·50
SB23 2 r. 60, booklet (cover, 125×90 mm, showing Huguenot Monument, Franschhoek) containing ten 16 c. + 10 c. (Nos. 641/2) in block of 10 (13.4.88) .. ..5·50

B 2 Stamp No. 787

1993 (7 May). *Aviation in South Africa. Multicoloured cover as Type B 2. Stamps attached by selvedge.*
SB24 4 r. 50, booklet containing 45 c. (Nos. 779/803) in block of 10 .. ..4·50
  Five versions of No. SB24 exist showing different combinations of Nos. 779/803, se-tenant in panes of 10 (2×5). The Philatelic Bureau sold the booklets in sets of ten, each pane being numbered at foot.

1993 (3 Sept). *Endangered Fauna. Multicoloured cover as Type B 2 but showing No. 821. Stamps attached by selvedge.*
SB25 4 r. 50, booklet containing "Standardised mail" stamp (No. 821) in block of 10 .. ..3·50

B 3 Lioness and Cubs Drinking
(Illustration further reduced. Actual size 142×64 mm)

1993 (12 Nov). *Tourism. Multicoloured covers as Type B 3. Stamps attached by selvedge. Five different cover designs:*
  (a) Type B 3
  (b) Luxury hotel
  (c) Table Mountain
  (d) Blue Train
  (e) Field of flowers
SB26 8 r. 50, booklet containing 85 c. (Nos. 826/30) in block of 10 (any cover) .. ..7·00
  Set of 5 different cover designs 32·00

B 4

1995 (14 Feb)–**96**. *Endangered Fauna. Ultramarine and bright scarlet cover as Type B 4. Stamps attached by selvedge with outer edges of pane imperf.*
SB27 (4 r. 50) booklet containing pane of 10 "Standardised mail" stamps (No. 821a) .. 3·00
  a. Containing booklet pane No. 821ba (9.4.96) 3·00
  No. SB27 as initially sold at 4 r. 50 which was increased to 5 r. on 30 September 1994, to 6 r. on 1 April 1995 and to 7 r. in August 1996.

1995 (Mar). *Tourism. Booklet No. SB26 with additional label inscr "FOR OVERSEAS POSTCARDS ONLY USE 1 × 85 c + 1 × 5 c = 90 c."*
SB28 9 r. booklet containing 85 c. (Nos. 826/30 in block of 10 plus 5 c. (No. 806) in strip of 10) (any cover) .. .. ..6·00
  a. With 5 c. (No. 656) in block of 10 (5×2) ..6·00
  b. With 5 c. (No. 806) in block of 10 (5×2) ..6·00

1995 (Apr). *Tourism. Booklet No. SB24 with additional label inscr "FOR OVERSEAS POSTCARDS" ONLY USE 2 × 45 c Stamps = 90 c."*
SB29 4 r. 50, booklet containing 45 c. (Nos. 799/803) in block of 10 .. ..5·00

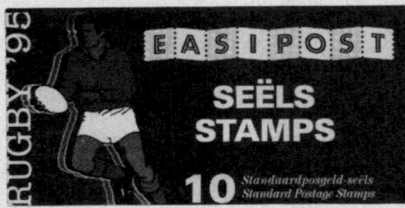

B 5 Player running with Ball

1995 (25 May). *World Cup Rugby Championship, South Africa. Multicoloured cover as Type B 5. Stamps attached by selvedge.*
SB30 (6 r.) booklet containing pane of 10 "STANDARDISED POSTAGE" stamps (No. 875ab) .. .. ..3·25
SB31 (6 r.) booklet containing pane of 10 "STANDARDISED POSTAGE" stamps (No. 876ab) .. .. ..3·25

1995 (16 Sept–1 Dec). *Masakhane Campaign. Bright scarlet and bright ultramarine covers as Type B 4. Stamps attached by selvedge.*
SB32 (6 r.) booklet containing pane of ten "STANDARD POSTAGE" stamps (No. 884a) .. ..2·00
SB33 (6 r.) booklet containing pane of ten "STANDARD POSTAGE" stamps (No. 884ba) (1 Dec) .. ..2·00

B 6 Jackass Penguin

1995 (1 Dec). *Endangered Fauna. Multicoloured cover as Type B 6. Stamps attached by selvedge.*
SB34 9 r. booklet containing pane of ten 90 c. (No. 816a) .. .. ..3·50

B 7 Lion

1996 (8 May–Dec). *Tourism. Multicoloured cover as Type B 7. Stamps attached by selvedge.*
SB35 (5 r.) booklet containing pane of 5 "Airmail postcard rate" stamps and five labels (No. 821cc) .. .. ..2·50
  a. As No. SB35, but with additional tab and hole at right (Dec) .. .. ..2·50

B 8 Drummer and Decorations

1996 (9 Oct). *Christmas. Multicoloured cover as Type B 8. Stamps attached by selvedge.*
SB36 7 r. booklet containing pane of ten 70 c. (No. 937a) .. .. ..3·00

1996 (Nov). *"Indaba '96" Tourism Exhibition, Durban. Multicoloured cover as Type B 7, but 210×75 mm with inscr at right. Stamps affixed by selvedge.*
SB37 (5 r.) booklet containing pane of 5 "Airmail postcard rate" stamps, 3 advertising and 2 airmail labels (No. 821cb) .. .. ..2·50

B 9 Landscape and Sunflower
(*Illustration reduced. Actual size 135×55 mm*)

1997 (25 Mar). *National Water Conservation. Multicoloured cover as Type B 9. Pane attached by selvedge.*
SB38 $7 booklet containing pane of ten 70 c. (No. 951a)   3·25
         a. Containing booklet pane No. 951ba   3·25

B 10 Black Rhinoceros
(*Illustration reduced. Actual size 135×55 mm*)

1997 (May). *Endangered Fauna. Multicoloured cover as Type B 10. "ILSAPEX '98" advertisement on the back. Stamps attached by selvedge.*
SB39   10 r. booklet containing 1 r. (No. 817) in block of
         10 . .   . .   4·00

1997 (June–Nov). *Endangered Fauna. Multicoloured cover as Type B 10. "ILSAPEX '98" advertisement on the back. Stamps attached by selvedge.*
SB40   (10 r.) booklet containing pane of 10 "Standardised mail" stamps (No. 821ba)   3·00
         a. Human Rights Commission advertisement on back (Nov)   3·00

B 11 Man holding Spear
(*Illustration reduced. Actual size 135×55 mm*)

1997 (27 July). *Thulamela National Heritage Site. Multicoloured cover as Type B 11. Pane attached by selvedge.*
SB41   ($6) booklet containing pane of 5 and 5 commemorative labels (No. 821cd) . .   2·50

B 12 Cultural Artefacts
(*Illustration reduced. Actual size 185×90 mm*)

1997 (8 Dec). *Year of Cultural Experiences. Multicoloured cover as Type B 12. Booklet contains text and illustrations on left-hand margins of panes and on interleaving pages. Stitched.*
SB42   (20 r.) booklet containing two panes of 10 "Standard Postage" stamps (No. 966ba)   6·50

B 13 Egyptian Geese
(*Illustration reduced. Actual size 185×90 mm*)

1997 (8 Dec). *World Environment Day. Waterbirds. Multicoloured cover as Type B 13. Booklet contains text and illustrations on left-hand margins of panes and on interleaving pages. Stitched.*
SB43   (20 r.) booklet containing two panes of 10 "STANDARD POSTAGE" stamps (No. 977ba)   6·50

B 15 Technology at Work
(*Illustration reduced. Actual size 135×55 mm*)

1998 (12 Feb). *Year of Science and Technology. Multicoloured cover as Type B 15. Stamps attached by selvedge.*
SB44   (10 r.) booklet containing pane of 10 "Standard Postage" stamps (No. 1029a) . .   . .   2·00

1998 (Mar). *Tourism. Multicoloured cover as Type B 10 showing lioness and inscr "10 AIRMAIL POSTCARD STAMPS". Stamps attached by selvedge.*
SB45   (12 r.) booklet containing pane of 10 "Airmail Postcard" stamps (No. 1040a) . .   2·50

B 16 Sable Antelope

1998 (Apr). *Centenary of Kruger National Park. Multicoloured cover as Type B 16. Pane attached by selvedge.*
SB46   (11 r.) booklet containing pane of 10 "standard postage" stamps (No. 1030a) . .   . .   2·25

B 17 Lydenburg Heads
(*Illustration reduced. Actual size 185×92 mm*)

1998 (28 June). *Early South African History. Multicoloured cover as Type B 17. Booklet contains text and illustrations on left-hand margins of panes and on interleaving pages. Stitched.*
SB47   (22 r.) booklet containing two panes of 10 "standard postage" stamps (No. 1055b) and two pre-paid postcards . .   . .   4·25

B 18 Cape Vultures
(*Illustration reduced. Actual size 185×92 mm*)

1998 (16 Aug). *South African Raptors. Multicoloured cover as Type B 18. Booklet contains text and illustrations on left-hand margins of panes and on interleaving pages. Stitched.*
SB48   (22 r.) booklet containing two panes of 10 "standard postage" stamps (No. 1065b) and two pre-paid postcards . .   . .   4·25

B 19

1998 (18 Aug). *Endangered Fauna. Ultramarine and scarlet cover as Type B 19. Self-adhesive.*
SB49   (11 r.) booklet containing pane of 10 "standard postage" stamps (No. 1075ab) . .   . .   2·25

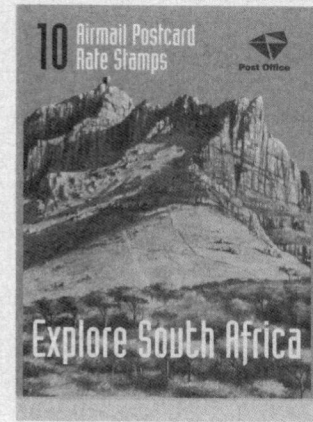

B 20 Table Mountain

1998 (28 Sept). *Explore South Africa. Multicoloured covers as Type B 20. Stamps attached by selvedge.*
SB50   (13 r.) booklet containing pane of 10 Western Cape "AIRMAIL POSTCARD" stamps (No. 1084a)   4·50
SB51   (13 r.) booklet containing pane of 10 KwaZulu-Natal "AIRMAIL POSTCARD" stamps (No. 1089a) (cover shows a rickshaw driver)   4·50

B 21 Rhinoceros (from *Beschryving van de Kaap de Goede Hoop*, Peter Kolbe, 1727)
(*Illustration reduced. Actual size 138×55 mm*)

1998 (Nov). *AIDS Awareness. Multicoloured cover as Type B 21. Stamps attached by selvedge.*
SB52   (11 r.) booklet containing "Standardised mail" (1 r. 10) (No. 821b) in block of 10 . .   2·25
The inside and back covers are printed with text and illustrations offering advice and telephone helpline numbers on AIDS.

B 22 The Blue Train

1998 (Nov). *Inauguration of Revived Blue Train Service. Multicoloured cover as Type B 22. Stamps attached by selvedge.*
SB53   (13 r.) booklet containing pane of 10 (1 r. 30) (No. 987ba) . .   . .   4·50

B 23 Couple with AIDS Ribbon

1999 (1 Apr). *AIDS Awareness Campaign. Multicoloured cover as Type B 23. Stamps attached by selvedge.*
SB54   (12 r.) booklet containing pane of 10 "Standard Postage" stamps (No. 1117a) . .   . .   2·25

SOUTH AFRICA

POSTAGE DUE STAMPS

D 1

UNION of SOUTH AFRICA	UNION of SOUTH AFRICA
(A)	(B)

(Typo D.L.R.)

1914–22. *Inscribed bilingually. Lettering as A. W 4. P 14.*

			Un single	Used single
D1	D 1	½d. black and green (19.3.15)	2·00	3·75
D2		1d. black and scarlet (19.3.15)	2·25	15
		a. Black ptd double	£1400	
		w. Wmk inverted	75·00	
D3		2d. black and reddish violet (12.12.14)	6·50	50
		a. Black and bright violet (1922)	7·00	60
		w. Wmk inverted	£110	
D4		3d. black and bright blue (2.2.15)	2·25	60
		w. Wmk inverted	25·00	
D5		5d. black and sepia (19.3.15)	4·00	20·00
D6		6d. black and slate (19.3.15)	7·00	24·00
D7		1s. red and black (19.3.15)	60·00	£140
D1/7		Set of 7	75·00	£170

There are interesting minor varieties in some of the above values, e.g. ½d. to 3d., thick downstroke to "d"; 1d., short serif to "1"; raised "d"; 2d., forward point of "2" blunted; 3d., raised "d"; very thick "d".

(Litho Govt Printer, Pretoria)

1922. *Lettering as A. No wmk. Rouletted.*

D 8	D 1	½d. black and bright green (6.6.22)	1·25	10·00
D 9		1d. black and rose-red (3.10.22)	1·00	1·00
D 10		1½d. black and yellow-brown (3.6.22)	1·25	1·75
D8/10		Set of 3	3·25	11·50

(Litho Govt Printer, Pretoria)

1922–26. *Type D 1 redrawn. Lettering as B. P 14.*

D11		½d. black and green (1.8.22)	80	1·75
D12		1d. black and rose (16.5.23)	90	15
D13		1½d. black and yellow-brown (12.1.24)	90	1·25
D14		2d. black and pale violet (16.5.23)	1·00	70
		a. Imperf (pair)	£225	£300
		b. Black and deep violet	9·50	3·25
D15		3d. black and blue (3.7.26)	8·00	17·00
D16		6d. black and slate (9.23)	12·00	6·00
D11/16		Set of 6	21·00	24·00

The locally printed stamps, perf 14, differ both in border design and in figures of value from the rouletted stamps. All values except the 3d. and 6d. are known with closed "G" in "POSTAGE" usually referred to as the "POSTADE" variety. This was corrected in later printings.

D 2	D 3	D 4

Blunt "2" (R. 3/6, 8/6)

(Typo Pretoria)

1927–28. *Inscribed bilingually. No wmk. P 13½×14.*

D17	D 2	½d. black and green	70	3·25
		a. Blunt "2"	8·00	
D18		1d. black and carmine	1·25	30
D19		2d. black and mauve	1·25	30
		a. Black and purple	12·00	80
D20		3d. black and blue	8·50	20·00
D21		6d. black and slate	21·00	6·00
D17/21		Set of 5	29·00	27·00

1932–42. *Type D 2 redrawn. W 9. P 15×14.*

(a) Frame roto, value typo

D22		½d. black and blue-green (1934)	2·75	1·75
		w. Wmk inverted	2·25	1·60
D23		2d. black and deep purple (10.4.33)	7·50	1·75
		w. Wmk inverted	8·50	1·75

(b) Whole stamp roto

D25		1d. black & carmine (wmk inverted) (3.34)	2·25	10
D26		2d. black and deep purple (1940)	22·00	10
		a. Thick (double) "2d." (R. 5/6, R. 18/2)	£190	20·00
		w. Wmk inverted	22·00	10
D27		3d. black and Prussian blue (3.8.32)	22·00	14·00
D28		3d. dp blue & blue (wmk inverted) (1935)	7·00	30
		a. Indigo and milky blue (wmk inverted) (1942)	55·00	2·75
		w. Wmk upright	32·00	
D29		6d. green and brown-ochre (wmk inverted) (7.6.33)	25·00	9·00
		a. Green & brt orge (wmk inverted) (1938)	11·00	4·00
D22/9a		Set of 7	70·00	19·00

In No. D26 the value, when magnified, has the meshed appearance of a photogravure screen, whereas in No. D23 the black of the value is solid.

1943–44. *Inscr bilingually. Roto. W 9. In units of three, perf 15 × 14 subdivided by roulette 6½.*

			Un unit	Us unit	Us single
D30	D 3	½d. blue-green (1944)	10·00	35·00	30
D31		1d. carmine	9·50	5·50	10
D32		2d. dull violet	6·50	11·00	15
		a. Bright violet	16·00	42·00	65
D33		3d. indigo (1943)	48·00	80·00	1·25
D30/3		Set of 4	65·00	£120	1·90

Split "D" (R. 7/5 on every fourth sheet)

1948–49. *New figure of value and capital "D". Whole stamp roto. W 9. P 15 × 14.*

D34	D 4	½d. black and blue-green	6·00	10·00
D35		1d. black and carmine	10·00	5·50
D36		2d. black and violet (1949)	10·00	5·50
		a. Thick (double) "2D." (R. 15/5–6, R. 16/5–6)	50·00	26·00
D37		3d. deep blue and blue	15·00	17·00
		a. Split "D"	£140	
D38		6d. green and bright orange (1949)	25·00	8·00
D34/8		Set of 5	60·00	42·00

1950–58. *As Type D 4, but "SUID-AFRIKA" hyphenated. Whole stamp roto. W 9. P 15 × 14.*

D39		1d. black and carmine (5.50)	70	30
D40		2d. black and violet (4.51)	50	20
		a. Thick (double) "2D." (R. 15/5–6, R. 16/5–6)	8·00	7·00
		b. Black and reddish violet (12.52)	70	20
		ba. Thick (double) "2D."	8·00	7·00
		bb. Black (value) omitted	£1700	
D41		3d. deep blue and blue (5.50)	4·50	2·00
		a. Split "D"	80·00	
D42		4d. deep myrtle-green and emerald (2.58)	12·00	15·00
D43		6d. green and bright orange (3.50)	7·00	9·00
D44		1s. black-brown and purple-brown (2.58)	12·00	15·00
D39/44		Set of 6	32·00	38·00

No. D40bb occurs in horizontal pair with a normal.

SOUTH AFRICA ... SUID-AFRIKA	REPUBLIEK VAN SUID-AFRIKA ... REPUBLIC OF SOUTH AFRICA	REPUBLIC OF SOUTH AFRICA ... REPUBLIEK VAN SUID-AFRICA
D 5	D 6 Afrikaans at top	D 7 English at top

1961 (14 Feb). *Values in cents as Type D 5. Whole stamp roto. W 102. P 15 × 14.*

D45		1 c. black and carmine	20	3·50
D46		2 c. black and violet	35	3·50
D47		4 c. deep myrtle-green and emerald	80	8·00
D48		5 c. deep blue and blue	1·75	8·00
D49		6 c. green and orange-red	8·50	8·50
D50		10 c. sepia and brown-lake	9·00	10·00
D45/50		Set of 6	19·00	38·00

1961 (31 May)**–69.** *Roto. W 102. P 15 × 14.*

D51	D 6	1 c. black and carmine	40	60
D52	D 7	1 c. black and carmine (6.62)	40	4·50
D53		2 c. black and deep reddish violet	40	55
D54	D 6	4 c. dp myrtle-green & light emerald	3·25	2·25
D54a	D 7	4 c. dp myrtle-grn & lt emerald (6.69)	17·00	22·00
D55		5 c. deep blue and grey-blue	2·75	4·25
D56		5 c. black and grey-blue (6.62)	1·75	7·50
D57	D 6	6 c. deep green and red-orange	8·00	5·50
D58	D 7	10 c. sepia and purple-brown	3·50	1·75
D51/8		Set of 9	35·00	45·00

1967 (Dec)**–71.** *Roto. W 127 (tête-bêche). P 15 × 14.*

D59	D 6	1 c. black and carmine	20	55
D60	D 7	1 c. black and carmine	20	30
D61	D 6	2 c. black and deep reddish violet	30	1·50
D62	D 7	2 c. black and deep reddish violet	30	1·50
D62b		4 c. dp myrtle-green & emerald (6.69)*	29·00	29·00
D62c	D 6	4 c. dp myrtle-green & emerald (6.69)*	£225	£225
D63		4 c. black and pale green (4.71)	27·00	27·00
D64	D 7	4 c. black and pale green (4.71)	27·00	27·00
D65	D 6	5 c. black and deep blue	50	50
D66	D 7	5 c. black and deep blue	50	50
D67	D 6	6 c. green and orange-red (1968)	5·00	8·50
D68	D 7	6 c. green and orange-red (1968)	5·00	8·50
D69	D 6	10 c. black and purple-brown	1·00	2·75
		a. Black and brown-lake (12.69)	1·00	2·75
D70	D 7	10 c. black and purple-brown	1·00	2·75
		a. Black and brown-lake (12.69)	1·00	2·75
D59/70a except D62b/c		Set of 12	60·00	70·00

Nos. D59/70 were printed in two panes, one with inscriptions as Type D 6 and the other as Type D 7.

*Nos. D54a, D62b/c and further supplies of D54 were part of a printing released in June 1969. Most sheets were printed on paper with the Arms watermark, but some were printed on RSA paper with the watermark upright and faint. Of these many were spoilt, but a few sheets were issued in Types D 7 and D 6, the latter being very scarce.

1971. *Roto. W 127 (tête-bêche). P 14.*

D71	D 6	2 c. black and deep reddish violet	23·00	7·00
D72	D 7	2 c. black and deep reddish violet	23·00	7·00
D74		4 c. deep myrtle-green & light emerald	45·00	40·00
D71/4		Set of 3	80·00	48·00

Nos. D71/4 were also printed in double panes as Nos. D59/70. Although the 4 c. as Type D 6 must have been printed it has not been possible to confirm that any were actually issued.

D 8

1972 (22 Mar). *English at right (1, 4 and 8 c.) or at left (others). W 127 (sideways tête-bêche). Chalk-surfaced paper (4 c. to 10 c.). P 14×13½.*

D75	D 8	1 c. deep yellowish green	50	2·25
D76		2 c. bright orange	70	3·00
D77		4 c. plum	1·75	3·50
D78		6 c. chrome-yellow	1·75	4·75
D79		8 c. ultramarine	2·00	5·00
D80		10 c. bright scarlet	6·00	7·50
D75/80		Set of 6	11·50	23·00

The 6 c. also exists on phosphorised paper.

The printing of Postage Due stamps ceased in 1978. Isolated examples are known used as late as 1980.

OFFICIAL STAMPS

OFFICIAL.	OFFISIEEL.	OFFISIEEL	OFFICIAL
(O 1)			(O 2)

(Approximate measurements of the space between the two lines of overprint are quoted in millimetres, either in the set headings or after individual listings)

1926 (1 Dec). *Optd with Type O 1 (reading upwards with stops and 12½ mm between lines of opt).*

(a) On 1913 issue (No. 6)

O1	3	2d. purple	18·00	1·75

			Un pair	Us pair	Us single

(b) On 1926 issue (Nos. 30/2)

O2	6	½d. black and green	6·00	14·00	1·50
O3	7	1d. black and carmine	3·25	4·75	50
O4	8	6d. green and orange	£550	75·00	10·00
		w. Wmk inverted	£900	£350	30·00

The overprint occurs on both the London and Pretoria printings of Nos. 30/2. For the lower two values the overprinted London printings are scarcer than the Pretoria, but for the 6d. the ratio is reversed.

1928–30. *Nos. 32 and 34 optd as Type O 1 (reading upwards without stops).*

O5	11	2d. grey & maroon (p 14) (17½ mm)	5·00	19·00	2·00
		a. Lines of opt 19 mm apart (1929)	4·00	13·00	1·50
		ab. On No. 34a (p 14×13½) (1930)	25·00	38·00	5·00
O6	8	6d. green and orange (11½–12 mm)	18·00	28·00	2·75

1929–31. *Optd with Type O 2. (a) On 1926 (Typo) issue (Nos. 30/2) (13½–15 mm between lines of opt).*

O7	6	½d. black and green	2·25	3·00	35
		a. Stop after "OFFISIEEL" on English inscr stamp (1930)	32·00	32·00	3·25
		b. Ditto, but on Afrikaans inscr stamp (1930)	40·00	40·00	3·25
O8	7	1d. black and carmine	3·00	4·00	45
O9	8	6d. green and orange	9·50	32·00	3·25
		a. Stop after "OFFISIEEL" on English inscr stamp (1930)	65·00	£110	10·00
		b. Ditto, but on Afrikaans inscr stamp (1930)	75·00	£120	12·00

(b) On 1927 (Recess) issue (Nos. 36a/7) (17½–19 mm between lines of opt)

O10	13	1s. brown and deep blue (1931)	32·00	90·00	9·50
		a. Stop after "OFFICIAL" on Afrikaans inscr stamp (R. 10/1, 10/7)	£100	£225	
		b. Lines of opt 22 mm apart	£250		
O11	14	2s. 6d. green and brown (1931)	60·00	£150	19·00
		a. Stop after "OFFICIAL" on Afrikaans inscr stamp (R. 10/1)	£275	£475	
O7/11		Set of 5	95·00	£250	29·00

The "stop" varieties for the ½d., and 6d. occur on R. 5/3, 5/11, 8/12, 15/3, 15/11, 18/12 with English inscriptions and R. 9/10, 9/12, 19/10, 19/12 with Afrikaans on the 1930 overprinting only.

As only the lefthand panes of the 2s. 6d. were overprinted in 1931 the stop variety only occurs once. A further overprinting in 1932 was on both panes, but did not include No. O11a.

1930–47. *Nos. 42/4 and 47/9 ("SUIDAFRIKA" in one word) optd with Type O 2.*

O12	6	½d. black and green (9½–12½ mm) (1931)	2·25	4·25	40
		a. Stop after "OFFISIEEL" on English inscr stamp	38·00	45·00	4·00
		b. Ditto, but on Afrikaans inscr stamp	32·00	40·00	3·50
		w. Wmk inverted (1934)	5·00	7·50	60

O13	7	1d. black & carm (I) (12½ mm)	4·50	4·50	55
		a. Stop after "OFFISIEEL" on English inscr stamp	42·00	48·00	4·00
		b. Ditto, but on Afrikaans inscr stamp	35·00	40·00	3·50
		cw. Wmk inverted (1931)	4·50	4·50	55
		d. On Type II (No. 43d) (12½–13½ mm) (1933)	12·00	9·00	90
		da. Opt double	£275	£300	
O14	11	2d. slate-grey and lilac (20½–22½ mm) (1931)	6·00	11·00	1·50
		w. Wmk inverted (1934)	50·00	85·00	8·00
O15		2d. blue and violet (20½–22½ mm) (1938)	£100	£100	9·00
O16	8	6d. green & orange (12½–13½ mm) (wmk inverted) (1931)	7·00	8·50	85
		a. Stop after "OFFISIEEL" on English inscr stamp	65·00	70·00	6·50
		b. Ditto, but on Afrikaans inscr stamp	55·00	60·00	5·50
		c. "OFFISIEEL" reading upwards (R. 17/12, 18/12, 19/12, 20/12) (1933)		£425	
		w. Wmk upright (1933)	50·00	75·00	7·00
O17	13	1s. brown and deep blue (19 mm) (wmk inverted) (1932)	45·00	80·00	8·50
		a. Lines of opt 21 mm apart (wmk inverted) (1933)	48·00	70·00	7·50
		ab. Twisted horn flaw		£225	
		aw. Wmk upright (1936)	60·00	£100	10·00
O18	14	2s. 6d. green and brown (17½–18½ mm) (1933)	75·00	£130	15·00
		a. Lines of opt 21 mm apart (1934)	48·00	75·00	8·50
		aw. Wmk inverted (1934)		£200	
O19		2s. 6d. blue and brown (19½–20 mm) (11.47)	32·00	70·00	6·50
		a. Diaeresis over second "E" of "OFFISIEEL" on Afrikaans inscr stamp (R. 6/2)	£750	£850	
		b. Ditto, but on English inscr stamp (R. 6/3)	£750	£850	

The stop varieties for the ½d. 1d. and 6d. occur on R. 9/10, 9/12, 19/10, 19/12 with English inscriptions and R. 5/3, 5/11, 8/12, 15/3, 15/11, 18/12 with Afrikaans on the 1930 and 1931 overprintings only.

1 Hands releasing Dove

2 African Buffalo (totem of Malete and Hwaduba tribes)

1935–49. Nos. 54, 56/8, 61/2 and 64a/b ("SUID-AFRIKA" hyphenated) optd.

(a) With Type O 2 (reading downwards with "OFFICIAL" at right)

O20	6	½d. grey and green (12½ mm) (wmk inverted) (1936)	4·25	20·00	1·75
		w. Wmk upright (1937)	4·25	20·00	1·25
O21	7	1d. grey and carmine (11½–13 mm) (wmk inverted)	3·00	3·00	35
		aw. Wmk upright (1937)	1·75	2·00	20
		b. Grey & bright rose-carmine (No. 56i) (1949)	2·50	3·25	30
O22	22	1½d. green and bright gold (20 mm) (wmk inverted) (1937)	32·00	24·00	1·75
		aw. Wmk upright (1939)	22·00	16·00	80
		b. Blue-green and dull gold (No. 57c) (1941)	45·00	11·00	1·10
O23	11	2d. blue & violet (20 mm) (1939)	£100	23·00	2·25
O24	8	6d. green and vermilion (I) (11½–13 mm) (1937)	80·00	45·00	3·75
		a. "Falling ladder" flaw		£300	
		b. Die II (No. 61b) (1938)	10·00	12·00	1·25
		c. Die III. Green & red-orange (No. 61c) (11.47)	4·00	8·50	85
O25	13	1s. brown and chalky blue (20 mm) (1939)	75·00	30·00	2·25
		a. Diaeresis over second "E" of "OFFISIEEL" on both English and Afrikaans inscr stamps (1941)	£1200	£850	
		b. Ditto, but on English inscr stamp only (11.47)	£1100	£750	
O26	15	5s. black and blue-green (20 mm) (6.48)	55·00	£130	13·00
O27	23	10s. blue and blackish brown (No. 64ba) (20 mm) (6.48)	85·00	£190	23·00

(b) With Type O 3 (reading downwards with "OFFICIAL" at left and 18–19 mm between lines of opt)

O28	15	5s. black and blue-green (1940)	85·00	£110	12·00
O29	23	10s. blue and green (1940)	£350	£350	38·00

(c) With Type O 4 (reading upwards with "OFFICIAL" at right and 18½ mm between lines of opt)

O30	11	2d. grey and dull purple (No. 58a) (1941)	8·00	24·00	2·25

No. O25a first appeared in the 1941 overprinting where the variety occurs on stamps 5 and 6 of an unidentified row. The variety reappears in the November 1947 overprinting where the stamps involved are R. 6/1 and 2. No. 25b occurs on R. 6/3 of the same overprinting.

Horizontal rows of 6 of the 1s. exist with "OFFICIAL" twice on the first stamp and "OFFISIEEL" twice on the last stamp. Such rows are believed to come from two half sheets which were overprinted in 1947, but not placed into normal stock.

MINIMUM PRICE

The minimum price quote is 10p which represents a handling charge rather than a basis for valuing common stamps. For further notes about prices see introductory pages.

1937–44. No. 75b (redrawn design) optd. (a) With Type O 2 (reading downwards with "OFFICIAL" at right and 11–12½ mm between lines of opt)

O31	25a	½d. grey and green	12·00	13·00	1·25
		a. Grey and blue-green (No. 75bd) (1944)	1·25	6·50	60

(b) With Type O 5 (reading up and down with "OFFICIAL" at left and diaeresis over the second "E" of "OFFISIEEL". 10 mm between lines of opt)

O32	25a	½d. grey and blue-green (No. 75bd) (1944)	22·00	21·00	2·00

1944–50. Nos. 87 and 134 optd. (a) With Type O 2 (reading downwards with "OFFICIAL" at right)

O33	34a	1½d. blue-green and yellow-buff (14½ mm)	2·50	9·00	80
		a. With diaeresis over second "E" of "OFFISIEEL"	£350	£190	
		b. Lines of opt 16½ mm apart (6.48)	2·25	7·50	50

(b) With Type O 6 (reading upwards with "OFFICIAL" at left and 16 mm between lines of opt)

O34	34a	1½d. bl-green & yell-buff (1949)	35·00	45·00	4·00
O35	68	2d. blue and violet (1950)	£1600	£1900	£170

Two different formes were used to overprint Type 34a between 1944 and 1946. The first, applied to the left halves of sheets only, had a diaeresis over the second "E" of "OFFISIEEL" on all positions of the setting, except for R. 1/2, 2/2 and 3/2. The second form, from which the majority of the stamps came, was applied twice to overprint complete sheets, had no diaeresis.

1947 (Nov)**–49.** No. 107 optd with Type O 2 (reading downwards with "OFFICIAL" at right and 20 mm between lines of opt).

O36	54	2d. slate and violet	3·00	19·00	1·75
		a. With diaeresis over second "E" of "OFFISIEEL" (R. 1/5-6, 11/5-6)	£300	£475	
		b. Slate-purple and bright violet (No. 107a) (1949)	5·50	14·00	1·60

1949–50. Nos. 114 and 120 optd with Type O 2 (reading downwards with "OFFICIAL" at right).

O37	25a	½d. grey and green (11 mm)	1·60	7·50	70
O38	13	1s. brown and chalky blue (17½–18½ mm) (1950)	9·00	28·00	2·50

1950 (June)**–54.** Optd as Type O 7 using stereo blocks measuring either 10 (½d., 1d., 6d.), 14½ (1½d., 2d.) or 19 mm (others) between the lines of opt.

O39	25a	½d. grey and green (No. 114c) (6.51)	70	1·50	15
O41	7	1d. grey & bright rose-carmine (No. 56i)	1·00	5·50	50
O42		1d. grey & car (No. 115) (3.51)	1·00	3·00	20
O43		1d. grey & car (No. 135) (6.52)	90	2·00	20
O44	34a	1½d. blue-green and yellow-buff (No. 87) (3.51)	1·40	4·00	30
O45	68	2d. blue and violet (No. 134)	1·00	2·00	20
		a. Opt inverted		£1200	
O46	8	6d. green & red-orge (No. 119)	1·00	3·50	35
		a. Green and brown-orange (No. 119a) (6.51)	1·50	3·50	35
O47	13	1s. brn & chalky bl (No. 120)	5·50	18·00	2·00
		a. Blackish brown and ultram (No. 120a) (1.54)	£150	£160	18·00
O48	14	2s. 6d. green & brn (No. 121)	8·50	35·00	3·50
O49	15	5s. black and blue-green (No. 64a) (3.51)	£180	90·00	9·00
O50		5s. black and pale blue-green (I) (No. 122) (2.53)	60·00	75·00	6·50
		a. Black & deep yellow-green (II) (No. 122a) (1.54)	70·00	90·00	9·00
O51	23	10s. blue and blackish brown (No. 64ba)	70·00	£170	22·00

The use of official stamps ceased in January 1955.

XI. BOPHUTHATSWANA

The Tswana Territory Authority was established by South Africa in 1968, and was granted internal self-government in 1972 under the Bantu Homelands Constitution Act. Bophuthatswana became fully independent on 6 December 1977. This independence did not receive international political recognition, but the stamps were accepted as valid on international mail.

PRINTERS. All the following stamps were printed in lithography by the South African Government Printer, Pretoria.

(Des A. H. Barrett)

1977 (6 Dec). *Independence. T 1 and similar horiz designs. Multicoloured. P 12½.*

1	4 c. Type 1		40	45
2	10 c. Leopard (national emblem)		90	70
3	15 c. Coat of arms		1·50	1·00
4	20 c. National flag		1·75	1·40
1/4		Set of 4	4·00	3·25

(Des A. H. Barrett)

1977 (6 Dec)**–82.** *Tribal Totems. T 2 and similar horiz designs. Multicoloured. P 12½.*

5	1 c. Type 2		30	15
	a. Perf 14 (15.4.81)		20	15
6	2 c. Bush Pig (Kolobeng)		30	15
	a. Perf 14 (21.6.82)		20	15
7	3 c. Chacma Baboon (Hurutshe and Tlharo)		30	15
	a. Perf 14 (18.8.82)		20	15
8	4 c. Leopard (national emblem)		3·00	1·25
	a. Perf 14 (6.7.79)		20	10
9	5 c. Crocodile (Kwena and Fokeng)		1·00	50
	a. Perf 14 (25.1.80)		20	10
10	6 c. Savanna Monkey (Kgatla)		20	10
11	7 c. Lion (Taung)		1·40	60
	a. Perf 14 (18.12.79)		30	15
12	8 c. Spotted Hyena (Phiring)		35	15
	a. Perf 14 (2.2.82)		20	15
13	9 c. Cape Porcupine (Rokologadi)		25	15
14	10 c. Aardvark (Tlokwa)		25	10
	a. Perf 14 (21.6.82)		25	10
15	15 c. Tilapia (fish) (Tlhaping)		30	15
16	20 c. Hunting Dog (Tlhalerwa)		25	20
17	25 c. Common Duiker (Mfatlha)		40	30
18	30 c. African Elephant (Tlhako, Tloung and Pô)		60	45
19	50 c. Python (Nogeng)		70	50
20	1 r. Hippopotamus (Kubung)		1·40	1·25
21	2 r. Greater Kudu (Rolong)		1·75	2·50
5/21		Set of 17 (cheapest)	6·00	5·75

3 Infected Kidney

(Des A. H. Barrett)

1978 (4 Apr). *World Hypertension Month. T 3 and similar horiz designs. Multicoloured. P 12×12½.*

22	4 c. Type 3		50	25
23	10 c. Heart and spoon of salt		70	70
24	15 c. Spoon reflecting skull, knife and fork		1·25	1·25
22/4		Set of 3	2·25	2·00

4 Skull behind Wheel of Car

5 Cutting Slabs of Travertine

1978 (12 July). *Road Safety. T 4 and similar horiz designs. Multicoloured. P 12×12½.*

25	4 c. Type 4		70	40
26	10 c. Child knocked off tricycle		1·10	80
27	15 c. Pedestrian stepping in front of car		1·25	1·10
28	20 c. Cyclist ignoring stop sign		1·75	1·75
25/8		Set of 4	4·25	3·50

(Des A. H. Barrett)

1978 (3 Oct). *Semi-precious Stones. T 5 and similar horiz designs. Multicoloured. P 12×12½.*

29	4 c. Type 5		65	25
30	10 c. Polishing travertine		1·25	85
31	15 c. Sorting semi-precious stones		1·50	1·25
32	20 c. Factory at Taung		2·25	1·60
29/32		Set of 4	5·00	3·50

6 Wright Flyer I

(Des A. H. Barrett)

1978 (1 Dec). *75th Anniv of First Powered Flight by Wright Brothers. T* **6** *and similar horiz design. P* 12½.

33	10 c. black, deep grey-blue and brown-red		1·25	1·00
34	15 c. black, deep grey-blue and brown-red		1·75	1·50

Design:—15 c. Orville and Wilbur Wright.

7 Pres. Lucas M. Mangope   8 Drying Germinated Wheat Sorghum

(Des A. H. Barrett)

1978 (6 Dec). *First Anniv of Independence. T* **7** *and similar vert design. Multicoloured. P* 12½.

35	4 c. Type **7**		20	20
36	15 c. Full face portrait of President		60	60

(Des A. H. Barrett)

1979 (28 Feb). *Sorghum Beer-making. T* **8** *and similar horiz designs. Multicoloured. P* 13½×14.

37	4 c. Type **8**		35	20
38	15 c. Cooking the ground grain		95	75
39	20 c. Sieving the liquid		1·10	85
40	25 c. Drinking the beer		1·50	1·25
37/40		*Set of* 4	3·50	2·75

9 Kallie Knoetze (South Africa)   10 Emblem and Drawing by Hendrick Sebapo of Local Fable

1979 (2 June). *Knoetze–Tate Boxing Match. T* **9** *and similar horiz design. Multicoloured. P* 13½×14.

41	15 c. Type **9**		65	75
	a. Pair. Nos. 41/2		1·25	1·50
42	15 c. John Tate (U.S.A.)		65	75

Nos. 41/2 were printed together, *se-tenant*, in pairs throughout the sheet.

1979 (7 June). *International Year of the Child. Children's Drawings of Local Fables. T* **10** *and similar horiz designs. Multicoloured. P* 14.

43	4 c. Type **10**		20	20
44	15 c. Family with animals (Daisy Morapedi)		25	35
45	20 c. Man's head and landscape (Peter Tladi)		35	45
46	25 c. Old man, boy and donkey (Hendrick Sebapo)		50	60
43/6		*Set of* 4	1·10	1·40

11 Miner and Molten Platinum   12 Cattle

(Des B. Sargent)

1979 (15 Aug). *Platinum Industry. T* **11** *and similar horiz designs. P* 13½×14.

47	4 c. multicoloured		25	10
48	15 c. multicoloured		35	30
49	20 c. multicoloured		45	45
50	25 c. black, grey and deep grey		60	65
47/50		*Set of* 4	1·50	1·40

Designs:—15 c. Platinum granules and industrial use; 20 c. Telecommunications satellite; 25 c. Jewellery.

(Des A. H. Barrett)

1979 (25 Oct). *Agriculture. T* **12** *and similar horiz designs. Multicoloured. P* 13½×14.

51	5 c. Type **12**		20	20
52	15 c. Picking cotton		25	25
53	20 c. Scientist examining maize		30	30
54	25 c. Catch of fish		35	35
51/4		*Set of* 4	1·00	1·00

13 Cigarettes forming Cross   14 *Landolphia capensis*   15 Pied Babbler

(Des A. H. Barrett)

1980 (5 Mar). *Anti-smoking Campaign. P* 14×13½.

55	**13** 5 c. multicoloured		40	20

(Des D. Findlay)

1980 (4 June). *Edible Wild Fruits. T* **14** *and similar vert designs. Multicoloured. P* 14×13½.

56	5 c. Type **14**		15	15
57	10 c. *Vangueria infausta*		30	30
58	15 c. *Bequaertiodendron magalismontanum*		40	40
59	20 c. *Sclerocarya caffra*		55	55
56/9		*Set of* 4	1·25	1·25

(Des D. Findlay)

1980 (10 Sept). *Birds. T* **15** *and similar vert designs. Multicoloured. P* 14×13½.

60	5 c. Type **15**		30	20
61	10 c. Carmine Bee Eater		40	35
62	15 c. Shaft-tailed Whydah		60	60
63	20 c. Meyer's Parrot		70	65
60/3		*Set of* 4	1·75	1·60

16 Sun City Hotel   17 Deaf Child

(Des P. Roos and G. Mynhardt)

1980 (5 Dec). *Tourism. Sun City. T* **16** *and similar horiz designs. Multicoloured. P* 13½×14.

64	5 c. Type **16**		10	15
65	10 c. Gary Player Country Club		40	30
66	15 c. Casino		45	50
67	20 c. Extravaganza		50	70
64/7		*Set of* 4	1·25	1·50

(Des H. Botha)

1981 (30 Jan). *International Year of Disabled Persons. T* **17** *and similar vert designs. Multicoloured. P* 14×13½.

68	5 c. Type **17**		15	10
69	15 c. Blind child		30	20
70	20 c. Archer in wheelchair		45	35
71	25 c. Tuberculosis X-ray		60	60
68/71		*Set of* 4	1·40	1·10

18 "Behold the Lamb of God..."   19 Siemens and Halske Wall Telephone, 1885

(Des J. Meyer)

1981 (1 Apr). *Easter. T* **18** *and similar horiz designs. Multicoloured. P* 13½×14.

72	5 c. Type **18**		10	10
73	15 c. Bread ("I am the bread of life")		25	25
74	20 c. Shepherd ("I am the good shepherd...")		35	35
75	25 c. Wheatfield ("Unless a grain of wheat falls into the earth and dies...")		45	45
72/5		*Set of* 4	1·00	1·00

(Des J. Hoekstra)

1981 (31 July). *History of the Telephone (1st series). T* **19** *and similar vert designs. Multicoloured. P* 14×13½.

76	5 c. Type **19**		10	10
77	15 c. Ericsson telephone, 1895		25	25
78	20 c. Hasler telephone, 1900		35	35
79	25 c. Mix and Genest wall telephone, 1904		45	45
76/9		*Set of* 4	1·00	1·00

See also Nos. 92/5, 108/11 and 146/9.

20 *Themeda triandra*   21 Boy Scout   22 Jesus arriving at Bethany (John 12:1)

(Des D. Findlay)

1981 (25 Nov). *Indigenous Grasses (1st series). T* **20** *and similar vert designs. Multicoloured. P* 14×13½.

80	5 c. Type **20**		10	10
81	15 c. *Rhynchelytrum repens*		25	25
82	20 c. *Eragrostis capensis*		30	30
83	25 c. *Monocymbium ceresiiforme*		40	40
80/3		*Set of* 4	95	95

See also Nos. 116/19.

(Des Sheila Nowers)

1982 (29 Jan). *75th Anniv of Boy Scout Movement. T* **21** *and similar vert designs. Multicoloured. P* 14×13½.

84	5 c. Type **21**		15	10
85	15 c. Mafeking siege stamps		35	35
86	20 c. Original cadet		40	40
87	25 c. Lord Baden-Powell		45	45
84/7		*Set of* 4	1·25	1·10

(Des J. Meyer)

1982 (1 Apr). *Easter. Palm Sunday. T* **22** *and similar vert designs. Multicoloured. P* 14×13½.

88	15 c. Type **22**		25	25
89	20 c. Jesus sending disciples for donkey (Matthew 21:1,2)		30	30
90	25 c. Disciples taking donkey (Mark 11:5,6)		40	40
91	30 c. Disciples with donkey and foal (Matthew 21:7)		45	45
88/91		*Set of* 4	1·25	1·25

23 Ericsson Telephone, 1878   24 Old Parliament Building

(Des J. Hoekstra)

1982 (3 Sept). *History of the Telephone (2nd series). T* **23** *and similar vert designs. Multicoloured. P* 14.

92	8 c. Type **23**		15	10
93	15 c. Ericsson telephone, 1885		20	20
94	20 c. Ericsson telephone, 1893		20	20
95	25 c. Siemens and Halske telephone, 1898		30	30
92/5		*Set of* 4	75	70

(Des A. H. Barrett)

1982 (12 Dec). *Fifth Anniv of Independence. T* **24** *and similar horiz designs. Multicoloured. P* 13½×14.

96	8 c. Type **24**		10	10
97	15 c. New government offices		20	20
98	20 c. University, Mmabatho		25	25
99	25 c. Civic Centre, Mmabatho		30	30
96/9		*Set of* 4	75	75

25 White Rhinoceros

(Des P. Bosman)

1983 (5 Jan). *Pilanesberg Nature Reserve. T* **25** *and similar horiz designs. Multicoloured. P* 13½×14.

100	8 c. Type **25**		30	10
101	20 c. Common Zebras		40	30
102	25 c. Sable Antelope		40	35
103	40 c. Hartebeest		60	60
100/3		*Set of* 4	1·50	1·10

26 Disciples bringing Donkeys to Jesus (Matthew 21:7)   27 Kori Bustard

(Des Sheila Nowers)

1983 (30 Mar). *Easter. Palm Sunday. T* **26** *and similar horiz designs. Multicoloured. P* 14×13½.

104	8 c. Type **26**	15	10
105	20 c. Jesus stroking colt (Mark 11:7)	35	30
106	25 c. Jesus enters Jerusalem on donkey (Matthew 21:8)	40	35
107	40 c. Crowd welcoming Jesus (Mark 11:9)	65	60
104/7	*Set of* 4	1·40	1·25

(Des I. Ellithorne)

1983 (22 June). *History of the Telephone* (3rd series). *Vert designs as T* **19**. *Multicoloured. P* 14×13½.

108	10 c. A.T.M. table telephone, *c.* 1920	15	10
109	20 c. A/S Elektrisk wall telephone, *c.* 1900	30	30
110	25 c. Ericsson wall telephone, *c.* 1900	35	35
111	40 c. Ericsson wall telephone, *c.* 1900 (*different*)	60	60
108/11	*Set of* 4	1·25	1·25

(Des D. Finlay)

1983 (14 Sept). *Birds of the Veld. T* **27** *and similar vert designs. Multicoloured. P* 14.

112	10 c. Type **27**	30	20
113	20 c. Little Black Bustard ("Black Korhaan")	45	45
114	25 c. Crested Bustard ("Red-crested Korhaan")	55	55
115	40 c. Barrow's Bustard ("Stanley Bustard")	70	80
112/15	*Set of* 4	1·75	1·75

(Des D. Findlay)

1984 (20 Jan). *Indigenous Grasses* (2nd series). *Vert designs as T* **20**. *Multicoloured. P* 14½×14.

116	10 c. *Panicum maximum*	15	10
117	20 c. *Hyparrhenia dregeana*	25	20
118	25 c. *Cenchrus ciliaris*	35	35
119	40 c. *Urochloa brachyura*	60	70
116/19	*Set of* 4	1·25	1·25

28 Money-lenders in the Temple (Mark 11:11)	**29** Car Upholstery, Ga-Rankuwa

(Des J. van Niekerk)

1984 (23 Mar). *Easter. T* **28** *and similar horiz designs. Multicoloured. P* 14½×14.

120	10 c. Type **28**	15	10
121	20 c. Jesus driving the money-lenders from the Temple (Mark 11:15)	25	20
122	25 c. Jesus and fig tree (Matthew 21:19)	35	35
123	40 c. The withering of the fig tree (Matthew 21:19)	60	70
120/3	*Set of* 4	1·25	1·25

(Des A. H. Barrett)

1984 (2 Apr)–**94**. *Industries. T* **29** *and similar horiz designs. Multicoloured. Chalk-surfaced paper (except Nos. 134/5). P* 14.

124	1 c. Textile mill (25.10.85)	10	10
	a. Ordinary paper (18.7.94)	30	30
125	2 c. Sewing sacks, Selosesha (25.10.85)	10	10
	a. Ordinary paper (5.6.92)	30	30
126	3 c. Ceramic tiles, Babelegi (25.10.85)	10	10
127	4 c. Sheepskin car seat covers (25.10.85)	10	10
	a. Ordinary paper (3.7.92)	30	30
128	5 c. Crossbow manufacture (25.10.85)	15	10
	a. Ordinary paper (16.11.92)	30	30
129	6 c. Automobile parts, Babelegi (25.10.85)	15	10
	a. Ordinary paper (26.6.92)	30	30
130	7 c. Hosiery, Babelegi (25.10.85)	15	10
	a. Ordinary paper (26.6.92)	30	30
131	8 c. Specialised bicycle factory, Babelegi (25.10.85)	30	10
132	9 c. Lawn mower assembly line (25.10.85)	30	15
133	10 c. Dress factory, Thaba 'Nchu (25.10.85)	20	10
134	11 c. Molten platinum (*ordinary paper*)	60	20
135	12 c. Type **29** (1.4.85) (*ordinary paper*)	40	15
	a. Chalk-surfaced paper (5.12.85)	40	15
136	14 c. Maize mill, Mafeking (1.4.86)	50	15
137	15 c. Plastic bags, Babelegi (25.10.85)	25	15
	a. Ordinary paper (3.7.92)	1·25	70
137*b*	16 c. Brick factory, Mmabatho (1.4.87)	60	15
137*c*	18 c. Cutlery manufacturing, Mogwase (3.7.89)	60	15
138	20 c. Men's clothing, Babelegi (25.10.85)	25	15
	a. Ordinary paper (26.6.92)	1·40	75
138*b*	21 c. Welding bus chassis (3.8.90)	50	50
	ba. Strip of five. Nos. 138*b*/*f*	2·25	
138*c*	21 c. Fitting engine to bus chassis (3.8.90)	50	50
138*d*	21 c. Bus body construction (3.8.90)	50	50
138*e*	21 c. Spraying and finishing bus (3.8.90)	50	50
138*f*	21 c. Finished buses (3.8.90)	50	50
139	25 c. Chromium plating pram parts (25.10.85)	30	20
	a. Ordinary paper (24.1.92)	60	30
140	30 c. Spray painting metal beds (25.10.85)	40	25
	a. Ordinary paper (1.2.89)	75	50
141	50 c. Milk processing plant (25.10.85)	65	40
	a. Ordinary paper (1.2.89)	85	75
142	1 r. Modern printing works (25.10.85)	1·25	75
143	2 r. Industrial complex, Babelegi (25.10.85)	3·00	2·75
124/43	*Set of* 27	11·50	8·00

Nos. 138*b*/*f* were printed together, *se-tenant*, in strips of five throughout the sheet.

(Des I. Ellithorne)

1984 (20 July). *History of the Telephone* (4th series). *Vert designs as T* **19**. *Multicoloured. P* 14.

146	11 c. Schuchhardt table telephone, 1905	15	10
147	20 c. Siemens wall telephone, 1925	25	20
148	25 c. Ericsson table telephone, 1900	30	30
149	30 c. Oki table telephone, 1930	40	50
146/9	*Set of* 4	1·00	1·00

30 Yellow-throated Plated Lizard	**31** Giving Oral Vaccine against Polio

(Des Sheila Nowers)

1984 (25 Sept). *Lizards. T* **30** *and similar horiz designs. Multicoloured. P* 14×14½.

150	11 c. Type **30**	20	10
151	25 c. Transvaal Girdled Lizard	30	30
152	30 c. Ocellated Sand Lizard	35	40
153	45 c. Bibron's Thick-toed Gecko	50	60
150/3	*Set of* 4	1·25	1·25

(Des D. Thorpe)

1985 (25 Jan). *Health. T* **31** *and similar vert designs. Multicoloured. P* 14.

154	11 c. Type **31**	35	10
155	25 c. Vaccinating against measles	45	30
156	30 c. Examining child for diphtheria	50	40
157	50 c. Examining child for whooping cough	70	65
154/7	*Set of* 4	1·75	1·25

32 Chief Montshiwa of Barolong booRatshidi	**33** The Sick flock to Jesus in the Temple (Matthew 21:14)

(Des A. H. Barrett)

1985 (11 Mar). *Centenary of Mafeking. T* **32** *and similar vert design. P* 14½×14.

158	11 c. black, grey and orange	20	10
159	25 c. black, grey and dull violet-blue	40	30

Design:—25 c. Sir Charles Warren.

(Des J. van Niekerk)

1985 (2 Apr). *Easter. T* **33** *and similar horiz designs. Multicoloured. P* 14.

160	12 c. Type **33**	20	10
161	25 c. Jesus cures the sick (Matthew 21:14)	30	20
162	30 c. Children praising Jesus (Matthew 21:15)	35	30
163	50 c. Community leaders discussing Jesus's acceptance of praise (Matthew 21:15,16)	50	60
160/3	*Set of* 4	1·25	1·10

34 *Faurea saligna* and Planting Sapling	**35** Jesus at the House of Mary and Martha, Bethany (John 12:2)

(Des B. Jackson)

1985 (4 July). *Tree Conservation. T* **34** *and similar vert designs. Multicoloured. P* 14.

164	12 c. Type **34**	20	10
165	25 c. *Boscia albitrunca* and Kudu	25	20
166	30 c. *Erythrina lysistemon* and Mariqua Sunbird	35	30
167	50 c. *Bequaertiondendron magalismontanum* and bee	55	50
164/7	*Set of* 4	1·25	1·00

COVER PRICES

Cover factors are quoted at the beginning of each country for most issues to 1945. An explanation of the system can be found on page x. The factors quoted do not, however, apply to philatelic covers.

(Des J. van Niekerk)

1986 (6 Mar). *Easter. T* **35** *and similar horiz designs. Multicoloured. P* 14½×14.

168	12 c. Type **35**	25	10
169	20 c. Mary anointing Jesus's feet (John 12:3)	30	20
170	25 c. Mary drying Jesus's feet with her hair (John 12:3)	35	25
171	30 c. Disciple condemns Mary for anointing Jesus's head with oil (Matthew 26:7)	45	50
168/71	*Set of* 4	1·25	95

PHILATELIC FOUNDATION MINIATURE SHEETS. These miniature sheets were issued by the Philatelic Foundation of Southern Africa and not by the postal administration. They could be purchased by post or from a limited number of philatelic offices at a premium in aid of various national and international stamp exhibitions.

36 "Wesleyan Mission Station and Residence of Moroka, Chief of the Barolong, 1834" (C. D. Bell)	**37** Farmer using Tractor (agricultural development)

1986 (15 May). *Paintings of Thaba 'Nchu. T* **36** *and similar horiz designs. Multicoloured. P* 14×14½.

172	14 c. Type **36**	25	15
173	20 c. "James Archbell's Congregation, 1834" (Charles Davidson Bell)	40	30
174	25 c. "Mission Station at Thaba 'Nchu, 1850" (Thomas Baines)	45	50
172/4	*Set of* 3	1·00	85

The 25 c. value exists as a Philatelic Foundation miniature sheet.

(Des Sheila Nowers)

1986 (6 Aug). *Temisano Development Project. T* **37** *and similar horiz designs. Multicoloured. P* 14.

175	14 c. Type **37**	20	10
176	20 c. Children at school (community development)	30	20
177	25 c. Repairing engine (training)	35	30
178	30 c. Grain elevator (secondary industries)	50	50
175/8	*Set of* 4	1·25	1·00

38 Stewardesses and Cessna Citation II of B.O.P. Airways	**39** Netball

(Des R. Smith)

1986 (16 Oct). *B.O.P. Airways. T* **38** *and similar horiz designs. Multicoloured. P* 14.

179	14 c. Type **38**	25	10
180	20 c. Passengers disembarking from Boeing 707	40	20
181	25 c. Mmabatho International Airport	50	35
182	30 c. B.O.P. Airways Cessna Citation II	60	50
179/82	*Set of* 4	1·60	1·10

(Des B. Jackson)

1987 (22 Jan). *Sports. T* **39** *and similar vert designs. Multicoloured. P* 14×14½.

183	14 c. Type **39**	20	15
184	20 c. Tennis	30	30
185	25 c. Football	30	30
186	30 c. Athletics	45	50
183/6	*Set of* 4	1·10	1·10

40 *Berkheya zeyheri*	**41** E. M. Mokgoko Farmer Training Centre

(Des Jeanette Stead)

1987 (23 Apr). *Wild Flowers. T* **40** *and similar vert designs. Multicoloured. P* 14×14½.

187	16 c. Type **40**	25	15
188	20 c. *Plumbago auriculata*	35	35
189	25 c. *Pterodiscus speciosus*	35	35
190	30 c. *Gazania krebsiana*	40	50
187/90	*Set of* 4	1·25	1·25

The 25 c. value exists as a Philatelic Foundation miniature sheet.

(Des E. Dias)

1987 (6 Aug). *Tertiary Education.* T **41** *and similar horiz designs. Multicoloured.* P 14½×14.
191	16 c. Type 41		20	15
192	20 c. Main lecture block, University of Bophuthatswana		30	35
193	25 c. Manpower Centre		30	35
194	30 c. Hotel Training School		30	50
191/4		*Set of 4*	1·00	1·25

42 Posts

43 Jesus entering Jerusalem on Donkey (John 12:12–14)

(Des J. van Niekerk)

1987 (4 Dec). *Tenth Anniv of Independence. Communications.* T **42** *and similar horiz designs. Multicoloured.* P 14½×14.
195	16 c. Type 42		25	15
196	30 c. Telephone		35	35
197	40 c. Radio		35	35
198	50 c. Television		40	50
195/8		*Set of 4*	1·25	1·25

(Des J. van Niekerk)

1988 (31 Mar). *Easter.* T **43** *and similar horiz designs. Multicoloured.* P 14½×14.
199	16 c. Type 43		25	15
200	30 c. Judas negotiating with chief priests (Mark 14:10–11)		35	35
201	40 c. Jesus washing the disciples' feet (John 13:5)		35	35
202	50 c. Jesus handing bread to Judas (John 13:26)		40	50
199/202		*Set of 4*	1·25	1·25

44 Environment Education

45 Sunflowers

(Des A. H. Barrett)

1988 (23 June). *National Parks Board.* T **44** *and similar horiz designs. Multicoloured.* P 14½×14.
203	16 c. Type 44		25	15
204	30 c. Rhinoceros (Conservation)		40	40
205	40 c. Catering workers		40	40
206	50 c. Cheetahs (Tourism)		55	65
203/6		*Set of 4*	1·40	1·40

The 50 c. value exists as a Philatelic Foundation miniature sheet.

(Des A. H. Barrett)

1988 (15 Sept). *Crops.* T **45** *and similar horiz designs. Multicoloured.* P 14½×14.
207	16 c. Type 45		25	15
208	30 c. Peanuts		35	35
209	40 c. Cotton		45	45
210	50 c. Cabbages		60	60
207/10		*Set of 4*	1·50	1·40

46 Ngotwane Dam

47 The Last Supper (Matthew 26:26)

(Des Estelle Marais)

1988 (17 Nov). *Dams.* T **46** *and similar horiz designs. Multicoloured.* P 14½×14.
211	16 c. Type 46		30	20
212	30 c. Groothoek dam		50	50
213	40 c. Sehujwane dam		50	50
214	50 c. Molatedi dam		70	70
211/14		*Set of 4*	1·75	1·75

(Des J. van Niekerk)

1989 (9 Mar). *Easter.* T **47** *and similar horiz designs. Multicoloured.* P 14½×14.
215	16 c. Type 47		35	20
216	30 c. Jesus praying in Garden of Gethsemane (Matthew 26:39)		50	50
217	40 c. Judas kissing Jesus (Mark 14:45)		60	60
218	50 c. Peter severing ear of High Priest's slave (John 18:10)		75	90
215/18		*Set of 4*	2·00	2·00

48 Cock (Thembi Atong)

49 Black-shouldered Kite

1989 (11 May). *Children's Art.* T **48** *and similar horiz designs depicting winning entries in National Children's Day Art Competition. Multicoloured.* P 14½×14.
219	18 c. Type 48		30	20
220	30 c. Traditional thatched hut (Muhammad Mahri)		40	40
221	40 c. Airplane, telephone wires and houses (Tshepo Mashokwi)		45	45
222	50 c. City scene (Miles Brown)		50	60
219/22		*Set of 4*	1·50	1·50

1989 (1 Sept). *Birds of Prey.* T **49** *and similar vert designs showing paintings by Claude Finch-Davies. Multicoloured.* P 14×14½.
223	18 c. Type 49		80	30
224	30 c. Pale Chanting Goshawk		1·00	75
225	40 c. Lesser Kestrel		1·25	1·10
226	50 c. Short-toed Eagle		1·60	1·50
223/6		*Set of 4*	4·25	3·25

The 50 c. value exists as a Philatelic Foundation miniature sheet.

50 Bilobial House

51 Early Learning Schemes

(Des A. George)

1989 (28 Nov). *Traditional Houses.* T **50** *and similar horiz designs. Multicoloured.* P 14½×14.
227	18 c. Type 50		25	20
228	30 c. House with courtyards at front and side	35	35
229	40 c. House with conical roof		35	35
230	50 c. House with rounded roof		40	50
227/30		*Set of 4*	1·25	1·25

(Des D. McLean)

1990 (11 Jan). *Community Services.* T **51** *and similar horiz designs. Multicoloured.* P 14.
231	18 c. Type 51		25	20
232	30 c. Clinics		35	35
233	40 c. Libraries		35	35
234	50 c. Hospitals		40	45
231/4		*Set of 4*	1·25	1·25

52 Lesser Climbing Mouse

53 Variegated Sandgrouse

(Des A. Ainslie)

1990 (11 Apr). *Small Mammals.* T **52** *and similar horiz designs. Multicoloured.* P 14.
235	21 c. Type 52		30	20
236	30 c. Zorilla		40	40
237	40 c. Transvaal Elephant Shrew		60	60
238	50 c. Large-toothed Rock Hyrax		80	85
235/8		*Set of 4*	1·90	1·90

The 50 c. value exists as a Philatelic Foundation miniature sheet.

1990 (12 July). *Sandgrouse.* T **53** *and similar horiz designs showing paintings by Claude Finch-Davies. Multicoloured.* P 14×14½.
239	21 c. Type 53		90	30
240	35 c. Double-banded Sandgrouse		1·10	75
241	40 c. Namaqua Sandgrouse		1·10	90
242	50 c. Yellow-throated Sandgrouse		1·40	1·40
239/42		*Set of 4*	4·00	3·00

54 Basketry

55 Sud Aviation SE 3130 Alouette II Helicopter

(Des Sheila Nowers)

1990 (4 Oct). *Traditional Crafts.* T **54** *and similar vert designs. Multicoloured.* P 14½.
243	21 c. Type 54		40	20
244	35 c. Tanning		60	60
245	40 c. Beer making		60	65
246	50 c. Pottery		65	75
243/6		*Set of 4*	2·00	2·00

1990 (12 Dec). *Bophuthatswana Air Force.* T **55** *and similar horiz designs. Multicoloured.* P 14½×14.
247	21 c. Type 55		1·00	1·00
	a. Horiz strip of 5. Nos. 247/51		4·50	
248	21 c. MBB-Kawasaki Bk-117 helicopter		1·00	1·00
249	21 c. Pilatus PC-7 Turbo Trainer		1·00	1·00
250	21 c. Pilatus PC-6 Turbo Porter		1·00	1·00
251	21 c. CASA C-212 Aviocar		1·00	1·00
247/51		*Set of 5*	4·50	4·50

Nos. 247/51 were printed together, *se-tenant*, in horizontal strips of 5 throughout the sheet.

56 Wild Custard Apple

57 Arrest of Jesus (Mark 14:46)

(Des Gillian Condy)

1991 (24 Jan). *Edible Wild Fruit.* T **56** *and similar vert designs. Multicoloured.* P 14×14½.
252	21 c. Type 56		35	25
253	35 c. Spine-leaved Monkey Orange		50	60
254	40 c. Sycamore Fig		55	65
255	50 c. Kei Apple		60	75
252/5		*Set of 4*	1·75	2·00

(Des J. van Niekerk)

1991 (21 Mar). *Easter.* T **57** *and similar horiz designs. Multicoloured.* P 14½×14.
256	21 c. Type 57		35	25
257	35 c. First trial by the Sanhedrin (Mark 14:53)		50	50
258	40 c. Assault and derision of Jesus after sentence (Mark 14:65)		55	55
259	50 c. Servant girl recognizing Peter (Mark 14:67)		60	70
256/9		*Set of 4*	1·75	1·75

58 Class 7A Locomotive No. 350, 1897

59 Caneiro Chart, 1502

(Des C. Becker)

1991 (4 July). *Steam Locomotives.* T **58** *and similar horiz designs. Multicoloured.* P 14.
260	25 c. Class 6A locomotive No. 194 with trucks and caboose, 1897 (71×25 mm)		75	55
261	40 c. Type 58		95	75
262	50 c. Double-boiler Class 6Z locomotives pulling Cecil Rhode's funeral train (71×25 mm)		1·10	1·10
263	60 c. Class 8 locomotive at Mafeking station, 1904		1·25	1·50
260/3		*Set of 4*	3·50	3·50

The 60 c. value exists as a Philatelic Foundation miniature sheet.
See also Nos. 293/6.

60 Fracanzano Map, 1508

61 Delivery of Jesus to Pilate (Mark 15:1)

(Des C. Becker (25, 40 c.), T. Marais (others))

1991 (12 Sept). *Old Maps (1st series).* T **59** *and similar vert designs. Multicoloured.* P 14×14½.
264	25 c. Type 59		75	40
265	40 c. Cantino Chart, 1502		1·10	85
266	50 c. Giovanni Contarini's map, 1506		1·25	1·25
267	60 c. Martin Waldseemüller's map, 1507		1·40	1·75
264/7		*Set of 4*	4·00	3·75

See also Nos. 268/71 and 297/300.

(Des Liza van der Wal)

1992 (9 Jan). *Old Maps* (2nd series). *T* **60** *and similar horiz designs. Multicoloured. P* 14¹/₂×14.
268	27 c. Type 60			75	40
269	45 c. Martin Waldseemüller's map (from edition of Ptolemy), 1513		1·10	85
270	65 c. Section of Waldseemüller's woodcut *Carta Marina Navigatora Portugallan Navigationes,* 1516		1·25	1·25
271	85 c. Map from Laurent Fries's *Geographia,* 1522		1·40	1·75
268/71			*Set of* 4	4·00	3·75

(Des J. van Niekerk)

1992 (1 Apr). *Easter. T* **61** *and similar horiz designs. Multicoloured. P* 14¹/₂×14.
272	27 c. Type 61			25	20
273	45 c. Scourging of Jesus (Mark 15:15)		40	40
274	65 c. Placing crown of thorns on Jesus's head (Mark 15:17–18)		50	70
275	85 c. Soldiers mocking Jesus (Mark 15:19)		60	90
272/5			*Set of* 4	1·60	2·00

62 Sweet Thorn 63 View of Palace across Lake

(Des Gillian Condy)

1992 (18 June). *Acacia Trees. T* **62** *and similar horiz designs. Multicoloured. P* 14¹/₂×14.
276	35 c. Type 62			30	25
277	70 c. Camel Thorn			50	60
278	90 c. Umbrella Thorn			60	80
279	1 r. 05, Black Thorn			70	1·00
276/9			*Set of* 4	1·90	2·40

The 70 c. value exists as a Philatelic Foundation miniature sheet.

1992 (19 Nov). *The Lost City Complex, Sun City. T* **63** *and similar horiz designs. Multicoloured. P* 14×14¹/₂.
280	35 c. Type 63			35	45
	a. Horiz strip of 5. Nos. 280/4		1·50	
281	35 c. Palace façade			35	45
282	35 c. Palace porte cochère			35	45
283	35 c. Palace lobby			35	45
284	35 c. Tusk Bar, Palace			35	45
280/4			*Set of* 5	1·50	2·00

Nos. 280/4 were printed together, *se-tenant,* in horizontal strips of 5 throughout the sheet.

64 Light Sussex 65 Pilate offering to release Barabbas (Luke 23:25)

(Des M. Ginn)

1993 (12 Feb). *Chickens. T* **64** *and similar horiz designs. Multicoloured. P* 14¹/₂×14.
285	35 c. Type 64			30	25
286	70 c. Rhode Island Red			50	50
287	90 c. Brown Leghorn			60	80
288	1 r. 05, White Leghorn			70	1·10
285/8			*Set of* 4	1·90	2·40

The 70 c. value exists as a Philatelic Foundation miniature sheet.

(Des J. van Niekerk)

1993 (5 Mar). *Easter. T* **65** *and similar horiz designs. Multicoloured. P* 14¹/₂×14.
289	35 c. Type 65			55	30
290	70 c. Jesus falling under cross (John 19:17)		85	75
291	90 c. Simon of Cyrene carrying cross (Mark 15:21)		1·00	1·00
292	1 r. 05, Jesus being nailed to cross (Mark 15:23)		1·25	1·60
289/92			*Set of* 4	3·25	3·25

66 Mafeking Locomotive Shed, 1933

(Des C. Becker)

1993 (18 June). *Steam Locomotives* (2nd series). *T* **66** *and similar multicoloured designs. P* 14.
293	45 c. Type 66			55	55
294	65 c. Rhodesian Railways steam locomotive No. 5, 1901 (34×25 *mm*)		65	65

295	85 c. Class 16B locomotive pulling "White Train" during Prince George's visit, 1934		85	85
296	1 r. 05, Class 19D locomotive, 1938 (34×25 *mm*)		1·10	1·25
293/6			*Set of* 4	2·75	3·00
MS297	127×113 mm. Nos. 293/6			2·75	3·25

67 Sebastian Münster's Map (from edition of Ptolemy), 1540 68 Crucifixion (Luke 23:33)

(Des C. Prinsloo)

1993 (20 Aug). *Old Maps* (3rd series). *T* **67** *and similar horiz designs. Multicoloured. P* 14¹/₂×14.
298	45 c. Type 67			50	40
299	65 c. Jacopo Gastaldi's map, 1564		65	65
300	75 c. Map from Mercator's *Atlas,* 1595		75	90
301	1 r. 05, Map from Ortelius's *Theatrum Orbis Terrarum,* 1570		90	1·25
298/301			*Set of* 4	2·50	2·75

(Des J. van Niekerk)

1994 (25 Mar). *Easter. T* **68** *and similar horiz designs. Multicoloured. P* 14¹/₂×14.
302	35 c. Type 68			55	45
303	65 c. Soldiers and Jews mocking Jesus (Luke 23:35–36)		85	75
304	85 c. Soldier offering Jesus vinegar (Luke 23:36)		95	95
305	1 r. 05, Jesus on cross and charge notice (Luke 23:38)		1·40	1·60
302/5			*Set of* 4	3·25	3·25

Bophuthatswana was reincorporated into the Republic of South Africa on 27 April 1994. Its postal service continued to operate, using South African stamps, until 1 April 1996 when it was integrated with that of the Republic.

XII. CISKEI

The Ciskei Territorial Authority was established in 1961 and autonomous government was granted in 1972 under the Bantu Homelands Constitution Act. Ciskei became fully independent on 4 December 1981. This independence did not receive international political recognition, but the stamps were accepted as valid on international mail.

PRINTERS. All the following stamps were printed in lithography by the South African Government Printer, Pretoria.

1 Dr. Lennox Sebe, Chief Minister 2 Knysna Turaco

(Des A. H. Barrett)

1981 (4 Dec). *Independence. T* **1** *and similar vert designs. Multicoloured. P* 14.
1	5 c. Type 1			10	10
2	15 c. Coat of arms			25	20
3	20 c. Flag			40	35
4	25 c. Mace			40	35
1/4			*Set of* 4	1·00	85

(Des D. Findlay)

1981 (4 Dec)**–90**. *Birds. T* **2** *and similar vert designs. Multicoloured. P* 14.
5	1 c. Type 2			20	15
6	2 c. Cape Wagtail			20	15
7	3 c. White-browed Coucal			30	15
8	4 c. Yellow-tufted Malachite Sunbird		50	15
9	5 c. Stanley Crane			50	15
10	6 c. African Red-winged Starling		50	15
11	7 c. Giant Kingfisher			50	15
12	8 c. Hadada Ibis			60	15
13	9 c. Black Cuckoo			50	15
14	10 c. Black-collared Barbet			50	15
14a	11 c. African Black-headed Oriole (2.4.84)		80	30
14b	12 c. Malachite Kingfisher (1.4.85)		1·10	50
14c	14 c. Hoopoe (1.4.86)			1·50	50
15	15 c. African Fish Eagle			60	30
15a	16 c. Cape Puff-back Flycatcher (1.4.87)		1·00	50
15b	18 c. Long-tailed Whydah (3.7.89)		1·50	60
16	20 c. Cape Longclaw			60	30
16a	21 c. Lemon Dove (3.7.90)			1·75	80

17	25 c. Cape Dikkop			50	40
18	30 c. African Green Pigeon		50	50
19	50 c. Cape Parrot			60	70
20	1 r. Narina Trogon			1·25	1·50
21	2 r. Cape Eagle Owl			2·50	2·75
5/21			*Set of* 23	16·00	10·00

3 Cecilia Makiwane (first Xhosa nurse) 4 Boom Sprayer

(Des A. H. Barrett)

1982 (30 Apr). *Nursing. T* **3** *and similar multicoloured designs. P* 14×13¹/₂ (*vert*) *or* 13¹/₂×14 (*horiz*).
22	8 c. Type 3			15	10
23	15 c. Operating theatre			30	30
24	20 c. Matron lighting nurse's lamp (*horiz*)	40	40
25	25 c. Nurses and patient (*horiz*)		50	50
22/5			*Set of* 4	1·25	1·10

(Des A. H. Barrett)

1982 (20 Aug). *Pineapple Industry. T* **4** *and similar horiz designs. Multicoloured. P* 13¹/₂×14.
26	8 c. Type 4			10	10
27	15 c. Harvesting			20	25
28	20 c. Despatch to cannery			25	30
29	30 c. Packing for local market		30	35
26/9			*Set of* 4	75	85

5 Brown Hare 6 Assegai

(Des A. H. Barrett)

1982 (29 Oct). *Small Mammals. T* **5** *and similar horiz designs. Multicoloured. P* 13¹/₂×14.
30	8 c. Type 5			15	15
31	15 c. Cape Fox			30	25
32	20 c. Cape Ground Squirrel			40	30
33	25 c. Caracal			50	35
30/3			*Set of* 4	1·25	95

(Des D. Findlay)

1983 (2 Feb). *Trees* (1st series). *T* **6** *and similar vert designs. Multicoloured. P* 14×13¹/₂.
34	8 c. Cabbage Tree			15	10
35	20 c. Type 6			30	30
36	25 c. Cape Chestnut			35	35
37	40 c. Outeniqua Yellowwood			50	55
34/7			*Set of* 4	1·10	1·10

See also Nos. 52/5.

7 Dusky Shark 8 Lovedale

(Des Sheila Nowers)

1983 (13 Apr). *Sharks. T* **7** *and similar horiz designs. Multicoloured. P* 14.
38	8 c. Type 7			15	15
39	20 c. Sand Tiger ("Ragged-tooth Shark")		40	40
40	25 c. Tiger Shark (57×21 *mm*)			45	45
41	30 c. Scalloped Hammerhead (57×21 *mm*)		50	50
42	40 c. Great White Shark (57×21 *mm*)		70	70
38/42			*Set of* 5	2·00	2·00

(Des A. H. Barrett)

1983 (6 July). *Educational Institutions. T* **8** *and similar horiz designs. P* 14.
43	10 c. stone, light brown and black		10	10
44	20 c. pale stone, olive-sepia and black		20	20
45	25 c. pale cinnamon, Venetian red and black	25	25
46	40 c. cinnamon, pinkish brown and black		40	45
43/6			*Set of* 4	80	85

Designs:—20 c. Fort Hare; 25 c. Healdtown; 40 c. Lennox Sebe.

9 White Drill
Uniform

10 Sandprawn

(Des A. May)

1983 (28 Sept). *British Military Uniforms (1st series). 6th (Warwickshire) Regiment of Foot, 1821–27. T* **9** *and similar vert designs. Multicoloured. P* 14.

47	20 c. Type **9**	..	..	40	40
	a. Horiz strip of 5. Nos. 47/51		..	1·75	
48	20 c. Light Company privates	..	..	40	40
49	20 c. Grenadier Company sergeants	..	40	40
50	20 c. Officers in undress blue frock-coats	..	40	40
51	20 c. Officer and field officer in parade order	..	40	40
47/51			*Set of* 5	1·75	1·75

Nos. 47/51 were printed together, *se-tenant*, in horizontal strips of 5 throughout the sheet.
See also Nos. 64/8 and 95/8.

(Des D. Findlay)

1984 (6 Jan). *Trees (2nd series). Vert designs as T* **6**. *Multicoloured. P* 14.

52	10 c. *Rhus chirindensis*	..	..	20	15
53	20 c. *Phoenix reclinata*	..	..	35	35
54	25 c. *Ptaeroxylon obliquum*	..	..	40	40
55	40 c. *Apodytes dimidiata*	..	..	55	55
52/5		..	*Set of* 4	1·40	1·25

(Des D. Thorpe)

1984 (12 Apr). *Fish-bait. T* **10** *and similar horiz designs. Multicoloured. P* 14×14½.

56	11 c. Type **10**	..	..	20	15
57	20 c. Coral Worm	..	..	30	30
58	25 c. Bloodworm	..	..	35	35
59	30 c. Red-bait	..	..	40	40
56/9		..	*Set of* 4	1·10	1·10

11 Banded Sand Martin

(Des Sheila Nowers)

1984 (17 Aug). *Migratory Birds. T* **11** *and similar horiz designs. Multicoloured. P* 14½×14.

60	11 c. Type **11**	..	..	25	20
61	25 c. House Martin	..	..	50	50
62	30 c. Greater Striped Swallow	..	60	60
63	45 c. Barn Swallow ("European Swallow")	..	80	85
60/3		..	*Set of* 4	1·90	1·90

(Des A. May)

1984 (26 Oct). *British Military Uniforms (2nd series). Cape Mounted Rifles. Vert designs as T* **9**. *Multicoloured. P* 14.

64	25 c. (1) Trooper in field and sergeant in undress uniforms, 1830	..	..	45	45
	a. Horiz strip of 5. Nos. 64/8	..	2·00	
65	25 c. (2) Trooper and sergeant in full dress, 1835	..	..	45	45
66	25 c. (3) Officers in undress, 1830	..	45	45
67	25 c. (4) Officers in full dress, 1827–34	..	45	45
68	25 c. (5) Officers in full dress, 1834	..	45	45
64/8			*Set of* 5	2·00	2·00

Nos. 64/8 were printed together, *se-tenant*, in horizontal strips of 5 throughout the sheet. Each stamp is inscribed at the foot with a number from "D1.5" to "D5.5". The first number is given in brackets in the listing to aid identification.

12 White Steenbras

13 Brownies holding
Handmade Doll

(Des D. Thorpe)

1985 (7 Mar). *Coastal Angling. T* **12** *and similar horiz designs. Multicoloured. P* 14.

69	11 c. Type **12**	..	..	30	20
70	25 c. Bronze Seabream	..	..	50	50
71	30 c. Kob	..	..	60	60
72	50 c. Spotted Grunt	..	..	85	85
69/72		..	*Set of* 4	2·00	1·90

(Des Sheila Nowers)

1985 (3 May). *International Youth Year. 75th Anniv of Girl Guide Movement. T* **13** *and similar horiz designs. Multicoloured. P* 14½×14.

73	12 c. Type **13**	..	..	15	10
74	25 c. Rangers planting trees	..	25	25
75	30 c. Guides with flag	..	..	30	30
76	50 c. Guides building fire	..	..	60	65
73/6			*Set of* 4	1·10	1·10

14 Furniture making

15 Antelope

(Des B. Jackson)

1985 (8 Aug). *Small Businesses. T* **14** *and similar horiz designs. Multicoloured. P* 14.

77	12 c. Type **14**	..	..	15	10
78	25 c. Dressmaking	..	..	30	30
79	30 c. Welding	..	..	30	30
80	50 c. Basketry	..	..	60	65
77/80		..	*Set of* 4	1·25	1·25

(Des R. Reynolds)

1985 (15 Nov). *Sail Troopships. T* **15** *and similar horiz designs. Multicoloured. P* 14.

81	12 c. Type **15**	..	..	20	15
82	25 c. Pilot	..	..	45	45
83	30 c. Salisbury	..	..	45	45
84	50 c. Olive Branch	..	..	80	85
81/4			*Set of* 4	1·75	1·75

16 Earth
showing Africa

17 Fifer in
Winter Dress

(Des J. van Ellinckhuijzen)

1986 (20 Mar). *Appearance of Halley's Comet. T* **16** *and similar vert designs. Multicoloured. P* 14.

85	12 c. (1) Earth showing South America	..	1·10	90
	a. Sheetlet. Nos. 85/94	..	10·00	
86	12 c. (2) Type **16**	..	..	1·10	90
87	12 c. (3) Stars and Moon	..	..	1·10	90
88	12 c. (4) Moon and Milky Way	..	1·10	90
89	12 c. (5) Milky Way and stars	..	1·10	90
90	12 c. (6) Earth showing Australia	..	1·10	90
91	12 c. (7) Earth and meteor	..	1·10	90
92	12 c. (8) Meteor, Moon and comet tail	..	1·10	90
93	12 c. (9) Comet head and Moon	..	1·10	90
94	12 c. (10) Sun	..	..	1·10	90
85/94			*Set of* 10	10·00	8·00

Nos. 85/94 were printed together, *se-tenant*, in sheetlets of 10 forming a composite design of the southern skies in April. Each stamp is inscribed with a number from "A1-10" to "A10-10". The first number is given in bracket in the listing to aid identification.

PHILATELIC FOUNDATION MINIATURE SHEETS.

These miniature sheets were issued by the Philatelic Foundation of Southern Africa and not by the postal administration. They could be purchased by post or from a limited number of philatelic offices at a premium in aid of various national and international stamp exhibitions.

(Des A. May)

1986 (12 June). *British Military Uniforms (3rd series). 98th Regiment of Foot. T* **17** *and similar vert designs. Multicoloured. P* 14.

95	14 c. Type **17**	..	..	20	15
96	20 c. Private in summer dress	..	30	30
97	25 c. Grenadier in full summer dress	..	35	35
98	30 c. Sergeant-major in full winter dress	..	50	50
95/8			*Set of* 4	1·25	1·10

The 30 c. value exists as a Philatelic Foundation miniature sheet.

18 Welding Bicycle
Frame

19 President Dr. Lennox
Sebe

(Des J. van Niekerk)

1986 (18 Sept). *Bicycle Factory, Dimbaza. T* **18** *and similar horiz designs. Multicoloured. P* 14½×14.

99	14 c. Type **18**	..	..	20	15
100	20 c. Spray-painting frame	..	30	30
101	25 c. Installing wheel-spokes	..	35	35
102	30 c. Final assembly	..	..	50	50
99/102			*Set of* 4	1·25	1·10

(Des J. van Niekerk)

1986 (4 Dec). *Fifth Anniv of Independence. T* **19** *and similar horiz designs. Multicoloured. P* 14×14½.

103	14 c. Type **19**	..	..	15	15
104	20 c. National Shrine, Ntaba kaNdoda	..	20	30
105	25 c. Legislative Assembly, Bisho	..	25	35
106	30 c. Automatic telephone exchange, Bisho	35	50
103/6			*Set of* 4	85	1·10

20 *Boletus edulis*

21 Nkone Cow and Calf

(Des H. Botha)

1987 (19 Mar). *Edible Mushrooms. T* **20** *and similar vert designs. Multicoloured. P* 14×14½.

107	14 c. Type **20**	..	..	25	15
108	20 c. *Macrolepiota zeyheri*	..	40	40
109	25 c. *Termitomyces spp*	..	..	50	50
110	30 c. *Russula capensis*	..	..	60	60
107/10			*Set of* 4	1·60	1·50

The 20 c. value exists as a Philatelic Foundation miniature sheet.

(Des D. Murphy)

1987 (18 June). *Nkone Cattle. T* **21** *and similar horiz designs. Multicoloured. P* 14½×14.

111	16 c. Type **21**	..	..	20	15
112	20 c. Nkone cow	..	..	25	30
113	25 c. Nkone bull	..	..	30	35
114	30 c. Herd of Nkone	..	..	40	55
111/14			*Set of* 4	1·00	1·25

22 Wire Windmill

23 Seven Birds

(Des A. H. Barrett)

1987 (17 Sept). *Homemade Toys. T* **22** *and similar multicoloured designs. P* 14×14½ (*vert*) *or* 14½×14 (*horiz*).

115	16 c. Type **22**	..	..	20	15
116	20 c. Rag doll	..	..	25	30
117	25 c. Clay horse (*horiz*)	..	30	35
118	30 c. Wire car (*horiz*)	..	..	40	55
115/18			*Set of* 4	1·00	1·25

(Des J. van Niekerk)

1987 (6 Nov). *Folklore (1st series). Sikulume. T* **23** *and similar horiz designs. Multicoloured. P* 14½×14.

119	16 c. Type **23**	..	..	20	15
120	20 c. Cannibals chasing Sikulume	..	25	30
121	25 c. Sikulume attacking the inabulele	..	30	35
122	30 c. Chief Mangangezulu chasing Sikulume and his bride	..	..	40	55
119/22			*Set of* 4	1·00	1·25

See also Nos. 127/36, 153/6 and 161/4.

24 Bush Lily
(*Clivia nobilis*)

25 Numbakatali crying and
Second Wife feeding Crows

(Des A. Batten)

1988 (17 Mar). *Protected Flowers. T* **24** *and similar vert designs. Multicoloured. P* 14×14½.

123	16 c. Type **24**	..	..	20	15
124	30 c. Harebell (*Dierama pulcherrimum*)	..	35	35

125	40 c. Butterfly Iris (*Moraea reticulata*)	..	40	40
126	50 c. Vlei Lily (*Crinum campanulatum*)	..	60	65
123/6		*Set of 4*	1·40	1·40

The 50 c. value exists as a Philatelic Foundation miniature sheet.

(Des J. van Niekerk)

1988 (27 May). *Folklore (2nd series). Mbulukazi. T 25 and similar horiz designs. Multicoloured.* P 14×14½.

127	16 c. Type 25	30	35
	a. Sheetlet. Nos. 127/36	2·75	
128	16 c. Numbakatali telling doves of her childlessness	30	35
129	16 c. Numbakatali finding children in earthenware jars	30	35
130	16 c. Broad Breast sees Mbulukazi and brother at river	30	35
131	16 c. Broad Breast asking to marry Mbulukazi	30	35
132	16 c. Broad Breast and his two wives, Mbulukazi and her half-sister Mahlunguluza	30	35
133	16 c. Mahlunguluza pushing Mbulukazi from precipice to her death ..	30	35
134	16 c. Mbulukazi's ox tearing down Mahlunguluza's hut ..	30	35
135	16 c. Ox licking Mbulukazi back to life ..	30	35
136	16 c. Mahlunguluza being sent back to her father in disgrace	30	35
127/36	*Set of 10*	2·75	3·25

Nos. 127/36 were printed together, *se-tenant*, in sheetlets of 10.

26 Oranges and Grafted Rootstocks in Nursery   **27** *Amanita phalloides*

(Des B. Jackson)

1988 (29 Sept). *Citrus Farming. T 26 and similar horiz designs. Multicoloured.* P 14×14½.

137	16 c. Type 26	20	15
138	30 c. Lemons and inarching rootstock onto mature tree	40	40
139	40 c. Tangerines and fruit being hand-picked	50	50
140	50 c. Oranges and fruit being graded	60	65
137/40	*Set of 4*	1·50	1·50

(Des H. Botha)

1988 (1 Dec). *Poisonous Fungi. T 27 and similar vert designs. Multicoloured.* P 14×14½.

141	16 c. Type 27	85	30
142	30 c. *Chlorophyllum molybdites*	1·25	75
143	40 c. *Amanita muscaria*	1·40	1·10
144	50 c. *Amanita pantherina*	1·60	1·25
141/4	*Set of 4*	4·50	3·00

28 Kat River Dam   **29** Taking Eggs from Rainbow Trout

(Des Sheila Nowers)

1989 (2 Mar). *Dams. T 28 and similar horiz designs. Multicoloured.* P 14½×14.

145	16 c. Type 28	35	25
146	30 c. Cata Dam	55	50
147	40 c. Binfield Park Dam	65	65
148	50 c. Sandile Dam ..	70	80
145/8	*Set of 4*	2·00	2·00

(Des B. Kent)

1989 (8 June). *Trout Hatcheries. T 29 and similar horiz designs. Multicoloured.* P 14½×14.

149	18 c. Type 29	25	15
150	30 c. Fertilized eyed trout ova and alevins	45	45
151	40 c. Five-week-old fingerlings	55	55
152	50 c. Adult male	60	65
149/52	*Set of 4*	1·75	1·60

The 50 c. value exists as a Philatelic Foundation miniature sheet.

30 Lion and Little Jackal killing Eland   **31** Cape Horse-cart

(Des J. van Niekerk)

1989 (21 Sept). *Folklore (3rd series). Little Jackal and the Lion. T 30 and similar horiz designs. Multicoloured.* P 14½×14.

153	18 c. Type 30	20	15
154	30 c. Little Jackal's children carrying meat to clifftop home	35	35
155	40 c. Little Jackal pretending to be trapped	40	40
156	50 c. Lion falling down cliff face	45	50
153/6	*Set of 4*	1·25	1·25

(Des J. Huntly)

1989 (7 Dec). *Animal-drawn Transport. T 31 and similar horiz designs. Multicoloured.* P 14×14½.

157	18 c. Type 31	20	15
158	30 c. Jubilee spider	35	35
159	40 c. Ballantine half-tent ox-drawn wagon	40	40
160	50 c. Voortrekker wagon	45	50
157/60	*Set of 4*	1·25	1·25

32 Mpunzikazi offering Food to Five Heads   **33** Handweaving on Loom

(Des J. van Niekerk)

1990 (15 Mar). *Folklore (4th series). The Story of Makanda Mahlanu (Five Heads). T 32 and similar horiz designs. Multicoloured.* P 14½×14.

161	18 c. Type 32	20	15
162	30 c. Five Heads killing Mpunzikazi with his tail	35	35
163	40 c. Mpunzanyana offering food to Five Heads	40	40
164	50 c. Five Heads transformed into a man ..	45	50
161/4	*Set of 4*	1·25	1·25

(Des I. Ellithorne)

1990 (14 June). *Handmade Carpets. T 33 and similar vert designs. Multicoloured.* P 14×14½.

165	21 c. Type 33	35	25
166	35 c. Spinning	55	55
167	40 c. Dyeing yarn	80	90
168	50 c. Knotting carpet	80	1·10
165/8	*Set of 4*	2·25	2·50

The 50 c. value exists as a Philatelic Foundation miniature sheet.

34 Wooden Beam Plough, 1855   **35** Prickly Pear Vendor

(Des J. Huntly)

1990 (6 Sept). *Ploughs. T 34 and similar horiz designs. Multicoloured.* P 14½×14.

169	21 c. Type 34	25	20
170	35 c. Triple disc plough, 1895	40	40
171	40 c. Reversible disc plough, 1895	50	55
172	50 c. "Het Volk" double furrow plough, 1910	60	80
169/72	*Set of 4*	1·60	1·75

(Des A. H. Barrett)

1990 (29 Nov). *Prickly Pear. T 35 and similar horiz designs. Multicoloured.* P 14½×14.

173	21 c. Type 35	30	20
174	35 c. Prickly pear bushes	50	50
175	40 c. Whole and opened fruits	60	60
176	50 c. Bushes in bloom	70	80
173/6	*Set of 4*	1·90	1·90

36 African Marsh Owl   **37** São Bras (now Mossel Bay) on Map, 1500

(Des D. Finlay)

1991 (7 Feb). *Owls. T 36 and similar vert designs. Multicoloured.* P 14×14½.

177	21 c. Type 36	90	40
178	35 c. African Scops Owl ..	1·25	90
179	40 c. Barn Owl	1·50	1·25
180	50 c. African Wood Owl	1·60	1·60
177/80	*Set of 4*	4·75	3·75

The 50 c. value exists as a Philatelic Foundation miniature sheet.

(Des J. van Niekerk)

1991 (11 May). *Stamp Day. D'Ataide's Letter of 1501. T 37 and similar horiz designs. Multicoloured.* P 14×14½.

181	25 c. Type 37	65	65
	a. Horiz strip of 5. Nos. 181/5	3·00	
182	25 c. Bartolomeo Dias's ship foundering off Cabo Tormentoso (now Cape of Good Hope) during voyage to India, 1500 ..	65	65
183	25 c. Captain Pedro d'Ataide landing at São Bras, 1501	65	65
184	25 c. D'Ataide leaving letter relating death of Dias on tree	65	65
185	25 c. Captain João da Nova finding letter, 1501 ..	65	65
181/5	*Set of 5*	3·00	3·00

Nos. 181/5 were printed together, *se-tenant*, in horizontal strips of 5 throughout the sheet.

The inscriptions at the foot of Nos. 181 and 182 are transposed.

38 Comet Nucleus   **39** Fort Armstrong and Xhosa Warrior

(Des J. van Ellinckhuijzen)

1991 (1 Aug). *The Solar System. T 38 and similar horiz designs. Multicoloured.* P 14.

186	1 c. Type 38	20	15
187	2 c. Trojan asteroids	20	15
188	5 c. Meteoroids	20	15
189	7 c. Pluto ..	30	15
190	10 c. Neptune	30	15
191	20 c. Uranus	50	20
192	25 c. Saturn	60	20
193	30 c. Jupiter	65	30
194	35 c. Planetoids in asteroid belt	65	40
195	40 c. Mars	80	50
196	50 c. The Moon	90	70
197	60 c. Earth	1·00	80
198	1 r. Venus	1·50	1·25
199	2 r. Mercury	2·50	2·25
200	5 r. The Sun	4·50	4·50
186/200	*Set of 15*	13·00	10·50
MS201	197×93 mm. Nos. 186/200	13·50	13·50

(Des D. Bagnall)

1991 (7 Nov). *19th-century Frontier Forts. T 39 and similar horiz designs. Multicoloured.* P 14×14½.

202	27 c. Type 39	40	30
203	45 c. Keiskamma Hoek Post and Sir George Grey (governor of Cape Colony, 1854–58)	55	55
204	65 c. Fort Hare and Xhosa Chief Sandile	70	70
205	85 c. Peddie Cavalry Barracks and cavalryman	1·10	1·25
202/5	*Set of 4*	2·50	2·50

40 Cumulonimbus   **41** "Intelsat VI" Communications Satellite

(Des J. Meyer)

1992 (19 Mar). *Cloud Formations. T 40 and similar vert designs. Multicoloured.* P 14.

206	27 c. Type 40	40	25
207	45 c. Altocumulus ..	65	65
208	65 c. Cirrus	80	80
209	85 c. Cumulus	1·00	1·10
206/9	*Set of 4*	2·50	2·50

(Des J. van Ellinckhuijzen)

1992 (4 June). *International Space Year. Satellites over Southern Africa. T 41 and similar horiz designs. Multicoloured.* P 14.

210	35 c. Type 41	40	25
211	70 c. "G P S Navstar" (navigation)	80	80
212	90 c. "Meteosat" (meteorology)	1·10	1·10
213	1 r. 05, "Landsat VI" (Earth resources survey)	1·25	1·40
210/13	*Set of 4*	3·25	3·25

The 70 c. value exists as a Philatelic Foundation miniature sheet.

42 Universal Disc-harrow,
1914

43 Mpekweni Sun Marine
Resort

(Des J. Huntly)

1992 (20 Aug). *Agricultural Tools. T* **42** *and similar horiz designs. Multicoloured. P* 14.
214	35 c. Type **42**		45	25
215	70 c. Clod crusher and pulveriser, 1914		90	75
216	90 c. Self-dump hay rake, 1910		1·10	1·10
217	1 r. 05, McCormick hay tedder, 1900		1·25	1·40
214/17		*Set of 4*	3·25	3·25

1992 (5 Nov). *Hotels. T* **43** *and similar horiz designs. Multicoloured. P* 14.
218	35 c. Type **43**		40	25
219	70 c. Katberg Protea Hotel		80	80
220	90 c. Fish River Sun Hotel		1·10	1·25
221	1 r. 05, Amatola Sun Hotel, Amatole Mountains		1·10	1·50
218/21		*Set of 4*	3·00	3·50

44 Vasco da Gama, *São Gabriel* and Voyage round Cape of Good Hope, 1497

45 Canary

(Des J. van Niekerk)

1993 (19 May). *Navigators. T* **44** *and similar horiz designs. Multicoloured. P* 14.
222	45 c. Type **44**		65	30
223	65 c. James Cook, H.M.S. *Endeavour* and first voyage, 1768–71		1·00	75
224	85 c. Ferdinand Magellan, *Vitoria* and circumnavigation, 1519		1·25	90
225	90 c. Sir Francis Drake, *Golden Hind* and circumnavigation, 1577–80		1·25	95
226	1 r. 05, Abel Tasman, *Heemskerk* and discovery of Tasmania, 1642		1·25	1·25
222/6		*Set of 5*	4·75	3·75

The ship on No. 222 is wrongly inscribed "San Gabriel", that on No. 224 "Victoria" and that on No. 226 "Heemskerck".

(Des J. Steyn (65 c.), M. Goetz (85 c.))

1993 (16 July). *Cage Birds. T* **45** *and similar vert designs. Multicoloured. P* 14.
227	45 c. Type **45**		45	30
228	65 c. Budgerigar		70	60
229	85 c. Peach-faced Lovebirds		90	80
230	90 c. Cockatiel		95	85
231	1 r. 05, Gouldian Finch		1·00	1·10
227/31		*Set of 5*	3·50	3·25

The 85 c. value exists as a Philatelic Foundation miniature sheet.

46 Goshen Church (Moravian Mission), Whittlesea

47 Jointed Cactus

(Des C. Meijer)

1993 (17 Sept). *Churches and Missions. T* **46** *and similar horiz designs. P* 14½×14.
232	45 c. stone, black and scarlet		35	20
233	65 c. azure, black and scarlet		60	60
234	85 c. cinnamon, black and scarlet		80	90
235	1 r. 05, pale olive-yellow, black and scarlet		90	1·25
232/5		*Set of 4*	2·40	2·75

Designs:—65 c. Kamastone Mission Church; 85 c. Richie Thompson Memorial Church (Hertzog Mission), nr. Seymour; 1 r. 05, Bryce Ross Memorial Church (Pirie Mission), nr. Dimbaza.

(Des Auriol Batten)

1993 (5 Nov). *Invader Plants. T* **47** *and similar vert designs. Multicoloured. P* 14.
236	45 c. Type **47**		40	30
237	65 c. Thorn Apple		70	60
238	85 c. Coffee Weed		90	90
239	1 r. 05, Poisonous Wild Tobacco		1·00	1·00
236/9		*Set of 4*	2·75	2·40
MS240	98×125 mm. Nos. 236/9		2·75	2·75

48 *Losna* (steamer) (near Fish River), 1921

49 "Herman Steyn"

(Des Sheila Nowers)

1994 (18 Feb). *Shipwrecks. T* **48** *and similar horiz designs. Multicoloured. P* 14.
241	45 c. Type **48**		65	30
242	65 c. *Catherine* (barque) (Waterloo Bay), 1846		1·00	70
243	85 c. *Bennebroek* (East Indiaman) (near Mtana River), 1713		1·25	1·10
244	1 r. 05, *São João Baptista* (galleon) (between Fish and Kei Rivers), 1622		1·40	1·50
241/4		*Set of 4*	3·75	3·25

1994 (15 Apr). *Hybrid Roses. T* **49** *and similar horiz designs. Multicoloured. P* 14.
245	45 c. Type **49**		35	30
246	70 c. "Esther Geldenhuys"		60	60
247	95 c. "Margaret Wasserfall"		80	90
248	1 r. 15, "Professor Fred Ziady"		1·00	1·25
245/8		*Set of 4*	2·50	2·75
MS249	149×114 mm. Nos. 245/8		2·50	2·75

Ciskei was reincorporated into the Republic of South Africa on 27 April 1994. Its postal service continued to operate, using South African stamps, until 1 April 1996 when it was integrated with that of the Republic.

XIII. TRANSKEI

The Natives Land Act of 1913 laid down that Transkei should be reserved entirely for Black ownership and occupation. In 1963 Transkei was granted internal self-government by the South African Parliament and subsequently the Republic of Transkei was established, on 26 October 1976, as the first of the independent "black homelands".

This independence did not receive international political recognition, but the stamps were accepted as valid on international mail.

PRINTERS. All the following stamps were printed in lithography by the South African Government Printer, Pretoria.

1 Lubisi Dam

2 K. D. Matanzima

(Des A. H. Barrett)

1976 (26 Oct)–**83.** *Transkei Scenes and Occupations. T* **1** *and similar horiz designs. Multicoloured. P* 12×12½.
1	1 c. Type **1**		10	10
	a. Perf 14 (28.3.83)		30	20
2	2 c. Soil cultivation		10	10
	a. Perf 14 (5.7.82)		15	10
3	3 c. Threshing sorghum		10	10
	a. Perf 14 (6.7.82)		15	10
4	4 c. Transkei matron		2·25	15
	a. Perf 14 (15.11.79)		15	10
5	5 c. Grinding maize		2·25	15
	a. Perf 14 (8.4.80)		15	10
6	6 c. Cutting *Phormium tenax*		15	15
	a. Perf 14 (8.7.82)		15	10
7	7 c. Herd-boy		40	10
8	8 c. Felling timber		20	10
	a. Perf 14 (20.1.82)		35	15
9	9 c. Agricultural schooling		15	15
	a. Perf 14 (13.7.82)		25	25
10	10 c. Tea picking		30	15
	a. Perf 14 (11.8.80)		20	15
11	15 c. Carrying wood		40	25
	a. Perf 14 (16.10.81)		30	15
12	20 c. Weaving industry		40	20
	a. Perf 14 (15.10.80)		35	15
13	25 c. Cattle		45	25
	a. Perf 14 (26.10.81)		60	50
14	30 c. Sledge transportation		85	50
	a. Perf 14 (13.8.80)		75	45
15	50 c. Coat of arms and map		1·25	50
	a. Perf 14 (13.11.81)		85	60
16	1 r. Administration building, Umtata		1·00	1·25
17	2 r. The Bunga (Parliamentary building), Umtata		1·75	2·25
1/17		*Set of 17 (cheapest)*	6·50	5·25

1976 (26 Oct). *Independence. T* **2** *and similar vert designs. Multicoloured. P* 12½.
18	4 c. Type **2**		25	20
19	10 c. Flag and mace		45	45
20	15 c. K. D. Matanzima, Paramount Chief (*different*)		85	85
21	20 c. Coat of arms		95	1·00
18/21		*Set of 4*	2·25	2·25

3 Beech 100 King Air of Transkei Airways

4 *Artemisia afra*

(Des A. H. Barrett)

1977 (11 Feb). *Transkei Airways' Inaugural Flight. T* **3** *and similar horiz design. Multicoloured. P* 12×12½.
22	4 c. Type **3**		30	25
23	15 c. Beech 100 King Air of Transkei Airways landing at Matanzima airport and on ground		1·25	1·50

(Des D. Findlay)

1977 (16 May). *Medicinal Plants (1st series). T* **4** *and similar vert designs. Multicoloured. P* 12½×12.
24	4 c. Type **4**		20	10
25	10 c. *Bulbine natalensis*		60	65
26	15 c. *Melianthus major*		70	80
27	20 c. *Cotyledon orbiculata*		90	1·25
24/7		*Set of 4*	2·25	2·50

See also Nos. 88/91.

5 Disc Jockey

6 Blind Basket Weaver

(Des A. H. Barrett)

1977 (26 Oct). *First Anniv of Transkei Radio. T* **5** *and similar horiz design. Multicoloured. P* 12×12½.
28	4 c. Type **5**		15	10
29	15 c. Announcer		60	60

(Des A. H. Barrett)

1977 (18 Nov). *Help for the Blind. T* **6** *and similar vert designs. P* 12½×12.
30	4 c. black, grey-lilac and gold		15	10
31	15 c. black, drab and gold		35	35
32	20 c. black, pinkish brown and gold		75	80
30/2		*Set of 3*	1·10	1·10

Designs:—15 c. Hands reading braille; 20 c. Blind woman spinning.

7 Men's Carved Pipes

(Des A. H. Barrett)

1978 (1 Mar). *Carved Pipes. T* **7** *and similar horiz designs. Multicoloured. P* 12×12½.
33	4 c. Type **7**		10	10
34	10 c. Two men's pipes		15	15
35	15 c. Multi-bowled men's pipes		45	55
36	20 c. Woman's pipe and witch-doctor's pipe		60	70
33/6		*Set of 4*	1·10	1·25

8 Angora Goat

9 *Carissa bispinosa*

(Des A. H. Barrett)

1978 (9 June). *Weaving Industry. T* **8** *and similar horiz designs. Multicoloured. P* 12×12½.
37	4 c. Type **8**		15	10
38	10 c. Spinning mohair		15	15
39	15 c. Dyeing mohair		30	35
40	20 c. Weaving mohair rug		45	55
37/40		*Set of 4*	95	1·00

(Des D. Findlay)

1978 (25 Sept). *Edible Wild Fruits.* T **9** *and similar vert designs. Multicoloured.* P 12½×12.

41	4 c. Type 9			15	10
42	10 c. *Dovyalis caffra*			30	25
43	15 c. *Harpephyllum caffrum*			55	55
44	20 c. *Syzygium cordatum*			60	70
41/4			Set of 4	1·40	1·40

10 Calipers   **11** Chi Cha Youth

(Des A. H. Barrett)

1978 (30 Nov). *Care of Cripples.* T **10** *and similar vert designs.* P 12½×12.

45	4 c. black, pale brown and gold			15	10
46	10 c. black, grey and gold			40	40
47	15 c. black, olive-yellow and gold			50	55
45/7			Set of 3	95	95

Designs:—10 c. Child in wheelchair; 15 c. Nurse examining child's leg.

1979 (3 Jan). *Abakwetha (coming-of-age ceremony of Xhosa males).* T **11** *and similar horiz designs. Multicoloured.* P 12½.

48	4 c. Type 11			15	10
49	10 c. Youths in three-month seclusion			30	25
50	15 c. Umtshilo dance			55	55
51	20 c. Burning of seclusion hut at end of final ceremony			60	70
48/51			Set of 4	1·40	1·40

12 President K. D. Matanzima   **13** Windpump   **14** Magwa Falls

1979 (20 Feb). *Inauguration of Second State President.* P 14×13½.

52	**12**	4 c. brown-red and gold		15	10
53		15 c. deep olive and gold		50	45

(Des K. De Beer)

1979 (13 Mar). *Water Resources.* T **13** *and similar multicoloured designs.* P 14.

54	4 c. Type 13			15	10
55	10 c. Woman ladling water into jar			30	25
56	15 c. Indwe River Dam (*horiz*)			55	55
57	20 c. Ncora Dam (*horiz*)			60	70
54/7			Set of 4	1·40	1·40

(Des A. H. Barrett)

1979 (4 Sept). *Waterfalls.* T **14** *and similar multicoloured designs.* P 14×13½ (*vert*) or 13½×14 (*horiz*).

58	4 c. Type 14			15	10
59	10 c. Bawa Falls			30	25
60	15 c. Waterfall Bluff (*horiz*)			55	55
61	20 c. Tsitsa Falls (*horiz*)			60	70
58/61			Set of 4	1·40	1·40

15 Expectant Mother pouring Milk   **16** Black Gnat (dry fly)

(Des A. H. Barrett)

1979 (3 Dec). *Child Health.* T **15** *and similar vert designs. Multicoloured.* P 14×13½.

62	5 c. Type 15			15	10
63	15 c. Mother breast-feeding baby			45	45
64	20 c. Immunising child			60	65
62/4			Set of 3	1·10	1·10

(Des A. H. Barrett)

1980 (15 Jan). *Fishing Flies (1st series).* T **16** *and similar horiz designs. Multicoloured.* P 14.

65	5 c. Type 16			35	35
	a. Strip of 5. Nos. 65/9			1·60	
66	5 c. Zug Bug (nymph)			35	35
67	5 c. March Brown (wet fly)			35	35
68	5 c. Durham Ranger (salmon fly)			35	35
69	5 c. Colonel Bates (streamer)			35	35
65/9			Set of 5	1·60	1·60

Nos. 65/9 were printed together, *se-tenant*, in strips of 5, both horizontally and vertically, within the sheet.
See also Nos. 83/7, 99/103, 116/20 and 133/7.

17 Rotary Emblem   **18** *Encephalartos altensteinii*   **19** Red-chested Cuckoo

(Des G. Mynhardt and H. De Klerk)

1980 (22 Feb). *75th Anniv of Rotary International.* P 14×13½.

70	**17**	15 c. bright blue and gold		35	30

(Des D. Findlay)

1980 (30 Apr). *Cycads.* T **18** *and similar vert designs. Multicoloured.* P 14×13½.

71	5 c. Type 18			15	10
72	10 c. *Encephalartos princeps*			25	25
73	15 c. *Encephalartos villosus*			40	40
74	20 c. *Encephalartos friderici-guilielmi*			50	55
71/4			Set of 4	1·10	1·10

(Des D. Findlay)

1980 (30 July). *Birds.* T **19** *and similar vert designs. Multicoloured.* P 14×13½.

75	5 c. Type 19			20	10
76	10 c. Cape Puff-back Flycatcher			45	25
77	15 c. South African Crowned Crane			65	60
78	20 c. Spectacled Weaver			70	70
75/8			Set of 4	1·75	1·50

20 Hole in the Wall

(Des A. H. Barrett)

1980 (29 Oct). *Tourism.* T **20** *and similar horiz designs. Multicoloured.* P 14.

79	5 c. Type 20			15	10
80	10 c. Port St. Johns			25	25
81	15 c. The Citadel (rock)			40	40
82	20 c. The Archway (rock)			50	55
79/82			Set of 4	1·10	1·10

(Des A. H. Barrett)

1981 (15 Jan). *Fishing Flies (2nd series). Horiz designs as* T **16**. *Multicoloured.* P 14.

83	10 c. Kent's Lightning (streamer)			25	25
	a. Strip of 5. Nos. 83/7			1·10	
84	10 c. Wickham's Fancy (dry fly)			25	25
85	10 c. Jock Scott (wet fly)			25	25
86	10 c. Green Highlander (salmon fly)			25	25
87	10 c. Tan Nymph			25	25
83/7			Set of 5	1·10	1·10

Nos. 83/7 were printed together, *se-tenant*, in strips of 5, both horizontally and vertically, within the sheet.

(Des D. Findlay)

1981 (15 Apr). *Medicinal Plants (2nd series). Vert designs as* T **4**. *Multicoloured.* P 14×13½.

88	5 c. *Leonotis leonurus*			15	10
89	15 c. *Euphorbia bupleurifolia*			35	35
90	20 c. *Pelargonium reniforme*			45	45
91	25 c. *Hibiscus trionum*			50	55
88/91			Set of 4	1·25	1·25

21 Eyamakhwenkwe

(Des A. H. Barrett)

1981 (28 Aug). *Xhosa Women's Headdresses.* T **21** *and similar horiz designs. Multicoloured.* P 14.

92	5 c. Type 21			10	10
93	15 c. Eyabafana			30	35
94	20 c. Umfazana			35	45
95	25 c. Ixhegokazi			40	55
92/5			Set of 4	1·00	1·25
MS96	126×91 mm. Nos. 92/5			1·00	1·25

22 State House, Umtata

(Des P. Semra'd)

1981 (26 Oct). *Fifth Anniv of Independence.* T **22** *and similar horiz design.* P 14.

97	5 c. black, lake-brown and emerald			15	10
98	15 c. black, lake-brown and emerald			45	30

Design:—15 c. University of Transkei.

(Des A. H. Barrett)

1982 (6 Jan). *Fishing Flies (3rd series). Horiz designs as* T **16**. *Multicoloured.* P 14.

99	10 c. Blue Charm			25	25
	a. Strip of 5. Nos. 99/103			1·10	
100	10 c. Royal Coachman			25	25
101	10 c. Light Spruce			25	25
102	10 c. Montana Nymph			25	25
103	10 c. Butcher			25	25
99/103			Set of 5	1·10	1·10

Nos. 99/103 were printed together, *se-tenant*, in strips of 5, both horizontally and vertically, within the sheet.

23 Cub Scout   **24** Hippocrates

(Des H. Botha)

1982 (14 May). *75th Anniv of Boy Scout Movement.* T **23** *and similar vert designs. Multicoloured.* P 14.

104	8 c. Type 23			15	10
105	10 c. Scout planting tree			15	10
106	20 c. Scout on raft			35	30
107	25 c. Scout with dog			35	30
104/7			Set of 4	90	70

(Des J. Meyer)

1982 (5 Oct). *Celebrities of Medicine (1st series).* T **24** *and similar vert designs. Multicoloured.* P 14.

108	15 c. Type 24			25	20
109	20 c. Antonie van Leeuwenhoek			35	30
110	25 c. William Harvey			45	40
111	30 c. Joseph Lister			50	45
108/11			Set of 4	1·40	1·25

See also Nos. 125/8, 160/3, 176/9, 249/52, 273/6, 281/4 and 305/8.

25 City Hall   **26** Hotel Complex, Mzamba

(Des A. H. Barrett)

1982 (10 Nov). *Centenary of Umtata.* T **25** *and similar horiz designs. Multicoloured.* P 13½×14.

112	8 c. Type 25			10	10
113	15 c. The Bunga			15	15
114	20 c. Botha Sigcau Building			20	20
115	25 c. Palace of Justice and K. D. Matanzima Building			25	30
112/15			Set of 4	65	65

(Des A. H. Barrett)

1983 (2 Mar). *Fishing Flies (4th series). Horiz designs as* T **16**. *Multicoloured.* P 14.

116	20 c. Alexandra			25	25
	a. Strip of 5. Nos. 116/20			1·10	
117	20 c. Kent's Marbled Sedge			25	25
118	20 c. White Marabou			25	25
119	20 c. Mayfly Nymph			25	25
120	20 c. Silver Wilkinson			25	25
116/20			Set of 5	1·10	1·10

Nos. 116/20 were printed together, *se-tenant*, in strips of 5, both horizontally and vertically, within the sheet.

(Des A. H. Barrett)

1983 (25 May). *Wildcoast Holiday Complex, Mzamba. T **26** and similar horiz designs. Multicoloured. P 14.*
121	10 c. Type **26**		15	15
122	20 c. Beach scene		25	25
123	25 c. Casino		35	35
124	40 c. Carousel		50	50
121/4		*Set of 4*	1·10	1·10

(Des J. Meyer)

1983 (17 Aug). *Celebrities of Medicine (2nd series). Vert designs as T **24**. Multicoloured. P 14.*
125	10 c. Edward Jenner		15	15
126	20 c. Gregor Mendel		30	30
127	25 c. Louis Pasteur		35	35
128	40 c. Florence Nightingale		55	55
125/8		*Set of 4*	1·25	1·25

27 Lady Frere Post Office

(Des A. H. Barrett)

1983 (9 Nov). *Transkei Post Offices (1st series). T **27** and similar horiz designs. Multicoloured. P 14.*
129	10 c. Type **27**		15	15
130	20 c. Idutywa		25	30
131	25 c. Lusikisiki		30	35
132	40 c. Cala		40	55
129/32		*Set of 4*	1·00	1·25

See also Nos. 156/9.

(Des A. H. Barrett)

1984 (10 Feb). *Fishing Flies (5th series). Horiz designs as T **16**. Multicoloured. P 14.*
133	20 c. Silver Grey		45	45
	a. Strip of 5. Nos. 133/7		2·00	
134	20 c. Ginger Quill		45	45
135	20 c. Hardy's Favourite		45	45
136	20 c. March Brown		45	45
137	20 c. Kent's Spectrum Mohawk		45	45
133/7		*Set of 5*	2·00	2·00

Nos. 133/7 were printed together, *se-tenant*, in strips of 5, both horizontally and vertically, within the sheet.

28 Amagqira	29 Soil Erosion by Overgrazing

(Des A. H. Barrett)

1984 (2 Apr)–**91**. *Xhosa Culture. T **28** and similar horiz designs. Multicoloured. Ordinary paper. P 14.*
138	1 c. Type **28** (6.7.84)		20	10
	a. Chalk-surfaced paper (7.1.91)		30	10
139	2 c. Horsemen (6.7.84)		20	10
140	3 c. Mat making (6.7.84)		20	10
141	4 c. Xhosa dancers (6.7.84)		20	10
142	5 c. Shopping with donkeys (6.7.84)		20	10
143	6 c. Young musicians (6.7.84)		30	15
144	7 c. Fingo brides (6.7.84)		30	20
145	8 c. Tasting the beer (6.7.84)		30	20
146	9 c. Thinning the maize (6.7.84)		30	30
147	10 c. Dancing demonstration (6.7.84)		30	15
148	11 c. Water from the river		30	15
148a	12 c. Preparing a meal (1.4.85)		30	15
148b	14 c. Weeding mealies (*chalk-surfaced paper*) (1.4.86)		30	20
149	15 c. National sport: stick fighting (6.7.84)		20	20
149a	16 c. Morning pasture (*chalk-surfaced paper*) (1.4.87)		30	20
150	20 c. Abakhwetha dance (6.7.84)		30	25
150a	21 c. Building of initiation hut (*chalk-surfaced paper*) (3.7.90)		85	20
151	25 c. Tribesman singing (6.7.84)		30	25
152	30 c. Jovial matrons (6.7.84)		70	35
153	50 c. Pipe making (6.7.84)		70	60
154	1 r. Intonjane (6.7.84)		80	1·10
155	2 r. Abakhwetha (6.7.84)		1·50	2·00
138/55		*Set of 22*	8·00	6·50

(Des A. H. Barrett)

1984 (11 May). *Transkei Post Offices (2nd series). Horiz designs as T **27**. Multicoloured. P 14.*
156	11 c. Umzimkulu		15	15
157	20 c. Mount Fletcher		25	25
158	25 c. Qumbu		25	25
159	30 c. Umtata		50	50
156/9		*Set of 4*	1·00	1·00

(Des J. Meyer)

1984 (12 Oct). *Celebrities of Medicine (3rd series). Vert designs as T **24**. Multicoloured. P 14.*
160	11 c. Nicholas of Cusa		20	15
161	25 c. William Morton		30	25
162	30 c. Wilhelm Röntgen		40	40
163	45 c. Karl Landsteiner		60	60
160/3		*Set of 4*	1·40	1·25

(Des A. H. Barrett)

1985 (7 Feb). *Soil Conservation. T **29** and similar horiz designs showing restoration of eroded landscape. Multicoloured. P 14½×14.*
164	11 c. Type **29**		20	15
165	25 c. Removal of stock and construction of walls as sediment collectors		30	25
166	30 c. Regeneration of vegetation		40	40
167	50 c. Cattle grazing in lush landscape		60	60
164/7		*Set of 4*	1·40	1·25

30 Tsitsa Bridge	31 Veneer-peeling Machine

(Des D. Bagnall)

1985 (18 Apr). *Bridges. T **30** and similar horiz designs. Multicoloured. P 14.*
168	12 c. Type **30**		20	15
169	25 c. White Kei Railway Bridge		25	25
170	30 c. Mitchell Bridge		35	35
171	50 c. Umzimvubu Bridge		55	60
168/71		*Set of 4*	1·25	1·25

(Des A. H. Barrett)

1985 (25 July). *Match Industry, Butterworth. T **31** and similar horiz designs. Multicoloured. P 14½×14.*
172	12 c. Type **31**		20	15
173	25 c. Cutting wood to match-size		25	25
174	30 c. Dipping splints in chemical to form match heads		35	35
175	50 c. Boxing matches		60	65
172/5		*Set of 4*	1·25	1·25

(Des J. Meyer)

1985 (20 Sept). *Celebrities of Medicine (4th series). Vert designs as T **24**. Multicoloured. P 14.*
176	12 c. Andreas Vesalius		20	15
177	25 c. Marcello Malpighi		40	40
178	30 c. Francois Magendie		45	45
179	50 c. William Stewart Halsted		65	70
176/9		*Set of 4*	1·50	1·50

32 Early Street Scene	33 Aloe ferox

(Des A. H. Barrett)

1986 (6 Feb). *Historic Port St. Johns. T **32** and similar horiz designs. Multicoloured. P 14½×14.*
180	12 c. Type **32**		20	15
181	20 c. Umzimvubu (coaster) anchored at old jetty		45	45
182	25 c. Wagons off-loading maize at jetty		50	50
183	30 c. View of town at end of 19th century		50	55
180/3		*Set of 4*	1·50	1·50
MS184	130×94 mm. Nos. 180/3		1·50	1·50

PHILATELIC FOUNDATION MINIATURE SHEETS.

These miniature sheets were issued by the Philatelic Foundation of Southern Africa and not the postal administration. They could be purchased by post or from a limited number of philatelic offices at a premium in aid of various national and international stamp exhibitions.

(Des D. Findlay)

1986 (1 May). *Aloes. T **33** and similar vert designs. Multicoloured. P 14½×14.*
185	14 c. Type **33**		20	15
186	20 c. Aloe arborescens		30	30
187	25 c. Aloe maculata		35	35
188	30 c. Aloe ecklonis		45	45
185/8		*Set of 4*	1·10	1·10

The 30 c. value exists as a Philatelic Foundation miniature sheet.

34 First Falls Station, Umtata River	35 Prime Minister George Matanzima

(Des R. Smith)

1986 (24 July). *Hydro-electric Power Stations. T **34** and similar horiz designs. Multicoloured. P 14½×14.*
189	14 c. Type **34**		20	15
190	20 c. Second Falls, Umtata River		25	25
191	25 c. Ncora, Qumanco River		40	40
192	30 c. Collywobbles, Mbashe River		50	50
189/92		*Set of 4*	1·25	1·10

(Des J. van Niekerk)

1986 (26 Oct). *Tenth Anniv of Independence. T **35** and similar horiz designs. Multicoloured. P 14½×14.*
193	14 c. Type **35**		15	15
194	20 c. Technical College, Umtata		25	30
195	25 c. University of Transkei, Umtata		30	40
196	30 c. Palace of Justice, Umtata		40	50
193/6		*Set of 4*	1·00	1·10

36 Piper PA-23 Apache 235 Ulundi flying through Clouds	37 Pondo Girl

(Des H. Botha)

1987 (5 Feb). *Tenth Anniv of Transkei Airways Corporation. T **36** and similar horiz designs. Multicoloured. P 14½×14.*
197	14 c. Type **36**		20	15
198	20 c. Tail fin of Ulundi		30	30
199	25 c. Beech 100 King Air		40	40
200	30 c. Control tower, K. D. Matanzima Airport		55	60
197/200		*Set of 4*	1·25	1·25

(Des A. H. Barrett)

1987 (22 May). *Transkei Beadwork. T **37** and similar vert designs. Multicoloured. P 14×14½.*
201	16 c. Type **37**		20	15
202	20 c. Bomvana woman		30	30
203	25 c. Xessibe woman		40	40
204	30 c. Xhosa man		55	60
201/4		*Set of 4*	1·25	1·25

The 25 c. value exists as a Philatelic Foundation miniature sheet.

38 Latrodectus indistinctus	39 Common Black Pigs

(Des Liza van der Wal (16, 30 c.), T. Marais (others))

1987 (27 Aug). *Spiders. T **38** and similar vert designs. Multicoloured. P 14×14½.*
205	16 c. Type **38**		20	15
206	20 c. Nephila pilipes		30	30
207	25 c. Lycosidae sp		40	40
208	30 c. Argiope nigrovittata		50	55
205/8		*Set of 4*	1·25	1·25

(Des B. Jackson)

1987 (22 Oct). *Domestic Animals. T **39** and similar horiz designs. Multicoloured. P 14×14½.*
209	16 c. Type **39**		20	15
210	30 c. Goats		30	30
211	40 c. Merino sheep		45	50
212	50 c. Cattle		55	65
209/12		*Set of 4*	1·40	1·40

40 Plocamium corallorhiza	41 Spinning

(Des D. Thorpe)

1988 (18 Feb). *Seaweed.* T **40** *and similar vert designs. Multicoloured.* P 14×14¹/₂.
213	16 c. Type **40**		20	15
214	30 c. *Gelidium amanzii*		30	30
215	40 c. *Ecklonia biruncinata*		40	40
216	50 c. *Halimeda cuneata*		50	55
213/16		Set of 4	1·25	1·25

(Des B. Jackson)

1988 (5 May). *Blanket Factory, Butterworth.* T **41** *and similar horiz designs. Multicoloured.* P 14¹/₂×14.
217	16 c. Type **41**		20	15
218	30 c. Warping		30	30
219	40 c. Weaving		40	40
220	50 c. Raising the nap		50	55
217/20		Set of 4	1·25	1·25

42 Map showing Wreck Site   **43** Small-spotted Cat

(Des Sheila Nowers)

1988 (4 Aug). *206th Anniv of Shipwreck of Grosvenor (East Indiaman).* T **42** *and similar horiz designs. Multicoloured.* P 14¹/₂×14.
221	16 c. Type **42**		40	20
222	30 c. "The Wreck of the *Grosvenor*" (R. Smirke)		50	50
223	40 c. Dirk hilt, divider and coins from wreck		55	55
224	50 c. "African Hospitality" (G. Morland)		60	70
221/4		Set of 4	1·90	1·75

The 50 c. value exists as a Philatelic Foundation miniature sheet.

(Des D. Murphy)

1988 (20 Oct). *Endangered Animals.* T **43** *and similar horiz designs. Multicoloured.* P 14¹/₂×14.
225	16 c. Type **43**		60	30
226	30 c. Blue Duiker		70	60
227	40 c. Oribi		85	75
228	50 c. Hunting Dog		1·00	1·00
225/8		Set of 4	2·75	2·40

44 Class 14 CRB Steam Locomotives   **45** Mat, Baskets and Jar

(Des D. Hall-Green)

1989 (19 Jan). *Trains.* T **44** *and similar multicoloured designs.* P 14×14¹/₂ (*horiz*) or 14¹/₂×14 (*vert*).
229	16 c. Type **44**		20	20
230	30 c. Class 14 CRB locomotive and passenger train at Toleni Halt		40	40
231	40 c. Double-headed steam train on Great Kei River Bridge (*vert*)		60	70
232	50 c. Double-headed steam train in Kei Valley (*vert*)		65	80
229/32		Set of 4	1·75	1·90

The 50 c. value exists as a Philatelic Foundation miniature sheet.

(Des Sheila Nowers)

1989 (20 Apr). *Basketry.* T **45** *and similar horiz designs. Multicoloured.* P 14¹/₂×14.
233	18 c. Type **45**		20	15
234	30 c. Basket and jar		30	30
235	40 c. Jars and bag		40	50
236	50 c. Dish and jars		55	75
233/6		Set of 4	1·25	1·50

46 Chub Mackerel   **47** Broom Cluster Fig

(Des D. Thorpe)

1989 (20 July). *Seafood.* T **46** *and similar horiz designs. Multicoloured.* P 14¹/₂×14.
237	18 c. Type **46**		40	15
238	30 c. Squid		55	45
239	40 c. Perna or Brown Mussels		65	55
240	50 c. Rock Lobster		80	85
237/40		Set of 4	2·25	1·75

(Des B. Jackson)

1989 (5 Oct). *Trees.* T **47** *and similar horiz designs. Multicoloured.* P 14×14¹/₂.
241	18 c. Type **47**		40	20
242	30 c. Natal Fig		65	55
243	40 c. Broad-leaved Coral		75	75
244	50 c. Cabbage Tree		1·00	1·10
241/4		Set of 4	2·50	2·40

48 *Ginkgo koningensis*   **49** Aretaeus (discoverer of diabetes)

(Des L. Kriedemann)

1990 (18 Jan). *Plant Fossils.* T **48** *and similar horiz designs. Multicoloured.* P 14.
245	18 c. Type **48**		60	25
246	30 c. *Pseudoctenis spatulata*		90	80
247	40 c. *Rissikia media*		1·00	1·00
248	50 c. *Taeniopteris anavolans*		1·25	1·40
245/8		Set of 4	3·25	3·00

(Des A. McBride)

1990 (29 Mar). *Celebrities of Medicine (5th series). Diabetes Research.* T **49** *and similar vert designs. Multicoloured.* P 14×14¹/₂.
249	18 c. Type **49**		50	20
250	30 c. Claude Bernard (discovered sugar formation by liver)		80	60
251	40 c. Oscar Minkowski (discovered pancreas removal caused diabetes)		90	80
252	50 c. Frederick Banting (discoverer of insulin)		1·10	1·00
249/52		Set of 4	3·00	2·40

50 Diviner dancing to Drum   **51** Soldier Lily

(Des A. H. Barrett)

1990 (28 June). *Diviners.* T **50** *and similar vert designs. Multicoloured.* P 14×14¹/₂.
253	21 c. Type **50**		50	20
254	35 c. Lecturing Imichetywa (novitiates)		80	60
255	40 c. Neophyte initiation		90	80
256	50 c. Diviner's induction ceremony		1·10	1·00
253/6		Set of 4	3·00	2·40

The 50 c. value exists as a Philatelic Foundation miniature sheet.

(Des A. Batten)

1990 (20 Sept). *Flowers.* T **51** *and similar vert designs. Multicoloured.* P 14.
257	21 c. Type **51**		40	20
258	35 c. *Disa crassicornis*		60	55
259	40 c. Christmas Bells		70	70
260	50 c. Port St. John's Creeper		80	1·00
257/60		Set of 4	2·25	2·25

52 Pink Ink Plant   **53** Common Dolphin

(Des A. Batten)

1991 (10 Jan). *Parasitic Plants.* T **52** *and similar vert designs. Multicoloured.* P 14×14¹/₂.
261	21 c. Type **52**		50	20
262	35 c. White Harveya		70	65
263	40 c. *Alectra sessiliflora*		80	90
264	50 c. *Hydnora africana*		1·00	1·25
261/4		Set of 4	2·75	2·75

(Des D. Thorpe)

1991 (4 Apr). *Dolphins.* T **53** *and similar horiz designs. Multicoloured.* P 14¹/₂×14.
265	25 c. Type **53**		70	25
266	40 c. Bottle-nosed Dolphin		1·00	75
267	50 c. Humpbacked Dolphin		1·10	1·10
268	60 c. Risso's Dolphin		1·25	1·40
265/8		Set of 4	3·50	3·25

54 South African Crowned Crane   **55** Emil von Behring and Shibasaburo Kitasako (diphtheria)

(Des A. Ainslie)

1991 (20 June). *Endangered Birds.* T **54** *and similar vert designs. Multicoloured.* P 14×14¹/₂.
269	25 c. Type **54**		55	30
270	40 c. Cape Vulture		80	70
271	50 c. Wattled Crane		1·00	90
272	60 c. Egyptian Vulture		1·25	1·25
269/72		Set of 4	3·25	2·75

The 60 c. value exists as a Philatelic Foundation miniature sheet.

(Des J. van Niekerk)

1991 (26 Sept). *Celebrities of Medicine (6th series). Vaccine Development.* T **55** *and similar horiz designs. Multicoloured.* P 14×14¹/₂.
273	25 c. Type **55**		60	25
274	40 c. Camille Guérin and Albert Calmette (tuberculosis)		1·00	80
275	50 c. Jonas Salk (poliomyelitis)		1·25	1·10
276	60 c. John Enders (measles)		1·40	1·25
273/6		Set of 4	3·75	3·00

56 *Eulophia speciosa*   **57** Thomas Weller (researcher into infectious viruses)

(Des A. Batten)

1992 (20 Feb). *Orchids.* T **56** *and similar vert designs. Multicoloured.* P 14.
277	27 c. Type **56**		25	20
278	45 c. *Satyrium sphaerocarpum*		40	40
279	65 c. *Disa scullyi*		60	70
280	85 c. *Disa tysonii*		80	1·00
277/80		Set of 4	1·90	2·10

(Des J. van Niekerk)

1992 (1 Apr). *Celebrities of Medicine (7th series).* T **57** *and similar horiz designs. Multicoloured.* P 14.
281	27 c. Type **57**		50	25
282	45 c. Ignaz Semmelweis		75	70
283	65 c. Sir James Simpson		1·00	1·00
284	85 c. René Laënnec		1·25	1·40
281/4		Set of 4	3·25	3·00

58 Red-billed Pintail   **59** *Pseudomelania sutherlandi* (gastropod)

1992 (16 July). *Waterfowl.* T **58** *and similar horiz designs. Multicoloured.* P 14.
285	35 c. Type **58**		50	50
	a. Pair. Nos. 285/6		1·00	1·00
286	35 c. Hottentot Teal		50	50
287	70 c. Maccoa Duck		80	80
	a. Pair. Nos. 287/8		1·60	1·60
288	70 c. White-backed Duck		80	80
289	90 c. African Black Duck		1·00	1·00
	a. Pair. Nos. 289/90		2·00	2·00
290	90 c. Egyptian Goose		1·00	1·00
291	1 r. 05, Cape Shoveler		1·25	1·25
	a. Pair. Nos. 291/2		2·25	2·25
292	1 r. 05, Cape Teal		1·25	1·25
285/92		Set of 8	6·25	6·25

The two designs of each value were printed together, *se-tenant*, in pairs within the sheets.

No. 287 exists as a Philatelic Foundation miniature sheet.

SOUTH AFRICA / *Transkei, Venda*

(Des L. Kriedemann)

1992 (17 Sept). *Marine Fossils. T 59 and similar horiz designs. Multicoloured. P 14.*
293	35 c. Type 59	85	35
294	70 c. *Gaudryceras denseplicatum* (ammonite)	1·25	95
295	90 c. *Neithea quinquecostata* (bivalve)	1·25	1·40
296	1 r. 05, *Pugilina acuticarinatus* (gastropod)	1·40	1·50
293/6	Set of 4	4·25	3·75

60 Papillon   **61** Fabrosaurus

(Des D. Murphy)

1993 (12 Feb). *Dogs. T 60 and similar horiz designs. Multicoloured. P 14.*
297	35 c. Type 60	50	30
298	70 c. Pekinese	80	80
299	90 c. Chihuahua	1·00	1·10
300	1 r. 05, Dachshund	1·25	1·40
297/300	Set of 4	3·25	3·25

The 70 c. value exists as a Philatelic Foundation miniature sheet.

(Des L. Kriedemann)

1993 (18 June). *Prehistoric Animals. T 61 and similar horiz designs. Multicoloured. P 14.*
301	45 c. Type 61	85	35
302	65 c. Diictodon	1·25	95
303	85 c. Chasmatosaurus	1·50	1·50
304	1 r. 05, Rubidgea	1·50	1·60
301/4	Set of 4	4·50	4·00

62 Sir Alexander Fleming and Howard Florey   **63** Laughing Doves

(Des J. van Niekerk)

1993 (20 Aug). *Celebrities of Medicine (8th series). T 62 and similar horiz designs. Multicoloured. P 14.*
305	45 c. Type 62	70	35
306	65 c. Alexis Carrel	1·10	95
307	85 c. James Lind	1·25	1·40
308	1 r. 05, Santiago Ramón y Cajal	1·40	1·50
305/8	Set of 4	4·00	3·75

(Des Julia Birkhead)

1993 (15 Oct). *Doves. T 63 and similar horiz designs. Multicoloured. P 14.*
309	45 c. Type 63	50	30
310	65 c. Tambourine Doves	80	80
311	85 c. Emerald-spotted Wood Doves	1·00	1·10
312	1 r. 05, Namaqua Doves	1·25	1·40
309/12	Set of 4	3·25	3·25
MS313	92×83 mm. Nos. 309/12	3·25	3·25

64 *Clan Lindsay* (steamer) on rocks, Mazeppa Bay, 1898

(Des J. van Niekerk)

1994 (18 Mar). *Shipwrecks. T 64 and similar horiz designs. Multicoloured. P 14.*
314	45 c. Type 64	85	55
315	65 c. *Horizon* (freighter) on rocks near River Mngazi, 1967	1·25	1·10
316	85 c. *Oceanos* (pleasure cruiser) sinking near Coffee Bay, 1991	1·40	1·50
317	1 r. 05, *Forresbank* (freighter) on fire near River Mtakatye, 1958	1·50	1·75
314/17	Set of 4	4·50	4·50

The 85 c. value exists as a Philatelic Foundation miniature sheet.

Transkei was reincorporated into the Republic of South Africa on 27 April 1994. Its postal service continued to operate, using South African stamps, until 1 April 1996 when it was integrated with that of the Republic.

XIV. VENDA

The Venda Territory Authority was established in 1969 and was granted internal self-government on 1 February 1973 under the Bantu Homelands Constitution Act. Venda became fully independent on 13 September 1979. This independence did not receive international political recognition, but the stamps were accepted as valid on international mail.

PRINTERS. All the following stamps were printed in lithography by the South African Government Printer, Pretoria.

1 Flag and Mace   **2** *Tecomaria capensis*

(Des A. H. Barrett)

1979 (13 Sept). *Independence. T 1 and similar horiz designs. Multicoloured. P 14.*
1	4 c. Type 1	25	25
2	15 c. Government Buildings, Thohoyandou	50	70
3	20 c. Chief Minister P. R. Mphephu	65	80
4	25 c. Coat of arms	1·00	1·40
1/4	Set of 4	2·25	2·75

(Des D. Findlay)

1979 (13 Sept)–**85**. *Flowers. T 2 and similar vert designs. Multicoloured. P 14 (11, 12 c.) or 12½ (others).*
5	1 c. Type 2	10	10
	a. Perf 14 (30.4.82)	10	10
6	2 c. *Catophractes alexandri*	30	15
	a. Perf 14 (6.5.81)	20	15
7	3 c. *Tricliceras longipedunculatum*	30	10
	a. Perf 14 (18.8.82)	30	15
8	4 c. *Dissotis princeps*	30	10
9	5 c. *Gerbera jamesonii*	1·75	45
	a. Perf 14 (15.1.80)	30	10
10	6 c. *Hibiscus mastersianus*	15	10
11	7 c. *Nymphaea caerulea*	20	10
12	8 c. *Crinum lugardiae*	45	25
	a. Perf 14 (27.1.82)	30	15
13	9 c. *Xerophyta retinervis*	20	15
14	10 c. *Hypoxis angustifolia*	40	25
	a. Perf 14 (4.3.83)	40	15
14b	11 c. *Combretum microphyllum* (2.4.84)	30	15
14c	12 c. *Clivia caulescens* (1.4.85)	30	15
15	15 c. *Pycnostachys urticifolia*	30	15
16	20 c. *Zantedeschia jucunda*	55	15
17	25 c. *Leonotis mollis*	2·00	1·00
	a. Perf 14 (22.1.80)	50	40
18	30 c. *Littonia modesta*	40	30
19	50 c. *Protea caffra*	40	40
	a. Perf 14 (17.2.84)	1·40	1·25
20	1 r. *Adenium multiflorum*	1·00	85
21	2 r. *Strelitzia caudata*	1·75	2·00
5/21	Set of 19 (cheapest)	7·00	5·00

3 Man drinking Beer   **4** Tea Plants in Nursery

(Des A. H. Barrett)

1980 (13 Feb). *Wood Carvings. T 3 and similar multicoloured designs. P 14.*
22	5 c. Type 3	15	15
23	10 c. Frying mealies in gourd	25	25
24	15 c. King Nebuchadnezzar (horiz)	40	40
25	20 c. Python squeezing woman to death (horiz)	50	60
22/5	Set of 4	1·10	1·25

(Des A. H. Barrett)

1980 (14 May). *Tea Cultivation. T 4 and similar horiz designs. Multicoloured. P 14.*
26	5 c. Type 4	15	10
27	10 c. Tea pluckers	20	20
28	15 c. Withering in the factory	35	35
29	20 c. Cut, twist, curl unit	40	45
26/9	Set of 4	1·00	1·00

ALTERED CATALOGUE NUMBERS

Any Catalogue numbers altered from the last edition are shown as a list in the introductory pages.

5 Young Banana Plants   **6** *Precis tugela*

(Des A. H. Barrett)

1980 (13 Aug). *Banana Cultivation. T 5 and similar horiz designs. Multicoloured. P 14.*
30	5 c. Type 5	15	10
31	10 c. Cutting "hands"	25	25
32	15 c. Sorting and dividing into clusters	30	30
33	20 c. Packing	40	45
30/3	Set of 4	1·00	1·00

(Des D. Findlay)

1980 (13 Nov). *Butterflies. T 6 and similar vert designs. Multicoloured. P 14.*
34	5 c. Type 6	20	15
35	10 c. *Charaxes bohemani*	40	40
36	15 c. *Catacroptera cloanthe*	55	55
37	20 c. *Papilio dardanus*	65	70
34/7	Set of 4	1·60	1·60

7 Collared Sunbird   **8** Nwanedi Dam

(Des J. Hoekstra)

1981 (16 Feb). *Sunbirds. T 7 and similar vert designs. Multicoloured. P 14.*
38	5 c. Type 7	20	15
39	15 c. Mariqua Sunbird	55	55
40	20 c. Southern White-bellied Sunbird	60	60
41	25 c. Scarlet-chested Sunbird	75	80
38/41	Set of 4	1·90	1·90

(Des A. H. Barrett)

1981 (6 May). *Lakes and Waterfalls. T 8 and similar horiz designs. Multicoloured. P 14.*
42	5 c. Type 8	15	10
43	15 c. Mahovhohovho Falls	30	30
44	20 c. Phiphidi Falls	35	35
45	25 c. Lake Fundudzi	35	40
42/5	Set of 4	1·00	1·00

9 *Cynorkis kassnerana*   **10** Mbila

(Des Jeannette Stead)

1981 (11 Sept). *Orchids. T 9 and similar vert designs. Multicoloured. P 14.*
46	5 c. Type 9	15	10
47	15 c. *Eulophia fridericii*	35	35
48	20 c. *Bonatea densiflora*	45	45
49	25 c. *Mystacidium brayoniae*	50	55
46/9	Set of 4	1·25	1·25
MS50	96×120 mm. Nos. 46/9	1·25	1·40

(Des J. Hoekstra)

1981 (13 Nov). *Musical Instruments. T 10 and similar horiz designs. P 14.*
51	5 c. yellow-orange and black	10	10
52	15 c. red-orange and black	25	25
53	20 c. orange-brown and black	30	35
54	25 c. brown-ochre and black	30	35
51/4	Set of 4	80	90

Designs:—15 c. Phalaphala; 20 c. Tshizambi; 25 c. Ngoma.

11 Gathering Sisal

(Des B. Ashton)

1982 (26 Feb). *Sisal Cultivation. T* **11** *and similar horiz designs. Multicoloured. P* 13½×14.

55	5 c. Type **11**	10	10
56	10 c. Drying	20	20
57	20 c. Grading	30	35
58	25 c. Baling	30	40
55/8	*Set of* 4	80	90

12 Bison Petrograph, Altamira, Spain

(Des H. Botha)

1982 (15 June). *History of Writing* (1st series). *T* **12** *and similar horiz designs. Multicoloured. P* 14.

59	8 c. Type **12**	15	10
60	15 c. Petroglyph, Eastern California	30	30
61	20 c. Pictograph script (Sumerian tablet)	40	40
62	25 c. Bushman burial stone, Humansdorp	45	45
59/62	*Set of* 4	1·10	1·10

No. 59 is inscribed "AHAMIRA" in error.
See also Nos. 75/8, 87/90, 107/10, 139/42, 171/4 and 203/6.

13 *Euphorbia ingens*   14 *Rana angolensis*

(Des D. Findlay)

1982 (17 Sept). *Indigenous Trees* (1st series). *T* **13** *and similar horiz designs. Multicoloured. P* 14.

63	8 c. Type **13**	15	10
64	15 c. *Pterocarpus angolensis*	30	30
65	20 c. *Ficus ingens*	40	40
66	25 c. *Adansonia digitata*	50	55
63/6	*Set of* 4	1·25	1·25

See also Nos. 79/82, 95/8 and 227/30.

(Des A. H. Barrett)

1982 (26 Nov). *Frogs. T* **14** *and similar horiz designs. Multicoloured. P* 14.

67	8 c. Type **14**	15	10
68	15 c. *Chiromantis xerampelina*	30	30
69	20 c. *Leptopelis* sp	40	40
70	25 c. *Ptychadena anchietae*	50	55
67/70	*Set of* 4	1·25	1·25

15 European Bee Eater

(Des Sheila Nowers)

1983 (16 Feb). *Migratory Birds* (1st series). *T* **15** *and similar horiz designs. Multicoloured. P* 14.

71	8 c. Type **15**	25	15
72	20 c. Tawny Eagle ("Steppe Eagle")	65	65
73	25 c. Violet Starling ("Plum-coloured Starling")	75	75
74	10 c. Abdim's Stork ("White-bellied Stork")	1·40	1·50
71/4	*Set of* 4	2·75	2·75

See also Nos. 91/4.

(Des H. Botha)

1983 (11 May). *History of Writing* (2nd series). *Multicoloured designs as T* **12**, *but vert. Multicoloured. P* 14.

75	10 c. Indus Valley script	15	10
76	20 c. Sumerian cuneiform	25	25
77	25 c. Egyptian hieroglyphics	30	30
78	40 c. Chinese handscroll	65	70
75/8	*Set of* 4	1·25	1·25

(Des D. Findlay)

1983 (3 Aug). *Indigenous Trees* (2nd series). *Horiz designs as T* **13**. *Multicoloured. P* 14.

79	10 c. *Gardenia spatulifolia*	15	10
80	20 c. *Hyphaene natalensis*	30	30
81	25 c. *Albizia adianthifolia*	40	40
82	40 c. *Sesamothamnus lugardii*	55	60
79/82	*Set of* 4	1·25	1·25

16 Avocado   17 African Paradise Flycatcher

(Des B. Jackson)

1983 (26 Oct). *Subtropical Fruit. T* **16** *and similar horiz designs. Multicoloured. P* 14.

83	10 c. Type **16**	15	10
84	20 c. Mango	30	30
85	25 c. Papaya	40	40
86	40 c. Litchi	55	60
83/6	*Set of* 4	1·25	1·25

(Des H. Botha)

1984 (17 Feb). *History of Writing* (3rd series). *Horiz designs as T* **12**. *Multicoloured. P* 14×14½.

87	10 c. Evolution of cuneiform sign	15	10
88	20 c. Evolution of Chinese character	30	30
89	25 c. Development of Cretan hieroglyphics	40	40
90	40 c. Development of Egyptian hieroglyphics	55	60
87/90	*Set of* 4	1·25	1·25

(Des Sheila Nowers)

1984 (26 Apr). *Migratory Birds* (2nd series). *T* **17** *and similar vert designs. Multicoloured. P* 14½×14.

91	11 c. White Stork	30	20
92	20 c. Type **17**	50	50
93	25 c. Black Kite ("Yellow-billed Kite")	60	60
94	30 c. Wood Sandpiper	70	85
91/4	*Set of* 4	1·90	1·90

(Des D. Findlay)

1984 (21 June). *Indigenous Trees* (3rd series). *Horiz designs as T* **13**. *Multicoloured. P* 14.

95	11 c. *Afzelia quanzensis*	15	10
96	20 c. *Peltophorum africanum*	30	30
97	25 c. *Gyrocarpus americanus*	40	40
98	30 c. *Acacia sieberana*	50	55
95/8	*Set of* 4	1·25	1·25

18 Dzata Ruins, Nzhelele Valley   19 White-browed Robin Chat

(Des B. Jackson)

1984 (13 Sept). *Fifth Anniv of Independence. T* **18** *and similar horiz designs. Multicoloured. P* 14.

99	11 c. Type **18**	15	10
100	25 c. Traditional hut	25	30
101	30 c. Sub-economical house	30	35
102	45 c. Modern home	45	65
99/102	*Set of* 4	1·00	1·25

(Des Sheila Nowers)

1985 (10 Jan). *Songbirds. T* **19** *and similar vert designs. Multicoloured. P* 14½×14.

103	11 c. Type **19** (inscr "Heuglin's Robin")	35	20
104	25 c. Black-collared Barbet	50	45
105	30 c. African Black-headed Oriole	65	55
106	50 c. Kurrichane Thrush	1·00	1·00
103/6	*Set of* 4	2·25	2·00

(Des H. Botha)

1985 (21 Mar). *History of Writing* (4th series). *Horiz designs as T* **12**. *Multicoloured. P* 14.

107	11 c. Southern Arabic characters	15	10
108	25 c. Phoenician characters	30	30
109	30 c. Aramaic characters	40	40
110	50 c. Canaanite characters	75	75
107/10	*Set of* 4	1·40	1·40

The new-issue supplement to this Catalogue appears each month in

GIBBONS
STAMP MONTHLY

—from your newsagent or by postal subscription— sample copy and details on request.

20 Transvaal Red Milkwood   21 *Pellaea dura*

(Des Sheila Nowers)

1985 (21 June). *Food from the Veld* (1st series). *T* **20** *and similar vert designs. Multicoloured. P* 14.

111	12 c. Type **20**	15	10
112	25 c. Buffalo Thorn	30	30
113	30 c. Wild Water Melon	35	35
114	50 c. Brown Ivory	55	60
111/14	*Set of* 4	1·25	1·25

See also Nos. 163/6.

(Des D. Findlay)

1985 (5 Sept). *Ferns. T* **21** *and similar vert designs. Multicoloured. P* 14.

115	12 c. Type **21**	15	10
116	25 c. *Actiniopteris radiata*	30	30
117	30 c. *Adiantum hispidulum*	40	40
118	50 c. *Polypodium polypodioides*	65	70
115/18	*Set of* 4	1·40	1·40

22 Three-lined Grass Snake   23 Etruscan Dish

1986 (16 Jan)–93. *Reptiles. T* **22** *and similar horiz designs. Multicoloured. Chalk-surfaced paper. P* 14.

119	1 c. Type **22**	10	10
	a. Ordinary paper (29.5.89)	30	30
120	2 c. Mole Snake	10	10
	a. Ordinary paper (29.5.89)	40	40
121	3 c. Ornate Scrub Lizard	10	10
122	4 c. Puff Adder	10	10
123	5 c. Three-lined Skink	10	10
	a. Ordinary paper (12.7.93)	40	40
124	6 c. Egyptian Cobra	15	10
125	7 c. Blue-tailed Kopje Skink	15	10
126	8 c. Spotted Bush Snake	20	20
	a. Ordinary paper (12.7.93)	40	40
127	9 c. Yellow-throated Plated Lizard	20	20
128	10 c. Northern Lined Shovelsnout	20	20
	a. Ordinary paper (20.7.93)	40	40
129	14 c. Transvaal Flat Lizard (1.4.86)	1·25	20
130	15 c. Soutpansberg Lizard	30	20
	a. Ordinary paper (13.9.89)	40	40
131	16 c. Iguana Water Leguan (1.4.87)	60	20
132	18 c. Black Mamba (*ordinary paper*) (3.7.89)	75	20
133	20 c. Transvaal Flat Gecko	30	20
	a. Ordinary paper (17.9.90)	1·25	70
133b	21 c. Flap-necked Chameleon (*ordinary paper*) (3.8.90)	75	20
134	25 c. Longtailed Garter Snake	40	30
135	30 c. Tigroid Thick-toed Gecko	45	35
	a. Ordinary paper (4.9.92)	75	75
136	50 c. Cape File Snake	70	50
137	1 r. Soutpansberg Girdled Lizard	1·25	1·00
	a. Ordinary paper (9.7.90)	2·25	2·25
138	2 r. African Python	1·75	2·25
	a. Ordinary paper (27.1.89)	3·75	3·75
119/38	*Set of* 21	8·50	6·00

(Des H. Botha)

1986 (10 Apr). *History of Writing* (5th series). *T* **23** *and similar vert designs. Multicoloured. P* 14×14½.

139	14 c. Type **23**	15	10
140	20 c. Greek inscription, AD 70	30	30
141	25 c. Roman inscription	40	40
142	30 c. Cyrillic inscription (Byzantine mosaic)	55	60
139/42	*Set of* 4	1·25	1·25

24 Planting Pine Seedlings

(Des B. Jackson)

1986 (26 June). *Forestry. T* **24** *and similar horiz designs. Multicoloured. P* 14.

143	14 c. Type **24**	20	15
144	20 c. Mule hauling logs	30	30
145	25 c. Off-loading logs at sawmill	40	40
146	30 c. Using timber in construction	55	60
143/6	*Set of* 4	1·25	1·25

PHILATELIC FOUNDATION MINIATURE SHEETS. These miniature sheets were issued by the Philatelic Foundation of Southern Africa and not the postal administration. They could be purchased by post or from a limited number of philatelic offices at a premium in aid of various national and international stamp exhibitions.

25 Maxwell, 1910   **26** Comb Duck

(Des A. H. Barrett)

1986 (4 Sept.). *FIVA International Veteran Car Rally. T* **25** *and similar horiz designs. Multicoloured. P* 14½×14.

147	14 c. Type 25		20	15
148	20 c. Bentley 4½ l., 1929		30	30
149	25 c. Plymouth Coupé, 1933		40	40
150	30 c. Mercedes Benz 220, 1958		55	60
147/50		*Set of* 4	1·25	1·25

The 30 c. value exists as a Philatelic Foundation miniature sheet.

(Des A. H. Barrett)

1987 (8 Jan.). *Waterfowl. T* **26** *and similar multicoloured designs. P* 14×14½ (*vert*) *or* 14½×14 (*horiz*).

151	14 c. Type 26		85	40
152	20 c. White-faced Whistling Duck		95	70
153	25 c. Spur-winged Goose (*horiz*)		1·10	90
154	30 c. Egyptian Goose (*horiz*)		1·40	1·25
151/4		*Set of* 4	3·75	3·00

The 25 c. value exists as a Philatelic Foundation miniature sheet.

27 "Iron Master"   **28** Tigerfish

(Des L. Kriedemann)

1987 (9 Apr.). *Wood Sculptures by Meshack Matamela Raphalalani. T* **27** *and similar vert designs. Multicoloured. P* 14½×14.

155	16 c. Type 27		15	15
156	20 c. "Distant Drums"		25	25
157	25 c. "Sunrise"		30	30
158	30 c. "Obedience"		40	40
155/8		*Set of* 4	1·00	1·00

(Des D. Thorpe)

1987 (2 July). *Freshwater Fishes. T* **28** *and similar horiz designs. Multicoloured. P* 14×14½.

159	16 c. Type 28		25	20
160	20 c. Barred Minnow		35	35
161	25 c. Mozambique Mouthbrooder		45	45
162	30 c. Sharp-toothed Catfish		55	60
159/62		*Set of* 4	1·40	1·40

29 Cross-berry   **30** Picking Berries

(Des Sheila Nowers)

1987 (2 Oct.). *Food from the Veld* (2nd series). *T* **29** *and similar vert designs. Multicoloured. P* 14×14½.

163	16 c. Type 29		20	15
164	30 c. Wild Date Palm		30	30
165	40 c. Tree Fuchsia		40	40
166	50 c. Wild Cucumber		50	55
163/6		*Set of* 4	1·25	1·25

(Des B. Jackson)

1988 (21 Jan.). *Coffee Industry. T* **30** *and similar horiz designs. Multicoloured. P* 14½×14.

167	16 c. Type 30		20	20
168	30 c. Weighing bags of berries		30	30
169	40 c. Drying beans in sun		35	35
170	50 c. Roasting graded beans		45	45
167/70		*Set of* 4	1·10	1·10

31 "Universal Love" in Chinese   **32** College

(Des H. Botha)

1988 (28 Apr.). *History of Writing* (6th series). *T* **31** *and similar horiz designs. P* 14½×14.

171	16 c. stone, black and bright scarlet		25	20
172	30 c. stone, black and bright scarlet		35	35
173	40 c. stone, black and deep rose-red		45	45
174	50 c. black and gold		55	60
171/4		*Set of* 4	1·40	1·40

Designs:—30 c. "Picture of a lion on a stone" in Devanagari (Indian script); 40 c. "Information" in Russian; 50 c. "Peace be upon you" in Thuluth (Arabic script).

(Des L. Kriedemann)

1988 (18 Aug.). *Fifth Anniv of Shayandima Nurses' Training College. T* **32** *and similar horiz designs. Multicoloured. P* 14½×14.

175	16 c. Type 32		25	20
176	30 c. Students using microscope		40	40
177	40 c. Anatomy class		50	50
178	50 c. Clinical training		55	60
175/8		*Set of* 4	1·50	1·50

33 "Fetching Water"   **34** Ndongwana (clay bowls)

1988 (6 Oct.). *Watercolours by Kenneth Thabo. T* **33** *and similar horiz designs. Multicoloured. P* 14½×14.

179	16 c. Type 33		25	20
180	30 c. "Grinding Maize"		40	40
181	40 c. "Offering Food"		50	50
182	50 c. "Kindling the Fire"		55	60
179/82		*Set of* 4	1·50	1·50

The 50 c. value exists as a Philatelic Foundation miniature sheet.

(Des L. Kriedemann)

1989 (5 Jan.). *Traditional Kitchenware. T* **34** *and similar horiz designs. Multicoloured. P* 14½×14.

183	16 c. Type 34		20	20
184	30 c. Ndilo (wooden porridge bowls)		30	30
185	40 c. Mufaro (basket with lid)		40	40
186	50 c. Muthatha (dish woven from ilala palm)		45	45
183/6		*Set of* 4	1·25	1·25

35 Domba   **36** Southern Ground Hornbill

(Des K. Thabo)

1989 (5 Apr.). *Traditional Dances. T* **35** *and similar horiz designs. Multicoloured. P* 14½×14.

187	18 c. Type 35		20	20
188	30 c. Tshinzerere		30	30
189	40 c. Malende		40	40
190	50 c. Malombo		45	45
187/90		*Set of* 4	1·25	1·25

(Des M. Enslin)

1989 (27 June). *Endangered Birds. T* **36** *and similar vert designs. Multicoloured. P* 14½×14.

191	18 c. Type 36		70	30
192	30 c. Lappet-faced Vulture		1·00	70
193	40 c. Bateleur		1·25	90
194	50 c. Martial Eagle		1·50	1·25
191/4		*Set of* 4	4·00	2·75

The 50 c. value exists as a Philatelic Foundation miniature sheet.

37 Pres. Gota F. N. Ravele   **38** Lion

(Des A. H. Barrett)

1989 (13 Sept.). *Tenth Anniv of Independence. T* **37** *and similar horiz designs. Multicoloured. P* 14½×14.

195	18 c. Type 37		20	20
196	30 c. Presidential offices		30	30
197	40 c. President's residence		40	40
198	50 c. Thohoyandou Sports Stadium		45	45
195/8		*Set of* 4	1·25	1·25

(Des D. Murphy)

1990 (1 Mar.). *Nwanedi National Park. T* **38** *and similar vert designs. Multicoloured. P* 14×14½.

199	18 c. Type 38		40	25
200	30 c. Common Zebra		70	55
201	40 c. Cheetah		75	65
202	50 c. White Rhinoceros		1·00	1·00
199/202		*Set of* 4	2·50	2·25

The 50 c. value exists as a Philatelic Foundation miniature sheet.

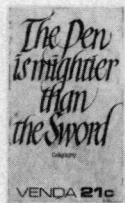

39 Calligraphy   **40** *Aloe globuligemma*

(Des H. Botha)

1990 (23 May). *History of Writing* (7th series). *T* **39** *and similar vert designs. P* 14½×14.

203	21 c. black and grey		20	15
204	30 c. black and reddish brown		40	40
205	40 c. black and yellowish green		50	50
206	50 c. blue, new blue and black		60	65
203/6		*Set of* 4	1·50	1·50

Designs:—30 c. Part of score for Beethoven's *Moonlight Sonata*; 40 c. Characters from personal computer; 50 c. Television picture of message transmitted into outer space from Arecibo 1000 radio telescope.

(Des G. Marx)

1990 (23 Aug.). *Aloes. T* **40** *and similar vert designs. Multicoloured. P* 14½×14.

207	21 c. Type 40		30	25
208	35 c. *Aloe aculeata*		50	50
209	40 c. *Aloe lutescens*		60	70
210	50 c. *Aloe angelica*		70	90
207/10		*Set of* 4	1·90	2·10

41 *Pseudacraea boisduvalii*   **42** Cape Puff-back Flycatchers

(Des E. Forbes)

1990 (15 Nov.). *Butterflies. T* **41** *and similar vert designs. Multicoloured. P* 14×14½.

211	21 c. Type 41		70	40
212	35 c. *Papilio nireus*		1·00	75
213	40 c. *Charaxes jasius*		1·10	1·00
214	50 c. *Aeropetes tulbaghia*		1·25	1·25
211/14		*Set of* 4	3·50	3·00

1991 (7 Mar.). *Birds. T* **42** *and similar horiz designs showing paintings by Claude Finch-Davies. Multicoloured. P* 14½×14.

215	21 c. Type 42		50	40
216	35 c. Red-capped Robin Chat		75	80
217	40 c. Collared Sunbirds		85	1·00
218	50 c. Yellow-streaked Greenbul		1·10	1·40
215/18		*Set of* 4	2·75	3·25

43 Paper made from Pulp   **44** Venda Sun Hotel Complex, Thohoyandou

(Des H. Botha)

1991 (6 June). *Inventions* (1st series). *T* **43** *and similar vert designs. Multicoloured. P* 14½×14.

219	25 c. Type 43		55	35
220	40 c. Magnetic compass		1·00	75
221	50 c. Abacus		1·10	1·00
222	60 c. Gunpowder		1·60	1·25
219/22		*Set of* 4	3·75	3·00

The 60 c. value exists as a Philatelic Foundation miniature sheet.
See also Nos. 239/42 and 259/62.

1991 (29 Aug). *Tourism. T* **44** *and similar horiz designs.*
Multicoloured. P 14½×14.
223	25 c. Type 44	..	..		55	35
224	40 c. Mphephu Resort	..	..		85	75
225	50 c. Sagole Spa	..	..		95	95
226	60 c. Luphephe-Nwanedi Resort				1·00	1·25
223/6				Set of 4	3·00	3·00

(Des D. Findlay)

1991 (21 Nov). *Indigenous Trees (4th series). Horiz designs as*
T **13**. *Multicoloured. P* 14½×14.
227	27 c. Fever Tree	..	..		60	35
228	45 c. Transvaal Beech	..			1·00	75
229	65 c. Transvaal Wild Banana	..			1·10	1·10
230	85 c. Sausage Tree	..	..		1·40	1·50
227/30		..	..	Set of 4	3·50	3·25

45 Setting the Web   46 *Apis mellifera*

1992 (5 Mar). *Clothing Factory. T* **45** *and similar horiz*
designs. Multicoloured. P 14.
231	27 c. Type 45	..	..		45	25
232	45 c. Knitting	..	..		60	55
233	65 c. Making up garment	..			90	1·00
234	85 c. Inspection of finished product			1·25	1·50
231/4		..	..	Set of 4	2·75	3·00

(Des A. Ainslie)

1992 (21 May). *Bees. T* **46** *and similar horiz designs.*
Multicoloured. P 14.
235	35 c. Type 46	..	..		60	40
236	70 c. *Anthidium cordiforme*	..		1·00	90
237	90 c. *Megachile frontalis*	..		1·40	1·25
238	1 r. 05, *Xylocopa caffra*	..		1·50	1·40
235/8		..	..	Set of 4	4·00	3·50
The 70 c. value exists as a Philatelic Foundation miniature
sheet.

47 Egyptian Plough   48 Nile Crocodile

(Des H. Botha)

1992 (13 Aug). *Inventions (2nd series). T* **47** *and similar horiz*
designs. Multicoloured. P 14.
239	35 c. Type 47	..	..		60	40
240	70 c. Early wheel, Mesopotamia	..		1·00	90
241	90 c. Making bricks, Egypt	..		1·40	1·25
242	1 r. 05, Early Egyptian sailing ship		1·50	1·40
239/42		..	..	Set of 4	4·00	3·50

(Des A. Ainslie)

1992 (15 Oct). *Crocodile Farming. T* **48** *and similar horiz*
designs. Multicoloured. P 14½×14.
243	35 c. Type 48	..	..		65	40
244	70 c. Egg laying	..	..		1·10	90
245	90 c. Eggs hatching	..	..		1·40	1·40
246	1 r. 05, Mother carrying young	..		1·50	1·60
243/6		..	..	Set of 4	4·25	3·75

49 Burmese   50 Green Heron

(Des Sheila Nowers)

1993 (19 May). *Domestic Cats. T* **49** *and similar horiz designs.*
Multicoloured. P 14.
247	45 c. Type 49	..	..		90	45
248	65 c. Tabby	..	..		1·25	1·00
249	85 c. Siamese	..	..		1·50	1·40
250	1 r. 05, Persian	..	..		1·60	1·75
247/50		..	..	Set of 4	4·75	4·25
The 65 c. value exists as a Philatelic Foundation miniature
sheet.

(Des Priscilla Henley)

1993 (16 July). *Herons. T* **50** *and similar horiz designs.*
Multicoloured. P 14.
251	45 c. Type 50	..	..		80	50
252	65 c. Black-crowned Night Heron ..		1·10	1·00
253	85 c. Purple Heron	..	..		1·40	1·40
254	1 r. 05, Black-headed Heron	..		1·60	1·90
251/4		..	..	Set of 4	4·50	4·25
MS255	86×132 mm. Nos. 251/4				4·50	4·75

51 Punching out   52 Axes
Sole Lining

1993 (17 Sept). *Shoe Factory. T* **51** *and similar horiz designs.*
Multicoloured. P 14×14½.
256	45 c. Type 51	..	..		30	25
257	65 c. Shaping heel ..	..			55	60
258	85 c. Joining the upper to inner sole	..	75	85
259	1 r. 05, Forming sole	..	..		90	1·25
256/9		..	..	Set of 4	2·25	2·75

(Des H. Botha)

1993 (5 Nov). *Inventions (3rd series). T* **52** *and similar horiz*
designs. Multicoloured. P 14.
260	45 c. Type 52	..	..		40	35
261	65 c. Armour	..	..		75	65
262	85 c. Arches	..	..		95	85
263	1 r. 05, Pont du Gard aqueduct	..	1·10	1·25
260/3		..	..	Set of 4	2·75	2·75

53 Cocker Spaniel   54 Savanna Monkey

(Des D. Murphy)

1994 (14 Jan). *Dogs. T* **53** *and similar horiz designs.*
Multicoloured. P 14.
264	45 c. Type 53	..	..		80	50
265	65 c. Maltese	..	..		1·00	1·00
266	85 c. Scottish Terrier	..	..		1·40	1·50
267	1 r. 05, Miniature Schnauzer	..		1·75	2·00
264/7		..	..	Set of 4	4·50	4·50
The 85 c. value exists as a Philatelic Foundation miniature
sheet.

(Des A. Ainslie)

1994 (4 Mar). *Monkeys. T* **54** *and similar horiz designs.*
Multicoloured. P 14½×14.
268	45 c. Type 54	..	..		75	55
269	65 c. Lesser Bushbaby	..	..		1·00	1·00
270	85 c. Diademed Monkey	..	..		1·25	1·50
271	1 r. 05, Thick-tailed Bushbaby	..		1·50	2·00
268/71		..	..	Set of 4	4·00	4·50
MS272	119×70 mm. Nos. 268/71				4·00	4·50

55 Red-shouldered
Glossy Starlings

(Des Julia Birkhead)

1994 (29 Apr). *Starlings. T* **55** *and similar horiz designs.*
Multicoloured. P 14.
273	45 c. Type 55	..	..		90	65
274	70 c. Violet Starlings	..	..		1·25	1·25
275	95 c. African Red-winged Starlings	..	1·50	1·60
276	1 r. 15, Wattled Starlings	..		1·75	2·00
273/6		..	..	Set of 4	4·75	5·00

Venda was reincorporated into the Republic of South Africa
on 27 April 1994. Its postal service continued to operate, using
South African stamps, until 1 April 1996 when it was integrated
with that of the Republic.

South Arabian Federation

ADEN

The first post office in Aden opened during January 1839, situated in what became known as the Crater district. No stamps were
initially available, but, after the office was placed under the
Bombay Postal Circle, stocks of the 1854 ½ a. and 1 a. stamps
were placed on sale in Aden from 10 October 1854. Supplies of
the 2 a. and 4 a. values did not arrive until December. Most
Indian issues from the 1854 lithographs up to 1935 Silver
Jubilee set can be found with Aden postmarks.
During January 1858 a further office, Aden Steamer Point,
was opened in the harbour area and much of the business was
transferred to it by 1869. The original Aden post office, in
Crater, was renamed Aden Cantonment, later to be changed
again to Aden Camp.
The first cancellation used with the Indian stamps was a plain
diamond of dots. This type was also used elsewhere so that attri-
bution to Aden is only possible when on cover. Aden was assigned
"124" in the Indian postal number system and this formed the main
feature of marks from 1858, either on its own or as part of a duplex.

1858 "124" Cancellation

1870 Aden Duplex

1872 Aden Steamer Point Duplex

Both post offices used this number until 1871 when Aden
Cantonment was assigned "125", only to have this swiftly amended
to "124A" in the same year.

1871 Aden Cantonment "125"   1871 Aden Cantonment "124A"
Cancellation   Cancellation

Cancellations inscribed "Aden Steamer Point" disappear after
1874 and this office was then known simply as Aden. Following
this change the office was given number "B-22" under the revised
Indian P.O. scheme and this number appears as a major part of the
cancellations from 1875 to 1886, either on its own or as part of a
duplex, Aden Camp, the alternative name for the Cantonment
office, became "B-22/1".

1875 Aden Duplex

Squared-circle types for Aden and Aden Cantonment were
introduced in 1884 and 1888 to be in turn replaced by standard
Indian double and single circle from 1895 onwards.
A number of other post offices were opened between 1891 and
1937:
Dthali (opened 1903, *initially using* "EXPERIMENTAL P.O. B-
84" *postmark; closed* 1907)
Kamaran (opened c 1915, *but no civilian postmarks known*
before 1925)
Khormaksar (opened 1892; *closed* 1915; *reopened* 1925)
Maalla (opened 1923; *closed* 1931)
Nobat-Dakim (opened 1904, *initially using* "EXPERI-
MENTAL P.O. B-84" *postmark; closed* 1905)
Perim (opened 1915; *closed* 1936)
Sheikh Othman (opened 1891; *closed* 1915; *reopened* 1922;
closed 1937)

PRICES FOR STAMPS ON COVER TO 1945	
Nos. 1/15	*from* × 6
Nos. 16/27	*from* × 3

(Currency. 12 pies = 1 anna; 16 annas = 1 rupee)

1 Dhow   3 Aidrus Mosque, Crater

Aden

(Recess D.L.R.)

1937 (1 Apr). *Wmk Mult Script CA sideways. P 13 × 12.*

1	1	½ a. yellow-green			..	..	3·75	1·40
2		9 p. deep green			..		3·75	1·60
3		1 a. sepia			..	..	3·75	70
4		2 a. scarlet			..	..	3·75	2·00
5		2½ a. bright blue			..	..	3·50	80
6		3 a. carmine			..	..	9·00	6·50
7		3½ a. grey-blue			..	..	7·50	2·00
8		8 a. pale purple			..	..	20·00	5·50
9		1 r. brown			..	..	29·00	6·00
10		2 r. yellow			..	..	48·00	16·00
11		5 r. deep purple			..	..	90·00	65·00
12		10 r. olive-green			..	..	£225	£275
1/12					..	Set of 12	£400	£350
1/12 Perf "Specimen"						Set of 12	£300	

1937 (12 May). *Coronation. As Nos. 118/20 of Jamaica. P 14.*

13	1 a. sepia			..	..	65	80
14	2½ a. light blue			..	..	75	1·40
15	3½ a. grey-blue			..	..	1·00	2·50
13/15					Set of 3	2·25	4·25
13/15 Perf "Specimen"					Set of 3	70·00	

(Recess Waterlow)

1939 (19 Jan)–48. *Horiz designs as T 3. Wmk Mult Script CA. P 12½.*

16	½ a. yellowish green			..	..	50	60
	a. Bluish green (9.48)			..		2·00	3·50
17	¾ a. red-brown			..	..	1·25	1·25
18	1 a. pale blue			..	..	20	30
19	1½ a. scarlet			..	..	55	60
20	2 a. sepia			..	..	20	25
21	2½ a. deep ultramarine			..	..	40	30
22	3 a. sepia and carmine			..	..	60	25
23	8 a. red-orange			..	..	55	40
23a	14 a. sepia and light blue (15.1.45)			..		2·25	1·00
24	1 r. emerald-green			..	..	2·25	2·00
25	2 r. deep blue and magenta			..		4·75	2·25
26	5 r. red-brown and olive-green			..		11·00	8·00
27	10 r. sepia and violet			..	..	29·00	11·00
16/27				Set of 13	48·00	25·00
16/27 Perf "Specimen"			Set of 13	£180	

Designs:—½ a., 2 a., Type 3; ¾ a., 5 r. Adenese Camel Corps; 1 a., 2 r. The Harbour; 1½ a., 1 r. Adenese Dhow; 2½ a., 8 a. Mukalla; 3 a., 14 a., 10 r. "Capture of Aden, 1839" (Capt. Rundle).

1946 (15 Oct). *Victory. As Nos. 141/2 of Jamaica.*

28	1½ a. carmine			..	..	15	1·00
29	2½ a. blue			..	..	15	30
	w. Wmk inverted			..	..	£400	
28/9 Perf "Specimen"			..	Set of 2	50·00	

1949 (7 Jan). *Royal Silver Wedding. As Nos. 143/4 of Jamaica.*

30	1½ a. scarlet (p 14×15)			..	40	80
31	10 r. mauve (p 11½×11)			..	27·00	30·00

1949 (10 Oct). *75th Anniv of U.P.U. As Nos. 145/8 of Jamaica, surch with new values by Waterlow.*

32	2½ a. on 20 c. ultramarine			..	75	1·50
33	3 a. on 30 c. carmine-red			..	1·75	1·50
34	8 a. on 50 c. orange			..	1·60	1·50
35	1 r. on 1 s. blue			..	2·10	2·75
32/5				Set of 4	5·75	6·50

(New Currency. 100 cents = 1 shilling)

5 CENTS

(12)

1951 (1 Oct). *Nos. 18 and 20/7 surch with new values, in cents or shillings, as T 12, or in one line between bars (30 c.) by Waterlow.*

36	5 c. on 1 a. pale blue		..		15	40
37	10 c. on 2 a. sepia			..	15	45
38	15 c. on 2½ a. deep ultramarine			20	1·25
	a. Surch double			..	£600	
39	20 c. on 3 a. sepia and carmine			30	40
40	30 c. on 8 a. red-orange (R.)			30	65
41	50 c. on 8 a. red-orange			..	30	35
42	70 c. on 14 a. sepia and light blue			1·75	1·50
43	1 s. on 1 r. emerald-green			35	30
44	2 s. on 2 r. deep blue and magenta			7·50	2·75
	a. Surch double			..	£375	
45	5 s. on 5 r. red-brown and olive-green		16·00	8·50
46	10 s. on 10 r. sepia and violet		..	24·00	11·00
36/46				Set of 11	45·00	24·00

1953 (2 June). *Coronation. As No. 153 of Jamaica.*

47	15 c. black and green			..	..	70	1·25

14 Minaret	25 "Aden in 1572" (F. Hogenberg)

Recess Waterlow, D.L.R. from 5 Dec 1961)

1953 (15 June)–63. *T 14 and similar designs, and T 25. Wmk Mult Script CA. P 13½×13 (No. 72), 12×13½ (Nos. 57, 64, 66, 68) or 12 (others).*

48	5 c. yellowish green			..	..	20	10
49	5 c. bluish green (1.6.55)			..	40	2·75
	a. Perf 12 × 13½ (12.4.56)			..	10	50
50	10 c. orange			..	..	40	10
51	10 c. vermilion (1.2.55)			..	10	30
52	15 c. blue-green			..	..	1·25	60
53	15 c. greenish grey (26.4.59)			..	3·75	4·50
	a. Deep greenish grey (16.1.62)			9·50	11·00
	b. Greenish slate (13.11.62)			11·00	13·00
54	25 c. carmine-red			..	..	85	55
55	25 c. deep rose-red (15.3.56)			2·00	1·25
	a. Rose-red (13.3.62)			..	10·00	4·00

56	35 c. deep ultramarine			..	..	2·50	2·00
57	35 c. deep blue (15.10.58)			..	4·50	3·50
	a. Violet-blue (17.2.59)			..	7·00	3·00
58	50 c. dull blue			..	..	20	10
59	50 c. deep blue (1.7.55)			..	75	1·25
	a. Perf 12×13½ (12.4.56)			..	75	20
	aw. Wmk inverted			..		
60	70 c. brown-grey			..	..	20	10
61	70 c. black (20.9.54)			..	..	85	35
	a. Perf 12×13½ (12.4.56)			..	90	20
62	1 s. sepia and reddish violet			30	10
63	1 s. black and violet (1.7.55)			1·50	10
64	1 s. 25, blue and black (16.7.56)			2·25	60
	a. Dull blue and black (16.1.62)			9·00	70
65	2 s. sepia and rose-carmine			1·25	50
66	2 s. black and carmine-red (1.3.56)			7·50	50
	aw. Wmk inverted					
	b. Black and carmine-rose (22.1.63)		21·00	10·00
67	5 s. sepia and dull blue			..	1·50	75
68	5 s. black and deep dull blue (11.4.56)		5·00	1·00
	a. Black and blue (11.12.62)			23·00	9·50
69	10 s. sepia and olive			..	1·75	8·00
70	10 s. black and bronze-green (20.9.54)		13·00	1·50
71	20 s. chocolate and reddish lilac			6·50	10·00
72	20 s. black and deep lilac (7.1.57)			40·00	14·00
	a. Deep black and deep lilac (14.5.58)		48·00	18·00
48/72				Set of 25	80·00	42·00

Designs: (as Type 14). *Horiz*—10 c. Camel transport; 15 c. Crater; 25 c. Mosque; 1 s. Dhow building. *Vert*—35 c. Dhow; 50 c. Map; 70 c. Salt works; 1 s. 25 Colony's badge; 2 s. Aden Protectorate levy; 5 s. Crater Pass; 10 s. Tribesman.

On No. 70 the tribesman's skirt is shaded with cross-hatching instead of with mainly diagonal lines as in No. 69.

1954 (27 Apr). *Royal Visit. As No. 62 but inscr "ROYAL VISIT 1954" at top.*

73	1 s. sepia and reddish violet ..		30	45

تعديل الدستور ١٩٥٩

(26)

REVISED CONSTITUTION 1959

(27)

1959 (26 Jan). *Revised Constitution. No. 53 optd with T 26, and No. 64 optd with T 27, in red, by Waterlow.*

74	15 c. slate-green			..	30	2·00
75	1 s. 25, blue and black			..	1·00	1·00

1963 (4 June). *Freedom from Hunger. As No. 80 of Lesotho.*

76	1 s. 25, bluish green			..	1·75	1·75

1964 (5 Feb)–65. *As Nos. 48, etc. but wmk w 12. P 12 (10 c., 15 c., 25 c., 1 s.) or 12×13½ (others).*

77	5 c. green (16.2.65)			..	1·00	4·00
78	10 c. bright orange			..	20	85
79	15 c. greenish grey ..			30	3·50
	w. Wmk inverted			..	85·00	
80	25 c. carmine-red			..	30	40
81	35 c. indigo-violet			..	3·25	3·00
82	50 c. indigo-blue			..	20	30
	a. Pale indigo-blue (16.2.65)			30	30
	aw. Wmk inverted					
83	70 c. black			..	..	30	1·75
	a. Brownish grey (16.2.65)			30	1·75
84	1 s. black and violet (10.3.64)			12·00	2·50
85	1 s. 25, ultramarine and black (10.3.64)		12·00	2·25
86	2 s. black and carmine-rose (16.2.65)		2·75	24·00
77/86				Set of 10	29·00	38·00

The stamps of Aden were withdrawn on 31 March 1965 and superseded by those of the South Arabian Federation.

ADEN PROTECTORATE STATES

KATHIRI STATE OF SEIYUN

> The stamps of ADEN were used in Kathiri State of Seiyun from 22 May 1937 until 1942. A further office was opened at Tarim on 11 December 1940.

> **PRICES FOR STAMPS ON COVER TO 1945**
> Nos. 1/11 *from* × 10

1 Sultan of Seiyun	2 Seiyun

(Recess D.L.R.)

1942 (July–Oct). *Designs as T 1/2. Wmk Mult Script CA. T 1, perf 14; others, perf 12 × 13 (vert) or 13 × 12 (horiz).*

1	½ a. blue-green			..	..	20	50
2	¾ a. brown			..	..	30	65
3	1 a. blue			..	..	60	50
4	1½ a. carmine			..	..	60	60
5	2 a. sepia			..	..	30	70
6	2½ a. blue			..	..	90	1·00
7	3 a. sepia and carmine			..	1·50	2·00

8	8 a. red			..	..	75	50
9	1 r. green			..	..	2·50	75
10	2 r. blue and purple			..	7·00	10·00
11	5 r. brown and green			..	20·00	14·00
1/11				Set of 11	30·00	28·00
1/11 Perf "Specimen"			Set of 11	£140	

Designs:—½ to 1 a. Type **1**. *Vert as T 2*—2 a. Tarim; 2½ a. Mosque, Seiyun; 1 r. South Gate, Tarim; 5 r. Mosque entrance, Tarim. *Horiz as T 2*—3 a. Fortress, Tarim; 8 a. Mosque, Seiyun; 2 r. A Kathiri house.

VICTORY ISSUE 8TH JUNE 1946

(10)

1946 (15 Oct). *Victory. No. 4 optd with T 10, and No. 6 optd similarly but in four lines, by De La Rue.*

12	1½ a. carmine			..	..	10	65
13	2½ a. blue (R.)			..	..	10	10
	a. Opt inverted			..	£400	
12/13 Perf "Specimen"			Set of 2	55·00	

No. 13 is known with overprint double but the second impression is almost coincident with the first.

1949 (17 Jan). *Royal Silver Wedding. As Nos. 143/4 of Jamaica.*

14	1½ a. scarlet			..	..	30	2·00
15	5 r. green			..	..	14·00	9·00

1949 (10 Oct). *75th Anniv of U.P.U. As Nos. 145/8 of Jamaica, surch with new values by Waterlow.*

16	2½ a. on 20 c. ultramarine			..	25	50
17	3 a. on 30 c. carmine-red			..	1·00	65
18	8 a. on 50 c. orange			..	40	75
19	1 r. on 1 s. blue			..	60	90
16/19				Set of 4	2·00	2·50

5 CTS (11) 50 CENTS (12) 5/- (13)

1951 (1 Oct). *Currency changed. Nos. 3 and 5/11 surch as T 11 (5 c.), 12 (10 c. ("CTS"), 15 c. ("CTS"), 20 c. and 50 c.) or 13 (1 s. to 5 s.), by Waterlow.*

20	5 c. on 1 a. blue (R.)			..	15	30
21	10 c. on 2 a. sepia			..	30	30
22	15 c. on 2½ a. blue			..	15	40
23	20 c. on 3 a. sepia and carmine			20	80
24	50 c. on 8 a. red			..	20	30
25	1 s. on 1 r. green			..	20	80
26	2 s. on 2 r. blue and purple			2·75	16·00
27	5 s. on 5 r. brown and green			16·00	32·00
20/27				Set of 8	18·00	45·00

1953 (2 June). *Coronation. As No. 153 of Jamaica.*

28	15 c. black and deep green			..	30	1·75

14 Sultan Hussein	15 Tarim

(Des Freya Stark and H. Ingram. Recess D.L.R.)

1954 (15 Jan). *As Nos. 1/11 (but with portrait of Sultan Hussein as in T 14/15). Wmk Mult Script CA. T 14, perf 12½; others, perf 12 × 13 (vert) or 13 × 12 (horiz).*

29	5 c. sepia			..	..	10	10
30	10 c. deep blue			..	..	15	10
31	15 c. deep bluish green			..	15	10
32	25 c. carmine-red			..	..	15	10
33	35 c. deep blue			..	..	15	10
34	50 c. deep brown and carmine-red			15	10
35	1 s. brown-orange			..	..	15	10
36	2 s. deep yellow-green			..	4·00	2·25
37	5 s. deep blue and violet			..	7·00	5·00
38	10 s. yellow-brown and violet ..			7·00	6·50
29/38				Set of 10	17·00	13·00

16 Qarn Adh Dhabi	17 Seiyun

(Recess D.L.R.)

1964 (1 July). *Designs as T 16/17. W w 12. P 12 × 13 (70 c.) or 13 × 12 (others).*

39	70 c. black			..	..	1·00	1·00
40	1 s. 25 c. blue-green			..	2·00	7·00
41	1 s. 50 c. deep reddish violet			2·00	7·00
39/41				Set of 3	5·50	13·50

Design: *Horiz as T 17*—1 s. 50 c. Gheil Omer.

(New Currency. 1000 fils = 1 dinar)

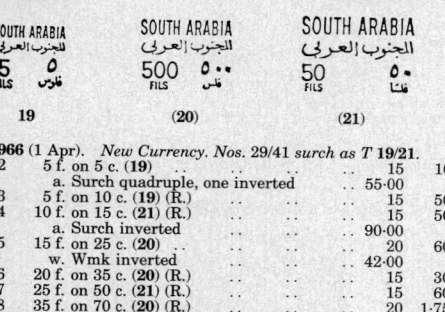

SOUTH ARABIA 5 FILS (19)
SOUTH ARABIA 500 FILS (20)
SOUTH ARABIA 50 FILS (21)

1966 (1 Apr). *New Currency. Nos. 29/41 surch as T 19/21.*

42	5 f. on 5 c. (19)	15	10
	a. Surch quadruple, one inverted	55·00	
43	5 f. on 10 c. (19) (R.)	15	50
44	10 f. on 15 c. (21) (R.)	15	50
	a. Surch inverted	90·00	
45	15 f. on 25 c. (20)	20	60
	w. Wmk inverted	42·00	
46	20 f. on 35 c. (20) (R.)	15	30
47	25 f. on 50 c. (21) (R.)	15	30
48	35 f. on 70 c. (20) (R.)	20	1·75
49	50 f. on 1 s. (21)	20	20
50	65 f. on 1 s. 25 (21)	20	20
51	75 f. on 1 s. 50 (21)	20	30
52	100 f. on 2 s. (20) (R.)	38·00	45·00
53	250 f. on 5 s. (21) (R.)	1·40	3·75
54	500 f. on 10 s. (20)	1·75	3·75
42/54		Set of 13 38·00	50·00

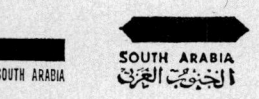

SOUTH ARABIA
5 FILS (22)
50 FILS (23)
15 FILS (24)

1966 (13 Aug). *Nos. 29/41 surch with T 22/4.*

55	5 f. on 5 c. (22) (B.)	1·25	30
	a. Surch inverted	65·00	
56	5 f. on 10 c. (22) (R.)	1·50	30
57	10 f. on 15 c. (23) (Y.)	1·50	60
	a. Surch inverted	50·00	
58	15 f. on 25 c. (24) (B.)	1·50	50
	a. Surch inverted	60·00	
59	20 f. on 35 c. (24) (Y.)	1·50	50
60	25 f. on 50 c. (23) (B.)	1·50	50
61	35 f. on 70 c. (24) (Br.)	1·50	60
62	50 f. on 1 s. (23) (G.)	1·50	80
	a. Stop after "FILS"	18·00	
63	65 f. on 1 s. 25 (23) (Y.)	1·50	1·50
64	75 f. on 1 s. 50 (23) (G.)	1·50	2·50
	a. Surch inverted	60·00	
65	100 f. on 2 s. (24) (Y.)	2·75	2·25
	a. Surch inverted	55·00	
66	250 f. on 5 s. (23) (Y.)	2·75	4·00
	a. Surch inverted	50·00	
67	500 f. on 10 s. (24) (G.)	2·75	8·50
55/67		Set of 13 20·00	20·00

HELSINKI 1952 (25)
INTERNATIONAL COOPERATION THROUGH OLYMPICS (26)

1966 (13 Aug). *History of Olympic Games. Nos. 57, 59 and 61/7 optd as T 25/6 in red.*

68	10 f. on 15 c. deep bluish green (25 ("LOS ANGELES 1932"))	35	25
	a. Optd as T 25 inverted		
69	20 f. on 35 c. deep blue (25 ("BERLIN 1936"))	45	35
70	35 f. on 70 c. black (26)	45	35
	a. Opt T 26 inverted	17·00	
71	50 f. on 1 s. brown-orange (25 ("LONDON 1948"))	50	40
	a. Stop after "FILS"	11·00	
72	65 f. on 1 s. 25, blue-green (25)	65	1·00
73	75 f. on 1 s. 50, deep reddish violet (25 ("MELBOURNE 1956"))	80	1·50
74	100 f. on 2 s. deep yellow-green (25 ("ROME 1960"))	90	1·60
75	250 f. on 5 s. deep blue and violet (25 ("TOKYO 1964"))	1·40	3·25
	a. Surch inverted	60·00	
76	500 f. on 10 s. yellow-brown and violet (25 ("MEXICO CITY 1968"))	1·75	3·75
68/76		Set of 9 6·50	11·00

CHAMPION: ENGLAND (27)
FOOTBALL 1966 (28)

1966 (19 Sept). *World Cup Football Championships. Nos. 57, 59, 61/2, 65/7 optd with T 27/8.*

77	10 f. on 15 c. deep bluish green (27)	70	30
78	20 f. on 35 c. deep blue (28)	90	40
79	35 f. on 70 c. black (28)	1·25	40
80	50 f. on 1 s. brown-orange (27)	1·40	20
	a. Stop after "FILS"	20·00	
81	100 f. on 2 s. deep yellow-green (28)	3·75	2·00
82	250 f. on 5 s. deep blue and violet (27)	7·50	5·00
83	500 f. on 10 s. yellow-brown and violet (28)	9·50	8·00
77/83		Set of 7 22·00	15·00

29 "Telstar"

(Photo State Ptg Wks, Vienna)

1966 (25 Oct). *I.T.U. Centenary (1965). T 29 and similar vert designs. P 13½.*

84	5 f. blackish green, black and reddish violet	1·25	25
85	10 f. maroon, black and bright green	1·40	30
86	15 f. Prussian blue, black and orange	1·75	40
87	25 f. blackish green, black and orange-red	2·50	50
88	35 f. maroon, black and deep olive-yellow	2·75	70
89	50 f. Prussian blue, black and orange-brown	3·25	1·10
90	65 f. blackish green, black and orange-yellow	3·75	1·25
84/90		Set of 7 15·00	4·00

Designs:—10, 35 f. "Relay"; 15, 50 f. "Ranger"; others, Type 29.

32 Churchill at Easel

(Photo State Ptg Wks, Vienna)

1966 (Dec). *Sir Winston Churchill's Paintings. T 32 and similar designs in black and gold (5 f.) or multicoloured (others). P 13½.*

91	5 f. Type 32	1·50	15
92	10 f. "Antibes"	1·75	15
93	15 f. "Flowers" (vert)	1·75	20
94	20 f. "Tapestries"	1·75	35
95	25 f. "Village, Lake Lugano"	1·75	35
96	35 f. "Church, Lake Como" (vert)	2·00	40
97	50 f. "Flowers at Chartwell" (vert)	2·25	65
98	65 f. Type 32	2·75	90
91/8		Set of 8 14·00	2·75

WORLD PEACE PANDIT NEHRU (39)

40 "Master Crewe as Henry VIII" (Sir Joshua Reynolds)

1967 (Jan). *"World Peace". Nos. 57, 59 and 61/7 optd as T 39 in various sizes of type.*

99	10 f. on 15 c. deep bluish green (Type 39) (R.)	1·25	85
100	20 f. on 35 c. deep blue ("WINSTON CHURCHILL") (R.)	4·50	2·25
101	35 f. on 70 c. black ("DAG HAMMARSKJOLD") (B.)	50	80
102	50 f. on 1 s. brown-orange ("JOHN F. KENNEDY") (R.)	60	90
	a. Stop after "FILS"	17·00	
103	65 f. on 1 s. 25, blue-green ("LUDWIG ERHARD") (Pk.)	70	1·10
104	75 f. on 1 s. 50 dp reddish violet ("LYNDON JOHNSON") (B.)	80	1·25
105	100 f. on 2 s. deep yellow-green ("ELEANOR ROOSEVELT") (B.)	1·00	1·75
106	250 f. on 5 s. dp blue and violet ("WINSTON CHURCHILL") (R.)	13·00	9·50
107	500 f. on 10 s. yellow-brown & violet ("JOHN F. KENNEDY") (R.)	5·00	10·00
99/107		Set of 9 24·00	25·00

(Photo State Ptg Wks, Vienna)

1967 (Feb). *Paintings. T 40 and similar multicoloured designs. P 13½.*

108	5 f. Type 40	30	25
109	10 f. "The Dancer" (Degas)	35	30
110	15 f. "The Fifer" (Manet)	40	30
111	20 f. "Stag at Sharkey's" (boxing match, G. Bellows)	45	40
112	25 f. "Don Manuel Osorio" (Goya)	50	45
113	35 f. "St. Martin distributing his Cloak" (A. van Dyck)	70	65
114	50 f. "The Blue Boy" (Gainsborough)	85	75
115	65 f. "The White Horse" (Gauguin)	1·10	1·00
116	75 f. "Mona Lisa" (Da Vinci) (45×62 mm)	1·40	1·25
108/16		Set of 9 5·50	4·75

SCOTT CARPENTER (49)

50 Churchill Crown

1967. *American Astronauts. Nos. 57, 59, 61/2 and 65/6 optd as T 49 in various sizes of type, in red.*

117	10 f. on 15 c. deep bluish green ("ALAN SHEPARD, JR.")	55	1·00
118	20 f. on 35 c. dp blue ("VIRGIL GRISSOM")	70	1·25
119	35 f. on 70 c. black ("JOHN GLENN, JR.")	95	1·50
120	50 f. on 1 s. brown-orange (Type 49)	95	1·50
	a. Stop after "FILS"	19·00	
121	100 f. on 2 s. deep yellow-green ("WALTER SCHIRRA, JR.")	2·25	3·50
122	250 f. on 5 s. deep blue & violet ("GORDON COOPER, JR.")	3·50	6·50
	a. Opt (as T 49) double	£100	
117/122		Set of 6 8·00	13·50

1967 (Mar). *Churchill Commemoration. Photo. P 13½.*

123	50	75 f. multicoloured	9·00 6·50

Appendix

The following stamps have either been issued in excess of postal needs, or have not been made available to the public in reasonable quantities at face value. Miniature sheets, imperforate stamps etc., are excluded from this section.

1967

Hunting. 20 f.
Olympic Games, Grenoble. Postage 10, 25, 35, 50, 75 f. Air 100, 200 f.
Scout Jamboree, Idaho. Air 150 f.
Paintings by Renoir. Postage 10, 35, 50, 65, 75 f. Air 100, 200, 250 f.
Paintings by Toulouse-Lautrec. Postage 10, 35, 50, 65, 75 f. Air 100, 200, 250 f.

The National Liberation Front is said to have taken control of Kathiri State of Seiyun on 1 October 1967.

QU'AITI STATE IN HADHRAMAUT

The stamps of ADEN were used in Qu'aiti State in Hadhramaut from 22 April 1937 until 1942. The main post office was at Mukalla. Other offices existed at Du'an (*opened* 1940), Gheil Ba Wazir (*opened* 1942), Haura (*opened* 1940), Shibam (*opened* 1940) and Shihr (*opened* 1939).

PRICES FOR STAMPS ON COVER TO 1945
Nos. 1/11 *from* × 6

I. ISSUES INSCR "SHIHR AND MUKALLA"

1 Sultan of Shihr and Mukalla
2 Mukalla Harbour
VICTORY ISSUE 8TH JUNE 1946 (10)

(Recess D.L.R.)

1942 (July)–46. *Wmk Mult Script CA. Designs as T 1 (½ to 1 a.) or T 2 (others). P 14 (½ to 1 a.), 12 × 13 (1½, 2, 3 a. and 1 r.) or 13 × 12 (others).*

1	½ a. blue-green	60	40
	a. Olive-green (12.46)	24·00	35·00
2	¾ a. brown	70	30
3	1 a. blue	80	90
4	1½ a. carmine	90	50
5	2 a. sepia	1·25	1·00
6	2½ a. blue	40	30
7	3 a. sepia and carmine	80	60
8	8 a. red	50	40
9	1 r. green	2·75	2·00
	a. "A" of "CA" missing from wmk	†	—
10	3 r. blue and purple	11·00	8·00
11	5 r. brown and green	14·00	11·00
1/11		Set of 11 30·00	23·00
1/11	Perf "Specimen"	Set of 11 £140	

Designs: *Vert*—2 a. Gateway of Shihr; 3 a. Outpost of Mukalla; 1 r. Du'an. *Horiz*—2½ a. Shibam; 8 a. 'Einat; 2 r. Mosque in Hureidha; 5 r. Meshhed.

1946 (15 Oct). *Victory. No. 4 optd. with T* **10** *and No. 6 optd similarly, but in three lines, by De La Rue.*

12	1½ a. carmine	..	..	..	10	65
13	2½ a. blue (R.)	..	..	..	10	10
12/13 Perf "Specimen"			*Set of* 2	55·00		

1949 (17 Jan). *Royal Silver Wedding. As Nos. 143/4 of Jamaica.*

14	1½ a. scarlet	..	..	..	50	2·25
15	5 r. green	..	..	15·00	9·00	

1949 (10 Oct). *75th Anniv of U.P.U. As Nos. 145/8 of Jamaica, surch with new values by Waterlow.*

16	2½ a. on 20 c. ultramarine	..	..	20	20	
17	3 a. on 30 c. carmine-red	..	..	1·10	50	
18	8 a. on 50 c. orange	..	..	55	60	
19	1 r. on 1s. blue	..	..	60	50	
	a. Surch omitted	..	..	£1200		
16/19	..	..	*Set of* 4	2·25	1·60	

1951 (1 Oct). *Currency changed. Surch with new values in cents or shillings as T* **11** *(5 c.),* **12** *(10 c. ("CTS"), 15 c., 20 c. and 50 c.) or* **13** *(1 s. to 5 s.) of Seiyun, by Waterlow.*

20	5 c. on 1 a. blue (R.)	..	..	15	15	
21	10 c. on 2 a. sepia	..	..	15	15	
22	15 c. on 2½ a. blue	..	..	15	15	
23	20 c. on 3 a. sepia and carmine	..	..	30	30	
	a. Surch double, one albino.	..	..	£170		
24	50 c. on 8 a. red	..	..	30	60	
25	1 s. on 1 r. green	..	..	1·00	30	
26	2 s. on 2 r. blue and purple	..	7·00	10·00		
27	5 s. on 5 r. brown and green	..	10·00	15·00		
20/27	..	..	*Set of* 8	17·00	24·00	

1953 (2 June). *Coronation. As No. 153 of Jamaica.*

28	15 c. black and deep blue	..	..	75	55	

II. ISSUES INSCR "HADHRAMAUT"

11 Metal Work **22** Metal Work

(Des Mme M. de Sturler Raemaekers. Recess D.L.R.)

1955 (1 Sept)–**63**. *T* **11** *and similar designs. Wmk Mult Script CA. P* 11½ × 13–13½ *(vert) or* 14 *(horiz).*

29	5 c. greenish blue	..	..	30	10	
30	10 c. grey-black	..	..	50	10	
31	15 c. deep green	..	..	50	10	
	a. Bronze-green (9.3.63)	..	..	40	40	
32	25 c. carmine-red	..	..	40	10	
33	35 c. blue	..	..	40	10	
34	50 c. orange-red	..	..	40	10	
	a. Red-orange (9.3.63)	..	..	40	30	
35	90 c. sepia	..	..	50	15	
36	1 s. black and deep lilac	..	..	50	10	
37	1 s. 25, black and red-orange	..	55	55		
38	2 s. black and indigo	..	..	4·00	60	
39	5 s. black and bluish green	..	5·00	1·75		
40	10 s. black and lake	..	..	5·50	7·50	
29/40			*Set of* 12	17·00	10·00	

Designs: *Vert*—10 c. Mat-making; 15 c. Weaving; 25 c. Pottery; 35 c. Building; 50 c. Date cultivation; 90 c. Agriculture. *Horiz*—1 s. Fisheries; 1 s. 25, 10 s. Lime-burning; 2 s. Dhow building; 5 s. Agriculture.

1963 (20 Oct). *As Nos. 29/40 but with inset portrait of Sultan Awadh bin Saleh el-Qu'aiti as in T* **22** *and wmk w* **12**.

41	5 c. greenish blue	..	..	10	70	
42	10 c. grey-black	..	..	10	70	
43	15 c. bronze-green	..	..	10	70	
44	25 c. carmine-red	..	..	10	40	
45	35 c. blue	..	..	10	90	
46	50 c. red-orange	..	..	10	50	
47	70 c. deep brown (as 90 c.)	..	15	50		
48	1 s. black and deep lilac	..	20	30		
49	1 s. 25, black and red-orange	..	45	2·75		
50	2 s. black and indigo-blue	..	3·25	1·25		
51	5 s. black and bluish green	..	13·00	20·00		
52	10 s. black and lake	..	..	16·00	20·00	
41/52			*Set of* 12	30·00	42·00	

(New Currency. 1000 fils = 1 dinar)

1966 (1 Apr). *New currency. Nos. 41/52 surch as T* **20/21** *of Kathiri State of Seiyun.*

53	5 f. on 5 c. greenish blue (**20**) (R.)	..	10	60		
54	5 f. on 10 c. grey-black (**20**) (R.)	..	10	60		
55	10 f. on 15 c. bronze-green (**20**) (R.)	..	10	30		
56	15 f. on 25 c. carmine-red (**20**)	..	10	60		
57	20 f. on 35 c. blue (**20**) (R.)	..	10	1·50		
58	25 f. on 50 c. red-orange (**20**).	..	10	60		
59	35 f. on 70 c. deep brown (**20**) (R.)	..	10	60		
60	50 f. on 1 s. black and deep lilac (**21**) (R.)	10	30			
61	65 f. on 1 s. 25, black and red-orange (**21**) (R.)	80	30			
62	100 f. on 2 s. black and indigo-blue (**21**) (R.).	1·50	75			
63	150 f. on 5 s. black and bluish green (**21**) (R.)..	1·50	60			
64	500 f. on 10 s. black and lake (**21**) (R.)	..	19·00	3·00		
53/64			*Set of* 12	21·00	9·50	

1874–1965	1917–1963
WINSTON CHURCHILL	**JOHN F. KENNEDY**
(23)	**(24)**

1966 (1 Apr). *Churchill Commemoration. Nos. 54/6 optd with T* **23**.

65	5 f. on 10 c. grey-black (R.)	..	5·50	7·50		
66	10 f. on 15 c. bronze-green (R.)	..	6·50	8·50		
	a. Opt *T* **23** inverted	..	..	75·00		
67	15 f. on 25 c. carmine-red (B.)	..	8·00	11·00		
65/7			*Set of* 3	18·00	24·00	

1966 (1 Apr). *President Kennedy Commemoration. Nos. 57/9 optd with T* **24**.

68	20 f. on 35 c. blue (R.)	..	..	2·00	6·00	
69	25 f. on 50 c. red-orange (B.)	..	2·50	6·50		
70	35 f. on 70 c. deep brown (B.)	..	3·50	7·50		
68/70			*Set of* 3	7·25	18·00	

25 World Cup Emblem

(Photo State Ptg Wks, Vienna)

1966 (11 Aug). *World Cup Football Championship, England. T* **25** *and similar diamond-shaped designs. P* 13½.

71	5 f. maroon and yellow-orange	..	1·75	25		
72	10 f. slate-violet and light green	..	2·00	25		
73	15 f. maroon and yellow-orange	..	2·25	30		
74	20 f. slate-violet and light green	..	2·50	40		
75	25 f. blackish green and orange-red	..	2·75	55		
76	35 f. blue and yellow	..	..	3·25	80	
77	50 f. blackish green and orange-red	..	3·75	1·10		
78	65 f. blue and yellow	..	..	4·50	1·40	
71/8			*Set of* 8	20·00	4·50	
MS78*a*	110×110 mm. Nos. 77/8	..	15·00	7·50		

Designs:—10, 35 f. Wembley Stadium; 15, 50 f. Footballers; 20 f. Jules Rimet Cup and football; 25, 65 f. Type **25**.

29 Mexican Hat and Blanket

(Photo State Ptg Wks, Vienna)

1966 (25 Oct). *Pre-Olympic Games, Mexico (1968). P* 13½.

79	**29**	75 f. sepia and light yellow-green		1·25	75	

30 Telecommunications Satellite

(Photo State Ptg Wks, Vienna)

1966 (Dec). *International Co-operation Year (1965). T* **30** *and similar horiz designs. P* 13½.

80	5 f. maroon, bright purple and emerald	2·25	35			
81	10 f. violet, orange, blue-green and new blue	2·50	35			
82	15 f. maroon, new blue and red	2·75	40			
83	20 f. Prussian blue, purple and red	3·00	45			
84	25 f. violet, olive-yellow, red and emerald	3·00	50			
85	35 f. maroon, rose-red and new blue	3·50	80			
	a. New blue (face values) omitted	£160				
86	50 f. maroon, green and red	4·50	1·25			
87	65 f. chocolate, bluish violet and red	5·00	1·75			
80/87			*Set of* 8	23·00	5·25	

Desig.s:—10 f. Olympic runner (inscribed "ROME 1960"); 15 f. Fishes; 25 f. Olympic runner (inscribed "TOKIO 1964"); 50 f. Tobacco plant; others, Type **30**.

NEW INFORMATION

The editor is always interested to correspond with people who have new information that will improve or correct the Catalogue.

Appendix

The following stamps have either been issued in excess of postal needs, or have not been made available to the public in reasonable quantities at face value. Miniature sheets, imperforate stamps etc. are excluded from this section.

1967

Stampex Stamp Exhibition, London. Postage 5, 10, 15, 20, 25 *f. Air* 50, 65 *f.*
Amphilex International Stamp Exhibition, Amsterdam. Air 75 *f.*
Olympic Games, Mexico (1968), 75 *f.*
Paintings. Postage 5, 10, 15, 20, 25 *f. Air* 50, 65 *f.*
Scout Jamboree, Idaho. Air 35 *f.*
Space Research. Postage 10, 25, 35, 50, 75 *f. Air* 100, 250 *f.*

The National Liberation Front is said to have taken control of Qu'aiti State in Hadhramaut on 17 September 1967.

MAHRA SULTANATE OF QISHN AND SOCOTRA

(Currency. 1000 fils = 1 dinar)

1 Mahra Flag

(Des and litho Harrison)

1967 (12 Mar). *Flag in green, black and vermilion; inscriptions in black; background colours given. P* 14 × 14½.

1	**1**	5 f. mauve		1·50	30	
2		10 f. buff	..	1·50	30	
3		15 f. sage-green		1·50	30	
4		20 f. red-orange		1·50	30	
5		25 f. yellow-brown		1·50	30	
6		35 f. turquoise-green		1·50	30	
7		50 f. new blue		1·50	30	
8		65 f. blackish brown		1·50	30	
9		100 f. violet		1·50	30	
10		250 f. rose-red		1·50	35	
11		500 f. grey-green		1·50	30	
1/11			*Set of* 11	15·00	3·25	

Appendix

The following stamps have either been issued in excess of postal needs, or have not been made available to the public in reasonable quantities at face value. Miniature sheets, imperforate stamps etc., are excluded from this section.

1967

Scout Jamboree, Idaho. 15, 75, 100, 150 *f.*
President Kennedy Commemoration. Postage 10, 15, 25, 50, 75, 100, 150 *f. Air* 250, 500 *f.*
Olympic Games, Mexico (1968). *Postage* 10, 25, 50 *f. Air* 250, 500 *f.*

The National Liberation Front is said to have taken control of Mahra Sultanate of Qishn and Socotra on 1 October 1967.

SOUTH ARABIAN FEDERATION

Comprising Aden and most of the territories of the former Western Aden Protectorate plus one from the Eastern Aden Protectorate.

(Currency. 100 cents=1 shilling)

1 Red Cross Emblem

1963 (25 Nov). *Red Cross Centenary. W w* **12**. *P* 13½.

1	**1**	15 c. red and black	..	..	40	30
2		1 s. 25, red and blue	..	..	85	95

(New Currency. 1000 fils=1 dinar)

2 Federal Crest **3** Federal Flag

(Des V. Whiteley. Photo Harrison)

1965 (1 Apr). *P* 14½ × 14 (*T* **2**) *or* 14½ (*T* **3**).

3	**2**	5 f. blue	..	..	20	10
4		10 f. violet-blue	..	..	20	10
5		15 f. turquoise-green	..	..	20	10
6		20 f. green	..	..	20	10
7		25 f. yellow-brown	..	..	20	10
8		30 f. yellow-bistre	..	..	20	10
9		35 f. chestnut	..	..	20	10
10		50 f. red	..	..	20	10
11		65 f. yellow-green	..	..	30	30
12		75 f. crimson	..	..	30	10

13	3	100 f. multicoloured	..	..	..	30	10
14		250 f. multicoloured	..	..	..	5·00	60
15		500 f. multicoloured	..	..	..	9·00	60
16		1 d. multicoloured	..	..	..	16·00	9·00
3/16				Set of 14		29·00	9·50

4 I.C.Y. Emblem

(Des V. Whiteley. Litho Harrison)

1965 (24 Oct). *International Co-operation Year. W w 12. P 14½.*

17	4	5 f. reddish purple and turquoise-green	20	10
18		65 f. deep bluish green and lavender	70	20

5 Sir Winston Churchill and St. Paul's Cathedral in Wartime

(Des Jennifer Toombs. Photo Harrison)

1966 (24 Jan). *Churchill Commemoration. No wmk. P 14.*

19	5	5 f. black, cerise, gold and new blue ..	10	10
20		10 f. black, cerise, gold and deep green	30	10
21		65 f. black, cerise, gold and brown	80	20
22		125 f. black, cerise, gold and bluish violet	1·25	1·75
19/22		.. Set of 4	2·25	1·90

6 Footballer's Legs, Ball and Jules Rimet Cup

(Des V. Whiteley. Litho Harrison)

1966 (1 July). *World Cup Football Championship, England. No wmk. P 14.*

23	6	10 f. violet, yellow-green, lake & yell-brn	50	10
24		50 f. chocolate, blue-grn, lake & yell-brn	1·50	20

7 W.H.O. Building

(Des M. Goaman. Litho Harrison)

1966 (20 Sept). *Inauguration of W.H.O. Headquarters, Geneva. No wmk. P 14.*

25	7	10 f. black, yellow-green and light blue	50	10
26		75 f. black, light purple and yellow-brown	1·25	45

8 "Education"

9 "Science"

10 "Culture"

(Des Jennifer Toombs. Litho Harrison)

1966 (15 Dec). *20th Anniv of U.N.E.S.C.O. No wmk. P 14.*

27	8	10 f. slate-violet, red, yellow and orange	30	20
28	9	65 f. orange-yellow, vio & dp olive	1·25	1·40
29	10	125 f. black, bright purple and orange	3·25	4·75
27/9		.. Set of 3	4·25	5·75

The South Arabian Federation became fully independent on 30 November 1967. Later issues for this area will be found listed in Part 19 (*Middle East*) of this catalogue under Yemen People's Democratic Republic.

South Australia
see Australia

Southern Cameroons
see Cameroon

Southern Nigeria
see Nigeria

Southern Rhodesia
see Zimbabwe

South Georgia and the South Sandwich Islands

As South Georgia was a dependency of the Falkland Islands between 1963 and 1980 stamps so inscribed are listed under FALKLAND ISLANDS DEPENDENCIES.

Under the new constitution, effective 3 October 1985, South Georgia and South Sandwich Islands ceased to be dependencies of the Falkland Islands.

(Des A. Theobald. Litho Questa)

1986 (21 Apr). *60th Birthday of Queen Elizabeth II. Vert designs as T 230a of Jamaica. Multicoloured. W w 16. P 14½×14.*

153	10p. Four generations of Royal Family at Prince Charles' christening, 1948	35	35
154	24p. With Prince Charles and Lady Diana Spencer, Buckingham Palace, 1981 ..	60	65
155	29p. In robes of Order of the British Empire, St. Paul's Cathedral, London ..	60	70
156	45p. At banquet, Canada, 1976 ..	80	95
157	58p. At Crown Agents Head Office, London, 1983	1·00	1·25
153/7	.. Set of 5	3·00	3·50

25a Prince Andrew and Miss Sarah Ferguson at Ascot

26 Southern Black-backed Gull

(Des D. Miller. Litho Questa)

1986 (10 Nov). *Royal Wedding. T 25a and similar vert designs. Multicoloured. W w 16. P 14½×14.*

158	17p. Type 25a	75	1·10
159	22p. Wedding photograph	85	1·25
160	29p. Prince Andrew with Westland WG-13 Lynx helicopter on board H.M.S. Brazen	1·50	1·50
158/60	.. Set of 3	2·75	3·50

(Des T. Chater. Litho Walsall)

1987 (24 Apr). *Birds. T 26 and similar multicoloured designs. W w 16 (sideways on horiz designs). P 14½.*

161	1p. Type 26	55	90
162	2p. Blue-eyed Cormorant	65	1·00
163	3p. Snowy Sheathbill (vert)	80	1·25
	w. Wmk inverted	£200	
164	4p. Great Skua (vert)	65	1·25
165	5p. Pintado Petrel ("Cape Pigeon")	65	1·25
166	6p. Georgian Diving Petrel	65	1·25
167	7p. South Georgia Pipit (vert)	75	1·40
168	8p. Georgian Teal ("South Georgian Pintail") (vert)	75	1·40
169	9p. Fairy Prion	75	1·40
170	10p. Chinstrap Penguin	1·00	1·40
171	20p. Macaroni Penguin (vert)	1·25	1·75
172	25p. Light-mantled Sooty Albatross (vert)	1·25	1·75
	w. Wmk inverted	£400	
173	50p. Giant Petrel (vert)	1·75	2·25
174	£1 Wandering Albatross	2·25	3·50
175	£3 King Penguin (vert)	6·00	7·50
161/75	Set of 15	18·00	26·00

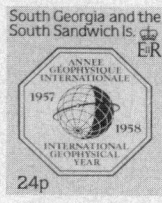

26a I.G.Y. Logo   27 Gaimardia trapesina

(Des L. Curtis. Litho Questa)

1987 (5 Dec). *30th Anniv of International Geophysical Year. T 26a and similar vert designs. W w 16. P 14½×14.*

176	24p. black and pale turquoise-blue ..	70	55
177	29p. multicoloured ..	75	60
178	58p. multicoloured ..	1·40	1·25
176/8	.. Set of 3	2·50	2·10

Designs:—29p. Grytviken; 58p. Glaciologist using hand-drill to take core sample.

(Des I. Strange. Litho Questa)

1988 (26 Feb). *Sea Shells. T 27 and similar horiz designs. Multicoloured. W w 16 (sideways*). P 14×14½.*

179	10p. Type 27	65	30
	w. Wmk Crown to right of CA ..		
180	24p. Margarella tropidophoroides	1·00	60
181	29p. Trophon geversianus	1·10	65
182	58p. Chlanidota densesculpta	1·60	1·25
	w. Wmk Crown to right of CA		†
179/82	.. Set of 4	3·75	2·50

*The normal sideways watermark shows Crown to left of CA, as seen from the back of the stamp.

(Des E. Nisbet and D. Miller (24p.), D. Miller (others). Litho Questa)

1988 (17 Sept). *300th Anniv of Lloyd's of London. Designs as T 167a of Malawi. W w 16 (sideways on 24, 29p.). P 14.*

183	10p. brownish black and brown ..	40	40
184	24p. multicoloured ..	75	75
185	29p. brownish black and emerald ..	80	80
186	58p. brownish black and carmine-red ..	1·40	1·40
183/6	.. Set of 4	3·00	3·00

Designs: Vert—10p. Queen Mother at opening of new Lloyd's building, 1957; 58p. Horatio (tanker) on fire, 1916. Horiz—24p. Lindblad Explorer (cruise liner); 29p. Whaling station, Leith Harbour.

28 Glacier Headwall   29 Retracing Shackleton's Trek

(Des I. Loe. Litho Questa)

1989 (31 July). *Glacier Formations. T 28 and similar horiz designs. Multicoloured. W w 16 (sideways). P 14.*

187	10p. Type 28	40	35
188	24p. Accumulation area	80	70
189	29p. Ablation area ..	90	80
190	58p. Calving front ..	1·60	1·40
187/90	.. Set of 4	3·25	3·00

(Des O. Bell. Litho Questa)

1989 (28 Nov). *25th Anniv of Combined Services Expedition to South Georgia. T 29 and similar horiz designs. Multicoloured. W w 16 (sideways). P 14×14½.*

191	10p. Type 29	40	35
192	24p. Surveying at Royal Bay ..	90	70

193	29p. H.M.S. *Protector* (ice patrol ship)		1·00	80
194	58p. Raising Union Jack on Mount Paget		1·60	1·40
191/4		*Set of 4*	3·50	3·00

(Des D. Miller. Litho Questa)

1990 (15 Sept). *90th Birthday of Queen Elizabeth the Queen Mother. Vert designs as T 107 (26p.) or 108 (£1) of Kenya.* W w 16. P 14×15 (26p.) or 14½ (£1).

195	26p. multicoloured		1·00	1·25
196	£1 black and dull ultramarine		2·75	3·25

Designs:—26p. Queen Mother; £1 King George VI and Queen Elizabeth with A.R.P. wardens, 1940.

30 *Brutus*, Prince Olav Harbour **31** Contest between two Bull Elephant Seals

(Des D. Miller. Litho Questa)

1990 (22 Dec). *Wrecks and Hulks. T 30 and similar vert designs. Multicoloured.* W w 16. P 14×14½.

197	12p. Type 30		55	40
198	26p. *Bayard*, Ocean Harbour		1·00	80
199	31p. *Karrakatta*, Husvik		1·10	95
200	62p. *Louise*, Grytviken		1·90	1·75
197/200		*Set of 4*	4·00	3·50

(Des D. Miller. Litho Questa)

1991 (2 July). *65th Birthday of Queen Elizabeth II and 70th Birthday of Prince Philip. Vert designs as T 58 of Kiribati. Multicoloured.* W w 16 (*sideways*). P 14½×14.

201	31p. Queen Elizabeth II		1·00	1·40
	a. Horiz pair. Nos. 201/2 separated by label		2·00	2·75
202	31p. Prince Philip in Grenadier Guards uniform		1·00	1·40

Nos. 201/2 were printed in a similar sheet format to Nos. 366/7 of Kiribati.

(Des D. Miller. Litho Questa)

1991 (2 Nov). *Elephant Seals. T 31 and similar horiz designs. Multicoloured.* W w 14 (*sideways*). P 14.

203	12p. Type 31		50	50
204	26p. Adult Elephant Seal		1·00	1·00
205	29p. Seal throwing sand		1·10	1·10
206	31p. Head of Elephant Seal		1·10	1·10
207	34p. Seals on beach		1·25	1·25
208	62p. Cow seal with pup		2·00	2·00
203/8		*Set of 6*	6·25	6·25

(Des D. Miller. Litho Questa (68p.), Walsall (others))

1992 (6 Feb). *40th Anniv of Queen Elizabeth II's Accession. Horiz designs as T 113 of Kenya. Multicoloured.* W w 14 (*sideways*). P 14.

209	17p. Ice-covered mountains		30	30
210	14p. Zavodovski Island		45	55
211	29p. Gulbrandsen Lake		80	95
212	34p. Three portraits of Queen Elizabeth		90	1·10
213	68p. Queen Elizabeth II		1·40	1·50
209/13		*Set of 5*	3·50	4·00

32 Adult Teal and Young Bird

(Des G. Drummond. Litho Questa)

1992 (12 Mar). *Endangered Species. Georgian Teal ("South Georgia Teal"). T 32 and similar horiz designs. Multicoloured.* W w 16 (*sideways*). P 14.

214	2p. Type 32		40	20
215	6p. Adult with eggs		50	30
216	12p. Teals swimming		70	50
217	20p. Adult and two chicks		90	90
214/17		*Set of 4*	2·25	1·75

(Des N. Shewring. Litho Questa)

1992 (20 June). *10th Anniv of Liberation. Square designs as T 169 of St. Helena. Multicoloured.* W w 16 (*sideways*). P 14.

218	14p. + 6p. King Edward Point		70	70
219	29p. + 11p. *Queen Elizabeth 2* (liner) in Cumberland Bay		1·25	1·25
220	34p. + 16p. Royal Marines hoisting Union Jack on South Sandwich Islands		1·60	1·60
221	68p. + 32p. H.M.S. *Endurance* (ice patrol ship) and Westland AS.1 Wasp helicopter		3·00	3·00
218/21		*Set of 4*	6·00	6·00
MS222	116×116 mm. Nos. 218/21		6·00	6·00

The premiums on Nos. 218/22 were for the S.S.A.F.A.

33 Disused Whale Factory, Grytviken **34** Pair of Swimming Penguins

(Des D. Miller. Litho B.D.T.)

1993 (29 June). *Opening of South Georgia Whaling Museum. T 33 and similar horiz designs. Multicoloured.* W w 14 (*sideways*). P 13½.

223	15p. Type 33		55	60
224	31p. Whaler's lighter and whale bones		1·00	1·10
225	36p. Aerial view of King Edward Cove		1·25	1·40
226	72p. Museum building		2·25	2·75
223/6		*Set of 4*	4·50	5·25

(Des N. Arlott. Litho Questa)

1993 (10 Dec). *Macaroni Penguin. T 34 and similar horiz designs. Multicoloured.* W w 14 (*sideways*). P 14½.

227	16p. Type 34		60	45
228	34p. Group of penguins		1·25	1·00
229	39p. Two juvenile penguins		1·40	1·25
230	78p. Two adult penguins		2·25	2·25
227/30		*Set of 4*	5·00	4·50

35 Hourglass Dolphin

(Des R. Watton. Litho B.D.T.)

1994 (24 Jan). *Whales and Dolphins. T 35 and similar horiz designs. Multicoloured.* W w 14 (*sideways*). P 14.

231	1p. Type 35		30	50
232	2p. Southern Right Whale Dolphin		40	60
233	5p. Long-finned Pilot Whale		50	70
234	8p. Southern Bottlenose Whale		65	80
235	9p. Killer Whale		70	80
236	10p. Minke Whale		70	80
237	20p. Sei Whale		1·00	1·10
238	25p. Humpback Whale		1·00	1·10
239	50p. Southern Right Whale		1·75	1·75
240	£1 Sperm Whale		2·75	3·00
241	£3 Fin Whale		6·50	7·00
242	£5 Blue Whale		10·00	11·00
231/42		*Set of 12*	23·00	26·00

1994 (18 Feb). *"Hong Kong '94" International Stamp Exhibition. Nos. 227/30 optd as T 272 of Jamaica.*

243	16p. Type 34		60	75
244	34p. Group of penguins		1·25	1·50
245	39p. Two juvenile penguins		1·40	1·60
246	78p. Two adult penguins		2·25	2·50
243/6		*Set of 4*	5·00	5·50

36 Bull Elephant Seals

(Des D. Miller. Litho Questa)

1994 (28 Sept). *"Life in the Freezer". T 36 and similar multicoloured designs showing scenes from the B.B.C. Natural History Unit series.* W w 16 (*sideways on* 17, 40p.). P 14½.

247	17p. Type 36		50	50
248	35p. Young Fur Seal (*vert*)		90	1·50
249	40p. Pair of Grey-headed Albatrosses		1·60	1·75
250	65p. King Penguins in courtship display (*vert*)		2·50	2·75
247/50		*Set of 4*	5·00	6·00

37 Map of Jason Harbour **38** *Damien II* (research schooner)

(Des R. Watton. Litho Walsall)

1994 (1 Dec). *Centenary of C.A. Larsen's First Voyage to South Georgia. T 37 and similar horiz designs. Multicoloured.* W w 16 (*sideways*). P 14×14½.

251	17p. Type 37		60	75
	w. Wmk Crown to right of CA		30·00	
252	35p. *Castor* (whaling ship), 1886		1·10	1·50
253	40p. *Hertha* (whaling ship), 1884		1·25	1·60
254	65p. *Jason* (whaling ship), 1881		1·75	2·75
251/4		*Set of 4*	4·75	6·00

*The normal sideways watermark shows Crown to left of CA, as seen from the back of the stamp.

(Des R. Watton. Litho Questa)

1995 (8 May). *50th Anniv of End of Second World War. Multicoloured designs as T 75 of Kiribati.* W w 16 (*sideways*). P 14.

255	50p. H.M.S. *Queen of Bermuda* (armed merchant cruiser), Leith Harbour, 1941		1·75	2·00
	a. Horiz pair. Nos. 255/6		3·50	4·00
256	50p. Norwegian Defence Force 4-inch coastal gun, Hansen Point		1·75	2·00
MS257	75×85 mm. £1 Reverse of 1939–45 War Medal (*vert*). W w 14		2·25	2·50

Nos. 255/6 were printed together, *se-tenant*, in horizontal pairs throughout the sheet, each pair forming composite design.

(Des N. Shewring. Litho Walsall)

1995 (16 Nov). *Sailing Ships. T 38 and similar vert designs. Multicoloured.* W w 16. P 14½.

258	35p. Type 38		1·25	1·75
259	40p. *Curlew* (cutter)		1·40	1·75
260	76p. *Mischief* (yacht)		2·25	2·75
258/60		*Set of 3*	4·50	5·50

39 Sir Ernest Shackleton and Ridge 2493 **40** Chinstrap Penguin swimming

(Des M. Skidmore. Litho Walsall)

1996 (20 May). *80th Anniv of Sir Ernest Shackleton's Trek across South Georgia. T 39 and similar horiz designs. Multicoloured.* W w 16 (*sideways*). P 14.

261	17p. Type 39		75	75
262	20p. Frank Worsley and King Haakon Bay		80	80
263	30p. Map of route		95	95
264	65p. Tom Crean and manager's villa, Stromness whaling station		1·40	1·40
261/4		*Set of 4*	3·50	3·50

(Des T. Chater. Litho Questa)

1996 (8 Nov). *Chinstrap Penguins. T 40 and similar vert designs. Multicoloured.* W w 14. P 14½×14.

265	17p. Type 40		55	55
266	35p. Mutual display		90	90
267	40p. Adult feeding chicks		1·10	1·10
268	76p. Feeding on krill		1·90	1·90
265/8		*Set of 4*	4·00	4·00

(Litho Walsall)

1997 (20 June). *Return of Hong Kong to China. Sheet 130×90 mm, containing design as No. 268, but with imprint date.* W w 14 (*sideways*). P 14½×14.

MS269	76p. Feeding on krill		1·75	2·00

(Des N. Shewring (No. MS276), D. Miller (others). Litho Questa)

1997 (10 July). *Golden Wedding of Queen Elizabeth and Prince Philip. Multicoloured designs as T 87 of Kiribati.* W w 16. P 14½.

270	15p. Queen Elizabeth wearing red hat, 1996		50	40
	a. Horiz pair. Nos. 270/1		1·00	80
271	15p. Prince Philip in carriage-driving at Royal Windsor Horse Show		50	40
272	17p. Queen Elizabeth with show jumping team, 1993		55	45
	a. Horiz pair. Nos. 272/3		1·10	90
273	17p. Prince Philip smiling		55	45
274	40p. Princess Anne on horseback and Queen Elizabeth		1·40	1·25
	a. Horiz pair. Nos. 274/5		2·75	2·50
275	40p. Zara Phillips horse riding and Prince Philip		1·40	1·25
270/5		*Set of 6*	4·50	3·75
MS276	110×70 mm. £1.50, Queen Elizabeth and Prince Philip in landau (*horiz*). W w 14 (*sideways*). P 14½×14½		3·50	3·75

Nos. 270/1, 272/3 and 274/5 were each printed together, *se-tenant*, in horizontal pairs throughout the sheets with the backgrounds forming composite designs.

MINIMUM PRICE

The minimum price quote is 10p which represents a handling charge rather than a basis for valuing common stamps. For further notes about prices see introductory pages.

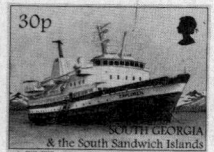

41 Reindeer   42 *Explorer* (cruise ship)

(Des Sonia Felton. Litho Questa)

1998 (16 Mar). *Wildlife. Sheet, 138×84 mm, containing T 41 and similar horiz designs. Multicoloured. W w 14 (sideways). P 14×13½.*
MS277 35p. Type 41; 35p. Antarctic Tern; 35p. Grey-headed Albatross; 35p. King Penguin; 35p. Prickly Burr; 35p. Fur Seal .. .. .. 5·00 5·00

(Des D. Miller. Litho Questa)

1998 (31 Mar). *Diana, Princess of Wales Commemoration. Sheet, 145×70 mm, containing vert designs as T 91 of Kiribati. Multicoloured. W w 14 (sideways). P 14½×14.*
MS278 35p. Laughing, 1983; 35p. In evening dress, 1996; 35p. Wearing red jacket, 1991; 35p. Wearing white jacket, 1996 (sold at £1.40 + 20p. charity premium) .. .. .. 3·25 3·50

(Des Kim Robertson. Litho Walsall)

1998 (28 Sept). *Tourism. T 42 and similar horiz designs. Multicoloured. W w 14 (sideways). P 14×14½.*
279 30p. Type 42 .. .. .. 1·10 1·00
280 35p. Wandering Albatross .. .. 1·25 1·10
281 40p. Elephant Seal .. .. 1·25 1·10
282 65p. Post Office at King Edward Point .. 1·75 1·75
279/82 .. .. .. Set of 4 4·75 4·50

43 Grytviken and Sugartop Mountain   44 H.M.S. *Resolution* in Antarctic, 1773

(Des J. Peck. Litho Walsall)

1999 (4 Jan). *Island Views. T 43 and similar horiz designs. Multicoloured. W w 16 (sideways). P 14.*
283 9p. Type 43 .. .. .. 45 45
284 17p. Dias and Albatross (abandoned sealing ships), Grytviken 65 65
285 35p. King Edward Point .. .. 1·10 1·10
286 40p. South Georgia from the sea .. 1·25 1·25
287 65p. Grytviken Church .. .. 1·50 1·50
283/7 .. .. Set of 5 4·50 4·50

(Des J. Batchelor. Litho B.D.T.)

1999 (5 Mar). *"Australia '99" World Stamp Exhibition, Melbourne. Sheet 120×83 mm. W w 16. P 13½.*
MS288 44 £1.50, multicoloured .. .. 3·25 3·25

(Des D. Miller. Litho Cartor)

1999 (18 Aug). *"Queen Elizabeth the Queen Mother's Century". Horiz designs as T 199 of St. Helena. Multicoloured (except 30p., £1). W w 16 (sideways). P 13½.*
289 25p. Visiting air-raid shelter, 1940 .. 65 65
290 30p. With grandchildren, 1970 (black) .. 75 75
291 35p. With Prince William, 1994 .. 85 85
292 40p. Presenting colour to Royal Anglian Regt 95 95
289/92 .. .. .. Set of 4 2·75 2·75
MS293 145×70 mm. £1 Lady Elizabeth Bowes-Lyon, 1914, and Funeral of Queen Victoria, 1901 (black) .. .. .. 2·75 3·00

45 Chinstrap Penguins   46 Sunrise

(Des Una Hurst. Litho Questa)

1999 (15 Nov). *Birds. T 45 and similar multicoloured designs. W w 16 (sideways on horiz designs). P 14.*
294 1p. Type 45 .. .. 10 10
295 2p. White-chinned Petrel (horiz) .. 10 10
296 5p. Grey-backed Storm Petrel 10 10

297 10p. South Georgia Pipit 20 25
298 11p. Grey-headed Albatross (horiz) .. 20 25
299 30p. Blue Petrel 60 65
300 35p. Black-browed Albatross (horiz) .. 70 75
301 40p. Georgian Diving Petrel (horiz) .. 80 85
302 50p. Macaroni Penguin .. .. 1·00 1·10
303 £1 Light-mantled Sooty Albatross (horiz) 2·00 2·10
304 £3 Georgian Teal ("South Georgia Pintail") (horiz) .. .. 6·00 6·25
305 £5 King Penguin .. .. 10·00 10·50
294/305 .. .. .. Set of 12 21·00 22·00

(Des G. Vasarhelyi. Litho Questa)

1999 (18 Dec). *New Millennium. T 46 and similar horiz designs. Multicoloured. W w 16 (sideways). P 14½.*
306 11p. Type 46 .. .. 20 25
307 11p. Grytviken Church 20 25
308 11p. Nesting Albatross 20 25
309 35p. Sunset 70 75
310 35p. Reindeer 70 75
311 35p. Penguins and chicks 70 75
306/11 .. .. Set of 6 2·50 3·00

47 Shackleton in *James Caird* crossing Scotia Sea

(Des M. Skidmore. Litho Questa)

2000 (10 Feb). *Shackleton's Trans-Antarctic Expedition, 1914–17, Commemoration. T 47 and similar horiz designs. Multicoloured. W w 14 (sideways). P 14.*
312 35p. Type 47 .. .. .. 70 75
313 40p. Shackleton and party approaching Stromness Whaling Station .. 80 85
314 65p. Shackleton's Cross at Hope Point .. 1·50 1·75
312/14 .. .. .. Set of 3 3·00 3·25

South West Africa
see Namibia

Sri Lanka
(*formerly* Ceylon)

CEYLON

PRICES FOR STAMPS ON COVER TO 1945

No. 1	from × 5
Nos. 2/12	from × 4
Nos. 16/17	from × 5
Nos. 18/59	from × 8
Nos. 60/2	from × 15
Nos. 63/72	from × 8
Nos. 121/38	from × 6
Nos. 139/41	†
Nos. 142/3	from × 10
Nos. 146/51	from × 6
Nos. 151a/2	†
Nos. 153/93	from × 8
Nos. 195/201	from × 12
Nos. 202/43	from × 6
Nos. 245/9	from × 4
Nos. 250/5	from × 5
Nos. 256/64	from × 4
Nos. 265/76	from × 3
Nos. 277/88	from × 4
Nos. 289/300	from × 8
Nos. 301/18	from × 2
Nos. 319/23	—
Nos. 330/7b	from × 2
Nos. 338/56	from × 2
Nos. 357/60	—
Nos. 361/2	from × 5
Nos. 363/7	from × 3
Nos. 368/78	from × 2
Nos. 379/82	from × 4
Nos. 383/5	from × 3
Nos. 386/97	from × 2
Nos. 398/9	from × 8
Nos. O1/17	from × 30

CROWN COLONY

PRICES. The prices of the imperf stamps of Ceylon vary greatly according to condition. The following prices are for fine copies with four margins.

Poor to medium specimens can be supplied at much lower prices.

1   2   3

NOTE. Beware of stamps of Type 2 which are often offered with corners added.

(Recess P.B.)

1857 (1 April). *Blued paper. Wmk Star W w 1. Imperf.*

1	1	6d. purple-brown			£750	£450

Collectors should beware of proofs with faked watermark, often offered as originals.

PERKINS BACON "CANCELLED". For notes on these handstamps, showing "CANCELLED" between horizontal bars forming an oval, see Catalogue Introduction.

1857 (2 July)–59. *Wmk Star, W w 1. White paper.* (a) *Imperf*

2	1	1d. deep turquoise-blue (24.8.57)		£650	24·00
		a. *Blue*		£750	40·00
		b. Blued paper		—	£180
3		2d. green (*shades*) (24.8.57)		£150	55·00
		a. *Yellowish green*		£500	90·00
4	2	4d. dull rose (23.4.59)		£50000	£4500
5	1	5d. chestnut		£1500	£150
6		6d. purple-brown (1859)		£1800	£130
		a. *Brown*		£6000	£450
		b. *Deep brown*		£7000	£1000
		c. *Light brown*		—	£850
7	2	8d. brown (23.4.59)		£22000	£1500
8		9d. purple-brown (23.4.59)		£32000	£900
9	3	10d. dull vermilion		£800	£300
10		1s. slate-violet		£4500	£200
11	2	1s. 9d. green (H/S "CANCELLED" in oval £5000)		£700	£800
		a. *Yellow-green*		£4000	£3000
12		2s. dull blue (23.4.59)		£5500	£1200

(b) *Unofficial perf 7½* (1s. 9d.) *or roul* (others)

13	1	1d. blue			£5500	
14		2d. green			£2250	£1200
15	2	1s. 9d. green			£5500	

Nos. 13/15 were privately produced, probably by commercial firms for their own convenience.

The 10d. also exists with "CANCELLED" in oval, but no examples are believed to be in private hands.

4

(Typo D.L.R.)

1857 (Oct)–64. *No wmk. Glazed paper.* (a) *Imperf*

16	4	½d. reddish lilac (*blued paper*)		£3250	£450
17		½d. dull mauve (1858)		£160	£160
		a. Private roul			£5500	

(b) *P 12½*

18	4	½d. dull mauve (1864)			£190	£150

(Recess P.B.)

1861–64. *Wmk Star, W w 1.*

(a) *Clean-cut and intermediate perf 14 to 15½*

19	1	1d. light blue		£750	£130
		a. *Dull blue* (H/S "CANCELLED" in oval £5000)		£120	12·00
20		2d. green (*shades*)		£120	28·00
		a. Imperf between (vert pair)		†	—
		b. *Yellowish green* (H/S "CANCELLED" in oval £5000)		£130	24·00
21	2	4d. dull rose (H/S "CANCELLED" in oval £5500)		£1800	£250
22	1	5d. chestnut (H/S "CANCELLED" in oval £3500)		75·00	8·00
23		6d. brown		£1700	95·00
		a. *Bistre-brown*		—	£160
24	2	8d. brown (H/S "CANCELLED" in oval £4500)		£1600	£475
25		9d. purple-brown		£5000	£225
26	3	1s. slate-violet (H/S "CANCELLED" in oval £5000)		80·00	13·00
27	2	2s. dull blue		£2250	£550

(b) *Rough perf 14 to 15½*

28	1	1d. dull blue		90·00	6·00
		a. Blued paper		£425	20·00
29		2d. green		£375	70·00
30	2	4d. rose-red		£325	60·00
		a. *Deep rose-red*		£350	70·00
31	1	6d. deep brown		£800	85·00
		a. *Light brown*		£1300	£110
		b. *Olive-sepia*		£750	75·00
32	2	8d. brown		£1200	£550
		a. *Yellow-brown*		£1200	£325
33		9d. deep brown (H/S "CANCELLED" in oval £4000)		65·00	50·00
		a. *Light brown*		£750	75·00
		b. *Olive-sepia*		£500	45·00
34	3	10d. dull vermilion		£225	20·00
		a. Imperf vert (horiz pair)		†	—
35		1s. slate-violet		£225	15·00
36	2	1s. 9d. light green (*prepared for use, but not issued*)		£550	
37		2s. dull blue (H/S "CANCELLED" in oval £4500)		£550	£110
		a. *Deep dull blue*		£750	£140

(c) *P 12½ by D.L.R.*

38	3	10d. dull vermilion (9.64)		£225	15·00

The line machine used for Nos. 19/37 produced perforations of variable quality due to wear, poor cleaning and faulty servicing, but it is generally accepted that the clean-cut and intermediate versions occurred on stamps perforated up to March 1861 and the rough variety when the machine was used after that date.

The 6d. with intermediate perforation also exists with "CANCELLED" in oval, but no complete examples are believed to be in private hands.

(Recess D.L.R.)

1862. *No wmk. Smooth paper.* (a) *P 13*

39	1	1d. dull blue		95·00	6·00
40		5d. lake-brown		£1200	£150
41		6d. brown		£120	25·00
		a. *Deep brown*		£120	23·00
42	2	9d. brown		£1200	90·00
43		1s. slate-purple		£1600	75·00

(b) *P 11½, 12*

44	1	1d. dull blue		£1100	£120
		a. Imperf between (horiz pair)		†	£8000

Nos. 39/44 were printed on paper showing a papermaker's watermark of "T H SAUNDERS 1862", parts of which can be found on individual stamps. Examples are rare and command a premium.

The 1s. is known imperforate, but was not issued in this condition.

The new-issue supplement to this Catalogue appears each month in

GIBBONS
STAMP MONTHLY

—from your newsagent or by postal subscription— sample copy and details on request.

---

5   **6**
(23 mm high. "CC" oval)   (21½ mm high. "CC" round and smaller)

(Typo (½d.) or recess (others) D.L.R.)

1863–66. *W 5. Paper medium thin and slightly soft.*

(a) *P 11½, 12*

45	1	1d. deep blue		£2500	£300
		x. Wmk reversed		£3000	£400

(b) *P 13*

46	1	6d. sepia		£1300	£140
		x. Wmk reversed		—	£120
		xw. Wmk inverted and reversed		£1700	£275
47	2	9d. sepia		£3000	£600

(c) *P 12½*

48	4	½d. dull mauve (1864)		30·00	22·00
		aw. Wmk inverted		£130	42·00
		b. *Reddish lilac*		48·00	35·00
		c. *Mauve*		23·00	24·00
49	1	1d. deep blue		30·00	3·50
		a. Imperf		†	22·00
		w. Wmk inverted		85·00	4·00
		x. Wmk reversed		†	27·00
		y. Wmk inverted and reversed		55·00	8·00
50		2d. grey-green (1864)		£150	32·00
		a. Imperf		†	65·00
		bw. Wmk inverted		†	£3500
		by. Wmk inverted and reversed		£7000	£400
		c. *Bottle-green*		†	£550
		d. *Yellowish green*		£100	90·00
		dx. Wmk reversed		£275	£160
		e. *Emerald* (*wmk reversed*)		£225	£225
		ew. Wmk inverted		£375	£375
51		2d. ochre (*wmk reversed*) (1866)		£300	£275
		w. Wmk inverted		£100	£275
		y. Wmk inverted and reversed		£450	£120
52	2	4d. rose-carmine (1865)		£550	
		ax. Wmk reversed		£275	60·00
		b. *Rose*		£325	80·00
		bx. Wmk reversed		£140	60·00
53	1	5d. red-brown (*shades*) (1865)		†	£110
		w. Wmk inverted		£160	48·00
		x. Wmk reversed		£1700	£300
54		5d. grey-olive (1866)		£1400	£250
		ax. Wmk reversed		£750	£200
		b. *Yellow-olive*		£750	£190
		bx. Wmk reversed		£100	4·00
55		6d. sepia		†	42·00
		aw Wmk inverted		£140	11·00
		b. *Reddish brown*		£100	9·00
		c. *Blackish brown*		†	£2250
		ca. Double print		†	38·00
		cw. Wmk inverted		£140	27·00
		cx. Wmk reversed		†	75·00
		cy. Wmk inverted and reversed		70·00	35·00
56	2	8d. reddish brown (*shades*) (1864)		95·00	48·00
		w. Wmk inverted		£170	60·00
		y. Wmk inverted and reversed		£275	35·00
57		9d. sepia		£375	55·00
58	3	10d. vermilion (1866)		£1500	55·00
		ax. Wmk reversed		†	95·00
		b. *Orange-red*		£3250	£300
		bx. Wmk reversed		†	£400
59	2	2s. steel-blue (*shades*) (1864)		£180	30·00
		x. Wmk reversed		†	65·00
		y. Wmk inverted and reversed		†	£110

Watermarks as Type 5 were arranged in four panes, each of 60, with the words "CROWN COLONIES" between the panes. Parts of this marginal watermark often appear on the stamps.

The ½d. dull mauve, 2d. ochre and 5d. grey-olive with this watermark also exist imperforate, but are not known used. The 6d. sepia and 2s. steel-blue also exist imperforate on wove paper without watermark.

One used example of the 2d. grey-green is known showing private roulettes added to an imperforate stamp (*Price* £2750).

7   **8**

(Typo D.L.R.)

1866–68. *Wmk Crown CC.* (a) *P 12½*

60	7	3d. rose		£160	70·00

(b) *P 14*

61	8	1d. blue (*shades*) (1868)		17·00	6·50
		w. Wmk inverted		†	65·00
62	7	3d. carmine-rose (1867)		60·00	30·00
		a. *Bright rose*		65·00	35·00

Nos. 60/1 exist imperforate.

(Recess D.L.R.)

1867–70. *W 6. Specially produced hand-made paper. P 12½.*

63	1	1d. dull blue		£110	8·00
		aw. Wmk inverted		£250	55·00
		ax. Wmk reversed		£110	8·00
		b. *Deep blue*		£100	6·50
		bx. Wmk reversed		£160	26·00

64	1	2d. ochre		85·00	9·00
		ax. Wmk reversed		—	26·00
		b. Bistre		40·00	7·00
		bw. Wmk inverted		90·00	
		c. Olive-bistre		£130	20·00
		cw. Wmk inverted		£130	
		d. Yellow		65·00	5·00
		dx. Wmk reversed		42·00	20·00
65	2	4d. rose		£180	55·00
		ax. Wmk reversed		£160	45·00
		b. Rose-carmine		42·00	13·00
		bw. Wmk inverted		†	55·00
		bx. Wmk reversed		42·00	13·00
		by. Wmk inverted and reversed		£250	80·00
66	1	5d. yellow-olive		65·00	9·50
		ax. Wmk reversed		55·00	15·00
		ay. Wmk inverted and reversed			
		b. Olive-green		85·00	10·00
		c. Bronze-green		25·00	40·00
67		6d. deep brown (1869)		55·00	10·00
		a. Blackish brown		75·00	8·50
		ax. Wmk reversed		95·00	15·00
		b. Red-brown		25·00	32·00
68	2	8d. chocolate		45·00	10·00
		ax. Wmk reversed		—	65·00
		b. Lake-brown		£100	60·00
		bx. Wmk reversed		—	75·00
69		9d. bistre-brown (1869)		£325	10·00
		ax. Wmk reversed		£275	25·00
		b. Blackish brown		35·00	6·00
70	3	10d. dull vermilion (*wmk reversed*)		£2000	£140
		ay. Wmk inverted and reversed		†	£225
		b. Red-orange		38·00	10·00
		bx. Wmk reversed		—	7·00
		by. Wmk inverted and reversed		£300	
		c. Orange		70·00	8·00
71		1s. reddish lilac (18″)		£275	27·00
		ax. Wmk reversed		£375	
		b. Reddish violet		70·00	5·50
		bw. Wmk inverted		†	80·00
		bx. Wmk reversed		£160	32·00
72	2	2s. steel-blue		£140	17·00
		ax. Wmk reversed		†	38·00
		b. Deep blue		90·00	12·00
		bx. Wmk reversed		£120	18·00

Watermarks as Type **6** were arranged in one pane of 240 (12×20) with the words "CROWN COLONIES" twice in each side margin.

Unused examples of the 1d. dull blue, 1d. deep blue, 5d. yellow-olive, 6d. deep brown, 9d. blackish brown and 10d. red-orange with this watermark exist imperforate.

PRINTERS. All stamps from No. 121 to 367 were typographed by De La Rue & Co. Ltd, London.

(New Currency. 100 cents = 1 rupee)

9   10   11   12   13   14   15   16   17

18   19

1872-80. Wmk Crown CC. (a) P 14.

121	9	2 c. pale brown (*shades*)		10·00	1·90
		w. Wmk inverted		75·00	40·00
122	10	4 c. grey		28·00	1·50
		w. Wmk inverted		†	40·00
123		4 c. rosy-mauve (1880)		45·00	1·50
124	11	8 c. orange-yellow		40·00	5·50
		a. Yellow		28·00	6·00
126	12	16 c. pale violet		65·00	2·75
		w. Wmk inverted		†	80·00
127	13	24 c. green		42·00	2·00
		w. Wmk inverted		†	
128	14	32 c. slate (1877)		£120	15·00
		w. Wmk inverted		£275	
129	15	36 c. blue		£110	16·00
		x. Wmk reversed		£225	
130	16	48 c. rose		60·00	5·00
		w. Wmk inverted		—	30·00
131	17	64 c. red-brown (1877)		£225	60·00
132	18	96 c. drab		£160	26·00
		w. Wmk inverted		†	£100
121/32			Set of 11	£800	£110

(b) P 14×12½

133	9	2 c. brown		£350	60·00
134	10	4 c. grey		£1000	25·00
135	11	8 c. orange-yellow		£375	45·00
		w. Wmk inverted		†	£130

(c) P 12½

136	9	2 c. brown		£1900	£150
137	10	4 c. grey		£1000	£200

(d) P 12½ × 14

138	19	2 r. 50 c. dull-rose (1879)		£450	£300

(e) Prepared for use and sent out to Ceylon, but not issued unsurcharged

139	14	32 c. slate (p 14 × 12½)		£800
140	17	64 c. red-brown (p 14 × 12½)		£950
141	19	2 r. 50, dull rose (p 12½)		£1200

FORGERIES.—Beware of forged overprint and surcharge varieties on Victorian issues.

SIXTEEN
16
CENTS
(20)

1882 (Oct). *Nos. 127 and 131 surch as T 20 by Govt Printer.*

142	13	16 c. on 24 c. green		21·00	6·50
		a. Surch inverted			
143	17	20 c. on 64 c. red-brown		9·00	4·75
		a. Surch double		†	£1100

1883-98. *Wmk Crown CA.* (a) P 14

146	9	2 c. pale brown		50·00	1·50
147		2 c. dull green (1884) (Optd S. £200)		2·00	15
		w. Wmk inverted		95·00	40·00
148	10	4 c. rosy mauve		2·50	30
149		4 c. rose (1884) (Optd S. £200)		3·50	11·00
150	11	8 c. orange		4·00	8·00
		a. Yellow (1898)		3·00	7·00
151	12	16 c. pale violet		£1200	£140

(b) Trial perforation. P 12

151a	9	2 c. dull green		£1900
151b	10	4 c. rose		£1900
151c	13	24 c. brown-purple		£2000

(c) Prepared for use and sent out to Ceylon, but not issued unsurcharged. P 14

152	13	24 c. brown-purple (Optd S. £425)		£950

Although delivered in 1884 it is believed that the 4 c. rose, No. 149, was not used until the early 1890s.

Postage &
FIVE
CENTS
Revenue
(21)

TEN
CENTS
(22)

Twenty
Cents
(23)

One Rupee
Twelve
Cents
(24)

1885. *T 10/19 surch locally as T 21/24.*

I. Wmk Crown CC. (a) P 14

153	21	5 c. on 16 c. pale violet		†	£2500
154		5 c. on 24 c. green		£1800	£100
155		5 c. on 32 c. slate		55·00	15·00
		a. Surch inverted		†	£1000
		b. Dark grey		95·00	30·00
156		5 c. on 36 c. blue		£180	8·00
		a. Surch inverted		†	£1600
		x. Wmk reversed		†	42·00
157		5 c. on 48 c. rose		£800	50·00
158		5 c. on 64 c. red-brown		80·00	4·50
		a. Surch double		†	£850
159		5 c. on 96 c. drab		£350	60·00
161	22	10 c. on 16 c. pale violet		£3750	£1500
162		10 c. on 24 c. green		£350	£100
163		10 c. on 36 c. blue		£325	£160
164		10 c. on 64 c. red-brown		£350	£120
165		20 c. on 24 c. green		48·00	18·00
166	23	20 c. on 32 c. slate		48·00	48·00
		a. Dark grey		48·00	40·00
167		25 c. on 32 c. slate		13·00	4·50
		a. Dark grey		23·00	8·00
168		28 c. on 48 c. rose		32·00	6·00
		a. Surch double		†	£950
169	22	30 c. on 36 c. blue		13·00	8·50
		x. Wmk reversed		10·00	8·50
		xa. Surch inverted		£200	£100
170		56 c. on 96 c. drab		19·00	16·00

(b) P 14 × 12½

172	21	5 c. on 32 c. slate		£450	45·00
173		5 c. on 64 c. red-brown		£450	35·00
174	22	10 c. on 64 c. red-brown		50·00	90·00
		a. Imperf between (vert pair)		£2500	
175	24	1 r. 12 c. on 2 r. 50 c. dull rose (p 12½)		£375	80·00
176		1 r. 12 c. on 2 r. 50 c. dull rose (p 12½ × 14)		75·00	42·00

II. Wmk Crown CA. P 14

178	21	5 c. on 4 c. rose		17·00	3·50
		a. Surch inverted		†	£275
179		5 c. on 8 c. orange-yellow		50·00	6·50
		a. Surch double		†	£1100
		b. Surch inverted		†	£1400
180		5 c. on 16 c. pale violet		75·00	9·50
		a. Surch inverted		†	£160
182		5 c. on 24 c. brown-purple		—	£500
184	22	10 c. on 16 c. pale violet		£3750	£850
185		10 c. on 24 c. brown-purple		11·00	5·50
186		15 c. on 16 c. pale violet		9·00	6·50

Only seven examples, all used, are recorded of No. 153.

The 5 c. on 4 c. rosy mauve and 5 c. on 24 c. green, both watermarked Crown CA, previously catalogued are now considered to be forgeries.

REVENUE AND POSTAGE

5 CENTS (25)   **10 CENTS** (26)   **1 R. 12 C.** (27)

1885. *T 11/15, 18 and 19 surch with T 25/7 by D.L.R. P 14.*

(a) Wmk Crown CA

187	25	5 c. on 8 c. lilac		12·00	1·40
		w. Wmk inverted		†	50·00
188	26	10 c. on 24 c. brown-purple		8·50	6·00
189		15 c. on 16 c. orange-yellow		50·00	7·50
190		28 c. on 32 c. slate		18·00	2·50
191		30 c. on 36 c. olive-green		28·00	14·00
192		56 c. on 96 c. drab		42·00	11·00

(b) Wmk Crown CC (sideways)

193	27	1 r. 12 on 2 r. 50, dull rose		38·00	80·00
187/93			Set of 7	£180	£110
187/93		Optd "Specimen"	Set of 7	£700	

28   29

1886. *Wmk Crown CA. P 14.*

195	28	5 c. dull purple		1·75	10
		w. Wmk inverted		†	60·00
196	29	15 c. sage-green		4·00	1·25
197		15 c. olive-green		4·25	1·25
198		25 c. yellow-brown		3·00	1·00
		a. Value in yellow		95·00	70·00
199		28 c. slate		14·00	1·40
195, 197/9		Optd "Specimen"	Set of 4	£190	

Six plates were used for the 5 c., No. 195, between 1885 and 1901, each being replaced by its successor as it became worn. Examples from the worn plates show thicker lines in the background and masses of solid colour under the chin, in front of the throat, at the back of the neck and at the base.

30

1887. *Wmk Crown CC (sideways). White or blued paper. P 14.*

201	30	1 r. 12, dull rose (Optd S. £95)		22·00	19·00
		a. Wmk upright		40·00	55·00
		aw. Wmk inverted		†	£120

TWO CENTS (31)   **TWO** (32)   **2 Cents** (33)

Two Cents (34)   **2 Cents** (35)

1888-90. *Nos. 148/9 surch with T 31/5.*

202	31	2 c. on 4 c. rosy mauve		1·00	70
		a. Surch inverted		19·00	18·00
		b. Surch double, one inverted		—	£160
203		2 c. on 4 c. rose		1·75	30
		a. Surch inverted		13·00	14·00
		b. Surch double		—	£170

204	32	2 (c). on 4 c. rosy mauve	60	30
		a. Surch inverted	28·00	30·00
		b. Surch double ..	48·00	48·00
		c. Surch double, one inverted	45·00	40·00
205		2 (c). on 4 c. rose	4·00	20
		a. Surch inverted ..	£170	
		b. Surch double ..	50·00	60·00
		c. Surch double, one inverted	55·00	65·00
206	33	2 c. on 4 c. rosy mauve	48·00	28·00
		a. Surch inverted ..	80·00	38·00
		b. Surch double, one inverted	95·00	
207		2 c. on 4 c. rose	2·25	75
		a. Surch inverted ..	9·50	8·50
		b. Surch double ..	95·00	95·00
		c. Surch double, one inverted	8·00	10·00
208	34	2 c. on 4 c. rosy mauve ..	42·00	16·00
		a. Surch inverted ..	95·00	30·00
209		2 c. on 4 c. rose	2·00	1·10
		a. Surch inverted ..	11·00	5·50
		b. Surch double ..	75·00	75·00
		c. Surch double, one inverted	11·00	5·50
210	35	2 c. on 4 c. rosy mauve ..	42·00	24·00
		a. Surch inverted ..	55·00	40·00
		b. Surch double, one inverted	65·00	65·00
		c. Surch double ..	—	£170
		d. "s" of "Cents" inverted	—	£325
		e. As d. Whole surch inverted		
211		2 c. on 4 c. rose	8·50	70
		a. Surch inverted ..	13·00	5·50
		b. Surch double ..	65·00	65·00
		c. Surch double, one inverted	15·00	8·50
		d. "s" of "Cents" inverted	—	£140
		x. Wmk reversed ..	†	65·00
		209, 211 Optd "Specimen" .. *Set of 2*	60·00	

The 4 c. rose and the 4 c. rosy mauve are found surcharged "Postal Commission 3 (or "Three") Cents". They denote the extra commission charged by the Post Office on postal orders which had not been cashed within three months of the date of issue. For a short time the Post Office did not object to the use of these stamps on letters.

POSTAGE

Five Cents

REVENUE

(36)

FIFTEEN CENTS

(37)

1890. *No.* 197 *surch with T* 36.

233		5 c. on 15 c. olive-green (Optd S. £30)	1·75	1·90
		a. Surch inverted ..	32·00	35·00
		b. Surch double ..	90·00	95·00
		c. "Flve" for "Five" (R. 1/1)	90·00	80·00
		d. Variety as c, inverted	—	£800
		e. "REVÉNUE" omitted ..	£120	£100
		f. Inverted "s" in "Cents" ..	45·00	50·00
		g. Variety as f, and whole surch inverted	£850	
		h. "REVÉNUE" omitted and inverted "s" in "Cents" ..	£700	
		i. "POSTAGE" spaced between "T" and "A" (R. 1/5) ..	50·00	55·00
		j. Variety as i, and whole surch inverted	—	£650

1891. *Nos.* 198/9 *surch with T* 37.

239	29	15 c. on 25 c. yellow-brown ..	7·50	10·00
240		15 c. on 28 c. slate	12·00	8·50

3 Cents

(38)

39

1892. *Nos.* 148/9 *and* 199 *surch with T* 38.

241	10	3 c. on 4 c. rosy mauve	85	3·00
242		3 c. on 4 c. rose (Optd S. £30) ..	2·50	6·00
243	29	3 c. on 28 c. slate ..	3·00	3·00
		a. Surch double ..	90·00	
241/3 ..		.. *Set of 3*	5·75	11·00

1893–99. *Wmk Crown CA. P* 14.

245	39	3 c. terracotta and blue-green ..	2·75	45
246	10	4 c. carmine-rose (1898) ..	7·50	8·00
247	29	30 c. bright mauve and chestnut ..	4·25	1·90
		a. Bright violet and chestnut ..	5·00	2·50
249	19	2 r. 50, purple/red (1899) ..	26·00	48·00
245/9 ..		.. *Set of 4*	35·00	55·00
245, 247/9 Optd "Specimen" ..		*Set of 3*	60·00	

Six Cents

(40)

2 R. 25 C.

(41)

1898 (Dec)**–99.** (*a*) *No.* 196 *surch with T* 40.

250	29	6 c. on 15 c. sage-green ..	70	75

(*b*) *As No.* 138, *but colour changed and perf* 14, *surch as T* 41 (1899)

254	19	1 r. 50 on 2 r. 50, slate ..	20·00	40·00
		w. Wmk inverted ..	80·00	
255		2 r. 25 on 2 r. 50, yellow	32·00	70·00
250/5 Optd "Specimen" ..		*Set of 3*	70·00	

43

1899–1900. *Wmk Crown CA* (1 *r.* 50, 2 *r.* 25 *wmk Crown CC*). *P* 14.

256	9	2 c. pale orange-brown ..	1·90	30
257	39	3 c. deep green	1·90	55
258	10	4 c. yellow	2·50	2·75
259	29	6 c. rose and black ..	1·00	45
260	39	12 c. sage-green and rose (1900)	3·00	6·50
261	29	15 c. blue	4·75	1·25
262	39	75 c. black and red-brown ..	4·25	5·00
263	43	1 r. 50, rose	18·00	35·00
264		2 r. 25, dull blue ..	30·00	35·00
256/64		*Set of 9*	60·00	75·00
256/64 Optd "Specimen"		*Set of 9*	£150	

44　　　　45　　　　46

47　　　　48

1903 (29 May)**–05.** *Wmk Crown CA. P* 14.

265	44	2 c. red-brown (21.7.03) ..	1·50	20
266	45	3 c. green (11.6.03) ..	1·50	1·00
267		4 c. orange-yellow and blue ..	1·50	3·25
268	46	5 c. dull purple (2.7.03) ..	1·50	60
269	47	6 c. carmine (5.11.03) ..	7·50	1·50
		w. Wmk inverted ..	45·00	
270	45	12 c. sage-green and rosine (13.8.03)	4·25	7·50
271	48	15 c. blue (2.7.03) ..	6·50	2·75
272		25 c. bistre (11.8.03) ..	4·00	7·50
273		30 c. dull violet and green ..	3·25	4·00
274	45	75 c. dull blue and orange (31.3.05)	2·75	17·00
275	48	1 r. 50, greyish slate (7.4.04)	65·00	55·00
276		2 r. 25, brown and green (12.4.04)	60·00	48·00
265/76		*Set of 12*	£140	£130
265/76 Optd "Specimen" ..		*Set of 12*	£150	

1904 (13 Sept)**–05.** *Wmk Mult Crown CA. Ordinary paper. P* 14.

277	44	2 c. red-brown (17.11.04) ..	75	10
278	45	3 c. green (17.11.04) ..	75	15
279		4 c. orange and ultramarine ..	1·00	1·25
280	46	5 c. dull purple (29.11.04) ..	1·75	1·25
		a. Chalk-surfaced paper (5.10.05)	3·00	70
281	47	6 c. carmine (11.10.04) ..	1·10	15
282	45	12 c. sage-green and rosine (29.9.04)	1·50	1·75
283	48	15 c. blue (1.12.04) ..	1·25	60
284		25 c. bistre (5.1.05) ..	6·00	3·75
285		30 c. violet and green (7.9.05) ..	2·50	2·50
286	45	75 c. dull blue and orange (25.5.05)	5·25	8·00
287	48	1 r. 50, grey (5.1.05) ..	22·00	10·00
288		2 r. 25, brown and green (22.12.04)	19·00	29·00
277/88		*Set of 12*	55·00	50·00

50　　　　51

1908. *Wmk Mult Crown CA. P* 14.

289	50	5 c. deep purple (26 May) ..	2·00	10
290		5 c. dull purple	3·00	30
291	51	6 c. carmine (6 June) ..	80	10
289, 291 Optd "Specimen"		*Set of 2*	55·00	

1910 (1 Aug)**–11.** *Wmk Mult Crown CA. P* 14.

292	44	2 c. brown-orange (20.5.11) ..	1·50	50
293	48	3 c. green (5.7.11) ..	1·00	75
294		10 c. sage-green and maroon ..	2·25	1·50
295		25 c. grey	2·50	1·00
296		50 c. chocolate	4·00	7·50
297		1 r. purple/yellow ..	7·50	10·00
298		2 r. red/yellow	15·00	27·00
299		5 r. black/green	35·00	65·00
300		10 r. black/red	70·00	£170
292/300		*Set of 9*	£120	£250
292/300 Optd "Specimen" ..		*Set of 9*	£190	

NEW INFORMATION

The editor is always interested to correspond with people who have new information that will improve or correct the Catalogue.

52

53

(A)

(B)

Most values in Type **52** were produced by two printing operations, using "Key" and "Duty" plates. Differences in the two Dies of the Key plate are described in the introduction to this catalogue.

In the Ceylon series, however, the 1 c. and 5 c. values, together with later printings of the 3 c. and 6 c., were printed from special plates at one operation. These plates can be identified by the large "C" in the value tablet (see illustration A). Examples of these values from Key and Duty plates printing have value tablet as illustration B. The 3 c. and 5 c. stamps from the single plate resemble Die I, and the 1 c. and 6 c. Die II, although in the latter case the inner top corners of the side panels are square and not curved.

1912–25. *Wmk Mult Crown CA. Chalk-surfaced paper* (30 *c. to* 100 *r.*). *P* 14.

(*a*) *Printed from single plates. Value tablet as* A

301	52	1 c. brown (1919) ..	90	10
		w. Wmk inverted ..	15·00	
302		3 c. blue-green (1919) ..	2·50	45
		w. Wmk inverted ..	15·00	25·00
		y. Wmk inverted and reversed ..	20·00	30·00
303		5 c. purple	5·50	2·75
		a. Wmk sideways (Crown to right of CA) ..	£225	
		y. Wmk inverted and reversed ..	55·00	
304		5 c. bright magenta ..	1·00	60
		w. Wmk inverted ..	—	50·00
305		6 c. pale scarlet (1919) ..	8·50	85
		a. Wmk sideways (Crown to left of CA) ..	29·00	55·00
		w. Wmk inverted ..	20·00	30·00
306		6 c. carmine	12·00	1·25
		a. Wmk sideways (Crown to right of CA) ..	38·00	
		y. Wmk inverted and reversed ..	20·00	

(*b*) *Printed from Key and Duty plates. Die I.* 3 *c. and* 6 *c. have value tablet as* B

307	52	2 c. brown-orange ..	40	30
		a. Deep orange-brown ..	30	20
308		3 c. yellow-green ..	6·50	2·25
		a. Deep green (1917) ..	4·25	1·10
309		6 c. scarlet (shades) ..	1·10	50
310		10 c. sage-green ..	3·00	1·75
		a. Deep sage-green (1917) ..	5·00	2·50
		w. Wmk inverted ..	60·00	
311		15 c. deep bright blue ..	2·50	1·25
		a. Ultramarine (1918) ..	1·50	1·25
		aw. Wmk inverted ..	20·00	
312		25 c. orange and blue ..	6·50	4·50
		a. Yellow and blue (1917) ..	1·75	1·75
		aw. Wmk inverted ..	60·00	60·00
313		30 c. blue-green and violet ..	4·00	2·75
		a. Yellow-green and violet (1915)	7·00	3·50
		ab. Wmk sideways (Crown to right of CA) ..	18·00	
		abw. Wmk Crown to left of CA	18·00	
		aw. Wmk inverted ..	32·00	
314		50 c. black and scarlet ..	1·25	1·75
		w. Wmk inverted ..	15·00	
315		1 r. purple/yellow ..	2·00	3·25
		a. White back (1913) (Optd S. £38)	1·75	4·25
		b. On lemon (1915) (Optd S. £38)	4·00	8·00
		c. On orange-buff (1918) ..	26·00	35·00
		cw. Wmk inverted ..	42·00	
		d. On pale yell (1922) (Optd S. £38)	4·50	10·00
316		2 r. black and red/yellow ..	3·25	9·50
		a. White back (1913) (Optd S. £38)	2·50	10·00
		b. On lemon (1915) (Optd S. £38)	20·00	27·00
		c. On orange-buff (1919) ..	35·00	42·00
		cw. Wmk inverted ..	42·00	
		d. On pale yellow (1921) ..	35·00	38·00
317		5 r. black/green ..	15·00	25·00
		a. White back (1914) (Optd S. £40)	17·00	30·00
		b. On blue-grn (olive back) (1917) (Optd S. £45) ..	15·00	28·00
		bw. Wmk inverted ..	42·00	55·00
		c. Die II. On emerald back (1923) (Optd S. £55) ..	45·00	85·00
318		10 r. purple and black/red ..	60·00	75·00
		aw. Wmk inverted ..	95·00	
		b. Die II (1923) ..	75·00	£110
		bw. Wmk inverted ..	£180	
319	53	20 r. black and red/blue ..	95·00	£110
320		50 r. dull purple (Optd S. £130) ..	£325	
		a. Break in scroll ..	£650	
		b. Broken crown and scroll ..	£650	
321		100 r. grey-black (Optd S. £250) ..	£1300	
		a. Break in scroll ..	£2250	
		b. Broken crown and scroll ..	£2250	
322		500 r. dull green (Optd S. £450) ..	£4000	
		a. Break in scroll ..	£6500	
		b. Broken crown and scroll ..	£6500	
323		1000 r. purple/red (1925) (Optd S. £850)	£14000	
		b. Broken crown and scroll ..	£19000	
301/18		*Set of 14*	85·00	£100
301/19 Optd "Specimen" ..		*Set of 15*	£275	

For illustrations of the varieties on Nos. 320/3 see above No. 58 of Leeward Islands.

The 2 c. and 5 c. exist in coils, constructed from normal sheets used in stamp-affixing machines introduced in 1915.

Sideways watermark varieties are described as seen *from the back of the stamp.*

WAR
STAMP

WAR
STAMP
ONE CENT

| | (54) | (55) |

1918 (18 Nov)–19. (a) *Optd with T 54 by Govt Printer, Colombo.*

330	52	2 c. brown-orange	20	40
		a. Opt inverted	30·00	35·00
		b. Opt double	24·00	28·00
		c. Opt omitted in pair with opt inverted	£325	
331		3 c. blue-green (No. 302) (1919)	1·40	40
332		3 c. deep green (No. 308a)	20	50
		a. Opt double	55·00	60·00
333		5 c. purple	40	30
		a. Opt double	30·00	35·00
		w. Wmk inverted	55·00	
334		5 c. bright magenta	1·60	1·90
		a. Opt inverted	30·00	35·00
		b. Opt double	24·00	32·00

(b) *Surch with T 55*

335	52	1 c. on 5 c. purple	50	30
		y. Wmk inverted and reversed	55·00	
336		1 c. on 5 c. bright magenta	1·10	20
330, 332/3, 335 Optd "Specimen"			Set of 4	90·00

Collectors are warned against forgeries of the errors in the "WAR STAMP" overprints.

1918. *Surch as T 55, but without "WAR STAMP".*

337	52	1 c. on 5 c. purple (Optd S. £30)	15	25
		a. Surch double	£120	
337b		1 c. on 5 c. bright magenta	1·60	2·50

1921–32. *Wmk Mult Script CA. Chalk-surfaced paper (30 c. to 100 r.). P 14.*

(a) *Printed from single plates. Value tablet as A*

338	52	1 c. brown (1927)	40	35
339		3 c. green (5.5.22)	2·50	75
		w. Wmk inverted	16·00	25·00
340		3 c. slate-grey (1923)	50	20
		a. Wmk sideways	£700	
		w. Wmk inverted	16·00	
341		5 c. purple (1927)	40	15
342		6 c. carmine-red (3.8.21)	1·75	75
		w. Wmk inverted	17·00	25·00
		y. Wmk inverted and reversed	26·00	
343		6 c. bright violet (1922)	60	15
		w. Wmk inverted	16·00	
		y. Wmk inverted and reversed	26·00	

(b) *Printed from Key and Duty plates*

344	52	2 c. brown-orange (Die II) (1927)	40	25
345		9 c. red/pale yellow (Die II) (1926)	50	30
346		10 c. sage-green (Die I) (16.9.21)	1·00	40
		aw. Wmk inverted	22·00	
		ay. Wmk inverted and reversed	16·00	25·00
		b. Die II (1924)	1·25	60
		c. Vert gutter pair. Die I and Die II. Nos. 346 and 346b	£150	
347		12 c. rose-scarlet (Die I) (1925)	3·50	5·00
		a. Die II (Optd S. £55)	90	2·25
		b. Vert gutter pair. Die I and Die II Nos. 347/a	85·00	
348		15 c. ultramarine (Die I) (30.5.22)	2·75	7·50
349		15 c. green/pale yellow (Die I) (1923)	1·25	1·25
		a. Die II (1924)	1·25	1·00
		aw. Wmk inverted	16·00	
		b. Vert gutter pair. Die I and Die II. Nos. 349/a	£150	
350		20 c. bright blue (Die I) (1922)	2·50	6·00
		aw. Wmk inverted	35·00	
		b. Die II (1924)	2·75	45
		c. Vert gutter pair. Die I and Die II. Nos. 350 and 350b	£150	
351		25 c. yellow and blue (Die I) (17.10.21)	1·00	1·90
		aw. Wmk inverted	40·00	
		b. Die II (1924)	2·50	1·25
		c. Vert gutter pair. Die I and Die II. Nos. 351/b	£100	
352		30 c. yellow-green & vio (Die I) (15.3.22)	1·40	2·50
		a. Die II (1924)	2·00	1·25
		b. Vert gutter pair. Die I and Die II. Nos. 352/a	£250	
353		50 c. black and scarlet (Die II) (1922)	1·25	80
		a. Die I (1932)	50·00	75·00
354		1 r. purple/pale yellow (Die I) (1923)	14·00	23·00
		a. Die II (1925)	11·00	21·00
		b. Vert gutter pair. Die I and Die II. Nos. 354/a	£200	
355		2 r. black & red/pale yell (Die II) (1923)	5·00	6·50
356		5 r. black/emerald (Die II) (1924)	25·00	42·00
357		20 r. black and red/blue (Die II) (1924)	£120	£140
358	53	50 r. dull purple (1924) (Optd S. £130)	£350	
		a. Break in scroll	£600	
		b. Broken crown and scroll	£600	
359		100 r. grey-black (1924) (Optd S. £300)	£1400	
		a. Break in scroll	£2000	
		b. Broken crown and scroll	£2000	
360		100 r. dull purple and blue (24.10.27) (Optd S. £300)	£1300	
		a. Break in scroll	£1900	
		b. Broken crown and scroll	£1900	
338/56			Set of 19	50·00	75·00
338/57 Optd "Specimen"			Set of 20	£400	

The 2 c. to 30 c. and 1 r. values produced from Key and Duty plates were printed in sheets of 240 using two plates one above the other. Nos. 346c, 347b, 349b, 350c, 351b, 353b and 354b come from printings in 1924 and 1925 which combined Key Plate 7 (Die I) with Key Plate 12 (Die II).

No. 353a, from Key Plate 23, was a mistake; the "retired" Die I being issued in error when it became necessary to replace Key Plate 21.

For illustrations of the varieties on Nos. 358/60 see above No. 58 of Leeward Islands.

| | (56) | | | | | | (57) |

2 Cents.

(Surch at Ceylon Govt Printing Works)

1926 (27 Nov). *Surch as T 56.*

361	52	2 c. on 3 c. slate-grey	70	1·00
		a. Surch double	70·00	
		b. Bar omitted	65·00	75·00
362		5 c. on 6 c. bright violet	50	40
361/2 Optd "Specimen"			Set of 2	50·00	

No. 361b comes from the bottom horizontal row of the sheet which was often partially obscured by the selvedge during surcharging.

1927 (27 Nov)–29. *Wmk Mult Script CA. Chalk-surfaced paper. P 14.*

363	57	1 r. dull and bright purple (1928)	2·00	1·25
364		2 r. green and carmine (1929)	3·75	2·75
365		5 r. green and dull purple (1928)	12·00	18·00
366		10 r. green and brown-orange	28·00	80·00
367		20 r. dull purple and blue	90·00	£180
363/7			Set of 5	£120	£250
363/7 Optd "Specimen"			Set of 5	£140	

No. 364. Collectors are warned against faked 2 r. stamps, showing what purports to be a double centre.

| 58 Tapping Rubber | 60 Adam's Peak |

(Recess D.L.R. (2, 3, 20, 50 c.), B.W. (others))

1935 (1 May)–36. *T 58/60 and similar designs. Wmk Mult Script CA (sideways on 10, 15, 25, 30 c. and 1 r.). Various perfs.*

368		2 c. black and carmine (p 12 × 13)	30	40
		a. Perf 14	9·00	40
369		3 c. blk & ol-green (p 13 × 12) (1.10.35)	35	40
		a. Perf 14	24·00	35
370		6 c. black & blue (p 11 × 11½) (1.1.36)	30	30
371		9 c. green & orange (p 11 × 11½) (1.1.36)	1·00	50
372		10 c. black & purple (p 11½ × 11) (1.6.35)	1·25	2·00
373		15 c. red-brown and green (p 11½ × 11)	1·00	50
374		20 c. black & grey-blue (p 12 × 13) (1.1.36)	1·75	2·25
375		25 c. deep blue & chocolate (p 11½ × 11)	1·40	1·25
376		30 c. carm & green (p 11½ × 11) (1.8.35)	3·00	2·25
377		50 c. black and mauve (p 14) (1.1.36)	8·00	1·60
378		1 r. vio-bl & chocolate (p 11½ × 11) (1.7.35)	15·00	14·00
368/78			Set of 11	30·00	23·00
368/78 Perf "Specimen"			Set of 11	£150	

Designs: *Vert*—6 c. Colombo Harbour; 9 c. Plucking tea; 20 c. Coconut Palms. *Horiz*—10 c. Hill paddy (rice); 15 c. River scene; 25 c. Temple of the Tooth, Kandy; 30 c. Ancient irrigation tank; 50 c. Wild elephants; 1 r. Trincomalee.

1935 (6 May). *Silver Jubilee. As Nos. 114/17 of Jamaica, but ptd by D.L.R. P 13½×14.*

379		6 c. ultramarine and grey	65	30
		f. Diagonal line by turret	48·00	
		g. Dot to left of chapel	70·00	
		h. Dot by flagstaff	70·00	
		i. Dash by turret	75·00	
380		9 c. green and indigo	70	80
		f. Diagonal line by turret	65·00	
		g. Dot to left of chapel	80·00	
		h. Dot by flagstaff	90·00	
381		20 c. brown and deep blue	4·25	2·75
		f. Diagonal line by turret	£150	
		g. Dot to left of chapel	£200	
382		50 c. slate and purple	5·25	7·50
		h. Dot by flagstaff	£250	
379/82			Set of 4	9·75	10·00
379/82 Perf "Specimen"			Set of 4	90·00	

For illustrations of plate varieties, see Omnibus section following Zimbabwe.

1937 (12 May). *Coronation. As Nos. 118/20 of Jamaica, but ptd by B.W. & Co. P 11×11½.*

383		6 c. carmine	65	15
384		9 c. green	2·50	3·25
385		20 c. blue	3·50	3·00
383/5			Set of 3	6·00	5·75
383/5 Perf "Specimen"			Set of 3	65·00	

| 69 Tapping Rubber | 70 Sigiriya (Lion Rock) |

| 71 Ancient Guard-stone, Anuradhapura | 72 King George VI |

COCONUT PALMS

Apostrophe flaw (Frame Pl 1A R.6/6) (ptg of 1 Jan 1943 only)

(Recess B.W. (stamps perf 11 × 11½ or 11½ × 11), D.L.R. (all others) T 72 typo D.L.R.)

1938–49. *T 69/72 and designs as 1935–36, but with portrait of King George VI instead of King George V, "POSTAGE & REVENUE" omitted and some redrawn. Wmk Mult Script CA (sideways on 10, 15, 25, 30 c. and 1 r.). Chalk-surfaced paper (5 r.). Various perfs.*

386	69	2 c. blk & carm (p 11½×13) (25.4.38)	10·00	1·75
		a. Perf 13½×13 (1938)	£120	1·75
		b. Perf 13½ (25.4.38)	2·00	10
		c. Perf 11×11½ (17.2.44)	65	85
		cw. Wmk inverted	—	£425
		d. Perf 12 (22.4.49)	2·00	3·50
387	60	3 c. black & dp blue-green (p 13×11½) (21.3.38)	10·00	50
		a. Perf 13×13½ (1938)	£250	7·50
		b. Perf 13½ (21.3.38)	3·50	10
		c. Perf 14 (7.41)	£120	95
		d. Perf 11½×11 (14.5.42)	80	10
		da. "A" of "CA" missing from wmk	£800	£800
		e. Perf 12 (14.1.46)	65	70
387f		5 c. sage-grn & orge (p 13½) (1.1.43)	30	10
		fa. Apostrophe flaw	48·00	
		g. Perf 12 (1947)	1·25	30
388		6 c. black and blue (p 11×11½) (1.1.38)	30	10
389	70	10 c. blk & light bl (p 11½×11) (1.2.38)	2·25	10
		a. Wmk upright (1.6.44)	2·50	40
390		15 c. grn & red-brn (p 11½×11) (1.1.38)	1·75	10
		a. Wmk upright (23.7.45)	2·75	60
391		20 c. blk & grey-bl (p 11½×11) (15.1.38)	3·25	10
392		25 c. dp bl & choc (p 11½×11) (15.1.38)	4·50	30
		a. Wmk upright (1944)	3·75	10
393		30 c. carm & grn (p 11½×11) (1.2.38)	11·00	1·25
		a. Wmk upright (16.4.45)	12·00	2·75
394		50 c. blk & mve (p 13×11½) (25.4.38)	£160	42·00
		a. Perf 13×13½ (1938)	£350	2·75
		b. Perf 13½ (25.4.38)	15·00	30
		c. Perf 14 (4.42)	£100	27·00
		d. Perf 11½×11 (14.5.42)	4·25	3·00
		e. Perf 12 (14.1.46)	3·75	20
395		1 r. blue-violet & chocolate (p 11½×11) (1.2.38)	15·00	85
		a. Wmk upright (1944)	13·00	2·25
396	71	2 r. black & carm (p 11×11½) (1.2.38)	13·00	2·25
		a. "A" of "CA" missing from wmk		
396b		2 r. black & violet (p 11×11½) (15.3.47)	1·75	1·60
397	72	5 r. green and purple (p 14) (1.7.38)	38·00	4·25
		a. Ordinary paper. Green and pale purple (19.2.43)	13·00	2·25
386/97a (cheapest)			Set of 14	65·00	7·50
386/97 Perf "Specimen"			Set of 14	£300	

Designs: *Vert*—5 c. Coconut Palms; 6 c. Colombo Harbour; 20 c. Plucking tea. *Horiz*—15 c. River scene; 25 c. Temple of the Tooth, Kandy; 30 c. Ancient irrigation tank; 50 c. Wild elephants; 1 r. Trincomalee.

3 CENTS   **3 CENTS**

=   **≡**

| | (73) | | | (74) |

1940–41. *Nos. 388 and 391 surch.*

398	73	3 c. on 6 c. (10.5.41)	10	10
399	74	3 c. on 20 c. (5.11.40)	2·00	1·50

1946 (10 Dec). *Victory. As Nos. 141/2 of Jamaica.*

400		6 c. blue	10	10
401		15 c. brown	10	40
400/1 Perf "Specimen"			Set of 2	55·00	

---

75 Parliament Building

76 Adam's Peak

(Des R. Tenison and M. S. V. Rodrigo. Recess B.W.)

1947 (25 Nov). *Inauguration of New Constitution. T* **75/6** *and similar designs. Wmk Mult Script CA. P* 11 × 12 (*horiz*) *or* 12 × 11 (*vert*).

402	6 c. black and blue	..	10	15
403	10 c. black, orange and carmine	..	10	20
404	15 c. green and purple..	..	10	80
405	25 c. ochre and emerald-green	..	10	20
402/5		Set of 4	35	1·25
402/5 Perf "Specimen"		Set of 4	85·00	

Designs: *Horiz*—15 c. Temple of the Tooth. *Vert*—25 c. Anuradhapura.

DOMINION

79 Lion Flag of Dominion

80 D. S. Senanayake

81 Lotus Flowers and Sinhalese Letters "Sri"

(Recess (flag typo) B.W.)

1949 (4 Feb–5 Apr). *First Anniv of Independence.* (*a*) *Wmk Mult Script CA* (*sideways on 4 c.*). *P* 12½ × 12 (4 c.) *or* 12 × 12½ (5 c.).

406	79	4 c. yellow, carmine and brown	..	10	20
407	80	5 c. brown and green	..	10	10

(*b*) *W* **81** (*sideways on 15 c.*). *P* 13 × 12½ (15 c.) *or* 12 × 12½ (25 c.).
(5 April)

408	79	15 c. yellow, carmine and vermilion	..	25	15
409	80	25 c. brown and blue	..	15	40
406/9			Set of 4	40	75

The 15 c. is larger, measuring 28 × 12 mm.

82 Globe and Forms of Transport

83

84

(Recess D.L.R.)

1949 (10 Oct). *75th Anniv of Universal Postal Union. W* **81**. *P* 13 (25 c.) *or* 12 (*others*).

410	82	5 c. brown and bluish green	..	75	10
411	83	15 c. black and carmine	..	1·40	1·75
412	84	25 c. black and ultramarine	..	1·40	1·10
410/12			Set of 3	3·25	2·50

85 Kandyan Dancer

88 Sigiriya (Lion Rock)

89 Octagon Library, Temple of the Tooth

90 Ruins at Madirigiriya

(Recess B.W.)

1950 (4 Feb). *T* **85**, **88/90** *and similar designs. W* **81**. *P* 11 × 11½ (75 c.), 11½ × 11 (1 r.), 12 × 12½ (*others*).

413	4 c. purple and scarlet	..	10	10
414	5 c. green	..	10	10
415	15 c. blue-green and violet	..	1·50	30
416	30 c. carmine and yellow	..	30	40
417	75 c. ultramarine and orange	..	3·00	10
418	1 r. deep blue and brown	..	1·75	30
413/18		Set of 6	6·00	95

Designs: *Vert* (*as T* **88**)—5 c. Kiri Vehera, Polonnaruwa; 15 c. Vesak Orchid.

For these values with redrawn inscriptions see Nos. 450/1, 454, 456, 460 and 462.

91 Sambars, Ruhuna National Park

92 Ancient Guard-stone, Anuradhapura

96 Star Orchid

97 Rubber Plantation

99 Tea Plantation

I. No. 424   II. No. 424a (Dot added)

(Photo Courvoisier)

1951 (1 Aug)**–54**. *T* **91/2**, **96/7**, **99** *and similar designs. No wmk. P* 11½.

419	2 c. brown and blue-green (15.5.54) ..		10	50
420	3 c. black and slate-violet (15.5.54) ..		10	50
421	6 c. brown-black & yellow-green (15.5.54)		10	30
422	10 c. green and blue-grey		75	65
423	25 c. orange-brown & bright blue (15.3.54)		10	20
424	35 c. red and deep green (I) (1.2.52)		1·50	1·50
	a. Type II (1954)		5·50	60
425	40 c. deep brown (15.5.54)		4·50	90
426	50 c. indigo and slate-grey (15.3.54)		30	10
427	85 c. black and deep blue-green (15.5.54)		50	10
428	2 r. blue and deep brown (15.5.54)		6·50	1·00
429	5 r. brown and orange (15.3.54)		4·75	1·25
430	10 r. red-brown and buff (15.3.54)		32·00	9·00
419/30		Set of 12	45·00	13·50

Designs: *Vert* (*as T* **91**)—6 c. Harvesting rice; 10 c. Coconut trees; 25 c. Sigiriya fresco. (*As T* **99**)—5 r. Bas-relief, Anuradhapura; 10 r. Harvesting rice. *Horiz* (*as T* **97**)—50 c. Outrigger canoe; (*as T* **99**)—2 r. River Gal Dam.

For these values with redrawn inscriptions see Nos. 448, etc.

103 Ceylon Mace and Symbols of Progress

(Photo Harrison)

1952 (23 Feb). *Colombo Plan Exhibition. Chalk-surfaced paper. W* **81** (*sideways*). *P* 14½ × 14.

431	103	5 c. green	10	10
432		15 c. ultramarine	20	40

104 Queen Elizabeth II

105 Ceremonial Procession

(Recess B.W.)

1953 (2 June). *Coronation. W* **81**. *P* 12 × 13.

433	104	5 c. green	90	10

(Recess D.L.R.)

1954 (10 Apr). *Royal Visit. W* **81** (*sideways*). *P* 13 × 12½.

434	105	10 c. deep blue	30	10

106 King Coconuts

107 Farm Produce

(Photo Courvoisier)

1954 (1 Dec). *No wmk. P* 11½.

435	106	10 c. orange, bistre-brown and buff	10	10

For this design with redrawn inscription see No. 453.

(Photo Harrison)

1955 (10 Dec). *Royal Agricultural and Food Exhibition. W* **81** (*sideways*). *P* 14 × 14½.

436	107	10 c. brown and orange	10	10

108 Sir John Kotelawala and House of Representatives

(Photo Courvoisier)

1956 (26 Mar). *Prime Minister's 25 Years of Public Service. P* 11½.

437	108	10 c. deep bluish green	10	10

109 Arrival of Vijaya in Ceylon

110 Lampstand and Dharmachakra

111 Hand of Peace and Dharmachakra

112 Dharmachakra encircling the Globe

(Photo Courvoisier)

1956. *Buddha Jayanti. P* 11½.

438	109	3 c. blue and brownish grey (23 May) ..		15	15
439	110	4 c. + 2 c. grnish yell & dp bl (10 May)		20	75
440	111	10 c. + 5 c. carm, yellow & grey (10 May)		20	75
441	112	15 c. bright blue (23 May)		25	10
438/41			Set of 4	70	1·50

113 Mail Transport

114 Stamp of 1857

(Photo Enschedé (4 c., 10 c.), Courvoisier (others))

1957 (1 Apr). *Centenary of First Ceylon Postage Stamp.*
P 12½ × 13 (4 c., 10 c.) or 11½ (others).

442	113	4 c. orange-red and deep bluish green	75	40
443		10 c. vermilion and blue	75	10
444	114	35 c. brown, yellow and blue	30	50
445		85 c. brown, yellow and grey-green	80	1·60
442/5		*Set of 4*	2·40	2·25

(115)   (116)   117 Kandyan Dancer

1958 (15 Jan). *Nos. 439/40 with premium obliterated as T 115* (4 c.) *or T 116* (10 c.).

446	110	4 c. greenish yellow and deep blue	10	10
		a. Opt inverted	13·00	15·00
		b. Opt double	17·00	20·00
447	111	10 c. carmine, yellow and grey	10	10
		a. Opt inverted	13·00	15·00

The 4 c. exists with opt misplaced to right so that some stamps show the vertical bar on the left (*Price £18 un.*).

(Recess B.W. (4 c., 5 c., 15 c., 30 c., 75 c., 1 r.). Photo Courvoisier (others))

1958 (14 May)–62. *As earlier types, but inscriptions redrawn as in T 117.* W 81 (4, 5, 15, 30, 75 c., 1 r.) *or no wmk (others).* P 11×11½ (75 c.), 11½×11 (1 r.), 12×12½ (4, 5, 15 , 30 c.), *or* 11½ (*others*).

448	91	2 c. brown and blue-green	10	50
449	92	3 c. black and slate-violet	10	70
450	117	4 c. purple and scarlet	10	10
451	—	5 c. green (1.10.58)	10	95
		a. Yellow-green (13.6.61)	40	1·50
		b. Deep green (19.6.62)	2·50	2·00
452	—	6 c. brown-black and yellow-green	10	65
453	106	10 c. orge, bistre-brown & buff (1.10.58)	10	10
454	—	15 c. blue-green and violet (1.10.58)	3·50	80
455	—	25 c. orange-brown and bright blue	10	10
456	88	30 c. carmine and yellow (1.5.59)	15	1·25
457	96	35 c. red and deep green (II) (15.7.58)	6·50	30
459	—	50 c. indigo and slate-grey (15.7.58)	30	10
460	89	75 c. ultramarine and orange (1.5.59)	9·00	2·50
		a. Ultramarine & brown-orge (3.4.62)	9·00	2·00
461	99	85 c. black and deep blue-green (1.5.59)	3·75	4·00
462	90	1 r. deep blue and brown (1.10.58)	60	10
463	—	2 r. blue and deep brown	1·00	30
464	—	5 r. brown and orange	3·00	10
465	—	10 r. red-brown and buff	9·00	30
448/65		*Set of 17*	32·00	11·50

Designs: *Vert (as T 117)*—5 c. Kiri Vehera Polonnaruwa; 6 c. Harvesting rice; 15 c. Vesak Orchid; 25 c. Sigiriya fresco. (*as T 99*)—5 r. Bas-relief, Anuradhapura; 10 r. Harvesting rice. *Horiz (as T 97)*—50 c. Outrigger canoe. (*as T 99*)—2 r. River Gal Dam.

118 "Human Rights"   119 Portraits of Founders and University Buildings

(Photo Enschedé)

1958 (10 Dec). *Tenth Anniv of Declaration of Human Rights.* P 13 × 12½.

466	118	10 c. vermilion and dull purple	10	10
467		85 c. vermilion and deep blue-green	30	45

(Photo Enschedé)

1959 (31 Dec). *Institution of Pirivena Universities.* P 13 × 12½.

468	119	10 c. red-orange and ultramarine	10	10

120 Uprooted Tree   121 S.W.R.D. Bandaranaike

(Des W. A. Ariyasena. Photo Courvoisier)

1960 (7 Apr). *World Refugee Year.* P 11½.

469	120	4 c. red-brown and gold	10	60
470		25 c. blackish violet and gold	10	15

(Photo Courvoisier)

1961 (8 Jan–15 June). *Prime Minister Bandaranaike Commemoration.* P 11½.

471	121	10 c. deep blue and greenish blue	10	10
		a. Portrait redrawn (15.6.61)*	10	10

*Earliest known postmark date.
No. 471a can be identified by Mr. Bandaranaike's dark hair at temples.

---

122 Ceylon Scout Badge   123 Campaign Emblem

(Des W. A. Ariyasena. Photo Courvoisier)

1962 (26 Feb). *Golden Jubilee of Ceylon Boy Scouts Association.* P 11½.

472	122	35 c. buff and blue	15	10

(Photo Harrison)

1962 (7 Apr). *Malaria Eradication.* W 81. P 14½ × 14.

473	123	25 c. red-orange and sepia	10	10

124 De Havilland D.H.85 Leopard Moth and Hawker Siddeley Comet 4   125 "Produce" and Campaign Emblem

(Photo Courvoisier)

1963 (28 Feb). *25th Anniv of Airmail.* P 11½.

474	124	50 c. black and light blue	40	50

(Photo Courvoisier)

1963 (21 Mar). *Freedom from Hunger.* P 11½.

475	125	5 c. vermilion and blue	30	2·00
476		25 c. brown and yellow-olive	1·50	30

(126)   127 "Rural Life"

1963 (1 June). *No. 450 surch with T 126.*

477	117	2 c. on 4 c. purple and scarlet	10	10
		a. Surch inverted	16·00	
		b. Surch double	25·00	

(Photo Harrison)

1963 (5 July). *Golden Jubilee of Ceylon Co-operative Movement* (1962). W 81. P 14 × 14½.

478	127	60 c. rose-red and black	80	60

128 S. W. R. D. Bandaranaike   129 Terrain, Elephant and Tree

(Recess Courvoisier)

1963 (26 Sept). P 11½.

479	128	10 c. light blue	10	10

(Photo Harrison)

1963 (9 Dec). *National Conservation Week.* W 81 (*sideways*). P 14 × 14½.

480	129	5 c. sepia and blue	60	40

130 S. W. R. D. Bandaranaike   131 Anagarika Dharmapala (Buddhist missionary)

(T 130/1. Photo Courvoisier)

1964 (1 July). P 11½.

481	130	10 c. deep violet-blue and greenish grey	10	10

1964 (16 Sept). *Birth Centenary of Anagarika Dharmapala* (*founder of Maha Bodhi Society*). P 11½.

482	131	25 c. sepia and olive-yellow	10	10

134 Southern Grackle   138 Ruins at Madirigiriya

135   D. S. Senanayake   136

146 Tea Plantation   149 Map of Ceylon

(Des A. Dharmasiri (5 r.); P. A. Miththapala (10 r.). Photo Courvoisier (10 c. (486), 20 c.), Harrison (10 c. (487), 60 c., 1 r., 5 r., 10 r.), D.L.R. (others incl sheet))

1964 (1 Oct)–72. *T 134/6, 138, 146, 149 and similar designs.* No wmk (Nos. 486, 489). W 81 (*others; sideways on Nos.* 487, 494, 499). P 11½ (*Nos.* 486, 489), 14½×14 (*No.* 494) *or* 14 (*others*).

485	134	5 c. multicoloured (5.2.66)	1·75	1·50
486	135	10 c. myrtle-green (22.3.66)	70	10
487	136	10 c. myrtle-green (23.9.68)	10	10
		a. Imperf (pair)	45·00	
		b. Horiz pair, one stamp imperf 3 sides	£100	
488	—	15 c. multicoloured (5.2.66)	2·75	30
489	138	20 c. brown-purple and buff	20	25
494	—	60 c. multicoloured (5.2.66)	3·50	1·00
		a. Red omitted	32·00	
		b. Blue and green omitted*	32·00	
495	—	75 c. multicoloured (5.2.66)	2·50	70
		a. No wmk (8.6.72)	11·00	11·00
497	146	1 r. brown and bluish green	1·00	30
		a. Brown (tea picker, etc) omitted	£180	
		b. Bluish green omitted	£250	
499	—	5 r. multicoloured (15.8.69)	5·00	3·25
500	149	10 r. multicoloured (1.10.69)	19·00	3·25
485/500		*Set of 10*	32·00	9·00

MS500a 148×174 mm. As Nos. 485, 488, 494 and 495. Imperf . . . . . 7·00 12·00

Designs: *Horiz (as T 134)*—15 c. Common Peafowl; 60 c. Ceylon Junglefowl; 75 c. Asian Black-headed Oriole. (*As T 138*)—5 r. Girls transplanting rice.
*Actually only the blue printing is omitted on this sheet, but where this was printed over the yellow to form the leaves it appeared as green.
The 5 c., 75 c. and 1 r. exist with PVA gum as well as gum arabic.
No. 487b comes from a sheet which showed stamps in the third vertical row imperforate at top, bottom and at right.
In the miniature sheet the inscriptions on the 60 c. have been rearranged to conform with the style of the other values.

150 Exhibition Buildings and Cogwheels   151 Trains of 1864 and 1964

(Photo State Printing Works, Budapest)

1964 (1 Dec). *Industrial Exhibition.* T 150 *and similar horiz design. No wmk.* P 11.

501	—	5 c. multicoloured	10	75
		a. Pair. Nos. 501/2	20	2·25
502	150	5 c. multicoloured	10	75

No. 501 is inscribed "INDUSTRIAL EXHIBITION" in Sinhala and Tamil, No. 502 in Sinhala and English. The stamps were issued together *se-tenant* in alternate vertical rows, producing horizontal pairs.

(Photo Harrison)

1964 (21 Dec). *Centenary of Ceylon Railways. T 151 and similar horiz design. W 81 (sideways). P 14 × 14½.*
503 – 60 c. blue, reddish purple & yellow-grn 2·75 40
   a. Pair. Nos. 503/4 .. .. 5·50 4·50
504 151 60 c. blue, reddish purple & yellow-grn 2·75 40
No. 503 is inscribed "RAILWAY CENTENARY" in Sinhala and Tamil, No. 504 in Sinhala and English. The stamps were issued together *se-tenant* in alternate horizontal rows, producing vertical pairs.

152 I.T.U. Emblem and Symbols   **153** I.C.Y. Emblem

(Photo Harrison)

1965 (17 May). *I.T.U. Centenary. W 81 (sideways). P 14½.*
505 152 2 c. bright blue and red .. .. 75 1·10
506 30 c. brown and red .. .. 3·00 45
   a. Value omitted £110
No. 506a was caused by the misplacement of the red.

(Photo Courvoisier)

1965 (26 June). *International Co-operation Year. T 153 and similar horiz design. P 11½.*
507 3 c. deep blue and rose-carmine .. 1·25 1·00
508 50 c. black, rose-carmine and gold .. 3·25 50
No. 508 is similar to T 153 but has the multilingual inscription "CEYLON" rearranged.

154 Town Hall, Colombo   **(155)**

(Photo Courvoisier)

1965 (29 Oct). *Centenary of Colombo Municipal Council. P 11 × 11½.*
509 154 25 c. myrtle-green and sepia 10 10

1965 (18 Dec). *No. 481 surch with T 155.*
510 130 5 c. on 10 c. dp vio-bl & greenish grey 10 30

157 Kandy and Council Crest   **158** W.H.O. Building

(Photo Harrison)

1966 (15 June). *Kandy Municipal Council Centenary. W 81. P 14 × 13½.*
512 157 25 c. multicoloured 10 10

(Litho D.L.R.)

1966 (8 Oct). *Inauguration of W.H.O. Headquarters. Geneva. P 14.*
513 158 4 c. multicoloured .. .. 1·75 3·00
514 1 r. multicoloured .. .. 6·75 1·50

159 Rice Paddy and Map of Ceylon   **160** Rice Paddy and Globe

(Photo Courvoisier)

1966 (25 Oct). *International Rice Year. P 11½.*
515 159 6 c. multicoloured 20 75
516 160 30 c. multicoloured 30 15

161 U.N.E.S.C.O. Emblem   **162** Water-resources Map

(Litho State Ptg Wks, Vienna)

1966 (3 Nov). *20th Anniv of U.N.E.S.C.O. P 12.*
517 161 3 c. multicoloured .. .. 2·00 1·75
518 50 c. multicoloured .. .. 5·50 30

(Litho D.L.R.)

1966 (1 Dec). *International Hydrological Decade. P 14.*
519 162 2 c. orange-brown, greenish yellow & bl 30 85
520 2 r. orge-brn, grnish yell, bl & yell-grn 1·25 2·25

163 Devotees at Buddhist Temple   **167** Galle Fort and Clock Tower

(Photo State Ptg Wks, Vienna)

1967 (2 Jan). *Poya Holiday System. T 163 and similar horiz designs. Multicoloured. P 12.*
521 5 c. Type 163 .. .. .. 10 60
522 20 c. Mihintale 10 10
523 35 c. Sacred Bo-tree, Anuradhapura .. 10 15
524 60 c. Adam's Peak 10 10
521/4 .. .. Set of 4 30 70

(Litho Rosenbaum Brothers, Vienna)

1967 (5 Jan). *Centenary of Galle Municipal Council. P 13½.*
525 167 25 c. multicoloured 70 20

168 Field Research

(Litho Rosenbaum Bros, Vienna)

1967 (1 Aug). *Centenary of Ceylon Tea Industry. T 168 and similar horiz designs. Multicoloured. P 13½.*
526 4 c. Type 168 .. .. 60 80
527 40 c. Tea-tasting equipment .. .. 1·75 1·50
528 50 c. Leaves and bud .. .. 1·75 20
529 1 r. Shipping tea .. .. 1·75 10
526/9 .. .. Set of 4 5·25 2·25

172 Elephant Ride   **173** Ranger, Jubilee Emblem and Flag

(Litho Rosenbaum Bros, Vienna)

1967 (15 Aug). *International Tourist Year. P 13½.*
530 172 45 c. multicoloured .. .. 2·25 80

1967 (16 Sept). *1st National Stamp Exhibition. No. MS500a optd "FIRST NATIONAL STAMP EXHIBITION 1967".*
MS531 148 × 174 mm. Nos. 485, 488, 494/5. Imperf 4·50 6·00

(Litho D.L.R.)

1967 (19 Sept). *Golden Jubilee of Ceylon Girl Guides Association. P 12½ × 13.*
532 173 3 c. multicoloured 40 20
533 25 c. multicoloured 70 10

174 Col. Olcott and Buddhist Flag

(Litho Rosenbaum Bros, Vienna)

1967 (8 Dec). *60th Death Anniv of Colonel H. S. Olcott (theosophist). P 13½.*
534 174 15 c. multicoloured 30 20

175 Independence Hall   **176** Lion Flag and Sceptre

(Photo Harrison)

1968 (2 Feb). *20th Anniv of Independence. W 81 (sideways). P 14.*
535 175 5 c. multicoloured 10 55
536 176 1 r. multicoloured 50 10

177 Sir D. B. Jayatilleke   **178** Institute of Hygiene

(Litho D.L.R.)

1968 (14 Feb). *Birth Centenary of Sir Baron Jayatilleke (scholar and statesman). P 14.*
537 177 25 c. yellow-brown and sepia .. 10 10

(Litho B.W.)

1968 (7 Apr). *20th Anniv of World Health Organization. W 81. P 12.*
538 178 50 c. multicoloured 10 10

179 Vickers Super VC-10 Aircraft over Terminal Building   **181** Open Koran and "1400"

(Des and litho B.W.)

1968 (5 Aug). *Opening of Colombo Airport. W 81. P 13½.*
539 179 60 c. grey-blue, chestnut, red and yellow 50 10

(Des M. I. M. Mohideen. Photo Harrison)

1968 (14 Oct). *1400th Anniv of the Holy Koran. W 81. P 14.*
541 181 25 c. multicoloured 10 10

182 Human Rights Emblem   **183** All Ceylon Buddhist Congress Headquarters

(Photo Pakistan Security Printing Corp)

1968 (10 Dec). *Human Rights Year. P 12½ × 13½.*
542 182 2 c. multicoloured 10 15
543 20 c. multicoloured 10 10
544 40 c. multicoloured 10 10
545 2 r. multicoloured .. .. 80 3·00
542/5 .. .. Set of 4 85 3·00

(Des A. Dharmasiri. Litho Rosenbaum Bros, Vienna)

1968 (19 Dec). *Golden Jubilee of All Ceylon Buddhist Congress. P 13½.*
546 183 5 c. multicoloured 10 40
A 50 c. value showing a footprint was prepared but its release was stopped the day before it was due for issue. However, some are known to have been released in error at rural offices (*Price £30 mint*).

184 E. W. Perera
(patriot)

185 Symbols of
Strength in Savings

(Photo Harrison)

1969 (17 Feb). *E. W. Perera Commemoration.* W 81. P 14 × 13½.
547 **184** 60 c. brown 10 10

(Des A. Dharmasiri. Photo Harrison)

1969 (20 Mar). *Silver Jubilee of National Savings Movement.* W 81. P 14.
548 **185** 3 c. multicoloured 10 30

186 Seat of Enlightenment
under Sacred Bodhi Tree

187 Buduresmala (Six
fold Buddha-Rays)

(Des L. T. P. Manjusree. Litho D.L.R.)

1969 (10 Apr). *Vesak Day* (inscr "Wesak"). W 81 (sideways). P 15.
549 **186** 4 c. multicoloured 10 40
550 **187** 6 c. multicoloured 10 40
551 **186** 35 c. multicoloured 10 10
549/51 .. .. *Set of 3* 15 80
No. 549 exists with the gold apparently omitted. Normally the gold appears (without a separate plate number) over an underlay of olive-green on carmine. In one sheet we have seen, the gold only shows as tiny specks under a strong magnifying glass and as there may be intermediate stages of faint printing we do not list this.

188 A. E. Goonesinghe

189 I.L.O. Emblem

(Des and photo Harrison)

1969 (29 Apr). *Commemoration of Goonesinghe* (founder of Labour Movement in Ceylon). W 81. P 14.
552 **188** 15 c. multicoloured 10 10

(Photo Harrison)

1969 (4 May). *50th Anniv of International Labour Organisation.* W 81 (sideways). P 14.
553 **189** 5 c. black and turquoise-blue .. 10 10
554 25 c. black and carmine-red .. 10 10

190 Convocation Hall,
University of Ceylon

192 Uranium Atom

(Des Ahangama Edward (35 c.); L. D. P. Jayawardena (50 c.); A. Dharmasiri (60 c.); 4 c. from photograph. Litho Rosenbaum Bros, Vienna)

1969 (1 Aug). *Educational Centenary.* T 190, 192 *and similar multicoloured designs.* P 13½.
555 4 c. Type 190 .. .. .. 10 80
556 35 c. Lamp of Learning, Globe and flags (horiz) 15 10
557 50 c. Type 192 .. .. .. 15 10
558 60 c. Symbols of Scientific education .. 20 10
555/8 .. .. *Set of 4* 50 1·00

194 Ath Pana
(Elephant Lamp)

195 Rock Fortress
of Sigiriya

(Des from photographs. Litho Rosenbaum Bros, Vienna)

1969 (1 Aug). *Archaeological Centenary.* P 13½.
559 **194** 6 c. multicoloured .. .. 25 1·50
560 **195** 1 r. multicoloured 25 10

196 Leopard

197 Emblem and Symbols

(Litho Rosenbaum Bros, Vienna)

1970 (11 May). *Wildlife Conservation.* T 196 *and similar horiz designs. Multicoloured.* P 13½.
561 5 c. Water Buffalo .. .. 40 1·25
562 15 c. Slender Loris 90 30
   a. Brown-black and orange-brown colours omitted .. .. .. 85·00
563 50 c. Spotted Deer .. .. 90 1·25
   a. Imperf (in vert pair with stamp perf 3 sides) £250
564 1 r. Type 196 .. .. .. 90 1·75
561/4 .. .. *Set of 4* 2·75 4·00
In No. 562a the sky is blue instead of violet and the animal is in green and yellow only.

(Des A. Dharmasiri. Litho Rosenbaum Bros, Vienna)

1970 (17 June). *Asian Productivity Year.* P 13½.
565 **197** 60 c. multicoloured 10 10

198 New U.P.U. H.Q.
Building

199 Oil Lamp and Caduceus

(Litho Rosenbaum Bros, Vienna)

1970 (14 Aug). *New U.P.U. Headquarters Building.* P 13½.
566 **198** 50 c. yellow-orange, black and new blue 20 10
   a. New blue (Building) omitted .. 85·00
567 1 r. 10, vermilion, black and new blue 2·25 30

(Des A. Dharmasiri. Litho Rosenbaum Bros, Vienna)

1970 (1 Sept). *Centenary of Colombo Medical School.* P 13½.
568 **199** 5 c. multicoloured 40 80
   a. Vert pair, bottom stamp imperf .. £190
569 45 c. multicoloured 40 60

200 Victory March and
S. W. R. D. Bandaranaike

201 U.N. Emblem and Dove
of Peace

(Des A. Dharmasiri. Litho D.L.R.)

1970 (25 Sept). *Definitive issue marking establishment of United Front Government.* P 13½.
570 **200** 10 c. multicoloured 10 10

(Des A. Dharmasiri. Photo Pakistan Security Printing Corp)

1970 (24 Oct). *25th Anniv of United Nations.* P 12½ × 13½.
571 **201** 2 r. multicoloured .. .. 2·00 2·50

202 Keppetipola
Dissawa

203 Ola Leaf Manuscript

(Des A. Dharmasiri. Litho Harrison)

1970 (26 Nov). *152nd Death Anniv of Keppetipola Dissawa* (Kandyan patriot). P 14 × 14½.
572 **202** 25 c. multicoloured 10 10

(Des A. Dharmasiri. Photo Pakistan Security Printing Corp)

1970 (21 Dec). *International Education Year.* P 13.
573 **203** 15 c. multicoloured .. .. 1·75 1·25

204 C. H. de Soysa

205 D. E. H. Pedris
(patriot)

206 Lenin

(Des L. D. P. Jayawardena. Litho Pakistan Security Printing Corp)

1971 (3 Mar). *135th Birth Anniv of C. H. de Soysa* (philanthropist). P 13½.
574 **204** 20 c. multicoloured 15 40

(Des L. D. P. Jayawardena. Litho Harrison)

1971 (8 July). *D. E. H. Pedris Commemoration.* P 14 × 14½.
575 **205** 25 c. multicoloured 15 50

(Des L. D. P. Jayawardena. Litho Harrison)

1971 (31 Aug). *Lenin Commemoration.* P 14½.
576 **206** 40 c. multicoloured 15 40

207 Ananda Rajakaruna

15

(208)

(Des A. Dharmasiri (Nos. 577 and 579), P. A. Miththapala (Nos. 578 and 580), L. D. P. Jayawardena (No. 581). Litho Harrison)

1971 (29 Oct). *Poets and Philosophers.* T 207 *and similar vert designs.* P 14 × 13½.
577 5 c. royal blue 10 15
578 5 c. lake-brown 10 15
579 5 c. red-orange 10 15
580 5 c. deep slate-blue 10 15
581 5 c. brown 10 15
577/81 .. .. *Set of 5* 30 70
Portraits: No. 577, Type 207; No. 578, Arumuga Navalar; No. 579, Rev. S. Mahinda; No. 580, Ananda Coomaraswamy; No. 581, Cumaratunga Munidasa.

1971 (26 Nov–2 Dec). *Nos. 549/50, 555, 559 and 570 surch as T 208* (obliterating shape differs).
582 **186** 5 c. on 4 c. multicoloured .. 5·00 1·75
   a. Surch inverted .. .. 5·50
   b. Pair, one with "X" omitted 60·00
   c. Surch double, one inverted 9·00
   d. Ditto. Pair, one with "X" omitted 38·00
583 **190** 5 c. on 4 c. multicoloured .. 10 1·00
   a. Surch inverted .. .. 2·75
   b. Surch double, one inverted 8·50
584 **200** 15 c. on 10 c. multicoloured (2 Dec) 10 30
   a. Surch inverted .. .. 2·75
   b. Surch double .. .. 6·50
   c. Surch and dot transposed
   d. Surch at right, dot omitted
585 **187** 25 c. on 6 c. multicoloured .. 30 60
   a. Surch double, one inverted 17·00
   b. Surch inverted .. .. 18·00
586 **194** 25 c. on 6 c. multicoloured .. 30 1·00
   a. Surch inverted .. .. 2·75
582/6 .. .. *Set of 5* 5·00 4·25
Nos. 584c/d were caused by a misplacement of the surcharge on one sheet.

209 Colombo Plan Emblem
and Ceylon

210 Globe and CARE Package

(Des P. A. Miththapala. Litho Harrison)

1971 (28 Dec). *20th Anniv of Colombo Plan.* P 14 × 14½.
587 **209** 20 c. multicoloured 15 30

(Des A. Dharmasiri. Litho Harrison)

1971 (28 Dec). *20th Anniv of CARE (Co-operative for American Relief Everywhere).* P 14 × 13½.
588 **210** 50 c. new blue, lilac and violet .. 35 30

211 W.H.O. Emblem and
Heart

212 Map of Asia and U.N.
Emblem

(Des A. Miththapala. Litho D.L.R.)

1972 (2 May). *World Health Day. P* 13 × 13½.
589 **211** 25 c. multicoloured .. .. 2·00 60

(Des L. D. P. Jayawardena. Litho B.W.)

1972 (2 May). *25th Anniv of ECAFE (Economic Commission for
Asia and the Far East). P* 13.
590 **212** 85 c. multicoloured .. .. 3·75 2·75

SRI LANKA

REPUBLIC

Ceylon became the Republic of Sri Lanka on 22 May 1972.

208 National Flower and
Mountain of the Illustrious Foot

209 Map of World with
Buddhist Flag

(Des L. D. P. Jayawardena. Litho D.L.R.)

1972 (22 May). *Inauguration of the Republic of Sri Lanka. P* 13.
591 **208** 15 c. multicoloured 30 30

(Des L. D. P. Jayawardena. Litho Harrison)

1972 (26 May). *Tenth Conference of the World Fellowship of
Buddhists. P* 14 × 13.
592 **209** 5 c. multicoloured 30 60
  a. "1972" ptd double 85
  b. "1972" ptd double, one inverted .. 20·00
This stamp was scheduled for release in May 1971, and when
finally released had the year "1972" additionally overprinted in
red. Sheets are known without this overprint but their status has
not been established.

210 Book Year Emblem

211 Emperor Angelfish

(Des L. D. P. Jayawardena. Photo Pakistan Security Printing Corp)

1972 (8 Sept). *International Book Year. P* 13.
593 **210** 20 c. light yellow-orange and lake-brown 20 50

(Des G. D. Kariyawasam. Litho Rosenbaum Bros, Vienna)

1972 (12 Oct). *T* **211** *and similar horiz designs showing fish.
Multicoloured. P* 13 × 13½.
594 2 c. Type **211** 10 80
  a. Plum colour omitted .. .. 3·00
595 3 c. Green Chromide 10 80
596 30 c. Skipjack Tuna .. .. 1·25 30
597 2 r. Black Ruby Barb .. .. 3·50 5·25
594/7 *Set of* 4 4·50 6·50
On No. 594a the stripes of the fish are in green instead of
plum.

212 Memorial Hall

(Des R. B. Mawilmada. Litho D.L.R.)

1973 (17 May). *Opening of Bandaranaike Memorial Hall. P* 14.
598 **212** 15 c. light cobalt and deep grey-blue 30 30

OMNIBUS ISSUES

Details, together with prices for complete sets,
of the various Omnibus issues from the 1935
Silver Jubilee series to date are included in a
special section following Zimbabwe at the end of
Volume 2.

213 King Vessantara giving
away his Children

214 Bandaranaike Memorial
Conference Hall

(Des P. Wanigatunga. Litho D.L.R.)

1973 (3 Sept). *Rock and Temple Paintings. T* **213** *and similar vert
designs. Multicoloured. P* 13½ × 14.
599 35 c. Type **213** 35 10
600 50 c. The Prince and the Grave-digger .. 40 10
601 90 c. Bearded old man 60 85
602 1 r. 55, Two female figures .. .. 70 1·75
599/602 *Set of* 4 1·90 2·50
MS603 115 × 141 mm. Nos. 599/602 .. 2·25 2·50

(Des and litho Harrison)

1974 (6 Sept). *20th Commonwealth Parliamentary Conference,
Colombo. P* 14½.
604 **214** 85 c. multicoloured 30 30

215 Prime Minister
Bandaranaike

216 "UPU" and "100"

(Des and photo Harrison)

1974 (25 Sept). *P* 14½.
605 **215** 15 c. multicoloured 15 10
  a. Red (face value) omitted .. 3·00
  b. Pale blue (background) omitted .. 4·00
  c. Ultramarine (country inscr)
    omitted £100
  d. Imperf (pair) £100

(Des P. Jayatillake. Litho German Bank Note Ptg Co, Leipzig)

1974 (9 Oct). *Centenary of Universal Postal Union. P* 13½ × 13.
606 **216** 50 c. multicoloured 75 75

217 Sri Lanka Parliament
Building

218 Sir Ponnambalam
Ramanathan (politician)

(Litho Toppan Printing Co, Japan)

1975 (1 Apr). *Inter-Parliamentary Meeting. P* 13.
607 **217** 1 r. multicoloured 30 50

(Des A. Rasiah. Litho Toppan Ptg Co, Japan)

1975 (4 Sep). *Ramanathan Commemoration. P* 13.
608 **218** 75 c. multicoloured 30 80

219 D. J. Wimalasurendra
(engineer)

220 Mrs. Bandaranaike,
Map and Dove

(Des A. Dharmasiri. Litho Toppan Ptg Co, Japan)

1975 (17 Sept). *Wimalasurendra Commemoration. P* 13.
609 **219** 75 c. blue-black and new blue 30 80

(Des B. U. Ananda Somatilaka. Litho Toppan Ptg Co, Japan)

1975 (22 Dec). *International Women's Year. P* 13.
610 **220** 1 r. 15, multicoloured .. .. 2·25 1·25

221 Ma-ratmal

222 Mahaweli Dam

(Des and litho Toppan Ptg Co, Japan)

1976 (1 Jan). *Indigenous Flora. T* **221** *and similar vert designs.
Multicoloured. P* 13.
611 25 c. Type **221** 10 10
  a. Imperf (pair) .. .. 65·00
612 50 c. Binara 10 10
613 75 c. Daffodil orchid 15 15
614 10 r. Diyapara .. .. 3·00 4·25
611/14 *Set of* 4 3·00 4·25
MS615 153 × 153 mm. Nos. 611/14 .. 9·50 13·00
A used example of No. 613 has been seen with the yellow printing
apparently omitted. This results in the leaves appearing blue
instead of green.

(Des R. B. Mawilmada. Litho German Bank Note Ptg Co, Leipzig)

1976 (8 Jan). *Diversion of the Mahaweli River. P* 13×12½.
616 **222** 85 c. turquoise, violet-blue and azure .. 30 80
Stamps in this design with a face value of 60 c. were not issued
to post offices.

223 Dish Aerial

224 Conception of the Buddha

(Des P. A. Miththapala. Litho German Bank Note Ptg Co, Leipzig)

1976 (6 May). *Opening of Satellite Earth Station, Padukka.
P* 14 × 13½.
617 **223** 1 r. multicoloured 65 85

(Des P. Wanigatunga. Litho Toppan Ptg Co, Japan)

1976 (7 May). *Vesak. T* **224** *and similar horiz designs showing
paintings from the Dambava Temple. Multicoloured. P* 13.
618 5 c. Type **224** 10 70
619 10 c. King Suddhodana and the astrologers .. 10 70
620 1 r. 50, The astrologers being entertained .. 80 80
621 2 r. The Queen in a palanquin .. 85 85
622 2 r. 25, Royal procession .. 95 1·60
623 5 r. Birth of the Buddha .. .. 1·50 2·75
618/23 *Set of* 6 3·75 6·75
MS624 161 × 95 mm. Nos. 618/23 .. 9·50 13·00

225 Blue Sapphire

226 Prime Minister
Mrs. S. Bandaranaike

(Des State Gem Corporation. Litho Toppan Ptg Co, Japan)

1976 (16 June). *Gems of Sri Lanka. T* **225** *and similar horiz
designs. Multicoloured. P* 12 × 12½.
625 60 c. Type **225** .. .. 3·75 30
626 1 r. 15, Cat's Eye .. .. 5·50 1·50
627 2 r. Star sapphire .. .. 6·00 3·25
628 5 r. Ruby .. .. 8·50 9·50
625/8 *Set of* 4 21·00 13·00
MS629 152 × 152 mm. Nos. 625/8 .. 27·00 24·00

(Photo Harrison)

1976 (3 Aug). *Non-aligned Summit Conference, Colombo.
P* 14×14½.
630 **226** 1 r. 15, multicoloured 25 25
631 2 r. multicoloured 40 55

227 Statue of Liberty

228 Bell, Early Telephone
and Telephone Lines

(Des A. Harischandra. Litho German Bank Note Ptg Co, Leipzig)

1976 (29 Nov). *Bicentenary of American Revolution.* P 13½.
632   227   2 r. 25, cobalt and indigo   65   1·25

(Des A. Harischandra. Litho German Bank Note Ptg Co, Leipzig)

1976 (21 Dec). *Telephone Centenary.* P 13.
633   228   1 r. multicoloured   60   20

229 Maitreya   230 Kandyan Crown
(pre-carnate Buddha)

(Des P. Wanigatunga. Litho German Bank Note Ptg Co, Leipzig)

1977 (1 Jan). *Centenary of Colombo Museum. T* **229** *and similar vert designs showing statues. Multicoloured.* P 12½.
634   50 c. Type 229 ..   25   15
635   1 r. Sundara Murti Swami (Tamil psalmist)   30   30
636   5 r. Tara (goddess)   ..   ..   2·25   4·25
634/6   ..   ..   *Set of 3*   2·50   4·25

(Des R. B. Mawilmada. Litho Toppan Ptg Co, Japan)

1977 (18 Jan). *Regalia of the Kings of Kandy. T* **230** *and similar vert design. Multicoloured.* P 13.
637   1 r. Type 230   35   40
638   2 r. Throne and footstool   75   2·40

231 Sri Rahula Thero   232 Sir Ponnambalam
(poet)   Arunachalam
                       (social reformer)

(Des S. Dissanayaka. Litho Toppan Ptg Co, Japan)

1977 (23 Feb). *Sri Rahula Commemoration.* P 13.
639   231   1 r. multicoloured   75   75

(Litho Toppan Ptg Co, Japan)

1977 (10 Mar). *Ponnambalam Arunachalam Commemoration.* P 13.
640   232   1 r. multicoloured   50   65

233 Brass Lamps   234 Siddi Lebbe (author
                   and educationalist)

(Des A. Harischandra. Litho Toppan Ptg Co, Japan)

1977 (7 Apr). *Handicrafts. T* **233** *and similar vert designs. Multicoloured.* P 13.
641   20 c. Type 233   15   15
642   25 c. Jewellery box   15   15
643   50 c. Caparisoned elephant   ..   30   20
644   5 r. Mask   ..   ..   ..   1·60   3·00
641/4   ..   ..   ..   *Set of 4*   2·00   3·25
MS645   205 × 89 mm. Nos. 641/4 ..   ..   3·50   4·25

(Des Sarasvati Rockwood. Litho Toppan Ptg Co, Japan)

1977 (11 June). *Siddi Lebbe Commemoration.* P 13½.
646   234   1 r. multicoloured   30   60

The new-issue supplement to this Catalogue appears each month in

GIBBONS STAMP MONTHLY

—from your newsagent or by postal subscription— sample copy and details on request.

---

235 Girl Guide   236 Parliament Building and
                        "Wheel of Life"

(Des and litho Asher & Co, Melbourne)

1977 (13 Dec). *60th Anniv of Sri Lanka Girl Guides Association.* P 14½ × 15.
647   235   75 c. multicoloured   85   30

(Des R. B. Mawilmada. Photo Enschedé)

1978 (4 Feb). *Election of New President.* P 12 × 12½.
648   236   15 c. gold, brt yellow-green & emerald   ..   20   10
      No. 648 was re-issued on 7 September 1978, additionally dated "1978.09.07" to mark the Promulgation of the Constitution for the Democratic Socialist Republic of Sri Lanka. This re-issue was only available on First Day Covers (*Price on F.D.C. £2*).
      See also Nos. 680/c.

237 Youths Running   238 Prince Siddhartha's
                       Renunciation

(Des M. Dissanayake. Litho Asher & Co, Melbourne)

1978 (27 Apr). *National Youth Service Council.* P 15 × 14½.
649   237   15 c. multicoloured   30   50

(Des P. Wanigatunga. Litho Metal Box Singapore Ltd)

1978 (16 May). *Vesak. Rock Carvings from Borobudur Temple. T* **238** *and similar horiz design in buff, brown and ultramarine.* P 13.
650   15 c. Type 238   75   30
651   50 c. Prince Siddhartha shaving his hair   1·00   1·50

•05

(239)   240 Veera Puran Appu

1978 (18 May–20 Nov). *Nos.* 559, 601/2, 605 *and* 648/9 *surch as T* **239**.
652   5 c. on 90 c. Bearded old man (26.6)   ..   1·25   2·50
    a. Surch inverted   ..   ..   12·00
    b. Surch double ..   ..
653   10 c. on 35 c. Type 213   50   50
    a. Surch inverted   ..   ..   12·00
654   25 c. on 15 c. Type 215 (20.11)   ..   3·50   3·50
    a. Dot after "25" (R.3/4) ..   ..   18·00
655   25 c. on 15 c. Type 236 (20.11)   ..   3·50   3·50
    a. Surch inverted   ..   ..   10·00
    b. Surch quadruple ..   ..
656   25 c. on 15 c. Type 237 (Blk & Pink) (20.11)   3·50   3·50
    a. Surch and obliterating square inverted   9·00
    ab. Surch only inverted   ..   10·00
657   1 r. on 1 r. 55, Two female figures (17.11)   1·25   45
    a. Surch inverted   ..   ..
652/7   ..   ..   ..   *Set of 6*   12·00   12·50
      No. 656 has the surcharge applied in black on a pink square, previously printed over the original face value.

(Des A. Dharmasiri. Litho Metal Box Singapore Ltd)

1978 (8 Aug). *130th Death Anniv of Veera Puran Appu (revolutionary).* P 13.
658   240   15 c. multicoloured   20   20

SRI LANKA

241 *Troides helena*   (242)

15

(Des G. Ratnavira. Litho J.W. or Questa (ptgs of 25 c. from 5 Jan 1990))

1978 (28 Nov). *Butterflies. T* **241** *and similar vert designs. Multicoloured.* P 14.
659   25 c. Type 241   55   10
660   50 c. *Cethosia nietneri*   1·00   10
661   5 r. *Kallima horsfieldi* (s sp *philarchus*) ..   1·75   1·25
662   10 r. *Papilio polymnestor*   ..   1·75   1·75
659/62   *Set of 4*   4·50   2·75
MS663   203×147 mm. Nos. 659/62   ..   11·00   7·00

1979 (22 Mar). *No.* 486 *surch with T* **242** *in black and turquoise-blue.*
664   15 c. on 10 c. myrtle-green   ..   1·75   1·40
    a. Surch double   ..   ..   12·00
    b. Turq-blue surch omitted..   ..   20·00
      Type **242** shows only part of the turquoise-blue section of the overprint ("SRI LANKA"), which also includes a rectangle obliterating the original face value. The new value is printed on this rectangle in black.

243 Prince Danta and   244 Piyadasa
Princess Hema Mala   Sirisena
bringing the Sacred
Tooth Relic from
Kalinga

(Des A. Dharmasiri. Litho J.W.)

1979 (3 May). *Vesak. Kelaniya Temple Paintings. T* **243** *and similar vert designs. Multicoloured.* P 13 × 13½.
665   25 c. Type 243   10   10
666   1 r. Theri Sanghamitta bringing the Bodhi
       Tree branch to Sri Lanka   ..   15   15
667   10 r. King Kirti Sri Rajasinghe offering fan of
       authority to the Sangha Raja   ..   1·50   2·75
665/7 ..   ..   ..   *Set of 3*   1·50   2·75
MS668   120 × 80 mm. Nos. 665/7 ..   ..   1·50   2·75

(Des P. Jayatillake. Litho Toppan Ptg Co, Japan)

1979 (22 May). *Piyadasa Sirisena (writer) Commemoration.* P 13.
669   244   1 r. 25, multicoloured   ..   40   40

245 Wrestlers   246 Dudley Senanayake

(Des R. B. Mawilmada. Litho Metal Box Singapore Ltd)

1979 (28 May). *Wood Carvings from Embekke Temple. T* **245** *and similar vert design.* P 14.
670   20 r. chocolate, ochre and deep green   ..   1·25   1·50
671   50 r. agate, bistre-yellow and deep green   2·00   3·25
Design:—50 r. Dancer.

(Photo Heraclio Fournier)

1979 (19 June). *Dudley Senanayake (former Prime Minister) Commemoration.* P 14.
672   246   1 r. 25, bottle green   15   20
      Examples of this design exist with a face value of 25 c., but there is no evidence that such stamps were issued for postal purposes.

247 Mother with Child   248 Ceylon 1857 6d. Stamp
                       and Sir Rowland Hill

(Des A. Dharmasiri and R. Mawilmada. Litho Metal Box Singapore Ltd)

1979 (31 July). *International Year of the Child. T* **247** *and similar horiz designs. Multicoloured.* P 12½.
673   5 c. Type 247 ..   10   10
674   3 r. Superimposed heads of children of
       different races   40   1·00
675   5 r. Children playing   50   1·10
673/5 ..   ..   ..   *Set of 3*   80   2·00

(Des A. Dharmasiri. Litho Toppan Ptg Co, Japan)

1979 (27 Aug). *Death Centenary of Sir Rowland Hill.* P 13.
676   248   3 r. multicoloured   30   55

249 Conference Emblem and Parliament Building   **250** Airline Emblem on Aircraft Tail-fin

(Des A. Harischandra. Litho Toppan Ptg Co, Japan)

1979 (28 Aug). *International Conference of Parliamentarians on Population and Development, Colombo.* P 13.
677   **249**   2 r. multicoloured   70   1·00

(Des S. Saparamadu. Litho Metal Box Singapore Ltd)

1979 (1 Sept). *Inauguration of "Airlanka" Airline.* P 12½.
678   **250**   3 r. black, deep blue-green & vermilion   80   1·25

251 Coconut Tree   **252** Swami Vipulananda

(Des G. Wathuwalagedara. Litho Metal Box Singapore Ltd)

1979 (10 Sept). *10th Anniv of Asian and Pacific Coconut Community.* P 14.
679   **251**   2 r. multicoloured   70   1·00

1979 (10 Oct)–**87**. *Design as No. 648 but smaller, 20 × 24 mm.* P 12½ × 13.
680   **236**   25 c. gold, brt yellow-green & emerald   30   20
680a   50 c. gold, brt yell-grn & emer (6.6.81)   2·50   10
680b   60 c. gold, bright yellow-green and emerald (30.12.83)   ..   6·00   1·25
680c   75 c. gold, bright yellow-green and emerald (1.7.87)   ..   10   10
680/c   ..   ..   *Set of 4*   8·00   1·50

(Des R. B. Mawilmada. Litho Metal Box Singapore Ltd)

1979 (18 Nov). *Swami Vipulananda (philosopher) Commemoration.* P 12½.
681   **252**   1 r. 25, multicoloured   30   30

253 Inscription and Crescent   **254** "The Great Teacher" (Institute emblem)

(Des Q. V. Saldin. Litho Metal Box Singapore Ltd)

1979 (22 Nov). *1500th Anniv of the Hegira (Mohammedan religion).* P 12½.
682   **253**   3 r. 75, black, deep green and blue-green   35   1·25

(Des H. P. Rupasinghe. Litho Metal Box Singapore Ltd)

1979 (29 Nov). *50th Anniv of Institute of Ayurveda (school of medicine).* P 13 × 12½.
683   **254**   15 c. multicoloured   30   50

255 Ceylon Blue Magpie   **256** Rotary International Emblem and Map of Sri Lanka

(Des G. Ratnavira. Litho German Bank Note Ptg Co, Leipzig)

1979 (13 Dec). *Birds (1st series). T 255 and similar vert designs. Multicoloured.* P 13½ × 14.
684   10 c. Type 255   10   75
685   15 c. Ceylon Hanging Parrot ("Ceylon Lorikeet")   ..   75   10
686   75 c. Ceylon Whistling Thrush ("Ceylon Arrenga")   ..   15   15
687   1 r. Ceylon Spurfowl   ..   15   15
688   5 r. Yellow-fronted Barbet   ..   60   1·75
689   10 r. Yellow-tufted Bulbul   ..   75   1·75
684/9   ..   ..   *Set of 6*   2·25   4·25
MS690   151 × 151 mm. Nos. 684/9   ..   4·25   4·25
See also Nos. 827/31, 985/9 and 1242/6.

(Des A. Harischandra. Litho Metal Box Singapore Ltd)

1979 (27 Dec). *50th Anniv of Sri Lanka Rotary Movement and 75th Anniv of Rotary International.* P 14.
691   **256**   1 r. 50, multicoloured   ..   70   1·25

257 A. Ratnayake   **(258)**   **259** Tank and Stupa (symbols of Buddhist culture)

(Photo Govt Ptg Works, Rome)

1980 (7 Jan). *80th Birth Anniv of A. Ratnayake (politician).* P 13½.
692   **257**   1 r. 25, deep grey-green   ..   20   30

1980 (17 Mar). *No. 680 surch with T 258.*
693   **236**   35 c. on 25 c. gold, brt yell-grn & emer   ..   15   15
   a. Surch ".33" (R. 6/1) ..   ..   15·00
   b. Dot omitted (R. 7/6)   ..   3·00

(Des R. B. Mawilmada. Photo Govt Ptg Works, Rome)

1980 (25 Mar). *60th Anniv of All Ceylon Buddhist Congress. T 259 and similar horiz design showing symbols of Buddhist culture. Multicoloured.* P 13½.
694   10 c. Type 259   25   90
695   35 c. Bo-leaf wheel and fan   ..   25   20

260 Colonel Olcott   **261** Patachara's Journey through Forest

(Des S. Senevirante. Litho J.W.)

1980 (17 May). *Centenary of Arrival of Colonel Olcott (campaigner for Buddhism).* P 14.
696   **260**   2 r. multicoloured   80   1·50

(Des A. Dharmasiri. Litho Metal Box Singapore Ltd)

1980 (23 May). *Vesak. Details from Temple Paintings, Purvaramaya, Kataluwa. T 261 and similar horiz design. Multicoloured.* P 13½.
697   35 c. Type 261   30   15
698   1 r. 60, Patachara crossing river   ..   1·25   2·00

262 George E. de Silva   **263** Dalada Maligawa

(Des A. Rasiah. Litho German Bank Note Ptg Co, Leipzig)

1980 (8 June). *George E. de Silva (politician) Commemoration.* P 13.
699   **262**   1 r. 60, multicoloured   ..   30   30

(Des A. Dharmasiri and R. B. Mawilmada. Litho Metal Box Singapore Ltd)

1980 (25 Aug). *U.N.E.S.C.O.—Sri Lanka Cultural Triangle Project. T 263 and similar horiz designs.* P 13.
700   35 c. claret   10   30
701   35 c. grey   10   30
702   35 c. rose-carmine   10   30
703   1 r. 60, olive-green   40   90
704   1 r. 60, slate-green   40   90
705   1 r. 60, sepia   40   90
700/5   ..   ..   *Set of 6*   1·40   3·25
MS706   215 × 115 mm. Nos. 700/5   ..   1·40   3·25
Designs:—No. 701, Dambulla; No. 702, Alahana Pirivena; No. 703, Jetavanarama; No. 704, Abhayagiri; No. 705, Sigiri.

264 Co-operation Symbols   **265** Lanka Mahila Samiti Emblem

---

(Des R. B. Mawilmada. Litho Metal Box Singapore Ltd)

1980 (1 Oct). *50th Anniv of Co-operative Department.* P 13.
707   **264**   20 c. multicoloured   10   30

(Des R. B. Mawilmada. Photo Govt Ptg Works, Rome)

1980 (7 Nov). *50th Anniv of Lanka Mahila Samiti (Rural Women's Movement).* P 14 × 13.
708   **265**   35 c. violet, rosine and yellow   ..   15   50

266 The Holy Family   **267** Colombo Public Library

(Des L. Priyantha Silva. Litho Metal Box Singapore Ltd)

1980 (20 Nov). *Christmas. T 266 and similar vert design. Multicoloured.* P 12 × 11½.
709   35 c. Type 266   10   10
710   3 r. 75, The Three Wise Men   ..   60   1·25
MS711   125 × 75 mm. Nos. 709/10. P 13½   60   1·50

(Des P. Jayatillake. Litho Toppan Ptg Co, Japan)

1980 (17 Dec). *Opening of Colombo Public Library.* P 12 × 12½.
712   **267**   35 c. multicoloured   10   10

268 Flag of Walapane Disawa   **269** Fishing Cat

(Des Mrs. J. L. M. Fernando. Litho Toppan Ptg Co, Japan)

1980 (18 Dec). *Ancient Flags. T 268 and similar horiz designs.* P 13.
713   10 c. black, green and brown-purple   ..   10   10
714   25 c. black, greenish yellow and brown-purple   10   10
715   1 r. 60, black, greenish yellow & brn-purple   15   20
716   20 r. black, greenish yellow and brown-purple   1·25   2·50
713/16   ..   *Set of 4*   1·40   2·50
MS717   215 × 140 mm. Nos. 713/16   ..   1·40   2·75
Designs:—25 c. Flag of the Gajanayaka, Huduhumpola, Kandy; 1 r. 60, Sinhala royal flag; 20 r. Sinhala royal flag, Ratnapura.

(Des L. Ranasinghe. Litho J.W.)

1981 (10 Feb). *Animals. T 269 and similar horiz designs. Multicoloured.* P 13½ × 14.
718   2 r. 50 on 1 r. 60, Type 269   15   15
719   3 r. on 1 r. 50, Golden Palm Civet   ..   15   20
720   4 r. on 2 r. Indian Spotted Chevrotain   ..   25   30
721   5 r. on 3 r. 75, Rusty-spotted Cat   ..   35   45
718/21   ..   *Set of 4*   80   1·00
MS722   165 × 89 mm. Nos. 718/21   ..   1·00   2·25
Nos. 718/21 are previously unissued stamps surcharged as in T 269.
For redrawn designs with revised face values see Nos. 780/3 and No. 1081.

270 Heads and Houses on Map of Sri Lanka   **271** Sri Lanka Light Infantry Regimental Badge

(Des D. Hemaratna. Litho Toppan Ptg Co, Japan)

1981 (2 Mar). *Population and Housing Census.* P 12½ × 12.
723   **270**   50 c. multicoloured   60   90

(Des D. Karunaratne. Litho Metal Box Singapore Ltd)

1981 (1 Apr). *Centenary of Sri Lanka Light Infantry.* P 12 × 11½.
724   **271**   2 r. multicoloured   ..   ..   1·00   75

ALTERED CATALOGUE NUMBERS

Any Catalogue numbers altered from the last edition are shown as a list in the introductory pages.

272 Panel from "The Great Stupa" in Honour of the Buddha, Sanci, India, 1st-century A.D.

273 St. John Baptist de la Salle

(Des P. Jayatillake. Litho German Bank Note Ptg Co, Leipzig)

1981 (5 May). *Vesak. T 272 and similar vert designs. P 13 × 13½.*
725	35 c. black, blackish green and sage-green	..	10	10
726	50 c. multicoloured	.. .. ..	10	10
727	7 r. black and flesh	.. .. ..	1·25	3·00
725/7		*Set of 3*	1·25	3·00
MS728	147 × 108 mm. Nos. 725/7. P 13 × 14.		3·50	3·75

Designs:—50 c. Silk banner representing a Bodhisattva from "Thousand Buddhas", Tun-Huang, Central Asia; 7 r. Bodhisattva from Fondukistan, Afghanistan.

(Des Grant Kenyon and Eckhardt Ltd. Litho State Printing Works, Moscow)

1981 (15 May). *300th Anniv of De La Salle Brothers (Religious Order of the Brothers of the Christian Schools). P 12½ × 12.*
729	**273**	2 r. brt rose, deep violet-blue & new blue	1·00	1·50

274 Rev. Polwatte Sri Buddadatta   **275** Dr. Al-Haj T. B. Jayah

(Des G. Fernando. Litho Metal Box Singapore Ltd)

1981 (22 May). *National Heroes. T 274 and similar vert designs, each showing scholar, writer and Buddhist campaigner. P 12.*
730	50 c. bistre	.. ..	50	80
731	50 c. brown-rose	.. ..	50	80
732	50 c. deep mauve	.. ..	50	80
730/2		*Set of 3*	1·40	2·25

Designs:—No. 731, Rev. Mohottiwatte Gunananda; No. 732, Dr. Gnanaprakasar.

(Des P. Jayatillake. Litho Metal Box Singapore Ltd)

1981 (31 May). *Dr. Al-Haj T. B. Jayah (statesman) Commemoration. P 12.*
733	**275**	50 c. grey-green	.. ..	50	70

276 Dr. N. M. Perera   **277** Stylised Disabled Person and Globe

(Des P. Jayatillake. Litho Metal Box Singapore Ltd)

1981 (6 June). *Dr. N. M. Perera (campaigner for social reform) Commemoration. P 12.*
734	**276**	50 c. rose-red	.. ..	50	70

(Des A. Adhikari. Litho State Printing Works, Moscow)

1981 (19 June). *International Year for Disabled Persons. P 12 × 12½.*
735	**277**	2 r. vermilion, black and grey	.. ..	85	1·50

278 Hand placing Vote into Ballot Box

(Des J. Vincent (50 c.), R. Mawilmada (7 r.). Litho State Printing Works, Moscow)

1981 (7 July). *50th Anniv of Universal Franchise. T 278 and similar multicoloured design. P 12½ × 12 (50 c.) or 12 × 12½ (7 r.)*
736	50 c. Type 278	.. ..	25	15
737	7 r. Ballot box, and people forming map of Sri Lanka (*vert*)	.. ..	1·50	2·00

279 T. W. Rhys Davids (founder)   **280** Federation Emblem and "25"

(Des P. Jayatillake. Litho State Printing Works, Moscow)

1981 (14 July). *Centenary of Pali Text Society. P 12½ × 12.*
738	**279**	35 c. stone, dp brown & orange-brown	..	50	20

(Des R. Mawilmada. Litho Secura, Singapore)

1981 (21 July). *25th Anniv of All Ceylon Buddhist Students' Federation. P 13½.*
739	**280**	2 r. black, greenish yellow & dull verm	60	60

281 "Plan for Happiness"   **282** Dove Symbol with Acupuncture Needle and "Yin-Yang" (Chinese universe duality emblem)

(Des D. Wijesinghe. Litho Secura, Singapore)

1981 (25 Sept). *Population and Family Planning. P 13½ × 13.*
740	**281**	50 c. multicoloured	.. ..	60	80

(Des F. Perera. Litho State Printing Works, Moscow)

1981 (20 Oct). *World Acupuncture Congress. P 12 × 12½.*
741	**282**	2 r. black, yellow and red-orange	..	2·50	2·75

283 Union and Sri Lanka Flags   **284** "Conserve our Forests"

(Des and litho J.W.)

1981 (21 Oct). *Royal Visit. P 14.*
742	**283**	50 c. multicoloured	.. ..	50	25
743		5 r. multicoloured	.. ..	1·75	3·25
MS744	165 × 90 mm. Nos. 742/3	.. ..	2·25	3·50

(Des Ravi Advertising. Litho German Bank Note Co, Leipzig)

1981 (27 Nov). *Forest Conservation. T 284 and similar horiz designs. P 13.*
745	35 c. multicoloured	.. ..	15	10
746	50 c. olive-brown and stone	.. ..	20	20
747	5 r. multicoloured	.. ..	1·90	3·75
745/7		*Set of 3*	2·00	3·75
MS748	180 × 90 mm. Nos. 745/7. P 14 × 13		2·00	3·75

Designs:—50 c. "Plant a tree"; 5 r. Jak (tree).

285 Sir James Peiris   **286** F. R. Senanayaka

(Des P. Jayatillake. Litho Metal Box Singapore Ltd)

1981 (20 Dec). *Birth Centenary of Sir James Peiris (politician). P 12.*
749	**285**	50 c. light brown	..	60	80

(Des M. Katugampola. Litho J.W.)

1982 (1 Jan). *Birth Centenary of F. R. Senanayaka (national hero). P 14.*
750	**286**	50 c. olive-brown	..	60	85

287 Philip Gunawardhane   **288** Department of Inland Revenue Building, Colombo

(Des P. Jayatillake. Litho J.W.)

1982 (11 Jan). *10th Death Anniv of Philip Gunawardhane (politician). P 14.*
751	**287**	50 c. cerise		60	85

(Des S. Mallikerachchi. Litho J.W.)

1982 (9 Feb). *50th Anniv of Department of Inland Revenue. P 14.*
752	**288**	50 c. black, blue-black & reddish orange	60	85

289 Rupavahini Emblem   **290** Cricketer and Ball

(Des G. Arthasad. Litho J.W.)

1982 (15 Feb). *Inauguration of Rupavahini (national television service). P 14.*
753	**289**	2 r. 50, lemon, purple-brown and grey	2·25	3·00

(Des R. Mawilmada. Litho J.W.)

1982 (17 Feb). *First Sri Lanka–England Cricket Test Match, Colombo. P 14.*
754	**290**	2 r. 50, multicoloured	.. ..	4·00	4·00

291 *Obsbeckia wightiana*   **292** Mother breast-feeding Child

(Des P. Jayatillake. Litho Security Printers (M), Malaysia)

1982 (1 Apr). *Flowers. T 291 and similar horiz designs. Multicoloured. P 12.*
755	35 c. Type 291	.. ..	10	10
756	2 r. *Mesua nagassarium*	.. ..	20	20
757	7 r. *Rhodomyrtus tomentosa*	.. ..	50	1·00
758	20 r. *Phaius tancarvilleae*	.. ..	1·40	3·25
755/8		*Set of 4*	2·00	4·00
MS759	180 × 110 mm. Nos. 755/8	.. ..	7·00	7·50

(Des A. Ratnapala. Litho Pakistan Security Printing Corp)

1982 (6 Apr). *Food and Nutrition Policy Planning. P 13.*
760	**292**	50 c. multicoloured	.. ..	95	95

293 Conference Emblem   **294** King Vessantara giving away magical, rain-making White Elephant

(Des M. Hussain. Litho J.W.)

1982 (21 Apr). *World Hindu Conference. P 14.*
761	**293**	50 c. multicoloured	..	85	85

(Des A. Dharmasiri. Litho J.W.)

1982 (23 Apr). *Vesak. Legend of Vessantara Jataka. Details of Cloth Painting from Arattana Rajamaha Vihara (temple), Hanguranketa, District of Nuwara Eliya. T 294 and similar horiz designs. Multicoloured. P 14.*
762	35 c. Type 294		45	10
763	50 c. King Vessantara with family in Vanka-giri Forest		55	15
764	2 r. 50, Vessantara giving away his children as slaves		2·00	2·25

765   5 r. Vessantara and family returning to Jetut-
       tara in royal chariot   .. .. .. 2·75 3·50
762/5 .. .. Set of 4 5·25 5·50
MS766 160 × 115 mm. Nos. 762/5 .. .. 7·00 7·00

295 Parliament Buildings,
Sri Jayawardanapura

296 Dr. C. W. W.
Kannangara

(Des M. Katugampola. Litho J.W.)

1982 (29 Apr). *Opening of Parliament Building Complex, Sri Jayawardanapura, Kotte. P* 14.
767 **295** 50 c. multicoloured 85 85

(Des M. Katugampola. Litho State Printing Works, Moscow)

1982 (22 May). *Dr. C. W. W. Kannangara ("Father of Free Education") Commemoration. P* 12 × 12½.
768 **296** 50 c. yellow-olive 85 85

297 Lord Baden-Powell

298 Dr. G. P. Malalasekara

(Des W. Rohana. Litho State Printing Works, Moscow)

1982 (24 May). *125th Birth Anniv of Lord Baden-Powell. P* 12½ × 12.
769 **297** 50 c. multicoloured .. .. .. 1·75 85

(Des A. Rasiah. Litho State Printing Works, Moscow)

1982 (26 May). *Dr. G. P. Malalasekara (founder of World Fellowship of Buddhists) Commemoration. P* 12 × 12½.
770 **298** 50 c. deep bluish green 85 85

299 Wheel encircling Globe

300 Wildlife

(Des A. Ratnapala. Litho State Printing Works, Moscow)

1982 (1 June). *World Buddhist Leaders Conference. P* 12½ × 12.
771 **299** 50 c. multicoloured 95 95

(Des U. Karunaratna. Litho State Printing Works, Moscow)

1982 (5 June). *World Environment Day. P* 12½ × 12.
772 **300** 50 c. multicoloured .. .. .. 1·60 1·10

301 Sir Waitialingam Duraiswamy

(Des A. Rasiah. Litho State Printing Works, Moscow)

1982 (14 June). *Sir Waitialingam Duraiswamy (statesman and educationalist) Commemoration. P* 12 × 12½.
773 **301** 50 c. blackish brown and brown .. 85 85

302 Y.M.C.A. Emblem

(Des R. Mawilmada. Litho State Printing Works, Moscow)
1982 (24 June). *Centenary of Colombo Y.M.C.A. P* 11½ × 11.
774 **302** 2 r. 50, multicoloured .. .. 3·00 3·50

303 Rev. Weliwita Sri
Saranankara Sangharaja

304 Maharagama Sasana
Sevaka Samithiya Emblem

(Des M. Katugampola. Litho State Printing Works, Moscow)
1982 (5 July). *Rev. Weliwita Sri Saranankara Sangharaja (Buddhist leader) Commemoration. P* 12 × 12½.
775 **303** 50 c. brown and yellow-orange .. 85 85

(Des A. Ratnapala. Litho Toppan Ptg Co, Japan)
1982 (4 Aug). *Silver Jubilee of Maharagama Sasana Sevaka Samithiya (Buddhist Social Reform Movement). P* 12 × 12½.
776 **304** 50 c. multicoloured 85 85

305 Dr. Robert Koch

306 Sir John Kotelawala

(Des W. Rohana. Litho Toppan Ptg Co, Japan)
1982 (21 Sept). *Centenary of Robert Koch's Discovery of Tubercle Bacillus. P* 12 × 12½.
777 **305** 50 c. multicoloured .. .. .. 1·75 1·00

(Des A. Rasiah. Litho State Printing Works, Moscow)
1982 (2 Oct). *2nd Death Anniv of Sir John Kotelawala. P* 12 × 12½.
778 **306** 50 c. deep olive 85 85

307 Eye Donation Society
and Lions Club Emblems

308 1859 4d. Dull Rose and 1948 15 c.
Independence Commemorative

(Des Grant Kenyon and Eckhardt Ltd. Litho State Printing Works, Moscow)
1982 (16 Nov). *World-Wide Sight Conservation Project. P* 12 × 12½.
779 **307** 2 r. 50, multicoloured .. .. 3·00 3·50

(Des L. Ranasinghe. Litho Questa (5 r.) or J.W. (others))
1982 (16 Nov)–**89**. *As Nos. 718/21, but without surcharges and showing revised face values. P* 14.
780   2 r. 50, Type **269** (1.6.83) 20 15
781   3 r. Golden Palm Civet (21.6.83) .. 2·25 2·25
782   4 r. Indian Spotted Chevrotain .. 25 30
783   5 r. Rusty-spotted Cat (1.12.89) .. 30 30
780/3 .. .. Set of 4 2·75 2·75
    For the 3 r. in similar design, but printed by Questa with imprint date see No. 1081.

(Des D. Karunaratne. Litho Security Printers (M), Malaysia)
1982 (2 Dec). *125th Anniv of First Postage Stamps. T* **308** *and similar horiz design. Multicoloured. P* 13 × 13½.
784   50 c. Type **308**. 50 50
785   2 r. 50, 1859 1s. 9d. green and 1981 50 c.
       "Just Society" stamp .. .. 1·50 2·50
MS786 59 × 84 mm. Nos. 784/5 (sold at 5 r.) 2·00 3·00

STANLEY GIBBONS
STAMP COLLECTING SERIES

Introductory booklets on *How to Start, How to Identify Stamps* and *Collecting by Theme.* A series of well illustrated guides at a low price.
Write for details.

---

309 Sir Oliver Goonetilleke

310 Sarvodaya Emblem

(Des A. Ratnapala. Litho State Printing Works, Moscow)
1982 (17 Dec). *4th Death Anniv of Sir Oliver Goonetilleke (statesman). P* 12 × 12½.
787 **309** 50 c. olive-grey, bistre-brown and black 60 75

(Des P. Gunasinghe. Litho Secura, Singapore)
1983 (1 Jan). *25th Anniv of Sarvodaya Movement. P* 13 × 13½.
788 **310** 50 c. multicoloured 90 90

311 Morse Key, Radio Aerial and
Radio Amateur Society Emblem

312 Customs Co-operation
Council Emblem
and Sri Lanka Flag

(Des W. Rohana. Litho Secura, Singapore)
1983 (17 Jan). *Amateur Radio Society. P* 13 × 13½.
789 **311** 2 r. 50, multicoloured .. .. 2·75 3·50

(Des W. Rohana. Litho Secura, Singapore)
1983 (26 Jan). *30th Anniv of International Customs Day. P* 12 × 11½.
790 **312** 50 c. multicoloured 50 40
791   5 r. multicoloured .. .. .. 3·00 4·50

313 Bottle-nosed Dolphin

314 *Lanka Athula*
(container ship)

(Des G. Ratnavira. Litho Harrison)
1983 (22 Feb). *Marine Mammals. T* **313** *and similar horiz designs. P* 14½ × 14.
792   50 c. black, new blue and grey-green .. 50 20
793   2 r. multicoloured 90 80
794   2 r. 50, black, dp grey-blue & dp bluish grey 2·25 2·00
795   10 r. multicoloured .. .. .. 5·50 6·00
792/5 .. .. Set of 4 8·25 8·00
    Designs:—2 r. Dugongs; 2 r. 50, Humpback Whale; 10 r. Sperm Whale.

(Des Vision Ltd. Litho Security Printers (M), Malaysia)
1983 (1 Mar). *Ships of the Ceylon Shipping Corporation. T* **314** *and similar horiz designs. Multicoloured. P* 11½ × 12.
796   50 c. Type **314**. 25 15
797   2 r. 50, Map of routes 90 70
798   5 r. *Lanka Kalyani* (freighter) .. 1·25 1·60
799   20 r. *Tammanna* (tanker) .. .. 2·00 4·50
796/9 .. .. Set of 4 4·00 6·25

315 Woman with I.W.D.
Emblem and Sri Lanka Flag

316 Waterfall

(Des R. Mawilmada. Litho Secura, Singapore)
1983 (8 Mar). *International Women's Day. T* **315** *and similar vert design. Multicoloured. P* 13.
800 **315** 50 c. Type **315**. 15 25
801   5 r. Woman, emblem, map and symbols of progress .. .. 70 2·00

(Des S. Lankatilake. Litho Secura, Singapore)

1983 (14 Mar). *Commonwealth Day.* T **316** *and similar horiz designs. Multicoloured. P* 13.
802	50 c. Type **316**..	..	..	10	10
803	2 r. 50, Tea plucking	..	..	15	25
804	5 r. Harvesting rice ..		..	25	40
805	20 r. Decorated elephants		..	80	2·00
802/5	.. .. ..	*Set of 4*		1·10	2·50

317 Lions Club International Badge   318 "The Dream of Queen Mahamaya"

(Des U. Karunaratna. Litho J.W.)

1983 (7 May). *25th Anniv of Lions Club International in Sri Lanka. P* 14.
806 317   2 r. 50, multicoloured .. .. 2·50 2·50

(Des G. Keyt and A. Dharmasiri. Litho Toppan Ptg Co, Japan)

1983 (13 May). *Vesak. Life of Prince Siddhartha from temple murals at Gotami Vihara.* T **318** *and similar vert designs. Multicoloured. P* 12½×12.
807	35 c. Type **318**..	..	..	10	10
808	50 c. "Prince Siddhartha given to Maha Brahma"..	..	..	10	10
809	5 r. "Prince Siddhartha and the Sleeping Dancers"..	..	..	55	1·25
810	10 r. "The Meeting with Mara"	..	90	2·25
807/10		*Set of 4*		1·40	3·25
MS811	150×90 mm. Nos. 807/10	..	..	1·50	3·25

319 First Telegraph Transmission Colombo to Galle, 1858   320 Henry Woodward Amarasuriya (philanthropist)

(Des W. Rohana. Litho Toppan Ptg Co, Japan)

1983 (17 May). *125th Anniv of Telecommunications in Sri Lanka* (2 r.) *and World Communications Year* (10 r.). T **319** *and similar horiz design. Multicoloured. P* 12×12½.
812	2 r. Type **319**.	..	..	50	60
813	10 r. World Communications Year emblem..		2·25	3·75

(Litho Security Printers (M), Malaysia (No. 810), Pakistan Security Printing Corp (others))

1983 (22 May). *National Heroes.* T **320** *and similar vert designs. P* 12×11½ (*No.* 814) *or* 13 (*others*).
814	50 c. bright emerald ..	..	..	30	80
815	50 c. new blue..	..	..	30	80
816	50 c. magenta ..	..	..	30	80
817	50 c. turquoise-green..	..	..	30	80
814/17		*Set of 4*		1·10	2·75

Designs:—No. 815, Father Simon Perera (historian); No. 816, Charles Lorenz (lawyer and newspaper editor); No. 817, Noordeen Abdul Cader (first President of All-Ceylon Muslim League).

A fifth design to commemorate C. W. Thamotheram Pillai was prepared for this set, but was withdrawn at the last moment when it was realised that the wrong portrait had been used. It is understood, however, that supplies were sold at some rural post offices where the instruction was not received in time. A corrected version was later issued, see No. 825.

321 Family and Village   322 Caravan of Bulls

(Des K. Gunasiri and U. Karunaratna. Litho Toppan Ptg Co, Japan)

1983 (23 June). *Gam Udawa (Village Re-awakening Movement).* T **321** *and similar horiz design. Multicoloured. P* 12×12½.
818	50 c. Type **321**..	..	..	10	25
819	5 r. Village view	..	..	40	1·50

(Des A. Rasiah (35 c., 2 r.), D. Hemaratna (2 r. 50), U. Karunaratna (5 r.). Litho State Printing Office, Budapest)

1983 (22 Aug). *Transport.* T **322** *and similar horiz designs. Multicoloured. P* 12
820	35 c. Type **322**.	..	..	10	10
821	2 r. Steam train	..	..	1·50	1·40
822	2 r. 50, Ox and cart ..	..	90	1·60
823	5 r. Ford motor car ..	..	1·75	3·50
820/3		*Set of 4*		3·75	6·00

323 Sir Tikiri Banda Panabokke   324 C. W. Thamotheram Pillai

(Des and litho Harrison)

1983 (2 Sept). *20th Death Anniv of Adigar Sir Tikiri Banda Panabokke. P* 14 × 14½.
824 323   50 c. Indian red 85 85

(Des and litho Pakistan Security Printing Corp)

1983 (1 Oct). *C. W. Thamotheram Pillai (Tamil scholar) Commemoration. P* 13.
825 324   50 c. orange-brown 85 85
See note below No. 817.

325 Arabi Pasha   326 Sri Lanka Wood Pigeon

(Des and litho Pakistan Security Printing Corp)

1983 (13 Nov). *Centenary of the Exile to Ceylon of Arabi Pasha (Egyptian nationalist). P* 13 × 13½.
826 325   50 c. green .. .. 1·00 1·00

(Des G. Ratnavira. Litho Format)

1983 (22 Nov)—**88**. *Birds (2nd series).* T **326** *and similar horiz designs. Multicoloured. P* 14½.
827	25 c. Type **326**	..	50	50
828	35 c. Large Sri Lanka White Eye	..	50	50
829	2 r. Sri Lanka Dusky Blue Flycatcher	..	50	20
829a	7 r. As 35 c. (28.9.88)	..	30	25
830	20 r. Ceylon Coucal	..	80	2·00
827/30		*Set of 5*	2·40	3·00
MS831	183×93 mm. Nos. 827/9 and 830	2·00	6·50

Special packs prepared for the S.A.A.R.C. "Philex 96" stamp exhibition at Colombo contained the block of stamps from No. **MS**831 with the sheet margins removed.
No. 829 exists imperforate from stock dispersed by the liquidator of Format International Security Printers Ltd.

327 Pelene Siri Vajiragnana   328 Mary praying over Jesus and St. Joseph welcoming Shepherds

(Des and litho Harrison)

1983 (25 Nov). *Pelene Siri Vajiragnana (scholar) Commemoration. P* 14 × 14½.
832 327   50 c. red-brown.. .. .. 90 90

(Des P. de Silva. Litho German Bank Note Co, Leipzig)

1983 (30 Nov). *Christmas. P* 12½ × 13.
833	328	50 c. multicoloured	..	10	15
834		5 r. multicoloured	..	25	85
MS835	85 × 141 mm. Nos. 833/4 ..	..	85	2·00

.60   .60

(329)   (330)

1983 (1 Dec). *No.* 680a *surch with* T **329**/30 *by Aitken Spence Ptg (Pte) Ltd, Sri Lanka.*
836	236	60 c. on 50 c. gold, bright yellow-green and emerald (surch T **329**)	2·00	1·50
		a. Surch inverted ..		
837		60 c. on 50 c. gold, bright yellow-green and emerald (surch T **330**) ..	4·00	3·50

331 Paddy Field, Globe and F.A.O. Emblem

(Des R. Mawilmada. Litho State Ptg Works, Moscow)

1984 (2 Jan). *World Food Day. P* 12½ × 12.
838 331   3 r. multicoloured .. .. 40 1·25

332 Modern Tea Factory   333 Students and University

(Des M. Ratnapala. Litho State Ptg Works, Moscow)

1984 (31 Jan). *Centenary of the Colombo Tea Auctions.* T **332** *and similar horiz designs. Multicoloured. P* 12½ × 12.
839	1 r. Type **332**..	..	..	15	15
840	2 r. Logo	..	..	30	45
841	5 r. Girl picking tea..	..	75	1·75
842	10 r. Auction in progress	..	1·50	2·75
839/42		*Set of 4*		2·40	4·50

(Des R. Mawilmada. Litho Security Printers (M), Malaysia)

1984 (10 Feb). *4th Anniv of Mahapola Scheme for Development and Education.* T **333** *and similar vert designs. Multicoloured. P* 12.
843	60 c. Type **333**..	..	..	10	15
844	1 r. Teacher with Gnana Darsana class	..	10	15
845	5 r. 50, Student with books and microscope	35	1·25
846	6 r. Mahapola lamp symbol	..	40	1·25
843/6		*Set of 4*		75	2·50

334 King Daham Sonda instructing Angels   335 Development Programme Logo

(Des A. Dharmasiri. Litho D.L.R.)

1984 (27 Apr). *Vesak. The Story of King Daham Sonda from ancient casket paintings.* T **334** *and similar horiz designs. Multicoloured. P* 14.
847	35 c. Type **334**	..	..	15	10
	a. Perf 13×13½	..	35	20
848	60 c. Elephant paraded with gift of gold ..	30	25
	a. Perf 13×13½	..	35	35
849	5 r. King Daham Sonda leaps into mouth of God Sakra		1·00	2·50
	a. Perf 13×13½		1·00	2·75
850	10 r. God Sakra carrying King Daham Sonda		1·40	3·50
	a. Perf 13×13½		1·50	4·00
847/50		*Set of 4*	2·50	5·75
847a/50a		*Set of 4*	2·75	6·50
MS851	154×109 mm. Nos. 847/50. P 13	1·00	2·50

(Des R. Mawilmada. Litho Harrison)

1984 (5 May). *Sri Lanka Lions Clubs' Development Programme. P* 14 × 14½.
852 335   60 c. multicoloured .. .. 1·40 90

336 Dodanduwe Siri Piyaratana Tissa Mahanayake Thero (Buddhist scholar)   337 Association Emblem

(Litho State Ptg Works, Moscow)

1984 (22 May). *National Heroes.* T **336** *and similar vert designs. P* 12×12½.
853	60 c. yellow-bistre ..	..	..	30	75
854	60 c. yellow-green	..	..	30	75

855		60 c. emerald-green	..	..	30	75
856		60 c. red	..	..	30	75
857		60 c. deep yellow-brown	..	..	30	75
853/7				Set of 5	1·40	3·25

Designs:—No. 853, Type **336**; 854, G. P. Wickremarachchi (physician); 855, Sir Mohamed Macan Markar (politician); 856, Dr. W. Arthur de Silva (philanthropist), 857, K. Balasingham (lawyer).

(Des A. Harischandra. Litho Govt Printing Bureau, Tokyo)

1984 (16 June). *Centenary of Public Service Mutual Provident Association.* P 13 × 13½.
858   **337**   4 r. 60, multicoloured ..   50   1·75

338 Sri Lanka Village   **339** World Map showing A.P.B.U. Countries

(Des S. Herath. Litho State Ptg Wks, Moscow)

1984 (23 June). *6th Anniv of "Gam Udawa" (Village Reawakening Movement).* P 12 × 12½.
859   **338**   60 c. multicoloured   30   65

(Des G. Arthasad. Litho State Ptg Wks, Moscow)

1984 (30 June). *20th Anniv of Asia-Pacific Broadcasting Union.* P 12½ × 12.
860   **339**   7 r. multicoloured ..   ..   2·00   3·00

340 Drummers and Elephant carrying Royal Instructions   **341** *Vanda memoria Ernest Soysa* (orchid)

(Des R. Mawilmada. Litho State Ptg Wks, Moscow)

1984 (11 Aug). *Esala Perahera (Procession of the Tooth), Kandy.* T **340** *and similar horiz designs. Multicoloured.* P 12½ × 12.
861		4 r. 60, Type **340**	..	..	1·00	1·75
	a.	Horiz strip of 4. Nos. 861/4			3·50	
862		4 r. 60, Dancers and elephants	..		1·00	1·75
863		4 r. 60, Elephant carrying Tooth Relic		1·00	1·75	
864		4 r. 60, Custodian of the Sacred Tooth and attendants		..	1·00	1·75
861/4				Set of 4	3·50	6·00
MS865		223×108 mm. Nos. 861/4		..	3·50	6·50

Nos. 861/4 were printed together, *se-tenant*, in horizontal strips of 4 throughout the sheet, forming a composite design.

(Des G. Ratnavira. Litho D.L.R.)

1984 (22 Aug). *50th Anniv of Ceylon Orchid Circle.* T **341** *and similar vert designs, showing orchids. Multicoloured.* P 14.
866		60 c. Type **341**	..	..	1·75	30
	a.	Perf 13½×13		..	75	1·25
867		4 r. 60, *Acanthephippium bicolor*		3·00	3·75	
	a.	Perf 13½×13		..	1·75	3·50
868		5 r. *Vanda tessellata* var. *rufescens*		3·75	3·75	
	a.	Perf 13½×13		..	1·00	3·50
869		10 r. *Anoectochilus setaceus*	..	3·75	5·50	
866/9		(cheapest)		Set of 4	6·50	11·50
MS870		115×110 mm. Nos. 866/9. P 13		7·00	10·00	

342 Symbolic Athletes and Stadium   **343** D. S. Senanayake, Temple and Fields

(Des M. Heenkenda. Litho Govt Printing Bureau, Tokyo)

1984 (5 Oct). *1st National School Games.* P 13½×13.
871   **342**   60 c. black, grey and bright new blue ..   1·50   1·50

(Des L. Jayawardena (35 c.), G. Fernando (60 c.), N. Lasantha (4 r. 60), R. Mawilmada (6 r.). Litho J.W.)

1984 (20 Oct). *Birth Centenary of D. S. Senanayake (former Prime Minister).* T **343** *and similar horiz designs. Multicoloured.* P 14.
872		35 c. Type **343**	..	..	10	10
873		60 c. Senanayake and statue	..		10	10
874		4 r. 60, Senanayake and irrigation project ..		35	50	
875		6 r. Senanayake and House of Representatives		..	40	60
872/5				Set of 4	80	1·10

344 Lake House   **345** Agricultural Workers and Globe

(Des Grant Kenyon and Eckhardt Ltd. Litho State Printing Office, Budapest)

1984 (19 Nov). *150th Anniv of the "Observer" Newspaper.* P 13×13½.
876   **344**   4 r. 60, multicoloured ..   ..   1·75   3·00

(Des M. Ratnapala. Litho German Bank Note Ptg Co, Leipzig)

1984 (10 Dec). *20th Anniv of World Food Programme.* P 13×13½.
877   **345**   7 r. multicoloured ..   ..   1·50   1·25

346 College Emblem   **347** Dove and Stylized Figures

(Des S. Herath. Litho J.W.)

1984 (24 Dec). *Centenary of Baari Arabic College, Weligama.* P 13×12½.
878   **346**   4 r. 60, blackish olive, turquoise-green and turquoise-blue ..   ..   1·25   2·50

(Des S. Chandrajeewa (4 r. 60), O. Weerakkody (20 r.). Litho J.W.)

1985 (1 Jan). *International Youth Year.* T **347** *and similar horiz design. Multicoloured.* P 12½×13.
879   4 r. 60, Type **347**   50   60
880   20 r. Dove, stylized figures and flower ..   2·00   3·00

348 Religious Symbols   **349** College Crest

(Des R. Mawilmada. Litho Security Printers (M), Malaysia)

1985 (20 Jan). *World Religion Day.* P 12.
881   **348**   4 r. 60, multicoloured ..   ..   1·50   1·75

(Des G. Arthasad. Litho J.W.)

1985 (29 Jan). *150th Anniv of Royal College, Colombo.* T **349** *and similar vert design.* P 13×12½.
882   60 c. bright yellow and deep ultramarine ..   10   25
883   7 r. multicoloured   70   2·25
Design:—7 r. Royal College.

350 Banknotes, Buildings, Ship and "Wheel of Life"   **351** Wariyapola Sri Sumangala Thero

(Des R. Mawilmada. Litho J.W.)

1985 (7 Feb). *5th Anniv of Mahapola Scheme.* P 14.
884   **350**   60 c. multicoloured   90   1·00

(Des G. Fernando. Litho State Printing Office, Budapest)

1985 (2 Mar). *Wariyapola Sri Sumangala Thero (Buddhist priest and patriot) Commemoration.* P 13×13½.
885   **351**   60 c. blk, reddish brn & greenish yell ..   70   1·00

352 Victoria Dam   **353** Cover of 50th Edition of International Buddhist Annual, *Vesak Sirisara*

(Des G. Arthasad. Litho State Ptg Wks, Moscow)

1985 (12 Apr). *Inauguration of Victoria Hydro-electric Project.* T **352** *and similar multicoloured design.* P 12½ × 12 (60 c.) or 12 × 12½ (7 r.).
886   60 c. Type **352**.   75   50
887   7 r. Map of Sri Lanka enclosing dam and power station (*vert*) ..   ..   3·50   4·50

(Des B. Harischandra (35 c.), R. Mawilmada (others). Litho J.W.)

1985 (26 Apr). *Centenary of Vesak Poya Holiday.* T **353** *and similar vert designs. Multicoloured.* P 13×12½.
888	35 c. Type **353**.	..	..	10	10
889	60 c. Buddhists worshipping at temple	..		10	10
890	6 r. Buddhist Theosophical Society Headquarters, Colombo	..	..	50	50
891	9 r. Buddhist flag	..	..	80	1·25
888/91			Set of 4	1·25	2·00
MS892	180×110 mm. Nos. 888/91 ..			4·00	6·00

354 Ven. Waskaduwe Sri Subhuthi (priest and scholar)   **355** Stylised Village and People

(Des S. Silva. Litho J.W.)

1985 (22 May). *Personalities.* T **354** *and similar vert designs.* P 13×12½.
893	60 c. black, yellow-orange and lake-brown ..			20	50
894	60 c. black, yellow-orange and deep mauve ..			20	50
895	60 c. black, yellow-orange and light brown ..			20	50
896	60 c. black, yellow-orange and emerald	..		20	50
893/6			Set of 4	70	1·75

Designs:— No. 893, Type **354**; 894, Revd. Fr. Peter A. Pillai (educationist and social reformer); 895, Dr. Senarath Paranavitane (scholar); 896, A. M. Wapche Marikar (architect and educationist).

(Des S. Herath. Litho German Bank Note Co, Leipzig)

1985 (23 June). *Gam Udawa '85 (Village Re-awakening Movement).* P 13½×13½.
897   **355**   60 c. multicoloured ..   ..   1·00   1·00

356 Emblem   **357** Kothmale Dam and Reservoir

(Des B. Harischandra. Litho German Bank Note Co, Leipzig)

1985 (25 June). *50th Anniv of Colombo Young Poets' Association.* P 14.
898   **356**   60 c. multicoloured   30   75

(Des R. Mawilmada. Litho J.W.)

1985 (24 Aug). *Inauguration of Kothmale Hydro-electric Project.* T **357** *and similar horiz design. Multicoloured.* P 14.
899   60 c. Type **357**.   65   25
900   6 r. Kothmale Power Station ..   ..   2·10   2·50

358 Federation Logo   **359** Breast Feeding

(Des R. Mawilmada. Litho J.W.)

1985 (2 Sept). *10th Asian and Oceanic Congress of Obstetrics and Gynaecology.* P 14.
901   **358**   7 r. multicoloured ..   ..   3·25   2·50

(Des B. Harischandra. Litho Cartor.)

1985 (5 Sept). *U.N.I.C.E.F. Child Survival and Development Programme.* T **359** *and similar vert designs. Multicoloured.* W w 17. P 13½.
902	35 c. Type **359**.	..	..	30	10
903	60 c. Child and oral rehydration salts	..		45	30
904	6 r. Weighing child (growth monitoring) ..			2·25	3·00
905	9 r. Immunization	..	..	2·75	4·00
902/5			Set of 4	5·25	6·50
MS906	99×180 mm. Nos. 902/5. P 12½			4·00	6·00
	w. Wmk inverted	..	..	4·00	6·00

MINIMUM PRICE

The minimum price quote is 10p which represents a handling charge rather than a basis for valuing common stamps. For further notes about prices see introductory pages.

360 Blowing Indian Chank   **361** Casket containing Land
Shell   Grant Deed

(Des G. Malaviachi. Litho Heraclio Fournier, Spain)

1985 (27 Sept). *10th Anniv of World Tourism Organization. T 360 and similar horiz designs. Multicoloured. P 14.*

907	1 r. Type 360.			20	10
908	6 r. Parliamentary Complex, Jayawardha-napura, Kotte		70	80
909	7 r. Tea plantation		80	1·00
910	10 r. Ruwanveliseya (Buddhist shrine), Anuradhapura		1·25	1·50
907/10			*Set of 4*	2·75	3·00
MS911	179×89 mm. Nos. 907/10. P 13½		2·75	2·75

(Des B. Harischandra. Litho Harrison)

1985 (15 Oct). *50th Anniv of Land Development Ordinance. P 14×15.*

912	**361**	4 r. 60, multicoloured		2·00	2·50

362 Koran and Map of Sri   **363** "Our Lady of Matara"
Lanka   Statue

(Des R. Mawilmada. Litho Cartor)

1985 (17 Oct). *Translation of The Koran into Sinhala. W w 17. P 13½.*

913	**362**	60 c. gold and bright violet		1·00	1·00

(Des S. Silva. Litho Security Printers (M), Malaysia)

1985 (5 Nov). *Christmas. T 363 and similar vert design. Multicoloured. P 12.*

914	60 c. Type 363.			30	15
915	9 r. "Our Lady of Madhu" statue		1·50	2·25
MS916	180×100 mm. Nos. 914/15		5·50	7·00

(364)   **365** Linked Arms and Map
                of S.A.A.R.C. Countries

1985 (1 Dec)–**86**. *Nos. 680b, 780, 823, 860 and 879 surch as T 364 by Aitken Spence Ptg (Pte) Ltd, Sri Lanka.*

917	236	75 c. on 60 c. gold, bright yellow-green and emerald (G.)	10	10
		a. Surch double		†	—
918	347	1 r. on 4 r. 60, mult (29.4.86)	2·25	1·75
919	339	1 r. on 7 r. multicoloured (20.1.86)	3·00	1·75
920	269	5 r. 75 on 2 r. 50, multicoloured (Br)	3·00	1·00
		a. Surch double			
921	—	7 r. on 35 c. mult (No. 828) (10.3.86)	3·00	1·25
		a. Surch inverted			
		b. Surch double			
		c. Surch triple			
917/21			*Set of 5*	10·00	5·25

(Des B. Harischandra. Litho J.W.)

1985 (8 Dec). *1st Summit Meeting of South Asian Association for Regional Co-operation, Dhaka, Bangladesh. T 365 and similar horiz design. Multicoloured. P 14.*

922	60 c. Type 365.			2·50	4·50
923	5 r. 50, Logo and flags of member countries		2·50	3·00

No 922 was, reportedly, withdrawn on 11 December after Pakistan objected to the boundaries shown on the map.

366 "Viceroy Special" Train

(Des G. Malaviachi. Litho Format)

1986 (2 Feb). *Inaugural Run of "Viceroy Special" Train from Colombo to Kandy. P 12½.*

924	366	1 r. multicoloured		60	1·50

367 Girl and Boy Students   **368** D. R. Wijewardena

(Des S. Silva. Litho Heraclio Fournier, Spain)

1986 (14 Feb). *6th Anniv of Mahapola Scheme. P 14.*

925	367	75 c. multicoloured		50	60

(Des S. Silva. Litho J.W.)

1986 (23 Feb). *Birth Centenary of D. R. Wijewardena (newspaper publisher). P 14×14½.*

926	368	75 c. orange-brown and deep olive	30	60

369 Ven Welitara   **370** Red Cross Flag and Personnel
Gnanatillake Maha
Nayake Thero

(Des S. Silva. Litho Cartor)

1986 (26 Feb). *Ven. Welitara Gnanatillake Maha Nayake Thero (scholar) Commemoration. W w 17. P 13½.*

927	369	75 c. multicoloured		70	80

(Des W. Rohana. Litho Format)

1986 (31 Mar). *50th Anniv of Sri Lanka Red Cross Society. P 12½.*

928	370	75 c. multicoloured		2·00	1·75

371 Comet depicted as   **372** Woman lighting
Goddess visiting Sun-god   Lamp

(Des W. Rohana. Litho Format)

1986 (5 Apr). *Appearance of Halley's Comet. T 371 and similar horiz designs. Multicoloured. P 12½.*

929	50 c. Type 371.			10	20
930	75 c. Comet and constellations of Scorpius and Sagittarius		10	20
931	6 r. 50, Comet's orbit		30	1·25
932	8 r. 50, Edmond Halley		55	1·75
929/32			*Set of 4*	75	3·00
MS933	180×115 mm. Nos. 929/32		4·00	8·00

(Des B. Harischandra. Litho Format)

1986 (10 Apr). *Sinhalese and Tamil New Year. T 372 and similar vert designs. Multicoloured. P 12½.*

934	50 c. Type 372.			10	20
935	75 c. Woman and festive foods		10	20
936	6 r. 50, Women playing drum		30	1·60
937	8 r. 50, Anointing and making offerings at temple		55	2·00
934/7			*Set of 4*	75	3·50
MS938	178×108 mm. Nos. 934/7		1·75	5·50

373 The King donating   **374** Ven. Kalukondayave
Elephant to the Brahmin   Sri Prajnasekhara Maha
                     Nayake Thero (Buddhist
                     leader and social reformer)

(Des N. Bulathsinhala. Litho Format)

1986 (16 May). *Vesak. Wall paintings from Samudragiri Temple, Mirissa. T 373 and similar horiz designs. Multicoloured. P 12½.*

939	50 c. Type 373.			10	20
940	75 c. The Bodhisattva in the Vasavarthi heaven		10	20
941	5 r. The offering of milk rice by Sujatha		30	1·75
942	10 r. The offering of parched corn and honey by Thapassu and Bhalluka		45	2·25
939/42			*Set of 4*	75	4·00

(Des S. Silva. Litho Format)

1986 (22 May). *National Heroes. T 374 and similar vert designs. Multicoloured. P 12½.*

943	75 c. Type 374.			15	60
944	75 c. Brahmachari Walisinghe Harischandra (social reformer) (birth centenary)		15	60
945	75 c. Martin Wickramasinghe (author and scholar)		15	60
946	75 c. G. G. Ponnambalam (politician)		15	60
947	75 c. A. M. A. Azeez (Islamic scholar) (75th birth anniv)		15	60
943/7			*Set of 5*	65	2·75

375 Stylised Village and   **376** Co-op Flag and Emblem
People

(Des S. Herath. Litho German Bank Note Co, Leipzig)

1986 (23 June). *Gam Udawa '86 (Village Re-awakening Movement). P 13½×13.*

948	375	75 c. multicoloured		1·50	1·50

(Des A. Harischandra. Litho Format)

1986 (5 July). *75th Anniv of Sri Lanka Co-operative Movement. P 12½.*

949	376	1 r. multicoloured		75	1·25

377 Arthur V. Dias   **378** Bull Elephant

(Des S. Silva. Litho Harrison)

1986 (31 July). *Birth Centenary of Arthur V. Dias (philanthropist). P 14×15.*

950	377	1 r. chestnut and dull violet-blue		1·50	1·50

(Des G. Ratnavira. Litho Harrison)

1986 (5 Aug). *Sri Lanka Wild Elephants. T 378 and similar horiz designs. Multicoloured. P 15×14.*

951	5 r. Type 378			6·00	5·00
	a. Horiz strip of 4. Nos. 951/4		22·00	
952	5 r. Cow elephant and calf		6·00	5·00
953	5 r. Cow elephant		6·00	5·00
954	5 r. Elephants bathing		6·00	5·00
951/4			*Set of 4*	22·00	18·00

Nos. 951/4 were printed, together, *se-tenant*, in horizontal strips of four throughout the sheet.

379 Congress Logo   **380** Map showing Route of Cable
                     and Telephone Receiver

(Des S. Silva. Litho Govt Printing Bureau, Tokyo)

1986 (14 Aug). *2nd Indo-Pacific Congress on Legal Medicine and Forensic Sciences. P 13½×13.*

955	379	8 r. 50, multicoloured		2·25	1·75

(Des R. Mawilmada. Litho Security Printers (M), Malaysia)

1986 (8 Sept). *SEA-ME-WE Submarine Cable Project. P 13½×14.*

956	380	5 r. 75, multicoloured		2·75	1·50

381 Anniversary Logo   **382** Logo on Flag

(Des R. Mawilmada. Litho Format)

1986 (20 Sept). *25th Anniv of Dag Hammarskjöld Award.*
P 12½.
957 **381** 2 r. multicoloured 50 65

(Des A. Harischandra. Litho Security Printers (M), Malaysia)
1986 (22 Sept). *2nd National School Games.* P 12.
958 **382** 1 r. multicoloured .. .. 2·75 1·90

383 Logo   **384** College Building and Crest

(Des W. Rohana. Litho Govt Printing Bureau, Tokyo)
1986 (27 Sept). *60th Anniv of Surveyors' Institute of Sri Lanka.*
P 13½ × 13.
959 **383** 75 c. red-brown and cinnamon .. 60 85

(Des W. Rohana. Litho Security Printers (M), Malaysia)
1986 (1 Nov). *Centenary of Ananda College, Colombo.* T **384**
and similar horiz designs. P 12.
960 75 c. multicoloured 10 10
961 5 r. multicoloured 30 50
962 5 r. 75, multicoloured 30 50
963 6 r. carmine-red, gold and rose-lilac 35 60
960/3 .. .. .. *Set of 4* 90 1·50
Designs:—5 r. Sports field and college crest; 5 r. 75, Col.
H. S. Olcott (founder), Ven. Migettuwatte Gunananda, Ven.
Hikkaduwe Sri Sumangala (Buddhist leaders) and Buddhist flag;
6 r. College flag.

385 Mangrove Swamp   **386** Family and Housing Estate

(Des G. Ratnavira. Litho Security Printers (M), Malaysia)
1986 (11 Nov). *Mangrove Conservation.* T **385** *and similar
horiz designs. Multicoloured.* P 12.
964 35 c. Type **385** 40 20
965 50 c. Mangrove tree 50 30
966 75 c. Germinating mangrove flower 60 30
967 6 r. Fiddler Crab .. .. 4·00 5·50
964/7 .. .. *Set of 4* 5·00 5·75

(Des R. Mawilmada. Litho Govt Printing Bureau, Tokyo)
1987 (1 Jan). *International Year of Shelter for the Homeless.*
P 13 × 13½.
968 **386** 75 c. multicoloured .. 1·75 50

387 Ven. Ambagahawatte   **388** Proctor John de
Indasabhawaragnanasamy Thero   Silva

(Des S. Silva. Litho Security Printers (M), Malaysia)
1987 (29 Jan). *Ven. Ambagahawatte Indasabhawaragnanasamy Thero (Buddhist monk) Commemoration.* P 12.
969 **387** 5 r. 75, multicoloured .. 2·50 1·00

(Des S. Silva. Litho Security Printers (M), Malaysia)
1987 (31 Jan). *Proctor John de Silva (playwright) Commemoration.* P 12.
970 **388** 5 r. 75, multicoloured .. 70 70

389 Mahapola Logo and   **390** Dr. R. L. Brohier
Aspects of Communication

(Des R. Mawilmada. Litho Security Printers (M), Malaysia)
1987 (6 Feb). *7th Anniv of Mahapola Scheme.* P 12.
971 **389** 75 c. multicoloured .. 75 75

(Des S. Silva. Litho Security Printers (M), Malaysia)
1987 (10 Feb). *Dr. Richard L. Brohier (historian and surveyor)
Commemoration.* P 12.
972 **390** 5 r. 75, multicoloured .. 2·00 90

391 Tyre Corporation Building, Kelaniya, and Logo

(Des A. Harischandra. Litho Questa)
1987 (23 Mar). *25th Anniv of Sri Lanka Tyre Corporation.* P 14.
973 **391** 5 r. 75, black, lake and bright orange .. 50 50

392 Logo   **393** Clasped Hands, Farmer
and Paddy Field

(Des A. Harischandra. Litho Govt Printing Bureau, Tokyo)
1987 (24 Mar). *Centenary of Sri Lanka Medical Association.*
P 13 × 13½.
974 **392** 5 r. 75, lake-brown, greenish yellow & blk 1·75 1·75

(Des B. Harischandra. Litho Questa)
1987 (29 Mar). *Inauguration of Farmers' Pension and Social
Security Benefit Scheme.* P 14.
975 **393** 75 c. multicoloured .. 65 65

394 Exhibition Logo   **395** Young Children with W.H.O.
and Immunization Logos

(Des W. Rohana. Litho Security Printers (M), Malaysia)
1987 (2 Apr). *Mahaweli Maha Goviya Contest and Agro
Mahaweli Exhibition.* P 12.
976 **394** 75 c. multicoloured .. 30 30

(Des B. Harischandra. Litho Questa)
1987 (7 Apr). *World Health Day.* P 14.
977 **395** 1 r. multicoloured .. 2·50 50

396 Girls playing on Swing   **397** Lotus Lanterns

(Des G. Fernando. Litho Security Printers (M), Malaysia)
1987 (9 Apr). *Sinhalese and Tamil New Year.* T **396** *and
similar vert design. Multicoloured.* P 12.
978 75 c. Type **396**. .. 10 10
979 5 r. Girls with oil lamp and sun symbol .. 50 50

(Des W. Rohana. Litho Security Printers (M), Malaysia)
1987 (4 May). *Vesak.* T **397** *and similar horiz designs. Multicoloured.* P 12.
980 50 c. Type **397**.. .. 10 10
981 75 c. Octagonal lanterns 10 10
982 5 r. Star lanterns 30 30
983 10 r. Gok lanterns 45 55
980/3 .. .. *Set of 4* 80 90
MS984 150×90 mm. Nos. 980/3 .. 80 1·00

398 Emerald-collared   **399** Ven. Heenatiyana Sri
Parakeet   Dhammaloka Maha Nayake
Thero (Buddhist monk)

(Des G. Ratnavira. Litho Questa)
1987 (18 May)–**91.** *Birds (3rd series).* T **398** *and similar horiz
designs. Multicoloured.* P 14. *A. With imprint date at bottom
right*
985A 50 c. Type **398** .. 50 10
986A 1 r. Legge's Flowerpecker .. 75 10
987A 5 r. Ceylon White-headed Starling .. 1·50 1·25
988A 10 r. Ceylon Jungle Babbler .. 1·75 2·00
985A/8A .. .. *Set of 4* 4·00 3·00
MS989A 140×80 mm. Nos. 985A/8A .. 4·00 3·00

B. Without imprint date
987B 5 r. Ceylon White-headed Starling
(27.2.91) .. 1·50 1·25
988B 10 r. Ceylon Jungle Babbler (9.10.90) .. 2·00 2·25
Imprint dates: "1987", Nos. 985A/9A; "1989", No. 986A;
"1990", No. 988A.

(Des S. Silva. Litho Security Printers (M), Malaysia)
1987 (22 May). *National Heroes.* T **399** *and similar vert
designs. Multicoloured.* P 12.
990 75 c. Type **399**.. .. 40 35
991 75 c. P. de S. Kularatne (educationist) .. 40 35
992 75 c. M. C. Abdul Rahuman (legislator) .. 40 35
990/2 .. .. *Set of 3* 1·10 95

400 Peasant Family and Village   **401** *Mesua nagassarium*

(Des J. Semage. Litho Security Printers (M), Malaysia)
1987 (23 June). *Gam Udawa '87 (Village Re-awakening Movement).* P 12.
993 **400** 75 c. multicoloured .. 30 30

(Des P. Hewabettage (75 c.), B. Harischandra (5 r.). Litho
Security Printers (M), Malaysia)
1987 (25 June). *Forest Conservation.* T **401** *and similar horiz
design. Multicoloured.* P 12.
994 75 c. Type **401**.. .. 10 10
995 5 r. Elephants in forest .. 1·25 90

402 Dharmaraja College,   **403** Youth Services Logo
Crest and
Col. H. Olcott (founder)

(Des C. Kandewela. Litho Security Printers (M), Malaysia)
1987 (30 June). *Centenary of Dharmaraja College, Kandy.*
P 12.
996 **402** 75 c. multicoloured .. 1·75 30

(Des H. Dayaratne. Litho Security Printers (M), Malaysia)
1987 (15 July). *20th Anniv of National Youth Services.* P 12.
997 **403** 75 c. multicoloured .. 20 20

404 Arm holding Torch   **405** Open Bible and Logo
and Mahaweli Logo

(Des W. Rohana. Litho Security Printers (M), Malaysia)
1987 (5 Sept). *Mahaweli Games. P 12.*
998 404 75 c. multicoloured .. .. .. 2·50 2·00

(Des C. Beling. Litho Security Printers (M), Malaysia)
1987 (2 Oct). *175th Anniv of Ceylon Bible Society. P 12.*
999 405 5 r. 75, multicoloured 40 40

406 Hurdler and Committee Symbol
407 Madonna and Child, Flowers and Oil Lamp

(Des R. Mawilmada. Litho Heraclio Fournier, Spain)
1987 (8 Oct). *50th Anniv of National Olympic Committee. P 13.*
1000 406 10 r. multicoloured .. .. 2·50 1·25

(Des B. Mendis. Litho Security Printers (M), Malaysia)
1987 (17 Nov). *Christmas. T 407 and similar vert design. Multicoloured. P 12 (75 c.) or 12½ × 13 (10 r.).*
1001 75 c. Type 407 .. .. 10 10
1002 10 r. Christ Child in manger, star and dove 35 40
MS1003 145 × 82 mm. Nos. 1001/2. P 12 .. 60 70

408 Sir Ernest de Silva
409 Society Logo

(Des P. Gunasinghe. Litho German Bank Note Co, Leipzig)
1987 (25 Nov). *Birth Centenary of Sir Ernest de Silva (philanthropist and philatelist). P 13 × 13½.*
1004 408 75 c. multicoloured 30 30

(Des W. Rohana. Litho German Bank Note Co, Leipzig)
1987 (28 Nov). *150th Anniv of Kandy Friend-in-Need Society. P 13½ × 13.*
1005 409 75 c. multicoloured 30 30

410 University Flag and Graduates
411 Father Joseph Vaz

(Des R. Samarasinghe. Litho Security Printers (M), Malaysia)
1987 (14 Dec). *First Convocation of Buddhist and Pali University. P 12.*
1006 410 75 c. multicoloured 30 30

(Des S. Silva. Litho Security Printers (M), Malaysia)
1987 (15 Dec). *300th Anniv of Arrival of Father Joseph Vaz in Kandy. P 12.*
1007 411 75 c. multicoloured 30 30

412 Wheel of Dhamma, Dagaba and Bo Leaf
413 Dharmayatra Lorry

(Des W. Rohana. Litho Security Printers (M), Malaysia)
1988 (1 Jan). *30th Anniv of Buddhist Publication Society, Kandy. P 12.*
1008 412 75 c. multicoloured 30 30

(Des B. Harischandra. Litho German Bank Note Co, Leipzig)
1988 (4 Jan). *5th Anniv of Mahapola Dharmayatra Service. P 13½ × 13.*
1009 413 75 c. multicoloured 30 30

414 Society Logo
415 National Youth Centre, Maharagama

(Des R. Samarasinghe. Litho Security Printers (M), Malaysia)
1988 (8 Jan). *Centenary of Ceylon Society of Arts. P 12.*
1010 414 75 c. multicoloured 30 30

(Des R. Chandrajeewa. Litho German Bank Note Co, Leipzig)
1988 (31 Jan). *Opening of National Youth Centre, Maharagama. P 13½ × 13.*
1011 415 1 r. multicoloured .. .. 2·50 30

416 Citizens with National Flag and Map of Sri Lanka
417 Graduates, Clay Lamp and Open Book

(Des R. Samarasinghe. Litho Security Printers (M), Malaysia)
1988 (4 Feb). *40th Anniv of Independence. T 416 and similar vert design. Multicoloured. P 12.*
1012 75 c. Type 416 .. .. .. 10 10
1013 8 r. 50, "40" in figures and lion emblem .. 70 70

(Des R. Samarasinghe. Litho Security Printers (M), Malaysia)
1988 (11 Feb). *8th Anniv of Mahapola Scheme. P 12.*
1014 417 75 c. multicoloured 20 20

418 Bus and Logo
419 Ven. Weligama Sri Sumangala Maha Nayake Thero

(Des W. Rohana. Litho Security Printers (M), Malaysia)
1988 (19 Feb). *30th Anniv of Sri Lanka Transport Board. P 12.*
1015 418 5 r. 75, multicoloured 55 55

(Des S. Silva. Litho Security Printers (M), Malaysia)
1988 (13 Mar). *Ven. Weligama Sri Sumangala Maha Nayake Thero (Buddhist monk) Commemoration. P 12.*
1016 419 75 c. multicoloured 20 20

420 Regimental Colour
421 Chevalier I. X. Pereira

(Des W. Rohana. Litho Security Printers (M), Malaysia)
1988 (20 Apr). *Centenary of Regiment of Artillery. P 12.*
1017 420 5 r. 75, multicoloured .. .. 2·50 80

(Des S. Silva. Litho Security Printers (M), Malaysia)
1988 (26 Apr). *Birth Centenary of Chevalier I. X. Pereira (politician). P 12.*
1018 421 5 r. 75, multicoloured 30 30

---

422 Invitation to the Deities and Brahmas
423 Father Ferdinand Bonnel (educationist)

(Des N. Bulathsinhala. Litho State Ptg Wks, Moscow)
1988 (13 May). *Vesak. Paintings from Narendrarama Rajamaha Temple, Suriyagoda. T 422 and similar horiz design. Multicoloured. P 12½ × 12.*
1019 50 c. Type 422 .. .. 15 15
1020 75 c. Bodhisathva at the Seventh Step .. 15 15
MS1021 150 × 92 mm. Nos. 1019/20 .. 50 50

(Des S. Silva. Litho State Ptg Wks, Moscow)
1988 (22 May). *National Heroes. T 423 and similar vert designs. Multicoloured. P 12 × 12½.*
1022 75 c. Type 423 .. .. 15 15
1023 75 c. Sir Razik Fareed (politician) .. 15 15
1024 75 c. W. F. Gunawardhana (scholar) .. 15 15
1025 75 c. Edward Nugawela (politician) .. 15 15
1026 75 c. Chief Justice Sir Arthur Wijeyewardene 15 15
1022/6 .. .. .. Set of 5 60 60

424 Stylized Figures and Reawakened Village
425 Maliyadeva College, Kurungala, and Crest

(Des P. Gunasinghe. Litho Security Printers (M), Malaysia)
1988 (23 June). *10th Anniv of Gam Udawa (Village Re-awakening Movement). P 12.*
1027 424 75 c. multicoloured 20 20

(Des W. Rohana. Litho German Bank Note Co, Leipzig)
1988 (30 June). *Centenary of Maliyadeva College, Kurunegala. P 13½ × 13.*
1028 425 75 c. multicoloured 20 20

426 M.J.M. Lafir, Billiard Game and Trophy
427 Flags of Australia and Sri Lanka, Handclasp and Map of Australia

(Des S. Silva. Litho State Ptg Wks, Moscow)
1988 (5 July). *Mohamed Junaid Mohamed Lafir (World Amateur Billiards Champion, 1973) Commemoration. P 12½ × 12.*
1029 426 5 r. 75, multicoloured 30 30

(Des R. Samarasinghe. Litho Security Printers (M), Malaysia)
1988 (19 July). *Bicentenary of Australian Settlement. P 12.*
1030 427 8 r. 50, multicoloured 40 40

428 Ven. Kataluwe Sri Gunaratana Maha Nayake Thero
429 Athlete, Rice and Hydro-electric Dam

(Des S. Silva. Litho State Ptg Wks, Moscow)
1988 (11 Aug). *Ven. Kataluwe Sri Gunaratana Maha Nayake Thero (Buddhist monk) Commemoration. P 12 × 12½.*
1031 428 75 c. multicoloured 20 20

(Des P. Gunasinghe. Litho Security Printers (M), Malaysia)
1988 (3 Sept). *Mahaweli Games. P 12.*
1032 429 75 c. multicoloured 20 20

430 Athletics

431 Outline Map of Sri Lanka and Anniversary Logo

(Des P. Gunasinghe. Litho State Ptg Wks, Moscow)

1988 (6 Sept). *Olympic Games, Seoul. T* **430** *and similar vert designs. Multicoloured.* P 12 × 12½.

1033	75 c. Type **430**			10	10
1034	1 r. Swimming			10	10
1035	5 r. 75, Boxing			40	40
1036	8 r. 50, Map of Sri Lanka and logos of Olympic Committee and Seoul Games			70	70
1033/6			*Set of 4*	1·10	1·10
MS1037	181 × 101 mm. Nos. 1033/6			1·10	1·40

(Des S. Silva. Litho Security Printers (M), Malaysia)

1988 (12 Sept). *40th Anniv of World Health Organization.* P 12.

1038	**431** 75 c. multicoloured		20	20

432 Games Logo

433 Mahatma Gandhi

(Des A. Harischandra. Litho Security Printers (M), Malaysia)

1988 (20 Sept). *3rd National School Games.* P 12.

1039	**432** 1 r. black, gold and mauve		1·60	20

(Des S. Silva. Litho Security Printers (M), Malaysia)

1988 (2 Oct). *40th Death Anniv of Mahatma Gandhi.* P 12.

1040	**433** 75 c. multicoloured		50	20

434 Globe with Forms of Transport and Communications

435 Woman with Rice Sheaf and Hydro-electric Project

(Des R. Samarasinghe. Litho State Ptg Wks, Moscow)

1988 (28 Oct). *Asia–Pacific Transport and Communications Decade. T* **434** *and similar horiz design.* P 12½ × 12.

1041	75 c. multicoloured	30	10
1042	5 r. 75, magenta, royal blue and black	1·10	50

Design:—5 r. 75, Antenna tower with dish aerials and forms of transport.

(Des B. Harischandra. Litho Security Printers (M), Malaysia)

1988 (31 Oct). *Commissioning of Randenigala Project. T* **435** *and similar horiz design. Multicoloured.* P 12.

1043	75 c. Type **435**	10	10
1044	5 r. 75, Randenigala Dam and reservoir	45	45

436 Handicrafts and Centre Logo in Cupped Hands

437 Angel, Dove, Olive Branch and Globe

(Des R. Samarasinghe. Litho Secura, Singapore)

1988 (17 Nov). *Opening of Gramodaya Folk Art Centre, Colombo.* P 13½.

1045	**436** 75 c. multicoloured		20	20

(Des B. Mendis. Litho State Ptg Wks, Moscow)

1988 (21 Nov). *Christmas. T* **437** *and similar vert design. Multicoloured.* P 12×12½.

1046	75 c. Type **437**	10	10
1047	8 r. 50, Shepherds and Star of Bethlehem	50	60
MS1048	175×100 mm. Nos. 1046/7	60	60

438 Dr. E. W. Adikaram

439 Open Book in Tree and Children reading

(Des S. Silva. Litho Security Printers (M), Malaysia)

1988 (28 Dec). *Dr. E. W. Adikaram (educationist) Commemoration.* P 12.

1049	**438** 75 c. multicoloured		20	20

(Des Lakmini Amararatne. Litho German Bank Note Co, Leipzig)

1989 (23 Jan). *10th Anniv of Free Distribution of School Text Books.* P 13½×13.

1050	**439** 75 c. multicoloured		20	20

440 Wimalaratne Kumaragama

441 Logo and New Chamber of Commerce Building

(Des S. Silva. Litho German Bank Note Co, Leipzig)

1989 (27 Jan). *Poets of Sri Lanka. T* **440** *and similar vert designs. Multicoloured.* P 13×13½.

1051	75 c. Type **440**		15	15
1052	75 c. G. H. Perera		15	15
1053	75 c. Sagara Palansuriya		15	15
1054	75 c. P. B. Alwis Perera		15	15
1051/4		*Set of 4*	50	50

(Des Mel Ads Ltd. Litho Security Printers (M), Malaysia)

1989 (25 Mar). *150th Anniv of Ceylon Chamber of Commerce.* P 12.

1055	**441** 75 c. multicoloured		20	20

442 Bodhisatva at Lunch and Funeral Pyre

443 Parawahera Vajiragnana Thero (Buddhist monk)

(Des N. Bulathsinhala. Litho State Ptg Wks, Moscow)

1989 (15 May). *Vesak. Wall Paintings from Medawala Monastery, Harispattuwa. T* **442** *and similar horiz designs. Multicoloured.* P 12½×12.

1056	50 c. Type **442**	10	10
1057	75 c. Rescue of King Vessantara's children by god Sakra	10	10
1058	5 r. Bodhisatva ploughing and his son attacked by snake	30	35
1059	5 r. 75, King Vessantara giving away his children	30	35
1056/9	*Set of 4*	70	80
MS1060	150×90 mm. Nos. 1056/9	75	75

(Des S. Silva. Litho Security Printers (M), Malaysia)

1989 (22 May). *National Heroes. T* **443** *and similar multicoloured designs.* P 12.

1061	75 c. Type **443**	15	15
1062	75 c. Father Maurice Jacques Le Goc (educationist)	15	15
1063	75 c. Hemapala Munidasa (author)	15	15
1064	75 c. Ananda Samarakoon (composer)	15	15
1065	75 c. Simon Casie Chitty (scholar) (*horiz*)	15	15
1061/5	*Set of 5*	65	65

444 College Crest

445 Dramachakra, Lamp, Buddhist Flag and Map

(Des W. Rohana. Litho Security Printers (M), Malaysia)

1989 (5 June). *150th Anniv of Hartley College, Point-Pedro* (1988). P 12.

1066	**444** 75 c. multicoloured		20	20

(Des P. Gunasinghe. Litho State Ptg Wks, Moscow)

1989 (18 June). *Establishment of Ministry of Buddha Sasana.* P 12½×12.

1067	**445** 75 c. multicoloured		20	20

446 Hands holding Brick and Trowel, House and Family

447 Two Families and Hand turning Cogwheel

(Des P. Gunasinghe. Litho State Ptg Wks, Moscow)

1989 (23 June). *Gam Udawa '89 (Village Re-awakening Movement).* P 12½×12.

1068	**446** 75 c. multicoloured		20	20

(Des P. Gunasinghe. Photo State Ptg Works, Moscow)

1989 (23 June)–**90**. *Janasaviya Development Programme.* "1989" (75 c.) or "1990" (1 r.) imprint date at bottom right. P 12×11½.

1069	**447** 75 c. multicoloured	20	20
1070	1 r. multicoloured (31.1.90)	20	20
	a. Without imprint date at bottom right (4.12.90)	10	10

448 Dunhinda Falls

449 Rev. James Chater (missionary) and Baptist Church

(Des S. Silva. Litho State Ptg Works, Moscow)

1989 (11 Aug). *Waterfalls. T* **448** *and similar vert designs. Multicoloured.* P 12.

1071	75 c. Type **448**	10	10
1072	1 r. Rawana Falls	10	10
1073	5 r. 75, Laxapana Falls	45	45
1074	8 r. 50, Diyaluma Falls	60	60
1071/4	*Set of 4*	1·10	1·10

(Des S. Silva. Litho State Ptg Works, Moscow)

1989 (19 Aug). *177th Anniv of Baptist Church in Sri Lanka.* P 12½×12.

1075	**449** 5 r. 75, multicoloured		30	30

450 Bicentenary Logo

451 Old and New Bank Buildings and Logo

(Des R. Samarasinghe. Litho German Bank Note Co, Leipzig)

1989 (26 Aug). *Bicentenary of French Revolution.* P 13½×13.

1076	**450** 8 r. 50, black, deep blue & brt carmine	70	70

(Des W. Rohana. Litho German Bank Note Co, Leipzig)

1989 (31 Aug). *50th Anniv of Bank of Ceylon. T* **451** *and similar horiz design. Multicoloured.* P 13½×13.

1077	75 c. Type **451**	10	10
1078	5 r. "Bank of Ceylon" orchid and logo	45	45

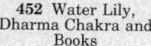

452 Water Lily, Dharma Chakra and Books

453 Wilhelm Geiger

(Des P. Gunasinghe. Litho Security Printers (M), Malaysia)

1989 (22 Sept). *State Literary Festival.* P 12.
1079 **452** 75 c. multicoloured 20 20

(Des S. Silva. Litho German Bank Note Co, Leipzig)

1989 (30 Sept). *Wilhelm Geiger (linguistic scholar) Commemoration.* P 13×13½.
1080 **453** 75 c. multicoloured 20 20

(Litho Questa)

1989 (11 Oct). *As No. 781, but different printer. Face value and inscriptions in black. "1989" imprint date.* P 14.
1081 3 r. Golden Palm Civet 75 30
No. 781 has face value and inscriptions in red-brown and is without imprint date.

454 H. V. Perera, Q.C.

455 Sir Cyril de Zoysa

(Des S. Silva. Litho Security Printers (M), Malaysia)

1989 (16 Oct). *Constitutional Pioneers.* T **454** *and similar vert design. Multicoloured.* P 12.
1082 75 c. Type **454** 20 20
1083 75 c. Prof. Ivor Jennings 20 20

(Des S. Silva. Litho German Bank Note Co, Leipzig)

1989 (26 Oct). *Sir Cyril de Zoysa (Buddhist philanthropist) Commemoration.* P 13×13½.
1084 **455** 75 c. multicoloured 20 20

456 Map of South-east Asia and Telecommunications Equipment

457 Members with Offerings and Water Lily on Map of Sri Lanka

(Des W. Rohana. Litho State Ptg Works, Moscow)

1989 (1 Nov). *10th Anniv of Asia-Pacific Telecommunity.* P 12×12½.
1085 **456** 5 r. 75, multicoloured 45 45

(Des P. Gunasinghe. Litho Security Printers (M), Malaysia)

1989 (9 Nov). *50th Anniv of Sri Sucharitha Welfare Movement.* P 13.
1086 **457** 75 c. multicoloured 20 20

458 "Apollo 11" Blast-off and Astronauts

459 Shepherds

(Des W. Rohana. Litho State Ptg Works, Moscow)

1989 (10 Nov). *20th Anniv of First Manned Landing on Moon.* T **458** *and similar vert designs. Multicoloured.* P 12×12½.
1087 75 c. Type **458** 15 10
1088 1 r. Armstrong leaving lunar module Eagle 20 10
1089 2 r. Astronaut on Moon 35 30
1090 5 r. 75, Lunar surface and Earth from Moon 60 70
1087/90 *Set of 4* 1·10 1·10
MS1091 100×160 mm. Nos. 1087/90 .. 1·40 1·40

(Des Father P. Silva. Litho Secura, Singapore)

1989 (21 Nov). *Christmas.* T **459** *and similar vert design. Multicoloured.* P 13½.
1092 75 c. Type **459** 10 10
1093 8 r. 50, Magi with gifts .. .. 60 1·50
MS1094 160×100 mm. Nos. 1092/3 .. 1·25 2·00

460 Ven. Sri Devananda Nayake Thero

461 College Building, Crest and Revd. William Ault (founder)

(Des S. Silva. Litho Security Printers (M), Malaysia)

1989 (25 Nov). *Ven. Sri Devananda Nayake Thero (Buddhist monk) Commemoration.* P 12.
1095 **460** 75 c. multicoloured 30 20

(Des W. Rohana. Litho Security Printers (M), Malaysia)

1989 (29 Nov). *175th Anniv of Methodist Central College, Batticaloa.* P 12.
1096 **461** 75 c. multicoloured 20 20

462 Golf Ball, Clubs and Logo

463 "Raja"

(Des G. Bozell. Litho Pakistan Security Ptg Corp, Karachi)

1989 (8 Dec). *Centenary of Nuwara Eliya Golf Club.* T **462** *and similar horiz design. Multicoloured.* P 13½.
1097 75 c. Type **462** .. .. 1·00 25
1098 8 r. 50, Course and club house .. .. 3·25 1·50

(Litho German Bank Note Co, Leipzig)

1989 (12 Dec). *"Raja" Royal Ceremonial Elephant, Kandy, Commemoration.* P 13×13½.
1099 **463** 75 c. multicoloured .. .. 2·50 65

464 College Building and G. Wickremarachchi (founder)

465 Ven. Udunuwara Sri Sarananda Thero

(Des S. Silva. Litho German Bank Note Co, Leipzig)

1989 (14 Dec). *60th Anniv of Gampaha Wickremarachchi Institute of Ayurveda Medicine.* P 13½×13.
1100 **464** 75 c. multicoloured 20 20

(Des S. Silva. Litho State Ptg Wks, Moscow)

1989 (20 Dec). *Ven. Udunuwara Sri Sarananda Thero (Buddhist monk) Commemoration.* P 12×12½.
1101 **465** 75 c. multicoloured 20 20

NEW INFORMATION

The editor is always interested to correspond with people who have new information that will improve or correct the Catalogue.

466 Diesel Train on Viaduct, Ella-Demodara Line

467 Cardinal Thomas Cooray

(Des R. Mawilmada. Litho Security Printers (M), Malaysia)

1989 (27 Dec). *125 Years of Sri Lanka Railways.* T **466** *and similar horiz designs. Multicoloured.* P 12.
1102 75 c. Type **466** 30 20
1103 2 r. Diesel train at Maradana Station .. 50 25
    a. Perf 13 .. .. 50 25
1104 3 r. Steam train and semaphore signal .. 55 30
    a. Perf 13 .. .. 55 30
1105 7 r. Steam train leaving station, 1864 .. 85 50
1102/5 *Set of 4* 2·00 1·00

(Des S. Silva. Litho German Bank Note Co, Leipzig)

1989 (28 Dec). *Cardinal Thomas Cooray Commemoration.* P 13×13½.
1106 **467** 75 c. multicoloured 85 30

468 Farmer and Wife with Dagaba and Dam

469 Justin Wijayawardena

(Des P. Gunasinghe. Litho Security Printers (M), Malaysia)

1989 (29 Dec). *Agro Mahaweli Development Programme.* P 12.
1107 **468** 75 c. multicoloured 20 20

(Des S. Silva. Litho State Ptg Wks, Moscow)

1990 (14 Jan). *Justin Wijayawardena (scholar) Commemoration.* P 12×12½.
1108 **469** 1 r. multicoloured .. .. 1·50 20

.25

(469a)

470 Ven. Induruwe Uttarananda Mahanayake Thero

1990 (16 Feb). *No. 1059 surch with T **469a**.*
1108a 25 c. on 5 r. 75, King Vessantara giving away his children 40 20

(Des S. Silva. Litho Security Printers (M), Malaysia)

1990 (15 Mar). *4th Death Anniv of Ven. Induruwe Uttarananda Mahanayake Thero (Buddhist theologian).* P 12.
1109 **470** 1 r. multicoloured .. .. 1·25 90

1.00

(470a)

471 Two Graduates, Lamp and Open Book

1990 (22 Mar). *No. 1069 surch with T **470a**.*
1109a 447 1 r. on 75 c. multicoloured 50 30

(Des P. Gunasinghe. Litho Secura, Singapore)

1990 (25 Mar). *9th Anniv of Mahapola Scheme.* P 13½.
1110 **471** 75 c. multicoloured 20 20

472 Traditional Drums

(Des R. Samarasinha. Litho Security Printers (M), Malaysia)

1990 (2 Apr). *25th Anniv of Laksala Traditional Handicrafts Organization. T 472 and similar horiz designs. Multicoloured. P 12.*

1111	1 r. Type 472	..	10	10
1112	2 r. Silverware	..	20	15
1113	3 r. Lacquerware	..	25	20
1114	8 r. Dumbara mats	..	50	40
1111/14	..	*Set of 4*	95	75

473 King Maha Prathapa visiting Queen Chandra

474 Father T. Long (educationist)

(Des N. Bulathsinhala. Litho State Ptg Wks, Moscow)

1990 (2 May). *Vesak. Wall Paintings from Buduraja Maha Viharaya, Wewurukannala. T 473 and similar horiz designs. Multicoloured. P 12½×12.*

1115	75 c. Type 473	..	10	10
1116	1 r. Execution of Prince Dharmapala	..	10	10
1117	2 r. Prince Mahinsasaka with the Water Demon		20	20
1118	8 r. King Dahamsonda with the God Sakra disguised as a demon		50	50
1115/18		*Set of 4*	70	70
MS1119	160×99 mm. Nos. 1115/18	..	80	80

(Des S. Silva. Litho Security Printers (M), Malaysia (No. 1120), State Ptg Wks, Moscow (others))

1990 (22 May). *National Heroes. T 474 and similar vert designs. Multicoloured. P 12 (No. 1120) or 12×12½ (others).*

1120	1 r. Type 474	..	25	20
1121	1 r. Prof. M. Ratnasuriya (37×25 mm)	..	25	20
1122	1 r. D. Wijewardene (patriot) (37×25 mm)	..	25	20
1123	1 r. L. Manjusri (artist) (37×25 mm)	..	25	20
1120/3		*Set of 4*	90	70

475 Janasaviya Workers

476 Gold Reliquary

(Des P. Dissanayake. Litho State Ptg Wks, Moscow)

1990 (23 June). *12th Anniv of Gam Udawa and Opening of Janasaviya Centre, Pallekele. P 12½×12.*

1124	475 1 r. multicoloured	1·25	30

(Des N. Bulathsinhala. Litho Security Printers (M), Malaysia)

1990 (7 July). *Centenary of Department of Archaeology. T 476 and similar vert designs. P 13 (8 r.) or 12 (others).*

1125	1 r. black and orange-yellow	..	15	10
1126	2 r. black and greenish grey	..	25	15
1127	3 r. black, apple-green and ochre	..	35	20
	a. Perf 13	..	35	20
1128	8 r. black and ochre	..	70	70
1125/8		*Set of 4*	1·25	1·00

Designs:—2 r. Statuette of Ganesh; 3 r. Terrace of the Bodhi-tree, Isurumuniya Vihara; 8 r. Inscription of King Nissankamalla.

477 Male Tennis Player at Left

478 Spotted Loach

(Des W. Rohana. Litho Pakistan Security Ptg Corp, Karachi)

1990 (14 Aug). *75th Anniv of Sri Lanka Tennis Association. T 477 and similar horiz designs. Multicoloured. P 13½.*

1129	1 r. Type 477	..	65	65
	a. Horiz pair. Nos. 1129/30	..	1·25	1·25
1130	1 r. Male tennis player at right	..	65	65
1131	8 r. Male tennis players	..	1·75	2·00
	a. Horiz pair. Nos. 1131/2	..	3·50	4·00
1132	8 r. Female tennis players	..	1·75	2·00
1129/32		*Set of 4*	4·25	4·75

Nos. 1129/30 and 1131/2 were each printed together, *se-tenant,* in horizontal pairs throughout the sheets, each pair forming a composite design of a singles (1 r.) or doubles (8 r.) match.

(Des R. Samarasinghe. Litho State Ptg Wks, Moscow)

1990 (14 Sept). *Endemic Fishes. T 478 and similar horiz designs. Multicoloured. P 11½.*

1133	25 c. Type 478	..	10	10
1134	2 r. Spotted Gourami ("Ornate Paradise Fish")		40	10
1135	8 r. Mountain Labeo	..	95	1·00
1136	20 r. Cherry Barb	..	1·75	2·25
1133/6		*Set of 4*	2·75	2·25
MS1137	150×90 mm. Nos. 1133/6		2·75	3·75

479 Rukmani Devi

480 Innkeeper turning away Mary and Joseph

(Litho Security Printers (M), Malaysia)

1990 (28 Oct). *12th Death Anniv of Rukmani Devi (actress and singer). P 12.*

1138	479 1 r. multicoloured	2·00	1·00

(Des P. Silva. Litho Security Printers (M), Malaysia)

1990 (28 Nov). *Christmas. T 480 and similar vert design. Multicoloured. P 13.*

1139	1 r. Type 480	..	30	10
1140	10 r. Adoration of the Magi	..	2·00	2·75
MS1141	190×114 mm. Nos. 1139/40. P 12		2·25	3·00

481 Health Worker talking to Villagers

482 Main College Building and Flag

(Des W. Rohana. Litho Security Printers (M), Malaysia)

1990 (30 Nov). *World Aids Day. T 481 and similar horiz design. Multicoloured. P 12.*

1142	1 r. Type 481	..	50	15
1143	8 r. Emblem and Aids virus	..	2·25	2·75

(Des P. Gunasinghe. Litho Security Printers (M), Malaysia)

1990 (8 Dec). *50th Anniv of Dharmapala College, Pannipitiya. P 12.*

1144	482 1 r. multicoloured	1·25	90

483 Peri Sundaram

484 Letter Box, Galle, 1904

(Des W. Rohana. Litho Security Printers (M), Malaysia)

1990 (14 Dec). *Birth Centenary of Peri Sundaram (lawyer and politician). P 12.*

1145	483 1 r. red-brown and yellow-green	1·25	90

(Des W. Rohana. Litho Security Printers (M), Malaysia)

1990 (26 Dec). *175th Anniv of Sri Lanka Postal Service. T 484 and similar vert designs. Multicoloured. P 12.*

1146	1 r. Type 484	..	45	10
1147	2 r. Mail runner, 1815	..	85	30
1148	5 r. Mail coach, 1832	..	1·50	1·75
1149	10 r. Nuwara-Eliya Post Office, 1894	..	2·25	3·00
1146/9		*Set of 4*	4·50	4·50

485 Chemical Structure Diagram, Graduating Students and Emblem

486 Kastavahana on Royal Elephant

(Des W. Rohana. Litho Security Printers (M), Malaysia)

1991 (25 Jan). *50th Anniv of Institute of Chemistry. P 12.*

1150	485 1 r. multicoloured	2·00	90

(Des U. Karunaratne. Litho Security Printers (M), Malaysia)

1991 (17 May). *Vesak. Temple Paintings from Karagampitiya Subodarama. T 486 and similar horiz designs. Multicoloured. P 12*

1151	75 c. Type 486	..	20	10
1152	1 r. Polo Janaka in prison	..	25	10
1153	2 r. Two merchants offering food to Buddha		55	35
1154	11 r. Escape of Queen	..	2·25	3·25
1151/4		*Set of 4*	2·75	3·25
MS1155	150×90 mm. Nos. 1151/4	..	3·00	3·75

487 Narada Thero (Buddhist missionary)

488 Society Building

(Des S. Silva. Litho State Ptg Works, Moscow)

1991 (22 May). *National Heroes. T 487 and similar vert designs. Multicoloured. P 12×12½.*

1156	1 r. Type 487	..	40	40
1157	1 r. Wallewatta Silva (novelist)	..	40	40
1158	1 r. Sir Muttu Coomaraswamy (lawyer and politician)		40	40
1159	1 r. Dr. Andreas Nell (opthalmic surgeon)		40	40
1156/9		*Set of 4*	1·40	1·40

(Des R. de Silva. Litho Security Printers (M), Malaysia)

1991 (31 May). *Centenary of Maha Bodhi Society. P 12.*

1160	488 1 r. multicoloured	1·00	80

489 Women working at Home

490 Globe and Plan Symbol

(Des T. Kariyawasam. Litho Security Printers (M), Malaysia)

1991 (23 June). *13th Anniv of Gam Udawa Movement. P 12½.*

1161	489 1 r. multicoloured	1·50	80

(Des R. Mawilmada. Litho Security Printers (M), Malaysia)

1991 (1 July). *40th Anniv of Colombo Plan. P 12.*

1162	490 1 r. bright violet and new blue	1·50	80

491 17th-century Map and Modern Satellite Photo of Sri Lanka

492 Ven. Henpitagedera Gnanaseeha Nayake Thero

(Des P. Miththapala. Litho Security Printers (M), Malaysia)

1991 (1 Aug). *190th Anniv of Sri Lanka Survey Department.*
P 12½.
1163 **491** 1 r. multicoloured .. .. 1·50 80

(Des S. Silva. Litho Security Printers (M), Malaysia)

1991 (1 Aug). *10th Death Anniv of Ven. Nayak Henpitagedera
Gnanaseeha Nayake Thero (Buddhist theologian).* P 12½.
1164 **492** 1 r. multicoloured .. .. 1·50 80

493 Police Officers of 1866
and 1991 with Badge

494 Kingswood College

(Des S. Silva. Litho Security Printers (M), Malaysia)

1991 (3 Sept). *125th Anniv of Sri Lankan Police Force.* P 12½.
1165 **493** 1 r. multicoloured 90 60

(Des W. Rohana. Litho State Ptg Wks, Moscow)

1991 (26 Oct). *Centenary of Kingswood College, Kandy.*
P 12½×12.
1166 **494** 1 r. multicoloured 50 30

495 The
Annunciation

496 Early Magneto
Telephone

(Des P. Silva. Litho Security Printers (M), Malaysia)

1991 (19 Nov). *Christmas. T 495 and similar vert design.
Multicoloured.* P 12½.
1167 **495** 1 r. Type **495** 20 20
1168 10 r. The Presentation of Jesus in the
Temple .. .. 75 1·25
MS1169 90×150 mm. Nos. 1167/8 .. 1·00 1·75

(Des W. Rohana. Litho Security Printers (M), Malaysia)

1991 (23 Nov). *Inauguration of Sri Lankan Telecom
Corporation. T 496 and similar vert designs. Multicoloured.*
P 12½.
1170 **496** 1 r. Type **496** 20 10
1171 2 r. Manual switchboard and telephonist 25 15
1172 8 r. Satellite communications system .. 55 80
1173 10 r. Fibre optics cable and mobile phone 70 90
1170/3 .. .. .. *Set of 4* 1·50 1·75

497 S.A.A.R.C. Logo and
Bandaranaike Memorial Hall

498 "Pancha" (Games
mascot)

(Des W. Rohana (1 r.), S. Silva (8 r.). Litho Security Printers (M),
Malaysia)

1991 (21 Dec). *Sixth South Asian Association for Regional
Cooperation Summit, Colombo. T 497 and similar horiz
design.* P 12½.
1174 **497** 1 r. Type **497** 15 10
1175 8 r. Logo and Hall surrounded by national
flags 45 75

(Des Sri Lanka National Design Centre. Litho Secura,
Singapore)

1991 (22 Dec). *5th South Asian Federation Games. T 498 and
similar horiz designs.* P 13½×14.
1176 **498** 1 r. Type **498** 25 10
1177 2 r. Games logo 45 20
1178 4 r. Sugathadasa Stadium .. 85 90
1179 11 r. Asia map on globe and national flags 1·75 2·50
1176/9 .. .. .. *Set of 4* 3·00 3·25

COVER PRICES

Cover factors are quoted at the beginning of each
country for most issues to 1945. An explanation of
the system can be found on page x. The factors
quoted do not, however, apply to philatelic covers.

---

499 Crate, Boeing
737-300/400 Airliner and
Container Ship

500 Plucking Tea

(Des W. Rohana. Litho Security Printers (M), Malaysia)

1992 (13 Jan). *Exports Year.* P 12.
1180 **499** 1 r. multicoloured .. .. 1·25 80

(Des R. Mawilmada. Litho Secura, Singapore)

1992 (12 Feb). *125th Anniv of Tea Industry. T 500 and similar
horiz designs. Multicoloured.* P 14.
1181 **500** 1 r. Type **500** 35 10
1182 2 r. Healthy family, tea and tea estate .. 65 20
1183 5 r. Ceylon tea symbol .. 1·75 2·00
1184 10 r. James Taylor (founder) .. 2·25 3·00
1181/4 .. .. .. *Set of 4* 4·50 4·75

501 General
Ranjan Wijeratne

502 Olcott Hall, Mahinda
College

(Des W. Rohana. Litho State Ptg Wks, Moscow)

1992 (2 Mar). *1st Death Anniv of General Ranjan Wijeratne.*
P 12×12½.
1185 **501** 1 r. multicoloured 30 20

(Des W. Rohana. Litho Security Printers (M), Malaysia)

1992 (2 Mar). *Centenary of Mahinda College, Galle.* P 12.
1186 **502** 1 r. multicoloured 20 20

503 Newstead College and
Logo

504 Student and Oil
Lamp

(Des S. Silva. Litho Security Printers (M), Malaysia)

1992 (13 Mar). *175th Anniv of Newstead Girls' College,
Negombo (1991).* P 12.
1187 **503** 1 r. multicoloured 20 20

(Des S. Perera. Litho Security Printers (M), Malaysia)

1992 (30 Mar). *11th Anniv of Mahapola Scholarship Fund.*
P 12.
1188 **504** 1 r. multicoloured 20 20

505 Sama's Parents
leaving for Forest

506 Ven. Devamottawe
Amarawansa (Buddhist
missionary)

(Des N. Bulathsinhala. Litho Security Printers (M), Malaysia)

1992 (5 May). *Vesak Festival. Sama Jataka Paintings from
Kottimbulwala Cave Temple. T 505 and similar horiz designs.
Multicoloured.* P 12.
1189 **505** 75 c. Type **505** 15 10
1190 1 r. Sama and parents in forest .. 15 10
1191 8 r. Sama leading blind parents .. 75 95
1192 11 r. Sama's parents grieving for wounded
son .. .. .. 1·25 1·75
1189/92 .. .. .. *Set of 4* 2·10 2·50
MS1193 151×91 mm. Nos. 1189/92 .. 2·10 2·75

(Des S. Silva. Litho Leigh-Mardon Ltd, Melbourne)

1992 (22 May). *National Heroes. T 506 and similar vert
designs. Multicoloured.* P 14.
1194 1 r. Type **506** 10 15
1195 1 r. Richard Mirando (Buddhist philanthropist) 10 15
1196 1 r. Gate Mudaliyar N. Canaganayagam
(Buddhist social reformer) .. 10 15
1197 1 r. Abdul Azeez (Moorish social reformer) 10 15
1194/7 .. .. .. *Set of 4* 30 50

507 Map of Sri
Lanka, Flag and
Symbol

508 Family in House

(Des S. Silva. Litho State Ptg Wks, Moscow)

1992 (14 June). *2300th Anniv of Arrival of Buddhism in Sri
Lanka.* P 12×12½.
1198 **507** 1 r. multicoloured 20 20

(Des P. Miranda. Litho Security Printers (M), Malaysia)

1992 (23 June). *14th Anniv of Gam Udawa Movement.* P 12.
1199 **508** 1 r. multicoloured 20 20

509 Postal Activities and
Award

510 Narilata Mask

(Des W. Rohana. Litho Leigh-Mardon Ltd, Melbourne)

1992 (11 July). *Postal Service Awards. T 509 and similar horiz
design. Multicoloured.* P 14.
1200 **509** 1 r. Type **509** 30 10
1201 10 r. Medals and commemorative cachet 2·00 2·25

(Des A. Dharmasiri. Litho Secura, Singapore)

1992 (19 Aug). *Kolam Dance Masks. T 510 and similar vert
designs. Multicoloured.* P 12½.
1202 **510** 1 r. Type **510** 10 10
1203 2 r. Mudali mask 20 10
1204 5 r. Queen mask 40 50
1205 10 r. King mask .. .. 75 1·00
1202/5 .. .. .. *Set of 4* 1·25 1·75
MS1206 150×90 mm. Nos. 1202/5 .. 1·25 1·75
Special packs prepared for the S.A.A.R.C. "Philex '96" stamp
exhibition at Colombo contained the strip of stamps from No.
MS1206 with the sheet margins removed.

511 19th and 20th-century
Players and Match of 1838

512 Running

(Des W. Rohana. Litho Secura, Singapore)

1992 (8 Sept). *160th Anniv of Cricket in Sri Lanka.* P 13.
1207 **511** 5 r. multicoloured .. .. 2·00 1·75

(Litho Questa)

1992 (15 Sept). *Olympic Games, Barcelona. T 512 and similar
vert designs. Multicoloured.* P 14.
1208 **512** 1 r. Type **512** 15 10
1209 11 r. Shooting .. .. 1·10 1·40
1210 13 r. Swimming .. .. 1·40 1·60
1211 15 r. Weight-lifting .. .. 1·50 2·00
1208/11 .. .. .. *Set of 4* 3·75 4·50
MS1212 91×151 mm. Nos. 1208/11 .. 3·75 4·75

513 Vijaya Kumaratunga

514 College Building and Crest

(Litho Secura, Singapore)

1992 (9 Oct). *Vijaya Kumaratunga (actor) Commemoration.* P 13.
1213 **513** 1 r. multicoloured 30 20

(Des W. Rohana. Litho Security Printers (M), Malaysia)

1992 (24 Oct). *Centenary of Al-Bahjathhul Ibraheemiyyah Arabic College.* P 12.
1214 **514** 1 r. multicoloured 30 20

515 Official Church Seal

516 Nativity

(Des W. Rohana. Litho Security Printers (M), Malaysia)

1992 (25 Oct). *350th Anniv of Dutch Reformed Church in Sri Lanka.* P 12.
1215 **515** 1 r. black, yellowish grn & greenish yell 70 40

(Des S. Purnajith. Litho Security Printers (M), Malaysia)

1992 (17 Nov). *Christmas. T* **516** *and similar vert design. Multicoloured.* P 12.
1216 1 r. Type **516** 10 10
1217 9 r. Family going to church .. .. 80 1·25
MS1218 150×90 mm. Nos. 1216/17 .. .. 80 1·60

517 Fleet of Columbus

2.00 ≡

(518)

(Des and litho Questa)

1992 (1 Dec). *500th Anniv of Discovery of America by Columbus. T* **517** *and similar horiz designs. Multicoloured.* P 14.
1219 1 r. Type **517** 40 10
1220 11 r. Columbus landing in New World 1·00 1·10
1221 13 r. Wreck of *Santa Maria* .. .. 1·25 1·50
1222 15 r. Columbus reporting to Queen Isabella and King Ferdinand .. 1·40 1·75
1219/22 .. .. *Set of* 4 3·50 4·00
MS1223 155×95 mm. Nos. 1219/22 .. .. 3·50 4·25

1992 (1 Dec). *No. 684 surch with T* **518**.
1224 **255** 2 r. on 10 c. multicoloured 70 50

519 Ven. Sumedhankara Thero and Dagoba

520 University Logo, Students and Building

(Des S. Silva. Litho Security Printers (M), Malaysia)

1992 (10 Dec). *Birth Centenary of Ven. Dambagasare Sumedhankara Nayake Thero.* P 12.
1225 **519** 1 r. multicoloured 20 20

(Des W. Rohana. Litho Security Printers (M), Malaysia)

1992 (22 Dec). *50th Anniv of University Education in Sri Lanka (1st issue).* P 12.
1226 **520** 1 r. multicoloured 20 20

521 University of Colombo Building and Logo

522 College Building and Crest

(Des W. Rohana. Litho Secura, Singapore)

1993 (23 Mar). *50th Anniv of University Education in Sri Lanka (2nd issue).* P 12½.
1227 **521** 1 r. multicoloured 30 20

(Des W. Rohana. Litho Secura, Singapore)

1993 (7 Apr). *Centenary of Zahira College, Colombo.* P 12½.
1228 **522** 1 r. multicoloured 40 30

523 Magandiya being presented to Buddha

524 Girl Guide, Badge and Camp

(Des S. Silva. Litho Security Printers (M), Malaysia)

1993 (30 Apr). *Vesak Festival. Verses from the Dhammapada. T* **523** *and similar vert designs. Multicoloured.* P 12.
1229 75 c. Type **523** 15 10
1230 1 r. Kisa Gotami carrying her dead baby 15 10
1231 3 r. Patachara and her dying family .. 35 45
1232 10 r. Angulimala praying .. .. 75 1·25
1229/32 .. .. *Set of* 4 1·25 1·60
MS1233 180×101 mm. Nos. 1229/32. P 12×12½ 1·25 2·00

(Des W. Rohana. Litho Security Printers (M), Malaysia)

1993 (10 May). *75th Anniv of Sri Lanka Girl Guides Association. T* **524** *and simlar vert design. Multicoloured.* P 12.
1234 1 r. Type **524** 40 10
1235 5 r. Girl Guide activities .. .. 1·10 1·50

525 Ven. Yagirala Pagnananda Maha Nayaka Thero (scholar)

526 Family arriving at New Home

(Des S. Silva. Litho Leigh-Mardon Ltd, Melbourne)

1993 (22 May). *National Heroes. T* **525** *and similar vert designs. Multicoloured.* P 14.
1236 1 r. Type **525** 15 15
1237 1 r. Charles de Silva (politician) .. 15 15
1238 1 r. Wilmot A. Perera (politician) .. 15 15
1239 1 r. Abdul Caffoor (philanthropist) .. 15 15
1236/9 .. .. *Set of* 4 55 55

(Des R. de Silva. Litho Secura, Singapore)

1993 (23 June). *"Gam Udawa '93".* P 12½.
1240 **526** 1 r. multicoloured 60 30

527 Consumer Movement Flag and Logo

528 Ashy-headed Laughing Thrush

(Des S. Perera. Litho Secura, Singapore)

1993 (3 July). *50th Anniv of Co-operative Consumer Movement (1992).* P 12½.
1241 **527** 1 r. multicoloured 60 30

(Des G. Ratnavira. Litho State Ptg Wks, Moscow)

1993 (14 July). *Birds (4th series). T* **528** *and similar horiz designs. Multicoloured.* P 12½×12.
1242 3 r. Type **528** 15 15
1243 4 r. Brown-capped Jungle Babbler .. 15 15
1244 5 r. Red-faced Malkoha 20 15
1245 10 r. Ceylon Grackle ("Ceylon Hill-Mynah") 50 50
1242/5 .. .. *Set of* 4 90 85
MS1246 151×121 mm. Nos. 1242/5 .. .. 1·75 2·50

529 Talawila Church

530 Rosette and Mail Delivery

(Des W. Rohana. Litho Secura, Singapore)

1993 (26 July). *150th Anniv of Talawila Church.* P 13.
1247 **529** 1 r. multicoloured 60 30

(Des W. Rohana. Litho Secura, Singapore)

1993 (22 Aug). *Sri Lanka Post Excellent Service Awards.* P 13.
1248 **530** 1 r. multicoloured 50 30

531 College and Flag

532 Presentation of Jesus in the Temple

(Des W. Rohana. Litho Secura, Singapore)

1993 (15 Nov). *Centenary of Musaeus College.* P 13.
1249 **531** 1 r. multicoloured 70 30

(Des S. Silva. Litho Pakistan Security Ptg Corporation, Karachi)

1993 (30 Nov). *Christmas. T* **532** *and similar horiz design. Multicoloured.* P 13½.
1250 1 r. Type **532** 10 10
1251 17 r. Boy Jesus with the Jewish teachers 70 1·50
MS1252 180×102 mm. Nos. 1250/1 .. .. 75 1·50

533 Healthy Youth and Drug Addict

(Des W. Rohana. Litho Pakistan Security Ptg Corp, Karachi)

1993 (16 Dec). *Youth and Health Campaign.* P 14.
1253 **533** 1 r. multicoloured 30 30

534 Maradana Technical College Building and Emblems

535 Trinity College Logo

(Des W. Rohana. Litho Secura, Singapore)

1993 (17 Dec). *Centenary of Technical Education.* P 13.
1254 **534** 1 r. multicoloured 50 30

(Des W. Rohana. Litho Secura, Singapore)

1994 (11 Feb). *Centenary of Trinity College, Kandy, Old Boys' Association.* P 13.
1255 535 1 r. multicoloured 30 20

536 College Flag

(Des W. Rohana. Litho Secura, Singapore)

1994 (10 Mar). *150th Anniv of St. Thomas' College, Matara.* P 13.
1256 536 1 r. lake-brown and pale new blue .. 30 20

537 Ven. Siyambalangamuwe Sri Gunaratana Thero

(Des S. Silva. Litho Secura, Singapore)

1994 (2 Apr). *Ven. Siyambalangamuwe Sri Gunaratana Thero (educationist) Commemoration.* P 12½.
1257 537 1 r. multicoloured 60 30

538 College Building and Arms

(Des S. Silva. Litho Secura Singapore)

1994 (4 Apr). *125th Anniv of St. Joseph's College, Trincomalee.* P 13.
1258 538 1 r. multicoloured 30 20

539 Man distributing Water   **540** I.L.O. Monument, Geneva, Logo and Workers

(Des S. Silva. Litho Secura, Singapore)

1994 (7 May). *Vesak Festival. Dasa Paramita (Ten Virtues).* T **539** *and similar horiz designs. Multicoloured.* P 13.
1259   1 r. Type **539** 10 10
1260   2 r. Man and elephant 50 30
1261   5 r. Man surrounded by women .. 65 75
1262   17 r. Ruler with snake charmer .. 1·50 2·25
1259/62   *Set of 4* 2·50 3·00
MS1263   162×88 mm. Nos. 1259/62 .. 2·50 3·00

(Des W. Rohana. Litho Secura, Singapore)

1994 (12 May). *75th Anniv of International Labour Organization.* P 13.
1264 540 1 r. multicoloured 40 30

541 Mahakavindra Dhammaratana Thero (Buddhist theologian)   **542** Conference Logo

(Des S. Silva. Litho Leigh-Mardon Ltd, Melbourne)

1994 (22 May). *National Heroes.* T **541** *and similar horiz designs. Multicoloured.* P 14.
1265   1 r. Type **541** 10 10
1266   1 r. Ranasinghe   Premadasa   (former President) .. 10 10
1267   1 r. Dr. Colvin de Silva (trade union leader) .. 10 10
1268   1 r. E. Periyathambipillai (Tamil poet) .. 10 10
1265/8   *Set of 4* 40 40

A 1 r. stamp for "Gam Udawa '94" was prepared for issue on 23 June 1994, but was not released due to the assassination of President Premadasa. Unused stamps exist from publicity examples circulated before the decision to cancel the issue was taken.

(Des R. de Silva. Litho Secura, Singapore)

1994 (9 July). *13th International Federation of Social Workers World Conference, Colombo.* P 13.
1269 542 8 r. multicoloured 70 75

543 Ven. Sri Somaratana Thero and Temple   **544** Communication Technology and Logo

(Des S. Silva. Litho Secura, Singapore)

1994 (2 Aug). *10th Death Anniv of Ven. Sri Somaratana Thero (Buddhist religious leader).* P 13.
1270 543 1 r. multicoloured 50 30

(Des W. Rohana. Litho Secura, Singapore)

1994 (8 Sept). *"INFOTEL LANKA '94" International Computers and Telecommunications Exhibition.* P 13.
1271 544 10 r. multicoloured .. .. 75 1·00

545 Veddah Tribesman stringing Bow   **546** Luca Pacioli (pioneer), Logo and Equipment inside "500"

(Des R. de Silva. Litho Security Printers (M), Malaysia)

1994 (12 Sept). *Year of Indigenous People (1993).* T **545** *and similar vert design. Multicoloured.* P 12.
1272   1 r. Type **545** 20 10
1273   17 r. Veddah artist and rock paintings .. 1·75 2·25

(Des W. Rohana. Litho Secura, Singapore)

1994 (11 Oct). *500th Anniv of Accountancy.* P 13.
1274 546 1 r. multicoloured 50 30

547 Society Emblem   **548** Airliner, I.C.A.O. Logo and Globe

(Des P. Miththapala. Litho Secura, Singapore)

1994 (24 Nov). *Centenary of Wildlife and Nature Society of Sri Lanka.* T **547** *and similar horiz designs.* P 13.
1275   1 r. bronze-green and black .. 15 10
1276   2 r. multicoloured 30 20
1277   10 r. multicoloured .. .. 1·00 1·25
1278   17 r. multicoloured .. .. 1·50 2·25
1275/8   *Set of 4* 2·75 3·25
MS1279   130×96 mm. Nos. 1275/8 .. 2·75 3·25
Designs:—2 r. Horned Lizard; 10 r. Giant Squirrel; 17 r. Sloth Bear.

(Des W. Rohana. Litho Secura, Singapore)

1994 (7 Dec). *50th Anniv of International Civil Aviation Organization.* P 13.
1280 548 10 r. multicoloured .. .. 1·25 1·40

NEW INFORMATION

The editor is always interested to correspond with people who have new information that will improve or correct the Catalogue.

549 Christmas Crib   **550** Map of Sri Lanka and Aspects of Science

(Des S. Silva. Litho Secura, Singapore)

1994 (8 Dec). *Christmas.* T **549** *and similar horiz design. Multicoloured.* P 13.
1281   1 r. Type **549** 10 10
1282   17 r. St. Joseph's carpentry workshop, Nazareth .. .. 75 1·25
MS1283   145×81 mm. Nos. 1281/2 .. 90 1·50

(Des D. Gunasekera. Litho Secura, Singapore)

1994 (19 Dec). *50th Anniv of Sri Lankan Association for the Advancement of Science.* P 13.
1284 550 1 r. multicoloured 50 30

551 College Building and Arms   **552** Dendrobium maccarthiae

(Des P. Nimal de Silva. Litho Secura, Singapore)

1994 (24 Dec). *Centenary of Richmond College Old Boys' Association.* P 13
1285 551 1 r. black, carmine-vermilion & violet-bl 20 20

(Des P. Miththapala. Litho Secura, Singapore)

1994 (27 Dec). *60th Anniv of Orchid Circle of Ceylon.* T **552** *and similar vert designs. Multicoloured.* P 13.
1286   50 c. Type **552** 10 10
1287   1 r. *Cottonia peduncularis* 15 10
1288   5 r. *Bulbophyllum wightii* 35 45
1289   17 r. *Habenaria crinifera* .. .. 80 1·25
1286/9   *Set of 4* 1·25 1·60
MS1290   127×95 mm. Nos. 1286/9 .. 2·00 2·50

553 Father Joseph Vaz and Pope John Paul II   **554** Blue Water Lily (*Nymphaea stellata*)

(Des S. Silva. Litho Japanese Govt Ptg Bureau, Tokyo)

1995 (20 Jan). *Papal Visit and Beatification of Father Joseph Vaz.* P 13.
1291 553 1 r. multicoloured 70 30

(Des S. Silva. Litho Leigh-Mardon Ltd, Melbourne)

1995 (22 Feb). P 14½×14.
1292 554 1 r. multicoloured 20 10

555 College Building and Arms   **556** Sirimavo Bandaranaike and National Flag

(Des W. Rohana. Litho Secura, Singapore)

1995 (2 Mar). *Centenary of St. Joseph's College, Colombo.* P 13.
1293 555 1 r. multicoloured 20 10

(Des W. Rohana. Litho Security Printers (M), Malaysia)

1995 (17 Apr). *Election of Sirimavo Bandaranaike as Prime Minister.* P 12½×12.
1294 556 2 r. multicoloured 60 40

557 Man offering Water to Crew of Outrigger Canoe

558 14th-century Map of Sri Lanka and Society Arms

(Des S. Silva. Litho Security Printers (M), Malaysia)

1995 (29 Apr). *Vesak Festival. Dasa Paramita (ten virtues). T 557 and similar vert designs. Multicoloured.* P 12×12½.

1295	1 r. Type 557	..	10	10
1296	2 r. Catching falling man	..	15	15
1297	10 r. Teacher with students	..	50	60
1298	17 r. Stopping man digging	..	90	1·10
1295/8		*Set of 4*	1·50	1·75
MS1299	170×90 mm. Nos. 1295/8. P 12½		1·75	2·25

(Litho Secura, Singapore)

1995 (17 May). *150th Anniv of Royal Asiatic Society of Sri Lanka.* P 12½.

1300	558	1 r. multicoloured	50	30

559 Abdul Cader

560 College Building

(Des S. Silva. Litho Bank Note Corporation of America, New York)

1995 (3 June). *120th Birth Anniv of Abdul Cader (lawyer).* P 11.

1301	559	2 r. multicoloured	50	35

(Des A. Hopman. Litho Security Printers (M), Malaysia)

1995 (21 June). *Centenary of St. Aloysius's College, Galle.* P 12½×12.

1302	560	2 r. multicoloured	50	35

561 Tikiri Ilangaratna

562 Lamps and Schools Flag

(Des S. Silva. Litho Secura, Singapore)

1995 (7 July). *Tikiri Bandara Ilangaratna (politician and author) Commemoration.* P 12½×13.

1303	561	2 r. multicoloured	50	35

(Des P. Gunasinghe. Litho Secura, Singapore)

1995 (3 Aug). *Centenary of Dhamma Schools Movement.* P 12½.

1304	562	2 r. multicoloured	50	35

563 G.P.O. Building

564 Young Hands surrounding Old Hand

(Des S. Silva. Litho Pakistan Security Ptg Corp, Karachi)

1995 (22 Aug). *Centenary of General Post Office, Colombo.* P 13½.

1305	563	1 r. multicoloured	30	20

(Des S. Purnajith. Litho Enschedé)

1995 (1 Oct). *International Day for the Elderly.* P 14×13½.

1306	564	2 r. multicoloured	50	35

565 Sri Lankan Parliament Building and C.P.A. Logo

566 Anniversary Emblem and Map of Sri Lanka

(Des W. Rohana. Litho Pakistan Security Ptg Corp, Karachi)

1995 (8 Oct). *41st Commonwealth Parliamentary Conference, Colombo.* P 13½.

1307	565	2 r. multicoloured	50	35

(Des S. Purnajith. Litho Pakistan Ptg Corp, Karachi)

1995 (24 Oct). *50th Anniv of United Nations.* P 13½.

1308	566	2 r. multicoloured	50	35

567 Money falling into Globe Money Box

568 Diocesan Arms of Colombo and Kurunegala

(Des S. Purnajith. Litho Pakistan Ptg Corp, Karachi)

1995 (31 Oct). *71st Anniv of World Thrift Day and 110th Anniv of National Savings Bank.* P 13½.

1309	567	2 r. multicoloured	50	35

(Des S. Purnajith. Litho Secura, Singapore)

1995 (30 Nov). *Christmas. 150th Anniv of Anglican Diocese of Colombo. T 568 and similar horiz design. Multicoloured.* P 13.

1310		2 r. Type 568	10	10
1311		20 r. Nativity scene and hands surrounding map	80	1·40
MS1312	150×90 mm. Nos. 1310/11		80	1·50

569 Flags of Member Countries

570 School Emblem

(Des S. Purnajith. Litho Secura, Singapore)

1995 (8 Dec). *10th Anniv of South Asian Association for Regional Co-operation.* P 12½×13.

1313	569	2 r. multicoloured	50	35

(Des S. Purnajith. Litho Secura, Singapore)

1996 (17 Jan). *175th Anniv of Vincent Girls' High School, Batticaloa.* P 12½×13.

1314	570	2 r. multicoloured	50	35

571 Little Basses Lighthouse

572 Traditional Sesath (umbrellas)

(Des S. Purnajith. Litho State Ptg Wks, Moscow)

1996 (22 Jan)–**97**. *Lighthouses. T 571 and similar vert designs. Multicoloured.* P 12.

1315	50 c. Type 571	..	..	10	10
1316	75 c. Great Basses	..	..	10	10
1317	2 r. Devinuwara	..	..	15	10
1317a	2 r. 50, As 2 r. (12.2.97)	..		15	10
1318	20 r. Galle	..	..	60	70
1315/18	..		*Set of 5*	90	90
MS1319	151×91 mm. Nos. 1315/17 and 1318		90	1·50

Nos. 1315/18 were printed in sheets of 50. During 1997 a printing of the 2 r. value appeared in sheets of 36.

Special packs for the S.A.A.R.C. "Philex '96" stamp exhibition at Colombo contained the strip of stamps from No. **MS**1319 with the sheet margins removed.

(Des P. Gunasinghe. Litho State Ptg Wks, Moscow)

1996 (13 Mar). *Traditional Handicrafts. T 572 and similar horiz designs. Multicoloured.* P 12.

1320	25 c. Type 572	..	10	10
1321	8 r. 50, Pottery		20	25
1322	10 r. 50, Mats		30	35
1323	17 r. Lace	..	55	70
1320/3		*Set of 4*	1·00	1·10
MS1324	150×90 mm. Nos. 1320/3		1·50	1·75

573 School Emblem and Trees

574 Upaka and Capa

(Des S. Purnajith. Litho Security Printers (M), Malaysia)

1996 (21 Mar). *Centenary of Chundikuli Girls' College, Jaffna.* P 12½×12½.

1325	573	2 r. multicoloured	50	35

(Des S. Silva. Litho Security Printers (M), Malaysia)

1996 (3 Apr). *Vesak Festival. T 574 and similar vert designs. Multicoloured.* P 12.

1326	1 r. Type 574	..	10	10
1327	2 r. Dantika and elephant	..	15	15
1328	5 r. Subha removing her eye	..	20	30
1329	10 r. Punna and the Brahmin	..	25	50
1326/9		*Set of 4*	60	95
MS1330	170×90 mm. Nos. 1326/9. P 12×12½		60	1·00

Some printings of the 2 r. have either luminescent fibres or luminescent paper visible under U.V. light.

575 Diving

576 Bowler

(Des S. Purnajith. Litho Enschedé)

1996 (22 July). *Olympic Games, Atlanta. T 575 and similar multicoloured designs.* P 14×13½ (vert) or 13½×14 (horiz).

1331	1 r. Type 575	..	15	10
1332	2 r. Volleyball	..	30	10
1333	5 r. Rifle shooting (horiz)	..	50	50
1334	17 r. Running (horiz)	..	1·00	1·60
1331/4	..	*Set of 4*	1·75	2·00

(Des S. Purnajith. Litho Enschedé)

1996 (18 Aug). *Sri Lanka's Victory in World Cup Cricket Tournament. T 576 and similar triangular designs. Multicoloured.* P 13½.

1335	2 r. Type 576	..	25	15
1336	10 r. 50, Wicket-keeper	..	55	65
1337	17 r. Batsman	..	90	1·25
1338	20 r. World Cup Trophy	..	1·10	1·40
1335/8		*Set of 4*	2·50	3·00
MS1339	150×90 mm. Nos. 1335/8		2·50	3·00

577 Main Building, Jaffna Central College

578 Globe in Flames and White Dove

(Des S. Purnajith. Litho Pakistan Security Printing Corp, Karachi)

1996 (7 Sept). *180th Anniv of Jaffna Central College.* P 13½×13.
1340 577 2 r. multicoloured 50 35
    a. Black ("SRI LANKA", upper and
    lower panels, etc) omitted .. 60·00

(Des S. Herath. Litho Pakistan Security Ptg Corp, Karachi)

1996 (4 Nov). *50th Anniv of U.N.E.S.C.O.* P 13½.
1341 578 2 r. multicoloured 50 35

579 Jesus washing   580 Cupped Hands
the Disciples' Feet   holding Child

(Litho Oriental Press, Bahrain)

1996 (2 Dec). *Christmas. T 597 and similar vert design showing murals by David Paynter from Trinity College Chapel, Kandy. Multicoloured.* P 13½×13.
1342 2 r. Type 579 .. .. 10 10
1343 17 r. Parable of the Good Samaritan .. 55 75
MS1344 150×90 mm. Nos. 1342/4 .. 65 85

(Des P. Gunasinghe. Litho Pakistan Security Ptg Corp, Karachi)

1996 (12 Dec). *50th Anniv of U.N.I.C.E.F.* P 13×13½.
1345 580 5 r. multicoloured 40 50

581 Swami Vivekananda
and Globe

(Des S. Silva. Litho Oriental Press, Bahrain)

1997 (15 Jan). *Centenary of Swami Vivekananda's Visit to Sri Lanka.* P 13½×13.
1346 581 2 r. 50, multicoloured 40 40

(582)	(583)	(584)	(585)
2.50	2.50	2.50	2.50

1997 (12 Feb). *No. 1317 surch with T 582/5.*
1347 582 2 r. 50 on 2 r. multicoloured .. 70 30
1348 583 2 r. 50 on 2 r. multicoloured .. 70 30
1349 584 2 r. 50 on 2 r. multicoloured .. 70 30
1350 585 2 r. 50 on 2 r. multicoloured .. 70 30
1347/50 .. .. .. Set of 4 2·50 1·10
Nos. 1347/50 occur in separate sheets. Nos. 1347 and 1349 were surcharged by the State Ptg Corporation and Nos. 1348 and 1350 by Lakmini Printers Ltd.

586 Venerable   (587)   (588)
Welivitiye Sorata
Thero (scholar)

	11.00	11.00

(Des S. Silva. Litho Oriental Press, Bahrain)

1997 (4 Apr). *National Heroes (1st series). T 586 and similar vert designs. Multicoloured.* P 13½×13.
1351 2 r. Type 586 .. .. 20 20
1352 2 r. Mahagama Sekera (writer and artist) 20 20
    a. Asterisk ovpt double .. ..
    b. Asterisk ovpt omitted .. ..
1353 2 r. Dr. S. A. Wickremasinghe (physician) 20 20
1354 2 r. Lt.-Gen. Denzil Kobbekaduwa .. 20 20
1351/4 .. .. .. Set of 4 70 70
No. 1352 was issued with the inscriptions at the top right and bottom left corners obliterated by rows of asterisks. A small quantity without the overprint is known to have been sold at one post office.
See also Nos. 1373/6.

1997 (6 May). *No. 1322 surch with T 587/8 by State Ptg Corporation.*
1355 583 11 r. on 10 r. 50, multicoloured .. 1·00 1·00
1356 584 11 r. on 10 r. 50, multicoloured .. 1·00 1·00
    a. Surch omitted (in horiz pair with
    normal) .. .. ..
The surcharge omitted error occurs in the last vertical row. The stamp next to it has the obliterating block missing.

589 Thuparama Stupa,   590 Don Johannes
3rd-century B.C.   Kumarage

(Des P. Gunasinghe. Litho Security Printers (M), Malaysia)

1997 (7 May). *Vesak Festival. Anauradhapura Sites. T 589 and similar vert designs. Multicoloured. No wmk.* P 12×12½ (2 r. 50) or 12 (others).
1357 1 r. Type 589 .. .. 10 10
    a. Perf 12×12½ 10 10
1358 2 r. 50, Ruwanvalisaya stupa, 161–137
    B.C. 10 10
1359 3 r. Abhayagiri Dagaba, 103–102 B.C .. 10 10
    a. Perf 12×12½ 10 10
1360 17 r. Jethavana Dagaba, 276–303 A.D. .. 45 65
1357/60 .. .. .. Set of 4 60 80
MS1361 170×90 mm. Nos. 1357/60. P 12×12½ 80 1·10
For 1 r. watermarked W 138 of Malaysia see No. 1421.

(Des W. Rohana. Litho Pakistan Security Ptg Corp, Karachi)

1997 (10 June). *Birth Centenary of D. J. Kumarage (Buddhist teacher).* P 13×13½.
1362 590 2 r. 50, multicoloured 50 30

591 Munronia pinnata   592 Tourist Board Logo,
Airliner and Holiday Resorts

(Des D. Gunatilake. Litho Pakistan Security Ptg Corp, Karachi)

1997 (17 June). *Medicinal Herbs. T 591 and similar vert design. Multicoloured.* P 13½×14.
1363 2 r. 50, Type 591 .. .. 20 10
1364 14 r. *Rauvolfia serpentina* .. 50 75

(Des S. Kalupahana. Litho Security Printers (M), Malaysia)

1997 (11 Sept). *Visit Sri Lanka.* P 12.
1365 592 20 r. multicoloured .. .. 1·00 1·25

1.00		
(593)	594 Lyre Head Lizard	

1997 (22 Sept). *No. 1321 surch with T 593 by State Ptg Corporation.*
1366 1 r. on 8 r. 50, Pottery 70 20

(Des V. Perera. Litho Security Printers (M), Malaysia)

1997 (18 Oct). *Reptiles. T 594 and similar horiz designs. Multicoloured.* P 12½×12 (20 r.) or 12 (others).
1367 2 r. 50, Type 594 .. .. 10 10
1368 5 r. Boie's Roughside (snake) .. 20 20
1369 17 r. Common Lanka Skink .. 55 70
1370 20 r. Great Forest Gecko 60 85
1367/70 .. .. .. Set of 4 1·25 1·60
MS1371 170×90 mm. Nos. 1367/70. P 12 1·25 1·60

OMNIBUS ISSUES

Details, together with prices for complete sets, of the various Omnibus issues from the 1935 Silver Jubilee series to date are included in a special section following Zimbabwe at the end of Volume 2.

---

595 St. Servatius' College,   596 The Nativity
Matara

(Des P. Gunasinghe. Litho Security Printers (M), Malaysia)

1997 (1 Nov). *Centenary of St. Servatius' College, Matara.* P 12½×12.
1372 595 2 r. 50, multicoloured 20 15
    a. Perf 12×12½ 20 15

(Des S. Silva. Litho Secura, Singapore)

1997 (11 Nov). *National Heroes (2nd series). Vert designs as T 586. Multicoloured.* P 12½×13.
1373 2 r. 50, Sri Indasara Nayake Thero
    (Buddhist leader) 10 15
    a. Block of 4. Nos. 1373/6 .. 30
1374 2 r. 50, Abdul Aziz (trade union leader) 10 15
1375 2 r. 50, Prof. Subramaniam
    Vithiananthan 10 15
1376 2 r. 50, Vivienne Goonewardene
    (politician) 10 15
1373/6 .. .. .. Set of 4 30 50
Nos. 1373/6 were printed together, *se-tenant*, in blocks of four throughout the sheet.

(Des S. Silva. Litho Security Printers (M), Malaysia)

1997 (20 Nov). *Christmas. T 596 and similar vert design. Multicoloured.* P 12½.
1377 2 r. 50, Type 596 .. .. 10 10
1378 20 r. Visit of the Three Kings .. 60 75
MS1379 170×90 mm. Nos. 1377/8 .. 60 80

597 Young Men's Buddhist
Association Building,
Colombo

(Des P. Ediriweera. Litho Security Printers (M), Malaysia)

1998 (8 Jan). *Centenary of Young Men's Buddhist Association, Colombo.* P 12½×13.
1380 597 2 r. multicoloured 20 15

598 Sri Jayawardenapura   599 Children and
Vidyalaya School   Mathematical Symbols

(Des P. Gunasinghe. Litho Security Printers (M), Malaysia)

1998 (28 Jan). *175th Anniv of Sri Jayawardenapura Vidyalaya School, Kotte.* P 12½.
1381 598 2 r. 50, multicoloured 20 15

(Des P. Gunasinghe (No. 1383), R. Mawilmada (others). Litho Pakistan Security Ptg Corp (No. 1383), Secura, Singapore (others))

1998 (4 Feb). *50th Anniv of Independence. T 599 and similar horiz designs. Multicoloured.* P 13½ (No. 1383) or 12½ (others).
1382 2 r. Type 599 .. .. 10 10
1383 2 r. 50, Flag and 1949 4 c. Independence
    stamp (38×28 mm) 15 15
1384 2 r. 50, People with technological and
    industrial symbols 15 15
1385 5 r. Dancers with arts and music symbols 20 25
1386 10 r. Women with cultural and historical
    symbols 25 45
1382/6 .. .. .. Set of 5 75 1·00

600 Scouts raising Flag and Jamboree Logo   **601** W.H.O. Emblem in "50" and Flag of Sri Lanka

(Des W. Rohana. Litho Pakistan Security Ptg Corp, Karachi)

1998 (18 Feb). *5th National Scout Jamboree, Kandy. T* **600** *and similar vert design. Multicoloured. P* 13½.
1387	2 r. 50, Type **600**	25	10
1388	17 r. Scout saluting and Jamboree emblem	1·00	1·25

(Des P. Gunasinghe. Litho Security Printers (M), Malaysia)

1998 (7 Apr). *50th Anniv of World Health Organization. P* 12½.
1389	**601** 2 r. 50, multicoloured	20	15

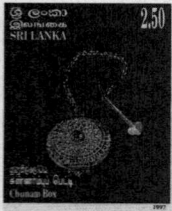

602 Chunam Box   **603** Kelani River and Stupa

(Des P. Ediriweera. Litho Pakistan Security Ptg Corp, Karachi)

1998 (24 Apr). *Traditional Jewellery and Crafts. T* **602** *and similar vert designs. Multicoloured. P* 13½.
1390	2 r. 50, Type **602**	15	10
1391	5 r. Agate necklace	25	20
1392	10 r. Bangle and hairpin	40	45
1393	17 r. Sigiri ear-ring	60	1·00
1390/3	Set of 4	1·25	1·50
MS1394	151×91 mm. Nos. 1390/3	1·25	1·50

(Des P. Gunasinghe. Litho Security Printers (M), Malaysia)

1998 (30 Apr). *Vesak Festival. Wall Paintings from Kelaniya Temple. T* **603** *and similar vert designs. Multicoloured. P* 12½.
1395	2 r. 50, Type **603**	10	10
1396	2 r. 50, Crown Prince Mahanaga and his court on way to Magampura	15	10
1397	4 r. Mahanaga and wife with baby Yatala Tissa	20	20
1398	17 r. Prince Mahanaga with King's minister	50	85
1395/8	Set of 4	80	1·10
MS1399	170×90 mm. Nos. 1395/8	80	1·10

604 School Building and Emblem

(Des P. Gunasinghe. Litho Thai British Security Ptg Co Ltd, Thailand)

1998 (7 May). *175th Anniv of St. John's College, Jaffna. P* 14½×14.
1400	**604** 2 r. 50, multicoloured	20	15

605 Elephants in River

(Des W. Perera. Litho Japanese Govt Ptg Bureau, Tokyo)

1998 (28 May). *Elephants. T* **605** *and similar horiz designs. Multicoloured. P* 13×13½.
1401	2 r. 50, Type **605**	20	10
1402	10 r. Cow and calf	35	35
1403	17 r. Family group	50	60
1404	50 r. Bull elephant	1·25	1·75
1401/4	Set of 4	2·10	2·50
MS1405	150×90 mm. Nos. 1401/4	2·10	2·50

606 S.A.A.R.C. Flags and Logo   **607** William Gopallawa

606a

(Des D. Paul. Litho Thai British Security Ptg Co Ltd, Thailand)

1998 (29 July). *10th Anniv of South Asian Association for Regional Co-operation. W* **606a** *(sideways). P* 14½×14.
1406	**606** 2 r. 50, multicoloured	20	15

(Des S. Silva. Litho Pakistan Security Ptg Corp, Karachi)

1998 (17 Sept). *William Gopallawa (first President of Sri Lanka) Commemoration. P* 13½.
1407	**607** 2 r. 50, multicoloured	20	15

608 Satellite and Computer   **609** Ven. Kotahene Pannakitti Nayaka Thero (Buddhist scholar)

(Des P. Gunasinghe. Litho Pakistan Security Ptg Corp, Karachi)

1998 (7 Oct). *Year of Information Technology. P* 13½.
1408	**608** 2 r. 50, multicoloured	15	15

(Des S. Silva. Litho Secura, Singapore)

1998 (11 Nov). *Distinguished Personalities. T* **609** *and similar vert designs. Multicoloured. P* 13.
1409	2 r. 50, Type **609**	15	15
1410	2 r. 50, Prof. Ediriweera Sarachchandra (scholar)	15	15
1411	2 r. 50, Sir Nicholas Attygalle (medical pioneer)	15	15
1412	2 r. 50, Dr. Samuel Fisk Green (Tamil scholar)	15	15
1409/12	Set of 4	55	55

610 Flag of Sri Lanka and Lions Club Emblem   **611** "50" and Meteorological Symbols

(Des P. Ediriweera. Litho Thai British Security Ptg Ltd, Thailand)

1998 (20 Nov). *Lions Clubs International 26th South Asia, Africa and Middle East Forum, Colombo. P* 14×14½.
1413	**610** 2 r. 50, multicoloured	30	20

(Des W. Rohana. Litho Pakistan Security Ptg Corp, Karachi)

1998 (7 Dec). *50th Anniv of Department of Meteorology. P* 13½.
1414	**611** 2 r. 50, multicoloured	15	15

612 Virgin Mary and the Infant Jesus   **613** S. W. Bandaranaike as a Young Man

(Des L. Priyantha Silva. Litho Pakistan Security Ptg Corp, Karachi)

1998 (10 Dec). *Christmas. T* **612** *and similar vert design. Multicoloured. P* 13½.
1415	2 r. 50, Type **612**	10	10
1416	20 r. The Annunciation	40	45
MS1417	90×150 mm. Nos. 1415/16	50	55

1998 (10 Dec). *Christmas. T* **612** *and similar vert design. Multicoloured. P* 13½.
1415	2 r. 50, Type **612**	10	10
1416	20 r. The Annunciation	40	55
	a. Black omitted		
MS1417	90×150 mm. Nos. 1415/16	50	65

The missing black, No. 1416a, shows on the hair, costumes and in the omission of the brown on the curtain.

(Des S. Silva. Litho Security Printers (M), Malaysia)

1999 (8 Jan). *Birth Centenary of S. W. Bandaranaike. T* **613** *and similar vert design. Multicoloured. P* 12.
1418	3 r. 50, Type **613**	15	15
1419	3 r. 50, Bandaranaike as Prime Minister	15	15
MS1420	81×100 mm. Nos. 1418/19. P 12½	30	35

(Litho Security Printers (M), Malaysia)

1999 (18 Jan). *No. 1357 redrawn with inscriptions in slightly different position. W* **138** *of Malaysia (sideways). P* 12½.
1421	1 r. Type **589**	10	10

614 Traditional Dancer   **615** Sir Arthur C. Clarke (author) and Spacecraft

(Des P. Ediriweera. Photo Courvoisier, Switzerland)

1999 (3 Feb). P 11½ (1 r. to 4 r.) or 11½×12 (5 r. to 20 r.).
1422	**614** 1 r. sepia	10	10
1423	2 r. greenish blue	10	10
1424	3 r. purple	10	10
1425	3 r. 50, ultramarine	10	10
1426	4 r. rose-carmine	10	10
1427	5 r. dull yellowish green	10	10
1428	10 r. bluish violet	20	25
1429	13 r. 50, bright vermilion	25	30
1430	17 r. deep turqoise-green	30	35
1431	20 r. bistre	40	45
1422/31	Set of 10	1·50	1·75

The 5 r. to 20 r. are larger, 21×26 mm.

(Des W. Rohana. Litho Security Printers (M), Malaysia)

1999 (19 Feb). *Fifty Years of Communications Improvement. T* **615** *and similar vert design. Multicoloured. P* 12.
1432	3 r. 50, Type **615**	15	15
	a. Horiz pair. Nos. 1432/3	30	30
1433	3 r. 50, Sir Arthur C. Clarke with spacecraft orbiting earth	15	15

Nos. 1432/3 were printed together, *se-tenant*, in horizontal pairs throughout the sheet, each pair forming a composite design.

616 Salvation Army Badge, Bible and Cross   **617** Activities of British Council

(Des P. Gunasinghe. Litho Security Printers (M), Malaysia)

1999 (28 Apr). *116th Anniv of Salvation Army in Sri Lanka. P* 12.
1434	**616** 3 r. 50, multicoloured	15	15

(Des A. Dharmasiri. Litho Security Printers (M), Malaysia)

1999 (20 May). *50th Anniv of British Council. P 12.*
1435 **617** 3 r. 50, multicoloured   15   15

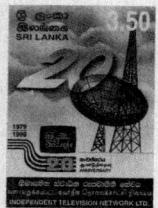

618 "Birth of Prince Siddhartha"   **619** Dish Aerial and Transmitting Tower

(Des P. Gunasinghe. Litho Security Printers (M), Malaysia)

1999 (25 May). *Vesak Festival. T* **618** *and similar vert designs. Multicoloured. P* 12½ (13 r. 50) or 12 (others).
1436	2 r. Type **618**	10	10
1437	3 r. 50, "The Enlightenment"	15	15
1438	13 r. 50, "The Maha Parinirvana"	35	40
1439	17 r. Celebrating Vesak	40	50
1436/9	Set of 4	80	1·00
MS1440	151×90 mm. Nos. 1436/9. P 12½	80	1·00

(Des P. Gunasinghe. Litho Secura, Singapore)

1999 (5 June). *20th Anniv of Independent Television. P 13.*
1441 **619** 3 r. 50, multicoloured   15   15

620 Sumithrayo Logo   **621** Scene from Handaya and Camera Crew

(Des W. Rohana. Litho Secura, Singapore)

1999 (14 June). *25th Anniv of Sumithrayo (humanitarian charity). P 13.*
1442 **620** 3 r. 50, multicoloured   15   15

(Des W. Rohana. Litho Secura, Singapore)

1999 (17 Sept). *Fifty Years of Sri Lankan Cinema. T* **621** *and similar vert designs. Multicoloured. P 13.*
1443	3 r. 50, Type **621**	10	10
1444	4 r. Scene from *Nidhanaya* and film societies' emblems	10	10
1445	10 r. Scene from *Gamperaliya* and camera crew	20	25
1446	17 r. Two scenes from *Kadawunu Poronduwa*	75	85
1443/6	Set of 4	60	70
MS1447	109×183 mm. Nos. 1443/6 ..	60	70

622 Vidyodaya Pirivena

(Des P. Gunasinghe. Litho Secura, Singapore)

1999 (17 Sept). *125th Anniv of Vidyodaya Pirivena (Buddhist education foundation). P 13.*
1448 **622** 3 r. 50, multicoloured   10   10

STAMP BOOKLETS

1905 (Oct). *Black on grey (No. SB1) or black on buff (No. SB1a) covers. Stapled.*
SB1   1 r. 21, booklet containing twenty-four 5 c. (No. 280) in blocks of 12 ..
SB1a   1 r. 45, booklet containing twenty-four 6 c. (No. 281) in blocks of 6 ..

1908. *Black on grey cover. Advertisement on back cover. Stapled.*
SB2   1 r. 20, booklet containing twenty-four 5 c. (No. 289) in blocks of 12 ..

1912. *Black on grey cover. Advertisement on back cover. Stapled.*
SB2a   1 r. 20, booklet containing twenty-four 5 c. (No. 304) in blocks of 12 ..

1919. *Black on orange covers. Telegraph details on back cover. Stapled.*
SB3   1 r. 44, booklet containing twenty-four 6 c. (No. 311) in blocks of 6 ..
   a. Black on grey cover. Advertisement on back cover ..
SB4   1 r. 44, booklet containing twenty-four 3 c. and twelve 6 c. (Nos. 310/11) in blocks of 6 ..
   a. Advertisement on back cover

1922. *Black on green covers. "Fiat" advertisement on back cover. Stapled.*
SB5   1 r. 44, booklet containing twenty-four 6 c. (No. 356) in blocks of 6 ..
SB6   1 r. 46, booklet containing twenty-four 3 c. and twelve 6 c. (Nos. 355/6) in blocks of 6 ..
   a. Black on orange cover. "Colombo Jewelry Store" advertisement on back cover ..

1926. *Black on green covers. Kennedy & Co. (No. SB7) or Fiat (No. SB8) advertisements on back cover. Stapled.*
SB7   2 r. 06, booklet containing twelve 3 c., 5 c. on 6 c. and 9 c. (Nos. 355, 362 and 357) in blocks of 6 £2500
SB8   2 r. 16, booklet containing twenty-four 9 c. (No. 357) in blocks of 6

1932. *Black on green covers. Stapled.*
SB9   1 r. 80, booklet containing thirty 6 c. (No. 356) in blocks of 6 and pane of three airmail labels £900
SB10   2 r. 70, booklet containing thirty 9 c. (No. 357) in blocks of 6 and pane of three airmail labels

1935 (May). *Silver Jubilee of King George V. Black on light blue (No. SB11) or light green (No. SB12) covers. Stapled.*
SB11   1 r. 80, booklet containing thirty 6 c. (No. 379) in blocks of 6 .. £1000
SB12   2 r. 70, booklet containing thirty 9 c. (No. 380) in blocks of 6 .. £1300

1935 (Dec)**–36.** *Black on blue (No. SB13) or green (No. SB14) covers. Stapled.*
SB13   1 r. 80, booklet containing thirty 6 c. (No. 370) in blocks of 6 and pane of four airmail labels
   a. Stamps in blocks of 10 .. £600
SB14   2 r. 70, booklet containing thirty 9 c. (No. 371) in blocks of 6 and pane of four airmail labels £700
   a. Stamps in blocks of 10 (1936) £700

1937 (Apr–June). *Coronation of King George VI. Black on blue (No. SB15) or olive-green (No. SB16) covers. Stapled.*
SB15   1 r. 80, booklet containing thirty 6 c. (No. 383) in blocks of 10 and pane of four airmail labels (June) £750
SB16   2 r. 70, booklet containing thirty 9 c. (No. 384) in blocks of 10 and pane of four airmail labels £800

1938. *Black on blue (No. SB17) or grey (No. SB18) covers. Stapled.*
SB17   1 r. 80, booklet containing thirty 6 c. (No. 388) in blocks of 10 and pane of four airmail labels
SB18   3 r. booklet containing fifteen 20 c. (No. 391) in blocks of 5 or 10 and pane of four airmail labels £900

1941. *Black on pink cover, with contents amended in manuscript. Stapled.*
SB19   1 r. 80, booklet containing sixty 3 c. on 6 c. (No. 398) in blocks of 10 ..
   a. Black on blue cover

1951 (5 Dec). *Black on buff cover. Stitched.*
SB20   1 r. booklet containing twenty 5 c. (No. 414) in blocks of four and pane of airmail labels .. 12·00
   a. Containing two blocks of ten 5 c. stamps and no airmail labels

1952 (21 Jan). *Black on green cover. Stitched.*
SB21   6 r. booklet containing eight 75 c. (No. 417) in blocks of 4 and two panes of four airmail labels .. 18·00

A limited edition stamp booklet was issued at the 20th Anniversary Exhibition for the Philatelic Society of Sri Lanka in 1998. This 14 r. booklet, which contained four examples of Nos. 1366 and 1406, was only available from the Philatelic Bureau and the Exhibition.

STANLEY GIBBONS STAMP COLLECTING SERIES

Introductory booklets on *How to Start, How to Identify Stamps* and *Collecting by Theme.* A series of well illustrated guides at a low price.
Write for details.

B 1

1999 (3 Feb). *Multicoloured cover as Type B* **1**. *Stamps attached by selvedge.*
SB22   10 r. booklet containing ten 1 r. (No. 1422) in block of 10 ..   50

OFFICIAL STAMPS

1869. *Issues of 1867–68 overprinted* "SERVICE" *in block letters. Although these stamps were prepared for use and sent out to the colony, they were never issued.*

Prices:
Narrow "SERVICE"		Wide "SERVICE"	
No. 64d, 2d. ..	65·00	No. 61, 1d. ..	55·00
67, 6d. ..	60·00	62, 3d. ..	95·00
68, 8d. ..	70·00		
71, 1s. ..	£110		
72, 2s. ..	£100		
72, 2s. imp ..	£700		

Until 1 October 1895 all Official mail was carried free. After that date postage was paid on Official letters to the general public, on certain interdepartmental mail and on all packets over 1lb in weight. Nos. O1/17 were provided for ths purpose.

On Service

(O 3)

1895. *Optd with Type O 3 by the Govt Printer, Colombo.*
O1	9	2 c. green (No. 147)	7·00	45
O2	39	3 c. terracotta and blue-green (No. 245)	10·00	55
O3	28	5 c. dull purple (No. 195)	3·25	30
O4	29	15 c. sage-green (No. 196)	12·00	50
O5		25 c. yellow-brown (No. 198)	10·00	1·00
O6		30 c. bright mauve and chestnut (No. 247)	13·00	50
O7	30	1 r. 12, dull rose (*wmk sideways*) (No. 201)	70·00	55·00
		a. Opt double, one albino	£200	
		b. Wmk upright	85·00	70·00
O1/7		Set of 7	£110	55·00

1899 (June)**–1900.** *Nos. 256/7 and 261/2 optd with Type O 3.*
O 8	9	2 c. pale orange-brown (3.00) ..	7·00	60
O 9	39	3 c. deep green (9.00) ..	8·00	1·90
O10	29	15 c. blue (9.00) ..	16·00	60
O11	39	75 c. black and red-brown (R.) ..	5·50	5·50
O8/11		Set of 4	32·00	7·75

1903 (26 Nov)**–04.** *Nos. 265/6, 268 and 271/3 optd with Type O 3.*
O12	44	2 c. red-brown (4.1.04) ..	11·00	85
O13	45	3 c. green ..	7·00	2·00
O14	46	5 c. dull purple ..	16·00	1·25
O15	48	15 c. blue ..	26·00	2·50
O16		25 c. bistre (15.7.04) ..	21·00	18·00
O17		30 c. dull violet and green (14.3.04) ..	10·00	1·50
O12/17		Set of 6	80·00	24·00

Stamps overprinted "On Service" were withdrawn on 1 October 1904.

POSTAL FISCALS

1952 (1 Dec). *As T* **72** *but inscr* "REVENUE" *at sides. Chalk-surfaced paper.*
F1   10 r. dull green and yellow-orange ..   60·00   28·00
This revenue stamp was on sale for postal use from 1 December 1952, until 14 March 1954.

F 1 Republic Crest

(Recess Harrison)

1979 (28 May)**–83.** *As Type F* **1**, *but with additional Sinhala and Tamil inscrs on either side of crest. W* **4** *of Maldive Islands. P 13×12.*
F2	20 r. blackish green ..	5·00	2·75
F3	50 r. deep slate-violet ..	12·00	7·00
F4	100 r. deep carmine-red (14.10.83) ..	22·00	22·00
F2/4	Set of 3	35·00	29·00
The above, together with 500 and 1000 r. values, were originally released for fiscal purposes on 24 June 1974. The dates quoted are those on which they were validated for postal use. All three were withdrawn on 6 August 1984.

F 2

(Litho Harrison)

1984 (15 Aug). *Wmk* F **2**. *P* 14½×14.
F5 F **1** 50 r. orange .. .. .. 28·00 13·00
F6 100 r. dull chocolate .. .. 45·00 45·00
  A 500 r. value also exists, but was not valid for postal purposes.

(Recess Harrison)

1984 (21 Sept). *Wmk* F **2**. *P* 14½×14.
F7 F **1** 50 r. orange-vermilion .. .. 1·25 1·50
F8 100 r. deep reddish purple .. .. 2·50 3·00
  Stamps in this series with face values of 500 or 1000 r. were not valid for postal purposes.

F 3

(Recess D.L.R.)

1998 (16 Dec)–**99**. *Wmk* F **3**. *P* 14½×14.
F 9 F **1** 50 r. orange (28.9.99) .. .. 1·00 1·10
F10 100 r. deep reddish brown .. .. 2·00 2·25

Sudan

ANGLO-EGYPTIAN CONDOMINIUM

An Egyptian post office was opened at Suakin in 1867 and the stamps of Egypt, including postage dues and the official (No. O64), were used in the Sudan until replaced by the overprinted "SOUDAN" issue of 1897.

Cancellations have been identified from eleven post offices, using the following postmark types:

A

B

C

D

E

F

G

H

I

J

K

L

BERBER (*spelt BARBAR*). *Open* 1 October 1873 *to* 20 May 1884. *Postmark type* G.
DABROUSSA. *Open* 1891 *onwards. Postmark as type J but with 11 bars in arcs.*
DONGOLA. *Open* 1 October 1873 *to* 13 June 1885 *and* 1896 *onwards. Postmark types* F, G, K, L.
GEDAREF. *Open* August 1878 *to* April 1884. *Postmark type* H.
KASSALA. *Open* 15 May 1875 *to* 30 July 1885. *Postmark type* G.
KHARTOUM. *Open* 1 October 1873 *to* 14 December 1885. *Postmark types* E (*spelt KARTUM*), G (*spelt HARTUM*), I (*with or without line of Arabic above date*).
KORTI. *Open* January *to* March 1885 *and* 1897. *Postmark type* K.
SUAKIN. *Open* November 1867 *onwards. Postmark types* A, B, C (*spelt SUAKIM*), D (*spelt SUAKIM and also with year replaced by concentric arcs*), I (*spelt SOUAKIN*), J (*spelt SAWAKIN, number of bars differs*).
TANI. *Open* 1885. *Postmark type* K.
TOKAR. *Open* 1891 *onwards. Postmark type* J (7 bars in arcs).
WADI HALFA. *Open* 1 October 1873 *onwards. Postmark types* F (*spelt WADI HALFE*), G (*spelt WADI HALFE*), I, J (*number of bars differs*).
WADI HALFA CAMP. *Open* 1896 *onwards. Postmark type* I.

Official records also list post offices at the following locations, but no genuine postal markings from them have yet been reported: Chaka, Dara, Debeira, El Abiad, El Fasher, El Kalabat, Faras, Fashoda, Fazogl, Ishkeit, Kalkal, Karkok, Mesellemia, Sara, Sennar and Taoufikia (not to be confused with the town of the same name in Egypt).

M

The post office at Kassala was operated by Italy from 1894 until 1896, using stamps of Eritrea cancelled with postmark type M.

From the last years of the nineteenth century that part of Sudan lying south of the 5 degree North latitude line was administered by Uganda (the area to the east of the Nile) (until 1912) or by Belgium (the area to the west of the Nile, known as the Lado Enclave) (until 1910).

Stamps of Uganda or East Africa and Uganda were used at Gondokoro and Nimuli between 1901 and 1911, usually cancelled with circular date stamps or, probably in transit at Khartoum, by a lozenge-shaped grid of 18 × 17 dots.

Stamps of Belgian Congo were used from the Lado Enclave between 1897 and 1910, as were those of Uganda (1901–10) and Sudan (1902–10), although no local postmarks were supplied, examples being initially cancelled in manuscript.

Stamps of Sudan were used at Gambeila (Ethiopia) between 1910 and 10 June 1940 and from 22 March 1941 until 15 October 1956. Sudan stamps were also used at Sabderat (Eritrea) between March 1910 and 1940.

PRICES FOR STAMPS ON COVER TO 1945	
Nos. 1/9	*from* × 20
Nos. 10/17	*from* × 6
Nos. 18/29	*from* × 5
Nos. 30/95	*from* × 2
Nos. D1/11	*from* × 30
Nos. O1/3	*from* × 10
Nos. O4/22	*from* × 15
Nos. A1/16	*from* × 6

(Currency. 10 milliemes = 1 piastre. 100 piastres = £1 Sudanese)

السودان
SOUDAN
(1)

1897 (1 Mar). *Nos.* 54b, 55a, 57/a, 58a, 59, 60, 62a *and* 63 *of Egypt optd as* T 1 *by Govt Ptg Wks, Bûlâq, Cairo.*

1	1 m. pale brown	1·50	2·00
	a. Opt inverted	£200	
	b. Opt omitted (in vert pair with normal)	£950	
	c. Deep brown	1·50	2·25
	w. Wmk inverted		
3	2 m. green	1·25	1·75
	a. Opt omitted (in vert pair with normal)	£3000	
4	3 m. orange-yellow	1·40	1·50
	a. Opt omitted (in vert pair with normal)	£3000	
5	5 m. rose-carmine	2·00	70
	a. Opt inverted	£200	£225
	b. Opt omitted (in vert pair with normal)	£1000	
6	1 p. ultramarine	7·00	2·00
7	2 p. orange-brown	50·00	14·00
	w. Wmk inverted	75·00	

8	5 p. slate	42·00	15·00
	a. Opt double	£2750	
	b. Opt omitted (in vert pair with normal)	£3000	
9	10 p. mauve	30·00	42·00
1/9	*Set of* 8	£120	70·00

Numerous forgeries exist including some which show the characteristics of the varieties mentioned below.

There are six varieties of the overprint on each value most of which can be supplied in vertical strips at double the catalogue price.

In some printings the large dot is omitted from the left-hand Arabic character on one stamp in the pane of 60.

Only two examples, one unused and the other used (in the Royal Collection), are known of No. 8a. In both instances one impression is partially albino.

PRINTERS. All stamps of Sudan were printed by De La Rue & Co, Ltd, London, *except where otherwise stated.*

2 Arab Postman

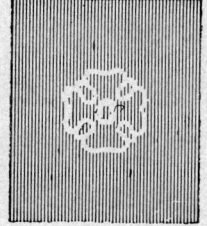

3

(Des E. A. Stanton. Typo)

1898 (1 Mar). W 3. P 14.

10	2	1 m. brown and pink	50	1·75
11		2 m. green and brown	1·75	2·25
12		3 m. mauve and green	2·00	2·25
13		5 m. carmine and black	1·75	10
14		1 p. blue and brown	5·50	4·00
15		2 p. black and blue	22·00	7·50
16		5 p. brown and green	27·00	12·00
17		10 p. black and mauve	25·00	2·25
10/17			*Set of* 8	75·00	29·00

5 Milliemes

4   (5)

1902–21. W 4. *Ordinary paper.* P 14.

18	2	1 m. brown and carmine (5.05)	1·25	30
19		2 m. green and brown (11.02)	1·75	10
20		3 m. mauve and green (7.03)	2·25	25
21		4 m. blue and bistre (20.1.07)	1·50	2·50
22		4 m. vermilion and brown (10.07)	1·50	75
23		5 m. scarlet and black (12.03)	2·00	10
		w. Wmk inverted	†	£100
24		1 p. blue and brown (12.03)	2·25	30
25		2 p. black and blue (2.08)	24·00	1·75
26		2 p. purple & orge-yellow (*chalk-surfaced paper*) (22.12.21)	3·75	9·00
27		5 p. brown and green (2.08)	22·00	30
		a. Chalk-surfaced paper	28·00	3·25
28		10 p. black and mauve (2.11)	22·00	3·75
		a. Chalk-surfaced paper	22·00	7·50
18/28			*Set of* 11	75·00	16·00

1903 (Sept). *No.* 16 *surch at Khartoum with* T 5, *in blocks of* 30.

29	2	5 m. on 5 pi. brown and green	6·50	9·00
		a. Surch inverted	£250	£225

6

7

1921–23. *Chalk-surfaced paper. Typo.* W 4. P 14.

30	6	1 m. black and orange (4.2.22)	80	3·50
31		2 m. yellow-orange and chocolate (1922)	9·00	11·00
		a. Yellow and chocolate (1923)..	11·00	11·00
32		3 m. mauve and green (25.1.22)	2·50	7·00
33		4 m. green and chocolate (21.3.22)	6·00	2·25
34		5 m. olive-brown and black (4.2.22)	2·25	10
35		10 m. carmine and black (1922)	2·25	10
36		15 m. bright blue and chestnut (14.12.21)	2·75	1·00
30/36			*Set of* 7	23·00	22·00

1927–41. W 7. *Chalk-surfaced paper.* P 14.

37	6	1 m. black and orange	60	10
		a. Ordinary paper (1941)	70	10
38		2 m. orange and chocolate	70	10
		a. Ordinary paper (1941)	1·50	10
39		3 m. mauve and green	50	10
		a. Ordinary paper (1941)	2·25	30
40		4 m. green and chocolate	40	10
		a. Ordinary paper (1941)	3·00	30
		aw. Wmk inverted	75·00	

41	6	5 m. olive-brown and black	..	..	30	10
		a. Ordinary paper (1941)	..	..	2·50	10
42		10 m. carmine and black	..	..	1·25	10
		a. Ordinary paper (1941)	..	..	3·00	10
43		15 m. bright blue and chestnut	..	..	80	10
		a. Ordinary paper (1941)	..	..	1·25	10
44	2	2 p. purple and orange-yellow	..	..	1·00	10
		a. Ordinary paper (1941)	..	..	3·50	10
44b		3 p. red-brown and blue (1.1.40)	..	..	2·75	10
		ba. Ordinary paper (1941)	..	..	16·00	10
44c		4 p. ultramarine and black (2.11.36)	..	..	3·50	10
45		5 p. chestnut and green	..	..	1·00	10
		a. Ordinary paper (1941)	..	..	3·75	40
45b		6 p. greenish blue and black (2.11.36)	..	..	4·75	40
		ba. Ordinary paper (1941)	..	..	27·00	1·25
45c		8 p. emerald and black (2.11.36)	..	..	5·50	2·25
		ca. Ordinary paper (1941)	..	..	27·00	3·50
46		10 p. black and reddish purple	..	..	2·25	10
		a. Ordinary paper. *Black and bright mauve* (1941)	..	..	8·00	70
46b		20 p. pale blue and blue (17.10.35)	..	..	2·25	10
		a. Ordinary paper (1941)	..	..	3·50	10
37/46b			*Set of 15*		25·00	3·00

The ordinary paper of this issue is thick, smooth and opaque and was a wartime substitute for chalk-surfaced paper.

For similar stamps, but with different Arabic inscriptions, see Nos. 96/111.

AIR MAIL	AIR MAIL	AIR
(8)	(9)	Extended foot to "R" (R.5/12)

1931 (15 Feb–Mar). *Air. Nos. 41/2 and 44 optd with T* **8** *or* **9** (2 p.).

47	6	5 m. olive-brown and black (Mar)	..		35	70
48		10 m. carmine and black	..		85	8·00
49	2	2 p. purple and orange-yellow	..		85	6·50
		a. Extended foot to "R"	..		21·00	
47/9			*Set of 3*		1·90	14·00

2½   2½

AIR MAIL

١٢/٧   ١٢/٧

10 Statue of Gen. Gordon   (11)

1931 (1 Sept)–37. *Air. Recess. W* **7** (*sideways**). *P* 14.

49b	10	3 m. green and sepia (1.1.33)	..	..	2·50	5·50
50		5 m. black and green	..		1·00	10
51		10 m. black and carmine	..		1·00	20
52		15 m. red-brown and sepia	..		40	10
		aw. Wmk top of G to right				
		b. Perf 11½×12½ (1937)			4·50	10
53		2 p. black and orange	..		30	10
		b. Perf 11½×12½ (1937)			4·50	15·00
53b		2½ p. magenta and blue (1.1.33)			3·50	10
		c. Perf 11½×12½ (1936)			3·00	10
		ca. *Aniline magenta and blue*			7·50	3·25
		cx. Wmk reversed				
		cy. Wmk top of G to right reversed				
54		3 p. black and grey	..		60	15
		a. Perf 11½×12½ (1937)			85	35
55		3½ p. black and violet	..		1·50	80
		a. Perf 11½×12½ (1937)			2·50	10·00
56		4½ p. red-brown and grey	..		10·00	15·00
57		5 p. black and ultramarine	..		1·00	30
		a. Perf 11½×12½ (1937)			3·75	35
57b		7½ p. green and emerald (17.10.35)			9·00	4·50
		by. Wmk top of G to right reversed				
57d		10 p. brown and greenish blue (17.10.35)			8·50	1·00
		e. Perf 11½×12½ (1937)			4·00	17·00
		ey. Wmk top of G to right reversed				
49b/57d			*Set of 12 (p 14)*		35·00	24·00
52b/7e			*Set of 8 (p 11½×12½)*		24·00	45·00

*The normal sideways watermark shows the top of the G pointing left *as seen from the back of the stamp*.

1932 (18 July). *Air. No. 44 surch with T* **11**.

58	2	2½ p. on 2 p. purple and orange-yellow			1·40	3·50

12 Gen. Gordon   13 Gordon Memorial College,
(after C. Ouless)   Khartoum

14 Gordon Memorial Service, Khartoum
(after R. C. Woodville)

1935 (1 Jan). *50th Death Anniv of General Gordon, Recess. W* **7**. *P* 14.

59	12	5 m. green	..	..	35	10
60		10 m. yellow-brown	..	..	85	25
61		13 m. ultramarine	..	..	85	9·00
62		15 m. scarlet	..	..	1·75	25

63	13	2 p. blue	..	..	1·25	20
64		5 p. orange-vermilion		..	1·25	40
65		10 p. purple	..	..	7·50	8·50
66	14	20 p. black	..	..	22·00	48·00
67		50 p. red-brown	..	..	80·00	£100
59/67			*Set of 9*		£100	£150

7½ PIASTRES   5 MILLIEMES
٧ ١/٢ قروش   ٥ مليمات
(15)   (16)

1935. *Air. Nos. 49b/51 and 56 surch as T* **15**.

68	10	15 m. on 10 m. black and carmine (Apr)		40	10
		a. Surch double			£600	£700
69		2½ p. on 3 m. green and sepia (Apr)		85	5·50
		a. Second arabic letter from left missing	65·00	£100
		b. Small "½"			2·75	20·00
70		2½ p. on 5 m. black and green (Apr)		40	1·50
		a. Second Arabic letter from left missing	35·00	55·00
		b. Small "½"			1·75	8·00
		c. Surch inverted			£600	£700
		d. Ditto with variety a.			£3000	
		e. Ditto with variety b.			£1200	
71		3 p. on 4½ p. red-brown and grey (Apr)	1·75	14·00
72		7½ p. on 4½ p. red-brown and grey (Mar)	6·50	45·00
73		10 p. on 4½ p. red-brown and grey (Mar)	6·50	45·00
68/73			*Set of 6*		15·00	£100

Nos. 69a and 70a occur in position 49 of the sheet of 50; the small "½" variety occurs in positions 17, 27, 32, 36, 41, 42 and 46.

The 15 m. on 10 m. surcharged in red and the 2½ p. on 3 m and 2½ p. on 5 m. in green are from proof sheets; the latter two items being known cancelled.

There were four proof sheets of the 7½ p. on 4½ p., two in red and two in black. The setting on these proof sheets showed three errors subsequently corrected before No. 72 was surcharged. Twelve positions showed an Arabic "⅓" instead of "½", one an English "¼" for "½" and another one of the Arabic letters inverted.

1938 (1 July). *Air. Nos. 53c, 55, 57b and 57d surch as T* **16**.

74	10	5 m. on 2½ p. mag & bl (p 11½×12½)	3·50	10
		w. Wmk top of G to right			
		x. Wmk reversed			
75		3 p. on 3½ p. black and violet (p 14)	35·00	48·00
		a. Perf 11½×12½		£425	£550
76		3 p. on 7½ p. green and emerald (p 14)	7·00	6·50
		ax. Wmk reversed			
		ay. Wmk top of G to right reversed	50·00	
		b. Perf 11½×12½		£425	£550
77		5 p. on 10 p. brown & greenish bl (p 14)	1·75	4·75
		a. Perf 11½×12½		£425	£550
74/7			*Set of 4*	42·00	55·00

A 5 p. on 2½ p., perf 11½×12½, exists either mint or cancelled from a trial printing (*Price* £350 *unused*).

5 Mills.
٥ مليم   مليم
(17)   Normal ("Malime")

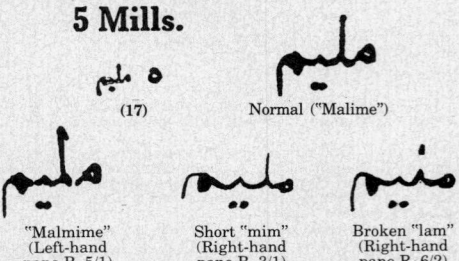

"Malmime"   Short "mim"   Broken "lam"
(Left-hand   (Right-hand   (Right-hand
pane R. 5/1)   pane R. 3/1)   pane R. 6/2)

5 M
Inserted "5"
(Bottom right-hand
pane R. 4/5)

1940 (25 Feb). *No. 42 surch with T* **17** *by McCorquodale (Sudan) Ltd, Khartoum*.

78	6	5 m. on 10 m. carmine and black	..	50	30
		a. "Malmime"			45·00	50·00
		b. Two dots omitted (Right-hand pane R. 8/6)		45·00	50·00
		c. Short "mim"	..		45·00	50·00
		d. Broken "lam"	..		45·00	50·00
		e. Inserted "5"	..		£130	

4½ Piastres
4½ PIASTRES   ٤ ١/٢ قرش
(18)   (19)

1940–1. *Nos. 41 and 45c surch as T* **18** *or* **19** *at Khartoum*.

79	6	4½ p. on 5 m. olive-brown & blk (9.2.41)	48·00	3·75
80	2	4½ p. on 8 p. emerald and black (12.12.40)	38·00	9·00

20 Tuti Island, R. Nile,   21 Tuti Island, R. Nile
near Khartoum   near Khartoum

(Des Miss H. M. Hebbert. Litho Security Printing Press, Nasik, India)

1941 (25 Mar–10 Aug). *P* 14 × 13½ (*T* **20**) *or P* 13½ × 14 (*T* **21**).

81	20	1 m. slate and orange (10.8)	..	1·00	3·50
82		2 m. orange and chocolate (10.8)	..	1·00	3·50
83		3 m. mauve and green (10.8)	..	1·00	20
84		4 m. green and chocolate (10.8)	..	80	50
85		5 m. olive-brown and black (10.8)	..	30	10
86		10 m. carmine and black (10.8)	..	7·00	1·75
87		15 m. bright blue and chestnut	..	70	10
88	21	2 p. purple and orange-yellow (10.8)	3·50	60
89		3 p. red-brown and blue	..	70	10
90		4 p. ultramarine and black	..	4·50	10
91		5 p. chestnut and green (10.8)	..	4·50	8·50
92		6 p. greenish blue and black (10.8)	18·00	40
93		8 p. emerald and black (10.8)	..	14·00	45
94		10 p. slate and purple (10.8)	..	50·00	75
95		20 p. pale blue and blue (10.8)	..	50·00	29·00
81/95			*Set of 15*		£140	45·00

22   23

1948 (1 Jan–June). *Arabic inscriptions below camel altered. Typo. W* **7**. *Ordinary paper* (8, 10, 20 p.) *or chalk-surfaced paper* (*others*). *P* 14.

96	22	1 m. black and orange	..	..	35	3·25
97		2 m. orange and chocolate	..	..	80	3·75
98		3 m. mauve and green	..	..	30	3·25
99		4 m. deep green and chocolate	..		30	10
100		5 m. olive-brown and black	..		5·00	1·75
101		10 m. rose-red and black	..		5·00	10
		a. Centre inverted	..	..	†	—
102		15 m. ultramarine and chestnut	..		4·50	10
103	23	2 p. purple and orange-yellow	..		6·50	1·50
104		3 p. red-brown and deep blue	..		6·00	20
105		4 p. ultramarine and black	..		4·00	1·75
106		5 p. brown-orange and deep green			4·00	1·75
107		6 p. greenish blue and black	..		4·50	3·00
108		8 p. bluish green and black	..		4·50	3·00
109		10 p. black and mauve	..		11·00	3·25
		a. Chalk-surfaced paper (June)	..	25·00	4·25
110		20 p. pale blue and deep blue	..		4·50	30
		a. Perf 13. Chalk-surfaced paper (June)		48·00	£130
111		50 p. carmine and ultramarine	..	6·50	2·00
96/111			*Set of 16*		60·00	26·00

A single used example is known of No. 101a.

For similar stamps, but with different Arabic inscriptions, see Nos. 37/46b.

24   25

1948 (1 Oct). *Golden Jubilee of "Camel Postman" design. Chalk-surfaced paper. Typo. W* **7**. *P* 13.

112	24	2 p. black and light blue	..	..	20	10

1948 (23 Dec). *Opening of Legislative Assembly, Chalk-surfaced paper. Typo. W* **7**. *P* 13.

113	25	10 m. rose-red and black	..		30	10
114		5 p. brown-orange and deep green	..	50	70

26 Blue Nile Bridge, Khartoum

(Des Col. W. L. Atkinson (2½ p., 6 p.), G. R. Wilson (3 p.), others from photographs. Recess)

1950 (1 July). *Air. T* **26** *and similar horiz designs. W* **7**. *P* 12.

115		2 p. black and blue-green	..		4·50	90
116		2½ p. light blue and red-orange	..	75	1·00
117		3 p. reddish purple and blue	..	3·00	60
118		3½ p. purple-brown and yellow-brown	1·25	2·50
119		4 p. brown and light blue	..	1·00	2·00
120		4½ p. black and ultramarine	..	2·50	3·50
		a. *Black and steel-blue*	..	5·50	5·50
121		6 p. black and carmine	..		1·00	2·50
122		20 p. black and purple	..		1·75	4·50
115/122			*Set of 8*		14·00	16·00

Designs:—2½ p. Kassala Jebel; 3 p. Sagia (water wheel); 3½ p. Port Sudan; 4 p. Gordon Memorial College; 4½ p. *Gordon Pasha* (Nile mail boat); 6 p. Suakin; 20 p. G.P.O., Khartoum.

34 Ibex

35 Cotton Picking

(Des Col. W. L. Atkinson (1 m., 2 m., 4 m., 5 m., 10 m., 3 p., 3½ p., 20 p.), Col. E. A. Stanton (50 p.) others from photographs. Typo)

1951 (1 Sept)–62? *Designs as T 34/5. Chalk-surfaced paper. W 7. P 14 (millieme values) or 13 (piastre values).*
123		1 m. black and orange		70	1·25
124		2 m. black and bright blue		1·50	50
125		3 m. black and green		5·00	2·25
126		4 m. black and yellow-green		1·00	2·50
127		5 m. black and purple		1·50	10
		a. Black and reddish purple (1962?)		4·50	40
128		10 m. black and pale blue		20	10
129		15 m. black and chestnut		3·00	10
		a. Black and brown-orange (1962?)		3·25	10
130		2 p. deep blue and pale blue		20	10
		a. Deep blue and very pale blue (1962?)		3·00	10
131		3 p. brown and dull ultramarine		5·00	10
		a. Brown and deep blue (1962?)		7·50	90
132		3½ p. bright green and red-brown		1·25	10
		a. Light emerald and red-brown (1962?)		2·75	10
133		4 p. ultramarine and black		60	10
		a. Deep blue and black (1962?)		5·50	10
134		5 p. orange-brown and yellow-green		30	10
135		6 p. blue and black		6·50	2·50
		a. Deep blue and black (1962?)		14·00	5·50
136		8 p. blue and brown		11·00	2·25
		a. Deep blue and brown (1962?)		14·00	2·00
137		10 p. black and green		1·25	10
138		20 p. blue-green and black		4·50	1·25
139		50 p. carmine and black		12·00	1·25
123/39		Set of 17		50·00	12·00

Designs: *Vert as T 34*—2 m. Whale-headed Stork; 3 m. Giraffe; 4 m. Baggara girl; 5 m. Shilluk warrior; 10 m. Hadendowa; 15 m. Policeman. *Horiz as T 35*—3 p. Ambatch reed canoe; 3½ p. Nuba wrestlers; 4 p. Weaving; 5 p. Saluka farming; 6 p. Gum tapping; 8 p. Darfur chief; 10 p. Stack Laboratory; 20 p. Nile Lechwe. *Vert as T 35*—50 p. Camel postman.

SELF-GOVERNMENT

51 Camel Postman

1954 (9 Jan). *Self-Government. Chalk-surfaced paper. Typo. W 7. P 13.*
140	51	15 m. orange-brown and bright green		50	1·00
141		3 p. blue and indigo		50	1·60
142		5 p. black and reddish purple		50	1·25
140/2		Set of 3		1·40	3·50

Stamps as Type 51, but dated "1953" were released in error at the Sudan Agency in London. They had no postal validity (*Price per set £16 un*).

Later issues of Sudan as an independent republic will be found in Part 14 (*Africa since Independence N–Z*) of this catalogue.

STAMP BOOKLETS

Nos. SB1/4 have one cover inscribed in English and one in Arabic.

1912. *Black on pink cover, size 74×29 mm. Stapled.*
SB1 100 m. booklet containing twenty 5 m. (No. 23) in pairs £650

1924. *Black on pink cover, size 45×50 mm. Stapled.*
SB2 105 m. booklet containing twenty 5 m. (No. 34) in blocks of 4

1926. *Black on pink cover, size 45×50 mm. Stapled.*
SB3 105 m. booklet containing twenty 5 m. (No. 41) in blocks of 4
No examples of No. SB3 are known to have survived.

1930. *Black on pink cover, size 45×50 mm. Stapled.*
SB4 100 m. booklet containing twenty 5 m. (No. 41) in blocks of 4 .. .. .. £950
Some supplies of No. SB4 included a page of air mail labels.

POSTAGE DUE STAMPS

1897 (1 Mar). *Type D 24 of Egypt, optd with T 1 at Bûlaq.*
D1		2 m. green		1·75	8·00
		a. Opt omitted (in horiz pair with normal) £2250		
D2		4 m. maroon		1·75	8·00
		a. Bisected (2 m.) (on cover)		†	
D3		1 p. ultramarine		10·00	5·00
D4		2 p. orange		10·00	11·00
		a. Bisected (1 p.) (on cover)		†	£1200
D1/4		Set of 4		21·00	29·00

In some printings the large dot is omitted from the left-hand Arabic character on one stamp in the pane.
No. D1 has been recorded used as a bisect.

D 1   Gunboat *Zafir*   D 2

1901 (1 Jan)–26. *Typo. W 4 (sideways). Ordinary paper. P 14.*
D5	D 1	2 m. black and brown		55	60
		a. Wmk upright (1912)		£150	60·00
		b. Chalk-surfaced paper (6.24*)		75	4·00
D6		4 m. brown and green		2·00	90
		a. Chalk-surfaced paper (9.26*)		5·00	1·40
D7		10 m. green and mauve		3·75	3·75
		a. Wmk upright (1912)		£100	50·00
		b. Chalk-surfaced paper (6.24*)		10·00	8·50
D8		20 m. ultramarine and carmine		3·25	3·25
D5/8		Set of 4		8·00	7·50

*Dates quoted for the chalk-surfaced paper printings are those of the earliest recorded postal use. These printings were despatched to the Sudan in March 1922 (10 m.) or September 1922 (others)).

The 4 m. is known bisected at Khartoum or Omdurman in November/December 1901 and the 20 m. at El Obeid in 1904–05.

1927–30. *W 7. Chalk-surfaced paper. P 14.*
D9	D 1	2 m. black and brown (1930)		2·50	2·50
D10		4 m. brown and green		90	80
D11		10 m. green and mauve		1·25	1·60
		a. Ordinary paper		18·00	
D9/11		Set of 3		4·25	4·50

1948 (1 Jan). *Arabic inscriptions at foot altered. Chalk-surfaced paper. Typo. W 7. P 14.*
D12	D 2	2 m. black and brown-orange		1·00	30·00
D13		4 m. brown and green		2·00	26·00
D14		10 m. green and mauve		18·00	18·00
D15		20 m. ultramarine and carmine		18·00	32·00
D12/15		Set of 4		35·00	95·00

The 10 and 20 m. were reissued in 1980 on Sudan arms watermarked paper.

OFFICIAL STAMPS

1900 (8 Feb). *5 mils of 1897 punctured "S G" by hand. The "S" has 14 and the "G" 12 holes.*
O1 5 m. rose-carmine .. .. .. 45·00 20·00

1901 (Jan). *1 m. wmk Quatrefoil, punctured as No. O1.*
O2 1 m. brown and pink .. .. 42·00 30·00
Nos. O1/2 are found with the punctured "SG" inverted, reversed or inverted and reversed.

O.S.G.S.   O.S.G.S.
(O 1)   ("On Sudan Government
(O 2)   Service")

1902. *No. 10 optd at Khartoum as Type O 1 in groups of 30 stamps.*
O3	2	1 m. brown and pink		2·00	8·50
		a. Oval "O" (No. 19)		40·00	£100
		b. Round stops. (Nos. 25 to 30)		7·50	35·00
		c. Opt inverted		£250	£350
		d. Ditto and oval "O"		£2500	
		e. Ditto and round stops		£600	£750
		f. Opt double		£350	
		g. Ditto and round stops		£800	
	|h. Ditto and oval "O"|		

1903–12. *T 2 optd as Type O 2, by D.L.R. in sheets of 120 stamps.*
(i) *Wmk Quatrefoil (3.06)*
O 4		10 p. black and mauve		13·00	23·00
		a. Malformed "O"		£120	

(ii) *Wmk Mult Star and Crescent*
O 5		1 m. brown and carmine (9.04)		50	10
	|a. Opt double|		
		b. Malformed "O"		19·00	
O 6		3 m. mauve and green (2.04)		2·50	15
		a. Opt double		£850	£850
		b. Malformed "O"		42·00	
O 7		5 m. scarlet and black (1.1.03)		2·50	10
		a. Malformed "O"		42·00	
O 8		1 p. blue and brown (1.1.03)		2·50	10
		a. Malformed "O"		42·00	
O 9		2 p. black and blue (1.1.03)		22·00	20
		a. Malformed "O"		£150	
O10		5 p. brown and green (1.1.03)		2·00	30
		a. Malformed "O"		45·00	
O11		10 p. black and mauve (9.12)		4·00	48·00
		a. Malformed "O"		65·00	
O4/11		Set of 8		45·00	60·00

The malformed "O" is slightly flattened on the left-hand side and occurs on position 7 of the lower pane.

1913 (Jan)–22. *Nos. 18/20 and 23/8 punctured "SG" by machine. The "S" has 12 holes and the "G" 13.*
O12	2	1 m. brown and carmine		5·50	25
O13		2 m. green and brown (1915)		8·00	6·50
O14		3 m. mauve and green		9·00	70
O15		5 m. scarlet and black		4·25	15
O16		1 p. blue and brown		6·00	35
O17		2 p. black and blue		13·00	65
O18		2 p. purple and orange-yellow (chalk-surfaced paper) (1922)		5·50	8·00
O19		5 p. brown and green		21·00	1·50
		a. Chalk-surfaced paper		21·00	3·25
O20		10 p. black and mauve (1914)		27·00	27·00
		a. Chalk-surfaced paper		27·00	27·00
O12/20		Set of 9		90·00	40·00

1922. *Nos. 32/5 punctured "SG" by machine. The "S" has 9 holes and the "G" 10.*
O21	6	3 m. mauve and green		16·00	12·00
O22		4 m. green and chocolate		16·00	7·50
O23		5 m. olive-brown and black		1·00	1·25
O24		10 m. carmine and black		2·00	1·25
O21/4		Set of 4		32·00	20·00

1927–30. *Nos. 39/42, 44, 45 and 46 punctured "SG" by machine. Nos. O25/8 have 9 holes in the "S" and 10 in the "G"; Nos. O29/31 12 holes in the "S" and 13 in the "G".*
O25	6	3 m. mauve and green (1928)		10·00	3·25
O26		4 m. green and chocolate (1930)		70·00	48·00
O27		5 m. olive-green and black		4·50	10
O28		10 m. carmine and black		9·00	35
O29	2	2 p. purple and orange-yellow		12·00	95
O30		5 p. chestnut and green		18·00	3·50
O31		10 p. black and reddish purple		35·00	60·00
O25/31		Set of 7		£140	60·00

The use of Nos. O25/31 on internal official mail ceased in 1932, but they continued to be required for official mail to foreign destinations until replaced by Nos. O32/46 in 1936.

S.G.   S.G.   S.G.
(O 3)   (O 4)   (O 4a)

1936 (19 Sept)–46. *Nos. 37a, 38a, 39/43 optd with Type O 3, and 44, 44ba, 44c, 45, 45ba, 45ca, 46 and 46ba with Type O 4. W 7. P 14.*
O32	6	1 m. black and orange (22.11.46)		1·60	9·00
		a. Opt double		†	£150
O33		2 m. orange and chocolate (ordinary paper) (4.45)		50	3·25
		a. Chalk-surfaced paper		—	70·00
O34		3 m. mauve and green (chalk-surfaced paper) (1.37)		2·50	10
O35		4 m. grn & choc (chalk-surfaced paper) (4.45)		3·00	2·50
O36		5 m. olive-brown and black (chalk-surfaced paper) (3.40)		1·00	10
		a. Ordinary paper		16·00	40
O37		10 m. carmine and black (chalk-surfaced paper) (6.46)		70	10
O38		15 m. bright blue and chestnut (chalk-surfaced paper) (21.6.37)		6·00	20
		a. Ordinary paper		32·00	1·75
O39	2	2 p. purple & orange-yellow (chalk-surfaced paper) (4.37)		11·00	10
		a. Ordinary paper		28·00	2·50
O39b		3 p. red-brown and blue (4.46)		5·50	1·75
O39c		4 p. ultramarine and black (chalk-surfaced paper) (4.46)		23·00	3·25
		ca. Ordinary paper		48·00	4·00
O40		5 p. chestnut and green (chalk-surfaced paper)		14·00	10
		a. Ordinary paper		48·00	4·50
O40b		6 p. greenish blue and black (4.46)		7·00	6·50
O40c		8 p. emerald and black (4.46)		5·00	24·00
O41		10 p. black and reddish purple (chalk-surfaced paper) (10.37)		25·00	7·50
		a. Ordinary paper. Black and bright mauve (1941)		40·00	2·75
O42		20 p. pale blue and blue (6.46)		24·00	19·00
O32/42		Set of 15		£110	65·00

1948 (1 Jan). *Nos. 96/102 optd with Type O 3, and 103/111 with Type O 4.*
O43	22	1 m. black and orange		30	3·25
O44		2 m. orange and chocolate		1·25	10
O45		3 m. mauve and green		2·50	5·00
O46		4 m. deep green and chocolate		2·50	2·75
O47		5 m. olive-brown and black		2·50	10
O48		10 m. rose-red and black		2·25	90
O49		15 m. ultramarine and chestnut		2·50	10
O50	23	2 p. purple and orange-yellow		2·50	10
O51		3 p. red-brown and deep blue		2·50	10
O52		4 p. ultramarine and black		2·50	10
		a. Perf 13 (optd Type O 4a)		13·00	15·00
O53		5 p. brown-orange and deep green		3·00	10
O54		6 p. greenish blue and black		2·25	10
O55		8 p. bluish green and black		2·25	2·25
O56		10 p. black and mauve		3·50	20
O57		20 p. pale blue and deep blue		4·00	25
O58		50 p. carmine and ultramarine		55·00	45·00
O43/58		Set of 16		80·00	55·00

1950 (1 July). *Air. Optd with Type O 4a.*
O59		2 p. black and blue-green (R.)		14·00	3·00
O60		2½ p. light blue and red-orange		1·50	1·75
O61		3 p. reddish purple and blue		80	6·50
O62		3½ p. purple-brown and yellow-brown		80	6·50
O63		4 p. brown and light blue		80	6·50
O64		4½ p. black and ultramarine (R.)		3·75	15·00
		a. Black and steel-blue		6·50	15·00
O65		6 p. black and carmine (R.)		1·00	4·25
O66		20 p. black and purple (R.)		1·50	10
O59/66		Set of 8		25·00	42·00

1951 (1 Sept)–62? *Nos. 123/9 optd with Type O 3, and 130/9 with Type O 4a.*
O67		1 m. black and orange (R.)		40	3·50
O68		2 m. black and bright blue (R.)		40	60
O69		3 m. black and green (R.)		3·00	14·00
O70		4 m. black and yellow-green (R.)		10	5·00
O71		5 m. black and purple (R.)		10	10
O72		10 m. black and pale blue (R.)		10	10
O73		15 m. black and chestnut (R.)		10	10
O74		2 p. deep blue and pale blue		10	10
		a. Opt inverted		£475	
		b. Deep blue and very pale blue (1962?)		75	10
O75		3 p. brown and dull ultramarine		4·50	10
		a. Brown and deep blue (1962?)		5·00	1·00
O76		3½ p. bright green and red-brown		25	10
		a. Light emerald & red-brown (1962?)		3·00	1·00
O77		4 p. ultramarine and black		30	10
		a. Deep blue and black (1962?)		1·50	10
O78		5 p. orange-brown and yellow-green		25	10
O79		6 p. blue and black		30	2·50
		a. Deep blue and black (1962?)		6·50	5·50

O80	8 p. blue and brown	45	10
	a. Deep blue and brown (1962?)	3·50	1·75
O81	10 p. black and green (R.)	50	10
O81a	10 p. black and green (Blk.) (1958)	13·00	1·50
O82	20 p. blue-green and black	1·25	30
	a. Opt inverted	—	£600
O83	50 p. carmine and black	3·50	1·25
O67/83	Set of 18	25·00	26·00

The 5, 10 and 15 m. values were later reissued with a thinner overprint.

ARMY SERVICE STAMPS

ARMY / **OFFICIAL** / **ARMY** / **OFFICIAL** / **Army**

Service

(A 1)   (A 2)   (A 3)

1905 (1 Jan). *T 2 optd at Khartoum as Types A 1 or A 2. Wmk Mult Star and Crescent.* (i) "ARMY" *reading up.*

A1	1 m. brown and carmine (A 1)	2·50	2·00
	a. "l" for "1"	48·00	30·00
	b. Opt Type A 2	38·00	23·00
	c. Pair. Types A 1 and A 2 se-tenant	75·00	

(ii) *Overprint horizontal*

A2	1 m. brown and carmine (A 1)		£325
	a. "l" for "1"		£3500
	b. Opt Type A 2		£2000

The horizontal overprint exists with either "ARMY" or "OFFICIAL" reading the right way up. It did not fit the stamps, resulting in misplacements where more than one whole overprint appears, or when the two words are transposed.

(iii) "ARMY" *reading down*

A3	1 m. brown and carmine (A 1)	70·00	60·00
	a. "l" for "1"	£700	£700
	b. Opt Type A 2	£600	£425

1905 (Nov). *As No. A1, but wmk Quatrefoil, W 3.*

A4	1 m. brown and pink (A 1)	£120	£130
	a. "l" for "1"	£2750	£1600
	b. Opt Type A 2	£1200	£1200
	c. Pair. Types A 1 and A 2 se-tenant	£2000	

The setting used for overprinting Nos. A1/4 was 30 (6×5). The "l" for "1" variety occurs on R. 5/4 and overprint Type A 2 on R. 1/6 and 2/6 of the setting.

Two varieties of the 1 millieme
A. 1st Ptg. 14 mm between lines of opt.
B. Later Ptgs. 12 mm between lines.
All other values are Type B.

1906 (Jan)–**11**. *T 2 optd as Type A 3.*

(i) *Wmk Mult Star and Crescent, W 4.*

A 5	1 m. brown and carmine (Type A)	£275	£225
A 6	1 m. brown and carmine (Type B)	1·50	20
	a. Opt double, one diagonal	†	£700
	b. Opt inverted	£400	£400
	c. Pair, one without opt		†
	d. "Service" omitted	†	£3500
	e. "Λ" for "A" in "Army"	£150	£150
A 7	2 m. green and brown	8·50	1·00
	a. Pair, one without opt	£2500	
	b. "Army" omitted	£3000	
A 8	3 m. mauve and green	17·00	40
	a. Opt inverted	£1900	
A 9	5 m. scarlet and black	1·50	10
	a. Opt. double	£190	£190
	ab. Opt double, one diagonal	£200	
	b. Opt inverted	†	£200
	c. "Amry"	†	£2250
	d. "Λ" for "A" in "Army"	—	£250
	e. Opt double, one inverted	£700	£350
A10	1 p. blue and brown	13·00	15
	a. "Army" omitted	†	£2000
A11	2 p. black and blue (1.09)	48·00	13·00
	a. Opt double	†	£3000
A12	5 p. brown and green (5.08)	£100	60·00
A13	10 p. black and mauve (5.11)	£450	£550
A6/10	Optd "Specimen" Set of 5	£110	

There are a number of printings of these Army Service stamps; the earlier are as Type A 3; the 1908 printing has a narrower "A" in "Army" and the 1910–11 printings have the tail of the "y" in "Army" much shorter.

(ii) *Wmk Quatrefoil, W 3.*

A14	2 p. black and blue	55·00	10·00
A15	5 p. brown and green	90·00	£140
A16	10 p. black and mauve	£120	£275
A14/16	Set of 3	£225	£375
A14/16	Optd "Specimen" Set of 3	£100	

1912 (1 Jan)–**22**. *Nos. 18/20 and 23/8 punctured "AS" by machine. The "A" has 12 holes and the "S" 11.*

A17	2 1 m. brown and carmine	24·00	3·00
A18	2 m. green and brown	6·00	70
A19	3 m. mauve and green	35·00	3·00
A20	5 m. scarlet and black	6·50	40
	a. On No. 13		
A21	1 p. blue and brown	16·00	75
A22	2 p. black and blue	38·00	3·75
A23	2 p. purple and orange-yellow (chalk-surfaced paper) (1922)	48·00	45·00
A24	5 p. brown and green	45·00	20·00
	a. Chalk-surfaced paper	45·00	20·00
A25	10 p. black and mauve (1914)	£400	£225
A17/25	Set of 9	£550	£275

1922–24. *Nos. 31a and 34/5 punctured "AS" by machine. The "A" has 8 holes and the "S" 9.*

A26	6 2 m. yellow and chocolate (1924)	55·00	35·00
A27	5 m. olive-brown and black (4.2.22)	8·50	3·00
A28	10 m. carmine and black	13·00	3·50
A26/8	Set of 3	70·00	38·00

The use of Nos. A17/28 on internal Army mail ceased when the Egyptian units were withdrawn at the end of 1924, but existing stocks continued to be used on Army mail to foreign destinations until supplies were exhausted.

Swaziland

TRIPARTITE GOVERNMENT

Following internal unrest and problems caused by the multitude of commercial concessions granted by the Swazi king the British and Transvaal governments intervened during 1889 to establish a tripartite administration under which the country was controlled by their representatives, acting with the agent of the Swazi king.

The Pretoria government had previously purchased the concession to run the postal service and, on the establishment of the tripartite administration, provided overprinted Transvaal stamps for use from a post office at Embekelweni and later at Bremersdorp and Darkton.

Swaziland
(1)

1889 (18 Oct)–**90**. *Stamps of Transvaal (South African Republic) optd with T 1, in black.* (a) *P 12½×12*

1	18	1d. carmine	17·00	16·00
		a. Opt inverted	£600	£650
2		2d. olive-bistre	85·00	20·00
		a. Opt inverted	—	£1000
		b. "Swazielan"	£950	£650
3		1s. green	10·00	13·00
		a. Opt inverted	£550	£450

(b) *P 12½*

4	18	½d. grey	9·00	18·00
		a. Opt inverted	£750	£600
		b. "Swazielan"	£950	£650
		c. "Swazielan" inverted	—	£3250
5		2d. olive-bistre	15·00	15·00
		a. Opt inverted	£700	£450
		b. "Swazielan"	£475	£450
		c. "Swazielan" inverted	£3000	£3000
		d. Opt double	£2000	
6		6d. blue	18·00	32·00
7		2s. 6d. buff (20.10.90)	£225	£250
8		5s. slate-blue (20.10.90)	£140	£180
		a. Opt inverted	£1600	£1800
		b. "Swazielan"	£4000	
		c. "Swazielan" inverted		
9		10s. fawn (20.10.90)	£4500	£3000

The variety without "d" occurs on the left-hand bottom corner stamp in each sheet of certain printings.

A printing of the ½d, 1d., 2d. and 10s. with stop after "Swazieland" was made in July 1894, but such stamps were not issued.

It is possible that the dates quoted above were those on which the overprinting took place in Pretoria and that the stamps were issued slightly later in Swaziland itself.

1892 (Aug). *Optd in carmine. P 12½.*

10	18	½d. grey	7·50	16·00
		a. Opt inverted	£475	
		b. Opt double	£425	£425
		c. Pair, one without opt	—	£1500

No. 10 was overprinted in Pretoria during August 1892 when Swaziland was under quarantine due to smallpox. It is unlikely that it saw much postal use before all the overprints were withdrawn, although cancelled-to-order examples are plentiful.

It appears likely that no further supplies of stamps overprinted "Swazieland" were provided by Pretoria after December 1892, although stocks held at post offices were used up. The overprinted stamps were declared to be invalid from 7 November 1894. They were replaced by unoverprinted issues of the Transvaal (South African Republic).

Stamps of TRANSVAAL (SOUTH AFRICAN REPUBLIC) used in Swaziland between December 1892 and January 1900.

1885–93. *(Nos. 175/87).*

Z1	½d. grey	20·00	
Z2	1d. carmine	20·00	
Z3	2d. olive-bistre	10·00	
Z4	2½d. mauve	20·00	
Z5	3d. mauve	20·00	
Z6	4d. bronze-green	20·00	
Z9	2s. 6d. orange-buff		

1893. *(Nos. 195/9).*

Z10	½d. on 2d. olive-bistre (Type A surch in red)		
Z11	½d. on 2d. olive-bistre (Type A surch in black)		
Z12	1d. on 6d. blue (Type A surch)	20·00	
	a. Surch Type B	20·00	
Z13	2½d. on 1s. green ("2½ Pence" in one line) (Type A surch)	20·00	
	a. Surch Type B	20·00	

1894. *(Nos. 200/4).*

Z16	1d. carmine	20·00	
Z17	2d. olive-bistre	20·00	

1895–96. *(Nos. 205/12a).*

Z20	½d. pearl-grey	20·00	
Z21	1d. rose-red	10·00	
Z22	2d. olive-bistre	10·00	
Z25	6d. pale dull blue	20·00	

1895. *(Nos. 213/14).*

Z27	½d. on 1s. green	

1895. *Introduction of Penny Postage (No. 215b)*

Z29	1d. red	

1896–97. *(Nos. 216/24).*

Z30	½d. green	20·00
Z31	1d. rose-red and green	10·00
Z35	4d. sage-green and green	20·00
Z36	6d. lilac and green	20·00
Z37	1s. ochre and green	

Prices are for clear and fairly complete postmarks. Examples dated in 1892 and 1893 are worth a premium. For list of post offices open during this period see boxed note below. Most known examples are from Bremersdorp (squared circle inscr "SWAZIEL" later replaced by "Z.A.R." or c.d.s.) or Darkton (c.d.s.).

Shortly after the outbreak of the Boer War in 1899 the Transvaal administration withdrew from Swaziland, although the post office at Darkton, which was on the border, was still operating in early 1900. There was, however, no further organised postal service in Swaziland until the country became a British Protectorate in March 1902. From that date, until the introduction of the 1933 definitives, the stamps of Transvaal and subsequently South Africa were in use.

BRITISH PROTECTORATE

2 King George V   3 King George VI

(Des Rev. C. C. Tugman. Recess D.L.R.)

1933 (2 Jan). *Wmk Mult Script CA. P 14.*

11	2	½d. green	30	30
12		1d. carmine	30	20
13		2d. brown	30	45
14		3d. blue	45	1·50
15		4d. orange	2·50	45
16		6d. bright purple	1·00	80
17		1s. olive	1·50	2·75
18		2s. 6d. bright violet	15·00	22·00
19		5s. grey	30·00	45·00
20		10s. sepia	80·00	£100
11/20		Set of 10	£120	£150
11/20 Perf "Specimen"		Set of 10	£225	

The ½d., 1d., 2d. and 6d. values exist overprinted "OFFICIAL", but authority for their use was withdrawn before any were actually used. However, some stamps had already been issued to the Secretariat staff before instructions were received to invalidate their use (Price £11000 per set un).

1935 (4 May). *Silver Jubilee. As Nos. 114/17 of Jamaica. P 11×12.*

21	1d. deep blue and scarlet	40	75
	a. Extra flagstaff	£200	
	b. Short extra flagstaff	£225	
	c. Lightning conductor	£225	
	d. Flagstaff on right-hand turret	80·00	
	e. Double flagstaff	80·00	
22	2d. ultramarine and grey-black	40	75
	a. Extra flagstaff	90·00	
	b. Short extra flagstaff	75·00	
	c. Lightning conductor	65·00	
23	3d. brown and deep blue	55	4·00
	a. Extra flagstaff	75·00	
	b. Short extra flagstaff	75·00	
	c. Lightning conductor	70·00	
24	6d. slate and purple	65	1·25
	a. Extra flagstaff	85·00	
	b. Short extra flagstaff	75·00	
	c. Lightning conductor	75·00	
21/4	Set of 4	1·75	6·00
21/4 Perf "Specimen"	Set of 4	80·00	

For illustrations of plate varieties see Omnibus section following Zimbabwe.

1937 (12 May). *Coronation. As Nos. 118/20 of Jamaica, but ptd by B.W. P 11×11½.*

25	1d. carmine	50	1·25
26	2d. yellow-brown	50	20
27	3d. blue	50	50
25/7	Set of 3	1·40	1·75
25/7 Perf "Specimen"	Set of 3	65·00	

(Recess D.L.R.)

1938 (1 Apr)–54. *Wmk Mult Script CA. P* 13½×13.

28	3	½d. green			1·50	80
		a. Perf 13½×14 (1.43)			20	2·25
		b. Perf 13½×14. *Bronze-green* (2.50)			95	4·00
29		1d. rose-red			1·50	70
		a. Perf 13½×14 (1.43)			80	1·40
30	1½d.	light blue			3·75	65
		a. Perf 14 (1941)			2·25	95
		b. Perf 13½×14 (1.43)			30	75
		ba. Printed on the gummed side			£2250	
31		2d. yellow-brown			2·50	85
		a. Perf 13½×14 (1.43)			30	50
32		3d. ultramarine			8·00	1·75
		a. *Deep blue* (10.38)			12·00	1·75
		b. Perf 13½×14. *Ultramarine* (1.43)			2·25	4·00
		c. Perf 13½×14. *Light ultram* (10.46)			16·00	10·00
		d. Perf 13½×14. *Deep blue* (10.47)			8·50	9·50
33		4d. orange			3·50	95
		a. Perf 13½×14 (1.43)			50	1·40
34		6d. deep magenta			8·00	2·00
		a. Perf 13½×14 (1.43)			3·50	3·50
		b. Perf 13½×14. *Reddish purple (shades)* (7.44)			3·50	1·25
		c. Perf 13½×14. *Claret* (13.10.54)			6·00	3·50
35		1s. brown-olive			8·00	1·50
		a. Perf 13½×14 (1.43)			1·25	65
36		2s. 6d. bright violet			24·00	4·00
		a. Perf 13½×14. *Violet* (1.43)			10·00	2·50
		b. Perf 13½×14. *Reddish violet* (10.47)			10·00	7·00
37		5s. grey			50·00	11·00
		a. Perf 13½×14. *Slate* (1.43)			55·00	50·00
		b. Perf 13½×14. *Grey* (5.44)			24·00	13·00
38		10s. sepia			50·00	5·00
		a. Perf 13½×14 (1.43)			6·50	6·00
28/38a				*Set of 11*	45·00	24·00
28/38 Perf "Specimen"				*Set of 11*	£225	

The above perforations vary slightly from stamp to stamp, but the average measurements are respectively: 13.3 × 13.2 comb (13½ × 13), 14.2 line (14) and 13.3 × 13.8 comb (13½ × 14).

Swaziland
(4)

1945 (3 Dec). *Victory. Nos. 108/10 of South Africa optd with T* 4.

				Un pair	Us pair	Us single
39	1d. brown and carmine			55	50	10
40	2d. slate-blue and violet			55	50	10
41	3d. deep blue and blue			55	2·00	20
39/41			*Set of 3*	1·50	2·75	30

1947 (17 Feb). *Royal Visit. As Nos. 32/5 of Lesotho.*

				Un	Us
42	1d. scarlet			10	10
43	2d. green			10	10
44	3d. ultramarine			10	10
45	1s. mauve			10	10
42/5			*Set of 4*	30	30
42/5 Perf "Specimen"			*Set of 4*	80·00	

1948 (1 Dec). *Royal Silver Wedding. As Nos. 143/4 of Jamaica.*

46	1½d. ultramarine			50	10
47	10s. purple-brown			23·00	25·00

1949 (10 Oct). *75th Anniv of U.P.U. As Nos. 145/8 of Jamaica.*

48	1½d. blue			20	10
49	3d. deep blue			1·75	90
50	6d. magenta			60	60
51	1s. olive			60	60
48/51			*Set of 4*	2·75	2·00

1953 (3 June). *Coronation. As No. 153 of Jamaica.*

52	2d. black and yellow-brown			20	20

5 Havelock Asbestos Mine

7 Swazi Married Woman

(Recess B.W.)

1956 (2 July). *T* 5, 7 *and similar designs. Wmk Mult Script CA. P* 13 × 13½ (*horiz*) *or* 13½ × 13 (*vert*).

53	5	½d. black and orange			10	10
54	—	1d. black and emerald			10	10
55	7	2d. black and brown			30	10
56	—	3d. black and rose-red			20	10
57	—	4½d. black and deep bright blue			60	10
58	—	6d. black and magenta			45	10
59	5	1s. black and deep olive			20	10
60	—	1s. 3d. black and sepia			1·00	2·00
61	—	2s. 6d. emerald and carmine-red			1·00	1·50
62	—	5s. deep lilac and slate-black			7·50	2·25
63	7	10s. black and deep lilac			15·00	8·00
64	—	£1 black and turquoise-blue			38·00	26·00
53/64				*Set of 12*	55·00	35·00

Designs: *Horiz*—1d., 2s. 6d. A Highveld view; *Vert*—3d., 1s. 3d. Swazi courting couple; 4½d., 5s. Swazi warrior; 6d., £1. Greater Kudu.

(New Currency. 100 cents = 1 rand)

½c (11)   **1c** (12)   **2c** (13)   **3½c** (14)

2½c (I)   **2½c** (II)   **4c** (I)   **4c** (II)

5c (I)   **5c** (II)   **25c** (I)   **25c** (II)

50c (I)   **50c** (II)   **50c** (III)

R1 (I)   **R1** (II)   **R1** (III)   **R2** (I)   **R2** (II)

1961 (14 Feb–May). *Nos. 53/64 surch as T* 11 *to* 14.

65	½ c. on ½d.			3·25	3·75
	a. Surch inverted			£650	
66	1 c. on 1d.			10	75
	a. Surch double*			£650	
67	2 c. on 2d.			10	90
68	2½ c. on 2d.			10	50
69	2½ c. on 3d. (Type I)			10	10
	a. Type II			10	15
70	3½ c. on 2d. (May)			10	30
71	4 c. on 4½d. (Type I)			10	10
	a. Type II			20	10
72	5 c. on 6d. (Type I)			10	10
	a. Type II			10	10
73	10 c. on 1s.			25·00	3·00
	a. Surch double*			£700	
74	25 c. on 2s. 6d. (Type I)			30	65
	a. Type II (central)			85	60
	b. Type II (bottom left)			£170	£190
75	50 c. on 5s. (Type I)			30	60
	a. Type II			4·50	2·25
	b. Type III			£325	£400
76	1 r. on 10s. (Type I)			1·50	60
	a. Type II			2·75	2·75
	b. Type III			42·00	50·00
77	2 r. on £1 (Type I)			7·00	9·00
	a. Type II (middle left)			4·50	6·50
	b. Type II (bottom)			50·00	95·00
65/77a			*Set of 13*	32·00	16·00

*On both Nos. 66a and 73a the second surcharge falls across the horizontal perforations.

No. 74b has the thin Type II surcharge at bottom left, in similar position to the thicker Type I, No. 74, with which it should not be confused.

No. 77b has the surcharge centrally placed at bottom. No. 77a has it at middle left, above "KUDU".

No. 66 with surcharge central (instead of bottom left) and No. 75a bottom left (instead of middle left) are believed to be from trial sheets released with the normal stocks. They do not represent separate printings. (No. 66 price £35 *un*, No. 75a price £120 *un*.).

(Recess B.W.)

1961. *As* 1956 *issue, but with values in cents and rands. Wmk Mult Script CA. P* 13 × 13½ (*horiz*) *or* 13½ × 13 (*vert*).

78	½ c. black and orange (as ½d.) (14.2)			10	50
79	1 c. black and emerald (as 1d.) (14.2)			10	10
80	2 c. black and brown (as 2d.) (10.9)			10	1·75
81	2½ c. black and rose-red (as 3d.) (14.2)			15	10
82	4 c. black & dp bright bl (as 4½d) (10.9)			15	75
83	5 c. black and magenta (as 6d.) (10.9)			30	15
84	10 c. black and deep olive (as 1s.) (14.2)			15	10
85	12½ c. black and sepia (as 1s 3d.) (14.2)			1·25	40
86	25 c. emerald and carmine-red (as 2s 6d.) (1.8)			2·25	2·50
87	50 c. deep lilac & slate-blk (as 5s.) (10.9)			2·00	1·40
88	1 r. black and deep lilac (as 10s.) (10.9)			4·00	8·00
89	2 r. black and turquoise-blue (as £1) (1.8)			9·00	11·00
78/89			*Set of 12*	17·00	24·00

15 Swazi Shields

16 Battle Axe

(Des Mrs. C. Hughes. Photo Enschedé)

1962 (24 Apr)–**66**. *Various designs as T* 15/16. *W w* 12. *P* 14×13 (*horiz*) *or* 13×14 (*vert*).

90	½ c. black, brown and yellow-brown			10	10
	w. Wmk inverted			11·00	
91	1 c. yellow-orange and black			10	10
	w. Wmk inverted			1·75	
92	2 c. dp bluish green, black & yellow-olive			10	65
	w. Wmk inverted			18·00	
93	2½ c. black and vermilion			10	10
	a. *Black and dull red* (5.66)			50	10
	w. Wmk inverted			2·25	
94	3½ c. yellow-green and deep grey			10	40
	w. Wmk inverted			5·00	

95	4 c. black and turquoise-green			10	10
	a. *Black & deep turquoise-green* (5.66)			80	10
	w. Wmk inverted			5·00	
96	5 c. black, red and orange-red			50	10
	w. Wmk inverted			8·00	
97	7½ c. deep brown and buff			80	50
	a. *Blackish brn & yellowish buff* (5.66)			3·00	2·50
	w. Wmk inverted			8·00	
98	10 c. black and light blue			2·50	20
	w. Wmk inverted			25·00	
99	12½ c. carmine and grey-olive			1·25	2·50
100	15 c. black and bright purple			1·50	70
101	20 c. black and green			40	90
102	25 c. black and bright blue			50	70
	w. Wmk inverted			25·00	
103	50 c. black and rose-red			10·00	4·00
104	1 r. emerald and ochre			2·50	2·25
105	2 r. carmine-red and ultramarine			14·00	8·50
90/105			*Set of 16*	30·00	19·00

Designs: *Vert*—2 c. Forestry; 2½ c. Ceremonial headdress; 3½ c. Musical instrument; 4 c. Irrigation; 5 c. Long-tailed Whydah; 7½ c. Rock paintings; 10 c. Secretary Bird; 12½ c. Pink Arum; 15 c. Swazi married woman; 20 c. Malaria control; 25 c. Swazi warrior; 1 r. Aloes. *Horiz*—50 c. Southern Ground Hornbill; 2 r. Msinsi in flower.

1963 (4 June). *Freedom from Hunger. As No.* 80 *of Lesotho.*

106	15 c. reddish violet			40	15

1963 (2 Sept). *Red Cross Centenary. As Nos.* 203/4 *of Jamaica.*

107	2½ c. red and black			30	10
108	15 c. red and blue			95	80

31 Goods Train and Map of Swaziland Railway

(Des R. A. H. Street. Recess B.W.)

1964 (5 Nov). *Opening of Swaziland Railway. W w* 12. *P* 11½.

109	31	2½ c. emerald-green and purple			55	10
110		3½ c. turquoise-blue & deep yellow-olive			55	90
111		15 c. red-orange and deep chocolate			70	70
112		25 c. olive-yellow and deep ultramarine			85	80
109/12				*Set of 4*	2·40	2·25

1965 (17 May). *I.T.U. Centenary. As Nos.* 98/9 *of Lesotho.*

113	2½ c. light blue and bistre			15	10
114	15 c. bright purple and rose			35	20

1965 (25 Oct). *International Co-operation Year. As Nos.* 100/1 *of Lesotho.*

115	½ c. reddish purple and turquoise-green			10	10
116	15 c. deep bluish green and lavender			40	20

1966 (24 Jan). *Churchill Commemoration. As Nos.* 102/5 *of Lesotho.*

117	½ c. new blue			10	90
118	2½ c. deep green			20	10
119	15 c. brown			35	25
	w. Wmk inverted				
120	25 c. bluish violet			50	70
117/20			*Set of 4*	1·00	1·75

1966 (1 Dec). *20th Anniv of U.N.E.S.C.O. As Nos.* 342/4 *of Mauritius.*

121	2½ c. slate-violet, red, yellow and orange			10	10
122	7½ c. orange-yellow, violet and deep olive			30	50
123	15 c. black, bright purple and orange			55	1·10
121/3			*Set of 3*	85	1·50

PROTECTED STATE

32 King Sobhuza II and Map

33 King Sobhuza II

(Des and photo Harrison)

1967 (25 Apr). *Protected State. W w* 12 (*sideways on horiz designs*). *P* 14½.

124	32	2½ c. multicoloured			10	10
125	33	7½ c. multicoloured			15	15
126	32	15 c. multicoloured			20	30
127	33	25 c. multicoloured			25	40
124/7				*Set of 4*	65	80

34 Students and University

(Des V. Whiteley. Photo Harrison)

1967 (7 Sept). *First Conferment of University Degrees.*
P 14 × 14½.

128	**34**	2½ c. sepia, ultramarine & lt yellow-orge		10	10
129		7½ c. sepia, ultramarine & lt greenish bl		15	15
130		15 c. sepia, ultramarine and rose		25	30
131		25 c. sepia, ultramarine and light violet		30	35
128/31			*Set of 4*	65	75

35 Incwala Ceremony   36 Reed Dance

(Des Mrs. G. Ellison. Photo Harrison)

1968 (5 Jan). *Traditional Customs.*

132	**35**	3 c. silver, vermilion and black		10	10
133	**36**	10 c. silver, light brown, orange and black		10	10
134	**35**	15 c. gold, vermilion and black		15	20
135	**36**	25 c. gold, light brown, orange and black		15	20
132/5			*Set of 4*	40	50

(37)   38 Cattle Ploughing

1968 (1 May). *No. 96 surch with T 37.*

136	3 c. on 5 c. black, red and orange-red		50	10
	w. Wmk inverted		4·50	1·75

INDEPENDENT

(Des Mrs. G. Ellison. Photo Enschedé)

1968 (6 Sept). *Independence. T* **38** *and similar horiz designs.*
W w **12** (*sideways*). P 14 × 12½.

137	3 c. multicoloured		10	10
	a. Imperf (pair)		£140	
138	4½ c. multicoloured		10	15
	a. Imperf (pair)		£140	
139	17½ c. yellow, green, black and gold		15	20
140	25 c. slate, black and gold		45	80
137/40		*Set of 4*	65	1·10
MS141	180 × 162 mm. Nos. 137/40 each × 5		14·00	22·00
	a. Error. Imperf		£1300	

Designs:—4½ c. Overhead cable carrying asbestos; 17½ c. Cutting sugar cane; 25 c. Iron ore mining and railway map.
Nos. 137/40 were printed in sheets of 50, but also in miniature sheets of 20 (4 × 5) containing *se-tenant* strips of each value.

INDEPENDENCE
1968
(42)   43 Cape Porcupine

1968 (6 Sept). *Nos. 90/105 optd as T* **42**, *and No. 93 additionally surch 3 c., by Enschedé. (a) Wmk upright.*

142	½ c. black, brown and yellow-brown		10	10
	a. Brown omitted		£225	
	b. Albino opt		40·00	
143	1 c. yellow-orange and black		10	10
	w. Wmk inverted		40·00	
144	2 c. dp bluish green, black & yellow-olive	10	10
	w. Wmk inverted		—	30·00
145	2½ c. black and vermilion		60	95
	a. Black and dull red		1·25	10
	w. Wmk inverted		35·00	
146	3 c. on 2½ c. black and vermilion		10	10
	a. Black and dull red		10	10
	w. Wmk inverted		35·00	
147	3½ c. yellow-green and deep grey		15	10
	w. Wmk inverted		27·00	
148	4 c. black and turquoise-green		10	10
	a. Black and deep turquoise-green		25	15
	b. Black and pale turquoise-green		20	1·50
149	5 c. black, red and orange-red		2·25	10
	w. Wmk inverted		40·00	
150	7½ c. deep brown and buff		50	10
151	10 c. black and light blue		2·50	10
152	12½ c. carmine and grey-olive		25	55
	w. Wmk inverted		2·00	3·00
153	15 c. black and bright purple		25	55
154	20 c. black and green		75	1·50
155	25 c. black and bright blue		35	50
156	50 c. black and rose-red		7·00	4·00
157	1 r. emerald and ochre		2·50	4·00
158	2 r. carmine-red and ultramarine		5·50	9·00

(b) Wmk sideways

159	50 c. black and rose-red		4·50	3·50
160	2 r. carmine-red and ultramarine		6·50	5·00
142/60		*Set of 19*	29·00	26·00

The 2½ c., 3½ c., 5 c., 12½ c., 50 c. (No. 156) and 2 r. (No. 158) exist with gum arabic only, the 1 c., 3 c., 4 c., and 15 c. with both gum arabic and PVA gum and the remainder with PVA gum only.

(Des and litho D.L.R.)

1969 (1 Aug)–75. *T* **43** *and similar designs showing animals. Multicoloured.* W w **12** (*sideways on 3 c., 3½ c., 1 r., 2 r.*).
P 13×13½ (3, 3½ c.), 12½×13 (1, 2 r.) or 13×12½ (*others*).

161	½ c. Caracal			10	10
162	1 c. Type **43**			10	10
163	2 c. Crocodile			20	10
	aw. Wmk inverted			4·00	
	b. Perf 12½×12 (29.9.75)			3·25	4·50
164	3 c. Lion			60	10
165	3½ c. African Elephant			75	10
166	5 c. Bush Pig			30	10
167	7½ c. Impala			35	10
168	10 c. Chacma Baboon			45	10
169	12½ c. Ratel			70	2·75
170	15 c. Leopard			1·25	70
171	20 c. Blue Wildebeest			95	60
172	25 c. White Rhinoceros			1·40	1·75
	w. Wmk inverted			3·25	
173	50 c. Common Zebra			1·50	3·25
174	1 r. Waterbuck (*vert*)			3·00	6·50
175	2 r. Giraffe (*vert*)			8·00	11·00
161/75			*Set of 15*	17·00	24·00

Nos. 161/73 are horizontal as Type **43** but the 3 c. and 3½ c. are larger, 35×24½ mm.
No. 163b was printed by the D.L.R. works in Bogotá, Colombia.
See also Nos. 219/20 and 229.

44 King Sobhuza II and Flags   45 King Sobhuza II, U.N. Building and Emblem

(Des D.L.R. Litho P.B.)

1969 (24 Sept). *Admission of Swaziland to the United Nations.* W w **12** (*sideways*). P 13½.

176	**44**	3 c. multicoloured		10	10
177	**45**	7½ c. multicoloured		15	10
178	**44**	12½ c. multicoloured		25	10
179	**45**	25 c. multicoloured		40	40
176/9			*Set of 4*	75	55

46 Athlete, Shield and Spears   47 *Bauhinia galpinii*

(Des L. Curtis. Litho Format)

1970 (16 July). *Ninth Commonwealth Games, Edinburgh. T* **46** *and similar vert designs. Multicoloured.* W w **12**. P 14.

180	3 c. Type **46**		10	10
181	7½ c. Runner		20	10
182	12½ c. Hurdler		25	10
183	25 c. Procession of Swaziland competitors	35	40
180/3		*Set of 4*	75	55

(Des L. Curtis from "Wild Flowers of Natal" by Dr. W. G. Wright. Litho Questa)

1971 (1 Feb). *Flowers. T* **47** *and similar vert designs. Multicoloured.* W w **12**. P 14½.

184	3 c. Type **47**		20	10
185	10 c. Crocosmia aurea		25	10
186	15 c. Gloriosa superba		40	15
187	25 c. Watsonia densiflora		55	35
184/7		*Set of 4*	1·25	60

48 King Sobhuza II in Ceremonial Dress   49 UNICEF emblem

(Des L. Curtis. Litho Format)

1971 (22 Dec). *Golden Jubilee of Accession of King Sobhuza II. T* **48** *and similar vert designs. Multicoloured.* W w **12**. P 14.

188	3 c. Type **48**		10	10
	w. Wmk inverted		50	
189	3½ c. Sobhuza II in medallion		10	10
190	7½ c. Sobhuza II attending Incwala ceremony		15	10
191	25 c. Sobhuza II and aides at opening of Parliament		30	35
	w. Wmk inverted		70	
188/91		*Set of 4*	45	40

(Des Sylvia Goaman. Litho J.W.)

1972 (17 Apr). *25th Anniv of UNICEF.* W w **12** (*sideways*). P 13½.

192	**49**	15 c. black and bright lilac		15	15
193		25 c. black and yellow-olive		20	35

The 25 c. value is as T **49**, but the inscription is rearranged.

50 Local Dancers

(Des G. Drummond. Litho Questa)

1972 (11 Sept). *Tourism. T* **50** *and similar horiz designs. Multicoloured.* W w **12**. P 13½ × 14.

194	**49**	3½ c. Type **50**	10	10
195		7½ c. Swazi beehive hut	15	15
196		15 c. Ezulwini Valley	20	50
197		25 c. Fishing, Usutu River	65	1·25
194/7		*Set of 4*	1·00	1·75

51 Spraying Mosquitoes

(Des PAD Studio. Litho Questa)

1973 (21 May). *25th Anniv of W.H.O. T* **51** *and similar horiz design. Multicoloured.* W w **12**. P 14.

198	3½ c. Type **51**		20	10
199	7½ c. Anti-malaria vaccination		40	70

52 Mining

(Des G. Drummond. Litho Questa)

1973 (21 June). *Natural Resources. T* **52** *and similar horiz designs. Multicoloured.* W w **12**. P 13½.

200	3½ c. Type **52**		55	10
201	7½ c. Cattle		25	15
202	15 c. Water		30	20
203	25 c. Rice		35	50
200/3		*Set of 4*	1·25	80

53 Coat of Arms   54 Flags and Mortar-board

(Des J.W. Litho Walsall)

1973 (7 Sept). *Fifth Anniv of Independence. T* **53** *and similar horiz designs. Multicoloured (except 3 c.).* W w **12**. P 14.

204	3 c. Type **53** (salmon and black)		10	10
205	10 c. King Sobhuza II saluting		15	10
206	15 c. Parliament Buildings		30	65
207	25 c. National Somhlolo Stadium		40	1·25
204/7		*Set of 4*	80	1·75

(Des P. Powell. Litho Format)

1974 (29 Mar). *Tenth Anniv of University of Botswana, Lesotho and Swaziland. T* **54** *and similar vert designs. Multicoloured.* W w **12** (*sideways*). P 14.

208	7½ c. Type **54**		20	10
209	12½ c. University campus		25	10
210	15 c. Map of Southern Africa		30	20
211	25 c. University badge		40	35
208/11		*Set of 4*	1·00	60

NEW INFORMATION

The editor is always interested to correspond with people who have new information that will improve or correct the Catalogue.

55 King Sobhuza as College Student

56 New Post Office, Lobamba

(Des Mary Nelson; adapted PAD Studio. Litho Enschedé)

1974 (22 July). *75th Birthday of King Sobhuza II. T* **55** *and similar vert designs. Multicoloured.* W w 12. P 13 × 10½.
212	3 c.	Type **55**		10	10
213	9 c.	King Sobhuza in middle-age		10	10
214	50 c.	King Sobhuza at 75 years of age		70	60
212/14			*Set of 3*	80	60

(Des R. Granger Barrett. Litho Questa)

1974 (9 Oct). *Centenary of Universal Postal Union. T* **56** *and similar horiz designs. Multicoloured.* W w 12 (*sideways*). P 14.
215	4 c.	Type **56**		10	10
216	10 c.	Mbabane Temporary Post Office, 1902		15	15
217	15 c.	Carrying mail by cableway		30	50
218	25 c.	Mule-drawn mail-coach		40	70
215/18			*Set of 4*	80	1·25

(New Currency. 100 cents = 1 lilangeni (*plural* emalangeni))

1975 (2 Jan). *New currency. As Nos. 174/5 but inscr in emalangeni.* W w 12 (*upright*). P 12½ × 13.
219	1 e.	Waterbuck		1·00	2·00
220	2 e.	Giraffe		2·00	4·00
	w.	Wmk inverted		70·00	

57 Umcwasho Ceremony

58 Control Tower, Matsapa Airport

(Des PAD Studio. Litho Kynoch Press)

1975 (20 Mar). *Swazi Youth. T* **57** *and similar multicoloured designs.* W w 12 (*sideways on 3, 10 and 25 c.*). P 14.
221	3 c.	Type **57**		10	10
222	10 c.	Butimba (hunting party)		15	10
223	15 c.	Lusekwane (sacred shrub) (*horiz*)		40	40
224	25 c.	Goina Regiment		60	70
221/4			*Set of 4*	1·10	1·10

(Des V. Whiteley Studio. Litho Questa)

1975 (18 Aug). *Tenth Anniv of Internal Air Service. T* **58** *and similar horiz designs. Multicoloured.* W w 14 (*sideways*). P 14.
225	4 c.	Type **58**		30	10
226	5 c.	Fire engine		70	20
227	15 c.	Douglas DC-3		1·75	1·40
228	25 c.	Hawker Siddeley H.S.748		2·50	2·00
225/8			*Set of 4*	4·75	3·25

(Litho De La Rue, Bogotá, Colombia)

1975 (29 Sept). *As No. 164 but* W w 12 *upright.*
229	3 c.	Lion		4·50	5·00

3c

(59)

1975 (15 Nov). *Nos. 167 and 169 surch as T* **59**.
230	3 c. on 7½ c. Impala			1·00	1·25
231	6 c. on 12½ c. Ratel			1·50	1·50

60 Elephant Symbol

(Des Mary-Jane Rostami. Litho Questa)

1975 (22 Dec). *International Women's Year. T* **60** *and similar designs.* W w 14 (*sideways on 4 and 5 c.*). P 14.
232	4 c.	light bluish grey, black & light brt blue		10	10
233	5 c.	multicoloured		10	10
234	15 c.	multicoloured		30	50
235	25 c.	multicoloured		50	80
232/5			*Set of 4*	80	1·40

Designs: *Horiz*—5 c. Queen Labotsibeni. *Vert*—15 c. Craftswoman; 25 c. "Women in Service".

61 African Black-headed Oriole

(Des C. Abbott. Litho Questa)

1976 (2 Jan)–**78**. *Birds. T* **61** *and similar multicoloured designs.* W w 14 (*sideways on 1 c., 3 c., 2 e.*). *Chalk-surfaced paper.* P 14.
236	1 c.	Type **61**		75	1·50
237	2 c.	African Green Pigeon (*vert*)		80	1·50
238	3 c.	Green-winged Pytilia		1·00	1·00
239	4 c.	Violet Starling (*vert*)		80	15
	aw.	Wmk inverted		†	2·00
	b.	Ordinary paper (31.7.78)		1·50	40
240	5 c.	Black-headed Heron (*vert*)		90	80
241	6 c.	Stonechat (*vert*)		1·50	1·50
242	7 c.	Chorister Robin Chat (*vert*)		1·40	1·75
243	10 c.	Four-coloured Bush-shrike (*vert*)		1·50	80
244	15 c.	Black-collared Barbet (*vert*)		2·25	55
245	20 c.	Grey Heron (*vert*)		3·25	2·00
246	25 c.	Giant Kingfisher (*vert*)		3·50	2·00
247	30 c.	Verreaux's Eagle (*vert*)		3·50	2·50
248	50 c.	Red Bishop (*vert*)		2·25	1·50
	a.	Ordinary paper (31.7.78)		90	1·00
249	1 e.	Pin-tailed Whydah (*vert*)		2·50	2·75
	a.	Ordinary paper (31.7.78)		1·75	2·50
250	2 e.	Lilac-breasted Roller		4·50	5·00
	a.	Ordinary paper (31.7.78)		2·00	5·00
236/50a			*Set of 15*	24·00	22·00

62 Blindness from Malnutrition

63 Marathon

(Des Jennifer Toombs. Litho Questa)

1976 (15 June). *Prevention of Blindness. T* **62** *and similar horiz designs. Multicoloured.* W w 14 (*sideways*). P 14.
251	5 c.	Type **62**		25	10
252	10 c.	Infected retina		30	10
253	20 c.	Blindness from trachoma		60	35
254	25 c.	Medicines		65	40
251/4			*Set of 4*	1·60	80

(Des PAD Studio. Litho Walsall)

1976 (17 July). *Olympic Games, Montreal. T* **63** *and similar vert designs. Multicoloured.* W w 14 (*inverted*). P 14.
255	5 c.	Type **63**		15	10
256	6 c.	Boxing		20	10
257	20 c.	Football		45	25
258	25 c.	Olympic torch and flame		55	35
255/8			*Set of 4*	1·25	65

64 Footballer Shooting

65 Alexander Graham Bell and Telephone

(Des J.W. Litho Questa)

1976 (13 Sept). *F.I.F.A. Membership. T* **64** *and similar vert designs. Multicoloured.* W w 14. P 14.
259	4 c.	Type **64**		20	10
260	6 c.	Heading		20	10
261	20 c.	Goalkeeping		50	25
262	25 c.	Player about to shoot		50	30
259/62			*Set of 4*	1·25	60

(Des J.W. Litho Walsall)

1976 (22 Nov). *Telephone Centenary. T* **65** *and similar horiz designs.* W w 14 (*sideways*). P 14.
263	4 c.	multicoloured		10	10
264	5 c.	multicoloured		10	10
265	10 c.	multicoloured		15	10
266	15 c.	multicoloured		30	20
267	20 c.	multicoloured		40	30
263/7			*Set of 5*	95	55

Nos. 264/7 are as T **65**, but show different telephones.

66 Queen Elizabeth II and King Sobhuza II

(Des Walsall. Litho Questa)

1977 (7 Feb). *Silver Jubilee. T* **66** *and similar horiz designs. Multicoloured.* W w 14 (*sideways*). P 13½.
268	20 c.	Type **66**		15	15
269	25 c.	Coronation Coach at Admiralty Arch		15	15
270	50 c.	Queen in coach		20	40
268/70			*Set of 3*	45	65

67 Matsapa College

(Des J. Cooter. Litho Questa)

1977 (2 May). *50th Anniv of Police Training. T* **67** *and similar multicoloured designs.* W w 14 (*upright on 20 c., sideways on others*). P 14.
271	5 c.	Type **67**		10	10
272	10 c.	Uniformed police and land rover		50	20
273	20 c.	Police badge (*vert*)		70	85
274	25 c.	Dog handling		80	95
271/4			*Set of 4*	1·90	1·90

68 Animals and Hunters

(Des BG Studio. Litho Questa)

1977 (8 Aug). *Rock Paintings. T* **68** *and similar horiz designs. Multicoloured.* W w 14 (*sideways**). P 14.
275	5 c.	Type **68**		25	10
276	10 c.	Four dancers in a procession		30	10
277	15 c.	Man with cattle		40	20
278	20 c.	Four dancers		45	30
275/8			*Set of 4*	1·25	55
MS279	103×124 mm. Nos. 275/8			2·00	2·75
	w.	Wmk Crown to right of CA		6·00	

*The normal sideways watermark shows Crown to left of CA, as seen from the back of the stamp.

69 Timber, Highveld Region

70 Timber, Highveld Region

(Des L. Curtis. Litho D.L.R.)

1977 (17 Oct). *Maps of the Regions. T* **69** *and similar horiz designs. Multicoloured.* W w 14 (*sideways*). P 13½.
280	5 c.	Type **69**		30	10
281	10 c.	Pineapple, Middleveld		35	10
282	15 c.	Orange and Lemon, Lowveld		55	65

283	20 c. Cattle, Lubombo region	..		75	95
280/3 ..			*Set of 4*	1·75	1·60

MS284 87 × 103 mm. Four 25 c. designs as T **70**,
together forming a composite map of Swaziland .. 1·40 1·60

71 Cabbage Tree

(Des Jennifer Toombs. Litho Walsall)

1978 (12 Jan). *Trees of Swaziland. T* **71** *and similar horiz
designs. Multicoloured (except 5 c.). W* w **14** *(sideways). P* 13½.

285	5 c. Type **71** (apple-green, ochre and black) ..	15	10
286	10 c. Marula ..	20	10
287	20 c. Kiaat ..	45	95
288	25 c. Lucky bean-tree ..	55	1·10
285/8	*Set of 4*	1·25	2·00

72 Rural Electrification at Lobamba   **73** Elephant

(Des G. Drummond. Litho Questa)

1978 (6 Mar). *Hydro-electric Power. T* **72** *and similar horiz
designs. W* w **14** *(sideways). P* 13½.

289	5 c. black and buff ..	10	10
290	10 c. black and light green ..	15	10
291	20 c. black and pale blue ..	25	30
292	25 c. black and magenta ..	30	35
289/92	*Set of 4*	70	65

Designs:—10 c. Edwaleni Power Station; 20 c. Switchgear,
Magudza Power Station; 25 c. Turbine Hall, Edwaleni.

(Des C. Abbott. Litho Questa)

1978 (2 June). *25th Anniv of Coronation. T* **73** *and similar vert
designs. P* 15.

293	25 c. chalky blue, black and sage-green ..	15	25
	a. Sheetlet. Nos. 293/5 × 2 ..	75	
294	25 c. multicoloured ..	15	25
295	25 c. chalky blue, black and sage-green ..	15	25
293/5	*Set of 3*	40	65

Designs:—No. 293, Queen's Lion; No. 294, Queen Elizabeth II;
No. 295, Type **73**.

Nos. 293/5 were printed together in small sheets of 6, containing
two *se-tenant* strips of 3, with horizontal gutter margin between.

74 Clay Pots

(Des C. Abbott. Litho Questa)

1978 (24 July). *Handicrafts (1st series). T* **74** *and similar horiz
designs. Multicoloured. W* w **14** *(sideways). P* 13½ × 14.

296	5 c. Type **74** ..	10	10
297	10 c. Basketwork ..	10	10
298	20 c. Wooden utensils ..	15	15
299	30 c. Wooden pot ..	25	30
296/9 ..	*Set of 4*	50	50

See also Nos. 310/13.

75 Defence Force

(Des BG Studio. Litho Questa)

1978 (6 Sept). *10th Anniv of Independence. T* **75** *and similar horiz
designs. Multicoloured. W* w **14** *(sideways). P* 14.

300	4 c. Type **75** ..	15	10
301	6 c. The King's Regiment ..	15	10
302	10 c. Tinkabi tractor (agricultural develop-ment) ..	15	10
303	15 c. Water-pipe laying (self-help scheme) ..	25	10
304	25 c. Sebenta adult literacy scheme ..	30	25
305	50 c. Fire emergency service ..	1·25	50
300/5 ..	*Set of 6*	2·00	85

76 Archangel Gabriel appearing   **77** Prospecting at
before Shepherds   Phophonyane

(Des V. Whiteley Studio. Litho Harrison)

1978 (12 Dec). *Christmas. T* **76** *and similar horiz designs. Multicoloured. W* w **14.** *P* 14½ × 14.

306	5 c. Type **76** ..	10	10
307	10 c. Three Wise Men paying homage to infant Jesus ..	10	10
308	15 c. Archangel Gabriel warning Joseph ..	10	10
309	25 c. Flight into Egypt ..	20	20
306/9 ..	*Set of 4*	30	35

(Des C. Abbott. Litho Walsall)

1979 (10 Jan). *Handicrafts (2nd series). Horiz designs as T* **74.**
Multicoloured. W w **14** *(sideways). P* 13½.

310	5 c. Sisal bowls ..	10	10
311	15 c. Pottery ..	15	10
312	20 c. Basket work ..	20	15
313	30 c. Hide shield ..	30	20
310/13 ..	*Set of 4*	60	45

(Des L. Curtis. Litho Questa)

1979 (27 Mar). *Centenary of Discovery of Gold in Swaziland. T* **77**
and similar vert designs. W w **14.** *P* 14.

314	5 c. gold and deep ultramarine ..	25	10
315	15 c. gold and deep brown ..	45	20
316	25 c. gold and deep green ..	65	30
317	50 c. gold and carmine-red ..	90	90
314/17 ..	*Set of 4*	2·00	1·25

Designs:—15 c. Early 3-stamp battery mill; 25 c. Cyanide tanks
at Piggs Peak; 50 c. Pouring off molten gold.

78 "Girls at the Piano"

(Des BG Studio. Litho Questa)

1979 (8 May). *International Year of the Child. Paintings by
Renoir. T* **78** *and similar horiz designs. Multicoloured. W* w **14**
(sideways). P 13½.

318	5 c. Type **78** ..	10	10
319	15 c. "Madame Charpentier and her Children" ..	25	10
320	25 c. "Girls picking Flowers" ..	35	15
321	50 c. "Girl with Watering Can" ..	70	55
318/21 ..	*Set of 4*	1·25	70
MS322 123 × 135 mm. Nos. 318/21		1·25	1·75

79 1933 1d. Carmine Stamp and Sir Rowland Hill

(Des J.W. Litho Walsall)

1979 (17 July). *Death Centenary of Sir Rowland Hill. T* **79** *and
similar horiz designs showing stamps and portrait of Sir
Rowland Hill. Multicoloured. W* w **14** *(sideways*). *P* 14½ × 14.

323	10 c. 1945 3d. Victory commemorative ..	15	10
324	20 c. Type **79** ..	25	25
325	25 c. 1968 25 c. Independence commemorative ..	25	30
323/5 ..	*Set of 3*	60	60
MS326 115×90 mm. 50 c. 1956 6d. Great Kudu Antelope definitive		75	85
	w. Wmk Crown to right of CA ..	7·50	

*The normal sideways watermark shows Crown to left of CA,
as seen from the back of of the stamp.

80 Obverse and Reverse of 5 Cents

(Des G. Hutchins. Litho Walsall)

1979 (6 Sept). *Coins. T* **80** *and similar horiz designs. W* w **14**
(sideways). P 13½.

327	5 c. black and light brown ..	15	10
328	10 c. black and new blue ..	20	10
329	20 c. black and yellowish green ..	35	20

330	50 c. black and yellow-orange ..	50	45
331	1 e. black and cerise ..	75	80
327/31	*Set of 5*	1·75	1·50

Designs:—10 c. Obverse and reverse of 10 cents; 20 c. Obverse
and reverse of 20 cents; 50 c. Reverse of 50 cents; 1 e. Reverse of
1 lilangeni.

81 Big Bend Post Office

(Des J. Cooter. Litho Questa)

1979 (22 Nov). *Post Office Anniversaries. T* **81** *and similar
designs. W* w **14** *(sideways on 5, 20 and 50 c.). P* 13½.

332	5 c. multicoloured ..	10	10
333	15 c. multicoloured ..	15	10
334	20 c. black, sage-green and magenta ..	20	15
335	50 c. multicoloured ..	40	60
332/5 ..	*Set of 4*	70	80

Designs and commemorations: Horiz—5 c. Type **81** (25th anniversary of Posts and Telecommunications Services); 20 c. 1949
75th anniversary of U.P.U. 1s. commemorative stamp (10th anniversary of U.P.U. membership); 50 c. 1974 centenary of U.P.U.
25 c. commemorative stamp (10th anniversary of U.P.U. membership). Vert—15 c. Microwave antenna. Mount Ntondozi (25th anniversary of Posts and Telecommunications Services).

82 Map of Swaziland   **83** *Brunsvigia radulosa*

(Des BG Studio. Litho Walsall)

1980 (23 Feb). *75th Anniv of Rotary International. T* **82** *and
similar vert designs in gold and bright blue. W* w **14.** *P* 13½.

336	5 c. Type **82** ..	25	10
337	15 c. Vitreous cutter and optical illuminator ..	45	10
338	50 c. Scroll ..	50	55
339	1 e. Rotary Headquarters, Evanston, U.S.A. ..	85	1·25
336/9 ..	*Set of 4*	1·90	1·75

(Des BG Studio. Litho Secura, Singapore)

1980 (28 Apr)–**83.** *Flowers. Multicoloured designs as T* **83**.

A. *Without imprint date below design. P* 13½.

340A	1 c. Type **83** ..	15	10
341A	2 c. *Aloe suprafoliata* ..	15	10
342A	3 c. *Haemanthus magnificus* ..	15	10
	c. Perf 12 ..	2·75	2·50
343A	4 c. *Aloe marlothii* ..	20	10
	c. Perf 12 ..	4·50	3·00
344A	5 c. *Dicoma zeyheri* ..	15	10
	c. Perf 12 ..	3·75	3·00
345A	6 c. *Aloe kniphofioides* ..	20	30
346A	7 c. *Cyrtanthus bicolor* ..	15	10
347A	10 c. *Eucomis autumnalis* ..	25	10
348A	15 c. *Leucospermum gerrardii* ..	15	10
	c. Perf 12 ..		
349A	20 c. *Haemanthus multiflorus* ..	40	25
350A	30 c. *Acridocarpus natalitius* ..	20	20
351A	50 c. *Adenium swazicum* ..	30	30
352A	1 e. *Protea simplex* ..	55	60
353A	2 e. *Calodendrum capense* ..	1·10	1·25
354A	5 e. *Gladiolus eckloni* ..	2·25	3·00
340A/54A	*Set of 15*	5·50	5·50

B. *With "1983" imprint date. P* 12 (12.83).

340B	1 c. Type **83** ..	1·00	1·00
341B	2 c. *Aloe suprafoliata* ..	1·00	1·00
343B	4 c. *Aloe marlothii.* ..	1·50	75
345B	6 c. *Aloe kniphofioides* ..	1·75	1·75
347B	10 c. *Eucomis autumnalis* ..	2·00	85
349B	20 c. *Haemanthus multiflorus* ..	2·25	2·00
340B/9B	*Set of 6*	8·50	6·50

Nos. 347/51 are horizontal, 42 × 25 mm, and Nos. 352/4 vertical,
28 × 38 mm.

84 Mail Runner

(Des A. Theobald. Litho Walsall)

1980 (6 May). *"London 1980" International Stamp Exhibition. T* **84** *and similar horiz designs. Multicoloured.* W w **14** *(sideways*). P* 14.

355	10 c.	Type 84	15	10
356	20 c.	Post Office mail truck	25	15
		w. Wmk Crown to right of CA	6·50	
357	25 c.	Mail sorting office	30	20
358	50 c.	Ropeway conveying mail at Bulembu	70	70
355/8		*Set of 4*	1·25	1·00

*The normal sideways watermark shows Crown to left of CA, as seen from the back of the stamp.

85 Scaly

(Des and litho Walsall)

1980 (25 Aug). *River Fishes. T* **85** *and similar horiz designs. Multicoloured.* W w **14** *(sideways).* P 13½.

359	5 c.	Type 85	30	10
360	10 c.	Silver Catfish ("Silver Barbel")	30	10
361	15 c.	Tiger Fish	55	15
362	30 c.	Brown Squeaker	85	30
363	1 e.	Red-breasted Tilapia ("Bream")	1·10	1·40
359/63		*Set of 5*	2·75	1·75

86 Oribi

(Des G. Drummond. Litho Harrison)

1980 (1 Oct). *Wildlife Conservation. T* **86** *and similar multi-coloured designs.* W w **14** *(sideways on 5 and 50 c.).* P 14.

364	5 c.	Type 86	15	10
365	10 c.	Nile Crocodile (*vert*)	30	10
366	50 c.	Temminck's Ground Pangolin	75	70
367	1 e.	Leopard (*vert*)	1·60	1·50
364/7		*Set of 4*	2·50	2·00

87 Public Bus Service

(Des G. Hutchins. Litho Format)

1981 (5 Jan). *Transport. T* **87** *and similar horiz designs. Multi-coloured.* W w **14** *(sideways).* P 14½.

368	5 c.	Type 87	10	10
369	25 c.	Royal Swazi National Airways	25	15
370	30 c.	Swaziland United Transport	30	20
371	1 e.	Swaziland Railway	1·25	1·75
368/71		*Set of 4*	1·60	2·00

88 Mantenga Falls   89 Prince Charles on Hike

(Des L. Curtis. Litho Format)

1981 (16 Mar). *Tourism. T* **88** *and similar horiz designs. Multi-coloured.* W w **14** *(sideways).* P 14.

372	5 c.	Type 88	10	10
373	15 c.	Mananga Yacht Club	15	10
374	30 c.	White Rhinoceros in Mlilwane Game Sanctuary	40	30
375	1 e.	Roulette wheel, playing cards and dice ("casinos")	1·10	1·60
372/5		*Set of 4*	1·50	1·90

(Des J.W. Litho Walsall)

1981 (21 July). *Royal Wedding. T* **89** *and similar vert designs. Multicoloured.* W w **14.** P 14.

376	10 c.	Wedding bouquet from Swaziland	10	10
377	25 c.	Type 89	15	10
378	1 e.	Prince Charles and Lady Diana Spencer	40	70
376/8		*Set of 3*	60	75

90 Installation of King Sobhuza II, 22 December 1921   91 "Physical Recreation"

(Des J.W. Litho Harrison)

1981 (24 Aug). *Diamond Jubilee of King Sobhuza II. T* **90** *and similar horiz designs. Multicoloured.* W w **14** *(sideways).* P 14½.

379	5 c.	Type 90	10	10
380	10 c.	Royal visit, 1947	10	10
381	15 c.	King Sobhuza II and Coronation of Queen Elizabeth II, 1953	15	15
382	25 c.	King Sobhuza taking Royal Salute, Independence, 1968	15	15
383	30 c.	King Sobhuza in youth	20	20
384	1 e.	King Sobhuza and Parliament Buildings	50	90
379/84		*Set of 6*	1·00	1·40

(Des BG Studio. Litho Questa)

1981 (5 Nov). *25th Anniv of Duke of Edinburgh Award Scheme. T* **91** *and similar vert designs. Multicoloured.* W w **14.** P 14.

385	5 c.	Type 91	10	10
386	20 c.	"Expeditions"	10	10
387	50 c.	"Skills"	25	25
388	1 e.	Duke of Edinburgh in ceremonial dress	50	80
385/8		*Set of 4*	80	1·00

92 Disabled Person in Wheelchair

(Des and litho Walsall)

1981 (16 Dec). *International Year of Disabled Persons. T* **92** *and similar multicoloured designs.* W w **14** *(sideways on 5 c. and 1 e.).* P 14×14½ *(5 c., 1 e.) or* 14½×14 *(others).*

389	5 c.	Type 92	30	10
390	15 c.	Teacher with disabled child (*vert*)	50	15
391	25 c.	Disabled craftsman (*vert*)	75	20
392	1 e.	Disabled driver in invalid carriage	2·25	1·75
389/92		*Set of 4*	3·50	2·00

93 *Papilio demodocus*   94 Man holding a Flower, after discarding Cigarettes

(Des I. Loe. Litho Rosenbaum Bros, Vienna)

1982 (6 Jan). *Butterflies. T* **93** *and similar horiz designs. Multicoloured.* W w **14** *(sideways*).* P 14.

393	5 c.	Type 93	50	10
		w. Wmk Crown to left of CA	1·10	
394	10 c.	*Charaxes candiope*	60	10
		w. Wmk Crown to right of CA	2·75	
395	50 c.	*Papilio nireus*	2·00	85
		w. Wmk Crown to right of CA		
396	1 e.	*Terias desjardinsii*	2·50	2·00
		w. Wmk Crown to left of CA		
393/6		*Set of 4*	5·00	2·75

*The normal sideways watermark shows Crown to left of CA on 10 c., 50 c. and to right on the other values, *all as seen from the back of the stamp.*

(Des PAD Studio. Litho Format)

1982 (27 Apr). *Pan-African Conference on Smoking and Health. T* **94** *and similar vert design. Multicoloured.* W w **14.** P 14.

397	5 c.	Type 94	50	85
398	10 c.	Smoker and non-smoker climbing stairs	60	90

95 Male Fishing Owl   96 Swaziland Coat of Arms

(Des G. Drummond. Litho J.W.)

1982 (16 June). *Wildlife Conservation* (1st series). *Pel's Fishing Owl. T* **95** *and similar vert designs. Multicoloured.* W w **14.** P 13½×13.

399	35 c.	Type 95	8·00	4·00
		a. Horiz strip of 5. Nos. 399/403	35·00	
400	35 c.	Female Fishing Owl at nest	8·00	4·00
401	35 c.	Pair of Fishing Owls	8·00	4·00
402	35 c.	Fishing Owl, nest and egg	8·00	4·00
403	35 c.	Adult Fishing Owl with youngster	8·00	4·00
399/403		*Set of 5*	18·00	

Nos. 399/403 were printed together, *se-tenant*, in horizontal and vertical strips of 5 throughout the sheet.
See also Nos. 425/9 and Nos. 448/52.

(Des C. Abbott. Litho W. S. Cowells Ltd)

1982 (1 July). *21st Birthday of Princess of Wales. T* **96** *and similar vert designs. Multicoloured.* W w **14.** P 14½.

404	5 c.	Type 96	10	10
		w. Wmk inverted	40·00	
405	20 c.	Princess leaving Eastleigh Airport, Southampton, August 1981	70	10
406	50 c.	Bride at Buckingham Palace	80	25
407	1 e.	Formal portrait	1·75	65
		w. Wmk inverted	80·00	
404/7		*Set of 4*	3·00	1·00

97 Irrigation

(Des G. Hutchins. Litho Walsall)

1982 (1 Sept). *Sugar Industry. T* **97** *and similar horiz designs. Multicoloured.* W w **14** *(sideways).* P 14 × 14½.

408	5 c.	Type 97	10	10
409	20 c.	Harvesting	25	15
410	30 c.	Mhlume mills	35	25
411	1 e.	Sugar transportation by train	1·00	1·40
408/11		*Set of 4*	1·50	1·75

98 Nurse with Child

(Des L. Curtis. Litho Questa)

1982 (9 Nov). *Swaziland Red Cross Society (Baphalali). T* **98** *and similar horiz designs. Multicoloured.* W w **14** *(sideways).*

412	5 c.	Type 98	10	10
413	20 c.	Juniors carrying stretcher	25	15
414	50 c.	Disaster relief	55	60
415	1 e.	Henri Dunant (founder of Red Cross)	1·25	1·60
412/15		*Set of 4*	1·90	2·25

99 Taking the Oath   100 Satellite View of Earth

(Des B. Melton. Litho Format)

1982 (6 Dec). *75th Anniv of Boy Scout Movement. T* **99** *and similar horiz designs. Multicoloured.* W w **14** *(sideways*).* P 14×13½.

416	5 c.	Type 99	10	10
417	10 c.	Hiking and exploration	15	10
418	25 c.	Community development	30	30
		w. Wmk Crown to right of CA	9·50	
419	75 c.	Lord Baden-Powell	1·00	1·25
		w. Wmk Crown to right of CA	9·50	
416/19		*Set of 4*	1·40	1·60
MS420		107×109 mm. 1 e. World Scout badge	1·25	1·40

*The normal sideways watermark shows Crown to left of CA, as seen from the back of the stamp.

(Des A. Theobald. Litho Harrison)

1983 (14 Mar). *Commonwealth Day. T* **100** *and similar multi-coloured designs.* W w **14** *(sideways on 50 c., 1 e.).* P 14.

421	6 c.	Type 100	10	10
422	10 c.	King Sobhuza II	10	10
423	50 c.	Swazi woman and beehive huts (*horiz*)	35	55
424	1 e.	Spraying sugar crops (*horiz*)	70	1·00
421/4		*Set of 4*	1·10	1·50

(Des G. Drummond. Litho J.W.)

1983 (16 May). *Wildlife Conservation* (2nd series). Lammergeier. Vert designs as T **95**. Multicoloured. W w 14. P 13½ × 13.
425	35 c. Adult male	..	2·50	2·50
	a. Horiz strip of 5. Nos. 425/9		11·00	
426	35 c. Pair	..	2·50	2·50
427	35 c. Nest and egg	..	2·50	2·50
428	35 c. Female at nest	..	2·50	2·50
429	35 c. Adult bird with fledgling	..	2·50	2·50
425/9		*Set of 5*	11·00	11·00

Nos. 425/9 were printed together, *se-tenant*, in horizontal strips of 5 throughout the sheet.

101 Swaziland National Football Team **102** Montgolfier Balloon

(Des G. Vasarhelyi. Litho Format)

1983 (20 Aug). *Tour of Swaziland by English Football Clubs.* Three sheets, 101 × 72 mm, each containing one 75 c. stamp as T **101**. Multicoloured. W w 14 (*sideways*). P 13½.
MS430	75 c. Type 101; 75 c. Tottenham Hotspur;			
	75 c. Manchester United	*Set of 3 sheets*	1·75	3·00

(Des D. Hartley-Marjoram. Litho Format)

1983 (22 Aug). *Bicentenary of Manned Flight.* T **102** and similar multicoloured designs. W w 14 (*sideways on 10 c. to 50 c.*). P 14.
431	5 c. Type 102	..	10	10
432	10 c. Wright brothers' Flyer I (*horiz*)	..	15	10
433	25 c. Fokker F.28 Fellowship (*horiz*)	..	30	35
434	50 c. Bell XS-1 (*horiz*)	..	60	65
431/4		*Set of 4*	95	1·00
MS435	73×73 mm. 1 e. Space shuttle *Columbia*		1·00	1·40

103 Dr. Albert Schweitzer (Peace Prize, 1952)

(Des G. Vasarhelyi. Litho Harrison)

1983 (21 Oct). *150th Birth Anniv of Alfred Nobel.* T **103** and similar horiz designs. Multicoloured. W w 14 (*sideways*). P 14.
436	6 c. Type 103	..	1·25	30
437	10 c. Dag Hammarskjöld (Peace Prize, 1961)	..	70	15
438	50 c. Albert Einstein (Physics Prize, 1921)	3·25	1·75	
439	1 e. Alfred Nobel ..	..	3·50	4·00
436/9		*Set of 4*	7·50	5·50

104 Maize

(Des Jennifer Toombs. Litho Harrison)

1983 (29 Nov). *World Food Day.* T **104** and similar horiz designs. Multicoloured. W w 14 (*sideways*). P 14.
440	6 c. Type 104 ..	..	10	10
441	10 c. Rice	..	10	10
442	50 c. Cattle herding	..	70	85
443	1 e. Ploughing	..	1·25	2·00
440/3		*Set of 4*	1·90	2·75

105 Women's College **106** Male on Ledge

(Des C. Abbott. Litho Format)

1984 (12 Mar). *Education.* T **105** and similar horiz designs. Multicoloured. W w 14 (*sideways*). P 14.
444	5 c. Type 105 ..	..	10	10
445	15 c. Technical Training School	..	15	15
446	50 c. University	..	35	60
447	1 e. Primary school	..	65	1·10
444/7 ..		*Set of 4*	1·10	1·75

(Des G. Drummond. Litho J.W.)

1984 (18 May). *Wildlife Conservation.* (3rd series) *Bald Ibis.* T **106** and similar vert designs. Multicoloured. W w 14. P 13½ × 13.
448	35 c. Type 106	..	3·00	3·00
	a. Horiz strip of 5. Nos. 448/52		13·50	
449	35 c. Male and female	..	3·00	3·00
450	35 c. Bird and egg	..	3·00	3·00
451	35 c. Female on nest of eggs	..	3·00	3·00
452	35 c. Adult and fledgling	..	3·00	3·00
448/52		*Set of 5*	13·50	13·50

Nos. 448/52 were printed together, *se-tenant*, in horizontal strips of 5 throughout the sheet.

107 Mule-drawn Passenger Coach

(Des A. Theobald. Litho Walsall)

1984 (15 June). *Universal Postal Union Congress, Hamburg.* T **107** and similar horiz designs. Multicoloured. W w 14 (*sideways*). P 14½.
453	7 c. Type 107 ..	..	30	10
454	15 c. Ox-drawn post wagon	..	45	15
455	50 c. Mule-drawn mail coach ..	..	90	60
456	1 e. Bristol to London mail coach	..	1·40	1·10
453/6		*Set of 4*	2·75	1·75

108 Running

(Des Harrison. Litho Walsall)

1984 (27 July). *Olympic Games, Los Angeles.* T **108** and similar horiz designs. Multicoloured. W w 14 (*sideways*). P 14.
457	7 c. Type 108 ..	..	10	10
458	10 c. Swimming	..	10	10
459	50 c. Shooting	..	45	75
460	1 e. Boxing	..	90	1·60
457/60		*Set of 4*	1·40	2·25
MS461	100 × 70 mm. Nos. 457/60	..	2·25	4·00

109 *Suillus bovinus*

(Des J. Spencer. Litho Format)

1984 (19 Sept). *Fungi.* T **109** and similar multicoloured designs. W w 14 (*sideways on 10 c., 1 e.*). P 14.
462	10 c. Type 109 ..	..	1·50	30
463	15 c. *Langermannia gigantea* (*vert*)		2·50	55
	w. Wmk inverted		10·00	
464	50 c. *Trametes versicolor* ("*Coriolus versicolor*") (*vert*)	..	2·75	2·75
465	1 e. *Boletus edulis*	..	3·25	5·25
462/5	..	*Set of 4*	9·00	8·00

110 King Sobhuza opening Railway, 1964 **(111)**

(Des W. Fenton. Litho Walsall)

1984 (5 Nov). *20th Anniv of Swaziland Railways.* T **110** and similar horiz designs. Multicoloured. W w 14 (*sideways*). P 14.
466	10 c. Type 110	..	30	15
467	25 c. Type 15A locomotive at Siweni Yard	65	40	
468	30 c. Container loading, Matsapha Station	65	40	
469	1 e. Locomotive No. 268 leaving Alto Tunnel	..	1·50	2·00
466/9		*Set of 4*	2·75	2·75
MS470	144×74 mm. Nos. 466/9	..	3·25	6·00

NEW INFORMATION

The editor is always interested to correspond with people who have new information that will improve or correct the Catalogue.

1984 (15 Dec). Nos. 340B, 341A, 342A, 343A, 345B and 346A surch as T **111**.
471	10 c. on 4 c. *Aloe marlothii* ..	..	50·00	
	a. Surch on No. 343Ac	..	50	10
	b. Surch on No. 343B		4·50	4·50
472	15 c. on 7 c. *Cyrtanthus bicolor*	..	60	20
473	20 c. on 3 c. *Haemanthus magnificus*	50	15	
	a. Surch on No. 342Ac		4·50	4·50
474	25 c. on 6 c. *Aloe kniphofioides*	..	60	20
	a. Surch triple	..		†
	b. Surch double			
475	30 c. on 1 c. Type 83	..	70	20
	a. Surch omitted (horiz pair with normal)	£375		
476	30 c. on 2 c. *Aloe suprafoliata*	..	2·50	3·00
	a. Surch on No. 341B		4·50	4·50
471a/6		*Set of 6*	4·75	3·50

112 Rotary International Logo and Map of World **113** Male Ground Hornbill

(Des G. Vasarhelyi. Litho Questa)

1985 (23 Feb). *80th Anniv of Rotary International.* T **112** and similar horiz designs. Multicoloured. W w 14 (*sideways*). P 14.
477	10 c. Type 112	..	30	10
478	15 c. Teacher and handicapped children	70	20	
479	50 c. Youth exchange	..	1·00	55
480	1 e. Nurse and children	..	2·00	1·10
477/80		*Set of 4*	3·50	1·75

(Des G. Drummond. Litho Harrison)

1985 (15 May). *Birth Bicentenary of John J. Audubon (ornithologist). Southern Ground Hornbills.* T **113** and similar vert designs. Multicoloured. W w 14. P 14.
481	25 c. Type 113	..	2·25	3·25
	a. Horiz strip of 5. Nos. 481/5	..	10·00	
482	25 c. Male and female Ground Hornbills	2·25	3·25	
483	25 c. Female at nest	..	2·25	3·25
484	25 c. Ground Hornbill in nest, and egg	2·25	3·25	
485	25 c. Adult and fledgling	..	2·25	3·25
481/5		*Set of 5*	10·00	14·00

Nos. 481/5 were printed together, *se-tenant*, in horizontal strips of 5 throughout the sheet.

114 The Queen Mother in 1975 **115** Buick "Tourer"

(Des A. Theobald (2 e.), C. Abbott (others). Litho Questa)

1985 (7 June). *Life and Times of Queen Elizabeth the Queen Mother.* T **114** and similar vert designs. Multicoloured. W w 16. P 14½ × 14.
486	10 c. The Queen Mother in South Africa, 1947	..	10	10
487	15 c. With the Queen and Princess Margaret, 1985 (from photo by Norman Parkinson)	..	10	10
488	50 c. Type 114	..	35	40
489	1 e. With Prince Henry at his christening (from photo by Lord Snowdon)		60	1·25
486/9		*Set of 4*	1·00	1·60
MS490	91×73 mm. 2 e. Greeting Prince Andrew. Wmk sideways..	..	1·90	1·40

(Des D. Hartley. Litho Walsall)

1985 (16 Sept). *Century of Motoring.* T **115** and similar horiz designs. Multicoloured. W w 14 (*sideways*). P 14.
491	10 c. Type 115 ..	..	50	10
492	15 c. Four cylinder Rover	..	70	20
493	50 c. De Dion Bouton ..	..	1·75	2·00
494	1 e. "Model T" Ford	..	2·25	3·75
491/4 ..		*Set of 4*	4·75	5·50

116 Youths building Bridge over Ravine

(Des Vrein Barlocher. Litho Format)

1985 (2 Dec). *International Youth Year* (10, 50 c.), *and 75th Anniv of Girl Guide Movement* (others). *T* **116** *and similar horiz designs. Multicoloured. W w* **16** (*sideways**). *P* 14.

495	10 c. Type **116**			15	10
496	20 c. Girl Guides in camp			20	15
	w. Wmk Crown to right of CA				
497	50 c. Youth making model from sticks			45	75
498	1 e. Guides collecting brushwood			80	1·50
495/8			*Set of 4*	1·40	2·25

*The normal sideways watermark shows Crown to left of CA, as seen from the back of the stamp.

117 Halley's Comet over Swaziland   **118** King Mswati III

(Des Jennifer Toombs. Litho B.D.T.)

1986 (27 Feb). *Appearance of Halley's Comet. W w* **14** (*sideways*). *P* 14.

499	**117** 1 e. 50, multicoloured			2·75	3·50

(Des A. Theobald. Litho Format)

1986 (21 Apr). *60th Birthday of Queen Elizabeth II. Vert designs as T* **230a** *of Jamaica. Multicoloured. W w* **16**. *P* 14×14½.

500	10 c. Christening of Princess Anne, 1950		10	10
501	30 c. On Palace balcony after wedding of Prince and Princess of Wales, 1981		15	25
502	45 c. Royal visit to Swaziland, 1947		15	30
503	1 e. At Windsor Polo Ground, 1984		30	60
504	2 e. At Crown Agents Head Office, London, 1983		60	1·25
500/4		*Set of 5*	1·10	2·25

(Des L. Curtis. Litho Walsall)

1986 (25 Apr). *Coronation of King Mswati III. T* **118** *and similar designs. W w* **16** (*sideways on 20 c. to 2 e.*). *P* 14½×14 (*10 c.*) *or* 14×14½ (*others*).

505	10 c. black and gold			35	10
506	20 c. multicoloured			70	30
507	25 c. multicoloured			80	35
508	30 c. multicoloured			90	50
509	40 c. multicoloured			2·00	1·75
510	2 e. multicoloured			3·50	6·00
505/10			*Set of 6*	7·50	8·00

Designs: *Horiz*—20 c. Prince with King Sobhuza II at Incwala ceremony; 25 c. At primary school; 30 c. At school in England; 40 c. Inspecting guard of honour at Matsapha Airport; 2 e. Dancing the Simemo.

119 Emblems of Round Table and Project Orbis (eye disease campaign)   **120** *Precis hierta*

(Des M. Kesson, adapted G. Vasarhelyi. Litho Walsall)

1986 (6 Oct). *50th Anniv of Round Table Organization. T* **119** *and similar vert designs showing branch emblems. Multicoloured. W w* **16**. *P* 14.

511	15 c. Type **119**			20	10
512	25 c. Ehlanzeni 51			30	20
513	55 c. Mbabane 30			65	60
514	70 c. Bulembu 54			75	85
515	2 e. Manzini 44			1·75	2·50
511/15			*Set of 5*	3·25	3·75

(Des I. Loe. Litho Questa)

1987 (17 Mar). *Butterflies (1st series). T* **120** *and similar horiz designs. Multicoloured. P* 14.

516	10 c. Type **120**			55	80
517	15 c. *Hamanumida daedalus*			65	50
518	20 c. *Charaxes boueti*			65	90
519	25 c. *Abantis paradisea*			65	80
520	30 c. *Acraea anemosa*			65	70
521	35 c. *Graphium leonidas*			65	75
522	45 c. *Graphium antheus*			70	1·00
523	50 c. *Precis orithya*			70	85
524	55 c. *Pinacopteryx eriphia*			70	85
525	70 c. *Precis octavia*			80	1·40
526	1 e. *Mylothris chloris*			1·00	2·50
527	5 e. *Colotis regina*			1·00	1·10
528	10 e. *Spindasis natalensis*			2·00	2·10
516/28			*Set of 13*	9·50	13·00

For these designs, and similar 5 c., with different portrait of King Mswati III see Nos. 606/17.

121 Two White Rhinoceroses   **122** Hybrid Tea Rose "Blue Moon"

(Des Doreen McGuinness. Litho Questa)

1987 (1 July). *White Rhinoceros. T* **121** *and similar horiz designs. Multicoloured. W w* **16** (*sideways*). *P* 14½.

529	15 c. Type **121**.			2·00	45
530	25 c. Female and calf.			2·75	1·00
531	45 c. Rhinoceros charging			4·25	3·25
532	70 c. Rhinoceros wallowing			6·50	7·00
529/32			*Set of 4*	14·00	10·50

(Des Josephine Martin. Litho Questa)

1987 (19 Oct). *Garden Flowers. T* **122** *and similar vert designs. Multicoloured. W w* **16**. *P* 14½.

533	15 c. Type **122**.			90	20
534	35 c. Rambler Rose "Danse du feu".			1·75	80
535	55 c. Pompon Dahlia "Odin".			2·25	1·50
536	2 e. *Lilium davidii* var. *willmottiae*			5·75	9·00
533/6			*Set of 4*	9·50	10·50

1987 (9 Dec). *Royal Ruby Wedding. Nos. 501/4 optd with T* **45a** *of Kiribati in silver.*

537	30 c. On Palace balcony after wedding of Prince and Princess of Wales, 1981		20	20
538	45 c. Royal visit to Swaziland, 1947		30	30
539	1 e. At Windsor Polo Ground, 1984		50	1·25
540	2 e. At Crown Agents Head Office, London, 1983		75	2·25
537/40		*Set of 4*	1·60	3·50

123 *Zabalius aridus* (grasshopper)

(Des I. Loe. Litho Questa)

1988 (14 Mar). *Insects. T* **123** *and similar horiz designs. Multicoloured. W w* **16** (*sideways*). *P* 14.

541	15 c. Type **123**			90	15
542	55 c. *Callidea bohemani* (shieldbug)		2·25	85
543	1 e. *Phymateus viridipes* (grasshopper)		3·50	4·00
544	2 e. *Nomadacris septemfasciata* (locust)		5·50	7·50
541/4			*Set of 4*	11·00	11·00

124 Athlete with Swazi Flag and Olympic Stadium

(Des C. Abbott. Litho Format)

1988 (22 Aug). *Olympic Games, Seoul. T* **124** *and similar horiz designs. Multicoloured. W w* **16** (*sideways*). *P* 14.

545	15 c. Type **124**			25	10
546	35 c. Taekwondo			80	45
547	1 e. Boxing			1·25	2·00
548	2 e. Tennis			2·75	4·25
545/8			*Set of 4*	4·50	6·00

125 Savanna Monkey ("Green Monkey")   **126** Dr. David Hynd (founder of Swazi Red Cross)

(Des I. Loe. Litho Questa)

1989 (16 Jan). *Small Mammals. T* **125** *and similar horiz designs. Multicoloured. W w* **16** (*sideways*). *P* 14.

549	35 c. Type **125**			1·25	30
550	55 c. Large-toothed Rock Hyrax ("Rock Dassie")		1·60	75
551	1 e. Zorilla			2·75	3·50
552	2 e. African Wild Cat			4·50	6·00
549/52			*Set of 4*	9·00	9·50

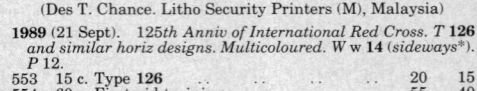

(Des T. Chance. Litho Security Printers (M), Malaysia)

1989 (21 Sept). *125th Anniv of International Red Cross. T* **126** *and similar horiz designs. Multicoloured. W w* **14** (*sideways**). *P* 12.

553	15 c. Type **126**			20	15
554	60 c. First aid training			55	40
555	1 e. Sigombeni Clinic			90	80
556	2 e. Refugee camp			1·40	1·40
	w. Wmk Crown to right of CA				
553/6			*Set of 4*	2·75	2·50

*The normal sideways watermark shows Crown to left of CA, as seen from the back of the stamp.

127 King Mswati III with Prince of Wales, 1987   **128** Manzini to Mahamba Road

(Des L. Curtis. Litho Harrison)

1989 (15 Nov). *21st Birthday of King Mswati III. T* **127** *and similar horiz designs. Multicoloured. P* 14×14½.

557	15 c. Type **127**			10	10
558	60 c. King with Pope John Paul II, 1988		30	35
559	1 e. Introduction of Crown Prince to people, 1983		50	55
560	2 e. King Mswati III and Queen Mother		95	1·00
557/60			*Set of 4*	1·60	1·75

(Des A. Theobald. Litho Questa)

1989 (18 Dec). *25th Anniv of African Development Bank. T* **128** *and similar horiz designs. Multicoloured. W w* **16** (*sideways*). *P* 14×14½.

561	15 c. Type **128**			10	10
562	60 c. Microwave Radio Receiver, Mbabane		30	40
563	1 e. Mbabane Government Hospital		50	85
564	2 e. Ezulwini Power Station switchyard		95	1·75
561/4			*Set of 4*	1·60	2·75

129 International Priority Mail Van

(Des G. Vasarhelyi. Litho Security Printers (M), Malaysia)

1990 (3 May). *"Stamp World London 90" International Stamp Exhibition. T* **129** *and similar horiz designs. Multicoloured. W w* **14** (*sideways*). *P* 12½.

565	15 c. Type **129**			15	10
566	60 c. Facsimile Service operators			40	40
567	1 e. Rural post office			75	1·00
568	2 e. Ezulwini Earth Station			1·40	2·25
565/8			*Set of 4*	2·40	3·25
MS569	105×85 mm. 2 e. Mail runner. Wmk upright.			2·25	3·25

No. **MS569** also commemorates the 150th anniversary of the Penny Black.

(Des D. Miller. Litho Questa)

1990 (4 Aug). *90th Birthday of Queen Elizabeth the Queen Mother. Vert designs as T* **107** (75 c.) *or* **108** (4 e.) *of Kenya. W w* **16**. *P* 14×15 (75 c.) *or* 14½ (4 e.).

570	75 c. multicoloured			50	50
571	4 e. brownish black & dp turquoise-green		2·25	3·00

Designs:—75 c. Queen Mother; 4 e. King George VI and Queen Elizabeth visiting Civil Resettlement Unit, Hatfield House.

130 Pictorial Teaching   **131** Rural Water Supply

(Des D. Aryeequaye. Litho Questa)

1990 (21 Sept). *International Literacy Year. T* **130** *and similar horiz designs. Multicoloured. W w* **14** (*sideways*). *P* 14.

572	15 c. Type **130**			10	10
573	75 c. Rural class			45	45
574	1 e. Modern teaching methods			60	95
575	2 e. Presentation of certificates			1·10	1·60
572/5			*Set of 4*	2·00	2·75

(Des D. Aryeequaye. Litho Cartor)

1990 (10 Dec). *40th Anniv of United Nations Development Programme. "Helping People to Help Themselves". T* **131** *and similar vert designs. Multicoloured. W w* **14**. *P* 13½×14.

576	60 c. Type **131**			35	35
577	1 e. Seed multiplication project			60	95
578	2 e. Low-cost housing project			1·25	1·75
576/8			*Set of 3*	2·00	2·75

10c ■

(132)   133 Lobamba Hot Spring

1990 (17 Dec). *Nos.* 519/20, 522 *and* 524 *surch as T* **132**.

579	10 c. on 25 c. *Abantis paradisea*			30	30
580	15 c. on 30 c. *Acraea anemosa*			40	40
580*a*	15 c. on 45 c. *Graphium antheus*			14·00	14·00
581	20 c. on 45 c. *Graphium antheus*			40	40
582	40 c. on 55 c. *Pinacopteryx eriphia*			55	55

(Des D. Aryeequaye. Litho Harrison)

1991 (11 Feb). *National Heritage. T* **133** *and similar horiz designs. Multicoloured. W* **77** *of Brunei (sideways). P* 14½.

583	15 c. Type **133**			15	10
584	60 c. Sibebe Rock			40	45
585	1 e. Jolobela Falls			70	80
586	2 e. Mantjolo Sacred Pool			1·25	1·60
583/6			*Set of 4*	2·25	2·75
MS587	80×60 mm. 2 e. Usushwana River. P 14			2·00	2·75

134 King Mswati III making Speech   135 *Xerophyta retinervis*

(Des D. Aryeequaye. Litho Cartor)

1991 (24 Apr). *5th Anniv of King Mswati III's Coronation. T* **134** *and similar horiz designs. Multicoloured. W w* **14** *(sideways). P* 14×13½.

588	15 c. Type **134**			15	10
589	75 c. Butimba Royal Hunt			50	60
590	1 e. King and visiting school friends from Sherborne, 1986			70	1·00
591	2 e. King opening Parliament			1·25	2·00
588/91			*Set of 4*	2·40	3·25

(Des D. Miller. Litho Questa)

1991 (17 June). *65th Birthday of Queen Elizabeth II and 70th Birthday of Prince Philip. Vert designs as T* **58** *of Kiribati. Multicoloured. W w* **16** *(sideways). P* 14½×14.

592	1 e. Prince Philip			70	1·00
	a. Horiz pair. Nos. 592/3 separated by label			1·90	2·40
593	2 e. Queen Elizabeth II			1·25	1·40

Nos. 592/3 were printed in a similar sheet format to Nos. 366/7 of Kiribati.

(Des D. Aryeequaye. Litho Questa)

1991 (30 Sept). *Indigenous Flowers. T* **135** *and similar vert designs. Multicoloured. W w* **14** *(sideways). P* 14.

594	15 c. Type **135**			25	10
595	75 c. *Bauhinia galpinii*			80	70
596	1 e. *Dombeya rotundifolia*			1·00	1·40
597	2 e. *Kigelia africana*			1·25	2·75
594/7			*Set of 4*	3·50	4·50

136 Father Christmas arriving with Gifts   137 Lubombo Flat Lizard

(Des D. Aryeequaye. Litho Cartor)

1991 (18 Dec). *Christmas. T* **136** *and similar vert designs. Multicoloured. W w* **14**. *P* 13½.

598	20 c. Type **136**			15	10
599	70 c. Singing carols			65	50
600	1 e. Priest reading from Bible			80	1·25
601	2 e. The Nativity			1·50	2·50
598/601			*Set of 4*	2·75	3·75

(Des D. Aryeequaye. Litho Cartor)

1992 (25 Feb). *Reptiles* (1st series). *T* **137** *and similar horiz designs. Multicoloured. W w* **14** *(sideways). P* 13½.

602	20 c. Type **137**			85	20
603	70 c. Natal Hinged Tortoise			2·00	1·25
604	1 e. Swazi Thick-toed Gecko			2·50	2·50
605	2 e. Nile Monitor			3·50	4·50
602/5			*Set of 4*	8·00	7·50

See also Nos. 658/61.

138 *Precis hierta*   139 Missionaries visiting King Sobhuza II and Queen Lomawa

(Des I. Loe. Litho Questa)

1992 (26 Aug). *Butterflies* (2nd series). *Designs as Nos.* 516/26 *and new value* (5 c.) *showing different portrait of King Mswati III as in T* **138**. *Multicoloured. Without imprint date* (5 c.) *or with "1991" imprint date below design* (others). *P* 14.

606	5 c. *Colotis antevippe*			10	10
607	10 c. Type **138**			10	10
608	15 c. *Hamanumida daedalus*			10	10
609	20 c. *Charaxes boueti*			10	10
610	25 c. *Abantis paradisea*			10	10
611	30 c. *Acraea anemosa*			10	10
612	35 c. *Graphium leonidas*			10	10
613	45 c. *Graphium antheus*			10	10
614	50 c. *Precis orithya*			10	10
615	55 c. *Pinacopteryx eriphia*			10	10
616	70 c. *Precis octavia*			15	20
617	1 e. *Mylothris chloris*			20	25
606/17			*Set of 12*	1·25	1·40

(Des D. Aryeequaye. Litho Cartor)

1992 (16 Dec). *Centenary of Evangelical Alliance Missions. T* **139** *and similar vert design. Multicoloured. P* 13½×14.

620	20 c. Type **139**			25	10
621	1 e. Pioneer missionaries			1·50	2·00

140 Calabashes   141 King Mswati III as Baby

(Des D. Aryeequaye. Litho Cartor)

1993 (18 Mar). *Archaeological and Contemporary Artifacts. T* **140** *and similar vert designs. Multicoloured. P* 13½×14.

622	20 c. Type **140**			35	10
623	70 c. Contemporary cooking pot			85	85
624	1 e. Wooden bowl and containers			1·25	1·50
625	2 e. Quern for grinding seeds			2·00	2·75
622/5			*Set of 4*	4·00	4·75

(Des D. Aryeequaye. Litho Cartor)

1993 (6 Sept). *25th Birthday of King Mswati III and 25th Anniv of Independence. T* **141** *and similar vert designs. Multicoloured. P* 13½×14.

626	25 c. Type **141**			15	10
627	40 c. King Mswati III addressing meeting			20	20
628	1 e. King Sobhuza II receiving Instrument of Independence			65	90
629	2 e. King Mswati III delivering Coronation speech			1·25	1·90
626/9			*Set of 4*	2·00	2·75

142 Male and Female Common Waxbills   143 Classroom and Practical Training

(Des D. Aryeequaye. Litho Cartor)

1993 (25 Nov). *Common Waxbill. T* **142** *and similar vert designs. Multicoloured. P* 13½.

630	25 c. Type **142**			40	20
631	40 c. Waxbill and eggs in nest			55	25
632	1 e. Waxbill on nest			1·25	1·50
633	2 e. Waxbill feeding chicks			2·00	2·75
630/3			*Set of 4*	3·75	4·25

(Des D. Aryeequaye. Litho Cartor)

1994 (22 Feb). *25th Anniv of U.S. Peace Corps in Swaziland. T* **143** *and similar vert designs. Multicoloured. P* 13½.

634	25 c. Type **143**			15	10
635	40 c. Rural water supply			25	20
636	1 e. Americans and Swazis in traditional costumes			80	1·00
637	2 e. Swazi-American co-operation			1·25	2·00
634/7			*Set of 4*	2·25	3·00

144 *Agaricus arvensis*   145 Emblem and Airliner on Runway

(Des D. Aryeequaye. Litho Cartor)

1994 (15 Sept). *Fungi. T* **144** *and similar vert designs. Multicoloured. P* 13½×14.

638	30 c. Type **144**			70	40
639	40 c. *Boletus edulis*			80	40
640	1 e. *Russula virescens*			1·50	1·75
641	2 e. *Armillaria mellea*			2·25	2·75
638/41			*Set of 4*	4·75	4·75

(Des D. Aryeequaye. Litho Walsall)

1994 (30 Nov). *50th Anniv of International Civil Aviation Organization. T* **145** *and similar horiz designs. Multicoloured. P* 14.

642	30 c. Type **145**			30	10
643	40 c. Control tower and dish aerial			35	20
644	1 e. Crash tenders			75	1·00
645	2 e. Air traffic controllers			1·25	2·00
642/5			*Set of 4*	2·40	3·00

146 Wooden Bowls   147 Harvesting Maize

(Des D. Aryeequaye. Litho Cartor)

1995 (7 Apr). *Handicrafts. T* **146** *and similar vert designs. Multicoloured. P* 13½×14.

646	35 c. Type **146**			20	20
647	50 c. Chicken nests			30	35
648	1 e. Leather crafts			50	70
649	2 e. Wood carvings			90	1·50
646/9			*Set of 4*	1·75	2·50

(Des D. Aryeequaye. Litho Cartor)

1995 (5 June). *50th Anniv of Food and Agriculture Organization. T* **147** *and similar vert designs. Multicoloured. P* 13½.

650	35 c. Type **147**			20	20
651	50 c. Planting vegetables			30	35
652	1 e. Herd of cattle			50	70
653	2 e. Harvesting sorghum			90	1·50
650/3			*Set of 4*	1·75	2·50

148 Knysna Turaco   149 Waterberry

(Des D. Aryeequaye. Litho Cartor)

1995 (27 Sept). *Turacos ("Louries"). T* 148 *and simlar horiz designs. Multicoloured. P* 13½×13.
654	35 c. Type 148			30	30
655	50 c. Knysna Turaco in flight		..	45	40
656	1 e. Violet-crested Turaco			70	90
657	2 e. Livingstone's Turaco	..		1·10	1·75
654/7		..	*Set of 4*	2·25	3·00

(Des D. Aryeequaye. Litho Cartor)

1996 (17 Jan). *Reptiles (2nd series). Horiz designs as T* 137 *with King's portrait at right. Multicoloured. P* 13½×13.
658	35 c. Chameleon			25	20
659	50 c. Rock Monitor		..	35	35
660	1 e. African Python			60	75
661	2 e. Tree Agama			90	1·50
658/61			*Set of 4*	1·90	2·50

(Des D. Aryeequaye. Litho Cartor)

1996 (23 Apr). *Trees. T* 149 *and similar vert designs. Multicoloured. P* 13×13½.
662	40 c. Type 149			15	15
663	60 c. Sycamore Fig			20	20
664	1 e. Stem Fruit			40	60
665	2 e. Wild Medlar			80	1·25
662/5		..	*Set of 4*	1·40	2·00

150 Mahamba Methodist Church

(Des D. Aryeequaye. Litho Cartor)

1996 (26 Aug). *Historic Monuments. T* 150 *and similar horiz designs. Multicoloured. P* 13½×13.
666	40 c. Type 150			15	15
667	60 c. Colonial Secretariat, Mbabane		20	20
668	1 e. King Sobhuza II Monument, Lobamba	40	60
669	2 e. First High Court Building, Hlatikulu	80	1·25
666/9			*Set of 4*	1·40	2·00

151 Children in Class   152 Klipspringer

(Litho Enschedé)

1996 (31 Dec). *50th Anniv of U.N.I.C.E.F. T* 151 *and similar multicoloured designs. P* 13½×14 (40 c.) *or* 14×13½ (*others*).
670	40 c. Type 151			15	15
671	60 c. Child being inoculated (*vert*)	..	20	20
672	1 e. Child on crutches (*vert*)		40	60
673	2 e. Mother and children (*vert*)		80	1·25
670/3			*Set of 4*	1·40	2·00

(Litho Enschedé)

1997 (22 Sept). *Mammals. T* 152 *and similar multicoloured designs. P* 14×13½ (*vert*) *or* 13½×14 (*horiz*).
674	50 c. Type 152			25	20
675	70 c. Grey Duiker			30	30
676	1 e. Antbear (*horiz*)			40	55
677	2 e. Cape Clawless Otter (*horiz*)		70	1·00
674/7			*Set of 4*	1·50	1·90

153 Umgaco Costume   154 Olive Toad

(Litho Cartor)

1997 (1 Dec). *Traditional Costumes. T* 153 *and similar vert designs. Multicoloured. P* 13×13½.
678	50 c. Type 153			15	15
679	70 c. Sigeja cloak			25	25
680	1 e. Umdada kilt			35	35
681	2 e. Ligcebesha costume	..		65	65
678/81			*Set of 4*	1·25	1·25

(Des K. Addai-Yinkah. Litho Enschedé)

1998 (1 June). *Amphibians. T* 154 *and similar horiz designs. P* 14½×14.
682	55 c. Type 154			15	15
683	75 c. African Bullfrog			25	25
684	1 e. Water Lily Frog			35	35
685	2 e. Bushveld Rain Frog			65	65
682/5			*Set of 4*	1·25	1·25

155 Aerial View of King Sobhuza II Memorial Park   156 Grinding Stone

(Des K. Addai-Yinkah. Litho Enschedé)

1998 (3 Sept). *30th Anniv of Independence and 30th Birthday of King Mswati III. T* 155 *and similar multicoloured designs. P* 14×13½ (75 c.) *or* 13½×14 (*others*).
686	55 c. Type 155			15	15
687	75 c. King Mswati III taking oath (*vert*)	25	25
688	1 e. King Mswati delivering speech		35	35
689	2 e. King Sobhuza II receiving Instrument of Independence		65	65
686/9			*Set of 4*	1·25	1·25

(Des D. Aryeequaye. Litho Cartor)

1999 (17 May). *Local Culinary Utensils. T* 156 *and similar vert designs. Multicoloured. Two phosphor bands. P* 13½.
690	60 c. Type 156			15	15
691	75 c. Stirring sticks		..	20	20
692	80 c. Clay pot			25	25
693	95 c. Swazi spoons	..		30	30
694	1 e. 75, Beer cups			50	50
695	2 e. 40, Mortar and pestle			60	60
690/5			*Set of 6*	1·75	1·75

157 Internet Service

(Des K. Addai-Yinkah. Litho Cartor)

1999 (9 Oct). *125th Anniv of Universal Postal Union. T* 157 *and similar multicoloured designs. Two phosphor bands. P* 13½.
696	60 c. Type 157			15	15
697	80 c. Cellular phone service			25	25
698	1 e. Two post vans exchanging mail (*horiz*)	30	30
699	2 e. 40, Training school (*horiz*)		60	60
696/9			*Set of 4*	1·10	1·10

POSTAGE DUE STAMPS

D 1   (D 2)   D 3

(Typo D.L.R.)

1933 (2 Jan)**—57.** *Wmk Mult Script CA. P* 14.
D1	D 1	1d. carmine		..		30	7·50
		a. Chalk-surfaced paper. *Dp carmine* (24.10.51)		20	11·00
		ac. Error. St Edward's Crown, W 9*b*		£180
D2		2d. pale violet		..		1·75	20·00
		a. Chalk-surfaced paper (22.2.57)		4·75	27·00
		ab. Large "d"	..		42·00
D1/2	Perf "Specimen"			*Set of 2*	42·00

For illustration of No. D2ab see above No. D1 of Lesotho.

1961 (8 Feb). *No.* 55 *surch with Type* D 2.
D3	7	2d. on 2d.		..		1·60	3·25

Another 2d. on 2d. Postage Due, with small surcharge as Type D 5, was produced *after the currency change*, to meet the philatelic demand (*Price 15p unused*).

(Typo D.L.R.)

1961 (14 Feb). *Chalk-surfaced paper. Wmk Mult Script CA. P* 14.
D4	D 3	1 c. carmine	..		..	15	75
D5		2 c. violet				15	1·10
D6		5 c. green			..	20	1·10
D4/6					*Set of 3*	45	2·75

Postage Due

1c (D 4)   Postage Due 1c (D 5)

1961. *No.* 55 *surcharged. A. As Type* D 4. (14 Feb.)
D 7	7	1 c. on 2d.	..		..	1·25	2·50
D 8		2 c. on 2d.			..	1·25	2·50
D 9		5 c. on 2d.			..	2·25	2·50
D7/9					*Set of 3*	4·25	6·75

B. *As Type* D 5. (Date?)
D10	7	1 c. on 2d.			..	70	2·75
D11		2 c. on 2d.			..	50	2·75
D12		5 c. on 2d.			..	90	2·25
D10/12					*Set of 3*	1·90	7·00

D 6

(Des and litho B.W.)

1971 (1 Feb). *Size* 18×23 *mm. W w* 12. *P* 11½.
D13	D 6	1 c. bright rose-red		..	65	3·25
D14		2 c. purple		..		75	3·25
D15		5 c. dull green		..		1·00	4·00
D13/15				*Set of 3*	2·25	9·50

1977 (17 Jan). *Size* 18×23 *mm. W w* 14 (*sideways*). *P* 11½.
D16	D 6	1 c. rose-red	..			75	3·50
D17		2 c. purple				1·00	4·00
D18		5 c. dull green				1·60	4·50
D16/18				*Set of 3*	3·00	11·00

(Litho Harrison)

1978 (20 Apr)**—85.** *Size* 17½×21 *mm. W w* 14. *P* 15×14.
D19	D 6	1 c. carmine		..		30	1·25
D19a		1 c. brown-red (13.3.85)			2·50	4·00
D20		2 c. purple			..	30	1·25
D21		5 c. blue-green	..			30	1·25
D19/21				*Set of 4*	2·75	7·00

(Litho Harrison)

1991 (17 July). *Size* 17½×21 *mm. With imprint date. W w* 14 (*sideways*). *P* 15×14.
D23	D 6	2 c. purple		..		10	10
D24		5 c. bright blue-green		..	10	10
D25		10 c. pale greenish blue		..	10	10
D26		25 c. red-brown		..		10	10
D23/6				*Set of 4*	25	25

Tanzania
(*formerly* Tanganyika)

TANGANYIKA

The stamps of GERMANY were used in the colony between October 1890 and July 1893 when issues for GERMAN EAST AFRICA were provided.

PRICES FOR STAMPS ON COVER TO 1945

The Mafia Island provisionals (No. M1/52) are very rare used on cover.

Nos. N1/5	*from* × 8
Nos. 45/59	*from* × 6
Nos. 60/2	—
Nos. 63/73	*from* × 6
Nos. 74/86	*from* × 8
Nos. 87/8	—
Nos. 89/92	*from* × 6
Nos. 93/106	*from* × 3
No. 107	—

MAFIA ISLAND
BRITISH OCCUPATION

Mafia Island was captured by the British from the Germans in January 1915. Letters were first sent out unstamped, then with stamps handstamped with Type M 1. Later the military were supplied with handstamps by the post office in Zanzibar. These were used to produce Nos. M11/52.

(Currency. 100 heller = 1 rupee)

G.B.
MAFIA
(M 1) (M 3)

1915 (Jan). *German East Africa Yacht types, handstamped with Type* M 1. *Wmk Lozenges, or no wmk* (1 r., 2 r.). A. *In black* (2½ h. *in blackish lilac*). B. *In deep purple*. C. *In reddish violet*.

		A	B	C
M 1	2½ h. brown	£425	†	£200
	a. Pair, one without handstamp		†	£1900
M 2	4 h. green	£550	£550	£250
	a. Pair, one without handstamp		†	£1800
M 3	7½ h. carmine	£400	£400	£100
	a. Pair, one without handstamp	£3250	†	£1500
M 4	15 h. ultramarine	£500	£500	£160
	a. Pair, one without handstamp		†	£1600
M 5	20 h. black and red/*yellow* ..	£550	£550	£300
	a. Pair, one without handstamp		†	£3250 £1900
M 6	30 h. black and carmine ..	£650	£800	£350
	a. Pair, one without handstamp	£3500	†	£1900
M 7	45 h. black and mauve ..	£750	£750	£400
	a. Pair, one without handstamp	£3500	†	£2250
M 8	1 r. carmine	£5000		† £3250
M 9	2 r. green	£5500		† £3750
M10	3 r. blue-black and red ..	£6500		† £4000

Prices are for unused examples.

A few contemporary Zanzibar stamps (1, 3, 6 and 15 c.) are known with the above handstamp.

(Currency. 100 cents = 1 rupee)

1915 (May). *German East Africa Yacht types with handstamped four-line surcharge* "G.R.—POST—6 CENTS—MAFIA" *in black, green or violet. Wmk Lozenges or no wmk* (1 r., 2 r.).

M11	6 c. on 2½ h. brown ..		£850 £1000
	a. Pair, one without handstamp ..		† £3500
M12	6 c. on 4 h. green ..		£850 £1000
	a. Pair, one without handstamp		£3500
M13	6 c. on 7½ h. carmine ..		£900 £1000
	a. Pair, one without handstamp		—
M14	6 c. on 15 h. ultramarine ..		£900 £1100
M15	6 c. on 20 h. black and red/*yellow*		£1000 £1200
M16	6 c. on 30 h. black and carmine		£1400 £1500
M17	6 c. on 45 h. black and mauve ..		£1400 £1500
	a. Pair, one without handstamp		—
M18	6 c. on 1 r. carmine ..		£7500
M19	6 c. on 2 r. green ..		£8500
M20	6 c. on 3 r. blue-black and red ..		£9500

The 5, 20 and 40 pesa values of the 1901 Yacht issue are also known with the above surcharge as are the contemporary 1 c. and 6 c. Zanzibar stamps.

1915 (Sept). (*a*) *German East African fiscal stamps.* "Statistik des Waaren-Verkehrs" (*Trade Statistical Charge*) *handstamped in bluish green or violet,* "O.H.B.M.S. Mafia" *in a circle, as Type* M 3.

M21	24 pesa, vermilion/*buff* ..	£650 £750
M22	12½ heller, drab ..	£600 £800
	a. Pair, one without handstamp ..	£2750
M23	25 heller, dull green ..	£600 £800
M24	50 heller, slate ..	£600 £800
	a. Pair, one without handstamp	£2750
M25	1 rupee, lilac ..	£600 £800

(*b*) *German East African* "Übersetzungs- Gebühren" *Fee*) *stamp, overprinted as before*

M26	25 heller, grey ..	£600 £800

G. R
POST
MAFIA
(M 4)

G. R.
Post
MAFIA.
(M 5)

(*c*) *Stamps as above, but with further opt as Type* M 4, *in bluish green or violet*

M27	24 pesa, vermilion/*buff* ..	£800
M28	12½ heller, drab ..	£800
M29	25 heller, dull green ..	£800
M30	50 heller, slate ..	£800
M31	1 rupee, lilac ..	£800
M32	25 heller, grey (No. M26) ..	£800
	a. Pair, one without handstamp Type M 4 £2750	

Type M 3 is also known handstamped on the 7½ h., 20 h. and 30 h. values of German East Africa 1905 Yacht issue and also on contemporary 1, 3, 6 and 25 c. Zanzibar stamps.

(Currency. 12 pies = 1 anna. 16 annas = 1 rupee)

1915 (Sept). *Nos.* E1/2, E4/9, E11 *and* E13 *of Indian Expeditionary Forces* (*India King George V optd* "I.E.F.") *with a further opt Type* M 4 *handstruck in green, greenish black or dull blue.*

M33	3 p. slate-grey	25·00	£100
	a. Pair, one stamp without opt	—	£700
M34	½ a. yellow-green	45·00	65·00
	a. Pair, one stamp without opt	—	£750
M35	1 a. carmine	48·00	65·00
M36	2 a. mauve	70·00	£100
M37	2½ a. ultramarine	90·00	£130
M38	3 a. orange-brown	95·00	£140
	a. Pair, one stamp without opt	—	£900
M39	4 a. olive-green	£120	£160
M40	8 a. purple	£180	£275
	a. Pair, one stamp without opt		£1100
M41	12 a. dull claret	£275	£375
M42	1 r. red-brown and blue-green ..	£325	£400
M33/42		*Set of* 10	£1100 £1500

All values exist with the overprint inverted, and several are known with overprint double or sideways.

1916 (Oct). *Nos.* E1/2, E4/9, E11 *and* E13 *of Indian Expeditionary Forces* (*India King George V optd* "I.E.F.") *with further opt Type* M 5 *handstruck in green, greenish black, dull blue or violet.*

M43	3 p. slate-grey	£100	£130
M44	½ a. yellow-green	£100	£120
M45	1 a. carmine	90·00	£100
M46	2 a. mauve	£140	£150
M47	2½ a. ultramarine	£150	£170
M48	3 a. orange-brown	£150	£170
M49	4 a. olive-green	£200	£250
M50	8 a. purple	£275	£375
M51	12 a. dull claret	£300	£450
M52	1 r. red-brown and blue-green ..	£350	£425
M43/52		*Set of* 10	£1600 £2000

Stamps with handstamp inverted are known.

NYASALAND-RHODESIAN FORCE

This issue was sanctioned for use by the Nyasaland-Rhodesian Force during operations in German East Africa, Mozambique and Nyasaland. Unoverprinted Nyasaland stamps were used by the Force prior to the introduction of Nos. N1/5 and, again, in 1918.

N. F.
(N 1)

1916 (7 Aug–18 Sept*). *Nos.* 83, 86, 90/1 *and* 93 *of Malawi* (*Nyasaland*) *optd with Type* N 1 *by Govt Printer, Zomba.*

N1	½d. green	1·50	7·50
N2	1d. scarlet	1·50	3·25
N3	3d. purple/*yellow* (15 Sept*) ..	6·50	16·00
	a. Opt double ..		† £7500
N4	4d. black and red/*yellow* (13 Sept*)	28·00	38·00
N5	1s. black/*green* (18 Sept*) ..	28·00	40·00
N1/5		*Set of* 5	60·00 95·00
N1/5 Optd "Specimen"		*Set of* 5	£200

* Earliest known dates of use.

Of No. N3a only six copies were printed, these being the bottom row on one pane issued at M'bamba Bay F.P.O., German East Africa in March 1918.

This overprint was applied in a setting of 60 (10 rows of 6) and the following minor varieties occur on all values: small stop after "N" (R. 1/1); broken "F" (R. 4/3); very small stop after "F" (R. 6/5); no serifs at top left and bottom of "N" (R. 10/1).

TANGANYIKA

BRITISH OCCUPATION OF GERMAN EAST AFRICA

Following the invasion of German East Africa by Allied forces civilian mail was accepted by the Indian Army postal service, using Indian stamps overprinted "I.E.F.". Some offices reverted to civilian control on 1 June 1917 and these used stamps of East Africa and Uganda until the "G.E.A." overprints were ready. The last field post offices, in the southern part of the country, did not come under civilian control until 15 March 1919.

(Currency. 100 cents = 1 rupee)

G.E.A. **G.E.A.** **G.E.A**
(1) (2) (3)

1917 (Oct)–21. *Nos.* 44/5, 46a/51, 52b, 53/9 *and* 61 *of Kenya, Uganda and Tanganyika optd with* T 1 *and* 2. *Wmk Mult Crown CA. Ordinary paper* (1 c. *to* 15 c.) *or chalk-surfaced paper* (*others*).

45	1 c. black (R.) ..	15	80
	aw. Wmk inverted		
	ay. Wmk inverted and reversed		85·00
	b. Vermilion opt ..	20·00	16·00
47	3 c. green ..	15	15
48	6 c. scarlet ..	15	10
	a. Wmk sideways ..	£1800	£1800
	w. Wmk inverted ..	†	£150
49	10 c. yellow-orange ..	40	50
50	12 c. slate-grey ..	40	1·75
	y. Wmk inverted and reversed ..	85·00	

51	15 c. bright blue ..	70	1·75
	w. Wmk inverted		£100
52	25 c. black and red/*yellow* ..	80	3·00
	a. On pale yellow (1921) (Optd S. £40)	1·40	4·50
53	50 c. black and lilac ..	80	3·25
54	75 c. black/*blue-green*, olive back (R.) ..	1·00	4·50
	a. On emerald back (1921) (Optd S. £50)	3·25	12·00
55	1 r. black/*green* (R.) ..	2·50	7·00
	a. On emerald back (1919) ..	4·50	42·00
56	2 r. red and black/*blue* ..	7·00	38·00
	x. Wmk reversed		
57	3 r. violet and green ..	13·00	65·00
58	4 r. red and green/*yellow* ..	17·00	80·00
59	5 r. blue and dull purple ..	32·00	80·00
60	10 r. red and green/*green* ..	60·00	£250
	a. On emerald back ..	65·00	£250
61	20 r. black and purple/*red* ..	£190	£325
62	50 r. carmine and green (Optd S. £160)	£475	£750
45/61		*Set of* 16	£300 £750
45/61 Optd "Specimen"		*Set of* 16	£375

Early printings of the rupee values exist with very large stop after the "E" in "G.E.A." (R. 5/3). There are round stops after "E" varieties, which in one position of later printings became a small stop.

The only known used example of No. 48a is cancelled at Tanga in August 1918.

1921. *Nos.* 69/74 *of Kenya, Uganda and Tanganyika optd with* T 1 *or* 2. *Wmk Mult Script CA. Chalk-surfaced paper* (50 c. *to* 5 r.).

63	12 c. slate-grey	6·50	80·00
64	15 c. bright blue ..	1·50	3·75
65	50 c. black and dull purple ..	8·50	80·00
66	2 r. red and black/*blue* ..	32·00	£110
67	3 r. violet and green ..	50·00	£130
68	5 r. blue and dull purple ..	70·00	£160
63/8		*Set of* 6	£150 £500
63/8 Optd "Specimen"		*Set of* 6	£200

1922. *Nos.* 65 *and* 68 *of Kenya, Uganda and Tanganyika optd by the Government Printer at Dar-es-Salaam with* T 3. *Wmk Mult Script CA.*

72	1 c. black (R.)	55	14·00
73	10 c. orange	55	14·00
	y. Wmk inverted and reversed ..	85·00	

BRITISH MANDATED TERRITORY
(New Currency. 100 cents = 1 shilling)

4 Giraffe 5

(Recess B.W.)

1922. *Head in black.* (*a*) *Wmk Mult Script CA.* P 15×14.

74	4	5 c. slate-purple ..	2·00	20
75		10 c. green ..	2·00	85
76		15 c. carmine-red ..	2·00	10
77		20 c. orange ..	1·75	10
78		25 c. black ..	5·50	6·00
79		30 c. blue ..	5·00	5·00
80		40 c. yellow-brown ..	2·50	4·50
81		50 c. slate-grey ..	2·00	1·50
82		75 c. yellow-bistre ..	3·25	17·00

(*b*) *Wmk Mult Script CA* (*sideways*). P 14.

83	5	1 s. green ..	3·00	13·00
		a. Wmk upright	2·50	11·00
84		2 s. purple ..	4·75	14·00
		a. Wmk upright	4·25	20·00
85		3 s. black ..	10·00	28·00
86		5 s. scarlet ..	22·00	80·00
		a. Wmk upright	13·00	70·00
87		10 s. deep blue ..	90·00	£170
		a. Wmk upright	48·00	90·00
88		£1 yellow-orange ..	£130	£275
		a. Wmk upright	£140	£250
74/88			*Set of* 15	£200 £450
74/88 Optd "Specimen"			*Set of* 15	£450

In the £1 stamp the words of value run across the stamp above the words "POSTAGE AND REVENUE".

1925. *As 1922. Frame colours changed.*

89	4	5 c. green ..	1·00	1·50
90		10 c. orange-yellow ..	3·25	1·50
91		25 c. blue ..	3·75	16·00
92		30 c. purple ..	3·75	10·00
89/92			*Set of* 4	10·50 26·00
89/92 Optd "Specimen"			*Set of* 4	70·00

6 7

(Typo D.L.R.)

1927–31. *Head in black. Wmk Mult Script CA. Chalk-surfaced paper* (5 s., 10 s., £1). P 14.

93	6	5 c. green ..	1·00	10
94		10 c. yellow ..	2·00	10
95		15 c. carmine-red ..	1·00	10
96		20 c. orange-buff ..	2·25	10

97	**6**	25 c. bright blue	.. ..	2·50 2·00
98		30 c. dull purple	.. ..	2·50 2·50
98a		30 c. bright blue (1931) ..		23·00 30
99		40 c. yellow-brown	.. ..	2·00 4·00
100		50 c. grey	.. ..	2·25 1·00
101		75 c. olive-green	.. ..	2·00 9·00
102	**7**	1 s. green	.. ..	3·25 2·50
103		2 s. deep purple	.. ..	12·00 4·25
104		3 s. black	.. ..	12·00 45·00
105		5 s. carmine-red	.. ..	12·00 15·00
106		10 s. deep blue ..	.. ..	8·00 85·00
107		£1 brown-orange	.. ..	£120 £190
93/107			Set of 16	£225 £325
93/107 Optd/Perf "Specimen"			Set of 16	£250

Tanganyika became part of the joint East African postal administration on 1 January 1933 and subsequently used the stamps of KENYA, UGANDA AND TANGANYIKA.

INDEPENDENT REPUBLIC

8 Teacher and Pupils

9 District Nurse and Child

14 "Maternity"

15 Freedom Torch over Mt Kilimanjaro

(Des V. Whiteley. Photo Harrison)

1961 (9 Dec)–**64**. *Independence. T* **8/9**, **14/15** *and similar designs.* P 14×15 (5 c., 30 c.), 15×14 (10 c., 15 c., 20 c., 50 c.) or 14½ (others).

108	5 c. sepia and light apple-green	..	10	10
109	10 c. deep bluish green	..	10	10
110	15 c. sepia and blue	..	10	10
	a. Blue omitted ..		£400	
111	20 c. orange-brown	..	10	10
112	30 c. black, emerald and yellow	..	10	10
	a. Inscr "UHURU 196" ..		£450	£160
	b. "1" inserted after "196" ..		14·00	
113	50 c. black and yellow	..	10	10
114	1 s. brown, blue and olive-yellow		15	10
115	1 s. 30, red, yellow, black, brown and blue		2·00	10
	a. Red, yellow, blk, brn & dp bl (10.3.64)		4·00	70
116	2 s. blue, yellow, green and brown	..	50	10
117	5 s. deep bluish green and orange-red	..	60	40
118	10 s. black, reddish purple and light blue		14·00	4·75
	a. Reddish purple (diamond) omitted	..	£150	
119	20 s. red, yellow, black, brown and green	..	3·50	7·50
108/19			Set of 12	18·00 11·50

Designs: *Vert (as T* **9**)—15 c. Coffee-picking; 20 c. Harvesting maize; 50 c. Serengeti lions. *Horiz (as T* **8**)—30 c. Tanganyikan flag. *(As T* **14**)—2 s. Dar-es-Salaam waterfront; 5 s. Land tillage; 10 s. Diamond and mine. *Vert*—20 s. Type **15**.

No. 112a. The missing "1" in "1961" occurs on emerald Plate 1C, R. 10/10. The "1" was later inserted but it is, however, very slightly shorter and the figure is more solid than normal.

19 Pres. Nyerere inaugurating Self-help Project

20 Hoisting Flag on Mt Kilimanjaro

(Photo Harrison)

1962 (9 Dec). *Inauguration of Republic. Vert designs as T* **19/20**. P 14½.

120	30 c. emerald	.. ..	10	10
121	50 c. yellow, black, green, red and blue	..	10	10
122	1 s. 30, multicoloured	.. ..	10	10
123	2 s. 50, black, red and blue ..	..	30	50
120/3		Set of 4	45	55

Designs:—1 s. 30, Presidential emblem; 2 s. 50, Independence Monument.

COVER PRICES

Cover factors are quoted at the beginning of each country for most issues to 1945. An explanation of the system can be found on page x. The factors quoted do not, however, apply to philatelic covers.

---

23 Map of Republic

24 Torch and Spear Emblem

(Des M. Goaman. Photo Harrison)

1964 (7 July). *United Republic of Tanganyika and Zanzibar Commemoration.* P 14 × 14½.

124	**23**	20 c. yellow-green and light blue	..	10 10
125	**24**	30 c. blue and sepia	..	10 10
126		1 s. 30, orange-brown and ultramarine		10 10
127	**23**	2 s. 50, purple and ultramarine		80 50
124/7			Set of 4	1·00 60

Despite the inscription on the stamps the above issue was only on sale in Tanganyika and had no validity in Zanzibar.

STAMP BOOKLETS

1922–25. *Black on red cover.*
SB1   3 s. booklet containing 5 c., 10 c., 15 c. and 20 c. (Nos. 74/7), each in block of 6
     a. As No. SB1, but contents changed (Nos. 89/90, 76/7) (1925)

1922–26. *Black on red cover. Stapled.*
SB2   3 s. booklet containing six 10 c., and twelve 5 c. and 15 c. (Nos. 74/6) in blocks of 6
     a. As No. SB2, but contents changed (Nos. 74, 90, 76) (1925)
     b. As No. SB2, but contents changed (Nos. 89/90, 76) (1926) £950

1927. *Black on red covers. Stapled.*
SB3   3 s. booklet containing six 10 c., and twelve 5 c. and 15 c. (Nos. 93/5) in blocks of 6 .. £550
SB4   3 s. booklet containing 5 c., 10 c. and 15 c. (Nos. 93/5), each in block of 10 .. ..

1961 (9 Dec). *Black on blue-green cover, size 48×46 mm. Stitched.*
SB5   5 s. booklet containing 10 c., 15 c., 20 c., 30 c. and 50 c. (Nos. 109/13), each in block of 4 .. 4·50

OFFICIAL STAMPS

OFFICIAL   **OFFICIAL**
(O 1)   (O 2) (3½ mm tall)

1961 (9 Dec). *Nos.* 108/14 *and* 117 *optd with Type* O 1 (10, 15, 20, 50 c. *or larger* (17 mm) 5, 30 c.) *or with Type* O 2 (1 s. *or larger* (22 mm) 5 s.).

O1	5 c. sepia and light apple-green	..	10	10
O2	10 c. deep bluish green	..	10	10
O3	15 c. sepia and blue	..	10	10
O4	20 c. orange-brown	..	10	10
O5	30 c. black, emerald and yellow		10	10
O6	50 c. black and yellow ..		10	10
O7	1 s. brown, blue and olive-yellow		10	10
O8	5 s. deep bluish green and orange-red		65	75
O1/8		Set of 8	90	90

ZANZIBAR

An Indian post office opened in Zanzibar in November 1868, but was closed for political reasons on 1 April of the following year. Little has survived from this period. Subsequently mail was forwarded via Seychelles or, later, Aden.

Stamps of INDIA were used in Zanzibar from 1 October 1875 until 10 November 1895, when the administration of the postal service was transferred from India to British East Africa. Separate cancellations for Zanzibar are known from 1 June 1878.

Z 1

Stamps of INDIA *cancelled with Type Z* 1 (1878–79).

1865. (*Nos.* 54/65).

Z1	1 a. deep brown	..	£120
Z2	2 a. orange	..	£120

1866–78. (*Nos.* 69/72).

Z3	4 a. blue-green (Die II) ..	..	£100

1873. (*Nos.* 75/6).

Z4	½ a. blue (Die II) ..	..	£100

Surviving covers show that Type Z 1 was normally used as a datestamp, struck clear of the stamps which were obliterated by a rhomboid of bars, but examples of the c.d.s. used as a cancel are known.

Z 2

Stamps of INDIA *cancelled with Type Z* 2 (1879–82).

1865. (*Nos.* 54/65).

Z10	8 p. mauve	..	£120
Z11	1 a. deep brown ..	.. ..	16·00
Z12	2 a. orange	.. ..	16·00

1866–78. (*Nos.* 69/72).

Z13	4 a. green (Die I)	..	85·00
Z14	4 a. blue-green (Die II)	..	22·00

1868. (*Nos.* 73/4).

Z15	8 a. rose (Die II) ..	..	55·00

1873. (*Nos.* 75/6).

Z16	½ a. blue (Die II) ..	..	16·00

1874. (*Nos.* 77/9).

Z17	1 r. slate	..	£130

1876. (*Nos.* 80/2).

Z18	6 a. pale brown ..	..	55·00
Z19	12 a. Venetian red	..	85·00

OFFICIAL STAMPS

1874–82. (*Nos.* O31/7).

Z20	2 a. orange	..	£120

Z 3

Stamps of INDIA *cancelled with Type Z* 3 (1882–84)

1865. (*Nos.* 54/65).

Z25	1 a. deep brown	.. ..	27·00
Z26	2 a. brown-orange	.. ..	22·00

1866–78. (*Nos.* 69/72).

Z27	4 a. blue-green (Die II)	..	27·00

1868. (*Nos.* 73/4).

Z28	8 a. rose (Die II)	..	38·00

1873. (*Nos.* 75/6).

Z29	½ a. blue (Die II)	..	22·00

1876. (*Nos.* 80/2).

Z30	6 a. pale brown	..	32·00
Z31	12 a. Venetian red	..	65·00

1882–83. (*Nos.* 84/101).

Z32	1 a. brown-purple	.. ..	22·00
Z33	1 a. 6 p. sepia	.. ..	27·00
Z34	3 a. orange	.. ..	27·00

Z 4

Z 5

Stamps of INDIA *cancelled with Type Z* 4 (June 1884–May 1887) (*between January and September 1885 the postmark was used without year numerals*).

1865. (*Nos.* 54/65).

Z39	1 a. deep brown	.. ..	50·00
Z40	2 a. brown-orange	.. ..	27·00

1866–78. (*Nos.* 69/72).

Z41	4 a. blue-green (Die II)	..	27·00

1868. (*Nos.* 73/4).

Z42	8 a. rose (Die II)	..	27·00

1873. (*Nos. 75/6*).
Z43   ½ a. blue (Die II)   ..   ..   27·00

1874. (*Nos. 77/9*).
Z44   1 r. slate   ..   ..   85·00

1876. (*Nos. 80/2*).
Z45   6 a. pale brown   ..   ..   45·00

1882–86. (*Nos. 84/101*).
Z46   ½ a. blue-green   ..   ..   ..   11·00
Z47   1 a. brown-purple   ..   ..   ..   22·00
Z48   1 a. 6 p. sepia   ..   ..   ..   17·00
Z49   2 a. blue   ..   ..   32·00
Z50   3 a. orange   ..   ..   ..   11·00
Z51   4 a. olive-green   ..   ..   ..   32·00
Z52   4 a. 6 p. yellow-green   ..   ..   16·00
Z53   8 a. dull mauve   ..   ..   ..   32·00
Z54   1 r. slate   ..   ..   32·00

OFFICIAL STAMPS

1867–73. (*Nos. O20/30a*).
Z55   2 a. orange £120

1874–82. (*Nos. O31/7*).
Z56   1 a. brown   ..   ..   70·00

1883–95. (*Nos. O37a/48*).
Z57   1 a. brown-purple   ..   ..   ..   70·00

Stamps of INDIA cancelled with Type Z 5 (1887–94).

1876. (*Nos. 80/2*).
Z60   6 a. pale brown   ..   ..   ..   16·00
Z61   12 a. Venetian red   ..   ..   ..   38·00

1882–88. (*Nos. 84/101*).
Z62   ½ a. blue-green   ..   ..   ..   5·00
Z63   9 p. aniline carmine   ..   ..   32·00
Z64   1 a. brown-purple   ..   ..   ..   5·00
Z65   1 a. 6 p. sepia   ..   ..   ..   7·00
Z66   2 a. blue   ..   ..   6·00
Z67   3 a. orange   ..   ..   ..   8·00
Z68   3 a. brown-orange   ..   ..   ..   6·00
Z69   4 a. olive-green   ..   ..   ..   32·00
Z70   4 a. 6 p. yellow-green   ..   ..   10·00
Z71   8 a. dull mauve   ..   ..   ..   16·00
Z72   12 a. purple/*red*   ..   ..   ..   32·00
Z73   1 r. slate   ..   ..   12·00

1891. (*No. 102*).
Z74   2½ a. on 4 a. 6 p. yellow-green   ..   7·00

1892–95. (*Nos. 103/6*).
Z75   2 a. 6 p. yellow-green   ..   ..   5·00

OFFICIAL STAMPS

1874. (*Nos. O31/7*).
Z76   ½ a. blue   ..   ..   60·00
Z77   1 a. brown   ..   ..   60·00

Z 6

Z 7

Stamps of INDIA cancelled with Type Z 6 (1888–95).

1876. (*Nos. 80/2*).
Z80   6 a. pale brown   ..   ..   ..   15·00

1882–88. (*Nos. 84/101*).
Z81   ½ a. blue-green   ..   ..   ..   27·00
Z82   9 p. aniline carmine   ..   ..   38·00
Z83   1 a. brown-purple   ..   ..   ..   7·00
Z84   1 a. 6 p. sepia   ..   ..   ..   7·00
Z85   2 a. blue   ..   ..   8·00
Z86   3 a. orange   ..   ..   ..   16·00
Z87   3 a. brown-orange   ..   ..   ..   12·00
Z88   4 a. olive-green   ..   ..   ..   12·00
Z89   4 a. 6 p. yellow-green   ..   ..   12·00
Z90   8 a. dull mauve   ..   ..   ..   15·00
Z91   12 a. purple/*red*   ..   ..   ..   32·00
Z92   1 r. slate   ..   ..   14·00

1891. (*No. 102*).
Z93   2½ a. on 4 a. 6 p. yellow-green   ..   16·00

1892–95. (*Nos. 103/6*).
Z94   2 a. 6 p. yellow-green   ..   ..   16·00

Stamps of INDIA cancelled with Type Z 7 (1894–95).

1876. (*Nos. 80/2*).
Z95   6 a. pale brown   ..   ..   ..   42·00

1882–88. (*Nos. 84/101*).
Z100   ½ a. blue-green   ..   ..   ..   15·00
Z101   9 p. aniline carmine   ..   ..   45·00
Z102   1 a. brown-purple   ..   ..   22·00
Z103   1 a. 6 p. sepia   ..   ..   32·00
Z104   2 a. blue   ..   ..   ..   15·00
Z105   3 a. brown-orange   ..   ..   32·00
Z106   4 a. olive-green   ..   ..   32·00
Z107   8 a. dull mauve   ..   ..   42·00
Z108   12 a. purple/*red*   ..   ..   45·00
Z109   1 r. slate   ..   ..   ..   42·00

1892–95. (*Nos. 103/6*).
Z110   2 a. 6 p. yellow-green   ..   ..   10·00

1895. (*Nos. 107/9*).
Z111   2 r. carmine and yellow-brown   ..   £170

> A French post office was opened on the island in January 1889 and this service used the stamps of FRANCE until 1894 when specific stamps for this office were provided. The French postal service on the island closed on 31 July 1904 and it is known that French stamps were again utilised during the final month.
> A German postal agency operated in Zanzibar between 27 August 1890 and 31 July 1891, using stamps of GERMANY.

PRICES FOR STAMPS ON COVER TO 1945

Nos. 1/2	—
Nos. 3/16	*from* × 30
No. 17	*from* × 8
No. 18	*from* × 25
Nos. 19/21	—
No. 22	*from* × 30
Nos. 23/5	—
No. 26	*from* × 40
Nos. 27/40	—
Nos. 41/6	*from* × 25
Nos. 156/68	*from* × 15
Nos. 169/77	—
Nos. 178/87	*from* × 20
Nos. 188/204	*from* × 15
Nos. 205/9	*from* × 20
Nos. 210/38	*from* × 15
Nos. 239/45	—
Nos. 246/59	*from* × 8
Nos. 260/*f*	—
Nos. 261/330	*from* × 4
Nos. D1/3	*from* × 8
No. D4	*from* × 1
No. D5	*from* × 15
No. D6	—
No. D7	*from* × 1
Nos. D8/12	*from* × 15
No. D13	*from* × 1
No. D14	—
Nos. D15/16	*from* × 6
No. D17	*from* × 4
Nos. D18/24	*from* × 15
Nos. D25/30	*from* × 30

PROTECTORATE

(Currency. 12 pies = 1 anna. 16 annas = 1 rupee)

Zanzibar

(1)

1895 (10 Nov)–**96.** *Nos. 81, 85, 90/6, 98/101, 103 and 106/9 of India (Queen Victoria) optd with T 1 by Zanzibar Gazette.*

(a) In blue
1   ½ a. blue-green   ..   £12000 £3500
2   1 a. plum £2250   £500
  j. "Zanzidar" (R. 4/6, 8/5)   ..   † £12000

(b) In black
3   ½ a. blue-green   ..   3·00   3·00
  j. "Zanzidar" (R. 4/6, 8/5)   ..   £950   £600
  k. "Zanibar" (R. 7/2)   ..   £1000 £1400
  l. Diaeresis over last "a" (R. 10/5)   £900   £900
  m. Opt double, one albino   £225
4   1 a. plum   ..   ..   3·25   3·00
  j. "Zanzidar" (R. 4/6, 8/5)   ..   — £2250
  k. "Zanibar" (R. 7/2)   ..   £1300 £1500
  l. Diaeresis over last "a" (R. 10/5)   £1200
5   1 a. 6 p. sepia   ..   4·00   3·00
  j. "Zanzidar" (R. 4/6, 8/5)   ..   £2750   £750
  k. "Zanibar" (R. 7/2)   ..   £1200 £1300
  l. "Zanzibar" (R. 1/9)   ..   —
  m. Diaeresis over last "a" (R. 10/5)   £900
6   2 a. pale blue   ..   4·25   4·00
7   2 a. blue   ..   ..   4·50   4·25
  j. "Zanzidar" (R. 4/6, 8/5)   £3000 £1500
  k. "Zanibar" (R. 7/2)   £3000 £1600
  l. Diaeresis over last "a" (R. 10/5)   £950
  m. Opt double   £250
8   2½ a. yellow-green   ..   6·00   4·25
  j. "Zanzidar" (R. 4/6, 8/5)   £2750 £1400
  k. "Zanibar" (R. 7/2)   ..   £550 £1000
  l. "Zapzibar"   —
  m. "Zanzipar"   —
  n. Diaeresis over last "a" (R. 10/5)   £950   £950
  o. Second "z" italic (R. 10/1)   £250   £375
  p. Opt double, one albino   £225
10   3 a. brown-orange   ..   9·00   8·50
  j. "Zanzidar" (R. 4/6, 8/5)   ..   £750 £1400
  k. "Zanibar" (R. 1/9)   ..   £3250 £3500
11   4 a. olive-green   ..   16·00 13·00
  j. "Zanzidar" ((R. 4/6, 8/5)   £4750 £3000
12   4 a. slate-green   ..   8·50 11·00
  l. Diaeresis over last "a" (R. 10/5)   £1300

---

13   6 a. pale brown   ..   16·00 11·00
  j. "Zanzidar" (R. 4/6, 8/5)   £5000 £3250
  k. "Zanibar" (R. 7/2)   ..   £650 £1200
  l. "Zanzibarr"   ..   £3500 £3500
  m. Opt double   —
  n. Opt double, one albino   £120
  o. Opt triple, two albino   £160
14   8 a. dull mauve   ..   20·00 18·00
  j. "Zanzidar" (R. 4/6, 8/5)   £4750 £4750
15   8 a. magenta (7.96)   ..   11·00 20·00
16   12 a. purple/*red*   ..   14·00 10·00
  j. "Zanzidar" (R. 4/6, 8/5)   £4500 £3250
17   1 r. slate   ..   ..   70·00 70·00
  j. "Zanzidar" (R. 4/6, 8/5)   £4500 £3750
18   1 r. green and aniline carmine (7.96)   10·00 24·00
  j. Opt vert downwards   £425
19   2 r. carmine and yellow-brown   45·00 65·00
  j. "r" omitted   £6000
  k. "r" inverted   £3500 £3500
20   3 r. brown and green   45·00 60·00
  j. "r" omitted   £6000
  k. "r" inverted   £3250 £3750
21   5 r. ultramarine and violet   48·00 70·00
  j. "r" omitted   £6000
  k. "r" inverted   £2750 £3750
  l. Opt double, one inverted   £800
3/21   *Set of 15*   £250   £325

There were a number of different settings for this overprint. Values to 1 r. were initially overprinted from settings of 120 (12×10) including one which showed "Zanzidar" on R.4/6 and R.8/5 (soon corrected) and "Zanibar" on R.1/9 (also soon corrected). Later supplies of these values were overprinted from settings of 80 (8×10) for the 6 a. only or 60 (6×10) for the others. One of these settings included "Zanibar" on R.7/2. Another late setting, size unknown, showed a diaeresis over last "a" on R.10/5.

Many forgeries of this overprint exist and also bogus errors.

MINOR VARIETIES. The following minor varieties of type exist on Nos. 1/21:

A. First "Z" antique (all values)
B. Broken "p" for "n" (all values to 1 r.)
C. Tall second "z" (all values)
D. Small second "z" (all values)
E. Small second "z" and inverted "q" for "b" (all values)
F. Second "z" Gothic (½ a. to 12 a. and 1 r.) (No. 18) (black opts only)
G. No dot over "i" (all values to 1 r.)
H. Inverted "q" for "b" (all values to 1 r.)
I. Arabic "2" for "r" (all values to 1 r.) (black opts only)

Varieties D and E are worth the same as normal examples, A (2, 3, 5 r.) and C normal plus 50%, G and I from 3 times normal, A (values to 1 r.), F and H from 4 times normal and B from 5 times normal.

2½ (2)   **2½** (3)   **2½** (4)   **2½** (5)

1895–98.   *Provisionals.* I. *Stamps used for postal purposes.*

(a) No. 5 surch in red (30.11.95)
22 2 2½ on 1½ a. sepia   ..   45·00 35·00
  j. "Zanzidar"   ..   £1200 £1100
  k. "Zanibar"   ..   £3500 £1800
  l. Inverted "1" in "½"   £1100   £900

(b) No. 4 surch in black (11.5.96)
23 3 2½ on 1 a. plum   ..   £130   £100
24 4 2½ on 1 a. plum   ..   £400   £275
  j. Inverted "1" in "½"   £2000
25 5 2½ on 1 a. plum   ..   £150   £110

2½ (6)   **2½** (7)   **2½** (8)

(c) No. 6 surch in red (15.8.96)
26 6 2½ on 2 a. pale blue   ..   50·00 25·00
  j. Inverted "1" in "½"   £375   £275
  k. Roman "I" in "½"   £225   £150
  l. "Zanzibar" double, one albino   £130
27 7 2½ on 2 a. pale blue   ..   £130 85·00
  j. "2" of "½" omitted   ..   £4000
  k. "2" for "2½"   ..   £5000
  l. "1" of "½" omitted   £4000 £3250
  m. Inverted "1" in "½"   £1600
  n. "Zanzibar" double, one albino   £275
28 8 2½ on 2 a. pale blue   £4000 £1600
No. 28 only exists with small "z" and occurs on R. 2/2 in the setting of 60.

(d) No. 5 surch in red (15.11.96)
29 6 2½ on 1½ a. sepia   ..   £130   £100
  j. Inverted "1" in "½"   ..   £1100   £950
  k. Roman "I" in "½"   ..   £800   £750
  l. Surch double, one albino   £225
30 7 2½ on 1½ a. sepia   ..   £375   £325
  l. Surch double, one albino   £600
31 8 2½ on 1½ a. sepia   ..   £9000 £6000
No. 31 only exists with small "z" and occurs on R. 2/2 in the setting of 60.

II. *Stamps prepared for official purposes. Nos. 4, 5 and 7 surch as before in red (1.98).*
32 3 2½ on 1 a. plum   ..   £225   £550
33 4 2½ on 1 a. plum   ..   £425   £850
34 5 2½ on 1 a. plum   ..   £250   £550
35 3 2½ on 1½ a. sepia   ..   75·00   £170
  j. Diaeresis over last "a"   £3500
36 4 2½ on 1½ a. sepia   ..   £170   £400
37 5 2½ on 1½ a. sepia   ..   £100   £225
38 3 2½ on 2 a. dull blue   ..   85·00   £200
39 4 2½ on 2 a. dull blue   ..   £170   £400
40 5 2½ on 2 a. dull blue   ..   95·00   £250
It is doubtful whether Nos. 32/40 were issued to the public.

1896. *Nos. 65/6, 68 and 71/3 of British East Africa (Queen Victoria), optd with T* **1.**
41 ½ a. yellow-green (23 May) .. .. 29·00 16·00
42 1 a. carmine-rose (1 June) .. .. 25·00 15·00
  j. Opt double £700 £750
  k. Opt double, one albino .. £250
43 2½ a. deep blue (R.) (24 May) .. 75·00 42·00
44 4½ a. orange-yellow (12 Aug) .. 42·00 48·00
45 5 a. yellow-bistre (12 Aug) .. 48·00 30·00
  j. "r" omitted .. .. — £2000
46 7½ a. mauve (12 Aug) .. .. 35·00 48·00
41/6 .. .. *Set of 6* £225 £180

MINOR VARIETIES. The various minor varieties of type detailed in the note below No. 21 also occur on Nos. 22 to 46 as indicated below:
A. Nos. 23, 25, 27, 30, 35, 38, 41/6
B. Nos. 22/3, 26, 29/30, 32/3, 36, 39, 44/6
C. Nos. 22, 25/6, 32, 36, 38, 40/6
D. Nos. 22/46
E. Nos. 22/46
F. Nos. 22, 25/6, 29, 41/6
G. Nos. 25/6, 29, 35, 37/8, 40/6
H. Nos. 22, 41/6 (on the British East Africa stamps this variety occurs in the same position as variety C)
I. Nos. 26, 29, 35, 38, 41/6

The scarcity of these varieties on the surcharges (Nos. 22/40) is similar to those on the basic stamps, but examples on the British East Africa values (Nos. 41/6) are more common.

PRINTERS. All Zanzibar stamps up to Type **37** were printed by De La Rue & Co.

12   13

14 Sultan Seyyid Hamed-bin-Thwain   No right serif to left-hand "4" (R. 1/1)

1896 (Dec). *Recess. Flags in red on all values. W* **12.** *P* 14.
156 **13** ½ a. yellow-green .. .. 3·50 1·75
157 1 a. indigo .. .. 1·40 1·50
158 1 a. violet-blue .. .. 4·00 4·00
159 2 a. red-brown .. .. 2·25 65
160 2½ a. bright blue .. .. 9·00 1·40
161 2½ a. pale blue .. .. 10·00 1·40
162 3 a. grey .. .. 7·00 4·25
163 3 a. bluish grey .. .. 8·00 6·50
164 4 a. myrtle-green .. .. 5·00 2·75
165 4½ a. orange .. .. 3·50 4·25
  a. No right serif to left-hand "4" 80·00 90·00
  b. No fraction bar at right (R. 2/1) 80·00 90·00
166 5 a. bistre .. .. 3·00 2·25
  a. Bisected (2½ a.) (on cover) .. †£3000
167 7½ a. mauve .. .. 2·50 2·25
168 8 a. grey-olive .. .. 9·50 7·00
169 **14** 1 r. blue .. .. 9·50 9·00
170 1 r. deep blue .. .. 17·00 13·00
171 2 r. green .. .. 23·00 9·50
172 3 r. dull purple .. .. 20·00 9·50
173 4 r. lake .. .. 16·00 13·00
174 5 r. sepia .. .. 21·00 13·00
156/74 .. .. *Set of 15* £120 75·00
156/74 Optd "Specimen" .. *Set of 15* £190
The ½, 1, 2, 2½, 3 and 8 a. are known without wmk, these being from edges of the sheets.

1897 (5 Jan). *No. 164 surch as before, in red.*
175 **3** 2½ on 4 a. myrtle-green .. 55·00 38·00
176 **4** 2½ on 4 a. myrtle-green .. £190 £170
177 **5** 2½ on 4 a. myrtle-green .. 75·00 50·00
175/7 .. .. *Set of 3* £275 £225

18

1898 (May). *Recess. W* **18.** *P* 14.
178 **13** ½ a. yellow-green .. .. 1·50 35
179 1 a. indigo .. .. 1·75 55
  a. Greenish black .. 4·25 1·50
180 2 a. red-brown .. .. 3·50 75
  a. Deep brown .. 4·50 1·75
181 2½ a. bright blue .. .. 1·75 30
182 3 a. grey .. .. 5·00 60
183 4 a. myrtle-green .. .. 2·75 1·00

184 **13** 4½ a. orange .. .. 5·50 70
  a. No right serif to left-hand "4" £110 38·00
  b. No fraction bar at right (R. 2/1) £110 38·00
185 5 a. bistre .. .. 12·50 1·75
  a. Pale bistre .. 12·50 2·00
186 7½ a. mauve .. .. 5·50 2·75
187 8 a. grey-olive .. .. 9·00 2·25
178/87 .. .. *Set of 10* 40·00 10·00

19   20 Sultan Seyyid Hamoud-bin-Mohammed bin Said

1899 (June)**–1901.** *Recess. Flags in red. W* **18** *(Nos. 188/99) or* **W 12** *(others). P* 14.
188 **19** ½ a. yellow-green .. .. 1·75 60
  a. Wmk sideways .. 9·50 4·25
189 1 a. indigo .. .. 4·00 20
  a. Wmk sideways .. 21·00 1·25
190 1 a. carmine (1901) .. .. 1·40 10
191 2 a. red-brown .. .. 2·00 50
192 2½ a. bright blue .. .. 1·50 60
193 3 a. grey .. .. 1·50 2·25
194 4 a. myrtle-green .. .. 2·75 1·00
195 4½ a. orange .. .. 7·50 2·25
196 4½ a. blue-black (1901) .. 12·00 12·00
197 5 a. bistre .. .. 2·50 1·25
198 7½ a. mauve .. .. 2·50 3·50
199 8 a. grey-olive .. .. 2·75 4·50
200 **20** 1 r. blue .. .. 17·00 14·00
201 2 r. green .. .. 16·00 18·00
202 3 r. dull purple .. .. 30·00 35·00
203 4 r. lake .. .. 42·00 50·00
204 5 r. sepia .. .. 50·00 60·00
188/204 .. .. *Set of 17* £170 £170
188/204 Optd "Specimen" .. *Set of 17* £190

One **(21)**
Two & Half **(22)**
Two & Half **(22a)** Thin open "w" (R. 2/2, 3/4)
Two & Half **(22b)** Serif to foot of "f" (R. 3/1)

1904. *Nos. 194/6 and 198/9 surch as T* **21** *and* **22,** *in black or lake (L.) by Zanzibar Gazette in setting of 30 (6×5).*
205 **19** 1 on 4½ a. orange .. .. 3·75 3·25
206 1 on 4½ a. blue-black (L.) .. 4·25 16·00
207 2 on 4 a. myrtle-green (L.) .. 13·00 16·00
208 2½ on 7½ a. mauve .. .. 12·00 18·00
  a. Opt Type 22a .. 75·00 95·00
  b. Opt Type 22b .. £110 £150
  c. "Hlaf" for "Half" .. £10000
209 2½ on 8 a. grey-olive .. .. 14·00 28·00
  a. Opt Type 22a .. £100 £150
  b. Opt Type 22b .. £150 £225
  c. "Hlaf" for "Half" .. £9500 £5500
205/9 .. .. *Set of 5* 42·00 70·00

23   24

Monogram of Sultan Seyyid Ali bin Hamoud bin Naherud

1904 (8 June). *Typo. Background of centre in second colour. W* **18.** *P* 14.
210 **23** ½ a. green .. .. 1·10 90
211 1 a. rose-red .. .. 1·10 10
212 2 a. brown .. .. 1·25 45
213 2½ a. blue .. .. 2·25 35
214 3 a. grey .. .. 2·25 2·25
215 4 a. deep green .. .. 2·25 1·60
216 4½ a. black .. .. 3·00 2·50
217 5 a. yellow-brown .. .. 3·25 1·25
218 7½ a. purple .. .. 4·00 7·00
219 8 a. olive-green .. .. 3·75 2·50
220 **24** 1 r. blue and red .. .. 20·00 10·00
  a. Wmk sideways .. 70·00 35·00
221 2 r. green and red .. .. 20·00 35·00
  a. Wmk sideways .. £120 £160
222 3 r. violet and red .. .. 40·00 75·00
223 4 r. claret and red .. .. 45·00 90·00
224 5 r. olive-brown and red .. 48·00 95·00
210/24 .. .. *Set of 15* £170 £275
210/24 Optd "Specimen" .. *Set of 15* £140

25   26

27 Sultan Ali bin Hamoud   28 View of Port

1908 (May)**–09.** *Recess. W* **18** *(sideways on 10 r. to 30 r.). P* 14.
225 **25** 1 c. pearl-grey (10.09) .. 1·75 30
226 3 c. yellow-green .. .. 3·50 10
  a. Wmk sideways .. 3·75 1·00
227 6 c. rose-carmine .. .. 6·50 10
  a. Wmk sideways .. 7·50 2·00
228 10 c. brown (10.09) .. .. 1·75 1·75
229 12 c. violet .. .. 9·00 2·25
  a. Wmk sideways .. 9·00 1·00
230 **26** 15 c. ultramarine .. .. 7·00 40
  a. Wmk sideways .. 8·00 5·50
231 25 c. sepia .. .. 2·75 80
232 50 c. blue-green .. .. 4·75 3·50
233 75 c. grey-black (10.09) .. 8·00 12·00
234 **27** 1 r. yellow-green .. .. 24·00 12·00
  a. Wmk sideways .. 45·00 9·00
235 2 r. violet .. .. 18·00 14·00
  a. Wmk sideways .. £110 60·00
236 3 r. orange-bistre .. .. 23·00 48·00
237 4 r. vermilion .. .. 42·00 75·00
238 5 r. steel-blue .. .. 40·00 55·00
239 **28** 10 r. blue-green and brown (S. £28) 95·00 £200
240 20 r. black and yellow-green (S. £35) £200 £400
241 30 r. black and sepia (S. £45) .. £275 £500
242 40 r. black and orange-brown (S. £55) £425
243 50 r. black and mauve (S. £65) £375
244 100 r. black and steel-blue (S. £100) £650
245 200 r. brown and greenish black (S. £150) £1000
225/38 .. .. *Set of 14* £160 £190
225/38 Optd "Specimen" .. *Set of 14* £160
Specimen copies of Nos. 239/45 are all overprinted.

29 Sultan Kalif bin Harub   30 Sailing Canoe

31 Dhow

1913. *Recess. W* **18** *(sideways on 75 c. and 10 r. to 200 r.). P* 14.
246 **29** 1 c. grey 30 20
247 3 c. yellow-green 50 20
248 6 c. rose-carmine .. .. 1·50 10
249 10 c. brown .. .. 1·10 1·60
250 12 c. violet .. .. 1·00 20
251 15 c. blue .. .. 1·25 30
252 25 c. sepia 90 45
253 50 c. blue-green .. .. 2·00 3·25
254 75 c. grey-black .. .. 2·00 2·75
  a. Wmk upright .. £150
255 **30** 1 r. yellow-green .. .. 5·00 7·50
256 2 r. violet .. .. 10·00 22·00
257 3 r. orange-bistre .. .. 11·00 32·00
258 4 r. scarlet .. .. 25·00 55·00
259 5 r. steel-blue .. .. 32·00 35·00
260 **31** 10 r. green and brown .. 85·00 £150
260a 20 r. black and green (S. £27) £120 £275
260b 30 r. black and brown (S. £38) £130 £350
260c 40 r. black and vermilion (S. £55) £275 £475
260d 50 r. black and purple (S. £60) £250 £475
260e 100 r. black and blue (S. £80) £325
260f 200 r. brown and black (S. £110) £600
246/60 .. .. *Set of 15* £150 £250
246/60 Optd "Specimen" .. *Set of 15* £170
Specimen copies of Nos. 260a/f are all overprinted.

1914–22. *Wmk Mult Crown CA (sideways on 10 r.). P* 14.
261 **29** 1 c. grey 70 25
262 3 c. yellow-green .. .. 1·10 10
  a. Dull green .. 3·25 15
263 6 c. deep carmine 85 10
  a. Bright rose-carmine .. 85 10
  aw. Wmk inverted .. † 85·00
264 8 c. purple/pale yellow (1922) 75 3·00
265 10 c. myrtle/pale yellow (1922) 75 10
266 15 c. deep ultramarine .. 1·10 4·00
268 50 c. blue-green .. .. 4·50 4·00
269 75 c. grey-black .. .. 3·00 18·00

270	30	1 r. yellow-green		4·00	3·50
271		2 r. violet		4·50	8·00
272		3 r. orange-bistre		16·00	27·00
273		4 r. scarlet		16·00	75·00
		y. Wmk inverted and reversed		85·00	
274		5 r. steel-blue		16·00	55·00
		w. Wmk inverted		85·00	
275	31	10 r. green and brown		90·00	£300
261/75			Set of 14	£140	£400
261/75 Optd "Specimen"			Set of 14	£180	

1921–29. *Wmk Mult Script CA (sideways on 10 r. to 30 r.).*
P 14.

276	29	1 c. slate-grey		20	7·00
277		3 c. yellow-green		50	2·75
278		3 c. yellow (1922)		30	10
		w. Wmk inverted			
279		4 c. green (1922)		50	60
280		6 c. carmine-red		30	50
281		6 c. purple/blue (1922)		35	10
282		10 c. brown		70	7·00
283		12 c. violet		40	30
		w. Wmk inverted			
284		12 c. carmine-red (1922)		40	40
285		15 c. blue		55	7·00
286		20 c. indigo (1922)		1·00	30
287		25 c. sepia		75	8·50
288		50 c. myrtle-green		1·25	3·25
		y. Wmk inverted and reversed		85·00	
289		75 c. slate		2·50	42·00
290	30	1 r. yellow-green		3·50	3·00
291		2 r. deep violet		3·00	6·50
292		3 r. orange-bistre		4·25	7·50
293		4 r. scarlet		11·00	32·00
294		5 r. Prussian blue		18·00	65·00
		w. Wmk inverted		£120	
295	31	10 r. green and brown		70·00	£200
296		20 r. black and green (Optd S. £70)		£150	£350
297		30 r. black & brown (1929) (Perf S. £80)		£170	£450
276/95			Set of 20	£100	£325
276/95 Optd "Specimen"			Set of 20	£225	

32   Sultan Kalif bin Harub   **33**

1926–27. *T* **32** ("CENTS" *in serifed capitals). Recess. Wmk Mult
Script CA. P* 14.

299	32	1 c. brown		40	10
300		3 c. yellow-orange		20	15
301		4 c. deep dull green		20	30
302		6 c. violet		20	10
303		8 c. slate		90	4·50
304		10 c. olive-green		85	40
305		12 c. carmine-red		1·50	40
306		20 c. bright blue		40	30
307		25 c. purple/yellow (1927)		4·00	2·50
308		50 c. claret		1·75	35
309		75 c. sepia (1927)		13·00	16·00
299/309			Set of 11	21·00	22·00
299/309 Optd "Specimen"			Set of 11	£110	

(New Currency. 100 cents = 1 shilling)

1936 (1 Jan). *T* **33** ("CENTS" *in sans-serif capitals), and
T* **30**/1, *but values in shillings. Recess. Wmk Mult Script CA.
P* 14 × 13½–14.

310	33	5 c. green		10	10
311		10 c. black		10	10
312		15 c. carmine-red		10	85
313		20 c. orange		10	10
314		25 c. purple/yellow		10	10
315		30 c. ultramarine		10	10
316		40 c. sepia		15	10
317		50 c. claret		30	10
318	30	1 s. yellow-green		50	10
319		2 s. slate-violet		65	1·25
320		5 s. scarlet		7·50	5·50
321		7 s. 50, light blue		19·00	20·00
322	31	10 s. green and brown		19·00	20·00
310/22			Set of 13	42·00	42·00
310/22 Perf "Specimen"			Set of 13	£130	

36 Sultan Kalif bin Harub

1936 (9 Dec). *Silver Jubilee of Sultan. Recess. Wmk Mult Script
CA. P* 14.

323	36	10 c. black and olive-green		70	30
324		20 c. black and bright purple		2·50	30
325		30 c. black and deep ultramarine		6·00	35
326		50 c. black and orange-vermilion		6·50	2·75
323/6			Set of 4	14·00	3·25
323/6 Perf "Specimen"			Set of 4	70·00	

---

37 Sham Alam   **(38)**
(Sultan's dhow)

1944 (20 Nov). *Bicentenary of Al Busaid Dynasty. Recess. Wmk
Mult Script CA. P* 14.

327	37	10 c. ultramarine		60	1·75
328		20 c. red		60	2·25
329		50 c. blue-green		60	30
330		1 s. dull purple		60	50
327/30			Set of 4	2·25	4·25
327/30 Perf "Specimen"			Set of 4	70·00	

1946 (11 Nov). *Victory. Nos. 311 and 315 optd with T* **38**.

331	33	10 c. black (R.)		20	20
332		30 c. ultramarine (R.)		20	40
331/2 Perf "Specimen"			Set of 2	45·00	

1949 (10 Jan). *Royal Silver Wedding. As Nos. 143/4 of
Jamaica.*

333	20 c. orange		30	1·25
334	10 s. brown		17·00	28·00

1949 (10 Oct). *75th Anniv of U.P.U. As Nos. 145/8 of Jamaica.*

335	20 c. red-orange		40	2·00
336	30 c. deep blue		1·40	80
337	50 c. magenta		1·50	2·00
338	1 s. blue-green		1·50	3·00
335/8		Set of 4	4·25	7·00

39 Sultan Kalif   **40** Seyyid Khalifa Schools,
bin Harub   Beit-el-Ras

1952 (26 Aug)–**55.** *Wmk Mult Script CA. P* 12½ (cent values)
or 13 (shilling values).

339	39	5 c. black		10	10
340		10 c. red-orange		10	10
341		15 c. green		40	1·75
		a. Yellow-green (12.11.53)		2·00	2·50
342		20 c. carmine-red		40	60
343		25 c. reddish purple		60	10
344		30 c. deep bluish green		60	10
		a. Deep green (29.3.55)		5·50	4·00
345		35 c. bright blue		50	3·00
346		40 c. deep brown		30	1·25
		a. Sepia (12.11.53)		2·00	1·75
347		50 c. violet		2·00	10
		a. Deep violet (29.3.55)		3·00	80
348	40	1 s. deep green and deep brown		30	10
349		2 s. bright blue and deep purple		1·75	2·00
350		5 s. black and carmine-red		1·75	3·00
351		7 s. 50, grey-black and emerald		18·00	23·00
352		10 s. carmine-red and black		9·50	9·00
339/52			Set of 14	32·00	40·00

41 Sultan Kalif bin Harub

(Photo Harrison)

1954 (26 Aug). *Sultan's 75th Birthday. Wmk Mult Script CA.
Chalk-surfaced paper. P* 13 × 12.

353	41	15 c. deep green		10	10
354		20 c. rose-red		10	10
355		30 c. bright blue		10	10
356		50 c. purple		15	10
357		1 s. 25, orange-red		15	60
353/7			Set of 5	50	80

42 Cloves   **43** *Ummoja Wema* (dhow)

44 Sultan's Barge   **45** Map of East African Coast

---

46 Minaret Mosque   **47** Dimbani Mosque   **48** Kibweni Palace

(Des W. J. Jennings (T **42**), A. Farhan (T **43**), Mrs. M. Broadbent
(T **44, 46**), R. A. Sweet (T **45**), A. S. B. New (T **47**), B. J. Woolley
(T **48**). Recess B.W.)

1957 (26 Aug). *W w* **12**. *P* 11½ (5 c., 10 c.), 11 × 11½ (15 c., 30 c.,
1 s. 25), 14 × 13½ (20 c., 25 c., 35 c., 50 c.,), 13½ × 14 (40 c., 1 s.,
2 s.) or 13 × 13½ (5 s., 7 s. 50, 10 s.).

358	42	5 c. orange and deep green		10	30
359		10 c. emerald and carmine-red		10	10
360	43	15 c. green and sepia		10	2·00
361	44	20 c. ultramarine		10	10
362	45	25 c. orange-brown and black		10	50
363	43	30 c. carmine-red and black		15	50
364	45	35 c. slate and emerald		15	20
365	46	40 c. brown and black		15	10
366	45	50 c. blue and grey-green		15	20
367	47	1 s. carmine and black		20	20
368	43	1 s. 25, slate and carmine		3·00	20
369	47	2 s. orange and deep green		3·00	2·00
370	48	5 s. deep bright blue		4·75	2·00
371		7 s. 50, green		5·50	4·00
372		10 s. carmine		5·50	4·75
358/72			Set of 15	20·00	15·00

49 Sultan Seyyid   **50** "Protein Foods"
Sir Abdulla bin Khalifa

(Recess B.W.)

1961 (17 Oct). *As T* **42**/8, *but with portrait of Sultan Sir Abdulla
as in T* **49**, *W w* **12**. *P* 13 × 13½ (20 s.), *others as before.*

373	49	5 c. orange and deep green		10	60
374		10 c. emerald and carmine-red		10	10
375	43	15 c. green and sepia		60	2·25
376	44	20 c. ultramarine		30	30
377	45	25 c. orange-brown and black		40	40
378	43	30 c. carmine-red and black		1·75	40
379	45	35 c. slate and emerald		1·50	2·00
380	46	40 c. brown and black		30	20
381	45	50 c. blue and grey-green		75	10
382	47	1 s. carmine and black		40	60
383	43	1 s. 25, slate and carmine		2·50	2·25
384	47	2 s. orange and deep green		50	2·25
385	48	5 s. deep bright blue		3·00	7·00
386		7 s. 50, green		3·00	15·00
387		10 s. carmine		3·00	9·00
388		20 s. sepia		17·00	28·00
373/88			Set of 16	32·00	60·00

(Des M. Goaman. Photo Harrison)

1963 (4 June). *Freedom from Hunger. W w* **12**. *P* 14 × 14½.
| 389 | 50 | 1 s. 30, sepia | | 90 | 50 |

INDEPENDENT

51 Zanzibar Clove   **53** "Religious Tolerance"
(mosques and churches)

(Photo Harrison)

1963 (10 Dec). *Independence. Portrait of Sultan Seyyid Jamshid
bin Abdulla. T* **51, 53** *and similar vert designs. P* 12½.

390		30 c. multicoloured		10	30
391		50 c. multicoloured		10	30
392		1 s. 30, multicoloured		15	3·75
393		2 s. 50, multicoloured		20	4·50
390/3			Set of 4	50	8·00

Designs:—50 c. "To Prosperity" (Zanzibar doorway); 2 s. 50,
"Towards the Light" (Mangapwani Cave).

REPUBLIC

When the Post Office opened on 14 January 1964, after the revolution deposing the Sultan, the stamps on sale had the portrait
cancelled by a manuscript cross. Stamps thus cancelled on cover or
piece used between January 14 and 17 are therefore of interest.

JAMHURI 1964

(55 = "Republic")

1964 (17 Jan). *Locally handstamped as T 55 in black.*

(i) *Nos. 373/88.*

394	49	5 c. orange and deep green	..	1·00	65
395		10 c. emerald and carmine-red	..	1·00	10
396	43	15 c. green and sepia	..	1·00	2·75
397	44	20 c. ultramarine	..	1·00	60
398	45	25 c. orange-brown and black	..	1·00	20
399	43	30 c. carmine-red and black	..	1·00	60
400	45	35 c. slate and emerald	..	1·00	1·50
401	46	40 c. brown and black	..	1·00	1·25
402	45	50 c. blue and grey-green	..	1·00	10
403	47	1 s. carmine and black	..	1·00	90
404	43	1 s. 25, slate and carmine	..	1·00	1·75
405	47	2 s. orange and deep green	..	1·75	1·75
406	48	5 s. deep bright blue	..	1·75	1·75
407		7 s. 50, green	..	2·00	1·75
408		10 s. carmine	..	2·00	1·75
409		20 s. sepia	..	2·50	5·50

(ii) *Nos. 390/3 (Independence)*

410		30 c. multicoloured		30	60
411		50 c. multicoloured	..	30	10
412		1 s. 30, multicoloured		60	80
413		2 s. 50, multicoloured		1·40	1·50
		a. Green omitted	..	£170	
394/413			*Set of 20*	21·00	23·00

T **55** occurs in various positions—diagonally, horizontally or vertically.

NOTE. Nos. 394 to 413 are the only stamps officially authorised to receive the handstamp but it has also been seen on Nos. 353/7, 389 and the Postage Dues. There are numerous errors but it is impossible to distinguish between cases of genuine oversight and those made deliberately at the request of purchasers.

JAMHURI

JAMHURI 1964	1964
(56)	(57)

1964 (28 Feb). *Optd by Bradbury, Wilkinson.*

(i) *As T 56 on Nos. 373/88.*

414	49	5 c. orange and deep green		10	10
415		10 c. emerald and carmine-red	..	10	10
416	43	15 c. green and sepia	..	10	10
417	44	20 c. ultramarine	..	10	10
418	45	25 c. orange-brown and black	..	10	10
419	43	30 c. carmine-red and black	..	10	10
420	45	35 c. slate and emerald	..	10	10
421	46	40 c. brown and black	..	10	10
422	45	50 c. blue and grey-green	..	10	10
423	47	1 s. carmine and black	..	10	10
424	43	1 s. 25, slate and carmine	..	1·50	20
425	47	2 s. orange and deep green	..	50	20
426	48	5 s. deep bright blue	..	50	35
427		7 s. 50, green	..	65	4·50
428		10 s. carmine	..	1·25	4·50
429		20 s. sepia	..	2·00	5·00

The opt T **56** is set in two lines on Types 46/8.

(ii) *As T 57 on Nos. 390/3 (Independence)*

430		30 c. multicoloured		10	10
431		50 c. multicoloured	..	10	10
432		1 s. 30, multicoloured	..	10	10
433		2 s. 50, multicoloured		15	30
		a. Green omitted	..	70·00	
414/33			*Set of 20*	6·50	14·00

The opt T **57** is set in one line on No. 432.

For the set inscribed "UNITED REPUBLIC OF TANGANYIKA AND ZANZIBAR" see Nos. 124/7 of Tanganyika.

58 Axe, Spear and Dagger

59 Zanzibari with Rifle

(Litho German Bank Note Ptg Co, Leipzig)

1964 (21 June). *T 58/9 and similar designs inscr. "JAMHURI ZANZIBAR 1964". Multicoloured. P 13 × 13½ (vert) or 13½ × 13 (horiz).*

434		5 c. Type 58		20	10
435		10 c. Bow and arrow breaking chains	..	30	10
436		15 c. Type 58	..	30	10
437		20 c. As 10 c.	..	50	10
438		25 c. Type 59	..	50	10
439		30 c. Zanzibari breaking manacles	..	50	10
440		40 c. Type 59	..	50	10
441		50 c. As 30 c.	..	30	10
442		1 s. Zanzibari, flag and Sun	..	30	10
443		1 s. 30, Hands breaking chains (*horiz*)	..	30	60
444		2 s. Hand waving flag (*horiz*)	..	30	30
445		5 s. Map of Zanzibar and Pemba on flag (*horiz*)	..	55	1·50
446		10 s. Flag on Map	..	3·00	3·00
447		20 s. National flag (*horiz*)	..	3·00	16·00
434/47			*Set of 14*	9·00	20·00

COVER PRICES

Cover factors are quoted at the beginning of each country for most issues to 1945. An explanation of the system can be found on page x. The factors quoted do not, however, apply to philatelic covers.

---

68 Soldier and Maps

69 Building Construction

(Litho German Bank Note Ptg Co, Leipzig)

1965 (12 Jan). *First Anniv of Revolution. P 13 × 13½ (vert) or 13½ × 13 (horiz).*

448	68	20 c. apple-green and deep green		10	10
449	69	30 c. chocolate and yellow-orange	..	10	10
450	68	1 s. 30, light blue and ultramarine	..	10	10
451	69	2 s. 50, reddish violet and rose	..	10	15
448/51			*Set of 4*	30	30

70 Planting Rice

(Litho German Bank Note Ptg Co, Leipzig)

1965 (17 Oct). *Agricultural Development. T 70 and similar horiz design. P 13 × 12½.*

452	70	20 c. sepia and blue	..	10	1·00
453	—	30 c. sepia and magenta	..	10	1·00
454	—	1 s. 30, sepia and yellow-orange	..	30	2·00
455	70	2 s. 50, sepia and emerald	..	50	3·75
452/5			*Set of 4*	85	7·00

Design:—30 c., 1 s. 30, Hands holding rice.

72 Freighter, Tractor, Factory, and Open Book and Torch

73 Soldier

(Litho German Bank Note Ptg Co, Leipzig)

1966 (12 Jan). *2nd Anniv of Revolution. P 12½ × 13.*

456	72	20 c. multicoloured	..	20	20
457	72	50 c. multicoloured	..	15	20
458	72	1 s. 30, multicoloured	..	15	20
459	73	2 s. 50, multicoloured	..	25	65
456/9			*Set of 4*	65	1·10

For stamps with similar inscription or inscribed "TANZANIA" only, and with commemorative date 26th April 1966, see Nos. Z142/5 of TANZANIA.

74 Tree-felling

75 Zanzibar Street

(Litho German Bank Note Ptg Co, Leipzig)

1966 (5 June). *Horiz designs as T 74, and T 75. P 12½ × 13 (50 c., 10 s.) or 13 × 12½ (others).*

460		5 c. maroon and yellow-olive		30	80
461		10 c. brown-purple and bright emerald	..	30	80
462		15 c. brown-purple and light blue	..	30	80
463		20 c. ultramarine and light orange	..	20	20
464		25 c. maroon and orange-yellow	..	20	30
465		30 c. maroon and ochre-yellow	..	30	20
466		40 c. purple-brown and rose-pink	..	50	20
467		50 c. green and pale greenish yellow	..	50	20
468		1 s. maroon and bright blue	..	50	20
469		1 s. 30, maroon and turquoise	..	50	2·00
470		2 s. brown-purple and light blue-green	..	50	30
471		5 s. rose-red and pale blue	..	1·00	4·25
472		10 s. crimson and pale yellow	..	2·25	16·00
473		20 s. deep purple-brown and magenta	..	4·25	25·00
460/473			*Set of 14*	10·50	45·00

Designs:—5 c., 20 s. Type 74; 10 c., 1 s. Clove cultivation; 15, 40 c. Chair-making; 20 c., 5 s. Lumumba College; 25 c., 1 s. 30, Agriculture; 30 c., 2 s. Agricultural workers; 50 c., 10 s. Type 75.

---

81 "Education"

(Litho D.L.R.)

1966 (25 Sept). *Introduction of Free Education. P 13½ × 13.*

474	81	50 c. black, light blue and orange		10	1·00
475		1 s. 30, black, lt blue and yellow-green		15	1·75
476		2 s. 50, black, light blue and pink		40	4·50
474/6			*Set of 3*	60	6·50

82 A.S.P. Flag

(Litho D.L.R.)

1967 (5 Feb). *Tenth Anniv of Afro-Shirazi Party (A.S.P.). T 82 and similar multicoloured design. P 14.*

477	82	30 c. Type 82		10	1·00
478		50 c. Vice-President M. A. Karume of Tanzania, flag and crowd (*vert*)		10	1·00
479		1 s. 30, As 50 c.		10	2·00
480		2 s. 50, Type 82		30	3·00
477/80			*Set of 4*	45	6·50

84 Voluntary Workers

(Photo Delrieu)

1967 (20 Aug). *Voluntary Workers Brigade. P 12½ × 12.*

481	84	1 s. 30, multicoloured	..	15	2·25
482		2 s. 50, multicoloured	..	40	5·50

POSTAGE DUE STAMPS

D 1

Insufficiently prepaid. Postage due. 1 cent.

Insufficiently prepaid Postage due. 6 cents.

D 2

(Types D **1** and D **2** typo by the Government Printer)

1926–30. *Rouletted 10, with imperf sheet edges. No gum.*

D 1	D 1	1 c. black/*orange*	..	..	11·00	90·00
D 2		2 c. black/*orange*	..	..	4·50	40·00
D 3		3 c. black/*orange*	..	..	5·00	38·00
		a. "cent.s" for "cents."	..		£110	
D 4		6 c. black/*orange*	..	..	—	£7000
		a. "cent.s" for "cents."	..		—	£16000
D 5		9 c. black/*orange*	..	..	2·75	18·00
		a. "cent.s" for "cents."	..		18·00	65·00
D 6		12 c. black/*orange*	..	..	£9000	£8500
		a. "cent.s" for "cents."	..			
D 7		12 c. black/*green*	..	..	£1400	£600
		a. "cent.s" for "cents."	..		£3750	£1700
D 8		15 c. black/*orange*	..	..	2·75	20·00
		a. "cent.s" for "cents."	..		17·00	70·00
D 9		18 c. black/*salmon*	..	..	4·00	32·00
		a. "cent.s" for "cents."	..		30·00	95·00
D10		18 c. black/*orange*	..	..	13·00	50·00
		a. "cent.s" for "cents."	..		55·00	£150
D11		20 c. black/*orange*	..	..	4·00	45·00
		a. "cent.s" for "cents."	..		32·00	£120
D12		21 c. black/*orange*	..	..	3·50	26·00
		a. "cent.s" for "cents."	..		26·00	90·00
D13		25 c. black/*magenta*	..	..	£2500	£1300
		a. "cent.s" for "cents."	..		£6500	£3750
D14		25 c. black/*orange*	..	..	£10000	£10000
		a. "cent.s" for "cents."	..			
D15		31 c. black/*orange*	..	..	9·50	60·00
		a. "cent.s" for "cents."	..		48·00	
D16		50 c. black/*orange*	..	..	21·00	£120
		a. "cent.s" for "cents."	..		90·00	
D17		75 c. black/*orange*	..	..	65·00	£200
		a. "cent.s" for "cents."	..		£250	

Initial printings, except the 1 c. and 2 c., contained the error "cent.s" for "cents" on R. 4/1 in the sheets of 10 (2×5). The error was corrected on subsequent supplies of the 3 c., 9 c. and 15 c.

It is known that examples of these stamps used before early 1929 were left uncancelled on the covers. Unused examples of Nos. D4, D6/7 and D13/14 which are not in very fine condition, must be assumed to have been used.

1930–33. *Rouletted 5. No gum.*

D18	D 2	2 c. black/*salmon*	..	..	11·00	24·00
D19		3 c. black/*rose* ..		..	3·00	42·00
D21		6 c. black/*yellow*		..	3·00	28·00
D22		12 c. black/*blue* ..		..	4·00	22·00
D23		25 c. black/*rose* ..		..	9·00	55·00
D24		25 c. black/*lilac*..		..	12·00	42·00
D18/24		..		*Set of 6*	35·00	£180

D 3

(Typo D.L.R.)

1936 (1 Jan)–**62.** *Wmk Mult Script CA. P* 14.

D25	D 3	5 c. violet	..	2·50	6·50
		a. Chalk-surfaced paper (18.7.56)		30	13·00
D26		10 c. scarlet	..	2·50	2·75
		a. Chalk-surfaced paper (6.3.62)		30	5·50
D27		20 c. green	..	1·75	4·25
		a. Chalk-surfaced paper (6.3.62)		30	13·00
D28		30 c. brown	..	6·00	15·00
		a. Chalk-surfaced paper (18.7.56)		30	10·00
D29		40 c. ultramarine	..	6·00	22·00
		a. Chalk-surfaced paper (18.7.56)		40	22·00
D30		1 s. grey	..	6·00	26·00
		a. Chalk-surfaced paper (18.7.56)		1·00	17·00
D25/30			*Set of 6*	22·00	70·00
D25a/30a			*Set of 6*	2·40	70·00
D25/30 Perf "Specimen"			*Set of 6*	60·00	

See footnote after No. 413.

All Zanzibar issues were withdrawn on 1 January 1968 and replaced by Tanzania issues. Zanzibar stamps remained valid for postage in Zanzibar for a limited period.

TANZANIA

The United Republic of Tanganyika and Zanzibar, formed 26 April 1964, was renamed the United Republic of Tanzania on 29 October 1964.

Issues to No. 176, except Nos. Z142/5, were also valid in Kenya and Uganda.

(Currency. 100 cents = 1 shilling)

25 Hale Hydro-Electric Scheme

26 Tanzanian Flag

27 National Servicemen

33 Dar-es-Salaam Harbour   38 Arms of Tanzania

(Des V. Whiteley. Photo Harrison)

1965 (9 Dec). *T* 25/7, 33, 38 *and similar designs. P* 14 × 14½ (5 *c.*, 10 *c.*, 20 *c.*, 50 *c.*, 65 *c.*), 14½ × 14 (15 *c.*, 30 *c.*, 40 *c.*), *or* 14 (*others*).

128	5 c. ultramarine and yellow-orange	..	10	10
129	10 c. black, greenish yellow, green & blue	..	10	10
130	15 c. multicoloured	..	10	10
131	20 c. sepia, grey-green and greenish blue	..	10	10
132	30 c. black and red-brown	..	10	10
133	40 c. multicoloured	..	65	20
134	50 c. multicoloured	..	30	10
135	65 c. green, red-brown and blue	..	2·50	2·00
136	1 s. multicoloured	..	1·00	10
137	1 s. 30, multicoloured	..	5·50	85
138	2 s. blue and orange-brown	..	6·00	90
139	5 s. lake-brown, yellow-green and blue	..	80	20
140	10 s. olive-yellow, olive-green and blue	..	1·00	2·75
141	20 s. multicoloured	..	6·00	15·00
128/41		*Set of 14*	21·00	20·00

Designs: *Horiz* (as T 25)—20 c. Road-building; 50 c. Common Zebras, Manyara National Park; 65 c. Mt Kilimanjaro. *Vert* (as T 27)—30 c. Drum, spear, shield and stool; 40 c. Giraffes, Mikumi National Park. *Horiz* (As T 33)—1 s. 30, Skull of *Zinjanthropus* and excavations, Olduvai Gorge, 2 s. 50, Fishing; 5 s. Sisal industry; 10 s. State House, Dar-es-Salaam.

MINIMUM PRICE

The minimum price quote is 10p which represents a handling charge rather than a basis for valuing common stamps. For further notes about prices see introductory pages.

Z 39 Pres. Nyerere and First Vice-Pres. Karume within Bowl of Flame

Z 40 Hands supporting Bowl of Flame

(Des J. Ahmed (Type Z 39), G. Vasarhelyi (Type Z 40). Photo Enschedé)

1966 (26 April). *2nd Anniv of United Republic. P* 14 × 13.

Z142	Z 39	30 c. multicoloured	..	30	45
Z143	Z 40	50 c. multicoloured	..	30	45
Z144		1 s. 30, multicoloured	..	30	45
Z145	Z 39	2 s. 50, multicoloured	..	45	1·25
Z142/5			*Set of 4*	1·25	2·40

Nos. Z142/5 were on sale in Zanzibar only.

39 Black-footed Cardinalfish

40 Sobrinus Mudskipper

41 Lionfish

(Des Rena Fennessy. Photo Harrison)

1967 (9 Dec)–**73.** *Designs as T* 39/41. *Chalk-surfaced paper. P* 14 × 15 (5 *c.* to 70 *c.*) *or* 14½ (*others*).

142	5 c. magenta, yellow-olive and black	..	10	1·25
	a. Glazed, ordinary paper (22.1.71)		30	1·50
143	10 c. brown and bistre	..	10	10
	a. Glazed, ordinary paper (27.9.72)		30	2·00
144	15 c. grey, turquoise-blue and black	..	10	75
	a. Glazed, ordinary paper (22.1.71)		30	3·00
145	20 c. brown and turquoise-green	..	10	10
	a. Glazed, ordinary paper (16.7.73)		30	4·50
146	30 c. sage-green and black	..	20	10
	a. Glazed, ordinary paper (3.5.71)		7·50	2·75
147	40 c. yellow, chocolate and bright green	..	70	10
	a. Glazed, ordinary paper (10.2.71)		70	30
148	50 c. multicoloured	..	20	10
	a. Glazed, ordinary paper (10.2.71)		30	1·50
149	65 c. orange-yellow, bronze-green and black	..	2·75	4·25
150	70 c. multicoloured (15.9.69)	..	1·00	2·50
	a. Glazed, ordinary paper (22.1.71)		4·25	6·50
151	1 s. orange-brown, slate-blue and maroon	..	30	10
	a. Glazed, ordinary paper (3.2.71)		1·00	10
152	1 s. 30, multicoloured	..	5·00	10
153	1 s. 50, multicoloured (15.9.69)	..	4·75	50
	a. Glazed, ordinary paper (27.9.72)		2·25	10
154	2 s. 50, multicoloured	..	2·75	2·75
	a. Glazed, ordinary paper (27.9.72)		11·00	10
155	5 s. greenish yellow, black & turquoise-grn	..	5·00	2·75
	a. Glazed, ordinary paper (12.12.70*)		3·25	10
156	10 s. multicoloured	..	1·25	2·75
	a. Glazed, ordinary paper (*dull blue-green background*) (12.12.70*)		1·50	10
	ab. Deep dull green background (12.9.73)		1·75	50
157	20 s. multicoloured	..	1·75	6·00
	a. Glazed, ordinary paper (12.12.70*)		7·00	15
142/57		*Set of 16*	22·00	21·00
142a/57a		*Set of 14*	35·00	20·00

*Earliest known postmark date.

Designs: *Horiz as T* 39/40—15 c. White-spotted Puffer; 20 c. Thorny Seahorse; 30 c. Dusky Batfish; 40 c. Black-spotted Sweetlips; 50 c. Blue Birdwrasse; 65 c. Bennett's Butterflyfish; 70 c. Black-tipped Grouper. *Horiz as T* 41:—1 s. 30, Powder-blue Surgeonfish; 1 s. 50, Yellow-finned Fusilier; 2 s. 50, Emperor Snapper; 5 s. Moorish Idol; 10 s. Painted Triggerfish; 20 s. Horned Squirrelfish.

On chalk-surfaced paper all values except the 30 c. exist with PVA gum as well as gum arabic, but the 70 c. and 1 s. 50 exist with PVA gum only. Stamps on glazed, ordinary paper come only with PVA gum.

53 *Papilio hornimani*

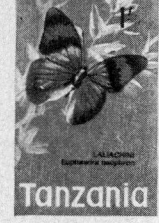
54 *Euphaedra neophron* (55)

(Des Rena Fennessy. Photo Harrison)

1973 (10 Dec)–**78.** *Various vert designs as T* 53/4.

(a) Size as T 53. *P* 14½ × 14.

158	5 c. light yellow-olive, lt violet-blue & black	60	30
159	10 c. multicoloured	60	15
160	15 c. light violet-blue and black	60	30
161	20 c. reddish cinnamon, orange-yellow & blk	70	15
162	30 c. yellow, orange and black	70	10
	a. Bistre-yellow, orange & black (20.4.78)	2·25	60
163	40 c. multicoloured	70	15
164	50 c. multicoloured	1·00	15
165	60 c. lt grey-brown, lemon & reddish brown	1·50	20
166	70 c. turquoise-green, pale orange and black	1·50	20

(b) Size as T 54. *P* 14.

167	1 s. multicoloured	1·50	15
168	1 s. 50, multicoloured	3·00	45
169	2 s. 50, multicoloured	3·25	80
170	5 s. multicoloured (*brt green background*)	3·00	95
	a. Apple-green background (20.4.78)	5·00	60
171	10 s. multicoloured	3·75	60
172	20 s. multicoloured	5·50	13·00
158/72		*Set of 15*	25·00	20·00

Butterflies:—10 c. *Colotis ione*; 15 c. *Amauris hyalites* (s sp *makuyuensis*); 20 c. *Libythea labdaca* (s sp *laius*); 30 c. *Danaus chrysippus*; 40 c. *Asterope rosa*; 50 c. *Axiocerses styx*; 60 c. *Terias hecabe*; 70 c. *Acraea insignis*; 1 s. 50, *Precis octavia*; 2 s. 50, *Charaxes eupale*; 5 s. *Charaxes pollux*; 10 s. *Salamis parhassus*; 20 s. *Papilio ophidicephalus*.

Nos. 159 and 164 exist in coils, constructed from normal sheets.

A used example of No. 167 has been seen apparently showing the yellow colour omitted.

1975 (17 Nov). *Nos.* 165, 168/9 *and* 172 *surch as T* 55.

173	80 c. on 60 c. *Terias hecabe*	..	2·00	2·00
174	2 s. on 1 s. 50, *Precis octavia*	..	3·75	6·00
175	3 s. on 2 s. 50, *Charaxes eupale*	..	14·00	27·00
176	40 s. on 20 s. *Papilio ophidicephalus*	..	6·50	12·00
173/6		*Set of 4*	24·00	42·00

1976 (15 Apr). *Telecommunications Development. As Nos.* 56/60 *of Kenya but inscr* "TANZANIA".

177	50 c. Microwave Tower	..	10	10
178	1 s. Cordless switchboard	..	15	10
179	2 s. Telephones	..	25	30
180	3 s. Message Switching Centre	..	30	40
177/80		*Set of 4*	70	70
MS181	120 × 120 mm. Nos. 177/80	..	1·10	1·50

Nos. 177/8 and 180 exist imperforate from stock dispersed by the liquidator of Format International Security Printers Ltd.

1976 (5 July). *Olympic Games, Montreal. As Nos* 61/5 *of Kenya but inscr* "TANZANIA".

182	50 c. Akii Bua, Ugandan hurdler	..	10	10
183	1 s. Filbert Bayi, Tanzanian runner	..	15	10
184	2 s. Steve Muchoki, Kenyan boxer	..	25	40
185	3 s. Olympic flame and East Africa flags	..	30	40
182/5		*Set of 4*	70	70
MS186	129 × 154 mm. Nos. 182/5	..	2·50	1·75

Nos. 182/4 exist imperforate from stock dispersed by the liquidator of Format International Security Printers Ltd.

1976 (4 Oct). *Railway Transport. As Nos.* 66/70 *of Kenya but inscr* "TANZANIA".

187	50 c. Diesel-hydraulic train, Tanzania–Zambia Railway	..	20	10
188	1 s. Nile Bridge, Uganda ..	..	30	10
189	2 s. Nakuru Station, Kenya	..	60	30
190	3 s. Uganda Railway Class A locomotive, 1896 ..	..	70	45
187/90		*Set of 4*	1·60	75
MS191	154×103 mm. Nos. 187/90	..	5·00	3·50

Nos. 187/91 exist imperforate from stock dispersed by the liquidator of Format International Security Printers Ltd.

1977 (10 Jan). *Game Fish of East Africa. As Nos.* 71/5 *of Kenya but inscr* "TANZANIA".

192	50 c. Nile Perch	..	30	10
193	1 s. Nile Mouthbrooder	..	35	10
194	3 s. Sailfish	..	1·00	40
195	5 s. Black Marlin ..	..	1·10	60
192/5		*Set of 4*	2·50	1·00
MS196	153×129 mm. Nos. 192/5	..	3·25	2·50

1977 (15 Jan). *Second World Black and African Festival of Arts and Culture, Nigeria. As Nos* 76/80 *of Kenya but inscr* "TANZANIA".

197	50 c. Maasai Manyatta (village), Kenya	15	10
198	1 s. "Heartbeat of Africa" (Ugandan dancers)	15	10
199	2 s. Makonde sculpture	40	70
200	3 s. "Early Man and Technology" (skinning hippopotamus)	45	1·00
197/200		*Set of 4*	1·00	1·75
MS201	132 × 190 mm. Nos. 197/200	1·10	3·00

1977 (5 Apr). *25th Anniv of Safari Rally. As Nos* 81/5 *of Kenya but inscr* "TANZANIA".

202	50 c. Rally-car and villagers	..	15	10
203	1 s. Pres. Kenyatta starting rally	..	15	10
204	2 s. Car fording river	..	30	40
205	5 s. Car and elephants	..	1·00	1·00
202/5		*Set of 4*	1·40	1·50
MS206	126 × 93 mm. Nos. 202/5 ..	..	1·75	2·00

1977 (30 June). *Centenary of Ugandan Church. As Nos* 86/90 *of Kenya but inscr* "TANZANIA".

207	50 c. Canon Kivebulaya	..	10	10
208	1 s. Modern Namirembe Cathedral	..	15	10
209	2 s. The first Cathedral	..	30	40
210	5 s. Early congregation, Kigezi	..	60	1·10
207/10		*Set of 4*	1·00	1·50
MS211	126 × 89 mm. Nos. 207/10 ..	..	1·00	1·75

1977 (26 Sept). *Endangered Species. As Nos. 96/101 of Kenya but inscr "TANZANIA".*

212	50 c. Pancake Tortoise	40	10
213	1 s. Nile Crocodile	45	10
214	2 s. Hunter's Hartebeest	1·40	55
215	3 s. Red Colobus monkey	2·00	40
216	5 s. Dugong	2·50	1·50
212/16		Set of 5	6·00	2·50
MS217	127 × 101 mm. Nos. 213/16	4·75	5·50

56 Prince Philip and President Nyerere

(Des G. Vasarhelyi. Litho Questa)

1977 (23 Nov). *Silver Jubilee. T 56 and similar horiz designs. Multicoloured. P 14 × 13½.*

218	50 c. Type **56**	10	10
219	5 s. Pres. Nyerere with Queen and Prince Philip	15	25
220	10 s. Jubilee emblem and Commonwealth flags	25	40
221	20 s. The Crowning	40	60
218/21		Set of 4	75	1·25
MS222	128 × 102 mm. Nos. 218/21	75	1·50

57 Improvements in Rural Living Standards

(Des P. Ndembo. Litho J.W.)

1978 (5 Feb). *First Anniv of Chama Cha Mapinduzi (New Revolutionary Party). T 57 and similar horiz designs. P 13½ × 14.*

223	50 c. multicoloured	10	10
224	1 s. multicoloured	10	10
225	3 s. multicoloured	35	60
226	5 s. black, light green and greenish yellow	55	85
223/6		Set of 4	1·00	1·40
MS227	142 × 106 mm. Nos. 223/6	1·00	1·40

Designs:—1 s. Flag raising ceremony, Zanzibar; 3 s. Handing over of TANU headquarters, Dodoma; 5 s. Chairman Julius Nyerere.

1978 (17 Apr). *World Cup Football Championship, Argentina. As Nos. 122/6 of Kenya but inscr "TANZANIA".*

228	50 c. Joe Kadenge and forwards	10	10
229	1 s. Mohamed Chuma and cup presentation	10	10
230	2 s. Omari Kidevu and goalmouth scene	30	60
231	3 s. Polly Ouma and forwards	40	75
228/31		Set of 4	75	1·25
MS232	136 × 81 mm. Nos. 228/31	2·00	1·75

25th **ANNIVERSARY** CORONATION	25th ANNIVERSARY CORONATION
(58)	(59)
2nd **JUNE** 1953	2nd JUNE 1953

1978 (2 June). *25th Anniv of Coronation. Nos. 218/22 optd.*

A. As T **58**. P 14×13½

233A	50 c. Type **56**	10	10
234A	5 s. Pres. Nyerere with Queen and Prince Philip	20	30
235A	10 s. Jubilee emblem and Commonwealth flags	25	40
236A	20 s. The Crowning	40	70
233A/6A		Set of 4	75	1·25
MS237A	128×102 mm. Nos. 233A/6A	75	1·25

B. As T **59**. P 12×11½.

233B	50 c. Type **56**	10	10
234B	5 s. Pres. Nyerere with Queen and Prince Philip	20	30
235B	10 s. Jubilee emblem and Commonwealth flags	25	40
236B	20 s. The Crowning	40	70
233B/6B		Set of 4	75	1·25
MS237B	128×102 mm. Nos. 233B/6B	75	1·25

60 "Do not Drink and Drive"

61 Lake Manyara Hotel

(Des and litho J.W.)

1978 (1 July). *Road Safety. T 60 and similar vert designs. P 13½ × 13.*

238	50 c. multicoloured	15	10
239	1 s. multicoloured	20	10
240	3 s. orange-red, black and light brown	70	65
241	5 s. multicoloured	1·00	1·25
238/41		Set of 4	1·90	1·75
MS242	92 × 129 mm. Nos. 238/41. P 14	2·00	2·00

Designs:—1 s. "Show courtesy to young, old and crippled"; 3 s. "Observe the Highway Code"; 5 s. "Do not drive a faulty vehicle".

(Des M. Raza. Litho B.W.)

1978 (11 Sept). *Game Lodges. T 61 and similar horiz designs. Multicoloured. P 13½×13.*

243	50 c. Type **61**	10	10
244	1 s. Lobo Wildlife Lodge	15	10
245	3 s. Ngorongoro Crater Lodge	25	35
246	5 s. Ngorongoro Wildlife Lodge	35	55
247	10 s. Mafia Island Lodge	50	90
248	20 s. Mikumi Wildlife Lodge	1·00	2·50
243/8		Set of 6	2·00	4·00
MS249	118 × 112 mm. Nos. 243/8	6·00	7·50

62 "Racial Suppression"

63 Fokker F.27 Friendship

(Des local artist; adapted G. Hutchins. Litho Harrison)

1978 (24 Oct). *International Anti-Apartheid Year. T 62 and similar vert designs. P 14½ × 14.*

250	50 c. multicoloured	10	10
251	1 s. black, yellowish green and yellow	10	10
252	2 s. 50, multicoloured	30	75
253	5 s. multicoloured	60	1·10
250/3		Set of 4	1·00	1·75
MS254	127 × 132 mm. Nos. 250/3	1·25	2·75

Designs:—1 s. "Racial division"; 2 s. 50, "Racial harmony"; 5 s. "Fall of suppression and rise of freedom".

(Des J. Mzinga; adapted J.W. Litho Walsall)

1978 (28 Dec). *75th Anniv of Powered Flight. T 63 and similar horiz designs. Multicoloured. P 13½.*

255	50 c. Type **63**	20	10
256	1 s. De Havilland D.H.84 Dragon Mk I on Zanzibar Island, 1930's	25	10
257	2 s. Concorde	1·00	60
258	5 s. Wright brothers' Flyer I, 1903	1·25	1·00
255/8		Set of 4	2·40	1·60
MS259	133×97 mm. Nos. 255/8	2·75	3·50

64 Corporation Emblem

(Des local artists; adapted BG Studio. Litho Harrison)

1979 (3 Feb). *1st Anniv of Tanzania Posts and Telecommunications Corporation. T 64 and similar horiz design. Multicoloured. P 14½ × 14.*

260	50 c. Type **64**	10	10
261	5 s. Headquarters buildings	50	70
MS262	82 × 97 mm. Nos. 260/1	1·00	1·50

65 Pres. Nyerere (patron of National I.Y.C. Committee) with Children
(66)

(Des J. Mzinga. Litho B.W.)

1979 (25 June). *International Year of the Child. T 65 and similar horiz designs. Multicoloured. P 14½.*

263	50 c. Type **65**	10	10
264	1 s. Day care centre	15	10
265	2 s. "Immunisation" (child being vaccinated)	25	45
266	5 s. National I.Y.C. Committee emblem	40	80
263/6		Set of 4	80	1·25
MS267	127 × 91 mm. Nos. 263/6	1·25	1·25

1979 (Aug–Sept*). *Nos. 159 and 166 surch as T 66 (No. 269 has horiz bar through original value).*

268	10 c. + 30 c. multicoloured	1·50	1·00
	a. Surch inverted	†	
269	50 c. on 70 c. turquoise-green, pale orge & bl.	2·50	2·25

* The earliest known postmark date for No. 268 is 15 September and for No. 269 30 August.

The face value of No. 268 was 40 c.; the 30 c. surcharge being added to the original 10 c., which was not obliterated. This method was adopted because of difficulties during the actual surcharging. On No. 269 the 70 c. face value is obliterated by a bar.

Examples of No. 268a were used at Singida in December 1979.

67 Planting Young Trees   **68** Mwenge Satellite Earth Station

(Des J. Mzinga. Litho J.W.)

1979 (24 Sept). *Forest Preservation. T 67 and similar vert designs. Multicoloured. P 14 × 14½.*

270	50 c. Type **67**	15	10
271	1 s. Replacing dead trees with saplings	15	10
272	2 s. Rainfall cycle	55	65
273	5 s. Forest fire warning	90	1·75
270/3		Set of 4	1·60	2·25

(Des and litho J.W.)

1979 (14 Dec). *Opening of Mwenge Satellite Earth Station. P 13½.*

274	**68** 10 c. multicoloured	10	10
275	40 c. multicoloured	15	10
276	50 c. multicoloured	15	10
277	1 s. multicoloured	25	20
274/7		Set of 4	55	40

69 Tabata Dispensary, Dar-es-Salaam

(Litho J.W.)

1980 (10 Apr). *75th Anniv of Rotary International. T 69 and similar horiz designs. Multicoloured. P 13.*

278	50 c. Type **69**	10	10
279	1 s. Ngomvu Village water project	15	10
280	5 s. Flying Doctor service (plane donation)	55	70
281	20 s. Torch and 75th Anniversary emblem	1·00	2·50
278/81		Set of 4	1·50	3·00
MS282	120 × 101 mm. Nos. 278/81. P 14	1·75	3·00

70 Zanzibar 1896 2 r. Stamp and 1964 25 c. Definitive
'LONDON 1980' PHILATELIC EXHIBITION (71)

(Des J.W. Litho Questa)

1980 (21 Apr). *Death Centenary of Sir Rowland Hill (1979). T 70 and similar multicoloured designs. P 14.*

283	40 c. Type **70**	10	10
284	50 c. Tanganyika 1962 Independence 50 c. commemorative and man attaching stamp to letter (vert)	10	10
285	10 s. Tanganyika 1922 25 c. stamp and 1961 1 s. 30, definitive	50	1·00
286	20 s. Penny Black and Sir Rowland Hill (vert)	80	1·60
283/6		Set of 4	1·25	2·50
MS287	158 × 120 mm. Nos. 283/6	1·25	2·50

1980 (5 May). *"London 1980" International Stamp Exhibition. Nos. 283/7 optd with T 71.*

288	40 c. Type **71**	10	10
289	50 c. Tanganyika 1962 Independence 50 c. commemorative and man attaching stamp to letter	10	10
290	10 s. Tanganyika 1922 25 c. stamp and 1961 1 s. 30, definitive	50	1·00
291	20 s. Penny Black and Sir Rowland Hill	80	1·60
288/91		Set of 4	1·25	2·50
MS292	158 × 120 mm. Nos. 288/91	1·25	2·50

District 920 - 55th Annual Conference, Arusha, Tanzania

(72)

1980 (23 June). *Annual Conference of District 920, Rotary International, Arusha. Nos. 278/82 optd as T* **72**.
293	50 c. Type **69**			20	10
294	1 s. Ngomvu Village water project			20	10
295	5 s. Flying Doctor service (plane donation)			45	70
296	20 s. Torch and 75th Anniversary of Rotary International Emblem			1·00	2·50
293/6			*Set of 4*	1·75	3·00
MS297	120 × 101 mm. Nos. 293/6			1·75	3·00

73 Conference, Tanzanian Posts and Telecommunications Corporation and U.P.U. Emblems

(Des and litho J.W.)

1980 (1 July). *P.A.P.U. (Pan-African Postal Union) Plenipotentiary Conference, Arusha. P* 13.
298	**73**	50 c. black and bright violet		10	10
299		1 s. black and ultramarine		10	10
300		5 s. black and orange-red		50	70
301		10 s. black and blue-green		1·00	1·60
298/301			*Set of 4*	1·50	2·25

74 Gidamis Shahanga (marathon)

(Litho J.W.)

1980 (18 Aug). *Olympic Games, Moscow. T* **74** *and similar horiz designs. Multicoloured. P* 13.
302	50 c. Type **74**			10	15
	a. Horiz strip of 4. Nos. 302/5			1·60	
303	1 s. Nzael Kyomo (sprints)			15	15
304	10 s. Zakayo Malekwa (javelin)			60	1·00
305	20 s. William Lyimo (boxing)			1·00	1·75
302/5			*Set of 4*	1·60	2·25
MS306	172 × 117 mm. Nos. 302/305. P 14			1·25	2·25

Nos. 302/305 were printed either in separate sheets or together, *se-tenant*, in horizontal strips of 4 throughout the sheet.

75 Spring Hare   **76** Impala

(Des Rena Fennessy)

1980 (1 Oct)–**85**. *Wildlife. Horiz designs as T* **75** (10 c. to 80 c.) *or T* **76** (1 s. to 40 s.). *Multicoloured.*

(*a*) Litho B.W. P 14 (10 c. to 80 c.) or 14½ (1 s. to 40 s.)
307	10 c. Type **75**			10	15
308	20 c. Large-spotted Genet			10	15
309	40 c. Banded Mongoose			10	10
310	50 c. Ratel (light blue panel at foot)			10	10
311	75 c. Large-toothed Rock Hyrax			20	15
312	80 c. Leopard (buff sky)			30	15
313	1 s. Type **76**			20	10
314	1 s. 50, Giraffe			30	20
315	2 s. Common Zebra			30	20
316	3 s. Buffalo			30	20
317	5 s. Lion			40	30
318	10 s. Black Rhinoceros			75	1·25
319	20 s. African Elephant			90	1·40
320	40 s. Cheetah			1·00	3·00
307/20			*Set of 14*	4·25	6·50

(*b*) Litho J.W. P 14 (50 c., 80 c.) or 14×14½ (others) (1984–85)
320*a*	50 c. Ratel (turquoise-blue panel at foot)			1·50	40
320*b*	80 c. Leopard (yellow sky)				
320*c*	1 s. Type **76**			1·50	40
	ca. Perf 13½			15·00	5·00
	cab. Booklet pane of 4 with margins on three sides			50·00	
320*d*	1 s. 50, Giraffe			7·00	4·00
320*e*	2 s. Common Zebra			4·00	3·25
	ea. Perf 13½			15·00	5·00
	eab. Booklet pane of 4 with margins on three sides			50·00	
320*f*	3 s. Buffalo			4·50	6·00
	fa. Perf 13½			15·00	5·00
	fab. Booklet pane of 4 with margins on three sides			50·00	
320*g*	5 s. Lion			7·50	9·00

Both formats of the Waddington printings are slightly smaller than the Bradbury Wilkinson stamps so that Nos. 320*a*/*b* measure 19½×16 mm, instead of 20×16½ mm, and the larger designs 40×23½ mm, instead of 40½×24 mm. The Swahili inscriptions on the 1 s. and 2 s. appear as one word on the Bradbury Wilkinson printings and as two words on those produced by Waddington.

Booklet panes Nos. 320cab, 320eab and 320fab have narrow margins at left, top and bottom.

1980 (22 Nov). *Nos. O41 and O43 with "OFFICIAL" opt Type* O 1 *obliterated by horizontal line.*
320*h*	10 c. multicoloured	
320*i*	40 c. multicoloured	

Nos. 320*h*/*i* exist on commercial mail from Morogoro. The date is that of the earliest postmark reported.

ROYAL WEDDING
H.R.H. PRINCE CHARLES
29th JULY 1981

77 Ngorongoro Conservation Area Authority Emblem   (**78**)

(Des D. Kyungu. Litho J.W.)

1981 (2 Feb). *60th Anniv of Ngorongoro and Serengeti National Parks. T* **77** *and similar horiz designs. P* 13.
321	50 c. multicoloured			10	10
322	1 s. black, gold and deep blue-green			10	10
323	5 s. multicoloured			30	60
324	20 s. multicoloured			80	2·25
321/4			*Set of 4*	1·10	2·75

Designs:—1 s. Tanzania National Parks emblem; 5 s. Friends of the Serengeti emblem; 20 s. Friends of Ngorongoro emblem.

Nos. 321/4 exist overprinted "75th ANNIVERSARY GIRL GUIDES 1910 1985" or "CONGRATULATIONS TO THE DUKE & DUCHESS OF YORK ON THE OCCASION OF THEIR MARRIAGE", but there is no evidence that these overprints were available from post offices in Tanzania.

1981 (29 July). *Royal Wedding. Nos. 220/1 optd with T* **78**.
325	10 s. Jubilee emblem and Commonwealth flags			35	60
326	20 s. Crowning			55	80
MS327	88×97 mm. Nos. 325/6			3·00	3·00

79 Mail Runner

(Des D. Kyungu. Litho State Printing Works, Moscow)

1981 (21 Oct). *Commonwealth Postal Administrations Conference, Arusha. T* **79** *and similar horiz designs. Multicoloured. P* 12½ × 12.
328	50 c. Type **79**			10	10
329	1 s. Letter sorting			15	15
330	5 s. Letter Post symbols			40	1·00
331	10 s. Flags of Commonwealth nations			75	2·00
328/31			*Set of 4*	1·25	3·00
MS332	130×100 mm. Nos. 328/31			1·40	3·00

80 Morris Nyunyusa (blind drummer)

(Des and litho Harrison)

1981 (30 Nov). *International Year for Disabled Persons. T* **80** *and similar horiz designs. Multicoloured. P* 14.
333	50 c. Type **80**			25	10
334	1 s. Mgulani Rehabilitation Centre, Dar-es-Salaam			30	10
335	5 s. Aids for disabled persons			1·50	2·25
336	10 s. Disabled children cleaning school compound			2·25	3·75
333/6			*Set of 4*	3·75	6·00

81 President Mwalimu Julius K. Nyerere   **82** Ostrich

(Litho J.W.)

1982 (13 Jan). *20th Anniv of Independence. T* **81** *and similar horiz designs. Multicoloured. P* 13 × 13½.
337	50 c. Type **81**			10	10
338	1 s. Electricity plant, Mtoni			10	10
339	3 s. Sisal industry			35	90
340	10 s. "Universal primary education"			80	2·25
337/40			*Set of 4*	1·25	3·00
MS341	120×85 mm. Nos. 337/40			1·25	3·00

(Des and litho J.W.)

1982 (25 Jan). *Birds. T* **82** *and similar vert designs. Multicoloured. P* 13½ × 13.
342	50 c. Type **82**			80	10
343	1 s. Secretary Bird			85	10
344	5 s. Kori Bustard			3·00	2·75
345	10 s. Saddle-bill Stork			3·75	5·50
342/5			*Set of 4*	7·50	7·50

83 Jella Mtaga

(Des P. Ndembo. Litho J.W.)

1982 (2 June). *World Cup Football Championship, Spain. T* **83** *and similar horiz designs. Multicoloured. P* 14.
346	50 c. Type **83**			30	10
347	1 s. Football stadium			35	10
348	10 s. Diego Maradona			3·00	3·00
349	20 s. FIFA emblem			4·75	5·00
346/9			*Set of 4*	7·50	7·50
MS350	130×100 mm. Nos. 346/9			8·00	8·00

Nos. 346/9 exist overprinted "CONGRATULATIONS TO THE DUKE & DUCHESS OF YORK ON THE OCCASION OF THEIR MARRIAGE", but there is no evidence that these overprints were available from post offices in Tanzania.

84 "Jade" of Seronera (cheetah) with Cubs

(Des and litho Harrison)

1982 (15 July). *Animal Personalities. T* **84** *and similar horiz designs. Multicoloured. P* 14.
351	50 c. Type **84**			20	10
352	1 s. Female Golden Jackal and cubs (incorrectly inscr "Wild dog")			30	10
353	5 s. "Fifi" and two sons of "Gombe" (chimpanzees)			50	1·75
354	10 s. "Bahati" of Lake Manyara with twins, "Rashidi" and "Ramadhani" (elephants)			1·25	2·75
351/4			*Set of 4*	2·00	4·25
MS355	120×89 mm. Nos. 351/4. P 14½			2·25	5·00

85 Brick-laying   **86** Ploughing Field

(Des P. Ndembo. Litho J.W.)

1982 (25 Aug). *75th Anniv of Boy Scout Movement. T* **85** *and similar horiz designs. Multicoloured. P* 14.
356	50 c. Type **85**			15	10
357	1 s. Camping			20	10
358	10 s. Tracing signs			1·25	2·00
359	20 s. Lord Baden-Powell			1·75	3·50
356/9			*Set of 4*	3·00	5·00
MS360	130×100 mm. Nos. 356/9			3·50	5·50

No. **MS**360 exists overprinted "75th ANNIVERSARY GIRL GUIDES 1910–1985", but there is no evidence that this overprint was available from post offices in Tanzania.

(Des P. Ndembo. Litho J.W.)

1982 (16 Oct). *World Food Day. T* **86** *and similar horiz designs. Multicoloured. P* 14.
361	50 c. Type **86**			10	10
362	1 s. Dairy farming			10	10
363	5 s. Maize farming			45	60
364	10 s. Grain storage			75	1·25
361/4			*Set of 4*	1·10	1·75
MS365	129×99 mm. Nos. 361/4			1·60	2·25

87 Immunization

(Des P. Ndembo. Litho State Printing Works, Moscow)

1982 (1 Dec). *Centenary of Robert Koch's Discovery of Tubercle Bacillus. T* **87** *and similar horiz designs. Multicoloured. P* 12½ × 12.
366	50 c. Type **87**			15	10
367	1 s. Dr. Robert Koch			20	10
368	5 s. International Union Against TB emblem			65	1·25
369	10 s. World Health Organization emblem			1·25	2·50
366/9			*Set of 4*	2·00	3·50

88 Letter Post

(Litho State Printing Works, Moscow)

1983 (3 Feb). *5th Anniv of Posts and Telecommunications Corporation. T 88 and similar horiz designs. Multicoloured. P 12.*

370	50 c. Type 88	..	10	10
371	1 s. Training institute	..	10	10
372	5 s. Satellite communications	..	45	90
373	10 s. U.P.U., I.T.U. and T.P.T.C.C. (Tanzania Posts and Telecommunications Corporation) emblems ..	..	75	2·00
370/3		*Set of* 4	1·25	2·75
MS374	126 × 96 mm. Nos. 370/3 ..	..	1·50	3·00

89 Pres. Mwalimu Julius Nyerere

(Litho J.W.)

1983 (14 Mar). *Commonwealth Day. T 89 and similar horiz designs. Multicoloured. P 14.*

375	50 c. Type 89	..	10	10
376	1 s. Athletics and boxing	..	15	10
377	5 s. Flags of Commonwealth countries	..	40	90
378	10 s. Pres. Nyerere and members of British Royal Family	..	70	1·90
375/8		*Set of* 4	1·10	2·75
MS379	121 × 100 mm. Nos. 375/8 ..	..	1·10	2·75

Nos. 375/8 exist overprinted "CONGRATULATIONS TO THE DUKE & DUCHESS OF YORK ON THE OCCASION OF THEIR MARRIAGE", but there is no evidence that these overprints were available from post offices in Tanzania.

90 Eastern and Southern African Management
Institute, Arusha, Tanzania

(Des P. Ndembo. Litho State Ptg Wks, Moscow)

1983 (12 Sept). *25th Anniv of the Economic Commission for Africa. T 90 and similar horiz designs. Multicoloured. P 12½ × 12.*

380	50 c. Type 90	..	15	10
381	1 s. 25th Anniversary inscription and U.N. logo	..	20	10
382	5 s. Mineral collections	..	2·75	2·75
383	10 s. E.C.A. Silver Jubilee logo and O.A.U. flag	..	2·75	3·50
380/3		*Set of* 4	5·25	5·75
MS384	132 × 102 mm. Nos. 380/3 ..	..	5·75	5·75

91 Telephone Cables

(Des P. Ndembo. Litho J.W.)

1983 (17 Oct). *World Communications Year. T 91 and similar horiz designs. Multicoloured. P 14.*

385	50 c. Type 91	..	15	10
386	1 s. W.C.Y. logo	..	15	10
387	5 s. Postal service	..	60	1·50
388	10 s. Microwave tower	..	80	2·50
385/8		*Set of* 4	1·50	3·75
MS389	102 × 92 mm. Nos. 385/88 ..	..	1·50	3·75

92 Bagamoyo Boma

(Des J. de Silva and P. Ndembo. Litho State Ptg Wks, Moscow)

1983 (12 Dec). *Historical Buildings. T 92 and similar horiz designs. Multicoloured. P 12½ × 12.*

390	1 s. Type 92	..	10	10
391	1 s. 50, Beit el Ajaib, Zanzibar	..	15	25
392	5 s. Anglican Cathedral, Zanzibar ..	..	40	1·00
393	10 s. Original German Government House and present State House, Dar-es-Salaam	..	75	2·00
390/3		*Set of* 4	1·25	3·00
MS394	130 × 100 mm. Nos. 390/3 ..	..	1·25	3·00

93 Sheikh Abeid Amani Karume
(founder of Afro-Shirazi Party)

(Des P. Ndembo. Litho J.W.)

1984 (18 June). *20th Anniv of Zanzibar Revolution. T 93 and similar horiz designs. Multicoloured. P 14.*

395	1 s. Type 93	..	10	10
396	1 s. 50, Clove farming	..	15	25
397	5 s. Symbol of Industrial Development	..	40	1·00
398	10 s. New housing schemes	..	75	2·00
395/8		*Set of* 4	1·25	3·00
MS399	130 × 100 mm. 15 s. *Mapinduzi* (ferry) and map		1·25	2·50

94 Boxing

(Des P. Ndembo. Litho State Ptg Wks, Moscow)

1984 (6 Aug). *Olympic Games, Los Angeles. T 94 and similar horiz designs. Multicoloured. P 12½ × 12.*

400	1 s. Type 94	..	10	10
401	1 s. 50, Running	..	15	10
402	5 s. Basketball	..	70	60
403	20 s. Football	..	1·60	2·25
400/3		*Set of* 4	2·25	2·75
MS404	130 × 100 mm. Nos. 400/3 ..	..	2·25	2·75

95 Icarus in Flight

(Des P. Ndembo. Litho J.W.)

1984 (15 Nov). *40th Anniv of International Civil Aviation Organization. T 95 and similar horiz designs. Multicoloured. P 13 × 12½.*

405	1 s. Type 95	..	10	10
406	1 s. 50, Douglas DC-10, Boeing 737 aircraft and air traffic controller	..	15	20
407	5 s. Boeing 737 undergoing maintenance	..	55	1·25
408	10 s. I.C.A.O. badge	..	1·10	2·00
405/8		*Set of* 4	1·75	3·25
MS409	130 × 100 mm. Nos. 405/8 ..	..	1·90	3·25

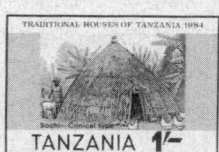

96 Sochi – Conical House

(Des P. Ndembo. Litho State Ptg Wks, Moscow)

1984 (20 Dec). *Traditional Houses. T 96 and similar horiz designs. Multicoloured. P 12½ × 12.*

410	1 s. Type 96	..	10	10
411	1 s. 50, Isyenga – circular type	..	15	20
412	5 s. Tembe – flatroofed type	..	40	1·25
413	10 s. Banda – coastal type	..	70	2·00
410/13		*Set of* 4	1·10	3·25
MS414	129 × 99 mm. Nos. 410/13 ..	..	1·50	3·25

97 Production of Cotton
Textiles

(Des P. Ndembo. Litho J.W.)

1985 (1 Apr). *5th Anniv of Southern African Development Co-ordination Conference. T 97 and similar horiz designs. Multicoloured. P 14.*

415	1 s. 50, Type 97	..	30	15
416	4 s. Diamond mining	..	2·00	1·50
417	5 s. Map of member countries and means of communication	..	2·00	1·50
418	20 s. Flags and signatures of member countries	..	2·75	4·00
415/18		*Set of* 4	6·25	6·50
MS419	110 × 104 mm. Nos. 415/18 ..	..	8·00	8·00

98 Tortoise

(Des P. Ndembo (15s., 20s.), J. de Silva (others). Litho J.W.)

1985 (8 May). *Rare Animals of Zanzibar. T 98 and similar multicoloured designs. P 12½ × 13 (17 s. 50) or 13 × 12½ (others).*

420	1 s. Type 98	..	50	15
421	4 s. Leopard ..	..	2·25	1·50
422	10 s. Civet Cat	..	2·75	3·75
423	17 s. 50, Red Colobus Monkey (*vert*).	..	3·50	5·50
420/3		*Set of* 4	8·00	9·75
MS424	110 × 93 mm. 15 s. Black Rhinoceros; 20 s. Giant Ground Pangolin		2·00	3·50

IMPERFORATE STAMPS. Nos. 425/9, 430/4, 456/68, 474/8, 508/11 and 517/21 exist imperforate from restricted printings reported as being unavailable in Tanzania.

99 The Queen Mother

(Litho Holders Press)

1985 (30 Sept). *Life and Times of Queen Elizabeth the Queen Mother. T 99 and similar horiz designs. Multicoloured. P 14.*

425	20 s. Type 99..	..	10	15
426	20 s. Queen Mother waving to crowd	..	10	15
427	100 s. Oval portrait with flowers	..	30	75
428	100 s. Head and shoulders portrait ..	..	30	75
425/8		*Set of* 4	70	1·60
MS429	Two sheets, each 125 × 63 mm. (a) Nos. 425 and 427; (b) Nos. 426 and 428.			
		Set of 2 *sheets*	80	2·75

Designs as Nos. 425/9, but inscr "H.R.H. The Queen Mother" were not issued in Tanzania.

100 Steam Locomotive No. 3022 (101)

GOLD MEDAL
HENRY TILLMAN
USA

(Litho Holders Press)

1985 (7 Oct). *Tanzanian Railway Steam Locomotives (1st series). T 100 and similar horiz designs. Multicoloured. P 14.*

430	5 s. Type 100..	..	10	15
431	10 s. Locomotive No. 3107	..	15	30
432	20 s. Locomotive No. 6004	..	25	60
433	30 s. Locomotive No. 3129	..	40	90
430/3		*Set of* 4	80	1·75
MS434	125 × 93 mm. Nos. 430/3 ..	..	80	2·75

See also Nos. 445/50.

1985 (22 Oct). *Olympic Games Gold Medal Winners, Los Angeles. Nos. 400/4 optd as T 101.*

435	1 s. Type 94 (optd with T 101)	..	15	15
436	1 s. 50, Running (optd "GOLD MEDAL USA")	..	20	20
437	5 s. Basketball (optd "GOLD MEDAL USA")	..	1·00	1·00
438	20 s. Football (optd "GOLD MEDAL FRANCE")	..	2·00	3·50
435/8		*Set of* 4	3·00	4·25
MS439	130 × 100 mm. Nos. 435/8 ..	..	8·00	10·00

102 Cooking and Water Pots   103 Class 64 Diesel
Locomotive

(Des J. Mzinga. Litho State Ptg Wks, Moscow)

1985 (4 Nov). *Pottery. T 102 and similar horiz designs. Multicoloured. P 12½ × 12.*

440	1 s. 50, Type 102	20	10
441	2 s. Large pot and frying pot with cover	25	15
442	5 s. Trader selling pots	60	35
443	40 s. Beer pot	2·25	4·25
440/3	*Set of 4*	3·00	4·25
MS444	129 × 98 mm. 30 s. Water pots	3·75	3·75

(Des P. Ndembo. Litho State Ptg Wks, Moscow)

1985 (25 Nov). *Tanzanian Railway Locomotives (2nd series). T 103 and similar horiz designs. P 12½ × 12.*

445	1 s. 50, multicoloured	40	20
446	2 s. multicoloured	40	30
447	5 s. multicoloured	55	75
448	10 s. multicoloured	80	1·60
449	30 s. black, brownish black and red	2·00	3·25
445/9	*Set of 5*	3·75	5·50
MS450	130 × 100 mm. 15 s. black, blackish brown and rose-pink; 20 s. black, blackish brown and rose-pink	7·00	7·00

Designs:—2 s. Class 36 diesel locomotive; 5 s. DFH1013 diesel shunter; 10 s. DE1001 diesel-electric locomotive; 15 s. Class 30 steam locomotive; 20 s. Class 11 steam locomotive; 30 s. Steam locomotive, Zanzibar, 1906.

Nos. 445/6 and 448/9 exist overprinted "CONGRAT-ULATIONS TO DUKE & DUCHESS OF YORK ON THE OCCASION OF THEIR MARRIAGE", but there is no evidence that these overprints were available from post offices in Tanzania.

104 Young Pioneers

(Des P. Ndembo. Litho J.W.)

1986 (20 Jan). *International Youth Year. T 104 and similar horiz designs. P 14.*

451	1 s. 50, multicoloured	15	15
452	4 s. reddish brown, pale brown and black	30	50
453	10 s. multicoloured	70	1·25
454	20 s. reddish brown, pale brown and black	1·40	2·50
451/4	*Set of 4*	2·25	4·00
MS455	130 × 100 mm. 30 s. reddish brown, pale brown and black	2·25	3·50

Designs:—4 s. Child health care; 10 s. Uhuru Torch Race; 20 s. Young workers and globe; 30 s. Young people farming.

105 Rolls-Royce "20/25" (1936)

(Litho Holders Press)

1986 (10 Mar). *Centenary of Motoring. T 105 and similar horiz designs. P 14.*

456	1 s. 50, Type 105	10	10
457	5 s. Rolls-Royce "Phantom II" (1933)	15	25
458	10 s. Rolls-Royce "Phantom I" (1926)	25	60
459	30 s. Rolls-Royce "Silver Ghost" (1907)	40	1·50
456/9	*Set of 4*	80	2·25
MS460	125 × 93 mm. Nos. 456/9	80	2·50

106 Rotary Logo and Staunton Queen Chess Piece

(Litho Holders Press)

1986 (17 Mar). *World Chess Championships, London and Leningrad. T 106 and similar horiz design. P 14.*

461	20 s. new blue and magenta	35	50
462	100 s. multicoloured	50	2·50
MS463	124 × 64 mm. Nos. 461/2	1·10	3·25

Design:—100 s. Hand moving Rook.

No. 461 also commemorates Rotary International.

Slightly different versions of Nos. 461/2, incorporating the Chess Championship emblem and with "TANZANIA" and face value at top on the 100 s., were not issued.

107 Mallard

(Litho Holders Press)

1986 (22 May). *Birth Bicentenary of John J. Audubon (ornithologist) (1985). T 107 and similar horiz designs. Multicoloured. P 14.*

464	5 s. Type 107	15	35
465	10 s. Eider	25	50
466	20 s. Scarlet Ibis	30	1·10
467	30 s. Roseate Spoonbill	40	1·25
464/7	*Set of 4*	1·00	2·75
MS468	122 × 91 mm. Nos. 464/7	1·00	3·50

108 Pearls

109

(Litho J.W.)

1986 (27 May). *Tanzanian Minerals. T 108 and similar horiz designs. Multicoloured. Phosphorised paper (Nos. 469/72). P 14.*

469	1 s. 50, Type 108	80	15
470	2 s. Sapphire	1·10	65
471	5 s. Tanzanite	2·00	1·25
472	40 s. Diamonds	7·25	10·00
469/72	*Set of 4*	10·00	11·00
MS473	130 × 100 mm. 30 s. Rubies. W 109	11·00	11·00

110 *Hibiscus calyphyllus*   **111** Oryx

(Litho Holders Press)

1986 (25 June). *Flowers of Tanzania. T 110 and similar vert designs. Multicoloured. P 14.*

474	1 s. 50, Type 110	10	10
475	5 s. Aloe graminicola	15	25
476	10 s. Nersium oleander	20	35
477	30 s. Nymphaea caerulea	40	1·75
474/7	*Set of 4*	75	2·25
MS478	90 × 119 mm. Nos. 474/7	75	2·50

(Litho Holders Press)

1986 (30 June). *Endangered Animals of Tanzania. T 111 and similar vert designs. Multicoloured. P 14.*

479	5 s. Type 111	15	15
480	10 s. Giraffe	20	35
481	20 s. Rhinoceros	25	75
482	30 s. Cheetah	25	1·25
479/82	*Set of 4*	75	2·25
MS483	91 × 121 mm. Nos. 479/82	75	3·25

Four stamps, 10, 20, 60 and 80 s., with accompanying miniature sheets, were prepared in 1986 for the Wedding of the Duke of York, but these were not placed on sale in Tanzania.

112 Immunization   **113** Angelfish

(Des P. Ndembo. Litho State Ptg Wks, Moscow)

1986 (29 July). *U.N.I.C.E.F. Child Survival Campaign. T 112 and similar horiz designs. Multicoloured. P 12½ × 12.*

484	1 s. 50, Type 112	25	10
485	2 s. Growth monitoring	35	15
486	5 s. Oral rehydration therapy	60	40
487	40 s. Breast feeding	2·25	4·00
484/7	*Set of 4*	3·00	4·25
MS488	110 × 101 mm. 30 s. Healthy baby	1·00	1·75

(Des P. Ndembo. Litho State Ptg Wks, Moscow)

1986 (28 Aug). *Marine Life. T 113 and similar horiz designs. Multicoloured. P 12½ × 12.*

489	1 s. 50, Type 113	70	10
490	4 s. Parrotfish	1·50	85
491	10 s. Turtle	2·25	2·75
492	20 s. Octopus	3·50	4·75
489/92	*Set of 4*	7·00	7·50
MS493	131 × 101 mm. 30 s. Corals	2·50	2·50

114 Team Captains shaking Hands   **115** Pres. Nyerere receiving Beyond War Award

(Litho Questa)

1986 (30 Oct). *World Cup Football Championship, Mexico. T 114 and similar horiz designs. Multicoloured. P 14.*

494	1 s. 50, Type 114	15	10
495	2 s. Referee sending player off	15	10
496	10 s. Goalkeeper and ball in net	60	90
497	20 s. Goalkeeper saving ball	1·00	2·00
494/7	*Set of 4*	1·75	2·75
MS498	95 × 72 mm. 30 s. Winning Argentine team	1·10	1·25

(Des P. Ndembo. Litho Mardon Printers Ltd, Zimbabwe)

1986 (20 Dec). *International Peace Year. T 115 and similar horiz designs. Multicoloured. P 14½.*

499	1 s. 50, Type 115	30	10
500	2 s. Children of many races	50	20
501	10 s. African cosmonaut and rocket launch	1·25	1·75
502	20 s. United Nations Headquarters, New York	1·75	3·00
499/502	*Set of 4*	3·50	4·50
MS503	109 × 86 mm. 30 s. International Peace Year symbols	2·25	3·25

116 Mobile Bank Service

(Des P. Ndembo. Litho Questa)

1987 (7 Feb). *20th Anniv of National Bank of Commerce. T 116 and similar horiz designs. Multicoloured. P 14.*

504	1 s. 50, Type 116	30	10
505	2 s. National Bank of Commerce Head Office	50	20
506	5 s. Pres. Mwinyi laying foundation stone	80	90
507	20 s. Cotton harvesting	2·00	3·25
504/7	*Set of 4*	3·25	4·00

117 Parade of Young Party Members

(Litho Holders Press)

1987 (10 Mar). *10th Anniv of Chama Cha Mapinduzi Party and 20th Anniv of Arusha Declaration. T 117 and similar horiz designs. Multicoloured. P 14.*

508	2 s. Type 117	15	10
509	5 s. Harvesting coffee	15	10
510	10 s. Pres. Nyerere addressing Second Peace Initiative Reunion	20	30
511	30 s. Presidents Julius Nyerere and Ali Hassan Mwinyi	35	1·25
508/11	*Set of 4*	75	1·50

118 Nungu Nungu Hair Style   **119**

(Litho Leigh-Mardon Ltd, Melbourne)

1987 (16 Mar). *Traditional Hair Styles. T 118 and similar vert designs. Multicoloured. W 119. P 14½.*

512	1 s. 50, Type 118	30	10
513	2 s. Upanga wa jogoo style	45	20
514	10 s. Morani style	80	1·25
515	20 s. Twende kilioni style	1·50	2·50
512/15	*Set of 4*	2·75	3·50
MS516	110 × 99 mm. 30 s. Hair plaiting	2·75	3·50

120 Royal Family on Buckingham Palace Balcony after Trooping the Colour

(Litho Holders Press)

1987 (24 Mar). *60th Birthday of Queen Elizabeth II (1986). T **120** and similar horiz designs. Multicoloured. P 14.*

517	5 s. Type 120		10	10
518	10 s. Queen and Prince Philip at Royal Ascot		15	20
519	40 s. Queen Elizabeth II		50	80
520	60 s. Queen Elizabeth with crowd		70	1·25
517/20		*Set of 4*	1·25	2·00
MS521	125×90 mm. Nos. 517/20		1·25	3·00

121 *Apis mellifera* (bee) **122** Crocodile

(Litho State Ptg Wks, Moscow)

1987 (22 Apr). *Insects. T **121** and similar horiz designs. Multicoloured. P 12½×12.*

522	1 s. 50, Type 121		60	15
523	2 s. *Prostephanus truncatus* (grain borer)		80	25
524	10 s. *Glossina palpalis* (tsetse fly)		1·50	2·00
525	20 s. *Polistes* sp (wasp)		2·25	4·25
522/5		*Set of 4*	4·50	6·00
MS526	110×101 mm. 30 s. *Anopheles* sp (mosquito)		3·00	4·00

(Des J. Mzinga (3 s., 30 s.), P. Ndembo (others). Litho State Ptg Wks, Moscow)

1987 (2 July). *Reptiles. T **122** and similar horiz designs. Multicoloured. P 12½×12.*

527	2 s. Type 122		65	25
528	3 s. Black-striped Grass-snake		70	30
529	10 s. Adder		1·25	1·50
530	20 s. Green Mamba		1·90	3·00
527/30		*Set of 4*	4·00	4·50
MS531	101×101 mm. 30 s. Tortoise		1·00	1·00

123 Emblems of Posts/ Telecommunications and Railways **124** Basketry

(Des and litho Questa)

1987 (27 July). *10th Anniv of Tanzania Communications and Transport Corporations. T **123** and similar horiz designs. Multicoloured. P 14.*

532	2 s. Type 123		30	25
533	8 s. Emblems of Air Tanzania and Harbours Authority		55	60
MS534	100×66 mm. 20 s. Methods of transport and communication		2·00	1·50

(Des P. Ndembo. Litho State Ptg Wks, Moscow)

1987 (15 Dec). *Traditional Handicrafts. T **124** and similar horiz designs. Multicoloured. P 12½×12.*

535	2 s. Type 124		15	10
536	3 s. Decorated gourds		15	15
537	10 s. Stools		25	20
538	20 s. Makonde carvings		40	45
535/8		*Set of 4*	85	80
MS539	89×89 mm. 40 s. Makonde carver at work		65	75

10th Anniversary of TANZANIA ZAMBIA RAILWAY AUTHORITY 1976-1986

(125)

1987 (30 Dec). *10th Anniv of Tanzania–Zambia Railway (1986). Nos. 445/9 optd with T **125**.*

540	**103**	1 s. 50, multicoloured	40	15
541	—	2 s. multicoloured	45	25
542	—	5 s. multicoloured	70	70
543	—	10 s. multicoloured	1·10	1·40
544	—	30 s. black, brownish black and red	2·25	3·50
540/4		*Set of 5*	4·50	5·50

126 Mdako (pebble game)

(Des P. Ndembo. Litho State Ptg Wks, Moscow)

1988 (15 Feb). *Traditional Pastimes. T **126** and similar horiz designs. Multicoloured. P 12½×12.*

545	2 s. Type 126		10	10
546	3 s. Wrestling		10	10
547	8 s. Bullfighting, Zanzibar		15	15
548	20 s. Bao (board game)		35	35
545/8		*Set of 4*	65	65
MS549	100×90 mm. 30 s. Archery		70	80

127 Plateosaurus

(Des G. Vasarhelyi. Litho Format)

1988 (22 Apr). *Prehistoric and Modern Animals. T **127** and similar trapezium-shaped designs. Multicoloured. P 12½.*

550	2 s. Type 127		20	40
	a. *Tête-bêche* (horiz pair)		40	80
551	3 s. Pteranodon		20	40
	a. *Tête-bêche* (horiz pair)		40	80
552	5 s. Apatosaurus ("Brontosaurus")		20	45
	a. *Tête-bêche* (horiz pair)		40	90
553	7 s. Lion		30	50
	a. *Tête-bêche* (horiz pair)		60	1·00
554	8 s. Tiger		30	50
	a. *Tête-bêche* (horiz pair)		60	1·00
555	12 s. Orang-utan		35	70
	a. *Tête-bêche* (horiz pair)		70	1·40
556	20 s. Elephant		70	1·25
	a. *Tête-bêche* (horiz pair)		1·40	2·50
557	100 s. Stegosaurus		1·75	3·00
	a. *Tête-bêche* (horiz pair)		3·50	6·00
550/7		*Set of 8*	3·50	6·50

Nos. 550/7 were issued in sheets which had the second and fourth stamps *tête-bêche* in each horizontal row of five.

128 Marchers with Party Flag **129** Population Symbols on Map

(Des P. Ndembo. Litho Questa)

1988 (1 July). *National Solidarity Walk. T **128** and similar horiz designs. Multicoloured. P 14×14½.*

558	2 s. + 1 s. Type 128		25	25
559	3 s. + 1 s. Pres. Mwinyi leading Walk		25	25
MS560	121×121 mm. 50 s. + 1 s. Pres. Ali Hassan Mwinyi (35×25 mm). P 14½		75	85

(Des P. Ndembo. Litho Questa)

1988 (8 Aug). *Third National Population Census. T **129** and similar horiz designs. Multicoloured. P 14.*

561	2 s. Type 129		10	10
562	3 s. Census official at work		10	10
563	10 s. Community health care		15	15
564	20 s. Population growth 1967–1988		30	30
561/4		*Set of 4*	55	55
MS565	96×91 mm. 40 s. Development of modern Tanzania		65	65

130 Javelin **131** Football

(Litho State Ptg Wks, Moscow)

1988 (5 Sept). *Olympic Games, Seoul (1st issue). T **130** and similar horiz designs. Multicoloured. P 12½×12.*

566	2 s. Type 130		50	10
567	3 s. Hurdling		50	10
568	7 s. Long distance running		85	30
569	12 s. Relay racing		1·00	45
566/9		*Set of 4*	2·50	80
MS570	100×70 mm. 40 s. Badminton		2·75	1·25

(Des D. Miller. Litho Questa)

1988 (5 Sept). *Olympic Games, Seoul (2nd issue). T **131** and similar vert designs. Multicoloured. P 14.*

571	10 s. Type 131		25	10
572	20 s. Cycling		60	25
573	50 s. Fencing		70	50
574	70 s. Volleyball		80	65
571/4		*Set of 4*	2·10	1·40
MS575	77×92 mm. 100 s. Gymnastics		1·50	2·00

(Des D. Miller. Litho Questa)

1988 (5 Sept). *Winter Olympic Games, Calgary. Vert designs as T **131**. Multicoloured. P 14.*

576	5 s. Cross-country skiing		35	10
577	25 s. Figure skating		75	25
578	50 s. Downhill skiing		1·25	50
579	75 s. Bobsleighing		1·40	70
576/9		*Set of 4*	3·25	1·40
MS580	77×92 mm. 100 s. Ice hockey sticks wrapped in Olympic and Canadian colours		2·25	1·25

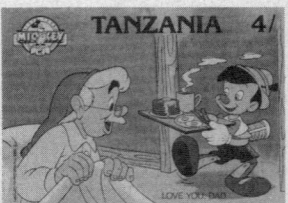

132 Goat **133** "Love You, Dad" (Pinocchio)

(Litho Questa)

1988 (9 Sept). *Domestic Animals. T **132** and similar multicoloured designs. P 14.*

581	4 s. Type 132		25	25
582	5 s. Rabbit (*horiz*)		25	25
583	8 s. Cows (*horiz*)		35	35
584	10 s. Kitten (*horiz*)		50	50
585	12 s. Pony		60	60
586	20 s. Puppy		90	90
581/6		*Set of 6*	2·50	2·50
MS587	102×73 mm. 100 s. Chicken (*horiz*)		1·75	1·75

(Des Walt Disney Company. Litho Questa)

1988 (9 Sept). *Greetings Stamps. T **133** and similar horiz designs showing Walt Disney cartoon characters. Multicoloured. P 14×13½.*

588	4 s. Type 133		10	10
589	5 s. "Happy Birthday" (Brer Rabbit and Chip n'Dale)		10	10
590	10 s. "Trick or Treat" (Daisy and Donald Duck)		15	15
591	12 s. "Be kind to Animals" (Ferdie and Mordie with Pluto)		15	15
592	15 s. "Love" (Daisy and Donald Duck)		20	20
593	20 s. "Let's Celebrate" (Mickey Mouse and Goofy)		30	30
594	30 s. "Keep in Touch" (Daisy and Donald Duck)		65	65
595	50 s. "Love you, Mom" (Minnie Mouse with Ferdie and Mordie)		1·25	1·25
588/95		*Set of 8*	2·50	2·50
MS596	Two sheets, each 127×101 mm. (a) 150 s. "Let's work together" (Goofy dressed as a fireman). (b) 150 s. "Have a super Sunday" (Goofy dressed as American footballer)			
		Set of 2 sheets	4·75	4·50

134 *Charaxes varanes* **135** Independence Torch and Mt Kilimanjaro

(Des Jennifer Toombs. Litho Questa)

1988 (17 Oct). *Butterflies. T **134** and similar horiz designs. Multicoloured. P 14½.*

597	8 s. Type 134		40	10
598	30 s. *Neptis melicerta*		80	30
599	40 s. *Mylothris chloris*		90	40
600	50 s. *Charaxes bohemani*		1·10	50
601	60 s. *Myrina silenus* (s sp *ficedula*)		1·25	70
602	75 s. *Papilio phorcas*		1·75	90
603	90 s. *Cyrestis camillus*		2·00	1·10
604	100 s. *Salamis temora*		2·00	1·25
597/604		*Set of 8*	9·00	4·75
MS605	Two sheets, each 80×50 mm. (a) 200 s. *Asterope rosa*. (b) 250 s. *Kallima rumia*			
		Set of 2 sheets	8·00	6·00

(Des R. Vigurs. Litho Questa)

1988 (1 Nov). *National Monuments. T **135** and similar vert designs. Multicoloured. P 14.*

606	5 s. Type 135		10	10
607	12 s. Arusha Declaration Monument		10	10
608	30 s. Askari Monument		25	30
609	60 s. Independence Monument		55	60
606/9		*Set of 4*	80	90
MS610	100×89 mm. 100 s. Askari Monument statue		1·25	1·40

136 Eye Clinic   **137** Loading Patient into Ambulance

(Des P. Ndembo. Litho National Printing & Packaging, Zimbabwe)

1988 (19 Dec). *25th Anniv of Dar-es-Salaam Lions Club. T* **136** *and similar horiz designs. Multicoloured. P* 14½.

611	2 s.	Type 136	20	15
612	3 s.	Family at shallow water well	20	15
613	7 s.	Rhinoceros and map of Tanzania	80	20
614	12 s.	Club presenting school desks	30	25
611/14		*Set of 4*	1·40	65
MS615	100×65 mm. 40 s. Lions International logo		90	80

(Des P. Ndembo. Litho State Ptg Wks, Moscow)

1988 (30 Dec). *125th Anniv of International Red Cross and Red Crescent. T* **137** *and similar horiz designs. Multicoloured. P* 12½×12.

616	2 s.	Type 137	20	15
617	3 s.	Mother and baby health clinic	20	15
618	7 s.	Red Cross flag	40	20
619	12 s.	Henri Dunant (founder)	45	30
616/19		*Set of 4*	1·10	70
MS620	90×90 mm. 40 s. Members of Red Cross International Committee, 1863		1·00	1·00

138 Paradise Whydah   **139** Bushbaby

(Des S. Barlowe. Litho B.D.T.)

1989 (15 Mar). *Birds. T* **138** *and similar vert designs. Multicoloured. P* 13½.

621	20 s.	Type 138	80	80
		a. Sheetlet. Nos. 621/40	14·00	
622	20 s.	Black-collared Barbet	80	80
623	20 s.	Bateleur	80	80
624	20 s.	Lilac-breasted Roller and African Open-bill Storks in flight	80	80
625	20 s.	Red-tufted Malachite Sunbird and African Open-bill Stork in flight	80	80
626	20 s.	Dark Chanting Goshawk	80	80
627	20 s.	White-fronted Bee Eater, Carmine Bee Eater and Little Bee Eaters	80	80
628	20 s.	Narina Trogon and Marabou Stork in flight	80	80
629	20 s.	Grey Parrot	80	80
630	20 s.	Hoopoe	80	80
631	20 s.	Masked Lovebird ("Yellow-collared Lovebird")	80	80
632	20 s.	Yellow-billed Hornbill	80	80
633	20 s.	Hammerkop	80	80
634	20 s.	Violet-crested Turaco and flamingos in flight	80	80
635	20 s.	Malachite Kingfisher	80	80
636	20 s.	Greater Flamingos	80	80
637	20 s.	Yellow-billed Storks	80	80
638	20 s.	Whale-headed Stork ("Shoebill Stork")	80	80
639	20 s.	Saddle-bill Stork and Blacksmith Plover	80	80
640	20 s.	South African Crowned Crane	80	80
621/40		*Set of 20*	14·00	14·00
MS641	Two sheets, each 105×75 mm. (a) 350 s. Helmet Guineafowl (28×42 mm). (b) 350 s. Ostrich (28×42 mm). P 14			
		Set of 2 sheets	9·00	5·50

Nos. 622/41 were printed together, *se-tenant*, in a sheetlet of 20 forming a composite design of birds at a waterhole.

(Des J. Barbaris (Nos. 642/4, 648, **MS**650a), S. Barlowe (others). Litho Questa)

1989 (20 Mar). *Fauna and Flora. T* **139** *and similar multicoloured designs. P* 14.

642	5 s.	Type 139	15	15
643	10 s.	Bushbaby holding insect (*horiz*)	20	20
644	20 s.	Bushbaby on forked branch	30	30
645	30 s.	Black Cobra on Umbrella Acacia	60	60
646	45 s.	Bushbaby at night (*horiz*)	60	60
647	70 s.	Red-billed Tropic Bird and Tree Ferns	2·75	2·75
648	100 s.	African Tree Frog on Cocoa Tree	2·75	2·75
649	150 s.	Black-headed Heron and Egyptian Papyrus	5·00	5·00
642/9		*Set of 8*	11·00	11·00
MS650	Two sheets. (a) 115×85 mm. 350 s. African Palm Civet (*horiz*). (b) 65×65 mm. 350 s. Pink-backed Pelican and Baobab Tree (*horiz*)			
		Set of 2 sheets	8·00	5·50

Nos. 645, 647/9 and **MS**650 are without the World Wildlife Fund logo.

---

140 Juma Ikangaa (marathon runner)   **141** Drums

(Des W. Storozuk. Litho Questa)

1989 (10 Apr). *International Sporting Personalities. T* **140** *and similar vert designs. Multicoloured. P* 14.

651	4 s.	Type 140	15	15
652	8 s.	50, Steffi Graf (tennis player)	1·00	30
653	12 s.	Yannick Noah (tennis player)	80	40
654	40 s.	Pelé (footballer)	90	65
655	100 s.	Erhard Keller (speed skater)	1·00	80
656	125 s.	Sadanoyama (sumo wrestler)	1·25	1·00
657	200 s.	Taino (sumo wrestler)	1·75	1·75
658	250 s.	T. Nakajima (golfer)	5·50	2·75
651/8		*Set of 8*	11·00	7·00
MS659	Two sheets. (a) 100×71 mm. 350 s. Joe Louis (boxer). (b) 100×76 mm. 350 s. I. Aoki (golfer)			
		Set of 2 sheets	8·00	5·50

The captions on Nos. 658 and MS659b are transposed.

(Des P. Ndembo. Litho Harrison)

1989 (29 June). *Musical Instruments. T* **141** *and similar horiz designs. Multicoloured. P* 14.

660	2 s.	Type 141	45	25
661	3 s.	Xylophones	45	25
662	10 s.	Thumbpiano	85	75
663	20 s.	Fiddles	1·40	1·75
660/3		*Set of 4*	2·75	2·75
MS664	91×80 mm. 40 s. Violins with calabash resonators		1·00	1·00

142 Chama Cha Mapinduzi Party Flag   **143** Class P36 Locomotive, Russia, 1953

(Des P. Ndembo. Litho Questa)

1989 (1 July). *National Solidarity Walk. T* **142** *and similar multicoloured designs. P* 14½.

665	5 s. + 1 s.	Type 142	25	25
666	10 s. + 1 s.	Marchers with party flag and President Mwinyi	25	25
MS667	122×122 mm. 50 s. + 1 s. President Mwinyi (*vert*)		60	60

(Des W. Wright. Litho B.D.T.)

1989 (22 Aug). *Steam Locomotives. T* **143** *and similar multi-coloured designs. P* 14.

668	10 s.	Type 143	45	35
669	25 s.	Class 12 streamlined locomotive, Belgium, 1939	55	45
670	60 s.	Class C62 locomotive, Japan, 1948	85	75
671	75 s.	Pennsylvania Railroad Class T1 streamlined locomotive, U.S.A., 1942	95	95
672	80 s.	Class WP locomotive, India, 1946	1·00	1·00
673	90 s.	East African Railways Class 59 Garratt locomotive No. 5919	1·25	1·25
674	150 s.	Class "People" locomotive No. 1206, China	1·75	2·00
675	200 s.	Southern Pacific "Daylight" express, U.S.A.	1·75	2·00
668/75		*Set of 8*	7·75	8·00
MS676	Two sheets, each 114×85 mm. (a) 350 s. Stephenson's *Planet*, Great Britain, 1830 (*vert*). (b) 350 s. L.M.S. *Coronation Scot*, Great Britain, 1937 (*vert*)			
		Set of 2 sheets	5·50	7·00

(Des Design Element. Litho Questa)

1989 (17 Nov). *"World Stamp Expo '89" International Stamp Exhibition, Washington. Landmarks of Washington. Sheet 78×62 mm containing horiz design as T* **193a** *of Lesotho. Multicoloured. P* 14.

MS677	500 s. Union Station		4·00	5·50

144 "Luna 3" Satellite orbiting Moon, 1959   (**145**)

(Des G. Vasarhelyi. Litho Questa)

1989 (22 Nov). *History of Space Exploration and 20th Anniv of First Manned Landing on Moon. T* **144** *and similar horiz designs. Multicoloured. P* 14.

678	20 s.	Type 144	45	35
679	30 s.	"Gemini 6" and "7", 1965	55	45
680	40 s.	Astronaut Edward White in space, 1965	65	55

681	60 s.	Astronaut Aldrin on Moon, 1969	85	75
682	70 s.	Aldrin performing experiment, 1969	90	80
683	100 s.	"Apollo 15" astronaut and lunar rover, 1971	1·25	1·00
684	150 s.	"Apollo 18" and "Soyuz 19" docking in space, 1975	1·50	1·75
685	200 s.	Spacelab, 1983	1·75	2·00
678/85		*Set of 8*	7·00	7·00
MS686	Two sheets, each 110×90 mm. (a) 250 s. Lunar module *Eagle* and "Apollo 11" emblem. (b) 250 s. Projected U.S. space station *Set of 2 sheets*		5·00	5·50

1989 (11 Dec). *Olympic Medal Winners, Calgary and Seoul. Optd as T* **145**. (a) *On Nos. 571/5*

687	10 s.	Type 131 (optd with T 145)	40	40
688	20 s.	Cycling (optd "Men's Match Sprint, Lutz Hesslich, DDR")	1·50	80
689	50 s.	Fencing (optd "Epee, Schmitt, W. Germany")	1·25	1·25
690	70 s.	Volleyball (optd "Men's Team, USA")	1·75	2·00
687/90		*Set of 4*	4·50	4·00
MS691	77×92 mm. 100 s. Gymnastics ("Women's Team, Gold – USSR")		2·00	3·00

(b) *On Nos. 576/80*

692	5 s.	Cross-country skiing (optd "Biathlon, Peter-Roetsch, DDR")	35	30
693	25 s.	Figure skating (optd "Pairs, Gordeeva & Grinkov, USSR")	75	65
694	50 s.	Downhill skiing (optd "Zurbriggen, Switzerland")	1·25	1·10
695	75 s.	Bobsleighing (optd "Gold – USSR Silver – DDR Bronze – DDR")	1·40	1·40
692/5		*Set of 4*	3·25	3·00
MS696	77×92 mm. 100 s. Ice hockey sticks wrapped in Olympic and Canadian colours (optd "Ice Hockey: Gold – USSR")		5·50	5·50

146 Spotted Tilapia

(Des W. Hanson Studio. Litho Questa)

1989 (14 Dec). *Reef and Freshwater Fishes of Tanzania. T* **146** *and similar multicoloured designs. P* 14.

697	9 s.	Type 146	60	40
698	13 s.	Painted Triggerfish	60	40
699	20 s.	Powder-blue Surgeonfish	80	50
700	40 s.	Red-tailed Butterflyfish	1·25	75
701	70 s.	Red-tailed Notho	1·50	1·25
702	100 s.	Ansorge's Neolebias	1·75	1·75
703	150 s.	Blue Panchax	2·00	2·50
704	200 s.	Regal Angelfish	2·00	2·50
697/704		*Set of 8*	9·50	9·00
MS705	Two sheets, each 112×83 mm. (a) 350 s. Jewel Cichlid (50×38 mm). P 14×13½. (b) 350 s. Dusky Batfish (38×50 mm). P 13½×14			
		Set of 2 sheets	9·50	9·50

 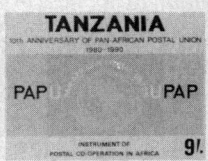

147 Rural Polling Station   **148** Logo

(Des P. Ndembo. Litho State Ptg Wks, Moscow)

1989 (22 Dec). *Centenary of Inter-Parliamentary Union. T* **147** *and similar horiz designs. P* 12½×12.

706	9 s.	multicoloured	10	10
707	13 s.	multicoloured	10	10
708	80 s.	multicoloured	40	55
709	100 s.	black, dull ultramarine and pale blue	50	75
706/9		*Set of 4*	90	1·40
MS710	90×90 mm. 40 s. multicoloured		70	1·25

Designs:—13 s. Parliament Building, Dar-es-Salaam; 40 s. Sir William Randal Cremer and Frederic Passy (founders); 80 s. Tanzania Parliament in session; 100 s. Logo.

(Des P. Ndembo. Litho Cartor)

1990 (10 Jan). *10th Anniv of Pan-African Postal Union. T* **148** *and similar horiz designs. P* 13½.

711	9 s.	greenish yellow, dull green and black	15	15
712	13 s.	multicoloured	15	15
713	70 s.	multicoloured	80	80
714	100 s.	multicoloured	1·50	1·50
711/14		*Set of 4*	2·40	2·40
MS715	90×90 mm. 40 s. multicoloured. P 12½		1·00	1·50

Designs:—13 s. Collecting mail from post office box; 40 s. Logos of Tanzania Posts and Telecommunications Corporation, P.A.P.U. and U.P.U.; 70 s. Taking mail to post office; 100 s. Mail transport.

149 Admiral's Flag and *Nina*

(Des T. Agans. Litho Questa)

1990 (12 Feb). *500th Anniv of Discovery of America by Columbus* (1992) (50, 60, 75, 200 s.) *and Modern Scientific Discoveries* (others). *T* **149** *and similar horiz designs. Multicoloured. P* 14.

716	9 a. Bell XS-1 aircraft (first supersonic flight, 1947)		50	40
717	13 s. *Trieste* (bathyscaphe) (first dive to depth of 35,000 ft, 1960)		50	40
718	50 s. Type **149**		90	80
719	60 s. Fleet flag and *Pinta*		1·00	90
720	75 s. Standard of Castile and León and *Santa Maria*		1·25	1·00
721	150 s. Transistor technology		1·25	1·50
722	200 s. Arms of Columbus and map of First Voyage		2·00	2·25
723	250 s. DNA molecule		2·00	2·25
716/23		*Set of 8*	8·50	8·50
MS724	Two sheets, each 106×78 mm. (a) 350 s. Caravels in the Caribbean. (b) 350 s. *Voyager II* and Neptune	*Set of 2 sheets*	5·50	7·00

150 Tecopa Pupfish

(Des J. Genzo. Litho Questa)

1990 (20 Feb). *Extinct Species. T* **150** *and similar multicoloured designs. P* 14.

725	25 s. Type **150**		60	60
726	40 s. Thylacine		90	90
727	50 s. Quagga		1·10	1·10
728	60 s. Passenger Pigeon		1·75	1·75
729	75 s. Rodriguez Saddleback Tortoise		1·75	1·75
730	100 s. Toolache Wallaby		1·75	1·75
731	150 s. Texas Red Wolf		1·90	1·90
732	200 s. Utah Lake Sculpin		1·90	1·90
725/32		*Set of 8*	10·50	10·50
MS733	Two sheets. (a) 102×74 mm. 350 s. South Island Whekau. (b) 71×99 mm. 350 s. Hawaii O-o (*vert*)	*Set of 2 sheets*	7·50	8·00

151 Camping

(Des P. Ndembo. Litho State Ptg Wks, Moscow)

1990 (22 Feb). *60th Anniv of Girl Guides Movement in Tanzania. T* **151** *and similar multicoloured designs. P* 12½×12.

734	9 s. Type **151**		15	15
735	13 s. Guides planting sapling		15	15
736	50 s. Guide teaching woman to write		40	60
737	100 s. Guide helping at child-care clinic		65	95
734/7		*Set of 4*	1·25	1·75
MS738	89×89 mm. 40 s. Guide teaching child to read (*vert*). P 12×12½		75	1·25

152 Fishing

153 Footballer

(Des P. Ndembo. Litho State Ptg Wks, Moscow)

1990 (25 Apr). *25th Anniv of Union of Tanganyika and Zanzibar. T* **152** *and similar multicoloured designs. P* 12½×12 (*horiz*) *or* 12×12½ (*vert*).

739	9 s. Type **152**		25	20
740	13 s. Vineyard		25	20
741	50 s. Cloves		95	95
742	100 s. Presidents Nyerere and Karume exchanging Union instruments (*vert*)		2·00	2·50
739/42		*Set of 4*	3·00	3·50
MS743	90×90 mm. 40 s. Arms (*vert*)		1·75	2·00

(Litho B.D.T.)

1990 (1 June). *World Cup Football Championship, Italy* (1st issue). *T* **153** *and similar vert designs. Multicoloured. P* 14.

744	25 s. Type **153**		1·00	80
745	60 s. Player passing ball		1·50	90
746	75 s. Player turning		1·75	1·00
747	200 s. Player kicking ball		4·00	3·75
744/7		*Set of 4*	7·50	5·50
MS748	Two sheets, each 105×76 mm. (a) 350 s. Two players fighting for possession. (b) 350 s. Player kicking ball	*Set of 2 sheets*	9·00	9·00

See also Nos. 789/93 and 794/8.

154 Miriam Makeba

155 Ring of People round Party Flag

(Des A. Fagbohun. Litho Questa)

1990 (29 June). *Famous Black Entertainers. T* **154** *and similar vert designs. Multicoloured. P* 14.

749	9 s. Type **154**		15	10
750	13 s. Manu Dibango		15	10
751	25 s. Fela		20	15
752	70 s. Smokey Robinson		75	40
753	100 s. Gladys Knight		85	55
754	150 s. Eddie Murphy		1·75	1·75
755	200 s. Sammy Davis Jnr.		2·00	2·25
756	250 f. Stevie Wonder		2·00	2·50
749/56		*Set of 8*	7·00	7·00
MS757	Two sheets, each 69×88 mm.(a) 350 s. Bill Cosby (30×39 *mm*). (b) 350 s. Michael Jackson (30×39 *mm*). P 14½	*Set of 2 sheets*	4·00	4·50

(Litho Cartor)

1990 (6 July). *Solidarity Walk,* 1990. *T* **155** *and similar multicoloured designs. P* 13½.

758	9 s. + 1 s. Type **155**		70	80
759	13 s. + 1 s. President Mwinyi		70	80
MS760	90×90 mm. 50 s. + 1 s. Handclasp on map (*vert*). P 12½		1·50	1·75

156 Diesel Train

157 Pope John Paul II

(Des P. Ndembo. Litho Cartor)

1990 (8 Aug). *10th Anniv of Southern African Development Co-ordination Conference. T* **156** *and similar horiz designs. Multicoloured. P* 13½.

761	8 s. Type **156**		65	30
762	11 s. 50, Paper-making plant		25	20
763	25 s. Tractor factory and ploughing		30	20
764	100 s. Map and national flags		2·25	2·50
761/4		*Set of 4*	3·00	2·75
MS765	89×89 mm. 50 s. Map of Southern Africa. P 12½		1·75	2·00

(Des P. Ndembo. Litho Questa)

1990 (1 Sept). *Papal Visit to Tanzania. T* **157** *and similar multicoloured designs. P* 14.

766	10 s. Type **157**		20	15
767	15 s. Pope in ceremonial robes		25	15
768	20 s. Pope giving blessing		30	15
769	100 s. Papal coat of arms		80	1·10
766/9		*Set of 4*	1·40	1·40
MS770	172×143 mm. 50 s. Pope John Paul II (*horiz*); 50 s. St. Joseph's Cathedral, Dar-es-Salaam (*horiz*); 50 s. Christ the King Cathedral, Moshi (*horiz*); 50 s. Saint Theresa's Cathedral, Tabora (*horiz*); 50 s. Cathedral of the Epiphany, Bugando Mwanza (*horiz*); 50 s. St. Mathias Mulumba Kalemba Cathedral, Songea (*horiz*)		3·50	3·75
a. Error. Imperf			†	—

158 Mickey and Minnie Mouse in Herby the Love Bug

(Des Walt Disney Co. Litho Questa)

1990 (7 Nov). *Motor Cars from Disney Films. T* **158** *and similar horiz designs. Multicoloured. P* 14×13½.

771	20 s. Type **158**		30	30
772	30 s. The Absent-minded Professor's car		35	35
773	45 s. Chitty-Chitty Bang-Bang		45	45
774	60 s. Mr. Toad's car		65	65
775	75 s. Scrooge's limousine		75	75
776	100 s. The Shaggy Dog's car		1·00	1·00
777	150 s. Donald Duck's nephews cleaning car		1·60	1·60
778	200 s. Fire engine from *Dumbo*		1·75	1·75
771/8		*Set of 8*	6·25	6·25
MS779	Two sheets, each 127×112, (a) 350 s. The Mickeymobile. (b) 350 s. Cruella De Vil and dog wagon from *101 Dalmations*	*Set of 2 sheets*	8·00	8·50

159 "St. Mary Magdalen in Penitence" (detail)

160 Klinsmann of West Germany

(Litho Questa)

1990 (7 Nov). *Paintings by Titian. T* **159** *and similar vert designs. Multicoloured. P* 13½×14.

780	5 s. Type **159**		10	10
781	10 s. "Averoldi Polyptych" (detail)		10	10
782	15 s. "Saint Margaret" (detail)		15	15
783	50 s. "Venus and Adonis" (detail)		40	40
784	75 s. "Venus and the Lutenist" (detail)		55	55
785	100 s. "Tarquin and Lucretia" (detail)		70	70
786	125 s. "Saint Jerome" (detail)		90	90
787	150 s. "Madonna and Child in Glory with Saints" (detail)		1·00	1·00
780/7		*Set of 8*	3·50	3·50
MS788	Three sheets. (a) 95×110 mm. 300 s. "Adoration of the Holy Trinity" (detail). (b) 95×110 mm. 300 s. "St. Catherine of Alexandria at Prayer" (detail). (c) 110×95 mm. 300 s. "The Supper at Emmaus" (detail)	*Set of 3 sheets*	7·50	8·50

(Des Young Phillips Studio. Litho Questa)

1990 (17 Nov). *World Cup Football Championship, Italy* (2nd issue). *T* **160** *and similar vert designs. Multicoloured. P* 14.

789	10 s. Type **160**		50	30
790	60 s. Serena of Italy		90	60
791	100 s. Nicol of Scotland		1·75	1·75
792	300 s. Susic of Yugoslavia		3·25	4·00
789/92		*Set of 4*	5·75	6·00
MS793	Two sheets, each 85×95 mm. (a) 400 s. Montero of Costa Rica. (b) 400 s. Seifo of Belgium	*Set of 2 sheets*	8·50	9·00

161 Throw-in

(Litho Questa)

1990 (17 Nov). *World Cup Football Championship, Italy* (3rd issue). *T* **161** *and similar horiz designs. Multicoloured. P* 14.

794	9 s. Type **161**		30	20
795	13 s. Penalty kick		30	20
796	25 s. Dribbling		45	25
797	100 s. Corner kick		1·75	2·00
794/7		*Set of 4*	2·50	2·40
MS798	82×82 mm. 50 s. World Cup and world map		1·75	2·25

162 Canoe

(Des M. Raza. Litho State Ptg Works, Moscow)

1990 (24 Nov). *Marine Transport. T* **162** *and similar horiz designs. Multicoloured. P* 12½×12.

799	9 s. Type **162**		15	15
800	13 s. Sailing canoe		20	15
801	25 s. Dhow		40	15
802	100 s. Freighter		1·75	1·75
799/802		*Set of 4*	2·25	2·25
MS803	90×90 mm. 40 s. Mashua dhow		1·75	2·25

ALTERED CATALOGUE NUMBERS

Any Catalogue numbers altered from the last edition are shown as a list in the introductory pages.

163 Lesser Masked Weaver   **164** Lesser Flamingo

(Litho Questa)

1990 (15 Dec)–**91.** *Birds. Horiz designs as T* **163** *(5 s. to 30 s.) or* **164** *(40 s. to 500 s.). Multicoloured. P* 14.

804	5 s.	Type **163**	15	10
	a. Booklet pane. Nos. 804/9 each × 2 with margins all round		2·00	
805	9 s.	African Emerald Cuckoo	20	10
806	13 s.	Little Bee Eater	30	10
807	15 s.	Red Bishop	30	10
808	20 s.	Bateleur	40	10
809	25 s.	Scarlet-chested Sunbird	40	10
809a	30 s.	African Wood Pigeon (1.7.91)	40	15
810	40 s.	Type **164**	40	15
811	70 s.	Helmet Guineafowl	45	30
812	100 s.	Eastern White Pelican	55	30
813	170 s.	Saddle-bill Stork	70	70
814	200 s.	South African Crowned Crane	80	80
814a	300 s.	Pied Crow (1.7.91)	90	1·00
814b	400 s.	White-headed Vulture (1.7.91)	1·00	1·40
815	500 s.	Ostrich	1·10	1·50
804/15		*Set of* 15	7·25	6·00
MS816	100×102 mm. 40 s. Superb Starling; 60 s. Lilac-breasted Roller		2·50	2·75

165 Athletics

(Des P. Ndembo. Litho Questa)

1990 (29 Dec). *14th Commonwealth Games, Auckland, New Zealand. T* **165** *and similar multicoloured designs. P* 14.

817	9 s.	Type **165**	25	15
818	13 s.	Netball (*vert*)	45	15
819	25 s.	Pole vaulting	60	20
820	100 s.	Long jumping (*vert*)	1·75	2·25
817/20		*Set of* 4	2·75	2·50
MS821	100×100 mm. 40 s. Boxing (*vert*)		1·00	1·50

166 Former German Post Office, Dar-es-Salaam

(Litho Questa)

1991 (10 Jan). *150th Anniv of the Penny Black and "Stamp World London '90" International Stamp Exhibition. T* **166** *and similar horiz designs. Multicoloured. P* 14.

822	50 s.	Type **166**	65	65
	a. Horiz pair. Nos. 822/3		1·25	1·25
823	50 s.	*Reichstag* (German mail steamer), 1890	65	65
824	75 s.	Dhows, Zanzibar	90	90
	a. Horiz pair. Nos. 824/5		1·75	1·75
825	75 s.	Cobham's Short S. 5 Singapore I flying boat, Mwanza, Lake Victoria, 1928	90	90
826	100 s.	Air Tanzania Fokker F. 27 Friendship over Livingstone's House, Zanzibar	1·25	1·25
	a. Horiz pair. Nos. 826/7		2·50	2·50
827	100 s.	Mail train at Moshi station	1·25	1·25
828	100 s.	English mail coach, 1840	1·25	1·25
829	150 s.	Stephenson's *Rocket* and mail coach, 1838	1·75	1·75
830	200 s.	Imperial Airways Handley Page H.P.42 at Croydon	1·90	1·90
822/30		*Set of* 9	9·50	9·50
MS831	Two sheets, each 85×65 mm. (a) 350 s. Sir Rowland Hill and Penny Black. (b) 350 s. Thurn and Taxis letter of 1860 . . *Set of* 2 *sheets*		7·00	8·00

Nos. 822/3, 824/5 and 826/7 were each printed together, *se-tenant,* in horizontal pairs throughout the sheets.

Nos. 822/7 and **MS**831a overprinted "40th Anniversary of the Accession H. M. Queen Elizabeth II 1952–1992" are reported as not being issued in Tanzania.

167 Petersberg Railway, Konigswinter, Germany

(Litho Questa)

1991 (10 Jan). *Cog Railways. T* **167** *and similar horiz designs. Multicoloured. P* 14.

832	8 s.	Type **167**	40	30
833	25 s.	Waumbek (locomotive), Mount Washington Railway, U.S.A.	60	60
834	50 s.	Sarajevo–Dubrovnik line, Yugoslavia	75	75
835	100 s.	Budapest Rack Railway, Hungary	1·00	1·00
836	150 s.	Steam locomotive No. 97218, Vordenberg–Eisenerz line, Austria	1·50	1·50
837	200 s.	Last train on Rimutaka Incline, New Zealand, 1955	1·60	1·60
838	250 s.	"John Stevens" rack and pinion drive locomotive, U.S.A., 1825	1·60	1·75
839	300 s.	Mt Pilatus Rack Railway steam railcar, Switzerland	1·75	1·75
832/9		*Set of* 8	8·25	8·25
MS840	Two sheets, each 117×87 mm. (a) 400 s. Sylvester Marsh and Presidential excursion train, Mt Washington Cog Railway, U.S.A. 1869 (51×38 mm). (b) 400 s. Steam locomotive, Schneeberg Railway, Austria (51×38 mm). P 13½×14 . . . . *Set of* 2 *sheets*		7·50	8·00

(Des Walt Disney Co. Litho Questa)

1991 (10 Jan). *International Literacy Year (1st issue). Designs as T* **246** *of Maldive Islands showing Walt Disney cartoon characters illustrating the Alphabet. Multicoloured. P* 13½×14.

841/67	1, 2, 3, 5, 10, 15, 18, 20, 25, 30, 35, 40, 45, 50, 55, 60, 75, 80, 90, 100, 120, 125, 145, 150, 160, 175, 200 s. . . . . *Set of* 27	12·00	14·00
MS868	Two sheets, each 128×112 mm. (a) 600 s. Tiger Lily and Lost Boys. P 14×13½. (b) 600 s. Mickey Mouse driving miniature railway locomotive (*vert*). P 13½×14 . . *Set of* 2 *sheets*	8·50	9·50

Nos. 841/67 were issued in three sheetlets, each of nine, the first containing Nos. 841/3, 846, 855, 858, 861, 863, 867, the second Nos. 845, 848, 850, 852, 854, 856, 860, 862, 864 and the third Nos. 844, 847, 849, 851, 853, 857, 859, 865/6.
See also Nos. 905/9.

(Litho Questa)

1991 (10 Jan). *Olympic Games, Barcelona (1st issue). Vert designs as T* **202** *of Lesotho. Multicoloured. P* 14.

869	5 s.	Archery	30	20
870	10 s.	Women's gymnastics	30	20
871	25 s.	Boxing	40	30
872	50 s.	Canoeing	60	50
873	100 s.	Volleyball	1·25	1·25
874	150 s.	Men's gymnastics	1·40	1·50
875	200 s.	4 × 100 metres relay	1·75	2·00
876	300 s.	Judo	2·00	2·25
869/76		*Set of* 8	7·25	7·25
MS877	Two sheets, each 102×71 mm. (a) 400 s. Cycling. (b) 400 s. 400 metres men's hurdles . . . . *Set of* 2 *sheets*		7·50	8·00

See also Nos. 1309/13 and 1404/12.

(Litho Questa)

1991 (18 Jan). *"EXPO '90" International Garden and Greenery Exhibition, Osaka. Orchids. Multicoloured designs as T* **198** *of Lesotho, but vert. P* 14.

878	10 s.	*Phalaenopsis* "Lipperose"	20	15
879	25 s.	*Lycoste* "Aquila"	30	20
880	30 s.	*Vuylstekeara* "Cambria Plush"	30	20
881	50 s.	*Vuylstekeara* "Monica Burnham"	45	35
882	90 s.	*Odontocidium* "Crowborough Plush"	85	85
883	100 s.	*Oncidioda* "Crowborough Chelsea"	85	85
884	250 s.	*Sophrolaeliocattleya* "Phena Saturn"	1·40	1·60
885	300 s.	*Laeliocattleya* "Lykas"	1·50	1·75
878/85		*Set of* 8	5·25	5·50
MS886	Two sheets, each 100×69 mm. (a) 400 s. *Cymbidium* "Baldoyle Melbury". (b) 400 s. *Cymbidium* "Tapestry Long Beach" . . . . *Set of* 2 *sheets*		5·50	6·50

168 Olympic "Soling" Class Yacht Racing

(Litho Questa)

1991 (18 Jan). *Record-breaking Sports Events. T* **168** *and similar multicoloured designs. P* 14.

887	5 s.	Type **168**	30	20
888	20 s.	Olympic downhill skiing	60	35
889	30 s.	"Tour de France" cycle race	1·00	50
890	40 s.	Le Mans 24-hour endurance motor race	1·00	60
891	75 s.	Olympic two-man bobsleighing	1·10	90
892	150 s.	Belgian Grand Prix motor cycle race	1·75	1·25
893	250 s.	Indianapolis 500 motor race	2·00	2·50
894	300 s.	Gold Cup power boat championship	2·00	2·25
887/94		*Set of* 8	8·75	8·00
MS895	Two sheets, each 85×64 mm. (a) 400 s. Colorado 500 motor cycle race (*vert*). (b) 400 s. Schneider Trophy air race (*vert*) *Set of* 2 *sheets*		8·50	9·00

169 Mickey Mouse as Cowboy

(Des Walt Disney Co. Litho Questa)

1991 (20 Feb). *Mickey Mouse in Hollywood. T* **169** *and similar horiz designs showing Walt Disney cartoon characters as actors. Multicoloured. P* 14×13½.

896	5 s.	Type **169**	30	30
897	10 s.	Mickey as boxer	30	30
898	15 s.	Mickey as astronaut	30	30
899	20 s.	Mickey and Minnie as lovers	30	30
900	100 s.	Mickey as pirate rescuing Minnie	1·25	1·25
901	200 s.	Mickey and Donald Duck as policemen arresting Big Pete	2·50	2·50
902	350 s.	Mickey and Donald with Goofy in historical drama	2·75	2·75
903	450 s.	Mickey, Donald and Goofy as sailors	2·75	2·75
896/903		*Set of* 8	9·50	9·50
MS904	Two sheets, each 127×96 mm. (a) 600 s. Mickey, Minnie and Donald in the mummy's tomb. (b) 600 s. Mickey as Canadian Mountie rescuing Minnie from Big Pete . . *Set of* 2 *sheets*		9·00	10·00

170 Women learning to Read

(Litho Questa)

1991 (15 Mar). *International Literacy Year (2nd issue). T* **170** *and similar horiz designs. Multicoloured. P* 14.

905	9 s.	Type **170**	20	15
906	13 s.	Teacher with blackboard	25	15
907	25 s.	Literacy aids	35	20
908	100 s.	Reading newspaper	1·75	2·00
905/8		*Set of* 4	2·25	2·25
MS909	104×73 mm. 50 s. Adult education class		1·25	1·75

171 Ngorongoro Crater   **172** Stegosaurus

(Litho National Printing and Packaging, Zimbabwe)

1991 (28 Mar). *Historical Craters and Caves. T* **171** *and similar horiz designs. Multicoloured. P* 14×14½.

910	3 s.	Type **171**	1·00	1·00
911	5 s.	Prehistoric rock painting, Kondoa Caves	1·00	1·00
912	9 s.	Inner crater, Mt Kilimanjaro	1·25	1·25
913	12 s.	Olduvai Gorge	1·75	1·75
910/13		*Set of* 4	4·50	4·50
MS914	91×92 mm. 10 s. Discarded bottles, Amboni Caves; 10 s. Rock paintings, Amboni Caves; 10 s. Entrance to Amboni Caves; 10 s. Rock formation, Amboni Caves		9·00	8·50

(Litho Questa)

1991 (28 Apr). *350th Death Anniv of Rubens. Cartoons for Decius Mus Tapestries. Multicoloured designs as T* **250** *of Maldive Islands. P* 14×13½.

915	85 s.	"Proclamation of the Vision"	1·40	1·40
	a. Sheetlet. Nos. 915/20		7·50	
916	85 s.	"Divining of the Entrails"	1·40	1·40
917	85 s.	"Dispatch of the Lictors"	1·40	1·40
918	85 s.	"Dedication to Death"	1·40	1·40
919	85 s.	"Victory and Death of Decius Mus"	1·40	1·40
920	85 s.	"Funeral Rites"	1·40	1·40
915/20		*Set of* 6	7·50	7·50
MS921	70×100 mm. 500 s. "Trophy of War" (detail) (*vert*). P 13½×14		7·50	8·00

(Litho State Ptg Wks, Moscow)

1991 (3 June). *Prehistoric Creatures. T* **172** *and similar vert designs. Multicoloured. P* 12×12½.

922	10 s.	Type **172**	25	25
923	15 s.	Triceratops	25	25
924	25 s.	Edmontosaurus	40	40
925	30 s.	Plateosaurus	40	40
926	35 s.	Diplodocus	45	45
927	100 s.	Iguanodon	1·40	1·40
928	200 s.	Silviasaurus	2·00	2·00
922/8		*Set of* 7	4·75	4·75
MS929	90×90 mm. 150 s. Rhamphorhynchus		2·25	2·75

173 Dairy Farming   **174** Pres. Mwinyi leading Walk

(Litho Questa)

1991 (7 June). *20th Anniv of Tanzania Investment Bank. T* **173** *and similar horiz designs. Multicoloured. P* 14.

930	10 s. Type **173**		20	15
931	13 s. Industrial development		25	15
932	25 s. Engineering		30	15
933	100 s. Tea picking ..		1·75	2·00
930/3		*Set of 4*	2·25	2·25
MS934	93×91 mm. Nos. 930/3		2·25	2·50

(Litho Cartor)

1991 (5 July). *National Solidarity Walk. T* **174** *and similar horiz designs. Multicoloured. P* 13½.

935	4 s. + 1 s. Type **174**		40	60
936	30 s. + 1 s. Pres. Mwinyi planting sapling		1·00	1·25
MS937	91×91 mm. 50 s. + 1 s. Pres. Mwinyi sorting cloves. P 12½ ..		1·75	2·00

(Des K. Gromell. Litho Questa)

1991 (15 Aug). *"Phila Nippon '91" International Stamp Exhibition, Tokyo. Japanese Railway Locomotives. Multicoloured designs as T* **257** *of Maldive Islands, but horiz. P* 14.

938	10 s. Class 150 steam locomotive, 1872 (first locomotive)		65	65
939	25 s. Class 4500 steam locomotive, 1902 ..		90	90
940	35 s. Class C62 steam locomotive, 1948 ..		1·00	1·00
941	50 s. Mikado steam locomotive		1·25	1·25
942	75 s. Class 6250 steam locomotive, 1915 ..		1·50	1·50
943	100 s. Class C11 steam locomotive, 1932 ..		1·75	1·75
944	200 s. Class E10 steam locomotive, 1948 ..		2·00	2·00
945	300 s. Class 8550 steam locomotive, 1899 ..		2·50	2·50
938/45		*Set of 8*	10·50	10·50
MS946	Four sheets, each 102×71 mm. (a) 400 s. Series 400 electric train. (b) 400 s. Class EH10 electric locomotive, 1954. (c) 400 s. Class DD51 diesel-hydraulic locomotive, 1962. (d) 400 s. Class EF58 electric locomotive .. *Set of 4 sheets*		9·00	10·00

175 Zebra and Golden-winged Sunbird, Ngorongoro Crater

176 *Eronia cleodora*

(Des Mary Walters. Litho Questa)

1991 (22 Aug). *National Game Parks. T* **175** *and similar horiz designs. Multicoloured. P* 14.

947	10 s. Type **175**		70	70
948	25 s. Greater Kudu and Elephant, Ruaha Park		1·00	1·00
949	30 s. Sable Antelope and Red and Yellow Barbet, Mikumi Park		1·00	1·00
950	50 s. Leopard and Wildebeest, Serengeti Park		1·25	1·25
951	90 s. Giraffe and Starred Robin, Ngurdoto Park		2·00	2·00
952	100 s. Eland and Abbott's Duiker, Kilimanjaro Park		1·75	1·75
953	250 s. Lion and Impala, Lake Manyara Park		3·00	3·00
954	300 s. Black Rhinoceros and Ostrich, Tarangire Park		3·75	3·75
947/54		*Set of 8*	13·00	13·00
MS955	Two sheets, each 99×68 mm. (a) 400 s. Blue-breasted Kingfisher and Defassa Waterbuck, Selous Game Reserve. (b) 400 s. Paradise Whydah and Oryx, Mkomazi Game Reserve .. *Set of 2 sheets*		11·00	10·00

(Des I. Maclaury. Litho Questa)

1991 (28 Aug). *Butterflies. T* **176** *and similar vert designs. Multicoloured. P* 14.

956	10 s. Type **176**		55	45
957	15 s. *Precis westermanni* ..		70	60
958	35 s. *Antanartia delius* ..		1·00	90
959	75 s. *Bematistes aganice* ..		1·75	1·60
960	100 s. *Kallima jacksoni* ..		1·90	1·75
961	150 s. *Apaturopsis cleocharis*		2·75	2·75
962	200 s. *Colotis aurigineus* ..		3·00	3·00
963	300 s. *Iolaus crawshayi* ..		3·25	3·50
956/63		*Set of 8*	13·00	13·00
MS964	Four sheets, each 117×76 mm. (a) 400 s. *Charaxes zoolina.* (b) 400 s. *Papilio phorcas.* (c) 400 s. *Charaxes ethalion.* (d) 400 s. *Papilio nobilis* .. *Set of 4 sheets*		14·00	15·00

177 Microwave Tower and Dish Aerial

178 Rice Cultivation

(Litho Questa)

1991 (5 Sept). *25th Anniv of Intelsat Satellite System. T* **177** *and similar horiz designs. Multicoloured. P* 14.

965	10 s. Type **177**		40	20
966	25 s. Satellite picture of Earth		55	30
967	100 s. Mwenge "B" Earth station		1·50	1·50
968	500 s. Mwenge "A" Earth station		4·50	5·50
965/8		*Set of 4*	6·25	6·75
MS969	90×86 mm. 50 s. Satellite links on world map ..		1·75	2·00

(Litho Cartor)

1991 (16 Sept). *40th Anniv of United Nations Development Programme. T* **178** *and similar designs. P* 13½.

970	10 s. multicoloured		10	10
971	15 s. multicoloured		15	10
972	100 s. multicoloured		1·25	1·50
973	500 s. multicoloured		3·75	5·50
970/3		*Set of 4*	4·75	6·50
MS974	90×90 mm. 40 s. pale new blue and black. P 12½ ..		1·10	1·50

Designs: Horiz—15 s. Vocational and Civil Service training; 100 s. Terrace farming. *Vert*—40 s. U.N.D.P. anniversary emblem; 500 s. Renovated Arab door.

179 Netball

180 "TELECOM '91" Logo

(Litho State Ptg Wks, Moscow)

1991 (20 Sept). *All-Africa Games, Cairo. T* **179** *and similar multicoloured designs. P* 12½×12 *(Nos. 976, 979) or* 12×12½ *(others).*

975	10 s. Type **179**		30	20
976	15 s. Football (*horiz*)		30	20
977	100 s. Tennis		1·75	1·50
978	200 s. Athletics		2·00	2·00
979	500 s. Baseball (*horiz*)		5·00	6·50
975/9		*Set of 5*	8·50	9·50
MS980	80×60 mm. 500 s. Basketball ..		6·00	6·50

(Litho Cartor)

1991 (1 Oct). *"TELECOM '91" International Telecommunication Exhibition, Geneva* (10, 15 *s.*) *and World Telecommunications Day (others). T* **180** *and similar multicoloured designs. P* 13½×14 *(vert) or* 14×13½ *(horiz).*

981	10 s. Type **180**		10	10
982	15 s. "TELECOM '91" logo and address on envelope (*horiz*)		15	10
983	35 s. Symbolic telecommunication signals		25	20
984	100 s. Symbolic telecommunication signals (*horiz*)		70	1·00
981/4		*Set of 4*	1·00	1·25

181 Japanese Bobtail Cat

(Des Mary Walters. Litho Questa)

1991 (28 Oct). *Cats. T* **181** *and similar horiz designs. Multicoloured. P* 14.

985	50 s. Type **181**		65	65
	a. Sheetlet. Nos. 985/1000		9·50	
986	50 s. Cornish Rex ..		65	65
987	50 s. Malayan		65	65
988	50 s. Tonkinese		65	65
989	50 s. Abyssinian		65	65
990	50 s. Russian Blue		65	65
991	50 s. Cymric		65	65
992	50 s. Somali		65	65
993	50 s. Siamese		65	65
994	50 s. Himalayan		65	65
995	50 s. Singapura		65	65
996	50 s. Manx		65	65
997	50 s. Oriental Shorthair ..		65	65
998	50 s. Maine Coon ..		65	65
999	50 s. Persian		65	65
1000	50 s. Birman		65	65
985/1000		*Set of 16*	9·50	9·50

Nos. 985/1000 were printed together, *se-tenant*, as a sheetlet of 16.

182 Shire Horse

(Des Mary Walters. Litho Questa)

1991 (28 Oct). *Horses and Ponies. T* **182** *and similar horiz designs. Multicoloured. P* 14.

1001	50 s. Type **182**		70	70
	a. Sheetlet. Nos. 1001/16		10·00	
1002	50 s. Thoroughbred		70	70
1003	50 s. Kladruber		70	70
1004	50 s. Appaloosa		70	70
1005	50 s. Hanoverian		70	70
1006	50 s. Arab		70	70
1007	50 s. Breton		70	70
1008	50 s. Exmoor		70	70
1009	50 s. Connemara		70	70
1010	50 s. Lipizzaner		70	70
1011	50 s. Shetland		70	70
1012	50 s. Percheron		70	70
1013	50 s. Pinto		70	70
1014	50 s. Orlov		70	70
1015	50 s. Palomino		70	70
1016	50 s. Welsh Cob		70	70
1001/16		*Set of 16*	10·00	10·00

Nos. 1001/16 were printed together, *se-tenant*, as a sheetlet of 16, with the backgrounds of each horizontal strip of 4 forming a composite design.

183 Yellow Tetra

184 African Elephant

(Des Mary Walters. Litho Questa)

1991 (28 Oct). *Aquarium Fishes. T* **183** *and similar horiz designs. Multicoloured. P* 14.

1017	75 s. Type **183**		70	70
	a. Sheetlet. Nos. 1017/32		10·00	
1018	75 s. Five-banded Barb ..		70	70
1019	75 s. Simpson Platy ..		70	70
1020	75 s. Guppy ..		70	70
1021	75 s. Zebra Danio		70	70
1022	75 s. Neon Tetra ..		70	70
1023	75 s. Siamese Fighting Fish ..		70	70
1024	75 s. Tiger Barb ..		70	70
1025	75 s. Two-striped Lyretail		70	70
1026	75 s. Fan-tailed Goldfish ..		70	70
1027	75 s. Pearl Gourami ..		70	70
1028	75 s. Freshwater Angelfish ..		70	70
1029	75 s. Clown Loach ..		70	70
1030	75 s. Red Swordtail ..		70	70
1031	75 s. Blue Discus ..		70	70
1032	75 s. Rosy Barb ..		70	70
1017/32		*Set of 16*	10·00	10·00

Nos. 1017/32 were printed together, *se-tenant*, as a sheetlet of 16, with the backgrounds of each stamp forming a composite design.

(Des Mary Walters. Litho Questa)

1991 (28 Oct). *African Elephants. T* **184** *and similar vert designs. Multicoloured. P* 14.

1033	75 s. Type **184**		90	90
	a. Sheetlet. Nos. 1033/48		13·00	
1034	75 s. Two elephants fighting		90	90
1035	75 s. Elephant facing forward and tree		90	90
1036	75 s. Elephant facing left and tree		90	90
1037	75 s. Cow elephant and calf facing right standing in water		90	90
1038	75 s. Cow watching over calf in water		90	90
1039	75 s. Two adults and calf in water		90	90
1040	75 s. Cow and calf facing left standing in water		90	90
1041	75 s. Elephant facing right		90	90
1042	75 s. Elephants feeding		90	90
1043	75 s. Elephant feeding		90	90
1044	75 s. Elephant and Zebra		90	90
1045	75 s. Cow and calf drinking		90	90
1046	75 s. Calf suckling		90	90
1047	75 s. Bull elephant		90	90
1048	75 s. Cow with small calf		90	90
1033/48		*Set of 16*	13·00	13·00

Nos. 1033/48 were printed together, *se-tenant*, as a sheetlet of 16, with each horizontal strip of 4 forming a composite design.

185 Budgerigar

186 Indian Elephant

(Des Mary Walters. Litho Questa)

1991 (28 Oct). *Pet Birds. T* **185** *and similar horiz designs. Multicoloured. P* 14.

1049	75 s. Type **185**		70	70
	a. Sheetlet. Nos. 1049/64		10·00	
1050	75 s. Orange-breasted Bunting ("Rainbow Bunting")		70	70
1051	75 s. Golden-fronted Leafbird ..		70	70

1052	75 s.	Black-headed Caique	.. ..	70	70
1053	75 s.	Java Sparrow	.. ..	70	70
1054	75 s.	Diamond Firetail Finch		70	70
1055	75 s.	Peach-faced Lovebird	..	70	70
1056	75 s.	Golden Conure	.. ..	70	70
1057	75 s.	Military Macaw	..	70	70
1058	75 s.	Yellow-faced Parrotlet	..	70	70
1059	75 s.	Sulphur-crested Cockatoo		70	70
1060	75 s.	White-fronted Amazon ("Spectacled Amazon Parrot")		70	70
1061	75 s.	Paradise Tanager	..	70	70
1062	75 s.	Gouldian Finch	..	70	70
1063	75 s.	Masked Lovebird	..	70	70
1064	75 s.	Hill Mynah	..	70	70
1049/64			Set of 16	10·00	10·00

Nos. 1049/64 were printed together, *se-tenant*, as a sheetlet of 16, forming a composite design.

(Litho Questa)

1991 (20 Nov). *Death Centenary of Vincent van Gogh (artist)* (1990). *Multicoloured designs as T 255 of Maldive Islands. P* 13½×14.

1065	10 s.	"Peasant Woman Sewing" ..		30	25
1066	15 s.	"Head of Peasant Woman with Greenish Lace Cap"		40	35
1067	35 s.	"Flowering Orchard" ..	..	70	60
1068	75 s.	"Portrait of a Girl" ..	..	1·25	1·00
1069	100 s.	"Portrait of a Woman with Red Ribbon"		1·50	1·25
1070	150 s.	"Vase with Flowers"	..	2·00	2·00
1071	200 s.	"Houses in Antwerp"	..	2·25	2·50
1072	400 s.	"Seated Peasant Woman with White Cap"		4·25	5·00
1065/72			Set of 8	11·50	11·50
MS1073	Two sheets, each 127×112 mm. (a) 400 s. "Bulb Fields" (*horiz*). (b) 400 s. "The Parsonage Garden at Nuenen in the Snow" (*horiz*). Imperf ..		Set of 2 sheets	11·00	12·00

(Des J. Puvilland. Litho State Ptg Wks, Moscow)

1991 (28 Nov). *Elephants. T 186 and similar multicoloured designs. P* 12×12½ (*vert*) or 12½×12 (*horiz*).

1074	10 s.	Type 186	..	50	50
1075	15 s.	Indian Elephant uprooting tree		65	65
1076	25 s.	Indian Elephant with calf	..	80	80
1077	30 s.	African Elephant	..	80	80
1078	35 s.	Head of African Elephant (*horiz*)		85	85
1079	100 s.	African Elephant and calf bathing (*horiz*)		1·75	1·75
1080	200 s.	Two African Elephants (*horiz*)		3·00	3·00
1074/80			Set of 7	7·50	7·50
MS1081	90×90 mm. 400 s. Mammoth (*horiz*)			4·00	4·50

187 Class Em Steam Locomotive, Russia, 1930,

(Litho State Ptg Wks, Moscow)

1991 (10 Dec). *Locomotives of the World. T 187 and similar multicoloured designs. P* 12½×12 (*horiz*) or 12×12½ (*vert*).

1082	10 s.	Type 187	..	25	25
1083	15 s.	"Hikari" express train, Japan, 1964		35	35
1084	25 s.	Russian steam locomotive, 1834 (*vert*)		45	45
1085	35 s.	TGV express train, France, 1979		55	55
1086	60 s.	Diesel railcar No. R16-01, France, 1972		80	80
1087	100 s.	High Speed Train 125, Great Britain, 1972		1·40	1·40
1088	300 s.	Russian steam locomotive, 1833 (*vert*)		3·00	3·00
1082/8			Set of 7	6·00	6·00
MS1089	91×91 mm. 100 s. French electric locomotive, 1952 (*vert*)			1·40	1·75

No. 1088 is inscribed "1837" in error.

(Des Walt Disney Co. Litho Questa)

1991 (24 Dec). *Christmas. Walt Disney Christmas Cards. Multicoloured designs as T 228 of St. Vincent. P* 14×13½ (*horiz*) or 13½×14 (*vert*).

1090	10 s.	Disney characters in "JOY", 1968 (*horiz*)		25	20
1091	25 s.	Mickey, Donald, Pluto and Goofy hanging up stockings, 1981 (*horiz*)		50	40
1092	35 s.	Characters from Disney film *Robin Hood*, 1973 (*horiz*)		55	45
1093	75 s.	Mickey looking at Christmas tree, 1967 (*horiz*)		1·00	90
1094	100 s.	Goofy, Mickey, Donald and Chip n' Dale on film set, 1969		1·40	1·25
1095	150 s.	Mickey on giant bauble, 1976		1·75	1·60
1096	200 s.	Clarabelle Cow with electric cow bell, 1935		2·00	2·25
1097	300 s.	Mickey's nephews with book, 1935		2·75	3·00
1090/7			Set of 8	9·00	9·00
MS1098	Two sheets, each 127×102 mm. (a) 500 s. Mickey handing out presents, 1935. (b) 500 s. Disney cartoon characters, 1968		Set of 2 sheets	11·00	12·00

MINIMUM PRICE

The minimum price quote is 10p which represents a handling charge rather than a basis for valuing common stamps. For further notes about prices see introductory pages.

---

188 Bruce Lee

189 Sand Tilefish

Malacanthus latovittatus

(Des J. Iskowitz. Litho Questa)

1992 (14 Feb). *Entertainers. T 188 and similar vert designs. P* 13½.

1099/134	75 s. × 36 multicoloured		Set of 36	20·00	22·00
MS1135	Four sheets, each 78×108 mm. 500 s. × 4 multicoloured (Bruce Lee, Marilyn Monroe, Elvis Presley, Kouyate & Kouyate, each 28×42 mm). P 14		Set of 4 sheets	20·00	22·00

Nos. 1099/134 were issued as four sheetlets, each of nine different designs, depicting Bruce Lee, Marilyn Monroe, Elvis Presley and black entertainers (Scott Joplin, Sammy Davis Jnr, Joan Armatrading, Louis Armstrong, Miriam Makeba, Lionel Ritchie, Whitney Houston, Bob Marley, Tina Turner).

(Des P. Ndembo. Litho State Ptg Wks, Moscow)

1992 (9 Mar). *Fishes. T 189 and similar horiz designs. Multicoloured. P* 12½×12.

1136	10 s.	Type 189	..	40	40
1137	15 s.	Five-banded Cichlid	..	45	45
1138	25 s.	Pearly Lamprologus	..	60	60
1139	35 s.	Jewel Cichlid	..	70	70
1140	60 s.	Two-striped Lyretail	..	1·00	1·00
1141	100 s.	Reef Stonefish	..	1·50	1·50
1142	300 s.	Ahl's Lyretail	..	3·75	3·75
1136/42			Set of 7	7·50	7·50
MS1143	90×90 mm. 100 s. Oarfish			1·40	1·60

190 Chimpanzee in Tree

191 Pope John Paul II in Dominican Republic, 1979

(Des Mary Walters. Litho Questa)

1992 (30 Mar). *Common Chimpanzee. T 190 and similar vert designs. Multicoloured. P* 14.

1144	10 s.	Type 190	..	50	50
1145	15 s.	Feeding	..	55	55
1146	35 s.	Two chimpanzees	..	85	85
1147	75 s.	Adult male with arms folded		1·25	1·25
1148	100 s.	Breaking branch	..	1·50	1·50
1149	150 s.	Young chimpanzee in tree		2·25	2·25
1150	200 s.	Female holding young	..	2·75	2·75
1151	300 s.	Chimpanzee sitting in tree		3·75	3·75
1144/51			Set of 8	12·00	12·00
MS1152	Two sheets, each 99×68 mm. (a) 400 s. Eating termites. (b) 400 s. Swinging through trees		Set of 2 sheets	7·00	7·00

(Litho Questa)

1992 (13 Apr). *Papal Visits. T 191 and similar vert designs. P* 14.

1153/272	100 s. × 120 multicoloured		Set of 120	85·00	75·00

Nos. 1153/272 were issued in ten sheetlets, each of 12 different designs arranged round a common block of four stamp-sized labels.

192 Balcony

193 Gogo Costume

(Des J. da Silva. Litho State Ptg Wks, Moscow)

1992 (15 Apr). *Zanzibar Stone Town. T 192 and similar multicoloured designs. P* 12½×12 (200 s.) or 12×12½ (*others*).

1273	10 s.	Type 192	..	30	20
1274	20 s.	Bahlnara Mosque	..	55	35
1275	30 s.	High Court Building	..	65	40
1276	200 s.	National Museum (*horiz*)		3·25	4·25
1273/6			Set of 4	4·25	4·75
MS1277	91×91 mm. 150 s. Old Fort (*horiz*); 300 s. Maruhubi ruins (*horiz*). P 12½×12			4·25	6·00

(Des P. Ndembo. Litho National Printing and Packaging, Zimbabwe)

1992 (30 Apr). *Traditional Costumes. T 193 and similar vert designs. Multicoloured. P* 14½.

1278	3 s.	Type 193	..	50	50
1279	5 s.	Swahili	..	50	50
1280	9 s.	Hehe and Makonde	..	60	60
1281	12 s.	Maasai	..	75	75
1278/81			Set of 4	2·10	2·10
MS1282	91×91 mm. 40 s. Mwarusha			2·25	2·50

194 Melisa and Mike (chimpanzees)

(Des P. Ndembo. Litho B.D.T.)

1992 (29 May). *Chimpanzees of the Gombe. Multicoloured. P* 14.

(a) *Horiz designs as T 194*

1283	10 s.	Type 194	..	40	40
1284	15 s.	Leakey and David Greybeard		50	50
1285	30 s.	Fifi termiting	..	70	70
1286	35 s.	Galahad	..	75	75
1283/6			Set of 4	2·10	2·10
MS1287	90×90 mm. 100 s. Fifi, Flo and Faben			2·00	2·50

(b) *Vert designs showing individual chimpanzees*

1288	10 s.	Leakey	..	70	70
		a. Sheetlet. Nos. 1288/95		5·50	
1289	15 s.	Fifi	..	70	70
1290	20 s.	Faben	..	70	70
1291	30 s.	David Greybeard	..	70	70
1292	35 s.	Mike	..	70	70
1293	50 s.	Galahad	..	70	70
1294	100 s.	Melisa	..	85	85
1295	200 s.	Flo	..	1·25	1·25
1288/95			Set of 8	5·50	5·50

Nos. 1288/95 were printed together, *se-tenant*, in sheetlets of 8.

195 Sorghum Farming, Serena

196 Giant Spider Conch (*Lambis truncata*)

(Des P. Ndembo. Litho Questa)

1992 (22 June). *25th Anniv of National Bank of Commerce. T 195 and similar multicoloured designs. P* 14.

1296	10 s.	Type 195	..	35	15
1297	15 s.	Samora Avenue Branch and computer operator (*vert*)		40	25
1298	35 s.	Training centre	..	65	65
1299	40 s.	Women dyeing textiles	..	70	90
1296/9			Set of 4	1·90	1·75
MS1300	111×117 mm. 30 s. Bank Head Office			1·00	1·50

(Litho State Ptg Wks, Moscow)

1992 (30 June). *Shells. T 196 and similar vert designs. Multicoloured. P* 12×12½.

1301	10 s.	Type 196	..	30	30
1302	15 s.	Bull-mouth Helmet (*Cypraecassis rufa*)		35	35
1303	25 s.	Rugose Mitre (*Vexillum rugosum*)		50	50
1304	30 s.	Lettered Cone (*Conus litteratus*)		50	50
1305	35 s.	True Heart Cockle (*Corculum cardissa*)		50	50
1306	50 s.	Ramose Murex (*Murex ramosus*) ..		70	70
1307	250 s.	Indian Volute (*Melo melo*)	..	2·75	3·25
1301/7			Set of 7	5·00	5·50
MS1308	91×91 mm. 300 s. Giant Clam (*Tridacna gigas*)			3·50	4·00

197 Basketball

198 British-designed Radar, Pearl Harbor

(Des A. Nabola. Litho State Ptg Wks, Moscow)

1992 (23 July). *Olympic Games, Barcelona (2nd issue). T* **197** *and similar vert designs. Multicoloured. P* 12×12½.

1309	40 s. Type **197**	..	..	..	45	30
1310	100 s. Billiards	..	..	..	75	60
1311	200 s. Table Tennis	..	..	1·25	1·40
1312	400 s. Darts	..	..	2·75	3·25
1309/12				*Set of 4*	4·75	5·00
MS1313	91×8 mm. 500 s. Weightlifting			3·00	4·25

(Des J. Batchelor. Litho Questa)

1992 (1 Aug). *50th Anniv of Japanese Attack on Pearl Harbor. T* **198** *and similar horiz designs. Multicoloured. P* 14½.

1314	75 s. Type **198**	..	..	1·25	1·25
	a. Sheetlet. Nos. 1314/23	..	11·00	
1315	75 s. Winston Churchill	..	1·25	1·25
1316	75 s. Sinking of H.M.S. *Repulse* (battle cruiser)	..	1·25	1·25
1317	75 s. Sinking of H.M.S. *Prince of Wales* (battleship)		1·25	1·25
1318	75 s. Surrender of Singapore		1·25	1·25
1319	75 s. Sinking of H.M.S. *Hermes* (aircraft carrier)		1·25	1·25
1320	75 s. Japanese attack on Malayan airfield	1·25	1·25
1321	75 s. Japanese gun crew, Hong Kong	1·25	1·25
1322	75 s. Japanese landing craft	1·25	1·25
1323	75 s. *Haguro* (Japanese cruiser)	1·25	1·25
1314/23				*Set of 10*	11·00	11·00

Nos. 1314/23 were printed together, *se-tenant*, in sheetlets of 10 with the stamps arranged in two horizontal strips of 5 separated by a gutter showing H.M.S. *Exeter* at Battle of Java Sea.

199 French Resistance
Monument and Medal

(Litho Questa)

1992 (1 Aug). *Birth Centenary of Charles de Gaulle (French statesman) (1990). T* **199** *and similar multicoloured designs. P* 14.

1324	25 s. Type **199**	..	..	50	40
1325	30 s. Free French tank on Omaha Beach, D-Day		50	40
1326	150 s. Concorde at Charles de Gaulle Airport		4·50	5·00
1324/6			*Set of 3*	5·00	5·25
MS1327	115×92 mm. 500 s. Free French local Cross of Lorraine opt on Petain 1 f. 50 and De Gaulle label postmarked 25 August 1944 (39×51 mm)	..	..	6·00	7·00

200 Scout Badge, Giraffe and
Elephant

(Litho Questa)

1992 (1 Aug). *50th Death Anniv of Lord Baden-Powell (founder of Boy Scout movement) (1991). T* **200** *and similar multicoloured designs. P* 14.

1328	10 s. Type **200**	..	..	70	30
1329	15 s. Scouts in boat	..	..	70	30
1330	400 s. John Glenn's space capsule	4·75	5·50
1328/30			*Set of 3*	5·50	5·50
MS1331	90×117 mm. 500 s. Tanzanian Scout (39×51 mm). P 13½	..	..	4·00	5·00

201 Marcella Sembrich as
Zerlina in *Don Giovanni*

202 Lucky Omens

(Litho Questa)

1992 (1 Aug). *Death Bicentenary of Mozart. T* **201** *and similar designs. P* 14.

1332	10 s. black and deep mauve	..	75	40
1333	50 s. multicoloured	..	1·75	1·10
1334	300 s. black and deep mauve	..	1·75	1·10
1332/4		*Set of 3*	6·25	6·00
MS1335	115×87 mm. 500 s. grey-brown, stone and black	..	6·50	7·00

Designs: *Horiz*—50 s. Planet Jupiter (Symphony No. 41); 300 s. Luciano Pavarotti as Idamente in *Idomeneo*. *Vert* (35×47 mm)—500 s. Wolfgang Amadeus Mozart.

(Litho B.D.T.)

1992 (1 Aug). *"Granada '92" International Stamp Exhibition, Spain. Paintings. Designs as T* **68** *of St. Kitts-Nevis (Nevis). P* 13.

1336	25 s. Indian red and black	..	..	40	40
1337	35 s. multicoloured	..	..	50	50
1338	50 s. multicoloured	..	..	60	60
1339	75 s. multicoloured	..	..	85	85
1340	100 s. black, brown and flesh	..	1·25	1·25
1341	150 s. Indian red and black	..	1·75	1·75
1342	200 s. Indian red and black	..	2·00	2·00
1343	300 s. multicoloured	..	2·50	2·50
1336/43			*Set of 8*	9·00	9·00
MS1344	Two sheets, each 121×95 mm. (a) 400 s. multicoloured. (b) 400 s. multicoloured. Imperf			
			Set of 2 sheets	6·25	6·75

Designs: *Horiz* (49½×36 *mm*)—25 s. "A Picador, mounted on a Chulo's Shoulders, spears a Bull" (Goya); 150 s. "Another Madness (of Martincho) in the Plaza de Zaragoza" (Goya); 200 s. "Recklessness of Martincho in the Plaza de Zaragoza" (Goya). (111×86 *mm*)—400 s. (No. **MS**1344a) "Two Men at Table" (Velasquez); 400 s. (No. **MS**1344b) "Seascape" (Mariana Salvador Maella). *Vert*—35 s. "Philip IV at Fraga" (Velasquez); 50 s. "Head of a Stag" (Velasquez); 75 s. "The Cardinal-Infante Ferdinand as a Hunter" (Velasquez); 100 s. "The Dream of Reason brings forth Monsters" (Goya); 300 s. "Pablo de Valladolid" (Velasquez).

(Des P. Ndembo. Litho State Ptg Wks, Moscow)

1992 (30 Sept). *500th Anniv of Discovery of America by Columbus. T* **202** *and similar multicoloured designs. P* 12½×12 (*vert*) or 12½×12 (*horiz*).

1345	10 s. Type **202**	..	..	20	20
1346	15 s. Map and compass	..	25	25
1347	25 s. Look-out in crow's nest	..	35	35
1348	30 s. Amerindians sighting ships (*horiz*)	40	40
1349	35 s. *Pinta* and *Nina* (*horiz*)	45	45
1350	75 s. *Santa Maria* (*horiz*)	..	70	70
1351	250 s. Wreck of *Santa Maria*	..	1·50	2·00
1345/51			*Set of 7*	3·50	4·00
MS1352	93×93 mm. 200 s. Columbus	..	1·50	2·00

TANZANIA

203 Superb
Starling

(204) 15th Anniversary

(Des P. Ndembo. Litho State Ptg Wks, Moscow)

1992 (15 Oct). *Birds. T* **203** *and similar multicoloured designs. P* 12×12½.

1353	5 s. Type **203**	..	..	30	25
1354	10 s. Golden Bishop ("Canary")	..	40	30
1355	15 s. Four-coloured Bush Shrike	..	50	40
1356	25 s. Grey-headed Kingfisher	..	55	45
1357	30 s. Common Kingfisher	..	55	45
1358	35 s. Yellow-billed Oxpecker	..	55	45
1359	150 s. Black-throated Honeyguide	1·40	1·40
1353/9			*Set of 7*	3·75	3·25
MS1360	93×92 mm. 300 s. European Cuckoo (*horiz*). P 12½×12	..	2·50	3·00

1992 (15 Oct). *15th Death Anniv of Elvis Presley. Nos.* 1117/25 *optd with T* **204**.

1361	75 s. Looking pensive	..	85	85
	a. Sheetlet. Nos. 1361/9	..	7·00	
1362	75 s. Wearing black and yellow striped shirt	..	85	85
1363	75 s. Singing into microphone	..	85	85
1364	75 s. Wearing wide-brimmed hat	..	85	85
1365	75 s. With microphone in right hand	85	85
1366	75 s. In Army uniform	..	85	85
1367	75 s. Wearing pink shirt	..	85	85
1368	75 s. In yellow shirt	..	85	85
1369	75 s. In jacket and bow tie	..	85	85
1361/9			*Set of 9*	7·00	7·00

TANZANIA

205 Iguanodon

(Des S. Barlowe. Litho Questa)

1992 (5 Nov). *African Dinosaurs. T* **205** *and similar horiz designs. Multicoloured. P* 14.

1370	100 s. Type **205**	..	..	80	80
	a. Sheetlet. Nos. 1370/85	..	11·00	
1371	100 s. Saltasaurus	..	..	80	80
1372	100 s. Cetiosaurus	..	..	80	80
1373	100 s. Camarasaurus	..	..	80	80
1374	100 s. Spinosaurus	..	..	80	80
1375	100 s. Stegosaurus	..	..	80	80
1376	100 s. Allosaurus	..	..	80	80
1377	100 s. Ceratosaurus	..	..	80	80
1378	100 s. Lesothosaurus	..	..	80	80
1379	100 s. Anchisaurus	..	..	80	80

1380	100 s. Ornithomimus	..	..	80	80
1381	100 s. Baronyx	..	..	80	80
1382	100 s. Pachycephalosaurus	..	80	80
1383	100 s. Heterodontosaurus	..	80	80
1384	100 s. Dryosaurus	..	..	80	80
1385	100 s. Coelophysis	..	..	80	80
1370/85			*Set of 16*	11·00	11·00

Nos. 1370/85 were printed together, *se-tenant*, in sheetlets of 16, forming a composite design.

Tilapia mariae

206 Spotted Tilapia

(Litho B.D.T.)

1992 (5 Nov). *Fishes. T* **206** *and similar horiz designs. Multicoloured. P* 13½.

1386	100 s. Type **206**	..	..	85	85
	a. Sheetlet. Nos. 1386/97	..	9·00	
1387	100 s. Butterfly Barb	..	..	85	85
1388	100 s. Blunthead Moliro Cichlid	..	85	85
1389	100 s. Angel Squeaker	..	..	85	85
1390	100 s. Dickfeld's Julie	..	..	85	85
1391	100 s. Nile Mouthbrooder	..	..	85	85
1392	100 s. Blue-finned Notho	..	..	85	85
1393	100 s. Crabro Mbuna	..	..	85	85
1394	100 s. Pearl-scaled Lamprologus	..	85	85
1395	100 s. Zebra Mbuna	..	..	85	85
1396	100 s. Marlier's Julie	..	..	85	85
1397	100 s. Brichard's Chalinochromis	..	85	85
1386/97			*Set of 12*	9·00	9·00
MS1398	Three sheets, each 71×55 mm. (a) 500 s. Palmqvist's Notho. (b) 500 s. Electric Blue Haplochromis. (c) 500 s. Short Lamprologus		
		Set of 3 sheets	11·00	12·00

Nos. 1386/97 were printed together, *se-tenant*, in sheetlets of 12, forming a composite design.

207 Hunting Birds with
Catapults

208 *Couroupita
guianensis*

(Litho Cartor)

1992 (25 Nov). *Traditional Hunting. T* **207** *and similar horiz designs. Multicoloured. P* 13½.

1399	20 s. Type **207**	..	..	50	30
1400	70 s. Hunting antelope with bow and arrow	..	75	55
1401	100 s. Hunting antelopes with dogs	1·00	90
1402	150 s. Hunting lion with spears and shields	1·75	2·25
1399/1402			*Set of 4*	3·50	3·50
MS1403	100×100 mm. 40 s. Traditional hunting weapons. P 12½×12	..	1·50	2·00

(Litho Questa)

1992 (30 Nov). *Olympic Games, Albertville and Barcelona (3rd issue). Multicoloured designs as T* **216** *of Lesotho. P* 14.

1404	20 s. Men's 4000 metre pursuit cycling	40	25
1405	40 s. Men's double sculls rowing (*horiz*)	30	20
1406	50 s. Waterpolo (*horiz*)	..	40	20
1407	70 s. Women's single luge (*horiz*)	40	30
1408	100 s. Marathon (*horiz*)	..	55	50
1409	150 s. Women's asymmetrical bars gymnastics (*horiz*)	..	1·25	1·25
1410	200 s. Ice hockey	..	..	2·00	1·50
1411	400 s. Men's rings gymnastics	..	2·75	3·25
1404/11			*Set of 8*	7·25	6·75
MS1412	Two sheets, each 100×71 mm. (a) 500 s. Tennis. (b) 500 s. Football	*Set of 2 sheets*	10·00	10·00

(Des Walt Disney & Co. Litho Questa)

1992 (30 Nov). *Mickey's Portrait Gallery. Multicoloured designs as T* **70** *of St. Kitts-Nevis (Nevis) showing Walt Disney cartoon characters. P* 13½×14.

1413	25 s. Donald Duck in *Sea Scouts*, 1939	30	30
1414	25 s. Minnie Mouse in *Hawaiian Holiday*, 1937	30	30
1415	25 s. Pluto in *Society Dog Show*, 1939	30	30
1416	35 s. Donald in *Fire Chief*, 1940	40	40
1417	50 s. Donald in *Truant Officer Donald*, 1941	50	50
1418	75 s. Goofy in *Clock Cleaners*, 1937	60	60
1419	100 s. Goofy in *Goofy and Wilbur*, 1939	70	70
1420	100 s. Mickey Mouse in *Magician Mickey*, 1937	70	70
1421	200 s. Minnie in *The Nifty Nineties*, 1941	1·25	1·25
1422	300 s. Mickey and Pluto in *Society Dog Show*, 1939	1·50	1·50
1423	400 s. Pluto and pups in *Pluto's Quin-Puplets*, 1937	1·60	1·60
1424	500 s. Daisy and Donald in *Mr. Duck Steps Out*, 1940	1·75	1·75
1413/24			*Set of 12*	9·00	9·00

MS1425 Three sheets. (a) 127×102 mm. 600 s. Goofy in *Forever Goofy*. P 13½×14. (b) 127×102 mm. 600 s. Daisy in *Don Donald*, 1937. P 13½×14. (c) 112×104 mm. 600 s. Mickey and Minnie in *Brave Little Tailor*, 1938 (*horiz*). P 14×13½ .. .. .. Set of 3 sheets 9·50 11·00

(Des Jennifer Toombs. Litho Questa)

1992 (1 Dec). *Botanical Gardens of the World. Rio de Janeiro. T 208 and similar vert designs showing African plants. Multicoloured. P 14½×14.*
1426/45 70 s.×20 .. .. Set of 20 12·00 14·00
MS1446 110×74 mm. 500 s. Avenue of Royal Palms .. .. 3·25 4·00
Nos. 1426/45 were issued as a *se-tenant* sheetlet of 20 (5×4).

209 Abyssinian Cat   210 Count Ferdinand von Zeppelin

(Litho State Ptg Wks, Moscow)

1992 (3 Dec). *Cats. T 209 and similar vert designs. Multicoloured. P 12×12½.*
1447 20 s. Type 209 .. .. .. 45 45
1448 30 s. Havana cat 45 45
1449 50 s. Persian black cat .. 55 55
1450 70 s. Persian blue cat .. 65 65
1451 100 s. European silver tabby cat .. 85 85
1452 150 s. Persian silver tabby cat .. 1·00 1·00
1453 200 s. Maine Coon cat .. .. 1·25 1·25
1447/53 .. .. .. Set of 7 4·75 4·75
MS1454 90×90 mm. 300 s. European cat .. 2·75 3·00

(Des W. Hanson. Litho B.D.T.)

1992 (10 Dec). *"Genova '92" International Stamp Exhibition. Toy Trains manufactured by Lionel. Horiz designs as T 253 of Sierra Leone. Multicoloured. P 14.*
1455 10 s. Baltimore & Ohio tunnel locomotive No. 5, 1904 .. .. 35 25
1456 20 s. "Liberty Bell" locomotive No. 385E, 1930 .. .. .. 45 35
1457 30 s. Armoured rail car No. 203, 1917 .. 50 40
1458 50 s. Open trolley No. 202, 1910–14 .. 70 60
1459 70 s. "Macy Special" electric locomotive No. 405 .. .. 80 70
1460 100 s. "Milwaukee Road" bi-polar electric locomotive, 1929 .. .. 90 80
1461 200 s. New York Central Type S locomotive, 1912 .. .. 1·50 1·50
1462 300 s. Locomotive No. 7, 1914 .. 1·75 2·00
1455/62 .. .. .. Set of 8 6·25 6·00
MS1463 Two sheets. (a) 91×75 mm. 500 s. Display model locomotive in clear plastic, 1947. (b) 71×89 mm. 500 s. Mickey and Minnie Mouse on clockwork handcar, 1936 .. Set of 2 sheets 5·50 6·50

(Des W. Wright and W. Hanson (Nos. 1464, 1471, MS1475a), W. Wright and L. Fried (Nos. 1466, 1473, MS1475c), J. Genzo (Nos. 1474, MS1475e), W. Wright (others). Litho B.D.T.)

1992 (15 Dec). *Anniversaries and Events. T 210 and similar multicoloured designs. P 14.*
1464 30 s. Type 210 .. .. 30 30
1465 70 s. *Santa Maria* 55 55
1466 70 s. "Apollo-Soyuz" link-up, 1975 55 55
1467 150 s. African Elephant .. .. 1·00 1·00
1468 150 s. Child being offered apple .. 1·00 1·00
1469 200 s. Zebra .. .. 1·10 1·10
1470 200 s. Trying on glasses .. .. 1·10 1·10
1471 300 s. Airship LZ-127 *Graf Zeppelin*, 1929 1·60 1·60
1472 300 s. Christopher Columbus .. 1·60 1·60
1473 400 s. Space shuttle .. .. 2·25 2·25
1474 400 s. Wolfgang Amadeus Mozart (*vert*) 2·00 2·25
1464/74 .. .. .. Set of 11 12·00 12·00
MS1475 Five sheets. (a) 110×82 mm. 500 s. LZ-5 Zeppelin airship. (b) 114×81 mm. 500 s. Head of Columbus. (c) 110×82 mm. 500 s. "Voyager 2" space probe. (d) 114×81 mm. 500 s. African Elephant (*different*). (e) 110×68 mm. 500 s. Queen of the Night from *The Magic Flute* (*vert*) .. .. .. Set of 5 sheets 15·00 16·00
Anniversaries and Events:—Nos. 1464, 1471, MS1475a, 75th death anniv of Count Ferdinand von Zeppelin; Nos. 1465, 1472, MS1475b, 500th anniv of Discovery of America by Columbus; Nos. 1466, 1473, MS1475c, International Space Year; No. 1467, 1469, MS1475d, Earth Summit '92, Rio; No. 1468, International Conference on Nutrition, Rome; No. 1470, 75th anniv of International Association of Lions Clubs; Nos. 1474, MS1475e, Death bicent of Mozart.

(Litho Walsall)

1992 (15 Dec). *Bicentenary of the Louvre, Paris. Paintings by Jean Chardin. Multicoloured designs as T 221 of Lesotho. P 12.*
1476 100 s. "Young Draughtsman sharpening Pencil" 75 75
a. Sheetlet. Nos. 1476/83 .. 5·50
1477 100 s. "The Buffet" 75 75
1478 100 s. "Return from the Market" .. 75 75
1479 100 s. "The Hard-working Mother" .. 75 75
1480 100 s. "Grace" 75 75
1481 100 s. "The Copper Water Urn" .. 75 75
1482 100 s. "The House of Cards" .. 75 75
1483 100 s. "Boy with a Top" .. 75 75
1476/83 .. .. .. Set of 8 5·50 5·50

MS1484 100×70 mm. 500 s. "The Ray" (85×52 mm). P 14½ .. .. 3·25 3·50
Nos. 1476/83 were printed together, *se-tenant*, in sheetlets of 8 stamps and one centre label.

211 Carved Head   212 Russian Cycle, 1813

(Litho State Ptg Wks, Moscow)

1992 (24 Dec). *Makonde Art. T 211 and similar vert designs showing various carvings. P 12×12½.*
1485 20 s. multicoloured 15 15
1486 30 s. multicoloured 15 15
1487 50 s. multicoloured 20 20
1488 70 s. multicoloured 30 30
1489 100 s. multicoloured 40 40
1490 150 s. multicoloured 70 70
1491 200 s. multicoloured 80 80
1485/91 .. .. .. Set of 7 2·40 2·40
MS1492 91×91 mm. 350 s. multicoloured .. 1·75 2·25

(Litho State Ptg Wks, Moscow)

1992 (30 Dec). *Bicycles of the World. T 212 and similar horiz designs. Multicoloured. P 12½×12.*
1493 20 s. Type 212 .. .. 20 20
1494 30 s. German, 1840 .. .. 20 20
1495 50 s. German, 1818 .. .. 30 30
1496 70 s. German, 1850 .. .. 30 40
1497 100 s. Italian, 1988 .. .. 35 50
1498 150 s. Swedish, 1982 .. .. 50 80
1499 300 s. Italian, 1989 .. .. 70 1·25
1493/9 .. .. .. Set of 7 2·25 3·25
MS1500 90×90 mm. 350 s. British penny-farthing, 1887 .. .. 1·00 2·50

213 Seal   214 Boxing

(Litho Questa)

1993 (1 Mar). *Large Sea Creatures. T 213 and similar horiz designs. Multicoloured. P 14.*
1501 20 s. Type 213 .. .. 50 50
1502 30 s. Whale .. .. 1·00 75
1503 70 s. Shark 90 90
1504 100 s. Walrus .. .. 1·00 1·00
1501/4 .. .. .. Set of 4 3·00 2·75
MS1505 99×91 mm. 500 s. Sea Turtle .. 4·50 5·00

(Litho State Ptg Wks, Moscow)

1993 (28 May). *Sports. T 214 and similar multicoloured designs. P 12½×12½.*
1506 20 s. Type 214 .. .. 15 15
1507 50 s. Hockey 50 20
1508 70 s. Show jumping 40 40
1509 100 s. Marathon running .. 45 45
1510 150 s. Football 60 60
1511 200 s. Diving 70 70
1512 400 s. Basketball .. .. 1·50 1·75
1506/12 .. .. .. Set of 7 3·75 3·75
MS1513 91×91 mm. 300 s. High jumping (*horiz*). P 12½×12 .. .. 1·75 2·25

(Des Kerri Schiff. Litho Questa)

1993 (10 June). *40th Anniv of Coronation. Vert designs as T 224 of Lesotho. P 13½×14.*
1514 100 s. multicoloured 65 65
a. Sheetlet. Nos. 1514/17×2 .. 7·00
1515 150 s. multicoloured 85 85
1516 200 s. blackish lilac and black .. 1·10 1·10
1517 300 s. multicoloured .. .. 1·25 1·25
1514/17 .. .. .. Set of 4 3·50 3·50
MS1518 102×70 mm. 500 s. multicoloured. P 14 2·75 3·00
Designs:—100 s. Queen Elizabeth II at Coronation (photograph by Cecil Beaton); 150 s. Gold salt-cellar; 200 s. Prince Philip at Coronation; 300 s. Queen Elizabeth II and Prince Andrew. (28½×42½ *mm*)—500 s. "Princess Elizabeth opening the New Broadgate, Coventry" (detail) (Dame Laura Knight).
Nos. 1514/17 were printed together in sheetlets of 8, containing two *se-tenant* blocks of 4.

---

215 *Macrolepiota rhacodes*   216 *Geochelone elephantopus* (tortoise)

(Des Mary Walters. Litho Questa)

1993 (18 June). *Fungi. T 215 and similar vert designs. Multicoloured. P 14.*
1519 20 s. Type 215 .. .. 40 35
1520 40 s. *Mycena pura* 60 50
1521 50 s. *Chlorophyllum molybdites* .. 60 50
1522 70 s. *Agaricus campestris* .. 70 60
1523 100 s. *Volvariella volvacea* .. 80 70
1524 150 s. *Leucoagaricus naucinus* .. 1·00 1·00
1525 200 s. *Oudemansiella radicata* .. 1·25 1·25
1526 300 s. *Clitocybe nebularis* .. 1·40 1·75
1519/26 .. .. .. Set of 8 6·00 6·00
MS1527 Two sheets, each 100×70 mm. (a) 500 s. *Omphalotus olearius*. (b) 500 s. *Lepista nuda* .. .. Set of 2 sheets 5·25 5·75

(Litho State Ptg Wks, Moscow)

1993 (28 June). *Reptiles. T 216 and similar multicoloured designs. P 12×12½ (vert) or 12½×12 (horiz).*
1528 20 s. Type 216 .. .. 20 20
1529 50 s. *Iguana iguana* 30 30
1530 70 s. *Varanus salvator* (lizard) (*horiz*) 40 40
1531 100 s. *Naja oxiana* (cobra) .. 45 45
1532 150 s. *Chamaeleo jacksoni* (*horiz*) .. 70 70
1533 200 s. *Eunectes murinus* (snake) (*horiz*) 80 80
1534 250 s. *Alligator mississippensis* (*horiz*) 90 90
1528/34 .. .. .. Set of 7 3·25 3·25
MS1535 90×90 mm. 500 s. *Vipera berus* (snake) 3·00 3·50

217 Pancake Tortoise on Rock   218 Elephant

(Des L. Birmingham. Litho Questa)

1993 (30 June). *Endangered Species. Pancake Tortoise. T 217 and similar horiz designs. Multicoloured. P 14.*
1536 20 s. Type 217 .. .. 35 35
1537 30 s. Drinking 40 40
1538 50 s. Under rock 60 60
1539 70 s. Tortoise hatching .. 75 75
1536/9 .. .. .. Set of 4 1·90 1·90

(Des L. Birmingham. Litho Questa)

1993 (30 June). *Wildlife. T 218 and similar multicoloured designs. P 14.*
1540/87 100 s.×48 .. .. Set of 48 20·00 22·00
MS1588 Two sheets, each 100×71 mm. (a) 500 s. Lion cub (*horiz*). (b) 500 s. Elephant calf (*horiz*) .. .. Set of 2 sheets 5·25 5·75
Nos. 1540/87 were issued together, *se-tenant*, as four sheetlets each of twelve different vertical designs. The species depicted are, in addition to Type 218, Gazelle, Hartebeest, Duiker, Genet, Civet, Eastern White Pelican, Waterbuck, Blacksmith Plover, Lesser Pied Kingfisher, Black-winged Stilt, Bush Pig, Brown-hooded Kingfisher, Sable Antelope, Impala, Buffalo, Leopard, Aardvark, Hippopotamus, Spotted Hyena, South African Crowned Crane, Crocodile, Greater Flamingo, Baboon, Potto, Lesser Flamingo, Grey-headed Kingfisher, Red Colobus Monkey, Dik-Dik, Aardwolf (incorrectly inscribed "ARDWOLF"), Black-backed Jackal, Tree Pangolin, Serval, Yellow-billed Hornbill, Pygmy Mongoose, Bat-eared Fox, Bushbaby, Egyptian Vulture, Ostrich, Greater Kudu, Diana Monkey, Giraffe, Cheetah, Wildebeest, Chimpanzee, Warthog, Zebra and Rhinoceros.

219 Grant's Zebra galloping   220 Valentina Tereshkova (first woman in space)

(Des P. Ndembo. Litho B.D.T.)

1993 (30 June). *Wild Animals. T* **219** *and similar horiz designs. Multicoloured. P* 14.
1589	100 s. Type 219	..	..	80	80
	a. Sheetlet. Nos. 1589/94			4·25	
1590	100 s. Grant's Zebra standing			80	80
1591	100 s. Grant's Gazelle doe			80	80
1592	100 s. Grant's Gazelle buck			80	80
1593	100 s. Thomson's Gazelle ..			80	80
1594	100 s. White-bearded Gnu with calf			80	80
1595	100 s. Female Cheetah with cubs			80	80
	a. Sheetlet. Nos. 1595/1600			4·25	
1596	100 s. Young Cheetah drinking			80	80
1597	100 s. Lioness carrying cub in mouth			80	80
1598	100 s. Pair of Hunting Dogs			80	80
1599	100 s. Three Hunting Dogs			80	80
1600	100 s. Four Hunting Dogs			80	80
1589/1600			*Set of 12*	8·50	8·50

MS1601 Two sheets, each 106×76 mm. (a) 500 s. African Elephant. (b) 500 s. Rhinoceros
	Set of 2 sheets	8·50	8·50

Nos. 1589/94 and 1595/1600 were printed together, *se-tenant*, in sheetlets of 6.

(Des J. Iskowitz. Litho Questa)

1993 (15 July). *Famous 20th-century Women. T* **220** *and similar vert designs. Multicoloured. P* 14.
1602	20 s. Type 220	..	..	45	45
	a. Sheetlet. Nos. 1602/9	..		6·75	
1603	40 s. Marie Curie (physicist)			80	80
1604	50 s. Indira Gandhi (Prime Minister of India)			80	80
1605	70 s. Wilma Rudolph (Olympic athlete) ..			80	80
1606	100 s. Margaret Mead (anthropologist)			80	80
1607	150 s. Golda Meir (Prime Minister of Israel)			1·00	1·00
1608	200 s. Dr. Elizabeth Blackwell (first female medical doctor)			1·00	1·00
1609	400 s. Margaret Thatcher (Prime Minister of Great Britain)			1·75	1·75
1602/9			*Set of 8*	6·75	6·75

MS1610 116×80 mm. 500 s. Mother Teresa (humanitarian)
		3·00	3·50

Nos. 1602/9 were printed together, *se-tenant*, in sheetlets of 8.

221 *Iolaus aphnaeoides*

222 Arthur Ashe (tennis)

(Des Jennifer Toombs. Litho Cartor)

1993 (15 July). *Butterflies. T* **221** *and similar horiz designs. Multicoloured. P* 13.
1611/54	20 s. × 44	*Set of 44*	35·00 30·00

MS1655 Four sheets, each 69×58 mm. (a) 500 s. *Cymothoe sangaris*. (b) 500 s. *Precis octavia*. (c) 500 s. *Charaxes violetta*. (d) 500 s. *Papilio nobilis*
Set of 4 sheets	13·00	13·00

Nos. 1611/54 were printed *se-tenant* in two sheetlets of 12 (Nos. 1611/34) and one of 20 (Nos. 1635/54). The species depicted are *Iolaus aphnaeoides, Charaxes eupale, Danaus formosa, Antanartia hippomene, Mylothris sagala, Charaxes anticlea, Salamis temora, Nepheronia argia, Acraea pseudolycia, Hypolimnas antevorta, Colotis hildebrandti, Acraea bonasia, Eurema desjardinsi, Myrina silenus, Iolaus ismenias, Charaxes candiope, Precis artaxia, Danaus chrysippus, Axiocerses bambana, Precis orithya, Pinacopteryx eriphia, Iolaus coecolus, Precis hierta, Colotis regina, Euphaedra neophron, Mylothris poppea, Aphaneus flavescens, Eronia leda, Charaxes zoolina, Papilio bromius, Cyrestis camillus, Hypolycaena buxtoni, Charaxes achaemenes, Asterope rosa, Graphium antheus, Charaxes acuminatus, Kallima rumia, Leptosia alcesta, Pseudacraea boisduvali, Iolaus sidus, Salamis parhassus, Charaxes protoclea azota, Charaxes bohemani* and *Papilio ophidicephalus.*

(Des J. Iskowitz. Litho Questa)

1993 (15 July). *Black Sporting Personalities. T* **222** *and similar multicoloured designs. P* 14.
1656	20 s. Type 222	..	..	40	40
	a. Sheetlet. Nos. 1656/63			4·50	
1657	40 s. Michael Jordan (basketball)			40	40
1658	50 s. Daley Thompson (decathlon)			40	40
1659	70 s. Jackie Robinson (baseball)			40	40
1660	100 s. Kareem Abdul-Jabbar (basketball)			50	50
1661	150 s. Florence Joyner (athletics)			60	60
1662	200 s. Jesse Owens (athletics)			70	70
1663	400 s. Jack Johnson (boxing)			1·50	1·50
1656/63			*Set of 8*	4·50	4·50

MS1664 72×101 mm. 500 s. Muhammad Ali (boxing) *(horiz)*
		2·50	2·75

Nos. 1656/63 were printed together, *se-tenant*, in sheetlets of 8.

223 Short-finned Mako

(Litho State Ptg Wks, Moscow)

1993 (27 July). *Sharks. T* **223** *and similar multicoloured designs. P* 12½×12.
1665	20 s. Type 223	..	..	15	15
1666	30 s. Lantern Shark			20	20
1667	50 s. Tiger Shark			25	25
1668	70 s. African Angelshark			35	35
1669	100 s. *Pristiophorus cirratus*			45	45
1670	150 s. White-tipped Reef Shark			65	65
1671	200 s. Scalloped Hammerhead			75	75
1665/71			*Set of 7*	2·50	2·50

MS1672 91×91 mm. 350 s. Six-gilled Shark *(vert)*
P 12×12½		1·75	2·00

224 Alpha Jet

225 Gordon Setter

(Litho State Ptg Wks, Moscow)

1993 (30 Aug). *Military Aircraft. T* **224** *and similar multicoloured designs. P* 12½×12.
1673	20 s. Type 224	..	..	20	20
1674	30 s. Northrop F-5E			20	25
1675	50 s. Dassault Mirage 3NG			25	30
1676	70 s. MB 339C			35	45
1677	100 s. MiG-31			35	50
1678	150 s. C-101 Aviojet			40	70
1679	200 s. General Dynamics F-16 Fighting Falcon			45	80
1673/9			*Set of 7*	2·00	3·00

MS1680 91×91 mm. 500 s. EAP fighter *(vert)*.
P 12×12½		1·40	2·00

(Litho State Ptg Wks, Moscow)

1993 (27 Sept). *Dogs. T* **225** *and similar vert designs. Multicoloured. P* 12×12½.
1681	20 s. Type 225	..	..	20	20
1682	30 s. Zwergschnauzer	..		25	25
1683	50 s. Labrador Retriever			30	30
1684	70 s. Wire Fox Terrier			45	45
1685	100 s. English Springer Spaniel			50	50
1686	150 s. Newfoundlander			70	70
1687	200 s. Moscow Toy Terrier			80	80
1681/7			*Set of 7*	3·00	3·00

MS1688 91×91 mm. 350 s. Dobermann Pinscher 1·75 2·00

226 Rhinoceros, Ngorongoro Crater

227 *Ansellia africana*

(Litho State Ptg Wks, Moscow)

1993 (29 Oct). *National Parks. T* **226** *and similar multicoloured designs. P* 12½×12.
1689	20 s. Type 226	..	..	20	20
1690	50 s. Buffalo, Ngurdoto Crater	..		20	20
1691	70 s. Leopard, Kilimanjaro			30	30
1692	100 s. Baboon, Gombe			35	35
1693	150 s. Lion, Selous			45	45
1694	200 s. Giraffe, Mikumi			65	65
1695	250 s. Zebra, Serengeti			70	70
1689/95			*Set of 7*	2·50	2·50

MS1696 91×91 mm. 500 s. Elephant, Lake Manyara *(vert)*. P 12×12½ 1·75 2·00

(Litho Cartor)

1993 (8 Nov). *Flowers. T* **227** *and similar vert designs. Multicoloured. P* 13½.
1697	20 s. Type 227	..	..	25	20
1698	30 s. *Saintpaulia ionantha*			30	25
1699	40 s. *Stapelia semota lutea*			35	30
1700	50 s. *Impatiens walleriana*			35	30
1701	60 s. *Senecio petraeus*			40	35
1702	70 s. *Kalanchoe velutina*			45	40
1703	100 s. *Kaempferia brachystemon*			55	50
1704	150 s. *Nymphaea colorata*			80	80
1705	200 s. *Thunbergia battiscombei*			90	90
1706	250 s. *Crossandra nilotica*			1·00	1·00
1707	300 s. *Spathodea campanulata*			1·10	1·25
1708	500 s. *Ruttya fruticosa*			1·10	1·25
1697/1708			*Set of 12*	6·75	6·75

MS1709 Two sheets, each 100×70 mm. (a) 500 s. *Streptocarpus saxorum*. (b) 500 s. *Glorioso verschurii*. P 13 .. | *Set of 2 sheets* | 5·25 | 6·50

228 Norman-Arab

229 Berts Warrior

(Litho State Ptg Wks, Moscow)

1993 (30 Nov). *Horses. T* **228** *and similar multicoloured designs. P* 12½×12.
1710	20 s. Type 228	..	..	30	30
1711	40 s. Nonius			40	40
1712	50 s. Boulonnais	..		40	40
1713	70 s. Arab			50	50
1714	100 s. Anglo-Arab			55	55
1715	150 s. Tarpon			70	70
1716	200 s. Thoroughbred			80	80
1710/16			*Set of 7*	3·25	3·25

MS1717 91×91 mm. 400 s. Anglo-Norman *(vert)*. P 12×12½ 1·75 2·00

No. 1716 is inscribed "THOROUGBLED" in error.

(Litho State Ptg Wks, Moscow)

1993 (30 Dec). *Traditional African Costumes. T* **229** *and similar vert designs. Multicoloured. P* 12×12½.
1718	20 s. Type 229	..	..	10	10
1719	40 s. Galla			15	15
1720	50 s. Guinean			15	15
1721	70 s. Goloff			20	25
1722	100 s. Peul			30	30
1723	150 s. Abyssinian			45	45
1724	200 s. Pahuin			55	55
1718/24			*Set of 7*	1·75	1·75

MS1725 91×91 mm. 350 s. Zulu | | 1·10 | 1·25

(Litho Questa)

1994 (10 Feb). *Hummel Figurines. Vert designs as T* **256** *of Maldive Islands. Multicoloured. P* 14.
1726	20 s. Boy playing accordion			25	25
1727	40 s. Girl with guitar and boy with lute			30	30
1728	50 s. Boy playing euphonium			30	30
1729	70 s. Boy playing mouth organ	..		35	35
1730	100 s. Boy with trumpet on fence			45	45
1731	150 s. Boy playing recorder			70	70
1732	200 s. Boy with trumpet and bird on feet			80	80
1733	300 s. Girl playing banjo			1·10	1·25
1734	350 s. Boy carrying double bass on back			1·25	1·50
1735	400 s. Girls with banjo and song sheet			1·25	1·50
1726/35			*Set of 10*	6·00	6·50

MS1736 Two sheets, each 70×101 mm. (a) 500 s. Carol singers. (b) 500 s. Angels with trumpets in bell tower .. | .. | *Set of 2 sheets* | 7·50 | 8·50

230 Downhill Skiing

231 Ruud Gullit (Netherlands)

(Litho State Ptg Wks, Moscow)

1994 (12 Feb). *Winter Olympic Games, Lillehammer, Norway. T* **230** *and similar vert designs. Multicoloured. P* 12×12½.
1737	40 s. Type 230	..	..	20	20
1738	50 s. Ice hockey			20	20
1739	70 s. Speed skating			30	30
1740	100 s. Bobsleighing			35	35
1741	120 s. Figure skating			40	40
1742	170 s. Free style skiing			55	55
1743	250 s. Biathlon			75	75
1737/43			*Set of 7*	2·50	2·50

MS1744 93×91 mm. 500 s. Cross-country skiing 1·50 2·00

(Litho Questa)

1994 (14 Feb). *World Cup Football Championship, U.S.A.* (1st issue). *T* **231** *and similar vert designs. Multicoloured. P* 14.
1745	20 s. Type 231	..	..	40	30
1746	30 s. Kevin Sheedy (Ireland)			40	30
1747	50 s. Giuseppe Giannini (Italy)			50	40
1748	70 s. Julio Cesar (Brazil)			55	45
1749	250 s. John Barnes (England) and Grun (Belgium)			1·50	1·50
1750	300 s. Chendo (Spain)			1·50	1·50
1751	350 s. Frank Rijkaard (Netherlands)			1·60	1·75
1752	400 s. Lothar Matthaeus (Germany)			1·60	1·75
1745/52			*Set of 8*	7·25	7·25

MS1753 Two sheets. (a) 76×106 mm. 500 s. Nicola Berti (Italy). (b) 106×76 mm. 500 s. Des Walker (England) .. | *Set of 2 sheets* | 7·00 | 7·50

See also Nos. 1838/46 and 1892/9.

(Des W. Hanson. Litho Questa)

1994 (18 Feb). *"Hong Kong '94" International Stamp Exhibition. Horiz designs as T 293 of Maldive Islands. Multicoloured.* P 14.

1754	350 s. Blue-barred Orange Parrotfish and Red Cap White Pearl-scale Goldfish at right	1·40	1·40
	a. Horiz pair. Nos. 1754/5	2·75	2·75
1755	350 s. Regal Angelfish and Red Cap White Pearl-scale Goldfish at left	1·40	1·40

Nos. 1754/5 were printed together, *se-tenant*, in horizontal pairs throughout the sheet with the centre part of each pair forming a composite design.

232 Mickey Mouse, Goofy, Pluto and Donald Duck boarding Airliner

(Des Rosemary DeFiglio. Litho Questa)

1994 (13 Mar). *65th Anniv of Mickey Mouse. T 232 and similar multicoloured designs showing Walt Disney cartoon characters on World Tour.* P 14×13½ (horiz) or 13½×14 (vert).

1756	10 s. Type 232	30	25
1757	20 s. Daisy Duck and Minnie Mouse dancing, Tonga	40	30
1758	30 s. Mickey and Goofy playing bowls, Australia	45	35
1759	40 s. Mickey, Donald and Goofy building igloo, Arctic Circle	50	40
1760	50 s. Pluto, Goofy, Mickey and Donald on guard at Buckingham Palace, London	50	40
1761	60 s. Pluto at Esna Bazaar, Egypt	55	45
1762	70 s. Donald being chased by Zsambox herders, Hungary (vert)	55	45
1763	100 s. Donald and Daisy on Grand Canal, Venice (vert)	70	60
1764	150 s. Goofy dancing, Bali (vert)	1·10	1·25
1765	200 s. Donald with monks, Thailand (vert)	1·25	1·40
1766	300 s. Goofy water skiing at Taj Mahal, India (vert)	1·50	1·75
1767	400 s. Mickey, Minnie, Goofy and Donald being carried by Sherpas, Nepal	1·75	2·00
1756/67	Set of 12	8·50	8·75

MS1768 Three sheets. (a) 127×102 mm. 500 s. Mickey at Livingstone's memorial, Ujiji (vert). (b) 127×102 mm. 500 s. Mickey at Kigoma railway station, Tanzania (vert). (c) 102×127 mm. 500 s. Mickey climbing Mt Kilimanjaro (vert).

	Set of 3 sheets	8·50	9·00

233 Bonelli's Eagle ("African Hawk Eagle")　　234 Henry Ford and Model "T"

(Des P. Ndembo. Litho Questa)

1994 (17 Apr). *Birds. T 233 and similar multicoloured designs.* P 14.

1769	20 s. Type 233	60	60
	a. Sheetlet. Nos. 1769/74	4·25	
1770	30 s. Whale-headed Stork ("Shoe-bill Stork")	60	60
1771	50 s. Brown Harrier Eagle	70	70
1772	70 s. Black-casqued Hornbill	80	80
1773	100 s. Crowned Cranes	90	90
1774	150 s. Greater Flamingos	1·00	1·00
1775	200 s. Pair of Eastern White Pelicans (horiz)	1·00	1·00
	a. Sheetlet. Nos. 1775/80	6·00	
1776	250 s. African Jacana and Black Crake (horiz)	1·00	1·00
1777	300 s. Pair of Ostriches (horiz)	1·10	1·10
1778	350 s. Pair of Helmet Guineafowl (horiz)	1·10	1·10
1779	400 s. Malachite Kingfisher (horiz)	1·10	1·10
1780	500 s. Pair of Saddle-bill Storks (horiz)	1·25	1·25
1769/80	Set of 12	10·00	10·00

Nos. 1769/74 and 1775/80 were printed together, *se-tenant*, in sheetlets of 6.

(Litho Questa)

1994 (25 Apr). *Centenaries of Henry Ford's First Petrol Engine (Nos. 1781, 1783, MS1785a) and Karl Benz's First Four-wheeled Car (others). T 234 and similar horiz designs. Multicoloured.* P 14.

1781	200 s. Type 234	1·10	1·10
1782	200 s. Benz, 1893, and "500 SEL", 1993	1·10	1·10
1783	400 s. Ford, 1893, Mustang Cobra and emblem	1·75	1·75

1784	400 s. Karl Benz and emblem	1·75	1·75
1781/4	Set of 4	5·00	5·00

MS1785 Two sheets, each 106×71 mm. (a) 500 s. Henry Ford outside first factory. (b) 500 s. Benz emblem and bonnet of 1937 "540k".

	Set of 2 sheets	5·00	6·00

235 Sopwith Pup Biplane　　236 Jahazi (sailing canoe)

(Litho Questa)

1994 (25 Apr). *Aviation Anniversaries. T 235 and similar multicoloured designs.* P 14.

1786	200 s. Type 235	1·00	1·00
1787	200 s. Inflating hot-air balloons	1·00	1·00
1788	400 s. Hawker Siddeley Harrier and design drawing	1·75	1·75
1789	400 s. Jean-Pierre Blanchard and his balloon	1·75	1·75
1786/9	Set of 4	5·00	5·00

MS1790 Two sheets, each 105×71 mm. (a) 500 s. Supermarine Spitfire. (b) 500 s. Hot-air balloons in flight (vert). Set of 2 sheets 5·50 6·00

Anniversaries:—Nos. 1786, 1788, MS1790a, 75th anniv of Royal Air Force; Nos. 1787, 1789, MS1790b, Bicentenary of first balloon flight in the U.S.A.

(Litho State Ptg Wks, Moscow)

1994 (20 May). *Sailing Ships. T 236 and similar vert designs. Multicoloured.* P 12½×12½.

1791	40 s. Type 236	15	15
1792	50 s. Caravel	15	15
1793	70 s. Pirate carrack	25	25
1794	100 s. Baltic galeass	25	30
1795	170 s. Frigate (inscr "Battle-ship")	35	55
1796	200 s. British ship of the line (inscr "Frigate")	40	65
1797	250 s. Brig	40	75
1791/7	Set of 7	1·75	2·50

MS1798 91×91 mm. 500 s. Clipper | 1·25 | 2·00

237 Diatryma　　238 Koala Bear with Cub

(Litho State Ptg Wks, Moscow)

1994 (30 June). *Prehistoric Animals. T 237 and similar vert designs. Multicoloured.* P 12½×12½.

1799	40 s. Type 237	30	30
1800	50 s. Tyrannosaurus rex	30	30
1801	100 s. Uintaterius	50	50
1802	120 s. Stiracosaurus	60	60
1803	170 s. Diplodocus	75	75
1804	250 s. Archaeopteryx	95	95
1805	300 s. Sordes	1·10	1·10
1799/1805	Set of 7	4·00	4·00

MS1806 91×91 mm. 500 s. Dimetrodon | 1·90 | 2·25

No. 1799 is inscribed "DIATRUMA" in error.

(Litho State Ptg Wks, Moscow)

1994 (29 July). *Endangered Species. T 238 and similar multicoloured designs.* P 12½×12.

1807	40 s. Type 238	25	25
1808	70 s. Giant Panda with cub	40	40
1809	100 s. Eagles	55	55
1810	120 s. African Elephant with calf	70	70
1811	250 s. Caribbean Monk Seals	90	90
1812	400 s. Dolphins	1·00	1·00
1813	500 s. Whales	1·50	1·50
1807/13	Set of 7	4·75	4·75

MS1814 90×90 mm. 500 s. Tiger (vert). P 12½×12½ | 2·00 | 2·50

No. 1808 shows the incorrect scientific species name.

239 Pres. Salmin Amour of Zanzibar　　240 Lorry at Customs Post

(Litho State Ptg Wks, Moscow)

1994 (1 Aug). *30th Anniv of Zanzibar Revolution. T 239 and similar multicoloured designs.* P 12½×12 (120 s.) or 12×12½ (others).

1815	40 s. Type 239	25	10
1816	70 s. Amani Karume (first President of Zanzibar)	35	20
1817	120 s. Harvesting cloves (horiz)	65	55
1818	250 s. Carved door	1·10	1·75
1815/18	Set of 4	2·10	2·25

MS1819 91×91 mm. 500 s. Hands clasped over map | 1·75 | 2·25

(Litho Cartor)

1994 (23 Aug). *81st/82nd Customs Co-Operation Council Meeting, Arusha. T 240 and similar multicoloured designs.* P 14×13½.

1820	20 s. Type 240	30	15
1821	50 s. Container ship	45	20
1822	100 s. Passengers and airliner	70	50
1823	150 s. Customs and U.P.U. logos	80	1·00
1820/3	Set of 4	2·00	1·75

MS1824 99×99 mm. 500 s. Customs arms (30×40 mm). P 12½ | 2·75 | 3·00

241 Tanzanian Family　　242 Trombidium sp

(Litho State Ptg Wks, Moscow)

1994 (30 Aug). *International Year of the Family. T 241 and similar multicoloured designs.* P 12½×12 (170 s.) or 12×12½ (others).

1825	40 s. Type 241	15	10
1826	120 s. Father playing with children	35	35
1827	170 s. Family clinic (horiz)	50	55
1828	250 s. Woman harvesting tobacco	70	80
1825/8	Set of 4	1·50	1·60

MS1829 91×91 mm. 300 s. Emblem | 1·60 | 1·75

(Litho State Ptg Wks, Moscow)

1994 (31 Aug). *Arachnids. T 242 and similar multicoloured designs.* P 12½×12 (horiz) or 12×12½ (vert).

1830	40 s. Type 242	20	20
1831	50 s. Eurypelma sp	20	20
1832	100 s. Salticus sp	30	30
1833	120 s. Micrommata rosea (vert)	35	35
1834	170 s. Araneus sp (vert)	50	50
1835	200 s. Micrathena sp (vert)	70	70
1836	300 s. Araneus diadematus (vert)	80	80
1830/6	Set of 7	2·75	2·75

MS1837 92×92 mm. 500 s. Claw of Hadogenes sp (vert) | 1·75 | 2·00

243 Giuseppe Signori (Italy)　　244 Bateleur

(Litho State Ptg Wks, Moscow)

1994 (26 Sept). *World Cup Football Championship, U.S.A. (2nd issue). T 243 and similar vert designs. Multicoloured. Litho.* P 14.

1838	300 s. Type 243	1·00	1·00
	a. Sheetlet. Nos. 1838/45	7·00	
1839	300 s. Ruud Gullit (Netherlands)	1·00	1·00
1840	300 s. Roberto Mancini (Italy)	1·00	1·00
1841	300 s. Marco van Basten (Netherlands)	1·00	1·00
1842	300 s. Dennis Bergkamp (Netherlands)	1·00	1·00
1843	300 s. Oscar Ruggeri (Argentina)	1·00	1·00
1844	300 s. Frank Rijkaard (Netherlands)	1·00	1·00
1845	300 s. Peter Schmeichel (Denmark)	1·00	1·00
1838/45	Set of 8	7·00	7·00

MS1846 100×70 mm. 1000 s. World Cup trophy | 4·00 | 4·50

Nos. 1838/45 were printed together, *se-tenant*, in sheetlets of 8.

(Litho State Ptg Wks, Moscow)

1994 (30 Sept). *Birds of Prey. T 244 and similar multicoloured designs.* P 12½×12 (170, 400 s.) or 12×12½ (others).

1847	40 s. Type 244	40	40
1848	50 s. Ornate Hawk Eagle	40	40
1849	100 s. Osprey	60	60
1850	120 s. Andean Condor	60	60
1851	170 s. African Fish Eagle (horiz)	70	70
1852	250 s. King Vulture	80	80
1853	400 s. Peregrine Falcon (horiz)	1·25	1·25
1847/53	Set of 7	4·25	4·25

MS1854 90×90 mm. 500 s. African White-backed Vulture | 1·75 | 2·25

245 Afghan Hound   246 Players and Flags from Group B

(Des G. Bibby. Litho B.D.T.)

1994 (30 Sept). *Dogs of the World. T* **245** *and similar vert designs. Multicoloured. P* 14.

1855/63	120 s. × 9 (Type **245**; Basenji; Siberian Husky; Irish Setter; Norwegian Elkhound; Bracco Italiano; Australian Cattle Dog; German Short-haired Pointer; Rhodesian Ridgeback)			
	a. Sheetlet. Nos. 1855/63		4·00	4·50
1864/72	120 s. × 9 (Alsatian; Japanese Chin; Shetland Sheepdog; Italian Spinone; Great Dane; English Setter; Welsh Corgi; St. Bernard; Irish Wolfhound)			
	a. Sheetlet. Nos. 1864/72		4·00	4·50
1873/81	120 s. × 9 (Doberman Pinscher; Chihuahua; Bloodhound; Keeshond; Tibetan Spaniel; Japanese Akita; Tervueren; Chow; Pharaoh Hound)			
	a. Sheetlet. Nos. 1873/81		4·00	4·50
1882/90	120 s. × 9 (Alaskan Malamute; Scottish Cairn Terrier; American Foxhound; British Bulldog; Boston Terrier; Borzoi; Shar Pei; Saluki; Bernese Mountain Dog)			
	a. Sheetlet. Nos. 1882/90		4·00	4·50
1855/90		*Set of 36*	14·00	16·00

MS1891 Two sheets, each 76×106 mm. 1000 s. As No. 1856. (b) 1000 s. As No. 1868

                Set of 2 sheets   8·00   9·00

Nos. 1855/63, 1864/72, 1873/81 and 1882/90 were printed together, *se-tenant*, in sheetlets of 9.

(Litho State Ptg Wks, Moscow)

1994 (30 Sept). *World Cup Football Championship, U.S.A. (3rd issue). T* **246** *and similar horiz designs. Multicoloured. P* 12½×12.

1892	40 s. Type **246**		45	45
1893	50 s. Players and flags from Group C		50	50
1894	70 s. Players and flags from Group D		60	60
1895	100 s. Players and flags from Group E		65	65
1896	170 s. Players and flags from Group A		90	90
1897	200 s. Players and World Cup		1·10	1·10
1898	250 s. Players and flags from Group F		1·40	1·40
1892/8		*Set of 7*	5·00	5·00

MS1899 92×92 mm. 500 s. Player heading ball   3·25   3·75

Nos. 1892/9 have been seen with cancelled-to-order postmarks of 17 June 1994.

247 *Rangaeris amaniensis*   248 *Dicentra spectabilis*

(Des Marilyn Abromowitz. Litho Questa)

1994 (7 Oct). *Orchids. T* **247** *and similar multicoloured designs. P* 14.

1900	200 s. Type **247**		65	65
	a. Sheetlet. Nos. 1900/7		4·75	
1901	200 s. *Eulophia macowanii*		65	65
1902	200 s. *Cytorchis arcuata*		65	65
1903	200 s. *Centrostigma occultans*		65	65
1904	200 s. *Cirrhopetalum umbellatum*		65	65
1905	200 s. *Ansellia gigantea*		65	65
1906	200 s. *Angraecum ramosum*		65	65
1907	200 s. *Disa englerana*		65	65
1908	200 s. *Nervilia stolziana*		65	65
	a. Sheetlet. Nos. 1908/15		4·75	
1909	200 s. *Satyrium orbiculare*		65	65
1910	200 s. *Schizochilus sulphureus*		65	65
1911	200 s. *Disa stolzii*		65	65
1912	200 s. *Platycornye mediocris*		65	65
1913	200 s. *Satyrium breve*		65	65
1914	200 s. *Eulophia nuttii*		65	65
1915	200 s. *Disa ornithantha*		65	65
1900/15		*Set of 16*	9·50	9·50

MS1916 Two sheets, each 106×76 mm. (a) 1000 s. *Phaius tankervilliae* (*horiz*). (b) 1000 s. *Eulophia thomsonii* (*horiz*)   *Set of 2 sheets*   7·50   8·00

Nos. 1900/7 and 1908/15 were printed together, *se-tenant*, in sheetlets of 8.

(Litho State Ptg Wks. Moscow)

1994 (31 Oct). *Flowers. T* **248** *and similar vert designs. Multicoloured. P* 12×12½.

1917	40 s. Type **248**		30	30
1918	100 s. *Thunbergia alata*		40	45
1919	120 s. *Cyrtanthus minimiflorus*		40	50
1920	170 s. *Nepenthes hybrida*		45	70
1921	250 s. *Allamanda cathartica*		50	80
1922	300 s. *Encyclia pentotis*		50	85
1923	400 s. *Protea lacticolor*		55	90
1917/23		*Set of 7*	2·75	4·00

MS1924   91×92 mm. 500 s. Tradescantia   1·25   1·75

249 *Limenitis sydyi*

(Des Mary Walters. Litho Questa)

1994 (19 Nov). *Butterflies. T* **249** *and similar horiz designs. Multicoloured. P* 14.

1925	120 s. Type **249**		55	55
	a. Sheetlet. Nos. 1925/33		4·50	
1926	120 s. *Agraulis vanillae*		55	55
1927	120 s. *Danaus chrysippus*		55	55
1928	120 s. *Eurytides marcellus*		55	55
1929	120 s. *Artopoetes pryeri*		55	55
1930	120 s. *Heliconius charitonius*		55	55
1931	120 s. *Limenitis weidemeyerii*		55	55
1932	120 s. *Phoebis sennae*		55	55
1933	120 s. *Timelaea albescens*		55	55
1934	120 s. *Papilio glaucus*		55	55
	a. Sheetlet. Nos. 1934/42		4·50	
1935	120 s. *Danaus plexippus*		55	55
1936	120 s. *Papilio troilus*		55	55
1937	120 s. *Hypolimnas antevorta*		55	55
1938	120 s. *Cirrhochroa imperatrix*		55	55
1939	120 s. *Vanessa atalanta*		55	55
1940	120 s. *Limenitis archippus*		55	55
1941	120 s. *Hypolimnas pandarus*		55	55
1942	120 s. *Anthocharis belia*		55	55
1925/42		*Set of 18*	9·00	9·00

MS1943 Two sheets, each 101×70 mm. (a) 1000 s. *Papilio polyxenes*. (b) 1000 s. *Vanessa cardui*   *Set of 2 sheets*   7·50   8·00

Nos. 1925/33 and 1934/42 were printed together, *se-tenant*, in sheetlets 9.

250 Donald Duck and Goofy with Safari Equipment

(Litho Questa)

1994 (26 Nov). *Mickey Mouse Safari Club. T* **250** *and similar multicoloured designs showing Walt Disney cartoon characters on safari. P* 14×13½.

1944	70 s. Type **250**		45	45
1945	70 s. Donald and Mickey Mouse with leopard cubs		45	45
1946	100 s. Donald photographing antelope		55	55
1947	100 s. Donald between elephant's legs		55	55
1948	120 s. Mickey with monkeys		60	60
1949	120 s. Donald with hippopotamuses		60	60
1950	150 s. Goofy carrying equipment		70	70
1951	150 s. Mickey, Donald and Goofy sheltering under elephant's ears		70	70
1952	200 s. Goofy with zebras		80	80
1953	200 s. Donald, Goofy and Mickey with lion		80	80
1954	250 s. Donald filming monkeys		90	90
1955	250 s. Giraffe licking Mickey		90	90
1944/55		*Set of 12*	7·25	7·25

MS1956 Three sheets, each 101×121 mm. (a) 1000 s. Goofy in tree with camera (*vert*). (b) 1000 s. Donald and Goofy with camera (*vert*). (c) 1000 s. Donald and Mickey with camera (*vert*). P 13½×14   *Set of 3 sheets*   11·00   12·00

251 Plan indicating Moon Landing Point

(Des G. Vasarhelyi. Litho Questa)

1994 (30 Nov). *25th Anniv of First Moon Landing. T* **251** *and similar horiz designs. Multicoloured. P* 14.

1957	150 s. Type **251**		75	75
	a. Sheetlet. Nos. 1957/65		6·00	
1958	150 s. Photograph showing Sea of Tranquility		75	75
1959	150 s. Lunar surface		75	75
1960	150 s. Lift-off		75	75
1961	150 s. Jettisoning first stage rocket		75	75
1962	150 s. Jettisoning second stage rocket		75	75
1963	150 s. Lunar module *Eagle* leaving command module		75	75
1964	150 s. *Eagle* descending towards lunar surface		75	75
1965	150 s. Armstrong and Aldrin (astronauts) inside *Eagle*		75	75
1966	150 s. "Apollo 11" crew in space suits		75	75
	a. Sheetlet. Nos. 1966/74		6·00	
1967	150 s. *Eagle* on lunar surface		75	75
1968	150 s. Armstrong descending to lunar surface		75	75
1969	150 s. Astronaut, *Eagle* and experiment		75	75
1970	150 s. Astronaut setting-up equipment		75	75
1971	150 s. Reflection in astronaut's visor		75	75
1972	150 s. Astronaut and U.S.A. flag		75	75
1973	150 s. Astronaut carrying equipment		75	75
1974	150 s. *Eagle* blasting off from Moon		75	75
1975	150 s. Command module		75	75
	a. Sheetlet. Nos. 1975/83		6·00	
1976	150 s. *Eagle* leaving Moon		75	75
1977	150 s. Capsule leaving Moon orbit		75	75
1978	150 s. Capsule heading for Earth		75	75
1979	150 s. Capsule re-entering Earth's atmosphere		75	75
1980	150 s. Capsule in sea		75	75
1981	150 s. Recovery crew opening hatch		75	75
1982	150 s. Transferring astronauts by helicopter		75	75
1983	150 s. Armstrong, Collins and Aldrin (astronauts) after recovery		75	75
1957/83		*Set of 27*	16·00	16·00

Nos. 1957/65, 1966/74 and 1975/83 were printed together, *se-tenant*, in sheetlets of 9.

252 *Astacus leptodactylus*

(Litho State Ptg Wks, Moscow)

1994 (30 Nov). *Crabs. T* **252** *and similar multicoloured designs. P* 12½×12 (*horiz*) or 12×12½ (*vert*).

1984	40 s. Type **252**		30	30
1985	100 s. *Eriocheir sinensis* (*vert*)		50	50
1986	120 s. *Cancer opillo* (*vert*)		55	55
1987	170 s. *Cardisoma quanhumi*		70	70
1988	250 s. *Birgus latro* (*vert*)		85	85
1989	300 s. *Menippe mercenaria*		90	90
1990	400 s. *Dromia vulgaris* (*vert*)		95	95
1984/90		*Set of 7*	4·25	4·25

MS1991 92×92 mm. 500 s. Coral and crab's claw   1·60   2·00

(Des Kerri Schiff. Litho Questa)

1994 (12 Dec). *Centenary of International Olympic Committee. Gold Medal Winners. Vert designs as T* **303** *of Maldive Islands. Multicoloured. P* 14.

1992	350 s. Kristin Otto (Germany) (50 metres freestyle swimming), 1988		1·00	1·00
1993	500 s. Carl Lewis (U.S.A.) (various track and field events), 1984 and 1988		1·40	1·40

MS1994 74×104 mm. 1000 s. Oksana Baiul (Ukraine) (figure skating), 1994   3·00   3·50

(Des J. Batchelor. Litho Questa)

1994 (12 Dec). *50th Anniv of D-Day (1st issue). Horiz designs as T* **304** *of Maldive Islands. Multicoloured. P* 14.

1995	350 s. Troops leaving landing craft		1·25	1·25
1996	600 s. Amphibious tank and troops, Omaha Beach		1·75	1·75

MS1997 104×74 mm. 1000 s. Loading landing ship in England   3·25   3·75

253 Supermarine Spitfire over Beaches   254 Deinonychus

(Des R. Vigurs. Litho Questa)

1994 (12 Dec). *50th Anniv of D-Day* (2nd issue). *T* **253** *and similar horiz designs. Multicoloured. P* 14.

1998	200 s. Type **253**			80	80
	a. Sheetlet. Nos. 1998/2003			4·25	
1999	200 s. D.U.K.W.s landing on Gold Beach			80	80
2000	200 s. Canadian troops landing on Juno Beach			80	80
2001	200 s. Canadian cyclists disembarking, Juno Beach			80	80
2002	200 s. Amphibious Sherman tank on beach			80	80
2003	200 s. German gun implacement			80	80
2004	200 s. General Montgomery and British troops on beach			80	80
	a. Sheetlet. Nos. 2004/9			4·25	
2005	200 s. British engineers with AVRE Churchill tank, Gold Beach			80	80
2006	200 s. U.S.S. *Thompson* (destroyer) being refuelled			80	80
2007	200 s. H.M.S. *Warspite* (battleship)			80	80
2008	200 s. Royal Marines on Juno Beach			80	80
2009	200 s. Sherman Mark 1 flail tank leaving landing craft			80	80
2010	200 s. General Eisenhower and U.S. troops on Omaha Beach			80	80
	a. Sheetlet. Nos. 2010/15			4·25	
2011	200 s. North American P-51 Mustang escorting ships			80	80
2012	200 s. U.S. coastguard cutter alongside landing craft			80	80
2013	200 s. U.S. troops in landing craft			80	80
2014	200 s. U.S. troops landing on Omaha Beach			80	80
2015	200 s. U.S. troops on Omaha Beach			80	80
1998/2015			*Set of* 18	12·50	12·50

MS2016 Two sheets, each 99×70 mm. (a) 1000 s. U.S. marines amongst beach obstacles. (b) 1000 s. U.S. troops landing on Utah Beach

Set of 2 *sheets* 7·00 8·00

Nos. 1998/2003, 2004/9 and 2010/15 were each printed together, *se-tenant*, in sheetlets of 6.

No. 2004 is inscribed "COMMANDER-IN-CHEIF" and No. 2010 "OPERATION OVERLOAD", both in error.

(Des G. Bibby. Litho Questa)

1994 (26 Dec). *Prehistoric Animals. T* **254** *and similar designs. P* 14.

2017/48	120 s. × 32 multicoloured			17·00	18·00
MS2049	80×110 mm. 1000 s. multicoloured			4·25	4·75

Designs: *Vert*—No. 2018, Styracosaurus; No. 2019, Anatosaurus; No. 2020, Plateosaurus; No. 2021, Iguanodon; No. 2022, Oviraptor; No. 2023, Dimorphodons; No. 2024, Ornithomimus; No. 2025, Lambeosaurus; No. 2026, Megalosaurus; No. 2027, Cetiosaurus; No. 2028, Hypsilophodon; No. 2029, Rhamphorynchus; No. 2030, Scelidosaurus; No. 2031, Antrodemus; No. 2032, Dimetrodon; No. **MS**2049, Brachiosaurus. *Horiz*—No. 2033, Brontosaurus; No. 2034, Albertosaurus; No. 2035, Parasaurolophus; No. 2036, Pteranodons; No. 2037, Stegosaurus; No. 2038, Tyrannosaurus rex; No. 2039, Triceratops; No. 2040, Ornitholestes; No. 2041, Camarasaurus; No. 2042, Ankylosaurus; No. 2043, Trachodon; No. 2044, Allosaurus; No. 2045, Corythosaurus; No. 2046, Struthiomimus; No. 2047, Camptosaurus; No. 2048, Heterodontosaurus.

Nos. 2017/32 and 2033/48 were printed together, *se-tenant*, in sheetlets of 16, Nos. 2033/48 forming a composite design.

255 "Hubble" Space Telescope

(Litho State Ptg Wks, Moscow)

1994 (30 Dec). *Space Research. T* **255** *and similar horiz designs. Multicoloured. P* 12½×12.

2050	40 s. Type **255**				30	30
2051	100 s. "Mariner"				50	50
2052	120 s. "Voyager 2"				55	55
2053	170 s. "Work Package-03"				70	70
2054	250 s. Orbiting solar observer				85	85
2055	300 s. "Magellan"				90	90
2056	400 s. "Galilei"				95	95
2050/6				*Set of* 7	4·25	4·25
MS2057	91×91 mm. 500 s. "Fobos"				1·90	2·25

STAMP BOOKLETS

1965 (9 Dec). *Black on blue (No. SB6) or buff (No. SB7) covers, size 48×46 mm. Stitched.*
SB6 3 s. booklet containing four 15 c. and eight 30 c.
  (Nos. 130, 132) in blocks of 4 .. .. .. 4·75
SB7 5 s. booklet containing four 15 c. and 50 c., and
  eight 30 c. (Nos. 130, 132, 134) in blocks of 4 .. 4·75

1967 (9 Dec). *Black on blue (No. SB8) or buff (No. SB9) covers, size 48×45 mm. Stitched.*
SB8 3 s. booklet containing four 15 c. and eight 30 c.
  (Nos. 144, 146) in blocks of 4 .. .. .. 3·00
SB9 5 s. booklet containing 10 c., 15 c., 20 c., 30 c. and
  50 c. (Nos. 143/6, 148), each in block of 4 .. 3·50

1971 (15 Dec). *Black printed (No. SB10) or black on claret (No. SB11) covers, size 48×46 mm. Stitched.*
SB10 5 s. booklet containing four 10 c., 15 c. and 40 c.,
  and eight 30 c. (Nos. 143, 144a, 146, 147a)
  in blocks of 4 .. .. 23·00
SB11 10 s. booklet containing four 10 c., 20 c., 30 c. and
  50 c., and eight 70 c. (Nos. 143, 145/6, 148a,
  150a) in blocks of 4 .. .. .. 26·00

1973 (13 June). *Black printed cover, size 48×46 mm. Stitched.*
SB12 5 s. booklet containing four 10 c., 15 c. and 40 c.,
  and eight 30 c. (Nos. 143a, 144a, 146a, 147a)
  in blocks of 4 .. .. 18·00

1973 (10 Dec). *Black on yellow (No. SB13) or blue (No. SB14) covers, size 54×41 mm. Stitched.*
SB13 5 s. booklet containing 5 c., 10 c., 20 c., 40 c. and
  50 c. (Nos. 158/9, 161, 163/4), each in block
  of 4 .. .. 12·00
SB14 10 s. booklet containing four 10 c., 20 c., 30 c. and
  50 c., and eight 70 c. (Nos. 159, 161/2, 164,
  166) in blocks of 4 .. .. .. 18·00

1980 (Nov). *Black printed (No. SB15) or black on red (No. SB16) covers, size 66×47 mm. Stitched.*
SB15 6 s. booklet containing eight 10 c. and 20 c., and
  four 40 c. and 50 c. (Nos. 307/10) in blocks
  of 4 .. .. 3·00
SB16 14 s. booklet containing four 1 s. and two 2 s. and
  3 s. (Nos. 313, 315/16) in pairs .. .. 3·50

1984. *Black on red cover, 98×63 mm. Stitched.*
SB17 24 s. booklet containing four 1 s., 2 s. and 3 s.
  Waddington printings in panes of 4 (Nos.
  320cab, 320eab, 320fab) £140

1990 (15 Dec). *Black on yellow cover, size 99×58 mm. Pane attached by selvedge.*
SB18 174 s. booklet containing se-tenant pane of twelve
  (No. 804a) .. .. 2·00

OFFICIAL STAMPS

(Opt photo Harrison)

1965 (9 Dec). *Nos. 128/32, 134, 136, 139 optd as Types O 1 (15 c., 30 c. or larger (17 mm) 5 c., 10 c., 20 c., 50 c.), or with O 2 of Tanganyika (1 s., 5 s.).*
O 9 5 c. ultramarine and yellow-orange .. 10 60
O10 10 c. black, greenish yellow, green & blue .. 10 60
O11 15 c. multicoloured 10 60
O12 20 c. sepia, grey-green and greenish blue .. 10 60
O13 30 c. black and red-brown 10 40
O14 50 c. multicoloured 15 60
O15 1 s. multicoloured 30 40
O16 5 s. lake-brown, yellow-green and blue .. 1·75 6·00
O9/16 .. .. *Set of 8* 2·25 8·75

OFFICIAL
(O 3) (3 mm tall)

(Opt litho Govt Printer, Dar-es-Salaam)

1967 (10–18 Nov). *Nos. 134, 136 and 139 optd as No. O14 (50 c.) or with Type O 3 (others).*
O17 50 c. multicoloured (18.11).. .. .. 16·00 4·50
O18 1 s. multicoloured (18.11).. .. .. — —
O19 5 s. lake-brown, yellow-green and blue .. 9·00 8·00
  The issue dates given are for the earliest known postmarked copies.
  Nos. O9/16 were overprinted by Harrison in photogravure and Nos. O17/19 have litho overprints by the Government Printer, Dar-es-Salaam. On No. O17 the overprint is the same size (17 mm long) as on No. O14.

1967 (9 Dec)–**71**. *Nos. 142/6, 148, 151 and 155 optd as Type O 1, but larger (measuring 17 mm) (5 c. to 50 c.) or as Type O 2 of Tanganyika (1 s. and 5 s.). Chalk-surfaced paper.*
O20 5 c. magenta, yellow-olive and black .. 10 1·75
  a. Glazed, ordinary paper (22.1.71) .. 1·50 4·25
O21 10 c. brown and bistre 10 50
O22 15 c. grey, turquoise-blue and black .. 10 1·75
  a. Glazed, ordinary paper (22.1.71) .. 1·50 5·00
O23 20 c. brown and turquoise-green .. 10 30
O24 30 c. sage-green and black 10 30
O25 50 c. multicoloured 15 80
  a. Glazed, ordinary paper (22.1.71) .. 1·50 5·00
O26 1 s. orange-brown, slate-blue and maroon .. 30 1·75
  a. Glazed, ordinary paper (3.2.71) .. 7·00 5·00
O27 5 s. greenish yellow, black & turquoise-grn .. 2·50 10·00
  a. Glazed, ordinary paper (3.2.71) .. 12·00 16·00
O20/7 .. .. *Set of 8* 3·00 15·00
O20a/7a .. .. .. *Set of 5* 21·00 32·00
  The chalk-surfaced paper exists with both PVA gum and gum arabic, but the glazed, ordinary paper exists PVA gum only.

OFFICIAL   OFFICIAL
(O 4)   *(O 5)*

1970 (10 Dec)–**73**. *Nos. 142/8, 151 and 155 optd locally by letterpress as Type O 4 (5 c. to 50 c.) or as Type O 2 of Tanganyika, but measuring 28 mm (1 s. and 5 s.).*

(a) Chalk-surfaced paper
O28 5 c. magenta, yellow-olive and black .. 10 2·00
  a. "OFFCIAL" (R.7/6) .. .. — —
O29 10 c. brown and bistre 10 90
  a. "OFFICIA" (R.7/6) .. .. — —
O30 20 c. brown and turquoise-green .. 20 1·00
O31 30 c. sage-green and black .. .. 25 1·00
O28/31 .. .. *Set of 4* 55 4·50

(b) Glazed, ordinary paper (1973)
O32 5 c. magenta, yellow-olive and black .. — 2·00
  a. "OFFCIAL" (R.7/6) .. .. — 35·00
  b. "OFFICIA" (R.10/9) .. .. — 40·00
O33 10 c. brown and bistre .. .. — —
  a. "OFFICIA" (R.7/6) .. .. — —
O34 15 c. grey, turquoise-blue and black .. — —
  a. "OFFICIA" (R.7/6) .. .. — —
O35 20 c. brown and turquoise-green .. — —
O36 40 c. yellow, chocolate and bright green .. — 2·50
  a. Opt double .. .. .. — —
  b. "OFFICIA" (R.10/9) .. .. — 55·00
O37 50 c. multicoloured .. .. .. — 2·00
  a. "OFFCIAL" (R.7/6) .. .. — 45·00
O38 1 s. orange-brown, slate-blue and maroon .. — 10·00
  a. Opt double .. .. .. — —
O39 5 s. greenish yellow, black & turquoise-grn .. — 25·00
  The letterpress overprint can be distinguished from the photogravure by its absence of screening dots and the overprint showing through to the reverse, apart from the difference in length.

1973 (10 Dec). *Nos. 158/9, 161, 163/4 and 166/70 optd with Type O 1 of Tanganyika (5 to 70 c.) or Type O 5 (others).*
O40 5 c. light yellow-olive, lt violet-blue & black .. 50 2·00
O41 10 c. multicoloured 65 30
O42 20 c. reddish cinnamon, orange-yellow & blk .. 80 30
O43 40 c. multicoloured .. .. .. 1·25 30
O44 50 c. multicoloured .. .. .. 1·25 30
O45 70 c. turquoise-green, pale orange and black .. 1·50 65
O46 1 s. multicoloured .. .. .. 1·50 30
O47 1 s. 50, multicoloured .. .. 3·50 3·00
  a. Pair, one without opt .. .. † —
O48 2 s. 50, multicoloured .. .. 4·00 6·50
O49 5 s. multicoloured .. .. .. 4·50 8·50
O40/9 .. .. *Set of 10* 17·00 20·00
  No. O47a is due to a paper fold and comes from a sheet used at Kigoma in 1974.

1977 (Feb). *Nos. 159, 161 and 163/4 optd locally by letterpress as Type O 4.*
O50 10 c. multicoloured .. .. .. — 2·50
  a. "OFFCIAL" (R. 7/6) .. .. — 45·00
O51 20 c. multicoloured .. .. .. — 2·50
  a. "OFFCIAL" (R. 7/6) .. .. — 45·00
  b. Opt inverted .. .. .. — —
  c. Opt double .. .. .. — —
O52 40 c. multicoloured .. .. .. — 2·75
  a. "OFFCIAL" (R. 7/6) .. .. — 55·00
O53 50 c. multicoloured .. .. .. — 2·75
  a. "OFFCIAL" (R. 7/6) .. .. — 55·00
  b. Opt inverted .. .. .. — —

OFFICIAL OFFICIAL OFFICIAL OFFICIAL
(O 6) *(O 6a)* *(O 7)* *(O 7a)*

1980 (Nov)–**85**. *(a) Bradbury Wilkinson printings. Nos. 307/12 optd with Type O 6 (10 mm long) and Nos. 313 and 315/17 optd with Type O 7 (13½ mm long).*
O54 10 c. Type 75 .. .. .. 20 60
O55 20 c. Large-spotted Genet 25 50
O56 40 c. Banded Mongoose 30 50
O57 50 c. Ratel (light blue panel at foot) .. 30 30
O58 75 c. Large-toothed Rock Hyrax .. 40 50
O59 80 c. Leopard 55 90
O60 1 s. Type 76 .. .. .. 55 30
O61 2 s. Common Zebra .. .. 85 2·00
O62 3 s. African Buffalo .. .. 1·00 2·25
O63 5 s. Lion .. .. .. 1·50 3·25
O54/63 .. .. *Set of 10* 5·50 10·00

(b) John Waddington printings. No. 320a optd with Type O 6a (8½ mm long) and Nos. 320c/g optd with Type O 7a (13 mm long) (1984–85)
O64 50 c. Ratel (turquoise-blue panel at foot) 1·75 1·75
O65 1 s. Type 76 .. .. .. 2·00 2·00
O66 1 s. 50, Giraffe .. .. .. 3·75 4·00
O67 2 s. Common Zebra .. .. 5·00 5·50
O68 3 s. African Buffalo .. .. 6·50 7·50
O69 5 s. Lion .. .. .. 9·50 11·00
O64/9 .. .. *Set of 6* 26·00 29·00
  On the Bradbury Wilkinson printings the overprint reads downwards on the 10 c., 50 c., 2 s., 5 s. and upwards on the others. All values of the John Waddington printing show the overprint reading upwards.

OFFICIAL   OFFICIAL
(O 8)   *(O 9)*

1990 (15 Dec)–**91**. *Nos. 804/12 optd with Type O 8 (5 s. to 30 s.) or Type O 9 (40 s. to 100 s.).*
O70 5 s. Type 163 .. .. .. 15 30
O71 9 s. African Emerald Cuckoo .. 20 30
O72 13 s. Little Bee Eater 20 30
O73 15 s. Red Bishop 20 30
O74 20 s. Bateleur 30 30
O75 25 s. Scarlet-chested Sunbird .. 30 30
O76 30 s. African Wood Pigeon (1.7.91) .. 30 30
O77 40 s. Type 164 .. .. .. 40 40
O78 70 s. Helmet Guineafowl 60 70
O79 100 s. Eastern White Pelican .. 90 1·25
O70/9 .. .. *Set of 10* 3·25 4·00
  Official overprints were reported as being used for normal postal purposes during 1992.

POSTAGE DUE STAMPS

Postage Due stamps of Kenya and Uganda were issued for provisional use as such in Tanganyika on 1 July 1933. The postmark is the only means of identification.
The Postage Due stamps of Kenya, Uganda and Tanganyika were used in Tanganyika until 2 January 1967.

D 1   D 2

(Litho D.L.R.)

1967 (3 Jan). *P 14 × 13½.*
D1 D 1 5 c. scarlet .. .. .. 35 5·50
D2 10 c. green .. .. .. 45 6·00
D3 20 c. deep blue .. .. .. 50 7·00
D4 30 c. red-brown .. .. .. 50 8·00
D5 40 c. bright purple .. .. 50 12·00
D6 1 s. orange .. .. .. 80 12·00
D1/6 .. .. *Set of 6* 2·75 45·00

1969 (12 Dec)–**71**. *Chalk-surfaced paper. P 14×15.*
D 7 D 1 5 c. scarlet .. .. .. 30 9·00
  a. Glazed, ordinary paper (13.7.71) 4·00 8·00
D 8 10 c. green .. .. .. 65 6·00
  a. Glazed, ordinary paper (13.7.71) 75 3·75
D 9 20 c. deep blue .. .. .. 40 9·00
  a. Glazed, ordinary paper (13.7.71) 2·50 9·00
D10 30 c. red-brown .. .. .. 50 14·00
  a. Glazed, ordinary paper (13.7.71) 85 6·50
D11 40 c. bright purple .. .. 2·00 14·00
  a. Glazed, ordinary paper (13.7.71) 6·50 25·00
D12 1 s. orange (glazed, ordinary paper)
  (13.7.71) .. .. .. 4·75 25·00
D7/12 .. .. *Set of 6* 7·75 60·00
  The stamps on chalk-surfaced paper exist only with gum arabic, but the stamps on glazed paper exist only with PVA gum.

1973 (12 Dec). *As Nos. D1/6, but glazed ordinary paper. P 15.*
D13 D 1 5 c. scarlet .. .. .. 50 8·00
D14 10 c. emerald .. .. .. 50 6·00
D15 20 c. deep blue .. .. .. 70 9·00
D16 30 c. red-brown .. .. .. 85 9·50
D17 40 c. bright mauve .. .. 90 14·00
D18 1 s. bright orange .. .. 1·25 15·00
D13/18 .. .. *Set of 6* 4·25 55·00

(Litho Questa)

1978 (31 July). *Chalk-surfaced paper. P 13½×14.*
D19 D 1 5 c. brown-red .. .. .. 15 2·00
D20 10 c. emerald .. .. .. 20 2·00
D21 20 c. steel-blue .. .. .. 30 2·25
D22 30 c. red-brown .. .. .. 45 3·00
D23 40 c. bright purple .. .. 50 4·25
D24 1 s. bright orange .. .. 70 4·75
D19/24 .. .. *Set of 6* 2·10 16·00

1984 (?). *Chalk-surfaced paper. P 15×14.*
D25 D 1 10 c. emerald .. .. ..
D26 20 c. deep dull blue .. ..
D27 30 c. reddish brown .. ..
D28 40 c. bright purple .. ..
D29 1 s. bright orange .. ..

(Litho Questa)

1990 (15 Dec). *P 14½×14.*
D30 D 2 50 c. myrtle-green 10 10
D31 80 c. ultramarine 10 10
D32 1 s. orange-brown 10 10
D33 2 s. yellow-olive 10 10
D34 3 s. purple 10 10
D35 5 s. grey-brown 10 10
D36 10 s. reddish brown 10 10
D37 20 s. brown-ochre 10 10
D30/7 .. .. *Set of 8* 40 40

Appendix

The following stamps have either been issued in excess of postal needs, or have not been made available to the public in reasonable quantities at face value. Miniature sheets, imperforate stamps, etc., are excluded from this section.

1985
Life and Times of Queen Elizabeth the Queen Mother. As Nos. 425/8 but embossed on gold foil. 20 s. × 2, 100 s. × 2.
Tanzanian Railway Locomotives (1st series). As Nos. 430/3, but embossed on gold foil. 5, 10, 20, 30 s.

1986
Caribbean Royal Visit. Optd in silver and gold on previous issues. (a) Nos. 425/8 20 s. × 2, 100 s. × 2. (b) On Nos. 430/3, 5, 10, 20, 30 s.
"Ameripex" International Stamp Exhibition, Chicago. Optd on Nos. 425/8. 20 s. × 2, 100 s. × 2.

1988
Centenary of Statue of Liberty (1986). 1, 2, 3, 4, 5, 6, 7, 8, 10, 12, 15, 18, 20, 25, 30, 35, 40, 45, 50, 60 s.
Royal Ruby Wedding. Optd on No. 378. 10 s.
125th Anniv of Red Cross. Optd on Nos. 486/7. 5, 40 s.
63rd Anniv of Rotary International in Africa. Optd on Nos. 422/3. 10 s., 17 s. 50.

Tasmania
see Australia

Togo

The stamps of GERMANY were used in the colony from March 1888 until June 1897 when issues for TOGO were provided.

PRICES FOR STAMPS ON COVER	
Nos. H1/7	*from* × 6
No. H8	—
No. H9	*from* × 6
No. H10	*from* × 2
No. H11	—
Nos. H12/13	*from* × 6
Nos. H14/16	—
Nos. H17/19	*from* × 12
Nos. H20/6	—
Nos. H27/8	*from* × 20
No. H29	—
Nos. H30/1	*from* × 6
Nos. H32/3	—
Nos. H34/58	*from* × 6

ANGLO-FRENCH OCCUPATION

French forces invaded southern Togo on 8 August 1914 and the British landed at Lomé on 12 August. The German administration surrendered on 26 August 1914.

The territory was jointly administered under martial law, but was formally divided between Great Britain and France, effective 1 October 1920. League of Nations mandates were issued for both areas from 20 July 1922.

(Currency. 100 pfennig = 1 mark)

Stamps of German Colonial issue Yacht Types 1900 and 1909–14 (5 pf. and 10 pf.)

TOGO
Anglo - French
Occupation (1)

Half penny (2)

SETTINGS. Nos. H1/33 were all overprinted or surcharged by the Catholic Mission, Lome.

The initial setting for the 3 pf. to 80 pf. was of 50 (10 × 5), repeated twice on each sheet of 100. Overprints from this setting, used for Nos. H1/9, had the lines of type 3 mm apart.

Nos. H1/2 were subsequently surcharged, also from a setting of 50, to form Nos. H12/13. The surcharge setting showed a thin dropped "y" with small serifs on R. 1/1–2, 2/1, 3/1, 4/1 and 5/1–2.

The type from the overprint and surcharge was then amalgamated in a new setting of 50 on which the lines of the overprint were only 2 mm apart. On this amalgamated setting, used for Nos. H27/8, the thin "y" varieties were still present and R. 4/7 showed the second "O" of "TOGO" omitted.

The surcharge was subsequently removed from this "2 mm" setting which was then used to produce Nos. H17/19. The missing "O" was spotted and corrected before any of the 30 pf. stamps were overprinted.

The remaining low values of the second issue, Nos. H14/16 and H20/2, were overprinted from settings of 25 (5 × 5), either taken from the last setting of 50 or from an amended version on which there was no space either side of the hyphen. This slightly narrower overprint was subsequently used for Nos. H29/33. It shows the top of the second "O" broken so that it resembles a "U" on R. 1/5.

The mark values were overprinted from settings of 20 (5 × 4), showing the same differences in the spacing of the lines as on the low values.

It is believed that odd examples of some German colonial values were overprinted from individual settings in either spacing.

1914 (17 Sept*). *Optd with T 1 by Catholic Mission, Lome. Wide setting. Lines 3 mm apart.*

H 1	3 pf. brown	£110	95·00
H 2	5 pf. green	£100	95·00
H 3	10 pf. carmine (Wmk Lozenges)	£120	£100
	a. Opt inverted	£7500	£3000
	b. Opt tête-bêche in vert pair	†	£7000
	c. No wmk	†	£5500
H 4	20 pf. ultramarine	28·00	35·00
H 5	25 pf. black and red/*yellow*	28·00	27·00
H 6	30 pf. black and orange/*buff*	30·00	45·00
H 7	40 pf. black and carmine	£225	£250
H 8	50 pf. black and purple/*buff*	£9000	£7000
H 9	80 pf. black and carmine/*rose*	£225	£275
H10	1 m. carmine	£5000	£2500
H11	2 m. blue	£8000	£8500
	a. "Occupation" double	£13000	£11000
	b. Opt inverted		£9500

*The post office at Lome was open for four hours on 17 September, before closing again on instructions from Accra. It finally reopened on 24 September.

The tête-bêche overprint on the 10 pf. is due to the sheet being turned round after the upper 50 stamps had been overprinted so that vertical pairs from the two middle rows have the overprint tête-bêche.

1914 (1 Oct). *Nos. H1 and H2 surch as T 2.*

H12	½d. on 3 pf. brown	£160	£140
	a. Thin "y" in "penny"	£400	£350
H13	1d. on 5 pf. green	£160	£140
	a. Thin "y" in "penny"	£400	£350

TOGO
Anglo-French
Occupation (3)

TOGO
Anglo-French
Occupation
Half penny (4)

1914 (Oct). *(a) Optd with T 3. Narrow Setting. Lines 2 mm apart. "Anglo-French" measures 16 mm.*

H14	3 pf. brown	£4500	£900
H15	5 pf. green	£1100	£700
H16	10 pf. carmine	†	£2750
H17	20 pf. ultramarine	16·00	12·00
	a. "TOG"	£4000	£4000
	b. Nos. H4 and H17 se-tenant (vert pair)		£6500
H18	25 pf. black and red/*yellow*	20·00	30·00
	a. "TOG"		£12000
H19	30 pf. black and orange/*buff*	19·00	29·00
H20	40 pf. black and carmine	£4500	£1500
H21	50 pf. black and purple/*buff*	†	£6000
H22	80 pf. black and carmine/*rose*	£1800	£1800
H23	1 m. carmine	£7000	£4000
H24	2 m. blue	†	£8500
H25	3 m. violet-black		† £38000
H26	5 m. lake and black		† £38000

(b) Narrow setting, but including value, as T 4.

H27	½d. on 3 pf. brown	32·00	26·00
	a. "TOG"	£425	£300
	b. Thin "y" in "penny"	60·00	60·00
H28	1d. on 5 pf. green	4·00	4·25
	a. "TOG"	£130	£110
	b. Thin "y" in "penny"	12·00	15·00

In the 20 pf. one half of a sheet was overprinted with the wide setting (3 mm), and the other half with the narrow setting (2 mm), so that vertical pairs from the middle of the sheet show the two varieties of the overprint.

TOGO
Anglo-French
Occupation (6)

TOGO
ANGLO-FRENCH
OCCUPATION (7)

TOGO
ANGLO-FRENCH
OCCUPATION (8)

1915 (7 Jan). *Optd as T 6. The words "Anglo-French" measure 15 mm instead of 16 mm as in T 3.*

H29	3 pf. brown	£7500	£2500
H30	5 pf. green	£200	£130
	a. "Occupation" omitted	£6500	
H31	10 pf. carmine	£200	£130
	a. No wmk	†	£7000
H32	20 pf. ultramarine	£1400	£475
H32a	40 pf. black and carmine	†	£7500
H33	50 pf. black and purple/*buff*	£12000	£9500

This printing was made on another batch of German Togo stamps, found at Sansane-Mangu.

Stamps of Ghana (Gold Coast) overprinted

1915 (May). *Nos. 70/81, 82a and 83/4 of Gold Coast (King George V) optd at Govt Press, Accra, with T 7 ("OCCUPATION" 14½ mm long).*

H34	½d. green	30	60
	a. Small "F" in "FRENCH"	1·50	2·50
	b. Thin "G" in "TOGO"	3·00	5·00
	c. No hyphen after "ANGLO"	3·00	5·00
	e. "CUPATION" for "OCCUPATION"	85·00	
	f. "CCUPATION" for "OCCUPATION"	48·00	
H35	1d. red	30	40
	a. Small "F" in "FRENCH"	1·75	4·50
	b. Thin "G" in "TOGO"	4·25	5·50
	c. No hyphen after "ANGLO"	4·25	5·50
	f. "CCUPATION" for "OCCUPATION"	£130	
	g. Opt double	£325	£450
	h. Opt inverted	£160	£250
	ha. Ditto. "TOGO" omitted	£5500	
H36	2d. grey	30	80
	a. Small "F" in "FRENCH"	1·75	3·00
	b. Thin "G" in "TOGO"	5·50	8·00
	c. No hyphen after "ANGLO"	65·00	
	d. Two hyphens after "ANGLO"	40·00	
	f. "CCUPATION" for "OCCUPATION"	£130	
H37	2½d. bright blue	50	2·50
	a. Small "F" in "FRENCH"	2·50	7·50
	b. Thin "G" in "TOGO"	8·50	20·00
	c. No hyphen after "ANGLO"	32·00	
	d. Two hyphens after "ANGLO"	45·00	
	f. "CCUPATION" for "OCCUPATION"	£110	
H38	3d. purple/*yellow*	65	80
	a. Small "F" in "FRENCH"	2·75	4·25
	b. Thin "G" in "TOGO"	9·00	13·00
	c. No hyphen after "ANGLO"	32·00	
	f. "CCUPATION" for "OCCUPATION"	£130	
	g. White back	3·50	13·00
	ga. Small "F" in "FRENCH"	15·00	35·00
	gb. Thin "G" in "TOGO"	50·00	80·00
H40	6d. dull and bright purple	65	1·75
	a. Small "F" in "FRENCH"	4·25	10·00
	b. Thin "G" in "TOGO"	9·50	20·00
	f. "CCUPATION" for "OCCUPATION"	£180	
H41	1s. black/*green*	1·25	4·00
	a. Small "F" in "FRENCH"	4·25	12·00
	b. Thin "G" in "TOGO"	10·00	30·00
	f. "CCUPATION" for "OCCUPATION"	£100	
	g. Opt double	£950	
H42	2s. purple and blue/*blue*	8·00	10·00
	a. Small "F" in "FRENCH"	26·00	38·00
	b. Thin "G" in "TOGO"	55·00	75·00
	c. No hyphen after "ANGLO"	£130	
	f. "CCUPATION" for "OCCUPATION"	£300	

H43	2s. 6d. black and red/*blue*	4·50	17·00
	a. Small "F" in "FRENCH"	18·00	55·00
	b. Thin "G" in "TOGO"	40·00	95·00
	c. No hyphen after "ANGLO"	£120	
	f. "CCUPATION" for "OCCUPATION"	£450	
H44	5s. green and red/*yellow (white back)*	8·00	15·00
	a. Small "F" in "FRENCH"	35·00	60·00
	b. Thin "G" in "TOGO"	60·00	£120
	c. No hyphen after "ANGLO"	£160	
	f. "CCUPATION" for "OCCUPATION"	£300	
H45	10s. green and red/*green*	32·00	55·00
	a. Small "F" in "FRENCH"	80·00	
	b. Thin "G" in "TOGO"	£170	
	f. "CCUPATION" for "OCCUPATION"	£425	
H46	20 s. purple and black/*red*	£120	£140
	a. Small "F" in "FRENCH"	£275	
	b. Thin "G" in "TOGO"	£475	
	f. "CCUPATION" for "OCCUPATION"	£650	
H34/46		Set of 12	£150	£225

Varieties (Nos. indicate positions in pane).
a. Small "F" in "FRENCH" (25, 58 and 59).
b. Thin "G" in "TOGO" (24).
c. No hyphen after "ANGLO" (5).
d. Two hyphens after "ANGLO" (5).
e. "CUPATION" for "OCCUPATION" (33).
f. "CCUPATION" for "OCCUPATION" (57).

Varieties c and e also occur together on position 28 of the ½d. value only.

The 1d. opt inverted (No. H35h) exists with small "F" (Price £1200 unused), thin "G" (Price £3250 unused) and "No hyphen" (Price £3250 unused).

Examples of all values, and especially the varieties, are known showing a forged Lome postmark dated "22 1 15".

1916 (Apr)–20. *Nos. 70/84 of Gold Coast (King George V) optd in London with T 8 ("OCCUPATION" 15 mm long). Heavy type and thicker letters showing through on back.*

H47	½d. green	15	2·00
H48	1d. red	15	85
H49	2d. grey	35	45
H50	2½d. bright blue	45	1·50
H51	3d. purple/*yellow*	1·00	70
H52	6d. dull and bright purple	70	1·00
	w. Wmk inverted	80·00	
H53	1s. black/*green*	1·75	3·50
	a. On blue-green (olive back) (1918)	4·00	9·00
	b. On emerald-green (olive back) (1920)	£375	
	c. On emer-grn (emer-grn back) (1920)	£225	£475
H54	2s. purple and blue/*blue*	4·50	8·50
	a. Wmk sideways	†	
H55	2s. 6d. black and red/*blue*	4·50	7·00
H56	5s. green and red/*yellow*	8·50	26·00
	a. On orange-buff (1919)	8·00	30·00
	b. On buff (1920)		
H57	10s. green and red/*green*	24·00	60·00
	a. On blue-green (olive back) (1920)	16·00	50·00
H58	20s. purple and black/*red*	£130	£150
H47/58		Set of 12	£150	£225
H47/58 Optd "Specimen"		Set of 12	£300	

Nos. H47/58 were withdrawn in October 1920 when Gold Coast stamps were introduced.

The mandates were transferred to the United Nations in January 1946. The inhabitants of the British mandate voted to join Ghana in 1957.

Tokelau
see after New Zealand

Tonga

The Tongan Post Office was established in 1885 and FIJI 2d. and 6d. stamps are recorded in use until the arrival of Nos. 1/4.

PRICES FOR STAMPS ON COVER TO 1945	
Nos. 1/4	*from* × 60
Nos. 5/9	*from* × 20
Nos. 10/28	*from* × 8
Nos. 29/31	*from* × 7
Nos. 32/7	*from* × 6
Nos. 38/54	*from* × 5
Nos. 55/63	*from* × 6
Nos. 64/70	*from* × 3
Nos. 71/87	*from* × 2
Nos. O1/10	*from* × 25

PROTECTORATE KINGDOM
King George I, 1845–93

1 King George I

2

(Eng Bock and Cousins. Plates made and typo Govt Ptg Office, Wellington)

1886–88. W **2**. P 12½ (line) or 12 × 11½ (comb)*.
1	**1**	1d. carmine (p 12½) (27.8.86)		£350	6·00
		a. Perf 12½ × 10			
		b. Perf 12 × 11½ (15.7.87)		10·00	3·25
		ba. Pale carmine (p 12 × 11½)		16·00	8·50
2		2d. pale violet (p 12½) (27.8.86)		50·00	10·00
		a. Bright violet		70·00	3·50
		b. Perf 12 × 11½ (15.7.87)		28·00	2·75
		ba. Bright violet (p 12 × 11½)		40·00	3·00
3		6d. blue (p 12½) (9.10.86)		60·00	2·25
		a. Perf 12 × 11½ (15.10.88)		50·00	2·25
		ab. Dull blue (p 12 × 11½)		27·00	2·25
4		1s. pale green (p 12½) (9.10.86)		85·00	4·50
		a. Deep green (p 12½)		95·00	2·25
		b. Perf 12 × 11½ (15.10.88)		55·00	6·00
		ba. Deep green (p 12 × 11½)		55·00	3·25

*See note after New Zealand, No. 186.

FOUR PENCE. (3)   **EIGHT PENCE.** (4)

(Surch Messrs Wilson & Horton, Auckland, N.Z.)

1891 (10 Nov). Nos. 1b and 2b surch.
5	**3**	4d. on 1d. carmine		2·75	11·00
		a. No stop after "PENCE"		45·00	£100
6	**4**	8d. on 2d. violet		35·00	90·00
		a. Short "T" in "EIGHT"		£150	£250

No. 5a occurred on R. 6/8 and 9, R. 10/11, all from the righthand pane.

1891 (23 Nov). Optd with stars in upper right and lower left corners. P 12½.
7	**1**	1d. carmine		42·00	50·00
		a. Three stars		£300	
		b. Four stars		£400	
		c. Five stars		£600	
		d. Perf 12 × 11½		£275	
		da. Three stars		£450	
		db. Four stars		£550	
		dc. Five stars		£800	
8		2d. violet		70·00	38·00
		a. Perf 12 × 11½		£350	

1892 (15 Aug). W **2**. P 12 × 11½.
9	**1**	6d. yellow-orange		16·00	26·00

5 Arms of Tonga   **6** King George I

Damaged "O" in "TONGA" (R. 1/1, later corrected)

(Dies eng A. E. Cousins. Typo at Govt Printing Office, Wellington, N.Z.)

1892 (10 Nov). W **2**. P 12 × 11½.
10	**5**	1d. pale rose		12·00	17·00
		a. Bright rose		12·00	17·00
		b. Bisected diag (½d.) (1893) (on cover)		†	£850
		c. Damaged "O"		£100	
11	**6**	2d. olive		15·00	16·00
12	**5**	4d. chestnut		48·00	70·00
13	**6**	8d. bright mauve		55·00	£150
14		1s. brown		75·00	£110
10/14			Set of 5	£180	£325

No. 10b was used from 31 May 1893 to provide a 2½d. rate before the arrival of No. 15, and on subsequent occasions up to 1895.

½d. (7)   **2½d.** (8)   **FIVE PENCE.** (9)   **7½d.** (10)

1893. Printed in new colours and surch with T **7/10** by Govt Printing Office, Wellington. (a) In carmine. P 12½ (21 Aug).
15	**5**	½d. on 1d. bright ultramarine		23·00	26·00
		a. Surch omitted			
16	**6**	2½d. on 2d. green		14·00	12·00
17	**5**	5d. on 4d. orange		4·00	6·50
18	**6**	7½d. on 8d. carmine		24·00	75·00

(b) In black. P 12 × 11½ (Nov)
19	**5**	½d. on 1d. dull blue		45·00	48·00
20	**6**	2½d. on 2d. green		17·00	17·00
		a. Surch double		—	£1700
		b. Fraction bar completely omitted (R. 3/3)			

King George II, 1893–1918

SURCHARGE. HALF-PENNY (11)   SURCHARGE, 2½d. (12)   HALF-PEI Small "F" in "HALF"

(Surch at the Star Office, Auckland, N.Z.)

1894 (June–Nov). Surch with T **11** or **12**.
21	**5**	½d. on 4d. chestnut (B.) (Nov)		1·75	7·00
		a. "SURCHARCE"		9·00	20·00
		b. Small "F"		9·00	20·00
22	**6**	½d. on 1s. brown		2·25	11·00
		a. "SURCHARCE"		10·00	38·00
		b. Small "F"		10·00	38·00
		c. Surch double		£275	
		d. Surch double with "SURCHARCE"		£900	
23		2½d. on 8d. bright mauve		5·00	8·00
		a. No stop after "SURCHARGE"		32·00	55·00
24		2½d. on 1s. deep green (No. 4a) (Nov)		55·00	24·00
		a. No stop after "SURCHARGE"		£170	
		b. Perf 12 × 11½		15·00	38·00
		ba. No stop after "SURCHARGE"		55·00	

Nos. 21/4 were surcharged in panes of 60 (6 × 10) with No. 21a occurring on R. 2/6, 4/6, 5/6, 8/6 and 10/6, No. 21b on R. 1/4, 3/4, 6/4, 7/4 and 9/4, No. 22a on R. 1/6, 4/6, 3/6, 5/6, 8/6 and 10/6, No. 22b on R. 2/4, 4/4, 6/4, 7/4 and 9/4 (both after the setting had been rearranged), No. 23a on R. 3/1–3 and Nos. 24a and 24ba on R. 6/3 and R. 7/3 or R. 7/1–2.

Sheets used for these provisionals were surcharged with the remains of the tissue interleaving still in place. This sometimes subsequently fell away taking parts of the surcharge with it.

Deformed "E" in "PENI" (R. 2/2)

(Design resembling No. 11 litho and surch at Star Office Auckland, N.Z.)

1895 (22 May*). As T **6** surch as T **11** and **12**. No wmk. P 12.
25	**11**	1d. on 2d. pale blue (C.)		45·00	22·00
		a. Deformed "E"		£110	
26	**12**	1½d. on 2d. pale blue (C.)		60·00	27·00
		a. Deformed "E"		£150	
		b. Perf 12 × 11		45·00	27·00
27		2½d. on 2d. pale blue (C.)†		40·00	45·00
		a. No stop after "SURCHARGE"		£225	£225
		b. Deformed "E"		£110	
28		7½d. on 2d. pale blue (C.)		£400	
		a. Deformed "E"			
		b. Perf 12 × 11		60·00	45·00
		ba. Deformed "E"		£150	

* Earliest known date of use.
†The 2½d. on 2d. is the only value which normally has a stop after the word "SURCHARGE".
No. 27a occurs on R.1/3 of the right-hand pane.

12a King George II   **13** King George II   **14**

Half Penny   VAEU OF BENI

"BU" joined (R. 1/1)   Missing eyebrow (R.2/4)

"7" for "1" in "½d." (R. 2/1)

1895 (20 June*). Unissued stamp surch as in T **12a**. No wmk. P 12.
29	**11**	½d. on 2½d. vermilion		30·00	32·00
		a. "BU" joined		75·00	
		b. "SURCHARCE"		70·00	
		c. Missing eyebrow		75·00	
		d. Stop after "POSTAGE" (R. 2/5)		75·00	
		e. "7" for "1" in "½d."		75·00	
30		1d. on 2½d. vermilion		55·00	35·00
		a. "BU" joined		£100	
		c. Missing eyebrow		£100	
		d. Stop after "POSTAGE" (R. 2/5)		£100	
		e. "7" for "1" in "½d."		£100	
31	**12**	7½d. on 2½d. vermilion		55·00	55·00
		a. "BU" joined		£100	
		c. Missing eyebrow		£100	
		d. Stop after "POSTAGE" (R. 2/5)		£100	
		e. "7" for "1" in "½d."		£100	

*Earliest known date of use.
No. 29b occurs on R. 1/6 and 3/6 of both the right and the left pane.
In the ½d. surcharge there is a stop after "SURCHARGE" and not after "PENNY". In the 1d. and 7½d. the stop is after the value only.

"Black Eye" flaw (Rt pane R. 2/4)

(Litho Star Office, Auckland, N.Z.)

1895 (9 July–Sept). No wmk. P 12.
32	**13**	1d. olive-green		17·00	26·00
		a. Bisected diagonally (½d.) (on cover) (9.95)		† £750	
		b. Imperf between (horiz pair)		—	£6000
33		2½d. rose		20·00	20·00
		a. Stop (flaw) after "POSTAGE" (R. 4/5)		60·00	60·00
34		5d. blue		21·00	48·00
		a. "Black eye" flaw		60·00	
		b. Perf 12 × 11		22·00	48·00
		ba. "Black eye" flaw		65·00	
		c. Perf 11		£350	
		ca. "Black eye" flaw			
35		7½d. orange-yellow		28·00	45·00
		a. Yellow		28·00	45·00

1896 (May). Nos. 26b and 28b with typewritten surcharge "Half-Penny-", in violet, and Tongan surcharge, in black, as T **14**.

A. Tongan surch reading downwards (right panes)
36A	**6**	½d. on 1½d. on 2d.		£450	
		a. Perf 12		£425	£425
		e. "Halef"		£4750	
		f. "H" over "G"			
37A		½d. on 7½d. on 2d.		85·00	£110
		a. "Hafl" for "Half"		£1500	£1600
		b. "Hafl" ("Penny" omitted)		£3250	
		c. "PPenny"		£600	
		d. Stops instead of hyphens		£900	
		e. "Halyf"			
		f. "Half-Penny-" inverted		£1900	
		g. No hyphen after "Penny"			
		l. Capital "P" over small "p"			
		p. Perf 12		£750	
		pa. No hyphen after "Half"			

B. Tongan surch reading upwards (left panes)
36B	**6**	½d. on 1½d. on 2d.		£425	£425
		a. Perf 12		£450	£450
		ab. "Haalf"		£1900	
		c. "H" double			
		d. Tongan surch omitted		£4250	
37B		½d. on 7½d. on 2d.		85·00	£110
		d. Stops instead of hyphens		£950	
		f. "Half-Penny-" inverted		£2750	
		h. "Hwlf"			
		i. No hyphen after "Half"		£800	
		j. "Penny" double			
		k. "Penny" twice, with "Half" on top of upper "Penny"		£3500	
		m. "Half H"		£750	
		n. Tongan surch double		£1200	
		o. Two hyphens between "Half" and "Penny"			
		p. Perf 12		£750	

Nos. 26b and 28b were in sheets of 48 (2 panes 6 × 4). The panes were separated before the surcharges were applied.
There are variations in the relative positions of the words "Half" and "Penny", both vertically and horizontally.

15 Arms

16 Ovava Tree, Kana-Kubolu

17 King George II

18 Prehistoric Trilith at Haamonga

19 Bread Fruit

20 Coral

21 View of Haapai

22 Red Shining Parrot

23 View of Vavau Harbour

24 Tortoises (upright)

Types of Type 17:

Type I. Top of hilt showing

Type II. No sword hilt

Normal

Lopped branch (R. 8/5) (ptgs from 1934 onwards)

Normal

Small "2" (R. 1/2, 1/4–5, 2/8, 4/4, 5/4 and 6/1)

Normal

Both "O"'s small in "HOGOFULU" (R. 1/7)

HOGOFULU

Small second "O" in "HOGOFULU" (R. 2/7)

WATERMARKS. Stamps with W 24 upright show all the tortoise heads pointing upwards, or downwards if inverted. On stamps with sideways watermark the heads point upwards or downwards alternately.

(Recess D.L.R.)

1897 (1 June). *W* **24.** *P* 14.

38	15	½d. indigo	..	..	3·75	2·75
		a. Wmk sideways	..		70	2·75
39	16	1d. black and scarlet	..	..	80	80
		a. Wmk sideways	..		5·00	3·25
		b. Lopped branch	..		35·00	
40	17	2d. sepia and bistre (I)	..	..	15·00	5·50
		a. Wmk sideways	..		13·00	3·50
		b. Small "2"	..		35·00	15·00
41		2d. sepia and bistre (II)		..	30·00	9·00
		a. Wmk sideways	..		20·00	9·00
		b. Small "2"	..		50·00	25·00
42		2d. grey and bistre (II)		..	30·00	3·25
		a. Wmk sideways	..		16·00	3·00
		b. Small "2"	..		38·00	5·50
43		2½d. black and blue	..		6·00	1·40
		a. No fraction bar in "½" (R. 2/10)		95·00	85·00
		a. Wmk sideways	..		3·50	1·60
		ba. No fraction bar in "½" (R. 2/10)		60·00	60·00
44	18	3d. black and yellow-green	..		3·50	7·00
		a. Wmk sideways	..		2·50	6·00
45	19	4d. green and purple	..		3·75	4·00
		a. Wmk sideways	..		4·00	4·50
46	17	5d. black with orange (II)	..		32·00	14·00
		a. Wmk sideways	..			
47	20	6d. red	..	..	13·00	5·50
		a. Wmk sideways	..		8·50	4·50
48	17	7½d. black and green (II)	..		16·00	23·00
		a. Centre inverted	..		£3750	
49		10d. black and lake (II)	..		45·00	45·00
		a. Wmk sideways	..			
		b. Both "O"'s small	..		£225	£225
		c. Small second "O"	..		£225	£225
50		1s. black and red-brown (II)	..		14·00	7·50
		a. No hyphen before "TAHA" (R. 3/5)		£140	£140
		b. Wmk sideways	..			
51	21	2s. black and ultramarine	..		60·00	65·00
		a. Wmk sideways	..		20·00	28·00
52	22	2s. 6d. deep purple	..		48·00	30·00
		a. Wmk sideways	..		65·00	48·00
53	23	5s. black and brown-red	..		48·00	45·00
		a. Wmk sideways	..		26·00	32·00
38a/53a				*Set of* 14	£200	£180

The 1d., 3d. and 4d. are known bisected and used for half their value.

T – L

1 June, 1899.

(25)

26 Queen Salote

1899 (1 June). *Royal Wedding. No. 39a optd with T* **25** *at* "Star" *Office, Auckland, N.Z.*

54	16	1d. black and scarlet (hyphen 2 mm long)		28·00	55·00
		a. "1889" for "1899" (R. 8/1, 8/4)	..	£200	£350
		b. Hyphen 3 mm long	..	..	42·00	80·00
		c. Wmk upright	..	..	50·00	85·00
		ca. "1889" for "1899" (R. 8/1, 8/4)		£375	£550
		cb. Hyphen 3 mm long	..		75·00	£130

The letters "T L" stand for Taufa'ahau, the King's family name, and Lavinia, the bride.

No. 54 was overprinted with a setting of 30 (3×10) applied twice to the sheets of 60. The setting contains twenty-one examples of the 2 mm hyphen and nine of the 3 mm.

PRICES OF SETS

Set prices are given for many issues, generally those containing three stamps or more. Definitive sets include one of each value or major colour change, but do not cover different perforations, die types or minor shades. Where a choice is possible the set prices are based on the cheapest versions of the stamps included in the listings.

Queen Salote, 1918–65

Dies of the 2d.:

Die I (As used for 1897 issue)

Die II

Normal	"2½" recut (note lines on "2" and different "½") (R. 1/1)

Retouched (small) hyphen (R. 3/5)

(Recess D.L.R.)

1920 (Apr)–**35.** *W* **24** (*sideways*). *P* 14.

55	15	½d. yellow-green (1934)	..	90	1·25
		a. Wmk upright	..	16·00	22·00
56	26	1½d. grey-black (1935)	..	30	3·00
57		2d. agate and aniline violet (Die I)		7·50	13·00
		a. Wmk upright	..	17·00	38·00
		b. Small "2"	..	60·00	85·00
		c. *Black and slate-violet* (1924)		7·00	2·25
		ca. Wmk upright	..		
		cb. Small "2"	..	55·00	20·00
		d. *Black and deep purple* (1925)			
		db. Small "2"	..		
57e		2d. black & blackish lilac (Die II) (1932)		4·00	5·50
58		2½d. black and blue (3.21)	..	4·50	35·00
59		2½d. bright ultramarine (1934)	..	20	80
		a. Recut "2½"	..	20·00	9·50
60		5d. black and orange-vermilion (1922)		3·25	4·50
61		7½d. black and yellow-green (1922)		1·75	1·75
62		10d. black and lake (1922)	..	2·50	4·75
		a. Both "O"'s small	..	28·00	45·00
		b. Small second "O"	..	28·00	45·00
		c. *Black and aniline carmine* (9.25)			
		ca. Both "O"'s small	..		
		cb. Small second "O"	..		
63		1s. black and red-brown (1922)	..	1·25	2·50
		a. Retouched (small) hyphen	..	15·00	24·00
		b. Wmk upright	..	22·00	22·00
		ba. Retouched (small) hyphen	..	£130	£130
55/63			*Set of* 10	25·00	55·00
55/63	Optd/Perf "Specimen"		*Set of* 9	£180	

In Die II the ball of the "2" is larger and the word "PENI-E-UA" is re-engraved and slightly shorter; the "U" has a spur on the left side.

For illustration of No. 62a see above No. 38.

TWO PENCE

TWO PENCE

PENI-E-UA

(27)

PENI-E-UA

(28)

1923 (20 Oct)–**24.** *Nos. 46, 48/9, 50, 51/2 and 53a surch as T* **27** (*vert stamps*) *or* **28** (*horiz stamps*).

64	17	2d. on 5d. black and orange (II) (B.)		1·00	85
		a. Wmk sideways	..	6·00	5·50
65		2d. on 7½d. black and green (II) (B.)		14·00	24·00
		a. Wmk sideways	..	45·00	55·00
66		2d. on 10d. black and lake (II) (B.)		8·00	48·00
		a. Wmk sideways	..	30·00	70·00
		b. Both "O"'s small	..	70·00	
		c. Small second "O"	..	70·00	
67		2d. on 1s. black and red-brown (II) (B.)		42·00	22·00
		a. No hyphen before "TAHA" (R. 3/5)		£275	£200
		b. Wmk sideways	..	60·00	55·00
68	21	2d. on 2s. black and ultramarine (R.)		15·00	16·00
		a. Wmk sideways	..	10·00	4·50
69	22	2d. on 2s. 6d. deep purple (R.)	..	29·00	6·50
		a. Wmk sideways	..	95·00	55·00
70	23	2d. on 5s. black and brown-red (R.)		11·00	11·00
		a. Wmk sideways	..	3·25	2·50
64/70a			*Set of* 7	95·00	95·00

29 Queen Salote

(Recess D.L.R.)

1938 (12 Oct). *20th Anniv of Queen Salote's Accession. Tablet at foot dated "1918–1938". W 24 (sideways). P 13½.*

71	**29**	1d. black and scarlet	..	60	3·00
72		2d. black and purple	..	7·00	2·25
73		2½d. black and ultramarine	..	7·00	3·00
71/3			*Set of 3*	13·00	7·50
71/3 Perf "Specimen"			*Set of 3*	70·00	

For Silver Jubilee issue in a similar design, see Nos. 83/87.

Further die of 2d.:

Die III

(Recess D.L.R.)

1942–49. *Wmk Mult Script CA (sideways on 5s.). P 14.*

74	**15**	½d. yellow-green	..	20	2·00
75	**16**	1d. black and scarlet	..	1·50	2·00
		a. Lopped branch		30·00	
76	**26**	2d. black and purple (Die II)	..	3·50	2·00
		a. Die III (4.49)		3·75	7·00
77		2½d. bright ultramarine	..	1·25	1·50
		a. Recut "2½"		25·00	
78	**18**	3d. black and yellow-green	..	50	2·50
79	**20**	4d. red	..	2·50	2·00
80	**26**	1s. black and red-brown	..	2·50	3·25
		a. Retouched (small) hyphen	..	32·00	38·00
81	**22**	2s. 6d. deep purple (1943)	..	26·00	20·00
82	**23**	5s. black and brown-red (1943)	..	16·00	42·00
74/82			*Set of 9*	48·00	70·00
74/82 Perf "Specimen"			*Set of 9*	£170	

In Die III the foot of the "2" is longer than in Die II and extends towards the right beyond the curve of the loop; the letters of "PENI-E-UA" are taller and differently shaped.

Damage to the "2" on R. 4/9 of No. 77 was frequently corrected by hand-painting.

For illustration of No. 75a see above No. 38 and of No. 77a see above No. 55.

The ½d., 1d., 3d. and 1s. exist perforated from either line or comb machines. The other values only come line perforated.

30

(Recess D.L.R.)

1944 (25 Jan). *Silver Jubilee of Queen Salote's Accession. As T 29, but inscr "1918–1943" at foot, as T 30. Wmk Mult Script CA. P 14.*

83		1d. black and carmine	..	15	80
84		2d. black and purple	..	15	80
85		3d. black and green	..	15	80
86		6d. black and orange	..	65	1·60
87		1s. black and brown	..	55	1·60
83/7			*Set of 5*	1·50	5·00
83/7 Perf "Specimen"			*Set of 5*	75·00	

1949 (10 Oct). *75th Anniv of U.P.U. As Nos. 145/8 of Jamaica.*

88		2½d. ultramarine	..	40	60
89		3d. olive	..	1·60	2·75
90		6d. carmine-red	..	50	50
91		1s. red-brown	..	50	50
88/91			*Set of 4*	2·75	4·00

31 Queen Salote **33**

32 Queen Salote

(Photo Waterlow)

1950 (1 Nov). *Queen Salote's Fiftieth Birthday. Wmk Mult Script CA. P 12½.*

92	**31**	1d. carmine	..	40	1·50
93	**32**	5d. green	..	40	1·75
94	**33**	1s. violet	..	40	2·00
92/4			*Set of 3*	1·10	4·75

34 Map   **35** Palace, Nuku'alofa

(Recess Waterlow)

1951 (2 July). *50th Anniv of Treaty of Friendship between Great Britain and Tonga. T 34/5 and similar designs. Wmk Mult Script CA. P 12½ (3d.), 13 × 13½ (½d.), 13½ × 13 (others).*

95		½d. green	..	20	2·25
96		1d. black and carmine	..	15	2·00
97		2½d. green and brown	..	30	2·25
98		3d. yellow and bright blue	..	1·25	2·25
99		5d. carmine and green	..	85	70
100		1s. yellow-orange and violet	..	85	70
95/100			*Set of 6*	3·25	9·00

Designs: *Horiz*—2½d. Beach scene; 5d. Flag; 1s. Arms of Tonga and G.B. *Vert*—3d. H.M.N.Z.S. *Bellona*.

40 Royal Palace, Nuku'alofa   **43** Swallows' Cave, Vava'u

52 Queen Salote   **53** Arms of Tonga

(Des J. Berry. Centre litho, frame recess (£1), recess (others) B.W.)

1953 (1 July). *T 40, 43, 52/3 and similar designs. W 24 (sideways). P 11×11½ (vert) or 11½×11 (horiz).*

101		1d. black and red-brown	..	10	10
102		1½d. blue and emerald	..	10	10
103		2d. deep turquoise-green and black	..	75	20
104		3d. blue and deep bluish green	..	75	20
105		3½d. yellow and carmine-red	..	50	70
106		4d. yellow and deep rose-carmine	..	1·40	40
107		5d. blue and red-brown	..	50	10
108		6d. black and deep blue	..	50	30
109		8d. emerald and deep reddish violet	..	1·25	40
110		1s. blue and black	..	70	10
111		2s. sage-green and brown	..	5·00	60
112		5s. orange-yellow and slate-lilac	..	24·00	7·00
113		10s. yellow and black	..	6·50	7·00
114		£1 yellow, scarlet, ultramarine & dp brt bl	8·00	6·50
101/14			*Set of 14*	45·00	21·00

Designs: *Horiz* (as T 40)—1½d. Shore fishing with throw-net; 2d. *Hifofua* and *Aoniu* (ketches); 3½d. Map of Tongatapu; 4d. Vava'u Harbour; 5d. Post Office, Nuku'alofa; 6d. Aerodrome, Fua'amotu; 8d. *Matua* (inter-island freighter) at Nuku'alofa wharf; 2s. Lifuka, Ha'apai; 5s. Mutiny on the *Bounty*. *Vert* (as T 43)—1s. Map of Tonga Islands.

54 Stamp of 1886   **55** Whaling Ship and Whaleboat

(Des D. Bakeley. Photo Harrison)

1961 (1 Dec). *75th Anniv of Tongan Postal Service. T 54/5 and similar horiz designs. W 24 (sideways). P 14½×13½.*

115		1d. carmine and brown-orange	..	10	10
116		2d. ultramarine	..	75	45
117		4d. blue-green	..	15	45
118		5d. violet	..	75	45
119		1s. red-brown	..	1·00	45
115/19			*Set of 5*	2·50	1·60

Designs:—4d. Queen Salote and Post Office, Nuku'alofa; 5d. *Aoniu II* (inter-island freighter); 1s. Douglas DC-4 mailplane over Tongatapu.

1862 TAU'ATAINA EMANCIPATION 1962
(59)   **60** "Protein Foods"

1962 (7 Feb). *Centenary of Emancipation. Nos. 101, 104, 107/10, 112, 117 optd with T 59 (No. 126 surch also), in red, by R. S. Wallbank, Govt Printer.*

120		1d. black and red-brown	..	10	50
121		4d. blue-green	..	10	60
122		5d. blue and red-brown	..	15	60
123		6d. black and deep blue	..	20	75
124		8d. emerald and deep reddish violet	..	40	1·25
125		1s. blue and black	..	20	70
		a. Opt inverted		£375	£190
126		2s. on 3d. blue and deep bluish green	40	3·00
		a. Missing fraction-bar in surch	10·00	
127		5s. orange-yellow and slate-lilac	6·00	3·00
		a. Opt inverted		£180	£275
120/127			*Set of 8*	6·50	9·50

(Des M. Goaman. Photo Harrison)

1963 (4 June). *Freedom from Hunger. W 24. P 14 × 14½.*

128	**60**	11d. ultramarine	..	50	15

61 Coat of Arms

62 Queen Salote

63 Queen Salote

(Des Ida West. Die-cut Walsall)

1963 (17 June). *First Polynesian Gold Coinage Commemoration. Circular designs. Embossed on gold foil, backed with paper, inscr overall "TONGA THE FRIENDLY ISLANDS". Imperf.*

(a) *Postage.* ¼ koula coin. Diameter 1⅝ in.

129	**61**	1d. carmine	..	10	10
130	**62**	2d. deep blue	..	10	10
131	**61**	6d. blue-green	..	15	15
132	**62**	9d. bright purple	..	15	15
133	**61**	1s. 6d. violet	..	25	25
134	**62**	2s. light emerald	..	30	30

(b) *Air.* (i) ½ koula coin. Diam 2⅛ in.

135	**63**	10d. carmine	..	20	20
136	**61**	11d. blue-green	..	20	20
137	**63**	1s. 1d. deep blue	..	20	20

(ii) 1 koula coin. Diam 3⅛ in.

138	**63**	2s. 1d. bright purple	..	35	30
139	**61**	2s. 4d. light emerald	..	40	35
140	**63**	2s. 9d. violet	..	40	40
129/140 *and* O17			*Set of 13*	7·50	8·50

Examples of a 9d. Postage value in the design of the 1s. 6d. exists, but these have been identified as proofs.

64 Red Cross Emblem

(Des V. Whiteley. Litho B.W.)

1963 (7 Oct). *Red Cross Centenary.* W **24** (sideways). P 13½.
141	**64**	2d. red and black	..	..	..	25	10
142		11d. red and blue	..	..	..	50	1·50

65 Queen Salote

66 Map of Tongatapu

(Des M. Meers. Die-cut Walsall)

1964 (19 Oct). *Pan-Pacific South-East Asia Women's Association Meeting, Nuku'alofa. Embossed on gold foil, backed with paper inscr overall "TONGA THE FRIENDLY ISLANDS". Imperf.*

(a) Postage.
143	**65**	3d. pink	..	..	..	15	15
144		9d. light blue	..	..	..	20	20
145		2s. yellow-green	..	..	..	35	35
146		5s. lilac	..	..	..	65	75

(b) Air
147	**66**	10d. blue-green	..	..	..	20	15
148		1s. 2d. black	..	..	..	30	35
149		3s. 6d. cerise	..	..	..	50	65
150		6s. 6d. violet	..	..	..	85	1·40
143/150		..	..	..Set of 8		2·75	3·50

(67)

1965 (18 Mar). *"Gold Coin" stamps of 1963 surch as T **67** by Walsall Lithographic Co. New figures of value in gold; obliterating colours shown in brackets. (a) Postage.*
151	**61**	1s. 3d. on 1s. 6d. violet (R.)	..		15	15
152	**62**	1s. 9d. on 9d. bright purple (W.)	..		15	20
153	**61**	2s. 6d. on 6d. blue-green (R.)	..		20	35
154		5s. on 1d. carmine	..		15·00	17·00
155	**62**	5s. on 2d. deep blue	..		2·50	3·25
156		5s. on 2s. light emerald	..		60	75

(b) Air
157	**63**	2s. 3d. on 10d. carmine.	..		15	25
158	**61**	2s. 9d. on 11d. blue-green (W.).	..		20	35
159	**63**	4s. 6d. on 2s. 1d. bright purple (R.)		12·00	13·00
160	**61**	4s. 6d. on 2s. 4d. light emerald (R.)		12·00	13·00
161	**63**	4s. 6d. on 2s. 9d. violet (R.)		7·00	8·00
151/161 and O18			Set of 12		45·00	55·00

King Taufa'ahau IV, 16 December 1965

1866-1966
TUPOU COLLEGE
& SECONDARY
EDUCATION

(68)

AIRMAIL
1866 CENTENARY 1966
TUPOU COLLEGE
&
SECONDARY EDUCATION
10d

(69)

XX

OU COLLE
&
ARY EDUC
Misplaced
"&" (R. 5/5)

1966 (18 June). *Centenary of Tupou College and Secondary Education. Nos. 115/16 and 118/19 optd or surch. (a) Postage. As T **68**.*
162		1d. carmine and brown-orange (P.)		..		10	10
163		3d. on 1d. carmine and brown-orange (P.)		..		10	10
		a. Misplaced "3d" (R.2/5)	..			2·50	
		b. Surch inverted	..			†	—
164		6d. on 2d. ultramarine (R.)	..			10	10
165		1s. 2d. on 2d. ultramarine (R.)	..			20	10
166		2s. on 2d. ultramarine (R.)	..			40	10
167		3s. on 2d. ultramarine (R.)	..			40	15

*(b) Air. As T **69***
168		5d. violet	..			10	10
		b. Misplaced "&"		..		2·50	
169		10d. on 1d. carmine and brown-orange			10	10
		b. Misplaced "&"		..		2·50	
170		1s. red-brown	..			30	10
		b. Misplaced "&"		..		2·50	
171		2s. 9d. on 2d. ultramarine		..		40	15
		a. Sideways second "X" (R.3/4)			8·50	
		b. Misplaced "&"		..		7·00	
172		3s. 6d. on 5d. violet		..		40	15
		a. Sideways second "X" (R.3/4)			8·50	
		b. Misplaced "&"		..		7·00	
173		4s. 6d. on 1s. red-brown	..			75	15
		a. Sideways second "X" (R.3/4)			8·50	
		b. Misplaced "&"		..		7·00	
162/173 and O19/20			Set of 14		4·25	1·75

On No. 163a the "d" is 20 mm from the "X" instead of the normal 22 mm.

(70)

(71)

1966 (16 Dec). *Queen Salote Commemoration. Nos. 143/4 and 147/8 optd as T **70/1**, or surch also, by Walsall Lithographic Co. Inscriptions and new figures of value in first colour and obliterating shapes in second colour given.*

*(a) Postage. Optd as T **70***
174	**65**	3d. (silver and ultramarine)		..		10	10
175		5d. on 9d. (silver and black)		..		15	10
176		9d. (silver and black)		..		20	10
177		1s. 7d. on 3d. (silver and ultramarine)			50	40
178		3s. on 9d. (silver and black)..			70	60
179		6s. 6d. on 3d. (silver and ultramarine)		1·25	1·40

*(b) Air. Optd as T **71***
180	**66**	10d. (silver and black)		..		20	10
181		1s. 2d. (black and gold)		..		25	20
182		4s. on 10d. (silver and black)		..		80	60
183		5s. 6d. on 1s. 2d. (black and gold)			1·10	1·25
184		10s. 6d. on 1s. 2d. (gold and black)			1·50	1·75
174/184			Set of 11		6·00	6·00

(New Currency. 100 seniti = 1 pa'anga)

10
Seniti

1 SENITI 1

(72)

10

(73)

1967 (25 Mar). *Decimal currency. Various stamps surch as T **72/3**.*
185	1 s. on 1d. (No. 101)	..	..	..	10	10
186	2 s. on 4d. (No. 106)	..	..	..	20	10
187	3 s. on 5d. (No. 107)	..	..	..	10	10
188	4 s. on 5d. (No. 107)	..	..	..	30	30
189	5 s. on 3½d. (No. 105)	..	..		10	10
190	6 s. on 8d. (No. 109)	..	..	..	30	10
191	7 s. on 1½d. (No. 102)	..	..		10	10
192	8 s. on 6d. (No. 108)	..	..	..	30	10
193	9 s. on 4d. (No. 104)	..	..	..	15	15
194	10 s. on 1s. (No. 110)	..	..		15	15
195	11 s. on 3d. on 1d. (No. 163)	..		30	20
	a. Misplaced "3d" (R. 2/5)	..		6·50	
196	21 s. on 3s. on 2d. (No. 167)	..		25	35
197	23 s. on 3s. (No. 101)	..	..		25	35
198	30 s. on 2s. (No. 111)* (R.)	..		2·25	2·50
199	30 s. on 2s. (No. 111)* (R.)	..		2·50	3·00
200	50 s. on 6d. (No. 108) (R.)	..		1·25	1·75
201	60 s. on 3s. (No. 103) (R.)	..		1·50	2·00
185/201 and O21		Set of 18		13·00	12·00

The above surcharges come in a variety of types and sizes.
*No. 198 has the surcharged value expressed horizontally; No. 199 has the figures "30" above and below "SENITI".

---

74 Coat of Arms (reverse)

75 King Taufa'ahau IV (obverse)

(Die-cut Walsall)

1967 (4 July). *Coronation of King Taufa'ahau IV. Circular designs. Embossed on palladium foil, backed with paper inscr overall "The Friendly Islands Tonga", etc. Imperf.*

Sizes
(a) Diameter 1½ in.	(d) Diameter 2³/₁₀ in.
(b) Diameter 1⁷/₁₀ in.	(e) Diameter 2⁷/₁₀ in.
(c) Diameter 2 in.	(f) Diameter 2⁹/₁₀ in.

(a) Postage
202	**74**	1 s. orange and greenish blue (b)	..	10	10
203	**75**	2 s. greenish blue and deep magenta (c)	10	10
204	**74**	4 s. emerald and bright purple (d)	..	10	10
205	**75**	15 s. turquoise and violet (e)	..	30	25
206	**74**	28 s. black and bright purple (a) ..	70	60
207	**75**	50 s. carmine-red and ultramarine (c)	1·00	1·00
208	**74**	1 p. blue and carmine (f)..	..	1·75	2·00

(b) Air
209	**75**	7 s. carmine-red and black (b)	..	15	10
210	**74**	9 s. brown-purple and emerald (c)	..	15	10
211	**75**	11 s. greenish blue and orange (d)	..	20	15
212	**74**	21 s. black and emerald (e)	..	40	30
213	**75**	23 s. bright purple and light emerald (a)	55	45
214	**74**	29 s. ultramarine and emerald (c)	..	70	60
215	**75**	2 p. bright purple and orange (f).	..	2·50	2·75
202/15			Set of 14	7·75	7·50

The commemorative coins depicted in reverse (Type **74**) are inscribed in various denominations as follows: 1 s.—"20 SENITI"; 4 s.—"PA'ANGA"; 9 s.—"50 SENITI"; 21 s.—"TWO PA'ANGA"; 28 s.—"QUARTER HAU"; 29 s.—"HALF HAU"; 1 p. "HAU".

The
Friendly Islands
welcome the
United States
Peace Corps

S

(76)

1967 (15 Dec). *Arrival of U.S. Peace Corps in Tonga. As Nos. 101/14, but imperf in different colours and surch as T **76**.*

(a) Postage.
216		1 s. on 1d. black and orange-yellow..		10	10
217		2 s. on 2d. ultramarine and carmine-red	..	10	10
218		3 s. on 3d. chestnut and yellow	..	10	10
219		4 s. on 4d. reddish violet and yellow	..	10	10
220		5 s. on 5d. green and yellow..	..	10	10
221		10 s. on 1s. carmine-red and yellow	..	10	10
222		20 s. on 2s. claret and new blue	..	30	15
223		50 s. on 5s. sepia and orange-yellow..		1·50	35
224		1 p. on 10s. orange-yellow	..	70	55

(b) Air
225		11 s. on 3½d. ultramarine (R.)	..	15	10
226		21 s. on 1½d. emerald	..	30	20
227		23 s. on 3½d. ultramarine	..	30	20
216/27 and O26/8			Set of 15	5·00	3·00

On Nos. 219 and 224 the opt is smaller, and in four lines instead of five. On Nos. 216/20 the surcharge takes the form of an alteration to the currency name as in T **76**.

10
SENITI

2 SENITI 2

(77)

10

(78)

1968 (6 Apr). *Various stamps surch as* T **77/8.**

(a) Postage

228	1 s. on 1d. (No. 101) (R.)	..	..	10	10
229	2 s. on 4d. (No. 106) (R.)	..	..	10	10
230	3 s. on 3d. (No. 104) (B.)	..	..	10	10
231	4 s. on 5d. (No. 107) (R.)	..	..	10	10
232	5 s. on 2d. (No. 103) (R.)	..	..	10	10
233	6 s. on 6d. (No. 108) (R.)	..	..	10	10
234	7 s. on 1½d. (No. 102) (R.)	..	..	10	15
235	8 s. on 8d. (No. 109) (R.)	..	..	10	15
236	9 s. on 3½d. (No. 105)	..	..	20	20
237	10 s. on 1s. (No. 110) (R.)	..	..	20	20
238	20 s. on 5s. (No. 112) (R.)	..	..	90	50
239	2 p. on 2s. (No. 111) (R.)	..	..	1·50	2·50

(b) Air. Surch as T **78** *with* "AIRMAIL" *added*

240	11 s. on 10s. (No. 113) (R.)	..	..	25	25
241	21 s. on 10s. (No. 113) (R.)	..	..	40	40
242	23 s. on 10s. (No. 113) (R.)	..	..	40	40
228/42 *and* O22/5		*Set of 19*		7·00	9·50

(79)

Friendly Islands
Field & Track Trials
South Pacific Games
Port Moresby
1969

S

(80)

1968 (4 July). *50th Birthday of King Taufa'ahua IV. Nos.* 202/15 *optd as* T **79.** (a) Postage.

243	74	1 s. orange and greenish blue (b) (R.)		10	10
244	75	2 s. greenish blue & dp magenta (b) (B.)		10	10
245	74	4 s. emerald and bright purple (d) (R.)		15	10
246	75	15 s. turquoise and violet (e) (B.)		40	15
247	74	28 s. black and bright purple (a) (R.)		80	30
248	75	50 s. carmine-red and ultramarine (c) (B.)		1·60	80
249	74	1 p. blue and carmine (f) (R.)		3·25	2·50

(b) Air

250	75	7 s. carmine-red and black (b) (B.)		20	10
251	74	9 s. brown-purple and emerald (c) (R.)		25	10
252	75	11 s. greenish blue and orange (d) (B.)		30	10
253	74	21 s. black and emerald (e) (R.)		65	25
		a. Opt (gold only) double		£275	
254	75	23 s. bright purple & lt emerald (a) (B.)		65	25
255	74	29 s. ultramarine and emerald (c) (R.)		85	35
256	75	2 p. bright purple and orange (f) (B.)		6·00	4·75
243/56 *and* O29/32			*Set of 18*	24·00	18·00

The overprints vary in size, but are all crescent-shaped as Type **79** and inscribed "H.M'S BIRTHDAY 4 JULY 1968" (Type **79**) or "HIS MAJESTY'S 50th BIRTHDAY" (others).

1968 (19 Dec). *South Pacific Games Field and Track Trials, Port Moresby, Papua New Guinea. Nos.* 101/13, *but imperf, in different colours and surch as* T **80.** (a) Postage.

257	5 s. on 5d. green and yellow (R.)		10	10
258	10 s. on 1s. carmine-red and yellow		10	10
259	15 s. on 2s. claret and new blue		15	15
260	25 s. on 2d. ultramarine and carmine-red		20	15
261	50 s. on 1d. black and orange-yellow		35	35
262	75 s. on 10s. orange-yellow		60	50

(b) Air

263	6 s. on 6d. black and yellow*		10	10
264	7 s. on 4d. reddish violet and yellow		10	10
265	8 s. on 8d. black and greenish yellow		10	10
	a. Surch 11½ mm as on 6d.		£140	£100
266	9 s. on 1½d. emerald		10	10
267	11 s. on 3d. chestnut and yellow		15	10
268	21 s. on 3½d. ultramarine		20	15
269	38 s. on 5s. sepia and orange-yellow		1·50	50
270	1 p. on 10s. orange-yellow		70	70
257/70 *and* O33/4		*Set of 16*	4·50	3·50

*On No. 263 the surcharge is smaller (11½ mm wide).

(81)   (82)

1969. *Emergency Provisionals. Various stamps (Nos.* 273/6 *are imperf and in different colours) surch as* T **81** *or* **82.** (a) Postage.

271	1 s. on 1s. 2d. on 2d. ultramarine (No. 165)		1·50	2·00
272	1 s. on 2s. on 2d. ultramarine (No. 166)		1·50	2·00
273	1 s. on 6d. black and yellow (as No. 108)		50	50
274	2 s. on 3½d. ultramarine (as No. 105)		55	50
275	3 s. on 1½d. emerald (as No. 102)		55	50
276	4 s. on 8d. blk & greenish yell (as No. 109)		80	80

(b) Air. Nos. 171/3 *surch with* T **82**

277	1 s. on 2s. 9d. on 2d. ultramarine		1·50	2·00
	a. Sideways second "X" (R.3/4)		14·00	
	b. Misplaced "&"		11·00	
278	1 s. on 3s. 6d. on 5d. violet		1·50	2·00
	a. Sideways second "X" (R.3/4)		14·00	
	b. Misplaced "&"		11·00	
279	1 s. on 4s. 6d. on 1s. red-brown		1·50	2·00
	a. Sideways second "X" (R.3/4)		14·00	
	b. Misplaced "&"		11·00	
271/9		*Set of 9*	9·00	11·00

SELF-ADHESIVE ISSUES. From No. 280 until No. 922 all stamps were manufactured by Walsall Security Printers Ltd and are self-adhesive. The backing paper is separated by roulette or perforations (from No. 780 onwards), and shows on its reverse the words "TONGA where time begins", or, from No. 568 onwards, various texts or illustrations. This also applies to the Official stamps.

83 Banana

1969 (21 Apr). *Coil stamps.*

280	83	1 s. scarlet, black and greenish yellow		70	80
281		2 s. brt green, black & greenish yellow		80	90
282		3 s. violet, black and greenish yellow		90	1·00
283		4 s. ultramarine, black and greenish yell		1·00	1·10
284		5 s. bronze-green, black & greenish yell		1·10	1·40
280/4			*Set of 5*	4·00	4·75

Nos. 280/4 were produced in rolls of 200, each even stamp having a number applied to the front of the backing paper, with the usual inscription on the reverse.
See also Nos. 325/9, 413/17 and 675/89.

84 Putting the Shot   86 Oil Derrick and Map

1969 (13 Aug). *Third South Pacific Games, Port Moresby.* T **84** *and similar design.* (a) Postage.

285	84	1 s. black, red and buff		10	10
286		3 s. bright green and buff		10	10
287		6 s. blue, red and buff		10	10
288		10 s. bluish violet, red and buff		10	10
289		30 s. blue, red and buff		20	20

(b) Air

290	—	9 s. black, violet and orange		10	10
291	—	11 s. black, ultramarine and orange		10	10
292	—	20 s. black, bright green and orange		20	20
293	—	60 s. black, cerise and orange		60	75
294	—	1 p. black, blue-green and orange		1·00	1·40
285/94 *and* O35/6			*Set of 12*	3·50	4·25

Design:—9, 11, 20, 60 s., 1 p. Boxing.

1969 (23 Dec). *First Oil Search in Tonga.* T **86** *and similar vert design.*

(a) Postage

295	86	3 s. multicoloured		15	10
296		7 s. multicoloured		20	15
297		20 s. multicoloured		50	40
298		25 s. multicoloured		55	45
299		35 s. multicoloured		80	80

(b) Air

300	—	9 s. multicoloured		30	20
301	—	10 s. multicoloured		30	20
302	—	24 s. multicoloured		60	45
303	—	29 s. multicoloured		70	70
304	—	38 s. multicoloured		80	80
295/304 *and* O37/8			*Set of 12*	10·00	10·00

Design:—Nos. 300/4, Oil derrick and island of Tongatapu.

87 Members of the British and Tongan Royal Families

1970 (7 Mar). *Royal Visit.* T **87** *and similar design. Multicoloured.*

(a) Postage

305	87	3 s. multicoloured		20	15
306		5 s. multicoloured		25	15
307		10 s. multicoloured		40	30
308		25 s. multicoloured		1·00	65
309		50 s. multicoloured		2·00	1·75

(b) Air

310	—	7 s. multicoloured		35	20
311	—	9 s. multicoloured		40	30
312	—	24 s. multicoloured		1·00	65
313	—	29 s. multicoloured		1·25	70
314	—	38 s. multicoloured		1·50	90
305/14 *and* O39/41			*Set of 13*	18·00	16·00

Design:—Nos. 310/14, Queen Elizabeth II and King Taufu'ahau Tupou IV.

89 Book, Tongan Rulers and Flag

1970 (4 June). *Entry into British Commonwealth.* T **89** *and similar design.* (a) Postage.

315	89	3 s. multicoloured		10	15
316		7 s. multicoloured		15	20
317		15 s. multicoloured		35	20
318		25 s. multicoloured		45	25
319		50 s. multicoloured		75	85

(b) Air

320	—	9 s. turquoise-blue, gold and scarlet		15	20
321	—	10 s. bright purple, gold and greenish blue		15	20
322	—	24 s. olive-yellow, gold and green		45	30
323	—	29 s. new blue, gold and orange-red		50	30
324	—	38 s. deep orange-yellow, gold & brt emer		60	40
315/24 *and* O42/4			*Set of 13*	7·50	7·50

Design: "*Star*" *shaped* (44 × 51 mm)—Nos. 320/4, King Taufa'ahau Tupou IV.

90 Coconut

1970 (9 June). *Coil stamps.* (a) *As* T **83** *but colours changed.*

325	83	1 s. greenish yellow, bright purple & blk		45	50
326		2 s. greenish yellow, ultramarine & black		55	60
327		3 s. greenish yellow, chocolate and black		55	60
328		4 s. greenish yellow, emerald and black		55	60
329		5 s. greenish yellow, orge-red & bl		60	65

(b) T **90.** *Multicoloured; colour of face value given*

330	90	6 s. rose-carmine		70	80
331		7 s. bright purple		75	85
332		8 s. bluish violet		85	95
333		9 s. turquoise		95	1·10
334		10 s. pale orange		95	1·10
325/34			*Set of 10*	6·25	7·00

Nos. 325/34 and O45/54 were produced in rolls of 200, each even stamp having a number applied to the front of the backing paper, with the usual inscription on the reverse.

91 "Red Cross"

(Litho (postage) or litho and die-stamped (air))

1970 (17 Oct). *Centenary of British Red Cross.* T **91** *and similar "cross" shaped design.* (a) Postage.

335	91	3 s. vermilion, black and light green		10	10
336		7 s. vermilion, black and ultramarine		15	15
337		15 s. vermilion and bright purple		40	40
338		25 s. vermilion, black and turquoise-blue		70	70
339		75 s. vermilion and deep red-brown		4·50	4·50

(b) Air

340	—	9 s. vermilion and silver		20	20
341	—	10 s. vermilion and bright purple		20	20
342	—	18 s. vermilion and green		50	50
343	—	38 s. vermilion and ultramarine		2·25	2·25
344	—	1 p. vermilion and turquoise-blue		5·50	5·50
335/44 *and* O55/7			*Set of 13*	22·00	22·00

Design: As T **91**—Nos. 340/4 as Nos. 335/9 but with inscription rearranged and coat of arms omitted.
On Nos. 335/6 and 338 the black colour is produced as a composite of the other two colours used.

MINIMUM PRICE

The minimum price quote is 10p which represents a handling charge rather than a basis for valuing common stamps. For further notes about prices see introductory pages.

(92)

(93)

1971 (30 Jan). *Fifth Death Anniv of Queen Salote. Nos. 174/84 surch as T **92**/3. Obliterating shapes in black; inscriptions and figures of value in colour given.* (a) *Postage. Surch as T **92**.*

345	**65**	2 s. on 5d. on 9d. (silver)	..	..	..	20	20
346		3 s. on 9d. (orange-red)	..	..	..	20	20
347		5 s. on 3d. (bright green)	..	..		30	20
348		15 s. on 3s. 6d. on 9d. (orange-brown)	..	1·00	35
		a. Surch double	..	..		—	30·00
349		25 s. on 6s. 6d. on 3d. (purple)	..		1·75	80
350		50 s. on 1s. 7d. on 3d. (gold)	..	..	2·75	2·00

*(b) Air. Surch as T **93***

351	**66**	9 s. on 10d. (silver)	..	..	..	75	20
352		24 s. on 4s. on 10d. (orange-brown)	..	1·75	75
353		29 s. on 5s. 6d. on 1s. 2d. (orange-red)	2·00	1·00
354		38 s. on 10s. 6d. on 1s. 2d. (bright green)	2·50	1·50
345/54 and O58/61	..	..	*Set of 14*	25·00	17·00

HONOURING JAPANESE POSTAL CENTENARY 1871-1971

(94)

(95)

1971 (17 Apr). *"Philatokyo 1971" Stamp Exhibition. As Nos. 101/2, 106 and 109/11, but imperf, colours changed and surch as T **94** (Nos. 355/6, 358/61 and 363), as T **95** (Nos. 357, 362) or with similar surcharge in four lines (No. 364).* (a) *Postage.*

355		3 s. on 8d. blk & greenish yellow (Blk. & R.)	10	10
356		7 s. on 4d. reddish violet & yellow (Blk. & R.)	15	10
357		15 s. on 1s. carmine, red and yellow	..	30	10
358		25 s. on 1d. black & orange-yellow (Blk. & R.)	40	30
359		75 s. on 2s. claret & new blue (Blk. & R.)	..	1·75	1·75

(b) Air. Additionally surch "AIRMAIL"

360		9 s. on 1½d. emerald (Blk. and R.)		15	10
361		10 s. on 4d. reddish violet & yellow (Blk. & R.)	15	10
362		18 s. on 1s. carmine-red and yellow (V.)	35	25
363		38 s. on 1d. black & orange-yellow (Blk. & R.)	75	50
364		1 p. on 2s. claret and new blue	..	1·75	2·00
355/64 and O62/4	..	..	*Set of 13*	9·50	8·50

96 Wristwatch   97 Pole-vaulter

1971 (20 July)–72. *Air. Backed with paper bearing advertisements.*

365	**96**	14 s. multicoloured	..	..		1·50	1·50
365a		17 s. multicoloured (20.7.72)	..		1·75	1·75
366		21 s. multicoloured	..	..		1·75	1·75
366a		38 s. multicoloured (20.7.72)	..		2·75	2·75
365/6a and O65/6a	..		*Set of 8*	14·00	14·00

1971 (20 July). *Fourth South Pacific Games, Tahiti. T **97** and similar design.* (a) *Postage.*

367	**97**	3 s. multicoloured	..	..	..	10	10
368		7 s. multicoloured	..	..	..	10	10
369		15 s. multicoloured	..	..	..	20	20
370		25 s. multicoloured	..	..	..	30	35
371		50 s. multicoloured	..	..	..	60	90

(b) Air

372	—	9 s. multicoloured	..	..	..	10	10
373	—	10 s. multicoloured	..	..	..	10	10
374	—	24 s. multicoloured	..	..	..	30	35
375	—	29 s. multicoloured	..	..	..	40	50
376	—	38 s. multicoloured	..	..	..	55	70
367/76 and O67/9	..	..	*Set of 13*	4·75	6·50

Design: *Horiz—Nos. 372/6, High-jumper.*

98 Medal of Merit   99 Child
  (reverse)

1971 (30 Oct). *Investiture of Royal Tongan Medal of Merit. T **98** and similar "medal" shaped design. Multicoloured; colour of medal given.*

(a) Postage

377	**98**	3 s. gold	..	..	..	10	10
378		24 s. silver ..	..	..	..	25	25
379	—	38 s. brown	..	..	..	50	50

(b) Air

380	—	10 s. gold	..	..	..	15	15
381	—	75 s. silver ..	..	..		90	1·00
382	**98**	1 p. brown	..	..		1·10	1·40
377/82 and O70/2	..		*Set of 9*	5·00	6·00

Design: *As T **98**—Nos. 379/81, Obverse of the Medal of Merit.*

1971 (31 Dec). *25th Anniv of UNICEF. T **99** and similar design.*

(a) Postage

383	**99**	2 s. multicoloured	..	..	..	10	10
384		4 s. multicoloured	..	..	..	10	10
385		8 s. multicoloured	..	..	..	10	10
386		16 s. multicoloured	..	..	..	25	25
387		30 s. multicoloured	..	..	..	45	45

(b) Air

388	—	10 s. multicoloured	..	..	..	15	15
389	—	15 s. multicoloured	..	..	..	25	25
390	—	25 s. multicoloured	..	..	..	40	40
391	—	50 s. multicoloured	..	..	..	85	1·00
392	—	1 p. multicoloured	..	..		1·75	2·00
383/92 and O73/5	..		*Set of 13*	8·00	9·00

Design: *Vert (21 x 42 mm)—Nos. 388/92, Woman.*

100 Map of South Pacific, and *Olovaha*

1972 (14 Apr). *Merchant Marine Routes. T **100** and similar design.*

(a) Postage

393	**100**	2 s. multicoloured	..	..	..	30	30
394		10 s. multicoloured	..	..	..	60	20
395		17 s. multicoloured	..	..	..	90	30
396		21 s. multicoloured	..	..		1·00	40
397		60 s. multicoloured	..	..		4·25	3·25

(b) Air

398	—	9 s. multicoloured	..	..	..	60	25
399	—	12 s. multicoloured	..	..	..	75	25
400	—	14 s. multicoloured	..	..	..	85	25
401	—	75 s. multicoloured	..	..		4·50	3·50
402	—	90 s. multicoloured	..	..		4·75	4·75
393/402 and O76/8	..		*Set of 13*	25·00	21·00

Design:—*Nos. 398/402, Map of South Pacific and Niuvakai.*

101 ¼ Hau Coronation Coin

1972 (15 July). *Fifth Anniv of Coronation. T **101** and similar design.*

(a) Postage

403	**101**	5 s. multicoloured	..	..	..	10	10
404		7 s. multicoloured	..	..	..	10	10
405		10 s. multicoloured	..	..	..	15	15
406		17 s. multicoloured	..	..	..	30	20
407		60 s. multicoloured	..	..		1·00	85

(b) Air

408	—	9 s. multicoloured	..	..	..	15	15
409	—	12 s. multicoloured	..	..	..	20	15
410	—	14 s. multicoloured	..	..	..	25	20
411	—	21 s. multicoloured	..	..	..	35	20
412	—	75 s. multicoloured	..	..		1·25	85
403/12 and O79/81	..		*Set of 13*	8·00	7·00

Design *(47 × 41 mm)*:—*Nos. 408/12, as T **101**, but with coins above inscription instead of beneath it.*

102 Water Melon

1972 (30 Sept). *Coil stamps.* (a) *As T **83**, but inscription altered, omitting "Best in the Pacific", and colours changed.*

413	**83**	1 s. light yellow, scarlet and black	25	10
414		2 s. light yellow, ultramarine and black	30	15
415		3 s. light yellow, yellow-green and black	35	20
416		4 s. light yellow, royal blue and black	35	20
417		5 s. light yellow, reddish brn & bl	35	20

*(b) As T **90** but colours changed. Colour of face value given*

418	**90**	6 s. dull orange	40	20
419		7 s. ultramarine	45	25
420		8 s. bright magenta	45	25
421		9 s. brown-orange	45	25
422		10 s. bright new blue	55	30

*(c) T **102**. Colour of face value given*

423	**102**	15 s. new blue	1·00	45
424		20 s. reddish orange	1·25	60
425		25 s. chocolate	1·40	70
426		40 s. yellow-orange	2·50	1·50
427		50 s. lemon	2·50	1·75
413/27	..	*Set of 15*	11·50	6·50

Nos. 413/27 and O82/96 were produced in rolls, each even stamp having a number applied to the front of the backing paper, with the usual inscription on the reverse.

█ 7s

NOVEMBER 1972 INAUGURAL Internal Airmail Nuku'alofa — Vava'u

(103)

1972 (2 Nov). *Inaugural Internal Airmail. No. 398 surch with T **103**.*

428		7 s. on 9 s. multicoloured		75	2·00

104 Hoisting Tongan Flag

1972 (9 Dec). *Proclamation of Sovereignty over Minerva Reefs. T **104** and similar design.* (a) *Postage.*

429	**104**	5 s. multicoloured	..	..	..	10	10
430		7 s. multicoloured	..	..	..	10	10
431		10 s. multicoloured	..	..	..	15	15
432		15 s. multicoloured	..	..	..	25	20
433		40 s. multicoloured	..	..	..	80	55

(b) Air

434	—	9 s. multicoloured	..	..	..	15	15
435	—	12 s. multicoloured	..	..	..	20	15
436	—	14 s. multicoloured	..	..	..	25	15
437	—	38 s. multicoloured	..	..	..	75	55
438	—	1 p. multicoloured	..	..		2·00	2·50
429/38 and O97/9	..		*Set of 13*	8·00	8·50

Design: *Spherical (52 mm diameter)—Nos. 434/8, Proclamation in Govt Gazette.*

105 Coins around Bank

1973 (30 Mar). *Foundation of Bank of Tonga.* T **105** *and similar design.* (a) *Postage.*

439	**105**	5 s. multicoloured	..	..	..	10	10
440		7 s. multicoloured				10	10
441		10 s. multicoloured				15	10
442		20 s. multicoloured				40	20
443		30 s. multicoloured				60	30

(b) *Air*

444	–	9 s. multicoloured				20	10
445	–	12 s. multicoloured				20	10
446	–	17 s. multicoloured				35	15
447	–	50 s. multicoloured				1·25	90
448	–	90 s. multicoloured				2·50	2·25
439/48 *and* O100/2					*Set of 13*	12·00	10·00

Design: *Horiz* (64 × 52 *mm*)—Nos. 444/8, Bank and banknotes.

106 Handshake and Scout in Outrigger Canoe

1973 (29 June). *Silver Jubilee of Scouting in Tonga.* T **106** *and similar design.* (a) *Postage.*

449	**106**	5 s. multicoloured	..	..	..	20	10
450		7 s. multicoloured				30	15
451		15 s. multicoloured				95	40
452		21 s. multicoloured				1·25	50
453		50 s. multicoloured				4·50	2·25

(b) *Air*

454	–	9 s. multicoloured				50	25
455	–	12 s. multicoloured				60	30
456	–	14 s. multicoloured				85	50
457	–	17 s. multicoloured				95	60
458	–	1 p. multicoloured				10·00	6·50
449/58 *and* O103/5					*Set of 13*	80·00	42·00

Design: *Square* (53 × 53 *mm*)—Nos. 454/8, Scout badge.

107 Excerpt from Cook's Log-book

1973 (2 Oct). *Bicentenary of Capt. Cook's Visit to Tonga.* T **107** *and similar design.* (a) *Postage.*

459	**107**	6 s. multicoloured	..	..	..	40	30
460		8 s. multicoloured				40	35
461		11 s. multicoloured				60	40
462		35 s. multicoloured				4·00	2·25
463		40 s. multicoloured				4·00	2·50

(b) *Air*

464	–	9 s. multicoloured				70	30
465	–	14 s. multicoloured				1·25	50
466	–	29 s. multicoloured				4·00	2·00
467	–	38 s. multicoloured				4·50	2·50
468	–	75 s. multicoloured				8·50	4·50
459/68 *and* O106/8					*Set of 13*	45·00	26·00

Design: *Vert*—Nos. 464/8, H.M.S. *Resolution.*

(108)   **109** Red Shining Parrot

1973 (19 Dec). *Commonwealth Games, Christchurch, New Zealand. Various stamps surch as* T **108** (No. 474 optd "AIRMAIL" in addition). (a) *Postage.*

469	5 s. on 50 s. (No. 371) (Blk. and Gold)		15	10
470	12 s. on 38 s. (No. 379) (R. and Silver)		30	15
471	14 s. on 75 s. (No. 381) (R. and Gold)		30	15
472	20 s. on 1 p. (No. 382) (Blk. and Gold)		50	30
473	50 s. on 24 s. (No. 378) (Blk. and Silver)		1·00	1·00

(b) *Air*

474	7 s. on 25 s. (No. 370) (Blk. and Silver)		15	10
475	9 s. on 38 s. (No. 376) (V.)		20	10
476	24 s. (No. 374)		60	30
477	29 s. on 9 s. (No. 454) (B.)		70	40
478	40 s. on 14 s. (No. 456)..		85	90
469/78 *and* O109/11		*Set of 13*	8·00	8·00

1974 (20 Mar). *Air.*

479	**109**	7 s. multicoloured	..	..	..	80	55
480		9 s. multicoloured				85	60
481		12 s. multicoloured				90	60
482		14 s. multicoloured				95	60
483		17 s. multicoloured				1·10	85
484		29 s. multicoloured				2·00	1·25
485		38 s. multicoloured				2·50	1·40
486		50 s. multicoloured				3·00	4·00
487		75 s. multicoloured				4·00	5·50
479/87					*Set of 9*	14·50	14·00

Nos. 479/87 and O112/20 were produced in rolls, each stamp having a number applied to the front of the backing paper, with the usual inscription on the reverse.

110 "Stamped Letter"

1974 (20 June). *Centenary of Universal Postal Union.* T **110** *and similar design.* (a) *Postage.*

488	**110**	5 s. multicoloured	..	..	..	10	15
489		10 s. multicoloured				15	15
490		15 s. multicoloured				25	25
491		20 s. multicoloured				30	30
492		50 s. multicoloured				1·00	1·50

(b) *Air*

493	–	14 s. multicoloured				25	25
494	–	21 s. multicoloured				35	35
495	–	60 s. multicoloured				1·10	1·60
496	–	75 s. multicoloured				1·25	1·75
497	–	1 p. multicoloured				1·50	2·00
488/97 *and* O121/3					*Set of 13*	7·50	10·50

Design: *Horiz*—Nos. 493/7, Carrier pigeon scattering letters over Tonga.

111 Girl Guide Badges

1974 (11 Sept). *Tongan Girl Guides.* T **111** *and similar design.*

(a) *Postage*

498	**111**	5 s. multicoloured	..	..	..	40	30
499		10 s. multicoloured				60	30
500		20 s. multicoloured				1·50	65
501		40 s. multicoloured				3·25	1·75
502		60 s. multicoloured				4·00	2·75

(b) *Air*

503	–	14 s. multicoloured				1·00	45
504	–	16 s. multicoloured				1·00	45
505	–	29 s. multicoloured				2·00	1·00
506	–	31 s. multicoloured				2·25	1·25
507	–	75 s. multicoloured				5·50	3·50
498/507 *and* O124/6 ..					*Set of 13*	32·00	20·00

Design: *Vert*—Nos. 503/7, Girl Guide leaders.

112 H.M.S. *Resolution*

1974 (11 Dec). *Establishment of Royal Marine Institute.* T **112** *and similar design.* (a) *Postage.*

508	**112**	5 s. multicoloured	..	..	..	1·25	50
509		10 s. multicoloured				1·40	50
		a. Vert roul omitted (horiz pair)				2·75	
510		25 s. multicoloured				2·75	80
511		50 s. multicoloured				4·00	3·00
512		75 s. multicoloured				5·50	4·50

(b) *Air*

513	–	9 s. multicoloured				1·25	30
514	–	14 s. multicoloured				1·75	55
515	–	17 s. multicoloured				2·00	60
516	–	60 s. multicoloured				4·25	3·75
517	–	90 s. multicoloured				6·00	5·00
508/17 *and* O127/9					*Set of 13*	35·00	25·00

Design: *Horiz* (51 × 46 *mm*)—Nos. 513/17, *James Cook* (bulk carrier).

113 Dateline Hotel, Nuku'alofa

1975 (11 Mar). *South Pacific Forum and Tourism.* T **113** *and similar vert designs.* (a) *Postage.*

518	**113**	5 s. multicoloured	..	..	..	10	10
519		10 s. multicoloured				10	10
520		15 s. multicoloured				20	20
521		30 s. multicoloured				45	45
522		1 p. multicoloured				1·60	2·00

(b) *Air*

523	–	9 s. multicoloured				10	10
524	–	12 s. multicoloured				15	15
525	–	14 s. multicoloured				20	20
526	–	17 s. multicoloured				20	20
527	–	38 s. multicoloured				55	65
518/27 *and* O130/2					*Set of 13*	8·00	8·00

Designs (46 × 60 *mm*):—9, 12, 14 s. Beach; 17, 38 s. Surf and sea.

114 Boxing

1975 (11 June). *Fifth South Pacific Games, Guam.* T **114** *and similar "star"-shaped design.* (a) *Postage.*

528	**114**	5 s. multicoloured	..	..	..	15	10
529		10 s. multicoloured				20	10
530		20 s. multicoloured				30	25
531		25 s. multicoloured				35	35
532		65 s. multicoloured				80	1·00

(b) *Air*

533	–	9 s. multicoloured				20	10
534	–	12 s. multicoloured				25	15
535	–	14 s. multicoloured				25	15
536	–	17 s. multicoloured				30	20
537	–	90 s. multicoloured				1·10	1·40
528/37 *and* O133/5					*Set of 13*	6·25	7·00

Design (37 × 43 *mm*):—Nos. 533/7, Throwing the Discus.

115 Commemorative Coin

1975 (3 Sept). *F.A.O. Commemoration.* T **115** *and similar designs.*

(a) *Postage*

538	5 s. multicoloured	..	..	..	15	10
539	20 s. multicoloured				35	15
540	50 s. new blue, black and silver			75	35
541	1 p. ultramarine, black and silver			1·50	1·25
542	2 p. black and silver				2·50	2·25

(b) Air
543	12 s. multicoloured	..	..	..		30	15
544	14 s. multicoloured	..	..	..		30	15
545	25 s. vermilion, black and silver	..		..		45	20
546	50 s. bright magenta, black and silver					70	50
547	1 p. black and silver ..	..	..	..		1·50	1·25
538/47				Set of 10		7·50	5·75

Nos. 539/47 are as **T 115** but show different coins. Nos. 542 and 544 are horiz, size 75 × 42 mm.

116 Commemorative Coin

1975 (4 Nov). *Centenary of Tongan Constitution.* **T 116** *and similar designs showing coinage. Multicoloured. (a) Postage.*
548	5 s. Type **116** ..				15	15
549	10 s. King George I				25	20
550	20 s. King Taufa'ahau IV				40	25
551	50 s. King George II				90	75
552	75 s. Tongan arms				1·50	1·60

(b) Air
553	9 s. King Taufa'ahau IV				25	20
554	12 s. Queen Salote				30	25
555	14 s. Tongan arms				30	25
556	38 s. King Taufa'ahau IV				70	40
557	1 p. Four monarchs				1·75	2·00
548/57 and O136/8 ..			Set of 13		9·00	9·00

Sizes:—60 × 40 mm, Nos. 549 and 551; 76 × 76 mm, Nos. 552 and 557; 57 × 56 mm, others.

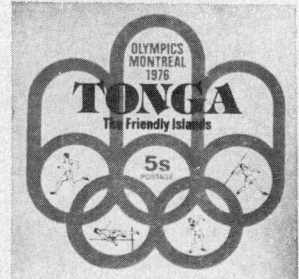
117 Montreal Logo

1976 (24 Feb). *First Participation in Olympic Games. (a) Postage.*
558	**117**	5 s. vermilion, black and blue ..			30	15
559		10 s. vermilion, black and emerald	..		35	15
560		25 s. vermilion, black and bistre	..		1·00	35
561		35 s. vermilion, black and mauve	..		1·25	45
562		70 s. vermilion, black and olive-yellow	..		2·75	2·00

(b) Air. Montreal logo optd on Girl Guide stamps (Nos. 500 etc)
563	**111**	12 s. on 20 s. multicoloured	..		60	25
564	–	14 s. on 16 s. multicoloured	..		60	25
565	–	16 s. multicoloured	..		70	25
566	**111**	38 s. on 40 s. multicoloured	..		2·00	45
567	–	75 s. multicoloured	..		3·50	2·00
558/67 and O139/41 ..			Set of 13		22·00	12·00

118 Signatories of Declaration of Independence

1976 (26 May). *Bicentenary of American Revolution.* **T 118** *and similar horiz designs showing signatories to the Declaration of Independence. (a) Postage.*
568	**118**	9 s. multicoloured	..		30	15
569	–	10 s. multicoloured	..		30	15
570	–	15 s. multicoloured	..		45	45
571	–	25 s. multicoloured	..		70	70
572	–	75 s. multicoloured	..		2·00	2·50

(b) Air
573	–	12 s. multicoloured	..		40	15
574	–	14 s. multicoloured	..		40	20
575	–	17 s. multicoloured	..		50	35
576	–	38 s. multicoloured	..		85	75
577	–	1 p. multicoloured	..		1·25	3·50
568/77 and O142/4 ..			Set of 13		11·50	13·00

119 Nathaniel Turner and John Thomas
(Methodist missionaries)

1976 (25 Aug). *150th Anniv of Christianity in Tonga.* **T 119** *and similar design. (a) Postage.*
578	**119**	5 s. multicoloured	..		..	20	25
579		10 s. multicoloured	..		..	30	25
580		20 s. multicoloured	..		..	50	40
581		25 s. multicoloured	..		..	55	45
582		85 s. multicoloured	..		..	2·25	2·75

(b) Air. Design showing Missionary Ship "Triton" (45×59 mm)
583	–	9 s. multicoloured	..		40	30
584	–	12 s. multicoloured	..		45	35
585	–	14 s. multicoloured	..		55	40
586	–	17 s. multicoloured	..		65	45
587	–	38 s. multicoloured	..		1·50	1·00
578/87 and O145/7 ..			Set of 10		13·00	13·00

120 Emperor Wilhelm I and King George Tupou I

1976 (1 Nov). *Centenary of Treaty of Friendship with Germany.*
(a) Postage
588	**120**	9 s. multicoloured	..		..	20	20
589		15 s. multicoloured	..		..	30	30
590		22 s. multicoloured	..		..	40	45
591		50 s. multicoloured	..		..	90	1·25
592		73 s. multicoloured	..		..	1·40	1·90

(b) Air. Circular design (52 mm diameter) showing Treaty Signing
593	–	11 s. multicoloured	..		25	25
594	–	17 s. multicoloured	..		40	45
595	–	18 s. multicoloured	..		40	45
596	–	31 s. multicoloured	..		60	80
597	–	39 s. multicoloured	..		70	90
588/97 and O148/50		..	Set of 13		9·50	11·50

121 Queen Salote and Coronation Procession

1977 (7 Feb). *Silver Jubilee. (a) Postage.*
598	**121**	11 s. multicoloured	..		..	50	30
599		20 s. multicoloured	..		..	40	30
600		30 s. multicoloured	..		..	40	30
601		50 s. multicoloured	..		..	60	65
602		75 s. multicoloured	..		..	75	85

(b) Air. Square design (59 × 59 mm) showing Queen Elizabeth and King Taufa'ahau
603	–	15 s. multicoloured	..		40	25
604	–	17 s. multicoloured	..		40	30
605	–	22 s. multicoloured	..		3·50	1·25
		a. Horiz roul omitted (vert pair) ..				
606	–	31 s. multicoloured	..		40	40
607	–	39 s. multicoloured	..		40	40
598/607 and O151/3 ..			Set of 13		8·50	5·50

122 Tongan Coins

1977 (4 July). *Tenth Anniv of King's Coronation. (a) Postage.*
608	**122**	10 s. multicoloured	..		..	20	20
609		15 s. multicoloured	..		..	25	25
610		25 s. multicoloured	..		..	35	45
611		50 s. multicoloured	..		..	75	90
612		75 s. multicoloured	..		..	1·00	1·50

(b) Air. Oval design (64 × 46 mm) showing 1967 Coronation Coin
613	–	11 s. multicoloured	..		25	20
614	–	17 s. multicoloured	..		30	30
615	–	18 s. multicoloured	..		30	30
616	–	39 s. multicoloured	..		45	60
617	–	1 p. multicoloured	..		1·50	2·25
608/17 and O154/6 ..			Set of 13		7·50	9·50

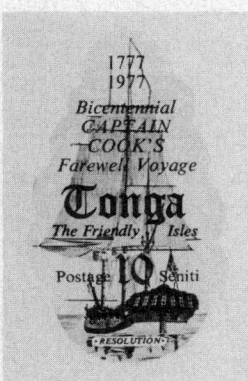
123 H.M.S. Resolution

1977 (28 Sept). *Bicentenary of Capt. Cook's Last Voyage.*
(a) Postage.
618	**123**	10 s. multicoloured	..		1·75	75
619		17 s. multicoloured	..		2·25	1·10
620		25 s. multicoloured	..		3·75	2·00
621		30 s. multicoloured	..		3·75	2·75
622		73 s. multicoloured	..		4·50	4·50

(b) Air. Horiz design (52×46 mm) showing medal and extract from Cook's journal
623	–	11 s. multicoloured	..		1·75	2·25
624	–	22 s. multicoloured	..		2·75	2·25
625	–	31 s. multicoloured	..		3·25	2·75
626	–	50 s. multicoloured	..		4·50	4·50
627	–	1 p. multicoloured	..		8·00	8·50
618/27 and O157/9 ..			Set of 13		48·00	45·00

124 Humpback Whale   (125)

1977 (16 Dec). *Whale Conservation. (a) Postage.*
628	**124**	15 s. black, grey and bright blue	..		2·75	80
629		22 s. black, grey and dull green..			3·00	1·25
630		31 s. black, grey and orange	..		3·50	1·75
631		38 s. black, grey and bright lilac	..		3·75	2·25
632		64 s. black, grey and red-brown..			6·00	5·50

(b) Air. Hexagonal design (66 × 51 mm) showing Sei and Fin Whales
633	–	11 s. multicoloured	..		2·75	75
634	–	17 s. multicoloured	..		3·00	90
635	–	18 s. multicoloured	..		3·00	1·00
636	–	39 s. multicoloured	..		4·00	2·25
637	–	50 s. multicoloured	..		5·00	3·25
628/37 and O160/2 ..			Set of 13		50·00	30·00

1978 (17 Feb). *Various stamps surch as* **T 125**. *(a) Postage.*
638	**115**	15 s. on 5 s. multicoloured	..		1·50	1·75
639	**119**	15 s. on 5 s. multicoloured (Br.).			1·50	1·75
640	**117**	15 s. on 10 s. verm, blk & emerald (G.)			1·50	1·75
641	**119**	15 s. on 10 s. multicoloured	..		1·50	1·75
642	**121**	15 s. on 11 s. multicoloured (Blk. & Sil.)			1·50	2·75
643	**114**	15 s. on 20 s. multicoloured	..		1·50	1·75
644	–	15 s. on 38 s. mult (No. O133) (V.)			1·50	1·75

(b) Air

645	–	17 s. on 9 s. multicoloured (No. 533) ..		1·75	2·00
646	–	17 s. on 9 s. multicoloured (583) (V.) ..		1·75	2·00
		a. Surch double ..			£150
647	–	17 s. on 12 s. multicoloured (534) (V.)		1·75	2·00
648	–	17 s. on 12 s. mult (573) (R. & Gold)		1·75	2·00
649	–	17 s. on 18 s. mult (595) (Olive & Br)		1·75	2·00
650	–	17 s. on 38 s. multicoloured (527) (G.)		1·75	2·00
651	–	17 s. on 38 s. multicoloured (556)		1·75	2·00
652	–	1 p. on 35 s. mult (O151) (Silver & B.)		20·00	27·00
653	–	1 p. on 38 s. mult (576) (V & Gold)		8·50	9·00
654	–	1 p. on 75 s. mult (572) (G. & Sil.)		8·50	9·00
638/54		Set of 17		55·00	65·00

The surcharges on Nos. 638/9 are formed by adding a figure "1" to the existing face value.

The surcharge on No. 644 includes the word "POSTAGE".

126 Flags of Canada and Tonga

1978 (5 May). *Commonwealth Games, Edmonton.* (a) *Postage.*

655	126	10 s. blue, red and black ..		15	15
656		15 s. multicoloured		25	25
657		20 s. turquoise-green, black and red		35	35
658		25 s. red, blue and black		40	40
659		45 s. black and red		90	1·00

(b) *Air. Leaf-shaped design (39 × 40 mm) showing Maple Leaf*

660	–	17 s. black and red		30	30
661	–	35 s. black, red and blue		60	65
662	–	38 s. black, red and turquoise-green		75	85
663	–	40 s. black, red and green		80	90
664	–	65 s. black, red and chestnut		1·40	1·60
655/64	and O163/5 ..	Set of 13		8·00	9·00

127 King Taufa'ahau Tupou IV

1978 (4 July). *60th Birthday of King Taufa'ahau Tupou IV.*

(a) *Postage*

665	127	2 s. black, deep blue and cobalt		10	20
666		5 s. black, deep blue and rose-pink ..		10	20
667		10 s. black, deep blue and mauve		20	20
668		25 s. black, deep blue and brownish grey		45	35
669		75 s. black, deep blue and yellow-ochre ..		1·10	1·25

(b) *Air. Star-shaped design (44 × 51 mm) showing portrait of King*

670	–	11 s. black, dp blue & greenish yellow		20	20
671	–	15 s. black, deep blue and cinnamon		30	25
672	–	17 s. black, deep blue and bright lilac		35	25
673	–	39 s. black, dp blue & turquoise-green		60	55
674	–	1 p. black, deep blue and pink		1·75	1·75
665/74	and O166/8 ..	Set of 13		7·00	7·00

128 Banana

1978 (29 Sept)–82. (a) *Coil stamps. Designs as T 128 showing bananas (the number coinciding with the face value).*

675		1 s. black and greenish yellow		20	50
676		2 s. deep blue and greenish yellow		20	50
677		3 s. purple-brown, yellow and greenish yellow		30	50
678		4 s. deep blue, yellow and greenish yellow		30	50
679		5 s. vermilion, yellow and greenish yellow		30	50

(b) *Coil stamps. Coconut-shaped design (18 × 26 mm)*

680		6 s. purple, emerald and bistre-brown		40	50
681		7 s. greenish blue, emerald and light brown ..		40	50
682		8 s. vermilion, emerald and light brown		40	50
683		9 s. deep mauve, emerald and light brown		40	50
684		10 s. emerald and light brown		40	50

(c) *Coil stamps. Pineapple-shaped design (17 × 30 mm)*

684a		13 s. deep mauve, emerald and cinnamon (17.12.82)..		7·50	5·00
685		15 s. blue-green, orange-brown and emerald ..		1·25	1·25
686		20 s. brown, orange-brown and emerald		1·40	1·40
687		30 s. magenta, orange-brown and emerald		1·60	1·60
688		50 s. black, orange-brown and emerald		2·00	2·00
689		1 p. purple, orange-brown and emerald		2·50	3·00

(d) *Mixed fruit oval design (55 × 29 mm)*

689a		2 p. multicoloured (17.12.82)		10·00	11·00
689b		3 p. multicoloured (17.12.82)		11·00	12·00
675/89b		Set of 18		38·00	38·00

Nos. 675/89 and O169/83 were produced in rolls, each even stamp having a number applied to the backing paper, with the usual inscription on the reverse.

129 Humpback Whale

1978 (15 Dec). *Endangered Wildlife Conservation. T 129 and similarly shaped designs. Multicoloured.* (a) *Postage.*

690		15 s. Type 129 ..		2·50	1·25
691		18 s. Insular Flying Fox		2·50	1·25
692		25 s. Turtle		2·50	1·50
693		28 s. Red Shining Parrot		4·00	2·00
694		60 s. Type 129		6·50	5·00

(b) *Air*

695		17 s. Type 129		2·50	1·25
696		22 s. As 18 s.		2·50	1·25
697		31 s. As 25 s.		2·50	2·00
698		39 s. As 28 s.		5·00	3·00
699		45 s. Type 129		5·50	3·50
690/9	and O184/6	Set of 13		48·00	32·00

130 Metrication Symbol

1979 (16 Feb). *Decade of Progress. T 130 and other multi-angular designs in ultramarine and gold (31 s.) or multicoloured (others).*

(a) *Postage*

700		5 s. Type 130		10	10
701		11 s. Map of South Pacific Islands		15	15
702		18 s. "Building wall of progress" with the assistance of the United States Peace Corps		25	20
703		22 s. New churches		35	25
704		50 s. Map showing air routes ..		80	50

(b) *Air*

705		15 s. As 50 s.		20	20
706		17 s. As 11 s.		25	20
707		31 s. Rotary International emblem		45	35
708		39 s. Government offices		60	40
709		1 p. "Communications"		1·60	1·25
700/9	and O187/9 ..	Set of 13		7·50	5·00

131 Various Envelopes bearing Self-adhesive Stamps

1979 (1 June). *Death Centenary of Sir Rowland Hill and 10th Anniv of Tongan Self-adhesive Stamps.* (a) *Postage.*

710	131	5 s. multicoloured		20	10
711		10 s. multicoloured		30	15
712		25 s. multicoloured		65	35
713		50 s. multicoloured		1·25	60
714		1 p. multicoloured		2·00	1·25
		a. Horiz roul omitted (vert pair)			

(b) *Air. Multi-angular design (53 × 53 mm) showing various self-adhesive stamps*

715		15 s. multicoloured		40	20
716		17 s. multicoloured		45	25
717		18 s. multicoloured		45	25
718		31 s. multicoloured		75	40
719		39 s. multicoloured		90	45
710/19	and O190/2 ..	Set of 13		10·50	6·00

132

(Des R. Edge and K. Jones)

1979 (17 Aug)–82. *Air. Coil stamps.*

720	132	5 s. black and cobalt		40	50
721		11 s. black and bright blue		50	50
722		14 s. black and violet		50	50
723		15 s. black and mauve		55	50
724		17 s. black and bright magenta ..		55	50
725		18 s. black and bright rose-red		55	50
726		22 s. black and orange-vermilion		65	50
726a		29 s. black and rose (17.12.82)		8·00	5·00
727		31 s. black and orange-yellow		85	1·00
727a		32 s. black and yellow-ochre (17.12.82)		9·00	5·50
728		39 s. black and bright yellow-green		1·00	1·00
728a		47 s. black and light brown (17.12.82)		9·00	6·50
729		75 s. black and bright blue-green		1·50	2·50
730		1 p. black and emerald		2·00	3·25
720/30		Set of 14		30·00	25·00

Nos. 720/30 and O193/203 were produced in rolls, each even stamp having a number applied to the backing paper, with the usual inscription on the reverse.

133 Rain Forest, Island of 'Eua

1979 (23 Nov). *Views as seen through the Lens of a Camera.*

(a) *Postage*

731	133	10 s. multicoloured		30	30
732		18 s. multicoloured		35	40
733		31 s. multicoloured		50	40
734		50 s. multicoloured		80	1·00
735		60 s. multicoloured		90	1·75

(b) *Air. Design as T 133 but showing Isle of Kao*

736	–	5 s. multicoloured		20	30
737	–	15 s. multicoloured		40	30
738	–	17 s. multicoloured		40	30
739	–	39 s. multicoloured		70	60
740	–	75 s. multicoloured		1·00	1·75
731/40	and O204/6 ..	Set of 13		7·50	10·00

1980 OLYMPIC GAMES

134 King George Tupou I, Admiral Du Bouzet and Map of Tonga

(135)

1980 (9 Jan). *125th Anniv of France–Tonga Treaty of Friendship.*

(a) *Postage*

741	134	7 s. multicoloured		15	15
742		10 s. multicoloured		20	20
743		14 s. multicoloured		30	30
744		50 s. multicoloured		1·25	1·25
745		75 s. multicoloured		1·75	2·00

(b) *Air. Design as T 134 but showing King George Tupou I, Napoleon III and "L'Aventure" (French warship)*

746	–	15 s. multicoloured		30	30
747	–	17 s. multicoloured		35	35
748	–	22 s. multicoloured		55	55
749	–	31 s. multicoloured		90	90
750	–	39 s. multicoloured		1·00	1·00
741/50	and O207/9 ..	Set of 13		10·50	11·00

1980 (30 Apr). *Olympic Games, Moscow. Nos. 710/19 surch or optd only (No. 755) as T 135 in black on silver background.*

(a) Postage

751	131	13 s. on 5 s. multicoloured	..	35	35
752		20 s. on 10 s. multicoloured	..	55	55
753		25 s. multicoloured	..	70	70
754		33 s. on 50 s. multicoloured	..	85	85
755		1 p. multicoloured	..	3·25	3·50

(b) Air

756	—	9 s. on 15 s. multicoloured	..	30	30
757	—	16 s. on 17 s. multicoloured	..	50	50
758	—	29 s. on 18 s. multicoloured	..	80	80
759	—	32 s. on 31 s. multicoloured	..	90	90
760	—	47 s. on 39 s. multicoloured	..	1·50	1·75
751/60 and O210/12 ..			*Set of 13*	14·00	14·50

136 Scout at Campfire

1980 (30 Sept). *South Pacific Scout Jamboree, Tonga and 75th Anniv of Rotary International. (a) Postage.*

761	136	9 s. multicoloured	..	30	20
762		13 s. multicoloured	..	40	20
763		15 s. multicoloured	..	40	20
764		30 s. multicoloured	..	75	50

(b) Air. Design as T 136 showing Scout activities and Rotary emblem

765	—	29 s. multicoloured	..	75	45
766	—	32 s. multicoloured	..	80	45
767	—	47 s. multicoloured	..	1·10	70
768	—	1 p. multicoloured	..	2·00	2·00
761/8 and O214/15 ..		..	*Set of 10*	9·50	8·25

9

(137)   138 Red Cross and Tongan Flags, with Map of Tonga

1980 (3 Dec)–**82**. *Various stamps surch as T 137. (a) Postage.*

769	117	9 s. on 35 s. vermilion, black and mauve		40	40
770	119	13 s. on 20 s. multicoloured	..	55	55
771		13 s. on 25 s. multicoloured	..	55	55
772	—	19 s. on 25 s. multicoloured (No. 571)	..	75	75
773	114	1 p. on 65 s. multicoloured	..	3·00	3·75
773a		5 p. on 25 s. multicoloured (No. O214) (B.) (4.1.82)		12·00	14·00
773b		5 p. on 2 p. multicoloured (No. O215) (B.) (4.1.82)		12·00	14·00
		ba. Stamp omitted (centre stamp of strip of 3) ..			

(b) Air

774	—	29 s. on 14 s. multicoloured (No. 585)	..	90	90
775	—	29 s. on 39 s. multicoloured (No. 597)	..	90	90
776	—	32 s. on 12 s. multicoloured (No. 554)	..	1·10	1·10
777	—	32 s. on 14 s. multicoloured (No. 574)	..	1·10	1·10
778	—	47 s. on 12 s. multicoloured (No. 524)	..	1·60	1·60
779	—	47 s. on 12 s. multicoloured (No. 584)	..	1·60	1·60
769/79 and O216		..	*Set of 14*	35·00	42·00

On No. 773ba the centre stamp in a vertical strip of 3 became detached so that the surcharge was applied to the white backing paper.

No. 773b exists with map on reverse or with plain back. No. 773a comes with map on back only.

1981 (9 Sept). *International Year of Disabled Persons.*

(a) Postage. P 14½ × 14.

780	138	2 p. multicoloured	..	2·00	1·25
781		3 p. multicoloured	..	2·25	1·50

(b) Air. Vert design (25 × 33 mm) showing Red Cross flag and map depicting Tongatapu and Eua. P 13½.

782	—	29 s. multicoloured	..	50	20
783	—	32 s. multicoloured	..	60	25
784	—	47 s. multicoloured	..	70	30
780/4 ..		..	*Set of 5*	5·50	3·25

139 Prince Charles and King Taufa'ahau Tupou IV

1981 (21 Oct). *Royal Wedding and Centenary of Treaty of Friendship between Tonga and Great Britain. T 139 and similar vert designs. Multicoloured. P 13½.*

785	13 s.	Type 139		30	20
786	47 s.	Prince Charles and Lady Diana Spencer		60	30
787	1 p. 50,	Prince Charles and Lady Diana (different)..		1·00	90
		a. Imperf backing paper (pair) ..		75·00	
788	3 p.	Prince and Princess of Wales after wedding ceremony		1·40	1·40
785/8 ..		..	*Set of 4*	3·00	2·50

140 Report of Printing in *Missionary Notices*

1981 (25 Nov). *Christmas. 150th Anniv of first Books Printed in Tonga. T 140 and similar horiz designs. Multicoloured. P 13½.*

789	9 s.	Type 140		25	25
790	13 s.	*Missionary Notices* report (different)	..	30	30
791	32 s.	Type in chase	..	85	85
792	47 s.	Bible class	..	1·40	1·40
789/92		..	*Set of 4*	2·50	2·50

141 Landing Scene

1981 (25 Nov). *Bicentenary of Maurelle's Discovery of Vava'u. T 141 and similar horiz designs. Multicoloured. P 14 × 14½.*

793	9 s.	Type 141	..	40	40
794	13 s.	Map of Vava'u	..	60	50
795	47 s.	*La Princesa*	..	2·75	1·50
796	1 p.	*La Princesa (different)*	..	5·00	6·50
793/6		..	*Set of 4*	8·00	8·00
MS797	100 × 78 mm. As No. 796. Imperf			8·50	11·00

The stamp from No. **MS**797 is as No. 796 but without inscription at foot of design.

142 Battle Scene

1981 (16 Dec). *175th Anniv of Capture of "Port au Prince" (ship). T 142 and similar horiz designs in black and new blue. P 13½.*

798	29 s.	Type 142	..	1·00	45
799	32 s.	Battle scene (different)	..	1·00	55
800	47 s.	Map of Ha'apai Group	..	1·50	1·25
801	47 s.	Native canoes preparing to attack	..	1·50	1·25
802	1 p.	*Port au Prince*	..	2·75	2·00
798/802		..	*Set of 5*	7·00	5·00

The 47 s. values were printed together, *se-tenant*, in horizontal and vertical pairs throughout the sheet.

143 Baden-Powell at Brownsea Island, 1907

CYCLONE RELIEF

T$1 +50s

POSTAGE & RELIEF

(144)

1982 (22 Feb). *75th Anniv of Boy Scout Movement and 125th Birth Anniv of Lord Baden-Powell. T 143 and similar vert designs. P 13½.*

803	29 s.	Type 143		1·00	30
804	32 s.	Baden-Powell on his charger "Black Prince"		1·10	35
805	47 s.	Baden-Powell at Imperial Jamboree, 1924		1·40	45
806	1 p. 50,	Cover of first *Scouting for Boys* journal		3·25	1·75
807	2 p. 50,	Newsboy, 1900 and Mafeking Siege 3d. stamp		5·50	4·00
803/7		..	*Set of 5*	11·00	6·00

1982 (14 Apr). *Cyclone Relief. No. 788 optd with T 144 in silver.*

808	1 p. + 50 s. on 3 p. Prince and Princess of Wales after wedding ceremony ..			80	2·00
	a. Imperf backing paper (pair) ..			£200	

145 Ball Control   146 Olovaha II (inter-island freighter)

1982 (7 July). *World Cup Football Championship, Spain. T 145 and similar vert designs. Multicoloured. P 13½.*

809	32 s.	Type 145	..	75	45
810	47 s.	Goalkeeping	..	95	60
811	75 s.	Heading	..	1·40	95
812	1 p. 50,	Shooting	..	2·50	1·75
809/12		..	*Set of 4*	5·00	3·25

1982 (11 Aug). *Inter-Island Transport. T 146 and similar horiz design. Multicoloured. P 14 × 14½.*

813	9 s.	Type 146	..	55	15
814	13 s.	Type 146	..	60	25
815	47 s.	SPIA De Havilland D.H.C.6 Twin Otter 300	..	1·50	1·00
816	1 p.	As 47 s.	..	2·40	3·00
813/16		..	*Set of 4*	4·50	4·00

147 Mail Canoe   148 Decathlon

1982 (29 Sept). *Tin Can Mail Centenary. T 147 and similar vert designs. P 13½ × 14.*

817	13 s.	multicoloured	..	15	15
818	32 s.	multicoloured	..	25	25
819	47 s.	multicoloured	..	35	35
820	2 p.	black and pale turquoise-green ..		1·40	1·40
817/20		..	*Set of 4*	2·00	2·00
MS821	135 × 90 mm. Nos. 817/19. Imperf			1·25	2·00
MS822	135 × 89 mm. As No. 820 but with gold inscriptions. Imperf			3·00	4·25

Designs:—32 s. Mail canoe and ship; 47 s. Collecting Tin Can mail; 2 p. Map of Niuafo'ou.

1982 (25 Oct). *Commonwealth Games, Brisbane. T 148 and similar multicoloured design. P 13½.*

823	32 s.	Type 148	..	50	50
824	1 p. 50,	Tongan Police band at opening ceremony (horiz) ..		4·50	5·00

149 Pupils   (150)

Christmas Greetings 1982

1982 (25 Oct). *Tonga College Centenary. T **149** and similar multicoloured designs. P 13½ (Nos. 825/6) or 14 × 14½ (others).*

825	5 s. Type **149** (Tongan inscription)		50	80
	a. Pair. Nos. 825/6		1·00	1·60
826	5 s. Type **149** (English inscription)		50	80
827	29 s. School crest and monument (Tongan inscr) (29×22 *mm*)		2·00	2·50
	a. Block of 4. Nos. 827/9		7·00	
828	29 s. As No. 827, but inscr in English		2·00	2·50
829	29 s. King George Tupou I (founder) and school (Tongan inscr) (29×22 *mm*)		2·00	2·50
830	29 s. As No. 829, but inscr in English		2·00	2·50
825/30		*Set of 6*	8·00	10·50

Nos. 825/6 were printed together, *se-tenant*, in horizontal and vertical pairs and Nos. 827/30 in different combinations throughout the sheet, giving four blocks of 4 and four single stamps.

1982 (17 Nov). *Christmas. Nos. 817/19 optd as T **150** in bright carmine (13 s.) or silver (others).*

831	13 s. Type **147**		25	50
	a. Bright purple opt			
832	32 s. Mail boat and ship		60	75
833	47 s. Collecting Tin Can mail		70	85
831/3		*Set of 3*	1·40	1·90

151 H.M.S. *Resolution*, and S. S. *Canberra*

1983 (22 Feb). *Sea and Air Transport. T **151** and similar horiz designs. Multicoloured. P 14.*

834	29 s. Type **151** (sage-green background)		3·00	1·75
835	32 s. Type **151** (buff background)		3·00	1·75
836	47 s. Montgolfier's balloon and Concorde (pale blue background)		4·25	3·00
837	1 p. 50, As No. 836 (lilac background)		6·50	9·00
834/7		*Set of 4*	15·00	14·00
MS838	120×165 mm. 2 p. 50, *Canberra* (liner) and Concorde		4·00	6·00

152 Globe and Inset of Tonga   153 SPIA De Havilland D.H.C.6 Twin Otter 300

1983 (14 Mar). *Commonwealth Day. T **152** and similar horiz designs. Multicoloured. P 14.*

839	29 s. Type **152**		35	45
840	32 s. Tongan dancers		6·00	4·00
841	47 s. Trawler		50	80
842	1 p. 50, King Taufa'ahau Tupou IV and flag		1·75	4·00
839/42		*Set of 4*	7·75	8·25

1983 (11 May). *Inauguration of Niuafo'ou Airport. T **153** and similar horiz design. Multicoloured. P 14 × 14½.*

843	32 s. Type **153**		1·00	30
844	47 s. Type **153**		1·10	35
845	1 p. SPIA Boeing 707		1·75	1·25
846	1 p. 50, As 1 p.		2·75	1·75
843/6		*Set of 4*	6·00	3·25

154 "Intelsat IV" Satellite   155 Obverse and Reverse of Pa'anga Banknote

1983 (22 June). *World Communications Year. T **154** and similar multicoloured designs. P 11 (2 p.) or 14 × 14½ (others).*

847	29 s. Type **154**		40	20
848	32 s. "Intelsat IVA" satellite		50	25
849	75 s. "Intelsat V" satellite		1·00	70
850	2 p. Moon post cover (45 × 32 *mm*)		2·00	
847/50		*Set of 4*	3·50	2·75

1983 (3 Aug). *10th Anniv of Bank of Tonga. P 14.*

851	**155** 1 p. multicoloured		1·25	1·50
852	2 p. multicoloured		2·25	2·75

STAMP DUTY. Stamps of Tonga and Niuafo'ou overprinted or surcharged "STAMP DUTY", "STAMP DUTY ONLY" or similar wording were for fiscal use and were not valid for postal purposes.

 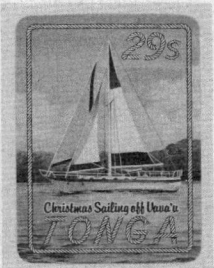

156 Early Printing Press   157 Yacht off Coast

(Des A. Benjamin and R. Edge)

1983 (22 Sept). *Printing in Tonga. T **156** and similar vert designs. Multicoloured. P 14.*

853	13 s. Type **156**		20	15
854	32 s. Arrival of W. Woon		40	30
855	1 p. Early Tongan print		95	95
856	2 p. *The Tonga Chronicle*		1·50	2·00
853/6		*Set of 4*	2·75	3·00

1983 (17 Nov). *Christmas. Yachting off Vava'u. T **157** and similar vert designs. Multicoloured. P 11.*

857	29 s. Type **157**		60	35
858	32 s. View of yacht from cave		60	35
859	1 p. 50, Anchored yacht		2·00	2·25
860	2 p. 50, Yacht off coast (*different*)		2·75	3·50
857/60		*Set of 4*	5·50	5·75

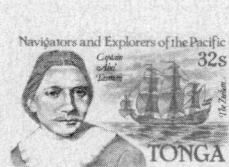

158 Abel Tasman and *Zeehan*   159 Chaste Mitre (*Scabrida casta*)

(Des R. Edge)

1984 (12 Mar). *Navigators and Explorers of the Pacific (1st series). T **158** and similar horiz designs. P 14.*

861	32 s. deep dull green and black		1·50	1·50
862	47 s. reddish violet and black		2·00	2·00
863	90 s. light brown and black		3·75	3·75
864	1 p. 50, royal blue and black		5·00	5·00
861/4		*Set of 4*	11·00	11·00

Designs:—47 s. Samuel Wallis and H.M.S. *Dolphin*; 90 s. William Bligh and H.M.S. *Bounty*; 1 p. 50, James Cook and H.M.S. *Resolution*.

See also Nos. 896/9.

STAMPS DIE-CUT OR PERFORATED. During 1985 developments took place in the production of Tonga and Niuafo'ou self-adhesive stamps. Since 1981 these had been produced in traditional formats on backing paper perforated in the usual way. The individual stamps were, however, separated by the removal of the margins between them by the die-cutting process.

As an experiment some supplies of Tonga Nos. 870, 896, MS904, 905/9, 915/18, O225 and Niuafo'ou Nos. 56/60, together with the entire printing of Tonga Nos. 910/14, were produced with the margins intact so that both stamps and backing paper were perforated through.

Such issues are usually inscribed "Bend forward and peel off backing paper" on the reverse.

1984 (10 Apr)–85. *Marine Life. T **159** and similar multicoloured designs. Stamps die-cut and backing paper perf 14 (1, 2, 3, 5 p.) or 14½ (others).*

865	1 s. Type **159**		40	80
866	2 s. *Porites* sp (26.6.84)		80	80
867	3 s. Red Squirrelfish (18.5.84)		80	90
868	5 s. Green Map Cowrie (*Cypraea mappa viridis*)		50	80
869	6 s. *Dardanus megistos* (crab) (17.9.84)		75	1·00
870	9 s. Variegated Shark (18.5.84)		75	55
	b. Stamp perforated (28.5.85)		1·75	85
871	10 s. Bubble Cone (*Conus bullatus*)		70	75
872	13 s. Lionfish (18.5.84)		1·00	65
873	15 s. Textile or Cloth of Gold Cone (*Conus textile*)		90	1·00
874	20 s. White-tailed Dascyllus (18.5.84)		1·75	1·50
875	29 s. Princely Cone (*Conus aulicus*)		1·75	80
876	32 s. Powder-blue Surgeonfish (18.5.84)		2·50	90
877	47 s. Giant Spider Conch (*Lambis truncata*)		2·50	1·60
878	1 p. *Millepora dichotama* (26.6.84)		9·00	8·00
879	2 p. *Birgus latro* (crab) (17.9.84)		11·00	12·00

880	3 p. Rose-branch Murex (*Chicoreus palma rosae*)		9·00	13·00
881	5 p. Yellow-finned Tuna (18.5.84)		11·00	15·00
865/81		*Set of 17*	50·00	55·00

Nos. 878/81 are horizontal, 38×23 mm.

For 1, 2, 5, 6, 10, 15, 20, 32 s., 2 p., 3 p. and 5 p. with normal gum and perforations see Nos. 976a/b, 999/1017a and 1087/95.

For some of these designs redrawn with face value at foot see Nos. 1218/34 and 1346/7.

160 Printer checking Newspaper   161 U.S.A. Flag and Running

1984 (26 June). *20th Anniv of Tonga Chronicle (newspaper). Die-cut.*

882	**160** 3 s. grey-brown and bright blue		15	20
	a. Sheetlet of 12		1·50	
883	32 s. grey-brown and vermilion		60	65
	a. Sheetlet of 12		6·00	

Nos. 882/3 were each printed in sheetlets of 12, the designs being superimposed on a reproduction of the front page from the first edition. This was printed in grey and is in Tongan for the 3 s. and English for the 32 s.

(Des R. Edge)

1984 (23 July). *Olympic Games, Los Angeles. T **161** and similar horiz designs, each showing U.S. flag. Each printed in black, scarlet-vermilion and bright new blue. P 14 × 14½.*

884	29 s. Type **161**		25	25
885	47 s. Javelin-throwing		30	30
886	1 p. 50, Shot-putting		1·00	1·00
887	3 p. Olympic torch		1·90	1·90
884/7		*Set of 4*	3·00	3·00

162 Sir George Airy and Dateline on World Map   163 Australia 1914 Laughing Kookaburra 6d. Stamp

(Des R. Edge)

1984 (20 Aug). *Centenary of International Dateline. T **162** and similar horiz design. Multicoloured. P 14.*

888	47 s. Type **162**		1·25	1·00
889	2 p. Sir Sandford Fleming and Map of Pacific time zones		4·25	4·50

1984 (17 Sept). *"Ausipex" International Stamp Exhibition, Melbourne. T **163** and similar vert design. Multicoloured. P 14.*

890	32 s. Type **163**		1·50	75
891	1 p. 50, Tonga 1897 Red Shining Parrot 2s. 6d. stamp		3·25	3·00
MS892	90×100 mm. As Nos. 890/1, but without exhibition logo and with "TONGA" and face values in gold. Die-cut		3·50	3·50

Examples of No. MS892 without face values are Exhibition Banquet souvenirs without postal validity.

164 Beach at Sunset ("Silent Night")   165 Section of Tonga Trench

(Des R. Edge)

1984 (12 Nov). *Christmas. Carols. T **164** and similar vert designs. Multicoloured. P 14.*

893	32 s. Type **164**		60	45
894	47 s. Hut and palm trees ("Away in a Manger")		85	65
895	1 p. Sailing boats ("I Saw Three Ships")		1·75	2·75
893/5		*Set of 3*	2·75	3·50

Nos. 893/5 were each issued in sheets of 20 stamps with 5 labels, in the central vertical row, showing progressive stages of the design.

(Des R. Edge)

85 (27 Feb). *Navigators and Explorers of the Pacific (2nd series). Horiz designs as T 158. Stamps die-cut and backing paper perf 14.*

6	32 s. black and turquoise-blue	2·75 1·25
	b. Stamp perforated	26·00 35·00
7	47 s. black and blue-green	3·00 1·50
8	90 s. black and scarlet	6·50 4·00
9	1 p. 50, black and buff	7·00 6·50
6/9	*Set of 4*	17·00 12·00

Designs:—32 s. Willem Schouten and *Eendracht*; 47 s. Jacob Maire and *Hoorn*; 90 s. Fletcher Christian and *Bounty*; p. 50, Francisco Maurelle and *La Princessa*.
No. 896b has no inscription on the reverse.

85 (10 Apr). *Geological Survey of the Tonga Trench. T 165 and similar multicoloured designs. Stamps die-cut and backing paper perf 14.*

0	29 s. Type 165.	1·25 1·00
1	32 s. Diagram of marine seismic survey ..	1·25 1·00
2	47 s. Diagram of aerial oil survey (*vert*) ..	1·50 1·50
3	1 p. 50, Diagram of sea bed survey (*vert*)	4·75 6·00
0/3	*Set of 4*	8·00 8·50
S904	100×100 mm. 1 p. 50, Bearded Angler	
(fish). Die-cut	7·00 5·00
	b. Stamp perforated	7·00 5·50

166 Port au Prince at Gravesend, 1805

167 Quintal (Byron Russell) and Capt. Bligh (Charles Laughton)

985 (18 June). *175th Anniv of Will Mariner's Departure for England. T 166 and similar horiz designs. Multicoloured.*

A. *Stamp die-cut and backing paper perf 14*

05A	29 s. Type 166	1·00 1·00
06A	32 s. Capture of *Port au Prince*, Tonga, 1806	1·00 1·00
07A	47 s. Will Mariner on Tongan canoe, 1807	1·10 1·10
08A	1 p. 50, Mariner boarding brig *Favourite*, 1810	2·50 3·50
09A	2 p. 50, *Cuffnells* in English Channel, 1811	4·00 5·00
05A/9A	*Set of 5*	8·75 10·50

B. *Both stamp and backing paper perf 14*

05B	29 s. Type 166	60 50
06B	32 s. Capture of *Port au Prince*, Tonga, 1806	60 50
07B	47 s. Will Mariner on Tongan canoe, 1807	80 70
08B	1 p. 50, Mariner boarding brig *Favourite*, 1810	2·25 2·75
09B	2 p. 50, *Cuffnells* in English Channel, 1811	3·50 4·25
05B/9B	*Set of 5*	7·00 8·00

985 (16 July). *50th Anniv of Film "Mutiny on the Bounty". T 167 and similar horiz designs showing film stills. Multicoloured. Both stamp and backing paper perf 14.*

10	47 s. Type 167.	7·00 7·00
	a. Horiz strip of 5. Nos. 910/14 ..	32·00
11	47 s. Captain Bligh and prisoners ..	7·00 7·00
12	47 s. Fletcher Christian (Clark Gable) ..	7·00 7·00
13	47 s. Mutineers threatening Bligh ..	7·00 7·00
14	47 s. Bligh and Roger Byam (Franchot Tone) in boat	7·00 7·00
10/14	*Set of 5*	32·00 32·00

Nos. 910/14 were printed together, *se-tenant*, in horizontal strips of 5 throughout the sheet.

168 Lady Elizabeth Bowes-Lyon 1910

169 Mary and Joseph arriving at Inn

985 (20 Aug). *Life and Times of Queen Elizabeth the Queen Mother and 75th Anniv of Girl Guide Movement. T 168 and similar horiz designs.*

A. *Stamp die-cut and backing paper perf 14*

915A	32 s. black, salmon-pink & reddish brown	1·10 1·10
916A	47 s. black, pale rose-lilac & reddish brown	1·40 1·40
917A	1 p. 50, black, olive-yellow & reddish brn	4·00 4·50
918A	2 p. 50, multicoloured	7·00 8·00
915A/18A	*Set of 4*	12·00 13·50

B. *Both stamp and backing paper perf 14*

915B	32 s. black, salmon-pink & reddish brown	1·75 1·00
916B	47 s. black, pale rose-lilac & reddish brown	2·25 1·50
917B	1 p. 50, black, olive-yellow & reddish brn	6·00 4·00
918B	2 p. 50, multicoloured	3·00 3·00
915B/18B	*Set of 4*	16·00 12·00

Designs:—47 s. Duchess of York at Hadfield Girl Guides' Rally, 1931; 1 p. 50, Duchess of York in Girl Guide uniform; 2 p. 50, Queen Mother in 1985 (from photo by Norman Parkinson).

1985 (12 Nov). *Christmas. T 169 and similar vert designs. Multicoloured. P 14.*

919	32 s. Type 169.	55 30
920	42 s. The shepherds	60 40
921	1 p. 50, The Three Wise Men ..	2·25 3·00
922	2 p. 50, The Holy Family ..	3·25 4·00
919/22	*Set of 4*	6·00 7·00

PRINTER AND PROCESS. All issues between Nos. 923 and 1420 were printed in lithography by Walsall Security Printers Ltd., *unless otherwise stated*, and have the normal form of gum, except for Nos. 972/6 which are self-adhesive.

170 Comet and Slogan "Maybe Twice in a Lifetime"

(171)

1986 (26 Mar). *Appearance of Halley's Comet. T 170 and similar horiz designs. Multicoloured. P 14.*

923	42 s. Type 170.	2·50 2·50
	a. Horiz strip of 5. Nos. 923/7 ..	11·00
924	42 s. Edmond Halley	2·50 2·50
925	42 s. Solar System	2·50 2·50
926	42 s. Telescope	2·50 2·50
927	42 s. *Giotto* spacecraft	2·50 2·50
928	57 s. Type 170.	2·75 2·75
	a. Horiz strip of 5. Nos. 928/32 ..	12·00
929	57 s. As No. 924	2·75 2·75
930	57 s. As No. 925	2·75 2·75
931	57 s. As No. 926	2·75 2·75
932	57 s. As No. 927	2·75 2·75
923/32	*Set of 10*	23·00 23·00

Nos. 923/7 and 928/32 were each printed together, *se-tenant*, in horizontal strips of five, forming composite designs, throughout the sheets.

1986 (16 Apr). *Nos. 866/7, 869/70, 872, 874, 879 and 881 surch as T 171.*

933	4 s. on 2 s. *Porites* sp.	80 1·00
934	4 s. on 13 s. Lionfish	80 1·00
935	42 s. on 3 s. Red Squirrelfish ..	1·50 1·00
936	42 s. on 9 s. Variegated Shark ..	1·50 1·00
937	57 s. on 6 s. *Dardanus megistos* ..	2·00 1·50
938	57 s. on 20 s. White-tailed Dascyllus ..	2·00 1·50
939	2 p. 50 on 2 p. *Birgus latro* ..	6·00 7·00
940	2 p. 50 on 5 p. Yellow-finned Tuna	6·00 7·00
933/40	*Set of 8*	18·00 19·00

172 King Taufa'ahau Tupou IV of Tonga

1986 (22 May). *Royal Links with Great Britain and 60th Birthday of Queen Elizabeth II. T 172 and similar designs. P 14.*

941	**172** 57 s. multicoloured	75 1·00
	a. Horiz pair. Nos. 941/2 ..	1·50 2·00
942	— 57 s. multicoloured	75 1·00
943	— 2 p. 50, reddish brown, blk & pale new bl	3·25 3·75
941/3	*Set of 3*	4·25 5·25

Designs: *Horiz* (as T 172)—No. 942, Queen Elizabeth II. *Square* (40×40 mm)—No. 943, Queen Elizabeth II and King Taufa'ahau Tupou IV, Tonga, 1970.

Nos. 941/2 were printed together, *se-tenant*, in horizontal pairs throughout the sheet, and No. 943 in sheetlets of five stamps and one stamp-size label.

173 Peace Corps Nurse giving Injection

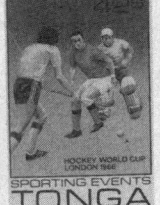
174 Hockey (World Hockey Cup for Men, London)

1986 (22 May). *"Ameripex '86" International Stamp Exhibition, Chicago. 25th Anniv of United States Peace Corps. T 173 and similar horiz design. Multicoloured. P 14.*

944	57 s. Type 173.	1·25 1·00
945	1 p. 50, Peace Corps teacher and pupil ..	2·25 2·75
MS946	90×90 mm. Nos. 944/5, magnifying glass and tweezers. Imperf	3·00 4·00

1986 (23 July). *Sporting Events. T 174 and similar vert designs. Multicoloured. P 14.*

947	42 s. Type 174.	1·75 1·00
948	57 s. Handball (13th Commonwealth Games, Edinburgh)	1·50 1·00
949	1 p. Boxing (13th Commonwealth Games, Edinburgh)	2·00 2·75
950	2 p. 50, Football (World Cup Football Championship, Mexico) ..	4·75 6·00
947/50	*Set of 4*	9·00 9·50

175 1886 1d. King George I Definitive

(Des A. Benjamin)

1986 (27 Aug). *Centenary of First Tonga Stamps. T 175 and similar multicoloured designs. P 14.*

951	32 s. Type 175.	1·50 1·10
952	42 s. 1897 7½d. King George II inverted centre error	1·75 1·25
953	57 s. 1950 Queen Salote's 50th Birthday 1d.	2·25 1·40
954	2 p. 50, 1986 Royal Links with Great Britain 2 p. 50	4·00 6·00
951/4	*Set of 4*	8·50 8·75
MS955	132×104 mm. 50 s. × 8 Vert designs forming montage of Tonga stamps	9·00 9·50

Nos. 951/5 were printed with an overall pattern similar to watermark W 24.

176 Girls wearing Shell Jewellery (177)

1986 (12 Nov). *Christmas. T 176 and similar multicoloured designs. P 14.*

956	32 s. Type 176.	1·50 70
957	42 s. Boy with wood carvings (*vert*) ..	1·75 75
958	57 s. Children performing traditional dance (*vert*)	2·00 1·10
959	2 p. Children in dugout canoe ..	4·75 7·50
956/9	*Set of 4*	9·00 9·00

1986 (2 Dec). *Scout Jamboree, Tongatapu. Nos. 957/8 optd with T 177 in silver.*

960	42 s. Boy with wood carvings (*vert*) ..	1·75 1·75
961	57 s. Children performing traditional dance (*vert*)	2·25 2·25

178 Dumont D'Urville and *L'Astrolabe*   **179** Noah's Ark

1987 (24 Feb). *150th Anniv of Dumont D'Urville's Second Voyage. T 178 and similar horiz designs. Multicoloured. P 14.*

962	32 s. Type 178.	3·00 1·75
963	42 s. Tongan girls (from *Voyage au Pole et dans l'Oceanie*)	3·00 1·75
964	1 p. Contemporary chart	6·50 6·00
965	2 p. 50, Wreck of *L'Astrolabe* ..	12·00 13·00
962/5	*Set of 4*	22·00 20·00

1987 (6 May). *World Wildlife Fund. Sheet 115×110 mm containing T 179 and similar vert designs. Multicoloured. P 13½.*

MS966	42 s. Type 179; 42 s. American Bald Eagles; 42 s. Giraffes and birds; 42 s. Gulls; 42 s. Ostriches and elephants; 42 s. Elephant; 42 s. Lions, zebras, antelopes and giraffes; 42 s. Chimpanzees; 42 s. Frogs and antelopes; 42 s. Lizard and tigers; 42 s. Snake and tiger; 42 s. *Papilio machaon* (butterfly)	32·00 32·00

The stamps within No. MS966 show a composite design of animals entering Noah's Ark.

PRICES OF SETS

Set prices are given for many issues, generally those containing three stamps or more. Definitive sets include one of each value or major colour change, but do not cover different perforations, die types or minor shades. Where a choice is possible the set prices are based on the cheapest versions of the stamps included in the listings.

180 Two Paddlers in Canoe

181 King Taufa'ahau Tupou IV

(Des C. Abbott. Litho Questa)

1987 (1 July). *"Siv'a'alo" (Tonga-Fiji-Samoa) Canoe Race.* T **180** *and similar square designs. Multicoloured.* P 14.
967	32 s. Type 180.		..	55	40
968	42 s. Five paddlers	..	..	65	50
969	57 s. Paddlers and canoe bow	..	..	80	65
	a. Value omitted (R. 3/2) ..			£350	
970	1 p. 50, Two paddlers (different)	..		2·10	2·75
967/70			*Set of 4*	3·50	3·75
MS971	153×59 mm. Nos. 967/70			3·50	4·25

The stamps within No. **MS971** show a composite design of two canoes racing.

No. 969a occurred on a batch of fifty sheets distributed to local post offices in Tonga. The remainder of the first printing was withdrawn and replaced, later in the month, by sheets showing the error corrected.

1987 (1 July)—88. *20th Anniv of Coronation of King Taufa'ahau Tupou IV. Self-adhesive. Stamps die-cut.*
972	181	1 s. black and olive-green	15	40
		a. Booklet pane. Nos. 972×2, 974×4, 975×2 and 976×4	3·00	
		b. Booklet pane. Nos. 972, 972d×2, 973×2, 974×4 and 975×3 (4.7.88)	6·50	
		c. Booklet pane. Nos. 972×4, 972d×2 and 976×6 (4.7.88)	7·00	
972d		2 s. black and pale orange (4.7.88) ..	2·00	2·50
973		5 s. black and pale magenta	15	40
		a. Booklet pane. Nos. 973×7, 974×2 and 975×3..	2·50	
974		10 s. black and reddish lilac	20	40
975		15 s. black and rose-red..	30	50
976		32 s. black and turquoise-blue ..	45	70
972/6		*Set of 6*	3·00	4·50

Nos. 972/6 were only available from stamp booklets. These are self-adhesive stamps and the backing card forms the booklet cover.

1987 (Sept). *As Nos. 871 and 876 (previously self-adhesive), but printed with normal gum and perforations. Multicoloured.* P 14½.
976a	10 s. *Conus bullatus*	..	5·00	5·00
976b	32 s. Powder-blue Surgeonfish	..	12·00	12·00

Nos. 976a/b were printed from the same plates as the self-adhesive issue. They are without imprint date at foot and show a space of 23 mm between the two horizontal lines across each design.

For redrawn versions of these stamps with imprint date see Nos. 1005 and 1008.

182 Arms and Tongan Citizens

183 Father Christmas Octopus and Rat with Sack of Presents

1987 (23 Sept). *125th Anniv of First Parliament.* P 14½×14.
977	182	32 s. multicoloured ..	40	30
978		42 s. multicoloured ..	50	40
979		75 s. multicoloured ..	90	1·00
980		2 p. multicoloured ..	2·25	2·75
977/80		*Set of 4*	3·50	4·00

1987 (25 Nov). *Christmas.* T **183** *and similar horiz designs showing cartoons. Multicoloured.* P 13½×14.
981	42 s. Type 183		85	50
982	57 s. Delivering presents by outrigger canoe	1·00	65
983	1 p. Delivering presents by motorised tricycle	..	2·00	2·25
984	3 p. Drinking cocktails	..	5·00	6·50
981/4		*Set of 4*	8·00	9·00

The new-issue supplement to this Catalogue appears each month in

GIBBONS STAMP MONTHLY

—from your newsagent or by postal subscription— sample copy and details on request.

184 King Taufa'ahau Tupou IV, Olovaha II (inter-island freighter), Oil Rig and Pole Vaulting

1988 (4 July). *70th Birthday of King Taufa'ahau Tupou IV.* T **184** *and similar horiz designs, each showing portrait. Multicoloured.* P 11½.
985	32 s. Type 184		1·25	80
986	42 s. Banknote, coins, Ha'amonga Trilithon and woodcarver	1·25	80
987	57 s. Rowing, communications satellite and Red Cross worker	1·40	90
988	2 p. 50, Scout emblem, 1982 47 s. Scout stamp and Friendly Islands Airways De Havilland D.H.C.6 Twin Otter 200/300 aircraft	6·00	7·50
985/8		*Set of 4*	9·00	9·00

Nos. 985/8 exist overprinted "XX U.P.U. CONGRESS WASHINGTON DC 1989" on the reverse in blue and come from albums distributed at this event.

For similar designs issued in 1990 for the King's Silver Jubilee see Nos. 1082/5.

185 Capt. Cook and Journal

186 Athletics

1988 (11 July). *Bicentenary of Australian Settlement. Sheet* 115 × 110 *mm containing* T **185** *and similar vert designs. Multicoloured.* P 13½.
MS989 42 s. Type 185; 42 s. Ships in Sydney Harbour and Governor Philip; 42 s. Australia 1952 2s. 6d. aborigine definitive and early settlement; 42 s. Burke and Wills (explorers); 42 s. Emu, opals and gold prospector's licence; 42 s. ANZAC cap badge and soldier; 42 s. Cover from first overland mail by Trans Continental; 42 s. Ross Smith, England–Australia flown cover and G.B. 1969 1s. 9d. commemorative stamp; 42 s. Don Bradman and Harold Larwood (cricketers); 42 s. World War II campaign medals; 42 s. Australia 1978 18 c. Flying Doctor Service stamp and sheep station; 42 s. Sydney Opera House .. .. 21·00 22·00
No. **MS989** exists overprinted on the reverse as described below Nos. 985/8.

1988 (11 Aug). *Olympic Games, Seoul.* T **186** *and similar vert designs. Multicoloured.* P 14.
990	57 s. Type 186	..	..	65	65
991	75 s. Sailing	..	..	95	95
992	2 p. Cycling	..	..	3·75	3·50
993	3 p. Tennis	..	..	4·75	4·75
990/3			*Set of 4*	9·00	9·00

187 Traditional Tongan Fale

1988 (9 Sept). *Music in Tonga.* T **187** *and similar horiz designs. Multicoloured.* P 14.
994	32 s. Type 187		30	35
995	42 s. Church choir		40	45
996	57 s. Tonga Police Band outside Royal Palace		75	80
997	2 p. 50, "The Jets" pop group		2·40	3·25
994/7		*Set of 4*	3·50	4·25

188 Olympic Flame

1988 (9 Sept). *"Sport Aid '88". Sheet* 105 × 75 *mm, containing* T **188** *and design as No. 997. Multicoloured.* P 14.
MS998 57 s. Type 188; 57 s. As No. 997 .. 1·40 1·75

Two types of 42 s.:

Type I. Background shading in bright blue extending to the perforation margin. Plumage is light brown.
Type II. Background shading in oval of new blue bleeding off at edges. Plumage is sepia.

1988 (4 Oct)—92. *Redrawn designs as Nos. 865/6, 868/9, 871/6, 879/81 (previously self-adhesive) and new values (7, 35, 42, 57 s., 1 p., 1 p. 50, 10 p.), all with normal gum, perforations and imprint date at foot. Multicoloured. Chalk-surfaced paper* (4, 7, 35, 42, 50, 57 s., 1 p., 1 p. 50, 2 p., 5 p., 10 p.). P 14 (1 p. to 10 p.) *or* 14½×14 *(others).*
999	1 s. Type 159		30	65
1000	2 s. *Porites* sp (18.10.88)		40	80
	a. Chalk-surfaced paper (4.90)		50	90
1001	4 s. Lionfish (2.3.89)		70	1·00
1002	5 s. Green Map Cowrie (*Cypraea mappa viridis*)		50	80
	a. Chalk-surfaced paper (4.90)		1·25	1·50
1003	6 s. *Dardanus megistos* (crab) (18.10.88)	70	1·50
1004	7 s. Wandering Albatross (2.3.89)		2·50	1·75
1005	10 s. Bubble Cone (*Conus bullatus*)		60	50
	a. Chalk-surfaced paper (4.90)		1·25	1·25
1006	15 s. Textile or Cloth of Gold Cone (*Conus textile*) (18.10.88)	60	70
1007	20 s. White-tailed Dascyllus		90	1·00
1008	32 s. Powder-blue Surgeonfish		1·00	70
	a. Chalk-surfaced paper (4.90)		1·25	1·25
1009	35 s. Seahorse (2.3.89)		2·25	2·00
1010	42 s. Lesser Frigate Bird (I) (18.10.88)	2·50	70
	a. Type II		25·00	
1011	50 s. Princely Cone (*Conus aulicus*) (2.3.89)	2·25	90
1012	57 s. Brown Booby (18.10.88)		3·00	90
1013	1 p. *Chelonia mydas* (turtle) (2.3.89)	3·50	3·50
1014	1 p. 50, Humpback Whale (2.3.89)	8·00	5·50
1015	2 p. *Birgus latro* (crab) (19.1.89)	5·50	5·50
1016	3 p. Rose-branch Murex (*Chicoreus palma rosae*) (18.10.88)	2·75	6·00
1017	5 p. Yellow-finned Tuna (19.1.89)	11·00	13·00
1017a	10 p. Variegated Shark (12.5.92)	15·00	18·00
999/1017a		*Set of 20*	55·00	60·00

Nos. 1013/17 are horizontal, 41×26 mm and No. 1017a vertical, 26×41 mm.

Imprint dates: "1988", Nos. 999/1000, 1002/3, 1005/8, 1010, 1012, 1016; "1989", Nos. 1001, 1004, 1009, 1013/15, 1017; "1990", Nos. 1000a, 1002a, 1005a, 1008a; "1992", No. 1017a.

On the redrawn designs there is a larger gap between the two horizontal lines on each design. On Nos. 1005 and 1008 this measures 25 mm. For these two values with a gap of 23 mm and no imprint date see Nos. 976a/b.

For 2, 5, 10, 15 and 32 s. values in a smaller format see Nos. 1087/95.

For some of these designs redrawn with face value at foot see Nos. 1218/34 and 1345/9.

189 Capt. Cook's H.M.S. Resolution

190 Girl in Hospital Bed

1988 (20 Oct). *Centenary of Tonga–U.S.A. Treaty of Friendship.* T **189** *and similar horiz designs. Multicoloured.* P 14.
1018	42 s. Type 189 ..		80	70
1019	57 s. *Santa Maria* ..		1·00	80
1020	2 p. Cook and Christopher Columbus	3·25	4·00
1018/20		*Set of 3*	4·50	5·00
MS1021	140 × 115 mm. Nos. 1018/20		4·50	5·50

Nos. 1018/21 exist overprinted on the reverse as described below Nos. 985/8.

1988 (17 Nov). *Christmas. 125th Anniv of International Red Cross and 25th Anniv of Tongan Red Cross.* T **123** *and similar horiz designs. Multicoloured.* P 14½.
1022	15 s. Type 190 (A)	..	15	20
	a. Horiz pair. Nos. 1022/3	..	30	40
1023	15 s. Type 190 (B)..		15	20
1024	32 s. Red Cross nurse reading to boy (A)	30	35
	a. Horiz pair. Nos. 1024/5.		60	70
1025	32 s. Red Cross nurse reading to boy (B)	30	35
1026	42 s. Red Cross nurse taking pulse (A)	40	45
	a. Horiz pair. Nos. 1026/7.		80	85
1027	42 s. Red Cross nurse taking pulse (B)	40	45
1028	57 s. Red Cross nurse with sleeping child (A)	55	60
	a. Horiz pair. Nos. 1028/9.		1·10	1·25
1029	57 s. Red Cross nurse with sleeping child (B)	55	60
1030	1 p. 50, Boy in wheelchair (A)	1·40	2·00
	a. Horiz pair. Nos. 1030/1.		2·75	4·00
1031	1 p. 50, Boy in wheelchair (B)	1·40	2·00
1022/31		*Set of 10*	4·50	6·50

Nos. 1022/3, 1024/5, 1026/7, 1028/9 and 1030/1 were printed together, *se-tenant,* in horizontal pairs throughout the sheets with the first stamp in each pair inscribed "INTERNATIONAL RED CROSS 125th ANNIVERSARY" (A) and the second "SILVER JUBILEE OF TONGAN RED CROSS" (B).

Nos. 1022, 1024, 1026, 1028 and 1030 exist overprinted on the reverse as described below Nos. 985/8.

191 Map of Tofua Island and Breadfruit

192 *Hypolimnas bolina*

1989 (28 Apr). *Bicentenary of Mutiny on the* Bounty. T **191** *and similar multicoloured designs.* P 13½×14.
1032	32 s. Type **191**	2·50	1·75
1033	42 s. H.M.S. *Bounty* and chronometer	4·00	2·00
1034	57 s. Captain Bligh and *Bounty*'s launch cast adrift	5·50	3·00
1032/4	*Set of 3*	10·00	6·00

MS1035 106×80 mm. 2 p. Fletcher Christian on H.M.S. *Bounty* (*vert*); 3 p. Bligh cast adrift. P 14×13½ (2 p.) or 13½×14×13½×13½ (3 p.) .. 7·50 9·00
Nos. 1032/5 exists overprinted on the reverse as described below Nos. 985/8.

1989 (18 May). *Butterflies.* T **192** *and similar vert designs. Multicoloured.* P 14½×14.
1036	42 s. Type **192**	1·00	80
1037	57 s. *Jamides bochus*	1·25	90
1038	1 p. 20, *Melanitis leda*	2·25	2·75
1039	2 p. 50, *Danaus plexippus*	3·75	5·50
1036/9	*Set of 4*	7·50	9·00

Nos. 1036/9 exist overprinted on the reverse as described below Nos. 985/8.

193 Football at Rugby School, 1870

194 Short S.30 Modified "G" Class Flying Boat *Aotearoa*, 1939 (50th anniv of first flight)

1989 (22 Aug). *Inauguration of National Sports Stadium and South Pacific Mini Games, Tonga.* T **193** *and similar horiz designs showing development of rugby, tennis and cricket. Multicoloured.* P 14.
1040	32 s. Type **193**	65	65
	a. Sheetlet. Nos. 1040/4×2	6·00	
1041	32 s. D. Gallaher (All Black's captain, 1905) and Springboks rugby match, 1906	65	65
1042	32 s. King George V with Cambridge team, 1922 and W. Wakefield (England captain, 1926)	65	65
1043	32 s. E. Crawford (Ireland captain, 1926) and players on cigarette cards	65	65
1044	32 s. S. Mafi (Tonga captain, 1970s) and modern rugby match	65	65
1045	42 s. Royal tennis, 1659	1·00	1·00
	a. Sheetlet. Nos. 1045/9×2	9·00	
1046	42 s. Major Wingfield and lawn tennis, 1873	1·00	1·00
1047	42 s. Oxford and Cambridge tennis teams, 1884	1·00	1·00
1048	42 s. Bunny Ryan, 1910, and players on cigarette cards	1·00	1·00
1049	42 s. Boris Becker and modern tennis match	1·00	1·00
1050	57 s. Cricket match, 1743, and F. Pilch memorial	1·75	1·75
	a. Sheetlet. Nos. 1050/4×2	16·00	
1051	57 s. W. G. Grace (19th-century cricketer)	1·75	1·75
1052	57 s. *Boys Own Paper* cricket article, 1909	1·75	1·75
1053	57 s. Australian cricket team, 1909, and players on cigarette cards	1·75	1·75
1054	57 s. The Ashes urn, and modern cricket match	1·75	1·75
1040/54	*Set of 15*	15·00	15·00

Nos. 1040/4, 1045/9 and 1050/4 were each issued in sheetlets of ten containing two horizontal strips of five separated by a central inscribed gutter.

1989 (23 Oct). *Aviation in Tonga.* T **194** *and similar horiz designs. Multicoloured.* P 14½×14.
1055	42 s. Type **194**	2·00	1·10
1056	57 s. Chance Vought F4U Corsair, 1943	2·50	1·50
1057	90 s. Boeing 737 at Fua'amotu Airport	4·50	4·50
1058	3 p. Montgolfier balloon, Wright Flyer I biplane, Concorde and space shuttle (97×26 *mm*)	9·50	11·00
1055/8	*Set of 4*	17·00	16·00

PRICES OF SETS

Set prices are given for many issues, generally those containing three stamps or more. Definitive sets include one of each value or major colour change, but do not cover different perforations, die types or minor shades. Where a choice is possible the set prices are based on the cheapest versions of the stamps included in the listings.

195 CASA C-212 Aviocar landing

196 Rowland Hill, Mulready Cover and Penny Blacks

(Des G. Bennett)

1989 (9 Nov). *Christmas. "Flying Home".* T **195** *and similar vert designs.* P 14×13½.
1059	32 s. blue-green, deep brown & dull orange	1·25	80
1060	42 s. blue-green, deep brown and emerald	1·40	80
1061	57 s. blue-green, deep brown and vermilion	1·60	90
1062	3 p. blue-green, deep brown & deep mauve	5·50	7·00
1059/62	*Set of 4*	8·75	8·50

Designs:—42 s. Villagers waving to CASA C-212 Aviocar aircraft; 57 s. Outrigger canoe and CASA C-212 Aviocar aircraft; 3 p. CASA C-212 Aviocar aircraft over headland.

1989 (17 Nov). *20th Universal Postal Union Congress, Washington. Sheet* 115×110 *mm containing* T **196** *and similar vert designs. Multicoloured.* P 13½.
MS1063 57 s. Type **196**; 57 s. Early train and steam ship; 57 s. Stage coach, Pony Express poster and rider; 57 s. French hot-air balloon and flown cover; 57 s. Samuel Morse and telegraph key; 57 s. Early British mail van and pillar box; 57 s. Unloading De Havilland D.H.4.M mail biplane; 57 s. *Queen Mary* (liner) and Airship LZ-127 *Graf Zeppelin* flown cover; 57 s. Westland Dragonfly helicopter and mail van; 57 s. Computer and fax machine; 57 s. "Apollo 11" emblem and space cover; 57 s. U.P.U. Monument and space shuttle .. .. 22·00 24·00
No. **MS**1063 exists overprinted on the reverse as described below Nos. 985/8.

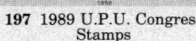
197 1989 U.P.U. Congress Stamps

198 Boxing

1989 (17 Nov). *"World Stamp Expo '89" International Stamp Exhibition, Washington.* P 14.
1064	**197** 57 s. multicoloured	1·75	1·50

No. 1064 exists overprinted on the reverse as described below Nos. 985/8.

1990 (14 Feb). *14th Commonwealth Games, Auckland.* T **198** *and similar vert designs. Multicoloured.* P 14.
1065	42 s. Type **198**	90	70
1066	57 s. Archery	1·50	1·10
1067	1 p. Bowls	2·00	2·50
1068	2 p. Swimming	3·50	4·50
1065/8	*Set of 4*	7·00	8·00

199 Wave Power Installation

200 Penny Black

1990 (11 Apr). *Alternative Sources of Electricity.* T **199** *and similar vert designs. Multicoloured.* P 14.
1069	32 s. Type **199**	1·00	65
1070	57 s. Wind farm	1·50	1·10
1071	1 p. 20, Experimental solar cell vehicle	3·00	4·75
1069/71	*Set of 3*	5·00	6·00

MS1072 110×90 mm. 2 p. 50, Planet Earth .. 7·00 8·00

1990 (1 May). *150th Anniv of the Penny Black.* T **200** *and similar horiz designs showing stamps.* P 14.
1073	42 s. multicoloured	1·25	1·25
	a. Horiz pair. Nos. 1073/4	2·50	2·50
1074	42 s. multicoloured	1·25	1·25
1075	57 s. scarlet and black	1·50	1·25
1076	1 p. 50, multicoloured	3·50	4·00
1077	2 p. 50, multicoloured	5·00	5·50
1073/7	*Set of 5*	11·00	12·00

Designs:—42 s. (No. 1074) Great Britain 1840 Twopence Blue; 57 s. Tonga 1886 1d.; 1 p. 50, 1980 South Pacific Scout Jamboree and Rotary 75th anniv 2 p. official stamp; 2 p. 50, 1990 Alternative Sources of Electricity 57 s.
Nos. 1073/4 were printed together, *se-tenant*, in horizontal pairs throughout the sheet.
Nos. 1073/7 show a faint grey pattern similar to W **24** in the background.

201 Departure of Canoe

202 Iguana searching for Food

(Des G. Bennett)

1990 (6 June). *Polynesian Voyages of Discovery.* T **201** *and similar vert designs.* P 14½.
1078	32 s. deep blue-green	75	65
1079	42 s. deep dull blue	1·00	80
1080	1 p. 20, reddish brown	2·75	3·00
1081	3 p. deep reddish violet	5·50	8·00
1078/81	*Set of 4*	9·00	11·00

Designs:—42 s. Navigating by night; 1 p. 20, Canoe and sea birds; 3 p. Landfall.

1990 (4 July). *Silver Jubilee of King Taufa'ahau Tupou IV. Designs as Nos. 985/8, but inscribed "Silver Jubilee of His Majesty King Taufa'ahau Tupou IV. 1965–1990" and with "TONGA" and values in silver.* P 11½.
1082	32 s. As Type **184**	1·00	70
1083	42 s. Banknote, coins, Ha'amonga Trilithon and woodcarver	1·10	75
1084	57 s. Rowing, communications satellite and Red Cross worker	1·40	85
1085	2 p. 50, Scout emblem, 1982 47 s. Scout stamp and Friendly Island Airways De Havilland D.H.C.6 Twin Otter aircraft	5·00	7·00
1082/5	*Set of 4*	7·75	8·50

1990 (6 July)–92. *Designs as Nos. 1000, 1002, 1003 (value changed), 1005 and 1008 redrawn smaller,* 19×22 *mm. Multicoloured. Chalk-surfaced paper.* P 14.
1087	2 s. *Porites sp*	40	50
	a. Booklet pane. No. 1087×10 (4.9.90)	3·50	
1089	5 s. Green Map Cowrie (*Cypraea mappa viridis*)	40	50
	a. Booklet pane. No. 1089×10 (4.9.90)	3·50	
1092	10 s. Bubble Cone (*Conus bullatus*)	40	50
	a. Booklet pane. No. 1092×10 (4.9.90)	3·50	
1093	15 s. *Dardanus megistos* (crab) (as No. 1003) (12.5.92)	80	60
1095	32 s. Powder-blue Surgeonfish	40	50
	a. Booklet pane. No. 1095×10 (4.9.90)	3·50	
1087/95	*Set of 5*	2·25	2·50

The outer edges of booklet panes Nos. 1087a, 1089a, 1092a, 1095a are imperforate so that stamps from them have one or two adjacent sides imperforate.
Imprint dates: "1990", Nos. 1087, 1089, 1092, 1095; "1992", Nos. 1087, 1089, 1092/3.

(Des G. Drummond)

1990 (12 Sept). *Endangered Species. Banded Iguana.* T **202** *and similar horiz designs. Multicoloured.* P 14.
1105	32 s. Type **202**	1·50	75
1106	42 s. Head of male	1·75	85
1107	57 s. Pair of iguanas during courtship	2·25	1·25
1108	1 p. 20, Iguana basking	5·00	6·50
1105/8	*Set of 4*	9·50	8·50

203 Tourism

204 Boy

(Des A. Benjamin and R. Edge)

1990 (25 Oct). *40th Anniv of United Nations Development Programme.* T **203** *and similar horiz designs. Multicoloured.* P 13½×14.
1109	57 s. Type **203**	1·25	1·50
	a. Pair. Nos. 1109/10	2·50	3·00
1110	57 s. Agriculture and Fisheries	1·25	1·50

1111	3 p. Education		6·00	7·50
	a. Pair. Nos. 1111/12		12·00	15·00
1112	3 p. Healthcare		6·00	7·50
1109/12		Set of 4	13·00	16·00

The two designs for each value were printed together, se-tenant, in horizontal and vertical pairs throughout the sheets.

1990 (28 Nov). *Christmas. Rotary International Interact Project. T 204 and similar vert designs. Multicoloured. P 14.*

1113	32 s. Type 204		70	40
1114	42 s. Young boys		90	55
1115	2 p. Girls in western clothes		3·50	4·25
1116	3 p. Girls in traditional costumes		4·50	5·50
1113/16		Set of 4	8·75	9·50

205 Safety at Work   206 Yacht at Dawn

(Des C. Abbott)

1991 (10 Apr–11 Aug). *Accident Prevention. T 205 and similar vert designs. Multicoloured. P 14½×14.*

1117	32 s. Type 205 (English inscription)		80	80
	a. Horiz pair. Nos. 1117/18		1·60	1·60
1118	32 s. Safety at home (English inscription)		80	80
1119	32 s. As No. 1118 (Tongan inscription)		80	80
	a. Horiz pair. Nos. 1119/20		1·60	1·60
	b. Horiz pair. Nos. 1119/20a (11 Aug)		18·00	18·00
1120	32 s. As Type 205 (Tongan inscription)		80	80
	a. Tongan inscription corrected to "Ngaue tokanga" (11 Aug)		18·00	18·00
1121	42 s. Safety in cars (English inscription)		1·25	1·25
	a. Horiz pair. Nos. 1121/2		2·50	2·50
1122	42 s. Safety on bikes (English inscription)		1·25	1·25
1123	42 s. As No. 1122 (Tongan inscription)		1·25	1·25
	a. Horiz pair. Nos. 1123/4		2·50	2·50
1124	42 s. As No. 1121 (Tongan inscription)		1·25	1·25
1125	57 s. Safety at sea (English inscription)		1·50	1·50
	a. Horiz pair. Nos. 1125/6		3·00	3·00
1126	57 s. Safety on the beach (English inscription)		1·50	1·50
1127	57 s. As No. 1126 (Tongan inscription)		1·50	1·50
	a. Horiz pair. Nos. 1127/8		3·00	3·00
1128	57 s. As No. 1125 (Tongan inscription)		1·50	1·50
1117/28		Set of 12	13·00	13·00

Nos. 1117/28 were printed in sheets of 20, two panes (2×5) separated by a vertical gutter, for each value with the left-hand panes containing se-tenant horizontal pairs of the designs with English inscriptions and the right-hand panes similar pairs inscribed in Tongan.

No. 1120 is incorrectly inscribed in Tongan "Ngauo tokanga".

(Des D. Miller)

1991 (2 July). *Around the World Yacht Race. Sheet 120×103 mm containing T 206 and similar vert designs. Multicoloured. P 14½×14.*

MS1129 1 p. Type 206; 1 p. Yacht in the morning; 1 p. Yacht at midday; 1 p. Yacht at night .. 6·75 7·50

207 Fishes in the Sea   208 Tonga Temple

(Des D. Miller)

1991 (2 July). *Heilala Week. T 207 and similar vert designs. Multicoloured. P 14½×14.*

1130	42 s. Type 207		70	55
1131	57 s. Island and yacht		90	65
1132	2 p. Pile of fruit		2·75	3·50
1133	3 p. Turtle on beach		3·50	4·00
1130/3		Set of 4	7·00	8·00

(Des R. Edge)

1991 (19 Aug). *Centenary of Church of Latter Day Saints in Tonga. T 208 and similar vert design. Multicoloured. P 14½.*

1134	42 s. Type 208		1·10	1·10
1135	57 s. Temple at night		1·40	1·40

209 Making T.V. Childcare Programme

(Des R. Edge)

1991 (15 Oct). *Telecommunications in Tonga. T 209 and similar horiz designs. Multicoloured. P 14½.*

1136	15 s. Type 209		35	35
	a. Horiz strip of 3. Nos. 1136/8		95	
1137	15 s. T.V. satellite		35	35
1138	15 s. Mothers watching programme		35	35
1139	32 s. Man on telephone and woman with computer		65	65
	a. Horiz strip of 3. Nos. 1139/41		1·75	
1140	32 s. Telecommunications satellite		65	65
1141	32 s. Overseas customer on telephone		65	65
1142	42 s. Sinking coaster		1·10	1·10
	a. Horiz strip of 3. Nos. 1142/4		3·00	
1143	42 s. Coastguard controller		1·10	1·10
1144	42 s. Maritime rescue		1·10	1·10
1145	57 s. Weather satellite above Southern Hemisphere		1·25	1·25
	a. Horiz strip of 3. Nos. 1145/7		3·25	
1146	57 s. Meteorologist collecting data		1·25	1·25
1147	57 s. T.V. weather map and storm		1·25	1·25
1136/47		Set of 12	9·00	9·00

The three designs for each value were printed together, se-tenant, in horizontal strips of three throughout the sheets.

210 Women's Rowing Eight

(Des D. Miller)

1991 (29 Oct). *"Siu'a'alo" Rowing Festival. T 210 and similar horiz designs. Multicoloured. P 14.*

1148	42 s. Type 210		85	45
1149	57 s. Longboat		1·00	55
1150	1 p. Outrigger canoe		2·00	2·00
1151	2 p. Stern of fautasi (large canoe)		3·25	4·00
	a. Horiz pair. No. 1152/3		6·50	8·00
1152	2 p. Bow of fautasi		3·25	4·00
1148/52		Set of 5	9·25	10·00

Nos. 1151/2 were printed together, se-tenant, in horizontal pairs throughout the sheet, forming a composite design

211 Turtles pulling Santa's Sledge   212 Pangai (patrol boat)

1991 (11 Nov). *Christmas. T 211 and similar horiz designs. Multicoloured. P 14.*

1153	32 s. Type 211		85	35
1154	42 s. Santa Claus on roof of fala (Tongan house)		95	45
1155	57 s. Family opening presents		1·10	60
1156	3 p. 50, Family waving goodbye to Santa		6·50	8·50
1153/6		Set of 4	8·50	9·00

(Des R. Edge)

1991 (15 Dec). *Royal Tongan Defence Force. T 212 and similar multicoloured designs. P 14.*

1157	42 s. Type 212		1·00	1·00
	a. Horiz pair. Nos. 1157/8		2·00	2·00
1158	42 s. Marine in battle dress		1·00	1·00
1159	57 s. Tonga Royal Guards		1·25	1·25
	a. Horiz pair. Nos. 1159/60		2·50	2·50
1160	57 s. Raising the ensign on Neiafu (patrol boat)		1·25	1·25
1161	2 p. Savea (patrol boat) (horiz)		3·00	3·50
	a. Horiz pair. Nos. 1161/2		6·00	7·00
1162	2 p. King Taufa'ahau Tupou IV inspecting parade (horiz)		3·00	3·50
1157/62		Set of 6	9·50	10·50

The two designs for each value were printed together, se-tenant, in horizontal pairs throughout the sheets.

XXX

 1s

(213)

214 Columbus and Signature

1992 (19 Mar). *No. 1007 surch with T 213.*

1163	1 s. on 20 s. White-tailed Dascyllus		55	55

(Des R. Edge)

1992 (28 Apr). *500th Anniv of Discovery of America by Columbus. Sheet 119×109 mm containing T 214 and similar vert designs. Multicoloured. P 13½.*

MS1164 57 s. Type 214; 57 s. Monastery of Santa Maria de la Chevas; 57 s. Obverse and reverse of coin of Ferdinand and Isabella; 57 s. Spain commemorative stamps of 1930; 57 s. Compass and astrolabe; 57 s. Model of Santa Maria; 57 s. Sketch map and signature; 57 s. 15th-century woodcut of Columbus arriving in New World; 57 s. Lucayan artefacts and parrot; 57 s. Pineapple, bird pendant and Indian nose ring; 57 s. Columbus reporting to Spanish Court; 57 s. Medal showing Columbus and signature .. 19·00 21·00

215 U.S.S. Arizona under attack, Pearl Harbor, 1941   216 Boxing

(Des R. Edge)

1992 (26 May). *50th Anniv of Outbreak of Pacific War. T 215 and similar horiz designs. Multicoloured. P 14.*

1165	42 s. Type 215		1·25	1·25
	a. Sheetlet. Nos. 1165/76		13·00	
1166	42 s. Japanese invasion of the Philippines		1·25	1·25
1167	42 s. U.S. landings in the Gilbert Islands		1·25	1·25
1168	42 s. Landing on Iwo Jima		1·25	1·25
1169	42 s. Admiral Nimitz and Battle of Midway map		1·25	1·25
1170	42 s. General MacArthur and liberation of Philippines map		1·25	1·25
1171	42 s. Lt-Gen. Holland Smith and map of landings on Saipan and Tinian		1·25	1·25
1172	42 s. Major-Gen. Curtis Lemay and bombing of Japan map		1·25	1·25
1173	42 s. Japanese Mitsubishi A6M Zero-Sen		1·25	1·25
1174	42 s. Douglas SBD Dauntless		1·25	1·25
1175	42 s. Grumman FM-2 Wildcat		1·25	1·25
1176	42 s. Supermarine Seafire Mk III		1·25	1·25
1165/76		Set of 12	13·00	13·00

Nos. 1165/76 were printed together, se-tenant, in sheetlets of 12 (4×3) on which the top row formed a composite design.

(Des J. Smith)

1992 (16 June). *Olympic Games, Barcelona. T 216 and similar vert designs. Multicoloured. P 14.*

1177	42 s. Type 216		75	50
1178	57 s. Diving		95	55
1179	1 p. 50, Tennis		4·00	4·25
1180	3 p. Cycling		6·00	6·50
1177/80		Set of 4	10·50	10·50

217 King Taufa'ahau Tupou IV and Queen Halaevalu   45s (218)

(Des R. Edge)

1992 (4 July). *25th Anniv of the Coronation of King Tupou IV. T 217 and similar horiz designs. P 13½×13 (45 s.) or 12 (others).*

1181	45 s. multicoloured		75	45
1182	80 s. multicoloured		1·50	1·75
	a. Horiz strip of 3. Nos. 1182/4		4·00	
1183	80 s. black and cinnamon		1·50	1·75
1184	80 s. multicoloured		1·50	1·75
1185	2 p. multicoloured		3·50	4·00
1181/5		Set of 5	8·00	8·75

Designs: (48×35 mm)—No. 1182, King Tupou IV and Crown; No. 1183, Extract from Investiture ceremony; No. 1184, King Tupou IV and 1967 Coronation 2 p. commemorative; No. 1185, As Type 217, but larger.

Nos. 1181/5 show the King's first name incorrectly spelt as "Tauf'ahau".

Nos. 1182/4 were printed together, se-tenant, in horizontal strips of 3 throughout the sheet.

1992 (11 Aug). *No. 1095 surch with T 218.*

1186	45 s. on 32 s. Powder-blue Surgeonfish		2·75	1·50

MINIMUM PRICE

The minimum price quote is 10p which represents a handling charge rather than a basis for valuing common stamps. For further notes about prices see introductory pages.

60
(219)

220 Bats flying Home

1992 (11 Aug). *Nos. 1121/4 surch with T 219 in black on red.*
1187 60 s. on 42 s. Safety in cars (English
            inscription) .. .. .. 2·25 2·50
     a. Horiz pair. Nos. 1187/8 .. 4·50 5·00
1188 60 s. on 42 s. Safety on bikes (English
            inscription) .. .. .. 2·25 2·50
1189 60 s. on 42 s. As No. 1187 (Tongan inscr) 2·25 2·50
     a. Horiz pair. Nos. 1189/90 .. 4·50 5·00
1190 60 s. on 42 s. As No. 1188 (Tongan inscr) 2·25 2·50
1187/90 .. .. .. *Set of 4* 8·00 9·00
  Nos. 1187/90 differ from the unsurcharged printing by
showing the order of the stamps in each horizontal pair
reversed.

(Des G. Bennett (Nos. 1191/5), D. Miller (No. **MS**1196))

1992 (20 Oct). *Sacred Bats of Kolovai. T 220 and similar
multicoloured designs. P 14.*
1191 60 s. Type 220 .. .. 1·60 1·75
     a. Horiz strip of 5. Nos. 1191/5 .. 7·25
1192 60 s. Tongan Fruit Bat .. 1·60 1·75
1193 60 s. Bats alighting on branches .. 1·60 1·75
1194 60 s. Bats hanging from tree .. 1·60 1·75
1195 60 s. Tongan Fruit Bat in tree .. 1·60 1·75
1191/5 .. .. *Set of 5* 7·25 8·00
MS1196 96×112 mm. 45 s. Kula leaving Tonga;
45 s. Kula watching Chief's daughter dancing;
2 p. Kula between fires and Hina; 2 p. Kula
leaving Samoa with bats (*each 38×30 mm*).
P 14×14½ .. .. .. 8·50 9·50
  Nos. 1191/5 were printed together, *se-tenant,* in horizontal
strips of five throughout the sheet each strip forming a
composite design.

60
Greetings
from
TONGA

221 Tongan Pearls

222 Tonga Flag and
Rotary Emblem (25th
anniv of Rotary
International in Tonga)

1992 (10 Nov). *Christmas. T 221 and similar horiz designs.
Multicoloured. P 14.*
1197 60 s. Type 221 .. .. 70 65
1198 80 s. Reef fish 90 80
1199 2 p. Pacific orchids .. .. 4·25 5·00
1200 3 p. Red Shining Parrots from Eua .. 5·50 7·00
1197/1200 .. *Set of 4* 10·00 12·00

1992 (15 Dec). *Anniversaries and Events. T 222 and similar
horiz designs. P 14×14½.*
1201 60 s. multicoloured .. .. 1·00 65
1202 80 s. multicoloured .. .. 1·25 90
1203 1 p. 50, deep violet, pale lilac and black 2·75 3·75
1204 3 p. 50, multicoloured .. 5·50 7·00
1201/4 .. .. *Set of 4* 9·50 11·00
  Designs:—80 s. Pres. Kennedy and Peace Corps emblem (25th
anniv of Peace Corps in Tonga); 1 p. 50, F.A.O. and W.H.O.
emblems (International Conference); 3 p. 50, Globe and Rotary
Foundation emblem (75th anniv of Rotary Foundation).

223 Mother and Child

(Des G. Bennett)

1993 (26 Jan). *Family Planning. T 223 and similar vert
designs. P 14×13½.*
1205 15 s. black, new blue & mag (English inscr) 40 50
     a. Horiz pair. Nos. 1205/6 .. 80 1·00
1206 15 s. black, new blue & mag (Tongan inscr) 40 50
1207 45 s. black, greenish yellow and bright
            yellow-green (English inscr) 90 1·00
     a. Horiz pair. Nos. 1207/8 .. 1·75 2·00

1208 45 s. black, greenish yellow and bright
            yellow-green (Tongan inscr) 90 1·00
1209 60 s. black, dull vermilion and chrome-
            yellow (English inscr) .. 1·90 2·00
     a. Horiz pair. Nos. 1209/10 .. 3·75 4·00
1210 60 s. black, dull vermilion and chrome-
            yellow (Tongan inscr) .. 1·90 2·00
1211 2 p. black, greenish yellow and red-orange
            (English inscr) .. .. 4·00 4·50
     a. Horiz pair. Nos. 1211/12 .. 8·00 9·00
1212 2 p. black, greenish yellow and red-orange
            (Tongan inscr) .. .. 4·00 4·50
1205/12 .. .. *Set of 8* 13·00 14·50
  Designs:—45 s. Child on bike; 60 s. Girl with cats; 2 p. Old
man and boy playing chess.
  The two designs for each value were printed in horizontal
se-tenant pairs throughout the sheets with those on the right
inscribed in Tongan and those on the left, which have the
designs reversed, in English.

224 Anti-smoking and Anti-drugs Symbols with Healthy Food

(Des D. Miller)

1993 (16 Mar). *Health and Fitness Campaign. T 224 and
similar horiz designs. Multicoloured. P 14.*
1213 60 s. Type 224 .. .. 1·25 90
1214 80 s. Anti-smoking symbol and weight
            training .. .. 1·60 1·10
1215 1 p. 50, Anti-drugs symbol and water
            sports .. .. 2·75 3·50
1216 2 p. 50, Healthy food with cyclist and
            jogger .. .. 5·00 6·00
1213/16 .. .. *Set of 4* 9·50 10·50

xx

10s
(225)

TONGA 1s

226 Chaste Mitre
(*Scabricola casta*)

1993 (29 Mar). *Nos. 1001 and 1087 surch as T 225 in blue by
Govt Printer.*
1217 10 s. on 2 s. *Porites* sp .. .. 50·00 15·00
1217a 20 s. on 4 s. Lionfish £400

I

II

Two types of 10, 20, 45, 60 and 80 s.:

Type I. Diffuse central oval extends to top perforations.
         Dated "1993".
Type II. Central design and oval with sharper outlines well
         clear of the perforations. Some in different shades.
         Dated "1995".

1993 (12 May)–**95**. *Multicoloured designs as Nos. 867, 872,
875, 877, 999, 1002, 1005, 1007, 1013, 1015/16 and 1017a,
some with new face values, redrawn as in T 226 with species
inscr at foot. Chalk-surfaced paper. P 13 (1, 5, 45, 60 s.) or 14
(others).*
1218 1 s. Type 226 .. .. 20 30
1219 3 s. Red Squirrelfish 30 40

1220 5 s. Green Map Cowrie (*Cypraea mappa
            viridis*) 30 30
1221 10 s. Bubble Cone (*Conus bullatus*) (I) (grey
            background) 65 65
     a. Type II (sage-green background)
        (25.9.95) 30 30
1223 20 s. White-tailed Dascyllus (I) (sage-green
            background) 85 85
     a. Type II (yell-ol background) (25.9.95) 50 50
1225 45 s. Giant Spider Conch (*Lambis truncata*)
            (as No. 877) (I) .. 1·25 90
     a. Perf 14. Type II (25.9.95) .. 60 60
1227 60 s. Princely Cone (*Conus aulicus*) (as No.
            875) (I) .. .. 1·75 1·75
     a. Perf 14. Type II (25.9.95) .. 80 80
1229 80 s. Lionfish (as No. 872) (I) .. 1·75 1·75
     a. Type II (25.9.95) .. 1·00 1·00
1230 1 p. *Chelonia mydas* (turtle) (21.6.94) 1·00 1·00
1231 2 p. *Birgus latro* (crab) (21.6.94) 1·75 2·00
1232 3 p. Rose-branch Murex (*Chicoreus palma
            rosae*) (21.6.94) .. 2·50 3·00
1233 5 p. Humpback Whale (as No. 1014)
            (21.9.94) .. .. 5·00 6·00
1234 10 p. Variegated Shark (18.1.95) .. 12·00 13·00
1218/34 .. .. *Set of 13* 24·00 26·00
  Nos. 1218/29 are 19×22 mm, Nos. 1230/3 40×28 mm and No.
1234 28×40 mm.
  Imprint dates: "1993", Nos. 1218/29; "1994", Nos. 1230/3;
"1995", Nos. 1221a, 1223a, 1225a, 1227a, 1229a, 1234.
  Nos. 1233/4 were each issued in sheets of 10 stamps and two
stamp-sized labels in the centre of the sheets.
  For 1 p. to 10 p. redrawn with species inscriptions at top left
see Nos. 1345/9.

227 Fire Brigade Badge

228 Old Map of
Islands

(Des D. Miller)

1993 (18 May). *25th Anniv of Police Training College and
Fire Service. T 227 and similar horiz designs. Multicoloured.
P 14.*
1235 45 s. Type 227 .. .. 1·50 1·75
     a. Horiz pair. Nos. 1235/6 .. 3·00 3·50
1236 45 s. Police badge and van .. 1·50 1·75
1237 60 s. Police band .. .. 1·75 2·00
     a. Horiz pair. Nos. 1237/8 .. 3·50 4·00
1238 60 s. Fire engine at fire .. 1·75 2·00
1239 2 p. Fire engine at station .. 4·00 5·00
     a. Horiz pair. Nos. 1239/40 .. 8·00 10·00
1240 2 p. Policeman and dog handler .. 4·00 5·00
1235/40 .. .. *Set of 6* 13·00 16·00
  The two designs for each value were printed together, *se-
tenant,* in horizontal pairs throughout the sheets.

(Des G. Bennett)

1993 (21 June). *350th Anniv of Abel Tasman's Discovery of
Eua. T 228 and similar vert designs. Multicoloured.
P 14×13½.*
1241 30 s. Type 228 .. .. 80 55
1242 60 s. *Heemskirk* and *Zeehaan* at sea .. 1·25 85
1243 80 s. Tongan canoes welcoming ships .. 1·60 1·25
1244 3 p. 50, Tasman landing on Eua .. 6·00 8·00
1241/4 .. .. *Set of 4* 8·75 9·50

TONGA 45

229 King
Taufa'ahau Tupou
IV and Musical
Instruments

230 Christmas
Feast

(Des D. Miller)

1993 (1 July). *75th Birthday of King Taufa'ahau Tupou IV.
T 229 and similar vert designs. Multicoloured. P 13×13½
(45 s.) or 12 (others).*
1245 45 s. Type 229 .. .. 60 45
1246 80 s. King Tupou IV and sporting events
            (38½ × 51 mm) .. 1·00 1·40
     a. Strip of 3. Nos. 1246/8 .. 2·75
1247 80 s. King Tupou IV and ancient
            landmarks (38½ × 51 mm) .. 1·00 1·40
1248 80 s. King Tupou IV and Royal Palace
            (38½ × 51 mm) .. 1·00 1·40
1249 2 p. As Type 229, but larger (38½ × 51
            mm) .. .. 2·50 3·25
1245/9 .. .. *Set of 5* 5·50 7·00
  Nos. 1246/8 were printed together, *se-tenant,* in horizontal
and vertical strips of 3 throughout the sheet of 9.

(Des G. Bennett)

1993 (10 Nov). *Christmas. T 230 and similar vert designs. Multicoloured. P 14.*
1250   60 s. Type **230** 90   60
1251   80 s. Firing home-made cannon .. 1.25   1.25
1252   1 p. 50, Band playing carols .. 2.50   3.25
1253   3 p. Going to church 5.00   6.00
1250/3   .. .. *Set of 4* 8.75   9.50

231 "Land of Sun, Sea and Sand" (Kiley and Peter Moala)

232 Boy holding Cockerel

1993 (1 Dec). *Winners of Children's Painting Competition. T 231 and similar vert designs. P 14.*
1254   **231**   10 s. multicoloured 30   50
    a. Horiz strip of 6. Nos. 1254/9 .. 1.60
1255   —   10 s. multicoloured 30   50
1256   —   10 s. multicoloured 30   50
1257   —   10 s. multicoloured 30   50
1258   —   10 s. black and grey-black .. 30   50
1259   —   10 s. black and grey-black .. 30   50
1260   **231**   80 s. multicoloured 1.40   1.60
    a. Horiz strip of 6. Nos. 1260/5 .. 7.50
1261   —   80 s. multicoloured 1.40   1.60
1262   —   80 s. multicoloured 1.40   1.60
1263   —   80 s. multicoloured 1.40   1.60
1264   —   80 s. multicoloured 1.40   1.60
1265   —   80 s. multicoloured 1.40   1.60
1254/65   .. .. *Set of 12* 9.00   11.00
Designs:—Nos. 1255 and 1261, "Maui, Fisher God of Tonga" (Kiley and Peter Moala); Nos. 1256 and 1262, "Traditional Island Transport" (Kiley and Peter Moala); Nos. 1257 and 1263, "Young Girl making Kava" (Pulotu Pole'o); Nos. 1258 and 1264, "Maui and his Hook" (Salome Tapou); Nos. 1259 and 1265, "Communications in the South Pacific" (Fe'ofa'aki Taufa).
Nos. 1254/9 and 1260/5 were each printed in sheetlets of 12, of one value, each sheetlet containing two *se-tenant* strips of six.

(Des G. Bennett)

1994 (14 Jan). *Animal Welfare. Sheet, 122×100 mm, containing T 232 and similar vert designs. Multicoloured. P 14½.*
MS1266   60 s. Type **232**; 60 s. Girl with butterfly; 60 s. Dog and puppies; 60 s. Boy with puppy; 80 s. Boy holding puppy; 80 s. Girl holding cat   6.00   7.00

233 Tiger Shark

(Des G. Bennett)

1994 (28 Feb). *Game Fishing. T 233 and similar horiz designs. Multicoloured. P 12½×12.*
1267   60 s. Type **233** 1.10   85
1268   80 s. Dolphin (fish) 1.50   1.10
1269   1 p. 50, Yellow-finned Tuna .. 2.75   3.50
1270   2 p. 50, Blue Marlin 3.50   4.50
1267/70   .. .. *Set of 4* 8.00   9.00

234 Hands holding World Cup

235 Policewoman

(Des D. Miller)

1994 (1 June). *World Cup Football Championship, U.S.A. T 234 and similar horiz designs. Multicoloured. P 14×14½.*
1271   80 s. Type **234** 1.50   1.50
    a. Pair. Nos. 1271/2 .. .. 3.00   3.00
1272   80 s. Player's legs 1.50   1.50
1273   2 p. German player (black shorts) .. 3.25   4.00
    a. Pair. Nos. 1273/4 .. .. 6.50   8.00
1274   2 p. American player 3.25   4.00
1271/4   .. .. *Set of 4* 8.50   10.00
Nos. 1271/2 and 1273/4 were printed together, *se-tenant*, in horizontal and vertical pairs throughout the sheets.

(Des D. Miller)

1994 (18 Aug). *Pan Pacific and South East Asia Women's Association Conference, Tonga. T 235 and similar vert designs. Multicoloured. P 14½.*
1275   45 s. Type **235** 1.50   1.50
    a. Pair. Nos. 1275/6 .. .. 3.00   3.00
1276   45 s. Woman barrister 1.50   1.50
1277   2 p. 50, Nurse 4.25   4.75
    a. Pair. Nos. 1277/8 .. .. 8.50   9.50
1278   2 p. 50, Woman doctor 4.25   4.75
1275/8   .. .. *Set of 4* 10.50   11.50
Nos. 1275/6 and 1277/8 were each printed together, *se-tenant*, in horizontal and vertical pairs throughout the sheets.

MERRY CHRISTMAS

(236)   (237)

1994 (10 Nov). *Christmas. No. MS1266 optd with T 236 or equivalent in Tongan.*
MS1279   60 s. Type **232**; 60 s. Girl with butterfly; 60 s. Dog and puppies; 60 s. Boy with puppy; 80 s. Boy holding puppy; 80 s. Girl holding cat   5.00   5.50
T **236** appears on five of the stamps from the miniature sheet. The 60 s. in the centre of the bottom row (dog and puppies) is overprinted "KILISIMASI FIEFIA".

1994 (17 Nov). *Visit South Pacific Year '95 (1st issue). No. 1204 surch with T 237 in blue.*
1280   60 s. on 3 p. 50, multicoloured .. 1.25   1.25
See also Nos. 1297/1308.

1994 (14 Dec). *25th Anniv of Tongan Self-adhesive Stamps.*
    (a) *Various previous self-adhesive designs, some in smaller size, with new values.* (i) *Postage*
1281   **128**   10 s. black & greenish yell (21×9 mm)   20   30
    a. Booklet pane. Nos. 1281×12 and 1284×3 .. .. .. 5.00
1282   **124**   60 s. black, grey and red-brown .. 1.40   1.75
    a. Booklet pane. Nos. 1282/3 and O243 .. .. .. 5.00
1283   —   60 s. multicoloured (as Nos. O214/15) 1.40   1.75
    (ii) *Air*
1284   **109**   25 s. multicoloured (27×36 mm) .. 1.00   1.25
    (b) *As Nos. 915A/18A, but new face value and inscr "SELF-ADHESIVE ANNIVERSARY 1969–1994"*
1285   **168**   45 s. black, salmon-pink & reddish brn   75   85
    a. Booklet pane. Nos. 1285/6 each × 3, 1287×2 and 1288 .. 5.00
1286   —   45 s. black, pale-rose lilac and reddish brown (as No. 916A) .. 75   85
1287   —   45 s. black, olive-yellow and reddish brown (as No. 917A) .. 1.25   1.50
1288   —   45 s. multicoloured (as No. 918A) .. 2.75   3.25
    (c) *Hologram design, 39×29 mm, showing Tongastar 1 satellite*
1289   —   2 p. multicoloured 5.00   6.00
    a. Booklet pane of 1 .. .. 5.00
1281/9   .. .. *Set of 9* 13.00   16.00
Nos. 1281/9 and O243 were only available from 10 p. self-adhesive booklets.

238 Farmer, Produce and Emblem

(Des K. McGee)

1995 (16 May). *50th Anniv of Food and Agriculture Organization. P 14.*
1290   **238**   5 p. multicoloured 7.00   8.00

239 Polynesian Girl with Bicycle on Beach

240 Three Players running with Ball

(Des K. McGee)

1995 (6 June). *25th Anniv of Tonga's Entry into Commonwealth. Children with Bicycles. T 239 and similar horiz designs. Multicoloured. P 14.*
1291   45 s. Type **239** 75   55
1292   60 s. Children and skyscrapers, Hong Kong   90   60
1293   80 s. Boy in African village 1.25   80
1294   2 p. Indian boy and palace .. 2.75   3.75
1295   2 p. 50, English children and village church 3.25   4.00
1291/5   .. .. *Set of 5* 8.00   8.75

(Des G. Bennett)

1995 (20 June). *World Cup Rugby Championship, South Africa. Two sheets, each 84×117 mm, containing T 240 and similar vert designs. P 14½.*
MS1296   (a) 80 s. × 2 Type **240**; 80 s. × 2 Two players running with ball. (b) 2 p. × 2 Player making pass; 2 p. × 2 Player receiving pass
    Set of 2 sheets 15.00   16.00
The miniature sheets contain two of each design.

WHERE TIME BEGINS

(241)

1995 (30 June). *Visit South Pacific Year '95 (2nd issue).*
    (a) *Nos. 1149/52 optd or surch as T 241, but inscr "VISIT SOUTH PACIFIC YEAR '95"*
1297   60 s. on 57 s. Longboat 75   60
1298   80 s. on 2 p. Stern of fautasi (large canoe)   1.00   1.50
    a. Horiz pair. Nos. 1298/9 .. 2.00   3.00
1299   80 s. on 2 p. Bow of fautasi .. 1.00   1.50
1300   1 p. Outrigger canoe 1.40   1.75
1297/1300   .. .. .. *Set of 4* 3.75   4.50
    (b) *Nos. 1197/1200 surch as T 241 inscr either (A) "WHERE TIME BEGINS" or (B) "THE 21st CENTURY STARTS HERE"*
1301   60 s. on 60 s. Type **221** (A) .. 75   1.00
    a. Horiz pair. Nos. 1301/2 .. 1.50   2.00
1302   60 s. on 60 s. Type **221** (B) .. 75   1.00
1303   60 s. on 80 s. Reef Fish (A) .. 75   1.00
    a. Horiz pair. Nos. 1303/4 .. 1.50   2.00
1304   60 s. on 80 s. Reef Fish (B) .. 75   1.00
1305   60 s. on 2 p. Pacific orchids (A) .. 75   1.00
    a. Horiz pair. Nos. 1305/6 .. 1.50   2.00
1306   60 s. on 2 p. Pacific orchids (B) .. 75   1.00
1307   60 s. on 3 p. Red Shining Parrots from Eua (A) 75   1.00
    a. Horiz pair. Nos. 1307/8 .. 1.50   2.00
1308   60 s. on 3 p. Red Shining Parrots from Eua (B) 75   1.00
1301/8   .. .. *Set of 8* 5.50   7.00
Nos. 1298/9, 1301/2, 1303/4, 1305/6 and 1307/8 were each printed together, *se-tenant*, in horizontal pairs throughout the sheets.

242 Soldier on Scrambling Net

243 1995 Commonwealth Stamp and Exhibition Emblem

(Des D. Miller)

1995 (1 Aug). *50th Anniv of End of Second World War in the Pacific. T 242 and similar vert designs. P 14½.*
1309   **242**   60 s. greenish yellow, black & new blue 1.25   1.25
    a. Sheetlet. Nos. 1309/18 .. 11.00
1310   —   60 s. greenish yellow, black & new blue 1.25   1.25
1311   —   60 s. greenish yellow, black & new blue 1.25   1.25
1312   —   60 s. multicoloured 1.25   1.25
1313   —   60 s. multicoloured 1.25   1.25
1314   **242**   80 s. greenish yellow, black and rosine 1.25   1.25
1315   —   80 s. greenish yellow, black and rosine 1.25   1.25
1316   —   80 s. greenish yellow, black and rosine 1.25   1.25
1317   —   80 s. multicoloured 1.25   1.25
1318   —   80 s. multicoloured 1.25   1.25
1309/18   .. .. .. *Set of 10* 11.00   11.00
Designs:—Nos. 1310 and 1315, U.S.S. *Nevada* (battleship) with troops in foreground; Nos. 1311 and 1316 U.S.S. *West Virginia* (battleship) and rear of landing craft; Nos. 1312 and 1317, U.S.S. *Idaho* (battleship) and front of landing craft; Nos. 1313 and 1318, Map of South-east Asia and Pacific.
Nos. 1309/18 were printed together, *se-tenant*, in sheetlets of 10 with the horizontal strips of 5 forming the same composite design.

(Des K. McGee)

1995 (1 Sept). *"Singapore '95" International Stamp Exhibition.*
T 243 and similar horiz designs. Multicoloured. P 12.
1319   45 s. Type 243 .. .. .. 1·00 1·25
    a. Horiz pair. Nos. 1319/20 .. 2·00 2·50
1320   60 s. 1995 Commonwealth 60 s. stamp and
    emblem .. .. .. 1·00 1·25
MS1321 110×70 mm. 2 p. Boy on bicycle and
Singapore skyscrapers .. .. 2·75 3·25
Nos. 1319/20 were printed together, *se-tenant* horizontally, in
sheets of 10.

244 Mt Song
(Illustration reduced. Actual size 84¹/₂×51¹/₂ mm)

(Des Li Defu)

1995 (14 Sept). *Beijing International Coin and Stamp Show
'95. Sheet 143×87 mm. P 14¹/₂.*
MS1322 **244** 1 p. 40, multicoloured .. .. 2·00 2·50

245 Holocaust Victims

(Des K. McGee)

1995 (20 Oct). *50th Anniv of United Nations and End of
Second World War. T 245 and similar designs. P 13×13¹/₂.*
1323   60 s. multicoloured .. .. 1·00 1·25
    a. Horiz strip of 3. Nos. 1323/5 .. 2·75
1324   60 s. black and bright blue .. 1·00 1·25
1325   60 s. multicoloured .. .. 1·00 1·25
1326   80 s. multicoloured .. .. 1·00 1·25
    a. Horiz strip of 3. Nos. 1326/8 .. 2·75
1327   80 s. bright blue and black .. 1·00 1·25
1328   80 s. multicoloured .. .. 1·00 1·25
1323/8 .. .. .. *Set of 6* 5·50 6·50
Designs: *Horiz (as Type 245)*—No. 1323, Type 245; No. 1325,
Children of Holocaust survivors with balloons; No. 1326, Atomic
explosion, Hiroshima; No. 1328, U.S. Space Shuttle. *Vert
(23×35 mm)*—Nos. 1324 and 1327, U.N. anniversary emblem.
Nos. 1323/5 and 1326/8 were printed together, *se-tenant*, in
horizontal strips of 3 throughout the sheets.

246 *Calanthe*
triplicata

247 Humpback Whale

(Des G. Bennett)

1995 (15 Nov). *Greetings Stamps. Orchids. T 246 and similar
square designs inscribed either "MERRY CHRISTMAS" (A) or
"A HAPPY 1996" (B). Multicoloured. P 14×14¹/₂.*
1329   20 s. Type 246 (A) 50 50
1330   45 s. *Spathoglottis plicata* (A) .. 75 75
1331   45 s. As No. 1330 (B) 75 75
1332   60 s. *Dendrobium platygastrium* (A) 90 90
1333   60 s. As No. 1332 (B) 90 90
1334   80 s. *Goodyera rubicunda* (B) .. 1·25 1·25
1335   2 p. *Dendrobium toki* (A) .. 2·75 3·25
1336   2 p. 50, *Phaius tankervillae* (A) .. 3·50 4·00
1329/36 .. .. .. *Set of 8* 10·00 11·00

(Des G. Bennett)

1996 (7 Feb). *Endangered Species. Humpback Whale. T 247
and similar horiz designs. Multicoloured. P 14.*
1337   45 s. Type 247 .. .. 1·40 75
1338   60 s. Whale and calf .. .. 1·75 80
1339   1 p. 50, Whale's tail and Herald Petrels 3·25 3·75
1340   2 p. 50, Whale breaking surface .. 4·75 6·00
1337/40 .. .. .. *Set of 4* 10·00 10·00

248 Rats and Top Left Quarter
of Clock Face

249 Running

Two types of 60 s.:

60   **60**
   I   II

(Des A. Benjamin)

1996 (7 Feb–27 June). *Chinese New Year ("Year of the Rat").
Sheets, 127×85 mm, containing T 248 and similar horiz
designs showing rats and quarter segments of clock face.
Multicoloured. P 14.*
MS1341 10 s. Type 248; 10 s. Top right quarter;
10 s. Bottom left quarter; 10 s. Bottom right
quarter (27 June) .. .. 75 1·00
MS1342 20 s. Type 248; 20 s. Top right quarter;
20 s. Bottom left quarter; 20 s. Bottom right
quarter (27 June) .. .. 1·50 1·75
MS1343 45 s. Type 248; 45 s. Top right quarter;
45 s. Bottom left quarter; 45 s. Bottom right
quarter (27 June) .. .. 3·00 3·50
MS1344 60 s. Type 248 (I); 60 s. Top right
quarter (I); 60 s. Bottom left quarter (I); 60 s.
Bottom right quarter (I) .. .. 4·00 4·50
    a. Face values as Type II (27 June) .. 5·00 6·00
On Nos. **MS**1341/3 and **MS**1344a the face values were applied
by typography. They also include "Sheet Value" inscriptions at
bottom right.
For similar designs for "Year of the Ox" see No. **MS**1370

1996 (31 May). *Multicoloured designs as Nos. 1230/4, but
redrawn with species inscriptions at top left. Chalk-surfaced
paper. P 14.*
1345   1 p. *Chelonia mydas* (turtle) .. 1·50 1·50
1346   2 p. *Birgus latro* (crab) .. .. 2·50 2·50
1347   3 p. Rose Branch Murex (*Chicoreus
palma-rosae*) .. .. 3·50 3·75
1348   5 p. Humpback Whale .. .. 7·00 7·50
1349   10 p. Variegated Shark (*vert*) .. 13·00 14·00
1345/9 .. .. .. *Set of 5* 25·00 26·00
Imprint date: "1996", Nos. 1345/9.
Nos. 1348/9 were each issued in sheets of 10 stamps and 2
stamp-size labels in the centre of the sheets.

(Des D. Miller)

1996 (2 July). *Centennial Olympic Games, Atlanta. T 249 and
similar vert designs showing ancient Greek and modern
athletes. Multicoloured. P 14.*
1350   45 s. Type 249 .. .. 90 65
1351   80 s. Throwing the discus .. 1·50 1·25
1352   2 p. Throwing the javelin .. 4·00 4·50
1353   3 p. Equestrian dressage .. 5·50 6·50
1350/3 .. .. .. *Set of 4* 10·50 11·50

250 Aspects of Prehistoric Life

(Des D. Miller)

1996 (5 Sept). *13th Congress of International Union of
Prehistoric and Protohistoric Sciences, Forli, Italy. T 250 and
similar horiz design. Multicoloured. P 12.*
1354   1 p. Type 250 .. .. 1·75 2·00
    a. Horiz pair. Nos. 1354/5 .. 3·50 4·00
1355   1 p. Aspects of Egyptian, Greek and
Roman civilisations .. .. 1·75 2·00
Nos. 1354/5 were printed together, *se-tenant*, in sheetlets of 6
(2×3).

PRICES OF SETS

Set prices are given for many issues, generally
those containing three stamps or more. Definitive
sets include one of each value or major colour
change, but do not cover different perforations,
die types or minor shades. Where a choice is
possible the set prices are based on the cheapest
versions of the stamps included in the listings.

251 "Virgin and Child"
(Sassoferrato)

252 Athletics and
Rugby

(Des D. Miller)

1996 (21 Oct). *Christmas. Religious Paintings. T 251 and
similar horiz designs. Multicoloured. P 14.*
1356   20 s. Type 251 .. .. 45 45
1357   60 s. "Adoration of the Shepherds"
(Murillo) .. .. .. 1·10 75
1358   80 s. "Virgin and Child" (Delaroche) .. 1·40 1·10
1359   3 p. "Adoration of the Shepherds"
(Champaigne) .. .. 4·50 6·00
1356/9 .. .. .. *Set of 4* 6·75 7·50

(Des D. Miller)

1996 (29 Oct). *50th Anniv of U.N.I.C.E.F. Children's Sports.
T 252 and similar vert designs. Multicoloured. P 14.*
1360   80 s. Type 252 .. .. 1·40 1·60
    a. Horiz strip of 3. Nos. 1360/2 .. 3·75
1361   80 s. Tennis .. .. 1·40 1·60
1362   80 s. Cycling .. .. 1·40 1·60
1360/2 .. .. .. *Set of 3* 3·75 4·25
Nos. 1360/2 were printed together, *se-tenant*, in horizontal
strips of three throughout the sheet, each strip forming a
composite design.

253 Queen Halaevalu Mata'aho and
Flag

(Des D. Miller and K. Jones)

1996 (27 Nov). *70th Birthday of Queen Halaevalu Mata'aho.
T 253 and similar horiz designs. Multicoloured. P 12.*
1363   60 s. Type 253 .. .. 1·00 65
1364   2 p. Queen and obverse (portrait) of
commemorative coin .. .. 3·25 4·00
    a. Horiz pair. Nos. 1364/5 .. 6·50 8·00
1365   2 p. Queen and reverse (arms) of
commemorative coin .. .. 3·25 4·00
1363/5 .. .. .. *Set of 3* 6·75 8·00
Nos. 1364/5 were printed together, *se-tenant*, as horizontal
pairs in sheets of 6.

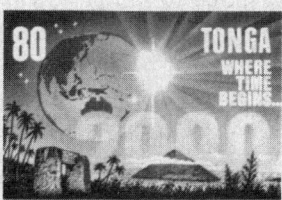

254 Globe, the Ha'amonga and Kao
Island

(Des D. Miller)

1996 (9 Dec). *"Towards the Millennium". T 254 and similar
horiz design. Multicoloured. P 12.*
1366   80 s. Type 254 .. .. 1·50 1·50
    a. Horiz pair. Nos. 1366/7 .. 3·00 3·00
1367   80 s. Mount Talau, Royal Palace and
satellite .. .. .. 1·50 1·50
1368   2 p. Type 254 .. .. 3·25 3·75
    a. Horiz pair. Nos. 1368/9 .. 6·50 7·50
1369   2 p. As No. 1367 .. .. 3·25 3·75
1366/9 .. .. .. *Set of 4* 8·50 9·50
Nos. 1366/7 and 1368/9 were printed together, *se-tenant*, as
horizontal pairs in sheets of 6.

(Des A. Benjamin)

1997 (24 Jan). *Chinese New Year ("Year of the Ox"). Sheet
126×85 mm, containing horiz designs as T 248, showing ox
and quarter segments of clock face. Multicoloured. P 14.*
MS1370 60 s. Top left quarter; 60 s. Top right
quarter; 80 s. Bottom left quarter; 2 p. Bottom
right quarter .. .. .. 5·50 6·50

(255)

10

1997 (3 Mar). *Nos. 1235/40 surch as T 255 in black by Govt Printer.*

1371	10 s. on 45 s. Type **227**	..	..	2·00	2·00
	a. Horiz pair. Nos. 1371/2	..	..	4·00	4·00
1372	10 s. on 45 s. Police badge and van	..	2·00	2·00
1373	10 s. on 60 s. Police band	..	..	2·00	2·00
	a. Horiz pair. Nos. 1373/4	..	..	4·00	4·00
1374	10 s. on 60 s. Fire engine at fire	..	2·00	2·00
1375	20 s. on 2 p. Fire engine at station	..	2·25	2·25
	a. Horiz pair. Nos. 1375/6	..	..	4·50	4·50
1376	20 s. on 2 p. Policeman and dog handler	..	2·25	2·25
1371/6			*Set of 6*	11·00	11·00

10

10

FAKAMANATU TA'U 75 'OE 'AKAPULU 'IUNIONI 'I TONGA

(256)

A SILVER FOR TONGA

(257)

1997 (24 Mar). *75th Anniv of Tongan Rugby Union No.* MS1296 *surch* (A) *as T* **256** *or* (B) *"75th ANNIVERSARY TONGA RUGBY FOOTBALL UNION" by Govt Printer.*

MS1377 Two sheets, each 84×117 mm. (a) 10 s. on 80 s. Type **240** (A); 10 s. on 80 s. Type **240** (B); 10 s. on 80 s. Two players running with ball (A); 10 s. on 80 s. Two players running with ball (B). (b) 1 p. on 2 p. Player making pass (A); 1 p. on 2 p. Player making pass (B); 1 p. on 2 p. Player receiving pass (A); 1 p. on 2 p. Player receiving pass (B) .. .. .. *Set of 2 sheets* 8·00 8·50

1997 (24 Mar). *Tongan Medal Winner at Atlanta Olympic Games. Nos. 1350/3 surch as T* **257** *or optd only* (3 p.) *by Govt Printer.*

1378	10 s. on 45 s. Type **249**	..	..	40	40
1379	10 s. on 80 s. Throwing the discus	..	40	40
1380	10 s. on 2 p. Throwing the javelin	..	40	40
1381	3 p. Equestrian dressage	..	..	3·50	4·00
1378/81			*Set of 4*	4·25	4·75

258 Captain James Wilson and *Duff* (full-rigged missionary ship)

(Des D. Miller)

1997 (28 Apr). *Birth Bicentenary of King George I and Bicentenary of Christianity in Tonga (1st issue). T* **258** *and similar horiz designs. Multicoloured. P* 14.

1382	10 s. Type **258**	..	..	1·50	1·50
	a. Sheetlet. Nos. 1382, 1383×3 and 1384/5			5·00	
1383	10 s. King George Tupou I	..	..	75	75
1384	10 s. Missionaries landing at Tongatapu	90	90
1385	10 s. Missionaries and Tongans	..	70	70
1386	60 s. Type **258**	..	..	1·00	1·00
	a. Horiz strip of 3. Nos. 1386/8	..	2·75	
1387	60 s. As No. 1384	..	..	1·00	1·00
1388	60 s. As No. 1385	..	..	1·00	1·00
1389	80 s. Type **258**	..	..	1·00	1·00
	a. Horiz strip of 3. Nos. 1389/91	..	2·75	
1390	80 s. As No. 1384	..	..	1·00	1·00
1391	80 s. As No. 1385	..	..	1·00	1·00
1382/91			*Set of 10*	9·50	9·50

Nos. 1382, 1383 x 3, and 1384/5 were printed together, *se-tenant*, in sheetlets of 6. Nos. 1386/8 and 1389/91 were each printed together, *se-tenant*, as horizontal strips of 3 in sheetlets of 9.

For 10 s. values as Nos. 1382/5, but smaller, 28×18 mm, see Nos. 1405/8.

259 Pacific Swallow

(Des D. Miller)

1997 (30 May). *"Pacific '97" International Stamp Exhibition, San Francisco. Sheet* 84×110 mm. *P* 14.

MS1392 **259** 2 p. multicoloured .. .. 2·75 3·25

---

260 Children and School Building

261 King and Queen of Tonga during Coronation

(Des D. Miller)

1997 (4 June). *50th Anniv of Tonga High School. T* **260** *and similar horiz designs. Multicoloured. P* 14.

1393	20 s. Type **260**	..	..	55	55
1394	60 s. Athletic team	..	..	1·10	75
1395	80 s. School band	..	..	1·50	1·00
1396	3 p. 50, Athletics meeting	..	4·25	6·00
1393/6			*Set of 4*	6·75	7·50

(Des D. Miller)

1997 (30 June). *King and Queen of Tonga's Golden Wedding and 30th Anniv of the Coronation. T* **261** *and similar vert designs. Multicoloured.* (a) *Size* 23×34 mm. *P* 13×13½.

1397	10 s. Type **261**	..	..	60	60
	a. Horiz strip of 3. Nos. 1397/9	..	1·60	
1398	10 s. Moment of Crowning and procession	60	60
1399	10 s. King and Queen of Tonga	..	60	60
1400	45 s. Royal Crown	..	..	1·00	75

(b) Size 50×37 mm. P 12

1401	60 s. As Type **261**	..	..	1·10	1·10
	a. Horiz strip of 3. Nos. 1401/3	..	3·00	
1402	60 s. As No. 1398	..	..	1·10	1·10
1403	60 s. As No. 1399	..	..	1·10	1·10
1404	2 p. As No. 1400	..	..	2·75	3·50
1397/1404			*Set of 8*	8·00	8·00

Nos. 1397/9 and 1400 were each printed in sheets of 9, the 10 s. as horiz *se-tenant* strips of three. Nos. 1401/3 and 1404 were in sheets of six, the 60 s. as horiz strips of three.

1997 (27 Aug). *Birth Bicentenary of King George I and Bicentenary of Christianity in Tonga (2nd issue). As Nos.* 1382/5, *but smaller,* 28×18 mm. *P* 14.

1405	10 s. Type **258**	..	..	60	60
	a. Sheetlet. Nos. 1405/7, each × 2, and 1408×6			5·00	
1406	10 s. As No. 1384	..	..	60	60
1407	10 s. As No. 1385	..	..	60	60
1408	10 s. As No. 1383	..	..	35	35
1405/8			*Set of 4*	1·90	1·90

Nos. 1405/8 were printed together, *se-tenant*, in sheetlets of 12.

262 *Lenzites elegans*

263 King Taufa'ahau Tupou IV

(Des D. Miller)

1997 (3 Oct). *Fungi. T* **262** *and similar vert designs. Multicoloured. P* 14. (a) *Size* 18 × 28 mm.

1409	10 s. Type **262**	..	..	60	60
	a. Horiz strip of 6. Nos. 1409/14	..	3·25	
1410	10 s. *Marasmiellus semiustus*	..	60	60
1411	10 s. *Aseroe rubra*	..	..	60	60
1412	10 s. *Podoscypha involuta*	..	60	60
1413	10 s. *Microporus xanthopus*	..	60	60
1414	10 s. *Lentinus tuber-regium*	..	60	60

(b) Size 28×42 mm

1415	20 s. Type **262**	..	..	1·00	1·00
	a. Horiz pair. Nos. 1415/16	..	2·00	2·00
	b. Sheetlet. Nos. 1415/20	..	9·50	
1416	20 s. As No. 1410	..	..	1·00	1·00
1417	60 s. As No. 1411	..	..	1·50	1·50
	a. Horiz pair. Nos. 1417/18	..	3·00	3·00
1418	60 s. As No. 1412	..	..	1·50	1·50
1419	2 p. As No. 1413	..	..	2·75	2·75
	a. Horiz pair. Nos. 1419/20	..	5·50	5·50
1420	2 p. As No. 1414	..	..	2·75	2·75
1409/20			*Set of 12*	12·50	12·50

Nos. 1409/14 were printed together, *se-tenant*, in horizontal strips of 6 throughout the sheet with the backgrounds forming a composite design. Nos. 1415/20 were printed in sheetlets of 6 (2×3) containing either *se-tenant* horizontal pairs of the two designs for each value or all six stamps.

(Des D. Miller. Litho Enschedé)

1998 (29 May). *Diana, Princess of Wales Commemoration. Sheet,* 145×70 mm, *containing vert designs as T* **91** *of Kiribati. Multicoloured. P* 13½×14.

MS1421 10 s. Princess Diana, 1992; 80 s. Wearing white jacket, 1992; 1 p. Wearing black jacket, 1991; 2 p. 50, Wearing white top, 1993 *(sold at* 4 p. 40 + 50 s. *charity premium)* .. 4·50 4·75

(Litho and die-stamped Southern Colour Print, Dunedin)

1998 (4 July). *80th Birthday of King Taufa'ahau Tupou IV. P* 14.

1422	**263**	2 p. 70, multicoloured	..	3·00	3·25
MS1423	80×90 mm. 2 p. 70, No. 1422; 2 p. 70, No. 276 of Niuafo'ou		..	5·00	5·50

(Des Karen Odiam. Litho Southern Colour Print, Dunedin)

1998 (23 July). *Chinese New Year ("Year of the Tiger"). Sheet,* 126×85 mm, *containing horiz designs as T* **248**, *each showing a tiger and quarter segment of clock face. Multicoloured. P* 14×14½.

MS1424 55 s. Top left quarter; 80 s. Top right quarter; 1 p. Bottom left quarter; 1 p. Bottom right quarter .. .. .. 3·25 3·50

No. MS1424 also includes the "SINGPEX '98" Stamp Exhibition, Singapore emblem on the sheet margin.

264 White Tern ("Fairy Tern")

(Des P. Martinson. Litho SNP Cambec, Melbourne)

1998 (26 Aug). *Birds. T* **264** *and similar multicoloured designs. P* 14×14½ (*vert*) *or* 14½×14 (*horiz*).

1425	5 s. Type **264**	..	..	10	10
1426	10 s. Tongan Whistler	..	..	10	10
1427	15 s. Common Barn Owl	..	..	10	15
1428	20 s. Purple Swamphen	..	..	15	20
1429	30 s. Red-footed Booby	..	..	25	30
1430	40 s. Banded Rail (*horiz*)	..	..	30	35
1431	50 s. Swamp Harrier (*horiz*)	..	40	45
1432	55 s. Blue-crowned Lorikeet	..	40	45
1433	60 s. Great Frigate Bird	..	..	45	50
1434	70 s. Friendly Ground Dove (*horiz*)	55	60
1435	80 s. Red-tailed Tropic Bird	..	60	65
1436	1 p. Red Shining Parrot	..	..	80	85
1437	2 p. Pacific Pigeon	..	..	1·60	1·75
1438	3 p. Pacific Golden Plover (*horiz*)	2·40	2·50
1439	5 p. Tongan Megapode (*horiz*)	..	4·00	4·25
1425/39			*Set of 15*	12·00	13·00

265 *Chaetodon pelewensis*

(Des Sue Wickison. Litho Southern Colour Print, Dunedin)

1998 (14 Oct). *International Year of the Ocean. T* **265** *and similar horiz designs. Multicoloured. P* 14.

1440	10 s. Type **265**	..	..	40	40
	a. Strip of 3. Nos. 1440/2	..	2·50	
1441	55 s. *Chaetodon lunula*	..	..	1·00	1·10
1442	1 p. *Chaetodon ephippium*	..	1·40	1·60
1440/2			*Set of 3*	2·50	2·75

Nos. 1440/2 were printed together, *se-tenant*, in horizontal and vertical strips of 3 throughout sheets of 9.

266 Angel (inscr in Tongan)

267 Rabbit and Segment of Flower

(Des Donna McKenna. Litho Southern Colour Print, Dunedin)

1998 (25 Nov). *Christmas. T* **266** *and similar vert designs. Multicoloured. P* 14×14½.

1443	10 s. Type **266**	..	..	30	20
1444	80 s. Angel (inscr in English)	..	1·00	65
1445	1 p. Boy with candle (inscr in Tongan)	1·25	90
1446	1 p. 60, Girl holding candle (inscr in English)	..	..	1·75	2·00
1443/6			*Set of 4*	3·75	3·25

(Des Julie Greig. Litho Southern Colour Print, Dunedin)

1999 (16 Feb). *Chinese New Year ("Year of the Rabbit"). Sheet 126×85 mm, containing horiz designs as T 267, showing rabbits and segments of flower. Multicoloured. P 14×14½.*
MS1447   10 s. Three rabbits; 55 s. Rabbit eating
leaf; 80 s. Type **267**; 1 p. Rabbit running   ..   1·75   1·90

268 Heemskerk (Tasman), 1643

(Des C. Abbott. Litho Southern Colour Print, Dunedin)

1999 (19 Mar). *Early Explorers. T 268 and similar horiz designs. Multicoloured. P 14.*
1448   55 s. Type **268**   65   50
1449   80 s. *L'Astrolabe* (La Perouse), 1788   ..   1·00   70
1450   1 p. H.M.S. *Bounty* (Bligh), 1789   ..   1·25   90
1451   2 p. 50, H.M.S. *Resolution* (Cook), 1777   2·50   3·00
1448/51   ..   ..   ..   *Set of 4*   4·75   4·50
MS1452   118×60 mm. No. 1451   ..   ..   2·25   2·50
No. **MS**1452 also includes the "Australia '99" emblem on the sheet margin.

269 Neiafu

(Des T. Crilley. Litho Southern Colour Print, Dunedin)

1999 (19 May). *Scenic Views of Vava'u. T 269 and similar horiz designs. Multicoloured. P 14½.*
1453   10 s. Type **269**   30   20
1454   55 s. Yachts at Port of Refuge   ..   60   50
1455   80 s. Port of Refuge from the air   ..   90   70
1456   1 p. Sunset at Neiafu   ..   ..   1·10   1·10
1457   2 p. 50, Mounu Island   ..   ..   2·50   3·00
1453/7   ..   ..   ..   *Set of 5*   4·75   5·00

270 Fagraea berteroana

(Des Sue Wickison. Litho Cartor)

1999 (29 Sept). *Fragrant Flowers. T 270 and similar multicoloured designs. P 13½×13 (horiz) or 13×13½ (vert).*
1458   10 s. Type **270**   15   15
1459   80 s. *Garcinia pseudoguttfera*   ..   80   65
1460   1 p. *Phaleria disperma* (vert)   ..   1·00   1·00
1461   2 p. 50, *Gardenia taitensis* (vert)   ..   2·40   2·75
1458/61   ..   ..   ..   *Set of 4*   4·00   4·00

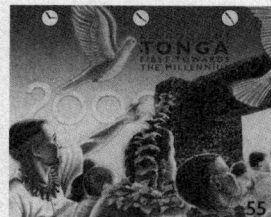

271 Crowd and Trilith at Ha'amonga

(Des Donna McKenna. Litho Cartor)

1999 (1 Dec). *New Millennium (1st issue). T 271 and similar horiz designs. Multicoloured. P 13½×13.*
1462   55 s. Type **271**   40   45
   a. Horiz strip of 4. Nos. 1462/5   ..   3·50
1463   80 s. Crowd and doves   60   65
1464   1 p. Tongans watching sunrise   ..   80   85
1465   2 p. 50, King Tauf'ahau Tupou IV, dove
   amd Millennium emblem   ..   ..   1·90   2·00
1462/5   ..   ..   ..   *Set of 4*   3·50   3·75
Nos. 1462/5 were printed together, *se-tenant*, in horizontal strips of 4 with the backgrounds forming a composite design.

272 Dove and Heilala (flowers)

(Des Donna McKenna. Litho and embossed (circular inscr) Southern Colour Print, Dunedin)

2000 (1 Jan). *New Millennium (2nd issue). T 272 and similar circular designs each incorporating a clock face and "FIRST TO SEE THE MILLENNIUM" inscription. Multicoloured. P 15 (and also around design).*
1466   10 s. Type **272**   10   10
1467   1 p. Ha'amonga Arch   80   85
1468   2 p. 50, Kalia (traditional canoe)   ..   1·90   2·00
1469   2 p. 70, Royal Crown   ..   ..   2·00   2·10
1466/9   ..   ..   *Set of 4*   4·75   5·00
MS1470   130×90 mm. Nos. 1468/9   ..   3·75   4·00
The outline of the dove extends beyond the perforations and is separated from the margin by die-cutting.

273 Dragon

(Des Helen Ngan. Litho and die-stamped Southern Colour Print, Dunedin)

2000 (4 Feb). *Chinese New Year ("Year of the Dragon"). Sheet, 126×85 mm, containing T 273 and similar horiz designs. Multicoloured. P 14½.*
MS1471   10 s. Type **273**; 55 s. Dragon blowing on
   sphere; 80 s. Dragon on hills; 1 p. Sea dragon   1·90   2·00

TONGA

STAMP BOOKLETS

1987 (1 July)–**88**. *20th Anniv of Coronation of King Taufa'ahau Tupou IV. Black, rosine and deep turquoise-green covers showing Royal Palace, 68×49 mm. Self-adhesive.*

SB1	1 p. booklet containing *se-tenant* pane of 12 (No. 973a)			2·50
	a. As No. SB1 but containing *se-tenant* pane No. 972b (4.7.88)			6·50
SB2	2 p. booklet containing *se-tenant* pane of 12 (No. 972a)			3·00
	a. As No. SB2 but containing *se-tenant* pane No. 972c (4.7.88)			7·00

1990 (4 Sept). *Turquoise printed covers, 131×41 mm, in four different designs showing marine life. Stitched.*
(a) *Dascyllus aruanus*
(b) *Cypraea mappa viridis*
(c) *Dardanus megistos*
(d) *Holocentrus ruber*

SB3	4 p. 90, booklet containing 2 s., 5 s., 10 s. and 32 s., each in pane of 10 (Nos. 1087a, 1089a, 1092a, 1095a) (*any cover*)		13·00
		Set of 4 different covers	45·00

1994 (14 Dec). *25th Anniv of Tongan Self-adhesive Stamps. Multicoloured cover showing photograph of Pacific from Space with cut out to show stamp on pane No. 1289a. Stitched.*

SB4	10 p. booklet containing panes Nos. 1281a/2a, 1285a and 1289a	17·00

EXPRESS STAMP

E 1 Short-eared Owl in Flight

1990 (21 Feb). *Air. P* 11½.

E1	E 1	10 p. black, vermilion and ultramarine		7·50	7·75

OFFICIAL STAMPS

(O 1) (O 2)

(G.F.B. = Gaue Faka Buleaga = On Government Service)

1893 (13 Feb). *Optd with Type O 1 by Govt Printing Office, Wellington, N.Z. W 2. P 12 × 11½.*

O1	5	1d. ultramarine (C.)			10·00	42·00
		a. Bisected diagonally (½d.) (on cover)				
O2	6	2d. ultramarine (C.)			27·00	48·00
O3	5	4d. ultramarine (C.)			45·00	90·00
O4	6	8d. ultramarine (C.)			85·00	£160
O5	5	1s. ultramarine (C.)			95·00	£180
O1/5			*Set of 5*		£225	£475

Above prices are for stamps in good condition and colour. Faded and stained stamps from the remainders are worth much less.

1893 (Dec). *Nos O1 to O5 variously surch with new value, sideways as Type O 2.*

O 6	5	½d. on 1d. ultramarine			17·00	48·00
O 7	6	2½d. on 2d. ultramarine			23·00	42·00
O 8	5	5d. on 4d. ultramarine			23·00	42·00
O 9	6	7½d. on 8d. ultramarine			23·00	75·00
		a. "D" of "7½D." omitted			£1200	
		b. Surch double			£1900	
O10		10d. on 1s. ultramarine			27·00	80·00
O6/10			*Set of 5*		£100	£250

OFFICIAL AIRMAIL

OFFICIAL AIR MAIL
1862
TAU'ATĀINA
EMANCIPATION
1962

(O 3)

40 SENITI

(O 4)

1962 (7 Feb). *Air. Centenary of Emancipation. Nos. 112/14, 116 and 118/19 optd with Type O 3 in red by R. S. Wallbank, Govt Printer.*

O11	—	2d. ultramarine		12·00	6·00
		a. "OFFICIAI"		22·00	11·00
		b. "MAII"		22·00	11·00
O12		5d. violet		13·00	6·50
		a. "OFFICIAI"		24·00	12·00
		b. "MAII"		24·00	12·00
O13	—	1s. red-brown		8·50	3·75
		a. "OFFICIAI"		27·00	11·00
		b. "MAII"		27·00	11·00
		c. Opt double		£350	
		ca. "OFFICIAI"		£600	
		cb. "MAII"		£600	

O14	—	5s. orange-yellow and slate-lilac		90·00	55·00
		a. "MAII"		£200	75·00
		b. "OFFICIAI"			
O15	52	10s. yellow and black		42·00	22·00
		a. "MAII"		£100	
O16	53	£1 yellow, scarlet, ultram & dp brt blue	70·00	35·00
		a. "MAII"		£150	
		b. "OFFICIAI"			
O11/16			*Set of 6*	£200	£120

SET PRICES. Official stamps from here onwards are included in the complete commemorative set prices given for any corresponding Postage issues.

1963 (15 July). *Air. First Polynesian Gold Coinage Commemoration. As T 63 but inscr "OFFICIAL AIRMAIL". 1 koula coin (diam 3½ in.). Imperf.*

O17	63	15s. black		5·50	6·50

1965 (18 Mar). *No. O17 surch as T 67.*

O18	63	30s. on 15s. black		3·00	3·75

1966 (18 June). *Air. Centenary of Tupou College and Secondary Education. No. 117 surch with "OFFICIAL AIRMAIL" and new value, with commemorative inscription as in T 69 but in italic capital letters.*

O19		10s. on 4d. blue-green		80	35
		a. Surch inverted		£300	£150
O20		20s. on 4d. blue-green		1·00	50

1967 (25 Mar). *Air. Decimal currency. No. 112 surch "OFFICIAL AIRMAIL ONE PA'ANGA" in three lines, in red.*

O21		1 p. on 5s.		4·50	2·25
		a. "AIRMAIL" above "OFFICIAL"		£150	

No. O21a occurred once in a number of sheets until it was corrected.

1967 (4 July). *Air. No. 114 surch in various denominations as Type O 4.*

O22	53	40 s. on £1		50	60
O23		60 s. on £1		70	80
O24		1 p. on £1		90	1·75
O25		2 p. on £1		1·50	2·25

Nos. O22/5 were first used on 4 July 1967, but supplies of unused stamps were not made available until April 1968.

The Friendly Islands welcome the United States Peace Corps *Official Airmail* 30s

(O 5)

Friendly Islands Trials Field & Track South Pacific Games Port Moresby 1969 T$ 1·00 OFFICIAL AIRMAIL

(O 6)

1967 (15 Dec). *Air. Arrival of U.S. Peace Corps in Tonga. As No. 114 but imperf, and background colour changed, and surch as Type O 5.*

O26	53	30 s. on £1 yellow, scarlet, ultramarine and emerald-green	50	25
O27		70 s. on £1 yellow, scarlet, ultramarine and emerald-green	70	45
O28		1 p. 50, on £1 yellow, scarlet, ultramarine and emerald-green	1·00	85

1968 (4 July). *Air. 50th Birthday of King Taufa'ahua IV. No. 207 surch "HIS MAJESTY'S 50th BIRTHDAY" (as T 79), "OFFICIAL AIRMAIL" and new value.*

O29	75	40 s. on 50 s. (Turq.)	1·50	70
O30		60 s. on 50 s. (G.)	2·00	1·25
O31		1 p. on 50 s. (V.)	3·00	3·00
O32		2 p. on 50 s. (P.)	5·50	5·50

1968 (19 Dec). *Air. South Pacific Games Field and Track Trials, Port Moresby, New Guinea. As No. 114, but imperf, background colour changed and surch as Type O 6.*

O33	53	20 s. on £1 yellow, scarlet, ultramarine and emerald-green	20	15
O34		1 p. on £1 yellow, scarlet, ultramarine and emerald-green	70	70

1969 (13 Aug). *Air. Third South Pacific Games, Port Moresby. Design as Nos. 290/4.*

O35		70 s. carmine-red, bright green and turquoise	65	90
O36		80 s. carmine-red, orange and turquoise	75	1·00

OFFICIAL AIRMAIL

Royal Visit
MARCH 1970

1969 OIL SEARCH 90s

(O 7)

OFFICIAL AIRMAIL

T$1·25

(O 8)

1969 (23 Dec). *Air. First Oil Search in Tonga. As No. 114 but imperf, background colour changed to emerald-green, and surch as Type O 7.*

O37	53	90 s. on £1 multicoloured	3·50	3·50
		a. "1966" for "1969" (R.3/5)	£140	
O38		1 p. 10 on £1 multicoloured (R.)	3·50	3·50
		a. "1966" for "1969" (R.3/5)	£140	

The "1966" error does not occur on every sheet. It is possible that Nos. O37/8 were surcharged in sheets of 120 containing two panes of 60 (6×10).

No. O38 is surch as Type O 7, but without "OFFICIAL AIRMAIL".

1970 (7 Mar). *Royal Visit. As No. 110 but imperf, colours changed, and surch as Type O 8.*

O39		75 s. on 1s. carmine-red and yellow	3·50	3·25
O40		1 p. on 1s. carmine-red and yellow (B.)	4·00	3·75
O41		1 p. 25 on 1s. carmine-red & yellow (G.)	4·75	5·00

OFFICIAL Commonwealth Member JUNE 1970 50s AIRMAIL

(O 9)

1970 (4 June). *Air. Entry into British Commonwealth. As No. 112 but imperf, background colour changed, and surch as Type O 9.*

O42		50 s. on 5s. orange-yellow and sepia	1·00	1·00
O43		90 s. on 5s. orange-yellow and sepia (R.)	1·40	1·60
O44		1 p. 50 on 5s. orange-yellow & sepia (G.)	2·25	2·75

1970 (4 June). *As Nos. 325/34, but inscr. "OFFICIAL POST". Colour of "TONGA" given for 6 to 10 s.*

O45	83	1 s. greenish yellow, brt purple & blk		45	50
O46		2 s. greenish yellow, ultram & black		55	60
O47		3 s. greenish yellow, chocolate & blk		55	60
O48		4 s. greenish yellow, emerald and black		55	60
O49		5 s. greenish yellow, orange-red & blk		60	65
O50	90	6 s. ultramarine		70	80
O51		7 s. deep mauve		75	85
O52		8 s. gold		85	95
O53		9 s. bright carmine		95	1·00
O54		10 s. silver		95	1·10
O45/54			*Set of 10*	6·25	7·00

The note after No. 334 also applies here.
See also Nos. O82/91.

Centenary British Red Cross 1870-1970

OFFICIAL AIRMAIL 30s

(O 10)

1970 (17 Oct). *Centenary of British Red Cross. As Nos. 102 and 112 but imperf, colours changed and surch as Type O 10.*

O55		30 s. on 1½d. emerald (Blk. and R.)	1·75	1·75
O56		80 s. on 5s. orange-yellow & sepia (B. & R.)	4·25	4·25
O57		90 s. on 5s. orange-yellow & sepia (B. & R.)	4·25	4·25

OFFICIAL AIRMAIL 20s

1971 (30 Jan). *Air. Fifth Death Anniv of Queen Salote. As No. 113, but imperf, colours changed and surch as Type O 11.*

O58	52	20 s. on 10s. orange-yellow	1·25	80
O59		30 s. on 10s. orange-yellow (V.)	1·50	1·00
O60		50 s. on 10s. orange-yellow	2·75	2·00
O61		2 p. on 10s. orange-yellow (G.)	9·00	8·00

1965 IN MEMORIAM 1970

(O 11)

PHILATOKYO 71

(O 12)

1971 (17 Apr). *Air. "Philatokyo 1971" Stamp Exhibition. Unissued Red Cross surcharges on No. 107, but imperf, colours changed and additionally surch as Type O 12.*

O62		30 s. on 5d. green and yellow (B. & R.)	90	65
O63		80 s. on 5d. green and yellow (Blk. & R.)	1·75	1·75
O64		90 s. on 5d. green and yellow (P. & R.)	2·00	2·00

1971 (20 July)–**72**. *Air. As Nos. 365/6a, but inscr "OFFICIAL AIRMAIL".*

O65	96	14 s. multicoloured	1·50	1·50
O65a		17 s. multicoloured (20.7.72)	1·75	1·75
O66		21 s. multicoloured	1·75	1·75
O66a		38 s. multicoloured (20.7.72)	2·75	2·75

O 13 Football

746

1971 (20 July). *Air. Fourth South Pacific Games, Tahiti.*
O67	O 13	50 s. multicoloured		..	..	60	90
O68		90 s. multicoloured			..	85	1·50
O69		1 p. 50, multicoloured		..	..	1·25	1·75

INVESTITURE   **1971**

✱✱✱   **60s**   ✱✱✱
OFFICIAL   **AIRMAIL**

(O 14)

(Illustration reduced. Actual size 61 × 13 mm)

1971 (30 Oct). *Air. Investiture of Royal Tongan Medal of Merit. Nos. 315, 318 and 316 surch as Type O 14.*
O70	89	60 s. on 3 s. multicoloured	..	70	90
O71		80 s. on 25 s. multicoloured	..	90	1·25
O72		1 p. 10 on 7 s. multicoloured	..	1·00	1·50

O 15 "UNICEF" and Emblem

1971 (31 Dec). *Air. 25th Anniv of UNICEF.*
O73	O 15	70 s. multicoloured	..	1·40	1·60
O74		80 s. multicoloured	..	1·50	1·75
O75		90 s. multicoloured	..	1·60	1·90

1972 (14 Apr). *Air. Merchant Marine Routes. Design similar to T 100, but inscr "OFFICIAL AIRMAIL".*
O76	20 s. multicoloured	..	1·25	80
O77	50 s. multicoloured	..	2·75	2·50
O78	1 p. 20, multicoloured	..	5·50	6·50

Design:—Nos. O76/8, Map of South Pacific, and *Aoniu.*

1972 (15 July). *Air. Fifth Anniv of Coronation. Design similar to T 101, but inscr "OFFICIAL AIRMAIL".*
O79	50 s. multicoloured	..	1·00	85
O80	70 s. multicoloured	..	1·40	1·25
O81	1 p. 50, multicoloured	..	2·75	3·00

Design (47 × 57 mm):—Nos. O79/81, As T 101, but with different background.

1972 (30 Sept). *As Nos. 413/27, but inscr "OFFICIAL POST".*

(a) As Nos. 413/17
O82	83	1 s. light yellow, scarlet and black		20	10
O83		2 s. light yellow, dp blue-green & black		25	15
O84		3 s. light yellow, yellow-green and black		30	20
O85		4 s. light yellow and black		30	20
O86		5 s. light yellow and black		30	20

(b) As Nos. O50/4, but colours changed. Colour of "TONGA" given
O87	90	6 s. light green	..	35	20
O88		7 s. light green	..	40	25
O89		8 s. light green	..	40	25
O90		9 s. light green	..	40	25
O91		10 s. light green	..	50	30

(c) As Nos. 423/7. Colour of face value given
O92	102	15 s. new blue		85	45
O93		20 s. reddish orange		1·00	60
O94		25 s. chocolate		1·10	70
O95		40 s. yellow-orange		2·25	1·50
O96		50 s. royal blue		2·50	1·75
O82/96			Set of 15	10·00	6·50

The note after No. 427 also applies here.

1972 (9 Dec). *Air. Proclamation of Sovereignty over Minerva Reefs. Design similar to T 104, but inscr "OFFICIAL AIRMAIL".*
O97	25 s. multicoloured	..	40	35
O98	75 s. multicoloured	..	1·25	1·50
O99	1 p. 50, multicoloured	..	2·50	3·00

Design: *Horiz* (64 × 39 mm)—Nos. O97/9, Flags and map.

TONGA
★
1973

**ESTABLISHMENT
BANK OF TONGA**
40s
OFFICIAL AIRMAIL

(O 16)

1973 (30 Mar). *Air. Foundation of Bank of Tonga. No. 396 surch as Type O 16.*
O100	100	40 s. on 21 s. mult (Blk. & G.)	1·50	1·25
O101		85 s. on 21 s. multicoloured (B. & G.)	2·75	2·50
O102		1 p. 25 on 21 s. multicoloured (Br.)	3·50	3·50

COVER PRICES

Cover factors are quoted at the beginning of each country for most issues to 1945. An explanation of the system can be found on page x. The factors quoted do not, however, apply to philatelic covers.

         30s

**SILVER JUBILEE
TONGAN SCOUTING
1948 - 1973**

(O 17)

1973 (29 June). *Silver Jubilee of Scouting in Tonga. Nos. O76, O74 and 319 variously optd or surch as Type O 17 in silver (Nos. O103/4) or silver and blue (No. O105).*
O103	–	30 s. on 20 s. multicoloured	..	10·00	2·75
O104	O 15	80 s. multicoloured	..	25·00	10·00
O105	89	1 p. 40 on 50 s. multicoloured	..	35·00	25·00

1973 (2 Oct). *Air. Bicentenary of Capt. Cook's Visit. Design similar to T 107, but inscr "OFFICIAL AIRMAIL".*
O106	25 s. multicoloured	..	..	3·25	1·50
O107	80 s. multicoloured	..	..	8·50	4·50
O108	1 p. 30, multicoloured	..		10·00	7·50

Design: *Horiz* (52 × 45 mm)—Nos. O106/8, James Cook (bulk carrier).

1974

**Commonwealth
Games
Christchurch**
OFFICIAL AIRMAIL
50s

(O 18)

1973 (19 Dec). *Air. Commonwealth Games. Nos. O67/9 optd with Type O 18.*
O109	O 13	50 s. multicoloured (B.)	..	80	1·10
O110		90 s. multicoloured (Blk.)	..	1·40	1·75
O111		1 p. 50, multicoloured (G.)	..	2·00	2·50
		a. Opt double	..	£150	

O 19 Dove of Peace

1974 (20 Mar). *Air.*
O112	O 19	7 s. turq-grn, reddish vio & orge-red	60	20	
O113		9 s. turq-grn, reddish vio & red-brn	65	25	
O114		12 s. turq-grn, reddish vio & yell-orge	70	35	
O115		14 s. turquoise-green, reddish violet and bistre-yellow	75	40	
O116		17 s. multicoloured	..	85	60
O117		29 s. multicoloured	..	1·50	1·00
O118		38 s. multicoloured	..	2·00	1·25
O119		50 s. multicoloured	..	2·50	2·75
O120		75 s. multicoloured	..	3·75	4·25
O112/120			Set of 9	12·00	10·00

1974 (20 June). *Air. Centenary of Universal Postal Union. Design similar to T 110, but inscr "OFFICIAL AIRMAIL".*
O121	25 s. dp red-orange, lt yellow-green & black	50	60
O122	35 s. lemon, magenta and black	60	75
O123	70 s. deep orange, bright blue and black	1·25	2·00

Design: *Square* (40 × 40 mm)—Letters "UPU".

1974 (11 Sept). *Air. Tongan Girl Guides. Design similar to T 111, but inscr "OFFICIAL AIRMAIL".*
O124	45 s. multicoloured	..	4·00	4·00
O125	55 s. multicoloured	..	4·25	2·25
O126	1 p. multicoloured	..	7·50	5·50

Design: *Oval* (35 × 52 mm)—Lady Baden-Powell.

(O 20)

1974 (11 Dec). *Air. Establishment of Royal Marine Institute. Nos. 446 and 451 surch as Type O 20, each obliterating the centre part of the original design.*
O127	30 s. on 15 s. multicoloured (Gold, B. & P.)	2·50	1·75
O128	35 s. on 15 s. multicoloured (Sil., B. & Blk.)	2·75	2·00
	a. Black ("TONGA TONGA") omitted	..	£150
O129	80 s. on 17 s. multicoloured (Blk. & R.)	..	4·25	4·50

1975 (11 Mar). *Air. South Pacific Forum and Tourism. Designs similar to T 113 but inscr "OFFICIAL AIRMAIL".*
O130	50 s. multicoloured		..	1·10	1·00
O131	75 s. multicoloured		..	1·75	1·50
O132	1 p. 25, multicoloured		..	2·50	2·25

Designs: (49 × 43 mm)—50 s. Jungle arch; others, Sunset scene.

1975 (11 June). *Air. Fifth South Pacific Games. Design similar to T 114 but inscr "OFFICIAL AIRMAIL".*
O133	38 s. multicoloured		..	55	50
O134	75 s. multicoloured		..	90	1·25
O135	1 p. 20, multicoloured		..	1·60	2·25

Design: *Oval* (51 × 27 mm):—Runners on track.

O 21 Tongan Monarchs

1975 (4 Nov). *Air. Centenary of Tongan Constitution.*
O136	O 21	17 s. multicoloured	..	55	40
O137		60 s. multicoloured	..	1·25	1·50
O138		90 s. multicoloured	..	1·75	2·00

1976 (24 Feb). *Air. First Participation in Olympic Games. Design similar to T 117 but inscr "OFFICIAL AIRMAIL".*
O139	45 s. multicoloured		..	3·00	1·00
O140	55 s. multicoloured		..	3·00	1·25
O141	1 p. multicoloured		..	5·50	4·50

Design: *Oval* (36 × 53 mm)—Montreal logo.

1976 (26 May). *Air. Bicentenary of American Revolution. Designs as T 118 showing signatories to the Declaration of Independence. Inscr "OFFICIAL AIRMAIL".*
O142	20 s. multicoloured	..	..	90	50
O143	50 s. multicoloured	..	..	1·25	1·50
O144	1 p. 15, multicoloured	..		2·75	3·50

1976 (25 Aug). *Air. 150th Anniv of Christianity in Tonga. Hexagonal design (65 × 52 mm) showing Lifuka Chapel.*
O145	65 s. multicoloured	..	2·00	2·00
O146	85 s. multicoloured	..	2·25	2·50
O147	1 p. 15, multicoloured	..	2·75	3·50

1976 (1 Nov). *Air. Centenary of Treaty of Friendship with Germany. Rectangular design (51 × 47 mm) showing text.*
O148	30 s. multicoloured	..	60	70
O149	60 s. multicoloured	..	1·40	1·75
O150	1 p. 25, multicoloured	..	2·75	3·50

1977 (7 Feb). *Air. Silver Jubilee. Vert design (57 × 66 mm) showing flags of Tonga and the U.K.*
O151	35 s. multicoloured	..	90	40
O152	45 s. multicoloured	..	40	30
O153	1 p. 10, multicoloured	..	55	50

1977 (4 July). *Air. Tenth Anniv of King's Coronation. Square design (50 × 50 mm) showing 1967 Coronation Coin.*
O154	20 s. multicoloured	..	40	45
O155	40 s. multicoloured	..	80	1·00
O156	80 s. multicoloured	..	1·75	2·25

1977 (28 Sept). *Air. Bicentenary of Capt. Cook's Last Voyage. Rectangular design (52 × 46 mm) showing text.*
O157	20 s. multicoloured	..	2·75	2·50
O158	55 s. on 20 s. multicoloured	..	6·00	6·50
O159	85 s. on 20 s. multicoloured (V. and Blk.)	..	8·50	9·00

The face values of Nos. O158/9 are surcharged on the stamps, the original face value being incorrect.

1977 (16 Dec). *Air. Whale Conservation. Hexagonal design (66 × 51 mm) showing Blue Whale.*
O160	45 s. multicoloured	..	5·00	3·00
O161	55 s. multicoloured	..	7·00	5·00
O162	85 s. multicoloured	..	8·50	6·00

1978 (5 May). *Air. Commonwealth Games, Edmonton. "Teardrop" design (35 × 52 mm) showing Games Emblem.*
O163	30 s. black, blue and red	..	45	50
O164	60 s. black, red and blue	..	1·00	1·25
O165	1 p. black, red and blue	..	1·60	1·75

1978 (4 July). *Air. 60th Birthday of King Taufa'ahau Tupou IV. Medal-shaped design (21 × 45 mm) showing portrait of King.*
O166	26 s. black, vermilion and yellow	..	35	30
O167	85 s. black, light brown and yellow	..	1·10	1·25
O168	90 s. black, bright violet and yellow	..	1·25	1·25

1978 (29 Sept). *Coil stamps. (a) Designs similar to Nos. 675/9 but inscr "OFFICIAL POST".*
O169	1 s. purple and greenish yellow	..	20	20
O170	2 s. brown and greenish yellow	..	20	20
O171	3 s. carmine, yellow and greenish yellow	..	30	30
O172	4 s. brown, yellow and greenish yellow	..	30	30
O173	5 s. blue-green, yellow and greenish yellow	..	30	30

(b) Designs similar to Nos. 680/4 but inscr "OFFICIAL POST"
O174	6 s. yellow-brown, emerald and light brown	..	40	40
O175	7 s. blue-black, emerald and light brown	..	40	40
O176	8 s. magenta, emerald and light brown	..	40	40
O177	9 s. red-brown, emerald and light brown	..	40	40
O178	10 s. deep green, emerald and light brown	..	40	40

TONGA

(c) *Designs similar to Nos. 685/9 but inscr "OFFICIAL POST"*

O179	15 s. grey-black, orange-brown and emerald		1·00	1·00
O180	20 s. vermilion, orange-brown and emerald		1·10	1·10
O181	30 s. emerald and orange-brown		1·25	1·50
O182	50 s. new blue, orange-brown and emerald		1·50	1·75
O183	1 p. reddish violet, orange-brown & emer.		2·25	2·75
O169/83		*Set of 15*	9·25	10·00

1978 (15 Dec). *Air. Endangered Wildlife Conservation. Designs as Nos. 690/2 but inscr "OFFICIAL AIRMAIL".*

O184	40 s. Type **129**		5·00	3·25
O185	50 s. Insular Flying Fox		5·00	3·25
O186	1 p. 10, Turtle		7·00	7·00

1979 (16 Feb). *Air. Decade of Progress. Designs similar to Nos. 700/9 but inscr "OFFICIAL AIRMAIL".*

O187	38 s. Tonga Red Cross emblem		65	40
O188	74 s. As No. 702		1·25	75
O189	80 s. As No. 701		1·40	80

1979 (1 June). *Air. Death Centenary of Sir Rowland Hill and 10th Anniv of Tongan Self-adhesive Stamps. Hand-shaped design (45 × 53 mm) showing self-adhesive stamps being removed from backing paper.*

O190	45 s. multicoloured		1·00	60
O191	65 s. multicoloured		1·40	85
O192	80 s. multicoloured		1·75	1·10

O **22** Blue-crowned Lory with foliage   O **23** Blue-crowned Lory without foliage

1979 (17 Aug). *Air. Coil stamps.*

O193	O **22** 5 s. mult (face value in black)		50	40
O194	11 s. multicoloured		55	40
O195	14 s. multicoloured		55	40
O196	15 s. multicoloured		60	40
O197	17 s. multicoloured		60	40
O198	18 s. multicoloured		60	40
O199	22 s. multicoloured		70	45
O200	31 s. multicoloured		75	65
O201	39 s. multicoloured		90	80
O202	75 s. multicoloured		1·75	2·50
O203	1 p. multicoloured		2·25	3·25
O193/203		*Set of 11*	8·75	9·00

See also No. O213.

1979 (23 Nov). *Air. Views as seen through the Lens of a Camera. Design as T **133** but showing Niuatoputapu and Tafahi.*

O204	35 s. multicoloured		65	65
O205	45 s. multicoloured		75	75
O206	1 p. multicoloured		1·60	2·50

1980 (9 Jan). *Air. 125th Anniv of France-Tonga Treaty of Friendship. Design as T **134** but showing the Establishment of the Principle of Religious Freedom in the Pacific Islands.*

O207	40 s. multicoloured		1·00	1·00
O208	55 s. multicoloured		1·25	1·25
O209	1 p. 25, multicoloured		2·50	2·75

1980 (30 Apr). *Air. Olympic Games, Moscow. Nos. O190/2 surch as T **135** in black on silver background.*

O210	26 s. on 45 s. multicoloured		85	85
O211	40 s. on 65 s. multicoloured		1·40	1·40
O212	1 p. 10, on 1 p. multicoloured		3·50	3·75

1980 (May). *No. O193 redrawn without foliage as Type O **23**.*

O213	O **23** 5 s. mult (face value in magenta)	£100	80·00

1980 (30 Sept). *Air. South Pacific Scout Jamboree, Tonga and 75th Anniv of Rotary International. Design showing Scout camp and Rotary emblem.*

O214	25 s. multicoloured		70	50
O215	2 p. multicoloured		3·50	4·00

Nos. O214/15 show maps of Tonga on the reverse.

T$2 OFFICIAL   **OFFICIAL**

(O **24**)   (O **25**)   (O **26**)

1980 (3 Dec). *Air. No. O145 surch with Type O **24**.*

O216	2 p. on 65 s. multicoloured		4·50	5·50

1983 (22 Feb–Mar). *Nos. 834/6 handstamped with Type O **25** (29 s., 32 s.) or optd with Type O **26** (47 s.).*

O217	29 s. Type **151**		3·50	3·75
O218	32 s. Type **151**		4·00	4·25
O219	47 s. Montgolfier's balloon and Concorde (Mar)		7·00	7·00
O217/19		*Set of 3*	13·00	13·50

STANLEY GIBBONS STAMP COLLECTING SERIES

Introductory booklets on *How to Start, How to Identify Stamps* and *Collecting by Theme.* A series of well illustrated guides at a low price. Write for details.

OFFICIAL   **OFFICIAL**   OFFICIAL

(O **27**)   (O **24**)   (O **25**)

1984 (10 Apr)–**85**. *Nos. 865/79 and 881 optd with Type O **27** (1, 5, 10, 15, 29, 47 s.) or with Type O **28** (others).*

O220	1 s. Type **159**		40	60
O221	2 s. *Porites sp* (26.6.84)		40	60
O222	3 s. Red Squirrelfish (18.5.84)		40	60
O223	5 s. Green Map Cowrie (*Cypraea mappa viridis*)		40	50
O224	6 s. *Dardanus megistos* (17.9.84)		40	70
O225	9 s. Variegated Shark (18.5.84)		55	55
b.	Optd on No. 870b (28.5.85)		1·50	1·50
O226	10 s. Bubble Cone (*Conus bullatus*)		55	50
O227	13 s. Lionfish (18.5.84)		70	50
O228	13 s. Textile or Cloth of Gold Cone (*Conus textile*)		80	80
O229	20 s. White-tailed Dascyllus (18.5.84)		90	90
O230	29 s. Princely Cone (*Conus aulicus*)		1·10	60
O231	32 s. Powder-blue Surgeonfish (18.5.84)		1·10	60
O232	47 s. Giant Spider Conch (*Lambis truncata*)		1·25	80
O233	1 p. *Millepora dichotama* (26.6.84)		2·75	2·50
O234	2 p. *Birgus latro* (17.9.84)		5·00	4·00
O235	5 p. Yellow-finned Tuna (28.5.85)		9·00	10·00
O220/35		*Set of 16*	23·00	22·00

Examples of the 3 p., No. 880, were also prepared with this overprint, but were not used for Official mail. It is believed that most examples were further overprinted "STAMP DUTY" for fiscal use.

1986 (16 Apr). *Nos. 933/9 optd with Type O **29**.*

O236	4 s. on 2 s. *Porites* sp.		80	1·10
O237	4 s. on 13 s. Lionfish		80	1·10
O238	42 s. on 3 s. Red Squirrelfish		2·00	2·00
O239	42 s. on 9 s. Variegated Shark		2·00	2·00
O240	57 s. on 6 s. *Dardanus megistos*		2·25	2·25
O241	57 s. on 20 s. White-tailed Dascyllus		2·25	2·25
O242	2 p. 50 on 2 p. *Birgus latro*		7·50	8·50
O236/42		*Set of 7*	16·00	17·00

1994 (14 Dec). *Air. 25th Anniv of Tongan Self-adhesive Stamps. Design as No. O192, but inscr "25th ANNIVERSARY OF THE INTRODUCTION OF SELFADHESIVE STAMPS 1969–1994 BERNARD MECHANICK: 1915–80 INVENTOR FREEFORM SELFADHESIVE STAMPS" at centre foot.*

O243	80 s. multicoloured		3·50	3·75

POSTAGE & REVENUE

TONGA 10s OFFICIAL
Conus bullatus

O **30** Bubble Cone (*Conus bullatus*)

1995 (25 Sept)–**96**. *Designs as Nos. 1221a, 1223a, 1225a, 1227a, 1229a and 1345/9, but inscr as Type O **30**. Chalk-surfaced paper. P 14.*

O247	10 s. Type O **30**		10	10
O249	20 s. White-tailed Dascyllus		15	20
O251	45 s. Giant Spider Conch (*Lambis truncata*)		35	40
O253	60 s. Princely Cone (*Conus aulicus*)		45	50
O255	80 s. Lionfish		60	65
O256	1 p. *Chelonia mydas* (turtle) (31.5.96)		80	85
O257	2 p. *Birgus latro* (crab) (31.5.96)		1·60	1·75
O258	3 p. Rose Branch Murex (*Chicoreus palma-rosae*) (31.5.96)		2·40	2·25
O259	5 p. Humpback Whale (31.5.96)		4·00	4·25
O260	10 p. Variegated Shark (*vert*) (31.5.96)		7·75	8·00
O247/60		*Set of 10*	18·00	19·00

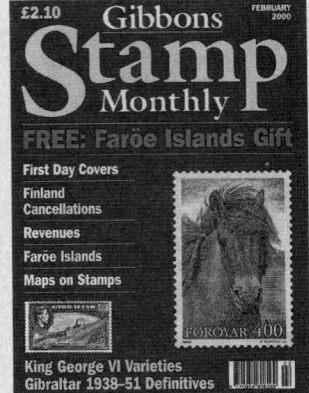

NIUAFO'OU

The following stamps were provided for the remote island of Niuafo'ou and were not valid for postage in the remainder of Tonga.

SELF-ADHESIVE ISSUES. Nos. 1/63 were manufactured by Walsall Security Printers using the self-adhesive system as described above Tonga No. 280.

T$1

1 Map of Niuafo'ou (2)

NIUAFO'OU
KINGDOM OF TONGA

1983 (11 May). (a) P 14.

1	1	1 s. pale stone, black and rosine		30	60
2		2 s. pale stone, black and light emerald		30	60
3		3 s. pale stone, black & dull ultram		30	70
4		3 s. pale stone, black and chestnut		30	70
5		5 s. pale stone, black and deep magenta		40	70
6		6 s. pale stone, black and greenish blue		40	70
7		9 s. pale stone, black & dull yell-grn		40	70
8		10 s. pale stone, black & dull ultram		40	70
9		13 s. pale stone, black and light emerald		65	75
10		15 s. pale stone, black and chestnut		70	1·00
11		20 s. pale stone, black and greenish blue		75	1·00
12		29 s. pale stone, black and deep magenta		1·00	80
13		32 s. pale stone, black & dull yellow-green		1·00	90
14		47 s. pale stone, black and rosine		1·40	1·40

(b) No. 820 of Tonga surch (No. 15) with T 2 by lithography or optd only (No. 16) by typography. P 13½.

15	1 p. on 2 p. pale turquoise-green & black (V.)		2·50	3·00
	a. Deep mauve surch in typography		12·00	13·00
16	2 p. pale turquoise-green (Gold)		3·50	4·50
1/16		Set of 16	13·00	17·00

Most examples of No. 15 have the surcharge printed by lithography. A small quantity did, however, receive a typography surcharge in a different shade to form No. 15a. In addition to the colour the typography printing can be identified by the white rims to the letters and figures. All examples of No. 16 were printed by typography.

1983 (11 May). *Inauguration of Niuafo'ou Airport. As T 153 of Tonga.* P 14 × 14½.

17	29 s. multicoloured		80	1·00
18	1 p. multicoloured		2·50	3·25

3s

(3)

4 Eruption of Niuafo'ou

1983 (30 May). *As T 1, but without value, surch with T 3 by Tonga Government Printer.*

19	3 s. pale stone, black and royal blue		20	20
20	5 s. pale stone, black and royal blue		20	20
21	32 s. pale stone, black and royal blue		1·50	1·25
	a. Surch inverted		£600	
	b. Surch double			
22	2 p. pale stone, black and royal blue		8·00	9·00
	a. Surch inverted		70·00	
	b. Surch double		£100	
	c. Albino surch			
19/22		Set of 4	9·00	9·50

At least one example of No. 21a was caused by the self-adhesive stamp in the last position of the bottom row being inverted when the sheet was surcharged.

STAMP DUTY. Stamps of Tonga and Niuafo'ou overprinted or surcharged "STAMP DUTY", "STAMP DUTY ONLY" or similar wording were for fiscal use and were not valid for postal purposes.

(Des R. Edge)

1983 (29 Sept). *25th Anniv of Re-settlement. T 4 and similar horiz designs.* Multicoloured. P 14.

23	5 s. Type 4		40	30
24	29 s. Lava flow		1·00	1·00
25	32 s. Islanders fleeing to safety		1·10	1·00
26	1 p. 50, Evacuation by canoe		3·50	5·00
23/6		Set of 4	5·50	6·50

5 Purple Swamphen

6 Green Turtle

(Des N. Arlott)

1983 (15 Nov). *Birds of Niuafo'ou. T 5 and similar designs.* P 11 (1 p., 2 p.), 14 (20 s. to 47 s.) or 14½ (others).

27	1 s. black and deep mauve			80	90
28	2 s. black and bright blue			80	90
29	3 s. black and blue-green			80	90
30	5 s. black and yellow			1·00	90
31	6 s. black and red-orange			1·25	1·10
32	9 s. multicoloured			1·60	1·10
33	10 s. multicoloured			1·60	1·60
34	13 s. multicoloured			2·00	1·60
35	15 s. multicoloured			2·00	2·00
36	20 s. multicoloured			2·25	2·25
37	29 s. multicoloured			2·50	1·50
38	32 s. multicoloured			2·50	1·60
39	47 s. multicoloured			3·00	2·25
40	1 p. multicoloured			5·50	7·50
41	2 p. multicoloured			7·50	10·00
27/41			Set of 15	32·00	32·00

Designs: Vert (22 × 29 mm)—2 s. White-collared Kingfisher; 3 s. Red-headed Parrot Finch; 5 s. Banded Rail; 6 s. Polynesian Scrub Hen ("Niuafo'ou Megapode"); 9 s. Green Honeyeater; 10 s. Purple Swamphen (different); (22 × 36 mm)—29 s. Red-headed Parrot Finch (different); 32 s. White-collared Kingfisher (different); (29 × 42 mm)—1 p. As 10 s. Horiz (29 × 22 mm)—13 s. Banded Rail (different); 15 s. Polynesian Scrub Hen ("Niuafo'ou Megapode") (different); (36 × 22 mm)—20 s. As 13 s.; 47 s. As 15 s.; (42 × 29 mm)—2 p. As 15 s.

(Des R. Edge)

1984 (7 Mar). *Wildlife and Nature Reserve. T 6 and similar multicoloured designs.* P 14.

42	29 s. Type 6		70	70
43	32 s. Insular Flying Fox (vert)		70	70
44	47 s. Humpback Whale		2·50	1·75
45	1 p. 50, Polynesian Scrub Hen ("Niuafo-ou Megapode") (vert)		4·50	6·00
42/5		Set of 4	7·50	8·25

7 Diagram of Time Zones

8 Australia 1913 £2 Kangaroo Definitive

(Des R. Edge)

1984 (20 Aug). *Centenary of International Dateline. T 7 and similar horiz design.* Multicoloured. P 14.

46	47 s. Type 7		60	50
47	2 p. Location map showing Niuafo'ou		1·90	2·75

1984 (17 Sept). *"Ausipex" International Stamp Exhibition, Melbourne. T 8 and similar vert design.* Multicoloured. P 14.

48	32 s. Type 8		75	60
49	1 p. 50, Niuafo'ou 1983 10 s. map definitive		2·25	3·00
MS50	90 × 100 mm. As Nos. 48/9, but without exhibition logo and with face value at foot. Die cut		1·75	2·50

Examples of No. MS50 without face values are Exhibition Banquet souvenirs without postal validity.

9 Dutch Brass Band entertaining Tongans

10 Ysabel, 1902

(Des R. Edge)

1985 (20 Feb). *400th Birth Anniv of Jacob Le Maire (discoverer of Niuafo'ou). T 9 and similar vert designs.* P 14.

51	13 s. purple-brown, pale cinnamon & brt orge	25	40
52	32 s. purple-brn, pale cinnamon & brt new bl	55	60
53	47 s. purple-brn, pale cinnamon & brt green	75	80
54	1 p. 50, purple-brn, pale cinnamon & lemon	2·25	3·00
51/4		Set of 4	3·50	4·25
MS55	90 × 90 mm. 1 p. 50, purple-brown, pale cinnamon and new blue. Imperf	1·50	2·00

Designs:—No. 52, Tongans preparing kava; No. 53, Tongan canoes and outriggers; Nos. 54/5, *Eendracht* at anchor off Tafahi Island.

1985 (22 May). *Mail Ships. T 10 and similar horiz designs.* Multicoloured.

A. Stamp die-cut and backing paper perf 14

56A	9 s. Type 10		60	50
57A	13 s. Tofua I, 1908		70	55
58A	47 s. Mariposa, 1934		1·50	1·25
59A	1 p. 50, Matua, 1936		3·25	9·00
56A/9A		Set of 4	5·50	5·25

B. Both stamp and backing paper perf 14

56B	9 s. Type 10		35	55
57B	13 s. Tofua I, 1908		50	80
58B	47 s. Mariposa, 1934		1·10	1·60
59B	1 p. 50, Matua, 1936		2·50	4·00
56B/9B		Set of 4	4·00	6·25

For description of the two forms of perforation see after Tonga No. 864.

---

11 Preparing to fire Rocket

12 Halley's Comet, 684 A.D.

1985 (5 Nov). *Niuafo'ou Rocket Mails. T 11 and similar horiz designs.* Multicoloured. P 14.

60	32 s. Type 11		1·00	80
61	42 s. Rocket in flight		1·25	1·00
62	57 s. Ship's crew watching rocket's descent	1·60	1·40
63	1 p. 50, Islanders reading mail		3·50	4·50
60/3		Set of 4	6·50	7·00

(Des and litho Walsall)

1986 (26 Mar). *Appearance of Halley's Comet. T 12 and similar vert designs.* Multicoloured. P 14.

64	42 s. Type 12		5·00	3·00
	a. Horiz strip of 5. Nos. 64/8		23·00	
65	42 s. Halley's Comet, 1066, from Bayeux Tapestry		5·00	3·00
66	42 s. Edmond Halley		5·00	3·00
67	42 s. Halley's Comet, 1910		5·00	3·00
68	42 s. Halley's Comet, 1986		5·00	3·00
69	57 s. Type 12		5·00	3·50
	a. Horiz strip of 5. Nos. 69/73		23·00	
70	57 s. As No. 65		5·00	3·50
71	57 s. As No. 66		5·00	3·50
72	57 s. As No. 67		5·00	3·50
73	57 s. As No. 68		5·00	3·50
64/73		Set of 10	45·00	29·00

Nos. 64/8 and 69/73 were each printed together, se-tenant, in horizontal strips of five, forming composite designs, throughout the sheets.

X X

4s

(13)

14 Swimmers with Mail

1986 (16 Apr). *Nos. 32/9 surch as T 13 in blue.*

74	4 s. on 9 s. Green Honeyeater		75	1·25
75	4 s. on 10 s. Purple Swamphen		75	1·25
76	42 s. on 13 s. Banded Rail		2·00	1·50
77	42 s. on 15 s. Polynesian Scrub Hen		2·00	1·50
78	57 s. on 29 s. Red-headed Parrot Finch		2·50	2·00
79	57 s. on 32 s. White-collared Kingfisher		2·50	2·00
80	2 p. 50 on 20 s. Banded Rail		7·00	8·00
81	2 p. 50 on 47 s. Polynesian Scrub Hen		7·00	8·00
74/81		Set of 8	22·00	23·00

(Des and litho Walsall)

1986 (22 May). *"Ameripex '86" International Stamp Exhibition, Chicago. 25th Anniv of United States Peace Corps. Horiz designs as T 173 of Tonga.* Multicoloured. P 14.

82	57 s. Peace Corps surveyor and pipeline	1·25	1·25
83	1 p. 50, Inspecting crops		2·25	2·75
MS84	90 × 90 mm. Nos. 82/3, magnifying glass and tweezers. Imperf		3·75	5·00

(Des Walsall. Litho Questa)

1986 (27 Aug). *Centenary of First Tonga Stamps. T 14 and similar horiz designs showing Niuafo'ou mail transport.* Multicoloured. P 14.

85	42 s. Type 14		90	90
86	57 s. Collecting tin can mail		1·10	1·10
87	1 p. Ship firing mail rocket		2·00	2·50
88	2 p. 50, "Collecting the Mails" (detail)			
	(C. Mayger)		3·50	4·50
85/8		Set of 4	6·75	8·00
MS89	135 × 80 mm. No. 88		5·00	7·00

Nos. 85/8 were issued in sheets of twenty stamps and five se-tenant labels, in the central vertical column, showing the colour separations of the designs.

PRINTER AND PROCESS. The following issues to No. 269 were lithographed by Walsall Security Printers Ltd, unless otherwise stated.

15 Woman with Nourishing Foods ("Eat a balanced diet")

16 Hammerhead

(Des C. Abbott)

1987 (11 Mar). *Red Cross. Preventive Medicine. T* **15** *and similar horiz designs. Multicoloured. P* 14×14½.

90	15 s. Type **15**		60	60
91	42 s. Nurse with baby ("Give them post-natal care")		1·60	1·60
92	1 p. Man with insecticide ("Insects spread disease")		2·50	3·00
93	2 p. 50, Boxer ("Say no to alcohol, drugs, tobacco")		4·00	4·75
90/3		*Set of 4*	8·00	9·00

1987 (29 Apr). *Sharks. T* **16** *and similar horiz designs. Multicoloured. P* 14.

94	29 s. Type **16**		2·00	1·75
95	32 s. Tiger Shark		2·00	1·75
96	47 s. Grey Nurse Shark		2·50	2·25
97	1 p. Great White Shark		4·00	5·50
94/7		*Set of 4*	9·50	10·00
MS98	90×90 mm. 2 p. Shark and fishes		11·00	12·00

17 Capt. E. C. Musick and
Sikorsky S.42A Flying Boat
Samoan Clipper

1987 (2 Sept). *Air Pioneers of the South Pacific. T* **17** *and similar horiz designs. Multicoloured. P* 14.

99	42 s. Type **17**		1·40	1·40
100	57 s. Capt. J. W. Burgess and Short S.30 modified "G" Class flying boat *Aotearoa*		1·75	1·75
101	1 p. 50, Sir Charles Kingsford Smith and Fokker F.VIIa/3m *Southern Cross*		2·50	3·00
102	2 p. Amelia Earhart and Lockheed 10E *Electra*		3·00	3·50
99/102		*Set of 4*	7·75	8·75

18 Polynesian Scrub Hen and
1983 1 s. Map Definitive

19 Sailing Ship and
Ship's Boat

1988 (18 May). *5th Anniversaries of First Niuafo'ou Postage Stamp* (42, 57 s.) *or Niuafo'ou Airport Inauguration* (1, 2 p.). *T* **18** *and similar horiz designs. Multicoloured. P* 14.

103	42 s. Type **18**		80	75
104	57 s. As Type **18** but with stamp at left		1·00	95
105	1 p. Concorde and 1983 Airport Inauguration 29 s. stamp		3·00	3·00
106	2 p. As 1 p., but with stamp at left		3·50	3·75
103/6		*Set of 4*	7·50	7·50

1988 (11 July). *Bicentenary of Australian Settlement. Sheet* 115 × 110 *mm containing T* **19** *and similar vert designs. Multicoloured. P* 13½.

MS107 42 s. Type **19**; 42 s. Aborigines; 42 s. Early settlement; 42 s. Marine and convicts; 42 s. Sheep station; 42 s. Mounted stockman; 42 s. Kangaroos and early Trans Continental locomotive; 42 s. Kangaroos and train carriages; 42 s. Flying Doctor aircraft; 42 s. Cricket match; 42 s. Wicket and Sydney skyline; 42 s. Fielders and Sydney Harbour Bridge .. 28·00 28·00

Each horizontal strip of 4 within No. **MS**107 shows a composite design.

No. **MS**107 exists overprinted on the reverse as described below Nos. 985/8 of Tonga.

20 Audubon's
Shearwaters and
Blowholes, Houma,
Tonga

21 Sextant

1988 (18 Aug). *Islands of Polynesia. T* **20** *and similar vert designs. Multicoloured. P* 14.

108	42 s. Type **20**		95	95
109	57 s. Brown Kiwi at Akaroa Harbour, New Zealand		1·40	1·40
110	90 s. Red-tailed Tropic Birds at Rainmaker Mountain, Samoa		2·00	2·25
111	2 p. 50, Laysan Albatross at Kapoho Volcano, Hawaii		4·50	5·50
108/11		*Set of 4*	8·00	9·00

1989 (28 Apr). *Bicentenary of Mutiny on the Bounty. Sheet* 115×110 *mm containing T* **21** *and similar vert designs. Multicoloured. P* 13½.

MS112 42 s. Type **21**; 42 s. Capt. Bligh; 42 s. Lieutenant, 1787; 42 s. Midshipman, 1787; 42 s. Tahitian woman and contemporary newspaper; 42 s. Breadfruit plant; 42 s. Pistol and extract from *Mutiny on the Bounty*; 42 s. Book illustration of Bligh cast adrift; 42 s. Profile of Tahitian woman and extract from contemporary newspaper; 42 s. Signatures of *Bounty* officers; 42 s. Fletcher Christian; 42 s. Tombstone of John Adams, Pitcairn Island .. .. .. 13·00 14·00

 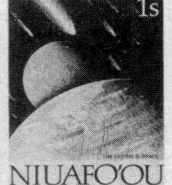

22 Spiny Hatchetfish

23 Formation of
Earth's Surface

1989 (2 June). *Fishes of the Deep. T* **22** *and similar horiz designs. Multicoloured. P* 14.

113	32 s. Type **22**		85	1·00
114	42 s. Snipe Eel		1·00	1·00
115	57 s. Viperfish		1·25	1·50
116	1 p. 50, Football Anglerfish		3·00	3·75
113/16		*Set of 4*	5·50	6·50

Nos. 113/16 exist overprinted on the reverse as described below Nos. 985/8 of Tonga.

(Des R. Edge)

1989 (6 June)–93. *The Evolution of the Earth. T* **23** *and similar vert designs. Multicoloured.*

(a) *Size* 27×35½ *mm. P* 14½

117	1 s. Type **23**		10	10
118	2 s. Cross-section of Earth's crust		10	10
119	5 s. Volcano		10	10
120	10 s. Cross-section of Earth during cooling		10	10
120a	13 s. Gem stones (3.5.93)		10	15
121	15 s. Sea		10	15
122	20 s. Mountains		15	20
123	32 s. River gorge		25	30
124	42 s. Early plant life, Silurian era		30	35
124a	45 s. Early marine life (3.5.93)		35	40
125	50 s. Fossils and Cambrian lifeforms		40	45
126	57 s. Carboniferous forest and coal seams		45	50
126a	60 s. Dinosaurs feeding (3.5.93)		45	50
126b	80 s. Tyrannosaurus fighting Triceratops (3.5.93)		60	65

(b) *Size* 25½×40 *mm. P* 14

127	1 p. Dragonfly and amphibians, Carboniferous era (1.8.89)		80	85
128	1 p. Dinosaurs, Jurassic era (1.8.89)		1·10	1·25
129	2 p. Archaeopteryx and mammals, Jurassic era (1.8.89)		1·60	1·75
130	5 p. Human family and domesticated dog, Pleistocene era (1.8.89)		4·00	4·25
130a	10 p. Mammoth and Sabre-tooth Tiger (14.9.93)		7·75	8·00
117/30a		*Set of 19*	19·00	20·00

Nos. 130/a were each printed in sheetlets of 12 (3×4) containing 10 stamps and 2 stamp-size labels in the centre of rows 2 and 3.

24 Astronaut on
Moon and Newspaper
Headline

25 Lake Vai Lahi

1989 (17 Nov). *"World Stamp Expo '89" International Stamp Exhibition, Washington. P* 14.

131	**24** 57 s. multicoloured		1·00	1·00

1989 (17 Nov). *20th Universal Postal Union Congress, Washington. Miniature sheet,* 185 × 150 *mm, containing designs as Nos.* 117/31, *but with U.P.U. emblem at top right and some new values. P* 14½×14 (*top two rows*) *or* 14 (*bottom row*).

MS132 32 s. × 5 (as Nos. 117/21); 42 s. × 5 (as Nos. 122/6); 57 s. × 5 (as Nos. 127/31) .. 17·00 19·00

On No. **MS**132 the row of five 57 s. values are at the foot of the sheet and are perforated in a different gauge from the top two rows.

No. **MS**132 exists overprinted on the reverse as described below Nos. 985/8 of Tonga.

1990 (4 Apr). *Niuafo'ou Crater Lake. T* **25** *and similar horiz designs. Multicoloured. P* 14.

133	42 s. Type **25**		70	90
	a. Sheetlet. Nos. 133/8		5·50	
134	42 s. Islands in centre of lake		70	90
135	42 s. South-west end of lake and islet		70	90
136	1 p. Type **25**		1·40	1·50
137	1 p. As No. 134		1·40	1·50
138	1 p. As No. 135		1·40	1·50
133/8		*Set of 6*	5·50	6·50

Nos. 133/8 were printed together, *se-tenant*, as a sheetlet of six containing horizontal strips of three of each value forming composite designs and separated by an inscribed horizontal gutter.

26 Penny Black and Tin Can
Mail Service

1990 (1 May). *150th Anniv of the Penny Black. T* **26** *and similar horiz designs, each showing stamp and Tin Can Mail. Multicoloured. P* 14.

139	42 s. Type **26**		80	80
140	57 s. U.S.A. 1847 10 c.		1·10	1·25
141	75 s. Western Australia 1854 1d.		1·25	1·50
142	2 p. 50, Mafeking Siege 1900 1d.		4·00	4·75
139/42		*Set of 4*	6·50	7·50

27 Humpback Whale surfacing

(Des G. Bennett)

1990 (6 June–4 Sept). *Polynesian Whaling. T* **27** *and similar horiz designs. Multicoloured. P* 11½.

143	15 s. Type **27**		1·75	1·60
144	42 s. Whale diving under canoe		2·25	1·90
145	57 s. Tail of Blue Whale		2·50	1·90
146	2 p. Old man and pair of whales		6·50	7·50
143/6		*Set of 4*	11·50	11·50
MS147	120×93 mm. 1 p. Pair of whales (38×30 mm). P 14×14½ (4 Sept)		10·00	11·00

No. **MS**147 shows "1990A" as an imprint on the 1p. stamp. Examples of this miniature sheet with "1990" as the imprint were mainly used for the surcharge, No. **MS**156, although a few unsurcharged examples with this imprint were used on Niuafo'ou in 1991.

(Des A. Benjamin and R. Edge)

1990 (25 Oct). *40th Anniv of United Nations Development Programme. Horiz designs as T* **203** *of Tonga. Multicoloured. P* 13½×14.

148	57 s. Agriculture and Fisheries		90	1·25
	a. Pair. Nos. 148/9		1·75	2·50
149	57 s. Education		90	1·25
150	2 p. 50, Healthcare		3·25	3·75
	a. Pair. Nos. 150/1		6·50	7·50
151	2 p. 50, Communications		3·25	3·75
148/51		*Set of 4*	7·50	9·00

The two designs for each value were printed together, *se-tenant*, in horizontal and vertical pairs throughout the sheets.

28 H.M.S. *Bounty* (29)

(Des D. Miller)

1991 (25 July). *Bicentenary of Charting of Niuafo'ou. T* **28** *and similar vert designs. Multicoloured. P* 14½×14.

152	32 s. Type **28**		1·00	1·50
	a. Horiz strip of 3. Nos. 152/4		3·00	
153	42 s. Chart of *Pandora's* course		1·10	1·50
154	57 s. H.M.S. *Pandora* (frigate)		1·25	1·50
152/4		*Set of 3*	3·00	4·00
MS155	120×93 mm. 2 p. Capt. Edwards of the *Pandora*; 3 p. Capt. Bligh of the *Bounty*		11·00	12·00

Nos. 152/4 were printed together, *se-tenant*, in horizontal strips of three throughout the sheet.

1991 (31 July). *Ornithological and Scientific Expedition to Niuafo'ou. No.* **MS**147 *surch with T* **29** *in blue by Govt. Printer, Tonga.*

MS156 120×93 mm. 1 p. on 1 p. multicoloured .. 2·75 3·50

No. **MS**156 shows "1990" as the imprint date.

30 Longhorned Beetle Grub	**31** Heina meeting the Eel

(Des G. Bennett)

1991 (11 Sept). *Longhorned Beetle. T* **30** *and similar vert designs. Multicoloured. P* 14½×14.

157	42 s. Type **30**		..	80	80
158	57 s. Adult beetle	..	..	90	90
159	1 p. 50, Grub burrowing	..	..	2·75	3·00
160	2 p. 50, Adult on treetrunk	..	..	4·00	4·25
157/60	.. ..		*Set of 4*	7·50	8·00

(Des D. Miller)

1991 (12 Nov). *Christmas. The Legend of the Coconut Tree. T* **31** *and similar horiz designs. Multicoloured. P* 14×14½.

161	15 s. Type **31**	..	..	35	40
162	42 s. Heina crying over the eel's grave			90	1·00
MS163	96×113 mm. 15 s. Type **31**; 42 s. No. 162; 1 p. 50, Heina's son collecting coconuts; 3 p. Milk flowing from coconut		..	9·00	10·00

(Des R. Edge)

1992 (28 Apr). *500th Anniv of Discovery of America by Columbus. Sheet* 119×109 *mm. containing vert designs as T* **214** *of Tonga. P* 13½.

MS164 57 s. Columbus; 57 s. Queen Isabella and King Ferdinand; 57 s. Columbus being blessed by Abbot of Palos; 57 s. 15th-century compass; 57 s. Wooden traverse, windrose and the *Nina*; 57 s. Bow of *Santa Maria*; 57 s. Stern of *Santa Maria*; 57 s. The *Pinta*; 57 s. Crew erecting cross; 57 s. Sailors and Indians; 57 s. Columbus reporting to King and Queen; 57 s. Coat of Arms .. 17·00 18·00

(Des R. Edge)

1992 (12 May). *50th Anniv of Outbreak of Pacific War. Horiz designs as T* **215** *of Tonga, each showing contemporary newspaper headline. Multicoloured. P* 14.

165	42 s. American battleship ablaze, Pearl Harbor		..	1·10	1·25
	a. Sheetlet. Nos. 165/76		..	12·00	
166	42 s. Destroyed American Douglas B-18 Bolo aircraft, Hawaii			1·10	1·25
167	42 s. Japanese Mitsubishi A6M Zero-Sen fighter			1·10	1·25
168	42 s. Pres. Roosevelt signing Declaration of War			1·10	1·25
169	42 s. Japanese T **95** light tank and Gen. MacArthur			1·10	1·25
170	42 s. Douglas SBD Dauntless dive bomber and Admiral Nimitz			1·10	1·25
171	42 s. Bren gun and Gen. Sir Thomas Blamey		1·10	1·25
172	42 s. Australian mortar crew, Kokoda	..	1·10	1·25
173	42 s. U.S.S. *Mississippi* (battleship) in action and Maj-Gen. Julian C. Smith			1·10	1·25
174	42 s. U.S.S. *Enterprise* (aircraft carrier)	..	1·10	1·25
175	42 s. American marine and Maj-Gen. Curtis Lemay			1·10	1·25
176	42 s. Boeing B-29 Superfortress bomber and Japanese surrender, Tokyo Bay			1·10	1·25
165/76	.. .. ..		*Set of 12*	12·00	13·50

Nos. 165/76 were printed together, *se-tenant*, in sheetlets of 12 (4×3) with each horizontal row forming a composite design.

(Des R. Edge)

1992 (4 July). *25th Anniv of the Coronation of King Tupou IV. Horiz designs as T* **217** *of Tonga. P* 13½×13 (45 s.) *or* 12 (*others*).

177	45 s. multicoloured	..	..	75	75
178	80 s. multicoloured	..	..	1·50	1·75
	a. Horiz strip of 3. Nos. 178/80		..	4·00	
179	80 s. black and cinnamon	..	..	1·50	1·75
180	80 s. multicoloured	..	..	1·50	1·75
181	2 p. multicoloured	..	..	2·75	3·00
177/81	.. ..		*Set of 5*	7·00	8·00

Designs: (34×23 *mm*)—No. 177, King Taufa'ahau Tupou IV and Queen Halaevalu during Coronation; (48×35 *mm*)—No. 178, King Tupou IV and Tongan national anthem; No. 179, Extract from Investiture ceremony; No. 180 Tongan choir; No. 181, As 45 s.

Nos. 177/81 show the King's first name incorrectly spelt as "Tauf'ahau".

Nos. 178/80 were printed together, *se-tenant*, in horizontal strips of 3 throughout the sheet.

32 Male and Female Scrub Hens searching for Food	**33** 1983 2s. Map and 1993 60s. Dinosaur Definitives

(Des G. Bennett)

1992 (15 Sept). *Endangered Species. Polynesian Scrub Hen. T* **32** *and similar horiz designs. P* 14.

182	45 s. Type **32**	..	..	1·00	1·25
183	60 s. Female guarding egg	..	..	1·25	1·40
184	80 s. Chick	..	..	1·60	1·75
185	1 p. 50, Head of male	..	..	2·75	3·50
182/5	.. ..		*Set of 4*	6·00	7·00

(Des D. Miller)

1993 (3 May). *10th Anniv of First Niuafo'ou Stamp. T* **33** *and similar horiz design. Multicoloured. P* 14×14½.

186	60 s. Type **33**	..	..	1·00	1·10
187	80 s. 1983 5 s. map and 1993 80 s. dinosaur definitives			1·25	1·40

34 De Havilland D.H.C.6 Twin Otter 200/300 of South Pacific Island Airways	**35** Blue-crowned Lory

(Des D. Miller)

1993 (3 May). *10th Anniv of First Flight to Niuafo'ou. T* **34** *and similar horiz designs. Multicoloured. P* 14×14½.

188	1 p. Type **34**	..	..	1·50	2·00
189	2 p. 50, De Havilland D.H.C.6 Twin Otter 200/300 of Friendly Islands Airways			3·50	4·25

(Des D. Miller)

1993 (1 July). *75th Birthday of King Taufa'ahau Tupou IV. Vert designs as T* **229** *of Tonga. Multicoloured. P* 13×13½ (45 s.) *or* 12 (*others*).

190	45 s. King Tupou IV and *Pangai* (patrol boat)			55	55
191	80 s. King Tupou IV and musical instruments (38½×51 *mm*)			1·25	1·75
	a. Strip of 3. Nos. 191/3			3·25	
192	80 s. King Tupou IV and sporting events (38½×51 *mm*)			1·25	1·75
193	80 s. King Tupou IV with De Havilland D.H.C.6 Twin Otter 200/300 aircraft and telecommunications (38½×51 *mm*)			1·25	1·75
194	2 p. As 45 s., but larger (38½×51 *mm*)			2·75	3·00
190/4	.. ..		*Set of 5*	6·50	8·00

Nos. 191/3 were printed together, *se-tenant*, in horizontal and vertical strips of 3 throughout the sheet of 9.

(Des G. Bennett)

1993 (10 Aug). *Natural History of Lake Vai Lahi. T* **35** *and similar vert designs. Multicoloured. P* 14.

195	60 s. Type **35**	..	..	1·00	1·25
	a. Horiz strip of 5. Nos. 195/9			4·50	
196	60 s. White-tailed Tropic Bird and Eastern Reef Heron			1·00	1·25
197	60 s. Black Admiral (butterfly) and Niuafo'ou Coconut Beetle			1·00	1·25
198	60 s. Niuafo'ou Dragonfly, Spotbill Ducks and Niuafo'ou Moths			1·00	1·25
199	60 s. Niuafo'ou Megapode	..	..	1·00	1·25
195/9	.. ..		*Set of 5*	4·50	5·50

Nos. 195/9 were printed together, *se-tenant*, in horizontal strips of five throughout the sheet, each strip forming a composite design.

1993 (1 Dec). *Children's Painting Competition Winners. Vert designs as T* **231** *of Tonga. P* 14.

200	10 s. multicoloured	..	..	40	55
	a. Pair. Nos. 200/1		..	80	1·10
201	10 s. black and grey-black	..	..	40	55
202	1 p. multicoloured	..	..	2·75	3·00
	a. Pair. Nos. 202/3		..	5·50	6·00
203	1 p. multicoloured	..	..	2·75	3·00
200/3	.. ..		*Set of 4*	5·75	6·50

Designs:—Nos. 200 and 202, "Crater Lake Megapode and Volcano" (Paea Puletau); Nos. 201 and 203, "Ofato Beetle Grubs of Niuafo'ou" (Peni Finau).

Nos. 200/1 and 202/3 were each printed together, *se-tenant*, in horizontal and vertical pairs throughout separate sheetlets of 12.

36 Scarabaeidea	**37** Stern of H.M.S. *Bounty*

(Des G. Bennett)

1994 (15 Mar). *Beetles. T* **36** *and similar horiz designs. Multicoloured. P* 14.

204	60 s. Type **36**	..	..	85	1·00
205	80 s. Coccinellidea	..	..	1·10	1·40
206	1 p. 50, Cerambycidea	..	..	2·00	2·50
207	2 p. 50, Pentatomidae	..	..	3·75	4·25
204/7	.. ..		*Set of 4*	7·00	8·25

(Des G. Bennett)

1994 (21 June). *Sailing Ships. T* **37** *and similar vert designs. Multicoloured. P* 14.

208	80 s. Type **37**	..	..	1·75	2·00
	a. Horiz strip of 5. Nos. 208/12			8·00	
209	80 s. Bow of H.M.S. *Bounty*	..	1·75	2·00
210	80 s. H.M.S. *Pandora* (frigate)	..	1·75	2·00
211	80 s. Whaling ship	..	..	1·75	2·00
212	80 s. Trading schooner	..	..	1·75	2·00
208/12	.. ..		*Set of 5*	8·00	9·00

Nos. 208/12 were printed together, *se-tenant*, in horizontal strips of 5 throughout the sheet.

SAVE THE WHALES

38 Blue-crowned Lory and Lava Flows	(**39**)

(Des D. Miller)

1994 (21 Sept). *Volcanic Eruptions on Niuafo'ou. T* **38** *and similar vert designs. Multicoloured. P* 14½.

213	80 s. Type **38**	..	..	1·25	1·50
	a. Horiz strip. Nos. 213/17			5·75	
214	80 s. Spotbill Ducks over lava flows		1·25	1·50
215	80 s. Megapodes and palm trees	..	1·25	1·50
216	80 s. White-tailed Tropic Birds and inhabitants			1·25	1·50
217	80 s. Eastern Reef Heron and evacuation, 1946			1·25	1·50
213/17	..		*Set of 5*	5·75	6·75

Nos. 213/17 were printed together, *se-tenant*, in horizontal strips of 5 throughout the sheet with the backgrounds forming a composite design.

1995 (30 June). *Visit South Pacific Year '95. Save the Whales. Nos.* 143/7 *surch as T* **39** *in blue.*

218	60 s. on 42 s. Whale diving under canoe	..	1·75	1·75
219	80 s. on 15 s. Type **27**	..	..	2·00	2·00
220	80 s. on 57 s. Tail of Blue Whale	..	2·00	2·00
221	2 p. on 2 p. Old man and pair of whales		3·75	3·75
218/21	.. ..		*Set of 4*	8·50	8·50
MS222	120×93 mm. 1 p. 50 on 1 p. Pair of whales (38×30 *mm*)		..	3·25	4·00

(Des D. Miller)

1995 (1 Aug). *50th Anniv of End of Second World War in the Pacific. Vert designs as T* **242** *of Tonga. P* 14½.

223	60 s. greenish yellow, black and new blue		1·25	1·25
	a. Sheetlet. Nos. 223/32			11·00	
224	60 s. greenish yellow, black and new blue		1·25	1·25
225	60 s. greenish yellow, black and new blue		1·25	1·25
226	60 s. greenish yellow, black and new blue		1·25	1·25
227	60 s. greenish yellow, black and new blue		1·25	1·25
228	80 s. greenish yellow, black and rosine		1·25	1·25
229	80 s. greenish yellow, black and rosine		1·25	1·25
230	80 s. greenish yellow, black and rosine		1·25	1·25
231	80 s. greenish yellow, black and rosine		1·25	1·25
232	80 s. greenish yellow, black and rosine		1·25	1·25
223/32	..		*Set of 10*	11·00	11·00

Designs:—Nos. 223 and 228, American marine; Nos. 224 and 229, Marine firing and side of tank; Nos. 225 and 230, Tank; Nos. 226 and 231, Marines leaving landing craft; Nos. 227 and 232, Beach assault and palm trees.

Nos. 223/32 were printed together, *se-tenant*, in sheetlets of 10 with the horizontal strips of 5 forming the same composite design.

(Des D. Miller)

1995 (1 Sept). *"Singapore '95" International Stamp Exhibition. Multicoloured designs as T* **243** *of Tonga each with exhibition emblem. P* 12.

233	45 s. Dinosaurs feeding (as No. 126a) (*vert*)		1·00	1·25
	a. Vert pair. Nos. 233/4			2·00	2·50
234	60 s. Tyrannosaurus fighting Triceratops (as No. 126b) (*vert*)			1·00	1·25
MS235	110×70 mm. 2 p. Plesiosaurus	..	2·50	3·25

Nos. 233/4 were printed together, *se-tenant* vertically, in sheets of 10.

(Des Li Defu)

1995 (14 Sept). *Beijing International Coin and Stamp Show '95. Sheet* 143×87 *mm. containing horiz design as T* **244** *of Tonga. Multicoloured. P* 14½.

MS236 1 p. 40, The Great Wall of China .. 2·00 2·50

(Des K. McGee)

1995 (20 Oct). *50th Anniv of United Nations and End of Second World War. Designs as T 245 of Tonga. P 13×13½.*

237	60 s. multicoloured	..	1·00	1·25
	a. Horiz strip of 3. Nos. 237/9	..	2·75	
238	60 s. black and bright blue	..	1·00	1·25
239	60 s. multicoloured	..	1·00	1·25
240	80 s. multicoloured	..	1·25	1·40
	a. Horiz strip of 3. Nos. 240/2	..	3·25	
241	80 s. bright blue and black	..	1·25	1·40
242	80 s. multicoloured	..	1·25	1·40
237/42		*Set of 6*	6·00	7·00

Designs: *Horiz* (as Type 245 of Tonga)—No. 237, St. Paul's Cathedral and searchlights; No. 239, Concorde; No. 240, Allied prisoners of war and Burma Railway; No. 242, Mt Fuji and express train. *Vert* (25×35 mm)—Nos. 238 and 241, U.N. anniversary emblem.

Nos. 237/9 and 240/2 were printed together, *se-tenant*, in horizontal strips of 3 throughout the sheets.

40 Charles Ramsay and Swimmers with Poles

41 Island and Two Canoes

(Des A. Benjamin (3 p.), G. Bennett (others))

1996 (21 Aug). *Tin Can Mail Pioneers. T 40 and similar horiz designs. Multicoloured. P 14.*

243	45 s. Type 40		90	90
244	60 s. Charles Ramsay and encounter with shark	..	1·25	1·25
245	1 p. Walter Quensell and transferring mail from canoes to ship	..	2·00	2·00
246	3 p. Walter Quensell and Tin Can Mail cancellations	..	6·00	6·00
243/6		*Set of 4*	9·00	9·00

(Des D. Miller)

1996 (5 Sept). *13th Congress of International Union of Prehistoric and Protohistoric Sciences, Forli, Italy. Horiz design as T 250 of Tonga. Multicoloured. P 12.*

247	1 p. Cave painting, lake village and hunter	2·25	2·25
	a. Horiz pair. Nos. 247/8	4·50	4·50
248	1 p. Egyptians with Pyramid, Greek temple, and Romans with Colosseum	2·25	2·25

Nos. 247/8 were printed together, *se-tenant*, in sheetlets of 6 (2×3).

(Des D. Miller)

1996 (29 Oct). *50th Anniv of U.N.I.C.E.F. Children's Toys. Vert designs as T 252 of Tonga. Multicoloured. P 14.*

249	80 s. Dolls, model truck and counting balls	1·25	1·50
	a. Horiz strip of 3. Nos. 249/51	3·50	
250	80 s. Teddy bear, tricycle and model car	1·25	1·50
251	80 s. Book, model helicopter, pedal car and roller skates	1·25	1·50
249/51		*Set of 3*	4·00	4·00

Nos. 249/51 were printed together, *se-tenant*, in horizontal strips of three throughout the sheet, each strip forming a composite design.

(Des G. Bennett)

1996 (2 Dec). *50th Anniv of Evacuation of Niuafo'ou. T 41 and similar vert designs. Multicoloured. P 14.*

252	45 s. Type 41		85	90
	a. Horiz strip of 5. Nos. 252/6	3·75	
253	45 s. Erupting volcano and canoes	85	90
254	45 s. End of island, volcanic cloud and canoe	85	90
255	45 s. Family and livestock in outrigger canoe	85	90
256	45 s. Islanders reaching *Matua* (inter-island freighter)	85	90
257	60 s. Type 41		95	1·00
	a. Horiz strip of 5. Nos. 257/61	4·25	
258	60 s. As No. 253	95	1·00
259	60 s. As No. 254	95	1·00
260	60 s. As No. 255	95	1·00
261	60 s. As No. 256	95	1·00
252/61		*Set of 10*	8·00	8·50

Nos. 252/6 and 257/61 were each printed together, *se-tenant*, in sheetlets of 10 with the horizontal strips of 5 forming the same composite design.

42 Plankton

43 Blue-crowned Lory Nestlings

(Des D. Miller)

1997 (19 May). *The Ocean Environment. T 42 and similar horiz designs showing different plankton. P 14.*

262	60 s. multicoloured	..	1·00	1·00
263	80 s. multicoloured	..	1·25	1·25
264	1 p. 50, multicoloured	..	2·25	2·50
265	2 p. 50, multicoloured	..	3·00	3·50
262/5		*Set of 4*	6·75	7·50

(Des D. Miller)

1997 (30 May). *"Pacific '97" International Stamp Exhibition, San Francisco. Sheet 85×110 mm, containing design as T 259 of Tonga. Multicoloured. P 14.*

MS266	2 p. Black-naped Tern	..	2·75	3·25

(Des D. Miller)

1997 (30 June). *King and Queen of Tonga's Golden Wedding and 30th Anniv of Coronation. Multicoloured designs as T 261 of Tonga, but 50×37 mm. P 12.*

267	80 s. King and Queen on wedding day	..	1·25	1·50
	a. Vert pair. Nos. 267/8	..	2·50	3·00
268	80 s. King Tupou in Coronation robes	..	1·25	1·50
MS269	82×70 mm. 5 p. King Tupou with pages (*horiz*)	..	7·00	7·50

Nos. 267/8 were printed together, *se-tenant*, as vertical pairs in sheets of 6.

(Des G. Bennett. Litho Southern Colour Print, Dunedin)

1998 (15 May). *Endangered Species. Blue-crowned Lory. T 43 and similar vert designs. Multicoloured. P 14½×15.*

270	10 s. Type 43		50	50
271	55 s. Feeding on flowers	..	1·00	85
272	80 s. Perched on branch	..	1·25	1·00
273	3 p. Pair on branch	..	4·00	4·50
270/3		*Set of 4*	6·00	6·25
MS274	160×112 mm. Nos. 270/3×2	..	11·00	11·00

(Des D. Miller. Litho Enschedé)

1998 (29 May). *Diana, Princess of Wales Commemoration. Sheet, 145×70 mm, containing vert designs as T 91 of Kiribati. Multicoloured. P 13½×14.*

MS275	10 s. Princess Diana in tartan jacket, 1987; 80 s. Wearing white dress, 1992; 1 p. Wearing check jacket, 1993; 2 p. 50, Wearing black jacket (*sold at 4 p. 40 + 50 s. charity premium*)	5·50	6·00

(Litho and die-stamped Southern Colour Print, Dunedin)

1998 (4 July). *80th Birthday of King Taufa'ahau Tupou IV. Portrait as T 263 of Tonga. P 14.*

276	2 p. 70, multicoloured	..	2·50	3·00

(Des Karen Odiam. Litho Southern Colour Print, Dunedin)

1998 (23 July). *Chinese New Year ("Year of the Tiger"). Sheet, 126×85 mm, containing horiz designs as T 248 of Tonga, each showing tiger and quarter segment of clock face. Multicoloured. P 14×14½.*

MS277	55 s. Top left quarter; 80 s. Top right quarter; 1 p. Bottom left quarter; 1 p. Bottom right quarter	3·00	3·25

No. **MS277** also includes "SINGPEX '98" Stamp Exhibition, Singapore emblem on the sheet margin.

(Des Sue Wickison. Litho Southern Colour Print, Dunedin)

1998 (14 Oct). *International Year of the Ocean. Horiz designs as T 265 of Tonga. Multicoloured. P 14.*

278	10 s. *Amphiprion melanopus*		40	50
	a. Strip of 3. Nos. 278/80	2·00	
279	55 s. *Amphiprion perideraion*	80	90
280	80 s. *Amphiprion chrysopterus*	1·00	1·10
278/80		*Set of 3*	2·00	2·25

No. 278/80 were printed together, *se-tenant*, in horizontal and vertical strips of 3 throughout the sheets of 9.

1998 (25 Nov). *Christmas. Vert designs as T 266 of Tonga. Multicoloured. P 14×14½.*

281	20 s. Angel playing lute (inscr in Tongan)	40	40
282	55 s. Angel playing violin (inscr in English)	75	55
283	1 p. Children and bells (inscr in Tongan)	1·10	1·10
284	1 p. 60, Children and candles (inscr in English)	1·50	2·00
281/4		*Set of 4*	3·25	3·50

(Des Julie Greig. Litho Southern Colour Print, Dunedin)

1999 (16 Feb). *Chinese New Year ("Year of the Rabbit"). Sheet 126×85 mm, containing horiz designs as T 267 of Tonga, showing rabbits and segments of flower (each red, greenish yellow and bluish grey). P 14×14½.*

MS285	10 s. Rabbit on hind legs and segment of flower; 55 s. Rabbit facing left; 80 s. Rabbit facing right; 1 p. Two rabbits	2·50	2·75

44 *Eendracht* (Le Maire)

45 Dove over Tafahi Island

(Des T. Crilley. Litho Southern Colour Print, Dunedin)

1999 (19 Mar). *Early Explorers. T 44 and similar horiz design. Multicoloured. P 14×14½.*

286	80 s. Type 44		1·00	90
287	2 p. 70, Tongiaki (outrigger canoe)	..	2·50	2·75
MS288	120×72 mm. Nos. 286/7	..	3·50	3·75

No. **MS288** also includes the "Australia '99" emblem on the sheet margin.

(Des R. Youmans. Litho Cartor)

1999 (29 Sept). *Fragrant Flowers. Multicoloured designs as T 270 of Tonga. P 13×13½ (horiz) or 13½×13 (vert).*

289	55 s. *Cananga odorata*		65	50
290	80 s. *Gardenia tannaensis* (vert)		85	80
291	1 p. *Coleus amboinicus* (vert)		1·10	1·10
292	2 p. 50, *Hernandia moerenhoutiana*		2·50	2·75
289/92		*Set of 4*	4·50	4·75

(Des D. Gunson. Litho Southern Colour Print, Dunedin)

2000 (1 Jan). *New Millennium. Sheet, 120×80 mm, containing T 45 and similar vert design. Multicoloured. P 14½×15.*

MS293	1 p. Type 45; 2 p. 50, Kalia (traditional canoe) passing island	2·50	2·75

(Des Helen Ngan. Litho Southern Colour Print, Dunedin)

2000 (4 Feb). *Chinese New Year ("Year of the Dragon"). Sheet, 126×85 mm, containing horiz designs as T 273 of Tonga. Multicoloured. P 14½.*

MS294	10 s. Dragon in the sky (facing right); 55 s. Dragon in the sky (facing left); 80 s. Sea dragon (facing right); 1 p. Sea dragon (facing left)	1·90	2·00

Transjordan

Transjordan was part of the Turkish Empire from 1516 to 1918.

Turkish post offices are known to have existed at Ajlun ("Adjiloun"), Amman ("Omman"), Amman Station, Kerak ("Kerek"), Ma'an ("Mohan" or "Maan"), Qatrana, Salt and Tafila ("Tafile"). Stamps cancelled "Ibin" may have been used at Ibbin.

The area was overrun by British and Arab forces, organised by Colonel T. E. Lawrence, in September 1918, and as Occupied Enemy Territory (East), became part of the Syrian state under the Emir Faisal, who was king of Syria from 11 March to 24 July 1920. During 1920 the stamps of the Arab Kingdom of Syria were in use. On 25 April 1920 the Supreme Council of the Allies assigned to the United Kingdom a mandate to administer both Palestine and Transjordan, as the area to the east of the Jordan was called. The mandate came into operation on 29 September 1923.

E.E.F. post offices, using the stamps of Palestine, operated in the area from September 1918.

BRITISH MANDATED TERRITORY

(Currency. 1000 milliemes = 100 piastres = £1 Egyptian)

"EAST". Where the word "East" appears in the Arabic overprints it is not used in its widest sense but as implying the land or government "East of Jordan".

("East of Jordan")
(1)   (1a)

(Optd at Greek Orthodox Convent, Jerusalem)

1920 (Nov). *T* 3 *of Palestine optd with* T 1. (a) P 15 × 14.
1	1	1 m. sepia		50	1·25
		a. Opt inverted		£120	£250
2		2 m. blue-green		7·50	8·50
		a. Silver opt			
3		3 m. yellow-brown		90	1·25
		a. Opt Type 1a		£1100	
4		4 m. scarlet		95	
5		5 m. yellow-orange		1·50	1·25
5a		1 p. deep indigo (Silver)		£2000	
6		2 p. olive		3·25	5·50
		a. Opt Type 1a		£850	
7		5 p. deep purple		25·00	28·00
		a. Opt Type 1a		£1400	
8		9 p. ochre		£800	£1400
1/7 (ex 5a)			Set of 7	35·00	42·00

(b) P 14
9	1	1 m. sepia		1·25	1·40
		a. Opt inverted		£150	
10		2 m. blue-green		50	70
		a. Silver opt		£550	£600
11		3 m. yellow-brown		16·00	16·00
12		4 m. scarlet		15·00	18·00
13		5 m. orange		2·00	80
14		1 p. deep indigo (Silver)		1·50	1·75
15		2 p. deep olive		3·50	3·00
16		5 p. purple		2·50	6·00
17		9 p. ochre		3·50	20·00
18		10 p. ultramarine		4·25	20·00
19		20 p. pale grey		8·00	35·00
9/19			Set of 11	50·00	£110

Nos. 1/9 were surcharged from five different settings of 120 (12×10) which produced eight sub-types of Type 1. Type 1a occurred on R. 8/12 from one setting. The 9 p. also exists with this overprint, but no example appears to have survived without further overprint or surcharge.

1b Moab District Seal (*full size*)

1920 (Nov). *Issued at Kerak. Handstamped. Manuscript initials "AK" in violet. Imperf.*
19a	1b	(1 p.) pale blue		£3500	£4000

No. 19a was issued in November 1920 by the political officer for Moab District, Captain (later Sir) Alex Kirkbride, and was used until supplies of Nos. 1/19 reached the area in March 1921. The local Turkish canceller was used as a postmark.

Emir Abdullah, 1 April 1921–22 May 1946

Abdullah, a son of the King of the Hejaz, was made Emir of Transjordan in 1921. On 26 May 1923 Transjordan was recognised as an autonomous state and on 20 February 1928 it was accorded a degree of independence.

("Tenth of a piastre")   ("Piastre")
(2)   (3)

1922 (Nov). *Nos.* 1/19 *additionally handstamped with steel dies at Amman as* T 2 *or* 3. (a) P 15 × 14.
20	2	1/10 p. on 1 m. sepia		25·00	45·00
		a. Red surch		70·00	70·00
		b. Violet surch		70·00	70·00
21		2/10 p. on 2 m. blue-green		28·00	28·00
		a. Error. Surch "3/10" for "2/10"		£110	£100
		b. Red surch		80·00	80·00
		c. Violet surch		£100	£100
		ca. Error. "3/10" for "2/10"			
22		3/10 p. on 3 m. yellow-brown		10·00	10·00
		a. Pair, one without surch		£750	
		b. Opt Type 1a		£1200	£1200
		c. Error. "2/10" for "3/10"			
		d. Violet surch		£150	£150
		da. Opt Type 1a		£2750	
23		4/10 p. on 4 m. scarlet		50·00	50·00
		a. Violet surch			
24		5/10 p. on 5 m. yellow-orange		£180	£100
		b. Violet surch		£250	£225
25	3	2 p. on 2 p. olive		£250	75·00
		a. Opt Type 1a		£1300	
		b. Red surch		£325	80·00
		ba. Opt Type 1a			
		c. Violet surch		£300	90·00
26		5 p. on 5 p. deep purple		50·00	70·00
		a. Opt Type 1a		£1500	
		b. Violet surch			
27		9 p. on 9 p. ochre		£300	£350
		a. Red surch		£130	£140
		b. Violet surch			

(b) P 14
28	2	1/10 p. on 1 m. sepia		20·00	25·00
		a. Pair, one without surch			
		b. Red surch		60·00	60·00
		c. Violet surch		£250	£300
29		2/10 p. on 2 m. blue-green		25·00	25·00
		a. Error. Surch "3/10" for "2/10"		£100	£100
		b. Red surch		80·00	80·00
		ba. Error. Surch "3/10" for "2/10"			
		c. Violet surch		80·00	80·00
30		5/10 p. on 5 m. orange		£225	£100
		a. Pair, one without surch		† £2000	
		b. Violet surch		£275	
31	3	1 p. on 1 p. deep indigo (R.)		£200	60·00
		a. Pair, one without surch		£1800	
		b. Violet surch		£400	
32		9 p. on 9 p. ochre (R.)		£500	£500
		a. Violet surch			
33		10 p. on 10 p. ultramarine		£850	£1000
		a. Violet surch inverted			
34		20 p. on 20 p. pale grey		£650	£850
		a. Violet surch		£900	£950

T 3 *of Palestine (perf* 15×14) *similarly surch*
35	3	10 p. on 10 p. ultramarine		£1800	£2500
36		20 p. on 20 p. pale grey		£2500	£3000

T 2 reads "tenths of a piastre" and T 3 "the piastre", both with Arabic figures below. These surcharges were applied in order to translate the Egyptian face values of the stamps into the currency of the Arab Kingdom of Syria, but the actual face value of the stamps remained unchanged.

Being handstamped the surcharge may be found either at the top or bottom of the stamp, and exists double on most values.

("Arab Government of the East, April 1921")
(4)

1922 (Dec). *Stamps of 1920, handstamped with a steel die as* T 4 *in red-purple, violet or black.* (a) P 15 × 14.
37	4	1 m. sepia (R.P.)		25·00	25·00
		a. Violet opt		28·00	28·00
		b. Black opt		22·00	22·00
38		2 m. blue-green (R.P.)		22·00	22·00
		a. Violet opt		20·00	20·00
		b. Black opt		18·00	18·00
39		3 m. yellow-brown (R.P.)		40·00	40·00
		a. Opt Type 1a		£1600	
		b. Violet opt		7·00	7·00
		ba. Pair, one without opt		£1200	
		bb. Opt Type 1a		£1500	£2000
		c. Black opt		8·00	8·00
		ca. Opt Type 1a			
40		4 m. scarlet (R.P.)		45·00	50·00
		b. Violet opt		45·00	50·00
		c. Black opt		45·00	50·00
41		5 m. yellow-orange (R.P.)		35·00	10·00
		a. Violet opt		15·00	10·00
42		2 p. olive (R.P.)		55·00	40·00
		a. Opt Type 1a		£1500	
		b. Violet opt		20·00	15·00
		ba. Opt Type 1a		£1500	£1300
		c. Black opt		12·00	10·00
43		5 p. deep purple (R.P.)		£100	£120
		a. Pair, one without opt		£1500	
		b. Violet opt		60·00	80·00
		c. Black opt			
44		9 p. ochre (R.P.)		£400	£450
		a. Violet opt		£200	£250
		ab. Opt Type 1a		£2250	
		b. Black opt		65·00	80·00

(b) P 14
45	4	1 m. sepia (R.P.)		12·00	15·00
		a. Pair, one without opt		£1200	
		b. Violet opt		22·00	20·00
		c. Black opt		18·00	18·00
46		2 m. blue-green (R.P.)		25·00	25·00
		a. Violet opt		8·00	10·00
		b. Black opt		10·00	10·00
46c		3 m. yellow-brown (V.)		£800	£350
47		5 m. orange (R.P.)		£300	75·00
		a. Violet opt		25·00	20·00
48		1 p. deep indigo (R.P.)		25·00	15·00
		a. Violet opt		15·00	9·00
49		2 p. deep olive (V.)		75·00	80·00
50		5 p. purple (R.P.)		90·00	£100
		a. Violet opt		£100	£110
		b. Black opt			
51		9 p. ochre (V.)		£900	£1000
52		10 p. ultramarine (R.P.)		£1800	£1900
		a. Violet opt		£1100	£1600
		b. Black opt			
53		20 p. pale grey (R.P.)		£1600	£2000
		a. Violet opt		£1100	£1800
		b. Black opt			

*The ink of the "black" overprint is not a true black, but is caused by a mixture of inks from different ink-pads. The colour is, however, very distinct from either of the others.

Most values are known with inverted and/or double overprints.

("Arab Government of the East, April 1921")
(5)

1923 (1 Mar). *Stamps of 1920, with typographed overprint,* T 5 *applied by Govt Printing Press, Amman.*
(a) P 15 × 14.
54	5	1 m. sepia (Gold)		£1400	£1800
55		2 m. blue-green (Gold)		20·00	22·00
56		3 m. yellow-brown (Gold)		12·00	15·00
		a. Opt double		£500	
		b. Opt inverted		£550	
		c. Black opt		75·00	85·00
57		4 m. scarlet		10·00	12·00
58		5 m. yellow-orange		50·00	45·00
		a. Opt Type 1 albino		£1200	£1400
59		2 p. olive (Gold)		15·00	15·00
		a. Opt Type 1a		£1200	£1000
		b. Black opt		£250	£250
		ba. Opt Type 1a			
60		5 p. deep purple (Gold)		60·00	80·00
		a. Opt inverted		£225	
		b. Opt Type 1a		£2000	
		ba. Opt inverted		£2500	
		c. Black opt inverted		£1500	

(b) P 14
62	5	1 m. sepia (Gold)		16·00	24·00
		a. Opt inverted		£600	
63		2 m. blue-green (Gold)		14·00	18·00
		a. Opt inverted		£350	£350
		b. Opt double		£275	
		c. Black opt		£300	
		ca. Opt double		£1500	
64		5 m. orange		10·00	12·00
65		1 p. deep indigo (Gold)		10·00	14·00
		a. Opt double		£450	£475
		b. Black opt		£800	£850
66		9 p. ochre		75·00	£100
		a. Gold opt		£3000	
67		10 p. ultramarine (Gold)		70·00	£100
68		20 p. pale grey (Gold)		70·00	£100
		a. Opt inverted		£350	
		b. Opt double		£425	
		c. Opt double, one inverted		£425	
		e. Opt double, one gold, one black, latter inverted		£700	
		f. Opt treble, one inverted		£1000	
		g. Black opt		£800	
		ga. Opt inverted		£1000	
		gb. Opt double, one inverted		£1200	

The gold overprints were created by sprinkling gold dust on wet black ink.

There are numerous constant minor varieties in this overprint in all values.

The 9 p. perforated 15×14 was also prepared with this overprint, but the entire stock was used for No. 85.

The 20 p. exists with top line of overprint only or with the lines transposed, both due to misplacement.

(6)   (7)

(8)   (9)

1923 (Apr–Oct). *Stamps of the preceding issues further surch by means of handstamps. (a) Issue of Nov 1920.*

70	—	2¹/₂/10ths p. on 5 m. (13) (B.–Blk.)		£160	£160
		a. Black surch		£160	£160
		b. Violet surch		£160	£160
70c	6	⁵/₁₀ p. on 3 m. (3)		† £5000	
70d		⁵/₁₀ p. on 5 m. (13)			
70e	9	2 p. on 20 p. (19)			

(b) Stamp of Palestine

71	6	⁵/₁₀ p. on 3 m. (p 15×14)		£3000	

(c) Issue of Nov 1922

72	6	⁵/₁₀ p. on 3 m. (22)		£7000	
73		⁵/₁₀ p. on 5 p. (26) (V.)		70·00	80·00
		a. Black surch		£1200	
		ab. Opt Type 3 omitted		£1200	
73b		⁵/₁₀ p. on 9 p. (27a)		£1200	
74	7	¹/₂ p. on 5 p. (26)		70·00	80·00
		a. Pair, one without surch		£750	
75		¹/₂ p. on 9 p. (27)		£3500	
		a. On No. 27a		£350	£400
		ab. Opt Type 1a		£3500	
76		¹/₂ p. on 9 p. (32)		—	£8000
77	8	1 p. on 5 p. (26)		80·00	£100

(d) Issue of Dec 1922

78	6	⁵/₁₀ p. on 3 m. (39) (V.)		85·00	£100
		a. Black surch			
		ab. Opt Type 1a		£750	
		b. On No. 39b		40·00	50·00
		ba. Pair, one without surch		£1400	
		bb. Without numeral of value			
		bc. Black surch			
79		⁵/₁₀ p. on 5 p. (43b) (Blk.)		8·00	14·00
		a. Opt Type 1a		£2000	
		b. Pair, one without surch		£500	
		c. Violet surch			
79d		⁵/₁₀ p. on 9 p. (44b)		—	£1200
		da. On No. 44a. Violet surch		—	£1300
80	7	¹/₂ p. on 2 p. (42)		£100	£120
		a. Opt Type 1a		£2000	
		b. On No. 42b		80·00	£110
		c. On No. 42c		60·00	£110
		ca. Pair, one without surch		£1000	
81		¹/₂ p. on 5 p. (43)		£3000	
		a. On No. 43a		£1000	
82		¹/₂ p. on 5 p. (50)		£1800	
		a. On No. 50a		£2500	
83	8	1 p. on 5 p. (43)		£3750	
		a. On No. 43a		£2000	£2250
83c		1 p. on 5 p. (50)		£2500	

(e) Issue of 1 March 1923

84	6	⁵/₁₀ p. on 3 m. (56)		25·00	30·00
		a. On No. 56c		£700	
85	7	¹/₂ p. on 9 p. (p 15×14)		90·00	£150
		a. Pair, one without surch		£5000	
86		¹/₂ p. on 9 p. (66)		£150	
87	9	1 p. on 10 p. (67)		£2250	£2500
		a. Violet surch		£2750	
88		2 p. on 20 p. (68)		60·00	80·00
88a		2 p. on 20 p. (68g)		£2000	

The handstamp on Nos. 70c, 88 and 88a has an Arabic "2" in place of the "1" shown in the illustration of Type **9**.

Being handstamped many of the above exist inverted or double.

TYPES OF SAUDI ARABIA. The following illustrations are repeated here for convenience from Saudi Arabia.

11   20

21   22

("Arab Government of the   ("Arab Government of
East, 9 Sha'ban 1341")   the East. Commemoration
                            of Independence,
(10)   25 May 1923")
                            (11)

It should be noted that as Arabic is read from right to left, the overprint described as reading downwards appears to the English reader as though reading upwards. Our illustration of Type **11** shows the overprint reading downwards.

1923 (April). *Stamps of Saudi Arabia. T 11, with typographed opt, T 10.*

89	10	¹/₈ p. chestnut		2·00	1·75
		a. Opt double		£200	
		b. Opt inverted		£110	
90		¹/₂ p. scarlet		2·00	1·75
		a. Opt inverted			
91		1 p. blue		1·25	80
		a. Opt inverted		£120	£140
92		1¹/₂ p. lilac		1·50	1·75
		a. Opt double		£150	
		b. Top line omitted		—	£250
		c. Pair, one without opt		£250	
93		2 p. orange		2·00	5·50
94		3 p. brown		3·00	8·00
		a. Opt inverted		£225	
		b. Opt double		£225	£250
		c. Pair, one without opt		£375	
95		5 p. olive		5·00	9·00
89/95			Set of 7	15·00	26·00

On same stamps, surcharged with new values (Saudi Arabia, Nos. 47 and 49)

96	10	¹/₄ p. on ¹/₈ p. chestnut		4·00	5·50
		a. Opt and surch inverted		£150	
		b. Ditto. but 2nd and 3rd lines of opt omitted		£200	
97		10 p. on 5 p. olive		15·00	22·00
		a. Top line omitted		£350	

In this setting the third line of the overprint measures 19–21 mm. On 35 stamps out of the setting of 36 the Arabic "9" (right-hand character in bottom line) is widely spaced from the rest of the inscription. Minor varieties of this setting exist on all values. For later setting, varying from the above, see Nos. 121/4.

Normal. "923"   Error. "933"

An error reading "933" instead of "923" occurs as No. 3 in the setting of 24 on all values. Only 24 stamps are believed to have been overprinted for each of Nos. 103A, 108A, 105B and 107B so that for these stamps only one example of the error can exist. No example has yet been confirmed for Nos. 103A or 105B.

1923 (25 May). *T 3 of Palestine optd with T 11, reading up or down, in black or gold by Govt Press, Amman, in a setting of 24 (12×2).*

A. Reading downwards

98A	1 m. (Blk.)			17·00	17·00
	a. Opt double, one inverted (Blk.)			£650	£650
	b. Arabic "933"			85·00	
	c. Gold opt			£150	£160
	ca. Opt double, one inverted (Gold)			£900	
	cb. Opt double (Blk. + Gold)			£900	£900
	cc. Arabic "933"			£300	
99A	2 m. (Blk.)			28·00	35·00
	a. Arabic "933"			£160	
100A	3 m. (Blk.)			10·00	12·00
	a. Arabic "933"			70·00	
101A	4 m. (Blk.)			10·00	12·00
	a. Arabic "933"			70·00	
102A	5 m. (Blk.)			50·00	60·00
	a. Arabic "933"			£300	
103A	1 p. (Gold)			£650	£750
	a. Opt double			£750	£850
104A	2 p. (Blk.)			50·00	70·00
	a. Arabic "933"			£275	
105A	5 p. (Gold)			60·00	70·00
	a. Opt double (Gold)			£650	
	b. Arabic "933"			£300	
	c. Opt double (Blk.)			£1500	
106A	9 p. (Blk.)			70·00	90·00
	a. Arabic "933"			£325	
107A	10 p. (Blk.)			60·00	80·00
	a. Arabic "933"			£300	
108A	20 p. (Blk.)			£700	
	a. Arabic "933"			£2500	

B. Reading upwards

98B	1 m. (Blk.)			90·00	£110
	b. Arabic "933"			£250	
	c. Gold opt			£150	£160
	cc. Arabic "933"			£350	
99B	2 m. (Blk.)			45·00	50·00
	a. Arabic "933"			£250	
100B	3 m. (Blk.)			90·00	£110
	a. Arabic "933"			£250	
101B	4 m. (Blk.)			25·00	32·00
	a. Arabic "933"			£130	
103B	1 p. (Gold)			50·00	60·00
	a. Opt double			£600	
	b. Black opt				
	c. Arabic "933"			£300	
105B	5 p. (Gold)			£750	£550
	a. Opt double			£600	
106B	9 p. (Blk.)			50·00	60·00
	a. Arabic "933"			£275	
107B	10 p. (Blk.)			£600	
	a. Arabic "933"			£2500	
108B	20 p. (Blk.)			70·00	90·00
	a. Arabic "933"			£325	

The 9 and 10 p. are perf 14, all the other values being perf 15×14.

No. 107A surch with T 9

109	1 p. on 10 p. ultramarine			£6000

(12)

1923 (Sept). *No. 92 surch with T 12. (a) Handstamped.*

110	12	¹/₂ p. on 1¹/₂ p. lilac		6·00	6·00
		a. Surch and opt inverted		55·00	
		b. Opt double		75·00	
		c. Opt double, one inverted		90·00	£100
		d. Pair, one without opt		£150	

This handstamp is known inverted, double and double, one inverted.

(b) Typographed

111	12	¹/₂ p. on 1¹/₂ p. lilac		50·00	50·00
		a. Surch inverted		£150	
		b. Surch double		£180	
		c. Pair, one without surch		£500	

(13a)   (13b)

("Arab Government of the East, 9 Sha'ban, 1341")

These two types differ in the spacing of the characters and in the position of the bottom line which is to the left of the middle line in T **13a** and centrally placed in T **13b**.

1923 (Oct). *T 11 of Saudi Arabia handstamped as T 13a or 13b.*

112	13a	¹/₂ p. scarlet		6·00	7·00
113	13b	¹/₂ p. scarlet		6·00	7·00

No. 112 exists with handstamp inverted.

(15 "Arab Government   ("Commemorating the coming
of the East")   of His Majesty the King of
                        the Arabs" and date)
                        (16)

1924 (Jan). *T 11 of Saudi Arabia with typographed opt T 15.*

114	15	¹/₂ p. scarlet		6·00	8·00
		a. Opt inverted		£180	
115		1 p. blue		£300	£200
116		1¹/₂ p. lilac		£350	
		a. Pair, one without opt		£1500	

The ¹/₂ p. exists with thick, brown gum, which tints the paper, and with white gum and paper.

The 2 p. in the same design was also overprinted, but was not issued without the subsequent Type **16** overprint.

1924 (18 Jan). *Visit of King Hussein of Hejaz. Nos. 114/16 and unissued 2 p. with further typographed opt T 16 in black.*

117	16	¹/₂ p. scarlet		1·00	1·00
		a. Type 15 omitted		£150	
		b. Type 16 inverted		£150	
		c. Imperf between (pair)		£110	
		d. Type 16 in gold		2·00	2·00
		dc. Imperf between (pair)		£250	
118		1 p. blue		1·25	1·25
		a. Type 15 omitted		£150	
		b. Both opts inverted		£200	
		c. Imperf between (pair)			
		d. Type 16 in gold		2·00	2·00
		db. Both opts inverted		£300	
		dc. Imperf between (pair)		£225	
119		1¹/₂ p. lilac		2·00	2·00
		a. Type 15 omitted			
		b. Type 15 inverted		£130	
		d. Type 16 in gold		3·00	3·00
		da. Type 15 inverted		£150	
120		2 p. orange		4·00	4·00
		d. Type 16 in gold			

The spacing of the lines of the overprint varies considerably, and a variety dated "432" for "342" occurs on the twelfth stamp in each sheet (*Price £75 un*).

(16a)

"Shaban"	"Shabal"	"Shabn"
(normal)	(R.4/6)	(R.5/3)

1924 (Mar–May). *T 11 of Saudi Arabia optd with T 16a (new setting of Type 10).*

121		¹/₈ p. chestnut		11·00	8·50
		a. Opt inverted		£100	
122		¹/₂ p. scarlet		3·25	3·25
		a. "Shabal"		50·00	
		b. "Shabn"		50·00	
		c. Opt inverted		£120	
123		1 p. blue		5·50	2·00
		a. "Shabal"		75·00	
		b. "Shabn"		75·00	
		c. Opt double		£120	

124 1½ p. lilac ... 8·00 9·00
  a. "Shabal" ... 90·00
  b. "Shabn" ... 90·00
  This setting is from fresh type with the third line measuring 18¼ mm.
  On all stamps in this setting (except Nos. 1, 9, 32 and 33) the Arabic "9" is close to the rest of the inscription.
  The dots on the character "Y" (the second character from the left in the second line) are on many stamps vertical (:) instead of horizontal (..).
  On some sheets of the ⅛ and ½ p. the right-hand character, "H", in the first line, was omitted from the second stamp in the first row of the sheet.

("Government of the Arab East, 1342") (17)   ("Government of the Arab East, 1343") (18)

"Hukumat" (normal)   "Jakramat" (R. 2/1)

"1342" (normal)   "1343" (R. 4/2)   "1242" (R. 6/1)

1924 (Sept–Nov). T 11 of Saudi Arabia with type-set opt as T 17 by Govt Press, Amman.

125 17 ⅛ p. chestnut ... 35 25
  a. Opt inverted ... £130
  b. "Jakramat" ... 25·00
  c. "1242" ... 25·00
126 ¼ p. green ... 30 30
  a. Tête-bêche (pair, both opts normal) 7·50 10·00
  b. Opt inverted ... 85·00
  c. Tête-bêche (pair, one with opt inverted) ... £300
  d. "Jakramat" ... 25·00
  e. "1242" ... 25·00
127 ½ p. bright scarlet ... 30 30
  a. Deep rose-red
  b. "1343" ... 25·00
129 1 p. blue ... 2·50 1·50
  a. Imperf between (horiz pair) ... £130
  b. Opt inverted
  c. "Jakramat" ... 35·00
  d. "1242" ... 35·00
130 1½ p. lilac ... 2·50 2·50
  a. "1343" ... 50·00
131 2 p. orange ... 2·00 2·00
  a. Opt double
  b. "1343" ... 50·00
132 3 p. brown-red ... 1·50 1·50
  a. Opt inverted ... £100
  b. Opt double ... £100
  c. "1343" ... 75·00
133 5 p. olive ... 2·00 2·50
  a. "Jakramat" ... 60·00
  b. "1242" ... 60·00
134 10 p. brown-purple and mauve (R.) 4·00 5·00
  a. Centre inverted ... £2000
  b. Black opt ... £200
  c. "Jakramat" ... 90·00
  d. "1242" ... 90·00
125/34 ... Set of 9 14·00 14·00

  Type 11 of Saudi Arabia was printed in sheets of 36 (6×6). The ¼ p. value had the bottom three rows inverted, giving six vertical tête-bêche pairs. A few sheets were overprinted with the normal setting of Type 17, with the result that the overprints on the bottom rows were inverted in relation to the stamp, including on one of the stamps in the tête-bêche pair (No. 126c). A corrected setting with the overprint inverted on the lower rows was used for the majority of the printing giving tête-bêche pairs with the overprints both normal in relation to the stamps (No. 126a).

1925 (2 Aug). T 20/2 of Saudi Arabia with lithographed opt T 18 applied in Cairo.

135 18 ⅛ p. chocolate ... 30 70
  a. Imperf between (horiz pair) ... £120 £140
  b. Opt inverted ... 60·00
136 ¼ p. ultramarine ... 30 70
  a. Opt inverted ... 60·00
137 ½ p. carmine ... 50 40
  a. Opt inverted ... 60·00
138 1 p. green ... 40 40
139 1½ p. orange ... 90 1·75
  a. Opt inverted ... 60·00
140 2 p. blue ... 1·25 2·00
  a. Opt treble ... £150 £200
141 3 p. sage-green (R.) ... 1·75 3·00
  a. Imperf between (horiz pair) ... £120 £160
  b. Opt inverted ... 80·00
  c. Black opt ... £120 £150
142 5 p. chestnut ... 2·00 7·00
  a. Opt inverted ... 80·00
135/42 ... Set of 8 6·75 14·00
  All values exist imperforate.
  No. 141 imperforate with gold overprint comes from a presentation sheet for the Emir.

("East of the Jordan") (19)

22 Emir Abdullah   23 Emir Abdullah

(Opt typo by Waterlow)

1925 (1 Nov)–26. Stamps of Palestine, 1922 (without the three-line Palestine opt), optd with T 19. Wmk Mult Script CA. P 14.

143 19 1 m. deep brown ... 10 65
144 2 m. yellow ... 10 30
145 3 m. greenish blue ... 20 30
146 4 m. carmine-pink ... 20 65
147 5 m. orange ... 20 30
  a. Yellow-orange ... 35·00 20·00
148 6 m. blue-green ... 20 50
149 7 m. yellow-brown ... 20 50
150 8 m. scarlet ... 30 30
151 13 m. ultramarine ... 50 60
152 1 p. grey ... 50 50
153 2 p. olive ... 1·00 1·25
  a. Olive-green ... £100 25·00
154 5 p. deep purple ... 3·00 4·00
155 9 p. ochre ... 6·00 8·00
  a. Perf 15×14 (1926) ... £850 £1200
156 10 p. light blue ... 12·00 14·00
  a. Error. "E.F.F." in bottom panel (R. 10/3) ... £750 £800
  b. Perf 15×14 (1926) ... 75·00 85·00
157 20 p. bright violet ... 20·00 25·00
  a. Perf 15×14 (1926) ... £850 £850
143/57 ... Set of 15 40·00 50·00
143/57 Optd "Specimen" ... Set of 15 £160

(New Currency. 1000 milliemes = £1 Palestinian)

(Recess Perkins, Bacon & Co)

1927 (1 Nov)–29. New Currency. Wmk Mult Script CA. P 14.

159 22 2 m. greenish blue ... 15 30
160 3 m. carmine-pink ... 60 70
161 4 m. green ... 70 1·25
162 5 m. orange ... 30 30
163 10 m. scarlet ... 50 1·00
164 15 m. ultramarine ... 60 30
165 20 m. olive-green ... 80 90
166 23 50 m. purple ... 2·50 4·00
167 90 m. bistre ... 6·00 12·00
168 100 m. blue ... 8·00 9·00
169 200 m. violet ... 17·00 24·00
170 500 m. brown (5.29) ... 60·00 85·00
171 1000 m. slate-grey (5.29) ... £100 £140
159/71 ... Set of 13 £180 £250
159/71 Optd/Perf "Specimen" ... Set of 13 £180

("Constitution") (24)   (27)

1928 (1 Sept). New Constitution of 20 February 1928. Optd with T 24 by Atwood, Morris & Co, Cairo.

172 22 2 m. greenish blue ... 80 2·00
173 3 m. carmine-pink ... 90 3·00
174 4 m. green ... 1·00 3·50
175 5 m. orange ... 1·00 4·00
176 10 m. scarlet ... 1·50 4·00
177 15 m. ultramarine ... 1·50 4·00
178 20 m. olive-green ... 3·00 8·00
179 23 50 m. purple ... 5·00 9·00
180 90 m. bistre ... 14·00 40·00
181 100 m. blue ... 22·00 45·00
182 200 m. violet ... 65·00 £100
172/82 ... Set of 11 £100 £190

1930 (1 Apr). Locust Campaign. Optd as T 27 by Whitehead, Morris & Co, Alexandria.

183 22 2 m. greenish blue ... 1·10 4·00
  a. Opt inverted ... £200 £500
184 3 m. carmine-pink ... 1·50 5·00
185 4 m. green ... 1·50 5·00
186 5 m. orange ... 15·00 14·00
  a. Opt double ... £300 £500
  b. Vert pair, top stamp double. Lower stamp without bottom line of opt ... £1000
187 10 m. scarlet ... 1·50 4·00
188 15 m. ultramarine ... 1·50 2·25
  a. Opt inverted ... £180 £350
189 20 m. olive-green ... 1·50 4·00
190 23 50 m. purple ... 5·00 9·50
191 90 m. bistre ... 10·00 40·00
192 100 m. blue ... 12·00 40·00
193 200 m. violet ... 30·00 85·00
194 500 m. brown ... 75·00 £170
  a. "C" of "LOCUST" omitted (R. 5/3) £700 £800
183/94 ... Set of 12 £140 £350
No. 186a was sold at Kerak.

MINIMUM PRICE

The minimum price quote is 10p which represents a handling charge rather than a basis for valuing common stamps. For further notes about prices see introductory pages.

---

28   29

(Re-engraved with figures of value at left only. Recess Perkins, Bacon)

1930 (1 June)–39. Wmk Mult Script CA. P 14.

194b 28 1 m. red-brown (6.2.34) ... 30 1·00
  c. Perf 13½×13 (1939) ... 3·00 3·50
195 2 m. greenish blue ... 30 50
  a. Perf 13½×13. Bluish grn (1939) 8·00 2·00
196 3 m. carmine-pink ... 40 70
196a 3 m. green (6.2.34) ... 1·75 85
  b. Perf 13½×13 (1939) ... 13·00 4·25
197 4 m. green ... 60 1·75
197a 4 m. carmine-pink (6.2.34) ... 2·25 90
  b. Perf 13½×13 (1939) ... 50·00 18·00
198 5 m. orange ... 40 40
  a. Coil stamp. Perf 13½×14 (29.2.36) ... 18·00 14·00
  b. Perf 13½×13 (1939) ... 50·00 3·00
199 10 m. scarlet ... 90 15
  a. Perf 13½×13 (1939) ... 80·00 4·25
200 15 m. ultramarine ... 65 20
  a. Coil stamp. Perf 13½×14 (29.2.36) ... 18·00 14·00
  b. Perf 13½×13 (1939) ... 32·00 3·75
201 20 m. olive-green ... 1·25 35
  a. Perf 13½×13 (1939) ... 55·00 12·00
202 29 50 m. purple ... 1·75 1·25
203 90 m. bistre ... 2·50 4·25
204 100 m. blue ... 3·75 4·25
205 200 m. violet ... 8·50 14·00
206 500 m. brown ... 20·00 38·00
207 £P1 slate-grey ... 45·00 80·00
194b/207 ... Set of 16 80·00 £130
194b/207 Perf "Specimen" ... Set of 16 £170
  For stamps perf 12 see Nos. 230/43, and for T 28 lithographed, perf 13½, see Nos. 222/9.

30 Mushetta   31 Threshing Scene

32 The Khazneh at Petra   33 Emir Abdullah

(Vignettes from photographs; frames des Yacoub Sukker. Recess Bradbury, Wilkinson)

1933 (1 Feb). As T 30 (various designs) and T 31/3. Wmk Mult Script CA. P 14.

208 1 m. black and maroon ... 50 1·40
209 2 m. black and claret ... 60 1·00
210 3 m. blue-green ... 75 1·40
211 4 m. black and brown ... 1·25 2·25
212 5 m. black and orange ... 1·25 1·25
213 10 m. carmine ... 1·50 3·00
214 15 m. blue ... 2·50 1·25
215 20 m. black and sage-green ... 3·50 5·00
216 50 m. black and purple ... 9·00 10·00
217 90 m. black and yellow ... 13·00 25·00
218 100 m. black and blue ... 13·00 25·00
219 200 m. black and red-brown ... 45·00 60·00
220 500 m. scarlet and red-brown ... £130 £170
221 £P1 black and yellow-green ... £350 £550
208/21 ... Set of 14 £500 £750
208/21 Perf "Specimen" ... Set of 14 £500
  Designs: As T 30—2 m. Nymphaeum, Jerash; 3 m. Kasr Kharana; 4 m. Kerak Castle; 5 m. Temple of Artemis, Jerash; 10 m. Ajlun Castle; 20 m. Allenby Bridge over the Jordan.
  The 90 m., 100 m. and 200 m. are similar to the 3 m., 5 m. and 10m. respectively, but are larger (33½ × 23½ mm). The 500 m. is similar to T 32, but larger (23½ × 33½ mm).

34

(Litho Survey Dept, Cairo)

1942 (18 May). T 28, but with Arabic characters above portrait and in top left circle modified as in T 34. No wmk. P 13½.

222 34 1 m. red-brown ... 80 3·35
223 2 m. green ... 1·50 1·50
224 3 m. yellow-green ... 2·00 2·25
225 4 m. carmine-pink ... 2·00 3·00
226 5 m. yellow-orange ... 3·25 1·00
227 10 m. scarlet ... 3·00 2·75
228 15 m. blue ... 6·00 1·75
229 20 m. olive-green ... 9·00 12·00
222/9 ... Set of 8 24·00 24·00
  Forgeries of the above exist on whiter paper with rough perforations.

(Recess Bradbury, Wilkinson)

1943 (1 Jan)–46. *Wmk Mult Script CA. P* 12.

230	28	1 m. red-brown		20	75
231		2 m. bluish green		70	75
232		3 m. green		1·75	1·25
233		4 m. carmine-pink		1·75	1·25
234		5 m. orange		1·25	20
235		10 m. red		3·00	1·25
236		15 m. blue		3·00	30
237		20 m. olive-green (26.8.46)		2·75	1·00
238	29	50 m. purple (26.8.46)		3·00	1·00
239		90 m. bistre (26.8.46)		4·75	4·00
240		100 m. blue (26.8.46)		5·00	1·75
241		200 m. violet (26.8.46)		9·00	6·50
242		500 m. brown (26.8.46)		13·00	12·00
243		£P1 slate-grey (26.8.46)		24·00	22·00
230/43			*Set of* 14	65·00	48·00

Nos. 237/43 were released in London by the Crown Agents in May 1944, but were not put on sale in Transjordan until 26 August 1946.

Printings of the 3, 4, 10, 12, 15 and 20 m. in changed colours were released on 12 May 1947.

POSTAGE DUE STAMPS

حكومة
مستحق
الشرق العربية
٩ شعبان ١٣٤١

مستحق

(D 12 "Due")   (D 13)

1923 (Sept). *Issue of April, 1923, with opt* T 10, *with further typographed opt Type* D 12 *(the 3 p. with handstamped surch as* T 12 *at top).*

D112	½ p. on 3 p. brown	13·00	16·00
	a. "Due" inverted	50·00	55·00
	b. "Due" double	50·00	60·00
	ba. "Due" double, one inverted	£150	
	c. Arabic "t" & "h" transposed (R. 1/2)	£100	
	ca. As c, inverted	£350	
	d. Surch at foot of stamp	26·00	
	da. Ditto, but with var. c	£120	
	e. Surch omitted	£200	
D113	1 p. blue	8·50	9·50
	a. Type 10 inverted	80·00	
	b. "Due" inverted	45·00	40·00
	c. "Due" double	50·00	
	d. "Due" double, one inverted	£150	
	e. Arabic "t" & "h" transposed (R. 1/2)	70·00	
	f. "Due" omitted (in vertical pair with normal)	£200	
D114	1½ p. lilac	8·50	9·50
	a. "Due" inverted	45·00	45·00
	b. "Due" double	50·00	
	ba. "Due" double, one diagonal	75·00	
	c. Arabic "t" & "h" transposed (R. 1/2)	70·00	
	ca. As c, inverted	£275	
	d. "Due" omitted (in pair with normal)	£200	
D115	2 p. orange	10·00	11·00
	a. "Due" inverted	60·00	60·00
	b. "Due" double	65·00	
	ba. "Due" double, one diagonal	£100	
	c. "Due" treble	£150	
	d. Arabic "t" & "h" transposed (R. 1/2)	70·00	
	e. Arabic "h" omitted	90·00	

The variety, Arabic "t" and "h" transposed, occurred on R. 1/2 of all values in the first batch of sheets printed. The variety, Arabic "h" omitted, occurred on every stamp in the first three rows of at least three sheets of the 2 p.

Handstamped in four lines as Type D 13 *and surch as on No.* D112.

D116	½ p. on 3 p. brown	42·00	50·00
	a. Opt and surch inverted	£200	
	b. Opt double	£200	
	c. Surch omitted	£225	
	d. Opt inverted. Surch normal, but at foot of stamp	£150	
	e. Opt omitted and opt inverted (pair)	£300	
	f. "Due" double, one inverted	£160	
	h. Surch double	£250	

حكومة
الشرق العربية
مستحق
٩ شعبان ١٣٤١
شرق الأردن

(D 14)   ("Due. East of the Jordan") (D 20)

1923 (Oct). T 11 *of Saudi Arabia handstamped with Type* D 14.

D117	½ p. scarlet	1·00	2·25
D118	1 p. blue	2·00	2·50
	a. Pair, one without handstamp		
D119	1½ p. lilac	2·00	3·25
D120	2 p. orange	2·75	3·75
D121	3 p. brown	4·00	7·50
	a. Pair, one without handstamp	£500	
D122	5 p. olive	7·00	11·00
D117/22		*Set of* 6	17·00 27·00

There are three types of this handstamp, differing in some of the Arabic characters. They occur inverted, double etc.

1923 (Nov). T 11 *of Saudi Arabia with opt similar to Type* D 14 *but first three lines typo and fourth handstruck.*

D123	1 p. blue	50·00	
D124	5 p. olive	7·00	
	a. Imperf between (vert pair)		

(Opt typo by Waterlow)

1925 (Nov). *Stamps of Palestine 1922 (without the three-line Palestine opt), optd with Type* D 20. *P* 14.

D159	1 m. deep brown	1·40	4·50
D160	2 m. yellow	1·75	3·25
D161	4 m. carmine-pink	2·75	5·50
D162	8 m. scarlet	3·75	8·50
D163	13 m. ultramarine	4·50	8·50
D164	5 p. deep purple	5·00	11·00
	a. Perf 15 × 14	40·00	55·00
D159/64		*Set of* 6	17·00 38·00
D159/64 Optd "Specimen"		*Set of* 6	65·00

Stamps as No. D164, but with a different top line to overprint Type D 20, were for revenue purposes.

مستحق

١ مليم   ٢ مليم   ٤ مليم
(1 m.)   (2 m.)   (4 m.)
(D 21)

٨ مليم   ١٣ مليم   ٥ قروش
(8 m.)   (13 m.)   (5 p.)

(Surch typo at Jerusalem)

1926 (Feb–May). *Postage stamps of 1 November 1925, surch "Due" and new value as Type* D 21 *by Greek Orthodox Printing Press, Jerusalem. Bottom line of surcharge differs for each value as illustrated.*

D165	1 m. on 1 m. deep brown	3·00	5·00
	a. Red opt	£100	
D166	2 m. on 1 m. deep brown	3·00	5·00
D167	4 m. on 3 m. greenish blue	3·25	6·00
D168	8 m. on 3 m. greenish blue	3·25	6·00
D169	13 m. on 13 m. ultramarine	3·75	7·00
D170	5 p. on 13 m. ultramarine	4·50	10·00
D165/70		*Set of* 6	19·00 35·00

استحق

مستحق

(D 25 "Due")   Extra Arabic character in opt (R. 4/10)

1929 (1 Jan). *Nos. 159 etc. optd only or surch in addition as Type* D 25 *by Whitehead, Morris & Co, Alexandria.*

D183	22	1 m. on 3 m. carmine-pink	70	3·50
		a. Extra Arabic character	25·00	
D184		2 m. greenish blue	80	3·50
		a. Pair, one without opt	£300	
D185		4 m. on 15 m. ultramarine	1·25	4·00
		a. Surch inverted	£120	£180
D186		10 m. scarlet	1·25	4·00
D187	23	20 m. on 100 m. blue	3·75	10·00
		a. Vert pair, one without surch	£375	
D188		50 m. purple	4·75	13·00
		a. Horiz pair, one without opt	£400	
D183/8			*Set of* 6	11·00 35·00

D 26   D 35

(Recess Perkins, Bacon)

1929 (1 Apr)–39. *Wmk Mult Script CA. P* 14.

D189	D 26	1 m. red-brown	60	3·50
		a. Perf 13½ × 13 (1939)	80·00	50·00
D190		2 m. orange-yellow	60	4·00
D191		4 m. green	90	4·50
D192		10 m. scarlet	2·25	4·50
D193		20 m. olive-green	6·50	11·00
D194		50 m. blue	7·50	17·00
D189/94			*Set of* 6	16·00 40·00
D189/94 Perf "Specimen"			*Set of* 6	65·00

(Litho Survey Dept, Cairo)

1942 (22 Dec). *Redrawn. Top line of Arabic in taller lettering. No wmk. P* 13½.

D230	D 35	1 m. red-brown	1·40	10·00
D231		2 m. orange-yellow	8·00	9·00
D232		10 m. scarlet	8·50	6·00
D230/2			*Set of* 3	16·00 23·00

Forgeries of the above exist on whiter paper with rough perforations.

(Recess Bradbury, Wilkinson)

1944–49. *Wmk Mult Script CA. P* 12.

D244	D 26	1 m. red-brown	15	2·75
D245		2 m. orange-yellow	30	3·25
D246		4 m. green	55	4·25
D247		10 m. carmine	1·10	4·75
D248		20 m. olive-green (1949)	25·00	40·00
D244/8			*Set of* 5	25·00 50·00

OFFICIAL STAMP

(حكومة)
الشرق العربي
١٣٤٢

("Arab Government of the East, 1342" = 1924)
(O 16)

1924. T 11 *of Saudi Arabia with typographed opt, Type* O 16.

O117	½ p. scarlet	20·00	£100
	a. Arabic "1242" (R. 2/2, 3/6, 4/5, 4/6)	£150	

By treaty of 22 March 1946 with the United Kingdom, Transjordan was proclaimed an independent kingdom on 25 May 1946.

Later issues are listed under JORDAN in Part 19 (*Middle East*) of this catalogue.

Transvaal
see South Africa

Trinidad and Tobago

TRINIDAD

CROWN COLONY

The first post office was established at Port of Spain in 1800 to deal with overseas mail. Before 1851 there was no post office inland service, although a privately-operated one along the coast did exist, for which rates were officially fixed (see No. 1). During 1851 the colonial authorities established an inland postal system which commenced operation on 14 August. Responsibility for the overseas mails passed to the local post authorities in 1858.

No. CC1 is recorded in the G.P.O. Record Book on 21 March 1852, but no examples have been recorded used on cover before February 1858. From March 1859 it was used with the early Britannia 1d. stamps to indicate prepayment of the additional overseas rate in cash or, later, to show that letters were fully franked with adhesive stamps. This is the normal usage of the handstamp and commands little, if any premium over the cover price quoted below for the stamps involved. The use of the handstamp without an adhesive is rare.

PORT OF SPAIN
CROWNED-CIRCLE HANDSTAMPS

CC 1

CC1 CC 1 TRINIDAD (R.) (*without additional adhesive stamp*) (21.3.52) *Price on cover* £500

PRICES FOR STAMPS ON COVER	
No. 1	*from* × 2
Nos. 2/12	*from* × 5
No. 8	
Nos. 13/20	*from* × 2
Nos. 25/9	*from* × 10
No. 30	
Nos. 31/44	*from* × 3
No. 45	
Nos. 46/59	*from* × 3
Nos. 60/3	*from* × 4
Nos. 64/8	*from* × 3
Nos. 69/79	*from* × 10
No. 87	
Nos. 98/102	*from* × 5
No. 103	
Nos. 104/5	*from* × 15
Nos. 106/12	*from* × 8
No. 113	
Nos. 114/21	*from* × 4
Nos. 122/4	
No. 125	*from* × 10
Nos. 126/30	*from* × 5
No. 131	
Nos. 132/43	*from* × 3
Nos. 144/5	
Nos. 146/8	*from* × 3
Nos. D1/17	*from* × 12

1   2 Britannia

1847 (16 Apr). *Litho. Imperf.*
1   1   (5 c.) blue £13000 £7000
The "LADY McLEOD" stamps were issued in April 1847, by
David Bryce, owner of the S.S. *Lady McLeod*, and sold at five cents
each for the prepayment of the carriage of letters by his vessel
between Port of Spain and San Fernando.
The price quoted for used examples of No. 1 is for pen-
cancelled. Stamps cancelled by having a corner skimmed-off are
worth less.

(Recess P.B.)

1851 (14 Aug)–**56.** *No value expressed. Imperf. Blued paper.*
2   2   (1d.) purple-brown (1851)   ..   ..   8·00 55·00
3   (1d.) blue *to* deep blue (12.51)   ..   8·00 40·00
4   (1d.) deep blue (1852)*   ..   .. £150 70·00
5   (1d.) grey (11.52)   ..   ..   45·00 50·00
6   (1d.) brownish grey (1853)   ..   28·00 60·00
7   (1d.) brownish red (1853)   ..   £300 45·00
8   (1d.) brick-red (1856)   ..   .. £120 50·00
*No. 4 shows the paper deeply and evenly blued, especially on the
back. It has more the appearance of having been printed on blue
paper rather than on white paper that has become blued.

1854–57. *Imperf. White paper.*
9   2   (1d.) deep purple (1854)   ..   .. 18·00 55·00
10   (1d.) dark grey (1854)   ..   .. 27·00 65·00
11   (1d.) blue (? date)   ..   ..   ..
12   (1d.) rose-red (1857)   ..   .. £1500 50·00

PRICES. Prices quoted for the unused of most of the above issues
and Nos. 25 and 29 are for "remainders" with original gum, found
in London. Old colours that have been out to Trinidad are of much
greater value.

3   Britannia   4

The following provisional issues were lithographed in the Colony
(from die engraved by Charles Petit), and brought into use to meet
shortages of the Perkins Bacon stamps during the following
periods:
(1) Sept 1852–May 1853; (2) March 1855–June 1855; (3) Dec
1856–Jan 1857; (4) Oct 1858–Jan 1859; (5) March 1860–June 1860.

1852–60. *No value expressed. Imperf.*
A. *First Issue* (Sept 1852). *Fine impression; lines of background
clear and distinct.* (i) *Yellowish paper*
13   3   (1d.) blue £8500 £1600
(ii) *Bluish cartridge paper* (Feb 1853)
14   3   (1d.) blue ..   ..   —£1800
B. *Second issue* (March 1855). *Thinner paper. Impression less
distinct than before*
15   3   (1d.) pale blue *to* greenish blue ..   — £900
C. *Third issue* (August 1856). *Background often of solid
colour, but with clear lines in places*
16   3   (1d.) bright blue *to* deep blue   .. £4500 £1000
D. *Fourth issue* (October 1858). *Impression less distinct, and rarely
showing more than traces of background lines*
17   3   (1d.) very deep greenish blue   ..   — £650
18   (1d.) slate-blue £4500 £650
E. *Fifth issue* (March 1860). *Impression shows no (or hardly any)
background lines*
19   3   (1d.) grey *to* bluish grey £4000 £400
20   (1d.) red (*shades*)   ..   ..   12·00 £450
In the worn impression of the fourth and fifth issues, the
impression varies according to the position on the stone. Generally
speaking, stamps of the fifth issue have a flatter appearance and
cancellations are often less well defined. The paper of both these
issues is thin or very thin. In all issues except 1853 (Feb) the gum
tends to give the paper a toned appearance.
Stamps in the slate-blue shade (No. 18) also occur in the fifth
issue, but are not readily distinguishable.

PERKINS BACON "CANCELLED". For notes on these
handstamps, showing "CANCELLED" between horizontal bars
forming an oval, see Catalogue Introduction.

(Recess P.B.)

1859 (9 May). *Imperf.*
25   4   4d. grey-lilac (H/S "CANCELLED" in oval
£3500)   ..   ..   ..   65·00 £275
28   6d. deep green (H/S "CANCELLED" in
oval £3500)   ..   ..   — £425
29   1s. indigo   ..   ..   ..   65·00 £275
30   1s. purple-slate ..   ..   ..   — £650
No. 30 may be of unissued status.

1859 (Sept). (*a*) *Pin-perf* 12½.
31   2   (1d.) rose-red   ..   ..   £500 45·00
32   (1d.) carmine-lake   ..   ..   £500 42·00
33   4   4d. dull lilac   ..   ..   ..   — £700
34   4d. dull purple £2750 £700
35   6d. yellow-green £1800 £150
36   6d. deep green £1800 £140
37   1s. purple-slate £2750 £850

(*b*) *Pin-perf* 13½–14
38   2   (1d.) rose-red   ..   ..   85·00 19·00
39   (1d.) carmine-lake   ..   ..   £120 17·00
40   4   4d. dull lilac   ..   ..   £650 65·00
40a   4d. brownish purple   ..   .. 65·00 85·00
41   4d. dull purple ..   ..   ..   £200 90·00
42   6d. yellow-green   ..   ..   £300 60·00
43   6d. deep green   ..   ..   £275 55·00
43a   6d. bright yellow-green   ..   65·00 70·00
    b. Imperf between (vert pair)   ..   £3500
44   1s. purple-slate £3000 £550

(*c*) *Compound pin-perf* 13½–14 × 12½
45   2   (1d.) carmine-lake   ..   ..   † £3000
45a   4   4d. dull purple ..   ..   ..   † —

PRICES. The Pin-perf stamps are very scarce with perforations on
all sides and the prices quoted above are for good average
specimens.
The note after No. 12 also applies to Nos. 38, 40a, 43a, 46, 47
and 50.

1860 (Aug). *Clean-cut perf* 14–16½.
46   2   (1d.) rose-red   ..   ..   85·00 48·00
    a. Imperf vert (horiz pair)   ..   £1100
47   4   4d. brownish lilac   ..   .. 90·00 70·00
48   4d. lilac   ..   ..   ..   — £225
49   6d. bright yellow-green ..   £300 75·00
50   6d. deep green £190 £120

1861 (June). *Rough perf* 14–16½.
52   2   (1d.) rose-red (H/S "CANCELLED" in oval
£3500)   ..   ..   75·00 23·00
53   (1d.) rose   ..   ..   ..   75·00 19·00
54   4   4d. brownish lilac   ..   ..   £160 60·00
55   4d. lilac..   ..   ..   ..   £375 65·00
    a. Imperf
56   6d. yellow-green   ..   ..   £160 65·00
57   6d. deep green   ..   ..   £350 55·00
58   1s. indigo £600 £160
59   1s. dp bluish purple (H/S "CANCELLED"
in oval £3500) £750 £250

(Recess D.L.R.)

1862–63. *Thick paper.* (*a*) *P* 11½, 12.
60   2   (1d.) crimson-lake   ..   ..   75·00 14·00
61   4   4d. deep purple ..   ..   ..   £120 48·00
62   6d. deep green   ..   ..   £650 65·00
63   1s. bluish slate   ..   ..   £750 65·00

(*b*) *P* 11½, 12, *compound with* 11
63a   2   (1d.) crimson-lake £1500 £350
63b   4   6d. deep green   ..   ..   —£5000

(*c*) *P* 13 (1863)
64   2   (1d.) lake   ..   ..   ..   32·00 15·00
65   4   6d. emerald-green   ..   ..   £275 48·00
67   1s. bright mauve £2750 £225

(*d*) *P* 12½ (1863)
68   2   (1d.) lake   ..   ..   ..   32·00 16·00

1863–76. *Wmk Crown CC.* (*a*) *P* 12½
69   2   (1d.) lake   ..   ..   ..   38·00 4·50
    a. Wmk sideways   ..   ..   £110 12·00
    b. Rose   ..   ..   ..   38·00 1·60
    ba. Imperf (pair)
    c. Scarlet   ..   ..   ..   38·00 1·50
    d. Carmine   ..   ..   ..   38·00 1·75
    w. Wmk inverted   ..   ..   † —
    x. Wmk reversed   ..   ..   — 2·00
70   4   4d. bright violet   ..   ..   90·00 8·00
    a. Pale mauve   ..   ..   £150 9·50
    b. Dull lilac   ..   ..   £110 11·00
    x. Wmk reversed
71   4d. grey (1872) ..   ..   ..   85·00 4·25
    a. Bluish grey   ..   ..   85·00 4·50
    x. Wmk reversed
72   6d. emerald-green   ..   ..   65·00 11·00
    a. Deep green   ..   ..   £200 7·50
    b. Yellow-green   ..   ..   50·00 3·00
    c. Apple-green   ..   ..   50·00 4·50
    d. Blue-green   ..   ..   85·00 6·00
    x. Wmk reversed   ..   ..   75·00 6·00
73   1s. bright deep mauve   ..   ..   £100 6·50
    a. Lilac-rose   ..   ..   85·00 6·00
    b. Mauve (aniline)   ..   ..   75·00 4·25
    bw. Wmk inverted
    bx. Wmk reversed   ..   ..   — 6·00
74   1s. chrome-yellow (1872)   ..   £110 1·00

(*b*) *P* 14 (1876)
75   2   (1d.) lake   ..   ..   ..   18·00 80
    a. Bisected (½d.) (on cover)   ..   † £550
    b. Rose-carmine   ..   ..   18·00 1·00
    c. Scarlet   ..   ..   ..   32·00 75
    x. Wmk reversed   ..   ..   — 1·00
76   4   4d. bluish grey ..   ..   ..   80·00 70
77   6d. bright yellow-green   ..   70·00 1·25
    a. Deep yellow-green   ..   ..   75·00 1·00
    w. Wmk inverted   ..   ..   † 60·00
    x. Wmk reversed
78   1s. chrome-yellow   ..   ..   85·00 2·50

(*c*) *P* 14×12½ (1876)
79   4   6d. yellow-green   ..   ..   —£4750
The 1s. perforated 12½ in purple-slate is a colour changeling.

5

(Typo D.L.R.)
1869. *Wmk Crown CC. P* 12½.
87   5   5s. rose-lake   ..   ..   £150 75·00

HALFPENNY   ONE PENNY
    (6)   (7)

1879–82. *Surch with T* **6** *or* **7**. *P* 14.
(*a*) *Wmk Crown CC* (June 1879)
98   2   ½d. lilac   ..   ..   ..   10·00 6·50
    w. Wmk inverted
    x. Wmk reversed   ..   ..   — 6·50
99   ½d. mauve   ..   ..   ..   10·00 6·50
    a. Wmk sideways   ..   ..   50·00 50·00
    w. Wmk inverted   ..   ..   †
(*b*) *Wmk Crown CA* (1882)
100   2   ½d. lilac..   ..   ..   £180 60·00
    x. Wmk reversed   ..   ..   £180 60·00
101   1d. rosy carmine   ..   ..   20·00 70
    a. Bisected (½d.) (on cover)   ..   † £475
    x. Wmk reversed

1882. *Wmk Crown CA. P* 14.
102   4   4d. bluish grey ..   ..   ..   £140 6·50
    x. Wmk reversed

    (8)   Various styles

1882 (9 May). *Surch by hand in various styles as T* **8** *in red or
black ink and the original value obliterated by a thick or thin bar
or bars, of the same colour.*
103   1d. on 6d. (No. 77) (Bk.)   ..   ..   —£1500
104   1d. on 6d. (No. 77) (R.)   ..   5·50 4·00
    x. Wmk reversed
105   1d. on 6d. (No. 77a) (R.)   ..   5·50 4·00
    a. Bisected (½d.) (on cover)   ..   † £300

10   11 Britannia   12 Britannia

(Typo D.L.R.)
1883–94. *P* 14. (*a*) *Wmk Crown CA.*
106   10   ½d. dull green   ..   ..   2·50 1·25
107   1d. carmine   ..   ..   8·00 50
    a. Bisected (½d.) (on cover)   ..   † £475
    w. Wmk inverted
108   2½d. bright blue   ..   ..   10·00 60
110   4d. grey   ..   ..   ..   2·25 50
    w. Wmk inverted
111   6d. olive-black (1884)   ..   3·00 3·75
112   1s. orange-brown (1884)   ..   3·00 2·00
(*b*) *Wmk Crown CC*
113   5   5s. maroon (1894)   ..   ..   48·00 75·00
106/13   Set of 7 70·00 75·00
106/12 Optd "Specimen"   ..   Set of 6 £400

Two types of 1d. value:

ONE PENNY   ONE PENNY
(I) (round "o")   (II) (oval "o")

(Typo D.L.R.)
1896 (17 Aug)–**1900.** *P* 14. (*a*) *Wmk Crown CA.*
114   11   ½d. dull purple and green   ..   3·25 30
115   1d. dull purple and rose (I)   ..   3·25 10
116   1d. dull purple and rose (II) (1900)   £180 4·00
117   2½d. dull purple and blue   ..   4·50 20
118   4d. dull purple and orange   ..   5·50 14·00
119   5d. dull purple and mauve   ..   5·50 13·00
120   6d. dull purple and black   ..   7·50 5·50
121   1s. green and brown   ..   ..   7·00 6·50
(*b*) *Wmk CA over Crown. Ordinary paper*
122   12   5s. green and brown   ..   ..   40·00 65·00
123   10s. green and ultramarine   ..   £130 £180
124   £1 green and carmine £110 £160
    a. Chalk-surfaced paper
114/24   Set of 10 £275 £400
114/24 Optd "Specimen"   Set of 10 £150
No. 119, surcharged "3d." was prepared for use but not issued
(*Price* £2750 *unused*). It also exists overprinted "Specimen"
(*Price* £75).
Collectors are warned against apparently postally used copies of
this issue which bear "REGISTRAR-GENERAL" obliterations and
are of very little value.

13 Landing of Columbus

(Recess D.L.R.)

1898. *400th Anniv of Discovery of Trinidad. Wmk Crown CC. P 14.*
125 13 2d. brown and dull violet .. .. 2·50 1·25
125 Optd "Specimen" .. .. 50·00

1901–06. *Colours changed. Wmk Crown CA or CA over Crown (5s.). Ordinary paper. P 14.*
126 11 ½d. grey-green (1902) .. .. 55 1·75
127 1d. black/*red* (II) .. .. 1·00 10
 a. Value omitted £10000
 w. Wmk inverted .. ..
128 2½d. purple and blue/*blue* (1902) .. 14·00 25
129 4d. green and blue/*buff* (1902) .. 1·75 11·00
 a. Chalk-surfaced paper .. 3·25 11·00
130 1s. black and blue/*yellow* (1903) .. 18·00 5·50
131 12 5s. lilac and mauve .. .. 40·00 60·00
 a. Deep purple and mauve (1906) .. 55·00 75·00
 ab. Chalk-surfaced paper .. 65·00 80·00
126/31 .. .. *Set of 6* 65·00 70·00
126/31 Optd "Specimen" .. *Set of 6* £100

A pane of sixty of No. 127a was found in a post office in Trinidad but not more than nine copies are believed to have been sold, and the rest withdrawn.

1904–09. *Wmk Mult Crown CA. Ordinary paper (½d., 1d., 2½d. (No. 137)) or chalk-surfaced paper (others). P 14.*
132 11 ½d. grey-green .. .. 2·00 90
 a. Chalk-surfaced paper .. 4·00 2·00
133 ½d. blue-green (1906) .. .. 8·00 2·25
134 1d. black/*red* (II) .. .. 3·25 10
 a. Chalk-surfaced paper .. 4·75 10
135 1d. rose-red (1907) .. .. 1·00 10
136 2½d. purple and blue/*blue* .. 19·00 90
137 2½d. blue (1906) .. .. 1·75 15
138 4d. grey and red/*yellow* (1906) .. 1·00 7·00
 a. Black and red/*yellow* .. 9·00 20·00
139 6d. dull purple and black (1905) .. 14·00 15·00
140 6d. dull and bright purple (1906) .. 6·50 7·50
141 1s. black and blue/*yellow* .. 20·00 8·00
142 1s. purple and blue/*golden yellow* .. 10·00 12·00
143 1s. black/*green* (1906) .. .. 1·50 1·25
144 12 5s. deep purple and mauve (1907) .. 42·00 75·00
145 £1 green and carmine (1907) .. £110 £180
132/45 .. .. *Set of 14* £200 £250
135, 137/8, 140, 142/3 Optd "Specimen" .. *Set of 6* £100

No. 135 is from a new die, the letters of "ONE PENNY" being short and thick, while the point of Britannia's spear breaks the uppermost horizontal line of shading in the background.

14   15   16

(Typo D.L.R.)

1909. *Wmk Mult Crown CA. P 14.*
146 14 ½d. green .. .. 2·50 10
147 15 1d. rose-red .. .. 1·50 10
148 16 2½d. blue .. .. 8·50 3·25
146/8 .. .. *Set of 3* 11·00 3·25
146/8 Optd "Specimen" .. *Set of 3* 50·00

TOBAGO

Although a Colonial Postmaster was appointed in January 1765 it was not until 1841 that the British G.P.O. established a branch office at Scarborough, the island capital, to handle the overseas mail.

The stamps of Great Britain were in use from May 1858 to the end of April 1860 when the control of the postal service passed to the local authorities.

From April 1860 Nos. CC1/2 were again used on overseas mail, pending the introduction of Tobago stamps in 1879.

SCARBOROUGH
CROWNED-CIRCLE HANDSTAMPS

CC 1   CC 2

CC1 CC 1 TOBAGO (R.) (31.10.1851) *Price on cover* £700
CC2 CC 2 TOBAGO (R.) (1875) *Price on cover* £2250

Stamps of GREAT BRITAIN cancelled "A 14" as Type Z 1 of Jamaica.

1858 to 1860.
Z 1 1d. rose-red (1857), *perf 14* £700
Z 2 4d. rose (1857) £250
Z 3 6d. lilac (1856) £225
Z 4 1s. green (1856) £1000

PRICES FOR STAMPS ON COVER	
Nos. 1/4	*from × 25*
Nos. 5/7	
Nos. 8/12	*from × 10*
Nos. 13/19	*from × 6*
Nos. 20/4	*from × 40*
Nos. 26/33	*from × 25*

CANCELLATIONS. Beware of early stamps of Tobago with fiscal endorsements removed and forged wide "A 14" postmarks added.

2½ PENCE (3)

1   2

(T 1 and 2 Typo D.L.R.)

1879 (1 Aug). *Fiscal stamps issued provisionally pending the arrival of stamps inscr "POSTAGE". Wmk Crown CC. P 14.*
1 1 1d. rose .. .. .. 75·00 60·00
2 3d. blue .. .. .. 70·00 45·00
3 6d. orange .. .. 35·00 48·00
 w. Wmk inverted .. .. 85·00 95·00
4 1s. green .. .. .. £350 60·00
 a. Bisected (6d.) (on cover) .. †
5 5s. slate £550 £500
6 £1 mauve £4000
The stamps were introduced for fiscal purposes on 1 July 1879. Stamps of T 1, watermark Crown CA, are fiscals which were never admitted to postal use.

1880 (Nov). *No. 3 bisected vertically and surch with pen and ink.*
7 1 1d. on half of 6d. orange £4500 £750
 w. Wmk inverted .. ..

1880 (20 Dec). *Wmk Crown CC. P 14.*
8 2 ½d. purple-brown .. .. 28·00 48·00
9 1d. Venetian red .. .. 85·00 48·00
 a. Bisected (½d.) (on cover) .. † £1600
10 4d. yellow-green .. .. £180 27·00
 a. Bisected (2d.) (on cover) .. † £1600
 b. Malformed "CE" in "PENCE" .. £1200 £400
 w. Wmk inverted .. .. — £100
11 6d. stone .. .. £250 90·00
12 1s. yellow-ochre .. .. 50·00 60·00
 w. Wmk inverted £110
For illustration of Nos. 10b, 18a, 22b, 30a, 31a and 33b see above No. 4 of Dominica.

1883 (Apr). *No. 11 surch with T 3.*
13 2 2½d. on 6d. stone .. .. 38·00 38·00
 a. Surch double £2750 £1300
 b. Large "2" with long tail .. £100 £110

"SLASH" FLAW. Stamps as Type 2 were produced from Key and Duty plates. On the Key plate used for consignments between 2 October 1892 and 16 December 1896, damage in the form of a large cut or "slash" shows after the "E" of "POSTAGE" on R.1/4.

After 1896 an attempt was made to repair the "slash". This resulted in its disappearance, but left an incomplete edge to the circular frame at right.

1882–84. *Wmk Crown CA. P 14.*
14 2 ½d. purple-brown (1882) .. .. 1·00 12·00
15 1d. Venetian red (1882) .. .. 2·50 1·75
 a. Bisected (½d.) (on cover) .. †
16 2½d. dull blue (1883) .. .. 24·00 1·10
 a. Bright blue .. .. 4·00 75
 b. Ultramarine .. .. 4·00 75
 c. "Slash" flaw .. .. 32·00 32·00
 ca. "Slash" flaw repaired .. 75·00
18 4d. yellow-green (1882) .. .. £170 90·00
 a. Malformed "CE" in "PENCE" .. £1100 £450
19 6d. stone (1884).. .. .. £500 £475

1885–96. *Colours changed and new value. Wmk Crown CA. P 14.*
20 2 ½d. dull green (1886) .. .. 1·00 40
 a. "Slash" flaw .. .. 18·00 24·00
 ab. "Slash" flaw repaired .. 35·00
 w. Wmk inverted .. ..
21 1d. carmine (1889) .. .. 1·75 30
 a. "Slash" flaw .. .. 26·00 26·00
 ab. "Slash" flaw repaired .. 45·00
22 4d. grey (1885) .. .. 1·75 80
 a. Imperf (pair) £1700
 b. Malformed "CE" in "PENCE" .. 50·00 80·00
 c. "Slash" flaw .. .. 60·00 90·00
 ca. "Slash" flaw repaired .. 90·00
23 6d. orange-brown (1886) .. .. 1·25 3·50
 a. "Slash" flaw .. .. 65·00 £100
 ab. "Slash" flaw repaired .. 90·00
24 1s. olive-yellow (1894) .. .. 1·50 13·00
 a. Pale olive-yellow .. .. 6·50
 b. "Slash" flaw .. .. 75·00 £160
 ba. "Slash" flaw repaired .. £100
24c 1s. orange-brown (1896) .. .. 6·00 50·00
 ca. "Slash" flaw £100
20, 21 and 23 Optd "Specimen" .. *Set of 3* £170
No. 24c was printed in the colour of the 6d. by mistake.

½d

½ PENNY	2½ PENCE	POSTAGE
(4)	(5)	(6)

1886–89. *Nos. 16, 19 and 23 surch as T 4.*
26 ½d. on 2½d. dull blue (4.86) .. .. 3·75 10·00
 a. Figure further from word .. 16·00 45·00
 b. Surch double £1600 £1300
 c. Surch omitted. Vert pair with No. 26 £8500
 d. Ditto with No. 26a £16000
27 ½d. on 6d. stone (1.86) .. .. 2·25 18·00
 a. Figure further from word .. 25·00 £110
 b. Surch inverted £1400
 c. Surch double £1600
28 ½d. on 6d. orange-brown (8.87) .. 90·00 £120
 a. Figure further from word .. £275 £300
 b. Surch double .. .. — £1100
29 1d. on 2½d. dull blue (7.89) .. 45·00 16·00
 a. Figure further from word .. £110 75·00
The surcharge is in a setting of 12 (two rows of 6) repeated five times in the pane. Nos. 7, 9 and 10 in the setting have a raised "P" in "PENNY", and No. 10 also shows the wider spacing between figure and word.

1891–92. *No. 22 surch with T 4 or 5.*
30 ½d. on 4d. grey (3.92) .. .. 12·00 40·00
 a. Malformed "CE" in "PENCE" .. £200 £350
 b. Surch double £1900
31 2½d. on 4d. grey (8.91) .. .. 4·00 6·50
 a. Malformed "CE" in "PENCE" .. £120 £200
 b. Surch double £1900 £1900

1896. *Fiscal stamp (T 1, value in second colour, wmk Crown CA, P 14), surch with T 6.*
33 ½d. on 4d. lilac and carmine .. .. 45·00 27·00
 a. Space between "½" and "d" .. 90·00 55·00
 b. Malformed "CE" in "PENCE" .. £425 £425

Tobago became a ward of Trinidad on 1 January 1899. Stamps of Trinidad were used until issues inscribed "TRINIDAD AND TOBAGO" appeared in 1913.

TRINIDAD AND TOBAGO

PRICES FOR STAMPS ON COVER	
Nos. 149/55	*from × 3*
Nos. 156/7	—
Nos. 174/89	*from × 10*
Nos. 206/56	*from × 2*
Nos. D18/25	*from × 12*

17   18

(Typo D.L.R.)

1913–23. *Wmk Mult Crown CA. Ordinary paper (½d. to 4d. and 1s.) or chalk-surfaced paper (others). P 14.*
149 17 ½d. green .. .. .. 3·00 10
 a. Yellow-green (1915) .. .. 3·50 20
 b. Blue-green (thick paper) (1917) .. 6·50 90
 ba. Wmk sideways .. .. † £1300
 c. Blue-green/bluish (3.18) .. 14·00 12·00
 w. Wmk inverted .. ..
150 1d. bright red .. .. 1·50 10
 a. Red (thick paper) (1916) .. 3·25 30
 b. Pink (1918) .. .. 16·00 2·25
 c. Carmine-red (5.18) .. .. 2·25 10
151 2½d. ultramarine .. .. 4·50 50
 a. Bright blue (thick paper) (1916) .. 5·50 50
 b. Bright blue (thin paper) (1918) .. 8·00 50

152	17	4d. black and red/*yellow*		70	5·50
		a. Chalk-surfaced paper			
		b. White back (12.13) (Optd S. £18)		1·75	10·00
		c. On lemon (1917)		10·00	
		d. On pale yellow (1923) (Optd S. £22)	5·00	8·50
153		6d. dull and reddish purple		7·50	6·00
		a. Dull and deep purple (1918)		7·50	3·75
		b. Dull purple and mauve (2.18)		10·00	8·00
154		1s. black/*green*		1·75	4·25
		a. White back (Optd S. £18)		1·00	4·50
		b. On blue-green, olive back		6·50	8·50
		c. On emerald back (Optd S. £22)		1·50	2·50
155	18	5s. dull purple and mauve (1914)	50·00	90·00
		a. Deep purple and mauve (1918)	50·00	90·00
		b. Lilac and violet		85·00	£120
		c. Dull purple and violet		90·00	£130
		d. Brown-purple and violet		40·00	90·00
156		£1 grey-green and carmine (1914)	£110	£150
		a. Deep yellow-green and carmine (1918)	£110	£150

149/56   *Set of 8* £150 £225
149/56 Optd "Specimen"   *Set of 8* £150
No. 156a is from a plate showing background lines very worn.

18a

1914 (18 Sept). *Red Cross Label authorised for use as ½d. stamp. Typo. P 11–12.*
157   18a   (½d.) Red   10·00 £190
The above was authorised for internal use on one day only, to raise funds for the Red Cross. The used price is for stamp on cover.

19.10.16.

21. 10. 15.

(19)   (19a)

1915 (21 Oct). *Optd with T 19. Cross in red with outline and date in black.*
174   17   1d. red   1·50 1·50
   a. Cross 2 mm to right   17·00 17·00
   b. "1" of "15" forked foot   8·50 12·00
   c. Broken "0" in "10"   12·00 14·00
The varieties occur in the following positions on the *pane* of 60: a. No. 11. b. No. 42. c. No. 45. Variety a. is only found on the right-hand pane.

1916 (19 Oct). *Optd with T 19a. Cross in red with outline and date in black.*
175   17   1d. scarlet   50 1·50
   a. No stop after "16"   7·00 23·00
   b. "19.10.16" omitted
   c. Red shading on cross omitted
No. 175a appears on stamp No. 36 on the right-hand pane only.

FORGERIES. Beware of forgeries of the "War Tax" errors listed below. There are also other unlisted errors which are purely fakes.

WAR TAX   **WAR TAX**   **WAR TAX**   **WAR TAX**
(19b)   (20)   (21)   (22)

1917 (2 Apr). *Optd with T 19b.*
176   17   1d. red   1·50 2·75
   a. Opt inverted   £150
   b. Scarlet   1·50 2·75
   w. Wmk inverted

1917 (May). *Optd with T 20.*
177   17   ½d. green   10 20
   a. Pair, one without opt   £275
178   1d. red   50 1·75
   a. Pair, one without opt   £275
   b. Scarlet   2·50 80
   ba. Opt double   90·00
The varieties without overprint were caused by the type being shifted over towards the left so that one stamp in the lowest row of each pane escaped.

1917 (21 June). *Optd with T 21.*
179   17   ½d. yellow-green   1·40 5·00
   a. Pale green   10 4·50
   b. Deep green   95 5·00
180   1d. red   10 75
   a. Pair, one without opt
No. 180a was caused by a shifting of the type to the left-hand side, but only a few stamps on the right-hand vertical row escaped the overprint and such pairs are very rare.

1917 (21 July–Sept). *Optd with T 22.*
181   17   ½d. yellow-green   4·00 6·00
   a. Deep green   10 2·50
182   1d. red (Sept)   2·50 95

WAR TAX   **WAR TAX**   **WAR TAX**
(23)   (24)   (25)

1917 (1 Sept). *Optd with T 23 (closer spacing between lines of opt).*
183   17   ½d. deep green   10 2·50
   a. Pale yellow-green
184   1d. red   27·00 21·00

1917 (31 Oct). *Optd with T 24.*
185   17   1d. scarlet   50 1·00
   a. Opt inverted   75·00

1918 (7 Jan). *Optd with T 25.*
186   17   1d. scarlet   1·00 15
   a. Opt double   £140 £140
   b. Opt inverted   85·00 85·00

War Tax   **War Tax**
(26)   (26a)   27

1918 (13 Feb–May). *Optd with T 26.*
187   17   ½d. bluish green   10 1·75
   a. Pair, one without opt   £450
188   1d. scarlet   60 1·25
   a. Opt double   80·00
   b. Rose-red (1.5.18)   10 60
The ½d. exists with "TAX" omitted caused by a paper fold.

1918 (14 Sept). *New printing as T 26, but 19 stamps on each sheet have the letters of the word "Tax" wider spaced, the "x" being to the right of "r" of "War" as T 26a. Thick bluish paper.*
189   17   1d. scarlet ("Tax" spaced)   35 4·00
   a. Opt double   £150

1921–22. *Wmk Mult Script CA. Chalk-surfaced paper (6d. to £1). P 14.*
206   17   ½d. green   1·60 2·00
207   1d. scarlet   30 30
208   1d. brown (17.2.22)   30 1·25
209   2d. grey (17.2.22)   1·00 1·25
210   2½d. bright blue   70 11·00
211   3d. bright blue (17.2.22)   2·50 2·75
212   6d. dull and bright purple   1·50 15·00
213   18   5s. dull purple and purple (1921)   48·00 £120
214   5s. deep purple and purple (1922)   48·00 £120
215   £1 green and carmine   75·00 £190
206/15   *Set of 9* £120 £300
206/15 Optd "Specimen"   *Set of 9* £200

(Typo D.L.R.)

1922–28. *P 14. Chalk-surfaced paper (4d. to £1).*

(a) Wmk Mult Crown CA
216   27   4d. black and red/*pale yellow*   2·75 5·50
217   1s. black/*emerald*   2·75 9·00

(b) Wmk Mult Script CA
218   27   ½d. green   30 10
219   1d. brown   30 10
   w. Wmk inverted   25·00
220   1½d. bright rose   2·00 20
   aw. Wmk inverted
   b. Scarlet   1·40 30
   bw. Wmk inverted
222   2d. grey   50 1·25
223   3d. blue   50 1·25
224   4d. black and red/*pale yellow* (1928)   3·00 3·25
225   6d. dull purple and bright magenta   2·00 24·00
226   6d. green and red/*emerald* (1924)   1·00 50
227   1s. black/*emerald*   5·00 1·75
228   5s. dull purple and mauve   20·00 35·00
229   £1 green and bright rose   90·00 £200
216/29   *Set of 13* £110 £250
216/29 Optd "Specimen"   *Set of 13* £225

(New Currency. 100 cents = 1 West Indian, later Trinidad and Tobago dollar)

28 First Boca   29 Imperial College of Tropical Agriculture

(Recess B.W.)

1935 (1 Feb)–**37.** *T 28/9 and similar horiz designs. Wmk Mult Script CA (sideways). P 12.*
230   1 c. blue and green   40 65
   a. Perf 13 × 12½ (1936)   20 10
231   2 c. ultramarine and yellow-brown   50 65
   a. Perf 13 × 12½ (1936)   60 10
232   3 c. black and scarlet   75 20
   a. Perf 13 × 12½ (1936)   2·00 20
233   6 c. sepia and blue   4·25 2·00
   a. Perf 13 × 12½ (1937)   4·50 2·50
234   8 c. sage-green and vermilion   3·50 3·50
   a. Perf 13 × 12½ (1937)   3·50 3·75
235   12 c. black and violet   3·25 1·50
   a. Perf 13 × 12½ (1937)   3·50 1·50
236   24 c. black and olive-green   2·50 1·50
   a. Perf 13 × 12½ (1937)   9·00 5·50

237   48 c. deep green   7·50 14·00
238   72 c. myrtle-green and carmine   28·00 29·00
230/8   *Set of 9* 45·00 45·00
230/8 Perf "Specimen"   *Set of 9* £110
Designs:—3 c. Mt Irvine Bay, Tobago; 6 c. Discovery of Lake Asphalt; 8 c. Queen's Park, Savannah; 12 c. Town Hall, San Fernando; 24 c. Government House; 48 c. Memorial Park; 72 c. Blue Basin.

1935 (6 May). *Silver Jubilee. As Nos. 114/17 of Jamaica. P 11×12.*
239   2 c. ultramarine and grey-black   30 60
   a. Extra flagstaff   32·00
   b. Short extra flagstaff   38·00
   c. Lightning conductor   27·00
   d. Flagstaff on right-hand turret   48·00
240   3 c. deep blue and scarlet   30 1·00
   a. Extra flagstaff   50·00
   c. Lightning conductor   35·00
241   6 c. brown and deep blue   1·50 2·25
   a. Extra flagstaff   85·00
   b. Short extra flagstaff   85·00
   c. Lightning conductor   70·00
242   24 c. slate and purple   5·00 15·00
   a. Extra flagstaff   £110
   c. Lightning conductor   90·00
   d. Flagstaff on right-hand turret   £140
   e. Double flagstaff   £150
239/42   *Set of 4* 6·50 17·00
239/42 Perf "Specimen"   *Set of 4* £75
For illustrations of plate varieties see Omnibus section following Zimbabwe.

1937 (12 May). *Coronation. As Nos. 118/20 of Jamaica.*
243   1 c. green   15 10
244   2 c. yellow-brown   35 10
245   8 c. orange   90 1·25
243/5   *Set of 3* 1·25 1·25
243/5 Perf "Specimen"   *Set of 3* 60·00

37 First Boca   47 King George VI

(Recess B.W.)

1938 (2 May)–**44.** *T 37 and similar horiz designs, and T 47. Wmk Mult Script CA (sideways on 1 c. to 60 c.).*

(a) P 11½×11
246   1 c. blue and green   55 20
247   2 c. blue and yellow-brown   55 20
248   3 c. black and scarlet   11·00 90
248a   3 c. green and purple-brown (1941)   30 20
   ab. "A" of "CA" missing from wmk
249   4 c. chocolate   29·00 1·00
249a   4 c. scarlet (1941)   40 70
249b   5 c. magenta (1.5.41)   30 15
250   6 c. sepia and blue   2·25 70
251   8 c. sage-green and vermilion   2·25 85
252   12 c. black and purple   16·00 1·75
   a. Black and slate-purple (1944)   2·50 10
253   24 c. black and olive-green   1·00 10
254   60 c. myrtle-green and carmine   8·50 1·25

(b) T 47. P 12
255   $1.20, blue-green (1.40)   10·00 1·25
256   $4.80, rose-carmine (1.40)   20·00 27·00
246/56   *Set of 14* 75·00 30·00
246/56 exc 249b Perf "Specimen"   *Set of 13* £190
Designs:—2 c. Imperial College of Tropical Agriculture; 3 c. Mt Irvine Bay, Tobago; 4 c. Memorial Park; 5 c. G.P.O. and Treasury; 6 c. Discovery of Lake Asphalt; 8 c. Queen's Park, Savannah; 12 c. Town Hall, San Fernando; 24 c. Government House; 60 c. Blue Basin.

1946 (1 Oct). *Victory. As Nos. 141/2 of Jamaica.*
257   3 c. chocolate   10 10
258   6 c. blue   10 90
257/8 Perf "Specimen"   *Set of 2* 48·00

1948 (22 Nov). *Royal Silver Wedding. As Nos. 143/4 of Jamaica, but $4.80 in recess.*
259   3 c. red-brown   10 10
260   $4.80, carmine   18·00 24·00

1949 (10 Oct). *75th Anniv of U.P.U. As Nos. 145/8 of Jamaica.*
261   5 c. bright reddish purple   40 50
262   6 c. deep blue   1·00 65
263   12 c. violet   40 75
264   24 c. olive   40 60
261/4   *Set of 4* 2·00 2·25

1951 (16 Feb). *University College of B.W.I. As Nos. 149/50 of Jamaica.*
265   3 c. green and red-brown   20 60
266   12 c. black and reddish violet   30 60

48 First Boca

49 Mt Irvine Bay, Tobago

(Recess B.W.)

1953 (20 Apr)–**59**. *Designs previously used for King George VI issue, but with portrait of Queen Elizabeth II as in T* **48** (1 c., 2 c., 12 c.) *or* **49** (*other values*). *Wmk Mult Script CA. P* 12 (*dollar values*) *or* 11½×11 (*others*).

267	1 c. blue and green		20	30
	a. *Blue and bluish green* (10.6.59)		4·00	3·75
268	2 c. indigo and orange-brown		20	30
269	3 c. deep emerald and purple-brown		20	10
270	4 c. scarlet		20	30
271	5 c. magenta		30	30
272	6 c. brown and greenish blue		50	30
273	8 c. deep yellow-green and orange-red		1·50	30
274	12 c. black and purple		30	10
275	24 c. black and yellow-olive		1·25	30
	a. *Black and olive* (16.11.55)		2·75	55
	b. *Black and greenish olive* (12.12.56)		4·75	1·00
276	60 c. blackish green and carmine		19·00	1·00
277	$1.20, bluish green		1·00	1·00
	a. Perf 11½ (19.1.55)		1·25	30
278	$4.80, cerise		7·00	20·00
	a. Perf 11½ (16.12.55)		8·50	13·00
267/78a		*Set of* 12	28·00	15·00

Designs: *Horiz*—2 c. Imperial College of Tropical Agriculture; 4 c. Memorial Park; 5 c. G.P.O. and Treasury; 6 c. Discovery of Lake Asphalt; 8 c. Queen's Park, Savannah; 12 c. Town Hall, San Fernando; 24 c. Government House; 60 c. Blue Basin. *Vert* (18 × 21 *mm*)—$1.20, $4.80, Queen Elizabeth II.

1953 (3 June). *Coronation. As No.* 153 *of Jamaica*.

279	3 c. black and green		20	10

ONE CENT

(50)

1956 (20 Dec). *No.* 268 *surch with T* **50**.

280	1 c. on 2 c. indigo and orange-brown		90	1·40

1958 (22 Apr). *Inauguration of British Caribbean Federation. As Nos.* 175/7 *of Jamaica*.

281	5 c. deep green		20	10
282	6 c. blue		25	1·50
283	12 c. scarlet		25	10
281/3		*Set of* 3	65	1·50

PRINTERS. Nos. 284 to 354 were printed in photogravure by Harrison & Sons, *unless otherwise stated*.

51 Cipriani Memorial

52 Queen's Hall

53 Copper-rumped Hummingbird

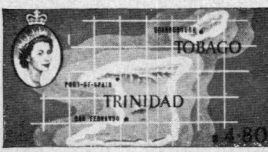

54 Map of Trinidad and Tobago

(Des V. Whiteley (1, 2, 12, 35, 60 c., $4.80), J. Matthews (5 c.), H. Baxter (6, 8, 10, 15 c.), M. Goaman (25 c., 50 c., $1.20))

1960 (24 Sept)–**67**. *Designs as T* **51**/4. *W w* **12** (*upright*). *P* 13½×14½ (1 c., 60 c., $1.20, $4.80) *or* 14½×13½ (*others*).

284	1 c. stone and black		10	10
285	2 c. bright blue		10	10
	a. *Blue* (23.6.64)		2·50	10
	b. *New blue* (18.4.67)		2·50	10
	w. Wmk inverted		4·00	
286	5 c. chalky blue		10	10
	w. Wmk inverted		4·50	1·25
287	6 c. red-brown		10	30
	a. *Pale chestnut* (13.4.67)		3·00	50
	w. Wmk inverted		22·00	
288	8 c. yellow-green		10	50
289	10 c. deep lilac		10	10
290	12 c. vermilion		10	20
291	15 c. orange		90	45
291a	15 c. orange (15.9.64)		2·75	10
292	25 c. rose-carmine and deep blue		80	10
	w. Wmk inverted		3·25	90

293	35 c. emerald and black		2·50	10
294	50 c. yellow, grey and blue		35	60
295	60 c. vermilion, yellow-green and indigo		55	30
	a. Perf 14½ (1.10.65)*		£100	35·00
296	$1.20, multicoloured		15·00	2·50
297	$4.80, apple-green and pale blue		15·00	5·00
284/97		*Set of* 15	28·00	13·00

Designs: *Vert as T* **51**—60 c. Anthurium Lilies. *Horiz as T* **52**—5 c. Whitehall; 6 c. Treasury Building; 8 c. Governor-General's House; 10 c. General Hospital, San Fernando; 12 c. Oil refinery; 15 c. (No. 291), Crest; 15 c. (No. 291a), Coat of arms; 25 c. Scarlet Ibis; 35 c. Pitch Lake; 50 c. Mohammed Jinnah Mosque.

*This is the earliest date reported to us. It comes from an unannounced printing which was despatched to Trinidad on 3 December 1964.

The 2, 5, 6, 12 and 25 c. exist with PVA gum as well as gum arabic.

See also No. 317.

65 Scouts and Gold Wolf Badge

1961 (4 Apr). *Second Caribbean Scout Jamboree. Design multicoloured; background colours below. W w* **12**. *P* 13½ × 14½.

298	65	8 c. light green	15	10
299		25 c. light blue	15	10
		w. Wmk inverted	—	60·00

INDEPENDENT

66 "Buccoo Reef" (painting by Carlisle Chang)

71 "Protein Foods"

1962 (31 Aug). *Independence. T* **66** *and similar horiz designs. W w* **12**. *P* 14½.

300	5 c. bluish green		10	10
301	8 c. grey		20	30
302	25 c. reddish violet		15	10
303	35 c. brown, yellow, green and black		2·25	15
304	60 c. red, black and blue		2·50	3·25
300/4		*Set of* 5	4·75	3·50

Designs:—8 c. Piarco Air Terminal; 25 c. Hilton Hotel, Port-of-Spain; 35 c. Greater Bird of Paradise and map; 60 c. Scarlet Ibis and map.

(Des M. Goaman)

1963 (4 June). *Freedom from Hunger. W w* **12**. *P* 14 × 13½.

305	71	5 c. brown-red	15	10
306		8 c. yellow-bistre	15	45
307		25 c. violet-blue	25	20
305/7		*Set of* 3	50	65

72 Jubilee Emblem

1964 (15 Sept). *Golden Jubilee of Trinidad and Tobago Girl Guides' Association. W w* **12**. *P* 14½×14.

308	72	6 c. yellow, ultramarine and rose-red	10	40
309		25 c. yellow, ultramarine and bright blue	15	20
310		35 c. yellow, ultramarine & emerald-grn	15	20
308/10		*Set of* 3	30	70

73 I.C.Y. Emblem

(Litho State Ptg Wks, Vienna)

1965 (15 Nov). *International Co-operation Year. P* 12.

311	73	35 c. red-brown, dp green & ochre-yell	65	20

74 Eleanor Roosevelt, Flag and U.N. Emblem

1965 (10 Dec). *Eleanor Roosevelt Memorial Foundation. W w* **12**. *P* 13½ × 14.

312	74	25 c. black, red and ultramarine	15	10

75 Parliament Building

5¢ FIFTH YEAR OF INDEPENDENCE 31st AUGUST 1967 (79)

1966 (8 Feb). *Royal Visit. T* **75** *and similar horiz designs. Multicoloured. W w* **12** (*sideways*). *P* 13½ × 14½.

313	5 c. Type **75**		15	10
314	8 c. Map, Royal Yacht *Britannia* and Arms		2·25	70
315	25 c. Map and flag		2·25	55
316	35 c. Flag and panorama		2·25	70
313/16		*Set of* 4	6·00	1·75

1966 (15 Nov). *As No.* 284 *but W w* **12** (*sideways**).

317	1 c. stone and black		10	70
	w. Wmk Crown to right of CA			

*The normal sideways watermark shows Crown to left of CA, as seen from the back of the stamp.

No. 317 exists with PVA gum as well as gum arabic.

1967 (31 Aug). *Fifth Year of Independence. Nos.* 288/9, 291a *and* 295 *optd as T* **79**.

318	8 c. yellow-green		10	10
319	10 c. deep lilac		10	10
320	15 c. orange		10	10
321	60 c. vermilion, yellow-green and indigo		25	15
318/21		*Set of* 4	30	30

On No. 321 the overprint is in five lines.

80 Musical Instruments

81 Calypso King

1968 (17 Feb). *Trinidad Carnival. Horiz designs as T* **80** (15 and 25 c.), *or vert designs as T* **81** (35 and 60 c.). *Multicoloured. P* 12.

322	5 c. Type **80**		10	10
323	10 c. Type **81**		10	10
324	15 c. Steel band		10	10
325	25 c. Carnival procession		20	10
326	35 c. Carnival King		20	10
327	60 c. Carnival Queen		35	1·25
322/7		*Set of* 6	75	1·50

86 Doctor giving Eye-Test

87 Peoples of the World and Emblem

1968 (7 May). *20th Anniv of World Health Organization. W w* **12** (*sideways*). *P* 14.

328	86	5 c. red, blackish brown and gold	15	10
329		25 c. orange, blackish brown and gold	25	10
330		35 c. bright blue, black and gold	40	15
328/30		*Set of* 3	80	30

1968 (5 Aug). *Human Rights Year. W w* **12** (*sideways*). *P* 13½ × 14.

331	87	5 c. cerise, black and greenish yellow	10	10
332		10 c. new blue, black and greenish yellow	15	10
333		25 c. apple-green, black & greenish yell	30	15
331/3		*Set of* 3	45	30

88 Cycling

(Des G. Vasarhelyi. Islands additionally die-stamped in gold (5 c. to 35 c.))

1968 (14 Oct). *Olympic Games, Mexico. T* **88** *and similar horiz designs. Multicoloured. W w* **12**. *P* 14.

334	5 c. Type **88**		30	10
	w. Wmk inverted		† £180	
335	15 c. Weightlifting		20	10
	w. Wmk inverted		7·50	
336	25 c. Relay-racing		20	10
337	35 c. Sprinting		20	10
338	$1.20 Maps of Mexico and Trinidad		90	45
334/8		*Set of* 5	1·60	65

93 Cocoa Beans   **94 Green Hermit**

(Des G. Vasarhelyi. Queen's profile die-stamped in gold (G.) or silver (S.), also the Islands on 20, 25 c.)

1969 (1 Apr)–72. *Designs as T 93/4. W w 12 (sideways* on 1 to 8 c., 40 c., 50 c.). Chalk-surfaced paper. P 14×14½ ($2.50, $5) or 14 (others).*

339	1 c. multicoloured (S.)	10	90
	a. Queen's head omitted		80·00
	bw. Wmk Crown to right of CA		
	cw. Wmk Crown to right of CA		
	c. Glazed, ordinary paper (24.3.72)	10	10
340	3 c. multicoloured (G.)	10	10
	aw. Wmk Crown to right of CA		
	b. Glazed, ordinary paper (24.3.72)	10	10
	bw. Wmk Crown to right of CA		
341	5 c. multicoloured (G.)	2·25	10
	a. Glazed, ordinary paper (24.3.72)	1·50	10
	ab. Queen's head omitted		
	ac. Imperf (pair)	£200	
	ad. Ditto and Queen's head omitted	£325	
	aw. Wmk Crown to right of CA	6·00	
342	6 c. multicoloured (G.)	10	10
	a. Queen's head omitted	£110	
	b. Imperf (pair)	£250	
	c. Glazed, ordinary paper (24.3.72)	2·75	3·50
	cw. Wmk Crown to right of CA	4·25	
343	8 c. multicoloured (S.)	1·50	1·50
344	10 c. multicoloured (G.)	2·00	10
	a. Glazed, ordinary paper (24.3.72)	2·00	10
	aw. Wmk inverted	7·00	
345	12 c. multicoloured (blue-green leaves) (S.)	15	1·50
	a. Myrtle-green leaves	4·25	4·25
	b. Glazed, ordinary paper (24.3.72)	50	2·25
346	15 c. multicoloured (S.)	10	10
	a. Queen's head omitted	£350	
	b. Glazed, ordinary paper (24.3.72)	20	10
347	20 c. scarlet, black and grey (G.)	15	10
	a. Glazed, ordinary paper (24.3.72)	50	30
348	25 c. scarlet, black and new blue (S.)	15	15
	a. Glazed, ordinary paper (24.3.72)	3·25	1·50
	ab. Silver (Queen's head and island) omitted	£120	
349	30 c. multicoloured (S.)	30	10
	a. Glazed, ordinary paper (24.3.72)	50	30
	aw. Wmk inverted	8·50	
350	40 c. multicoloured (G.)	5·00	10
	a. Glazed, ordinary paper (24.3.72)	6·50	60
351	50 c. multicoloured (S.)	30	1·75
	a. Glazed, ordinary paper (24.3.72)	1·50	3·75
	aw. Wmk Crown to right of CA	6·00	
352	$1 multicoloured (G.)	60	15
	a. Gold (Queen's head) omitted	£130	
	b. Glazed, ordinary paper (24.3.72)	1·50	3·75
	ba. Gold (Queen's head) omitted		
353	$2.50, multicoloured (G.)	1·00	3·50
	a. Perf 14 (1972)	7·50	15·00
	aw. Wmk inverted	38·00	
354	$5 multicoloured (G.)	1·50	3·75
	a. Gold (Queen's head) omitted	£300	
	b. Perf 14 (1972)	15·00	25·00
	bw. Wmk inverted	38·00	50·00
339/54	*Set of 16*	12·50	11·50

Designs: *Horiz as T 93*—3 c. Sugar refinery; 5 c. Rufous-vented Chachalaca; 6 c. Oil refinery; 8 c. Fertilizer plant; 40 c. Scarlet Ibis; 50 c. Maracas Bay; $2.50, Fishing; $5 Red House. *Vert as T 94*—12 c. Citrus fruit; 15 c. Arms of Trinidad and Tobago; 20 c, 25 c. Flag and outline of Trinidad and Tobago; 30 c. Chaconia plant; $1, Poui tree.

*The normal sideways watermark shows the Crown to the left of CA, *as seen from the back of the stamp.*

The date quoted for the glazed, ordinary paper printings is that of receipt at the G.P.O.; the dates of issue are not known.

The listed missing die-stamped heads have the heads completely omitted and, except for No. 352a which results from a shift, show a blind impression of the die. They should not be confused with stamps from sheets containing a row of partially missing heads progressing down to mere specks of foil. The 20 c. value also exists with the gold omitted from the map only. We have also seen stamps with an additional "blind" profile cutting into the rear of the head but without a second die-stamped impression. Varieties of this nature are outside the scope of this catalogue.

See also Nos. 428/30 and 473.

108 Captain A. A. Cipriani (labour leader) and Entrance to Woodford Square

(Photo State Ptg Works, Vienna)

1969 (1 May). *50th Anniv of International Labour Organization. T 108 and similar horiz design. P 12.*

355	6 c. black, gold and carmine-red	15	25
356	15 c. black, gold and new blue	15	25

Design:—15 c. Arms of Industrial Court and entrance to Woodford Square.

110 Cornucopia and Fruit   **111** Map showing "CARIFTA" Countries

(Des and photo State Ptg Works, Vienna)

1969 (1 Aug). *First Anniv of CARIFTA (Caribbean Free Trade Area). T 110/11 and similar multicoloured designs. P 13½.*

357	6 c. Type 110	10	10
358	10 c. British and member nations' flags (horiz)	10	10
359	30 c. Type 111	30	20
360	40 c. Boeing 727-100 "Sunjet" in flight (horiz)	55	90
357/60	*Set of 4*	90	1·10

114 Space Module landing on Moon

(Des G. Vasarhelyi. Litho D.L.R.)

1969 (2 Sept). *First Man on the Moon. T 114 and similar multi-coloured designs. P 14.*

361	6 c. Type 114	15	10
362	40 c. Space module and astronauts on Moon (vert)	20	10
363	$1 Astronauts seen from inside space module	50	35
361/3	*Set of 3*	75	50

The above were released by the Philatelic Agency in the U.S.A. on 1 September, but not sold locally until 2 September.

117 Parliamentary Chamber, Flags and Emblems

(Photo Harrison)

1969 (23 Oct*). *15th Commonwealth Parliamentary Association Conference, Port-of-Spain. T 117 and similar horiz designs. Multicoloured. W w 12. P 14½ × 13½.*

364	10 c. Type 117	10	10
365	15 c. J.F. Kennedy College	10	10
366	30 c. Parliamentary maces	25	50
367	40 c. Cannon and emblem	25	50
364/7	*Set of 4*	60	1·00

*This was the local release date; the Philatelic Agency in New York released the stamps ten days earlier.

121 Congress Emblem   **122** Emblem and Islands at Daybreak

(Photo Rosenbaum Bros, Vienna)

1969 (3 Nov). *International Congress of the Junior Chamber of Commerce. T 121/2 and similar vert design. P 13½.*

368	6 c. black, red and gold	10	10
369	30 c. gold, lake and light blue	25	40
370	40 c. black, gold and ultramarine	25	40
368/70	*Set of 3*	50	75

Design:—40 c. Emblem, palm-trees and ruin.
The above were released by the Philatelic Agency in the U.S.A. on 2 November, but not sold locally until 3 November.

PRICES OF SETS

Set prices are given for many issues, generally those containing three stamps or more. Definitive sets include one of each value or major colour change, but do not cover different perforations, die types or minor shades. Where a choice is possible the set prices are based on the cheapest versions of the stamps included in the listings.

124 "Man in the Moon"   **129** Statue of Gandhi

(Des V. Whiteley. Litho Questa)

1970 (6 Feb). *Carnival Winners. T 124 and similar multicoloured designs. W w 12 (sideways on 40 c.). P 14.*

371	5 c. Type 124	10	10
372	6 c. "City beneath the Sea"	10	10
373	15 c. "Antelope" God Bamibara	15	10
	w. Wmk inverted	—	13·00
374	30 c. "Chanticleer" Pheasant Queen of Malaya	25	10
375	40 c. Steel Band of the Year (horiz)	25	30
371/5	*Set of 5*	70	50

The above were released by the Philatelic Agency in the U.S.A. on 2 February, but not sold locally until 6 February.

(Photo State Printing Works, Vienna)

1970 (2 Mar). *Gandhi Centenary Year (1969). T 129 and similar multicoloured design. P 12.*

376	10 c. Type 129	25	10
377	30 c. Head of Gandhi and Indian flag (horiz)	45	20

131 Symbols of Culture, Science, Arts and Technology

132 New U.P.U. H.Q. Building

(Des G. Lee. Photo State Printing Works, Vienna)

1970 (26 June). *25th Anniv of United Nations. T 131/2 and similar designs. Multicoloured. P 12 (30 c.), 13½ × 14 (10 c.) or 13½ (others).*

378	5 c. Type 131	10	10
379	10 c. Children of different races, map and flag (34 × 25 mm)	25	10
380	20 c. Noah's Ark, rainbow and dove (35 × 24 mm)	35	45
381	30 c. Type 132	35	30
378/81	*Set of 4*	95	75

NATIONAL
COMMERCIAL
BANK
ESTABLISHED
1.7.70

(133)   **134** "East Indian Immigrants" (J. Cazabon)

1970 (1 July). *Inauguration of National Commercial Bank. No. 341 optd with T 133.*

382	5 c. multicoloured	30	10

(Des from paintings by Cazabon. Litho Questa)

1970 (Oct). *125th Anniv of San Fernando. T 134 and similar designs. W w 12 (sideways on 5 c. and 40 c.). P 13½.*

383	3 c. multicoloured	10	90
	w. Wmk inverted	—	32·00
384	5 c. black, blue and yellow-ochre	10	10
385	40 c. black, blue and yellow-ochre	60	20
383/5	*Set of 3*	70	1·10

Designs: *Horiz*—5 c. "San Fernando Town Hall"; 40 c. "San Fernando Harbour, 1860".

135 "The Adoration of the Shepherds"
(detail, School of Seville)

(Des G. Drummond. Litho Format)

1970 (8 Dec). *Christmas. Paintings. T* **135** *and similar vert designs. Multicoloured. P* 13½.
386	3 c. Type **135**			10	10
387	5 c. "Madonna and Child with Saints" (detail, Titian)			10	10
388	30 c. "The Adoration of the Shepherds" (detail, Le Nain)			20	20
389	40 c. "The Virgin and Child, St. John and an Angel" (Morando)			20	10
390	$1 "The Adoration of the Kings" (detail, Veronese)			50	1·75
386/90			*Set of 5*	80	2·00
MS391	114 × 153 mm. Nos. 386/9			1·25	2·75

136 Red Brocket

(Des State Printing Works, Vienna. Litho Questa)

1971 (9 Aug). *Trinidad Wildlife. T* **136** *and similar horiz designs. Multicoloured. W w* **12** *(sideways*). P* 13½.
392	3 c. Type **136**			20	30
393	5 c. Collared Peccary ("Quenk")			25	15
394	6 c. Paca ("Lappe")			30	50
	w. Wmk Crown to left of CA				
395	30 c. Brazilian Agouti			1·00	3·50
396	40 c. Ocelot			1·00	2·75
392/6			*Set of 5*	2·50	6·50

*The normal sideways watermark shows Crown to right of CA, *as seen from the back of the stamp.*

137 A. A. Cipriani   **138** "Virgin and Child with St. John" (detail, Bartolommeo)

(Litho D.L.R.)

1971 (30 Aug*). *Ninth Anniv of Independence. T* **137** *and similar vert design. Multicoloured. W w* **12**. *P* 14.
397	5 c. Type **137**			10	10
398	30 c. Chaconia medal			30	60

*This was the local release date, but the New York agency issued the stamps on 25 August.

(Litho Harrison)

1971 (25 Oct). *Christmas. T* **138** *and similar vert designs. Multicoloured. W w* **12** *(sideways* on 10 and 15 c.). P* 14×14½.
399	3 c. Type **138**			15	15
400	5 c. Local crèche			20	10
401	10 c. "Virgin and Child with Saints Jerome and Dominic" (detail, Lippi)			25	10
402	15 c. "Virgin and Child with St. Anne" (detail, Gerolamo dai Libri)			30	20
	w. Wmk Crown to right of CA			16·00	
399/402			*Set of 4*	80	40

*The normal sideways watermark shows Crown to left of CA, *as seen from the back of the stamp.*

139 Satellite Earth Station, Matura

(Litho Harrison)

1971 (18 Nov). *Satellite Earth Station. T* **139** *and similar vert designs. Multicoloured. W w* **12** *(sideways* on 10 c.). P* 14 (10 c.) or 14 × 13½ (others).
403	10 c. Type **139**			10	10
404	30 c. Dish antennae			25	50
405	40 c. Satellite and the earth			55	50
403/5			*Set of 3*	65	1·00
MS406	140 × 76 mm. Nos. 403/5 (wmk sideways). Imperf			90	2·00
	a. Yellow and pale blue omitted				

140 *Morpho peleides × achilleana*

(Des G. Drummond. Photo Harrison)

1972 (18 Feb). *Butterflies. T* **140** *and similar horiz designs. Multicoloured. W w* **12** *(sideways* on 5 c.). P* 14.
407	3 c. Type **140**			75	50
	w. Wmk inverted			25·00	
408	5 c. *Eryphanis polyxena*			80	10
409	6 c. *Phoebis philea*			85	50
	w. Wmk inverted			13·00	
410	10 c. *Prepona laertes*			1·00	15
411	20 c. *Eurytides telesilaus*			1·75	2·00
	w. Wmk inverted			2·00	
412	30 c. *Eurema proterpia*			2·00	2·50
407/12			*Set of 6*	6·50	5·00

141 *Lady McLeod* (paddle-steamer)   **142** Trinity Cross
and McLeod Stamp

(Des J. Cooter. Litho Harrison)

1972 (24 Apr*). *125th Anniv. of First Trinidad Postage Stamp. T* **141** *and similar horiz designs. W w* **12**. *P* 14.
413	5 c. multicoloured			15	10
414	10 c. multicoloured			25	10
415	30 c. greenish blue, reddish chestnut & blk			70	45
	w. Wmk inverted			20·00	
413/15			*Set of 3*	1·00	55
MS416	83×140 mm. Nos. 413/15			1·00	1·25
	a. Wmk sideways			16·00	25·00
	w. Wmk inverted			22·00	

Designs:—10 c. Map and Lady McLeod stamp and inscription; 30 c. Lady McLeod stamp.
*This was the local release date, but the New York Agency issued the stamps on 12 April.

(Des G. Drummond. Photo Enschedé)

1972 (28 Aug). *Tenth Anniv of Independence. T* **142** *and similar vert designs. Multicoloured. W w* **12**. *P* 13½ × 13.
417	5 c. Type **142**			10	10
418	10 c. Chaconia Medal			10	10
419	20 c. Hummingbird Medal			15	15
420	30 c. Medal of Merit			15	20
417/20			*Set of 4*	40	40
MS421	93 × 121 mm. Nos. 417/20			60	1·00

One example of MS421 has been seen with the blue (background and frame) omitted from the 10 c. Another example has been seen with carmine (background and frame) omitted from the 30 c.
See also Nos. 440/4.

143 Bronze Medal, 1964 Relay

(Des G. Drummond. Litho Questa)

1972 (7 Sept). *Olympic Games, Munich. T* **143** *and similar horiz designs. Multicoloured. W w* **12**. *P* 14.
422	10 c. Type **143**			15	10
423	20 c. Bronze, 1964 200 metres			25	25
424	30 c. Silver, 1952 weightlifting			35	25
425	40 c. Silver, 1964 400 metres			35	25
426	50 c. Silver, 1948 weightlifting			35	1·75
422/6			*Set of 5*	1·25	2·25
MS427	153×82 mm. Nos. 422/6			1·75	2·25
	w. Wmk inverted			20·00	

1972–74. *Nos. 340/2, but W w* **12** *(upright). Glazed, ordinary paper.*
428	3 c. multicoloured (7.11.72*)			4·50	10·50
429	5 c. multicoloured (1973)			7·50	1·75
	a. Yellow (background) omitted			£130	
430	6 c. multicoloured (1974)			3·50	4·25
	w. Wmk inverted				
428/30			*Set of 3*	14·00	15·00

*Earliest known postmark date.

---

144 "Adoration of the Kings" (detail, Dosso)

(Des G. Drummond. Photo J.W.)

1972 (9 Nov). *Christmas. T* **144** *and similar horiz design. Multicoloured. W w* **12**. *P* 14.
431	3 c. Type **144**			10	10
432	5 c. "The Holy Family and a Shepherd" (Titian)			10	10
433	30 c. As 5 c.			70	55
431/3			*Set of 3*	80	60
MS434	73×99 mm. Nos. 431/3			90	1·50
	w. Wmk inverted				

145 E.C.L.A. Building, Chile

(Des G. Drummond. Litho Questa)

1973 (15 Aug). *Anniversaries. Events described on stamps. T* **145** *and similar horiz designs. Multicoloured. W w* **12**. *P* 14.
435	10 c. Type **145**			10	10
	w. Wmk inverted			12·00	
436	20 c. Interpol emblem			45	30
437	30 c. W.M.O. emblem			45	30
438	40 c. University of the West Indies			45	80
435/8			*Set of 4*	1·25	80
MS439	155×92 mm. Nos. 435/8			1·25	1·25
	w. Wmk inverted			20·00	

(Des J. Cooter. Litho Harrison)

1973 (30 Aug). *Eleventh Anniv of Independence. Vert designs as T* **142**. *Multicoloured. W w* **12**. *P* 14½ × 14.
440	10 c. Trinity Cross			10	10
441	20 c. Medal of Merit			20	35
442	30 c. Chaconia Medal			20	40
443	40 c. Hummingbird Medal			30	40
440/3			*Set of 4*	70	1·10
MS444	75×122 mm. Nos. 440/3. P 14			70	1·25
	w. Wmk inverted			27·00	

146 G.P.O., Port-of-Spain   **147** "Madonna with Child" (Murillo)

(Des J. Cooter. Photo J.W.)

1973 (8 Oct). *Second Commonwealth Conference of Postal Administrations, Trinidad. T* **146** *and similar horiz design. Multicoloured. W w* **12** *(sideways*). P* 14.
445	30 c. Type **146**			20	50
446	40 c. Conference Hall, Chaguaramas			30	50
MS447	115×115 mm. Nos. 445/6			90	1·00
	w. Wmk Crown to right of CA			18·00	

No. 446 is wrongly inscribed "CHAGARAMAS".
*The normal sideways watermark shows Crown to left of CA, *as seen from the back of the stamp.*

(Des PAD Studio. Photo Harrison)

1973 (22 Oct). *Christmas. W w* **12**. *P* 14½×14.
448	**147**	5 c. multicoloured		10	10
		w. Wmk inverted		30·00	
449		$1 multicoloured		75	1·25
MS450	94×88 mm. Nos. 448/9. Wmk sideways*. P 14			85	1·40
	w. Wmk Crown to right of CA			15·00	

*The normal sideways watermark shows Crown to left of CA, *as seen from the back of the stamp.*

148 Berne H.Q. within U.P.U. Emblem

(Des PAD Studio. Photo Harrison)

1974 (18 Nov). *Centenary of Universal Postal Union. T* **148** *and similar horiz design. Multicoloured. W w* **12** *(sideways). P* 13 × 14.
451	40 c. Type **148**			45	15
452	50 c. Map within emblem			45	85
MS453	117 × 104 mm. Nos. 451/2. P 13 × 14½			15·00	20·00

149 *Humming Bird I* (ketch)
crossing Atlantic Ocean (1960)

(Des and photo Harrison)

1974 (2 Dec). *First Anniv of World Voyage by H. and K. La Borde.*
T **149** *and similar horiz design. Multicoloured. W w* **12** *(sideways). P* 14.
454	40 c. Type **149**		50	15
455	50 c. *Humming Bird II* (ketch) crossing globe		60	95
MS456	109×84 mm. Nos. 454/5. Wmk upright.		1·50	4·00
	w. Wmk inverted		3·25	4·50

150 "Sex Equality"

(Des Hetty J. Mejias de Grannes; adapted V. Whiteley. Litho
Harrison)

1975 (23 June). *International Women's Year. W w* **14** *(sideways).*
P 14.
457	**150**	15 c. multicoloured	15	20
458		30 c. multicoloured	35	70

151 Common Vampire Bat,
Microscope and Syringe

(Des PAD Studio. Photo Harrison)

1975 (23 Sept). *Isolation of Rabies Virus. T* **151** *and similar horiz*
design. Multicoloured. W w **14**. *P* 14 × 14½.
459	25 c. Type **151**		40	40
460	30 c. Dr. Pawan, instruments and book		50	50
	w. Wmk inverted		6·50	

152 Route-map and Tail of Boeing 707

(Des C. Abbott. Litho Walsall)

1975 (27 Nov). *35th Anniv of British West Indian Airways.*
T **152** *and similar horiz designs. W w* **14** *(sideways*). P* 14.
461	20 c. Type **152**		40	20
462	30 c. 707 on ground		60	85
463	40 c. 707 in flight		70	1·00
	w. Wmk Crown to right of CA			
461/3		Set of 3	1·50	1·90
MS464	119×110 mm. Nos. 461/3.		1·50	2·00

*The normal sideways watermark shows Crown to left of CA,
as seen from the back of the stamp.

153 "From the Land of the Humming Bird"

1976 (12 Jan). *Carnival. 1974 Prizewinning Costumes. T* **153**
and similar horiz design. Multicoloured. W w **14** *(sideways*).*
P 14.
465	30 c. Type **153**		10	10
466	$1 "The Little Carib"		40	50
MS467	83×108 mm. Nos. 465/6.		1·10	1·10
	w. Wmk Crown to right of CA		5·00	

*The normal sideways watermark shows Crown to left of CA,
as seen from the back of the stamp.

ALTERED CATALOGUE NUMBERS

Any Catalogue numbers altered from the last
edition are shown as a list in the introductory
pages.

154 Angostura Building, Port-of-Spain

(Des Jennifer Toombs. Litho J.W.)

1976 (14 July). *150th Anniv. of Angostura Bitters. T* **154** *and*
similar horiz designs. Multicoloured. W w **14** *(sideways). P* 13.
468	5 c. Type **154**		10	10
469	35 c. Medal, New Orleans 1885/6		20	35
470	45 c. Medal, Sydney 1879		25	40
471	50 c. Medal, Brussels 1897		25	80
468/71		Set of 4	65	1·50
MS472	119×112 mm. Nos. 468/71. P 14		90	1·50

REPUBLIC

1976 (2 Aug). *As No.* 344a *but W w* **14**.
473	10 c. multicoloured		75	1·00
	w. Wmk inverted		7·50	

1976 (4 Oct). *West Indian Victory in World Cricket Cup. As*
Nos. 419/20 *of Jamaica.*
474	35 c. Caribbean map		45	40
475	45 c. Prudential Cup		55	40
MS476	80 × 80 mm. Nos. 474/5		1·75	2·75

155 "Columbus sailing through
the Bocas" (Campins)

(Des J.W. Litho Questa)

1976 (1 Nov)–78. *Paintings, Hotels and Orchids. Horiz designs*
as T **155**. *Multicoloured. W w* **14**. *P* 14.
479	5 c. Type **155**		1·50	10
	w. Wmk inverted		3·50	
480	6 c. Robinson Crusoe Hotel, Tobago (17.1.78)		20	1·75
482	10 c. "San Fernando Hill" (J. Cazabon)		20	10
483	12 c. *Paphinia cristata* (7.6.78)		2·00	2·75
484	15 c. Turtle Beach Hotel (17.1.78)		50	1·75
485	20 c. "East Indians in a Landscape" (J. Cazabon)		70	10
486	25 c. Mt Irvine Hotel (17.1.78)		60	10
487	30 c. *Caularthon bicornutum* (7.6.78)		2·00	1·50
488	35 c. "Los Gallos Point" (J. Cazabon)		1·00	10
	w. Wmk inverted		6·50	
489	40 c. *Miltassia* (7.6.78)		2·00	10
490	45 c. "Corbeaux Town" (J. Cazabon)		1·00	10
491	50 c. *Oncidium ampliatum* (7.6.78)		2·00	20
	w. Wmk inverted		†	—
492	70 c. Beach facilities, Mt Irvine Hotel (17.1.78)		70	1·00
494	$2.50, *Oncidium papilio* (7.6.78)		2·25	1·00
495	$5 Trinidad Holiday Inn (17.1.78)		1·25	6·00
479/95		Set of 15	15·00	14·00
MS497	171 × 100 mm. Nos. 479, 482, 485, 488 and 490. Wmk sideways		2·00	1·50
MS498	171 × 88 mm. Nos. 480, 484, 486, 492 and 495. Wmk sideways (17.1.78)		2·25	6·50
MS499	170 × 90 mm. Nos. 483, 487, 489, 491 and 494. Wmk sideways (7.6.78)		3·75	4·00

156 Hasely Crawford and
Olympic Gold Medal

(Des J.W. Litho D. L. R.)

1977 (4 Jan). *Hasely Crawford Commemoration. W w* **14** *(sideways). P* 12 × 12½.
501	**156**	25 c. multicoloured	30	50
MS502	93 × 70 mm. No. 501		80	1·25

157 Lindbergh's Sikorsky
"S–38", 1929

158 National Flag

(Des and litho J.W.)

1977 (4 Apr). *50th Anniv of Airmail Service. T* **157** *and similar*
horiz designs. Multicoloured. W w **14** *(sideways). P* 13.
503	20 c. Type **157**		40	20
504	35 c. Arrival of Charles and Anne Lindbergh		50	35
505	45 c. Boeing "707", c. 1960		60	60
506	50 c. Boeing "747", 1969		1·00	3·25
503/6		Set of 4	2·25	4·00
MS507	130 × 100 mm. Nos. 503/6. P 14		3·75	4·25

(Des and litho J.W.)

1977 (26 July). *Inauguration of the Republic. T* **158** *and similar*
vert designs. Multicoloured. W w **14**. *P* 13.
508	20 c. Type **158**		40	15
509	35 c. Coat of Arms		60	65
510	45 c. Government House		70	85
508/10		Set of 3	1·50	1·50
MS511	125×84 mm. Nos. 508/10. P 14		1·00	2·25

159 White Poinsettia **160** Miss Janelle (Penny)
Commissioning with Trophy

(Des J.W. Litho Walsall)

1977 (11 Oct). *Christmas. T* **159** *and similar vert design. Multi-*
coloured. W w **14**. *P* 14 × 14½.
512	10 c. Type **159**		20	10
513	35 c. Type **159**		35	10
514	45 c. Red Poinsettia		45	30
515	50 c. As 45 c.		55	2·00
512/15		Set of 4	1·40	2·25
MS516	112 × 142 mm. Nos. 512/15		1·40	2·75

(Des BG Studio. Litho Questa)

1978 (2 Aug). *Miss Janelle (Penny) Commissiong ("Miss Universe*
1977") Commemoration. T **160** *and similar vert designs showing*
Miss Commissiong. Multicoloured. W w **14**. *P* 14½.
517	10 c. Type **160**		25	10
	w. Wmk inverted		†	11·00
518	35 c. Portrait		50	60
519	45 c. In evening dress		60	75
517/19		Set of 3	1·25	1·25
MS520	186×120 mm. Nos. 517/19		1·25	1·75
	a. 45 c. value imperf on three sides		£500	

161 Tayra **162** "Burst of Beauty"

(Des G. Drummond. Litho Walsall)

1978 (7 Nov). *Wildlife. T* **161** *and similar horiz designs. Multi-*
coloured. W w **14** *(sideways). P* 13½.
521	15 c. Type **161**.		20	20
522	25 c. Ocelot		30	30
523	40 c. Brazilian Tree Porcupine		50	30
524	70 c. Tamandua		65	2·50
521/4		Set of 4	1·50	3·00
MS525	128×101 mm. Nos. 521/4		1·50	3·25

(Des C. Abbott. Litho Format)

1979 (1 Feb). *Carnival 1978. T* **162** *and similar vert designs.*
P 13½.
526	5 c. multicoloured		10	10
527	10 c. multicoloured		10	10
528	35 c. multicoloured		10	10
529	45 c. multicoloured		10	10
530	50 c. yellow-brown, rosine and deep lilac		10	15
531	$1 multicoloured		20	65
526/31		Set of 6	50	85

Designs:—10 c. Rain worshipper; 35 c. "Zodiac"; 45 c. Praying
mantis; 50 c. "Eye of the Hurricane"; $1 Steel orchestra.

163 Day Care **164** Geothermal Exploration

(Des BG Studio. Litho J.W.)

1979 (5 June). *International Year of the Child. T 163 and similar vert designs. Multicoloured. P 13.*

532	5 c. Type **163**		10	10
533	10 c. School feeding programme		10	10
534	35 c. Dental care		30	15
535	45 c. Nursery school		30	20
536	50 c. Free bus transport		30	40
537	$1 Medical care		65	1·50
532/7		*Set of 6*	1·60	2·25
MS538	114 × 132 mm. Nos. 532/7. P 14 × 13½		1·60	2·25

(Des local artist; adapted L. Curtis. Litho Format)

1979 (3 July). *4th Latin American Geological Congress. T 164 and similar horiz designs. Multicoloured. W w 14 (sideways). P 13½.*

539	10 c. Type **164**		20	10
540	35 c. Hydrogeology		35	35
541	45 c. Petroleum exploration		40	40
542	70 c. Environmental preservation		55	1·60
539/42		*Set of 4*	1·40	2·25
MS543	185 × 89 mm. Nos. 539/42		1·50	2·00

165 1879 1d. rose and Map of Tobago

(Des J. Cooter. Litho Format)

1979 (1 Aug). *Tobago Stamp Centenary. T 165 and similar horiz designs in black, rose-lilac and dull orange ($1) or multicoloured (others). W w 14 (sideways*). P 13½×14.*

544	10 c. Type **165**		10	10
545	15 c. 1879 3d. and 1880 ½d. surcharged on half of 6d.		15	10
546	35 c. 1879 6d. and 1886 ½d. surcharged on 6d.		25	20
547	45 c. 1879 1s. and 1886 ½d. surcharged on 2½d.		25	20
548	70 c. 1879 5s. and Great Britain 1856 1s. with "A14" (Scarborough, Tobago) postmark		30	1·50
549	$1 1879 £1 and General Post Office, Scarborough, Tobago		40	1·75
544/9		*Set of 6*	1·25	3·25
MS550	165×155 mm. Nos. 544/9		2·00	4·00
	w. Wmk Crown to right of CA		32·00	

*The normal sideways watermark on Nos. 544/50 shows Crown to left of CA, *as seen from the back of the stamp.*

166 1962 60 c. Independence Commemorative and Sir Rowland Hill

(Des and litho J.W.)

1979 (4 Oct). *Death Centenary of Sir Rowland Hill. T 166 and similar horiz designs showing stamps and Sir Rowland Hill. Multicoloured. W w 14 (sideways*). P 13.*

551	25 c. Type **166**		30	15
552	45 c. 1977 35 c. Inauguration of Republic commemorative		35	20
553	$1 1879 Trinidad ½d. surcharge and Tobago 1880 4d.		45	1·25
551/3		*Set of 3*	1·00	1·40
MS554	115×125 mm. Nos. 551/3. P 13½×14		1·25	1·50
	w. Wmk Crown to left of CA		30·00	

*The normal sideways watermark on Nos. 551/4 shows Crown to right of CA, *as seen from the back of the stamp.*

1844–1980 POPULATION CENSUS 12th MAY 1980
(168)

167 Poui Tree in Churchyard

(Des G. Hutchins. Litho Format)

1980 (21 Jan). *Centenary of Princes Town. T 167 and similar horiz designs. Multicoloured. W w 14 (sideways). P 14½ × 14.*

555	5 c. Type **167**		10	10
556	10 c. Princes Town Court House		10	10
557	50 c. Locomotive of the Royal Train, 1880		60	90
558	$1.50, H.M.S. *Bacchante* (screw corvette)		1·00	2·00
555/8		*Set of 4*	1·60	2·75
MS559	177×102 mm. Nos. 555/8		1·90	2·75

1980 (8 Apr). *Population Census. Nos. 479/80 and 482 optd with T 168.*

560	5 c. Type **155**		20	20
561	6 c. Robinson Crusoe Hotel, Tobago		20	80
562	10 c. "San Fernando Hill" (Cazabon)		20	20
560/2		*Set of 3*	55	1·10

169 Scarlet Ibis (male)
170 Silver and Bronze Medals for Weightlifting, 1948 and 1952

(Des G. Drummond. Litho Questa)

1980 (6 May). *Scarlet Ibis. T 169 and similar vert designs. Multicoloured. W w 14. P 14.*

563	50 c. Type **169**		1·10	1·40
	a. Strip of 5. Nos. 563/7		5·00	
564	50 c. Male and female		1·10	1·40
565	50 c. Hen and nest		1·10	1·40
566	50 c. Nest and eggs		1·10	1·40
567	50 c. Chick in nest		1·10	1·40
563/7		*Set of 5*	5·00	6·00

Nos. 563/7 were printed together, *se-tenant*, in horizontal and vertical strips of 5 throughout.

(Des G. Hutchins. Litho Walsall)

1980 (22 July). *Olympic Games, Moscow. T 170 and similar designs. W w 14 (sideways). P 14.*

568	10 c. multicoloured		10	10
569	15 c. multicoloured		10	10
570	70 c. multicoloured		45	65
568/70		*Set of 3*	50	70
MS571	110 × 149 mm. $2.50, black, silver and orange-vermilion (wmk upright)		1·50	2·25

Designs: *Horiz*—15 c. Hasely Crawford (100 metres sprint winner, 1976) and gold medal; 70 c. Silver medal for 400 metres and bronze medals for 4 × 400 metres relay, 1964. *Vert*—$2.50, Olympic Games emblems for Moscow, 1980, Olympia, 776 B.C. and Athens, 1896.

171 Charcoal Production

(Des J. Cooter. Litho Walsall)

1980 (8 Sept). *11th Commonwealth Forestry Conference. T 171 and similar horiz designs. Multicoloured. W w 14 (sideways). P 14.*

572	10 c. Type **171**		10	10
573	55 c. Logging		25	25
574	70 c. Teak plantation		35	60
575	$2.50, Watershed management		85	2·25
572/5		*Set of 4*	1·40	2·75
MS576	135 × 87 mm. Nos. 572/5		1·50	2·75

172 Beryl McBurnie (dance and culture) and Audrey Jeffers (social worker)

(Des BG Studio. Litho Questa)

1980 (29 Sept). *Decade for Women (1st issue). T 172 and similar horiz designs. Multicoloured. W w 14 (sideways). P 14.*

577	$1 Type **172**		45	55
578	$1 Elizabeth Bourne (judiciary) and Isabella Teshier (government)		45	55
579	$1 Dr. Stella Abidh (public health) and Louise Horne (nutrition)		45	55
577/9		*Set of 3*	1·25	1·50

See also Nos. 680/2.

173 Netball Stadium

(Des BG Studio. Litho Format)

1980 (21 Oct). *World Netball Tournament. W w 14 (sideways). P 13½ × 14.*

580	**173** 70 c. multicoloured		30	45

174 I.Y.D.P. Emblem, Athlete and Disabled Person
175 "Our Land Must Live"

(Des BG Studio. Litho Format)

1981 (23 Mar). *International Year for Disabled Persons. T 174 and similar horiz designs. W w 14. P 14½.*

581	10 c. black, vermilion and dull yellowish green		15	10
582	70 c. black, vermilion and buff		40	70
583	$1.50, black, vermilion and cobalt		60	1·40
584	$2 black, vermilion and flesh		60	1·75
581/4		*Set of 4*	1·60	3·50

Designs:—70 c. I.Y.D.P. emblem and doctor with disabled person; $1.50, Emblem, and blind man and woman; $2 Emblem and inscription.

(Des Debbie Galt; adapted G. Vasarhelyi. Litho J.W.)

1981 (7 July). *Environmental Preservation. T 175 and similar horiz designs. Multicoloured. W w 14 (sideways). P 13 × 13½.*

585	10 c. Type **175**		15	10
586	55 c. "Our seas must live"		45	30
587	$3 "Our skies must live"		1·60	1·60
585/7		*Set of 3*	2·00	1·75
MS588	142 × 89 mm. Nos. 585/7		2·50	4·50

176 "Food or Famine"
177 "First Aid Skills"

(Des and litho Harrison)

1981 (16 Oct). *World Food Day. T 176 and similar horiz designs. Multicoloured. W w 14 (sideways*). P 14½×14.*

589	10 c. Type **176**		10	10
	w. Wmk Crown to right of CA			
590	15 c. "Produce more" (threshing and milling rice)		10	10
	w. Wmk Crown to right of CA			
591	45 c. "Fish for food" (Bigeye)		30	20
592	55 c. "Prevent hunger"		35	25
593	$1.50, "Fight malnutrition"		85	90
	w. Wmk Crown to right of CA		20·00	
594	$2 "Fish for food" (Small-mouthed Grunt)		1·10	1·25
589/94		*Set of 6*	2·40	2·40
MS595	164×98 mm. Nos. 589/94		2·75	4·25

*The normal sideways watermark shows Crown to left of CA, *as seen from the back of the stamp.*

(Des L. Curtis. Litho Format)

1981 (17 Nov). *President's Award Scheme. T 177 and similar vert designs. Multicoloured. W w 14. P 14.*

596	10 c. Type **177**		20	10
597	70 c. "Motor mechanics"		40	45
598	$1 "Expedition"		50	55
599	$2 Presenting an award		90	1·40
596/9		*Set of 4*	1·75	2·25

178 Pharmacist at Work
179 "Production"

(Des C. Abbott. Litho Questa)

1982 (12 Feb). *Commonwealth Pharmaceutical Conference. T 178 and similar vert designs. W w 14. P 14½ × 14.*

600	10 c. Type **178**		15	10
601	$1 Gerritoute (plant)		1·75	2·25
602	$2 Rachette (plant)		2·75	4·25
600/2		*Set of 3*	4·25	6·00

(Des Debbie Galt; adapted G. Vasarhelyi. Litho Questa)

1982 (28 June). *75th Anniv of Boy Scout Movement. T 179 and similar vert designs. Multicoloured. W w 14. P 14.*

603	15 c. Type **179**		60	10
604	55 c. "Tolerance"		1·50	30
605	$5 "Discipline"		5·50	7·00
603/5		*Set of 3*	7·00	7·00

NEW INFORMATION

The editor is always interested to correspond with people who have new information that will improve or correct the Catalogue.

180 Charlotteville   181 "Pa Pa Bois"

(Des Harrison. Litho Format)

1982 (18 Oct).   *25th Anniv of Tourist Board.* T **180** *and similar vert designs. Multicoloured.* W w **14**. P 13½ × 14.
606	55 c. Type **180**			30	25
607	$1 Boating			40	55
608	$3 Fort George			1·25	2·25
606/8			*Set of 3*	1·75	2·75

(Des D. Louison. Litho Harrison)

1982 (8 Nov).   *Folklore. Local Spirits and Demons.* T **181** *and similar horiz designs. Multicoloured.* W w **14** (*sideways*). P 14.
609	10 c. Type **181**			10	10
610	15 c. "La Diablesse"			10	10
611	65 c. "Lugarhoo", "Phantom" and "Soucou-yant"			35	30
612	$5 "Bois de Soleil", "Davens" and "Mamma de l'Eau"			2·50	3·25
609/12			*Set of 4*	2·75	3·25
MS613	133 × 100 mm. Nos. 609/12			4·25	6·00

182 Cane Harvesting

((Des W. Fenton. Litho Harrison)

1982 (13 Dec).   *Canefarmers' Association Centenary.* T **182** *and similar horiz designs. Multicoloured.* W w **14** (*sideways*). P 14.
614	30 c. Type **182**			30	15
615	70 c. Farmers loading bullock cart			60	85
616	$1.50, Cane field in bloom			1·10	1·75
614/16			*Set of 3*	1·75	2·50
MS617	72 × 117 mm. Nos. 614/16. P 14½.			1·40	1·50

183 National Stadium

(Des McCombie Skinner. Litho Harrison)

1982 (28 Dec).   *20th Anniv of Independence.* T **183** *and similar horiz designs. Multicoloured.* W w **14** (*sideways**). P 13×14.
618	10 c. Type **183**			15	10
	w. Wmk Crown to right of CA			7·50	
619	35 c. Caroni water treatment plant			35	15
620	50 c. Mount Hope Maternity Hospital			70	25
621	$2 National Insurance Board Mall, Tobago			1·00	2·00
618/21			*Set of 4*	2·00	2·25

The normal sideways watermark shows Crown to left of CA, as seen from the back of the stamp.

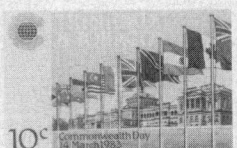

184 Commonwealth Flags

(Des C. Abbott. Litho Harrison)

1983 (14 Mar).   *Commonwealth Day.* T **184** *and similar multi-coloured designs.* W w **14** (*sideways on* 10, 55 *c.*). P 14.
622	10 c. Type **184**			10	10
623	55 c. Satellite view of Trinidad and Tobago			25	20
624	$1 "Nodding donkey" oil pump (*vert*)			40	60
625	$2 Map of Trinidad and Tobago (*vert*)			85	1·25
622/5			*Set of 4*	1·40	1·90

185 Lockheed L-1011 TriStar
500 *Flamingo*

(Des D. Miller. Litho Format)

1983 (11 July).   *10th Anniv of CARICOM.* W w **14** (*sideways*). P 14.
626	185	35 c. multicoloured		80	1·25

186 V.D.U. Operator

(Des G. Vasarhelyi. Litho Harrison)

1983 (5 Aug).   *World Communications Year.* T **186** *and similar horiz designs. Multicoloured.* W w **14** (*sideways*). P 14.
627	15 c. Type **186**			20	10
628	55 c. Scarborough Post Office, Tobago			30	20
629	$1 Textel building			60	70
630	$3 Morne Blue E.C.M.S. station			1·10	2·50
627/30			*Set of 4*	2·00	3·25

187 Financial Complex

(Des D. Miller. Litho Format)

1983 (19 Sept).   *Conference of Commonwealth Finance Ministers.* W w **14** (*sideways*). P 14.
631	187	$2 multicoloured		60	1·25

188 King Mackerel   189 Bois Pois

(Des N. Weaver. Litho Format)

1983 (17 Oct).   *World Food Day.* T **188** *and similar horiz designs. Multicoloured.* W w **14** (*sideways*). P 14 × 13½ (10 c., 55 c.) or 13½ (*others*).
632	10 c. Type **188**			20	10
633	55 c. Four-winged Flyingfish			1·00	40
634	70 c. Queen or Pink Conch			1·25	1·40
635	$4 Red Shrimp			4·50	7·00
632/5			*Set of 4*	6·25	8·00

(Des I. Loe. Litho Questa)

1983 (14 Dec)–84.   *Flowers.* T **189** *and similar multicoloured designs.* W w **14** (*sideways on* 5 c. *to* $1.50). P 14.

A. *Without imprint date*
636A	5 c. Type **189**			80	1·00
637A	10 c. Maraval Lily			80	50
638A	15 c. Star Grass			80	30
639A	20 c. Bois Caco			30	15
640A	25 c. Strangling Fig			90	1·25
641A	30 c. *Cassia moschata*			40	15
642A	50 c. Chalice Flower			30	30
643A	65 c. Black Stick			55	30
644A	80 c. *Columnea scandens*			65	85
645A	95 c. Cat's Claw			80	1·00
646A	$1 Bois L'agli			1·00	50
647A	$1.50, *Eustoma exaltatum*			1·25	1·25
648A	$2 Chaconia (39×29 *mm*)			1·50	1·75
649A	$2.50, *Chrysothemis pulchella* (39×29 mm)			1·25	2·50
650A	$5 *Centratherum punctatum* (39×29 mm)			2·75	6·50
651A	$10 Savanna Flower (39×29 *mm*)			3·75	8·50
636A/51A			*Set of 16*	16·00	24·00

B. *With imprint date* (10.84)
636B	5 c. Type **189**			1·50	2·00
637B	10 c. Maraval Lily			75	80
638B	15 c. Star Grass			1·25	1·75
640B	25 c. Strangling Fig			1·50	2·25
636B/40B			*Set of 4*	4·50	6·00

The 10 c. value shows an incorrect botanical name. This should read "*Spathiphyllum cannaefolium*".
Imprint dates: "1984", Nos. 636B/8B, 640B; "1985", No. 637B; "1987", No. 637B; "1989", No. 637B.
For these designs watermarked w **16** see Nos. 686/701.

---

190 Rook Chess Pieces in Staunton and 17th-century Styles   191 Swimming

(Des L. Curtis. Litho Questa)

1984 (14 Sept).   *60th Anniv of International Chess Federation.* T **190** *and similar vert designs. Multicoloured.* W w **14**. P 14.
652	50 c. Type **190**			2·75	50
653	70 c. Staunton and 12th-century Lewis Bishops			3·00	2·00
654	$1.50, Staunton and 13th-century Swedish Queens			4·00	5·00
655	$2 Staunton and 19th-century Chinese Kings			5·00	6·50
652/5			*Set of 4*	13·50	12·50

(Des Garden Studio. Litho Harrison)

1984 (21 Sept).   *Olympic Games, Los Angeles.* T **191** *and similar vert designs. Multicoloured.* W w **14**. P 14 × 14½.
656	15 c. Type **191**			10	10
	w. Wmk inverted			85	1·25
657	55 c. Track and field events			30	20
658	$1.50, Sailing			1·00	1·75
659	$4 Cycling			4·25	4·75
656/9			*Set of 4*	5·00	6·00
MS660	132×85 mm. Nos. 656/9			6·00	7·00

192 Slave Schooner and Shackles   193 Children's Band

(Des O. Bell. Litho Walsall)

1984 (22 Oct).   *150th Anniv of Abolition of Slavery.* T **192** *and similar vert designs. Multicoloured.* W w **14**. P 13½ × 13.
661	35 c. Type **192**			85	30
662	55 c. Slave and "Slave Triangle" map			1·25	50
663	$1 *Capitalism and Slavery* (book by Dr. Eric Williams)			2·00	1·75
664	$2 Toussaint l'Ouverture (Haitian revolutionary)			2·50	4·75
661/4			*Set of 4*	6·00	6·50
MS665	95 × 100 mm. Nos. 661/4			6·50	8·00

(Des G. Vasarhelyi. Litho J.W.)

1984 (13 Nov).   *125th Anniv of St. Mary's Children's Home.* T **193** *and similar horiz designs. Multicoloured.* W w **14** (*sideways*). P 13½.
666	10 c. Type **193**			15	10
667	70 c. St. Mary's Children's Home			50	50
668	$3 Group of children			2·25	2·75
666/8			*Set of 3*	2·50	3·00

194 Parang Band   195 Capt. A. A. Cipriani and T. U. B. Butler

(Des D. Miller. Litho Questa)

1984 (26 Nov).   *Parang Festival.* T **194** *and similar horiz designs. Multicoloured.* W w **14** (*sideways*). P 14 × 14½.
669	10 c. Type **194**			20	10
670	30 c. Bandola, bandolin and cuatro (musical instruments)			50	15
671	$1 Bandola, bandolin and cuatro (musical instruments)			1·50	90
672	$3 Double bass, fiddle and guitar (musical instruments)			2·50	3·75
669/72			*Set of 4*	4·25	4·50

(Des G. Vasarhelyi. Litho Questa)

1985 (17 June).   *Labour Day. Labour Leaders.* T **195** *and similar horiz designs.* W w **14**. P 14.
673	55 c. black and bright rose			80	80
674	55 c. black and orange-yellow			80	80
675	55 c. black and emerald			80	80
673/5			*Set of 3*	2·25	2·25

Designs:—No. 674, C. P. Alexander and Q. O'Connor; 675, A. Cola Rienzi and C. T. W. E. Worrell.

196 *Lady Nelson* (1928)

(Des E. Nisbet. Litho Format)

1985 (20 Aug). *Ships. T* **196** *and similar horiz designs. Multicoloured. W w* **14**. *P* 14½ × 14.

676	30 c. Type **196**.	..	70	25
677	95 c. *Lady Drake* (1928)	..	1·50	1·75
678	$1.50, *Federal Palm* (1961)	..	1·50	3·00
679	$2 *Federal Maple* (1961)	..	1·75	3·50
676/9	..	*Set of* 4	4·75	7·75

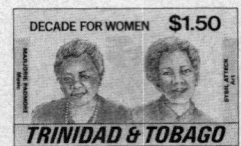

197 Marjorie Padmore (music) and Sybil Atteck (art)

(Des Julijana Zappin. Litho Walsall)

1985 (11 Nov). *Decade for Women* (2nd issue). *T* **197** *and similar horiz designs. Multicoloured. W w* **16** (*sideways*). *P* 14.

680	$1.50, Type **197**	..	1·40	1·75
681	$1.50, May Cherrie (medical social worker) and Evelyn Tracey (social worker)	..	1·40	1·75
682	$1.50, Umilta McShine (education) and Jessica Smith-Phillips (public service)	..	1·40	1·75
680/2	..	*Set of* 3	3·75	4·75

198 Badge of Trinidad and Tobago Cadet Force (75th Anniv) **199** Anne-Marie Javouhey (foundress)

(Des D. Slater. Litho Harrison)

1985 (9 Dec). *International Youth Year. T* **198** *and similar horiz designs. Multicoloured. W w* **16** (*sideways*). *P* 14 × 14½.

683	10 c. Type **198**.	..	45	10
684	65 c. Guide badges (75th anniv of Girl Guide movement)	..	2·00	2·25
685	95 c. Young people of Trinidad	..	2·50	2·75
683/5	..	*Set of* 3	4·50	4·50

1985 (Dec)–89. *As Nos.* 636/7, 639/41 *and* 643/51, *but W w* **16** (*sideways on* 5, 10, 20, 25, 30, 65, 80, 95 c.), $1, $1.50). *With imprint date. P* 14.

686	5 c. Type **189**	..	2·75	1·00
687	10 c. Maraval Lily (4.8.86)	..	30	30
689	20 c. Bois Caco (8.88)	..	75	1·50
690	25 c. Strangling Fig (8.88)	..	75	1·50
691	30 c. *Cassia moschata* (5.87)	..	1·25	1·50
693	65 c. Black Stick (5.87)	..	1·25	2·00
694	80 c. *Columnea scandens* (5.87)	..	3·00	3·50
695	95 c. Cat's Claw	..	50	70
696	$1 Bois L'agli	..	65	30
697	$1.50, *Eustoma exaltatum* (5.87)	..	4·00	4·50
698	$2 Chaconia (39×29 *mm*) (5.87)	..	1·75	3·25
699	$2.50, *Chrysothemis pulchella* (39×29 *mm*) (5.89)	..	9·00	9·00
700	$5 *Centratherum punctatum* (39×29 *mm*)	..	1·75	2·00
	w. Wmk inverted		4·50	
701	$10 Savanna Flower (39×29 *mm*)	..	3·50	4·50
	w. Wmk inverted		9·50	
686/701	..	*Set of* 14	28·00	32·00

Imprint dates: "1985", Nos. 686. 695/6, 700/1; "1986", No. 687; "1987", Nos. 687, 691, 693/8, 700/1; "1988", Nos. 687, 689/91, 693/6, 700/1; "1989", Nos. 687, 689/91, 693, 696/701.

(Des Joan Thompson. Litho Format)

1986 (19 Mar). 150*th Anniv of Arrival of Sisters of St. Joseph de Cluny. T* **199** *and similar vert designs. Multicoloured. W w* **16** (*sideways*). *P* 14 × 14½.

702	10 c. Type **199**	..	10	10
703	65 c. St. Joseph's Convent, Port-of-Spain	..	45	90
704	95 c. Children and statue of Anne-Marie Javouhey	..	65	1·25
702/4	..	*Set of* 3	1·10	2·00

ALTERED CATALOGUE NUMBERS

Any Catalogue numbers altered from the last edition are shown as a list in the introductory pages.

 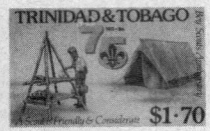

200 Tank Locomotive *Arima* **201** Scout Camp

(Des J.W. Litho Format)

1986 (26 May). *"Ameripex '86" International Stamp Exhibition, Chicago. Trinidad Railway Locomotives. T* **200** *and similar horiz designs. W w* **16**. *P* 14½ × 14.

705	65 c. Type **200**	..	25	35
706	95 c. Canadian-built steam locomotive No. 22	..	35	60
707	$1.10, Steam tender engine	..	40	95
708	$1.50, Saddle tank locomotive	..	60	1·25
705/8	..	*Set of* 4	1·40	2·75
MS709	105×80 mm. Nos. 705/8	..	1·40	2·75

(Des N. Shewring. Litho Questa)

1986 (21 July). 75*th Anniv of Trinidad and Tobago Boy Scouts. T* **201** *and similar horiz design. Multicoloured. W w* **16** (*sideways*). *P* 14.

710	$1.70, Type **201**	..	1·00	1·60
711	$2 Scouts of 1911 and 1986	..	1·25	1·90

202 Queen and Duke of Edinburgh laying Wreath at War Memorial **203** Eric Williams at Graduation, 1935

(Des C. Abbott. Litho Walsall)

1986 (16 Sept). 60*th Birthday of Queen Elizabeth II. T* **202** *and similar vert designs. Multicoloured. W w* **16**. *P* 14½ × 14.

712	10 c. Type **202**	..	35	10
713	15 c. Queen with Trinidadian dignitaries aboard *Britannia*	..	1·00	30
714	30 c. With President Ellis Clarke	..	65	30
715	$5 Receiving bouquet	..	3·00	6·50
712/15	..	*Set of* 4	4·50	6·50

(Des D. Miller. Litho Format)

1986 (25 Sept). 75*th Birth Anniv of Dr. Eric Williams. T* **203** *and similar multicoloured designs. W w* **14** (*sideways* on* 95 c., $5). *P* 14.

716	10 c. Type **203**	..	30	10
717	30 c. Premier Eric Williams (wearing red tie)	..	55	20
	w. Wmk inverted			
718	30 c. As No. 717, but wearing black and orange tie	..	55	20
719	95 c. Arms of University of West Indies and Dr. Williams as Pro-Chancellor (*horiz*)	..	1·00	1·25
720	$5 Prime Minister Williams and Whitehall (*horiz*)	..	2·25	4·75
	w. Wmk Crown to right of CA		24·00	
716/20	..	*Set of* 5	4·25	6·00
MS721	105×100 mm. Nos. 716/17 and 719/20. Wmk sideways	..	5·00	8·50

*The normal sideways watermark shows Crown to left of CA, as seen from the back of the stamp.

204 "PEACE" Slogan and Outline Map of Trinidad and Tobago **205** Miss Giselle La Ronde and BWIA Airliner

(Adapted L. Curtis. Litho Questa)

1986 (3 Nov). *International Peace Year. T* **204** *and similar horiz design. Multicoloured. W w* **16** (*sideways*). *P* 14.

722	95 c. Type **204**.	..	40	50
723	$3 Peace dove with olive branch	..	1·25	2·25

(Des D. Miller. Litho Walsall)

1987 (27 July). *Miss World* 1986. *T* **205** *and similar vert designs. Multicoloured. W w* **16**. *P* 14.

724	10 c. Type **205**	..	60	10
725	30 c. In swimsuit on beach	..	1·25	30
726	95 c. Miss Giselle La Ronde	..	2·75	2·50
727	$1.65, Wearing Miss World sash	..	3·75	4·75
	w. Wmk inverted		17·00	
724/7	..	*Set of* 4	7·50	7·00

---

206 Colonial Bank, Port-of-Spain **207** Sergeant in Parade Order and Soldiers in Work Dress and Battle Dress

(Des J.W. Litho Walsall)

1987 (21 Dec). 150*th Anniv of Republic Bank. T* **206** *and similar horiz designs. Multicoloured. W w* **14** (*sideways*). *P* 14.

728	10 c. Type **206**.	..	10	10
729	65 c. Cocoa plantation	..	50	70
730	95 c. Oil field	..	1·25	1·75
731	$1.10, Belmont Tramway Company tramcar	..	1·25	2·25
728/31	..	*Set of* 4	2·75	4·25

(Des C. Abbott. Litho Questa)

1988 (29 Feb). 25*th Anniv of Defence Force. T* **207** *and similar vert designs. Multicoloured. W w* **16** (*sideways*). *P* 14.

732	10 c. Type **207**.	..	75	15
733	30 c. Women soldiers	..	1·75	30
734	$1.10, Defence Force officers	..	2·75	2·75
735	$1.50, Naval ratings and patrol boat	..	3·75	3·50
732/5	..	*Set of* 4	8·00	6·00

(Des D. Hartley and L. Curtis. Litho Walsall)

1988 (6 June). *West Indian Cricket. Horiz designs as T* **243***a of Jamaica, each showing portrait, cricket equipment and early belt buckle. Multicoloured. W w* **14** (*sideways**). *P* 14.

736	30 c. George John	..	1·25	40
	w. Wmk Crown to right of CA			
737	65 c. Learie Constantine	..	2·25	1·00
	w. Wmk Crown to right of CA		25·00	
738	95 c. Sonny Ramadhin	..	2·50	1·75
739	$1.50, Gerry Gomez	..	3·00	3·50
740	$2.50, Jeffrey Stollmeyer	..	4·00	5·50
736/40	..	*Set of* 5	12·00	11·00

*The normal sideways watermark shows Crown to left of CA, as seen from the back of the stamp.

 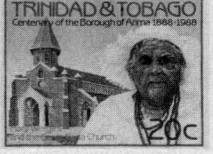

208 Uriah Butler (labour leader) **209** Mary Werges and Santa Rosa Church

(Des G. Vasarhelyi. Litho Walsall)

1988 (11 July). 50*th Anniv of Oilfield Workers Trade Union* (1987). *T* **208** *and similar vert designs. Multicoloured. W w* **16**. *P* 14½ × 14.

741	10 c. Type **208**	..	10	10
742	30 c. Adrian Rienzi (O.W.T.U. president, 1937-42)	..	10	10
743	65 c. John Rojas (O.W.T.U. president, 1943-62)	..	15	25
744	$5 George Weekes (O.W.T.U. president, 1962-87)	..	1·25	2·25
741/4	..	*Set of* 4	1·40	2·40

(Des O. Bell. Litho Walsall)

1988 (22 Aug). *Centenary of Borough of Arima. T* **209** *and similar horiz designs. Multicoloured. W w* **16** (*sideways*). *P* 14 × 14½.

745	20 c. Type **209**	..	15	10
746	30 c. Governor W. Robinson and Royal Charter	..	15	10
747	$1.10, Arrival of Governor Robinson at railway station	..	60	95
748	$1.50, Mayor J. F. Wallen and Centenary logo	..	90	1·50
745/8	..	*Set of* 4	1·60	2·40

(Des D. Miller (30 c.), S. Noon and D. Miller (others). Litho Questa)

1988 (21 Nov). 300*th Anniv of Lloyd's of London. Multicoloured designs as T* **167***a of Malawi. W w* **16** (*sideways on* $1.10, $1.55). *P* 14.

749	30 c. Queen Mother at Topping-out of new building, 1984	..	75	20
750	$1.10, BWIA Lockheed L-1011 TriStar 500 *Flamingo* airliner (*horiz*)	..	2·00	1·40
751	$1.55, Steel works, Trinidad (*horiz*)	..	1·75	1·75
752	$2 *Atlantic Empress* (tanker) on fire off Tobago, 1979	..	3·75	2·75
749/52	..	*Set of* 4	7·50	5·50

210 Colonial Arms of Trinidad &
Tobago and 1913 1d. Stamp

(Des W. Carr, adapted D. Miller. Litho Questa)

1989 (20 Mar). *Centenary of Union of Trinidad and Tobago.
T 210 and similar horiz designs. Multicoloured. W w 16
(sideways). P 14½.*

753	40 c. Type 210		60	10
754	$1 Pre-1889 Tobago emblem and Tobago 1896 ½d. on 4d. stamp		1·75	1·00
755	$1.50, Pre-1889 Trinidad emblem and Trinidad 1883 4d. stamp		2·25	3·00
756	$2.25, Current Arms of Trinidad and Tobago and 1977 45 c. Republic stamp		2·75	3·75
753/6	.. .. .. *Set of 4*		6·50	7·00

211 Common Piping Guan   **212** Blind Welfare
(75th Anniversary)

(Des Doreen McGuinness. Litho Walsall)

1989 (31 July). *Rare Fauna of Trinidad and Tobago. T 211
and similar horiz designs. Multicoloured. W w 14 (sideways).
P 14×14½.*

757	$1 Type 211		3·25	3·50
	a. Vert strip of 5. Nos. 757/61		14·00	
758	$1 *Phyllodytes auratus* (frog)		3·25	3·50
759	$1 *Cebus albifrons trinitatis* (monkey)		3·25	3·50
760	$1 Tamandua		3·25	3·50
761	$1 *Lutra longicaudis* (otter)		3·25	3·50
757/61	*Set of 5*		14·00	15·00

Nos. 757/61 were printed together, *se-tenant*, in vertical strips
of 5 throughout the sheet, forming a composite background
design.

(Des S. Noon. Litho Walsall)

1989 (2 Oct). *Anniversaries. T 212 and similar vert designs.
Multicoloured. W w 14. P 14½×14.*

762	10 c. Type 212		60	15
	w. Wmk inverted		5·50	
763	40 c. Port-of-Spain City Hall (75th anniv)		40	20
	w. Wmk inverted			
764	$1 Guides and Brownies (75th anniv)		2·00	60
765	$2.25, Red Cross members (50th anniv)		2·75	2·75
762/5	*Set of 4*		5·25	3·25

213 Tenor Pan   **214** *Xeromphalina
tenuipes*

(Des T. Mussio, adapted D. Miller. Litho Questa)

1989 (30 Nov). *Steel Pans (1st series). T 213 and similar vert
designs. Multicoloured. W w 16. P 14½×14.*

766	10 c. Type 213		10	10
767	40 c. Guitar pans		15	15
768	$1 Cello pans		45	60
769	$2.25, Bass pans		85	1·75
766/9	*Set of 4*		1·40	2·40

See also Nos. 828/31.

(Des McCombie Skinner. Litho Questa)

1990 (3 May). *"Stamp World London 90" International Stamp
Exhibition, London. Fungi. T 214 and similar horiz designs.
Multicoloured. W w 16 (sideways). P 14×13½.*

770	10 c. Type 214		35	20
771	40 c. *Phallus indusiatus* ("Dictyophora indusiata")		65	25
772	$1 *Leucocoprinus birnbaumii*		1·25	1·00
773	$2.25, *Crinipellis perniciosa*		2·00	3·75
770/3	*Set of 4*		3·75	4·75

COVER PRICES

Cover factors are quoted at the beginning of each
country for most issues to 1945. An explanation of
the system can be found on page x. The factors
quoted do not, however, apply to philatelic covers.

215 Scarlet Ibis in Immature   **216** Princess Alice and
Plumage   Administration Building

(Litho Questa)

1990 (7 Sept). *Scarlet Ibis. T 215 and similar horiz designs.
Multicoloured. W w 16 (sideways). P 14.*

774	40 c. Type 215		1·50	30
775	80 c. Pair in pre-nuptial display		1·75	1·40
776	$1 Male in breeding plumage		1·75	1·40
777	$2.25, Adult on nest with chick		2·75	4·25
774/7	*Set of 4*		7·00	6·50

(Des L. Curtis. Litho B.D.T.)

1990 (15 Oct). *40th Anniv of University of West Indies. T 216
and similar horiz designs. Multicoloured. W w 14 (sideways).
P 13½×14.*

778	40 c. Type 216		40	15
779	80 c. Sir Hugh Wooding and Library		70	70
780	$1 Sir Allen Lewis and Faculty of Engineering		90	90
781	$2.25, Sir Shridath Ramphal and Faculty of Medical Sciences		2·25	3·25
778/81	*Set of 4*		3·75	4·50

217 Lockheed L.18 Lodestar   **218** Yellow Oriole

(Des E. Nisbet. Litho B.D.T)

1990 (27 Nov). *50th Anniv of British West Indies Airways.
T 217 and similar horiz designs. Multicoloured. W w 14
(sideways). P 14.*

782	40 c. Type 217		1·25	30
783	80 c. Vickers Viking 1A		1·75	1·25
784	$1 Vickers Viscount 702		2·00	1·25
785	$2.25, Boeing 707		3·25	4·50
782/5	*Set of 4*		7·50	6·50
MS786	77×52 mm. $5 Lockheed L-1011 TriStar			
500			4·25	5·00

(Des D. Miller. Litho Questa)

1990 (17 Dec). *Birds. T 218 and similar vert designs.
Multicoloured. W w 16 (sideways). P 14.*

787	20 c. Type 218		10	10
788	25 c. Green-rumped Parrotlet		65	30
789	40 c. Fork-tailed Flycatcher		10	10
790	50 c. Copper-rumped Hummingbird		85	50
791	$1 Bananaquit		1·00	50
792	$2 Violaceous Euphonia		1·50	1·50
793	$2.25, Channel-billed Toucan		45	50
794	$2.50, Bay-headed Tanager		1·25	1·25
795	$5 Green Honeycreeper		3·00	3·50
796	$10 Cattle Egret		3·00	3·50
797	$20 Golden-olive Woodpecker		5·00	6·00
798	$50 Peregrine Falcon		10·00	10·50
787/98	*Set of 12*		24·00	25·00

For some of these values watermarked w 14 (sideways) see
Nos. 837/46.

219 *Lygodium volubile*

(Des T. Musio. Litho B.D.T)

1991 (1 July). *Ferns. T 219 and similar horiz designs.
Multicoloured. W w 14 (sideways). P 13½×14.*

799	40 c. Type 219		40	15
800	80 c. *Blechnum occidentale*		75	70
801	$1 *Gleichenia bifida*		85	85
802	$2.25, *Polypodium lycopodioides*		2·00	3·50
799/802	*Set of 4*		3·50	4·75

220 Trinidad and Tobago   **221** H. E. Rapsey
Regiment Anti-aircraft Battery   (founder)

(Des A. Theobald. Litho Questa)

1991 (7 Dec). *50th Anniv of Second World War. T 220 and
similar horiz designs. Multicoloured. W w 16 (sideways).
P 13½×14.*

803	40 c. Type 220		1·00	30
804	80 c. Fairey Barracuda Mk III attacking U-boat		1·50	1·00
805	$1 Avro Type 683 Lancaster		1·75	1·00
806	$2.25, H.M.S. *Wye* (frigate) escorting convoy		2·75	4·25
803/6	*Set of 4*		6·25	6·00
MS807	117×85 mm. $2.50. Presentation Supermarine Spitfire; $2.50. Presentation Vickers-Armstrong Wellington bomber		7·50	7·50

(Des G. Vasarhelyi. Litho B.D.T.)

1992 (30 Mar). *Anniversaries. T 221 and similar vert designs.
Multicoloured. W w 14. P 14.*

808	40 c. Type 221 (centenary of Trinidad Building and Loan Assoc)		30	15
809	80 c. *Inca clathrata quesneli* (beetle) (Trinidad & Tobago Field Naturalists' Club)		1·00	1·10
810	$1 Holy Name Convent (centenary)		1·10	1·25
808/10	*Set of 3*		2·25	2·25

222 Baptism   **223** McDonnell Douglas
(Baptist)   MD-83

(Des Jennifer Toombs. Litho Questa)

1992 (21 Apr). *Religions of Trinidad and Tobago. T 222 and
similar vert designs. Multicoloured. W w 14. P 14.*

811	40 c. Type 222		60	60
812	40 c. Minaret with star and crescent (Islam)		60	60
813	40 c. Logo (Hinduism)		60	60
814	40 c. Cross (Christian)		60	60
815	40 c. Logo (Baha'i)		60	60
811/15	*Set of 5*		2·75	2·75

(Des G. Vasarhelyi. Litho B.D.T.)

1992 (6 Aug). *Aircraft. T 223 and similar horiz design.
Multicoloured. W w 14 (sideways). P 14.*

816	$2.25, Type 223		2·25	2·50
817	$2.25, Lockheed L-1011 TriStar aircraft		2·25	2·50

224 *Trinidad Guardian* Title
(75th anniv of newspaper)

(Des Jennifer Toombs (No. 819), N. Shewring (others). Litho
Questa)

1992 (7–30 Dec). *Anniversaries. T 224 and similar
multicoloured designs. W w 16 (sideways on horiz designs).
P 14½.*

818	40 c. Type 224		10	10
819	40 c. Nativity scene (Christmas) (*vert*) (21 Dec)		10	10
820	$1 National Museum and Art Gallery (centenary) (23 Dec)		35	40
821	$2.25, Cover to St. James Internment Camp, 1942 (50th anniv of Trinidad and Tobago Philatelic Society) (30 Dec)		80	1·25
818/21	*Set of 4*		1·25	1·60

225 Derek Walcott, Sir Shridath Ramphal and
William Demas with Caribbean Maps
(*illustration reduced. Actual size 100×22 mm*)

(Des O. Ball and D. Miller. Litho B.D.T.)

1994 (31 Jan). *20th Anniv of CARICOM (Caribbean Economic Community). Recipients of Order of the Caribbean Community. T 225 and similar design. W w 14 (sideways). P 13×13½.*

822	**225**	50 c. multicoloured	..	20	20
823		$1.50, multicoloured	..	45	60
824		$2.75, multicoloured	..	85	1·10
825		$3 multicoloured	..	1·00	1·40
822/5			Set of 4	2·25	3·00

MS826 90×90 mm. $6 multicoloured (Insignia of the Order (34½×51½ mm)). Wmk upright. P 13½×13 .. 2·00 3·00

226 Aldwyn Roberts Kitchener (bass player)

227 Quadrophonic Pans

(Des G. Vasarhelyi. Litho Walsall)

1994 (11 Feb). *"Land of Calypso". W w 14. P 14.*

827 **226** 50 c. multicoloured 70 70

(Des D. Miller. Litho B.D.T.)

1994 (11 Feb). *Steel Pans (2nd series). T 227 and similar horiz designs. W w 16 (sideways). P 14×15.*

828	50 c. Type **227**	..		20	20
829	$1 Tenor base pans	..	..	35	30
830	$2.25, Six pans	..	..	80	1·25
831	$2.50, Rocket pans	..	..	90	1·25
828/31			Set of 4	2·00	2·75

1994 (18 Feb). *"Hong Kong '94" International Stamp Exhibition. Nos. 789, 792, 837 and 845 optd as T 272 of Jamaica.*

832	25 c. Green-rumped Parrotlet	..	30	20
833	40 c. Fork-tailed Flycatcher	..	35	20
834	$2 Violaceous Euphonia	..	95	1·25
835	$10 Cattle Egret ..	..	3·25	4·50
832/5		Set of 4	4·25	5·50

1994 (Aug)–**98**. *As Nos. 788, 790/2 and 794/7, but W w 14 (sideways). P 14.*

837	25 c. Green-rumped Parrotlet	..	10	10
839	50 c. Copper-rumped Hummingbird (4.95)	..	10	10
840	$1 Bananaquit (3.3.97)	..	20	25
841	$2 Violaceous Euphonia (3.3.97)	..	40	45
843	$2.50, Bay-headed Tanager (14.10.98)	..	50	55
844	$5 Green Honeycreeper (6.96)	..	1·00	1·10
845	$10 Cattle Egret (14.10.98)	..	2·00	2·10
846	$20 Golden-olive Woodpecker (14.10.98)	..	4·00	4·25
837/46		Set of 8	8·25	8·75

On some sheets from the April 1995 printing of Nos. 837 and 839 the watermark is indistinct.

For miniature sheet containing the $5 see No. MS872.

228 Trinidad Hilton
229 Boa Constrictor

(Des D. Miller. Litho Walsall)

1994 (10 Aug). *Hotels and Lodgings. T 228 and similar horiz designs. Multicoloured. W w 14 (sideways). P 14×14½.*

848	$3 Type **228**	..	90	1·25
849	$3 Sandy Point Village, Tobago	..	90	1·25
850	$3 Asa Wright Nature Centre and Lodge	90	1·25
851	$3 M.L.'s Bed and Breakfast	..	90	1·25
848/51		Set of 4	3·25	4·50

(Des R. Watton. Litho Walsall)

1994 (19 Sept). *Snakes. T 229 and similar horiz designs. Multicoloured. W w 14 (sideways). P 14.*

852	50 c. Type **229**	..	20	20
853	$1.25, Vine Snake	..	45	55
854	$2.50, Bushmaster	..	80	1·10
855	$3 Large Coral Snake	..	95	1·25
852/5		Set of 4	2·25	2·75

PRICES OF SETS

Set prices are given for many issues, generally those containing three stamps or more. Definitive sets include one of each value or major colour change, but do not cover different perforations, die types or minor shades. Where a choice is possible the set prices are based on the cheapest versions of the stamps included in the listings.

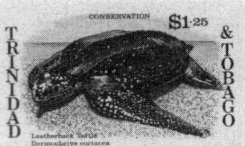

230 "Snowballman" (painting, Mahmoud Alladin)

231 Loggerhead Turtle

(Des D. Miller. Litho Walsall)

1995 (6 Mar). *50th Anniv of the Trinidad Art Society. T 230 and similar vert designs. Multicoloured. W w 16. P 13½.*

856	50 c. Type **530**	35	45
857	50 c. "Fishermen" (painting, Sybil Atteck)	35	45
858	50 c. Copper sculpture (Ken Morris)	35	45
856/8		Set of 3	95	1·25

(Des D. Miller. Litho Walsall)

1995 (7 Aug). *Conservation. T 231 and similar multicoloured designs. W w 16 (sideways on horiz designs). P 14½.*

859	$1.25, Type **231** ..		40	50
860	$2.50, Port-of-Spain Lighthouse (vert)	80	1·00
861	$3 "Knowsley" (location of Ministry of Foreign Affairs)	1·00	1·25
859/61		Set of 3	2·00	2·50

232 Brian Lara
233 Red Cross Economy Label on Envelope

(Des S. Noon. Litho Cartor)

1996 (15 May). *Brian Lara (cricketer) Commemoration. T 232 and similar vert designs showing cricket scenes. W w 14. P 13×13½.*

862	50 c. multicoloured	..	20	10
863	$1.25, multicoloured	..	45	35
864	$2.50, multicoloured	..	75	1·25
865	$3 multicoloured	..	90	1·40
862/5		Set of 4	2·10	2·75

MS866 62×75 mm. $3.75, multicoloured; $5.01, multicoloured .. .. 2·75 3·25

(Des R. Watton. Litho Cot Printery Ltd, Barbados)

1996 (7 June). *50th Anniv of End of Second World War (1995). T 233 and similar horiz designs. Multicoloured. W w 14 (sideways). P 14.*

867	50 c. Type **233**		20	10
868	$1.25, U.S.S. Missouri (battleship), 1944	45	35
869	$2.50, U.S. servicemen playing baseball, 1942	75	1·25
870	$3 Fleet Air Arm Fulmar 1 (fighter)	90	1·40
867/70		Set of 4	2·10	2·75

MS871 116×85 mm. $3 Fleet Air Arm Grumman Mackinnon G-21C Goose flying boat; $3 U.S. Navy airship .. .. 1·90 2·25

1997 (3 Feb). *"HONG KONG '97" International Stamp Exhibition. Sheet 130×90 mm, containing design as No. 795. Multicoloured. W w 14 (sideways). P 14.*

MS872 $5 Green Honeycreeper .. .. 1·25 1·50

234 Wendy Fitzwilliam
235 Bottle of Angostura Bitters

(Litho Cot Printery Ltd, Barbados)

1999 (3 May). *Wendy Fitzwilliam ("Miss Universe 1998"). T 234 and similar vert designs. Multicoloured. W w 14. P 14.*

873	50 c. Type **234**	..	15	15
874	$1.25, Lying on beach	..	40	30
875	$2.50, In national costume	..	70	75
876	$3 In white evening gown	..	80	90
873/6		Set of 4	1·90	1·90

MS877 70×100 mm. $5 Wearing "Miss Universe" sash. Wmk sideways .. 1·75 2·00

(Des Sea Sky Design. Litho Southern Colour Print, Dunedin)

2000 (27 Jan). *175th Anniv of Angostura Bitters. T 235 and similar bottle-shaped designs. Multicoloured. Self-adhesive. Roul 10.*

878	75 c. Type **235**	15	15
879	$3 Angostura Building inside bottle	60	65
880	$4.50, Cocktails and Angostura inside bottle (horiz)	95	1·00
878/80		Set of 3	1·60	1·75

MS881 120×80 mm. Nos. 878/80. Imperf 1·60 1·75

Nos. 878/80 have die-cut perforations around the shape of the bottle and individual stamps are separated from the sheet by roulettes.

STAMP BOOKLETS

1925.
SB1   2s. booklet containing eight ½d., 1d. and 1½d.
(Nos. 218/20) in blocks of 4   ..   ..   ..

1931–32. *Black on pink covers.*
SB2   1s. 8d. booklet containing eight ½d. and sixteen
1d. (Nos. 218/19) in blocks of 8   ..   ..
SB3   2s. booklet containing eight ½d., 1d. and 1½d.
(Nos. 218/20) in blocks of 8 (1932)   ..   ..

1935.
SB4   48 c. booklet containing eight 1, 2 and 3 c. (Nos.
230/2) in blocks of 4   ..   ..

1970 (8 Dec). *Christmas. Olive-green printed cover inscr*
"CHRISTMAS GREETINGS".
SB5 $1.78, booklet containing six 3 c., four 5 c. and two
30 c. and 40 c. (Nos. 386/9) in pairs ..   ..   4·25

POSTAGE DUE STAMPS

D 1

D 2

Row 4   Row 5

The degree of inclination of the stroke on the 1s. value varies
for each vertical row of the sheet: Rows 1, 2 and 6 104°, Row 3
108°, Row 4 107° and Row 5 (Nos. D9a, D17a, D25a) 100°.

(Typo D.L.R.)

1885 (1 Jan). *Wmk Crown CA. P* 14.

D1	D 1	½d. slate-black	..	..	15·00	45·00
D2		1d. slate-black	..	..	4·50	20
D3		2d. slate-black	..	..	21·00	20
D4		3d. slate-black	..	..	48·00	40
D5		4d. slate-black	..	..	28·00	3·00
D6		5d. slate-black	..	..	23·00	60
D7		6d. slate-black	..	..	38·00	4·00
D8		8d. slate-black	..	..	55·00	3·00
D9		1s. slate-black	..	..	55·00	5·00
		a. Upright stroke	..	..	£110	15·00
D1/9			..	*Set of* 9	£250	55·00

1905–06. *Wmk Mult Crown CA. P* 14.

D10	D 1	1d. slate-black	..	..	3·25	20
D11		2d. slate-black	..	..	15·00	20
		w. Wmk inverted			†	—
D12		3d. slate-black	..	..	8·50	2·75
		w. Wmk inverted				
D13		4d. slate-black	..	..	11·00	9·50
		w. Wmk inverted				
D14		5d. slate-black	..	..	11·00	9·00
D15		6d. slate-black	..	..	6·00	9·50
D16		8d. slate-black	..	..	12·00	14·00
D17		1s. slate-black	..	..	12·00	27·00
		a. Upright stroke	..	..	25·00	55·00
D10/17			..	*Set of* 8	70·00	65·00

1923–45. *Wmk Mult Script CA. P* 14.

D18	D 1	1d. black	..	..	70	1·50
D19		2d. black	..	..	1·00	1·50
D20		3d. black (1925)	..	..	70	2·25
D21		4d. black (1929)	..	..	2·75	17·00
D22		5d. black (1944)	..	..	35·00	80·00
D23		6d. black (1945)	..	..	42·00	27·00
D24		8d. black (1945)	..	..	42·00	£130
D25		1s. black (1945)	..	..	60·00	95·00
		a. Upright stroke	..	..	£120	£180
D18/25			..	*Set of* 8	£160	£325
D18/25	Optd/Perf "Specimen"			*Set of* 8	£140	

1947 (1 Sept)**–61.** *Values in cents. Wmk Mult Script CA.*
Ordinary paper. P 14.

D26	D 1	2 c. black	..		1·50	2·25
		a. Chalk-surfaced paper (20.1.53)	..		20	3·75
		ab. Error. Crown missing. W 9a	..		70·00	
		ac. Error. St. Edward's Crown. W 9b			25·00	
D27		4 c. black	..	..	85	3·00
		a. Chalk-surfaced paper (10.8.55)	..		2·25	4·50
D28		6 c. black	..	..	1·10	6·00
		a. Chalk-surfaced paper (20.1.53)	..		30	7·50
		ab. Error. Crown missing. W 9a	..		£180	
		ac. Error. St. Edward's Crown. W 9b			60·00	
D29		8 c. black	..	..	1·10	18·00
		a. Chalk-surfaced paper (10.9.58)	..		35	16·00
D30		10 c. black	..	..	1·10	2·75
		a. Chalk-surfaced paper (10.8.55)	..		3·25	15·00
D31		12 c. black	..	..	1·10	15·00
		a. Chalk-surfaced paper (20.1.53)	..		40	17·00
		ab. Error. Crown missing. W 9a	..		£225	
		ac. Error. St. Edward's Crown. W 9b			90·00	

D32	D 1	16 c. black	..	..	2·00	35·00
		a. Chalk-surfaced paper (22.8.61)	..		8·50	40·00
D33		24 c. black	..	..	7·00	7·50
		a. Chalk-surfaced paper (10.8.55)	..		3·00	30·00
D26/33			..	*Set of* 8	14·00	80·00
D26/33a			..	*Set of* 8	16·00	£110
D26/33	Perf "Specimen"	..		*Set of* 8	£140	

(Litho B.W.)

1969 (25 Nov)**–70.** *Size* 19 × 24 *mm. P* 14 × 13½.

D34	D 2	2 c. pale blue-green			15	2·50
D35		4 c. magenta (1970)	..		25	3·25
D36		6 c. brown (1970)	..		50	4·50
D37		8 c. slate-lilac (1970)	..		65	4·75
D38		10 c. dull red (1970)	..		65	4·75
D39		12 c. pale orange (1970)	..		80	4·75
D40		16 c. bright apple-green (1970)			90	3·25
D41		24 c. grey (1970)	..		90	3·50
D42		50 c. grey-blue (1970)	..		1·00	4·00
D43		60 c. sage-green (1970)	..		1·00	4·00
D34/43			..	*Set of* 10	6·00	35·00

(Litho Questa)

1976 (3 May)*–**77.** *Redrawn in smaller size* (17 × 21 *mm*).
P 13½ × 14.

D44	D 2	2 c. pale blue-green (31.3.77)	..		20	1·25
D45		4 c. light claret ..			25	1·25
D46		6 c. brown (31.3.77)	..		25	1·50
D47		8 c. bright lilac (31.3.77)	..		30	1·50
D48		10 c. dull red (31.3.77)	..		30	1·25
D49		12 c. pale orange ..	..		50	2·00
D44/9	..			*Set of* 6	1·60	8·00

*The date for the 4 and 12 c. is the local date; the Crown Agents
released the stamps on 19 March.

"TOO LATE" STAMPS

A handstamp with the words "TOO LATE" was used upon letters
on which a too-late fee had been paid, and was sometimes used for
cancelling the stamps on such letters.

OFFICIAL STAMPS

O S   OFFICIAL   OFFICIAL
(O 1)   (O 2)   (O 3)

1894. *Optd with Type* O 1. (*a*) *On Nos.* 106/12. *Wmk Crown*
CA. P 14.

O1	10	½d. dull green	..	..	30·00	50·00
O2		1d. carmine	..	..	32·00	55·00
O3		2½d. bright blue	..	..	42·00	80·00
O4		4d. grey	..	..	42·00	85·00
O5		6d. olive-black	..	..	42·00	85·00
O6		1s. orange-brown	..	..	60·00	£110

(*b*) *On No.* 87. *Wmk Crown CC. P* 12½.

O7	5	5s. rose-lake	..	..	£150	£325

1909. *Nos.* 133 *and* 135 *optd with Type* O 2. *Wmk Mult Crown*
CA. P 14.

O8	11	½d. blue-green	..	..	50	4·50
O9		1d. rose-red	..	..	50	4·50
		a. Opt double	..	..	—	£225
		b. Opt vertical	..	..	55·00	
		c. Opt inverted	..	..	—	£160

1910. *No.* 146 *optd with Type* O 2. *Wmk Mult Crown CA. P* 14.

O10	14	½d. green	..	..	3·00	4·50

1913. *No.* 149 *optd with Type* O 3.

O11	17	½d. green	..	..	60	4·25
		a. Opt vertical				

OFFICIAL   OFFICIAL   OFFICIAL
(O 4)   (O 5)   (O 6)

1914. *No.* 149 *optd with Type* O 4.

O12	17	½d. green	..	..	1·10	9·00

1914–17. *No.* 149 *optd with Type* O 5 (*without stop*).

O13	17	½d. green	..	..	2·25	10·00
		a. Blue-green (thick paper) (1917)	..		50	6·00

1916. *No.* 149a *optd with Type* O 5 (*with stop*).

O14	17	½d. yellow-green	..	..	80	1·50
		a. Opt double	..	..	24·00	

1917 (22 Aug). *No.* 149 *optd with Type* O 6.

O15	17	½d. green	..	..	2·00	12·00
		a. Yellow-green	..	..	2·75	15·00
		b. Blue-green (thick paper)	..		90	13·00

Tristan Da Cunha

Although first settled in 1817 no surviving mail is known from Tristan da Cunha until two whaler's letters written in 1836 and 1843, these being carried home in other whaling ships. Then there is a long gap until the late 1800's when other letters are known—surprisingly only some seven in number, up to 1908 when the first of the island cachet handstamps came into use.

The collecting of postal history material from 1908 to 1952, when Tristan's first stamps were issued, revolves around the numerous cachets of origin which were struck on mail from the island during these 44 years. The handstamps producing these cachets were supplied over the years by various people particularly interested in the island and the islanders, and were mostly used by the clergymen who volunteered to go and serve as the community's ministers.

The postal cachets are illustrated below. The use of the different cachets on mail frequently overlapped, at one period in 1930 there were five different types of handstamp in use. As there was no official source for providing them they appeared on the island from various donors; then disappeared without trace once they became worn out. Only one of these early rubber handstamps has apparently survived, Cachet Va.

Covers bearing the cachets are recognised collector's items, but are difficult to value in general terms. As elsewhere the value is discounted by poor condition of the cover, and may be increased by use on a scarce date or with additional postal markings.

Cachet Types V and VII on cover are the commonest, Type Va, used only for three months, and Type IVa are the scarcest, equalling the scarcest use of Type I examples. All cacheted covers, particularly if non-philatelic, are desirable forerunner items. Even a philatelic cover of Type V is, at present, worth in the region of £35.

Dates given are of the first recorded use.

Cachet I   Cachet II

				Value on cover
C1	**1908** (May).	Cachet I	..	..*from* £4000
C2	**1919** (31 July).	Cachet II	..	..*from* £425

Cachet III

C3	**1921** (8 Feb).	Cachet III	..	..	..*from* £275

Cachet IVa

C4	**1927** (1 Oct).	Cachet IV (as IVa, *but without*		
		centre label)	..	..	..*from* £800
C5	**1928** (28 Oct).	Cachet IVa	..	..*from* £5500

Cachet V   Cachet VI

C6	**1929** (24 Feb).	Cachet V	..*from* 35·00
C7	**1929** (15 May).	Cachet Va (as V, *but without*	
		break in inner ring. Shows "T"	
		"C" and "N" damaged)..	..*from* £6500
C8	**1936** (Aug).	Cachet VI	..*from* 60·00

Cachet VII

C9	**1936** (1 Feb).	Cachet VII	..	..*from* 22·00

During World War II there was little mail from the island as its function as a meteorological station was cloaked by security. Such covers as are known are generally struck with the "tombstone" naval censor mark and postmarked "maritime mail" or have South African postal markings. A few philatelic items from early in the war bearing cachets exist, but this usage was soon stopped by the military commander and the handstamps were put away until peace returned. Covers from the period would be worth from £75 to, at least, £350.

Cachet VIII

C10	**1946** (8 May).	Cachet VIII	..	..*from* 85·00

Cachet IX

C11	**1948** (2 Feb).	Cachet IX	..	.. *from* 45·00

Cachet X

C12	**1948** (29 Feb).	Cachet X ..	..	.. *from* 55·00

Cachet XI

Cachet XII

Cachet XIII

Cachets XI to XIII from the 1961/63 "volcano eruption" and "return to the island" period vary in value from £30 to £120, due to philatelic usage on the one hand and scarce mailings from the small survey parties on shore during this period on the other.

TRISTAN DA CUNHA

(1)

1952 (1 Jan). Nos. 131, 135a/40 and 149/51 of St. Helena optd with T 1.

1	½d. violet	..	..	15	1·25
2	1d. black and green	..	..	70	1·25
3	1½d. black and carmine	..	..	70	1·25
4	2d. black and scarlet	..	..	70	1·50
5	3d. grey	..	..	1·00	1·25
6	4d. ultramarine	..	..	3·25	2·00
7	6d. light blue	..	..	4·25	2·50
8	8d. olive-green	..	..	3·50	3·50
9	1s. sepia	..	..	4·25	2·00
10	2s. 6d. maroon	..	..	17·00	14·00
11	5s. chocolate	..	..	21·00	23·00
12	10s. purple	..	..	35·00	38·00
1/12		Set of 12	80·00	80·00

1953 (2 June). Coronation. As No. 153 of Jamaica.
13	3d. black and grey-green	..	50	1·25

2 Tristan Crawfish   3 Carting Flax for Thatching

(Recess D.L.R.)

1954 (2 Jan). T 2/3 and similar designs. Wmk Mult Script CA. P 12½ × 13 (horiz) or 13 × 12½ (vert).

14	½d. red and deep brown	..	..	10	10
15	1d. sepia and bluish green	..	..	10	50
16	1½d. black and reddish purple	..	..	1·75	90
17	2d. grey-violet and brown-orange	..	..	30	20
18	2½d. black and carmine-red	..	..	1·50	60
19	3d. ultramarine and olive-green	..	..	80	95
20	4d. turquoise-blue and deep blue	..	..	90	90
21	5d. emerald and black	..	..	90	70
22	6d. deep green and violet	..	..	90	75
23	9d. reddish violet and Venetian red	..	..	90	45
24	1s. deep yellow-green and sepia	..	..	90	45
25	2s. 6d. deep brown and light blue	..	..	21·00	10·00
26	5s. black and red-orange	..	..	48·00	16·00
27	10s. brown-orange and purple	..	..	22·00	20·00
14/27		Set of 14	90·00	45·00

Designs: Vert—1½d. Rockhopper Penguin; 3d. Island longboat. Horiz—2d. Big Beach factory; 2½d. Yellow-nosed Albatross; 4d. Tristan from the south-west; 5d. Girls on donkeys; 6d. Inaccessible Island from Tristan; 9d. Nightingale Island; 1s. St. Mary's Church; 2s. 6d. Southern Elephant-Seal at Gough Island; 5s. Inaccessible Island Rail; 10s. Island spinning wheel.

16 Starfish   17 Concha Wrasse

(Des Mr. and Mrs. G. F. Harris. Recess Waterlow)

1960 (1 Feb). Marine Life. Vert designs as T 16/17. W w 12. P 13.

28	½d. black and orange	..	..	15	40
29	1d. black and bright purple..	..	..	15	20
30	1½d. black and light turquoise-blue ..	..	15	70
31	2d. black and bluish green	..	..	20	70
32	2½d. black and sepia	..	..	30	60
33	3d. black and brown-red	..	..	75	50
34	4d. black and yellow-olive ..	..	75	50
35	5d. black and orange-yellow	..	..	90	60
36	6d. black and blue	..	..	1·00	60
37	9d. black and rose-carmine ..	..	1·25	60
38	1s. black and light brown ..	..	1·25	50
39	2s. 6d. black and ultramarine	..	..	10·00	15·00
40	5s. black and light emerald	..	..	11·00	20·00
41	10s. black and violet	..	..	35·00	40·00
28/41		Set of 14	50·00	70·00

Designs:—1½d. Two-spined Thornfish; 2d. Atlantic Saury; 2½d. Bristle Snipefish; 3d. Tristan Crawfish; 4d. False Jacopever; 5d. Five-fingered Morwong; 6d. Long-finned Scad; 9d. Christophersen's Medusafish; 1s. Blue Medusafish; 2s. 6d. Snoek; 5s. Blue Shark; 10s. Black Right Whale.

NEW INFORMATION

The editor is always interested to correspond with people who have new information that will improve or correct the Catalogue.

1961 (15 Apr). *As Nos. 28/30 and 32/41 but values in South African decimal currency.*

42	½ c. black and orange (as ½d.)		10	90
43	1 c. black and bright purple (as 1d.)		15	90
44	1½ c. black and light turquoise-blue (as 1½d.)		35	90
45	2 c. black and sepia (as 2½d.)		40	90
46	2½ c. black and brown-red (as 3d.)		50	90
47	3 c. black and yellow-olive (as 4d.)		65	90
48	4 c. black and orange-yellow (as 5d.)		80	90
49	5 c. black and blue (as 6d)		85	90
50	7½ c. black and rose-carmine (as 9d.)		90	90
51	10 c. black and light brown (as 1s.)		1·75	90
52	25 c. black and ultramarine (as 2s. 6d.)		6·00	11·00
53	50 c. black and light emerald (as 5s.)		11·00	20·00
54	1 r. black and violet (as 10s.)		35·00	40·00
42/54		*Set of 13*	50·00	70·00

Following a volcanic eruption the island was evacuated on 10 October 1961, but resettled in 1963.

TRISTAN DA CUNHA RESETTLEMENT 1963

(30)

1963 (12 Apr). *Tristan Resettlement. As Nos. 176/88 of St. Helena, but Wmk Mult Script CA (sideways on 1d., 2d., 7d., 10d., 2s. 6d., 10s.), optd with T 30.*

55	1d. bright blue, dull violet, yellow & carmine		15	70
56	1½d. yellow, green, black and light drab		20	60
57	2d. scarlet and grey		25	80
58	3d. light blue, black, pink and deep blue		30	70
	a. Black printed double*		£275	
	w. Wmk inverted		£350	
59	4½d. yellow-green, green, brown and grey		50	50
60	6d. red, sepia and light yellow-olive		85	30
61	7d. red-brown, black and violet		50	30
62	10d. brown-purple and light blue		50	30
63	1s. greenish yellow, bluish green & brown		50	30
64	1s. 6d. grey, black and slate-blue		4·00	80
65	2s. 6d. red, pale yellow and turquoise		1·00	45
66	5s. yellow, brown and green		6·00	1·25
	w. Wmk inverted		70·00	
67	10s. orange-red, black and blue		6·50	1·25
55/67		*Set of 13*	18·00	7·00

*No. 58a shows the outline round the Queen's head printed double.

1963 (2 Oct). *Freedom from Hunger. As No. 80 of Lesotho.*

68	1s. 6d. carmine		50	30

1964 (1 Feb). *Red Cross Centenary. As Nos. 203/4 of Jamaica.*

69	3d. red and black		25	15
70	1s. 6d. red and blue		50	20

31 South Atlantic Map   32 Queen Elizabeth II

(Queen's portrait by Anthony Buckley. Des, eng and recess B.W.)

1965 (17 Feb)–67. *Designs as T 31/2. W w 12 (sideways on £1). P 11½ × 11 (vert) or 11 × 11½ (horiz).*

71	½d. black and ultramarine		15	15
72	1d. black and emerald-green		50	15
73	1½d. black and blue		50	15
74	2d. black and purple		50	15
75	3d. black and turquoise-blue		50	15
75a	4d. black and orange (1.9.67)		5·50	4·00
76	4½d. black and brown		50	15
77	6d. black and green		50	15
78	7d. black and rose-red		50	30
79	10d. black and chocolate		50	55
80	1s. black and carmine		50	30
81	1s. 6d. black and yellow-olive		3·50	2·50
82	2s. 6d. black and orange-brown		2·75	2·75
83	5s. black and violet		5·00	3·50
84	10s. deep blue and carmine		1·75	1·25
84a	10s. black and deep turquoise-blue (1.9.67)		17·00	15·00
84b	£1 deep blue and orange-brown (1.9.67)		17·00	19·00
71/84b		*Set of 17*	48·00	45·00

Designs: *Horiz as T* 31—1d. Flagship of Tristão da Cunha, 1506; 1½d. Heemstede (Dutch East Indiaman), 1643; 2d. Edward (American whaling ship), 1864; 3d. Shenandoah (Confederate warship), 1862; 4d. H.M.S. Challenger (survey ship), 1873; 4½d. H.M.S. Galatea (screw frigate), 1867; 6d. H.M.S. Cilicia (transport), 1942; 7d. Royal Yacht Britannia; 10d. H.M.S. Leopard (frigate); 1s. Tjisadane (liner); 1s. 6d. Tristania (crayfish trawler); 2s. 6d. Boissevain (cargo liner); 5s. Bornholm (liner); 10s. (No. 84a), R.S.A. (research vessel). *Vert*—10s. (No. 84), £1, Type 32.

1965 (11 May*). *I.T.U. Centenary. As Nos. 98/9 of Lesotho.*

85	3d. orange-red and grey		30	15
86	6d. reddish violet and yellow-orange		40	15

*This is the local date of issue; the stamps were not released in London until 17 May.

1965 (25 Oct). *International Co-operation Year. As Nos. 100/1 of Lesotho.*

87	1d. reddish purple and turquoise-green		20	15
88	6d. deep bluish green and lavender		75	25

1966 (24 Jan). *Churchill Commemoration. As Nos. 102/5 of Lesotho.*

89	1d. new blue		35	40
	a. Value omitted		£475	
90	3d. deep green		1·25	50
91	6d. brown		1·50	65
92	1s. 6d. bluish violet		2·00	70
89/92		*Set of 4*	4·50	2·00

No. 89a was caused by misplacement of the gold and also shows the country inscription moved to the right.

45 H.M.S. *Falmouth* (frigate) at Tristan and Soldier of 1816

(Des V. Whiteley. Litho Harrison)

1966 (15 Aug). *150th Anniv of Tristan Garrison. W w 12 (sideways*). P 14½.*

93	**45**	3d. multicoloured	20	10
		w. Wmk Crown to right of CA	5·50	
94		4d. multicoloured	20	15
95		1s. 6d. multicoloured	30	25
96		2s. 6d. multicoloured	30	25
93/6		*Set of 4*	90	65

*The normal sideways watermark shows Crown to left of CA, as seen from the back of the stamp.

1966 (1 Oct*). *World Cup Football Championships. As Nos. 57/8 of Pitcairn Islands.*

97	3d. violet, yellow-grn, lake & yell-brn		20	10
98	2s. 6d. chocolate, blue-grn, lake & yellow-brn		50	20

*Released in St. Helena on 1 July in error.

1966 (1 Oct). *Inauguration of W.H.O. Headquarters, Geneva. As Nos. 185/6 of Montserrat.*

99	6d. black, yellow-green and light blue		50	30
100	5s. black, light purple and yellow-brown		75	70

1966 (1 Dec). *20th Anniv of U.N.E.S.C.O. As Nos. 342/4 of Mauritius.*

101	10d. slate-violet, red, yellow and orange		45	15
	w. Wmk Crown to right of CA		38·00	
102	1s. 6d. orange-yellow, violet and deep olive		50	20
103	2s. 6d. black, bright purple and orange		70	25
101/3		*Set of 3*	1·50	55

*The normal sideways watermark shows Crown to left of CA, as seen from the back of the stamp.

46 Calshot Harbour

(Des V. Whiteley. Litho D.L.R.)

1967 (2 Jan). *Opening of Calshot Harbour. P 14 × 14½.*

104	**46**	6d. multicoloured	10	10
105		10d. multicoloured	10	10
106		1s. 6d. multicoloured	10	15
107		2s. 6d. multicoloured	15	20
104/7		*Set of 4*	30	45

(47)   48 Prince Alfred, First Duke of Edinburgh

1967 (10 May). *No. 76 surch with T 47.*

108	4d. on 4½d. black and brown		10	10

(Des M. Goaman. Litho Harrison)

1967 (10 July). *Centenary of First Duke of Edinburgh's Visit to Tristan. W w 12. P 14½.*

109	**48**	3d. multicoloured	10	10
110		6d. multicoloured	10	10
111		1s. 6d. multicoloured	10	10
112		2s. 6d. multicoloured	15	15
109/12		*Set of 4*	30	30

---

49 Wandering Albatross

(Des V. Whiteley. Photo Harrison)

1968 (15 May). *Birds. T 49 and similar horiz designs. Multicoloured. W w 12. P 14 × 14½.*

113	**49**	4d. Type 49	40	30
114		1s. Wilkins's Finch	45	30
115		1s. 6d. Tristan Thrush	50	55
116		2s. 6d. Greater Shearwater	90	65
113/16		*Set of 4*	2·00	1·60

53 Union Jack and Dependency Flag

(Des Jennifer Toombs. Litho D.L.R.)

1968 (1 Nov). *30th Anniv of Tristan da Cunha as a Dependency of St. Helena. T 53 and similar horiz design. W w 12 (sideways). P 14.*

117	**53**	6d. multicoloured	10	25
118		9d. sepia, blue and turquoise-blue	10	30
119	**53**	1s. 6d. multicoloured	15	35
120		2s. 6d. carmine, blue and turquoise-blue	20	35
117/20		*Set of 4*	50	1·10

Design:—9d., 2s. 6d. St. Helena and Tristan on chart.

55 Frigate

(Des and recess B.W.)

1969 (1 June). *Clipper Ships. T 55 and similar horiz designs. W w 12. P 11 × 11½.*

121	4d. new blue		40	30
122	1s. carmine (full-rigged ship)		40	35
123	1s. 6d. blue-green (barque)		45	70
124	2s. 6d. chocolate (full-rigged clipper)		50	75
121/4		*Set of 4*	1·60	1·90

59 Sailing Ship off Tristan da Cunha

(Des Jennifer Toombs. Litho Format)

1969 (1 Nov). *United Society for the Propagation of the Gospel. T 59 and similar horiz designs. Multicoloured. W w 12 (sideways). P 14½ × 14.*

125	**59**	6d. Type 59	40	30
126		9d. Islanders going to first Gospel service	15	30
127		1s. 6d. Landing of the first minister	15	40
128		2s. 6d. Procession outside St. Mary's Church	20	40
125/8		*Set of 4*	80	1·25

63 Globe and Red Cross Emblem

(Des and litho B.W.)

1970 (1 June). *Centenary of British Red Cross. T 63 and similar designs. W w 12 (sideways on vert designs). P 13.*

129	**63**	4d. lt emerald, scarlet & dp bluish green	10	20
130		9d. bistre, scarlet and deep bluish green	15	25
131	–	1s. 9d. light drab, scarlet & ultramarine	25	40
132	–	2s. 6d. reddish purple, scarlet & ultram	30	50
129/32		*Set of 4*	70	1·25

Design: *Vert*—1s. 9d., 2s. 6d., Union Jack and Red Cross Flag.

MINIMUM PRICE

The minimum price quote is 10p which represents a handling charge rather than a basis for valuing common stamps. For further notes about prices see introductory pages.

64 Crawfish and Longboat   (65)

(Des Harrison. Litho Enschedé)

1970 (1 Nov). *Crawfish Industry.* T **64** *and similar horiz design. Multicoloured.* W w **12**. P 12½ × 13.

133	4d. Type **64**		25	30
134	10d. Packing and storing Crawfish		30	35
135	1s. 6d. Type **64**		50	60
136	2s. 6d. As 10d.		50	70
133/6		Set of 4	1·40	1·75

1971 (14 Feb).* *Decimal Currency. As Nos. 72/4, 75a, 77/83 and 84a surch as T* **65**, *by B.W. in typo. Glazed paper.*

137	½p. on 1d. black and emerald-green	15	15
138	1p. on 2d. black and purple	15	15
139	1½p. on 4d. black and orange	30	15
140	2½p. on 6d. black and green	30	15
141	3p. on 7d. black and rose-red	30	15
142	4p. on 10d. black and chocolate	30	20
143	5p. on 1s. black and carmine	30	20
144	7½p. on 1s. 6d. black and yellow-olive	1·75	1·75
145	12½p. on 2s. 6d. black and orange-brown	2·50	2·50
146	15p. on 1½d. black and blue	2·50	3·00
147	25p. on 5s. black and violet	2·50	5·50
148	50p. on 10s. black and deep turquoise-blue	3·50	11·00
137/48	Set of 12	13·00	22·00

*This was the local release date, but the Crown Agents issued the stamps one day later.

66 Quest

(Des V. Whiteley. Litho J.W.)

1971 (1 June). *50th Anniv of Shackleton–Rowett Expedition.* T **66** *and similar horiz designs.* W w **12** (sideways). P 13½ × 14.

149	1½p. multicoloured	70	30
150	4p. sepia, pale green and apple-green	70	40
151	7½p. black, bright purple and pale green	70	40
152	12½p. multicoloured	75	45
149/52	Set of 4	2·50	1·40

Designs:—4p. Presentation of Scout Troop flag; 7½p. Cachet on pair of 6d. G.B. stamps; 12½p. Shackleton, postmarks and longboat taking mail to the *Quest.*

67 H.M.S. *Victory* at Trafalgar and Thomas Swain catching Nelson   **68** Cow Pudding

(Des R. Granger Barrett. Litho Questa)

1971 (1 Nov). *Island Families.* T **67** *and similar horiz designs showing ships and the names of families associated with them. Multicoloured.* W w **12** (sideways). P 13½.

153	1½p. Type **67**	20	40
154	2½p. *Emily of Stonington* (American schooner) (P. W. Green)	25	50
155	4p. *Italia* (barque) (Lavarello and Repetto)	30	60
156	7½p. H.M.S. *Falmouth* (frigate) (William Glass)	40	70
157	12½p. American whaling ship (Rogers and Hagan)	40	85
153/7	Set of 5	1·40	2·75

(Des M. and Sylvia Goaman. Recess and litho B.W. (50p., £1); Litho A. & M. (others))

1972 (29 Feb). T **68** *and similar multicoloured designs showing flowering plants.* W w **12** (sideways* on horiz designs). P 13.

158	½p. Type **68**	20	15
	w. Wmk inverted	30	30
159	1p. Peak Berry	40	15
	w. Wmk inverted	40	40
160	1½p. Sand Flower (*horiz*)	40	20
161	2½p. N.Z. Flax (*horiz*)	40	20
	w. Wmk Crown to right of CA	70	70
162	3p. Island Tree	40	20
	w. Wmk inverted	70	70
163	4p. Bog Fern	40	25
	w. Wmk inverted	90	90
164	5p. Dog Catcher	85	25
	w. Wmk inverted	1·50	1·00

165	7½p. Celery			3·00	1·00
	w. Wmk inverted			3·00	1·25
166	12½p. Pepper Tree			1·75	60
	w. Wmk inverted			29·00	29·00
167	25p. Foul Berry (*horiz*)			1·75	1·50
	w. Wmk Crown to right of CA			3·00	3·50
168	50p. Tussock			7·00	2·50
169	£1 Tussac (*horiz*)			2·25	2·50
158/69		Set of 12		17·00	8·50

*The normal sideways watermark shows Crown to left of CA, as seen from the back of the stamp.

69 Launching

(Des R. Svensson. Litho Walsall)

1972 (1 June). *Tristan Longboats.* T **69** *and similar multicoloured designs.* W w **12** (sideways on 2½p. and 4p.). P 14.

170	2½p. Type **69**	25	15
171	4p. Under oars	30	15
172	7½p. Coxswain Arthur Repetto (*vert*)	30	20
173	12½p. Under sail for Nightingale Island (*vert*)	35	25
170/73	Set of 4	1·10	65

70 Tristan Thrushes and Wandering Albatrosses

(Des (from photographs by D. Groves) and photo Harrison)

1972 (20 Nov). *Royal Silver Wedding. Multicoloured; background colours given.* W w **12**. P 14 × 14½.

174	**70** 2½p. red-brown	25	30
	w. Wmk inverted	9·00	
175	7½p. dull ultramarine	10	30
	w. Wmk inverted	85·00	

71 Church Altar

(Des J. Cooter. Litho Questa)

1973 (8 July). *Golden Jubilee of St. Mary's Church.* W w **12**. P 13½.

176	**71** 25p. multicoloured	40	40

72 H.M.S. *Challenger's* Laboratory

(Des V. Whiteley Studio. Litho Questa)

1973 (15 Oct). *Centenary of H.M.S. Challenger's Visit.* T **72** *and similar horiz designs. Multicoloured.* W w **12**. P 13½.

177	4p. Type **72**	20	25
178	5p. H.M.S. *Challenger* off Tristan	20	25
179	7½p. *Challenger's* pinnace off Nightingale Is	20	30
180	12½p. Survey route	30	40
177/80	Set of 4	80	1·10
MS181	145 × 96 mm. Nos. 177/80	1·10	2·75

73 Approaching English Port

(Des Jennifer Toombs. Litho Questa)

1973 (10 Nov). *Tenth Anniv of Return to Tristan da Cunha.* T **73** *and similar horiz designs. Multicoloured* (except 4p.). W w **12**. P 14.

182	4p. Type **73** (reddish brn, lemon & gold)	20	25
183	5p. Survey party	20	25
184	7½p. Embarking on *Bornholm*	20	35
	w. Wmk inverted	£150	
185	12½p. Approaching Tristan	30	45
	w. Wmk inverted	1·50	
182/5	Set of 4	80	1·10

1973 (14 Nov). *Royal Wedding. As Nos. 322/3 of Montserrat.*

186	7½p. bright blue	15	10
187	12½p. light turquoise-green	15	10

74 Rockhopper Penguin and Egg

(Des R. Granger Barrett. Litho Questa)

1974 (1 May). *Rockhopper Penguins.* T **74** *and similar horiz designs.* W w **12**. P 14.

188	2½p. Type **74**	2·50	1·00
189	5p. Rockhopper Colony, Inaccessible Island	3·00	1·40
190	7½p. Penguin fishing	3·50	1·60
	w. Wmk inverted		
191	25p. Adult and fledgling	4·00	2·00
188/91	Set of 4	11·50	5·50

75 Map with Rockhopper Penguin and Wandering Albatross

(Des J.W. Litho Questa)

1974 (1 Oct). *"The Lonely Island". Sheet* 154×104 mm. W w **12** (sideways*). P 13½.

MS192	**75** 35p. multicoloured	3·00	3·50
	w. Wmk Crown to right of CA	£225	

*The normal sideways watermark shows Crown to left of CA as seen from the back of the stamp.

76 Blenheim Palace

(Des Sylvia Goaman. Litho Questa)

1974 (30 Nov). *Birth Centenary of Sir Winston Churchill.* T **76** *and similar horiz design.* W w **14** (sideways). P 14.

193	7½p. pale yellow and black	10	10
194	25p. black, sepia and grey	30	25
MS195	93 × 93 mm. Nos. 193/4. W w **12** (sideways)	55	1·60

Design:—25p. Churchill with Queen Elizabeth II.

77 *Plocamium fuscorubrum*

(Des Sylvia Goaman. Litho Harrison)

1975 (16 Apr). *Sea Plants.* T **77** *and similar horiz designs.* W w **12** (sideways*). P 13×13½.

196	4p. rose-carmine, light lilac and black	15	10
197	5p. apple-green, light violet-blue and deep bluish green	15	15
198	10p. red-orange, stone and brown-purple	20	15
	w. Wmk Crown to right of CA	80·00	
199	20p. multicoloured	30	25
196/9	Set of 4	70	60

Designs:—5p. *Ulva lactua*; 10p. *Epymenia flabellata*; 20p. *Macrocystis pyrifera.*

*The normal sideways watermark shows Crown to left of CA as seen from the back of the stamp.

78 Killer Whale

(Des G. Drummond. Litho Walsall)

1975 (1 Nov). *Whales. T* **78** *and similar horiz designs. Multicoloured. W w* 12 (*sideways*). *P* 13½.

200	2p. Type **78**			75	35
201	3p. Rough-toothed Dolphin			75	35
202	5p. Black Right Whale			90	40
203	20p. Fin Whale			1·60	85
200/3			Set of 4	3·50	1·75

79 ½d. Stamp of 1952   **80** Island Cottage

(Des C. Abbott. Litho J.W.)

1976 (27* May). *Festival of Stamps, London. T* **79** *and similar designs. W w* 14 (*sideways on 5 and 25p*). *P* 13½.

204	5p. black, violet and light lilac			20	15
205	9p. black, deep green and turquoise			25	15
206	25p. multicoloured			40	40
204/6			Set of 3	75	65

Designs: *Vert*—9p. 1953 Coronation stamp. *Horiz*—25p. Mail carrier *Tristania II*.
*This is the local date of issue. The stamps were released by the Crown Agents on 4 May.
For miniature sheet containing No. 206 see No. **MS218** of Ascension.

(Des C. Abbott. Litho Questa)

1976 (4 Oct). *Paintings by Roland Svensson* (1st series). *T* **80** *and similar multicoloured designs. W w* 14 (*sideways on 5p., 10p. and* **MS211**). *P* 14.

207	3p. Type **80**			15	15
208	5p. The potato patches (*horiz*)			15	15
209	10p. Edinburgh from the sea (*horiz*)			20	20
210	20p. Huts, Nightingale Island			30	35
207/10			Set of 4	70	70
MS211	125 × 112 mm. Nos. 207/10			90	1·75

See also Nos. 234/8 and 272/6.

81 The Royal Standard

(Des and litho J.W.)

1977 (7 Feb). *Silver Jubilee. T* **81** *and similar horiz designs. Multicoloured. W w* 14 (*sideways*). *P* 13.

212	10p. Royal Yacht *Britannia*			15	20
213	15p. Type **81**			15	20
214	25p. Royal family			20	20
212/14			Set of 3	45	55

For Nos. 213/14 surcharged, see Nos. 232/3.

82 H.M.S. *Eskimo* (frigate)

(Des L. Curtis. Litho Walsall)

1977 (1 Oct). *Ships' Crests. T* **82** *and similar horiz designs. Multicoloured. W w* 14 (*sideways*). *P* 14.

215	5p. Type **82**			15	15
216	10p. H.M.S. *Naiad* (frigate)			20	15
217	15p. H.M.S. *Jaguar* (frigate)			25	25
218	20p. H.M.S. *London* (destroyer)			30	30
215/18			Set of 4	80	75
MS219	142×140 mm. Nos. 215/18			80	1·50

83 Great-winged Petrel

(Des BG Studio. Litho Walsall)

1977 (1 Dec). *Multicoloured designs as T* **83** *showing birds. W w* 14 (*sideways on 1 and 2p.*). *P* 13½.

220	1p. Type **83**			15	60
221	2p. White-faced Storm Petrel			20	90
222	3p. Hall's Giant Petrel			20	90
223	4p. Soft-plumaged Petrel			60	1·00
224	5p. Wandering Albatross			60	1·00
225	10p. Kerguelen Petrel			60	1·00
226	15p. Swallow-tailed Tern			60	1·25
227	20p. Greater Shearwater			1·00	1·25
228	25p. Broad-billed Prion			1·25	1·25
229	50p. Great Skua			1·50	1·25
230	£1 Common Diving Petrel			2·00	2·25
231	£2 Yellow-nosed Albatross			4·50	3·50
220/31			Set of 12	12·00	14·50

The 3p. to £2 are vertical designs.

4p

  (84)   Normal   Straight top
to serif in
"½" (Pl 1C
R. 5/1–5)

1978 (19 Jan*). *Provisional definitives. Nos. 213/14 surch as T* **84**.

232	4p. on 15p. Type **81**			1·50	4·00
233	7½p. on 25p. Royal family			1·50	4·00
	a. Straight top to serif				13·00

*This is the local date of issue. Covers dated 26 November 1977 are philatelic mail forwarded to the island for cancellation, the stamps having been released in London on 31 October 1977. Supplies for the island population did not arrive until 19 January.

(Des C. Abbott. Litho Questa)

1978 (1 Mar). *Paintings by Roland Svensson* (2nd series). *Horiz designs as T* **80**. *Multicoloured. W w* 14 (*sideways**). *P* 14.

234	5p. St. Mary's Church			15	15
235	10p. Longboats			15	15
236	15p. A Tristan home			20	25
237	20p. The harbour, 1970			20	25
	w. Wmk Crown to right of CA			75·00	
234/7			Set of 4	65	70
MS238	115×128 mm. Nos. 234/7			1·10	2·00

*The normal sideways watermark shows Crown to left of CA, as seen from the back of the stamp.

85 King's Bull   **86** Sodalite

(Des Jennifer Toombs. Litho Questa)

1978 (21 Apr). *25th Anniv of Coronation. T* **85** *and similar vert designs. W w* 14. *P* 15.

239	25p. bistre, bright violet and silver			25	30
	aw. Wmk inverted			17·00	
	b. Sheetlet. Nos. 239/41×2			1·10	
	bw. Wmk inverted			90·00	
240	25p. multicoloured			25	30
	aw. Wmk inverted			17·00	
241	25p. bistre, bright violet and silver			25	30
	aw. Wmk inverted			17·00	
239/41			Set of 3	65	80

Designs:—No. 239, Type **85**; No. 240, Queen Elizabeth II; No. 241, Tristan crawfish.
Nos. 239/41 were printed together in small sheets of 6, containing two *se-tenant* strips of 3, with horizontal gutter margin between.

(Des J.W. Litho Questa)

1978 (9 June). *Local Minerals. T* **86** *and similar horiz designs. Multicoloured. W w* 14 (*sideways*). *P* 13½.

242	3p. Type **86**			25	25
243	5p. Aragonite			30	30
244	10p. Sulphur			45	45
245	20p. Lava containing pyroxene crystal			65	65
242/5			Set of 4	1·50	1·50

87 Two-spined Thornfish

(Des R. Granger Barrett. Litho Harrison)

1978 (29 Sept). *Fish. T* **87** *and similar horiz designs. W w* 14 (*sideways*). *P* 14.

246	5p. black, yellow-brown and yellow-green			10	10
247	10p. black, yellow-brown and emerald			15	15
248	15p. multicoloured			20	20
249	20p. multicoloured			30	25
246/9			Set of 4	65	60

Designs:—10p. Five-fingered Morwong; 15p. Concha Wrasse; 20p. Tristan Jacopever.

88 R.F.A. *Orangeleaf*   **89** Southern
(tanker)   Elephant Seal

(Des R. Granger Barrett. Litho Cartor)

1978 (24 Nov). *Royal Fleet Auxiliary Vessels. T* **88** *and similar horiz designs. Multicoloured. W w* 14 (*sideways*). *P* 12½ × 12.

250	5p. Type **88**			15	10
251	10p. R.F.A. *Tarbatness* (store carrier)			20	10
252	20p. R.F.A. *Tidereach* (tanker)			30	25
253	25p. R.F.A. *Reliant* (store carrier)			35	30
250/3			Set of 4	90	65
MS254	136×140 mm. Nos. 250/3 (Wmk inverted)			90	2·75

(Des J.W. Litho Questa)

1979 (3 Jan). *Wildlife Conservation. T* **89** *and similar vert designs. Multicoloured. W w* 14. *P* 14.

255	5p. Type **89**			10	10
256	10p. Afro-Australian Fur Seal			15	15
257	15p. Tristan Thrush			25	20
258	20p. Nightingale Finch			35	25
255/8			Set of 4	75	60

90 Tristan Longboat

(Des R. Granger Barrett. Litho Questa)

1979 (8 Feb). *Visit of Queen Elizabeth 2. T* **90** *and similar horiz designs. Multicoloured. W w* 14 (*sideways**). *P* 14½.

259	5p. Type **90**			15	20
	w. Wmk Crown to right of CA			2·00	
260	10p. *Queen Mary* (liner)			15	20
261	15p. *Queen Elizabeth* (liner)			20	30
262	20p. *Queen Elizabeth 2* (liner)			20	30
259/62			Set of 4	65	90
MS263	148×96 mm. 25p. *Queen Elizabeth 2*				
	(liner) (131×27 mm)			75	1·50
	w. Wmk Crown to right of CA			7·00	

*The normal watermark for both stamps and minature sheet has Crown to left of CA, as seen from the back of the stamp.

91 1952 "TRISTAN DA CUNHA" overprinted
St. Helena 10s. Definitive

(Des J.W. Litho Questa)

1979 (27 Aug). *Death Centenary of Sir Rowland Hill. T* **91** *and similar designs showing stamps. W w* 14 (*sideways** on 5 and 10p.). *P* 14.

264	5p. black, lilac and bistre-yellow			10	15
	w. Wmk Crown to right of CA			10·00	
265	10p. black, red and apple-green			15	20
266	25p. multicoloured			30	30
	w. Wmk inverted				
264/6			Set of 3	50	60
MS267	83×103 mm. 50p. black and vermilion			60	70

Designs: *Horiz*—10p. 1954 5s. definitive. *Vert*—25p. 1963 3d. Tristan da Cunha Resettlement commemorative; 50p. 1946 1d. 4 Potatoes local label.
*The normal sideways watermark shows Crown to left of CA, as seen from the back of the stamp.

92 "The Padre's House" | **93** *Tristania II* (crayfish trawler)

(Des G. Hutchins. Litho Questa)

1979 (26 Nov). *International Year of the Child. Children's Drawings. T 92 and similar horiz designs. Multicoloured. W w 14 (sideways). P 14.*

268	5p. Type **92**		10	10
269	10p. "Houses in the Village"		15	15
270	15p. "St. Mary's Church"		15	15
271	20p. "Rockhopper Penguins"		20	25
268/71		*Set of 4*	50	60

(Des C. Abbott. Litho Questa)

1980 (29 Feb). *Paintings by Roland Svensson (3rd series). Landscapes. Multicoloured designs as T 80. W w 14 (sideways on 5 and 10p). P 14.*

272	5p. "Stoltenhoff Island" [*horiz*]		10	10
273	10p. "Nightingale from the East" (*horiz*)		15	20
274	15p. "The Administrator's Abode"		15	25
275	20p. "Ridge where the Goat jump off"		20	30
272/5		*Set of 4*	50	75
MS276	126 × 109 mm. Nos. 272/5 (wmk sideways)		70	1·25

(Des C. Abbott. Litho Walsall)

1980 (6 May). *"London 1980" International Stamp Exhibition. T 93 and similar vert designs. Multicoloured. W w 14. P 14.*

277	5p. Type **93**		10	10
278	10p. Unloading mail at Calshot Harbour		15	15
279	15p. Tractor transporting mail to Post Office		15	20
280	20p. Ringing the "dong" to summons people to Post Office		20	20
281	25p. Distributing mail		25	25
277/81		*Set of 5*	70	80

94 Queen Elizabeth the Queen Mother at Royal Opera House, 1976 | **95** *Golden Hind*

(Des Harrison. Litho Questa)

1980 (11 Aug*). *80th Birthday of Queen Elizabeth the Queen Mother. W w 14 (sideways). P 14.*

282 **94**	14p. multicoloured		25	25

*This is the local date of issue. The Crown Agents released this stamp in London on 4 August.

(Des G. Vasarhelyi. Litho Walsall)

1980 (6 Sept). *400th Anniv of Sir Francis Drake's Circumnavigation of the World. T 95 and similar vert designs. Multicoloured. W w 14. P 14½ × 14.*

283	5p. Type **95**		10	10
284	10p. Drake's route		15	15
285	20p. Sir Francis Drake		20	20
286	25p. Queen Elizabeth I		25	25
283/6		*Set of 4*	65	65

96 "Humpty Dumpty" | **97** South Atlantic Ocean showing Islands on Mid-Atlantic Ridge

---

(Des G. Vasarhelyi. Litho J.W.)

1980 (31 Oct). *Christmas. Scenes from Nursery Rhymes. T 96 and similar horiz designs. Multicoloured. W w 14 (sideways). P 13.*

287	15p. Type **96**		15	25
	a. Sheetlet Nos. 287/95		1·25	
288	15p. "Mary had a little Lamb"		15	25
289	15p. "Little Jack Horner"		15	25
290	15p. "Hey Diddle Diddle"		15	25
291	15p. "London Bridge"		15	25
292	15p. "Old King Cole"		15	25
293	15p. "Sing a Song of Sixpence"		15	25
294	15p. "Tom, Tom the Piper's Son"		15	25
295	15p. "The Owl and the Pussy Cat"		15	25
287/95		*Set of 9*	1·25	1·75

Nos. 287/95 were printed together, *se-tenant*, within a small sheet of 9 stamps.

(Des A. Crawford, adapted BG Studio. Litho Rosenbaum Bros, Vienna)

1980 (15 Dec). *150th Anniv of Royal Geographical Society. Maps. T 97 and similar vert designs. Multicoloured. W w 14. P 13½.*

296	5p. Type **97**		15	20
297	10p. Tristan da Cunha group (Beauforts Survey, 1806)		15	25
298	15p. Tristan Island (Crawford, 1937–38)		20	30
299	20p. Gough Island (1955–56)		25	40
296/9		*Set of 4*	65	1·00

98 Revd. Edwin Dodgson as Young Man | **99** Detail from Captain Denham's Plan, 1853

(Des Jennifer Toombs. Litho Questa)

1981 (23 Mar). *Centenary of Revd. Edwin Dodgson's Arrival on Tristan da Cunha. T 98 and similar multicoloured designs. W w 14 (sideways on 20p). P 14.*

300	10p. Type **98**		15	15
301	20p. Dodgson and view of Tristan da Cunha (*horiz*)		25	30
302	30p. Dodgson with people of Tristan da Cunha		35	45
300/2		*Set of 3*	65	80
MS303	140×134 mm. Nos. 300/2. Wmk sideways*		75	1·40
	w. Wmk Crown to right of CA		25·00	

*The normal sideways watermark on No. MS303 shows Crown to left of CA, *as seen from the back of the stamp.*

(Des L. McCombie. Litho Questa)

1981 (22 May). *Early Maps. T 99 and similar horiz designs. Multicoloured. W w 14 (sideways*). P 13½×14.*

304	5p. Type **99**		15	10
	w. Wmk Crown to right of CA		45·00	
305	14p. Detail from map by A. Dalrymple, 17 March 1781		30	20
306	21p. Detail from Captain Denham's plan, 1853 (*different*)		40	30
304/6		*Set of 3*	75	55
MS307	110×70 mm. 35p. Detail from map by J. van Keulen, *circa* 1700		50	60
	w. Wmk Crown to right of CA		65·00	

*The normal sideways watermark shows Crown to left of CA, *as seen from the back of the stamp or miniature sheet.*

100 Wedding Bouquet from Tristan da Cunha | **101** Explorer with Rucksack

(Des J.W. Litho Walsall)

1981 (22 July). *Royal Wedding. T 100 and similar vert designs. Multicoloured. W w 14. P 14.*

308	10p. Type **100**		10	10
309	20p. Prince of Wales at Investiture		15	15
310	50p. Prince Charles and Lady Diana Spencer		45	45
308/10		*Set of 3*	60	60

(Des BG Studio. Litho Questa)

1981 (14 Sept). *25th Anniv of Duke of Edinburgh Award Scheme. T 101 and similar vert designs. Multicoloured. W w 14. P 14.*

311	5p. Type **101**		10	10
312	10p. Explorer at campsite		10	10
313	20p. Explorer map reading		20	20
314	25p. Duke of Edinburgh		25	25
311/14		*Set of 4*	55	55

---

102 Inaccessible Island Rail on Nest

(Des R. Granger Barrett. Litho Walsall)

1981 (1 Nov). *Inaccessible Island Rail. T 102 and similar horiz designs. Multicoloured. W w 14 (sideways*). P 13½×14.*

315	10p. Type **102**		25	30
	a. Strip of 4. Nos. 315/18		90	
	aw. Wmk Crown to right of CA (strip of 4)		£140	
316	10p. Inaccessible Island Rail eggs		25	30
317	10p. Rail chicks		25	30
318	10p. Adult Rail		25	30
315/18		*Set of 4*	90	1·10

*The normal sideways watermark shows Crown to left of CA, *as seen from the back of the stamp.*

Nos. 315/18 were printed together, *se-tenant*, in horizontal and vertical strips of 4 throughout the sheet.

103 Six-gilled Shark

(Des I. Loe. Litho Enschedé)

1982 (8 Feb). *Sharks. T 103 and similar horiz designs. Multicoloured. W w 14 (sideways*). P 13½.*

319	5p. Type **103**		30	10
	w. Wmk Crown to right of CA		65·00	
320	14p. Porbeagle		40	20
	w. Wmk Crown to right of CA		65·00	
321	21p. Blue Shark		45	35
322	35p. Golden Hammerhead		55	50
319/22		*Set of 4*	1·50	1·50

*The normal sideways watermark shows Crown to left of CA, *as seen from the back of the stamp.*

104 *Marcella* (barque) | **105** Lady Diana Spencer at Windsor, July 1981

(Des J. Cooter. Litho Questa)

1982 (5 Apr). *Sailing Ships (1st series). T 104 and similar horiz designs. Multicoloured. W w 14 (sideways). P 13½.*

323	5p. Type **104**		25	30
324	15p. *Eliza Adams* (full-rigged ship)		30	40
325	30p. *Corinthian* (American whaling ship)		45	60
326	50p. *Samuel and Thomas* (American whaling ship)		70	80
323/6		*Set of 4*	1·50	1·90

See also Nos. 341/4.

(Des Jennifer Toombs. Litho Walsall)

1982 (1 July). *21st Birthday of Princess of Wales. T 105 and similar vert designs. Multicoloured. W w 14. P 14½ × 14.*

327	5p. Tristan da Cunha coat of arms		10	10
328	15p. Type **105**		40	20
329	30p. Prince and Princess of Wales in wedding portrait		45	40
330	50p. Formal portrait		1·25	60
327/30		*Set of 4*	2·00	1·10

106 Lord Baden-Powell | (**107**)

(Des C. Abbott. Litho J.W.)

1982 (20 Sept). *75th Anniv of Boy Scout Movement. T* **106** *and similar multicoloured designs.* W w **14** *(sideways on No. 333).* P 13 × 13½ (50p.) or 13½ × 13 (others).

331	5p. Type **106**			15	15
332	20p. First Scout camp, Brownsea, 1907			30	35
333	50p. Local Scouts on parade (horiz)			65	75
331/3			Set of 3	1·00	1·10
MS334	88 × 104 mm. 50p. Moral of the Acorn and the Oak. P 14			1·10	1·40

1982 (28 Sept). *Commonwealth Games, Brisbane. Nos.* 224 *and* 228 *optd with T* **107**.

335	5p. Wandering Albatross			15	10
336	25p. Broad-billed Prion			40	30
	w. Wmk inverted			27·00	

108 Formation of Island   109 Tractor pulling Trailer

(Des J.W. Litho Questa)

1982 (1 Nov). *Volcanoes. T* **108** *and similar horiz designs. Multicoloured.* W w **14** *(sideways).* P 14 × 14½.

337	5p. Type **108**			15	15
338	15p. Plan of surface cinder cones and cross-section of volcano showing feeders			30	35
339	25p. Eruption			45	50
340	35p. 1961 Tristan eruption			65	70
337/40			Set of 4	1·40	1·50

(Des J. Cooter. Litho Questa)

1983 (1 Feb). *Sailing Ships* (2nd series). *Multicoloured designs as T* **104**. W w **14** *(sideways on 20p., 35p.).* P 13½.

341	5p. *Islander* (barque) (vert)			25	15
342	20p. *Roscoe* (full-rigged ship)			45	35
343	35p. *Columbia* (whaling ship)			60	55
344	50p. *Emeline* (schooner) (vert)			80	80
341/4			Set of 4	1·90	1·75

(Des C. Abbott. Litho Format)

1983 (2 May). *Land Transport. T* **109** *and similar horiz designs. Multicoloured.* W w **14** *(sideways).* P 14.

345	5p. Type **109**			10	15
346	15p. Pack donkeys			15	25
347	30p. Bullock cart			30	40
348	50p. Landrover			50	60
345/8			Set of 4	90	1·25

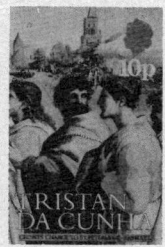

110 Early Chart of South Atlantic   111 "Christ's Charge to St. Peter" (detail) (Raphael)

(Des L. Curtis. Litho Questa)

1983 (1 Aug). *Island History. T* **110** *and similar horiz designs. Multicoloured (except 50p. black, bright scarlet and buff).* W w **14** *(sideways*).* P 14.

349	1p. Type **110**			30	30
350	3p. Tristao da Cunha's caravel			40	30
351	4p. Notice left by Dutch on first landing, 1643			40	30
352	5p. 17th-century views of the island			40	30
353	10p. British army landing party, 1815			45	40
354	15p. 19th-century view of the settlement			55	50
355	18p. Governor Glass's house			55	50
356	20p. The Revd. W. F. Taylor and Peter Green			65	65
357	25p. *John and Elizabeth* (American whaling ship)			85	75
358	50p. Letters Patent declaring Tristan da Cunha a dependency of St. Helena			1·10	1·25
359	£1 Commissioning H.M.S. *Atlantic Isle*, 1944			1·25	2·50
	w. Wmk Crown to right of CA			1·25	
360	£2 Evacuation, 1961			2·00	4·00
	w. Wmk Crown to right of CA			2·00	
349/60			Set of 12	8·00	10·50

*The normal sideways watermark shows Crown to left of CA, as seen from the back of the stamp.

(Des and litho Walsall)

1983 (27 Oct). *500th Birth Anniv of Raphael. T* **111** *and similar designs, showing different details of "Christ's Charge to St. Peter".* W w **14**. P 14½.

361	10p. multicoloured			15	20
362	25p. multicoloured			25	35
363	40p. multicoloured			45	60
361/3			Set of 3	75	1·00
MS364	115 × 90 mm. 50p. multicoloured (horiz). Wmk sideways			70	80

On No. **MS**364 the Queen's head has been replaced by the Royal Cypher.

---

112 1952 6d. Stamp   113 *Agrocybe praecox var. cutefracta*

(Des C. Abbott. Litho Questa)

1984 (1 Jan). *150th Anniv of St. Helena as a British Colony. T* **112** *and similar horiz designs showing 1952 overprints on St. Helena stamps. Multicoloured.* W w **14** *(sideways).* P 14.

365	10p. Type **112**			25	35
366	15p. 1952 1s. stamp			35	45
367	25p. 1952 2s. 6d. stamp			40	70
368	60p. 1952 10s. stamp			85	1·25
365/8			Set of 4	1·60	2·50

(Des McCombie Skinner Studio. Litho Questa)

1984 (25 Mar). *Fungi. T* **113** *and similar multicoloured designs.* W w **14** *(sideways on 30 p., 50 p.).* P 14.

369	10p. Type **113**			65	85
370	20p. *Laccaria tetraspora*			95	1·25
371	30p. *Agrocybe cylindracea* (horiz)			1·10	1·40
372	50p. *Sacoscypha coccinea* (horiz)			1·40	1·75
369/72			Set of 4	3·75	4·75

114 Constellation of "Orion"   115 Sheep-shearing

(Des Harrison. Litho Questa)

1984 (30 July). *The Night Sky. T* **114** *and similar vert designs. Multicoloured.* W w **14**. P 14½ × 14.

373	10p. Type **114**			45	80
374	20p. "Scorpius"			55	90
375	25p. "Canis Major"			65	95
376	50p. "Crux"			85	1·10
373/6			Set of 4	2·25	3·25

(Des G. Wilby. Litho Walsall)

1984 (1 Oct). *Tristan Woollens Industry. T* **115** *and similar vert designs. Multicoloured.* W w **14**. P 14½.

377	9p. Type **115**			20	45
378	17p. Carding wool			25	50
379	29p. Spinning			35	80
380	45p. Knitting			55	90
377/80			Set of 4	1·25	2·40
MS381	120 × 85 mm. As Nos. 377/80, but without white borders around the designs.			1·25	3·00

116 "Christmas Dinner-table"   117 "H.M.S. *Julia* (sloop) Ashore, 1817" (Midshipman C. W. Browne)

(Des G. Vasarhelyi. Litho Questa)

1984 (3 Dec). *Christmas. Children's Drawings. T* **116** *and similar horiz designs. Multicoloured.* W w **14** *(sideways).* P 14.

382	10p. Type **116**			20	35
383	20p. "Santa Claus in ox cart"			25	40
384	30p. "Santa Claus in longboat"			30	70
385	50p. "The Nativity"			50	80
382/5			Set of 4	1·10	2·00

(Des A. Crawford, adapted G. Vasarhelyi. Litho Questa)

1985 (4 Feb). *Shipwrecks* (1st series). *T* **117** *and similar designs.* W w **14** *(sideways on 35p.).* P 14×13½ (10, 25p.) or 13½×14 (35, 60p.).

386	10p. royal blue and light grey-blue			70	80
387	25p. red-brown and emerald			1·25	1·40
388	35p. yellow-brown and orange-yellow			1·40	1·60
386/8			Set of 3	3·00	3·50
MS389	142×101 mm. 60p. multicoloured. Wmk sideways			1·00	2·25

Designs: *Vert*—25p. Mabel Clark's bell, St. Mary's Church. *Horiz*—35p. "Barque *Glenhuntley* foundering, 1898" (John Hagan); 60p. Map of Tristan da Cunha showing sites of shipwrecks.

See also Nos. 411/14 and 426/9.

---

118 The Queen Mother at Ascot with Princess Margaret   119 Jonathan Lambert and "Isles of Refreshment" Flag, 1811

(Des A. Theobald (80p.), C. Abbott (others). Litho Questa)

1985 (7 June). *Life and Times of Queen Elizabeth the Queen Mother. T* **118** *and similar vert designs. Multicoloured.* W w **16**. P 14½×14.

390	10p. The Queen Mother and Prince Charles, 1954			20	30
	w. Wmk inverted			8·00	10·00
391	20p. Type **118**			30	60
	w. Wmk inverted			8·00	10·00
392	30p. Queen Elizabeth the Queen Mother			40	85
393	50p. With Prince Henry at his christening			70	1·25
390/3			Set of 4	1·40	2·75
MS394	91×73 mm. 80p. The Queen Mother and the young Princess Anne at Trooping the Colour. Wmk sideways			1·75	2·75

(Des D. Slater. Litho J.W.)

1985 (30 Sept). *Flags. T* **119** *and similar multicoloured designs.* W w **16** *(sideways on 10p., inverted on others).* P 14.

395	10p. Type **119**			70	80
396	15p. 21st Light Dragoons guidon and cannon from Fort Malcolm (1816–17) (vert)			80	90
397	25p. White Ensign and H.M.S. *Falmouth* (frigate) offshore, 1816 (vert)			1·00	1·25
398	60p. Union Jack and Tristan da Cunha (vert)			2·00	2·50
395/8			Set of 4	4·00	5·00

120 Lifeboat heading for Barque *West Riding*   121 Halley's Comet, 1066, from Bayeux Tapestry

(Des D. Miller. Litho Format)

1985 (28 Nov). *Centenary of Loss of Island Lifeboat. T* **120** *and similar vert designs. Multicoloured.* W w **14**. P 14×13½.

399	10p. Type **120**			25	60
	w. Wmk inverted			75	
400	30p. Map of Tristan da Cunha			40	1·25
	w. Wmk inverted			1·25	
401	50p. Memorial plaque to lifeboat crew			60	1·75
399/401			Set of 3	1·10	3·25

(Des D. Miller. Litho Walsall)

1986 (3 Mar). *Appearance of Halley's Comet. T* **121** *and similar horiz designs. Multicoloured.* W w **16** *(sideways).* P 14.

402	10p. Type **121**			40	65
403	20p. Path of Comet			65	1·00
404	30p. Comet over Inaccessible Island			85	1·40
405	50p. H.M.S. *Paramour* (pink) and map of South Atlantic			1·40	1·75
402/5			Set of 4	3·00	4·25

(Des A. Theobald. Litho Questa)

1986 (21 Apr). *60th Birthday of Queen Elizabeth II. Vert designs as T* **230a** *of Jamaica. Multicoloured.* W w **16**. P 14½×14.

406	10p. With Prince Charles, 1950			15	30
	w. Wmk inverted			90	
407	15p. Queen at Trooping the Colour			20	40
408	25p. In robes of Order of the Bath, Westminster Abbey, 1972			35	60
	a. Silver (cypher and logo) omitted			£275	
409	45p. In Canada, 1977			55	1·00
	w. Wmk inverted			1·75	
410	65p. At Crown Agents Head Office, London, 1983			75	1·50
406/10			Set of 5	1·75	3·50

The new-issue supplement to this Catalogue appears each month in

GIBBONS STAMP MONTHLY

—from your newsagent or by postal subscription—
sample copy and details on request.

122 "*Allanshaw* wrecked on East Beach, 1893" (drawing by John Hagan)

123 Wandering Albatross

(Des A. Crawford, adapted G. Vasarhelyi. Litho J.W.)

1986 (2 June). *Shipwrecks (2nd series). T* **122** *and similar designs. W* w **16** (*sideways on* 9p.) *P* 13½×13 (9p.) *or* 13×13½ (*others*).

411	9p. dp turquoise-blue, dp grey-blue & black	30	80
412	20p. grey-olive, olive-yellow and black	60	1·40
413	40p. bright blue, bright violet and black	1·10	1·90
411/13	Set of 3	1·75	3·50
MS414	142×80 mm. 65p. orange-brown and black. Wmk sideways*. *P* 13½×13	1·75	3·25
	w. Wmk Crown to left of CA	22·00	

Designs: *Vert*—20p. Church font from wreck of *Edward Vittery*, 1881; 40p. Ship's figurehead. *Horiz*—65p. Gaetano Lavarello and Andrea Repetto, survivors from *Italia*, 1892.

*The normal sideways watermark on the miniature sheet shows Crown to right of CA, *as seen from the back of the sheet.*

(Des D. Miller. Litho Questa)

1986 (23 July). *Royal Wedding. Square designs as T* **231***a of Jamaica. Multicoloured. W* w **16**. *P* 14.

415	10p. Prince Andrew and Miss Sarah Ferguson	20	50
	w. Wmk inverted	35·00	
416	40p. Prince Andrew piloting helicopter, Digby, Canada, 1985	80	1·50
	w. Wmk inverted	40·00	

(Des A. Theobald. Litho Questa)

1986 (30 Sept). *Flora and Fauna of Inaccessible Island. T* **123** *and similar vert designs. Multicoloured. W* w **16**. *P* 14.

417	5p. Type **123**	50	70
418	10p. *Lagenophora nudicaulis* (daisy)	50	80
	w. Wmk inverted	25·00	
419	20p. *Cynthia virginiensis* (butterfly)	1·00	1·50
420	25p. Wilkin's Finch	1·10	1·50
	w. Wmk inverted	23·00	
421	50p. White-chinned Petrel	1·50	2·00
417/21	Set of 5	4·25	6·00

124 *Dimorphinoctua cunhaensis* (flightless moth) and Edinburgh

125 Castaways from *Blenden Hall* attacking Sea Elephant, 1821

(Des C. Abbott. Litho Walsall)

1987 (23 Jan). *Island Flightless Insects and Birds. T* **124** *and similar vert designs. Multicoloured. W* w **14**. *P* 14½.

422	10p. Type **124**	25	60
423	25p. *Tristanomyia frustilifera* (fly) and Crater Lake	55	1·25
424	35p. Inaccessible Island Rail and Inaccessible Island	1·25	2·00
425	50p. Gough Island Moorhen and Gough Island	1·75	2·25
422/5	Set of 4	3·50	5·50

(Des A. Crawford, adapted G. Vasarhelyi. Litho Walsall)

1987 (2 Apr*). *Shipwrecks (3rd series). T* **125** *and similar designs. W* w **16** (*sideways on* 17p.) *P* 13½×14 (17p.) *or* 14×13½ (*others*).

426	11p. black and olive-brown	85	1·25
427	17p. black and bright lilac	1·10	1·60
428	45p. black and deep blue-green	1·40	2·00
426/8	Set of 3	3·00	4·25
MS429	131×70 mm. 70p. royal blue, bright green and pale blue. Wmk sideways†. *P* 13½×14	2·75	3·00
	w. Wmk Crown to right of CA	35·00	

Designs: *Horiz*—17p. Barquentine *Henry A. Paull* stranded at Sandy Point, 1879; 70p. Map of Inaccessible Island showing sites of shipwrecks. *Vert*—45p. Gustav Stoltenhoff, 1871, and Stoltenhoff Island.

*This is the local date of issue. The Crown Agents placed the stamps on the sale on 2 February 1987.

†The normal sideways watermark on the miniature sheet shows Crown to left of CA, *as seen from the back of the sheet.*

126 Rockhopper Penguin swimming

127 Microscope and Published Report

(Des I. Strange. Litho Questa)

1987 (22 June). *Rockhopper Penguins. T* **126** *and similar horiz designs. Multicoloured. W* w **16** (*sideways*). *P* 14½.

430	10p. Type **126**	85	95
431	20p. Adult with egg	1·25	1·50
432	30p. Adult with juvenile	1·60	1·90
433	50p. Head of Rockhopper Penguin	1·90	2·25
430/3	Set of 4	5·00	6·00

(Des N. Shewring. Litho Questa)

1987 (7 Dec). *50th Anniv of Norwegian Scientific Expedition. T* **127** *and similar square designs. Multicoloured. W* w **16** (10p., 20p.) *or* w **14** (30p., 50p.) (*all sideways*). *P* 14.

434	10p. Type **127**	90	1·00
435	20p. Scientists ringing Yellow-nosed Albatross	1·90	2·00
436	30p. Expedition hut, Little Beach Point	2·25	2·50
437	50p. S.S. *Thorshammer* (whale factory ship)	3·25	3·50
434/7	Set of 4	7·50	8·00

1988 (9 Mar). *Royal Ruby Wedding. Nos.* 406/10 *optd with T* **45***a of Kiribati in silver.*

438	10p. Princess Elizabeth with Prince Charles, 1950	20	25
439	15p. Queen Elizabeth II at Trooping the Colour	30	35
440	25p. In robes of Order of the Bath, Westminster Abbey, 1972	50	55
441	45p. In Canada, 1977	95	95
442	65p. At Crown Agents Head Office, London, 1983	1·00	1·40
438/42	Set of 5	2·75	3·25

128 Nightingale Finch ("Tristan Bunting")

129 Painted Penguin Eggs

(Des A. Theobald. Litho Questa)

1988 (21 Mar). *Fauna of Nightingale Island. T* **128** *and similar vert designs. Multicoloured. W* w **16**. *P* 14.

443	5p. Type **128**	50	50
444	10p. Tristan Thrush (immature)	65	65
445	20p. Yellow-nosed Albatross (chick)	85	90
446	25p. Greater Shearwater	85	1·00
447	50p. Elephant Seal	1·40	2·00
443/7	Set of 5	3·75	4·50

(Des O. Bell. Litho Questa)

1988 (30 May). *Tristan da Cunha Handicrafts. T* **129** *and similar horiz designs. Multicoloured. W* w **16** (*sideways**). *P* 14×14½.

448	10p. Type **129**	25	35
	w. Wmk Crown to right of CA	35·00	
449	15p. Moccasins	35	50
	w. Wmk Crown to right of CA	25·00	
450	35p. Knitwear	75	1·00
	w. Wmk Crown to right of CA	35·00	
451	50p. Model longboat	1·10	1·40
	w. Wmk Crown to right of CA	25·00	
448/51	Set of 4	2·25	3·00

*The normal sideways watermark show Crown to left of CA, *as seen from the back of the stamp.*

130 Processing Blubber

(Des N. Shewring. Litho Questa)

1988 (6 Oct). *19th-century Whaling. T* **130** *and similar horiz designs. Multicoloured. W* w **16** (*sideways**). *P* 14×14½.

452	10p. Type **130**	75	65
	w. Wmk Crown to right of CA		
453	20p. Harpoon guns	95	85
454	30p. Scrimshaw (carved whale bone)	1·25	1·00
455	50p. Whaling ships	2·00	2·00
	w. Wmk Crown to right of CA	60·00	
452/5	Set of 4	4·50	4·00
MS456	76×56 mm. £1 Right Whale	3·00	2·75

*The normal sideways watermark shows Crown to left of CA, *as seen from the back of the stamp.*

(Des E. Nisbet and D. Miller (25, 35p.), D. Miller (others). Litho Harrison)

1988 (7 Nov). *300th Anniv of Lloyd's of London. Designs as T* **167***a of Malawi. W* w **16** (*sideways on* 25, 35p.). *P* 14.

457	10p. multicoloured	30	40
458	25p. multicoloured	1·10	1·10
459	35p. brownish black and emerald	1·50	1·50
460	50p. brownish black and carmine-red	1·90	1·90
457/60	Set of 4	4·25	4·50

Designs: *Vert*—10p. New Lloyd's Building, 1988; 50p. *Kobenhavn* (cadet barque), 1928. *Horiz*—25p. *Tristania II* (crayfish trawler); 35p. *St. Helena* (mail ship).

131 "Government House"

132 Hall's Giant Petrel

(Des N. Harvey. Litho Walsall)

1988 (10 Dec). *Augustus Earle's Paintings, 1824. T* **131** *and similar horiz designs. Multicoloured. W* w **16** (*sideways**). *P* 14.

461	1p. Type **131**	30	60
462	3p. "Squall off Tristan"	45	60
463	4p. "Rafting Blubber"	50	60
464	5p. "View near Little Beach"	50	60
465	10p. "Man killing Albatross"	70	70
466	15p. "View on The Summit"	90	1·00
467	20p. "Nightingale Island"	1·00	1·10
468	25p. "Earle on Tristan"	1·25	1·40
469	35p. "Solitude–Watching the Horizon"	1·40	1·50
470	50p. "Northeaster"	1·75	2·00
	w. Wmk Crown to right of CA	40·00	
471	£1 "Tristan Village"	2·75	3·00
472	£2 "Governor Glass at Dinner"	4·25	4·50
461/72	Set of 12	14·00	16·00

*The normal sideways watermark shows Crown to left of CA, *as seen from the back of the stamp.*

Examples of Nos. 461/72 showing Earle's dates as "1793–1835" were sold by the U.S.A. agents, and by the authorities on Ascension, in error. Supplies sent to Tristan Cunha show the correct dates "1793–1838".

(Des A. Theobald. Litho Walsall)

1989 (6 Feb). *Fauna of Gough Island. T* **132** *and similar vert designs. Multicoloured. W* w **16**. *P* 14.

473	5p. Type **132**	75	75
474	10p. Gough Island Moorhen	85	85
475	20p. Gough Island Finch ("Gough Bunting")	1·10	1·10
476	25p. Sooty Albatross	1·25	1·25
477	50p. Amsterdam Fur Seal	1·60	2·00
473/7	Set of 5	5·00	5·50

133 *Eriosorus cheilanthoides*

134 Surgeon's Mortar

(Des Jane Fern. Litho Walsall)

1989 (22 May). *Ferns. T* **133** *and similar vert designs. Multicoloured. W* w **14**. *P* 14×13½.

478	10p. Type **133**	65	65
479	25p. *Asplenium alvarezense*	1·10	1·10
480	35p. *Elaphoglossum hybridum*	1·40	1·40
481	50p. *Ophioglossum opacum*	1·60	1·60
478/81	Set of 4	4·25	4·25

(Des Jennifer Toombs. Litho Questa)

1989 (25 Sept). *Nautical Museum Exhibits. T* **134** *and similar horiz designs. Multicoloured. W* w **16** (*sideways*). *P* 14.

482	10p. Type **134**	65	65
483	20p. Parts of darting-gun harpoon	1·10	1·10
484	30p. Ship's compass with binnacle-hood	1·40	1·40
485	60p. Rope-twisting device	1·75	1·75
482/5	Set of 4	4·50	4·50

135 Cattle Egret   **136** *Peridroma saucia*

(Des Josephine Martin and Sally Hynard. Litho Questa)

1989 (20 Nov). *Vagrant Birds. T* **135** *and similar vert designs. Multicoloured.* W w **16**. P 14.

486	10p. Type 135		1·50	1·25
487	25p. Spotted Sandpiper		2·25	2·25
488	35p. Purple Gallinule		2·50	2·50
489	50p. Barn Swallow		2·75	3·00
486/9		Set of 4	8·00	8·00

(Des I. Loe. Litho Questa)

1990 (1 Feb). *Moths. T* **136** *and similar horiz designs. Multicoloured.* W w **14** (*sideways*). P 14.

490	10p. Type 136		90	80
491	15p. *Ascalapha odorata*		1·25	1·25
492	35p. *Agrius cingulata*		2·00	2·00
493	60p. *Eumorpha labruscae*		2·75	3·00
490/3		Set of 4	6·25	6·25

137 Sea Urchin   **138** H.M.S. *Pyramus* (frigate), 1829

(Des Anna Hecht. Litho Questa)

1990 (12 June). *Echinoderms. T* **137** *and similar vert designs showing starfishes.* W w **14**. P 13½×14.

494	10p. multicoloured		90	80
495	20p. multicoloured		1·50	1·50
496	30p. multicoloured		1·90	1·90
497	60p. multicoloured		2·50	3·00
494/7		Set of 4	6·25	6·50

(Des D. Miller. Litho Questa)

1990 (4 Aug). *90th Birthday of Queen Elizabeth the Queen Mother. Vert designs as T* **107** (25p.) *or* **108** (£1) *of Kenya.* W w **16**. P 14×15 (25p.) *or* 14½ (£1).

498	25p. multicoloured		1·25	1·25
499	£1 agate and Prussian blue		3·25	3·00

Designs:—25p. Queen Mother at the London Coliseum; £1 Queen Elizabeth broadcasting to women of the Empire, 1939.

(Des L. Curtis. Litho Walsall)

1990 (13 Sept). *Maiden Voyage of St. Helena II. Horiz designs as T* **162** *of St. Helena. Multicoloured.* W w **14** (*sideways*). P 14×14½.

500	10p. *Dunnottar Castle* (liner), 1942		1·00	1·00
501	15p. *St. Helena* (mail ship) at Tristan		1·60	1·60
502	35p. Launch of *St. Helena II* (mail ship)		2·25	2·50
503	60p. Duke of York launching *St. Helena II*		3·00	3·50
500/3		Set of 4	7·00	7·75
MS504	100×100 mm. £1 *St. Helena II* and outline map of Tristan da Cunha		3·75	5·50

No. MS504 also contains two preliminary designs of similar stamps from Ascension and St. Helena without face values.

(Des E. Nisbet. Litho Questa)

1990 (30 Nov). *Ships of the Royal Navy (1st series). T* **138** *and similar horiz designs. Multicoloured.* W w **14** (*sideways*). P 14.

505	10p. Type 138		1·50	1·25
506	25p. H.M.S. *Penguin* (sloop), 1815		2·50	2·50
507	35p. H.M.S. *Thalia* (screw corvette), 1886		2·75	2·75
508	50p. H.M.S. *Sidon* (paddle frigate), 1858		3·25	3·50
505/8		Set of 4	9·00	9·00

See also Nos. 509/12 and 565/8.

(Des E. Nisbet. Litho Questa)

1991 (4 Feb). *Ships of the Royal Navy (2nd series). Horiz designs as T* **138**. *Multicoloured.* W w **14** (*sideways*). P 14.

509	10p. H.M.S. *Milford* (sloop), 1938		1·50	1·25
510	25p. H.M.S. *Dublin* (cruiser), 1923		2·50	2·50
511	35p. H.M.S. *Yarmouth* (cruiser), 1919		2·75	2·75
512	50p. H.M.S. *Carlisle* (cruiser), 1937		3·25	3·50
509/12		Set of 4	9·00	9·00

No. 512 is inscribed "1938" in error.

139 *Royal Viking Sun* (cruise liner)

(Des L. Curtis. Litho B.D.T.)

1991 (1 Apr). *Visit of Royal Viking Sun. Sheet* 62×47 *mm.* W w **16** (*sideways*). P 14.

MS513	139 £1 multicoloured		5·50	6·50

140 Prince Alfred and H.M.S. *Galatea* (screw frigate), 1867

(Des D. Miller. Litho Questa)

1991 (10 June). *70th Birthday of Prince Philip, Duke of Edinburgh. T* **140** *and similar horiz designs.* W w **16** (*sideways*). P 14.

514	10p. brownish black, pale blue & dp dull bl		1·75	1·75
515	25p. brownish black, pale blue-green and myrtle-green		2·25	2·50
516	30p. black, deep brown & pale bistre-yellow		3·00	3·25
517	50p. multicoloured		3·50	3·75
514/17		Set of 4	9·50	10·00

Designs:—25p. Prince Philip meeting local inhabitants, 1957; 30p. Prince Philip and Royal Yacht *Britannia*, 1957; 50p. Prince Philip and Edinburgh settlement.

141 Pair of Gough Island Moorhens   **142** Coats' Perch

(Des G. Vasarhelyi. Litho Questa)

1991 (1 Oct). *Endangered Species. Birds. T* **141** *and similar horiz designs. Multicoloured.* W w **14** (*sideways*). P 14.

518	8p. Type 141		1·75	1·75
519	10p. Gough Island Finch		1·75	1·75
520	12p. Gough Island Moorhen on nest		1·90	1·90
521	15p. Gough Island Finch feeding chicks		1·90	1·90
518/21		Set of 4	6·50	6·50

(Des R. Watton. Litho Walsall)

1992 (23 Jan). *500th Anniv of Discovery of America by Columbus and Re-enactment Voyages. Horiz designs as T* **168** *of St. Helena. Multicoloured.* W w **14** (*sideways*). P 13½×14.

522	10p. Map of re-enactment voyages and *Eye of the Wind* (cadet brig)		1·00	1·00
523	15p. Compass rose and *Soren Larsen* (cadet brigantine)		1·50	1·50
524	35p. Ships of Columbus		2·50	2·75
525	60p. Columbus and *Santa Maria*		2·75	3·00
522/5		Set of 4	7·00	7·50

(Des D. Miller. Litho Questa (65p.), Walsall (others))

1992 (6 Feb). *40th Anniv of Queen Elizabeth II's Accession. Horiz designs as T* **113** *of Kenya. Multicoloured.* W w **14** (*sideways*). P 14.

526	10p. Tristan from the sea		60	60
527	20p. Longboat under sail		90	90
528	25p. Aerial view of Edinburgh		1·00	1·00
529	35p. Three portraits of Queen Elizabeth		1·25	1·25
530	65p. Queen Elizabeth II		2·25	2·25
526/30		Set of 5	5·50	5·50

(Des Ann Hecht. Litho Questa)

1992 (1 June). *Fishes. T* **142** *and similar horiz designs. Multicoloured.* W w **14** (*sideways*). P 14×13½.

531	10p. Type 142		80	80
532	15p. Lined Trumpeter		1·25	1·25
533	35p. Karrer's Morid Cod		2·25	2·50
534	60p. Long-finned Scad		2·75	3·00
531/4		Set of 4	6·25	6·75

143 *Italia* leaving Greenock   **144** *Stenoscelis hylastoides*

(Des E. Nisbet. Litho Questa)

1992 (16 Sept). *Centenary of the Wreck of Barque* Italia. *T* **143** *and similar horiz designs.* W w **14** (*sideways*). P 13½×14.

535	10p. Type 143		1·00	1·00
536	45p. In mid-Atlantic		2·50	3·00
537	65p. Driving ashore on Stony Beach		3·00	3·50
535/7		Set of 3	6·00	6·75
MS538	101×75 mm. £1 *Italia* becalmed		6·00	7·00

Nos. MS538 also commemorates "Genova '92" International Thematic Stamp Exhibition.

(Des G. Marx. Litho Questa)

1993 (2 Feb). *Insects. T* **144** *and similar vert designs. Multicoloured.* W w **16**. P 14×13½.

539	15p. Type 144		1·25	1·25
540	45p. *Trogloscaptomyza brevilamellata*		2·50	2·75
541	60p. *Senilites tristanicola*		3·00	3·50
539/41		Set of 3	6·00	6·75

145 Ampulla and Anointing Spoon

(Des D. Miller. Litho Walsall)

1993 (14 June). *40th Anniv of Coronation. T* **145** *and similar vert designs.* W w **16**. P 14½×14.

542	10p. emerald and black		90	90
543	15p. magenta and black		1·40	1·50
544	35p. violet and black		1·90	2·25
545	60p. new blue and black		2·50	3·00
542/5		Set of 4	6·00	7·00

Designs:—15p. Orb; 35p. Imperial State Crown; 60p. St. Edward's Crown.

146 *Tristania* and *Frances Repetto* (crayfish trawlers)

(Des E. Nisbet. Litho Questa)

1993 (10 Nov). *30th Anniv of Resettlement of Tristan. T* **146** *and similar horiz designs. Multicoloured.* W w **16** (*sideways*). P 13½×14.

546	35p. Type 146		2·25	2·50
	a. Horiz pair. Nos. 546/7		4·50	5·00
547	35p. *Boissevain* (cargo liner)		2·25	2·50
548	50p. *Bornholm* (liner) and longboat		2·75	3·50
546/8		Set of 3	6·50	7·75

Nos. 546/7 were printed together, *se-tenant*, in horizontal pairs throughout the sheet.

147 "Madonna with Child" (School of Botticelli)   **148** *Duchess of Atholl* (liner)

(Des D. Miller. Litho Cartor)

1993 (30 Nov). *Christmas. Religious Paintings. T* **147** *and similar vert designs. Multicoloured.* W w **14**. P 13.

549	5p. Type 147		80	80
550	15p. "The Holy Family" (Daniel Gran)		1·75	1·75
551	35p. "The Holy Virgin and Child" (Rubens)		2·75	3·00
552	65p. "The Mystical Marriage of St. Catherine with the Holy Child" (Jan van Balen)		3·50	4·25
549/52		Set of 4	8·00	9·00

(Des R. Watton. Litho Questa)

1994 (3 Feb). *Ships. T* **148** *and similar horiz designs. Multicoloured.* W w **16** (*sideways*). P 14.

553	1p. Type 148		10	10
554	3p. *Empress of Australia* (liner)		10	10
555	5p. *Anatolia* (freighter)		10	10
556	8p. *Viceroy of India* (liner)		15	20
557	10p. *Rangitata* (transport)		20	25
558	15p. *Caronia* (liner)		30	35
559	20p. *Rotterdam* (liner)		40	45
560	25p. *Leonardo da Vinci* (liner)		50	55

561	35p. *Vistafjord* (liner)			70	75
562	£1 *World Discoverer* (liner)			2·00	2·10
563	£2 *Astor* (liner)			4·00	4·25
564	£5 *St. Helena II* (mail ship)			10·00	10·50
553/64			*Set of 12*	18·00	19·00

(Des E. Nisbet. Litho Questa)

1994 (2 May). *Ships of the Royal Navy (3rd series). Horiz designs as T* **138**. *Multicoloured. W w* **14** *(sideways). P* 14×14½.

565	10p. H.M.S. *Nigeria* (cruiser), 1948			1·00	1·00
566	25p. H.M.S. *Phoebe* (cruiser), 1949			2·00	2·00
567	35p. H.M.S. *Liverpool* (cruiser), 1949			2·25	2·25
568	50p. H.M.S. *Magpie* (frigate), 1955			3·00	3·00
565/8			*Set of 4*	7·50	7·50

149 Blue Shark

(Des Anne Hecht. Litho Questa)

1994 (8 Aug). *Sharks. T* **149** *and similar horiz designs. Multicoloured. W w* **16** *(sideways). P* 14½.

569	10p. Type **149**			90	1·00
570	45p. Seven-gilled Shark			2·50	3·00
571	65p. Short-finned Mako			3·25	3·75
569/71			*Set of 3*	6·00	7·00

150 Pair of Donkeys

(Des Josephine Martin. Litho Questa)

1994 (21 Nov). *Island Livestock (1st series). T* **150** *and similar horiz designs. Multicoloured. W w* **14** *(sideways). P* 13½×14.

572	10p. Type **150**			90	90
573	20p. Cattle			1·25	1·25
574	35p. Ducks and geese			2·25	2·50
575	60p. Girl bottle-feeding lamb			3·25	3·75
572/5			*Set of 4*	7·00	7·50

See also Nos. 620/3.

151 Pick-up Truck   152 Queen Elizabeth the Queen Mother

(Des A. Theobald. Litho Walsall)

1995 (27 Feb). *Local Transport. T* **151** *and similar horiz designs. Multicoloured. W w* **16** *(sideways). P* 14.

576	15p. Type **151**			1·10	1·10
577	20p. Sherpa van			1·50	1·50
578	45p. Scooter and Yamaha motorcycle			2·50	2·75
579	60p. Administrator's Landrover			3·00	3·25
576/9			*Set of 4*	7·25	7·75

(Des R. Watton. Litho Cartor (Nos. 580/3) or Questa (No. MS584))

1995 (10 July). *50th Anniv of End of Second World War. Multicoloured designs as T* **75** *of Kiribati. W w* **14** *(sideways). P* 13½.

580	15p. Sailors training on Lewis guns			1·25	1·25
581	20p. Tristan Defence Volunteers			1·50	1·50
582	45p. Wireless and meteorological station			2·25	2·50
583	60p. H.M.S. *Birmingham* (cruiser)			3·00	3·25
580/3			*Set of 4*	7·25	7·75
MS584	75×85 mm. £1 Reverse of 1939–45 War Medal (*vert*). Wmk upright. P 14			2·00	2·50

(Des Jennifer Toombs. Litho Questa)

1995 (4 Aug). *95th Birthday of Queen Elizabeth the Queen Mother. Sheet 75×103 mm. W w* **14** *(sideways). P* 14½×14.

| MS585 | **152** £1.50, multicoloured | | | 4·50 | 5·50 |

COVER PRICES

Cover factors are quoted at the beginning of each country for most issues to 1945. An explanation of the system can be found on page x. The factors quoted do not, however, apply to philatelic covers.

153 Sub-Antarctic Fur Seal on Rock

(Des R. Watton. Litho Cartor)

1995 (3 Nov). *Seals. T* **153** *and similar horiz designs. Multicoloured. W w* **14** *(sideways). P* 14×13½.

586	10p. Type **153**			90	90
587	35p. Sub-Antarctic Fur Seals with pups			2·00	2·00
588	45p. Southern Elephant Seal asleep with pups			2·50	2·50
589	50p. Southern Elephant Seals in water			2·50	2·50
586/9			*Set of 4*	7·00	7·00

(Des A. Theobald. Litho Cartor)

1996 (23 Jan). *50th Anniv of United Nations. Horiz designs as T* **284** *of Jamaica. Multicoloured. W w* **14** *(sideways). P* 13½×13.

590	20p. Bedford 4-ton lorry			1·25	1·25
591	30p. Saxon armoured personnel carrier			1·50	1·50
592	45p. Mi26 heavy lift helicopter			2·75	2·75
593	50p. R.F.A. *Sir Tristram* (landing ship)			2·75	2·75
590/3			*Set of 4*	7·50	7·50

(Des D. Miller. Litho Cartor)

1996 (22 Apr). *70th Birthday of Queen Elizabeth II. Vert designs as T* **55** *of New Zealand (Tokelau), each incorporating a different photograph of the Queen. W w* **14**. *P* 13½×14.

594	15p. Tristan from the sea			70	80
595	20p. Traditional cottage			80	90
596	45p. The Residency			1·75	2·00
597	60p. The Queen and Prince Philip			2·25	2·50
594/7			*Set of 4*	5·00	5·50

154 Old Harbour and *St. Helena I* (mail ship)

(Des C. Abbott. Litho Cartor)

1996 (5 July). *Construction of New Harbour. T* **154** *and similar horiz designs. Multicoloured. W w* **14** *(sideways). P* 13 (15, 60p.) *or* 14×13½ (20, 45p.).

598	15p. Type **154**			1·00	1·00
599	20p. Excavator and dump truck (44×27 mm)			1·10	1·10
600	45p. Construction of new mole (44×27 mm)			2·00	2·25
601	60p. New harbour and *St. Helena II* (mail ship)			3·00	3·25
598/601			*Set of 4*	6·25	7·00

155 Gough Island Moorhen   156 19th-century Map

(Des I. Loe. Litho Walsall)

1996 (1 Oct). *Declaration of Gough Island as World Heritage Site. Birds. T* **155** *and similar vert designs. Multicoloured. W w* **14**. *P* 14.

602	15p. Type **155**			85	85
603	20p. Wandering Albatross			95	95
604	45p. Sooty Albatross			1·75	2·00
605	60p. Gough Island Finch ("Gough Bunting")			2·25	2·75
602/5			*Set of 4*	5·25	6·00

For 60p. design in miniature sheet see No. MS619.

(Des G. Vasarhelyi. Litho Cartor)

1996 (18 Dec). *Centenary of the Presentation of the Queen Victoria Portrait to Tristan. T* **156** *and similar vert designs. Multicoloured. W w* **14**. *P* 13½.

606	20p. Type **156**			1·25	1·25
607	30p. H.M.S. *Magpie* (gunboat)			1·75	1·75
608	45p. Governor Peter Green			1·90	2·00
609	50p. "Queen Victoria" (H. von Angeli) (detail)			2·00	2·25
606/9			*Set of 4*	6·25	6·50

157 Archelon (turtle)

(Des N. Shewring. Litho B.D.T.)

1997 (10 Feb). *Atlantic Marine Fauna (1st series). Cretaceous Period. Sheet 92×100 mm containing T* **157** *and similar horiz designs. Multicoloured. W w* **16** *(sideways). P* 14.

| MS610 | 35p. Type **157**; 35p. Trinacromerum; 35p. Platecarpus; 35p. Clidastes | | | 3·25 | 4·00 |

See also No. MS638.

158 Smoke Signals   159 *Hilary* and *Melodie*

(Des D. Miller. Litho Walsall)

1997 (1 May). *Visual Communications. T* **158** *and similar horiz designs. Multicoloured. W w* **16** *(sideways). P* 14×14½.

611	10p. Type **158**			30	45
	a. Horiz pair. Nos. 611/12			60	90
612	10p. H.M.S. *Eurydice* (frigate)			30	45
613	15p. H.M.S. *Challenger* (survey ship)			50	80
	a. Horiz pair. Nos. 613/14			1·00	1·60
614	15p. Flag hoists			50	80
615	20p. Semaphore			65	80
	a. Horiz pair. Nos. 615/16			1·25	1·60
616	20p. H.M.S. *Carlisle* (cruiser)			65	80
617	35p. Aldis lamp			80	1·00
	a. Horiz pair. Nos. 617/18			1·60	2·00
618	35p. H.M.S. *Cilicia* (transport)			80	1·00
611/18			*Set of 8*	4·00	5·50

Nos. 611/12, 613/14, 615/16 and 617/18 were each printed together, *se-tenant*, in horizontal pairs forming composite designs.

(Litho Walsall)

1997 (20 June). *Return of Hong Kong to China. Sheet, 130×90 mm, containing designs as No. 605, but with "1997" imprint date. W w* **14**. *P* 14.

| MS619 | 60p. Gough Island Finch ("Gough Bunting") | | | 1·50 | 2·00 |

(Des Josephine Martin. Litho Walsall)

1997 (26 Aug). *Island Livestock (2nd series). Horiz designs as T* **150**. *Multicoloured. W w* **16** *(sideways). P* 13½×14.

620	20p. Chickens			70	70
621	30p. Bull			90	1·00
622	45p. Sheep			1·40	1·60
623	50p. Collie dogs			1·75	1·75
620/3			*Set of 4*	4·25	4·50

(Des N. Shewring (No. MS630), D. Miller (others). Litho Questa (No. MS630), B.D.T. (others))

1997 (20 Nov). *Golden Wedding of Queen Elizabeth and Prince Philip. Multicoloured designs as T* **87** *of Kiribati. W w* **14**. *P* 13½.

624	15p. Queen Elizabeth			45	55
	a. Horiz pair. Nos. 624/5			90	1·10
625	15p. Prince Philip playing polo			45	55
626	20p. Queen Elizabeth with horse			55	65
	a. Horiz pair. Nos. 626/7			1·10	1·25
627	20p. Prince Philip			55	65
628	45p. Queen Elizabeth with Prince Philip in R.A.F. uniform			1·25	1·40
	a. Horiz pair. Nos. 628/9			2·25	2·75
629	45p. Princess Anne on horseback			1·25	1·40
624/9			*Set of 6*	3·75	4·50
MS630	110×70 mm. £1.50, Queen Elizabeth and Prince Philip in landau (*horiz*). Wmk sideways. P 14×14½			3·75	4·25

Nos. 624/5, 626/7 and 628/9 were each printed together, *se-tenant*, in horizontal pairs throughout the sheetlets with the backgrounds forming composite designs.

(Des N. Shewring. Litho Questa)

1998 (6 Feb). *50th Anniv of First Lobster Survey. Lobster Trawlers. T* **159** *and similar vert designs. Multicoloured. W w* **14**. *P* 14½×14.

631	15p. Type **159**			55	60
632	20p. *Tristania II* and *Hekla*			65	70
633	30p. *Pequena* and *Frances Repetto*			85	95
634	45p. *Tristania* and *Gillian Gaggins*			1·40	1·50
635	50p. *Kelso* and *Edinburgh*			1·40	1·50
631/5			*Set of 5*	4·25	4·75
MS636	100×80 mm. £1.20, Revd. C. P. Lawrence and lobster			4·00	4·50

(Des D. Miller. Litho Questa)

1998 (15 May). *Diana, Princess of Wales Commemoration. Sheet,* 145×70 *mm, containing vert designs as T* **91** *of Kiribati. Multicoloured.* W **14** (*sideways*). P 14½×14.
MS637 35p. Wearing pink jacket, 1993; 35p. Wearing white jacket, 1990; 35p. Laughing, in striped dress, 1991; 35p. Wearing blue and white dress, 1989 (*sold at* £1.40 + 20p. *charity premium*) .. .. 3·25 3·75

(Des N. Shewring. Litho B.D.T.)

1998 (8 July). *Atlantic Marine Fauna* (2nd series). *Miocene Epoch. Sheet,* 92×100 *mm, containing horiz designs as T* **157**. *Multicoloured.* W **16** (*sideways*). P 14.
MS638 45p. Carcharodon (shark); 45p. Orycterocetus (sperm whale); 45p. Eurhinodelphis (dolphin); 45p. Hexanchus (shark) and Myliobatis (ray) .. .. 4·75 5·50

160 *Livonia*

(Des J. Batchelor. Litho B.D.T.)

1998 (15 Sept). *Cruise Ships. T* **160** *and similar horiz designs. Multicoloured.* W w **14** (*sideways*). P 14.
639 15p. Type **160** 75 75
640 20p. *Professor Molchanov* 90 90
641 45p. *Explorer* .. .. .. 1·75 1·75
642 60p. *Hanseatic* .. .. .. 2·00 2·00
639/42 .. .. .. *Set of* 4 4·75 4·75

161 *H. G. Johnson* (barque)

(Des J. Batchelor. Litho Questa)

1998 (23 Nov). *Maritime Heritage* (1st series). *T* **161** *and similar horiz designs. Multicoloured.* W w **16** (*sideways*). P 14½.
643 15p. Type **161** 75 75
644 35p. *Theodore* (full-rigged ship) .. 1·50 1·50
645 45p. *Hesperides* (full-rigged ship) .. 1·60 1·60
646 50p. *Bessfield* (barque) .. .. 1·75 1·75
643/6 .. .. .. *Set of* 4 5·00 5·00

(Des J. Batchelor. Litho Questa)

1999 (19 Mar). *Maritime Heritage* (2nd series). *Horiz designs as T* **161**. *Multicoloured.* W w **16** (*sideways*). P 14½.
647 20p. *Derwent* (full-rigged ship) .. 75 75
648 30p. *Strathgryfe* (full-rigged ship) .. 1·40 1·40
649 50p. *Celestial Empire* (full-rigged ship) 1·75 1·75
650 60p. *Lamorna* (full-rigged ship) .. 1·75 1·75
647/50 .. .. .. *Set of* 4 5·00 5·00

162 *Wandering Albatross Courtship Dance*

(Des Josephine Martin. Litho Walsall)

1999 (27 Apr). *Endangered Species. Wandering Albatross. T* **162** *and similar horiz designs. Multicoloured.* W w **14** (*sideways**). P 14.
651 5p. Type **162** 40 40
  a. Strip of 4. Nos. 651/4 .. 1·40
  b. Panda emblem printed twice
  w. Wmk Crown to left of CA .. 40 40
  wa. Strip of 4. Nos. 651w/4w .. 1·40
652 8p. Adult and chick 40 40
  w. Wmk Crown to left of CA .. 40 40
653 12p. Adult with spread wings .. 40 40
  w. Wmk Crown to left of CA .. 40 40
654 15p. Two adults in flight 40 40
  w. Wmk Crown to left of CA .. 40 40
651/4 .. .. .. *Set of* 6 1·40 1·40
*The normal sideways watermark shows Crown to right of CA, *as seen from the back of the stamp.*
Nos. 651/4 were printed in sheets of individual values, or in sheets of 16 containing the four stamps *se-tenant*, both horizontally and vertically.
No. 651a occurs on R. 2/4 of those *se-tenant* sheets with the watermark sideways Crown to right. There is a second image of the W.W.F. Panda emblem shown over the left-hand bird in addition to the normal position at bottom right.

(Des D. Miller. Litho Walsall)

1999 (18 June). *Royal Wedding. Vert designs as T* **153** *of Pitcairn Islands. Multicoloured.* W w **16**. P 14.
655 45p. Photographs of Prince Edward and Miss Sophie Rhys-Jones .. 1·10 1·10
656 £1.20, Engagement photograph .. 2·75 3·00

(Des D. Miller. Litho Cartor)

1999 (18 Aug). *"Queen Elizabeth the Queen Mother's Century". Horiz designs as T* **199** *of St. Helena. Multicoloured* (*except* £1.50). W w **16** (*sideways*). P 13½.
657 20p. With King George VI and Princess Elizabeth, 1944 .. .. 50 50
658 30p. King George and Queen Elizabeth at Balmoral, 1951 .. .. 70 70
659 50p. Family group outside Clarence House, 1994 .. .. .. 1·25 1·25
660 60p. Inspecting The Black Watch .. 1·50 1·50
657/60 .. .. .. *Set of* 4 3·50 3·50
MS661 145×70 mm. £1.50, Lady Elizabeth Bowes-Lyon, 1905, and Hurricane squadron, Battle of Britain, 1940 (black) .. 3·50 4·00

163 *Winter Sunrise*

164 *King Manuel I of Portugal*

(Des D. Miller. Litho Questa)

2000 (1 Jan). *New Millennium. T* **163** *and similar horiz designs. Multicoloured.* W w **14** (*sideways*). P 14.
662 20p. Type **163** 40 45
663 30p. Spring sunrise 60 65
664 50p. Summer sunrise .. .. 1·00 1·10
665 60p. Autumn sunrise .. .. 1·25 1·40
662/5 .. .. .. *Set of* 4 3·25 3·50

(Des Crown Agents. Litho Questa)

2000 (1 Feb). *Monarchs connected with Tristan da Cunha. T* **164** *and similar vert designs. Multicoloured* (*except* 1p. *and* 5p.). W w **16**. P 14.
666 1p. Type **164** (black, stone and olive-brown) 10 10
667 3p. Frederick Henry, Prince of Orange .. 10 10
668 5p. Empress Maria Theresa of Austria (blackish olive, stone and black) .. 10 10
669 8p. King George III 15 20
670 10p. King George IV 20 25
671 15p. King William IV 30 35
672 20p. Queen Victoria 40 45
673 25p. King Edward VII 50 55
674 35p. King George V 70 75
675 £1 King Edward VIII .. .. 2·00 2·10
676 £2 King George VI .. .. 4·00 4·25
677 £5 Queen Elizabeth II .. .. 10·00 10·50
666/77 .. .. .. *Set of* 12 18·00 19·00

STAMP BOOKLETS

1957 (30 May)–58. *Black on blue cover. Postmarked* "MY 30 57" *on back cover. Stapled.*
SB1 3s. 6d. booklet containing eight ½d. and four 1d., 1½d., 3d. and 4d. (Nos. 14/16, 19/20) in blocks of 4 .. .. £350
  a. Postmarked "JA 24 58" on back cover (24.1.58) £300
  b. Without postmark £300

1958 (Jan). *Black on red cover. Without postmark. Stapled.*
SB2 3s. 6d. Contents as No. SB1 .. 65·00

1960 (Feb). *Black on green cover. Stitched.*
SB3 3s. 6d. booklet containing eight ½d. and four 1d., 1½d., 3d. and 4d. (Nos. 28/30, 33/4) in blocks of 4 .. .. 40·00

1965 (17 Feb). *Black on green cover. Stapled.*
SB4 4s. 2d. booklet containing eight ½d. and four 1d., 1½d., 3d. and 6d. (Nos. 71/3, 75, 77) in blocks of 4 .. .. 7·00
The booklet covers were reprinted with amended postage rates and released by the Crown Agents on 21 September 1970.

POSTAGE DUE STAMPS

D 1

3d Normal

3d Lower serif at left of "3" missing (R. 9/1)

(Typo D.L.R.)

1957 (1 Feb). *Chalk-surfaced paper. Wmk Mult Script CA.* P 14.
D1 D 1 1d. scarlet .. .. 1·75 10·00
D2 2d. orange-yellow .. 3·00 4·75
  a. Large "d" .. .. 22·00
D3 3d. green .. .. 3·50 5·50
  a. Missing serif .. .. 38·00
D4 4d. ultramarine .. .. 7·00 7·00
D5 5d. lake .. .. 5·00 23·00
D1/5 .. .. .. *Set of* 5 18·00 45·00
For illustration of No. D2a see above No. D1 of Lesotho.

D 2

D 3 *Outline Map of Tristan da Cunha*

(Des J.W. Litho Questa)

1976 (27 May*). W w **12** (*sideways*). P 13½×14.
D 6 D 2 1p. magenta 10 30
D 7 2p. dull emerald 15 40
D 8 4p. bluish violet 20 40
D 9 5p. new blue 20 40
D10 10p. chestnut 20 50
D6/10 .. .. .. *Set of* 5 75 1·75
*This is the local date of issue; the Crown Agents released the stamps four days later.

1976 (3 Sept). W w **14** (*sideways**). P 13½×14.
D11 D 2 1p. magenta 10 30
D12 2p. dull emerald 15 30
D13 4p. bluish violet 20 35
D14 5p. new blue 20 40
D15 10p. chestnut 20 45
  w. Wmk Crown to right of CA .. 90·00
D11/15 .. .. .. *Set of* 5 75 1·60
*The normal sideways watermark shows Crown to left of CA, *as seen from the back of the stamp.*

(Des L. Curtis. Litho Questa)

1986 (20 Nov). W w **16**. P 14½×14.
D16 D 3 1p. deep brown and cinnamon .. 10 10
D17 2p. deep brown and bright orange .. 10 10
D18 5p. deep brown and orange-vermilion 10 15
D19 7p. black and bright reddish violet .. 15 20
D20 10p. black and violet-blue .. 20 25
D21 25p. black and pale emerald .. 50 55
D16/21 .. .. .. *Set of* 6 95 1·10

POSTAL FISCAL STAMPS

NATIONAL SAVINGS **2½P**

(F 1) (F 2)

1970 (15 May). *No. 77 optd with Type F 1 in red.*
F1 6d. black and green 20 30
No. F1 was originally intended as a National Savings Stamp, but also retained postal validity.

(Handstamped locally by rubber handstamp)

1971 (14 Feb). *Decimal currency. No. F 1 handstamped with Type F 2, in violet.*
F2 2½p. on 6d. black and green .. 3·50 5·00
  a. Pair, one without handstamp .. £400 £400
Beware of forgeries of this handstamp.

Trucial States

The Trucial States consisted of Abu Dhabi, Ajman (with Manama), Dubai, Fujeira, Ras al Khaima, Sharjah and Umm al Qiwain. However the following issue of stamps was only put into use in Dubai, despite the inscription "TRUCIAL STATES".

The first organised postal service in Dubai commenced on 19 August 1909 when an Indian Branch Office, administered from Karachi, was opened, using the unoverprinted stamps of India, principally the ½ a. and 1 a. values.

The initial cancellation was a single-ring type inscribed "DUBAI B.O. PERSIAN GULF", which remained in use until 1933.

1909 Cancellation

Its replacement was of the Indian double-circle type showing a similar inscription.

Dubai was upgraded to Sub-Post Office status on 1 April 1942 and this change was reflected in a new double-ring mark inscribed "DUBAI" only. At the same time the office was provided with a single-ring handstamp which also incorporated a cancelling device of seven wavy lines.

1942 Handstamp

(illustration reduced: actual size 65 × 27 mm)

A further version of the double-ring type appeared in 1946, showing the "PERSIAN GULF" inscription restored to the lower segment of the postmark.

In October 1947 control of the Dubai Post Office passed to Pakistan whose stamps were used there until the end of March 1948.

On 1 April 1948 the post office was transferred, yet again, to British control and Great Britain stamps surcharged for use in the British Postal Agencies in Eastern Arabia were then sold in Dubai until 6 January 1961, being cancelled with British style single and double-ring postmarks.

(Currency. 100 naye paise = 1 rupee)

1 Palms

2 Dhow

(Des M. Goaman. Photo Harrison (T **1**). Des M. Farrar-Bell. Recess D.L.R. (T **2**))

1961 (7 Jan). *P* 15 × 14 (*T* **1**) or 13 × 12½ (*T* **2**).

1	**1**	5 n.p. green		60	10
2		15 n.p. red-brown		30	10
3		20 n.p. bright blue		60	10
4		30 n.p. orange-red		40	10
5		40 n.p. reddish violet		40	10
6		50 n.p. bistre		40	10
7		75 n.p. grey		60	10
8	**2**	1 r. green		4·00	2·00
9		2 r. black		3·00	12·00
10		5 r. carmine-red		5·50	18·00
11		10 r. deep ultramarine		12·00	21·00
1/11			Set of 11	25·00	48·00

The Dubai Post Department took over the postal services on 14 June 1963. Later issues for Dubai will be found in Part 19 (*Middle East*) of this catalogue.

Turks and Caicos Islands

TURKS ISLANDS

DEPENDENCY OF JAMAICA

A branch of the British Post Office opened at Grand Turk on 11 December 1854 replacing an earlier arrangement under which mail for the islands was sorted by local R.M.S.P. agents. No. CC1 is known used between 22 October 1857 and 20 April 1862.

GRAND TURK
CROWNED-CIRCLE HANDSTAMPS

CC 1

CC1 CC **1** TURKS-ISLANDS (Oct 1857) *Price on cover £5000*

PRICES FOR STAMPS ON COVER TO 1945	
Nos. 1/5	*from* × 30
No. 6	—
Nos. 7/20	*from* × 50
Nos. 20*a*/48	—
Nos. 49/52	*from* × 12
Nos. 53/7	*from* × 10
Nos. 58/65	*from* × 20
Nos. 66/9	*from* × 5
Nos. 70/2	*from* × 10
Nos. 101/9	*from* × 8
Nos. 110/26	*from* × 6
Nos. 129/39	*from* × 4
Nos. 140/53	*from* × 12
Nos. 154/90	*from* × 3
Nos. 191/3	*from* × 10
Nos. 194/205	*from* × 2

1

Throat flaw (R.3/4)

(Recess P.B.)

1867 (4 Apr). *No wmk. P* 11–12.

1	**1**	1d. dull rose		48·00	48·00
		a. Throat flaw		£140	£150
2		6d. black		85·00	£110
3		1s. dull blue		80·00	60·00

1873–79. *Wmk Small Star.* W w **2** (sideways on Nos. 5 and 6). *P* 11–12 × 14½–15½.

4	**1**	1d. dull rose-lake (7.73)		48·00	48·00
		a. Throat flaw		£150	£160
		b. Wmk sideways		80·00	80·00
		ba. Throat flaw		£250	£250
5		1d. dull red (1.79)		55·00	60·00
		a. Imperf between (horiz pair)		£12000	
		b. Throat flaw		£170	£180
		c. Wmk upright			
6		1s. lilac (1.79)		£5000	£2000

1881 (1 Jan). *Stamps of the preceding issues surcharged locally, in black.*

There are twelve different settings of the ½d., nine settings of the 2½d., and six settings of the 4d.

½ (2)   ½ (3)

Setting 1. *T* **2**. *Long fraction bar. Two varieties repeated fifteen times in the sheet.*

7		½ on 6d. black		70·00	£100

Setting 2. *T* **3**. *Short fraction bar. Three varieties in a vertical strip repeated ten times in sheet.*

Setting 3. *Similar to setting 2, but the middle stamp of the three varieties has a longer bar.*

8	½ on 6d. black (setting 2 only)		60·00	90·00
9	½ on 1s. dull blue		85·00	£140
	a. Surch double		£5000	

½ (4)   ½ (5)   ½ (6)

Three varieties in a vertical strip repeated ten times in sheet.
Section 4. Types 4, 5, 6.
Setting 5. Types 4 (*without bar*), 5, 6.
Setting 6. Types 4, 5, 6 (*without bar*).
Setting 7. Types 4 (*shorter thick bar*), 6, 6.

10	½ on 1d. dull red (*setting 7 only*) (T **6**)			
	a. Type 4 (shorter thick bar)		£7000	
11	½ on 1s. dull blue (*setting 6 and 7*) (T **4**)		£950	
	a. Type 4 (shorter thick bar)		£1300	
	b. Type 5		£950	
	c. Type 6		£850	
	d. Type 6 (without bar)		£1100	
	e. Surch double (T **6** without bar)			
12	½ on 1s. lilac (T **4**)		£250	£375
	a. Without bar		£500	
	b. With short thick bar		£475	
	c. Surch double		£3000	
	cb. Surch double and short thick bar		£5500	
13	½ on 1s. lilac (T **5**)		£120	£200
	a. Surch double		£2750	
14	½ on 1s. lilac (T **6**)		£120	£200
	a. Without bar		£550	
	b. Surch double		£4000	
	ba. Surch double and without bar		£5500	

Care should be taken in the identification of Types 6 and 7 which are very similar. For the 1s. value some varieties of No. 9 are often confused with Nos. 11b/c.

½ (7)   ½ (8)   ½ (9)   ½ (10)

Setting 8. *T* **7**. *Three varieties in a vertical strip. All have a very short bar.*

15	½ on 1d. dull red		60·00	90·00
	a. Throat flaw		£190	

Setting 9. *T* **8**. *Three varieties in a vertical strip. Bars long and thick and "1" leaning a little to left.*

16	½ on 1d. dull red		£180	£225
	a. Surch double		£3250	
	b. Throat flaw		£475	

Setting 10. *T* **9** *and* **10**. *Fifteen varieties repeated twice in a sheet. Ten are of T* **9** (*Rows 1 and 2*), *five of T* **10** (*Row 3*).

17	½ on 1d. dull red (T **9**)		50·00	95·00
	a. Surch double		£3000	
18	½ on 1d. dull red (T **10**)		80·00	£140
	a. Surch double		£5000	
	b. Throat flaw		£225	
19	½ on 1s. lilac (T **9**)		85·00	£150
20	½ on 1s. lilac (T **10**)		£150	£275
20*a*	½ on 1s. dull blue (T **9**)		£7000	
20*b*	½ on 1s. dull blue (T **10**)		£11000	

Types 9 and 11. The difference is in the position of the "2" in relation to the "1". In setting 10 the "2" is to the left of the "1" except on No. 10 (where it is directly below the "1") and in setting 11 it is to the right except on No. 2 (where it is to the left, as in setting 10).

½ (11)   ½ (12)   ½ (13)   ½ (14)

Setting 11. *T* **9** *and* **11** *to* **14**. *Fifteen varieties repeated twice in a sheet. Nine of T* **11**, *three of T* **12**, *and one each of T* **9**, **13** *and* **14**.

Setting 12. *Similar to last, but T* **13** *replaced by another T* **12**.

21	½ on 1d. dull red (T **11**)		£100	£160
22	½ on 1d. dull red (T **12**)		£200	
	a. Throat flaw		£950	
23	½ on 1d. dull red (T **13**)		£1000	
	a. Throat flaw		£1000	
24	½ on 1d. dull red (T **14**)		£500	
24*a*	½ on 1s. dull blue (T **11**)		£11000	

Type **9** from these settings, where it occurs on position 2, can only be distinguished from similar stamps from setting 10 when *se-tenant* with Type 11.

2½ (15)   2½ (16)

Setting 1. *T* **15**. *Fraction in very small type.*

25	2½ on 6d. black		£7500	

Setting 2. *T* **16**. *Two varieties repeated fifteen times in a sheet. Large "2" on level with top of the "1", long thin bar.*

26	2½ on 6d. black		£300	£375
	a. Imperf between (horiz pair)		£11000	
	b. Surch double		£6500	

2½ **2½** **2½**

(17) (18) (19)

Setting 3. T **17**, *but large "2" not so high up.*
27   2½ on 1s. lilac £2000

Setting 4. T **18**. *Three varieties in a vertical strip repeated ten times in sheet. Large "2" placed lower and small bar.*
28   2½ on 6d. black £150 £250
      a. Surch double £6500

Setting 5. T **19**. *Three varieties in a vertical strip repeated ten times in sheet "2" further from "½", small fraction bar.*
29   2½ on 1s. lilac £550 £850

2½ **2½**

(20) (21)

Setting 6. T **20** *and* **21**. *Fifteen varieties. Ten of T* **20** *and five of* T **21**, *repeated twice in a sheet.*
30   2½ on 1s. lilac (T **20**) £6500
31   2½ on 1s. lilac (T **21**) £10000

2½ **2½** **2½**

(22) (23) (24)

Setting 7. T **22**. *Three varieties in a vertical strip, repeated ten times in a sheet.*
32   2½ on 6d. black £7500
33   2½ on 1s. dull blue £11000

Setting 8. T **23** *and* **24**. *Fifteen varieties. Ten of T* **23** *and five of* T **24**, *repeated twice in a sheet.*
34   2½ on 1d. dull red (T **23**) £600
35   2½ on 1d. dull red (T **24**) £1200
      a. Throat flaw £550 £700
36   2½ on 1s. lilac (T **23**) £550 £700
      a. Surch "½" double £2750
37   2½ on 1s. lilac (T **24**) £1200
      a. Surch "½" double £4500

2½ **2½** **2½**

(25) (26) (27)

Setting 9. T **25**, **26**, *and* **27**. *Fifteen varieties. Ten of T* **25**, *three of* T **26**, *one of T* **26** *without bar, and one of T* **27**, *repeated twice in a sheet.*
38   2½ on 1s. dull blue (T **25**) £700
39   2½ on 1s. dull blue (T **26**) £1700
40   2½ on 1s. dull blue (T **26**) (without bar)   .. £6000
41   2½ on 1s. dull blue (T **27**) £6000

4 **4** **4**

(28) (29) (30)

Setting 1. T **28**. *"4" 8 mm high, pointed top.*
42   4 on 6d. black £375 £300

Settings 2–6. T **29** *and* **30**.
43   4 on 6d. black (T **29**)   .. .. 70·00 95·00
44   4 on 6d. black (T **30**) £325 £425
45   4 on 1s. lilac (T **29**) £400
      a. Surch double   .. ..
46   4 on 1s. lilac (T **30**) £2000
      a. Surch double   .. ..
47   4 on 1d. dull red (T **29**) £700 £475
48   4 on 1d. dull red (T **28**) £800 £550

The components of these settings can only be distinguished when in blocks. Details are given in the handbook by John J. Challis.

One Penny

31 (32)

(Typo D.L.R.)

1881. *Wmk Crown CC (sideways* on T* 1). *P* 14.
49   1   1d. brown-red (Oct)   .. .. 55·00 80·00
      a. Throat flaw £160 £190
50   31   4d. ultramarine (Die I) (Aug)   .. 95·00 60·00
51   1   6d. olive-black (Oct)   .. .. 90·00 £120
52   1s. slate-green (Oct) £120 £110
      *The normal sideways watermark shows Crown to right of CC, *as seen from the back of the stamp.*
      Nos. 49 and 52 also exist showing Crown to left of CC, but due to the position of the watermark such varieties are difficult to detect on single stamps.

1882–85. *Wmk Crown CA (reversed on 1d.). P* 14.
53   31   ½d. blue-green (Die I) (2.82)   .. 8·00 20·00
      a. Pale green (2.82)   .. .. 2·25 3·50
      b. Top left triangle detached   .. 85·00
55   1   1d. orange-brown (10.83)   .. 55·00 30·00
      a. Bisected (½d.) (on cover)   .. † £4000
      b. Throat flaw   .. .. £150 80·00
      x. Wmk normal (not reversed)   .. 80·00
56   31   2½d. red-brown (Die I) (2.82)   .. 15·00 10·00
57   4d. grey (Die I) (10.84)   .. 13·00 2·00
      a. Bisected (2d.) (on cover)   .. † £4000
      For illustration of "top left triangle detached" variety see above No. 6 of Montserrat.

1887 (July)–89. *Wmk Crown CA.* (a) *P* 12
58   1   1d. crimson-lake   .. .. 12·00 3·00
      a. Imperf between (horiz pair)   .. £10000
      b. Throat flaw   .. .. 35·00 10·00
      x. Wmk reversed   .. .. 10·00 2·50

(b) *P* 14
59   1   6d. yellow-brown (2.89) (Optd S. £60)   2·50 2·75
60   1s. sepia   .. .. 4·00 2·75

> During a shortage of 1d. stamps a supply of JAMAICA No. 27 was sent to the Turks and Caicos Islands in April 1889 and used until replaced by No. 61.

1889 (May). *Surch at Grand Turk with T* **32**.
61   31   1d. on 2½d. red-brown   .. .. 6·50 9·50
      a. "One" omitted (12.85)   .. £1500
      b. Bisected (½d.) (on cover)   .. † £4500
      No. 61a was caused by misplacement of the surcharge. Stamps from the same sheet can be found with the surcharge reading "Penny One".

Neck flaw (R.3/2)

1889–93. *Wmk Crown CA. P* 14.
62   1   1d. crimson-lake (7.89)   .. .. 3·00 3·50
      a. Bisected (½d.) (on cover)   .. † £4000
      b. Throat flaw   .. .. 13·00 14·00
      c. Neck flaw   .. .. 17·00 19·00
      x. Wmk reversed   .. .. 35·00
63   1d. lake   .. .. 2·00 2·25
      a. Bisected (½d.) (on cover)   .. † £4000
      b. Throat flaw   .. .. 8·00 8·50
      c. Neck flaw   .. .. 11·00 13·00
64   1d. pale rosy lake   .. .. 1·60 4·00
      b. Throat flaw   .. .. 6·00 6·50
      c. Neck flaw   .. .. 8·50 18·00
65   31   2½d. ultram (Die II) (4.93) (Optd S. £55)   2·25 1·50

(33) 34

1893 (10 June). *No. 57 surch at Grand Turk with T* **33**.
Setting 1. Bars between "1d." and "2" separate, instead of continuous across the rows of stamps.
66   ½d. on 4d. grey £1800 £750
Setting 2. Continuous bars. Thin and thick bar 10¾ mm apart. "2" under the "1".
67   ½d. on 4d. grey £150 £130
Setting 3. As last, but bars 11¾ mm apart.
68   ½d. on 4d. grey £130 £140
Setting 4. Bars 11 mm apart. Five out of the six varieties in the strip have the "2" below the space between the "1" and "d".
69   ½d. on 4d. grey £150 £140
There is a fifth setting, but the variation is slight.

(Typo D.L.R.)
1893–95. *Wmk Crown CA. P* 14.
70   31   ½d. dull green (Die II) (12.93)   .. 1·75 1·75
71   4d. dull purple & ultram (Die II) (5.95)   8·00 12·00
72   34   5d. olive-green and carmine (6.94)   3·25 11·00
      a. Bisected (2½d.) (on cover)   .. † £3750
70/2   .. .. Set of 3 11·50 22·00
71/2 Optd "Specimen"   .. .. Set of 2 £100

---

35   Badge of the Islands   36

The dates on the stamps have reference to the political separation from Bahamas.

(Recess D.L.R.)
1900 (10 Nov)–04. *Wmk Crown CA (½d. to 1s.) or Wmk Crown CC (2s., 3s.). P* 14.
101   35   ½d. green   .. .. 2·75 4·00
      x. Wmk reversed   .. ..
102   1d. red   .. .. 3·50 75
      w. Wmk inverted   .. .. 60·00
103   2d. sepia   .. .. 75 1·25
      w. Wmk inverted   .. ..
      x. Wmk reversed   .. ..
104   2½d. blue   .. .. 7·50 16·00
      a. Greyish blue (1904)   .. .. 1·75 1·00
      aw. Wmk inverted   .. .. 60·00
      ay. Wmk inverted and reversed   .. ..
105   4d. orange   .. .. 3·50 7·00
106   6d. dull mauve   .. .. 2·00 6·50
107   1s. purple-brown   .. .. 2·75 16·00
108   36   2s. purple   .. .. 40·00 55·00
109   3s. lake   .. .. 50·00 75·00
101/9   .. .. Set of 9 95·00 £150
101/9 Optd "Specimen"   .. .. Set of 9 £225

1905–08. *Wmk Mult Crown CA. P* 14.
110   35   ½d. green   .. .. 4·00 15
111   1d. red   .. .. 13·00 50
      w. Wmk inverted   .. ..
112   3d. purple/yellow (1908) (Optd S. £50)   1·50 6·00
      w. Wmk inverted   .. ..
110/12   .. .. Set of 3 17·00 6·00

37 Turk's-head Cactus   38

(Recess D.L.R.)
1909 (2 Sept)–11. *Wmk Mult Crown CA. P* 14.
115   37   ¼d. rosy mauve (1910)   .. .. 1·50 1·00
      w. Wmk inverted   .. ..
116   ¼d. red (1911) 40 30
      w. Wmk inverted   .. ..
117   38   ½d. yellow-green 55 30
      w. Wmk inverted   .. ..
      x. Wmk reversed   .. .. 42·00
      y. Wmk inverted and reversed   .. ..
118   1d. red   .. .. 1·00 30
      w. Wmk inverted   .. ..
119   2d. greyish slate   .. .. 1·50 1·40
120   2½d. blue   .. .. 1·50 3·75
      w. Wmk inverted   .. ..
      x. Wmk reversed   .. .. 55·00
121   3d. purple/yellow   .. .. 1·75 2·00
122   4d. red/yellow   .. .. 3·25 7·00
123   6d. purple   .. .. 6·50 7·00
124   1s. black/green   .. .. 6·50 8·50
      w. Wmk inverted   .. ..
125   2s. red/green   .. .. 27·00 48·00
126   3s. black/red   .. .. 27·00 40·00
115/26   .. .. Set of 12 70·00 £110
115/26 Optd "Specimen"   .. .. Set of 12 £200
      See also Nos. 154 and 162.

WAR TAX

39 (40)

1913 (1 Apr)–21. *Wmk Mult Crown CA. P* 14.
129   39   ½d. green   .. .. 40 1·75
      w. Wmk inverted   .. ..
130   1d. red   .. .. 1·00 2·25
      a. Bright rose-scarlet   .. .. 1·10 2·00
      ax. Wmk reversed   .. .. 40·00
      b. Rose-carmine (1918)   .. .. 3·75 5·50
131   2d. greyish slate   .. .. 1·75 3·25
132   2½d. ultramarine   .. .. 2·25 2·75
      aw. Wmk inverted   .. ..
      b. Bright blue (1918)   .. .. 4·00 2·50
133   3d. purple/yellow   .. .. 2·25 9·00
      a. On lemon   .. .. 16·00
      b. On yellow-buff   .. .. 4·00 8·50
      c. On orange-buff   .. .. 1·75
      cx. Wmk reversed   .. .. 60·00
      d. On pale yellow   .. .. 2·00 8·00
134   4d. red/yellow   .. .. 1·00 9·00
      a. On orange-buff (Optd S. £48)   .. 1·60 7·00
      ab. "A" of "CA" missing from wmk   .. ..
      b. Carmine on pale yellow   .. 7·50 16·00
135   5d. pale olive-green (18.5.16)   .. 6·50 20·00
136   6d. dull purple   .. .. 2·25 3·25
      w. Wmk inverted   .. ..
      x. Wmk reversed   .. ..

137	39	1s. brown-orange	..	..	1·50	4·00
		w. Wmk inverted				
138		2s. red/blue-green		..	7·50	25·00
		a. On greenish white (1919)	..	24·00	70·00
		b. On emerald (3.21) (Optd S. £48)	48·00	70·00
		bx. Wmk reversed				£110
139		3s. black/red	..	..	15·00	25·00
129/39				Set of 11	35·00	90·00
129/39 Optd "Specimen"		Set of 11	£180	

1917 (3 Jan). *Optd with T 40 at bottom of stamp.*

140	39	1d. red	..	..	10	1·50
		a. Opt double	..	..	£180	£180
		b. "TAX" omitted	..		£375	
		c. "WAR TAX" omitted in vert pair with normal	£375	
		d. Opt inverted at top	..		65·00	
		e. Opt double, one inverted*	£110	
		f. Opt inverted only, in pair with No. 140e*	£475	
141		3d. purple/yellow-buff	..	85	3·50
		a. Opt double	..	..	80·00	
		b. Purple/lemon	..	..	1·75	4·75
		ba. Opt double	..	80·00	90·00
		bb. Opt double, one inverted	£325	

*In Nos. 140e/f the inverted overprint is at foot and reads "TAX WAR" owing to displacement. No. 140e also exists with "WAR" omitted from the inverted overprint.

In both values of the first printings the stamp in the bottom left-hand corner of the sheet has a long "T" in "TAX", and on the first stamp of the sixth row the "X" is damaged and looks like a reversed "K".

1917 (Oct). *Second printing with overprint at top or in middle of stamp.*

143	39	1d. red	..	..	10	1·00
		a. Inverted opt at bottom or centre	45·00	
		c. Opt omitted (in pair with normal)	£375	
		d. Opt double, one at top, one at bottom	55·00	
		e. As d., but additional opt in top margin	£110	
		f. Horiz pair, one as d., the other normal	£250	
		g. Pair, one opt inverted, one normal	£375	
		h. Double opt at top (in pair with normal)	£200	
		i. Opt double	..	40·00	40·00
144		3d. purple/yellow	..	60	1·50
		a. Opt double	..	..	35·00	
		b. Opt double, one inverted	£300	
		c. Purple/lemon	..	..	3·00	

1918. *Overprinted with T 40.*

145	39	3d. purple/yellow (R.)	..	8·50	22·00
		a. Opt double	..	..	£300	

WAR

WAR

WAR	WAR	TAX
TAX	TAX	
(41)	(42)	(43)

1918. *Optd with T 41 in London by D.L.R.*

146	39	1d. rose-carmine	..	20	1·25
		a. Bright rose-scarlet	..	15	1·25
		aw. Wmk inverted	..	60·00	
147		3d. purple/yellow	..	1·50	3·50
146/7 Optd "Specimen"	..	Set of 2	80·00	

1919. *Optd with T 41 in London by D.L.R.*

148	39	3d. purple/orange-buff (R.)	..	10	2·00
148 Optd "Specimen"	..	..	40·00	

1919. *Local overprint. T 40, in violet.*

149	39	1d. bright rose-scarlet	..	15	3·00
		a. "WAR" omitted	..	..	£150	
		b. Opt double	..	..	21·00	
		c. Opt double in pair with normal	£120	
		d. Opt double, one inverted	£120	
		e. Rose-carmine	..	..	6·50	14·00
		ea. Opt double	..	..	30·00	
		w. Wmk inverted	..	..	30·00	

1919. *Optd with T 42.*

150	39	1d. scarlet	..	..	10	90
		a. Opt double	..	..	£140	£160
		b. Opt double, one albino and reversed		
151		3d. purple/orange-buff	..	30	2·50
		w. Wmk inverted	..	..	30·00	
		x. Wmk reversed	..	..	30·00	

1919 (17 Dec). *Optd with T 43.*

152	39	1d. scarlet	..	..	10	2·25
		a. Opt inverted	..			
153		3d. purple/orange-buff	..	30	2·50
		w. Wmk inverted	..	..	30·00	
		x. Wmk reversed	..	..	25·00	
		y. Wmk inverted and reversed	12·00	

The two bottom rows of this setting have the words "WAR" and "TAX" about 1 mm further apart.

1921 (23 Apr). *Wmk Mult Script CA. P 14.*

154	37	¼d. rose-red	..	..	2·50	10·00
155	39	½d. green	..	..	2·75	5·50
156		1d. carmine-red	..	..	1·00	5·50
157		2d. slate-grey	..	..	1·00	16·00
		y. Wmk inverted and reversed	45·00	
158		2½d. bright blue	..	..	1·75	7·50
159		5d. sage-green	..	..	7·50	40·00

160	39	6d. purple	..	..	6·50	40·00
		w. Wmk inverted	..			
		x. Wmk reversed	..	..	48·00	
161		1s. brown-orange	..	6·50	22·00
154/61				Set of 8	26·00	£130
154/61 Optd "Specimen"	..	Set of 8	£140	

44	45

(Recess D.L.R.)

1922 (20 Nov)–26. *P 14. (a) Wmk Mult Script CA*

162	37	¼d. black (11.10.26)	..	80	1·00
163	44	½d. yellow-green	..	1·75	2·50
		a. Bright green	..	..	1·75	2·25
		b. Apple-green	..	..	5·00	10·00
164		1d. brown	..	..	50	3·00
165		1½d. scarlet (24.11.25)	..	6·00	13·00
166		2d. slate	..	..	50	4·75
167		2½d. purple/pale yellow	..	50	1·50
168		3d. bright blue	..	..	50	4·75
169		4d. red/pale yellow	..	1·00	12·00
		ax. Wmk reversed	..	..	45·00	
		b. Carmine/pale yellow	..	4·50	15·00
170		5d. sage-green	..	..	75	20·00
		y. Wmk inverted and reversed	48·00	
171		6d. purple	..	..	60	4·00
		x. Wmk reversed	..	..	50·00	
172		1s. brown-orange	..	70	15·00
173		2s. red/emerald	..	2·00	8·50

(b) Wmk Mult Crown CA

174	44	2s. red/emerald (24.11.25)	..	25·00	65·00
175		3s. black/red (24.11.25)	..	5·00	23·00
162/75				Set of 14	40·00	£160
162/75 Optd "Specimen"	..	Set of 14	£200	

1928 (1 Mar). *Inscr "POSTAGE & REVENUE". Wmk Mult Script CA. P 14.*

176	45	½d. green	..	..	60	50
177		1d. brown	..	..	60	70
178		1½d. scarlet	..	..	60	3·00
179		2d. grey	..	..	60	50
180		2½d. purple/yellow	..	60	4·00
181		3d. bright blue	..	..	60	5·00
182		6d. purple	..	..	60	7·00
183		1s. brown-orange	..	3·75	7·00
184		2s. red/emerald	..	6·00	35·00
185		5s. green/yellow	..	11·00	35·00
186		10s. purple/blue	..	45·00	95·00
176/86				Set of 11	65·00	£170
176/86 Optd "Specimen"	..	Set of 11	£140	

1935 (6 May). *Silver Jubilee. As Nos. 114/17 of Jamaica, but ptd by Waterlow. P 11×12.*

187		½d. black and green	..	30	75
		k. Kite and vertical log	..	30·00	
		l. Kite and horizontal log	..	25·00	
188		3d. brown and deep blue	..	2·75	4·50
		k. Kite and vertical log	..	70·00	
189		6d. light blue and olive-green	..	1·75	4·75
		k. Kite and vertical log	..	70·00	
190		1s. slate and purple	..	1·75	3·25
		k. Kite and vertical log	..	70·00	
187/90				Set of 4	6·00	12·00
187/90 Perf "Specimen"	..	Set of 4	75·00	

For illustrations of plate varieties see Omnibus section following Zimbabwe.

1937 (12 May). *Coronation. As Nos. 118/20 of Jamaica.*

191		½d. myrtle-green	..	10	10
		a. Deep green	..	..	40·00	
192		2d. grey-black	..	..	50	40
193		3d. bright blue	..	..	60	40
191/3				Set of 3	1·00	75
191/3 Perf "Specimen"	..	Set of 3	55·00	

46 Raking Salt	47 Salt Industry

(Recess Waterlow)

1938 (18 June)–45. *Wmk Mult Script CA. P 12½.*

194	46	¼d. black	..	..	10	10
195		½d. yellowish green	..	4·00	15
		a. Deep green (6.11.44)	..	80	70
196		1d. red-brown	..	..	60	10
197		1½d. scarlet	..	..	60	15
198		2d. grey	..	..	60	30
199		2½d. yellow-orange	..	4·25	80
		a. Orange (6.11.44)	..	2·00	1·50
200		3d. bright blue	..	..	50	30
201		6d. mauve	..	..	9·50	1·25
201a		6d. sepia (9.2.45)	..	20	20
202		1s. yellow-bistre	..	3·75	7·50
202a		1s. grey-olive (9.2.45)	..	20	20
203	47	2s. deep rose-carmine	..	42·00	11·00
		a. Bright rose-carmine (6.11.44)	17·00	16·00
204		5s. yellowish green	..	48·00	13·00
		a. Deep green (6.11.44)	..	35·00	20·00
205		10s. bright violet	..	12·00	5·50
194/205				Set of 14	75·00	35·00
194/205 Perf "Specimen"	..	Set of 14	£200	

1946 (4 Nov). *Victory. As Nos. 141/2 of Jamaica.*

206		2d. black	..	..	10	10
207		3d. blue	..	..	15	10
206/7 Perf "Specimen"	..	Set of 2	55·00	

1948 (13 Sept). *Royal Silver Wedding. As Nos. 143/4 of Jamaica.*

208		1d. red-brown	..	..	15	10
209		10s. mauve	..	..	7·00	11·00

50 Badge of the Islands	53 Queen Victoria and King George VI

(Recess Waterlow)

1948 (14 Dec). *Centenary of Separation from Bahamas. T 50, 53 and similar designs. Wmk Mult Script CA. P 12½.*

210	50	½d. blue-green	..	70	15
211		2d. carmine	..	..	1·25	15
212	—	3d. blue	..	..	1·50	15
213	—	6d. violet	..	..	50	30
214	53	2s. black and bright blue	..	75	65
215		5s. black and green	..	90	2·75
216		10s. black and brown	..	90	3·25
210/16				Set of 7	5·75	6·75

Designs: Horiz—3d. Flag of Turks and Caicos Islands; 6d. Map of islands.

1949 (10 Oct). *75th Anniv of U.P.U. As Nos. 145/8 of Jamaica.*

217		2½d. red-orange	..	30	55
218		3d. deep blue	..	..	1·75	50
219		6d. brown	..	..	40	50
220		1s. olive	..	..	40	35
217/20				Set of 4	2·50	1·75

65 Bulk Salt Loading

66 Dependency's Badge

(Recess Waterlow)

1950 (1 Aug). *T 65 and similar horiz designs, and T 66. Wmk Mult Script CA. P 12½.*

221		½d. green	..	..	60	40
222		1d. red-brown	..	..	50	75
223		1½d. deep carmine	..	90	55
224		2d. red-orange	..	..	30	40
225		2½d. grey-olive	..	..	70	50
226		3d. bright blue	..	..	30	40
227		4d. black and rose	..	2·50	70
228		6d. black and blue	..	2·00	50
229		1s. black and blue-green	..	80	40
230		1s. 6d. black and scarlet	..	6·50	3·25
231		2s. emerald and ultramarine	..	2·50	3·50
232		5s. blue and black	..	16·00	7·50
233		10s. black and violet	..	16·00	17·00
221/33				Set of 13	45·00	32·00

Designs:—1d. Salt Cay; 1½d. Caicos mail; 2d. Grand Turk; 2½d. Sponge diving; 3d. South Creek; 4d. Map; 6d. Grand Turk Light; 1s. Government House; 1s. 6d. Cockburn Harbour; 2s. Government Offices; 5s. Loading salt.

1953 (2 June). *Coronation. As No. 153 of Jamaica, but ptd by B.W. & Co.*

234		2d. black and orange-red	..	30	1·00

67 M.V. Kirksons

(Recess Waterlow)

1955 (1 Feb). *T 67 and similar horiz design. Wmk Mult Script CA. P 12½.*

235		5d. black and bright green	..	30	55
236		8d. black and brown	..	2·25	50

Design:—8d. Greater Flamingoes in flight.

69 Queen Elizabeth II
(after Annigoni)

70 Bonefish

82 Dependency's Badge

(Recess B.W.)

1957 (25 Nov.). T **69/70**, **82** and similar horiz designs as T **70**.
W w 12. P 13½×14 (1d.), 14 (10s.) or 13½ (others).

237	1d. deep blue and carmine		15	20
238	1½d. grey-green and orange		15	30
239	2d. red-brown and olive		15	15
240	2½d. carmine and green		15	15
241	3d. turquoise-blue and purple		15	15
242	4d. lake and black		60	15
243	5d. slate-green and brown		75	40
244	6d. carmine-rose and blue		2·00	55
245	8d. vermilion and black		3·00	20
246	1s. deep blue and black		60	10
247	1s. 6d. sepia and deep ultramarine		8·50	1·25
248	2s. deep ultramarine and brown		9·50	2·50
249	5s. black and carmine		2·00	2·00
250	10s. black and purple		13·00	8·00
237/250 and 253		Set of 15	70·00	29·00

Designs:—2d. Red Grouper; 2½d. Spiny Lobster; 3d. Albacore;
4d. Mutton Snapper; 5d. Permit; 6d. Queen or Pink Conch; 8d.
Greater Flamingoes; 1s. Spanish Mackerel; 1s. 6d. Salt Cay; 2s.
Uakon (Caicos sloop); 5s. Cable Office.

83 Map of the Turks and Caicos Islands

(Photo D.L.R.)

1959 (4 July). New Constitution. Wmk Mult Script CA.
P 13½ × 14.

251	**83**	6d. deep olive and light orange	45	70
252		8d. violet and light orange	45	40

84 Brown Pelican

(Des Mrs. S. Hurd. Photo Harrison)

1960 (1 Nov.). W w 12. P 14 × 14½.

253	**84**	£1 sepia and deep red	40·00	16·00

CROWN COLONY

1963 (4 June). Freedom from Hunger. As No. 80 of Lesotho.

254	8d. carmine	30	15

1963 (2 Sept.). Red Cross Centenary. As Nos. 203/4 of Jamaica.

255	2d. red and black	15	35
256	8d. red and blue	30	35

1964 (23 Apr). 400th Birth Anniv of William Shakespeare. As
No. 156 of Montserrat.

257	8d. green	30	10

1965 (17 May). I.T.U. Centenary. As Nos. 98/9 of Lesotho.

258	1d. vermilion and brown	10	10
259	2s. light emerald and turquoise-blue	20	20

1965 (25 Oct). International Co-operation Year. As Nos. 100/1
of Lesotho.

260	1d. reddish purple and turquoise-green	10	15
261	8d. deep bluish green and lavender	20	15

1966 (24 Jan.). Churchill Commemoration. As Nos. 102/5 of
Lesotho.

262	1d. new blue	10	10
263	2d. deep green	20	10
264	8d. brown	25	10
	a. Gold ptg double	£120	
265	1s. 6d. bluish violet	30	75
262/5	Set of 4	70	90

1966 (4 Feb). Royal Visit. As Nos. 183/4 of Montserrat.

266	8d. black and ultramarine	25	10
267	1s. 6d. black and magenta	45	20

85 Andrew Symmer going ashore

(Des V. Whiteley. Photo D.L.R.)

1966 (1 Oct). Bicentenary of "Ties with Britain" T **85** and similar
horiz designs. P 13½.

268	1d. deep blue and orange		10	10
269	8d. red, blue and orange-yellow		20	15
270	1s. 6d. multicoloured		25	20
268/70		Set of 3	50	40

Designs:—8d. Andrew Symmer and Royal Warrant; 1s. 6d. Arms
and Royal Cypher.

1966 (1 Dec). 20th Anniv of U.N.E.S.C.O. As Nos. 342/4 of
Mauritius.

271	1d. slate-violet, red, yellow and orange		10	10
272	8d. orange-yellow, violet and deep olive		15	15
273	1s. 6d. black, bright purple and orange		20	40
271/3		Set of 3	35	50

88 Turk's-head Cactus

89 Boat-building

90 Arms of Turks and Caicos
Islands

91 Queen Elizabeth II

(Des V. Whiteley. Photo Harrison)

1967 (1 Feb). Designs as T **88/91**. W w 12. P 14½ × 14 (vert) or
14 × 14½ (horiz).

274	1d. olive-yellow, vermilion & brt bluish vio		10	10
275	1½d. brown and orange-yellow		40	10
276	2d. deep slate and deep orange-yellow		20	10
277	3d. agate and dull green		20	10
278	4d. bright mauve, black and turquoise		1·50	10
279	6d. sepia and new blue		40	10
280	8d. yellow, turquoise-blue and deep blue		40	10
281	1s. maroon and turquoise		20	10
282	1s. 6d. orange-yellow, lake-brn & dp turq-bl		50	20
283	2s. multicoloured		60	1·75
284	3s. maroon and turquoise-blue		55	40
285	5s. ochre, blue and new blue		1·25	2·75
286	10s. multicoloured		1·75	3·00
287	£1 Prussian blue, silver and crimson		3·50	6·50
274/287		Set of 14	10·50	13·50

Designs: Vert as T **88**—2d. Donkey; 3d. Sisal industry; 6d. Salt
industry; 8d. Skin-diving; 1s. 6d. Water-skiing. Horiz as T **89**—4d.
Conch industry; 1s. Fishing; 2s. Crawfish industry; 3s. Maps of
Turks and Caicos Islands and West Indies; 5s. Fishing industry.

102 Turks Islands 1d. Stamp of 1867

(Des R. Granger Barrett. Photo Harrison)

1967 (1 May). Stamp Centenary. T **102** and similar horiz
designs. W w 12. P 14½.

288	1d. black and light magenta		15	10
	w. Wmk inverted		32·00	
289	6d. black and bluish grey		25	15
290	1s. black and turquoise-blue		25	15
288/90		Set of 3	60	30

Designs:—6d. Queen Elizabeth "stamp" and Turks Islands 6d.
stamp of 1867; 1s. Turks Islands 1s. stamp of 1867.

104 Human Rights Emblem and Charter

(Des R. Granger Barrett. Photo Harrison)

1968 (1 Apr). Human Rights Year. W w 12. P 14 × 14½.

291	**104**	1d. multicoloured		10	10
292		8d. multicoloured		15	15
293		1s. 6d. multicoloured		15	15
291/3			Set of 3	30	30

105 Dr Martin Luther King and
"Freedom March"

(Des V. Whiteley. Photo Harrison)

1968 (1 Oct). Martin Luther King Commemoration. W w 12.
P 14 × 14½.

294	**105**	2d. yellow-brown, blackish brn & dp bl	10	10
295		8d. yellow-brown, blackish brn & lake	15	15
296		1s. 6d. yellow-brn, blackish brn & vio	15	15
294/6			Set of 3	30	30

(New Currency. 100 cents=1 dollar)

(106) **1c**

107 "The Nativity with
John the Baptist"

1969 (8 Sept)–**71**. Decimal currency. Nos. 274/87 surch as
T **106** by Harrison & Sons, and new value (¼ c.) as T **90**.

297	¼ c. pale greenish grey and multicoloured		10	10
	a. Bronze-green & multicoloured (2.2.71)		1·25	30
298	1 c. on 1d. olive-yell, verm & brt bluish vio		10	10
	a. Wmk sideways		10	10
299	2 c. on 2d. deep slate & deep orange-yellow		10	10
	a. Wmk sideways		10	10
300	3 c. on 3d. agate and dull green		10	10
	a. Wmk sideways		10	10
301	4 c. on 4d. bright mauve, black & turquoise		1·25	10
302	5 c. on 6d. sepia and new blue		10	10
	a. Wmk sideways		10	10
303	7 c. on 8d. yellow, turquoise-blue & dp blue		10	10
	a. Wmk sideways		10	10
304	8 c. on 1½d. brown and orange-yellow		10	10
	w. Wmk inverted		18·00	
305	10 c. on 1s. maroon and turquoise		20	10
306	15 c. on 1s. 6d. orange-yellow, lake-brown			
	and deep turquoise-blue		25	10
	a. Wmk sideways		20	25
307	20 c. on 2s. multicoloured		30	25
308	30 c. on 3s. maroon and turquoise-blue		55	35
309	50 c. on 5s. ochre, blue and new blue		1·25	45
310	$1 on 10s. multicoloured		2·50	1·00
311	$2 on £1 Prussian blue, silver and crimson		2·75	9·00
	a. Wmk sideways		2·00	3·00
297/311		Set of 15	8·00	10·50
298a/311a		Set of 7	2·25	3·25

The 4, 8, 10, 20, 30, 50 c., and $1 exist with PVA gum as well
as gum arabic.

No. 311 was only on sale through the Crown Agents.

(Des adapted by V. Whiteley. Litho D.L.R.)

1969 (20 Oct). Christmas. Scenes from 16th-cent Book of Hours.
T **107** and similar vert design. Multicoloured. W w 12.
P 13 × 12½.

312	1 c. Type **107**		10	10
313	3 c. "The Flight into Egypt"		10	10
314	15 c. Type **107**		15	10
315	30 c. As 3 c.		25	20
312/15		Set of 4	40	40

109 Coat of Arms

110 "Christ bearing the Cross"

(Des L. Curtis. Litho B.W.)

1970 (2 Feb). New Constitution. Multicoloured; background
colours given. W w 12 (sideways). P 13 × 12½.

316	**109**	7 c. brown	20	25
317		35 c. deep violet-blue	35	25

For similar $10 design, but without commemorative
inscription, see No. 946.

(Des, recess and litho Enschedé)

1970 (17 Mar). *Easter. Details from the "Small Engraved Passion" by Dürer. T* **110** *and similar vert designs. W w* **12** *(sideways). P* 13 × 13½.

318	5 c. olive-grey and blue			10	10
319	7 c. olive-grey and vermilion			10	10
320	50 c. olive-grey and red-brown			50	90
318/20			*Set of 3*	60	1·00

Designs:—7 c. "Christ on the Cross"; 50 c. "The Lamentation of Christ".

113 Dickens and Scene from *Oliver Twist*

(Des Sylvia Goaman. Recess and litho D.L.R.)

1970 (17 June). *Death Centenary of Charles Dickens. T* **113** *and similar horiz designs. W w* **12** *(sideways). P* 13.

321	1 c. black and yellow-brown/*yellow*			10	30
322	3 c. black and Prussian blue/*flesh*			10	10
323	15 c. black and grey-blue/*flesh*			20	20
324	30 c. black and drab/*blue*			40	40
321/4			*Set of 4*	60	1·00

Designs (each incorporating portrait of Dickens as in T **113**, and a scene from one of his novels):—3 c. *A Christmas Carol*; 15 c. *Pickwick Papers*; 30 c. *The Old Curiosity Shop*.

114 Ambulance—1870

(Des Harrison. Litho B.W.)

1970 (4 Aug). *Centenary of British Red Cross. T* **114** *and similar horiz design. Multicoloured. W w* **12**. *P* 13½ × 14.

325	1 c. Type **114**			10	20
326	5 c. Ambulance—1970			20	10
	a. Wmk sideways			20	
	ab. Grey omitted			£250	
327	15 c. Type **114**			40	15
	a. Wmk sideways			40	10
328	30 c. As 5 c.			50	20
	a. Wmk sideways			55	40
325/8			*Set of 4*	1·00	55

115 Duke of Albemarle and Coat of Arms

(Des V. Whiteley. Litho Enschedé)

1970 (1 Dec). *Tercentenary of Issue of Letters Patent. T* **115** *and similar horiz design. Multicoloured. W w* **12**. *P* 12½ × 13½.

329	1 c. Type **115**			10	30
330	8 c. Arms of Charles II and Elizabeth II			20	40
331	10 c. Type **115**			20	15
332	35 c. As 8 c.			40	75
329/32			*Set of 4*	75	1·40

116 Boat-building   **117** Lined Seahorse

1971 (2 Feb). *Designs as T* **88/91** *etc., but inscr in decimal currency as in T* **116**. *W w* **12** *(sideways on 1 c., 2 c., 3 c., 5 c., 7 c., 15 c. and $2).*

333	1 c. olive-yell, verm & brt bluish vio (as 1d.)		10	10
334	2 c. deep slate & deep orange-yell (as 2d.)		10	10
335	3 c. agate and dull green (as 3d.)		15	10
336	4 c. brt mauve, black & turquoise (as 4d.)		1·25	10
337	5 c. sepia and new blue (as 6d.)		40	10
338	7 c. yellow, turquoise-blue & dp bl (as 8d.)		30	10
339	8 c. brown and orange-yellow		1·25	10
340	10 c. maroon and turquoise (as 1s.)		75	10
341	15 c. orange-yellow, lake-brown and deep turquoise-blue (as 1s. 6d.)		1·00	65

342	20 c. multicoloured (as 2s.)			1·50	2·50
343	30 c. maroon and turquoise-blue (as 3s.)			2·00	1·00
344	50 c. ochre, blue and new blue (as 5s.)			3·00	2·00
345	$1 multicoloured (as 10s.)			3·00	3·00
	a. Green omitted				
	w. Wmk inverted			4·00	5·00
346	$2 Prussian blue, silver & crimson (as £1)		4·00	7·50
333/46			*Set of 14*	16·00	15·00

The ¼ c. value was also re-issued and is listed as No. 297a.

(Des G. Vasarhelyi. Litho J.W.)

1971 (4 May). *Tourist Development. T* **117** *and similar multi-coloured designs. W w* **12** *(sideways on Nos. 348/50). P* 14 × 14½ *(1 c.) or* 14½ × 14 *(others).*

347	1 c. Type **117**			10	10
348	3 c. Queen or Pink Conch Shell (*horiz*)		15	10
349	15 c. Oystercatcher (*horiz*)			80	20
350	30 c. Sailfish ("Blue Marlin") (*horiz*)		65	25
347/50			*Set of 4*	1·50	55

118 Pirate Sloop   **119** The Wilton Diptych (Left Wing)

(Des and litho J.W.)

1971 (27 July). *Pirates. T* **118** *and similar horiz designs. Multi-coloured. W w* **12** *(sideways). P* 14.

351	2 c. Type **118**			10	10
352	3 c. Pirate treasure			10	10
353	15 c. Marooned sailor			45	15
354	30 c. Buccaneers			70	45
351/4			*Set of 4*	1·25	70

(Des J.W. Litho Questa)

1971 (12 Oct). *Christmas. T* **119** *and similar vert design. Multi-coloured. W w* **12**. *P* 13½.

355	2 c. Type **119**			10	10
	a. Horiz pair. Nos. 355/6			10	10
356	2 c. The Wilton Diptych (Right Wing)		10	10
357	8 c. Type **119**			20	20
	a. Horiz pair. Nos. 357/8			20	20
358	8 c. As No. 356			10	10
359	15 c. Type **119**			20	10
	a. Horiz pair. Nos. 359/60			40	20
360	15 c. As No. 356			20	10
355/60			*Set of 6*	65	45

The two stamps of each denomination were printed in horizontal *se-tenant* pairs throughout the sheet.

120 Cape Kennedy Launching Area   **121** "Christ before Pilate" (Rembrandt)

(Des V. Whiteley. Litho A. & M.)

1972 (21 Feb). *Tenth Anniv of Colonel Glenn's Splashdown. T* **120** *and similar multicoloured designs. W w* **12** *(sideways* on 5, 10 and 15 c.). P* 13½.

361	5 c. Type **120**			10	10
	w. Wmk Crown to right of CA		20	20
362	10 c. "Friendship 7" space capsule		10	10
	w. Wmk Crown to right of CA		30	30
363	15 c. Map of Islands and splashdown		15	10
	w. Wmk Crown to right of CA		30	30
364	20 c. N.A.S.A. Space Medal (*vert*)		15	10
	w. Wmk inverted			30	30
361/4			*Set of 4*	40	30

*The normal sideways watermark shows Crown to left of CA, as seen from the back of the stamp.

(Des and litho J.W.)

1972 (21 Mar). *Easter. T* **121** *and similar designs. W w* **12** *(sideways on 15 c.). P* 13½.

365	2 c. black and lilac			10	10
366	15 c. black and rose-pink			20	10
367	30 c. black and greenish yellow		30	15
365/7			*Set of 3*	50	30

Designs: *Horiz*—15 c. "The Three Crosses" (Rembrandt). *Vert*—30 c. "The Descent from the Cross" (Rembrandt).

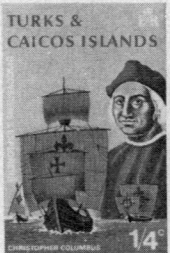

122 Christopher Columbus   **123** Turk's-head Cactus and Spiny Lobster

(Des P. Powell. Litho J.W.)

1972 (28 July*). *Discoverers and Explorers. T* **122** *and similar multicoloured designs. W w* **12** *(sideways on 8 and 30 c.). P* 13½.

368	¼ c. Type **122**			15	10
369	8 c. Sir Richard Grenville (*horiz*)		70	10
370	10 c. Capt. John Smith			80	10
371	30 c. Juan Ponce de Leon (*horiz*)		1·50	90
368/71			*Set of 4*	2·75	1·00

*This was the local date of issue; the Crown Agents released the stamps on 4 July.

(Des (from photograph by D. Groves) and photo Harrison)

1972 (20 Nov). *Royal Silver Wedding. Multicoloured; background colour given. W w* **12**. *P* 14 × 14½.

372	**123**	10 c. dull ultramarine		15	10
373		20 c. myrtle-green		15	10
		w. Wmk inverted		£250	

124 Treasure Hunting, *circa* 1700   **125** Arms of Jamaica and Turks & Caicos Islands

(Des C. Abbott. Litho Questa)

1973 (18 Jan). *Treasure. T* **124** *and similar vert designs. W w* **12** *(sideways*). P* 14 × 14½.

374	3 c. multicoloured			10	10
375	5 c. reddish purple, silver and black		10	10
376	10 c. magenta, silver and black		20	10
	w. Wmk Crown to right of CA			
377	30 c. multicoloured			60	30
374/7			*Set of 4*	85	35
MS378	127 × 108 mm. Nos. 374/7		1·10	2·00

Designs:—5 c. Silver Bank medallion (obverse); 10 c. Silver Bank medallion (reverse); 30 c. Treasure hunting, 1973.

*The normal sideways watermark shows Crown to left of CA, as seen from the back of the stamp.

(Des PAD Studio. Litho Walsall)

1973 (16 Apr). *Centenary of Annexation to Jamaica. W w* **12** *(sideways). P* 13½ × 14.

379	**125**	15 c. multicoloured		25	10
380		35 c. multicoloured		45	20

126 Sooty Tern   **127** Bermuda Sloop

(Des R. Granger Barrett. Litho Questa)

1973 (1 Aug). *Birds. T* **126** *and similar vert designs. W w* **12** *(sideways*). P* 14.

381	¼ c. Type **126**			10	40
382	1 c. Magnificent Frigate Bird		30	60
383	2 c. Common Noddy			30	60
	w. Wmk Crown to right of CA		48·00	
384	3 c. Blue-grey Gnatcatcher		85	50
385	4 c. Little Blue Heron			35	1·25
	w. Wmk Crown to right of CA		75·00	
386	5 c. Catbird			30	30
	w. Wmk Crown to right of CA		1·00	
387	7 c. Black-whiskered Vireo		4·50	30
	w. Wmk Crown to right of CA		80·00	
388	8 c. Osprey			5·00	2·50
389	10 c. Greater Flamingo		70	90
390	15 c. Brown Pelican			1·25	50
	w. Wmk Crown to right of CA		85·00	
391	20 c. Parula Warbler			3·50	1·25
392	30 c. Northern Mockingbird		1·75	90
393	50 c. Ruby-throated Hummingbird		3·25	3·75

394	$1 Bananaquit	3·50	4·00
	w. Wmk Crown to right of CA	8·00	
395	$2 Cedar Waxwing	4·50	5·50
381/95	Set of 15	27·00	21·00

*The normal sideways watermark shows Crown to left of CA, as seen from the back of the stamp.
See also Nos. 411/14 and 451/64.

(Des R. Granger Barrett. Litho Questa)

1973 (14 Aug). *Vessels.* T **127** *and similar horiz designs. Multicoloured.* W w **12**. P 13½.

396	2 c. Type **127**	20	60
397	5 c. H.M.S. *Blanche* (screw sloop)	35	10
398	8 c. *Grand Turk* (American privateer) and *Hinchinbrook II* (British packet), 1813	40	60
399	10 c. H.M.S. *Endymion* (frigate), 1790	40	15
400	15 c. *Medina* (paddle-steamer)	45	70
401	20 c. H.M.S. *Daring* (brig), 1804	50	1·25
396/401	Set of 6	2·10	3·00
MS402	198×101 mm. Nos. 396/401	2·10	3·00

1973 (14 Nov). *Royal Wedding. As Nos. 322/3 of Montserrat.*

403	12 c. light turquoise-blue	10	10
	w. Wmk Crown to right of CA	42·00	
404	18 c. dull indigo	10	10

*The normal sideways watermark shows Crown to left of CA, as seen from the back of the stamp.

128 Duho (stool)

(Des Jennifer Toombs. Litho Questa)

1974 (17 July). *Lucayan Remains.* T **128** *and similar horiz designs. Multicoloured.* W w **12** (*sideways**). P 14½×14.

405	6 c. Type **128**	10	10
406	10 c. Broken wood bowl	15	10
	w. Wmk Crown to right of CA	1·75	
407	12 c. Greenstone axe	15	10
408	18 c. Wood bowl	15	10
409	35 c. Fragment of duho	20	20
405/9	Set of 5	65	40
MS410	240×90 mm. Nos. 405/9	1·10	1·75

*The normal sideways watermark shows Crown to left of CA, as seen from the back of the stamp.

1974–75. *As Nos. 381 etc, but* W w **12** (*upright*).

411	1 c. Magnificent Frigate Bird (11.6.75)	1·00	1·50
412	2 c. Common Noddy (27.9.74)	1·50	1·00
413	3 c. Blue-grey Gnatcatcher (19.3.75)	2·25	1·00
	w. Wmk inverted	11·00	
414	20 c. Parula Warbler (11.6.75)	1·75	3·75
411/14	Set of 4	6·00	6·50

Nos. 415/25 vacant.

129 G.P.O., Grand Turk

(Des G. Drummond. Litho Questa)

1974 (9 Oct). *Centenary of Universal Postal Union.* T **129** *and similar horiz designs. Multicoloured.* W w **12**. P 14.

426	4 c. Type **129**	10	10
427	12 c. Sloop and island map	20	10
428	18 c. "U.P.U." and globe	20	10
429	55 c. Posthorn and emblem	35	35
426/9	Set of 4	75	55

130 Churchill and Roosevelt   **131** Spanish Captain, circa 1492

(Des V. Whiteley. Litho Questa)

1974 (30 Nov). *Birth Centenary of Sir Winston Churchill.* T **130** *and similar horiz design. Multicoloured.* W w **14** (*sideways*). P 14.

430	12 c. Type **130**	15	15
431	18 c. Churchill and vapour-trails	15	15
MS432	85 × 85 mm. Nos. 430/1	40	55

(Des J.W. Litho Questa)

1975 (26 Mar). *Military Uniforms.* T **131** *and similar vert designs. Multicoloured.* W w **14**. P 14.

433	5 c. Type **131**	10	10
434	20 c. Officer, Royal Artillery, 1783	20	15
435	25 c. Officer, 67th Foot, 1798	25	15
436	35 c. Private, 1st West India Regt, 1833	35	25
433/6	Set of 4	80	50
MS437	145 × 88 mm. Nos. 433/6	1·00	2·00

132 Ancient Windmill, Salt Cay   **133** Star Coral

(Des P. Powell. Litho Questa)

1975 (16 Oct). *Salt-raking Industry.* T **132** *and similar multicoloured designs.* W w **12** (*sideways on 10 and 20 c.*). P 14.

438	6 c. Type **132**	15	10
439	10 c. Salt pans drying in sun (*horiz*)	15	10
440	20 c. Salt-raking (*horiz*)	25	25
441	25 c. Unprocessed salt heaps	30	30
	w. Wmk inverted	30·00	
438/41	Set of 4	75	60

(Des C. Abbott. Litho Questa)

1975 (4 Dec). *Island Coral.* T **133** *and similar horiz designs. Multicoloured.* W w **14** (*sideways**). P 14.

442	6 c. Type **133**	15	10
443	10 c. Elkhorn Coral	20	10
444	20 c. Brain Coral	35	15
	w. Wmk Crown to right of CA	50·00	
445	25 c. Staghorn Coral	40	20
442/5	Set of 4	1·00	40

*The normal sideways watermark shows Crown to left of CA, as seen from the back of the stamp.

134 American Schooner   **135** 1s. 6d. Royal Visit Stamp of 1966

(Des J.W. Litho Questa)

1976 (28 May). *Bicentenary of American Revolution.* T **134** *and similar vert designs. Multicoloured.* W w **14**. P 13½.

446	6 c. Type **134**	25	15
447	20 c. British ship of the line	30	20
448	25 c. American privateer *Grand Turk*	30	25
	w. Wmk inverted	65·00	
449	55 c. British ketch	40	65
	w. Wmk inverted	4·25	
446/9	Set of 4	1·10	1·10
MS450	95×151 mm. Nos. 446/9	1·25	4·50

Each value depicts, at the top, the engagement between the *Grand Turk* and the P.O. Packet *Hinchinbrooke*, as in T **134**.

1976–77. *As Nos. 381/95, and new value ($5), but* W w **14** (*upright*).

451	¼ c. Type **126** (12.77)	75	3·00
452	1 c. Magnificent Frigate Bird (12.77)	75	2·00
453	2 c. Common Noddy (12.77)	75	3·00
454	3 c. Blue-grey Gnatcatcher (14.6.76)	90	70
455	4 c. Little Blue Heron (12.77)	1·75	2·25
456	5 c. Catbird (12.77)	1·25	3·00
457	10 c. Greater Flamingo (12.77)	1·25	3·00
458	15 c. Brown Pelican (12.77)	1·50	2·50
459	20 c. Parula Warbler (30.11.76)	1·50	75
460	30 c. Northern Mockingbird (12.77)	1·25	2·25
461	50 c. Ruby-throated Hummingbird (12.77)	1·50	2·25
462	$1 Bananaquit (12.77)	2·25	2·75
463	$2 Cedar Waxwing (12.77)	5·50	4·50
464	$5 Painted Bunting (24.11.76)	1·75	2·25
451/64	Set of 14	19·00	30·00

No. 465 vacant.

(Des V. Whiteley Studio. Litho Walsall)

1976 (14 July). *Tenth Anniv of Royal Visit.* T **135** *and similar horiz design. Multicoloured.* W w **14** (*sideways*). P 14½ × 14.

466	20 c. Type **135**	30	30
467	25 c. 8d. Royal Visit stamp	40	30

136 "The Virgin and Child with Flowers" (C. Dolci)   **137** Balcony Scene, Buckingham Palace

(Des G. Drummond. Litho Questa)

1976 (10 Nov). *Christmas.* T **136** *and similar vert designs. Multicoloured.* W w **14**. P 13½.

468	6 c. Type **136**	10	10
469	10 c. "Virgin and Child with St. John and an Angel" (Studio of Botticelli)	10	10
470	20 c. "Adoration of the Magi" (Master of Paraiso)	30	15
471	25 c. "Adoration of the Magi" (French miniature)	30	20
468/71	Set of 4	65	35

(Des J.W. (MS475), C. Abbott (others) Litho Questa)

1977 (7 Feb–6 Dec). *Silver Jubilee.* T **137** *and similar vert designs. Multicoloured.* W w **14**. P 14 × 13½ (MS475) *or* 13½ (*others*).

472	6 c. Queen presenting O.B.E. to E.T. Wood	10	10
	w. Wmk inverted	15·00	
473	25 c. The Queen with regalia	15	20
474	55 c. Type **137**	30	45
472/4	Set of 3	40	60
MS475	120×97 mm. $5 Queen Elizabeth II (6.12.77)	90	80

138 Col. Glenn's "Mercury" Capsule   **139** "Flight of the Holy Family" (Rubens)

(Des and litho J.W.)

1977 (20 June). *25th Anniv of U.S. Tracking Station.* T **138** *and similar multicoloured designs.* W w **14** (*sideways on horiz designs*). P 13½.

476	1 c. Type **138**	10	10
477	3 c. Moon buggy "Rover" (*vert*)	10	10
478	6 c. Tracking Station, Grand Turk	10	10
479	20 c. Moon landing craft (*vert*)	15	15
480	25 c. Col. Glenn's rocket launch (*vert*)	20	20
481	50 c. "Telstar 1" satellite	30	40
476/81	Set of 6	70	80

(Des J.W. Litho Questa)

1977 (23 Dec). *Christmas and 400th Birth Anniv of Rubens.* T **139** *and similar vert designs. Multicoloured.* P 14.

482	¼ c. Type **139**	10	10
483	½ c. "Adoration of the Magi" (1634)	10	10
484	1 c. "Adoration of the Magi" (1624)	10	10
485	6 c. "Virgin within Garland"	10	10
486	20 c. "Madonna and Child Adored by Angels"	15	10
487	$2 "Adoration of the Magi" (1618)	1·25	1·25
482/7	Set of 6	1·40	1·25
MS488	100 × 81 mm. $1 detail of 20 c.	1·10	1·40

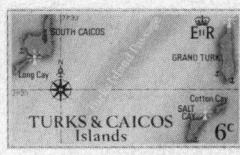

140 Map of Passage

(Des R. Granger Barrett. Litho J.W.)

1978 (2 Feb). *Turks Islands Passage.* T **140** *and similar horiz designs. Multicoloured.* P 13½. A. *No wmk*

489A	6 c. Type **140**	15	15
490A	20 c. Caicos sloop passing Grand Turk Lighthouse	45	65
491A	25 c. Motor cruiser	45	75
492A	55 c. *Jamaica Planter* (freighter)	95	2·00
489A/92A	Set of 4	1·75	3·25
MS493A	136×88 mm. Nos. 489A/92A. P 14½	1·10	2·50

B. W w **14** (*sideways*)

489B	6 c. Type **140**	15	15
490B	20 c. Caicos sloop passing Grand Turk Lighthouse	45	65
491B	25 c. Motor cruiser	45	75
492B	55 c. *Jamaica Planter* (freighter)	95	2·00
489B/92B	Set of 4	1·75	3·25
MS493B	136×88 mm. Nos. 489B/92B. P 14½	25·00	

141 "Queen Victoria" (Sir George Hayter)   **142** Ampulla and Anointing Spoon

(Manufactured by Walsall (Nos. 499/501). Des PAD Studio. Litho Questa (others))

1978 (2 June–July). *25th Anniv of Coronation. Multicoloured.*

(a) *Sheet stamps. Vert designs as T **141** showing British monarchs in coronation robes.* P 14

494	6 c. Type **141**		10	10
495	10 c. "King Edward VII" (Sir Samuel Fildes)		10	10
496	25 c. King George V		20	10
497	$2 King George VI		50	70
494/7		*Set of 4*	75	75
MS498	161 × 113 mm. $2.50, Queen Elizabeth II		75	75

(b) *Booklet stamps. Vert designs as T **142**. Imperf × roul 5*.* Self-adhesive (July)*

499	15 c. Type **142**		15	30
	a. Booklet pane. Nos. 499/501		1·10	
	b. Booklet pane. Nos. 499/500, each × 3		80	
500	25 c. St. Edward's Crown		15	30
501	$2 Queen Elizabeth II in coronation robes		1·00	2·25
499/501		*Set of 3*	1·10	2·50

Nos. 494/7 also exist perf 12 (*Price for set of 4 75p mint or used*) from additional sheetlets of 3 stamps and 1 label. Stamps perforated 14 are from normal sheets of 50.

Nos. 499/501 are separated by various combinations of rotary-knife (giving a straight edge) and roulette.

143 Wilbur Wright and
Wright Type A

(Des Curtis Design. Litho Format)

1978 (29 June). *75th Anniv of Powered Flight. T **143** and similar horiz designs. Multicoloured.* P 14½.

502	1 c. Type **143**		10	10
503	6 c. Wright brothers and Cessna 337 Super Skymaster		10	10
504	10 c. Orville Wright and Lockheed L.188 Electra		10	10
505	15 c. Wilbur Wright and Douglas C-47 Skytrain		15	15
506	35 c. Wilbur Wright and Britten Norman Islander		35	35
507	$2 Wilbur Wright and Wright Type A		1·00	1·75
502/7		*Set of 6*	1·50	2·25
MS508	111×84 mm. $1 Orville Wright and Wright glider No. III		60	1·40

No. 502 is inscribed "FLYER III" in error.

144 Hurdling

(Des J.W. Litho Format)

1978 (3 Aug). *Commonwealth Games, Edmonton. T **144** and similar horiz designs. Multicoloured.* P 14½.

509	6 c. Type **144**		10	10
510	20 c. Weightlifting		15	15
511	55 c. Boxing		20	30
512	$2 Cycling		50	1·25
509/12		*Set of 4*	75	1·50
MS513	105 × 79 mm. $1 Sprinting		55	1·25

145 Indigo Hamlet

146 "Madonna of the Siskin"

(Des G. Drummond. Litho Questa)

1978 (17 Nov)–83. *Fishes. Horiz designs as T **145**. Multicoloured.*

A. *No imprint date.* P 14

514A	1 c. Type **145**		15	50
515A	2 c. Tobacco Fish (19.1.79)		75	50
516A	3 c. Bar Jack		30	30
517A	4 c. Porkfish (19.1.79)		75	50
518A	5 c. Spanish Grunt		30	40
519A	7 c. Yellow-tailed Snapper (19.1.79)		1·00	1·00
520A	8 c. Four-eyed Butterflyfish (19.1.79)		1·00	15
521A	10 c. Yellow-finned Grouper		30	15
522A	15 c. Beau Gregory		30	30
523A	20 c. Queen Angelfish		30	30
524A	30 c. Hogfish (19.1.79)		1·75	40
525A	50 c. Royal Gramma ("Fairy Basslet") (19.1.79)		1·00	65
526A	$1 Fin-spot Wrasse (19.1.79)		1·50	1·60
527A	$2 Stoplight Parrotfish (19.1.79)		2·25	2·50
528A	$5 Queen Triggerfish (19.1.79)		2·25	6·50
514A/28A		*Set of 15*	12·00	13·50

B. *With imprint date at foot of design.* P 14 (15 c.) or 12 (others)

514B	1 c. Type **145** (15.12.81)		2·25	2·25
518B	5 c. Spanish Grunt (15.12.81)		2·75	2·75
521B	10 c. Yellow-finned Grouper (15.12.81)		2·75	2·75
522B	15 c. Beau Gregory (25.1.83)		2·50	2·25
523B	20 c. Queen Angelfish (15.12.81)		1·25	1·00
	a. Perf 14 (25.1.83)		85	1·25
525B	50 c. Royal Gramma ("Fairy Basslet") (15.12.81)		7·00	6·00
526B	$1 Fin-spot Wrasse (15.12.81)		3·25	3·00
	a. Perf 14 (25.1.83)		2·00	2·00
527B	$2 Stoplight Parrotfish (15.12.81)		5·50	5·00
	a. Perf 14 (25.1.83)		2·50	4·50
528B	$5 Queen Triggerfish (15.12.81)		9·50	11·00
	a. Perf 14 (25.1.83)		5·50	9·00
514B/28B		*Set of 9*	25·00	30·00

Imprint dates: "1981", Nos. 514B, 518B, 521B, 523B, 525B/8B; "1983", Nos. 522B, 523Ba, 526Ba, 527Ba, 528Ba.

(Des BG Studio. Litho Questa)

1978 (11 Dec). *Christmas. Paintings by Dürer. T **146** and similar multicoloured designs.* P 14.

529	6 c. Type **146**		15	10
530	20 c. "The Virgin and Child with St. Anne"		20	15
531	35 c. "Paumgärtner Nativity" (horiz)		35	15
532	$2 "Praying Hands"		85	1·40
529/32		*Set of 4*	1·40	1·60
MS533	137 × 124 mm. $1 "Adoration of the Magi" (horiz)		2·25	3·25

147 Osprey

(Des G. Drummond. Litho Questa)

1979 (29 May). *Endangered Wildlife. T **147** and similar horiz designs. Multicoloured.* P 14.

534	6 c. Type **147**		75	20
535	10 c. Green Turtle		65	20
536	25 c. Queen or Pink Conch		75	25
537	55 c. Rough-toothed Dolphin		90	50
538	$1 Humpback Whale		2·00	2·00
534/8		*Set of 5*	4·50	2·75
MS539	117×85 mm. $2 Iguana		2·50	3·75

148 "The Beloved" (painting by D. G. Rossetti)

(Des G. Vasarhelyi. Litho Questa)

1979 (2 July). *International Year of the Child. T **148** and similar horiz designs showing paintings and I.Y.C. emblem. Multicoloured.* P 14.

540	6 c. Type **148**		10	10
541	25 c. "Tahitian Girl" (P. Gauguin)		15	10
542	55 c. "Calmady Children" (Sir Thomas Lawrence)		25	20
543	$1 "Mother and Daughter" (detail, P. Gauguin)		45	45
540/3		*Set of 4*	80	70
MS544	112 × 85 mm. $2 "Marchesa Elena Grimaldi" (A. van Dyck)		55	1·25

149 Medina (paddle-steamer)
and Handstamped Cover

150 Cuneiform Script

(Des J.W. Litho Questa (Nos. 545/51). Des and litho Walsall (Nos. 552/64))

1979 (27 Aug)–80. *Death Centenary of Sir Rowland Hill.*

(a) *Sheet stamps. Horiz designs as T **149**. Multicoloured.* P 12 ($2) or 14 (others)

545	6 c. Type **149**		10	10
546	20 c. Sir Rowland Hill and map of Caribbean		15	15
547	45 c. Orinoco I (mail paddle-steamer) and cover bearing Penny Black stamp		20	20
548	75 c. Shannon (screw steamer) and letter to Grand Turk		30	30
549	$1 Trent I (paddle-steamer) and map of Caribbean		35	35
550	$2 Turks Islands 1867 and Turks and Caicos Islands 1900 1d. stamps (6.5.80)		2·50	2·25
545/50		*Set of 6*	3·25	3·00
MS551	170×113 mm. As No. 550. P 14		75	1·50

Nos. 545/9 also exist perf 12 (*Price for set of 5 £1·10 mint or used*) from additional sheetlets of 5 stamps and 1 label. No. 550 only exists in this format and has the inscription "International Stamp Exhibition Earls Court—London 6–14 May 1980. LONDON 1980" overprinted on the sheet margin. The individual stamps are not overprinted. Stamps perforated 14 are from normal sheets of 40.

(b) *Booklet stamps. Designs as T **150**. Imperf × roul 5*.* Self-adhesive (27.9.79)*

552	5 c. black and bright emerald		10	10
	a. Booklet pane. Nos. 552/7		80	
553	5 c. black and bright emerald		10	10
554	5 c. black and bright emerald		10	10
555	15 c. black and light blue		20	20
556	15 c. black and light blue		20	20
557	15 c. black and light blue		20	20
558	25 c. black and light blue		30	30
	a. Booklet pane. Nos. 558/63		2·25	
559	25 c. black and light blue		60	45
560	25 c. black and light blue		30	30
561	40 c. black and bright rosine		45	45
562	40 c. black and bright rosine		45	45
563	40 c. black and bright rosine		45	45
564	$1 black and lemon		70	1·25
	a. Booklet pane of 1		70	

Designs: Horiz—No. 552. Type **150**; No. 553, Egyptian papyrus; No. 554, Chinese paper; No. 555, Greek runner; No. 556, Roman post horse; No. 557, Roman post ship; No. 558, Pigeon post; No. 559, Railway post; No. 560, Packet paddle-steamer; No. 561, Balloon post; No. 562, First airmail; No. 563, Supersonic airmail. Vert—No. 564, Original stamp press.

*Nos. 552/63 are separated by various combinations of rotary knife (giving a straight edge) and roulette. No. 564 exists only with straight edges.

152 "St. Nicholas",
Prikra, Ukraine

BRASILIANA 79
(**151**)

1979 (10 Sept). *"Brasiliana 79" International Stamp Exhibition, Rio de Janeiro. No. MS551 optd with T **151**.*

MS565	170 × 113 mm. $2 Turks Islands 1867 and Turks and Caicos Islands 1900 1d. stamps	65	1·50

Stamps from Nos. MS551 and MS565 are identical as the overprint on MS565 appears on the margin of the sheet.

(Des M. Diamond. Litho Questa)

1979 (19 Oct). *Christmas. Art. T **152** and similar vert designs. Multicoloured.* P 13½ × 14.

566	1 c. Type **152**		10	10
567	3 c. "Emperor Otto II with Symbols of Empire" (Master of the Registrum Gregorii)		10	10
568	6 c. "Portrait of St. John" (Book of Lindisfarne)		10	10
569	15 c. "Adoration of the Majestas Domini" (Prayer Book of Otto II)		10	10
570	20 c. "Christ attended by Angels" (Book of Kells)		15	15
571	25 c. "St. John the Evangelist" (Gospels of St. Medard of Soissons), Charlemagne		20	15
572	65 c. "Christ Pantocrator", Trocany, Ukraine		30	25
573	$1 "Portrait of St. John" (Canterbury Codex Aureus)		45	45
566/73		*Set of 8*	1·10	1·10
MS574	106 × 133 mm. $2 "Portrait of St. Matthew" (Book of Lindisfarne)		70	1·50

153 Pluto and Starfish

(Litho Format)

1979 (2 Nov). *International Year of the Child. Walt Disney Cartoon Characters. T **153** and similar vert designs showing characters at the seaside. Multicoloured.* P 11.

575	¼ c. Type **153**		10	10
576	½ c. Minnie Mouse in summer outfit		10	10
577	1 c. Mickey Mouse underwater		10	10
578	2 c. Goofy and turtle		10	10
579	3 c. Donald Duck and dolphin		10	10

580	4 c. Mickey Mouse fishing		10	10
581	5 c. Goofy surfing		10	10
582	25 c. Pluto and crab		45	20
583	$1 Daisy water-skiing		1·50	2·25
575/83		*Set of 9*	2·00	2·50

MS584 126 × 96 mm. $1.50, Goofy after water-skiing accident. P 13½ .. .. 1·25 1·60
    a. Error. Imperf £180

154 "Christina's World"
(painting by Andrew Wyeth)

(Des J.W. Litho Format)

1979 (19 Dec). *Works of Art. T 154 and similar multicoloured designs.* P 13½.

585	6 c. Type 154		10	10
586	10 c. Ivory Leopards, Benin (19th-cent)		10	10
587	20 c. "The Kiss" (painting by Gustav Klimt) (vert)		15	15
588	25 c. "Portrait of a Lady" (painting by R. van der Weyden) (vert)		15	15
589	80 c. Bull's head harp, Sumer, c. 2600 B.C. (vert)		30	30
590	$1 "The Wave" (painting by Hokusai)		45	45
585/90		*Set of 6*	95	95

MS591 110 × 140 mm. $2 "Holy Family" (painting by Rembrandt) (vert) .. .. 70 1·25

 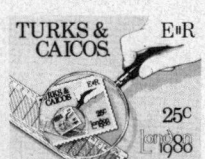

155 Pied-billed Grebe   **156** Stamp, Magnifying Glass and Perforation Gauge

(Des G. Drummond. Litho Questa)

1980 (20 Feb). *Birds. T 155 and similar horiz designs. Multicoloured.* P 14.

592	20 c. Type 155		70	30
593	25 c. Ovenbirds at nest		75	30
594	35 c. Hen Harrier		1·00	45
595	55 c. Yellow-bellied Sapsucker		1·25	50
596	$1 Blue-winged Teal		1·50	1·75
592/6		*Set of 5*	4·75	3·00

MS597 107 × 81 mm. $2 Glossy Ibis .. 2·75 2·25

(Des BG Studio. Litho Questa)

1980 (6 May). *"London 1980" International Stamp Exhibition. T 156 and similar horiz designs.* P 14.

598	25 c. black and chrome-yellow		15	15
599	40 c. black and bright green		15	25

MS600 76 × 97 mm. $2 vermilion, black and blue 70 1·10
Designs:—40 c. Stamp, tweezers and perforation gauge; $2, Earls Court Exhibition Centre.

157 Atlantic Trumpet Triton   **158** Queen Elizabeth the
(*Charonia variegata*)   Queen Mother

(Des G. Drummond. Litho Questa)

1980 (26 June). *Shells. T 157 and similar horiz designs. Multicoloured.* P 14.

601	15 c. Type 157		20	20
602	20 c. Measled Cowrie (*Cypraea zebra*)		25	25
603	35 c. True Tulip (*Fasciolaria tulipa*)		35	35
604	45 c. Lion's-paw Scallop (*Lyropecten nodosa*)		45	45
605	55 c. Sunrise Tellin (*Tellina radiata*)		55	55
606	70 c. Crown Cone (*Conus regius*)		70	70
601/6		*Set of 6*	2·25	2·25

(Des G. Vasarhelyi. Litho Questa)

1980 (4 Aug). *80th Birthday of Queen Elizabeth the Queen Mother.* P 14.

607	**158** 80 c. multicoloured		50	1·40

MS608 57 × 80 mm. **158** $1.50, multicoloured. P 12. 80 2·00

COVER PRICES

Cover factors are quoted at the beginning of each country for most issues to 1945. An explanation of the system can be found on page x. The factors quoted do not, however, apply to philatelic covers.

---

159 Doctor examining Child and Lions
International Emblem

(Des Design Images. Litho Questa)

1980 (29 Aug). *"Serving the Community". T 159 and similar horiz designs. Multicoloured.* P 14.

609	10 c. Type 159		15	10
610	15 c. Students receiving scholarships and Kiwanis International emblem		20	10
611	45 c. Teacher with students and Soroptimist emblem		40	35
612	$1 Lobster trawler and Rotary International emblem		75	80
609/12		*Set of 4*	1·40	1·25

MS613 101 × 74 mm. $2 School receiving funds and Rotary International emblem .. .. 1·25 2·00
No. **MS613** also commemorates the 75th anniversary of Rotary International.

(Litho Walsall)

1980 (30 Sept). *Christmas. Scenes from Walt Disney's Cartoon Film "Pinocchio". Horiz designs as T 153. Multicoloured.* P 11.

614	¼ c. Scene from *Pinocchio*		10	10
615	½ c. As puppet		10	10
616	1 c. Pinocchio changed into a boy		10	10
617	2 c. Captured by fox		10	10
618	3 c. Pinocchio and puppeteer		10	10
619	4 c. Pinocchio and bird's nest nose		10	10
620	5 c. Pinocchio eating		10	10
621	75 c. Pinocchio with ass ears		1·00	90
622	$1 Pinocchio underwater		1·25	1·00
614/22		*Set of 9*	2·25	2·00

MS623 127 × 102 mm. $2 Pinocchio dancing (*vert*) 2·50 2·50

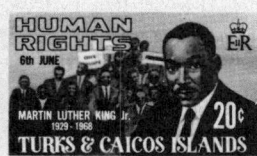

160 Martin Luther King Jr

(Des Design Images. Litho Questa)

1980 (22 Dec). *Human Rights. Personalities. T 160 and similar horiz designs. Multicoloured.* P 14 × 13½.

624	20 c. Type 160		15	10
625	30 c. John F. Kennedy		30	25
626	45 c. Roberto Clemente (baseball player)		45	35
627	70 c. Sir Frank Worrel (cricketer)		90	90
628	$1 Harriet Tubman		1·10	1·25
624/8		*Set of 5*	2·50	2·50

MS629 103 × 80 mm. $2 Marcus Garvey 1·10 1·25

161 Yachts   **162** Night Queen Cactus

(Litho Questa)

1981 (29 Jan). *South Caicos Regatta. T 161 and similar horiz designs. Multicoloured.* P 14.

630	6 c. Type 161		10	10
631	15 c. Trophy and yachts		15	15
632	35 c. Spectators watching speedboat race		25	20
633	$1 Caicos sloops		60	60
630/3		*Set of 4*	90	90

MS634 113 × 85 mm. $2 Queen Elizabeth II and map of South Caicos (*vert*) .. .. 80 1·75

(Des J. Cooter. Litho Questa)

1981 (10 Feb). *Flowering Cacti. T 162 and similar vert designs. Multicoloured.* P 13½ × 14.

635	25 c. Type 162		20	25
636	35 c. Ripsaw Cactus		25	35
637	55 c. Royal Strawberry Cactus		30	60
638	80 c. Caicos Cactus		40	1·00
635/8		*Set of 4*	1·00	2·00

MS639 72 × 86 mm. $2 Turks Head Cactus. P 14½ 1·00 2·00

(Litho Format)

1981 (16 Feb). *50th Anniv of Walt Disney's Cartoon Character, Pluto. Vert designs as T 153. Multicoloured.* P 13½.

640	10 c. Pluto playing on beach with Queen or Pink Conch shell		10	10
641	75 c. Pluto on raft, and porpoise		75	90

MS642 127 × 101 mm. $1.50 Pluto in scene from film *Simple Things* .. .. .. 1·60 2·25

(Litho Format)

1981 (20 Mar). *Easter. Walt Disney Cartoon Characters. Vert designs as T 153. Multicoloured.* P 11.

643	10 c. Donald Duck and Louie		20	20
644	25 c. Goofy and Donald Duck		40	40
645	60 c. Chip and Dale		60	1·00
646	80 c. Scrooge McDuck and Huey		70	1·40
643/6		*Set of 4*	1·75	2·75

MS647 126 × 101 mm. $4 Chip (or Dale). P 13½ 4·00 3·50

163 "Woman with Fan"   **164** Kensington Palace

(Des J.W. Litho Questa)

1981 (28 May). *Birth Centenary of Picasso. T 163 and similar vert designs. Multicoloured.* P 13½ × 14.

648	20 c. Type 163		20	15
649	45 c. "Woman with Pears"		25	30
650	80 c. "The Accordionist"		45	50
651	$1 "The Aficionado"		60	80
648/51		*Set of 4*	1·40	1·60

MS652 102 × 127 mm. $2 "Girl with a Mandolin" 1·40 1·25

(Des J.W. Litho Questa)

1981 (23 June). *Royal Wedding. T 164 and similar vert designs. Multicoloured.* P 14.

653	35 c. Prince Charles and Lady Diana Spencer		15	10
654	65 c. Type 164		20	20
655	90 c. Prince Charles as Colonel of the Welsh Guards		25	30
653/5		*Set of 3*	50	50

MS656 96 × 82 mm. $2 Glass Coach .. 50 55
Nos. 653/5 also exist perforated 12 (*price for set of 3 50p. mint or used*) from additional sheetlets of five stamps and one label. The 65 c. and 90 c. values from these sheetlets have changed background colours.

165 Lady Diana Spencer   **166** Marine Biology Observation

(Manufactured by Walsall)

1981 (7 July). *Royal Wedding. T 165 and similar vert designs. Multicoloured. Roul 5 × imperf*. Self-adhesive.*

657	20 c. Type 165		25	30
	a. Booklet pane. Nos. 657/8, each × 3		1·60	
658	$1 Prince Charles		35	70
659	$2 Prince Charles and Lady Diana Spencer		1·10	2·25
	a. Booklet pane of 1		1·10	
657/9		*Set of 3*	1·50	3·00

*The 20 c. and $1 values were each separated by various combinations of rotary knife (giving a straight edge) and roulette. The $2 value exists only with straight edges. Nos. 657/9 were only issued in $5.60 stamp booklets.

(Des G. Drummond. Litho Questa)

1981 (21 Aug). *Diving. T 166 and similar horiz designs. Multicoloured.* P 14.

660	15 c. Type 166		20	15
661	40 c. Underwater photography		50	35
662	75 c. Wreck diving		90	70
663	$1 Diving with dolphins		1·25	1·00
660/3		*Set of 4*	2·50	2·00

MS664 91 × 75 mm. $2 Diving flag .. 1·75 2·25

(Litho Questa)

1981 (2 Nov). *Christmas. Horiz designs as T 153 showing scenes from Walt Disney's cartoon film "Uncle Remus".* P 13½.

665	¼ c. multicoloured		10	10
666	½ c. multicoloured		10	10
667	1 c. multicoloured		10	10
668	2 c. multicoloured		10	10
669	3 c. multicoloured		10	10
670	4 c. multicoloured		10	10
671	5 c. multicoloured		10	10
672	75 c. multicoloured		1·00	80
673	$1 multicoloured		1·25	1·00
665/73		*Set of 9*	1·90	1·90

MS674 128 × 103 mm. $2 multicoloured .. 1·75 2·25

167 Map of Grand Turk, and Lighthouse   **168** *Junonia evarete*

(Des J.W. Litho Questa)

1981 (1 Dec). *Tourism. T* **167** *and similar horiz designs. Multicoloured.* P 14.

675	20 c. Type **167**		40	45
	a. Vert strip of 10. Nos. 675/84		3·50	
676	20 c. Map of Salt Cay, and "industrial archaeology"		40	45
677	20 c. Map of South Caicos, and "island flying"		40	45
678	20 c. Map of East Caicos, and "beach combing"		40	45
679	20 c. Map of Grand Caicos (middle), and cave exploring		40	45
680	20 c. Map of North Caicos, and camping and hiking		40	45
681	20 c. Map of North Caicos, Parrot Cay, Dellis Cay, Fort George Cay, Pine Cay and Water Cay, and "environmental studies"		40	45
682	20 c. Map of Providenciales, and scuba diving		40	45
683	20 c. Map of West Caicos, and "cruising and bird sanctuary"		40	45
684	20 c. Turks and Caicos Islands flag		40	45
675/84		*Set of 10*	3·50	4·00

Nos. 675/84 were printed together, *se-tenant*, in vertical strips of 10 throughout the sheet of 40, the two panes (2 × 10), separated by a gutter margin, being *tête-bêche*.

(Des J. Cooter. Litho Questa)

1982 (21 Jan). *Butterflies. T* **168** *and similar vert designs. Multicoloured.* P 14.

685	20 c. Type **168**		30	30
686	35 c. *Strymon maesites*		50	55
687	65 c. *Agraulis vanillae*		90	1·25
688	$1 *Eurema dina*		1·40	2·00
685/8		*Set of 4*	2·75	3·75
MS689	72×56 mm. $2 *Anaea intermedia*		2·75	3·75

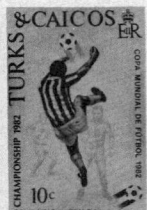

169 Flag Salute on Queen's Birthday   **170** Footballer

(Litho Questa)

1982 (17 Feb). *75th Anniv of Boy Scout Movement. T* **169** *and similar vert designs. Multicoloured.* P 14.

690	40 c. Type **169**		50	50
691	50 c. Raft building		60	60
692	75 c. Sea scout cricket match		1·10	1·60
693	$1 Nature study		1·50	1·75
690/3		*Set of 4*	3·25	4·00
MS694	100 × 70 mm. $2 Lord Baden-Powell and scout salute		2·50	3·00

(Des G. Vasarhelyi. Litho Questa)

1982 (30 Apr). *World Cup Football Championship, Spain. T* **170** *and similar designs showing footballers.* P 14.

695	10 c. multicoloured		15	15
696	25 c. multicoloured		20	20
697	45 c. multicoloured		25	25
698	$1 multicoloured		80	80
695/8		*Set of 4*	1·25	1·25
MS699	117 × 83 mm. $2 multicoloured (*horiz*)		1·25	2·00

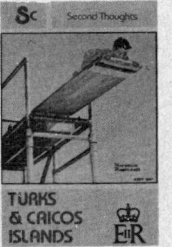

171 Washington crossing the Delaware and Phillis Wheatley (poetess)   **172** "Second Thoughts"

(Des Design Images. Litho Questa)

1982 (3 May). *250th Birth Anniv of George Washington* (20, 35 c.) *and Birth Centenary of Franklin D. Roosevelt* (65, 80 c.). *T* **171** *and similar horiz designs. Multicoloured.* P 14.

700	20 c. Type **171**		25	30
701	35 c. George Washington and Benjamin Banneker (surveyor)		35	45
702	65 c. Franklin D. Roosevelt meeting George Washington Carver (agricultural researcher)		50	80
703	80 c. Roosevelt as stamp collector		60	1·00
700/3		*Set of 4*	1·50	2·25
MS704	100 × 70 mm. $2 Roosevelt with stamp showing profile of Washington		1·50	2·50

(Litho Questa)

1982 (23 June). *Norman Rockwell* (painter) *Commemoration. T* **172** *and similar vert designs. Multicoloured.* P 14 × 13½.

705	8 c. Type **172**		15	10
706	15 c. "The Proper Gratuity"		20	20
707	20 c. "Doctor's Office" (inscr "Before the Shot")		25	30
708	25 c. "Bottom of the Sixth" (inscr "The Three Umpires")		25	30
705/8		*Set of 4*	75	80

173 Princess of Wales   **174** Cessna 337 Super Skymaster over Caicos Cays

(Des PAD Studio. Litho Questa)

1982 (1 July–18 Nov). *21st Birthday of Princess of Wales. T* **173** *and similar vert designs. Multicoloured.* P 14½ × 14.

(a) Sheet stamps. Pale green frames

709	55 c. Sandringham		35	45
710	70 c. Prince and Princess of Wales		60	55
711	$1 Type **173**		90	80
709/11		*Set of 3*	1·75	1·75
MS712	102 × 76 mm. $2 Princess Diana (*different*)		1·50	1·75

(b) Booklet stamps. As Nos. 709/11 *but printed with new values and blue frame* (18.11.82)

713	8 c. Sandringham		15	35
714	35 c. Prince and Princess of Wales		55	1·00
715	$1.10, Type **173**		80	2·00
713/15		*Set of 3*	1·40	3·00

Nos. 713/15 also exist from sheets printed in horizontal *tête-bêche* pairs throughout.

(Des MBI Studios. Litho Questa)

1982 (23 Aug). *Aircraft. T* **174** *and similar horiz designs. Multicoloured.* P 14.

716	8 c. Type **174**		15	15
717	15 c. Lockheed JetStar II over Grand Turk		20	25
718	65 c. Sikorsky S.58 helicopter over South Caicos		65	80
719	$1.10, Cessna 182 Skylane seaplane over Providenciales		1·10	1·25
716/19		*Set of 4*	1·90	2·25
MS720	99×69 mm. $2 Boeing 727-200 over Turks and Caicos Islands		2·00	2·50

(Litho Questa)

1982 (1 Dec). *Christmas. Scenes from Walt Disney's Cartoon Film "Mickey's Christmas Carol". Horiz designs as T* **153**. *Multicoloured.* P 13½.

721	1 c. Donald Duck, Mickey Mouse and Scrooge		10	10
722	1 c. Goofy (Marley's ghost) and Scrooge		10	10
723	2 c. Jiminy Cricket and Scrooge		10	10
724	2 c. Huey, Dewey and Louie		10	10
725	3 c. Daisy Duck and youthful Scrooge		10	10
726	3 c. Giant and Scrooge		10	10
727	4 c. Two bad wolves, a wise pig and a reformed Scrooge		10	10
728	65 c. Donald Duck and Scrooge		1·00	75
729	$1.10, Mortie and Scrooge		1·60	1·25
721/9		*Set of 9*	2·50	2·00
MS730	126 × 101 mm. $2 Mickey and Minnie Mouse with Mortie		2·75	2·50

175 West Caicos Mule-drawn Wagon

(Des N. Waldman. Litho Questa)

1983 (18 Jan). *Trams and Locomotives. T* **175** *and similar horiz designs. Multicoloured.* P 14.

731	15 c. Type **175**		20	25
732	55 c. West Caicos steam locomotive		65	70
733	90 c. East Caicos mule-drawn sisal train		90	1·00
734	$1.60, East Caicos steam locomotive		1·75	1·90
731/4		*Set of 4*	3·25	3·50
MS735	99×69 mm. $2.50, Steam sisal train		2·25	2·25

176 Policewoman on Traffic Duty   **177** "St. John and the Virgin Mary" (detail)

(Des N. Waldman. Litho Questa)

1983 (14 Mar). *Commonwealth Day. T* **176** *and similar horiz designs. Multicoloured.* P 14

736	1 c. Type **176**		15	20
	a. Vert strip of 4. Nos. 736/9		2·40	
737	8 c. Stylised sun and weather vane		15	20
738	65 c. Yacht		85	90
739	$1 Cricket		1·50	1·60
736/9		*Set of 4*	2·40	2·50

Nos. 736/9 were printed together, *se-tenant*, in vertical strips of four throughout the sheet.

(Des Design Images. Litho Questa)

1983 (7 Apr). *Easter. T* **177** *and similar vert designs showing details from the "Mond Crucifixion" by Raphael. Multicoloured.* P 13½ × 14.

740	35 c. Type **177**		20	25
741	50 c. "Two Women"		30	35
742	95 c. "Angel with two jars"		40	60
743	$1.10, "Angel with one jar"		60	80
740/3		*Set of 4*	1·40	2·00
MS744	100 × 130 mm. $2.50, "Christ on the Cross"		1·60	2·00

178 Minke Whale   **179** First Hydrogen Balloon *The Globe*, 1783

(Des D. Hamilton. Litho Questa)

1983 (16 May–11 July). *Whales. T* **178** *and similar horiz designs. Multicoloured.* P 13½.

745	50 c. Type **178**		2·00	2·00
746	65 c. Black Right Whale (11.7.83)		2·25	2·25
747	70 c. Killer Whale (13.6.83)		2·50	2·50
748	95 c. Sperm Whale (13.6.83)		2·75	2·75
749	$1.10, Cuvier's Beaked Whale (11.7.83)		3·00	3·00
750	$2 Blue Whale (13.6.83)		5·00	5·00
751	$2.20, Humpback Whale		5·50	5·50
752	$3 Long-finned Pilot Whale		6·25	6·25
745/52		*Set of 8*	26·00	26·00
MS753	112×82 mm. $3 Fin Whale (11.7.83)		5·50	5·00

Nos. 745/52 were each issued in sheetlets of four.

(Des BG Studio. Litho Questa)

1983 (30 Aug). *Bicentenary of Manned Flight. T* **179** *and similar vert designs. Multicoloured.* P 14.

754	25 c. Type **179**		20	25
755	35 c. *Friendship 7*		30	35
756	70 c. First hot air balloon *Le Martial*, 1783		50	70
757	95 c. Space shuttle *Columbia*		70	90
754/7		*Set of 4*	1·50	2·00
MS758	112×76 mm. $2 Montgolfier balloon and Space shuttle		1·50	2·00

180 Fiddler Pig   **181** Bermuda Sloop

(Litho Format)

1983 (4 Oct). *Christmas. Walt Disney Cartoon Characters. T* **180** *and similar vert designs. Multicoloured.* P 11.

759	1 c. Type **180**		10	10
760	1 c. Fifer Pig		10	10
761	2 c. Practical Pig		10	10
762	2 c. Pluto		10	10
763	3 c. Goofy		10	10

764	3 c. Mickey Mouse	10	10
765	35 c. Gyro Gearloose	45	35
766	50 c. Ludwig von Drake	70	60
767	$1.10, Huey, Dewey and Louie	1·00	1·25
759/67	Set of 9	2·00	2·00

MS768 127 × 102 mm. $2.50, Mickey and Minnie
Mouse with Huey, Dewey and Louie. P 13½ .. 3·25 4·00

(Des G. Drummond. Litho Questa)

1983 (5 Oct)–85. *Ships. T 181 and similar horiz designs. Multicoloured. P 14.*

769	4 c. Arawak dug-out canoe (9.1.84)	40	1·50
	a. Perf 12½×12 (3.85)	2·00	2·50
770	5 c. Santa Maria (9.1.84)	65	1·50
	a. Perf 12½×12 (12.8.85)	70	1·50
771	8 c. British and Spanish ships in battle (16.12.83)	2·00	1·50
	a. Perf 12½×12 (3.85)	2·75	1·50
772	10 c. Type 181	2·00	90
	a. Perf 12½×12 (3.85)	2·75	1·25
773	20 c. U.S. privateer Grand Turk (9.1.84)	70	1·50
	a. Perf 12½×12 (12.8.85)	50	1·25
774	25 c. H.M.S. Boreas (frigate) (16.12.83)	3·00	1·25
	a. Perf 12½×12 (12.8.85)	50	1·25
775	30 c. Endymion (frigate) attacking French ship, 1790s	3·00	90
	a. Perf 12½×12 (3.85)	3·00	1·25
776	35 c. Caesar (barque) (9.1.84)	1·25	2·00
	a. Perf 12½×12 (12.8.85)	60	1·50
777	50 c. Grapeshot (American schooner) (16.12.83)	3·50	1·25
	a. Perf 12½×12 (3.85)	60	1·25
778	65 c. H.M.S. Invincible (battle cruiser)	4·50	2·50
	a. Perf 12½×12 (3.85)	2·50	2·75
779	95 c. H.M.S. Magicienne (cruiser) (16.12.83)	4·50	2·50
	a. Perf 12½×12 (3.85)	2·50	2·75
780	$1.10, H.M.S. Durban (cruiser)	5·50	3·75
	a. Perf 12½×12 (3.85)	8·00	4·00
781	$2 Sentinel (cable ship)	7·00	4·00
	a. Perf 12½×12 (12.8.85)	2·50	4·00
782	$3 H.M.S. Minerva (frigate)	7·50	7·50
	a. Perf 12½×12 (12.85)	8·00	15·00
783	$5 Caicos sloop (9.1.84)	7·50	11·00
	a. Perf 12½×12 (3.85)	15·00	16·00
769/83	Set of 15	48·00	38·00
769a/83a	Set of 15	45·00	48·00

182 President Kennedy and Signing
of Civil Rights Legislation

(Des Design Images. Litho Questa)

1983 (22 Dec). *20th Death Anniv of President J. F. Kennedy. P 14.*

784	**182**	20 c. multicoloured	20	15
785		$1 multicoloured	70	1·25

183 Clarabelle Cow Diving

(Litho Questa)

1984 (21 Feb–Apr). *Olympic Games, Los Angeles. T 183 and similar horiz designs showing Disney cartoon characters in Olympic events. Multicoloured. A. Inscr "1984 LOS ANGELES". P 14×13½*

786A	1 c. Type 183	10	10
787A	1 c. Donald Duck in 500 m kayak race	10	10
788A	2 c. Huey, Dewey and Louie in 1000 m kayak race	10	10
789A	2 c. Mickey Mouse in single kayak	10	10
790A	3 c. Donald Duck highboard diving	10	10
791A	3 c. Minnie Mouse in kayak slalom	10	10
792A	25 c. Mickey Mouse freestyle swimming	70	45
793A	75 c. Donald Duck playing water-polo	2·00	2·00
794A	$1 Uncle Scrooge and Donald Duck yachting	2·00	2·00
786A/94A	Set of 9	4·50	4·25

MS795A 117×90 mm. $2 Pluto platform diving. 4·00 4·50

B. Inscr "1984 OLYMPICS LOS ANGELES" and Olympic emblem. P 12 (4.84)

786B	1 c. Type 183	10	10
787B	1 c. Donald Duck in 500 m kayak race	10	10
788B	2 c. Huey, Dewey and Louie in 1000 m kayak race	10	10
789B	2 c. Mickey Mouse in single kayak	10	10
790B	3 c. Donald Duck highboard diving	10	10
791B	3 c. Minnie Mouse in kayak slalom	10	10
792B	25 c. Mickey Mouse freestyle swimming	70	45
793B	75 c. Donald Duck playing water-polo	2·00	2·00
794B	$1 Uncle Scrooge and Donald Duck yachting	2·00	2·00
786B/94B	Set of 9	4·50	4·25

MS795B 117×90 mm. $2 Pluto platform diving.
P 14×13½ .. 4·00 5·50

184 "Cadillac V–16", 1933 **185** "Rest during the Flight to Egypt, with St. Francis"

(Des N. Waldman. Litho Questa)

1984 (15 Mar). *Classic Cars and 125th Anniv of first Commercial Oil Well. T 184 and similar horiz designs. Multicoloured. P 14.*

796	4 c. Type 184	20	10
797	8 c. Rolls-Royce "Phantom III", 1937	30	15
798	10 c. Saab "99", 1969	30	15
799	25 c. Maserati "Bora", 1973	70	40
800	40 c. Datsun "260Z", 1970	1·00	65
801	55 c. Porsche "917", 1971	1·25	80
802	80 c. Lincoln "Continental", 1939	1·40	90
803	$1 Triumph "TR3A", 1957	1·50	1·25
796/803	Set of 8	6·00	4·00

MS804 70 × 100 mm. $2 Daimler, 1886 .. 2·00 2·50

(Des S. Karp. Litho Walsall)

1984 (9 Apr). *Easter. 450th Death Anniv of Correggio (painter). T 185 and similar vert designs. Multicoloured. P 14.*

805	15 c. Type 185	20	15
806	40 c. "St. Luke and St. Ambrose"	45	40
807	60 c. "Diana and her Chariot"	65	65
808	95 c. "The Deposition of Christ"	80	80
805/8	Set of 4	1·90	1·75

MS809 100 × 79 mm. $2 "The Nativity with Saints
Elizabeth and John the younger" (horiz) .. 2·00 2·50

**19TH UPU CONGRESS,
HAMBURG, WEST GERMANY.
1874–1984**

(186)

1984 (19 June). *Universal Postal Union Congress, Hamburg. Nos. 748/9 and MS753 optd with T 186.*

810	95 c. Sperm Whale	2·50	2·00
811	$1.10, Cuvier's Beaked Whale	2·50	2·00

MS812 112 × 82 mm. $3 Fin Whale .. 4·25 4·25

187 "The Adventure of the **188** Orange Clownfish
Second Stain"

(Des S. Karp. Litho Walsall)

1984 (16 July). *125th Birth Anniv of Sir Arthur Conan Doyle (author). T 187 and similar horiz designs showing scenes from Sherlock Holmes stories. Multicoloured. P 14.*

813	25 c. Type 187	2·25	1·50
814	45 c. "The Adventure of the Final Problem"	3·00	2·25
815	70 c. "The Adventure of the Empty House"	4·50	3·50
816	85 c. "The Adventure of the Greek Interpreter"	5·50	4·00
813/16	Set of 4	13·50	10·00

MS817 100×70 mm. $2 Sir Arthur Conan Doyle 9·00 10·00

(Des Susan David. Litho Walsall)

1984 (22 Aug). *"Ausipex" International Stamp Exhibition, Melbourne. 175th Birth Anniv of Charles Darwin. T 188 and similar vert designs. Multicoloured. P 14×13½.*

818	5 c. Type 188	55	40
819	35 c. Monitor Lizard	2·00	1·75
820	50 c. Rainbow Lory	2·75	2·75
821	$1.10, Koalas	3·50	3·75
818/21	Set of 4	8·00	8·00

MS822 100×70 mm. $2 Eastern Grey Kangaroo .. 3·00 4·50

189 Donald Duck cutting down
Christmas Tree

(Litho Questa)

1984 (8 Oct–26 Nov). *Christmas. Walt Disney Cartoon Characters. T 189 and similar horiz designs showing scenes from "Toy Tinkers". Multicoloured. P 12 (75 c.) or 14×13½ (others).*

823	20 c. Type 189	85	45
824	35 c. Donald Duck and Chip n'Dale playing with train set	1·10	75
825	50 c. Donald Duck and Chip n'Dale playing with catapult	1·60	1·10
826	75 c. Donald Duck, Chip n'Dale and Christmas tree (26.11)	2·25	1·75
827	$1.10, Donald Duck, toy soldier and Chip n'Dale	2·50	2·50
823/7	Set of 5	7·50	6·00

MS828 126×102 mm. $2 Donald Duck as Father
Christmas .. 3·25 4·00

No. 826 was printed in sheetlets of 8 stamps.

190 Magnolia Warbler **191** Leonardo da Vinci and
Illustration of Glider Wing
(15th century)

(Des Susan David. Litho Walsall)

1985 (28 Jan). *Birth Bicentenary of John J. Audubon (ornithologist). T 190 and similar vert designs. Multicoloured. P 14.*

829	25 c. Type 190	2·00	75
830	45 c. Short-eared Owl	3·00	1·50
831	70 c. Mourning Dove and eggs	3·50	2·75
832	85 c. Caribbean Martin	3·50	3·00
829/32	Set of 4	11·00	7·25

MS833 100×70 mm. $2 Oystercatcher and
chicks .. 4·50 4·50

(Des K. Gromol. Litho Walsall)

1985 (22 Feb). *40th Anniv of International Civil Aviation Organization. Aviation Pioneers. T 191 and similar horiz designs. Multicoloured. P 14.*

834	8 c. Type 191	50	30
835	25 c. Sir Alliott Verdon Roe and Avro (Canada) CF-102 jetliner (1949)	1·50	40
836	65 c. Robert H. Goddard and first liquid fuel rocket (1926)	2·50	1·60
837	$1 Igor Sikorsky and Vought-Sikorsky VS-300 helicopter prototype (1939)	4·75	3·25
834/7	Set of 4	8·25	5·00

MS838 100×70 mm. $2 Amelia Earhart's
Lockheed 10E Electra (1937) .. 2·75 3·25

192 Benjamin Franklin and
Marquis de Lafayette

(Des Susan David. Litho Walsall)

1985 (28 Mar). *Centenary of the Statue of Liberty's Arrival in New York. T 192 and similar horiz designs. Multicoloured. P 14.*

839	20 c. Type 192	80	80
840	30 c. Frederic Bartholdi (designer) and Gustave Eiffel (engineer)	1·10	80
841	65 c. Isere (French screw warship) arriving in New York with statue, 1885	2·50	1·75
842	$1.10, United States fund raisers Louis Agassiz, Charles Sumner, H. W. Longfellow and Joseph Pulitzer	2·50	2·00
839/42	Set of 4	6·25	4·75

MS843 99×69 mm. $2 Dedication ceremony,
1886 .. 3·00 3·50

193 Sir Edward Hawke and
H.M.S. Royal George (ship of
the line), 1782

(Des Susan David. Litho Walsall)

1985 (17 Apr). *Salute to the Royal Navy. T* **193** *and similar multicoloured designs. P* 14.

844	20 c. Type **193**		2·25	1·75
845	30 c. Lord Nelson and H.M.S. *Victory* (ship of the line), 1805		2·75	2·25
846	65 c. Admiral Sir George Cockburn and H.M.S. *Albion* (ship of the line), 1802		3·75	3·00
847	95 c. Admiral Sir David Beatty and H.M.S. *Indefatigable* (battle cruiser), 1916		4·75	4·25
844/7		Set of 4	12·00	10·00
MS848	99×69 mm. $2 18th-century sailor and cannon (*vert*)		3·25	4·00

194 Mark Twain riding on Halley's Comet

195 The Queen Mother outside Clarence House

(Des J. Iskowitz. Litho Walsall)

1985 (17 May). *International Youth Year. Birth Annivs of Mark Twain (150th) and Jakob Grimm (Bicentenary). T* **194** *and similar multicoloured designs. P* 13½ × 14 (25, 35 c., $2) or 14 × 13½ (50, 95 c.).

849	25 c. Type **194**		1·00	40
850	35 c. *Grand Turk* (Mississippi river steamer)		1·50	55
851	50 c. Hansel and Gretel and gingerbread house (*vert*)		1·75	85
852	95 c. Rumpelstiltskin (*vert*)		2·50	2·00
849/52		Set of 4	6·00	3·50
MS853	99×68 mm. $2 Mark Twain and the Brothers Grimm		3·50	5·00

(Des J.W. Litho Questa)

1985 (15 July). *Life and Times of Queen Elizabeth the Queen Mother. T* **195** *and similar multicoloured designs. P* 14.

854	30 c. Type **195**		45	45
855	50 c. Visiting Biggin Hill airfield (*horiz*)		1·50	75
856	$1.10, 80th birthday portrait		1·75	1·90
854/6		Set of 3	3·25	2·75
MS857	56×85 mm. $2 With Prince Charles at Garter ceremony, Windsor Castle, 1968		2·00	3·00

196 King George II and Score of "Zadok the Priest" (1727)

197 Harley-Davidson Dual Cylinder (1915) on Middle Caicos

(Des Susan David. Litho Format)

1985 (17 July). *300th Birth Anniv of George Frederick Handel (composer). T* **196** *and similar vert designs. P* 15.

858	4 c. multicoloured		65	50
859	10 c. multicoloured		1·00	50
860	50 c. multicoloured		2·50	2·50
861	$1.10, multicoloured		3·00	5·50
858/61		Set of 4	6·50	8·00
MS862	101×76 mm. $2 black, deep dull purple and dull violet-blue		5·00	7·50

Designs:—10 c. Queen Caroline and score of "Funeral Anthem" (1737); 50 c. King George I and score of "Water Music" (1714); $1.10, Queen Anne and score of "Or la Tromba" from *Rinaldo* (1711); $2 George Frederick Handel.

(Des Susan David. Litho Format)

1985 (17 July). *300th Birth Anniv of Johann Sebastian Bach (composer). Vert designs as T* **204***a of Maldive Islands. Multicoloured. P* 15.

863	15 c. Bassoon		1·00	40
864	40 c. Natural Horn		1·50	85
865	60 c. Viola D'Amore		2·00	1·25
866	95 c. Clavichord		2·25	2·25
863/6		Set of 4	6·00	4·25
MS867	102×76 mm. $2 Johann Sebastian Bach		4·00	4·00

(Des Mary Walters. Litho Questa)

1985 (4 Sept). *Centenary of the Motor Cycle. T* **197** *and similar multicoloured designs. P* 14.

868	8 c. Type **197**		75	30
869	25 c. Triumph "Thunderbird" (1950) on Grand Turk		1·50	70
870	55 c. BMW "K100RS" (1985) on North Caicos		2·50	1·75
871	$1.20, Honda "1100 Shadow" (1985) on South Caicos		3·50	6·00
868/71		Set of 4	7·50	8·00
MS872	106×77 mm. $2 Daimler single track (1885) (*vert*)		4·00	4·00

Turks & Caicos Islands

198 Pirates in Prison

(Des Walt Disney Productions. Litho Questa)

1985 (4 Oct). *30th Anniv of Disneyland, U.S.A. T* **198** *and similar horiz designs showing scenes from "Pirates of the Caribbean" exhibition. Multicoloured. P* 14 × 13½.

873	1 c. Type **198**		10	10
874	1 c. The fate of Captain William Kidd		10	10
875	2 c. Bartholomew Roberts		10	10
876	2 c. Two buccaneers		10	10
877	3 c. Privateers looting		10	10
878	3 c. Auction of captives		10	10
879	35 c. Singing pirates		1·50	80
880	75 c. Edward Teach—"Blackbeard"		3·00	3·25
881	$1.10, Sir Henry Morgan		3·50	4·00
873/81		Set of 9	7·50	7·50
MS882	123×86 mm. $2.50, Mary Read and Anne Bonney		4·50	4·50

199 Brownies from China, Turks and Caicos and Papua New Guinea

(Des Mary Walters. Litho Questa)

1985 (4 Nov). *75th Anniv of Girl Guide Movement and 35th Anniv of Grand Turk Company. T* **199** *and similar horiz designs. Multicoloured. P* 14.

883	10 c. Type **199**		75	40
884	40 c. Brownies from Surinam, Turks and Caicos and Korea		1·75	1·25
885	70 c. Guides from Australia, Turks and Caicos and Canada		2·50	3·00
886	80 c. Guides from West Germany, Turks and Caicos and Israel		2·75	3·00
883/6		Set of 4	7·00	7·00
MS887	107×76 mm. $2 75th anniversary emblem		3·00	3·50

200 Iguana and Log

201 Duke and Duchess of York after Wedding

(Des I. MacLaury. Litho Questa)

1986 (20 Nov). *Turks and Caicos Ground Iguana. T* **200** *and similar horiz designs. Multicoloured. P* 14.

888	8 c. Type **200**		2·25	1·25
889	10 c. Iguana on beach		2·25	1·25
890	20 c. Iguana at nest		3·50	2·50
891	35 c. Iguana eating flowers		6·50	4·50
888/91		Set of 4	13·00	8·50
MS892	105×76 mm. $2 Map showing habitat		12·00	14·00

(Litho Questa)

1986 (19 Dec). *Royal Wedding. T* **201** *and similar vert designs. Multicoloured. P* 14.

893	35 c. Type **201**		85	55
894	65 c. Miss Sarah Ferguson in wedding carriage		1·60	1·40
895	$1.10, Duke and Duchess of York on Palace balcony after wedding		2·00	2·75
893/5		Set of 3	4·00	4·25
MS896	85×85 mm. $2 Duke and Duchess of York leaving Westminster Abbey		3·50	4·00

The new-issue supplement to this Catalogue appears each month in

GIBBONS STAMP MONTHLY

—from your newsagent or by postal subscription— sample copy and details on request.

---

202 "The Prophecy of the Birth of Christ to King Achaz"

203 H.M.S. *Victoria* (ship of the line), 1859, and Victoria Cross

(Litho Questa)

1987 (9 Dec). *Christmas. T* **202** *and similar vert designs, each showing illuminated illustration by Giorgio Clovio from "Farnese Book of Hours". Multicoloured. P* 14.

897	35 c. Type **202**		1·25	85
898	50 c. "The Annunciation"		1·75	1·75
899	65 c. "The Circumcision"		2·25	2·25
900	95 c. "Adoration of the Kings"		3·25	4·00
897/900		Set of 4	7·75	8·00
MS901	76×106 mm. $2 "The Nativity"		4·25	5·50

(Litho Questa)

1987 (24 Dec). *150th Anniv of Accession of Queen Victoria. T* **203** *and similar horiz designs. Multicoloured. P* 14.

902	8 c. Type **203**		1·75	1·00
903	35 c. *Victoria* (paddle-steamer) and gold sovereign		2·75	2·25
904	55 c. Royal Yacht *Victoria and Albert I* and 1840 Penny Black stamp		3·00	2·75
905	95 c. Royal Yacht *Victoria and Albert II* and Victoria Public Library		4·00	5·00
902/5		Set of 4	10·50	10·00
MS906	129×76 mm. $2 *Victoria* (barque)		6·00	7·50

(Des and litho Questa)

1987 (31 Dec). *Bicentenary of U.S. Constitution. Multicoloured designs as T* **210***a of Sierra Leone. P* 14.

907	10 c. State Seal, New Jersey		25	35
908	35 c. 18th-century family going to church ("Freedom of Worship") (*vert*)		75	75
909	65 c. U.S. Supreme Court, Judicial Branch, Washington (*vert*)		1·40	1·75
910	80 c. John Adams (statesman) (*vert*)		1·60	2·25
907/10		Set of 4	3·50	4·50
MS911	105×75 mm. $2 George Mason (Virginia delegate) (*vert*)		2·40	3·75

Nos. 907/10 were each printed in sheetlets of five stamps and one stamp-size label, which appears in the centre of the bottom row.

204 *Santa Maria*

205 Arawak Artifact and Scouts in Cave, Middle Caicos

(Litho Questa)

1988 (20 Jan). *500th Anniv of Discovery of America by Columbus (1992) (1st issue). T* **204** *and similar horiz designs. Multicoloured. P* 14.

912	4 c. Type **204**		45	30
913	25 c. Columbus meeting Tainos Indians		95	60
914	70 c. *Santa Maria* anchored off Indian village		2·75	3·25
915	$1 Columbus in field of grain		2·75	3·25
912/15		Set of 4	6·25	6·75
MS916	105 × 76 mm. $2 *Santa Maria, Pinta* and *Nina*		3·50	4·50

See also Nos. 947/51, 1028/36, 1072/80 and 1166/76.

(Litho Questa)

1988 (12 Feb). *World Scout Jamboree, Australia. T* **205** *and similar multicoloured designs. P* 14.

917	8 c. Type **205**		20	15
918	35 c. *Santa Maria*, scouts and Hawks Nest Island (*horiz*)		55	55
919	65 c. Scouts diving to wreck of galleon		95	1·25
920	95 c. Visiting ruins of 19th-century sisal plantation (*horiz*)		1·40	1·75
917/20		Set of 4	2·75	3·25
MS921	118 × 82 mm. $2 Splashdown of John Glenn's "Mercury" capsule, 1962		3·75	5·00

No. **MS**921 is inscribed "Sight" in error.

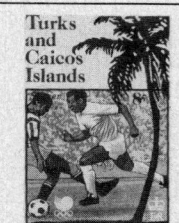

40TH WEDDING ANNIVERSARY

H.M. QUEEN ELIZABETH II

H.R.H. THE DUKE OF EDINBURGH

(206)   207 Football

1988 (14 Mar). *Royal Ruby Wedding. Nos. 772A, 774A and 781A optd with T 206.*

922	10 c. Type **181**		50	50
923	25 c. H.M.S. *Boreas* (frigate)		90	55
924	$2 *Sentinel* (cable ship)		3·25	4·25
922/4		*Set of 3*	4·25	4·75

(Des L. Fried. Litho B.D.T.)

1988 (29 Aug). *Olympic Games, Seoul. T 207 and similar vert designs. Multicoloured. P 14.*

925	8 c. Type **207**		40	15
926	30 c. Yachting		70	50
927	70 c. Cycling		2·25	2·00
928	$1 Athletics		1·75	2·25
925/8		*Set of 4*	4·50	4·50
MS929	102 × 71 mm. $2 Swimming		2·75	3·50

208 Game-fishing Launch and Swordfish

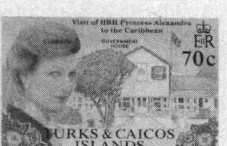

209 Princess Alexandra and Government House

(Des L. Birmingham. Litho Questa)

1988 (5 Sept). *Billfish Tournament. T 208 and similar multicoloured designs. P 14.*

930	8 c. Type **208**		55	30
931	10 c. Competitors with swordfish catch		55	30
932	70 c. Game-fishing launch		2·25	3·00
933	$1 Atlantic Blue Marlin		2·75	3·50
930/3		*Set of 4*	5·50	6·25
MS934	119×85 mm. $2 Stylized Sailfish (*horiz*)		4·00	5·50

(Litho Questa)

1988 (24 Oct). *Christmas. 500th Birth Anniv of Titian (artist). Vert designs as T **186**a of Lesotho inscr "CHRISTMAS 1988" and with royal cypher at top right. Multicoloured. P 13½×14.*

935	15 c. "Madonna and Child with Saint Catherine"		40	30
936	25 c. "Madonna with a Rabbit"		50	40
937	35 c. "Virgin and Child with Saints"		60	50
938	40 c. "The Gypsy Madonna"		70	60
939	50 c. "The Holy Family and a Shepherd"		80	70
940	65 c. "Madonna and Child"		95	85
941	$3 "Madonna and Child with Saints"		4·25	6·00
935/41		*Set of 7*	7·50	8·50
MS942	Two sheets, each 110 × 95 mm. (a) $2 "Adoration of the Magi" (detail). (b) $2 "The Annunciation" (detail)	*Set of 2 sheets*	6·00	7·50

(Des and litho Questa)

1988 (14 Nov). *Visit of Princess Alexandra. T 209 and similar multicoloured designs. P 14.*

943	70 c. Type **209**		1·75	1·50
944	$1.40, Princess Alexandra and map of islands		3·75	4·00
MS945	92 × 72 mm. $2 Princess Alexandra (*vert*)		7·00	7·50

210 Coat of Arms

210a Andrew Jackson and Railway Locomotive *De Witt Clinton*

(Des and litho Questa)

1988 (15 Dec). *P 14½×15.*

946	210 $10 multicoloured		11·00	13·00

(Des D. Miller. Litho Questa)

1989 (15 May). *500th Anniv of Discovery of America by Columbus (1992) (2nd issue). Pre-Columbian Carib Society. Multicoloured designs as T **69** of St. Vincent Grenadines. P 14.*

947	10 c. Cutting tree bark for canoe		15	15
948	50 c. Body painting (*horiz*)		80	80
949	65 c. Religious ceremony (*horiz*)		95	1·10
950	$1 Canoeing		1·50	1·50
947/50		*Set of 4*	3·00	3·50
MS951	84×70 mm. $2 Cave pictograph (*horiz*)		3·50	4·50

(Des Design Element. Litho Questa)

1989 (17 Nov). *"World Stamp Expo '89" International Stamp Exhibition, Washington (1st issue). Sheet 77×62 mm containing horiz design as T **193**a of Lesotho. Multicoloured. P 14.*

MS952	$1.50, Lincoln Memorial		2·50	3·25

(Des W. Hanson Studio. Litho Questa)

1989 (19 Nov). *"World Stamp Expo '89" International Stamp Exhibition, Washington (2nd issue). Bicentenary of the U.S. Presidency. T **210**a and similar horiz designs. Multicoloured. P 14.*

953	50 c. Type **210**a		90	90
	a. Sheetlet. Nos. 953/8		4·75	
954	50 c. Martin van Buren, Moses Walker and early baseball game		90	90
955	50 c. William H. Harrison and campaign parade		90	90
956	50 c. John Tyler, Davy Crockett and the Alamo, Texas		90	90
957	50 c. James K. Polk, California gold miner and first U.S. postage stamp		90	90
958	50 c. Zachary Taylor and Battle of Buena Vista, 1846		90	90
959	50 c. Rutherford B. Hayes and end of Confederate Reconstruction		90	90
	a. Sheetlet. Nos. 959/64		4·75	
960	50 c. James A. Garfield and Battle of Shiloh		90	90
961	50 c. Chester A. Arthur and opening of Brooklyn Bridge, 1883		90	90
962	50 c. Grover Cleveland, Columbian Exposition, Chicago, 1893, and commemorative stamp		90	90
963	50 c. Benjamin Harrison, Pan-American Union Building and map of Americas		90	90
964	50 c. William McKinley and Rough Rider Monument		90	90
965	50 c. Herbert Hoover, Sonya Heine (skater) and Ralph Metcalf (athlete)		90	90
	a. Sheetlet. Nos. 965/70		4·75	
966	50 c. Franklin D. Roosevelt with dog and in wheelchair		90	90
967	50 c. Statue of Washington by Frazer and New York World's Fair, 1939		90	90
968	50 c. Harry S. Truman, Veterans Memorial Building, San Francisco, and U.N. emblem		90	90
969	50 c. Dwight D. Eisenhower and U.S. troops landing in Normandy, 1944		90	90
970	50 c. John F. Kennedy and "Apollo 11" astronauts on Moon, 1969		90	90
953/70		*Set of 18*	14·00	14·00

Nos. 953/8, 959/64 and 965/70 were each printed together, *se-tenant*, in sheetlets of six stamps.

(Litho Questa)

1989 (18 Dec). *Christmas. Paintings by Bellini. Vert designs as T **193**b of Lesotho. Multicoloured. P 14.*

971	15 c. "Madonna and Child"		50	50
972	25 c. "The Madonna of the Shrubs"		60	50
973	35 c. "The Virgin and Child"		70	60
974	40 c. "The Virgin and Child with a Greek Inscription"		80	70
975	50 c. "The Madonna of the Meadow"		90	80
976	65 c. "The Madonna of the Pear"		1·75	1·75
977	70 c. "The Virgin and Child" (*different*)		2·00	2·00
978	$1 "Madonna and Child" (*different*)		2·75	2·75
971/8		*Set of 8*	9·00	8·50
MS979	Two sheets, each 96 × 72 mm. (a) $2 "The Virgin and Child enthroned". (b) $2 "The Madonna with John the Baptist and another Saint"	*Set of 2 sheets*	11·00	13·00

211 Lift-off of "Apollo 11"

212 *Zephyranthes rosea*

(Des W. Hanson Studio. Litho Questa)

1990 (8 Jan). *20th Anniv of First Manned Landing on Moon. T **211** and similar vert designs. Multicoloured. P 14.*

980	50 c. Type **211**		70	90
	a. Sheetlet. Nos. 980/4 and 5 labels		3·25	
981	50 c. Lunar module *Eagle* on Moon		70	90
982	50 c. Aldrin gathering dust sample		70	90
983	50 c. Neil Armstrong with camera		70	90
984	50 c. *Eagle* re-united with command module *Columbia*		70	90
980/4		*Set of 5*	3·25	4·00

Nos. 980/4 were printed together, *se-tenant*, in sheetlets of five stamps, and five stamp-size labels, with Nos. 981/3 forming a composite design.

(Des C. Abbott. Litho Questa)

1990 (11 Jan)–94. *Island Flowers. T **212** and similar vert designs. Multicoloured. P 14.*

985	8 c. Type **212**		30	20
	a. Perf 12 (1994)		30	20
986	10 c. *Sophora tomentosa*		30	20
	a. Perf 12 (1994)		30	20
987	15 c. *Coccoloba uvifera*		40	25
	a. Perf 12 (1994)		40	25
988	20 c. *Encyclia gracilis*		40	30
	a. Perf 12 (1994)		40	30
989	25 c. *Tillandsia streptophylla*		50	35
	a. Perf 12 (1994)		50	35
990	30 c. *Maurandella antirrhiniflora*		70	70
	a. Perf 12 (1994)		70	60
991	35 c. *Tillandsia balbisiana*		60	50
	a. Perf 12 (1994)		60	50
992	50 c. *Encyclia rufa*		1·25	1·25
	a. Perf 12 (1994)		1·00	1·00
993	65 c. *Aechmea lingulata*		1·40	1·50
	a. Perf 12 (1994)		1·25	1·25
994	80 c. *Asclepias curassavica*		1·40	1·50
	a. Perf 12 (1994)		1·40	1·50
995	$1 *Caesalpinia bahamensis*		1·50	1·60
	a. Perf 12 (1994)		1·50	1·60
996	$1.10, *Capparis cynophallophora*		2·00	2·75
	a. Perf 12 (1994)		2·00	2·75
997	$1.25, *Stachytarpheta jamaicensis*		2·50	3·00
	a. Perf 12 (1994)		2·50	3·00
998	$2 *Cassia biflora*		3·00	4·00
	a. Perf 12 (1994)		3·00	4·00
999	$5 *Clusia rosea*		7·00	9·00
	a. Perf 12 (1994)		7·00	9·00
1000	$10 *Opuntia bahamana* (21.5.90)		14·00	17·00
	a. Perf 12 (1994)		14·00	17·00
985/1000		*Set of 16*	35·00	40·00
985a/1000a		*Set of 16*	35·00	40·00

213 Queen Parrotfish

(Des J. Barbaris. Litho B.D.T.)

1990 (12 Feb). *Fishes. T **213** and similar horiz designs. Multicoloured. P 14.*

1001	8 c. Type **213**		25	20
1002	10 c. Queen Triggerfish		25	20
1003	25 c. Sergeant Major		60	45
1004	40 c. Spotted Goatfish		85	75
1005	50 c. Neon Goby		1·00	85
1006	75 c. Nassau Grouper		1·50	1·50
1007	80 c. Yellow-headed Jawfish		1·75	2·00
1008	$1 Blue Tang		1·75	2·00
1001/8		*Set of 8*	7·00	7·00
MS1009	Two sheets, each 115×80 mm. (a) $2 Butter Hamlet. (b) $2 Queen Angelfish	*Set of 2 sheets*	13·00	14·00

214 Yellow-billed Cuckoo

215 *Anartia jatrophae*

(Des W. Wright. Litho B.D.T.)

1990 (19 Feb). *Birds (1st series). T **214** and similar horiz designs. Multicoloured. P 14.*

1010	10 c. Type **214**		70	50
1011	15 c. White-tailed Tropic Bird		85	50
1012	20 c. Kirtland's Warbler		1·10	75
1013	30 c. Yellow-crowned Night Heron		1·25	75
1014	50 c. Black-billed Whistling Duck ("West Indian Tree Duck")		1·90	1·00
1015	80 c. Yellow-bellied Sapsucker		2·50	2·25
1016	$1 American Kestrel		2·50	2·25
1017	$1.40, Northern Mockingbird		3·25	3·75
1010/17		*Set of 8*	12·50	10·50
MS1018	Two sheets, each 104×78 mm. (a) $2 Yellow Warbler. (b) $2 Osprey	*Set of 2 sheets*	15·00	15·00

See also Nos. 1050/8.

(Des Linda Vorovik. Litho Questa)

1990 (19 Mar). *Butterflies (1st series). T **215** and similar multicoloured designs. P 14.*

1019	15 c. Type **215**		80	45
1020	25 c. *Phoebis sennae* (*horiz*)		1·00	60
1021	35 c. *Euptoieta hegesia* (*horiz*)		1·25	75
1022	40 c. *Hylephila phylaeus* (*horiz*)		1·40	80
1023	50 c. *Eurema chamberlaini* (*horiz*)		1·40	1·00
1024	60 c. *Brephidium exilis*		1·60	1·40
1025	90 c. *Papilio aristodemus* (*horiz*)		2·75	3·00
1026	$1 *Marpesia eleucha*		2·75	3·00
1019/26		*Set of 8*	11·50	10·00
MS1027	Two sheets, each 106×76 mm. (a) $2 *Hemiargus thomasi* (*horiz*). (b) $2 *Danaus gilippus* (*horiz*)	*Set of 2 sheets*	11·00	12·00

See also Nos. 1081/9.

(Des Mary Walters. Litho Questa)

1990 (2 Apr). *500th Anniv of Discovery of America by Columbus (1992) (3rd issue). New World Natural History – Fishes. Horiz designs as T **60** of Nevis (St. Kitts-Nevis). Multicoloured. P 14.*

1028	10 c. Rock Beauty	50	30
1029	15 c. Coney	60	40
1030	25 c. Red Hind	85	60
1031	50 c. Banded Butterflyfish	1·40	1·25
1032	60 c. French Angelfish	1·75	1·50
1033	75 c. Black-barred Soldierfish	1·90	1·90
1034	90 c. Stoplight Parrotfish	2·00	2·25
1035	$1 French Grunt	2·25	2·40
1028/35	*Set of 8*	10·00	9·50
MS1036	Two sheets, each 109×75 mm. (a) $2 Blue Chromis. (b) $2 Grey Angelfish		
	Set of 2 sheets	9·00	10·00

216 Penny "Rainbow Trial" in Blue   **217** Pillar Box No. 1, 1855

(Des M. Pollard. Litho B.D.T.)

1990 (3 May). *150th Anniv of the Penny Black. T **216** and similar vert designs. P 14.*

1037	25 c. deep violet-blue	1·00	60
1038	75 c. lake-brown	2·25	2·00
1039	$1 blue	2·75	2·75
1037/9	*Set of 3*	5·50	4·75
MS1040	144×111 mm. $2 brownish black	5·00	5·50

Designs:—75 c. 1d. red-brown colour trial of December, 1840; $1 2d. blue of 1840; $2 Penny Black.

(Des M. Pollard. Litho B.D.T.)

1990 (3 May). *"Stamp World London 90" International Stamp Exhibition. British Pillar Boxes. T **217** and similar vert designs. P 14.*

1041	35 c. purple-brown and brownish grey	65	65
1042	50 c. deep violet-blue and brownish grey	90	1·00
1043	$1·25, dull ultramarine & brownish grey	2·25	3·25
1041/3	*Set of 3*	3·50	4·50
MS1044	143×111 mm. $2 brown-lake and black	4·50	5·00

Designs:—50 c. Penfold box, 1866; $1·25, Air mail box, 1935; $2 "K" type box, 1979.

218 Queen Elizabeth the Queen Mother   **219** Stripe-headed Tanager

(Des D. Miller. Litho Questa)

1990 (20 Aug). *90th Birthday of Queen Elizabeth the Queen Mother. T **218** and similar vert designs showing recent photographs of the Queen Mother. P 14.*

1045	10 c. multicoloured	35	15
1046	25 c. multicoloured	75	50
1047	75 c. multicoloured	1·40	1·60
1048	$1·25, multicoloured	2·00	2·00
1045/8	*Set of 4*	4·00	4·25
MS1049	70×73 mm. $2 multicoloured	4·00	5·00

(Des Tracy Pedersen. Litho Questa)

1990 (24 Sept). *Birds (2nd series). T **219** and similar multicoloured designs. P 14.*

1050	8 c. Type 219	70	55
1051	10 c. Black-whiskered Vireo (horiz)	70	55
1052	25 c. Blue-grey Gnatcatcher (horiz)	1·00	60
1053	40 c. Lesser Scaup (horiz)	1·75	1·00
1054	50 c. Bahama Pintail (horiz)	1·75	1·10
1055	75 c. Black-necked Stilt (horiz)	2·25	2·25
1056	80 c. Oystercatcher (horiz)	2·25	2·50
1057	$1 Louisiana Heron (horiz)	2·75	3·00
1050/7	*Set of 8*	12·00	10·50
MS1058	Two sheets, each 98×69 mm. (a) $2 American Coot (horiz). (b) $2 Bahama Woodstar (horiz)		
	Set of 2 sheets	7·50	8·50

ALTERED CATALOGUE NUMBERS

Any Catalogue numbers altered from the last edition are shown as a list in the introductory pages.

220 "Triumph of Christ over Sin and Death" (detail, Rubens)   **221** Canoeing

(Litho Questa)

1990 (17 Dec). *Christmas. 350th Death Anniv of Rubens. T **220** and similar vert designs. Multicoloured. P 13½×14.*

1059	10 c. Type 220	25	20
1060	35 c. "St. Theresa Praying" (detail)	70	45
1061	45 c. "St. Theresa Praying" (different detail)	80	60
1062	50 c. "Triumph of Christ over Sin and Death" (different detail)	90	65
1063	65 c. "St. Theresa Praying" (different detail)	1·25	1·00
1064	75 c. "Triumph of Christ over Sin and Death" (different detail)	1·40	1·25
1065	$1·25, "St. Theresa Praying" (different detail)	1·90	2·50
1059/65	*Set of 7*	6·50	6·00
MS1066	Two sheets, each 70×100 mm. (a) $2 "Triumph of Christ over Sin and Death" (different detail). (b) $2 "St. Theresa Praying" (different detail)		
	Set of 2 sheets	8·00	9·00

(Des D. Miller. Litho Questa)

1991 (7 Jan). *Olympic Games, Barcelona (1992). T **221** and similar vert designs. Multicoloured. P 14.*

1067	10 c. Type 221	25	20
1068	25 c. 100 metre sprint	60	50
1069	75 c. Pole vaulting	1·40	1·50
1070	$1·25, Javelin	2·00	2·50
1067/70	*Set of 4*	3·75	4·25
MS1071	109×70 mm. $2 Baseball	4·00	4·50

(Des T. Agans. Litho Questa)

1991 (15 Apr). *500th Anniv of Discovery of America by Columbus (1992) (4th issue). History of Exploration. Multicoloured designs as T **64** of Nevis (St. Kitts-Nevis). P 14.*

1072	5 c. Henry Hudson in Hudson's Bay, 1611	35	20
1073	10 c. Roald Amundsen's airship N.1 *Norge*, 1926	35	20
1074	15 c. Amundsen's *Gjoa* in the Northwest Passage, 1906	60	35
1075	50 c. U.S.S. *Nautilus* (submarine) under North Pole, 1958	90	65
1076	75 c. Robert Scott's *Terra Nova*, 1911	1·50	1·10
1077	$1 Byrd and Bennett's Fokker F.VIIIa/3m *Josephine Ford* aircraft over North Pole, 1926	1·75	1·50
1078	$1·25, Lincoln Ellsworth's Northrop Gamma *Polar Star* on trans-Antarctic flight, 1935	2·25	2·75
1079	$1·50, Capt. James Cook in the Antarctic, 1772–1775	2·50	3·25
1072/9	*Set of 8*	9·00	9·00
MS1080	Two sheets, each 116×76 mm. (a) $2 *Santa Maria* (vert). (b) $2 Bow of *Nina* (vert)		
	Set of 2 sheets	8·50	9·00

222 *Anartia jatrophae*

(Des D. Miller. Litho Questa)

1991 (13 May). *Butterflies (2nd series). T **222** and similar horiz designs. Multicoloured. P 14.*

1081	5 c. Type 222	35	30
1082	25 c. *Historis osius*	80	50
1083	35 c. *Agraulis vanillae*	90	65
1084	45 c. *Junonia evarete*	1·10	90
1085	55 c. *Dryas julia*	1·25	1·25
1086	65 c. *Siproeta stelenes*	1·60	1·60
1087	70 c. *Appias drusilla*	1·75	1·75
1088	$1 *Ascia monuste*	1·90	2·00
1081/8	*Set of 8*	8·75	8·00
MS1089	Two sheets, each 114×72 mm. (a) $2 *Phoebis philea*. (b) $2 *Pseudolycaena marsyas*		
	Set of 2 sheets	10·00	11·00

223 *Protohydrochoerus*

(Des R. Frank. Litho Questa)

1991 (3 June). *Extinct Species of Fauna. T **223** and similar horiz designs. Multicoloured. P 14.*

1090	5 c. Type 223	40	40
1091	10 c. *Phororhacos*	40	40
1092	15 c. *Prothylacynus*	55	40
1093	50 c. *Borhyaena*	1·25	75
1094	75 c. *Smilodon*	1·60	1·40
1095	$1 *Thoatherium*	1·75	1·60
1096	$1·25, *Cuvieronius*	2·00	2·25
1097	$1·50, *Toxodon*	2·25	2·50
1090/7	*Set of 8*	9·00	8·75
MS1098	Two sheets, each 79×59 mm. (a) $2 *Astrapotherium*. (b) $2 *Mesosaurus*		
	Set of 2 sheets	9·00	9·50

(Des D. Miller. Litho Walsall)

1991 (8 June). *65th Birthday of Queen Elizabeth II. Horiz designs as T **210** of Lesotho. Multicoloured. P 14.*

1099	25 c. Queen and Prince Philip at St. Paul's Cathedral, 1988	65	45
1100	35 c. Queen and Prince Philip	80	60
1101	65 c. Queen and Prince Philip at Garter Ceremony, 1988	1·40	1·40
1102	80 c. Queen at Windsor, May 1988	1·75	2·00
1099/1102	*Set of 4*	4·25	4·00
MS1103	68×90 mm. $2 Separate photographs of Queen and Prince Philip	4·00	4·50

224 *Pluteus chrysophlebius*

(Des Wendy Smith-Griswold. Litho Questa)

1991 (24 June). *Fungi. T **224** and similar multicoloured designs. P 14.*

1104	10 c. Type 224	40	30
1105	15 c. *Leucopaxillus gracillimus*	55	30
1106	20 c. *Marasmius haematocephalus*	65	40
1107	35 c. *Collybia subpruinosa*	85	45
1108	50 c. *Marasmius atrorubens* (vert)	1·25	75
1109	65 c. *Leucocoprinus birnbaumii* (vert)	1·50	1·25
1110	$1·10, *Trogia cantharelloides* (vert)	2·00	2·50
1111	$1·25, *Boletellus cubensis* (vert)	2·00	2·75
1104/11	*Set of 8*	8·25	8·00
MS1112	Two sheets, each 85×59 mm. (a) $2 *Pyrrhoglossum pyrrhum* (vert). (b) $2 *Gerronema citrinum*		
	Set of 2 sheets	9·00	9·50

(Des D. Miller. Litho Walsall)

1991 (29 July). *10th Wedding Anniv of Prince and Princess of Wales. Horiz designs as T **210** of Lesotho. Multicoloured. P 14.*

1113	10 c. Prince and Princess of Wales, 1987	45	25
1114	45 c. Separate photographs of Prince, Princess and sons	1·75	90
1115	50 c. Prince Henry in fire engine and Prince William applauding	2·00	1·25
1116	$1 Princess Diana in Derbyshire, 1990, and Prince Charles	2·50	2·75
1113/16	*Set of 4*	6·00	4·75
MS1117	68×90 mm. $2 Prince, Princess and family, Majorca, 1990	4·50	5·00

(Litho B.D.T.)

1991 (26 Aug). *Death Centenary of Vincent van Gogh (artist) (1990). Multicoloured designs as T **255** of Maldive Islands. P 13.*

1118	15 c. "Weaver with Spinning Wheel" (horiz)	45	30
1119	25 c. "Head of a Young Peasant with Pipe"	60	40
1120	35 c. "Old Cemetery Tower at Nuenen"	70	50
1121	45 c. "Cottage at Nightfall" (horiz)	85	60
1122	50 c. "Still Life with Open Bible" (horiz)	90	65
1123	65 c. "Lane, Jardin du Luxembourg" (horiz)	1·25	1·25
1124	80 c. "Pont du Carrousel and Louvre, Paris" (horiz)	1·50	2·00
1125	$1 "Vase with Poppies, Cornflowers, Peonies and Chrysanthemums"	1·60	2·00
1118/25	*Set of 8*	7·00	7·00
MS1126	Two sheets, each 117×80 mm. (a) $2 "Ploughed Field" (horiz). (b) $2 "Entrance to the Public Park" (horiz). Imperf		
	Set of 2 sheets	8·50	9·00

225 Series 8550 Steam Locomotive, 1899

(Litho Questa)

1991 (4 Nov). *"Phila Nippon '91" International Stamp Exhibition, Tokyo. Japanese Steam Locomotives. T **225** and similar horiz designs. Multicoloured. P 14.*

1127	8 c. Type 225	30	30
1128	10 c. Class C57, 1937	30	30
1129	45 c. Series 4110, 1913	90	70
1130	50 c. Class C55, 1935	95	70
1131	65 c. Series 6250, 1915	1·25	1·25
1132	80 c. Class E10, 1948	1·50	1·60
1133	$1 Series 4500, 1902	1·60	1·90
1134	$1·25, Class C11, 1932	2·00	2·25
1127/34	*Set of 8*	8·00	8·00
MS1135	Two sheets, each 112×80 mm. (a) $2 Class C58, 1938. (b) $2 Class C62, 1948		
	Set of 2 sheets	8·00	8·50

(Litho Walsall)

1991 (23 Dec). *Christmas. Religious Paintings by Gerard David. Vert designs as T* **211** *of Lesotho. Multicoloured. P* 12.

1136	8 c. "Adoration of the Shepherds" (detail)	25	15
1137	15 c. "Virgin and Child Enthroned with Two Angels"	45	25
1138	35 c. "The Annunciation" (outer wings)	80	50
1139	45 c. "The Rest on the Flight to Egypt"	90	75
1140	50 c. "The Rest on the Flight to Egypt" (different)	1·00	90
1141	65 c. "Virgin and Child with Angels"	1·40	1·25
1142	80 c. "Adoration of the Shepherds"	1·75	2·25
1143	$1.25, "Perussis Altarpiece" (detail)	2·25	2·75
1136/43	*Set of 8*	8·00	8·00
MS1144	Two sheets, each 102×127 mm. (a) $2 "The Nativity". (b) $2 "Adoration of the Kings". P 14 *Set of 2 sheets*	8·00	9·00

(Des D. Miller. Litho Questa)

1992 (6 Feb). *40th Anniv of Queen Elizabeth II's Accession. Horiz designs as T* **214** *of Lesotho. Multicoloured. P* 14.

1145	10 c. Garden overlooking sea	45	40
1146	20 c. Jetty	80	55
1147	25 c. Small bay	90	60
1148	35 c. Island road	95	75
1149	50 c. Grand Turk	1·40	1·00
1150	65 c. Beach	1·60	1·60
1151	80 c. Marina	1·75	2·00
1152	$1.10, Grand Turk (different)	1·90	2·25
1145/52	*Set of 8*	8·75	8·25
MS1153	Two sheets, each 75×97 mm. (a) $2 Beach (different). (b) $2 Foreshore, Grand Turk *Set of 2 sheets*	8·00	9·00

(Litho B.D.T.)

1992 (26 May). *"Granada '92" International Stamp Exhibition, Spain. Religious Paintings. Vert designs as T* **68** *of St. Kitts-Nevis (Nevis). Multicoloured. P* 13.

1154	8 c. "St. Monica" (Luis Tristán)	30	20
1155	20 c. "The Vision of Ezekiel: The Resurrection of the Flesh" (detail) (Francisco Collantes)	60	30
1156	45 c. "The Vision of Ezekiel: The Resurrection of the Flesh" (different detail) (Collantes)	90	65
1157	50 c. "The Martyrdom of St. Phillip" (José de Ribera)	1·00	65
1158	65 c. "St. John the Evangelist" (Juan Ribalta)	1·25	1·25
1159	80 c. "Archimedes" (De Ribera)	1·50	1·75
1160	$1 "St. John the Baptist in the Desert" (De Ribera)	1·60	1·75
1161	$1.25, "The Martyrdom of St. Phillip" (detail) (De Ribera)	1·90	2·25
1154/61	*Set of 8*	8·00	8·00
MS1162	Two sheets, each 95×120 mm. (a) $2 "The Baptism of Christ" (Juan Fernández Navarrete). (b) $2 "Battle at El Sotillo" (Francisco Zurbarán). Imperf *Set of 2 sheets*	8·00	9·00

226 Boy Scout on Duty at New York World's Fair, 1964

(Des W. Hanson Studio. Litho Questa)

1992 (6 July). *17th World Scout Jamboree, Korea. T* **226** *and similar multicoloured designs. P* 14.

1163	$1 Type **226**	2·25	2·50
1164	$1 Lord Baden-Powell (vert)	2·25	2·50
MS1165	117×89 mm. $2 Silver Buffalo award	4·25	5·50

227 Nina and Commemorative Coin

(Litho Questa)

1992 (12 Oct). *500th Anniv of Discovery of America by Columbus (5th issue). T* **227** *and similar horiz designs, each showing a commemorative coin. Multicoloured. P* 14.

1166	10 c. Type **227**	20	20
1167	15 c. Departure from Palos	35	25
1168	20 c. Coat of Arms of Columbus	35	30
1169	25 c. Ships of Columbus	50	35
1170	30 c. Pinta	50	40
1171	35 c. Landfall in the New World	60	45
1172	50 c. Christopher Columbus	70	65
1173	65 c. Santa Maria	1·10	1·10
1174	80 c. Erecting commemorative cross	1·25	1·40
1175	$1.10, Columbus meeting Amerindian	1·40	1·50
1166/75	*Set of 10*	6·25	6·00
MS1176	Two sheets, each 70×100 mm. (a) $2 Coins showing ships of Columbus. (b) $2 Coins showing landing in the New World *Set of 2 sheets*	8·00	8·00

(Litho Questa)

1992 (7 Dec). *Christmas. Religious Paintings. Vert designs as T* **218** *of Lesotho. Multicoloured. P* 13½×14.

1177	10 c. "Nativity" (detail) (Simon Bening)	30	15
1178	15 c. "Circumcision" (detail) (Bening)	50	30
1179	35 c. "Flight to Egypt" (detail) (Bening)	85	60

1180	50 c. "Massacre of the Innocents" (detail) (Bening)	1·00	80
1181	65 c. "The Annunciation" (Dieric Bouts)	1·40	1·25
1182	80 c. "The Visitation" (Bouts)	1·75	2·00
1183	$1.10, "Adoration of the Angels" (Bouts)	1·90	2·25
1184	$1.25, "Adoration of the Wise Men" (Bouts)	2·00	2·25
1177/84	*Set of 8*	8·75	8·75
MS1185	Two sheets, each 77×102 mm. (a) $2 "The Virgin seated with the Child" (detail) (Bouts). (b) $2 "The Virgin and Child" (detail) (Bouts) *Set of 2 sheets*	9·50	10·00

228 American Astronaut repairing Satellite (229)

Royal Visit
HRH Duke of Edinburgh
20th March 1993

(Des W. Wright and L. Fried (Nos. 1186, 1191, **MS**1192a), W. Wright (others). Litho Questa)

1993 (8 Mar). *Anniversaries and Events. T* **228** *and similar horiz designs. Multicoloured. P* 14.

1186	25 c. Type **228**	85	60
1187	50 c. Dead and flourishing trees	1·25	80
1188	65 c. Food and World map	1·60	1·40
1189	80 c. Polluted and clean seas	2·25	2·50
1190	$1 Lions Club emblem	2·50	2·50
1191	$1.25, Projected orbiting quarantine modules	2·75	3·25
1186/91	*Set of 6*	10·00	10·00
MS1192	Two sheets, each 107×80 mm. (a) $2 Projected orbital Martian vehicle. (b) $2 Industrialised town and clean beach *Set of 2 sheets*	10·00	11·00

Anniversaries and Events:—Nos. 1186, 1191, **MS**1192a, International Space Year; Nos. 1187, 1189, **MS**1192b, Earth Summit '92, Rio; No. 1188, International Conference on Nutrition, Rome; No. 1190, 75th anniv of International Association of Lions Clubs.

1993 (20 Mar). *Visit of the Duke of Edinburgh. Nos.* 1100/1 *and* **MS**1103 *optd with T* **229**.

1193	35 c. Queen and Prince Philip (R.)	85	60
1194	65 c. Queen and Prince Philip at Garter Ceremony, 1988 (R.)	1·40	1·25
MS1195	68×90 mm. $2 Separate photographs of Queen and Prince Philip	3·75	4·00

(Des Kerri Schiff. Litho Questa)

1993 (2 June). *40th Anniv of Coronation. Vert designs as T* **224** *of Lesotho. P* 13½×14.

1196	15 c. multicoloured	40	40
	a. Sheetlet. Nos. 1196/9×2	7·50	
1197	50 c. multicoloured	90	90
1198	$1 deep emerald and black	1·40	1·50
1199	$1.25, multicoloured	1·50	1·60
1196/9	*Set of 4*	3·75	4·00
MS1200	70×100 mm. $2 multicoloured. P 14	3·25	3·50

Designs:—15 c. Communion Chalice and Plate; 50 c. Queen Elizabeth II at Coronation (photograph by Cecil Beaton); $1 Queen Elizabeth during Coronation ceremony; $1.25, Queen Elizabeth and Prince Philip. (28½×42½ mm)—$2 "Queen Elizabeth II" (detail).

Nos. 1196/9 were printed together in sheetlets of 8, containing two *se-tenant* blocks of 4.

230 Omphalosaurus

(Litho Questa)

1993 (15 Nov). *Prehistoric Animals. T* **230** *and similar horiz designs. Multicoloured. P* 14.

1201	8 c. Type **230**	30	30
1202	15 c. Coelophysis	40	30
1203	20 c. Triceratops	45	30
1204	35 c. Dilophosaurus	65	50
1205	50 c. Pterodactyl	80	65
1206	65 c. Elasmosaurus	1·10	1·00
1207	80 c. Stegosaurus	1·25	1·40
1208	$1.25, Euoplocephalus	1·60	2·00
1201/8	*Set of 8*	6·00	5·75
MS1209	Two sheets, each 100×70 mm. (a) $2 As 20 c. (b) $2 As 35 c. *Set of 2 sheets*	8·50	9·00

(Litho Questa)

1993 (29 Nov). *Christmas. Religious Paintings. Designs as T* **76** *of Nevis (St. Kitts–Nevis). Black, pale lemon and red (Nos.* 1210/12, 1217 *and* **MS**1218) *or multicoloured (others). P* 13½×14.

1210	8 c. "Mary, Queen of the Angels" (detail) (Dürer)	30	10
1211	20 c. "Mary, Queen of the Angels" (different detail) (Dürer)	60	30
1212	35 c. "Mary, Queen of the Angels" (different detail) (Dürer)	85	50
1213	50 c. "Virgin and Child with St. John the Baptist" (Raphael)	1·00	70
1214	65 c. "The Canagiani Holy Family" (detail) (Raphael)	1·40	1·25
1215	80 c. "The Holy Family with the Lamb" (detail) (Raphael)	1·60	1·75

1216	$1 "Virgin and Child with St. John the Baptist" (different detail) (Raphael)	2·00	2·00
1217	$1.25, "Mary, Queen of the Angels" (different detail) (Dürer)	2·25	2·75
1210/17	*Set of 8*	9·00	8·50
MS1218	Two sheets, each 102×127 mm. (a) $2 "Mary, Queen of the Angels" (different detail) (Dürer). P 13½×14. (b) $2 "The Canagiani Holy Family" (different detail) (Raphael) (horiz). P 14×13½ *Set of 2 sheets*	8·00	9·00

231 Blue-headed Wrasse

(Des J. Genzo. Litho Questa)

1993 (15 Dec). *Fishes. T* **231** *and similar horiz designs. Multicoloured. P* 14.

1219	10 c. Type **231**	30	20
1220	20 c. Honeycomb Cowfish	50	40
1221	25 c. Glass-eyed Snapper	50	40
1222	35 c. Spotted Drum	65	50
1223	50 c. Jolt-headed Porgy	90	70
1224	65 c. Small-mouthed Grunt	1·10	1·00
1225	80 c. Candy Basslet ("Peppermint Bass")	1·25	1·50
1226	$1.10, Indigo Hamlet	1·75	2·25
1219/26	*Set of 8*	6·25	6·25
MS1227	Two sheets, each 106×75 mm. (a) $2 Bonnethead. (b) $2 Atlantic Sharp-nosed Shark *Set of 2 sheets*	7·50	8·00

The captions on No. **MS**1227 have been transposed in error.

232 Killdeer

(Des I. MacLaury. Litho Questa)

1993 (30 Dec). *Birds. T* **232** *and similar multicoloured designs. P* 14.

1228	10 c. Type **232**	50	50
1229	15 c. Yellow-crowned Night Heron (vert)	75	50
1230	35 c. Northern Mockingbird	1·10	60
1231	50 c. Eastern Kingbird (vert)	1·25	75
1232	65 c. Magnolia Warbler	1·75	1·25
1233	80 c. Cedar Waxwing (vert)	2·00	2·25
1234	$1.10, Ruby-throated Hummingbird	2·25	2·25
1235	$1.25, Painted Bunting (vert)	2·50	2·75
1228/35	*Set of 8*	11·00	9·75
MS1236	Two sheets, each 100×70 mm. (a) $2 Ruddy Duck. (b) $2 American Kestrel (vert) *Set of 2 sheets*	9·50	9·50

233 Sergio Goycoechea (Argentina) **234** Xerocomus guadelupae

(Litho Questa)

1994 (26 Sept). *World Cup Football Championship, U.S.A. T* **233** *and similar multicoloured designs. P* 14.

1237	8 c. Type **233**	30	20
1238	10 c. Bodo Illgner (Germany)	30	20
1239	50 c. Nico Claesen (Belgium), Bossis and Amoros (France)	1·25	70
1240	65 c. German players celebrating	1·50	1·10
1241	80 c. French players celebrating	1·75	2·00
1242	$1 Cuciuffo (Argentina), Santin and Francescoli (Uruguay)	2·00	2·00
1243	$1.10, Hugo Sanchez (Mexico)	2·00	2·25
1237/43	*Set of 7*	8·25	7·75
MS1244	Two sheets, each 100×70 mm. (a) $2 The Silverdome, Michigan. (b) $2 Michel Platini (France) (vert) *Set of 2 sheets*	5·25	5·75

No. 1237 is inscribed "Segio Goycoechea" and No. 1238 "Bado Illgner", both in error.

(Litho Questa)

1994 (10 Oct). *Fungi. T* **234** *and similar multicoloured designs. P* 14.

1245	5 c. Type **234**	30	30
1246	10 c. Volvariella volvacea	30	30
1247	35 c. Hygrocybe atrosquamosa (horiz)	65	50
1248	50 c. Pleurotus ostreatus (horiz)	90	65
1249	65 c. Marasmius pallescens (horiz)	1·25	1·00
1250	80 c. Coprinus plicatilis	1·40	1·50
1251	$1.10, Bolbitius vitellinus (horiz)	1·60	1·90
1252	$1.50, Pyrrhoglossum lilaceipes	2·00	2·50
1245/52	*Set of 8*	7·75	7·75
MS1253	Two sheets, each 102×72 mm. (a) $2 Russula cremeolilacina. (b) $2 Lentinus edodes (horiz) *Set of 2 sheets*	7·50	8·00

235 "The Annunciation"

(Litho Questa)

1994 (5 Dec). *Christmas. Illustrations from 15th-century French Book of Hours. T 235 and similar vert designs. P 14.*
1254	25 c. Type 235	70	35
1255	50 c. "The Visitation"	1·25	75
1256	65 c. "Annunciation to the Shepherds"	1·50	1·25
1257	80 c. "The Nativity"	1·75	2·00
1258	$1 "Flight into Egypt"	2·00	2·00
1254/8	*Set of 5*	6·50	5·75
MS1259	63×86 mm. $2 "The Adoration of the Magi"	5·00	5·50

236 *Dryas julia*

(Litho Questa)

1994 (12 Dec). *Butterflies. T 236 and similar horiz designs. Multicoloured. P 14.*
1260	15 c. Type 236	40	35
1261	20 c. *Urbanus proteus*	45	40
1262	25 c. *Colobura dirce*	50	40
1263	50 c. *Papilio homerus*	90	65
1264	65 c. *Chiodes catillus*	1·25	1·00
1265	80 c. *Eurytides zonaria*	1·50	1·75
1266	$1 *Hypolymnas misippus*	1·60	1·75
1267	$1.25, *Phoebis avellaneda*	1·75	2·00
1260/7	*Set of 8*	7·50	7·50
MS1268	Two sheets, each 100×70 mm. (a) $2 *Eurema adamsi*. (b) $2 *Morpho peleides*		
	Set of 2 sheets	5·50	6·00

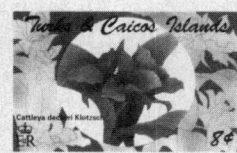

237 General Montgomery and British Troops landing on Juno Beach

(Des J. Iskowitz. Litho Questa)

1994 (19 Dec). *50th Anniv of D-Day. T 237 and similar horiz designs. Multicoloured. P 14.*
1269	10 c. Type 237	30	30
1270	15 c. Admiral Ramsay and British commandos at Sword Beach	45	35
1271	35 c. Gun crew on H.M.S. *Belfast* (cruiser)	65	45
1272	50 c. Montgomery and Eisenhower with Air Chief Marshal Tedder	90	65
1273	65 c. General Eisenhower and men of U.S. 101st Airborne Division	1·25	1·00
1274	80 c. Lt-Gen. Bradley and U.S. troops landing on Omaha Beach	1·40	1·50
1275	$1.10, Arrival of U.S. reinforcements	1·60	1·75
1276	$1.25, Eisenhower at briefing	1·75	1·90
1269/76	*Set of 8*	7·50	7·00
MS1277	Two sheets, each 100×70 mm. (a) $2 Landing craft and barrage balloon. (b) $2 Eisenhower and Montgomery		
	Set of 2 sheets	5·00	5·25

238 *Cattleya deckeri*

(Des Dorothy Novak. Litho Questa)

1995 (5 Jan). *Orchids. T 238 and similar horiz designs. Multicoloured. P 14.*
1278	8 c. Type 238	50	20
1279	20 c. *Epidendrum carpophorum*	70	30
1280	25 c. *Epidendrum ciliare*	70	35
1281	50 c. *Encyclia phoenicea*	95	70
1282	65 c. *Bletia patula*	1·25	1·10

1283	80 c. *Brassia caudata*	1·40	1·50
1284	$1 *Brassavola nodosa*	1·60	1·60
1285	$1.25, *Bletia purpurea*	1·90	2·25
1278/85	*Set of 8*	8·00	7·25
MS1286	Two sheets, each 100×70 mm. (a) $2 *Vanilla planifolia*. (b) $2 *Ionopsis utricularioides*		
	Set of 2 sheets	7·50	8·00

(Des W. Hanson. Litho Questa)

1995 (9 Jan). *25th Anniv of First Moon Landing. Multi-coloured designs as T 302 of Maldive Islands. P 14.*
1287	10 c. "Apollo 11"	30	30
1288	20 c. Moon landing simulation	45	35
1289	25 c. "Astronauts on the Moon" (detail) (Kovales)	50	35
1290	35 c. First human foot on Moon	65	45
1291	50 c. Astronaut Aldrin conducting solar wind experiment	90	65
1292	65 c. Astronauts planting U.S.A. flag	1·25	1·00
1293	80 c. Space module *Columbia* over lunar surface	1·40	1·50
1294	$1.10, "Apollo 11" after splashdown	1·60	1·90
1287/94	*Set of 8*	6·25	6·00
MS1295	Two sheets, each 104×84 mm. (a) $2 Sample of Moon rock. (b) $2 "Apollo 11" lift-off, Cape Canaveral (*vert*)		
	Set of 2 sheets	7·00	7·50

239 Elasmosaurus

240 Fencing

(Des Mary Walters. Litho Questa)

1995 (23 Jan). *Jurassic Marine Reptiles. T 239 and similar horiz designs. Multicoloured. P 14.*
1296	35 c. Type 239	65	65
	a. Sheetlet. Nos. 1296/307	7·00	
1297	35 c. Plesiosaurus	65	65
1298	35 c. Ichthyosaurus	65	65
1299	35 c. Archelon	65	65
1300	35 c. Askeptosaurus	65	65
1301	35 c. Macroplata	65	65
1302	35 c. Ceresiosaurus	65	65
1303	35 c. Lipoleurodon	65	65
1304	35 c. Henodus	65	65
1305	35 c. Muraenosaurus	65	65
1306	35 c. Placodus	65	65
1307	35 c. Kronosaurus	65	65
1296/1307	*Set of 12*	7·00	7·00

Nos. 1296/307 were printed together, *se-tenant*, in sheetlets of 12 forming a composite design.

(Des D. Miller. Litho Questa)

1995 (6 Feb). *Centenary of International Olympic Committee. T 240 and similar vert designs. Multicoloured. P 14.*
1308	8 c. Type 240	20	15
1309	10 c. Speed skating	20	15
1310	15 c. Diving	30	25
1311	20 c. Cycling	70	30
1312	25 c. Ice hockey	70	35
1313	35 c. Figure skating	65	50
1314	50 c. Football	80	70
1315	65 c. Bob-sleighing	1·10	1·10
1316	80 c. Supergiant slalom	1·25	1·40
1317	$1.25, Show jumping	1·75	2·00
1308/17	*Set of 10*	6·75	6·25
MS1318	Two sheets, 89×110 mm. (a) $2 Downhill skiing. (b) $2 Gymnastics		
	Set of 2 sheets	6·50	7·50

Both miniature sheets are incorrectly dated "1984–1994" on the margin.

241 Cat and Kitten

242 Belted Kingfisher

(Des Mary Walters. Litho Questa)

1995 (3 July). *Cats. T 241 and similar horiz designs. Multi-coloured. P 14.*
1319	15 c. Type 241	40	30
1320	20 c. Tabby on branch	45	30
1321	35 c. Cat and ladybird	65	45
1322	50 c. Black and white cat	90	65
1323	65 c. Red cat with flower in paw	1·25	1·10
1324	80 c. White cat on pink pillow	1·40	1·60
1325	$1 Siamese with flower in paws	1·60	1·75
1326	$1.25, Cats preening	2·00	2·50
1319/26	*Set of 8*	7·75	7·75
MS1327	Two sheets, each 106×76 mm. (a) $2 Kitten and ladybirds. (b) $2 Kittens asleep		
	Set of 2 sheets	7·00	7·50

(Des Helen Bultfield. Litho B.D.T.)

1995 (2 Aug). *Birds. T 242 and similar multicoloured designs. P 13½×13.*
1328	10 c. Type 242	10	10
1329	15 c. Clapper Rail	20	25
1330	20 c. American Redstart	25	30
1331	25 c. Roseate Tern	30	35
1332	35 c. Purple Gallinule	40	45
1333	45 c. Turnstone	55	60
1334	50 c. Barn Owl	60	65
1335	60 c. Brown Booby	70	75
1336	80 c. Great Blue Heron	1·00	1·10
1337	$1 Antillean Nighthawk	1·25	1·40
1338	$1.25, Thick-billed Vireo	1·50	1·60
1339	$1.40, American Flamingo	1·75	1·90
1340	$2 Wilson's Plover	2·40	2·50
1341	$5 Blue-winged Teal	6·00	6·25
1342	$10 Pair of Reddish Egrets (50×28 *mm*)	12·00	12·50
1328/42	*Set of 15*	29·00	30·00

(Des and litho Questa)

1995 (4 Aug). *95th Birthday of Queen Elizabeth the Queen Mother. Vert designs as T 321 of Maldive Islands. P 13½×14.*
1344	50 c. orange-brown, pale brown and black	90	1·00
	a. Sheetlet. Nos. 1344/7×2	6·50	
1345	50 c. multicoloured	90	1·00
1346	50 c. multicoloured	90	1·00
1347	50 c. multicoloured	90	1·00
1344/7	*Set of 4*	3·25	3·50
MS1348	102×127 mm. $2 multicoloured	3·50	3·75

Designs:—No. 1344, Queen Elizabeth the Queen Mother (pastel drawing); No. 1345, Wearing tiara; No. 1346, At desk (oil painting); No. 1347, Wearing blue dress; No. MS1348, Wearing pale blue dress and hat

Nos. 1344/7 were printed together in sheetlets of 8, containing two *se-tenant* horizontal strips of 4.

(Des R. Sauber. Litho Questa)

1995 (14 Aug). *50th Anniv of End of Second World War in Europe. Horiz designs as T 317 of Maldive Islands. Multi-coloured. P 14.*
1349	10 c. Churchill, Roosevelt and Stalin at Yalta Conference	30	30
1350	15 c. Liberated Allied prisoners of war	40	30
1351	20 c. Meeting of American and Soviet soldiers at River Elbe	45	30
1352	25 c. Pres. Roosevelt's funeral cortege	50	35
1353	60 c. U.S. bugler sounding cease-fire	1·00	1·00
1354	80 c. U.S. sailor kissing nurse, New York	1·40	1·50
1355	$1 Nuremburg Trials	1·60	1·75
1349/55	*Set of 7*	5·00	5·00
MS1356	104×74 mm. $2 Fireworks over Allied capitals	2·40	2·50

243 William James Scuba, 1825

(Des L. Birmingham. Litho Questa)

1995 (1 Sept). *"Singapore '95" International Stamp Exhibition. Deep Sea Diving. T 243 and similar horiz designs. Multi-coloured. P 14×14½.*
1357	60 c. Type 243	75	80
	a. Sheetlet. Nos. 1357/65	6·25	
1358	60 c. Rouquayrol apparatus, 1864	75	80
1359	60 c. Fluess oxygen-rebreathing apparatus, 1878	75	80
1360	60 c. Armoured diving suit, 1900	75	80
1361	60 c. Diving on the *Lusitania* in Peress armoured diving suit, 1935	75	80
1362	60 c. Cousteau Gagnan aqualung, 1943	75	80
1363	60 c. Underwater camera, 1955	75	80
1364	60 c. Sylvia Earle's record dive, 1979	75	80
1365	60 c. Spider propeller-driven rigid suit, 1984	75	80
1357/65	*Set of 9*	6·25	6·50
MS1366	Two sheets, each 107×77 mm. (a) $2 Helmet diver, 1935. (b) $2 Jacques-Yves Cousteau (aqualung pioneer) *Set of 2 sheets*	4·75	5·00

Nos. 1357/65 were printed together, *se-tenant*, in sheetlets of 9.

(Litho Questa)

1995 (29 Dec). *Christmas. Religious Paintings by Piero di Cosimo. Vert designs as T 98 of St. Kitts-Nevis (Nevis). Multicoloured. P 13½×14.*
1367	20 c. "Madonna and Child with St. Giovannino"	40	40
1368	25 c. "Adoration of the Child"	45	35
1369	60 c. "Madonna and Child with St. Giovannino, St. Margherita and Angel"	1·00	85
1370	$1 "Madonna and Child with Angel"	1·50	1·50
1367/70	*Set of 4*	3·00	2·75
MS1371	76×106 mm. $2 "Madonna and Child with Angels and Saints" (detail)	3·50	4·00

244 Daisies and Female Symbol
("Rights of Women and Children")

(Litho Questa)

1996 (26 Feb). *50th Anniv of the United Nations. T 244 and similar horiz designs. Multicoloured. P 14×13½.*
1372	15 c. Type **244**		30	25
1373	60 c. Peace dove escaping from prison		80	80
1374	80 c. Symbolic candles ("Human Rights")	1·10	1·40
1375	$1 People on open book		1·40	1·60
1372/5		*Set of 4*	3·25	3·75
MS1376	107×78 mm. $2 National flags forming "50"		3·00	3·50

245 Farmer on Tractor

(Litho Questa)

1996 (26 Feb). *50th Anniv of Food and Agriculture Organization. Sheet 111×80 mm. P 14×13½.*
MS1377 **245** $2 multicoloured		2·40	2·50

(Litho Questa)

1996 (21 Apr). *70th Birthday of Queen Elizabeth II. Vert designs as T 334 of Maldive Islands. Multicoloured. P 13½×14.*
1378	80 c. As Type **334** of Maldive Islands		1·10	1·25
	a. Strip of 3. Nos. 1378/80		3·00	
1379	80 c. In blue coat and hat		1·10	1·25
1380	80 c. At Trooping the Colour		1·10	1·25
1378/80		*Set of 3*	3·00	3·25
MS1381	125×104 mm. $2 In yellow dress and hat		2·40	2·50

Nos. 1378/80 were printed together, *se-tenant*, in horizontal or vertical strips of 3 throughout the sheet.

246 Glaucus, God of Divers, 2500 B.C.

247 Show Jumping

(Des L. Birmingham. Litho Questa)

1996 (13 May). *"China '96" Asian International Philatelic Exhibition, Beijing. Underwater Exploration (1st series). T 246 and similar horiz designs. Multicoloured. P 14×14½.*
1382	55 c. Type **246**		70	75
	a. Sheetlet. Nos. 1382/90		5·75	
1383	55 c. Alexander the Great, 332 B.C.		70	75
1384	55 c. Salvage diver, 1430		70	75
1385	55 c. Borelli's rebreathing device, 1680		70	75
1386	55 c. Edmund Halley's diving bell, 1690		70	75
1387	55 c. John Lethbridge's diving machine, 1715		70	75
1388	55 c. Klingert's diving apparatus, 1789		70	75
1389	55 c. Drieberg's triton, 1808		70	75
1390	55 c. Seibe's diving helmet, 1819		70	75
1382/90		*Set of 9*	5·75	6·25
MS1391	Two sheets, each 102×77 mm. (a) $2 12th-century Arab diver, 1498. (b) $2 Caribbean pearl diver, 1498	*Set of 2 sheets*	4·75	5·00

Nos. 1382/90 were printed together, *se-tenant*, in sheetlets of 9.

See also Nos. 1392/1401 and 1460/9.

(Des L. Birmingham. Litho Questa)

1996 (13 May). *"Capex '96" World Stamp Exhibition, Toronto. Underwater Exploration (2nd series). Multicoloured designs as T 246. P 14×14½.*
1392	60 c. Jim Jarrat exploring *Lusitania*, 1935		75	80
	a. Sheetlet. Nos. 1392/1400		6·25	
1393	60 c. Cousteau's first use of scuba gear for exploration, 1952		75	80

1394	60 c. Discovery of oldest shipwreck, 1959	75	80
1395	60 c. Raising of the *Vasa*, 1961	75	80
1396	60 c. Mel Fisher discovering *Atocha*, 1971	75	80
1397	60 c. Barry Clifford discovering *Whydah*, 1984	75	80
1398	60 c. Argo robot over the *Bismarck*, 1989	75	80
1399	60 c. Discovery of *Land Tortoise* in Lake George, New York, 1991	75	80
1400	60 c. Nuclear submarine recovering artefacts from Roman shipwreck, 1994	75	80
1392/1400	*Set of 9*	6·25	6·75

MS1401 Two sheets, each 102×77 mm. (a) $2 Diver investigates the *Edmund Fitzgerald*. (b) $2 *Alvin* exploring the *Titanic* .. *Set of 2 sheets* 4·75 5·00

Nos. 1392/1400 were printed together, *se-tenant*, in sheetlets of 9.

(Litho Questa)

1996 (27 May). *Olympic Games, Atlanta. T 247 and similar vert designs showing sports on medals. Multicoloured. P 13½×14.*
1402	55 c. Type **247**		70	75
	a. Sheetlet. Nos. 1402/11			
1403	55 c. Cycling		70	75
1404	55 c. Fencing		70	75
1405	55 c. Gymnastics		70	75
1406	55 c. Pole vaulting		70	75
1407	55 c. Sprinting		70	75
1408	55 c. Swimming		70	75
1409	55 c. Diving		70	75
1410	55 c. Hurdling		70	75
1411	55 c. Long-distance running		70	75
1402/11		*Set of 10*	6·50	7·00

Nos. 1402/11 were printed in individual sheets of each design and, *se-tenant*, as a sheetlet of 10.

248 James McCartney (First Chief Minister)

249 Space Dog

1996 (8 July). *20th Anniv of Ministerial Government. Litho. P 14.*
1412	**248** 60 c. multicoloured		70	75

No. 1412 was printed in sheetlets of 9 with a large illustrated margin at right.

(Des Mary Walters. Litho Questa)

1996 (8 Sept). *Working Dogs. T 249 and similar vert designs. Multicoloured. P 14.*
1413	25 c. Type **249**		35	40
	a. Sheetlet. Nos. 1413/24		3·75	
1414	25 c. Greyhound		35	40
1415	25 c. St. Bernard		35	40
1416	25 c. Dog with medals		35	40
1417	25 c. Retriever		35	40
1418	25 c. Dog with bone		35	40
1419	25 c. "Hearing ear" dog		35	40
1420	25 c. Husky		35	40
1421	25 c. Police Alsatian		35	40
1422	25 c. Guard dog		35	40
1423	25 c. Boxer		35	40
1424	25 c. Sniffer dog		35	40
1413/24		*Set of 12*	3·75	4·25

MS1425 Two sheets, each 106×76 mm. (a) $2 Labrador guide dog. (b) $2 Border sheep dog *Set of 2 sheets* 4·75 5·00

Nos. 1413/24 were printed together, *se-tenant*, in sheetlets of 12.

250 Winnie the Pooh asleep in Chair

251 Giant Milkweed

1996 (25 Nov). *Christmas. Winnie the Pooh. T 250 and similar vert designs. Multicoloured. Litho. P 13½×14.*
1426	15 c. Type **250**		30	30
1427	20 c. Piglet holding star decoration		35	35
1428	35 c. Tigger carrying presents		55	55
1429	50 c. Pooh, Tigger and Piglet singing carols		75	75
1430	60 c. Winnie and Rabbit		90	90
1431	80 c. Tigger and Roo		1·25	1·25
1432	$1 Santa Pooh filling stockings		1·40	1·60
1433	$1.25, Christopher Robin and Winnie the Pooh		1·60	2·00
1426/33		*Set of 8*	6·50	7·00

MS1434 Two sheets. (a) 124×98 mm. $2 Piglet decorating biscuits. (b) 98×124 mm. $2.60, Piglet placing star on tree .. *Set of 2 sheets* 7·00 7·50

1997 (10 Feb). *Flowers. T 251 and similar vert designs. Multicoloured. Litho. P 14.*
1435	20 c. Type **251**		30	35
	a. Sheetlet. Nos. 1435/8, each × 2		2·25	
1436	20 c. Geiger Tree		30	35
1437	20 c. Passion Flower		30	35
1438	20 c. Hibiscus		30	35
1439	60 c. Yellow Elder		75	80
	a. Sheetlet. Nos. 1439/42, each × 2		6·00	
1440	60 c. Prickly Poppy		75	80
1441	60 c. Frangipani		75	80
1442	60 c. Seaside Mahoe		75	80
1435/42		*Set of 8*	3·75	4·25

MS1443 Two sheets, each 105×76 mm. (a) $2 Firecracker. (b) $2 Chain of Love *Set of 2 sheets* 4·75 5·00

Nos. 1435/8 and 1439/42 were each printed together, *se-tenant*, in sheetlets of 8 containing two of each design.

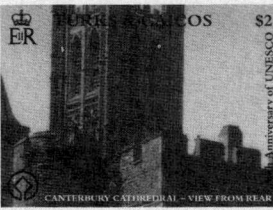

252 Canterbury Cathedral Tower

(Litho Questa)

1997 (24 Mar). *50th Anniv of U.N.E.S.C.O. Two sheets, each 127×102 mm, containing T 252 and similar horiz design. Multicoloured. P 14×13½.*

MS1444 (a) $2 Type **252**; (b) $2 High Altar, Canterbury Cathedral .. *Set of 2 sheets* 4·75 5·00

The miniature sheets of No. **MS**1444 are inscribed "CATHREDRAL" in error.

253 White Dove (face value at right)

254 "Adoration of an Angel" (detail) (studio of Fra Angelico)

(Des Claire Fejes. Litho)

1997 (24 Mar). *50th Anniv of U.N.I.C.E.F. T 253 and similar vert designs. Multicoloured. P 14.*
1445	60 c. Type **253**		75	80
	a. Sheetlet. Nos. 1445/8		2·75	
1446	60 c. White dove (with face value at left)		75	80
1447	60 c. Three children		75	80
1448	60 c. Two children with pets		75	80
1445/8		*Set of 4*	2·75	3·00

Nos. 1445/8 were printed together, *se-tenant*, in sheetlets of 4

(Litho Questa)

1997 (21 Apr). *Golden Wedding of Queen Elizabeth and Prince Philip. Horiz designs as T 350 of Maldive Islands. Multicoloured. P 14.*
1449	60 c. Queen Elizabeth II		90	1·00
	a. Sheetlet. Nos. 1449/54		4·75	
1450	60 c. Royal coat of arms		90	1·00
1451	60 c. Queen Elizabeth and Prince Philip in carriage		90	1·00
1452	60 c. Queen Elizabeth and Prince Philip on royal visit		90	1·00
1453	60 c. Windsor Castle		90	1·00
1454	60 c. Prince Philip		90	1·00
1449/54		*Set of 6*	4·75	5·50

MS1455 100×70 mm. $2 Princess Elizabeth and Duke of Edinburgh on wedding day .. 3·50 4·00

Nos. 1449/54 were printed together, *se-tenant*, in sheetlets of 6.

(Des J. Iskowitz. Litho Questa)

1997 (1 July). *"Pacific '97" International Stamp Exhibition, San Francisco. Death Centenary of Heinrich von Stephan (founder of the U.P.U.). Horiz designs as T 351 of Maldive Islands. P 14.*
1456	50 c. mauve		65	70
	a. Sheetlet. Nos. 1456/8		1·75	
1457	50 c. chestnut		65	70
1458	50 c. deep blue		65	70
1456/8		*Set of 3*	1·75	1·90

MS1459 80×117 mm. $2 bright mauve and black 2·40 2·50

Designs:—No. 1456, British mail coach, 1700s; No. 1457, Von Stephan and Mercury; No. 1458, Space Shuttle; No. **MS**1459, Von Stephan and Ancient Greek messenger.

Nos. 1456/8 were printed together, *se-tenant*, in sheets of 3 with enlarged right-hand margin.

1997 (21 Aug). *"STAMPSHOW '97" 111th Annual A.P.S. Convention, Milwaukee. Underwater Exploration (3rd series). Horiz designs as T 246. Multicoloured. Litho.* P 14×13½.

1460	20 c. Edgerton underwater camera, 1954	30	35
	a. Sheetlet. Nos. 1460/8		2·25
1461	20 c. Conshelf Habitat, 1963	30	35
1462	20 c. *Sealab II,* 1965	30	35
1463	20 c. Research Habitat Tektite, 1970	30	35
1464	20 c. Galapagos Volcanic rift, 1974	30	35
1465	20 c. Epaulard robot survey craft, 1979	30	35
1466	20 c. Underwater sealife, 1995	30	35
1467	20 c. One-man research vessel, 1996	30	35
1468	20 c. Okhotsk Tower, Japan, 1996	30	35
1460/8	*Set of 9*	2·25	2·50

MS1469 Two sheets, each 72×103 mm. (a) $2 Coelacanth. (b) $2 John Williamson making underwater movie. P 14×14½ .. *Set of 2 sheets* 4·75 5·00
Nos. 1460/8 were printed together, *se-tenant*, in sheetlets of 9.

(Litho Questa)

1997 (8 Dec). *Christmas. Religious Paintings. T 254 and similar multicoloured designs. Multicoloured.* P 13½×14.

1470	15 c. Type 254	25	25
1471	20 c. "Scenes from the life of St. John the Baptist" (detail) (Master of Saint Severin)	30	30
1472	35 c. "Archangel Gabriel" (Masolino de Panicale)	50	45
1473	50 c. "Jeremiah with two Angels" (detail) (Gherardo Starnina)	70	65
1474	60 c. "Jeremiah with Two Angels" (different detail) (Starnina)	80	75
1475	80 c. "The Annunciation" (detail) (Giovanni di Palo di Grazia)	1·00	1·40
1476	$1 "The Annunciation" (detail) (Carlo di Braccesco)	1·25	1·50
1477	$1.25, "The Nativity" (detail) (Benvenuto di Giovanni Guasta)	1·50	2·00
1470/7	*Set of 8*	5·75	6·50

MS1478 Two sheets. (a) 130×105 mm. $2 "The Journey of the Magi" (detail) (Benozzo Gozzoli). (b) 105×130 mm. $2 "The Wilton Diptych" (right panel) (anon) .. *Set of 2 sheets* 4·75 5·00

255 Black-finned Snapper

(Des H. Friedman. Litho)

1998 (24 Feb). *Endangered Species. International Year of the Reef. Fishes. T 255 and similar horiz designs. Multicoloured.* P 14.

1479	25 c. Type 255	30	35
	a. Block of 4. Nos. 1479/82		1·10
1480	25 c. Dog Snapper	30	35
1481	25 c. Cubera Snapper	30	35
1482	25 c. Mahogany Snapper	30	35
1479/82	*Set of 4*	1·10	1·40

Nos. 1479/82 were printed together, *se-tenant*, in blocks of 4 throughout the sheet.

256 Spotted Flamingo Tongue (John Petrak)   257 Bird and Logo

(Litho B.D.T.)

1998 (1 May). *First World Open Underwater Photographic Competition Prizewinners (1997). T 256 and similar horiz designs. Multicoloured.* P 14.

1483	20 c. Type 256	25	30
1484	50 c. Feather Duster (Dave Bothwell)	60	65
1485	60 c. Squirrel Fish (Waldemar Seifert)	70	75
1486	80 c. Queen Angelfish (Ralph Oberlander)	1·00	1·10
1487	$1 Barracuda (Steve Rosenburg)	1·25	1·40
1488	$1.25, Royal Gramma ("Fairy Basslet") (John Petrak)	1·50	1·60
1483/8	*Set of 6*	5·25	5·75

MS1489 Two sheets, each 148×85 mm. (a) $2 Spotted Cleaning Shrimp (Michael Boyer). (b) $2 Rough File Clam (Steve Rosenburg) .. *Set of 2 sheets* 4·75 5·00

1998 (30 July). *International Year of the Ocean. T 257 and similar vert designs. Multicoloured. Litho.* P 14.

1490	50 c. Type 257	60	65
	a. Sheetlet. Nos. 1490/3		2·40
1491	50 c. Stylised crab	60	65
1492	50 c. Fish	60	65
1493	50 c. Logo in cloverleaf	60	65
1490/3	*Set of 4*	2·40	2·50

MS1494 102×71 mm. $2 Ocean and globe logo 2·40 2·50
Nos. 1490/3 were printed together, *se-tenant*, in sheetlets of 4.

258 University Arms on Banner (50th anniv of University of West Indies)   259 S.E. 5A Aircraft

(Des L. Fried. Litho Questa)

1998 (30 July). *Anniversaries and Events. T 258 and similar vert designs. Multicoloured.* P 14.

1495	20 c. Type 258	25	30
1496	60 c. Global logo (U.N.E.S.C.O. World Solar Energy Programme Summit)	70	75
1497	80 c. Flame (50th anniv of Universal Declaration of Human Rights)	1·00	1·10
1498	$1 John Glenn (astronaut) (second space flight)	1·25	1·40
1495/8	*Set of 4*	3·00	3·50

MS1499 100×72 mm. $2 Space shuttle (John Glenn's second space flight) 2·40 2·50

(Des K. Gromell. Litho Questa)

1998 (18 Aug). *80th Anniv of Royal Air Force. T 259 and similar horiz designs. Multicoloured.* P 14.

1500	20 c. Type 259	25	30
1501	50 c. Sopwith Camel	60	65
1502	60 c. Supermarine Spitfire	70	75
1503	80 c. Avro Lancaster	1·00	1·10
1504	$1 Panavia Tornado	1·25	1·40
1505	$1.25, Hawker Hurricane	1·50	1·60
1500/5	*Set of 6*	5·25	5·75

MS1506 Two sheets, each 110×80 mm. (a) $2 Hawker Siddley Harrier. (b) $2 Avro Vulcan *Set of 2 sheets* 4·75 5·00

260 Diana, Princess of Wales   261 "Magi's Visit"

(Des D. Miller. Litho Questa)

1998 (31 Aug). *1st Death Anniv of Diana, Princess of Wales.* P 14.

1507	260 60 c. multicoloured	70	75
	a. Sheetlet of 6		4·00

No. 1507 was printed in sheetlets of 6 with a large illustrated margin at right.

(Des Rosemary DeFiglio. Litho Questa)

1998 (30 Nov). *Christmas. Paintings by Thomasita Fessler. T 261 and similar multicoloured designs.* P 14.

1508	50 c. Type 261	60	65
	a. Sheetlet. Nos. 1508/13		3·50
1509	50 c. "Flight into Egypt"	60	65
1510	50 c. "Wedding Feast"	60	65
1511	50 c. "Maria"	60	65
1512	50 c. "Annunciation and Visitation" (57×46 mm)	60	65
1513	50 c. "Nativity" (57×46 mm)	60	65
1508/13	*Set of 6*	3·50	3·75

MS1514 105×130 mm. $2 "Queen of Mothers" 2·40 2·50
Nos. 1508/13 were printed together, *se-tenant*, in sheetlets of 6.

262 Flamingos   263 Prince Edward and Miss Sophie Rhys-Jones

(Des L. Birmingham. Litho)

1999 (7 June). *Marine Life. T 262 and similar horiz designs. Multicoloured.* P 14½.

1515	20 c. Type 262	25	30
	a. Sheetlet. Nos. 1515/38		6·00
1516	20 c. Sailing dinghies	25	30
1517	20 c. Seagulls and lighthouse	25	30
1518	20 c. House on beach	25	30
1519	20 c. Yellowtail Snapper and Pillar Coral	25	30
1520	20 c. Yellowtail Snapper and Elliptical Star Coral	25	30
1521	20 c. Porkfish	25	30
1522	20 c. Spotted Eagle Ray	25	30
1523	20 c. Large Ivory Coral	25	30
1524	20 c. Shy Hamlet and Mustard Hill Coral	25	30
1525	20 c. Blue Crust Coral	25	30
1526	20 c. Fused Staghorn Coral	25	30
1527	20 c. Queen Angelfish and Massive Starlet Coral	25	30
1528	20 c. Pinnate Spiny Sea Fan	25	30
1529	20 c. Knobby Star Coral	25	30
1530	20 c. Lowridge Cactus Coral	25	30
1531	20 c. Orange Telesto Coral	25	30
1532	20 c. Spanish Hogfish and Knobby Ten-Ray Star Coral	25	30
1533	20 c. Clown Wrasse and Boulder Brain Coral	25	30
1534	20 c. Rainbow Parrotfish and Regal Sea Fan	25	30
1535	20 c. Bluestriped Grunt and Great Star Coral	25	30
1536	20 c. Blue Tang and Stinging Coral	25	30
1537	20 c. Lavender Thin Finger Coral	25	30
1538	20 c. Juvenile French Grunt and Brilliant Sea Fingers	25	30
1515/38	*Set of 24*	6·00	7·00

MS1539 Two sheets, each 100×70 mm. (a) $2 Elkhorn Coral. (b) $2 Sea Fan .. *Set of 2 sheets* 4·75 5·00
Nos. 1515/38 were printed together, *se-tenant*, in sheetlets of 24, with the backgrounds forming a composite design. No. 1520 is inscribed "ELIPTICAL STAR CORAL" in error.

1999 (19 June). *Royal Wedding. T 263 and similar vert designs. Multicoloured. Litho.* P 14.

1540	60 c. Type 263	70	75
	a. Sheetlet. Nos. 1540/3		2·75
1541	60 c. Prince Edward	70	75
1542	60 c. Miss Sophie Rhys-Jones	70	75
1543	60 c. Prince Edward and Miss Sophie Rhys-Jones (different)	70	75
1540/3	*Set of 4*	2·75	3·00

MS1544 Two sheets, each 76×60 mm. (a) $2 Prince Edward and Miss Sophie Rhys Jones in front of building. (b) $2 Prince Edward and Miss Sophie Rhys-Jones in front of tree *Set of 2 sheets* 4·75 5·00
Nos. 1540/3 were printed together, *se-tenant*, in sheetlets of 4 with an enlarged illustrated left-hand margin.

264 Painted Tunicates (S. Genkins)   265 Constellations over Earth and "2000"

1999 (11 Nov). *Winning Entries from Second World Open Underwater Photographic Competition. T 264 and similar horiz designs. Multicoloured. Litho.* P 14½×14.

1545	10 c. Type 264	10	15
1546	20 c. Peacock Flounder (M. Lynn)	25	30
1547	50 c. Squat Anemone Shrimps (M. Boyer)	60	65
1548	60 c. Juvenile Drum (N. Army)	70	75
1549	80 c. Batwing Coral Crab (R. Jarnutowski)	1·00	1·10
1550	$1 Moon Jellyfish (R. Kaufman)	1·25	1·40
1545/50	*Set of 6*	3·75	4·25

MS1551 Two sheets, each 85×68 mm. (a) $2 Christmas Tree Worms (B. Joubert) (48½×36 mm). (b) $2 Longhorn Nudibranch (Trina Locklear) (48½×36 mm). P 14×13½
Set of 2 sheets 4·75 5·00

(Des A. Pichkhadze. Litho Questa)

1999 (15 Nov). *New Millennium. T 265 and similar vert designs. Multicoloured.* P 14½ (20 c., $1) or 14×13½ (50 c.).

1552	20 c. Type 265	25	30
1553	50 c. Big Ben, London (30×47 mm)	60	65
	a. Sheetlet. Nos. 1553/8		3·50
1554	50 c. Flamingo, Turks and Caicos Islands (30×47 mm)	60	65
1555	50 c. Empire State Building, New York (30×47 mm)	60	65
1556	50 c. Coliseum, Rome (30×47 mm)	60	65
1557	50 c. Dome of the Rock, Jerusalem (30×47 mm)	60	65
1558	50 c. Eiffel Tower, Paris (30×47 mm)	60	65
1559	$1 Type 265	1·25	1·40
1552/9	*Set of 8*	5·00	5·25

MS1560 Two sheets, each 106×86 mm. (a) $2 Part of globe and Turks and Caicos Islands flag (30×47 mm). (b) $2 Part of globe and Turks and Caicos Islands coat of arms (30×47 mm). P 14×13½ .. *Set of 2 sheets* 4·75 5·00
Nos. 1553/8 were printed together, *se-tenant*, in sheetlets of 6 with each design incorporating a clock face together with a map of the country depicted.

266 "The Mystic Marriage
of St. Catherine"
(Anthony Van Dyck)

(Litho Questa)

1999 (7 Dec). *Christmas. T **266** and similar vert designs.
Multicoloured. P 13½×14.*
1561	20 c. Type **266**	25	30
1562	50 c. "Rest on the Flight into Egypt"	60	65
1563	$2 "Holy Family with Saints John and Elizabeth"	2·25	2·50
1561/3	Set of 3	3·00	3·25
MS1564	102×122 mm. $2 "The Madonna of the Rosary"	2·40	2·50

No. 1561 is inscribed "Marrige" in error.

STAMP BOOKLETS

1977 (7 Feb). *Silver Jubilee. Multicoloured cover, 80×55 mm.
Stapled.*
SB1 $1.60, booklet containing 25 c. and 55 c. (Nos.
473/4), each in pair .. .. .. 1·10

1978 (July). *25th Anniv of Coronation. Cover, 165×92 mm,
black and purple on front showing Westminster Abbey and
multicoloured on back. Stitched.*
SB2 $3.60, booklet containing *se-tenant* panes of 3 and
6 (Nos. 499a/b) .. .. .. 1·90

1979 (27 Sept). *Death Centenary of Sir Rowland Hill.
Multicoloured cover, 165×92 mm, showing Penny Black
stamp and Sir Rowland Hill. Stitched.*
SB3 $3.55, booklet containing two different *se-tenant*
panes of 6 and pane of 1 $1 (Nos. 552a, 558a,
564a) .. .. 3·25

1981 (7 July). *Royal Wedding. Cover, 165×90 mm; blue, gold
and black on front showing Prince of Wales emblem and
multicoloured on back. Stitched.*
SB4 $5.60, booklet containing *se-tenant* pane of 6 and
pane of 1 $2 (Nos. 657a, 659a) .. .. 2·40

1981 (1 Dec). *Tourism. Multicoloured cover, 114×58 mm,
showing tourist attractions. Stapled.*
SB5 $4 booklet containing twenty 20 c. (Nos. 675/84),
in *se-tenant* blocks of 4 .. .. 6·00

1982 (18 Nov). *21st Birthday of Princess of Wales.
Multicoloured cover, 101×49 mm, showing rainbow over
South Caicos Harbour. Stapled.*
SB6 $4.60, booklet containing 8 c., 35 c. and $1.10
(Nos. 713/15), each in strip of 3 .. .. 5·50

CAICOS ISLANDS

CAICOS ISLANDS
(1)

1981 (24 July). *Nos. 514A, 518A, 520A, 523A and 525A/7A of Turks and Caicos Islands optd with T* 1.

1	1 c. Indigo Hamlet	..	15	15
2	5 c. Spanish Grunt	.. ..	20	20
3	8 c. Four-eyed Butterflyfish	..	20	20
4	20 c. Queen Angelfish	..	45	30
5	50 c. Royal Gramma ("Fairy Basslet")		70	1·00
6	$1 Fin-spot Wrasse	.. ..	1·00	1·75
7	$2 Stoplight Parrotfish	..	2·00	3·25
1/7	.. .. *Set of* 7		4·25	6·00

(2)   (3)

1981 (24 July). *Royal Wedding. Nos. 653/6 of Turks and Caicos Islands optd with T* 1.
A. With T 2 in London

8A	35 c. Prince Charles and Lady Diana Spencer		20	25
9A	65 c. Kensington Palace	..	30	40
10A	90 c. Prince Charles as Colonel of the Welsh Guards		40	50
8A/10A	*Set of* 3		80	1·00
MS11A	96×82 mm. $2 Glass Coach	..	1·00	2·00

B. With T 3 in New York

8B	35 c. Prince Charles and Lady Diana Spencer		40	70
	a. Opt inverted	..	£110	
9B	65 c. Kensington Palace	..	55	1·00
	a. Opt inverted ..		80·00	
10B	90 c. Prince Charles as Colonel of the Welsh Guards		75	1·50
	a. Opt inverted ..		90·00	
	b. Opt double	..	90·00	
8B/10B	*Set of* 3		1·50	3·00
MS11B	96×82 mm. $2 Glass Coach	..	1·00	2·50
	a. Opt inverted			

Nos. 8B/10 come either in sheets of 40 (2 panes 4×5) or in sheetlets of 5 stamps and one label. Examples of Nos. 8Ba, 9Ba and 10Ba are known from both formats, but No. 10Bb only exists from sheetlets.

Nos. 8/10 also exist perforated 12 (*Price for set of 3 with London opt £2 or with New York opt £5, mint or used*) from additional sheetlets of five stamps and one label.

1981 (29 Oct). *Royal Wedding. Booklet stamps. As Nos. 657/9 of Turks and Caicos Islands, but each inscr "Caicos Islands". Multicoloured. Roul* 5×*imperf*. Self-adhesive.*

12	20 c. Lady Diana Spencer	..	30	40
	a. Booklet pane. Nos. 12/13, each ×3		3·00	
13	$1 Prince Charles	..	80	1·25
14	$2 Prince Charles and Lady Diana Spencer		5·50	5·50
	a. Booklet pane of 1		5·50	
12/14	*Set of* 3		6·00	6·50

*The 20 c. and $1 values were each separated by various combinations of rotary knife (giving a straight edge) and roulette. The $2 value exists only with straight edges.

4 Queen or Pink Conch and Lobster Fishing, South Caicos

(Des J. Cooter (8 c. to 20 c.). Litho)

1983 (6 June)—**84.** *T* 4 *and similar horiz designs. Multicoloured. P* 14.

15	8 c. Type 4	.. ..	80	50
16	10 c. Hawksbill Turtle, East Caicos	..	80	50
17	20 c. Arawak Indians and idol, Middle Caicos		80	50
18	35 c. Boat-building, North Caicos		1·25	85
19	50 c. Marine biologist at work, Pine Cay		2·00	90
20	95 c. Boeing 707 airliner at new airport, Providenciales		4·00	2·25
21	$1.10, Columbus' Pinta, West Caicos		4·00	2·50
22	$2 Fort George Cay (18.5.84)		3·50	3·75
23	$3 Pirates Anne Bonny and Calico Jack at Parrot Cay (18.5.84)		6·00	4·75
15/23	.. .. *Set of* 9		21·00	15·00

OMNIBUS ISSUES

Details, together with prices for complete sets, of the various Omnibus issues from the 1935 Silver Jubilee series to date are included in a special section following Zimbabwe at the end of Volume 2.

---

5 Goofy and Patch   **6** "Leda and the Swan"

(Litho Walsall)

1983 (7 Nov). *Christmas. T* 5 *and similar vert designs showing Disney cartoon characters. Multicoloured. P* 11.

30	1 c. Type 5	..	10	10
31	1 c. Chip and Dale	..	10	10
32	2 c. Morty	..	10	10
33	2 c. Morty and Ferdie	..	10	10
34	3 c. Goofy and Louie	..	10	10
35	3 c. Donald Duck, Huey, Dewey and Louie	..	10	10
36	50 c. Uncle Scrooge	..	3·00	2·25
37	70 c. Mickey Mouse and Ferdie		3·25	2·75
38	$1.10, Pinocchio, Jiminy Cricket and Figaro		3·75	3·50
30/8	*Set of* 9		9·00	8·00
MS39	126 × 101 mm. $2 Morty and Ferdie. P 13½ × 14		3·75	3·50

(Des and litho Questa)

1983 (15 Dec). *500th Birth Anniv of Raphael. T* 6 *and similar vert designs. Multicoloured. P* 14.

40	35 c. Type 6	..	75	50
41	50 c. "Study of Apollo for Parnassus"	..	1·00	70
42	95 c. "Study of two figures for the battle of Ostia"		2·00	1·25
43	$1.10, "Study for the Madonna of the Goldfinch"		2·00	1·50
40/3	*Set of* 4		5·25	3·50
MS44	71 × 100 mm. $2.50, "The Garvagh Madonna"		3·50	3·25

7 High Jumping   **8** Horace Horsecollar and Clarabelle Cow

(Litho Questa)

1984 (1 Mar). *Olympic Games, Los Angeles. T* 7 *and similar designs. P* 14.

45	4 c. multicoloured	..	10	10
46	25 c. multicoloured	..	20	20
47	65 c. black, deep grey-blue and new blue		80	50
48	$1.10, multicoloured	..	85	85
45/8	*Set of* 4		1·75	1·50
MS49	105 × 75 mm. $2 multicoloured		2·25	3·00

Designs: *Vert*—25 c. Archery; 65 c. Cycling; $1.10, Football. *Horiz*—$2 Show jumping.

(Des Walt Disney Productions. Litho Questa)

1984 (23 Apr). *Easter. Walt Disney Cartoon Characters. T* 8 *and similar horiz designs. Multicoloured. P* 14 × 13½.

50	35 c. Type 8	..	80	60
51	45 c. Mickey and Minnie Mouse, and Chip		95	75
52	75 c. Gyro Gearloose, Chip 'n Dale		1·60	1·25
53	85 c. Mickey Mouse, Chip 'n Dale		1·60	1·40
50/3	*Set of* 4		4·50	3·50
MS54	127 × 101 mm. $2.20, Donald Duck		5·50	3·75

 AUSIPEX 1984
(9)   (10)

1984 (19 June). *Universal Postal Union Congress, Hamburg. Nos.* 20/1 *optd with T* 9.

55	95 c. Boeing 707 airliner at new airport, Providenciales		1·00	1·25
56	$1.10, Columbus' Pinta, West Caicos		1·25	1·50

1984 (22 Aug). *"Ausipex" International Stamp Exhibition, Melbourne. No.* 22 *optd with T* 10.

57	$2 Fort George Cay	..	2·40	2·50

11 Seamen sighting American Manatees

(Des L. Lightbourne. Litho Walsall)

1984 (12 Sept). *492nd Anniv of Columbus' First Landfall. T* 11 *and similar horiz designs. Multicoloured. P* 14.

58	10 c. Type 11	..	85	60
59	70 c. Fleet of Columbus	..	3·00	2·75
60	$1 First landing in West Indies		3·50	3·25
58/60	*Set of* 3		6·50	6·00
MS61	99×69 mm. $2 Fleet of Columbus(*different*)		2·75	3·00

12 Donald Duck and Mickey Mouse with Father Christmas

(Litho Questa)

1984 (26 Nov). *Christmas. Walt Disney Cartoon Characters. T* 12 *and similar vert designs. Multicoloured. P* 12 ($2) *or* 13½ × 14 (*others*).

62	20 c. Type 12	..	1·00	75
63	35 c. Donald Duck opening refrigerator	..	1·40	1·00
64	50 c. Mickey Mouse, Donald Duck and toy train		1·90	1·50
65	75 c. Donald Duck and parcels		2·50	2·25
66	$1.10, Donald Duck and carol singers		2·75	2·75
62/6	*Set of* 5		8·50	7·50
MS67	127 × 102 mm. $2 Donald Duck as Christmas tree		3·75	4·00

No. 65 was printed in sheetlets of 8 stamps.

13 Thick-billed Vireo   **14** Two Children learning to Read and Write (Education)

(Des Susan David. Litho Walsall)

1985 (12 Feb). *Birth Bicentenary of John J. Audubon (ornithologist). T* 13 *and similar horiz designs. Multicoloured. P* 14.

68	20 c. Type 13	..	1·75	50
69	35 c. Black-faced Grassquit	..	2·00	75
70	50 c. Pearly-eyed Thrasher	..	2·25	1·10
71	$1 Greater Antillean Bullfinch		2·75	1·90
68/71	*Set of* 4		8·00	3·75
MS72	100 × 70 mm. $2 Stripe-headed Tanager		3·50	3·50

(Des C. Walters. Litho Walsall)

1985 (8 May). *International Youth Year and 40th Anniv of United Nations. T* 14 *and similar vert designs. Multicoloured. P* 14.

73	16 c. Type 14	..	20	25
74	35 c. Two children on playground swings (Health)		50	55
75	70 c. Boy and girl (Love)	..	1·00	1·10
76	90 c. Three children (Peace) ..		1·25	1·40
73/6	*Set of* 4		2·75	3·00
MS77	101×71 mm. $2 Child, dove carrying ears of wheat and map of the Americas		2·75	3·00

15 Air Caicos Douglas DC-3 on Ground   **16** The Queen Mother visiting Foundation for the Disabled, Leatherhead

(Des K. Gromell. Litho Walsall)

1985 (23 May). *40th Anniv of International Civil Aviation Organization. T* 15 *and similar horiz designs. Multicoloured. P* 14.

78	35 c. Type 15	..	1·90	55
79	75 c. Air Caicos Convair CV 440 Metropolitan		3·25	1·25
80	90 c. TCNA Britten Norman Islander		3·25	1·40
78/80	*Set of* 3		7·50	3·00
MS81	100×70 mm. $2.20, Hang-gliding over the Caicos Islands		3·00	3·25

(Des J.W. Litho Questa)

1985 (8 July). *Life and Times of Queen Elizabeth the Queen Mother. T* **16** *and similar multicoloured designs.* P 14.
82	35 c. Type 16		60	55
83	65 c. With Princess Anne (*horiz*)	1·00	95
84	95 c. At Epsom, 1961	1·60	1·60
82/4		*Set of 3*	2·75	2·75
MS85	56×85 mm. $2 Visiting Royal Hospital, Chelsea	3·50	3·00

(Des Walt Disney Productions. Litho Questa)

1985 (5 Dec). *150th Birth Anniv of Mark Twain (author). Multicoloured designs as T* **160a** *of Lesotho, but horiz, showing Walt Disney cartoon characters in scenes from "Tom Sawyer, Detective".* P 14×13½.
86	8 c. Huckleberry Finn (Goofy) and Tom Sawyer (Mickey Mouse) reading reward notice	60	20
87	35 c. Huck and Tom meeting Jake Dunlap	1·75	65
88	95 c. Huck and Tom spying on Jubiter Dunlap	3·25	2·00
89	$1.10, Huck and Tom with hound (Pluto)	3·25	2·25
86/9		*Set of 4*	8·00	4·75
MS90	127×101 mm. $2 Tom unmasking Jubiter Dunlap	4·75	4·25

(Des Walt Disney Productions. Litho Questa)

1985 (5 Dec). *Birth Bicentenaries of Grimm Brothers (folklorists). Multicoloured designs as T* **160b** *of Lesotho, but horiz, showing Walt Disney cartoon characters in scenes from "Six Soldiers of Fortune".* P 14×13½.
91	16 c. The Soldier (Donald Duck) with his meagre pay	1·00	30
92	25 c. The Soldier meeting the Strong Man (Horace Horsecollar)	1·25	45
93	65 c. The Soldier meeting the Marksman (Mickey Mouse)	2·75	1·25
94	$1.35, The Fast Runner (Goofy) winning the race against the Princess (Daisy Duck)	3·50	2·25
91/4		*Set of 4*	7·75	3·75
MS95	126×101 mm. $2 The Soldier and the Strong Man with sack of gold	4·75	4·00

STAMP BOOKLET

1981 (29 Oct). *Royal Wedding. As No.* SB4 *of Turks and Caicos Islands.*
SB1	$5.60, booklet containing *se-tenant* pane of 6 and pane of 1 $2 (Nos. 12a, 14a)	8·00

Tuvalu

Formerly known as the Ellice Islands when they shared a joint administration with the Gilbert group. On 1 January 1976 the two island-groups separated and the Ellice Islands were renamed Tuvalu.

CROWN COLONY

(Currency. 100 cents = 1 Australian dollar)

1 Gilbertese and Tuvaluan

(Des Iakopo Nivatui; adapted J. Cooter. Litho Questa)

1976 (1 Jan). *Separation of the Islands. T* **1** *and similar multicoloured designs.* W w **14** (*sideways** on 4 and 35 c.). P 13½.
1	4 c. Type 1		35	80
2	10 c. Map of the islands (*vert*)	50	1·00
3	35 c. Canoes	70	1·50
	w. Wmk Crown to right of CA	3·75	
1/3		*Set of 3*	1·40	3·00

*The normal sideways watermark shows Crown to left of CA, as seen from the back of the stamp.

(2)

(Des G. Drummond. Litho Walsall)

1976 (21 Apr). *New Coinage. Vert designs, each showing coin as in T* **3**. *Multicoloured.* W w **14** (*inverted*). P 13½.
26	5 c. Type 3		30	15
27	10 c. Red-eyed Crab	40	20
28	15 c. Flying Fish	55	25
29	35 c. Green Turtle	70	45
26/9		*Set of 4*	1·75	95

3 50 c. Coin and Octopus

1976 (1 Jan). *Nos. 173 etc. of Gilbert & Ellice Is optd as T* **2** *in silver (35 c.) or blue (others).* (*a*) W w **12** (*upright*).
4	2 c. Lagoon fishing		£900	£140
5	5 c. Gilbertese canoe	40	60
6	8 c. Weaving pandanus fronds	40	60
7	10 c. Weaving a basket	40	80
	w. Wmk inverted	3·50	
8	50 c. Local handicrafts	13·00	11·00
9	$1 Weaving coconut screen	50·00	65·00

(*b*) W w **12** (*sideways*)
10	2 c. Lagoon fishing		£140	22·00
11	3 c. Cleaning pandanus leaves	60	60
12	5 c. Gilbertese canoe	1·25	65
	w. Wmk Crown to right of CA	3·25	
13	25 c. Loading copra	2·50	1·75

(*c*) W w **14** (*inverted*)
14	1 c. Cutting toddy		30	30
15	6 c. De-husking coconuts	40	40
16	15 c. Tiger Shark	60	50
17	50 c. Local handicrafts	40	65
18	$1 Weaving coconut screen	40	85
19	$2 Coat of arms	50	85

(*d*) W w **14** (*sideways**)
20	2 c. Lagoon fishing		40	40
	w. Wmk Crown to right of CA	70·00	
21	3 c. Cleaning pandanus leaves	40	40
22	4 c. Casting nets	40	45
23	20 c. Beating a rolled pandanus leaf	40	60
24	25 c. Loading copra	40	60
25	35 c. Fishing at night	60	70
5/7 and 14/25		*Set of 15*	5·50	7·50

*The normal sideways watermark shows Crown to left of CA, as seen from the back of the stamp.

4 Niulakita and Seven-ridged Leathery Turtle

5 Title page of New Testament

(Des J. Cooter. Litho Questa)

1976 (1 July–1 Sept). *Vert designs showing maps (1 to 25 c.) or horiz designs showing scenes (others). Multicoloured.* W w **14** (*sideways* on 35 c. to $5). P 13½.
30	1 c. Type 4		85	70
31	2 c. Nukulaelae and sleeping mat	40	55
32	4 c. Nui and taro (vegetable)	40	50
33	5 c. Nanumanga and grass skirt	80	50
34	6 c. Nukufetau and Coconut Crab	70	55
35	8 c. Funafuti and Banana tree	75	70
36	10 c. Map of Tuvalu	50	40
37	15 c. Niutao and Flying fish	75	20
38	20 c. Vaitupu and Maneapa (meeting hall)	50	45
39	25 c. Nanumea and fish-hook	50	90
	w. Wmk inverted	60·00	
40	35 c. Te Ano (game)	45	20
41	50 c. Canoe pole fishing	45	30
42	$1 Reef fishing by flare	45	30
43	$2 Living house	45	30
44	$5 M.V. *Nivanga* (1.9.76)	5·50	6·00
30/44		*Set of 15*	12·00	11·00

See also Nos. 58/69.

(Des G. Drummond. Litho Harrison)

1976 (6 Oct). *Christmas. T* **5** *and similar horiz designs. Multicoloured.* W w **14**. P 14 × 14½.
45	5 c. Type 5		20	25
46	20 c. Lotolelei Church	20	25
47	25 c. Kelupi Church	20	25
48	30 c. Mataloa o Tuvalu Church	25	25
49	35 c. Palatasio o Keliso Church	25	25
45/9		*Set of 5*	1·00	1·10

Nos. 45/9 were each printed in sheets of ten stamps and two *se-tenant* stamp-size labels.

6 Queen Elizabeth and Prince Philip

(Des G. Vasarhelyi. Litho Format)

1977 (9 Feb). *Silver Jubilee. T* **6** *and similar horiz designs. Multicoloured.* P 13½.
50	15 c. Type 6		15	10
51	35 c. Prince Philip carried ashore at Vaitupu	20	15
52	50 c. Queen and attendants	30	20
50/2		*Set of 3*	60	40
MS53	98 × 144 mm. Nos. 50/2. P 15	1·00	1·00

7 "Health"

(Des I. Oliver. Litho Format)

1977 (4 May). *30th Anniv of South Pacific Commission. T* **7** *and similar horiz designs. Multicoloured.* P 13½.
54	5 c. Type 7		15	20
55	20 c. "Education"	15	20
56	30 c. "Fruit-growing"	15	20
57	35 c. Map of S.P.C. area	20	25
54/7		*Set of 4*	60	75

1977 (13 June)–78. *As Nos. 30/6, 38/9 and 44, but no wmk, or new values and designs (30, 40 c.).*
58	1 c. Type 4 (4.78)		50	15
59	2 c. Nukulaelae and sleeping mat (4.78)	20	25
60	4 c. Nui and taro (vegetable) (4.78)	20	15
61	5 c. Nanumanga and grass skirt (9.77)	25	15
62	6 c. Nukufetau and Coconut Crab (3.78)	20	35
63	8 c. Funafuti and Banana tree (4.78)	20	25
64	10 c. Map of Tuvalu (4.78)	20	20
65	20 c. Vaitupu and Maneapa (meeting house) (9.77)	50	1·25
66	25 c. Nanumea and fish hook (9.77)	80	20
67	30 c. Fatele (local dancing) (19.4.78)	30	20
68	40 c. Screw Pine (19.4.78)	30	15
69	$5 M.V. *Nivanga*	1·50	2·50
58/69		*Set of 12*	4·75	5·00

Examples of the 15 c. and 35 c. values are known on unwatermarked paper, but there is no evidence that such printings were issued without the Independence overprint of 1 October 1978 (Nos. 94/100).

8 Scout Promise

(Des I. Oliver. Litho Format)

1977 (10 Aug). *50th Anniv of Scouting in the Central Pacific. T* **8** *and similar horiz designs. Multicoloured.* P 13½.
73	5 c. Type 8		15	20
74	20 c. Canoeing	15	20
75	30 c. Scout shelter	20	25
76	35 c. Lord Baden-Powell	20	25
73/6		*Set of 4*	65	80

9 Hurricane Beach (Expedition photo)

(Des I. Oliver. Litho Format)

1977 (2 Nov). *Royal Society Expeditions, 1896/7. T* **9** *and similar designs.* P 13½ × 14 (5 and 35 c.) or 14 × 13½ (*others*).
77	5 c. multicoloured		15	15
78	20 c. black and light blue	15	20
79	30 c. black and light blue	20	20
80	35 c. multicoloured	20	20
77/80		*Set of 4*	65	65

Designs: *Vert*—20 c. Boring apparatus on H.M.S. *Porpoise*; 30 c. Dredging chart. *Horiz*—35 c. Charles Darwin and H.M.S. *Beagle*.

10 Pacific Pigeon

11 *Lawedua* (inter-island coaster)

(Des G. Drummond. Litho Format)

1978 (25 Jan). *Wild Birds. T 10 and similar vert designs. Multicoloured. P 14 × 13½.*

81	8 c. Type **10**	..	40	25
82	20 c. Eastern Reef Heron	..	55	40
83	30 c. White Tern	..	65	50
84	40 c. Lesser Frigate Bird	..	65	55
	a. Magenta offset from 20 c. value on back			
81/4		*Set of 4*	2·00	1·50

No. 84a shows an inverted impression of the magenta plate used for the 20 c. on the reverse.

(Des I. Oliver. Litho Format)

1978 (5 Apr). *Ships. T 11 and similar horiz designs. Multicoloured. P 13½ × 14.*

85	8 c. Type **11**	..	25	15
86	10 c. *Wallacia* (tug)	..	25	15
87	30 c. *Cenpac Rounder* (freighter)	..	25	20
88	40 c. *Pacific Explorer* (freighter)	..	30	20
85/8		*Set of 4*	95	65

(Des G. Drummond. Litho Format)

1978 (2 June). *25th Anniv of Coronation. Horiz designs as Nos. 422/5 of Montserrat. Multicoloured. P 13½ × 14.*

89	8 c. Canterbury Cathedral	..	10	10
90	30 c. Salisbury Cathedral	..	10	10
91	40 c. Wells Cathedral	..	10	10
92	$1 Hereford Cathedral	..	30	30
89/92		*Set of 4*	40	40
MS93	137 × 108 mm. Nos. 89/92. P 15		60	90

Nos. 89/92 were each printed in sheets containing 2 *se-tenant* stamp-size labels.

INDEPENDENT

INDEPENDENCE
1ST OCTOBER
1978
(12)

13 White Frangipani

1978 (1 Oct). *Independence. Nos. 63/4, 65, 67/8 and as Nos. 37 and 40, but without wmk, optd as T 12.*

94	8 c. Funafuti and Banana tree	..	10	10
95	10 c. Map of Tuvalu	..	10	10
96	15 c. Niutao and Four-winged Flyingfish	..	10	10
97	20 c. Vaitupu and Maneapa (house)	..	15	15
98	30 c. Fatele (local dancing)	..	15	15
99	35 c. Te Ano (game)	..	20	20
100	40 c. Screw Pine	..	20	20
94/100		*Set of 7*	75	75

(Des J. Cooter. Litho Format)

1978 (4 Oct). *Wild Flowers. T 13 and similar vert designs. Multicoloured. P 14.*

101	8 c. Type **13**	..	10	10
102	20 c. Susana	..	10	10
103	30 c. Tiale	..	15	15
104	40 c. Inato	..	20	25
101/4		*Set of 4*	50	55

14 Squirrelfish

(Des G. Drummond. Litho Format)

1979 (24 Jan)—**81.** *Fishes (1st series). Multicoloured designs as T 14. P 14.*

105	1 c. Type **14**	..	10	10
106	2 c. Band-tailed Goatfish	..	10	10
107	4 c. Regal Angelfish	..	10	10
108	5 c. Melon Butterflyfish	..	15	10
109	6 c. Semi-circle Angelfish	..	15	10
110	8 c. Blue-striped Snapper	..	15	10
111	10 c. Clown Anemonefish	..	25	10
112	15 c. Chevron Butterflyfish	..	25	10
113	20 c. Yellow-edged Lyretail ("Fairy Cod")	..	35	15
114	25 c. Clown Triggerfish	..	35	20
115	30 c. Long-nosed Butterflyfish	..	35	10
116	35 c. Yellow-finned Tuna	..	40	20
117	40 c. Spotted Eagle Ray	..	40	10
117b	45 c. Black-tipped Grouper (16.6.81)	..	1·50	2·00
118	50 c. Hammerhead	..	40	20
119	70 c. Lionfish (*vert*)	..	40	30
120	$1 Painted Triggerfish (*vert*)	..	40	40
121	$2 Copper-banded Butterflyfish ("Beaked Coralfish") (*vert*)	..	70	55
122	$5 Tiger Shark (*vert*)	..	90	55
105/22		*Set of 19*	6·50	4·25

Nos. 105/22 were each printed in sheets containing 2 *se-tenant* stamp-size printed labels.

Both fine (300 lines of dots per linear inch) and coarse (175 lines of dots per linear inch) screens were used to produce plates for this issue. Examples of the 1, 5, 8, 10, 30 and 40 c. values exist with either screen, the 2, 4, 6, 20, 70 c., $1, $2, $5 only with the fine screen, and the 15, 25, 35, 45 and 50 c. only with the coarse.

See also Nos. 770/81.

---

15 "Explorer of the Pacific"

(Des J. Cooter. Litho Format)

1979 (14 Feb). *Death Bicentenary of Captain Cook. T 15 and similar horiz designs. Multicoloured. P 14 × 14½.*

123	8 c. Type **15**		15	20
	a. Horiz strip of 4. Nos. 123/6		75	
124	30 c. "A new island is discovered"		20	20
125	40 c. "Transit of Venus, Tahiti, 3 June, 1769"		20	20
126	$1 Death of Captain Cook, Hawaii, 14 February, 1779		30	30
123/6		*Set of 4*	75	80

Nos. 123/6 were printed together, *se-tenant*, in horizontal strips of 4 throughout the sheet.

Nos. 123/6 exist imperforate from stock dispersed by the liquidator of Format International Security Printers Ltd.

16 Grumman Mackinnon G-21C Goose Flying Boat and Nukulaelae Island

(Des J. Cooter. Litho Format)

1979 (16 May). *Internal Air Service. T 16 and similar horiz designs. Multicoloured. P 13½.*

127	8 c. Type **16**	..	15	15
128	20 c. Goose and Vaitupu	..	15	20
129	30 c. Goose and Nui	..	20	30
130	40 c. Goose and Funafuti	..	25	35
127/30		*Set of 4*	65	90

17 Sir Rowland Hill, 1976 4 c. Separation Commemorative and London's First Pillar Box, 1855

18 Child's Face

(Des J. Cooter. Litho Format)

1979 (27 Aug). *Death Centenary of Sir Rowland Hill. T 17 and similar horiz designs. Multicoloured. P 13½ × 14.*

131	30 c. Type **17**	..	15	15
132	40 c. Sir Rowland Hill, 1976 10 c. Separation commemorative and Penny Black	..	15	15
133	$1 Sir Rowland Hill, 1976 35 c. Separation commemorative and mail coach	..	35	30
131/3		*Set of 3*	60	55
MS134	148 × 140 mm. Nos. 131/3. P 15	..	70	1·25

(Des G. Vasarhelyi. Litho Format)

1979 (20 Oct). *International Year of the Child. T 18 and similar vert designs showing children's faces. P 14 × 13½.*

135	8 c. multicoloured	..	10	10
136	20 c. multicoloured	..	10	10
137	30 c. multicoloured	..	10	15
138	40 c. multicoloured	..	15	25
135/8		*Set of 4*	40	55

19 Eyed Cowrie (*Cypraea argus*)

(Des J. Cooter. Litho Format)

1980 (20 Feb). *Cowrie Shells. T 19 and similar horiz designs. Multicoloured. P 13½ × 14.*

139	8 c. Type **19**	..	10	10
140	20 c. Jester Cowrie (*Cypraea scurra*)	..	10	10
141	30 c. Closely-related Carnelian Cowrie (*Cypraea carneola propinqua*)	..	15	15
142	40 c. Golden Cowrie (*Cypraea aurantium*)	..	25	20
139/42		*Set of 4*	55	45

---

20 Philatelic Bureau, Funafuti, and 1976 8 c. Definitive

21 Queen Elizabeth the Queen Mother at Royal Variety Performance, 1978

(Des J. Cooter. Litho Questa)

1980 (30 Apr). *"London 1980" International Stamp Exhibition. T 20 and similar horiz designs. Multicoloured. P 13½ × 14.*

143	10 c. Type **20**	..	10	10
144	20 c. Gilbert and Ellice Islands stamp with Nukulaelae postmark of 1946 and 1976 2 c. definitive	..	15	15
145	30 c. Fleet Post Office, U.S. Navy, airmail letter of 1943	..	15	20
146	$1 Tuvalu coat of arms and map	..	35	40
143/6		*Set of 4*	65	75
MS147	160 × 136 mm. Nos. 143/6	..	65	1·10

(Des G. Drummond. Litho Format)

1980 (14 Aug). *80th Birthday of Queen Elizabeth the Queen Mother. P 13½.*

148	**21** 50 c. multicoloured	..	25	20

22 Aethaloessa calidalis

(Des J. Cooter. Litho Format)

1980 (20 Aug). *Moths. T 22 and similar horiz designs. Multicoloured. P 14.*

149	8 c. Type **22**	..	10	10
150	20 c. *Parotis suralis*	..	15	10
151	30 c. *Dudua aprobola*	..	20	15
152	40 c. *Decadarchis simulans*	..	20	15
149/52		*Set of 4*	60	45

23 Air Pacific De Havilland D.H.114 Heron 2 **(24)**

(Des G. Drummond. Litho Format)

1980 (5 Nov). *Aviation Commemorations. T 23 and similar horiz designs. Multicoloured. P 13½ × 14.*

153	8 c. Type **23**	..	10	10
154	20 c. Hawker Siddeley H.S.748	..	15	10
155	30 c. Short S.25 Sunderland flying boat	..	15	15
156	40 c. Orville Wright and Wright Flyer III	..	20	15
153/6		*Set of 4*	55	45

Commemorations:—8 c. 1st regular air service to Tuvalu, 1964; 20 c. Air service to Tuvalu; 30 c. War time R.N.Z.A.F. flying boat service to Funafuti, 1945; 40 c. Wright Brothers' 1st flight, 17 December 1903.

TWO TYPES OF SURCHARGE FOR NO. 157

Type I

Type II

Type I. Applied by lithography. Clean lines with an even distribution of the ink.

Type II. Applied by typography. Ragged lines with an uneven distribution of the ink, especially at the edges of the figures and bars. On some stamps the impression of the surcharge is visible on the back.

1981 (19 Jan). *No. 118 surch with T 24.*
157	45 c. on 50 c. Hammerhead (I)				25	40
	a. Type II (typo) surch				2·75	2·75

25 *Hypolimnas bolina* (male)

26 *Elizabeth* (brig), 1809

(Des J. Cooter. Litho Questa)

1981 (3 Feb). *Butterflies. T 25 and similar horiz designs. Multicoloured. P 14 × 14½.*
158	8 c. Type 25				15	10
159	20 c. *Hypolimnas bolina* (female)			20	15
160	30 c. *Hypolimnas bolina* (female) (*different*)		20	20
161	40 c. *Precis villida*				25	20
158/61				Set of 4	70	60

(Des R. Granger Barrett. Litho Format)

1981 (13 May). *Ships (1st series). T 26 and similar horiz designs. Multicoloured. W w 15 (sideways). P 14.*
162	10 c. Type 26				20	20
163	25 c. *Rebecca* (brigantine), 1819			20	25
164	35 c. *Independence II* (whaling ship), 1821	25	30
165	40 c. H.M.S. *Basilisk* (paddle-sloop), 1872	30	35
166	45 c. H.M.S. *Royalist* (screw-corvette), 1890	35	40
167	50 c. *Olivebank* (barque), 1920		35	40
162/7				Set of 6	1·50	1·75

Nos. 162/7 were each produced in sheets of six stamps and two labels, these occurring in the second horizontal row.
See also Nos. 235/40, 377/80, 442/5, 809/12 and 832/6.

(Des D. Shults. Litho Questa)

1981 (10 July–26 Nov). *Royal Wedding. Horiz designs as T 26/27 of Kiribati. Multicoloured.* (a) W w 15. P 14.
168	10 c. *Carolina*				10	15
	a. Sheetlet. No. 168 × 6 and No. 169			90	
169	10 c. Prince Charles and Lady Diana Spencer		35	50
170	45 c. *Victoria and Albert III*			10	15
	a. Sheetlet. No. 170 × 6 and No. 171			90	
171	45 c. As No. 169				40	65
172	$2 *Britannia*				25	50
	a. Sheetlet No. 172 × 6 and No. 173		2·00	
173	$2 As No. 169				75	1·50
168/73				Set of 6	1·75	3·00
MS174	120 × 109 mm. $1.50, As No. 169. Wmk sideways. P 12 (26 Nov)		50	75

(b) Booklet stamps. No wmk. P 12 (26 No
175	10 c. As No. 168				10	15
	a. Booklet pane. No. 175×4 with margins all round			35	
176	45 c. As No. 171				30	80
	a. Booklet pane. No. 176×2 with margins all round			60	

Nos. 168/73 were printed in sheetlets of seven stamps of the same face value, each containing six of the "Royal Yacht" design and one of the larger design showing Prince Charles and Lady Diana.
Nos. 175/6 come from $1.70 stamp booklets.

27 U.P.U. Emblem

28 Map of Funafuti and Anchor

(Des, eng and recess Harrison)

1981 (19 Nov). *U.P.U. Membership. W 4 of Maldive Islands. P 14½ × 14.*
177	27	70 c. deep ultramarine			20	30
178		$1 red-brown			30	45
		w. Wmk inverted			6·00	7·50
MS179	86×71 mm. Nos. 177/8. No wmk		90	2·25

(Des J. Cooter. Litho Questa)

1982 (17 Feb). *Amatuku Maritime School. T 28 and similar horiz designs. Multicoloured. W w 15 (sideways). P 13½ × 14.*
180	10 c. Type 28				10	10
181	25 c. Motor launch				20	20
182	35 c. School buildings and jetty			25	30
183	45 c. School flag and freighters			30	35
180/3				Set of 4	75	85

29 Caroline of Brandenburg–Ansbach, Princess of Wales, 1714

TONGA CYCLONE
RELIEF
1982 +20c
(30)

(Des D. Shults and J. Cooter. Litho Format)

1982 (19 May). *21st Birthday of Princess of Wales. T 29 and similar vert designs. Multicoloured. W w 15. P 13½ × 14.*
184	10 c. Type 29				10	10
185	45 c. Coat of arms of Caroline of Brandenburg-Ansbach		10	10
	w. Wmk inverted				12·00	
186	$1.50, Diana, Princess of Wales			50	30
	w. Wmk inverted				16·00	
184/6				Set of 3	60	40

1982 (20 May). *Tonga Cyclone Relief. Nos. 170/1 surch as T 30 (words in one line on No. 188).*
187	45 c. + 20 c. *Victoria and Albert III*		15	30
	a. Sheetlet. No. 187 × 6 and No. 188		1·25	
	b. Surch inverted				3·00	
	c. Surch inverted (horiz pair)			5·50	
	d. Surch double				2·75	
188	45 c. + 20 c. Prince Charles and Lady Diana Spencer			45	95
	a. Surch inverted				11·00	
	b. Surch double				11·00	

No. 187c shows the long surcharge, intended for No. 188, inverted and struck across a horizontal pair of No. 187. No. 188a shows two examples of Type 30 inverted on the same stamp.

1982 (14 July). *Birth of Prince William of Wales. Nos. 184/6 optd with T 19 of St. Kitts.*
189	10 c. Type 29				10	10
190	45 c. Coat of arms of Caroline of Brandenburg-Ansbach		10	10
	a. Opt inverted				17·00	
	w. Wmk inverted				12·00	
191	$1.50, Diana, Princess of Wales			30	30
189/91				Set of 3	40	40

31 Tuvalu and World Scout Badges

32 Tuvalu Crest and Duke of Edinburgh's Standard

(Des J. Cooter. Litho Walsall)

1982 (18 Aug). *75th Anniv of Boy Scout Movement. T 31 and similar horiz designs. Multicoloured. W w 15 (sideways). P 13½ × 14.*
192	10 c. Type 31				15	15
193	25 c. Camp-fire				40	40
194	35 c. Parade				45	45
195	45 c. Boy Scout				55	55
192/5				Set of 4	1·40	1·40

(Des J. Cooter. Litho Format)

1982 (26 Oct). *Royal Visit. T 32 and similar vert designs. Multicoloured. W w 15. P 14.*
196	25 c. Type 32				15	20
197	45 c. Tuvalu flag and Royal Standard		25	30
198	50 c. Portrait of Queen Elizabeth II		25	30
196/8				Set of 3	60	70
MS199	104×85 mm. Nos. 196/8. Wmk inverted		60	1·50

33 Fisherman's Hat and Equipment

(Des G. Drummond. Litho Walsall)

1983 (14 Mar)–84. *Handicrafts. T 33 and similar multicoloured designs. W w 15 (sideways on 1 c. to 45 c.). P 14.*
200	1 c. Type 33				30	10
201	2 c. Cowrie shell handbags			30	10
202	5 c. Wedding and babyfood baskets		30	10
203	10 c. Model canoe				30	10
203a	15 c. Ladies' sun hats (30.4.84)		2·25	1·75
204	20 c. Palm climbing rope and platform with toddy pot			30	20
205	25 c. Pandanus baskets			30	20
205a	30 c. Basket tray and coconut stands (18.4.84)	2·00	1·40
206	35 c. Pandanus pillows and shell necklaces	40	30
207	40 c. Round baskets and fans			30	35
208	45 c. Reef sandals and fish trap		35	40
209	50 c. Rat trap (*vert*)			40	45
209a	60 c. Fisherman's waterproof boxes (*vert*) (18.4.84)		2·75	1·40
210	$1 Pump drill and adze (*vert*)		45	45
211	$2 Fisherman's hat and canoe bailers (*vert*)	60	55
212	$5 Fishing rod, lures and scoop nets (*vert*)	1·00	75
200/12				Set of 16	11·00	7·50

34 *Te Tautai* (trawler)

(Des G. Drummond. Litho Format)

1983 (14 Mar). *Commonwealth Day. T 34 and similar horiz designs. Multicoloured. W w 15 (sideways). P 14.*
213	20 c. Type 34				15	15
214	35 c. Traditional dancing, Motufoua School	15	25
215	45 c. Satellite view of Pacific		20	30
216	50 c. *Morning Star* (container ship)	25	40
213/16				Set of 4	65	1·00

No. 214 is incorrectly inscribed "MOTOFOUA SCHOOL".

35 *Pantala flavescens*

(Des J. Cooter. Litho Format)

1983 (25 May). *Dragonflies. T 35 and similar horiz designs. Multicoloured. W w 15 (sideways). P 14.*
217	10 c. Type 35				15	10
218	35 c. *Anax guttatus*			35	35
219	40 c. *Tholymis tillarga*			35	40
220	50 c. *Diplacodes bipunctata*			40	50
217/20				Set of 4	1·10	1·25

36 Brigade Members Racing
(37)

(Des J. Cooter. Litho Format)

1983 (10 Aug). *Centenary of Boys' Brigade. T 36 and similar multicoloured designs. W w 15 (sideways on 10 c., 35 c.). P 13½.*
221	10 c. Type 36				10	10
222	35 c. B. B. members in outrigger canoe		25	30
223	$1 On parade (*vert*)			65	1·00
221/3				Set of 3	90	1·25

1983 (26 Aug). *No. 210 surch with T 37.*
224	60 c. on $1 Pump drill and adze			70	70

IMPERFORATES AND MISSING COLOURS. Various issues between Nos. 225 and 529 exist either imperforate or with colours omitted. Such items are not listed as there is no evidence that they fulfil the criteria outlined on page xi of this catalogue.

38 Montgolfier Balloon, 1783   39 Early Communications

(Des A. Theobald. Litho Format)

1983 (21 Sept). *Bicentenary of Manned Flight.* T **38** *and similar multicoloured designs.* W w 15 *(sideways on 35 c., 45 c.).* P 14.

225	25 c. Type **38**	20	20
	w. Wmk inverted	25·00	
226	35 c. Grumman Mackinnon G-21E Turbo Goose (*horiz*)	20	25
	a. No wmk		
227	45 c. Beech 200 Super King Air (*horiz*)	25	30
228	50 c. *Double Eagle II* balloon	25	35
	w. Wmk inverted	35·00	
225/8	*Set of 4*	80	1·00
MS229	114×145 mm. Nos. 225/8. Wmk sideways	70	1·00

(Des J.W. Litho Questa)

1983 (18 Nov). *World Communications Year.* T **39** *and similar horiz designs. Multicoloured.* W w 15. P 14.

230	25 c. Type **39**	20	20
231	35 c. Radio operator	25	25
232	45 c. Modern telephone	25	25
233	50 c. Funafuti transmitting station	30	30
230/3	*Set of 4*	90	90

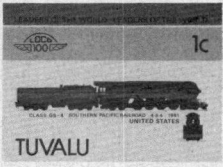

(40)

1984 (1 Feb). *No. 208 surch with* T **40**.

234	30 c. on 45 c. Reef sandals and fish trap	35	40

(Des R. Granger Barrett. Litho Format)

1984 (16 Feb). *Ships (2nd series). Horiz designs as* T **26**. *Multicoloured.* W w 15 *(sideways*).* P 14.

235	10 c. *Titus* (freighter), 1897	25	15
	w. Wmk POST OFFICE reading upwards	50·00	
236	20 c. *Malaita* (freighter), 1905	25	15
	w. Wmk POST OFFICE reading upwards	90·00	
237	25 c. *Aymeric* (freighter), 1906	25	15
	w. Wmk POST OFFICE reading upwards	50·00	
238	35 c. *Anshun* (freighter), 1965	30	25
239	45 c. *Beaverbank* (freighter), 1970	30	30
240	50 c. *Benjamin Bowring* (freighter), 1981	30	30
235/40	*Set of 6*	1·50	1·10

*The normal sideways watermark shows "POST OFFICE" reading downwards.

Nos. 235/40 were each produced in sheets of six stamps and two labels, these occurring in the second horizontal row.

41 Southern Pacific Railroad Class GS-4

(Des J.W. Litho Format)

1984 (29 Feb). *Leaders of the World. Railway Locomotives (1st series).* T **41** *and similar horiz designs, the first in each pair showing technical drawings and the second the locomotive at work.* P 12½.

241	1 c. multicoloured	10	10
	a. Vert pair. Nos. 241/2	10	10
242	1 c. multicoloured	10	10
243	15 c. multicoloured	20	25
	a. Vert pair. Nos. 243/4	40	50
244	15 c. multicoloured	20	25
245	40 c. multicoloured	25	30
	a. Vert pair. Nos. 245/6	50	60
246	40 c. multicoloured	25	30
247	60 c. multicoloured	35	40
	a. Vert pair. Nos. 247/8	70	80
248	60 c. multicoloured	35	40
241/8	*Set of 8*	1·40	1·75

Designs:—Nos. 241/2, Southern Pacific Railroad Class GS-4, U.S.A. (1941); 243/4, New South Wales Govt Class AD60, Australia (1952); 245/6, New South Wales Govt Class C38, Australia (1943); 247/8, Class "Achilles" *Lord of the Isles*, Great Britain (1892).

See also Nos. 253/68, 273/80, 313/20 and 348/55.

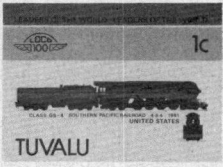

42 *Ipomoea pes-caprae*

(Des Michael and Sylvia Goaman. Litho Questa)

1984 (30 May). *Beach Flowers.* T **42** *and similar horiz designs. Multicoloured.* W w 15. P 14.

249	25 c. Type **42**	25	25
250	45 c. *Ipomoea macrantha*	40	40
251	50 c. *Triumfetta procumbens*	45	45
252	60 c. *Portulaca quadrifida*	50	50
249/52	*Set of 4*	1·40	1·40

(Des J.W. Litho Format)

1984 (27 June). *Leaders of the World, Railway Locomotives (2nd series). Designs as* T **41** *in each pair showing technical drawings and the second the locomotive at work.* P 12½.

253	10 c. multicoloured	10	10
	a. Vert pair. Nos. 253/4	10	15
254	10 c. multicoloured	10	10
255	15 c. multicoloured	10	15
	a. Vert pair. Nos. 255/6	15	30
256	15 c. multicoloured	10	15
257	20 c. multicoloured	10	15
	a. Vert pair. Nos. 257/8	15	30
258	20 c. multicoloured	10	15
259	25 c. multicoloured	10	15
	a. Vert pair. Nos. 259/60	15	30
260	25 c. multicoloured	10	15
261	40 c. multicoloured	10	20
	a. Vert pair. Nos. 261/2	20	40
262	40 c. multicoloured	10	20
263	50 c. multicoloured	10	20
	a. Vert pair. Nos. 263/4	20	40
264	50 c. multicoloured	10	20
265	60 c. multicoloured	10	20
	a. Vert pair. Nos. 265/6	20	40
266	60 c. multicoloured	10	20
267	$1 multicoloured	15	25
	a. Vert pair. Nos. 267/8	30	50
268	$1 multicoloured	15	25
253/68	*Set of 16*	1·25	2·50

Designs:—Nos. 253/4, Illinois Central Railroad "Casey Jones" type locomotive No. 382, U.S.A. (1896); 255/6, Erie Railroad Triplex type, U.S.A. (1914); 257/8, Class 370 Advanced Passenger Train, Great Britain (1981); 259/60, LMS Class 4F, Great Britain (1924); 261/2, GWR Class "Tornado Rover", Great Britain (1888); 263/4, Class 73 electric locomotive *Broadlands*, Great Britain (1967); 265/6, *Locomotion*, Great Britain (1825); 267/8, Class C57, Japan, (1937).

Nos. 253/68 were issued in a similar sheet format to Nos. 241/8.

43 Exhibition Emblem

44 A. Shrewsbury

(Des G. Drummond. Litho Format)

1984 (21 Aug). *"Ausipex" International Stamp Exhibition, Melbourne (Nos. 269/70) and 15th South Pacific Forum (others).* T **43** *and similar horiz designs. Multicoloured,* W w 15 *(sideways).* P 14.

269	60 c. Type **43**	20	30
270	60 c. Royal Exhibition Building, Melbourne	20	30
271	60 c. Arms of Tuvalu	20	30
272	60 c. Tuvalu flag	20	30
269/72	*Set of 4*	70	1·10

(Des J.W. Litho Format)

1984 (4 Oct). *Leaders of the World. Railway Locomotives (3rd series). Horiz designs as* T **41**, *the first in each pair showing technical drawings and the second the locomotive at work.* P 12½.

273	1 c. multicoloured	10	10
	a. Vert pair. Nos. 273/4	10	10
	b. Error. Wmk w 15	2·25	
	ba. Vert pair. Nos. 273b/4b	4·50	
274	1 c. multicoloured	10	10
	b. Error. Wmk w 15	2·25	
275	15 c. multicoloured	15	20
	a. Vert pair. Nos. 275/6	30	40
276	15 c. multicoloured	15	20
277	30 c. multicoloured	20	25
	a. Vert pair. Nos. 277/8	40	50
	b. Error. Wmk w 15	2·25	
	ba. Vert pair. Nos. 277b/8b	4·50	
278	30 c. multicoloured	20	25
	b. Error. Wmk w 15	2·25	
279	$1 multicoloured	40	65
	a. Vert pair. Nos. 279/80	80	1·25
	b. Error. Wmk w 15	3·75	
	ba. Vert pair. Nos. 279b/80b	7·50	
280	$1 multicoloured	40	65
	b. Error. Wmk w 15	3·75	
273/80	*Set of 8*	1·40	2·00

Designs:—Nos. 273/4, Class 9700, Japan (1897); 275/6, Paris–Lyon–Mediterranee Class 231C/K, France (1909); 277/8, Class 640, Italy (1907); 279/80, Paris–Orleans Class 4500, France (1906).

Nos. 273/80 were issued together in a similar sheet format to Nos. 241/8.

(Des Court House Studio. Litho Format)

1984 (5 Nov). *Leaders of the World. Cricketers.* T **44** *and similar vert designs, the first listed in each pair showing the cricketer in action and the second a head portrait.* P 12½.

281	5 c. multicoloured	10	10
	a. Horiz pair. Nos. 281/2	10	20
282	5 c. multicoloured	10	10
283	30 c. multicoloured	20	30
	a. Horiz pair. Nos. 283/4	40	60
284	30 c. multicoloured	20	30
285	50 c. multicoloured	20	30
	a. Horiz pair. Nos. 285/6	40	60
286	50 c. multicoloured	20	30
287	60 c. multicoloured	25	35
	a. Horiz pair. Nos. 287/8	50	70
288	60 c. multicoloured	25	35
281/8	*Set of 8*	1·25	1·90

Designs:—Nos. 281/2, A. Shrewsbury; 283/4, H. Verity; 285/6, E. H. Hendren; 287/8, J. Briggs.

Nos. 281/2, 283/4, 285/6 and 287/8 were printed together, se-tenant, in horizontal pairs throughout the sheets.

Similar stamps showing Close (5 c.), (Boycott (15 c.), Bairstow (30 c.), and Evans ($1) were prepared, but not issued. They exist imperforate from stock dispersed by the liquidator of Format International Security Printers Ltd.

45 Trees and Stars

(Des Jennifer Toombs. Litho Format)

1984 (14 Nov). *Christmas. Children's Drawings.* T **45** *and similar horiz designs. Multicoloured.* W w 15 *(sideways).* P 14½ × 14.

289	15 c. Type **45**	10	10
290	40 c. Fishing from outrigger canoes	20	20
291	50 c. Three Wise Men bearing gifts	25	25
292	60 c. The Holy Family	35	35
289/92	*Set of 4*	75	75

46 Morris Minor

47 Common Flicker

(Des J.W. ($1), Artists International (others). Litho Format)

1984 (7 Dec). *Leaders of the World. Automobiles (1st series).* T **46** *and similar horiz designs, the first in each pair showing technical drawings and the second paintings.* P 12½.

293	1 c. black, pale cinnamon and yellow-ochre	10	10
	a. Vert pair. Nos. 293/4	10	10
294	1 c. multicoloured	10	10
295	15 c. black, pale flesh and brown-lilac	10	15
	a. Vert pair. Nos. 295/6	20	30
296	15 c. multicoloured	10	15
297	50 c. black, pale cinnamon and dull mauve	20	20
	a. Vert pair. Nos. 297/8	40	60
298	50 c. multicoloured	20	30
299	$1 black, pale green and cobalt	30	40
	a. Vert pair. Nos. 299/300	60	80
300	$1 multicoloured	30	40
293/300	*Set of 8*	1·10	1·60

Designs:—Nos. 293/4, Morris "Minor"; 295/6, Studebaker "Avanti"; 297/8, Chevrolet "International Six"; 299/300, Allard "J2".

Nos. 293/4, 295/6, 297/8 and 299/300 were printed together, se-tenant, in vertical pairs throughout the sheets.

See also Nos. 321/8, 356/71, 421/32 and 446/70.

(Des R. Vigurs. Litho Format)

1985 (12 Feb). *Leaders of the World. Birth Bicentenary of John J. Audubon (ornithologist).* T **47** *and similar vert designs. Multicoloured.* P 12½.

301	1 c. Type **47**	10	10
	a. Horiz pair. Nos. 301/2	10	10
302	1 c. Say's Phoebe	10	10
303	25 c. Townsend's Warbler	30	30
	a. Horiz pair. Nos. 303/4	60	60
304	25 c. Bohemian Waxwing	30	30
305	50 c. Prothonotary Warbler	30	50
	a. Horiz pair. Nos. 305/6	60	1·00
306	50 c. Worm-eating Warbler	30	50
307	70 c. Broad-winged Hawk	35	65
	a. Horiz pair. Nos. 307/8	70	1·25
308	70 c. Hen Harrier	35	65
301/8	*Set of 8*	1·75	2·50

Nos. 301/2, 303/4, 305/6 and 307/8 were printed together, se-tenant, in horizontal pairs throughout the sheets.

48 Black-naped Tern

(Des G. Drummond. Litho Format)

1985 (27 Feb). *Birds and their Eggs.* T **48** *and similar horiz designs. Multicoloured.* W w 15 *(sideways).* P 14.

309	15 c. Type **48**	50	20
310	40 c. White-capped Noddy	85	50
311	50 c. White-tailed Tropicbird	95	60
312	60 c. Sooty Tern	1·00	70
309/12	*Set of 4*	3·00	1·75

(Des J.W. (5 c., $1), T. Hadler (others). Litho Format)

1985 (19 Mar). *World War II. Railway Locomotives (4th series). Horiz designs as T 41 the first in each pair showing technical drawings and the second the locomotive at work.* P 12½.

313	5 c. multicoloured	10	10
	a. Vert pair. Nos. 313/14	10	10
314	5 c. multicoloured	10	10
315	10 c. multicoloured	10	10
	a. Vert pair. Nos. 315/16	20	20
316	10 c. multicoloured	10	10
317	30 c. multicoloured	30	35
	a. Vert pair. Nos. 317/18	60	70
318	30 c. multicoloured	30	35
319	$1 multicoloured	50	80
	a. Vert pair. Nos. 319/20	1·00	1·60
320	$1 multicoloured	50	80
313/20	*Set of 8*	1·60	2·40

Designs:—Nos. 313/14, GWR Class "Churchward 28XX", Great Britain (1905); 315/16, Class KF No. 605, China (1935); 317/18, Class 99.77 No. 99773, Germany (1952); 319/20, Pearson type, Great Britain (1853).
Nos. 313/20 were issued in a similar sheet format to Nos. 241/8.

(Des Artists International. Litho Format)

1985 (3 Apr). *Leaders of the World. Automobiles (2nd series). Horiz designs as T 46, the first in each pair showing technical drawings and the second paintings.* P 12½.

321	1 c. black, apple green and deep dull green	10	10
	a. Vert pair. Nos. 321/2	10	10
322	1 c. multicoloured	10	10
323	20 c. black, pink and rose-red	15	20
	a. Vert pair. Nos. 323/4	30	40
324	20 c. multicoloured	15	20
325	50 c. black, dull violet-blue & brt reddish vio	20	30
	a. Vert pair. Nos. 325/6	40	60
326	50 c. multicoloured	20	30
327	70 c. black, dull pink and grey-brown	20	35
	a. Vert pair. Nos. 327/8	40	70
328	70 c. multicoloured	20	35
321/8	*Set of 8*	1·00	1·50

Designs:—Nos. 321/2, Rickenbacker (1923); 323/4, Detroit-Electric Two Door Brougham (1914); 325/6, Packard "Clipper" (1941); 327/8, Audi "Quattro" (1982).
Nos. 321/8 were issued in a similar sheet format to Nos. 293/300.

49 Curtiss P-40N Warhawk

50 Queen Elizabeth the Queen Mother

(Des A. Theobald. Litho Questa)

1985 (29 May). *World War II Aircraft. T 49 and similar horiz designs. Multicoloured. W w 15. P 14.*

329	15 c. Type 49	1·75	80
330	40 c. Consolidated B-24 Liberator	2·25	1·50
331	50 c. Lockheed PV-1 Ventura	2·25	1·75
332	60 c. Douglas C-54	2·25	2·00
329/32	*Set of 4*	7·75	5·50
MS333	110×108 mm. Nos. 329/32. Wmk sideways	4·00	2·75

(Des D. Ewart ($1.20), Maxine Marsh (others). Litho Format)

1985 (4 July). *Leaders of the World. Life and Times of Queen Elizabeth the Queen Mother. Various vertical portraits as T 50.* P 12½.

334	5 c. multicoloured	10	10
	a. Horiz pair. Nos. 334/5	10	10
335	5 c. multicoloured	10	10
336	30 c. multicoloured	15	15
	a. Horiz pair. Nos. 336/7	30	30
337	30 c. multicoloured	15	15
338	60 c. multicoloured	15	20
	a. Horiz pair. Nos. 338/9	30	40
339	60 c. multicoloured	15	20
340	$1 multicoloured	15	35
	a. Horiz pair. Nos. 340/1	30	70
341	$1 multicoloured	15	35
334/41	*Set of 8*	70	1·40
MS342	85×114 mm. $1.20, multicoloured; $1.20, multicoloured	60	1·50

The two designs of each value were issued, *se-tenant*, in horizontal pairs within the sheets.
Each *se-tenant* pair shows a floral pattern across the bottom of the portraits which stops short of the left-hand edge on the left-hand stamp and of the right-hand edge on the right-hand stamp.
Designs as Nos. 336/7 and 338/9, but with face values of $3×2 and $2×2, also exist in additional miniature sheets from a restricted printing issued 10 January 1986.

51 Guide playing Guitar

52 Stalk-eyed Ghost Crab

(Des Jennifer Toombs. Litho Format)

1985 (28 Aug). *75th Anniv of Girl Guide Movement. T 51 and similar vert designs. Multicoloured. W w 15 (sideways).* P 15.

343	15 c. Type 51	15	20
344	40 c. Building camp-fire	40	45
345	50 c. Patrol Leader with Guide flag	50	55
346	60 c. Guide saluting	60	65
343/6	*Set of 4*	1·50	1·60
MS347	141×77 mm. Nos. 343/6. Wmk upright	1·50	2·00

(Des J.W. (10 c.), T. Hadler (others). Litho Format)

1985 (18 Sept). *Leaders of the World. Railway Locomotives (5th series). Horiz designs as T 41, the first in each pair showing technical drawings and the second the locomotive at work.* P 12½.

348	10 c. multicoloured	10	15
	a. Vert pair. Nos. 348/9	15	30
349	10 c. multicoloured	10	15
350	40 c. multicoloured	20	30
	a. Vert pair. Nos. 350/1	40	60
351	40 c. multicoloured	20	30
352	65 c. multicoloured	25	40
	a. Vert pair. Nos. 352/3	50	80
353	65 c. multicoloured	25	40
354	$1 multicoloured	30	55
	a. Vert pair. Nos. 354/5	60	1·10
355	$1 multicoloured	30	55
348/55	*Set of 8*	1·50	2·50

Designs:—Nos. 348/9, LNER *Green Arrow*, Great Britain (1936); 350/1 Conrail Class SD-50 diesel locomotive No. 6729, U.S.A. (1982); 352/3, "Flying Hamburger", Germany (1932); 354/5, Class 1070, Japan (1925. Dated "1908" in error).
Nos. 348/55 were issued in a similar sheet format to Nos. 241/8.

(Des Artists International. Litho Format)

1985 (8 Oct). *Leaders of the World. Automobiles (3rd series). Horiz designs as T 46, the first in each pair showing technical drawings and the second paintings.* P 12½.

356	5 c. black, grey and bright mauve	10	10
	a. Vert pair. Nos. 356/7	10	15
357	5 c. multicoloured	10	10
358	10 c. black, pale salmon-pink and Indian red	10	15
	a. Vert pair. Nos. 358/9	15	30
359	10 c. multicoloured	10	15
360	15 c. black, light brown and Indian red	10	15
	a. Vert pair. Nos. 360/1	15	30
361	15 c. multicoloured	10	15
362	35 c. black, brown-red & light turq-blue	15	25
	a. Vert pair. Nos. 362/3	30	50
363	35 c. multicoloured	15	25
364	40 c. black, dull yellow-grn & yellowish grn	15	25
	a. Vert pair. Nos. 364/5	30	50
365	40 c. multicoloured	15	25
366	55 c. black, pale stone and brown-olive	15	25
	a. Vert pair. Nos. 366/7	30	50
367	55 c. multicoloured	15	25
368	$1 black, brown and lake-brown	25	35
	a. Vert pair. Nos. 368/9	50	70
369	$1 multicoloured	25	35
370	$1.50, black, flesh and dull scarlet	30	45
	a. Vert pair. Nos. 370/1	60	90
371	$1.50, multicoloured	30	45
356/71	*Set of 16*	2·25	3·50

Designs:—Nos. 356/7, Cord "L-29" (1929); 358/9, Horch "670 V-12" (1932); 360/1, Lanchester (1901); 362/3, Citroen "2 CV" (1950); 364/5, MGA (1957); 366/7, Ferrari "250 GTO" (1962); 368/9, Ford "V-8" (1932); 370/1, Aston Martin "Lagonda" (1977).
Nos. 356/71 were issued in a similar sheet format to Nos. 293/300.

(Des G. Drummond. Litho Format)

1986 (7 Jan). *Crabs. T 52 and similar horiz designs. Multicoloured.* P 15.

372	15 c. Type 52	60	70
373	40 c. Red and White Painted Crab	80	95
374	50 c. Red-spotted Crab	85	1·40
375	60 c. Red Hermit Crab	85	1·75
372/5	*Set of 4*	2·75	4·25

53 Chess Knight on Board and Flags of U.S. and U.S.S.R. (World Chess Championships)

54 Peace Dove carrying Wreath and Rainbow

(Des Court House Studio. Litho Format)

1986 (19 Mar). *International Events. Sheet 148×127 mm, containing T 53 and similar vert design. Multicoloured.* P 12½.

MS376	$3 Type 53: $3 Emblem (80th anniv of Rotary	5·00	7·00

The margins of No. MS376 are inscribed "TUVALU" and "Anniversary of Scouting" with two emblems either on a plain apple-green background or with illustrations of types of fungi added.
Overprints on this miniature sheet commemorating "Capex 87" International Stamp Exhibition, Toronto, were not authorised by the Tuvalu administration.

(Des R. Granger Barrett. Litho Format)

1986 (14 Apr). *Ships (3rd series). Missionary Vessels. Horiz designs as T 26. Multicoloured. W w 15.* P 15.

377	15 c. *Messenger of Peace* (schooner)	40	50
378	40 c. *John Wesley* (brig)	55	80
379	50 c. *Duff* (full-rigged ship)	60	90
380	60 c. *Triton* (brigantine)	65	1·25
377/80	*Set of 4*	2·00	3·00

(Des Court House Studio. Litho Format)

1986 (21 Apr–14 June). *60th Birthday of Queen Elizabeth II. Multicoloured designs as T 117a of Montserrat.* P 12½.

381	10 c. Queen wearing ceremonial cloak, New Zealand, 1977	10	10
382	90 c. Before visit to France, 1957	25	35
383	$1.50, Queen in 1982	35	65
384	$3 In Canberra, 1982 (*vert*)	60	1·25
381/4	*Set of 4*	1·10	2·10
MS385	85×115 mm. $4 Queen carrying bouquet (14.6)	2·75	5·00

The 10 c., 90 c. and $1.50 values exist with PVA gum as well as gum arabic.

(Des Gloria McConnaghy. Litho Questa)

1986 (22 May). *25th Anniv of United States Peace Corps. W w 15.* P 14.

386	54	50 c. multicoloured	80	90

55 Island and Flags of Tuvalu and U.S.A.

56 South Korean Player

(Des Court House Studio. Litho Questa)

1986 (22 May). *"Ameripex" International Stamp Exhibition, Chicago. W w 15.* P 14×13½.

387	55	60 c. multicoloured	85	95

(Des Court House Studio. Litho Format)

1986 (30 June). *World Cup Football Championship, Mexico. T 56 and similar multicoloured designs.* P 15 (1 c. to 40 c.) or 12½ (others).

388	1 c. Type 56	10	10
389	5 c. French player	10	10
390	10 c. West German captain with World Cup trophy, 1974	10	10
391	40 c. Italian player	50	50
392	60 c. World Cup final, 1974 (59×39 mm)	65	65
393	$1 Canadian team (59×39 mm)	80	1·00
394	$2 Northern Irish team (59×39 mm)	1·25	2·00
395	$3 English team (59×39 mm)	1·75	3·00
388/95	*Set of 8*	4·50	6·50
MS396	Two sheets, each 85×114 mm. (a) $1.50, As No. 393; (b) $2.50, As No. 394 *Set of 2 sheets*	3·75	6·00

(Litho Format)

1986 (18 July–15 Oct). *Royal Wedding (1st issue). Multicoloured designs as T 118a of Montserrat.* P 12½.

397	60 c. Prince Andrew and Miss Sarah Ferguson	25	35
	a. Pair. Nos. 397/8	50	70
398	60 c. Prince Andrew with prizewinning bull	25	35
399	$1 Prince Andrew at horse trials (*horiz*)	30	65
	a. Pair. Nos. 399/400	60	1·25
400	$1 Miss Sarah Ferguson and Princess Diana (*horiz*)	30	65
397/400	*Set of 4*	1·00	1·75
MS401	85×115 mm. $6 Duke and Duchess of York after wedding (*horiz*) (15.10)	1·25	4·00

Nos. 397/8 and 399/400 were printed together, *se-tenant*, in horizontal and vertical pairs throughout the sheets.
Nos. 397/400 imperforate come from souvenir stamp booklets.
See also Nos. 433/6.

57 Mourning Gecko

(58)

(Des Jennifer Toombs. Litho Questa)

1986 (30 July). *Lizards. T 57 and similar horiz designs. Multicoloured. W w 15.* P 14.

402	15 c. Type 57	55	55
403	40 c. Oceanic Stump-toed Gecko	1·00	1·00
404	50 c. Azure-tailed Skink	1·25	1·50
405	60 c. Moth Skink	1·50	2·00
402/5	*Set of 4*	4·00	4·50

1986 (4 Aug). *"Stampex '86" Stamp Exhibition, Adelaide. No. 386 optd with T 58.*

406	54	50 c. multicoloured	55	65

59 Map and Flag of Australia

(Des G. Drummond. Litho Format)

1986 (4 Aug). *15th Anniv of South Pacific Forum. T* **59** *and similar horiz designs showing maps and national flags. Multicoloured. W w* 15. *P* 15.

407	40 c. Type 59	..	..	55	60
	a. Sheetlet. Nos. 407/20			6·50	
408	40 c. Cook Islands	..	..	55	60
409	40 c. Micronesia	..	..	55	60
410	40 c. Fiji	..	..	55	60
411	40 c. Kiribati	..	..	55	60
412	40 c. Western Samoa	..	..	55	60
413	40 c. Nauru	..	..	55	60
414	40 c. Vanuatu	..	..	55	60
415	40 c. New Zealand	..	..	55	60
416	40 c. Tuvalu	..	..	55	60
417	40 c. Tonga	..	..	55	60
418	40 c. Solomon Islands	..	..	55	60
419	40 c. Papua New Guinea	..	..	55	60
420	40 c. Niue	..	..	55	60
407/20			Set of 14	6·50	7·50

Nos. 407/20 were printed together, *se-tenant*, as a sheetlet of fourteen stamps arranged round a central label.

(Des Court House Studio. Litho Format)

1986 (13 Oct). *Automobiles (4th series). Horiz designs as T* **46**, *the first in each pair showing technical drawings and the second paintings. P* 12½.

421	15 c. multicoloured	..	..	15	15
	a. Vert pair. Nos. 421/2			30	30
422	15 c. multicoloured	..	..	15	15
423	40 c. multicoloured	..	..	20	25
	a. Vert pair. Nos. 423/4			40	50
424	40 c. multicoloured	..	..	20	25
425	50 c. multicoloured	..	..	20	30
	a. Vert pair. Nos. 425/6			40	60
426	50 c. multicoloured	..	..	20	30
427	60 c. multicoloured	..	..	20	35
	a. Vert pair. Nos. 427/8			40	70
428	60 c. multicoloured	..	..	20	35
429	90 c. multicoloured	..	..	25	35
	a. Vert pair. Nos. 429/30			50	70
430	90 c. multicoloured	..	..	25	35
431	$1.50, multicoloured	..	..	30	45
	a. Vert pair. Nos. 431/2			60	90
432	$1.50 multicoloured	..	..	30	45
421/32			Set of 12	2·40	3·25

Designs:—Nos. 421/2, Cooper "500" (1953); 423/4, Rover "2000" (1964); 425/6, Ruxton (1930); 427/8, Jowett "Jupiter" (1950); 429/30, Cobra "Daytona Coupe" (1964); 431/2, Packard Model F "Old Pacific" (1903).

Nos. 421/32 were issued in a similar sheet format to Nos. 293/300.

1986 (28 Oct). *Royal Wedding (2nd issue). Nos.* 397/400 *optd as* **T** 121 *of Montserrat in silver.*

433	60 c. Prince Andrew and Miss Sarah Ferguson	..	..	70	1·25
	a. Pair. Nos. 433/4	..		1·40	2·50
434	60 c. Prince Andrew with prizewinning bull		70	1·25
435	$1 Prince Andrew at horse trials (*horiz*)	..	1·25	1·40
	a. Pair. Nos. 435/6	..		2·50	2·75
436	$1 Miss Sarah Ferguson and Princess Diana (*horiz*)		1·25	1·40
433/6		..	Set of 4	3·50	4·75

60 Sea Star

61 *Nephrolepis saligna*

(Des G. Drummond. Litho Questa)

1986 (5 Nov). *Coral Reef Life (1st series). T* **60** *and similar horiz designs. Multicoloured. P* 14.

437	15 c. Type 60	..	..	85	85
438	40 c. Pencil Urchin	..	..	1·60	1·90
439	50 c. Fragile Coral	..	..	1·75	2·00
440	60 c. Pink Coral	..	..	2·00	2·25
437/40			Set of 4	5·50	6·25

See also Nos. 498/501, 558/62 and 822/6.

(Des Court House Studio. Litho Format)

1986 (24 Nov). *Centenary of Statue of Liberty. Vert views of Statue as T* **121a** *of Montserrat in separate miniature sheets. Multicoloured. P* 14×13½.

MS441	Nine sheets, each 85×115 mm. $1.25; $1.50; $1.80; $2; $2.25; $2.50; $3; $3.25; $3.50			
		Set of 9 sheets	5·00	9·00

(Des R. Granger Barrett. Litho Questa)

1987 (4 Feb). *Ships (4th series). Missionary Steamers. Horiz designs as T* **26**. *Multicoloured. P* 14.

442	15 c. *Southern Cross IV*	..	..	95	95
443	40 c. *John Williams VI*	..	..	2·00	2·25
444	50 c. *John Williams IV*	..	..	2·25	2·50
445	60 c. *M.S. Southern Cross*	..	..	2·25	2·50
442/5		..	Set of 4	6·75	7·50

(Litho Format)

1987 (7 May–6 June). *Automobiles (5th series). Horiz designs as T* **46**, *the first in each pair showing technical drawings and the second paintings. P* 12½.

446	1 c. multicoloured	..	..	10	10
	a. Vert pair. Nos. 446/7			10	10
447	1 c. multicoloured	..	..	10	10
448	2 c. multicoloured	..	..	10	10
	a. Vert pair. Nos. 448/9			10	10
449	2 c. multicoloured	..	..	10	10
450	5 c. multicoloured	..	..	10	10
	a. Vert pair. Nos. 450/1			10	15
451	5 c. multicoloured	..	..	10	10
452	10 c. multicoloured	..	..	15	20
	a. Vert pair. Nos. 452/3			30	40
453	10 c. multicoloured	..	..	15	20
454	20 c. multicoloured	..	..	20	25
	a. Vert pair. Nos. 454/5			40	50
455	20 c. multicoloured	..	..	20	25
456	30 c. multicoloured	..	..	25	30
	a. Vert pair. Nos. 456/7			50	60
457	30 c. multicoloured	..	..	25	30
458	40 c. multicoloured	..	..	30	35
	a. Vert pair. Nos. 458/9			60	70
459	40 c. multicoloured	..	..	30	35
460	50 c. multicoloured	..	..	30	40
	a. Vert pair. Nos. 460/1			60	80
461	50 c. multicoloured	..	..	30	40
462	60 c. multicoloured	..	..	30	40
	a. Vert pair. Nos. 462/3			60	80
463	60 c. multicoloured	..	..	30	40
464	70 c. multicoloured	..	..	30	45
	a. Vert pair. Nos. 464/5			60	90
465	70 c. multicoloured	..	..	30	45
466	75 c. multicoloured	..	..	30	45
	a. Vert pair. Nos. 466/7			60	90
467	75 c. multicoloured	..	..	30	45
468	$1 multicoloured	..	..	40	70
	a. Vert pair. Nos. 468/9			80	1·40
469	$1 multicoloured	..	..	40	70
446/9			Set of 24	4·50	6·50
MS470	100×85 mm. Nos. 468/9 (6.6)			2·25	3·25

Designs:—Nos. 446/7, Talbot-Lago (1938); 448/9, Du Pont "Model G" (1930); 450/1, Riley "RM" (1950); 452/3, Chevrolet "Baby Grand" (1915); 454/5, Shelby "Mustang GT 500 KR" (1968); 456/7, Ferrari "212 Export Barchetta" (1952); 458/9, Peerless "Model 48-Six" (1912); 460/1, Sunbeam "Alpine" (1954); 462/3, Matra-Ford "MS 80" (1969); 464/5, Squire 1½ Litre (1934); 466/7, Talbot "105" (1931); 468/9, Plymouth "Model Q" (1928).

Nos. 446/69 were issued in a similar sheet format to Nos. 293/300.

(Des J. Cooter. Litho Questa)

1987 (7 July). *Ferns. T* **61** *and similar vert designs. Multicoloured. W w* 15 (*sideways*). *P* 14.

471	15 c. Type 61	..	..	40	55
472	40 c. *Asplenium nidus*	..	..	70	90
473	50 c. *Microsorum scolopendria*	..	85	1·10
474	60 c. *Pteris tripartita*	..	..	95	1·25
471/4			Set of 4	2·50	3·50
MS475	62×62 mm. $1.50, *Psilotum nudum*.			
	Wmk upright			2·25	3·50

62 Floral Arrangement **63** Queen Victoria, 1897 (photo by Downey)

(Des Jennifer Toombs. Litho Questa)

1987 (12 Aug). *Flowers and "Fous". T* **62** *and similar vert designs showing either floral arrangements or "fous" (women's headdresses). Multicoloured. W w* 15 (*sideways*). *P* 14.

476	15 c. Type 62	..	..	25	35
	a. Horiz pair. Nos. 476/7			50	70
477	15 c. "Fou"	..	..	25	35
478	40 c. "Fou"	..	..	55	75
	a. Horiz pair. Nos. 478/9			1·10	1·50
479	40 c. Floral arrangement	..	55	75
480	50 c. Floral arrangement	..	65	80
	a. Horiz pair. Nos. 480/1			1·25	1·60
481	50 c. "Fou"	..	..	65	80
482	60 c. "Fou"	..	..	75	90
	a. Horiz pair. Nos. 482/3			1·50	1·75
483	60 c. Floral arrangement	..	75	90
476/83			Set of 8	4·00	5·00

The two designs of each value were printed together, *se-tenant*, in horizontal pairs throughout the sheets.

(Litho Format)

1987 (15 Oct). *Royal Ruby Wedding and 150th Anniv of Queen Victoria's Accession. T* **63** *and similar square designs. P* 15.

484	40 c. brownish black, black and deep olive	..	45	50
485	60 c. purple-black, black and deep blue-green	..	65	75
486	80 c. brownish black, black and deep dull blue	85	1·00
487	$1 brownish black, black and deep claret	..	1·10	1·25
488	$2 multicoloured	..	..	1·90	2·50
484/8			Set of 5	4·50	5·50
MS489	86×101 mm. $3 brownish black	..	2·25	3·50

Designs:—60 c. Wedding of Princess Elizabeth and Duke of Edinburgh, 1947; 80 c. Queen, Duke of Edinburgh and Prince Charles, c. 1950; $1 Queen with Princess Anne, 1950; $2 Queen Elizabeth II, 1970; $3 Queen and Prince Charles at Princess Anne's christening, 1950.

64 Coconut Crab

(Des M. Pollard. Litho Questa)

1987 (11 Nov). *Crustaceans. T* **64** *and similar diamond-shaped designs. Multicoloured. W w* 15. *P* 14.

490	40 c. Type 64	..	..	1·00	1·25
491	50 c. Painted Crayfish	..	..	1·25	1·50
492	60 c. Ocean Crayfish	..	..	1·40	1·75
490/2			Set of 3	3·25	4·00

65 Aborigine and Ayers Rock

(Des Young Philips. Litho Format)

1987 (2 Dec). *World Scout Jamboree, Australia, and Bicent of Australian Settlement. T* **65** *and similar horiz designs. Multicoloured. P* 12½.

493	40 c. Type 65	..	..	30	45
494	60 c. Capt. Cook and H.M.S. *Endeavour*	..	70	90
495	$1 Scout saluting and Scout Park entrance	..	70	95
	a. Copyright symbol alongside Australia Bicent emblem omitted (R. 1/1)		12·00	
496	$1.50, Koala and kangaroo	..	80	1·25
493/6			Set of 4	2·25	3·25
MS497	115×85 mm. $2.50, Lord and Lady Baden-Powell	..	2·00	3·25

(Des G. Drummond. Litho Format)

1988 (29 Feb). *Coral Reef Life (2nd series). Horiz designs as T* **60**. *Multicoloured. P* 15.

498	15 c. Spanish Dancer (*Hexabranchus sanguineus*)	..	85	85
499	40 c. Hard corals	..	..	1·00	1·40
500	50 c. Feather Stars	..	..	1·00	1·60
501	60 c. Staghorn corals	..	..	1·00	1·60
498/501			Set of 4	3·50	5·00

66 Red Junglefowl **67** Henri Dunant (founder)

(Des Jennifer Toombs. Litho Format)

1988 (2 Mar). *Birds. T* **66** *and similar horiz designs. Multicoloured. P* 15.

502	5 c. Type 66	..	..	15	15
503	10 c. White Tern	..	..	20	20
504	15 c. Common Noddy	..	..	30	20
505	20 c. Phoenix Petrel	..	..	40	40
506	25 c. American Golden Plover	..	45	45
507	30 c. Crested Tern	..	..	50	45
508	35 c. Sooty Tern	..	..	50	45
509	40 c. Bristle-thighed Curlew	..	50	40
510	45 c. Bar-tailed Godwit	..	..	50	45
511	50 c. Eastern Reef Heron	..	50	50
512	55 c. Great Frigate Bird	..	60	70
513	60 c. Red-footed Booby	..	..	60	60
514	70 c. Rufous-necked Sandpiper ("Red-necked Stint")	..	60	1·00
515	$1 Long-tailed Koel ("Long-tailed Cuckoo")	..	60	1·50
516	$2 Red-tailed Tropic Bird	..	60	3·00
517	$5 Banded Rail	..	..	90	6·00
502/17		..	Set of 16	7·00	15·00

(Des M. Pollard. Litho Format)

1988 (9 May). *125th Anniv of International Red Cross. T* **67** *and similar horiz designs. P* 12½.

518	15 c. vermilion and pale reddish brown	10	20
519	40 c. vermilion and ultramarine	..	20	40
520	50 c. vermilion and turquoise-green	..	25	50
521	60 c. vermilion and purple	..	35	70
518/21			Set of 4	80	1·60
MS522	96 × 66 mm. $1.50, vermilion & emerald	90	2·50

Designs:—40 c. Junior Red Cross members on parade; 50 c. Red Cross worker with boy in wheelchair; 60 c. First aid training; $1.50, Lecture.

68 H.M.S. *Endeavour*

(Litho Format)

1988 (15 June). *Voyages of Captain Cook. T* **68** *and similar horiz designs. Multicoloured. P* 12½.
523	20 c. Type **68**		75	80
524	40 c. Stern of H.M.S. *Endeavour*		90	1·10
525	50 c. Cook preparing to land at Tahiti (*vert*)		1·00	1·25
526	60 c. Maori chief (*vert*)		1·00	1·40
527	80 c. H.M.S. *Resolution* and Hawaiian canoe		1·25	1·75
528	$1 "Captain Cook" (after Nathaniel Dance) (*vert*)		1·40	1·90
523/8		*Set of 6*	5·50	7·50
MS529	115 × 85 mm. $2.50, H.M.S. *Resolution* in Antarctica		6·00	8·00

69 *Ganoderma applanatum*

(Des J. Cooter. Litho Format)

1988 (25 July). *Fungi* (1st series). *T* **69** *and similar vert designs. Multicoloured. P* 15.
530	40 c. Type **69**		1·25	1·40
531	50 c. *Pseudoepicoccum cocos* (brown leaf spot)		1·40	1·50
532	60 c. *Rigidoporus lineatus* ("*Rigidoporus zonalis*")		1·60	1·75
533	90 c. *Rigidoporus microporus*		1·75	2·00
530/3		*Set of 4*	5·50	6·00

See also 554/7.

70 Rifle-shooting

(Litho Format)

1988 (19 Aug). *Olympic Games, Seoul. T* **70** *and similar horiz designs. Multicoloured. P* 12½.
534	10 c. Type **70**		25	55
535	20 c. Judo		35	65
536	40 c. Canoeing		60	85
537	60 c. Swimming		80	1·25
838	80 c. Sailing		1·00	1·60
539	$1 Gymnastics		1·25	1·60
534/9		*Set of 6*	3·75	6·00

71 Queen Elizabeth II in Ceremonial Canoe

72 Virgin Mary

(Des and litho Questa)

1988 (28 Sept). *10th Anniv of Independence. T* **71** *and similar designs showing scenes from Royal Visit of 1982. W w* 15 (*sideways on* 60, 90 *c.*, $1.20). *P* 14.
540	60 c. multicoloured		60	70
541	90 c. multicoloured		90	1·10
542	$1 multicoloured (*horiz*)		1·00	1·40
543	$1.20, multicoloured		1·25	1·75
540/3		*Set of 4*	3·50	4·50

MS544 Designs as Nos. 540/3 in separate miniature sheets, each 85 × 85 mm
Set of 4 sheets 3·50 5·00

(Des M. Pollard. Litho Questa)

1988 (5 Dec). *Christmas. T* **72** *and similar diamond-shaped designs. Multicoloured. P* 14.
545	15 c. Type **72**		55	55
546	40 c. Christ Child		90	80
547	60 c. Joseph		1·10	1·75
545/7		*Set of 3*	2·25	2·75
MS548	73 × 99 mm. $1.50, Angel		1·75	2·50

73 Dancing Skirt and Dancer

(Des Jennifer Toombs. Litho Questa)

1989 (31 Mar). *Traditional Dancing Skirts. T* **73** *and similar designs showing skirts and dancer silhouettes. P* 14½.
549	40 c. multicoloured		70	90
550	50 c. multicoloured		80	1·00
551	60 c. multicoloured		90	1·25
552	90 c. multicoloured		1·40	1·75
549/52		*Set of 4*	3·50	4·50
MS553	110×75 mm. $1.50, multicoloured (dancer) (*vert*)		3·75	5·50

(Litho Questa)

1989 (24 May). *Fungi* (2nd series). *Vert designs as T* **69**. *Multicoloured. P* 14.
554	40 c. *Trametes marianna* ("*Trametes muelleri*")		1·75	1·75
555	50 c. *Pestalotiopsis palmarum* (grey leaf spot)		1·90	1·90
556	60 c. *Trametes cingulata*		2·00	2·00
557	90 c. *Schizophyllum commune*		2·75	2·75
554/7		*Set of 4*	7·50	7·50

(Des G. Drummond. Litho Questa)

1989 (31 July). *Coral Reef Life* (3rd series). *Horiz designs as T* **60**. *Multicoloured. P* 14.
558	40 c. Pennant Coralfish		1·75	1·75
559	50 c. Orange-finned Anemonefish		2·00	2·00
560	60 c. Narrow-banded Batfish		2·25	2·25
561	90 c. Thread-finned Butterflyfish		2·75	2·75
558/61		*Set of 4*	8·00	8·00
MS562	110×85 mm. Nos. 558/61		8·00	9·00

74 *Nivaga II*

75 Trumpet Triton Shell

(Des M. Pollard. Litho Questa)

1989 (9 Oct). *Delivery of Nivaga II* (*new inter-island ship*). *Sheet* 116×85 *mm. P* 14.
MS563	74 $1.50, multicoloured		4·00	5·50

(Des Jennifer Toombs. Litho Questa)

1989 (29 Nov). *Christmas. T* **75** *and similar vert designs. Multicoloured. P* 14.
564	40 c. Type **75**		85	85
565	50 c. Posy of flowers		1·00	1·00
566	60 c. Germinating coconut		1·25	1·25
567	90 c. Jewellery		2·25	2·75
564/7		*Set of 4*	4·75	5·25

76 *Cocus nucifera*

77 Penny Black with "Stamp World London 90" Emblem

(Des M. Pollard. Litho Questa)

1990 (28 Feb). *Tropical Trees. T* **76** *and similar vert designs. Multicoloured. P* 14½.
568	15 c. Type **76**		80	80
569	30 c. *Rhizophora samoensis*		1·25	1·25
570	40 c. *Messerschmidia argentea*		1·40	1·40
571	50 c. *Pandanus tectorius*		1·60	1·75
572	60 c. *Hernandia nymphaeifolia*		1·75	1·90
573	90 c. *Pisonia grandis*		2·25	2·75
568/73		*Set of 6*	8·25	9·00

(Des M. Pollard. Litho Questa)

1990 (3 May). *150th Anniv of the Penny Black, and "Stamp World London 90" International Stamp Exhibition. P* 14.
574	77 15 c. multicoloured		1·50	1·50
575	40 c. multicoloured		2·75	2·75
576	90 c. multicoloured		4·50	5·00
574/6		*Set of 3*	8·00	8·25
MS577	115×85 mm. **77** $2 multicoloured		6·00	7·00

78 Japanese Camouflaged Freighter

79 *Erythrina fusca*

(Litho Questa)

1990 (25 July). *Second World War Ships* (1st series). *T* **78** *and similar horiz designs. Multicoloured. P* 14.
578	15 c. Type **78**		1·25	1·25
579	30 c. U.S.S *Unimack* (seaplane tender)		1·75	1·75
580	40 c. *Amagiri* (Japanese destroyer)		1·90	1·90
581	50 c. U.S.S *Platte* (attack transport)		2·00	2·00
582	60 c. Japanese "Shumushu" Class escort		2·25	2·25
583	90 c. U.S.S *Independence* (aircraft carrier)		3·00	3·00
578/83		*Set of 6*	11·00	11·00

See also Nos. 613/16.

(Des Jennifer Toombs. Litho Questa)

1990 (21 Sept). *Flowers. T* **79** *and similar vert designs. Multicoloured. P* 14½×14.
584	15 c. Type **79**		30	50
585	30 c. *Capparis cordifolia*		50	70
586	40 c. *Portulaca pilosa*		60	80
587	50 c. *Cordia subcordata*		75	90
588	60 c. *Scaevola taccada*		80	1·00
589	90 c. *Suriana maritima*		1·25	2·00
584/9		*Set of 6*	3·75	5·50

80 Land Resources Survey

81 Mary and Joseph travelling to Bethlehem

(Litho Questa)

1990 (20 Nov). *40th Anniv of United Nations Development Programme. T* **80** *and similar horiz designs. P* 14.
590	40 c. Type **80**		80	80
591	60 c. Satellite earth station		1·50	1·50
592	$1.20, *Te Tautai* (trawler)		3·25	4·25
590/2		*Set of 3*	5·00	6·00

(Des M. Pollard. Litho Questa)

1990 (20 Nov). *Christmas. T* **81** *and similar square designs. Multicoloured. P* 14.
593	15 c. Type **81**		55	55
594	40 c. The Nativity		1·00	1·00
595	60 c. Shepherds with flock		1·50	1·50
596	90 c. Wise Men bearing gifts		2·00	2·50
593/6		*Set of 4*	4·50	5·00

82 Ramose Murex (*Murex ramosus*)

83 *Cylas formicarius* (beetle)

(Des D. Miller. Litho Questa)

1991 (18 Jan). *Sea Shells. T* **82** *and similar vert designs. Multicoloured. P* 14.
597	40 c. Type **82**		1·50	1·50
598	50 c. Marble Cone (*Conus marmoreus marmoreus*)		1·60	1·60
599	60 c. Commercial Trochus (*Trochus niloticus*)		1·75	1·75
600	$1.50, Green Map Cowrie (*Cypraea mappa viridis*)		3·50	4·00
597/600		*Set of 4*	7·50	8·00

(Des D. Miller. Litho Questa)

1991 (22 Mar). *Insects. T 83 and similar horiz designs. Multicoloured. P 14.*

601	40 c. Type 83			1·75	1·60
602	50 c. *Heliothis armiger* (moth)			2·00	1·75
603	60 c. *Spodoptera litura* (moth)			2·25	2·00
604	$1.50, *Agrius convolvuli* (moth)			5·50	7·00
601/4			*Set of 4*	10·50	11·00

84 Green Turtle

85 Football

(Des D. Miller. Litho Questa)

1991 (31 May). *Endangered Marine Life. T 84 and similar vert designs. Multicoloured. P 14.*

605	40 c. Type 84			1·25	1·00
606	50 c. Humpback Whale			1·75	1·25
607	60 c. Hawksbill Turtle			1·75	1·60
608	$1.50, Sperm Whale			3·50	5·50
605/8			*Set of 4*	7·50	8·50

(Des D. Miller. Litho Questa)

1991 (31 July). *9th South Pacific Games. T 85 and similar vert designs. Multicoloured. P 14.*

609	40 c. Type 85			1·40	1·10
610	50 c. Volleyball			1·90	1·75
611	60 c. Lawn tennis			2·75	2·50
612	$1.50, Cricket			5·50	6·25
609/12			*Set of 4*	10·50	10·50

86 U.S.S. *Tennessee* (battleship)

87 Traditional Dancers

(Des D. Miller. Litho Questa)

1991 (15 Oct). *Second World War Ships (2nd series). T 86 and similar horiz designs. Multicoloured. P 14.*

613	40 c. Type 86			2·25	1·75
614	50 c. *Haguro* (Japanese cruiser)			2·50	1·75
615	60 c. H.M.N.Z.S. *Achilles* (cruiser)			2·75	2·25
616	$1.50, U.S.S. *North Carolina* (battleship)			6·00	7·50
613/16			*Set of 4*	12·00	12·00

(Des D. Miller. Litho Questa)

1991 (13 Dec). *Christmas. T 87 and similar vert designs. Multicoloured. P 14.*

617	40 c. Type 87			1·75	1·25
618	50 c. Solo dancer			2·00	1·50
619	60 c. Dancers in green costumes			2·50	1·75
620	$1.50, Dancers in multicoloured costumes			5·00	7·00
617/20			*Set of 4*	10·00	10·50

88 Southern Fish Constellation

89 King George VI and Cargo Liner

(Des D. Miller. Litho Questa)

1992 (29 Jan). *Pacific Star Constellations. T 88 and similar vert designs. Multicoloured. P 14.*

621	40 c. Type 88			2·00	1·75
622	50 c. Scorpion			2·25	1·75
623	60 c. Archer			2·75	2·25
624	$1.50, Southern Cross			5·00	7·00
621/4			*Set of 4*	11·50	11·50

(Des D. Miller. Litho Questa)

1992 (23 Mar). *Centenary of British Occupation of Tuvalu. T 89 and similar horiz designs. P 14.*

625	40 c. Type 89			2·00	1·75
626	50 c. King George V and freighter with barges at wharf			2·25	1·75
627	60 c. King Edward VII and freighter			2·50	2·00
628	$1.50, Queen Victoria and warship			4·50	6·00
625/8			*Set of 4*	10·00	10·50

It is probable that the ship shown on No. 628 is intended to be H.M.S. *Royalist* (corvette) launched 1883, but the vessel depicted appears to be H.M.S. *Royalist* (cruiser) launched 1915.

90 Columbus with King Ferdinand and Queen Isabella of Spain

(Des D. Miller. Litho Questa)

1992 (22 May). *500th Anniv of Discovery of America by Columbus. T 90 and similar horiz designs. P 14.*

629	40 c. deep new blue and black			70	80
630	50 c. brown-purple and black			80	90
631	60 c. myrtle-green and black			90	1·10
632	$1.50, deep purple and black			2·25	3·25
629/32			*Set of 4*	4·25	5·50

Designs:—50 c. Columbus and Polynesians; 60 c. Columbus and South American Indians; $1.50, Columbus and North American Indians.

91 Blue-spotted Butterflyfish   92 Discus Throwing

(Des D. Miller. Litho Questa)

1992 (15 July). *Fishes. T 91 and similar multicoloured designs. P 14.*

633	15 c. Type 91			40	40
634	20 c. Bridled Parrotfish			45	40
635	25 c. Clown Surgeonfish			45	50
636	30 c. Moon Wrasse			55	50
637	35 c. Harlequin Filefish			60	50
638	40 c. Bird Wrasse			70	50
639	45 c. Black-finned Pigfish			75	50
640	50 c. Blue Damselfish			80	60
641	60 c. Hump-headed Wrasse			90	70
642	70 c. Ornate Butterflyfish (*vert*)			1·00	1·25
643	90 c. Saddle Butterflyfish (*vert*)			1·25	1·50
644	$1 Vagabond Butterflyfish (*vert*)			1·40	1·60
645	$2 Pennant Coralfish (*vert*)			2·25	3·00
646	$3 Moorish Idol (*vert*)			3·00	4·00
633/46			*Set of 14*	13·00	14·50

(Des D. Miller. Litho Questa)

1992 (27 July). *Olympic Games, Barcelona. T 92 and similar vert designs. Multicoloured. P 14.*

647	40 c. Type 92			1·25	1·00
648	50 c. Javelin throwing			1·50	1·25
649	60 c. Shotput			1·75	1·50
650	$1.50, Competitor's foot			3·25	4·50
647/50			*Set of 4*	7·00	7·50
MS651	100×71 mm. $2 Olympic stadium, Barcelona			3·50	5·00

93 Blue Coral   (94)

(Des G. Drummond. Litho Questa)

1992 (1 Sept). *Endangered Species. Blue Coral. T 93 and similar horiz designs showing different coral formations. P 14.*

652	10 c. multicoloured			1·00	1·00
653	25 c. multicoloured			2·00	2·00
654	30 c. multicoloured			2·00	2·00
655	35 c. multicoloured			2·25	2·25
652/5			*Set of 4*	6·50	6·50

1992 (1 Sept). *"Kuala Lumpur '92" International Philatelic Exhibition. Nos. 636, 638 and 640/1 optd with T 94.*

656	30 c. Moon Wrasse			1·60	1·60
657	40 c. Bird Wrasse			1·75	1·75
658	50 c. Blue Damselfish			2·00	2·00
659	60 c. Hump-headed Wrasse			2·00	2·00
656/9			*Set of 4*	6·50	6·50

COVER PRICES

Cover factors are quoted at the beginning of each country for most issues to 1945. An explanation of the system can be found on page x. The factors quoted do not, however, apply to philatelic covers.

95 Fishermen and Angel   96 *Calophyllum inophyllum*

(Des D. Miller. Litho Questa)

1992 (25 Dec). *Christmas. T 95 and similar vert designs. Multicoloured. P 14.*

660	40 c. Type 95			90	70
661	50 c. Fishing canoes following star			1·00	80
662	60 c. Nativity scene			1·25	1·00
663	$1.50, Christmas gifts			2·25	3·25
660/3			*Set of 4*	4·75	5·25

(Des D. Miller. Litho Questa)

1993 (2 Feb). *Flowers. T 96 and similar vert designs. Multicoloured. P 14.*

664	40 c. Type 96			1·00	90
665	50 c. *Hibiscus tiliaceus*			1·25	1·00
666	60 c. *Lantana camara*			1·50	1·25
667	$1.50, *Plumeria rubra*			3·00	4·00
664/7			*Set of 4*	6·00	6·50

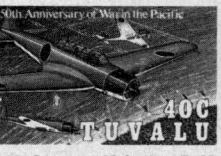

97 Japanese Nakajima B5N "Kate" Bombers attacking Island   98 *Cepora perimale*

(Des D. Miller. Litho Questa)

1993 (23 Apr). *50th Anniv of War in the Pacific. T 97 and similar multicoloured designs. P 14.*

668	40 c. Type 97			1·75	1·50
669	50 c. Japanese anti-aircraft gun (*vert*)			2·00	1·50
670	60 c. American troops storming beach			2·00	1·75
671	$1.50, Map of Funafuti Atoll (*vert*)			4·25	4·75
668/71			*Set of 4*	9·00	8·50

(Des Patricia Altman. Litho and die-stamped Southern Colour Print, Dunedin)

1993 (29 May). *"Indopex '93" International Stamp Exhibition", Surabaya, Indonesia. Sheet 81×111 mm. P 14.*

MS672 98	$1.50 multicoloured			3·50	3·75

See also Nos. MS682, MS683 and MS693.

99 Fluted Giant Clam (*Tridacna squamosa*)   100 Queen Elizabeth II and Prince Philip in Land Rover

(Des D. Miller. Litho Questa)

1993 (29 June). *Marine Life. T 99 and similar horiz designs. Multicoloured. P 14.*

673	40 c. Type 99			75	75
674	50 c. Anemone Crab			85	85
675	60 c. Octopus			95	95
676	$1.50, Green Turtle			2·25	3·00
673/6			*Set of 4*	4·25	5·00

(Litho Questa)

1993 (5 July). *40th Anniv of Coronation. T 100 and similar horiz designs. P 14.*

677	40 c. multicoloured			85	75
678	50 c. multicoloured			95	90
679	60 c. multicoloured			1·10	1·10
680	$1.50, multicoloured			2·50	3·00
677/80			*Set of 4*	4·75	5·25
MS681	88×88 mm. $2 blackish olive, pale lemon and black			6·00	7·00

Designs:—50 c. Queen Elizabeth drinking kava; 60 c. Queen Elizabeth with parasol; $1.50, Ceremonial welcome; $2 Crowning of Queen Elizabeth II, 1953.

(Des Patricia Altman. Litho and die-stamped Southern Colour Print, Dunedin)

1993 (14 Aug). *"Taipei '93" International Stamp Exhibition, Taiwan. Sheet, 85×85 mm, containing multicoloured design as T 98. P 14½×14.*

MS682	$1.50, *Geoffroyi godart* (*vert*)			3·75	5·00

(Des Patricia Altman. Litho and die-stamped Southern Colour Print, Dunedin)

1993 (1 Oct). *"Bangkok 1993" International Stamp Exhibition, Thailand. Sheet, 86×86 mm, containing horiz design as T **98**. P 14.*
MS683 $1.50, *Paradisea staudinger* .. .. 2·00 3·00

101 Hermit Crab and Shells on Beach
102 Virgin and Child with Christmas Tree

(Des Patricia Altman. Litho Southern Colour Print, Dunedin)

1993 (2 Nov). *Environmental Protection. T **101** and similar vert designs. Multicoloured. P 13½.*
684 40 c. Type **101** 85 75
685 50 c. Conch shell and starfish 95 90
686 60 c. Crab, seaweed and shells .. .. 1·10 1·10
687 $1.50, Herring Gull and human footprint on beach .. .. 2·50 3·25
684/7 .. .. *Set of 4* 4·75 5·50
MS688 126×80 mm. Nos. 684/7. P 14½×14 .. 5·50 6·50

(Des Patricia Altman. Litho Southern Colour Print, Dunedin)

1993 (3 Dec). *Christmas. T **102** and similar vert designs. Multicoloured. P 13½.*
689 40 c. Type **102** 90 80
690 50 c. Candle .. .. 1·00 90
691 60 c. Angel .. .. 1·25 1·25
692 $1.50, Decorated palm tree .. .. 2·50 3·75
689/92 .. .. *Set of 4* 5·00 6·00

(Des Patricia Altman. Litho Southern Colour Print, Dunedin)

1994 (18 Feb). *"Hong Kong '94" International Stamp Exhibition. Sheet 85×85 mm containing multicoloured design as T **98**. P 14½×14.*
MS693 $2 *Danaus plexippus* (vert) .. .. 4·25 5·00

103 Beach
104 Irish Red Setter

(Des D. Miller. Litho Questa)

1994 (18 Feb). *Island Scenery. T **103** and similar horiz designs. Multicoloured. P 14.*
694 40 c. Type **103** 90 80
695 50 c. Lagoon .. .. 1·00 90
696 60 c. Distant island .. .. 1·25 1·25
697 $1.50, Launch and outrigger canoes on beach .. .. 2·50 3·75
694/7 .. .. *Set of 4* 5·00 6·00

(Des D. Miller. Litho Questa)

1994 (23 Apr). *Chinese New Year ("Year of the Dog"). T **104** and similar vert designs. Multicoloured. P 14.*
698 40 c. Type **104** .. .. 1·00 1·00
699 50 c. Golden Retriever .. .. 1·10 1·10
700 60 c. West Highland Terrier .. .. 1·25 1·25
701 $1.50, German Shepherd .. .. 2·75 4·25
698/701 .. .. *Set of 4* 5·50 7·00

105 World Cup, Australian Player and Sydney Opera House
106 Giant Button Top (*Umbonium giganteum*)

(Des D. Miller. Litho Questa)

1994 (7 June). *World Cup Football Championship, U.S.A. T **105** and similar vert designs. Multicoloured. P 14.*
702 40 c. Type **105** 50 50
703 50 c. English player and Big Ben, London 60 60
704 60 c. Argentinian player and House of Assembly, Buenos Aires 70 75
705 $1.50, German player and Brandenburg Gate, Berlin .. .. .. 2·00 2·75
702/5 .. .. *Set of 4* 3·50 4·25
MS706 105×99 mm. $2 American player and Statue of Liberty, New York .. .. 5·50 6·00

(Des D. Miller. Litho Questa)

1994 (16 Aug). *Sea Snails. T **106** and similar vert designs. Multicoloured. P 14.*
707 40 c. Type **106** .. .. 1·00 85
708 50 c. Tapestry Turban (*Turbo petholatus*) 1·25 95
709 60 c. *Planaxis savignyi* .. .. 1·50 1·25
710 $1.50, Green-lined Paper Bubble (*Hydatina physis*) .. .. 3·00 4·00
707/10 .. .. *Set of 4* 6·00 6·25

107 Pekingese and Logo
(**108**)

(Des D. Miller. Litho Questa)

1994 (16 Aug). *"Philakorea '94" International Stamp Exhibition, Seoul. Sheet 106×72 mm. P 14.*
MS711 **107** $1.50, multicoloured .. .. 3·50 4·50

1994 (31 Aug). *"Singpex '94" Stamp Exhibition, Singapore. Nos. 502/3 and 509/10 optd with T **108**.*
712 5 c. Type 66 .. .. .. 35 50
713 10 c. White Tern 35 50
714 40 c. Bristle-thighed Curlew .. 70 85
715 45 c. Bar-tailed Godwit 80 95
712/15 .. .. *Set of 4* 2·00 2·50

109 "Saturn V" Launch
110 Boys swimming with Log

(Des D. Miller. Litho Questa)

1994 (21 Oct). *25th Anniv of First Moon Landing. T **109** and similar vert designs. Multicoloured. P 14.*
716 40 c. Type **109** .. .. 1·40 1·40
a. Horiz strip of 4. Nos. 716/19 .. 6·00
717 50 c. "Apollo 11" capsule .. .. 1·50 1·50
718 60 c. Neil Armstrong and American flag .. 1·60 1·60
719 $1.50, Capsule re-entry .. .. 2·00 2·00
716/19 .. .. *Set of 4* 6·00 6·00
Nos. 716/19 were printed together, *se-tenant*, in horizontal strips of 4 throughout the sheet of 16.

(Des D. Miller. Litho Questa)

1994 (15 Dec). *Christmas. Local Customs. T **110** and similar horiz designs. Multicoloured. P 14.*
720 40 c. Type **110** .. .. 1·00 75
721 50 c. Fishermen landing catch .. 1·10 85
722 60 c. Christmas dinner .. .. 1·25 1·10
723 $1.50, Traditional dancers .. 2·50 3·50
720/3 .. .. *Set of 4* 5·25 5·50

111 Pig asleep

(Des D. Miller. Litho Questa)

1995 (30 Jan). *Chinese New Year ("Year of the Pig"). T **111** and similar horiz designs. Multicoloured. P 14.*
724 40 c. Type **111** 65 60
725 50 c. Two pigs and vegetation .. 75 70
726 60 c. Three pigs 85 85
727 $1.50, Sow suckling piglets .. 1·75 2·75
724/7 .. .. *Set of 4* 3·50 4·50

112 Emblem and Man with Produce in Wheelbarrow

(Litho Questa)

1995 (31 Mar). *50th Anniv of Food and Agriculture Organization. T **112** and similar horiz designs. Multicoloured. P 14.*
728 40 c. Type **112** 90 80
729 50 c. Man holding basket of food .. 1·00 90
730 60 c. Woman slicing produce .. 1·25 1·25
731 $1.50, Woman mixing food .. 2·50 3·25
728/31 .. .. *Set of 4* 5·00 5·50

113 Beach and Lagoon

(Litho Questa)

1995 (26 May). *Visit South Pacific Year. T **113** and similar horiz designs. Multicoloured. P 14.*
732 40 c. Type **113** 70 70
733 50 c. Catamaran 80 80
734 60 c. Traditional hut .. .. 90 1·00
735 $1.50, Village on beach .. .. 2·00 3·00
732/5 .. .. *Set of 4* 4·00 5·00

114 *Dendrobium comptonii*

(Des Sue Wickison. Litho Questa)

1995 (28 July). *Pacific Coastal Orchids. T **114** and similar horiz designs. Multicoloured. P 14.*
736 40 c. Type **114** .. .. 1·00 85
737 50 c. *Dendrobium involutum* .. 1·10 90
738 60 c. *Dendrobium rarum* .. .. 1·25 1·10
739 $1.50, *Grammatophyllum scriptum* .. 2·75 3·50
736/9 .. .. *Set of 4* 5·50 5·75

115 Japanese Soldier and Maps of Tuvalu and Japan
116 Tuvalu Dancer

(Des D. Miller. Litho Questa)

1995 (19 Aug). *50th Anniv of End of Second World War. T **115** and similar horiz designs. Multicoloured. P 14.*
740 40 c. Type **115** .. .. 1·50 1·00
741 50 c. American soldier and beach landing 1·60 1·10
742 60 c. American marine and tree .. 1·75 1·25
743 $1.50, American soldier and atomic explosion .. .. 3·50 4·25
740/3 .. .. *Set of 4* 7·50 7·00

(Litho and die-stamped Southern Colour Print, Dunedin)

1995 (19 Aug). *"JAKARTA '95" Stamp Exhibition, Indonesia. Sheet 85×85 mm. P 12.*
MS744 **116** $1 multicoloured .. .. 2·00 2·50

OMNIBUS ISSUES

Details, together with prices for complete sets, of the various Omnibus issues from the 1935 Silver Jubilee series to date are included in a special section following Zimbabwe at the end of Volume 2.

117 *Phalaenopsis amabillis*

118 Tuvaluans in Outrigger Canoes

(Litho and die-stamped Southern Colour Print, Dunedin)

1995 (1 Sept). *"Singapore '95" International Stamp Exhibition. Sheet 85×85 mm. P 12.*
MS745 **117** $1 multicoloured .. .. .. 2·50 2·75

(Des D. Miller. Litho Questa)

1995 (24 Oct). *50th Anniv of United Nations. Sheet 83×70 mm, containing T 118 and similar vert design. Multicoloured. P 15×14½.*
MS746 $1 Type **118**; $1 U.N. headquarters, New York .. .. 2·50 3·25

119 "Silent Night" and Aerial View of Airfield

(Des D. Miller. Litho Questa)

1995 (15 Dec). *Christmas. T 119 and similar horiz designs showing Christmas carols. Multicoloured. P 14.*
747	40 c. Type **119**			80	70
748	50 c. "O Come all ye Faithful" and choir boys		95	85
749	60 c. "The First Nowell" and choir girls ..	1·10	1·10
750	$1.50, "Hark the Herald Angels sing" and angel ..		2·75	3·50
747/50			*Set of 4*	5·00	5·50

120 1976 Separation 4 c. Stamp

121 Rat with Jar

(Des D. Miller. Litho Questa)

1996 (1 Jan). *20th Anniv of Separation from Gilbert Islands and of First Tuvalu Postage Stamps. Sheet 108×82 mm, containing T 120 and similar horiz designs showing values from 1976 Separation issue. P 14.*
MS751 40 c. Type **120**; 60 c. 1976 10 c. stamp; $1 1976 35 c. stamp .. .. .. 4·00 4·50

(Des Sophie Zhang. Litho Questa)

1996 (23 Feb). *Chinese New Year ("Year of the Rat"). Sheet 130×87 mm containing T 121 and similar vert design. Multicoloured. P 14×14½.*
MS752 50 c. Type **121**; 50 c. Rat drinking from jar .. .. 1·40 1·75

1996 (23 Feb). *"HONGPEX '96" International Stamp Exhibition. Sheet as No. MS752, but additionally inscr with "HONGPEX '96" emblem on sheet margin. P 14×14½.*
MS753 50 c. Type **121**; 50 c. Rat drinking from jar .. .. 1·40 1·75

(122)

123 Volleyball

1996 (21 Mar). *"indonesia 96" International Youth Stamp Exhibition, Bandung. No. MS744 optd with T 122 in gold.*
MS754 85×85 mm. **116** $1 multicoloured .. 1·40 1·75
A further overprint as Type **122** appears on the sheet margin.

1996 (18 May). *"CHINA '96" 9th Asian International Stamp Exhibition, Peking. Sheet as No. MS752, but additionally inscr with "CHINA '96" emblem and puppet holding envelope on sheet margin. P 14×14½.*
MS755 50 c. Type **121**; 50 c. Rat drinking from jar .. .. 1·40 1·75

(Des D. Miller. Litho Questa)

1996 (11 Sept). *Olympic Games, Atlanta. T 123 and similar horiz designs. Multicoloured. P 14.*
756	40 c. Type **123**			70	70
757	50 c. Swimming			80	80
758	60 c. Weightlifting ..			90	90
759	$1.50, Boxing			2·00	2·50
756/9			*Set of 4*	4·00	4·50

$1.00

TAIPEI '96
21-27 OCTOBER

(124)

1996 (21 Oct). *"TAIPEI 96" 10th Asian International Stamp Exhibition, Taiwan. No. 639 surch with T 124.*
760 $1 on 45 c. Black-finned Pigfish .. 1·25 1·50

125 Children being Immunised

126 Wise Men following Star

(Des D. Miller. Litho Questa)

1996 (28 Oct). *50th Anniv of U.N.I.C.E.F. T 125 and similar horiz designs. Multicoloured. P 14.*
761	40 c. Type **125**			55	55
762	50 c. Teacher and children			65	65
763	60 c. Domestic water tanks and child		75	75
764	$1.50, Children in hydroponic greenhouse	1·90	2·75
761/4			*Set of 4*	3·50	4·25

(Litho Walsall)

1996 (25 Nov). *Christmas. T 126 and similar vert designs. Multicoloured. P 14½.*
765	40 c. Type **126**			55	45
766	50 c. Shepherds and star			65	55
767	60 c. Wise men presenting gifts		75	75
768	$1.50, The Nativity			1·90	2·75
765/8			*Set of 4*	3·50	4·00

127 Ox ploughing

128 White Pekin Ducks

(Des Colleen Corlett. Litho Walsall)

1997 (12 Feb). *"HONG KONG '97" International Stamp Exhibition. Chinese New Year ("Year of the Ox"). Sheet 97×83 mm. P 14.*
MS769 **127** $2 multicoloured .. .. 2·40 3·25

(Des G. Drummond. Litho Questa)

1997 (15 Mar). *Fishes (2nd series). Horiz designs as T 14. Multicoloured. P 14.*
770	25 c. Sehel's Grey Mullet ..			20	25
771	30 c. Leatherback ..			25	30
772	40 c. Hump-backed Snapper ("Paddletail")	30	35
773	45 c. Long-nosed Emperor ..		35	40
774	50 c. Blue-spined Unicornfish ..		40	45
775	55 c. Oblique-banded Snapper ..		40	45
776	60 c. Twin-spotted Snapper ("Red Bass") ..	45	50
777	70 c. Rusty Jobfish ..			55	60
778	90 c. Leopard Flounder ..			70	75
779	$1 Ruby Snapper ..			80	85
780	$2 Yellow-striped Snapper ..		1·60	1·75
781	$3 Black Jack ..			2·40	2·50
770/81			*Set of 12*	8·25	8·50

(Des Colleen Corlett. Litho Walsall)

1997 (29 May). *"Pacific '97" International Stamp Exhibition, San Francisco. Ducks. T 128 and similar horiz designs. Multicoloured. P 14½.*
782	40 c. Type **128**			65	55
783	50 c. Muscovy Ducks			75	65
784	60 c. Pacific Black Ducks ..		85	85
785	$1.50, Mandarin Ducks ..		2·00	2·75
782/5			*Set of 4*	3·75	4·25

129 Korat King Cat

(Des Colleen Corlett. Litho Walsall)

1997 (20 June). *Cats. T 129 and similar horiz designs. Multicoloured. P 14½.*
786	40 c. Type **129**			60	50
787	50 c. Long-haired ginger kitten		70	60
788	60 c. Shaded Cameo			80	80
789	$1.50, Maine Coon			2·00	2·75
786/9			*Set of 4*	3·50	4·25

(Litho Walsall)

1997 (20 June). *Return of Hong Kong to China. Sheet, 130×90 mm, containing design as No. 780, but with imprint date. W w 14 (sideways). P 14.*
MS790 $2 Yellow-striped Snapper .. .. 2·40 3·00

(Des N. Shewring (No. MS797), D. Miller (others). Litho Questa (No. MS797) or Walsall (others))

1997 (1 Oct). *Golden Wedding of Queen Elizabeth and Prince Philip. Multicoloured designs as T 87 of Kiribati. W w 14. P 14½.*
791	40 c. Queen Elizabeth and Prince Philip in Land Rover ..		40	65
	a. Horiz pair. Nos. 791/2 ..		80	1·25
792	40 c. Queen Elizabeth			40	65
793	50 c. Queen Elizabeth accepting ceremonial gift ..		50	70
	a. Horiz pair. Nos. 793/4 ..		1·00	1·40
794	50 c. Prince Philip ..			50	70
795	60 c. Three portraits of Queen Elizabeth	65	75
	a. Horiz pair. Nos. 795/6 ..		1·25	1·50
796	60 c. Queen Elizabeth and Prince Philip leaving Philatelic Bureau ..	65	75
791/6			*Set of 6*	2·75	3·75
MS797	110×70 mm. $2 Queen Elizabeth and Prince Philip in landau (horiz). Wmk sideways. P 14×14½ ..		2·10	2·50

Nos. 791/2, 793/4 and 795/6 were each printed together, *se-tenant*, in horizontal pairs throughout the sheets with the backgrounds forming composite designs.

130 Turtle Hunting

(Des O. Bell. Litho Cartor)

1997 (25 Nov). *Christmas. T 130 and similar horiz designs. Multicoloured. W w 14 (sideways). P 13½×13.*
798	40 c. Type **130**			55	50
799	50 c. Pole fishing			65	55
800	60 c. Canoe racing			75	65
801	$1.50, Traditional dancing		1·50	2·25
798/801			*Set of 4*	3·00	3·50

131 Tiger

(Des V. Ambrus. Litho Cartor)

1998 (2 Feb). *Chinese New Year ("Year of the Tiger"). Sheet 110×69 mm. W w 14 (sideways). P 13.*
MS802 **131** $1.40, multicoloured .. .. 1·50 2·00

(Des D. Miller. Litho Questa)

1998 (31 Mar). *Diana, Princess of Wales Commemoration. Sheet, 145×70 mm, containing vert designs as T 91 of Kiribati. Multicoloured. W w 14 (sideways). P 14½×14.*
MS803 80 c. Wearing pearl drop earrings, 1990; 80 c. Wearing black evening dress, 1995; 80 c. Wearing tiara, 1992; 80 c. Wearing beige coat (sold at $3.20 + 20 c. charity premium) .. 3·00 3·25

(Des A. Theobald. Litho Cartor)

1998 (1 Apr). *80th Anniv of the Royal Air Force. Horiz designs as T 270 of Samoa. Multicoloured. W w 14 (sideways). P 13½.*
804	40 c.	Hawker Woodcock			65	65
805	50 c.	Vickers Victoria			75	75
806	60 c.	Bristol Brigand			85	85
807	$1.50,	De Havilland D.H.C.1 Chipmunk			1·75	2·25
804/7				Set of 4	3·50	4·00

MS808 110×77 mm. $1 Sopwith Pup; $1 Armstrong Whitworth F.K.8; $1 North American Harvard; $1 Vultee Vengeance .. 3·75 4·00

132 *Los Reyes* and *Santiago* (Alvare Mendana)

(Des J. Batchelor. Litho Questa)

1998 (19 May). *Ships (5th series). T 132 and similar horiz designs. Multicoloured. W w 14 (sideways). P 13½×14.*
809	40 c.	Type 132			55	50
810	50 c.	Morning Star II (missionary schooner)			65	55
811	60 c.	The Light (missionary brigantine)			75	70
812	$1.50,	New Zealand missionary schooner			1·40	2·00
809/12				Set of 4	3·00	3·25

133 Bottlenose Dolphin

(Des Wendy Russell. Litho Cartor)

1998 (21 Aug). *Dolphins and Porpoises. T 133 and similar horiz designs. Multicoloured. W w 14 (sideways). P 13½×13.*
813	40 c.	Type 133			55	50
814	50 c.	Dall's Porpoise			65	55
815	60 c.	Harbour Porpoise			75	70
816	$1.50,	Common Dolphin			1·40	2·00
813/16				Set of 4	3·00	3·25

134 Bikenibeu Paeniu, Teacher and Class

135 *Psammocra digitata* and Bleached *Platygyra daedalea*

(Des G. Vasarhelyi. Litho Questa)

1998 (1 Oct). *20th Anniv of Independence. Prime Ministers of Tuvalu. T 134 and similar horiz designs. Multicoloured. W w 14 (sideways). P 14.*
817	40 c.	Type 134			50	45
818	60 c.	Kamuta Latasi and diagram of communications network			60	50
819	90 c.	Sir Tomasi Puapua and emblem of Trust Fund			85	85
820	$1.50,	Sir Toaripi Lauti and emblem of Maritime School			1·40	1·75
817/20				Set of 4	3·00	3·25

MS821 115×81 mm. Nos. 817/20 .. .. 3·00 3·25

(Des A. Robinson. Litho Questa)

1998 (6 Nov). *Coral Reef Life (4th series). T 135 and similar horiz designs. Multicoloured. W w 16 (sideways). P 14½.*
822	20 c.	Type 135			30	30
823	30 c.	Bleached Acropora robusta			45	45
824	50 c.	Bleached Acropora hyacinthus			70	70
825	$1	Bleached Acropora danai and Montastrea curta			1·00	1·25
822/5				Set of 4	2·25	2·40

MS826 74×54 mm. $1.50, Bleached *Seriatopora* and Bleached *Stylophora* .. 1·60 1·75
Nos. 822/6 include the "GREENPEACE" save our seas logo and No. MS826 additionally shows the "UNESCO International Year of the Ocean" emblem on the sheet margin.

136 Mary and Joseph travelling to Bethlehem

(Des V. Ambrus. Litho Walsall)

1998 (20 Nov). *Christmas. T 136 and similar horiz designs. Multicoloured. W w 14 (sideways). P 14½×14.*
827	40 c.	Type 136			50	45
828	50 c.	Shepherds and Angel			55	50
829	60 c.	The Nativity			60	55
830	$1.50,	Visit of Wise Men			1·40	1·75
827/30				Set of 4	2·75	3·00

137 Rabbit playing Pipa and Chinese Lantern

138 *Heemskerk* (Tasman), 1642

(Des O. Bell. Litho Questa)

1999 (16 Feb). *Chinese New Year ("Year of the Rabbit"). Sheet 115×75 mm. W w 14 (sideways). P 14½.*

MS831 137 $2 multicoloured .. .. 2·00 2·25

(Des J. Batchelor. Litho Questa)

1999 (19 Mar). *"Australia '99" World Stamp Exhibition, Melbourne. Ships (6th series). T 138 and similar horiz designs. Multicoloured. W w 14 (sideways). P 14.*
832	40 c.	Type 138			50	45
833	50 c.	H.M.S. Endeavour (Cook), 1769			60	55
834	90 c.	Sophia Jane (paddle-steamer), 1831			90	95
835	$1.50,	Chusan I (screw steamer), 1852			1·40	1·60
832/5				Set of 4	3·00	3·25

MS836 135×75 mm. $2 H.M.S. *Supply* (brig), 1788. Wmk upright .. .. 2·00 2·25

Kosovo Relief Fund

(139)

1999 (11 June). *Kosovo Relief Campaign. Nos. 505, 508, 512 and 515 optd with T 139.*
837	20 c.	Phoenix Petrel			25	30
838	35 c.	Sooty Tern			45	50
839	55 c.	Great Frigate Bird			60	65
840	$1	Long-tailed Koel			1·00	1·10
837/40				Set of 4	2·10	2·25

(Des N. Shewring. Litho Walsall)

1999 (20 July). *30th Anniv of the First Manned Landing on Moon. Multicoloured designs as T 296 of Jamaica. W w 16. P 14.*
841	40 c.	Lift-off			45	50
842	60 c.	Lander approaches Moon			60	65
843	90 c.	Lander leaving Moon			85	90
844	$1.50,	Crew recovery			1·25	1·40
841/4				Set of 4	2·75	3·00

MS845 90×80 mm. $2 Earth as seen from Moon (circular, 40 mm diameter). Wmk sideways. P 14 2·00 2·75

(Des D. Miller. Litho Cartor)

1999 (16 Aug). *"Queen Elizabeth the Queen Mother's Century". Horiz designs as T 199 of St. Helena. Multicoloured. W w 16 (sideways). P 13½.*
846	40 c.	King George VI and Queen Elizabeth inspecting bomb damage, 1940			45	50
847	60 c.	Queen Elizabeth with her daughters, 1951			60	65
848	90 c.	With Princes William and Harry, 1995			85	90
849	$1.50,	Inspecting the Queen's Dragoon Guards			1·25	1·40
846/9				Set of 4	2·75	3·00

MS850 145×70 mm. $2 Lady Elizabeth Bowes-Lyon aged 6, and Yuri Gagarin (first cosmonaut) 2·00 2·25

140 *Solandra maxima* (flower)

(Des R. Sauber Litho Cartor)

1999 (22 Nov). *Flowers. T 140 and similar multicoloured designs. P 14×13½.*
851	90 c.	Type 140			70	75
		a. Sheetlet. Nos. 851/6			4·00	
852	90 c.	Cistus sp.			70	75
853	90 c.	Pandorea jasminoides			70	75
854	90 c.	Grewia caffra			70	75
855	90 c.	Mandevilla × amabilis			70	75
856	90 c.	Punica granatum (open flowers)			70	75
857	90 c.	Cassytha filiformis			70	75
		a. Sheetlet. Nos. 857/62			4·00	

858	90 c.	Wollastonia biflora			70	75
859	90 c.	Portulacacae lueta (without local inscr)			70	75
860	90 c.	Portulacacae lueta (also inscr "TAMOLOC")			70	75
861	90 c.	Vigna marina			70	75
862	90 c.	Punica granatum (closed flowers)			70	75
851/62				Set of 12	8·00	9·00

MS863 97×104 mm. $3 *Cassia surattensis* (vert). P 13½×14 .. .. .. 3·50 3·75
Nos. 851/6 and 857/62 were each printed together, *se-tenant*, in sheetlets of 6 with the backgrounds forming composite designs.
No. MS863 is inscribed "SCRAMBLED EGGES" in error.

TUVALU

STAMP BOOKLETS

1978 (20 July). *25th Anniv of Coronation. Multicoloured cover, 85×52 mm, showing Coronation ceremony on front and Westminster Abbey on reverse. Stapled.*

SB1	$3.56, booklet containing 8 c., 30 c., 40 c. and $1 (Nos. 89/92), each in pair	1·00

1980 (20 Feb). *Brown and blue-green cover, 100×60 mm, showing Lionfish. Stapled.*

SB2	$3.92, booklet containing 8 c., 20 c., 30 c. and 40 c. (Nos. 110, 113, 115, 117), each in block of 4	1·50

1981 (16 June). *Violet on blue cover, 100×63 mm, showing stylized shark. Stapled.*

SB3	$4.60, booklet containing 10 c., 25 c., 35 c. and 45 c. (Nos. 111, 114, 116, 117b), each in block of 4	5·50

1981 (26 Nov). *Royal Wedding. Multicoloured cover, 105×65 mm, showing The Carolina. Stitched.*

SB4	$1.70, booklet containing two panes of four 10 c. (No. 175a) and pane of two 45 c. (No. 176a)	1·00

1984 (18 Apr). *Vermilion printed cover, 98×50 mm, showing Tuvalu crest. Stamps attached by selvedge.*

SB5	$1.20, booklet containing two 30 c. and one 60 c. (Nos. 205a, 209a)	4·75

1986 (18 July). *Royal Wedding. Silver (No. SB6) or gold (No. SB7) on rosine covers, 152×80 mm. Stapled.*

SB6	$6.40, booklet (State Coach) containing 60 c. and $1 (Nos. 397/400, but imperf) each value in block of 4	2·75
SB7	$7.20, booklet (Westminster Abbey) containing twelve 60 c. (Nos. 397/8) in blocks of 4	3·00

1997 (13 June). *Fishes. Multicoloured cover, 99×65 mm, showing fishes and coral. Stamps attached by selvedge.*

SB8	$5.60, booklet containing 25 c., 30 c., 40 c. and 45 c. (Nos. 770/3), each in block of 4	4·25

POSTAGE DUE STAMPS

D 1 Tuvalu Crest

(Des G. Drummond. Litho Questa)

1981 (3 May). *P 13½×14.*

D1	D 1	1 c. black and bright purple		10	10
D2		2 c. black and greenish blue		10	10
D3		5 c. black and ochre		10	10
D4		10 c. black and blue-green		10	15
D5		20 c. black and purple-brown		15	25
D6		30 c. black and bright orange		20	30
D7		40 c. black and blue		25	40
D8		50 c. black and yellow-green		30	45
D9		$1 black and deep mauve		50	50
D1/9			*Set of 9*	1·50	2·25

1982 (25 Nov)–**83**. *As Nos. D1/9 but P 14½ × 15 and with imprint date at foot.*

D10	D 1	1 c. black and bright purple		10	20
D11		2 c. black and greenish blue		10	20
D12		5 c. black and ochre		10	20
D13		10 c. black and blue-green		10	20
D14		20 c. black and purple-brown		15	30
D15		30 c. black and bright orange (25.5.83)		35	40
D16		40 c. black and blue (25.5.83)		45	50
D17		50 c. black and yellow-green (25.5.83)		55	60
D18		$1 black and deep mauve (25.5.83)		85	90
D10/18			*Set of 9*	2·25	3·25

The imprint date on Nos. D10/14 is "1982" and on Nos. D15/18 "1983".

OFFICIAL STAMPS

For the use of the Philatelic Bureau.

OFFICIAL   OFFICIAL

(O 1)   (O 2)

TWO TYPES OF OVERPRINT FOR NOS. O1/19

This issue was overprinted using two different processes.

All values, except for the 35, 45 and 50 c., come with the overprint applied by typography. This process results in ragged lines, uneven distribution of the ink, especially at the edges of the letters, and often has the impression of the letters visible from the reverse.

In addition nine of these values have been found with overprints applied by lithography. These show clean lines and an even distribution of the ink.

The 35, 45 and 50 c. values have only been seen with overprints applied by lithography.

1981 (2 July). *Nos. 105/22 optd with Type O 1.*

O 1	1 c. Type 14			10	10
	a. Litho opt			1·25	
O 2	2 c. Band-tailed Goatfish			10	10
O 3	4 c. Regal Angelfish			10	10
O 4	5 c. Melon Butterflyfish			10	10
O 5	6 c. Semi-circle Angelfish			10	10
	a. Litho opt			1·25	1·25

O 6	8 c. Blue-striped Snapper			10	10
O 7	10 c. Clown Anemonefish			15	15
	a. Litho opt			1·25	1·25
O 8	15 c. Chevron Butterflyfish			20	20
O 9	20 c. Yellow-edged Lyretail ("Fairy Cod")			25	25
O10	25 c. Clown Triggerfish			25·00	
	a. Litho opt			30	30
O11	30 c. Long-nosed Butterflyfish			30	30
O12	35 c. Yellow-finned Tuna (*litho opt*)			30	30
O13	40 c. Spotted Eagle Ray			30	30
O14	45 c. Black-tipped Grouper (*litho opt*)			35	35
O15	50 c. Hammerhead (*litho opt*)			40	40
O16	70 c. Lionfish			50	50
	a. Litho opt			3·25	3·00
O17	$1 Painted Triggerfish			50	50
	a. Litho opt			2·50	2·50
O18	$2 Copper-banded Butterflyfish			1·25	1·00
	a. Litho opt			1·10	1·00
O19	$5 Tiger Shark			1·40	1·00
	a. Litho opt			15·00	12·00
O1/19			*Set of 19*	5·50	5·50

The 1 c. (typo opt), 8 c. and 30 c. exist with either screen, the 2 c., 4 c., 6 c. (both opts), 10 c. (typo opt), 20 c., 70 c. (both opts), $1 (both opts), $2 (both opts) and $5 (both opts) with the fine screen and the 1 c. (litho opt), 5 c., 10 c. (litho opt), 15 c., 25 c. (both opts), 35 c., 40 c., 45 c. and 50 c. with the coarse.

1983 (26 Aug)–**85**. *Nos. 202/3a, 205/12, 224 and 234 optd as Type O 1, but 20½×4 mm, (5 c.) or as Type O 2 (others), both applied by lithography.*

O20	5 c. Wedding and baby food baskets (1.2.84)		10	40
	a. Optd as Type O 2 (5.85)		30	40
O21	10 c. Hand-carved model of canoe (1.2.84)		10	40
O22	15 c. Ladies' sun hats (30.4.84)		15	70
O23	25 c. Pandanus baskets (1.2.84)		25	60
O24	30 c. on 45 c. Reef sandals and fish trap (1.2.84)		50	70
O25	30 c. Basket tray and coconut stand (30.4.84)		30	70
O26	35 c. Pandanus pillows and shell necklaces (1.2.84)		40	75
O27	40 c. Round baskets and fans (1.2.84)		45	75
O28	45 c. Reef sandals and fish trap (1.2.84)		45	75
O29	50 c. Rat trap (1.2.84)		50	75
O30	60 c. on $1 Pump drill and adze		75	75
O31	60 c. Fisherman's waterproof boxes (30.4.84)		60	1·00
	a. Typo opt (19.2.85*)		75	1·00
O32	$1 Pump drill and adze (1.2.84)		75	1·00
O33	$2 Fisherman's hat and canoe bailers (1.2.84)		1·25	1·00
O34	$5 Fishing rod, lures and scoop nets (1.2.84)		3·00	2·50
O20/34		*Set of 15*	8·50	11·00

*No. O31a comes from an emergency overprinting by typography undertaken in Fiji to meet Tuvalu government requirements for this value. Examples are known used between 19 February 1985 and August 1988. Further supplies of the lithography overprint were subsequently obtained from Great Britain.

For the different characteristics of litho and typo overprints see above No. O1.

OFFICIAL

(O 3)

1989 (22 Feb). *Nos. 502/17 optd with Type O 3.*

O35	5 c. Type 66		30	55
O36	10 c. White Tern		30	55
O37	15 c. Common Noddy		45	55
O38	20 c. Phoenix Petrel		45	55
O39	25 c. American Golden Plover		50	75
O40	30 c. Crested Tern		50	75
O41	35 c. Sooty Tern		55	80
O42	40 c. Bristle-thighed Curlew		55	80
O43	45 c. Bar-tailed Godwit		65	85
O44	50 c. Eastern Reef Heron		70	90
O45	55 c. Great Frigate Bird		70	90
O46	60 c. Red-footed Booby		70	90
O47	70 c. Rufous-necked Sandpiper ("Red-necked Stint")		80	1·00
O48	$1 Long-tailed Koel ("Long-tailed Cuckoo")		1·10	1·10
O49	$2 Red-tailed Tropic Bird		2·00	1·90
O50	$5 Banded Rail		4·25	4·50
O35/50		*Set of 16*	13·00	15·00

Appendix

The following issues for individual islands of Tuvalu fall outside the criteria for full listing as detailed on page xi of this edition.

FUNAFUTI

1984

Leaders of the World. Railway Locomotives (1st series). Two designs for each value, the first showing technical drawings and the second the locomotive at work. 15, 20, 30, 40, 50, 60 c., *each × 2*

Leaders of the World. Automobiles (1st series). Two designs for each value, the first showing technical drawings and the second the car in action. 1, 10, 40 c., $1, *each × 2*

Leaders of the World. Railway Locomotives (2nd series). Two designs for each value, the first showing technical drawings and the second the locomotive at work. 5, 15, 25, 35, 40, 55, 60 c., $1, *each × 2*

1985

Leaders of the World. Automobiles (2nd series). Two designs for each value, the first showing technical drawings and the second the car in action. 1, 30, 55, 60 c., *each × 2*

Leaders of the World. Railway Locomotives (3rd series). Two designs for each value, the first showing technical drawings and the second the locomotive at work. 5, 15, 35, 40, 50 c., $1, *each × 2*

Leaders of the World. Life and Times of Queen Elizabeth the Queen Mother. Two designs for each value, showing different portraits. 5, 25, 80 c., $1.05, *each × 2*

1986

60th Birthday of Queen Elizabeth II. 10, 50 c., $1.50, $3.50

Royal Wedding (1st issue). 60 c., $1, *each × 2*

Royal Wedding (2nd issue). Previous Royal Wedding stamps optd "Congratulations T.R.H. The Duke & Duchess of York". 60 c., $1, *each × 2*

Railway Locomotives (4th series). Two designs for each value, the first showing technical drawings and the second the locomotive at work. 20, 40, 60 c., $1.50, *each × 2*

1987

Automobiles (3rd series). Two designs for each value, the first showing technical drawings and the second the car in action. 10, 20, 40, 60, 75, 80 c., $1, $1.50, *each × 2*

Royal Ruby Wedding. 20, 50, 75 c., $1.20, $1.75

1988

Olympic Games, Seoul. 10, 20, 40, 50, 80, 90 c.

NANUMAGA

1984

Leaders of the World. Automobiles (1st series). Two designs for each value, the first showing technical drawings and the second the car in action. 5, 10, 25, 30, 40 c., $1, *each × 2*

Leaders of the World. British Monarchs. Two designs for each value, forming a composite picture. 10, 20, 30, 40, 50 c., $1, *each × 2*

Leaders of the World. Automobiles (2nd series). Two designs for each value, the first showing technical drawings and the second the car in action. 5, 10, 50 c., $1, *each × 2*

1985

Leaders of the World. Railway Locomotives. Two designs for each value, the first showing technical drawings and the second the locomotive at work. 10, 25, 50, 60 c., *each × 2*

Leaders of the World. Flowers. 25, 30, 40, 50 c., *each × 2*

Leaders of the World. Automobiles (3rd series). Two designs for each value, the first showing technical drawings and the second the car in action. 10, 25, 75 c., $1, *each × 2*

Leaders of the World. Life and Times of Queen Elizabeth the Queen Mother. Two designs for each value, showing different portraits. 15, 55, 65, 90 c., *each × 2*

1986

60th Birthday of Queen Elizabeth II. 5 c., $1, $1.75, $2.50

World Cup Football Championship, Mexico. 1, 5, 5, 10, 20, 35, 50, 60, 75 c., $1, $2, $4

Royal Wedding (1st issue). 60 c., $1, *each × 2*

Royal Wedding (2nd issue). Previous Royal Wedding stamps optd as for Funafuti. 60 c., $1, *each × 2*

1987

Automobiles (4th series). Two designs for each value, the first showing technical drawings and the second the car in action. 5, 10, 15, 20, 25, 40, 60 c., $1, *each × 2*

Royal Ruby Wedding. 15, 35, 60 c., $1.50, $1.75

NANUMEA

1984

Leaders of the World. Railway Locomotives (1st series). Two designs for each value, the first showing technical drawings and the second the locomotive at work. 15, 20, 30, 40, 50, 60 c., *each × 2*

Leaders of the World. Famous Cricketers. Two designs for each value, the first showing a portrait and the second the cricketer in action. 1, 10, 40 c., $1, *each × 2*

1985

Leaders of the World. Automobiles (1st series). Two designs for each value, the first showing technical drawings and the second the car in action. 5, 40, 50, 60 c., *each × 2*

Leaders of the World. Railway Locomotives (2nd series). Two designs for each value, the first showing technical drawings and the second the locomotive at work. 1, 35, 50, 60 c., *each × 2*

Leaders of the World. Automobiles (2nd series). Two designs for each value, the first showing technical drawings and the second the car in action. 15, 20, 50, 60 c., *each × 2*

Leaders of the World. Cats. 5, 30, 50 c., $1, *each × 2*

Leaders of the World. Life and Times of Queen Elizabeth the Queen Mother. Two designs for each value, showing different portraits. 5, 30, 75 c., $1.05, *each × 2*

1986

60th Birthday of Queen Elizabeth II. 10, 80 c., $1.75, $3

World Cup Football Championship, Mexico. 1, 2, 5, 10, 25, 40, 50, 75, 90 c., $1, $2.50, $4

Royal Wedding (1st issue). 60 c., $1, *each × 2*

Royal Wedding (2nd issue). Previous Royal Wedding stamps optd as for Funafuti. 60 c., $1, *each × 2*

Automobiles (3rd series). Two designs for each value, the first showing technical drawings and the second the car in action. 10, 20, 35, 50, 75 c., $2, *each × 2*

1987

Royal Ruby Wedding. 40, 60, 80 c., $1, $2

NIUTAO

1984

Leaders of the World. Automobiles (1st series). Two designs for each value, the first showing technical drawings and the second the car in action. 15, 30, 40, 50 c., *each × 2*

Leaders of the World. Railway Locomotives (1st series). Two designs for each value, the first showing technical drawings and the second the locomotive at work. 5, 10, 20, 40, 50 c., $1, *each × 2*

1985

Leaders of the World. Famous Cricketers. Two designs for each value, the first showing a portrait and the second the cricketer in action. 1, 15, 50 c., $1, *each × 2*

Leaders of the World. Birth Bicent of John J. Audubon (ornithologist). Birds. 5, 15, 25 c., $1, *each × 2*

Leaders of the World. Automobiles (2nd series). Two designs for each value, the first showing technical drawings and the second the car in action. 20, 25, 40, 60 c., *each × 2*

Leaders of the World. Railway Locomotives (2nd series). Two designs for each value, the first showing technical drawings and the second the locomotive at work. 10, 30, 45, 60, 75 c., $1.20, *each × 2*

Leaders of the World. Life and Times of Queen Elizabeth the Queen Mother. Two designs for each value, showing different portraits. 15, 35, 70, 95 c., *each × 2*

1986

60th Birthday of Queen Elizabeth II. 5, 60 c., $1.50, $3.50

Royal Wedding (1st issue). 60 c., $1, *each × 2*

Royal Wedding (2nd issue). Previous Royal Wedding stamps optd as for Funafuti. 60 c., $1, *each × 2*

1987

Royal Ruby Wedding. 60th Birthday of Queen Elizabeth II issue of 1986 optd "40th WEDDING ANNIVERSARY OF H.M. QUEEN ELIZABETH II". 5, 60 c., $1.50, $3.50

NUI

1984

Leaders of the World. Railway Locomotives (1st series). Two designs for each value, the first showing technical drawings and the second the locomotive at work. 15, 25, 30, 50 c., *each × 2*

Leaders of the World. British Monarchs. Two designs for each value, forming a composite picture. 1, 5, 15, 40, 50 c., $1, *each × 2*

1985

Leaders of the World. Railway Locomotives (2nd series). Two designs for each value, the first showing technical drawings and the second the locomotive at work. 5, 15, 25 c., $1, *each × 2*

Leaders of the World. Automobiles (1st series). Two designs for each value, the first showing technical drawings and the second the car in action. 25, 30, 40, 50 c., *each × 2*

Leaders of the World. Famous Cricketers. Two designs for each value, the first showing a portrait and the second the cricketer in action. 1, 40, 60, 70 c., *each × 2*

Leaders of the World. Life and Times of Queen Elizabeth the Queen Mother. Two designs for each value, showing different portraits. 5, 50, 75, 85 c., *each × 2*

Leaders of the World. Automobiles (2nd series). Two designs for each value, the first showing technical drawings and the second the car in action. 5, 15, 40, 60, 90 c., $1.10, *each × 2*

1986

60th Birthday of Queen Elizabeth II. 10, 80 c., $1.75, $3

Royal Wedding (1st issue). 60 c., $1, *each × 2*

Royal Wedding (2nd issue). Previous Royal Wedding stamps optd as for Funafuti. 60 c., $1, *each × 2*

1987

Railway Locomotives (3rd series). Two designs for each value, the first showing technical drawings and the second the locomotive at work. 10, 25, 35, 40, 60, 75 c., $1, $1.25, *each × 2*

Royal Ruby Wedding. 20, 50, 75 c., $1.20, $1.75

1988

Railway Locomotives (4th series). Two designs for each value, the first showing technical drawings and the second the locomotive at work. 5, 10, 20, 25, 40, 50, 60, 75 c., *each × 2*

NUKUFETAU

1984

Leaders of the World. Automobiles (1st series). Two designs for each value, the first showing technical drawings and the second the car in action. 10, 25, 30, 50, 60 c.. *each × 2*

Leaders of the World. British Monarchs. Two designs for each value, forming a composite picture. 1, 10, 30, 50, 60 c., $1, *each × 2*

1985

Leaders of the World. Famous Cricketers. Two designs for each value, the first showing a portrait and the second the cricketer in action. 1, 10, 55 c., $1, *each × 2*

Leaders of the World. Railway Locomotives (1st series). Two designs for each value, the first showing technical drawings and the second the locomotive at work. 1, 10, 60, 70 c., *each × 2*

Leaders of the World. Automobiles (2nd series). Two designs for each value, the first showing technical drawings and the second the car in action. 5, 10, 15, 20, 50, 60, 75 c., $1.50, *each × 2*

Leaders of the World. Life and Times of Queen Elizabeth the Queen Mother. Two designs for each value, showing different portraits. 10, 45, 65 c., $1, *each × 2*

1986

Leaders of the World. Railway Locomotives (2nd series). Two designs for each value, the first showing technical drawings and the second the locomotive at work. 20, 40, 60 c., $1.50, *each × 2*

60th Birthday of Queen Elizabeth II. 5, 40 c., $2, $4

Royal Wedding (1st issue). 60 c., $1, *each × 2*

Royal Wedding (2nd issue). Previous Royal Wedding stamps optd as for Funafuti. 60 c., $1, *each × 2*

1987

Railway Locomotives (3rd series). Two designs for each value, the first showing technical drawings and the second the locomotive at work. 5, 10, 15, 25, 30, 50, 60 c., $1, *each × 2*

Royal Ruby Wedding. 60th Birthday of Queen Elizabeth II issue of 1986 optd as for Niutao. 5, 40 c., $2, $4

NUKULAELAE

1984

Leaders of the World. Railway Locomotives (1st series). Two designs for each value, the first showing technical drawings and the second the locomotive at work. 5, 15, 40 c., $1, *each × 2*

Leaders of the World. Famous Cricketers. Two designs for each value, the first showing a portrait and the second the cricketer in action. 5, 15, 30 c., $1, *each × 2*

Leaders of the World. Railway Locomotives (2nd series). Two designs for each value, the first showing technical drawings and the second the locomotive at work. 5, 20, 40 c., $1, *each × 2*

1985

Leaders of the World. Automobiles. Two designs for each value, the first showing technical drawings and the second the car in action. 5, 35, 50, 70 c., *each × 2*

Leaders of the World. Dogs. 5, 20, 50, 70 c., *each × 2*

Leaders of the World. Railway Locomotives (3rd series). Two designs for each value, the first showing technical drawings and the second the locomotive at work. 10, 25, 50 c., $1, *each × 2*

Leaders of the World. Automobiles (2nd series). Two designs for each value, the first showing technical drawings and the second the car in action. 10, 25, 35, 50, 75 c., $1, *each × 2*

Leaders of the World. Life and Times of Queen Elizabeth the Queen Mother. Two designs for each value, showing different portraits. 5, 25, 85 c., $1, *each × 2*

1986

60th Birthday of Queen Elizabeth II. 10 c., $1, $1.50, $3

Railway Locomotives (4th series). Two designs for each value, the first showing technical drawings and the second the locomotive at work. 10, 15, 25, 40, 50, 80 c., $1, $1.50, *each × 2*

Royal Wedding (1st issue). 60 c., $1, *each × 2*

Royal Wedding (2nd issue). Previous Royal Wedding stamps optd as for Funafuti. 60 c., $1, *each × 2*

1987

Royal Ruby Wedding. 15, 35, 60 c., $1.50, $1.75

VAITUPU

1984

Leaders of the World. Automobiles (1st series). Two designs for each value, the first showing technical drawings and the second the car in action. 15, 25, 30, 50 c., *each × 2*

Leaders of the World. British Monarchs. Two designs for each value, forming a composite picture. 1, 5, 15, 40, 50 c., $1, *each × 2*

Leaders of the World. Automobiles (2nd series). Two designs for each value, the first showing technical drawings and the second the car in action. 5, 15, 25, 30, 40, 50, 60 c., $1, *each × 2*

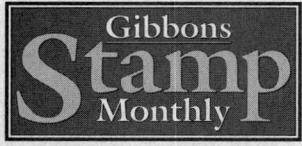

1985

Leaders of the World. Railway Locomotives (1st series). Two designs for each value, the first showing technical drawings and the second the locomotive at work. 10, 25, 50, 60 c., each ×2

Leaders of the World, Butterflies. 5, 15, 50, 75 c., each×2

Leaders of the World. Automobiles (3rd series). Two designs for each value, the first showing technical drawings and the second the car in action. 15, 30, 40, 60 c., each×2

Leaders of the World. Life and Times of Queen Elizabeth the Queen Mother. Two designs for each value, showing different portraits. 15, 40, 65, 95 c., each × 2

1986

Leaders of the World. Railway Locomotives (2nd series). Two designs for each value, the first showing technical drawings and the second the locomotive at work. 5, 25, 80 c., $1, each×2

60th Birthday of Queen Elizabeth II. 5, 60 c., $2, $3.50

Royal Wedding (1st issue). 60 c., $1, each×2

Royal Wedding (2nd issue). Previous Royal Wedding stamps optd as for Funafuti. 60 c., $1, each×2

1987

Railway Locomotives (3rd series). Two designs for each value, the first showing technical drawings and the second the locomotive at work. 10, 15, 25, 35, 45, 65, 85 c., $1, each×2

Royal Ruby Wedding. 60th Birthday of Queen Elizabeth II issue of 1986 optd as for Niutao. 5, 60 c., $2, $3.50

Uganda

PRICES FOR STAMPS ON COVER TO 1945

The type-written stamps of Uganda, Nos. 1/53, are very rare used on cover.

Nos. 54/60	*from × 20*
No. 61	—
Nos. 70/5	*from × 12*
No. 76	—
Nos. 84/90	*from × 20*
No. 91	—
Nos. 92/3	*from × 40*

PROTECTORATE

Following a period of conflict between Islamic, Protestant and Roman Catholic factions, Uganda was declared to be in the British sphere of influence by the Anglo-German Agreement of July 1890. The British East Africa Company exercised a variable degree of control until 27 August 1894 when the country was declared a British Protectorate.

Before the introduction of Nos. 84/91 the stamps of Uganda were only valid for internal postage. Letters for overseas were franked with British East Africa issues on arrival at Mombasa.

(Currency. 200 cowries = 1 rupee)

U G	U G
50	20
1	**2**

TYPE-WRITTEN STAMPS. Nos. 2/53 were type-written by the Revd. E. Millar at Mengo for the Uganda administration. For all "printings" a thin laid paper was used, and all issues were imperforate.

The original typewriter used had wide letters, but in late April, 1895 Millar obtained a new machine on which the type face was in a narrower fount.

Each sheet was made up of whatever values were required at the time, so that different values can be found se-tenant or tête-bêche. These last were caused by the paper being inverted in the machine so that space at the foot could be utilised.

For the first issue the sheets were of 117 (9 × 13), but with the introduction of the narrower width (Nos. 17 onwards) a larger number of stamps per sheet, 143 (11 × 13), was adopted.

The manuscript provisionals, Nos. 9a/16, come from the Mission at Ngogwe, most of the manuscript surcharges including the initials of the Revd. G. R. Blackledge stationed there.

1895 (20 Mar). *Wide letters. Wide stamps, 20 to 26 mm wide.*

2	1	10 (c.) black					£2500	£1200
4		20 (c.) black					£3750	£1200
		a. "U A" for "U G"					†	£2500
6		30 (c.) black					£1400	£1400
7		40 (c.) black					£2250	£1200
8		50 (c.) black					£1200	£1000
		a. "U A" for "U G"					†	£4000
9		60 (c.) black					£1600	£1600

It is now believed that the 5, 15 and 25 cowries values in this width, previously Nos. 1, 3 and 5, do not exist.

A strip of three of No. 2 is known on cover of which one stamp has the value "10" altered to "5" in manuscript and initialled "E.M.".

1895 (May). *Wide stamps with pen-written surcharges, in black.*

9a	1	10 on 30 (c.) black				†	£30000
10		10 on 50 (c.) black				†	£30000
11		15 on 10 (c.) black				†	£22000
12		15 on 20 (c.) black				†	£26000
13		15 on 40 (c.) black				†	£26000
14		15 on 50 (c.) black				†	£30000
15		25 on 50 (c.) black				†	£30000
16		50 on 60 (c.) black				†	£30000

1895 (April). *Wide letters. Narrow stamps, 16 to 18 mm wide.*

17	1	5 (c.) black				£1400	£950
18		10 (c.) black				£1400	£1000
19		15 (c.) black				£1000	£1000
20		20 (c.) black				£1200	£650
21		25 (c.) black				£950	£950
22		30 (c.) black				£7000	£7000
23		40 (c.) black				£6500	£6500
24		50 (c.) black				£3000	
25		60 (c.) black				£5000	

1895 (May). *Narrow letters. Narrow stamps 16 to 18 mm wide.*

26	2	5 (c.) black				£750	
27		10 (c.) black				£700	
28		15 (c.) black				£700	
29		20 (c.) black				£550	
30		25 (c.) black				£700	
31		30 (c.) black				£700	
32		40 (c.) black				£800	
33		50 (c.) black				£650	
34		60 (c.) black				£1300	

1895 (Nov). *Narrow letters. Narrow stamps, 16–18 mm wide. Change of colour.*

35	2	5 (c.) violet				£475	£475
36		10 (c.) violet				£450	£450
37		15 (c.) violet				£550	£400
38		20 (c.) violet				£350	£275
		a. "G U" for "U G"					
39		25 (c.) violet				£650	£650
40		30 (c.) violet				£900	£650
41		40 (c.) violet				£750	£750
42		50 (c.) violet				£750	£800
43		100 (c.) violet				£2500	£2500

Stamps of 35 (c.) and 45 (c.) have been recorded in violet. They were never prepared for postal use, and did not represent a postal rate, but were type-written to oblige a local official. (*Price £2500 each, unused*)

```
'V.96.R'
   25
'Uganda'
    3
```

1896 (June).

44	3	5 (c.) violet				£450	£475
45		10 (c.) violet				£400	£375
46		15 (c.) violet				£450	£475
47		20 (c.) violet				£275	£200
48		25 (c.) violet				£450	
49		30 (c.) violet				£500	£650
50		40 (c.) violet				£500	£650
51		50 (c.) violet				£600	£650
52		60 (c.) violet				£1400	
53		100 (c.) violet				£1200	£1400

(New Currency. 16 annas = 1 rupee)

UGANDA	UGANDA
POSTAGE	POSTAGE
V†R	*V†R*
1 ANNA	1 ANNA
PROTECTORATE	PROTECTORATE
4 (Thin "1")	**5 (Thick "1")**

UGANDA	UGANDA
POSTAGE	POSTAGE
V÷R	V L R*
4 ANNAS	4 ANNAS
PROTECTORATE	PROTECTORATE
6	**7**

In the 2 a. and 3 a. the dagger points upwards; the stars in the 2 a. are level with the top of "VR". The 8 a. is as T 6 but with left star at top and right star at foot. The 1 r. has three stars at foot. The 5 r. has central star raised and the others at foot.

(Type-set by the Revd. F. Rowling at Lubwa's, in Usoga)

1896 (7 Nov). *Thick white wove paper (Nos. 54/8) or thin yellowish paper ruled with vertical lines 9 mm apart (Nos. 59/61).* (a) *Types 4/6*

54	4	1 a. black				90.00	80.00
		a. Small "o" in "POSTAGE"				£425	£400
55	5	1 a. black				14.00	18.00
		a. Small "o" in "POSTAGE"				55.00	65.00
56	6	2 a. black				20.00	22.00
		a. Small "o" in "POSTAGE"				75.00	80.00
57		3 a. black				20.00	23.00
		a. Small "o" in "POSTAGE"				75.00	90.00
58		4 a. black				20.00	23.00
		a. Small "o" in "POSTAGE"				75.00	90.00
59		8 a. black				23.00	24.00
		a. Small "o" in "POSTAGE"				90.00	100
60		1 r. black				65.00	80.00
		a. Small "o" in "POSTAGE"				£250	£325
61		5 r. black				£170	£250
		a. Small "o" in "POSTAGE"				£550	£650

(b) *Optd "L", in black as in T 7 for local use, by a postal official, R. R. Racey, at Kampala*

70	4	1 a. black				£150	£130
		a. Small "o" in "POSTAGE"			£800	£700
71	6	2 a. black				70.00	90.00
		a. Small "o" in "POSTAGE"			£250	£325
72		3 a. black				£170	£190
		a. Small "o" in "POSTAGE"			£850	£950
73		4 a. black				80.00	£130
		a. Small "o" in "POSTAGE"			£375	
74		8 a. black				£140	£180
		a. Small "o" in "POSTAGE"			£750	£900
75		1 r. black				£275	£325
		a. Small "o" in "POSTAGE"			£1000	
76		5 r. black				£8000	£8000

Tête-bêche pairs of all values may be found owing to the settings of 16 (4 × 4) being printed side by side or above one another. They are worth a premium. The variety with small "O" occurs on R. 3/1.

8	**9**	**UGANDA** **(10)**

(Recess D.L.R.)

1898 (Nov)–**1902.** *P* 14. (a) *Wmk Crown CA.*

84	8	1 a. scarlet				1·75	2·00
		a. Carmine-rose (1902)			1·75	1·00
86		2 a. red-brown				1·50	5·00
87		3 a. pale grey				6·50	20·00
		a. Bluish grey				7·00	13·00
88		4 a. deep green				2·75	6·50
89		8 a. pale olive				6·50	24·00
		a. Grey-green				7·50	26·00

(b) *Wmk Crown CC*

90	9	1 r. dull blue				28·00	38·00
		a. Bright blue				40·00	40·00
91		5 r. brown				65·00	95·00
84/91				*Set of 7*	£100	£160
84/91		Optd "Specimen"		*Set of 7*	£150	

On 1 April 1901 the postal administrations of British East Africa and Uganda were merged. Subsequent issues to 1962 are listed under KENYA, UGANDA and TANGANYIKA.

1902 (Feb). *T 11 of British East Africa (Kenya, Uganda, and Tanganyika) optd with T 10.*

92		½ a. yellow-green				2·00	1·40
		a. Opt omitted (in pair with normal)		£3250	
		b. Opt inverted (at foot)		£1300	
		c. Opt double				£1400	
93		2½ a. deep blue (R.)				2·00	3·00
		a. Opt double				£600	
		b. Inverted "S" (R. 1/1)			45·00	75·00

The Eastern Province of Uganda was transferred to British East Africa on 1 April 1902.

SELF-GOVERNMENT

(New Currency. 100 cents = 1 East African, later Uganda shilling)

11 Ripon Falls and Speke Memorial

(Des S. Scott. Recess B.W.)

1962 (28 July). *Centenary of Speke's Discovery of Source of the Nile.* W w 12. *P* 14.

95	11	30 c. black and red				15	10
96		50 c. black and slate-violet				15	10
97		1 s. 30, black and green				30	20
98		2 s. 50, black and blue				1·60	1·60
95/8				*Set of 4*	2·00	1·75

INDEPENDENT

12 Murchison Falls	**13** Tobacco-growing

14 Mulago Hospital

(Des V. Whiteley. Photo Harrison)

1962 (9 Oct)–**64**. *Independence. Various designs as T* **12/14**. *P* 15×14 (5 c. to 50 c.) *or* 14½ (*others*).

99	5 c. deep bluish green		10	10
100	10 c. reddish brown		10	10
	a. Brown (coil)		10	10
	b. Deep yellow-brown (17.10.64)		10	10
101	15 c. black, red and green		10	10
102	20 c. plum and buff		10	10
103	30 c. blue		10	10
104	50 c. black and turquoise-green		10	10
105	1 s. sepia, red and turquoise-green		15	10
106	1 s. 30, yellow-orange and violet		20	10
107	2 s. black, carmine and light blue		40	40
108	5 s. vermilion and deep green		4·00	1·00
109	10 s. slate and chestnut		1·75	2·25
110	20 s. brown and blue		4·50	11·00
99/110		Set of 12	10·50	13·50

Designs: *As T* **12/13**—10 c. Tobacco growing; 15 c. Coffee growing; 20 c. Ankole cattle; 30 c. Cotton; 50 c. Mountains of the Moon. *As T* **14**—1 s. 30, Cathedrals and Mosque; 2 s. Makerere College; 5 s. Copper mining; 10 s. Cement industry; 20 s. Parliament Buildings.

15 South African
Crowned Crane

(Photo Harrison)

1965 (20 Feb). *International Trade Fair, Kampala. P* 14½ × 14.

111	**15** 30 c. multicoloured		10	10
112	1 s. 30, multicoloured		20	10

16 Black Bee Eater   **17** African Jacana

18 Ruwenzori Turaco

(Des Mrs. R. Fennessy. Photo Harrison)

1965 (9 Oct). *Birds. Various designs as T* **16/18**. *P* 15 × 14 (5 c., 15 c., 20 c., 40 c.), 14 × 15 (10 c., 30 c., 65 c.) *or* 14½×14 (*others*).

113	5 c. multicoloured		10	10
114	10 c. chestnut, black and light blue		10	10
115	15 c. yellow and sepia		20	10
116	20 c. multicoloured		20	10
117	30 c. black and brown-red		1·50	10
118	40 c. multicoloured		90	75
119	50 c. grey-blue and reddish violet		25	10
	a. White bird (grey-blue omitted)		£275	
120	65 c. orange-red, black and light grey		2·50	2·25
121	1 s. multicoloured		50	10
122	1 s. 30, chestnut, black and yellow		5·50	30
123	2 s. 50, multicoloured		4·25	65
124	5 s. multicoloured		7·00	4·00
125	10 s. multicoloured		11·00	11·00
126	20 s. multicoloured		21·00	35·00
113/26		Set of 14	48·00	48·00

Designs: *Vert as T* **16**—15 c. Orange Weaver; 20 c. Narina Trogon; 40 c. Blue-breasted Kingfisher; 50 c. Whale-headed Stork. *Horiz as T* **17**—30 c. Sacred Ibis; 65 c. Red-crowned Bishop. *As T* **18**. *Vert*—1 s. 30, African Fish Eagle; 5 s. Lilac-breasted Roller. *Horiz*—2 s. 50, Great Blue Turaco; 10 s. Black-collared Lovebird; 20 s. South African Crowned Crane.

The 15 c., 40 c., 65 c., and 1s. exist with PVA gum as well as gum arabic.

19 Carved Screen

(Des Mrs. R. Fennessy. Photo Harrison)

1967 (26 Oct). *13th Commonwealth Parliamentary Association Conference. T* **19** *and similar horiz designs. Multicoloured. P* 14.

127	**19** 30 c. Type **19**		10	10
128	50 c. Arms of Uganda		10	10
129	1 s. 30, Parliamentary Building		10	10
130	2 s. 50, Conference Chamber		15	1·50
127/30		Set of 4	30	1·50

20 Cordia
abyssinica

21 Acacia
drepanolobium

(Des Mrs. R. Fennessy. Photo Harrison)

1969 (9 Oct)–**74**. *Flowers. Various designs as T* **20/1**. *Chalk-surfaced paper. P* 14½×14 (5 c. to 70 c.) *or* 14 (*others*).

131	5 c. brown, green and light olive-yellow		10	85
	a. Glazed, ordinary paper (11.4.73)		40	10
132	10 c. multicoloured		10	10
	a. Glazed, ordinary paper (27.9.72)		40	10
133	15 c. multicoloured		40	10
134	20 c. bluish violet, yellow-ol & pale sage-grn		15	10
	a. Glazed, ordinary paper (27.9.72)		40	10
135	30 c. multicoloured		20	10
136	40 c. reddish violet, yell-grn & pale ol-grey		20	10
137	50 c. multicoloured		20	10
138	60 c. multicoloured		45	90
	a. Glazed, ordinary paper (9.5.73)		8·50	40
139	70 c. multicoloured		35	30
	a. Glazed, ordinary paper (27.9.72)		1·00	45
140	1 s. multicoloured		20	10
	a. Glazed, ordinary paper (22.1.71)		80	10
141	1 s. 50, multicoloured (cobalt background)		35	10
	a. Glazed, ordinary paper (3.2.71)		50	10
	b. Azure background (chalk-surfaced paper) (21.1.74)		55	20
142	2 s. 50, multicoloured		50	1·25
	a. Glazed, ordinary paper (3.2.71)		1·25	10
143	5 s. multicoloured		50	1·60
	a. Glazed, ordinary paper (3.2.71)		1·75	10
144	10 s. multicoloured		75	4·00
	a. Glazed, ordinary paper (3.2.71)		3·75	10
145	20 s. multicoloured		1·25	5·00
	a. Glazed, ordinary paper (22.1.71)		11·00	15
131/45		Set of 15	4·50	13·00
131a/45a		Set of 11	27·00	1·40

Designs: *As T* **20**—10 c. Grewia similis; 15 c. Cassia didymobotrya; 20 c. Coleus barbatus; 30 c. Ochna ovata; 40 c. Ipomoea spathulata; 50 c. Spathodea nilotica; 60 c. Oncoba spinosa; 70 c. Carissa edulis. *As T* **21**—1 s. 50, Clerodendrum myricoides; 2 s. 50, Acanthus arboreus; 5 s. Kigelia aethiopium; 10 s. Erythrina abyssinica; 20 s. Monodora myristica.

Some of the glazed ordinary paper printings were available in Uganda some time before the London release dates which are quoted in the listings.

2⁵

(22)

1975 (29 Sept). *Nos. 141/2 and 145a surch as T* **22**.

146	1 s. on 1 s. 50, multicoloured		2·00	1·50
147	3 s. on 2 s. 50, multicoloured		20·00	40·00
148	40 s. on 20 s. multicoloured		5·50	3·50
	a. Surch on No. 145		6·50	3·50
146/8		Set of 3	25·00	40·00

23 Millet   **24** Maize

(Des Mrs. R. Fennessy. Photo Harrison)

1975 (9 Oct). *Ugandan Crops. T* **23/4** *and similar horiz designs. P* 14 × 14½ (10 to 80 c.) *or* 14 (*others*).

149	10 c. black, apple-green and yellow-brown		10	10
150	20 c. multicoloured		10	10
151	30 c. multicoloured		10	10
152	40 c. multicoloured		10	10
153	50 c. multicoloured		10	10
154	70 c. black, apple-green and light blue-green		10	15
155	80 c. multicoloured		10	15
156	1 s. multicoloured		10	10
157	2 s. multicoloured		30	30
158	3 s. multicoloured		50	45
159	5 s. multicoloured		50	75
160	10 s. multicoloured		50	1·25
161	20 s. apple-green, black and bright purple		70	2·50
162	40 s. apple-green, black and yellow-orange		1·10	4·50
149/62		Set of 14	3·50	9·00

Designs: *As T* **23**—20 c. Sugar; 30 c. Tobacco; 40 c. Onions; 50 c. Tomatoes; 70 c. Tea; 80 c. Bananas. *As T* **24**—2 s. Pineapples; 3 s. Coffee; 5 s. Oranges; 10 s. Groundnuts; 20 s. Cotton; 40 s. Runner Beans.

Face value colours: 5 s. green; 10 s. brown; 20 s. bright purple; 40 s. yellow-orange. For 5 s. to 40 s. with colours changed see No. 220/3.

Nos. 149 and 153 exist in coils constructed from normal sheets.

1976 (15 Apr). *Telecommunications Development. As Nos. 56/60 of Kenya, but inscr* "UGANDA".

163	50 c. Microwave tower		10	10
164	1 s. Cordless switchboard		10	10
165	2 s. Telephone		20	25
166	3 s. Message Switching Centre		30	45
163/6		Set of 4	60	70
MS167	120 × 120 mm. Nos. 163/6		90	1·25

Nos. 164 and 166 exist imperforate from stock dispersed by the liquidator of Format International Security Printers Ltd.

1976 (5 July). *Olympic Games, Montreal. As Nos. 61/5 of Kenya, but inscr* "UGANDA".

168	50 c. Akii Bua, hurdler		10	10
169	1 s. Filbert Bayi, runner		10	10
170	2 s. Steve Muchoki, boxer		30	30
171	3 s. East African flags		40	45
168/71		Set of 4	40	45
MS172	129 × 154 mm. Nos. 168/71		4·00	5·00

Nos. 168/70 exist imperforate from stock dispersed by the liquidator of Format International Security Printers Ltd.

1976 (4 Oct). *Railway Transport. As Nos. 66/70 of Kenya, but inscr* "UGANDA".

173	50 c. Diesel-hydraulic train, Tanzania–Zambia railway		15	10
174	1 s. Nile Bridge, Uganda		15	10
175	2 s. Nakuru Station, Kenya		50	45
176	3 s. Uganda Railway Class A locomotive, 1896		55	55
173/6		Set of 4	1·25	1·00
MS177	154×103 mm. Nos. 173/6		2·25	2·50

Nos. 173/7 exist imperforate from stock dispersed by the liquidator of Format International Security Printers Ltd.

1977 (10 Jan). *Game Fish of East Africa. As Nos. 71/5 of Kenya, but inscr* "UGANDA".

178	50 c. Nile Perch		15	10
179	1 s. Nile Mouthbrooder		20	10
180	3 s. Sailfish		60	40
181	5 s. Black Marlin		80	60
178/81		Set of 4	1·60	1·00
MS182	153×129 mm. Nos. 178/81		4·25	2·00

1977 (15 Jan). *Second World Black and African Festival of Arts and Culture, Nigeria. As Nos. 76/80 of Kenya, but inscr* "UGANDA".

183	50 c. Maasai Manyatta (village)		10	10
184	1 s. "Heartbeat of Africa" (Ugandan dancers)		10	10
185	2 s. Makonde sculpture		25	55
186	3 s. "Early Man and Technology" (skinning hippopotamus)		35	85
183/6		Set of 4	75	1·40
MS187	132 × 109 mm. Nos. 183/6		1·25	2·25

1977 (5 Apr). *25th Anniv of Safari Rally. As Nos. 81/5 of Kenya, but inscr* "UGANDA".

188	50 c. Rally-car and villagers		10	10
189	1 s. Starting-line		10	10
190	2 s. Car fording river		25	35
191	5 s. Car and elephants		80	1·00
188/91		Set of 4	1·10	1·40
MS192	126 × 93 mm. Nos. 188/91		1·50	2·50

1977 (30 June). *Centenary of Ugandan Church. As Nos. 86/90 of Kenya, but inscr* "UGANDA".

193	50 c. Canon Kivebulaya		10	10
194	1 s. Modern Namirembe Cathedral		10	10
195	2 s. Old Namirembe Cathedral		20	40
196	5 s. Early congregation, Kigezi		45	90
193/6		Set of 4	75	1·25
MS197	126 × 89 mm. Nos. 193/6		1·00	1·75

80c **(25)**   **26** Shot Putting

1977 (22 Aug). *Design as No. 155 surch with T* **25** *in mauve by Harrison*.

198	80 c. on 60 c. multicoloured		30	20
	a. Surch omitted		£180	

A 60 c. stamp was to have been added to Nos. 149/62 using the design of the 80 c. (bananas), but it was cancelled and those already printed were surcharged to make No. 198.

1977 (26 Sept). *Endangered Species. As Nos. 96/101 of Kenya, but inscr* "UGANDA".

199	50 c. Pancake Tortoise		30	10
200	1 s. Nile Crocodile		45	10
201	2 s. Hunter's Hartebeest		2·00	40
202	3 s. Red Colobus monkey		2·50	75
203	5 s. Dugong		2·50	1·00
199/203		Set of 5	7·00	2·00
MS204	127 × 101 mm. Nos. 200/3		5·50	4·00

1978 (10 Apr). *World Cup Football Championship, Argentina* (1st issue). *As Nos. 122/6 of Kenya but inscr* "UGANDA".

205	50 c. Joe Kadenge and forwards		15	10
206	1 s. Mohamed Chuma and cup presentation		15	10
207	2 s. Omari Kidevu and goalmouth scene		30	40
208	5 s. Polly Ouma and forwards		50	1·10
205/8		Set of 4	1·40	
MS209	136 × 81 mm. Nos. 205/8		2·00	2·75

(Litho Questa)

1978 (28 Aug). *Commonwealth Games, Edmonton. T* **26** *and similar horiz designs. Multicoloured. P* 14.

210	50 c. Type **26**		10	10
211	1 s. Long jumping		15	10
212	2 s. Running		20	35
213	5 s. Boxing		40	95
210/13		Set of 4	75	1·25
MS214	114×85 mm. Nos. 210/13. P 12½×12		1·50	3·00

1978 (11 Sept). *World Cup Football Championship, Argentina (2nd issue). Designs as Nos. 205/8 but additionally inscr* "WORLD CUP 1978".

215	50 c. Polly Ouma and forwards		15	10
216	2 s. Omari Kidevu and goalmouth scene		30	40
217	5 s. Joe Kadenge and forwards		60	90
218	10 s. Mohamed Chuma and cup presentation		90	1·60
215/18		*Set of 4*	1·75	2·75
MS219	140×87 mm. Nos. 215/18. P 12×11½		2·00	2·75

1978. *As Nos. 159/62 but printing process and colours changed.*

220	5 s. multicoloured (face value in blue)		50	70
221	10 s. multicoloured (face value in magenta)		50	85
222	20 s. multicoloured (face value in brown)		55	85
223	40 s. multicoloured (face value in red)		65	1·10
220/3		*Set of 4*	2·00	3·25

27 Measurements of High Blood Pressure

(Litho Questa)

1978 (25 Sept). *"Down with High Blood Pressure". T* **27** *and similar horiz designs. Multicoloured. P* 14 × 13½.

224	50 c. Type **27**		15	10
225	1 s. Hypertension and the heart		15	10
226	2 s. Fundus of the eye in hypertension		40	40
227	5 s. Kidney and high blood pressure		75	1·25
224/7		*Set of 4*	1·25	1·60
MS228	180 × 115 mm. Nos. 224/7		1·50	2·75

28 Off Loading Cattle

(Litho Questa)

1978 (16 Dec). *75th Anniv of Powered Flight. T* **28** *and similar horiz designs. Multicoloured. P* 14.

229	1 s. Type **28**		15	10
230	1 s. 50, "Domestic services" (passengers boarding Britten Norman Islander light aircraft)		25	15
231	2 s. 70, Export of Uganda coffee		25	35
232	10 s. "Time machines in the air" (Wright Flyer III and Concorde)		75	1·25
229/32		*Set of 4*	1·25	1·60
MS233	166×110 mm. Nos. 229/32		2·25	2·75

29 Queen Elizabeth II leaving Owen Falls Dam

(Des BG Studio. Litho Ashton-Potter)

1979 (15 Feb). *25th Anniv of Coronation (1978). T* **29** *and similar horiz designs. Multicoloured. P* 12½ × 12.

234	1 s. Type **29**		15	10
235	1 s. 50, Regalia		20	10
236	2 s. 70, Coronation ceremony		45	20
237	10 s. Royal family on balcony of Buckingham Palace		80	1·10
234/7		*Set of 4*	1·40	1·25
MS238	150 × 102 mm. Nos. 234/7		1·40	1·25

30 Dr. Joseph Kiwanuka (first Ugandan bishop)

(Des G. Vasarhelyi. Litho Questa)

1979 (15 Feb). *Centenary of Catholic Church in Uganda. T* **30** *and similar horiz designs. Multicoloured. P* 14.

239	1 s. Type **30**		10	10
240	1 s. 50, Lubaga Cathedral		10	10
241	2 s. 70, Ugandan pilgrimage to Rome, Holy Year, 1975		15	25
242	10 s. Friar Lourdel-Mapeera (early missionary)		50	80
239/42		*Set of 4*	75	1·10
MS243	128 × 91 mm. Nos. 239/42		1·00	2·00

31 Immunisation of Children

(Des J.W. Litho Questa)

1979 (28 June). *International Year of the Child. T* **31** *and similar horiz designs. Multicoloured. P* 14.

244	1 s. Type **31**		10	10
245	1 s. 50, Handicapped children at play		15	20
246	2 s. 70, Ugandan I.Y.C. emblem		20	35
247	10 s. Children in class		60	90
244/7		*Set of 4*	85	1·40
MS248	136 × 113 mm. Nos. 244/7		1·10	2·00

UGANDA LIBERATED 1979	UGANDA LIBERATED 1979	UGANDA LIBERATED 1979
(32)	(33)	(34)

1979 (12 July–16 Aug?). *Liberation.*

(*a*) *Nos.* 149/55 *optd with T* **32** *and* 156/62 *with T* **33** (12 July)

249	10 c. black, apple-green and yellow-brown		10	10
250	20 c. multicoloured		10	10
251	30 c. multicoloured		10	10
252	40 c. multicoloured		10	10
253	50 c. multicoloured		10	10
254	70 c. black, apple-green and light blue-green		10	10
255	80 c. multicoloured		10	10
	a. Opt double		£110	
256	1 s. multicoloured		15	15
257	2 s. multicoloured		20	25
258	3 s. multicoloured		35	40
259	5 s. multicoloured		55	60
260	10 s. multicoloured		80	1·25
261	20 s. apple-green, black and bright purple		1·50	2·40
262	40 s. apple-green, black and yellow-orange		3·00	4·75
	a. Opt double		£130	

(*b*) *Nos.* 210/13 (*Commonwealth Games*) *optd with T* **34** (1 Aug)

263	50 c. Type **26**		10	10
264	1 s. Long jumping		15	20
265	2 s. Running		25	30
266	5 s. Boxing		60	65

(*c*) *Nos.* 207, 215 *and* 217/18 (*World Cup Football Championships*) *optd with T* **34** (1 Aug)

267	50 c. Polly Ouma and forwards		10	10
268	2 s. Omari Kidevu and goal-mouth scene		20	30
	a. Optd on No. 216		8·00	17·00
269	5 s. Joe Kadenge and forwards		55	65
270	10 s. Mohamed Chuma and cup presentation		1·00	1·40

(*d*) *Nos.* 220/3 *optd with T* **33** (1979)

271	5 s. multicoloured		55	60
272	10 s. multicoloured		80	1·25
273	20 s. multicoloured		80	2·40
274	40 s. multicoloured		1·00	4·75

(*e*) *Nos.* 229/32 (*75th Anniv of Powered Flight*) *optd with T* **34** (1 Aug)

275	1 s. Type **28**		35	20
276	1 s. 50, "Domestic services" (passengers boarding Britten Norman Islander light aircraft)		45	25
277	2 s. 70, Export of Uganda coffee		55	55
278	10 s. "Time machines in the air" (Wright Flyer III and Concorde)		2·50	2·00

(*f*) *Nos.* 234/7 (*25th Anniv of Coronation*) *optd as T* **33** *or surch also and No.* **MS**238 *additionally inscr* "Diplomatic Relations Normalised" *with Ugandan and British flags replacing portrait of Amin* (12 July)

279	1 s. Type **29**		10	20
280	1 s. 50, Regalia		15	20
281	2 s. 70, Coronation ceremony		20	30
282	15 s. on 10 s. Royal family on balcony of Buckingham Palace		85	1·50
MS283	150×102 mm. Nos. 234/6 and 15 s. as No. 237*		1·50	3·25

* The sheet contains unoverprinted stamps; the additional inscriptions and changes in design appear only on the sheet margin.

(*g*) *Nos.* 239/42 (*Centenary of Catholic Church in Uganda*) *optd with T* **34** *and No.* **MS**243 *with additional inscr* "FREEDOM OF WORSHIP DECLARED" *replacing part of the margin decoration* (1 Aug)

284	1 s. Type **30**		10	20
285	1 s. 50, Lubaga Cathedral		15	25
286	2 s. 70, Ugandan pilgrimage to Rome, Holy Year, 1975		30	45
287	10 s. Friar Lourdel-Mapeera (early missionary)		90	1·60
MS288	128×91 mm. Nos. 239/42*. P 12½×12 (1979)		1·75	2·75

* The sheet contains the original unoverprinted stamps; the additional inscription appears on the sheet margin.

(*h*) *Nos.* 244/8 (*International Year of the Child*) *optd with T* **34** (16 Aug)

289	1 s. Type **31**		15	20
290	1 s. 50, Handicapped children at play		20	25
291	2 s. 70, Ugandan I.Y.C. emblem		40	45
292	10 s. Children in class		1·25	1·40
MS293	136×113 mm. Nos. 289/92		2·00	3·25
249/82, 284/7 and 289/92		*Set of 42*	20·00	29·00

MINIMUM PRICE

The minimum price quote is 10p which represents a handling charge rather than a basis for valuing common stamps. For further notes about prices see introductory pages.

---

35 Radio Wave Symbol

(Des G. Vasarhelyi. Litho Questa)

1979 (11 Sept). *50th Anniv of International Consultative Radio Committee and International Telecommunications Union. P* 14.

294	**35** 1 s. multicoloured		10	10
295	1 s. 50, multicoloured		15	10
296	2 s. 70, multicoloured		20	35
297	10 s. multicoloured		60	1·10
294/7		*Set of 4*	90	1·50

36 20s. Definitive Stamp of 1965 and Sir Rowland Hill

(Des BG Studio. Litho Questa)

1979 (Oct). *Death Centenary of Sir Rowland Hill. T* **36** *and similar horiz designs showing stamps and Sir Rowland Hill. Multicoloured. P* 14.

298	1 s. Type **36**		10	10
299	1 s. 50, 1967 13th Commonwealth Parliamentary Association Conference 50 c. commemorative		15	10
300	2 s. 70, 1962 Independence 20 s. commemorative		20	30
301	10 s. Uganda Protectorate 1898 1 a.		60	1·25
298/301		*Set of 4*	85	1·40
MS302	154×98 mm. Nos. 298/301		90	1·50

37 Impala   **38** Lions with Cub

(Des G. Drummond. Litho Questa)

1979 (3 Dec)–**82**. *Wildlife. Horiz designs as T* **37** (10 to 80 c.) *or T* **38** (1 to 40 s.). *Multicoloured. P* 14×13½ (10 to 80 c.) *or* 14 (1 to 40 s). A. *Without imprint date*

303A	10 c. Type **37**		10	20
304A	20 c. Large-spotted Genet		10	20
305A	30 c. Thomson's Gazelle		15	20
306A	50 c. Lesser Bushbaby		15	10
307A	50 c. Hunting Dog		20	10
308A	1 s. Type **38**		30	10
309A	1 s. 50, Gorilla		50	10
310A	2 s. Common Zebra		50	20
311A	2 s. 70, Leopard with cub		50	20
312A	3 s. 50, Black Rhinoceros		50	55
313A	5 s. Waterbuck		50	55
314A	10 s. African Buffalo		50	1·00
315A	20 s. Hippopotamus		80	2·00
316A	40 s. African Elephant		1·40	3·50
303A/16A		*Set of 14*	5·50	8·00

B. *With imprint date* ("1982") *at foot of design* (1982)

308B	1 s. Type **38**		20	10
310B	2 s. Common Zebra		30	20
313B	5 s. Waterbuck		40	85
308B/13B		*Set of 3*	80	1·00

For designs as Nos. 308/12 and 315/16, but with face values in revalued currency, see Nos. 433/9.

LONDON 1980

(39)   **40** Rotary Emblem

1980 (6 May). *"London 1980" International Stamp Exhibition. Nos.* 298/302 *optd as T* **39**.

317	1 s. Type **36**		15	10
318	1 s. 50, 1967 13th Commonwealth Parliamentary Association Conference 50 c. commemorative		20	10
319	2 s. 70, 1962 Independence 20s. commemorative		35	25
320	10 s. Uganda Protectorate 1898 1a.		80	80
317/20		*Set of 4*	1·40	1·25
MS321	154×99 mm. Nos. 317/20		1·40	1·75

(Des BG Studio. Litho Questa)

1980 (25 Aug). *75th Anniv of Rotary International. T* **40** *and similar multicoloured design. P* 14.

322	1 s. Type **40**		10	10
323	20 s. Paul Harris (founder) with wheel-barrow containing "Rotary projects" (*horiz*)		1·50	2·00
MS324	100 × 76 mm. Nos. 322/3. Imperf.		1·75	2·50

FOOTBALL
GOLD MEDALISTS, C.S.S.R.

41 Football   (**42**)

(Des G. Vasarhelyi. Litho Questa)

1980 (29 Dec). *Olympic Games, Moscow. T* **41** *and similar horiz designs. Multicoloured. P* 14.

325	1 s. Type **41**		10	10
326	2 s. Relay		10	10
327	10 s. Hurdles		45	75
328	20 s. Boxing		75	2·00
325/8		*Set of* 4	1·25	2·50
MS329	118 × 90 mm. 2 s. 70, 3 s., 5 s., 25 s. As Nos. 325/8		1·25	2·25

1980 (29 Dec). *Olympic Games, Moscow. Medal Winners. Nos. 325/9 optd as T* **42**.

330	1 s. Type **41**		10	10
331	2 s. Relay		10	15
332	10 s. Hurdles		35	60
333	20 s. Boxing		60	1·25
330/3		*Set of* 4	1·00	1·75
MS334	118 × 90 mm. 2 s. 70, 3 s., 5 s., 25 s. As Nos. 330/3		1·00	2·50

Overprints:—2s. "RELAY GOLD MEDALIST U.S.S.R."; 10s. "HURDLES 110 m. GOLD MEDALIST THOMAS MUNKLET, D.D.R."; 20s. "BOXING WELTERWEIGHT SILVER MEDALIST JOHN MUGABI, UGANDA".

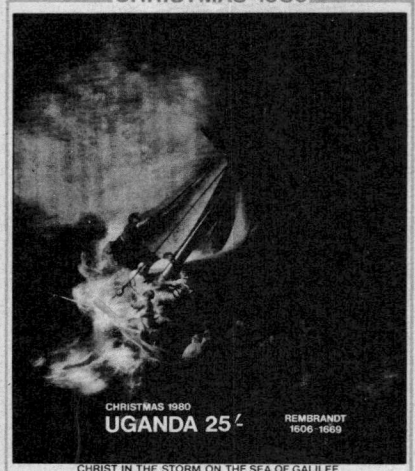

CHRISTMAS 1980

43 "Christ in the Storm on the Sea of Galilee" (painting, Rembrandt)

1980 (31 Dec). *Christmas. Sheet* 79 × 101 *mm. Litho. Imperf.*

MS335	**43** 25 s. multicoloured		4·25	4·75

44 Heinrich von Stephan and U.P.U. Emblem   **45** Tower of London

(Des BG Studio. Litho Questa)

1981 (2 June). *150th Birth Anniv of Heinrich von Stephan (founder of U.P.U.). T* **44** *and similar horiz designs. Multicoloured. P* 14.

336	1 s. Type **44**		10	10
337	2 s. U.P.U. Headquarters		15	15
338	2 s. 70, Air mail, 1935		40	20
339	10 s. Mail transport by train, 1927		1·10	80
336/9		*Set of* 4	1·60	1·10
MS340	112 × 95 mm. Nos. 336/9		2·25	1·90

(**46**)   (**47**)

(Des J.W. Litho Questa)

1981 (July). *Royal Wedding. T* **45** *and similar vert designs. Multicoloured. P* 14. (*a*) *Unissued stamps surch as T* **46** (13 July).

341	10 s. on 1 s. Prince Charles and Lady Diana Spencer		20	50
	a. Surch on 5 s. value		20·00	
	b. Surch on 20 s. value		19·00	
	c. Surch omitted		50·00	
	d. Surch inverted			
	e. Surch as Type **47**		15	20
342	50 s. on 5 s. Type **45**		30	70
	a. Surch omitted		30·00	
	e. Surch as Type **47**		20	30
343	200 s. on 20 s. Prince Charles at Balmoral		60	2·00
	a. Surch omitted		75·00	
	b. Surch inverted		22·00	
	c. Surch inverted on 1 s. value		22·00	
	d. Surch inverted on 5 s. value		22·00	
	e. Surch as Type **47**		45	80
341/3		*Set of* 3	1·00	2·75
341e/3e		*Set of* 3	70	1·10
MS344	95 × 80 mm. 250 s. on 25 s. Royal Mews		3·00	5·50
	a. Surch omitted			
	e. Surch as Type **47**		1·00	1·00

(*b*) *Redrawn with new face values. Background colours changed* (29 July)

345	10 s. As No. 341		10	15
346	50 s. Type **45**		15	20
347	200 s. As No. 343		30	40
345/7		*Set of* 3	40	65
MS348	95 × 80 mm. 250 s. As No. MS344		50	65

Nos. 345/7 also exist perforated 12 (*price for set of 3 40p mint or used*) from additional sheetlets of 5 stamps and one label. These stamps have changed background colours.

The issue was originally printed with face values of 1, 5 and 20 s. and 25 s. for the miniature sheet. Before it could be placed on sale the Uganda currency was devalued and the stamps were surcharged, and later reprinted with corrected face values.

48 "Sleeping Woman before Green Shutters"

(Des J.W. Litho Questa)

1981 (21 Sept). *Birth Centenary of Picasso. T* **48** *and similar multicoloured designs. P* 14 × 13½.

349	10 s. Type **48**		10	10
350	20 s. "Bullfight"		20	20
351	30 s. "Detail of a Nude asleep in a Landscape"		25	30
352	200 s. "Interior with a Girl Drawing"		2·25	3·25
349/52		*Set of* 4	2·50	3·50
MS353	120 × 146 mm. 250 s. "Minotaure" (112 × 139 *mm*). Imperf		3·50	4·00

49 Deaf People using Sign Language

(Des Design Images. Litho Format)

1981 (28 Dec). *International Year of Disabled Persons. T* **49** *and similar horiz designs. Multicoloured. P* 15.

354	1 s. Type **49**		10	10
355	10 s. Disabled teacher in classroom		15	10
356	50 s. Teacher and disabled children		70	50
357	200 s. Blind person with guide dog		1·40	2·00
354/7		*Set of* 4	2·00	2·25
MS358	122 × 93 mm. Nos. 354/7		3·00	4·00

50 Footballers

(Des G. Vasarhelyi. Litho Questa)

1982 (11 Jan). *World Cup Football Championship, Spain. T* **50** *and similar horiz designs showing World Cup (250 s.) or footballers (others). P* 14.

359	1 s. multicoloured		10	10
360	10 s. multicoloured		15	10
361	50 s. multicoloured		70	50
362	200 s. multicoloured		2·00	2·00
359/62		*Set of* 4	2·50	2·25
MS363	116 × 77 mm. 250 s. multicoloured		3·00	3·00

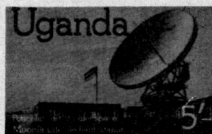

51 Mpoma Satellite Earth Station

(Des Artists International. Litho Format)

1982 (10 May). *"Peaceful Use of Outer Space". T* **51** *and similar horiz designs. Multicoloured. P* 15.

364	5 s. Type **51**		25	15
365	10 s. *Pioneer II* (satellite)		35	35
366	50 s. Space Shuttle		1·50	2·00
367	100 s. *Voyager 2* (satellite)		2·00	4·00
364/7		*Set of* 4	3·50	6·00
MS368	118 × 89 mm. 150 s. Space Shuttle (*different*)		3·75	2·00

No. 364 exists imperforate from stock dispersed by the liquidator of Format International Security Printers Ltd.

52 Dr. Robert Koch   (**53**)

(Des R. Vigurs. Litho Questa)

1982 (14 June). *Centenary of Robert Koch's Discovery of Tubercle Bacillus. T* **52** *and similar multicoloured designs. P* 14.

369	1 s. Type **52**		30	10
370	10 s. Microscope		1·25	40
371	50 s. Ugandans receiving vaccinations		3·00	2·50
372	100 s. Tubercle virus		4·50	4·25
369/72		*Set of* 4	8·00	6·50
MS373	85 × 64 mm. 150 s. Medical College classroom scene (*horiz*).		4·50	2·00

1982 (7 July). *21st Birthday of Princess of Wales. Nos. 345/8 optd with T* **53**. *P* 14.

374	10 s. Prince Charles and Lady Diana Spencer		20	10
375	50 s. Type **45**		50	40
376	200 s. Prince Charles at Balmoral		1·50	1·25
374/6		*Set of* 3	2·00	1·50
MS377	95 × 82 mm. 250 s. Royal Mews		2·00	2·00

Nos. 374/6 also exist perforated 12 (*price for set of 3 £1·25 mint or used*) from additional sheetlets of 5 stamps and one label. These stamps have changed background colours.

Nos. 374/7, and the sheetlets, also exist with the top line of the overprint shown as "21st Birthday" instead of "21st BIRTHDAY" as in Type **53** (*Price for set of 3 and miniature sheet £4 mint*).

Examples of an unissued miniature sheet for the 20th Anniversary of Independence, containing a single 150 s. stamp showing the State Arms, exist from stock dispersed by the liquidator of Format International Security Printers Ltd.

54 Yellow-billed Hornbill   **55** Scout Band

(Des Artists International. Litho Questa)

1982 (12 July). *Birds. T* **54** *and similar vert designs. Multicoloured. P* 14.

378	1 s. Type **54**		15	10
379	20 s. Superb Starling		60	35
380	50 s. Bateleur		1·25	1·75
381	100 s. Saddle-bill Stork		2·00	2·50
378/81		*Set of* 4	3·50	4·25
MS382	115 × 85 mm. 200 s. Laughing Dove		9·00	9·00

(Des G. Vasarhelyi. Litho Questa)

1982 (23 Aug). *75th Anniv of Boy Scout Movement. T* **55** *and similar horiz designs. Multicoloured. P* 14.

383	5 s. Type **55**		40	10
384	20 s. Scout receiving Bata Shoe trophy		1·10	45
385	50 s. Scouts with wheelchair patient		2·25	2·25
386	100 s. First aid instruction		3·00	3·50
383/6		*Set of* 4	6·00	5·75
MS387	112 × 85 mm. 150 s. Lord Baden-Powell		4·00	3·00

NEW INFORMATION

The editor is always interested to correspond with people who have new information that will improve or correct the Catalogue.

56 Swearing-in of Roosevelt

(Des Design Images. Litho Format)

1982 (8 Nov). *250th Birth Anniv of George Washington (Nos. 389/90) and Birth Centenary of Franklin D. Roosevelt (others). T 56 and similar horiz designs. Multicoloured. P 15.*
388	50 s. Type 56	30	30
389	200 s. Swearing-in of Washington	75	1·25
MS390	100×69 mm. 150 s. Washington at Mt Vernon	1·00	1·25
MS391	100×70 mm. 150 s. Roosevelt at Hyde Park Mansion	1·00	1·25

Nos. 388/91 exist imperforate from stock dispersed by the liquidator of Format International Security Printers Ltd.

57 Italy v West Germany

(Des D. Miller. Litho Format)

1982 (30 Dec). *World Cup Football Championship Winners. T 57 and similar horiz designs. Multicoloured. P 14½.*
392	10 s. Type 57	30	25
393	200 s. Victorious Italian team	1·50	3·50
MS394	97×117 mm. 250 s. Espana '82 emblem with Spanish and Italian flags	1·50	2·00

Nos. 392/4 exist imperforate from stock dispersed by the liquidator of Format International Security Printers Ltd.

58 Dancers **59** "St. George and the Dragon" (Raphael)

(Des and litho Questa)

1983 (14 Mar). *Commonwealth Day. Cultural Art. T 58 and similar horiz designs. Multicoloured. P 14.*
395	5 s. Type 58	10	10
396	20 s. Traditional currency	15	20
397	50 s. Homestead	35	55
398	100 s. Drums	70	1·10
395/8	Set of 4	1·10	1·75

(Des Design Images. Litho Questa)

1983 (16 Apr). *500th Birth Anniv of Raphael (painter). T 59 and similar vert designs. Multicoloured. P 13½.*
399	5 s. Type 59	10	10
400	20 s. "St. George and the Dragon" (different)	30	20
401	50 s. "Crossing the Red Sea" (detail)	60	60
402	200 s. "The Expulsion of Heliodorus" (detail)	1·25	3·00
399/402	Set of 4	2·00	3·50
MS403	126×101 mm. 250 s. "The Meeting of Pope Leo the Great and Attila the Hun" (detail)	1·40	1·40

60 Map showing Namibia and U.N. Flag

(Des R. Vigurs. Litho Format)

1983 (15 Aug). *Commemorations. T 60 and similar horiz design. Multicoloured. P 15.*
404	5 s. Type 60	10	10
405	200 s. 7th Non-aligned Summit Conference logo	80	2·50

Nos. 404/5 exist imperforate from stock dispersed by the liquidator of Format International Security Printers Ltd.

61 Elephants in Grassland **(62)**

(Des J. Iskowitz. Litho Format)

1983 (22 Aug). *Endangered Species (1st series). T 61 and similar multicoloured designs. P 15.*
406	5 s. Elephants in "Elephants' Graveyard"	1·50	50
407	10 s. Type 61	1·75	50
408	30 s. Elephants at waterhole	3·75	2·50
409	70 s. Elephants having dust bath	6·00	7·00
406/9	Set of 4	11·50	9·50
MS410	87×64 mm. 300 s. Grevy's Zebra drinking (vert)	6·00	3·25

Nos. 406/9 also exist perforated 14, but have only been seen mint or used on first day covers. There is some evidence that such stamps were produced around 1990.
No. MS410 exists imperforate from stock dispersed by the liquidator of Format International Security Printers Ltd.
See also No. 642 for the 10 s. redrawn and Nos. 988/92 for these designs with different face values.

1983 (19 Sept). *Centenary of Boys' Brigade. Nos. 383/7 optd with T 62 or surch also.*
411	5 s. Type 55	10	10
412	20 s. Scout receiving Bata Shoe trophy	15	15
413	50 s. Scouts with wheelchair patient	25	30
414	400 s. on 100 s. First aid instruction	2·40	2·75
411/14	Set of 4	2·50	3·00
MS415	112×85 mm. 150 s. Lord Baden-Powell	90	1·25

63 Mpoma Satellite Earth Station **(64)**

(Des D. Dorfman. Litho Format)

1983 (3 Oct). *World Communications Year. T 63 and similar horiz designs. Multicoloured. P 15.*
416	20 s. Type 63	25	15
417	50 s. Railroad computer and operator	55	85
418	70 s. Cameraman filming lions	60	1·50
419	100 s. Aircraft cockpit	70	2·00
416/19	Set of 4	1·90	4·00
MS420	128×103 mm. 300 s. Communications satellite	1·00	1·75

No. 416 has the "o" omitted from "Station".

1983 (7 Oct). *Nos. 303, 305/7, 308A, 309 and 313A surch as T 64.*
421	100 s. on 10 c. Type 37	75	60
422	135 s. on 1 s. Type 38	90	80
423	175 s. on 30 c. Thomson's Gazelle	1·10	1·25
424	200 s. on 50 c. Lesser Bushbaby	1·25	1·40
425	400 s. on 80 c. Hunting Dog	2·25	2·75
426	700 s. on 5 s. Waterbuck	3·50	5·00
427	1000 s. on 1 s. 50, Gorilla	6·00	8·50
421/7	Set of 7	14·00	18·00

65 The Nativity

(Des PAD Studio. Litho Questa)

1983 (12 Dec). *Christmas. T 65 and similar horiz designs. Multicoloured. P 14.*
428	10 s. Type 65	10	10
429	50 s. Shepherds and Angels	25	30
430	175 s. Flight into Egypt	70	1·25
431	400 s. Angels blowing trumpets	1·25	2·75
428/31	Set of 4	2·00	4·00
MS432	85×57 mm. 300 s. The Three Kings	1·40	1·75

1983 (19 Dec). *Designs as Nos. 308/12 and 315/16 but with face values in revalued currency. Without imprint date.*
433	100 s. Type 38	90	35
434	135 s. Gorilla	1·25	50
435	175 s. Common Zebra	1·40	80
436	200 s. Leopard with cub	1·75	90
437	400 s. Black Rhinoceros	3·00	3·25
438	700 s. African Elephant	6·00	6·50
439	1000 s. Hippopotamus	5·50	7·50
433/9	Set of 7	17·00	18·00

66 Ploughing with Oxen

(Des J.W. Litho Questa)

1984 (16 Jan). *World Food Day. T 66 and similar horiz design. Multicoloured. P 14.*
440	10 s. Type 66	15	10
441	300 s. Harvesting bananas	4·25	5·50

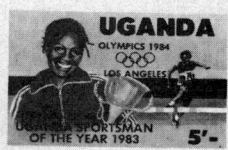

67 Ruth Kyalisiima, Sportsman of the Year 1983

(Des J. Iskowitz. Litho Format)

1984 (1 Oct). *Olympic Games, Los Angeles. T 67 and similar designs. P 15.*
442	5 s. Type 67	10	10
443	115 s. Javelin-throwing	65	90
444	155 s. Wrestling	70	1·25
445	175 s. Rowing	70	1·25
442/5	Set of 4	1·90	3·00
MS446	108×79 mm. 500 s. Fund-raising walk (vert)	90	1·25

68 Entebbe Airport

(Des BG Studio. Litho Format)

1984 (29 Oct). *40th Anniv of International Civil Aviation Organization. T 68 and similar horiz designs. Multicoloured. P 15.*
447	5 s. Type 68	15	10
448	115 s. Loading cargo plane	1·50	1·75
449	155 s. Uganda police helicopter	2·50	2·75
450	175 s. East African Civil Flying School, Soroti	2·75	3·25
447/50	Set of 4	6·25	7·00
MS451	100×70 mm. 250 s. Balloon race	2·00	1·75

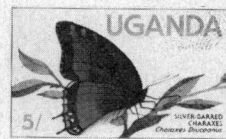

69 *Charaxes druceanus*

(Des J. Johnson. Litho Questa)

1984 (19 Nov). *Butterflies. T 69 and similar horiz designs. Multicoloured. P 14.*
452	5 s. Type 69	30	10
453	115 s. Papilio lormieri	2·50	2·00
454	155 s. Druryia antimachus	3·00	2·50
455	175 s. Salamis temora	4·25	3·25
452/5	Set of 4	9·00	7·00
MS456	127×90 mm. 250 s. Colotis protomedia	3·00	2·50

70 Blue-finned Notho

(Des Associated Creative Designers. Litho Format)

1985 (1 Apr–10 June). *Lake Fishes. T 70 and similar horiz designs. Multicoloured. P 15.*
457	5 s. Type 70	30	40
458	10 s. Semutundu	40	40
459	50 s. Grey Bichir	75	30
460	100 s. Walking Catfish	85	30
461	135 s. Elephant-snout Fish (10 June)	1·25	1·00
462	175 s. Lake Victoria Squeaker	1·25	1·60
463	205 s. Brown's Haplochromis	1·25	2·00
464	400 s. Nile Perch	1·25	2·25
465	700 s. African Lungfish	1·25	2·75
466	1000 s. Radcliffe's Barb	1·25	3·00
467	2500 s. Electric Catfish (10 June)	1·50	3·75
457/67	Set of 11	10·00	16·00

Nos. 459/67 exist imperforate from stock dispersed by the liquidator of Format International Security Printers Ltd.

71 The Last Supper

(Des Associated Creative Designers. Litho Questa)

1985 (13 May). *Easter. T* **71** *and similar horiz designs. Multicoloured. P* 14.

468	5 s. Type **71**		10	10
469	115 s. Christ showing the nail marks to Thomas		1·25	1·25
470	155 s. The raising of the Cross		1·40	2·00
471	175 s. Pentecost		1·75	2·50
468/71		*Set of 4*	4·00	5·25
MS472	99×70 mm. 250 s. The last prayer in the Garden		80	1·25

72 Breast Feeding

73 Queen Elizabeth the Queen Mother

(Des Associated Creative Designers. Litho Questa)

1985 (29 July). *U.N.I.C.E.F. Child Survival Campaign. T* **72** *and similar horiz designs. Multicoloured. P* 14.

473	5 s. Type **72**		10	10
474	115 s. Growth monitoring		1·75	1·75
475	155 s. Immunisation		2·25	2·25
476	175 s. Oral re-hydration therapy		2·50	2·50
473/6		*Set of 4*	6·00	6·00
MS477	75×55 mm. 500 s. Pregnant woman preparing nourishing food		4·25	5·00

(Des J.W. Litho Questa)

1985 (21 Aug). *Life and Times of Queen Elizabeth the Queen Mother and Decade for Women. T* **73** *and similar vert design. Multicoloured. P* 14.

478	1000 s. Type **73**		1·40	2·10
MS479	57×81 mm. 1500 s. The Queen Mother inspecting Kings African Rifles, Kampala		2·25	3·50

74 Sedge Warbler

GOLD MEDALIST BENITA BROWN-FITZGERALD USA

(75)

(Des S. Heinmann. Litho Questa)

1985 (21 Aug). *Birth Bicentenary of John J. Audubon (ornithologist) (1st issue). T* **74** *and similar vert designs. Multicoloured. P* 14.

480	115 s. Type **74**		2·00	1·50
481	155 s. Cattle Egret		2·25	1·75
482	175 s. Crested Lark		2·50	2·25
483	500 s. Tufted Duck		3·25	4·50
480/3		*Set of 4*	9·00	9·00
MS484	99×69 mm. 1000 s. Tawny Owl		11·00	10·00

See also Nos. 494/8.

1985 (21 Aug). *Olympic Gold Medal Winners, Los Angeles. Nos.* 442/6 *optd or surch as T* **75** *in gold.*

485	5 s. Type 67 (optd T **75**)		10	10
486	115 s. Javelin-throwing (optd "GOLD MEDALIST ARTO HAERKOENEN FINLAND")		50	30
487	155 s. Wrestling (optd "GOLD MEDALIST ATSUJI MIYAHARA JAPAN")		60	40
488	1000 s. on 175 s. Rowing (surch "GOLD MEDALIST WEST GERMANY")		2·25	2·00
485/8		*Set of 4*	3·00	2·50
MS489	108×79 mm. 1200 s. on 500 s. Fund-raising walk (surch "MEN'S HURDLES EDWIN MOSES USA")		2·25	2·50

On No. MS489 only the new value appears on the stamp, the remainder of the surcharge is on the sheet margin.

76 Women carrying National Women's Day Banner

77 Man beneath Tree laden with Produce (F.A.O.)

(Des and litho Questa)

1985 (1 Nov). *Decade for Women. T* **76** *and similar multicoloured designs. P* 14.

490	5 s. Type **76**		10	10
491	115 s. Girl Guides (*horiz*)		1·75	2·00
492	155 s. Mother Teresa (Nobel Peace Prize winner, 1979)		3·00	3·25
490/2		*Set of 3*	4·25	4·75
MS493	85×59 mm. 1500 s. As 115 s.		4·00	4·00

Nos. 491 and MS493 also commemorate the 75th anniversary of the Girl Guide movement.

(Litho Questa)

1985 (23 Dec). *Birth Bicentenary of John J. Audubon (ornithologist) (2nd issue). Multicoloured designs as T* **201** *of Maldive Islands, but horiz, showing original paintings. P* 12.

494	5 s. Rock Ptarmigan		1·75	1·75
495	155 s. Sage Grouse		2·00	1·75
496	175 s. Lesser Yellowlegs		2·00	2·50
497	175 s. Brown-headed Cowbird		3·25	4·50
494/7		*Set of 4*	7·00	8·00
MS498	72×102 mm. 1000 s. Whooping Crane. P 14		9·50	9·50

Nos. 494/7 were each printed in sheetlets of 5 stamps and one stamp-size label which appears in the centre of the bottom row.

(Des BG Studio. Litho Format)

1986 (1 Apr). *40th Anniv of United Nations Organization. T* **77** *and similar designs. P* 15.

499	10 s. multicoloured		10	10
500	180 s. multicoloured		40	30
501	200 s. new blue, agate and bright green		40	35
502	250 s. new blue, brownish blk & scar-verm		40	40
503	2000 s. multicoloured		1·25	5·00
499/503		*Set of 5*	2·25	5·50
MS504	69×69 mm. 2500 s. multicoloured		1·75	2·75

Designs: *Horiz*—180 s. Soldier of U.N. Peace-Keeping Force; 250 s. Hands releasing peace dove. *Vert*—200 s. U.N. emblem; 2000 s. Flags of U.N. and Uganda; 2500 s. U.N. Building, New York, and flags of member nations.

78 Goalkeeper catching Ball

NRA LIBERATION 1986

(79)

(Des Shelley Haas. Litho Questa)

1986 (17 Apr). *World Cup Football Championship, Mexico. T* **78** *and similar multicoloured designs. P* 14.

505	10 s. Type **78**		10	10
506	180 s. Player with ball		85	55
507	250 s. Two players competing for ball		1·00	65
508	2500 s. Player running with ball		5·50	6·00
505/8		*Set of 4*	6·75	6·50
MS509	87×66 mm. 3000 s. Player kicking ball (*vert*)		4·75	3·50

1986 (30 Apr). *Liberation by National Resistance Army. Nos.* 462, 464/7 *and* MS493 *optd with T* **79** *or larger (22×8 mm) (No.* MS493).

510	175 s. Lake Victoria Squeaker (Sil.)		70	70
511	400 s. Nile Perch		1·25	1·25
512	700 s. African Lungfish (Sil.)		1·75	2·50
513	1000 s. Radcliffe's Barb		2·00	3·00
514	2500 s. Electric Catfish		3·00	6·00
510/14		*Set of 5*	8·00	12·00
MS514a	85×59 mm. 1500 s. Girl Guides		4·00	2·50

Nos. 510/14 also exist with the overprint colours transposed.

(Des W. Hanson. Litho Questa)

1986 (30 Apr). *Appearance of Halley's Comet (1st issue). Horiz designs as T* **162a** *of Lesotho. Multicoloured. P* 14.

515	50 s. Tycho Brahe and Arecibo Radio Telescope, Puerto Rico		20	10
516	100 s. Recovery of astronaut John Glenn from sea, 1962		35	15
517	140 s. "The Star in the East" (painting by Giotto)		50	30
518	2500 s. Death of Davy Crockett at the Alamo, 1835		3·75	6·00
515/18		*Set of 4*	4·25	6·00
MS519	102×70 mm. 3000 s. Halley's Comet over Uganda		5·50	4·00

See also Nos. 544/8.

80 Niagara Falls

81 *Glo*: (Colombia)

(Des Mary Walters. Litho Format)

1986 (22 May). *"Ameripex '86" International Stamp Exhibition, Chicago. American Landmarks. T* **80** *and similar horiz designs. Multicoloured. P* 15.

520	50 s. Type **80**		15	10
521	100 s. Jefferson Memorial, Washington D.C.		25	15
522	250 s. Liberty Bell, Philadelphia		50	35
523	1000 s. The Alamo, San Antonio, Texas		1·50	2·25
524	2500 s. George Washington Bridge, New York–New Jersey		2·25	5·00
520/4		*Set of 5*	4·25	7·00
MS525	87×64 mm. 3000 s. Grand Canyon		2·00	3·25

Nos. 520/4 exist imperforate from stock dispersed by the liquidator of Format International Security Printers Ltd.

(Litho Questa)

1986 (24 May). *60th Birthday of Queen Elizabeth II. Vert designs as T* **163a** *of Lesotho. P* 14.

526	100 s. black and yellow		50	15
527	140 s. multicoloured		50	20
528	2500 s. multicoloured		3·25	4·25
526/8		*Set of 3*	3·75	4·25
MS529	120×85 mm. 3000 s. black & grey-brown		3·25	4·00

Designs:—100 s. Princess Elizabeth at London Zoo; 140 s. Queen Elizabeth at race meeting, 1970; 2500 s. With Prince Philip at Sandringham, 1982; 3000 s. Engagement photograph, 1947.

(Des J. Iskowitz. Litho Questa)

1986 (2 July). *Centenary of Statue of Liberty. T* **81** *and similar multicoloured designs showing cadet sailing ships. P* 14.

530	50 s. Type **81**		60	20
531	100 s. *Mircea* (Rumania)		95	30
532	140 s. *Sagres II* (Portugal) (*horiz*)		1·60	1·00
533	2500 s. *Gazela Primiero* (U.S.A.) (*horiz*)		7·00	10·50
530/3		*Set of 4*	9·00	10·50
MS534	113×82 mm. 3000 s. Statue of Liberty		3·25	3·50

No. 533 is inscribed "Primero" in error.

(Des and litho Questa)

1986 (23 July). *Royal Wedding. Multicoloured designs as T* **170a** *of Lesotho. P* 14.

535	50 s. Prince Andrew and Miss Sarah Ferguson (*horiz*)		10	10
536	140 s. Prince Andrew with Princess Anne at shooting match (*horiz*)		20	20
537	2500 s. Prince Andrew and Miss Sarah Ferguson at Ascot (*horiz*)		2·75	3·75
535/7		*Set of 3*	2·75	3·75
MS538	88×88 mm. 3000 s. Prince Andrew and Miss Sarah Ferguson (*different*)		3·00	3·25

WINNERS

Argentina 3 W.Germany 2

(82)

1986 (15 Sept). *World Cup Football Championship Winners, Mexico. Nos.* 505/9 *optd as T* **82**, *or surch also, in gold.*

539	50 s. on 10 s. Type **78**		10	10
540	180 s. Player with ball		25	25
541	250 s. Two players competing for ball		35	35
542	2500 s. Player running with ball		2·75	4·00
539/42		*Set of 4*	3·00	4·25
MS543	87×66 mm. 3000 s. Player kicking ball (*vert*)		4·50	3·25

1986 (15 Oct). *Appearance of Halley's Comet (2nd issue). Nos.* 515/19 *optd with T* **213b** *of Maldive Islands (in silver on* 3000 *s.).*

544	50 s. Tycho Brahe and Arecibo Radio Telescope, Puerto Rico		20	15
545	100 s. Recovery of astronaut John Glenn from sea, 1962		35	20
546	140 s. "The Star in the East" (painting by Giotto)		55	40
547	2500 s. Death of Davy Crockett at the Alamo, 1835		5·50	7·50
544/7		*Set of 4*	6·00	7·50
MS548	102×70 mm. 3000 s. Halley's Comet over Uganda		4·00	4·00

83 St. Kizito

(Des Associated Creative Designers. Litho Questa)

1986 (15 Oct). *Christian Martyrs of Uganda. T* **83** *and similar horiz designs. Multicoloured. P* 14.

549	50 s. Type **83**		10	10
550	150 s. St. Kizito instructing converts		25	20
551	200 s. Martyrdom of Bishop James Hannington, 1885.		30	30
552	1000 s. Burning of Bugandan Christians, 1886		1·50	2·75
549/52		*Set of 4*	1·90	3·00
MS553	89×59 mm. 1500 s. King Mwanga of Buganda passing sentence on Christians		1·50	2·25

NEW INFORMATION

The editor is always interested to correspond with people who have new information that will improve or correct the Catalogue.

84 "Madonna of the Cherries" (Titian)

(Litho Questa)

1986 (26 Nov). *Christmas. Religious Paintings. T **84** and similar multicoloured designs. P* 14.

554	50 s. Type **84**	25	15
555	150 s. "Madonna and Child" (Dürer) (*vert*)..	60	30
556	200 s. "Assumption of the Virgin" (Titian) (*vert*)	70	40
557	2500 s. "Praying Hands" (Dürer) (*vert*)	5·50	8·00
554/7	*Set of 4*	6·25	8·00

MS558 Two sheets, each 102×76 mm. (a) 3000 s. "Presentation of the Virgin in the Temple" (Titian). (b) 3000 s. "Adoration of the Magi" (Dürer) .. .. .. *Set of 2 sheets* 6·50 7·50

85 Red-billed Fire Finch and Glory Lily

(Litho Format)

1987 (22 July). *Flora and Fauna. T **85** and similar horiz designs. Multicoloured. P* 15.

559	2 s. Type **85**..	35	30
560	5 s. African Pygmy Kingfisher and Nandi Flame	45	30
561	10 s. Scarlet-chested Sunbird and Crown of Thorns ..	55	30
562	25 s. White Rhinoceros and Yellow-billed Oxpecker ..	1·00	80
563	35 s. Lion and Elephant Grass ..	1·00	1·10
564	45 s. Cheetahs and Doum Palm ..	1·25	1·50
565	50 s. Red-cheeked Cordon Bleu and Desert Rose..	1·40	2·00
566	100 s. Giant Eland and Acacia	2·25	3·50
559/66	*Set of 8*	7·50	8·75

MS567 Two sheets, each 98×67 mm. (a) 150 s. Carmine Bee Eaters and Sausage Tree. (b) 150 s. Cattle Egret and Zebras .. *Set of 2 sheets* 6·50 7·50

Nos. 559 and 561/6 exist imperforate from stock dispersed by the liquidator of Format International Security Printers Ltd.

86 Tremml's *Eagle* (longest man-powered flight), 1987

(Des W. Hanson. Litho Format)

1987 (14 Aug). *Milestones of Transportation. T **86** and similar horiz designs. Multicoloured. P* 15.

568	2 s. Type **86**	20	20
569	3 s. Junkers W.33 *Bremen* (first east-west transatlantic flight), 1928 ..	20	20
570	5 s. Lockheed Vega 5 *Winnie Mae* (Post's first solo round-the-world flight), 1933	30	30
571	10 s. *Voyager* (first non-stop round-the-world flight), 1986 ..	40	40
572	15 s. Chanute biplane glider, 1896	60	60
573	25 s. Airship N.1 *Norge* and Polar Bear (first transpolar flight), 1926	90	90
574	35 s. Curtiss Golden Flyer biplane and U.S.S. *Pennsylvania* (battleship) (first take-off and landing from ship), 1911	1·25	1·25
575	45 s. Shepard and *"Freedom 7"* spacecraft (first American in space), 1961	1·40	1·50
576	100 s. Concorde (first supersonic passenger flight) ..	4·25	5·50
568/76	*Set of 9*	8·50	9·75

Nos. 568/76 exist imperforate from stock dispersed by the liquidator of Format International Security Printers Ltd.

87 Olympic Torch-bearer

(Litho Questa)

1987 (5 Oct). *Olympic Games, Seoul (1988) (1st issue). T **87** and similar horiz designs. Multicoloured. P* 14.

577	5 s. Type **87**..	10	10
578	10 s. Swimming ..	20	25
579	50 s. Cycling..	1·00	1·25
580	100 s. Gymnastics	2·00	2·50
577/80	*Set of 4*	3·00	3·75

MS581 100×75 mm. 150 s. Boxing .. 3·00 4·00

See also Nos. 628/32.

88 Child Immunization   **89** Golden-backed Weaver

(Des Associated Creative Designers. Litho Questa)

1987 (8 Oct). *25th Anniv of Independence. T **88** and similar horiz designs. P* 14.

582	5 s. multicoloured ..	15	10
583	10 s. multicoloured ..	30	25
584	25 s. multicoloured ..	70	70
585	50 s. multicoloured ..	1·25	1·50
582/5	*Set of 4*	2·25	3·25

MS586 90×70 mm. 100 s. black, bright scarlet and greenish yellow .. .. 2·00 2·75

Designs:—10 s. Mulago Hospital, Kampala; 25 s. Independence Monument, Kampala City Park; 50 s. High Court, Kampala; 100 s. Stylized head of Crested Crane, "25" and Ugandan flag.

(Des Jennifer Toombs. Litho Questa)

1987 (19 Oct). *Birds of Uganda. T **89** and similar multicoloured designs. P* 14.

587	5 s. Type **89** ..	75	70
588	10 s. Hoopoe ..	1·50	1·00
589	15 s. Red-throated Bee Eater ..	1·60	1·00
590	25 s. Lilac-breasted Roller ..	2·25	1·60
591	35 s. African Pygmy Goose ..	2·25	1·75
592	45 s. Scarlet-chested Sunbird ..	2·50	2·00
593	50 s. South African Crowned Crane	2·50	2·50
594	100 s. Long-tailed Fiscal ..	4·25	4·50
587/94	*Set of 8*	16·00	14·00

MS595 Two sheets, each 80×60 mm. (a) 150 s. African Fish Eagle. (b) 150 s. Barn Owl
Set of 2 sheets 6·50 8·00

90 Hippocrates (physician) and Surgeons performing Operation

(Des L. Nelson. Litho Questa)

1987 (2 Nov). *Great Scientific Discoveries. T **90** and similar multicoloured designs. P* 14.

596	5 s. Type **90** ..	50	30
597	25 s. Einstein and Deep Space (Theory of Relativity) ..	1·75	1·75
598	35 s. Isaac Newton and diagram from *Opticks* (Theory of Colour and Light) ..	2·00	2·50
599	45 s. Karl Benz, early Benz and modern Mercedes cars ..	2·50	3·00
596/9	*Set of 4*	6·00	6·75

MS600 97×70 mm. 150 s. *Challenger* (space shuttle) (*vert*) .. .. .. 3·75 4·00

91 Scout with Album and Uganda Stamps

(Des Mary Walters. Litho Questa)

1987 (20 Nov). *World Scout Jamboree, Australia. T **91** and similar horiz designs. Multicoloured. P* 14.

601	5 s. Type **91** ..	20	10
602	25 s. Scouts planting tree ..	70	70
603	35 s. Canoeing on Lake Victoria ..	1·25	85
604	45 s. Hiking ..	1·75	1·10
601/4	*Set of 4*	3·50	2·50

MS605 95×65 mm. 150 s. Jamboree and Uganda scout emblems .. .. .. 3·00 4·00

92 "The Annunciation"

(Litho Questa)

1987 (18 Dec). *Christmas. T **92** and similar multicoloured designs showing scenes from French diptych, c.* 1250. *P* 14.

606	5 s. Type **92**..	10	10
607	10 s. "The Nativity"..	20	25
608	50 s. "Flight into Egypt"	1·00	1·25
609	100 s. "The Adoration of the Magi" ..	2·00	2·50
606/9	*Set of 4*	3·00	3·50

MS610 76×105 mm. 150 s. "Mystic Wine" (tapestry detail) (*vert*) .. .. 3·00 4·00

93 Class 12 Light Shunter Locomotive   **94** Columbite-Tantalite

(Des BG Studio. Litho Questa)

1988 (18 Jan). *Locomotives of East Africa Railways. T **93** and similar horiz designs. Multicoloured. P* 14.

611	5 s. Type **93** ..	45	35
612	10 s. Class 92 diesel-electric ..	55	45
613	15 s. Steam locomotive No. 2506 ..	70	60
614	25 s. Class 11 tank locomotive No. 126 ..	95	85
615	35 s. Class 24 steam locomotive ..	1·25	1·10
616	45 s. Class 21 steam locomotive ..	1·50	1·40
617	50 s. Class 59 Garratt steam locomotive, 1955	1·75	1·60
618	100 s. Class 87 diesel-electric locomotive ..	2·75	2·40
611/18	*Set of 8*	9·00	8·00

MS619 Two sheets, each 100×74 mm. (a) 150 s. Class 31 steam locomotive. (b) 150 s. Class 59 Garratt steam locomotive .. *Set of 2 sheets* 6·00 6·50

(Des Mary Walters. Litho Questa)

1988 (18 Jan). *Minerals. T **94** and similar vert designs. Multicoloured. P* 14.

620	1 s. Type **94** ..	15	15
621	2 s. Galena ..	20	20
622	5 s. Malachite ..	35	35
623	10 s. Cassiterite ..	55	55
624	35 s. Ferberite ..	1·50	1·50
625	50 s. Emerald ..	2·00	2·00
626	100 s. Monazite ..	3·00	3·00
627	150 s. Microcline ..	4·00	4·00
620/7	*Set of 8*	10·50	10·50

95 Hurdling

(Des BG Studio. Litho Questa)

1988 (16 May). *Olympic Games, Seoul (2nd issue). T **95** and similar horiz designs. Multicoloured. P* 14.

628	5 s. Type **95** ..	10	10
629	25 s. High jumping ..	40	50
630	35 s. Javelin throwing ..	45	55
631	45 s. Long jumping ..	55	70
628/31	*Set of 4*	1·25	1·60

MS632 85×114 mm. 150 s. Olympic medals .. 1·00 1·50

96 *Spathodea campanulata*

(Des L. Nelson. Litho Format)

1988 (29 July). *Flowers. T **96** and similar multicoloured designs. P* 15.

633	5 s. Type **96** ..	15	15
634	10 s. *Gloriosa simplex* ..	15	15
635	20 s. *Thevetica peruviana* (*vert*) ..	20	20
636	25 s. *Hibiscus schizopetalus* ..	20	25
637	35 s. *Aframomum sceptrum* ..	20	30
638	45 s. *Adenium obesum* ..	20	35
639	50 s. *Kigelia africana* (*vert*) ..	25	40
640	100 s. *Clappertonia ficifolia* ..	35	75
633/40	*Set of 8*	1·50	2·25

MS641 Two sheets, each 109×79 mm. (a) 150 s. *Costus spectabilis*. (b) 150 s. *Canarina abyssinica* (*vert*) .. .. *Set of 2 sheets* 2·00 2·75

Nos. 633/41 exist imperforate from stock dispersed by the liquidator of Format International Security Printers Ltd.

97 Elephants in Grassland (Type 61 redrawn)

(Litho Questa)

1988 (29 July). *Endangered Species (2nd series). P* 14.

642	**97** 10 s. multicoloured ..	60·00	4·00

98 Red Cross Worker vaccinating Baby

99 Giraffes, Kidepo Valley National Park

(Des Associated Creative Art Designers. Litho Questa)

1988 (28 Oct). *125th Anniv of International Red Cross. T 98 and similar designs. P 14.*

643	10 s. bright scarlet, pale yellow and black	25	15
644	40 s. multicoloured	70	70
645	70 s. multicoloured	1·50	2·00
646	90 s. multicoloured	2·00	2·25
643/6	*Set of 4*	4·00	4·50
MS647	110 × 78 mm. 150 s. multicoloured	1·00	1·60

Designs: *Horiz*—10 s. "AIDS" with test tube as "I"; 70 s. Distributing food to refugees; 90 s. Red Cross volunteers with accident victim. *Vert*—150 s. Henri Dunant (founder).

(Litho Questa)

1988 (31 Oct). *500th Birth Anniv of Titian (artist). Vert designs as T 186a of Lesotho. Multicoloured. P 13½×14.*

648	10 s. "Portrait of a Lady"	15	15
649	20 s. "Portrait of a Man"	20	20
650	40 s. "Isabella d'Este"	35	35
651	50 s. "Vincenzo Mosti"	45	45
652	70 s. "Pope Paul III Farnese"	50	60
653	90 s. "Violante"	60	75
654	100 s. "Titian's Daughter Lavinia"	70	85
655	250 s. "Dr. Parma"	1·40	1·90
648/55	*Set of 8*	4·00	4·75
MS656	Two sheets, each 110 × 95 mm. (a) 350 s. "The Speech of Alfonso D'Avalos" (detail). (b) 350 s. "Cain and Abel" (detail) *Set of 2 sheets*	6·50	7·50

(Des Mary Walters. Litho Questa)

1988 (18 Nov). *National Parks of Uganda. T 99 and similar vert designs. Multicoloured. P 14.*

657	10 s. Type 99	50	20
658	25 s. Zebras, Lake Mburo National Park	1·00	30
659	100 s. African Buffalo, Murchison Falls National Park	2·00	2·00
660	250 s. Eastern White Pelicans, Queen Elizabeth National Park	5·00	6·50
657/60	*Set of 4*	7·75	8·50
MS661	97×68 mm. 350 s. Roan Antelopes, Lake Mburo National Park	2·50	3·75

100 Doctor examining Child's Eyes

(Des L. Watkins. Litho Questa)

1988 (1 Dec). *40th Anniv of World Health Organization. T 100 and similar horiz designs. Multicoloured. P 14.*

662	10 s. Type 100	20	15
663	25 s. Mental health therapist with patient	40	30
664	45 s. Surgeon performing operation	60	60
665	100 s. Dentist treating girl	1·25	1·50
666	200 s. Doctor examining child	2·00	2·50
662/6	*Set of 5*	4·00	4·50
MS667	107 × 88 mm. 350 s. Delegates approving Declaration of Alma-Ata, 1978	2·50	3·50

100a Father Christmas with List

(101)

110 M HURDLES
R. KINGDOM
USA

(Des Walt Disney Co. Litho Questa)

1988 (2 Dec). *Christmas. "Santa's Helpers". T 100a and similar vert designs showing Walt Disney cartoon characters. Multicoloured. P 13½×14.*

668	50 s. Type 100a	85	1·00
	a. Sheetlet. Nos. 668/75	6·00	
669	50 s. Goofy carrying presents	85	1·00
670	50 s. Mickey Mouse on toy train	85	1·00
671	50 s. Reindeer at window	85	1·00

672	50 s. Donald Duck's nephew with building blocks	85	1·00
673	50 s. Donald Duck holding sack	85	1·00
674	50 s. Chip n'Dale on conveyor belt	85	1·00
675	50 s. Donald Duck's nephew operating conveyor belt	85	1·00
668/75	*Set of 8*	6·00	7·00
MS676	Two sheets, each 127×102 mm. (a) 350 s. Mickey Mouse loading sack of toys on sleigh (*horiz*). P 14×13½. (b) 350 s. Mickey Mouse and Chip n'Dale grooming reindeer. P 13½×14 *Set of 2 sheets*	7·50	8·50

Nos. 668/75 were printed together, *se-tenant* as a composite design, in sheetlets of eight.

102 Goalkeeper with Ball

103 1895 5 Cowries Stamp

1989 (30 Jan). *Olympic Gold Medal Winners, Seoul. Nos. 628/32 optd as T 101 or surch also.*

677	5 s. Type 95 (optd with T 101)	10	10
678	25 s. High jumping (optd "HIGH JUMP G. AVDEENKO USSR")	20	25
679	35 s. Javelin throwing (optd "JAVELIN T. KORJUS FINLAND")	25	30
680	300 s. on 45 s. Long jumping (optd "LONG JUMP C. LEWIS USA")	2·25	2·75
677/80	*Set of 4*	2·50	3·00
MS681	85×114 mm. 350 s. on 150 s. Olympic medals with medal table optd on sheet margin	3·00	4·00

(Des J. Genzo. Litho Questa)

1989 (24 Apr). *World Cup Football Championship, Italy (1990) (1st issue). T 102 and similar multicoloured designs. P 14.*

682	10 s. Type 102	25	15
683	25 s. Player kicking ball (*horiz*)	55	40
684	75 s. Heading ball towards net (*horiz*)	1·25	1·10
685	200 s. Tackling	2·25	2·75
682/5	*Set of 4*	3·75	4·00
MS686	118×87 mm. 300 s. Football and World Cup trophy (*horiz*)	2·50	3·25

See also Nos. 849/53.

(Litho Questa)

1989 (15 May). *Japanese Art. Paintings by Hokusai. Horiz designs as T 187a of Lesotho. Multicoloured. P 14×13½.*

687	10 s. "Fuji and the Great Wave off Kanagawa"	20	20
688	15 s. "Fuji from Lake Suwa"	30	30
689	20 s. "Fuji from Kajikazawa"	30	30
690	60 s. "Fuji from Shichirigahama"	70	70
691	90 s. "Fuji from Ejiri in Sunshu"	90	90
692	120 s. "Fuji above Lightning"	1·10	1·10
693	200 s. "Fuji from Lower Meguro in Edo"	1·90	1·90
694	250 s. "Fuji from Edo"	2·10	2·10
687/94	*Set of 8*	6·75	6·75
MS695	Two sheets, each 102×76 mm. (a) 500 s. "The Red Fuji from the Foot". (b) 500 s. "Fuji from Umezawa" *Set of 2 sheets*	7·50	8·00

Nos. 687/94 were each printed in sheetlets of 10 containing two horizontal strips of 5 stamps separated by printed labels commemorating Emperor Hirohito.

(Des U. Purins. Litho B.D.T.)

1989 (7 July). *"Philexfrance 89" International Stamp Exhibition, Paris. T 103 and similar vert designs. P 14.*

696	20 s. black, brt scarlet & pale grey-brown	40	35
697	70 s. black, yellowish green and azure	1·00	1·00
698	100 s. black, dull violet and pale brown-rose	1·25	1·50
699	250 s. black, orange-yell & pale greenish yell	2·25	2·75
696/9	*Set of 4*	4·50	5·00
MS700	176×131 mm. Nos. 696/9 (*sold at 500 s.*)	6·00	7·00

Designs:—70 s. 1895 10 on 50 cowries stamp; 100 s. 1896 25 cowries stamp; 250 s. 1896 1 rupee stamp.

104 Scout advising on Immunization

105 *Suillus granulatus*

(Des Associated Creative Designers. Litho Questa)

1989 (3 Aug). *2nd All African Scout Jamboree, Uganda, and 75th Anniv of Ugandan Scout Movement. T 104 and similar multicoloured designs. P 14.*

701	10 s. Type 104	30	15
702	70 s. Poultry keeping	1·10	90
703	90 s. Scout on crutches leading family to immunization centre	1·50	1·75
704	100 s. Scouts making bricks	1·50	1·75
701/4	*Set of 4*	4·00	4·00
MS705	99×67 mm. 500 s. Ugandan Scout logo (*vert*)	3·25	4·25

(Des Mary Walters. Litho B.D.T.)

1989 (14 Aug). *Fungi. T 105 and similar vert designs. Multicoloured. P 14.*

706	10 s. Type 105	40	30
707	15 s. *Omphalotus olearius*	55	40
708	45 s. *Oudemansiella radicata*	1·25	1·00
709	50 s. *Clitocybe nebularis*	1·25	1·10
710	60 s. *Macrolepiota rhacodes*	1·40	1·25
711	75 s. *Lepista nuda*	1·60	1·40
712	150 s. *Suillus luteus*	2·75	3·00
713	200 s. *Agaricus campestris*	3·00	3·25
706/13	*Set of 8*	11·00	10·50
MS714	Two sheets, each 100×68 mm. (a) 350 s. *Bolbitius vitellinus*. (b) 350 s. *Schizophyllum commune* *Set of 2 sheets*	11·00	11·00

106 Saddle-bill Stork

107 Rocket on Launch Pad

(Des S. Barlowe. Litho Questa)

1989 (12 Sept). *Wildlife at Waterhole. T 106 and similar vert designs. Multicoloured. P 14½×14.*

715	30 s. Type 106	70	70
	a. Sheetlet. Nos. 715/34	12·00	
716	30 s. Eastern White Pelican	70	70
717	30 s. Marabou Stork	70	70
718	30 s. Egyptian Vulture	70	70
719	30 s. Bateleur	70	70
720	30 s. African Elephant	70	70
721	30 s. Giraffe	70	70
722	30 s. Goliath Heron	70	70
723	30 s. Black Rhinoceros	70	70
724	30 s. Common Zebra and Oribi	70	70
725	30 s. African Fish Eagle	70	70
726	30 s. Hippopotamus	70	70
727	30 s. Black-backed Jackal and Eastern White Pelican	70	70
728	30 s. African Buffalo	70	70
729	30 s. Olive Baboon	70	70
730	30 s. Bohar Reedbuck	70	70
731	30 s. Lesser Flamingo and Serval	70	70
732	30 s. Whale-headed Stork ("Shoebill Stork")	70	70
733	30 s. South African Crowned Crane	70	70
734	30 s. Impala	70	70
715/34	*Set of 20*	12·00	12·00
MS735	Two sheets, each 99×68 mm. (a) 500 s. Lion. (b) 500 s. Long-crested Eagle *Set of 2 sheets*	6·50	8·00

Nos. 715/34 were printed together, *se-tenant*, in a sheetlet of 20 stamps, forming a composite design showing wildlife at a waterhole.

(Des T. Agans. Litho Questa)

1989 (20 Oct). *20th Anniv of First Manned Landing on Moon. T 107 and similar multicoloured designs. P 14.*

736	10 s. Type 107	20	20
737	20 s. Lunar module *Eagle* on Moon	30	30
738	30 s. "Apollo 11" command module	40	40
739	50 s. *Eagle* landing on Moon	60	60
740	70 s. Astronaut Aldrin on Moon	85	85
741	250 s. Neil Armstrong alighting from *Eagle* (*vert*)	2·75	2·50
742	300 s. *Eagle* over Moon	2·75	2·50
743	350 s. Astronaut Aldrin on Moon (*vert*)	2·75	2·75
736/43	*Set of 8*	9·50	9·00
MS744	Two sheets, each 77×104 mm. (a) 500 s. "Saturn" rocket (*vert*). (b) 500 s. "Apollo 11" capsule on parachutes (*vert*) *Set of 2 sheets*	7·50	8·50

108 *Aphniolaus pallene*

109 John Hanning Speke and Map of Lake Victoria

(Des S. Heimann. Litho Questa)

1989 (13 Nov). *Butterflies. T 108 and similar vert designs showing "UGANDA" in black. Multicoloured. Without imprint date. P 14.*

745	5 s. Type 108	30	20
746	10 s. *Hewitsonia boisduvali*	40	25
747	20 s. *Euxanthe wakefieldi*	60	30
748	30 s. *Papilio echerioides*	70	30
749	40 s. *Acraea semivitrea*	75	40
750	50 s. *Colotis antevippe*	75	40
751	70 s. *Acraea perenna*	90	70
752	90 s. *Charaxes cynthia*	90	70
753	100 s. *Euphaedra neophron*	90	70
754	150 s. *Cymothoe beckeri*	1·25	1·00
755	200 s. *Vanessula milca*	1·25	1·25
756	400 s. *Mimacraea marshalli*	1·75	2·50
757	500 s. *Axiocerses amanga*	2·00	2·75
758	1000 s. *Precis hierta*	2·50	4·00
745/58	*Set of 14*	13·50	14·00

For these, and similar, designs showing "UGANDA" in blue, see Nos. 864/80.

(Des A. Granberg. Litho Questa)

1989 (15 Nov). *Exploration of Africa. T 109 and similar horiz designs. Multicoloured. P 14.*

760	10 s. Type 109	55	35
761	25 s. Sir Richard Burton and map of Lake Tanganyika	75	50
762	40 s. Richard Lander and Bakota bronze	80	65
763	90 s. René Caillié and mosque, Timbuktu	1·25	1·00
764	125 s. Sir Samuel Baker and Dorcas Gazelle	1·40	1·50
765	150 s. Pharaoh Necho and ancient Phoenician merchant ship	1·60	1·75
766	250 s. Vasco da Gama and 15th-century caravel	2·50	2·75
767	300 s. Sir Henry Morton Stanley and *Lady Alice* (sectional boat)	2·75	3·00
760/7	*Set of 8*	10·50	10·50

MS768 Two sheets, each 73×103 mm. (a) 500 s. Dr. David Livingstone and steam launch *Ma Robert;* (b) 500 s. Mary Kingsley and map of Ogooué River .. .. *Set of 2 sheets* 8·50 9·50

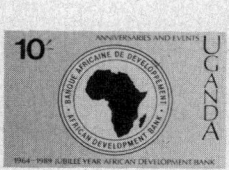

110 Logo (25th anniv of African Development Bank)

111 *Aerangis kotschyana*

(Des D. Miller. Litho Questa)

1989 (12 Dec). *Anniversaries. T 110 and similar horiz designs. Multicoloured. P 14.*

769	10 s. Type 110	15	15
770	20 s. Arrows and dish aerials (World Telecommunications Day)	20	20
771	75 s. Two portraits of Nehru (birth centenary)	1·50	1·50
772	90 s. Pan Am Boeing 314A flying boat *Dixie Clipper* (50th anniv of first scheduled trans-Atlantic airmail flight)	1·50	1·50
773	100 s. George Stephenson and *Locomotion, 1825* (175th anniv of first practical steam locomotive)	1·60	1·60
774	150 s. Concorde cockpit (20th anniv of first test flight)	2·75	2·75
775	250 s. *Wapen von Hamburg* and *Leopoldus Primus* (galleons) (800th anniv of Port of Hamburg)	2·75	2·75
776	300 s. Concorde and cockpit interior (20th anniv of first test flight)	3·00	3·00
769/76	*Set of 8*	12·00	12·00

MS777 Two sheets (a) 91×87 mm. 500 s. Revolutionary with musket and Bastille, Paris (bicentenary of French Revolution). (b) 110×82 mm. 500 s. Emperor Frederick I Barbarossa and Hamburg charter (800th anniv of Port of Hamburg) .. .. *Set of 2 sheets* 6·50 7·50

(Des W. Wright. Litho Questa)

1989 (18 Dec). *Orchids. T 111 and similar vert designs. Multicoloured. P 14.*

778	10 s. Type 111	25	25
779	15 s. *Angraecum infundibulare*	30	30
780	45 s. *Cyrtorchis chailluana*	70	70
781	50 s. *Aerangis rhodosticta*	75	75
782	100 s. *Eulophia speciosa*	1·50	1·50
783	200 s. *Calanthe sylvatica*	2·25	2·25
784	250 s. *Vanilla imperialis*	2·40	2·40
785	350 s. *Polystachya vulcanica*	2·75	2·75
778/85	*Set of 8*	9·75	9·75

MS786 Two sheets, each 110×82 mm. (a) 500 s. *Ansellia africana.* (b) 500 s. *Ancistrochilus rothschildianus* .. .. *Set of 2 sheets* 7·00 8·00

(Litho Questa)

1989 (21 Dec). *Christmas. Paintings by Fra Angelico Vert designs as T 193b of Lesotho. Multicoloured. P 14.*

787	10 s. "Madonna and Child"	15	10
788	20 s. "Adoration of the Magi"	20	15
789	40 s. "Virgin and Child enthroned with Saints"	40	30
790	75 s. "The Annunciation"	70	60
791	100 s. "Virgin and Child" (detail, "St. Peter Martyr" triptych)	85	75
792	150 s. "Virgin and Child enthroned with Saints" (*different*)	1·25	1·50
793	250 s. "Virgin and Child enthroned"	1·75	2·25
794	350 s. "Virgin and Child" (from Annalena altarpiece)	2·00	3·25
787/94	*Set of 8*	6·50	8·00

MS795 Two sheets, each 72×96 mm. (a) 500 s. "Virgin and Child" (from Bosco ai Frati altarpiece). (b) 500 s. "Madonna and Child with Twelve Angels" .. .. *Set of 2 sheets* 5·00 6·00

---

112 *Thevetia peruviana*

(113)

(Des Jennifer Toombs. Litho B.D.T.)

1990 (17 Apr). *"EXPO '90" International Garden and Greenery Exhibition, Osaka (1st issue). Flowering Trees. T 112 and similar vert designs. Multicoloured. P 14.*

796	10 s. Type 112	15	15
797	20 s. *Acanthus eminens*	20	20
798	90 s. *Gnidia glauca*	50	50
799	150 s. *Oncoba spinosa*	70	70
800	175 s. *Hibiscus rosa-sinensis*	75	75
801	400 s. *Jacaranda mimosifolia*	1·25	1·75
802	500 s. *Erythrina abyssinica*	1·40	1·90
803	700 s. *Bauhinia purpurea*	1·60	2·25
796/803	*Set of 8*	6·00	7·50

MS804 Two sheets, each 93×85 mm. (a) 1000 s. *Delonix regia.* (b) 1000 s. *Cassia didymobotrya* .. .. *Set of 2 sheets* 8·50 9·50

See also Nos. 820/8.

(Des W. Wright. Litho Questa)

1990 (8 June). *50th Anniv of Second World War. Multicoloured designs as T 242 of Maldive Islands. P 14.*

805	5 s. Allied penetration of German West Wall, 1944	25	25
806	10 s. Flags of the Allies, VE Day, 1945	35	35
807	20 s. Capture of Okinawa, 1945	45	45
808	75 s. Appointment of Gen. De Gaulle to command all Free French forces, 1944	60	60
809	100 s. Invasion of Saipan, 1944	75	75
810	150 s. Airborne landing, Operation Market Garden, 1944	1·25	1·25
811	200 s. MacArthur's return to Philippines, 1944	1·40	1·40
812	300 s. *Shoho* (Japanese aircraft carrier) under attack, Coral Sea, 1942	1·50	1·50
813	350 s. First Battle of El Alamein, 1942	1·60	1·60
814	500 s. Naval Battle of Guadalcanal, 1942	2·00	2·00
805/14	*Set of 10*	9·00	9·00

MS815 112×83 mm. 1000 s. Battle of Britain, 1940 (*vert*) .. .. 3·75 4·50

(Des Young Phillips Studio. Litho Questa)

1990 (5 July). *90th Birthday of Queen Elizabeth the Queen Mother. Vert designs as T 198a of Lesotho, showing portraits, 1940–49. P 14.*

816	250 s. black, deep magenta and new blue	95	1·00
	a. Strip of 3. Nos. 816/18	2·50	
817	250 s. black, deep magenta and new blue	95	1·00
818	250 s. black, deep magenta and new blue	95	1·00
816/18	*Set of 3*	2·50	2·75

MS819 90×75 mm. 1000 s. multicoloured .. 2·75 3·25
Designs:—No. 816, Queen Elizabeth with corgi; No. 817, **MS819**, Queen Elizabeth wearing feathered hat; No. 818, Queen Elizabeth at wartime inspection.

Nos. 816/18 were printed together, horizontally and vertically *se-tenant*, in sheetlets of 9 (3×3).

1990 (30 July). *"EXPO 90" International Garden and Greenery Exhibition, Osaka (2nd issue). Nos. 778/86 optd as T 113 in silver.*

820	10 s. Type 111	40	30
821	15 s. *Angraecum infundibulare*	40	30
822	45 s. *Cyrtorchis chailluana*	75	45
823	50 s. *Aerangis rhodosticta*	75	45
824	100 s. *Eulophia speciosa*	1·00	70
825	200 s. *Calanthe sylvatica*	1·40	1·40
826	250 s. *Vanilla imperialis*	1·40	2·00
827	350 s. *Polystachya vulcanica*	1·60	2·50
820/7	*Set of 8*	7·00	7·25

MS828 Two sheets, each 110×82 mm. (a) 500 s. *Ansellia africana.* (b) 500 s. *Ancistrochilus rothschildianus* .. .. *Set of 2 sheets* 8·00 8·50
The overprint on No. **MS828** occurs on the sheet margin and includes an additional inscription.

114 P.A.P.U. Emblem

115 Unissued G. B. "V R" Penny Black

(Des L. Fried. Litho B.D.T.)

1990 (3 Aug). *Tenth Anniv of Pan-African Postal Union (80 s.) and Second United Nations Conference on Least Developed Countries, Paris (750 s.). T 114 and similar horiz design. P 14.*

829	80 s. multicoloured	60	60

MS830 97×67 mm. 750 s. black and new blue 2·75 3·50
Design:—750 s. Clasped hands.

(Des and litho B.D.T.)

1990 (6 Aug). *150th Anniv of the Penny Black. T 115 and similar vert designs. P 14.*

831	25 s. multicoloured	20	15
832	50 s. brown-lake, blk & pale turquoise-grn	35	25
833	100 s. multicoloured	55	45
834	150 s. multicoloured	80	85
835	200 s. multicoloured	90	95
836	300 s. multicoloured	1·25	1·40
837	500 s. multicoloured	1·50	1·75
838	600 s. multicoloured	1·50	2·00
831/8	*Set of 8*	6·25	7·00

MS839 Two sheets (a) 107×77 mm. 1000 s. multicoloured. (b) 119×85 mm. 1000 s. black and rosine .. .. *Set of 2 sheets* 6·50 7·50
Designs:—50 s. Canada 1858-59 3d. Beaver; 100 s. Baden 1851 9 k. on green error; 150 s. Basel 1845 2½ r. Dove; 200 s. U.S.A. 1918 24 c. Inverted "Jenny" error; 300 s. Western Australia 1854 1d. Black Swan; 500 s. Uganda 1895 20 c. "narrow" typewritten stamp; 600 s. Great Britain Twopenny blue; 1000 s. (No. **MS839a**), Uganda 1895 20 c. "wide" typewritten stamp; 1000 s. (No. **MS839b**), Sir Rowland Hill.
No. **MS839** also commemorates "Stamp World London 90" International Stamp Exhibition.

116 African Jacana

(Des P. Gonzalez. Litho Questa)

1990 (3 Sept). *Wild Birds of Uganda. T 116 and similar multicoloured designs. P 14.*

840	10 s. Type 116	60	35
841	15 s. Southern Ground Hornbill	60	35
842	45 s. Kori Bustard (*vert*)	85	50
843	50 s. Secretary Bird	85	50
844	100 s. Egyptian Geese	1·25	85
845	300 s. Goliath Heron (*vert*)	2·25	2·75
846	500 s. Ostrich with chicks (*vert*)	2·75	3·50
847	650 s. Saddle-bill Stork (*vert*)	3·00	4·00
840/7	*Set of 8*	11·00	11·50

MS848 Two sheets, each 98×69 mm. (a) 1000 s. Lesser Flamingo (*vert*). (b) 1000 s. Vulturine Guineafowl (*vert*) .. .. *Set of 2 sheets* 7·50 8·50

117 Roger Milla of Cameroun

(Des Young Phillips Studio. Litho Questa)

1990 (21 Sept). *World Cup Football Championship, Italy (2nd issue). T 117 and similar horiz designs. Multicoloured. P 14.*

849	50 s. Type 117	35	25
850	100 s. Ramzy of Egypt	55	45
851	250 s. David O'Leary of Ireland	1·50	1·25
852	600 s. Littbarsky of West Germany	2·00	2·50
849/52	*Set of 4*	4·00	4·00

MS853 Two sheets, each 75×90 mm. (a) 1000 s. Ali McCoist of Scotland. (b) 1000 s. Ekstrom of Sweden .. .. *Set of 2 sheets* 7·00 8·00

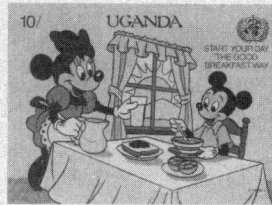

118 Mickey and Minnie Mouse at Breakfast

(Des Walt Disney Co. Litho B.D.T.)

1990 (19 Oct). *Health and Safety Campaign. T 118 and similar multicoloured designs showing Walt Disney cartoon characters. P 13.*

854	10 s. Type 118	20	10
855	20 s. Donald Duck's nephews doing kerb drill	25	15
856	50 s. Donald and Mickey stopping Big Pete smoking	55	35
857	90 s. Mickey stopping Donald choking	85	40
858	100 s. Mickey and Goofy using seat belts	90	45
859	250 s. Mickey and Minnie dancing	1·75	1·75
860	500 s. Donald Duck's fitness class	2·75	3·50
861	600 s. Mickey's nephews showing lights at night	3·00	4·00
854/61	*Set of 8*	9·25	9·50

MS862 Two sheets, each 135×115 mm. (a) 1000 s. Mickey weighing nephew (*vert*). (b) 1000 s. Mickey and Pluto walking (*vert*) .. .. *Set of 2 sheets* 7·50 8·50

(Litho Questa)

1990 (1 Nov)–**92**. *As Nos. 746/55 and new values, showing butterflies, as T 108 with "UGANDA" in blue. Multicoloured. P 14.* **A. Without imprint date**

864A	10 s. Hewitsonia boisduvali	30	15
865A	20 s. Euxanthe wakefieldi	40	20
866A	30 s. Papilio echerioides	40	20
867A	40 s. Acraea semivitrea	40	20
869A	70 s. Acraea perenna	50	30
870A	90 s. Charaxes cynthia	60	30
871A	100 s. Euphaedra neophron	60	40
872A	150 s. Cymothoe beckeri	80	40
873A	200 s. Vanessula milca	1·00	60
877A	2000 s. Precis hierta	6·00	6·50
878A	3000 s. Euphaedra eusemoides (9.10.92)	7·50	8·00
879A	4000 s. Acraea natalica (9.10.92)	8·00	9·00
880A	5000 s. Euphaedra themis (9.10.92)	8·00	10·00
864A/80A	*Set of 13*	30·00	32·00

B. With "1991" imprint date (4.11.91)

865B	20 s. Euxanthe wakefieldi	50	30
868B	50 s. Colotis antevippe	50	30
871B	100 s. Euphaedra neophron	65	40
873B	200 s. Vanessula milca	85	60
874B	400 s. Mimacraea marshalli	1·25	1·25
875B	500 s. Axiocerses amanga	1·25	1·25
876B	1000 s. Precis hierta	2·50	2·50
877B	2000 s. Precis hierta	3·25	4·75
865B/77B	*Set of 8*	9·50	10·00

(Litho Questa)

1990 (17 Dec). *Christmas. 350th Death Anniv of Rubens. Multicoloured designs as T 250 of Maldive Islands, but inscr "CHRISTMAS 1990". P 13½×14.*

881	10 s. "Baptism of Christ" (detail) (vert)	10	10
882	20 s. "St. Gregory the Great and other Saints" (detail) (vert)	15	10
883	100 s. "Saints Nereus, Domitilla and Achilleus" (detail) (vert)	65	35
884	150 s. "St. Gregory the Great and other Saints" (different detail) (vert)	90	60
885	300 s. "Saint Augustine" (detail) (vert)	1·50	1·50
886	400 s. "St. Gregory the Great and other Saints" (different detail) (vert)	1·60	1·75
887	500 s. "Baptism of Christ" (different detail) (vert)	1·75	1·90
888	600 s. "St. Gregory the Great and other Saints" (different detail) (vert)	1·90	2·50
881/8	*Set of 8*	7·50	8·00

MS889 Two sheets, each 110×71 mm. (a) 1000 s. "The Triumph of Faith" (detail). (b) 1000 s. "The Victory of Eucharistic Truth over Heresy" (detail). P 14×13½ .. *Set of 2 sheets* 8·50 9·50

119 Census Emblem   **120** Damselfly

(Litho Questa)

1990 (28 Dec). *National Population and Housing Census. T 119 and similar horiz design. Multicoloured. P 14.*

890	20 s. Type 119	30	30

MS891 105×73 mm. 1000 s. Symbolic people and dwellings .. .. .. 4·00 4·50

(Des I. Maclaury. Litho B.D.T.)

1991 (8 Jan). *Fauna of Uganda's Wetlands. T 120 and similar multicoloured designs. P 14.*

892	70 s. Type 120	55	55
	a. Sheetlet of 16. Nos. 892/907	8·00	
893	70 s. Purple Swamphen ("Gallinule")	55	55
894	70 s. Sitatunga	55	55
895	70 s. Western Reef Heron ("Purple Heron")	55	55
896	70 s. Bushpig	55	55
897	70 s. Vervet Monkey	55	55
898	70 s. Long Reed Frog	55	55
899	70 s. Malachite Kingfisher	55	55
900	70 s. Marsh Mongoose	55	55
901	70 s. Painted Reed Frog	55	55
902	70 s. African Jacana	55	55
903	70 s. Charaxes butterfly	55	55
904	70 s. Nile Crocodile	55	55
905	70 s. Herald Snake	55	55
906	70 s. Dragonfly	55	55
907	70 s. Lungfish	55	55
892/907	*Set of 16*	8·00	8·00

MS908 118×78 mm. 1000 s. Nile Monitor (horiz) 5·25 5·75

Nos. 892/907 were printed together, se-tenant, in sheetlets of 16 forming a composite design.

121 Slug Haplochromis

(Des Susan Fuller. Litho B.D.T.)

1991 (18 Jan). *Fishes of Uganda. T 121 and similar horiz designs. Multicoloured. P 14.*

909	10 s. Type 121	10	10
910	20 s. Palmquist's Notho	15	15
911	40 s. Silver Distichodus	20	20
912	90 s. Sauvage's Haplochromis	40	40
913	100 s. Blue Calliurum	45	45
914	350 s. Johnston's Haplochromis	1·10	1·25
915	600 s. Colour-tailed Haplochromis	2·25	2·50
916	800 s. Jewel Cichlid	2·50	3·00
909/16	*Set of 8*	6·50	7·25

MS917 Two sheets, each 100×74 mm. (a) 1000 s. Haplochromis. (b) 1000 s. Striped Panchax *Set of 2 sheets* 9·50 11·00

(Des B. Grout. Litho Questa)

1991 (25 Feb). *Olympic Games, Barcelona (1992). Multicoloured designs as T 202 of Lesotho. P 14.*

918	20 s. Women's 100 metres hurdles	30	15
919	40 s. Long jump	40	20
920	125 s. Table tennis	90	80
921	250 s. Football	1·25	1·50
922	500 s. Men's 800 metres	1·75	2·50
918/22	*Set of 5*	4·25	4·75

MS923 Two sheets, each 110×71 mm. (a) 1200 s. Opening Ceremony at Seoul Games (horiz). (b) 1200 s. Women's 4 × 100 metres relay (horiz) .. .. .. *Set of 2 sheets* 9·00 10·00

122 South African Railways Class 15f Steam Locomotive,1938–48

(Des O. Fernandez. Litho Walsall)

1991 (2 Apr). *African Railway Locomotives. T 122 and similar horiz designs. Multicoloured. P 14.*

924	10 s. Type 122	40	30
925	20 s. Rhodesian Railways 12th Class steam locomotive, 1900s	55	45
926	80 s. Class "Tribal" steam locomotive, Tanzam Railway, 1951–56	1·00	80
927	200 s. Steam locomotive, Egypt, 1905	1·75	1·50
928	300 s. Mikado steam locomotive, Sudan, 1930	1·90	1·90
929	400 s. East African Railways Class 59 Garratt steam locomotive, 1955	1·90	1·90
930	500 s. East African Railways Mallet steam locomotive, 1900	2·00	2·00
931	1000 s. Type 5 F 1 electric locomotive, South Africa, 1970	2·50	2·75
924/31	*Set of 8*	11·00	10·50

MS932 Four sheets, each 100×70 mm. (a) 1200 s. Atlantic steam locomotive, Egypt, 1900s. (b) 1200 s. Rhodesian Railways 12th Class steam locomotive, 1930. (c) 1200 s. Benguela Railway Class 11 steam locomotive, Angola, 1920. (d) 1200 s. Natal Govt Mallet steam locomotive, 1905–19 .. .. .. *Set of 4 sheets* 14·00 15·00
No. 924 is incorrectly captioned as a Rhodesia Railways 10th Class locomotive.

123 Lord Baden-Powell and Scout Emblem   **124** General Charles de Gaulle

(Des W. Hanson Studio. Litho Questa)

1991 (27 May). *World Scout Jamboree Mount Sorak, Korea. T 123 and similar horiz designs. P 14.*

933	20 s. multicoloured	30	30
934	80 s. multicoloured	65	65
935	100 s. multicoloured	75	75
936	150 s. black and pale yellow-olive	1·00	1·00
937	300 s. multicoloured	1·50	1·50
938	400 s. multicoloured	1·60	1·60
939	500 s. multicoloured	1·75	1·75
940	1000 s. multicoloured	2·50	2·50
933/40	*Set of 8*	9·00	9·00

MS941 Two sheets. (a) 76×115 mm. 1200 s. black and stone. (b) 115×76mm. 1200 s. black and dull violet-blue .. *Set of 2 sheets* 9·50 10·00
Designs:—80 s. Scouts and Uganda 1982 100 s. anniversary stamp; 100 s. Scout encampment, New York World's Fair, 1939; 150 s. Cover and illustration from *Scouting for Boys*; 300 s. Cooking on campfire; 400 s. Aldrin and Armstrong on Moon; 500 s. Scout salutes; 1000 s. Statue to the Unknown Scout, Gillwell Park; 1200 s. (MS941a) Jamboree emblem; 1200 s. (MS941b) Lord Baden-Powell, W. Boyce and Revd. L. Hadley.

(Des Walt Disney Co. Litho Questa)

1991 (29 May). *"Phila Nippon '91" International Stamp Exhibition, Tokyo. Multicoloured designs as T 204 of Lesotho showing Walt Disney cartoon characters and Japanese traditions. P 14×13½.*

942	10 s. Uncle Scrooge celebrating Ga-No-Iwai	15	15
943	20 s. Mickey Mouse removing shoes	25	20

944	70 s. Goofy leading cart-horse	60	50
945	80 s. Daisy Duck and Minnie Mouse exchanging gifts	70	60
946	300 s. Minnie kneeling at doorway	1·75	1·75
947	400 s. Donald Duck and Mickey taking a hot volcanic sand bath	1·90	1·90
948	500 s. Clarabelle Cow burning incense	2·00	2·00
949	1000 s. Mickey and Minnie writing New Year cards	2·75	3·00
942/9	*Set of 8*	9·00	9·00

MS950 Two sheets, each 127×112 mm. (a) 1200 s. Mickey conducting (vert). (b) 1200 s. Mickey in public bath (vert). P 13½×14 *Set of 2 sheets* 11·00 11·00

(Litho Walsall)

1991 (26 June). *Death Centenary of Vincent van Gogh (artist) (1990). Multicoloured designs as T 255 of Maldive Islands. P 13½.*

951	10 s. "Snowy Landscape with Arles" (horiz)	20	20
952	20 s. "Peasant Woman binding Sheaves"	30	30
953	60 s. "The Drinkers" (horiz)	50	50
954	80 s. "View of Auvers" (horiz)	65	65
955	200 s. "Mourning Man"	1·25	1·25
956	400 s. "Still Life: Vase with Roses" (horiz)	1·75	1·75
957	800 s. "The Raising of Lazarus" (horiz)	2·50	2·50
958	1000 s. "The Good Samaritan"	2·50	2·50
951/8	*Set of 8*	8·75	8·75

MS959 Two sheets, each 102×76 mm. (a) 1200 s. "First Steps" (95×71 mm). (b) 1200 s. "Village Street and Steps in Auvers" (95×71 mm). Imperf *Set of 2 sheets* 9·00 10·00

(Des D. Miller. Litho Walsall)

1991 (5 July). *65th Birthday of Queen Elizabeth II. Horiz designs as T 210 of Lesotho. Multicoloured. P 14.*

960	70 s. Queen and Prince Charles after polo match	60	45
961	90 s. Queen at Balmoral, 1976	60	55
962	500 s. Queen with Princess Margaret, August 1980	2·25	2·00
963	600 s. Queen and Queen Mother leaving St. George's Chapel, Windsor	2·25	2·00
960/3	*Set of 4*	5·00	4·50

MS964 68×90 mm. 1200 s. Separate photographs of Queen and Prince Philip 3·25 3·75

(Des D. Miller. Litho Walsall)

1991 (5 July). *10th Wedding Anniv of Prince and Princess of Wales. Horiz designs as T 210 of Lesotho. Multicoloured. P 14.*

965	20 s. Prince and Princess of Wales in July 1986	40	15
966	100 s. Separate photographs of Prince, Princess and sons	90	45
967	200 s. Prince Henry and Prince William	1·25	1·00
968	1000 s. Separate photographs of Prince and Princess in 1988	4·25	4·25
965/8	*Set of 4*	6·00	5·25

MS969 68×90 mm. 1200 s. Princes William and Henry on Majorca and Prince and Princess of Wales in Cameroun .. .. 4·50 4·50

(Litho Questa)

1991 (15 July). *Birth Centenary of Charles de Gaulle (French statesman) (1990). T 124 and similar multicoloured designs. P 14.*

970	20 s. Type 124	20	20
971	70 s. Liberation of Paris, 1944	45	45
972	90 s. De Gaulle with King George VI, 1940	55	50
973	100 s. Reviewing Free French troops, 1940 (horiz)	60	60
974	200 s. Broadcasting to France, 1940 (horiz)	1·00	1·00
975	500 s. De Gaulle in Normandy, 1944 (horiz)	1·75	1·75
976	600 s. De Gaulle at Albert Hall, 1940 (horiz)	1·75	2·00
977	1000 s. Inauguration as President, 1959	2·50	2·75
970/7	*Set of 8*	8·00	8·50

MS978 Two sheets. (a) 104×76 mm. 1200 s. De Gaulle entering Paris, 1944. (b) 107×76 mm. 1200 s. De Gaulle with Eisenhower, 1942 (horiz) *Set of 2 sheets* 8·00 9·00

125 Volvariella bingensis   **126** Anigozanthos manglesii

(Des K. Botis. Litho Questa)

1991 (19 July). *Fungi. T 125 and similar multicoloured designs. P 14.*

979	20 s. Type 125	30	30
980	70 s. Agrocybe broadwayi	55	55
981	90 s. Camarophyllus olidus	65	65
982	140 s. Marasmius arborescens	90	90
983	180 s. Marasmiellus subcinereus	1·00	1·00
984	200 s. Agaricus campestris	1·25	1·25
985	500 s. Chlorophyllum molybdites	2·25	2·25
986	1000 s. Agaricus bingensis	3·50	3·50
979/86	*Set of 8*	9·50	9·50

MS987 Two sheets, each 96×65 mm. (a) 1200 s. Leucocoprinus cepaestipes (horiz). (b) 1200 s. Laccaria ohiensis ("Laccaria lateritia") (horiz) *Set of 2 sheets* 8·50 9·00

(Des J. Iskowitz (Nos. 988/91), O. Fernandez (No. **MS**992). Litho Questa (Nos. 988/91) or Cartor (No. **MS**992))

1991 (1 Aug). *Endangered Species (3rd series). As Nos. 406/9, but with changed face values, and additional horiz designs as T* **61**. *Multicoloured. P* 14.

988	100 s. Elephants in "Elephants' Graveyard"	65	45
989	140 s. Type **61**	85	75
990	200 s. Elephants at waterhole	1·25	1·10
991	600 s. Elephants having dust bath	2·50	3·75
	988/91 *Set of 4*	4·75	5·50

MS992 Two sheets, each 102×74 mm. (a) 1200 s. Giraffe. (b) 1200 s. Rhinoceros and Red-billed Oxpecker. P 13×12 . . *Set of 2 sheets* 13·00 14·00

(Des Jennifer Toombs. Litho Questa)

1991 (25 Nov). *Botanical Gardens of the World. T* **126** *and similar vert designs. Multicoloured. P* 14½.

993/1032	90 s. × 20, 100 s. × 20	*Set of 40*	15·00	17·00

MS1033 Two sheets, each 110×75 mm. (a) 1400 s. The Pagoda, Kew. (b) 1400 s. Temple of the Winds, Melbourne . . *Set of 2 sheets* 10·00 12·00

Nos. 993/1032 were issued together, *se-tenant*, as two sheetlets of 20. The 90 s. values show *Anigozanthos manglesii, Banksia grandis, Clianthus formosus, Gossypium sturtianum, Callistemon lanceolatus, Saintpaulia ionantha, Calodendrum capense, Aloe ferox × arborescens, Bolusanthus speciousus, Lithops schwantesii, Protea repens, Plumbago capensis, Clerodendrum thomsoniae, Thunbergia alata, Schotia latifolia, Epacris impressa, Acacia pycnantha, Telopea speciosissima, Wahlenbergia gloriosa, Eucalyptus globulus* from Melbourne, and the 100 s. *Cypripedium calceolus, Rhododendron thomsonii, Ginkgo biloba, Magnolia campbellii, Wisteria sinensis, Clerodendrum ugandense, Eulophia horsfallii, Aerangis rhodosticta, Abelmoschus moschatus, Gloriosa superba, Carissa edulis, Ochna kirkii, Canarina abyssinica, Nymphaea caerulea, Ceropegia succulenta, Strelitzia reginae, Strongylodon macrobotrys, Victoria amazonica, Orchis militaris* and *Sophora microphylla* from Kew.

20/-

(127)

1991 (4 Dec). *Nos. 573, 597 and 614 surch as T* **127**.

1034	20 s. on 25 s. Airship N.1 *Norge* and Polar Bear (first transpolar flight), 1926		
1035	20 s. on 25 s. Einstein and Deep Space (Theory of Relativity)		
1035a	20 s. on 25 s. Tank locomotive No. 126 . .		

(Litho Walsall)

1991 (18 Dec). *Christmas. Paintings by Piero della Francesca. Vert designs as T* **211** *of Lesotho. Multicoloured. P* 12.

1036	20 s. "Madonna with Child and Angels"	30	15
1037	50 s. "The Baptism of Christ" . .	50	15
1038	80 s. "Polyptych of Mercy"	70	40
1039	100 s. "Polyptych of Mercy" (detail)	70	40
1040	200 s. "The Annunciation" from "The Legend of the True Cross"	1·25	80
1041	500 s. "Pregnant Madonna" . .	2·25	2·25
1042	1000 s. "The Annunciation" from "Polyptych of St. Anthony" . .	3·25	3·75
1043	1500 s. "The Nativity" . .	4·25	6·00
	1036/43 *Set of 8*	12·00	12·50

MS1044 Two sheets, each 102×127 mm. (a) 1800 s. "The Brera Altarpiece". (b) 1800 s. "Madonna and Child" from "Polyptych of St. Anthony". P 14 . . *Set of 2 sheets* 11·00 12·00

128 Boy Scout Monument, New York, and Ernest Thompson (first Chief Scout of U.S.A.)

(Des W. Hanson (Nos. 1045/6, **MS**1050b). W. Wright (Nos. 1047, **MS**1050a). Litho Questa)

1992 (6 Jan). *Anniversaries and Events. T* **128** *and similar multicoloured designs. P* 14.

1045	20 s. Type **128** . .	60	30
1046	50 s. Treehouse design and Daniel Beard (*vert*)	75	40
1047	400 s. Lilienthal's signature and *Flugzeug Nr. 8*	1·50	1·75
1048	500 s. Demonstrator demolishing Berlin Wall	1·60	2·25
1049	700 s. *The Magic Flute* . .	3·00	3·25
	1045/9 *Set of 5*	6·75	7·25

MS1050 Two sheets. (a) 114×85 mm. 1200 s. Class VL8 electric locomotive leaving tunnel. (b) 117×89 mm. 1500 s. Ugandan Boy Scout badge *Set of 2 sheets* 8·00 9·00

Anniversaries and Events:—Nos. 1045/6, **MS**1050b, 50th death anniv of Lord Baden-Powell and World Scout Jamboree, Korea; No. 1047, Centenary of Otto Lilienthal's first gliding experiments; No. 1048, Centenary of Brandenburg Gate, Berlin; No. 1049, Death bicentenary of Mozart; No. **MS**1050a, Centenary of Trans-Siberian Railway.

COVER PRICES

Cover factors are quoted at the beginning of each country for most issues to 1945. An explanation of the system can be found on page x. The factors quoted do not, however, apply to philatelic covers.

---

129 U.S.S. *Vestal* (repair ship) under Attack

(Des W. Hanson Studio. Litho Questa)

1992 (6 Jan). *50th Anniv of Japanese Attack on Pearl Harbor. T* **129** *and similar horiz designs. Multicoloured. P* 14½.

1051	200 s. Type **129**	90	90
	a. Sheetlet. Nos. 1051/60	8·00	
1052	200 s. Japanese Mitsubishi A6M Zero-Sen	90	90
1053	200 s. U.S.S. *Arizona* (battleship) on fire	90	90
1054	200 s. U.S.S. *Nevada* (battleship) passing burning ships	90	90
1055	200 s. Japanese Aichi D3A "Val" bomber attacking	90	90
1056	200 s. Douglas SBD Dauntless bombers attacking *Hiryu* (carrier) at Midway	90	90
1057	200 s. Japanese Mitsubishi A6M Zero-Sen aircraft attacking Midway Island	90	90
1058	200 s. U.S. Marine Brewster F2A Buffalo (fighter) defending Midway	90	90
1059	200 s. American Grumman F6F Hellcat aircraft and carrier	90	90
1060	200 s. U.S.S. *Yorktown* (carrier) torpedoed	90	90
	1051/60 *Set of 10*	8·00	8·00

Nos. 1051/60 were printed together, *se-tenant*, in sheetlets of 10 with the stamps arranged in two horizontal strips of 5 forming composite designs separated by a gutter showing photograph of Pearl Harbor model and text.

130 Three Modern Hot Air Balloons

(Litho Questa)

1992 (6 Jan). *120th Anniv of Paris Balloon Post (1990). T* **130** *and similar horiz designs. Multicoloured. P* 14.

1061	200 s. Type **130**	80	80
	a. Sheetlet. Nos. 1061/9	6·50	
1062	200 s. Sport balloons and top of *Double Eagle II*	80	80
1063	200 s. Pro Juventute balloon and top of Branson's *Virgin Otsuka Pacific Flyer*	80	80
1064	200 s. Blanchard and Jeffries' balloon	80	80
1065	200 s. Nadar's *Le Geant* and centre of *Double Eagle II*	80	80
1066	200 s. Branson's *Virgin Otsuka Pacific Flyer*	80	80
1067	200 s. Montgolfier balloon	80	80
1068	200 s. *Double Eagle II* basket and Paris balloons of 1870	80	80
1069	200 s. Henri Giffard's balloon *Le Grand Ballon Captif*	80	80
	1061/9 *Set of 9*	6·50	6·50

Nos. 1061/9 were printed together, *se-tenant*, as a sheetlet of 9 forming a composite design.

(Des Walt Disney Co. Litho B.D.T.)

1992 (20 Feb). *Mickey's World Tour. Multicoloured designs as T* **264** *of Maldive Islands showing Walt Disney cartoon characters in different countries. P* 13.

1070	20 s. Mickey Mouse and Goofy on African safari (*horiz*)	25	15
1071	50 s. Mickey charming Pluto's tail, India (*horiz*)	40	15
1072	80 s. Minnie Mouse, Donald and Daisy Duck as Caribbean calypso band (*horiz*)	60	25
1073	200 s. Goofy pulling Donald and Daisy in rickshaw, China (*horiz*)	1·00	60
1074	500 s. Mickey and Minnie on camel, Egypt (*horiz*)	1·50	1·50
1075	800 s. Donald and Pete sumo wrestling, Japan (*horiz*)	1·75	2·00
1076	1000 s. Goofy bullfighting, Spain (*horiz*) . .	1·90	2·25
1077	1500 s. Mickey playing football, Italy (*horiz*)	2·50	3·25
	1070/7 *Set of 8*	9·00	9·00

MS1078 Two sheets, each 83×104 mm. (a) 2000 s. Mickey as Cossack dancer, Russia. (b) 2000 s. Daisy as Wagnerian diva, Germany *Set of 2 sheets* 8·50 9·50

(Des D. Miller. Litho Questa)

1992 (26 Feb). *40th Anniv of Queen Elizabeth II's Accession. Horiz designs as T* **214** *of Lesotho. Multicoloured. P* 14.

1079	100 s. Lake Victoria	60	25
1080	200 s. Lake and mountains	90	50
1081	500 s. Lakeside fields	2·00	2·25
1082	1000 s. River Nile	3·00	3·50
	1079/82 *Set of 4*	6·00	6·00

MS1083 Two sheets, each 74×97 mm. (a) 1800 s. Waterfalls. (b) 1800 s. Owen Falls Dam *Set of 2 sheets* 9·00 9·50

(Des D. Burkhart, Litho Walsall)

1992 (8 Apr). *Prehistoric Animals. Horiz designs as T* **217** *of Lesotho. Multicoloured. P* 14.

1084	50 s. Kentrosaurus	50	30
1085	200 s. Iguanodon	1·00	80
1086	250 s. Hypsilophodon	1·10	90
1087	300 s. Brachiosaurus	1·25	1·10
1088	400 s. Peloneustes	1·40	1·40
1089	500 s. Pteranodon	1·50	1·50
1090	800 s. Tetralophodon	2·00	2·00
1091	1000 s. Megalosaurus	2·00	2·50
	1084/91 *Set of 8*	9·75	10·00

MS1092 Two sheets, each 100×70 mm. (a) 2000 s. As 250 s. (b) 2000 s. As 1000 s. *Set of 2 sheets* 11·00 12·00

131 "The Entry into Jerusalem" (detail) (Giotto)   132 Adungu

(Litho Questa)

1992 (7 May). *Easter. Religious Paintings. T* **131** *and similar vert designs. Multicoloured. P* 13½×14.

1093	50 s. Type **131**	35	15
1094	100 s. "Pilate and the Watch" (Psalter of Robert de Lisle)	45	25
1095	200 s. "The Kiss of Judas" (detail) (Giotto)	75	55
1096	250 s. "Christ washing the Feet of the Disciples" (Vita Christi manuscript)	85	75
1097	300 s. "Christ seized in the Garden" (Melissende Psalter)	95	85
1098	500 s. "Doubting Thomas" (Vita Christi manuscript)	1·40	1·60
1099	1000 s. "The Marys at the Tomb" (detail) (anon)	2·25	3·00
1100	2000 s. "The Ascension" (Florentine manuscript)	3·75	5·00
	1093/100 *Set of 8*	9·75	11·00

MS1101 Two sheets, each 72×102 mm. (a) 2500 s. "The Piercing of Christ's Side" (detail) (Limoges enamel). (b) 2500 s. "Agony at Gethsemane" (detail) (Limoges enamel) *Set of 2 sheets* 11·00 12·00

(Des R. Sauber. Litho Questa)

1992 (20 July). *Traditional Musical Instruments. T* **132** *and similar vert designs. Multicoloured. P* 14.

1102	50 s. Type **132**	20	20
1103	100 s. Endingidi	35	35
1104	200 s. Akogo	60	60
1105	250 s. Nanga	65	65
1106	300 s. Engoma	75	75
1107	400 s. Amakondere	80	80
1108	500 s. Akakyenkye	1·10	1·25
1109	1000 s. Ennanga	2·25	2·75
	1102/9 *Set of 8*	6·00	6·50

133 Map of Known World, 1486

(Des A. Granberg. Litho Questa)

1992 (27 July). *500th Anniv of Discovery of America by Columbus and "World Columbian Stamp Expo '92" Exhibition, Chicago. T* **133** *and similar multicoloured designs. P* 14.

1110	50 s. Type **133** . .	20	20
1111	100 s. Map of Africa, 1508	30	30
1112	150 s. Map of West Indies, 1500	50	50
1113	200 s. *Nina* and astrolabe	60	60
1114	600 s. *Pinta* and quadrant	1·50	1·50
1115	800 s. Sand glass	1·60	1·60
1116	900 s. 15th-century compass	1·75	1·75
1117	2000 s. Map of World, 1492	3·50	3·50
	1110/17 *Set of 8*	9·00	9·00

MS1118 Two sheets, each 95×75 mm. (a) 2500 s. Sections of globe, 1492. (b) 2500 s. Europe and Africa from map by Henricus Martellus, 1490 (*vert*) . . *Set of 2 sheets* 9·25 10·00

(Litho Questa)

1992 (28 Aug). *Hummel Figurines. Vert designs as T* **256** *of Maldive Islands. Multicoloured. P* 14.

1119	50 s. Girl with washing	25	20
1120	200 s. Girl scrubbing floor	60	50
1121	250 s. Girl sweeping floor	70	60
1122	300 s. Girl with baby	80	70
1123	600 s. Boy mountaineer	1·75	1·75
1124	900 s. Girl knitting	2·25	2·50
1125	1000 s. Boy on stool	2·50	2·75

1126	1500 s.	Boy with telescope			2·75	3·00
1119/26				*Set of 8*	10·50	11·00

MS1127 Two sheets, each 97×122 mm. (a) 500 s. As No. 1119; 500 s. As No. 1120; 500 s. As No. 1121; 500 s. As No. 1122. (b) 500 s. As No. 1124; 500 s. As No. 1123; 500 s. As No. 1125; 500 s. As No. 1126 .. .. *Set of 2 sheets* 9·50 11·00

134 Spotted Hyena   **135** Red-headed Falcon

(Litho Questa)

1992 (25 Sept). *Wildlife. T* **134** *and similar horiz designs. Multicoloured. P* 14.

1128	50 s.	Type **134**			20	15
1129	100 s.	Impala			30	25
1130	200 s.	Giant Forest Hog			45	35
1131	250 s.	Pangolin			50	45
1132	300 s.	Golden Monkey			60	50
1133	800 s.	Serval			1·60	1·75
1134	1000 s.	Small-spotted Genet ("Bush Genet")			1·75	1·90
1135	3000 s.	Waterbuck			4·50	6·00
1128/35				*Set of 8*	9·00	10·00

MS1136 Two sheets, each 100×70 mm. (a) 2500 s. Gorilla. (b) 2500 s. Hippopotamus *Set of 2 sheets* 9·00 9·50

(Litho Questa)

1992 (2 Oct). *Olympic Games, Barcelona. Multicoloured designs as T* **216** *of Lesotho. P* 14.

1137	50 s.	Men's javelin			25	20
1138	100 s.	Men's highjump (*horiz*)			35	30
1139	200 s.	Fencing (Pentathlon)			50	45
1140	250 s.	Men's volleyball			60	60
1141	300 s.	Women's platform diving			60	60
1142	500 s.	Men's team cycling			2·00	1·75
1143	1000 s.	Women's tennis			3·00	3·00
1144	2000 s.	Boxing (*horiz*)			3·75	4·50
1137/44				*Set of 8*	10·00	10·00

MS1145 Two sheets, each 100×70 mm. (a) 2500 s. Men's basketball. (b) 2500 s. Baseball *Set of 2 sheets* 11·00 12·00

(Litho Questa)

1992 (9 Oct). *Birds. T* **135** *and similar vert designs. Multicoloured. P* 15×14.

1146	20 s.	Type **135**			35	20
1147	30 s.	Yellow-billed Hornbill			40	20
1148	50 s.	Purple Heron			40	20
1149	100 s.	Regal Sunbird			50	20
1150	150 s.	White-browed Robin Chat			60	25
1151	200 s.	Shining-blue Kingfisher			70	30
1152	250 s.	Great Blue Turaco			80	40
1153	300 s.	African Emerald Cuckoo			90	60
1154	500 s.	Abyssinian Roller			1·25	1·00
1155	800 s.	South African Crowned Crane			1·75	1·75
1156	1000 s.	Doherty's Bush Shrike			2·00	2·00
1157	2000 s.	Splendid Glossy Starling			3·25	3·75
1158	3000 s.	Little Bee Eater			4·50	6·00
1159	4000 s.	Red-faced Lovebird ("Red-headed Lovebird")			6·00	7·50
1146/59				*Set of 14*	21·00	22·00

(Des Kerri Schiff. Litho Questa)

1992 (28 Oct). *Postage Stamp Mega Event, New York. Sheet* 100×70 mm. *containing vert design as T* **219** *of Lesotho. Multicoloured. P* 14.

MS1160 2500 s. United Nations Headquarters 3·25 3·75

136 Goofy in *Hawaiian Holiday, 1937*   **137** "The Annunciation" (Zurbaran)

(Des Walt Disney Co. Litho Questa)

1992 (2 Nov). *60th Anniv of Goofy. T* **136** *and similar multicoloured designs. P* 13½.

1162	50 s.	Type **136**			30	20
1163	100 s.	Riding pennyfarthing cycle, 1941			40	20
1164	200 s.	Goofy and Mickey Mouse as firemen, 1935			60	35
1165	250 s.	Skiing, 1941 (*horiz*)			65	40
1166	300 s.	One man band, 1937 (*horiz*)			70	60
1167	1000 s.	Asleep against boat, 1938 (*horiz*)			2·25	2·50
1168	1500 s.	Ancient Olympic champion, 1942			3·25	3·75
1169	2000 s.	Pole vaulting, 1942			3·50	3·75
1162/9				*Set of 8*	10·50	10·50

MS1170 Two sheets. (a) 105×115 mm. 3000 s. Goofy and Wilbur the grasshopper, 1939 (*horiz*). (b) 92×116 mm. 3000 s. Wyatt Goofy and Goofy today .. .. *Set of 2 sheets* 10·00 11·00

(Litho Questa)

1992 (16 Nov). *Christmas. Religious Paintings by Francisco Zurbaran. T* **137** *and similar vert designs. Multicoloured. P* 13½×14.

1171	50 s.	Type **137**		25	15
1172	200 s.	"The Annunciation" (*different*)		55	35
1173	250 s.	"The Virgin of the Immaculate Conception"		65	45
1174	300 s.	"The Virgin of the Immaculate Conception" (*detail*)		75	50
1175	800 s.	"Holy Family with Saints Anne, Joachim and John the Baptist"		2·00	2·25
1176	900 s.	"Holy Family with Saints Anne, Joachim and John the Baptist" (*detail*)		2·25	2·50
1177	1000 s.	"Adoration of the Magi"		2·25	2·50
1178	2000 s.	"Adoration of the Magi" (*detail*)		3·75	4·75
1171/8			*Set of 8*	11·00	12·00

MS1179 Two sheets, each 76×102 mm. (a) 2500 s. "The Virgin of the Immaculate Conception (*different*). (b) 2500 s. "The Virgin of the Immaculate Conception" (*different*) *Set of 2 sheets* 11·00 12·00

138 Man cleaning Granary

(Des W. Wright and L. Fried (Nos. 1184, 1189, MS1191a). Litho Questa)

1992 (7 Dec). *Anniversaries and Events. T* **138** *and similar horiz designs. Multicoloured. P* 14.

1180	50 s.	Type **138**			15	15
1181	200 s.	Mother breast feeding			40	40
1182	250 s.	Mother feeding baby			50	50
1183	300 s.	Boy collecting water from pump			60	60
1184	300 s.	"Voyager 2" passing Jupiter			1·25	1·00
1185	800 s.	Mother and baby			1·40	1·75
1186	800 s.	Impala			1·40	1·75
1187	1000 s.	Mountain Zebra			2·25	2·50
1188	1000 s.	Count Ferdinand von Zeppelin and airship			2·25	2·50
1189	2000 s.	"Voyager 2" passing Neptune			5·00	5·00
1190	3000 s.	Count Ferdinand von Zeppelin and Clement-Bayard airship *Fleurus*			6·00	7·00
1180/90				*Set of 11*	19·00	21·00

MS1191 Four sheets, each 115×85 mm. (a) 2500 s. "Voyager 2" and Jupiter. (b) 2500 s. Warthog. (c) 2500 s. Count Ferdinand von Zeppelin with Robert Brothers and Colin Hullin balloon. (d) 2500 s. Doctor inoculating boy *Set of 4 sheets* 17·00 18·00

Anniversaries and Events—Nos. 1180/3, 1185, United Nations World Health Organization Projects; Nos. 1184, 1189, MS1191a, International Space Year; Nos. 1186/7, MS1191b, Earth Summit '92, Rio; Nos. 1188, 1190, MS1191c, 75th death anniv of Count Ferdinand von Zeppelin (airship pioneer); MS1191d, 75th anniv of International Association of Lions Clubs.

139 Hands releasing Dove with Lubaga and Kampala Catholic Cathedrals

(Des Susan Rini. Litho Questa)

1993 (1 Feb). *Visit of Pope John Paul II. T* **139** *and similar multicoloured designs. P* 14.

1192	50 s.	Type **139**			30	10
1193	200 s.	Pope and Kampala Cathedral			55	30
1194	250 s.	Pope and Catholic worshipper			60	35
1195	300 s.	Ugandan bishops and Pope			65	40
1196	800 s.	Pope John Paul II waving			1·75	1·90
1197	900 s.	Pope and Kampala Cathedral (*different*)			1·75	1·90
1198	1000 s.	Pope, national flag and Kampala Cathedral			1·75	1·90
1199	2000 s.	Pope and national flag			3·25	4·00
1192/9				*Set of 8*	9·50	9·75

MS1200 Two sheets, each 100×70 mm. (a) 3000 s. Pope on aircraft steps (*vert*). (b) 3000 s. Pope delivering blessing (*vert*) . *Set of 2 sheets* 10·00 11·00

A 5000 s. value embossed on gold foil exists from a limited printing.

(Litho Walsall)

1993 (5 Apr). *Bicentenary of the Louvre, Paris. Paintings by Rembrandt. Multicoloured designs as T* **221** *of Lesotho. P* 12.

1201	500 s.	"Self-portrait at Easel"			95	95
		a. Sheetlet. Nos. 1201/8			7·00	
1202	500 s.	"Birds of Paradise"			95	95
1203	500 s.	"The Carcass of Beef"			95	95
1204	500 s.	"The Supper at Emmaus"			95	95
1205	500 s.	"Hendrickje Stoffels"			95	95
1206	500 s.	"The Artist's Son, Titus"			95	95
1207	500 s.	"The Holy Family" (left detail)			95	95
1208	500 s.	"The Holy Family" (right detail)			95	95
1201/8				*Set of 8*	7·00	7·00

MS1209 100×70 mm. 2500 s. "The Philosopher in Meditation" (89×57 mm). P 14½ .. 4·00 4·50

Nos. 1201/8 were printed together, *se-tenant*, in sheetlets of 8 stamps and one centre label.

140 Afghan Hound   **141** Gutierrez (Uruguay) and Voeller (Germany)

(Des J. Barbaris. Litho Questa)

1993 (28 May). *Dogs of the World. T* **140** *and similar multicoloured designs. P* 14.

1210	50 s.	Type **140**			40	20
1211	100 s.	Newfoundland			55	20
1212	200 s.	Siberian Huskies			85	40
1213	250 s.	Briard			90	55
1214	300 s.	Saluki			95	70
1215	800 s.	Labrador guide-dog (*vert*)			2·00	2·25
1216	1000 s.	Greyhound			2·25	2·50
1217	1500 s.	Pointer			2·50	3·50
1210/17				*Set of 8*	9·50	9·50

MS1218 Two sheets, each 103×80 mm. (a) 2500 s. Cape Hunting Dog. (b) 2500 s. Norwegian Elkhound pup . *Set of 2 sheets* 13·00 13·00

(Des Kerri Schiff. Litho Questa)

1993 (2 June). *40th Anniv of Coronation. Vert designs as T* **224** *of Lesotho. Multicoloured. P* 13½.

1219	50 s.	Queen Elizabeth II at Coronation (photograph by Cecil Beaton)			25	30
		a. Sheetlet. Nos. 1219/22×2			6·00	
1220	200 s.	Orb and Sceptre			40	50
1221	500 s.	Queen Elizabeth during Coronation			80	95
1222	1500 s.	Queen Elizabeth II and Princess Margaret			2·00	2·25
1219/22				*Set of 4*	3·00	3·50

MS1223 69×100 mm. 2500 s. "The Crown" (detail) (Grace Wheatley) (28½×42½ mm). P 14 3·75 4·00

Nos. 1219/22 were printed in sheetlets of 8, containing two *se-tenant* blocks of 4.

(Des Kerri Schiff. Litho Questa)

1993 (22 Sept). *Asian International Stamp Exhibitions. Multicoloured designs as T* **263** *of St. Vincent, but vert. P* 13½×14.

(a) "Indopex '93", Surabaya, Indonesia. Javanese Wayang Puppets

1224	600 s.	Bupati karma, Prince of Wangga			1·00	1·25
		a. Sheetlet. Nos. 1224/9			5·50	
1225	600 s.	Rahwana			1·00	1·25
1226	600 s.	Sondjeng Sandjata			1·00	1·25
1227	600 s.	Raden Damar Wulan			1·00	1·25
1228	600 s.	Unidentified puppet			1·00	1·25
1229	600 s.	Hanaman			1·00	1·25
1224/9				*Set of 6*	5·50	6·50

MS1230 135×105 mm. 2500 s. Candi Mendut Temple, Java .. .. 4·50 5·00

(b) "Taipei '93", Taiwan. Funerary Pottery Figures

1231	600 s.	Tomb guardian god in green armour			1·00	1·25
		a. Sheetlet. Nos. 1231/6			5·50	
1232	600 s.	Civil official and shrine			1·00	1·25
1233	600 s.	Tomb guardian god in green and gold armour			1·00	1·25
1234	600 s.	Civil official in red robe			1·00	1·25
1235	600 s.	Chimera (tomb guardian)			1·00	1·25
1236	600 s.	Civil official in red and green robe			1·00	1·25
1231/6				*Set of 6*	5·50	6·50

MS1237 135×105 mm. 2500 s. Statue of the Sacred Mother, Taiyuan .. .. 4·50 5·00

(c) "Bangkok '93", Thailand. Sculptured Figures

1238	600 s.	Standing Buddha in gilded red sandstone, 13th–15th century			1·00	1·25
		a. Sheetlet. Nos. 1238/43			5·50	
1239	600 s.	Crowned Buddha in bronze, 13th century			1·00	1·25
1240	600 s.	Thepanom in stone, 15th century			1·00	1·25
1241	600 s.	Crowned Buddha in bronze, 12th century			1·00	1·25
1242	600 s.	Avalokitesvara in bronze, 9th century			1·00	1·25
1243	600 s.	Lop Buri standing Buddha in bronze, 13th–century			1·00	1·25
1238/43				*Set of 6*	5·50	6·50

MS1244 135×105 mm. 2500 s. Buddha, Wat Mahathat .. .. 4·50 5·00

Nos. 1224/9, 1231/6 and 1238/43 were each printed together, *se-tenant*, in sheetlets of 6.

(Des Rosemary DeFiglio. Litho Questa)

1993 (1 Oct). *World Cup Football Championship, U.S.A. (1994) (1st issue). T* **141** *and similar multicoloured designs. P* 14.

1245	50 s.	Type **141**			30	15
1246	200 s.	Tomas Brolin (Sweden)			80	40
1247	250 s.	Gary Lineker (England)			90	45
1248	300 s.	Munoz and Butragueno (Spain)			95	55
1249	800 s.	Carlos Valderrama (Colombia)			2·00	2·25
1250	900 s.	Diego Maradona (Argentina)			2·00	2·25
1251	1000 s.	Pedro Troglio (Argentina)			2·00	2·25
1252	2000 s.	Enzo Scifo (Belgium)			3·25	3·25
1245/52				*Set of 8*	11·00	11·00

MS1253 Two sheets, each 103×72 mm. (a) 2500 s. Brazilians celebrating. (b) 2500 s. De Napoli (Italy) and Skuhravy (Czechoslovkia) (*horiz*) .. .. .. *Set of 2 sheets* 11·00 12·00

See also Nos. 1322/8.

142 York Minster,
England

143 Mickey Mouse asleep on
Stegosaurus

(Des G. Bibby. Litho Questa)

1993 (3 Nov). *Cathedrals of the World. T **142** and similar vert designs. Multicoloured. P 14.*

1254	50 s. Type **142**	..	..	..	25	15
1255	100 s. Notre Dame, Paris	..		35	20
1256	200 s. Little Metropolis, Athens	..	65	40
1257	250 s. St. Patrick's, New York	..	70	45
1258	300 s. Ulm, Germany	..	..	75	50
1259	800 s. St. Basil's, Moscow	..	2·00	2·25
1260	1000 s. Roskilde, Denmark	..	2·00	2·25
1261	2000 s. Seville, Spain	..	..	3·50	4·25
1254/61		..	..	*Set of 8*	9·25	9·50

MS1262 Two sheets, each 70×100 mm. (a) 2500 s. Namirembe, Uganda. (b) 2500 s. St. Peter's, Vatican City .. *Set of 2 sheets* 9·00 9·50

(Litho Questa)

1993 (19 Nov). *Christmas. Religious Paintings. Vert designs as T **76** of Nevis (St. Kitts–Nevis). Black, pale lemon and red (Nos. 1263, 1265, 1267, 1270 and **MS**1271a) or multicoloured (others).*

1263	50 s. "Virgin with Carthusian Monks" (detail) (Dürer)	..	25	10
1264	100 s. "Sacred Family" (detail) (Raphael)		35	10
1265	200 s. "Virgin with Carthusian Monks" (different detail) (Dürer)		55	30
1266	250 s. "The Virgin of the Rose" (Raphael)		60	35
1267	300 s. "Virgin with Carthusian Monks" (different detail) (Dürer)		65	40
1268	800 s. "Sacred Family" (different detail) (Raphael)	..	1·75	2·00
1269	1000 s. "Virgin with Beardless Joseph" (Raphael)	..	2·00	2·25
1270	2000 s. "Virgin with Carthusian Monks" (different detail) (Dürer)	..	3·25	4·50
1263/70		*Set of 8*	8·50	9·00

MS1271 Two sheets, each 102×127 mm. (a) 2500 s. "Virgin with Carthusian Monks" (different detail) (Dürer). (b) 2500 s. "Sacred Family" (different detail) (Raphael)
Set of 2 sheets 10·00 11·00

Nos. **MS**1271 is inscribed "Canthusian Monks" in error.

(Des Walt Disney Co. Litho Questa)

1993 (22 Dec). *Prehistoric Animals. T **143** and similar horiz designs showing Walt Disney cartoon characters. Multicoloured. P 14×13½.*

1272	50 s. Type **143**	..	..	35	20
1273	100 s. Minnie Mouse on pteranodon	..	45	20
1274	200 s. Mickey being licked by mamenchisaurus	..	70	40
1275	250 s. Mickey doing cave painting	..	80	45
1276	300 s. Mickey wind-surfing on dinosaur	85	60
1277	500 s. Mickey and Donald Duck sliding on diplodocus	..	1·25	1·25
1278	800 s. Mamenchisaurus carrying Mickey	1·90	2·25
1279	1000 s. Pluto on triceratops	..	2·00	2·25
1272/9		*Set of 8*	7·50	7·00

MS1280 Two sheets, each 128×102 mm. (a) 2500 s. Mickey and Minnie. (b) 2500 s. Mickey feeding tyrannosaurus rex .. *Set of 2 sheets* 9·50 10·00

No. 1273 is inscribed "PTERANDOM" and No. 1278 "MAMENSHISAURUS", both in error.

144 "Woman in
Yellow" (Picasso)

145 Passion Fruit

(Litho Questa)

1993 (29 Dec). *Anniversaries and Events. T **144** and similar multicoloured designs. P 14.*

1281	100 s. Type **144**	..	..	30	15
1282	200 s. Head of cow and syringe	..	50	30
1283	250 s. "Gertrude Stein" (Picasso)	..	60	35
1284	500 s. Early telescope	..	1·25	1·25
1285	800 s. "Creation" (S. Witkiewicz after J. Glogowski)	..	1·75	2·00
1286	1000 s. Modern telescope	..	2·00	2·25
1287	1000 s. "For the Right to Work" (A. Strumillo)	..	2·00	2·25
1281/7		*Set of 7*	7·75	7·75

MS1288 Three sheets. (a) 75×105 mm. 2500 s. "Woman by a Window" (detail) (Picasso). (b) 105×75 mm. 2500 s. Copernicus. (c) 105×75 mm. 2500 s. "Temptation of Saint Antony I" (detail) (S. Witkiewicz) (horiz) .. *Set of 3 sheets* 13·00 14·00

Anniversaries and Events:—Nos. 1281, 1283, **MS**1288a, 20th death anniv of Picasso (artist); No. 1282, Pan African Rinderpest Campaign; Nos. 1284, 1286, **MS**1288b, 450th death anniv of Copernicus (astronomer); Nos. 1285, 1287, **MS**1288c, "Polska '93" International Stamp Exhibition, Poznań.

(Litho Questa)

1994 (13 Jan). *Fruits and Crops. T **145** and similar multicoloured designs. P 14.*

1289	50 s. Type **145**	..	..	25	10
1290	100 s. Sunflower	..	..	30	10
1291	150 s. Bananas	..	..	45	25
1292	200 s. Runner beans	..	..	55	30
1293	250 s. Pineapple	..	..	60	50
1294	300 s. Jackfruit	..	..	70	60
1295	500 s. Sorghum	..	..	1·25	1·40
1296	800 s. Maize	..	..	1·75	2·25
1289/96		*Set of 8*	5·25	5·00

MS1297 Two sheets, each 101×71 mm. (a) 2000 s. Sesame. (b) 2000 s. Coffee (horiz)
Set of 2 sheets 7·50 8·00

146 Ford Model "A", 1903

(Litho Questa)

1994 (18 Jan). *Centenaries of Henry Ford's First Petrol Engine (Nos. 1298/1301, **MS**1306a) and Karl Benz's First Four-wheeled Car (others). T **146** and similar multicoloured designs. P 14.*

1298	700 s. Type **146**	..	1·25	1·50
	a. Horiz strip of 4. Nos. 1298/1301	4·50	
1299	700 s. Ford Model "T" snowmobile, 1932	1·25	1·50
1300	700 s. Ford "Mustang"	..	1·25	1·50
1301	700 s. Lotus-Ford racing car, 1965	1·25	1·50
1302	800 s. Mercedes-Benz "S600" coupe, 1994	1·25	1·50
	a. Horiz strip of 4. Nos. 1302/5	4·50	
1303	800 s. Mercedes-Benz "W196" racing car, 1955	1·25	1·50
1304	800 s. Mercedes-Benz "W125" road speed record car, 1938	1·25	1·50
1305	800 s. Benz "Viktoria", 1893	1·25	1·50
1298/1305		*Set of 8*	9·00	11·00

MS1306 Two sheets, each 85×85 mm. (a) 2500 s. Henry Ford (vert). (b) 2500 s. Karl Benz (vert)
Set of 2 sheets 9·00 10·00

Nos. 1298/1301 and 1302/5 were printed together, se-tenant, in horizontal strips of 4 throughout the sheet.

(Des W. Hanson. Litho Questa)

1994 (18 Feb). *"Hong Kong '94" International Stamp Exhibition (1st issue). Horiz designs as T **293** of Maldive Islands. Multicoloured. P 14.*

1307	500 s. Hong Kong 1988 60 c. Catholic Cathedral stamp and Religious shrines, Repulse Bay	..	80	90
	a. Horiz pair. Nos. 1307/8	..	1·60	1·75
1308	500 s. Uganda 1993 2500 s. Namirembe Cathedral stamp and Religious shrines, Repulse Bay (different)	..	80	90

Nos. 1307/8 were printed together, se-tenant, in horizontal pairs throughout the sheet with the centre part of each pair forming a composite design.

(Des Kerri Schiff. Litho Questa)

1994 (18 Feb). *"Hong Kong '94" International Stamp Exhibition (2nd issue). Ching Dynasty Snuff Boxes. Vert designs as T **294** of Maldive Islands. Multicoloured. P 14.*

1309	200 s. Glass box with pavilion design	..	35	40
	a. Sheetlet. Nos. 1309/14	..	1·90	
1310	200 s. Porcelain box with quail design	35	40
1311	200 s. Porcelain box with floral design	35	40
1312	200 s. Porcelain box with openwork design	35	40
1313	200 s. Agate box with carved Lion-dogs	35	40
1314	200 s. Agate box with man on donkey design	..	35	40
1309/14		*Set of 6*	1·90	2·25

Nos. 1309/14 were printed together, se-tenant, in sheetlets of 6.

Captions for Nos. 1310/11 are transposed.

147 Meteorological Weather
Station

(Des Associated Creative Designs. Litho Questa)

1994 (15 Mar). *World Meteorological Day. T **147** and similar multicoloured designs. P 14.*

1315	50 s. Type **147**	..	..	30	15
1316	200 s. Weather observatory at training school, Entebbe (vert)	75	40
1317	250 s. Satellite link	..	85	50
1318	300 s. Recording temperatures	..	90	60
1319	400 s. Automatic weather station (vert)	1·25	1·25
1320	800 s. Crops damaged by hailstorms	2·00	2·75
1315/20		*Set of 6*	5·50	5·00

MS1321 105×75 mm. 2500 s. Barograph | 5·00 | 5·50

(Des J. Iskowitz. Litho Questa)

1994 (27 June). *World Cup Football Championship, U.S.A. (2nd issue). Horiz designs as T **268** of Sierra Leone. Multicoloured. P 14.*

1322	500 s. Georges Grun (Belgium)	..	1·00	1·25
	a. Sheetlet. Nos. 1322/7	..	5·50	
1323	500 s. Oscar Ruggeri (Argentina)	..	1·00	1·25
1324	500 s. Frank Rijkaard (Netherlands)	..	1·00	1·25
1325	500 s. Magid "Tyson" Musisi (Uganda)	..	1·00	1·25
1326	500 s. Ronald Koeman (Netherlands)	..	1·00	1·25
1327	500 s. Igor Shalimov (Russia)	..	1·00	1·25
1322/7		*Set of 6*	5·50	6·50

MS1328 Two sheets, each 70×100 mm. (a) 2500 s. Ruud Gullit (Netherlands). (b) 2500 s. Player and R.F.K. Stadium, Washington D.C.
Set of 2 sheets 9·00 9·50

Nos. 1322/7 were printed together, se-tenant, in sheetlets of 6. No. 1326 is inscribed "DONALD KOEMAN" in error.

148 Milking Cow

(Des Associated Creative Designs. Litho Questa)

1994 (29 June). *50th Anniv of Heifer Project International. P 14.*

1329	**148**	100 s. multicoloured	..	60	40

149 Lobobunaea
goodii (wings
spread)

150 Wooden Stool

(Des D. Burkhart. Litho Questa)

1994 (13 July). *Moths. T **149** and similar vert designs. Multicoloured. P 14.*

1330	100 s. Type **149**	..	..	35	20
1331	200 s. Bunaeopsis hersilia	..	65	40
1332	300 s. Rufoglanis rosea	..	80	60
1333	350 s. Acherontia atropos	..	85	75
1334	400 s. Rohaniella pygmaea	..	95	95
1335	450 s. Euchloron megaera	..	1·00	1·25
1336	500 s. Epiphora rectifascia	..	1·10	1·25
1337	1000 s. Polyphychus coryndoni	..	1·90	2·50
1330/7		*Set of 8*	7·00	7·00

MS1338 Two sheets, each 117×88 mm. (a) 2500 s. As Type **149**. (b) 2500 s. Lobobunaea goodii (wings folded) .. *Set of 2 sheets* 9·50 10·00

(Litho Questa)

1994 (18 July). *Crafts. T **150** and similar vert designs. Multicoloured. P 14.*

1339	100 s. Type **150**	..	..	25	10
1340	200 s. Wood and banana fibre chair	..	45	30
1341	250 s. Raffia and palm leaves basket	..	50	35
1342	300 s. Wool tapestry showing tree planting	..	55	45
1343	450 s. Wool tapestry showing hair grooming	..	85	90
1344	500 s. Wood sculpture of a drummer	..	95	95
1345	800 s. Gourds	..	..	1·75	2·00
1346	1000 s. Bark cloth handbag	..	2·00	2·25
1339/46		*Set of 8*	6·50	6·50

MS1347 Two sheets, each 100×70 mm. (a) 2500 s. Raffia baskets. (b) 2500 s. Papyrus hats
Set of 2 sheets 8·50 9·00

151 Turkish Angora Cat and
Blue Mosque

152 Child carrying
Building Block

(Des J. Genzo. Litho Questa)

1994 (22 July). *Cats. T **151** and similar multicoloured designs. P 14.*

1348	50 s. Type **151**	..	..	30	15
1349	100 s. Japanese Bobtail and Mt Fuji	..	40	15
1350	200 s. Norwegian Forest Cat and windmill, Holland	..	60	35

1351	300 s. Egyptian Mau and Pyramids (vert)	70	55
1352	450 s. Rex and Stonehenge, England (vert)	90	90
1353	500 s. Chartreux and Eiffel Tower, France	95	95
1354	1000 s. Burmese and Shwe Dagon Pagoda (vert)	1·75	2·00
1355	1500 s. Maine Coon and Pemaquid Point Lighthouse (vert)	2·50	3·00
1348/55	Set of 8	7·25	7·25
MS1356	Two sheets, each 100×76 mm. (a) 2500 s. Russian Blue. (b) 2500 s. Manx		
	Set of 2 sheets	8·50	9·00

(Des Associated Creative Designs. Litho Questa)

1994 (29 July). *75th Anniv of International Labour Organization.* P 14.

1357	**152** 350 s. multicoloured	75	75

(Des W Hanson. Litho B.D.T.)

1994 (11 Aug). *25th Anniv of First Moon Landing. Astronauts. Horiz designs as T **302** of Maldive Islands. Multicoloured.* P 14.

1358	50 s. Alan Shepard Jnr	40	40
	a. Sheetlet. Nos. 1358/64	4·75	
1359	100 s. M. Scott Carpenter	50	50
1360	200 s. Virgil Grissom	70	70
1361	300 s. L. Gordon Cooper Jnr	80	80
1362	400 s. Walter Schirra Jnr	85	85
1363	500 s. Donald Slayton	90	90
1364	600 s. John Glenn Jnr	1·00	1·00
1358/64	Set of 7	4·75	4·75
MS1365	88×91 mm. 3000 s. "Apollo 11" anniversary emblem	5·00	5·50

Nos. 1358/64 were printed together, se-tenant, in sheetlets of 7 with 2 stamp-size labels depicting rocket launches.

(Des Kerri Schiff. Litho Questa)

1994 (11 Aug). *Centenary of International Olympic Committee. Gold Medal Winners. Multicoloured designs as T **303** of Maldive Islands.* P 14.

1366	350 s. John Akii-Bua (Uganda) (400 metres hurdles), 1972 (horiz)	60	45
1367	900 s. Heike Herkel (Germany) (high jump), 1992 (horiz)	1·25	1·50
MS1368	107×76 mm. 2500 s. Aleski Urmanov (Russia) (figure skating), 1994	4·00	4·50

(Des J. Batchelor. Litho Questa)

1994 (11 Aug). *50th Anniv of D-Day. Horiz designs as T **304** of Maldive Islands. Multicoloured.* P 14.

1369	300 s. Mulberry Harbour pier	50	40
1370	1000 s. Mulberry Harbour floating bridge	1·50	2·00
MS1371	105×76 mm. 2500 s. Aerial view of Mulberry Harbour	3·75	4·00

(Litho Questa)

1994 (11 Aug). *"Philakorea '94" International Stamp Exhibition, Seoul. Horiz designs as T **305** of Maldive Islands. Multicoloured.* P 14.

1372	100 s. Sari Pagoda, Paekyangsa	10	10
1373	350 s. Ch'omsongdae	40	45
1374	1000 s. Pulguksa Temple	1·25	1·40
1372/4	Set of 3	1·75	2·00
MS1375	76×106 mm. 2500 s. Bronze mural, Pagoda Park, Seoul	3·00	3·25

153 Ugandan Family

(Litho Questa)

1994 (11 Aug). *International Year of the Family.* P 14.

1376	**153** 100 s. multicoloured	30	20

154 Baby Simba

(Des Alvin White Studios. Litho Questa)

1994 (30 Sept). *The Lion King. T **154** and similar multicoloured designs showing characters from Walt Disney's cartoon film.* P 14.

1377	100 s. Type **154**	30	30
	a. Sheetlet. Nos. 1377/85	2·40	
1378	100 s. Mufasa, Simba and Sarabi	30	30
1379	100 s. Young Simba and Nala	30	30
1380	100 s. Timon	30	30
1381	100 s. Rafiki	30	30
1382	100 s. Pumbaa	30	30
1383	100 s. The Hyenas	30	30
1384	100 s. Scar	30	30
1385	100 s. Zazu	30	30
1386	200 s. Rafiki and Mufasa	35	35
	a. Sheetlet. Nos. 1386/94	2·75	

1387	200 s. Rafiki holding Simba with Mufasa and Sarabi	35	35
1388	200 s. Rafiki holding Simba aloft	35	35
1389	200 s. Scar and Zazu	35	35
1390	200 s. Rafiki having vision	35	35
1391	200 s. Simba and Scar	35	35
1392	200 s. Simba and Nala	35	35
1393	200 s. Simba with mane of leaves	35	35
1394	200 s. Simba, Nala and Zazu	35	35
1395	250 s. Scar and Simba	40	40
	a. Sheetlet. Nos. 1395/1403	3·25	
1396	250 s. Mufasa rescues Simba	40	40
1397	250 s. Scar killing Mufasa	40	40
1398	250 s. Simba falling off cliff	40	40
1399	250 s. Timon, Pumbaa and Simba at pool	40	40
1400	250 s. Simba, Timon and Pumbaa	40	40
1401	250 s. Rafiki with staff	40	40
1402	250 s. Simba and Nala	40	40
1403	250 s. Simba looking into pool	40	40
1377/1403	Set of 27	8·00	8·00
MS1404	Three sheets. (a) 127×94 mm. 2500 s. Jungle animals. P 14×13½. (b) 127×102 mm. 2500 s. Simba and Timon on branch. P 14×13½. (c) 127×94 mm. 2500 s. Simba with parents and Rafiki (vert). P 13½×14 … Set of 3 sheets	13·00	14·00

Nos. 1377/85, 1386/94 and 1395/1403 were each printed together, se-tenant, in sheetlets of 9.

A 5000 s. in a similar design, embossed on gold foil, also exists from a limited printing.

(Des Kerri Schiff. Litho B.D.T.)

1994 (9 Nov). *Centenary of Sierra Club (environmental protection society) (1992). Endangered Species. Multicoloured designs as T **296** of Maldive Islands.* P 14.

(a) Vert designs

1405	100 s. Chimpanzee with arms folded	50	55
	a. Sheetlet. Nos. 1405/12	6·25	
1406	200 s. Head of Chimpanzee	70	80
1407	250 s. Head of African Wild Dog	70	80
1408	300 s. Head of Cheetah	80	90
1409	500 s. Geleda Baboon	90	1·00
1410	600 s. Geleda Baboon from back	1·00	1·10
1411	800 s. Head of Grevy's Zebra	1·10	1·25
1412	1000 s. Geleda Baboon sitting on rock	1·25	1·40

(b) Horiz designs

1413	200 s. Pair of Cheetahs	70	80
	a. Sheetlet. Nos. 1413/19 plus label	5·50	
1414	250 s. Cheetah cubs	70	80
1415	300 s. African Wild Dog at rest	80	90
1416	500 s. Head of African Wild Dog	90	1·00
1417	600 s. Grevy's Zebra	1·00	1·10
1418	800 s. Chimpanzee lying down	1·10	1·25
1419	1000 s. Grevy's Zebra feeding	1·25	1·40
1405/19	Set of 15	12·00	13·50

Nos. 1405/12 and 1413/19 were each printed together, se-tenant, in sheetlets of 8 stamps (Nos. 1405/12) or 7 stamps and one label (at top left) (Nos. 1413/19).

155 Terminal Building, Entebbe International Airport

156 Game Poachers

(Des Creative Graphics. Litho B.D.T.)

1994 (14 Nov). *50th Anniv of International Civil Aviation Organization. T **155** and similar horiz design. Multicoloured.* P 14.

1420	100 s. Type **155**	45	20
1421	250 s. Control tower, Entebbe International Airport	95	90

(Des Creative Graphics. Litho B.D.T.)

1994 (15 Nov). *Ecology. T **156** and similar vert designs. Multicoloured.* P 14.

1422	100 s. Type **156**	25	10
1423	250 s. Villagers at rubbish dump	60	45
1424	350 s. Fishermen	80	80
1425	500 s. Deforestation	1·40	1·60
1422/5	Set of 4	2·75	2·75

157 "Adoration of the Christ Child" (Filippino Lippi)

158 "Self-portrait" (Tintoretto)

(Litho Questa)

1994 (5 Dec). *Christmas. Religious Paintings. T **157** and similar vert designs. Multicoloured.* P 13½×14.

1426	100 s. Type **157**	30	10
1427	200 s. "The Holy Family rests on the Flight into Egypt" (Annibale Carracci)	50	30
1428	300 s. "Madonna with Christ Child and St. John" (Piero di Cosimo)	70	40
1429	350 s. "The Conestabile Madonna" (Raphael)	80	65
1430	450 s. "Madonna and Child with Angels" (after Antonio Rossellino)	90	1·00
1431	500 s. "Madonna and Child with St. John" (Raphael)	1·00	1·00
1432	900 s. "Madonna and Child" (Luca Signorelli)	2·00	2·50
1433	1000 s. "Madonna with the Child Jesus, St. John and an Angel" (pseudo Pier Francesco Fiorentino)	2·00	2·50
1426/33	Set of 8	7·50	7·50
MS1434	Two sheets, each 115×95 mm. (a) 2500 s. "The Madonna of the Magnificat" (detail) (Sandro Botticelli). (b) 2500 s. "Adoration of the Magi" (detail) (Fra Angelico and Filippo Lippi)		
	Set of 2 sheets	9·00	10·00

No. 1426 is inscribed "Fillipino" in error.

(Des Pauline Cianciolo. Litho B.D.T.)

1995 (7 Feb). *400th Death Anniv of Jacopo Tintoretto (painter) (1994). T **158** and similar multicoloured designs.* P 13.

1435	100 s. Type **158**	25	10
1436	300 s. "A Philosopher"	65	45
1437	400 s. "The Creation of the Animals" (detail) (horiz)	80	80
1438	450 s. "The Feast of Belshazzar" (detail) (horiz)	85	85
1439	500 s. "The Raising of the Brazen Serpent"	95	95
1440	1000 s. "Elijah fed by the Angel"	1·90	2·50
1435/40	Set of 6	4·75	5·00
MS1441	Two sheets. (a) 114×124 mm. 2000 s. "Moses striking Water from a Rock" (detail). (b) 124×114 mm. 200 s. "Finding of Moses" (detail)		
	Set of 2 sheets	8·00	8·50

159 White-faced Whistling Duck ("White-faced Tree-duck")

1995 (24 Apr). *Waterfowl and Wetland Birds of Uganda. T **159** and similar horiz designs. Multicoloured. Litho.* P 14.

1442	200 s. Type **159**	45	45
	a. Sheetlet. Nos. 1442/57	6·50	
1443	200 s. Common Shoveler ("European Shoveler")	45	45
1444	200 s. Hartlaub's Duck	45	45
1445	200 s. Verreaux's Eagle Owl ("Milky Eagle-owl")	45	45
1446	200 s. Avocet	45	45
1447	200 s. African Fish Eagle	45	45
1448	200 s. Spectacled Weaver	45	45
1449	200 s. Black-headed Gonolek	45	45
1450	200 s. Great Crested Grebe	45	45
1451	200 s. Red-knobbed Coot	45	45
1452	200 s. Woodland Kingfisher	45	45
1453	200 s. Pintail	45	45
1454	200 s. Squacco Heron	45	45
1455	200 s. Purple Swamphen ("Purple Gallinule")	45	45
1456	200 s. African Darter	45	45
1457	200 s. African Jacana	45	45
1442/57	Set of 16	6·50	6·50
MS1458	Two sheets, each 106×76 mm. (a) 2500 s. African Pygmy Goose. (b) 2500 s. Fulvous Whistling Duck ("Fulvous Tree-duck")		
	Set of 2 sheets	7·50	8·00

Nos. 1442/57 were printed together, se-tenant, in sheetlets of 16 forming a composite design.

18th World Scout Jamboree Mondial, Holland, August 1995

(160)

1995 (1 June). *18th World Scout Jamboree, Netherlands. Nos. 701/4 and MS941b optd or surch as T **160**.*

1459	100 s. Scouts making bricks	20	10
1460	450 s. on 70 s. Poultry keeping	85	55
1461	800 s. on 90 s. Scout on crutches leading family to immunization centre	1·40	1·60
1462	1500 s. on 10 s. Type **104**	2·25	2·50
1459/62	Set of 4	4·25	4·25
MS1463	115×76 mm. 2500 s. on 1200 s. Lord Baden-Powell, W. Boyce and Revd. L. Hadley	3·75	4·00

No. **MS**1463 is overprinted "18th World Scout Jamboree, August 1995, The Netherlands" on the sheet margin with the surcharge appearing on the stamp.

(Des W. Wright. Litho Questa)

1995 (6 July). *50th Anniv of End of Second World War in Europe. Horiz designs as T* **317** *of Maldive Islands. Multicoloured. P* 14.

1464	500 s.	Soviet artillery in action	85	85
	a.	Sheetlet. Nos. 1464/71	6·00	
1465	500 s.	Soviet tanks on the Moltke Bridge	85	85
1466	500 s.	Kaiser Wilhelm Memorial Church, Berlin	85	85
1467	500 s.	Soviet tanks and Brandenburg Gate	85	85
1468	500 s.	U.S. Boeing B-17 Flying Fortress	85	85
1469	500 s.	Soviet tanks enter Berlin	85	85
1470	500 s.	Ruins of the Chancellery	85	85
1471	500 s.	The Reichstag on fire	85	85
1464/71		*Set of* 8	6·00	6·00

MS1472 104×74 mm. 2500 s. Hoisting the Soviet flag on the Reichstag (57×42½ *mm*) .. 3·50 4·00

Nos. 1464/71 were printed together, *se-tenant*, in sheetlets of 8 with the stamps arranged in two horizontal strips of 4 separated by a gutter showing map of the Soviet advance.

161 Dove, Child, Dish Aerial, Food and Emblem

162 Australian Flag in Form of "VJ"

(Litho Questa)

1995 (6 July). *50th Anniv of United Nations. T* **161** *and similar multicoloured designs. P* 14.

1473	450 s.	Type **161**	55	45
1474	1000 s.	Hands releasing bird and insects	1·25	1·50

MS1475 100×70 mm. 2000 s. Child's hand holding adult's finger (*horiz*) .. 2·50 3·00

(Litho Questa)

1995 (6 July). *50th Anniv of Food and Agriculture Organization. Vert designs as T* **320** *of Maldive Islands. Multicoloured. P* 14.

1476	350 s.	Woman peeling maize	55	65
	a.	Horiz strip of 3. Nos. 1476/8	1·50	
1477	350 s.	Woman and child with maize	55	65
1478	350 s.	Woman and baby with maize	55	65
1476/8		*Set of* 3	1·50	1·75

MS1479 100×70 mm. 2000 s. Child and head of cow .. 2·50 3·00

Nos. 1476/8 were printed together, *se-tenant*, as horizontal strips of 3 in sheets of 9, each strip forming a composite design.

(Litho Questa)

1995 (6 July). *90th Anniv of Rotary International. Designs as T* **299** *of St. Vincent, but vert. Multicoloured. P* 14.

1480	2000 s.	Paul Harris (founder) and logo	2·00	2·50

MS1481 70×100 mm. 2000 s.. National flag and logo .. 2·00 2·50

(Litho Questa)

1995 (6 July). *95th Birthday of Queen Elizabeth the Queen Mother. Vert designs as T* **321** *of Maldive Islands. P* 13½×14.

1482	500 s.	orange-brown, pale brown and black	90	1·00
	a.	Sheetlet. Nos. 1482/5×2	6·50	
1483	500 s.	multicoloured	90	1·00
1484	500 s.	multicoloured	90	1·00
1485	500 s.	multicoloured	90	1·00
1482/5		*Set of* 4	3·25	3·50

MS1486 102×127 mm. 2500 s. multicoloured 4·00 4·00

Designs:—No. 1482, Queen Elizabeth the Queen Mother (pastel drawing); No. 1483, With bouquet of flowers; No. 1484, At desk (oil painting); No. 1845, Wearing turquoise-blue dress; No. **MS**1486, Wearing pale blue dress.

Nos. 1482/5 were printed together in sheetlets of 8, containing two *se-tenant* horizontal strips of 4.

(Des J. Batchelor. Litho Questa)

1995 (6 July). *50th Anniv of End of Second World War in the Pacific. T* **162** *and similar horiz designs showing national flags as "VJ". P* 14.

1487	600 s.	scarlet-vermilion, bluish violet & blk	90	1·00
	a.	Sheetlet. Nos. 1487/92	4·75	
1488	600 s.	scarlet-vermilion, bluish violet & blk	90	1·00
1489	600 s.	scarlet-vermilion, bluish violet & blk	90	1·00
1490	600 s.	multicoloured	90	1·00
1491	600 s.	scarlet-vermilion, pale orange & blk	90	1·00
1492	600 s.	scarlet-vermilion and black	90	1·00
1487/92		*Set of* 6	4·75	5·50

MS1493 108×76 mm. 2500 s. multicoloured 3·50 4·00

Designs:—No. 1487, Type **162**; No. 1488, Great Britain; No. 1489, New Zealand; No. 1490, United States of America; No. 1491, People's Republic of China; No. 1492, Canada; No. **MS**1493 American soldier and flag.

Nos. 1487/92 were printed together, *se-tenant*, in sheetlets of 6 with the stamps arranged in two horizontal strips of 3 separated by a gutter showing the raising of the U.S.A. flag on Iwo Jima.

MINIMUM PRICE

The minimum price quote is 10p which represents a handling charge rather than a basis for valuing common stamps. For further notes about prices see introductory pages.

163 Veloceraptor

(Des B. Regal. Litho B.D.T.)

1995 (15 July). *Prehistoric Animals. T* **163** *and similar multicoloured designs. P* 14.

1494	150 s.	Type **163**	45	45
1495	200 s.	Head of Psittacosaurus	45	45
1496	300 s.	Archaeopteryx (*vert*)	60	60
	a.	Sheetlet. Nos. 1496/1507	6·50	
1497	300 s.	Quetzalcoatlus and volcano (*vert*)	60	60
1498	300 s.	Pteranodon and volcano (*vert*)	60	60
1499	300 s.	Brachiosaurus (*vert*)	60	60
1500	300 s.	Tsintaosaur (*vert*)	60	60
1501	300 s.	Allosaur (*vert*)	60	60
1502	300 s.	Tyrannosaurus (*vert*)	60	60
1503	300 s.	Apatosaur (*vert*)	60	60
1504	300 s.	Giant Dragonfly (*vert*)	60	60
1505	300 s.	Dimorphodon (*vert*)	60	60
1506	300 s.	Triceratops (*vert*)	60	60
1507	300 s.	Compsognathus (*vert*)	60	60
1508	350 s.	Head of Dilophosaurus	65	65
1509	400 s.	Kentrosaurus	70	70
1510	500 s.	Stegosaurus	75	75
1511	1500 s.	Pterodaustro	1·50	2·00
1494/1511		*Set of* 18	10·50	11·00

MS1512 Two sheets, each 106×75 mm. (a) 2000 s. Head of Parasaurolophus. (b) 2000 s. Head of Shunosaurus .. *Set of* 2 *sheets* 6·00 7·00

Nos. 1496/1507 were printed together, *se-tenant*, in sheetlets of 12 with the backgrounds forming a composite design.
No. 1502 is inscribed "Tyranosaur" and No. 1506 "Tricreatops", both in error.

164 Rough-scaled Bush Viper

165 Bell's Hinged Tortoise

(Des R. Rundo. Litho Questa)

1995 (21 Aug)–98. *Reptiles. T* **164/5** *and similar multicoloured designs. P* 14×15 (50, 100, 150, 200, 350, 400, 450, 500 s.), 13½×13 (300, 600, 700 s. (*No.* 1521a) *or* 14 (*others*).

1513	50 s.	Type **164**	10	10
1514	100 s.	Pygmy Python	10	10
1515	150 s.	Three-horned Chameleon	15	20
1516	200 s.	African Rock Python	15	20
1516a	300 s.	Armadillo Girdled Lizard (21.4.98)	25	30
1517	350 s.	Nile Monitor	30	35
1518	400 s.	Savannah Monitor	35	40
1519	450 s.	Bush Viper	40	45
1520	500 s.	Nile Crocodile	45	50
1520a	600 s.	Spotted Sandveld Lizard (21.4.98)	55	60
1521	700 s.	Type **165**	1·25	1·25
1521a	700 s.	Bell's Hinged Tortoise (21.4.98)	60	65
1522	900 s.	Rhinoceros Viper	80	85
1523	1000 s.	Gaboon Viper	90	95
1524	2000 s.	Spitting Cobra	1·75	1·90
1525	3000 s.	Leopard Tortoise (20.11.95)	2·50	2·75
1526	4000 s.	Puff Adder (20.11.95)	3·50	3·75
1527	5000 s.	Common House Gecko (20.11.95)	4·50	4·75
1528	6000 s.	Dwarf Chameleon (20.11.95)	5·25	5·50
1529	10000 s.	Boomslang (snake) (20.11.95)	8·75	9·00
1513/29		*Set of* 20	30·00	32·00

Sizes:—21×21 *mm* 50, 100, 150, 200, 350, 400, 450, 500 s; 18×20 *mm* 300, 600, 700 s. (*No.* 1521a); 38½×24½ *mm* 700 s. (*No.* 1521), 900 s. to 10000 s.

166 Nsambya Church

(Litho Questa)

1995 (7 Sept). *Local Anniversaries. T* **166** *and similar horiz designs. Multicoloured. P* 14.

1530	150 s.	Type **166**	25	20
1531	450 s.	Namilyango College	60	55
1532	500 s.	Figures with symbolic wheel	65	60
1533	1000 s.	Volunteers with food sacks	1·25	1·50
1530/3		*Set of* 4	2·50	2·50

Anniversaries:—Nos. 1530/1, Centenary of Mill Hill Missionaries in Uganda; No. 1532, Centenary of International Co-operative Alliance; No. 1533, 25th anniversary of U.N. volunteers.

167 Bwindi Forest

(Litho Questa)

1995 (14 Sept). *Landscapes. T* **167** *and similar horiz designs. Multicoloured. P* 14.

1534	50 s.	Type **167**	20	20
1535	100 s.	Karamoja	20	20
1536	450 s.	Sunset, Lake Mburo National Park	60	55
1537	500 s.	Sunset, Gulu District	70	60
1538	900 s.	Mist, Kabale District	1·25	1·50
1539	1000 s.	Ruwenzori Mountains	1·40	1·50
1534/9		*Set of* 6	4·00	4·00

(Litho Questa)

1995 (14 Sept). *Waterfalls. Multicoloured designs as T* **167**. *P* 14.

1540	50 s.	Sipi Falls (*vert*)	20	20
1541	100 s.	Murchison Falls	20	20
1542	450 s.	Bujagali Falls	60	55
1543	500 s.	The Two Falls at Murchison	70	60
1544	900 s.	Falls, Ruwenzori Mountains (*vert*)	1·25	1·50
1545	1000 s.	Falls, Ruwenzori Mountains (*different*) (*vert*)	1·40	1·50
1540/5		*Set of* 6	4·00	4·00

168 Peter Rono (1500 metres), 1988

(Des R. Sauber. Litho Questa)

1995 (21 Sept). *Olympic Games, Atlanta* (1996). *T* **168** *and similar multicoloured designs. P* 14.

1546	50 s.	Type **168**	15	10
1547	350 s.	Reiner Klimke (dressage), 1984	50	40
1548	450 s.	German team (cycling time trials), 1988	1·00	70
1549	500 s.	Grace Birungi (athlete)	80	70
1550	900 s.	Francis Ogola (athlete)	1·25	1·50
1551	1000 s.	Nyakana Godfrey (boxer)	1·40	1·50
1546/51		*Set of* 6	4·50	4·50

MS1552 Two sheets, each 106×76 mm. (a) 2500 s. Sebastian Coe (1500 metres), 1980 and 1984. (b) 2500 s. Rolf Dannenberg (discus), 1984 (*vert*) .. *Set of* 2 *sheets* 6·00 6·50

169 Peacock

170 Scouts putting Child on Scales

(Litho Questa)

1995 (2 Oct). *Domestic Animals. T* **169** *and similar horiz designs. Multicoloured. P* 14.

1553	200 s.	Type **169**	40	40
	a.	Sheetlet. Nos. 1553/68	5·75	
1554	200 s.	Pouter Pigeon	40	40
1555	200 s.	Rock Doves	40	40
1556	200 s.	Rouen Duck	40	40
1557	200 s.	Guineafowl	40	40
1558	200 s.	Donkey	40	40
1559	200 s.	Shetland ponies	40	40
1560	200 s.	Palomino horse	40	40
1561	200 s.	Pigs	40	40
1562	200 s.	Border Collie	40	40
1563	200 s.	Merino sheep	40	40
1564	200 s.	Milch goat	40	40
1565	200 s.	Black Dutch rabbit	40	40
1566	200 s.	Lop rabbit	40	40
1567	200 s.	Somali cat	40	40
1568	200 s.	Asian cat	40	40
1553/68		*Set of* 16	5·75	5·75

MS1569 Two sheets, each 106×76 mm. (a) 2500 s. Saddle-bred horses. (b) 2500 s. Oxen *Set of* 2 *sheets* 7·50 7·50

Nos. 1553/68 were printed together, *se-tenant*, in sheetlets of 16 forming a composite design.

(Litho Questa)

1995 (18 Oct). *Uganda Boy Scouts in the Community. T* **170** *and similar multicoloured designs. P* 14.

1570	150 s.	Type **170**	30	30
1571	350 s.	Scouts carrying children	60	40
1572	450 s.	Checking health cards (*horiz*)	65	60
1573	800 s.	Holding child for immunization (*horiz*)	1·25	1·50
1574	1000 s.	Weighing child before immunization	1·40	1·50
1570/4		*Set of* 5	3·75	3·75

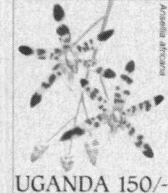

171 Hermann
Staudinger (1953
Chemistry)

172 *Ansellia africana*

(Des R. Cassila. Litho Questa)

1995 (31 Oct). *Centenary of Nobel Prize Trust Fund. T* **171** *and similar vert designs. Multicoloured. P* 14.

1575	300 s.	Type **171**	45	45
	a. Sheetlet. Nos. 1575/86		4·75	
1576	300 s.	Fritz Haber (1918 Chemistry)	45	45
1577	300 s.	Bert Sakmann (1991 Medicine)	45	45
1578	300 s.	Adolf Windaus (1926 Chemistry)	45	45
1579	300 s.	Wilhelm Wien (1911 Physics)	45	45
1580	300 s.	Ernest Hemingway (1954 Literature)	45	45
1581	300 s.	Richard Willstätter (1915 Chemistry)	45	45
1582	300 s.	Stanley Cohen (1986 Medicine)	45	45
1583	300 s.	Hans Jensen (1963 Physics)	45	45
1584	300 s.	Otto Warburg (1931 Medicine)	45	45
1585	300 s.	Heinrich Wieland (1927 Chemistry)	45	45
1586	300 s.	Albrecht Kossel (1910 Medicine)	45	45
1587	300 s.	Hideki Yukawa (1949 Physics)	45	45
	a. Sheetlet. Nos. 1587/98		4·75	
1588	300 s.	F. W. de Klerk (1993 Peace)	45	45
1589	300 s.	Nelson Mandela (1993 Peace)	45	45
1590	300 s.	Odysseus Elytis (1979 Literature)	45	45
1591	300 s.	Ferdinand Buisson (1927 Peace)	45	45
1592	300 s.	Lev Landau (1962 Physics)	45	45
1593	300 s.	Halldor Laxness (1955 Literature)	45	45
1594	300 s.	Wole Soyinka (1986 Literature)	45	45
1595	300 s.	Desmond Tutu (1984 Peace)	45	45
1596	300 s.	Susumu Tonegawa (1987 Medicine)	45	45
1597	300 s.	Louis de Broglie (1929 Physics)	45	45
1598	300 s.	George Seferis (1963 Literature)	45	45
1575/98		*Set of 24*	9·50	9·50

MS1599 Two sheets, each 105×76 mm. (a) 2000 s. Nelly Sachs (1966 Literature). (b) 2000 s. Werner Forssmann (1956 Medicine).
Set of 2 sheets 6·50 7·00
Nos. 1575/86 and 1587/98 were each printed together, *se-tenant*, in sheetlets of 12 forming composite designs.

(Litho Questa)

1995 (30 Nov). *Christmas. Religious Paintings. Vert designs as T* **98** *of St. Kitts-Nevis (Nevis). Multicoloured. P* 13½×14.

1600	150 s.	"The Virgin and Child" (Holbein the Younger)	25	20
1601	350 s.	"Madonna" (Procaccini)	50	35
1602	500 s.	"The Virgin and Child" (Pisanello)	70	50
1603	1000 s.	"Madonna and Child" (Crivelli)	1·40	1·40
1604	1500 s.	"The Nativity of the Virgin" (Le Nain)	1·75	2·25
1600/4		*Set of 5*	4·25	4·25

MS1605 Two sheets, each 102×127 mm. (a) 2500 s. "Madonna and Child" (detail) (Bellini). (b) 2500 s. "The Holy Family" (detail) (Andrea del Sarto) ... *Set of 2 sheets* 7·50 7·50

(Litho Questa)

1995 (8 Dec). *Orchids. T* **172** *and similar vert designs. Multicoloured. P* 14½×14.

1606	150 s.	Type **172**	30	30
1607	350 s.	*Aerangis iuteoalba*	50	50
	a. Sheetlet. Nos. 1607/15		4·00	
1608	350 s.	*Satyrium sacculatum*	50	50
1609	350 s.	*Bolusiella maudiae*	50	50
1610	350 s.	*Habenaria attenuata*	50	50
1611	350 s.	*Cyrtorchis arcuata*	50	50
1612	350 s.	*Eulophia angolensis*	50	50
1613	350 s.	*Tridactyle bicaudata*	50	50
1614	350 s.	*Eulophia horsfallii*	50	50
1615	350 s.	*Diaphananthe fragrantissima*	50	50
1616	350 s.	*Satyricum crassicaule*	65	65
1617	500 s.	*Polystachya cultriformis*	70	70
1618	800 s.	*Disa erubescens*	1·10	1·10
1606/18		*Set of 13*	6·50	6·50

MS1619 Two sheets, each 66×76 mm. (a) 2500 s. *Rangaeris amaniensis*. (b) 2500 s. *Diaphananthe pulchella*. P 13½×14 ... *Set of 2 sheets* 7·00 7·50
Nos. 1607/15 were printed together, *se-tenant*, in sheetlets of 9.

173 Rat and Purple Grapes

(Des Y. Lee. Litho B.D.T.)

1996 (29 Jan). *Chinese New Year ("Year of the Rat"). T* **173** *and similar horiz designs. Multicoloured. P* 14.

1620	350 s.	Type **173**	30	35
	a. Block of 4. Nos. 1620/3		1·10	
1621	350 s.	Rat and radishes	30	35
1622	350 s.	Rat eating corn	30	35
1623	350 s.	Rat eating cucumber	30	35
1620/3		*Set of 4*	1·10	1·40

MS1624 100×74 mm. Nos. 1620/3 1·10 1·40
MS1625 106×76 mm. 2000 s. Rat and green grapes 1·75 1·90
Nos. 1620/3 were printed together, *se-tenant*, as blocks of 4 in sheets of 16.

174 Wild Dog and Pup

(Des R. Rundo. Litho Questa)

1996 (27 Mar). *Wildlife of Uganda. Multicoloured designs as T* **174**. P 14.

(a) *Horiz designs*

1626	150 s.	Type **174**	15	20
	a. Sheetlet. Nos. 1626/33		2·50	
1627	200 s.	African Fish Eagle	15	20
1628	250 s.	Hippopotamus	20	25
1629	350 s.	Leopard	30	35
1630	400 s.	Lion	35	40
1631	450 s.	Lioness	40	45
1632	500 s.	Meerkats	45	50
1633	550 s.	Pair of Black Rhinoceroses	50	55

(b) *Vert designs*

1634	150 s.	Gorilla	15	20
	a. Sheetlet. Nos. 1634/41		2·50	
1635	200 s.	Cheetah	15	20
1636	250 s.	African Elephant	20	25
1637	350 s.	Thomson's Gazelle	30	35
1638	400 s.	Crowned Crane	35	40
1639	450 s.	Saddlebill	40	45
1640	500 s.	Vulture	45	50
1641	550 s.	Zebra	50	55
1626/41		*Set of 16*	5·00	5·75

MS1642 Two sheets. (a) 72×102 mm. 2000 s. Grey Heron (*horiz*). (b) 102×72 mm. 2000 s. Giraffe ... *Set of 2 sheets* 3·50 3·75
Nos. 1626/33 and 1634/41 were each printed together, *se-tenant*, in sheetlets of 8 with enlarged left or top margin.

175 Mickey Mouse and Goofy on Platform at Calais

176 "Autumn Pond"

(Des Walt Disney Co. Litho Questa)

1996 (15 Apr). *Mickey's Orient Express. T* **175** *and similar horiz designs showing Walt Disney cartoon characters. Multicoloured. P* 14×13½.

1643	50 s.	Type **175**	20	20
1644	100 s.	Mickey and Goofy at Athens	25	20
1645	150 s.	Mickey showing Donald Duck his Pullman ticket	40	25
1646	200 s.	Daisy and Donald Duck in Pullman car	55	30
1647	250 s.	Mickey and Minnie Mouse in dining car	65	35
1648	300 s.	Goofy as guard assisting Mickey and Minnie	75	40
1649	600 s.	Mickey and Donald preparing for bed	1·25	1·50
1650	700 s.	Mickey and Minnie at Orient Express accident, Frankfurt, 1901	1·40	1·75
1651	800 s.	Mickey and Goofy building snowman and Orient Express in snowdrift, 1929	1·50	1·75
1652	900 s.	Disney characters filming *Murder on the Orient Express*	1·60	2·00
1643/52		*Set of 10*	7·75	8·00

MS1653 Two sheets, each 132×106 mm. (a) 2500 s. Donald driving Orient Express. (b) 2500 s. Mickey, Minnie and Goofy on observation platform ... *Set of 2 sheets* 8·50 9·00

(Litho Questa)

1996 (8 May). *"CHINA '96" 9th Asian International Stamp Exhibition, Peking (1st issue). Paintings by Qi Baishi. T* **176** *and similar vert designs. Multicoloured. P* 15×14.

1654	50 s.	Type **176**	10	10
	a. Sheetlet. Nos. 1654/63		2·40	
1655	100 s.	"Partridge and Smartweed"	10	10
1656	150 s.	"Begonias and Mynah"	15	20
1657	200 s.	"Chrysanthemums, Cocks and Hens"	15	20
1658	250 s.	"Crabs"	20	25
1659	300 s.	"Wisterias and Bee"	25	30
1660	350 s.	"Smartweed and Ink-drawn Butterflies"	30	35
1661	400 s.	"Lotus and Mandarin Ducks"	35	40
1662	450 s.	"Lichees and Locust"	40	45
1663	500 s.	"Millet and Praying Mantis"	45	50
1654/63		*Set of 10*	2·40	2·75

MS1664 135×114 mm. 800 s. "Morning Glories and Locust" (50×38 *mm*); 800 s. "Shrimps" (50×38 *mm*). P 14×13½ ... 1·25 1·40
The painting titles on 150 s. and 200 s. are transposed in error with "CHRYSANTHEMUMS" shown as "RYSANTHEMUMS".
Nos. 1654/63 were printed together, *se-tenant*, in sheetlets of 10.

177 Tomb Mural, Xi'an

1996 (13 May). *"CHINA '96" 9th Asian International Stamp Exhibition, Peking (2nd issue). Sheet* 140×90 *mm. Litho. P* 13½×14.
MS1664*a* **177** 500 s. multicoloured ... 45 50

178 *Coprinus disseminatus*

179 *Catopsilia philea*

(Litho Questa)

1996 (24 June). *African Fungi. T* **178** *and similar vert designs. Multicoloured. Litho. P* 14.

1665	150 s.	Type **178**	15	20
	a. Sheetlet. Nos. 1665/72		3·25	
1666	300 s.	*Coprinus radians*	25	30
1667	350 s.	*Hygrophorus coccineus*	30	35
1668	400 s.	*Marasmius siccus*	35	40
1669	450 s.	*Cortinarius collinitus*	40	45
1670	500 s.	*Cortinarius cinnabarinus*	45	50
1671	550 s.	*Coltricia cinnamomea*	50	55
1672	1000 s.	*Mutinus elegans*	90	95
1665/72		*Set of 8*	3·25	3·50

MS1673 Two sheets, each 110×80 mm. (a) 2500 s. *Inocybe sororia*. (b) 2500 s. *Flammulina velutipes* ... *Set of 2 sheets* 4·50 4·75
Nos. 1665/72 were printed together, *se-tenant*, in sheetlets of 8.

(Des D. Burkhardt. Litho Questa)

1996 (26 June). *Butterflies. T* **179** *and similar horiz designs. Multicoloured. P* 14.

1674	50 s.	Type **179**	10	10
	a. Sheetlet. Nos. 1674/85		3·50	
1675	100 s.	*Dione vanillae*	10	10
1676	150 s.	*Metamorpha dido*	15	20
1677	200 s.	*Papilio sesostris*	15	20
1678	250 s.	*Papilio neophilus*	20	25
1679	300 s.	*Papilio thoas*	25	30
1680	350 s.	*Diorina periander*	30	35
1681	400 s.	*Morpho cipris*	35	40
1682	450 s.	*Catonephele numilia*	40	45
1683	500 s.	*Heliconius doris*	45	50
1684	550 s.	*Prepona antimache*	50	55
1685	600 s.	*Eunica alcmena*	55	60
1674/85		*Set of 12*	3·50	4·00

MS1686 Two sheets, each 100×70 mm. (a) 2500 s. *Caligo martia*. (b) 2500 s. *Heliconius doris* (different) ... *Set of 2 sheets* 4·50 4·75
Nos. 1674/85 were printed together, *se-tenant*, in sheetlets of 12.

(Litho Questa)

1996 (10 July). *70th Birthday of Queen Elizabeth II. Vert designs as T* **334** *of Maldive Islands showing different photographs. Multicoloured. P* 13½×14.

1687	500 s.	As Type **334** of Maldive Islands	45	50
	a. Strip of 3. Nos. 1687/9		1·25	
1688	500 s.	In evening dress	45	50
1689	500 s.	Wearing red coat and hat	45	50
1687/9		*Set of 3*	1·25	1·50

MS1690 125×103 mm. 2000 s. Queen Elizabeth II ... 1·75 1·90
Nos. 1687/9 were printed together, *se-tenant*, in horizontal and vertical strips of 3 throughout sheets of 9.

(Litho Questa)

1996 (10 July). *50th Anniv of U.N.I.C.E.F. Multicoloured designs as T 335 of Maldive Islands. P 14.*

1691	450 s. Asian children (*horiz*)	..	40	45
1692	500 s. South American children (*horiz*)	..	45	50
1693	550 s. Boy holding pencil (*horiz*)	..	50	55
1691/3		*Set of 3*	1·25	1·50
MS1694	74×104 mm. 2000 s. African mother and child	..	1·75	1·90

(Des M. Freedman and Dena Rubin. Litho Questa)

1996 (10 July). *50th Anniv of U.N.E.S.C.O. Horiz designs as T 348 of Maldive Islands. Multicoloured. P 14×13½.*

1695	450 s. Darien National Park, Panama		40	45
1696	500 s. Los Glaciares National Park, Argentina		45	50
1697	550 s. Tubbaha Reef Marine Park, Philippines		50	55
1695/7		*Set of 3*	1·25	1·50
MS1698	104×74 mm. 2500 s. Ruwenzori Mountains National Park, Uganda		2·25	2·40

No. **MS**1698 is inscribed "RWENZORI" in error.

180 Statue of
Menorah, Knesset

(Des R. Sauber. Litho Questa)

1996 (10 July). *3000th Anniv of Jerusalem. T 180 and similar vert designs. Multicoloured. P 14.*

MS1699	114×95 mm. 300 s. Type **180**, 500 s. Jerusalem Theatre. 1000 s. Israel Museum		1·50	1·60
MS1700	104×74 mm. 2000 s. Grotto of the Nativity	..	1·75	1·90

(Des R. Sauber. Litho Questa)

1996 (10 July). *Centenary of Radio. Entertainers. Vert designs as T 326 of St. Vincent. Multicoloured. P 13½×14.*

1701	200 s. Ella Fitzgerald	..	15	20
1702	300 s. Bob Hope	..	25	30
1703	500 s. Nat "King" Cole	..	45	50
1704	800 s. George Burns and Gracie Allen		70	75
1701/4		*Set of 4*	1·50	1·75
MS1705	74×104 mm. 2000 s. Jimmy Durante		1·75	1·90

181 Electric Locomotive, 1968 (Japan)

(Des J. Puvilland. Litho B.D.T.)

1996 (25 July). *Railway Locomotives. T 181 and similar horiz designs. Multicoloured. P 14.*

1706	450 s. Type **181**	..	40	45
	a. Sheetlet. Nos. 1706/11		2·40	
1707	450 s. Stephenson's *Rocket*, 1829		40	45
1708	450 s. William Norris's *Austria*, 1843		40	45
1709	450 s. Early American steam locomotive		40	45
1710	450 s. Steam locomotive, 1947 (India)		40	45
1711	450 s. Class 103 electric locomotive (Germany)		40	45
1712	550 s. GWR steam locomotive *Lady of Lynn* (England)		50	55
	a. Sheetlet. Nos. 1712/17		3·00	
1713	550 s. Steam locomotive, 1930 (China)		50	55
1714	550 s. Meyer-Kitson steam locomotive (Chile)		50	55
1715	550 s. Union Pacific "Centennial" diesel locomotive No. 6900 (U.S.A.)		50	55
1716	550 s. Type 581 diesel locomotive (Japan)		50	55
1717	550 s. Class 120 electric locomotive (Germany)		50	55
1706/17		*Set of 12*	5·25	6·00
MS1718	Two sheets, each 106×76 mm. (a) 2500 s. Type 99 steam locomotive (Germany); (b) 2500 s. LNER Class A4 steam locomotive *Mallard*, (Great Britain)	*Set of 2 sheets*	4·50	4·75

Nos. 1706/11 and 1712/17 were each printed, *se-tenant*, in sheetlets of 6.

ALTERED CATALOGUE NUMBERS

Any Catalogue numbers altered from the last edition are shown as a list in the introductory pages.

182 Postal and
Telecommunications
Corporation Emblem

(Litho Questa)

1996 (30 Aug). *Centenary of Postal Services. T 182 and similar horiz designs. Multicoloured. P 14.*

1719	150 s. Type **182**	..	15	20
1720	450 s. Loading postbus	..	40	45
1721	500 s. Modern postal transportation		45	50
1722	550 s. 1896 25 c. violet and 1 r. black stamps		50	55
1719/22		*Set of 4*	1·50	1·60

183 Two American River
Steamers and 1904 Games,
St. Louis

184 Mango

(Litho B.D.T.)

1996 (23 Sept). *Olympic Games, Atlanta (1st issue). T 183 and similar multicoloured designs. P 14.*

1723	350 s. Type **183**	..	30	35
1724	450 s. George Finnegan (U.S.A.) (boxing), 1904		40	45
1725	500 s. Chariot racing	..	45	50
1726	800 s. John Flanagan (U.S.A.) (hammer), 1904 (*vert*)		70	75
1723/6		*Set of 4*	1·75	2·00

See also Nos. 1764/81.

(Litho B.D.T.)

1996 (8 Oct). *Fruit. T 184 and similar multicoloured designs. P 14.*

1727	150 s. Type **184**	..	15	20
1728	350 s. Orange	..	30	35
1729	450 s. Pawpaw	..	40	45
1730	500 s. Avocado	..	45	50
1731	550 s. Watermelon (*horiz*)		50	55
1727/31		*Set of 5*	1·75	2·00

(Litho Questa)

1996 (18 Nov). *Christmas. Religious Paintings. Multicoloured designs as T 337 of St. Vincent. P 13½×14.*

1732	150 s. "Annunciation" (Lorenzo di Credi)	15	20
1733	350 s. "Madonna of the Loggia" (detail) (Botticelli)	30	35
1734	400 s. "Virgin in Glory with Child and Angels" (Lorenzetti)	35	40
1735	450 s. "Adoration of the Child" (Lippi)	40	45
1736	500 s. "Madonna of the Loggia" (Botticelli)	45	50
1737	550 s. "The Strength" (Botticelli)	50	55
1732/7	*Set of 6*	2·10	2·40
MS1738	Two sheets, each 106×76 mm. (a) 2500 s. "Holy Allegory" (Bellini) (*horiz*); (b) 2500 s. "The Virgin on the Throne with Child and the Saints" (Ghirlandaio) (*horiz*). P 14×13½ *Set of 2 sheets*	4·50	4·75

(Des Shannon. Litho Questa)

1996 (21 Nov). *20th Anniv of Rocky (film). Sheet 143×182 mm, containing vert design as T 338 of St. Vincent. Multicoloured. P 14×13½.*

MS1739 800 s. × 3 Sylvester Stallone in *Rocky III* 2·10 2·25

185 Traditional
Costume from
Western Uganda

186 Ox

(Litho B.D.T.)

1997 (2 Jan). *Traditional Costumes. T 185 and similar multicoloured designs. P 14.*

1740	150 s. Type **185**	..	15	20
1741	300 s. Acholi headdress	..	25	30
	a. Sheetlet. Nos. 1741/6		1·50	
1742	300 s. Alur headdress	..	25	30
1743	300 s. Bwola dance headdress		25	30
1744	300 s. Madi headdress	..	25	30
1745	300 s. Karimojong headdress with plume		25	30
1746	300 s. Karimojong headdress with two feathers		25	30
1747	350 s. Karimojong women		30	35
1748	450 s. Ganda traditional dress (*horiz*)		40	45
1749	500 s. Acholi traditional dress (*horiz*)		45	50
1740/9		*Set of 10*	2·75	3·25

Nos. 1741/6 were printed together, *se-tenant*, in sheetlets of 6.

(Des Y. Lee. Litho Questa)

1997 (24 Jan). *Chinese New Year ("Year of the Ox"). T 186 and similar multicoloured designs. P 14.*

1750	350 s. Type **186**	..	30	35
	a. Vert strip of 4. Nos. 1750/3		1·10	
1751	350 s. Cow suckling calf		30	35
1752	350 s. Cow and calf lying down		30	35
1753	350 s. Ox lying down	..	30	35
1750/3		*Set of 4*	1·10	1·40
MS1754	111×83 mm. Nos. 1750/3		1·10	1·40
MS1755	76×106 mm. 1500 s. Young calf (*vert*)		1·10	1·40

Nos. 1750/3 were printed together, *se-tenant*, as vertical strips of 4 in sheets of 16.

187 Giraffe running

188 "The Constitution" on Open Book

(Des D. Burkhart. Litho Questa)

1997 (12 Feb). *Endangered Species. Rothschild's Giraffe. T 187 and similar multicoloured designs. P 14.*

1756	300 s. Type **187**	..	25	30
	a. Horiz strip of 4. Nos. 1756/9		1·00	
1757	300 s. Two adult giraffes		25	30
1758	300 s. Head of giraffe	..	25	30
1759	300 s. Giraffe with calf		25	30
1756/9		*Set of 4*	1·00	1·10
MS1760	75×109 mm. 2500 s. Head of giraffe (*different*) (*horiz*)		2·10	2·25

Nos. 1756/9 were printed together, *se-tenant*, both horizontally and vertically in sheets of 12 containing three of each design.

(Litho Questa)

1997 (25 Feb). *Promulgation of New Constitution (8 Oct 1995). T 188 and similar multicoloured designs. P 13½×14 (550 s.) or 14×13½ (others).*

1761	150 s. Type **188**	..	15	20
1762	350 s. "The Constitution" on scroll		30	35
1763	550 s. "THE CONSTITUTION" on closed book (*vert*)		50	55
1761/3		*Set of 3*	95	1·10

189 Kitel Son (Japan)
(marathon), 1936

190 "Red Plum
Blossom and Daffodil"

(Des J. Puvilland. Litho Questa)

1997 (3 Mar). *Olympic Games, Atlanta (2nd issue). Previous Gold Medal Winners. T 189 and similar vert designs. Multicoloured. P 14.*

1764	150 s. Type **189**	15	20
	a. Sheetlet. Nos. 1764, 1766, 1768, 1770, 1772, 1774, 1776, 1778, 1780	2·50	
1765	150 s. Bob Hayes (U.S.A.) (100m), 1964	15	20
	a. Sheetlet. Nos. 1765, 1767, 1769, 1771, 1773, 1775, 1777, 1779, 1781	2·50	
1766	200 s. Walter Davis (U.S.A.) (high jump), 1952	15	20

1767	200 s.	Rod Milburn (110m hurdles), 1972	15	20
1768	250 s.	Matthes (swimming), 1968	20	25
1769	250 s.	Filbert Bayi (Tanzania) (athletics), 1976	20	25
1770	300 s.	Akii Bua (Uganda) (400m hurdles), 1972	25	30
1771	300 s.	H. Kipchoge Keino (Kenya) (steeple chase), 1972	25	30
1772	350 s.	Nordwig (Germany) (pole vault), 1972	30	35
1773	350 s.	Ron Ray (U.S.A.) (athletics), 1976	30	35
1774	400 s.	Wilma Rudolph (U.S.A.) (100m relay), 1960	35	40
1775	400 s.	Joe Frazer (U.S.A.) (boxing), 1976	35	40
1776	450 s.	Abebe Bikila (Ethiopia) (marathon), 1964	40	45
1777	450 s.	Carl Lewis (U.S.A.) (100m), 1984	40	45
1778	500 s.	Edwin Moses (U.S.A.) (400m hurdles), 1984	45	50
1779	500 s.	Gisela Mauermayer (Germany) (discus), 1936	45	50
1780	550 s.	Rady Williams (U.S.A.) (long jump), 1972	50	55
1781	550 s.	Dietmar Mogenburg (Germany) (high jump), 1984	50	55
1764/81		Set of 18	5·50	6·25

Nos. 1764, 1766, 1768, 1770, 1772, 1774, 1776, 1778 and 1780 and 1765, 1767, 1769, 1771, 1773, 1775, 1777, 1779 and 1781 were each printed together, *se-tenant*, in sheetlets of 9 with the backgrounds forming composite designs.

No. 1769 is incorrectly inscribed "Eiilbert" and is dated "1976"; Filbert Bayi did not participate in the 1976 Games. No. 1779 is incorrectly inscribed "Mauemayer" and wrongly identifies the event as the shotput.

(Des Y. Lee. Litho B.D.T.)

1997 (5 Mar). *"HONG KONG '97" International Stamp Exhibition. Paintings by Wu Changshuo. T **190** and similar multicoloured designs. P 14×15.*

1782	50 s.	Type **190**	10	10
		a. Sheetlet. Nos. 1782/91	2·40	
1783	100 s.	"Peony"	10	15
1784	150 s.	"Rosaceae"	15	20
1785	200 s.	"Pomegranate"	15	20
1786	250 s.	"Peach, Peony and Plum Blossom"	20	25
1787	300 s.	"Calyx Canthus"	25	30
1788	350 s.	"Chrysanthemum"	30	35
1789	400 s.	"Calabash"	35	40
1790	450 s.	"Chrysanthemum" (different)	40	45
1791	500 s.	"Cypress Tree"	45	50
1782/91		Set of 10	2·40	2·75
MS1792		137×105 mm. 550 s. "Litchi" (50×37 mm); 1000 s. "Water Lily" (50×37 mm). P 14	90	95

Nos. 1782/91 were printed together, *se-tenant*, in sheetlets of 10.

191 Woody

192 "Pioneer 10"

(Des Rosemary DeFiglio. Litho Questa)

1997 (2 Apr). *Disney's Toy Story (cartoon film). T **191** and similar multicoloured designs. P 13¹/₂×14 (vert) or 14×13¹/₂ (others).*

1793	100 s.	Type **191**	35	35
		a. Sheetlet. Nos. 1793/8	1·90	
1794	100 s.	Buzz Lightyear	35	35
1795	100 s.	Bo Peep	35	35
1796	100 s.	Hamm	35	35
1797	100 s.	Slinky	35	35
1798	100 s.	Rex	35	35
1799	150 s.	Woody on bed (horiz)	50	50
		a. Sheetlet. Nos. 1799/1807	4·00	
1800	150 s.	Woody at microphone (horiz)	50	50
1801	150 s.	Bo Peep (horiz)	50	50
1802	150 s.	Buzz Lightyear (horiz)	50	50
1803	150 s.	Slinky and Rex (horiz)	50	50
1804	150 s.	Woody hiding (horiz)	50	50
1805	150 s.	"Halt ! Who goes there" (horiz)	50	50
1806	150 s.	Rex, Slinky and Buzz Lightyear (horiz)	50	50
1807	150 s.	"You're just an action figure!" (horiz)	50	50
1808	200 s.	"I'm the only sheriff in these parts" (horiz)	50	50
		a. Sheetlet. Nos. 1808/16	4·00	
1809	200 s.	Green toy soldiers (horiz)	50	50
1810	200 s.	Woody and Buzz (horiz)	50	50
1811	200 s.	Woody pointing (horiz)	50	50
1812	200 s.	Buzz Lightyear (horiz)	50	50
1813	200 s.	Green aliens (horiz)	50	50
1814	200 s.	"This is an intergalactic emergency" (horiz)	50	50
1815	200 s.	Buzz and Woody argue (horiz)	50	50
1816	200 s.	Buzz and Woody in buggy (horiz)	50	50
1793/1816		Set of 24	9·50	9·50
MS1817		Three sheets, each 133×108 mm. (a) 133×108 mm. 2000 s. Woody; (b) 108×133 mm. 2000 s. Buzz Lightyear, Rex and other toys; (c) 2000 s. Buzz Lightyear ... Set of 3 sheets	12·00	12·00

Nos. 1793/8, 1799/1807 and 1808/16 were each printed, *se-tenant*, in sheetlets of 6 (Nos. 1793/8) or 9.

(Des W. Wright. Litho Questa)

1997 (16 Apr). *Space Exploration. T **192** and similar multi-coloured designs. P 14.*

1818	250 s.	Type **192**	20	25
		a. Sheetlet. Nos. 1818/25	1·60	
1819	250 s.	"Voyager 1"	20	25
1820	250 s.	"Viking Orbiter"	20	25
1821	250 s.	"Pioneer – Venus 1"	20	25
1822	250 s.	"Mariner 9"	20	25
1823	250 s.	"Galileo" Entry Probe	20	25
1824	250 s.	"Mariner 10"	20	25
1825	250 s.	"Voyager 2"	20	25
1826	300 s.	"Sputnik 1"	25	30
		a. Sheetlet. Nos. 1826/33	2·00	
1827	300 s.	"Apollo" space craft	25	30
1828	300 s.	"Soyuz" space craft	25	30
1829	300 s.	"Intelsat 1"	25	30
1830	300 s.	Manned manoeuvring Unit	25	30
1831	300 s.	"Skylab"	25	30
1832	300 s.	"Telstar 1"	25	30
1833	300 s.	Hubble Telescope	25	30
1818/33		Set of 16	3·50	4·25
MS1834		Two sheets, each 103×73 mm. (a) 2000 s. Space Shuttle Challenger (35×61 mm). (b) 2000 s. "Viking Lander" on Mars (61×35 mm) ... Set of 2 sheets	3·50	3·75

Nos. 1818/25 and 1826/33 were each printed together, *se-tenant*, in sheetlets of 8 with the backgrounds forming composite designs.

193 Deng Xiaoping and Port

194 Water Hyacinth and Pebbles

(Des Y. Lee. Litho Questa)

1997 (9 May). *Deng Xiaoping (Chinese statesman) Commemoration. T **193** and similar horiz design. P 14.*

1835	**193**	500 s. multicoloured	45	50
		a. Sheetlet. Nos. 1835/7	1·75	
1836		550 s. multicoloured	50	55
1837		1000 s. multicoloured	50	55
1835/7		Set of 3	1·75	2·00
MS1838		100×70 mm. 2000 s. multicoloured (Deng Xiaoping and Shenzhen)	1·75	2·00

Nos. 1835/7 were printed together, *se-tenant*, in sheetlets of 3 with an enlarged illustrated margin at right.

(Des R. Martin. Litho Questa)

1997 (14 May). *Environmental Protection. T **194** and similar vert designs. Multicoloured. P 14.*

1839	500 s.	Water hyacinth and Lake Victoria (inscr at top left)	45	50
		a. Sheetlet. Nos. 1839/42	1·75	
1840	500 s.	Water hyacinth and Lake Victoria (inscr at top right)	45	50
1841	500 s.	Type **194**	45	50
1842	500 s.	Larger clump of Water hyacinth and pebbles	45	50
1843	550 s.	Buffalo	50	55
		a. Sheetlet. Nos. 1843/6	2·00	
1844	550 s.	Uganda Kob	50	55
1845	550 s.	Guinea Fowl	50	55
1846	550 s.	Marabou Stork	50	55
1839/46		Set of 8	3·75	4·00
MS1847		106×76 mm. 2500 s. Gorilla	2·25	2·50

Nos. 1839/42 and 1843/6 were each printed together, *se-tenant*, in sheetlets of 4 with the backgrounds forming composite designs, and an enlarged illustrated margin at right. No. 1845 is inscribed "GUINEA FOWEL" and No. 1846 "MALIBU STORK", both in error.

(Litho Questa)

1997 (21 May). *10th Anniv of Chernobyl Nuclear Disaster. Vert designs as T **347** of St. Vincent. P 13¹/₂×14.*

1848	500 s.	As Type **347** of St. Vincent	45	50
1849	700 s.	As No. 1848 but inscribed "CHABAD'S CHILDREN OF CHERNOBYL" at foot	60	65

(Des J. Iskowitz. Litho Questa)

1997 (2 June). *50th Death Anniv of Paul Harris (founder of Rotary International). Horiz designs as T **113** of St. Kitts-Nevis (Nevis). Multicoloured. P 14.*

1850	1000 s.	Paul Harris and child drinking	90	95
MS1851		78×107 mm. 2500 s. The first Rotarians	2·25	2·40

(Litho Questa)

1997 (2 June). *Golden Wedding of Queen Elizabeth and Prince Philip. Horiz designs as T **350** of Maldive Islands. Multicoloured. P 14.*

1852	200 s.	Queen Elizabeth II	15	20
		a. Sheetlet. Nos. 1852/7	90	
1853	200 s.	Royal coat of arms	15	20
1854	200 s.	Queen Elizabeth and Prince Philip at reception	15	20
1855	200 s.	Queen Elizabeth and Prince Philip on royal visit	15	20
1856	200 s.	Buckingham Palace	15	20
1857	200 s.	Prince Philip in military uniform	15	20
1852/7		Set of 6	90	1·10
MS1858		100×70 mm. 2000 s. Princess Elizabeth in wedding dress	1·75	1·90

Nos. 1852/7 were printed together, *se-tenant*, in sheetlets of 6.

(Des J. Iskowitz. Litho Questa)

1997 (2 June). *"Pacific '97" International Stamp Exhibition, San Francisco. Death Centenary of Heinrich von Stephan (founder of the U.P.U.). Horiz designs as T **351** of Maldive Islands. P 14.*

1859	800 s.	deep blue	70	75
		a. Sheetlet. Nos. 1859/61	2·10	
1860	800 s.	chestnut	70	75
1861	800 s.	blue-green	70	75
1859/61		Set of 3	2·10	2·25
MS1862		82×119 mm. 2500 s. dull blue and grey-blue		

Designs:—No. 1859, Chinese post boat; No. 1860, Von Stephan and Mercury; No. 1861, Russian post cart; No. **MS**1862, Von Stephan and French postman on stilts.

Nos. 1859/61 were printed together, *se-tenant*, in sheets of 3 with enlarged right-hand margin.

195 Men's Slalom

196 Main Building, Makerere University

(Litho Questa)

1997 (23 June). *Winter Olympic Games, Nagano, Japan (1998). T **195** and similar multicoloured designs. P 14.*

1863	350 s.	Type **195**	30	35
1864	450 s.	Two-man bobsled	40	45
1865	500 s.	Ski-jumping (horiz)	45	50
		a. Sheetlet. Nos. 1865/70	2·50	
1866	500 s.	Giant slalom (horiz)	45	50
1867	500 s.	Cross-country skiing (horiz)	45	50
1868	500 s.	Ice hockey (horiz)	45	50
1869	500 s.	Pairs figure skating (man) (horiz)	45	50
1870	500 s.	Pairs figure skating (woman) (horiz)	45	50
1871	800 s.	Women's slalom (horiz)	70	75
1872	2000 s.	Men's speed skating (horiz)	1·75	1·90
1863/72		Set of 10	5·75	6·25
MS1873		Two sheets, each 103×72 mm. (a) 2500 s. Downhill skiing (horiz). (b) 2500 s. Women's figure skating (horiz) ... Set of 2 sheets	4·50	4·75

Nos. 1865/70 were printed together, *se-tenant*, in sheetlets of 6 with the backgrounds forming a composite design.

(Litho Questa)

1997 (31 July). *75th Anniv of Makerere University. T **196** and similar multicoloured designs. P 14×13¹/₂ (horiz) or 13¹/₂×14 (vert).*

1874	150 s.	Type **196**	15	20
1875	450 s.	East African School of Librarianship building (vert)	40	45
1876	500 s.	Buyana Stock Farm, Makerere University	45	50
1877	550 s.	Ceramic dish from School of Architecture and Fine Arts	50	55
1874/7		Set of 4	1·50	1·60

1997 (3 Oct). *World Cup Football Championship, France (1998). Multicoloured (except Nos. 1878, 1880, 1883 and 1886) designs as T **246** of Lesotho. P 13¹/₂×14 (vert) or 14×13¹/₂ (horiz).*

1878	200 s.	Fritz Walter, Germany (agate)	15	20
		a. Sheetlet. Nos. 1878 and 1896/1900	2·50	
1879	250 s.	Paulo Rossi (horiz)	20	25
		a. Sheetlet. Nos. 1879/87	1·75	
1880	250 s.	Mario Kempes (black) (horiz)	20	25
1881	250 s.	Gerd Muller (horiz)	20	25
1882	250 s.	Grzegorz Lato (horiz)	20	25
1883	250 s.	Joseph Gaetjens (black) (horiz)	20	25
1884	250 s.	Eusebio Ferreica da Silva (horiz)	20	25
1885	250 s.	Salvatore Schillaci (horiz)	20	25
1886	250 s.	Leonidas da Silva (black) (horiz)	20	25
1887	250 s.	Gary Lineker (horiz)	20	25
1888	250 s.	Argentine and West German player chasing ball (horiz)	20	25
		a. Sheetlet. Nos. 1888/95 and central label	1·60	
1889	250 s.	Azteca Stadium (horiz)	20	25
1890	250 s.	Maradona holding World Cup (horiz)	20	25
1891	250 s.	Argentine and West German players with goal keeper (horiz)	20	25
1892	250 s.	West German player tackling Argentine player (horiz)	20	25
1893	250 s.	Ball in back of net (horiz)	20	25
1894	250 s.	Argentine team (horiz)	20	25
1895	250 s.	Players competing to head ball (horiz)	20	25
1896	300 s.	Daniel Pasarella, Argentina	25	30
1897	450 s.	Dino Zoff, Italy	40	45
1898	500 s.	Bobby Moore, England	45	50
1899	550 s.	Franz Beckenbauer, West Germany	50	55
1900	600 s.	Diego Maradona, Argentina	55	60
1878/1900		Set of 23	5·75	6·75
MS1901		Two sheets. (a) 102×127 mm. 2000 s. Celebrating West German players, 1990 (horiz). (b) 127×102 mm. 2000 s. Bobby Moore, 1966 (horiz) ... Set of 2 sheets	3·50	3·50

Nos. 1878 with 1896/1900, 1879/87 and 1888/95 were each printed together in sheets of 6 (Nos. 1878 with 1896/1900), 9 (Nos. 1879/87) or 8 stamps and 1 central label (Nos. 1888/95) (depicts 1986 World Cup final between Argentina and West Germany).

No. 1883 is inscribed "ADEMIR" in error.

197 Mahatma
Gandhi

198 "Cupid and Dolphin"
(Andrea del Verrocchio)

(Des J. Iskowitz. Litho Questa)

1997 (5 Oct). *50th Death Anniv of Mahatma Gandhi* (1998) *(1st issue). T* **197** *and similar vert designs showing different portraits. P* 14.

1902	600 s. reddish brown and black	..	..	55	60
1903	700 s. reddish brown and black	..	..	60	65
MS1904	73×103 mm. 1000 s. multicoloured	..	90	95

See also Nos. 2021/2.

(Litho B.D.T.)

1997 (1 Dec). *Christmas. Paintings and Sculptures. T* **198** *and similar multicoloured designs. P* 14.

1905	200 s. Type **198**	..	..	15	20
1906	300 s. "The Fall of the Rebel Angels" (Pieter Brueghel the Elder)	..	..	25	30
1907	400 s. "The Immaculate Conception" (Bartolome Murillo)	..	..	35	40
1908	500 s. "Music-making Angel" (Rosso Fiorentino)	..	..	45	50
1909	600 s. "Cupid and Psyche" (Adolphe-William Bouguereau)	..	..	55	60
1910	700 s. "Cupid and Psyche" (Antonio Canova)	..	..	60	65
1905/10	.. .. ..	*Set of 6*	2·25	2·50

MS1911 Two sheets, each 105×96 mm. (a) 2500 s. Mary and Angels (detail, "The Assumption of the Virgin") (El Greco) (*horiz*). (b) 2500 s. Angel holding baby (detail, "The Assumption of the Virgin") (El Greco) (*horiz*)

Set of 2 sheets 4·50 4·75

199 Diana, Princess
of Wales

200 Tiger

(Des Deb Hoeffner. Litho Questa)

1997 (8 Dec). *Diana, Princess of Wales Commemoration. P* 14.

1912	**199** 600 s. multicoloured	..	55	60
	a. Sheetlet. No. 1912×6	..	3·25	

No. 1912 were printed in sheetlets of 6 stamps with an enlarged illustrated right-hand margin.

(Litho Cartor)

1998 (16 Jan). *Chinese New Year ("Year of the Tiger"). T* **200** *and similar horiz designs. Multicoloured. P* 13½.

1913	350 s. Type **200**	..	..	30	35
	a. Sheetlet. Nos. 1913/16	..	1·10	
1914	350 s. Tiger leaping	..	..	30	35
1915	350 s. Tiger resting	..	..	30	35
1916	350 s. Tiger yawning	..	..	30	35
1913/16		*Set of 4*	1·10	1·40
MS1917	106×76 mm. 1500 s. Tiger	..	1·10	1·40

Nos. 1913/16 were printed together, *se-tenant*, in sheetlets of 4.

201 Mountain Gorilla

202 Namugongo
Martyrs Shrine,
Kampala

(Litho Questa)

1998 (18 Jan). *18th Anniv of Pan African Postal Union. P* 14.

1918	**201** 300 s. + 150 s. multicoloured	..	40	45

(Des M. Friedman. Litho Questa)

1998 (6 Feb). *Tourist Attractions. T* **202** *and similar multicoloured designs. P* 14.

1919	300 s. Type **202**	..	..	25	30
1920	400 s. Kasubi Tombs, Kampala (*horiz*)	..	35	40
1921	500 s. Tourist launch in Kazinga Channel, Queen Elizabeth Park (*horiz*)	..	45	50
1922	600 s. Elephant, Queen Elizabeth Park (*horiz*)	..	55	60
1923	700 s. Bujagali Falls, River Nile at Jinja (*horiz*)	..	60	65
1919/23	.. ..	*Set of 5*	2·10	2·40

203 Mother
Teresa, 1928

204 Child in Wheelchair

(Des Zina Saunders. Litho B.D.T.)

1998 (9 Feb). *Mother Teresa Commemoration. T* **203** *and similar multicoloured designs. P* 14.

1924	300 s. Type **203**	..	..	25	30
	a. Sheetlet. Nos. 1924/31	..	2·00	
1925	300 s. Holding child (56×42 *mm*)	..	25	30
1926	300 s. Mother Teresa at United Nations, 1975 (56×42 *mm*)	..	25	30
1927	300 s. Facing left	..	..	25	30
1928	300 s. Full face portrait	..	..	25	30
1929	300 s. With children (56×42 *mm*)	..	25	30
1930	300 s. Mother Teresa rescuing child (56×42 *mm*)	..	..	25	30
1931	300 s. Smiling	..	..	25	30
1924/31		*Set of 8*	2·00	2·40

MS1932 95×81 mm. 2000 s. Mother Teresa with Diana, Princess of Wales (50×37 *mm*) | 1·75 | 1·90

Nos. 1924/31 were printed together, *se-tenant*, in sheetlets of 8.

(Des R. Sempagala-Mpagi. Litho Questa)

1998 (6 Mar). *30th Anniv of U.N.I.C.E.F. T* **204** *and similar vert designs. Multicoloured. P* 13½×14.

1933	300 s. Type **204**	..	..	25	30
1934	400 s. Child receiving oral vaccination against polio	..	..	35	40
1935	600 s. Children outside toilet	..	55	60
1936	700 s. Children in class	..	60	65
1933/6		*Set of 4*	1·75	1·90

205 Pteranodon

206 Rita Dove

(Des G. Bibby. Litho Questa)

1998 (24 Mar). *Prehistoric Animals. T* **205** *and similar multicoloured designs. P* 14.

1937	300 s. Type **205**	..	..	25	30
1938	400 s. Diplodocus	..	..	35	40
1939	500 s. Lambeosaurus	..	..	45	50
1940	600 s. Centrosaurus	..	..	55	60
1941	600 s. Cetiosaurus (*vert*)	..	55	60
	a. Sheetlet. Nos. 1941/6	..	3·25	
1942	600 s. Brontosaurus (*vert*)	..	55	60
1943	600 s. Brachiosaurus (*vert*)	..	55	60
1944	600 s. Deinonychus (*vert*)	..	55	60
1945	600 s. Dimetrodon (*vert*)	..	55	60
1946	600 s. Megalosaurus (*vert*)	..	55	60
1947	700 s. Parasaurolophus	..	60	65
1937/47		*Set of 11*	5·25	6·00

MS1948 Two sheets, each 73×103 mm. (a) 2500 s. Tyrannosaurus rex (42×56 *mm*). (b) 2500 s. Iguanodon (42×56 *mm*) .. *Set of 2 sheets* 4·50 4·75

Nos. 1941/6 were printed together, *se-tenant*, in sheetlets of 6 with the backgrounds forming a composite design.

(Des G. Aagaard. Litho Questa)

1998 (6 Apr). *U.N.E.S.C.O. World Literacy Campaign. 20th-century Afro-American Writers. T* **206** *and similar vert designs. Multicoloured. P* 14.

1949	300 s. Type **206**	..	..	25	30
	a. Sheetlet. Nos. 1949/54	..	1·50	
1950	300 s. Mari Evans	..	..	25	30
1951	300 s. Sterling A. Brown	..	..	25	30
1952	300 s. June Jordan	..	..	25	30
1953	300 s. Stephen Henderson	..	25	30
1954	300 s. Zora Neale Hurston	..	25	30
1949/54		*Set of 6*	1·50	1·75

Nos. 1949/54 were printed together, *se-tenant*, in sheetlets of 6.

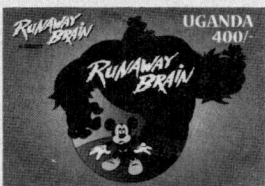

207 Mickey Mouse and Monster (**208**)

(Litho Questa)

1998 (4 May). *70th Birthday of Mickey Mouse. T* **207** *and similar multicoloured designs showing scenes from cartoon film* Runaway Brain. *P* 14×13½.

1955	400 s. Type **207**	..	..	70	70
	a. Sheetlet. Nos. 1955/63	..	5·50	
1956	400 s. Mickey and Pluto with newspaper	70	70
1957	400 s. Mickey and Pluto in front of television	..	..	70	70
1958	400 s. Mickey and Minnie fleeing	..	70	70
1959	400 s. Mickey on television screen	..	70	70
1960	400 s. Monster and hostage Minnie Mouse clinging to skyscraper	..	70	70
1961	400 s. Mickey Mouse throwing lasso	..	70	70
1962	400 s. Mickey circling Monster on lasso	..	70	70
1963	400 s. Mickey and Minnie on rope	..	70	70
1955/63		*Set of 9*	5·50	5·50

MS1964 Two sheets, each 127×102 mm. (a) 3000 s. Mickey and Minnie hugging on roof. P 14×13½. (b) 3000 s. Mickey and Minnie on liferaft (*vert*). P 13½×14 .. *Set of 2 sheets* 7·50 7·50

Nos. 1955/63 were printed together, *se-tenant*, in sheetlets of 9.

1998 (13 May). *"Israel 98" International Stamp Exhibition, Tel-Aviv. Nos.* **MS**1699/1700 *optd with T* **208** *and each further optd* "ISRAEL 98 – WORLD STAMP EXHIBITION TEL-AVIV 13–21 MAY 1998" *on margin.*

MS1965	114×95 mm. 300 s. Type **180**; 500 s. Jerusalem Theatre; 1000 s. Israel Museum	1·60	1·75
MS1966	104×74 mm. 2000 s. Grotto of the Nativity	..	1·75	1·90

209 *Santa Maria* (Columbus)

(Des L. Schwinger. Litho Cartor)

1998 (2 June). *Ships of the World. T* **209** *and similar multicoloured designs. P* 13×13½.

1967	1000 s. Type **209**	..	..	90	95
	a. Sheetlet. Nos. 1967/9	..	2·50	
1968	1000 s. *Mayflower* (Pilgrim Fathers)	..	90	95
1969	1000 s. Barque	..	..	90	95
1970	1000 s. Fishing schooner	..	..	90	95
	a. Sheetlet. Nos. 1970/2	..	2·50	
1971	1000 s. Chesapeake oyster boat	..	90	95
1972	1000 s. Java Sea schooner	..	90	95
1967/72		*Set of 6*	5·00	5·50

MS1973 Two sheets, each 100×70 mm. (a) 3000 s. Thames barge (27×41 *mm*); (b) 3000 s. Felucca (41×27 *mm*). P 13½/2

Set of 2 sheets 5·25 5·50

Nos. 1967/9 and 1970/2 were each printed together, *se-tenant*, in sheetlets of 3 with enlarged illustrated left-hand margins.

210 Grumman F4F Wildcat
(U.S.A.)

211 *Onosma* sp.

(Des B. Regal. Litho Questa)

1998 (24 July). *Aircraft. T* **210** *and similar horiz designs. Multicoloured. P* 14.

1974	500 s. Type **210**	..	..	45	50
	a. Sheetlet. Nos. 1974/9	..	2·50	
1975	500 s. Mitsubishi A6M Zero-Sen (Japan)	45	50
1976	500 s. Supermarine Seafire ("Spitfire") (Great Britain)	..	..	45	50
1977	500 s. Hawker Siddeley Harrier (Great Britain)	..	..	45	50
1978	500 s. S3A Viking (U.S.A.)	..	45	50
1979	500 s. Corsair (U.S.A.)	..	..	45	50
1980	600 s. Dornier Do-X (flying boat) (1929)	55	60
	a. Sheetlet. Nos. 1980/5	..	3·25	
1981	600 s. German Zucker mail rocket (1930)	55	60
1982	600 s. North American X-15 rocket plane (1959)	..	..	55	60
1983	600 s. Goddard's rocket (1930s)	..	55	60
1984	600 s. Wright Brothers' Flyer I (1903)	55	60

1985 600 s. 160R Sikorsky (first helicopter)
(1939) 55 60
1974/85 .. .. Set of 12 5·75 6·50
MS1986 Two sheets. (a) 85×110 mm. 2500 s.
P-40 Tomahawk (U.S.A.) (1940). (b) 110×85
mm. 2500 s. SH-346 Seabat recovery helicopter
(U.S.A.) .. .. Set of 2 sheets 4·50 4·75
Nos. 1974/9 and 1980/5 were each printed together, *se-tenant*,
in sheetlets of 6, forming composite designs.

1998 (23 Sept). *Flowers of the Mediterranean. T* **211** *and
similar multicoloured designs. Litho. P* 14.
1987 300 s. Type **211** 25 30
   a. Sheetlet. Nos. 1987/95 .. .. 2·25
1988 300 s. Rhododendron luteum 25 30
1989 300 s. Paeonia mascula 25 30
1990 300 s. Geranium macrorrhizum .. 25 30
1991 300 s. Cyclamen graecum 25 30
1992 300 s. Lilium rhodopaedum .. 25 30
1993 300 s. Narcissus pseudonarcissus .. 25 30
1994 300 s. Paeonia rhodia 25 30
1995 300 s. Aquilegia amaliae 25 30
1996 600 s. Paeonia peregrina (horiz) .. 55 60
   a. Sheetlet. Nos. 1996/2004 .. 4·75
1997 600 s. Muscari comutatum (horiz) .. 55 60
1998 600 s. Sternbergia sp. (horiz) .. 55 60
1999 600 s. Dianthus sp. (horiz) .. 55 60
2000 600 s. Verbascum sp. (horiz) .. 55 60
2001 600 s. Aubrieta gracilis (horiz) .. 55 60
2002 600 s. Galanthus nivalis (horiz) .. 55 60
2003 600 s. Campanula incurva (horiz) .. 55 60
2004 600 s. Crocus sieberi (horiz) .. 55 60
1987/2004 .. .. .. Set of 18 7·00 8·00
MS2005 Two sheets. (a) 70×100 mm. 2000 s.
Paeonia parnassica. (b) 100×70 mm. 2000 s.
Pancratium maritimum .. Set of 2 sheets 3·50 3·75
Nos. 1987/95 and 1996/2004 were each printed together,
se-tenant, in sheetlets of 9.

212 Bohemian Waxwing

213 Diana, Princess
of Wales

(Litho B.D.T.)

1998 (3 Dec). *Christmas. Birds. T* **212** *and similar multicoloured designs. P* 14.
2006 300 s. Type **212** 25 30
2007 400 s. House Sparrow 35 40
2008 500 s. Black-capped Chickadee .. 45 50
2009 600 s. Eurasian Bullfinch 55 60
2010 700 s. Painted Bunting 60 65
2011 1000 s. Common Cardinal ("Northern
Cardinal") 90 95
2006/11 .. .. .. Set of 6 3·00 3·25
MS2012 Two sheets, each 70×97 mm. (a) 2500 s.
Winter Wren (*vert*). (b) 2500 s. Red-winged
Blackbird (*vert*) .. .. Set of 2 sheets 4·50 4·75
No. MS2012a is inscribed "Winter Wreu" in error.

(Des Diana Catherines. Litho Questa)

1998 (28 Dec). *25th Death Anniv of Pablo Picasso* (painter).
Multicoloured designs as T **373** *of St. Vincent. P* 14½.
2013 500 s. "Woman Reading" (*vert*) .. 45 50
2014 600 s. "Portrait of Dora Maar" (*vert*) 55 60
2015 700 s. "Les Demoiselles d'Avignon" .. 60 65
2013/15 .. .. .. Set of 3 1·60 1·75
MS2016 127×101 mm. 2500 s. "Night Fishing at
Antibes" (*vert*) .. .. .. 2·25 2·40
No. 2015 is inscribed "Des Moiselles D'Avignon" in error.

(Des J. Iskowitz. Litho Questa)

1998 (28 Dec). *19th World Scout Jamboree, Chile. Multicoloured* (except No. **MS2020**) *designs as T* **130** *of St. Kitts-
Nevis* (Nevis). *P* 14.
2017 700 s. Cub Scouts greeting President
Eisenhower, 1956 .. .. 60 65
   a. Sheetlet. Nos. 2017/19 .. 1·75
2018 700 s. Scout with "Uncle Dan" Beard, 1940 60 65
2019 700 s. Vice-President Hubert Humphrey as
Scout leader, 1934 .. .. 60 65
2017/19 .. .. .. Set of 3 1·75 1·90
MS2020 70×100 mm. 2000 s. Scout with pet
beaver (dull pur, bluish grey & dp reddish brn) 1·75 1·90
Nos. 2017/19 were printed together, *se-tenant*, in sheetlets of 3
with enlarged illustrated margins at top and right.

(Des J. Iskowitz. Litho Questa)

1998 (28 Dec). *50th Death Anniv of Mahatma Gandhi* (2nd
issue). *Designs as T* **131** *of St. Kitts-Nevis* (Nevis). *P* 14.
2021 600 s. multicoloured 55 60
   a. Sheetlet of 4 .. .. 2·10
MS2022 98×58 mm. 2500 s. orange-brown, dull
mauve and black .. .. .. 2·25 2·40
Designs: *Vert*—600 s. Gandhi as a young man. *Horiz*—2500 s.
Gandhi in Bombay law office
No. 2021 was printed in sheetlets of 4 with enlarged
illustrated margins at top and left.

1998 (28 Dec). *1st Death Anniv of Diana, Princess of Wales.
Litho. P* 14½×14.
2023 **213** 700 s. multicoloured .. 60 65
   a. Sheetlet of 6 .. .. 3·50
No. 2023 was printed in sheetlets of 6 with an enlarged
illustrated right-hand margin.

214 Rabbit

(Des Wong Kang. Litho Questa)

1999 (4 Jan). *Chinese New Year* ("Year of the Rabbit"). *T* **214**
and similar horiz designs. Multicoloured. P 14.
2024 350 s. White rabbit 30 35
   a. Sheetlet. Nos. 2024/7 .. 1·10
2025 350 s. Rabbit with carrot 30 35
2026 350 s. Brown and white rabbit .. 30 35
2027 350 s. Type **214** 30 35
2024/7 .. .. .. Set of 4 1·10 1·25
MS2028 106×76 mm. 1500 s. Rabbit .. 1·10 1·25
Nos. 2024/7 were printed together, *se-tenant*, in sheetlets of 4.

215 Post Office Emblem and
Slogan

216 Iru Hairstyle

(Litho Questa)

1999 (18 Jan). *Uganda Post Limited Commemoration. P* 14.
2029 **215** 300 s. multicoloured 25 30

(Litho B.D.T.)

1999 (1 Feb). *Hairstyles. T* **216** *and similar vert designs.
Multicoloured. P* 14.
2030 300 s. Type **216** 25 30
2031 500 s. Enshunju hairstyle 45 50
2032 550 s. Elemungole hairstyle 50 55
2033 600 s. Lango hairstyle 55 60
2034 700 s. Ekikuura hairstyle 60 65
2030/4 .. .. .. Set of 5 2·25 2·50

217 Blue Marlin

1999 (13 Mar). *International Year of the Ocean. T* **217** *and
similar horiz designs. Multicoloured. P* 14.
2035 500 s. Type **217** 45 50
   a. Sheetlet. Nos. 2035/43 .. 4·00
2036 500 s. Arctic Tern 45 50
2037 500 s. Common Dolphin 45 50
2038 500 s. Blacktip Shark 45 50
2039 500 s. Manta Ray 45 50
2040 500 s. Blackedge Moray 45 50
2041 500 s. Loggerhead Turtle 45 50
2042 500 s. Sail-finned Tang 45 50
2043 500 s. Two-spotted Octopus 45 50
2044 500 s. Atlantic Wolffish 45 50
   a. Sheetlet of 4. Nos. 2044/7 .. 1·75
2045 500 s. Equal Sea Star 45 50
2046 500 s. Purple Sea Urchin 45 50
2047 500 s. Mountain Crab 45 50
2035/47 .. .. .. Set of 13 5·75 6·50
MS2048 Two sheets, each 110×85 mm. (a)
2500 s. Sea Nettle Jellyfish. (b) 2500 s.
Decatopecten striatus (scallop) .. Set of 2 sheets 4·50 4·75
Nos. 2035/43 and Nos. 2044/7 were each printed together,
se-tenant, in sheetlets of 9 (with the backgrounds forming a
composite design) or 4.
No. 2036 is inscribed "ARTIC TERN" in error.

218 Cows feeding (income
generation)

219 L'Hoest's Monkey

(Litho Cartor)

1999 (19 July). *International Year of the Elderly. T* **218** *and
similar horiz designs. Multicoloured. P* 13×13½.
2049 300 s. Type **218** 25 30
2050 500 s. Elderly man reading with child .. 45 50
2051 600 s. Playing board game 55 60
2052 700 s. Food distribution 60 65
2049/52 .. .. .. Set of 4 1·75 2·00

1999 (19 Nov). *Primates. T* **219** *and similar multicoloured
designs. Litho. P* 13½×14.
2053 300 s. Type **219** 25 30
2054 400 s. Diademed Monkey ("Sykes/Blue
Monkey") 35 40
2055 500 s. Patas Monkey 45 50
2056 600 s. Red-tailed Monkey 55 60
2057 700 s. Eastern Black and White Colobus 60 65
2058 1000 s. Mountain Gorilla 90 95
2053/8 .. .. .. Set of 6 3·00 3·25
MS2059 73×54 mm. 2500 s. Olive Baboon
(35×26 *mm*). P 13½ .. .. 2·25 2·40

(Litho Questa)

1999 (24 Nov). *150th Death Anniv of Katsushika Hokusai*
(Japanese artist). *Multicoloured designs as T* **263** *of Lesotho,
but vert. P* 13½×14.
2060 700 s. "Dragon flying over Mount Fuji"
(detail) 60 65
   a. Sheetlet. Nos. 2060/5 .. 3·50
2061 700 s. "Famous Poses from the Kabuki
Theatre" (one woman) 60 65
2062 700 s. "Kitsune No Yomeiri" 60 65
2063 700 s. "Dragon flying over Mount Fuji"
(complete picture) 60 65
2064 700 s. "Famous Poses from the Kabuki
Theatre" (man and woman) .. 60 65
2065 700 s. "Girl holding Cloth" 60 65
2060/5 .. .. .. Set of 6 3·50 3·75
MS2066 100×70 mm. 3000 s. "Japanese Spaniel" 2·50 2·75
Nos. 2060/5 were printed together, *se-tenant*, in sheetlets of 6.
No. 2065 is inscribed "GIRL HOLDING CLOTHE" in error.

(Litho Questa)

1999 (24 Nov). *"Queen Elizabeth the Queen Mother's Century".
Vert designs as T* **267** *of Lesotho. P* 14.
2067 1200 s. multicoloured .. .. 95 1·00
   a. Sheetlet. Nos. 2067/70 .. 3·75
2068 1200 s. black and gold .. .. 95 1·00
2069 1200 s. black and gold .. .. 95 1·00
2070 1200 s. multicoloured .. .. 95 1·00
2067/70 .. .. .. Set of 4 3·75 4·00
MS2071 152×155 mm. 3000 s. multicoloured.
P 13½×14 .. .. .. 2·50 2·75
Designs (*As Type* **267** *of Lesotho*)—No. 2067, Duchess of York
wearing evening cape; No. 2068, Wedding of Duke and Duchess
of York, 1923; No. 2069, Formal portrait of Queen Mother; No.
2070, Queen Mother at evening reception. (37×50 *mm*)—No.
MS2071, Queen Mother visiting Cambridge, 1961.
Nos. 2067/70 were printed together, *se-tenant*, as a sheetlet of
4 stamps and a central label with inscribed and embossed
margins.
No. MS2071 also shows the Royal Arms embossed in gold.

220 Saturn V Rocket
Launch

221 Penduline Tit

(Litho Questa)

1999 (24 Nov). *30th Anniv of First Manned Landing on Moon.
T* **220** *and similar vert designs. Multicoloured. P* 14×13½.
2072 600 s. Type **220** 55 60
   a. Sheetlet. Nos. 2072/7 .. 3·25
2073 600 s. Command and service module
Columbia 55 60
2074 600 s. Edwin E. Aldrin descending ladder 55 60
2075 600 s. Saturn V rocket on launch pad .. 55 60
2076 600 s. Lunar module Eagle 55 60
2077 600 s. Edwin E. Aldrin on Moon's surface 55 60
2078 700 s. Mercury mission "Freedom 7", 1961 60 65
   a. Sheetlet. Nos. 2078/83 .. 3·50
2079 700 s. "Gemini 4", 1965 .. .. 60 65
2080 700 s. "Apollo 11" command and service
module Columbia 60 65
2081 700 s. "Vostok 1", 1961 .. .. 60 65
2082 700 s. Saturn V rocket 60 65
2083 700 s. Apollo 11 lunar module Eagle .. 60 65
2072/83 .. .. .. Set of 12 6·75 7·50
MS2084 Two sheets, each 76×106 mm. (a)
3000 s. Edwin E. Aldrin with scientific
experiment. (b) 3000 s. "Apollo 11" command
module re-entering Earth's atmosphere
.. .. .. Set of 2 sheets 5·25 5·50
Nos. 2072/7 and 2078/83 were each printed together,
se-tenant, in sheetlets of 6 with enlarged illustrated margins
with the backgrounds of Nos. 2078/83 forming a composite
design.

(Litho Questa)

1999 (1 Dec). *Birds of Uganda. T 221 and similar vert designs.*
Multicoloured. P 14.

2085	300 s. Type 221 ..	..	25	30
2086	500 s. Grey-headed Kingfisher ..	..	45	50
	a. Sheetlet. Nos. 2086/93	..	3·50	
2087	500 s. Green-headed Sunbird ..	..	45	50
2088	500 s. Speckled Pigeon ..	..	45	50
2089	500 s. Grey Parrot ..	..	45	50
2090	500 s. Barn Owl ..	..	45	50
2091	500 s. South African Crowned Crane ("Grey Crowned Crane") ..	..	45	50
2092	500 s. Whale-headed Stork ("Shoebill") ..		45	50
2093	500 s. Black Heron ..	..	45	50
2094	600 s. Scarlet-chested Sunbird ..	..	55	60
	a. Sheetlet. Nos. 2094/101 ..	..	4·25	
2095	600 s. Lesser Honeyguide ..	..	55	60
2096	600 s. African Palm Swift ..	..	55	60
2097	600 s. Swamp Flycatcher ..	..	55	60
2098	600 s. Lizard Buzzard ..	..	55	60
2099	600 s. Osprey ..	..	55	60
2100	600 s. Cardinal Woodpecker ..	..	55	60
2101	600 s. Pearl-spotted Owlet ..	..	55	60
2102	700 s. Speke's Weaver ("Fox's Weaver") ..		60	65
	a. Sheetlet. Nos. 2102/9 ..	..	4·75	
2103	700 s. Chin-spot Flycatcher ..	..	60	65
2104	700 s. Blue Swallow ..	..	60	65
2105	700 s. Purple-breasted Sunbird ..		60	65
2106	700 s. Comb Duck ("Knob-billed Duck") ..		60	65
2107	700 s. Red-collared Whydah ("Widowbird") ..		60	65
2108	700 s. Ruwenzori Turaco ..	..	60	65
2109	700 s. African Cuckoo Hawk ..	..	60	65
2110	1000 s. Yellow-fronted Tinkerbird ..		90	95
2111	1200 s. Zebra Waxbill ..	..	95	1·00
2112	1800 s. Sooty Anteater Chat ..	..	1·50	1·60
2085/112		*Set of 28*	16·00	17·00

MS2113 Two sheets, each 76×106 mm. (a)
3000 s. Four-banded Sandgrouse. (b) 3000 s.
Paradise Whydah .. .. .. *Set of 2 sheets* 5·25 5·50
Nos. 2086/93, 2094/101 and 2102/9 were each printed
together, *se-tenant*, in sheetlets of 8 with the backgrounds
forming composite designs.
Nos. 2100/1 are inscribed "Cardinal Woopecker" or
"*Glaucidium periatum*", both in error.

222 *Epiphora bauhiniae*   **223** Postman with
    (moth)   Women and Child

(Litho Cartor)

2000 (19 Jan). *Moths. T 222 and similar multicoloured*
designs. P 13½.

2114	300 s. Type 222 ..	..	25	30
2115	400 s. *Phylloxiphia formosa* (*horiz*) ..		35	40
2116	500 s. *Bunaea alcinoe* ..	..	45	50
2117	600 s. *Euchloron megaera* (*horiz*) ..		55	60
2118	700 s. *Argema mimosae* ..	..	60	65
2119	1800 s. *Denephila nerii* (*horiz*) ..		1·50	1·60
2114/19		*Set of 6*	3·50	4·00

MS2120 75×52 mm. 3000 s. *Lobobunaea*
angasana (*horiz*) .. .. .. 2·50 2·75

2000 (28 Jan). *125th Anniv of Universal Postal Union. T 223*
and similar vert designs. Multicoloured. Litho. P 14.

2121	600 s. Type 223 ..	..	55	60
2122	700 s. American mother and child reading letter by post box ..		60	65
2123	1200 s. Mail coach ..	..	95	1·00
2121/3		*Set of 3*	2·10	2·25

STAMP BOOKLETS

1962 (9 Oct). *Black on buff cover. Stitched.*
SB1 5 s. booklet containing 10 c., 15 c., 20 c., 30 c. and
50 c. (Nos. 100/4), each in block of 4 .. 6·50

1965. *Black on blue (No. SB2) or buff (No. SB3) covers.*
Stitched.
SB2 3 s. booklet containing four 15 c. and eight 30 c.
(Nos. 115, 117) in blocks of 4 .. .. 10·00
SB3 5 s. booklet containing four 15 c. and 50 c., and
eight 30 c. (Nos. 115, 117, 119) in blocks of 4 11·00

1970. *Black on blue (No. SB4) or buff (No. SB5) covers.*
Stitched.
SB4 3 s. booklet containing four 5 c. and 10 c., and
eight 30 c. (Nos. 131/2, 135) in blocks of 4 .. 7·50
SB5 5 s. booklet containing four 5 c., 10 c. and 50 c.,
and eight 30 c. (Nos. 131/2, 135, 137) in blocks
of 4 .. .. 7·50

1971 (15 Dec). *Black on salmon (No. SB6) or lilac (No. SB7)*
covers. Stitched.
SB6 5 s. booklet containing four 10 c., 15 c. and 40 c.,
and eight 30 c. (Nos. 132/3, 135/6) in blocks
of 4 .. .. 7·50
SB7 10 s. booklet containing four 10 c., 20 c., 30 c. and
50 c., and eight 70 c. (Nos. 132, 134/5, 137,
139) in blocks of 4 .. .. .. 11·00

1975 (9 Oct). *Black on blue (No. SB8) or yellow (No. SB9)*
covers. Stitched.
SB8 5 s. booklet containing ten 50 c. (No. 153) in two
blocks of 4 and one pair .. .. 4·00
SB9 10 s. booklet containing four 10 c., 20 c., 40 c. and
80 c., and eight 50 c. (Nos. 149/50, 152/3, 155)
in blocks of 4 .. .. .. 4·75

POSTAGE DUE STAMPS

The Postage Due stamps of Kenya, Uganda and Tanganyika
were used in Uganda until 2 January 1967.

    D 1   LIBERATED   D 3 Lion
             1979
            (D 2)

(Litho D.L.R.)

1967 (3 Jan). *Chalk-surfaced paper. P 14 × 13½.*

D1	D 1	5 c. scarlet	..	20	4·25
D2		10 c. green	..	20	4·25
D3		20 c. deep blue ..	..	35	4·25
D4		30 c. red-brown ..	..	40	6·00
D5		40 c. bright purple ..		60	9·00
D6		1 s. orange ..	..	1·50	13·00
D1/6	..		*Set of 6*	3·00	38·00

1970 (31 Mar). *As Nos. D1/6, but on glazed ordinary paper.*
P 14 × 15.

D 7	D 1	5 c. scarlet	..	15	2·50
D 8		10 c. green	..	15	2·50
D 9		20 c. deep blue	..	25	3·00
D10		30 c. red-brown	..	35	4·00
D11		40 c. bright purple ..		55	4·50
D7/11			*Set of 5*	1·25	15·00

1973 (12 Dec). *Glazed, ordinary paper. P 15.*

D12	D 1	5 c. scarlet	..	80	5·00
D13		10 c. emerald	..	80	5·00
D14		20 c. deep blue	..	1·25	6·00
D15		30 c. red-brown	..	1·50	8·00
D16		40 c. bright mauve ..		2·00	11·00
D17		1 s. bright orange ..		2·75	11·00
D12/17			*Set of 6*	8·00	42·00

"UGANDA LIBERATED" OVERPRINTS. Nos. D1/17 were
overprinted "UGANDA LIBERATED 1979", in very limited
quantities, using a style of overprint similar to Type **32** (*Prices:*
Nos. D1/6 set of 6 £225; D7/11 set of 5 £75; D12, 14/17 set of 5
£60; D13 £80, all mint).

(Litho Questa)

1979 (Dec). *Liberation. As Nos. D1/6 optd with Type D* **2**. *Chalk-*
surfaced paper. P 13½ × 14.

D18	D 1	5 c. scarlet	..	20	40
D19		10 c. green	..	20	40
D20		20 c. dull ultramarine ..		25	40
D21		30 c. red-brown	..	25	60
D22		40 c. bright purple	..	30	60
D23		1 s. orange	..	30	60
D18/23			*Set of 6*	1·40	2·75

(Litho Questa)

1985 (11 Mar). *Animals. Type D* **3** *and similar vert designs.*
P 14½ × 14.

D24	5 s. black and bright turquoise-green ..		15	20
D25	10 s. black and dull rose-lilac ..		15	20
D26	20 s. black and dull orange ..		30	40
D27	40 s. black and bright lilac ..		60	75
D28	50 s. black and pale greenish blue ..		60	75
D29	100 s. black and mauve ..		1·00	1·25
D24/9		*Set of 6*	2·50	3·25

Designs:—10 s. African Buffalo; 20 s. Kob; 40 s. African
Elephant; 50 s. Common Zebra; 100 s. Black Rhinoceros.

Vanuatu
(*formerly* New Hebrides)

NEW HEBRIDES

Stamps of NEW SOUTH WALES were used by various Postal Agencies in the New Hebrides from August 1891 onwards. From late 1892 the N.S.W. agency at Port Vila was run by the Australian New Hebrides Company who, from 1897, issued local 1d. and 2d. stamps for the carriage of mail on the Company's ships. These can be found used in combination with N.S.W. issues. Similar Postal Agencies supplying the stamps of NEW CALEDONIA were opened from 1903 onwards. The use of New South Wales and New Caledonia stamps was prohibited after 1 December 1908.

PRICES FOR STAMPS ON COVER TO 1945	
Nos. 1/8 (F1/5)	*from* × 10
No. 9	*from* × 2
Nos. 10/16 (F6/10)	*from* × 8
Nos. 18/28 (F11/32)	*from* × 6
Nos. 30/4 (F33/7)	*from* × 4
No. 35 (F32a)	—
Nos. 36/9	*from* × 3
Nos. 40/2 (F38/41)	*from* × 4
Nos. 43/51 (F42/52)	*from* × 5
Nos. 52/63 (F53/64)	*from* × 3
Nos. D1/10 (FD53/69)	*from* × 8

ANGLO-FRENCH CONDOMINIUM

The New Hebrides, an island group in the south-west Pacific, were recognised as an area of joint Anglo-French influence in 1878. The position was regularised by the Convention of 20 October 1906 which created a Condominium, the two nations having equal rights and shares in the administration of the islands.

Stamps inscribed in English or French were issued concurrently and had equal validity throughout the islands. A common currency was reflected in the face values from 1938.

Where common designs were used the main differences between stamps inscribed in English and those in French are as follows:

(a) Inscriptions in English or French.
(b) Position of cyphers. French issues normally have "RF" to the right or above the British royal cypher.
(c) French issues are without watermark, *unless otherwise stated.*

Inscriptions in English

Inscriptions in French

I. STAMPS INSCRIBED IN ENGLISH

NEW HEBRIDES.   NEW HEBRIDES

CONDOMINIUM.   CONDOMINIUM
(1)   (2)

1908 (29 Oct). *T* **23** *and* **24** *of Fiji optd with T* **1** *by Govt Printing Establishment, Suva. On the bicoloured stamps the word "FIJI" obliterated by a bar in the colour of the stamp.* P 14.

(a) Wmk Multiple Crown CA. Ordinary paper (½d., 1d.) *or chalk-surfaced paper* (1s.)

1	½d. green and pale green (No. 115)	..		3·00	14·00
1a	½d. green (No. 118)	..		40	7·00
2	1d. red	..		45	40
	a. Opt omitted (in vert pair with normal)		£5500	
3	1s. green and carmine	..	..	19·00	4·50

(b) Wmk Crown CA

4	½d. green and grey-green	..	..	50·00	80·00
5	2d. dull purple and orange			60	70
6	2½d. dull purple and blue/*blue*			60	70
7	5d. dull purple and green			80	2·00
8	6d. dull purple and carmine			70	1·25
9	1s. green and carmine	..		£150	£200
1/9			*Set of 9*	£180	£250

1910 (15 Dec). *Types as last optd with T* **2** *by D.L.R. Wmk Multiple Crown CA. Ordinary paper* (½d. *to* 2½d.) *or chalk-surfaced paper* (5d., 6d., 1s.). P 14.

10	½d. green	..	..	3·50	24·00
11	1d. red	..		10·00	8·50
12	2d. grey	..		60	3·00
13	2½d. bright blue	..		65	3·75
14	5d. dull purple and olive-green			1·00	5·50
15	6d. dull and deep purple			1·00	5·00
16	1s. black/*green* (R.)			1·00	7·50
10/16			*Set of 7*	16·00	50·00
10/16 Optd "Specimen"			*Set of 7*	£250	

3 Weapons and Idols   (**4**)

1d.

(Des J. Giraud. Recess D.L.R.)

1911 (25 July). *Wmk Mult Crown CA.* P 14.

18	**3**	½d. green	..	..	..	85	1·75
19		1d. red	..	..	..	3·50	2·00
20		2d. grey	..	..	..	7·00	4·00
21		2½d. ultramarine	..	..		3·00	5·50
24		5d. sage-green	..	..		4·50	6·50
25		6d. purple	..	..		3·00	5·00
26		1s. black/*green*	..	..		2·25	13·00
27		2s. purple/*blue*	..	..		17·00	22·00
28		5s. green/*yellow*	..	..		32·00	48·00
18/28				*Set of 9*	65·00	95·00	
18/28 Optd "Specimen"				*Set of 9*	£180		

1920 (June)–**21**. *Surch with T* **4** *at Govt Printing Establishment, Suva.*

(a) On Nos. **24** *and* **26/8**

30	**3**	1d. on 5d. sage-green (10.3.21)	..		7·00	60·00
		a. Surch inverted	..		£1700	
31	**3**	1d. on 1s. black/*green*	..		1·25	13·00
32		1d. on 2s. purple/*blue*	..		1·00	10·00
33		1d. on 5s. green/*yellow*	..		1·00	10·00

(b) On No. **F16**

34	**3**	2d. on 40 c. red/*yellow*	..		1·00	15·00

(c) On No. **F27**

35	**3**	2d. on 40 c. red/*yellow*	..		£120	£450

1921 (Sept–Oct). *Wmk Mult Script CA.* P 14.

36	**3**	1d. scarlet	..		2·00	14·00
37		2d. slate-grey	..		4·00	32·00
39		6d. purple	..		14·00	70·00
36/9			*Set of 3*	18·00	£100	
36/9 Optd "Specimen"			*Set of 3*	70·00		

1924 (1 May). *Surch as T* **4**, *at Suva.*

40	**3**	1d. on ½d. green (No. 18)	..		4·00	20·00
41		3d. on 1d. scarlet (No. 36)	..		4·00	11·00
42		5d. on 2½d. ultramarine (No. 21)			7·50	20·00
		a. Surch inverted	..		£1500	
40/2			*Set of 3*	14·00	45·00	

5

(Recess D.L.R.)

1925 (June). *Wmk Mult Script CA.* P 14.

43	**5**	½d. (5 c.) black	..		1·25	9·00
44		1d. (10 c.) green	..		1·00	9·00
45		2d. (20 c.) slate-grey	..		1·75	2·50
46		2½d. (25 c.) brown	..		1·00	12·00
47		5d. (50 c.) ultramarine	..		2·75	2·50
48		6d. (60 c.) purple	..		3·50	11·00
49		1s. (1.25 fr.) black/*emerald*			3·25	19·00
50		2s. (2.50 fr.) purple/*blue*	..		6·00	22·00
51		5s. (6.25 fr.) green/*yellow*	..		6·00	25·00
43/51			*Set of 9*	23·00	£100	
43/51 Optd "Specimen"			*Set of 9*	£180		

(New Currency. 100 gold centimes = 1 gold franc)

The currency used for the face values of issues to 1977 was an artificial, rather than an actual, monetary unit. The actual currencies in use were Australian dollars and the local franc.

6 Lopevi Is and Outrigger Canoe

(Des J. Kerhor. Eng J. G. Hall. Recess B.W.)

1938 (1 June). *Gold Currency. Wmk Mult Script CA.* P 12.

52	**6**	5 c. blue-green	..		2·50	3·00
53		10 c. orange	..		1·25	1·50
54		15 c. bright violet	..		3·00	3·25
55		20 c. scarlet	..		1·60	2·00
56		25 c. reddish brown	..		1·60	2·00
57		30 c. blue	..		1·90	1·50
58		40 c. grey-olive	..		4·50	4·25
59		50 c. purple	..		1·60	1·50
60		1 f. red/*green*	..		4·00	7·50
61		2 f. blue/*green*	..		30·00	17·00
62		5 f. red/*yellow*	..		70·00	48·00
63		10 f. violet/*blue*	..		£200	75·00
52/63			*Set of 12*	£300	£150	
52/63 Perf "Specimen"			*Set of 12*	£225		

(Recess Waterlow)

1949 (10 Oct). *75th Anniv of U.P.U. As No.* 148 *of Jamaica. Wmk Mult Script CA.* P 13½×14.

64		10 c. red-orange	..		30	40
65		15 c. violet	..		30	40
66		30 c. ultramarine	..		30	40
67		50 c. purple	..		30	40
64/7			*Set of 4*	1·10	1·40	

NEW INFORMATION

The editor is always interested to correspond with people who have new information that will improve or correct the Catalogue.

7 Outrigger Sailing Canoes

(Des C. Hertenberger (1 f. to 5 f.), R. Serres (others). Recess Waterlow)

1953 (30 Apr). *T* **7** *and similar horiz designs. Wmk Mult Script CA.* P 12½.

68		5 c. green	..		60	10
69		10 c. scarlet	..		60	10
70		15 c. yellow-ochre	..		60	10
71		20 c. ultramarine	..		60	10
72		25 c. olive	..		60	10
73		30 c. brown	..		60	10
74		40 c. blackish brown	..		60	10
75		50 c. violet	..		1·00	10
76		1 f. orange	..		7·50	10
77		2 f. reddish purple	..		7·50	9·00
78		5 f. scarlet	..		12·00	32·00
68/78			*Set of 11*	29·00	38·00	

Designs:—5 to 20 c. Type **7**; 25 to 50 c. Native carving; 1 to 5 f. Two natives outside hut.

1953 (2 June). *Coronation. As No.* 153 *of Jamaica.*

79		10 c. black and carmine	..		60	50

10 San Pedro y San Paulo (Quiros)

(Photo Harrison)

1956 (20 Oct). *50th Anniv of Condominium. T* **10** *and similar horiz design. Wmk Mult Script CA.* P 14½ × 14.

80		5 c. emerald	..		15	10
81		10 c. scarlet	..		15	10
82		20 c. deep bright blue	..		10	10
83		50 c. deep lilac	..		15	15
80/3			*Set of 4*	45	30	

Designs:—5, 10 c. Type **10**; 20, 50 c. "Marianne", "Talking Drum" and "Britannia".

12 Port Vila: Iririki Islet

13 River Scene and Spear Fisherman

(Des H. Cheffer (T **12**), P Gandon (others). Recess Waterlow)

1957 (3 Sept). *Wmk Mult Script CA. T* **12/13** *and similar horiz design.* P 13½.

84	**12**	5 c. green	..		40	75
85		10 c. scarlet	..		30	10
86		15 c. yellow-ochre	..		50	75
87		20 c. ultramarine	..		40	10
88	**13**	25 c. olive	..		45	10
89		30 c. brown	..		45	10
90		40 c. sepia	..		45	10
91		50 c. violet	..		45	10
92	—	1 f. orange	..		1·00	80
93	—	2 f. mauve	..		6·00	4·50
94	—	5 f. black	..		15·00	6·00
84/94			*Set of 11*	23·00	12·00	

Design:—1 to 5 f. Woman drinking from coconut.

1963 (2 Sept). *Freedom from Hunger. As No.* 80 *of Lesotho.*

95		60 c. green	..		50	15

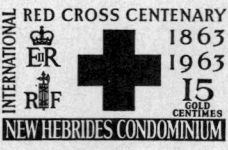
15 Red Cross Emblem

(Des V. Whiteley. Litho B.W.)

1963 (2 Sept). *Red Cross Centenary. W w* **12**. P 13½.

96	**15**	15 c. red and black	..		35	10
97		45 c. red and blue	..		45	20

16 Exporting Manganese, Forari

17 Cocoa Beans

(Des V. Whiteley, from drawings by J. White (10 c., 20 c.), K. Penny (40 c.), C. Robin (3 f.). Photo Harrison. Des C. Robin (5 c., 1 f.), J. White (15 c.), G. Vasarhelyi (25 c., 5 f.), A. Larkins, Turrell and Thomas (30 c., 50 c., 2 f.). Recess Govt Printing Works, Paris)

1963 (25 Nov)–72.   *T* **16/17** *and similar horiz designs. W* w **12** (10 c., 20 c., 40 c., 3 f.) *or no wmk* (others). *P* 14 (3 f.), 12½ (10 c., 20 c., 40 c.) *or* 13 (others).

98	5 c. lake, purple-brn & greenish bl (15.8.66)		1·00	50
	a. *Lake and greenish blue** (29.2.72)		35·00	35·00
99	10 c. light brown, buff and emerald		15	10
100	15 c. yellow-bistre, red-brown & deep violet		15	10
101	20 c. black, olive-grn & greenish bl (16.8.65)		55	10
102	25 c. reddish violet, orange-brown & crimson (15.8.66)		50	70
103	30 c. chestnut, bistre and violet		75	10
104	40 c. vermilion and deep blue (16.8.65)		80	1·40
105	50 c. green, yellow and greenish blue		60	10
106	1 f. red, black & deep bluish green (15.8.66)		2·50	3·25
107	2 f. black, brown-purple and yellow-olive		2·50	1·75
108	3 f. deep violet, orange-brown, emerald and black (16.8.65)		12·00	8·00
	w. Wmk inverted		15·00	
109	5 f. blue, deep blue and black (24.1.67)		14·00	21·00
98/109		*Set of* 12	30·00	32·00

Designs:—15 c. Copra; 20 c. Fishing from Palikulo Point; 25 c. Painted Triggerfish; 30 c. New Caledonian Nautilus shell; 40 c. Lionfish; 50 c. Clown Surgeonfish; 1 f. Cardinal Honeyeater; 2 f. Buff-bellied Flycatcher; 3 f. Thicket Warbler; 5 f. White-collared Kingfisher.

*In No. 98*a* the globe is printed in the same colour as the centre, instead of in purple-brown.

See also No. 129.

28 I.T.U. Emblem

(Des M. Goaman. Litho Enschedé)

1965 (17 May).   *I.T.U. Centenary. W* w **12**. *P* 11 × 11½.

110	**28**	15 c. scarlet and drab	20	10
111		60 c. blue and light red	35	20

29 I.C.Y. Emblem

(Des V. Whiteley. Litho Harrison)

1965 (24 Oct).   *International Co-operation Year. W* w **12**. *P* 14½.

112	**29**	5 c. reddish purple and turquoise-green	15	10
113		55 c. deep bluish green and lavender	20	20

30 Sir Winston Churchill and St. Paul's Cathedral in Wartime

(Des Jennifer Toombs. Photo Harrison)

1966 (24 Jan).   *Churchill Commemoration. W* w **12**. *P* 14.

114	**30**	5 c. black, cerise, gold and new blue	20	10
115		15 c. black, cerise, gold and deep green	40	10
116		25 c. black, cerise, gold and brown	50	10
117		30 c. black, cerise, gold and bluish violet	50	10
114/17		*Set of* 4	1·40	35

31 Footballer's Legs, Ball and Jules Rimet Cup

(Des V. Whiteley. Litho Harrison)

1966 (1 July).   *World Cup Football Championships. W* w **12** (sideways). *P* 14.

118	**31**	20 c. violet, yellow-green, lake & yell-brn	20	15
119		40 c. chocolate, blue-grn, lake & yell-brn	30	15

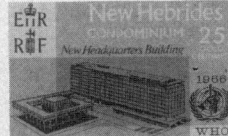

32 W.H.O. Building

(Des M. Goaman. Litho Harrison)

1966 (20 Sept).   *Inauguration of W.H.O. Headquarters, Geneva. W* w **12** (sideways). *P* 14.

120	**32**	25 c. black, yellow-green and light blue	20	10
121		60 c. black, light purple and yellow-brown	55	20

33 "Education"

(Des Jennifer Toombs. Litho Harrison)

1966 (1 Dec).   *20th Anniv of U.N.E.S.C.O. W* w **12** (sideways). *T* **33** *and similar horiz designs. P* 14.

122	15 c. slate-violet, red, yellow and orange		20	10
123	30 c. orange-yellow, violet and deep olive		50	10
124	45 c. black, bright purple and orange		60	15
122/4		*Set of* 3	1·10	30

Designs:—30 c. "Science"; 45 c. "Culture".

36 The Coast Watchers

(Des R. Granger Barrett. Photo Enschedé)

1967 (26 Sept).   *25th Anniv of the Pacific War. T* **36** *and similar horiz designs. Multicoloured. W* w **12**. *P* 14 × 13.

125	15 c. Type **36**		15	10
126	25 c. Map of war zone, U.S. marine and Australian soldier		50	20
127	60 c. H.M.A.S. *Canberra* (cruiser)		60	30
128	1 f. Boeing B-17 Flying Fortress		70	60
125/8		*Set of* 4	1·75	1·10

1967 (5 Dec).   *New value with W* w **12** sideways.

129	60 c. vermilion and deep blue (as No. 104)	40	15

40 Globe and Hemispheres

(Des and eng J. Combet. Recess Govt Printing Works, Paris)

1968 (23 May).   *Bicentenary of Bougainville's World Voyage. T* **40** *and similar horiz designs. P* 13.

130	15 c. emerald, slate-violet and red		15	10
131	25 c. deep olive, maroon and ultramarine		30	10
132	60 c. bistre-brown, brown-pur & myrtle-grn		35	10
130/2		*Set of* 3	70	30

Designs:—25 c. Ships *La Boudeuse* and *L'Etoile*, and map; 60 c. Bougainville, ship's figure-head and bougainvillea flowers.

43 Concorde and Vapour Trails   45 Kauri Pine

(Des S. W. Moss (25 c.), R. Granger Barrett (60 c.). Litho D.L.R.)

1968 (9 Oct).   *Anglo-French Concorde Project. T* **43** *and similar horiz design. W* w **12** (sideways). *P* 14.

133	25 c. lt blue, orange-red & deep violet-blue		50	20
134	60 c. red, black and bright blue		60	25

Design:—60 c. Concorde in flight.

(Des V. Whiteley. Litho Format)

1969 (30 June).   *Timber Industry. W* w **12**. *P* 14½.

135	**45**	20 c. multicoloured (shades)	10	10

No. 135 was issued in small sheets of 9 (3 × 3) printed on a simulated wood-grain background and with a decorative border showing various stages of the local timber industry. There is a wide range of shades on the printing.

ALTERED CATALOGUE NUMBERS

Any Catalogue numbers altered from the last edition are shown as a list in the introductory pages.

46 Cyphers, Flags and Relay Runner   48 Diver on Platform
receiving Baton

(Des C. Haley. Photo Delrieu)

1969 (13 Aug).   *Third South Pacific Games, Port Moresby. T* **46** *and similar horiz design. Multicoloured. P* 12½.

136	25 c. Type **46**		10	10
137	1 f. Cyphers, flags and relay runner passing baton		20	20

(Des V. Whiteley. Litho P.B.)

1969 (15 Oct).   *Pentecost Island Land Divers. T* **48** *and similar vert designs. Multicoloured. W* w **12** (sideways). *P* 12½.

138	15 c. Type **48**		10	10
139	25 c. Diver jumping		10	10
140	1 f. Diver at end of fall		20	20
138/40		*Set of* 3	30	30

51 U.P.U. Emblem and New   52 General Charles
Headquarters Building   de Gaulle

(Des and eng J. Gauthier. Recess Govt Ptg Wks, Paris)

1970 (20 May).   *Inauguration of New U.P.U. Headquarters Building. P* 13.

141	**51**	1 f. 05, slate, red-orange & bright purple	15	15

(Des V. Whiteley. Photo Govt Ptg Wks, Paris)

1970 (20 July).   *30th Anniv of New Hebrides' Declaration for the Free French Government. P* 13.

142	**52**	65 c. multicoloured	35	70
143		1 f. 10, multicoloured	45	70

35
≡

(53)   54 "The Virgin and Child"
(Bellini)

1970 (15 Oct).   *As No. 101, but W* w **12** (sideways) *and surch with T* **53**.

144	35 c. on 20 c. black, ol-grn & greenish black		30	30

(Des V. Whiteley. Litho Harrison)

1970 (30 Nov).   *Christmas. T* **54** *and similar vert design. Multicoloured. W* w **12** (sideways). *P* 14½ × 14.

145	15 c. Type **54**		10	10
146	50 c. "The Virgin and Child" (Cima)		20	20

1890-1970

IN MEMORIAM
9-11-70

(55)

1971 (19 Jan). *Death of General Charles de Gaulle. Nos. 142/3 optd with T 55, vertical bars in black, inscriptions in gold.*
147 **52** 65 c. multicoloured 15 10
148 1 f. 10, multicoloured 15 20

56 Football

(Des G. Bétemps. Photo Delrieu)

1971 (13 July). *Fourth South Pacific Games, Papeete, French Polynesia. T 56 and similar multicoloured design. P 12½.*
149 20 c. Type **56** 10 10
150 65 c. Basketball (*vert*) 30 20

57 Kauri Pine, Cone and Arms of Royal Society   **58** "The Adoration of the Shepherds" (detail, Louis le Nain)

(Des P. Powell. Litho Harrison)

1971 (7 Sept). *Royal Society Expedition to New Hebrides, 1971. W w 12 (sideways). P 14½ × 14.*
151 **57** 65 c. multicoloured 20 15

(Des G. Drummond. Litho Questa)

1971 (23 Nov). *Christmas. T 58 and similar vert design. Multicoloured. W w 12. P 14 × 13½.*
152 25 c. Type **58** 10 10
153 50 c. "The Adoration of the Shepherds" (detail, Tintoretto) 30 60

59 De Havilland D.H.A.3 Drover 3   **60** Ceremonial Headdress, South Malekula

(Des M. Goaman. Photo Delrieu)

1972 (29 Feb). *Aircraft. T 59 and similar horiz designs. Multicoloured. P 13.*
154 20 c. Type **59** 40 15
155 25 c. Short S.25 Sandringham 4 flying boat 40 15
156 30 c. De Havilland D.H.89 Dragon Rapide 40 15
157 65 c. Sud Aviation SE210 Caravelle .. 1·00 1·25
154/7 .. .. *Set of 4* 2·00 1·50

(Des Odette Baillais (bird designs), Pierrette Lambert (others). Photo Govt Printing Works, Paris)

1972 (24 July). *T 60 and similar vert designs. Multicoloured. P 12½ × 13.*
158 5 c. Type **60** 10 10
159 10 c. Baker's Pigeon 25 10
160 15 c. Gong and carving, North Ambrym .. 15 15
161 20 c. Red-headed Parrot Finch .. 40 25
162 25 c. Gaskoin's Cowrie (*Cypraea gaskoini*) (shell) 40 25
163 30 c. Red-lip Olive (*Oliva rubrolabiata*) (shell) 50 30
164 35 c. Chestnut-bellied Kingfisher .. 65 40
165 65 c. Pretty Conch (*Strombus plicatus pulchellus*) (shell) 75 60
166 1 f. Gong (North Malekula) and carving (North Ambrym) .. .. .. 70 1·00
167 2 f. Palm Lorikeet .. .. .. 4·00 4·50
168 3 f. Ceremonial headdress, South Malekula (*different*) .. .. .. 2·00 6·00
169 5 f. Great Green Turban (*Turbo marmoratus*) (shell) .. .. .. 5·50 14·00
158/69 *and* 199 .. .. *Set of 13* 22·00 42·00

NEW INFORMATION

The editor is always interested to correspond with people who have new information that will improve or correct the Catalogue.

---

61 "Adoration of the Kings" (Spranger)   **62** Royal and French Cyphers

(Des G. Drummond. Litho J.W.)

1972 (25 Sept). *Christmas. T 61 and similar vert design. Multicoloured. W w 12. P 14.*
170 25 c. Type **61** 10 10
171 70 c. "The Virgin and Child in a Landscape" (Provoost) 20 20

(Des (from photographs by D. Groves) and photo Harrison)

1972 (20 Nov). *Royal Silver Wedding. Multicoloured; background colour given. W w 12. P 14 × 14½.*
172 **62** 35 c. violet-black 15 10
    w. Wmk inverted .. .. 23·00
173 65 c. yellow-olive 20 10

63 *Dendrobium teretifolium*   **64** New Wharf at Vila

(Des Jennifer Toombs. Litho Questa)

1973 (26 Feb). *Orchids. T 63 and similar vert designs. Multicoloured. W w 12 (sideways*). P 14×14½.*
174 25 c. Type **63** 30 10
    w. Wmk Crown to right of CA .. 1·75
175 30 c. *Ephemerantha comata* .. 35 10
    w. Wmk Crown to right of CA .. 8·50
176 35 c. *Spathoglottis petri* .. 40 10
177 65 c. *Dendrobium mohlianun* .. 75 55
174/7 .. .. .. *Set of 4* 1·60 70
*The normal sideways watermark shows Crown to left of CA, as seen from the back of the stamp.

(Des PAD Studio. Litho Questa)

1973 (14 May). *Opening of New Wharf at Vila. P 14 × 14½ (25 c.) or 14½ × 14 (70 c.).*
178 **64** 25 c. multicoloured 20 10
179 – 70 c. multicoloured 40 30
The 70 c. is as T **64**, but in a horizontal format.

65 Wild Horses   **66** Mother and Child

(Des Pierrette Lambert. Photo Govt Printing Works, Paris)

1973 (13 Aug). *Tanna Island. T 65 and similar horiz design. Multicoloured. P 13 × 12½.*
180 35 c. Type **65** 30 15
181 70 c. Yasur Volcano 55 20

(Des Moutouh (35 c.), Tatin d'Avesnières (70 c.); adapted PAD Studio. Litho Questa)

1973 (19 Nov). *Christmas. T 66 and similar vert design. Multicoloured. W w 12 (sideways). P 13½.*
182 35 c. Type **66** 10 10
183 70 c. Lagoon scene 20 20

67 Pacific Pigeon   **ROYAL VISIT 1974**   (**68**)

(Des J. and H. Bregulla. Photo Govt Printing Works, Paris)

1974 (11 Feb). *Wild Life. T 67 and similar horiz designs. Multicoloured. P 13 × 12½.*
184 25 c. Type **67** 80 35
185 35 c. *Lyssa curvata* (moth) 80 60
186 70 c. Green Sea Turtle 80 70
187 1 f. 15, Grey-headed Flying Fox .. 1·00 1·50
184/7 .. .. .. *Set of 4* 3·00 2·75

1974 (11 Feb). *Royal Visit of Queen Elizabeth II. Nos. 164 and 167 optd with T 68.*
188 35 c. Chestnut-bellied Kingfisher (R.) .. 30 10
189 2 f. Palm Lorikeet 50 40

69 Old Post Office

(Des Odette Baillais. Photo Govt Printing Works, Paris)

1974 (6 May). *Inauguration of New Post Office, Vila. T 69 and similar triangular design. Multicoloured. P 12.*
190 35 c. Type **69** 15 50
    a. *Tête-bêche* (pair). Nos. 190/1 .. 30 1·10
191 70 c. New Post Office 15 60
Nos. 190/1 were printed together, in *tête-bêche* pairs throughout the sheet.

70 Capt. Cook and Map

(Des J. Cooter. Litho J.W.)

1974 (1 Aug). *Bicentenary of Discovery. T 70 and similar horiz designs. Multicoloured. W w 12 (sideways on 1 f. 15). P 11 (1 f. 15) or 13 (others).*
192 35 c. Type **70** .. .. .. 1·25 2·00
    a. Horiz strip of 3. Nos. 192/4 .. 3·25
193 35 c. William Wales and beach landing .. 1·25 2·00
194 35 c. William Hodges and island scene .. 1·25 2·00
195 1 f. 15, Capt Cook, map and H.M.S. *Resolution* (59 × 34 mm) .. .. 2·50 3·50
192/5 .. .. .. *Set of 4* 5·50 8·50
Nos. 192/4 were printed together, *se-tenant*, in horizontal strips of 3 throughout the sheet forming a composite design.

71 U.P.U. Emblem and Letters   **72** "Adoration of the Magi" (Velazquez)

(Des Pierrette Lambert. Photo Govt Printing Works, Paris)

1974 (9 Oct). *Centenary of Universal Postal Union. P 13 × 12½.*
196 **71** 70 c. multicoloured 30 70

(Des J. Cooter. Litho Questa)

1974 (14 Nov). *Christmas. T 72 and similar multicoloured design. W w 12 (sideways* on 70 c.). P 14×13½ (35 c.) or 13½×14 (70 c.).*
197 35 c. Type **72** 10 10
198 70 c. "The Nativity" (Gerard van Honthorst) (*horiz*) 20 20
    w. Wmk Crown to right of CA .. 2·50
*The normal sideways watermark shows Crown to left of CA, as seen from the back of the stamp.

73 Charolais Bull   **74** Canoeing

(Des and eng J. Pheulpin. Recess Govt Printing Works, Paris)

1975 (29 Apr). *P 13 × 12½.*
199 **73** 10 f. bistre-brown, green & dull ultram 9·50 20·00

(Des J. Cooter. Litho Questa)

1975 (5 Aug). _World Scout Jamboree, Norway. T **74** and similar vert designs. Multicoloured. P 13½._

200	25 c. Type 74	20	10
201	35 c. Preparing meal	20	10
202	1 f. Map-reading	50	15
203	5 f. Fishing	1·75	2·50
200/3	_Set of 4_	2·40	2·50

75 "Pitti Madonna" (Michelangelo)

(Des PAD Studio. Litho Harrison)

1975 (11 Nov). _Christmas. Michelangelo's Sculptures. T **75** and similar vert designs. Multicoloured. W w 12 (sideways*). P 14½×14._

204	35 c. Type 75	10	10
205	70 c. "Bruges Madonna"	15	10
206	2 f. 50, "Taddei Madonna"	70	50
	w. Wmk Crown to right of CA	32·00	
204/6	_Set of 3_	85	55

*The normal sideways watermark shows Crown to left of CA, as seen from the back of the stamp.

76 Concorde

(Des J. B. F. Chesnot. Typo Edila)

1976 (30 Jan). _First Commercial Flight of Concorde. P 13._

207	76 5 f. multicoloured	5·00	5·00

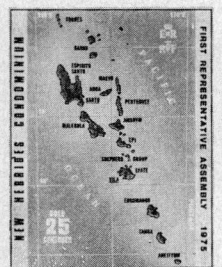

77 Telephones of 1876 and 1976   **78** Map of the Islands

(Des J. Gauthier. Photo Delrieu)

1976 (31 Mar). _Telephone Centenary. T **77** and similar vert designs. Multicoloured. P 13½._

208	25 c. Type 77	15	10
209	70 c. Alexander Graham Bell	30	10
210	1 f. 15, Satellite and Nouméa Earth Station	50	50
208/10	_Set of 3_	85	60

(Des Odette Baillais. Photo Govt Printing Works, Paris)

1976 (29 June). _Constitutional Changes. T **78** and similar multicoloured designs. P 13 (25 c.) or 13 × 12½ (others)._

211	25 c. Type 78	40	15
212	1 f. View of Santo (36 × 27 mm)	75	60
213	2 f. View of Vila (36 × 27 mm)	1·10	1·75
211/13	_Set of 3_	2·00	2·25

No. 211 shows the incorrect longitude, 116°E instead of 166°E.

Nos. 212/13 are inscribed "MUNICIPAL COUNCIL". Similar designs exist inscribed "FIRST REPRESENTATIVE ASSEMBLY 1975" and the name of the town. These stamps were not available in the New Hebrides.

79 "The Flight into Egypt" (Lusitano)   **80** Royal Visit, 1974

(Des J. Cooter. Litho Walsall)

1976 (8 Nov). _Christmas. T **79** and similar vert designs. Multicoloured. W w 14. P 13½._

214	35 c. Type 79	10	10
215	70 c. "Adoration of the Shepherds"	15	10
216	2 f. 50, "Adoration of the Magi"	45	50
214/16	_Set of 3_	60	55

Nos. 215/16 show retables by the Master of Santos-o-Novo.

(Des BG Studio. Litho Walsall)

1977 (7 Feb). _Silver Jubilee. T **80** and similar vert designs. Multicoloured. W w 14. P 13½._

217	35 c. Type 80	10	10
218	70 c. Imperial State Crown	15	10
	w. Wmk inverted	40·00	
219	2 f. The Blessing	30	65
217/19	_Set of 3_	45	70

(New Currency: 100 centimes=1 New Hebrides franc)

FNH	**FNH**	**FNH**	**25** **FNH**
(81) (5 f.)	**(82)** (10 f., 20 f.)	**(83)** (15 f.)	**(84)**

1977 (1 July). _Currency change. Surch by Govt. Ptg Works, Paris. Nos. 220/3 as T 81/3, others as T 84._

220	5 f. on 5 c. Type 60	40	55
221	10 f. on 10 c. Baker's Pigeon	80	35
222	15 f. on 15 c. Gong and carving	60	80
223	20 f. on 20 c. Red-headed Parrot Finch	1·25	55
224	25 f. on 25 c. Gaskoin's Cowrie (_Cypraea gaskoini_) (shell)	1·00	1·00
225	30 f. on 30 c. Red-lip Olive (_Oliva rubro-labiata_) (shell)	1·25	50
226	35 f. on 35 c. Chestnut-bellied Kingfisher	1·75	1·25
227	40 f. on 65 c. Pretty Conch (_Strombus plicatus pulchellus_) (shell)	1·25	1·50
228	50 f. on 1 f. Gong and carving	1·00	1·50
229	70 f. on 2 f. Palm Lorikeet	3·00	75
230	100 f. on 3 f. Ceremonial headdress	1·25	3·50
231	200 f. on 5 f. Great Green Turban (_Turbo marmoratus_) (shell)	6·00	12·00
232	500 f. on 10 f. Type 73	8·00	20·00
220/32	_Set of 13_	24·00	38·00

FNH	**FNH**	**FNH**
(85) (5 f.)	**(86)** (10 f.)	**(87)** (15 f.)

Two settings of 35 f. and 200 f. surcharges:
Setting I. Space of 1.4 mm between figures and "FNH".
Setting II. Space of 2.1 mm between figures and "FNH".

1977 (18 July)–78. _Nos. 158/60, 162/5 and 169 surch by I.P.V., Port Vila, in typography with T **85**/7 or similar surcharges._

233	5 f. on 5 c. Type 60 (10.8.77)	50	15
	a. Surch double	£350	
234	10 f. on 10 c. Baker's Pigeon (10.7.77)	50	15
235	15 f. on 15 c. Gong and carving (18.7.77)	3·00	1·25
	b. Short bar in surcharge (5.8.77)	1·50	90
	ba. Surch inverted		
236	25 f. on 25 c. Gaskoin's Cowrie (_Cypraea gaskoini_) (shell) (10.9.77)	50·00	20·00
	a. "FHN" for "FNH" (R. 5/1)	£400	
237	30 f. on 30 c. Red-lip Olive (_Oliva rubro-labiata_) (shell) (10.9.77)	£250	75·00
	a. "FHN" for "FNH" (R. 5/1)	£1300	£600
238	35 f. on 35 c. Chestnut-bellied Kingfisher (Setting I) (10.9.77)	2·50	55
	a. Setting II (6.1.78)		
239	40 f. on 65 c. Pretty Conch (_Strombus plicatus pulchellus_) (shell) (12.9.77)	1·50	55
240	200 f. on 5 f. Great Green Turban (_Turbo marmoratus_) (shell) (Setting I) (22.8.77)	17·00	13·00
	a. Setting II (13.1.78)		
241	500 f. on 10 f. Type 73 (14.9.77)	19·00	13·00
233/41	_Set of 9_	£300	£110

50 f. and 100 f. local surcharges were also prepared but these were not put on general sale, being available from the Philatelic Bureau only (_Price for set of 2_ £50 mint, £35 used).

Dates are those on which the various values were surcharged.

Surcharges on Nos. 236/41 are similar to Type 84, but with new currency inscription as Type 86.

89 Island of Erromango and Kauri Pine   **90** "Tempi Madonna" (Raphael)

(Des L. Curtis. Litho J.W. (15, 30, 40 f.), Walsall (10, 35, 70, 500 f.), Questa (others))

1977 (6 Sept)–78. _Maps of the Islands. T **89** and similar vert designs. Multicoloured. W w 14. P 13½ × 13 (15, 30, 40 f.) or 14 (others)._

242	5 f. Type 89	30	10
243	10 f. Territory map and copra-making (9.5.78)	40	30
244	15 f. Espiritu Santo and cattle (23.11.77)	30	30
245	20 f. Efate and Vila P.O.	30	25
246	25 f. Malekula and headdresses (23.11.77)	40	40
247	30 f. Aoba, Maewo and pigs' tusks (23.11.77)	45	50
248	35 f. Pentecost and land diver (9.5.78)	50	65
249	40 f. Tanna and John Frum cross (23.11.77)	70	60
250	50 f. Shepherd Island and canoe	1·00	40
251	70 f. Banks Island and dancers (9.5.78)	1·75	2·75
252	100 f. Ambrym and idols	1·75	90
253	200 f. Aneityum and baskets	1·75	2·50
254	500 f. Torres Islands and archer fisherman (9.5.78)	4·00	7·50
242/54	_Set of 13_	12·00	15·00

(Des J.W. Litho Cartor)

1977 (8 Dec). _Christmas. T **90** and similar vert designs. Multicoloured. W w 14. P 12._

255	10 f. Type 90	20	15
	w. Wmk inverted	65	
256	15 f. "The Flight into Egypt" (Gerard David)	30	20
	w. Wmk inverted	85	
257	30 f. "Virgin and Child" (Batoni)	40	70
	w. Wmk inverted	1·25	
255/7	_Set of 3_	80	95

91 Concorde over New York   **92** White Horse of Hanover

(Des BG Studio. Litho Rosenbaum Bros, Vienna)

1978 (9 May). _Concorde Commemoration. T **91** and similar horiz designs. Multicoloured. W w 14 (sideways*). P 13½._

258	10 f. Type 91	1·00	75
	w. Wmk Crown to right of CA	10·00	
259	20 f. Concorde over London	1·25	1·00
	w. Wmk Crown to right of CA	10·00	
260	30 f. Concorde over Washington	1·60	1·40
	w. Wmk Crown to right of CA	10·00	
261	40 f. Concorde over Paris	1·90	1·60
	w. Wmk Crown to right of CA	12·00	
258/61	_Set of 4_	5·25	4·25

*The normal sideways watermark shows Crown to left of CA, as seen from the back of the stamp.

(Des Jennifer Toombs. Litho Questa)

1978 (2 June). _25th Anniv of Coronation. T **92** and similar vert designs. P 15._

262	40 f. sepia, turquoise-blue and silver	15	30
	a. Sheetlet. Nos. 262/4, each × 2	75	
263	40 f. multicoloured	15	30
264	40 f. sepia, turquoise-blue and silver	15	30
262/4	_Set of 3_	40	80

Designs:—No. 262, Type 92. No. 263, Queen Elizabeth II; No. 264, Gallic Cock.

Nos. 262/4 were printed together in small sheets of 6, containing two _se-tenant_ strips of 3 with horizontal gutter margin between.

93 "Madonna and Child"   **(94)**

(Des C. Abbott. Litho Questa)

1978 (1 Dec). _Christmas. Paintings by Dürer. T **93** and similar vert designs. Multicoloured. W w 14. P 14 × 13½._

265	10 f. Type 93	10	10
266	15 f. "The Virgin and Child with St. Anne"	10	10
267	30 f. "Madonna of the Siskin"	15	10
268	40 f. "The Madonna of the Pear"	20	15
265/8	_Set of 4_	50	30

1979 (11 Jan). _1st Anniv of Internal Self-Government. As No. 211 surch as T **94**._

269	78 10 f. on 25 c. multicoloured (blue background)	10	10
270	40 f. on 25 c. multicoloured (pale blue-green background)	20	20

95 1938 5 c. Stamp and
Sir Rowland Hill

96 Chubwan Mask

(Des J.W. Litho Questa)

1979 (10 Sept). *Death Centenary of Sir Rowland Hill. T* **95** *and similar horiz designs showing stamps and Sir Rowland Hill. Multicoloured. W w* **14** (*sideways*). *P* 14.

271	10 f. Type **95**		15	10
272	20 f. 1969 25 c. Pentecost Island Land Divers commemorative		20	10
273	40 f. 1925 2d. (20 c.)		25	20
271/3		*Set of 3*	55	30
MS274	143 × 94 mm. No. 272 and as No. F286, but W w **14** (sideways)		75	90

(Des BG Studio. Litho Format)

1979 (16 Nov). *Festival of Arts. T* **96** *and similar vert designs. Multicoloured. W w* **14**. *P* 14.

275	5 f. Type **96**		10	10
276	10 f. Nal-Nal clubs and spears		10	10
277	20 f. Ritual puppet		15	10
278	40 f. Neqatmalow headdress		25	15
275/8		*Set of 4*	55	30

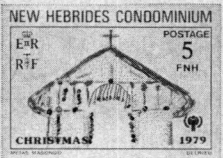

97 "Native Church" (Metas Masongo)

(Litho Delrieu)

1979 (4 Dec). *Christmas and International Year of the Child. Children's Drawings. T* **97** *and similar multicoloured designs. No wmk. P* 13 × 13½ (*horiz*) *or* 13½ × 13 (*vert*).

279	5 f. Type **97**		10	10
280	10 f. "Priest and Candles" (Herve Rutu)		10	10
281	20 f. "Cross and Bible" (Mark Deards) (*vert*)		10	10
282	40 f. "Green Candle and Santa Claus" (Dev Raj) (*vert*)		15	15
279/82		*Set of 4*	30	30

98 White-bellied Honeyeater

(Des G. Drummond. Litho Walsall)

1980 (27 Feb). *Birds. T* **98** *and similar horiz designs. Multicoloured. W w* **14** (*sideways*). *P* 14.

283	10 f. Type **98**		50	10
284	20 f. Scarlet Robin		70	10
285	30 f. Yellow-fronted White Eye		90	45
286	40 f. Fan-tailed Cuckoo		1·00	70
283/6		*Set of 4*	2·75	1·25

STAMP BOOKLETS

1980. *Multicoloured cover,* 109×74 *mm. Stamps attached by selvedge.*

SB1	200 f. booklet containing 5 f., 10 f., 15 f. and 20 f. (Nos. 242/5), each in block of 4		10·00

POSTAGE DUE STAMPS

POSTAGE DUE (D 1)　　POSTAGE DUE (D 2)　　POSTAGE DUE (D 3)

1925 (June). *Optd with Type* D **1**, *by D.L.R.*

D1	5	1d. (10 c.) green	40·00	1·00
D2		2d. (20 c.) slate-grey	48·00	1·00
D3		3d. (30 c.) red	50·00	2·50
D4		5d. (50 c.) ultramarine	55·00	4·50
D5		10d. (1 f.) carmine/*blue*	60·00	5·50
D1/5		*Set of 5*	225	13·00
D1/5 Optd "Specimen"		*Set of 5*	225	

1938 (1 June). *Optd with Type* D **2**, *by B.W.*

D 6	**6**	5 c. blue-green	22·00	29·00
D 7		10 c. orange	22·00	29·00
D 8		20 c. scarlet	28·00	45·00
D 9		40 c. grey-olive	35·00	60·00
D10		1 f. red/*green*	45·00	70·00
D6/10		*Set of 5*	£140	£200
D6/10 Perf "Specimen"		*Set of 5*	£120	

1953 (30 Apr). *Nos. 68/9, 71, 74 and 76 optd with Type* D **3**, *by Waterlow.*

D11	5 c. green		5·00	11·00
D12	10 c. scarlet		1·75	8·00
D13	20 c. ultramarine		6·00	17·00
D14	40 c. blackish brown		8·50	27·00
D15	1 f. orange		6·00	27·00
D11/15		*Set of 5*	24·00	80·00

1957 (3 Sept). *Nos. 84/5, 87, 90 and 92 optd with Type* D **3**, *by Waterlow.*

D16	**12**	5 c. green	30	1·50
D17		10 c. scarlet	30	1·50
D18		20 c. ultramarine	1·25	2·00
D19	**13**	40 c. sepia	2·00	3·75
D20	—	1 f. orange	3·00	7·00
D16/20		*Set of 5*	6·00	14·00

II. STAMPS INSCRIBED IN FRENCH

(Currency. 100 centimes = 1 French franc)

NOUVELLES HEBRIDES (F 1)　　NOUVELLES-HEBRIDES (F 2)

1908 (21 Nov). *T* **15**/**17** *of New Caledonia optd with Types* F **1** *or* F **2** (1 *f*.), *by Govt Ptg Wks, Paris.*

F1	5 c. green		2·75	3·50
F2	10 c. carmine		3·25	3·50
F3	25 c. blue/*greenish* (R.)		4·00	3·75
F4	50 c. red/*orange*		5·50	6·00
F5	1 f. blue/*green* (R.)		11·50	11·50
F1/5		*Set of 5*	24·00	25·00

CONDOMINIUM (F 3)　　10c. (F 4)

1910 (Aug)–**11**. *Nos.* F1/5 *further optd with Type* F **3**, *or larger* (1 *f*.), *by Govt Ptg Wks, Paris.*

F 6	5 c. green		2·00	2·00
F 7	10 c. carmine		2·00	80
F 8	25 c. blue/*greenish* (R.) (1911)		2·25	3·75
F 9	50 c. red/*orange* (1911)		6·50	7·00
F10	1 f. blue/*green* (R.)		13·00	16·00
F6/10		*Set of 5*	23·00	26·00

All the above were released in Paris on 16 March 1910. The 5 c., 10 c. and 1 f. were issued in New Hebrides in August but the 25 c. and 50 c. were not received until 1911 after the issue of the definitive stamps and they were placed in reserve, although some may have been issued on request.

1911 (12 July). *Wmk Mult Crown CA. P* 14.

F11	**3**	5 c. green	1·00	2·75
F12		10 c. carmine	45	1·25
F13		20 c. greyish slate	1·10	2·25
F14		25 c. ultramarine	3·50	7·00
F15		30 c. brown/*yellow*	6·50	4·00
F16		40 c. red/*yellow*	1·40	3·75
F17		50 c. sage-green	2·00	3·25
F18		75 c. orange	6·75	17·00
F19		1 f. red/*blue*	2·50	2·50
F20		2 f. violet	8·50	19·00
F21		5 f. red/*green*	12·00	25·00
F11/21		*Set of 11*	40·00	75·00

1913. *As last but wmk* "R F" *in sheet or without wmk.*

F22	**3**	5 c. green	80	4·25
F23		10 c. carmine	80	3·75
F24		20 c. greyish slate	90	3·00
F25		25 c. ultramarine	85	4·00
F26		30 c. brown/*yellow*	2·50	8·50
F27		40 c. red/*yellow*	32·00	48·00
F28		50 c. sage-green	14·00	20·00
F29		75 c. orange	14·00	32·00
F30		1 f. red/*blue*	7·00	8·00
F31		2 f. violet	13·00	25·00
F32		5 f. red/*green*	16·00	40·00
F22/32		*Set of 11*	90·00	£180

The above were placed on sale in Paris on 29 April 1912.

1920–21. *Surch as Type* F **4**, *at Govt Printing Establishment, Suva, Fiji.* (*a*) *On stamps of* 1908–11 (June 1920).

F32a	5 c. on 50 c. red/*orange* (F4)		£425	£425
F33	5 c. on 50 c. red/*orange* (F9)		2·50	70·00
F33a	10 c. on 25 c. blue/*greenish* (F8)		50	1·25

(*b*) *On stamps of* 1911–13 (10.3.21)

F34	**3**	5 c. on 40 c. red/*yellow* (F27)	26·00	75·00
F35		20 c. on 30 c. brown/*yellow* (F15)	11·00	50·00
F36		20 c. on 30 c. brown/*yellow* (F26)	14·00	60·00

(*c*) *On Inscr in English* (10.3.21)

F37	**3**	10 c. on 5d. sage-green (24)	15·00	42·00

1924 (1 May). *Stamps of* 1911–13 *surch as Type* F **4**, *at Suva.*

F38	**3**	10 c. on 5 c. green (F22)	1·60	4·00
F39		30 c. on 10 c. carmine (F23)	1·75	2·25
F40		50 c. on 25 c. ultramarine (F14)	32·00	70·00
F41		50 c. on 25 c. ultramarine (F25)	3·25	22·00
F38/41		*Set of 4*	35·00	90·00

F 5　　(F 6) **France Libre**

(Recess D.L.R.)

1925 (June). *Wmk* "R F" *in sheet or without wmk. P* 14.

F42	**5**	5 c. (½d.) black	1·50	9·50
F43		10 c. (1d.) green	1·50	9·00
F44		20 c. (2d.) greyish slate	1·75	2·75
F45		25 c. (2½d.) brown	2·25	11·00
F46		30 c. (3d.) red	1·50	5·00
F47		40 c. (4d.) red/*yellow*	1·50	5·00
F48		50 c. (5d.) ultramarine	1·50	3·25
F49		75 c. (7½d.) yellow-brown	2·00	11·00
F50		1 f. (10d.) carmine/*blue*	2·00	3·00
F51		2 f. (1/8) violet	4·25	20·00
F52		5 f. (4s.) carmine/*green*	5·50	21·00
F42/52		*Set of 11*	22·00	90·00
F42/52 Optd "Specimen"		*Set of 11*	£250	

In July 1929 a batch of mail was carried by aircraft from Port Vila to the French cruiser *Tourville* for sorting and forwarding at Nouméa, New Caledonia. Stamps of the above issue (including those with English inscriptions) were affixed to covers and hand-stamped "PAR AVION" before cancellation.

(New Currency. 100 gold centimes = 1 gold franc)

1938 (1 June). *Gold Currency. Wmk* "R F" *in sheet or without wmk. P* 12.

F53	**6**	5 c. blue-green	1·60	3·25
F54		10 c. orange	1·60	2·75
F55		15 c. bright violet	1·25	3·25
F56		20 c. scarlet	1·60	2·75
F57		25 c. reddish brown	4·00	3·25
F58		30 c. blue	4·00	2·50
F59		40 c. grey-olive	1·25	6·50
F60		50 c. purple	1·25	2·25
F61		1 f. lake/*pale green* (shades)	1·60	3·75
F62		2 f. blue/*pale green* (shades)	26·00	28·00
F63		5 f. red/*yellow*	50·00	45·00
F64		10 f. violet/*blue*	£120	90·00
F53/64		*Set of 12*	£190	£170
F53/64 Perf "Specimen"		*Set of 12*	£300	

1941 (15 Apr). *Adherence to General de Gaulle. Optd with Type* F **6**, *at Nouméa, New Caledonia.*

F65	**6**	5 c. blue-green	2·50	22·00
F66		10 c. orange	4·00	21·00
F67		15 c. bright violet	6·00	30·00
F68		20 c. scarlet	14·00	27·00
F69		25 c. reddish brown	14·00	35·00
F70		30 c. blue	14·00	28·00
F71		40 c. grey-olive	14·00	32·00
F72		50 c. purple	14·00	27·00
F73		1 f. lake/*pale green*	14·00	32·00
F74		2 f. blue/*pale green*	14·00	32·00
F75		5 f. red/*yellow*	14·00	32·00
F76		10 f. violet/*blue*	14·00	32·00
F65/76		*Set of 12*	£120	£300

1949 (10 Oct). *75th Anniv of U.P.U. As Nos.* 64/7. *Wmk* "R F" *in sheet or without wmk. P* 13½.

F77	10 c. red-orange		2·25	4·25
F78	15 c. violet		3·50	7·00
F79	30 c. ultramarine		5·00	10·00
F80	50 c. purple		6·00	10·00
F77/80		*Set of 4*	15·00	28·00

1953 (30 Apr). *As Nos.* 68/78. *Wmk* "R F" *in sheet or without wmk. P* 12½.

F81	**7**	5 c. green	40	1·50
F82		10 c. scarlet	90	1·00
F83		15 c. yellow-ochre	90	1·50
F84		20 c. ultramarine	90	1·00
F85	—	25 c. olive	70	1·00
F86	—	30 c. brown	70	1·00
F87		40 c. blackish brown	70	1·50
F88		50 c. violet	70	1·00
F89		1 f. orange	19·00	6·50
F90		2 f. reddish purple	21·00	45·00
F91		5 f. scarlet	28·00	75·00
F81/91		*Set of 11*	65·00	£120

1956 (20 Oct). *Fiftieth Anniv of Condominium. As Nos.* 80/3. *Wmk* "R F" *in sheet or without wmk. P* 14½ × 14.

F92	**10**	5 c. emerald	1·50	1·25
F93		10 c. scarlet	1·50	1·25
F94		20 c. deep bright blue	1·50	1·50
F95		50 c. deep lilac	1·50	2·00
F92/5		*Set of 4*	5·50	5·50

1957 (3 Sept). *As Nos.* 84/94. *Wmk* "R F" *in sheet or without wmk. P* 13½.

F 96	**12**	5 c. green	80	60
F 97		10 c. scarlet	80	40
F 98		15 c. orange-yellow	1·25	60
F 99		20 c. ultramarine	1·25	50
F100	**13**	25 c. yellow-olive	1·25	50
F101		30 c. brown	1·25	60
F102		40 c. sepia	1·25	60
F103		50 c. reddish violet	1·25	50
F104	—	1 f. red-orange	8·00	2·75
F105	—	2 f. mauve	22·00	27·00
F106	—	5 f. black	32·00	35·00
F96/106		*Set of 11*	65·00	65·00

F 7 Emblem and Globe　　F 8 Centenary Emblem

(Des and eng J. Derrey. Recess Govt Ptg Wks, Paris)

1963 (2 Sept). *Freedom from Hunger.* P 13.
F107 F 7 60 c. deep bluish green and chestnut .. 17·00 11·00

(Des and eng J. Combet. Recess Govt Ptg Wks, Paris)

1963 (2 Sept). *Red Cross Centenary.* P 13.
F108 F 8 15 c. red, grey and orange .. .. 10·00 6·00
F109 45 c. red, grey and yellow-bistre .. 18·00 18·00

1963 (25 Nov)–**72.** *As Nos. 98/109 and 129. No wmk.*
P 12½ (10, 20, 40, 60 c.), 14 (3 f.) or 13 (others).
F110 5 c. lake, purple-brown and greenish blue
(15.8.66) 60 30
  a. *Lake and greenish blue* (29.2.72) .. 50·00 50·00
F111 10 c. lt brown, buff & emerald* (16.8.65) .. 80 1·00
F112 10 c. lt brown, buff and emerald (5.8.68) .. 65 15
F113 15 c. yellow-bistre, red-brown & dp violet .. 10·00 40
F114 20 c. black, ol-green & grnsh bl* (16.8.65) .. 2·25 3·00
F115 20 c. black, ol-green & grnsh bl (5.8.68) .. 2·50 25
F116 25 c. reddish violet, orange-brown and
crimson (15.8.66) 60 60
F117 30 c. chestnut, bistre and violet .. 11·00 60
F118 40 c. vermilion and deep blue* (16.8.65) .. 3·50 60
F119 50 c. green, yellow and greenish blue .. 11·00 60
F120 60 c. vermilion and deep blue (5.12.67) .. 1·50 80
F121 1 f. red, black & dp bluish grn (15.8.66) .. 2·00 3·50
F122 2 f. black, brown-purple & yellow-olive .. 24·00 10·00
F123 3 f. multicoloured* (16.8.65) .. 12·00 20·00
F124 3 f. multicoloured (5.8.68) .. 12·00 12·00
F125 5 f. blue, deep blue and black (24.1.67) .. 22·00 28·00
F110/25 *Set of 16* £100 75·00

*Normally all French New Hebrides issues have the "RF" inscription on the right to distinguish them from the British New Hebrides stamps which have it on the left. The stamps indicated by an asterisk have "RF" wrongly placed on the left.

F 9 "Syncom" Communications Satellite,
Telegraph Poles and Morse Key

(Des and eng J. Combet. Recess Govt Ptg Wks, Paris)

1965 (17 May). *Air. I.T.U. Centenary.* P 13.
F126 F 9 15 c. blue, chocolate and emerald .. 10·00 6·00
F127 60 c. carmine, dp bluish green & slate .. 22·00 22·00

1965 (24 Oct). *International Co-operation Year. As Nos. 112/13.* P 14½.
F128 29 5 c. dp reddish purple & turquoise-grn 4·00 3·00
F129 55 c. deep bluish green and lavender .. 10·00 9·00

1966 (24 Jan). *Churchill Commemoration. As Nos. 114/17.* P 14.
F130 30 5 c. black, cerise, gold and new blue .. 1·00 75
F131 15 c. black, cerise, gold and deep green .. 2·75 1·00
F132 25 c. black, cerise, gold and brown .. 3·00 3·50
F133 30 c. black, cerise, gold and bluish violet .. 3·75 4·50
F130/3 *Set of 4* 9·50 8·75

1966 (1 July). *World Cup Football Championships. As Nos. 118/19.* P 14.
F134 31 20 c. violet, yellow-grn, lake & yell-brn 2·75 2·75
F135 40 c. chocolate, bl-grn, lake & yell-brn 4·25 4·25

1966 (20 Sept). *Inauguration of W.H.O. Headquarters, Geneva. As Nos. 120/1.* P 14.
F136 32 25 c. black, yellow-green and light blue 3·00 2·00
F137 60 c. black, mauve and yellow-ochre .. 5·00 5·00

1966 (1 Dec). *20th Anniv of U.N.E.S.C.O. As Nos. 122/4.* P 14.
F138 33 15 c. slate-violet, red, yellow and orange 1·75 1·75
F139 – 30 c. orange-yellow, violet & dp olive .. 2·75 2·50
F140 – 45 c. black, bright purple and orange 3·00 3·00
F138/40 *Set of 3* 6·75 6·00

1967 (26 Sept). *25th Anniv of the Pacific War. As Nos. 125/8.* P 14 × 13.
F141 15 c. Type 36 .. .. .. 85 40
F142 25 c. Map of war zone, U.S. marine and
Australian soldier .. .. 1·40 60
F143 60 c. H.M.A.S. Canberra (cruiser) .. 2·00 1·25
F144 1 f. Boeing B-17 Flying Fortress .. 2·25 2·00
F141/4 *Set of 4* 6·00 3·75

1968 (23 May). *Bicentenary of Bougainville's World Voyage. As Nos. 130/2.* P 13.
F145 40 15 c. emerald, slate-violet and red .. 20 20
F146 – 25 c. dp olive, maroon & ultramarine .. 40 40
F147 – 60 c. bistre-brn, brn-pur & myrtle-grn .. 90 90
F145/7 *Set of 3* 1·40 1·40

1968 (9 Oct). *Anglo-French Concorde Project. As Nos. 133/4.* P 14.
F148 43 25 c. lt blue, orange-red & dp violet-bl .. 2·25 1·50
F149 – 60 c. red, black and bright blue .. 3·75 3·00

1969 (30 June). *Timber Industry. As No. 135.* P 14½.
F150 45 20 c. multicoloured (shades) .. 20 30

1969 (13 Aug). *3rd South Pacific Games, Port Moresby, Papua New Guinea. As Nos. 136/7. Multicoloured.* P 12½.
F151 25 c. Type 46 .. .. .. 50 30
F152 1 f. Runner passing baton, and flags .. 2·00 2·00

1969 (15 Oct). *Pentecost Island Land Divers. As Nos. 138/40. Multicoloured.* P 12½.
F153 15 c. Type 48 .. .. .. 30 30
F154 25 c. Diver jumping 40 40
F155 1 f. Diver at end of fall .. 1·40 1·40
F153/5 *Set of 3* 1·90 1·90

1970 (20 May). *Inauguration of New U.P.U. Headquarters Building, Berne. As No. 141.* P 13.
F156 51 1 f. 05, slate, red-orange & brt purple 50 70

1970 (20 July). *30th Anniv of New Hebrides' Declaration for the Free French Government. As Nos. 142/3.* P 13.
F157 52 65 c. multicoloured 85 85
F158 1 f. 10, multicoloured .. 1·40 1·40

1970 (15 Oct). *No. F115 surch with T 53.*
F159 35 c. on 20 c. black, ol-green & greenish blue 60 50

1970 (30 Nov). *Christmas. As Nos. 145/6. Multicoloured.* P 14½ × 14.
F160 15 c. Type 54 .. .. .. 15 15
F161 50 c. "The Virgin and Child" (G. Cima) .. 25 20

1971 (19 Jan). *Death of General Charles de Gaulle. Nos. F157/8 optd with T 55, the vertical bars in black and inscriptions in gold.*
F162 52 65 c. multicoloured 75 55
  a. Gold opt omitted
F163 1 f. 10, multicoloured .. 1·50 1·50
On No. F162a the vertical black bars are still present.

1971 (13 July). *4th South Pacific Games, Papeete, French Polynesia. As Nos. 149/50. Multicoloured.* P 12½.
F164 20 c. Type 56 .. .. .. 35 20
F165 65 c. Basketball (vert) 95 80

1971 (7 Sept). *Royal Society's Expedition to New Hebrides. As No. 151.* P 14½ × 14.
F166 57 65 c. multicoloured 50 50

1971 (23 Nov). *Christmas. As Nos. 152/3. Multicoloured.* P 14 × 13½.
F167 25 c. Type 58 .. .. 15 20
F168 50 c. "Adoration of the Shepherds" (J. Tintoretto) .. 30 35

1972 (29 Feb). *Aircraft. As Nos. 154/7. Multicoloured.* P 13.
F169 20 c. Type 59 .. .. 1·00 60
F170 25 c. Short S.25 Sandringham 4 flying boat 1·00 70
F171 30 c. De Havilland D.H.89 Dragon Rapide 1·10 40
F172 65 c. Sud Aviation SE 210 Caravelle .. 4·50
F169/72 *Set of 4* 5·50 6·00

1972 (24 July). *As Nos. 158/69. Multicoloured.* P 12½ × 13.
F173 5 c. Type 60 .. .. 40 10
F174 10 c. Baker's Pigeon .. 1·75 50
F175 15 c. Gong and carving, North Ambrym 50 15
F176 20 c. Red-headed Parrot Finch .. 2·25 30
F177 25 c. Gaskoin's Cowrie (Cypraea gaskoini) (shell) .. 1·75 30
F178 30 c. Red-lip Olive (Oliva rubrolabiata) (shell) .. 1·75 30
F179 35 c. Chestnut-bellied Kingfisher .. 3·00 40
F180 65 c. Pretty Conch (Strombus plicatus pulchellus) (shell) .. 2·50 60
F181 1 f. Gong, North Malekula and carving, North Ambrym .. 2·50 1·75
F182 2 f. Palm Lorikeet .. 15·00 10·00
F183 3 f. Ceremonial headdress, South Malekula (different) .. 9·50 13·00
F184 5 f. Great Green Turban (Turbo marmoratus) (shell) .. 17·00 22·00
F173/84 and F213 *Set of 13* 75·00 75·00

1972 (25 Sept). *Christmas. As Nos. 170/1. Multicoloured.* P 14.
F185 25 c. Type 61 .. .. 25 20
F186 70 c. "Virgin and Child" (Provoost) .. 50 45

1972 (20 Nov). *Royal Silver Wedding. As Nos. 172/3. W w 12.* P 14 × 14½.
F187 62 35 c. multicoloured 40 40
F188 65 c. multicoloured .. .. 50 1·00

1973 (26 Feb). *Orchids. As Nos. 174/7. Multicoloured.* P 14 × 14½.
F189 25 c. Type 63 .. .. 2·25 60
F190 30 c. Ephemerantha comata .. 2·25 80
F191 35 c. Spathoglottis petri .. 2·25 95
F192 65 c. Dendrobium mohlianum .. 4·75 4·75
F189/92 *Set of 4* 9·50 6·50

1973 (14 May). *Opening of New Wharf, Vila. As Nos. 178/9. Multicoloured.* P 14 × 14½ (25 c.) or 14½ × 14 (70 c.).
F193 25 c. Type 64 .. .. 60 50
F194 70 c. View of wharf (horiz) .. 90 1·50

1973 (13 Aug). *Tanna Island. As Nos. 180/1. Multicoloured.* P 13 × 12½.
F195 35 c. Type 65 .. .. 2·25 1·25
F196 70 c. Yasur Volcano .. 3·25 3·25

1973 (19 Nov). *Christmas. As Nos. 182/3. Multicoloured.* P 14 × 13½.
F197 35 c. Type 66 .. .. 40 35
F198 70 c. Lagoon scene .. 70 75

1974 (11 Feb). *Wild Life. As Nos. 184/7. Multicoloured.* P 13 × 12½.
F199 25 c. Type 67 .. .. 3·75 1·50
F200 35 c. Lyssa curvata .. 5·50 1·75
F201 70 c. Green Sea Turtle .. 5·50 4·00
F202 1 f. 15, Grey-headed Flying Fox .. 6·00 10·00
F199/202 *Set of 4* 15·00 15·00

VISITE ROYALE
1974

(F 10)

1974 (11 Feb). *Royal Visit of Queen Elizabeth II. Nos. F179 and F182 optd with Type T 10.*
F203 35 c. Chestnut-bellied Kingfisher (R.) .. 2·50 50
F204 2 f. Palm Lorikeet .. 6·00 6·50

1974 (6 May). *Inauguration of New Post Office, Vila. As Nos. 190/1. Multicoloured.* P 12.
F205 35 c. Type 69 .. .. 50 65
  a. Tête-bêche (pair). Nos. F205/6 .. 1·10 1·50
F206 70 c. New Post Office .. 60 85

1974 (1 Aug). *Bicentenary of Discovery. As Nos. 192/5. Multicoloured.* P 11 (1 f. 15) or 13 × 13½ (others).
F207 35 c. Type 70 .. .. 4·50 4·00
  a. Horiz strip of 3. Nos. F207/9 .. 12·00
F208 35 c. William Wales and beach landing .. 4·50 4·00
F209 35 c. William Hodges and island scene .. 4·50 4·00
F210 1 f. 15, Capt. Cook, Resolution and map of islands (64 × 39 mm) .. 10·00 8·50
F207/10 *Set of 4* 21·00 18·00

1974 (9 Oct). *Centenary of Universal Postal Union. As No. 196.* P 13 × 12½.
F210a 71 70 c. dp turquoise-blue, rosine & black 1·50 1·75

1974 (4 Nov). *Christmas. As Nos. 197/8. Multicoloured.* P 14 × 13½ (35 c.) or 13½ × 14 (70 c.).
F211 35 c. Type 72 .. .. 25 20
F212 70 c. "The Nativity" (G. van Honthorst) (horiz) .. 55 45

1975 (29 Apr). *As No. 199.* P 13 × 12½.
F213 73 10 f. bistre-brown, yellow-green & blue 28·00 35·00

1975 (5 Aug). *World Scout Jamboree, Norway. As Nos. 200/3. Multicoloured.* P 14 × 13½.
F214 25 c. Type 74 .. .. 55 20
F215 35 c. Preparing meal .. 65 30
F216 1 f. Map-reading .. 1·25 1·10
F217 5 f. Fishing .. 5·50 9·00
F214/17 *Set of 4* 7·00 9·50

1975 (11 Nov). *Christmas. As Nos. 204/6. Multicoloured.* P 14½ × 14.
F218 35 c. Type 75 .. .. 25 15
F219 70 c. "Bruges Madonna" .. 40 25
F220 2 f. 50, "Taddei Madonna" .. 1·75 2·75
F218/20 *Set of 3* 2·25 2·75

1976 (30 Jan). *First Commercial Flight of Concorde. As No. 207.* P 13.
F221 76 5 f. multicoloured .. .. 15·00 14·00

1976 (31 Mar). *Telephone Centenary. As Nos. 208/10. Multicoloured.* P 13½.
F222 25 c. Type 77 .. .. 55 40
F223 70 c. Alexander Graham Bell .. 1·40 1·50
F224 1 f. 15, Satellite and Earth Station, Nouméa 1·75 2·50
F222/4 *Set of 3* 3·50 4·00

1976 (29 June). *Constitutional Changes. As Nos. 211/13. Multicoloured.* P 13 (25 c.) or 13 × 12½ (others).
F225 25 c. Type 78 .. .. 50 30
F226 1 f. Luganville (36 × 27 mm) .. 1·50 1·25
F227 2 f. Vila (36 × 27 mm) .. 2·50 2·25
F225/7 *Set of 3* 4·00 3·50
No. F225 shows the incorrect longitude, 116°E, instead of 166°E.
Nos. F226/7 are inscribed "PREMIERE MUNICIPALITE". Similar designs exist with the inscription "PREMIERE ASSEMBLEE REPRESENTATIVE 1975" and the name of the town. These stamps were not available in the New Hebrides.

1976 (8 Nov). *Christmas. As Nos. 214/16. Multicoloured.* P 13½.
F228 35 c. Type 79 .. .. 25 15
F229 70 c. "Adoration of the Shepherds" .. 40 25
F230 2 f. 50, "Adoration of the Magi" .. 1·75 2·75
F228/30 *Set of 3* 2·25 2·75

1977 (7 Feb). *Silver Jubilee. As Nos. 217/19. Multicoloured.* P 13½.
F231 35 c. Type 80 .. .. 30 15
F232 70 c. Imperial State Crown .. 50 25
F233 2 f. The Blessing .. 60 60
F231/3 *Set of 3* 1·25 90

(New Currency. 100 centimes = 1 New Hebrides franc)

1977 (1 July). *Currency Change. Nos. F173/84 and F214 surch as T 81/3 (No. F234/7) or as T 84 (others) by Govt Ptg Wks, Paris.*
F234 5 f. on 5 c. Type 60 .. 40 40
F235 10 f. on 10 c. Baker's Pigeon .. 85 40
F236 15 f. on 15 c. Gong and carving, North Ambrym .. 70 60
F237 20 f. on 20 c. Red-headed Parrot Finch 1·50 85
F238 25 f. on 25 c. Gaskoin's Cowrie (Cypraea gaskoini) (shell) .. 1·50 1·00
F239 30 f. on 30 c. Red-lip Olive (Oliva rubrolabiata) (shell) .. 1·75 1·50
F240 35 f. on 35 c. Chestnut-bellied Kingfisher 2·50 1·50
F241 40 f. on 65 c. Pretty Conch (Strombus plicatus pulchellus) (shell) .. 2·50 2·00
F242 50 f. on 1 f. Gong, North Malekula, and carving, North Ambrym .. 2·00 2·00
F243 70 f. on 2 f. Palm Lorikeet .. 4·25 2·75
  a. Surch double
F244 100 f. on 3 f. Ceremonial headdress, South Malekula .. 3·25 4·50
F245 200 f. on 5 f. Great Green Turban (Turbo marmoratus) (shell) .. 13·00 19·00
F246 500 f. on 10 f. Type 73 .. 22·00 35·00
F234/46 *Set of 13* 50·00 65·00

1977 (18 July)–78. *Nos. F173/5, F177/180, F184 and F213 surch by I.P.V., Port Vila, in typography with T **85/7** or similar surcharges.*

F247	5 f. on 5 c. Type **60** (10.8.77)		1·25	1·00
F248	10 f. on 10 c. Baker's Pigeon (20.7.77)		2·50	55
F249	15 f. on 15 c. Gong and carving (18.7.77)		3·25	1·50
	a. Short bar in surcharge (5.8.77)		2·75	2·25
F250	25 f. on 25 c. Gaskoin's Cowrie (*Cypraea gaskoini*) (shell) (10.9.77)		£130	65·00
	a. "FHN" for "FNH" (R. 5/1)		£750	
F251	30 f. on 30 c. Red-lip Olive (*Oliva rubrolabiata*) (shell) (10.9.77)		£375	75·00
	a. "FHN" for "FNH" (R. 5/1)		£1500	£600
F252	35 f. on 35 c. Chestnut-bellied Kingfisher (Setting I) (10.9.77)		6·00	4·25
	a. "NH" for "FNH" (R. 4/2)		£500	
	b. Setting II (6.1.78)		24·00	14·00
F253	40 f. on 65 c. Pretty Conch (*Strombus plicatus pulchellus*) (shell) (12.9.77)		4·50	4·50
F254	200 f. on 5 f. Great Green Turban (*Turbo marmoratus*) (shell) (Setting I) (22.8.77)		40·00	48·00
	a. Setting II (13.1.78)		45·00	48·00
F255	500 f. on 10 f. Type **73** (14.9.77)		42·00	48·00
F247/55		*Set of 9*	£550	£225

Dates are those on which the various values were surcharged. 50 f., 70 f. and 100 f. local surcharges were also prepared, but were not put on general sale, being available from the Philatelic Bureau only (Price £70 each mint).

1977 (7 Sept)–78. *Maps of the Islands. As Nos. 242/54. Multi-coloured. P 13½×13 (15, 30, 40 f.) or 14 (others).*

F256	5 f. Type **89**		65	20
F257	10 f. Territory map and copra-making (9.5.78)		75	20
F258	15 f. Espiritu Santo and cattle (23.11.77)		75	20
F259	20 f. Efate and Vila Post Office		1·00	30
F260	25 f. Malekula and headdresses (23.11.77)		80	40
F261	30 f. Aoba, Maewo and pigs' tusks (23.11.77)		80	45
F262	35 f. Pentecost and land diver (9.5.78)		2·25	60
F263	40 f. Tanna and John Frum cross (23.11.77)		75	75
F264	50 f. Shepherd Island and canoe		2·00	75
F265	70 f. Banks Island and dancers (9.5.78)		4·50	3·25
F266	100 f. Ambrym and idols		3·00	2·50
F267	200 f. Aneityum and baskets		4·75	9·00
F268	500 f. Torres Islands and archer fisherman (9.5.78)		11·00	15·00
F256/68		*Set of 13*	30·00	30·00

1977 (8 Dec). *Christmas. As Nos. 255/7. Multicoloured. P 12.*

F269	10 f. Type **90**		20	20
F270	15 f. "The Flight into Egypt" (G. David)		35	35
F271	20 f. "Virgin and Child" (Pompeo Batoni)		1·25	1·25
F269/71		*Set of 3*	1·25	1·25

1978 (9 May). *Concorde Commemoration. As Nos. 258/61. Multicoloured. P 13½.*

F272	10 f. Type **91**		2·50	1·00
F273	20 f. Concorde over London		2·75	1·50
F274	30 f. Concorde over Washington		3·25	2·00
F275	40 f. Concorde over Paris		3·75	3·25
F272/5		*Set of 4*	11·00	7·00

1978 (2 June). *25th Anniv of Coronation. As Nos. 262/4. P 15.*

F276	**92** 40 f. sepia, turquoise-blue and silver		25	60
	a. Sheetlet. Nos. F276/8 × 2		1·25	
F277	– 40 f. multicoloured		25	60
F278	– 40 f. sepia, turquoise-blue and silver		25	60
F276/8		*Set of 3*	65	1·60

Nos. F276/278 were printed together in small sheets of 6, containing two *se-tenant* strips of 3, with horizontal gutter margin between.

1978 (1 Dec). *Christmas. As Nos. 265/8. Multicoloured. P 14 × 13½.*

F279	10 f. Type **93**		15	20
F280	15 f. "The Virgin and Child with St. Anne"		20	30
F281	30 f. "The Madonna with the Goldfinch"		30	60
F282	40 f. "The Madonna with the Child"		35	70
F279/82		*Set of 4*	90	1·60

1979 (11 Jan). *1st Anniv of Internal Self-Government. As No. F225 surch as Type F **11**.*

F283	**78** 10 f. on 25 c. multicoloured (blue background)		55	30
F284	40 f. on 25 c. multicoloured (pale blue-green background)		1·25	1·50

1979 (10 Sept). *Death Centenary of Sir Rowland Hill. As Nos. 271/3. Multicoloured. P 14.*

F285	10 f. Type **95**		25	35
F286	20 f. 1969 Land Divers 25 c. commemorative		30	55
F287	40 f. 1925 20 c. (2d.)		40	75
F285/7		*Set of 3*	85	1·50

For miniature sheet containing No. F286, see No. **MS274**.

1979 (16 Nov). *Festival of Arts. As Nos. 275/8. Multicoloured. P 14.*

F288	5 f. Type **96**		20	10
F289	10 f. Nal-Nal clubs and spears		25	15
F290	20 f. Ritual puppet		35	40
F291	40 f. Neqatmalow headdress		60	1·00
F288/91		*Set of 4*	1·25	1·50

1979 (4 Dec). *Christmas and International Year of the Child. As Nos. 279/82. Multicoloured. P 13 × 13½ (horiz) or 13½ × 13 (vert).*

F292	5 f. Type **97**		65	35
F293	10 f. "Priest and Candles" (Herve Rutu)		85	35
F294	20 f. "Cross and Bible" (Mark Deards) (*vert*)		1·25	1·00
F295	40 f. "Green Candle and Santa Claus" (Dev Raj) (*vert*)		2·00	2·00
F292/5		*Set of 4*	4·25	3·25

1980 (27 Feb). *Birds. As Nos. 283/6. Multicoloured. P 14.*

F296	10 f. Type **98**		1·50	45
F297	20 f. Scarlet Robin		1·75	1·00
F298	30 f. Yellow-fronted White Eye		2·25	1·75
F299	40 f. Fan-tailed Cuckoo		2·25	2·25
F296/9		*Set of 4*	7·00	5·00

STAMP BOOKLETS

1980. *Cover as No. SB1.*

FSB1	200 f. As No. SB1, but containing Nos. F256/9	35·00	

POSTAGE DUE STAMPS

CHIFFRE TAXE	CHIFFRE TAXE	TIMBRE-TAXE
(FD 1)	(FD 2)	(FD 3)

1925 (June). *Optd with Type FD **1**, by D.L.R.*

FD53	**F 5** 10 c. (1d.) green		48·00	3·50
FD54	20 c. (2d.) greyish slate		48·00	3·50
FD55	30 c. (3d.) red		48·00	3·50
FD56	50 c. (5d.) ultramarine		48·00	3·50
FD57	1 f. (10d.) carmine/*blue*		48·00	3·50
FD53/7		*Set of 5*	£225	16·00
FD53/7 Optd "Specimen"		*Set of 5*	£225	

Although on sale in Paris, the Postmaster would not issue any in unused condition for about a year and most copies are cancelled-to-order.

1938 (1 June). *Optd with Type FD **2**, by Bradbury, Wilkinson.*

FD65	**6** 5 c. blue-green		14·00	38·00
FD66	10 c. orange		17·00	38·00
FD67	20 c. scarlet		23·00	48·00
FD68	40 c. grey-olive		45·00	£100
FD69	1 f. lake/*pale green*		48·00	£110
FD65/9		*Set of 5*	£130	£300
FD65/9 Perf "Specimen"		*Set of 5*	£200	

1941 (15 Apr). *Nos. FD65/9 optd with Type F **6** at Nouméa, New Caledonia.*

FD77	**6** 5 c. blue-green		8·75	38·00
FD78	10 c. orange		8·75	38·00
FD79	20 c. scarlet		8·75	38·00
FD80	40 c. grey-olive		8·75	38·00
FD81	1 f. lake/*pale green*		17·00	38·00
FD77/81		*Set of 5*	48·00	£170

1953 (30 Apr). *Optd with Type FD **3**, by Waterlow.*

FD92	**7** 5 c. green		4·50	18·00
FD93	10 c. scarlet		4·50	15·00
FD94	20 c. ultramarine		13·00	23·00
FD95	– 40 c. blackish brown		15·00	48·00
FD96	– 1 f. orange		25·00	48·00
FD92/6		*Set of 5*	55·00	£140

1957 (3 Sept). *Optd with Type FD **3**, by Waterlow.*

FD107	**12** 5 c. green		2·25	7·00
FD108	10 c. scarlet		2·25	7·00
FD109	20 c. ultramarine		5·50	9·50
FD110	**13** 40 c. sepia		11·00	17·00
FD111	– 1 f. red-orange		13·00	20·00
FD107/11		*Set of 5*	30·00	55·00

VANUATU

The former Condominium of the New Hebrides became the Republic of Vanuatu on 30 July 1980 and was admitted as a member of the Commonwealth.

99 Island of Erromango and Kauri Pine

100 Rotary International

(Des L. Curtis. Litho J.W. (15, 30, 40 f.), Walsall (10, 35, 70, 500 f.), Questa (others))

1980 (30 July). *As Nos. 242/54 of New Hebrides but inscr "VANUATU" and without cyphers as in T **99**. P 13 (15, 30, 40 f.) or 14 (others). E. Inscr in English. W w **14***

287E	5 f. Type **99**		15	15
288E	10 f. Territory map and copra making		15	15
289E	15 f. Espiritu Santo and cattle		25	25
290E	20 f. Efate and Vila P.O.		30	30
291E	25 f. Malakula and headdresses		35	35
292E	30 f. Aoba, Maewo and pigs' tusks		45	45
293E	35 f. Pentecost and land diver		50	50
294E	40 f. Tanna and John Frum cross		50	70
295E	50 f. Shepherd Island and outrigger canoe		55	80
296E	70 f. Banks Island and custom dancers		1·00	1·50
297E	100 f. Ambrym and idols		1·00	80
298E	200 f. Aneityum and baskets		1·10	1·40
299E	500 f. Torres Island and archer fisherman		2·00	3·00
287E/99E		*Set of 13*	7·50	9·00

F. Inscr in French. No wmk

287F	5 f. Type **99**		35	15
288F	10 f. Territory map and copra making		40	15
289F	15 f. Espiritu Santo and cattle		45	25
290F	20 f. Efate and Vila P.O.		50	30
291F	25 f. Malakula and headdresses		55	40
292F	30 f. Aoba, Maewo and pigs' tusks		55	55
293F	35 f. Pentecost and land diver		60	60
294F	40 f. Tanna and John Frum cross		90	60
295F	50 f. Shepherd Island and outrigger canoe		1·00	80
296F	70 f. Banks Island and custom dancers		1·40	1·50
297F	100 f. Ambrym and idols		1·50	1·10
298F	200 f. Aneityum and baskets		1·75	1·75
299F	500 f. Torres Island and archer fisherman		4·00	3·50
287F/99F		*Set of 13*	12·50	10·00

(Des L. Curtis. Litho Walsall)

1980 (16 Sept). *75th Anniv of Rotary International. T **100** and similar multicoloured design. P 14. E. Inscr in English. W w **14** (sideways on 10 f.)*

300E	10 f. Type **100**		10	10
301E	40 f. Rotary emblem (*vert*)		30	30

F. Inscr in French. No wmk

300F	10 f. Type **100**		15	15
301F	40 f. Rotary emblem (*vert*)		45	45

101 Kiwanis Emblem and Globe

102 "The Virgin and Child enthroned with Saints and Angels" (Umkreis Michael Pacher)

(Des L. Curtis. Litho Walsall)

1980 (16 Sept). *Kiwanis International (service club), New Zealand District Convention, Port Vila. T **101** and similar design. P 14. E. Inscr in English. W w **14** (sideways on 40 f.)*

302E	10 f. gold, ultramarine and chestnut		10	10
303E	40 f. gold, blue-green and bright blue		30	55

F. Inscr in French. No wmk

302F	10 f. gold, ultramarine and chestnut		40	45
303F	40 f. gold, blue-green and bright blue		85	85

Design: *Horiz*—40 f. Kiwanis and Convention emblems.

(Des BG Studio. Litho Questa)

1980 (12 Nov). *Christmas. Details from Paintings. T **102** and similar vert designs. Multicoloured. W w **14**. P 14 × 13½.*

304	10 f. Type **102**		10	10
305	15 f. "The Virgin and Child with Saints, Angels and Donors" (Hans Memling)		10	10
306	30 f. "The Rest on the Flight to Egypt" (Adriaen van der Werff)		20	20
304/6		*Set of 3*	35	35

103 Blue-faced Parrot Finch

104 Tribesman with Portrait of Prince Philip

(Des G. Drummond. Litho Questa)

1981 (18 Feb). *Birds (1st series). T **103** and similar vert designs. Multicoloured. W w **14**. P 14.*

307	10 f. Type **103**		70	25
308	20 f. Emerald Dove		90	45
309	30 f. Golden Whistler		1·10	80
310	40 f. Silver-shouldered Fruit Dove		1·25	1·00
307/10		*Set of 4*	3·50	2·25

See also Nos. 327/30.

(New Currency. Vatus)

(Des A. Theobald. Litho Format)

1981 (10 June). 60th Birthday of Prince Philip, Duke of Edinburgh. T 104 and similar vert designs. Multicoloured. W w 14. P 14 × 14½.
311 15 v. Type 104 .. .. 10 15
312 25 v. Prince Philip in casual dress .. 15 20
313 35 v. Queen and Prince Philip with Princess Anne and Master Peter Phillips .. 15 25
314 45 v. Prince Philip in ceremonial dress .. 20 35
311/14 .. .. .. Set of 4 55 85

105 Prince Charles with his Dog, Harvey
106 National Flag and Map of Vanuatu

(Des J.W. Litho Walsall)

1981 (22 July). Royal Wedding. T 105 and similar vert designs. Multicoloured. W w 14. P 14.
315 15 v. Wedding bouquet from Vanuatu .. 10 10
316 45 v. Type 105 .. .. 20 15
317 75 v. Prince Charles and Lady Diana Spencer 35 45
315/17 .. .. .. Set of 3 55 60

(Des C. Abbott. Litho Format)

1981 (30 July). First Anniv of Independence. T 106 and similar designs. W w 14 (sideways on 25 and 45 v.). P 14.
318 15 v. multicoloured 15 15
w. Wmk inverted .. .. 30·00
319 25 v. multicoloured 15 15
320 45 v. greenish yellow and brown-lake .. 20 20
321 75 v. multicoloured 35 70
w. Wmk inverted .. .. 4·50
318/21 .. .. .. Set of 4 75 1·10
Designs: Horiz—25 v. Vanuatu emblem; 45 v. Vanuatu national anthem. Vert—75 v. Vanuatu coat of arms.

 VANUATU 15

107 Three Shepherds
108 New Caledonian Myiagra Flycatcher

(Adapted G. Vasarhelyi. Litho Questa)

1981 (11 Nov). Christmas. Children's Paintings. T 107 and similar multicoloured designs. W w 14 (sideways on 25 and 45 v.). P 14.
322 15 v. Type 107 .. .. 10 10
323 25 v. Vanuatu girl with lamb (vert) .. 15 15
324 35 v. Angel as butterfly .. 15 20
325 45 v. Boy carrying torch and gifts (vert) 25 30
322/5 .. .. .. Set of 4 60 65
MS326 133 × 94 mm. Nos. 322/5 (wmk sideways) 80 1·25

(Des G. Drummond. Litho Questa)

1982 (8 Feb). Birds (2nd series). T 108 and similar vert designs. Multicoloured. W w 14. P 14½ × 14.
327 15 v. Type 108 .. .. 55 20
w. Wmk inverted .. ..
328 20 v. Rainbow Lorys 60 30
w. Wmk inverted .. ..
329 25 v. Buff-bellied Flycatchers .. 70 35
330 45 v. Collared Grey Fantails .. 80 65
327/30 .. .. .. Set of 4 2·40 1·40

109 Flickingeria comata
110 Scouts round Campfire

(Des Jennifer Toombs. Litho Enschedé)

1982 (15 June). Orchids. Multicoloured designs as T 109. W w 14 (sideways* on 35, 45, 50 and 75 v.). P 13½.
331 1 v. Type 109 .. .. 10 50
332 2 v. Calanthe triplicata .. 10 50
333 10 v. Dendrobium sladei .. 15 10
334 15 v. Dendrobium mohlianum .. 20 20

335 20 v. Dendrobium macrophyllum .. 25 30
336 25 v. Dendrobium purpureum .. 30 35
337 30 v. Robiquetia mimus .. 35 40
338 35 v. Dendrobium mooreanum (horiz) 50 50
339 45 v. Spathoglottis plicata (horiz) 55 70
340 50 v. Dendrobium seemannii (horiz) 60 80
341 95 v. Dendrobium conanthum (horiz) 95 1·50
w. Wmk Crown to right of CA .. — 10·00
342 100 v. Dendrobium macranthum .. 1·25 1·50
343 200 v. Coelogyne lamellata .. 2·25 2·75
344 500 v. Bulbophyllum longioscapum .. 5·00 6·50
331/44 .. .. Set of 14 11·00 15·00
*The normal sideways watermark shows Crown to left of CA, as seen from the back of the stamp.

(Des L. Curtis. Litho Questa)

1982 (1 Sept). 75th Anniv of Boy Scout Movement. T 110 and similar horiz designs. Multicoloured. W w 14 (sideways). P 14.
345 15 v. Type 110 .. .. 50 20
346 20 v. First aid 55 25
347 25 v. Constructing tower .. 60 40
348 45 v. Constructing raft .. 90 70
349 75 v. Scout saluting .. 1·25 1·25
345/9 .. .. Set of 5 3·50 2·50

111 Baby Jesus
112 Euploea sylvester

(Des G. Vasarhelyi. Litho Questa)

1982 (1 Nov). Christmas. Nativity Scenes. T 111 and similar multicoloured designs. W w 14 (sideways on 15, 25 v.). P 14.
350 15 v. Type 111 .. .. 40 15
351 25 v. Mary and Joseph .. 60 45
352 35 v. Shepherds (vert) .. 75 1·00
353 45 v. Kings bearing gifts (vert) 80 1·40
350/3 .. .. Set of 4 2·25 2·75
MS354 132 × 92 mm. As Nos. 350/3 but without yellow borders 1·75 3·25

(Des J. Cooter. Litho Questa)

1983 (17 Jan). Butterflies. T 112 and similar horiz designs. Multicoloured. W w 14 (sideways). P 14 × 14½.
355 15 v. Type 112 .. .. 90 65
a. Pair. Nos. 355/6 .. 1·75 1·25
356 15 v. Hypolimnas octocula .. 90 65
357 20 v. Papilio canopus .. 95 80
a. Pair. Nos. 357/8 .. 1·90 1·60
358 20 v. Polyura sacco .. 95 80
359 25 v. Luthrodes cleotas .. 1·25 80
a. Pair. Nos. 359/60 .. 2·25 1·60
360 25 v. Danaus pumila .. 1·25 80
355/60 .. .. Set of 6 5·25 4·00
Nos. 355/6, 357/8 and 359/60 were each printed in se-tenant pairs, horizontally and vertically throughout the sheets.

 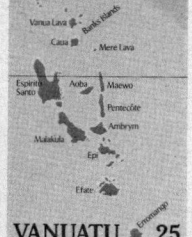

113 President Afi George Sokomanu
114 Map of Northern Vanuatu

(Des L. Curtis. Litho Enschedé)

1983 (14 Mar). Commonwealth Day. T 113 and similar horiz designs. Multicoloured. W w 14 (sideways*). P 13½×14.
361 15 v. Type 113 .. .. 15 10
362 20 v. Fisherman and liner Oriana .. 20 15
w. Wmk Crown to right of CA .. 1·00
363 25 v. Herdsman and cattle .. 25 15
364 75 v. World map showing position of Vanuatu with Commonwealth and Vanuatu flags .. 50 70
w. Wmk Crown to right of CA .. 11·00
361/4 .. .. Set of 4 1·00 1·00
*The normal sideways watermark shows Crown to left of CA, as seen from the back of the stamp.

(Des A. Theobald. Litho Harrison)

1983 (23 May). Economic Zone. Sheet 120 × 120 mm containing T 114 and similar vert designs. Multicoloured. W w 14. P 13½ × 13.
MS365 25 v. × 6 Yellow-finned Tuna; Type 114; Map of Matthew Island; Map of Hunter Island; Cornet Grouper; Skipjack Tuna .. 2·75 2·75

NEW INFORMATION
The editor is always interested to correspond with people who have new information that will improve or correct the Catalogue.

 VANUATU 15

115 Montgolfier Balloon of De Rozier and D'Arlandes, 1783
116 Mail at Bauerfield Airport

(Des A. Theobald. Litho Questa)

1983 (4 Aug). Bicentenary of Manned Flight. T 115 and similar multicoloured designs, each with manned flight logo. W w 14 (sideways on 35, 40 and 45 v.). P 13½.
366 15 v. Type 115 .. .. 15 15
367 20 v. J. A. C. Charles hydrogen balloon (first use of hydrogen), 1783 .. 25 25
368 25 v. Blanchard and Jeffries crossing English Channel, 1785 .. 30 30
369 35 v. Giffard's steam-powered dirigible airship, 1852 (horiz) .. 40 40
370 40 v. La France (airship of Renard and Krebs), 1884 (horiz) .. 45 45
371 45 v. LZ-127 Graf Zeppelin (first aerial circumnavigation), 1929 (horiz) .. 55 55
366/71 .. .. Set of 6 1·90 1·90

(Des L. McCombie. Litho Questa)

1983 (10 Oct). World Communications Year. T 116 and similar horiz designs. Multicoloured. W w 14 (sideways). P 14.
372 15 v. Type 116 .. .. 20 25
373 20 v. Switchboard operator .. 30 35
374 25 v. Telex operator .. 35 40
375 45 v. Satellite Earth station .. 65 70
372/5 .. .. Set of 4 1·40 1·50
MS376 138 × 95 mm. Nos. 372/5 .. 2·00 2·75

 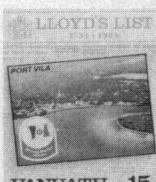

117 Cymatoderma elegans var lamellatum
118 Port Vila

(Des P. Cox. Litho Questa)

1984 (9 Jan). Fungi. T 117 and similar multicoloured designs. W w 14 (sideways on 35 v., inverted on 45 v.). P 14.
377 15 v. Type 117 .. .. 70 45
378 25 v. Lignosus rhinocerus .. 90 85
379 35 v. Stereum ostrea (horiz) .. 1·25 1·25
380 45 v. Ganoderma boninense .. 1·60 1·90
377/80 .. .. Set of 4 4·00 4·00

(Des D. Miller. Litho Questa)

1984 (30 Apr). 250th Anniv of "Lloyd's List" (newspaper). T 118 and similar vert designs. Multicoloured. W w 14. P 14½ × 14.
381 15 v. Type 118 .. .. 20 25
382 20 v. Induna (container ship) .. 30 35
383 25 v. Air Vanuatu Boeing 737 aircraft .. 35 40
384 45 v. Brahman Express (container ship) .. 65 70
381/4 .. .. Set of 4 1·40 1·50

(Des A. Theobald. Litho Questa)

1984 (11 June). Universal Postal Union Congress, Hamburg. As No. 371 but inscribed "UPU CONGRESS HAMBURG" and with U.P.U. logo. W w 14 (sideways). P 13½ × 14.
385 45 v. multicoloured 80 80

119 Charolais

(Des Doreen McGuinness. Litho J.W.)

1984 (24 July). Cattle. T 119 and similar horiz designs. Multicoloured. W w 14 (sideways). P 14.
386 15 v. Type 119 .. .. 20 25
387 25 v. Charolais-afrikander .. 30 40
388 45 v. Friesian 50 70
389 75 v. Charolais-brahman .. 90 1·25
386/9 .. .. Set of 4 1·75 2·40

120 *Makambo*

(Des L. Dunn. Litho Walsall)

1984 (7 Sept). *"Ausipex" International Stamp Exhibition, Melbourne. T 120 and similar horiz designs showing inter-island freighters. Multicoloured. W w 14 (sideways). P 14.*

390	25 v. Type **120**	..	..	70	50
391	45 v. *Rockton* ..	..	..	1·10	90
392	100 v. *Waroonga*	..	..	2·00	3·50
390/2			*Set of 3*	3·50	4·50
MS393	140 × 70 mm. Nos. 390/2 ..			4·00	5·00

5

121 Father Christmas (**122**)
in Children's Ward

(Des D. Slater. Litho Questa)

1984 (19 Nov). *Christmas. T 121 and similar horiz designs. Multicoloured. W w 14 (sideways). P 14.*

394	25 v. Type **121**	..	..	45	40
395	45 v. Nativity play	..	..	80	70
396	75 v. Father Christmas distributing presents		1·40	1·25
394/6			*Set of 3*	2·40	2·10

1985 (16 Jan). *No. 331 surch with T 122.*

397	5 v. on 1 v. Type **109** ..	..	..	65	50

123 Ambrym Island   **124** Peregrine
Ceremonial Dance   Falcon diving

(Des D. Slater. Litho Questa)

1985 (22 Jan). *Traditional Costumes. T 123 and similar vert designs. Multicoloured. W w 14. P 14.*

398	20 v. Type **123**	..	..	35	35
399	25 v. Pentecost Island marriage ceremony ..		40	40
400	45 v. Women's grade ceremony, South West Malakula				75	70
401	75 v. Ceremonial dance, South West Malakula			1·10	1·25
398/401			*Set of 4*	2·40	2·40

(Des N. Arlott. Litho Questa)

1985 (26 Mar). *Birth Bicentenary of John J. Audubon (ornithologist). Peregrine Falcon. T 124 and similar vert designs. Multicoloured. W w 14. P 14.*

402	20 v. Type **124**	..	..	60	35
403	35 v. Peregrine Falcon in flight	..	75	50
404	45 v. Peregrine Falcon perched on branch			90	80
405	100 v. "Peregrine Falcon" (John J. Audubon)			1·60	1·75
402/5	..		*Set of 4*	3·50	3·00

125 The Queen   **126** *Mala* (patrol boat)
Mother on her 80th
Birthday

(Des A. Theobald (100 v.), C. Abbott (others). Litho Questa)

1985 (7 June). *Life and Times of Queen Elizabeth the Queen Mother. T 125 and similar vert designs. Multicoloured. W w 16. P 14½ × 14.*

406	5 v. Duke and Duchess of York on wedding day, 1923		15	30
	w. Wmk inverted		†	—
407	20 v. Type **125**		40	40
408	35 v. At Ancona, Italy		60	60
409	55 v. With Prince Henry at his christening (from photo by Lord Snowdon)		85	90
406/9		*Set of 4*	1·75	2·00
MS410	91×73 mm. 100 v. At Royal Opera House, Covent Garden. Wmk sideways ..		1·40	1·50

(Des A. Theobald. Litho Format)

1985 (26 July). *5th Anniv of Independence and "Expo '85" World Fair, Japan. T 126 and similar horiz designs. Multicoloured. W w 16 (sideways). P 14.*

411	35 v. Type **126**		45	50
412	45 v. Japanese fishing fleet ..		55	70
413	55 v. Vanuatu Mobile Force Band ..		60	85
414	100 v. Prime Minister Fr. Walter H. Lini		65	1·75
411/14		*Set of 4*	2·00	3·50
MS415	116×102 mm. Nos. 411/14		2·50	4·25

127 "Youth Activities"
(Alain Lagaliu)

(Des D. Miller. Litho Questa)

1985 (16 Sept). *International Youth Year. Children's Paintings. T 127 and similar horiz designs. Multicoloured. W w 14 (sideways*). P 14.*

416	20 v. Type **127**		55	35
	w. Wmk Crown to right of CA	17·00		
417	30 v. "Village" (Peter Obed)		65	45
	w. Wmk Crown to right of CA	17·00		
418	50 v. "Beach and "PEACE" Slogan" (Mary Estelle)		1·10	75
	w. Wmk Crown to right of CA	5·50		
419	100 v. "Youth Activities" (*different*) (Abel Merani)		1·75	1·50
	w. Wmk Crown to right of CA	11·00		
416/19		*Set of 4*	3·50	2·75

*The normal sideways watermark shows Crown to left of CA, as seen from the back of the stamp.

128 Map of Vanuatu with   **129** Elizabeth's
National and U.N. Flags   Nudibranch
                          (*Chromodoris*
                          elisabethina)

(Des D. Hartley. Litho Questa)

1985 (24 Oct). *4th Anniv of United Nations Membership. W w 14 (sideways). P 14.*

420	**128** 45 v. multicoloured ..	..	80	70

(Des A. Riley. Litho Questa)

1985 (11 Nov). *Marine Life (1st series). Sea Slugs. T 129 and similar multicoloured designs. W w 14 (sideways on 35, 55 v.). P 14½ × 14 (20, 100 v.) or 14 × 14½ (others).*

421	20 v. Type **129**		30	35
422	35 v. Tessellated Nudibranch (*Halgerda aurantiomaculata*) (horiz)		45	50
423	55 v. *Chromodoris kuniei* (horiz) ..		75	80
424	100 v. *Notodoris minor* ..		1·40	1·50
421/4		*Set of 4*	2·50	2·75

See also Nos. 442/5 and 519/22.

130 Scuba Diving   **131** Liner S.S. *President
Coolidge* leaving San
Francisco

(Des O. Bell. Litho Walsall)

1986 (22 Jan). *Tourism. T 130 and similar vert designs. Multicoloured. W w 16. P 14.*

425	30 v. Type **130**	..	70	40
	w. Wmk inverted		1·50	
426	35 v. Yasur volcano, Tanna	..	1·00	45
	w. Wmk inverted		2·25	
427	55 v. Land diving, Pentecost Island		1·00	70
428	100 v. Windsurfing	..	1·25	1·75
425/8		*Set of 4*	3·50	2·75

For miniature sheet containing Nos. 427/8 with additional Australian Bicentenary symbol see No. MS501.

(Des A. Theobald. Litho Format)

1986 (21 Apr). *60th Birthday of Queen Elizabeth II. Vert designs as T 230a of Jamaica. Multicoloured. W w 16. P 14½×14½.*

429	20 v. With Prince Charles and Princess Anne, 1951		15	30
430	35 v. Prince William's Christening, 1982		20	45
	w. Wmk inverted		6·50	
431	45 v. In New Hebrides, 1974		25	60
432	55 v. On board Royal Yacht *Britannia*, Mexico, 1974		30	70
433	100 v. At Crown Agents Head Office, London, 1983		40	1·25
429/33		*Set of 5*	1·10	3·00

(Des L. Curtis. Litho Walsall)

1986 (19 May). *"Ameripex '86" International Stamp Exhibition, Chicago. Sinking of S.S. President Coolidge. T 131 and similar horiz designs. Multicoloured. W w 16 (sideways). P 14.*

434	45 v. Type **131**		1·00	60
435	55 v. S.S. *President Coolidge* as troopship, 1942		1·10	70
436	135 v. Map of Espiritu Santo showing site of sinking, 1942		2·00	1·75
434/6		*Set of 3*	3·50	2·75
MS437	80×105mm. Nos. 434/6 ..		4·25	3·00

132 Halley's Comet and
Vanuatu Statue

(Des Jennifer Toombs. Litho Questa)

1986 (23 June). *Appearance of Halley's Comet. T 132 and similar horiz designs. Multicoloured. W w 16 (sideways). P 14½.*

438	30 v. Type **132**	..	90	50
439	45 v. Family watching Comet	..	1·25	1·00
440	55 v. Comet passing Earth ..		1·40	1·25
441	100 v. Edmond Halley	..	2·00	3·25
438/41	..	*Set of 4*	5·00	5·50

133 Daisy Coral

(Des I. Loe. Litho Walsall)

1986 (27 Oct). *Marine Life (2nd series). Corals. T 133 and similar horiz designs. Multicoloured. W w 16 (sideways). P 14.*

442	20 v. Type **133**		65	40
443	45 v. Organ Pipe Coral	..	1·00	75
444	55 v. Sea Fan	..	1·25	1·10
445	135 v. Soft Coral	..	2·50	3·50
442/5		*Set of 4*	4·75	5·25

 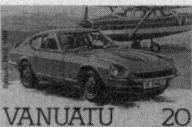

134 Children of Different   **135** Datsun "240Z" (1969)
Races

(Des C. Austin. Litho Harrison)

1986 (3 Nov). *Christmas. International Peace Year. T 134 and similar horiz designs. Multicoloured. W w 14 (sideways). P 14.*

446	30 v. Type **134**		90	50
447	45 v. Church and boy praying		1·25	85
448	55 v. U.N. discussion and Headquarters Building, New York ..		1·40	1·40
449	135 v. People of different races at work		2·75	5·00
446/9		*Set of 4*	5·75	7·00

(Des J.W. Litho Questa)

1987 (22 Jan). *Motor Vehicles. T 135 and similar horiz designs. Multicoloured. W w 14 (sideways). P 14.*

450	20 v. Type **135**		30	30
451	45 v. Ford "Model A" (1927)		60	60
452	55 v. Unic lorry (1924–5) ..		70	70
453	135 v. Citroen "DS19" (1975)		1·60	2·25
450/3		*Set of 4*	3·00	3·50

Hurricane Relief Fund +10

(136)   137 Young Coconut Plants

1987 (12 May). *Hurricane Relief Fund. No. 332, already surch as T* **122**, *and Nos.* 429/33, *all surch as T* **136**.

454	20 v. + 10 v. on 2 v. Calanthe triplicata	45	70
455	20 v. + 10 v. Princess Elizabeth with Prince Charles and Princess Anne, 1951	45	70
456	35 v. + 15 v. Prince William's Christening, 1982	75	1·00
457	45 v. + 20 v. Queen in New Hebrides, 1974	90	1·25
458	55 v. + 25 v. Queen on board Royal Yacht Britannia, Mexico, 1974	1·50	1·60
459	100 v. + 50 v. Queen at Crown Agents Head Office, London, 1983	1·75	2·75
454/9	*Set of 6*	5·25	7·25

The surcharge as T **136** on No. 454 includes the word "Surcharge" in addition to the inscription illustrated.

(Des R. Corrigne. Litho Format)

1987 (13 May). *25th Anniv of I.R.H.O. Coconut Research Station. T* **137** *and similar horiz designs. Multicoloured. W w* **16** *(sideways). P* 14.

460	35 v. Type **137**	40	45
461	45 v. Coconut flower and fronds	50	60
462	100 v. Coconuts	85	1·40
463	135 v. Research Station	1·10	2·00
460/3	*Set of 4*	2·50	4·00

The inscriptions on Nos. 462/3 are in French.

138 Spotted Hawkfish   139 Xylotrupes gideon (beetle)

(Des N. Harvey. Litho Questa)

1987 (15 July). *Fishes. T* **138** *and similar horiz designs. Multicoloured. W w* **16** *(sideways*). P* 14×14½.

464	1 v. Type **138**	10	10
465	5 v. Moorish Idol	15	10
466	10 v. Black-saddled Pufferfish	15	10
467	15 v. Dusky Anemonefish	20	20
468	20 v. Striped Surgeonfish	30	25
469	30 v. Six-barred Wrasse	40	35
470	35 v. Yellow-striped Anthias ("Purple Queenfish")	45	40
471	40 v. Squirrelfish	50	45
472	45 v. Clown Triggerfish	60	55
473	50 v. Dragon Wrasse	65	65
474	55 v. Regal Angelfish	70	70
475	65 v. Lionfish	80	80
476	100 v. Freckled Hawkfish	1·40	1·40
477	300 v. Undulate Triggerfish	3·50	4·00
	w. Wmk Crown to right of CA	55·00	
478	500 v. Saddle Butterflyfish	5·50	6·00
464/78	*Set of 15*	14·00	14·50

*The normal sideways watermark shows Crown to left of CA, as seen from the back of the stamp.

(Des I. Loe. Litho Questa)

1987 (22 Sept). *Insects. T* **139** *and similar horiz designs. Multicoloured. W w* **16** *(sideways). P* 14.

479	45 v. Type **139**	55	60
480	55 v. Phyllodes imperialis (moth)	65	70
481	65 v. Cyphogastra sp (beetle)	75	85
482	100 v. Othreis fullonia (moth)	1·10	1·75
479/82	*Set of 4*	2·75	3·50

140 "Away in a Manger"   141 Dugong Cow and Calf

(Des Josephine Martin. Litho Security Printers (M), Malaysia)

1987 (10 Nov). *Christmas. Christmas Carols. T* **140** *and similar vert designs. Multicoloured. W w* **14**. *P* 13½×14.

483	20 v. Type **140**	50	30
484	45 v. "Once in Royal David's City"	85	65
485	55 v. "While Shepherds watched their Flocks"	95	90
486	65 v. "We Three Kings of Orient Are"	1·00	1·00
483/6	*Set of 4*	3·00	2·50

1987 (9 Dec). *Royal Ruby Wedding. Nos.* 429/33 *optd with T* **45**a *of Kiribati in silver.*

487	20 v. Princess Elizabeth with Prince Charles and Princess Anne, 1951	30	30
488	35 v. Prince William's Christening, 1982	45	45
	w. Wmk inverted	11·00	
489	45 v. Queen in New Hebrides, 1974	60	60
490	55 v. Queen on board Royal Yacht Britannia, Mexico, 1974	70	70
491	100 v. Queen at Crown Agents Head Office, London, 1983	1·25	1·25
487/91	*Set of 5*	3·00	3·00

(Des Doreen McGuinness. Litho Walsall)

1988 (29 Feb). *Endangered Species. Dugong. T* **141** *and similar horiz designs. Multicoloured. W w* **16** *(sideways). P* 13×13½.

492	5 v. Type **141**	90	35
493	10 v. Dugong underwater	1·40	35
494	20 v. Two dugongs surfacing to breathe	1·90	1·00
495	45 v. Four dugongs swimming	3·25	2·50
492/5	*Set of 4*	6·75	3·75

142 Tambo   143 Captain James Cook

(Des E. Nisbet. Litho Security Printers (M), Malaysia)

1988 (18 May). *Bicentenary of Australian Settlement. Freighters. T* **142** *and similar horiz designs. Multicoloured. W w* **14** *(sideways*). P* 12.

496	20 v. Type **142**	20	25
	w. Wmk Crown to right of CA	7·00	
497	45 v. Induna	50	55
	w. Wmk Crown to left of CA	8·00	
498	55 v. Morinda	60	65
499	65 v. Marsina	70	75
	w. Wmk Crown to right of CA	15·00	
496/9	*Set of 4*	1·75	2·00

*The normal sideways watermark shows Crown to left of CA on the 20 v. and 65 v. and to right of CA on 45 v. and 55 v., *all as seen from the back of the stamp.*

(Des A. Theobald. Litho Format)

1988 (29 July). *"Sydpex '88" National Stamp Exhibition, Sydney. W w* **16**. *P* 14.

500	143 45 v. black and rosine	75	75

No. 500 was printed in small sheets of 10 (5 × 2), the two strips separated by a horizontal gutter of five illustrated stamp-size labels. The outer edges of the sheet are imperforate so that the stamps have one or two adjacent sides imperforate.

(Des O. Bell, adapted D. Miller. Litho Walsall)

1988 (24 Aug). *"Expo '88" World Fair, Brisbane. Sheet 100 × 80 mm. containing designs as Nos.* 427/8, *but with addition of Australian Bicentenary symbol and imprint date. Multicoloured. W w* **14**. *P* 14.

MS501	55 v. Land diving, Pentecost Island; 100 v. Windsurfing	2·50	1·90

144 Boxer in training   145 Agricultural Crops

(Des S. Noon. Litho Security Printers (M), Malaysia)

1988 (19 Sept). *Olympic Games, Seoul. T* **144** *and similar vert designs. Multicoloured. W w* **14**. *P* 13½ × 14.

502	20 v. Type **144**	20	25
	w. Wmk inverted	3·00	
503	45 v. Athletics	50	55
504	55 v. Signing Olympic agreement	60	65
505	65 v. Soccer	70	75
	w. Wmk inverted	3·50	
502/5	*Set of 4*	1·75	2·00
MS506	54×66 mm. 150 v. Tennis. P 13½	2·75	2·40

(Des O. Bell and D. Miller (55, 65 v.), D. Miller (20, 145 v.). Litho Questa)

1988 (25 Oct). *300th Anniv of Lloyd's of London. Multicoloured designs as T* **167**a *of Malawi. W w* **16** *(sideways on 55, 65 v.). P* 14.

507	20 v. Interior of new Lloyd's Building, 1988	30	25
508	55 v. Shirrabank (freighter) (horiz)	1·25	65
509	65 v. Adela (ferry) (horiz)	1·40	75
510	145 v. General Slocum (excursion paddle-steamer) on fire, New York, 1904	2·25	2·25
507/10	*Set of 4*	4·75	3·50

(Des A. Edmonston. Litho Format)

1988 (14 Nov). *Food and Agriculture Organization. T* **145** *and similar multicoloured designs. W w* **16** *(sideways on 45, 120 v.). P* 14½ × 14 *(horiz)* or 14 × 14½ *(vert).*

511	45 v. Type **145**	40	55
512	55 v. Fisherman with catch (vert)	45	65
513	65 v. Livestock on smallholding (vert)	50	75
514	120 v. Market women with produce	60	1·40
511/14	*Set of 4*	1·75	3·00

146 Virgin and Child ("Silent Night")   147 Periclimenes brevicarpalis

(Des Josephine Martin. Litho Format)

1988 (1 Dec). *Christmas. Carols. T* **146** *and similar horiz designs. Multicoloured. W w* **16** *(sideways*). P* 14½×14.

515	20 v. Type **146**	25	25
516	45 v. Angels ("Angels from the Realms of Glory")	45	55
517	65 v. Shepherd boy with lamb ("O Come all ye Faithful")	55	75
	w. Wmk Crown to right of CA	2·25	
518	155 v. Baby ("In that Poor Stable how Charming Jesus Lies")	1·50	1·90
	w. Wmk Crown to right of CA	2·25	
515/18	*Set of 4*	2·50	3·00

*The normal sideways watermark shows Crown to left of CA, as seen from the back of the stamp.

(Des A. Riley. Litho Questa)

1989 (1 Feb). *Marine Life (3rd series). Shrimps. T* **147** *and similar horiz designs. Multicoloured. W w* **16** *(sideways). P* 14.

519	20 v. Type **147**	50	25
520	45 v. Lysmata grabhami	80	55
521	65 v. Rhynchocinetes sp	95	75
522	150 v. Stenopus hispidus	2·25	2·50
519/22	*Set of 4*	4·00	3·50

148 Consolidated PBY-5 Catalina Flying Boat   149 Porte de Versailles Hall No. 1

(Des A. Theobald. Litho Security Printers (M), Malaysia)

1989 (5 Apr). *Economic and Social Commission for Asia and the Pacific. Aircraft. T* **148** *and similar horiz designs. W w* **14** *(sideways). P* 12.

523	20 v. black and cobalt	85	30
524	45 v. black and turquoise-green	1·25	65
525	55 v. black and orange-yellow	1·50	80
526	200 v. black and orange-red	4·25	3·00
523/6	*Set of 4*	7·00	4·25

Designs:—45 v. Douglas DC-3; 55 v. Embraer EMB-110 Bandeirante; 200 v. Boeing 737-300.

(Des O. Bell (Nos. 527/8), D. Miller (No. **MS529**). Litho Security Printers, Malaysia (Nos. 527/8), B.D.T. (No. **MS529**))

1989 (5 July). *"Philexfrance '89" International Stamp Exhibition, Paris. T* **149** *and similar horiz designs. W w* **14**. *P* 12.

527	**149** 100 v. multicoloured	2·00	1·40
	a. Horiz pair. Nos. 527/8	4·00	2·75
528	100 v. multicoloured (Eiffel Tower)	2·00	1·40
MS529	115×101 mm. 100 v. black, grey and scarlet (Revolt of French troops, Nancy, 1790 (42×28 mm)). W w **16** (sideways). P 14	1·40	1·50

Nos. 527/8 were printed together, *se-tenant*, in horizontal pairs throughout the sheet, each pair forming a composite design.

(Des A. Theobald (100 v.), D. Miller (others). Litho Questa)

1989 (20 July). *20th Anniv of First Manned Landing on Moon. Multicoloured designs as T* **51**a *of Kiribati. W w* **16** *(sideways on 55, 65 v.). P* 14×13½ *(45, 120 v.)* or 14 *(others).*

530	45 v. Command module seen from lunar module	1·25	80
531	55 v. Crew of "Apollo 17" (30×30 mm)	1·25	90
532	65 v. "Apollo 17" emblem (30×30 mm)	1·40	1·00
533	120 v. Launch of "Apollo 17"	2·50	2·00
530/3	*Set of 4*	5·75	4·25
MS534	99×82 mm. 100 v. Recovery of "Apollo 11". Wmk inverted. P 14×13½	1·75	1·75

100

(150)   151 New Hebrides 1978 Concorde 30 f. (French inscr) Stamp

1989 (18 Oct). *"Melbourne Stampshow '89". No. 332 surch with T 150.*
535   100 v. on 2 v. *Calanthe triplicata* .. .. 3·50   4·00

(Des A. Theobald. Litho Leigh-Mardon Ltd, Melbourne)

1989 (6 Nov). *"World Stamp Expo '89", International Stamp Exhibition, Washington. T 151 and similar horiz designs. Multicoloured. W w 16 (inverted). P 13½.*
536   65 v. Type 151 .. .. .. 2·50   2·50
MS537   105×100 mm. 65 v. New Hebrides 1978 Concorde 10 f. (English inscr) stamp; 100 v. White House, Washington .. .. 7·00   7·50

152 *Alocasia macrorrhiza*   153 Kava (National plant)

(Des Jennifer Toombs. Litho Security Printers (M), Malaysia)

1990 (5 Jan). *Flora. T 152 and similar vert designs. Multicoloured. W w 14. P 12.*
538   45 v. Type 152 60   55
539   55 v. *Acacia spirorbis* 70   70
540   65 v. *Metrosideros collina* .. 80   80
541   145 v. *Hoya australis* .. .. 1·75   2·50
538/41   .. .. .. *Set of 4* 3·50   4·00

(Des O. Bell. Litho Security Printers (M), Malaysia)

1990 (30 Apr). *"Stamp World London 90" International Stamp Exhibition. T 153 and similar vert designs. Multicoloured. W w 14 (sideways). P 13½.*
542   45 v. Type 153 80   55
543   65 v. Luganville Post Office .. 1·00   95
544   100 v. Embraer EMB-110 Bandeirante mail plane and sailing packet .. 1·90   2·00
545   200 v. Penny Black and Vanuatu 1980 10 f. definitive .. .. 3·00   3·75
542/5   .. .. .. *Set of 4* 6·00   6·50
MS546   110×70 mm. 150 v. New Hebrides 1974 New Post Office *tête-bêche* pair with first day postmark. Wmk upright .. .. 4·50   5·00

154 National Council of Women Logo

(Des D. Ashby. Litho Security Printers (M), Malaysia)

1990 (30 July). *10th Anniv of Independence. T 154 and similar horiz designs. W w 14 (sideways). P 14×13½.*
547   25 v. black and pale blue .. 35   30
548   50 v. multicoloured 60   70
549   55 v. bright purple, black and buff .. 65   70
550   65 v. multicoloured 70   90
551   80 v. multicoloured 85   1·25
547/51   .. .. .. *Set of 5* 2·75   3·50
MS552   109×82 mm. 150 v. multicoloured. Wmk upright .. .. .. 4·50   5·50
Designs:—50 v. President Frederick Kalomuana Timakata; 55 v. Preamble to the Constitution; 65 v. Vanuaaku Pati party flag; 80 v. Reserve Bank of Vanuatu; 150 v. Prime Minister Fr. Walter Lini taking oath.
No. MS552 also commemorates the South Pacific Forum, Port Vila, 1990.

155 General De Gaulle at Bayeux, 1944   156 Angel facing Right

(Des G. Vasarhelyi. Litho B.D.T)

1990 (22 Nov). *Birth Centenary of General Charles de Gaulle (French statesman). T 155 and similar horiz designs. Multicoloured. W w 14 (sideways). P 14.*
553   20 v. Type 155 .. .. 2·25   2·50
   a. Sheetlet. Nos. 553/4, and 555/8 each × 2 .. .. .. 10·00
554   25 v. Generals De Lattre de Tassigny, De Gaulle, Devers and Patch in Alsace, 1945 .. .. .. 2·25   2·50

555   30 v. De Gaulle as President of the French Republic 75   80
556   45 v. De Gaulle at Biggin Hill, 1942 .. 80   90
557   55 v. Roosevelt, De Gaulle and Churchill, Casablanca, 1943 .. 85   95
558   65 v. General De Gaulle and Liberation of Paris, 1944 90   1·00
553/8   .. .. .. *Set of 6* 7·00   7·75
Nos. 553/8 were printed together, *se-tenant*, in sheetlets of 12 (4×3) containing one each of the 20 c. and 25 c. values and two each of the others plus two labels, showing the Cross of Lorraine, at each end of the centre row.

(Des Jennifer Toombs. Litho Cartor)

1990 (2 Dec). *Christmas. T 156 and similar vert designs. Multicoloured. W w 14 (sideways). P 13.*
559   25 v. Type 156 45   55
   a. Horiz strip of 5. Nos. 559/63 .. 3·25
560   50 v. Shepherds 70   90
561   65 v. Nativity 80   1·00
562   70 v. Three Kings 85   1·10
563   80 v. Angel facing left .. 85   1·25
559/63   .. .. .. *Set of 5* 3·25   4·25
Nos. 559/63 were printed together, *se-tenant*, in horizontal strips of 5 throughout the sheet, forming a composite design.

157 *Parthenos sylvia*   158 Dance Troupe from South-west Malakula

(Des I. Loe. Litho Questa)

1991 (9 Jan). *Butterflies. T 157 and similar horiz designs. Multicoloured. W w 16. P 14×14½.*
564   25 v. Type 157 55   30
565   55 v. *Euploea leucostictus* .. 95   60
566   80 v. *Lampides boeticus* .. 1·40   1·25
567   150 v. *Danaus plexippus* .. 2·25   3·25
564/7   .. .. .. *Set of 4* 4·75   4·75
Nos. 564/7 were each printed in sheets of 10 with the two horizontal rows of five being separated by a row of labels illustrating the butterfly's life cycle.

(Des Sue Wickison. Litho Cartor)

1991 (2 May). *Second National Art Festival, Luganville. T 158 and similar vert designs. Multicoloured. W w 14. P 13½×14.*
568   25 v. Type 158 35   30
569   65 v. Women weavers and baskets .. 85   85
570   80 v. Woodcarver and carved animals, masks, dish and ceremonial figures .. 1·10   1·25
571   150 v. Musicians playing bamboo flute, youtatau and pan pipes .. 1·90   2·25
568/71   .. .. .. *Set of 4* 3·75   4·25

160 White-collared Kingfisher

20 (159)   20 (159a)

Type 159.   Surch by Mercury-Walch Pty, Hobart. 2½ mm between "20" and bars. Bars 5½ mm long.
Type 159a.   Surch by Southern Colour Print, Dunedin. 2 mm between "20" and bars. Bars 6½ mm long.

1991 (12 June–3 Dec). *Nos. 332/4 and 337 surch as T 159 by Mercury-Walch Pty, Hobart.*
572   20 v. on 2 v. *Calanthe triplicata* .. 50   50
   a. Surch with Type 159a (3 Dec) .. 85   85
573   60 v. on 10 v. *Dendrobium sladei* .. 1·25   1·60
574   70 v. on 15 v. *Dendrobium mohlianum* .. 1·40   1·75
575   80 v. on 30 v. *Robiquetia mimus* .. 1·40   1·75
572/5   .. .. .. *Set of 4* 4·00   5·00
See also No. 622.

(Des D. Miller. Litho Questa)

1991 (17 June). *65th Birthday of Queen Elizabeth II and 70th Birthday of Prince Philip. Vert designs as T 58 of Kiribati. Multicoloured. W w 16 (sideways). P 14½×14.*
576   65 v. Queen Elizabeth II .. 1·00   1·25
   a. Horiz pair. Nos. 576/7 separated by label .. .. 2·00   2·50
577   70 v. Prince Philip .. .. 1·00   1·25
Nos. 576/7 were printed in a similar sheet format as Nos. 366/7 of Kiribati.

(Des N. Arlott. Litho Questa)

1991 (15 Nov). *"Phila Nippon '91" International Stamp Exhibition, Tokyo. Birds. T 160 and similar vert designs. Multicoloured. W w 14. P 14½×14.*
578   50 v. Type 160 65   70
579   55 v. Palm Lorikeet 70   75
580   80 v. Scarlet Robin 95   1·10
581   100 v. Pacific Swallow .. 1·10   1·75
578/81   .. .. .. *Set of 4* 3·25   3·75
MS582   75×56 mm. 150 v. Eastern Reef Heron 2·25   3·00

161 Group of Islanders

(Des C. Bulewal and Sue Wickison (80 v.), Sue Wickison (others). Litho Questa)

1991 (29 Nov). *World AIDS Day. T 161 and similar horiz designs. Multicoloured. W w 16 (sideways). P 14.*
583   25 v. Type 161 55   30
584   65 v. Caring for AIDS victim .. 1·00   85
585   80 v. AIDS Shark .. .. 1·25   1·50
586   150 v. Children's playground .. 2·25   3·00
583/6   .. .. .. *Set of 4* 4·50   5·00

(Des D. Miller. Litho Questa (70 v.), Leigh-Mardon Ltd, Melbourne)

1992 (6 Feb). *40th Anniv of Queen Elizabeth II's Accession. Horiz designs as T 113 of Kenya. Multicoloured. W w 14 (sideways) (70 v.) or w 16 (sideways) (others). P 14.*
587   20 v. Reserve Bank of Vanuatu building, Port Vila 30   30
588   25 v. Port Vila 40   30
589   60 v. Mural, Parliament House .. 85   75
590   65 v. Three portraits of Queen Elizabeth .. 90   80
591   70 v. Queen Elizabeth II .. 95   1·50
587/91   .. .. .. *Set of 5* 3·00   3·25

162 Grumman F4F Wildcat   163 Meteorological Station, Port Vila

(Des E. Nisbet, Litho Enschedé)

1992 (22 May). *50th Anniv of Outbreak of the Pacific War (1st issue). T 162 and similar horiz designs, Multicoloured. W w 16 (sideways). P 13½×14.*
592   50 v. Type 162 .. .. 1·75   1·00
593   55 v. Douglas SBD-3 Dauntless .. 1·75   1·10
594   65 v. Consolidated PBY-5A Catalina .. 2·00   1·50
595   80 v. U.S.S. *Hornet* (aircraft carrier) .. 2·75   3·00
592/5   .. .. .. *Set of 4* 7·50   6·00
MS596   94×62 mm. 200 v. Vought-Sikorsky OS-2-3 Kingfisher over Port Vila .. 7·00   6·50
See also Nos. 623/7.

(Des Sue Wickison. Litho Leigh-Mardon Ltd, Melbourne)

1992 (24 June). *10th Anniv of Vanuatu's Membership of World Meteorological Organization. T 163 and similar horiz designs. Multicoloured. W w 14. P 14.*
597   25 v. Type 163 40   30
598   60 v. Satellite picture of tropical cyclone .. 80   80
599   80 v. Weather chart of Pacific showing cyclone .. .. 1·00   1·25
600   105 v. Radio Vanuatu broadcasting cyclone warning .. .. 1·25   1·75
597/600   .. .. .. *Set of 4* 3·00   3·50

164 Vanuatu National Football Team   165 Breast-feeding

(Des S. Noon. Litho Questa)

1992 (20 July). *Vanuatu's Participation in Melanesian Football Cup and Olympic Games, Barcelona. T 164 and similar horiz designs. Multicoloured. W w 14 (sideways). P 13½×14.*
601   20 v. Type 164 55   40
602   65 v. Melanesian Cup Final, 1990 .. 1·40   1·25
603   70 v. Baptiste Firiam (800 metres) .. 1·60   1·50
604   80 v. Mary Estelle Kapalu (400, 400 hurdles and 800 metres) .. 1·75   2·00
601/4   .. .. .. *Set of 4* 4·75   4·75

(Des Sue Wickison. Litho B.D.T.)

1992 (16 Oct). *World Food Day. T* **165** *and similar vert designs. Each reddish brown and bronze-green.* W w **16.** P 14×13½.
605	20 v. Type **165**	..	..	30	25
606	70 v. Central Hospital, Port Vila	..		95	90
607	80 v. Children eating	..	..	1·10	1·00
608	150 v. Nutritious food	..	..	1·75	2·50
605/8			*Set of 4*	3·50	4·25

166 Leatherback Turtle

167 *Hibiscus rosa-sinensis* "Agnes Goult"

(Des Sue Wickison. Litho Questa)

1992 (15 Dec). *Turtles. T* **166** *and similar horiz designs. Multicoloured.* W w **16** (*sideways*). P 14×14½.
609	5 v. Type **166**	..	..	1·25	1·10
610	65 v. Loggerhead Turtle laying eggs	..	1·40	1·25
611	70 v. Hawksbill Turtle swimming	..	1·60	1·40
612	80 v. Green Turtle under water	..	2·25	2·00
609/12			*Set of 4*	6·00	5·25
MS613	81×96 mm. 200 v. Green Turtle				
	hatchlings on beach. Wmk upright	..		3·75	4·50

(Des Jennifer Toombs. Litho Questa)

1993 (3 Mar). *Hibiscus Flowers* (1st series). *T* **167** *and similar vert designs. Multicoloured.* W w **16.** P 14.
614	25 v. Type **167**	..	..	30	30
615	55 v. *Hibiscus tiliaceus*	..	..	70	70
616	80 v. *Hibiscus rosa-sinensis linnaeus*	..	95	1·00
617	150 v. *Hibiscus rosa-sinensis* "Rose of China"	1·60	2·25
614/17			*Set of 4*	3·25	3·75

See also Nos. 682/5 and 736/9.

WORLD ORCHID CONFERENCE 1993

20

40

(168) (169)

1993 (2 Apr). *14th World Orchid Conference, Glasgow. Nos. 339 and 341/3 surch as T* **168.**
618	40 v. on 45 v. *Spathoglottis plicata* (*horiz*)	50	50
619	55 v. on 75 v. *Dendrobium conanthum*		
	(*horiz*)		70	75
620	65 v. on 100 v. *Dendrobium macranthum*	75	80
621	150 v. on 200 v. *Coelogyne lamellata*	1·60	2·50
618/21		*Set of 4*	3·25	4·00

1993 (30 Apr*). *No. 338 surch with T* **169.**
622	20 v. on 35 v. *Dendrobium mooreanum*	..	3·75	50

*Earliest known date of use.

(Des E. Nisbet. Litho B.D.T.)

1993 (30 June). *50th Anniv of Outbreak of the Pacific War* (2nd issue). *Horiz designs as T* **162.** *Multicoloured.* W w **14** (*sideways*). P 13½.
623	20 v. Grumman F6F Hellcat	..	..	90	55
624	55 v. Lockheed P-38F Lightning	..	1·75	1·50
625	65 v. Grumman TBF Avenger	..	1·75	1·60
626	80 v. U.S.S. *Essex* (aircraft carrier)	..	2·00	2·50
623/6			*Set of 4*	5·75	5·50
MS627	82×58 mm. 200 v. Douglas C-47				
	Skytrain			5·50	5·50

170 Port Vila and Iririki Island

171 Commercial Trochus (*Trochus niloticus*)

(Des D. Miller. Litho Leigh-Mardon Ltd, Melbourne)

1993 (7 July). *Local Scenery. T* **170** *and similar multicoloured designs.* W w **14** (*sideways on vert designs*). P 14×14½ (*horiz*) or 14½×14 (*vert*).
628	5 v. Type **170**	..	..	20	30
629	10 v. Yachts and Iririki Island	..	30	30
630	15 v. Court House, Port Vila	..	40	40
631	20 v. Two girls, Pentecost Island	..	40	40
632	25 v. Women dancers, Tanna Island	..	45	30
633	30 v. Market, Port Vila	..	..	50	35
634	45 v. Man in canoe, Erakor Island (*vert*)	..	60	45

635	50 v. Coconut trees, Champagne Beach	..	60	50
636	55 v. Coconut trees, North Efate Islands	..	70	55
637	60 v. Underwater shoal of fishes, Banks			
	Group			75	60
638	70 v. Sea Fan, Tongoa Island (*vert*)	..	1·00	90
639	75 v. Santo Island	..	..	1·00	95
640	80 v. Sunset, Port Vila harbour (*vert*)	..	1·10	1·00
641	100 v. Mele Waterfall (*vert*)	..	1·50	1·25
642	300 v. Yasur Volcano, Tanna Island (*vert*)	3·25	4·25
643	500 v. Aerial view of Erakor Island	..	4·75	6·00
628/43			*Set of 16*	16·00	17·00

For miniature sheet containing Nos. 629, 636/7 and 639 see No. **MS673.**

(Des Sue Wickison. Litho Walsall)

1993 (15 Sept). *Shells* (1st series). *T* **171** *and similar vert designs. Multicoloured.* W w **14.** P 14½.
644	55 v. Type **171**	..	1·10	85
645	65 v. Camp Pitar Venus (*Lioconcha*		
	castrensis)	..	1·25	95
646	80 v. Tapestry Turban (*Turbo petholatus*)	1·60	1·75
647	150 v. Trapezium Horse Conch (*Fasciolaria*		
	trapezium)	..	2·75	3·75
644/7		*Set of 4*	6·00	6·50

See also Nos. 665/8 and 692/5.

172 "St. Joseph the Carpenter" (detail) (De La Tour)

(Des D. Miller. Litho B.D.T.)

1993 (10 Nov). *Christmas. Bicentenary of the Louvre, Paris. Religious Paintings by Georges de la Tour. T* **172** *and similar horiz designs. Multicoloured.* W w **14** (*sideways*). P 14.
648	25 v. Type **172**	..	..	35	30
649	70 v. "Holy Child" (detail)	..	70	65
650	80 v. "Adoration of the Shepherds" (detail)	90	1·00
651	150 v. "Adoration of the Shepherds"		
	(different detail)	..	1·60	2·25
648/51			*Set of 4*	3·25	3·75

VANUATU

SOUTH PACIFIC MINI GAMES PORT VILA DECEMBER 1993

15

(173)

174 Charity Horse Race and Kiwanis Emblem

1993 (6 Dec). *South Pacific Mini Games, Port Vila. Nos.* 602, 604, 631 *and* 633 *surch as T* **173.**
652	15 v. on 10 v. Two girls, Pentecost Island	..	25	25
653	25 v. on 30 v. Market, Port Vila	..	35	35
654	55 v. on 65 v. Melanesian Cup Final, 1990	75	75
655	70 v. on 80 v. Mary Estelle Kapalu (400, 400		
	hurdles and 800 metres)	..	80	1·10
652/5			*Set of 4*	1·90	2·25

(Des E. Nisbet. Litho B.D.T.)

1994 (18 Feb). *"Hong Kong '94" International Stamp Exhibition. Charitable Organizations. T* **174** *and similar multicoloured designs.* W w **14** (*sideways on horiz designs*). P 14×15 (*vert*) or 15×14 (*horiz*).
656	25 v. Type **174**	..	..	35	30
657	60 v. Twin Otter airplane and Lions Club		
	emblem (*horiz*)	..	70	75
658	75 v. Mosquito and Rotary International		
	emblem	..	90	1·00
659	150 v. Blood donor service ambulance and		
	Red Cross emblem (*horiz*)	..	1·60	2·25
656/9			*Set of 4*	3·25	3·75
MS660	126×96 mm. 200 v. Charity emblems				
	(*horiz*)			2·00	3·00

175 Silhouetted Family

176 Traditional Sculpture and Hut

(Des Sue Wickison. Litho Questa)

1994 (2 Mar). *International Year of the Family.* W w **14.** P 14.
661	**175** 25 v. purple-brown and bluish violet	..	35	30
662	60 v. myrtle-green and vermilion	..	70	75
663	90 v. deep brown and emerald	..	1·00	1·10
664	150 v. bluish violet and yellow-brown	..	1·60	2·00
661/4			*Set of 4*	3·25	3·75

(Des Sue Wickison. Litho Southern Colour Print, Dunedin)

1994 (31 May). *Shells* (2nd series). *Vert designs as T* **171.** *Multicoloured.* P 12.
665	60 v. Eyed Cowrie (*Cypraea argus*)	..	1·75	1·00
666	70 v. Marble Cone (*Conus marmoreus*)	..	1·75	1·25
667	85 v. Chiragra Spider Conch (*Lambis*		
	chiragra)	..	1·90	1·90
668	155 v. Adusta Murex (*Murex brunneus*)	..	2·50	3·50
665/8			*Set of 4*	7·00	7·00

(Des C. Abbott. Litho Southern Colour Print, Dunedin)

1994 (27 July). *Tourism. T* **176** *and similar vert designs. Multicoloured.* P 13½.
669	25 v. Type **176**	..	..	70	80
	a. Horiz strip of 4. Nos. 669/72	..	6·00	
670	75 v. Outrigger canoe and inflatable dinghy	1·40	1·50
671	90 v. Yachts, airliner and parrot	..	1·75	1·90
672	200 v. Helicopter and local woman with fruit	2·75	3·00
669/72			*Set of 4*	6·00	6·50

Nos. 669/72 were printed together, *se-tenant*, in horizontal strips of 4 forming a composite design.

(Des D. Miller. Litho Leigh-Mardon Ltd, Melbourne)

1994 (10 Aug). *"Philakorea '94" International Stamp Exhibition. Sheet* 130×68 *mm, containing Nos.* 629, 636/7 *and* 639. *Multicoloured.* P 14×14½.
MS673	10 v. Yachts and Iririki Island; 55 v.				
	Coconut trees, North Efate Islands; 60 v.				
	Underwater shoal of fishes, Banks Group; 75 v.				
	Santo Island			2·75	3·50

VANUATU 25

VANUATU 55

177 Pink Anemonefish

178 Consolidated PBY-5 Catalina Flying Boat

(Des Sue Wickison. Litho Southern Colour Print, Dunedin)

1994 (16 Aug). *Anemonefish. T* **177** *and similar horiz designs. Multicoloured.* P 12.
674	55 v. Type **177**	..	..	1·50	80
675	70 v. Yellow-tailed Anemonefish	..	1·75	1·00
676	80 v. Fire Anemonefish	..	2·00	1·75
677	140 v. Orange-finned Anemonefish	..	3·50	4·50
674/7			*Set of 4*	8·00	7·25
MS678	80×60 mm. No. 677	..	..	3·25	4·00

No. **MS678** shows the "Philakorea '94" International Stamp Exhibition logo on the sheet margin.

(Des C. Abbott. Litho Southern Colour Print, Dunedin)

1994 (7 Dec). *50th Anniv of International Civil Aviation Organization. T* **178** *and similar horiz designs. Multicoloured.* P 12.
679	25 v. Type **178**	..	..	65	45
680	60 v. Douglas DC-3	..	..	1·10	90
681	75 v. De Havilland D.H.A.3 Drover	..	1·25	1·40
682	90 v. Boeing 737 on runway	..	1·50	2·00
679/82			*Set of 4*	4·00	4·25

Vanuatu **25**

179 *Hibiscus rosa-sinensis* "The Path"

180 *Emoia nigromarginata*

(Des Patricia Altman. Litho Southern Colour Print, Dunedin)

1995 (1 Feb). *Hibiscus Flowers* (2nd issue). *T* **179** *and similar horiz designs. Multicoloured.* P 12.
683	25 v. Type **179**	..	..	60	45
684	60 v. *Hibiscus rosa-sinensis* "Old Frankie"	1·10	1·00
685	90 v. *Hibiscus sinensis* "Fijian White"	..	1·60	1·75
686	200 v. *Hibiscus rosa-sinensis* "Surfrider"	..	3·25	4·00
683/6			*Set of 4*	6·00	6·50

(Des Sue Wickison. Litho Southern Colour Print, Dunedin)

1995 (12 Apr). *Lizards. T* **180** *and similar horiz designs. Multicoloured.* P 12.
687	25 v. Type **180**	..	..	60	45
688	55 v. *Nactus multicarinatus*	..	1·25	1·00
689	70 v. *Lepidodactylus*	..	1·40	1·40
690	80 v. *Emoia caeruleocauda*	..	1·50	1·50
691	140 v. *Emoia sanfordi*	..	3·25	3·25
687/91			*Set of 5*	6·50	7·00

(Des Sue Wickison. Litho Southern Colour Print, Dunedin)

1995 (1 June). *Shells* (3rd series). *Vert designs as T* **171.** *Multicoloured.* P 12.
692	25 v. *Epitonium scalare*	..	..	60	50
693	55 v. *Strombus latissimus*	..	1·25	1·25
694	90 v. *Conus bullatus*	..	1·75	1·75
695	200 v. *Pterynotus pinnatus*	..	3·50	4·00
692/5			*Set of 4*	6·25	6·75

181 "Tanna Girls" (A. Toni)   **182** Children with Doves and Flags

(Des Red Cactus Design Ltd. Litho Enschedé)

1995 (28 July). *15th Anniv of Independence. T* **181** *and similar multicoloured designs. P* 14×13½ (*horiz*) *or* 13½×14 (*vert*).

696	25 v. Type **181**		45	40
697	55 v. "Black Coral Dancers" (sculpture, E. Watt) (*vert*)		90	90
698	75 v. Erromango tapestry by Juliet Peta (*vert*)		1·25	1·25
699	90 v. "Parade Day" (H. Di-Donna)		1·40	1·75
700	140 v. "Banks Dancers" (J. John)		2·00	3·00
696/700		*Set of 5*	5·50	6·50
MS701	100×75 mm. No. 699		2·75	3·50

No. **MS701** also includes the "Singapore '95" International Stamp Exhibition logo on the sheet margin.

(Des G. Vasarhelyi, adapted Red Cactus Design Ltd. Litho Enschedé)

1995 (28 July). *50th Anniv of United Nations. P* 13½×14.

702	**182** 60 v. multicoloured		1·25	1·00

(Des E. Nisbet (Nos. 703/6), G. Vasarhelyi (No. **MS707**). Litho Enschedé)

1995 (1 Sept). *50th Anniv of End of Second World War in the Pacific. Horiz designs as T* **162** *showing aircraft. Multicoloured. P* 12½.

703	60 v. Curtiss SB2C Helldiver		1·75	1·50
704	70 v. Supermarine Spitfire Mk VIII		1·75	1·75
705	75 v. Chance Vought F4U-1A Corsair		1·90	1·75
706	80 v. Lockheed PV-1 Ventura		1·90	1·75
703/6		*Set of 4*	6·50	6·00
MS707	94×68 mm. 140 v. Japanese delegation at signing of Unconditional Surrender, Tokyo Bay. P 13½×14		4·00	4·50

No. **MS707** also includes the "Singapore '95" International Stamp Exhibition logo on the sheet margin.

183 Rambaramp (effigy), Malakula   **184** Boy throwing Cast Net

(Des C. Abbott. Litho Enschedé)

1995 (22 Nov). *Vanuatu Culture (1st series). Opening of New National Museum. Artefacts. T* **183** *and similar vert designs. Multicoloured. P* 13½×13.

708	25 v. Type **183**		35	30
	a. Horiz strip of 4. Nos. 708/11		3·00	
709	60 v. Pot from Wusi, Espiritu Santo		75	75
710	75 v. Slit gong from Mele, Efate		90	1·00
711	90 v. Tapa cloth, Erromango		1·25	1·60
708/11		*Set of 4*	3·00	3·25

In addition to separate sheets of 50, Nos. 708/11 were also available in sheets of 48 with the stamps *se-tenant* horizontally. See also Nos. 772/6.

(Des R. Youmans. Litho Questa)

1996 (1 Feb). *Fishing. T* **184** *and similar multicoloured designs. P* 14.

712	55 v. Type **184**		75	65
713	75 v. Fishing canoes		1·00	90
714	80 v. *Etelis* (fishing boat) and deep water fish (*vert*)		1·10	1·10
715	140 v. Game fisherman catching sailfish (*vert*)		2·25	2·75
712/15		*Set of 4*	4·50	4·75

185 *Pteropus anetianus*   **186** Immunization Programme

(Des Sue Wickison. Litho Southern Colour Print, Dunedin)

1996 (3 Apr). *Endangered Species. Flying Foxes. T* **185** *and similar multicoloured designs. P* 14.

716	25 v. Type **185**		40	50
717	25 v. *Notopteris macdonaldi* upside down eating fruit (*horiz*)		40	50
718	25 v. *Pteropus anetianus* hanging on branch		40	50
719	25 v. *Notopteris macdonaldi* on branch (*horiz*)		40	50
716/19		*Set of 4*	1·40	1·75

(Des C. Abbott (No. **MS720**), Sue Wickison (No. **MS721**). Litho Southern Colour Print, Dunedin)

1996 (18 May). *"CHINA '96" 9th Asian International Stamp Exhibition, Peking. P* 14.

MS720	75×85 mm. No. 711		1·75	2·00
MS721	75×85 mm. 90 v. *Pteropus tonganus* (flying fox); 140 v. *Pteropus tonganus* (*different*)		3·75	4·25

(Des Karen Odiam. Litho Questa)

1996 (5 June). *50th Anniv of U.N.I.C.E.F. T* **186** *and similar horiz design. Multicoloured. P* 14.

722	55 v. Type **186**		90	90
723	60 v. Breast-feeding programme		90	90

187 Airliner and Radio Waves

(Des C. Abbott. Litho Questa)

1996 (5 June). *Centenary of Radio. T* **187** *and similar horiz designs. Multicoloured. P* 14½.

724	60 v. Type **187**		80	90
	a. Block of 4. Nos. 724/7		3·50	
725	75 v. Radio Vanuatu broadcaster		95	1·10
726	80 v. Guglielmo Marconi		1·00	1·25
727	90 v. Cruise liner and radio waves		1·10	1·40
724/7		*Set of 4*	3·50	4·25

In addition to separate sheets of 50, Nos. 724/7 were also available in sheets of 48 with the stamps in *se-tenant* blocks of 4, forming a composite aerial view of Port Vila.

188 Marie Kapalu, Tawai Keiruan, Baptiste Firiam and Tava Kalo

(Des S. Coburn. Litho Southern Colour Print, Dunedin)

1996 (17 July). *Centenary of Modern Olympics Games. T* **188** *and similar horiz designs. Multicoloured. P* 14.

728	25 v. Type **188**		35	30
	a. Horiz strip of 4. Nos. 728/31		4·50	
729	70 v. Athletes training		95	95
730	75 v. Athletes from 1950s		1·00	1·00
731	200 v. Athletes in 1896		2·75	3·25
728/31		*Set of 4*	4·50	5·00

In addition to separate sheets of 50, Nos. 728/31 were also available in sheets of 48 with the stamps *se-tenant* horizontally.

189 Children in Front of Presbyterian Church and Roman Catholic Cathedral   **190** *Hibiscus rosa-sinensis* "Lady Cilento"

(Des Josephine Martin. Litho Southern Colour Print, Dunedin)

1996 (11 Sept). *Christmas. Religious Buildings. T* **189** *and similar vert designs. Multicoloured. P* 14.

732	25 v. Type **189**		45	30
	a. Horiz strip of 4. Nos. 732/5		3·25	
733	60 v. Children and Church of Christ		90	80
734	75 v. Children and Seventh Day Adventist and Apostolic churches		95	1·00
735	90 v. Children and Anglican church		1·25	1·60
732/5		*Set of 4*	3·25	3·25

In addition to separate sheets of 50, Nos. 732/5 were also available in sheets of 48 with the stamps *se-tenant* horizontally.

(Des Sue Wickison. Litho Walsall)

1996 (13 Nov). *Hibiscus Flowers (3rd issue). T* **190** *and similar horiz designs. Multicoloured. P* 13½.

736	25 v. Type **190**		40	30
737	60 v. *Hibiscus rosa-sinensis* "Kinchen's Yellow"		90	70
738	90 v. *Hibiscus rosa-sinensis* "D. J. O'Brien"		1·25	1·25
739	200 v. *Hibiscus rosa-sinensis* "Cuban Variety"		3·00	3·75
736/9		*Set of 4*	5·00	5·50

For miniature sheet containing Nos. 736 and 739 see No. **MS745**.

191 Coral Garden

(Des G. Ryan. Litho Questa)

1997 (15 Jan). *Diving. T* **191** *and similar horiz designs. Multicoloured. P* 14½×14.

740	70 v. Type **191**		90	80
741	75 v. Carving on the *President Coolidge*		95	85
742	90 v. "Boris" (Giant Grouper)		1·25	1·25
743	140 v. Wreck of the *President Coolidge*		2·25	3·25
740/3		*Set of 4*	4·75	5·50
MS744	124×75 mm. Nos. 740/3		4·75	5·50

For further miniature sheet containing Nos. 741 and 743 see No. **MS750**.

(Des Sue Wickison. Litho Walsall)

1997 (12 Feb). *"HONG KONG '97" International Stamp Exhibition. Sheet,* 100×85 *mm, containing Nos.* 736 *and* 739. *Multicoloured. P* 13½.

MS745	25 v. Type **190**; 200 v. *Hibiscus rosa-sinensis* "Cuban Variety"		3·25	4·00

192 View from Cockpit

(Des C. Abbott. Litho Enschedé)

1997 (2 Apr). *10th Anniv of Air Vanuatu. T* **192** *and similar horiz designs. Multicoloured. P* 15×14.

746	25 v. Type **192**		55	30
747	60 v. 737-400 airliner being serviced, Bauerfield International Airport, Port Vila (81×31 *mm*)		1·00	70
748	90 v. Air stewardess serving drinks		1·50	1·40
749	200 v. Passengers disembarking		2·50	3·50
746/9		*Set of 4*	5·00	5·50

(Des G. Ryan. Litho Questa)

1997 (29 May). *"Pacific '97" International Philatelic Exhibition, San Francisco. Sheet,* 100×86 *mm, containing Nos.* 741 *and* 743. *Multicoloured. P* 14½×14.

MS750	75 v. Carving on the *President Coolidge*; 140 v. Wreck of the *President Coolidge*		3·00	3·50

193 Sharp-tailed Sandpiper

(Des P. Martinson. Litho Enschedé)

1997 (4 June). *Birds (1st issue). Coastal Birds. T* **193** *and similar multicoloured designs. P* 13½×14 (*horiz*) *or* 14×13½ (*vert*).

751	25 v. Type **193**		35	30
752	55 v. Crested Tern		70	70
753	60 v. Little Pied Cormorant		75	75
754	75 v. Brown Booby		90	90
755	80 v. Reef Heron (*vert*)		95	1·10
756	90 v. Red-tailed Tropic Bird (*vert*)		1·10	1·40
751/6		*Set of 6*	4·25	4·75

See also Nos. 804/8.

NEW INFORMATION

The editor is always interested to correspond with people who have new information that will improve or correct the Catalogue.

194 Thomas Edison and Light Bulb   **195** Yellow-faced Angelfish

(Des C. Abbott. Litho Southern Colour Print, Dunedin)

1997 (27 Aug). *150th Birth Anniv of Thomas Edison (inventor). T* **194** *and similar horiz designs. Multicoloured. P* 12.

757	60 v. Type **194**				1·25	1·50
	a. Horiz pair. Nos. 757/8					2·50
758	70 v. Hydro-electric dam, Espiritu Santo			1·25	1·50
759	200 v. Port Vila at dusk (80×29 *mm*)			2·40	2·75
757/9				*Set of 3*	4·50	5·25

Nos. 757/9 were printed together, *se-tenant*, in blocks of 3 showing the two smaller designs separated from the 200 v. by an inscribed gutter. Each sheet contained six such blocks.

(Des Sue Wickison. Litho Questa)

1997 (12 Nov). *Angelfish. T* **195** *and similar vert designs. Multicoloured. P* 14×13½.

760	25 v. Type **195**				30	30
761	55 v. Flame Angelfish				70	70
762	60 v. Lemonpeel Angelfish			75	75
763	70 v. Emperor Angelfish			85	90
764	140 v. Multi-barred Angelfish			1·75	2·25
760/4				*Set of 5*	4·00	4·50

(196)   **197** Fale, Espiritu Santo

1998 (26 Jan). *No.* 638 *surch with T* **196** *by I.P.V., Port Vila.*

765	5 v. on 70 v. Sea Fan, Tongoa Island (*vert*)		30	30

For similar 5 v. surcharge see No. 795.

(Des C. Abbott. Litho Southern Colour Print, Dunedin)

1998 (12 Feb). *Local Architecture. T* **197** *and similar square designs. Multicoloured. P* 14½.

766	30 v. Type **197**				35	35
767	65 v. National Cultural Centre			80	80
768	80 v. University of South Pacific			95	95
769	200 v. Chiefs' Nakamal			1·90	2·25
766/9				*Set of 4*	3·50	4·00

(Des D. Miller. Litho Questa)

1998 (31 Mar). *Diana, Princess of Wales Commemoration. Vert designs as T* **91** *of Kiribati. Multicoloured. P* 14½×14.

770	95 v. Wearing black jacket, 1997			1·00	1·10

MS771 145×70 mm. 75 v. Wearing green jacket, 1987; 85 v. Wearing cream jacket and hat, 1991; 95 v. No. 769; 145 v. Wearing red dress, 1992 (*sold at 400 v. + 50 v. charity premium*) .. .. 3·75 5·00

198 Nalawan Headdresses from South West Bay, Malakula

(Des C. Abbott. Litho Southern Colour Print, Dunedin)

1998 (3 June). *Vanuatu Culture (2nd series). Masks. T* **198** *and similar vert designs. Multicoloured. P* 14½×15.

772	30 v. Type **198**				50	35
	a. Horiz strip of 5. Nos. 772/6				3·75	
773	65 v. Rom mask from North Ambrym			75	65
774	75 v. Tamate mask from Gaua Island			85	85
775	85 v. Banglulu headdress from Uripiv Island, north-east Malakula			95	1·00
776	95 v. Chubwan masks from Vao Island, Malakula, and from Pentecost			1·10	1·40
772/6				*Set of 5*	3·75	3·75

In addition to separate sheets of 40, Nos. 772/6 were also available in sheets of 50 with the stamps *se-tenant* horizontally.

199 *Danaus plexippus*

(Des Sue Wickison. Litho Premier Business Print, Auckland)

1998 (23 July). *Butterflies. T* **199** *and similar horiz designs. Multicoloured. Self-adhesive. Stamps die-cut perf* 14* *and backing paper roul.*

777	30 v. Type **199**				30	35
778	60 v. *Hypolimnas bolina*			55	60
779	65 v. *Eurema hecabe*			60	65
780	75 v. *Nymphalidae* sp.			70	75
781	95 v. *Precis villida*			95	1·00
782	205 v. *Tirumala hamata*			2·00	2·10
777/82			*Set of 6*	5·00	5·25
MS783	105×79 mm. No. 782			2·00	2·10

*Nos. 777/83 are die-cut perforated 14 with the wing of the butterfly, which extends out to the right of the design, separated from the backing paper by die-cutting around the outline.

No. MS783 also commemorates "SINGPEX '98" International Stamp Exhibition, Singapore.

Used examples of Nos. 777/83 should be retained on paper as the stamps disintegrate if soaked.

200 Yasur, Tanna

(Litho Southern Colour Print, Dunedin)

1998 (23 Oct). *Volcanoes in Vanuatu. T* **200** *and similar horiz designs. Multicoloured. P* 14½×14.

784	30 v. Type **200**				30	35
785	60 v. Marum and Benbow, Ambrym			55	60
786	75 v. Mount Garet, Gaua			70	75
787	80 v. Lopevi			75	80
788	145 v. Lake Manaro Voui, Ambae			1·40	1·50
784/8				*Set of 5*	3·50	4·00

═ 4   **═ 4**   **═ 5**   **34 ═**   **34 ═**
(201)   **(201a)**   **(202)**   **(203)**   **(203a)**

1998 (18 Dec)–**2000**. *Nos.* 631, 634 *and* 636/41 *surch as T* 201/3.

789	1 v. on 100 v. Mele Waterfall (*vert*)				
790	2 v. on 45 v. Man in canoe, Erakor Island (*vert*) (1999)			
791	2 v. on 55 v. Coconut trees, North Efate Islands			
792	3 v. on 60 v. Underwater shoal of fishes, Banks Group			
793	3 v. on 75 v. Santo Island (27.4.99)			
794	4 v. on 45 v. Man in canoe, Erakor Island (*vert*) (surch Type **201** (litho)			
	a. Surch Type **201a** (typo) (3.3.99*)			
795	5 v. on 70 v. Sea Fan, Tongoa Island (*vert*) (14.5.99*)			
796	34 v. on 20 v. Two girls, Pentecost Island (surch Type **203**) (1999)		
	a. Surch Type **203a** (17.2.2000)			
797	73 v. on 80 v. Sunset, Port Vila harbour (*vert*) (17.2.2000)		

*Earliest known postmark date.

Nos. 789/97 were produced as a result of the addition of VAT at 13% to postal rates from 14 September 1998.

204 De Quiros and *San Pedro y Paulo*   **205** Vanuatu Kingfisher

(Des S. Noon. Litho Southern Colour Print, Dunedin)

1999 (17 Feb). *Early Explorers. T* **204** *and similar horiz designs. Multicoloured. P* 14×14½.

798	34 v. Type **204**				60	50
799	73 v. De Bougainville and *La Boudeuse*		1·00	90
800	84 v. Cook and H.M.S. *Resolution*		1·10	1·10
801	90 v. La Pérouse and *L'Astrolabe*		1·25	1·25
802	96 v. Dumont d'Urville and *L'Astrolabe*		1·25	1·50
798/802			*Set of 5*	4·75	4·75

No. 802 is inscribed "1788" in error.

(Des S. Noon. Litho Southern Colour Print, Dunedin)

1999 (19 Mar). *"Australia '99" World Stamp Exhibition, Melbourne. Multicoloured. P* 14×14½.

MS803	95×82 mm. Nos. 800/2				2·00	2·50

(Des P. Martinson. Litho Southern Colour Print, Dunedin)

1999 (12 May). *Birds (2nd series). Bush and Lowland Birds. T* **205** *and similar vert designs. Multicoloured. P* 14.

804	34 v. Type **205**				50	40
805	67 v. Shining Cuckoo			85	70
806	73 v. Peregrine Falcon			90	75
807	107 v. Rainbow Lorikeet			1·25	1·60
804/7				*Set of 4*	3·25	3·00
MS808	111×95 mm. No. 807 (sold at 214 v.)		2·40	2·75

No. MS808 has the frame, series inscription and artist's signature shown in gold die-stamping on the sheet margins.

(Litho Southern Colour Print, Dunedin)

1999 (2 July). *"PhilexFrance '99" International Stamp Exhibition, Paris. Multicoloured. P* 14×14½.

MS809	105×82 mm. Nos. 799 and 801/2		3·00	3·25

206 Banks Islands Dancers   **207** *Pterois antennata*

(Litho Southern Colour Print, Dunedin)

1999 (14 July). *Vanuatu Dances. T* **206** *and similar vert designs. Multicoloured. Phosphorised paper. P* 14.

810	1 v. Type **206**				10	10
811	2 v. Small Nambas, Lamap-Malakula		10	10
812	3 v. Small Nambas, Malakula			10	10
813	5 v. Smol Bag Theatre			10	10
814	107 v. South West Bay, Malakula			95	1·00
815	200 v. Big Nambas, Malakula			1·90	2·00
816	500 v. Pentecost Island			4·00	4·25
810/16				*Set of 7*	7·25	7·50

(Litho Southern Colour Print, Dunedin)

1999 (18 Aug). *"China '99" International Stamp Exhibition, Beijing. Sheet as No.* MS808, *but* 100×80 *mm without gold die-stamped features, with "China '99" logo added to the margin in carmine. P* 14.

MS822	107 v. No. 807				95	1·00

(Des Sue Wickison. Litho Southern Colour Print, Dunedin)

1999 (13 Oct). *Lionfish. T* **207** *and similar vert designs. Multicoloured. Phosphorised paper. P* 14½×14.

823	34 v. Type **207**				35	40
824	84 v. Head of *Pterois antennata*			75	80
825	90 v. *Pterois volitans*			80	85
826	96 v. Head of *Pterois volitans*			85	95
823/6				*Set of 4*	2·75	3·00

208 Clown Triggerfish

(Des G. Ryan. Litho Southern Colour Print, Dunedin)

1999 (1 Dec). *New Millennium. Sheet,* 165×75 *mm, containing T* **208** *and similar multicoloured designs. Phosphorised paper. P* 14½.

MS827 165×75 mm. 34 v. Type **208**; 68 v. Young boy and Pentecost Island land diver (*vert*); 84 v. Statue and pig's tusk (*vert*); 90 v. Vanuatu Kingfisher; 96 v. Tanna islander blowing Triton shell and Yasur volcano .. .. .. 3·00 3·25

STAMP BOOKLETS

1980 (July). *Multicoloured cover,* 110×75 *mm, showing Vanuatu flag. Stamps attached by selvedge. E. Stamps inscr in English. F. Stamps inscr in French.*

SB2 200 f. As No. SB1, but containing Nos. 287E/90E and 287F/90F, each in pair .. .. 3·75

1982 (15 June). *Multicoloured cover,* 92×74 *mm, showing orchid. Stamps attached by selvedge.*

SB3 230 v. booklet containing 20 v. (No. 335) in block of 4, and 10 v. and 15 v. (Nos. 333/4) in blocks of 6 .. .. 3·75

1987 (15 July). *Multicoloured cover,* 90×85 *mm, showing diver and coral reef. Stamps attached by selvedge.*

SB4 360 v. booklet containing 5 v., 10 v., 35 v. and 40 v. (Nos. 465/6, 470/1), each in block of 4 .. 4·00

1993 (7 July). *Local Scenery. Multicoloured cover,* 90×85 *mm, showing view of Champagne Beach. Stamps attached by selvedge.*

SB5 440 v. booklet containing 5 v., 10 v., 45 v. and 50 v. (Nos. 628/9, 634/5), each in block of 4 .. 4·75

Victoria
see Australia

Virgin Islands
see British Virgin Islands

Western Australia
see Australia

Western Samoa
see Samoa

Zambia
(*formerly* Northern Rhodesia)

NORTHERN RHODESIA

The north-eastern and north-western provinces of Rhodesia, previously administered by the British South Africa Company, became a Crown Colony on 1 April 1924.

The current stamps of Rhodesia (the "Admiral design" first issued in 1913) remained in use until 31 March 1925 and continued to be valid for postal purposes until 30 September of that year.

PRICES FOR STAMPS ON COVER TO 1945	
Nos. 1/21	from × 2
Nos. 22/4	from × 5
Nos. 25/45	from × 2
Nos. D1/4	from × 15

1   2

(Eng W. G. Fairweather. Recess Waterlow)

1925 (1 April)–**29.** *Wmk Mult Script CA. P* 12½.

1	1	½d. green				1·50	60
2		1d. brown				1·50	10
3		1½d. carmine-red				1·50	30
4		2d. yellow-brown				2·00	10
5		3d. ultramarine				2·00	1·25
6		4d. violet				3·50	50
7		6d. slate-grey				3·50	40
8		8d. rose-purple				3·75	38·00
9		10d. olive-green				4·00	38·00
10	2	1s. yellow-brown and black				3·25	1·50
11		2s. brown and ultramarine				14·00	21·00
12		2s. 6d. black and green				15·00	6·50
13		3s. violet and blue (1929)				23·00	16·00
14		5s. slate-grey and violet				26·00	17·00
15		7s. 6d. rose-purple and black				90·00	£140
16		10s. green and black				65·00	70·00
17		20s. carmine-red and rose-purple				£140	£160
1/17					*Set of 17*	£350	£450
1/17 Optd/Perf "Specimen"					*Set of 17*	£750	

A used example of the 4d. exists imperforate between the stamp and a fragment of another below it.

1935 (6 May). *Silver Jubilee. As Nos. 114/17 of Jamaica, but ptd by D.L.R. P* 13½×14.

18	1d. light blue and olive-green			70	1·25
	f. Diagonal line by turret			42·00	
	h. Dot by flagstaff			70·00	
	i. Dash by turret			70·00	
19	2d. green and indigo			70	1·25
	f. Diagonal line by turret			55·00	
	g. Dot to left of chapel			85·00	
20	3d. brown and deep blue			2·50	5·00
	f. Diagonal line by turret			85·00	
	g. Dot to left of chapel			£150	
21	6d. slate and purple			3·00	1·25
	f. Frame printed double, one albino			£1700	
	h. Dot by flagstaff			£160	
18/21			*Set of 4*	6·25	8·00
18/21 Perf "Specimen"			*Set of 4*	90·00	

For illustrations of plate varieties see Omnibus section following Zimbabwe.

THERN_RHODE

Hyphen between "NORTHERN" AND "RHODESIA" (R. 9/6)

1937 (12 May). *Coronation. As Nos. 118/20 of Jamaica, but ptd by B.W. P* 11×11½.

22	1½d. carmine					30	35
23	2d. buff					40	35
24	3d. blue					60	1·25
	a. Hyphen flaw					£140	
22/4					*Set of 3*	1·10	1·75
22/4 Perf "Specimen"					*Set of 3*	65·00	

3   4

"Tick bird" flaw (R. 7/1 of ptgs from Sept 1938 onwards)

(Recess Waterlow)

1938 (1 Mar)–**52.** *Wmk Mult Script CA. P* 12½.

25	3	½d. green				10	10
		a. "C" of "CA" missing from wmk					
26		½d. chocolate (15.11.51)				10	80
		a. Perf 12½×14 (22.10.52)				1·40	5·00
27		1d. brown				10	10
		a. *Chocolate* (1948)				1·60	60
28		1d. green (15.11.51)				60	90
29		1½d. carmine-red				45·00	40
		a. Imperf between (horiz pair)				£12000	
		b. "Tick bird" flaw				£2250	£170
30		1½d. yellow-brown (10.1.41)				30	10
		b. "Tick bird" flaw				50·00	23·00
31		2d. yellow-brown				45·00	1·25
32		2d. carmine-red (10.1.41)				30	30
33		2d. purple (1.12.51)				45	90
34		3d. ultramarine				30	10
35		3d. scarlet (1.12.51)				50	2·00
36		4d. dull violet				30	40
37		4½d. blue (5.5.52)				40	4·50
38		6d. grey				30	10
39		9d. violet (5.5.52)				40	2·25
40	4	1s. yellow-brown and black				2·25	40
41		2s. 6d. black and green				7·00	2·25
42		3s. violet and blue				13·00	4·00
43		5s. grey and dull violet				9·00	6·00
44		10s. green and black				12·00	12·00
45		20s. carmine-red and rose-purple				38·00	45·00
25/45					*Set of 21*	£160	70·00
25/45 Perf "Specimen"					*Set of 15*	£275	

Nos. 26a and 28 exist in coils, constructed from normal sheets.

1946 (26 Nov). *Victory. As Nos. 141/2 of Jamaica. P* 13½×14.

46	1½d. red-orange				10	10
	a. Perf 13½				11·00	12·00
47	2d. carmine				10	40
46/7 Perf "Specimen"				*Set of 2*	55·00	

The decimal perforation gauge for Nos. 46/7 is 13.7×14.1 and for No. 46a 13.7×13.4.

1948 (1 Dec). *Royal Silver Wedding. As Nos. 143/4 of Jamaica, but* 20s. *ptd in recess.*

48	1½d. orange				30	10
49	20s. brown-lake				42·00	45·00

1949 (10 Oct). *75th Anniv of U.P.U. As Nos. 145/8 of Jamaica.*

50	2d. carmine				30	30
51	3d. deep blue				1·90	1·25
52	6d. grey				1·00	1·25
53	1s. red-orange				1·00	1·25
50/3				*Set of 4*	3·75	3·50

5 Cecil Rhodes and Victoria Falls

(Recess D.L.R.)

1953 (30 May). *Birth Centenary of Cecil Rhodes. Wmk Mult Script CA. P* 12 × 11½.

54	5	½d. brown				50	50
55		1d. green				40	50
56		2d. mauve				40	15
57		4½d. blue				40	3·25
58		1s. orange and black				75	4·00
54/8					*Set of 5*	2·25	7·50

6 Arms of the Rhodesias and Nyasaland

(Recess Waterlow)

1953 (30 May). *Rhodes Centenary Exhibition. Wmk Mult Script CA. P* 14 × 13½.

59	6	6d. violet				40	75

1953 (2 June). *Coronation. As No. 153 of Jamaica.*

60	1½d. black and yellow-orange				40	10

7   8

(Recess Waterlow)

1953 (15 Sept). *Wmk Mult Script CA. P* 12½ × 14 (*pence values*) or 12½ × 13½ (*shilling values*).

61	7	½d. deep brown				65	10
62		1d. bluish green				65	10
63		1½d. orange-brown				80	10
64		2d. reddish purple				75	10
65		3d. scarlet				60	10
66		4d. slate-lilac				1·25	1·25
67		4½d. deep blue				90	3·75
68		6d. grey-black				1·25	10
		w. Wmk inverted				£2500	£1000
69		9d. violet				60	3·75
70	8	1s. orange-brown and black				60	10
71		2s. 6d. black and green				6·50	2·75
72		5s. grey and dull purple				6·50	12·00
73		10s. green and black				6·00	22·00
74		20s. rose-red and rose-purple				20·00	26·00
61/74					*Set of 14*	40·00	60·00

For issues from 1954 to 1963, see RHODESIA AND NYASALAND.

9   Arms   10

(Photo Harrison)

1963 (10 Dec). *Arms black, orange and blue; portrait and inscriptions black; background colours below. P* 14½ (*T* 9) *or* 13½ × 13 (*T* 10).

75	9	½d. bright violet				40	60
		a. Value omitted				£650	
76		1d. light blue				70	10
		a. Value omitted				12·00	
77		2d. brown				30	10
78		3d. yellow				20	10
		a. Value omitted				75·00	
		b. Value and orange (eagle) omitted				£150	
		c. Eagle printed double				£2000	
		d. Orange (eagle) omitted				£1000	
79		4d. green				30	20
		a. Value omitted				90·00	
80		6d. light olive-green				30	10
		a. Value omitted				£450	
81		9d. yellow-brown				30	90
		a. Value omitted				£400	
		b. Value and orange (eagle) omitted				£275	
82		1s. slate-purple				30	10
83		1s. 3d. bright purple				1·75	10
84	10	2s. orange				1·25	2·50
85		2s. 6d. lake-brown				1·25	1·00
86		5s. magenta				5·50	5·50
		a. Value omitted				£1400	
87		10s. bright magenta				5·00	13·00
88		20s. blue				6·00	14·00
		a. Value omitted				£850	
75/88					*Set of 14*	21·00	35·00

Nos. 75/6 exist in coils, constructed from normal sheets.

The stamps of Northern Rhodesia were withdrawn on 23 October 1964 when the territory attained independence as the Republic of Zambia.

ZAMBIA
INDEPENDENT

11 Pres. Kaunda and Victoria Falls   12 College of Further Education, Lusaka

(Des M. Goaman (3d., 6d.), Gabriel Ellison (1s. 3d.). Photo Harrison)

1964 (24 Oct). *Independence. T 11/12 and similar vert design. P 13½ × 14½ (6d.) or 14½ × 13½ (others).*

91	3d. sepia, yellow-green and blue	..	10	10
92	6d. deep violet and yellow	..	15	20
93	1s. 3d. red, black, sepia and orange		20	25
91/3		*Set of 3*	40	50

Design:—1s. 3d. Barotse dancer.

14 Maize—Farmer and Silo

15 Health— Radiographer

21 Fishing at Mpulungu   22 Tobacco Worker

(Des Gabriel Ellison. Photo Harrison)

1964 (24 Oct). *T 14/15, 21/2 and similar designs. P 14½ (½d. to 4d.), 14½ × 13½ (1s. 3d., 2s. and £1) or 13½ × 14½ (others).*

94	½d. red, black and yellow-green	..	10	50
95	1d. brown, black and bright blue	..	10	10
96	2d. red, deep brown and orange	..	10	10
97	3d. black and red	..	10	10
98	4d. black, brown and orange	..	15	10
99	6d. orange, deep brown & deep bluish green		15	10
100	9d. carmine, black and bright blue..		15	10
101	1s. black, yellow-bistre and blue	..	15	10
102	1s. 3d. light red, yellow, black and blue		20	10
103	2s. bright blue, black, deep brown & orange		25	30
104	2s. 6d. black and orange-yellow	..	60	35
105	5s. black, yellow and green..	..	1·00	50
106	10s. black and orange	..	3·50	3·75
107	£1 black, brown, yellow and red	..	2·00	4·25
94/107		*Set of 14*	7·50	8·50

Designs: *Vert* (as *T* 15)—2d. Chinyau dancer; 3d. Cotton-picking. (As *T* 22)—2s. Tonga basket-making; £1 Makishi dancer. *Horiz* (as *T* 14)—4d. Angoni bull. (As *T* 21)—6d. Communications, old and new; 9d. Zambezi sawmills and Redwood flower; 2s. 6d. Luangwa Game Reserve; 5s. Education—student; 10s. Copper mining.
Nos. 94/5 and 97 exist in coils, constructed from normal sheets.

28 I.T.U. Emblem and Symbols

29 I.C.Y. Emblem

(Photo Harrison)

1965 (26 July). *I.T.U. Centenary. P 14 × 14½.*

108	28	6d. light reddish violet and gold .	15	10
109		2s. 6d. brownish grey and gold ..	85	1·50

(Photo Harrison)

1965 (26 July). *International Co-operation Year. P 14½.*

110	29	3d. turquoise and gold ..	10	10
111		1s. 3d. ultramarine and gold ..	35	45

30 State House, Lusaka

34 W.H.O. Building and U.N. Flag

(Des Gabriel Ellison. Photo Harrison)

1965 (18 Oct). *First Anniv of Independence. T 30 and similar multicoloured designs. No wmk. P 13½ × 14½ (3d.), 14 × 13½ (6d.) or 13½ × 14 (others).*

112	3d. Type 30	..	10	10
113	6d. Fireworks, Independence Stadium		10	10
	a. Bright purple (fireworks) omitted		85·00	
114	1s. 3d. Clematopsis (*vert*)		15	10
115	2s. 6d. Tithonia diversifolia (*vert*)		30	1·25
112/15		*Set of 4*	50	1·25

(Des M. Goaman. Photo Harrison)

1966 (18 May). *Inauguration of W.H.O. Headquarters, Geneva. P 14½.*

116	34	3d. lake-brown, gold and new blue	20	10
		a. Gold omitted	£100	
117		1s. 3d. gold, new blue & deep bluish vio	80	80

35 University Building

36 National Assembly Building

(Des Gabriel Ellison. Photo Harrison)

1966 (12 July). *Opening of Zambia University. P 14½.*

118	35	3d. blue-green and copper-bronze	..	10	10
119		1s. 3d. reddish violet and copper-bronze		20	10

(Des Gabriel Ellison. Photo Harrison)

1967 (2 May). *Inauguration of National Assembly Building. P 14½.*

120	36	3d. black and copper-bronze	..	10	10
121		6d. olive-green and copper-bronze	..	10	10

37 Airport Scene

(Des Gabriel Ellison. Photo Harrison)

1967 (2 Oct). *Opening of Lusaka International Airport. P 13½ × 14½.*

122	37	6d. violet-blue and copper-bronze		15	10
123		2s. 6d. brown and copper-bronze	..	60	1·00

38 Youth Service Badge

39 "Co-operative Farming"

(Des Gabriel Ellison. Photo Harrison)

1967 (23 Oct). *National Development. T 38/9 and similar designs. P 13½ × 14½ (6d., 1s. 6d.) or 14½ × 13½ (others).*

124	4d. black, red and gold		10	10
125	6d. black, gold and violet-blue		10	10
126	9d. black, grey-blue and silver		15	40
127	1s. multicoloured		50	10
128	1s. 6d. multicoloured		70	2·00
124/8 ..		*Set of 5*	1·40	2·25

Designs: *Vert*—9d. "Communications"; 1s. Coalfields. *Horiz*—1s. 6d. Road link with Tanzania.

(New Currency. 100 ngwee=1 kwacha)

43 Lusaka Cathedral

44 Baobab Tree

52 Chokwe Dancer

53 Kafue Railway Bridge

(Des Gabriel Ellison. Photo Harrison)

1968 (16 Jan). *Decimal Currency. T 43/4, 52/3 and similar designs. P 13½ × 14½ (1, 3, 15, 50 n.) or 14½ × 13½ (others).*

129	1 n. multicoloured	..	10	10
	a. Copper-bronze (including value) omitted	£100	
	b. Ultramarine (windows) omitted	£100	
130	2 n. multicoloured	..	10	10
131	3 n. multicoloured	..	10	10

132	5 n. bistre-brown and copper-bronze		10	10
133	8 n. multicoloured		15	10
	a. Copper-bronze (background) omitted			
	b. Blue (of costumes) omitted	..	80·00	
134	10 n. multicoloured	..	25	10
135	15 n. multicoloured		2·75	10
136	20 n. multicoloured		4·50	10
137	25 n. multicoloured		25	10
138	50 n. chocolate, red-orange & copper-bronze		30	15
139	1 k. royal blue and copper-bronze		4·00	20
140	2 k. black and copper-bronze		2·25	1·25
129/40		*Set of 12*	13·00	1·75

Designs: *Horiz* (as *T* 43)—3 n. Zambia Airways Vickers VC-10 jetliner. (As *T* 53)—15 n. *Imbrasia zambesina* (moth); 2 k. Eland. *Vert* (as *T* 44)—5 n. National Museum, Livingstone; 8 n. Vimbuza dancer; 10 n. Tobacco picking. (As *T* 52)—20 n. South African Crowned Cranes; 25 n. Angoni warrior.
All values exist with PVA gum as well as gum arabic.
Nos. 129/30 and 132 exist in coils, constructed from normal sheets.

55 Ndola on Outline of Zambia

56 Human Rights Emblem and Heads

(Des Gabriel Ellison. Photo Harrison)

1968 (29 June). *Trade Fair, Ndola. P 14.*

141	55	15 n. green and gold	..	10	10

(Des Gabriel Ellison. Photo and die-stamped (gold emblem) Harrison)

1968 (23 Oct). *Human Rights Year. P 14.*

142	56	3 n. deep blue, pale violet and gold		10	10

57 W.H.O. Emblem

58 Group of Children

(Des Gabriel Ellison. Photo and die-stamped (gold staff and "20") Harrison)

1968 (23 Oct). *20th Anniv of World Health Organization. P 14.*

143	57	10 n. gold and bluish violet	..	10	10

(Des Gabriel Ellison. Photo and die-stamped (gold children) Harrison)

1968 (23 Oct). *22nd Anniv. of U.N.I.C.E.F. P 14.*

144	58	25 n. black, gold and ultramarine	..	15	70

59 Copper Miner

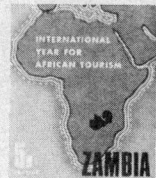
61 Zambia outlined on Map of Africa

(Des Gabriel Ellison. Photo Harrison)

1969 (18 June). *50th Anniv of International Labour Organization. T 59 and similar design. P 14½ × 13½ (3 n.) or 13½ × 14½ (25 n.).*

145	3 n. copper-bronze and deep violet	..	25	10
146	25 n. pale yell, copper-bronze & blackish brn	1·00	1·00

Design: *Horiz*—25 n. Poling a furnace.
A used example of No. 145 exists with the copper-bronze omitted.

(Des Gabriel Ellison. Photo Harrison)

1969 (23 Oct). *International African Tourist Year. T 61 and similar multicoloured designs. P 14 × 14½ (5 n., 25 n.) or 14½ × 14 (others).*

147	5 n. Type 61		10	10
148	10 n. Waterbuck (*horiz*)		15	10
149	15 n. Kasaba Bay Golden Perch (*horiz*)		35	40
150	25 n. Carmine Bee Eater		1·00	1·75
147/50		*Set of 4*	1·40	2·00

The new-issue supplement to this Catalogue appears each month in

GIBBONS STAMP MONTHLY

—from your newsagent or by postal subscription— sample copy and details on request.

PREVENTIVE MEDICINE

65 Satellite "Nimbus 3" orbiting the Earth

66 Woman collecting Water from Well

(Des Gabriel Ellison. Litho Enschedé)

1970 (23 Mar). *World Meteorological Day.* P 13 × 10½.
151 **65** 15 n. multicoloured 20 50

(Des V. Whiteley (from local designs). Litho B.W.)

1970 (4 July). *Preventive Medicine.* T **66** *and similar vert designs.*
P 13½ × 12.
152 3 n. multicoloured 15 10
153 15 n. multicoloured 40 25
154 25 n. greenish blue, rosine and sepia .. 80 35
152/4 .. .. *Set of 3* 1·25 65
Designs:—15 n. Child on scales; 25 n. Child being immunized.

67 "Masks" (mural by Gabriel Ellison)

68 Ceremonial Axe

(Des Gabriel Ellison. Litho Harrison)

1970 (8 Sept). *Conference of Non-Aligned Nations.* P 14 × 14½.
155 **67** 15 n. multicoloured 30 30

(Des Gabriel Ellison. Litho D.L.R.)

1970 (30 Nov). *Traditional Crafts.* T **68** *and similar multicoloured designs.* P 13½ (15 n.), 12½ (25 n.) or 14 (others).
156 3 n. Type **68** 10 10
157 5 n. Clay Smoking-Pipe Bowl 15 10
158 15 n. Makishi Mask (30 × 47 *mm*) .. 35 45
159 25 n. Kuomboka Ceremony (72 × 19 *mm*) 60 1·25
156/9 .. .. *Set of 4* 1·10 1·75
MS160 133 × 83 mm. Nos. 156/9. Imperf. .. 7·50 13·00

69 Dag Hammarskjöld and U.N. General Assembly

(Des J.W. Litho Questa)

1971 (18 Sept). *Tenth Death Anniv of Dag Hammarskjöld.* T **69** *and similar horiz designs, each with portrait of Hammarskjöld. Multicoloured.* P 13½.
161 4 n. Type **69** 10 10
162 10 n. Tail of aircraft 20 10
163 15 n. Dove of Peace 25 25
164 25 n. Memorial tablet .. .. .. 45 1·50
161/4 .. .. *Set of 4* 85 1·75

70 Red-breasted Tilapia

71 North African Crested Porcupine

(Des G. Drummond. Litho J.W.)

1971 (10 Dec). *Fish.* T **70** *and similar horiz designs. Multicoloured.* P 13½.
165 4 n. Type **70** 50 10
166 10 n. Long-finned Tilapia ("Green-headed Bream") 75 40
167 15 n. Tigerfish .. .. 1·00 2·50
165/7 .. .. *Set of 3* 2·00 2·75

(Des and litho J.W.)

1972 (15 Mar). *Conservation Year (1st issue).* T **71** *and similar multicoloured designs.* P 13½.
168 4 n. Cheetah (58 × 21 *mm*) 20 25
169 10 n. Lechwe (58 × 21 *mm*) 35 60
170 15 n. Type **71** 50 85
171 25 n. African Elephant .. .. .. 1·75 3·00
168/71 .. .. *Set of 4* 2·50 4·25

(Des and litho J.W.)

1972 (30 June). *Conservation Year (2nd issue). Designs similar to* T **71**. *Multicoloured.* P 13½.
172 4 n. Soil conservation 15 20
173 10 n. Forestry 20 30
174 15 n. Water (58 × 21 *mm*) 30 70
175 25 n. Maize (58 × 21 *mm*) .. .. 65 1·40
172/5 .. .. *Set of 4* 1·10 2·40

72 Giraffe and Common Zebra

(Des and litho J.W.)

1972 (30 June). *National Parks. Sheet* 114 × 140 *mm containing* T **72** *and similar vert designs. Multicoloured.* P 13½.
MS176 10 n. (× 4). Type **72**; Black Rhinoceros; Hippopotamus and Common Panther; Lion .. 8·00 14·00
Each design includes part of a map showing Zambian National Parks, the four forming a composite design.

73 Zambian Flowers

(Des and litho J.W.)

1972 (22 Sept). *Conservation Year (3rd issue).* T **73** *and similar horiz designs. Multicoloured.* P 13½.
177 4 n. Type **73** 30 30
178 10 n. *Papilio demodocus* (butterfly) .. 90 80
179 15 n. *Apis mellifera* (bees) .. .. 1·10 1·40
180 25 n. *Nomadacris septemfasciata* (locusts) 1·75 2·25
177/80 .. .. *Set of 4* 3·50 4·25

74 Mary and Joseph

75 Oudenodon and Rubidgea

(Des V. Whiteley. Litho Questa)

1972 (1 Dec). *Christmas.* T **74** *and similar horiz designs. Multicoloured.* P 14.
181 4 n. Type **74** 10 10
182 9 n. Mary, Joseph and Jesus 10 10
183 15 n. Mary, Jesus and the shepherds .. 10 10
184 25 n. The Three Wise Men 20 40
181/4 .. .. *Set of 4* 35 50

(Des Gabriel Ellison; adapted J.W. Litho Questa)

1973 (1 Feb). *Zambian Prehistoric Animals.* T **75** *and similar horiz designs. Multicoloured.* P 14 × 13½ (4 n.) or 13½ × 14 (others).
185 4 n. Type **75** 85 85
186 9 n. Broken Hill Man 90 90
187 10 n. Zambiasaurus .. .. .. 1·00 1·50
188 15 n. *Luangwa drysdalli* .. .. 1·10 2·00
189 25 n. Glossopteris .. .. .. 1·25 3·00
185/9 .. .. *Set of 5* 4·50 7·50
Nos. 186/9 are smaller, 38×21 mm.

76 "Dr. Livingstone, I Presume"

(Des J.W. Litho Format)

1973 (1 May). *Death Centenary of Dr. Livingstone.* T **76** *and similar horiz designs. Multicoloured.* P 13½.
190 3 n. Type **76** 20 15
191 4 n. Scripture Lesson 20 15
192 9 n. Victoria Falls 40 40
193 10 n. Scattering slavers 30 45
194 15 n. Healing the sick .. .. .. 40 1·60
195 25 n. Burial place of Livingstone's heart .. 45 2·75
190/5 .. .. *Set of 6* 1·75 5·00

77 Parliamentary Mace

(Des Gabriel Ellison. Litho Questa)

1973 (24 Sept). *Third Commonwealth Conference of Speakers and Presiding Officers, Lusaka.* P 13½.
196 **77** 9 n. multicoloured 60 65
197 15 n. multicoloured .. .. .. 75 1·50
198 25 n. multicoloured .. .. .. 85 2·00
196/8 .. .. *Set of 3* 2·00 3·75

78 Inoculation

79 U.N.I.P. Flag

(Des Gabriel Ellison. Litho Questa)

1973 (16 Oct). *25th Anniv of W.H.O.* T **78** *and similar multicoloured designs.* P 14.
199 4 n. Mother washing baby (*vert*) .. 48·00 23·00
200 9 n. Nurse weighing baby (*vert*) .. 45 2·25
201 10 n. Type **78** .. .. 50 3·00
202 15 n. Child eating meal .. .. .. 90 5·00
199/202 .. .. *Set of 4* 48·00 30·00
Only a small quantity of No. 199 was produced, and most examples were issued to post offices for local use.

(Des Gabriel Ellison. Litho Questa)

1973 (13 Dec). *1st Anniv of Second Republic.* T **79** *and similar vert designs. Multicoloured.* P 14 × 13½.
203 4 n. Type **79** .. .. 7·00 7·00
204 9 n. Freedom House .. .. .. 30 1·50
205 10 n. Army band .. .. 30 2·00
206 15 n. "Celebrations" (dancers) .. .. 50 3·25
207 25 n. Presidential chair .. .. .. 75 5·00
203/7 .. .. *Set of 5* 8·00 17·00

80 President Kaunda at Mulungushi

81 Nakambala Sugar Estate

(Des Gabriel Ellison. Litho Harrison)

1974 (28 Apr). *President Kaunda's 50th Birthday.* T **80** *and similar horiz designs. Multicoloured.* P 14½ × 14 (4 n.) or 14 × 14½ (others).
208 4 n. Type **80** 40 40
209 9 n. President's former residence .. 20 20
210 15 n. President holding Independence flame .. 50 1·25
208/10 .. .. *Set of 3* 1·00 1·75

(Des G. Vasarhelyi. Litho Questa)

1974 (23 Oct). *Tenth Anniv of Independence.* T **81** *and similar horiz designs. Multicoloured.* P 13½.
211 3 n. Type **81** 15 10
212 4 n. Local market 15 10
213 9 n. Kapiri glass factory 20 10
214 10 n. Kafue hydro-electric scheme .. 25 10
215 15 n. Kafue Railway Bridge 50 95
216 25 n. Non-aligned Conference, Lusaka, 1970 60 1·25
211/16 .. .. *Set of 6* 1·60 2·25
MS217 141 × 105 mm. 15 n. (× 4) Academic Education; Teacher Training College; Technical Education; Zambia University .. .. 6·00 8·50

82 Mobile Post-van

(Des Gabriel Ellison. Litho Format)

1974 (15 Nov). *Centenary of Universal Postal Union. T* **82** *and similar horiz designs. Multicoloured. P* 13½.
218	4 n.	Type 82		..	20	15
219	9 n.	Hawker Siddeley H.S.748 airplane on tarmac			30	30
220	10 n.	Chipata Post Office		..	30	40
221	15 n.	Modern training centre		..	45	1·75
218/21				*Set of 4*	1·10	2·40

83 Dish Aerial

(Des Gabriel Ellison. Litho Questa)

1974 (16 Dec). *Opening of Mwembeshi Earth Station (21 October). T* **83** *and similar horiz designs. Multicoloured. P* 13½.
222	4 n.	Type 83		..	25	20
223	9 n.	View at dawn		..	35	30
224	15 n.	View at dusk		..	40	70
225	25 n.	Aerial view		..	50	1·50
222/5				*Set of 4*	1·40	2·40

84 Black Rhinoceros and Calf   85 Independence Monument

(Des Gabriel Ellison. Litho J.W.)

1975 (3 Jan). *T* **84/5** *and similar horiz designs. Multicoloured.*

(a) *Size as T* **84**. *P* 13½ × 14
226	1 n.	Type 84		..	50	50
227	2 n.	Helmet Guineafowl		..	50	50
228	3 n.	National Dancing Troupe		..	15	50
229	4 n.	African Fish Eagle		..	60	10
230	5 n.	Knife-edge Bridge		..	85	60
231	8 n.	Sitatunga (antelope)		..	85	50
232	9 n.	African Elephant, Kasaba Bay		..	85	30
233	10 n.	Temminck's Ground Pangolin		..	20	10

(b) *Size as T* **85**. *P* 13
234	15 n.	Type 85		..	30	10
	a.	Magenta omitted..			£700	
235	20 n.	Harvesting groundnuts		..	85	95
236	25 n.	Tobacco-growing		..	1·25	30
237	50 n.	Flying-Doctor service		..	2·00	1·75
238	1 k.	Lady Ross's Turaco		..	3·75	1·75
239	2 k.	Village scene		..	5·50	5·50
226/39				*Set of 14*	14·00	11·50

No. 234a shows much of the design in yellow-green due to the omission of the magenta which was used as an overlay on other colours.

Nos. 226/7 exist in coils, constructed from normal sheets.

86 Map of Namibia   87 Erection of Sprinkler Irrigation

(Des PAD Studio. Litho Questa)

1975 (26 Aug). *Namibia Day. P* 13½.
240	**86**	4 n. green and light yellow-green			20	20
241		9 n. steel-blue and light turquoise-green			25	30
242		15 n. orange-yellow and greenish yellow			40	75
243		25 n. orange and light orange			50	1·25
240/3				*Set of 4*	1·25	2·25

(Des and litho J.W.)

1975 (16 Dec). *Silver Jubilee of the International Commission on Irrigation and Drainage. T* **87** *and similar horiz designs. Multicoloured. P* 13.
244	4 n.	Type 87		..	15	15
245	9 n.	Sprinkler irrigation (*different*)		..	30	40
246	15 n.	Furrow irrigation		..	65	1·25
244/6				*Set of 3*	1·00	1·60

88 Mutondo

(Des A. Chimfwembe. Litho J.W.)

1976 (22 Mar). *World Forestry Day. T* **88** *and similar horiz designs showing trees. Multicoloured. P* 13.
247	3 n.	Type 88		..	25	10
248	4 n.	Mukunyu		..	25	10
249	9 n.	Mukusi		..	45	25
250	10 n.	Mopane		..	45	25
251	15 n.	Musuku		..	70	1·40
252	25 n.	Mukwa		..	85	1·75
247/52				*Set of 6*	2·75	3·50

89 Passenger Train

(Des A. Chimfwembe. Litho J.W.)

1976 (10 Dec). *Opening of Tanzania-Zambia Railway. T* **89** *and similar horiz designs. Multicoloured. P* 13½ (**MS**257) *or* 13 (*others*).
253	4 n.	Type 89		..	30	30
254	9 n.	Copper exports		..	55	55
255	15 n.	Machinery imports		..	90	95
256	25 n.	Goods train		..	1·40	1·75
253/6				*Set of 4*	2·75	3·25
MS257	140 × 106 mm. 10 n. Clearing bush; 15 n. Laying track; 20 n. Railway workers; 25 n. Completed track				3·50	4·00

90 Kayowe Dance   91 Grimwood's Longclaw

(Des BG Studio. Litho Questa)

1977 (18 Jan). *Second World Black and African Festival of Arts and Culture, Nigeria. T* **90** *and similar horiz designs. Multicoloured. P* 13½.
258	4 n.	Type 90		..	15	10
259	9 n.	Lilombola dance		..	15	15
260	15 n.	Initiation ceremony		..	30	40
261	25 n.	Munkhwele dance		..	55	1·00
258/61				*Set of 4*	1·00	1·50

(Des Gabriel Ellison. Litho Questa)

1977 (1 July). *Birds of Zambia. T* **91** *and similar vert designs. Multicoloured. P* 14½.
262	4 n.	Type 91		..	40	10
263	9 n.	Shelley's Sunbird		..	55	60
264	10 n.	Black-cheeked Lovebird		..	55	60
265	15 n.	Locust Finch		..	1·25	2·00
266	20 n.	Black-chinned Tinkerbird		..	1·40	2·25
267	25 n.	Chaplin's Barbet		..	1·50	2·75
262/7				*Set of 6*	5·00	7·50

92 Girls with Building Blocks

(Des Gabriel Ellison. Litho Questa)

1977 (20 Oct). *Decade for Action to Combat Racism and Racial Discrimination. T* **92** *and similar horiz designs. Multicoloured. P* 14 × 14½.
268	4 n.	Type 92		..	10	10
269	9 n.	Women dancing		..	15	20
270	15 n.	Girls with dove		..	25	70
268/70				*Set of 3*	45	90

---

93 Angels and Shepherds

(Des Gabriel Ellison. Litho J.W.)

1977 (20 Dec). *Christmas. T* **93** *and similar horiz designs. Multicoloured. P* 14.
271	4 n.	Type 93		..	10	10
272	9 n.	The Holy Family		..	10	10
273	10 n.	The Magi		..	10	15
274	15 n.	Jesus presented to Simeon		..	20	60
271/4				*Set of 4*	40	85

94 African Elephant and Road Check   (95)

(Des Gabriel Ellison. Litho Questa)

1978 (1 Aug). *Anti-Poaching Campaign. T* **94** *and similar horiz designs. Multicoloured. P* 14 × 14½.
275	8 n.	Type 94		..	45	20
276	18 n.	Lechwe and canoe patrol		..	40	65
277	28 n.	Warthog and Bell 206 JetRanger helicopter			1·00	1·10
278	32 n.	Cheetah and game guard patrol		..	1·00	1·50
275/8				*Set of 4*	2·50	3·00

1979 (15 Mar). *Nos.* 228, 232, 234 *and* 236 *surch as T* **95**.
279	8 n. on 9 n. African Elephant, Kasaba Bay				70	10
	a. Surch inverted				50·00	
280	10 n. on 3 n. National Dancing Troupe				10	10
	a. Surch inverted				50·00	
	b. Surch omitted (in pair with normal)					
281	18 n. on 25 n. Tobacco-growing				15	15
	a. Surch inverted					
282	28 n. on 15 n. Type 85				20	25
	a. Surch inverted				8·00	
	b. Albino surch					
279/82				*Set of 4*	1·00	55

No. 280b was caused by a corner paper fold.

96 Kayowe Dance   97 "Kalulu and the Tug of War"

(Des Gabriel Ellison. Litho Questa)

1979 (1 Aug). *Commonwealth Summit Conference, Lusaka. T* **96** *and similar horiz designs. Multicoloured. P* 14.
283	18 n.	Type 96		..	15	25
284	32 n.	Kutambala dance		..	20	40
285	42 n.	Chitwansombo drummers		..	20	60
286	58 n.	Lilombola dance		..	25	80
283/6				*Set of 4*	70	1·90

(Des Gabriel Ellison. Litho Questa)

1979 (21 Sept). *International Year of the Child. Illustrations from Children's Books. T* **97** *and similar vert designs. Multicoloured. P* 14.
287	18 n.	Type 97		..	20	30
288	32 n.	"Why the Zebra has no Horns"		..	30	55
289	42 n.	"How the Tortoise got his Shell"		..	40	85
290	58 n.	"Kalulu and the Lion"		..	50	1·10
287/90				*Set of 4*	1·25	2·50
MS291	90 × 120 mm. Nos. 287/90				2·25	2·75

98 Children of Different Races holding Anti-Apartheid Emblem

(Des Gabriel Ellison. Litho Questa)

1979 (13 Nov). *International Anti-Apartheid Year. T* **98** *and similar horiz designs showing children of different races together. Multicoloured. P* 14½.
292	18 n.	Type 98		..	15	25
293	32 n.	Children with toy car		..	25	40
294	42 n.	Young children with butterfly		..	35	60
295	58 n.	Children with microscope		..	50	80
292/5				*Set of 4*	1·10	1·90

99 Sir Rowland Hill and 2s. Definitive Stamp of 1964 (100)

LONDON 1980

(Des Gabriel Ellison. Litho Format)

1979 (20 Dec). *Death Centenary of Sir Rowland Hill. T* **99** *and similar horiz designs. Multicoloured. P* 14½.
296	18 n.	Type **99**		20	25
297	32 n.	Sir Rowland Hill and mailman		25	55
298	42 n.	Sir Rowland Hill and Northern Rhodesia 1963 ½d. definitive stamp		25	70
299	58 n.	Sir Rowland Hill and mail-carrying oxwaggon		30	1·10
296/9			*Set of* 4	90	2·40
MS300	112 × 89 mm. Nos. 296/9			1·25	2·50

1980 (16 May). *"London 1980" International Stamp Exhibition. Nos.* 296/300 *optd with T* **100**.
301	18 n.	Type **99**		25	40
302	32 n.	Sir Rowland Hill and mailman		30	60
303	42 n.	Sir Rowland Hill and Northern Rhodesia 1963 ½d. definitive stamp		40	75
304	58 n.	Sir Rowland Hill and mail-carrying oxwaggon		60	90
301/4			*Set of* 4	1·40	2·40
MS305	112 × 89 mm. Nos. 301/4			3·00	3·75

101 Rotary Anniversary Emblem

(Des J.W. Litho Questa)

1980 (18 June). *75th Anniv of Rotary International. P* 14.
306	101	8 n. multicoloured		10	10
307		32 n. multicoloured		30	40
308		42 n. multicoloured		35	50
309		58 n. multicoloured		45	80
306/9			*Set of* 4	1·00	1·60
MS310	115 × 89 mm. Nos. 306/9			1·50	2·25

102 Running

(Des Gabriel Ellison. Litho J.W.)

1980 (19 July). *Olympic Games, Moscow. T* **102** *and similar horiz designs. Multicoloured. P* 13.
311	18 n.	Type **102**		25	25
312	32 n.	Boxing		40	45
313	42 n.	Football		50	80
314	58 n.	Swimming		80	1·25
311/14			*Set of* 4	1·75	2·50
MS315	142 × 144 mm. Nos. 311/14. P 14.			2·00	3·00

103 *Euphaedra zaddachi*   104 Zambia Coat of Arms

(Des Gabriel Ellison. Litho Questa)

1980 (27 Aug). *Butterflies. T* **103** *and similar horiz designs. Multicoloured. P* 14.
316	18 n.	Type **103**		15	15
317	32 n.	*Aphnaeus questiauxi*		25	40
318	42 n.	*Abantis zambesiaca*		40	80
319	58 n.	*Spindasis modesta*		60	1·60
316/19			*Set of* 4	1·25	2·75
MS320	114 × 86 mm. Nos. 316/19			4·25	3·25

(Des Gabriel Ellison. Litho Format)

1980 (27 Sept). *26th Commonwealth Parliamentary Association Conference, Lusaka. P* 14.
321	104	18 n. multicoloured		15	25
322		32 n. multicoloured		25	45
323		42 n. multicoloured		30	65
324		58 n. multicoloured		40	1·25
321/4			*Set of* 4	1·00	2·40

105 Nativity and St. Francis of Assisi (stained glass window, Ndola Church)   106 Musikili

(Des Gabriel Ellison. Litho Questa)

1980 (3 Nov). *50th Anniv of Catholic Church on the Copperbelt. P* 13½.
325	105	8 n. multicoloured		10	10
326		28 n. multicoloured		30	70
327		32 n. multicoloured		30	70
328		42 n. multicoloured		45	95
325/8			*Set of* 4	1·00	2·25

(Des Gabriel Ellison. Litho Questa)

1981 (21 Mar). *World Forestry Day. Seedpods. T* **106** *and similar horiz designs. Multicoloured. P* 14.
329	8 n.	Type **106**		10	10
330	18 n.	Mupapa		20	45
331	28 n.	Mulunguti		25	80
332	32 n.	Mulama		25	1·25
329/32			*Set of* 4	70	2·25

107 I.T.U. Emblem   108 Mask Maker

(Des J.W. Litho Format)

1981 (15 May). *World Telecommunications and Health Day. T* **107** *and similar vert design. Multicoloured. P* 14½.
333	8 n.	Type **107**		20	10
334	18 n.	W.H.O. emblems		25	35
335	28 n.	Type **107**		30	60
336	32 n.	As 18 n.		35	75
333/6			*Set of* 4	1·00	1·60

Nos. 333/6 exist imperforate from stock dispersed by the liquidator of Format International Security Printers Ltd.

(Des Gabriel Ellison. Litho Harrison)

1981 (2 June)**–83.** *Multicoloured designs as T* **108**. *P* 14 × 13½ (50 n., 75 n., 1 k., 2 k.) *or* 14½ (*others*).
337	1 n.	Type **108**		10	10
338	2 n.	Blacksmith		10	10
339	5 n.	Pottery making		10	10
340	8 n.	Straw-basket fishing		10	10
341	10 n.	Thatching		10	10
342	12 n.	Mushroom picking (17.2.83)		3·00	1·75
343	18 n.	Millet grinding on stone		30	10
344	20 n.	Royal Barge paddler (11.11.81)		50	10
345	30 n.	Makishi tightrope dancer (11.11.81)		50	10
346	35 n.	Tonga Ila granary and house (11.11.81)		55	10
347	42 n.	Cattle herding (11.11.81)		55	80
348	50 n.	Traditional healer (38 × 26 *mm*) (11.11.81)		55	10
349	75 n.	Women carrying water (38 × 26 *mm*) (17.2.83)		55	60
350	1 k.	Pounding maize (38 × 26 *mm*) (17.2.83)		55	60
351	2 k.	Pipe-smoking, Gwembe Valley Belle (38 × 26 *mm*)		55	60
337/51			*Set of* 15	7·00	4·50

Nos. 338/9 and 341 exist in coils, constructed from normal sheets.

109 Kankobele   110 Banded Ironstone

(Des Gabriel Ellison. Litho Format)

1981 (30 Sept*). *Traditional Musical Instruments. T* **109** *and similar vert designs. Multicoloured. P* 15.
356	8 n.	Type **109**		25	10
357	18 n.	Inshingili		30	50
358	28 n.	Ilimba		40	1·50
359	32 n.	Bango		40	1·75
356/9			*Set of* 4	1·25	3·50

*It has been reported that the Ndola Philatelic Bureau inadvertently sold some of these stamps some days earlier, and that cancelled-to-order examples exist postmarked 14 or 15 September.

Nos. 356 and 358/9 exist imperforate from stock dispersed by the liquidator of Format International Security Printers Ltd.

(Des Gabriel Ellison. Litho Questa)

1982 (5 Jan). *Minerals* (1st series). *T* **110** *and similar vert designs. Multicoloured. P* 14.
360	8 n.	Type **110**		1·00	10
361	18 n.	Cobaltocalcite		2·00	80
362	28 n.	Amazonite		2·75	2·00
363	32 n.	Tourmaline		3·00	2·50
364	42 n.	Uranium ore		3·25	3·50
360/4			*Set of* 5	11·00	8·00

See also Nos. 370/4.

111 Zambian Scouts

(Des Gabriel Ellison. Litho Questa)

1982 (30 Mar). *75th Anniv of Boy Scout Movement. T* **111** *and similar horiz designs. Multicoloured. P* 14.
365	8 n.	Type **111**		30	10
366	18 n.	Lord Baden-Powell and Victoria Falls		70	40
367	28 n.	African Buffalo and Zambian Scout patrol pennant		70	50
368	1 k.	African Fish Eagle and Zambian Conservation badge		2·25	4·50
365/8			*Set of* 4	3·50	5·00
MS369	105 × 78 mm. Nos. 365/8			3·50	5·00

(Des Gabriel Ellison. Litho Questa)

1982 (1 July). *Minerals* (2nd series). *Vert designs as T* **110**. *Multicoloured. P* 14.
370	8 n.	Bornite		95	10
371	18 n.	Chalcopyrite		2·25	90
372	28 n.	Malachite		2·75	3·00
373	32 n.	Azurite		2·75	3·00
374	42 n.	Vanadinite		3·25	4·25
370/4			*Set of* 5	11·00	10·00

112 Drilling Rig, 1926

(Des Gabriel Ellison. Litho Harrison)

1983 (26 Jan). *Early Steam Engines. T* **112** *and similar horiz designs. Multicoloured. P* 14 × 14½.
375	8 n.	Type **112**		60	10
376	18 n.	Fowler road locomotive, 1900		80	70
377	28 n.	Borsig ploughing engine, 1925		1·25	2·25
378	32 n.	Rhodesian Railways 7th Class steam locomotive, 1900		1·60	2·50
375/8			*Set of* 4	3·75	5·00

113 Cotton Picking   114 *Eulophia cucullata*

(Des Gabriel Ellison. Litho Harrison)

1983 (10 Mar). *Commonwealth Day. T* **113** *and similar horiz designs. Multicoloured. P* 14 × 13½.
379	12 n.	Type **113**		20	10
380	18 n.	Mining		40	30
381	28 n.	Ritual pot and traditional dances		30	50
382	1 k.	Violet-crested Turaco and Victoria Falls		2·75	5·00
379/82			*Set of* 4	3·25	5·50

(Des Gabriel Ellison. Litho Questa)

1983 (26 May). *Wild Flowers. T* **114** *and similar vert designs. Multicoloured. P* 14.
383	12 n.	Type **114**		25	10
384	18 n.	*Kigelia africana*		35	40
385	35 n.	*Protea gaguedi*		40	80
386	50 n.	*Leonotis nepetifolia*		60	2·00
383/6			*Set of* 4	1·40	3·00
MS387	141 × 71 mm. Nos. 383/6. P 12			1·50	3·25

115 Giraffe

(Des Gabriel Ellison. Litho Harrison)

1983 (21 July). *Zambia Wildlife. T 115 and similar horiz designs. Multicoloured. P 14 × 13½.*

388	12 n. Type 115	70	10
	a. Orange-brown and brown (inscr and face value) omitted	£300	
389	28 n. Blue Wildebeest	90	70
390	35 n. Lechwe	1·25	90
391	1 k. Yellow-backed Duiker	2·50	4·25
388/91	Set of 4	4·75	5·50

116 Tigerfish | 117 The Annunciation

(Des Gabriel Ellison. Litho J.W.)

1983 (29 Sept). *Zambia Fishes. T 116 and similar horiz designs. Multicoloured. P 14.*

392	12 n. Type 116	40	15
393	28 n. Silver Catfish	70	65
394	35 n. Large-spotted Squeaker	80	1·50
395	38 n. Red-breasted Tilapia	90	1·50
392/5	Set of 4	2·50	3·50

(Des Gabriel Ellison. Litho J.W.)

1983 (12 Dec). *Christmas. T 117 and similar vert designs. Multicoloured. P 14.*

396	12 n. Type 117	15	10
397	28 n. The Shepherds	30	40
398	35 n. Three Kings	40	1·00
399	38 n. Flight into Egypt	45	1·50
396/9	Set of 4	1·10	2·75

118 Boeing 737

(Des Gabriel Ellison. Litho Harrison)

1984 (26 Jan). *Air Transport. T 118 and similar horiz designs. Multicoloured. P 14 × 13½.*

400	12 n. Type 118	25	10
401	28 n. De Havilland D.H.C.2 Beaver	45	40
402	35 n. Short S.45A Solent 3 flying boat	55	70
403	1 k. De Havilland D.H.66 Hercules *City of Basra*	1·00	2·50
400/3	Set of 4	2·00	3·25

119 Receiving Flowers | 120 Football

(Des and litho J.W.)

1984 (28 Apr). *60th Birthday of President Kaunda. T 119 and similar multicoloured designs. P 14½ × 14 (12 n., 60 n.) or 14 × 14½ (others).*

404	12 n. Type 119	25	10
405	28 n. Swearing-in ceremony (*vert*)	35	40
406	60 n. Planting cherry tree	70	2·00
407	1 k. Opening of 5th National Assembly (*vert*)	90	3·00
404/7	Set of 4	2·00	5·00

(Des Gabriel Ellison. Litho Format)

1984 (18 July). *Olympic Games, Los Angeles. T 120 and similar vert designs. Multicoloured. P 14½ × 14.*

408	12 n. Type 120	25	10
409	28 n. Running	30	50
410	35 n. Hurdling	40	80
411	50 n. Boxing	45	1·40
408/11	Set of 4	1·25	2·50

121 Gaboon Viper

(Des Gabriel Ellison. Litho Harrison)

1984 (5 Sept). *Reptiles. T 121 and similar horiz designs. Multicoloured. P 14.*

412	12 n. Type 121	20	10
413	28 n. Chameleon	40	50
414	35 n. Nile Crocodile	50	70
415	1 k. Blue-headed Agama	1·00	2·75
412/15	Set of 4	1·90	3·50
MS416	120 × 101 mm. Nos. 412/15	2·00	4·00

122 Pres. Kaunda and Mulungushi Rock | 123 *Amanita flammeola*

(Des Gabriel Ellison. Litho Harrison)

1984 (22 Oct). *26th Anniv of United National Independence Party (12 n.) and 20th Anniv of Independence (others) (1st issue). T 122 and similar horiz designs. Multicoloured. P 14.*

417	12 n. Type 122	25	10
418	28 n. Freedom Statue	35	50
419	1 k. Pres. Kaunda and agricultural produce ("Lima Programme")	1·00	3·00
417/19	Set of 3	1·40	3·25

See also Nos. 438/40.

(Des Gabriel Ellison. Litho J.W.)

1984 (12 Dec). *Fungi. T 123 and similar vert designs. Multicoloured. P 14 × 14½.*

420	12 n. Type 123	1·10	30
421	28 n. *Amanita zambiana*	1·50	1·25
422	32 n. *Termitomyces letestui*	2·00	2·25
423	75 n. *Cantharellus miniatescens*	3·25	4·50
420/3	Set of 4	7·00	7·50

(124) | 125 Chacma Baboon

1985 (5 Mar). *No. 237 surch with T 124.*

424	5 k. on 50 n. Flying-doctor service	1·75	2·00

(Des Gabriel Ellison. Litho Harrison)

1985 (25 Apr). *Zambian Primates. T 125 and similar horiz designs. Multicoloured. P 14.*

425	12 n. Type 125	55	10
426	20 n. Diademed Monkey	75	40
427	45 n. Diademed Monkey (*different*)	1·50	1·25
428	1 k. Savanna Monkey	2·50	4·25
425/8	Set of 4	4·75	5·50

126 Map showing S.A.D.C.C. Member States | 127 The Queen Mother in 1980

(Des Gabriel Ellison. Litho Harrison)

1985 (9 July). *5th Anniv of Southern African Development Co-ordination Conference. T 126 and similar horiz designs. P 14.*

429	20 n. multicoloured	75	15
430	45 n. black, new blue and pale blue	1·75	1·10
431	1 k. multicoloured	2·00	3·25
429/31	Set of 3	4·00	4·00

Designs:—45 n. Mining; 1 k. Flags of member states and Mulungushi Hall.

(Des and litho Harrison)

1985 (2 Aug). *Life and Times of Queen Elizabeth the Queen Mother. T 127 and similar designs. P 14.*

432	25 n. multicoloured	10	10
433	45 n. deep violet-blue and gold	10	15
434	55 n. deep violet-blue and gold	15	25
435	5 k. multicoloured	1·25	2·25
432/5	Set of 4	1·40	2·50

Designs: *Vert*—45 n. The Queen Mother at Clarence House, 1963. *Horiz*—55 n. With the Queen and Princess Margaret, 1980; 5 k. At Prince Henry's christening, 1984.

(128) | 129 Postman and Lusaka Post Office, 1958

1985 (12 Sept–25 Nov). *Nos. 340 and 342 surch as T 128 in chestnut (20 n.) or greenish blue (25 n.).*

436	20 n. on 12 n. Mushroom picking	2·75	30
	a. Horiz pair, one without surch	£500	
437	25 n. on 8 n. Straw-basket fishing (25.11)	1·00	65

1985 (23 Oct). *26th Anniv of United National Independence Party (No. 438) and 20th Anniv of Independence (others) (2nd issue). Designs as Nos. 417/19 but larger, 55 × 34 mm, embossed on gold foil. P 10.*

438	5 k. Type 122	60	1·75
439	5 k. Freedom Statue	60	1·75
440	5 k. Pres. Kaunda and agricultural produce ("Lima Programme")	60	1·75
438/40	Set of 3	1·60	4·75

(Des Gabriel Ellison. Litho J.W.)

1985 (12 Dec). *10th Anniv of Posts and Telecommunication Corporation. T 129 and similar horiz designs. Multicoloured. P 13 × 12½.*

441	20 n. Type 129	55	10
442	45 n. Postman and Livingstone Post Office, 1950	85	25
443	55 n. Postman and Kalomo Post Office, 1902	1·00	70
444	5 k. Africa Trans-Continental Telegraph Line under construction, 1900	3·25	5·50
441/4	Set of 4	5·00	6·00

130 Boy in Maize Field | 131 *Mylabris tricolor*

(Des Gabriel Ellison. Litho Harrison)

1985 (19 Dec). *40th Anniv of United Nations Organization. T 130 and similar vert designs. P 14.*

445	20 n. multicoloured	30	10
446	45 n. black, new blue and brownish black	50	20
447	1 k. multicoloured	1·00	2·00
448	2 k. multicoloured	1·40	3·00
445/8	Set of 4	2·75	4·75

Designs:—45 n. Logo and "40"; 1 k. President Kaunda addressing U.N. General Assembly, 1970; 2 k. Signing of U.N. Charter, San Francisco, 1945.

(Des Gabriel Ellison. Litho Harrison)

1986 (20 Mar). *Beetles. T 131 and similar horiz designs. Multicoloured. P 14.*

449	35 n. Type 131	15	10
450	1 k. *Phasgonocnema melanianthe*	20	20
451	1 k. 70, *Amaurodes passerinii*	30	50
452	5 k. *Ranzania petersiana*	85	2·00
449/52	Set of 4	1·40	2·50

(Des A. Theobald. Litho Format)

1986 (21 Apr). *60th Birthday of Queen Elizabeth II. Vert designs as T 230a of Jamaica. Multicoloured. W w 16. P 14×14½ (1 k. 95) or 14×13½ (others).*

453	35 n. Princess Elizabeth at Flower Ball, Savoy Hotel, 1951	10	10
	a. Perf 14×14½	1·00	
454	1 k. 25, With Prince Andrew, Lusaka Airport, 1979	15	20
	a. Perf 14×14½	6·00	
455	1 k. 70, With President Kaunda	15	25
	a. Perf 14×14½	10·00	
456	1 k. 95, In Luxembourg, 1976	15	30
457	5 k. At Crown Agents Head Office, London, 1983	40	85
453/7	Set of 5	85	1·50

(Des D. Miller. Litho Questa)

1986 (23 July). *Royal Wedding. Square designs as T 231a of Jamaica. Multicoloured. W w 16. P 14.*

458	1 k. 70, Prince Andrew and Miss Sarah Ferguson	30	35
459	5 k. Prince Andrew in Zambia, 1979	80	1·40

ALTERED CATALOGUE NUMBERS

Any Catalogue numbers altered from the last edition are shown as a list in the introductory pages.

132 Goalkeeper saving Goal   **133** Sculpture of Edmond Halley by Henry Pegram

(Des Gabriel Ellison. Litho Mardon Printers Ltd, Zimbabwe)

1986 (30 July). *World Cup Football Championship, Mexico. T* **132** *and similar vert designs. Multicoloured.* P 14½.

460	35 n. Type 132		85	15
461	1 k. 25, Player kicking ball..		2·00	1·40
462	1 k. 70, Two players competing for ball		2·25	1·90
463	5 k. Player scoring goal		3·25	6·00
460/3		*Set of 4*	7·50	8·50

(Des Jennifer Toombs. Litho Mardon Printers Ltd, Zimbabwe)

1986 (6 Aug). *Appearance of Halley's Comet. T* **133** *and similar horiz designs.* P 14½.

464	1 k. 25, multicoloured		1·00	55
465	1 k. 70, multicoloured		1·25	85
466	2 k. multicoloured		1·75	1·75
467	5 k. light blue and blue-black		3·50	6·00
464/7		*Set of 4*	6·75	8·00

Designs:—1 k. 70, *Giotto* spacecraft approaching nucleus of Comet; 2 k. Studying Halley's Comet in 1682 and 1986; 5 k. Part of Halley's chart of southern sky.

134 The Nativity

(Des and litho Harrison)

1986 (15 Dec). *Christmas. Children's Paintings. T* **134** *and similar horiz designs. Multicoloured.* P 14.

468	35 n. Type 134		40	10
469	1 k. 25, The Visit of the Three Kings		1·50	75
470	1 k. 60, The Holy Family with Shepherd and King		1·75	1·60
471	5 k. Angel and Christmas Tree		3·75	6·50
468/71		*Set of 4*	6·75	8·00

135 Diesel Train in Kasama Cutting

(Des G. Vasarhelyi. Litho Questa)

1986 (22 Dec). *10th Anniv of Tanzania-Zambia Railway. T* **135** *and similar horiz designs. Multicoloured.* P 14.

472	35 n. Type 135		25	10
473	1 k. 25, Passenger train leaving Tunnel No. 21		45	50
474	1 k. 70, Train between Tunnels Nos. 6 and 7		50	70
475	5 k. Trains near Mpika Station		1·00	2·50
472/5		*Set of 4*	2·00	3·50

136 President Kaunda and Graduate   **137** Arms of Kitwe

(Litho Harrison)

1987 (27 Jan). *20th Anniv of University of Zambia. T* **136** *and similar multicoloured designs.* P 14.

476	35 n. Type 136		25	10
477	1 k. 25, University Badge (*vert*)		55	60
478	1 k. 60, University Statue (*vert*)		60	1·00
479	5 k. President Kaunda laying foundation stone (*vert*)		2·00	5·50
476/9		*Set of 4*	3·00	6·50

(Litho Harrison)

1987 (26 Mar). *Arms of Zambian Towns. T* **137** *and similar vert designs. Multicoloured.* P 14.

480	35 n. Type 137		10	10
481	1 k. 25, Ndola		15	20
482	1 k. 70, Lusaka		20	25
483	20 k. Livingstone		2·75	5·00
480/3		*Set of 4*	2·75	5·00

138 Chestnut-headed Crake   **139** Look-out Tree, Livingstone

Two types of surcharge for 20 n., 75 n.:

20n	20n	75n	75n
=	=	=	=
I	II	I	II

I   Surch by Format in Great Britain
II   Surch in Zambia

(Des Gabriel Ellison. Litho Questa)

1987 (16 Apr)–**88**. *Birds* (1st series). *T* **138** *and similar vert designs, some additionally surch as T* **128**. *Multicoloured.* P 11×13. (5 n. to 40 n., 75 n., 1 k. 65) or 14 (*others*).

484	5 n. Cloud-scraping Cisticola (8.10.87)		10	10
485	10 n. White-winged Starling (8.10.87)		10	10
486	20 n. on 1 n. Yellow Swamp Warbler (I) (10.3.88)		30	20
	a. Surch Type II		20	20
	b. Surch omitted			
487	25 n. Type 138		2·00	1·00
488	30 n. Red-fronted Barbet ("Miombo Pied Barbet") (8.10.87)		10	10
489	35 n. Black and Rufous Swallow		2·25	1·50
490	40 n. Wattled Crane (8.10.87)		10	10
491	50 n. Red-throated Heron ("Slaty Egret") (8.10.87)		10	10
492	75 n. on 2 n. Olive-flanked Robin Chat (I) (10.3.88)		30	60
	a. Surch Type II		30	60
	b. Surch omitted			
493	1 k. Bradfield's Hornbill		2·25	40
494	1 k. 25, Boulton's Puff-back Flycatcher ("Margaret's Batis")		2·25	2·00
495	1 k. 60, Anchieta's Sunbird		2·25	1·50
496	1 k. 65 on 30 n. Red-fronted Barbet (10.3.88)		30	60
497	1 k. 70, Boehm's Bee Eater		2·50	2·00
498	1 k. 95, Perrin's Bush Shrike		2·50	2·00
499	2 k. Whale-headed Stork ("Shoebill") (8.10.87)		35	35
500	5 k. Taita Falcon ..		3·00	80
501	10 k. on 50 n. Red-throated Heron (10.3.88)		1·10	2·00
502	20 k. on 2 k. Whale-headed Stork (10.3.88)		2·10	3·75
484/502		*Set of 19*	21·00	17·00

Nos. 491, 493/5 and 497/502 are larger, size 24×39 mm.

It was not intended that the 1 n. and 2 n. should be issued without surcharge, but it is believed examples were placed on sale with the surcharged versions in error. C-t-o examples without surcharge cancelled 10 March 1988 also exist.

No. 502 is surcharged "K 20" only. For "K 20·00" surcharge see No. 594.

For further surcharges see Nos. 587/95, and for different designs see Nos. 625/38.

(Litho Questa)

1987 (30 June). *Tourism. T* **139** *and similar horiz designs. Multicoloured.* P 14.

503	35 n. Type 139		30	15
504	1 k. 25, Rafting on Zambezi		30	25
505	1 k. 70, Tourists photographing lions, Luangwa Valley		1·75	90
506	10 k. Eastern White Pelicans		6·50	7·50
503/6		*Set of 4*	8·00	8·00

(140)   **141** De Havilland D.H.C.2 Beaver

═══ K3

1987 (14 Sept). *Various stamps surch as T* **140**.

(a) On Nos. 432/5 in gold

507	127	3 k. on 25 n. multicoloured	65	65
508	—	6 k. on 45 n. deep violet-blue and gold	1·25	1·25
509	—	10 k. on 55 n. deep violet-blue and gold	1·75	1·75
510	—	20 k. on 5 k. multicoloured	3·75	4·50

(b) On Nos. 453/7

511	3 k. on 35 n. Princess Elizabeth at Flower Ball, Savoy Hotel, 1951	55	55
512	4 k. on 1 k. 25, With Prince Andrew, Lusaka Airport, 1979	65	65
513	6 k. on 1 k. 70, With President Kaunda	1·00	1·00
514	10 k. on 1 k. 95, In Luxembourg, 1976	1·60	1·60
515	20 k. on 5 k. At Crown Agents Head Office, London, 1983	3·50	3·75

(c) On Nos. 460/3

516	3 k. on 35 n. Type 132	55	55
517	6 k. on 1 k. 25, Player kicking ball	1·00	1·00
518	10 k. on 1 k. 70, Two players competing for ball	1·60	1·60
519	20 k. on 5 k. Player scoring goal	3·25	3·75

(d) On Nos. 464/7 in gold

520	133	3 k. on 1 k. 25, multicoloured	1·00	80
		a. Surch omitted (in horiz pair with normal)	80·00	
521	—	6 k. on 1 k. 70, multicoloured	1·75	1·50
522	—	10 k. on 2 k. multicoloured	3·00	3·00
523	—	20 k. on 15 k. light blue and blue-black	5·50	6·00
507/23		*Set of 17*	29·00	30·00

(Des and litho Questa)

1987 (21 Sept). *20th Anniv of Zambia Airways. T* **141** *and similar horiz designs showing aircraft. Multicoloured.* P 14.

524	35 c. Type 141		65	10
525	1 k. 70, Douglas DC-10		1·50	70
526	5 k. Douglas DC-3		3·50	3·50
527	10 k. Boeing 707		5·50	6·50
524/7		*Set of 4*	10·00	9·75

142 Friesian/Holstein Cow   **143** Mpoloto Ne Mikobango

(Des Gabriel Ellison. Litho Format)

1987 (1 Oct). *40th Anniv of Food and Agriculture Organization. T* **142** *and similar horiz designs. Multicoloured.* P 14½×15.

528	35 n. Type 142		10	10
529	1 k. 25, Simmental bull		20	25
530	1 k. 70, Sussex bull ..		20	30
531	20 k. Brahman bull		1·00	3·00
528/31		*Set of 4*	1·25	3·25

Nos. 528/31 exist imperforate from stock dispersed by the liquidator of Format International Security Printers Ltd.

(Litho Format)

1987 (3 Nov). *People of Zambia. T* **143** *and similar vert designs. Multicoloured.* P 12½.

532	35 n. Type 143		10	10
533	1 k. 25, Zintaka		20	25
534	1 k. 70, Mufuluhi		25	30
535	10 k. Ntebwe		75	1·50
536	20 k. Kubangwa Aa Mbulunga		1·25	3·00
532/6		*Set of 5*	2·25	5·00

Nos. 532/6 exist imperforate from stock dispersed by the liquidator of Format International Printers Ltd.

144 Black Lechwe at Waterhole   **145** Cassava Roots

(Des Gabriel Ellison. Litho Questa)

1987 (21 Dec). *Black Lechwe. T* **144** *and similar multicoloured designs.* P 14.

537	50 n. Type 144		65	10
538	2 k. Black Lechwe resting by pool (*horiz*)	1·75	40
539	2 k. 50, Running through water (*horiz*)	1·75	80
540	10 k. Watching for danger		4·50	6·00
537/40		*Set of 4*	7·75	6·50

MS541 Two sheets, each 105×74 mm. (a) 20 k. Caracal (predator). (b) 20 k. Cheetah (predator)

	Set of 2 sheets 9·00	8·00

(Des Gabriel Ellison. Litho Questa)

1988 (20 May). *International Fund for Agricultural Development. T* **145** *and similar horiz designs. Multicoloured.* P 14.

542	50 n. Type 145		10	10
543	2 k. 50, Fishing		60	50
544	2 k. 85, Farmer and cattle		65	55
545	10 k. Picking coffee beans		1·25	1·75
542/5		*Set of 4*	2·40	2·50

146 Breast feeding   **147** Asbestos Cement

(Des Gabriel Ellison. Litho Format)

1988 (12 Sept). *U.N.I.C.E.F. Child Survival Campaign. T* **146** *and similar vert designs. Multicoloured.* P 12½.

546	50 n. Type 146		20	10
547	2 k. Growth monitoring		50	30
548	2 k. 85, Immunization		60	60
549	10 k. Oral rehydration		1·25	3·00
546/9		*Set of 4*	2·25	3·50

Nos. 546/9 exist imperforate from stock dispersed by the liquidator of Format International Security Printers Ltd.

(Des Gabriel Ellison. Litho Format)

1988 (10 Oct). *Preferential Trade Area Fair. T* **147** *and similar vert designs. Multicoloured. P* 12½.

550	50 n. Type **147**		10	10
551	2 k. 35, Textiles		20	30
552	2 k. 50, Tea		20	40
553	10 k. Poultry		75	2·50
550/3		*Set of* 4	1·10	3·00

Nos. 550/3 exist imperforate from stock dispersed by the liquidator of Format International Security Printers Ltd.

148 Emergency Food Distribution

(Des Gabriel Ellison. Litho Questa)

1988 (20 Oct). *125th Anniv of International Red Cross. T* **148** *and similar horiz designs. Multicoloured. P* 14.

554	50 n. Type **148**		20	10
555	2 k. 50, Giving first aid		50	60
556	2 k. 85, Practising bandaging		55	70
557	10 k. Henri Dunant (founder)		1·75	3·00
554/7		*Set of* 4	2·75	4·00

149 Aardvark

(Des Gabriel Ellison. Litho Questa)

1988 (5 Dec). *Endangered Species of Zambia. T* **149** *and similar horiz designs. Multicoloured. P* 14.

558	50 n. Type **149**		25	10
559	2 k. Temminck's Ground Pangolin		50	40
560	2 k. 85, Hunting Dog		60	75
561	20 k. Black Rhinoceros and calf		6·00	7·00
558/61		*Set of* 4	6·50	7·50

150 Boxing

151 Red Toad

(Des Gabriel Ellison. Litho Questa)

1988 (30 Dec). *Olympic Games, Seoul. T* **150** *and similar horiz designs. Multicoloured. P* 14.

562	50 n. Type **150**		15	10
563	2 k. Athletics		35	40
564	2 k. 50, Hurdling		40	70
565	20 k. Football		3·75	6·50
562/5		*Set of* 4	4·25	7·00
MS566	Two sheets, each 97×72 mm. (a) 30 k. Tennis. (b) 30 k. Karate	*Set of 2 sheets*	8·00	11·00

(Des Gabriel Ellison. Litho Format)

1989 (25 Jan). *Frogs and Toads. T* **151** *and similar horiz designs. Multicoloured. P* 12½.

567	50 n. Type **151**		15	10
568	2 k. 50, Puddle Frog		50	50
569	2 k. 85, Marbled Reed Frog		55	65
570	10 k. Young Reed Frogs		1·60	3·00
567/70		*Set of* 4	2·50	3·75

Nos. 567/70 exist imperforate from stock dispersed by the liquidator of Format International Security Printers Ltd.

152 Common Slit-faced Bat

153 Pope John Paul II and Map of Zambia

(Des Gabriel Ellison. Litho Questa)

1989 (22 Mar). *Bats. T* **152** *and similar horiz designs. Multicoloured. P* 12½.

571	50 n. Type **152**		15	10
572	2 k. 50, Little Free-tailed Bat		45	55
573	2 k. 85, Hildebrandt's Horseshoe Bat		55	75
574	10 k. Peters' Epauletted Fruit Bat		1·50	3·00
571/4		*Set of* 4	2·40	4·00

Nos. 571/4 exist imperforate from stock dispersed by the liquidator of Format International Security Printers Ltd.

(Des and litho Harrison)

1989 (2 May). *Visit of Pope John Paul II. T* **153** *and similar vert designs each with inset portrait. Multicoloured. P* 12½.

575	50 k. Type **153**		75	20
576	6 k. 85, Peace dove with olive branch		2·75	2·75
577	7 k. 85, Papal arms		3·00	3·25
578	10 k. Victoria Falls		4·50	4·50
575/8		*Set of* 4	10·00	9·75

K19.50 = K20.00 =

(154) (155)

1989 (1 July–1 Nov). *Various stamps surch.*

(a) *Nos.* 339, 341/3, 345/6, 349 *and* 351 *surch as T* **154** (1 *k.* 20, 19 *k.* 50, 20 *k.* 50) *or as T* **155** (*others*)

579	1 k. 20 on 35 n. Tonga Ila granary and house (Br.) (1 Nov)		15	15
580	3 k. 75 on 5 n. Pottery making		20	20
581	8 k. 11 on 10 n. Thatching		40	50
582	9 k. on 30 n. Makishi tightrope dancer		40	50
583	10 k. on 75 n. Women carrying water (38×26 mm)		40	50
584	18 k. 50 on 2 k. Pipe-smoking Gwembe Valley belle (38×26 mm)		1·00	1·50
585	19 k. 50 on 12 k. Mushroom picking (Br.) (1 Nov)		2·25	2·25
	a. Two stops between "K19" and "50" (R.8/1)			
586	20 k. 50 on 18 n. Millet grinding on stone (V.) (1 Nov)		1·00	1·50

(b) *Nos.* 484, 489, 493/5 *and* 497/500 *surch as T* **155**

587	70 n. on 35 n. Black and Rufous Swallow		60	15
	a. Bars printed twice		†	—
588	3 k. on 5 n. Cloud-scraping Cisticola		80	30
589	8 k. on 1 k. 25, Boulton's Puff-back Fly-catcher		1·00	60
590	9 k. 90 on 1 k. 70, Boehm's Bee Eater		1·10	90
591	10 k. 40 on 1 k. 60, Anchieta's Sunbird		1·10	90
	a. Error. Surch on 1 k. 95, Perrin's Bush Shrike (No. 498)			
592	12 k. 50 on 1 k. Bradfield's Hornbill		1·25	1·25
593	15 k. on 1 k. 95, Perrin's Bush Shrike		1·25	1·50
594	20 k. on 2 k. Whale-headed Stork		1·75	2·25
595	20 k. 35 on 5 k. Taita Falcon		1·75	2·25
579/95		*Set of* 17	14·50	15·00

No. 587a shows a second pair of bars applied by typography, the original surcharge in lithography being misplaced. One example of this error includes an extraneous "7".

No. 594 shows the surcharge as "K20·00". The previously listed 20 k. on 2 k., No. 502, is surcharged "K20" only.

156 *Parinari curatellifolia*

157 *Lamarckiana* sp

(Des Gabriel Ellison. Litho Questa)

1989 (26 July). *Edible Fruits. T* **156** *and similar vert designs. Multicoloured. P* 14½.

596	50 n. Type **156**		15	10
597	6 k. 50, *Uapaca kirkiana*		1·25	1·50
598	6 k. 85, Wild Fig		1·25	1·75
599	10 k. Bottle Palm		2·25	2·75
596/9		*Set of* 4	4·50	5·50

(Des Gabriel Ellison. Litho Cartor)

1989 (8 Nov). *Grasshoppers. T* **157** *and similar horiz designs. Multicoloured. P* 14×13½.

600	70 n. Type **157**		15	10
601	10 k. 40, *Dictyophorus* sp		1·25	1·50
602	12 k. 50, *Cymantomera* sp		1·50	2·25
603	15 k. *Phymateus iris*		2·00	2·75
600/3		*Set of* 4	4·50	6·00

158 Fireball

159 Postvan, Postman on Bicycle and Main Post Office, Lusaka

(Des Gabriel Ellison. Litho National Printing & Packaging, Zimbabwe)

1989 (6 Dec). *Christmas. Flowers. T* **158** *and similar vert designs. Multicoloured. P* 14½.

604	70 n. Type **158**		15	10
605	10 k. 40, Flame Lily		1·00	1·25
606	12 k. 50, Foxglove Lily		1·40	1·75
607	20 k. Vlei Lily		2·40	3·50
604/7		*Set of* 4	4·50	6·00

(Des D. Miller. Litho Questa)

1990 (2 May). *"Stamp World London 90" International Stamp Exhibition. T* **159** *and similar horiz designs. Multicoloured. P* 14.

608	1 k. 20, Type **159**		10	10
609	19 k. 50, Zambia 1980 18 n. butterflies stamp		2·00	2·50
610	20 k. 50, Rhodesia and Nyasaland 1962 9d. and Northern Rhodesia 1925 ½d. stamps		2·00	2·50
611	50 k. 1840 Penny Black and Maltese Cross cancellation		4·25	5·00
608/11		*Set of* 4	7·50	9·00

160 Footballer and Ball

161 Road Tanker

(Des R. Vigurs. Litho Questa)

1990 (7 July). *World Cup Football Championship, Italy. T* **160** *and similar vert designs showing football scenes. P* 14.

612	1 k. 20, multicoloured		10	10
613	18 k. 50, multicoloured		2·00	2·50
614	19 k. 50, multicoloured		2·00	2·50
615	20 k. 50, multicoloured		2·00	2·50
612/15		*Set of* 4	5·50	6·50
MS616	100×73 mm. 50 k. multicoloured		7·00	7·50

No. **MS**616 also exists imperforate from a limited printing.

(Litho Harrison)

1990 (23 July). *10th Anniv of Southern African Development Co-ordination Conference. T* **161** *and similar horiz designs, each showing map of Southern Africa. Multicoloured. P* 12½.

617	1 k. 20, Type **161**		15	10
618	19 k. 50, Telecommunications		1·50	2·00
619	20 k. 50, "Regional Co-operation"		1·50	2·00
620	50 k. Transporting coal by cable		5·50	6·50
617/20		*Set of* 4	7·75	9·50

162 Irrigation

163 The Bird and the Snake

(Des Gabriel Ellison. Litho Questa)

1990 (23 Oct). *26th Anniv of Independence. T* **162** *and similar horiz designs. Multicoloured. P* 14.

621	1 k. 20, Type **162**		10	10
622	19 k. 50, Shoe factory		1·10	1·40
623	20 k. 50, Mwembeshi II satellite earth station		1·25	1·60
624	50 k. "Mother and Child" (statue)		2·50	3·75
621/4		*Set of* 4	4·50	6·00

(Des Gabriel Ellison. Litho Questa)

1990 (30 Oct)–**91**. *Birds (2nd series). Vert designs as T* **138**. *Multicoloured. P* 11×13 (10, 15, 30, 50 n., 1 k., 1 k. 20, 2 k., 3 k., 5 k.) *or* 14 (*others*).

625	10 n. Livingstone's Flycatcher		20	20
626	15 n. Bar-winged Weaver		20	20
627	30 n. Purple-throated Cuckoo Shrike		30	20
628	50 n. Retz's Red-billed Helmet Shrike		30	20
629	50 n. As 10 n. (7.5.91)		1·10	40
630	1 k. As 15 n. (7.5.91)		1·10	40
631	1 k. 20, Bronze-naped Pigeon		30	10
632	2 k. As 30 n. (7.5.91)		1·10	50
633	3 k. As 50 n. (No. 628) (7.5.91)		1·10	50
634	5 k. As 1 k. 20 (7.5.91)		1·25	60
635	15 k. Corncrake		30	40
636	20 k. Dickinson's Kestrel (7.5.91)		1·50	1·25
637	20 k. 50, As 20 k.		30	40
638	50 k. Barrow's Bustard ("Denham's Bustard")		50	75
625/38		*Set of* 14	8·50	5·50

Nos. 635/8 are larger, size 23×39 mm.

(Des Gabriel Ellison. Litho Questa)

1991 (11 Jan). *International Literacy Year. Folklore. T* **163** *and similar vert designs. Multicoloured. P* 14.

639	1 k. 20, Type **163**		20	10
640	18 k. 50, Kalulu and the Leopard		2·25	2·50
641	19 k. 50, The Mouse and the Lion		2·25	2·50
642	20 k. 50, Kalulu and the Hippopotamus		2·25	2·50
639/42		*Set of* 4	6·25	6·75

K2

164 Genet   (165)

(Des Gabriel Ellison. Litho Questa)

1991 (25 Jan). *Small Carnivores. T* **164** *and similar horiz designs. Multicoloured. P* 14.
643   1 k. 20, Type **164** 20   10
644   18 k. 50, Civet .. .. 2·50   3·00
645   19 k. 50, Serval .. .. 2·50   3·00
646   20 k. 50, African Wild Cat .. .. 2·50   3·00
643/6   .. .. .. *Set of* 4   7·00   8·00

1991 (4 Mar). *Nos.* 441/4 *surch with T* **165**.
647   2 k. on 20 n. Type **129** .. .. 2·25   2·75
648   2 k. on 45 n. Postman and Livingstone Post
         Office, 1950 .. .. .. 2·25   2·75
649   2 k. on 55 n. Postman and Kalomo Post
         Office, 1902 .. .. .. 2·25   2·75
650   2 k. on 5 k. African Trans-Continental
         Telegraph Line under construction,
         1900 .. .. 2·25   2·75
647/50   .. .. .. *Set of* 4   8·00   10·00

166 Woman   167 Chilubula Church
    Cooking   near Kasama

(Des A. Mwansa and Daniela Schepp. Litho Cartor)

1991 (28 June). *Soya Promotion Campaign. T* **166** *and similar vert designs. Multicoloured. P* 13½.
651   1 k. Type **166** 10   10
652   2 k. Soya bean and field 10   10
653   5 k. Mother feeding child 20   15
654   20 k. Healthy and malnourished children .. 1·25   1·75
655   50 k. President Kaunda holding child .. 2·25   3·00
651/5   .. .. .. *Set of* 5   3·50   4·50

1991 (5 July). *Various stamps surch as T* **165**.
656   **130** 2 k. on 20 n. multicoloured .. 30·00   5·00
657   **127** 2 k. on 25 n. multicoloured (Gold) .. 75·00   5·00
658   —   2 k. on 28 n. multicoloured (No. 344) .. 30·00   5·00
659   —   2 k. on 28 n. multicoloured (No. 393) .. 40·00   5·00
660   —   2 k. on 28 n. multicoloured (No. 401) .. —   5·00
661   —   2 k. on 28 n. multicoloured (No. 418) .. —   5·00
662   —   2 k. on 32 n. multicoloured (No. 422) .. 25·00   5·00
663   —   2 k. on 35 n. multicoloured (No. 453) .. —   5·00
664   **134** 2 k. on 35 n. multicoloured .. 65·00   5·00
665   **137** 2 k. on 35 n. multicoloured .. 40·00   5·00
666   —   2 k. on 45 n. multicoloured (No. 427) .. 40·00   5·00
667   —   2 k. on 45 n. black, new blue and pale
              blue (No. 430) .. .. 50·00   5·00
668   —   2 k. on 45 n. deep violet-blue and gold
              (No. 433) .. .. 75·00   5·00
669   —   2 k. on 45 n. black, new blue & brownish
              black (No. 446) (Gold + Blk.) .. 40·00   5·00
670   —   2 k. on 1 k. 60, multicoloured (No. 470) 65·00   5·00
671   —   2 k. on 1 k. 70, multicoloured (No. 451) 40·00   5·00
672   —   2 k. on 1 k. 70, multicoloured (No. 482) .. —   5·00
673   —   2 k. on 5 k. multicoloured (No. 435) .. 15·00   5·00
674   —   2 k. on 5 k. multicoloured (No. 452) .. 15·00   5·00
675   —   2 k. on 6 k. 85, multicoloured (No. 597) 40·00   5·00
676   —   2 k. on 6 k. 85, multicoloured (No. 576) 50·00   5·00
677   —   2 k. on 6 k. 85, multicoloured (No. 598) 15·00   5·00
678   —   2 k. on 7 k. 85, multicoloured (No. 577) .. 2·25   5·00
The surcharge for No. 669 shows "K2" in gold and the bars in
black over gold.

(Des Gabriel Ellison. Litho Cartor)

1991 (18 July). *500th Birth Anniv of St. Ignatius Loyola. T* **167** *and similar vert designs. Multicoloured. P* 13½.
679   1 k. Type **167** 10   10
680   2 k. Chikuni Church near Monze .. 15   15
681   20 k. Bishop Joseph du Pont .. .. 2·25   2·50
682   50 k. Saint Ignatius Loyola .. .. 4·00   4·75
679/82   .. .. .. *Set of* 4   5·75   6·75

168 Adansonia digitata   169 Disa
                                  hamatopetala

(Des Gabriel Ellison. Litho Cartor)

1991 (28 Nov). *Flowering Trees. T* **168** *and similar horiz designs. Multicoloured. P* 13½.
683   1 k. Type **168** 20   10
684   2 k. *Dichrostachys cinerea* 25   15

---

685   10 k. *Stereospermum kunthianum* .. 1·50   1·40
686   30 k. *Azana garckeana* .. .. 3·00   3·75
683/6   .. .. .. *Set of* 4   4·50   4·75
No. 685 is inscribed "Sterospermum" in error.

(Des D. Miller. Litho Cartor)

1992 (6 Feb). *40th Anniv of Queen Elizabeth II's Accession. Horiz designs as T* **113** *of Kenya. Multicoloured. W w* 14 *(sideways). P* 13½.
687   4 k. Queen's House 10   10
688   32 k. Traditional village .. .. 1·00   70
689   35 k. Fishermen hauling nets .. .. 1·00   90
690   38 k. Three portraits of Queen Elizabeth 1·25   1·25
691   50 k. Queen Elizabeth II .. .. 1·60   2·75
687/91   .. .. .. *Set of* 5   4·50   5·00

(Des Gabriel Ellison. Litho Cartor)

1992 (28 Feb). *Orchids. T* **169** *and similar vert designs. Multicoloured. P* 13½.
692   1 k. Type **169** 50   15
693   2 k. *Eulophia paivaeana* 50   20
694   5 k. *Eulophia quartiniana* 85   40
695   20 k. *Aerangis verdickii* .. .. 3·50   5·00
692/5   .. .. .. *Set of* 4   4·75   5·25

170 Kasinja Mask   171 Bushbuck

(Des Gabriel Ellison. Litho Cartor)

1992 (10 Mar). *Tribal Masks. T* **170** *and similar vert designs. Multicoloured. P* 13½.
696   1 k. Type **170** 15   10
697   2 k. Chizaluke 20   10
698   10 k. Mwanapweu 65   50
699   30 k. Maliya .. .. .. 2·00   2·75
696/9   .. .. .. *Set of* 4   2·75   3·00

(Des Gabriel Ellison. Litho Questa)

1992 (14 Sept). *Antelopes. T* **171** *and similar horiz designs. Multicoloured. P* 14.
700   4 k. Type **171** 10   10
701   40 k. Eland 50   40
702   45 k. Roan Antelope 50   45
703   100 k. Sable Antelope .. .. 1·25   2·00
700/3   .. .. .. *Set of* 4   2·00   2·75

172 De Havilland D.H.66
    Hercules *City of Basra*

(Des Gabriel Ellison. Litho Questa)

1992 (24 Nov). *60th Anniv of Airmail Service. T* **172** *and similar horiz designs. Multicoloured. P* 14.
704   4 k. Type **172** 40   20
705   40 k. Vickers Super VC-10 .. .. 1·75   85
706   45 k. Short S.45A Solent 3 flying boat
         Severn .. .. .. 1·75   85
707   100 k. Douglas DC-10 .. .. 3·00   4·25
704/7   .. .. .. *Set of* 4   6·25   5·50

173 Wise Men with Gifts   174 Hurdling

(Litho Questa)

1992 (23 Dec). *Christmas. T* **173** *and similar horiz designs. Multicoloured. P* 14.
708   10 k. Type **173** 20   10
709   80 k. Nativity .. .. .. 1·60   1·75
710   90 k. Angelic choir .. .. 1·75   1·75
711   100 k. Angel and shepherds .. .. 1·75   1·90
708/11   .. .. .. *Set of* 4   4·75   5·00
MS712   209×57 mm. Nos. 708/11 .. .. 7·00   8·00

(Des R. Vigurs. Litho Questa)

1992 (28 Dec). *Olympic Games, Barcelona. T* **174** *and similar vert designs. Multicoloured. P* 14.
713   10 k. Type **174** 20   10
714   40 k. Boxing 60   40
715   80 k. Judo .. .. .. 1·25   1·60
716   100 k. Cycling .. .. .. 2·50   2·75
713/16   .. .. .. *Set of* 4   4·00   4·25

---

175 Nkundalila Falls   176 Athlete and
                              Cardiograph

(Des Gabriel Ellison. Litho Cartor)

1993 (30 Sept). *Waterfalls. T* **175** *and similar horiz designs. Multicoloured. P* 13½.
717   50 k. Type **175** 15   10
718   200 k. Chishimba Falls 55   60
719   250 k. Chipoma Falls 60   65
720   300 k. Lumangwe Falls 60   65
717/20   .. .. .. *Set of* 4   1·75   1·75

(Litho National Printing & Packaging, Zimbabwe)

1993 (20 Oct). *Heartbeat Campaign. T* **176** *and similar vert design. Multicoloured. P* 14½.
721   (O) Type **176** 50   55
722   (P) Heart and cardiograph 50   55
These stamps were initially sold at 50 k. (No. 721) for ordinary
post and 80 k. (No. 722) for priority mail. These face values were
increased to reflect postage rates increases. See note below Nos.
723/38.

177 Bronze Sunbird   178 Tiger Snake

(Des Gabriel Ellison. Litho Cartor)

1994 (30 May). *Sunbirds. T* **177** *and similar horiz designs. Multicoloured. P* 13. (*a*) *Face values as T* **177**.
723   20 k. Type **177** 20   10
724   50 k. Violet-backed Sunbird 30   10
725   100 k. Scarlet-chested Sunbird .. 40   10
726   150 k. Bannerman's Sunbird 50   20
727   200 k. Oustalet's White-bellied Sunbird .. 55   25
728   250 k. Anchieta's Sunbird ("Red and Blue
              Sunbird") 60   30
729   300 k. Olive Sunbird 70   35
730   350 k. Green-headed Sunbird 70   40
731   400 k. Red-tufted Malachite Sunbird .. 75   45
732   500 k. Variable Sunbird 80   55
733   800 k. Coppery Sunbird .. .. 1·00   1·10
734   1000 k. Orange-tufted Sunbird .. .. 1·25   1·50
735   1500 k. Amethyst Sunbird ("Black Sunbird") 1·75   2·25
736   2000 k. Green-throated Sunbird .. .. 2·00   2·50
       (*b*) *Face values shown as capital letters*
737   (O) Mariqua Sunbird ("Marico Sunbird") .. 80   55
738   (P) Eastern Double-collared Sunbird .. 80   55
723/38   .. .. .. *Set of* 16   12·00   10·50
Nos. 737/8 were initially sold at 50 k. for ordinary post (No.
737) and 80 k. for priority mail (No. 738). These rates were
increased to 100 k. for ordinary post and 150 k. for priority mail
on 20 June 1994. On 1 March 1995 the difference between the
two rates was abolished and both "O" and "P" stamps were sold
at 500 k. This was reduced to 400 k. each on 1 April 1995, but
the rate reverted to 500 k. on 8 February 1996.

(Litho Questa)

1994 (28 Sept). *Snakes. T* **178** *and similar vert designs. Multicoloured. P* 14.
739   50 k. Type **178** 20   10
740   200 k. Egyptian Cobra 70   45
741   300 k. African Python 90   80
742   500 k. Green Mamba .. .. 1·25   1·50
739/42   .. .. .. *Set of* 4   2·75   3·00

179 Women working on Road

(Des Gabriel Ellison. Litho Questa)

1995 (3 Apr). *75th Anniv of International Labour Organization. T* **179** *and similar horiz design. Multicoloured. P* 14.
743   100 k. Type **179** 25   10
744   450 k. Women making cement blocks .. 1·00   1·25

180 Angel playing Kalimba and Flowers

181 Anniversary Emblem, Rainbow and Map

(Des Gabriel Ellison. Litho Walsall)

1995 (29 Aug). *Christmas* (1994). *T* **180** *and similar diamond-shaped designs. Multicoloured. P* 14×14½.
745 100 k. Type **180** 10 10
746 300 k. Angel at prayer and animals .. 30 35
747 450 k. Angel with flute and birds 45 50
748 500 k. Angel with drum and Baobab trees 50 55
745/8 .. .. *Set of* 4 1·40 1·50

(Photo Courvoisier)

1995 (30 Dec). 50*th Anniv of United Nations. Granite paper. P* 11½.
749 **181** 700 k. multicoloured 70 85

182 David Livingstone (missionary) and Memorial

183 Saddle-bill Stork

(Des Gabriel Ellison. Litho Questa)

1996 (21 Feb). *Monuments. T* **182** *and similar vert designs. Multicoloured. P* 14.
750 100 k. Type **182** 10 10
751 300 k. Mbereshi Mission 40 40
752 450 k. Von Lettow-Vorbeck Monument .. 60 70
753 500 k. Niamkolo Church 65 75
750/3 .. .. *Set of* 4 1·60 1·75

(Des Gabriel Ellison. Litho Walsall)

1996 (27 Nov). *Endangered Species. Birds. T* **183** *and similar horiz designs. Multicoloured. P* 14×14½.
754 200 k. Type **183** 30 25
755 300 k. Black-cheeked Lovebird 45 35
756 500 k. Pair of Black-cheeked Lovebirds .. 70 70
757 900 k. Saddle-bill Stork and chicks .. 1·25 1·75
754/7 .. .. *Set of* 4 2·40 2·75
MS758 120×90 mm. Nos. 754/7 .. .. 50·00 50·00

(**184**)

185 *Precis octavia sesamus*

1996 (18 Dec). *Christmas. Nos.* 709/10 *surch as T* **184**.
759 (O) on 90 k. Angelic Choir 50 55
760 900 k. on 80 k. Nativity 85 90
No. 759 was sold at 500 k., which was the minimum local postage rate for ordinary post.

(Des Gabriel Ellison. Litho Questa)

1997 (8 Aug). *Butterflies and Moths. T* **185** *and similar vert designs. Multicoloured. P* 14.
761 300 k. Type **185** 40 35
762 500 k. *Argema mimosae* 65 60
763 700 k. *Imbrasia dione* 95 95
764 900 k. *Papilio ophidicephalus cotterell* .. 1·10 1·25
761/4 .. .. *Set of* 4 2·75 2·75
MS765 85×120 mm. As Nos. 761/4, but each with face value of 900 k. .. .. .. 4·00 4·50

O

(**186**)

187 Verreaux's Eagle Owl

1997 (19 Sept). *Nos.* 688/90 *surch as T* **186**.
766 (O) on 32 k. Traditional village .. 60 55
767 500 k. on 35 k. Fishermen hauling nets .. 60 55
768 900 k. on 38 k. Three portraits of Queen Elizabeth .. .. 1·40 1·60
766/8 .. .. *Set of* 3 2·40 2·40
No. 766 was sold at 500 k. which was the minimum local postage rate for ordinary post.

(Des Gabriel Ellison. Litho Walsall)

1997 (18 Dec). *Owls of Zambia. T* **187** *and similar vert designs. Multicoloured. P* 14.
769 300 k. Type **187** 45 35
770 500 k. Pel's Fishing Owl 70 60
771 700 k. Barn Owl 90 90
772 900 k. Spotted Eagle Owl .. .. .. 1·25 1·50
769/72 .. .. *Set of* 4 3·00 3·00
MS773 128×85 mm. As Nos. 769/72, but each with face value of 900 k. .. .. .. 4·75 4·75

188 Gandhi as Law Student, London, 1888

189 Dove and Map of Zambia

1998 (30 Jan). 50*th Death Anniv of Mahatma Gandhi. T* **188** *and similar multicoloured designs. Litho. P* 13½.
774 250 k. Type **188** 40 35
775 (O) Gandhi at Red Fort, Delhi 60 55
776 500 k. Gandhi with Nehru, 1946 (*horiz*) .. 60 55
777 900 k. Gandhi at prayer .. .. .. 1·25 1·50
774/7 .. .. *Set of* 4 2·50 2·75
MS778 70×100 mm. 2000 k. At Second Round Table Conference, London, 1931 .. .. 3·00 3·00
No. 775 was sold at 500 k. which was the minimum local postage rate for ordinary post.

(Des Gabriel Ellison. Litho Questa)

1998 (14 July). 18*th Anniv of Pan African Postal Union. T* **189** *and similar horiz designs. P* 14½.
779 (O) multicoloured 60 55
780 500 k. multicoloured 60 55
781 900 k. black, vermilion and reddish orange 1·25 1·50
779/81 .. .. *Set of* 3 2·25 2·40
Designs:—500 k. Lechwe at Kafue Flats; 900 k. Dove with "18th" note in beak.
No. 779 was sold at 500 k. which was the minimum local postage rate for ordinary post.

190 Traveller and Dog ("Luchele nganga")

191 "U20C" Diesel-electric Locomotive, 1967

(Des Gabriel Ellison. Litho Cartor)

1998 (2 Dec). *Christmas. Traditional Stories. T* **190** *and similar vert design. Multicoloured. P* 14.
782 300 k. Type **190** 15 20
783 500 k. Man feeding crocodile ("Kasuli") .. 25 30
MS784 111×70 mm. 2000 k. Type **190**; 2000 k. As 500 k. .. .. 1·90 2·00

(Des Gabriel Ellison. Litho Questa)

1999 (1 Feb). *Trains. T* **191** *and similar horiz designs. Multicoloured. P* 14½×15.
785 (O) Type **191** 25 30
786 800 k. Beyer-Garratt Class 15A No. 401 steam locomotive, 1950 .. .. 35 40
787 800 k. Class 7 No. 70 steam locomotive, 1900 35 40
788 900 k. Class 20 No. 708 steam locomotive, 1954 .. .. 40 45
789 900 k. H.P. diesel-electric railcar, 1966 .. 40 45
785/9 .. .. *Set of* 5 1·75 2·00
MS790 112×85 mm. 1000 k. Class 7 No. 955 steam locomotive, 1892 .. .. .. 45 50
No. 785 was sold at 500 k. which was the minimum local postage rate for ordinary post.

K500

(**192**)

1999 (1 June). *No.* 743 *surch with T* **192**.
791 500 k. on 100 k. Type **179** 25 30

193 Conference Emblem and Dam

194 Blacksmith Plover

(Des Gabriel Ellison. Litho Walsall)

1999 (20 Aug). 11*th International Conference on AIDS and STDs in Africa, Lusaka. T* **193** *and similar horiz design. Multicoloured. P* 14.
792 500 k. Type **193** 25 30
793 900 k. Conference emblem and Victoria Falls 40 45

(Des Gabriel Ellison. Litho Questa)

1999 (20 Dec). *Water Birds. T* **194** *and similar horiz designs. Multicoloured. P* 14½.
794 50 k. Type **194** 10 10
795 100 k. Sacred Ibis 10 10
796 200 k. Purple Swamphen ("Purple Gallinule") 10 15
797 250 k. Purple Heron 10 15
798 300 k. Glossy Ibis 15 20
799 400 k. Marabou Stork 15 20
800 450 k. African Spoonbill 20 25
801 500 k. Peters's Finfoot ("African Finfoot") 25 30
802 (O) Comb Duck ("Knob-billed Duck") .. 25 30
803 600 k. African Darter 30 35
804 700 k. African Skimmer 30 35
805 800 k. Spur-winged Goose 35 40
806 900 k. Hammerkop 40 45
807 1000 k. Eastern White Pelican 45 50
808 1500 k. Black-winged Stilt 70 75
809 2000 k. Black-crowned Night Heron .. 90 95
794/809 .. .. *Set of* 16 4·75 5·50
No. 802 was sold at 500 k. which was the minimum local postage rate for ordinary post.
No. 794 is inscribed "Sarkidiomis melamotos" and No. 805 "Plectroterus gambensis", both in error.

STAMP BOOKLETS

B 1

1964. *Black on blue cover as Type B 1. Stitched.*
SB1   1s. booklet containing 3d. (No.78) in block of 4   11·00

B 2

1968. *Black on buff covers as Type B 2 (No. SB2), or size 82×58 mm (No. SB3). Stitched.*
SB2   20 n. booklet containing eight 1 n. and four 3 n.
        (Nos. 129, 131) in blocks of 4   ..   4·25
SB3   30 n. booklet containing twelve 1 n. and six 3 n.
        (Nos. 129, 131) in blocks of 6   ..   ..   4·25

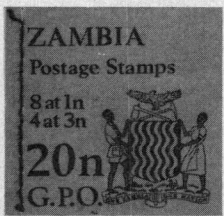

B 3

1970 (26 Aug). *Black on green cover as Type B 3 (No. SB4) or black on rose cover, size 82×58 mm (No. SB5). Stitched.*
SB4   20 n. booklet containing eight 1 n. and four 3 n.
        (Nos. 129, 131) in blocks of 4   ..   4·25
SB5   30 n. booklet containing twelve 1 n. and six 3 n.
        (Nos. 129, 131) in blocks of 6   ..   ..   4·25

B 4

1976. *Black on green cover as Type B 4, (No. SB6), or black on blue cover, size 101×54 mm (No. SB7). Stitched.*
SB6   44 n. booklet containing four 3 n. and eight 4 n.
        (Nos. 228/9) in blocks of 4   ..   ..   8·00
SB7   78 n. booklet containing 4 n. and 9 n. (Nos. 229,
        232), each in block of 6   ..   ..   9·00

B 5

1981 (2 June). *Black on emerald (No. SB8) or orange (No. SB9) covers as Type B 5. Stitched.*
SB8   66 n. booklet containing 1 n., 2 n. and 8 n. (Nos.
        337/8, 340), each in block of 6   ..   3·75
SB9   1 k. 08, booklet containing 8 n. and 10 n. (Nos.
        340/1), each in block of 6   ..   ..   4·25

POSTAGE DUE STAMPS

D 1   **D 2**

(Typo D.L.R.)

1929–52. *Wmk Mult Script CA. Ordinary paper. P 14.*
D1   D 1   1d. grey-black   ..   ..   2·50   2·50
            a. Chalk-surfaced paper. *Blk* (22.1.52)   20·00   75·00
            ab. Error. St. Edward's Crown, W9b   £1400
D2   2d. grey-black   ..   ..   3·00   3·00
D3   3d. grey-black   ..   ..   3·00   24·00
            a. Chalk-surfaced paper. *Blk* (22.1.52)   7·00   65·00
            ab. Error. Crown missing, W9a   ..   £225
            ac. Error. St. Edward's Crown, W9b   ..   £150
D4   4d. grey-black   ..   ..   9·50   28·00
D1/4   Set of 4   16·00   50·00
D1/4 Perf "Specimen"   ..   ..   Set of 4   85·00

The 2d. is known bisected and used as a 1d. at Luanshya or Nkana on various dates between 1937 and 1951 and on understamped letters from South Africa at Chingola in May 1950 (*Price on cover £425*).

Following the increase in the internal letter rate from 1½d. to 2d. on 1 July 1953 stocks of postage due stamps at Mkushi became exhausted. As an emergency measure the sub-postmaster was authorised to surcharge examples of Nos. 28 and 55 "POSTAGE DUE (or "postage due") 1d." in red by typewriter. Examples properly used on cover between 6 July and 15 September 1953 are of considerable scarcity (*Price on cover £2000*). No unused examples exist.

(Des D. Smith. Litho Govt Ptr, Lusaka)

1963 (10 Dec).   *P 12½.*
D 5   D 2   1d. orange   90   3·75
D 6   2d. deep blue   90   4·00
D 7   3d. lake   ..   ..   ..   1·00   4·50
D 8   4d. ultramarine   ..   ..   1·00   6·50
D 9   6d. purple   ..   ..   5·50   8·00
D10   1s. light emerald   ..   ..   6·50   19·00
            a. Imperf (vert pair) £180
            b. Block of four imperf horiz and imp
                between vert £700
D5/10   ..   ..   ..   Set of 6   14·00   40·00

In all values the stamps in the right-hand vertical row of the sheet are imperforate on the right.

D 3

(Des D. Smith. Litho Govt Printer, Lusaka)

1964 (24 Oct).   *P 12½.*
D11   D 3   1d. orange   30   1·00
D12   2d. deep blue   35   1·60
D13   3d. lake   45   1·60
D14   4d. ultramarine   45   2·00
D15   6d. purple   45   2·25
D16   1s. light emerald   55   4·25
D11/16   Set of 6   2·25   11·50

In all values the left-hand vertical row of the sheet is imperf at left and the bottom horizontal row is imperf at foot. The above were crudely perforated, resulting in variations in the sizes of the stamps.

The above were withdrawn on 15 January 1968 and thereafter decimal currency postage stamps were used for postage due purposes with appropriate cancellations.

Appendix

The following stamps have either been issued in excess of postal needs, or have not been made available to the public in reasonable quantities at face value. Miniature sheets, imperforate stamps etc., are excluded from this section.

1984

Olympic Games, Los Angeles. 90 n. × 5, *each embossed on gold foil.*

1987

Classic Cars. 1 k. 50×25, *each embossed on gold foil.*

The following issues are reported by the Zambia Postal Services Corporation as being available from Philatelic Counters only.

1997

Disney's Chinese New Year. 250 k., 400 k., 500 k. × 7, 600 k., 750 k., 1000 k.
Endangered Species. 500 k. × 6, 1000 k. × 6
Trains of the World. 200 k., 300 k., 500 k. × 7, 900 k., 1000 k., 1500 k.
Golden Wedding of Queen Elizabeth II and Prince Philip. 500 k. × 6
50th Death Anniv of Paul P. Harris (founder of Rotary International). 1000 k.
"Pacific '97" International Stamp Exhibition, San Francisco. Death Centenary of Heinrich von Stephan (founder of the U.P.U.) 1000 k. × 3
Christmas. Religious Paintings. 50 k. × 2, 100 k. × 2, 500 k., 1000 k.

1998

Diana, Princess of Wales Commemoration. 500 k. × 6, 700 k. × 6
Flowers. 500 k. × 13
Chinese New Year ("Year of the Tiger"). 700 k. × 4
Indian Landmarks. 900 k. × 3
Indian Art. 700 k. × 4
World Cup Football Championship, France. 450 k. × 8, 500 k. × 16
Muhammed Ali (boxing champion). 500 k. × 6
Parrots. Lories and Cockatoos. 500 k. × 6, 1000 k. × 6
Mushrooms. 250 k. × 2, 450 k. × 2, 500 k. × 2, 900 k. × 14, 1000 k. × 2
Cars. 300 k., 500 k., 900 k. × 13, 1000 k.

1999

Lunar New Year ("Year of the Rabbit"). 700 k. × 4
Orchids. 100 k. × 2, 500 k. × 2, 900 k. × 18, 1000 k. × 2
"China '99" International Stamp Exhibition, Beijing. Hang Dagian Paintings. 500 k. × 10
"Queen Elizabeth the Queen Mother's Century". 2000 k. × 4
Prehistoric Animals. 50 k., 100 k., 500 k., 900 k. × 19, 1000 k., 1800 k.
Fauna and Flora. 50 k., 100 k., 500 k. × 5, 700 k. × 36, 900 k., 1000 k., 1800 k.
250th Birth Anniv of Johann von Goethe (German writer). 2000 k. × 3
Royal Wedding. 500 k., 900 k., 1000 k.
"iBra '99" International Stamp Exhibition. Nuremberg. 1000 k., 3200 k. × 3
Cats and Dogs. 50 k., 100 k. × 2, 500 k. × 2, 900 k. × 2, 1000 k. × 25
Princess Diana Photomosaic. 1000 k. × 8
New Millennium. Events of Second Half of 20th Century. 500 k. × 18

Zanzibar
see **Tanzania**

Zimbabwe
(formerly Rhodesia)

SOUTHERN RHODESIA

> **PRICES FOR STAMPS ON COVER TO 1945**
> Nos. 1/61 *from* × 2

SELF-GOVERNMENT

The southern part of Rhodesia, previously administered by the British South Africa Company, was annexed by the British Government and granted the status of a self-governing colony from 1 October 1923.

The existing stamps of Rhodesia (the "Admiral" design first issued in 1913) remained in use until 31 March 1924 and continued to be valid for postal purposes until 30 April of that year.

1   **2** King George V   **3** Victoria Falls

(Recess Waterlow)

1924 (1 Apr)–**29**. *P* 14.

1	1	½d. blue-green ..	..	1·50	10
		a. Imperf between (horiz pair)	..	£700	£800
		b. Imperf between (vert pair)	..	£700	£800
		c. Imperf vert (horiz pair)	..	£750	
2		1d. bright rose	..	1·60	10
		a. Imperf between (horiz pair)	..	£600	£700
		b. Imperf between (vert pair)	..	£1000	
		c. Perf 12½ (coil) (1929)	..	2·75	80·00
3		1½d. bistre-brown	..	1·25	55
		a. Imperf between (horiz pair)	..	£7500	
		b. Imperf between (vert pair)	..	£4500	
		c. Printed double, once albino	..	£325	
4		2d. black and purple-grey	..	2·25	50
		a. Imperf between (horiz pair)	..	£9000	
5		3d. blue	..	2·25	2·25
6		4d. black and orange-red	..	2·50	2·75
7		6d. black and mauve	..	2·00	3·25
		a. Imperf between (horiz pair)	..	£30000	
8		8d. purple and pale green	..	11·00	42·00
9		10d. blue and rose	..	11·00	42·00
10		1s. black and light blue	..	5·00	4·50
11		1s. 6d. black and yellow	..	19·00	32·00
12		2s. black and brown	..	17·00	17·00
13		2s. 6d. blue and sepia	..	35·00	60·00
14		5s. blue and blue-green	..	60·00	£120
1/14			Set of 14	£150	£300

Prices for "imperf between" varieties are for adjacent stamps from the same pane and not for those separated by wide gutter margins between vertical or horizontal pairs, which come from the junction of two panes.

(T **2** recess by B.W.; T **3** typo by Waterlow)

1931 (1 April)–**37**. T **2** (*line perf* 12 *unless otherwise stated*) *and* **3** (*comb perf* 15 × 14). (*The* 11½ *perf is comb.*).

15	2	½d. green	..	85	1·00
		a. Perf 11½ (1933)	..	65	20
		b. Perf 14 (1935)	..	1·60	30
16		1d. scarlet	..	1·00	70
		a. Perf 11½ (1933)	..	1·75	20
		b. Perf 14 (1935)	..	50	20
16c		1½d. chocolate (3.3.33)	..	60·00	42·00
		d. Perf 11½ (1.4.32)	..	2·50	80
17	3	2d. black and sepia	..	3·75	1·40
18		3d. deep ultramarine	..	10·00	11·00
19	2	4d. black and vermilion	..	1·25	1·50
		a. Perf 11½ (1935)	..	17·00	5·00
		b. Perf 14 (10.37)	..	32·00	48·00
20		6d. black and magenta	..	2·25	2·50
		a. Perf 11½ (1933)	..	15·00	1·50
		b. Perf 14 (1936)	..	10·00	60
21		8d. violet and olive-green	..	1·75	3·25
		a. Perf 11½ (1934)	..	17·00	32·00
21b		9d. vermilion and olive-green (1.9.34)	6·00	9·00
22		10d. blue and scarlet	..	7·00	3·00
		a. Perf 11½ (1933)	..	6·00	13·00
23		1s. black and greenish blue	..	2·00	2·50
		a. Perf 11½ (1935)	..	95·00	60·00
		b. Perf 14 (10.37)	..	£200	£140
24		1s. 6d. black and orange-yellow	..	10·00	16·00
		a. Perf 11½ (1936)	..	50·00	95·00
25		2s. black and brown	..	21·00	6·00
		a. Perf 11½ (1933)	..	35·00	30·00
26		2s. 6d. blue and drab	..	32·00	35·00
		a. Perf 11½ (1933)	..	28·00	45·00
27		5s. blue and blue-green	..	48·00	48·00
		a. Printed on gummed side	..	£3750	
15/27			Set of 15	£120	£110

No. 16c was only issued in booklets.

PRINTERS. All stamps from Types **4** to **29** were recess-printed by Waterlow and Sons, Ltd, London, except where otherwise stated.

4

1932 (1 May). *P* 12½.

29	4	2d. green and chocolate ..	..	3·75	75
30		3d. deep ultramarine ..	..	4·00	1·75
		a. Imperf horiz (vert pair) ..	£6000	£8000
		b. Imperf between (vert pair) ..	£14000	

5 Victoria Falls

1935 (6 May). *Silver Jubilee. P* 11×12.

31	5	1d. olive and rose-carmine	..	3·25	1·75
32		2d. emerald and sepia	..	5·50	5·00
33		3d. violet and deep blue ..	..	5·50	10·00
34		6d. black and purple ..	..	8·00	14·00
31/4			Set of 4	20·00	28·00

1935–41. *Inscr* "POSTAGE AND REVENUE".

35	4	2d. green and chocolate (p 12½) ..	2·50	8·50
		a. Perf 14 (1941)..		1·50	10
35b		3d. deep blue (p 14) (1938)	..	3·00	10

6 Victoria Falls and Railway Bridge   **7** King George VI

1937 (12 May). *Coronation. P* 12½.

36	6	1d. olive and rose-carmine	..	80	60
37		2d. emerald and sepia	..	80	1·50
38		3d. violet and blue	..	3·75	7·00
39		6d. black and purple	..	2·25	3·25
36/9			Set of 4	7·00	11·00

1937 (25 Nov). *P* 14.

40	7	½d. green	..	50	10
41		1d. scarlet	..	40	10
42		1½d. red-brown	..	1·00	20
43		4d. red-orange	..	1·50	10
44		6d. grey-black	..	1·50	40
45		8d. emerald-green	..	2·00	1·50
46		9d. pale blue	..	1·50	50
47		10d. purple	..	2·25	2·00
48		1s. black and blue-green	..	1·75	10
		a. Double print of frame	..	£1100	
49		1s. 6d. black and orange-yellow	10·00	2·00
50		2s. black and brown	..	14·00	55
51		2s. 6d. ultramarine and purple	9·00	4·75
52		5s. blue and blue-green	..	26·00	2·00
40/52			Set of 13	60·00	12·50

Nos. 40/1 exist in coils, constructed from normal sheets.

8 British South Africa Co's Arms   **9** Fort Salisbury, 1890

10 Cecil John Rhodes (after S. P. Kendrick)

15 Lobengula's Kraal and Govt House, Salisbury

MINIMUM PRICE

The minimum price quote is 10p which represents a handling charge rather than a basis for valuing common stamps. For further notes about prices see introductory pages.

Recut shirt collar (R. 6/1)

"Cave" flaw (R. 6/6)

(Des Mrs. L. E. Curtis (½d., 1d., 1½d., 3d.), Mrs I. Mount (others))

1940 (3 June). *British South Africa Company's Golden Jubilee. T* 8/10, 15 *and similar designs. P* 14.

53		½d. slate-violet and green	..	10	55
54		1d. violet-blue and scarlet	..	10	10
55		1½d. black and red-brown	..	15	80
		a. Recut shirt collar	..	20·00	
56		2d. green and bright violet	..	30	70
57		3d. black and blue	..	30	1·50
		a. Cave flaw	..	30·00	
58		4d. green and brown	..	2·00	2·50
59		6d. chocolate and green	..	50	2·00
60		1s. blue and green	..	50	2·00
53/60			Set of 8	3·50	9·00

Designs: *Horiz* (as T **8**)—2d. Fort Victoria; 3d. Rhodes makes peace. *Vert* (as T **10**)—4d. Victoria Falls Bridge; 6d. Statue of Sir Charles Coghlan.

16 Mounted Pioneer   Hat brim retouch (P1 1B R. 1/8)

(Roto South African Govt Printer, Pretoria)

1943 (1 Nov). *50th Anniv of Occupation of Matabeleland. W* **9** *of South Africa (Mult Springbok) sideways. P* 14.

61	16	2d. brown and green	..	20	50
		a. Hat brim retouch	..	17·00	

17 Queen Elizabeth II when Princess and Princess Margaret

1947 (1 Apr). *Royal Visit. T* 17 *and similar horiz design. P* 14.

62		½d. black and green ..	..	15	60
63		1d. black and scarlet ..		15	60

Design:—1d. King George VI and Queen Elizabeth.

19 Queen Elizabeth   **20** King George VI   **21** Queen Elizabeth II when Princess

22 Princess Margaret

Damage to
right-hand frame
(R.1/10)

1947 (8 May). *Victory. P* 14.
64	19	1d. carmine	..	..	..	10	10
65	20	2d. slate	..	..	..	10	10
		a. Double print	..	..	..	£1000	
		b. Damaged frame	..	..	20·00	
66	21	3d. blue	..	..	..	55	50
67	22	6d. orange	..	..	..	30	90
64/7				*Set of 4*	90	1·40

(Recess B.W.)

1949 (10 Oct). *75th Anniv of U.P.U. As Nos. 146/7 of Jamaica.*
| 68 | | 2d. slate-green | .. | .. | .. | 80 | 20 |
| 69 | | 3d. blue | .. | .. | .. | 1·10 | 3·25 |

23 Queen Victoria, Arms and King George VI

1950 (12 Sept). *Diamond Jubilee of Southern Rhodesia. P* 14.
| 70 | 23 | 2d. green and brown | .. | .. | 40 | 80 |

24 "Medical Services"

(Des A. R. Winter (2d.), Mrs. J. M. Enalim (others))

1953 (15 Apr). *Birth Centenary of Cecil Rhodes. T* 24 *and
similar horiz designs. P* 14.
71		½d. pale blue and sepia	..	..	15	2·00
72		1d. chestnut and blue-green	..	..	15	10
73		2d. grey-green and violet	..	..	15	10
74		4½d. deep blue-green & deep ultramarine	..	75	2·75
75		1s. black and red-brown	..	..	3·00	80
71/5				*Set of 5*	3·75	5·00

Designs:—1d. "Agriculture"; 2d. "Building"; 4½d. "Water
Supplies"; 1s. "Transport".
No. 74 also commemorates the Diamond Jubilee of
Matabeleland.

1953 (30 May). *Rhodes Centenary Exhibition, Bulawayo. As
No. 59 of Zambia, but without watermark.*
| 76 | | 6d. violet | .. | .. | .. | 30 | 60 |

30 Queen Elizabeth II

(Recess D.L.R.)

1953 (1 June). *Coronation. P* 12 × 12½.
| 77 | 30 | 2s. 6d. carmine | .. | .. | .. | 4·50 | 6·00 |

31 Sable Antelope

33 Rhodes's Grave

---

34 Farm Worker

42 Basket Maker

43 Balancing Rocks

44 Coat of Arms

(Recess, centre typo (4d.), B.W.)

1953 (31 Aug). *T* 31, 33/4, 42/4 *and similar designs. P* 13½ × 14
(2d., 6d., 5s.), 14 (10s., £1) *or* 14 × 13½ *(others).*
78		½d. grey-green and claret	..	..	30	40
79		1d. green and brown	..	..	30	10
80		2d. deep chestnut and reddish violet	..	30	10
81		3d. chocolate and rose-red	..	..	55	80
82		4d. red, green and indigo	..	..	3·25	10
83		4½d. black and deep bright blue	..	..	2·00	2·75
84		6d. brown-olive & deep turquoise-green	..	3·00	60
85		9d. deep blue and reddish brown	..	3·50	2·75
86		1s. reddish violet and light blue	..	1·25	10
87		2s. purple and scarlet	..	..	11·00	3·50
88		2s. 6d. yellow-olive and orange-brown	..	5·00	3·75
89		5s. yellow-brown and deep green	..	10·00	8·50
90		10s. red-brown and olive	..	..	14·00	35·00
91		£1 rose-red and black	..	..	22·00	35·00
78/91				*Set of 14*	65·00	80·00

Designs: *Vert (as T* 31*)*—1d. Tobacco planter. (*As T* 33)—6d.
Baobab tree. *Horiz (as T* 34)—4d. Flame Lily; 4½d. Victoria Falls;
9d. Lion; 1s. Zimbabwe Ruins; 2s. Birchenough Bridge; 2s. 6d.
Kariba Gorge.

For issues from 1954 to 1963 see under RHODESIA AND
NYASALAND.

45 Maize

50 Flame Lily

56 Cattle

58 Coat of Arms

(Des V. Whiteley. Photo Harrison)

1964 (19 Feb). *T* 45, 50, 56, 58 *and similar horiz designs. P* 14½
(½d. *to* 4d.), 13½ × 13 (6d. *to* 2s. 6d.) *or* 14½ × 14 *(others).*
92		½d. yellow, yellow-green and light blue	..	20	1·75
93		1d. reddish violet and yellow-ochre	..	15	10
		a. Reddish violet omitted	..	£1700	
94		2d. yellow and deep violet	..	..	60	10
95		3d. chocolate and pale blue	..	..	20	10
96		4d. yellow-orange and deep green	..	30	10
97		6d. carmine-red, yellow & deep dull green	40	10
98		9d. red-brown, yellow and olive-green	..	2·50	90
99		1s. blue-green and ochre	..	..	4·00	10
		a. Blue-green (Queen and emeralds) omitted	..	£1900	
100		1s. 3d. red, violet and yellow-green	..	3·75	10
101		2s. blue and ochre	..	..	3·00	1·40
102		2s. 6d. ultramarine and vermilion	..	5·00	70
		a. Vermilion omitted	..	£2250	
		b. Ultramarine omitted	..	£5000	
103		5s. light brown, bistre-yellow & light blue	5·00	2·25
104		10s. black, yell-brown lt blue & carmine-red	13·00	6·50
105		£1 brown, yellow-grn, buff & salmon-pink	7·00	16·00
92/105				*Set of 14*	40·00	26·00

Designs: (*As T* 45)—1d. African Buffalo; 2d. Tobacco; 3d.
Greater Kudu; 4d. Citrus. (*As T* 50)—9d. Ansellia Orchid; 1s.
Emeralds; 1s. 3d. Aloe; 2s. Lake Kyle; 2s. 6d. Tigerfish. (*As
T* 56)—10s. Helmet Guineafowl.
Nos. 92 and 93 exist in coils constructed from normal sheets.
Nos. 102a and 102b occur on different sheets and involve one
vertical row of stamps in each instance. They were caused by the
printing press being stopped and then restarted. Three such
sheets showing No. 102a have been reported.
See also Nos. 359/72 of Rhodesia.

In October 1964 Southern Rhodesia was renamed Rhodesia.

NEW INFORMATION

The editor is always interested to correspond with
people who have new information that will
improve or correct the Catalogue.

RHODESIA

59 "Telecommunications"

60 Bangala Dam

(Des V. Whiteley. Photo Harrison)

1965 (17 May). *I.T.U. Centenary. P* 14½.
351	59	6d. violet and light yellow-olive	..	1·50	40
352		1s. violet and light yellow-olive	..	1·50	40
353		2s. 6d. violet and light brown	..	2·50	4·50
351/3				*Set of 3*	5·00	4·75

(Des V. Whiteley. Photo Harrison)

1965 (19 July). *Water Conservation. T* 60 *and similar vert designs.
Multicoloured. P* 14.
354		3d. Type **60**	..	..	30	10
355		4d. Irrigation canal	..	..	1·00	1·25
356		2s. 6d. Cutting sugar cane	..	..	2·25	3·50
354/6				*Set of 3*	3·25	4·25

63 Sir Winston Churchill, Quill, Sword and
Houses of Parliament

(Des H. Baxter. Photo Harrison)

1965 (16 Aug). *Churchill Commemoration. P* 14½.
| 357 | 63 | 1s. 3d. black and bright blue | .. | 60 | 35 |

UNILATERAL DECLARATION OF INDEPENDENCE

Independence was declared by Rhodesia on 11 November 1965
but this was not recognised by the British Government. Following
a conference in London during 1979 it was agreed that the British
Government should resume control, pending elections to be held in
February 1980.
After the elections Rhodesia became an independent republic
within the Commonwealth on 18 April 1980, as ZIMBABWE.

64 Coat of Arms

(Des Col. C. R. Dickenson. Litho Mardon Printers, Salisbury)

1965 (8 Dec). *"Independence". P* 11.
| 358 | 64 | 2s. 6d. multicoloured | .. | .. | 15 | 15 |
| | | a. Imperf (pair) | .. | .. | £600 | |

INDEPENDENCE
11th November
1965

INDEPENDENCE ═ 5/-
11th November 1965

(65) (66)

1966 (17 Jan). (*a*) *Nos. 92/105 optd with T* 65 *or larger (5s. to
£1) by Mardon Printers, Salisbury.*
359		½d. yellow, yellow-green and light blue	..	10	10
		a. Pair, one stamp without opt.	..	£2750	
360		1d. reddish violet and yellow-ochre	..	10	10
361		2d. yellow and deep violet	..	..	10	10
362		3d. chocolate and pale blue	..	..	10	10
363		4d. yellow-orange and deep green	..	15	10
364		6d. carmine-red, yellow & dp dull green	..	15	10
365		9d. red-brown, yellow and olive-green	..	30	10
		a. Opt double	..	..	£350	
366		1s. blue-green and ochre	..	..	40	10
		a. Opt double	..	..	£350	
367		1s. 3d. red, violet and yellow-green	..	80	20
368		2s. blue and ochre	..	..	90	3·25
369		2s. 6d. ultramarine and vermilion	..	60	1·00
370		5s. light brown, bistre-yellow & lt blue	..	2·00	5·50
		a. Opt double	..	..	£450	
371		10s. black, yellow-ochre, lt bl & carm-red	3·00	2·25
372		£1 brown, yell-green, buff & salmon-pink	1·25	2·25
		(*b*) *No.* 357 *surch with T* 66		
373		5s. on 1s. 3d. black and bright blue (R.)	6·50	16·00
		a. "5/-" omitted			
359/73				*Set of 15*	14·50	27·00

Owing to the existence of forgeries, No. 370a should only be
purchased when accompanied by a certificate of genuineness.
Other overprint errors exist from the clandestine use of the
original settings.

67 Emeralds   **68** Zeederberg Coach, *circa* 1895

(Des V. Whiteley. Photo Harrison)

1966 (9 Feb). *As Nos. 92/105, but inscr "RHODESIA" as T* **67**. *Some designs and colours changed. P* 14½ (1d. to 4d.), 13½×13 (6d. to 2s. 6d) or 14½×14 (5s. to £1).

374	–	1d. reddish violet and yellow-ochre	..	10	10
375	–	2d. yellow-orange and dp grn (as No. 96)		10	10
		a. Yellow-orange omitted		£1200	
376	–	3d. chocolate and pale blue	..	10	10
		a. Chocolate omitted	..	£2250	
		b. Pale blue omitted	..	£1700	
377	**67**	4d. emerald and sepia	..	70	10
378	**50**	6d. carmine-red, yellow & dp dull green		15	10
379	–	9d. yellow and deep violet (as No. 94)		15	20
380	**45**	1s. yellow, yellow-green and light blue		15	10
381	–	1s. 3d. blue and ochre (as No. 101)	..	25	15
		a. Ochre omitted	..	£1900	
382	–	1s. 6d. red-brn, yell & ol-grn (as No. 98)	1·75	25
383	–	2s. red, violet and yell-grn (as No. 100)	40	80
384	–	2s. 6d. blue, vermilion & turquoise-blue	60	20
385	**56**	5s. light brown, bistre-yellow & lt blue	40	90
386	–	10s. black, yell-ochre, lt blue & carm-red	2·25	4·00
387	**58**	£1 brown, yell-grn, buff & salmon-pink	8·00	8·00
374/87			*Set of* 14	12·00	13·00

Nos. 379/80 are in larger format, as T **50**.

No. 374 exists in coils constructed from normal sheets. Coil-vending machines were withdrawn from service in 1967.

No. 375a occured on single rows from two separate sheets, No. 376a in the bottom row of a sheet, No. 376b in the top two rows of a sheet and No. 381a in the third vertical row on two sheets.

For stamps printed by lithography, see Nos. 397/407.

PRINTERS. All the following stamps were printed by lithography by Mardon Printers, Salisbury.

(Des V. Whiteley (Nos. 388/90))

1966 (2 May). *28th Congress of Southern Africa Philatelic Federation* ("Rhopex"). *T* **68** *and similar horiz designs. P* 14½.

388	3d. multicoloured	..	25	10
389	9d. grey-buff, sepia and grey-green	..	30	40
390	1s. 6d. pale blue and black	..	50	50
391	2s. 6d. salmon-pink, pale dull grn & blk	55	80
388/91		*Set of* 4	1·40	1·50
MS392	126×84 mm. Nos. 388/91 (toned paper)	9·00	16·00
	a. White paper		13·00	20·00

Designs:—9d. Sir Rowland Hill; 1s. 6d. The Penny Black; 2s. 6d. Rhodesian stamp of 1892 (No. 12).

The 3d., 2s. 6d. and miniature sheet exist imperforate from sheets prepared for presentation purposes.

69 De Havilland D.H.89   **70** Kudu
Dragon Rapide (1946)

1966 (1 June). *20th Anniv of Central African Airways. T* **69** *and similar horiz designs. P* 14½ × 14.

393	6d. black, blue, yellow and green	..	75	50
394	1s. 3d. blue, yellow-orange, black and green	1·25	55
395	2s. 6d. black, blue, yellow and green	3·00	2·50
396	5s. black and blue	..	5·00	5·50
393/6		*Set of* 4	9·00	8·00

Aircraft:—1s. 3d. Douglas DC-3 (1953); 2s. 6d. Vickers Viscount 748 *Matopos* (1956); 5s. B.A.C. One Eleven 200.

The 6d., 2s. 6d. and 5s. values exist imperforate from sheets prepared for presentation purposes.

1966–69. *As Nos. 374/87 but litho. P* 14½ (1d. to 2s.) or 14½ × 14 (others).

397	1d. reddish violet and yellow-ochre (shades) (2.6.66)	..	15	10
398	2d. orange and green (1.11.67)	..	85	65
399	3d. chocolate-brn & pale grnsh bl (29.1.68)	1·25	10
400	4d. emerald, bistre-brown & drab (21.9.66)	65	10
401	6d. carmine-red, yell & ol-grey (1.11.66)	60	50
402	9d. yellow and light violet (20.11.67)	..	30	10
403	1s. 3d. blue and ochre (1.11.66)	..	2·00	10
404	2s. dull red, violet & sage-green (18.7.66)	2·00	4·00
405	5s. yellow-brown, deep bistre-yellow and light blue (25.6.66)	2·75	4·50
406	10s. black, buff, lt bl & carm-red (10.8.66)	10·00	17·00
407	£1 pale brown, yellow-green, brown-ochre and salmon (10.8.66)	10·00	19·00
397/407		*Set of* 11	27·00	42·00

In addition to the change in printing process from photogravure to lithography and the difference in perforation in the 6d. to 2s. values (14½ instead of 13½ × 13) and shade variations, the oval portrait frame is larger (and in some values thicker) in the 1d. to 2s., and in the 1s. 3d. the Queen's head is also larger.

Trial printings, made in June 1966, exist of the 5s., 10s. and £1 values on a slightly thinner paper. These are rare.

The 1d., 3d. and 5s. values exist imperforate from sheets prepared for presentation purposes.

1967–68. *Dual Currency Issue. As Nos. 376, 380 and 382/4 but value in decimal currency in addition as in T* **70**. *P* 14½. *White gum (No. 408) or cream gum (others).*

408	3d./2½ c. chocolate-brown and pale greenish blue (15.3.67)	60	20
409	1s./10 c. yell, grn & greenish bl (1.11.67)	70	45
410	1s. 6d./15 c. red-brown, yellow and yellow-green (11.3.68)	4·00	50
411	2s./20 c. dull red, viol and sage-grn (11.3.68)	2·75	5·00
412	2s. 6d./25 c. ultramarine-blue, vermilion and bright turquoise-blue (9.12.68)	30·00	40·00
408/12		*Set of* 5	35·00	42·00

71 Dr. Jameson (administrator)

(Des from painting by F. M. Bennett)

1967 (17 May). *Famous Rhodesians (1st issue) and 50th Death Anniv of Dr. Jameson. P* 14½.

413	**71**	1s. 6d. multicoloured	..	30	35

See also Nos. 426, 430, 457, 458, 469, 480, 488 and 513.

72 Soapstone Sculpture (Joram Mariga)

1967 (12 July). *Tenth Anniv of Opening of Rhodes National Gallery. T* **72** *and similar vert designs. P* 14½ × 14 (3d., 9d.) or 14 (others).

414	3d. reddish chestnut, yellow-olive and black	10	10
415	9d. lt greenish blue, dp olive-brown & black	20	20
	a. Perf 13½		7·50	18·00
416	1s. 3d. multicoloured	..	20	25
417	2s. 6d. multicoloured	..	25	35
414/17		*Set of* 4	65	75

Designs:—9d. "The Burgher of Calais" (detail, Rodin); 1s. 3d. "The Knight" (stamp design wrongly inscr) (Roberto Crippa); 2s. 6d. "John the Baptist" (M. Tossini).

73 Baobab Tree

1967 (6 Sept). *Nature Conservation. T* **73** *and similar designs. P* 14½.

418	4d. light brown and black	..	25	25
419	4d. yellow-olive and black	..	25	25
420	4d. deep grey and black	..	25	25
421	4d. yellow-orange and black	..	25	25
418/21		*Set of* 4	90	90

Designs:—*Horiz*—No. 418, Type **73**; No. 419, White Rhinoceros; No. 420, African Elephants. *Vert*—No. 421, Wild Gladiolus.

74 Wooden Hand Plough

(Des Rose Martin)

1968 (26 Apr). *15th World Ploughing Contest, Norton, Rhodesia. T* **74** *and similar horiz designs. P* 14½.

422	3d. pale orange, orange-verm & lake-brown	10	10
423	9d. multicoloured	..	20	25
424	1s. 6d. multicoloured	..	25	65
425	2s. 6d. multicoloured	..	30	95
422/5		*Set of* 4	75	1·75

Designs:—9d. Early wheel plough; 1s. 6d. Steam powered tractor, and ploughs; 2s. 6d. Modern tractor, and plough.

---

75 Alfred Beit (national   **76** Raising the Flag,
benefactor)   Bulawayo, 1893

(Des from painting by A. Haywood)

1968 (15 July). *Famous Rhodesians (2nd issue). P* 14½.

426	**75**	1s. 6d. pale orange, black and brown	..	30	30

(Des Rose Martin)

1968 (4 Nov). *75th Anniv of Matabeleland. T* **76** *and similar vert designs. P* 14½.

427	3d. pale orange, red-orange and black	..	15	10
428	9d. multicoloured	..	25	20
429	1s. 6d. pale turquoise-green, deep emerald and blackish green	25	60
427/9		*Set of* 3	60	80

Designs:—9d. View and coat of arms of Bulawayo; 1s. 6d. Allan Wilson (combatant in the Matabele War).

77 Sir William Henry Milton (administrator)

(Des from painting by S. Kendrick)

1969 (15 Jan). *Famous Rhodesians (3rd issue). P* 14½.

430	**77**	1s. 6d. multicoloured	..	..	20	55

78 2 ft Gauge Steam Locomotive No. 15, 1897

(Des Rose Martin)

1969 (22 May). *70th Anniv of Opening of Beira-Salisbury Railway. T* **78** *and similar horiz designs showing locomotives. Multicoloured. P* 14½.

431	3d. Type **78**	..	75	20
432	9d. 7th Class steam locomotive No. 43, 1903	1·25	75
433	1s. 6d. Beyer Peacock 15th Class steam locomotive No. 413, 1951	3·50	3·25
434	2s. 6d. Class DE2 diesel-electric locomotive No. 1203, 1955	4·50	7·00
431/4		*Set of* 4	9·00	10·00

79 Low Level Bridge

(Des Rose Martin)

1969 (18 Sept). *Bridges of Rhodesia. T* **79** *and similar horiz designs. Multicoloured. P* 14½.

435	3d. Type **79**	..	75	20
436	9d. Mpudzi bridge	..	1·00	30
437	1s. 6d. Umniati bridge	..	2·50	2·00
438	2s. 6d. Birchenough bridge	..	3·50	3·00
435/8		*Set of* 4	7·00	5·00

(New Currency. 100 cents = 1 dollar)

80 Harvesting   **81** Devil's Cataract,
Wheat   Victoria Falls

(Des from colour-transparencies (3, 6 c.), Rose Martin (others))

1970 (17 Feb). *Decimal Currency. T* **80/1** *and similar horiz designs. P* 14½.

439	1 c. multicoloured	..	10	10
	a. Booklet pane of 4		30	
440	2 c. multicoloured	..	10	10
441	2½ c. multicoloured	..	10	10
	a. Booklet pane of 4		35	

441c	3 c. multicoloured (1.1.73)			1·25	10
	ca. Booklet pane of 4			4·50	
442	3½ c. multicoloured			10	10
	a. Booklet pane of 4			65	
442b	4 c. multicoloured (1.1.73)			1·75	40
	ba. Booklet pane of 4			6·00	
443	5 c. multicoloured			15	10
443b	6 c. multicoloured (1.1.73)			4·00	3·75
443c	7½ c. multicoloured (1.1.73)			7·50	80
444	8 c. multicoloured			1·25	20
445	10 c. multicoloured			60	10
446	12½ c. multicoloured			1·00	10
446a	14 c. multicoloured (1.1.73)			15·00	90
447	15 c. multicoloured			2·50	15
448	20 c. multicoloured			1·75	15
449	25 c. multicoloured			5·00	90
450	50 c. turquoise and ultramarine			2·25	55
451	$1 multicoloured			5·00	1·75
452	$2 multicoloured			10·00	23·00
439/52			*Set of 19*	48·00	28·00

Designs: *Size as T 80*—2 c. Pouring molten metal; 2½ c. Zimbabwe Ruins; 3 c. Articulated lorry; 3½ and 4 c. Statue of Cecil Rhodes; 5 c. Mine headgear. *Size as T 81*—6 c. Hydrofoil *Seaflight*; 7½ c. As 8 c.; 10 c. Yachting on Lake McIlwaine; 12½ c. Hippopotamus in river; 14 c. and 15 c. Kariba Dam; 20 c. Irrigation canal. *As T 80/1 but larger (31×26 mm)*—25 c. Bateleurs; 50 c. Radar antenna and Vickers Viscount 810; $1 "Air Rescue"; $2 Rhodesian flag.

Booklet panes Nos. 439a, 441a, 441ca, 442a and 442ba have margins all round.

82 Despatch Rider, *circa* 1890

(Des Rose Martin)

1970 (1 July). *Inauguration of Posts and Telecommunications Corporation. T 82 and similar horiz designs. Multicoloured. P 14½.*

453	2½ c. Type **82**			35	10
454	3½ c. Loading mail at Salisbury airport			75	50
455	15 c. Constructing telegraph line, *circa* 1890			1·25	2·25
456	25 c. Telephone and modern telecommunications equipment			1·75	4·00
453/6			*Set of 4*	3·50	6·00

83 Mother Patrick (Dominican nurse and teacher)

(Des Rose Martin from photograph)

1970 (16 Nov). *Famous Rhodesians (4th issue). P 14½.*

457	**83**	15 c. multicoloured		60	50

84 Frederick Courteney Selous (big-game hunter, explorer and pioneer)

(Des from painting by L. C. Dickinson)

1971 (1 Mar). *Famous Rhodesians (5th issue). P 14½.*

458	**84**	15 c. multicoloured		40	70

85 Hoopoe   **86** Porphyritic Granite

(Des from photographs by Peter Ginn)

1971 (1 June). *Birds of Rhodesia (1st series). T 85 and similar multicoloured designs. P 14½.*

459	2 c. Type **85**			1·00	20
460	2½ c. Half-collared Kingfisher (*horiz*)			1·00	20
461	5 c. Golden-breasted Bunting			2·75	70
462	7½ c. Carmine Bee Eater			3·00	1·25
463	8 c. Red-eyed Bulbul			3·00	1·50
464	25 c. Senegal Wattled Plover (*horiz*)			6·00	3·25
459/64			*Set of 6*	15·00	6·50

See also Nos. 537/42.

(Des from photographs by University of Rhodesia and Dept of Geological Survey)

1971 (30 Aug). *"Granite 71" Geological Symposium. T 86 and similar vert designs. Multicoloured. P 14.*

465	2½ c. Type **86**			85	10
466	7½ c. Muscovite mica seen through microscope			1·75	1·25
467	15 c. Granite seen through microscope			2·25	3·25
468	25 c. Geological map of Rhodesia			3·00	4·50
465/8			*Set of 4*	7·00	8·00

87 Dr. Robert Moffat (missionary)

1972 (14 Feb). *Famous Rhodesians (6th issue). P 14½.*

469	**87**	13 c. multicoloured		65	1·40

88 Bird ("Be Airwise")   **89** "The Three Kings"

(Des C. Lawton)

1972 (17 July). *"Prevent Pollution". T 88 and similar horiz designs. Multicoloured. P 14½.*

470	2½ c. Type **88**			20	10
471	3½ c. Antelope ("Be Countrywise")			20	20
472	7 c. Fish ("Be Waterwise")			30	45
473	13 c. City ("Be Citywise")			45	70
470/3			*Set of 4*	1·00	1·25

1972 (28 Aug). *"Rhophil '72". As Nos. 439a, 441a and 442a with commemorative inscr in margins. Each 66 × 78 mm.*

MS474	1 c. multicoloured			1·40	2·50
MS475	2½ c. multicoloured			1·40	2·50
MS476	3½ c. multicoloured			1·40	2·50
MS474/6			*Set of 3 sheets*	3·75	6·75

(Des Rose Martin)

1972 (18 Oct). *Christmas. P 14.*

477	**89**	2 c. multicoloured		10	10
478		5 c. multicoloured		20	25
479		13 c. multicoloured		50	75
477/9			*Set of 3*	70	1·00

90 Dr. David Livingstone   **91** W.M.O. Emblem

1973 (2 Apr). *Famous Rhodesians (7th issue). P 14.*

480	**90**	14 c. multicoloured		70	1·00

(Des S. J. Ivey)

1973 (2 July). *I.M.O./W.M.O. Centenary. P 14.*

481	**91**	3 c. multicoloured		15	10
482		14 c. multicoloured		65	65
483		25 c. multicoloured		90	2·25
481/3			*Set of 3*	1·50	2·75

92 Arms of Rhodesia

1973 (10 Oct). *50th Anniv of Responsible Government. P 14.*

484	**92**	2½ c. multicoloured		15	10
485		5 c. multicoloured		25	20
486		7½ c. multicoloured		40	80
487		14 c. multicoloured		70	2·50
484/7			*Set of 4*	1·40	3·25

93 George Pauling (construction engineer)

(Des P. Birch)

1974 (15 May). *Famous Rhodesians (8th issue). P 14.*

488	**93**	14 c. multicoloured		80	1·75

94 Greater Kudu   **95** Thunbergia   **96** *Charaxes varanes*

(Des J. Huntly)

1974 (14 Aug)–**76**. *Various vert designs as T 94/6. Multicoloured. P 14½ (1 to 14 c.) or 14 (others). (a) Antelopes. Size as T 94.*

489	1 c. Type **94**			10	10
490	2½ c. Eland			75	10
	a. Booklet pane of 4			2·75	
491	3 c. Roan Antelope			10	10
	a. Booklet pane of 4			70	
492	4 c. Reedbuck			30	10
	a. Booklet pane of 4			1·00	
493	5 c. Bushbuck			40	10

(b) Wild Flowers. Size as T 95

494	6 c. Type **95**			40	10
495	7½ c. Flame Lily			2·25	35
496	8 c. As 7½ c. (1.7.76)			40	10
497	10 c. Devil Thorn			40	10
498	12 c. Hibiscus (1.7.76)			70	2·50
499	12½ c. Pink Sabi Star			3·00	50
500	14 c. Wild Pimpernel			3·00	50
501	15 c. As 12½ c. (1.7.76)			70	75
502	16 c. As 14 c. (1.7.76)			70	45

(c) Butterflies. Size as T 96

503	20 c. Type **96**			2·50	35
504	24 c. *Precis hierta* (s sp *cebrene*) (1.7.76)			85	40
505	25 c. As 24 c.			4·00	3·50
506	50 c. *Colotis regina*			70	90
507	$1 *Graphium antheus*			70	1·50
508	$2 *Hamanumida daedalus*			80	2·25
489/508			*Set of 20*	19·00	13·00

97 Collecting Mail   **98** Thomas Baines (artist)

(Des M. Chase)

1974 (20 Nov). *Centenary of Universal Postal Union. T 97 and similar horiz designs. Multicoloured. P 14.*

509	3 c. Type **97**			15	10
510	4 c. Sorting mail			15	10
511	7½ c. Mail delivery			40	60
512	14 c. Weighing parcel			70	1·75
509/12			*Set of 4*	1·25	2·25

(Des from self-portrait)

1975 (12 Feb). *Famous Rhodesians (9th issue). P 14.*

513	**98**	14 c. multicoloured		90	1·25

99 *Euphorbia confinalis*   **100** Prevention of Head Injuries

(Des Nancy Abrey)

1975 (16 July). *International Succulent Congress, Salisbury ("Aloe '75"). T 99 and similar vert designs. Multicoloured. P 14½.*

514	2½ c. Type **99**			20	10
515	3 c. *Aloe excelsa*			20	10
516	4 c. *Hoodia lugardii*			20	10
517	7½ c. *Aloe ortholopha*			25	10
518	14 c. *Aloe musapana*			50	20
519	25 c. *Aloe saponaria*			75	3·00
514/19			*Set of 6*	1·90	3·00

(Des Val Bond)

1975 (15 Oct). *Occupational Safety.* T **100** *and similar horiz designs. Multicoloured. P* 14.
520	2½ c. Type **100**		10	10
521	4 c. Bandaged hand and gloved hand		20	10
522	7½ c. Broken glass and eye		30	30
523	14 c. Blind man and welder with protective mask		35	1·00
520/3		*Set of* 4	80	1·25

101 Telephones, 1876 and 1976 (**102**)

(Des M. Chase)

1976 (10 Mar). *Telephone Centenary.* T **101** *and similar vert design. P* 14.
524	3 c. grey-black and pale blue		10	10
525	14 c. brownish black and light stone		20	55

Design:—14 c. Alexander Graham Bell.

1976 (1 July). *Nos.* 495, 500 *and* 505 *surch as* T **102**.
526	8 c. on 7½ c. Flame Lily		15	15
	a. Surch double, one albino			
527	16 c. on 14 c. Wild Pimpernel		20	15
528	24 c. on 25 c. *Precis hierta* (s sp *cebrene*)		30	80
526/8		*Set of* 3	60	1·00

103 Roan Antelope   **104** Msasa

(Des N. Pedersen)

1976 (21 July). *Vulnerable Wildlife.* T **103** *and similar horiz designs. Multicoloured. P* 14.
529	4 c. Type **103**		15	10
530	6 c. Brown Hyena		15	40
531	8 c. Hunting Dog		25	20
532	16 c. Cheetah		35	45
529/32		*Set of* 4	80	1·00

(Des Nancy Abrey)

1976 (17 Nov). *Trees of Rhodesia.* T **104** *and similar vert designs. Multicoloured. P* 14.
533	4 c. Type **104**		15	10
534	6 c. Red Mahogany		15	10
535	8 c. Mukwa		20	15
536	16 c. Rhodesian Teak		25	65
533/6		*Set of* 4	65	75

105 Common Bulbul   **106** "Lake Kyle" (Joan Evans)

(Des B. Finch)

1977 (16 Mar). *Birds of Rhodesia (2nd series).* T **105** *and similar vert designs. Multicoloured. P* 14.
537	3 c. Type **105**		20	10
538	4 c. Yellow-mantled Whydah		20	10
539	6 c. Cape Longclaw		25	35
540	8 c. Eastern Long-tailed Shrike		30	50
541	16 c. Lesser Blue-eared Glossy Starling		35	80
542	24 c. Green Wood Hoopoe		40	1·25
537/42		*Set of* 6	1·50	2·75

1977 (20 July). *Landscape Paintings.* T **106** *and similar horiz designs. Multicoloured. P* 14.
543	3 c. Type **106**		10	10
544	4 c. "Chimanimani Mountains" (Joan Evans)		10	10
545	6 c. "Rocks near Bonsor Reef", (Alice Balfour)		15	40
546	8 c. "A Dwala near Devil's Pass" (Alice Balfour)		20	10
547	16 c. "Zimbabwe" (Alice Balfour)		25	40
548	24 c. "Victoria Falls" (Thomas Baines)		30	75
543/8		*Set of* 6	1·00	1·50

107 Virgin and Child   **108** Fair Spire

(Des Dianne Deudney)

1977 (16 Nov). *Christmas. P* 14.
549	**107** 3 c. multicoloured		10	10
550	6 c. multicoloured		10	20
551	8 c. multicoloured		15	10
552	16 c. multicoloured		30	75
549/52		*Set of* 4	60	95

1978 (15 Mar). *Trade Fair Rhodesia, Bulawayo.* T **108** *and similar vert design. Multicoloured. P* 14.
553	4 c. Type **108**		15	10
554	8 c. Fair Spire (*different*)		20	25

109 Morganite   **110** White Rhinoceros

111 Odzani Falls

(Des N. Pedersen (1 to 17 c.), D. Myles (21 c. to $2))

1978 (16 Aug). *Multicoloured.*

(a) *Horiz designs as* T **109** *showing gemstones.* P 14½
555	1 c. Type **109**		20	10
556	3 c. Amethyst		20	10
557	4 c. Garnet		20	10
558	5 c. Citrine		20	10
559	7 c. Blue Topaz		20	10

(b) *Horiz designs as* T **110** *showing wild animals.* P 14½
560	9 c. Type **110**		15	10
561	11 c. Lion		15	30
562	13 c. Warthog		15	55
563	15 c. Giraffe		15	30
564	17 c. Common Zebra		15	10

(c) *Horiz designs as* T **111** *showing waterfalls.* P 14
565	21 c. Type **111**		15	40
566	25 c. Goba Falls		15	20
567	30 c. Inyangombi Falls		20	20
568	$1 Bridal Veil Falls		20	60
569	$2 Victoria Falls		30	75
555/69		*Set of* 15	2·50	3·25

112 Wright Flyer I

(Des C. Herbert)

1978 (18 Oct). *75th Anniv of Powered Flight.* T **112** *and similar horiz designs. Multicoloured. P* 14.
570	4 c. Type **112**		10	10
571	5 c. Bleriot XI		10	10
572	7 c. Vickers Vimy *Silver Queen II*		10	10
573	9 c. Armstrong Whitworth A.W.15 Atlanta		10	10
574	17 c. Vickers Viking 1B *Zambezi*		15	10
575	25 c. Boeing 720B		20	50
570/5		*Set of* 6	65	85

STANLEY GIBBONS STAMP COLLECTING SERIES

Introductory booklets on *How to Start, How to Identify Stamps* and *Collecting by Theme.* A series of well illustrated guides at a low price.
Write for details.

ZIMBABWE

REPUBLIC

Rhodesia became independent under majority rule on 18 April 1980 and was renamed Zimbabwe.

PRINTERS. All stamps of Zimbabwe were printed in lithography by Mardon Printers (Pvt) Ltd, subsequently (from Nos. 724/7) National Printing and Packaging, Harare, *unless otherwise stated.*

113 Morganite   **114** Rotary Anniversary Emblem

1980 (18 Apr)–**83**. *As Nos.* 555/69 *and new value* (40 c.)*, all inscr* "ZIMBABWE" *as in* T **113**.
576	1 c. Type **113**		20	30
577	3 c. Amethyst		30	30
578	4 c. Garnet		30	10
	a. Imperf (pair)		£120	
579	5 c. Citrine		35	10
580	7 c. Blue Topaz		35	10
581	9 c. White Rhinoceros		15	10
582	11 c. Lion		15	15
583	13 c. Warthog		15	15
584	15 c. Giraffe		15	20
585	17 c. Common Zebra		15	20
586	21 c. Odzani Falls		20	25
587	25 c. Goba Falls		25	30
588	30 c. Inyangombi Falls		30	50
588a	40 c. Bundi Falls (14.3.83)		6·00	4·50
589	$1 Bridal Veil Falls		50	2·00
590	$2 Victoria Falls		75	3·75
576/90		*Set of* 16	9·25	11·50

1980 (18 June). *75th Anniv of Rotary International. P* 14½.
591	**114** 4 c. multicoloured		10	10
592	13 c. multicoloured		15	30
593	21 c. multicoloured		20	55
594	25 c. multicoloured		20	80
591/4		*Set of* 4	50	1·60
MS595	140 × 84 mm. Nos. 591/4.		75	1·60

115 Olympic Rings

(Des Nancy Abrey)

1980 (19 July). *Olympic Games, Moscow. P* 14½.
596	**115** 17 c. multicoloured		30	40

116 Gatooma Post Office, 1912   **117** Stylised Blind Person

(Des Mortimer Tiley and Partners Ltd)

1980 (17 Oct). *75th Anniv of Post Office Savings Bank.* T **116** *and similar horiz designs. Multicoloured. P* 14.
597	5 c. black and yellow-brown		10	10
598	7 c. black and red-orange		10	10
599	9 c. black and olive-yellow		10	10
600	17 c. black and light blue		25	25
597/600		*Set of* 4	40	40
MS601	125 × 84 mm. Nos. 597/600		55	1·25

Designs:—7 c. Salisbury Post Office, 1912; 9 c. Umtali Post Office, 1901; 17 c. Bulawayo Post Office, 1895.

(Des Rose Martin)

1981 (23 Sept). *International Year of Disabled Persons.* T **117** *and similar vert designs showing stylised figures. Multicoloured. P* 14.
602	5 c. Type **117**		15	10
603	7 c. Deaf person		15	10
604	11 c. Person with one leg		20	15
605	17 c. Person with one arm		25	35
602/5		*Set of* 4	65	60

118 Msasa

119 Painting from Gwamgwadza Cave, Mtoko Area

(Des Nancy Abrey)

1981 (4 Dec). *National Tree Day. T **118** and similar vert designs. Multicoloured. P 14½.*

606	5 c. Type **118**	10	10
607	7 c. Mopane	15	15
608	21 c. Flat-crowned Acacia	45	65
609	30 c. Pod Mahogany	60	1·10
606/9	Set of 4	1·10	1·75

1982 (17 Mar). *Rock Paintings. T **119** and similar horiz designs showing paintings from various locations. Multicoloured. P 14½.*

610	9 c. Type **119**	75	20
611	11 c. Epworth Mission, near Harare	1·00	20
612	17 c. Diana's Vow, near Harare	1·00	50
613	21 c. Gwamgwadza Cave, Mtoko Area (different)	1·40	1·00
614	25 c. Mucheka Cave, Msana Communal Land	1·75	1·75
615	30 c. Chinzwini Shelter, Chiredzi Area	2·00	2·00
610/15	Set of 6	7·00	5·00

120 Scout Emblem

121 Dr. Robert Koch

(Des Rose Martin)

1982 (21 July). *75th Anniv of Boy Scout Movement. T **120** and similar vert designs. Multicoloured. P 14½ × 14.*

616	9 c. Type **120**	35	15
617	11 c. Scouts around campfire	35	15
618	21 c. Scouts map-reading	55	90
619	30 c. Lord Baden-Powell	65	1·50
616/19	Set of 4	1·75	2·40

(Des Rose Martin)

1982 (17 Nov). *Centenary of Dr. Robert Koch's Discovery of Tubercle Bacillus. T **121** and similar horiz design. P 14.*

620	11 c. salmon, black and greenish grey	85	25
621	30 c. multicoloured	1·40	3·25

Design:—30 c. Man looking through microscope.

122 "Wing Woman" (Henry Mudzengerere)

123 Traditional Ploughing Team (moving right)

1983 (14 Mar). *Commonwealth Day. Sculptures. T **122** and similar multicoloured designs. P 14.*

622	9 c. Type **122**	10	10
623	11 c. "Telling Secrets" (Joseph Ndandarika) (horiz)	10	10
624	30 c. "Hornbill Man" (John Takawira) (horiz)	30	40
625	$1 "The Chief" (Nicholas Mukomberanwa)	55	1·75
622/5	Set of 4	80	2·00

(Des Rose Martin)

1983 (13 May). *30th World Ploughing Contest, Zimbabwe. T **123** and similar horiz designs. Multicoloured. P 14.*

626	21 c. Type **123**	25	35
	a. Horiz pair. Nos. 626/7	50	70
627	21 c. Traditional ploughing team (moving left)	25	35
628	30 c. Tractor ploughing	40	65
	a. Horiz pair. Nos. 628/9	80	1·25
629	30 c. Modern plough	40	65
626/9	Set of 4	1·25	1·75

The two designs of each value were issued in horizontal *se-tenant* pairs, forming composite designs, throughout the sheets.

NEW INFORMATION

The editor is always interested to correspond with people who have new information that will improve or correct the Catalogue.

124 Postman on Cycle

125 Map of Africa showing Zimbabwe

(Des R. Phillips)

1983 (12 Oct). *World Communications Year. T **124** and similar multicoloured designs. P 14.*

630	9 c. Type **124**	20	10
631	11 c. Aircraft controller directing airliner	25	10
632	15 c. Switchboard operator	30	30
633	17 c. Printing works	35	30
634	21 c. Road transport (horiz)	50	60
635	30 c. Rail transport (horiz)	75	1·25
630/5	Set of 6	2·10	2·40

(Des Bunty Woods and Nancy Abrey)

1984 (11 Apr). *Zimbabwe International Trade Fair. T **125** and similar vert designs. Multicoloured. P 14½.*

636	9 c. Type **125**	10	10
637	11 c. Globe	15	10
638	30 c. Zimbabwe flag and Trade Fair logo	45	50
636/8	Set of 3	65	60

126 Cycling

(Des Vivienne Fick (11 c.), Joanna Hogg (21 c.), Blessing Chikoore (30 c.), Wayne Gubb (40 c.))

1984 (18 July). *Olympic Games, Los Angeles. Children's Pictures. T **126** and similar horiz designs. Multicoloured. P 14½.*

639	11 c. Type **126**	35	15
640	21 c. Swimming	45	50
641	30 c. Running	65	85
642	40 c. Hurdling	80	1·75
639/42	Set of 4	2·00	3·00

127 Liberation Heroes

128 African Fish Eagle

(Des N. Pearce (11 c.), J. Akester (others))

1984 (8 Aug). *Heroes' Days. T **127** and similar multicoloured designs showing various aspects of Heroes' Acre. P 14½.*

643	9 c. Type **127**	25	10
644	11 c. Symbolic tower and flame (vert)	25	10
645	17 c. Bronze sculpture (vert)	40	60
646	30 c. Section of bronze mural	55	95
643/6	Set of 4	1·25	1·50

(Des B. Finch)

1984 (10 Oct). *Birds of Prey. T **128** and similar vert designs. Multicoloured. P 14½.*

647	9 c. Type **128**	50	20
648	11 c. Long-crested Eagle	50	20
649	13 c. Bateleur	65	55
650	17 c. Verreaux's Eagle	80	55
651	21 c. Martial Eagle	90	1·40
652	30 c. Bonelli's Eagle	1·25	2·25
647/52	Set of 6	4·25	4·75

129 9th Class Locomotive No. 86

130 "Intelsat V" Telecommunications Satellite

(Des G. Cameron)

1985 (15 May). *"Zimbabwe Steam Safaris". Railway Locomotives. T **129** and similar horiz designs. Multicoloured. P 14½.*

653	9 c. Type **129**	85	20
654	11 c. 12th Class locomotive No. 190	85	20
655	17 c. 15th Class Beyer-Garratt locomotive No. 424 *Isilwane*	1·50	1·00
656	30 c. 20th Class Garratt locomotive No. 726 *Gwaai*	2·50	3·00
653/6	Set of 4	5·25	4·00

1985 (8 July). *Earth Satellite Station, Mazowe. T **130** and similar multicoloured design. P 14½ × 14 (26 c.) or 14½ (57 c.).*

657	26 c. Type **130**	1·50	60
658	57 c. Earth Satellite Station, Mazowe (65 × 25 mm)	3·00	6·00

131 Tobacco

132 Chief Mutapa Gatsi Rusere and 17th-century Seal

(Des Rose Rigden)

1985 (21 Aug)–88. *National Infrastructure. T **131** and similar horiz designs. Multicoloured. P 14½.*

659	1 c. Type **131**	10	10
	a. Perf 14	—	40
660	3 c. Maize	10	10
	a. Perf 14	—	40
661	4 c. Cotton	15	10
	a. Perf 14	—	40
662	5 c. Tea	30	10
	a. Perf 14	—	40
663	10 c. Cattle	30	10
	a. Perf 14	—	40
664	11 c. Birchenough Bridge	75	10
665	12 c. Ore stamp mill	1·25	10
666	13 c. Gold pouring	2·25	15
	a. Perf 14	—	75
667	15 c. Dragline coal mining	1·75	15
	a. Perf 14	—	75
668	17 c. Uncut amethyst	2·25	40
669	18 c. Electric locomotive	2·25	60
670	20 c. Kariba Dam	1·50	30
	a. Perf 14	—	75
671	23 c. Elephants at water hole	2·50	45
672	25 c. Sunset over Zambezi	65	30
	a. Perf 14	—	1·00
673	26 c. Baobab tree	65	20
674	30 c. Ruins of Great Zimbabwe	75	70
675	35 c. Traditional dancing	60	30
676	45 c. Village women crushing maize	75	40
677	57 c. Woodcarving	75	70
678	$1 Playing Mbira (musical instrument)	1·25	90
	a. Perf 14	—	—
679	$2 Mule-drawn Scotch cart	2·00	3·00
680	$5 Zimbabwe coat-of-arms	3·75	5·00
659/80	Set of 22	23·00	13·00

The stamps perforated 14 date from the introduction of a new perforating head in 1988.

(Des C. Herbert)

1985 (18 Sept). *50th Anniv of National Archives. T **132** and similar horiz designs. Multicoloured. P 14½.*

681	12 c. Type **132**	20	15
682	18 c. Chief Lobengula, seal and 1888 Treaty	25	40
683	26 c. Exhibition gallery	35	45
684	35 c. National Archives building	45	75
681/4	Set of 4	1·10	1·60

MACHINE LABELS. From 24 October 1985 gummed labels in the above design varying in value from 1 c. to $99.99, were available from four automatic machines located at the Philatelic Bureau and at post offices in Bulawayo, Gwelo and Harare. Two further machines were installed at Harare offices in 1985–86, but by this time the Bureau example had ceased to function. Paper showing an overall pattern of rhinoceroses appeared briefly in 1991, but it is reported that all machines were withdrawn by the end of March that year.

133 Computer Operator

(Des C. Herbert)

1985 (13 Nov). *United Nations Decade for Women. T **133** and similar horiz designs. Multicoloured. P 14½.*

685	10 c. Type **133**	40	10
686	17 c. Nurse giving injection	75	70
687	26 c. Woman student	1·25	2·50
685/7	Set of 3	2·25	3·00

134 Harare Conference Centre

(Des C. Herbert)

1986 (29 Jan). *Harare International Conference Centre. T 134 and similar horiz design. Multicoloured. P 14½.*
688 26 c. Type 134.. .. .. .. 60 30
689 35 c. Interior of conference hall .. .. 1·00 1·40

135 Grain Storage Silo   **136** *Bunaeopsis jacksoni*

(Des C. Herbert)

1986 (1 Apr). *6th Anniv of Southern African Development Co-ordination Conference. T 135 and similar horiz designs. Multicoloured. P 14½.*
690 12 c. Type 135.. .. .. .. 55 20
691 18 c. Rhinoceros and hawk at sunset .. 2·50 1·50
692 26 c. Map showing S.A.D.C.C. member states, and Boeing "737".. .. 2·50 2·00
693 35 c. Map and national flags of S.A.D.C.C. members.. .. .. .. 2·75 2·25
690/3 .. .. *Set of 4* 7·50 5·50

1986 (18 June). *Moths of Zimbabwe. T 136 and similar horiz designs. Multicoloured. P 14½×14.*
694 12 c. Type 136.. .. .. .. 1·10 20
695 18 c. *Deilephila nerii* .. .. .. 1·60 1·10
696 26 c. *Bunaeopsis zaddachi* .. .. 2·00 1·50
697 35 c. *Heniocha apollonia* .. .. 2·40 4·25
694/7 .. .. *Set of 4* 6·50 6·25

137 Victoria Falls   **138** Sopwith Motorcycle (1921)

(Des C. Herbert)

1986 (26 Aug). *8th Non-Aligned Summit Conference. T 137 and similar horiz design. Multicoloured. P 14½×14 (26 c.) or 14½ ($1).*
698 26 c. Type 137.. .. .. .. 1·75 30
699 $1 Ruins of Great Zimbabwe (62×24 mm) .. .. 4·25 5·50

(Des G. Cameron)

1986 (8 Oct). *Centenary of Motoring. T 138 and similar horiz designs. Multicoloured. P 14½.*
700 10 c. Type 138.. .. .. .. 65 10
701 12 c. Gladiator motor car (1902) 65 30
702 17 c. Douglas motorcycle (1920) .. 1·00 40
703 26 c. Ford "Model A" (1930) .. .. 1·40 70
704 35 c. Schacht motor car (1909) .. 1·75 2·25
705 40 c. Benz three-wheeled car (1886) .. 1·75 2·25
700/5 .. .. *Set of 6* 6·50 5·50

139 Growth Monitoring   **140** Barred Owlet

(Des Barbara Chalk)

1987 (11 Feb). *Child Survival Campaign. T 139 and similar vert designs. Multicoloured. P 14×14½.*
706 12 c. Type 139.. .. .. .. 1·50 1·75
 a. Block of 4. Nos. 706/9 .. .. 5·50
707 12 c. Breast-feeding .. .. .. 1·50 1·75
708 12 c. Oral rehydration therapy .. 1·50 1·75
709 12 c. Immunization .. .. .. 1·50 1·75
706/9 .. .. *Set of 4* 5·50 6·25
Nos. 706/9 were printed together, *se-tenant*, in blocks of four throughout the sheet.

(Des B. Finch)

1987 (15 Apr). *Owls (1st series). T 140 similar vert designs. Multicoloured. P 14½.*
710 12 c. Type 140.. .. .. .. 2·00 30
711 18 c. Pearl-spotted Owlet .. .. 2·50 1·25
712 26 c. White-faced Scops Owl .. .. 3·00 1·75
713 35 c. African Scops Owl .. .. 4·00 4·50
710/13 .. .. *Set of 4* 10·50 7·00
See also Nos. 850/3 and 988/91.

141 Brownie, Guide and Ranger saluting ("Commitment")   **142** Common Grey Duiker

(Des Barbara Connelly)

1987 (24 June). *75th Anniv of Girl Guides' Association of Zimbabwe. T 141 and similar horiz designs. Multicoloured. P 14½.*
714 15 c. Type 141.. .. .. .. 55 15
715 23 c. Guides preparing meal over campfire ("Adventure") 75 30
716 35 c. Guide teaching villagers to read ("Service") 85 45
717 $1 Handshake and globe ("International Friendship") .. .. 2·00 3·00
714/17 .. .. *Set of 4* 3·75 3·50

(Des Patricia Wilson)

1987 (7 Oct). *Duikers of Africa Survey. T 142 and similar horiz designs, each showing duiker and distribution map. Multicoloured. P 14½×14.*
718 15 c. Type 142.. .. .. .. 70 15
719 23 c. Zebra Duiker 80 25
720 25 c. Yellow-backed Duiker 80 90
721 30 c. Blue Duiker .. .. .. 95 1·10
722 35 c. Jentink's Duiker .. .. 95 1·25
723 38 c. Red Duiker .. .. .. 1·00 1·75
718/23 .. .. *Set of 6* 4·75 4·75

143 *Pseudocreobotra wahlberghi* (mantid)   **144** "Cockerel" (Arthur Azevedo)

(Des Janet Duff)

1988 (12 Jan). *Insects. T 143 and similar horiz designs. Multicoloured. P 14½.*
724 15 c. Type 143.. .. .. .. 70 15
725 23 c. *Dicranorrhina derbyana* (beetle) .. 85 30
726 35 c. *Dictyophorus spumans* (grasshopper) 1·10 85
727 45 c. *Chalcocoris rutilus* (bug) .. 1·40 2·00
724/7 .. .. *Set of 4* 3·50 3·00

1988 (14 Apr). *30th Anniv of National Gallery of Zimbabwe. T 144 and similar multicoloured designs showing painting (38 c.) or sculptures (others). P 14 × 14½ (vert) or 14½ × 14 (horiz).*
728 15 c. Type 144.. .. .. .. 20 10
729 23 c. "Man into Hippo" (Bernard Matemera) 30 20
730 30 c. "Spirit Python" (Henry Munyaradzi) .. 35 30
731 35 c. "Spirit Bird carrying People" (Thomas Mukarobgwa) (horiz) 35 30
732 38 c. "The Song of the Herd Boy" (George Nene) (horiz) 35 40
733 45 c. "War Victim" (Joseph Muzondo) (horiz) 40 50
728/33 .. .. *Set of 6* 1·75 1·60

145 *Aloe cameronii var. bondana*   **146** White-faced Whistling Duck

(Des Nancy Abrey)

1988 (14 July). *Aloes. T 145 and similar vert designs. Multicoloured. P 14½.*
734 15 c. Type 145.. .. .. .. 20 10
735 23 c. *Orbeopsis caudata* 35 20
736 25 c. *Euphorbia wildii* 35 35
737 30 c. *Euphorbia fortissima* 40 45
738 35 c. *Aloe aculeata* 40 55
739 38 c. *Huernia zebrina* 45 70
734/9 .. .. *Set of 6* 2·00 2·00

(Des B. Finch and C. Herbert)

1988 (6 Oct). *Wild Ducks and Geese of Zimbabwe. T 146 and similar horiz designs. Multicoloured. P 14½ × 14.*
740 15 c. Type 146.. .. .. .. 75 20
741 23 c. African Pygmy Goose 85 20
742 30 c. Hottentot Teal 95 85
743 35 c. Comb Duck ("Knob-billed Duck") .. 1·10 95
744 38 c. White-backed Duck .. .. 1·10 1·00
745 45 c. Maccoa Duck .. .. .. 1·60 2·00
740/5 .. .. *Set of 6* 5·75 4·75

147 O'Shaughnessy's Banded Gecko   **148** Spotted Leaved Arum-Lily

(Des C. Herbert)

1989 (10 Jan). *Geckos. T 147 and similar horiz designs. Multicoloured. P 14½.*
746 15 c. Type 147.. .. .. .. 70 15
747 23 c. Tiger Rock Gecko 85 40
748 35 c. Tasman's Gecko .. .. 1·25 1·25
749 45 c. Bibron's Gecko .. .. .. 1·50 2·00
746/9 .. .. *Set of 4* 3·75 3·50

1989 (12 Apr). *Wild Flowers. T 148 and similar vert designs. Multicoloured. P 14½.*
750 15 c. Type 148.. .. .. .. 35 10
751 23 c. Grassland Vlei-lily 45 25
752 30 c. Manica Protea 45 40
753 35 c. Flame Lily 50 40
754 38 c. Poppy Hibiscus 55 55
755 45 c. Blue Sesbania 65 65
750/5 .. .. *Set of 6* 2·75 2·00

149 Red-breasted Tilapia   **150** Black Rhinoceros

(Des C. Herbert)

1989 (12 July). *Fishes (1st series). T 149 and similar horiz designs. Multicoloured. P 14½.*
756 15 c. Type 149.. .. .. .. 60 15
757 23 c. Chessa 80 25
758 30 c. Eastern Bottlenose 90 70
759 35 c. Vundu 90 70
760 38 c. Large-mouthed Black Bass .. 1·00 1·00
761 45 c. Lesser Tigerfish .. .. 1·40 1·75
756/61 .. .. *Set of 6* 5·00 4·00
See also Nos. 864/9.

1989 (10 Oct). *Endangered Species. T 150 and similar horiz designs. Multicoloured. P 14½×14.*
762 15 c. Type 150.. .. .. .. 1·25 40
763 23 c. Cheetah .. .. 1·25 45
764 30 c. Wild Dog .. .. .. 1·40 90
765 35 c. Pangolin .. .. .. 1·40 1·25
766 38 c. Brown Hyena .. .. .. 1·50 2·00
767 45 c. Roan Antelope .. .. .. 1·60 2·25
762/7 .. .. *Set of 6* 7·50 6·50

151 Giant Tigerfish   **152** Headrest

153 Bicycles

(Des Janet Duff (1 to 9 c.), Rose Rigden (15 to 30 c.), Nancy Abrey (33 c. to $2))

1990 (2 Jan). *Multicoloured.*

(a) *Horiz designs as T 151 showing wildlife. P 14*
768 1 c. Type 151 .. .. 15 10
 a. Perf 14½ 75 10
769 2 c. Helmet Guineafowl 20 10
 a. Perf 14½ 75 10
770 3 c. Scrub Hare 20 10
 a. Perf 14½ 75 10
771 4 c. Temminck's Ground Pangolin .. 20 10
 a. Perf 14½ 60 10

772	5 c. Greater Kudu					30	10
	a. Perf 14½					75	10
	b. Imperf (pair)					£160	
773	9 c. Black Rhinoceros					75	30
	a. Perf 14½					75	30

(b) Horiz designs as T 152 showing cultural artifacts.
P 14½×14.

774	15 c. Type 152					20	20
775	20 c. Hand axe and adze					20	20
776	23 c. Gourd and water pot					20	20
777	25 c. Snuff container					20	20
778	26 c. Winnowing tray and basket					30	30
779	30 c. Grinding stone					30	30

(c) Horiz designs as T 153 showing transport. P 14½.

780	33 c. Type 153					40	30
781	35 c. Buses					70	40
782	38 c. Diesel train					70	40
783	45 c. Mail motorcycle and trailer					70	40
784	$1 Air Zimbabwe Boeing 737 airliner					1·50	90
785	$2 Lorry					1·50	1·60
768/85					Set of 18	7·50	5·50

154 Pres. Mugabe and Joshua Nkomo at Signing of Unity Accord, 1987

155 Runhare House, 1986

(Adapted Nancy Abrey)

1990 (17 Apr). *10th Anniv of Independence. T 154 and similar horiz designs. Multicoloured. P 14½×14.*

786	15 c. Type 154					40	10
787	23 c. Conference Centre, Harare					45	20
788	30 c. Children in class					50	40
789	35 c. Intelsat aerial, Mazowe Earth Satellite Station					60	70
790	38 c. National Sports Stadium					60	80
791	45 c. Maize field					90	1·40
786/91					Set of 6	3·00	3·25

1990 (11 July). *Centenary of the City of Harare. T 155 and similar horiz designs. Multicoloured. P 14½.*

792	15 c. Type 155					30	10
793	23 c. Market Hall, 1894					50	20
794	30 c. Charter House, 1959					55	35
795	35 c. Supreme Court, 1927					60	80
796	38 c. Standard Chartered Bank, 1911					60	90
797	45 c. The Town House, 1933					80	1·40
792/7					Set of 6	3·00	3·25

156 Speaker's Mace

157 Small-spotted Genet

1990 (17 Sept). *36th Commonwealth Parliamentary Conference, Harare. T 156 and similar vert design. Multicoloured. P 14½.*

798	35 c. Type 156					50	25
799	$1 Speaker's chair					1·25	2·00

(Des Barbara Chalk)

1991 (15 Jan). *Small Mammals. T 157 and similar horiz designs. Multicoloured. P 14½×14.*

800	15 c. Type 157					80	20
801	23 c. Red Squirrel					85	30
802	35 c. Night-ape					1·25	1·25
803	45 c. Bat-eared Fox					1·75	2·25
800/3					Set of 4	4·25	3·50

158 Hosho (rattles)

159 Snot-apple

(Des R. Pletts)

1991 (16 Apr). *Traditional Musical Instruments. T 158 and similar vert designs. Multicoloured. P 14½.*

804	15 c. Type 158					45	10
805	23 c. Mbira (thumb piano)					50	15
806	30 c. Ngororombe (pan pipes)					55	40

807	35 c. Chipendani (mouth bow)					65	70
808	38 c. Marimba (xylophone)					65	80
809	45 c. Ngoma (drum)					75	1·10
804/9					Set of 6	3·25	2·75

(Des Barbara Chalk)

1991 (17 July). *Wild Fruits. T 159 and similar vert designs. Multicoloured. P 14×14½.*

810	20 c. Type 159					50	10
811	39 c. Marula					55	30
812	51 c. Mobola Plum					60	80
813	60 c. Water Berry					70	85
814	65 c. Northern Dwaba Berry					75	85
815	77 c. Mahobohobo					85	1·10
810/15					Set of 6	3·50	3·50

160 Bridal Veil Falls

161 Lion

(Des R. Jeffrey)

1991 (16 Oct). *Commonwealth Heads of Government Meeting, Harare. T 160 and similar vert designs. Multicoloured. P 14½.*

816	20 c. Type 160					55	15
817	39 c. Meeting logo					55	35
818	51 c. Chinhoyi Caves					70	75
819	60 c. Kariba Dam					80	1·00
820	65 c. Victoria Falls					90	1·25
821	77 c. Balancing rocks					95	1·50
816/21					Set of 6	4·00	4·50

(Des R. Pletts)

1992 (8 Jan). *Wildlife Conservation. Big Cats. T 161 and similar horiz designs. Multicoloured. P 14½×14.*

822	20 c. Type 161					65	15
823	39 c. Leopard					95	40
824	60 c. Cheetah					1·40	1·75
825	77 c. Serval					1·75	2·00
822/5					Set of 4	4·25	3·75

162 Amanita zambiana

163 Common Bulbul

(Des R. Pletts)

1992 (8 Apr). *Edible Mushrooms. T 162 and similar vert designs. Multicoloured. P 14×14½.*

826	20 c. Type 162					50	20
827	39 c. Boletus edulis					70	40
828	51 c. Termitomyces sp					75	75
829	60 c. Cantharellus densifolius					90	1·00
830	65 c. Cantharellus longisporus					1·00	1·25
831	77 c. Cantharellus cibarius					1·25	1·50
826/31					Set of 6	4·50	4·50

(Des R. Pletts)

1992 (7 July). *Birds. T 163 and similar vert designs. Multicoloured. P 14½.*

832	25 c. Type 163					45	15
833	59 c. Fiscal Shrike					65	45
834	77 c. Forktailed Drongo					75	80
835	90 c. Cardinal Woodpecker					80	95
836	98 c. Yellow-billed Hornbill					80	95
837	$1.16, Crested Francolin					95	1·40
832/7					Set of 6	4·00	4·25

164 Charaxes jasius

165 Uranium

(Des R. Pletts)

1992 (15 Oct). *Butterflies. T 164 and similar horiz designs. Multicoloured. P 14½×14.*

838	25 c. Type 164					75	20
839	59 c. Eronia leda					1·25	75
840	77 c. Princeps ophidicephalus					1·50	1·25
841	90 c. Junonia oenone					1·75	1·75
842	98 c. Danaus chrysippus					1·90	1·90
843	$1.16, Junonia octavia					2·00	2·25
838/43					Set of 6	8·25	7·25

(Des R. Jeffrey)

1993 (12 Jan). *Minerals. T 165 and similar horiz designs. Multicoloured. P 14½×14.*

844	25 c. Type 165					90	20
845	59 c. Chrome					1·40	55
846	77 c. Copper					1·75	1·00
847	90 c. Coal					2·00	1·50
848	98 c. Gold					2·25	1·75
849	$1.16, Emerald					2·40	2·25
844/9					Set of 6	9·75	6·50

(Des B. Finch)

1993 (6 Apr). *Owls (2nd series). Vert designs as T 140. Multicoloured. P 14½.*

850	25 c. African Wood Owl					1·25	40
851	59 c. Pel's Fishing Owl					2·00	85
852	90 c. Spotted Eagle Owl					2·75	2·75
853	$1.16, Verreaux's Eagle Owl ("Giant Eagle Owl")					3·00	3·75
850/3					Set of 4	8·00	7·00

166 Hadyana (relish pot)

167 Polystachya dendrobiflora

(Des Dianne Deudney)

1993 (13 July). *Household Pottery. T 166 and similar horiz designs. Multicoloured. P 14½×14.*

854	25 c. Type 166					40	10
855	59 c. Chirongo (water jar)					55	30
856	77 c. Mbiya (relish bowl)					65	60
857	90 c. Pfuko (water jar)					75	85
858	98 c. Tsaya (cooking pot)					75	85
859	$1.16, Gate (beer pot)					85	1·00
854/9					Set of 6	3·50	3·50

(Des Paula Ware)

1993 (12 Oct). *Orchids. T 167 and similar vert designs. Multicoloured. P 14×14½.*

860	35 c. Type 167					75	20
861	$1 Diaphananthe subsimplex					1·50	75
862	$1.50, Ansellia gigantea					2·00	1·90
863	$1.95, Vanilla polyepis					2·25	2·50
860/3					Set of 4	6·00	4·75

(Des C. Herbert)

1994 (20 Jan). *Fishes (2nd series). Horiz designs as T 149. Multicoloured. P 14½.*

864	35 c. Manyame Labeo ("Hunyani Salmon")					35	10
865	$1 Sharp-toothed Catfish ("Barbel")					65	30
866	$1.30, Rainbow Trout					75	65
867	$1.50, African Mottled Eel					80	70
868	$1.65, Common Carp					85	85
869	$1.95, Nembwe ("Robustus Bream")					95	1·00
864/9					Set of 6	4·00	3·25

168 City Hall, 1940

169 Strelitzia

(Des Janet Duff)

1994 (5 Apr). *Centenary of Bulawayo. T 168 and similar horiz designs. Multicoloured. P 14½.*

870	35 c. Type 168					15	10
871	80 c. Cresta Churchill Hotel, 1974					30	20
872	$1.15, High Court, 1938					40	40
873	$1.75, Douslin House, 1902					50	70
874	$1.95, Goldfields Building, 1895					60	90
875	$2.30, Parkade Centre, 1975					85	1·25
870/5					Set of 6	2·50	3·00

(Des Dianne Deudney)

1994 (12 July). *Export Flowers. T 169 and similar vert designs. Multicoloured. P 14½.*

876	35 c. Type 169					35	10
877	80 c. Protea					65	25
878	$1.15, Phlox					80	60
879	$1.75, Chrysanthemum					90	1·00
880	$1.95, Ullum					1·10	1·50
881	$2.30, Rose					1·40	2·00
876/81					Set of 6	4·75	4·75

170 The Annunciation

171 Harvesting Maize

(Des Paula Ware)

1994 (11 Oct). *Christmas. T* **170** *and similar vert designs. Multicoloured. P* 14½.

882	35 c. Type **170**	.. ..	25	10
883	80 c. Journey to Bethlehem	..	45	15
884	$1.15, The Nativity	..	60	40
885	$1.75, Shepherds	.. ..	80	1·00
886	$1.95, Wise Men	.. ..	90	1·25
887	$2.30, Mary and Jesus	..	1·10	1·60
882/7	.. ..	*Set of* 6	3·50	4·00

(Des R. Pletts (1 c. to 4 c.), C. Herbert (5 c. on 50 c.), D. Hobert (70 c. to $10))

1995 (17 Jan)–**96**. *Zimbabwe Culture. T* **171** *and similar horiz designs. Multicoloured. P* 14.

888	1 c. Type **171**	..	10	10
889	2 c. Loading sugar cane	..	10	10
890	3 c. Sunflowers	..	10	10
891	4 c. Sorghum	.. ..	10	10
892	5 c. Miners	.. ..	20	10
893	10 c. Drilling for gold	..	30	10
894	20 c. Opencast coal mining, Wankie		40	10
895	30 c. Chrome smelting, Kwekwe	..	50	20
896	40 c. Opencast iron extraction, Redcliff		50	20
896a	45 c. Underground mining team (3.6.96)		50	20
897	50 c. Gold smelting	..	50	20
898	70 c. Bogie Clock Tower, Gweru	..	20	20
899	80 c. Masvingo Watchtower	..	20	20
900	$1 Hanging Tree, Harare	..	20	20
901	$2 Cecil House, Harare	..	20	20
902	$5 The Toposcope, Harare	..	35	45
903	$10 Paper House, Kwekwe	..	60	75
888/903	.. ..	*Set of* 17	4·25	2·75

172 Spider-hunting Wasp

173 Football

(Des Janet Duff)

1995 (4 Apr). *Insects. T* **172** *and similar horiz designs. Multicoloured. P* 14½.

904	35 c. Type **172**	..	35	10
905	$1.15, Emperor Dragonfly	..	85	45
906	$1.75, Foxy Charaxes (butterfly)	..	1·10	1·25
907	$2.30, Antlion	.. ..	1·50	2·00
904/7	.. ..	*Set of* 4	3·50	3·50

(Des Paula Ware)

1995 (11 July). *6th All-Africa Games, Harare. T* **173** *and similar vert designs, each showing sport within map of Africa. Multicoloured. P* 14×14½.

908	35 c. Type **173**	..	25	10
909	80 c. Running	..	35	20
910	$1.15, Boxing	..	40	30
911	$1.75, Swimming	..	60	70
912	$1.95, Hockey	..	1·50	1·40
913	$2.30, Volleyball	..	1·10	1·60
908/13	.. ..	*Set of* 6	3·75	3·75

174 Weighing Baby (Health)

175 Fernandoa Tree

(Des Jane Debney)

1995 (17 Oct). *50th Anniv of United Nations. T* **174** *and similar horiz designs. Multicoloured. P* 14½×14½.

914	35 c. Type **174**	..	15	10
915	$1.15, Women at pump (Environment)		30	35
916	$1.75, Workers on lorry (Food Distribution)		50	60
917	$2.30, Teacher and children (Education)		60	90
914/17	.. ..	*Set of* 4	1·40	1·75

(Des Janet Duff)

1996 (24 Jan). *Indigenous Flowering Trees. T* **175** *and similar vert designs. Multicoloured. P* 14½.

918	45 c. Type **175**	..	15	10
919	$1 Round Leaf Mukwa	..	30	20
920	$1.50, Luckybean Tree	..	45	45
921	$2.20, Winter Cassia	..	60	65
922	$2.50, Sausage Tree	..	65	80
923	$3 Sweet Thorn ..	..	75	1·00
918/23	..	*Set of* 6	2·50	2·75

176 Mazvikadei Dam

(Des R. Pletts)

1996 (9 Apr). *Dams of Zimbabwe. T* **176** *and similar horiz designs. Multicoloured. P* 14½.

924	45 c. Type **176**	..	15	10
925	$1.50, Mutirikwi Dam	..	45	35
926	$2.20, Ncema Dam	..	65	80
927	$3 Odzani Dam ..	..	75	1·25
924/7	..	*Set of* 4	1·75	2·25

177 Matusadonha National Park at Sunset

178 Carved Frog

(Des Paula Ware)

1996 (18 July). *Scenic Views. T* **177** *and similar horiz designs. Multicoloured. P* 14½.

928	45 c. Type **177**	..	15	10
929	$1.50, Juliasdale rocky outcrop	..	45	35
930	$2.20, Honde Valley	..	75	90
931	$3 Finger Rocks at Morgenster Mission		85	1·50
928/31	..	*Set of* 4	2·00	2·50

(Des M. Nyoni)

1996 (15 Oct). *Animal Wood Carvings. T* **178** *and similar horiz designs. Multicoloured. P* 14½×14.

932	45 c. Type **178**	..	15	10
933	$1.50, Tortoise	..	30	20
934	$1.70, Kudu	..	35	35
935	$2.20, Chimpanzee	..	50	60
936	$2.50, Porcupine	..	55	70
937	$3 Rhinoceros	..	60	85
932/7	..	*Set of* 6	2·25	2·50

179 Mashona Cow

(Des R. Pletts)

1997 (7 Jan). *Cattle Breeds. T* **179** *and similar horiz designs. Multicoloured. P* 14½.

938	45 c. Type **179**	..	20	10
939	$1.50, Tuli cow	..	40	20
940	$2.20, Nkoni bull	..	55	60
941	$3 Brahman bull	..	80	1·00
938/41	..	*Set of* 4	1·75	1·75

180 Cycad

(Des Paula Ware)

1997 (15 Apr). *10th Meeting of Convention on International Trade in Endangered Species Members, Harare. T* **180** *and similar horiz designs. Multicoloured. P* 14½.

942	45 c. Type **180**	..	10	10
943	$1.50, Peregrine Falcon	..	50	40
944	$1.70, Temminck's Ground Pangolin		30	30
945	$2.20, Black Rhinoceros	..	60	70
946	$2.50, African Elephant	..	60	70
947	$3 Python	..	60	80
942/7	..	*Set of* 6	2·40	2·75

181 Wood Carving

(Des Dianne Deudney)

1997 (22 July). *Rural Life. T* **181** *and similar horiz designs. Multicoloured. P* 14½.

948	65 c. Type **181**	..	15	10
949	$1 Winnowing	..	15	10
950	$2.40, Dancing	..	25	30
951	$2.50, Ploughing	..	25	30
952	$3.10, Stamping cereals	..	30	40
953	$4.20, Fetching water	..	45	60
948/53	..	*Set of* 6	1·40	1·60

182 Passenger Coach No. 1826

(Des Janet Duff)

1997 (28 Oct). *Centenary of Zimbabwe Railways. T* **182** *and similar horiz designs. Multicoloured. P* 14½.

954	65 c. Type **182**	..	20	15
955	$1 Class 12 steam locomotive No. 257	..	20	15
956	$2.40, Class 16A steam locomotive No. 605		25	25
957	$2.50, Class EL 1 electric locomotive No. 4107		25	25
958	$3.10, Steam locomotive No. 7 *Jack Tar*		30	35
959	$4.20, Class DE 2 diesel-electric locomotive No. 1211	..	40	60
954/9	..	*Set of* 6	1·40	1·60

183 Aardwolf

184 Honeybee on Flower

(Des C. Herbert)

1998 (20 Jan). *Lesser Known Animals of Zimbabwe. T* **183** *and similar horiz designs. Multicoloured. P* 14½.

960	65 c. Type **183**	..	20	10
961	$2.40, Large Grey Mongoose	..	25	25
962	$3.10, Clawless Otter	..	25	30
963	$4.20, Antbear	..	35	45
960/3	..	*Set of* 4	95	1·00

(Des Jan Desmond and Gaye Dixon)

1998 (14 Apr). *Bees and Bee-keeping. T* **184** *and similar vert designs. Multicoloured. P* 14×14½.

964	$1.20, Type **184**	..	15	10
965	$4.10, Queen, worker and drone	..	20	20
966	$4.70, Queen and retinue	..	20	20
967	$5.60, Rural bee-keeper	..	25	25
968	$7.40, Commercial bee-keepers	..	35	50
969	$9.90, Products of the hive	..	45	70
964/9	..	*Set of* 6	1·40	1·75

185 Fossil Fish

186 Yellow-bellied Sunbird

(Des Janet Duff)

1998 (21 July). *Fossils. T* **185** *and similar horiz designs. Multicoloured. P* 14½×14.

970	$1.20, Type **185**	..	25	10
971	$5.60, Allosaurus footprints	..	50	45
972	$7.40, Left foot of Massospondylus	..	60	60
973	$9.90, Fossil wood	..	70	90
970/3	..	*Set of* 4	1·90	1·90

(Des Paula Ware)

1998 (20 Oct). *Birds. T* **186** *and similar vert designs. Multicoloured. P* 14×14½.

974	$1.20, Type **186**		20	15
975	$4.10, Lesser Blue-eared Starling		30	25
976	$4.70, Grey-headed Kingfisher ("Grey-hooded Kingfisher")		30	30
977	$5.60, Miombo Grey Tit		40	40
978	$7.40, Chirinda Apalis		50	60
979	$9.90, Swynnerton's Robin		60	70
974/9		*Set of* 6	2·10	2·25

187 Philatelic Counter   188 Serval

(Des Paula Ware)

1999 (19 Jan). *125th Anniv of Universal Postal Union. T* **187** *similar horiz designs. Multicoloured. P* 14½×14.

980	$1.20, Type **187**		10	10
981	$5.60, Postman delivering letters		15	20
982	$7.40, 19th-century runner, motorcycle and truck		25	30
983	$9.90, Harare Central Sorting Office		30	35
980/3		*Set of* 4	80	95

(Des D. Herbert)

1999 (16 Mar). *Cats. T* **188** *and similar vert designs. Multicoloured. P* 14×14½.

984	$1.20, Type **188**		15	10
985	$5.60, Cheetah		30	25
986	$7.40, Caracal		40	40
987	$9.90, Leopard		70	70
984/7		*Set of* 4	1·40	1·25

(Des B. Finch and C. Herbert)

1999 (8 June). *Owls (3rd series). Vert designs as T* **140**. *Multicoloured. P* 14½.

988	$1.20, Cape Eagle Owl		25	15
989	$5.60, Grass Owl		50	35
990	$7.40, Barn Owl		65	65
991	$9.90, Marsh Owl		75	80
988/91		*Set of* 4	1·90	1·75

189 Canoe Safari   190 Family Reunion

(Des Janet Duff)

1999 (10 Aug). *Tourism in Zimbabwe. T* **189** *and similar horiz designs. Multicoloured. P* 14½×14.

992	$2 Type **189**		15	10
993	$6.70, Rock climbing		40	40
994	$7.70, Flying microlight		45	45
995	$9.10, White water rafting		60	50
996	$12 Mountain scenery		70	75
997	$16 Game watching		1·00	1·10
992/7		*Set of* 6	3·00	3·00

No. 997 is inscribed "Game Veiwing" in error.

(Des Margaret Tredgold)

1999 (12 Oct). *Christmas. T* **190** *and similar vert designs. Multicoloured. P* 14×14½.

998	$2 Type **190**		10	10
999	$6.70, Elephants around Christmas tree		20	25
1000	$7.70, Children and dog with balloons		20	25
1001	$9.10, Flame Lily		25	30
1002	$12 Madonna and Child		40	45
1003	$16 The Nativity		50	55
998/1003		*Set of* 6	1·60	1·90

191 Nyala

(Des C. Herbert, Paula Ware and R. Pletts)

2000 (25 Jan). *Fauna, Industry and Development. T* **191** *and similar horiz designs. Multicoloured. P* 14½.

1004	1 c. Type **191**		10	10
1005	10 c. Building development		10	10
1006	30 c. Timber yard		10	10
1007	50 c. Tobacco auction		10	10
1008	70 c. Central Sorting Office, Harare		10	10
1009	80 c. Harare New International Airport		10	10
1010	$1 Westgate Shopping Complex		10	10
1011	$2 Nile Crocodile		10	10
1012	$3 Pungwe River Water Project		10	15
1013	$4 Zebra		10	15
1014	$5 Mining		15	20
1015	$7 National University of Science and Technology		20	25
1016	$10 Ostrich		30	35
1017	$15 Cape Parrot		45	50
1018	$20 Leather products		60	65
1019	$30 Lilac-breasted Roller		90	1·00
1020	$50 Victoria Falls		1·50	1·60
1021	$100 Mukorsi Dam, Tokwe River		3·00	3·25
1004/21		*Set of* 18	7·50	8·50

STAMP BOOKLETS

1928 (1 Jan). *Black on blue cover. Stitched.*
SB1   2s. 6d. booklet containing twelve ½d. and twenty-four 1d. (Nos. 1/2) in blocks of 6 .. £2750

1931. *Black on blue cover. Stitched.*
SB2   2s. 6d. booklet containing twelve ½d. and twenty-four 1d. (Nos. 15/16) in blocks of 6 .. £3250

1933 (3 Mar). *Black on red cover, size 69×53 mm. Stitched.*
SB3   3s. booklet containing twelve ½d., 1d. and 1½d. (Nos. 15, 16, 16c) in blocks of 6 .. £2000

1938 (31 Mar). *Black on yellow cover. Stitched.*
SB4   2s. 6d. booklet containing twenty-four ½d. and eighteen 1d. (Nos. 40/1) in blocks of 6 .. £225

1954 (Jan). *Black on yellow cover, size 71×54 mm. Stitched.*
SB5   2s. 6d. booklet containing twelve ½d. and twenty-four 1d. (Nos. 78/9) in blocks of 6 .. 70·00

1964 (19 Feb). *Black on orange cover, size 57×45 mm. Stitched.*
SB6   1s. booklet containing 3d. (No. 95) in block of 4 .. 4·25

1967 (Feb). *Black on orange cover, size 57×45 mm. Stitched.*
SB7   1s. booklet containing 3d. (No. 376) in block of 4   5·50
Although not issued in Rhodesia until February 1967, No. SB7 was released in London in June 1966.

1968 (21 Dec). *Black on yellow cover, size 51×94 mm. Stapled.*
SB8   5s. booklet containing twelve 1d. and 3d., and six 2d. (Nos. 397/9) in blocks of 6 .. 22·00

1970 (17 Feb). *Red on yellow cover. Stapled.*
SB9   46 c. booklet containing twelve 1 c., eight 2½ c. and four 3½ c. in panes of 4 (Nos. 439a, 441a, 442a) .. .. 5·00

1972 (10 Apr). *Green on yellow cover. Stapled.*
SB10   48 c. booklet containing eight 1 c. and sixteen 2½ c. in panes of 4 (Nos. 439a, 441a) .. 13·00

1973 (7 May). *Blue on yellow cover. Stapled.*
SB11   50 c. booklet containing four 2½ c. and 4 c., and eight 3 c. in panes of 4 (Nos. 441a, 441ca, 442ba) .. .. 18·00

1974 (14 Aug). *White on blue cover. Stapled.*
SB12   50 c. booklet containing four 2½ c. and 4 c., and eight 3 c. in panes of 4 (Nos. 490a, 491a, 492a) .. .. 6·00

POSTAGE DUE STAMPS

SOUTHERN RHODESIA
(D 1)

POSTAGE DUE
1D
ONE PENNY
RHODESIA
D 2

1951 (1 Oct). *Postage Due stamps of Great Britain optd with Type D 1.*
D1	D 1	½d. emerald (No. D27)	..	3·25	14·00
D2		1d. violet-blue (No. D36)	..	3·00	2·75
D3		2d. agate (No. D29)	..	4·00	1·75
D4		3d. violet (No. D30)	..	2·75	2·25
D5		4d. blue (No. D38)	..	1·75	3·50
D6		4d. dull grey-green (No. D31)	..	£180	£550
D7		1s. deep blue (No. D33)	..	3·00	2·75
D1/5, 7			*Set of 6*	16·00	24·00

No. D6 is reported to have been issued to Fort Victoria and Gwelo main post offices only.

(Typo Printing and Stationery Dept, Salisbury)
1965 (17 June). *Roul 9.*
D 8	D 2	1d. orange-red (*roul 5*)	..	70	12·00
		a. Roul 9	..	3·75	12·00
D 9		2d. deep blue	..	50	8·00
D10		4d. green	..	60	8·00
D11		6d. plum	..	60	6·00
D8a/11			*Set of 4*	2·25	30·00

The 2d. has a stop below the "D".

D 3 Zimbabwe Bird (soapstone sculpture)   D 4 Zimbabwe Bird (soapstone sculpture)

(Litho Mardon Printers, Salisbury)
1966 (15 Dec). *P 14½.*
D12	D 3	1d. red	..	1·00	3·25
D13		2d. bluish violet	..	1·25	2·50
D14		4d. pale green	..	1·25	4·25
D15		6d. reddish violet	..	1·25	2·25
D16		1s. red-brown	..	1·25	2·25
D17		2s. black	..	1·50	5·00
D12/17			*Set of 6*	6·50	18·00

1970 (17 Feb)–**73.** *Decimal Currency. As Type D 3, but larger (26 × 22½ mm). P 14½.*
D18	D 3	1 c. bright green	..	1·00	2·00
D19		2 c. ultramarine	..	1·00	80
		a. Printed on the gummed side		65·00	
D20		5 c. bright reddish violet	..	2·50	3·25
D21		6 c. pale lemon (7.5.73)	..	4·25	4·50
D22		10 c. cerise	..	2·50	4·50
D18/22			*Set of 5*	10·00	13·50

1980. *P 14½.*
D23	D 4	1 c. bright green	..	25	1·00
D24		2 c. ultramarine	..	30	1·00
D25		5 c. bright reddish violet	..	40	1·00
		a. Imperf (pair)		90·00	
D26		6 c. pale lemon	..	50	1·75
D27		10 c. cerise	..	65	2·25
D23/7			*Set of 5*	1·90	6·25

D 5   (D 6)

1985 (21 Aug). *P 14½.*
D28	D 5	1 c. yellow-orange	..	20	50
D29		2 c. magenta	..	20	50
D30		6 c. blue-green	..	45	65
D31		10 c. orange-brown	..	55	65
D32		13 c. new blue	..	55	65
D28/32			*Set of 5*	1·75	2·75

1990 (2 Jan). *No. D27 surch with Type D 6.*
D33	D 4	25 c. on 10 c. cerise	..	6·00	6·00

No. D33 is reported to have been issued to the main post offices at Bulawayo, Gweru, Harare and Mutare.

D 7

1995 (17 Jan). *P 14½.*
D34	D 7	1 c. lemon	..	10	10
D35		2 c. yellow-orange	..	10	10
D36		5 c. mauve	..	10	10
D37		10 c. pale blue	..	10	10
D38		25 c. bright reddish violet	..	10	10
D39		40 c. bright blue-green	..	10	10
D40		60 c. red-orange	..	10	10
D41		$1 brown	..	10	10
D34/41			*Set of 8*	45	45

Zululand
see South Africa

Note: The first Supplement recording new stamps not in this catalogue appeared in the September 2000 number of *Gibbons Stamp Monthly.*

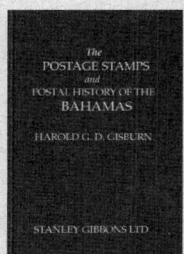

Set Prices for British Commonwealth Omnibus Issues

The composition of these sets is in accordance with the tables on the following pages. Only such items considered basic stamps are included; varieties such as shades, perforation changes and watermark changes are excluded. Great Britain issues which come on both ordinary paper and on paper with phosphor bands are however covered.

Stamps issued in connection with any of the events by countries which are no longer in the British Commonwealth and which are not listed in the Part 1 Catalogue are omitted.

	Price Un	Used
1935. Silver Jubilee. *Complete set of 250 stamps*	£950	£1200

The concept initiated by the 1935 Silver Jubilee omnibus issue has provided a pattern for a series of Royal commemoratives over the past 50 years which have introduced countless collectors to the hobby.

The Crown Colony Windsor Castle design by Harold Fleury is, surely, one of the most impressive produced in the 20th-century and its reproduction in the recess process by three of the leading stamp-printing firms of the era has provided a subject for philatelic research which has yet to be exhausted.

Each of the three, Bradbury, Wilkinson & Co. and Waterlow and Sons, who both produced fifteen issues, together with De La Rue & Co. who printed fourteen, used a series of vignette (centre) plates coupled with individual frame plates for each value. All were taken from dies made by Waterlow. Several worthwhile varieties exist on the frame plates, but most interest has been concentrated on the centre plates, each of which was used to print a considerable number of different stamps.

Sheets printed by Bradbury, Wilkinson were without printed plate numbers, but research has now identified eleven centre plates which were probably used in permanent pairings. A twelfth plate awaits confirmation. Stamps from some of these centre plates have revealed a number of prominent plate flaws, the most famous of which, the extra flagstaff, has been eagerly sought by collectors for many years.

Extra flagstaff (Plate "1" R.9/1)

Short extra flagstaff (Plate "2" R.2/1)

Lightning conductor (Plate "3" R.2/5)

Flagstaff on right-hand turret (Plate "5" R.7/1)

Double flagstaff (Plate "6" R.5/2)

De La Rue sheets were initially printed with plate numbers, but in many instances these were subsequently trimmed off. Surviving examples do, however, enable a positive identification of six centre plates, 2A, 2B, (2A), (2B), 4 and 4/ to be made. The evidence of sheet markings and plate flaws clearly demonstrates that there were two different pairs of plates numbered 2A 2B. The second pair is designated (2A) (2B) by specialist collectors to avoid further confusion. The number of major plate flaws is not so great as on the Bradbury, Wilkinson sheets, but four examples are included in the catalogue.

Diagonal line by turret (Plate 2A R.10/1 and 10/2)

Dot to left of chapel (Plate 2B R.8/3)

Dot by flagstaff (Plate 4 R.8/4)

Dash by turret (Plate 4/ R.3/6)

Much less is known concerning the Waterlow centre plate system as the sheets did not show plate numbers. Ten individual plates have, so far, been identified and it is believed that these were used in pairs. The two versions of the kite and log flaw from plate "2" show that this plate exists in two states.

Damaged turret (Plate "1" R.5/6)

Kite and vertical log (Plate "2A" R.10/6)

Kite and horizontal log (Plate "2B" R.10/6)

Bird by turret (Plate "7" R.1/5)

1937. Coronation. *Complete set of 202 stamps* £120 £120

1945–46. Victory. *Complete set of 164 stamps* 30·00 30·00

1948–49. Royal Silver Wedding. *Complete set of 138 stamps* £1600 £1600

1949. U.P.U. 75th Anniversary *Complete set of 310 stamps* £325 £325

1951. B.W.I. University College *Complete set of 28 stamps* 9·50 13·00

1953. Coronation. *Complete set of 106 stamps* £100 80·00

1953–54. Royal Visit. *Complete set of 13 stamps* 3·25 3·50

1958. Caribbean Federation. *Complete set of 30 stamps* 16·00 18·00

1963. Freedom from Hunger.
Complete set of 77 stamps £190 90·00

1963. Red Cross Centenary.
Complete set of 108 stamps and 2 miniature sheets £275 £190

1964. Shakespeare. 400th Birth Anniversary.
Complete set of 25 stamps 21·00 19·00

1965. I.T.U. Centenary.
Complete set of 112 stamps and 1 miniature sheet £160 95·00

1965. I.C.Y.
Complete set of 107 stamps and 2 miniature sheets £130 80·00

1965–67. Churchill. *Complete set of 182 stamps* £250 £140

1966. Royal Visit to the Caribbean.
Complete set of 34 stamps 30·00 14·00

1966. World Cup Football Championship.
Complete set of 68 stamps and 1 miniature sheet £100 70·00

1966. W.H.O. New Headquarters.
Complete set of 58 stamps and 1 miniature sheet 90·00 50·00

1966–67. U.N.E.S.C.O. 20th Anniversary.
Complete set of 110 stamps and 1 miniature sheet £170 £110

1972. Royal Silver Wedding.
Complete set of 78 stamps 27·00 25·00

1973. Royal Wedding.
Complete set of 72 stamps and 6 miniature sheets 24·00 19·00

1977. Silver Jubilee. *Set of 220 stamps* 50·00 55·00
Set of 24 miniature sheets 18·00 26·00

1977. Royal Visit. *Set of 46 stamps* 9·00 12·00
Set of 8 miniature sheets 7·00 12·00

1978. Coronation. 25th Anniversary.
Set of 195 stamps 42·00 50·00
Set of 21 sheetlets 22·00
Set of 27 miniature sheets 32·00 22·00

1980. Queen Mother's Birthday.
Set of 41 stamps 21·00 25·00
Set of 12 miniature sheets 26·00 24·00

1981. Royal Wedding. *Set of 244 stamps* 90·00 £100
Set of 35 miniature sheets 40·00 45·00

1982. Princess Diana's 21st Birthday.
Set of 162 stamps £100 90·00
Set of 19 miniature sheets 48·00 42·00

1982. Birth of Prince William.
Set of 124 stamps   £100   90·00
Set of 22 miniature sheets   55·00   55·00

The Life and Times of
Her Majesty Queen Elizabeth The Queen Mother

(Illustration reduced)

1985. Life and Times of Queen Elizabeth the Queen Mother.
Set of 226 stamps   £110   £140
Set of 47 miniature sheets   90·00   £110

1986. 60th Birthday of Queen Elizabeth II.
Set of 233 stamps   £130   £170
Set of 28 miniature sheets   90·00   £120

1986. Royal Wedding.
Set of 142 stamps   £100   £120
Set of 24 miniature sheets   75·00   £100

1987. Royal Ruby Wedding.
Set of 117 stamps   £110   £130
Set of 14 miniature sheets   40·00   50·00

1990. 90th Birthday of Queen Elizabeth the Queen Mother.
Set of 127 stamps   £180   £190
Set of 22 miniature sheets   £120   £130

1991. 65th Birthday of Queen Elizabeth II and 70th Birthday of Prince Philip.
Set of 99 stamps   £120   £140
Set of 14 miniature sheets   45·00   50·00

1992. 40th Anniversary of Queen Elizabeth II's Accession.
Set of 195 stamps   £190   £190
Set of 30 miniature sheets   £110   £140

Coronation Anniversary
1953-1993

Coronation Anniversary
1953-1993

Coronation Anniversary
1953-1993

Coronation Anniversary
1953-1993

1993. 40th Anniv of Coronation.
Set of 135 stamps   £140   £160
Set of 18 miniature sheets   65·00   75·00

1994. Royal Visit. *Set of 27 stamps* 30·00 32·00
Set of 2 miniature sheets 8·50 8·50

1995. 95th Birthday of Queen Elizabeth the Queen Mother.
Set of 64 stamps 65·00 70·00
Set of 18 miniature sheets 65·00 70·00

1996. Queen Elizabeth II's 70th Birthday.
Set of 89 stamps 95·00 £100
Set of 21 miniature sheets 55·00 60·00

1997. Royal Golden Wedding.
Set of 222 stamps £140 £150
Set of 39 miniature sheets £110 £120

1997–98. Diana, Princess of Wales Commemoration.
Set of 166 stamps 95·00 £100
Set of 48 miniature sheets £150 £160

1999. Royal Wedding.
Set of 65 stamps 75·00 75·00
Set of 10 miniature sheets 26·00 28·00

1999–2000. Queen Elizabeth the Queen Mother's Century.
Set of 108 stamps 75·00 80·00
Set of 23 miniature sheets 55·00 60·00

1935 SILVER JUBILEE TO 1973 ROYAL WEDDING

Issuing Countries	1935 Silver Jubilee	1937 Corona-tion	1945–46 Victory	1948 Silver Wedding	1949 U.P.U.	1951 B.W.I. Univ	1953 Corona-tion	1953–54 Royal Visit	1958 Carib-bean Fed.	1963 F.F.H.	1963 Red Cross	1964 Shake-speare	1965 I.T.U.	1965 I.C.Y.	1965–66 Churchill	1966 Royal Visit	1966 Foot-ball Cup	1966 W.H.O.	1966–67 UNESCO	1972 Silver Wedding	1973 Royal Wedding
Great Britain	4	1	2	—	4	—	4	—	—	2+2	3+3	5+4	2+2	2+2	2+2	—	3+3	—	—	✗	2
Guernsey	—	—	—	—	—	—	—	—	—	—	—	—	—	—	—	—	—	—	—	✗	1
Isle of Man	—	—	—	—	—	—	—	—	—	—	—	—	—	—	—	—	—	—	—	✗	1
Jersey	—	—	—	—	—	—	—	—	—	—	—	—	—	—	—	—	—	—	—	✗	2
Anguilla	—	—	—	—	—	—	—	—	—	—	—	—	—	—	—	—	—	—	—	✗	2+MS
Antigua	4	3	2	2	4	2	1	—	3	1	2	1	2	2	4	2	2	2	3	✗	2+MS
Barbuda	—	—	—	—	—	—	—	—	—	—	—	—	—	—	—	—	—	—	—	✗	2
Ascension	4	3	2	—	4	—	1	—	—	1	2	—	2	2	4	—	2	2	3	✗	2
Australia	3	—	3	—	1	—	3	3	—	—	1	—	1	1	1	—	—	—	—	—	—
Bahamas	4	3	2	2	4	—	1	—	—	1	2	1	2	2	4	2	2	2	3	✗	—
Bahrain	—	—	—	2	4	—	4	—	—	—	—	—	—	—	—	—	—	—	—	—	—
Barbados	4	3	2	2	4	2	1	—	3	—	2	—	2	—	4	2	—	—	3	—	—
Belize/British Honduras	4	3	2	2	4	2	1	—	—	1	2	—	2	2	4	—	2	2	3	—	2
Bermuda	4	3	2	2	4	—	1	1	—	1	2	—	2	2	4	—	—	2	3	✗	2
Botswana/Bechuanaland	4	3	3×2	2	4	—	1	—	—	1	2	1	2	2	4	—	—	—	—	—	—
British Antarctic Territory	—	—	—	—	—	—	—	—	—	—	—	—	—	—	4	—	—	—	—	✗	2
British Indian Ocean Terr.	—	—	—	—	—	—	—	—	—	—	—	—	—	—	—	—	—	—	—	✗	—
British P.A.'s in Eastern Arabia	—	—	—	2	4	—	4	—	—	—	—	—	—	—	—	—	—	—	—	—	—
British Virgin Islands	4	3	2	2	4	2	1	—	—	1	2	2	2	2	4	2	—	—	—	✗	2
Brunei	—	—	—	—	4	—	—	—	—	1	—	—	2	2	4	—	2	2	3	✗	2
Burma	—	—	4	—	—	—	—	—	—	—	—	—	—	—	—	—	—	—	—	—	—
Canada	6	1	—	—	—	—	1	—	—	—	—	—	—	1	1	—	—	—	—	—	—
Newfoundland	4	14	—	—	—	—	—	—	—	—	—	—	—	—	—	—	—	—	—	—	—
Cayman Islands	4	3	2	2	4	—	1	—	—	1	2	1	2	2	4	2	2	2	3	✗	2
Cook Islands	3	3	4	—	—	—	2	—	—	—	—	—	—	—	6	—	—	—	—	✗	3 +MS
Aitutaki	—	—	—	—	—	—	—	—	—	—	—	—	—	—	—	—	—	—	—	2	2 +MS
Penrhyn	—	—	—	—	—	—	—	—	—	—	—	—	—	—	—	—	—	—	—	—	3
Cyprus	4	3	2	2	4	—	1	—	—	2	2	4	3	—	—	—	—	—	1	—	—
Dominica	4	3	2	2	4	2	1	—	3	1	2	1	2	2	4	2	2	2	3	✗	2+MS
Egypt/British Forces in Egypt	1	—	—	—	—	—	—	—	—	—	—	—	—	—	—	—	—	—	—	—	—
Falkland Islands	4	3	2	2	4	—	1	—	—	1	2	1	2	2	4	—	—	—	—	✗	2
Falkland Islands Dependencies	—	—	2	2	4	—	1	—	—	—	—	—	—	—	—	—	—	—	—	—	—
South Georgia	—	—	—	—	—	—	—	—	—	—	—	—	—	—	—	—	—	—	—	✗	2
Fiji	4	3	2	2	4	—	1	1	—	1	2	—	2	2	4	—	2	2	—	—	—
Gambia	4	3	2	2	4	—	1	—	—	1	2	1	2	—	3	—	—	—	—	—	—
Ghana/Gold Coast	4	3	2	2	4	—	1	—	—	3	4+MS	—	4+MS	4+MS	—	5+MS	4+MS	5+MS	—	—	—
Gibraltar	4	3	2	2	4	—	1	1	—	1	2	1	2	2	4	—	2	2	3	✗	2
Gilbert and Ellice Islands	4	3	2	2	4	—	1	—	—	1	2	—	2	2	4	—	2	2	3	✗	2
Grenada	4	3	2	2	4	2	1	—	3	1	2	—	2	2	4	2	2	2	3	—	2+MS
Grenadines	—	—	—	—	—	—	—	—	—	—	—	—	—	—	—	—	—	—	—	—	2+MS
Guyana/British Guiana	4	3	2	2	4	—	1	—	—	1	2	—	2	2	2	—	—	—	—	—	—
Hong Kong	4	3	2	—	4	—	1	—	—	1	2	—	2	2	4	—	2	2	3	✗	—
India	7	—	4	—	4	—	1	—	—	1	1	—	2	1	1	—	—	—	—	—	—
Hyderabad	—	—	1	—	—	—	—	—	—	—	—	—	—	—	—	—	—	—	—	—	—
Ireland	—	—	—	—	—	—	—	—	—	2	2	—	2	2	—	—	—	—	—	—	—
Jamaica	4	3	2	2	4	—	1	1	3	2	2	—	1	—	2	4	—	—	—	—	—
K.U.T./East Africa	4	3	2	2	4	—	1	1	—	4	2	—	4	4	4	—	—	—	4	—	—
Kuwait	—	—	—	2	4	—	4	—	—	—	—	—	—	—	—	—	—	—	—	—	—
Leeward Islands	4	3	2	2	4	2	1	—	—	—	—	—	—	—	—	—	—	—	—	—	—
Lesotho/Basutoland	4	3	3×2	2	4	—	1	—	—	1	2	—	2	2	4	—	—	—	4	—	—
Malawi/Nyasaland	4	3	—	2	4	—	1	—	—	—	—	—	—	—	—	—	—	—	—	—	—
Malayan States, etc.	4	3	—	22	44	—	11	—	—	3	—	—	3	—	—	—	—	—	—	—	—
North Borneo	—	—	—	2	4	—	1	—	—	1	—	—	—	—	—	—	—	—	—	—	—
Sarawak	—	—	—	2	4	—	1	—	—	1	—	—	—	—	—	—	—	—	—	—	—
Maldive Islands	—	—	—	—	—	—	—	—	—	7	5	—	—	—	5+MS	6	—	—	6	—	—
Malta	4	3	2	2	4	—	1	1	—	1	2	—	2	2	4	—	—	—	—	—	—
Mauritius	4	3	2	2	4	—	1	—	—	1	2	—	2	2	4	—	—	—	3	—	—
Montserrat	4	3	2	2	4	2	1	—	3	1	2	1	2	2	4	2	—	2	3	✗	2
Morocco Agencies/Tangier	15	3	—	2	4	—	4	—	—	—	—	—	—	—	—	—	—	—	—	—	—
Namibia/South West Africa	4	8×2	3×2	1×2	3×2	—	5	—	—	—	2	—	—	—	—	—	—	—	—	—	—
Nauru	4	4	—	—	—	—	—	—	—	—	—	—	—	—	—	—	—	—	—	—	—
New Zealand	3	3	11	—	—	—	5	2	—	—	—	—	1	1	1	—	—	—	—	—	—
Tokelau Islands	—	—	—	—	—	—	1	—	—	—	—	—	—	—	—	—	—	—	—	—	—
Nigeria	4	3	2	2	—	—	1	—	—	2	3+MS	—	3	3	—	—	—	—	3	—	—
Niue	3	3	4	—	—	—	2	—	—	—	—	—	—	—	—	—	—	—	—	—	—
Pakistan	—	—	—	—	—	—	—	—	—	2	1	—	1	2	—	—	—	—	1	—	—
Bahawalpur Postage and Officials	—	—	1	—	4+4	—	—	—	—	—	—	—	—	—	—	—	—	—	—	—	—
P.N.G./Papua	4	4	—	—	—	—	—	—	—	—	1	—	—	—	—	—	—	—	—	—	—
New Guinea	2	4	—	—	—	—	—	—	—	—	—	—	—	—	—	—	—	—	—	—	—
Pitcairn Islands	—	—	2	2	4	—	1	—	—	1	2	—	2	2	4	—	2	2	3	✗	2
Rhodesia and Nyasaland	—	—	—	—	—	—	—	—	—	—	1	—	—	—	—	—	—	—	—	—	—
St. Helena	4	3	2	2	4	—	1	—	—	1	2	—	2	2	4	—	2	2	3	✗	2
St. Kitts-Nevis	4	3	2	2	4	2	1	—	3	1	2	—	2	2	4	2	2	2	3	✗	2
St. Lucia	4	3	2	2	4	2	1	—	3	1	2	—	2	2	4	2	2	2	3	✗	2
St. Vincent	4	3	2	2	4	2	1	—	3	1	2	—	2	2	4	2	2	2	3	✗	2
Grenadines	—	—	—	—	—	—	—	—	—	—	—	—	—	—	—	—	—	—	—	—	2
Samoa	3	—	4	—	—	—	2	—	—	—	—	—	—	—	—	—	—	4	—	—	—
Seychelles	4	3	2	2	4	—	1	—	—	1	2	—	2	2	4	—	2	2	3	✗	—
Sierra Leone	4	3	2	2	4	—	1	—	—	2	3	—	—	—	11	—	—	—	—	—	—
Singapore	—	—	—	2	4	—	1	—	—	—	—	—	—	—	—	—	—	—	—	—	—
Solomon Islands	4	3	2	2	4	—	1	—	—	1	2	—	2	2	4	—	2	2	3	✗	—
Somaliland Protectorate	4	3	2	2	4	—	1	—	—	—	—	—	—	—	—	—	—	—	—	—	—
South Africa	4×2	5×2	3×2	1×2	3×2	—	1	—	—	—	2	—	2	—	—	—	—	—	—	—	—
South Arabian Fed./Aden	—	3	2	2	4	—	1	1	—	1	2	—	—	2	4	—	2	2	3	—	2
Seiyun	—	—	2	2	4	—	1	—	—	—	—	—	7	—	1	—	7	—	—	—	—
Shihr and Mukalla	—	—	2	2	4	—	1	—	—	—	—	—	8	—	3	—	8	—	—	—	—
Sri Lanka/Ceylon	4	3	2	—	3	—	1	1	—	2	—	—	2	2	4	—	2	2	3	—	—
Swaziland	4	3	3×2	2	4	—	1	—	—	1	2	—	2	2	4	—	—	—	—	—	—
Tanzania/Zanzibar	—	—	2	2	4	—	—	—	—	—	—	—	—	—	—	—	—	—	—	—	—
Tonga	—	—	—	—	4	—	—	—	—	—	—	—	—	—	—	—	—	—	—	—	—
Trinidad and Tobago	4	3	2	2	4	2	1	—	3	3	—	—	—	—	1	—	4	—	—	—	—
Tristan da Cunha	—	—	—	—	—	—	—	—	—	1	2	—	2	2	4	2	2	2	3	—	2
Turks and Caicos Islands	4	3	2	2	4	—	1	—	—	1	2	—	2	2	4	—	2	2	3	✗	2
Vanuatu/New Hebrides (English & French inscr)	—	—	—	—	4+4	—	1	—	—	1+1	2+2	—	2+2	2+2	4+4	—	2+2	2+2	3+3	✗+2	—
Zambia/Northern Rhodesia	4	3	2	2	—	—	1	—	—	—	—	—	—	—	—	—	—	2	—	—	—
Zimbabwe/Southern Rhodesia	4	4	4	—	2	—	1	—	—	—	—	—	2	—	1	—	—	—	—	—	—
Total number of stamps	250	202	164	138	310	28	106	13	30	77	108 +2 MS	25	112 +MS	107 +2 MS	182	34	68 + MS	58 + MS	110 + MS	78	72 +6 MS

NOTE Countries marked with an asterisk are those which comprise the Crown Agents Omnibus issue.

1977 SILVER JUBILEE

Country	Catalogue Nos.	Stamps	MS
Great Britain	1033/7	5	—
Guernsey	149/50	2	—
Isle of Man	94/6	3	—
Jersey	168/70	3	—
Anguilla	269/73	4	1
Antigua	526/31	5	1
Barbuda	298/304, 323/28	11	2
Ascension*	222/4	3	—
Australia	645/6	2	—
Christmas Island	83	1	—
Norfolk Island	196	1	—
Bahamas	488/92	4	1
Bangladesh	93/6	3	1
Barbados*	574/6	3	—
Belize*	449/51	3	—
Bermuda*	371/3	3	—
Botswana*	391/3	3	—
British Antarctic Territory*	83/5	3	—
British Virgin Islands*	364/6	3	—
Brunei	264/6	3	—
Canada	855	1	—
Cayman Islands*	427/9	3	—
Cook Islands	564/70	6	1
Aitutaki	225/9	4	1
Penrhyn	100/3	3	1
Cyprus	485	1	—
Dominica	562/7	5	1
Falkland Islands*	325/7	3	—
South Georgia*	50/2	3	—
Fiji*	536/8	3	—
Gambia*	365/7	3	—
Gibraltar	371/3	2	1
Grenada	857/62	5	1
Grenadines of Grenada	215/18	3	1
Hong Kong*	361/3	3	—
Kenya	91/5	4	2
Kiribati / Gilbert Islands*	48/50	3	—
Maldive Islands	673/9	6	1
Mauritius*	516/18	3	—
Montserrat	396/8	3	—
New Zealand	MS1137	—	1
Niue	213/15	2	1
Papua New Guinea	330/2	3	—
Pitcairn Islands*	171/3	3	—
St. Helena*	332/4	3	—
St. Kitts-Nevis*	367/9	3	—
St. Lucia	443/7	4	1
St. Vincent	502/14	12	1
Grenadines of St. Vincent	93/5	3	—
Samoa	479/82	4	—
Seychelles	393/401	8	1
Sierra Leone	597/8	2	—
Solomon Islands*	334/6	3	—
Swaziland*	268/70	3	—
Tanzania	218/22	4	1
Tonga	598/607, O151/3	13	—
Tristan da Cunha*	212/14	3	—
Turks and Caicos Islands*	472/5	3	1
Tuvalu	50/3	3	1
Vanuatu/New Hebrides* (English & French inscr)	F231/3	3+3	—
Total number of items		**220**	**24**

The Turks and Caicos Islands miniature sheet, MS475, did not form part of the Crown Agents Omnibus issue.

1977 ROYAL VISIT

Country	Catalogue Nos.	Stamps	MS
Anguilla	298/302	4	1
Antigua	548/53	5	1
Barbuda	345/54	8	2
Bahamas	500/4	4	1
Barbados	590/2	3	—
British Virgin Islands	371/3	3	—
Dominica	591/6	5	1
Grenada	894/9	5	1
Grenadines of Grenada	239/42	3	—
Montserrat	409/11	3	—
St. Vincent	540	1	—
Grenadines of St. Vincent	104/5	2	—
Total number of items		**46**	**8**

1978 CORONATION ANNIVERSARY

Country	Catalogue Nos.	Stamps	Sheetlets	MS
Great Britain	1059/62	4	—	—
Guernsey	167	1	—	—
Isle of Man	132	1	—	—
Jersey	195/6	2	—	—
Anguilla	320/4	4	—	1
Antigua	581/6	5	—	1
Barbuda	408/20, 445/6	12	1	3
Ascension*	233/5	3	1	—
Australia				
Christmas Island*	96/8	3	1	—
Norfolk Island	207/8	2	—	—
Bahamas	515/17	2	—	1
Bangladesh	116/20	4	—	1
Barbados*	597/9	3	1	—
Belize*	464/6, 495/503	11	1	2
Bermuda	384/6	3	—	—
British Antarctic Territory*	86/8	3	1	—
British Virgin Islands*	384/6	3	1	—
Brunei	267/9	3	—	—
Cayman Islands*	468/70	3	1	—

Country	Catalogue Nos.	Stamps	Sheetlets	MS
Cook Islands	593/601	8	—	1
Aitutaki	257/60	3	—	1
Penrhyn	121/4	3	—	1
Dominica	612/15	3	—	1
Falkland Islands*	348/50	3	1	—
South Georgia*	67/9	3	1	—
Fiji*	549/51	3	1	—
Gambia*	397/9	3	1	—
Gibraltar	400/3	4	—	—
Grenada	946/9	3	—	1
Grenadines of Grenada	272/5	3	—	1
Hong Kong	373/4	2	—	—
Kiribati/Gilbert Islands*	68/70	3	1	—
Maldive Islands	755/61	6	—	1
Mauritius*	549/51	3	1	—
Montserrat	422/6	4	—	1
New Zealand				
Tokelau	61/4	4	—	—
Niue	245/8	3	—	1
Pitcairn Islands	MS189	—	—	1
St. Helena*	338/40	3	1	—
St. Kitts-Nevis*	389/91	3	1	—
St. Lucia	468/72	4	—	1
St. Vincent	556/60	4	—	1
Grenadines of St. Vincent	130/4	4	—	1
Samoa*	508/10	3	1	—
Seychelles	428/32	4	—	1
Sierra Leone	601/3	3	—	—
Solomon Islands*	357/9	3	1	—
Swaziland	293/5	3	1	—
Tanzania	233/7	4	—	1
Tristan da Cunha*	239/41	3	1	—
Turks and Caicos Islands	494/8	4	—	1
Tuvalu	89/93	4	—	1
Uganda	234/8	4	—	1
Vanuatu/New Hebrides* (English & French inscr)	F276/8	3+3	1+1	—
Total number of items		**195**	**21**	**27**

The Crown Agents Omnibus issue was printed in matching sheetlets, each containing two se-tenant strips of the three designs.
Barbuda Nos. 445/6 form part of a general anniversaries issue.
Belize Nos. 495/503 were not part of the Crown Agents Omnibus issue.

1980 QUEEN MOTHER's 80th BIRTHDAY

Country	Catalogue Nos.	Stamps	MS
Great Britain	1129	1	—
Anguilla	411/15	4	1
Antigua	663/5	2	1
Barbuda	533/5	2	1
Ascension*	269	1	—
Australia			
Norfolk Island	252/3	2	—
Bangladesh	172/4	2	1
Belize	592/3	1	1
Bermuda*	425	1	—
Cayman Islands*	506	1	—
Cook Islands	701/2	1	1
Penrhyn	150/1	1	1
Dominica	732/4	2	1
Falkland Islands*	383	1	—
Gambia*	440	1	—
Gibraltar*	436	1	—
Hong Kong*	390	1	—
Lesotho	423/5	3	—
Maldive Islands	886/7	1	1
Niue	364/5	1	1
Pitcairn Islands*	206	1	—
St. Helena*	366	1	—
St. Kitts-Nevis			
St. Kitts	48	1	—
Nevis	50	1	—
St. Lucia	534/6	2	1
Samoa*	572	1	—
Solomon Islands*	421	1	—
Tristan da Cunha*	282	1	—
Turks and Caicos Islands	607/8	1	—
Tuvalu	148	1	—
Total number of items		**41**	**12**

1981 ROYAL WEDDING

Country	Catalogue Nos.	Stamps	MS
Great Britain	1160/1	2	—
Guernsey	232/9	7	1
Isle of Man	202/4	2	1
Jersey	284/5	2	—
Anguilla	464/7	3	1
Antigua	702/5	3	1
Barbuda	565/75	9	2
Ascension*	302/4	2	—
Australia	821/2	2	—
Cocos (Keeling) Islands	70/1	2	—
Norfolk Island*	262/4	3	—
Bahamas	586/8	2	1
Barbados*	674/6	3	—
Belize	614/20	6	1
Bermuda*	436/8	3	—
British Virgin Islands*	463/5	3	—
Brunei*	304/6	3	—
Cayman Islands*	534/6	3	—
Cook Islands	812/14	2	1
Aitutaki	391/3	3	—
Penrhyn	223/8	5	1
Cyprus	580	1	—
Turkish Cypriot Posts	121	1	—
Dominica	747/50	3	1
Falkland Islands*	402/4	3	—
Dependencies*	95/7	3	—
Fiji*	612/14	3	—
Gambia*	454/6	3	—
Ghana	948/54	6	1
Gibraltar	450	1	—
Grenada	1130/5	5	1
Grenadines of Grenada	444/9	5	1
Guyana	769/70, 841/3, 930/6	12	—
Hong Kong*	399/401	3	—

Country	Catalogue Nos.	Stamps	MS
Jamaica	516/20	4	1
Kenya	207/11	4	1
Kiribati	149/55	6	1
Lesotho*	451/4	3	1
Maldive Islands	918/21	3	1
Mauritius*	615/17	3	—
Montserrat	510/15	6	1
New Zealand	1247/8	2	—
Niue	430/3	3	1
Pitcairn Islands*	219/21	3	—
St. Helena*	378/80	3	—
St. Kitts-Nevis			
St. Kitts	75/81	6	1
Nevis	72/8	6	1
St. Lucia	576/9	3	1
St. Vincent	668/74	6	1
Grenadines of St. Vincent	195/201	6	1
Samoa	599/601	3	—
Seychelles	505/10	6	1
Zil Elwagne Sesel	23/9	6	1
Sierra Leone*	668/74	6	1
Solomon Islands*	445/7	3	—
Swaziland*	376/8	3	—
Tanzania	325/7	2	1
Tonga	785/8	4	—
Tristan da Cunha*	308/10	3	—
Turks and Caicos Islands	653/6	3	1
Caicos Islands	8/11	3	1
Tuvalu	168/74	6	1
Uganda	341/8	6	2
Vanuatu*	315/17	3	—
Total number of items		**244**	**35**

The Lesotho miniature sheet, No. MS454, and Sierra Leone Nos. 671/3 do not form part of the Crown Agents Omnibus issue.

1982 PRINCESS DIANA'S 21st BIRTHDAY

Country	Catalogue Nos.	Stamps	MS
Anguilla	507/14	6	2
Antigua	748/51	3	1
Barbuda	624/30	6	2
Ascension*	322/5	4	—
Bahamas*	622/5	4	—
Barbados*	705/8	4	—
Belize	680/6	6	1
British Antarctic Territory*	109/12	4	—
British Virgin Islands*	488/91	4	—
Cayman Islands*	549/52	4	—
Cook Islands	833/7	4	1
Aitutaki	411/14	3	1
Penrhyn	250/5	3	1
Dominica	821/4	3	1
Falkland Islands*	426/9	4	—
Dependencies*	108/11	4	—
Fiji*	640/3	4	—
Gambia*	476/9	4	—
Grenada	1188/94	6	1
Grenadines of Grenada	493/9	6	1
Guyana	979/81	3	—
Jamaica	551/7	6	1
Kiribati	183/5	3	—
Lesotho*	514/17	3	—
Maldive Islands	964/7	3	1
Mauritius*	643/6	4	—
Montserrat	542/4	3	—
Niue	454/7	3	1
Pitcairn Islands*	226/9	4	—
St. Helena*	397/400	4	—
St. Kitts-Nevis			
St. Kitts	95/7	3	—
Nevis	85/7	3	—
St. Lucia	625/8	3	1
St. Vincent	694/6	3	—
Grenadines of St. Vincent	229/31	3	1
Sierra Leone	707/10	3	1
Solomon Islands*	467/70	4	—
Swaziland*	404/7	4	—
Tristan da Cunha*	327/30	4	—
Turks and Caicos Islands	709/12	3	1
Tuvalu	184/6	3	—
Uganda	374/7	1	1
Total number of items		**162**	**19**

1982 BIRTH OF PRINCE WILLIAM

Country	Catalogue Nos.	Stamps	MS
Great Britain			
Isle of Man	MS227	—	1
Antigua	757/60	3	1
Barbuda	613/16, 632/5	6	2
Belize	707/20	12	2
Cook Islands	838/47, 856/61	13	3
Aitutaki	415/24	9	1
Penrhyn	256/72	15	2
Dominica	830/3	3	1
Grenada	1200/6	6	1
Grenadines of Grenada	505/11	6	1
Guyana	982/7	6	—
Jamaica	558/64	6	1
Kiribati	186/8	3	—
Lesotho	521/2	2	—
Maldive Islands	968/72	4	1
Mauritius	647	1	—
Niue	458/74	13	4
St. Kitts-Nevis			
St. Kitts	98/100	3	—
Nevis	88/90	3	—
St. Vincent	699/701	3	—
Grenadines of St. Vincent	234/6	3	—
Sierra Leone	711/14	3	1
Tuvalu	189/91	3	—
Total number of items		**124**	**22**

BRITISH COMMONWEALTH OMNIBUS ISSUES

1985 LIFE AND TIMES OF QUEEN ELIZABETH THE QUEEN MOTHER

Country	Catalogue Nos.	Stamps	MS
Anguilla	655/8	3	1
Antigua	946/9	3	1
Barbuda	776/82, 809/15 826/9	17	1
Ascension*	376/80	4	1
Australia			
Norfolk Island*	364/8	4	1
Bahamas*	712/16	4	1
Barbados*	779/83	4	1
Belize	827/31	4	1
Bermuda*	494/8	4	1
British Virgin Islands	579/87	8	1
Cook Islands	1035/9	4	1
Aitutaki	523/7	4	1
Penrhyn	378/82	4	1
Dominica	949/52	3	1
Falkland Islands*	505/9	4	1
Dependencies*	129/33	4	1
Fiji*	701/5	4	1
Gambia	586/9	3	1
Ghana	1140/3	3	1
Grenada	1426/9	3	1
Grenadines of Grenada	689/92	3	1
Guyana	1536/9	3	1
Hong Kong*	493/6	4	—
Jamaica*	625/9	4	1
Lesotho	635/9	4	1
Maldive Islands	1099/102	4	1
Mauritius*	699/703	4	1
Montserrat	636/44	8	1
Niue	587/90	3	1
Pitcairn Islands*	268/72	4	1
St. Helena*	454/8	4	1
St. Kitts-Nevis			
Nevis	309/17	8	1
St. Lucia	832/40	8	1
St. Vincent	910/18	8	1
Grenadines of St. Vincent	403/11	8	1
Samoa*	700/4	4	1
Seychelles*	614/18	4	1
Zil Elwannyen Sesel*	115/19	4	1
Sierra Leone	872/5	3	1
Solomon Islands*	538/42	4	1
Swaziland*	486/90	4	1
Tanzania	425/9	4	1
Tonga	915/18	4	—
Tristan da Cunha*	390/4	4	1
Turks and Caicos Islands	854/7	3	1
Caicos Islands	82/5	3	1
Tuvalu	334/42	8	1
Uganda	478/9	1	1
Vanuatu*	406/10	4	1
Zambia	432/5	4	—
Trinidad and Tobago	712/15	4	—
Tristan da Cunha*	406/10	5	—
Tuvalu	381/5	4	1
Uganda	526/9	3	1
Vanuatu*	429/33	5	—
Zambia*	453/7	5	—
Total number of items		**233**	**28**

(partial total shown in first column: **226 47**)

1986 QUEEN ELIZABETH II's 60th BIRTHDAY

Country	Catalogue Nos.	Stamps	MS
Great Britain	1316/19	4	—
Guernsey	365	1	—
Isle of Man	328/30	3	—
Jersey	389	1	—
Anguilla	711/14	3	1
Antigua	1005/8	3	1
Barbuda	861/4, 872/5	6	2
Ascension*	397/401	5	—
Australia	1009	1	—
Norfolk Island	389/92	4	—
Bahamas*	741/5	5	—
Barbados*	810/14	5	—
Belize	905/9	4	1
Bermuda*	524/8	5	—
British Virgin Islands	600/4	4	1
Cayman Islands*	621/5	5	—
Cook Islands	1065/8	3	1
Aitutaki	542/3	1	1
Penrhyn	394/6	3	—
Cyprus—Turkish Cypriot Posts	201	1	—
Dominica	998/1001	3	1
Falkland Islands*	522/6	5	—
Fiji*	714/18	5	—
Gambia	641/4	3	1
Gibraltar	540	1	—
Grenada	1499/502	3	1
Grenadines of Grenada	753/6	3	1
Guyana	1684/5	1	1
Hong Kong*	512/16	5	—
Jamaica*	646/50	5	—
Kiribati*	251/5	5	—
Lesotho	701/4	3	1
Maldive Islands	1170/3	3	1
Mauritius*	724/8	5	—
Montserrat	677/81	4	1
Niue	615/19	3	2
Papua New Guinea*	520/4	5	—
Pitcairn Islands*	285/9	5	—
St. Helena*	477/81	5	—
St. Kitts-Nevis			
St. Kitts	185/8	4	—
Nevis	384/8	4	1
St. Lucia	876/85	8	2
St. Vincent	978/82, 996/1000	8	2
Grenadines of St. Vincent	459/63	4	1
Samoa*	726/30	5	—
Seychelles*	639/43	5	—
Zil Elwannyen Sesel*	128/32	5	—
Sierra Leone	937/40	3	1
Solomon Islands*	562/6	5	—
South Georgia and South Sandwich Islands*	153/7	5	—
Swaziland*	500/4	5	—
Tanzania	517/21	4	1
Tonga	941/3	3	—

1986 ROYAL WEDDING

Country	Catalogue Nos.	Stamps	MS
Great Britain	1333/4	2	—
Guernsey	369/70	2	—
Isle of Man	326/7	2	—
Jersey	395/6	2	—
Anguilla	720/4	4	1
Antigua	1019/22	3	1
Barbuda	891/4	3	1
Ascension*	407/8	2	—
Australia			
Christmas Island*	220/1	2	—
Bahamas*	756/7	2	—
Barbados*	822/3	2	—
Belize	941/4	3	1
British Virgin Islands	605/9	4	1
Cayman Islands*	633/4	2	—
Cook Islands	1075/7	3	—
Aitutaki	547/8	1	1
Penrhyn	400/1	1	—
Cyprus—Turkish Cypriot Posts	200	1	—
Dominica	1018/21	3	1
Falkland Islands	536/8	3	1
Gambia	664/7	3	1
Gibraltar	MS545	—	1
Grenada	1512/15	3	1
Grenadines of Grenada	762/5	3	1
Jamaica*	656/7	2	—
Lesotho	736/9	3	1
Maldive Islands	1179/82	3	1
Montserrat	691/5, 705/8	8	1
Niue	625/6	1	1
Pitcairn Islands*	290/1	2	—
St. Helena*	486/7	2	—
St. Kitts-Nevis			
St. Kitts*	189/90	2	—
Nevis	406/10, 454/7	8	1
St. Lucia	890/3, 897/901	8	1
St. Vincent	1009/13, 1022/5	8	1
Grenadines of St. Vincent	481/5, 486/9	8	1
Seychelles*	651/2	2	—
Zil Elwannyen Sesel*	133/4	2	—
Sierra Leone	946/9	3	1
Solomon Islands*	568/9	2	—
South Georgia and South Sandwich Islands*	158/60	3	—
Tristan da Cunha*	415/16	2	—
Turks and Caicos Islands	893/6	3	1
Tuvalu	397/401, 433/6	8	1
Uganda	535/8	3	1
Zambia*	458/9	2	—
Total number of items		**142**	**24**

1987 ROYAL RUBY WEDDING

Country	Catalogue Nos.	Stamps	MS
Anguilla	788/91	4	—
Antigua	1149/53	4	1
Barbuda	1029/33	4	1
Ascension*	447/51	5	—
Belize	980/4	4	1
Cook Islands	1193/4	2	—
Aitutaki	572/4	3	—
Penrhyn	413/14	2	—
Dominica	1109/13	4	1
Gambia	770/4	4	1
Grenada	1737/41	4	1
Grenadines of Grenada	928/32	4	1
Guyana	2233/4	5	1
Kiribati*	279/83	5	—
Lesotho	806/9	3	1
Maldive Islands	1282/5	3	1
Montserrat	739/42	8	—
Niue	657/8	2	—
St. Helena*	514/18	5	—
St. Vincent	1079/84	5	1
Grenadines of St. Vincent	536/41	5	1
Seychelles*	674/8	5	—
Zil Elwannyen Sesel*	157/61	5	—
Sierra Leone	1116/20	4	1
Swaziland*	537/40	4	—
Tristan da Cunha*	438/42	5	—
Turks and Caicos Islands	922/4	3	—
Tuvalu	484/9	5	—
Vanuatu*	487/91	5	—
Total number of items		**117**	**14**

1990 QUEEN MOTHER'S 90th BIRTHDAY

Country	Catalogue Nos.	Stamps	MS
Great Britain	1507/10	4	—
Isle of Man	448	1	—
Anguilla	859	1	—
Antigua	1415/19	4	1
Barbuda	1206/10	4	1
Ascension*	525/6	2	—
Bahamas*	880/1	2	—
Barbados*	919/20	2	—
British Antarctic Territory*	186/7	2	—
British Indian Ocean Territory*	106/7	2	—
British Virgin Islands	746/50	4	1
Cayman Islands*	711/12	2	—
Cook Islands	1246/7	1	1
Aitutaki	MS614	—	1
Penrhyn	445/6	1	1
Dominica	1373/7	4	1
Falkland Islands*	606/7	2	—
Gambia	1060/3	3	1
Grenada	2131/4	3	1
Grenadines of Grenada	1262/5	3	1
Guyana	2754/61, EMS31/3	8	3
Kenya*	545/6	2	—
Kiribati*	341/2	2	—
Lesotho	967/70	3	1
Maldive Islands	1396/9	3	1
Niue	689/90	1	1
Pitcairn Islands*	378/9	2	—
St. Helena*	570/1	2	—
St. Kitts-Nevis			
Nevis	555/8	3	1
St. Lucia*	1053/4	2	—
St. Vincent	1536/9	3	1
Grenadines of St. Vincent	705/32	27	1
Seychelles*	782/3	2	—
Zil Elwannyen Sesel*	212/13	2	—
Sierra Leone	1493/6	3	1
Solomon Islands*	675/6	2	—
South Georgia and South Sandwich Islands*	195/6	2	—
Swaziland*	570/1	2	—
Tristan da Cunha*	498/9	2	—
Turks and Caicos Islands	1045/9	4	1
Uganda	816/19	3	1
Total number of items		**127**	**22**

1991 65th BIRTHDAY OF QUEEN ELIZABETH II AND 70th BIRTHDAY OF PRINCE PHILIP

Country	Catalogue Nos.	Stamps	MS
Antigua	1534/8	4	1
Barbuda	1303/12	4	1
Ascension*	539/40	2	—
Australia	1286	1	—
Bahamas*	913/14	2	—
Belize*	1104/5	2	—
Bermuda*	634/5	2	—
Cook Islands	1255	1	—
Aitutaki	622	1	—
Penrhyn	456	1	—
Dominica	1433/7	4	1
Gambia	1165/9	4	1
Grenada	2299/303	4	1
Grenada Grenadines	1393/7	4	1
Guyana	3146/52	6	1
Kiribati*	366/7	2	—
Maldive Islands	1506/10	4	1
Mauritius*	849/50	2	—
Niue	706	1	—
Pitcairn Islands*	399/400	2	—
St. Helena*	591/2	2	—
St. Kitts-Nevis			
St. Kitts*	336/7	2	—
Nevis	622/6	4	1
St. Vincent	1686/90	4	1
Grenadines of St. Vincent	750/4	4	1
Samoa*	861/2	2	—
Seychelles*	799/800	2	—
Zil Elwannyen Sesel*	234/5	2	—
Sierra Leone	1639/43	4	1
Solomon Islands*	692/5	2	—
South Georgia and South Sandwich Islands*	201/2	2	—
Swaziland*	592/3	2	—
Tristan da Cunha	514/17	4	—
Turks and Caicos Islands	1099/1103	4	1
Uganda	960/4	4	—
Vanuatu*	576/7	2	—
Total number of items		**99**	**14**

1992 40th ANNIVERSARY OF QUEEN ELIZABETH II'S ACCESSION

Country	Catalogue Nos.	Stamps	MS
Great Britain	1602/6	5	—
Guernsey	552/5	4	—
Isle of Man	508/12	5	—
Antigua	1604/8	4	2
Barbuda	1384/8	4	2
Ascension*	569/73	5	—
Bahamas*	928/32	5	—
Bermuda*	640/4	5	—
British Indian Ocean Territory*	119/23	5	—
British Virgin Islands	813/17	4	1
Cayman Islands*	737/41	5	—
Cook Islands	1324/7	4	—
Dominica	1515/19	4	2
Falkland Islands*	647/51	5	—
Gambia	1284/8	4	2
Gibraltar*	673/7	5	—
Grenada	2375/9	4	2
Grenada Grenadines	1469/73	4	2
Guyana	3294/8	4	2
Hong Kong*	691/5	5	—
Kenya*	565/9	5	—
Kiribati*	377/81	5	—
Lesotho	1084/8	4	1
Maldive Islands	1622/6	4	2
Niue	759/62	4	—

Country	Catalogue Nos.	Stamps	MS
Pitcairn Islands*	409/13	5	—
St. Helena*	607/11	5	—
St. Kitts-Nevis			
St. Kitts*	350/4	5	—
Nevis	655/9	4	2
St. Vincent	1858/62	4	2
St. Vincent Grenadines	803/7	4	2
Samoa*	876/80	5	—
Seychelles*	810/14	5	—
Zil Elwannyen Sesel*	240/4	5	—
Sierra Leone	1790/4	4	2
Solomon Islands*	713/17	5	—
South Georgia and South Sandwich Islands*	209/13	5	—
Tristan da Cunha*	526/30	5	—
Turks and Caicos Islands	1145/53	8	2
Uganda	1079/83	4	2
Vanuatu*	587/91	5	—
Zambia*	687/91	5	—
Total number of items		**195**	**30**

1993 40th ANNIVERSARY OF CORONATION

Country	Catalogue Nos.	Stamps	MS
Great Britain			
Jersey	634	1	—
Anguilla	917/21	4	1
Antigua	1772/6	4	1
	1777/1808	32	—
Bahamas	962/5	4	—
British Virgin Islands	841/5	4	1
Cook Islands	1328/30	3	—
Aitutaki	650/2	3	—
Penrhyn	480	1	—
Dominica	1700/4	4	1
Gambia	1521/5	4	1
Ghana	1844/8	4	2
Grenada	2518/22	4	1
Grenada Grenadines	1623/7	4	1
Guyana	3551/5	4	1
Hong Kong	741/4	4	—
Lesotho	1159/63	4	1
Maldive Islands	1805/8	4	—
Montserrat	913/14	2	—
New Zealand			
Tokelau	197/200	4	—
Niue	773	1	—
Pitcairn Islands	430	1	—
St. Kitts-Nevis			
St. Kitts	378/81	4	—
Nevis	753/7	4	1
St. Vincent	2264/8	4	1
Sierra Leone	2059, 2061, 2064, MS2067b	3	1
Tanzania	1514/18	4	1
Tristan da Cunha	542/5	4	—
Turks and Caicos Islands	1196/1200	4	1
Tuvalu	677/81	4	1
Uganda	1219/23	4	1
Total number of items		**135**	**18**

1994 ROYAL VISIT

Country	Catalogue Nos.	Stamps	MS
Bahamas	999/1002	4	—
Belize	1157/60	4	—
Bermuda	699/701	3	—
Cayman Islands	774/7	4	—
Dominica	1844/8	4	1
Guyana	3873/7	4	1
Jamaica	843/6	4	—
Total number of items		**27**	**2**

1995 QUEEN MOTHER'S 95th BIRTHDAY

Country	Catalogue Nos.	Stamps	MS
Antigua	2127/31	4	1
Barbuda	1662, 1814/18	5	1
Cayman Islands	MS810	—	1
Cook Islands	1378	1	—
Aitutaki	688	1	—
Penrhyn	515	1	—
Dominica	1993/7	4	1
Gambia	2025/9	4	1
Ghana	2191/5	4	1
Grenada	2902/6	4	1
Grenada Grenadines	1980/4	4	1
Guyana	4414/18	4	1
Jamaica	MS883	—	1
Maldive Islands	2274/8	4	1
Pitcairn Islands	MS478	—	1
St. Kitts-Nevis			
Nevis	923/7	4	1
St. Vincent	2927/31	4	1
Seychelles	852/5	4	—
Sierra Leone	2335/9	4	1
Tristan da Cunha	MS585	—	1
Turks and Caicos Islands	1344/8	4	1
Uganda	1482/6	4	1
Total number of items		**64**	**18**

1996 QUEEN ELIZABETH II's 70th BIRTHDAY

Country	Catalogue Nos.	Stamps	MS
Great Britain			
Jersey	738	1	—
Antigua	2355/8	3	1
Barbuda	1782/5	3	1
Ascension*	671/4	4	—
Australia	1589	1	—
British Antarctic Territory*	270/3	4	—
British Indian Ocean Territory*	180/4	4	1
British Virgin Islands*	920/4	4	1
Cook Islands	1392/5	3	1
Aitutaki	694	1	—
Penrhyn	521	1	—
Dominica	2118/21	3	1
Falkland Islands*	761/5	4	1
Gambia	2247/50	3	1
Ghana	2325/8	3	1
Grenada	3078/81	3	1
Grenadines of Grenada	2126/9	3	1
Guyana	4707/10	3	1
Maldive Islands	2489/92	3	1
New Zealand			
Tokelau*	240/4	4	1
Pitcairn Islands*	493/6	4	—
St. Helena*	716/20	4	1
St. Kitts-Nevis			
Nevis	1018/21	3	1
St. Vincent	3326/9	3	1
Samoa*	983/7	4	1
Sierra Leone	2559/62	3	1
Tristan da Cunha*	594/7	4	—
Turks and Caicos Islands	1378/81	3	1
Uganda	1687/90	3	1
Total number of items		**89**	**21**

1997 ROYAL GOLDEN WEDDING

Country	Catalogue Nos.	Stamps	MS
Great Britain	1978/9, 2011/14	6	—
Guernsey	754/9	6	—
Isle of Man	768/72	4	1
Jersey	840/2	2	1
Antigua	2474/80	6	1
Barbuda	1894/9	6	1
Ascension*	719/24	6	1
Australia			
Norfolk Island*	647/51	4	1
Bahamas*	1114/20	6	1
Bermuda*	778/80	2	1
Botswana*	870/6	6	1
British Indian Ocean Territory*	195/200	6	1
British Virgin Islands*	959/64	6	1
Cayman Islands*	841/7	6	1
Cook Islands	1424/5	1	1
Aitutaki	697/8	1	1
Penrhyn	523/4	1	1
Dominica	2296/302	6	1
Falkland Islands*	785/90	6	1
Gambia	2595/601	6	1
Ghana	2441/7	6	1
Gibraltar*	810/11	2	—
Grenada	3352/8	6	1
Grenadines of Grenada	2316/22	6	1
Kiribati*	535/41	6	1
Maldive Islands	2753/9	6	1
Nauru	469/71	2	1
New Zealand	2117	1	—
Papua New Guinea*	813/19	6	1
Pitcairn Islands*	516/21	6	—
St. Helena*	746/52	6	1
St. Kitts-Nevis			
St. Kitts*	485/91	6	1
Nevis	1083/9	6	1
St. Lucia*	1160/6	6	1
St. Vincent	3694/700	6	1
Samoa*	1007/13	6	1
Seychelles*	876/82	6	1
Sierra Leone	2697/703	6	1
Solomon Islands*	889/93	4	1
South Georgia and South Sandwich Islands*	270/6	6	1
Tristan da Cunha*	624/30	6	1
Turks and Caicos Islands	1449/55	6	1
Tuvalu*	791/7	6	1
Uganda	1852/8	6	1
Total number of items		**222**	**39**

1997–98 DIANA, PRINCESS OF WALES COMMEMORATION

Country	Catalogue Nos.	Stamps	MS
Great Britain	2021/5	5	—
Isle of Man	813/16	4	—
Anguilla	1012/15	4	—
Antigua	2573/85	12	1
Barbuda	1973/84	12	1
Ascension*	MS741	—	1
Australia			
Norfolk Island*	664/5	1	1
Bahamas*	1130/1	1	1
Bangladesh	681/3	3	—
Barbados*	MS1121	—	1
Belize*	MS1226	—	1
Bermuda*	MS787	—	1
Botswana*	885/9	4	1
British Antarctic Territory*	MS280	—	1
British Indian Ocean Territory*	MS214	—	1
British Virgin Islands*	MS989	—	1
Cayman Islands*	856/8	2	1
Cook Islands	1426/7	1	1
Aitutaki	699/700	1	1
Penrhyn	525/6	1	1

Country	Catalogue Nos.	Stamps	MS
Dominica	2392/6	4	1
Falkland Islands*	MS803	—	1
Fiji*	1014/15	1	1
Gambia	2814/18	4	1
Ghana	2591/603	12	1
Gibraltar*	MS828	—	1
Grenada	3497/503	6	1
Grenada Grenadines	2497/503	6	1
Jamaica	918/19	1	1
Kiribati*	557/8	1	1
Lesotho	1341/7	6	1
Malawi*	973/7	4	1
Maldive Islands	2860/78	18	1
Montserrat	1109/12	3	1
Namibia*	MS789	—	1
Nauru	477/82	6	—
New Zealand			
Tokelau*	275/6	1	1
Niue*	MS835	—	1
Papua New Guinea*	MS829	—	1
Pitcairn Islands*	MS534	—	1
St. Helena*	MS761	—	1
St. Kitts-Nevis			
St. Kitts*	514/15	1	1
Nevis	1127/35	9	—
St. Lucia	1179	1	—
St. Vincent	3910/18	8	1
Samoa*	1027/8	1	1
Seychelles*	MS883	—	1
Sierra Leone	2844/62	18	1
Solomon Islands*	907/8	1	1
South Georgia and South Sandwich Islands*	MS278	—	1
Tonga*	MS1421	—	1
Niuafo'ou*	MS275	—	1
Tristan da Cunha*	MS638	—	1
Turks & Caicos Islands	1507	1	—
Tuvalu*	MS803	—	1
Uganda	1912	1	—
Vanuatu*	770/1	1	1
Total number of items		**166**	**48**

1999 ROYAL WEDDING

Country	Catalogue Nos.	Stamps	MS
Great Britain	2096/7	2	—
Guernsey	MS837	—	1
Isle of Man	851/5	5	—
Jersey	903/4	2	—
Antigua	2912/15	3	1
Ascension*	774/5	2	—
British Virgin Islands*	1019/20	2	—
Cayman Islands*	892/3	2	—
Dominica	2628/31	3	1
Falkland Islands*	838/9	2	—
Gambia	3014/17	3	1
Gibraltar	890/3	4	—
Grenada	3833/6	3	1
Grenada Grenadines	2779/82	3	1
Pitcairn Islands*	553/4	2	—
St. Helena*	783/4	2	—
St. Kitts-Nevis			
Nevis	1354/62	8	1
St. Vincent	4321/4	3	1
Samoa*	1042/3	2	—
Seychelles	895/6	2	—
Sierra Leone	3212/16	4	1
Tristan da Cunha*	655/6	2	—
Turks and Caicos Islands	1540/4	4	1
Total number of items		**65**	**10**

1999–2000 QUEEN ELIZABETH THE QUEEN MOTHER'S CENTURY

Country	Catalogue Nos.	Stamps	MS
Great Britain			
Guernsey	817/26	10	—
Isle of Man	875/81	6	—
Ascension*	781/5	4	1
Australia			
Norfolk Island*	712/16	4	1
Bahamas*	1184/8	4	1
Cayman Islands*	899/903	4	1
Dominica	2666/70	4	1
Falkland Islands*	843/7	4	1
Fiji*	1059/63	4	1
Gambia	3220/4	4	1
Ghana	2934/8	4	1
Grenada	3846/50	4	1
Grenada Grenadines	2783/7	4	1
Lesotho	1644/8	4	1
Maldive Islands	3124/8	4	1
St. Helena*	790/4	4	1
St. Kitts-Nevis			
Nevis	1386/90	4	1
St. Vincent	4371/5	4	1
Samoa*	1049/53	4	1
Sierra Leone	3195/9	4	1
Solomon Islands*	941/5	4	1
South Georgia & South Sandwich Islands*	289/93	4	1
Tristan da Cunha*	657/61	4	1
Tuvalu*	846/50	4	1
Uganda	2067/71	4	1
Total number of items		**108**	**23**

Index

References to Vol. 1 = *Vol 1 317*
References to Vol. 2 = **545**

Collectors Bookshelf
Commonwealth Titles

After many months of busily accumulating new stocks of literature, from interesting private collections, and philatelic auctions in the U.K. and abroad, Stanley Gibbons have great pleasure in presenting a sample from our new and updated Commonwealth Bookshelf Listing.

Please note that for many of the titles listed we may have only single copies available.

Aden
The Postal History Of British Aden 1839-1967,
1st Edition, 1985, Hardback, "Major, Pratt.R.W", ...£27.50
Imperial Outpost-Aden,
1st Edition, 1964, Softback, "King, Gillian", ...£9.50
The Southern Gates Of Arabia,
1st Edition, 1936, Hardback, "Stark, Freya", "Murray, John"...£9.00

Antigua And Barbuda
The "Codrington" Correspondence 1974-1851 Including Antigua And Barbuda,
1st Edition, 1951, Softback, Robson Lowe Ltd, ...£15.00

Ascension
The History And Postage Stamps Of Ascension Island,
1st Edition, 1933, Hardback, "Ford, E.H", ...£100.00

Australia
History Of The Australian Military Postal Services 1914-1950,
1st Edition, 1991, Hardback, "Proud, E.B.", ...£65.00
History Of The Australian Military Postal Services 1914-1950,
1st Edition, 1991, Hardback, "Proud, E.B.", ...£65.00
The Chapman Collection Of Australia Commonwealth Stamps,
1st Edition, 1999, Hardback, "Chapman, R.", ...£45.00
"Australian Imperial Forces Postal History 1914-1918, Including Supplement",
1st Edition, 1984, Hardback, ...£60.00
Australasian Wreck Mail,
1st Edition, 1997, Hardback, "Pearce,B.R.", ...£90.00
The Postal History Of The Australian Army During World War II,
1st Edition, 1986, Hardback, "Collas,P.", ...£35.00
The Catalogue Of Australian Pre-Stamped Envelopes,
1st Edition, 1981, Softback, "Parker, C.", ...£7.25
Explore Australia Through Stamps, 1st Edition, Softback, "Hornadge,B.", ...£4.00
The Australian Commonwealth George V Halfpenny,
1st Edition, 1959, Softback, "Dix,V.W. Rowntree, A.W.", ...£10.00
The Postal History Of Internees And Prisoners Of War In Australia During World War II,
1st Edition, 1982, Hardback, "Collas,P.", ...£26.50

New South Wales
History Of The Post Office And Of The Issue Of Postage Stamps In New South Wales 1890,
Reprint, 1983, Hardback, "Housion, A.", ...£45.00
New South Wales Numeral Cancellations,
1st Edition, Softback, "Brown, A.G. Campbell, H.M.", ...£12.50
New South Wales Numeral Cancellations, 2nd Edition, 1977, Hardback, "Brown,A.G. Campbell, H.M.", ...£16.00
The Postal History Of New South Wales 1788-1901,
1st Edition, 1988, Hardback, "White, J.S. Editor", ...£60.00
The Revenue Stamps Of New South Wales, Looseleaf Pages
1st Edition, 1983, Softback, "Osborn,D.", ...£10.00

Norfolk Island
Norfolk Island A Postal And Philatelic History 1788-1969,
1st Edition, Softback, "Collas, P. Breckon,.R.", ...£19.95
Norfolk Island Cancellations And Postal Markings,
1st Edition, 1974, Softback, "Murray Brown,D.A.R.", ...£12.00
Norfolk Island Cancellations And Postal Markings, Looseleaf Pages
2nd Edition , 1983, Softback, "Murray Brown,D.A.R.", ...£8.95

Pitcairn Islands
Pitcairn Islands Philately A Handbook,
2nd Edition , 1999, Hardback, "Hume,D.E.", ...£12.50
Pitcairn Islands Postal Markings 1883-1984,
1st Edition, 1985, Softback, "Kitching,Cy.", ...£15.00
Pitcairn Islands Stamps And Postal History,
1st Edition, Softback, "Foxwell,F.W.", ...£15.00

Queensland
Queensland Postal Stationery,
1st Edition, 1979, Softback, "Collas, P.", ...£15.00

The Revenue Stamps Of Queensland,
1st Edition, 1982, Softback, "Craig, W.D.", ...£9.00
Queensland Cancellations And Other Postal Markings 1860-1913,
1st Edition, 1977, Hardback, "Campbell, H.M.", ...£35.00

South Australia
The Personal Touch: A Look At South Australia's Postal History From Proclamation Day To Present Day,
1st Edition, 1986, Softback, The Australian Post Office........£8.00
South Australia:The Squared Circle Cancellations,
1st Edition, Softback, "Cox, D.G", ...£18.00
South Australia,
Reprint, Softback, Postilion Publications £15.00
The Departmental Stamps Of South Australia,
1st Edition, 1978, Hardback, "Butler,A.R.", ...£40.00

Tasmania
The Pictorial Stamps Of Tasmania 1899-1912,
1st Edition, 1986, Hardback, "Lancaster,K.E.", ...£27.00
Tasmania: The Postal History And Postal Markings,
1st Edition, 1962, Hardback, "Campbell,H.M.", ...£40.00
Tasmania: The Postal History And Postal Markings Part II,
1st Edition, 1975, Hardback, "Ingles,O.G Editor", ...£30.00

Victoria
The Postal History Of Port Phillip District 1835-1851,
1950, Hardback, "Purves,J.R.W", ...£23.00
Victoria: The Registered And Too Late Stamps 1854-58,
1st Edition, 1966, Hardback, "Purves,J.R.W" £30.00
Victoria: The Barred Numeral Cancellations 1856-1912,
1st Edition, 1963, Hardback, "Purves,J.R.W", ...£70.00
The Stamps Of Victoria,
1st Edition, 1990, Hardback, "Kellow,G.N.", ...£61.00
Victoria: The Butterfly And Barred Oval Cancellations 1850-1855,
1st Edition, 1965, Softback, "Purves,J.R.W" £20.00
Victoria: The Butterfly Postmarks,
1st Edition, 1949, Softback, "Purves, J.R.W", ...£7.00
The Post Offices And Hand-Held Datestamps Of Victoria Vol I,
1st Edition, 1989, Hardback, "Watson, G.Wood,D. Webster,J.", ...£45.00

Western Australia
Western Australia: The Slogan Postmarks To 1983,
1st Edition, 1984, Softback, "Whittaker, B.", ...£9.50
Western Australia: The Machine Date Cases To 1983. Part 1 Offices Other Than Perth,
1st Edition, 1984, Softback, "Creaser, A.", ...£8.00
Western Australia: The 4d Lithograph 1854-1864,
1st Edition, 1984, Softback, "Poole, B.W.H.", ...£12.50
The Local Posts Of Western Australia,
1st Edition, 1960, Softback, "Collas,P.", ...£8.00
Place And Date Stamps Of Western Australia With Rarity Guide,
1st Edition, 1976, Softback, "Dzelme,J.", ...£15.00
Western Australia: The Postal Stationery To 1914,
1st Edition, 1982, Hardback, "Pope,.B Thomas,P.", ...£20.00
Western Australia: The Stamps And Postal History,
1st Edition, 1979, Hardback, "Hamilton, M. Editor", ...£36.00
Western Australia: The Forces, Prisoner Of War And Censor Mail,
1st Edition, 1997, Hardback, "Haynes,B. Pope, B.", ...£80.00

Bahamas
The Postage Stamps And Postal History Of The Bahamas,
1st Edition, 1950, Hardback, "Gisburn Harold, G.D.", ...£18.00
The Postage Stamps And Postal History Of The Bahamas,
2nd Edition, 1998, Hardback, "Gisburn Harold, G.D.", ...£25.00
The Bahama Islands,
1st Edition, 1968, Hardback, "Ludington, M.H. & Raymond, ...£17.50

The Postage Stamps And Postal History Of The Bahamas,
Reprint, Hardback, "Gisburn,H.G.D. ", ...£25.00

Barbados
The Postal Censorship In Barbados During The First And Second World Wars,
1st Edition, 1984, Softback, "Shepherd, Anthony", ...£7.50
The Postal Markings Of Barbados,
1st Edition, 1961, Softback, "Benwell, Basil B. & Britnor, L.E.", ...£18.00
The Stamps Of Barbados,
1st Edition, 1989, Hardback, "Bayley,E.A.", "Bayley,E.A." £65.00

Basutoland
Basutoland: Some Historical Notes With Special Reference To Postal Matters,
2nd Edition, 1973, Softback, "Gilbert, G.N.", Harry Hayes...£7.50
The Postal History Of Basutoland And Bechuanaland Protectorate,
1st Edition, 1996, Hardback, "Proud, E.B.", Edward B. Proud £35.00

Bechuanalands
The Bechuanalands - A Brief History Of The Countries And Their Postal Services To 1895,
1st Edition, 1945, Hardback, "Jurgens, A. A.", ...£150.00
"The Postage Stamps, Postal Stationery And Postmarks Of The Bechuanalands", 1st Edition, 1971, Hardback, "Holmes, H.R.", ...£120.00
The Postage Stamps Postal Stationery And Postmarks Of The Bechuanalands,
1st Edition, 1971, Hardback, "Holmes, H.R.", ...£125.00

Bermuda
The Postal History And Stamps Of Bermuda,
2nd Edition, 1978, Hardback, "Ludington, M.H.", ...£65.00
Bermuda Mails To 1865 - An Inventory Of The Postal Markings,
1st Edition, 1995, Softback, "Forand, M. & Freeland, C.", ...£16.00
"The King George V High Value Stamps Of Bermuda, 1917-1938",
1st Edition, 1994, Hardback, "Glazer, M.", ...£55.00

British Columbia
The Stamps And Postal History Of Vancouver Island And British Columbia 1849-1871: The Gerald Wellburn Collection,
1st Edition, 1987, Hardback, "Wellburn, G.E", ...£95.00

British Columbia/Vancouver
The Postage Stamps And Postal History Of Colonial Vancouver Island And British Columbia,
1st Edition, 1987, Hardback, "Wellburn, G. E.", ...£85.00

British East Africa
History Of The East African Army Postal Service,
1st Edition, Hardback, "Rossiter,S.", ...£30.00
The Stamps And Postal Stationery Of British East Africa,
1st Edition, 1981, Hardback, "Minns, J", ...£27.50

British Guiana
Postal Registration In British Guiana,
1st Edition, 1981, Softback, "Rego, M.R.", ...£10.00
The Postage Stamps And Postal History Of British Guiana,
1st Edition, 1970, Hardback, "Townsend,T.A Howe, F.G.",...£220.00

Burma
A Catalogue For Telegraph And Revenue Stamps For Burma And Myanmar, 1st Edition, 1998, Softback, "Davis, G", Alan Meech £16.00

Burma (Independ)
The Postal Stationery Of Burma & Myanmar,
1st Edition, 1998, Softback, "Warren, R.", ...£7.50
A Catalogue Of Telegraph And Revenue Stamps For Burma And Myanmar,
1st Edition, 1998, Softback, "Davis, G. & Meech, A.", Alan Meech £16.00

Canada
The Postage Stamps And Postal History Of Canada Volume 1 And 2, 1st Edition, 1945, Hardback, "Boggs, W.S.", Chambers Publishing Company..........................£75.00
Canada Specialized Postage Stamp Catalogue, 1st Edition, 1979, Softback, Philatelic Publishers Company.......£2.00
Canada's Decimal Era 1859-1868, 1st Edition, 1996, Hardback, "Arfken, G.B. & Leggett, A.W.", The Vincent G. Greene Philatelic Research Foundation...........................£55.00
The Handbook And Catalogue Of Canadian Transportation Postmarks, 1st Edition, 1963, Hardback, "Shaw, T.P.G.", Royal Philatelic Society Of Canada...........£21.00
Canada Notes On The 1911-1925 Issue,
1st Edition, 1949, Hardback, "Marler, G.C.", Committee On Philatelic Research And Literature Of The American Philatelic Society..£18.00
The Centennial Definitives Of Canada, 1st Edition, 1972, Softback, "Gronbeck-Jones, D.",......................£8.00

For further information on any of the titles listed, to enquire about the availability of titles not currently included, or to receive our FREE BROCHURE please contact ADRIAN DUNNE, Stanley Gibbons Ltd., 399 Strand, London, WC2R 0LX, UK. Tel: +44 (0)20 7836 8444 Fax: +44 (0)20 7836 7342 Why not email your order? mailorder@stanleygibbons.co.uk Or visit our website: www.stanleygibbons.com